SCOTT®

2012
STANDARD POSTAGE
STAMP CATALOGUE

ONE HUNDRED AND SIXTY-EIGHTH EDITION IN SIX VOLUMES

VOLUME 2
COUNTRIES OF THE WORLD
C-F

EDITOR	James E. Kloetzel
ASSISTANT EDITOR	Charles Snee
ASSISTANT EDITOR /NEW ISSUES & VALUING	Martin J. Frankevicz
ASSOCIATE EDITORS	David Akin, Donna Houseman
VALUING ANALYST	Steven R. Myers
ADMINISTRATIVE ASSISTANT/IMAGE COORDINATOR	Eric Wiessinger
CREATIVE DIRECTOR	Mark Potter
ADVERTISING	Angela Nolte
CIRCULATION/PRODUCT PROMOTION MANAGER	Tim Wagner
VICE PRESIDENT/EDITORIAL AND PRODUCTION	Steve Collins
PRESIDENT	William Fay

Released May 2011

Includes New Stamp Listings through the May 2011 *Linn's Stamp News Special Edition* Catalogue Update

Copyright© 2011 by

Scott Publishing Co.

911 Vandemark Road, Sidney, OH 45365-0828

A division of AMOS PRESS, INC., publishers of *Linn's Stamp News, Linn's Stamp News Special Edition, Coin World* and *Coin World Special Edition.*

Table of Contents

See Volume 1 for United States, United Nations and Countries of the World A-B
See Volume 3 through 6 for Countries of the World, G-Z

Volume 3: G-I
Volume 4: J-M
Volume 5: N-Sam
Volume 6: San-Z

Scott Publishing Mission Statement

The Scott Publishing Team exists to serve the recreational,
educational and commercial hobby needs of stamp collectors and dealers.

We strive to set the industry standard for philatelic information and products by developing and
providing goods that help collectors identify, value, organize and present their collections.

Quality customer service is, and will continue to be, our highest priority.
We aspire toward achieving total customer satisfaction.

Vol. 2 Number Additions, Deletions & Changes

Cambodia

Number in 2011 Catalogue	Number in 2012 Catalogue
new	1074
new	1076A
new	C39a
new	C41a
new	C43a

Canada

Number in 2011 Catalogue	Number in 2012 Catalogue
197a	deleted
new	2083a
new	2139b
new	2239b

China, People's Republic of

Number in 2011 Catalogue	Number in 2012 Catalogue
new	1607e
new	2208a
new	2209a
new	2210a
new	2242a
new	2243a
new	2258b
new	2323a
new	2324a
new	2346a
new	2431a
new	2432a
new	2463a
new	2464a

Costa Rica

Number in 2011 Catalogue	Number in 2012 Catalogue
new	390a

Croatia

Number in 2011 Catalogue	Number in 2012 Catalogue
new	J2b

Czechoslovakia

Number in 2011 Catalogue	Number in 2012 Catalogue
256	Bohemia and Moravia 1A
C18	Bohemia and Moravia C1
C55	Slovakia 23A

Epirus

Number in 2011 Catalogue	Number in 2012 Catalogue
new	4A-4Z
new	4AA-4GG
new	28
new	29
new	30
new	31
new	31a
new	32
new	32a
new	33
new	33A
new	33B
new	33Ba
new	33C
new	33D
new	42
new	42a-56a
new	42b-44b
new	43
new	44
new	45
new	46
new	47
new	47b-56b
new	48
new	48c-49c
new	49
new	49d
new	50
new	51
new	52
new	53
new	54
new	55
new	56
new	56c
new	N1b
new	N1c
new	N1d
new	N2c
new	N2d
new	N2e
new	N2f
new	N2g
new	N4b
new	N4c
new	N4d
new	N5b
new	N6a
new	N6b
new	N7a
new	N7b
new	N12a
new	N12b
new	N17a
new	N18a
new	N22a-N27a
new	N22b
new	N30a

Fiji

Number in 2011 Catalogue	Number in 2012 Catalogue
1153b	1153B
new	1155b
new	1196a
new	1197d
new	1197e
new	1197f
new	1223b
1215a	1215A
1217a	1217A
1218a	1218A
1222a	1222A
1223a	1223A

Finland

Number in 2011 Catalogue	Number in 2012 Catalogue
new	138a
new	414B
new	907a-d
new	927a-d
new	941a-j
new	960a-d
new	1191a-b
new	1192a-f
new	1214a-f

Fiume

Number in 2011 Catalogue	Number in 2012 Catalogue
new	104a-b
new	105a-b
new	106a-b
new	107a-b
new	108a-b
new	109a-b
new	110a-b
new	111a-b
new	112a
new	113a
new	113c
new	114a
new	115a
new	116a-b
new	117a-b
new	118b
new	119a-b
new	120a-b
new	121a-b
new	134a-b
new	135a-b
new	136a-b
new	137a-b
new	138a-b
new	139a-b
new	140a-b
new	141a
new	142a
new	143a
new	148a-b
new	150a
new	154a
new	156a
new	157a
new	160a
new	161a
new	162a-b
new	164a-c
new	165a
new	168a-b
new	184a-b
new	185a
new	186a
new	187a-b
new	189a
new	190a
new	191a
new	192a
new	193a
new	B1b
new	B2b
new	E1a
new	E4a-b
new	E5a-c
new	E7a
new	E9a
new	E10a-b
new	E11a-b
new	J1ca
new	J2ca
new	J3a
new	J5a-b
new	J7a-b
new	J8a
new	J11a
new	P1a-b
new	P4a

Scott Publishing Co.

SCOTT 911 VANDEMARK ROAD, SIDNEY, OHIO 45365 937-498-0802

Dear Scott Catalogue User:

China, again?

In last year's Letter From the Editor for Volume 2 of the *Scott Standard Postage Stamp Catalogue*, we indicated that China was the stand-out country for value changes for the volume. The only difference between last year and this year is that in this 2012 Volume 2, values for myriad China issues have gone up still further. And very often the increases have not been small but are quite large. Where are China values headed in the future? We will not try to gaze into the future; it is quite enough to try to get our heads and hands around the present state of the market.

China contributed mightily to the high number of value changes in this year's Volume 2. More than 14,600 occur in the three China sections. Imperial China accounts for 827 value changes, the Republic of China adds 5,327 more, and People's Republic of China totals 8,475.

Classic China stamps show many value increases, several of them quite large. China's first stamp, the 1878 1c green Imperial Dragon, Scott 1, sets the tempo with an increase to $600 unused and $475 used, from $400 unused and $325 used in the 2011 Volume 2. Issues up to 1894 move in a similar fashion, with smaller increases thereafter.

There are frequent value increases in the Republic of China period, though not as great a percentage as in Imperial China or People's Republic of China. One item that shows a large increase in value is the 1951 Election souvenir sheet, Scott 1041, which moves to $575 unused and $400 used, from $425 unused and $350 used last year. As the large number of value changes during this period would suggest, there are frequent increases throughout the Republic period, continuing right through the back-of-the-book issues of Taiwan and Japanese occupation.

The People's Republic of China stamps show the most value increases and the largest increases. A key stamp collectors and dealers look to to gauge the China market is the 1980 8f Year of the Monkey New Year stamp, Scott 1586. From $1,000 mint, never hinged and $250 used in the 2011 Volume 2, this stamp soars to $1,950 mint, never hinged and $750 used in the 2012 catalogue edition. Another set often consulted to show China trends is the 1952 series of blocks of four representing setting-up exercises, Scott 141-150. From $80 unused and $35 used per block in 2011, they move to $175 unused and $57.50 used per block this year.

Large increases are the rule rather than the exception throughout People's Republic of China, most notably in the Cultural Revolution period. Typical is the 1967 8f Mao, 'Sun of the Revolution' set of two, Scott 965-966. From $120 mint, never hinged and $31.50 used last year, this set jumps to $250 mint, never hinged and $77.50 used in the 2012 Volume 2.

Where are the other value changes in the 2012 Volume 2?

For all of the Volume 2 listings in this 2012 edition, which covers countries of the world alphabetically C through F, almost 40,000 value changes appear. This is more than the average number of changes seen each year for about the past decade.

Following China, the country with the most value changes is Finland and the Aland Islands, with 2,384 changes. Other countries with high numbers of value changes include Denmark (2,157), Costa Rica (2,135), Cuba (2,105), Canada (1,975), Czechoslovakia (1,462), Cambodia (1,153) and Christmas Island (1,085).

The great majority of the Canada changes flow from the strength of the Canadian dollar, which has grown considerably against the United States dollar during the past year. There seems to be little reason to believe this will change appreciably any time soon.

The general weakness in worldwide economies has contin-

ued throughout the past year, and that certainly has dampened most upward pressure on values. The results of a weak United States economy, from the perspective of U.S. catalogue editors, are threefold. First, economic weakness harms hobby-related fields generally because it is relatively easy to put hobby expenses on hold for a period of time, whereas it is not possible to put necessities such as food and housing on hold. It follows that the more common philatelic material in the marketplace would be expected to show a pretty lethargic sales pattern, and that is what we have been seeing. Nothing terribly upsetting, but also very little showing strength in the market.

Second, as usual during such uncertain periods, true rarities and condition rarities show strength.

The third pattern we see often during difficult economic times is a swing in the relative value for different currencies. If all countries experienced the same weakness, currencies could be expected to remain relatively stable in relation to each other. That pattern, however, is seldom the case. There are strong currencies and there are weak currencies, and with Scott being a retail-value catalogue, these relative shifts have an impact on values. If an important country experiences a stronger currency in relation to the United States dollar's value, it will tend to cause prices to rise in the United States, because more dollars are needed to compete with the stronger home-country currency.

Some interesting editorial changes.

Proceeding on the axiom that a picture is worth a thousand words, the Scott editors have expanded the illustrations in two interesting areas of Volume 2. The Epirus listings have been completely revamped, with many new major and minor numbers added, and as part of this project multiple new illustrations have been added for the 1914 surcharges on Turkish stamps, generally called the Argyrokastro issues.

A similar treatment of showing illustrations for every stamp listed, in this case both major numbers and minor numbers, appears in the 2007-10 Fiji surcharges on the Bird stamps, Scott 1149-1160, 1191-1197C and 1214-1223A. These most interesting stamps are now much easier to distinguish, and the full array in illustrations makes quite a presentation.

A very large number of additions for classic errors in Fiume appear for the first time in this 2012 Volume 2.

To see these and all other listing changes that have been made this year, consult the 2012 Volume 2 Number Additions, Deletions & Changes list. In this volume, it is on page 4A in the introduction.

Final thoughts.

Dr. Hsien-Ming Meng, a great Scott friend and benefactor, passed away Feb. 8, 2011, at age 84. Longtime catalogue users might recognize his name. When Scott began converting catalogue images from black and white to color in 2001, we began by scanning all of the stamps in our own reference collection. But this left a huge number of earlier stamps in black and white. Recognizing the benefit of Scott's color project, Dr. Meng stepped forward with an offer to loan us his massive collection of unused stamps for scanning purposes. The time and effort saved by having this immense resource made available proved invaluable, and we will forever remember the kindness and generosity shown by this wonderful Ohio collector. Thank you again, Dr. Meng.

And speaking of our color project, there are only 122 images in this Volume 2 remaining to be converted to color. Other volumes have more or less. We still have staff and outside contributors on the lookout for the stamps not currently shown in color.

A hobby is a great gift. Happy collecting.

James E. Kloetzel

James E. Kloetzel/Catalogue Editor

Acknowledgments

Our appreciation and gratitude go to the following individuals who have assisted us in preparing information included in this year's Scott Catalogues. Some helpers prefer anonymity. These individuals have generously shared their stamp knowledge with others through the medium of the Scott Catalogue.

Those who follow provided information that is in addition to the hundreds of dealer price lists and advertisements and scores of auction catalogues and realizations that were used in producing the catalogue values. It is from those noted here that we have been able to obtain information on items not normally seen in published lists and advertisements. Support from these people goes beyond data leading to catalogue values, for they also are key to editorial changes.

A special acknowledgment to Liane and Sergio Sismondo of The Classic Collector for their extraordinary assistance and knowledge sharing that has aided in the preparation of this year's Standard and Classic Specialized Catalogues.

A. R. Allison (Orange Free State Study Circle)
Roland Austin
Robert Ausubel (Great Britain Collectors Club)
Jack Hagop Barsoumian (International Stamp Co.)
George G. Birdsall
John Birkinbine II
Roger S. Brody
Keith & Margie Brown
Mahdi Bseiso
Paul Buchsbayew
Bernard Bujnak
Timothy Bryan Burgess
Mike Bush (Joseph V. Bush, Inc.)
Tina & John Carlson (JET Stamps)
Richard A. Champagne (Richard A. Champagne, Inc.)
Henry Chlanda
Bob Coale
Leroy P. Collins III (United Postal Stationery Society)
Frank D. Correl
Tom Cossaboom
Francis J. Crown, Jr.
Tony L. Crumbley (Carolina Coin & Stamp, Inc.)
Stephen R. Datz
Tony Davis
Kenneth E. Diehl
Bob Dumaine
Sister Theresa Durand
Mark Eastzer (Markest Stamp Co.)
Esi Ebrani (Iran Philatelic Study Circle)
Paul G. Eckman
George Epstein
Mehdi Esmaili
Leon Finik
Robert A. Fisher
Geoffrey Flack
Jeffrey M. Forster
Ken Fowler
Ernest E. Fricks (France & Colonies Philatelic Society)
Phillip F. Gallagher
Bob Genisol (Sultan Stamp Center)
Stan Goldfarb
Daniel E. Grau
Jan E. Gronwall
Bruce Hecht (Bruce L. Hecht Co.)
Robert R. Hegland
Clifford O. Herrick (Fidelity Trading Co.)
Peter Hoffman

Armen Hovsepian
Philip J. Hughes
Doug Iams
Thomas Jackson (Stamp Parlor)
N. M. Janoowalla
Peter Jeannopoulos
Stephen Joe (International Stamp Service)
Richard A. Johnson
Allan Katz (Ventura Stamp Co.)
Stanford M. Katz
Lewis Kaufman
Patricia A. Kaufmann
William V. Kriebel
Dr. Ingert (Ihor) Kuzych-Berlzovsky
Frederick P. Lawrence
John R. Lewis (The William Henry Stamp Co.)
Ulf Lindahl
Pedro Llach (Filatelia Llach S.L.)
George Luzitano
Dennis Lynch
Robert L. Markovits (Quality Investors, Ltd.)
Marilyn R. Mattke
William K. McDaniel
Gary McLean
Mark S. Miller (India Study Circle)
Allen Mintz (United Postal Stationery Society)
Gary Morris (Pacific Midwest Co.)
Peter Mosiondz, Jr.
Bruce M. Moyer (Moyer Stamps & Collectibles)
Richard H. Muller
Gregg Nelson
Robert Odenweller
Marc Parren
John E. Pearson (Pittwater Philatelic Service)
Donald J. Peterson (International Philippine Philatelic Society)
Stanley M. Piller (Stanley M. Piller & Associates)
Todor Drumev Popov
Peter W. W. Powell
Stephen Radin (Albany Stamp Co.)
Siddique Mahmudur Rahman
Dr. Reuben A. Ramkissoon
Ghassan D. Riachi
Eric Roberts
Omar Rodriguez
Michael Rogers (Michael Rogers, Inc.)
Robert G. Rufe
Michael Ruggiero
Andrew Sader
Mehrdad Sadri (Persiphila)
Alex Schauss (Schauss Philatelics)

Jacques C. Schiff, Jr. (Jacques C. Schiff, Jr., Inc.)
Bernard Seckler (Fine Arts Philatelists)
Guy Shaw
Jeff Siddiqui
Sergio & Liane Sismondo (The Classic Collector)
Jay Smith
Frank J. Stanley, III
Alfred E. Staubus
Scott R. Trepel (Siegel Auction Galleries)
Philip T. Wall
Giana Wayman
William R. Weiss, Jr. (Weiss Expertizing)
Ed Wener (Indigo)
Don White (Dunedin Stamp Centre)
Kirk Wolford (Kirk's Stamp Company)
Robert F. Yacano (K-Line Philippines)
Ralph Yorio
Val Zabijaka
Michal Zika
Alfonso G. Zulueta, Jr.

Addresses, Telephone Numbers, Web Sites, E-Mail Addresses of General & Specialized Philatelic Societies

Collectors can contact the following groups for information about the philately of the areas within the scope of these societies, or inquire about membership in these groups. Aside from the general societies, we limit this list to groups that specialize in particular fields of philately, particular areas covered by the Scott Standard Postage Stamp Catalogue, and topical groups. Many more specialized philatelic society exist than those listed below. These addresses are updated yearly, and they are, to the best of our knowledge, correct and current. Groups should inform the editors of address changes whenever they occur. The editors also want to hear from other such specialized groups not listed.

Unless otherwise noted all website addresses begin with http://

American Philatelic Society
100 Match Factory Place
Bellefonte PA 16823-1367
Ph: (814) 933-3803
www.stamps.org
E-mail: apsinfo@stamps.org

American Stamp Dealers Association, Inc.
Joe Savarese
217-14 Northern Blvd.
Bayside NY 11361
Ph: (718) 224-2500
www.asdaonline.com
E-mail: asda@erols.com

National Stamp Dealers Association
Dick Keiser, president
2916 NW Bucklin Hill Rd #136
Silverdale WA 98383-8514
Ph: (800) 875-6633
www.nsdainc.org
E-mail: gail@nsdainc.org

International Society of Worldwide Stamp Collectors
Joanne Berkowitz, MD
P.O. Box 19006
Sacramento CA 95819
www.iswsc.org
E-mail: executivedirector@iswsc.org

Royal Philatelic Society
41 Devonshire Place
London, W1G 6JY
UNITED KINGDOM
www.rpsl.org.uk
E-mail: secretary@rpsl.org.uk

Royal Philatelic Society of Canada
P.O. Box 929, Station Q
Toronto, ON, M4T 2P1
CANADA
Ph: (888) 285-4143
www.rpsc.org
E-mail: info@rpsc.org

Young Stamp Collectors of America
Janet Houser
100 Match Factory Place
Bellefonte PA 16823-1367
Ph: (814) 933-3820
www.stamps.org/ysca/intro.htm
E-mail: ysca@stamps.org

Philatelic Research Resources

(Scott editors are encouraging any additional research organizations to submit data for inclusion in this new listing category)

The Western Philatelic Library
P.O. Box 2219
1500 Partridge Avenue
Sunnyvale CA 94087
Ph: (408) 733-0336
www.fwpf.org

Groups focusing on fields or aspects found in worldwide philately (some may cover U.S. area only)

American Air Mail Society
Stephen Reinhard
P.O. Box 110
Mineola NY 11501
www.americanairmailsociety.org
E-mail: sreinhard1@optonline.net

American First Day Cover Society
Douglas Kelsey
P.O. Box 16277
Tucson AZ 85732-6277
Ph: (520) 321-0880
www.afdcs.org
E-mail: afdcs@aol.com

American Revenue Association
Eric Jackson
P.O. Box 728
Leesport PA 19533-0728
Ph: (610) 926-6200
www.revenuer.org
E-mail: eric@revenuer.com

American Topical Association
Vera Felts
P.O. Box 8
Carterville IL 62918-0008
Ph: (618) 985-5100
www.americantopicalassn.org
E-mail: americantopical@msn.com

Christmas Seal & Charity Stamp Society
John Denune
234 East Broadway
Granville OH 43023
Ph: (740) 587-0276
http://www.charityseals.org
E-mail: jdenune@roadrunner.com

Errors, Freaks and Oddities Collectors Club
Don David Price
5320 Eastchester Drive
Sarasota FL 34134-2711
Ph: (717) 445-9420 Nor. Am. Phone No.
www.efocc.org
E-mail: ddprice98@hotmail.com

First Issues Collectors Club
Clark Buchi
P.O. Box 453
Brentwood TN 37024-0453
www.firstissues.org
E-mail: orders@firstissues.org

International Society of Reply Coupon Collectors
Peter Robin
P.O. Box 353
Bala Cynwyd PA 19004
E-mail: peterrobin@verizon.net

The Joint Stamp Issues Society
Richard Zimmermann
124, Avenue Guy de Coubertin
Saint Remy Les Chevreuse, F-78470
FRANCE
www.jointstampissues.net
E-mail: contact@jointstampissues.net

National Duck Stamp Collectors Society
Anthony J. Monico
P.O. Box 43
Harleysville PA 19438-0043
www.ndscs.org
E-mail: ndscs@ndscs.org

No Value Identified Club
Albert Sauvanet
Le Clos Royal B, Boulevard des Pas Enchantes
St. Sebastien-sur Loire, 44230
FRANCE
E-mail: alain.vailly@irin.univ nantes.fr

The Perfins Club
Jerry Hejduk
P.O. Box 490450.
Leesburg FL 34749-0450
Ph: (352) 326-2117
E-mail: flprepers@comcast.net

Postage Due Mail Study Group
John Rawlins
13, Longacre
Chelmsford, CM1 3BJ
UNITED KINGDOM
E-mail: john.rawlins2@ukonline.co.uk.

Post Mark Collectors Club
Beverly Proulx
7629 Homestead Drive
Baldwinsville NY 13027
Ph: (315) 638-0532
www.postmarks.org
E-mail: stampdance@yahoo.com

Postal History Society
Kalman V. Illyefalvi
869 Bridgewater Drive
New Oxford PA 17350-8206
Ph: (717) 624-5941
www.stampclubs.com
E-mail: kalphyl@juno.com

Precancel Stamp Society
Jerry Hejduk
P.O. Box 490450.
Leesburg FL 34749-0450
Ph: (352) 326-2117
www.precancels.com
E-mail: psspromosec@comcast.net

United Postal Stationery Society
Stuart Leven
P.O. Box 24764
San Jose CA 95154-4764
www.upss.org
E-mail: poststat@gmail.com

United States Possessions Philatelic Society
Geoffrey Brewster
6453 E. Stallion Rd.
Paradise Valley AZ 85253
Ph: (480) 607-7184
www.uspps.com
E-mail: patlabb@aol.com

Groups focusing on U.S. area philately as covered in the Standard Catalogue

Canal Zone Study Group
Richard H. Salz
60 27th Ave.
San Francisco CA 94121-1026

Carriers and Locals Society
Martin Richardson
P.O. Box 74
Grosse Ile MI 48138
www.pennypost.org
E-mail: martinr362@aol.com

Confederate Stamp Alliance
Patricia A. Kaufmann
10194 N. Old State Road
Lincoln DE 19960
Ph. (302) 422-2656
www.csalliance.org
E-mail: csaas@comcast.net

Hawaiian Philatelic Society
Kay H. Hoke
P.O. Box 10115
Honolulu HI 96816-0115
Ph: (808) 521-5721

Plate Number Coil Collectors Club
Gene Trinks
16415 W. Desert Wren Ct.
Surprise AZ 85374
Ph: (623) 322-4619
www.pnc3.org
E-mail: gctrinks@cox.net

Ryukyu Philatelic Specialist Society
Laura Edmonds, Secy.
P.O. Box 240177
Charlotte NC 28224-0177
Ph: (704) 519-5157
www.ryukyustamps.org
E-mail: secretary@ryukyustamps.org

United Nations Philatelists
Blanton Clement, Jr.
P.O. Box 146
Morrisville PA 19067-0146
www.unpi.com
E-mail: bclemjr@yahoo.com

United States Stamp Society
Executive Secretary
P.O. Box 6634
Katy TX 77491-6631
www.usstamps.org
E-mail: webmaster@usstamps.org

U.S. Cancellation Club
Roger Rhoads
6160 Brownstone Ct.
Mentor OH 44060
http://bob.trachimowicz.org/indfk.html
E-mail: rrrhoads@aol.com

U.S. Philatelic Classics Society
Rob Lund
2913 Fulton
Everett WA 98201-3733
www.uspcs.org
E-mail: membershipchairman@uspcs.org

Groups focusing on philately of foreign countries or regions

Aden & Somaliland Study Group
Gary Brown
P.O. Box 106
Briar Hill, Victoria, 3088
AUSTRALIA
E-mail: garyjohn951@optushome.com.au

American Society of Polar
  Philatelists (Antarctic areas)
Alan Warren
P.O. Box 39
Exton PA 19341-0039
www.polarphilatelists.org
E-mail: alanwar@att.net

Andorran Philatelic Study Circle
D. Hope
17 Hawthorn Dr.
Stalybridge, Cheshire, SK15 1UE
UNITED KINGDOM
apsc.free.fr
E-mail: apsc@free.fr

Australian States Study Circle of
  The Royal Sydney Philatelic Club
Ben Palmer
GPO 1751
Sydney, N.S.W., 2001
AUSTRALIA

Austria Philatelic Society
Ralph Schneider
P.O. Box 23049
Belleville IL 62223
Ph: (618) 277-6152
www.austriaphilatelicsociety.com
E-mail: rschneider39@charter.net

American Belgian Philatelic Society
Edward de Bary
11 Wakefield Dr. Apt. 2105
Asheville NC 28803
E-mail: belgam@charter.net

Bechuanalands and Botswana Society
Neville Midwood
69 Porlock Lane
Furzton, Milton Keynes, MK4 1JY
UNITED KINGDOM
www.nevsoft.com
E-mail: bbsoc@nevsoft.com

Bermuda Collectors Society
Thomas J. McMahon
P.O. Box 1949
Stuart FL 34995
www.bermudacollectorssociety.org
E-mail: science29@comcast.net

Brazil Philatelic Association
William V. Kriebel
1923 Manning St.
Philadelphia PA 19103-5728
Ph: (215) 735-3697
E-mail: kriebewv@drexel.edu

British Caribbean Philatelic Study
  Group
Dr. Reuben A. Ramkissoon
11075 Benton Street #236
Loma Linda CA 92354-3182
www.bcpsg.com
E-mail: rramkissoon@juno.com

The King George VI Collectors
  Society (British Commonwealth)
Brian Livingstone
21 York Mansions, Prince of Wales
Drive
London, SW11 4DL
UNITED KINGDOM
www.kg6.info
E-mail: livingstone484@btinternet.com

British North America Philatelic
  Society (Canada & Provinces)
David G. Jones
184 Larkin Dr.
Nepean, ON, K2J 1H9
CANADA
www.bnaps.org
E-mail: shibumi.management@gmail.com

British West Indies Study Circle
John Seidl
4324 Granby Way
Marietta GA 30062
Ph: (770) 642-6424
www.bwisc.org
jseidl@mindspring.com

Burma Philatelic Study Circle
Michael Whittaker
1, Ecton Leys, Hillside
Rugby, Warwickshire, CV22 5SL
UNITED KINGDOM
www.burmastamps.homecall.co.uk
E-mail: whittaker2004@btinternet.com

Cape and Natal Study Circle
Dr. Guy Dillaway
P.O. Box 181
Weston MA 02493
www.nzsc.demon.co.uk

Ceylon Study Group
R. W. P. Frost
42 Lonsdale Road, Cannington
Bridgewater, Somerset, TA5 2JS
UNITED KINGDOM
E-mail: rodney.frost@tiscali.co.uk

Channel Islands Specialists Society
Moira Edwards
86, Hall Lane, Sandon,
Chelmsford, Essex, CM2 7RQ
UNITED KINGDOM
www.ciss1950.org.uk
E-mail: membership@ciss1950.org.uk

China Stamp Society
Paul H. Gault
P.O. Box 20711
Columbus OH 43220
www.chinastampsociety.org
E-mail: secretary@chinastampsociety.org

Colombia/Panama Philatelic Study
  Group (COPAPHIL)
Thomas P. Myers
P.O. Box 522
Gordonsville VA 22942
www.copaphil.org
E-mail: tpmphil@hotmail.com

Association Filatelic de Costa Rica
Giana Wayman
c/o Interlink 102, P.O. Box 52-6770
Miami, FL 33152
E-mail: scotland@racsa.co.cr

Society for Costa Rica Collectors
Dr. Hector R. Mena
P.O. Box 14831
Baton Rouge LA 70808
www.socorico.org
E-mail: hrmena@aol.com

International Cuban Philatelic
  Society
Ernesto Cuesta
P.O. Box 34434
Bethesda MD 20827
www.cubafil.org
E-mail: ecuesta@philat.com

Cuban Philatelic Society of America
P.O. Box 141656
Coral Gables FL 33114-1656
www.cubapsa.com
E-mail: cpsa.usa@gmail.com

Cyprus Study Circle
Colin Dear
10 Marne Close, Wem
Shropshire, SY4 5YE
UNITED KINGDOM
www.cyprusstudycircle.org/index.htm
E-mail: colindear@talktalk.net.

Society for Czechoslovak Philately
Phil Rhoade
905 E. Oakside St.
South Bend IN 46614
www.csphilately.org
E-mail: philip.rhoade@mnsu.edu

Danish West Indies Study Unit of
  the Scandinavian Collectors Club
Arnold Sorensen
7666 Edgedale Drive
Newburgh IN 47630
Ph: (812) 480-6532
www.scc-online.org
E-mail: valbydwi@hotmail.com

East Africa Study Circle
Jonathan Smalley
1 Lincoln Close
Tweeksbury, B91 1AE
UNITED KINGDOM
easc.org.uk
E-mail: jpasmalley@tiscali.co.uk

Egypt Study Circle
Mike Murphy
109 Chadwick Road
London, SE15 4PY
UNITED KINGDOM
Dick Wilson: North American Agent
egyptstudycircle.org.uk
E-mail: egyptstudycircle@hotmail.com

Estonian Philatelic Society
Juri Kirsimagi
29 Clifford Ave.
Pelham NY 10803
Ph: (914) 738-3713

Ethiopian Philatelic Society
Ulf Lindahl
21 Westview Place
Riverside CT 06878
Ph: (203) 866-3540
home.comcast.net/~fbheiser/ethiopia5.
htm
E-mail: ulindahl@optonline.net

Falkland Islands Philatelic Study
  Group
Carl J. Faulkner
Williams Inn, On-the-Green
Williamstown MA 01267-2620
www.fipsg.org.uk
Ph: (413) 458-9371

Faroe Islands Study Circle
Norman Hudson
40 Queenís Road, Vicarís Cross
Chester, CH3 5HB
UNITED KINGDOM
www.faroeislandssc.org.
E-mail: jntropics@hotmail.com

Former French Colonies Specialist
  Society
BP 628
75367 Paris, Cedex 08
FRANCE
www.colfra.com
E-mail: clubcolfra@aol.com

France & Colonies Philatelic Society
Edward Grabowski
111 Prospect St., 4C
Westfield NJ 07090
www.franceandcolonies.org
E-mail: edjjg@alum.mit.edu

Germany Philatelic Society
P.O. Box 6547
Chesterfield MO 63006
www.gps.nu

Gibraltar Study Circle
David R. Stirrups
34 Glamis Drive
Dundee, DD2 1QP
UNITED KINGDOM
E-mail: drstirrups@dundee.ac.uk

Great Britain Collectors Club
Steve McGill
10309 Brookhollow Circle
Highlands Ranch CO 80129
www.gbstamps.com/gbcc
E-mail: steve.mcgill@comcast.net

International Society of Guatemala
  Collectors
Jaime Marckwordt
449 St. Francis Blvd.
Daly City CA 94015-2136
www.guatemalastamps.com

Haiti Philatelic Society
Ubaldo Del Toro
5709 Marble Archway
Alexandria VA 22315
www.haitiphilately.org
E-mail: u007ubi@aol.com

Hong Kong Stamp Society
Ming W. Tsang
P.O. Box 206
Glenside PA 19038

Society for Hungarian Philately
Robert Morgan
2201 Roscomare Rd.
Los Angeles CA 90077-2222
www.hungarianphilately.org
E-mail: bwilson1951@aol.com

India Study Circle
John Warren
P.O. Box 7326
Washington DC 20044
Ph: (202) 564-6876
www.indiastudycircle.org
E-mail: warren.john@epa.gov

Indian Ocean Study Circle
Mrs. S. Hopson
Field Acre, Hoe Benham
Newbury, Berkshire, RG20 8PD
UNITED KINGDOM

Society of Indo-China Philatelists
Ron Bentley
2600 North 24th Street
Arlington VA 22207
www.sicp-online.org
E-mail: ron.bentley@verizon.net

Iran Philatelic Study Circle
Mehdi Esmaili
P.O. Box 750096
Forest Hills NY 11375
www.iranphilatelic.org
E-mail: m.esmaili@earthlink.net

Eire Philatelic Association (Ireland)
David J. Brennan
P.O. Box 704
Bernardsville NJ 07924
eirephilatelicassoc.org
E-mail: brennan704@aol.com

Society of Israel Philatelists
Michael Bass
P.O. Box 507
Northfield OH 44067
www.israelstamps.com
israelstamps@gmail.com

Italy and Colonies Study Circle
Andrew DíAnneo
1085 Dunweal Lane
Calistoga CA 94515
www.icsc.pwp.blueyonder.co.uk
E-mail: audanneo@napanet.net

International Society for Japanese
  Philately
William Eisenhauer
P.O. Box 230462
Tigard OR 97281
www.isjp.org
E-mail: secretary@isjp.org\

Korea Stamp Society
John E. Talmage
P.O. Box 6889
Oak Ridge TN 37831
www.pennfamily.org/KSS-USA
E-mail: jtalmage@usit.net

Latin American Philatelic Society
Jules K. Beck
30 1/2 Street #209
St. Louis Park MN 55426-3551

Liberian Philatelic Society
William Thomas Lockard
P.O. Box 106
Wellston OH 45692
Ph: (740) 384-2020
E-mail: tlockard@zoomnet.net

Liechtenstudy USA (Liechtenstein)
Paul Tremaine
410 S. W. Ninth St.
Dundee OR 97115
Ph: (503) 538-4500
www.liechtenstudy.org
E-mail: editor@liechtenstudy.org

Lithuania Philatelic Society
John Variakojis
3715 W. 68th St.
Chicago IL 60629
Ph: (773) 585-8649
http://lithuanianphilately.com/lps
E-mail: variakojis@sbcglobal.net

Luxembourg Collectors Club
Gary B. Little
7319 Beau Road
Sechelt, BC, VON 3A8
CANADA
lcc.luxcentral.com
E-mail: gary@luxcentral.com

Malaya Study Group
David Tett
P.O. Box 34
Wheathampstead, Herts, AL4 8JY
UNITED KINGDOM
www.m-s-g/org/uk
E-mail: davidtett@aol.com

Malta Study Circle
Alec Webster
50 Worcester Road
Sutton, Surrey, SM2 6QB
UNITED KINGDOM
E-mail: alecwebster50@hotmail.com

Mexico-Elmhurst Philatelic Society
  International
David Pietsch
P.O. Box 50997
Irvine CA 92619-0997
E-mail: mepsi@msn.com

Asociacion Mexicana de Filatelia
AMEXFIL
Ave. 16 de Septiembre #6-401, Col.
Centro
Mexico City DF, 06000
MEXICO
www.amexfil.org.mx
E-mail: carlosfet@prodigy.net.mx

Society for Moroccan and Tunisian
  Philately
206, bld. Pereire
75017 Paris
FRANCE
members.aol.com/Jhaik5814
E-mail: splm206@aol.com

Nepal & Tibet Philatelic Study Group
Roger D. Skinner
1020 Covington Road
Los Altos CA 94024-5003
Ph: (650) 968-4163
fuchs-online.com/ntpsc/
E-mail: colinhepper@hotmail.co.uk

American Society for Netherlands
  Philately
Hans Kremer
50 Rockport Ct.
Danville CA 94526
Ph: (925) 820-5841
www.angelfire.com/ca2/asnp
E-mail: hkremer@usa.net

New Zealand Society of Great Britain
Keith C. Collins
13 Briton Crescent
Sanderstead, Surrey, CR2 0JN
UNITED KINGDOM
www.cs.stir.ac.uk/~rgc/nzsgb
E-mail: rgc@cs.stir.ac.uk

Nicaragua Study Group
Erick Rodriguez
11817 S.W. 11th St.
Miami FL 33184-2501
clubs.yahoo.com/clubs/nicara-
guastudygroup
E-mail: nsgsec@yahoo.com

Society of Australasian Specialists/
  Oceania
Stuart Leven
P.O. Box 24764
San Jose CA 95154-4764
Ph: (408) 978-0193
www.sasoceania.org
E-mail: sas_oceania@yahoo.com

Orange Free State Study Circle
J. R. Stroud
28 Oxford St.
Burnham-on-sea, Somerset, TA8 1LQ
UNITED KINGDOM
orangefreestatephilately.org.uk
E-mail: richardstroudph@gofast.co.uk

Pacific Islands Study Circle
John Ray
24 Woodvale Avenue
London, SE25 4AE
UNITED KINGDOM
www.pisc.org.uk
E-mail: info@pisc.org.uk

Pakistan Philatelic Study Circle
Jeff Siddiqui
P.O. Box 7002
Lynnwood WA 98046
E-mail: jeffsiddiqui@msn.com

Centro de Filatelistas
  Independientes de Panama
Vladimir Berrio-Lemm
Apartado 0823-02748
Plaza Concordia Panama,
PANAMA
E-mail: panahistoria@gmail.com

Papuan Philatelic Society
Steven Zirinsky
P.O. Box 49, Ansonia Station
New York NY 10023
Ph: (718) 706-0616
www.communigate.co.uk/york/pps
E-mail: szirinsky@cs.com

International Philippine Philatelic
  Society
Donald J. Peterson
7408 Alaska Ave., NW
Washington DC 20012
Ph: (202) 291-6229
www.theipps.info
E-mail: dpeterson@comcast.net

Pitcairn Islands Study Group
Dr. Everett L. Parker
249 NW Live Oak Place
Lake City FL 32055-8906
Ph: (386) 754-8524
www.pisg.net
E-mail: eparker@hughes.net

Polonus Philatelic Society (Poland)
Chris Kulpinski
9350 E. Palm Tree Dr.
Scottsdale AZ 85255
Ph: (480) 585-7114
www.polonus.org
E-mail: ctk@kulpinski.net

International Society for
  Portuguese Philately
Clyde Homen
1491 Bonnie View Rd.
Hollister CA 95023-5117
www.portugalstamps.com
E-mail: cjh1491@sbcglobal.net

Rhodesian Study Circle
William R. Wallace
P.O. Box 16381
San Francisco CA 94116
www.rhodesianstudycircle.org.uk
E-mail: bwall8rscr@earthlink.net

Rossica Society of Russian Philately
Edward J. Laveroni
P.O. Box 320997
Los Gatos CA 95032-0116
www.rossica.org
E-mail: ed.laveroni@rossica.org

St. Helena, Ascension & Tristan Da
  Cunha Philatelic Society
Dr. Everett L. Parker
249 NW Live Oak Place
Lake City FL 32055-8906
Ph: (386) 754-8524
www.atlanticislands.org
E-mail: eparker@hughes.net

St. Pierre & Miquelon Philatelic
  Society
James R. (Jim) Taylor
2335 Paliswood Rd. SW
Calgary, AB, T2V 3P6
CANADA

Associated Collectors of El Salvador
Joseph D. Hahn
1015 Old Boalsburg Rd. Apt G-5
State College PA 16801-6149
www.elsalvadorphilately.org
E-mail: joehahn2@yahoo.com

Fellowship of Samoa Specialists
Donald Mee
23 Leo Street
Christchurch, 8051
NEW ZEALAND
www.samoaexpress.org
E-mail: donanm@xtra.co.nz

Sarawak Specialists' Society
Stu Leven
P.O. Box 24764
San Jose CA 95154-4764
Ph: (408) 978-0193
www.britborneostamps.org.uk
www.s-s-s.org.uk
E-mail: stulev@ix.netcom.com

Scandinavian Collectors Club
Donald B. Brent
P.O. Box 13196
El Cajon CA 92020
www.scc-online.org
E-mail: dbrent47@sprynet.com

Slovakia Stamp Society
Jack Benchik
P.O. Box 555
Notre Dame IN 46556

Philatelic Society for Greater
  Southern Africa
Alan Hanks
34 Seaton Drive
Aurora, ON, L4G 2KI
CANADA
Ph: (905) 727-6993
www.psgsa.thestampweb.com
Email: alan.hanks@sympatico.ca

Spanish Philatelic Society
Robert H. Penn
1108 Walnut Drive
Danielsville PA 18038
Ph: (610) 767-6793
E-mail: roberthpenn@aol.com

Sudan Study Group
c/o North American Agent
Richard S. Wilson
53 Middle Patent Road
Bedford NY 10506
www.sudanstamps.org
E-mail: dadu1@verizon.net

American Helvetia Philatelic
  Society (Switzerland,
  Liechtenstein)
Richard T. Hall
P.O. Box 15053
Asheville NC 28813-0053
www.swiss-stamps.org
E-mail: secretary2@swiss-stamps.org

Tannu Tuva Collectors Society
Ken Simon
513 Sixth Ave. So.
Lake Worth FL 33460-4507
Ph: (561) 588-5954
www.tuva.tk
E-mail: yurttuva@yahoo.com

Society for Thai Philately
H. R. Blakeney
P.O. Box 25644
Oklahoma City OK 73125
E-mail: HRBlakeney@aol.com

Transvaal Study Circle
J. Woolgar
P.O. Box 379
Gravesend, DA11 9EW
UNITED KINGDOM
www.transvaal.org.uk

Ottoman and Near East Philatelic
  Society (Turkey and related areas)
Bob Stuchell
193 Valley Stream Lane
Wayne PA 19087
www.oneps.org
E-mail: rstuchell@msn.com

Ukrainian Philatelic & Numismatic
  Society
George Slusarczuk
P.O. Box 303
Southfields NY 10975-0303
www.upns.org
E-mail: Yurko@frontiernet.net

Vatican Philatelic Society
Sal Quinonez
1 Aldersgate, Apt. 1002
Riverhead NY 11901-1830
Ph: (516) 727-6426
www.vaticanphilately.org

British Virgin Islands Philatelic
  Society
Giorgio Migliavacca
P.O. Box 7007
St. Thomas VI 00801-0007
www.islandsun.com/FEATURES/
bviphil9198.html
E-mail: issun@candwbvi.net

West Africa Study Circle
Dr. Peter Newroth
Suite 603
5332 Sayward Hill Crescent
Victoria, BC, V8Y 3H8
CANADA
www.wasc.org.uk/

Western Australia Study Group
Brian Pope
P.O. Box 423
Claremont, Western Australia, 6910
AUSTRALIA
www.wastudygroup.com
E-mail: black5swan@yahoo.com.au

Yugoslavia Study Group of the
  Croatian Philatelic Society
Michael Lenard
1514 North 3rd Ave.
Wausau WI 54401
Ph: (715) 675-2833
E-mail: mjlenard@aol.com

Topical Groups

Americana Unit
Dennis Dengel
17 Peckham Rd.
Poughkeepsie NY 12603-2018
www.americanaunit.org
E-mail: info@americanaunit.org

Astronomy Study Unit
John W. G. Budd
29203 Coharie Loop
San Antonio FL 33576-4643
Ph: (352) 588-4706
www.astronomystudyunit.com
E-mail: jwgbudd@earthlink.net

Bicycle Stamp Club
Tony Teideman
P.O. Box 90
Baulkham Hills, NSW, 1755
AUSTRALIA
members.tripod.com/~bicyclestamps
E-mail: tonimaur@bigpond.com

Biology Unit
Alan Hanks
34 Seaton Dr.
Aurora, ON, L4G 2K1
CANADA
Ph: (905) 727-6993

Bird Stamp Society
Graham Horsman
23 A East Main Street
Blackburn West Lothian
Scotland, EH47 7QR
UNITED KINGDOM
www.bird-stamps.org/bss
E-mail: graham_horsman7@msn.com

Canadiana Study Unit
John Peebles
P.O. Box 3262, Station ìBî
London, ON, N6A 4K3
CANADA
E-mail: c.s.u@sympatico.ca

Captain Cook Study Unit
Brian P. Sandford
173 Minuteman Dr.
Concord MA 01742-1923
www.captaincooksociety.com
E-mail: US@captaincooksociety.com

Casey Jones Railroad Unit
Dr. Roy Menninger
85 SW Pepper Tree Lane
Topeka KS 66611-2072
www.uqp.de/cjr/index.htm
E-mail: roymenn@sbcglobal.net

Cats on Stamps Study Unit
Mary Ann Brown
3006 Wade Rd.
Durham NC 27705
www.catsonstamps.org
E-mail: mabrown@nc.rr.com

Chemistry & Physics on Stamps Study Unit
Dr. Roland Hirsch
20458 Water Point Lane
Germantown MD 20874
www.cpossu.org
E-mail: rfhirsch@cpossu.org

Chess on Stamps Study Unit
Ray C. Alexis
608 Emery St.
Longmont CO 80501
E-mail: chessstuff911459@aol.

Christmas Philatelic Club
Linda Lawrence
312 Northwood Drive
Lexington KY 40505
www.web.295.ca/cpc/
E-mail: stamplinda@aol.com

Christopher Columbus Philatelic Society
Donald R. Ager
P.O. Box 71
Hillsboro NH 03244-0071
ccps.maphist.nl/
Ph: (603) 464-5379
E-mail: meganddon@tds.net

Collectors of Religion on Stamps
Verna Shackleton
425 North Linwood Avenue #110
Appleton WI 54914
www://my.vbe.com/~cmfourl/coros1.htm
E-mail: corosec@sbcglobal.net

Dogs on Stamps Study Unit
Morris Raskin
202A Newport Rd.
Monroe Township NJ 08831
Ph: (609) 655-7411
www.dossu.org
E-mail: mraskin@cellurian.com

Earth's Physical Features Study Group
Fred Klein
515 Magdalena Ave.
Los Altos CA 94024
epfsu.jeffhayward.com

Ebony Society of Philatelic Events and Reflections, Inc (African-American topicals)
Manuel Gilyard
800 Riverside Drive, Ste 4H
New York NY 10032-7412
www.esperstamps.org
E-mail: gilyardmani@aol.com

Europa Study Unit
Donald W. Smith
P.O. Box 576
Johnstown PA 15907-0576
www.europastudyunit.org/
E-mail: eunity@aol.com or donsmith65@msn.com

Fine & Performing Arts
Deborah L. Washington
6922 So. Jeffery Boulevard
#7 - North
Chicago IL 60649
E-mail: brasslady@comcast.net

Fire Service in Philately
Brian R. Engler, Sr.
726 1/2 W. Tilghman St.
Allentown PA 18102-2324
Ph: (610) 433-2782
www.firestamps.com

Gay & Lesbian History on Stamps Club
Joe Petronie
P.O. Box 190842
Dallas TX 75219-0842
www.glhsc.org
E-mail: glhsc@aol.com

Gems, Minerals & Jewelry Study Unit
George Young
P.O. Box 632
Tewksbury MA 01876-0632
Ph: (978) 851-8283
www.rockhounds.com/rockshop/gmjsuapp.txt
E-mail: george-young@msn.com

Graphics Philately Association
Mark H Winnegrad
P.O. Box 380
Bronx NY 10462-0380
www.graphics-stamps.org
E-mail: indybruce1@yahoo.com

Journalists, Authors & Poets on Stamps
Ms. Lee Straayer
P.O. Box 6808
Champaign IL 61826
E-mail: lstraayer@dcbnet.com

Lighthouse Stamp Society
Dalene Thomas
8612 West Warren Lane
Lakewood CO 80227-2352
Ph: (303) 986-6620
www.lighthousestampsociety.org
E-mail: dalene@lighthousestampsociety.org

Lions International Stamp Club
John Bargus
108-2777 Barry Rd. RR 2
Mill Bay, BC, V0R 2P2
CANADA
Ph: (250) 743-5782

Mahatma Gandhi On Stamps Study Circle
Pramod Shivagunde
Pratik Clinic, Akluj
Solapur, Maharashtra, 413101
INDIA
E-mail: drnanda@bom6.vsnl.net.in

Mask Study Unit
Carolyn Weber
1220 Johnson Drive, Villa 104
Ventura CA 93003-0540
E-mail: cweber@venturalink.net

Masonic Study Unit
Stanley R. Longenecker
930 Wood St.
Mount Joy PA 17552-1926
Ph: (717) 669-9094
E-mail: natsco@usa.net

Mathematical Study Unit
Estelle Buccino
5615 Glenwood Rd.
Bethesda MD 20817-6727
Ph: (301) 718-8898
www.math.ttu.edu/msu/
E-mail: montystrauss@gmail.com

Medical Subjects Unit
Dr. Frederick C. Skvara
P.O. Box 6228
Bridgewater NJ 08807
E-mail: fcskvara@optonline.net

Military Postal History Society
Ed Dubin
One South Wacker Drive, Suite 3500
Chicago IL 60606
www.militaryPHS.org
E-mail: dubine@comcast.net

Mourning Stamps and Covers Club
James Bailey, Jr.
P.O. Box 937
Brownwood TX 76804
E-mail: jfbailey238@earthlink.net

Napoleonic Age Philatelists
Ken Berry
7513 Clayton Dr.
Oklahoma City OK 73132-5636
Ph: (405) 721-0044
www.nap-stamps.org
E-mail: krb2@earthlink.net

Old World Archeological Study Unit
Caroline Scannel
11 Dawn Drive
Smithtown NY 11787-1761
www.owasu.org
E-mail: editor@owasu.org

Petroleum Philatelic Society International
Dr. Chris Coggins
174 Old Bedford Road
Luton, England, LU2 7HW
UNITED KINGDOM
E-mail: WAMTECH@Luton174.fsnet.co.uk

Philatelic Computing Study Group
Robert de Violini
P.O. Box 5025
Oxnard CA 93031-5025
www.pcsg.org
E-mail: dviolini@adelphia.net

Philatelic Lepidopterists' Association
Alan Hanks
34 Seaton Dr.
Aurora, ON, L4G 2K1
CANADA
Ph: (905) 727-6933
E-mail: alan.hanks@sympatico.ca

Rotary on Stamps Unit
Gerald L. Fitzsimmons
105 Calla Ricardo
Victoria TX 77904
rotaryonstamps.org
E-mail: glfitz@suddenlink.net

Scouts on Stamps Society International
Lawrence Clay
P.O. Box 6228
Kennewick WA 99336
Ph: (509) 735-3731
www.sossi.org
E-mail: lclay3731@charter.net

Ships on Stamps Unit
Les Smith
302 Conklin Avenue
Penticton, BC, V2A 2T4
CANADA
Ph: (250) 493-7486
www.shipsonstamps.org
E-mail: lessmith440@shaw.ca

Space Unit
Carmine Torrisi
P.O. Box 780241
Maspeth NY 11378
Ph: (917) 620-5687
stargate.1usa.com/stamps/
E-mail: ctorrisi1@nyc.rr.com

Sports Philatelists International
Margaret Jones
705 S Laclede Station Rd S, Apt 163.
St. Louis MO 63119-4969
www.sportstamps.org

Stamps on Stamps Collectors Club
Alf Jordan
156 West Elm Street
Yarmouth ME 04096
www.stampsonstamps.org
E-mail: ajordan1@maine.rr.com

Windmill Study Unit
Walter J. Hollien
P.O. Box 346
Long Valley NJ 07853-0346
Ph: (862) 812-0030
E-mail: whollien@earthlink.net

Wine On Stamps Study Unit
Bruce L. Johnson
115 Raintree Drive
Zionsville IN 46077
www.wine-on-stamps.org
E-mail: indybruce@yahoo.com

Women on Stamps Study Unit
Hugh Gottfried
2232 26th St.
Santa Monica CA 90405-1902
E-mail: hgottfried@adelphia.net

Zeppelin Collectors Club
Cheryl Ganz
P.O. Box 77196
Washington DC 20013
www.americanairmailsociety.org

Expertizing Services

The following organizations will, for a fee, provide expert opinions about stamps submitted to them. Collectors should contact these organizations to find out about their fees and requirements before sub-miting philatelic material to them. The listing of these groups here is not intended as an endorsement by Scott Publishing Co.

General Expertizing Services

American Philatelic Expertizing
Service (a service of the
American Philatelic Society)
100 Match Factory Place
Bellefonte PA 16823-1367
Ph: (814) 237-3803
Fax: (814) 237-6128
www.stamps.org
E-mail: ambristo@stamps.org
Areas of Expertise: Worldwide

B. P. A. Expertising, Ltd.
P.O. Box 137
Leatherhead, Surrey, KT22 0RG
UNITED KINGDOM
E-mail: sec.bpa@tcom.co.uk
Areas of Expertise: British
Commonwealth, Great Britain,
Classics of Europe, South America and
the Far East

Philatelic Foundation
70 West 40th St., 15th Floor
New York NY 10018
Ph: (212) 221-6555
Fax: (212) 221-6208
www.philatelicfoundation.org
E-mail:philatelicfoundation@verizon.net
Areas of Expertise: U.S. & Worldwide

Philatelic Stamp Authentication
and Grading, Inc.
P.O. Box 56-2111
Miami FL 33256-2111
Customer Service: (305) 345-9864
www.stampauthentication.com
E-mail: info@stampauthentication.com

Professional Stamp Experts
P.O. Box 6170
Newport Beach CA 92658
Ph: (877) STAMP-88
Fax: (949) 833-7955
www.collectors.com/pse
E-mail: pseinfo@collectors.com
Areas of Expertise: Stamps and
covers of U.S., U.S. Possessions,
British Commonwealth

Royal Philatelic Society Expert
Committee
41 Devonshire Place
London, W1N 1PE
UNITED KINGDOM
www.rpsl.org.uk/experts.html
E-mail: experts@rpsl.org.uk
Areas of Expertise: All

Expertizing Services Covering Specific Fields Or Countries

China Stamp Society Expertizing
Service
1050 West Blue Ridge Blvd
Kansas City MO 64145
Ph: (816) 942-6300
E-mail: hjmesq@aol.com
Areas of Expertise: China

Confederate Stamp Alliance
Authentication Service
Gen. Frank Crown, Jr.
P.O. Box 278
Capshaw AL 35742-0396
Ph: (302) 422-2656
Fax: (302) 424-1990
www.csalliance.org
E-mail: csaas@knology.net
Areas of Expertise: Confederate stamps
and postal history

Errors, Freaks and Oddities
Collectors Club
Expertizing Service
138 East Lakemont Dr.
Kingsland GA 31548
Ph: (912) 729-1573
Areas of Expertise: U.S. errors, freaks
and oddities

Estonian Philatelic Society
Expertizing Service
39 Clafford Lane
Melville NY 11747
Ph: (516) 421-2078
E-mail: esto4@aol.com
Areas of Expertise: Estonia

Hawaiian Philatelic Society
Expertizing Service
P.O. Box 10115
Honolulu HI 96816-0115
Areas of Expertise: Hawaii

Hong Kong Stamp Society
Expertizing Service
P.O. Box 206
Glenside PA 19038
Fax: (215) 576-6850
Areas of Expertise: Hong Kong

International Association of
Philatelic Experts
United States Associate members:

Paul Buchsbayew
119 W. 57th St.
New York NY 10019
Ph: (212) 977-7734
Fax: (212) 977-8653
Areas of Expertise: Russia, Soviet
Union

William T. Crowe
P.O. Box 2090
Danbury CT 06813-2090
E-mail: wtcrowe@aol.com
Areas of Expertise: United States

John Lievsay
(see American Philatelic Expertizing
Service and Philatelic Foundation)
Areas of Expertise: France

Robert W. Lyman
P.O. Box 348
Irvington on Hudson NY 10533
Ph and Fax: (914) 591-6937
Areas of Expertise: British North
America, New Zealand

Robert Odenweller
P.O. Box 401
Bernardsville NJ 07924-0401
Ph and Fax: (908) 766-5460
Areas of Expertise: New Zealand,
Samoa to 1900

Sergio Sismondo
10035 Carousel Center Dr.
Syracuse NY 13290-0001
Ph: (315) 422-2331
Fax: (315) 422-2956
Areas of Expertise: British East
Africa, Camerouns,
Cape of Good Hope, Canada, British
North America

International Society for Japanese
Philately Expertizing Committee
132 North Pine Terrace
Staten Island NY 10312-4052
Ph: (718) 227-5229
Areas of Expertise: Japan and
related areas, except WWII Japanese
Occupation issues

International Society for
Portuguese Philately
Expertizing Service
P.O. Box 43146
Philadelphia PA 19129-3146
Ph: (215) 843-2106
Fax: (215) 843-2106
E-mail: s.s.washburne@worldnet.
att.net
Areas of Expertise: Portugal and
Colonies

Mexico-Elmhurst Philatelic
Society International Expert
Committee
P.O. Box 1133
West Covina CA 91793
Areas of Expertise: Mexico

Ukrainian Philatelic &
Numismatic Society
Expertizing Service
30552 Dell Lane
Warren MI 48092-1862
Areas of Expertise: Ukraine, Western
Ukraine

V. G. Greene Philatelic Research
Foundation
P.O. Box 204, Station Q
Toronto, ON, M4T 2M1
CANADA
Ph: (416) 921-2073
Fax: (416) 921-1282
E-mail: vggfoundation@on.aibn.com
www.greenefoundation.ca
Areas of Expertise: British North
America

Information on Catalogue Values, Grade and Condition

Catalogue Value

The Scott Catalogue value is a retail value; that is, an amount you could expect to pay for a stamp in the grade of Very Fine with no faults. Any exceptions to the grade valued will be noted in the text. The general introduction on the following pages and the individual section introductions further explain the type of material that is valued. The value listed for any given stamp is a reference that reflects recent actual dealer selling prices for that item.

Dealer retail price lists, public auction results, published prices in advertising and individual solicitation of retail prices from dealers, collectors and specialty organizations have been used in establishing the values found in this catalogue. Scott Publishing Co. values stamps, but Scott is not a company engaged in the business of buying and selling stamps as a dealer.

Use this catalogue as a guide for buying and selling. The actual price you pay for a stamp may be higher or lower than the catalogue value because of many different factors, including the amount of personal service a dealer offers, or increased or decreased interest in the country or topic represented by a stamp or set. An item may occasionally be offered at a lower price as a "loss leader," or as part of a special sale. You also may obtain an item inexpensively at public auction because of little interest at that time or as part of a large lot.

Stamps that are of a lesser grade than Very Fine, or those with condition problems, generally trade at lower prices than those given in this catalogue. Stamps of exceptional quality in both grade and condition often command higher prices than those listed.

Values for pre-1900 unused issues are for stamps with approximately half or more of their original gum. Stamps with most or all of their original gum may be expected to sell for more, and stamps with less than half of their original gum may be expected to sell for somewhat less than the values listed. On rarer stamps, it may be expected that the original gum will be somewhat more disturbed than it will be on more common issues. Post-1900 unused issues are assumed to have full original gum. From breakpoints in most countries' listings, stamps are valued as never hinged, due to the wide availability of stamps in that condition. These notations are prominently placed in the listings and in the country information preceding the listings. Some countries also feature listings with dual values for hinged and never-hinged stamps.

Grade

A stamp's grade and condition are crucial to its value. The accompanying illustrations show examples of Very Fine stamps from different time periods, along with examples of stamps in Fine to Very Fine and Extremely Fine grades as points of reference. When a stamp seller offers a stamp in any grade from fine to superb without further qualifying statements, that stamp should not only have the centering grade as defined, but it also should be free of faults or other condition problems.

FINE stamps (illustrations not shown) have designs that are quite off center, with the perforations on one or two sides very close to the design but not quite touching it. There is white space between the perforations and the design that is minimal but evident to the unaided eye. Imperforate stamps may have small margins, and earlier issues may show the design just touching one edge of the stamp design. Very early perforated issues normally will have the perforations slightly cutting into the design. Used stamps may have heavier than usual cancellations.

FINE-VERY FINE stamps will be somewhat off center on one side, or slightly off center on two sides. Imperforate stamps will have two margins of at least normal size, and the design will not touch any edge. For perforated stamps, the perfs are well clear of the design, but are still noticeably off center. *However, early issues of a country may be printed in such a way that the design naturally is very close to the edges. In these cases, the perforations may cut*

into the design very slightly. Used stamps will not have a cancellation that detracts from the design.

VERY FINE stamps will be just slightly off center on one or two sides, but the design will be well clear of the edge. The stamp will present a nice, balanced appearance. Imperforate stamps will be well centered within normal-sized margins. *However, early issues of many countries may be printed in such a way that the perforations may touch the design on one or more sides. Where this is the case, a boxed note will be found defining the centering and margins of the stamps being valued.* Used stamps will have light or otherwise neat cancellations. This is the grade used to establish Scott Catalogue values.

EXTREMELY FINE stamps are close to being perfectly centered. Imperforate stamps will have even margins that are slightly larger than normal. Even the earliest perforated issues will have perforations clear of the design on all sides.

Scott Publishing Co. recognizes that there is no formally enforced grading scheme for postage stamps, and that the final price you pay or obtain for a stamp will be determined by individual agreement at the time of transaction.

Condition

Grade addresses only centering and (for used stamps) cancellation. *Condition* refers to factors other than grade that affect a stamp's desirability.

Factors that can increase the value of a stamp include exceptionally wide margins, particularly fresh color, the presence of selvage, and plate or die varieties. Unusual cancels on used stamps (particularly those of the 19th century) can greatly enhance their value as well.

Factors other than faults that decrease the value of a stamp include loss of original gum, regumming, a hinge remnant or foreign object adhering to the gum, natural inclusions, straight edges, and markings or notations applied by collectors or dealers.

Faults include missing pieces, tears, pin or other holes, surface scuffs, thin spots, creases, toning, short or pulled perforations, clipped perforations, oxidation or other forms of color changelings, soiling, stains, and such man-made changes as reperforations or the chemical removal or lightening of a cancellation.

Grading Illustrations

On the following two pages are illustrations of various stamps from countries appearing in this volume. These stamps are arranged by country, and they represent early or important issues that are often found in widely different grades in the marketplace. The editors believe the illustrations will prove useful in showing the margin size and centering that will be seen on the various issues.

In addition to the matters of margin size and centering, collectors are reminded that the very fine stamps valued in the Scott catalogues also will possess fresh color and intact perforations, and they will be free from defects.

Examples shown are computer-manipulated images made from single digitized master illustrations.

Stamp Illustrations Used in the Catalogue

It is important to note that the stamp images used for identification purposes in this catalogue may not be indicative of the grade of stamp being valued. Refer to the written discussion of grades on this page and to the grading illustrations on the following two pages for grading information.

Fine-Very Fine →

SCOTT
CATALOGUES
VALUE
STAMPS IN
THIS GRADE

Very Fine →

Extremely Fine →

Fine-Very Fine →

SCOTT
CATALOGUES
VALUE
STAMPS IN
THIS GRADE

Very Fine →

Extremely Fine →

For purposes of helping to determine the gum condition and value of an unused stamp, Scott Publishing Co. presents the following chart which details different gum conditions and indicates how the conditions correlate with the Scott values for unused stamps. Used together, the Illustrated Grading Chart on the previous pages and this Illustrated Gum Chart should allow catalogue users to better understand the grade and gum condition of stamps valued in the Scott catalogues.

Gum Categories:	MINT N.H.	ORIGINAL GUM (O.G.)				NO GUM
	Mint Never Hinged *Free from any disturbance*	**Lightly Hinged** *Faint impression of a removed hinge over a small area*	**Hinge Mark or Remnant** *Prominent hinged spot with part or all of the hinge remaining*	**Large part o.g.** *Approximately half or more of the gum intact*	**Small part o.g.** *Approximately less than half of the gum intact*	**No gum** *Only if issued with gum*
Commonly Used Symbol:	★★	★	★	★	★	(★)
Pre-1900 Issues (Pre-1881 for U.S.)	*Very fine pre-1900 stamps in these categories trade at a premium over Scott value*			Scott Value for "Unused"		Scott "No Gum" listings for selected unused classic stamps
From 1900 to breakpoints for listings of never-hinged stamps	Scott "Never Hinged" listings for selected unused stamps	Scott Value for "Unused" (Actual value will be affected by the degree of hinging of the full o.g.)				
From breakpoints noted for many countries	Scott Value for "Unused"					

Never Hinged (NH; ★★): A never-hinged stamp will have full original gum that will have no hinge mark or disturbance. The presence of an expertizer's mark does not disqualify a stamp from this designation.

Original Gum (OG; ★): Pre-1900 stamps should have approximately half or more of their original gum. On rarer stamps, it may be expected that the original gum will be somewhat more disturbed than it will be on more common issues. Post-1900 stamps should have full original gum. Original gum will show some disturbance caused by a previous hinge(s) which may be present or entirely removed. The actual value of a post-1900 stamp will be affected by the degree of hinging of the full original gum.

Disturbed Original Gum: Gum showing noticeable effects of humidity, climate or hinging over more than half of the gum. The significance of gum disturbance in valuing a stamp in any of the Original Gum categories depends on the degree of disturbance, the rarity and normal gum condition of the issue and other variables affecting quality.

Regummed (RG; (★)): A regummed stamp is a stamp without gum that has had some type of gum privately applied at a time after it was issued. This normally is done to deceive collectors and/or dealers into thinking that the stamp has original gum and therefore has a higher value. A regummed stamp is considered the same as a stamp with none of its original gum for purposes of grading.

Understanding the Listings

On the opposite page is an enlarged "typical" listing from this catalogue. Below are detailed explanations of each of the highlighted parts of the listing.

① Scott number — Scott catalogue numbers are used to identify specific items when buying, selling or trading stamps. Each listed postage stamp from every country has a unique Scott catalogue number. Therefore, Germany Scott 99, for example, can only refer to a single stamp. Although the Scott catalogue usually lists stamps in chronological order by date of issue, there are exceptions. When a country has issued a set of stamps over a period of time, those stamps within the set are kept together without regard to date of issue. This follows the normal collecting approach of keeping stamps in their natural sets.

When a country issues a set of stamps over a period of time, a group of consecutive catalogue numbers is reserved for the stamps in that set, as issued. If that group of numbers proves to be too few, capital-letter suffixes, such as "A" or "B," may be added to existing numbers to create enough catalogue numbers to cover all items in the set. A capital-letter suffix indicates a major Scott catalogue number listing. Scott generally uses a suffix letter only once. Therefore, a catalogue number listing with a capital-letter suffix will seldom be found with the same letter (lower case) used as a minor-letter listing. If there is a Scott 16A in a set, for example, there will seldom be a Scott 16a. However, a minor-letter "a" listing may be added to a major number containing an "A" suffix (Scott 16Aa, for example).

Suffix letters are cumulative. A minor "b" variety of Scott 16A would be Scott 16Ab, not Scott 16b.

There are times when a reserved block of Scott catalogue numbers is too large for a set, leaving some numbers unused. Such gaps in the numbering sequence also occur when the catalogue editors move an item's listing elsewhere or have removed it entirely from the catalogue. Scott does not attempt to account for every possible number, but rather attempts to assure that each stamp is assigned its own number.

Scott numbers designating regular postage normally are only numerals. Scott numbers for other types of stamps, such as air post, semipostal, postal tax, postage due, occupation and others have a prefix consisting of one or more capital letters or a combination of numerals and capital letters.

② Illustration number — Illustration or design-type numbers are used to identify each catalogue illustration. For most sets, the lowest face-value stamp is shown. It then serves as an example of the basic design approach for other stamps not illustrated. Where more than one stamp use the same illustration number, but have differences in design, the design paragraph or the description line clearly indicates the design on each stamp not illustrated. Where there are both vertical and horizontal designs in a set, a single illustration may be used, with the exceptions noted in the design paragraph or description line.

When an illustration is followed by a lower-case letter in parentheses, such as "A2(b)," the trailing letter indicates which overprint or surcharge illustration applies.

Illustrations normally are 70 percent of the original size of the stamp. Oversized stamps, blocks and souvenir sheets are reduced even more. Overprints and surcharges are shown at 100 percent of their original size if shown alone, but are 70 percent of original size if shown on stamps. In some cases, the illustration will be placed above the set, between listings or omitted completely. Overprint and surcharge illustrations are not placed in this catalogue for purposes of expertizing stamps.

③ Paper color — The color of a stamp's paper is noted in italic type when the paper used is not white.

④ Listing styles — There are two principal types of catalogue listings: major and minor.

Major listings are in a larger type style than minor listings. The catalogue number is a numeral that can be found with or without a capital-letter suffix, and with or without a prefix.

Minor listings are in a smaller type style and have a small-letter suffix or (if the listing immediately follows that of the major number) may show only the letter. These listings identify a variety of the major item. Examples include perforation and shade differences, multiples (some

souvenir sheets, booklet panes and se-tenant combinations), and singles of multiples.

Examples of major number listings include 16, 28A, B97, C13A, 10N5, and 10N6A. Examples of minor numbers are 16a and C13Ab.

⑤ Basic information about a stamp or set — Introducing each stamp issue is a small section (usually a line listing) of basic information about a stamp or set. This section normally includes the date of issue, method of printing, perforation, watermark and, sometimes, some additional information of note. *Printing method, perforation and watermark apply to the following sets until a change is noted.* Stamps created by overprinting or surcharging previous issues are assumed to have the same perforation, watermark, printing method and other production characteristics as the original. Dates of issue are as precise as Scott is able to confirm and often reflect the dates on first-day covers, rather than the actual date of release.

⑥ Denomination — This normally refers to the face value of the stamp; that is, the cost of the unused stamp at the post office at the time of issue. When a denomination is shown in parentheses, it does not appear on the stamp. This includes the non-denominated stamps of the United States, Brazil and Great Britain, for example.

⑦ Color or other description — This area provides information to solidify identification of a stamp. In many recent cases, a description of the stamp design appears in this space, rather than a listing of colors.

⑧ Year of issue — In stamp sets that have been released in a period that spans more than a year, the number shown in parentheses is the year that stamp first appeared. Stamps without a date appeared during the first year of the issue. Dates are not always given for minor varieties.

⑨ Value unused and Value used — The Scott catalogue values are based on stamps that are in a grade of Very Fine unless stated otherwise. Unused values refer to items that have not seen postal, revenue or any other duty for which they were intended. Pre-1900 unused stamps that were issued with gum must have at least most of their original gum. Later issues are assumed to have full original gum. From breakpoints specified in most countries' listings, stamps are valued as never hinged. Stamps issued without gum are noted. Modern issues with PVA or other synthetic adhesives may appear ungummed. Unused self-adhesive stamps are valued as appearing undisturbed on their original backing paper. Values for used self-adhesive stamps are for examples either on piece or off piece. For a more detailed explanation of these values, please see the "Catalogue Value," "Condition" and "Understanding Valuing Notations" sections elsewhere in this introduction.

In some cases, where used stamps are more valuable than unused stamps, the value is for an example with a contemporaneous cancel, rather than a modern cancel or a smudge or other unclear marking. For those stamps that were released for postal and fiscal purposes, the used value represents a postally used stamp. Stamps with revenue cancels generally sell for less.

Stamps separated from a complete se-tenant multiple usually will be worth less than a pro-rated portion of the se-tenant multiple, and stamps lacking the attached labels that are noted in the listings will be worth less than the values shown.

⑩ Changes in basic set information — Bold type is used to show any changes in the basic data given for a set of stamps. These basic data categories include perforation gauge measurement, paper type, printing method and watermark.

⑪ Total value of a set — The total value of sets of three or more stamps issued after 1900 are shown. The set line also notes the range of Scott numbers and total number of stamps included in the grouping. The actual value of a set consisting predominantly of stamps having the minimum value of twenty cents may be less than the total value shown. Similary, the actual value or catalogue value of se-tenant pairs or of blocks consisting of stamps having the minimum value of twenty cents may be less than the catalogue values of the component parts.

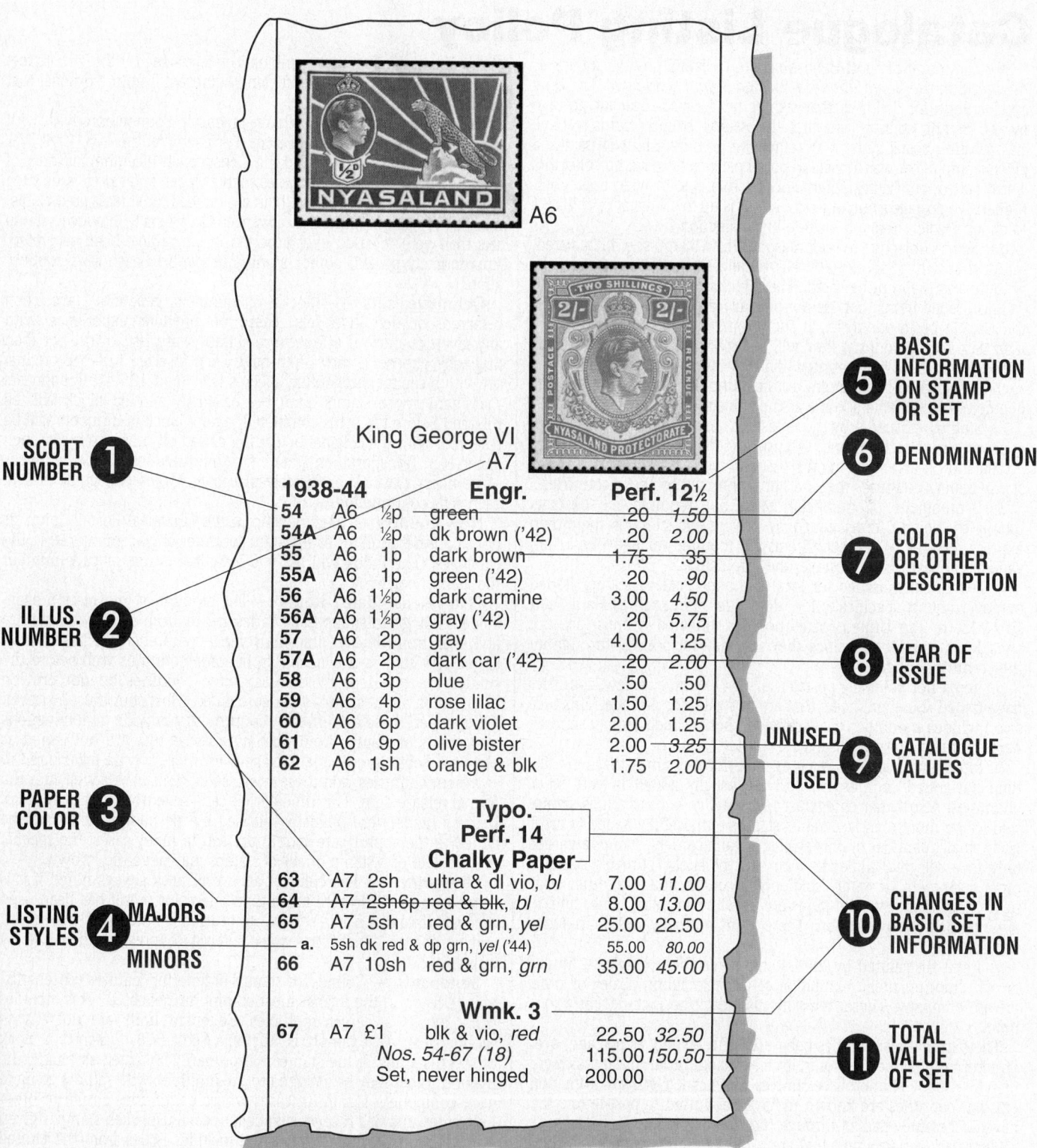

SCOTT NUMBER **1**

ILLUS. NUMBER **2**

PAPER COLOR **3**

LISTING STYLES **4** MAJORS

MINORS

A6

King George VI
A7

5 BASIC INFORMATION ON STAMP OR SET

6 DENOMINATION

7 COLOR OR OTHER DESCRIPTION

8 YEAR OF ISSUE

9 CATALOGUE VALUES

UNUSED

USED

1938-44 **Engr.** **Perf. 12½**

Scott	Illus	Denom	Description	Unused	Used
54	A6	½p	green	.20	1.50
54A	A6	½p	dk brown ('42)	.20	2.00
55	A6	1p	dark brown	1.75	.35
55A	A6	1p	green ('42)	.20	.90
56	A6	1½p	dark carmine	3.00	4.50
56A	A6	1½p	gray ('42)	.20	5.75
57	A6	2p	gray	4.00	1.25
57A	A6	2p	dark car ('42)	.20	2.00
58	A6	3p	blue	.50	.50
59	A6	4p	rose lilac	1.50	1.25
60	A6	6p	dark violet	2.00	1.25
61	A6	9p	olive bister	2.00	3.25
62	A6	1sh	orange & blk	1.75	2.00

Typo.
Perf. 14
Chalky Paper

Scott	Illus	Denom	Description	Unused	Used
63	A7	2sh	ultra & dl vio, *bl*	7.00	11.00
64	A7	2sh6p	red & blk, *bl*	8.00	13.00
65	A7	5sh	red & grn, *yel*	25.00	22.50
a.			5sh dk red & dp grn, *yel* ('44)	55.00	80.00
66	A7	10sh	red & grn, *grn*	35.00	45.00

Wmk. 3

Scott	Illus	Denom	Description	Unused	Used
67	A7	£1	blk & vio, *red*	22.50	32.50
			Nos. 54-67 (18)	115.00	150.50
			Set, never hinged	200.00	

10 CHANGES IN BASIC SET INFORMATION

11 TOTAL VALUE OF SET

Catalogue Listing Policy

It is the intent of Scott Publishing Co. to list all postage stamps of the world in the *Scott Standard Postage Stamp Catalogue*. The only strict criteria for listing is that stamps be decreed legal for postage by the issuing country and that the issuing country actually have an operating postal system. Whether the primary intent of issuing a given stamp or set was for sale to postal patrons or to stamp collectors is not part of our listing criteria. Scott's role is to provide basic comprehensive postage stamp information. It is up to each stamp collector to choose which items to include in a collection.

It is Scott's objective to seek reasons why a stamp should be listed, rather than why it should not. Nevertheless, there are certain types of items that will not be listed. These include the following:

1. Unissued items that are not officially distributed or released by the issuing postal authority. If such items are officially issued at a later date by the country, they will be listed. Unissued items consist of those that have been printed and then held from sale for reasons such as change in government, errors found on stamps or something deemed objectionable about a stamp subject or design.

2. Stamps "issued" by non-existent postal entities or fantasy countries, such as Nagaland, Occusi-Ambeno, Staffa, Sedang, Torres Straits and others. Also, stamps "issued" in the names of legitimate, stamp-issuing countries that are not authorized by those countries.

3. Semi-official or unofficial items not required for postage. Examples include items issued by private agencies for their own express services. When such items are required for delivery, or are valid as prepayment of postage, they are listed.

4. Local stamps issued for local use only. Postage stamps issued by governments specifically for "domestic" use, such as Haiti Scott 219-228, or the United States non-denominated stamps, are not considered to be locals, since they are valid for postage throughout the country of origin.

5. Items not valid for postal use. For example, a few countries have issued souvenir sheets that are not valid for postage. This area also includes a number of worldwide charity labels (some denominated) that do not pay postage.

6. Intentional varieties, such as imperforate stamps that look like their perforated counterparts and are usually issued in very small quantities. Also, other egregiously exploitative issues such as stamps sold for far more than face value, stamps purposefully issued in artificially small quantities or only against advance orders, stamps awarded only to a selected audience such as a philatelic bureau's standing order customers, or stamps sold only in conjunction with other products. All of these kinds of items are usually controlled issues and/or are intended for speculation. These items normally will be included in a footnote.

7. Items distributed by the issuing government only to a limited group, club, philatelic exhibition or a single stamp dealer or other private company. These items normally will be included in a footnote.

The fact that a stamp has been used successfully as postage, even on international mail, is not in itself sufficient proof that it was legitimately issued. Numerous examples of so-called stamps from non-existent countries are known to have been used to post letters that have successfully passed through the international mail system.

There are certain items that are subject to interpretation. When a stamp falls outside our specifications, it may be listed along with a cautionary footnote.

A number of factors are considered in our approach to analyzing how a stamp is listed. The following list of factors is presented to share with you, the catalogue user, the complexity of the listing process.

Additional printings — "Additional printings" of a previously issued stamp may range from an item that is totally different to cases where it is impossible to differentiate from the original. At least a minor number (a small-letter suffix) is assigned if there is a distinct change in stamp shade, noticeably redrawn design, or a significantly different perforation measurement. A major number (numeral or numeral and capital-letter combination) is assigned if the editors feel the "additional printing" is sufficiently different from the original that it constitutes a different issue.

Commemoratives — Where practical, commemoratives with the same theme are placed in a set. For example, the U.S. Civil War Centennial set of 1961-65 and the Constitution Bicentennial series of 1989-90 appear as sets. Countries such as Japan and Korea issue such material on a regular basis, with an announced, or at least predictable, number of stamps known in advance. Occasionally, however, stamp sets that were released over a period of years have been separated. Appropriately placed footnotes will guide you to each set's continuation.

Definitive sets — Blocks of numbers generally have been reserved for definitive sets, based on previous experience with any given country. If a few more stamps were issued in a set than originally expected, they often have been inserted into the original set with a capital-letter suffix, such as U.S. Scott 1059A. If it appears that many more stamps than the originally allotted block will be released before the set is completed, a new block of numbers will be reserved, with the original one being closed off. In some cases, such as the U.S. Transportation and Great Americans series, several blocks of numbers exist. Appropriately placed footnotes will guide you to each set's continuation.

New country — Membership in the Universal Postal Union is not a consideration for listing status or order of placement within the catalogue. The index will tell you in what volume or page number the listings begin.

"No release date" items — The amount of information available for any given stamp issue varies greatly from country to country and even from time to time. Extremely comprehensive information about new stamps is available from some countries well before the stamps are released. By contrast some countries do not provide information about stamps or release dates. Most countries, however, fall between these extremes. A country may provide denominations or subjects of stamps from upcoming issues that are not issued as planned. Sometimes, philatelic agencies, those private firms hired to represent countries, add these later-issued items to sets well after the formal release date. This time period can range from weeks to years. If these items were officially released by the country, they will be added to the appropriate spot in the set. In many cases, the specific release date of a stamp or set of stamps may never be known.

Overprints — The color of an overprint is always noted if it is other than black. Where more than one color of ink has been used on overprints of a single set, the color used is noted. Early overprint and surcharge illustrations were altered to prevent their use by forgers.

Se-tenants — Connected stamps of differing features (se-tenants) will be listed in the format most commonly collected. This includes pairs, blocks or larger multiples. Se-tenant units are not always symmetrical. An example is Australia Scott 508, which is a block of seven stamps. If the stamps are primarily collected as a unit, the major number may be assigned to the multiple, with minors going to each component stamp. In cases where continuous-design or other unit se-tenants will receive significant postal use, each stamp is given a major Scott number listing. This includes issues from the United States, Canada, Germany and Great Britain, for example.

Special Notices

Classification of stamps

The *Scott Standard Postage Stamp Catalogue* lists stamps by country of issue. The next level of organization is a listing by section on the basis of the function of the stamps. The principal sections cover regular postage, semi-postal, air post, special delivery, registration, postage due and other categories. Except for regular postage, catalogue numbers for all sections include a prefix letter (or number-letter combination) denoting the class to which a given stamp belongs. When some countries issue sets containing stamps from more than one category, the catalogue will at times list all of the stamps in one category (such as air post stamps listed as part of a postage set).

The following is a listing of the most commonly used catalogue prefixes.

Prefix...	Category
C	Air Post
M	Military
P	Newspaper
N	Occupation - Regular Issues
O	Official
Q	Parcel Post
J	Postage Due
RA	Postal Tax
B	Semi-Postal
E	Special Delivery
MR	War Tax

Other prefixes used by more than one country include the following:

H	Acknowledgment of Receipt
I	Late Fee
CO	Air Post Official
CQ	Air Post Parcel Post
RAC	Air Post Postal Tax
CF	Air Post Registration
CB	Air Post Semi-Postal
CBO	Air Post Semi-Postal Official
CE	Air Post Special Delivery
EY	Authorized Delivery
S	Franchise
G	Insured Letter
GY	Marine Insurance
MC	Military Air Post
MQ	Military Parcel Post
NC	Occupation - Air Post
NO	Occupation - Official
NJ	Occupation - Postage Due
NRA	Occupation - Postal Tax
NB	Occupation - Semi-Postal
NE	Occupation - Special Delivery
QY	Parcel Post Authorized Delivery
AR	Postal-fiscal
RAJ	Postal Tax Due
RAB	Postal Tax Semi-Postal
F	Registration
EB	Semi-Postal Special Delivery
EO	Special Delivery Official
QE	Special Handling

New issue listings

Updates to this catalogue appear each month in the *Scott Stamp Monthly* magazine. Included in this update are additions to the listings of countries found in the *Scott Standard Postage Stamp Catalogue* and the *Specialized Catalogue of United States Stamps*, as well as corrections and updates to current editions of this catalogue.

From time to time there will be changes in the final listings of stamps from the *Scott Stamp Monthly* to the next edition of the catalogue. This occurs as more information about certain stamps or sets becomes available.

The catalogue update section of the *Scott Stamp Monthly* is the most timely presentation of this material available. Annual subscriptions to the *Scott Stamp Monthly* are available from Scott Publishing Co., Box 828, Sidney, OH 45365-0828.

Number additions, deletions & changes

A listing of catalogue number additions, deletions and changes from the previous edition of the catalogue appears in each volume. See Catalogue Number Additions, Deletions & Changes in the table of contents for the location of this list.

Understanding valuing notations

The *minimum catalogue value* of an individual stamp or set is 20 cents. This represents a portion of the cost incurred by a dealer when he prepares an individual stamp for resale. As a point of philatelic-economic fact, the lower the value shown for an item in this catalogue, the greater the percentage of that value is attributed to dealer mark up and profit margin. In many cases, such as the 20-cent minimum value, that price does not cover the labor or other costs involved with stocking it as an individual stamp. The sum of minimum values in a set does not properly represent the value of a complete set primarily composed of a number of minimum-value stamps, nor does the sum represent the actual value of a packet made up of minimum-value stamps. Thus a packet of 1,000 different common stamps — each of which has a catalogue value of 20-cents — normally sells for considerably less than 200 dollars!

The *absence of a retail value* for a stamp does not necessarily suggest that a stamp is scarce or rare. A dash in the value column means that the stamp is known in a stated form or variety, but information is either lacking or insufficient for purposes of establishing a usable catalogue value.

Stamp values in *italics* generally refer to items that are difficult to value accurately. For expensive items, such as those priced at $1,000 or higher, a value in italics indicates that the affected item trades very seldom. For inexpensive items, a value in italics represents a warning. One example is a "blocked" issue where the issuing postal administration may have controlled one stamp in a set in an attempt to make the whole set more valuable. Another example is an item that sold at an extreme multiple of face value in the marketplace at the time of its issue.

One type of warning to collectors that appears in the catalogue is illustrated by a stamp that is valued considerably higher in used condition than it is as unused. In this case, collectors are cautioned to be certain the used version has a genuine and contemporaneous cancellation. The type of cancellation on a stamp can be an important factor in determining its sale price. Catalogue values do not apply to fiscal, telegraph or non-contemporaneous postal cancels, unless otherwise noted.

Some countries have released back issues of stamps in canceled-to-order form, sometimes covering as much as a 10-year period. The Scott Catalogue values for used stamps reflect canceled-to-order material when such stamps are found to predominate in the marketplace for the issue involved. Notes frequently appear in the stamp listings to specify which items are valued as canceled-to-order, or if there is a premium for postally used examples.

Many countries sell canceled-to-order stamps at a marked reduction of face value. Countries that sell or have sold canceled-to-order stamps at *full* face value include United Nations, Australia, Netherlands, France and Switzerland. It may be almost impossible to identify such stamps if the gum has been removed, because official government canceling devices are used. Postally used copies of these items on cover, however, are usually worth more than the canceled-to-order stamps with original gum.

Abbreviations

Scott Publishing Co. uses a consistent set of abbreviations throughout this catalogue to conserve space, while still providing necessary information.

COLOR ABBREVIATIONS

amb	amber	crim	crimson	ol	olive
anil	aniline	cr	cream	olvn	olivine
ap	apple	dk	dark	org	orange
aqua	aquamarine	dl	dull	pck	peacock
az	azure	dp	deep	pnksh	pinkish
bis	bister	db	drab	Prus	Prussian
bl	blue	emer	emerald	pur	purple
bld	blood	gldn	golden	redsh	reddish
blk	black	grysh	grayish	res	reseda
bril	brilliant	grn	green	ros	rosine
brn	brown	grnsh	greenish	ryl	royal
brnsh	brownish	hel	heliotrope	sal	salmon
brnz	bronze	hn	henna	saph	sapphire
brt	bright	ind	indigo	scar	scarlet
brnt	burnt	int	intense	sep	sepia
car	carmine	lav	lavender	sien	sienna
cer	cerise	lem	lemon	sil	silver
chlky	chalky	lil	lilac	sl	slate
cham	chamois	lt	light	stl	steel
chnt	chestnut	mag	magenta	turq	turquoise
choc	chocolate	man	manila	ultra	ultramarine
chr	chrome	mar	maroon	Ven	Venetian
cit	citron	mv	mauve	ver	vermilion
cl	claret	multi	multicolored	vio	violet
cob	cobalt	mlky	milky	yel	yellow
cop	copper	myr	myrtle	yelsh	yellowish

When no color is given for an overprint or surcharge, black is the color used. Abbreviations for colors used for overprints and surcharges include: "(B)" or "(Blk)," black; "(Bl)," blue; "(R)," red; and "(G)," green.

Additional abbreviations in this catalogue are shown below:

Adm	Administration
AFL	American Federation of Labor
Anniv.	Anniversary
APS	American Philatelic Society
Assoc.	Association
ASSR	Autonomous Soviet Socialist Republic
b.	Born
BEP	Bureau of Engraving and Printing
Bicent.	Bicentennial
Bklt.	Booklet
Brit.	British
btwn.	Between
Bur.	Bureau
c. or ca.	Circa
Cat.	Catalogue
Cent.	Centennial, century, centenary
CIO	Congress of Industrial Organizations
Conf.	Conference
Cong.	Congress
Cpl.	Corporal
CTO	Canceled to order
d.	Died
Dbl	Double
EDU	Earliest documented use
Engr.	Engraved
Exhib.	Exhibition
Expo.	Exposition
Fed.	Federation
GB	Great Britain
Gen.	General
GPO	General post office
Horiz.	Horizontal
Imperf.	Imperforate
Impt.	Imprint

Intl.	International
Invtd.	Inverted
L.	Left
Lieut., lt.	Lieutenant
Litho.	Lithographed
LL	Lower left
LR	Lower right
mm	Millimeter
Ms.	Manuscript
Natl.	National
No.	Number
NY	New York
NYC	New York City
Ovpt.	Overprint
Ovptd.	Overprinted
P	Plate number
Perf.	Perforated, perforation
Phil.	Philatelic
Photo.	Photogravure
PO	Post office
Pr.	Pair
P.R.	Puerto Rico
Prec.	Precancel, precanceled
Pres.	President
PTT	Post, Telephone and Telegraph
Rio	Rio de Janeiro
Sgt.	Sergeant
Soc.	Society
Souv.	Souvenir
SSR	Soviet Socialist Republic, see ASSR
St.	Saint, street
Surch.	Surcharge
Typo.	Typographed
UL	Upper left
Unwmkd.	Unwatermarked
UPU	Universal Postal Union
UR	Upper Right
US	United States
USPOD	United States Post Office Department
USSR	Union of Soviet Socialist Republics
Vert.	Vertical
VP	Vice president
Wmk.	Watermark
Wmkd.	Watermarked
WWI	World War I
WWII	World War II

Examination

Scott Publishing Co. will not comment upon the genuineness, grade or condition of stamps, because of the time and responsibility involved. Rather, there are several expertizing groups that undertake this work for both collectors and dealers. Neither will Scott Publishing Co. appraise or identify philatelic material. The company cannot take responsibility for unsolicited stamps or covers sent by individuals.

All letters, E-mails, etc. are read attentively, but they are not always answered due to time considerations.

How to order from your dealer

When ordering stamps from a dealer, it is not necessary to write the full description of a stamp as listed in this catalogue. All you need is the name of the country, the Scott catalogue number and whether the desired item is unused or used. For example, "Japan Scott 422 unused" is sufficient to identify the unused stamp of Japan listed as "422 A206 5y brown."

Basic Stamp Information

A stamp collector's knowledge of the combined elements that make a given stamp issue unique determines his or her ability to identify stamps. These elements include paper, watermark, method of separation, printing, design and gum. On the following pages each of these important areas is briefly described.

Paper

Paper is an organic material composed of a compacted weave of cellulose fibers and generally formed into sheets. Paper used to print stamps may be manufactured in sheets, or it may have been part of a large roll (called a web) before being cut to size. The fibers most often used to create paper on which stamps are printed include bark, wood, straw and certain grasses. In many cases, linen or cotton rags have been added for greater strength and durability. Grinding, bleaching, cooking and rinsing these raw fibers reduces them to a slushy pulp, referred to by paper makers as "stuff." Sizing and, sometimes, coloring matter is added to the pulp to make different types of finished paper.

After the stuff is prepared, it is poured onto sieve-like frames that allow the water to run off, while retaining the matted pulp. As fibers fall onto the screen and are held by gravity, they form a natural weave that will later hold the paper together. If the screen has metal bits that are formed into letters or images attached, it leaves slightly thinned areas on the paper. These are called watermarks.

When the stuff is almost dry, it is passed under pressure through smooth or engraved rollers - dandy rolls - or placed between cloth in a press to be flattened and dried.

Wove   Laid   Granite

Quadrille   Oblong Quadrille   Laid Batonne

Stamp paper falls broadly into two types: wove and laid. The nature of the surface of the frame onto which the pulp is first deposited causes the differences in appearance between the two. If the surface is smooth and even, the paper will be of fairly uniform texture throughout. This is known as *wove paper*. Early papermaking machines poured the pulp onto a continuously circulating web of felt, but modern machines feed the pulp onto a cloth-like screen made of closely interwoven fine wires. This paper, when held to a light, will show little dots or points very close together. The proper name for this is "wire wove," but the type is still considered wove. Any U.S. or British stamp printed after 1880 will serve as an example of wire wove paper.

Closely spaced parallel wires, with cross wires at wider intervals, make up the frames used for what is known as *laid paper*. A greater thickness of the pulp will settle between the wires. The paper, when held to a light, will show alternate light and dark lines. The spacing and the thickness of the lines may vary, but on any one sheet of paper they are all alike. See Russia Scott 31-38 for examples of laid paper.

Batonne, from the French word meaning "a staff," is a term used if the lines in the paper are spaced quite far apart, like the printed ruling on a writing tablet. Batonne paper may be either wove or laid. If laid, fine laid lines can be seen between the batons.

Quadrille is the term used when the lines in the paper form little squares. *Oblong quadrille* is the term used when rectangles, rather than squares, are formed. See Mexico-Guadalajara Scott 35-37 for examples of oblong quadrille paper.

Paper also is classified as thick or thin, hard or soft, and by color if dye is added during manufacture. Such colors may include yellowish, greenish, bluish and reddish.

Brief explanations of other types of paper used for printing stamps, as well as examples, follow.

Pelure — Pelure paper is a very thin, hard and often brittle paper that is sometimes bluish or grayish in appearance. See Serbia Scott 169-170.

Native — This is a term applied to handmade papers used to produce some of the early stamps of the Indian states. Stamps printed on native paper may be expected to display various natural inclusions that are normal and do not negatively affect value. Japanese paper, originally made of mulberry fibers and rice flour, is part of this group. See Japan Scott 1-18.

Manila — This type of paper is often used to make stamped envelopes and wrappers. It is a coarse-textured stock, usually smooth on one side and rough on the other. A variety of colors of manila paper exist, but the most common range is yellowish-brown.

Silk — Introduced by the British in 1847 as a safeguard against counterfeiting, silk paper contains bits of colored silk thread scattered throughout. The density of these fibers varies greatly and can include as few as one fiber per stamp or hundreds. U.S. revenue Scott R152 is a good example of an easy-to-identify silk paper stamp.

Silk-thread paper has uninterrupted threads of colored silk arranged so that one or more threads run through the stamp or postal stationery. See Great Britain Scott 5-6 and Switzerland Scott 14-19.

Granite — Filled with minute cloth or colored paper fibers of various colors and lengths, granite paper should not be confused with either type of silk paper. Austria Scott 172-175 and a number of Swiss stamps are examples of granite paper.

Chalky — A chalk-like substance coats the surface of chalky paper to discourage the cleaning and reuse of canceled stamps, as well as to provide a smoother, more acceptable printing surface. Because the designs of stamps printed on chalky paper are imprinted on what is often a water-soluble coating, any attempt to remove a cancellation will destroy the stamp. *Do not soak these stamps in any fluid.* To remove a stamp printed on chalky paper from an envelope, wet the paper from underneath the stamp until the gum dissolves enough to release the stamp from the paper. See St. Kitts-Nevis Scott 89-90 for examples of stamps printed on this type of chalky paper.

India — Another name for this paper, originally introduced from China about 1750, is "China Paper." It is a thin, opaque paper often used for plate and die proofs by many countries.

Double — In philately, the term double paper has two distinct meanings. The first is a two-ply paper, usually a combination of a thick and a thin sheet, joined during manufacture. This type was used experimentally as a means to discourage the reuse of stamps.

The design is printed on the thin paper. Any attempt to remove a cancellation would destroy the design. U.S. Scott 158 and other Banknote-era stamps exist on this form of double paper.

The second type of double paper occurs on a rotary press, when the end of one paper roll, or web, is affixed to the next roll to save time feeding the paper through the press. Stamp designs are printed over the joined paper and, if overlooked by inspectors, may get into post office stocks.

Goldbeater's Skin — This type of paper was used for the 1866 issue of Prussia, and was a tough, translucent paper. The design was printed in reverse on the back of the stamp, and the gum applied over the printing. It is impossible to remove stamps printed on this type of paper from the paper to which they are affixed without destroying the design.

Ribbed — Ribbed paper has an uneven, corrugated surface made by passing the paper through ridged rollers. This type exists on some copies of U.S. Scott 156-165.

Various other substances, or substrates, have been used for stamp manufacture, including wood, aluminum, copper, silver and gold foil, plastic, and silk and cotton fabrics.

Watermarks

Watermarks are an integral part of some papers. They are formed in the process of paper manufacture. Watermarks consist of small designs, formed of wire or cut from metal and soldered to the surface of the mold or, sometimes, on the dandy roll. The designs may be in the form of crowns, stars, anchors, letters or other characters or symbols. These pieces of metal - known in the paper-making industry as "bits" - impress a design into the paper. The design sometimes may be seen by holding the stamp to the light. Some are more easily seen with a watermark detector. This important tool is a small black tray into which a stamp is placed face down and dampened with a fast-evaporating watermark detection fluid that brings up the watermark image in the form of dark lines against a lighter background. These dark lines are the thinner areas of the paper known as the watermark. Some watermarks are extremely difficult to locate, due to either a faint impression, watermark location or the color of the stamp. There also are electric watermark detectors that come with plastic filter disks of various colors. The disks neutralize the color of the stamp, permitting the watermark to be seen more easily.

Multiple watermarks of Crown Agents and Burma

Watermarks of Uruguay, Vatican City and Jamaica

WARNING: Some inks used in the photogravure process dissolve in watermark fluids (Please see the section on Soluble Printing Inks). Also, see "chalky paper."

Watermarks may be found normal, reversed, inverted, reversed and inverted, sideways or diagonal, as seen from the back of the stamp. The relationship of watermark to stamp design depends on the position of the printing plates or how paper is fed through the press. On machine-made paper, watermarks normally are read from right to left. The design is repeated closely throughout the sheet in a "multiple-watermark design." In a "sheet watermark," the design appears only once on the sheet, but extends over many stamps. Individual stamps may carry only a small fraction or none of the watermark.

"Marginal watermarks" occur in the margins of sheets or panes of stamps. They occur on the outside border of paper (ostensibly outside the area where stamps are to be printed). A large row of letters may spell the name of the country or the manufacturer of the paper, or a border of lines may appear. Careless press feeding may cause parts of these letters and/or lines to show on stamps of the outer row of a pane.

Soluble Printing Inks

WARNING: Most stamp colors are permanent; that is, they are not seriously affected by short-term exposure to light or water. Many colors, especially of modern inks, fade from excessive exposure to light. There are stamps printed with inks that dissolve easily in water or in fluids used to detect watermarks. Use of these inks was intentional to prevent the removal of cancellations. Water affects all aniline inks, those on so-called safety paper and some photogravure printings - all such inks are known as *fugitive colors. Removal from paper of such stamps requires care and alternatives to traditional soaking.*

Separation

"Separation" is the general term used to describe methods used to separate stamps. The three standard forms currently in use are perforating, rouletting and die-cutting. These methods are done during the stamp production process, after printing. Sometimes these methods are done on-press or sometimes as a separate step. The earliest issues, such as the 1840 Penny Black of Great Britain (Scott 1), did not have any means provided for separation. It was expected the stamps would be cut apart with scissors or folded and torn. These are examples of imperforate stamps. Many stamps were first issued in imperforate formats and were later issued with perforations. Therefore, care must be observed in buying single imperforate stamps to be certain they were issued imperforate and are not perforated copies that have been altered by having the perforations trimmed away. Stamps issued imperforate usually are valued as singles. However, imperforate varieties of normally perforated stamps should be collected in pairs or larger pieces as indisputable evidence of their imperforate character.

PERFORATION

The chief style of separation of stamps, and the one that is in almost universal use today, is perforating. By this process, paper between the stamps is cut away in a line of holes, usually round, leaving little bridges of paper between the stamps to hold them together. Some types of perforation, such as hyphen-hole perfs, can be confused with roulettes, but a close visual inspection reveals that paper has been removed. The little perforation bridges, which project from the stamp when it is torn from the pane, are called the teeth of the perforation.

As the size of the perforation is sometimes the only way to differentiate between two otherwise identical stamps, it is necessary to be able to accurately measure and describe them. This is done with a perforation gauge, usually a ruler-like device that has dots or graduated lines to show how many perforations may be counted in the space of two centimeters. Two centimeters is the space universally adopted in which to measure perforations.

Perforation gauge

perce en arc   perce en lignes

perce en points   oblique roulette

perce en scie   perce serpentin

To measure a stamp, run it along the gauge until the dots on it fit exactly into the perforations of the stamp. If you are using a graduated-line perforation gauge, simply slide the stamp along the surface until the lines on the gauge perfectly project from the center of the bridges or holes. The number to the side of the line of dots or lines that fit the stamp's perforation is the measurement. For example, an "11" means that 11 perforations fit between two centimeters. The description of the stamp therefore is "perf. 11." If the gauge of the perforations on the top and bottom of a stamp differs from that on the sides, the result is what is known as *compound perforations.* In measuring compound perforations, the gauge at top and bottom is always given first, then the sides. Thus, a stamp that measures 11 at top and bottom and 10 1/2 at the sides is "perf. 11 x 10 1/2." See U.S. Scott 632-642 for examples of compound perforations.

Stamps also are known with perforations different on three or all four sides. Descriptions of such items are clockwise, beginning with the top of the stamp.

A perforation with small holes and teeth close together is a "fine perforation." One with large holes and teeth far apart is a "coarse perforation." Holes that are jagged, rather than clean-cut, are "rough perforations." *Blind perforations* are the slight impressions left by the perforating pins if they fail to puncture the paper. Multiples of stamps showing blind perforations may command a slight premium over normally perforated stamps.

The term *syncopated perfs* describes intentional irregularities in the perforations. The earliest form was used by the Netherlands from 1925-33, where holes were omitted to create distinctive patterns. Beginning in 1992, Great Britain has used an oval perforation to help prevent counterfeiting. Several other countries have started using the oval perfs or other syncopated perf patterns.

A new type of perforation, still primarily used for postal stationery, is known as microperfs. Microperfs are tiny perforations (in some cases hundreds of holes per two centimeters) that allows items to be intentionally separated very easily, while not accidentally breaking apart as easily as standard perforations. These are not currently measured or differentiated by size, as are standard perforations.

ROULETTING

In rouletting, the stamp paper is cut partly or wholly through, with no paper removed. In perforating, some paper is removed. Rouletting derives its name from the French roulette, a spur-like wheel. As the wheel is rolled over the paper, each point makes a small cut. The number of cuts made in a two-centimeter space determines the gauge of the roulette, just as the number of perforations in two centimeters determines the gauge of the perforation.

The shape and arrangement of the teeth on the wheels varies. Various roulette types generally carry French names:

Perce en lignes - rouletted in lines. The paper receives short, straight cuts in lines. This is the most common type of rouletting. See Mexico Scott 500.

Perce en points - pin-rouletted or pin-perfed. This differs from a small perforation because no paper is removed, although round, equidistant holes are pricked through the paper. See Mexico Scott 242-256.

Perce en arc and *perce en scie* - pierced in an arc or saw-toothed designs, forming half circles or small triangles. See Hanover (German States) Scott 25-29.

Perce en serpentin - serpentine roulettes. The cuts form a serpentine or wavy line. See Brunswick (German States) Scott 13-18.

Once again, no paper is removed by these processes, leaving the stamps easily separated, but closely attached.

DIE-CUTTING

The third major form of stamp separation is die-cutting. This is a method where a die in the pattern of separation is created that later cuts the stamp paper in a stroke motion. Although some standard stamps bear die-cut perforations, this process is primarily used for self-adhesive postage stamps. Die-cutting can appear in straight lines, such as U.S. Scott 2522, shapes, such as U.S. Scott 1551, or imitating the appearance of perforations, such as New Zealand Scott 935A and 935B.

Printing Processes

ENGRAVING (Intaglio, Line-engraving, Etching)

Master die — The initial operation in the process of line engraving is making the master die. The die is a small, flat block of softened steel upon which the stamp design is recess engraved in reverse.

Master die

Photographic reduction of the original art is made to the appropriate size. It then serves as a tracing guide for the initial outline of the design. The engraver lightly traces the design on the steel with his graver, then slowly works the design until it is completed. At various points during the engraving process, the engraver hand-inks the die and makes an impression to check his progress. These are known as progressive die proofs. After completion of the engraving, the die is hardened to withstand the stress and pressures of later transfer operations.

Transfer roll

Transfer roll — Next is production of the transfer roll that, as the name implies, is the medium used to transfer the subject from the master die to the printing plate. A blank roll of soft steel, mounted on a mandrel, is placed under the bearers of the transfer press to allow it to roll freely on its axis. The hardened die is placed on the bed of the press and the face of the transfer roll is applied to the die, under pressure. The bed or the roll is then rocked back and forth under increasing pressure, until the soft steel of the roll is forced into every engraved line of the die. The resulting impression on the roll is known as a "relief" or a "relief transfer." The engraved image is now positive in appearance and stands out from the steel. After the required number of reliefs are "rocked in," the soft steel transfer roll is hardened.

Different flaws may occur during the relief process. A defective relief may occur during the rocking in process because of a minute piece of foreign material lodging on the die, or some other cause. Imperfections in the steel of the transfer roll may result in a breaking away of parts of the design. This is known as a relief break, which will show up on finished stamps as small, unprinted areas. If a damaged relief remains in use, it will transfer a repeating defect to the plate. Deliberate alterations of reliefs sometimes occur. "Altered reliefs" designate these changed conditions.

Plate — The final step in pre-printing production is the making of the printing plate. A flat piece of soft steel replaces the die on the bed of the transfer press. One of the reliefs on the transfer roll is positioned over this soft steel. Position, or layout, dots determine the correct position on the plate. The dots have been lightly marked on

the plate in advance. After the correct position of the relief is determined, the design is rocked in by following the same method used in making the transfer roll. The difference is that this time the image is being transferred from the transfer roll, rather than to it. Once the design is entered on the plate, it appears in reverse and is recessed. There are as many transfers entered on the plate as there are subjects printed on the sheet of stamps. It is during this process that double and shifted transfers occur, as well as re-entries. These are the result of improperly entered images that have not been properly burnished out prior to rocking in a new image.

Modern siderography processes, such as those used by the U.S. Bureau of Engraving and Printing, involve an automated form of rocking designs in on preformed cylindrical printing sleeves. The same process also allows for easier removal and re-entry of worn images right on the sleeve.

Transferring the design to the plate

Following the entering of the required transfers on the plate, the position dots, layout dots and lines, scratches and other markings generally are burnished out. Added at this time by the siderographer are any required *guide lines, plate numbers* or other *marginal markings.* The plate is then hand-inked and a proof impression is taken. This is known as a plate proof. If the impression is approved, the plate is machined for fitting onto the press, is hardened and sent to the plate vault ready for use.

On press, the plate is inked and the surface is automatically wiped clean, leaving ink only in the recessed lines. Paper is then forced under pressure into the engraved recessed lines, thereby receiving the ink. Thus, the ink lines on engraved stamps are slightly raised, and slight depressions (debossing) occur on the back of the stamp. Prior to the advent of modern high-speed presses and more advanced ink formulations, paper had to be dampened before receiving the ink. This sometimes led to uneven shrinkage by the time the stamps were perforated, resulting in improperly perforated stamps, or misperfs. Newer presses use drier paper, thus both *wet* and *dry printings* exist on some stamps.

Rotary Press — Until 1914, only flat plates were used to print engraved stamps. Rotary press printing was introduced in 1914, and slowly spread. Some countries still use flat-plate printing.

After approval of the plate proof, older *rotary press plates* require additional machining. They are curved to fit the press cylinder. "Gripper slots" are cut into the back of each plate to receive the "grippers," which hold the plate securely on the press. The plate is then hardened. Stamps printed from these bent rotary press plates are longer or wider than the same stamps printed from flat-plate presses. The stretching of the plate during the curving process is what causes this distortion.

Re-entry — To execute a re-entry on a flat plate, the transfer roll is re-applied to the plate, often at some time after its first use on the press. Worn-out designs can be resharpened by carefully burnishing out the original image and re-entering it from the transfer roll. If the original impression has not been sufficiently removed and the transfer roll is not precisely in line with the remaining impression, the resulting double transfer will make the re-entry obvious. If the registration is true, a re-entry may be difficult or impossible to distinguish. Sometimes a stamp printed from a successful re-entry is identified by having a much sharper and clearer impression than its neighbors. With the advent of rotary presses, post-press re-entries were not possible. After a plate was curved for the rotary press, it was impossible to make a re-entry. This is because the plate had already been bent once (with the design distorted).

However, with the introduction of the previously mentioned modern-style siderography machines, entries are made to the preformed cylindrical printing sleeve. Such sleeves are dechromed and softened. This allows individual images to be burnished out and re-entered on the curved sleeve. The sleeve is then rechromed, resulting in longer press life.

Double Transfer — This is a description of the condition of a transfer on a plate that shows evidence of a duplication of all, or a portion of the design. It usually is the result of the changing of the registration between the transfer roll and the plate during the rocking in of the original entry. Double transfers also occur when only a portion of the design has been rocked in and improper positioning is noted. If the worker elected not to burnish out the partial or completed design, a strong double transfer will occur for part or all of the design.

It sometimes is necessary to remove the original transfer from a plate and repeat the process a second time. If the finished re-worked image shows traces of the original impression, attributable to incomplete burnishing, the result is a partial double transfer.

With the modern automatic machines mentioned previously, double transfers are all but impossible to create. Those partially doubled images on stamps printed from such sleeves are more than likely re-entries, rather than true double transfers.

Re-engraved — Alterations to a stamp design are sometimes necessary after some stamps have been printed. In some cases, either the original die or the actual printing plate may have its "temper" drawn (softened), and the design will be re-cut. The resulting impressions from such a re-engraved die or plate may differ slightly from the original issue, and are known as "re-engraved." If the alteration was made to the master die, all future printings will be consistently different from the original. If alterations were made to the printing plate, each altered stamp on the plate will be slightly different from each other, allowing specialists to reconstruct a complete printing plate.

Dropped Transfers — If an impression from the transfer roll has not been properly placed, a dropped transfer may occur. The final stamp image will appear obviously out of line with its neighbors.

Short Transfer — Sometimes a transfer roll is not rocked its entire length when entering a transfer onto a plate. As a result, the finished transfer on the plate fails to show the complete design, and the finished stamp will have an incomplete design printed. This is known as a "short transfer." U.S. Scott No. 8 is a good example of a short transfer.

TYPOGRAPHY (Letterpress, Surface Printing, Flexography, Dry Offset, High Etch)

Although the word "Typography" is obsolete as a term describing a printing method, it was the accepted term throughout the first century of postage stamps. Therefore, appropriate Scott listings in this catalogue refer to typographed stamps. The current term for this form of printing, however, is "letterpress."

As it relates to the production of postage stamps, letterpress printing is the reverse of engraving. Rather than having recessed areas trap the ink and deposit it on paper, only the raised areas of the design are inked. This is comparable to the type of printing seen by inking and using an ordinary rubber stamp. Letterpress includes all printing where the design is above the surface area, whether it is wood, metal or, in some instances, hardened rubber or polymer plastic.

For most letterpress-printed stamps, the engraved master is made in much the same manner as for engraved stamps. In this instance, however, an additional step is needed. The design is transferred to another surface before being transferred to the transfer roll. In this way, the transfer roll has a recessed stamp design, rather than one done in relief. This makes the printing areas on the final plate raised, or relief areas.

For less-detailed stamps of the 19th century, the area on the die not used as a printing surface was cut away, leaving the surface area raised. The original die was then reproduced by stereotyping or electrotyping. The resulting electrotypes were assembled in the required number and format of the desired sheet of stamps. The plate used in printing the stamps was an electroplate of these assembled electrotypes.

Once the final letterpress plates are created, ink is applied to the raised surface and the pressure of the press transfers the ink impression to the paper. In contrast to engraving, the fine lines of letterpress are impressed on the surface of the stamp, leaving a debossed surface. When viewed from the back (as on a typewritten page), the corresponding line work on the stamp will be raised slightly (embossed) above the surface.

PHOTOGRAVURE (Gravure, Rotogravure, Heliogravure)

In this process, the basic principles of photography are applied to a chemically sensitized metal plate, rather than photographic paper. The design is transferred photographically to the plate through a halftone, or dot-matrix screen, breaking the reproduction into tiny dots. The plate is treated chemically and the dots form depressions, called cells, of varying depths and diameters, depending on the degrees of shade in the design. Then, like engraving, ink is applied to the plate and the surface is wiped clean. This leaves ink in the tiny cells that is lifted out and deposited on the paper when it is pressed against the plate.

Gravure is most often used for multicolored stamps, generally using the three primary colors (red, yellow and blue) and black. By varying the dot matrix pattern and density of these colors, virtually any color can be reproduced. A typical full-color gravure stamp will be created from four printing cylinders (one for each color). The original multicolored image will have been photographically separated into its component colors.

Modern gravure printing may use computer-generated dot-matrix screens, and modern plates may be of various types including metal-coated plastic. The catalogue designation of Photogravure (or "Photo") covers any of these older and more modern gravure methods of printing.

For examples of the first photogravure stamps printed (1914), see Bavaria Scott 94-114.

LITHOGRAPHY (Offset Lithography, Stone Lithography, Dilitho, Planography, Collotype)

The principle that oil and water do not mix is the basis for lithography. The stamp design is drawn by hand or transferred from engraving to the surface of a lithographic stone or metal plate in a greasy (oily) substance. This oily substance holds the ink, which will later be transferred to the paper. The stone (or plate) is wet with an acid fluid, causing it to repel the printing ink in all areas not covered by the greasy substance.

Transfer paper is used to transfer the design from the original stone or plate. A series of duplicate transfers are grouped and, in turn, transferred to the final printing plate.

Photolithography — The application of photographic processes to lithography. This process allows greater flexibility of design, related to use of halftone screens combined with line work. Unlike photogravure or engraving, this process can allow large, solid areas to be printed.

Offset — A refinement of the lithographic process. A rubber-covered blanket cylinder takes the impression from the inked lithographic plate. From the "blanket" the impression is *offset* or transferred to the paper. Greater flexibility and speed are the principal reasons offset printing has largely displaced lithography. The term "lithography" covers both processes, and results are almost identical.

EMBOSSED (Relief) Printing

Embossing, not considered one of the four main printing types, is a method in which the design first is sunk into the metal of the die. Printing is done against a yielding platen, such as leather or linoleum. The platen is forced into the depression of the die, thus forming the design on the paper in relief. This process is often used for metallic inks.

Embossing may be done without color (see Sardinia Scott 4-6); with color printed around the embossed area (see Great Britain Scott 5 and most U.S. envelopes); and with color in exact registration with the embossed subject (see Canada Scott 656-657).

HOLOGRAMS

For objects to appear as holograms on stamps, a model exactly the same size as it is to appear on the hologram must be created. Rather than using photographic film to capture the image, holography records an image on a photoresist material. In processing, chemicals eat away at certain exposed areas, leaving a pattern of constructive and destructive interference. When the phororesist is developed, the result is a pattern of uneven ridges that acts as a mold. This mold is then coated with metal, and the resulting form is used to press copies in much the same way phonograph records are produced.

A typical reflective hologram used for stamps consists of a reproduction of the uneven patterns on a plastic film that is applied to a reflective background, usually a silver or gold foil. Light is reflected off the background through the film, making the pattern present on the film visible. Because of the uneven pattern of the film, the viewer will perceive the objects in their proper three-dimensional relationships with appropriate brightness.

The first hologram on a stamp was produced by Austria in 1988 (Scott 1441).

FOIL APPLICATION

A modern tecnique of applying color to stamps involves the application of metallic foil to the stamp paper. A pattern of foil is applied to the stamp paper by use of a stamping die. The foil usually is flat, but it may be textured. Canada Scott 1735 has three different foil applications in pearl, bronze and gold. The gold foil was textured using a chemical-etch copper embossing die. The printing of this stamp also involved two-color offset lithography plus embossing.

COMBINATION PRINTINGS

Sometimes two or even three printing methods are combined in producing stamps. In these cases, such as Austria Scott 933 or Canada 1735 (described in the preceding paragraph), the multiple-printing technique can be determined by studying the individual characteristics of each printing type. A few stamps, such as Singapore Scott 684-684A, combine as many as three of the four major printing types (lithography, engraving and typography). When this is done it often indicates the incorporation of security devices against counterfeiting.

INK COLORS

Inks or colored papers used in stamp printing often are of mineral origin, although there are numerous examples of organic-based pigments. As a general rule, organic-based pigments are far more subject to varieties and change than those of mineral-based origin.

The appearance of any given color on a stamp may be affected by many aspects, including printing variations, light, color of paper, aging and chemical alterations.

Numerous printing variations may be observed. Heavier pressure or inking will cause a more intense color, while slight interruptions in the ink feed or lighter impressions will cause a lighter appearance. Stamps printed in the same color by water-based and solvent-based inks can differ significantly in appearance. This affects several stamps in the U.S. Prominent Americans series. Hand-mixed ink formulas (primarily from the 19th century) produced under different conditions (humidity and temperature) account for notable color variations in early printings of the same stamp (see U.S. Scott 248-250, 279B, for example). Different sources of pigment can also result in significant differences in color.

Light exposure and aging are closely related in the way they affect stamp color. Both eventually break down the ink and fade colors, so that a carefully kept stamp may differ significantly in color from an identical copy that has been exposed to light. If stamps are exposed to light either intentionally or accidentally, their colors can be faded or completely changed in some cases.

Papers of different quality and consistency used for the same stamp printing may affect color appearance. Most pelure papers, for example, show a richer color when compared with wove or laid papers. See Russia Scott 181a, for an example of this effect.

The very nature of the printing processes can cause a variety of differences in shades or hues of the same stamp. Some of these shades are scarcer than others, and are of particular interest to the advanced collector.

Luminescence

All forms of tagged stamps fall under the general category of luminescence. Within this broad category is fluorescence, dealing with forms of tagging visible under longwave ultraviolet light, and phosphorescence, which deals with tagging visible only under shortwave light. Phosphorescence leaves an afterglow and fluorescence does not. These treated stamps show up in a range of different colors when exposed to UV light. The differing wavelengths of the light activates the tagging material, making it glow in various colors that usually serve different mail processing purposes.

Intentional tagging is a post-World War II phenomenon, brought about by the increased literacy rate and rapidly growing mail volume. It was one of several answers to the problem of the need for more automated mail processes. Early tagged stamps served the purpose of triggering machines to separate different types of mail. A natural outgrowth was to also use the signal to trigger machines that faced all envelopes the same way and canceled them.

Tagged stamps come in many different forms. Some tagged stamps have luminescent shapes or images imprinted on them as a form of security device. Others have blocks (United States), stripes, frames (South Africa and Canada), overall coatings (United States), bars (Great Britain and Canada) and many other types. Some types of tagging are even mixed in with the pigmented printing ink (Australia Scott 366, Netherlands Scott 478 and U.S. Scott 1359 and 2443).

The means of applying taggant to stamps differs as much as the intended purposes for the stamps. The most common form of tagging is a coating applied to the surface of the printed stamp. Since the taggant ink is frequently invisible except under UV light, it does not interfere with the appearance of the stamp. Another common application is the use of phosphored papers. In this case the paper itself either has a coating of taggant applied before the stamp is printed, has taggant applied during the papermaking process (incorporating it into the fibers), or has the taggant mixed into the coating of the paper. The latter method, among others, is currently in use in the United States.

Many countries now use tagging in various forms to either expedite mail handling or to serve as a printing security device against counterfeiting. Following the introduction of tagged stamps for public use in 1959 by Great Britain, other countries have steadily joined the parade. Among those are Germany (1961); Canada and Denmark (1962); United States, Australia, France and Switzerland (1963); Belgium and Japan (1966); Sweden and Norway (1967); Italy (1968); and Russia (1969). Since then, many other countries have begun using forms of tagging, including Brazil, China, Czechoslovakia, Hong Kong, Guatemala, Indonesia, Israel, Lithuania, Luxembourg, Netherlands, Penrhyn Islands, Portugal, St. Vincent, Singapore, South Africa, Spain and Sweden to name a few.

In some cases, including United States, Canada, Great Britain and Switzerland, stamps were released both with and without tagging. Many of these were released during each country's experimental period. Tagged and untagged versions are listed for the aforementioned countries and are noted in some other countries' listings. For at least a few stamps, the experimentally tagged version is worth far more than its untagged counterpart, such as the 1963 experimental tagged version of France Scott 1024.

In some cases, luminescent varieties of stamps were inadvertently created. Several Russian stamps, for example, sport highly fluorescent ink that was not intended as a form of tagging. Older stamps, such as early U.S. postage dues, can be positively identified by the use of UV light, since the organic ink used has become slightly fluorescent over time. Other stamps, such as Austria Scott 70a-82a (varnish bars) and Obock Scott 46-64 (printed quadrille lines), have become fluorescent over time.

Various fluorescent substances have been added to paper to make it appear brighter. These optical brightners, as they are known, greatly affect the appearance of the stamp under UV light. The brightest of these is known as Hi-Brite paper. These paper varieties are beyond the scope of the Scott Catalogue.

Shortwave UV light also is used extensively in expertizing, since each form of paper has its own fluorescent characteristics that are impossible to perfectly match. It is therefore a simple matter to detect filled thins, added perforation teeth and other alterations that involve the addition of paper. UV light also is used to examine stamps that have had cancels chemically removed and for other purposes as well.

Gum

The Illustrated Gum Chart in the first part of this introduction shows and defines various types of gum condition. Because gum condition has an important impact on the value of unused stamps, we recommend studying this chart and the accompanying text carefully.

The gum on the back of a stamp may be shiny, dull, smooth, rough, dark, white, colored or tinted. Most stamp gumming adhesives use gum arabic or dextrine as a base. Certain polymers such as polyvinyl alcohol (PVA) have been used extensively since World War II.

The *Scott Standard Postage Stamp Catalogue* does not list items by types of gum. The *Scott Specialized Catalogue of United States Stamps* does differentiate among some types of gum for certain issues.

Reprints of stamps may have gum differing from the original issues. In addition, some countries have used different gum formulas for different seasons. These adhesives have different properties that may become more apparent over time.

Many stamps have been issued without gum, and the catalogue will note this fact. See, for example, United States Scott 40-47. Sometimes, gum may have been removed to preserve the stamp. Germany Scott B68, for example, has a highly acidic gum that eventually destroys the stamps. This item is valued in the catalogue with gum removed.

Reprints and Reissues

These are impressions of stamps (usually obsolete) made from the original plates or stones. If they are valid for postage and reproduce obsolete issues (such as U.S. Scott 102-111), the stamps are *reissues*. If they are from current issues, they are designated as *second, third,* etc., *printing*. If designated for a particular purpose, they are called *special printings*.

When special printings are not valid for postage, but are made from original dies and plates by authorized persons, they are *official reprints*. *Private reprints* are made from the original plates and dies by private hands. An example of a private reprint is that of the 1871-1932 reprints made from the original die of the 1845 New Haven, Conn., postmaster's provisional. *Official reproductions* or imitations are made from new dies and plates by government authorization. Scott will list those reissues that are valid for postage if they differ significantly from the original printing.

The U.S. government made special printings of its first postage stamps in 1875. Produced were official imitations of the first two stamps (listed as Scott 3-4), reprints of the demonetized pre-1861 issues (Scott 40-47) and reissues of the 1861 stamps, the 1869 stamps and the then-current 1875 denominations. Even though the official imitations and the reprints were not valid for postage, Scott lists all of these U.S. special printings.

Most reprints or reissues differ slightly from the original stamp in some characteristic, such as gum, paper, perforation, color or watermark. Sometimes the details are followed so meticulously that only a student of that specific stamp is able to distinguish the reprint or reissue from the original.

Remainders and Canceled to Order

Some countries sell their stock of old stamps when a new issue replaces them. To avoid postal use, the *remainders* usually are canceled with a punch hole, a heavy line or bar, or a more-or-less regular-looking cancellation. The most famous merchant of remainders was Nicholas F. Seebeck. In the 1880s and 1890s, he arranged printing contracts between the Hamilton Bank Note Co., of which he was a director, and several Central and South American countries. The contracts provided that the plates and all remainders of the yearly issues became the property of Hamilton. Seebeck saw to it that ample stock remained. The "Seebecks," both remainders and reprints, were standard packet fillers for decades.

Some countries also issue stamps *canceled-to-order (CTO)*, either in sheets with original gum or stuck onto pieces of paper or envelopes and canceled. Such CTO items generally are worth less than postally used stamps. In cases where the CTO material is far more prevalent in the marketplace than postally used examples, the catalogue value relates to the CTO examples, with postally used examples noted as premium items. Most CTOs can be detected by the presence of gum. However, as the CTO practice goes back at least to 1885, the gum inevitably has been soaked off some stamps so they could pass as postally used. The normally applied postmarks usually differ slightly from standard postmarks, and specialists are able to tell the difference. When applied individually to envelopes by philatelically minded persons, CTO material is known as *favor canceled* and generally sells at large discounts.

Cinderellas and Facsimiles

Cinderella is a catch-all term used by stamp collectors to describe phantoms, fantasies, bogus items, municipal issues, exhibition seals, local revenues, transportation stamps, labels, poster stamps and many other types of items. Some cinderella collectors include in their collections local postage issues, telegraph stamps, essays and proofs, forgeries and counterfeits.

A *fantasy* is an adhesive created for a nonexistent stamp-issuing authority. Fantasy items range from imaginary countries (Occusi-Ambeno, Kingdom of Sedang, Principality of Trinidad or Torres

Straits), to non-existent locals (Winans City Post), or nonexistent transportation lines (McRobish & Co.'s Acapulco-San Francisco Line).

On the other hand, if the entity exists and could have issued stamps (but did not) or was known to have issued other stamps, the items are considered *bogus* stamps. These would include the Mormon postage stamps of Utah, S. Allan Taylor's Guatemala and Paraguay inventions, the propaganda issues for the South Moluccas and the adhesives of the Page & Keyes local post of Boston.

Phantoms is another term for both fantasy and bogus issues.

Facsimiles are copies or imitations made to represent original stamps, but which do not pretend to be originals. A catalogue illustration is such a facsimile. Illustrations from the Moens catalogue of the last century were occasionally colored and passed off as stamps. Since the beginning of stamp collecting, facsimiles have been made for collectors as space fillers or for reference. They often carry the word "facsimile," "falsch" (German), "sanko" or "mozo" (Japanese), or "faux" (French) overprinted on the face or stamped on the back. Unfortunately, over the years a number of these items have had fake cancels applied over the facsimile notation and have been passed off as genuine.

Forgeries and Counterfeits

Forgeries and counterfeits have been with philately virtually from the beginning of stamp production. Over time, the terminology for the two has been used interchangeably. Although both forgeries and counterfeits are reproductions of stamps, the purposes behind their creation differ considerably.

Among specialists there is an increasing movement to more specifically define such items. Although there is no universally accepted terminology, we feel the following definitions most closely mirror the items and their purposes as they are currently defined.

Forgeries (also often referred to as *Counterfeits*) are reproductions of genuine stamps that have been created to defraud collectors. Such spurious items first appeared on the market around 1860, and most old-time collections contain one or more. Many are crude and easily spotted, but some can deceive experts.

An important supplier of these early philatelic forgeries was the Hamburg printer Gebruder Spiro. Many others with reputations in this craft included S. Allan Taylor, George Hussey, James Chute, George Forune, Benjamin & Sarpy, Julius Goldner, E. Oneglia and L.H. Mercier. Among the noted 20th-century forgers were Francois Fournier, Jean Sperati and the prolific Raoul DeThuin.

Forgeries may be complete replications, or they may be genuine stamps altered to resemble a scarcer (and more valuable) type. Most forgeries, particularly those of rare stamps, are worth only a small fraction of the value of a genuine example, but a few types, created by some of the most notable forgers, such as Sperati, can be worth as much or more than the genuine. Fraudulently produced copies are known of most classic rarities and many medium-priced stamps.

In addition to rare stamps, large numbers of common 19th- and early 20th-century stamps were forged to supply stamps to the early packet trade. Many can still be easily found. Few new philatelic forgeries have appeared in recent decades. Successful imitation of well-engraved work is virtually impossible. It has proven far easier to produce a fake by altering a genuine stamp than to duplicate a stamp completely.

Counterfeit (also often referred to as *Postal Counterfeit* or *Postal Forgery*) is the term generally applied to reproductions of stamps that have been created to defraud the government of revenue. Such items usually are created at the time a stamp is current and, in some cases, are hard to detect. Because most counterfeits are seized when the perpetrator is captured, postal counterfeits, particularly used on cover, are usually worth much more than a genuine example to specialists. The first postal counterfeit was of Spain's 4-cuarto carmine of 1854 (the real one is Scott 25). Apparently, the counterfeiters were not satisfied with their first version, which is now very scarce,

and they soon created an engraved counterfeit, which is common. Postal counterfeits quickly followed in Austria, Naples, Sardinia and the Roman States. They have since been created in many other countries as well, including the United States.

An infamous counterfeit to defraud the government is the 1-shilling Great Britain "Stock Exchange" forgery of 1872, used on telegraph forms at the exchange that year. The stamp escaped detection until a stamp dealer noticed it in 1898.

Fakes

Fakes are genuine stamps altered in some way to make them more desirable. One student of this part of stamp collecting has estimated that by the 1950s more than 30,000 varieties of fakes were known. That number has grown greatly since then. The widespread existence of fakes makes it important for stamp collectors to study their philatelic holdings and use relevant literature. Likewise, collectors should buy from reputable dealers who guarantee their stamps and make full and prompt refunds should a purchased item be declared faked or altered by some mutually agreed-upon authority. Because fakes always have some genuine characteristics, it is not always possible to obtain unanimous agreement among experts regarding specific items. These students may change their opinions as philatelic knowledge increases. More than 80 percent of all fakes on the philatelic market today are regummed, reperforated (or perforated for the first time), or bear forged overprints, surcharges or cancellations.

Stamps can be chemically treated to alter or eliminate colors. For example, a pale rose stamp can be re-colored to resemble a blue shade of high market value. In other cases, treated stamps can be made to resemble missing color varieties. Designs may be changed by painting, or a stroke or a dot added or bleached out to turn an ordinary variety into a seemingly scarcer stamp. Part of a stamp can be bleached and reprinted in a different version, achieving an inverted center or frame. Margins can be added or repairs done so deceptively that the stamps move from the "repaired" into the "fake" category.

Fakers have not left the backs of the stamps untouched either. They may create false watermarks, add fake grills or press out genuine grills. A thin India paper proof may be glued onto a thicker backing to create the appearance an issued stamp, or a proof printed on cardboard may be shaved down and perforated to resemble a stamp. Silk threads are impressed into paper and stamps have been split so that a rare paper variety is added to an otherwise inexpensive stamp. The most common treatment to the back of a stamp, however, is regumming.

Some in the business of faking stamps have openly advertised foolproof application of "original gum" to stamps that lack it, although most publications now ban such ads from their pages. It is believed that very few early stamps have survived without being hinged. The large number of never-hinged examples of such earlier material offered for sale thus suggests the widespread extent of regumming activity. Regumming also may be used to hide repairs or thin spots. Dipping the stamp into watermark fluid, or examining it under longwave ultraviolet light often will reveal these flaws.

Fakers also tamper with separations. Ingenious ways to add margins are known. Perforated wide-margin stamps may be falsely represented as imperforate when trimmed. Reperforating is commonly done to create scarce coil or perforation varieties, and to eliminate the naturally occurring straight-edge stamps found in sheet margin positions of many earlier issues. Custom has made straight-edged stamps less desirable. Fakers have obliged by perforating straight-edged stamps so that many are now uncommon, if not rare.

Another fertile field for the faker is that of overprints, surcharges and cancellations. The forging of rare surcharges or overprints began in the 1880s or 1890s. These forgeries are sometimes difficult to detect, but experts have identified almost all. Occasionally, overprints or cancellations are removed to create non-overprinted stamps or seemingly unused items. This is most commonly done by removing a manuscript cancel to make a stamp resemble an unused example. "SPECIMEN" overprints may be removed by scraping and repainting to create non-overprinted varieties. Fakers use inexpensive revenues or pen-canceled stamps to generate unused stamps for further faking by adding other markings. The quartz lamp or UV lamp and a high-powered magnifying glass help to easily detect removed cancellations.

The bigger problem, however, is the addition of overprints, surcharges or cancellations - many with such precision that they are very difficult to ascertain. Plating of the stamps or the overprint can be an important method of detection.

Fake postmarks may range from many spurious fancy cancellations to a host of markings applied to transatlantic covers, to adding normally appearing postmarks to definitives of some countries with stamps that are valued far higher used than unused. With the increased popularity of cover collecting, and the widespread interest in postal history, a fertile new field for fakers has come about. Some have tried to create entire covers. Others specialize in adding stamps, tied by fake cancellations, to genuine stampless covers, or replacing less expensive or damaged stamps with more valuable ones. Detailed study of postal rates in effect at the time a cover in question was mailed, including the analysis of each handstamp used during the period, ink analysis and similar techniques, usually will unmask the fraud.

Restoration and Repairs

Scott Publishing Co. bases its catalogue values on stamps that are free of defects and otherwise meet the standards set forth earlier in this introduction. Most stamp collectors desire to have the finest copy of an item possible. Even within given grading categories there are variances. This leads to a controversial practice that is not defined in any universal manner: stamp *restoration.*

There are broad differences of opinion about what is permissible when it comes to restoration. Carefully applying a soft eraser to a stamp or cover to remove light soiling is one form of restoration, as is washing a stamp in mild soap and water to clean it. These are fairly accepted forms of restoration. More severe forms of restoration include pressing out creases or removing stains caused by tape. To what degree each of these is acceptable is dependent upon the individual situation. Further along the spectrum is the freshening of a stamp's color by removing oxide build-up or the effects of wax paper left next to stamps shipped to the tropics.

At some point in this spectrum the concept of *repair* replaces that of restoration. Repairs include filling thin spots, mending tears by reweaving or adding a missing perforation tooth. Regumming stamps may have been acceptable as a restoration or repair technique many decades ago, but today it is considered a form of fakery.

Restored stamps may or may not sell at a discount, and it is possible that the value of individual restored items may be enhanced over that of their pre-restoration state. Specific situations dictate the resultant value of such an item. Repaired stamps sell at substantial discounts from the value of sound stamps.

Terminology

Booklets — Many countries have issued stamps in small booklets for the convenience of users. This idea continues to become increasingly popular in many countries. Booklets have been issued in many sizes and forms, often with advertising on the covers, the panes of stamps or on the interleaving.

The panes used in booklets may be printed from special plates or made from regular sheets. All panes from booklets issued by the United States and many from those of other countries contain stamps that are straight edged on the sides, but perforated between. Others are distinguished by orientation of watermark or other identifying features. Any stamp-like unit in the pane, either printed or blank, that is not a postage stamp, is considered to be a *label* in the catalogue listings.

Scott lists and values booklet panes. Modern complete booklets also are listed and valued. Individual booklet panes are listed only when they are not fashioned from existing sheet stamps and, therefore, are identifiable from their sheet stamp counterparts.

Panes usually do not have a used value assigned to them because there is little market activity for used booklet panes, even though many exist used and there is some demand for them.

Cancellations — The marks or obliterations put on stamps by postal authorities to show that they have performed service and to prevent their reuse are known as cancellations. If the marking is made with a pen, it is considered a "pen cancel." When the location of the post office appears in the marking, it is a "town cancellation." A "postmark" is technically any postal marking, but in practice the term generally is applied to a town cancellation with a date. When calling attention to a cause or celebration, the marking is known as a "slogan cancellation." Many other types and styles of cancellations exist, such as duplex, numerals, targets, fancy and others. See also "precancels," below.

Coil Stamps — These are stamps that are issued in rolls for use in dispensers, affixing and vending machines. Those coils of the United States, Canada, Sweden and some other countries are perforated horizontally or vertically only, with the outer edges imperforate. Coil stamps of some countries, such as Great Britain and Germany, are perforated on all four sides and may in some cases be distinguished from their sheet stamp counterparts by watermarks, counting numbers on the reverse or other means.

Covers — Entire envelopes, with or without adhesive postage stamps, that have passed through the mail and bear postal or other markings of philatelic interest are known as covers. Before the introduction of envelopes in about 1840, people folded letters and wrote the address on the outside. Some people covered their letters with an extra sheet of paper on the outside for the address, producing the term "cover." Used airletter sheets, stamped envelopes and other items of postal stationery also are considered covers.

Errors — Stamps that have some major, consistent, unintentional deviation from the normal are considered errors. Errors include, but are not limited to, missing or wrong colors, wrong paper, wrong watermarks, inverted centers or frames on multicolor printing, inverted or missing surcharges or overprints, double impressions, missing perforations, unintentionally omitted tagging and others. Factually wrong or misspelled information, if it appears on all examples of a stamp, are not considered errors in the true sense of the word. They are errors of design. Inconsistent or randomly appearing items, such as misperfs or color shifts, are classified as freaks.

Color-Omitted Errors — This term refers to stamps where a missing color is caused by the complete failure of the printing plate to deliver ink to the stamp paper or any other paper. Generally, this is caused by the printing plate not being engaged on the press or the ink station running dry of ink during printing.

Color-Missing Errors — This term refers to stamps where a color or colors were printed somewhere but do not appear on the finished stamp. There are four different classes of color-missing errors, and the catalog indicates with a two-letter code appended to each such listing what caused the color to be missing. These codes are used only for the United States' color-missing error listings.

FO = A *foldover* of the stamp sheet during printing may block ink from appearing on a stamp. Instead, the color will appear on the back of the foldover (where it might fall on the back of the selvage or perhaps on the back of the stamp or another stamp). FO also will be used in the case of foldunders, where the paper may fold underneath the other stamp paper and the color will print on the platen.

EP = A piece of *extraneous paper* falling across the plate or stamp paper will receive the printed ink. When the extraneous paper is removed, an unprinted portion of stamp paper remains and shows partially or totally missing colors.

CM = A misregistration of the printing plates during printing will result in a *color misregistration*, and such a misregistraion may result in a color not appearing on the finished stamp.

PS = A *perforation shift* after printing may remove a color from the finished stamp. Normally, this will occur on a row of stamps at the edge of the stamp pane.

Measurements – When measurements are given in the Scott catalogues for stamp size, grill size or any other reason, the first measurement given is always for the top and bottom dimension, while the second measurement will be for the sides (just as perforation gauges are measured). Thus, a stamp size of 15mm x 21mm will indicate a vertically oriented stamp 15mm wide at top and bottom, and 21mm tall at the sides. The same principle holds for measuring or counting items such as U.S. grills. A grill count of 22x18 points (B grill) indicates that there are 22 grill points across by 18 grill points down.

Overprints and Surcharges — Overprinting involves applying wording or design elements over an already existing stamp. Overprints can be used to alter the place of use (such as "Canal Zone" on U.S. stamps), to adapt them for a special purpose ("Porto" on Denmark's 1913-20 regular issues for use as postage due stamps, Scott J1-J7) or to commemorate a special occasion (United States Scott 647-648).

A *surcharge* is a form of overprint that changes or restates the face value of a stamp or piece of postal stationery.

Surcharges and overprints may be handstamped, typeset or, occasionally, lithographed or engraved. A few hand-written overprints and surcharges are known.

Personalized Stamps — In 1999, Australia issued stamps with se-tenant labels that could be personalized with pictures of the customer's choice. Other countries quickly followed suit, with some offering to print the selected picture on the stamp itself within a frame that was used exclusively for personalized issues. As the picture used on these stamps or labels vary, listings for such stamps are for *any* picture within the common frame (or any picture on a se-tenant label), be it a "generic" image or one produced especially for a customer, almost invariably at a premium price.

Precancels — Stamps that are canceled before they are placed in the mail are known as precancels. Precanceling usually is done to expedite the handling of large mailings and generally allow the affected mail pieces to skip certain phases of mail handling.

In the United States, precancellations generally identified the point of origin; that is, the city and state. This information appeared across the face of the stamp, usually centered between parallel lines. More recently, bureau precancels retained the parallel lines, but the city and state designations were dropped. Recent coils have a service inscription that is present on the original printing plate. These show the mail service paid for by the stamp. Since these stamps are not intended to receive further cancellations when used as intended, they are considered precancels. Such items often do not have parallel lines as part of the precancellation.

In France, the abbreviation *Affranchts* in a semicircle together with the word *Postes* is the general form of precancel in use. Belgian precancellations usually appear in a box in which the name of the city appears. Netherlands precancels have the name of the city enclosed between concentric circles, sometimes called a "lifesaver." Precancellations of other countries usually follow these patterns, but may be any arrangement of bars, boxes and city names.

Precancels are listed in the Scott catalogues only if the precancel changes the denomination (Belgium Scott 477-478); if the precanceled stamp is different from the non-precanceled version (such as untagged U.S. precancels); or if the stamp exists only precanceled (France Scott 1096-1099, U.S. Scott 2265).

Proofs and Essays — Proofs are impressions taken from an approved die, plate or stone in which the design and color are the same as the stamp issued to the public. Trial color proofs are impressions taken from approved dies, plates or stones in colors that vary from the final version. An essay is the impression of a design that differs in some way from the issued stamp. "Progressive die proofs" generally are considered to be essays.

Provisionals — These are stamps that are issued on short notice and intended for temporary use pending the arrival of regular issues. They usually are issued to meet such contingencies as changes in government or currency, shortage of necessary postage values or military occupation.

During the 1840s, postmasters in certain American cities issued stamps that were valid only at specific post offices. In 1861, postmasters of the Confederate States also issued stamps with limited validity. Both of these examples are known as "postmaster's provisionals."

Se-tenant — This term refers to an unsevered pair, strip or block of stamps that differ in design, denomination or overprint.

Unless the se-tenant item has a continuous design (see U.S. Scott 1451a, 1694a) the stamps do not have to be in the same order as shown in the catalogue (see U.S. Scott 2158a).

Specimens — The Universal Postal Union required member nations to send samples of all stamps they released into service to the International Bureau in Switzerland. Member nations of the UPU received these specimens as samples of what stamps were valid for postage. Many are overprinted, handstamped or initial-perforated "Specimen," "Canceled" or "Muestra." Some are marked with bars across the denominations (China-Taiwan), punched holes (Czechoslovakia) or back inscriptions (Mongolia).

Stamps distributed to government officials or for publicity purposes, and stamps submitted by private security printers for official approval, also may receive such defacements.

The previously described defacement markings prevent postal use, and all such items generally are known as "specimens."

Tete Beche — This term describes a pair of stamps in which one is upside down in relation to the other. Some of these are the result of intentional sheet arrangements, such as Morocco Scott B10-B11. Others occurred when one or more electrotypes accidentally were placed upside down on the plate, such as Colombia Scott 57a. Separation of the tete-beche stamps, of course, destroys the tete beche variety.

Currency Conversion

Country	Dollar	Pound	S Franc	Yen	HK $	Euro	Cdn $	Aus $
Australia	1.0151	1.6049	1.0355	0.0121	0.1306	1.3427	1.0057	—
Canada	1.0093	1.5957	1.0296	0.0120	0.1298	1.3351	—	0.9943
European Union	0.7560	1.1952	0.7712	0.0090	0.0973	—	0.7490	0.7448
Hong Kong	7.7731	12.289	7.9293	0.0926	—	10.282	7.7015	7.6575
Japan	83.942	132.71	85.629	—	10.799	111.03	83.169	82.693
Switzerland	0.9803	1.5499	—	0.0117	0.1261	1.2967	0.9713	0.9657
United Kingdom	0.6325	—	0.6452	0.0075	0.0814	0.8367	0.6267	0.6231
United States	—	1.5810	1.0201	0.0119	0.1286	1.3228	0.9908	0.9851

Country	Currency	U.S. $ Equiv.
Cambodia	riel	.0002
Cameroun	Community of French Africa (CFA) franc	.0020
Canada	dollar	.9908
Cape Verde	escudo	.0120
Cayman Islands	dollar	1.2345
Central African Republic	CFA franc	.0020
Chad	CFA franc	.0020
Chile	peso	.0021
China (Taiwan)	dollar	.0331
China (People's Republic)	yuan	.1503
Christmas Island	Australian dollar	.9851
Cocos Island	Australian dollar	.9851
Colombia	peso	.0005
Comoro Islands	franc	.0027
Congo Republic	CFA franc	.0020
Cook Islands	New Zealand dollar	.7481
Costa Rica	colon	.0020
Croatia	kuna	.1786
Cyprus	euro	1.3228
Czech Republic	koruna	.0525
Denmark	krone	.1775
Djibouti	franc	.0057
Dominica	East Caribbean dollar	.3724
Dominican Republic	peso	.0268
Ecuador	US dollar	1.00
Egypt	pound	.1727
Equatorial Guinea	CFA franc	.0020
Eritrea	nakfa	.0662
Estonia	kroon	.0845
Ethiopia	birr	.0603
Falkland Islands	pound	1.5810
Faroe Islands	krone	.1775
Fiji	dollar	.5381
Finland	euro	1.3228
Aland Islands	euro	1.3228
France	euro	1.3228
French Polynesia	Community of French Pacific (CFP) franc	.0112
French So. & Antarctic Terr.	euro	1.3228

*Source: **Wall Street Journal** Dec. 11, 2010. Figures reflect values as of Dec. 10, 2010.*

COMMON DESIGN TYPES

Pictured in this section are issues where one illustration has been used for a number of countries in the Catalogue. Not included in this section are overprinted stamps or those issues which are illustrated in each country.

EUROPA
Europa, 1956

The design symbolizing the cooperation among the six countries comprising the Coal and Steel Community is illustrated in each country.

Belgium	496-497
France	805-806
Germany	748-749
Italy	715-716
Luxembourg	318-320
Netherlands	368-369

Europa, 1958

"E" and Dove — CD1

European Postal Union at the service of European integration.

1958, Sept. 13

Belgium	527-528
France	889-890
Germany	790-791
Italy	750-751
Luxembourg	341-343
Netherlands	375-376
Saar	317-318

Europa, 1959

6-Link Enless Chain — CD2

1959, Sept. 19

Belgium	536-537
France	929-930
Germany	805-806
Italy	791-792
Luxembourg	354-355
Netherlands	379-380

Europa, 1960

19-Spoke Wheel CD3

First anniversary of the establishment of C.E.P.T. (Conference Europeenne des Administrations des Postes et des Telecommunications.) The spokes symbolize the 19 founding members of the Conference.

1960, Sept.

Belgium	553-554
Denmark	379
Finland	376-377
France	970-971
Germany	818-820
Great Britain	377-378
Greece	688
Iceland	327-328

Ireland	175-176
Italy	809-810
Luxembourg	374-375
Netherlands	385-386
Norway	387
Portugal	866-867
Spain	941-942
Sweden	562-563
Switzerland	400-401
Turkey	1493-1494

Europa, 1961

19 Doves Flying as One — CD4

The 19 doves represent the 19 members of the Conference of European Postal and Telecommunications Administrations C.E.P.T.

1961-62

Belgium	572-573
Cyprus	201-203
France	1005-1006
Germany	844-845
Great Britain	383-384
Greece	718-719
Iceland	340-341
Italy	845-846
Luxembourg	382-383
Netherlands	387-388
Spain	1010-1011
Switzerland	410-411
Turkey	1518-1520

Europa, 1962

Young Tree with 19 Leaves CD5

The 19 leaves represent the 19 original members of C.E.P.T.

1962-63

Belgium	582-583
Cyprus	219-221
France	1045-1046
Germany	852-853
Greece	739-740
Iceland	348-349
Ireland	184-185
Italy	860-861
Luxembourg	386-387
Netherlands	394-395
Norway	414-415
Switzerland	416-417
Turkey	1553-1555

Europa, 1963

Stylized Links, Symbolizing Unity — CD6

1963, Sept.

Belgium	598-599
Cyprus	229-231
Finland	419
France	1074-1075
Germany	867-868
Greece	768-769
Iceland	357-358
Ireland	188-189
Italy	880-881
Luxembourg	403-404
Netherlands	416-417
Norway	441-442
Switzerland	429
Turkey	1602-1603

Europa, 1964

Symbolic Daisy — CD7

5th anniversary of the establishment of C.E.P.T. The 22 petals of the flower symbolize the 22 members of the Conference.

1964, Sept.

Austria	738
Belgium	614-615
Cyprus	244-246
France	1109-1110
Germany	897-898
Greece	801-802
Iceland	367-368
Ireland	196-197
Italy	894-895
Luxembourg	411-412
Monaco	590-591
Netherlands	428-429
Norway	458
Portugal	931-933
Spain	1262-1263
Switzerland	438-439
Turkey	1628-1629

Europa, 1965

Leaves and "Fruit" CD8

1965

Belgium	636-637
Cyprus	262-264
Finland	437
France	1131-1132
Germany	934-935
Greece	833-834
Iceland	375-376
Ireland	204-205
Italy	915-916
Luxembourg	432-433
Monaco	616-617
Netherlands	438-439
Norway	475-476
Portugal	958-960
Switzerland	469
Turkey	1665-1666

Europa, 1966

Symbolic Sailboat — CD9

1966, Sept.

Andorra, French	172
Belgium	675-676
Cyprus	275-277
France	1163-1164
Germany	963-964
Greece	862-863
Iceland	384-385
Ireland	216-217
Italy	942-943
Liechtenstein	415
Luxembourg	440-441
Monaco	639-640
Netherlands	441-442
Norway	496-497
Portugal	980-982
Switzerland	477-478
Turkey	1718-1719

Europa, 1967

Cogwheels CD10

1967

Andorra, French	174-175
Belgium	688-689
Cyprus	297-299
France	1178-1179
Germany	969-970
Greece	891-892
Iceland	389-390
Ireland	232-233
Italy	951-952
Liechtenstein	420
Luxembourg	449-450
Monaco	669-670
Netherlands	444-447
Norway	504-505
Portugal	994-996
Spain	1465-1466
Switzerland	482
Turkey	B120-B121

Europa, 1968

Golden Key with C.E.P.T. Emblem CD11

1968

Andorra, French	182-183
Belgium	705-706
Cyprus	314-316

France......1209-1210
Germany......983-984
Greece......916-917
Iceland......395-396
Ireland......242-243
Italy......979-980
Liechtenstein......442
Luxembourg......466-467
Monaco......689-691
Netherlands......452-453
Portugal......1019-1021
San Marino......687
Spain......1526
Turkey......1775-1776

Europa, 1969

"EUROPA" and "CEPT" CD12

Tenth anniversary of C.E.P.T.

1969

Andorra, French......188-189
Austria......837
Belgium......718-719
Cyprus......326-328
Denmark......458
Finland......483
France......1245-1246
Germany......996-997
Great Britain......585
Greece......947-948
Iceland......406-407
Ireland......270-271
Italy......1000-1001
Liechtenstein......453
Luxembourg......475-476
Monaco......722-724
Netherlands......475-476
Norway......533-534
Portugal......1038-1040
San Marino......701-702
Spain......1567
Sweden......814-816
Switzerland......500-501
Turkey......1799-1800
Vatican......470-472
Yugoslavia......1003-1004

Europa, 1970

Interwoven Threads CD13

1970

Andorra, French......196-197
Belgium......741-742
Cyprus......340-342
France......1271-1272
Germany......1018-1019
Greece......985, 987
Iceland......420-421
Ireland......279-281
Italy......1013-1014
Liechtenstein......470
Luxembourg......489-490
Monaco......768-770
Netherlands......483-484
Portugal......1060-1062
San Marino......729-730
Spain......1607
Switzerland......515-516
Turkey......1848-1849
Yugoslavia......1024-1025

Europa, 1971

"Fraternity, Cooperation, Common Effort" CD14

1971

Andorra, French......205-206

Belgium......803-804
Cyprus......365-367
Finland......504
France......1304
Germany......1064-1065
Greece......1029-1030
Iceland......429-430
Ireland......305-306
Italy......1038-1039
Liechtenstein......485
Luxembourg......500-501
Malta......425-427
Monaco......797-799
Netherlands......488-489
Portugal......1094-1096
San Marino......749-750
Spain......1675-1676
Switzerland......531-532
Turkey......1876-1877
Yugoslavia......1052-1053

Europa, 1972

Sparkles, Symbolic of Communications CD15

1972

Andorra, French......210-211
Andorra, Spanish......62
Belgium......825-826
Cyprus......380-382
Finland......512-513
France......1341
Germany......1089-1090
Greece......1049-1050
Iceland......439-440
Ireland......316-317
Italy......1065-1066
Liechtenstein......504
Luxembourg......512-513
Malta......450-453
Monaco......831-832
Netherlands......494-495
Portugal......1141-1143
San Marino......771-772
Spain......1718
Switzerland......544-545
Turkey......1907-1908
Yugoslavia......1100-1101

Europa, 1973

Post Horn and Arrows CD16

1973

Andorra, French......219-220
Andorra, Spanish......76
Belgium......839-840
Cyprus......396-398
Finland......526
France......1367
Germany......1114-1115
Greece......1090-1092
Iceland......447-448
Ireland......329-330
Italy......1108-1109
Liechtenstein......528-529
Luxembourg......523-524
Malta......469-471
Monaco......866-867
Netherlands......504-505
Norway......604-605
Portugal......1170-1172
San Marino......802-803
Spain......1753
Switzerland......580-581
Turkey......1935-1936
Yugoslavia......1138-1139

Europa, 2000

CD17

2000

Albania......2621-2622
Andorra, French......522
Andorra, Spanish......262
Armenia......610-611
Austria......1814
Azerbaijan......698-699
Belarus......350
Belgium......1818
Bosnia & Herzegovina (Moslem)......358
Bosnia & Herzegovina (Serb)......111-112
Croatia......428-429
Cyprus......959
Czech Republic......3120
Denmark......1189
Estonia......394
Faroe Islands......376
Finland......1129
Aland Islands......166
France......2771
Georgia......228-229
Germany......2086-2087
Gibraltar......837-840
Great Britain (Guernsey)......805-809
Great Britain (Jersey)......935-936
Great Britain (Isle of Man)......883
Greece......1959
Greenland......363
Hungary......3699-3700
Iceland......910
Ireland......1230-1231
Italy......2349
Latvia......504
Liechtenstein......1178
Lithuania......668
Luxembourg......1035
Macedonia......187
Malta......1011-1012
Moldova......355
Monaco......2161-2162
Poland......3519
Portugal......2358
Portugal (Azores)......455
Portugal (Madeira)......208
Romania......4370
Russia......6589
San Marino......1480
Slovakia......355
Slovenia......424
Spain......3036
Sweden......2394
Switzerland......1074
Turkey......2762
Turkish Rep. of Northern Cyprus......500
Ukraine......379
Vatican City......1152

The Gibraltar stamps are similar to the stamp illustrated, but none have the design shown above. All other sets listed above include at least one stamp with the design shown, but some include stamps with entirely different designs. Bulgaria Nos. 4131-4132 and Yugoslavia Nos. 2485-2486 are Europa stamps with completely different designs.

PORTUGAL & COLONIES
Vasco da Gama

Fleet Departing CD20

Fleet Arriving at Calicut — CD21

Embarking at Rastello CD22

Muse of History CD23

San Gabriel, da Gama and Camoens CD24

Archangel Gabriel, the Patron Saint CD25

Flagship San Gabriel — CD26

Vasco da Gama — CD27

Fourth centenary of Vasco da Gama's discovery of the route to India.

1898

Azores......93-100
Macao......67-74
Madeira......37-44
Portugal......147-154
Port. Africa......1-8
Port. Congo......75-98
Port. India......189-196
St. Thomas & Prince Islands...170-193
Timor......45-52

Pombal
POSTAL TAX
POSTAL TAX DUES

Marquis de Pombal — CD28

Planning Reconstruction of Lisbon, 1755 — CD29

Pombal Monument, Lisbon — CD30

Sebastiao Jose de Carvalho e Mello, Marquis de Pombal (1699-1782), statesman, rebuilt Lisbon after earthquake of 1755. Tax was for the erection of Pombal monument. Obligatory on all mail on certain days throughout the year. Postal Tax Dues are inscribed "Multa."

1925

Angola..............RA1-RA3, RAJ1-RAJ3
Azores.............RA9-RA11, RAJ2-RAJ4
Cape Verde......RA1-RA3, RAJ1-RAJ3
Macao..............RA1-RA3, RAJ1-RAJ3
Madeira...........RA1-RA3, RAJ1-RAJ3
Mozambique.....RA1-RA3, RAJ1-RAJ3

Nyassa............. RA1-RA3, RAJ1-RAJ3
Portugal RA11-RA13, RAJ2-RAJ4
Port. Guinea RA1-RA3, RAJ1-RAJ3
Port. India........ RA1-RA3, RAJ1-RAJ3
St. Thomas & Prince
Islands RA1-RA3, RAJ1-RAJ3
Timor RA1-RA3, RAJ1-RAJ3

Vasco da Gama
CD34

Mousinho de
Albuquerque
CD35

Dam
CD36

Prince Henry
the Navigator
CD37

Affonso de
Albuquerque
CD38

Plane over
Globe
CD39

1938-39

Angola 274-291, C1-C9
Cape Verde 234-251, C1-C9
Macao......................... 289-305, C7-C15
Mozambique................ 270-287, C1-C9
Port. Guinea 233-250, C1-C9
Port. India.................. 439-453, C1-C8
St. Thomas & Prince
Islands ... 302-319, 323-340, C1-C18
Timor 223-239, C1-C9

Lady of Fatima

Our Lady of the
Rosary, Fatima,
Portugal — CD40

1948-49

Angola 315-318
Cape Verde 266
Macao.....................................336
Mozambique.......................325-328
Port. Guinea 271
Port. India..............................480
St. Thomas & Prince Islands 351
Timor 254

A souvenir sheet of 9 stamps was issued in 1951 to mark the extension of the 1950 Holy Year. The sheet contains: Angola No. 316, Cape Verde No. 266, Macao No. 336, Mozambique No. 325, Portuguese Guinea No. 271, Portuguese India Nos. 480, 485, St. Thomas & Prince Islands No. 351, Timor No. 254. The sheet also contains a portrait of Pope Pius XII and is inscribed "Encerramento do Ano Santo, Fatima 1951." It was sold for 11 escudos.

Holy Year

Church Bells and
Dove
CD41

Angel Holding
Candelabra
CD42

Holy Year, 1950.

1950-51

Angola 331-332
Cape Verde 268-269
Macao.................................339-340
Mozambique.........................330-331
Port. Guinea 273-274
Port. India................ 490-491, 496-503
St. Thomas & Prince Islands ...353-354
Timor 258-259

A souvenir sheet of 8 stamps was issued in 1951 to mark the extension of the Holy Year. The sheet contains: Angola No. 331, Cape Verde No. 269, Macao No. 340, Mozambique No. 331, Portuguese Guinea No. 275, Portuguese India No. 490, St. Thomas & Prince Islands No. 354, Timor No. 258, some with colors changed. The sheet contains doves and is inscribed 'Encerramento do Ano Santo, Fatima 1951.' It was sold for 17 escudos.

Holy Year Conclusion

Our Lady of
Fatima — CD43

Conclusion of Holy Year. Sheets contain alternate vertical rows of stamps and labels bearing quotation from Pope Pius XII, different for each colony.

1951

Angola 357
Cape Verde 270
Macao.......................................352
Mozambique...............................356
Port. Guinea 275
Port. India.................................506
St. Thomas & Prince Islands 355
Timor 270

Medical Congress

CD44

First National Congress of Tropical Medicine, Lisbon, 1952. Each stamp has a different design.

1952

Angola 358
Cape Verde 287
Macao.......................................364
Mozambique...............................359
Port. Guinea 276
Port. India.................................516
St. Thomas & Prince Islands 356
Timor 271

Postage Due Stamps

CD45

1952

Angola J37-J42
Cape Verde J31-J36

Macao.................................J53-J58
Mozambique.........................J51-J56
Port. Guinea J40-J45
Port. India...........................J47-J52
St. Thomas & Prince Islands ...J52-J57
Timor J31-J36

Sao Paulo

Father Manuel
da Nobrega
and View of
Sao
Paulo — CD46

Founding of Sao Paulo, Brazil, 400th anniv.

1954

Angola 385
Cape Verde 297
Macao.......................................382
Mozambique...............................395
Port. Guinea 291
Port. India.................................530
St. Thomas & Prince Islands 369
Timor 279

Tropical Medicine Congress

CD47

Sixth International Congress for Tropical Medicine and Malaria, Lisbon, Sept. 1958. Each stamp shows a different plant.

1958

Angola 409
Cape Verde 303
Macao.......................................392
Mozambique...............................404
Port. Guinea 295
Port. India.................................569
St. Thomas & Prince Islands 371
Timor 289

Sports

CD48

Each stamp shows a different sport.

1962

Angola 433-438
Cape Verde 320-325
Macao...................................394-399
Mozambique...........................424-429
Port. Guinea 299-304
St. Thomas & Prince Islands ...374-379
Timor 313-318

Anti-Malaria

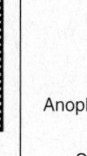

Anopheles Funestus
and Malaria
Eradication
Symbol — CD49

World Health Organization drive to eradicate malaria.

1962

Angola 439
Cape Verde 326
Macao.......................................400
Mozambique...............................430
Port. Guinea 305
St. Thomas & Prince Islands 380
Timor 319

Airline Anniversary

Map of Africa, Super
Constellation and Jet
Liner — CD50

Tenth anniversary of Transportes Aereos Portugueses (TAP).

1963

Angola 490
Cape Verde 327
Mozambique...............................434
Port. Guinea 318
St. Thomas & Prince Islands 381

National Overseas Bank

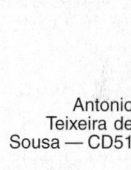

Antonio
Teixeira de
Sousa — CD51

Centenary of the National Overseas Bank of Portugal.

1964, May 16

Angola 509
Cape Verde 328
Port. Guinea 319
St. Thomas & Prince Islands 382
Timor 320

ITU

ITU Emblem and
the Archangel
Gabriel — CD52

International Communications Union, Cent.

1965, May 17

Angola 511
Cape Verde 329
Macao.......................................402
Mozambique...............................464
Port. Guinea 320
St. Thomas & Prince Islands 383
Timor 321

National Revolution

CD53

40th anniv. of the National Revolution. Different buildings on each stamp.

1966, May 28

Angola 525
Cape Verde 338
Macao.......................................403
Mozambique...............................465
Port. Guinea 329
St. Thomas & Prince Islands 392
Timor 322

Navy Club

CD54

Centenary of Portugal's Navy Club. Each stamp has a different design.

1967, Jan. 31

Angola 527-528
Cape Verde 339-340
Macao..................................412-413
Mozambique........................478-479
Port. Guinea........................330-331
St. Thomas & Prince Islands ...393-394
Timor 323-324

Admiral Coutinho

CD55

Centenary of the birth of Admiral Carlos Viegas Gago Coutinho (1869-1959), explorer and aviation pioneer. Each stamp has a different design.

1969, Feb. 17

Angola 547
Cape Verde 355
Macao..417
Mozambique...............................484
Port. Guinea...............................335
St. Thomas & Prince Islands 397
Timor 335

Administration Reform

Luiz Augusto Rebello da Silva — CD56

Centenary of the administration reforms of the overseas territories.

1969, Sept. 25

Angola 549
Cape Verde 357
Macao..419
Mozambique...............................491
Port. Guinea...............................337
St. Thomas & Prince Islands 399
Timor 338

Marshal Carmona

CD57

Birth centenary of Marshal Antonio Oscar Carmona de Fragoso (1869-1951), President of Portugal. Each stamp has a different design.

1970, Nov. 15

Angola 563
Cape Verde 359
Macao..422
Mozambique...............................493
Port. Guinea...............................340
St. Thomas & Prince Islands 403
Timor 341

Olympic Games

CD59

20th Olympic Games, Munich, Aug. 26-Sept. 11. Each stamp shows a different sport.

1972, June 20

Angola 569
Cape Verde 361
Macao..426
Mozambique...............................504
Port. Guinea...............................342
St. Thomas & Prince Islands 408
Timor 343

Lisbon-Rio de Janeiro Flight

CD60

50th anniversary of the Lisbon to Rio de Janeiro flight by Arturo de Sacadura and Coutinho, March 30-June 5, 1922. Each stamp shows a different stage of the flight.

1972, Sept. 20

Angola 570
Cape Verde 362
Macao..427
Mozambique...............................505
Port. Guinea...............................343
St. Thomas & Prince Islands 409
Timor 344

WMO Centenary

WMO Emblem — CD61

Centenary of international meterological cooperation.

1973, Dec. 15

Angola 571
Cape Verde 363
Macao..429
Mozambique...............................509
Port. Guinea...............................344
St. Thomas & Prince Islands 410
Timor 345

FRENCH COMMUNITY
Upper Volta can be found under Burkina Faso in Vol. 1
Madagascar can be found under Malagasy in Vol. 3
Colonial Exposition

People of French Empire CD70

Women's Heads CD71

France Showing Way to Civilization CD72

"Colonial Commerce" CD73

International Colonial Exposition, Paris.

1931

Cameroun..................................213-216
Chad..60-63
Dahomey.....................................97-100
Fr. Guiana 152-155
Fr. Guinea 116-119
Fr. India 100-103
Fr. Polynesia.................................76-79
Fr. Sudan..................................102-105
Gabon.......................................120-123
Guadeloupe...............................138-141
Indo-China.................................140-142
Ivory Coast..................................92-95
Madagascar...............................169-172
Martinique.................................129-132
Mauritania....................................65-68
Middle Congo................................61-64
New Caledonia...........................176-179
Niger..73-76
Reunion.....................................122-125
St. Pierre & Miquelon.................132-135
Senegal.....................................138-141
Somali Coast.............................135-138
Togo..254-257
Ubangi-Shari................................82-85
Upper Volta...................................66-69
Wallis & Futuna Isls. 85-88

Paris International Exposition
Colonial Arts Exposition

"Colonial Resources" CD74   CD77

Overseas Commerce CD75

Exposition Building and Women CD76

"France and the Empire" CD78

Cultural Treasures of the Colonies CD79

Souvenir sheets contain one imperf. stamp.

1937

Cameroun...................................217-222A
Dahomey 101-107
Fr. Equatorial Africa 27-32, 73

Fr. Guiana 162-168
Fr. Guinea 120-126
Fr. India 104-110
Fr. Polynesia.............................117-123
Fr. Sudan..................................106-112
Guadeloupe...............................148-154
Indo-China.................................193-199
Inini...41
Ivory Coast................................152-158
Kwangchowan..............................132
Madagascar...............................191-197
Martinique.................................179-185
Mauritania....................................69-75
New Caledonia...........................208-214
Niger..72-83
Reunion.....................................167-173
St. Pierre & Miquelon.................165-171
Senegal.....................................172-178
Somali Coast.............................139-145
Togo..258-264
Wallis & Futuna Isls. 89

Curie

Pierre and Marie Curie CD80

40th anniversary of the discovery of radium. The surtax was for the benefit of the Intl. Union for the Control of Cancer.

1938

Cameroun...................................... B1
Cuba..B1-B2
Dahomey B2
France B76
Fr. Equatorial Africa B1
Fr. Guiana B3
Fr. Guinea B2
Fr. India B6
Fr. Polynesia................................. B5
Fr. Sudan...................................... B1
Guadeloupe................................... B3
Indo-China................................... B14
Ivory Coast................................... B2
Madagascar.................................. B2
Martinique.................................... B2
Mauritania.................................... B3
New Caledonia.............................. B4
Niger... B1
Reunion.. B4
St. Pierre & Miquelon.................... B3
Senegal.. B3
Somali Coast................................ B2
Togo... B1

Caillie

Rene Caillie and Map of Northwestern Africa — CD81

Death centenary of Rene Caillie (1799-1838), French explorer. All three denominations exist with colony name omitted.

1939

Dahomey 108-110
Fr. Guinea 161-163
Fr. Sudan..................................113-115
Ivory Coast................................160-162
Mauritania.................................109-111
Niger..84-86
Senegal.....................................188-190
Togo..265-267

New York World's Fair

Natives and New York Skyline CD82

1939

Cameroun...................................223-224
Dahomey 111-112
Fr. Equatorial Africa 78-79
Fr. Guiana 169-170

Fr. Guinea	164-165
Fr. India	111-112
Fr. Polynesia	124-125
Fr. Sudan	116-117
Guadeloupe	155-156
Indo-China	203-204
Inini	42-43
Ivory Coast	163-164
Kwangchowan	121-122
Madagascar	209-210
Martinique	186-187
Mauritania	112-113
New Caledonia	215-216
Niger	87-88
Reunion	174-175
St. Pierre & Miquelon	205-206
Senegal	191-192
Somali Coast	179-180
Togo	268-269
Wallis & Futuna Isls.	90-91

French Revolution

Storming of
the Bastille
CD83

French Revolution, 150th anniv. The surtax was for the defense of the colonies.

1939

Cameroun	B2-B6
Dahomey	B3-B7
Fr. Equatorial Africa	B4-B8, CB1
Fr. Guiana	B4-B8, CB1
Fr. Guinea	B3-B7
Fr. India	B7-B11
Fr. Polynesia	B6-B10, CB1
Fr. Sudan	B2-B6
Guadeloupe	B4-B8
Indo-China	B15-B19, CB1
Inini	B1-B5
Ivory Coast	B3-B7
Kwangchowan	B1-B5
Madagascar	B3-B7, CB1
Martinique	B3-B7
Mauritania	B4-B8
New Caledonia	B5-B9, CB1
Niger	B2-B6
Reunion	B5-B9, CB1
St. Pierre & Miquelon	B4-B8
Senegal	B4-B8, CB1
Somali Coast	B3-B7
Togo	B2-B6
Wallis & Futuna Isls.	B1-B5

Plane over
Coastal
Area
CD85

All five denominations exist with colony name omitted.

1940

Dahomey	C1-C5
Fr. Guinea	C1-C5
Fr. Sudan	C1-C5
Ivory Coast	C1-C5
Mauritania	C1-C5
Niger	C1-C5
Senegal	C12-C16
Togo	C1-C5

Defense of the Empire

Colonial
Infantryman — CD86

1941

Cameroun	B13B
Dahomey	B13

Fr. Equatorial Africa	B8B
Fr. Guiana	B10
Fr. Guinea	B13
Fr. India	B13
Fr. Polynesia	B12
Fr. Sudan	B12
Guadeloupe	B10
Indo-China	B19B
Inini	B7
Ivory Coast	B13
Kwangchowan	B7
Madagascar	B9
Martinique	B9
Mauritania	B14
New Caledonia	B11
Niger	B12
Reunion	B11
St. Pierre & Miquelon	B8B
Senegal	B14
Somali Coast	B9
Togo	B10B
Wallis & Futuna Isls.	B7

Colonial Education Fund

CD86a

1942

Cameroun	CB3
Dahomey	CB4
Fr. Equatorial Africa	CB5
Fr. Guiana	CB4
Fr. Guinea	CB4
Fr. India	CB3
Fr. Polynesia	CB4
Fr. Sudan	CB4
Guadeloupe	CB3
Indo-China	CB5
Inini	CB3
Ivory Coast	CB4
Kwangchowan	CB4
Malagasy	CB5
Martinique	CB3
Mauritania	CB4
New Caledonia	CB4
Niger	CB4
Reunion	CB4
St. Pierre & Miquelon	CB3
Senegal	CB5
Somali Coast	CB3
Togo	CB3
Wallis & Futuna	CB3

Cross of
Lorraine &
Four-motor
Plane
CD87

1941-5

Cameroun	C1-C7
Fr. Equatorial Africa	C17-C23
Fr. Guiana	C9-C10
Fr. India	C1-C6
Fr. Polynesia	C3-C9
Fr. West Africa	C1-C3
Guadeloupe	C1-C2
Madagascar	C37-C43
Martinique	C1-C2
New Caledonia	C7-C13
Reunion	C18-C24
St. Pierre & Miquelon	C1-C7
Somali Coast	C1-C7

Transport
Plane
CD88

Caravan
and Plane
CD89

1942

Dahomey	C6-C13
Fr. Guinea	C6-C13
Fr. Sudan	C6-C13
Ivory Coast	C6-C13
Mauritania	C6-C13
Niger	C6-C13
Senegal	C17-C25
Togo	C6-C13

Red Cross

Marianne
CD90

The surtax was for the French Red Cross and national relief.

1944

Cameroun	B28
Fr. Equatorial Africa	B38
Fr. Guiana	B12
Fr. India	B14
Fr. Polynesia	B13
Fr. West Africa	B1
Guadeloupe	B12
Madagascar	B15
Martinique	B11
New Caledonia	B13
Reunion	B15
St. Pierre & Miquelon	B13
Somali Coast	B13
Wallis & Futuna Isls.	B9

Eboue

CD91

Felix Eboue, first French colonial administrator to proclaim resistance to Germany after French surrender in World War II.

1945

Cameroun	296-297
Fr. Equatorial Africa	156-157
Fr. Guiana	171-172
Fr. India	210-211
Fr. Polynesia	150-151
Fr. West Africa	15-16
Guadeloupe	187-188
Madagascar	259-260
Martinique	196-197
New Caledonia	274-275
Reunion	238-239
St. Pierre & Miquelon	322-323
Somali Coast	238-239

Victory

Victory — CD92

European victory of the Allied Nations in World War II.

1946, May 8

Cameroun	C8
Fr. Equatorial Africa	C24

Fr. Guiana	C11
Fr. India	C7
Fr. Polynesia	C10
Fr. West Africa	C4
Guadeloupe	C3
Indo-China	C19
Madagascar	C44
Martinique	C3
New Caledonia	C14
Reunion	C25
St. Pierre & Miquelon	C8
Somali Coast	C8
Wallis & Futuna Isls.	C1

Chad to Rhine

Leclerc's Departure from
Chad — CD93

Battle at Cufra Oasis — CD94

Tanks in Action, Mareth — CD95

Normandy Invasion — CD96

Entering Paris — CD97

Liberation of Strasbourg — CD98

"Chad to the Rhine" march, 1942-44, by Gen. Jacques Leclerc's column, later French 2nd Armored Division.

1946, June 6

Cameroun	C9-C14
Fr. Equatorial Africa	C25-C30
Fr. Guiana	C12-C17
Fr. India	C8-C13
Fr. Polynesia	C11-C16
Fr. West Africa	C5-C10
Guadeloupe	C4-C9
Indo-China	C20-C25
Madagascar	C45-C50
Martinique	C4-C9
New Caledonia	C15-C20
Reunion	C26-C31
St. Pierre & Miquelon	C9-C14
Somali Coast	C9-C14

Wallis & Futuna Isls. C2-C7

UPU

French Colonials, Globe and
Plane — CD99

Universal Postal Union, 75th anniv.

1949, July 4

Cameroun	C29
Fr. Equatorial Africa	C34
Fr. India	C17
Fr. Polynesia	C20
Fr. West Africa	C15
Indo-China	C26
Madagascar	C55
New Caledonia	C24
St. Pierre & Miquelon	C18
Somali Coast	C18
Togo	C18
Wallis & Futuna Isls.	C10

Tropical Medicine

Doctor
Treating
Infant
CD100

The surtax was for charitable work.

1950

Cameroun	B29
Fr. Equatorial Africa	B39
Fr. India	B15
Fr. Polynesia	B14
Fr. West Africa	B3
Madagascar	B17
New Caledonia	B14
St. Pierre & Miquelon	B14
Somali Coast	B14
Togo	B11

Military Medal

Medal, Early Marine
and Colonial
Soldier — CD101

Centenary of the creation of the French Military Medal.

1952

Cameroun	322
Comoro Isls.	39
Fr. Equatorial Africa	186
Fr. India	233
Fr. Polynesia	179
Fr. West Africa	57
Madagascar	286
New Caledonia	295
St. Pierre & Miquelon	345
Somali Coast	267
Togo	327
Wallis & Futuna Isls.	149

Liberation

Allied Landing, Victory Sign and Cross
of Lorraine — CD102

Liberation of France, 10th anniv.

1954, June 6

Cameroun	C32
Comoro Isls.	C4
Fr. Equatorial Africa	C38
Fr. India	C18
Fr. Polynesia	C22
Fr. West Africa	C17
Madagascar	C57
New Caledonia	C25
St. Pierre & Miquelon	C19
Somali Coast	C19
Togo	C19
Wallis & Futuna Isls.	C11

FIDES

Plowmen
CD103

Efforts of FIDES, the Economic and Social
Development Fund for Overseas Possessions
(Fonds d' Investissement pour le Developpe-
ment Economique et Social). Each stamp has
a different design.

1956

Cameroun	326-329
Comoro Isls.	43
Fr. Equatorial Africa	189-192
Fr. Polynesia	181
Fr. West Africa	65-72
Madagascar	292-295
New Caledonia	303
St. Pierre & Miquelon 350	
Somali Coast	268
Togo	331

Flower

CD104

Each stamp shows a different flower.

1958-9

Cameroun	333
Comoro Isls.	45
Fr. Equatorial Africa	200-201
Fr. Polynesia	192
Fr. So. & Antarctic Terr.	11
Fr. West Africa	79-83
Madagascar	301-302
New Caledonia	304-305
St. Pierre & Miquelon	357
Somali Coast	270
Togo	348-349
Wallis & Futuna Isls.	152

Human Rights

Sun, Dove
and U.N.
Emblem
CD105

10th anniversary of the signing of the Universal Declaration of Human Rights.

1958

Comoro Isls.	44
Fr. Equatorial Africa	202
Fr. Polynesia	191
Fr. West Africa	85
Madagascar	300
New Caledonia	306
St. Pierre & Miquelon	356
Somali Coast	274
Wallis & Futuna Isls.	153

C.C.T.A.

CD106

Commission for Technical Cooperation in
Africa south of the Sahara, 10th anniv.

1960

Cameroun	339
Cent. Africa	3
Chad	66
Congo, P.R.	90
Dahomey	138
Gabon	150
Ivory Coast	180
Madagascar	317
Mali	9
Mauritania	117
Niger	104
Upper Volta	89

Air Afrique, 1961

Modern and Ancient Africa, Map and
Planes — CD107

Founding of Air Afrique (African Airlines).

1961-62

Cameroun	C37
Cent. Africa	C5
Chad	C7
Congo, P.R.	C5
Dahomey	C17
Gabon	C5
Ivory Coast	C18
Mauritania	C17
Niger	C22
Senegal	C31
Upper Volta	C4

Anti-Malaria

CD108

World Health Organization drive to eradicate malaria.

1962, Apr. 7

Cameroun	B36
Cent. Africa	B1
Chad	B1
Comoro Isls.	B1
Congo, P.R.	B3
Dahomey	B15
Gabon	B4
Ivory Coast	B15
Madagascar	B19
Mali	B1
Mauritania	B16
Niger	B14
Senegal	B16
Somali Coast	B15
Upper Volta	B1

Abidjan Games

CD109

Abidjan Games, Ivory Coast, Dec. 24-31,
1961. Each stamp shows a different sport.

1962

Chad	83-84
Cent. Africa	19-20
Congo, P.R.	103-104
Gabon	163-164, C6
Niger	109-111
Upper Volta	103-105

African and Malagasy Union

Flag of
Union
CD110

First anniversary of the Union.

1962, Sept. 8

Cameroun	373
Cent. Africa	21
Chad	85
Congo, P.R.	105
Dahomey	155
Gabon	165
Ivory Coast	198
Madagascar	332
Mauritania	170
Niger	112
Senegal	211
Upper Volta	106

Telstar

Telstar and Globe Showing Andover
and Pleumeur-Bodou — CD111

First television connection of the United
States and Europe through the Telstar satellite, July 11-12, 1962.

1962-63

Andorra, French	154
Comoro Isls.	C7
Fr. Polynesia	C29
Fr. So. & Antarctic Terr.	C5
New Caledonia	C33
Somali Coast	C31
St. Pierre & Miquelon	C26
Wallis & Futuna Isls.	C17

Freedom From Hunger

World Map
and Wheat
Emblem
CD112

U.N. Food and Agriculture Organization's
"Freedom from Hunger" campaign.

1963, Mar. 21

Cameroun	B37-B38
Cent. Africa	B2
Chad	B2
Congo, P.R.	B4
Dahomey	B16
Gabon	B5
Ivory Coast	B16
Madagascar	B21
Mauritania	B17
Niger	B15

Senegal B17
Upper Volta................................... B2

Red Cross Centenary

CD113

Centenary of the International Red Cross.

1963, Sept. 2

Comoro Isls. 55
Fr. Polynesia...................................205
New Caledonia 328
St. Pierre & Miquelon.....................367
Somali Coast 297
Wallis & Futuna Isls. 165

African Postal Union, 1963

UAMPT Emblem, Radio Masts, Plane and Mail CD114

Establishment of the African and Malagasy Posts and Telecommunications Union.

1963, Sept. 8

Cameroun...................................... C47
Cent. Africa C10
Chad.. C9
Congo, P.R.................................... C13
Dahomey C19
Gabon.. C13
Ivory Coast................................... C25
Madagascar C75
Mauritania C22
Niger.. C27
Rwanda 36
Senegal C32
Upper Volta..................................... C9

Air Afrique, 1963

Symbols of Flight — CD115

First anniversary of Air Afrique and inauguration of DC-8 service.

1963, Nov. 19

Cameroun...................................... C48
Chad.. C10
Congo, P.R.................................... C14
Gabon.. C18
Ivory Coast................................... C26
Mauritania C26
Niger.. C35
Senegal C33

Europafrica

Europe and Africa Linked — CD116

Signing of an economic agreement between the European Economic Community and the African and Malagasy Union, Yaounde, Cameroun, July 20, 1963.

1963-64

Cameroun......................................402
Chad.. C11
Cent. Africa C12
Congo, P.R.................................... C16
Gabon.. C19
Ivory Coast...................................217
Niger.. C43
Upper Volta................................... C11

Human Rights

Scales of Justice and Globe CD117

15th anniversary of the Universal Declaration of Human Rights.

1963, Dec. 10

Comoro Isls. 58
Fr. Polynesia...................................206
New Caledonia 329
St. Pierre & Miquelon.....................368
Somali Coast 300
Wallis & Futuna Isls. 166

PHILATEC

Stamp Album, Champs Elysees Palace and Horses of Marly CD118

Intl. Philatelic and Postal Techniques Exhibition, Paris, June 5-21, 1964.

1963-64

Comoro Isls. 60
France..1078
Fr. Polynesia...................................207
New Caledonia 341
St. Pierre & Miquelon.....................369
Somali Coast 301
Wallis & Futuna Isls. 167

Cooperation

CD119

Cooperation between France and the French-speaking countries of Africa and Madagascar.

1964

Cameroun................................409-410
Cent. Africa 39

Chad..103
Congo, P.R.....................................121
Dahomey 193
France...1111
Gabon..175
Ivory Coast....................................221
Madagascar 360
Mauritania 181
Niger..143
Senegal 236
Togo...495

ITU

Telegraph, Syncom Satellite and ITU Emblem CD120

Intl. Telecommunication Union, Cent.

1965, May 17

Comoro Isls. C14
Fr. Polynesia................................ C33
Fr. So. & Antarctic Terr. C8
New Caledonia C40
New Hebrides......................124-125
St. Pierre & Miquelon.................. C29
Somali Coast C36
Wallis & Futuna Isls. C20

French Satellite A-1

Diamant Rocket and Launching Installation — CD121

Launching of France's first satellite, Nov. 26, 1965.

1965-66

Comoro Isls. C15-C16
France.............................1137-1138
Fr. Polynesia........................ C40-C41
Fr. So. & Antarctic Terr. C9-C10
New Caledonia C44-C45
St. Pierre & Miquelon........... C30-C31
Somali Coast C39-C40
Wallis & Futuna Isls. C22-C23

French Satellite D-1

D-1 Satellite in Orbit — CD122

Launching of the D-1 satellite at Hammaguir, Algeria, Feb. 17, 1966.

1966

Comoro Isls. C17
France...1148
Fr. Polynesia................................ C42
Fr. So. & Antarctic Terr. C11
New Caledonia C46
St. Pierre & Miquelon.................. C32
Somali Coast C49
Wallis & Futuna Isls. C24

Air Afrique, 1966

Planes and Air Afrique Emblem — CD123

Introduction of DC-8F planes by Air Afrique.

1966

Cameroun...................................... C79
Cent. Africa C35
Chad.. C26
Congo, P.R.................................... C42
Dahomey C42
Gabon.. C47
Ivory Coast................................... C32
Mauritania C57
Niger.. C63
Senegal C47
Togo.. C54
Upper Volta................................... C31

African Postal Union, 1967

Telecommunications Symbols and Map of Africa — CD124

Fifth anniversary of the establishment of the African and Malagasy Union of Posts and Telecommunications, UAMPT.

1967

Cameroun...................................... C90
Cent. Africa C46
Chad.. C37
Congo, P.R.................................... C57
Dahomey C61
Gabon.. C58
Ivory Coast................................... C34
Madagascar C85
Mauritania C65
Niger.. C75
Rwanda C1-C3
Senegal C60
Togo.. C81
Upper Volta................................... C50

Monetary Union

Gold Token of the Ashantis, 17-18th Centuries — CD125

West African Monetary Union, 5th anniv.

1967, Nov. 4

Dahomey 244
Ivory Coast....................................259
Mauritania 238
Niger..204
Senegal 294
Togo...623
Upper Volta....................................181

WHO Anniversary

Sun, Flowers and WHO Emblem CD126

World Health Organization, 20th anniv.

1968, May 4

Afars & Issas	317
Comoro Isls.	73
Fr. Polynesia	241-242
Fr. So. & Antarctic Terr.	31
New Caledonia	367
St. Pierre & Miquelon	377
Wallis & Futuna Isls.	169

Human Rights Year

Human Rights
Flame — CD127

1968, Aug. 10

Afars & Issas	322-323
Comoro Isls.	76
Fr. Polynesia	243-244
Fr. So. & Antarctic Terr.	32
New Caledonia	369
St. Pierre & Miquelon	382
Wallis & Futuna Isls.	170

2nd PHILEXAFRIQUE

CD128

Opening of PHILEXAFRIQUE, Abidjan, Feb. 14. Each stamp shows a local scene and stamp.

1969, Feb. 14

Cameroun	C118
Cent. Africa	C65
Chad	C48
Congo, P.R.	C77
Dahomey	C94
Gabon	C82
Ivory Coast	C38-C40
Madagascar	C92
Mali	C65
Mauritania	C80
Niger	C104
Senegal	C68
Togo	C104
Upper Volta	C62

Concorde

Concorde in
Flight
CD129

First flight of the prototype Concorde supersonic plane at Toulouse, Mar. 1, 1969.

1969

Afars & Issas	C56
Comoro Isls.	C29
France	C42
Fr. Polynesia	C50
Fr. So. & Antarctic Terr.	C18
New Caledonia	C63
St. Pierre & Miquelon	C40
Wallis & Futuna Isls.	C30

Development Bank

Bank
Emblem — CD130

African Development Bank, fifth anniv.

1969

Cameroun	499
Chad	217
Congo, P.R.	181-182
Ivory Coast	281
Mali	127-128
Mauritania	267
Niger	220
Senegal	317-318
Upper Volta	201

ILO

ILO Headquarters, Geneva, and
Emblem — CD131

Intl. Labor Organization, 50th anniv.

1969-70

Afars & Issas	337
Comoro Isls.	83
Fr. Polynesia	251-252
Fr. So. & Antarctic Terr.	35
New Caledonia	379
St. Pierre & Miquelon	396
Wallis & Futuna Isls.	172

ASECNA

Map of
Africa,
Plane and
Airport
CD132

10th anniversary of the Agency for the Security of Aerial Navigation in Africa and Madagascar (ASECNA, Agence pour la Securite de la Navigation Aerienne en Afrique et a Madagascar).

1969-70

Cameroun	500
Cent. Africa	119
Chad	222
Congo, P.R.	197
Dahomey	269
Gabon	260
Ivory Coast	287
Mali	130
Niger	221
Senegal	321
Upper Volta	204

U.P.U. Headquarters

CD133

New Universal Postal Union headquarters, Bern, Switzerland.

1970

Afars & Issas	342
Algeria	443
Cameroun	503-504
Cent. Africa	125
Chad	225
Comoro Isls.	84

Congo, P.R.	216
Fr. Polynesia	261-262
Fr. So. & Antarctic Terr.	36
Gabon	258
Ivory Coast	295
Madagascar	444
Mali	134-135
Mauritania	283
New Caledonia	382
Niger	231-232
St. Pierre & Miquelon	397-398
Senegal	328-329
Tunisia	535
Wallis & Futuna Isls.	173

De Gaulle

CD134

First anniversary of the death of Charles de Gaulle, (1890-1970), President of France.

1971-72

Afars & Issas	356-357
Comoro Isls.	104-105
France	1322-1325
Fr. Polynesia	270-271
Fr. So. & Antarctic Terr.	52-53
New Caledonia	393-394
Reunion	377, 380
St. Pierre & Miquelon	417-418
Wallis & Futuna Isls.	177-178

African Postal Union, 1971

UAMPT Building, Brazzaville,
Congo — CD135

10th anniversary of the establishment of the African and Malagasy Posts and Telecommunications Union, UAMPT. Each stamp has a different native design.

1971, Nov. 13

Cameroun	C177
Cent. Africa	C89
Chad	C94
Congo, P.R.	C136
Dahomey	C146
Gabon	C120
Ivory Coast	C47
Mauritania	C113
Niger	C164
Rwanda	C8
Senegal	C105
Togo	C166
Upper Volta	C97

West African Monetary Union

African Couple, City, Village and
Commemorative Coin — CD136

West African Monetary Union, 10th anniv.

1972, Nov. 2

Dahomey	300
Ivory Coast	331
Mauritania	299
Niger	258
Senegal	374
Togo	825
Upper Volta	280

African Postal Union, 1973

Telecommunications Symbols and Map
of Africa — CD137

11th anniversary of the African and Malagasy Posts and Telecommunications Union (UAMPT).

1973, Sept. 12

Cameroun	574
Cent. Africa	194
Chad	294
Congo, P.R.	289
Dahomey	311
Gabon	320
Ivory Coast	361
Madagascar	500
Mauritania	304
Niger	287
Rwanda	540
Senegal	393
Togo	849
Upper Volta	297

Philexafrique II — Essen

CD138

CD139

Designs: Indigenous fauna, local and German stamps. Types CD138-CD139 printed horizontally and vertically se-tenant in sheets of 10 (2x5). Label between horizontal pairs alternately commemorates Philexafrique II, Libreville, Gabon, June 1978, and 2nd International Stamp Fair, Essen, Germany, Nov. 1-5.

1978-1979

Benin	C285-C286
Central Africa	C200-C201
Chad	C238-C239
Congo Republic	C245-C246
Djibouti	C121-C122
Gabon	C215-C216
Ivory Coast	C64-C65
Mali	C356-C357
Mauritania	C185-C186
Niger	C291-C292
Rwanda	C12-C13
Senegal	C146-C147
Togo	C363-C364

BRITISH COMMONWEALTH OF NATIONS

The listings follow established trade practices when these issues are offered as units by dealers. The Peace issue, for example, includes only one stamp from the Indian state of Hyderabad. The U.P.U. issue includes the Egypt set. Pairs are included for those varieties issues with bilingual designs se-tenant.

Silver Jubilee

Windsor
Castle
and King
George V
CD301

Reign of King George V, 25th anniv.

1935

Antigua 77-80
Ascension 33-36
Bahamas 92-95
Barbados 186-189
Basutoland 11-14
Bechuanaland Protectorate.....117-120
Bermuda 100-103
British Guiana 223-226
British Honduras 108-111
Cayman Islands 81-84
Ceylon 260-263
Cyprus 136-139
Dominica 90-93
Falkland Islands 77-80
Fiji 110-113
Gambia 125-128
Gibraltar 100-103
Gilbert & Ellice Islands................33-36
Gold Coast 108-111
Grenada 124-127
Hong Kong 147-150
Jamaica 109-112
Kenya, Uganda, Tanganyika 42-45
Leeward Islands 96-99
Malta 184-187
Mauritius 204-207
Montserrat 85-88
Newfoundland 226-229
Nigeria 34-37
Northern Rhodesia 18-21
Nyasaland Protectorate...............47-50
St. Helena 111-114
St. Kitts-Nevis 72-75
St. Lucia 91-94
St. Vincent 134-137
Seychelles 118-121
Sierra Leone 166-169
Solomon Islands 60-63
Somaliland Protectorate..............77-80
Straits Settlements 213-216
Swaziland 20-23
Trinidad & Tobago 43-46
Turks & Caicos Islands 71-74
Virgin Islands 69-72

The following have different designs but are included in the omnibus set:

Great Britain 226-229
Offices in Morocco 67-70, 226-229,
    422-425, 508-510
Australia 152-154
Canada 211-216
Cook Islands 98-100
India 142-148
Nauru 31-34
New Guinea 46-47
New Zealand 199-201
Niue 67-69
Papua 114-117
Samoa 163-165
South Africa 68-71
Southern Rhodesia 33-36
South-West Africa 121-124

249 stamps

Coronation

Queen
Elizabeth
and King
George VI
CD302

1937

Aden 13-15
Antigua 81-83
Ascension 37-39
Bahamas 97-99
Barbados 190-192
Basutoland 15-17
Bechuanaland Protectorate.....121-123
Bermuda 115-117
British Guiana 227-229

British Honduras......................112-114
Cayman Islands..........................97-99
Ceylon 275-277
Cyprus 140-142
Dominica 94-96
Falkland Islands 81-83
Fiji 114-116
Gambia 129-131
Gibraltar 104-106
Gilbert & Ellice Islands...............37-39
Gold Coast 112-114
Grenada 128-130
Hong Kong 151-153
Jamaica 113-115
Kenya, Uganda, Tanganyika 60-62
Leeward Islands 100-102
Malta 188-190
Mauritius 208-210
Montserrat 89-91
Newfoundland 230-232
Nigeria 50-52
Northern Rhodesia 22-24
Nyasaland Protectorate...............51-53
St. Helena 115-117
St. Kitts-Nevis 76-78
St. Lucia 107-109
St. Vincent 138-140
Seychelles 122-124
Sierra Leone 170-172
Solomon Islands 64-66
Somaliland Protectorate.............81-83
Straits Settlements 235-237
Swaziland 24-26
Trinidad & Tobago 47-49
Turks & Caicos Islands 75-77
Virgin Islands 73-75

The following have different designs but are included in the omnibus set:

Great Britain 234
Offices in Morocco 82, 439, 514
Canada 237
Cook Islands 109-111
Nauru 35-38
Newfoundland 233-243
New Guinea 48-51
New Zealand 223-225
Niue 70-72
Papua 118-121
South Africa 74-78
Southern Rhodesia 38-41
South-West Africa 125-132

202 stamps

Peace

King
George VI
and
Parliament
Buildings,
London
CD303

Return to peace at the close of World War II.

1945-46

Aden 28-29
Antigua 96-97
Ascension 50-51
Bahamas 130-131
Barbados 207-208
Bermuda 131-132
British Guiana 242-243
British Honduras 127-128
Cayman Islands 112-113
Ceylon 293-294
Cyprus 156-157
Dominica 112-113
Falkland Islands 97-98
Falkland Islands Dep...........1L9-1L10
Fiji 137-138
Gambia 144-145
Gibraltar 119-120
Gilbert & Ellice Islands...............52-53
Gold Coast 128-129
Grenada 143-144
Jamaica 136-137
Kenya, Uganda, Tanganyika 90-91
Leeward Islands 116-117
Malta 206-207
Mauritius 223-224
Montserrat 104-105
Nigeria 71-72
Northern Rhodesia 46-47
Nyasaland Protectorate..............82-83
Pitcairn Island 9-10
St. Helena 128-129
St. Kitts-Nevis 91-92
St. Lucia 127-128

St. Vincent 152-153
Seychelles 149-150
Sierra Leone 186-187
Solomon Islands 80-81
Somaliland Protectorate..........108-109
Trinidad & Tobago 62-63
Turks & Caicos Islands 90-91
Virgin Islands 88-89

The following have different designs but are included in the omnibus set:

Great Britain 264-265
    Offices in Morocco 523-524
Aden
    Kathiri State of Seiyun............12-13
    Qu'aiti State of Shihr and Mukalla
   12-13
Australia 200-202
Basutoland 29-31
Bechuanaland Protectorate......137-139
Burma 66-69
Cook Islands 127-130
Hong Kong 174-175
India 195-198
    Hyderabad 51
New Zealand 247-257
Niue 90-93
Pakistan-Bahawalpur...................O16
Samoa 191-194
South Africa 100-102
Southern Rhodesia 67-70
South-West Africa 153-155
Swaziland 38-40
Zanzibar 222-223

164 stamps

Silver Wedding

King George VI and Queen
Elizabeth
CD304   CD305

1948-49

Aden 30-31
    Kathiri State of Seiyun..............14-15
    Qu'aiti State of Shihr and Mukalla .....
   14-15
Antigua 98-99
Ascension 52-53
Bahamas 148-149
Barbados 210-211
Basutoland 39-40
Bechuanaland Protectorate......147-148
Bermuda 133-134
British Guiana 244-245
British Honduras 129-130
Cayman Islands 116-117
Cyprus 158-159
Dominica 114-115
Falkland Islands 99-100
Falkland Islands Dep..........1L11-1L12
Fiji 139-140
Gambia 146-147
Gibraltar 121-122
Gilbert & Ellice Islands...............54-55
Gold Coast 142-143
Grenada 145-146
Hong Kong 178-179
Jamaica 138-139
Kenya, Uganda, Tanganyika 92-93
Leeward Islands 118-119
Malaya
    Johore 128-129
    Kedah 55-56
    Kelantan 44-45
    Malacca 1-2
    Negri Sembilan 36-37
    Pahang 44-45
    Penang 1-2
    Perak 99-100
    Perlis 1-2
    Selangor 74-75
    Trengganu 47-48
Malta 223-224
Mauritius 229-230
Montserrat 106-107
Nigeria 73-74
North Borneo 238-239
Northern Rhodesia 48-49

Nyasaland Protectorate...............85-86
Pitcairn Island 11-12
St. Helena 130-131
St. Kitts-Nevis 93-94
St. Lucia 129-130
St. Vincent 154-155
Sarawak 174-175
Seychelles 151-152
Sierra Leone 188-189
Singapore 21-22
Solomon Islands 82-83
Somaliland Protectorate..........110-111
Swaziland 48-49
Trinidad & Tobago 64-65
Turks & Caicos Islands 92-93
Virgin Islands 90-91
Zanzibar 224-225

The following have different designs but are included in the omnibus set:

Great Britain 267-268
    Offices in Morocco..... 93-94, 525-526
Bahrain 62-63
Kuwait 82-83
Oman 25-26
South Africa 106
South-West Africa 159

138 stamps

U.P.U.

Mercury and Symbols of
Communications — CD306

Plane, Ship and
Hemispheres — CD307

Mercury
Scattering
Letters over
Globe
CD308

U.P.U.
Monument,
Bern
CD309

Universal Postal Union, 75th anniversary.

1949

Aden 32-35
    Kathiri State of Seiyun..............16-19
    Qu'aiti State of Shihr and Mukalla .....
   16-19
Antigua 100-103
Ascension 57-60
Bahamas 150-153
Barbados 212-215
Basutoland 41-44
Bechuanaland Protectorate......149-152
Bermuda 138-141
British Guiana 246-249
British Honduras 137-140
Brunei 79-82
Cayman Islands 118-121
Cyprus 160-163
Dominica 116-119
Falkland Islands 103-106
Falkland Islands Dep..........1L14-1L17
Fiji 141-144
Gambia 148-151
Gibraltar 123-126
Gilbert & Ellice Islands...............56-59
Gold Coast 144-147

Grenada..................................147-150
Hong Kong 180-183
Jamaica..................................142-145
Kenya, Uganda, Tanganyika 94-97
Leeward Islands 126-129
Malaya
  Johore..................................151-154
  Kedah......................................57-60
  Kelantan..................................46-49
  Malacca...................................18-21
  Negri Sembilan 59-62
  Pahang....................................46-49
  Penang....................................23-26
  Perak...................................101-104
  Perlis..3-6
  Selangor..................................76-79
  Trengganu................................49-52
Malta.....................................225-228
Mauritius................................231-234
Montserrat.............................108-111
New Hebrides, British 62-65
New Hebrides, French 79-82
Nigeria.....................................75-78
North Borneo..........................240-243
Northern Rhodesia.....................50-53
Nyasaland Protectorate...............87-90
Pitcairn Islands 13-16
St. Helena..............................132-135
St. Kitts-Nevis...........................95-98
St. Lucia................................131-134
St. Vincent.............................170-173
Sarawak.................................176-179
Seychelles..............................153-156
Sierra Leone...........................190-193
Singapore.................................23-26
Solomon Islands........................84-87
Somaliland Protectorate...........112-115
Southern Rhodesia 71-72
Swaziland.................................50-53
Tonga.......................................87-90
Trinidad & Tobago 66-69
Turks & Caicos Islands 101-104
Virgin Islands............................92-95
Zanzibar................................226-229

The following have different designs but are
included in the omnibus set:

Great Britain...........................276-279
  Offices in Morocco.................546-549
Australia..223
Bahrain.....................................68-71
Burma.....................................116-121
Ceylon...................................304-306
Egypt.....................................281-283
India......................................223-226
Kuwait......................................89-92
Oman.......................................31-34
Pakistan-Bahawalpur   26-29, O25-O28
South Africa.............................109-111
South-West Africa 160-162

319 stamps

University

Arms of
University
College
CD310

Alice, Princess
of Athlone
CD311

1948 opening of University College of the
West Indies at Jamaica.

1951

Antigua 104-105
Barbados................................228-229
British Guiana..........................250-251
British Honduras......................141-142
Dominica................................120-121
Grenada..................................164-165
Jamaica..................................146-147
Leeward Islands 130-131
Montserrat 112-113
St. Kitts-Nevis.........................105-106
St. Lucia................................149-150
St. Vincent.............................174-175
Trinidad & Tobago 70-71
Virgin Islands............................96-97

28 stamps

Coronation

Queen Elizabeth
II — CD312

1953

Aden..47
  Kathiri State of Seiyun.................28
  Qu'aiti State of Shihr and Mukalla .....
 28
Antigua.......................................106
Ascension.....................................61
Bahamas.....................................157
Barbados.....................................234
Basutoland....................................45
Bechuanaland Protectorate.............153
Bermuda......................................142
British Guiana...............................252
British Honduras...........................143
Cayman Islands.............................150
Cyprus..167
Dominica.....................................141
Falkland Islands............................121
Falkland Islands Dependencies ...1L18
Fiji...145
Gambia..152
Gibraltar......................................131
Gilbert & Ellice Islands....................60
Gold Coast...................................160
Grenada......................................170
Hong Kong...................................184
Jamaica.......................................153
Kenya, Uganda, Tanganyika 101
Leeward Islands 132
Malaya
  Johore.....................................155
  Kedah..82
  Kelantan.....................................71
  Malacca......................................27
  Negri Sembilan 63
  Pahang.......................................71
  Penang.......................................27
  Perak.......................................126
  Perlis...28
  Selangor...................................101
  Trengganu...................................74
Malta...241
Mauritius......................................250
Montserrat...................................127
New Hebrides, British 77
Nigeria..79
North Borneo................................260
Northern Rhodesia..........................60
Nyasaland Protectorate...................96
Pitcairn..19
St. Helena...................................139
St. Kitts-Nevis..............................119
St. Lucia.....................................156
St. Vincent..................................185
Sarawak......................................196
Seychelles...................................172
Sierra Leone................................194
Singapore.....................................27
Solomon Islands.............................88
Somaliland Protectorate.................127
Swaziland.....................................54
Trinidad & Tobago 84
Tristan da Cunha............................13
Turks & Caicos Islands 118
Virgin Islands...............................114

The following have different designs but are
included in the omnibus set:

Great Britain...........................313-316
  Offices in Morocco.................579-582
Australia.................................259-261
Bahrain.....................................92-95
Canada..330
Ceylon...317
Cook Islands............................145-146
Kuwait....................................113-116
New Zealand............................280-284
Niue......................................104-105
Oman.......................................52-55
Samoa....................................214-215
South Africa..................................192
Southern Rhodesia 80
South-West Africa 244-248
Tokelau Islands................................4

106 stamps

Royal Visit 1953

Separate designs for each country for the
visit of Queen Elizabeth II and the Duke of
Edinburgh.

1953

Aden..62
Australia.................................267-269
Bermuda......................................163
Ceylon...318
Fiji...146
Gibraltar......................................146
Jamaica.......................................154
Kenya, Uganda, Tanganyika 102
Malta...242
New Zealand............................286-287

13 stamps

West Indies Federation

Map of the
Caribbean
CD313

Federation of the West Indies, April 22,
1958.

1958

Antigua...................................122-124
Barbados................................248-250
Dominica................................161-163
Grenada..................................184-186
Jamaica..................................175-177
Montserrat..............................143-145
St. Kitts-Nevis.........................136-138
St. Lucia................................170-172
St. Vincent.............................198-200
Trinidad & Tobago 86-88

30 stamps

Freedom from Hunger

Protein Food
CD314

U.N. Food and Agricultural Organization's
"Freedom from Hunger" campaign.

1963

Aden..65
Antigua..133
Ascension.....................................89
Bahamas.....................................180
Basutoland....................................83
Bechuanaland Protectorate.............194
Bermuda......................................192
British Guiana...............................271
British Honduras...........................179
Brunei...100
Cayman Islands.............................168
Dominica.....................................181
Falkland Islands............................146
Fiji...198
Gambia..172
Gibraltar......................................161
Gilbert & Ellice Islands....................76
Grenada......................................190
Hong Kong...................................218
Malta...291
Mauritius......................................270
Montserrat...................................150
New Hebrides, British 93
North Borneo................................296
Pitcairn..35
St. Helena...................................173
St. Lucia.....................................179
St. Vincent..................................201
Sarawak......................................212
Seychelles...................................213
Solomon Islands.............................109
Swaziland.....................................108
Tonga...127
Tristan da Cunha............................68
Turks & Caicos Islands 138
Virgin Islands...............................140
Zanzibar......................................280

37 stamps

Red Cross Centenary

Red Cross
and
Elizabeth
II
CD315

1963

Antigua 134-135
Ascension...................................90-91
Bahamas................................183-184
Basutoland................................84-85
Bechuanaland Protectorate...195-196
Bermuda................................193-194
British Guiana..........................272-273
British Honduras......................180-181
Cayman Islands.......................169-170
Dominica................................182-183
Falkland Islands......................147-148
Fiji.......................................203-204
Gambia..................................173-174
Gibraltar................................162-163
Gilbert & Ellice Islands................77-78
Grenada.................................191-192
Hong Kong..............................219-220
Jamaica..................................203-204
Malta.....................................292-293
Mauritius................................271-272
Montserrat.............................151-152
New Hebrides, British 94-95
Pitcairn Islands 36-37
St. Helena..............................174-175
St. Kitts-Nevis........................143-144
St. Lucia................................180-181
St. Vincent.............................202-203
Seychelles..............................214-215
Solomon Islands......................110-111
South Arabia 1-2
Swaziland...............................109-110
Tonga.....................................134-135
Tristan da Cunha.......................69-70
Turks & Caicos Islands 139-140
Virgin Islands...........................141-142

70 stamps

Shakespeare

Shakespeare Memorial Theatre,
Stratford-on-Avon — CD316

400th anniversary of the birth of William
Shakespeare.

1964

Antigua 151
Bahamas 201
Bechuanaland Protectorate.............197
Cayman Islands..............................171
Dominica......................................184
Falkland Islands............................149
Gambia..192
Gibraltar......................................164
Montserrat 153
St. Lucia.....................................196
Turks & Caicos Islands 141
Virgin Islands...............................143

12 stamps

ITU

ITU
Emblem
CD317

Intl. Telecommunication Union, cent.

1965

Antigua 153-154
Ascension...................................92-93
Bahamas................................219-220
Barbados................................265-266
Basutoland.............................101-102
Bechuanaland Protectorate.....202-203

Intl. Cooperation Year

ICY Emblem CD318 — BRUNEI 4 CENTS

1965

Churchill Memorial

Winston Churchill and St. Paul's, London, During Air Attack CD319 — ANTIGUA ½ CENT

1966

Royal Visit, 1966

Queen Elizabeth II and Prince Philip CD320 — Royal Visit to the Caribbean 1966 ANTIGUA 6c

Caribbean visit, Feb. 4 - Mar. 6, 1966.

1966

World Cup Soccer

Soccer Player and Jules Rimet Cup CD321 — NEW HEBRIDES CONDOMINIUM 20

World Cup Soccer Championship, Wembley, England, July 11-30.

1966

WHO Headquarters

World Health Organization Headquarters, Geneva — CD322

1966

UNESCO Anniversary

"Education" — CD323

"Science" (Wheat ears & flask enclosing globe). "Culture" (lyre & columns). 20th anniversary of the UNESCO.

1966-67

Silver Wedding, 1972

Queen Elizabeth II and Prince Philip — CD324

Designs: borders differ for each country.

1972

Princess Anne's Wedding

Princess Anne and Mark Phillips — CD325

Wedding of Princess Anne and Mark Phillips, Nov. 14, 1973.

1973

Elizabeth II Coronation Anniv.

CD326   CD327

CD328

Designs: Royal and local beasts in heraldic form and simulated stonework. Portrait of Elizabeth II by Peter Grugeon. 25th anniversary of coronation of Queen Elizabeth II.

1978

Ascension	229
Barbados	474
Belize	397
British Antarctic Territory	71
Cayman Islands	404
Christmas Island	87
Falkland Islands	275
Fiji	384
Gambia	380
Gilbert Islands	312
Mauritius	464
New Hebrides, British	258
St. Helena	317
St. Kitts-Nevis	354
Samoa	472
Solomon Islands	368
South Georgia	51
Swaziland	302
Tristan da Cunha	238
Virgin Islands	337

20 sheets

Queen Mother Elizabeth's 80th Birthday

CD330

Designs: Photographs of Queen Mother Elizabeth. Falkland Islands issued in sheets of 50; others in sheets of 9.

1980

Ascension	261
Bermuda	401
Cayman Islands	443
Falkland Islands	305
Gambia	412
Gibraltar	393
Hong Kong	364
Pitcairn Islands	193
St. Helena	341
Samoa	532
Solomon Islands	426
Tristan da Cunha	277

12 stamps

Royal Wedding, 1981

Prince Charles and Lady Diana — CD331

CD331a

Wedding of Charles, Prince of Wales, and Lady Diana Spencer, St. Paul's Cathedral, London, July 29, 1981.

1981

Antigua	623-625
Ascension	294-296
Barbados	547-549
Barbuda	497-499
Bermuda	412-414

Brunei	268-270
Cayman Islands	471-473
Dominica	701-703
Falkland Islands	324-326
Falkland Islands Dep.	1L59-1L61
Fiji	442-444
Gambia	426-428
Ghana	759-761
Grenada	1051-1053
Grenada Grenadines	440-443
Hong Kong	373-375
Jamaica	500-503
Lesotho	335-337
Maldive Islands	906-908
Mauritius	520-522
Norfolk Island	280-282
Pitcairn Islands	206-208
St. Helena	353-355
St. Lucia	543-545
Samoa	558-560
Sierra Leone	509-517
Solomon Islands	450-452
Swaziland	382-384
Tristan da Cunha	294-296
Turks & Caicos Islands	486-488
Caicos Island	8-10
Uganda	314-316
Vanuatu	308-310
Virgin Islands	406-408

Princess Diana

CD332

CD333

Designs: Photographs and portrait of Princess Diana, wedding or honeymoon photographs, royal residences, arms of issuing country. Portrait photograph by Clive Friend. Souvenir sheet margins show family tree, various people related to the princess. 21st birthday of Princess Diana of Wales, July 1.

1982

Antigua	663-666
Ascension	313-316
Bahamas	510-513
Barbados	585-588
Barbuda	544-546
British Antarctic Territory	92-95
Cayman Islands	486-489
Dominica	773-776
Falkland Islands	348-351
Falkland Islands Dep.	1L72-1L75
Fiji	470-473
Gambia	447-450
Grenada	1101A-1105
Grenada Grenadines	485-491
Lesotho	372-375
Maldive Islands	952-955
Mauritius	548-551
Pitcairn Islands	213-216
St. Helena	372-375
St. Lucia	591-594
Sierra Leone	531-534
Solomon Islands	471-474
Swaziland	406-409
Tristan da Cunha	310-313
Turks and Caicos Islands	530A-534
Virgin Islands	430-433

250th anniv. of first edition of Lloyd's List (shipping news publication) & of Lloyd's marine insurance.

CD335

Designs: First page of early edition of the list; historical ships, modern transportation or harbor scenes.

1984

Ascension	351-354
Bahamas	555-558
Barbados	627-630
Cayes of Belize	10-13
Cayman Islands	522-525
Falkland Islands	404-407
Fiji	509-512
Gambia	519-522
Mauritius	587-590
Nauru	280-283
St. Helena	412-415
Samoa	624-627
Seychelles	538-541
Solomon Islands	521-524
Vanuatu	368-371
Virgin Islands	466-469

Queen Mother 85th Birthday

CD336

Designs: Photographs tracing the life of the Queen Mother, Elizabeth. The high value in each set pictures the same photograph taken of the Queen Mother holding the infant Prince Henry.

1985

Ascension	372-376
Bahamas	580-584
Barbados	660-664
Bermuda	469-473
Falkland Islands	420-424
Falkland Islands Dep.	1L92-1L96
Fiji	531-535
Hong Kong	447-450
Jamaica	599-603
Mauritius	604-608
Norfolk Island	364-368
Pitcairn Islands	253-257
St. Helena	428-432
Samoa	649-653
Seychelles	567-571
Solomon Islands	543-547
Swaziland	476-480
Tristan da Cunha	372-376
Vanuatu	392-396
Zil Elwannyen Sesel	101-105

Queen Elizabeth II, 60th Birthday

CD337

1986, April 21

Ascension	389-393
Bahamas	592-596
Barbados	675-679
Bermuda	499-503
Cayman Islands	555-559

Falkland Islands	441-445
Fiji	544-548
Hong Kong	465-469
Jamaica	620-624
Kiribati	470-474
Mauritius	629-633
Papua New Guinea	640-644
Pitcairn Islands	270-274
St. Helena	451-455
Samoa	670-674
Seychelles	592-596
Solomon Islands	562-566
South Georgia	101-105
Swaziland	490-494
Tristan da Cunha	388-392
Vanuatu	414-418
Zambia	343-347
Zil Elwannyen Sesel	114-118

Royal Wedding

Marriage of Prince Andrew and Sarah Ferguson CD338

1986, July 23

Ascension	399-400
Bahamas	602-603
Barbados	687-688
Cayman Islands	560-561
Jamaica	629-630
Pitcairn Islands	275-276
St. Helena	460-461
St. Kitts	181-182
Seychelles	602-603
Solomon Islands	567-568
Tristan da Cunha	397-398
Zambia	348-349
Zil Elwannyen Sesel	119-120

Queen Elizabeth II, 60th Birthday

Queen Elizabeth II & Prince Philip, 1947 Wedding Portrait — CD339

Designs: Photographs tracing the life of Queen Elizabeth II.

1986

Anguilla	674-677
Antigua	925-928
Barbuda	783-786
Dominica	950-953
Gambia	611-614
Grenada	1371-1374
Grenada Grenadines	749-752
Lesotho	531-534
Maldive Islands	1172-1175
Sierra Leone	760-763
Uganda	495-498

Royal Wedding, 1986

CD340

Designs: Photographs of Prince Andrew and Sarah Ferguson during courtship, engagement and marriage.

1986

Antigua	939-942
Barbuda	809-812
Dominica	970-973
Gambia	635-638

Grenada..............................1385-1388
Grenada Grenadines...............758-761
Lesotho...................................545-548
Maldive Islands....................1181-1184
Sierra Leone..........................769-772
Uganda..................................510-513

Lloyds of London, 300th Anniv.

CD341

Designs: 17th century aspects of Lloyds, representations of each country's individual connections with Lloyds and publicized disasters insured by the organization.

1986

Ascension.................................454-457
Bahamas..................................655-658
Barbados.................................731-734
Bermuda..................................541-544
Falkland Islands.......................481-484
Liberia...................................1101-1104
Malawi....................................534-537
Nevis......................................571-574
St. Helena..............................501-504
St. Lucia................................923-926
Seychelles..............................649-652
Solomon Islands.......................627-630
South Georgia..........................131-134
Trinidad & Tobago....................484-487
Tristan da Cunha......................439-442
Vanuatu...................................485-488
Zil Elwannyen Sesel..................146-149

Moon Landing, 20th Anniv.

CD342

Designs: Equipment, crew photographs, spacecraft, official emblems and report profiles created for the Apollo Missions. Two stamps in each set are square in format rather than like the stamp shown; see individual country listings for more information.

1989

Ascension Is.............................468-472
Bahamas..................................674-678
Belize......................................916-920
Kiribati...................................517-521
Liberia...................................1125-1129
Nevis......................................586-590
St. Kitts.................................248-252
Samoa.....................................760-764
Seychelles..............................676-680
Solomon Islands.......................643-647
Vanuatu...................................507-511
Zil Elwannyen Sesel..................154-158

Queen Mother, 90th Birthday

CD343   CD344

Designs: Portraits of Queen Elizabeth, the Queen Mother. See individual country listings for more information.

1990

Ascension Is.............................491-492
Bahamas..................................698-699
Barbados.................................782-783
British Antarctic Territory.........170-171
British Indian Ocean Territory.......106-107
Cayman Islands........................622-623
Falkland Islands.......................524-525
Kenya......................................527-528
Kiribati...................................555-556
Liberia...................................1145-1146
Pitcairn Islands.......................336-337
St. Helena..............................532-533
St. Lucia................................969-970
Seychelles..............................710-711
Solomon Islands.......................671-672
South Georgia..........................143-144
Swaziland................................565-566
Tristan da Cunha......................480-481
Zil Elwannyen Sesel..................171-172

Queen Elizabeth II, 65th Birthday, and Prince Philip, 70th Birthday

CD345

CD346

Designs: Portraits of Queen Elizabeth II and Prince Philip differ for each country. Printed in sheets of 10 + 5 labels (3 different) between. Stamps alternate, producing 5 different triptychs.

1991

Ascension Is.............................505-506
Bahamas..................................730-731
Belize......................................969-970
Bermuda..................................617-618
Kiribati...................................571-572
Mauritius................................733-734
Pitcairn Islands.......................348-349
St. Helena..............................554-555
St. Kitts.................................318-319
Samoa.....................................790-791
Seychelles..............................723-724
Solomon Islands.......................688-689
South Georgia..........................149-150
Swaziland................................586-587
Vanuatu...................................540-541
Zil Elwannyen Sesel..................177-178

Royal Family Birthday, Anniversary

CD347

Queen Elizabeth II, 65th birthday, Charles and Diana, 10th wedding anniversary: Various photographs of Queen Elizabeth II, Prince Philip, Prince Charles, Princess Diana and their sons William and Henry.

1991

Antigua...................................1446-1455
Barbuda..................................1229-1238
Dominica.................................1328-1337
Gambia....................................1080-1089
Grenada...................................2006-2015
Grenada Grenadines...........1331-1340
Guyana....................................2440-2451
Lesotho...................................871-875
Maldive Islands.......................1533-1542
Nevis......................................666-675
St. Vincent..............................1485-1494

St. Vincent Grenadines............769-778
Sierra Leone..........................1387-1396
Turks & Caicos Islands..........913-922
Uganda...................................918-927

Queen Elizabeth II's Accession to the Throne, 40th Anniv.

CD348

CD349

Various photographs of Queen Elizabeth II with local Scenes.

1992 - CD348

Antigua...................................1513-1518
Barbuda..................................1306-1309
Dominica.................................1414-1419
Gambia....................................1172-1177
Grenada...................................2047-2052
Grenada Grenadines...........1368-1373
Lesotho...................................881-885
Maldive Islands.......................1637-1642
Nevis......................................702-707
St. Vincent..............................1582-1587
St. Vincent Grenadines............829-834
Sierra Leone..........................1482-1487
Turks and Caicos Islands......978-987
Uganda...................................990-995
Virgin Islands.........................742-746

1992 - CD349

Ascension Islands...................531-535
Bahamas..................................744-748
Bermuda..................................623-627
British Indian Ocean Territory......119-123
Cayman Islands........................648-652
Falkland Islands.......................549-553
Gibraltar.................................605-609
Hong Kong...............................619-623
Kenya......................................563-567
Kiribati...................................582-586
Pitcairn Islands.......................362-366
St. Helena..............................570-574
St. Kitts.................................332-336
Samoa.....................................805-809
Seychelles..............................734-738
Solomon Islands.......................708-712
South Georgia..........................157-161
Tristan da Cunha......................508-512
Vanuatu...................................555-559
Zambia....................................561-565
Zil Elwannyen Sesel..................183-187

Royal Air Force, 75th Anniversary

CD350

1993

Ascension.................................557-561
Bahamas..................................771-775
Barbados.................................842-846
Belize......................................1003-1008
Bermuda..................................648-651
British Indian Ocean Territory......136-140
Falkland Is..............................573-577
Fiji...687-691
Montserrat..............................830-834
St. Kitts.................................351-355

Royal Air Force, 80th Anniv.

Design CD350 Re-inscribed

1998

Ascension.................................697-701
Bahamas..................................907-911
British Indian Ocean Terr........198-202
Cayman Islands........................754-758
Fiji...814-818
Gibraltar.................................755-759
Samoa.....................................957-961
Turks & Caicos Islands........1258-1265
Tuvalu.....................................763-767
Virgin Islands.........................879-883

End of World War II, 50th Anniv.

CD351

CD352

1995

Ascension.................................613-617
Bahamas..................................824-828
Barbados.................................891-895
Belize......................................1047-1050
British Indian Ocean Territory......163-167
Cayman Islands........................704-708
Falkland Islands.......................634-638
Fiji...720-724
Kiribati...................................662-668
Liberia...................................1175-1179
Mauritius................................803-805
St. Helena..............................646-654
St. Kitts.................................389-393
St. Lucia................................1018-1022
Samoa.....................................890-894
Solomon Islands.......................799-803
South Georgia & S. Sandwich Is..........198-200
Tristan da Cunha......................562-566

UN, 50th Anniv.

CD353

1995

Bahamas..................................839-842
Barbados.................................901-904
Belize......................................1055-1058
Jamaica...................................847-851
Liberia...................................1187-1190
Mauritius................................813-816
Pitcairn Islands.......................436-439
St. Kitts.................................398-401
St. Lucia................................1023-1026

Samoa 900-903
Tristan da Cunha....................568-571
Virgin Islands.......................807-810

Queen Elizabeth, 70th Birthday

CD354

1996

Ascension 632-635
British Antarctic Territory..........240-243
British Indian Ocean Territory 176-180
Falkland Islands 653-657
Pitcairn Islands.......................446-449
St. Helena 672-676
Samoa 912-916
Tokelau 223-227
Tristan da Cunha.....................576-579
Virgin Islands.........................824-828

Diana, Princess of Wales (1961-97)

CD355

1998

Ascension 696
Bahamas 901A-902
Barbados 950
Belize 1091
Bermuda 753
Botswana 659-663
British Antarctic Territory.............258
British Indian Ocean Terr. 197
Cayman Islands....................752A-753
Falkland Islands 694
Fiji 819-820
Gibraltar...............................754
Kiribati 719A-720
Namibia 909
Niue 706
Norfolk Island 644-645
Papua New Guinea 937
Pitcairn Islands.......................487
St. Helena 711
St. Kitts 437A-438
Samoa 955A-956
Seychelles 802
Solomon Islands....................866-867
South Georgia & S. Sandwich Islands
....................................220
Tokelau 252B-253
Tonga.................................980
Niuafo'ou 201
Tristan da Cunha.......................618
Tuvalu 762
Vanuatu 719
Virgin Islands.........................878

Wedding of Prince Edward and Sophie Rhys-Jones

CD356

1999

Ascension 729-730
Cayman Islands.......................775-776
Falkland Islands 729-730
Pitcairn Islands.......................505-506
St. Helena 733-734
Samoa 971-972
Tristan da Cunha.....................636-637
Virgin Islands.........................908-909

1st Manned Moon Landing, 30th Anniv.

CD357

1999

Ascension 731-735
Bahamas 942-946
Barbados 967-971
Bermuda 778
Cayman Islands.......................777-781
Fiji 853-857
Jamaica 889-893
Kirbati 746-750
Nauru 465-469
St. Kitts 460-464
Samoa 973-977
Solomon Islands....................875-879
Tuvalu 800-804
Virgin Islands.........................910-914

Queen Mother's Century

CD358

1999

Ascension 736-740
Bahamas 951-955
Cayman Islands.......................782-786
Falkland Islands 734-738
Fiji 858-862
Norfolk Island 688-692
St. Helena 740-744
Samoa 978-982
Solomon Islands....................880-884
South Georgia & South
  Sandwich Islands 231-235
Tristan da Cunha.....................638-642
Tuvalu 805-809

Prince William, 18th Birthday

CD359

2000

Ascension 755-759
Cayman Islands.......................797-801
Falkland Islands 762-766
Fiji 889-893
South Georgia 257-261
  and South Sandwich Islands
Tristan da Cunha.....................664-668
Virgin Islands.........................925-929

Reign of Queen Elizabeth II, 50th Anniv.

CD360

2002

Ascension 790-794
Bahamas 1033-1037
Barbados 1019-1023
Belize 1152-1156
Bermuda 822-826
British Antarctic Territory..........307-311
British Indian Ocean Territory 239-243
Cayman Islands.......................844-848
Falkland Islands 804-808
Gibraltar...............................896-900
Jamaica 952-956
Nauru 491-495
Norfolk Island 758-762
Papua New Guinea 1019-1023
Pitcairn Islands.......................552
St. Helena 788-792
St. Lucia 1146-1150
Solomon Islands....................931-935
South Georgia & So. Sandwich Is. ....
....................................274-278
Swaziland 706-710
Tokelau 302-306
Tonga.................................1059
Niuafo'ou 239
Tristan da Cunha.....................706-710
Virgin Islands.........................967-971

Queen Mother Elizabeth (1900-2002)

CD361

2002

Ascension 799-801
Bahamas 1044-1046
Bermuda 834-836
British Antarctic Territory..........312-314
British Indian Ocean Territory 245-247
Cayman Islands.......................857-861
Falkland Islands 812-816
Nauru 499-501
Pitcairn Islands.......................561-565
St. Helena 808-812
St. Lucia 1155-1159
Seychelles 830
Solomon Islands....................945-947
South Georgia & So. Sandwich Isls. .....
....................................281-285
Tokelau 312-314
Tristan da Cunha.....................715-717
Virgin Islands.........................979-983

Head of Queen Elizabeth II

CD362

2003

Ascension 822
Bermuda 865
British Antarctic Territory...............322
British Indian Ocean Territory 261
Cayman Islands.......................878
Falkland Islands 828
St. Helena 820
South Georgia & South Sandwich
  Islands 294

Tristan da Cunha.......................731
Virgin Islands.........................1003

Coronation of Queen Elizabeth II, 50th Anniv.

CD363

2003

Ascension 823-825
Bahamas 1073-1075
Bermuda 866-868
British Antarctic Territory..........323-325
British Indian Ocean Territory 262-264
Cayman Islands.......................879-881
Jamaica 970-972
Kiribati 825-827
Pitcairn Islands.......................577-581
St. Helena 821-823
St. Lucia 1171-1173
Tokelau 320-322
Tristan da Cunha.....................732-734
Virgin Islands.........................1004-1006

Prince William, 21st Birthday

CD364

2003

Ascension 826
British Indian Ocean Territory 265
Cayman Islands.......................882-884
Falkland Islands 829
South Georgia & South Sandwich
  Islands 295
Tokelau 323
Tristan da Cunha.......................735
Virgin Islands.........................1007-1009

British Commonwealth of Nations

Dominions, Colonies, Territories, Offices and Independent Members

Comprising stamps of the British Commonwealth and associated nations.

A strict observance of technicalities would bar some or all of the stamps listed under Burma, Ireland, Kuwait, Nepal, New Republic, Orange Free State, Samoa, South Africa, South-West Africa, Stellaland, Sudan, Swaziland, the two Transvaal Republics and others but these are included for the convenience of collectors.

1. Great Britain

Great Britain: Including England, Scotland, Wales and Northern Ireland.

2. The Dominions, Present and Past

AUSTRALIA

The Commonwealth of Australia was proclaimed on January 1, 1901. It consists of six former colonies as follows:

New South Wales   Victoria
Queensland   Tasmania
South Australia   Western Australia

The following islands and territories are, or have been, administered by Australia: Australian Antarctic Territory, Christmas Island, Cocos (Keeling) Islands, Nauru, New Guinea, Norfolk Island, Papua.

CANADA

The Dominion of Canada was created by the British North America Act in 1867. The following provinces were former separate colonies and issued postage stamps:

British Columbia and   Newfoundland
Vancouver Island   Nova Scotia
New Brunswick   Prince Edward Island

FIJI

The colony of Fiji became an independent nation with dominion status on Oct. 10, 1970.

GHANA

This state came into existence Mar. 6, 1957, with dominion status. It consists of the former colony of the Gold Coast and the Trusteeship Territory of Togoland. Ghana became a republic July 1, 1960.

INDIA

The Republic of India was inaugurated on January 26, 1950. It succeeded the Dominion of India which was proclaimed August 15, 1947, when the former Empire of India was divided into Pakistan and the Union of India. The Republic is composed of about 40 predominantly Hindu states of three classes: governor's provinces, chief commissioner's provinces and princely states. India also has various territories, such as the Andaman and Nicobar Islands.

The old Empire of India was a federation of British India and the native states. The more important princely states were autonomous. Of the more than 700 Indian states, these 43 are familiar names to philatelists because of their postage stamps.

CONVENTION STATES

Chamba   Jhind
Faridkot   Nabha
Gwalior   Patiala

NATIVE FEUDATORY STATES

Alwar	Jammu and Kashmir
Bahawalpur	Jasdan
Bamra	Jhalawar
Barwani	Jhind (1875-76)
Bhopal	Kashmir
Bhor	Kishangarh
Bijawar	Kotah
Bundi	Las Bela
Bussahir	Morvi
Charkhari	Nandgaon
Cochin	Nowanuggur
Dhar	Orchha
Dungarpur	Poonch
Duttia	Rajasthan
Faridkot (1879-85)	Rajpeepla
Hyderabad	Sirmur
Idar	Soruth
Indore	Tonk
Jaipur	Travancore
Jammu	Wadhwan

NEW ZEALAND

Became a dominion on September 26, 1907. The following islands and territories are, or have been, administered by New Zealand:

Aitutaki	Ross Dependency
Cook Islands (Rarotonga)	Samoa (Western Samoa)
Niue	Tokelau Islands
Penrhyn	

PAKISTAN

The Republic of Pakistan was proclaimed March 23, 1956. It succeeded the Dominion which was proclaimed August 15, 1947. It is made up of all or part of several Moslem provinces and various districts of the former Empire of India, including Bahawalpur and Las Bela. Pakistan withdrew from the Commonwealth in 1972.

SOUTH AFRICA

Under the terms of the South African Act (1909) the self-governing colonies of Cape of Good Hope, Natal, Orange River Colony and Transvaal united on May 31, 1910, to form the Union of South Africa. It became an independent republic May 3, 1961.

Under the terms of the Treaty of Versailles, South-West Africa, formerly German South-West Africa, was mandated to the Union of South Africa.

SRI LANKA (CEYLON)

The Dominion of Ceylon was proclaimed February 4, 1948. The island had been a Crown Colony from 1802 until then. On May 22, 1972, Ceylon became the Republic of Sri Lanka.

3. Colonies, Past and Present; ControlledTerritory and Independent Members of the Commonwealth

Aden	Bechuanaland
Aitutaki	Bechuanaland Prot.
Antigua	Belize
Ascension	Bermuda
Bahamas	Botswana
Bahrain	British Antarctic Territory
Bangladesh	British Central Africa
Barbados	British Columbia and
Barbuda	Vancouver Island
Basutoland	British East Africa
Batum	British Guiana

British Honduras
British Indian Ocean Territory
British New Guinea
British Solomon Islands
British Somaliland
Brunei
Burma
Bushire
Cameroons
Cape of Good Hope
Cayman Islands
Christmas Island
Cocos (Keeling) Islands
Cook Islands
Crete,
  British Administration
Cyprus
Dominica
East Africa & Uganda
  Protectorates
Egypt
Falkland Islands
Fiji
Gambia
German East Africa
Gibraltar
Gilbert Islands
Gilbert & Ellice Islands
Gold Coast
Grenada
Griqualand West
Guernsey
Guyana
Heligoland
Hong Kong
Indian Native States
  (see India)
Ionian Islands
Jamaica
Jersey

Kenya
Kenya, Uganda & Tanzania
Kuwait
Labuan
Lagos
Leeward Islands
Lesotho
Madagascar
Malawi
Malaya
  Federated Malay States
  Johore
  Kedah
  Kelantan
  Malacca
  Negri Sembilan
  Pahang
  Penang
  Perak
  Perlis
  Selangor
  Singapore
  Sungei Ujong
  Trengganu
Malaysia
Maldive Islands
Malta
Man, Isle of
Mauritius
Mesopotamia
Montserrat
Muscat
Namibia
Natal
Nauru
Nevis
New Britain
New Brunswick
Newfoundland
New Guinea

New Hebrides
New Republic
New South Wales
Niger Coast Protectorate
Nigeria
Niue
Norfolk Island
North Borneo
Northern Nigeria
Northern Rhodesia
North West Pacific Islands
Nova Scotia
Nyasaland Protectorate
Oman
Orange River Colony
Palestine
Papua New Guinea
Penrhyn Island
Pitcairn Islands
Prince Edward Island
Queensland
Rhodesia
Rhodesia & Nyasaland
Ross Dependency
Sabah
St. Christopher
St. Helena
St. Kitts
St. Kitts-Nevis-Anguilla
St. Lucia
St. Vincent
Samoa
Sarawak
Seychelles
Sierra Leone
Solomon Islands
Somaliland Protectorate
South Arabia
South Australia
South Georgia

Southern Nigeria
Southern Rhodesia
South-West Africa
Stellaland
Straits Settlements
Sudan
Swaziland
Tanganyika
Tanzania
Tasmania
Tobago
Togo
Tokelau Islands
Tonga
Transvaal
Trinidad
Trinidad and Tobago
Tristan da Cunha
Trucial States
Turks and Caicos
Turks Islands
Tuvalu
Uganda
United Arab Emirates
Victoria
Virgin Islands
Western Australia
Zambia
Zanzibar
Zululand

**POST OFFICES IN
FOREIGN COUNTRIES**
Africa
  East Africa Forces
  Middle East Forces
Bangkok
China
Morocco
Turkish Empire

Colonies, Former Colonies, Offices, Territories Controlled by Parent States

Belgium
Belgian Congo
Ruanda-Urundi

Denmark
Danish West Indies
Faroe Islands
Greenland
Iceland

Finland
Aland Islands

France
COLONIES PAST AND PRESENT, CONTROLLED TERRITORIES
Afars & Issas, Territory of
Alaouites
Alexandretta
Algeria
Alsace & Lorraine
Anjouan
Annam & Tonkin
Benin
Cambodia (Khmer)
Cameroun
Castellorizo
Chad
Cilicia
Cochin China
Comoro Islands
Dahomey
Diego Suarez
Djibouti (Somali Coast)
Fezzan
French Congo
French Equatorial Africa
French Guiana
French Guinea
French India
French Morocco
French Polynesia (Oceania)
French Southern & Antarctic Territories
French Sudan
French West Africa
Gabon
Germany
Ghadames
Grand Comoro
Guadeloupe
Indo-China
Inini
Ivory Coast
Laos
Latakia
Lebanon
Madagascar
Martinique
Mauritania
Mayotte
Memel
Middle Congo
Moheli
New Caledonia
New Hebrides
Niger Territory
Nossi-Be

Obock
Reunion
Rouad, Ile
Ste.-Marie de Madagascar
St. Pierre & Miquelon
Senegal
Senegambia & Niger
Somali Coast
Syria
Tahiti
Togo
Tunisia
Ubangi-Shari
Upper Senegal & Niger
Upper Volta
Viet Nam
Wallis & Futuna Islands

POST OFFICES IN FOREIGN COUNTRIES
China
Crete
Egypt
Turkish Empire
Zanzibar

Germany
EARLY STATES
Baden
Bavaria
Bergedorf
Bremen
Brunswick
Hamburg
Hanover
Lubeck
Mecklenburg-Schwerin
Mecklenburg-Strelitz
Oldenburg
Prussia
Saxony
Schleswig-Holstein
Wurttemberg

FORMER COLONIES
Cameroun (Kamerun)
Caroline Islands
German East Africa
German New Guinea
German South-West Africa
Kiauchau
Mariana Islands
Marshall Islands
Samoa
Togo

Italy
EARLY STATES
Modena
Parma
Romagna
Roman States
Sardinia
Tuscany
Two Sicilies
  Naples
  Neapolitan Provinces
  Sicily

FORMER COLONIES, CONTROLLED TERRITORIES, OCCUPATION AREAS
Aegean Islands
  Calimno (Calino)
  Caso
  Cos (Coo)
  Karki (Carchi)
  Leros (Lero)
  Lipso
  Nisiros (Nisiro)
  Patmos (Patmo)
  Piscopi
  Rodi (Rhodes)
  Scarpanto
  Simi
  Stampalia
Castellorizo
Corfu
Cyrenaica
Eritrea
Ethiopia (Abyssinia)
Fiume
Ionian Islands
  Cephalonia
  Ithaca
  Paxos
Italian East Africa
Libya
Oltre Giuba
Saseno
Somalia (Italian Somaliland)
Tripolitania

POST OFFICES IN FOREIGN COUNTRIES
"ESTERO"*
Austria
China
  Peking
  Tientsin
Crete
Tripoli
Turkish Empire
  Constantinople
  Durazzo
  Janina
Jerusalem
Salonika
Scutari
Smyrna
Valona
*Stamps overprinted "ESTERO" were used in various parts of the world.

Netherlands
Aruba
Netherlands Antilles (Curacao)
Netherlands Indies
Netherlands New Guinea
Surinam (Dutch Guiana)

Portugal
COLONIES PAST AND PRESENT, CONTROLLED TERRITORIES
Angola
Angra
Azores
Cape Verde
Funchal

Horta
Inhambane
Kionga
Lourenco Marques
Macao
Madeira
Mozambique
Mozambique Co.
Nyassa
Ponta Delgada
Portuguese Africa
Portuguese Congo
Portuguese Guinea
Portuguese India
Quelimane
St. Thomas & Prince Islands
Tete
Timor
Zambezia

Russia
ALLIED TERRITORIES AND REPUBLICS, OCCUPATION AREAS
Armenia
Aunus (Olonets)
Azerbaijan
Batum
Estonia
Far Eastern Republic
Georgia
Karelia
Latvia
Lithuania
North Ingermanland
Ostland
Russian Turkestan
Siberia
South Russia
Tannu Tuva
Transcaucasian Fed. Republics
Ukraine
Wenden (Livonia)
Western Ukraine

Spain
COLONIES PAST AND PRESENT, CONTROLLED TERRITORIES
Aguera, La
Cape Juby
Cuba
Elobey, Annobon & Corisco
Fernando Po
Ifni
Mariana Islands
Philippines
Puerto Rico
Rio de Oro
Rio Muni
Spanish Guinea
Spanish Morocco
Spanish Sahara
Spanish West Africa

POST OFFICES IN FOREIGN COUNTRIES
Morocco
Tangier
Tetuan

Dies of British Colonial Stamps

        DIE A   DIE B   DIE I   DIE II

DIE A:
1. The lines in the groundwork vary in thickness and are not uniformly straight.
2. The seventh and eighth lines from the top, in the groundwork, converge where they meet the head.
3. There is a small dash in the upper part of the second jewel in the band of the crown.
4. The vertical color line in front of the throat stops at the sixth line of shading on the neck.

DIE B:
1. The lines in the groundwork are all thin and straight.
2. All the lines of the background are parallel.
3. There is no dash in the upper part of the second jewel in the band of the crown.
4. The vertical color line in front of the throat stops at the eighth line of shading on the neck.

DIE I:
1. The base of the crown is well below the level of the inner white line around the vignette.
2. The labels inscribed "POSTAGE" and "REVENUE" are cut square at the top.
3. There is a white "bud" on the outer side of the main stem of the curved ornaments in each lower corner.
4. The second (thick) line below the country name has the ends next to the crown cut diagonally.

        DIE Ia.   DIE Ib.
        1 as die II.   1 and 3 as die II.
        2 and 3 as die I.   2 as die I.

DIE II:
1. The base of the crown is aligned with the underside of the white line around the vignette.
2. The labels curve inward at the top inner corners.
3. The "bud" has been removed from the outer curve of the ornaments in each corner.
4. The second line below the country name has the ends next to the crown cut vertically.

Wmk. 1	Wmk. 2	Wmk. 3	Wmk. 4
Crown and C C	Crown and C A	Multiple Crown and C A	Multiple Crown and Script C A

       Wmk. 4a   Wmk. 314
                           St. Edward's Crown
                         and C A Multiple

      Wmk. 373   Wmk. 384

             Wmk. 406

British Colonial and Crown Agents Watermarks

Watermarks 1 to 4, 314, 373, 384 and 406, common to many British territories, are illustrated here to avoid duplication.

The letters "CC" of Wmk. 1 identify the paper as having been made for the use of the Crown Colonies, while the letters "CA" of the others stand for "Crown Agents." Both Wmks. 1 and 2 were used on stamps printed by De La Rue & Co.

Wmk. 3 was adopted in 1904; Wmk. 4 in 1921; Wmk. 314 in 1957; Wmk. 373 in 1974; Wmk. 384 in 1985; Wmk 406 in 2008.

In Wmk. 4a, a non-matching crown of the general St. Edwards type (bulging on both sides at top) was substituted for one of the Wmk. 4 crowns which fell off the dandy roll. The non-matching crown occurs in 1950-52 printings in a horizontal row of crowns on certain regular stamps of Johore and Seychelles, and on various postage due stamps of Barbados, Basutoland, British Guiana, Gold Coast, Grenada, Northern Rhodesia, St. Lucia, Swaziland and Trinidad and Tobago. A variation of Wmk. 4a, with the non-matching crown in a horizontal row of crown-CA-crown, occurs on regular stamps of Bahamas, St. Kitts-Nevis and Singapore.

Wmk. 314 was intentionally used sideways, starting in 1966. When a stamp was issued with Wmk. 314 both upright and sideways, the sideways varieties usually are listed also – with minor numbers. In many of the later issues, Wmk. 314 is slightly visible.

Wmk. 373 is usually only faintly visible.

CAMBODIA

kam-'bō-dē-ə

(Kampuchea)

(Khmer Republic)

LOCATION — Southern Indo-China
GOVT. — Republic
AREA — 69,898 sq. mi.
POP. — 11,626,520 (1999 est.)
CAPITAL — Phnom Penh

Before 1951, Cambodia used stamps of Indo-China. In October, 1970, the Kingdom of Cambodia became the Khmer Republic.

From 1978 to 1980 money was abolished.

100 Cents = 1 Piaster
100 Cents = 1 Riel (1955)

Imperforates

Most Cambodia stamps exist imperforate in issued and trial colors, and also in small presentation sheets in issued colors.

Catalogue values for all unused stamps in this country are for Never Hinged items.

Apsaras — A1

King Norodom Sihanouk — A3

Enthronement Hall — A2

1951-52		Unwmk.	Engr.	Perf. 13	
1	A1	10c dk blue green		1.25	4.25
2	A1	20c cl & org brn		.75	1.75
3	A1	30c pur & indigo		.75	.70
4	A1	40c ultra & brt bl grn		1.00	1.10
5	A2	50c dk grn & dk ol grn		.85	1.00
6	A3	80c bl blk & dk bl		2.50	5.00
7	A2	1pi indigo & purple		2.00	.95
8	A3	1.10pi dp car & brt red		2.75	5.00
9	A3	1.50pi blk brn & red brn ('51)		2.75	1.75
10	A1	1.50pi dp car & cerise		2.75	2.75
11	A2	1.50pi indigo & dp ultra		2.75	2.25
12	A3	1.90pi indigo & dp ultra		4.75	7.25
13	A2	2pi dp car & org brn		3.75	1.25
14	A3	3pi dp car & org brn		5.25	2.75
15	A1	5pi indigo & purple		16.00	10.00
a.		Souvenir sheet of 1		55.00	
16	A2	10pi purple & indigo		18.00	15.00
a.		Souvenir sheet of 1		55.00	
17	A3	15pi dk pur & purple		42.50	30.00
a.		Souvenir sheet of 1		55.00	
		Nos. 1-17 (17)		110.35	92.75

Nos. 15a, 16a, 17a sold in a booklet. Value, $300.

Stamps with completely white gum and no toning sell for a premium.

For surcharges see Nos. B1-B4.

Phnom Daun Penh — A4

East Gate, Angkor Thom — A5

Arms of Cambodia — A6

Methods of Mail Transport — A7

1954-55		Unwmk.	Perf. 13	
18	A4	10c rose carmine	.20	.20
a.		Souvenir sheet of 5 ('55)	47.50	47.50
19	A4	20c dark green	.20	.20
20	A4	30c indigo	.20	.20
21	A4	40c dark purple	.25	.25
22	A4	50c dk violet brn	.25	.25
23	A5	70c chocolate	.45	.75
a.		Souvenir sheet of 5 ('55)	47.50	47.50
24	A5	1pi red violet	.55	.55
25	A5	1.50pi red	.50	.45
26	A6	2pi rose red	.85	.65
a.		Souvenir sheet of 5 ('55)	47.50	47.50
27	A6	2.50pi green	1.25	.80
28	A7	2.50pi blue green	1.50	1.00
a.		Souvenir sheet of 5 ('55)	47.50	47.50
29	A6	3pi ultra	1.75	1.50
30	A7	4pi black brown	1.90	1.50
31	A6	4.50pi purple	2.25	1.50
32	A7	5pi rose red	3.00	1.50
33	A6	6pi chocolate	3.50	1.75
34	A7	10pi purple	3.75	2.00
35	A7	15pi deep blue	6.00	3.75
36	A5	20pi ultra	12.50	6.00
37	A5	30pi blue green	20.00	11.00
		Nos. 18-37 (20)	60.85	35.80
		Nos. 18a//28a, Set of 4	190.00	

The 4 souvenir sheets each contain 5 stamps: #18a (10c, 20c, 30c, 40c, 50c); #23a (70c, 1pi, 1.50pi, 20pi, 30pi); #26a (2pi, 2.50pi green, 3pi, 4.50pi, 6pi); #28a (2.50pi blue green, 4pi, 5pi, 10pi, 15pi). Size of #18a, 26a and 28a: 120x120mm. Size of #23a: 160x92mm. Values are for very fine, unblemished sheets. Examples with toning and/or gum bends sell for less.

For overprints see Nos. 99-100.

King Norodom Suramarit — A8

King Norodom Suramarit and Queen Kossamak Nearirat Serey Vathana A9

Portraits: 50c (No. 39), 2.50r, 4r, 6r, 15r, Queen Kossamak Nearirat Serey Vathana.

Perf. 14x13(A8), 13(A9)

1955, Nov. 24		Engr.	Unwmk.	
38	A8	50c violet	.40	.40
39	A8	50c indigo	.40	.40
40	A8	1r car lake	.55	.50
41	A9	1.50r dk brown	.90	.55
42	A9	2r black & indigo	.80	.50
43	A8	2r dp ultra	.90	.65
44	A8	2.50r dk vio brn	1.25	.65
45	A9	3r brn org & car	1.10	.65
46	A8	4r dark green	1.60	1.00
47	A9	5r blk & dk grn	1.75	1.25
48	A8	6r deep plum	2.00	1.25
49	A8	7r dark brown	2.50	1.25
50	A9	10r brn car & vio	3.00	1.40
51	A8	15r purple	3.75	2.50
52	A8	20r deep green	5.50	3.25
		Nos. 38-52 (15)	26.40	16.20

Coronation of King Norodom Suramarit and Queen Kossamak Nearirat Serey Vathana. See #74-75. For surcharge see #122.

King Norodom Suramarit — A10

Prince Sihanouk, Globe and Flags — A11

Portrait: 3r, 5r, 50r, Queen Kossamak Nearirat Serey Vathana.

1956, Mar. 8			Perf. 13	
53	A10	2r dark red	2.25	2.00
54	A10	3r dark blue	3.00	2.75
55	A10	5r yellow green	4.50	4.00
56	A10	10r dark green	10.00	9.00
57	A10	30r dark violet	22.50	21.00
58	A10	50r rose lilac	45.00	40.00
		Nos. 53-58 (6)	87.25	78.75

Coronation of King Norodom Suramarit and Queen Kossamak Nearirat Serey Vathana.

1957, Mar. 1			Perf. 13	
59	A11	2r green, ultra & car	1.50	1.10
60	A11	4.50r ultra	1.50	1.10
61	A11	8.50r carmine	1.50	1.10
		Nos. 59-61 (3)	4.50	3.30

Admission to the UN, 1st anniv. (in 1956).

Type of Semi-Postal Stamps, 1957

1957, May 12		Unwmk.	Perf. 13	
62	SP1	1.50r vermilion	1.00	1.00
63	SP1	6.50r bluish violet	1.25	1.25
64	SP1	8r dark green	1.50	1.50
		Nos. 62-64 (3)	3.75	3.75

2500th anniv. of the birth of Buddha.

King Ang Duong A12

1958, Mar. 4				
65	A12	1.50r purple & brown	.60	.60
66	A12	5r olive gray & olive	.80	.80
67	A12	10r claret & dull brn	1.50	1.50
a.		Souvenir sheet of 3, #65-67	6.00	5.25
		Nos. 65-67 (3)	2.90	2.90

King Ang Duong (1795-1860). No. 67a sold for 25r.

King Norodom I — A13

1958-59		Engr.	Perf. 12½x13	
68	A13	2r ultra & olive	.70	.50
69	A13	6r orange & sl grn	1.00	.70
70	A13	15r green & ol gray	2.00	1.40
a.		Souv. sheet of 3, #68-70 ('59)	6.00	5.00
		Nos. 68-70 (3)	3.70	2.60

King Norodom I (1835-1904). No. 70a sold for 32r. Issued: #68-70, 11/3/58; #70a, 1/31/59. For surcharge see No. 184.

Children of the World — A14

1959, Dec. 9		Unwmk.	Perf. 13	
71	A14	20c rose violet	.30	.30
72	A14	50c blue	.55	.55
73	A14	80c rose carmine	1.10	1.10
		Nos. 71-73 (3)	1.95	1.95

Issued to promote friendship among the children of the world.
For surcharges see Nos. 115, B8-B10.

Nos. 49 and 52 with Black Border

1960			Perf. 14x13	
74	A8	7r dk brown & blk	4.50	4.50
75	A8	20r dp green & blk	4.50	4.50

Death of King Norodom Suramarit.

Port of Sihanoukville, Prince Sihanouk and Serpent Naga — A15

20r (double size)

1960, Apr.			Perf. 13x12½	
76	A15	2r carmine & sepia	.65	.65
a.		Cambodian 20r	3.00	3.00
77	A15	5r ultra & dp brown	.65	.65
a.		Cambodian 20r	3.25	3.25
78	A15	20r lilac & dk blue	2.40	2.40
		Nos. 76-78 (3)	3.70	3.70

Opening of the port of Sihanoukville. By error the denomination in Cambodian on the 2r and 5r was engraved as 20r; it was corrected later.

Ceremonial Plow — A16

1960			Perf. 12	
79	A16	1r magenta	.65	.65
80	A16	2r brown	.90	.90
81	A16	3r bluish green	1.25	1.25
		Nos. 79-81 (3)	2.80	2.80

Feast of the Sacred Furrow.

Fight Against Illiteracy A17

Water Conservation, Dam at Chhouksar — A18

Dove, Factory
and Books
A19

Buddhist
Ceremony
A20

Works of Sangkum: 6r, Workman and
house. 10r, Woman in rice field.

1960, Sept. 1   Engr.   Perf. 13
82 A17 2r dk grn, brn & dk
            bl   .65   .40
  a.   Souvenir sheet of 3   8.00 8.00
83 A18 3r brown & green   .80   .40
  a.   Souvenir sheet of 3   8.00 8.00
84 A19 4r rose car, vio &
            grn   .80   .55
85 A17 6r brown, org & grn   .90   .70
86 A17 10r ultra, grn & bis 2.25 1.40
87 A20 25r dk car, red & mag 4.50 2.75
        Nos. 82-87 (6)   9.90 6.20

No. 82a contains one each of Nos. 82, 85
and 87, and sold for 42r. No. 83a contains one
each of Nos. 83, 84 and 86, and sold for 23r.
Nos. 82a-83a were issued Dec. 5, 1960.

Cambodian Flag
and Dove
A21

Frangipani
A22

1960, Dec. 24   Engr.   Perf. 13
Flag in Ultramarine and Red
88 A21 1.50r brown & green   .40   .25
89 A21 5r orange red   .60   .35
90 A21 7r green & ultra   1.25 1.00
  a.   Souvenir sheet of 3, #88-90 17.50 17.50
  b.   Souv. sheet of 3 (colors
        changed)   12.50 12.50
        Nos. 88-90 (3)   2.25 1.60

Peace propaganda. No. 90a sold for 16r.
No. 90b contains one of each denomination
with colors changed to: 1.50r orange red, 5r
green & ultramarine, 7r brown & green and
sold for 20r.

1961, July 1   Unwmk.   Perf. 13
91 A22 2r shown   .65   .65
92 A22 5r Oleander   1.10 1.10
93 A22 10r Amaryllis   2.75 2.75
  a.   Souvenir sheet of 3, #91-93 8.00 8.00
        Nos. 91-93 (3)   4.50 4.50

No. 93a sold for 20r.

Krishna in Chariot,
Khmer Frieze — A23

1961-63   Typo.   Perf. 14x13½
94 A23 1r lilac   .40   .20
94A A23 2r blue ('63)   3.25 1.60
95 A23 3r emerald   .90   .40
96 A23 6r orange   .90   .40
  a.   Souvenir sheet of 3   7.50 7.50
        Nos. 94-96 (4)   5.45 2.60

Issued to honor Cambodian armed forces.
No. 94A issued in coils. No. 96a contains
one each of Nos. 94, 95, 96. Sold for 12r.

Independence Monument — A24

1961, Nov. 9   Engr.   Perf. 13x12½
97 A24 2r green   .50   .50
98 A24 4r gray brown   .50   .50
  a.   Souvenir sheet of 2, #97-98 5.00 5.00
        Nos. 97-98,C15-C17 (5) 8.55 5.15

10th anniv. of Independence.
For surcharge see No. 116.

Nos. 27 and 31 Overprinted in Red:
"VIe CONFERENCE MONDIALE
BOUDDIQUE 12-11-1961"

1961, Nov. 11   Perf. 13
99 A6 2.50pi green   1.10   .65
100 A6 4.50pi purple   1.75 1.00

Sixth World Conference of Buddhism.

Highway
(American
Aid) — A25

Foreign Aid: 2r, Power station (Czech aid).
4r, Textile factory (Chinese aid). 5r, Hospital
(Russian aid). 6r, Airport (French aid).

1961, Dec.   Engr.   Perf. 13
101 A25 2r org & rose car   .45   .30
102 A25 3r bl, grn & org brn .45   .30
103 A25 4r dl bl, org brn & mag .45 .40
104 A25 5r dl grn & lil rose .65   .40
105 A25 6r dk bl & org brn 1.25   .55
  a.   Souvenir sheet of 5, #101-105 7.00 7.00
        Nos. 101-105 (5)   3.25 1.95

Malaria Eradication
Emblem — A26

1962, Apr. 7   Unwmk.   Perf. 13
106 A26 2r magenta & brown   .50   .40
107 A26 4r green & dk brown .50   .40
108 A26 6r violet & olive bister .75 .45
        Nos. 106-108 (3)   1.75 1.25

WHO drive to eradicate malaria.
For surcharges see Nos. B11-B12.

Fruits
A27

1962, June 4   Engr.
109 A27 2r Turmeric   .60   .45
110 A27 4r Cinnamon   1.10   .75
111 A27 6r Mangosteens   1.10   .75
  a.   Souvenir sheet of 3, #109-111 6.00 6.00
        Nos. 109-111 (3)   2.80 1.95

Nos. 111a sold for 15r.

Pineapples — A28

1962   Unwmk.   Perf. 13
112 A28 2r shown   .90   .50
113 A28 5r Sugar cane   1.40   .75
114 A28 9r Sugar palms   1.75   .70
        Nos. 112-114 (3)   4.05 1.95

No. 73 Surcharged
1962, Nov. 9   Perf. 13
115 A14 50c on 80c rose car .70   .40

**No. 97 Surcharged in Red and
Overprinted in Black**

1962
116 A24 3r on 2r green   1.00   .40

Dedication of Independence Monument.
See No. C18.

Corn, Rice
and FAO
Emblem
A29

1963, Mar. 21   Engr.   Perf. 13
117 A29 3r multicolored   .70   .55
118 A29 6r org red, vio bl &
            ocher   .70   .55

FAO "Freedom from Hunger" campaign.

Preah Vihear,
Ancient
Temple — A30

Tonsay
Lake — A31

1963, June 15   Perf. 12½x13
119 A30 3r claret, brown & sl
            grn   .50   .40
120 A30 6r org, sl grn & grnsh
            blk   .90   .65
121 A30 15r blue, choc & green 1.40 1.10
        Nos. 119-121 (3)   2.80 2.15

Return by Thailand of Preah Vihear on the
Mekong River.
For overprint see No. 176.

No. 44 Surcharged

1963   Engr.   Perf. 14x13
122 A8 3r on 2½r dk violet brn .90 .55

Perf. 12½x12½, 12½x12
1963, Aug. 1   Photo.

7r, Popokvil Falls. 20r, Beach, horiz.

123 A31 3r multicolored   .50   .50
124 A31 7r multicolored   .80   .70
125 A31 20r multicolored   2.50 1.10
        Nos. 123-125 (3)   3.80 2.30

UNESCO
Emblem,
Scales and
Globe
A32

1963, Dec. 10   Engr.   Perf. 13
126 A32 1r vio bl, rose cl & grn .50 .50
127 A32 3r yel grn, vio bl &
            rose cl   .90   .90
128 A32 12r rose cl, yel grn & vio
            bl   1.60 1.60
        Nos. 126-128 (3)   3.00 3.00

15th anniversary of the Universal Declaration of Human Rights.
For surcharge see No. 183.

Kouprey
A33

1964, Mar. 3   Unwmk.   Perf. 13
129 A33 50c grn, dk brn & org
            brn   .95   .55
130 A33 3r org, brn, dk brn &
            grn   1.40   .70
131 A33 6r blue, dk brn & grn 2.10 1.40
        Nos. 129-131 (3)   4.45 2.65

Black-billed
Magpie — A34

1964, May 2   Engr.   Perf. 13
132 A34 3r shown   1.40   .65
133 A34 6r Kingfisher   2.10 1.00
134 A34 12r Gray heron   3.75 2.00
        Nos. 132-134 (3)   7.25 3.65

For overprint & surcharge see #303, B16.

Emblem of
Royal
Cambodian
Airline
A35

1964   Unwmk.   Perf. 13x12½
135 A35 1.50r rose car & purple .40 .25
136 A35 3r ver & dk blue   .55   .40
137 A35 7.50r ultra & car   1.25   .60
        Nos. 135-137 (3)   2.20 1.25

8th anniv. of the Royal Cambodian Airline.

Prince Norodom
Sihanouk — A36

1964   Engr.   Perf. 12½x13
138 A36 2r purple   .55   .40
139 A36 3r red brown   .80   .50
140 A36 10r dark blue   1.60   .90
        Nos. 138-140 (3)   2.95 1.80

10th anniv. of the Sangkum (political party).
For overprints see Nos. 144-145.

A set of three stamps, imperf, showing clasped hands, was prepared for International Cooperation Year but were never issued. Value, $40.

Woman Weaver A37

Khmer Handicrafts: 3r, Metal worker. 5r, Basket maker.

1965, Feb. 1   *Perf. 13x12½*
141 A37 1r multicolored .40 .40
142 A37 3r red lil, red brn & gray ol .65 .40
143 A37 5r green, dk brn & car 1.10 .85
    Nos. 141-143 (3) 2.15 1.65

Nos. 139-140 Overprinted in Black or Red

1965, Mar. 1   *Perf. 12½x13*
144 A36 3r red brown .70 .40
145 A36 10r dark blue (R) 1.00 .55
Conference of the people of Indo-China.

ITU Emblem, Old and New Communication Equipment — A38

1965, May 17   Engr.   *Perf. 13*
146 A38 3r green & olive bister .40 .30
147 A38 4r red & blue .70 .40
148 A38 10r violet & rose lilac 1.00 .70
    Nos. 146-148 (3) 2.10 1.40
Centenary of the ITU.

Cotton Plant — A39

3r, Peanut plant. 7.50r, Coconut palm.

1965, Aug. 2   *Perf. 12½x13*
149 A39 1.50r orange, sl grn & pur .55 .40
150 A39 3r blue, yel, grn & brn .90 .60
151 A39 7.50r orange brn & sl grn 1.50 1.00
    Nos. 149-151 (3) 2.95 2.00

Preah Ko Temple, Rolouoh — A40

Temples at Angkor: 5r, Baksei Chamkrong, Rolouoh. 7r, Banteay Srei (Citadel of Women). 9r, Angkor Wat. 12r, Bayon, Angkor Thom.

1966, Feb. 1   Engr.   *Perf. 13*
152 A40 3r gray ol, sal & dl grn 1.25 .80
153 A40 5r lil, dk grn & redsh brn 1.50 .85
154 A40 7r dk grn, redsh brn & bis 2.00 1.60
155 A40 9r vio bl, pur & dk grn 2.75 2.10
156 A40 12r dk grn, rose car & ver 3.25 2.75
    Nos. 152-156 (5) 10.75 8.10
For overprints see Nos. 172-175, 177.

WHO Headquarters, Geneva — A41

1966, July 1   Photo.   *Perf. 12½x13*
WHO Emblem in Blue and Yellow
157 A41 2r black & pale rose .40 .25
158 A41 3r black & yel grn .50 .40
159 A41 5r black & lt bl .80 .55
    Nos. 157-159 (3) 1.70 1.20
Inauguration of WHO Headquarters, Geneva.

Tree Planting — A42

UNESCO Emblem — A43

1966, July 22   Engr.   *Perf. 12½x13*
160 A42 1r brn, dull brn & brt grn .30 .25
161 A42 3r org, dull brn & brt grn .55 .30
162 A42 7r gray, dull brn & brt grn .85 .40
    Nos. 160-162 (3) 1.70 .95
Issued for Arbor Day.

1966   Photo.   *Perf. 13*
163 A43 3r multicolored .50 .40
164 A43 7r multicolored .75 .55
20th anniv. of UNESCO.

Wrestlers and Games' Emblem A44

GANEFO Games (Games Emblem and): 3r, Stadium, Phnom Penh. 7r, Swordsmen. 10r, Indian club swingers. Bas-reliefs from Angkor Wat.

1966, Nov. 25   Engr.   *Perf. 13*
165 A44 3r violet blue .40 .20
166 A44 4r green .45 .30
167 A44 7r dk car rose .70 .50
168 A44 10r dark brown 1.10 .65
    Nos. 165-168 (4) 2.65 1.65

Indian Wild Boar A45

Perf. 13x12½, 12½x13
1967, Feb. 20   Engr.
169 A45 3r shown 1.25 .40
170 A45 5r Muntjac, vert. 1.60 .65
171 A45 7r Elephant 2.25 .95
    Nos. 169-171 (3) 5.10 2.00

Nos. 152-153, 155-156 and 121 Overprinted in Red

1967, Apr. 27   Engr.   *Perf. 13*
172 A40 3r multicolored .95 .75
173 A40 5r multicolored 1.00 .75
174 A40 9r multicolored 1.60 1.25
175 A40 12r multicolored 2.00 1.50
176 A30 15r multicolored 2.40 1.75
    Nos. 172-176 (5) 7.95 6.00
International Tourist Year, 1967.

No. 154 Overprinted in Red

1967, Apr. 27
177 A40 7r multicolored 2.00 .75
Banteay Srei Temple at Angkor, millennium.

Royal Ballet Dancer — A46

Various Dancers

1967, June   Engr.   *Perf. 13*
178 A46 1r orange .60 .60
179 A46 3r Prus blue 1.40 .80
180 A46 5r ultra 1.75 1.10
181 A46 7r carmine rose 2.75 1.50
182 A46 10r multicolored 3.50 2.10
    Nos. 178-182 (5) 10.00 6.10
Cambodian Royal Ballet.

Nos. 128 and 70 Surcharged in Red

1967, Sept. 8   Engr.
183 A32 6r on 12r multi .90 .40
184 A13 7r on 15r grn & olive gray 1.10 .60
Intl. Literacy Day, Sept. 8. The surcharge on #184 is adapted to fit the shape of the stamp.

Symbolic Water Cycle — A47

1967, Nov. 1   Typo.   *Perf. 13x14*
185 A47 1r black, bl & org .30 .20
186 A47 6r lilac, lt bl & org .60 .30
187 A47 10r dk blue, emer & org .90 .50
    Nos. 185-187 (3) 1.80 1.00
Hydrological Decade (UNESCO), 1965-74.

Royal University, Kompong Cham A48

6r, Engineering School, Phnom Penh. 9r, University Center, Sangkum Reastr Niyum.

1968, Mar. 1   Engr.   *Perf. 13*
188 A48 4r violet bl & multi .50 .40
189 A48 6r slate & multi .65 .40
190 A48 9r Prus blue & multi .90 .55
    Nos. 188-190 (3) 2.05 1.35

Vaccination and WHO Emblem A49

WHO, 20th Anniv.: 7r, Malaria control and WHO emblem (man spraying DDT).

1968, July 8   Engr.   *Perf. 13*
191 A49 3r ultramarine .60 .40
192 A49 7r deep blue .90 .55

Stadium, Mexico City — A50

1968, Oct. 12   Engr.   *Perf. 13*
193 A50 1r shown .50 .40
194 A50 2r Wrestling .55 .40
195 A50 3r Bicycling .75 .40
196 A50 5r Boxing, vert. .95 .40
197 A50 7.50r Torch bearer, vert. 1.10 .55
    Nos. 193-197 (5) 3.85 2.15
19th Olympic Games, Mexico City, 12/12-27.

Red Cross Team A51

1968, Nov. 1   Engr.   *Perf. 13*
198 A51 3r Prus bl, grn & red 1.10 .40
Issued to honor the Cambodian Red Cross.

Prince Norodom Sihanouk A52

8r, Soldiers wading through swamp.

1968, Nov. 9
199 A52 7r emer, ultra & pur .50 .40
200 A52 8r bl, grn & dp brn .75 .55
15th anniversary of independence.

Human Rights Flame and Prince Sihanouk A53

1968, Dec. 10   Engr.   Perf. 13
201 A53 3r blue   .45   .25
202 A53 5r bright plum   .80   .35
203 A53 7r multicolored   1.10   .55
    Nos. 201-203 (3)   2.35   1.15

International Human Rights Year.

ILO Emblem A54

1969, May 1   Engr.   Perf. 13
204 A54 3r ultra   .40   .25
205 A54 6r dp carmine   .70   .40
206 A54 9r blue green   1.00   .55
    Nos. 204-206 (3)   2.10   1.20

ILO, 50th anniversary.

Globe, Red Cross, Crescent, Lion and Sun Emblems A55

1969, May 8
207 A55 1r blue, red & yel   .40   .25
208 A55 3r sl grn, red & vio brn .60   .40
209 A55 10r brt lil, red & brn   1.25   .60
    Nos. 207-209 (3)   2.25   1.25

50th anniv. of the League of Red Cross Societies.

Papilio Oeacus A56

Butterflies: 4r, Papilio agamenon. 8r, Danaus plexippus.

1969, Oct. 10   Engr.   Perf. 13
210 A56 3r lilac, blk & yel   5.00   1.25
211 A56 4r ver, blk & grn   8.50   2.00
212 A56 8r yel grn, dk brn & org 11.50   3.00
    Nos. 210-212 (3)   25.00   6.25

Map of Cambodia and Diesel Engine A57

Various railroad stations and trains.

1969, Nov. 27   Engr.   Perf. 13
213 A57 3r multicolored   1.00   .75
214 A57 6r slate grn & lt brn   2.00   1.50
215 A57 8r black   3.25   2.25
216 A57 9r dk green & blue   3.75   2.40
    Nos. 213-216 (4)   10.00   6.90

Issued to publicize the new rail link between Phnom Penh and Sihanoukville.

Fish — A58

1970, Jan. 29   Photo.   Perf. 13
217 A58 3r Tripletail   2.40   1.40
218 A58 7r Sleeper goby   4.50   2.40
219 A58 9r Snakehead   6.00   3.00
    Nos. 217-219 (3)   12.90   6.80

Wat Maniratanaram — A59

Monasteries: 2r, Wat Tepthidaram, vert. 6r, Wat Patumavati. 8r, Wat Unnalom.

1970, Apr. 29   Photo.   Perf. 13
220 A59 2r multicolored   .35   .40
221 A59 4r multicolored   .40   .40
222 A59 6r multicolored   .85   .40
223 A59 8r multicolored   1.60   .55
    Nos. 220-223 (4)   3.20   1.75

UPU Headquarters and Monument, Bern — A60

1970, May 20
224 A60 1r green & multi   .30   .20
225 A60 3r scarlet & multi   .50   .20
226 A60 4r dp blue & multi   .65   .25
227 A60 10r brown & multi   1.40   .40
    Nos. 224-227 (4)   2.85   1.05

New UPU Headquarters in Bern.

Open Book and Satellite Earth Receiving Station — A61

1970, May 17   Photo.   Perf. 13
228 A61 3r dk vio bl & multi   .30   .20
229 A61 4r sl grn & multi   .40   .25
230 A61 9r brn ol & multi   .85   .35
    Nos. 228-230 (3)   1.55   .80

World Telecommunications Day.

Nelumbium Speciosum A62

Flowers: 4r, Eichhornia crassipes. 13r, Nymphea lotus.

1970, Aug. 17   Photo.   Perf. 13
231 A62 3r multicolored   .70   .30
  a.   Cambodian and Arabic 3's
         transposed   25.00 30.00
232 A62 4r multicolored   1.40   .45
233 A62 13r multicolored   3.00   .70
    Nos. 231-233 (3)   5.10   1.45

Elephant God, Bas relief at Banteay Srei — A63

1970, Sept. 21   Engr.   Perf. 13
234 A63 3r lil rose & dp grn   .30   .25
235 A63 4r bl grn, grn & lil rose .55   .25
236 A63 7r bl grn, dk brn & grn   .80   .40
    Nos. 234-236 (3)   1.65   .90

Issued for World Meteorological Day.

Khmer Republic

Globe, Rocket, Dove and UN Emblem A64

1970, Nov. 9   Photo.   Perf. 12½x12
237 A64 3r black & multi   .30   .20
238 A64 5r brown red & multi   .45   .25
239 A64 10r dp violet & multi   .90   .50
    Nos. 237-239 (3)   1.65   .95

25th anniversary of the United Nations.

Education Year Emblem A65

1970, Nov. 9   Engr.   Perf. 13x12½
240 A65 1r blue   .25   .20
241 A65 3r brt rose lilac   .30   .20
242 A65 8r blue green   .70   .45
    Nos. 240-242 (3)   1.25   .85

Issued for International Education Year.

Chuon-Nath — A66

1971, Jan. 27   Photo.   Perf. 13
243 A66 3r ol grn & multi   .35   .20
244 A66 8r purple & multi   .75   .35
245 A66 9r violet & multi   1.00   .55
    Nos. 243-245 (3)   2.10   1.10

In memory of Chuon-Nath (1883-1969), Cambodian language expert.
For surcharge see No. 322.

Soldiers in Battle A67

1971, Mar. 18   Photo.   Perf. 13
246 A67 1r gray & multi   .50   .20
247 A67 3r bister & multi   .50   .40
248 A67 10r blue & multi   2.50   .75
    Nos. 246-248 (3)   3.50   1.35

National territorial defense.
For overprint see No. 321.

UN Emblem, Men of Four Races A68

1971, Mar. 21
249 A68 3r blue & multi   .35   .20
250 A68 7r green & multi   .55   .30
251 A68 8r brt rose & multi   1.25   .50
    Nos. 249-251 (3)   2.15   1.00

Intl. year against racial discrimination.

General Post Office, Phnom Penh — A69

1971, Apr. 19
252 A69 3r blue & multi   .20   .20
253 A69 9r lilac rose & multi   .65   .35
254 A69 10r black & multi   .85   .40
    Nos. 252-254 (3)   1.70   .95

Symbolic Globe and Waves A70

Design: 7r, 8r, ITU emblem and waves.

1971, May 17   Photo.   Perf. 13
255 A70 3r green, blk & bl   .25   .20
256 A70 4r yellow & multi   .30   .25
257 A70 7r lilac, blk & red   .40   .25
258 A70 8r sal pink, blk & red   .60   .30
    Nos. 255-258 (4)   1.55   .95

3rd World Telecommunications Day.

Erythrina Indica A71

Wild Flowers: 3r, Bauhinia variegata. 6r, Butea frondosa. 10r, Lagerstroemia floribunda, vert.

1971, July 5   Perf. 13x12½, 12½x13
259 A71 2r lt ultra & multi   .55   .45
260 A71 3r yel grn & multi   .65   .55
261 A71 6r blue & multi   1.40   1.10
262 A71 10r brown & multi   1.75   1.40
    Nos. 259-262 (4)   4.35   3.50

Khmer Coat of Arms — A72   Flag and Square of the Republic — A73

1971, Oct. 9   Engr.   Perf. 13
263 A72 3r brt grn & bis   .25   .20
264 A73 3r purple & multi   .30   .20
265 A73 4r dp claret & multi   .40   .20
266 A72 8r orange & bis   .50   .25
267 A72 10r lt brn & bis   .80   .30
  a. Souv. sheet of 3, #263, 266-267   3.00 3.00
268 A73 10r slate grn & multi   .80   .35
  a. Souv. sheet of 3, #264-265, 268   3.00 3.00
    Nos. 263-268 (6)   3.05   1.50

Republic, 1st anniv.
#267a sold for 25r, #268a for 20r.
For overprints and surcharges see Nos. 301-302, B13-B14.

UNICEF Emblem — A74

1971, Dec. 11
269 A74 3r black brown   .35   .20
270 A74 5r ultra   .50   .25
271 A74 9r dk pur & brn red   1.00   .45
    Nos. 269-271 (3)   1.85   .90

25th anniv. of UNICEF.
This set and others exist with overprint "RPK," both with and without frame. Status has not been determined.

Book Year
Emblem
A75

1972, Feb. 7

272	A75	3r blue, grn & vio	.40	.20
273	A75	8r violet, grn & bl	.60	.30
274	A75	9r emerald & multi	1.00	.50
a.		Souvenir sheet of 3, #272-274	2.75	2.75
		Nos. 272-274 (3)	2.00	1.00

Intl. Book Year. No. 274a sold for 23r.

Lion of St.
Mark
A76

Designs: 5r, Waves engulfing St. Mark's
Basilica. 10r, Bridge of Sighs, vert.

1972, Feb. 7   Engr.   Perf. 13

275	A76	3r lil rose & org brn	.50	.20
276	A76	5r yel grn & org brn	.90	.30
277	A76	9r org brn, bl & yel grn	1.50	.50
a.		Souvenir sheet of 3, #275-277	3.50	3.50
		Nos. 275-277 (3)	2.90	1.00

UNESCO campaign to save Venice. No.
277a sold for 23r.

UN
Emblem
A77

1972, Mar. 28

278	A77	3r deep carmine	.40	.20
279	A77	6r deep blue	.60	.30
280	A77	9r deep orange	.90	.50
a.		Souvenir sheet of 3, #278-280	2.25	2.25
		Nos. 278-280 (3)	1.90	1.00

25th anniv. UN Economic Commission for
Asia and the Far East (ECAFE). No. 280a sold
for 23r.

Dancing
Apsarases — A78

"UIT"
A79

1972, May 5   Engr.   Perf. 13

281	A78	1r golden brn	.25	.20
282	A78	3r violet	.35	.20
283	A78	7r rose claret	.45	.30
284	A78	8r olive brn	.60	.30
285	A78	9r blue grn	.70	.30
286	A78	10r ultra	1.10	.30
287	A78	12r purple	1.40	.30
288	A78	14r Prus blue	1.75	.30
		Nos. 281-288 (8)	6.60	2.35

1972, May 17   Litho.

289	A79	3r blk, yel & grnsh bl	.40	.20
290	A79	9r blk, dp lil rose & bl grn	.75	.30
291	A79	14r blk, brn & bl grn	1.10	.45
		Nos. 289-291 (3)	2.25	.95

4th World Telecommunications Day.

"Human
Environment" — A80

1972, June 5   Engr.

292	A80	3r org, plum & grn	.40	.20
293	A80	12r brt grn & plum	.60	.30
294	A80	15r plum & brt grn	.90	.40
a.		Souvenir sheet of 3, #292-294	3.25	3.25
		Nos. 292-294 (3)	1.90	.90

UN Conf. on Human Environment, Stockholm, June 5-16. No. 294a sold for 35r.
For overprints and surcharges see Nos.
304-305, B15, B17.

Javan
Rhinoceros
A81

1972, Aug. 1   Engr.   Perf. 13

295	A81	3r shown	.60	.20
296	A81	4r Serow	.70	.20
297	A81	6r Malayan sambar	1.40	.30
298	A81	7r Banteng	2.00	.30
299	A81	8r Water buffalo	2.50	.50
300	A81	10r Gaur	3.25	.60
		Nos. 295-300 (6)	10.45	2.10

Nos. 263, 267, 134, 293, 294
Overprinted in Red

1972, Sept. 9   Engr.   Perf. 13

301	A72	3r brt grn & bister	.75	.30
302	A72	10r orange & bister	1.50	.65
303	A34	12r multicolored	1.50	.80
304	A80	12r brt grn & plum	1.60	.80
305	A80	15r plum & brt grn	2.10	1.00
		Nos. 301-305 (5)	7.45	3.55

20th Olympic Games, Munich, 8/26-9/11.

Stupa and
Crest — A83

Apsaras — A84

1973, May 12   Engr.   Perf. 13

309	A83	3r ocher & multi	.35	.20
310	A83	12r yel grn & multi	.35	.20
311	A83	14r blue & multi	.60	.30
a.		Souvenir sheet of 3, #309-311	3.00	3.00
		Nos. 309-311 (3)	1.30	.70

New Constitution. No. 311a sold for 34r.

1973, July 23   Engr.   Perf. 13

Sculptures from Angkor Wat: 8r, 10r,
Devata, diff.

312	A84	3r brown black	.60	.25
313	A84	8r Prus green	1.00	.30
314	A84	10r olive bister	1.50	.50
a.		Souvenir sheet of 3, #312-314	3.00	3.00
		Nos. 312-314 (3)	3.10	1.05

No. 314a sold for 25r.

INTERPOL
Emblem — A85

Marshal Lon
Nol — A86

1973, Oct. 2   Engr.   Perf. 13

315	A85	3r green & multi	.45	.20
316	A85	7r red brn & multi	.55	.30
317	A85	10r olive & multi	.75	.45
a.		Souvenir sheet of 3, #315-317	3.25	3.25
		Nos. 315-317 (3)	1.75	.95

50th anniv. of the Intl. Criminal Police Org.
No. 317a sold for 30r.

1973, Oct. 9

318	A86	3r lt grn, blk & brn	.40	.20
319	A86	8r brown, ol & blk	.60	.30
320	A86	14r black & brn	1.00	.40
a.		Souvenir sheet of 3	5.00	5.00
		Nos. 318-320 (3)	2.00	.90

Marshal Lon Nol, 1st pres. of the Republic.
No. 320a contains stamps similar to Nos. 318-
320 in changed colors. Sold for 50r.

Nos. 248, 243 and 307 Surcharged &
Overprinted in Red or Silver

1974   Photo.   Perf. 13, 12½x13

321	A67	10r multi (R)	1.25	.75
322	A66	50r on 3r multi	2.75	1.75
323	A82	100r on 5r multi	8.00	4.75
		Nos. 321-323 (3)	12.00	7.25

4th anniversary of the Republic.

Copernicus and "Nerva" — A87

Copernicus, various spacecraft and events.

1974, Sept. 10   Litho.   Perf. 13

324	A87	1r shown		
325	A87	5r Mariner II		
326	A87	10r Apollo		
327	A87	25r Telstar		
328	A87	50r Space walk		
329	A87	100r Moon landing		
330	A87	150r Separation of spaceship and module		
		Nos. 324-330 (7)	45.00	
		Nos. 324-330, C46-C47 (9)	55.00	

500th anniversary of the birth of Nicolaus
Copernicus (1473-1543), Polish astronomer.

Carrier Pigeon and UPU
Emblem — A88

Design: 60r, Sailing ship and UPU emblem.

1974, Nov. 2

331	A88	10r multicolored	1.00	.20
332	A88	60r multicolored	3.00	.20
		Nos. 331-332, C50 (3)	14.00	10.40

Cent. of UPU. A souvenir sheet containing
one No. 332 exists.

A set of 8 stamps picturing musical
instruments, overprinted and
surcharged for use by the Khmer
Republic just before the fall of the government in Apr. 1975, exists. Value,
$1,100. Value for same set without
surcharge, $500.

A89

1976 Summer Olympic Games,
Montreal — A90

1r, 18th cent. swordsmen. 5r, Modern fencers. 10r, Ancient Olympic runner. 25r, Modern
runner. 50r, Ancient rowers. 100r, Modern
kayakers. 150r, Ancient horseman. 200r, Modern equestrian competitor. 250r, Buildings,
Olympic flame.

1975, Jan. 2   Litho.   Perf. 13½

333-341	A89	Set of 9	15.00	

Litho. & Embossed

342	A90	1200r gold & multi	35.00	

Souvenir Sheets

343	A89	200r silver & multi	7.50	
344	A89	250r silver & multi	7.50	

Nos. 337-344 are airmail.
A number has been reserved for another
souvenir sheet released with this set.

A91

1974 World Cup Soccer
Championships — A92

Soccer players and arms of: 1r, Hamburg.
5r, Gelsenkirchen. 10r, Dortmund. 25r, Stuttgart. 50r, Dusseldorf. 100r, Hannover. 150r,
Frankfurt. 200r, Munich. 250r, Berlin.

Litho. (#346-354, 356-357)
Litho. & Embossed (#355, 358)
1975, Feb. 13
346-354 A91 Set of 9   7.50
355 A92 1200r gold & multi   37.50
         Souvenir Sheets
356 A91 200r gold & multi   6.00
357 A91 250r gold & multi   6.00
358 A92 1200r gold & multi   13.00

Nos. 350-358 are airmail. Nos. 346-354
exist in imperforate souvenir sheets.

UPU, Cent. — A93

Designs: 15r, Letter carrier, pack mule. 20r,
Biplane. 70r, Post coach. 160r, Biplane, Concorde. 180r, Steam-powered wagon. 235r,
Postrider, tail of mailplane. 500r, Railway mail
car. 1000r, Airship. 2000r, Caravel.

1975, Apr. 12
359-367 A93 Set of 9   10.00
366a   Souvenir sheet of 1   10.00
367a   Souvenir sheet of 1   10.00

Nos. 365-367 are airmail. Nos. 366a and
367a exist imperf. Values, each $25.

People's Republic of Kampuchea

Soldiers — A94

Designs, horiz.: 20c, People, flag. 50c, Fishermen. 1r, Soldiers passing flag.

1980, Apr. 10   Litho.   Perf. 11
368-371 A94 Set of 4   47.50 47.50

Soviet Union,
60th
Anniv. — A95

Designs: 50c, Globe, Kremlin. 1r, Buildings,
map of USSR.

1982, Dec. 30   Perf. 12x12½
372-373 A95 Set of 2   1.00 .55

People's Republic of Kampuchea, 4th
Anniv. — A96

Designs: 50c, Natl. arms, vert. 1r, shown.
3r, Map, stylized figures, vert. 6r, Temple, vert.

1983, Jan. 7   Litho.   Perf. 13
374-376 A96 Set of 3   4.00 1.25
         Souvenir Sheet
377 A96 6r multicolored   5.50 2.25

1984
Summer
Olympic
Games,
Los
Angeles
A97

Designs: 20c, Runner with torch. 50c, Javelin. 80c, Pole vault. 1r, Discus. 1.50r, Relay
race. 2r, Swimming. 3r, Basketball.
20c-1r, 3r are vert.

1983, Jan. 20   Litho.   Perf. 13
378-384 A97 Set of 7   7.00 1.50
         Souvenir Sheet
385 A97 6r Soccer   5.25 3.00

No. 385 contains one 32x40mm stamp.

Butterflies — A98

20c, Salatura genutia. 50c, Euploea
althaea. 80c, Byasa polyeuctes. 1r,
Stichophthalma howqua. 1.50r, Kallima
inachus. 2r, Precis orithya. 3r, Catopsilia
pomona.
20c, 50c, 1.50r, 2r, 3r are vert.

1983, Feb. 18   Litho.   Perf. 13
386-392 A98 Set of 7   12.00 2.00

Khmer
Culture
A99

Designs: 20c, Ruins, Srah Srang. 50c, Tem-
ple, Bakong. 80c, Ta Son. 1r, North Gate,
Angkor Thom. 1.50r, Two winged figures. 2r,
Apsara, Angkor. 3r, Statue of Banteai Srei.

80c-3r are vert.

1983, Mar. 15
393-399 A99 Set of 7   6.50 1.75

Folk Dances
A100

Various dances. Denominations 50c, 1r, 3r.

1983, Apr. 17   Litho.   Perf. 13
400-402 A100 Set of 3   3.75 1.25
         Souvenir Sheet
403 A100 6r Native, "buffalo" 6.50 1.40

No. 403 contains one 32x40mm stamp.

Raphael (1483-1520) — A101

Parnassus (details): #404, 20c, Dante,
Ennius, Homer. #406, 80c, Horace, Ovid,
others. #409, 2r, The Muses. #410, 3r,
Alcaeus, Petrarch, others.
School at Athens (details): #407, 1r, Euclid,
disciples. #408, 1.50r, Telange, Pythagoras.
Details from: #405, 50c, Mass of Bolsena).
6r, Angels from Dispute of the Holy Sacrament, horiz.

1983, May 10   Litho.   Perf. 12½x13
404-410 A101 Set of 7   6.50 2.25
         Souvenir Sheet
             Perf. 13
411 A101 6r multicolored   6.50 2.00

No. 411 contains one 40x32mm stamp.

1st Hot Air
Balloon
Ascension,
Bicent.
A102

Designs: 20c, Montgolfier. 30c, Ville
d'Orleans. 50c, Hydrogen balloon. 1r,
Blanchard & Jeffries, 1785. 1.50r, Ascension
in Arctic. 2r, Stratosphere balloon. 3r, Balloon
race. 6r, Balloons over town.

1983, June 3   Perf. 12½
412-418 A102 Set of 7   6.00 2.00
         Souvenir Sheet
             Perf. 13
419 A102 6r multicolored   6.75 1.50

Reptiles — A103

Designs: 20c, Iguana. 30c, Cobra. 80c,
Trionyx turtle. 1r, Chameleon. 1.50r, Boa constrictor. 2r, Crocodile. 3r, Turtle.

30c, 1r, 1.50r are vert.

1983, June 28
420-426 A103 Set of 7   6.50 2.25

Birds
A104

Designs: 20c, Lorikeet. 50c, Swallow. 80c,
Eagle. 1r, Vulture. 1.50r, Turtle dove. 2r, Magpie. 3r, Hornbill.
20c-50c, 2r-3r are vert.

1983, Sept. 20
427-433 A104 Set of 7   10.00 2.00

Flowers — A105

20c, Sunflower. 50c, Caprifoliacae. 80c,
Bougainvillea. 1r, Renonculacae. 1.50r,
Nyctaginaceae. 2r, Cockscomb. 3r, Roses.

1983, Oct. 18   Perf. 13
434-440 A105 Set of 7   6.00 1.75

1984 Winter Olympic Games,
Sarajevo — A106

Designs: 1r, Luge. 2r, Biathlon. 4r, Ski jumping. 5r, Two-man bobsled. 7r, Hockey.

1983, Nov. 10   Perf. 12½
441-445 A106 Set of 5   10.00 2.75
         Souvenir Sheet
446 A106 6r Cross-country ski-
             ing   5.50 1.75

No. 446 contains one 40x32mm stamp.

Fish
A107

20c, 1.50r, 2r, 3r, Various Cyprinidae. 50c,
Trout. 80c, Catfish. 1r, Moray eel.

1983, Nov. 16   Perf. 13
447-453 A107 Set of 7   7.50 2.00

Festival of Rebirth — A108

50c, Factory. 1r, Bull, tractor. 3r, Bridge
ship, train. 6r, Radio antenna. 50c, 1r are vert.

Perf. 12½x13, 13x12½
1983, Dec. 2   Litho.
454-456 A108 Set of 3   3.50 1.00
Souvenir Sheet
457 A108 6r multicolored   5.50 1.40
No. 457 contains one 32x40mm stamp.

People's
Republic of
Kampuchea,
5th
Anniv. — A109

Designs: 50c, Red Cross. 1r, Soldiers. 3r, People celebrating. 6r, Man carrying water.
1984, Jan. 7   Litho.   **Perf. 13**
458-460 A109 Set of 3   3.75 1.25
Souvenir Sheet
461 A109 6r multicolored   5.50 1.50
No. 461 contains one 32x40mm stamp.
For surcharges see Nos. 775-776.

1984 Winter
Olympics,
Sarajevo
A110

Designs: 20c, Speed skating. 50c, Hockey. 80c, Slalom skiing. 1r, Ski jumping. 1.50r, Biathlon. 2r, Cross-country skiing. 3r, Pairs figure skating. 6r, Women's figure skating.
1984, Jan. 6   Litho.   **Perf. 13**
462-468 A110 Set of 7   6.50 2.00
Souvenir Sheet
469 A110 6r multicolored   5.00 1.40
No. 469 contains one 32x40mm stamp.

Birds — A111

Designs: 10c, Bubulcus ibis. 40c, Lanius schach. 80c, Psittacula himalayana. 1r, Chloropsis aurifrons. 1.20r, Clamator coromandus. 2r, Motacilla cinerea. 2.50r, Dendronanthus indicus.
1984, Feb. 2
470-476 A111 Set of 7   10.00 3.00

Intl. Peace in
Southeast Asia
Forum — A112

Background color: 50c, Green. 1r, Blue. 3r, Violet.
1984, Feb. 25   **Perf. 13x12½**
477-479 A112 Set of 3   3.75 1.00

Space Exploration — A113

Designs: 10c, Luna 1. 40c, Luna 2. 80c, Luna 3. 1r, Soyuz 6. 1.20r, Soyuz 7. 2r, Soyuz 8. 2.50r, Book, rocket, S.P. Koralev. 6r, Salyut space station.
1r-2.50r are vert.
1984, Mar. 8   **Perf. 12½**
480-486 A113 Set of 7   6.50 2.00
Souvenir Sheet
487 A113 6r multicolored   5.50 1.75
No. 487 contains one 40x32mm stamp.

1984 Summer
Olympic
Games, Los
Angeles
A114

Designs: 20c, Discus. 50c, Long jump. 80c, Hurdles. 1r, Relay race. 1.50r, Pole vault. 2r, Javelin. 3r, High jump. 6r, Sprint race.
1984, Apr. 20   **Perf. 13**
488-494 A114 Set of 7   5.50 2.00
Souvenir Sheet
495 A114 6r multicolored   5.50 2.00
No. 495 contains one 32x40mm stamp.

Souvenir Sheet

ESPAÑA '84, Madrid — A115

1984, Apr. 24   **Perf. 12½**
496 A115 5r 1933 Hispano-Suiza K6   5.50 1.50

Wild
Animals
A116

Designs: 10c, Canis latrans. 40c, Canis dingo. 80c, Lycaon pictus. 1r, Canis aureus. 1.20r, Vulpes vulpes. 2r, Chrysocyon brachyurus, vert. 2.50r, Canis lupus.
1984, May 5   **Perf. 13**
497-503 A116 Set of 7   7.00 1.60

Locomotives — A117

Designs: 10c, BB-1002, France, 1966. 40c, BB-1052, France, 1966. 80c, Franco-Belgian,

1945. 1r, #231-505, Franco-Belgian, 1929. 1.20r, #803, Germany, 1968. 2r, BDE-405, France, 1957. 2.50r, DS-01, France, 1979.
1984, June 15   Litho.   **Perf. 12½**
504-510 A117 Set of 7   6.50 1.75

Flowers
A118

Designs: 10c, Magnolia. 40c, Plumeria. 80c, Himenoballis. 1r, Peltophorum roxburghii. 1.20r, Couroupita guianensis. 2r, Lagerstroemia. 2.50r, Thevetia perubiana.
1984, July 10   Litho.   **Perf. 13**
511-517 A118 Set of 7   7.00 2.00

Classic Automobiles — A119

Designs: 20c, Mercedes-Benz. 50c, Bugatti. 80c, Alfa Romeo. 1r, Franklin. 1.50r, Hispano-Suiza. 2r, Rolls Royce. 3r, Tatra. 6r, Mercedes Benz, diff.
1984, Sept. 15   **Perf. 13x12½**
518-524 A119 Set of 7   6.50 1.50
Souvenir Sheet
Perf. 12½
525 A119 6r multicolored   5.50 1.25
No. 525 contains one 40x32mm stamp.

Musical Instruments — A120

Designs: 10c, Sra Lai. 40c, Skor drum. 80c, Skor thom. 1r, Thro khmer. 1.20r, Raneat ek. 2r, Raneat kong. 2.50r, Thro khe.
10c, 80c are vert.
1984, Oct. 10   **Perf. 13**
526-532 A120 Set of 7   5.75 1.75

Wild
Animals
A121

Designs: 10c, Gazelle. 40c, Capreolus capreolus. 80c, Lepus. 1r, Cervus elaphus. 1.20r, Elephas maximus. 2r, Genet. 2.50r, Bibos sauveli.
10c-40c, 1r-1.20r are vert.
1984, Nov. 11   **Perf. 13**
533-539 A121 Set of 7   6.50 1.75

Correggio (1489-1534) — A122

Details from paintings: 20c, Rest on Flight into Egypt. 50c, Martyrdom of the Four Saints. 80c, Mystic Marriage of St. Catherine with Saints Francis and Dominic. 1r, Madonna & Child with Saints John the Baptist, Geminian, Peter Martyr and George. 1.50r, Mystic Marriage of St. Catherine. 2r, The Deposition. 2.50r, The Deposition, diff. 6r, Virgin Crowned by Christ.
1984, Dec. 10   **Perf. 12½x13**
540-546 A122 Set of 7   4.50 1.00
Souvenir Sheet
Perf. 12½
547 A122 6r multicolored   4.50 1.00
No. 547 contains one 40x32mm stamp.

Natl. Festival — A123

50c, Oxcart. 1r, Horse-drawn cart. 3r, Elephants. 6r, Oxcart with passengers, vert.
1985, Jan. 5   **Perf. 12½x12**
548-550 A123 Set of 3   4.25 1.00
Souvenir Sheet
Perf. 12½
551 A123 6r multicolored   4.50 1.00
No. 551 contains one 32x40mm stamp.

1986 World Cup Soccer
Championships, Mexico — A124

Various soccer players; 20c, vert. 50c, vert. 80c, vert. 1r. 1.50r. 2r, vert. 3r, vert.
1985, Feb. 4   **Perf. 13**
552-558 A124 Set of 7   4.50 1.25
Souvenir Sheet
559 A124 6r multicolored   4.50 1.00
No. 559 contains one 40x32mm stamp.

Motorcycles — A125

20c, 1939 Eska-Mofa. 50c, 1939 Wanderer. 80c, 1929 Premier. 1r, 1939 Ardie. 1.50r, 1932 Jawa. 2r, 1983 Simson. 3r, 1984 CZ-125.
1985, Mar. 8   Litho.   **Perf. 13**
560-566 A125 Set of 7   4.50 1.75
Souvenir Sheet
567 A125 6r 1984 MBA   4.50 1.50
No. 567 contains one 40x32mm stamp.

Mushrooms — A126

Designs: 20c, Gymnopilus spectabilis. 50c, Coprinus micaceus. 80c, Amanita panterina. 1r, Hebelona crustuliniforme. 1.50r, Amanita muscaria. 2r, Coprinus comatus. 3r, Amanita caesarea.
Nos. 569-574 are vert.

1985, Apr. 4   **Perf. 13**
568-574 A126 Set of 7   6.50 1.40

Soviet Space Achievements — A127

Designs: 20c, Sputnik. 50c, Yuri Gagarin, rocket. 80c, Valentina Tereshkova, Vostok 6. 1r, Cosmonaut walking in space. 1.50r, Soyuz 4 docked with Soyuz 5. 2r, Lunar rover. 3r, Apollo-Soyuz mission. 6r, Soyuz capsule.

1985, Apr. 12   **Perf. 13**
575-581 A127 Set of 7   4.50 1.25
         Souvenir Sheet
582 A127 6r multicolored   4.50 1.00
   No. 582 contains one 40x32mm stamp.

Traditional Dances — A128

Designs: 50c, Four dancers. 1r, Three dancers. 3r, One dancer, vert.

1985, Apr. 13   **Litho.**   **Perf. 12½**
583-585 A128 Set of 3   3.50 1.25

End of World War II, 40th Anniv. A129

Designs: 50c, Soldiers celebrating. 1r, Victory parade, Moscow. 3r, Tank battle.

1985, May 9   **Litho.**   **Perf. 12x12½**
586-588 A129 Set of 3   4.25 1.50

Cats — A130

Various cats: 20c, 50c, 80c, 1r, 1.50r, 2r, 3r.

1985, May 16   **Litho.**   **Perf. 12x12½**
589-595 A130 Set of 7   6.50 1.50

Flowers — A131

20c, Lilium Black Dragon. 50c, Iris delavayi. 80c, Crocus aureus. 1r, Cyclamen persicum, wild form. 1.50r, Primula malacoides. 2r, Viola tricolor. 3r, Crocus purpureus.

1985, June 5   **Litho.**   **Perf. 13**
596-602 A131 Set of 7   4.50 1.25

Intl. Music Year — A132

Paintings: 20c, Mezzetin, by Watteau. 50c, St. Cecilia and the Angel, by Saraceni. 80c, Still Life with Violin, Flute and Guitar, by Oudry, horiz. 1r, Three Musicians, by F. Leger. 1.50r, Opera Orchestra, by Degas. 2r, St. Cecilia, by Schedoni. 3r, Young Harlequin with Violin, by Caillard. 6r, The Fifer, by Manet.

1985, June 13   **Perf. 13**
603-609 A132 Set of 7   3.75 1.25
         Souvenir Sheet
610 A132 6r multicolored   3.75 1.25
   No. 610 contains one 32x40mm stamp.

Lenin (1870-1924) A133

1r, Portrait. 3r, Lenin standing, map of Soviet Union.

1985, June 20   **Litho.**   **Perf. 13**
611-612 A133 Set of 2   3.50 1.00

ARGENTINA '85 — A134

Birds: 20c, Xanthopsar flavus. 50c, Sicalis flaveola. 80c, Thraupis bonariensis. 1r, Amblyramphus holosericeus. 1.50r, Chiloroceryle amazona. 2r, Ramphastos toco. 3r, Turdus rufiventris.
20c-80c, 1.50r-2r are vert.

1985, July 5   **Litho.**   **Perf. 12½**
613-619 A134 Set of 7   8.75 2.00

Ships A135

Designs: 10c, River boat, 1942. 40c, River boat, 1948. 80c, Tugboat, Japan, 1913. 1r, Dredge. 1.20r, Tugboat, US. 2r, Freighter. 2.50r, Tanker, Panama.

1985, Aug. 8
620-626 A135 Set of 7   4.50 1.40

ITALIA 85 — A136

Paintings: 20c, The Flood, by Michelangelo. 50c, Virgin & St. Margaret, by Il Parmigianino (Filippo Mazzola). 80c, Martyrdom of St. Peter Martyr, by Domenichino. 1r, Spring, by Botticelli. 1.50r, Sacrifice of Abraham, by Veronese. 2r, Meeting of St. Joachim and St. Anne, by Giotto. 3r, Bacchus, by Caravaggio.
6r, Early train.

1985, Oct. 25
627-633 A136 Set of 7   4.50 1.10
         Souvenir Sheet
634 A136 6r multicolored   4.50 1.25
   No. 634 contains one 32x40mm stamp.

Son Ngoc Minh — A137

1985, Dec. 2   **Litho.**   **Perf. 12x12½**
635-637 A137 Set of 3, 50c, 1r,
    3r   3.50 1.25

Fish A138

20c, Barbus tetrazona. 50c, Ophiocephalus micropeltes. 80c, Carassius auratus. 1r, Trichogaster leeri. 1.50r, Puntius hexazona. 2r, Betta splendens. 3r, Datnioides microlepis.

1985, Dec. 28   **Litho.**   **Perf. 13**
638-644 A138 Set of 7   6.25 1.50

1986 World Cup Soccer Championships, Mexico — A139

Various soccer players: 20c, 50c, 80c, 1r, 1.50r, 2r, 3r.

1986, Jan. 29
645-651 A139 Set of 7   4.25 1.25
         Souvenir Sheet
652 A139 6r multicolored   4.00 1.00
   No. 652 contains one 32x40mm stamp.

Horses A140

Designs: 20c, Cob. 50c, Arabian. 80c, Australian pony. 1r, Appaloosa. 1.50r, Quarter horse. 2r, Vladimir heavy draft. 3r, Andalusian.

1986, Feb. 15
653-659 A140 Set of 7   4.75 1.50

27th Soviet Communist Party Congress A141

Designs: 50c, Space capsules. 1r, Lenin. 5r, Statue, rocket lift-off.

1986, Feb. 25   **Perf. 12x12½**
660-662 A141 Set of 3   3.50 1.25

Prehistoric Animals — A142

Designs: 20c, Edaphosaurus, horiz. 50c, Sauroctonus, horiz. 80c, Mastodonsaurus, horiz. 1r, Rhamphorhynchus. 1.50r, Brachiosaurus. 2r, Tarbosaurus. 3r, Indricotherium.

1986, Mar. 20   **Perf. 12½**
663-669 A142 Set of 7   9.00 3.00

Manned Space Flight, 25th Anniv. — A143

10c, Luna 16. 40c, Luna 3. 80c, Vostok. 1r, Alexei Leonov walking in space. 1.20r, Apollo-Soyuz mission. 2r, Soyuz capsule docking with Salyut station. 2.50r, Yuri Gagarin.

1986, Apr. 12   **Perf. 12½**
670-676 A143 Set of 7   7.00 2.00

Khmer
Culture — A144

20c, Temple. 50c, Head of Buddha. 80c, Temple entrance. 1r, 1.50r, 2r, 3r, Various fans.

1986, Apr. 12   *Perf. 13*
677-683 A144 Set of 7   4.50 1.60

Mercedes-Benz Automobiles — A145

20c, 1885 3-wheel. 50c, 1935 sedan. 80c, 1907 open touring car. 1r, 1920 convertible. 1.50r, 1932 cabriolet. 2r, 1938 2-door. 3r, 1985 sedan.

1986, May 14   *Perf. 13x12½*
684-690 A145 Set of 7   4.75 1.50

Butterflies
A146

Designs: 20c, Danaus genutia. 50c, Graphium amtiphates. 80c, Papilio demoleus. 1r, Danaus sita. 1.50r, Idea blanchardi. 2r, Papilio polytes. 3r, Dabasa payeni.

1986, June 19   *Perf. 13*
691-697 A146 Set of 7   7.00 1.75

Ships
A147

20c, English cog. 50c, Cog. 80c, Nile barge. 1r, Galley. 1.50r, Viking long ship. 2r, Two-masted lateen-rigged ship. 3r, Cog, diff.

1986, July 7   *Perf. 13*
698-704 A147 Set of 7   4.25 1.50

Halley's
Comet — A148

Designs: 10c, Solar system, Copernicus, Galileo, Brahe. 20c, Comet above Adoration of the Magi in painting by Giotto. 50c, Comet, observatory. 80c, Edmond Halley. 1.20r,

Giotto probe. 1.50r, Vega probe. 2r, Computer-enhanced images of comet. 6r, Vega probe, diff.

1986, July 21 Litho.   *Perf. 12x12½*
705-711 A148 Set of 7   3.75 1.40
Souvenir Sheet
Perf. 13
712 A148 6r multicolored   3.25 1.25
No. 712 contains one 32x40mm stamp.

STOCKHOLMIA 86 — A149

Chess masters: 20c, Ruy Lopez. 50c, Francois Philador. 80c, Adolph Anderssen. 1r, Wilhelm Steinetz. 1.50r, Emanuel Lasker. 2r, José Capablanca. 3r, Alexander Alekhine. 6r, Chess pieces.

1986, Aug. 28 Litho.   *Perf. 12½*
713-719 A149 Set of 7   4.50 1.40
Souvenir Sheet
Perf. 13
720 A149 6r multicolored   4.25 1.40
No. 720 contains one 40x32mm stamp.

Cactus — A150

20c, Parodia maasii. 50c, Rebutia marsoneri. 80c, Melocactus evae. 1r, Gymnocalycium valnicekianum. 1.50r, Discocactus silichromus. 2r, Neochilenia simulans. 3r, Weingartia chiqichuquensis.

1986, Sept. 25   *Perf. 13*
721-727 A150 Set of 7   4.50 1.40

Fruit — A151

1986, Oct. 4   *Perf. 12½*
Designs: 10c, Bananas. 40c, Papayas. 80c, Mangos. 1r, Breadfruit. 1.20r, Litchi. 2r, Pineapple. 2.50r, Grapefruit, horiz.
728-734 A151 Set of 7   3.50 1.50

Aircraft — A152

20c, Concorde. 50c, DC-10. 80c, 747. 1r, IL-62. 1.50r, IL-86. 2r, AN-124. 3r, A-300. Illustration reduced.

1986, Nov. 21
735-741 A152 Set of 7   4.50 1.50

Silverware — A153

Designs: 50c, Elephant, containers. 1r, Covered bowl. 3r, Serving dish.

1986, Dec. 2   *Perf. 13*
742-744 A153 Set of 3   4.00 1.40

World
Wildlife
Fund
A154

Designs: No. 745, 20c, Kouprey. No. 746, 20c, Gaur. 80c, Banteng. 1.50r, Buffalo.

1986, Dec. 30 Litho.   *Perf. 13*
745-748 A154 Set of 4   20.00 4.00

Tou Samouth
A155

Denominations and background colors: 50c, green. 1r, blue, 3r, yellow.

1987, Jan. 7 Litho.   *Perf. 13*
749-751 A155 Set of 3   3.00 1.00

1988 Winter Olympic Games,
Calgary — A156

Designs: 20c, Biathlon. 50c, Women's figure skating. 80c, Speed skating. 1r, Hockey. 1.50r, Luge. 2r, Two-man bobsled. 3r, Cross-country skiing. 6r, Slalom skiing.

1987, Jan. 14   *Perf. 13x12½*
752-758 A156 Set of 7   3.50 1.25
Souvenir Sheet
Perf. 12½
759 A156 6r multicolored   3.00 1.10
No. 759 contains one 40x32mm stamp.

1988 Summer Olympic Games,
Seoul — A157

Designs: 20c, Weight lifting, vert. 50c, Archery. 80c, Fencing. 1r, Gymnastics, vert. 1.50r, Discus. 2r, Javelin, vert. 3r, Hurdles. 6r, Wrestling.

1987, Feb. 2   *Perf. 12½x13, 13x12½*
760-766 A157 Set of 7   3.50 1.25
Souvenir Sheet
Perf. 13
767 A157 6r multicolored   3.00 1.00
No. 767 contains one 40x32mm stamp.

Dogs
A158

Designs: 20c, shown. 50c, Greyhound. 80c, Great Dane. 1r, Doberman pinscher. 1.50r, Samoyed. 2r, Borzoi. 3r, Collie.

1987, Mar. 3   *Perf. 13*
768-774 A158 Set of 7   5.50 1.50

Nos. 458, 463 Surcharged

1987, Mar. Litho.   *Perf. 13*
775 A110 35r on 50c #463   5.00
776 A109 50r on 50c #458   5.00

Soviet
Spacecraft
A159

Designs: 20c, Sputnik. 50c, Weather satellite. 80c, Proton. 1r, Vostok 1. 1.50r, Electron-2. 2r, Kosmos. 3r, Luna 2. 6r, Electron-4.

1987, Apr. 12 Litho.   *Perf. 13*
777-783 A159 Set of 7   4.25 1.50
Souvenir Sheet
784 A159 6r multicolored   3.50 1.10
No. 784 contains one 40x32mm stamp.

Silverware — A159a

Designs: 50c, Long-necked pot, vert. 1r, Box. 1.50r, Tea set. 3r, Sword.

1987, Apr. 13   *Perf. 13*
785-788 A159a Set of 4   3.25 1.00

CAPEX 87 — A160

Birds: 20c, Merops nubicus. 50c, Upupa epops. 80c, Balearica pavonina. 1r, Tyto alba. 1.50r, Halcyon leucocephala. 2r, Pycnonotus jocosus. 3r, Ardea purpurea. 6r, Terpsiphone paradisi.
50c-1.50r, 3r are vert.

1987, May 5   *Perf. 13*
789-795 A160 Set of 7   4.25 1.25
Souvenir Sheet
796 A160 6r multicolored   4.25 1.25
No. 796 contains one 32x40mm stamp.

Early Aircraft Designs A161

Designs by: 20c, Horatio F. Phillips, 1893. 50c, John Stringfellow, 1848. 80c, Thomas Moy, 1875. 1r, Leonardo da Vinci, 1490. 1.50r, Sir George Cayley, 1840. 2r, Sir Hiram Maxim, 1894. 3r, William S. Henson, 1842. 6r, Da Vinci, diff.

1987, Aug. 7   *Perf. 13*
797-803 A161 Set of 7   4.25 1.40

Souvenir Sheet
Perf. 12½
804 A161 6r multicolored   3.25 1.00
No. 804 contains one 32x40mm stamp.

Reptiles A162

Designs: 20c, Testudo gigantea. 50c, Uromastix acanthinuros. 80c, Cyclura macleayi. 1r, Phrynosoma coronatum. 1.50r, Sauromalus obesus. 2r, Ophisaurus apodus. 3r, Thamnophis sirtalis.

1987, Sept. 9   *Perf. 13*
805-811 A162 Set of 7   5.00 1.50

HAFNIA 87 — A163

Helicopters: 20c, Kamov KA-15. 50c, Kamov KA-18. 80c, Westland Lynx WG-13. 1r, Sud Aviation Gazelle. 1.50r, Sud Aviation Puma. 2r, Boeing CH-47 Chinook. 3r, Boeing UTTAS. 6r, Fairey Rotodyne.

1987, Oct. 16   *Perf. 12½x12*
812-818 A163 Set of 7   4.25 1.40

Souvenir Sheet
Perf. 13
819 A163 6r multicolored   3.25 1.10
No. 819 contains one 40x32mm stamp.

Russian October Revolution, 70th Anniv. A164

1987   **Litho.**   *Perf. 12x12¼*
820 A164 2r Soldiers, horse   1.25 .30
821 A164 3r Soldiers   1.75 .50
822 A164 5r Lenin, aides   3.50 .80
Two additional stamps were issued in this set. The editors would like to examine them.

Fire Trucks A165

1987, Nov. 24   **Litho.**   *Perf. 13*
823-829 A165   20c, 50c, 80c, 1r, 1.50r, 2r, 3r, set of 7   6.50 2.00

Telecommunications — A166

50c, Dish antenna, vert. 1r, Broadcast center, vert. 3r, Dish antenna, broadcast center.

Perf. 13x12½, 12x12½, 12½x12
1987, Dec. 2
830-832 A166 Set of 3   3.00 1.10
No. 830 is 29x40mm. No. 831 is 28x44mm. No. 832 printed with se-tenant label.

1988 Winter Olympic Games, Calgary A167

Designs: 20c, Speed skating. 50c, Hockey. 80c, Downhill skiing. 1r, Ski jumping. 1.50r, Biathlon. 2r, Pairs figure skating. 3r, Cross-country skiing. 6r, Four-man bobsled.

1988, Jan. 7   *Perf. 12½*
833-839 A167 Set of 7   3.25 1.00

Souvenir Sheet
Perf. 13
840 A167 6r multicolored   2.75 .90
No. 840 contains one 32x40mm stamp.

Water Projects A168

Designs: 50c, Canal. 1r, Dam under construction. 3r, Dam, bridge.

1988, Jan. 7   **Litho.**   *Perf. 13*
841-843 A168 Set of 3   4.00 1.25

1988 Summer Olympic Games, Seoul — A169

Designs: 20c, Balance beam, vert. 50c, Uneven bars. 80c, Rhythmic gymnastics ribbon, vert. 1r, Rhythmic gymnastics hoop, vert. 1.50r, Rhythmic gymnastics clubs, vert. 2r, Rhythmic gymnastics ball. 3r, Floor exercise.

Perf. 12½x13, 13x12½
1988, Feb. 2   **Litho.**
844-850 A169 Set of 7   4.00 1.50

Souvenir Sheet
Perf. 12½
851 A169 6r Rhythmic gymnastics, diff.   3.25 1.50
No. 851 contains one 32x40mm stamp.

JUVALUX 88 A170

Various cats. Denominations: 20c, 50c, 80c, 1r, 1.50r, 2r, 3r. Nos. 853-854, 856-858 are vert.

1988, Mar. 15   *Perf. 12½*
852-858 A170 Set of 7   4.25 1.25

Souvenir Sheet
Perf. 13
859 A170 6r multicolored   4.50 1.25
No. 859 contains one 40x32mm stamp.

ESSEN 88 — A171

Ships: 20c, Passenger liner. 50c, Passenger liner, diff. 80c, Research ship. 1r, Communications ship. 1.50r, Tanker. 2r, Hydrofoil. 3r, Hovercraft.

1988, Apr. 14   **Litho.**   *Perf. 12½*
860-866 A171 Set of 7   4.00 1.50

Souvenir Sheet
Perf. 13
867 A171 6r Hydrofoil   3.75 1.10

Satellites — A172

Various satellites. Denominations: 20c, 50c, 80c, 1r, 1.50r, 2r, 3r. Nos. 868-870 are vert.

1988, Apr. 24   *Perf. 12½x13, 13x12½*
868-874 A172 Set of 7   4.00 1.50

Souvenir Sheet
Perf. 13
875 A172 6r multicolored   6.00 2.25
No. 875 contains one 40x32mm stamp.

FINLANDIA 88 — A173

Fish: 20c, Xiphophorus helleri. 50c, Hemigrammus ocellifer. 80c, Macropodus opercularis. 1r, Carassius auratus. 1.50r, Hyphessobrycon inesi. 2r, Corynopoma riisei. 3r, Mollienisia latipinna.

6r, Pterophyllum scalare.

1988, Jun 10   **Litho.**   *Perf. 13x12½*
876-882 A173 Set of 7   4.50 1.50

Souvenir Sheet
Perf. 12½
883 A173 6r multicolored   4.25 1.25
No. 883 contains one 32x40mm stamp.

Shells — A174

Designs: 20c, Helicostyla florida. 50c, Helicostyla marinduquensis. 80c, Helicostyla fulgens. 1r, Helicostyla woodiana. 1.50r, Chloraea sirena. 2r, Helicostyla mirabilis. 3r, Helicostyla limansauensis.

1988, Aug. 5   **Litho.**   *Perf. 13x12½*
884-890 A174 Set of 7   5.25 1.50

Insects — A175

Designs: 20c, Coccinellidae. 50c, Zonabride geminata. 80c, Carabus auronitens. 1r, Apis mellifera. 1.50r, Praying mantis. 2r, Odonata. 3r, Malachius aeneus.

1988, Sept. 6   *Perf. 13x12½*
891-897 A175 Set of 7   5.50 1.40

Orchids A176

Designs: 20c, Cattleya aclandiae. 50c, Odontoglossum Royal Sovereign. 80c, Cattleya labiata. 1r, Ophrys apifera. 1.50r, Laelia anceps. 2r, Laelia pumila. 3r, Stanhopea tigrina, horiz.

1988, Oct. 10   *Perf. 12½x13, 13x12½*
898-904 A176 Set of 7   7.50 1.75

Reptiles — A177

Designs: 20c, Naja haje, vert. 50c, Iguana iguana, vert. 80c, Dryophis nasuta. 1r, Terrapene carolina. 1.50r, Cyclura macleayi. 2r, Bothrops bicolor. 3r, Naja naja, with hood spread, vert.

1988, Nov. 7   *Perf. 12x12½, 12½x12*
905-911 A177 Set of 7   6.00 1.75

Dance of the Peacock
A178

50c, 3 dancers, vert. 1r, shown. 3r, 2 dancers.

1988, Dec. 2 **Perf. 13**
912-914 A178 Set of 3 4.00 1.25

For surcharges see Nos. 1195-1196.

Bridges — A179

1989 **Perf. 13x12½**
915-917 A179 50c, 1r, 3r, set of 3 3.25 1.40

Decade of Progress — A180

3r, Telecommunications station. 12r, Central Electrical Plant No. 4. 30r, Cement plant, vert.

1989
918-920 A180 Set of 3 3.50 1.50

1990 World Cup Soccer Championships, Italy — A181

Various soccer players. Denominations: 2r, 3r, 5r, 10r, 15r, 20r, 35r.

1989 **Perf. 12½x13**
921-927 A181 Set of 7 5.00 1.50
Souvenir Sheet
Perf. 13
928 A181 45r multicolored 3.50 1.00

No. 928 contains one 32x40mm stamp.

Trains
A182

Various locomotives. Denominations: 2r, 3r, 5r, 10r, 15r, 20r, 35r.

1989 **Perf. 13**
929-935 A182 Set of 7 4.75 1.50
Souvenir Sheet
Perf. 12½
936 A182 45r multicolored 3.75 1.00

No. 936 contains one 40x32mm stamp.

A183

A184

1989 **Perf. 13**
937 A183 12r red & black 1.25 .55

Cuban Revolution, 30th anniv.

1989

Birds: 20c, Ara macao. 80c, Kakatoe galerita. 3r, Psittacula krameri. 6r, Ara ararauna. 10r, Poicephalus robustus. 15r, Amazona aestiva. 25r, Pionus senilis, horiz. 45r, Cyanoramphus novaezelandiae.

938-944 A184 Set of 7 5.00 1.25
Souvenir Sheet
Perf. 12½
945 A184 45r multicolored 4.00 1.00

No. 945 contains one 40x32mm stamp.

1992 Winter Olympic Games, Albertville
A185

2r, Slalom skiing. 3r, Biathlon. 5r, Cross-country skiing. 10r, Ski jumping. 15r, Speed skating. 20r, Hockey. 35r, Bobsled. 45r, Pairs figure skating.

1989, Mar. 30 **Perf. 13**
946-952 A185 Set of 7 4.75 1.50
Souvenir Sheet
Perf. 12½
953 A185 45r multicolored 3.00 1.00

No. 953 contains one 32x40mm stamp.

Water Lilies
A186

20c, Nymphaea capensis (pink). 80c, Nymphaea capensis (purple). 3r, Nymphaea lotus. 6r, Nymphaea Dir. Geo. T. Moore. 10r, Nymphaea Sunrise. 15r, Nymphaea Escarboncie. 25r, Nymphaea Cladstoniana. 45r, Nymphaea Paul Hariot.

1989 **Perf. 12½x13**
954-960 A186 Set of 7 4.50 1.25
Souvenir Sheet
Perf. 12½
961 A186 45r multicolored 3.50 1.00

No. 961 contains one 32x40mm stamp.

1992 Summer Olympic Games, Barcelona — A187

Designs: 2r, Wrestling. 3r, Pommel horse, vert. 5r, Shot put. 10r, Running, vert. 15r, Fencing. 20r, Canoeing, vert. 35r, Steeplechase, vert. 45r, Weight lifting, vert.

1989 **Perf. 13**
962-968 A187 Set of 7 4.50 1.50
Souvenir Sheet
Perf. 12½
969 A187 45r multicolored 4.00 1.50

No. 969 contains one 32x40mm stamp.

Mushrooms
A188

Designs: 20c, Xerocomus subtomentosus. 80c, Inocybe patouillardii. 3r, Armillaria mellea. 6r, Agaricus campestris. 10r, Paxillus involutus. 15r, Coprinus comatus. 25r, Lepiota procera.

1989 **Perf. 12½x13**
970-976 A188 Set of 7 4.50 1.10

Horses — A189

Designs: 2r, Shire. 3r, Brabant. 5r, Bolounais. 10r, Breton. 15r, Vladimir heavy draft. 20r, Italian heavy draft. 35r, Freiberger. 45r, Horse-drawn cart.

1989 **Perf. 12½**
977-983 A189 Set of 7 4.75 1.50
Souvenir Sheet
984 A189 45r multicolored 3.75 1.10

Nos. 977-983 printed with se-tenant label. No. 984 contains one 40x32mm stamp.

Angkor Wat — A190

Denominations: 35r, 50r, 80r, 100r.

1989, May 15 **Litho.** **Perf. 13¼**
985-988 A190 Set of 4 100.00 100.00

Cambodia

PHILEXFRANCE 89 — A191

Mail coaches: 2r, 17th cent. 3r, Paris-Lyon, 1720. 5r, 1793. 10r, 1805. 15r, Royal Mail. 20r, 1843. 35r, Paris-Lille, 1837, vert. 45r, 1815, vert.

1989 **Litho.** **Perf. 13**
989-995 A191 Set of 7 4.75 1.50
Souvenir Sheet
Perf. 12½
996 A191 45r multicolored 3.25 1.50

No. 996 contains one 23x40mm stamp.

BRASILIANA 89 — A192

Butterflies: 2r, Papilio zagreus. 3r, Morpho catenarius. 5r, Morpho aega. 10r, Callithea sapphira. 15r, Catagramma sorana. 20r, Pierella nereis. 35r, Papilio brasiliensis. 45r, Thacia marsyas, horiz.

1989 **Perf. 13**
997-1003 A192 Set of 7 12.00 1.50
Souvenir Sheet
1004 A192 45r multicolored 7.50 1.50

No. 1004 contains one 40x32mm stamp.

Khmer Boats
A193

Various pirogues. Denominations: 3r, 12r, 30r.

1989, Dec. 2 **Litho.** **Perf. 12½**
1005-1007 A193 Set of 3 3.50 1.25

Natl. Organizations — A194

3r, Youth, vert. 12r, Labor. 30r, Natl. Front.

1990, Jan. 7 **Litho.** **Perf. 13**
1008-1010 A194 Set of 3 3.50 1.25

1990 World Cup Soccer Championships, Italy — A195

Various soccer players. Denominations: 2r, 3r, 5r, 10r, 15r, 20r, 35r.

1990, Jan. 5   Litho.   *Perf. 13*
1011-1017 A195 Set of 7   4.50 1.50
Souvenir Sheet
1018 A195 45r multicolored   3.25 1.00
No. 1018 contains one 32x40mm stamp.
For surcharges see Nos. 1072-1076A.

STAMPWORLD LONDON 90 — A196

Various mail coaches. Denominations: 2r, 3r, 5r, 10r, 15r, 20r, 35r.
45r, Single horse van for rural deliveries.

1990   *Perf. 12½x12*
1019-1025 A196 Set of 7   4.25 1.25
Souvenir Sheet
Perf. 13
1026 A196 45r multicolored   4.25 1.00
Nos. 1019-1025 are printed with se-tenant label. No. 1026 contains one 40x32mm stamp.

Rice — A197

Designs: 3r, Woman, rice. 12r, People hauling rice, horiz. 30r, Women threshing rice.

1990, June 19   Litho.   *Perf. 13*
1027-1029 A197 Set of 3   3.50 1.25

1992 Winter Olympic Games, Albertville A198

2r, 4-man bobsled. 3r, Speed skating. 5r, Pairs figure skating. 10r, Hockey. 15r, Biathlon. 20r, Luge. 35r, Ski jumping. 45r, Hockey goalie.

1990   Litho.   *Perf. 13*
1030-1036 A198 Set of 7   4.75 1.50
Souvenir Sheet
1037 A198 45r multicolored   3.00   .90
No. 1037 contains one 32x40mm stamp.

1992 Summer Olympic Games, Barcelona A199

Designs: 2r, Shooting. 3r, Shot put. 5r, Weight lifting. 10r, Boxing. 15r, Pole vault. 20r, Basketball. 35r, Fencing. 45r, Rhythmic gymnastics.

1990
1038-1044 A199 Set of 7   4.75 1.50
Souvenir Sheet
1045 A199 45r multicolored   2.75   .90
No. 1045 contains one 32x40mm stamp.

Khmer Culture A200

Designs: 3r, Facade, Bantey Srei. 12r, Relief. 30r, Ruins, Banon.

Perf. 12½, 12½x13 (#1048)
1990, Dec. 2   Litho.
1046-1048 A200 Set of 3   3.25 1.25
No. 1048 is 36x21mm.

Dogs A201

20c, Poodle. 80c, Shetland. 3r, Samoyed. 6r, Springer spaniel. 10r, Fox terrier. 15r, Afghan. 25r, Dalmatian. 45r, Bernese.

1990   Litho.   *Perf. 13*
1049-1055 A201 Set of 7   4.50 1.25
Souvenir Sheet
1056 A201 45r multicolored   3.50 1.00
No. 1056 contains one 40x32mm stamp.

Cacti — A202

Designs: 20c, Cereus hexagonus. 80c, Arthrocereus rondonianus. 3r, Matucana multicolor. 6r, Hildewintera aureispina. 10r, Opuntia retrosa. 15r, Erdisia tenuicula. 25r, Mamillaria yaquensis.

1990
1057-1063 A202 Set of 7   4.25 1.50

NEW ZEALAND 90 — A203

Butterflies: 2r, Zizina oxleyi. 3r, Cupha prosope. 5r, Heteronympha merope. 10r, Dodonidia helmsi. 15r, Argirophenga antipodum. 20r, Tysonotis danis. 35r, Pyrameis gonnarilla. 45r, Pyrameis itea.

1990   *Perf. 13*
1064-1070 A203 Set of 7   8.00 1.50
Souvenir Sheet
Perf. 12½
1071 A203 45r multicolored   5.00 1.25
No. 1071 contains one 40x32mm stamp.

Nos. 1012, 1013, 1015, 1016 Surcharged in Red
1990   Litho.   *Perf. 13*
1072 A195 200r on 3r #1012
1073 A195 300r on 5r multi
1074 A195 500r on 10r multi

1075   A195   800r on 15r multi
1076   A195   1000r on 20r multi
1076A A195   2000r on 35r multi

Intl. Literacy Year — A204

Denominations: 3r, 12r, 30r.

1990   Litho.   *Perf. 13*
1077-1079 A204 Set of 3   3.75 1.50

Ships A205

Designs: 20c, English, 1200. 80c, Spanish galleon, 16th cent. 3r, Dutch ship, 1627. 6r, La Couronne, 1638. 10r, L'Astrolabe, 1826. 15r, French packet, Louisiana, 1864. 25r, Clipper ship, 1900, vert. 45r, Merchant ship, 1800.

1990   Litho.   *Perf. 13*
1080-1086 A205 Set of 7   4.50 1.50
Souvenir Sheet
Perf. 12½
1087 A205 45r multicolored   3.25 1.00
No. 1087 contains one 32x40mm stamp.

Natl. Building Campaign — A206

3r, Railroad. 12r, Cargo ship, Kampong Som. 30r, Fishing boats, Kampong Som.

1990   Litho.   *Perf. 13*
1088-1090 A206 Set of 3   3.25 1.25

PARIS 90 — A207

Chess pieces and: 2r, Sacré Coeur. 3r, Equestrian statue. 5r, Winged Victory of Samothrace. 10r, Chateau, Azay le Riddeau. 15r, Sculpture, "The Dance." 20r, Eiffel Tower. 35r, Arc de Triomphe.
45r, Chess pieces, horiz.

1990, Nov. 15   Litho.   *Perf. 13*
1091-1097 A207 Set of 7   6.50 2.00
Souvenir Sheet
1098 A207 45r multicolored   4.75 1.50
No. 1098 contains one 40x32mm stamp.

Space Day — A208

Designs: 2r, Vostok. 3r, Soyuz. 5r, Artificial satellite. 10r, Luna 10. 15r, Mars 1. 20r, Venus 3. 35r, Mir. 45r, Energia, Buran.

1990   Litho.   *Perf. 13*
1099-1105 A208 Set of 7   5.00 1.50
Souvenir Sheet
1106 A208 45r multicolored   3.25 1.00
No. 1106 contains one 32x40mm stamp.
For surcharges see Nos. 1145-1151.

Discovery of America, 500th Anniv. (in 1992) — A209

Designs: 2r, Columbus. 3r, Queen Isabella's jewelry chest. 5r, Queen Isabella. 10r, Santa Maria. 15r, Juan de la Cosa. 20r, Columbus Monument. 35r, Pyramid, Yucatan. 45r, Columbus, diff.

1990, Oct. 12   Litho.   *Perf. 13*
1107-1113 A209 Set of 7   6.50 2.00
Souvenir Sheet
1114 A209 45r multicolored   4.25 1.25
No. 1114 contains one 32x40mm stamp.

Natl. Festival A210

Designs: 100r, Tire production. 300r, Rural infirmary. 500r, Fisherman, vert.

Perf. 12½, 13 (#1117)
1991, Jan. 7   Litho.
1115-1117 A210 Set of 3   4.50 1.75
No. 1117 is 28x40mm.

1994 World Cup Soccer Championships, US — A211

Various soccer players. Denominations: 5r, 25r, 70r, 100r, 200r, 400r, 1000r.

1991, Feb. 15   Litho.   *Perf. 13*
1118-1124 A211 Set of 7   5.75 1.75
Souvenir Sheet
1125 A211 900r multicolored   3.25 1.10
No. 1125 contains one 32x40mm stamp.

1992 Winter Olympic Games, Albertville A212

Designs: 5r, Speed skating. 25r, Slalom skiing. 70r, Hockey. 100r, Bobsled. 200r, Freestyle skiing. 400r, Pairs figure skating. 1000r, Downhill skiing.
900r, Ski jumping.

1991, Mar. 30   **Litho.**   **Perf. 12½**
1126-1132 A212 Set of 7   6.00   2.00
Souvenir Sheet
Perf. 13
1133 A212 900r multicolored   3.25   1.00
No. 1133 contains one 32x40mm stamp.

Khmer Culture A213

Statues: 100r, Garuda, 10th cent. 300r, Torso of Vishnu reclining, 11th cent. 500r, Reclining Nandin, 7th cent.

1991, Apr. 13   **Litho.**   **Perf. 12½**
1134-1136 A213 Set of 3   3.50   1.50

1992 Summer Olympic Games, Barcelona A214

Designs: 5r, Pole vault. 25r, Table tennis. 70r, Women's running. 100r, Wrestling. 200r, Women's gymnastics. 400r, Tennis. 1000r, Boxing.
900r, Balance beam.

1991, Apr. 25   **Litho.**   **Perf. 12½x13**
1137-1143 A214 Set of 7   5.00   1.50
Souvenir Sheet
Perf. 13
1144 A214 900r multicolored   3.50   1.00
No. 1144 contains one 32x40mm stamp.

Nos. 1099-1105 Surcharged in Red
1991   **Litho.**   **Perf. 13**
1145 A208 100r on 2r #1099
1146 A208 150r on 3r #1100   —
1147 A208 200r on 5r #1101   —
1148 A208 300r on 10r #1102   —
1149 A208 500r on 15r #1103   —
1150 A208 1500r on 20r #1104   —
1151 A208 2000r on 35r #1105   —

Aircraft — A215

Designs: 5r, DC-10-30. 25r, MD-11. 70r, IL-6-300. 100r, A-310. 200r, YAK-42. 400r, TU-54. 1000r, DC-9

1991, June 15   **Litho.**   **Perf. 13x12½**
1152-1158 A215 Set of 7   5.50   1.75

ESPAMER 91 — A216

Pre-Columbian pottery: 5r, Catamarca. 25r, Catamarca, vert. 70r, Tucuman, vert. 100r, Santiago del Estero. 200r, Santiago del Estero, diff. 400r, Tucuman, diff., vert. 1000r, Catamarca, diff.
900r, Catamarca, diff.

1991, July 10   **Perf. 13**
1159-1165 A216 Set of 7   6.00   2.00
Souvenir Sheet
Perf. 12½
1166 A216 900r multicolored   4.25   1.25
No. 1166 contains one 40x32mm stamp.

Discovery of America, 500th Anniv. (in 1992) — A217

Designs: 5r, Pinta, vert. 25r, Niña, vert. 70r, Santa Maria, vert. 100r, Landing of Columbus. 200r, Encountering new cultures. 400r, First European settlement in Americas. 1000r, Native village.
900r, Columbus.

1991, Oct. 12   **Perf. 12½x13, 13x12½**
1167-1173 A217 Set of 7   6.50   2.00
Souvenir Sheet
Perf. 12½
1174 A217 900r multicolored   3.50   1.10
No. 1174 contains one 40x32mm stamp.

PHILANIPPON 91 — A218

Butterflies: 5r, Neptis pryeri. 25r, Papilio xuthus. 70r, Cyrestis thyodamas. 100r, Argynnis anadiomene. 200r, Lethe marginalis. 400r, Artopoetes pryeri. 1000r, Danaus chrysippus.
900r, Ochlodes subhyalina.

1991, Nov. 16   **Perf. 13**
1175-1181 A218 Set of 7   8.00   2.00
Souvenir Sheet
Perf. 12½
1182 A218 900r multicolored   6.50   1.25
No. 1182 contains one 40x32mm stamp.

Natl. Building Campaign A219

Designs: 100r, Fishing port. 300r, Preparing palm sugar, vert. 500r, Harvesting peppers.

1991, Dec. 2   **Litho.**   **Perf. 12½**
1183-1185 A219 Set of 3   4.50   1.25

Natl. Festival — A220

Traditional costumes: 150r, Chakdomuk. 350r, Longvek. 1000r, Angkor.

1992, Jan. 7   **Perf. 13**
1186-1188 A220 Set of 3   4.00   1.25

1992 Summer Olympic Games, Barcelona A221

5r, Wrestling. 15r, Soccer. 80r, Weight lifting. 400r, Archery. 1500r, Balance beam. 1000r, Equestrian.

1992, Jan.   **Litho.**   **Perf. 13**
1189-1193 A221 Set of 5   4.00   1.25
Souvenir Sheet
Perf. 12½
1194 A221 1000r multicolored   3.25   .95
No. 1194 contains one 32x40mm stamp.

Nos. 913-914 Surcharged in Red
1992, Jan.   **Litho.**   **Perf. 13**
1195 A178 200r on 3r #914
1196 A178 300r on 1r #913

Fish A222

Designs: 5r, Hyphessobrycon innesi. 15r, Betta splendens. 80r, Nematobrycon palmen. 400r, Colisa lalia. 1500r, Hoplosternum thoracatum.
1000r, Pterophyllum scalare.

1992, Feb. 8   **Litho.**   **Perf. 12½**
1197-1201 A222 Set of 5   5.00   1.50
Souvenir Sheet
1202 A222 1000r multicolored   3.75   1.00
No. 1202 contains one 40x32mm stamp.

1994 World Cup Soccer Championships, US — A223

Various soccer plays. Denominations: 5r, 15r, 80r, 400r, 1500r. Nos. 1203, 1205-1207 are vert.

1992, Mar. 6   **Litho.**   **Perf. 12½**
1203-1207 A223 Set of 5   4.25   1.50
Souvenir Sheet
1208 A223 1000r multicolored   3.00   .90
No. 1208 contains one 40x32mm stamp.

Khmer Culture — A224

19th cent. structures: 150r, Monument. 350r, Stupa. 1000r, Library of Mandapa.

1992, Apr. 13   **Litho.**   **Perf. 12½**
1209-1211 A224 Set of 3   4.75   2.25

Leonardo da Vinci (1452-1519) — A225

Designs: 5r, Automobile. 15r, Container ship. 80r, Helicopter. 400r, Scuba gear. 1500r, Parachute, vert.
1000r, Portrait.

1992, Apr. 15   **Litho.**   **Perf. 12x12½**
1212-1216 A225 Set of 5   7.50   1.50
Souvenir Sheet
Perf. 13
1217 A225 1000r multicolored   4.75   1.00
Nos. 1212-1216 each printed with se-tenant labels showing Da Vinci's conceptions of the items shown on the stamps. No. 1217 contains one 32x40mm stamp.

EXPO 92, Seville A226

Inventors, builders: 5r, De la Cierva, autogyro. 15r, Edison, electric light bulb. 80r, Morse, telegraph. 400r, Monturiol, submarine. No. 1222, 1500r, Bell, telephone. No. 1223, 1500r, Fulton, steamship.

1992, Apr. 23   **Perf. 12½**
1218-1222 A226 Set of 5   4.50   1.25
Souvenir Sheet
Perf. 13
1223 A226 1000r pink & black   3.00   .90
No. 1223 contains one 32x40mm stamp.

1992 Summer Olympic Games, Barcelona — A227

Designs: 5r, Weight lifting. 15r, Boxing. 80r, Basketball. 400r, Sprints. 1500r, Water polo. 1000r, Women's gymnastics.

1992, May 15   **Perf. 13**
1224-1228 A227 Set of 5   7.50   1.50
Souvenir Sheet
Perf. 12½
1229 A227 1000r multicolored   4.25   1.25
No. 1229 contains one 40x32mm stamp.

Environmental Protection — A228

Designs: 5r, Women filling water jars. 15r, Pagoda. 80r, Palm trees. 400r, Boy riding water buffalo. 1500r, Lake, swimmers. 1000r, Angkor Wat.

1992, June 16	**Litho.**	**Perf. 12½**	
1230-1234 A228	Set of 5	6.25	1.75
	Souvenir Sheet		
	Perf. 13		
1235 A228	1000r multicolored	5.00	1.25

No. 1235 contains one 42x32mm stamp.

GENOA 92 — A229

Explorers, ship: 5r, Bougainville, Boudeuse. 15r, Cook, Endeavour. 80r, Darwin, Beagle. 400r, Cousteau, Calypso. 1500r, Heyerdahl, Kon Tiki. 1000r, Columbus.

1992, Aug. 1	**Litho.**	**Perf. 12x12½**	
1236-1240 A229	Set of 5	4.75	1.50
	Souvenir Sheet		
	Perf. 12½		
1241 A229	1000r multicolored	3.00	.90

No. 1241 contains one 32x40mm stamp.

Mushrooms A230

Designs: 5r, Albatrellus confluens. 15r, Boletus calopus. 80r, Stropharia aeruginosa. 400r, Telamonia armillata. 1500r, Cortinarius traganus.

1992, Sept. 25		**Perf. 13**	
1242-1246 A230	Set of 5	5.00	1.50

Seaplanes — A231

Designs: 5r, Bellanca Pacemaker, 1930. 15r, Canadair CL-215, 1965. 80r, G-21A Goose, 1937. 400r, Sealand SA-6, 1947. 1500r, Short S-23, 1936. 1000r, G-44 Widgeon, 1940.

1992, Oct. 16		**Perf. 12½x12**	
1247-1251 A231	Set of 5	4.25	1.25
	Souvenir Sheet		
	Perf. 13		
1252 A231	1000r multicolored	3.00	.90

No. 1252 contains one 32x40mm stamp.

Natl. Development A232

Designs: 150r, Dish antenna. 350r, Dish antenna, flags. 1000r, Hotel Cambodiana.

1992, Dec. 2	**Litho.**	**Perf. 12½**	
1253-1255 A232	Set of 3	4.25	1.25

Natl. Festival A233

Designs: 50r, Sociological Institute. 450r, Motel Cambodiana. 1000r, Theater.

1993, Jan. 7	**Litho.**	**Perf. 12½**	
1256-1258 A233	Set of 3	4.50	1.25

Dolphin, Bathyscaph — A234

Fauna, machine: 150r, shown. 200r, Falcon, jet fighter. 250r, Beaver, dam. 500r, Bat, satellite. 900r, Hummingbird, helicopter.

1993, Feb. 5	**Litho.**	**Perf. 13**	
	Without Gum		
1259-1263 A234	Set of 5	4.50	1.25

Flowers — A235

Designs: 150r, Datura suaveolens. 200r, Convolvulus tricolor. 250r, Hippeastrum hybrid. 500r, Camellia hybrid. 900r, Lilium speciosum. 1000r, Datura suaveolens, camellia, lilium speciosum.

1993, Mar. 15		**Perf. 13**	
	Without Gum		
1264-1268 A235	Set of 5	5.50	1.25
	Souvenir Sheet		
	Perf. 12½		
1269 A235	1000r multicolored	3.00	1.00

No. 1269 contains one 40x32mm stamp.

Khmer Culture A236

Designs: 50r, Statue of a Nandin. 450r, Temple Vihear. 1000r, Man with offerings.

1993, Apr. 13	**Litho.**	**Perf. 12½**	
1270-1272 A236	Set of 3	4.25	1.75

Wildlife — A237

150r, Cynocephalus volans. 200r, Petuarista petuarista. 250r, Ptychozoon homalocephalum. 500r, Rhacophorus nigropalmatus. 900r, Draco volans.

1993, May 4	**Litho.**	**Perf. 12½x12**	
	Without Gum		
1273-1277 A237	Set of 5	4.75	1.40

BRASILIANA 93 — A238

Butterflies: 250r, Symbrenthia hypselis. 350r, Sithon nedymond. 600r, Geitoneura minyas. 800r, Argyreus hyperbius. 1000r, Argyrophenga antipodum. 1500r, Pararge schakra.

1993, June 15		**Perf. 12½x12**	
	Without Gum		
1278-1282 A238	Set of 5	8.00	1.50
	Souvenir Sheet		
	Perf. 12½		
1283 A238	1500r multicolored	5.50	1.25

No. 1283 contains one 40x32mm stamp.

UN Transitional Authority in Cambodia (UNTAC) Pacification Program A239

150r, Cambodian soldiers approaching UN base. 200r, Cambodians entering camp. 250r, Cambodians surrendering weapons to UN. 500r, Vocational training. 900r, Cambodians re-entering society. 1000r, Returning to homes and family.

1993, Aug. 4	**Litho.**	**Perf. 12½**	
1284-1288 A239	Set of 5	5.50	1.50
	Souvenir Sheet		
	Perf. 13		
1289 A239	1000r blue & black	4.00	1.25

No. 1289 contains one 32x40mm stamp.

Ships A240

150r, Venetian caravel. 200r, Phoenician galley. 250r, Egyptian merchantman. 500r, Genoese merchantman. 900r, English merchantman.

1993, Aug. 27	**Litho.**	**Perf. 13**	
	Without Gum		
1290-1294 A240	Set of 5	4.50	1.25

Alberto Santos-Dumont (1873-1932) — A241

Designs: 150r, Portrait, Balloon, Eiffel Tower, vert. 200r, 14-bis, 1906. 250r, Demoiselle. 500r, EMB-201A. 900r, EMB-111.

1993, Sept. 10		**Perf. 13**	
	Without Gum		
1295-1299 A241	Set of 5	4.50	1.25

1994 World Cup Soccer Championships, US — A242

Various soccer plays. Denominations: 250r, 350r, 600r, 800r, 1000r, vert.

1993, Sept. 23	**Litho.**	**Perf. 12½**	
1300-1304 A242	Set of 5	5.50	1.75
	Souvenir Sheet		
1305 A242	1500r multicolored	4.75	1.50

No. 1305 contains one 40x32mm stamp.

BANGKOK 93 — A243

Ducks: 250r, Anas penelope. 350r, Anas formosa. 600r, Aix galericulata. 800r, Aix sponsa. 1000r, Histrionicus histrionicus. 1500r, Head of Aix galericulata.

1993, Oct. 1	**Litho.**	**Perf. 12½**	
	Without Gum		
1306-1310 A243	Set of 5	5.75	1.75
	Souvenir Sheet		
1311 A243	1500r multicolored	3.50	1.10

No. 1311 contains one 40x32mm stamp.

Vertical Take-Off Aircraft — A244

Designs: 150r, First helicopter model, France, 1784, vert. 200r, Steam helicopter model, 1863, vert. 250r, New York-Atlanta-Miami autogyro flight, 1927. 500r, Sikorsky helicopter, 1943. 900r, French VTOL jet. 1000r, Juan de la Cierva's autogyro C-1923.

	Perf. 12x12½, 12½x12		
1993, Nov. 6		**Without Gum**	
1312-1316 A244	Set of 5	4.50	1.25
	Souvenir Sheet		
	Perf. 12½		
1317 A244	1000r multicolored	3.25	.90

No. 1317 contains one 40x32mm stamp.

Insects — A245

Designs: 50r, Cnaphalocrosis medinalis. 450r, Cicadelle brune. 500r, Scirpophaga incertulas. No. 1321, 1000r, Diopsis macrophthlalma.

No. 1322, Leptocorisa oratorius.

1993, Dec. 2   *Perf. 13*
1318-1321 A245   Set of 4   4.00 1.25
Souvenir Sheet
Perf. 12½
1322 A245   1000r multicolored   3.25 .90
Issued without gum.
No. 1322 contains one 32x40mm stamp.

Independence, 40th Anniv. — A246

Designs: 300r, Ministry of Posts and Telecommunications. 500r, Independence Monument, 1953, vert. 700r, Natl. flag.

1993   Litho.   *Perf. 12½*
1323-1325 A246   Set of 3   3.50 1.50

Hummel Figurines A247

Designs: 50r, Boy riding pony. 100r, Girl with baby carriage. 150r, Girl bathing doll. 200r, Girl holding doll. 250r, Boys playing. 300r, Girls pulling boy in cart. 350r, Girls playing ring-around-the-rosie. 600r, Boys with stick and drum.

1993   Litho.   *Perf. 12½*
1326-1333 A247   Set of 8   5.50 1.75

1994 Winter Olympic Games, Lillehammer — A248

150r, Women's figure skating, vert. 250r, Two-man luge. 400r, Downhill skiing. 700r, Biathlon. 1000r, Speed skating, vert. 1500r, Curling, vert.

1994, Jan. 23   *Perf. 13*
1334-1338 A248   Set of 5   5.75 1.50
Souvenir Sheet
1339 A248   1500r multicolored   3.75 1.25
No. 1339 contains one 32x40mm stamp.

Classic Automobiles — A249

Designs: 150r, 1924 Opel. 200r, 1901 Mercedes. 250r, 1927 Model T Ford. 500r, 1907 Rolls Royce. 900r, 1908 Hutton. 1000r, 1931 Duesenberg.

1994, Feb. 20   *Perf. 13*
1340-1344 A249   Set of 5   5.00 1.50
Souvenir Sheet
1345 A249   1000r multicolored   3.75 .90
No. 1345 contains one 32x40mm stamp.

1996 Summer Olympic Games, Atlanta — A250

Designs: 150r, Women's gymnastics. 200r, Soccer. 250r, Javelin. 300r, Canoeing. 600r, Running. 1000r, Diving, horiz. 1500r, Equestrian.

1994, Mar. 20   *Perf. 13*
1346-1351 A250   Set of 6   5.25 1.50
Souvenir Sheet
1352 A250   1500r multicolored   4.50 1.25
No. 1352 contains one 32x40mm stamp.

Khmer Statues — A251

Designs: 300r, Siva and Uma. 500r, Vishnu. 700r, King Jayavarman VII.

1994, Apr. 13
1353-1355 A251   Set of 3   5.00 2.00

Intl. Olympic Committee, Cent. — A252

Designs: 100r, Olympic Flag. 300r, Flag, Torch. 600r, Flag, Baron de Coubertin.

1994, Apr. 23   *Perf. 12½*
1356-1358 A252   Set of 3   3.25 1.40

Prehistoric Animals — A253

150r, Mesonyx. 250r, Doedicurus. 400r, Mylodon. 700r, Uintatherium. 1000r, Hyrachyus.

1994, May 10   *Perf. 12½*
1359-1363 A253   Set of 5   5.50 1.75

1994 World Cup Soccer Championships, U.S. — A254

Various soccer plays. Denominations: 150r, 250r, 400r, 700r, 1000r.

1994, June 17   *Perf. 12½*
1364-1368 A254   Set of 5   5.50 1.50
Souvenir Sheet
1369 A254   1500r multicolored   4.00 1.25
No. 1369 contains one 32x40mm stamp.

Statues A255

Designs: 300r, shown. 500r, Soldiers in combat, vert. 700r, Lions, vert.

1994   *Perf. 13*
1370-1372 A255   Set of 3   4.00 1.50

Beetles A256

Designs: 150r, Chlorophanus viridis. 200r, Chrysochroa fulgidissima. 250r, Lytta vesicatoria. 500r, Purpuricenus kaehleri. 900r, Dynastes hercules.
1000r, Timarcha tenebricosa.

1994, July 7   *Perf. 12½*
1373-1377 A256   Set of 5   5.00 1.50
Souvenir Sheet
1378 A256   1000r multicolored   3.00 .90
No. 1378 contains one 40x32mm stamp.

Submarines — A257

Designs: 150r, Halley's diving bell, 1690, vert. 200r, Gimnote, 1886. 250r, Peral, 1888. 500r, Nuclear-powered Nautilus, 1954. 900r, Bathyscaphe Trieste, 1953.
1000r, Ictineo, 1885.

1994, Aug. 12   *Perf. 13*
1379-1383 A257   Set of 5   5.50 1.50
Souvenir Sheet
Perf. 12½
1384 A257   1000r multicolored   3.50 1.00
No. 1384 contains one 40x32mm stamp.

Chess Champions — A258

Designs: 150r, Francois-André Philador, 1795. 200r, Louis de la Bourdonnais, 1821. 250r, Adolph Anderssen, 1851. 500r, Paul Morphy, 1858. 900r, Wilhelm Steinitz, 1866. 1000r, Emanuel Lasker, 1894.

1994, Sept. 20   *Perf. 13*
1385-1389 A258   Set of 5   5.00 1.50
Souvenir Sheet
1390 A258   1000r multicolored   3.25 1.00
No. 1390 contains one 32x40mm stamp.

Aircraft A259

Designs: 150r, Sikorsky S-42 flying boat. 200r, Vought-Sikorsky VS-300A helicopter. 250r, Sikorsky S-37 biplane. 500r, Sikorsky S-35 biplane. 900r, Sikorsky S-43 amphibian. 1000r, 1st 4-engine bomber, Ilya Mourometz.

1994, Oct. 6   *Perf. 13*
1391-1395 A259   Set of 5   5.00 1.50
Souvenir Sheet
Perf. 12½
1396 A259   1000r multicolored   3.50 1.00
No. 1396 contains one 40x32mm stamp.

Birds A260

Designs: 150r, Remiz pendulinus, vert. 250r, Panurus biarmicus. 400r, Emberiza rustica. 700r, Emberiza schoeniclus. 1000r, Regulus regulus.
1500r, Pitta angolensis.

1994, Nov. 20   *Perf. 12½*
1397-1401 A260   Set of 5   6.50 1.50
Souvenir Sheet
Perf. 13
1402 A260   1500r multicolored   4.50 1.40
No. 1402 contains one 32x40mm stamp.

Independence Festival — A261

Designs: 300r, Postal Service float. 500r, Soldiers marching. 700r, Army unit marching.

1994, Dec. 9   *Perf. 13*
1403-1405 A261   Set of 3   5.00 1.75

Natl. Development — A262

Designs: 300r, Chruoi Changwar Bridge. 500r, Olympic Commercial Center. 700r, Sakamony Chedei Temple.

1994, Dec. 10
1406-1408 A262 Set of 3   5.00 1.50

Prehistoric Animals — A263

100r, Psittacosaurus. 200r, Protoceratops. 300r, Montanoceraptors. 400r, Centrosaurus. 700r, Styracosaurus. 800r, Triceratops.

1995, Jan. 10
1409-1414 A263 Set of 6   6.50 1.50

Butterflies
A264

100r, Anthocharis cardamines. 200r, Iphiclides podalirius. 300r, Mesoacidalia aglaja. 600r, Vanessa atalanta. 800r, Inachis io.

1995, Feb. 12
1415-1419 A264 Set of 5   7.00 1.50

1996 Summer Olympic Games, Atlanta A265

Designs: 100r, Swimming. 200r, Rhythmic gymnastics. 400r, Basketball. 800r, Soccer. 1000r, Cycling. 1500r, Running. 200r-1500r are vert.

1995, Mar. 9
1420-1424 A265 Set of 5   6.00 1.50
Souvenir Sheet
1425 A265 1500r multicolored   3.75 1.00
No. 1425 contains one 32x40mm stamp.

Mushrooms
A266

Designs: 100r, Amanita phalloides. 200r, Cantharellus cibarius. 300r, Armillaria mellea. 600r, Agaricus campestris. 800r, Amanita muscaria.

1995, Mar. 23
1426-1430 A266 Set of 5   5.50 1.50

Statues — A267

Designs: 300r, Kneeling ascetic. 500r, Parasurama. 700r, Siva.

1995, Apr. 13   **Perf. 12½**
1431-1433 A267 Set of 3   4.50 1.40

Protected Wildlife — A268

Designs: 300r, Bos gaurus. 500r, Bos sauveli, vert. 700r, Grus antigone, vert.

1995, May 5   **Perf. 13**
1434-1436 A268 Set of 3   4.00 1.25

Parrots — A269

Designs: 100r, Lorus lory. 200r, Polytelis alexandrae. 400r, Eclectus voratus. 800r, Ara macao. 1000r, Melopsittacus undulatus. 1500r, Amazona ochrocephala.

1995, May 23   **Perf. 13**
1437-1441 A269 Set of 5   6.50 1.50
Souvenir Sheet
                                  Perf. 12½
1442 A269 1500r multicolored   5.00 1.50
No. 1442 contains one 32x40mm stamp.

Tourism
A270

Public gardens: 300r, Sculpture of Garuda. 500r, Fountain. 700r, Sculpture of mythological figures.

1995, July 15   **Perf. 12½**
1443-1445 A270 Set of 3   3.50 1.40

Locomotives — A271

100r, Richard Trevithick's steam locomotive, 1804. 200r, George Stephenson's Rocket, 1830. 300r, Stephenson's Locomotion, 1825. 600r, Lafayette, 1837. 800r, Best Friend of Charleston, 1830. 1000r, Stephenson, vert.

1995, Aug. 17
1446-1450 A271 Set of 5   5.00 1.50
Souvenir Sheet
1451 A271 1000r multicolored   3.25 1.25
No. 1451 contains one 32x40mm stamp.

World War II Aircraft A272

100r, Bristol Blenheim II, vert. 200r, North American B-25. 300r, Avro Anson. 600r, Avro Manchester. 800r, Consolidated B-24. 1000r, Boeing B-17E.

Perf. 12x12½, 12½x12
1995, Sept. 15
1452-1456 A272 Set of 5   5.00 1.50
Souvenir Sheet
                                  Perf. 12½
1457 A272 1000r multicolored   3.50 1.00
No. 1457 contains one 32x40mm stamp.

FAO, 50th Anniv. A273

Designs: 300r, Separating rice plants. 500r, Transplanting rice. 700r, Model rice farm.

1995, Oct. 24   **Perf. 13**
1458-1460 A273 Set of 3   3.25 1.00

UN, 50th Anniv. A274

Designs: 300r, Bridge. 500r, People on bridge. 700r, Central spans of bridge.

1995, Oct. 24   **Perf. 12½**
1461-1463 A274 Set of 3   4.00 1.40

Queen Monineath A275

700r, shown. 800r, King Norodom Sihanouk.

1995, Nov. 9   **Perf. 12½x13**
1464-1465 A275 Set of 2   3.75 1.25

Fish
A276

100r, Heniochus acuminatus. 200r, Chelmon rostratus. 400r, Amphiprion percula. 800r, Paracanthurus hepatus. 1000r, Holocanthus ciliaris. 1500r, Coris angulata, vert.

1995, Nov. 19   **Perf. 12½**
1466-1470 A276 Set of 5   6.00 1.50
Souvenir Sheet
1471 A276 1500r multicolored   4.50 1.00

Main Post Office, Cent. A277

Denominations: 300r, 500r, 700r.

1995, Dec. 2   **Perf. 12½**
1472-1474 A277 Set of 3   6.00 1.40

Admission to UN, 40th Anniv. — A278

300r, Independence Monument. 400r, Angkor Wat. 800r, Natl. flag, vert.

Perf. 12½x13, 13x12½
1995, Dec. 14   **Litho.**
1475-1477 A278 Set of 3   5.50 1.25

1996 Summer Olympic Games, Atlanta — A279

Designs: 100r, Tennis. 200r, Volleyball. 300r, Soccer. #1480A, 500r, Running. 900r, Baseball. 1000r, Basketball. 1500r, Windsurfing.

1996, Jan. 10 Litho. Perf. 12½x13
1478-1482 A279 Set of 6   6.00 1.50
Souvenir Sheet
                                  Perf. 12½
1483 A279 1500r multicolored   3.50 1.00
No. 1483 contains one 32x40mm stamp.

A280

1996, Jan. 30   **Perf. 12½**
1484 A280   50r Kep State
                 Chalet   .20 .20
1485 A280 100r Power station   .20 .20
1486 A280 200r Wheelchair   .30 .20
1487 A280 500r Wheelchair
                 basketball   .60 .20
1488 A280 800r Making
                 crutches,
                 vert.   .85 .25
1489 A280 1000r Kep beach   1.00 .35
1490 A280 1500r Serpent Island 1.75 .45
         Nos. 1484-1490 (7)   4.90 1.85

Wild Cats
A281

100r, Felis libyca, vert. 200r, Felis silvestris. 300r, Felis caracal. 500r, Felis geoffroyi. 900r, Felis nigripes. 1000r, Felis planiceps.

1996, Feb. 8 — *Perf. 13*
1491-1496 A281 Set of 6 — 6.00 2.00

1998 World Cup Soccer Championships, France — A282

Various soccer players. Denominations: 100r, 200r, 300r, 500r, 900r, 1000r. No. 1502 is horiz.

1996, Mar. 15 — *Perf. 13*
1497-1502 A282 Set of 6 — 6.00 1.50
Souvenir Sheet
1503 A282 1500r multicolored — 4.00 1.00
No. 1503 contains one 32x40mm stamp.

Khmer Culture — A283

100r, Tusmukh. 500r, Ream Iso. 900r, Isei.

1996, Apr. 13 Litho. — *Perf. 12½x13*
1504-1506 A283 Set of 3 — 3.00 1.00

Locomotives — A284

100r, Pacific Type. 200r, Unidentified, 1902. 300r, Unidentified, 1930. 500r, Unidentified, 1914. 900r, LMS #6202, 1930. 1000r, Snake, 1864.
1500r, Canadian Pacific.

1996, Apr. 20
1507-1512 A284 Set of 6 — 4.75 1.50
Souvenir Sheet
1513 A284 1500r multicolored — 3.25 1.00
No. 1513 contains one 40x32mm stamp.
CAPEX 96 (#1513).

Birds A285

Designs: 100r, Kittacinela malabarica, vert. 200r, Leiothrix lutea. 300r, Parus varius, vert. 500r, Oriolus chinensis. 900r, Cettia diphone. 1000r, Cyanoptila cyanomelana, vert.

1996, May 7
1514-1519 A285 Set of 6 — 5.00 1.50

Olymphilex '96 — A286

Designs: 100r, Rhythmic gymnastics. 200r, Judo. 300r, High jump. 500r, Wrestling. 900r, Weight lifting. 1000r, Soccer.
1500r, Diving.

1996, June 14 Litho. — *Perf. 13x12½*
1520-1525 A286 Set of 6 — 4.25 1.25
Souvenir Sheet — *Perf. 12½*
1526 A286 1500r multicolored — 2.75 .90
No. 1526 contains one 32x40mm stamp.

Early Aircraft — A287

100r, Douglas M-2, 1926. 200r, Pitcairn PA-5 Mailwing, 1928. 300r, Boeing 40 B, 1928. 500r, Potez 25, 1925. 900r, Stearman C-3MB, 1927. 1000r, De Havilland DH4, 1918.
1500r, Standard JR-1B, 1918.

1996, July 5 — *Perf. 12½x12*
1527-1532 A287 Set of 6 — 4.50 1.50
Souvenir Sheet — *Perf. 13*
1533 A287 1500r multicolored — 3.00 .90
No. 1533 contains one 40x32mm stamp.

Historic Sites — A288

50r, 100r, 200r, Diff. Apsaras, Tonle Bati. #1537, Statue, Angkor Wat. #1538, Statue of a Goddess. 500r, Carved wall, Tonle Bati. #1540, 1000r, Various structures, Tonle Bati. #1541, #1544, 1700r, 2500r, 3000r, Various views of Angkor Wat.
Nos. 1539, 1543, 1545-1547 are horiz.

1996-97 Litho. — *Perf. 12½*
1534 A288 50r black & yel org	.25	.20
1535 A288 100r black & blue	.25	.20
1536 A288 200r black & tan	.25	.20
1537 A288 300r blk & light bl	.25	.20
1538 A288 300r black & red	.25	.20
1539 A288 500r blk & bright bl	.35	.20
1540 A288 800r black & yel grn	.45	.20
1541 A288 800r black & yel grn	.45	.20
1542 A288 1000r black & green	.60	.20
1543 A288 1500r black & bister	.90	.25
1544 A288 1500r black & brown	.90	.25
1545 A288 1700r black & org brn	1.10	.30
1546 A288 2500r black & blue	1.60	.40
1547 A288 3000r black & dk grn	2.00	.50
Nos. 1534-1547 (14)	9.60	3.50

Issued: 50r, 100r, 200r, 500r, No. 1540, 1000r, No. 1543, 7/30/96; others, 3/26/97.
See Nos. 1686-1692, 1846-1852.

Dinosaurs — A289

No. 1548: a, 50r, Coelophysis. b, 100r, Euparkeria. c, 150r, Plateosaurus. d, 200r, Herrerasaurus.
No. 1549: a, 250r, Dilophosaurus. b, 300r, Tuojiangosaurus. c, 350r, Camarasaurs. d, 400r, Ceratosaurus.
No. 1550: a, 500r, Spinosaurus. b, 700r, Ouranosaurus. c, 800r, Avimimus. d, 1200r, Deinonychus.

1996, Aug. 8 Litho. — *Perf. 13*
Sheets of 4
1548 A289 #a.-d. — 1.00 .25
1549 A289 #a.-d. — 2.75 .60
1550 A289 #a.-d. — 6.75 1.50

Chess Champions A290

100r, José Raul Capablanca. 200r, Alexander Alekhine. 300r, Vassily Smyslov. 500r, Mikhail Tal. 900r, Bobby Fischer. 1000r, Anatoly Karpov.
1500r, Garry Kasparov.

1996, Sept. 10 — *Perf. 13*
1551-1556 A290 Set of 6 — 5.00 1.50
Souvenir Sheet — *Perf. 12½*
1557 A290 1500r multicolored — 3.00 .90
No. 1557 contains one 32x40mm stamp.

Wild Animals A291

Designs: 100r, Ursus arctos. 200r, Panthera leo. 300r, Tapirus indicus. 500r, Camelus ferus. 900r, Capra ibex. 1000r, Zalophus californianus.

1996, Oct. 3 — *Perf. 13x12½*
1558-1563 A291 Set of 6 — 4.50 1.25

Dogs — A292

Designs: 200r, Collie. 300r, Labrador retriever. 500r, Doberman pinscher. 900r, German shepherd. 1000r, Boxer.

1996, Nov. 8 — *Perf. 12½x13*
1564-1568 A292 Set of 5 — 4.50 1.25

Independence — A293

100, 500, 900r, Various water treatment plants.

1996, Nov. 9 — *Perf. 13*
1569-1571 A293 Set of 3 — 3.25 1.25

Ships A294

Designs: 200r, Chinese junk. 300r, Galley. 500r, Roman galley. 900r, Clipper ship, 19th cent. 1000r, Paddle steamer Sirius, 1838. 1500r, Great Eastern, 1858.

1996, Dec. 15 — *Perf. 12½x13*
1572-1576 A294 Set of 5 — 4.50 1.25
Souvenir Sheet — *Perf. 12½*
1577 A294 1500r multicolored — 3.00 .90
No. 1577 contains one 40x32mm stamp.

Cambodia's Admission to UPU, 45th Anniv. — A295

Denominations: 200r, 400r, 900r.

1996, Dec. 21 — *Perf. 12½*
1578-1580 A295 Set of 3 — 2.75 1.00

New Year 1997 (Year of the Ox) — A296

Paintings of oxen, attributed to Han Huang 723-87): a, Facing left. b, Looking right. c, Brown & white spotted. d, Facing left, head down.

1996, Dec. 28 — *Perf. 13x12½*
1581 A296 500r Strip of 4, #a.-d. + label — 3.00 .90

UN Intl. Day of Volunteers — A297

Designs: 100r, Phnom Kaun Sat Dam. 900r, Chrey Krem Dam. 1500r, Angkrung Canal.

1996, Dec. 30
1582-1584 A297 Set of 3 — 3.75 1.10

Greenpeace, 25th Anniv. — A298

Helicopter: 200r, Hovering over cargo. 300r, Hovering over ship. 500r, On helipad. 900r, Lifting cargo.
1000r, Close-up of helicopter.

1996, Dec. 30
1585-1588 A298 Set of 4   6.00 1.75
Souvenir Sheet
Perf. 12½
1589 A298 1000r multicolored   3.50 1.00

No. 1589 contains one 32x40mm stamp.

1998 World Cup
Soccer
Championships,
France — A299

Various soccer plays. Denominations: 100r,
200r, 300r, 500r, 900r, 1000r.

1997, Jan. 6 **Litho.** **Perf. 12½x13**
1590-1595 A299 Set of 6   5.00 1.50
Souvenir Sheet
Perf. 13
1596 A299 2000r multicolored   3.00 .90

No. 1596 contains one 40x32mm stamp.

Elephas Maximus — A300

World Wildlife Fund: a, 300r, Two walking. b,
500r, Three standing. c, 900r, Two fighting. d,
1000r, Adult, calf.

1997, Feb. 12 **Perf. 12½x12**
1597 A300 Strip of 4, #a.-d.   8.00 3.00

Birds — A301

600r, Bombycilla garrulus. 900r, Lanius
excubitor. 1000r, Passer montanus. 2000r,
Phoenicurus phoenicurus. 2500r, Emberiza
schoeniclus. 3000r, Emberiza hortulana.

1997, Feb. 20 **Perf. 13x12½**
1598-1603 A301 Set of 6   13.50 4.50
Express mail service.

Fire
Fighting
Vehicles
A302

Designs: 200r, English, 1731. 500r, Putnam,
1863. 900r, Merryweather, 1894. 1000r,
Shand Mason Co., 1901. 1500r, Maxim Motor
Co., Ford, 1949. 4000r, Merryweather, 1950.
5400r, Mack Truck Co., 1953.

1997, Mar. 11 **Perf. 12½x13**
1604-1609 A302 Set of 6   8.00 1.50
Souvenir Sheet
Perf. 13
1610 A302 5400r multicolored   4.50 1.10

No. 1610 contains one 40x32mm stamp.

Ducks
A303

Designs: 200r, Polystieta stelleri. 500r, Alopochen aegyptiacus. 900r, Anas americana.
1000r, Anas falcata. 1500r, Melanitta perspicillata. 4000r, Anas discors.
5400r, Anas formosa, vert.

1997, Apr. 7 **Perf. 12½x13**
1611-1616 A303 Set of 6   5.00 1.50
Souvenir Sheet
Perf. 12½
1617 A303 5400r multicolored   3.50 1.10

No. 1617 contains one 32x40mm stamp.

Heinrich Von
Stephan (1831-
1897), Founder
of UPU — A304

Denominations: 500r, 1500r, 2000r.

1997, Apr. 8 **Perf. 12½x13**
1618-1620 A304 Set of 3   3.50 1.00

Khmer
Culture — A305

Various views of Bantea Srei Temple.
Denominations: 500r, 1500r, 2000r.

1997, Apr. 13 **Perf. 13x12½**
1621-1623 A305 Set of 3   3.75 1.00

Cats — A306

Designs: 200r, Birman. 500r, Exotic shorthair. 900r, Persian. 1000r, Turkish. 1500r,
American short-hair. 4000r, Scottish fold.
5400r, Sphinx.

1997, May 8 **Perf. 13x12½**
1624-1629 A306 Set of 6   11.00 2.00
Souvenir Sheet
Perf. 13
1630 A306 5400r multicolored   4.00 1.10

No. 1630 contains one 32x40mm stamp.

Trains
A307

200r, 4-4-2T, #488. 500r, Frederick Smith 4-
6-0. 900r, 0-8-0, #3131. 1000r, Transport #1,
London #L44, 0-4-4. 1500r, 0-6-2, #1711.
4000r, 4-6-2, #60523.
5400r, North Yorkshire Moor (K1), 2-6-0,
#2005.

1997, Jun 9 **Perf. 12½x12**
1631-1636 A307 Set of 6   5.00 1.50
Souvenir Sheet
Perf. 13
1637 A307 5400r multicolored   3.50 1.00

No. 1637 contains one 40x32mm stamp.

Dogs
A308

Designs: 200r, Shar-pei. 500r, Tchin-tchin.
900r, Pekinese. 1000r, Chow-chow, vert.
1500r, Pug, vert. 4000r, Akita, vert.
5400r, Tufted Chinese, vert.

1997, July 4 **Perf. 12½x13, 13x12½**
1638-1643 A308 Set of 6   4.75 1.50
Souvenir Sheet
Perf. 12½
1644 A308 5400r multicolored   3.50 1.25

No. 1644 contains one 32x40mm stamp.

ASEAN,
30th
Anniv.
A309

Designs: 500r, Dunalom Wat. 1500r, Royal
Palace. 2000r, Natl. Museum.

1997, Aug. 5 **Perf. 12½x13**
1645-1647 A309 Set of 3   4.00 1.00

Ships
A310

Designs: 200r, Caravelle, 15th cent. 500r,
Spanish galleon, 16th cent. 900r, Galleon
"Great Harry," 16th cent. 1000r, Galleon "Le
Couronne," 17th cent. 1500r, Cargo ship, 18th
cent. 4000r, Clipper ship, 19th cent.
5400r, HMS Victory.

1997, Sept. 10 **Perf. 12½x12**
1648-1653 A310 Set of 6   5.00 1.50
Souvenir Sheet
Perf. 13
1654 A310 5400r multicolored   3.50 1.10

No. 1654 contains one 40x32mm stamp.

A311

#1655-1658, Various public gardens.
#1659-1661, Various dams. #1657 is vert.

1997, Sept. 30 **Perf. 12½**
1655 A311 300r black & yel grn   .25 .20
1656 A311 300r black & red   .25 .20
1657 A311 800r black & citron   .50 .20
1658 A311 1500r black & org brn   .90 .30
1659 A311 1700r blk & red brn   1.10 .35
1660 A311 2500r blk & grn bl   1.50 .50
1661 A311 3000r black & blue   1.75 .65
      Nos. 1655-1661 (7)   6.25 2.40

Mushrooms
A312

Designs: 200r, Boletus satanas. 500r, Amanita regalis. 900r, Morchella semilibera. 1000r,
Gomphus clavatus. 1500r, Hygrophorus
hypothejus. 4000r, Albatrellus confluens.
5400r, Boletus chrysenteron.

1997, Oct. 5 **Perf. 12½x13**
1662-1667 A312 Set of 6   5.25 1.50
Souvenir Sheet
Perf. 12½
1668 A312 5400r multicolored   3.75 1.10

No. 1668 contains one 32x40mm stamp.

Fish
A313

200r, Betta imbellis. 500r, Colisa fasciata.
900r, Puntius conchonius. 1000r, Macropodus
concolor. 1500r, Epalzeorhynchos frenatus.
4000r, Capoeta tetrazona.
5400r, Rasbora heteromorpha.

1997, Nov. 8 **Perf. 12½x13**
1669-1674 A313 Set of 6   5.00 1.50
Souvenir Sheet
Perf. 13
1675 A313 5400r multicolored   3.50 1.00

No. 1675 contains one 40x32mm stamp.

Independence, 44th Anniv. — A314

Post Offices: 1000r, Kampot. 3000r, Prey
Veng.

1997, Nov. 9 **Perf. 13**
1676-1677 A314 Set of 2   3.00 .90

Orchids — A315

200r, Orchis milicaris. 500r, Orchiaceras
bivonae. 900r, Orchiaceras spuria. 1000r,
Gymnadenia conopsea. 1500r, Serapias
neglecta. 4000r, Pseudorhiza bruniana.
5400r, Dactylodenia wintonii.

1997, Dec. 12 **Perf. 13**
1678-1683 A315 Set of 6   10.00 2.00
Souvenir Sheet
1684 A315 5400r multicolored   6.50 1.10

No. 1684 contains one 32x40mm stamp.

Princess Diana
(1961-97)
A316

Designs: a, 100r, In dark blue jacket. b, 200r, In black dress. c, 300r, Holding hand to throat. d, 500r, Wearing face shield. e, 1000r, Watching mine clearing operation. f, 1500r, With Elizabeth Dole. g, 2000r, Holding land mine. h, 2500r, With members of Mother Teresa's Order.

1997, Dec. 30   *Perf. 12x12½*
1685 A316 Sheet of 8, #a.-h. +
    label   7.50 1.90

Historic Sites Type of 1996-97
Temples: 300r, Prasat Suorprat. 500r, Preah Kumlung, horiz. 1200r, Prasat Bapuon, horiz. 1500r, Palilai. 1700r, Prasat Prerup, horiz. 2000r, Prasat Preah Khan, horiz. 3000r, Prasat Bayon.

1998   **Litho.**   *Perf. 12½*
1686 A288 300r black & orange   .20   .20
1687 A288 500r black & pink   .30   .20
1688 A288 1200r black & buff   .70   .25
1689 A288 1500r black & buff   .90   .30
1690 A288 1700r black & blue   1.00   .35
1691 A288 2000r black & green   1.25   .45
1692 A288 3000r black & violet   1.75   .65
    Nos. 1686-1692 (7)   6.10 2.40

New Year 1998 (Year of the Tiger) A317

Various pictures of panthera tigris: 200r, vert., 500r, vert., 900r, vert., 1000r, 1500r, 4000r.
5400r, Tiger, vert.

1998   *Perf. 13*
1693-1698 A317 Set of 6   5.25 1.50
Souvenir Sheet
Perf. 12½
1699 A317 5400r multicolored   4.50 1.00
No. 1699 contains one 32x40mm stamp.

1998 World Cup Soccer Championships, France — A318

Designs showing portion of soccer player at left, various plays at right, stadium: 200r, 500r, 900r, 1000r, 1500r, 4000r.
5400r, Two players kicking ball.

1998   *Perf. 13*
1700-1705 A318 Set of 6   4.75 1.50
Souvenir Sheet
1706 A318 5400r multicolored   3.50 1.00
No. 1706 contains one 40x32mm stamp.

Domestic Cats A319

Designs: 200r, Scottish fold. 500r, Ragdoll. 900r, Welsh. 1000r, Devon rex. 1500r, American curl. 4000r, Sphinx.
5400r, Japanese bobtail.

1998
1707-1712 A319 Set of 6   5.00 1.50
Souvenir Sheet
1713   A319 5400r multi   3.50 1.00
No. 1713 contains one 40x32mm stamp.

Italia '98, Intl. Philatelic Exhibition A320

Paintings: 200r, Baptism of Christ from triptych, Jean de Trompes, by Gerard David. 500r, The Virgin of Martin van Niuwenhoven, by Hans Memling. 900r, Baptism of Christ, by Hendrich Goltzius. 1000r, Christ Carrying the Cross, by Luis de Morales. 1500r, Angel in the Desert, by Dirk Bouts. 4000r, The Virgin, by Petrus Christus.
5400r, The Immaculate Conception, by Bartolomé Esteban Murillo.

1998   **Litho.**   *Perf. 12½x13*
1714-1719 A320 Set of 6   5.00 1.50
Souvenir Sheet
Perf. 12½
1720 A320 5400r multicolored   3.50 1.00
No. 1720 contains one 40x32mm stamp.

Butterflies — A321

200r, Phyciodes tharos. 500r, Pararge mergera. 900r, Danaus plexippus. 1000r, Parnassius apollo. 1500r, Papilio machaon. 4000r, Eumenis semele.
5400r, Morpho rhetenor.

1998   *Perf. 12½*
1721-1726 A321 Set of 6   5.50 1.50
Souvenir Sheet
1727 A321 5400r multicolored   5.00 1.00
No. 1727 contains one 40x32mm stamp.

Mail Boxes — A322

Designs: 1000r, 1997. 3000r, 1951.

1998   **Litho.**   *Perf. 13*
1728-1729 A322 Set of 2   2.75 1.00

Trains — A323

#1730a, 200r, Oakland, Antioch & Eastern. #1730b, 500r, New York, Westchester & Boston. #1731a, 900r, Spokane & Inland. #1731b, 1000r, International Railway. #1732a, 1500r, British columbia Electric Railway. #1732b, 4000r, Southern Pacific.
5400r, Storage battery locomotive.

1998, Mar. 2   **Litho.**   *Perf. 12½*
1730-1732 A323 Set of 3 pairs,
    #a.-b.   5.50 1.50
Souvenir Sheet
1733 A323 5400r multicolored   3.75 1.25

Dogs — A324

200r, Rottweiler. 500r, Beauceron. 900r, Boxer. 1000r, Siberian husky. 1500r, Welsh corgi (Pembroke). 4000r, Basset hound.
5400r, Schnauzer.

1998, Mar. 30   **Litho.**   *Perf. 12¼*
1734-1739 A324 Set of 6   5.00 1.50
Souvenir Sheet
Perf. 12½
1740 A324 5400r multicolored   3.50 1.00

Insects A325

200r, Lucanus cervus. 500r, Carabus auronitens. 900r, Rosalia alpina. 1000r, Geotrupes. 1500r, Megasoma elephas. 4000r, Chalcosoma.
5400r, Leptura rubra.

1998, Apr. 10   **Litho.**   *Perf. 12½*
1741-1746 A325 Set of 6   5.50 1.50
Souvenir Sheet
1747 A325 5400r multicolored   4.75 1.25

Khmer Culture A326

Designs: 500r, Prasat Prerup. 1500r, Prasat Bayon. 2000r, Angkor Wat.

1998, Apr. 13   **Litho.**   *Perf. 12¾*
1748-1750 A326 Set of 3   3.75 1.10

Historic Ships A327

200r, Cutter. 500r, Steamship "Britannia." 900r, Viking ship. 1000r, Steamship "Great Britain." 1500r, Coaster. 4000r, Frigate.
5400r, Tartan.

1998, May 7   **Litho.**   *Perf. 12¾*
1751-1756 A327 Set of 6   5.25 1.50
Souvenir Sheet
Perf. 13
1757 A327 5400r multicolored   3.50 1.00
No. 1757 contains one 40x32mm stamp.

Flowers — A328

200r, Petasites japonica. 500r, Gentiana triflora. 900r, Doronicum cordatum. 1000r, Scabiosa japonica. 1500r, Magnolia sieboldii. 4000r, Erythronium japonica.
5400r, Callistephus chinensis.

1998   **Litho.**   *Perf. 12¾*
1758-1763 A328 Set of 6   5.00 1.50
Souvenir Sheet
Perf. 13
1764 A328 5400r multicolored   3.50 1.00
No. 1764 contains one 32x40mm stamp.

Turtles A329

200r, Platysternon megacephalum. 500r, Chelonia mydas. 900r, Trionyx spiniferus. 1000r, Eretmochelys imbricata. 1500r, Megalochelys gigantea. 4000r, Dermochelys coriacea.

1998, Nov. 8   **Litho.**   *Perf. 12¾*
1765-1770 A329 Set of 6   5.00 1.50
Souvenir Sheet
Perf. 13x13¼
1771 A329 5400r Chelus fim-
    briatus   4.50 1.00
No. 1771 contains one 40x32mm stamp.

Independence, 45th Anniv. — A330

Various dancers: 500r, 1500r, 2000r.

1998, Nov. 9   **Litho.**   *Perf. 12½x12¼*
1772-1774 A330 Set of 3   3.00 1.00

Gemstones A331

Designs: 200r, Aquamarine. 500r, Cat's eye. 900r, Malachite. 1000r, Emerald. 1500r, Turquoise. 4000r, Ruby.
5400r, Diamond, horiz.

1998, Dec. 28   **Litho.**   *Perf. 12¾*
1775-1780 A331 Set of 6   5.00 1.50
Souvenir Sheet
Perf. 13
1781 A331 5400r multi   4.00 1.00
No. 1781 contains one 40x32mm stamp.

Wild Cats A332

Designs: 200r, Acinonyx juabatus. 500r, Panthera uncia. 900r, Felis pardalis. 1000r, Panthera pardus. 1500r, Felis serval. 4000r, Panthera onca.
5400r, Panthera tigris.

1998	Litho.	Perf. 12½x12¼
1782-1787 A332	Set of 6	5.00 1.50

Souvenir Sheet
Perf. 13

1788 A332 5400r multi 4.00 1.00
No. 1788 contains one 32x40mm stamp.

New Year 1999 (Year of the Rabbit) A333

Various rabbits: 200r, 500r, 900r, 1000r, 1500r, 4000r. 4000r is vert.

1999, Jan. 5	Litho.	Perf. 12¾
1790-1795 A333	Set of 6	7.00 1.50

Souvenir Sheet
Perf. 13

1796 A333 5400r Rabbit, diff. 6.00 1.00
No. 1796 contains one 40x32mm stamp.

Trains — A334

Designs: 200r, Stourbridge Lion. 500r, Atlantic. 900r, 035. 100r, Iron Duke. 1500r, 4-6-0. 4000r, 4-4-2.

Perf. 12½x12¼

1999, Nov. 20		Litho.
1797-1802 A334	Set of 6	5.00 1.50

Souvenir Sheet
Perf. 12½

1803 A334 5400r Firefly 3.50 1.00
No. 1803 contains one 40x32mm stamp.

Dogs A335

Designs: 200r, Shiba inu, vert. 500r, Shih tzu. 900r, Tibetan spaniel. 1000r, Ainu, vert. 1500r, Lhasa apso. 4000r, Tibetan terrier.

Perf. 12¼x12½ (200, 1000r), 12¾

1999, Feb. 3		Litho.
1804-1809 A335	Set of 6	5.50 1.50

Souvenir Sheet
Perf. 12½

1810 A335 5400r Tosa inu, vert. 3.50 1.00
Size of Nos. 1804, 1807: 48x30mm. No. 1810 contains one 32x40mm stamp.

Antique Automobiles — A336

Designs: 200r, 1881 La Rapide. 500r, 1895 Duryea. 900r, 1898 Barbarou. 1000r, 1898 Panhard. 1500r, 1901 Mercedes-Benz. 4000r, 1915 Ford.
5400r, 1875 Siegfried Marcus.

1999, Mar. 5	Litho.	Perf. 13x12¾
1811-1816 A336	Set of 6	5.00 1.50

Souvenir Sheet
Perf. 13

1817 A336 5400r multi 3.50 1.00
No. 1817 contains one 40x32mm stamp.

Cats — A337

Designs: 200r, Ragdoll. 500r, Russian blue. 900r, Bombay. 1000r, Snowshoe. 1500r, Oriental. 4000r, Somali.

1999, Mar. 30	Litho.	Perf. 13
1818-1823 A337	Set of 6	5.50 1.50

Souvenir Sheet

1824 A337 5400r Egyptian mau 3.50 1.00
No. 1824 contains one 32x40mm stamp.

Butterflies A338

Designs: 200r, Araschnia levana. 500r, Vanessa cardui, horiz. 900r, Clossiana euphrosyne. 1000r, Coenonympha hero. 1500r, Parnassius apollo, horiz. 4000r, Plebejus argus.
5400r, Palaeochrysophanus hippothoe.

1999, Apr. 25		Perf. 12¾
1825-1830 A338	Set of 6	7.00 1.50

Souvenir Sheet
Perf. 12½

1831 A338 5400r multi 5.00 1.00
No. 1831 contains one 32x40mm stamp.

Dinosaurs — A339

Designs: 200r, Saurornitholestes. 500r, Prenocephalus. 900r, Wuerhosaurus. 1000r, Muttaburrasaurus. 1500r, Shantungosaurus. 4000r, Microceratops.
5400r, Daspletosaurus.

1999, May 10	Litho.	Perf. 12¾
1832-1837 A339	Set of 6	5.25 1.50

Souvenir Sheet
Perf. 13

1838 A339 5400r multi 3.50 1.00
No. 1838 contains one 40x32mm stamp.

Molluscs A340

Designs: 200r, Flabellina affinis. 500r, Octopus macropus. 900r, Helix hortensis. 1000r, Lima hians. 1500r, Arion empiricorum. 4000r, Anodonta cygnaea.
5400r, Eledone aldrovandii.

1999, May 31	Litho.	Perf. 12¾
1839-1844 A340	Set of 6	5.25 1.50

Souvenir Sheet
Perf. 12½

1845 A340 5400r multi 3.50 1.00
No. 1845 contains one 32x40mm stamp.

Historic Sites Type of 1996-97

Designs: 100r, Prasat Neak Poan, horiz. 300r, Statue, Prasat Neak Poan, horiz. 500r, Prasat Banteay Srey. 1400r, Prasat Banteay Samré, horiz. 1600r, Prasat Banteay Srey, horiz. 1800r, Bas-relief, Angkor Wat. 1900r, Prasat Takeo, horiz.

1999		Litho.	Perf. 12½
	Vignette Colors		
1846	A288	100r blue	.30 .20
1847	A288	300r red	.30 .20
1848	A288	500r olive green	.40 .20
1849	A288	1400r bright green	1.00 .30
1850	A288	1600r pink	1.25 .30
1851	A288	1800r violet	1.40 .35
1852	A288	1900r brown	1.60 .45
	Nos. 1846-1852 (7)		6.25 2.00

Khmer Culture A341

Designs: 500r, Dragon Bridge. 1500r, Temple with 100 columns, Kratie. 2000r, Krapum Chhouk stupa, Kratie.

1999, Apr. 13		Perf. 13
1853-1855 A341	Set of 3	3.00 .85

UPU, 125th Anniv. A342

1999	Litho.	Perf. 12½x12¼
1856 A342	1600r multi	1.50 .75

Independence — A343

People and: 500r, Map. 1500r, Ship, airplane, dove, public works. 2000r, Buildings.

1999, Nov. 9		Perf. 12½
1857-1859 A343	Set of 3	2.75 1.00

Snakes A344

Designs: 200r, Aspidelaps lubricus. 500r, Epicrates cenchria. 900r, Eunectes notaeus. 1000r, Diadophus punctatus. 1500r, Micrurus fulvius. 4000r, Telescopus semiannulatus.
5400r, Chondropython viridis.

1999, Dec. 6	Litho.	Perf. 12¾
1860-1865 A344	Set of 6	5.25 1.50

Souvenir Sheet
Perf. 13

1866 A344 5400r multi 3.50 1.00
No. 1866 contains one 39x31mm stamp.

Birds of Prey A345

Designs: 200r, Harpia harpyja. 500r, Terthopius ecaudatus, vert. 900r, Neophron pernopterus, vert. 1000r, Falco peregrinus, vert. 1500r, Buteo jamaicensis, vert. 4000r, Haliaetus leucocephalus.
5400r, Milvus milvus.

1999, Oct. 5	Litho.	Perf. 12¾
1867-1872 A345	Set of 6	5.50 1.50

Souvenir Sheet
Perf. 12½

1873 A345 5400r multi 3.75 1.00
No. 1873 contains one 31x39mm stamp.

Philex France 99 — A346

Still life paintings by: 200r, Henri Fantin-Latour. 500r, Paul Cézanne. 900r, André Derain. 1000r, Henri Matisse. 1500r, Othon Friesz. 4000r, Matisse, diff.
5400r, Cézanne, diff.

1999, June 10	Litho.	Perf. 12½
1874-1879 A346	Set of 6	7.50 1.50

Souvenir Sheet
Perf. 13

1880 A346 5400r multi 5.25 1.00

Souvenir Sheet

China 1999 World Philatleic Exhibition — A347

Pagodas: a, 200r, Tongzhou. b, 500r, Tianing Temple. c, 900r, Summer Palace. d, 900r, Temple of the Clouds. e, 1000r, Bei Hai. f, 1000r, Perfumed Hill. g, 1500r, Yunju. h, 4000r, Miaoying Temple.

Perf. 12¼x12½
1999, Aug. 12   **Litho.**
1881 A347   Sheet of 8, #a-h, +
       label   7.00 2.00

Orchids
A348

Designs: 200r, Cymbidium insigne. 500r, Papillonanthe teres. 900r, Panisea uniflora. 1000r, Euanthe sanderiana. 1500r, Dendrobium trigonopus. 4000r, Vanda coerulea. 5400r, Paphiopedilum callosum.

1999, Aug. 5   **Litho.**   **Perf. 12¾**
1889-1894 A348   Set of 6   6.00 1.50
Souvenir Sheet
Perf. 12½
1895 A348   5400r multi   5.25 1.25
No. 1895 contains one 32x40mm stamp.

Birds
A349

Designs: 200r, Pyrrhula pyrrhula. 500r, Coccothraustes coccothraustes. 900r, Carduelis chloris. 1000r, Dendroica petechia. 1500r, Lanius excubitor. 4000r, Parus caeruleus. 5400r, Erithacus rubecula.

1999, Sept. 5   **Litho.**   **Perf. 12¾**
1896-1901 A349   Set of 6   7.00 1.50
Souvenir Sheet
Perf. 13
1902 A349   5400r multi   4.50 1.25
No. 1902 contains one 40x32mm stamp.

Fish
A350

Designs: 200r, Capoeta tetrazona. 500r, Epalzeorhynchus frenatus. 900r, Rasbora kalochroma. 1000r, Etroplus maculatus. 1500r, Betta imbellis. 4000r, Colisa sota. 5400r, Tetraodon biocellatus.

Perf. 12½x12¼
1999, Sept. 20   **Litho.**
1903-1908 A350   Set of 6   7.00 1.50
Souvenir Sheet
Perf. 13
1909 A350   5400r multi   4.50 1.00
No. 1909 contains one 40x32mm stamp.

Wildlife — A351

Designs: 200r, Ailuropada melanoleuca. 500r, Bos mutus. 900r, Hydropotes inermis. 1000r, Neomys fodiens, horiz. 1500r, Lutra lutra, horiz. 4000r, Panthera tigris, horiz. 5400r, Elaphurus davidianus, vert.

1999, Nov. 20   **Litho.**   **Perf. 12¾**
1910-1915 A351   Set of 6   5.50 1.50
Souvenir Sheet
Perf. 12½
1916 A351   5400r multi   4.50 1.00
No. 1916 contains one 32x40mm stamp.

Bangkok 2000 Stamp
Exhibition — A352

Turtle-shaped objects and turtles: 200r, Cuora amboinensis, vert. 500r, Cuora flavomarginata, vert. 900r, Geoemyda spengleri. 1000r, Manouria impressa. 1500r, Chinemys reevesi. 4000r, Heosemys spinosa. 4500r, Hieremys annandalei.

2000, Feb. 27   **Perf. 12¾**
1917-1922 A352   Set of 6   7.00 1.50
Souvenir Sheet
Perf. 13
1923 A352   4500r multi   5.00 1.00
No. 1923 contains one 40x32mm stamp.

Dinosaurs — A353

Designs: 200r, Iguanodon. 500r, Euoplocephalus, vert. 900r, Dilophosaurus. 1000r, Diplodocus. 1500r, Stegoceras. 4000r, Stegosaurus. 4500r, Brachiosaurus, vert. Illustration reduced.

2000, Jan. 30   **Litho.**   **Perf. 12½x12¼**
1924-1929 A353   Set of 6   5.00 1.00
Souvenir Sheet
Perf. 12½
1930 A353   4500r multi   3.50 1.00
No. 1930 contains one 32x40mm stamp.

Beetles
A354

Designs: 200r, Calosoma sycophanta. 500r, Oryctes nasicornis. 900r, Diochrysa fastuosa. 1000r, Blaps gigas. 1500r, Cincindela campestris. 4000r, Cissistes cephalotes. 4500r, Scarabeus aegyptiorum.

2000, Feb. 5   **Litho.**   **Perf. 12¾**
1931-1936 A354   Set of 6   6.50 1.50

Souvenir Sheet
Perf. 13
1937 A354   4500r multi   3.00 1.00
No. 1937 contains one 40x32mm stamp.

New Year 2000
(Year of the
Dragon) — A355

Various dragons. Denominations: 200r, 500r, 900r, 1000r, 1500r, 4000r.

2000, Jan. 20   **Litho.**   **Perf. 12¼x12½**
1938-1943 A355   Set of 6   5.50 1.50
Souvenir Sheet
Perf. 13
1944 A355   4500r multi   3.25 1.00
No. 1944 contains one 32x40mm stamp.

Bettas — A356

Designs: 200r, Unimaculata, Pugnax. 500r, Macrostoma, Taeniata. 900r, Foerschi, Imbellis. 1000r, Tessyae, Picta. 1500r, Edithae, Bellica. 4000r, Smaragdina. 4500r, Splendens. Illustration reduced.

2000, Apr. 10   **Litho.**   **Perf. 12½x12¼**
1945-1950 A356   Set of 6   5.00 1.50
Souvenir Sheet
Perf. 13
1951 A356   4500r multi   3.75 1.00
No. 1951 contains one 40x32mm stamp.

Mushrooms
A357

Designs: 200r, Amanita muscaria. 500r, Amanita pantherina. 900r, Clitocybe oleana. 1000r, Lactarius scrobiculatus. 1500r, Scleroderma vulgare. 4000r, Amanita verna. 4500r, Amanita phalloides.

2000, Mar. 20   **Litho.**   **Perf. 12¾**
1952-1957 A357   Set of 6   5.00 1.50
Souvenir Sheet
Perf. 13
1958 A357   4500r multi   3.25 1.00
No. 1958 contains one 32x40mm stamp.

Khmer
Culture — A358

Designs: 500r, Srei Snam. 1500r, Srei Snam, diff. 2000r, Srei Krub Lakhna,

2000, Apr. 13   **Litho.**   **Perf. 13**
1959-1961 A358   Set of 3   3.00 1.10

Growing
Rice — A359

Designs: 100r, Transporting seedlings. 300r, Harrowing. 500r, Threshing. 1400r, Winnowing. 1600r, Transplanting. 1900r, Plowing. 2200r, Harvesting.

2000, Mar. 1   **Perf. 12¼x12½**
Vignette Color
1962 A359   100r brt yel grn   .25   .20
1963 A359   300r brt blue   .30   .20
1964 A359   500r brt pink   .40   .20
1965 A359   1400r brn orange   1.10   .25
1966 A359   1600r dull blue   1.25   .30
1967 A359   1900r bister brn   1.50   .35
1968 A359   2200r red   1.75   .40
     Nos. 1962-1968 (7)   6.55 1.90

Locomotives — A360

Designs: 200r, Jules Petiet. 500r, Longue Chaudiere. 900r, Les Grand Chocolats. 1000r, Glehn du Bousquet. 1500r, Le Pendule Français. 4000r, TGV 001. 4500r, Le Shuttle.

2000, Mar. 5   **Litho.**   **Perf. 12½x12¼**
1969-1974 A360   Set of 6   7.25 1.50
Souvenir Sheet
Perf. 13
1975 A360   4500r multi   3.25 1.00
WIPA 2000 Philatelic Exhibition, Vienna (#1975). No. 1975 contains one 80x32mm stamp.

Birds
A361

Designs: 200r, Diomedea irrorata. 500r, Charadrius alexandrinus, vert. 900r, Sula nebouxii. 1000r, Sterna hirundo. 1500r, Larus argentatus, vert. 4000r, Chlidonia hybrida. 4500r, Sula bassana.

2000, May 8   **Perf. 12¾**
1976-1981 A361   Set of 6   5.25 1.50
Souvenir Sheet
Perf. 13
1982 A361   4500r multi   3.50 1.00
No. 1982 contains one 40x32mm stamp.

Orchids — A362

Designs: 200r, Cypripedium macranthum. 500r, Vandopsis gigantea. 900r, Calypso bulbosa. 1000r, Vanda luzonica. 1500r, Paphiopedilum villosum. 4000r, Vanda merrillii. 4500r, Paphiopedilum victoria.

2000, May 30   **Perf. 12¾**
1983-1988 A362   Set of 6   6.50 1.50

Souvenir Sheet
Perf. 13
1989 A362 4500r multi   4.00 1.00

No. 1989 contains one 32x40mm stamp.

Children's Stories — A363

Designs: 200r, The Courageous Little Tailor, vert. 500r, Tom Thumb, vert. 900r, Thumbelina, vert. 1000r, Pinocchio. 1500r, The Crayfish. 4000r, Peter Pan.
4500r, The Pied Piper, vert.

2000, Nov. 20   Litho.   Perf. 12¾
1990-1995 A363   Set of 6   5.25 5.25

Souvenir Sheet
Perf. 12½
1996 A363 4500r multi   3.00 3.00

No. 1996 contains one 32x40mm stamp.

Water Festival and Tourism A364

Designs: 500r, Men rowing canoe. 1500r, Men at canoe prow. 2000r, Temples, elephant, woman.

2000, June 1   Litho.   Perf. 13
1997-1999 A364   Set of 3   2.75 2.75

Fire Trucks A365

Designs: 200r, Metz DLK 23-6. 500r, Iveco-Magirus SLF24/100. 900r, Metz SLF 7000 WS. 1000r, Iveco-Magirus TLF 24/50. 1500r, Saval-Kronenburg RFF 11000. 4000r, Metz TLF 24/50.
4500r, Metz TLF 16/25.

2000, July 30   Perf. 12¾
2000-2005 A365   Set of 6   5.25 5.25

Souvenir Sheet
Perf. 13
2006 A365 4500r multi   3.50 3.50

No. 2006 contains one 40x32mm stamp.

Independence, 47th Anniv. — A366

Flag, temple and: 500r, Flowers. 1500r, Dove. 2000r, People carrying torch.

2000, Oct. 9   Perf. 12¾
2007-2009 A366   Set of 3   2.75 2.75

Antique Automobiles — A367

Designs: 200r, 1912 Rover 12C. 500r, 1907, Austin 30CV. 900r, 1909 Rolls-Royce Silver Ghost. 1000r, 1929 Graham Paige Phaeton DC. 1500r, 1937 Austin 12. 4000r, 1957 Mercedes-Benz 300SL.
4500r, 1936 MG.

2000, Sept. 30   Perf. 12¾
2010-2015 A367   Set of 6   5.25 5.25

Souvenir Sheet
Perf. 13
2016 A367 4500r multi   4.25 4.25

España 2000 Intl. Philatelic Exhibition (#2016). No. 2016 contains one 40x32mm stamp.

Dachshunds — A368

Designs: 200r, Smooth-haired dachshund. 500r, Wire-haired dachshund. 900r, Long-haired dachshund. 1000r, Two dachshunds. 1500r, Dachshund with pups. 4000r, Dachshunds resting.
4500r, Wire-haired dachshund, vert.

2000, Aug. 30   Perf. 13
2017-2022 A368   Set of 6   5.25 5.25

Souvenir Sheet
Perf. 12½
2023 A368 4500r multi   3.00 3.00

No. 2023 contains one 32x40mm stamp.

Cats and Art A369

Cat or cats and: 200r, Korean silk painting, 18th cent. 500r, Portuguese tile, 18th cent. 900r, Japanese ceramic cat. 1000r, Egyptian metallic cat. 1500r, Scandinavian engraving. 4000r, Japanese painting.
4500r, Cat on hind legs.

2000, Oct. 5   Perf. 12½x12¼
2024-2029 A369   Set of 6   5.00 5.00

Souvenir Sheet
Perf. 13x13¼
2030 A369 4500r multi   3.00 3.00

No. 2030 contains one 40x32mm stamp.

Birds A370

Designs: 200r, Creatophora cinerea. 500r, Sturnus vulgaris. 900r, Leiothrix lutea. 1000r, Rupicola rupicola. 1500r, Prunella collaris. 4000r, Panurus biarnicus.
4500r, Muscicapula pallipes, vert.

2000, Dec. 10   Perf. 13
2031-2036 A370   Set of 6   5.50 5.50

Souvenir Sheet
2037 A370 4500r multi   3.50 3.50

No. 2037 contains one 32x40mm stamp.

Sports — A371

Designs: 200r, Weight lifting. 500r, Rhythmic gymnastics. 900r, Baseball. 1000r, Women's tennis. 1500r, Basketball. 4000r, Women's high jump.

Perf. 12¾, 12½ (#2044)
2000, June 30   Litho.
2038-2043 A371   Set of 6   5.00 5.00

Souvenir Sheet
2044 A371 4500r Runners   3.00 3.00

No. 2044 contains one 32x40mm stamp.

New Year 2001 (Year of the Snake) — A372

Various stylized snakes with background colors of: 200r, Beige. 500r, Dull bister. 900r, Light blue. 1000r, Greenish blue. 1500r, Dull green. 4000r, Blue.
5400r, Blue, horiz.

2001, Jan. 15   Litho.   Perf. 12¼x12½
2045-2050 A372   Set of 6   6.00 6.00

Souvenir Sheet
Perf. 13x13¼
2051 A372 5400r multi   4.75 4.75

No. 2051 contains one 40x32mm stamp.

Millennium — A373

Designs: 200r, Johannes Gutenberg, printers. 500r, Michael Faraday, electric motor. 900r, Samuel F. B. Morse, telegraph. 1000r, Alexander Graham Bell, telephone. 1500r, Enrico Fermi, nuclear energy. 4000r, Edward Roberts, computer.
No. 2058: a, Christopher Columbus, ships. b, Neil Armstrong, lunar module.

2001, Jan. 5   Litho.   Perf. 12¾
2052-2057 A373   Set of 6   7.50 7.50

Souvenir Sheet
Perf. 12½
2058 A373 5400r Sheet of 2, #a-
              b + label   8.00 8.00

No. 2058 contains two 40x32mm stamps.

Fire and Rescue Equipment A374

Designs: 200r, 1910 Sandou ladder wagon. 500r, 1899 Gallo cart. 900r, Merryweather pumper, 1950s. 1000r, 1940 Merryweather ambulance. 1500r, 1972 Man-Metz pumper. 4000r, Roman Diesel pumper, 1970s.
5400r, 1898 Metropolitan steam pumper.

2001, Feb. 5   Perf. 12¾
2059-2064 A374   Set of 6   7.50 7.50

Souvenir Sheet
Perf. 13x13¼
2065 A374 5400r multi   4.00 4.00

No. 2065 contains one 40x32mm stamp.

Mushrooms — A375

Designs: 200r, Lycoperdon perlatum. 500r, Trametes versicolor. 900r, Hipholoma sublateritium. 1000r, Amanita muscaria. 1500r, Lycoperdon umbrinum. 4000r, Cortinarius orellanus.
5400r Amanita phalloides, vert.

2001, Feb. 25   Perf. 12¾
2066-2071 A375   Set of 6   7.50 7.50

Souvenir Sheet
Perf. 12½
2072 A375 5400r multi   4.00 4.00

No. 2072 contains one 32x40mm stamp.

Belgica 2001 Intl. Stamp Exhibition, Brussels — A376

Butterflies: 200r, Nymphalis polychloros. 500r, Cethosia hypsea. 900r, Papilio palinurus. 1000r, Apatura ilia. 1500r, Parthenos sylvia. 4000r, Morpho grandensis.
5400r, Heliconius melpomene.

2001, Apr. 5   Perf. 12¾
2073-2078 A376   Set of 6   7.00 7.00

Souvenir Sheet
Perf. 13x13¼
2079 A376 5400r multi   4.00 4.00

Film Personalities A377

Designs: 200r, Gary Cooper. 500r, Marlene Dietrich. 900r, Walt Disney. 1000r, Clark Gable. 1500r, Jeanette MacDonald. 4000r, Melvyn Douglas.
No. 2086: a, Rudolph Valentino. b, Marilyn Monroe.

2001, Apr. 25   Litho.   Perf. 12¾
2080 A377   200r multi   .25 .25
2081 A377   500r multi   .50 .50
2082 A377   900r multi   .70 .70
2083 A377   1000r multi   .90 .90
2084 A377   1500r multi   1.25 1.25
2085 A377   4000r multi   3.25 3.25
       Nos. 2080-2085 (6)   6.85 6.85

Souvenir Sheet
Perf. 13
2086 A377 5400r Sheet of 2,
              #a-b   9.00 9.00

Natl. Culture Day A378

Sculptures: 500r, Angkor. 1500r, Bayon. 2000r, Bayon, diff.

2001, Apr. 3 Litho. Perf. 12¾
2087-2089 A378 Set of 3 3.50 3.50

Temples — A379

Designs: 200r, Preah Vihear. 300r, Thonmanom. 600r, Tasom. 1000r, Kravan. 1500r, Takeo. 1700r, Mebon. 2200r, Banteay Kdei.

2001, Mar. 15 Perf. 12¼x12½
2090-2096 A397 Set of 7 6.00 6.00

Automobiles — A380

Designs: 200r, 1972 TVR Series M. 500r, 1958 Ferrari 410. 900r, 1995 Peugeot 405. 1000r, 1953 Fiat 8VZ. 1500r, 1997 Citroen Xsara. 4000r, 1997 Renault Espace. 5400r, 1963 Ferrari 250 GT SWB.

2001, June 5 Litho. Perf. 12¾
2097-2102 A380 Set of 6 7.50 7.50
Souvenir Sheet
Perf. 13x13¼
2103 A380 5400r multi 3.75 3.75
No. 2103 contains one 40x32mm stamp.

Tourism A381

Designs: 500r, Sourire de Bayon. 1500r, Bayon. 2000r, Bayon, diff.

2001, June 5 Perf. 12¾
2104-2106 A381 Set of 3 3.50 3.50

Philanippon '01 — A382

Locomotives: 200r, 4-6-0. 500r, 4-6-4. 900r, 4-4-0. 1000r, 4-6-4, diff. 1500r, 4-6-2. 4000r, 4-8-2.
5400r, Undescribed locomotive.

2001, July 5 Perf. 12½x12¼
2107-2112 A382 Set of 6 7.50 7.50
Souvenir Sheet
Perf. 13x13¼
2113 A380 5400r multi 5.00 5.00
No. 2113 contains one 40x32mm stamp.

Penguins A383

Designs: 200r, Aptenodytes forsteri. 500r, Spheniscus demersus. 900r, Spheniscus humboldti. 1000r, Eudypes cristatus. 1500r, Aptenodytes patagonica. 4000r, Pygoscelis antarctica.
5400r, Pygoscelis papua.

2001, Aug. 5 Perf. 12¾
2114-2119 A383 Set of 6 8.00 8.00
Souvenir Sheet
Perf. 13x13¼
2120 A383 5400r multi 7.00 7.00
No. 2120 contains one 40x32mm stamp.

Cats A384

Designs: 200r, Singapura. 500r, Cymric. 900r, Exotic shorthair. 1000r, Ragdoll. 1500r, Manx. 4000r, Somali.
5400r, Egyptian Mau.

2001, Aug. 25 Perf. 12½x12¼
2121-2126 A384 Set of 6 7.50 7.50
Souvenir Sheet
Perf. 13x13¼
2127 A384 5400r multi 5.50 5.50
No. 2127 contains one 40x32mm stamp.

Kites A385

Designs: 300r, Khleng Chak. 500r, Khleng Kanton. 1000r, Khleng Phnong. 1500r, Khleng Kaun Morn. 3000r, Khleng Me Ambao.

2001, Sept. 7 Perf. 12¾
2128-2132 A385 Set of 5 6.00 6.00

Cacti — A386

Designs: 200r, Parodia cintiensis. 500r, Astrophytum astenas. 900r, Parodia faustiana. 1000r, Coryphantha sulcolanata. 1500r, Neochilenia hankena. 4000r, Mammilaria boolii.
5400r, Mammilaria swinglei.

2001, Sept. 15 Perf. 12¾
2133-2138 A386 Set of 6 7.00 7.00
Souvenir Sheet
Perf. 12½
2139 A386 5400r multi 5.50 5.50
No. 2139 contains one 32x40mm stamp.

Khmer Culture A387

Designs: 500r, Fish Dance. 1500r, Red Fish Ballet. 2000r, Apsara Ballet.

2001, Oct. 9 Perf. 12¾
2140-2142 A387 Set of 3 4.25 4.25

Wolves and Foxes A388

Designs: 200r, Canis lupus occidentalis. 500r, Canis lupus tundrorum, vert. 900r, Vulpes fulvas. 1000r, Canis latrans. 1500r, Vulpes zerda, vert. 4000r, Alopex lagopus.
5400r, Canis lupus signatus, vert.

2001, Oct. 15 Perf. 12¾
2143-2148 A388 Set of 6 5.25 5.25
Souvenir Sheet
Perf. 12½
2149 A388 5400r multi 3.50 3.50
No. 2103 contains one 32x40mm stamp.

Human Evolution — A389

Designs: 100r, Australopithecus anamensis. 200r, Australopithecus afarensis. 300r, Australopithecus africanus. No. 2153, 500r, Australopithecus rudolfensis. No. 2154, 500r, Australopithecus boisei. 1000r, Homo habilis. 1500r, Homo erectus. 4000r, Homo sapiens neanderthalensis.
5400r, Homo sapiens sapiens.

2001, Oct. 25 Perf. 13
2150-2157 A389 Set of 8 9.00 9.00
Souvenir Sheet
2158 A389 5400r multi 6.50 6.50
No. 2158 contains one 40x32mm stamp.

King Norodom Sihanouk, 80th Birthday (in 2002) A389a

Various photos: 100r, 200r, 300r, 400r, 500r, 600r, 700r, 800r, 900r, 1000r, 1500r, 2000r, 3000r.

2001, Oct. 31 Litho. Perf. 13
2158A-2158M A389a Set of 13 15.00 15.00

Chess A390

Designs: 200r, Rook. 500r, Pawn. 900r, King. 1000r, Bishop. 1500r, Queen. 4000r, Knight.
5400r, Pieces of Oriental chess-like game.

2001, Dec. 25 Perf. 12¾
2159-2164 A390 Set of 6 5.00 5.00
Souvenir Sheet
Perf. 13
2165 A390 5400r multi 3.75 3.75
No. 2165 contains one 40x32mm stamp.

Italian Soccer A391

Designs: 200r, 1934 World Cup championship team. 500r, 1938 World Cup championship team. 900r, 1968 European Cup championship team. 1000r, 1982 World Cup championship team. 1500r, 2002 World Cup team. 4000r, Italian soccer federation emblem.

2001 Perf. 12¾
2166-2171 A391 Set of 6 5.25 5.25

ASEAN Post, 10th Anniv A392

Temples: 500r, Prasat Preah Vihear. 1000r, Prasat Preah Ko. 1500r, Prasat Banteay Srei. 2500r, Prasat Bayon. 3500r, Prasat Angkor Wat.

2002, July 9 Perf. 13
2172-2176 A392 Set of 5 10.00 10.00

Sugar Palm — A393

Designs: 300r, Tree. 500r, Female flower. 700r, Male flower. 1500r, Fruit.

2003, June 20 Litho.
2177-2180 A393 Set of 4 7.00 7.00

Japanese Grant Aid — A394

Designs: 100r, Drawing of Bridge No. 26, Highway 6A. 200r, Bridge No. 26, Highway 6A. 400r, Chroy Changvar Bridge. 800r, Kizuna Bridge. 3500r, Monument, vert.

2003, Apr. 25
2181-2185 A394 Set of 5 6.00 6.00

Cambodian Red Cross — A395

Designs: 100r, Ox cart. 200r, Woman carrying rice bag, vert. 300r, Queen with Red Cross volunteers. 400r, Queen and women. 500r, Queen and elderly people. 700r, Queen and women, diff. 800r, Queen and Prime Minister's wife giving items to people. 1000r, Like 800r, diff. 1900r, Like 800r, diff., vert. 2100r, Like 800r, diff., vert. 4000r, Queen and Prime Minister's wife with baby.

2003, May 8
2186-2196 A395　Set of 11　10.00 10.00

Cambodia/People's Republic of China Diplomatic Relations, 50th Anniv. — A396

No. 2197: a, Angkor Wat. b, Great Wall of China.
Illustration reduced.

2003, July 19　　　**Perf. 12¼x12**
2197 A396 2000r Horiz. pair,
　　　#a-b　　　　4.50 4.50

Association of South East Asian Nations, 36th Anniv. — A397

Designs: 400r, Conference emblem. 500r, Apsara dancer. 600r, Apsara dancer, diff. 1600r, Apsara dancer, diff. 1900r, Temonorom dancers.

2003, Aug. 8　　　　**Perf. 13**
2198-2202 A397　Set of 5　6.00 6.00

King Norodom Sihanouk — A398

Designs: 200r, Pointing at map. 400r, Meeting rural Cambodians, vert. 500r, Sitting in forest, vert. 800r, Pointing in forest, vert. 1000r, Saluting, vert. 2000r, Saluting, with flag and Independence Monument, vert. 5000r, With handicapped people.

2003, Nov. 9
2203-2209 A398　Set of 7　10.00 10.00

Khmer Culture A399

Sculptures: 100r, Bayon. 200r, Banteay Srei. 400r, Banteay Srei, diff. 800r, Bayon, vert. 3500r, Banteay Srei, vert.
2000r, Unattributed sculpture, vert.

2004, Apr. 3
2210-2214 A399　Set of 5　4.50 4.50
Souvenir Sheet
2215 A399 2000r multi　　2.50 2.50

Rural Areas A400

Designs: 600r, Mill. 900r, House, field and cattle. 2000r, House and trees.
2000r, Ox cart and driver.

2004, Apr. 13
2216-2218 A400　Set of 3　4.50 3.50
Souvenir Sheet
2219 A400 2000r multi　　2.50 2.50

Tepmonorum Dancers — A401

Dancers with: 400r, Yellow costumes. 1000r, Blue costumes. 2100r, Blue and yellow costumes.
2100r, Blue and yellow costumes, diff.

2004, May 5
2220-2222 A401　Set of 3　5.00 4.00
Souvenir Sheet
2223 A401 2000r multi　　2.50 2.50

Flowers — A402

Designs: 600r, Cassia fistula. 700r, Butea monosperma. 900r, Couroupita quianensis. 1000r, Delonix regia, horiz. 1800r, Lagerstroemia floribunda.
2000r, Lagerstroemia floribunda, horiz.

2004, Aug. 25　**Litho.**　**Perf. 13**
2224-2228 A402　Set of 5　5.00 5.00
Souvenir Sheet
2229 A402 2000r multi　　2.75 2.75

Tourism — A403

Designs: 200r, Prasat Preah Khan. 500r, Prasat Preup. 600r, PrasatBanteay Samre. 1600r, Prasat Bayon. 1900r, Angkor Wat. 2000r, Prasat Bayon, vert.

2004, Sept. 27　**Litho.**　**Perf. 13**
2230-2234 A403　Set of 5　4.00 4.00
Souvenir Sheet
2235 A403 2000r multi　　2.50 2.50

Coronation of King Norodom Shiamoni A404

Various photos: 100r, 400r, 500r, 600r, 700r, 900r, 2100r, 2200r, 4000r. 700r-4000r are horiz.

2004, Oct. 29
2236-2244 A404　Set of 9　7.50 7.50

Ancient Fishing Tools A405

Various scoops and baskets: 100r, 200r, 800r, 1700r, 2200r. 1700r and 2200r are vert. 2000r, Child with basket, vert.

2004, Dec. 5
2245-2249 A405　Set of 5　5.00 5.00
Souvenir Sheet
2250 A405 2000r multi　　3.00 3.00

Cambodian Red Cross, 50th Anniv. — A406

Designs: 400r, Emblem. 700r, Volunteers, horiz. 800r, Volunteers, diff., horiz. 1900r, Volunteers, diff., horiz. 2100r, Volunteers, diff. horiz. 2200r, Royalty on dais, horiz.

2005, Feb. 18
2251-2256 A406　Set of 6　7.25 7.25

Apsaras Dance — A407

Dancer with background color of: 800r, Pink. 900r, Light blue. 1400r, Green. 1600r, Rose. 2000r, Blue.
4000r, Brown.

2005, Apr. 12
2257-2261 A407　Set of 5　6.00 6.00
Souvenir Sheet
2262 A407 4000r multi　　4.00 4.00

Khmer Culture A408

Designs: 500r, Banteay Kdei. 700r, Elephant Terrace. 1000r, Thommanon. 2000r, Ta Prohm. 2500r, Angkor Wat.

4000r, Ta Reach, vert.

2005, May 16
2263-2267 A408　Set of 5　6.00 6.00
Souvenir Sheet
2268 A408 4000r multi　　4.00 4.00

Flowers — A409

Nymphaea lotus in: 100r, Purple. 500r, White. 1200r, Blue. 2000r, Yellow. 2500r, Red. 4000r, Red flowers in canoe, horiz.

2005, July 25　**Litho.**　**Perf. 13**
2269-2273 A409　Set of 5　5.75 5.75
Souvenir Sheet
2274 A409 4000r multi　　4.00 4.00

Fish A410

Designs: 700r, Pangasionodon gigas. 800r, Catlocarpio siamensis. 1000r, Mekongina erythrospila. 1900r, Probarbus labeaminor, vert. 2200r, Wallago leeri, vert.
4000r, Scleropages formosus.

2005, Sept. 5　　　　**Perf. 13**
2275-2279 A410　Set of 5　6.00 6.00
Souvenir Sheet
2280 A410 4000r multi　　4.25 4.25

Coronation of King Norodom Sihamoni, 1st Anniv. — A411

Frame colors: 500r, Green. 1500r, Blue. 2200r, Red.

2005, Oct. 29　**Litho.**　**Perf. 13**
2281-2283 A411　Set of 3　3.25 3.25

Miniature Sheet

Birds — A412

No. 2284: a, 200r, Great egret. b, 400r, Great-billed heron. c, 1000r, Painted stork. d, 1200r, Spot-billed pelican. e, 1800r, Sarus crane, horiz. f, 3500r, Greater adjutant, horiz.

2005, Dec. 5
2284 A412　Sheet of 6, #a-f　7.50 7.50

Khmer Culture A413

Women at work: 100r, Scooping dyes. 800r, Washing clothes. 1500r, Weaving. 2200r, Spinning thread. 3500r, Weaving, diff. 5400r, Weaving, diff.

2006, Jan. 26
2285-2289 A413 Set of 5   6.00 6.00
Souvenir Sheet
2290 A413 5400r multi   3.75 3.75

Marine Mammals — A414

Designs: 500r, Sousa chinensis. 900r, Neophocaena phocaenoides. 1400r, Dolphinus capensis tropicalis. 2100r, Stenella longirostris roseinventris. 3500r, Tursiops aduncus. 5400r, Neophocaena phocaenoides and boat.

2006, Mar. 9
2291-2295 A414 Set of 5   7.50 7.50
Souvenir Sheet
2296 A414 5400r multi   4.00 4.00

Reamker Legend — A415

Designs: 1000r, Jup Leak and Ream Leak. 1400r, Preah Ream, vert. 1600r, Neang Seda, vert. 1900r, Krong Reap, vert. 2100r, Hanuman, vert. 5400r, Two characters in water.

2006, Apr. 13
2297-2301 A415 Set of 5   6.00 6.00
Souvenir Sheet
2302 A415 5400r multi   4.00 4.00

Elephants — A416

Designs: 400r, Adult and juvenile elephant. 700r, Elephants in water. 1600r, Elephant, vert. 2200r, Elephant facing right. 3500r, Elephant facing left. 5400r, Elephants in water, diff.

2006, June 15   Litho.   *Perf. 13*
2303-2307 A416 Set of 5   6.00 6.00
Souvenir Sheet
2308 A416 5400r multi   4.00 4.00

Dances — A417

Designs: 600r, Chhai Yaim dance. 1900r, Sacrifice of Buffalo dance. 2200r, Mouth Organ dance. 3500r, Rice Harvest dance.

2006, Aug. 17
2309-2312 A417 Set of 4   6.00 6.00

Birds A418

Designs: 600r, Threskionis melanocephalus. 800r, Plegadis facinellus. 1500r, Houbaropsis bengalensis. 2100r, Pseudibis gigantea. 3500r, Pseudibis davisoni. 5400r, Pseudibis gigantea, vert.

2006, Nov. 8   Litho.   *Perf. 13*
2313-2317 A418 Set of 5   8.00 8.00
Souvenir Sheet
2318 A418 5400r multi   7.00 7.00

Condom Use Program — A419

Designs: 300r, Man, woman, program emblem. 500r, Man, motorcycle, program emblem. 2200r, Men on boat, flag with program emblem.

2006, Dec. 1   Litho.   *Perf. 13*
2319-2321 A419 Set of 3   2.25 2.25
World AIDS Day.

Cambodian Red Cross HIV/AIDS Campaign — A420

Campaign leader Bun Rany, wife of Prime Minister Hun Sen and captions: 1500r, Caring. 1900r, Stop discrimination, vert. 2000r, Give hope to families. 2100r, National and Asia-Pacific Leadership Forum Champion. 2200r, National and Asia-Pacific Leadership Forum Champion, diff.

2007   Litho.   *Perf. 13*
2322-2326 A420 Set of 5   6.00 6.00

Sculpture A421

Flags of Viet Nam and Cambodia A422

2007, June 24
2327 A421 500r shown   .40 .40
2328 A421 800r Sculpture, diff.   .60 .60
2329 A421 1000r Sculpture, diff.   .70 .70
2330 A421 1500r Sculpture, diff.   1.00 1.00
2331 A422 1900r shown   1.25 1.25
   Nos. 2327-2331 (5)   3.95 3.95

Diplomatic relations between Cambodia and Viet Nam, 40th anniv.

Handicap International, 25th Anniv. — A423

Denominations: 1000r, 1500r.

2007, July 25
2332-2333 A423 Set of 2   2.00 2.00

Dancers — A424

Architecture — A425

Various dancers with denominations of: 800r, 900r, 1400r, 1600r, 2000r.

No. 2339: a, Secretariat Building, Bandar Seri Begawan, Brunei. b, National Museum of Cambodia. c, Fatahillah Museum, Jakarta, Indonesia. d, Typical house, Laos. e, Malayan Railway Headquarters Building, Kuala Lumpur, Malaysia. f, Yangon Post Office, Myanmar (Burma). g, Malacañang Palace, Philippines. h, National Museum of Singapore. i, Vimanmek Mansion, Bangkok, Thailand. j, Presidential Palace, Hanoi, Viet Nam.

2007, Aug. 8
2334-2338 A424 Set of 5   5.00 5.00
2339 A425 1000r Sheet of 10, #a-j   7.75 7.75

Association of South East Asian Nations (ASEAN), 40th anniv. See Brunei No. 607, Burma No. 370, Indonesia Nos. 2120-2121, Laos Nos. 1717-1718, Malaysia No. 1170, Philippines Nos. 3103-3105, Singapore No. 1265, Thailand No. 2315, and Viet Nam Nos. 3302-3311.

SEMI-POSTAL STAMPS

Nos. 8, 12, 14 and 15 Surcharged in Black

1952, Oct. 20   Unwmk.   *Perf. 13*
B1 A3 1.10pi + 40c   4.75 4.75
B2 A3 1.90pi + 60c   4.75 4.75
B3 A3 3pi + 1pi   4.75 4.75
B4 A1 5pi + 2pi   4.75 4.75
   Nos. B1-B4 (4)   19.00 19.00
For students assistance.

Preah Stupa — SP1

1957, Mar. 15   Engr.   *Perf. 13*
B5 SP1 1.50r + 50c ind, ol & red   1.60 1.60
B6 SP1 6.50r + 1.50r red lil, ol & red   2.40 2.40
B7 SP1 8r + 2r bl, ol & red   4.00 4.00
   Nos. B5-B7 (3)   8.00 8.00
Birth of Buddha, 1500th anniv. See #62-64.

Type of Regular Issue, 1959, with Red Typographed Surcharge

1959, Dec. 9
B8 A14 20c + 20c rose vio   .50 .50
B9 A14 50c + 30c blue   .80 .80
B10 A14 80c + 50c rose car   1.60 1.60
   Nos. B8-B10 (3)   2.90 2.90
The surtax was for the Red Cross.

Nos. 107-108 Surcharged and Overprinted in Red

1963, Oct. 1   Unwmk.   *Perf. 13*
B11 A26 4r + 40c grn & dk brn   .90 .90
B12 A26 6r + 60c vio & ol bis   1.25 1.25
Centenary of International Red Cross.

Nos. 263, 267, 293-294, 134 Surcharged in Red

1972, Nov. 15   Engr.   Perf. 13

B13	A72	3r + 2r multi	.40 .40
B14	A72	10r + 6r multi	.80 .80
B15	A80	12r + 7r multi	.90 .90
B16	A34	12r + 7r multi	.90 .90
B17	A80	15r + 8r multi	1.60 1.60
		Nos. B13-B17 (5)	4.60 4.60

Surtax was for war victims. Surcharge arranged differently on Nos. B15-B17.

AIR POST STAMPS

Kinnari — AP1

Unwmk.

1953, Apr. 16   Engr.   Perf. 13

C1	AP1	50c deep green	.80 .75
a.		Souv. sheet of 4, #C1, C3, C5, C9	90.00 90.00
C2	AP1	3pi red brown	1.10 .80
a.		Souv. sheet of 3, #C2, C4, C8	90.00 90.00
C3	AP1	3.30pi rose violet	1.25 1.00
C4	AP1	4pi dk brn & dp bl	1.60 1.10
C5	AP1	5.10pi brn, red & org	3.00 2.50
C6	AP1	6.50pi dk brn & lil rose	3.00 2.50
a.		Souv. sheet of 2, #C6-C7	90.00 90.00
C7	AP1	9pi lil rose & dp grn	4.25 3.50
C8	AP1	11.50pi multi	13.00 7.25
C9	AP1	30pi dk brn, bl grn & org	21.00 10.00
		Nos. C1-C9 (9)	49.00 29.40

#C1a sold for 50pi, #C2a for 25pi, #C6a for 20pi.

Souvenir sheets with completely white gum, no toning and no gum bends sell for a premium.

AP2

1957, Dec. 11

C10	AP2	50c maroon	.40 .20
C11	AP2	1r emerald	.70 .20
C12	AP2	4r ultra	2.25 .75
C13	AP2	50r carmine rose	8.75 4.00
C14	AP2	100r grn, bl & car	16.00 6.00
a.		Souv. sheet of 5, #C10-C14	35.00 35.00
		Nos. C10-C14 (5)	28.10 11.15

No. C14a sold for 160r.
See note after #C9.

Independence Type of 1961

1961, Nov. 9   Perf. 13x12½

C15	A24	7r multicolored	.80 .40
C16	A24	30r grn, car & ultra	2.75 1.25
C17	A24	50r ind, grn & ol	4.00 2.50
a.		Souv. sheet of 3, #C15-C17	11.00 11.00
		Nos. C15-C17 (3)	6.65 3.70

No. C15 Surcharged in Red and Overprinted in Black

C18ovpt

1962, Nov. 9

C18	A24	12r on 7r multi	2.25 1.25

Dedication of Independence Monument.

Hanuman, Monkey God — AP3

1964, Sept. 1   Engr.   Perf. 13

C19	AP3	5r multicolored	1.10 .55
C20	AP3	10r ol bis, lil rose & grn	1.60 .65
C21	AP3	20r vio, bl & ol bis	2.50 1.40
C22	AP3	40r bl, ol bis & dk grn	6.00 2.25
C23	AP3	80r multicolored	10.00 6.00
		Nos. C19-C23 (5)	21.20 10.85

Nos. C19-C22 Surcharged in Red

1964, Oct.

C24	AP3	3r on 5r multi	.90 .55
C25	AP3	6r on 10r multi	1.40 .85
C26	AP3	9r on 20r multi	1.75 1.10
C27	AP3	12r on 40r multi	3.00 1.75
		Nos. C24-C27 (4)	7.05 4.25

18th Olympic Games, Tokyo, Oct. 10-25.

1972 Summer Olympic Games, Munich — AP4

Designs: No. C28, shown. No. C29, Munich churches, Olympic emblem, vert. Illustration reduced.

Litho. & Embossed

1972, Sept. 28   Perf. 13½

C28	AP4	900r gold & multi	30.00 30.00
C29	AP4	900r gold & multi	30.00 30.00
a.		Souvenir sheet of 2, #C28-C29	70.00

No. C29a exists imperf. Value, $85.

Apollo 16 AP5

Designs: No. C30, Astronauts in Lunar Rover. No. C31, Astronaut walking on moon.

1972, Sept. 28

C30	AP5	900r gold & multi	35.00 35.00
C31	AP5	900r gold & multi	35.00 35.00
a.		Souvenir sheet of 2, #C30-C31	75.00

No. C31a exists imperf. Value, $110.

Pres. Nixon's Visit to the People's Republic of China — AP6

Nixon, Mao Zedong: No. C32, Large portraits (shown). No. C33, Small portraits.

1972, Sept. 28   Perf. 12½

C32	AP6	900r gold & multi	75.00 75.00
C33	AP6	900r gold & multi	75.00 75.00

Garuda, 12th Century, Angkor Thom — AP7

1973, Jan. 18   Engr.   Perf. 13

C34	AP7	3r carmine	.35 .20
C35	AP7	30r violet blue	1.75 .95
C36	AP7	50r dull purple	3.25 1.75
C37	AP7	100r dull green	5.00 2.75
		Nos. C34-C37 (4)	10.35 5.65

1972 Summer Olympic Games, Munich AP8

Gold medalists: No. C38, Heide Rosendahl. No. C39, Mark Spitz.

Litho. & Embossed

1973, May 18   Perf. 13½

C38	AP8	900r gold & multi	30.00 30.00
C39	AP8	900r gold & multi	30.00 30.00
a.		Souvenir sheet, #C38-C39	70.00

No. C39a exists imperf. Value $85.

Nos. C38-C39 Overprinted

1973, Nov. 19

C40	AP8	900r on C38	37.50 37.50
C41	AP8	900r on C39	37.50 37.50
a.		Souvenir sheet, #C40-C41	80.00

No. C41a exists imperf. Value, $160.

1974 World Cup Soccer Championships, Munich — AP9

Designs: No. C42, Trophy, players. No. C43, Trophy, players, vert.

1973, Nov. 19   Litho. & Embossed

C42	AP9	900r gold & multi	37.50 37.50
C43	AP9	900r gold & multi	37.50 37.50
a.		Souvenir sheet, #C42-C43	80.00

No. C43a exists imperf. Value, $95.

John F. Kennedy, Apollo 11 — AP10

#C44, shown. #C45, Kennedy, Apollo 17.

1974, Feb. 18

C44	AP10	1100r gold & multi	80.00 80.00
C45	AP10	1100r gold & multi	80.00 80.00
a.		Souv. sheet of 2, #C44-C45	175.00

Nos. C44-C45a exist imperf. Values same.

Copernicus Type of 1974 and

Copernicus, Sun — AP11

200r, Copernicus and Skylab III. 250r, Copernicus, Concorde and solar eclipse. No. C48, shown. No. C49, Moon, Skylab, hand holding symbol of sun.

1974, Sept. 10   Litho.   Perf. 13

C46	A87	200r multi	10.00 4.00
C47	A87	250r multi	16.00 10.00

Litho. & Engraved

Perf. 13½

C48	AP11	1200r gold & multi	27.50 27.50

Souvenir Sheet of 1

C49	AP11	1200r gold & multi	27.50 27.50

Nos. C46-C47 exist in perf or imperf souvenir sheets of 1. Values, each $40.

AP12

700r, Rocket, globe and UPU emblem. No. C51, UPU Headquarters. No. C52, US #1434-1435.

1974, Nov. 2   Litho.   Perf. 13
C50 A88   700r gold & multi   10.00 10.00
Litho. & Embossed
Perf. 13½
C51 AP12 1200r gold & multi 25.00 25.00
Souvenir Sheet
C52 AP12 1200r gold & multi 45.00

Nos. C50-C51 exist in souvenir sheets of one. Nos. C51-C52 exist imperf.

#C53-C54, UPU Centennial, 4/12/75.

Post Aerienne at
Right — AP14

Post Aerienne at
Left — AP15

Denominations: 5r, 10r, 15r, 25r.

1984, Feb. 1   Litho.   Perf. 12x12½
C55-C58 AP14 Set of 4   42.50 7.50

1986, Mar. 4   Litho.   Perf. 12x12½
Denominations: 5r, 10r, 15r, 25r.
C59-C62 AP15 Set of 4   37.50 7.50

POSTAGE DUE STAMPS

D1

Frieze, Angkor
Wat — D2

1957   Unwmk.   Typo.   Perf. 13½
Denomination in Black
J1 D1 10c ver & pale blue   .30 .30
J2 D1 50c ver & pale blue   .55 .55
J3 D1 1r ver & pale blue   .85 .85
J4 D1 3r ver & pale blue   1.25 1.25
J5 D1 5r ver & pale blue   1.90 1.90
     Nos. J1-J5 (5)   4.85 4.85

1974, Feb. 18   Engr.   Perf. 12½x13
J6 D2 2r ocher   .30 .30
J7 D2 6r green   .45 .45
J8 D2 8r deep carmine   .70 .70
J9 D2 10r violet blue   1.10 1.10
     Nos. J6-J9 (4)   2.55 2.55

CAMEROONS

ˌka-mə-'rüns

LOCATION — West coast of Africa, north of equator
GOVT. — British Trust Territory
AREA — 34,081 sq. mi.
POP. — 868,637 (estimated)
CAPITAL — Buea

Prior to World War I, Cameroons (Kamerun) was a German Protectorate. It was occupied during the War by Great Britain and France and in 1922 was mandated to these countries by the League of Nations. Stamps of Nigeria were used in the British part until 1960. The northern section of the British Cameroons became part of the independent state of Nigeria in 1960, and the southern section became a United Kingdom Trust Territory. After a referendum, this U.K.T.T. joined the independent State of Cameroun to form the Federal Republic of Cameroun, Oct. 1, 1961.

Stamps of the German Protectorate, the French Mandate, the independent state and the Cameroun Federal Republic are listed under Cameroun.

> Catalogue values for unused stamps in this country are for Never Hinged items.

United Kingdom Trust Territory

Stamps and Type of Nigeria, 1953, Overprinted in Red

Perf. 13½, 14
1960, Oct. 1   Wmk. 4   Engr.
Size: 35½x22½mm
66 A17 ½p red org & black   .20 1.75
67 A17 1p ol gray & black   .20 .90
68 A17 1½p blue green   .20 .25
69 A17 2p gray (II)   .30 .50
70 A17 3p purple & black   .20 .20
71 A17 4p ultra & black   .25 1.75
72 A18 6p blk & org brn, perf. 14   .60 .25
a.   Perf. 13x13½ ('61)   .45 2.25
73 A17 1sh brown vio & blk   .25 .20
Size: 40½x24½mm
74 A17 2sh6p green & black   1.75 1.50
75 A17 5sh ver & black   2.50 4.50
76 A17 10sh red brn & blk   3.75 8.50
Size: 42x31½mm
77 A17 £1 violet & black   12.00 27.50
     Nos. 66-77 (12)   22.20 47.80

Nos. 66-77 were withdrawn in Northern Cameroons on May 31, 1961, when that territory joined Nigeria and in Southern Cameroons Sept. 30, 1961, when that territory joined the Cameroun Federal Republic.

CAMEROUN

ˌka-mə-'rün

(Kamerun)

LOCATION — On the west coast of Africa, north of the equator
GOVT. — Republic

AREA — 183,520 sq. mi.
POP. — 15,456,092 (1999 est.)
CAPITAL — Yaounde

Before World War I, Cameroun (Kamerun) was a German Protectorate. It was occupied during the war by Great Britain and France and in 1922 was mandated to these countries by the League of Nations. The French-mandated part became the independent State of Cameroun on January 1, 1960. The Southern Cameroons, a United Kingdom Trust Territory, joined this state to form the Federal Republic of Cameroun on October 1, 1961. The name was changed to United Republic of Cameroon on May 20, 1972.

Stamps of Southern Cameroons are listed under Cameroons.

100 Pfennig = 1 Mark
12 Pence = 1 Shilling
100 Centimes = 1 Franc

> Catalogue values for unused stamps in this country are for Never Hinged items, beginning with Scott 296 in the regular postage section, Scott B29 in the semipostal section, Scott C8 in the airpost section, Scott J24 in the postage due section, and Scott M1 in the military stamp section.

Watermark

Wmk. 125 —
Lozenges

C ЯOT
CARTO
ЯOT
CARTO   Wmk. 385

Issued under German Dominion

Stamps of Germany
Overprinted in Black

1897   Unwmk.   Perf. 13½x14½
1 A9   3pf yel brn   11.00 17.00
a.   3pf red brown   62.50 240.00
b.   3pf dark brown   18.00 42.50
c.   3pf olive brown   10.00 42.50
2 A9   5pf green   6.00 8.50
3 A10 10pf carmine   4.25 5.00
4 A10 20pf ultra   4.00 8.00
a.   Diagonal half used as 10pf on cover   18,750.
5 A10 25pf orange   20.00 42.50
6 A10 50pf red brn   16.00 29.00
     Nos. 1-6 (6)   61.25 110.00

A3

Kaiser's Yacht "Hohenzollern" — A4

1900   Unwmk.   Typo.   Perf. 14
7 A3 3pf brown   1.40 1.75
8 A3 5pf green   13.50 1.40
9 A3 10pf carmine   40.00 1.50
10 A3 20pf ultra   25.00 2.40
a.   Vertical half used as 10pf on cover (Longji, '11)   7,500.
11 A3 25pf org & blk, yel   1.50 5.50
12 A3 30pf org & blk, sal   2.00 4.75
13 A3 40pf lake & blk   2.00 4.25
14 A3 50pf pur & blk, sal   2.00 6.25
15 A3 80pf lake & blk, rose   2.75 11.00
Engr.   Perf. 14½x14
16 A4 1m carmine   67.50 77.50
17 A4 2m blue   5.50 77.50
18 A4 3m blk vio   5.50 125.00
19 A4 5m slate & car   160.00 575.00
     Nos. 7-19 (13)   328.65 893.80

1905-18   Wmk. 125   Typo.
20 A3 3pf brown ('18)   .85
21 A3 5pf green   .85 1.75
a.   Bklt. pane of 6   15.00
b.   Bklt. pane of 6, 2 #21 + 4 #22   62.50
c.   Booklet pane of 5 + label   375.00
22 A3 10pf carmine ('06)   2.40 1.75
a.   Bklt pane of 6   17.50
b.   Booklet pane of 5 + label   500.00
23 A3 20pf ultra ('14)   3.25 125.00
24 A4 1m carmine ('15)   11.00
25 A4 5m slate & car ('13)   50.00 4,250.
     Nos. 20-25 (6)   68.35
     Nos. 20-25 (6)   66.95

The 3pf and 1m were not placed in use. Nos. 21a, 22a were made from sheet stamps.

Issued under British Occupation
Stamps of German Cameroun
Surcharged

#53

#62

Wmk. Lozenges (125) (#54-56, 65);
Unwmk. (Other Values)
1915   Perf. 14, 14½
Blue Surcharge
53 A3 ½p on 3pf brn   15.00 45.00
54 A3 ½p on 5pf grn   4.00 16.50
a.   Double surcharge   1,000.
b.   Black surcharge   —
55 A3 1p on 10pf car   2.50 12.00
a.   "1" with thin serifs   15.00 75.00
b.   Double surcharge   375.00
c.   Black surcharge   20.00 82.50
d.   As "c," "1" with thin serifs   275.00
Black Surcharge
56 A3 2p on 20pf ultra   5.00 26.00
57 A3 2½p on 25pf org & blk, yel   18.00 65.00
a.   Double surcharge   12,000.
58 A3 3p on 30pf org & blk, sal   18.00 65.00
59 A3 4p on 40pf lake & blk   18.00 65.00
60 A3 6p on 50pf pur & blk, sal   18.00 65.00
61 A3 8p on 80pf lake & blk, rose   18.00 65.00
62 A4 1sh on 1m car   200.00 900.00
a.   "S" inverted   1,000. 3,500.
63 A4 2sh on 2m bl   200.00 900.00
a.   "S" inverted   1,000. 3,500.
64 A4 3sh on 3m blk vio   200.00 900.00
a.   "S" inverted   1,000. 3,500.
b.   Double surcharge   12,000.
65 A4 5sh on 5m sl & car   275.00 925.00
a.   "S" inverted   1,200. 3,750.
     Nos. 53-65 (13)   991.50 4,049.

The letters "C. E. F." are the initials of "Cameroons Expeditionary Force."

Numerous overprint varieties exist for #53-65.
Counterfeits exist of Nos. 54a, 54b.

See Cameroons for Nos. 66-77.

Issued under French Occupation
Gabon Nos. 37, 49-52, 54, 57-58, 60, 62-64, 66, 69-70 Overprinted

1915   Unwmk.   Perf. 13½x14
Inscribed "Congo Français"
101	A10	10c red & car	32.50	24.00

Inscribed "Afrique Equatoriale"
102	A10	1c choc & org	110.00	47.50
103	A10	2c blk & choc	200.00	150.00
104	A10	4c vio & dp bl	200.00	150.00
105	A10	5c ol gray & grn	40.00	24.00
105A	A10	10c red & car	22,500.	25,000.
106	A10	20c ol brn & dk vio	210.00	210.00
107	A11	25c dp bl & choc	60.00	47.50
108	A11	30c gray blk & red	200.00	200.00
109	A11	35c dk vio & grn	67.50	45.00
a.		Double overprint	1,900.	
110	A11	40c choc & ultra	200.00	200.00
111	A11	45c car & vio	225.00	225.00
112	A11	50c bl grn & gray	225.00	225.00
113	A11	75c grn & choc	275.00	225.00
114	A12	1fr dk brn & bis	260.00	225.00
115	A12	2fr car & brn	300.00	260.00
Nos. 101-105,106-115 (15)			2,605.	2,258.

The overprint is vertical, reading up, on #101-106, 114-115, and horizontal on #107-113.

Stamps of Middle Congo, Issue of 1907, Overprinted

1916   Unwmk.
116	A1	1c ol gray & brn	110.00	110.00
117	A1	2c violet & brn	110.00	110.00
118	A1	4c blue & brown	120.00	120.00
119	A1	5c dk green & blue	32.50	32.50
120	A2	35c violet brn & bl	110.00	75.00
121	A2	45c violet & red	87.50	75.00

The overprint is vert., reading down, on #120-121.

Same Overprint On Stamps of French Congo, 1900
Wmk. Branch of Thistle (122)
122	A4	15c dull vio & ol grn	120.00	120.00
a.		Inverted overprint	200.00	180.00

Wmk. Branch of Rose Tree (123)
123	A5	20c yellow grn & org	140.00	92.50
124	A5	30c car rose & org	110.00	87.50
125	A5	40c org brn & brt grn	105.00	80.00
126	A5	50c gray vio & lil	110.00	87.50
127	A5	75c red vio & org	110.00	85.00

Wmk. Branch of Olive (124)
128	A6	1fr gray lilac & ol	125.00	120.00
129	A6	2fr carmine & brn	160.00	120.00
Nos. 116-129 (14)			1,550.	1,315.

The overprint is horiz. on No. 122. The overprint is vert., reading down or up, on Nos. 123-129. Values are for the cheaper variety. See the Scott Classic Specialized Catalogue of Stamps & Covers for detailed listings.

Values are for stamps centered in the grade of fine.
Counterfeits exist of Nos. 101-129.

Stamps of Middle Congo, Issue of 1907 Overprinted

1916-17   Unwmk.
130	A1	1c ol gray & brn	.40	.40
131	A1	2c violet & brn	.50	.50
132	A1	4c blue & brn	.85	.55
133	A1	5c dk green & bl	.50	.40
134	A1	10c carmine & bl	1.25	.80
135	A1	15c brn vio & rose ('17)	2.25	.80
136	A1	20c brown & bl	.90	.80
137	A2	25c blue & grn	.90	.80
a.		Triple overprint	550.00	700.00
138	A2	30c scarlet & grn	1.25	.80
a.		Double overprint	400.00	575.00
139	A2	35c vio brn & bl	.90	.80
140	A2	40c dull grn & brn	2.75	1.60
141	A2	45c violet & red	2.75	1.60
142	A2	50c blue grn & red	2.75	1.60
143	A2	75c brown & blue	2.75	1.60
144	A3	1fr dp grn & vio	2.00	1.60
145	A3	2fr vio & gray grn	8.25	6.75
146	A3	5fr blue & rose	13.50	11.00
Nos. 130-146 (17)			44.45	32.40

Nos. 130-146 exist on ordinary paper and, with the exception of No. 135, on chalk surfaced paper. Nos. 137-146 are known with inverted 'S' in 'Francaise' and without period after 'Francaise.' See the Scott Classic Specialized Catalogue of Stamps & Covers for detailed listings.
On Nos. 137-146 there is 7mm between "Cameroun" and "Occupation."

Provisional French Mandate

Types of Middle Congo, 1907, Overprinted

1921
147	A1	1c ol grn & org	.35	.30
148	A1	2c brown & rose	.35	.30
149	A1	4c gray & lt grn	.55	.55
150	A1	5c dl red & org	.55	.55
a.		Double overprint	1,200.	
151	A1	10c bl grn & lt grn	1.25	.90
152	A1	15c blue & org	.55	.55
153	A1	20c red brn & ol	.85	.80
154	A2	25c slate & org	1.20	.80
155	A2	30c rose & ver	1.25	.80
156	A2	35c gray & ultra	.85	.80
157	A2	40c ol grn & org	1.25	.80
158	A2	45c brown & rose	.85	.80
159	A2	50c blue & ultra	1.25	.80
160	A2	75c red brn & lt grn	1.25	.80
161	A3	1fr slate & org	2.40	2.40
162	A3	2fr ol grn & rose	6.50	5.50
163	A3	5fr dull red & gray	9.50	8.00
Nos. 147-163 (17)			30.75	25.45

The 1c, 2c, 4c, 15c, 20c, 25c and 50c exist with overprint omitted. For listings, see the Scott Specialized Catalogue of Stamps & Covers.

Nos. 152, 162, 163, 158, 160 Surcharged with New Value and Bars

1924-25
164	A1	25c on 15c bl & org ('25)	1.25	1.25
165	A3	25c on 2fr ol grn & rose	1.75	1.75
166	A3	25c on 5fr red & gray	1.75	1.75
a.		Pair, one without new value and bars		
167	A2	65c on 45c brn & rose ('25)	2.00	2.00
168	A2	85c on 75c red brn & lt grn ('25)	3.00	3.00
Nos. 164-168 (5)			9.75	9.75

French Mandate

Herder and Cattle Crossing Sanaga River — A5

Tapping Rubber Tree — A6

Rope Suspension Bridge A7

1925-38   Typo.   Perf. 14x13½
170	A5	1c ol grn & brn vio, lav	.25	.25
171	A5	2c rose & grn, grnsh	.25	.25
172	A5	4c blue & blk	.25	.25
173	A5	5c org & red vio, lav	.25	.25
174	A5	10c red brn & org, yel	.45	.40
175	A5	15c sl grn & grn	.45	.40
176	A5	15c lilac & red ('27)	1.00	.80

Perf. 13½x14
177	A6	20c ol brn & red brn	.70	.40
178	A6	20c green ('26)	.65	.50
179	A6	20c brn red & ol brn ('27)	.65	.65
180	A6	25c lt green & blk	.95	.50
181	A6	30c bluish grn & ver	.50	.30
182	A6	30c dk grn & grn ('27)	.90	.70
183	A6	35c brown & black	1.10	.50
184	A6	35c dl grn & grn ('38)	1.90	1.20
185	A6	40c orange & vio	2.00	1.20
186	A6	45c dp rose & cer	.80	.50
187	A6	45c vio & org brn ('27)	2.25	1.60
188	A6	50c lt green & cer	.80	.30
189	A6	55c ultra & car ('38)	1.60	1.60
190	A6	60c red vio & blk	.80	.55
191	A6	60c brown red ('26)	.95	.55
192	A6	65c indigo & brn	1.20	1.20
193	A6	75c indigo & dp bl	.80	.80
194	A6	75c org brn & red vio ('27)	1.40	1.10
195	A6	80c carmine & brn ('38)	1.40	1.20
196	A6	85c dp rose & bl	1.60	1.20
197	A6	90c brn red & cer ('27)	2.75	1.20

Perf. 14x13½
198	A7	1fr indigo & brn	1.20	1.20
199	A7	1fr dull bl ('26)	.80	.55
200	A7	1fr ol brn & red vio ('27)	1.10	.80
201	A7	1fr grn & dk brn ('29)	2.50	1.20
202	A7	1.10fr rose red & dk brn ('28)	4.75	6.50
203	A7	1.25fr gray & dp bl ('33)	5.50	3.50
204	A7	1.50fr dull bl ('27)	1.20	.80
205	A7	1.75fr brn & org ('33)	1.60	1.20
206	A7	1.75fr dk bl & lt bl ('38)	2.50	1.60
207	A7	2fr dl grn & brn org	2.00	1.20
208	A7	3fr ol brn & red vio ('27)	7.25	2.75
209	A7	5fr brn & blk, bluish	3.50	2.00
a.		Cliché of 2fr in plate of 5fr	1,450.	
b.		As "a," in pair with #209	1,700.	
210	A7	10fr org & vio ('27)	14.50	7.25
211	A7	20fr rose & ol grn ('27)	21.00	15.00
Nos. 170-211 (42)			98.00	65.90

Shades exist for several values.
For overprints and surcharge see Nos. 212, 264, 276, 278, 279, B7-B9, B21.

No. 199 Surcharged with New Value and Bars in Red

1926
212	A7	1.25fr on 1fr dull blue	1.20	.80

Common Design Types pictured following the introduction.

Colonial Exposition Issue
Common Design Types
Name of Country in Black

1931   Engr.   Perf. 12½
213	CD70	40c deep green	5.50	4.00
214	CD71	50c violet	5.50	4.75
215	CD72	90c red orange	5.50	4.75
216	CD73	1.50fr dull blue	6.50	4.75
Nos. 213-216 (4)			23.00	18.25

Paris International Exposition Issue
Common Design Types

1937   Perf. 13
217	CD74	20c deep violet	1.75	1.75
218	CD75	30c dark green	1.75	1.75
219	CD76	40c carmine rose	1.75	1.75
220	CD77	50c dark brown	1.90	1.90
221	CD78	90c red	1.90	1.90
222	CD79	1.50fr ultramarine	1.90	1.90
Nos. 217-222 (6)			10.95	10.95

French Colonial Art Exhibition
Common Design Type
Souvenir Sheet

1937   Imperf.
222A	CD77	3fr org red & blk	8.00	9.50

New York World's Fair Issue
Common Design Type

1939   Perf. 12½x12
223	CD82	1.25fr carmine lake	1.40	1.20
224	CD82	2.25fr ultra	1.40	1.20

For overprints and surcharges see Nos. 280-281, B14-B17, B23, B25.

Mandara Woman — A19

Falls on M'bam River near Banyo — A20

Elephants A21

Man in Yaré — A22

1939-40   Engr.   Perf. 13
225	A19	2c black brn	.25	.25
226	A19	3c magenta ('40)	.25	.25
227	A19	4c deep violet	.25	.25
228	A19	5c red brown	.25	.25
229	A19	10c dp bl grn	.25	.25
230	A19	15c rose red	.30	.30
231	A19	20c plum	.30	.30
232	A20	25c black brn	.65	.65
233	A20	30c dk red	.80	.70
234	A20	40c ultra ('40)	.80	.80
235	A20	45c slate green ('40)	2.60	2.25
236	A20	50c brown car	.90	.70
237	A20	60c pck blue ('40)	.75	.50
238	A20	70c plum ('40)	3.25	2.90
239	A21	80c Prus blue	2.60	2.25
240	A21	90c Prus blue	.95	.75
241	A21	1fr car rose	1.90	.95
242	A21	1fr choc ('40)	1.40	.80
243	A21	1.25fr car rose	4.00	3.25
244	A21	1.40fr org red ('40)	1.25	.95
245	A21	1.50fr chocolate	1.20	.95
246	A21	1.60fr black brn ('40)	2.50	2.25
247	A21	1.75fr dk blue	1.40	.95
248	A21	2fr dk green	.90	.90
249	A21	2.25fr dk blue	1.40	.95
250	A21	2.50fr brt red vio ('40)	1.20	1.00
251	A21	3fr dk violet	1.40	.80
252	A22	5fr black brn	1.40	.95
253	A22	10fr brt red vio	2.00	1.60
254	A22	20fr dk green	4.00	3.25
Nos. 225-254 (30)			41.10	32.85

For overprints and surcharges see Nos. 255-263, 265-275, 277, 278A, 279A, B10-B13, B22, B24.

Stamps of 1925-40 Overprinted in Black or Orange "CAMEROUN FRANCAIS 27.8.40."

1940		Perf. 14x13½, 13½x14, 13	
255	A19	2c blk brn (O)	1.60	1.60
256	A19	3c magenta	2.40	2.40
257	A19	4c dp ultra (O)	1.60	1.60
258	A19	5c red brn	5.50	5.50
259	A19	10c dp bl grn (O)	1.60	1.60
260	A19	15c rose red	2.40	2.40
260A	A19	20c plum (O)	13.50	13.50
261	A20	25c blk brn	1.60	1.60
b.		Inverted overprint	260.00	260.00
261A	A20	30c dk red	14.50	14.50
262	A20	40c ultra	5.50	5.50
263	A20	45c slate green	4.00	4.00
264	A6	50c lt grn & cer	2.40	1.60
a.		Inverted overprint	225.00	
265	A20	60c pck bl	6.50	6.50
266	A20	70c plum	3.25	3.25
267	A21	80c Prus bl (O)	5.50	5.50
268	A21	90c Prus bl (O)	1.60	1.60
269	A21	1.25fr car rose	1.60	1.60
270	A21	1.40fr org red	4.75	4.75
271	A21	1.50fr chocolate	1.60	1.60
272	A21	1.60fr blk brn (O)	3.25	3.25
273	A21	1.75fr dk bl (O)	2.40	2.40
274	A21	2.25fr dk bl (O)	1.60	1.60
275	A21	2.50fr brt red vio	1.60	1.60
276	A7	5fr brn & blk, bluish	16.00	14.00
277	A22	5fr black brn	24.00	16.00
278	A7	10fr org & vio	27.50	26.00
278A	A22	10fr brt red vio	65.00	45.00
279	A7	20fr rose & ol grn	52.50	47.50
279A	A22	20fr dk green	190.00	190.00

Same Overprint on Stamps of 1939
Perf. 12½x12

280	CD82	1.25fr car lake	8.75	8.75
281	CD82	2.25fr ultra	8.75	8.75
		Nos. 255-281 (31)	482.75	445.45

Issued to note Cameroun's affiliation with General de Gaulle's "Free France" movement. Numerous overprint varieties exist.

Cattle Fording Sanaga River and Marshal Petain A22a

1941		Engr.	Perf. 12½x12
281A	A22a	1fr green	.80
281B	A22a	2.50fr dark blue	.80

Nos. 281A-281B were issued by the Vichy government in France, but were not placed on sale in Cameroun.
For surcharges, see Nos. B25A-B25B.

Lorraine Cross and Joan of Arc Shield — A23

1941		Photo.	Perf. 14x14½
282	A23	5c brown	.25	.25
283	A23	10c dk blue	.25	.25
284	A23	25c emerald	.25	.25
285	A23	30c dp orange	.25	.25
286	A23	40c dk slate green	.25	.25
287	A23	80c red brown	.50	.25
288	A23	1fr dp red lilac	.50	.50
289	A23	1.50fr brt red	.50	.50
290	A23	2fr gray black	.75	.50
291	A23	2.50fr brt ultra	.80	.50
292	A23	4fr dull violet	.90	.75
293	A23	5fr bister	.95	.90
294	A23	10fr dp brown	.95	.90
295	A23	20fr dp green	1.90	1.40
		Nos. 282-295 (14)	9.00	7.45

For surcharges see Nos. 297A-303.

Catalogue values for unused stamps in this section, from this point to the end of the section, are for Never Hinged items.

Eboue Issue
Common Design Type

1945		Unwmk.	Engr.	Perf. 13
296	CD91	2fr black	.80	.55
297	CD91	25fr Prus green	1.75	1.40

Nos. 282, 284, 291 Surcharged with New Values and Bars in Red, Carmine or Black

1946		Perf. 14x14½
297A	A23	50c on 5c (R)	.75	.50
298	A23	60c on 5c (C)	.75	.55
a.		Inverted surcharge	200.00	
299	A23	70c on 5c (R)	1.00	.75
300	A23	1.20fr on 5c (C)	1.00	.75
301	A23	2.40fr on 25c	.95	.75
302	A23	3fr on 25c	1.40	1.00
302A	A23	4.50fr on 25c	1.90	1.40
303	A23	15fr on 2.50fr (C)	2.00	1.50
		Nos. 297A-303 (8)	9.75	7.20

Zebu and Herder A25

Tikar Women — A26

Porters Carrying Bananas — A27

Bowman A28

Lamido Horsemen A29

Farmer — A30

1946		Engr.	Perf. 12½x12, 12x12½
304	A25	10c blue grn	.50	.30
305	A25	30c brown org	.50	.30
306	A25	40c brt ultra	.50	.30
307	A26	50c olive brn	.50	.30
308	A26	60c dp plum	.65	.30
309	A26	80c chnt brn	.80	.50
310	A27	1fr org red	.50	.25
311	A27	1.20fr dp green	.90	.50
312	A27	1.50fr dk car	2.25	1.75
313	A28	2fr black	.50	.25
314	A28	3fr dk carmine	.65	.30
314A	A28	3.60fr red brn	1.60	1.10
315	A28	4fr dp blue	.90	.40
316	A29	5fr brown car	1.00	.65
317	A29	6fr ultra	1.00	.55
318	A29	10fr slate green	1.75	.50
319	A30	15fr grnsh blue	2.40	.90
320	A30	20fr dk green	3.25	.90
321	A30	25fr black	3.25	1.40
		Nos. 304-321 (19)	23.40	11.45

Shades exist for most values.
For surcharges see Nos. 343-344, 346.

Imperforates
Most Cameroun stamps from 1952 onward exist imperforate in issued and trial colors, and also in small presentation sheets in issued colors.

Military Medal Issue
Common Design Type
Engraved and Typographed

1952		Unwmk.	Perf. 13
322	CD101	15fr multicolored	7.25	3.25

Porters Carrying Bananas — A32

Picking Coffee Beans — A33

1954			Engr.
323	A32	8fr red vio, org brn & vio bl	1.20	.80
324	A32	15fr brn red, yel & blk brn	1.60	.80
325	A33	40fr blk brn, org brn & lil rose	2.00	.80
		Nos. 323-325 (3)	4.80	2.40

FIDES Issue
Common Design Type

Designs: 5fr, Plowmen. 15fr, Wouri bridge. 20fr, Technical instruction. 25fr, Mobile medical station.

1956		Unwmk.	Perf. 13
326	CD103	5fr org brn & dk brn	1.20	.50
327	CD103	15fr aqua, slate & blk	1.60	.80
328	CD103	20fr grnsh bl & dp ultra	1.60	.80
329	CD103	25fr dp ultra	2.50	1.10
		Nos. 326-329 (4)	6.90	3.20

For surcharges see Nos. 345, 347.

Coffee Issue

Coffee A35

1956		Engr.	Perf. 13
330	A35	15fr car & brt red	1.60	.80

For surcharge see No. 348.

Autonomous Government

Flag and Woman Holding Child A36

1958			
331	A36	20fr multicolored	1.60	.80

Anniv. of the installation of the 1st autonomous government of Cameroun.

Men Looking to the Sun — A37

1958			
332	A37	20fr sepia & brn red	1.60	.80

10th anniv. of the signing of the Universal Declaration of Human Rights.

Flower Issue
Common Design Type

Design: 20fr, Randia malleifera.

1959		Photo.	Perf. 12½x12
333	CD104	20fr dp grn, yel & rose	1.60	.80

Loading Bananas A38

Harvesting Bananas — A39

1959		Engr.	Perf. 13
334	A38	20fr dk grn & org	1.20	.40
335	A39	25fr maroon & slate grn	1.60	.80

For surcharge see No. 349.

Independent State

Map and Flag of Cameroun — A40

Prime Minister Ahmadou Ahidjo — A41

1960		Unwmk.	Engr.	Perf. 13
336	A40	20fr multicolored	.80	.20
337	A41	25fr blk, grn & pale lem	.85	.20

Declaration of independence, Jan. 1, 1960.
For surcharge see No. 350.

Uprooted Oak Emblem A42

1960			
338	A42	30fr red brn, ultra & yel grn	1.10	.40

World Refugee Year, 7/1/59-6/30/60.
For surcharge see No. 351.

C.C.T.A. Issue
Common Design Type

1960			
339	CD106	50fr dull claret & slate	1.60	.40

UN Headquarters, NYC, and Flag — A43

1961, May 20			Perf. 13
Flag in Green, Red and Yellow			
340	A43	15fr grn, dk bl & brn	.60	.25
341	A43	25fr dk blue & grn	.75	.25
342	A43	85fr red, dk bl & vio brn	2.40	.80
		Nos. 340-342 (3)	3.75	1.30

Cameroun's admission to the UN, Sept. 20, 1960.

Federal Republic

Stamps of 1946-60
Surcharged in Red
or Black:

Two types of 2sh6p:
I — Large figures. "2/6" measures 8x3¾mm.
II — Small figures. "2/6" measures 6x2½mm.

Perf. 12x12½, 13

			Engr.
1961, Oct. 1			
343	A27	½p on 1fr (#310)	.35 .20
344	A28	1p on 2fr (#313)	.45 .30
345	CD103	1½p on 5fr (#326)	.55 .35
346	A29	2p on 10fr (#318)	1.00 .45
347	CD103	3p on 15fr (#327)	1.40 .60
348	A35	4p on 15fr (Bk) (#330)	1.10 .70
349	A38	6p on 20fr (#334)	2.40 1.00
350	A41	1sh on 25fr (#337)	2.75 1.50
351	A42	2sh6p on 30fr (#338) (I)	5.00 5.00
a.		Type II	21.00 21.00
		Nos. 343-351 (9)	15.00 10.10

Issued for use in the former United Kingdom Trust Territory of Southern Cameroons.
The "Republique Federale" overprint is in one line on Nos. 345, 347-349, in two vertical lines on No. 350. See Nos. C38-C40.

President Ahidjo and Prime Minister Foncha A45

Unwmk.

			Engr.	Perf. 13
1962, Jan. 1				
352	A45	20fr vio & choc	8.00	7.00
353	A45	25fr dk grn & brn	14.00	11.00
354	A45	60fr car & dl grn	40.00	32.50
		Nos. 352-354 (3)	62.00	50.50

Same Surcharged for Use in Southern Cameroons

355	A45	3p on 20fr	175.00 160.00
356	A45	6p on 25fr	175.00 160.00
357	A45	2sh6p on 60fr	175.00 160.00
		Nos. 355-357 (3)	525.00 480.00

Reunification of the former French and British Sections of Cameroun. It is reported that Nos. 352-357 were withdrawn after a few days and destroyed.

Mustache Monkey A46

Designs: 1fr, 4fr, Elephant, Ntem Falls. 1.50fr, 3fr, Buffon's kob, Dschang. 2fr, 5fr, Hippopotamus. 6fr, 15fr, Mustache monkey. 8fr, 30fr, Manatee, Lake Ossa. 10fr, 25fr, Buffalo, Batouri. 20fr, 40fr, Giraffes, Waza Reservation, vert.

			Engr.	Perf. 12
1962	**Unwmk.**			
358	A46	50c brn, brt grn & bl	.20	.20
359	A46	1fr gray brn, bl grn & org	.20	.20
360	A46	1.50fr brn, lt grn & sl grn	.20	.20

361	A46	2fr dk gray, grnsh bl & grn	.20	.20
362	A46	3fr brn, org & lil rose	.20	.20
363	A46	4fr brn, yel grn & bl grn	.25	.20
364	A46	5fr gray brn, grn & sal	.25	.20
365	A46	6fr brn, yel & bl	.45	.20
366	A46	8fr dk bl, red & grn	.90	.50
367	A46	10fr ol blk, org & brt bl	.75	.20
368	A46	15fr brn, Prus bl & bl	1.00	.40
369	A46	20fr brn & gray	1.25	.40
370	A46	25fr red brn, grn & yel	3.25	1.00
371	A46	30fr blk, org & bl	4.50	1.10
372	A46	40fr dp cl, yel grn & blk	7.50	1.50
		Nos. 358-372 (15)	21.10	6.70

See Nos. 396-397.

African and Malagasy Union Issue
Common Design Type

			Perf. 12½x12
1962, Sept. 8	**Photo.**		
373	CD110	30fr multicolored	2.00 .45

Village and Map of Cameroun A48

Designs: 20fr, 25fr, Sun rising over city. 50fr, Hands holding scroll.

			Engr.	Perf. 13
1962, Oct. 1				
374	A48	9fr pur, olive & dk brn	.40	.20
375	A48	18fr grn, org brn & dk bl	.50	.20
376	A48	20fr lil rose, ol bis & ind	.50	.20
377	A48	25fr bl, red org & sep	.60	.20
378	A48	50fr dk red, sepia & bl	1.75	.50
		Nos. 374-378 (5)	3.75	1.30

1st anniv. of the reunification of Cameroun.

"School under the Trees" — A49

			Photo.	Perf. 12x12½
1962, Nov. 5				
379	A49	20fr ver, emerald & yel	1.00	.90

Literacy and popular education campaign.

Telstar and Globe A50

			Engr.	Perf. 13
1963, Feb. 9				
		Size: 36x22mm		
380	A50	1fr dk bl, olive & pur	.20	.20
381	A50	2fr dk bl, claret & grn	.20	.20
382	A50	3fr dk grn, ol & dp cl	.25	.20
383	A50	25fr grn, dp cl & brt bl	1.10	.40
		Nos. 380-383,C45 (5)	4.25	1.65

1st TV connection of the US and Europe through the Telstar satellite, July 11-12, 1962.

High Frequency Transmission Station, Mt. Bankolo — A51

Design: 20fr, Station and wiring plan.

			Photo.	Perf. 12x12½
1963, May 18				
384	A51	15fr multicolored	.45	.20
385	A51	20fr multicolored	.60	.20
		Nos. 384-385,C46 (3)	3.55	1.05

Issued to publicize the high frequency telegraph connection Douala-Yaounde.

"Yaoundé-Regional Center of Textbook Production" — A52

			Unwmk.	Perf. 12½
1963, Aug. 10				
386	A52	20fr emer, blk & red	.45	.20
387	A52	25fr org, blk & red	.55	.20
388	A52	100fr gold, blk & red	2.10	.60
		Nos. 386-388 (3)	3.10	1.00

UNESCO regional center for the production of school books at Yaounde.

Pres. Ahmadou Ahidjo and Flag — A53

Design: 18fr, Flag and map of Cameroun.

			Perf. 12x12½
1963, Oct. 1			
Flag in Green, Red and Yellow			
389	A53	9fr grn, bl & dk brn	.45 .20
390	A53	18fr grn, bl & lil	.65 .20
391	A53	20fr grn, blk & yel grn	.70 .20
		Nos. 389-391 (3)	1.80 .60

Second anniversary of reunification.

Scales, Globe, UNESCO Emblem A54

			Photo.	Perf. 12½x12
1963, Dec. 10				
392	A54	9fr ultra, blk & sal	.35	.20
393	A54	18fr brt yel grn, blk & rose red	.45	.20
394	A54	25fr rose red, blk & brt yel grn	.60	.20
395	A54	75fr yel, blk & ultra	1.75	.50
		Nos. 392-395 (4)	3.15	1.10

Universal Declaration of Human Rights, 15th anniv.

Animal Type of 1962

Design: 10fr, 25fr, Lion, Waza National Park, North Cameroun.

			Engr.	Perf. 13
1964, June 20				
396	A46	10fr red brn, bis & grn	1.25	.40
397	A46	25fr green & bister	3.00	1.25

Soccer Game in Stadium A55

18fr, Pile of sports equipment. 30fr, Stadium (outside), flags and map of Africa.

			Engr.	Perf. 13
1964, July 11				
398	A55	10fr grn, bl & red brn	.55	.20
399	A55	18fr car, grn & vio	.65	.20
400	A55	30fr blk, dk bl & org brn	1.10	.20
		Nos. 398-400 (3)	2.30	.60

Tropics Cup Games, Yaounde, July 11-19.

Europafrica Issue, 1964
Common Design Type and

Palace of Justice, Yaounde — A56

40fr, Emblems of Science, Agriculture, Industry and Education and two sunbursts.

			Photo.	Perf. 12x13
1964, July 20				
401	A56	15fr multicolored	1.25	.25
402	CD116	40fr multicolored	2.25	.60

1st anniv. of the economic agreement between the European Economic Community and the African and Malgache Union.

Hurdling and Olympic Flame — A57

Design: 10fr, Runners, vert.

			Engr.	Perf. 13
1964, Oct. 10				
403	A57	9fr red, yel grn & blk	1.50	.40
404	A57	10fr red, vio & ol gray	2.25	.40
		Nos. 403-404,C49 (3)	11.25	2.80

18th Olympic Games, Tokyo, Oct. 10-25.

Bamileke Dance Dress — A58   Ntem Falls, Ebolowa Region — A59

Designs: 18fr, Dance mask, Bamenda region. 25fr, Fulani horseman, North Cameroun, horiz.

				Perf. 13
1964	**Unwmk.**			
405	A58	9fr red, yel grn & bl	.55	.20
406	A58	18fr bl, red & brn	.70	.20
407	A59	20fr dk car, grn & ol	.90	.20
408	A58	25fr dk brn, org & car	1.40	.20
		Nos. 405-408,C50 (5)	4.55	1.15

Cooperation Issue
Common Design Type

			Engr.
1964, Nov. 7			
409	CD119	18fr dk bl, yel grn & dk brn	1.00 .20
410	CD119	30fr red brn, bl grn & dk brn	2.00 .20

Memorial Stone — A60

Diesel Train
A61

1965, Jan. 1   Engr.   Perf. 13
411 A60 12fr bl, indigo & grn   1.00   .20

Typo.   Perf. 14x13
412 A61 20fr rose car, yel & grn   2.50   .20

Laying of the 1st rail of the Mbanga-Kumba Railroad, Mar. 28, 1964.

Red Cross Station and Ambulance A62

50fr, Red Cross nurse and infant, vert.

1965, May 8   Engr.   Perf. 13
413 A62 25fr car, slate grn &
             ocher   .65   .20
414 A62 50fr gray, red & red brn 1.50   .30

Issued for the Cameroun Red Cross.

Coins Inserted in Map of Cameroun, and Bankbook — A63

Savings Bank Building — A64

Design: 20fr, Bankbook and coins inserted in cacao pod-shaped bank, vert.

1965, June 10
    Size: 22x37mm
415 A63 9fr grn, red & org   .45   .20
    Size: 48x27mm, 27x48mm
416 A64 15fr choc, ultra & grn   .55   .20
417 A63 20fr ocher, brt grn & brn .65   .20
    Nos. 415-417 (3)   1.65   .60

Federal Postal Savings Banks.

Soccer Players and Africa Cup — A65

Unwmk.
1965, June 26   Engr.   Perf. 13
418 A65 9fr car, brn & yel   .55   .20
419 A65 20fr car, slate bl & yel 1.40   .20

Cameroun Oryx Club, winner of the club champions' Africa Cup, February 1965.

Symbolic Map of Europe and Africa — A66

40fr, Delegates around conference table.

1965, July 20   Photo.   Perf. 12x12½
420 A66 5fr car, blk & lilac   .30   .20
421 A66 40fr brn, buff, grn & ul-
             tra   1.50   .35

2nd, anniv. of the economic agreement between the European Economic Community and the African and Malgache Union.

UPU Monument, Bern A67

1965, July 26   Engr.   Perf. 13
422 A67 30fr black & red   .80   .25

Cameroun's admission to the UPU, 5th anniv.

ICY Emblem — A68

1965, Sept. 11   Unwmk.   Perf. 13
423 A68 10fr dk bl & car rose   .45   .20

Issued for the International Cooperation Year, 1964-65. See No. C57.

Pres. Ahidjo and Government House — A69

Design: 9fr, 20fr, Pres. Ahidjo and Government House, vert.

Perf. 12x12½, 12½x12
1965, Oct. 1   Photo.   Unwmk.
424 A69 9fr multicolored   .25   .20
425 A69 18fr multicolored   .55   .20
426 A69 20fr multicolored   .65   .20
427 A69 25fr multicolored   .80   .20
    Nos. 424-427 (4)   2.25   .80

Reelection of Pres. Ahmadou Ahidjo.

National Tourist Office, Yaoundé A70

Designs: 9fr, Pouss Musgum houses. 18fr, Great Calao's dance (North Cameroon). 20fr, Gate of Sultan's Palace, Foumban, vert.

1965   Engr.   Perf. 13
428 A70 9fr brn, rose red & grn   .45   .20
429 A70 18fr brt bl, brn & grn   .65   .20
430 A70 20fr bl, brn & choc   1.00   .20
431 A70 25fr mar, emer & gray   .90   .20
    Nos. 428-431 (4)   3.00   .80

See No. C58.

Mountain Hotel, Buea — A71

Designs: 20fr, Hotel of the Deputies, Yaoundé. 35fr, Dschang Health Center.

1966
432 A71 9fr sl grn, rose cl &
             brn   .35   .20
433 A71 20fr brt bl, sl grn & blk .45   .20
434 A71 35fr brn, sl grn & car .80   .30
    Nos. 432-434,C63-C69 (10) 15.10 4.75

Bas-relief, Foumban A72

Designs: 18fr, Ekoi mask, vert. 20fr, Mother and child, carving, Bamiléké, vert. 25fr, Ceremonial stool, Bamoun.

1966, Apr. 15   Unwmk.
435 A72 9fr red & blk   .55   .20
436 A72 18fr brt grn, org brn &
             choc   .65   .20
437 A72 20fr brt bl, red brn & pur 1.00   .20
438 A72 25fr pur & dk brn   1.10   .20
    Nos. 435-438 (4)   3.30   .80

Intl. Negro Arts Festival, Dakar, Senegal, 4/1-24.

New WHO Headquarters, Geneva — A73

1966, May 3   Photo.   Perf. 12½x13
439 A73 50fr ultra, red brn & yel 1.40   .35

ITU Headquarters, Geneva — A74

1966, May 3   Photo.   Perf. 12½x13
440 A74 50fr ultra & yellow   1.40   .35

Phaeomeria Magnifica — A75

"6" and Men Dancing around UN Emblem — A76

Flowers: 18fr, Hibiscus (rose of China). 20fr, Mountain rose.

1966, May 20   Perf. 12x12½
    Flowers in Natural Colors
       Size: 22x36mm
441 A75 9fr red brown   .55   .20
442 A75 18fr green   .70   .20
443 A75 20fr dark green   .70   .20
    Nos. 441-443,C70-C72 (6) 7.55 1.25

See No. 469.

1966, Sept. 20   Engr.   Perf. 13
Design: 50fr, UN General Assembly, horiz.
444 A76 50fr ultra, grn & vio brn .90   .20
445 A76 100fr red brn, grn & ul-
             tra   2.00   .50

6th anniv. of Cameroun's admission to the UN.

Prime Minister's Residence, Buea — A77

Designs (Prime Minister's Residences): 18fr, at Yaoundé, front view. 20fr, at Yaoundé, side view. 25fr, at Buea, front view.

1966, Oct. 1   Photo.
446 A77 9fr multicolored   .45   .20
447 A77 18fr multicolored   .65   .20
448 A77 20fr multicolored   .65   .20
449 A77 25fr multicolored   .80   .20
    Nos. 446-449 (4)   2.55   .80

5th anniversary of re-unification.

Learning to Write and UNESCO Emblem A78

#451, Children's heads & UNICEF emblem.

1966, Nov. 24   Engr.   Perf. 13
450 A78 50fr red lil, bl & brn   1.40   .30
451 A78 50fr red lil, blk & brt bl 1.40   .30

20th anniv. of UNESCO, 20th anniv. of UNICEF.

Independence Proclamation — A79

1967, Jan. 1   Engr.   Perf. 13
452 A79 20fr grn, red & yel   2.25   .60

7th anniversary of independence.

Map of Africa and Madagascar, Railroad Tracks and Symbols — A80

25fr, Map of Africa and Madagascar and train.

1967, Feb. 21   Photo.   Perf. 13
453 A80 20fr multicolored   4.00   .20
454 A80 25fr multicolored   6.00   .20

5th Conf. of African and Madagascan Railroad Technicians.

Lions Emblem and Forest — A81

Design: 100fr, Lions emblem and palms.

1967, Mar. 3
455 A81 50fr multicolored .90 .35
456 A81 100fr multicolored 2.10 .65

Lions International, 50th anniversary.

Jet and I.C.A.O. Emblem — A82

Dove and I.A.E.A. Emblem A83

Perf. 13x12½, 12½x13
457 A82 50fr ultra, lt bl, brn & gold 1.40 .35   **Photo.**
458 A83 50fr ultra & emer 1.40 .35

UN agencies: No. 457, the ICAO; No. 458, the Intl. Atomic Energy Agency.

Rotary International Emblem — A84

1967, Apr. 17   Photo.   *Perf. 12½*
459 A84 25fr crim, vio bl & gold 1.25 .20

10th anniversary of the Douala, Cameroun, branch of Rotary International.

Grapefruit — A85   Bird of Paradise Flower — A86

1967, May 10   Photo.   *Perf. 12x12½*
460 A85 1fr shown .20 .20
461 A85 2fr Papaya .20 .20
462 A85 3fr Custard apple .20 .20
463 A85 4fr Breadfruit .20 .20
464 A85 5fr Coconut .35 .20
465 A85 6fr Mango .45 .20
466 A85 8fr Avacado .90 .20
467 A85 10fr Pineapple 1.40 .20
468 A85 30fr Bananas 3.50 .20
Nos. 460-468 (9) 7.40 1.80

For surcharges see Nos. 550, 593.

1967, June 22   Photo.   *Perf. 12x12½*
Size: 22x36mm
469 A86 15fr lt blue & multi .90 .20

Sanaga Falls and ITY Emblem — A87

1967, Aug. 14   Photo.   *Perf. 13x12½*
470 A87 30fr multicolored .85 .25

Issued for International Tourist Year 1967.

Art of Cameroun: Coconut Harvest A88

Carved Bas-relief: 20fr, Lion hunt. 30fr, Women carrying baskets. 100fr, Carved chest.

1967, Sept. 22   *Perf. 12½x13*
471 A88 10fr brn, bl & car .35 .20
472 A88 20fr brn, yel & grn .55 .20
473 A88 30fr emer, brn & car .90 .20
474 A88 100fr red org, brn & emer 2.25 .40
Nos. 471-474 (4) 4.05 1.00

Coat of Arms A89

1968, Jan. 1   Litho.   *Perf. 12½x13*
475 A89 30fr gold & multi 1.00 .20

Spiny Lobster A90

Designs (Fish and Crustaceans): 10fr, River crayfish. 15fr, Nile mouth-breeder. 20fr, Sole. 25fr, Common pike. 30fr, Crab. 40fr, Spadefish, vert. 50fr, Shrimp, vert. 55fr, African snakehead. 60fr, Threadfin.

1968, July 25   Engr.   *Perf. 13*
476 A90 5fr brn, vio bl & dl grn .20 .20
477 A90 10fr ultra, brn ol & slate .20 .20
478 A90 15fr sal, red lil & sepia .70 .20
479 A90 20fr red brn, dp bl & sep .80 .20
480 A90 25fr lt brn, emer & slate .90 .20
481 A90 30fr mag, dk bl & dk brn 1.25 .20
482 A90 40fr slate bl & org 1.75 .20
483 A90 50fr emer, gray & rose car 2.50 .20
484 A90 55fr lt brn, Prus bl & dk brn 3.50 .25
485 A90 60fr brn, bl grn & indigo 5.50 .35
Nos. 476-485 (10) 17.30 2.20

Tanker, Refinery and Map of Area Served — A91

1968, July 30   Photo.   *Perf. 12½*
486 A91 30fr multicolored 1.10 .20

Port Gentil (Gabon) Refinery opening, 6/12/68.

Human Rights Flame A92

1968, Sept. 14   Photo.   *Perf. 12½x13*
487 A92 15fr blue & salmon .65 .20

Intl. Human Rights Year. See No. C110.

Pres. Ahmadou Ahidjo A93

1969, Apr. 10   Photo.   *Perf. 12½x12*
488 A93 30fr carmine & multi .80 .20

Chocolate Vat — A94

Designs: 30fr, Chocolate factory. 50fr, Candy making, vert.

1969, Apr. 24   Engr.   *Perf. 13*
489 A94 15fr red brn, ind & choc .50 .20
490 A94 30fr grn, blk & red brn .80 .20
491 A94 50fr brown & multi 1.10 .20
Nos. 489-491 (3) 2.40 .60

Cameroun chocolate industry.

Fertility Symbol, Abbia — A95

Diesel Train on Bridge — A96

Art and Folklore from Abbia: 10fr, Two toucans, horiz. 15fr, Forest symbol. 30fr, Vulture attacking monkey, horiz. 70fr, Oliphant player.

1969, May 30   Engr.   *Perf. 13*
492 A95 5fr ultra, Prus bl & brt rose lil .25 .20
493 A95 10fr bl, ol gray & org .35 .20
494 A95 15fr ultra, dk red & blk .50 .20
495 A95 30fr brt bl, lem & org .90 .25
496 A95 70fr brt bl, dk grn & ver 1.90 .50
Nos. 492-496 (5) 3.90 1.35

Perf. 12½x13, 13x12½
1969, July 11   Photo.
Design: 30fr, Kumba Railroad station, horiz.
497 A96 30fr blue & multi 1.25 .30
498 A96 50fr black & multi 2.75 .60

Opening of Mbanga-Kumba Railroad.

Development Bank Issue
Common Design Type
1969, Sept. 10   Engr.   *Perf. 13*
499 CD130 30fr vio bl, grn & ocher .80 .20

African Development Bank, 5th anniv.

ASECNA Issue
Common Design Type
1969, Dec. 12   Engr.   *Perf. 13*
500 CD132 100fr slate green 2.00 .60

Red Sage — A99

Design: 30fr, Passionflower.

1970, Mar. 24   Photo.   *Perf. 12x12½*
Size: 22x36½mm
501 A99 15fr yel grn & multi .45 .20
502 A99 30fr multicolored 1.00 .20
Nos. 501-502,C140-C141 (4) 5.60 1.05

UPU Headquarters Issue
Common Design Type
1970, May 20   Engr.   *Perf. 13*
503 CD133 30fr blue, pur & grn 1.00 .20
504 CD133 50fr gray, red & bl 1.60 .30

Brewery A100

Design: 30fr, Cellar with barrels.

1970, July 9   Engr.   *Perf. 13*
505 A100 15fr brn, gray & dk grn .75 .20
506 A100 30fr bl grn, dk brn & brn red 1.50 .30

Cameroun brewing industry.

Ozila Dancers — A101

Cameroun Doll — A102

Design: 50fr, Ozila dancer and drummer.

1970, Oct. 19   Engr.   *Perf. 13*
507 A101 30fr multicolored 1.00 .20
508 A101 50fr red & multi 2.75 .40

1970, Nov. 2

Designs: 15fr, Doll in short skirt. 30fr, Doll with basket on back.

509	A102	10fr car & multi	.60	.20
510	A102	15fr dk grn & multi	.70	.20
511	A102	30fr brn red & multi	1.90	.30
		Nos. 509-511 (3)	3.20	.70

Cogwheels and Grain — A103

1970, Feb. 9   Photo.   Perf. 13
512 A103 30fr multicolored   .85   .20

Europafrica Economic Conference.

Federal University, Yaoundé — A104

1971, Jan. 19   Engr.
513 A104 50fr multicolored   1.00   .20

Inauguration of Federal University at Yaoundé.

Presidents Ahidjo and Pompidou, Flags of Cameroun and France — A105

1971, Feb. 9   Photo.   Perf. 13
514 A105 30fr multicolored   1.50   .35

Visit of Georges Pompidou, Pres. of France.

Young People, Globe, Map of Cameroun — A106

1971, Feb. 11
515 A106 30fr blue & multi   .95   .20

Fifth National Youth Festival, Feb. 11.

Gerbera Hybrida — A107

Men of Four Races — A108

Designs: 40fr, Opuntia polyantha (cactus). 50fr, Hemerocallis hybrida (lily).

1971, Mar. 14   Photo.
516	A107	20fr multicolored	.60	.20
517	A107	40fr green & multi	1.50	.20
518	A107	50fr blue & multi	2.10	.20
		Nos. 516-518 (3)	4.20	.60

1971, Mar. 21   Perf. 13x12½

Design: 30fr, Hands and globe.

519	A108	20fr green & multi	.55	.20
520	A108	30fr ultra & multi	.75	.20

Intl. year against racial discrimination.

Crowned Cranes at Waza Camp A109

20fr, Canoe on Sanaga River. 30fr, Sanaga River.

1971, Apr. 9.   Engr.   Perf. 13
521	A109	10fr red, grn & blk	1.50	.25
522	A109	20fr dk grn, brn & red	1.00	.25
523	A109	30fr red, dk grn & brt bl	1.50	.25
		Nos. 521-523 (3)	4.00	.75

International Court, The Hague — A110

1971, June 14   Engr.   Perf. 13
524 A110 50fr ultra, org brn & sl grn   1.25   .20

25th anniversary of the International Court in The Hague, Netherlands.

Liana Bridge — A111

Bamoun Horseman A113

Local Market A112

1971, Aug. 16   Photo.   Perf. 13
525	A111	40fr multicolored	1.25	.20
526	A112	45fr multicolored	1.50	.20

1971, Sept. 18

African Art: 15fr, Animal fetish statuette.

527	A113	10fr brown & yellow	.50	.50
528	A113	15fr dp brn & org yel	.50	.50

Communications Satellite and Globe — A114

1971, Oct. 14   Perf. 13x12½
529 A114 40fr Prus bl, sl grn & org   .80   .20

Pan-African telecommunications system.

UNICEF Emblem A115

50fr, UNICEF emblem and grain, vert.

1971, Dec. 11   Engr.   Perf. 13
530	A115	40fr sl grn, bl grn & plum	.95	.20
531	A115	50fr dp bl, dk red & lt grn	1.25	.25

25th anniv. of UNICEF.

Houses from South-Central Region — A116

Design: 15fr, Adamaua round houses.

1972, Jan. 15   Photo.   Perf. 13
532	A116	10fr dk blue & multi	.25	.20
533	A116	15fr black & multi	.55	.20

Giraffe — A117

Designs: 5fr, Home industries. 10fr, Smith, horiz. 15fr, Women carrying burdens.

Perf. 13x13½, 13½x13
1972, Feb. 18   Litho.
534	A117	2fr multicolored	.30	.20
535	A117	5fr black, org & red	.30	.20
536	A117	10fr multicolored	.30	.20
537	A117	15fr multicolored	.30	.20
		Nos. 534-537 (4)	1.20	.80

Youth Day 1972.

Soccer Players and Field — A118

Designs: 20fr, African Soccer Cup, vert. 45fr, Team captains shaking hands, vert.

1972, Feb. 22   Perf. 13½
538	A118	20fr gray & multi	.55	.20
539	A118	40fr gray & multi	.95	.20
540	A118	45fr yellow & multi	1.50	.25
		Nos. 538-540 (3)	3.00	.65

African Soccer Cup, Yaoundé, 2/23-3/5.

Government Building, Yaoundé, and Laurel — A119

1972, Apr. 6   Photo.   Perf. 12½x12
541 A119 40fr multicolored   .80   .20

110th session of Inter-Parliamentary Council, Yaoundé, Apr. 1972.

"Fantasia," North Cameroun A120

Bororo Woman — A121

40fr, Boat on Wouri River & Mt. Cameroun.

1972, Apr. 24   Perf. 13x12½, 12½x13
542	A120	15fr dk vio & multi	.35	.20
543	A121	20fr multicolored	.45	.20
544	A120	40fr multicolored	1.50	.20
		Nos. 542-544 (3)	2.30	.60

Chemical Apparatus A122

1972, May 15   Engr.   Perf. 13
545 A122 40fr lilac, red & green   .80   .20

President Ahmadou Ahidjo Prize.

United Republic

Solanum Macranthum A123

Design: 45fr, Wax plant.

1972, July 20   Photo.   Perf. 13
546	A123	40fr multicolored	.95	.20
547	A123	45fr yellow & multi	1.25	.20

Charaxes Ameliae A124

Design: 45fr, Papilio tynderaeus.

1972, Aug. 20   Photo.   Perf. 13
548	A124	40fr bl, dk bl & gold	3.25	.40
549	A124	45fr lt grn, blk & gold	4.25	.60

No. 468 Surcharged

1972, Aug. 30 Photo. Perf. 12x12½
550 A85 40fr on 30fr multicolored   1.00 .20

Resurrection
Lily — A125

Great Blue
Touraco — A126

Flowers: 45fr, Candlestick cassia. 50fr,
Amaryllis.

1972, Sept. 16   Perf. 13
551 A125 40fr lt green & multi   1.00 .20
552 A125 45fr multicolored   1.50 .20
553 A125 50fr lt blue & multi   2.10 .20
      Nos. 551-553 (3)   4.60 .60

Perf. 12½x13, 13x12½
1972, Nov. 20   Litho.

Design: 45fr, Red-faced lovebirds, horiz.

554 A126 10fr yellow & multi   1.75 .20
555 A126 45fr yellow & multi   3.75 .20

Cotton
(North) — A127

10fr, Cacao (south central). 15fr, Logging
(southeast & southern coast). 20fr, Coffee
(west). 45fr, Tea (northwest & southwest).

1973, Mar. 26 Photo. Perf. 12½x13
556 A127 5fr black & multi   .25 .20
557 A127 10fr black & multi   .25 .20
558 A127 15fr black & multi   .75 .20
559 A127 20fr black & multi   1.50 .20
560 A127 45fr black & multi   3.25 .20
      Nos. 556-560 (5)   6.00 1.00
     Third 5-Year Plan.
    For surcharge see No. 568.

Flag and Map of Cameroun, Pres.
Ahidjo and No. 331 — A128

Design: 20fr, Proclamation of independence, Pres. Ahidjo and No. 336.

1973, May 20   Engr.   Perf. 13
561 A128 10fr ultra & multi   .65 .20
562 A128 20fr multicolored   1.00 .20
    Nos. 561-562,C200-C201 (4) 3.45 .85
United Republic of Cameroun, 1st anniv.

Bamoun   Dr.
Mask — A129   Hansen — A130

Designs: Various Bamoun masks.

1973, July 10   Engr.   Perf. 13
563 A129 5fr green, brn & blk   .20 .20
564 A129 10fr lilac, brn & blk   .25 .20
565 A129 45fr red, brn & blk   .75 .20
566 A129 100fr ultra, brn & blk 2.00 .40
    Nos. 563-566 (4)   3.20 1.00

1973, July 25   Engr.   Perf. 13
567 A130 45fr multicolored   1.60 .20
Centenary of the discovery by Dr. Armauer
G. Hansen of the Hansen bacillus, the cause
of leprosy.

No. 556 Surcharged with New Value,

1973, Aug. 16 Photo. Perf. 12½x13
568 A127 100fr on 5fr multicolored 1.75 .40
African solidarity in drought emergency.

Dancers, South   WMO
West   Emblem — A132
Africa — A131

Designs: Southwest African dances.

1973, Aug. 17   Perf. 13
569 A131 10fr multicolored   .20 .20
570 A131 25fr multicolored   .55 .20
571 A131 45fr multicolored 1.10 .20
    Nos. 569-571 (3)   1.85 .60

1973, Sept. 1   Engr.   Perf. 13
572 A132 45fr green & ultra   1.60 .20
Cent. of intl. meteorological cooperation.

Garoua Party Headquarters — A133

1973, Sept. 1   Photo.
573 A133 40fr multicolored   .80 .20
7th anniv. of Cameroun National Union.

African Postal Union Issue, 1973
Common Design Type
1973, Sept. 12   Engr.
574 CD137 100fr brt bl, bl & sl grn 1.75 .40

Avocados — A135

1973, Sept. 20
575 A135 10fr shown   .70 .20
576 A135 20fr Mangos   .80 .20
577 A135 45fr Plums   2.00 .20
578 A135 50fr Custard apple 2.50 .20
    Nos. 575-578 (4)   6.00 .80

Kirdi Village
A136

45fr, Mabas village. 50fr, Fishing village.

1973, Oct. 25   Engr.   Perf. 13
579 A136 15fr black, bis & grn   .25 .20
580 A136 45fr magenta, brn &
         org   .90 .20
581 A136 50fr green, blk & org 1.25 .20
    Nos. 579-581 (3)   2.40 .60

Handshake on
Map of
Africa — A137

1974, May 15   Engr. Perf. 12½x13
582 A137 40fr carmine & multi .55 .20
583 A137 45fr indigo & multi   .70 .20
Organization for African Unity, 10th anniv.

Spinning
Mill — A138

1974, May 25   Engr. Perf. 13x12½
584 A138 45fr multicolored   .80 .20
CICAM Industrial Complex.

Carved
Panel from
Bilinga
A139

Cameroun Art (Carvings): 40fr, Detail from
Bubinga chair. 45fr, Detail Acajou Ngollon
panel.

1974, May 30
585 A139 10fr brt grn & ocher   .25 .20
586 A139 40fr red & brown   .80 .20
587 A139 45fr blue & rose brn 1.10 .20
    Nos. 585-587 (3)   2.15 .60

Zebu — A140

1974, June 1   Perf. 13½
588 A140 40fr multicolored   1.40 .20
North Cameroun cattle raising. See No.
C210.

Laying Rail
Section
A141

Designs: 5fr, Map showing line Yaoundé to
Ngaoundéré, vert. 40fr, Welding rail joint, vert.
100fr, Train on Djerem River Bridge.

Perf. 12½x13, 13x12½
1974, June 10   Engr.
589 A141 5fr multicolored   .65 .20
590 A141 20fr multicolored 1.25 .30
591 A141 40fr multicolored 2.00 .60
592 A141 100fr multicolored 3.25 .90
    Nos. 589-592 (4)   7.15 2.00
Opening of Yaoundé-Ngaoundéré railroad
line.
For surcharge see No. 596.

No. 466 Surcharged

1974, June 1 Photo. Perf. 12x12½
593 A85 40fr on 8fr multi   .80 .25

UPU
Emblem,
Hands
Holding
Letters
A142

1974, Oct. 8   Engr.   Perf. 13
594 A142 40fr multicolored   .90 .20
    Nos. 594,C218-C219 (3) 5.90 1.10
     Cent. of the UPU.

Presidents and Flags of Cameroun,
CAR, Congo, Gabon and Meeting
Center — A143

1974, Dec. 8   Photo.   Perf. 13
595 A143 40fr gold & multi   1.50 .20
10th anniversary of Central African Customs
and Economic Union (Union Douanière et
Economique de l'Afrique Centrale, UDEAC).
See No. C223.

No. 589
Surcharged in
Violet Blue

1974, Dec. 10   Engr.   Perf. 12½x13
596 A141 100fr on 5fr multi   1.90   .45

Virgin of
Autun, 15th
Century
Sculpture
A144

Christmas: 45fr, Virgin and Child, by Luis de Morales (c. 1509-1586).

1974, Dec. 20   Photo.   Perf. 13
597 A144 40fr gold & multi   .95   .20
598 A144 45fr gold & multi   1.25   .20

Tropical
Plants — A145

1975, Mar. 10   Photo.   Perf. 13
599 A145 5fr Cockscomb   .30   .20
600 A145 40fr Costus spectabilis 1.50 .25
601 A145 45fr Mussaenda er-
         ythrophylla   1.90   .35
         Nos. 599-601 (3)   3.70   .80

Fishing by Night — A146

1975, Apr. 1   Engr.   Perf. 13
602 A146 40fr shown   1.60   .20
603 A146 45fr Fishing by day   2.10   .20

Afo Akom Statue
and Chief's
Stool — A147

Tree
Fungus — A148

1975, Apr. 1   Photo.
604 A147 40fr multicolored   .65   .20
605 A147 45fr multicolored   .85   .20
606 A147 200fr multicolored   2.50   .75
         Nos. 604-606 (3)   4.00 1.15

1975, Apr. 14
607 A148 15fr shown   150.00   .20
608 A148 40fr Chrysalis   90.00   .20

Ministry of Posts and
Telecommunications — A149

1975, July 21   Engr.   Perf. 13
609 A149 40fr brn, grn & Prus bl .65 .20
610 A149 45fr Prus bl, brn & grn .90 .20

Presbyterian Church, Elat — A150

Designs: No. 612, Foumban Mosque. 45fr, Catholic Church, Ngaoundere.

1975, Aug. 20   Engr.   Perf. 13
611 A150 40fr multicolored   .45   .20
612 A150 40fr multicolored   .45   .20
613 A150 45fr multicolored   .65   .20
         Nos. 611-613 (3)   1.55   .60

Plowing
A151

Design: No. 615, Corn harvest, vert.

Perf. 13x12½, 12½x13
1975, Dec. 15   Photo.
614 A151 40fr deep grn & multi .80 .20
615 A151 40fr deep grn & multi .80 .20
         Green revolution.

Zamengoe Satellite Monitoring
Station — A152

1976, May 20   Litho.   Perf. 13
616 A152 40fr shown   .60   .20
617 A152 100fr Radar, vert.   1.10   .40

Porcelain
Rose — A153

Design: 50fr, Flower of North Cameroon.

1976, July 20   Litho.   Perf. 12½
618 A153 40fr multicolored   1.00   .20
619 A153 50fr multicolored   1.40   .20

Leopard
Dance — A154

Telephone
Exchange
A155

1976, Sept. 15   Litho.   Perf. 12
620 A154 40fr gray & multi   .80   .20
         Nos. 620,C233-C234 (3) 2.55   .75

1976, Oct. 5   Litho.   Perf. 13
621 A155 50fr multicolored   .80   .20
Centenary of first telephone call by Alexander Graham Bell, Mar. 10, 1876.

Young Men Building House — A156

Design: 45fr, Young women working in field.

1976, Oct. 10   Litho.   Perf. 12
622 A156 40fr multicolored   .35   .20
623 A156 45fr multicolored   .60   .20
         10th National Youth Day.

Konrad Adenauer
(1876-1967),
German
Chancellor,
Cologne
Cathedral
A157

1976, Oct. 20
624 A157 100fr multicolored   .95   .40

Party Headquarters, Douala — A158

No. 626, Party Headquarters, Yaoundé.

1976, Dec. 28   Litho.   Perf. 12
625 A158 50fr orange & multi   .45   .20
626 A158 50fr blue & multi   .45   .20
10th anniv. of the Cameroun National Union.

Bamoun Copper
Pipe — A159

Ostrich — A160

1977, Feb. 4   Litho.   Perf. 12½
627 A159 50fr multicolored   .70   .20
2nd World Black and African Festival, Lagos, Nigeria, 1/15-2/12. See No. C239.

1977, Mar. 20   Litho.   Perf. 12
628 A160 30fr shown   2.50   .35
629 A160 50fr Crowned cranes 3.00   .50

Cameroun No. 609 and Switzerland
No. 3L1 — A161

1977, June 5   Litho.   Perf. 12
630 A161 50fr multicolored   1.00   .20
         Nos. 630,C252-C253 (3) 4.35   .85
Jufilex Philatelic Exhibition, Bern, Switzerland. See Nos. C252-C253.

Winter Olympics 1976, set of five, 40, 50fr, airmail 140, 200, 350fr, and airmail souv. sheet, 500fr, issued Aug. 10, 1977. Nos. 7701-7706. Value, set $7.50, souvenir sheet $5.

Apollo-Soyuz — A163

Designs: 40fr, Astronaut Thomas P. Stafford, Apollo lifting off. 60fr, Cosmonaut Alexei Leonov, Soyuz lifting off.

1977, Aug. 10   Litho.   *Perf. 14x13½*
633   A163   40fr multicolored   .45   .25
634   A163   60fr multicolored   .70   .50
    Nos. 633-634,C256-C258 (5)   7.55   6.60

No. 617 Overprinted in French and
English

1977, Aug. 22   Litho.   *Perf. 13*
635   A152   100fr multicolored   .90   .40

Palestinian fighters and their families.

Chairman
Mao and
Great Wall
A164

1977, Sept. 9   Engr.   *Perf. 13*
636   A164   100fr olive & brown   3.00   .55

Mao Tse-tung (1893-1976), Chinese communist leader, first death anniversary.

Nativity, by
Albrecht
Altdorfer
A165

50fr, Madonna of the Grand Duke, by
Raphael.

1977, Dec. 15   Litho.   *Perf. 12½x12*
637   A165   30fr multicolored   .55   .20
638   A165   50fr multicolored   1.10   .20
    Nos. 637-638,C264-C265 (4)   7.65   2.40

Christmas 1977.

Gazelle and
Rotary
Emblem — A166

Pres. Ahidjo, Flag
and Map of
Cameroun
A167

1978, Feb. 11   Litho.   *Perf. 12*
639   A166   50fr orange & multi   .70   .20

Rotary Club of Yaounde, 20th anniversary.

1978, Apr. 3   Litho.   *Perf. 12½*
640   A167   50fr multicolored   .90   .20

New flag of Cameroun. See No. C266.

Cardioglossa Escalerae — A168

Design: 60fr, Cardioglossa elegans.

1978, Apr. 5
641   A168   50fr multicolored   1.75   .20
642   A168   60fr multicolored   2.75   .25
    Nos. 641-642,C267 (3)   8.25   .85

Jules Verne and
"From Earth to
Moon" — A169

1978, Oct. 10   Litho.   *Perf. 12*
643   A169   250fr multicolored   2.25   1.40

Jules Verne (1828-1905), science fiction
writer, birth sesquicentennial. See No. C276.

Hypolimnas Salmacis Drury — A170

Butterflies: 25fr, Euxanthe trajanus ward.
30fr, Euphaedra cyparissa cramer.

1978, Oct. 15
644   A170   20fr multicolored   2.75   .35
645   A170   25fr multicolored   3.00   .35
646   A170   30fr multicolored   5.00   .35
    Nos. 644-646 (3)   10.75   1.05

Men Planting
Seedlings
A171

Carved Bamun
Drum
A172

1978, Oct. 30   *Perf. 12½*
647   A171   10fr multicolored   .25   .20
648   A171   15fr multicolored   .35   .20

Green barrier against the desert.

1978, Nov. 20   Litho.   *Perf. 12½*
60fr, String instrument (Gueguerou), horiz.
649   A172   50fr multicolored   .45   .20
650   A172   60fr multicolored   .65   .25
    Nos. 649-650,C277 (3)   2.35   .85

Pres. Ahidjo, Giscard D'Estaing, Flags
of Cameroun and France — A173

1979, Feb. 8   Photo.   *Perf. 13*
651   A173   60fr multicolored   1.50   .25

Visit of Pres. Valery Giscard D'Estaing of
France to Cameroun.

Human Rights Emblem, Globe, Scroll
and African — A174

1979, Feb. 11   Litho.   *Perf. 12x12½*
652   A174   5fr multicolored   .25   .20

Universal Declaration of Human Rights,
30th anniversary (in 1978). See No. C278.
See No. 803.

Boy and Girl
Greeting
Sun — A175

1979, Aug. 15   Litho.   *Perf. 12*
653   A175   50fr multicolored   .80   .20

International Year of the Child.

Protected
Animals
A176

Nos. 655, 658 vert.

1979, Sept. 20   *Perf. 12½*
654   A176   50fr Rhinoceros   1.50   .25
655   A176   60fr Giraffe   2.25   .35
656   A176   60fr Gorilla   2.25   .45
657   A176   100fr Leopard   3.50   .55
658   A176   100fr Elephant   3.50   .65
    Nos. 654-658 (5)   13.00   2.25

Eugene
Jamot, Map
of
Cameroun,
Tsetse
Fly — A177

1979, Nov. 5   Engr.   *Perf. 13*
659   A177   50fr multicolored   3.00   .40

Eugene Jamot (1879-1937), discoverer of
sleeping sickness cure.

Annunciation, by Fra Filippo
Lippi — A178

Paintings; 50fr, Rest During the Flight to
Egypt, c. 1620. No. 622, Flight into Egypt, by
Jan Joest, No. 663, Nativity, by Joest. 100fr,
Nativity, by Botticelli.

1979, Dec. 6   Litho.   *Perf. 12½x12*
660   A178   10fr multicolored   .20   .20
661   A178   50fr multicolored   .60   .25
662   A178   60fr multicolored   .75   .30
663   A178   60fr multicolored   .75   .30
   a.   Pair, #662-663   1.50   .65
664   A178   100fr multicolored   1.50   .40
    Nos. 660-664 (5)   3.80   1.45

Christmas 1979.

Piper
Capense
A179

Medicinal Plants: 60fr, Bracken fern.

1979, Dec. 15   Litho.   *Perf. 12½*
665   A179   50fr multicolored   1.25   .20
666   A179   60fr multicolored   1.50   .35

Pres.
Ahidjo,
Cameroun
Map, Arms
and No.
331
A180

1980, Feb. 12   Litho.   *Perf. 12½*
667   A180   50fr multicolored   .65   .20

Independence, 20th anniversary.

Congress
Building,
Bafoussam
A181

1980, Feb. 12
668   A181   50fr multicolored   .65   .20

Cameroun National Union, 3rd Ordinary
Congress, Bafoussam, Feb. 12-17.

Rotary Emblem,
Map of
Cameroun
A182

Rotary Intl., 75th Anniv.: #670, Anniv.
emblem.

1980, Mar. 15   Litho.   Perf. 12½
669 A182 200fr multicolored   2.40   .80
670 A182 200fr multicolored   2.40   .80
  a.   Souvenir sheet of 2, #669-670   5.25   4.00

Voacanga
Medicinal
Beans
A183

1980, Dec. 3   Litho.   Perf. 12½
671 A183 50fr shown   1.00   .20
672 A183 60fr Voacanga tree,
            vert.   1.25   .25
673 A183 100fr Voacanga flower,
            vert.   1.75   .40
      Nos. 671-673 (3)   4.00   .85

Violet
Mellowstone
A184

1980, Dec. 5
674 A184 50fr shown   .70   .20
675 A184 60fr Patula   1.00   .25
676 A184 100fr Cashmere bou-
            quet   1.60   .40
      Nos. 674-676 (3)   3.30   .85

Occupation of Mecca by Mohammed,
1350th Anniversary — A185

1980, Dec. 9
677 A185 50fr multicolored   1.00   .30

African Slender-snouted Crocodile
(Endangered Species) — A186

1980, Dec. 24
678 A186 200fr shown   3.25   .80
679 A186 300fr Buffon's ante-
            lope, vert.   4.25   1.20
      See Nos. 888-889.

Bororo Girls and Roumsiki
Peaks — A187

1980, Dec. 29
680 A187 50fr shown   .55   .20
681 A187 60fr Dschang tourist
            center   .55   .25

Banana
Tree
A188

1981, Feb. 5
682 A188 50fr shown   .65   .30
683 A188 60fr Cattle, vert.   .80   .40

Girl on
Crutches — A189

1981, Feb. 20   Litho.   Perf. 12½
684 A189 60fr shown   .55   .25
685 A189 150fr Boy in motorized
            wheelchair   1.25   .65
      International Year of the Disabled.

Air Terminal, Douala Airport — A190

1981, Apr. 4   Litho.   Perf. 12½
686 A190 100fr shown   1.00   .55
687 A190 200fr Boeing 747   2.00   1.10
688 A190 300fr Douala Intl. Air-
            port   3.00   1.60
      Nos. 686-688 (3)   6.00   3.25
      Cameroun Airlines, 10th anniv.

Scaly
Anteater
A192

Designs: Endangered species.

1981, July 20   Litho.   Perf. 12½
691 A192 50fr Moutourou   1.50   .20
692 A192 50fr Tortoise   1.50   .20
693 A192 100fr shown   3.00   .40
      Nos. 691-693 (3)   6.00   .80

Prince Charles
and Lady Diana,
St. Paul's
Cathedral
A193

1981, July 29   Litho.   Perf. 12½
694 A193 500fr shown   4.50   2.00
695 A193 500fr Couple, royal
            coach   4.50   2.00
  a.   Souvenir sheet of 2, #694-695   10.00   4.00
      Royal wedding.

Bafoussam-Bamenda Highway — A194

1981, Sept. 10   Litho.   Perf. 12½
696 A194 50fr multicolored   .55   .20

Freighter
Cam Iroko
(Cameroun
Shipping
Line)
A195

1981, Sept. 25
697 A195 60fr multicolored   1.00   .40

20th Anniv. of Reunification — A196

1981, Oct. 10   Perf. 12½x13
698 A196 50fr multicolored   .65   .20

Medicinal
Plants — A197

1981, Dec. 31   Litho.   Perf. 12½
699 A197 60fr Voacanga thouarsii   1.25   .30
700 A197 70fr Cassia alata   1.75   .40

Easter 1982 — A198

Paintings: 100fr, Christ in the Garden of
Olives, by Delacroix. 200fr, Descent from the
Cross, by Giotto. 250fr, Pieta in the Country-
side, by Bellini.

1982, Apr. 10   Litho.   Perf. 13
701 A198 100fr multicolored   .90   .35
702 A198 200fr multicolored   1.75   .65
703 A198 250fr multicolored   2.25   .90
      Nos. 701-703 (3)   4.90   1.90

PHILEXFRANCE '82 Stamp Exhibition,
Paris, June 11-21 — A199

1982, Apr. 25   Perf. 12
704 A199 90fr multicolored   2.10   .40

Snakeskin
Handbag — A200

1982, Apr. 30   Perf. 12½
705 A200 60fr shown   .70   .25
706 A200 70fr Clay water jug   .80   .35

10th Anniv. of Republic — A201

1982, May 20   Perf. 13
707 A201 500fr multicolored   5.25   2.00

Pres. Ahidjo
Presenting Trophy
to Canon Soccer
Team — A191

1981, Apr. 20
689 A191 60fr shown   .90   .40
690 A191 60fr Union team captain   .90   .40
      1979 African Soccer Cup champions.

Town Hall, Douala — A202

1982, June 15   Litho.   Perf. 12½
708	A202	40fr shown	.45	.20
709	A202	60fr Yaounde	.65	.25

See Nos. 730-731, 757-758, 790-791, 867.

1982 World Cup — A203

1982, July 10   Perf. 13
710	A203	100fr Natl. team	1.40	.40
711	A203	200fr Semi-finalists	2.75	.75
712	A203	300fr Players, vert.	4.50	1.25
713	A203	400fr Natl. team 2nd lineup	5.75	1.60
a.		Souvenir sheet of 2, #713	14.50	3.50
		Nos. 710-713 (4)	14.40	4.00

Partridge — A204

1982   Perf. 12½x13
714	A204	10fr shown	2.75	.35
715	A204	15fr Turtle dove	3.00	.55
716	A204	20fr Swallow	4.50	.75
717	A204	200fr Bongo antelope	4.00	.80
718	A204	300fr Black colobus	6.25	1.25
		Nos. 714-718 (5)	20.50	3.70

Issued: 200fr, 300fr, July 20; others Aug. 10.
See No. 804.

Scouting Year A205

1982, Sept. 30   Litho.   Perf. 13x12½
719	A205	200fr Campfire	2.25	.80
720	A205	400fr Baden-Powell	4.00	1.60

25th Anniv. of the Presbyterian Church in Cameroun — A206

1982, Oct. 30   Perf. 13x12½, 12½x13
721	A206	45fr Buea Chapel	.55	.20
722	A206	60fr Nyasoso Chapel, vert.	.65	.20

ITU Plenipotentiaries Conference, Nairobi, Sept. — A207

1982, Oct. 5   Litho.   Perf. 12½x13
723	A207	70fr multicolored	.70	.25

Italy's Victory in 1982 World Cup — A208

1982, Nov.   Perf. 13
724	A208	500fr multicolored	5.50	2.00
725	A208	1000fr multicolored	10.50	4.00

30th Anniv. of Customs Cooperation Council — A209

1983, Jan. 10   Perf. 12½x13
726	A209	250fr Emblem	2.25	.80
727	A209	250fr Headquarters, Brussels	2.25	.80

2nd Yaoundé Medical Conference — A210

1983, Jan. 23   Litho.   Perf. 13
728	A210	60fr grn & multi	.70	.20
729	A210	70fr brn & multi	.90	.25

City Hall Type of 1982

1983, Feb. 25   Litho.   Perf. 12½
730	A202	60fr Bafoussam	.60	.25
731	A202	70fr Garoua	.70	.30

Homage to Women — A211

1983, Apr. 25   Litho.   Perf. 12½
733	A211	60fr Nurse	.75	.20
734	A211	70fr Lawyer	.75	.25

11th Anniv. of Independence — A212

Flag and Pres. Paul Biya.

1983, May 18   Litho.   Perf. 13
735	A212	60fr dk grn & multi	.55	.25
736	A212	70fr dk bl & multi	.70	.30

25th Anniv. of Intl. Maritime Org. A213

1983, May 23   Perf. 13x12½
737	A213	500fr multicolored	4.50	1.50

Eagle — A214

1983, June 15   Litho.   Perf. 12½x13
738	A214	25fr shown	1.75	.35
739	A214	30fr Sparrowhawk	2.50	.50
740	A214	50fr Purple heron	4.50	.75
		Nos. 738-740 (3)	8.75	1.60

See Nos. 798-800, 873, 882, 886.

A215

1983, July 25   Litho.   Perf. 12
741	A215	60fr Pearl mask, by Wery-Nwen-Nto, 1899	.70	.25
742	A215	70fr Basket with lid	.90	.30

A216

1983, Aug. 20   Litho.   Perf. 12
743	A216	90fr Mobile Post Office, horiz	.90	.20
744	A216	150fr Telegraph Operator	1.40	.35
745	A216	250fr Tom-tom	2.75	.55
		Nos. 743-745 (3)	5.05	1.10

World Communications Year.

Endangered Species — A217

1983, Sept. 22   Perf. 12
746	A217	200fr Civet Cat	2.75	.40
747	A217	200fr Gorilla, vert	2.75	.40
748	A217	350fr Cobaya, vert	5.50	.80
		Nos. 746-748 (3)	11.00	1.60

See No. 887.

Lake Tizon — A218

1983, Nov. 25   Litho.   Perf. 13
749	A218	60fr shown	.55	.20
750	A218	70fr Mt. Cameroon	.70	.20

Human Rights Declaration, 35th Anniv — A219

1983, Dec. 20   Litho.   Perf. 12½x13
751	A219	60fr multicolored	.55	.20
752	A219	70fr multicolored	.70	.20

Christmas 1983 — A220

60fr, Christmas tree. 200fr, Stained glass window, Yaoundé Cathedral. #755, Rest during Flight into Egypt, by Philipp Otto Runge. #756, Angel of the Annunciation. 60fr, 200fr, #756 vert.

1983, Dec. 20   Litho.   Perf. 12½
753	A220	60fr multicolored	.45	.20
754	A220	200fr multicolored	1.75	.50
755	A220	500fr multicolored	4.50	1.25
756	A220	500fr multicolored	4.50	1.25
a.		Souvenir sheet of 3, #754-756	12.00	10.00
		Nos. 753-756 (4)	11.20	3.20

City Hall Type of 1982

1984, Apr. 20   Litho.   Perf. 12½
757	A202	60fr Bamenda	.55	.20
758	A202	70fr Mbalmayo	.70	.25

Catholic Church, Zoetele — A221

1984, July 25   Litho.   Perf. 13
759	A221	60fr shown	.55	.25
760	A221	70fr Protestant Church, Yaounde	.70	.25

Endangered Species — A222

1984, Aug. 15
761 A222 250fr Wild pig   4.00 .65
762 A222 250fr Deer   4.00 .65

1984, Oct. 10   Litho.   Perf. 13½
763 A222 60fr Nightingale   5.00 5.00
764 A222 60fr Vultures   5.00 5.00

See No. 883.

Bamenda Farming Fair — A223

1984, Dec. 10   Litho.   Perf. 13
765 A223 60fr Corn   .60 .20
766 A223 70fr Cattle   .90 .25
767 A223 300fr Potatoes   3.50 .90
   Nos. 765-767 (3)   5.00 1.35

International Civil Aviation Organization, 40th Anniv. — A224

1984, Dec. 20   Litho.   Perf. 12½
768 A224 200fr Icarus   1.75 .60
769 A224 200fr ICAO emblem, vert.   1.75 .60
770 A224 300fr Boeing 747   2.75 .90
771 A224 300fr Solar Princess painting   3.25 .90
   Nos. 768-771 (4)   9.50 3.00

Olymphilex '85, Lausanne — A225

Wmk. 385
1985, Apr. 5   Photo.   Perf. 13
772 A225 150fr Wrestlers, exhibition emblem   1.50 .40

Domestic Musical Instruments A226

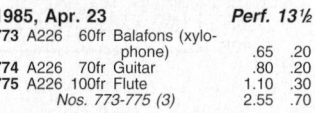

1985, Apr. 23   Perf. 13½
773 A226 60fr Balafons (xylophone)   .65 .20
774 A226 70fr Guitar   .80 .20
775 A226 100fr Flute   1.10 .30
   Nos. 773-775 (3)   2.55 .70

INTELSAT Org., 20th Anniv. — A227

1985, May 8   Perf. 13
776 A227 125fr Intelsat V   1.60 .35
777 A227 200fr Intelcam, Yaounde   2.10 .60

New York Headquarters — A228

1985, May 30
778 A228 250fr multicolored   2.40 1.10
779 A228 500fr multicolored   4.50 2.25

UN, 40th anniv.

Pres. Mitterand, Biya — A229

1985, June 20
780 A229 60fr multicolored   1.40 .20
781 A229 70fr multicolored   1.60 .25

Visit of Pres. Mitterand of France.

UNICEF A230

UN Infant Survival Campaign A231

1985, July 15
782 A230 60fr multicolored   .55 .20
783 A231 300fr multicolored   2.75 1.00

Visit of Pope John Paul II, Aug. 10-14 — A232

1985, Aug. 9   Perf. 13x12½
784 A232 60fr Pope, papal arms   1.50 .40
785 A232 70fr Pope, crosier   2.00 .55
   Size: 55x38mm
786 A232 200fr Pres. Biya, John Paul II   6.25 2.25
  a.   Souv. sheet of 3, #784-786   11.50 10.00
   Nos. 784-786 (3)   9.75 3.20

Landscapes — A233

1985, July 25   Litho.   Perf. 12½
787 A233 60fr Lake Barumbi, Kumba   .70 .20
788 A233 70fr Bonando Pygmy Village, Doume   .70 .20
789 A233 150fr Cameroun River   1.40 .40
   Nos. 787-789 (3)   2.80 .80

City Hall Type of 1982
1985, July 30
790 A202 60fr Ngaoundere   .55 .20
791 A202 60fr D'Ebolowa   .55 .20

Wildlife — A234

Wood Sculptures A235

1985, Aug. 20   Perf. 13½
792 A234 125fr Porcupine   1.50 .40
793 A234 200fr Squirrel   2.50 .60
794 A234 350fr Hedgehog   4.00 1.10
   Nos. 792-794 (3)   8.00 2.10

1985, Sept. 15
795 A235 60fr Mask   .65 .20
796 A235 70fr Mask, diff.   .90 .25
797 A235 100fr Wood bas-relief, horiz.   1.25 .30
   Nos. 795-797 (3)   2.80 .75

Bird Type of 1983
Inscribed Republic of Cameroon
1985, Nov. 10
798 A214 140fr Toucans   2.25 .50
799 A214 150fr Rooster   2.25 .55
800 A214 200fr Red-throated bee-eater   3.25 .70
   Nos. 798-800 (3)   7.75 1.75

See No. 873. For surcharge see No. 871.

American Peace Corps in Cameroun, 25th Anniv. — A237

1986, Jan. 1   Litho.   Perf. 12½
801 A237 70fr multicolored   .70 .25
802 A237 100fr multicolored   1.00 .30

Stamps of 1979-1982 Redrawn
1986, Mar.   Perf. 13, 13½
803 A174 5fr multicolored   .35 .35
804 A204 10fr multicolored   .35 .35

Nos. 803-804 inscribed "Republic of Cameroon" instead of "United Republic of Cameroon."

Easter — A238

Insects — A239

Paintings: 210fr, Head of the Virgin, by Pierre-Paul Prud'Hon (1758-1823). 350fr, The Stoning of St. Steven, by Van Scorel (1495-1562).

1986, Apr. 15   Perf. 13½
805 A238 210fr multicolored   1.75 .60
806 A238 350fr multicolored   2.75 1.00

1986, Apr. 20
807 A239 70fr Honeybee   1.50 .40
808 A239 70fr Dragonfly   1.50 .40
809 A239 100fr Grasshopper   2.50 .55
   Nos. 807-809 (3)   5.50 1.35

Nos. 808-809 horiz.

Flags, Conference Center — A240

1986, Apr. 25   Litho.   Perf. 13
810 A240 100fr Map, vert.   1.00 .30
811 A240 175fr shown   2.00 .60

Conference of Ministers of the Economic Commission for Africa, Apr. 9-29.

Statues — A241

1986, July 5   Litho.   Perf. 13½
812 A241 70fr Bronze earth
mother .85 .25
813 A241 100fr Wood funerary
figure .95 .30
814 A241 130fr Wood equestrian
figure 1.60 .40
Nos. 812-814 (3) 3.40 .95

Queen Elizabeth II, 60th
Birthday — A242

1986, July 15   Litho.   Perf. 13
815 A242 100fr Elizabeth 1.00 .40
816 A242 175fr Elizabeth, Pres.
Biya 1.40 .60
817 A242 210fr Elizabeth, diff. 2.00 .75
Nos. 815-817 (3) 4.40 1.75

Natl. Democratic Party, 1st
Anniv. — A243

1986, July 25   Perf. 12½
818 A243 70fr Party headquarters, Bamenda .70 .25
819 A243 70fr Pres. Biya, vert. .70 .25
820 A243 100fr Presidential address, vert. 1.00 .35
Nos. 818-820 (3) 2.40 .85

Kwem Mask
Dancers of the
Northeast — A244

1986, Aug. 1   Perf. 13½
821 A244 100fr multicolored 1.00 .35
822 A244 130fr multicolored 1.25 .45

Endangered Species — A245

1986, Aug. 20
823 300fr Varanus niloticus 3.50 1.00
824 300fr Panthera pardus 3.50 1.00

For surcharge see No. 872.

A246

A247

Intl. Peace Year: 175fr, 200fr, Desmond
Tutu, South Africa, Nobel Peace Prize winner.
250fr, UN and IPY emblems.

1986, Sept. 7   Litho.   Perf. 13½
825 A246 175fr multicolored 1.60 1.10
826 A246 200fr multicolored 2.10 1.25
827 A246 250fr multicolored 2.75 1.50
Nos. 825-827 (3) 6.45 3.85

1986, Oct. 30   Litho.   Perf. 13½
828 A247 70fr multicolored .65 .25
Natl. Fed. of Associations for the
Handicapped.

A248

A249

1986, Nov. 9
829 A248 70fr Family under umbrella .90 .25
830 A248 100fr Child immunization 1.10 .35

African Vaccination Year.

1986, Dec. 20   Litho.   Perf. 13½
831 A249 70fr Afforestation map .90 .25
832 A249 100fr Hands, seedling 1.10 .35

Arbor Day.

Agricultural Development — A250

1986, Dec. 24
833 A250 70fr ONCPB seminar .75 .40
834 A250 70fr Coconut farming,
Dibombari .75 .40
835 A250 200fr Pineapple farm 2.00 1.10
Nos. 833-835 (3) 3.50 1.90

Insects
Destructive
to
Agriculture
A251

1987, Sept. 25   Litho.   Perf. 13½
836 A251 70fr Antestiopsis
lineaticollis intri-
cata 1.50 .50
837 A251 100fr Distantiella theobroma 2.00 .70

4th African Games, Nairobi — A252

1987, Oct. 1   Perf. 12½
838 A252 100fr Shot put .90 .70
839 A252 140fr Pole vault 1.25 1.00

Maroua Agricultural Show — A253

1988, Jan. 6
840 A253 70fr Millet field .90 .50
841 A253 100fr Cotton 1.10 .70
842 A253 150fr Cattle 1.60 1.10
Nos. 840-842 (3) 3.60 2.30

World Wildlife Fund — A254

Baboons, Papio leucophaeus.

1988, Apr. 25   Litho.   Perf. 13
843 A254 30fr Adult 2.75 2.00
844 A254 40fr Adult grooming
young 3.25 2.00
845 A254 70fr Baboon on
branch 4.75 3.25
846 A254 100fr Adult carrying
young 7.50 4.00
Nos. 843-846 (4) 18.25 11.25

Interparliamentary Union,
Cent. — A255

1989   Litho.   Perf. 13½
847 A255 50fr Natl. Assembly .60 .30

World Cup Soccer Championships,
Italy — A256

1990, Oct. 27   Litho.   Perf. 11½
Granite Paper
848 A256 200fr shown 1.75 1.00
849 A256 250fr Players, diff. 2.25 1.25
850 A256 250fr Goalkeeper, flags 2.25 1.25
851 A256 300fr Team 3.00 1.50
a. Souv. sheet of 4, #848-851 9.00 6.50
Nos. 848-851 (4) 9.25 5.00

Roger Milla,
World Cup
Soccer Player
A257

1990, July 4   Litho.   Perf. 11½
Granite Paper
852 A257 500fr multicolored 5.50 3.50
a. Souv. sheet of 1 9.00 6.00

Agriculture
A258

70fr, Treating cacao plants. 100fr, Sheep.

1990, Dec. 1   Litho.   Perf. 13½
853 A258 70fr multicolored 1.25 .55
854 A258 100fr multicolored 1.75 .80
a. Sheet of 2, #853-854, perf. 12½ 8.00 3.50

For surcharges see Nos. 894-895.

UN Development Program, 40th
Anniv. — A259

1990, Dec. 31   Litho.   Perf. 13½
855 A259 50fr multicolored .60 .40

Intl.
Literacy
Year
A260

1990, Dec. 31
856 A260 200fr bl, blk, & lt bl 1.75 .75

Independence, 30th Anniv. — A261

1991, Jan. 1   Perf. 13
857 A261 150fr shown 1.60 1.25
858 A261 1000fr Flag, Palace, #336 9.00 8.00
a. Souv. sheet of 2, #857-858 12.50 10.00

Fight
Against
AIDS
A262

1991, Jan. 15
859 A262 15fr Hearts, map, vert. .20 .20
860 A262 25fr shown .35 .20

See Nos. 884-885.

Designs: Nos. 861, 864, Pie grieche, vert. Nos. 862, 863, Picathartes chauve.

Birds
A263

1991, May 3   Litho.   Perf. 13½
861 A263 70fr grn & multi .60 .35
862 A263 70fr bl & multi .60 .40
863 A263 300fr blk & multi 3.25 2.00
864 A263 350fr blk & multi 3.50 2.25
a. Souv. sheet of 2, #863-864 9.00 5.50
Nos. 861-864 (4) 7.95 5.00

Wild Animals
A264

1991, May 8   Perf. 13½
865 A264 125fr Elephant 1.60 1.00
866 A264 250fr Water buffalo 3.00 2.00
a. Souvenir sheet of 2, #865-866, perf. 12½ 9.00 3.50

City Hall Type of 1982 Redrawn

1991   Perf. 13
867 A202 40fr multicolored .60 .20

No. 867 inscribed "Republic of Cameroon" instead of "United Republic of Cameroon."

Cameroun Catholic Church, Cent. (in 1990)
A265

1991, Dec. 8   Litho.   Perf. 13½
868 A265 125fr Mvolye church 1.25 .75
a. Booklet pane of 4 #868a —
Complete booklet, #868a —
869 A265 250fr Akono church 2.25 1.75
a. Souvenir sheet of 2, #868-869, perf. 12½x13 4.00 3.00
b. Booklet pane of 4 —
Complete booklet, #869a —

Issued: Nos. 868a, 869b, 1993.

Intl. Savings Banks Institute, 7th Meeting of the African Group
A266

1991, Dec. 9
870 A266 250fr multicolored 2.40 1.60
a. Souv. sheet of 1, perf. 12½x13 3.00 2.00

Nos. 799 & 824 Surcharged

1992   Perf. 13½
871 A214 20fr on 150fr #799 1.75 .20
872 A245 70fr on 300fr #824 5.75 .55

Bird Type of 1983

1992   Litho.   Perf. 13½
873 A214 125fr like #800 1.40 .95

Dated 1985.

Cameroun Soccer League
A267

125fr, Mbappe Mbappe Samuel (1936-85), soccer player, vert. 250fr, Linafoote League emblem, vert. 400fr, Linafoote emblem, diff. 500fr, Stadium.

1992, Aug.   Perf. 11½
874 A267 125fr multicolored 1.25 .75
875 A267 250fr multicolored 2.40 1.75
876 A267 400fr multicolored 3.50 2.75
877 A267 500fr multicolored 5.50 3.50
Nos. 874-877 (4) 12.65 8.75

See Nos. 896-896B.

Discovery of America, 500th Anniv.
A268

Columbus and: 125fr, Fleet of ships. 250fr, Landing in New World. 400fr, Meeting with natives. 500fr, Map, ships.

1992, Aug.
878 A268 125fr multicolored 1.40 .75
879 A268 250fr multicolored 2.10 1.75
880 A268 400fr multicolored 3.50 2.75
881 A268 500fr multicolored 5.00 3.50
Nos. 878-881 (4) 12.00 8.75

Types of 1983-84 Redrawn and Inscribed "Republic of Cameroon"

1992   Litho.   Perf. 13½
882 A214 200fr like #739 2.25 1.40
a. Booklet pane of 5 —
Complete booklet, #882a —
883 A222 350fr like #763 3.75 2.50

AIDS Type of 1991

1993   Litho.   Perf. 13½
884 A262 100fr like #859 1.10 .70
885 A262 175fr like #860 1.90 1.25

Types of 1983 Redrawn and Inscribed "Republic of Cameroon"
886 A214 370fr like #738 3.50 2.50

Perf. 13
887 A217 410fr like #746 4.50 2.90

Wild Animal Type of 1980 Inscribed "Republique du Cameroun"

1993   Litho.   Serpentine Die Cut 9½
Booklet Stamps
Self-Adhesive
888 A186 125fr Crocodile 1.40 .65
a. Booklet pane of 4 5.75
889 A186 250fr Buffon's ante-lope, vert. 2.75 1.25
a. Booklet pane of 4 11.50

By their nature, Nos. 888a, 889a are complete booklets. The peelable backing serves as a booklet cover.

1994 World Cup Soccer Championships, US — A270

Designs: 125fr, Pres. Paul Biya holding soccer ball, lion. 250fr, Logo, lion, player, map. 450fr, Players, globe, World Cup, flag. 500fr, US eagle, Cameroun lion, soccer ball.

1994, Mar. 28   Litho.   Perf. 13
890 A270 125fr multicolored .75 .40
891 A270 250fr multicolored 1.50 .75
892 A270 450fr multicolored 2.75 1.50
893 A270 500fr multicolored 3.00 1.75
a. Min. sheet of 4, #890-893 90.00 7.00
Nos. 890-893 (4) 8.00 4.40

Nos. 853-854 Surcharged in Gold and Black

1993   Litho.   Perf. 13½
894 A258 125fr on 70fr #853 — —
895 A258 125fr on 100fr #854 — —

Cameroun Soccer League Type of 1992

1992-93   Litho.   Perf. 11½
896 A267 10fr like #876 — —
896A A267 25fr like #875 — —
896B A267 50fr like #874 — —

Nos. 896-896A dated 1993.
Issued: 50fr, 8/1/92; others, 1993.

Psittacus Erithacus — A271

1995   Litho.   Perf. 11½
Granite Paper
897 A271 125fr multicolored 1.50 .50

Visit of Pope John Paul II
A272

1995, Sept. 14   Perf. 12½
898 A272 55fr shown .35 .20
a. Souvenir sheet of 1 —
899 A272 125fr Pope, open text, cross .95 .50
a. Souvenir sheet of 1 —

UN, 50th Anniv.
A273

1995, Oct. 24   Perf. 11½
900 A273 200fr shown 1.25 .60
901 A273 250fr "50," people 1.50 .80

Conf. of Heads of State & Govt., Yaounde
A274

Perf. 12½, 14¾x14 (200fr, 250fr)
1996-97   Litho.
902 A274 125fr blue & multi —
c. A274 125fr Perf. 14¾x14 —
902A A274 200fr lt grn & multi ('97) —
902B A274 250fr yel & multi ('97) —
903 A274 410fr pink & multi, vert. —

No. 902c is dated "1997."

World Records Set at 1996 Summer Olympic Games, Atlanta
A275

1996   Perf. 11½
904 A275 125fr Baily, M. Johnson .55 .45
905 A275 250fr Harrison, Galfione, Perec, vert. 1.00 .90

Universal Declaration of Human Rights, 50th Anniv. — A279

1998   Litho.   Perf. 14x14¾
918 A279 370fr multi — —

1998 World Cup Soccer Championships, France — A280

Design: 125fr, Flag of Cameroon, World Cup trophy, vert.

1998   Litho.   Perf. 13
922 A280 125fr multi — —
923 A280 250fr multicolored — —

Shrike
A281

1998   Litho.   Perf. 13x13½
926 A281 125fr multicolored — —

Economic and Monetary Community of Central Africa Week — A281a

Design: 125fr, Flags surrounding map of Africa. 225fr, Flags above map of Africa.

1999   Litho.   Perf. 14½
927 A281a 125fr multi   —   —
928 A281a 225fr multi   —   —

Flora & Fauna — A282

2000   Litho.   Perf. 14x14½
929   A282 100fr Pineapple
930   A282 125fr Pineapple
930A A282 150fr Coffee beans
930B A282 175fr Crowned crane
931   A282 200fr Baboon
932   A282 250fr Coffee beans
934   A282 410fr Crowned crane

Dated 1998.

Peace, Work, Country A283

Map and Scenes — A284

Airplane and Wildlife — A285

2000   Litho.   Perf. 11¾
935 A283 125fr multi   —   —
936 A284 200fr multi   —   —
937 A285 250fr multi   —   —

Palais des Congrés, Yaounde A286

Perf. 11¾x11½
2001, Mar. 26   Litho.
938 A286 125fr multi   —   —

Cooperation between Cameroun and People's Republic of China, 30th anniv.

Campaign Against AIDS — A287

Design: 125fr, Woman vaccinating child, Chantal Biya Foundation emblem. 250fr, Chantal Biya Foundation emblem, globe, ribbon, woman with fetus.

2001   Litho.   Perf. 13¼x13
939 A287 125fr multi   —   —
941 A287 250fr multi   —   —
  a.   Souvenir sheet, #939, 941   —   —

2002 World Cup Soccer Championships, Japan and Korea — A287a

Indomitable Lions Soccer Team, 20th Anniv. of Success A288

2002, June 20   Litho.   Perf. 13¾
943 A287a 125fr multi   —   —
            Perf. 13x13¼
944 A288 250fr multi   —   —
            Souvenir Sheet
945   Sheet of 2,
                 #943, 945a   —   —
  a.   As #944, 40x44mm, perf. 13½ —

71st Interpol General Assembly, Yaounde — A289

2002   Litho.   Perf. 13¼x13
946 A289 125fr multi   —   —
  a.   Souvenir sheet of 1   —   —

Cooperation Between Cameroun and Japan — A290

2005   Litho.   Perf. 13
948 A290 100fr multi   —   —
949 A290 125fr multi   —   —
950 A290 200fr multi   —   —
951 A290 250fr multi   —   —
952 A290 370fr multi   —   —
953 A290 410fr multi   —   —
954 A290 500fr multi   —   —
955 A290 1000fr multi   —   —

Nos. 948-951, 954-955 exist with "2005" year date.

Cameroun postal officials have declared as illegal a stamp inscribed "Republic of Cameroon" dated "2005" marking the 70th birthday of Elvis Presley.

Postal Savings Bank — A291

2006   Litho.   Perf. 15x14
956 A291 500fr multi   4.50 4.50

No. 956 was issued in 1997 as a stamp to pay fees for opening an account with the Postal Savings Bank. It was made available for postal use in 2006.

Visit of Pope Benedict XVI to Cameroun A292

Flags of Vatican City and Cameroun, Pope Benedict XVI, Pres. Paul Biya and background color of: 200fr, Yellow. 250fr, Bright pink.

2009   Litho.   Perf. 13x13¼
957-958 A292 Set of 2   4.25 4.25

New Challenges for Africa Conference, Yaounde — A293

Colors: 125fr, Black & gray. 250fr, Multicolored.

2010   Litho.   Perf. 13½
959-960 A293 Set of 2   —   —

Reunification and Independence, 50th Anniv. — A294

Designs: 125fr, Cameroun flag shown rotated 90 degrees clockwise. 200fr, 50th anniversary emblem. 250fr, Arms of Cameroun. 500fr, Pres. Paul Biya in black. 1000fr, Pres. Biya in color.

2010
961-964 A294 Set of 4   —   —
964a   Horiz. strip of 4, #961-964   —
964b   Booklet pane of 8, 2 each
        #961-964   —
        Complete booklet, #964b   —
            Souvenir Sheet
965 A294 1000fr multi   —   —

No. 965 sold for 1500fr.

SEMI-POSTAL STAMPS

Curie Issue
Common Design Type
1938   Unwmk.   Perf. 13
B1 CD80 1.75fr + 50c brt ul-
                    tra   10.00 10.00

French Revolution Issue
Common Design Type
Photogravure; Name and Value Typographed in Black

1939
B2 CD83 45c + 25c green   11.50 11.50
B3 CD83 70c + 30c brown   11.50 11.50
B4 CD83 90c + 35c red
                    org   11.50 11.50
B5 CD83 1.25fr + 1fr rose
                    pink   11.50 11.50
B6 CD83 2.25fr + 2fr blue 14.00 14.00
        Nos. B2-B6 (5)   60.00 60.00

Stamps of 1925-33 Surcharged in Black

1940   Perf. 14x13½
B7 A7 1.25fr + 2fr gray & dp
                bl   27.50 24.00
B8 A7 1.75fr + 3fr brn & org 27.50 24.00
B9 A7 2fr + 5fr dl grn &
                brn org   27.50 24.00
        Nos. B7-B9 (3)   82.50 72.00

The surtax was used for war relief work.

Regular Stamps of 1939 Surcharged in Black

1940   Perf. 13
B10 A20 25c + 5fr blk brn   130.00 110.00
B11 A20 45c + 5fr slate grn 130.00 110.00
B12 A20 60c + 5fr peacock
                bl   130.00 120.00
B13 A20 70c + 5fr plum   130.00 120.00
        Nos. B10-B13 (4)   520.00 460.00

The surtax was used to purchase Spitfire planes for the Free French army.

Common Design Type and

Military Doctor SP2

Cameroun Militiaman — SP4

1941   Photo.   Perf. 13½
B13A SP2 1fr + 1fr red   1.60
B13B CD86 1.50fr + 3fr maroon   1.60
B13C SP4 2.50fr + 1fr dk bl   1.60
        Nos. B13A-B13C (3)   4.80

Nos. B13A-B13C were issued by the Vichy government in France, but were not placed on sale in Cameroun.

New York World's Fair Stamps, 1939 Surcharged in Black

1941   Perf. 12½x12
B14 CD82 1.25fr + 10fr car
                    lake   120.00 120.00
B15 CD82 2.25fr + 10fr ultra 120.00 120.00

New York World's Fair Stamps, 1939,
Surcharged in Black or Blue

1941
B16 CD82 1.25fr + 10fr car
lake (Bl)   30.00 30.00
B17 CD82 2.25fr + 10fr ultra
(Bk)   30.00 30.00

The surtax was used to purchase ambulances for the Free French army.

Regular
Stamps of
1933-39
Surcharged
in Black

1943   *Perf. 14x13½, 13, 12½x12*
B21 A7   1.25fr + 100 gray
    & dp bl   20.00 20.00
B22 A21   1.25fr + 100fr car
    rose   20.00 20.00
B23 CD82 1.25fr + 100fr car
    lake   20.00 20.00
B24 A21   1.50fr + 100fr
    choc   20.00 20.00
B25 CD82 2.25fr + 100fr ul-
    tra   20.00 20.00
   Nos. B21-B25 (5)   100.00 100.00

Nos. 281A-281B
Surcharged in Black or Red

1944   Engr.   *Perf. 12½x12*
B25A   50c + 1.50fr on 2.50fr
    deep blue (R)   .80
B25B   + 2.50fr on 1fr green   .80

Colonial Development Fund.
Nos. B25A-B25B were issued by the Vichy government in France, but were not placed on sale in Cameroun.

Red Cross Issue
Common Design Type
1944   Photo.   *Perf. 14½x14*
B28 CD90 5fr + 20fr rose   2.00 1.60

The surtax was for the French Red Cross and national relief.

> Catalogue values for unused stamps in this section, from this point to the end of the section, are for Never Hinged items.

Tropical Medicine Issue
Common Design Type
1950   Engr.   *Perf. 13*
B29 CD100 10fr + 2fr dk bl grn
    & dk grn   7.25 5.50

The surtax was for charitable work.

Independent State

Map and
Flag — SP7

Unwmk.
1961, Mar. 25   Engr.   *Perf. 13*
B30 SP7 20fr + 5fr grn, car &
    yel   1.00 1.00
B31 SP7 25fr + 10fr multi   1.25 1.25
B32 SP7 30fr + 15fr car, yel &
    grn   1.75 1.75
   Nos. B30-B32 (3)   4.00 4.00

The surtax was for the Red Cross.

Federal Republic

Map of Cameroun, Lions Emblem and
Physician Helping Leper
SP8

1962, Jan. 28
B33 SP8 20fr + 5fr multi   .70 .40
B34 SP8 25fr + 10fr multi   .90 .50
B35 SP8 50fr + 15fr multi   1.75 .85
   Nos. B33-B35 (3)   3.35 1.75

Issued for leprosy relief work.

Anti-Malaria Issue
Common Design Type
1962, Apr. 7   *Perf. 12½x12*
B36 CD108 25fr + 5fr rose lilac   1.00 .45

WHO drive to eradicate malaria.

Freedom from Hunger Issue
Common Design Type
1963, Mar. 21   Engr.   *Perf. 13*
B37 CD112 18fr + 5fr multi   1.00 .35
B38 CD112 25fr + 5fr multi   1.25 .40

Antelopes — SP9

Designs: 125fr+10fr, Ourebia ourebi.
250fr+20fr, Kobus defassa.

1991, Apr. 30   Litho.   *Perf. 13½x13*
B39 SP9 125fr + 10fr multi   2.00 1.10
B40 SP9 250fr + 20fr multi   3.00 2.25
   a.   Souvenir sheet of 2, #B39-B40,
     perf. 12½   8.00 3.50

AIR POST STAMPS

Common Design Type
1942 Unwmk. Photo. Perf. 14½x14
C1 CD87   1fr dk orange   .30 .30
C2 CD87   1.50fr brt red   .30 .30
C3 CD87   5fr brown red   .65 .65
C4 CD87   10fr black   .80 .80
C5 CD87   25fr ultra   1.10 1.10
C6 CD87   50fr dk green   1.40 1.40
C7 CD87   100fr plum   1.75 1.75
   Nos. C1-C7 (7)   6.30 6.30

Types AP9 and AP10 without "RF" and

Plane Over
Coast
AP3

1943-44   Photo.   *Perf. 13, 13½*
C7A AP9   25c brown red   .25
C7B AP9   50c green   .25
C7C AP9   1fr brt violet   .30
C7D AP10   5fr red brown   .55
C7E AP10   10fr black   .65
C7F AP10   12fr orange   .70
C7G AP10   20fr crimson   .95

C7H AP10   50fr blue   1.10
C7I AP3   100fr lilac brown   1.25
   Nos. C7A-C7I (9)   6.00

Nos. C7A to C7I were issued by the Vichy Government in France, but were not placed on sale in Cameroun.
For Types AP9 and AP10 inscribed RF, see Nos. C15-C24.

> Catalogue values for unused stamps in this section are for Never Hinged items.

Victory Issue
Common Design Type
1946, May 8   Engr.   *Perf. 12½*
C8 CD92 8fr dk violet brn   1.60 1.20

European victory of the Allied Nations in WWII.

Chad to Rhine Issue
Common Design Types
1946, June 6
C9   CD93   5fr dk blue grn   1.60 1.25
C10 CD94   10fr dk rose vio   1.60 1.25
C11 CD95   15fr red   2.00 1.60
C12 CD96   20fr brt blue   2.00 1.60
C13 CD97   25fr orange red   2.10 1.75
C14 CD98   50fr gray   2.75 2.25
   Nos. C9-C14 (6)   12.05 9.70

Plane and Map — AP9

Seaplane
Alighting
AP10

Plane and
Freighters
AP11

1946   Photo.   *Perf. 13, 13½*
C15 AP9   25c brown red   .40 .25
C16 AP9   50c green   .40 .25
C17 AP9   1fr brt violet   .50 .30
C18 AP10   2fr olive grn   .65 .50
C19 AP10   3fr chocolate   .65 .50
C20 AP10   4fr deep ultra   .65 .50
C21 AP10   6fr blue grn   .65 .50
C22 AP10   7fr brt violet   1.10 .80
C23 AP10   12fr orange   5.50 3.50
C24 AP10   20fr crimson   1.90 1.40
C25 AP11   50fr dk ultra   2.75 1.90
   Nos. C15-C25 (11)   15.15 10.40

Nos. C15 to C25 were issued in 1941 in France by the Vichy Government, but were not sold in Cameroun until 1946.

Birds over Mountains — AP12

Cavalry and Plane — AP13

Warrior, Dance
Mask and Nose
of Plane — AP14

   Perf. 12½
1947, Feb. 10   Unwmk.   Engr.
C26 AP12   50fr dk green   3.25 1.20
C27 AP13   100fr brn red   4.75 1.20
C28 AP14   200fr black   7.25 2.40
   Nos. C26-C28 (3)   15.25 4.80

UPU Issue
Common Design Type
1949, July   *Perf. 13*
C29 CD99 25fr multicolored   8.00 4.75

Rhumsiki
Peak — AP16

1953, Feb. 16
C30 AP16 500fr grnsh blk, dk
    vio & vio bl   26.00 4.00

For surcharge see No. C40.

Edéa Dam and Sacred Ibis — AP17

1953, Nov. 18
C31 AP17 15fr choc, brn lake &
    ultra   5.50 1.60

Dedication of Edea Dam on the Sanaga River.

Liberation Issue
Common Design Type
1954, June 6
C32 CD102 15fr dk grnsh bl &
    bl grn   7.25 4.75

Dr. Eugene Jamot, Research
Laboratory and Tsetse Flies — AP19

1954, Nov. 29
C33 AP19 15fr dk grn, ind & dk
    brn   4.75 2.75

75th anniv. of the birth of Dr. Eugene Jamot.

Logging — AP20

100fr, Giraffes. 200fr, Port of Douala.

1955, Jan. 24
C34	AP20	50fr ol grn, brn & vio brn	4.00	.80
C35	AP20	100fr grnsh bl, brn & dk brn	8.00	1.60
C36	AP20	200fr dk grn, choc & dp ultra	10.50	2.40
		Nos. C34-C36 (3)	22.50	4.80

For surcharges see Nos. C38-C39.

Federal Republic
Air Afrique Issue
Common Design Type

1962, Feb. 17   Engr.   Perf. 13
Unwmk.
C37	CD107	25fr mar, pur & lt grn	1.00	.50

Nos. C35-C36 and C30 Surcharged in Red

Type I

Two types of 5sh:
I — "5/-" measures 6½x4mm.
II — "5/" measures 3¾x3mm, No dash after diagonal line.

Three types of 10sh:
I — "10/-" measures 9x3¾mm.
II — "10/-" measures 7x2½-3mm.
III — "1" of "10/" vertically in line with last "E" of "FEDERALE".

Two types of £1:
I — "REPUBLIQUE / FEDERALE" 17¼mm wide.
II — "REPUBLIQUE / FEDERALE" 22mm wide.

1961, Oct. 1   Engr.   Perf. 13
C38	AP20	5sh on 100fr (I)	10.00	6.00
a.		Type II	32.50	18.00
C39	AP20	10sh on 200fr (I)	22.00	13.00
a.		Type II	77.50	42.50
b.		Type III	32.50	30.00
C40	AP16	£1 on 500fr (I)	35.00	22.00
a.		Type II	60.00	35.00
		Nos. C38-C40 (3)	67.00	41.00

Issued for use in the former United Kingdom Trust Territory of Southern Cameroons.

Kapsikis Mokolo — AP21

Designs: 50fr, Cocotieres Hotel, Douala. 100fr, Cymothoe sangaris butterflies. 200fr, Ostriches, Waza Reservation.

1962, June 15
C41	AP21	50fr sl grn, bl & dl red	.90	.25
C42	AP21	100fr multicolored	5.75	.60
C43	AP21	200fr dk grn, blk & bis	8.00	1.40
C44	AP21	500fr vio brn, bl & ocher	9.00	2.25
		Nos. C41-C44 (4)	23.65	4.50

Telstar Type of Regular Issue

1963, Feb. 9
Size: 48x27mm
C45	A50	100fr dk grn & red brn	2.50	.65

Edéa Relay Station — AP22

1963, May 18   Photo.   Perf. 12x12½
C46	AP22	100fr multicolored	2.50	.65

Issued to publicize the high frequency telegraph connection Douala-Yaoundé.

African Postal Union Issue
Common Design Type

1963, Sept. 8   Unwmk.   Perf. 12½
C47	CD114	85fr ultra, ocher & red	2.25	1.00

Air Afrique Issue, 1963
Common Design Type

1963, Nov. 19   Perf. 13x12
C48	CD115	50fr pink, gray, blk & grn	1.25	.40

Olympic Games Type of 1964

300fr, Greco-Roman wrestlers (ancient).

1964, Oct. 10   Engr.   Perf. 13
C49	A57	300fr red, dk brn & dl grn	7.50	2.00
a.		Sheet of 3, #403-404, C49	13.50	4.25

Kribi Port — AP25

1964, Oct. 26   Unwmk.   Perf. 13
C50	AP25	50fr red brn, ultra & grn	1.00	.35

Black Rhinoceros — AP26

1964, Dec. 15   Engr.   Perf. 13
C51	AP26	250fr brn red, grn & dk brn	10.00	1.10

Pres. John F. Kennedy — AP27

1964, Dec. 8   Photo.   Perf. 12½
C52	AP27	100fr grn, yel grn & brn	2.50	1.10
a.		Souvenir sheet of 4	10.00	4.50

Pres. John F. Kennedy (1917-63).

Abraham Lincoln — AP28

1965, Apr. 20   Unwmk.   Perf. 13
C53	AP28	100fr multicolored	2.50	.80

Abraham Lincoln, death centenary.

Syncom Satellite and ITU Emblem — AP29

1965, May 17   Engr.
C54	AP29	70fr red, dk bl, & blk	1.60	.60

Cent. of the ITU.

Sir Winston Spencer Churchill, Statesman and World War II Leader — AP30

Designs: 12fr, Churchill giving V sign. 18fr, Churchill, battleship and oak leaves with acorns. Image reduced.

Perf. 13x12½
			Unwmk.	
1965, May 28		**Photo.**		
C55		12fr multicolored	1.00	.50
C56		18fr multicolored	1.00	.50
a.		AP40 Strip of 2, #C55-C56 + label	2.75	1.40

ICY Type of Regular Issue

1965, Sept. 11   Engr.   Perf. 13
C57	A68	100fr dk red & dk bl	2.25	.70

Racing Boat, Sanaga River, Edéa — AP31

1965, Oct. 27   Unwmk.   Perf. 13
C58	AP31	50fr brn, dk grn & sl	1.75	.35

Edward H. White Floating in Space and Gemini IV — AP32

Designs: 50fr, Vostok 6. 200fr, Gemini V and REP (rendezvous evaluation pod). 500fr, Gemini VI & VII rendezvous.

1966, Mar. 30   Engr.   Perf. 13
C59	AP32	50fr car rose & dk sl grn	.90	.35
C60	AP32	100fr red lil & vio bl	2.10	.65
C61	AP32	200fr ultra & dk pur	3.75	1.40
C62	AP32	500fr brt bl & indigo	9.00	3.00
		Nos. C59-C62 (4)	15.75	5.40

Man's conquest of space.

Hotel Type of Regular Issue

18fr, Mountain Hotel, Buea. 25fr, Hotel Akwa Palace, Douala. 50fr, Terminus Hotel, Yaoundé. 60fr, Imperial Hotel, Yaoundé. 85fr, Independence Hotel, Yaoundé. 100fr, Hunting Lodge, Mora, vert. 150fr, Boukarous (round huts), Waza Camp.

1966
C63	A71	18fr sl grn, brt bl & blk	.45	.20
C64	A71	25fr car, ultra & sl	.65	.25
C65	A71	50fr choc, grn & ocher	2.50	.90
C66	A71	60fr choc, grn & brt bl	1.50	.50
C67	A71	85fr dk car rose, dl bl & grn	1.90	.60
C68	A71	100fr brn, grn & sl	2.75	.70
C69	A71	150fr brn, dl bl & ocher	3.75	.90
		Nos. C63-C69 (7)	13.50	4.05

Issued: #C63-C64, 4/6; #C65-C69, 6/4.

Flower Type of Regular Issue

Flowers: 25fr, Hibiscus mutabilis. 50fr, Delonix regia. 100fr, Bougainvillea.

1966, May 20   Photo.   Perf. 12½
Flowers in Natural Colors
Size: 26x45mm
C70	A75	25fr slate green	.75	.20
C71	A75	50fr brt grnsh bl	1.60	.20
C72	A75	100fr gold	3.25	.25
		Nos. C70-C72 (3)	5.60	.65

Military Police — AP33

25fr, "Army," soldier, tanks & parachutes. 60fr, "Navy," & "Vigilante." 100fr, "Air Force," plane.

1966, June 21   Engr.   Perf. 13
C73	AP33	20fr vio bl, org brn & dl pur	.55	.20
C74	AP33	25fr dk grn, dl pur & brn	.55	.20
C75	AP33	60fr bl grn, bl & ind	1.60	.30
C76	AP33	100fr brn, Prus bl & car rose	2.75	.65
		Nos. C73-C76 (4)	5.45	1.35

Issued to honor Cameroun's armed forces.

Wembley Stadium, London — AP34

1966, July 20
C77	AP34	50fr shown	1.40	.25
C78	AP34	200fr Soccer	4.00	1.10

8th World Cup Soccer Championship, Wembley, England, July 11-30.

Air Afrique Issue, 1966
Common Design Type

1966, Aug. 31   Photo.   Perf. 13
C79	CD123	25fr red lil, blk & gray	.80	.20

Yaoundé Cathedral — AP35

18fr, Buea Cathedral. 30fr, Orthodox Church, Yaoundé. 60fr, Mosque, Garoua.

1966, Dec. 19   Engr.   Perf. 13
C80 AP35 18fr choc, bl & grn .45 .20
C81 AP35 25fr brn, grn & brt vio .55 .20
C82 AP35 30fr lil, grn & dl red .70 .20
C83 AP35 60fr mar, brt grn & grn 1.40 .35
Nos. C80-C83 (4) 3.10 .95

Pioneer A and Moon — AP36

1967, Apr. 30   Engr.   Perf. 13
C84 AP36 25fr shown .45 .20
C85 AP36 50fr Ranger 6 .90 .35
C86 AP36 100fr Luna 9 2.10 .65
C87 AP36 250fr Luna 10 4.50 2.00
Nos. C84-C87 (4) 7.95 3.20

"Conquest of the Moon."

Flower Type of Regular Issue
1967, June 22   Photo.   Perf. 12½
Size: 26x46mm
C88 A86 200fr Thevetia Peruviana 4.50 .90
C89 A86 250fr Amaryllis 5.50 1.10

African Postal Union Issue, 1967
Common Design Type
1967, Sept. 9   Engr.   Perf. 13
C90 CD124 100fr red brn, Prus bl & brt lil 2.40 .65

Skis, Ice Skates, Olympic Flame and Emblem — AP38

1967, Oct. 11   Engr.   Perf. 13
C91 AP38 30fr ultra & sepia 1.60 .20

Issued to publicize the 10th Winter Olympic Games, Grenoble, Feb. 6-8, 1968.

Cameroun Exhibit, EXPO '67 — AP39

100fr, Bangwa house poles carved with ancestor figures. 200fr, Canadian Pavilions.

1967, Oct. 18
C92 AP39 50fr mag, ol & mar 1.00 .25
C93 AP39 100fr dk grn, mar & dk brn 3.25 .70
C94 AP39 200fr brn, lil rose & sl grn 4.25 1.25
Nos. C92-C94 (3) 8.50 2.20

EXPO '67, International Exhibition, Montreal, Apr. 28-Oct. 27, 1967.
See note after No. C116 regarding 1969 moon overprint.

Konrad Adenauer (1876-1967), Chancellor of West Germany (1949-63) and Cologne Cathedral AP40

70fr, Adenauer and Chancellery, Bonn.

1967, Dec. 1   Photo.   Perf. 12½
C95 AP40 30fr multi .90 .20
C96 AP40 70fr multi 1.50 .40
a. Pair, #C95-C96 + label 3.50 .65

Pres. Ahidjo, King Faisal and View of Mecca — AP41

60fr, Pres. Ahidjo, Pope Paul VI & view of Rome.

1968, Feb. 18   Photo.   Perf. 12½
C97 AP41 30fr multi .90 .20
C98 AP41 60fr multi 2.10 .30

Issued to commemorate President Ahidjo's Pilgrimage to Mecca and visit to Rome.

Earth on Television Transmitted by Explorer VI — AP42

30fr, Molniya spacecraft. 40fr, Earth on television screen transmitted by Molniya.

1968, Apr. 20   Engr.   Perf. 13
C99 AP42 20fr multi .55 .20
C100 AP42 30fr multi .80 .20
C101 AP42 40fr multi 1.10 .20
Nos. C99-C101 (3) 2.45 .60

Telecommunication by satellite.

Forge — AP43

Boxing — AP44

#C103, Tea harvest. #C104, Trans-Cameroun railroad (diesel train emerging from tunnel). 40fr, Rubber harvest. 60fr, Douala Harbor, horiz.

1968, June 5   Engr.   Perf. 13
C102 AP43 20fr red brn, dk grn & ind .65 .20
C103 AP43 30fr dk brn, grn & ultra 1.10 .20
C104 AP43 30fr ind, sl grn & bis brn 7.50 .20
C105 AP43 40fr ol bis, dk grn & bl grn 1.10 .20
C106 AP43 60fr ultra, dk brn & sl 3.00 .40
Nos. C102-C106 (5) 13.35 1.20

Second Economic Development Five-Year Plan.

1968, Aug. 19   Engr.   Perf. 13
50fr, Long jump. 60fr, Athlete on rings.
C107 AP44 30fr brt grn, dk grn & choc .65 .20
C108 AP44 50fr brt grn, brn red & choc 1.25 .30
C109 AP44 60fr brn, grn, ultra & choc 1.50 .35
a. Min. sheet of 3, #C107-C109 4.00 1.50
Nos. C107-C109 (3) 3.40 .85

19th Olympic Games, Mexico City, 10/12-27.

Human Rights Type of Regular Issue
1968, Sept. 14   Photo.   Perf. 12½x13
C110 A92 30fr grn & brt pink .80 .20

Martin Luther King, Jr. — AP45

Portraits: No. C112, Mahatma Gandhi and map of India. 40fr, John F. Kennedy. 60fr, Robert F. Kennedy. No. C115, Rev. Martin Luther King, Jr. No. C116, Mahatma Gandhi.

1968, Dec. 5   Photo.   Perf. 12½
C111 AP45 30fr bl & blk .55 .20
C112 AP45 30fr multi .55 .20
C113 AP45 40fr pink & blk .90 .25
C114 AP45 60fr bluish lil & blk 1.10 .40
C115 AP45 70fr yel grn & blk 1.25 .45
a. Souvenir sheet of 4, #C112-C115 8.00 2.00
C116 AP45 70fr multi 1.25 .50
Nos. C111-C116 (6) 5.60 2.00

Issued to honor exponents of non-violence. The 2 King stamps (Nos. C111 and C115), the 2 Gandhi stamps (Nos. C112 and C116) and the 2 Kennedy stamps (Nos. C113-C114) are each printed as triptychs with a descriptive label between.
In 1969 Nos. C111-C116 and C94 were overprinted in carmine capitals: "Premier Homme / sur la Lune / 20 Juillet 1969" or "First Man / Landing on Moon / 20 July 1969". Values: on No. C94, $50; on #C111-C116, $275; on No. C115 (2 souvenir sheets, with both overprint types), $300.

PHILEXAFRIQUE Issue

The Letter, by Armand Cambon AP46

1968, Dec. 10
C117 AP46 100fr multi 3.25 .80

PHILEXAFRIQUE, Philatelic Exhibition in Abidjan, Feb. 14-23, 1969. Printed with alternating light green label.

2nd PHILEXAFRIQUE Issue
Common Design Type
Design: Cameroun #199 and Wouri Bridge.

1969, Feb. 14   Engr.   Perf. 13
C118 CD128 50fr multi 3.25 .55

Caladium Bicolor — AP47

Flowers: 50fr, Aristolochia elegans. 100fr, Gloriosa simplex.

1969, May 14   Photo.   Perf. 12½
C119 AP47 30fr lil & multi .70 .20
C120 AP47 50fr grn & multi 1.40 .35
C121 AP47 100fr grn & multi 3.25 .55
Nos. C119-C121 (3) 5.35 1.10

3rd Intl. Flower Show, Paris, Apr. 23-Oct. 5.

Douala Post Office — AP48

50fr, Buèa P.O. 100fr, Bafoussam P.O.

1969, June 19   Engr.   Perf. 13
C122 AP48 30fr grn, vio bl & brn .55 .20
C123 AP48 50fr sl, emer & red brn .90 .25
C124 AP48 100fr dk brn, brt grn & brn 1.75 .50
Nos. C122-C124 (3) 3.20 .95

Coronation of Napoleon I, by Jacques Louis David — AP49

Napoleon Crossing Saint Bernard, after J. L. David — AP50

1969, July 4   Photo.   Perf. 12x12½
C125 AP49 30fr vio bl & multi 1.00 .20
Die-cut Perf. 10
Embossed on Gold Foil
C126 AP50 1000fr gold 45.00 16.00
Bicentenary of birth of Napoleon I.

William E. B. Du Bois (1868-1963), American Writer — AP51

15fr, Dr. Price Mars, Haiti (1876-1969). #C128, Aimé Cesaire, Martinique (1913-). #C130, Langston Hughes, US (1902-67). #C131, Marcus Garvey, Jamaica (1887-1940). 100fr, René Maran, Martinique (1887-1960).

1969, Sept. 25   Photo.   Perf. 12½

C127	AP51	15fr lt bl & blk	.45	.20
C128	AP51	30fr lem & blk	.55	.20
C129	AP51	30fr rose brn & blk	.55	.20
C130	AP51	50fr gray & blk	.80	.25
C131	AP51	50fr emer & blk	.80	.25
C132	AP51	100fr yel & blk	2.00	.60
a.		Min. sheet of 6, #C127-C132	6.75	2.50
		Nos. C127-C132 (6)	5.15	1.70

Issued to honor Negro writers.

ILO Emblem — AP52

1969, Oct. 29   Photo.   Perf. 13

C133	AP52	30fr blk, bl grn & gray	.80	.20
C134	AP52	50fr blk, dp lil rose & gray	1.40	.25

50th anniv. of the ILO.

Armstrong, Collins and Aldrin Splashdown in the Pacific — AP53

Design: 500fr, Landing module and Neil A. Armstrong's first step on moon.

1969, Nov. 29   Photo.   Perf. 12½

C135	AP53	200fr multi	5.00	1.25
C136	AP53	500fr multi	11.50	2.25

See note after Algeria No. 427.

Pres. Ahidjo, Arms and Map of Cameroun — AP54

Embossed on Gold Foil

1970, Jan. 1   Die-cut Perf. 10

C137	AP54	1000fr gold & multi	26.00	8.25

10th anniversary of independence.

Hotel Mont Fébé, Yaoundé — AP55

1970, Jan. 15   Engr.   Perf. 13

C138	AP55	30fr lt brn, sl grn & gray	.80	.20

Lenin — AP56

1970, Jan. 25   Photo.   Perf. 12½

C139	AP56	50fr org & blk	2.00	.25

Plant Type of Regular Issue

Designs: 50fr, Cleome speciosa (caper). 100fr, Mussaenda erythrophylla (madder).

1970, Mar. 24   Photo.   Perf. 12½
Size: 26x46mm

C140	A99	50fr blk & multi	1.40	.25
C141	A99	100fr multi	2.75	.40

Map of Africa and Lions Emblem Pinpointing Yaoundé — AP57

1970, May 2   Photo.   Perf. 12½

C142	AP57	100fr multi	2.25	.50

13th Lions International Congress of District 13, Yaoundé, May 2, 1970.

UN Emblem and Doves — AP58

Design: 50fr, UN emblem and dove, vert.

1970, June 26   Engr.   Perf. 13

C143	AP58	30fr brn & org	1.00	.20
C144	AP58	50fr Prus bl & sl bl	1.25	.25

25th anniversary of the United Nations.

Japanese Pavilion and EXPO Emblem — AP59

Designs (EXPO Emblem and): 100fr, Map of Japan, vert. 150fr, Australian pavilion.

1970, Aug. 1   Engr.   Perf. 13

C145	AP59	50fr ind, lt grn & ver	.90	.25
C146	AP59	100fr bl, lt grn & red	2.00	.40
C147	AP59	150fr choc, bl & gray	3.25	.65
		Nos. C145-C147 (3)	6.15	1.30

EXPO '70 International Exhibition, Osaka, Japan, Mar. 15-Sept. 13.

Charles de Gaulle — AP60

Design: 200fr, de Gaulle in unifrom.

1970, Aug. 27

C148		100fr grn, vio bl & ol brn	2.25	.50
C149		200fr ol brn, vio bl & grn	4.50	.90
a.		AP60 Pair, #C148-C149 + label	8.00	1.60

Rallying of the Free French, 30th anniv. For overprints see Nos. C159-C160.

Pelé and Team — AP61

1970, Oct. 14   Photo.   Perf. 12½

Designs: 50fr, Aztec Stadium, Mexico City, horiz. 100fr, Mexican soccer team, horiz.

C150	AP61	50fr multi	.90	.25
C151	AP61	100fr multi	2.00	.50
C152	AP61	200fr multi	3.50	1.00
		Nos. C150-C152 (3)	6.40	1.75

9th World Soccer Championships for the Jules Rimet Cup, Mexico City, May 30-June 21, and the final victory of Brazil over Italy.

Ludwig van Beethoven (1770-1827), Composer AP62

1970, Nov. 23   Engr.   Perf. 13

C153	AP62	250fr multi	5.75	1.00

Christ at Emmaus, by Rembrandt — AP63

150fr, The Anatomy Lesson, by Rembrandt.

1970, Dec. 5   Photo.   Perf. 12x12½

C154	AP63	70fr grn & multi	1.40	.25
C155	AP63	150fr multi	2.75	.60

Charles Dickens — AP64

Designs: 50fr, Scenes from David Copperfield. 100fr, Dickens holding quill.

1970, Dec. 22   Perf. 13

C156	AP64	40fr blk & rose	.95	.20
C157	AP64	50fr bis & multi	1.00	.20
C158	AP64	100fr rose & multi	2.00	.40
a.		Strip of 3, #C156-C158	5.00	1.00

Charles Dickens (1812-1870), English novelist.

De Gaulle Type of 1970 Overprinted

Charles de Gaulle

1971, Jan. 15   Engr.   Perf. 13

C159		100fr vio bl, emer & brn red	2.75	.40
C160		200fr brn red, emer & vio bl	5.75	.80
a.		AP60 Pair, #C159-C160 + label	9.00	1.40

In memory of Gen. Charles de Gaulle (1890-1970), President of France.

Timber Storage, Douala — AP65

Industrialization: 70fr, ALUCAM aluminum plant, Edea, vert. 100fr, Mbakaou Dam.

1971, Feb. 14   Engr.   Perf. 13

C161	AP65	40fr dk red, bl grn & ol brn	.55	.20
C162	AP65	70fr ol brn, sl grn & brt bl	1.10	.25
C163	AP65	100fr Prus bl, yel grn & red brn	1.75	.40
		Nos. C161-C163 (3)	3.40	.85

Relay Race — AP66

50fr, Torch bearer, vert. 100fr, Discus.

1971, Apr. 24   Engr.   Perf. 13

C164	AP66	30fr dk brn, ver & ind	.65	.20
C165	AP66	50fr blk, bl & choc	.80	.25
C166	AP66	100fr multi	1.75	.35
		Nos. C164-C166 (3)	3.20	.80

75th anniv. of revival of Olympic Games.

Fishing Trawler — AP67

Designs: 40fr, Local fishermen, Northern Cameroun. 70fr, Fishing harbor, Douala. 150fr, Shrimp boats, Douala.

1971, May 14   **Engr.**   **Perf. 13**
C167 AP67 30fr lt brn, bl & grn   .70 .20
C168 AP67 40fr sl grn, bl & dk brn   .90 .20
C169 AP67 70fr dk brn, bl & red org   2.00 .25
C170 AP67 150fr multi   4.25 .60
Nos. C167-C170 (4)   7.85 1.25

Cameroun fishing industry.

Cameroun No. 123 and War Memorial, Yaoundé — AP68

Designs (Cameroun Stamps): 25fr, No. C33 and Jamot memorial. 40fr, No. 431 and government buildings, Yaoundé. 70fr, No. 19 and Imperial German postal emblem. 100fr, No. 101 and World War II memorial.

1971, Aug. 1   **Engr.**   **Perf. 13**
C171 AP68 20fr grn, ocher & dk brn   .35 .20
C172 AP68 25fr dk brn, vio bl & sl grn   .55 .20
C173 AP68 40fr grn, mar & sl   .70 .20
C174 AP68 50fr dk brn, blk & ver   1.00 .20
C175 AP68 100fr mar, sl grn & org   1.75 .40
Nos. C171-C175 (5)   4.35 1.20

PHILATECAM 1971 Philatelic Exhibition.

Cameroun Flag, Pres. Ahidjo and Reunification Highway — AP69

Typographed, Silk Screen, Embossed
1971, Oct. 1   **Perf. 12½**
C176 AP69 250fr gold & multi   5.75 2.00
PHILATECAM Philatelic Exhibition, Yaoundé-Douala.

African Postal Union Issue, 1971
Common Design Type
1971, Nov. 13   **Photo.**   **Perf. 13x13½**
C177 CD135 100fr bl & multi   2.00 .40

Annunciation, by Fra Angelico — AP71

Christmmas (Paintings): 45fr, Virgin and Child, by Andrea del Sarto. 150fr, Christ Child with Lamb, detail from Holy Family, by Raphael, vert.

1971, Dec. 19   **Perf. 13x13½, 13½x13**
C178 AP71 40fr multi   .55 .20
C179 AP71 45fr multi   .70 .20
C180 AP71 150fr multi   3.25 .60
Nos. C178-C180 (3)   4.50 1.00

Cameroun Airlines Emblem AP72

1972, Feb. 2   **Photo.**   **Perf. 12½x12**
C181 AP72 50fr lt bl & multi   .80 .20

Inauguration of Cameroun Airlines.

Doge's Palace, by Ippolito Caffi AP73

100fr, 200fr, Details from "Regatta on the Grand Canal," by School of Canaletto.

1972   **Photo.**   **Perf. 13**
C182 AP73 40fr gold & multi   .70 .20
C183 AP73 100fr gold & multi   1.75 .40
C184 AP73 200fr gold & multi   3.75 .80
Nos. C182-C184 (3)   6.20 1.40

UNESCO campaign to save Venice.

Cosmonauts Patsayev, Dobrovolsky and Volkov — AP74

1972, May 1   **Photo.**   **Perf. 13x13½**
C185 AP74 50fr multi   1.00 .20

Salute-Soyuz 11 space mission, and in memory of the Russian cosmonauts Victor I. Patsayev, Georgi T. Dobrovolsky and Vladislav N. Volkov, who died during Soyuz 11 space mission, June 6-30, 1971.

UN Headquarters, Chinese Flag and Gate of Heavenly Peace — AP75

1972, May 19   **Perf. 13**
C186 AP75 50fr blk, scar & gold   3.25 .20

Admission of People's Republic of China to UN.

United Republic

Olympic Rings, Swimming AP76

Designs (Olympic Rings and): No. C188, Boxing, vert. 200fr, Equestrian.

1972, Aug. 1   **Engr.**   **Perf. 13**
C187 AP76 50fr lake & slate grn   .90 .20
C188 AP76 50fr choc & slate   .90 .20

C189 AP76 200fr cl, gray & dk brn   3.50 .70
a. Min. sheet of 3   5.75 2.25
Nos. C187-C189 (3)   5.30 1.10

20th Olympic Games, Munich, Aug. 26-Sept. 11. No. C189a contains stamps similar to Nos. C187-C189, but in changed colors. The 50fr (swimming) is Prussian blue, violet & brown; the 50c (boxing) lilac, Prussian blue & brown; the 200fr, Prussian blue & brown.

Nos. C187-C189 Overprinted in Red or Black

a

b

c

1972, Oct. 23   **Engr.**   **Perf. 13**
C190 AP76(a) 50fr (R)   .90 .20
C191 AP76(b) 50fr   .90 .20
C192 AP76(c) 200fr   3.50 .80
Nos. C190-C192 (3)   5.30 1.20

Gold Medal Winners in 20th Olympic Games: Mark Spitz, US, swimming (#C190); Dieter Kottysch, West Germany, light middle-weight boxing (#C191); Richard Meade, Great Britain, 3-day equestrian (#C192).

Madonna with Angels, by Cimabue AP77

Christmas: 140fr, Madonna of the Rose Arbor, by Stefan Lochner.

1972, Dec. 21   **Photo.**   **Perf. 13**
C193 AP77 45fr gold & multi   1.00 .20
C194 AP77 140fr gold & multi   2.75 .45

St. Teresa, the Little Flower — AP78

100fr, Lisieux Cathedral and St. Teresa.

1973, Jan. 2   **Engr.**
C195 AP78 45fr vio bl, pur & mar   .70 .20
C196 AP78 100fr mag, ultra & brn   1.75 .40
Centenary of the birth of St. Teresa of Lisieux (1873-1897); Carmelite nun.

African Unity Hall, Addis Ababa and Emperor Haile Selassie — AP79

1973, Mar. 14   **Photo.**   **Perf. 13**
C197 AP79 45fr yellow & multi   1.00 .20

80th birthday of Emperor Haile Selassie of Ethiopia.

Corn, Grain, Healthy and Starving People — AP80

1973, Apr. 10   **Typo.**   **Perf. 13**
C198 AP80 45fr multi   .80 .20

World Food Program, 10th anniversary.

Hearts and Blood Vessels — AP81

1973, May 5   **Engr.**
C199 AP81 50fr dk car rose & dk vio bl   1.00 .20

"Your Heart is Your Health" and for the 25th anniv. of the WHO.

Scout Emblem and Flags — AP82

Type of Regular Issue

Designs: 45fr, Map of Cameroun, Pres. Ahidjo and No. C176. 70fr, National colors and commemorative inscriptions.

1973, May 20   **Engr.**   **Perf. 13**
C200 A128 45fr grn & multi   .80 .20
C201 A128 70fr red & multi   1.00 .25

1973, July 31   **Typo.**   **Perf. 13**
C202 AP82 40fr multi   1.00 .20
C203 AP82 45fr multi   1.25 .20
C204 AP82 100fr multi   3.25 .40
Nos. C202-C204 (3)   5.50 .80

Cameroun's admission to the World Scout Conference, Mar. 26, 1971.

African Weeks Issue

Head and City Hall, Brussels — AP83

1973, Sept. 17   Engr.   *Perf. 13*
C205 AP83 40fr dp brn & rose claret   .80   .20

African Weeks, Brussels, Sept. 15-30.

Map of Africa with Cameroun — AP84

1973, Sept. 29   Engr.   *Perf. 13*
C206 AP84 40fr blk, red & grn   .80   .20

Help for handicapped children.

Zamengoe Radar Station AP85

1973, Dec. 8   Engr.   *Perf. 13*
C207 AP85 100fr bl, lt brn & grn   1.50   .40

Chancellor Rolin Madonna, by Van Eyck AP86

Christmas: 140fr, Nativity, by Federigo Barocei.

1973, Dec. 11   Photo.   *Perf. 13*
C208 AP86 45fr gold & multi   1.00   .20
C209 AP86 140fr gold & multi   2.75   .70

Zebu Type of 1974

1974, June 1   Litho.   *Perf. 13*
C210 A140 45fr Zebu herd   1.40   .20

Churchill and Union Jack AP87

1974, July 10   Engr.   *Perf. 13*
C211 AP87 100fr blk, bl & red   1.60   .40

Winston Churchill (1874-1965).

Soccer, Arms of Frankfurt, Dortmund, Gelsenkirchen and Stuttgart — AP88

100fr, Soccer & arms of Berlin, Hamburg, Hanover & Düsseldorf. 200fr, Soccer cup & game.

1974, Aug. 5   Photo.   *Perf. 13*
C212 AP88 45fr gray, sl & org   .65   .20
C213 AP88 100fr gray, sl & org   1.25   .40
C214 AP88 200fr org, slate & bl   2.50   .65
  a.   Strip of 3, Nos. C212-C214   5.00   1.40

World Cup Soccer Championship, Munich, June 13-July 7.

Nos. C212-C214 Overprinted in Dark Blue

1974, Sept. 16   Photo.   *Perf. 13*
C215 AP88 45fr multi   .65   .20
C216 AP88 100fr multi   1.25   .40
C217 AP88 200fr multi   2.40   .80
  a.   Strip of 3, Nos. C215-C217   5.50   1.50

World Cup Soccer Championship, 1974, victory of German Federal Republic.

UPU Type of 1974

100fr, Cameroun #503. 200fr, Cameroun #C29.

1974, Oct. 8   Engr.   *Perf. 13*
C218 A142 100fr blue & multi   1.75   .30
C219 A142 200fr red & multi   3.25   .60

Copernicus and Planets Circling Sun — AP89

1974, Oct. 15   Engr.   *Perf. 13*
C220 AP89 250fr multi   3.50   1.00

500th anniversary of the birth of Nicolaus Copernicus (1473-1543), Polish astronomer.

21st Chess Olympiad, Nice, France, June 6-30 — AP90

1974, Nov. 3   Photo.   *Perf. 13x12½*
C221 AP90 100fr Chess pieces   5.25   1.00

Mask and ARPHILA Emblem — AP91

1974, Nov. 30   Engr.   *Perf. 13*
C222 AP91 50fr choc & magenta   .80   .25

ARPHILA 75, Paris, June 6-16, 1975.

Presidents and Flags of Cameroun, CAR, Gabon and Congo — AP92

1974, Dec. 8   Photo.
C223 AP92 100fr gold & multi   2.40   .40
See note after No. 595.

Man Landing on Moon — AP93

1974, Dec. 15   Engr.
C224 AP93 200fr brn, bl & car   3.25   .80

5th anniv. of man's 1st landing on the moon.

Charles de Gaulle and Félix Eboué — AP94

1975, Feb. 24   Typo.   *Perf. 13*
C225 AP94 45fr multi   1.50   .20
C226 AP94 200fr multi   5.00   .80

Felix A. Eboué (1884-1944), Governor of Chad, first colonial governor to join Free French in WWII, 30th death anniversary.

Marquis de Lafayette AP95

American Bicentennial: 140fr, Washington and soldiers. 500fr, Franklin and Independence Hall.

1975, Oct. 20   Engr.   *Perf. 13*
C227 AP95 100fr vio bl & multi   2.10   .40
C228 AP95 140fr brn & multi   2.25   .60
C229 AP95 500fr grn & multi   7.25   1.60
  Nos. C227-C229 (3)   11.60   2.60

The Burning Bush, by Nicolas Froment AP96

Painting: 500fr, Adoration of the Kings, by Gentile da Fabriano, horiz.

1975, Dec. 25   Photo.   *Perf. 13*
C230 AP96 50fr gold & multi   .90   .20
C231 AP96 500fr gold & multi   7.25   1.60

Christmas 1975.

Concorde and Route: Paris-Dakar-Rio de Janeiro — AP97

1976, July 20   Litho.   *Perf. 13*
C232 AP97 500fr lt bl & multi   6.50   1.60
  a.   Souvenir sheet of 1   9.00   3.75

1st commercial flight of supersonic jet Concorde from Paris to Rio de Janeiro, Jan. 21. No. C232a sold for 600fr.
For overprint see No. C263.

Dance Type of 1976

50fr, Dancers & drummer. 100fr, Woman dancer.

1976, Sept. 15   Litho.   *Perf. 12*
C233 A154 50fr gray & multi   .65   .20
C234 A154 100fr gray & multi   1.10   .35

Virgin and Child, by Giovanni Bellini — AP98

Paintings: 30fr, Adoration of the Shepherds, by Le Brun. 60fr, Adoration of the Kings, by Rubens. 500fr, The Newborn, by Georges de la Tour.

1976, Dec. 15   Litho.   *Perf. 12½*
C235 AP98 30fr gold & multi   .70   .20
C236 AP98 60fr gold & multi   .90   .25
C237 AP98 70fr gold & multi   1.25   .35
C238 AP98 500fr gold & multi   9.00   1.60
  a.   Souv. sheet of 4, #C235-C238   12.50   3.75
  Nos. C235-C238 (4)   11.85   2.30

Christmas 1976.

Festival Type of 1977

Traditional Chief on his throne, sculpture.

1977, Feb. 4   Litho.   *Perf. 12½*
C239 A159 60fr multi   1.10   .25

Crucifixion, by Matthias Grunewald — AP99

125fr, Christ on the Cross, by Velazquez, vert. 150fr, The Deposition, by Titian.

1977, Apr. 2   Litho.   Perf. 12½
C240 AP99 50fr gold & multi   .90   .20
C241 AP99 125fr gold & multi   1.75   .40
C242 AP99 150fr gold & multi   2.50   .55
a. Souv. sheet of 3, #C240-
    C242, perf. 12   6.75   1.75
  Nos. C240-C242 (3)   5.15   1.15
Easter 1977. No. C242a sold for 350fr.

Lions Emblem, Map of Africa — AP100

Rotary Emblem AP101

1977, Apr. 29   Litho.   Perf. 12½
C243 AP100 250fr multi   3.00   1.00
Lions Club of Douala, 19th Cong., 4/29-30.

1977, May 18
C244 AP101 60fr multi   .70   .25
Rotary Club of Douala, 20th anniversary.

Antoine de Saint-Exupéry AP102

Charles Lindbergh and Spirit of St. Louis — AP103

Designs: 50fr, Jean Mermoz and his plane. 80fr, Maryse Bastié and her plane. 100fr, Sikorsky S-43. 300fr, Concorde.

1977, May 20   Engr.   Perf. 13
C245 AP103 50fr org & bl   .80   .20
C246 AP102 60fr mag & org   .95   .25
C247 AP103 80fr mag & bl   1.25   .30
a. Souv. sheet, #C245-C247   3.25   1.10
C248 AP103 100fr grn & yel   1.50   .40
C249 AP103 300fr multi   5.50   1.25
C250 AP103 500fr multi   14.50   6.00
a. Souv. sheet, #C248-C250   14.50   6.00
  Nos. C245-C250 (6)   18.00   4.15
Aviation pioneers and events. No. C247a sold for 200fr. No. C250a sold for 1000fr. For overprint see No. C262.

Sassenage Castle, Grenoble — AP104

1977, May 21   Litho.   Perf. 12½
C251 AP104 70fr multi   1.60   1.00
10th anniv. of Intl. French Language Council.

Jufilex Type of 1977
Designs: 70fr, Switzerland (Zurich) No. 1L1 and Cameroun No. 16. 100fr, Switzerland (Geneva) No. 2L1 and Cameroun No. 254.

1977, June 5   Litho.   Perf. 12
C252 A161 70fr multi   1.25   .25
C253 A161 100fr multi   2.10   .40

Apollo-Soyuz Type
100fr, Astronaut Vance Brand, Apollo in orbit. 250fr, Apollo and Soyuz docking. 350fr, Cosmonaut Valery Kubasov, Soyuz in orbit. 500fr, Astronaut Donald Slayton, handshake.

1977, Aug. 10   Litho.   Perf. 14x13½
C256 A163 100fr multicolored   .90   .75
C257 A163 250fr multicolored   2.25   2.10
C258 A163 350fr multicolored   3.25   3.00
  Nos. C256-C258 (3)   6.40   5.85

Souvenir Sheet
C259 A163 500fr multicolored   5.00   4.25

Diseased Knee, WHO Emblem AP105

1977, Oct. 15   Engr.   Perf. 13
C260 AP105 70fr multi   .70   .25
World Rheumatism Year.

Nos. C249 and C232 Overprinted in Red

Engraved, Lithographed
1977, Nov. 22   Perf. 13
C262 AP103 300fr multi   3.25   1.25
C263 AP97 500fr multi   5.00   2.00
Concorde, 1st commercial flight Paris to NY.

Christmas Type of 1977
Paintings: 60fr, Virgin and Child with 4 Saints, by Bellini, horiz. 400fr, Adoration of the Shepherds, by George de la Tour, horiz.

1977, Dec. 15   Litho.   Perf. 12x12½
C264 A165 60fr multi   1.00   .25
C265 A165 400fr multi   5.00   1.75

Flag Type of 1978
60fr, New flag, Pres. Ahidjo and spear.

1978, Apr. 3   Litho.   Perf. 12½
C266 A167 60fr multi   .55   .20

Frog Type of 1978
Design: 100fr, Cardioglossa trifasciata.

1978, Apr. 5
C267 A168 100fr multi   3.75   .40

L'Arlesienne, by Van Gogh — AP106

#C269, Burial of Christ, by Albrecht Dürer.

1978, May 15   Litho.   Perf. 12½
C268 AP106 200fr multi   3.00   1.10
C269 AP106 200fr multi   4.00   1.10

Leprosy Distribution on World Map, Raoul Follereau — AP107

1978, June 6   Litho.   Perf. 12
C270 AP107 100fr multi   1.00   .55
25th World Leprosy Day.

Capt. Cook and Siege of Quebec — AP108

Design: 250fr, Capt. Cook, Adventure and Resolution, map of voyages.

1978, July 26   Engr.   Perf. 13
C271 AP108 100fr multi   2.10   .55
C272 AP108 250fr multi   5.00   1.40
Capt. James Cook (1728-1779), explorer.

Argentine Soccer Team, Coat of Arms and Rimet Cup — AP109

200fr, Two soccer players, vert. 1000fr, Soccer ball illuminating world map, vert.

1978, Sept. 1   Litho.   Perf. 13
C273 AP109 100fr multi   1.00   .55
C274 AP109 200fr multi   1.75   1.10
C275 AP109 1000fr multi   10.00   5.50
  Nos. C273-C275 (3)   12.75   7.15
11th World Cup Soccer Championship, Argentina, June 1-25.

Jules Verne Type of 1978
Design: 400fr, Jules Verne and "20,000 Leagues Under the Sea," horiz.

1978, Oct. 10   Litho.   Perf. 12
C276 A169 400fr multi   4.00   2.00

Musical Instrument Type of 1978
Design: 100fr, Man playing Mvet zither.

1978, Nov. 20   Litho.   Perf. 12½
C277 A172 100fr multi   1.25   .40

Human Rights Type of 1979
1979, Feb. 11   Litho.   Perf. 12x12½
C278 A174 500fr multi   5.50   2.50

Lions Emblem, Map of District 403 — AP110

1979, Apr. 26   Litho.   Perf. 12½
C279 AP110 60fr multi   .70   .25
21st Congress of Lions Club of Yaoundé.

Penny Black, Hill, Cameroun No. 9 — AP111

1979, Oct. 10   Engr.   Perf. 13
C280 AP111 100fr multi   1.00   .40
Sir Rowland Hill (1795-1879), originator of penny postage.

"TELECOM 79" — AP112

Pope Paul VI — AP113

1979, Sept. 26   Litho.   Perf. 13x12½
C281 AP112 100fr multi   1.10   .40
3rd World Telecommunications Exhibition, Geneva, Sept. 20-26.

1979, Oct. 23   Engr.   Perf. 12½x13
C282 AP113 100fr shown   2.25   .50
C283 AP113 100fr John Paul I   2.25   .50
C284 AP113 100fr John Paul II   2.25   .50
  Nos. C282-C284 (3)   6.75   1.50

"Double Eagle" over French Coastline AP114

Design: No. C286, Balloonists and balloon.

1979, Dec. 15   Litho.   Perf. 12½
C285 AP114 500fr multi   5.00   2.25
C286 AP114 500fr multi   5.00   2.25
First Transatlantic balloon crossing.

100-Meter Race — AP115

Designs: 150fr, Figure skating pairs. 200fr, Javelin. 300fr, Wrestling.

1980, Dec. 18   Litho.   Perf. 12½
C287	AP115	100fr yel brn & brn	.90	.50
C288	AP115	150fr bl & brn	1.25	.70
C289	AP115	200fr grn & brn	1.75	1.00
C290	AP115	300fr red & brn	2.50	1.40
	Nos. C287-C290 (4)		6.40	3.60

22nd Summer Olympic Games, Moscow, July 19-Aug. 3; 13th Winter Olympic Games, Lake Placid, Feb. 12-24 (150fr).

Alan Shepard and Freedom 7 — AP116

1981, Sept. 15   Litho.   Perf. 12½
C291	AP116	500fr shown	6.00	4.00
C292	AP116	500fr Yuri Gagarin, Vostok I	6.00	4.00

Manned space flight, 20th anniv.

4th African Scouting Conference, Abidjan, June — AP117

1981, Oct. 5
C293	AP117	100fr Emblem, salute, badge	.70	.40
C294	AP117	500fr Scout saluting	4.50	2.00

Guernica (detail), by Pablo Picasso (1881-1973) — AP118

#C296, Landscape, by Paul Cezanne (1839-1906).

1981, Nov. 10   Litho.   Perf. 12½
C295	AP118	500fr multi	6.00	2.00
C296	AP118	500fr multi	6.00	2.00

Christmas 1981 — AP119

Designs: 50fr, Virgin and Child, by Froment, vert. 60f, San Zeno Altarpiece, by Mantegna, vert. 400fr, Flight into Egypt, by Giotto.

1981, Dec. 1   Litho.   Perf. 12½
C297	AP119	50fr multi	.45	.25
C298	AP119	60fr multi	.65	.30
C299	AP119	400fr multi	3.50	2.00
a.	Souv. sheet of 3, #C297-C299, perf. 13x13½		9.00	2.75
	Nos. C297-C299 (3)		4.60	2.55

Still Life, by Georges Braque (1882-1963) — AP120

Paintings: No. C301, Olympia, by Edouard Manet (1832-1883).

1982, Dec. 5   Litho.   Perf. 13
C300	AP120	500fr multi	5.00	2.00
C301	AP120	500fr multi	5.00	2.00

Pres. John F. Kennedy (1917-63) AP121

Lions District 403 (Douala), 2nd Convention, May — AP122

1983, Mar. 15   Litho.   Perf. 13
C302	AP121	500fr multi	4.50	2.00

1983, May 5   Litho.   Perf. 12½
C303	AP122	70fr multi	.55	.30
C304	AP122	150fr multi	1.25	.65

Jeanne of Aragon by Raphael AP123

No. C306, Massacre of Scio by Delacroix.

1983, Oct. 15   Litho.   Perf. 13
C305	AP123	500fr multi	5.00	1.00
C306	AP123	500fr multi	5.00	1.00

Easter 1984 — AP124

200fr, Pieta, by G. Hernandez. 500fr, Martyrdom of St. John the Evangelist, by C. Le Brun.

1984, Mar. 30   Litho.   Perf. 13
C307	AP124	200fr multi	1.75	.50
C308	AP124	500fr multi	4.50	1.40
a.	Souv. sheet of 2, #C307-C308		7.25	2.00

1984 Summer Olympics AP125

European Soccer Championship, June 12-27 — AP126

1984, Apr. 30   Perf. 12½
C309	AP125	100fr High jump	.90	.25
C310	AP125	150fr Volleyball	1.25	.30
C311	AP125	250fr Handball	2.25	.55
C312	AP125	500fr Bicycling	4.50	1.10
	Nos. C309-C312 (4)		8.90	2.20

See Nos. C321-C324.

1984, June 5   Litho.   Perf. 12½
C313	AP126	250fr Player in red shorts	2.25	.65
C314	AP126	250fr Yellow shorts	2.25	.65
C315	AP126	500fr Players	4.50	1.25
a.	Souvenir sheet of 3		10.00	2.75
	Nos. C313-C315 (3)		9.00	2.55

No. C315a contains Nos. C313-C315 in changed panel colors.

Presidential Oath — AP127

1984   Litho.   Perf. 13
C316	AP127	60fr French inscription	.55	.20
a.	English inscription		.55	.20
C317	AP127	70fr French inscription	.55	.20
a.	English inscription		.55	.20
C318	AP127	200fr French inscription	1.75	.40
a.	English inscription		1.75	.40
	Nos. C316-C318 (3)		2.85	.80

Issue dates: French, Sept. 15; English, Nov.

Famous Men — AP128

#C316, Diana in the Bath, by Watteau (1684-1721). #C317, Portrait of Diderot (1713-1784).

1984, Sept. 20   Litho.   Perf. 13
C319	AP128	500fr Watteau	5.00	1.00
C320	AP128	500fr Diderot, vert.	5.00	1.00

Nos. C309-C312 in Changed Colors with Added Inscriptions
100fr: MOEGENBURG (R.F.A.) 11-08-84
150fr: U.S.A. 11-08-84
250fr: YOUGOSLAVIE 9-08-84
500fr: GORSKI (U.S.A.) 3-08-84

1984, Sept. 25   Litho.   Perf. 12½
C321	AP125	100fr multi	.90	.20
C322	AP125	150fr multi	1.25	.30
C323	AP125	250fr multi	2.25	.50
C324	AP125	500fr multi	4.50	1.00
	Nos. C321-C324 (4)		8.90	2.00

Moon Landing, 15th Anniv. — AP129

1984, Nov. 15   Litho.   Perf. 12½
C325	AP129	500fr Neil Armstrong	4.50	1.50
C326	AP129	500fr Apollo 12 launching	4.50	1.50

Louis Pasteur (1822-1895), Chemist, Microbiologist — AP130

#328, Mourning Woman (detail), Mausoleum of Henri Claude d'Harcourt, by sculptor Jean Baptiste Pigalle (1714-1785).

1985, Oct. 10   Litho.   Perf. 13
C327	AP130	500fr multi	6.00	1.75
C328	AP130	500fr multi	6.00	1.75

Christmas AP131

250fr, Children's gifts. 300fr, Akono Church. 400fr, Holy Family & drummer boy. 500fr, The Virgin with the Blue Diadem, by Raphael.

1985, Dec. 20   Litho.   Perf. 13
C329	AP131	250fr multi	2.25	.90
C330	AP131	300fr multi	2.50	1.10
C331	AP131	400fr multi	3.25	1.50
C332	AP131	500fr multi	5.00	2.00
	Nos. C329-C332 (4)		13.00	5.50

1986 World Cup Soccer Championships, Mexico — AP132

1986 Perf. 13½

C333	AP132	250fr Argentina, winner	2.75	1.40
C334	AP132	300fr Stadium	2.75	1.60
C335	AP132	400fr Mexican team	3.50	2.25
		Nos. C333-C335 (3)	9.00	5.25

Famous Men — AP133

#C336, Pierre Curie (1859-1906), chemist, atom, and elements. #C337, Jean Mermoz (1901-1936), aviator, and aircraft.

1986, Sept. 10 Litho. Perf. 12½

C336	AP133	500fr multi	6.25	2.00
C337	AP133	500fr multi	6.25	2.00

AIR POST SEMI-POSTAL STAMPS

Doctor Examining Child — SPAP1

Unwmk.

1942, June 22 Engr. Perf. 13

CB1	SPAP1	1.50fr + 50c green	1.00
CB2	SPAP1	2fr + 6fr brn & red brn	1.00

Native children's welfare fund. Nos. CB1-CB2 were issued by the Vichy government in France, but were not placed on sale in Cameroun.

Colonial Education Fund
Common Design Type

1942, June 22

CB3	CD86a	1.20fr + 1.80fr blue & red	1.10

No. CB3 was issued by the Vichy government in France, but was not placed on sale in Cameroun.

POSTAGE DUE STAMPS

Man Felling Tree — D1

Perf. 14x13½

1925-27 Unwmk. Typo.

J1	D1	2c lt bl & blk	.30	.50
J2	D1	4c ol bis & red vio	.30	.50
J3	D1	5c vio & blk	.65	.80
J4	D1	10c red & blk	.65	.80
J5	D1	15c gray & blk	.75	.95
J6	D1	20c olive grn & blk	.75	.95
J7	D1	25c yel & blk	1.40	1.60
J8	D1	30c blue & org	1.60	1.90
J9	D1	50c brn & blk	2.00	2.40
J10	D1	60c bl grn & rose red	2.00	2.40
J11	D1	1fr dl red & grn, grnsh	2.40	3.25
J12	D1	2fr red & vio ('27)	4.75	5.50
J13	D1	3fr org brn & ultra ('27)	7.25	8.00
		Nos. J1-J13 (13)	24.80	29.55

Shades occur for several values.

Carved Figures — D2

1939 Engr. Perf. 14x13

J14	D2	5c brt red vio	.25	.80
J15	D2	10c Prus blue	.75	.90
J16	D2	15c car rose	.25	.40
J17	D2	20c blk brn	.25	.40
J18	D2	30c ultra	.50	.65
J19	D2	50c dk grn	.50	.65
J20	D2	60c brn vio	.85	1.00
J21	D2	1fr dk vio	1.10	1.20
J22	D2	2fr org red	1.60	1.60
J23	D2	3fr dark blue	2.25	2.40
		Nos. J14-J23 (10)	8.30	10.00

Type D2 without "RF"

1944

J23A	D2	10c Prussian blue	.80

No. J23A was issued by the Vichy government in France, but was not placed on sale in Cameroun.

Catalogue values for unused stamps in this section, from this point to the end of the section, are for Never Hinged items.

D3

1947 Unwmk. Perf. 13

J24	D3	10c dark red	.40	.30
J25	D3	30c dp org	.40	.30
J26	D3	50c grnsh blk	.40	.30
J27	D3	1fr dark car	.50	.40
J28	D3	2fr dp yel grn	.65	.55
J29	D3	3fr dp red lil	.65	.55
J30	D3	4fr dp ultra	.90	.70
J31	D3	5fr red brn	1.00	.90
J32	D3	10fr peacock bl	1.90	1.60
J33	D3	20fr sepia	2.75	2.25
		Nos. J24-J33 (10)	9.55	7.85

Federal Republic

Hibiscus D4

Flowers: No. J35, Erythrina. No. J36, Plumeria lutea. No. J37, Ipomoea. No. J38, Hoodia gordonii. No. J39, Crinum. No. J40, Ochna. No. J41, Gloriosa. No. J42, Costus spectabilis. No. J43, Bougainvillea spectabilis. No. J44, Delonix regia. No. J45, Haemanthus. No. J46, Ophthalmophyllum. No. J47, Titanopsis. No. J48, Amorphophallus. No. J49, Zingiberaceae.

Unwmk.

1963, Apr. 10 Engr. Perf. 11

J34	D4	50c car, bl, grn & yel	.25	.20
J35	D4	50c car, bl, grn & yel	.25	.20
a.		Pair, #J34-J35	.55	.45
J36	D4	1fr mag, grn & yel	.25	.20
J37	D4	1fr mag, grn & yel	.25	.20
a.		Pair, #J36-J37	.55	.45
J38	D4	1.50fr dk grn, lil & yel	.25	.20
J39	D4	1.50fr dk grn, lil & yel	.25	.20
a.		Pair, #J38-J39	.55	.45
J40	D4	2fr org ver, yel & grn	.25	.20
J41	D4	2fr org ver, yel & grn	.25	.20
a.		Pair, #J40-J41	.55	.45
J42	D4	5fr mag, grn & yel	.25	.20
J43	D4	5fr mag, grn & yel	.25	.20
a.		Pair, #J42-J43	.55	.45
J44	D4	10fr crim, grn & yel	.50	.20
J45	D4	10fr crim, grn & yel	.50	.20
a.		Pair, #J44-J45	1.20	.45
J46	D4	20fr grn, yel & lil	1.10	.45
J47	D4	20fr grn, yel & lil	1.10	.45
a.		Pair, #J46-J47	2.40	1.00
J48	D4	40fr lilac & yel	2.00	.80
J49	D4	40fr lilac & yel	2.00	.80
a.		Pair, #J48-J49	4.25	1.75
		Nos. J34-J49 (16)	9.70	4.90

The pairs are se-tenant at the base.

MILITARY STAMPS

Catalogue values for unused stamps in this section are for Never Hinged items.

M1

Unwmk.

1963, July 1 Typo. Perf. 13

M1	M1	rose claret	3.00	3.00

Type of 1963 Inscribed "REPUBLIC UNIE DU CAMEROUN / UNITED REPUBLIC OF CAMEROUN"

1982? Litho. Perf. 13x13½

M2	M1	rose claret

CANADIAN PROVINCES

BRITISH COLUMBIA & VANCOUVER IS.

'bri-tish kə-'ləm-bē-ə

and van-'kü-vər 'ī-lənd

LOCATION — On the northwest coast of North America
GOVT. — British Colony
AREA — 355,900 sq. mi.
POP. — 694,300

In 1871 the colony became a part of the Canadian Confederation and the postage stamps of Canada have since been used.

12 Pence = 1 Shilling
20 Shillings = 1 Pound
100 Cents = 1 Dollar (1865)

Values for unused stamps are for examples with original gum as defined in the catalogue introduction. Very fine examples of Nos. 2 and 5-18 will have perforations touching the design on at least one side due to the narrow spacing of the stamps on the plates. Stamps with perfs clear of the design on all four sides are extremely scarce and will command much higher prices.

Queen Victoria — A1

1860   Unwmk.   Typo.   Imperf.
1   A1   2½p dull rose   ·15,000.

No. 1 was not placed in use. It is ungummed and may be a proof or reprint.

Perf. 14
2   A1   2½p dull rose   900.   250.

VANCOUVER ISLAND

A2   A3

1865   Wmk. 1   Imperf.
3   A2   5c rose   40,000.   11,000.
4   A3   10c blue   5,000.   1,250.

Perf. 14
5   A2   5c rose   340.   225.
6   A3   10c blue   300.   215.

BRITISH COLUMBIA

Seal of British Columbia — A4

1865, Nov. 1
7   A4   3p blue   120.00   100.00

Type A4 of 1865 Surcharged in Various Colors

1867-69   Perf. 14
8   2c on 3p brown (Bk)   175.00   160.00
9   5c on 3p brt red (Bk) ('69)   230.00   200.00
10   10c on 3p lilac rose (Bl)   1,600.
11   25c on 3p orange (V) ('69)   275.00   210.00
12   50c on 3p violet (R)   875.00   1,150.
13   $1 on 3p green (G)   1,500.
Nos. 10 and 13 were not placed in use.

1869   Perf. 12½
14   5c on 3p brt red (Bk)   2,000.   1,400.
15   10c on 3p lilac rose (Bl)   1,300.   1,100.
16   25c on 3p orange (V)   725.00   725.00
17   50c on 3p violet (R)   1,100.   900.00
18   $1 on 3p green (G)   1,900.   1,900.

NEW BRUNSWICK

'nü 'brənz-ˌwik

LOCATION — Eastern Canada, bordering on the Bay of Fundy and the Gulf of St. Lawrence.
GOVT. — British Province
AREA — 27,985 sq. mi.
POP. — 285,594 (1871)
CAPITAL — Fredericton

At one time a part of Nova Scotia, New Brunswick became a separate province in 1784. Upon joining the Canadian Confederation in 1867 its postage stamps were superseded by those of Canada.

12 Pence = 1 Shilling
100 Cents = 1 Dollar (1860)

Crown of Great Britain and Heraldic Flowers of the United Kingdom A1

1851   Unwmk.   Engr.   Imperf.
Blue Paper
1   A1   3p red   3,500.   575.
   a.   3p dark red   3,750.   600.
   b.   Half used as 1½p on cover   4,750.
2   A1   6p olive yellow   6,000.   1,150.
   a.   6p orange yellow   6,000.   1,200.
   b.   Half used as 3p on cover   3,500.
   c.   Quarter used as 1½p on cover   30,000.
   d.   6p mustard yellow   8,000.   1,500.
3   A1   1sh brt red violet   25,000.   6,500.
   a.   Half used as 6p on cover   24,000.
   b.   Quarter used as 3p on cover   24,000.
4   A1   1sh dull violet   30,000.   7,500.
   a.   Half used as 6p on cover   24,000.
   b.   Quarter used as 3p on cover   24,000.

The reprints are on stout white paper. The 3p is printed in orange and the 6p and 1sh in violet black. Value about $275 per set of 3.

Charles Connell — A2

1860   Perf. 12
5   A2   5c brown   11,000.
No. 5 was prepared for use but not issued. Most examples of No. 5 have creases or other faults. Value of an average example is about half that shown here.

Locomotive   Victoria
A3   A4

A5   A6

Steam and Sailing Ship — A7   Edward VII as Prince of Wales — A8

1860-63   White Paper   Perf. 12
6   A3   1c red lilac   37.50   37.50
   a.   1c brown violet   70.00   55.00
   b.   Horiz. pair, imperf. vert.   700.00
7   A4   2c orange ('63)   15.00   14.00
   a.   Vertical pair, imperf. horiz.   750.00
8   A5   5c yellow green   22.50   22.50
   a.   5c blue green   22.50   22.50
   b.   5c olive green   150.00   37.50
9   A6   10c vermilion   47.50   47.50
   a.   Half used as 5c on cover   800.00
   b.   Double impression   350.00   175.00
10   A7   12½c blue   77.50   77.50
11   A8   17c black   47.50   47.50
   Nos. 6-11 (6)   247.50   246.50
   Set, never hinged   440.00

NEWFOUNDLAND

'nü-fən-ˌd-lənd

LOCATION — Island in the Atlantic Ocean off the coast of Canada, and Labrador, a part of the mainland
GOVT. — British Dominion
AREA — 42,734 sq. mi.
POP. — 321,177 (1945)
CAPITAL — St. John's

Newfoundland was a self-governing Dominion of the British Empire from 1855 to 1933, when it became a Crown Colony. In 1949 it united with Canada.

12 Pence = 1 Shilling
100 Cents = 1 Dollar (1866)

Values for unused stamps are for examples with original gum as defined in the catalogue introduction. However, very fine examples of Nos. 2-7, 9, 11, 12, 13 and 15 without gum are often traded at values very close to those for examples with original gum.

Watermark

Wmk. 224
Coat of Arms

As the watermark 224 does not show on every stamp in the sheet, pairs are found one with and one without watermark. This applies to all stamps with watermark 224.

Crown of Great Britain and Heraldic Flowers of the United Kingdom — A1

Rose, Thistle and Shamrock — A3

A2   A4

A5   A6

A7   A8

1857   Unwmk.   Engr.   Imperf.
Thick Porous Wove Paper with Mesh
1   A1   1p brown vio   120.00   190.00
   a.   Half used as ½p on cover   15,000.
2   A2   2p scarlet ver   17,500.   5,500.
   a.   Vert. half used as 1p on cover   19,000.
3   A3   3p green   475.00   475.00
4   A4   4p scarlet ver   11,500.   3,750.
   a.   Half used as 2p on cover   20,000.
5   A1   5p brown vio   300.00   375.00
6   A5   6p scarlet ver   22,500.   4,750.
7   A6   6½p scarlet ver   4,500.   3,750.
8   A7   8p scarlet ver   450.00   475.00
   a.   Half used as 4p on cover   6,000.
9   A8   1sh scarlet ver   35,000.   10,000.
   a.   Half used as 6p on cover   20,000.

1860
Thin to Thick Wove Paper, No Mesh
11   A2   2p orange   400.00   475.00
11A   A3   3p green   77.50   105.00
12   A4   4p orange   3,000.   1,150.
   b.   Half used as 2p on cover   15,000.
12A   A1   5p vio brown   77.50   135.00
13   A5   6p orange   4,500.   1,000.

15	A8	1sh orange	30,000.	11,500.
b.		Half used as 6p on cover		17,500.

A 6½p orange exists as a souvenir item.
A 1sh exists in orange on horizontally or vertically laid paper. Most authorities consider these to be proofs. Value, $10,500.

1861-62

15A	A1	1p vio brown	160.00	225.00
16	A1	1p reddish brown	11,000.	
17	A2	2p rose	160.00	175.00
18	A4	4p rose	35.00	70.00
a.		Half used as 2p on cover		
19	A1	5p reddish brown	62.50	77.50
20	A5	6p rose	22.50	62.50
a.		Half used as 3p on cover		10,000.
21	A6	6½p rose	77.50	275.00
22	A7	8p rose	77.50	300.00
23	A8	1sh rose	37.50	275.00
a.		Half used as 6p on cover		18,000.

Some sheets of Nos. 11-23 are known with the papermaker's watermark "STACEY WISE 1858" in large capitals. Values unused and used about 25% more than values shown, except about 50% more for unused Nos. 12 and 13.
No. 16 was prepared but not issued.
False cancellations are found on Nos. 1, 3, 5, 8, 11, 11A, 12A and 17-23.
Forgeries exist of most or all of Nos. 1-23.

Codfish — A9

Harp Seal — A10

Prince Albert — A11

Victoria — A12

Fishing Ship — A13

Victoria — A14

1865-94
White Paper(#24, 27, 28)
Thin Yellowish Paper (#25-26, 29-31)

Perf. 12

24	A9	2c green	77.50	30.00
a.		Thin yellowish paper	95.00	40.00
b.		Half used as 1c on cover		4,000.
25	A10	5c brown	550.00	375.00
a.		Half used as 2c on cover		5,250.
26	A10	5c black ('68)	350.00	150.00
27	A11	10c black	325.00	60.00
a.		Thin yellowish paper	375.00	115.00
b.		Half used as 5c on cover		4,250.
28	A12	12c pale red brn	57.50	47.50
a.		Thin yellowish paper	500.00	190.00
b.		Half used as 6c on cover		3,250.
29	A12	12c brn, *white* ('94)	57.50	45.00

30	A13	13c orange	225.00	115.00
31	A14	24c blue, thin transluscent paper	52.50	30.00
a.		Thicker white paper ('70)	375.00	300.00

See Nos. 38, 40.

Edward VII as Prince of Wales — A15

Queen Victoria — A16

1868-94

32	A15	1c violet	75.00	60.00
32A	A15	1c brown lilac (re-engr. '71)	115.00	75.00
33	A16	3c ver ('70)	375.00	190.00
34	A16	3c blue ('73)	375.00	75.00
35	A16	6c dull rose ('70)	22.50	15.00
36	A16	6c car lake ('94)	37.50	22.50
		Nos. 32-36 (6)	1,000.	437.50

In the re-engraved 1c the top of the letters "N" and "F" are about ½mm from the ribbon with "ONE CENT." In No. 32 they are fully 1mm away. There are many small differences in the engraving.

1876-79

Rouletted

37	A15	1c brn lilac ('77)	160.00	52.50
38	A9	2c green ('79)	200.00	52.50
39	A16	3c blue ('77)	425.00	14.00
40	A10	5c blue	250.00	14.00
		Nos. 37-40 (4)	1,035.	133.00

A17

A19

A18

A20

1880-96

Perf. 12

41	A17	1c violet brown	42.50	11.50
42	A17	1c gray brown	42.50	11.50
43	A17	1c brown ('96)	100.00	57.50
44	A17	1c deep green ('87)	19.00	3.75
45	A17	1c green ('97)	19.00	4.00
46	A19	2c yellow green	45.00	14.00
47	A19	2c green ('96)	87.50	27.50
48	A19	2c red org ('87)	32.50	9.50
a.		Imperf., pair	325.00	
49	A18	3c blue	52.50	6.75
51	A18	3c umber brn ('87)	37.50	4.75
52	A18	3c vio brown ('96)	115.00	90.00
53	A20	5c pale blue	375.00	10.00
54	A20	5c dark blue ('87)	160.00	8.50
55	A20	5c bright bl ('94)	45.00	6.50
		Nos. 41-55 (14)	1,173.	265.75

Newfoundland Dog — A21

Schooner — A22

1887-96

56	A21	½c rose red	9.50	7.25
57	A21	½c orange red ('96)	75.00	45.00
58	A21	½c black ('94)	9.00	7.25
59	A22	10c black	120.00	67.50
		Nos. 56-59 (4)	213.50	127.00

Queen Victoria — A23

1890

60	A23	3c slate	30.00	1.60
a.		3c gray lilac	30.00	1.60
b.		3c brown lilac	50.00	1.60
c.		3c lilac	30.00	1.60
d.		3c slate violet	75.00	3.00
e.		Vert. pair, imperf. horiz.	650.00	

For surcharges see Nos. 75-77.

Victoria — A24

Cabot (John?) — A25

Cape Bonavista A26

Caribou Hunting A27

Mining — A28

Logging — A29

Fishing — A30

Cabot's Ship "Matthew" A31

Willow Ptarmigan A32

Seals — A33

Salmon Fishing — A34

Colony Seal — A35

Iceberg off St. John's — A36

Henry VII — A37

1897, June 24

61	A24	1c deep green	1.75	1.75
62	A25	2c carmine lake	2.20	1.35
63	A26	3c ultramarine	3.75	1.40
64	A27	4c olive green	5.25	2.75
65	A28	5c violet	9.00	2.75
66	A29	6c red brown	5.75	3.25
67	A30	8c red orange	17.50	14.00
68	A31	10c black brown	17.50	7.50
69	A32	12c dark blue	22.50	14.00
70	A33	15c scarlet	22.50	13.00
71	A34	24c gray violet	30.00	12.00
72	A35	30c slate	55.00	55.00
73	A36	35c red	120.00	60.00
74	A37	60c black	19.00	11.50
		Nos. 61-74 (14)	331.70	200.25
		Set, never hinged	580.00	

400th anniv. of John Cabot's discovery of Newfoundland; 60th year of Victoria's reign. The ship on the 10c was previously used by the American Bank Note Co. as the "Flagship of Columbus" on US No. 232. The portrait on the 2c, intended to be of John Cabot, is said to be a Holbein painting of his son, Sebastian.

For surcharges and overprints see Nos. 127-130, C2-C4.

No. 60a Surcharged with Bars and

No. 75

ONE CENT
No. 76

No. 77

1897, Oct.

75	A23	1c on 3c gray lilac	60.00	30.00
a.		Dbl. surch., one diagonal	*1,500.*	
b.		Vert. pair, "ONE CENT" and lower bar omitted on bottom stamp	*4,250.*	
76	A23	1c on 3c gray lilac	225.00	190.00
77	A23	1c on 3c gray lilac	750.00	700.00
		Nos. 75-77 (3)	1,035.	920.00
		Set, never hinged	2,250.	

Most examples of Nos. 75-77 are poorly centered. Fine examples sell for about 60% of the values given. No. 75b is valued in the grade of fine.

Trial surcharges of Nos. 75-77 exist with red surcharge and with double surcharge, one in red and one in black, but these were not issued.

Edward VIII as a Child — A38   Victoria — A39

Edward VII as Prince of Wales — A40

Queen Alexandra as Princess of Wales — A41

Queen Mary as Duchess of York — A42

George V as Duke of York — A43

1897-1901   **Engr.**

78	A38	½c olive green	3.75	2.25
79	A39	1c carmine rose	4.75	4.75
80	A39	1c yel grn ('98)	4.50	.25
b.		Vert. pair, imperf. horiz.	500.00	
81	A40	2c orange	6.25	4.25
82	A40	2c ver ('98)	11.50	.60
b.		Pair, imperf. between	475.00	
83	A41	3c orange ('98)	26.00	.75
a.		Vert. pair, imperf. horiz.	425.00	
84	A42	4c violet ('01)	37.50	4.50
85	A43	5c blue ('99)	47.50	3.00
		Nos. 78-85 (8)	141.75	20.35
		Set, never hinged	220.00	

No. 80b is valued in the grade of fine.

Imperf., Pairs

78a	A38	½c	475.00	
81a	A40	2c		*400.00*
82a	A40	2c	325.00	
83b	A41	3c	425.00	
84a	A42	4c	350.00	

Imperf., Pairs

Newfoundland imperforates virtually always are proofs on stamp paper or "postmaster's perquisites." Most part-perforate varieties also are "postmaster's perquisites." These items were not regularly issued, but rather were sold or given to favored persons.

Map of Newfoundland — A44

1908, Sept.

86	A44	2c rose carmine	47.50	1.90
		Never hinged	85.00	

Guy Issue

James I — A45

Arms of the London and Bristol Co. — A46

John Guy — A47   Lord Bacon — A50

Guy's Ship, the "Endeavour" A48

View of Cupids — A49

View of Mosquito — A51

Edward VII — A54

Logging Camp — A52

George V — A55

Paper Mills — A53

SIX CENT TYPES
I — "Z" of "COLONIZATION" reversed.
II — "Z" of normal.

1910, Aug. 15   **Litho.**   *Perf. 12*

87	A45	1c deep green, perf. 12x11	2.30	1.10
a.		Perf. 12	4.75	1.90
b.		Perf. 12x14	3.60	2.25
c.		Horiz. pair, imperf. btwn.	400.00	
d.		Vert. pair, imperf. btwn.	350.00	
88	A46	2c carmine	7.50	1.15
a.		Perf. 12x14	6.25	.85
b.		As "a," horiz. pair, imperf. between	300.00	
c.		Perf. 12x11½	475.00	350.00
89	A47	3c brown olive	15.00	14.00
90	A48	4c dull violet	15.00	11.50
91	A49	5c ultramarine, perf. 14x12	15.00	4.50
a.		Perf. 12	22.50	11.50
92	A50	6c claret, type I	77.50	65.00
92A	A50	6c claret, type II	37.50	37.50
b.		Imperf., pair	350.00	
93	A51	8c pale brown	60.00	55.00
94	A52	9c olive green	60.00	55.00
95	A53	10c vio black	60.00	55.00
96	A54	12c lilac brown	60.00	55.00
a.		Imperf., pair	375.00	
97	A55	15c gray black	77.50	65.00
		Nos. 87-97 (12)	487.30	419.75
		Set, never hinged	950.00	

Tercentenary of the Colonization of Newfoundland.

On No. 87 printing flaws such as "NFW" and "JANES" exist.

1911   **Engr.**   *Perf. 14*

98	A50	6c brown vio	32.50	22.50
99	A51	8c bister brn	75.00	67.50
100	A52	9c olive grn	60.00	57.50
101	A53	10c violet blk	95.00	95.00
102	A54	12c red brown	75.00	75.00
103	A55	15c slate grn	75.00	75.00
b.		Horiz. pair, imperf. btwn.	325.00	
		Nos. 98-103 (6)	412.50	392.50
		Set, never hinged	750.00	

Nos. 100 and 103 are known with papermaker's watermark "E. TOWGOOD FINE."

Imperf., Pairs

98a	A50	6c	325.00
99a	A51	8c	325.00
100a	A52	9c	325.00
101a	A53	10c	325.00
102a	A54	12c	325.00
103a	A55	15c	325.00

Nos. 98a-103a were made with and without gum. Values the same.

Royal Family Issue

Queen Mary — A56

George V — A57

Prince of Wales (Edward VIII) — A58

Prince Albert (George VI) — A59

Princess Mary — A60

Prince Henry — A61

Prince George A62

Prince John A63

Queen Alexandra A64

Duke of Connaught A65

Seal of Colony — A66

1911, June 19   Perf. 13½x14, 14

104	A56	1c yellow grn	3.00	.25
105	A57	2c carmine	2.60	.80
106	A58	3c red brown	22.50	19.00
107	A59	4c violet	19.00	13.50
108	A60	5c ultra	11.00	1.90
109	A61	6c black	22.50	22.50
110	A62	8c blue (paper colored through)	75.00	65.00
a.		8c peacock blue	80.00	70.00
111	A63	9c bl violet	22.50	20.00
112	A64	10c dark green	40.00	37.50
113	A65	12c plum	37.50	37.50
114	A66	15c magenta	30.00	37.50
		Nos. 104-114 (11)	285.60	255.45
		Set, never hinged	500.00	

Coronation of King George V.

Imperf., Pairs
Without Gum

104a	A56	1c	325.00
105a	A57	2c	325.00
108a	A60	5c	325.00
113a	A65	12c	325.00
114a	A66	15c	125.00

Trail of the Caribou Issue

Caribou
A67   A68

1919, Jan. 2   Perf. 14

115	A67	1c green	2.25	.35
116	A68	2c scarlet	2.75	.50
117	A67	3c red brown	3.00	.30
118	A67	4c violet	4.50	1.40
119	A68	5c ultramarine	5.75	1.40
120	A67	6c gray	22.50	22.50
121	A68	8c magenta	22.50	19.00
122	A67	10c dark green	11.00	5.50
123	A68	12c orange	65.00	45.00
124	A67	15c dark blue	42.50	42.50
125	A67	24c bister	45.00	42.50
126	A67	36c olive green	37.50	35.00
		Nos. 115-126 (12)	264.25	215.95
		Set, never hinged	425.00	

Services of the Newfoundland contingent in WWI.

Each denomination of type A67 is inscribed with the name of a different action in which Newfoundland troops took part.

For overprint and surcharge see Nos. C1, C5.

Imperf., Pairs
Without Gum

115a	A67	1c	280.00
116a	A68	2c	280.00
117a	A67	3c red brown	280.00
118a	A67	4c	280.00
119a	A67	5c	280.00
120a	A67	6c	280.00
121a	A68	8c	280.00
122a	A67	10c	280.00
123a	A68	12c	280.00
124a	A67	15c	280.00
125a	A67	24c	280.00
126a	A67	36c	280.00

No. 72 Surcharged in Black

1920   Perf. 12

127	A35	2c on 30c slate	5.75	5.50
		Never hinged	8.75	
a.		Inverted surcharge	950.00	

No. 127 with red surcharge is an unissued color trial. 25 examples are known. Value, $1,000.

Also known reading "TWO / 2 / CENTS," with surcharge in red. 50 stamps were so surcharged, including examples with double surcharge. Value, $1,000.

Nos. 70 and 73 Surcharged in Black

THREE CENTS
Type I — Bars 10½mm apart.
Type II — Bars 13½mm apart.

128	A33	3c on 15c scar (I)	230.00	225.00
a.		Inverted surcharge	2,300.	
129	A33	3c on 15c scar (II)	19.00	11.00
130	A36	3c on 35c red	11.50	9.50
a.		Lower bar omitted	135.00	135.00
b.		Inverted surcharge	1,750.	

All examples of the former No. 130c ("THREE" omitted) examined show part of the tops or bottoms of the letters. It is probable that no examples with "THREE" completely omitted exist.

Twin Hills, Tor's Cove — A70

South West Arm, Trinity — A71

War Memorial, St. John's A72

Humber River A73

Coast of Trinity — A74

Upper Steadies, Humber River — A75

Quidi Vidi, near St. John's — A76

Caribou Crossing Lake — A77

Humber River Canyon A78

Shell Bird Island A79

Mt. Moriah, Bay of Islands A80

Humber River near Little Rapids A81

Placentia, from Mt. Pleasant A82

Topsail Falls near St. John's A83

1923-24   Engr.   Perf. 14, 13½x14

131	A70	1c gray green	1.90	.30
a.		Booklet pane of 8	450.00	
132	A71	2c carmine	1.90	.25
a.		Booklet pane of 8	300.00	
133	A72	3c brown	2.50	.25
134	A73	4c brn violet	2.75	1.80
135	A74	5c ultramarine	4.50	2.25
136	A75	6c gray black	5.25	5.25
137	A76	8c dull violet	4.50	4.25
138	A77	9c slate green	37.50	27.50
139	A78	10c dark violet	4.25	2.50
140	A79	11c olive green	7.00	7.00
141	A80	12c lake	7.50	7.50
142	A81	15c deep blue	9.50	8.00
143	A82	20c red brn ('24)	13.00	7.50
144	A83	24c blk brn ('24)	60.00	45.00
		Nos. 131-144 (14)	162.05	119.35
		Set, never hinged	250.00	

For surcharge see No. 160.

Imperf., Pairs

131b	A70	1c	200.00
132b	A71	2c	200.00
134a	A73	4c	200.00
135a	A74	5c	200.00
136a	A75	6c	200.00
137a	A76	8c	200.00
138a	A77	9c	200.00
139a	A78	10c	200.00
140a	A79	11c	200.00
141a	A80	12c	200.00
142a	A81	15c	160.00

Nos. 134a-139a, 141a-142a are without gum. Others are either with or without gum; values about the same.

Map of New-foundland A84

Steamship "Caribou" A85

Queen Mary, George V — A86

Prince of Wales — A87

Express Train — A88

Newfoundland Hotel, St. John's — A89

Heart's Content — A90

Cabot Tower, St. John's — A91

War Memorial, St. John's — A92

GPO, St. John's — A93

First Nonstop Transatlantic Flight, 1919 — A94

Colonial Building, St. John's — A95

Grand Falls, Labrador — A96

Perf. 14, 13½x13, 13x13½
1928, Jan. 3

145	A84	1c deep green	1.40	.75
146	A85	2c deep carmine	2.50	.70
a.		Imperf., pair	300.00	
147	A86	3c brown	2.75	.50
148	A87	4c lilac rose	3.50	1.80
149	A88	5c slate green	10.00	4.25
150	A89	6c ultramarine	5.75	3.50
151	A90	8c lt red brown	7.25	4.50
152	A91	9c myrtle green	7.00	6.75
153	A92	10c dark violet	9.00	4.25
154	A93	12c brn carmine	5.50	4.00
155	A91	14c red brown	10.50	6.75
156	A94	15c dark blue	9.25	7.00
157	A95	20c gray black	11.50	6.00
158	A93	28c gray green	27.50	22.50
159	A96	30c olive brown	14.00	7.50
		Nos. 145-159 (15)	127.40	80.75
		Set, never hinged	215.00	

See Nos. 163-182.

No. 136 Surcharged in Red or Black

THREE CENTS

Type I — 5mm between "CENTS" and bar.
Type II — 3mm between "CENTS" and bar.

1929　　　　　　　　　　　　　　*Perf. 14x13½*

160	A75	3c on 6c gray black		
		(II) (R)	4.25	4.25
		Never hinged	6.75	
a.		Inverted surcharge (II)	950.00	

The stamps with black surcharge, type I and II, were 1st or trial printings, and were not issued. There were 50 examples of each. Value, each $1,000.

Types of 1928 Issue
Re-engraved

1c — On No. 145 the lines of the engraving are thinner and the impression is clearer than on No. 163. On the former "C. BAULD" is above "C. NORMAN." On the latter these words are transposed.

2c — On the 1928 stamp the "D" of "NEW-FOUNDLAND" is 1mm from the scroll at the right; the flag at the stern is lower than the top of the boat davit. On the 1929 stamp the "D" is ½mm from the scroll and the flag rises above the davits.

3c — On the 1928 stamp the pearls at the top of the crown, the jewels of the tiara and the pillars flanking the portraits are all unshaded. On the reengraved stamp there are small curved lines inside the pearls, the jewels of the tiara are in solid color, and the pillars have vertical shading lines. On the 1928 stamps the tablets with "THREE" and "CENTS" have a background of crossed lines (vertical and horizontal). On the 1929 stamp the background is of horizontal lines only.

4c — On the 1928 stamp the figures "4" have shading of horizontal and diagonal crossed lines. There are six circles at each side of the portrait.
On the 1929 stamp the "4s" have shading of horizontal lines only. There are five roses at each side of the portrait.

5c — The crossbars of the telegraph pole touch the frame at the left on the 1929 stamp but just clear it on the 1928 stamp. In the 1928 issue the foliate ornaments beside and below the figures "5" end in small scrolls and a small spur. These spurs are omitted on the 1929 stamp.

6c — On the re-engraved stamp the columns at right and left of the picture have heavy wavy outlines on the inner sides. There is no period after "JOHNS." The numerals in the lower corners are 1½mm wide instead of 1¼mm.

8c — The impression of the 1928 stamp is clear, that of 1931 is slightly blurred. The 1928 stamp has three horizontal lines above "EIGHT CENTS" and four berries on the laurel branch at the right side. On the 1931 stamp there are two horizontal lines and three berries.

10c — On the re-engraved stamp there is no period after "ST. JOHN'S." The letters of "TEN CENTS" are slightly larger and the numerals "10" slightly smaller than in 1928. Inside the "0" of "10" at the right there are two vertical lines instead of three. The clouds are fainter in 1929 and the cross upheld by the figure on the monument is more distinct. On the 1928 stamp the torch at the left side terminates in a single tongue of flame. On the 1929-30 stamp it terminates in two tongues.

15c — On the 1928 stamp the "N" of "NEW-FOUNDLAND" is 1½mm from the left frame, the "L" of "LEAVING" is under the first "A" of "AIRPLANE" and the apostrophe in "JOHN'S" breaks the first line above it.
On the 1929 stamp the "N" of "NEW-FOUNDLAND" is 1mm from the left frame, the "L" of "LEAVING" is below the "T" of "FIRST" and the apostrophe in "JOHN'S" does not touch the line above it.

20c — On the 1928 stamp the points of the "W" of "NEWFOUNDLAND" are truncated. The "O" is wide and nearly round. The columns that form the sides of the frame have a shading of evenly spaced horizontal lines at their inner sides.
On the 1929-31 stamp the points of the "W" form sharp angles. The "O" is narrow and has a small opening. Many lines have been added to the shading on the inner sides of the columns, making it almost solid.

30c — 1928 stamp. Size: 19¼x24½mm. At the outer side of the right column there are three strong and two faint vertical lines. Faint period after "FALLS."
1931 stamp. Size: 19x25mm. At the outer side of the right column there are two strong vertical lines and a fragment of the lower end of a faint one. Clear period after "FALLS." A great many of the small lines of the design have been deepened making the whole stamp appear darker.

1929-31　　　　Unwmk.　　*Perf. 13½ to 14*

163	A84	1c green	2.25	.65
a.		Double impression	325.00	
b.		Vert. pair, imperf. btwn.	210.00	
164	A85	2c deep carmine	2.25	.35
165	A86	3c dp red brown	2.50	.35
166	A87	4c magenta	3.75	1.25
167	A88	5c slate green	7.25	1.60
168	A89	6c ultramarine	9.75	9.00
169	A92	10c dark violet	8.75	2.25

170	A94	15c deep blue ('30)	45.00	37.50
171	A95	20c gray blk ('31)	75.00	27.50
		Nos. 163-171 (9)	156.50	80.45
		Set, never hinged	250.00	

Imperf., Pairs

163c	A84	1c	120.00
164a	A85	2c pale carmine,	
		cream	145.00
b.		2c dark carmine	120.00
165a	A86	3c	120.00
166a	A87	4c	145.00

No. 164b is without gum, others with gum.

Types of 1928 Issue
Perf. 13½x14

1931　　Re-engraved　　**Wmk. 224**

172	A84	1c green, perf.		
		13½	2.25	1.25
a.		Horiz. pair, imperf. btwn.	425.00	
173	A85	2c red	5.50	1.30
174	A86	3c red brown	3.50	1.25
175	A87	4c rose	4.25	2.00
176	A88	5c grnsh gray	15.00	7.00
177	A89	6c ultramarine	22.50	16.00
178	A90	8c lt red brn	22.50	16.00
179	A92	10c dk violet	15.00	9.00
180	A94	15c deep blue	45.00	27.50
181	A95	20c gray black	57.50	17.50
182	A96	30c olive brown	45.00	25.00
		Nos. 172-182 (11)	238.00	123.80
		Set, never hinged	365.00	

Codfish — A97

George V — A98

Queen Mary — A99

Prince of Wales — A100

Caribou A101

Princess Elizabeth A102

Salmon Leaping Falls — A103

Newfoundland Dog — A104

Harp Seal Pup — A105

Cape Race — A106

Sealing Fleet — A107

Fishing Fleet Leaving for "The Banks" — A108

FIVE CENT
Die I — Antlers even, or equal in height.
Die II — Antler under "T" higher.

1932-37　　Engr.　　*Perf. 13½, 14*

183	A97	1c green	2.25	.50
a.		Booklet pane of 4, perf. 13	75.00	
c.		Vert. pair, imperf. btwn.	200.00	
184	A97	1c gray black	.35	.20
a.		Bklt. pane of 4, perf. 13½	57.50	
b.		Booklet pane of 4, perf. 14	72.50	
185	A98	2c rose	2.25	.35
a.		Booklet pane of 4, perf. 13½	35.00	
b.		Booklet pane of 4, perf. 13	47.50	
186	A98	2c green	1.10	.25
a.		Bklt. pane of 4, perf. 13½	55.00	
b.		Booklet pane of 4, perf. 14	35.00	
d.		Horiz. pair, imperf. btwn.	160.00	
187	A99	3c orange brn	1.10	.35
a.		Bklt. pane of 4, perf. 13½	55.00	
b.		Booklet pane of 4, perf. 14	67.50	
c.		Booklet pane of 4, perf. 13	75.00	
e.		Vert. pair, imperf. btwn.	160.00	
188	A100	4c deep violet	5.50	1.60
189	A100	4c rose lake	.75	.35
b.		Vert. pair, imperf. btwn.	120.00	
c.		Horiz. pair, imperf. btwn.	120.00	
190	A101	5c vio brn, perf.		
		13½ (Die II)	9.50	1.25
191	A101	5c dp vio, perf.		
		13½ (Die II)	1.10	.20
a.		5c dp vio, perf. 13½ (Die I)	11.00	1.00
c.		Horiz. pair, imperf. btwn.		
		(I)	240.00	
g.		Horiz. pair, imperf. btwn.		
		(II)	240.00	
192	A102	6c dull blue	11.00	11.00
193	A103	10c olive black	1.40	.85
194	A104	14c int black	3.25	2.75
195	A105	15c magenta	2.50	2.25
196	A106	20c gray green	2.50	1.00
197	A107	25c gray	2.60	2.00
b.		Horiz. pair, imperf. btwn.	275.00	
c.		Vert. pair, imperf. btwn.	375.00	
198	A108	30c ultra	27.50	24.00
b.		Vert. pair, imperf. btwn.	475.00	
199	A108	48c red brn ('37)	11.00	5.25
		Nos. 183-199 (17)	85.65	54.15
		Set, never hinged	125.00	

Two dies were used for 2c green, one for 2c rose.
See Nos. 253-266.

Imperf., Pairs

183b	A97	1c	240.00
184c	A97	1c	47.50
185c	A98	2c	160.00
186c	A98	2c	47.50
187d	A99	3c	95.00
189a	A100	4c	60.00
190a	A101	5c	160.00
191b	A101	5c (II)	60.00
191d	A101	5c (I)	95.00
192a	A102	6c	145.00
193a	A103	10c	95.00
194a	A103	14c	120.00
195a	A103	15c	120.00
196a	A106	20c	160.00
197a	A107	25c	160.00
198a	A108	30c	550.00
199a	A108	48c	120.00

All with gum. Nos. 186c, 187d, 192a, 193a and 196a also made without gum; values about 10% less.

Queen Elizabeth when Duchess of York — A109

Corner Brook Paper Mills — A110

Loading Iron Ore at Bell Island — A111

1932

208	A109	7c red brown	1.40	1.25
a.		Imperf., pair	160.00	
b.		Horiz. pair, imperf. between	475.00	
209	A110	8c orange red	1.40	1.10
a.		Imperf., pair	120.00	
210	A111	24c light blue	2.75	2.75
a.		Imperf., pair	200.00	
b.		Double impression	1,200.	
		Nos. 208-210 (3)	5.55	5.10
		Set, never hinged	7.75	

No. 208a was made both with and without gum. Values about the same.
See Nos. 259, 264.

No. C9 Overprinted Bars and

1933, Feb. 9　　Wmk. 224　　*Perf. 14*

211	AP6	15c brown	11.00	9.50
a.		Vert. pair, one without overprint	6,500.	
b.		Overprint reading up	4,500.	

"L. & S." stands for "Land and Sea."

Sir Humphrey Gilbert Issue

Sir Humphrey Gilbert — A112

Compton Castle, Home of the Gilbert Family — A113

Gilbert Coat of Arms — A114

Eton College — A115

Token from Queen Elizabeth I — A116

Sir Humphrey Receiving Royal Patents for Colonization A117

Sir Humphrey's Ships Leaving Plymouth, 1583 — A118

The Ships Arriving at St. John's — A119

Annexation of Newfoundland, Aug. 5, 1583 — A120

Coat of Arms
of England
A121

Sir Humphrey
on the Deck of
the "Squirrel"
A122

Capt. John
Mason's Map of
Newfoundland,
1626 — A123

Queen
Elizabeth I
A124

Gilbert Statue
at Truro
A125

Wmk. 224

1933, Aug. 3   Engr.   Perf. 13½

212	A112	1c gray black	1.10	.75
213	A113	2c green	1.10	.75
b.		Double impression	575.00	
214	A114	3c yellow brn	1.90	.75
215	A115	4c carmine	1.90	.75
216	A116	5c dull violet	2.75	1.10
217	A117	7c blue	19.00	12.50
218	A118	8c orange red	7.50	7.00
219	A119	9c ultramarine	8.00	7.50
220	A120	10c red brown	8.00	6.25
221	A121	14c black	16.00	14.00
222	A122	15c claret	14.00	14.00
223	A123	20c deep green	13.00	10.00
224	A124	24c vio brown	22.50	22.50
225	A125	32c gray	22.50	22.50
		Nos. 212-225 (14)	139.25	120.35
		Set, never hinged	205.00	

350th anniv. of annexation of Newfoundland
to England, Aug. 5, 1583, by authority of Letters Patent issued by Queen Elizabeth I to Sir
Humphrey Gilbert.

Imperf., Pairs

212a	A112	1c	47.50
213a	A113	2c	47.50
214a	A114	3c	240.00
215a	A115	4c	50.00
216a	A116	5c	280.00
219a	A119	9c	280.00
220a	A120	10c	280.00
221a	A120	14c	400.00
222a	A120	15c	200.00
224a	A124	24c	200.00

Common Design Types
pictured following the introduction.

Silver Jubilee Issue
Common Design Type

1935, May 6   Wmk. 4   Perf. 11x12

226	CD301	4c bright rose	1.75	.70
227	CD301	5c violet	1.75	.85
228	CD301	7c dark blue	4.00	3.50
229	CD301	24c olive green	9.00	7.00
		Nos. 226-229 (4)	16.50	12.05
		Set, never hinged	24.00	

Coronation Issue
Common Design Type

1937, May 12   Perf. 11x11½

230	CD302	2c deep green	1.75	.70
231	CD302	4c carmine rose	1.75	.70
232	CD302	5c dark violet	3.50	1.40
		Nos. 230-232 (3)	7.00	2.80
		Set, never hinged	9.75	

Codfish
A126

Map of Newfoundland — A127

Caribou
A128

Corner
Brook
Paper Mills
A129

Salmon
A130

Newfoundland Dog — A131

Harp Seal
Pup
A132

Cape Race
A133

Loading
Iron Ore at
Bell Island
A134

Sealing
Fleet
A135

Fishing
Fleet
Leaving for
"The
Banks"
A136

Two dies of the 3c
Die I — Fine impression; no lines on bridge
of nose.
Die II — Coarse impression; lines on bridge
of nose.

Perf. 13½, 14 (#234-235)

1937, May 12   Wmk. 224

233	A126	1c gray black	.40	.30
234	A127	3c org brn, die I	2.50	1.10
a.		Die II	1.75	1.10
b.		Vert. pair, imperf. btwn. (I)	575.00	
c.		Vert. pair, imperf. btwn. (II)	575.00	
d.		Horiz. pair, imperf. btwn. (I)	575.00	
e.		Horiz. pair, imperf. btwn. (II)	575.00	
f.		Imperf., pair	240.00	
235	A128	7c blue	2.50	2.50
236	A129	8c orange red	2.50	2.50
a.		Imperf., pair	275.00	
b.		Vert. pair, imperf. between	675.00	
c.		Horiz. pair, imperf. between	675.00	
237	A130	10c olive gray	4.25	4.25
a.		Double impression	280.00	

238	A131	14c black	3.50	3.50
a.		Imperf., pair	400.00	
239	A132	15c rose lake	3.50	3.50
a.		Vert. pair, imperf. between	550.00	
240	A133	20c green	2.75	2.25
a.		Vert. pair, imperf. between	850.00	
241	A134	24c turq blue	3.50	3.25
a.		Vert. pair, imperf. between	1,200.	
242	A135	25c gray	3.50	3.25
a.		Imperf., pair	200.00	
243	A136	48c dark violet	4.25	3.50
a.		Imperf., pair	1,200.	
b.		Imperf., pair	240.00	
		Nos. 233-243 (11)	33.15	29.90
		Set, never hinged	45.00	

Imperfs are with gum. No. 243b also made
without gum; value the same.

Princess
Elizabeth — A139

Designs: 2c, King George VI. 3c, Queen
Elizabeth. 7c, Queen Mother Mary.

1938, May 12   Perf. 13½

245	A139	2c green	1.75	.20
246	A139	3c dark carmine	1.75	.20
247	A139	4c light blue	2.40	.20
248	A139	7c dark ultra	1.60	1.10
		Nos. 245-248 (4)	7.50	1.70
		Set, never hinged	9.50	

See Nos. 254-256, 258, 269.

Imperf., Pairs

245a	A139	2c	120.00
246a	A139	3c	120.00
247a	A139	4c	120.00
248a	A139	7c	120.00
		Set, never hinged	700.00

George VI
and Queen
Elizabeth
A141

1939, June 17   Unwmk.

249	A141	5c violet blue	1.25	1.10

Visit of King George and Queen Elizabeth.

No. 249 Surcharged in Brown or Red

1939, Nov. 20

250	A141	2c on 5c vio blue (Br)	1.25	1.00
251	A141	4c on 5c vio blue (R)	1.10	1.00
		Set, never hinged	3.10	

There are many varieties of broken letters
and figures in the settings of the surcharges.

Sir Wilfred Grenfell and
"Strathcona II" — A142

1941, Dec. 1   Perf. 12

252	A142	5c dull blue	.40	.30
		Never hinged	.50	

Grenfell Mission, 50th anniv.

Types of 1931-38

1941-44   Wmk. 224   Perf. 12½

253	A97	1c dark gray	.35	.20
a.		Imperf., pair	150.00	
254	A139	2c deep green	.35	.20
255	A139	3c rose carmine	.45	.20
256	A139	4c blue	.70	.30

257	A101	5c violet (Die I)	1.10	.20
a.		Imperf., pair	175.00	
b.		Horiz. pair, imperf. vert.	475.00	
c.		Double impression	400.00	
258	A139	7c vio blue ('42)	1.20	1.00
259	A110	8c red	1.30	.65
260	A103	10c brownish blk	1.30	.60
261	A104	14c black	2.10	1.75
a.		Imperf., pair	240.00	
c.		Vert. pair, imperf. horiz.	240.00	
262	A105	15c pale rose vio	2.00	1.40
263	A106	20c green	2.00	1.10
264	A111	24c deep blue	2.25	2.00
265	A107	25c slate	2.25	2.00
266	A108	48c red brown ('44)	3.00	1.75
		Nos. 253-266 (14)	20.35	13.35
		Set, never hinged	26.00	

Nos. 254 and 255 are re-engraved.

Memorial
University
College
A143

1943, Jan. 2   Unwmk.   Perf. 12

267	A143	30c carmine	1.40	1.00
		Never hinged	1.85	

No. 267
Surcharged
in Black

1946, Mar. 23

268	A143	2c on 30c carmine	.30	.30
		Never hinged	.40	

Princess
Elizabeth — A144

Deck of the
Matthew
A145

Wmk. 224

1947, Apr. 21   Engr.   Perf. 12½

269	A144	4c light blue	.30	.20
		Never hinged	.40	
a.		Imperf., pair	240.00	
b.		Horiz. pair, imperf. vert.	325.00	

Princess Elizabeth's 21st birthday.

1947, June 23

270	A145	5c rose violet	.30	.25
		Never hinged	.40	
a.		Horiz. pair, imperf. between	1,200.	
b.		Imperf., pair	240.00	

Cabot's arrival off Cape Bonavista, 450th
anniv.

AIR POST STAMPS

No. 117 Overprinted
in Black

1919, Apr. 12   Unwmk.   Perf. 14

C1	A67	3c red brown	25,000.	16,000.
		Never hinged	37,500.	

No. 70 Surcharged
in Black

Trans-Atlantic
AIR POST,
1919.
ONE DOLLAR.

1919, June 9   *Perf. 12*
C2	A33 $1 on 15c scarlet	225.00	225.00
	Never hinged	375.00	
a.	Without comma after "Post"	240.00	*275.00*
b.	As "a," without period after "1919"	450.00	450.00

No. 73
Overprinted in
Black

AIR MAIL
to Halifax, N.S.
1921

1921, Nov. 7
C3	A36 35c red, 2½mm between "AIR" and "MAIL"	145.00	*180.00*
a.	Inverted overprint	6,000.	
b.	With period after "1921"	160.00	*200.00*
c.	As "b," inverted overprint	6,250.	

No. C3 was printed in sheets of twenty-five, containing varieties of wide and narrow space between "AIR" and "MAIL," date shifted to right, and with and without period after date.

No. 74 Overprinted in
Red

Air Mail
DE PINEDO
1927

1927, May 21
C4	A37 60c black	*42,500.*	*17,500.*
	Never hinged	*57,500.*	

No. 126 Surcharged
in Black

Trans-Atlantic
AIR MAIL
By B. M.
"Columbia"
September
1930
Fifty Cents

1930, Sept. 25   *Perf. 14*
C5	A67 50c on 36c ol grn	*9,500.*	*9,500.*
	Never hinged	*13,750.*	

Dog Sled and
Airplane — AP6

First Transatlantic Mail Airplane and
Packet Ship — AP7

Routes of Historic Transatlantic
Flights — AP8

1931, Jan. 2   Engr.   Unwmk.
C6	AP6 15c brown	11.00	7.50
a.	Horiz. pair, imperf. between	950.00	

b.	Vert. pair, imperf. between		
c.	Imperf., pair	950.00	
		625.00	
C7	AP7 50c green	35.00	25.00
a.	Horiz. pair, imperf. between	1,350.	825.00
b.	Vert. pair, imperf. between	1,350.	
c.	Imperf., pair	725.00	
C8	AP8 $1 blue	70.00	55.00
a.	Horiz. pair, imperf. between	1,000.	
b.	Vert. pair, imperf. between	1,000.	
c.	Imperf., pair	725.00	
	Nos. C6-C8 (3)	116.00	87.50
	Set, never hinged	195.00	

1931   **Wmk. 224**
C9	AP6 15c brown	11.00	7.50
a.	Horiz. pair, imperf. between	950.00	
b.	Vert. pair, imperf. between	1,100.	
c.	Imperf., pair	600.00	
C10	AP7 50c green	45.00	35.00
a.	Horiz. pair, imperf. between	950.00	
b.	Vert. pair, imperf. between	950.00	
c.	Horiz. pair, imperf. vert.	950.00	
C11	AP8 $1 blue	110.00	90.00
a.	Horiz. pair, imperf. between	1,000.	
c.	Horiz. pair, imperf. between	1,000.	
d.	Vert. pair, imperf. horiz.	1,000.	
e.	Imperf., pair	600.00	
	Nos. C9-C11 (3)	166.00	132.50
	Set, never hinged	280.00	

As the watermark 224 does not show on every stamp in the sheet, pairs are found one with and one without watermark.
For overprint and surcharge see Nos. 211, C12.

No. C11 Surcharged in Red

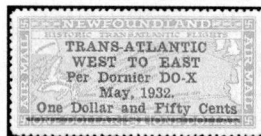

NEWFOUNDLAND
HISTORIC TRANSATLANTIC FLIGHTS
TRANS-ATLANTIC
WEST TO EAST
Per Dornier DO-X
May, 1932.
One Dollar and Fifty Cents

1932, May 19
C12	AP8 $1.50 on $1 blue	290.00	275.00
	Never hinged	450.00	
a.	Inverted surcharge	18,500.	
	Never hinged	25,000.	

A stamp of this design was produced in the US in 1932 by a private company under contract with Newfoundland authorities. The government canceled the contract and the stamp was not valid for prepayment of postage. Value, $35.

"Put to
Flight" — AP9

"Land of
Heart's
Delight"
AP10

"Spotting the
Herd"
AP11

"News from
Home"
AP12

"Labrador,
The Land of
Gold"
AP13

Perf. 11½ (10, 60c), 14 (5, 30, 75c)
1933, June 9   Engr.
C13	AP9 5c lt brown	11.00	11.00
b.	Horiz. pair, imperf. between	1,250.	
c.	Vert. pair, imperf. between	1,250.	
C14	AP10 10c yellow	19.00	17.50
C15	AP11 30c blue	30.00	30.00
C16	AP12 60c green	60.00	57.50
C17	AP13 75c bister	60.00	57.50
b.	Horiz. pair, imperf. between	1,250.	
c.	Vert. pair, imperf. between	1,250.	
	Nos. C13-C17 (5)	180.00	173.50
	Set, never hinged	265.00	

Beware of clever forgeries of Nos. C13b, C13c, C17b and C17c. Certificates of authenticity are highly recommended.

Imperf., Pairs

C13a	AP9	5c	275.00
C14a	AP10	10c	200.00
C15a	AP11	30c	600.00
C16a	AP12	60c	675.00
C17a	AP13	75c	650.00
	Set, never hinged		3,150.

No. C17 Surcharged in Black

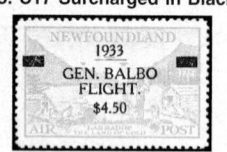

NEWFOUNDLAND
1933
GEN. BALBO
FLIGHT.
$4.50

1933, July 24   *Perf. 14*
C18	AP13 $4.50 on 75c bister	350.00	*375.00*
	Never hinged	550.00	
a.	Inverted surcharge	*120,000.*	
	Never hinged	—	

Return flight from Chicago to Rome of the squadron of Italian seaplanes under the command of Gen. Italo Balbo.
No. C18a was not regularly issued. The $4.50 on No. C14, 10c yellow, is a proof.

View of St.
John's
AP14

1943, June 1   Unwmk.   *Perf. 12*
C19	AP14 7c bright ultra	.35	.30
	Never hinged	.45	

POSTAGE DUE STAMPS

POSTAGE DUE
1
CENT
NEWFOUNDLAND
D1

Perf. 10-10½, Compound
1939-49   Litho.   Unwmk.
J1	D1 1c yellow green, perf. 11 ('49)	4.25	5.50
a.	Perf. 10-10½	7.25	5.50
J2	D1 2c vermilion	7.00	5.50
a.	Perf. 11x9 ('46)	7.00	5.50
J3	D1 3c ultramarine	7.00	5.50
a.	Perf. 11x9 ('49)	7.50	7.50
b.	Perf. 9	1,500.	
J4	D1 4c yel org, perf. 11x9 ('49)	9.50	9.50
a.	Perf 10-10½	15.00	15.00

J5	D1 5c pale brown	15.00	4.25
J6	D1 10c dark violet	6.00	5.00
	Nos. J1-J6 (6)	48.75	35.25
	Set, never hinged	78.75	

1949   **Wmk. 224**   *Perf. 11*
J7	D1 10c dark violet	11.00	*14.00*
	Never hinged	19.00	
a.	Vert. pair, imperf. between	800.00	

For used examples of Nos. J1-J7 with dated cancels from 1939-49, triple the values shown.

NOVA SCOTIA

ˌnō-və-ˈskō-shə

LOCATION — Eastern coast of Canada between the Gulf of St. Lawrence and the Atlantic Ocean
GOVT. — British Crown Colony
AREA — 21,428 sq. mi.
POP. — 386,500 (1871)
CAPITAL — Halifax

Nova Scotia joined the Canadian Confederation in 1867 and is now a province of the Dominion. Postage stamps of Canada are used.

12 Pence = 1 Shilling
100 Cents = 1 Dollar (1860)

Values for unused stamps are for examples with original gum as defined in the catalogue introduction except for Nos. 4-7, which are rarely found with any remaining original gum.

Queen Victoria — A1

Crown of
Great Britain
and Heraldic
Flowers of
the
Empire — A2

1851-57   Unwmk.   Engr.   *Imperf.*
Blue Paper
1	A1 1p red brown ('53)	3,250.	650.
a.	Half used as ½p on cover		
2	A2 3p bright blue	1,250.	240.
a.	Half used as 1½p on cover		*3,750.*
b.	3p pale blue ('57)	1,250.	240.
c.	As "b," half used as 1½p on cover		*3,750.*
3	A2 3p dark blue	1,600.	300.
a.	Half used as 1½p on cover		*4,500.*
4	A2 6p yellow green	4,750.	675.
a.	Half used as 3p on cover		*4,500.*
5	A2 6p dark green ('57)	9,250.	1,900.
a.	Half used as 3p on cover		*5,000.*
b.	Quarter used as 1½p on cover		*47,500.*
6	A2 1sh reddish pur ('57)	25,000.	5,250.
a.	Half used as 6p on cover		*32,500.*
b.	1sh deep purple	25,000.	5,250.
7	A2 1sh dull violet	25,000.	6,500.
a.	Half used as 6p on cover		*47,500.*
b.	Quarter used as 3p on cover		*60,000.*

Reprints are on thin hard white paper. 1p in brown, 3p in blue, 6p dark green. 1sh violet black. Value about $300 per set.
No. 6 was reproduced by the collotype process in a souvenir sheet distributed at the London International Stamp Exhibition 1950.

Queen
Victoria — A3   A5

A6

1860-63   *Perf. 12*
White or Yellowish Paper

8	A3	1c black	12.00	7.50
a.	White paper		12.00	7.50
b.	Half used as ½c on cover			
				5,750.
c.	Horiz. pair, imperf. vert.		325.00	
9	A3	2c lilac	12.00	10.00
a.	Yellowish paper		12.00	10.00
b.	Half used as 1c on cover			
				2,750.
10	A3	5c blue	400.00	9.00
a.	Yellowish paper		400.00	9.00
b.	Half used as 2½c on cover			—
11	A5	8½c green	12.00	16.00
a.	White paper		12.00	13.50
12	A5	10c vermilion	12.00	12.00
a.	Yellowish paper		12.00	12.00
b.	Half used as 5c on cover			1,200.
13	A6	12½c black	37.50	37.50
a.	White paper		37.50	37.50
	Nos. 8-13 (6)		485.50	92.00
	Set, never hinged		1,075.	

The stamps of Nova Scotia were replaced by those of Canada.

PRINCE EDWARD ISLAND

'prin̯t̯s 'ed-wərd 'ī-ləns

LOCATION — In the Gulf of St. Lawrence, opposite the provinces of New Brunswick and Nova Scotia
GOVT. — British Crown Colony
AREA — 2,184 sq. mi.
POP. — 92,000 (estimated)
CAPITAL — Charlottetown

Originally annexed to Nova Scotia, Prince Edward Island was a separate colony from 1769 to 1873, when it became a part of the Canadian Confederation. Postage stamps of Canada are now used.

12 Pence = 1 Shilling
100 Cents = 1 Dollar (1872)

A1   A2

Queen Victoria — A3

1861, Jan. 1   Unwmk. Typo.   *Perf. 9*

1	A1	2p dull rose	600.	300.
a.	2p deep rose		700.	350.
b.	Rouletted			22,500.
c.	Horiz. pair, imperf. between		6,000.	
d.	Diagonal half used as 1p on cover			1,900.

2	A2	3p blue	1,150.	650.
a.	Diagonal half used as 1½p on cover			2,250.
b.	Double impression		4,750.	

No. 2b is valued with very small faults.

3	A3	6p yellow green	1,900.	1,150.

A4   A5

1862-65   *Perf. 11½-12*
White or Yellowish Paper

4	A4	1p yellow orange	37.50	35.00
a.	1p brown orange. perf. 11		37.50	35.00
b.	Imperf., pair		200.00	
c.	Half used as ½p on cover			1,500.
5	A1	2p rose	8.50	7.50
a.	Yellowish paper		8.50	7.50
b.	Imperf., pair		72.50	
c.	Horiz. pair, imperf. vert.		275.00	
d.	Vert. pair, imperf. horiz.		375.00	
e.	Diagonal half used as 1p on cover			1,900.
f.	"TWC" for "TWO"		60.00	30.00
6	A2	3p blue	12.50	15.00
a.	Yellowish paper		17.50	15.00
b.	Imperf., pair		85.00	
c.	Vert. pair, imperf. horiz.		240.00	
d.	Horiz. pair, imperf. vert.		240.00	
e.	Diagonal half used as 1½p on cover			250.00
7	A3	6p yellow green	115.00	95.00
a.	6p blue green		115.00	95.00
b.	Imperf.			
c.	Diagonal half used as 3p on cover			3,000.
8	A5	9p violet	95.00	80.00
a.	Imperf., pair		300.00	
b.	Horiz. pair, imperf. vert.		325.00	
c.	Diagonal half used as 4½p on cover			2,250.
	Nos. 4-8 (5)		268.50	232.50

Queen Victoria
A6   A7

1868

9	A6	4p black	9.50	19.00
a.	Yellowish paper		15.00	22.50
b.	Horiz. pair, imperf. vert.		190.00	
c.	Diagonal half used as 2p on cover			2,250.
d.	Imperf., pair		115.00	
e.	Horiz. pair, imperf. between		160.00	

1870, June 1   Engr.   *Perf. 12*

10	A7	4½p brown	60.00	60.00

A8   A9

A10   A11

A12   A13

1872, Jan. 1   Typo.   *Perf. 12, 12½*

11	A8	1c brown orange	5.25	7.50
a.	Imperf., pair		240.00	
12	A9	2c ultra	24.00	30.00
a.	Imperf., pair		300.00	
b.	Diagonal half used as 1c on cover			—
13	A10	3c rose	24.00	24.00
a.	Imperf., pair		240.00	
b.	Diagonal half used as 1½c on cover			—
c.	Horiz. or vert. pair, imperf. between		240.00	
14	A11	4c green	7.00	13.00
a.	Imperf., pair		240.00	
b.	Diagonal half used as 2c on cover			2,000.
15	A12	6c black	6.00	13.00
a.	Horiz. pair, imperf. btwn.		275.00	
b.	Half used as 3c on cover			900.00
16	A13	12c violet	7.75	30.00
a.	Imperf., pair		240.00	
b.	Half used as 6c on cover			—
	Nos. 11-16 (6)		74.00	117.50

CANADA

'ka-nə-də

LOCATION — Northern part of North American continent, except for Alaska
GOVT. — Self-governing dominion in the British Commonwealth of Nations
AREA — 3,851,809 sq. mi.
POP. — 28,846,761 (1996)
CAPITAL — Ottawa

Included in the dominion are British Columbia, Vancouver Island, Prince Edward Island, Nova Scotia, New Brunswick and Newfoundland, all of which formerly issued stamps.

12 Pence = 1 Shilling
100 Cents = 1 Dollar (1859)

Catalogue values for unused stamps in this country are for Never Hinged items, beginning with Scott 268 in the regular postage section, Scott B1 in the semi-postal section, Scott C9 in the air post section, Scott CE3 in the air post special delivery section, Scott CO1 in the air post official section, Scott E11 in the special delivery section, Scott EO1 in the special delivery official section, Scott J15 in the postage due section, and Scott O1 in the official section.

Values for unused stamps of #1-33 are for examples with partial original gum. Stamps without gum often trade at prices very close to those of stamps with partial gum. Examples with full original gum and lightly hinged are extremely scarce and generally sell for substantially more than the values listed.

Very fine examples of the perforated issues between Nos. 11-20 will have perforations touching the design or frameline on at least one side due to the narrow spacing of the stamps on the plates. Stamps with perfs clear of the designs on all four sides are extremely scarce and will command much higher prices.

Province of Canada

Beaver — A1   Prince Albert — A2

Queen Victoria — A3

1851   Unwmk.   Engr.   *Imperf.*
Laid Paper

1	A1	3p red	30,000.	1,000.
2	A2	6p slate violet	35,000.	1,750.
a.	Diagonal half used as 3p on cover			32,500.
3	A3	12p black	160,000.	140,000.

On some stamps the laid lines of Nos. 1-3 are practically invisible.

1852-57   Wove Paper

4	A1	3p red	1,400.	225.
a.	3p brown red ('53)		1,600.	250.
b.	Diagonal half used as 1½p on cover			32,500.
c.	Ribbed paper		4,000.	550.
d.	Thin paper		1,500.	225.

5	A2	6p slate gray ('55)	27,500.	1,500.
a.		6p brownish gray	35,000.	2,000.
b.		6p greenish gray	27,500.	1,500.
c.		Diagonal half used as 3p on cover		17,500.
d.		Thick hard paper (gray vio) ('57)	27,500.	3,000.

Re-entries of the 3p are numerous. The main re-entry is distinguishable most easily by the line through "EE" and "PEN".

Most authorities believe the 12p black does not exist on wove paper.

Jacques Cartier — A4

1855

7	A4	10p blue	9,000.	1,750.
a.		Thick paper	10,000.	2,250.

Queen Victoria
A5   A6

1857

8	A5	½p rose	1,000.	700.
a.		Horizontally ribbed paper	10,000.	2,500.
b.		Vertically ribbed paper	10,000.	3,750.
9	A6	7½p green		3,500.

Very Thick Soft Wove Paper

10	A2	6p reddish pur	20,000.	6,000.
a.		Half used as 3p on cover		22,500.

1858-59   Wove Paper   *Perf. 12*

11	A5	½p rose	3,250.	1,800.
12	A1	3p red	15,000.	1,250.
13	A2	6p brown vio ('59)	17,500.	6,750.
a.		6p gray violet	18,000.	7,250.
b.		Diagonal half used as 3p on cover		17,500.

Nos. 11-13 values are for examples with perfs touching the design.

A7   A8

A9   A10

A11   A12

1859

14	A7	1c rose	425.00	90.00
a.		Imperf., pair	5,000.	
b.		1c deep rose	575.00	140.00
15	A8	5c ver	525.00	37.50
		On cover		47.50
a.		Imperf., pair	14,000.	—
b.		Diagonal half used as 2½c on cover		6,000.
c.		5c brick red	625.00	42.50

16	A9	10c black brn	11,500.	5,500.
a.		Half used as 5c on cover		8,000.
17	A9	10c red lilac	1,100.	150.00
a.		10c violet	1,300.	160.00
b.		10c brown	1,200.	140.00
c.		Imperf., pair	11,000.	
d.		Diagonal half used as 5c on cover		3,750.
e.		10c deep red purple	3,250.	1,500.
18	A10	12½c yel green	875.00	120.00
a.		12½c blue green	1,050.	125.00
b.		Imperf., pair	5,000.	
19	A11	17c blue	1,250.	190.00
a.		17c slate blue	1,250.	210.00
b.		Imperf., pair	4,750.	

No. 15b was used with a 10c for a 12½c rate.

Imperfs. are without gum.

Re-entries of the 5c are numerous. Many of them are slight and have only small premium value. The major re-entry has many lines of the design double, especially the outlines of the ovals and frame at left. Value, used, about $700.

Nos. 14-19 values are for examples with perfs touching the design.

1864

20	A12	2c rose	725.00	300.00
a.		2c deep claret rose	775.00	350.00
b.		Imperf., pair	3,500.	

Imperfs. are without gum.
Values are for examples with perfs touching the design.

Dominion of Canada

Queen Victoria
A13   A14

A15   A16

A17   A18

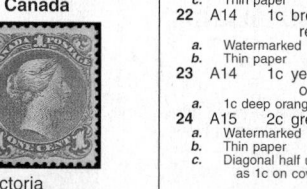

A19   A20

1868-76   *Perf. 12, 11½x12 (5c)*

21	A13	½c black	100.00	75.00
a.		Perf. 11½x12 ('73)	125.00	85.00
b.		Watermarked	18,500.	11,000.
c.		Thin paper	125.00	75.00
22	A14	1c brown red	750.00	100.00
a.		Watermarked	3,000.	450.00
b.		Thin paper	800.00	100.00
23	A14	1c yellow org	1,500.	200.00
a.		1c deep orange	2,250.	240.00
24	A15	2c green	850.00	95.00
a.		Watermarked	3,000.	375.00
b.		Thin paper	900.00	100.00
c.		Diagonal half used as 1c on cover		4,000.

No.	Type	Description			
25	A16	3c red		1,900.	35.00
a.		Watermarked		4,750.	375.00
b.		Thin paper		2,000.	40.00
26	A17	5c ol grn ('75)		1,600.	200.00
a.		Perf. 12		3,250.	900.00
b.		Imperf., pair		12,000.	
27	A18	6c dark brown		2,000.	125.00
a.		6c yellow brown		1,750.	125.00
b.		Watermarked		6,250.	2,000.
c.		Thin paper		1,900.	160.00
d.		Diagonal half used as 3c on cover			3,000.
e.		Vert. half used as 3c on cover			—
f.		6c black brown, thin paper (Mar. '68, 1st printing)		2,750.	240.00
28	A19	12½c blue		1,200.	100.00
a.		Watermarked		4,000.	375.00
b.		Thin paper		1,100.	125.00
c.		Horiz. pair, imperf. vert.			—
d.		Vert. pair, imperf. horiz.			16,000.
29	A20	15c gray violet		95.00	50.00
a.		Perf. 11½x12 ('74)		1,600.	375.00
b.		15c red lilac		950.00	115.00
c.		Wmk. (Clutha Mills)		6,000.	1,150.
d.		Imperf., pair		1,500.	
		Never hinged		3,000.	
e.		Thin paper		725.00	135.00
30	A20	15c gray		95.00	55.00
a.		Perf. 11½x12 ('73)		1,200.	375.00
b.		15c blue gray ('75)		115.00	60.00
c.		Very thick paper (dp vio)		4,750.	1,350.
d.		Script wmk., Perf. 11½x12, ('76)		22,500.	5,500.
e.		15c deep blue		1,650.	375.00

The watermark on Nos. 21b, 22a, 24a, 25a, 27b, 28a and 29c consists of double-lined letters reading: "E. & G. BOTHWELL CLUTHA MILLS." The script watermark on No. 30d reads in full: "Alexr. Pirie & Sons." Values for all these watermarked stamps are for fine examples. Very fine examples are rare, seldom traded, and generally command premiums of about 100% over the values listed.

No. 26a unused is valued in the grade of fine. No. 26b is a unique pair.

The existence of No. 28c has been questioned.

1868 — Laid Paper

No.	Type	Description			
31	A14	1c brown red		22,500.	7,250.
32	A15	2c green			200,000.
33	A16	3c bright red		20,000.	2,000.

Only two examples of No. 32 are known, neither being very fine.

Montreal and Ottawa Printings

A21

A22

A23

A24

A25

A26   A27

1870-89 — Wove Paper — Perf. 12

No.	Type	Description			
34	A21	½c black ('82)		15.00	10.00
a.		Imperf., pair		600.00	
b.		Horiz. pair, imperf. between		800.00	
35	A22	1c yellow		47.50	1.10
a.		1c orange ('70)		175.00	9.50
b.		Imperf., pair		475.00	
c.		Diagonal half used as ½c on circular			4,000.
36	A23	2c green ('72)		75.00	2.25
a.		Imperf., pair		725.00	
b.		Diagonal half used as 1c on cover			2,000.

No.	Type	Description			
c.		Vertical half used as 1c on cover			2,000.
d.		2c blue green ('89)		100.00	4.50
f.		Double impression		—	
37	A24	3c orange red ('73)		120.00	2.00
a.		3c rose ('71)		600.00	15.00
b.		3c copper red ('70)		1,500.	60.00
c.		3c dull red ('72)		125.00	3.00
38	A25	5c sl green ('76)		925.00	22.50
39	A26	6c yel brn ('72)		725.00	22.50
a.		Diagonal half used as 3c on cover			600.00
c.		Imperf., pair		2,750.	
40	A27	10c dull rose lilac ('77)		1,100.	75.00
a.		10c magenta ('80)		1,150.	80.00
b.		10c deep lilac rose		1,100.	75.00

No. 34a was made with and without gum; values the same.

Examples of Nos. 36b and 36c postmarked "Halifax" are a private speculation.

1870 — Perf. 12½

No.	Type	Description			
37d	A24	3c copper red (Ottawa)		9,500.	1,400.

1873-79 — Perf. 11½x12

No.	Type	Description			
35d	A22	1c orange		350.00	18.50
36e	A23	2c green		525.00	22.50
37e	A24	3c red		275.00	11.00
38a	A25	5c slate green		1,100.	50.00
39b	A26	6c yellow brown		900.00	60.00
40c	A27	10c dull rose lilac		1,600.	240.00

The gum on Nos. 35d-40c is always dull and usually blotchy or streaky. It is distinct from the earlier clear, smooth gum and from the bright shiny gums of the later periods.

Nos. 38 and 40 were printed at Montreal. Printings of Nos. 34 to 37, and 39 were made at Ottawa or Montreal and can be separated only by differences in paper and gum.

Ottawa Printing

A28

A29

1888-97 — Perf. 12

No.	Type	Description			
41	A24	3c brt vermilion		60.00	.75
a.		3c rose carmine		475.00	11.00
42	A25	5c gray		200.00	4.75
43	A26	6c red brown		190.00	11.00
a.		6c chocolate ('90)		225.00	27.50
44	A28	8c violet black ('93)		220.00	4.50
a.		8c blue gray		350.00	5.75
b.		8c slate		240.00	4.50
c.		8c gray		240.00	4.50
45	A27	10c brown red ('97)		625.00	55.00
a.		10c dull rose		600.00	50.00
b.		10c pink		600.00	55.00
46	A29	20c ver ('93)		425.00	100.00
47	A29	50c dp blue ('93)		425.00	75.00

Stamps of the 1870-93 issues are found on paper varying from very thin to thick, also occasionally on paper showing a distinctly ribbed surface.

The gum on Nos. 41-47 appears bright and shiny, often with a yellowish tint.

Imperf., Pairs

No.	Type	Description		
41b	A24	3c		475.
42a	A25	5c		725.
43b	A26	6c		600.
44d	A28	8c		800.
45c	A27	10c		600.
46a	A29	20c		1,400.
47a	A29	50c		1,400.

Nos. 41b-45c made with and without gum. Without gum sell for the same as the unused hinged price.

Imperforates and Part-Perforates

From 1859 through 1943 (Nos. 14a/262a), imperforate stamps were printed. The earliest imperforates through perhaps 1917 most likely were from imprimatur sheets (i.e. the first sheets from the approved plates, normally kept in government files) or proof sheets on stamp paper that once were in the post office archives. The imperforates from approximately 1927 to 1943 (often made both with and without gum) were specially created and traded for classic stamps needed for the post office museum, given as gifts to governmental or other dignitaries, or sold or given to favored persons.

The only imperforates from this entire period that were issued to the public were Nos. 90a and 136-138.

Similarly, almost all stamps that are known part-perforate (i.e. horizontal pairs imperforate vertically and vertical pairs imperforate horizontally) were specially made for trading purposes or as presentation items to be given to favored persons. These part-perforates are not listed here, but they are listed in *Scott Classic Specialized Catalogue of Stamps & Covers.* Part-perforate error stamps that are believed to have been actually issued to the public are listed in this catalogue.

See the similar imperforates in the air post, Nos. CE1a and CE2a, special delivery, No. F2c (but not No. F1c which was an issued error), postage dues, and Nos. MR4b and MR4c.

Jubilee Issue

Queen Victoria, "1837" and "1897" — A30

1897, June 19 — Unwmk. — Perf. 12

No.	Type	Description			
50	A30	½c black		120.00	120.00
		Never hinged		300.00	
51	A30	1c orange		22.50	8.00
		Never hinged		57.50	
52	A30	2c green		25.00	15.00
		Never hinged		62.50	
53	A30	3c bright rose		17.50	2.50
		Never hinged		45.00	
54	A30	5c deep blue		60.00	45.00
		Never hinged		160.00	
55	A30	6c yellow brown		230.00	175.00
		Never hinged		575.00	
56	A30	8c dark violet		120.00	65.00
		Never hinged		300.00	
57	A30	10c brown violet		120.00	120.00
		Never hinged		300.00	
58	A30	15c steel blue		260.00	190.00
		Never hinged		650.00	
59	A30	20c vermilion		275.00	190.00
		Never hinged		625.00	
60	A30	50c ultra		375.00	190.00
		Never hinged		775.00	
61	A30	$1 lake		1,000.	700.00
		Never hinged		2,650.	
62	A30	$2 dk purple		1,400.	525.00
		Never hinged		3,750.	
63	A30	$3 yel bister		1,400.	1,000.
		Never hinged		3,750.	
64	A30	$4 purple		1,400.	1,000.
		Never hinged		3,750.	
65	A30	$5 olive green		1,500.	1,000.
		Never hinged		3,900.	
		Nos. 50-60 (11)		1,625.	1,120.
		Nos. 50-60, never hinged		3,840.	

60th year of Queen Victoria's reign.
Roller and smudged cancels on Nos. 61-65 sell for less.

A31

A32

1897-98

No.	Type	Description			
66	A31	½c black		13.00	6.50
		Never hinged		32.50	
67	A31	1c blue green		40.00	1.40
		Never hinged		100.00	
68	A31	2c purple		40.00	2.25
		Never hinged		100.00	
69	A31	3c carmine ('98)		65.00	1.00
		Never hinged		165.00	

No.	Type	Description			
70	A31	5c dk bl, *bluish*		150.00	9.00
		Never hinged		375.00	
71	A31	6c brown		130.00	35.00
		Never hinged		325.00	
72	A31	8c orange		250.00	12.50
		Never hinged		625.00	
73	A31	10c brown vio ('98)		500.00	80.00
		Never hinged		1,250.	
		Nos. 66-73 (8)		1,188.	147.65
		Nos. 66-73, never hinged		2,968.	

For surcharge see No. 87.

Imperf., Pairs

No.	Type	Description		
66a	A31	½c		400.
		Never hinged		750.
67a	A31	1c		400.
		Never hinged		750.
68a	A31	2c		400.
		Never hinged		750.
69a	A31	3c		800.
		Never hinged		1,450.
70a	A31	5c		400.
		Never hinged		750.
71a	A31	6c		800.
		Never hinged		1,450.
72a	A31	8c		600.
		Never hinged		1,100.
73a	A31	10c		600.
		Never hinged		1,100.

Nos. 66a, 67a, 68a and 70a made with and without gum. Specialists can distinguish printings made with and without gum by shade and paper quality. Without gum sell for about 95% of the unused hinged price.

1898-1902

TWO CENTS:
Type I — Frame of four very thin lines.
Type II — Frame of a thick line between two thin ones.

No.	Type	Description			
74	A32	½c black		9.00	2.25
		Never hinged		18.00	
75	A32	1c gray green		35.00	.35
		Never hinged		70.00	
76	A32	2c purple (I)		35.00	.35
		Never hinged		70.00	
a.		Thick paper ('99)		175.00	12.00
		Never hinged		350.00	
77	A32	2c car (I) ('99)		35.00	.35
		Never hinged		70.00	
a.		2c carmine (II) ('99)		47.50	.60
		Never hinged		95.00	
b.		Booklet pane of 6 (II) ('00)		1,600.	—
		Never hinged		3,000.	
78	A32	3c carmine		65.00	1.10
		Never hinged		130.00	

79	A32	5c blue, *bluish*			
		('99)	220.00	2.25	
		Never hinged	440.00		
80	A32	6c brown	190.00	45.00	
		Never hinged	380.00		
81	A32	7c ol yel ('02)	150.00	22.50	
		Never hinged	300.00		
82	A32	8c orange	300.00	25.00	
		Never hinged	600.00		
83	A32	10c brown vio	400.00	20.00	
		Never hinged	800.00		
84	A32	20c ol grn ('00)	600.00	100.00	
		Never hinged	1,200.		
		Nos. 74-84 (11)	2,039.	219.15	
		Nos. 74-84, never hinged	4,078.		

For surcharges see Nos. 88-88C.

Imperf., Pairs

74a	A32	½c	475.	
		Never hinged	775.	
75a	A32	1c	1,200.	
		Never hinged	1,900.	
77c	A32	2c (I)	475.	
		Never hinged	775.	
77d	A32	2c (II)	1,800.	
e.		As No. 77b, imperf., 2 panes tete beche ('00)	15,000.	
79a	A32	5c	1,200.	
		Never hinged	1,900.	
80a	A32	6c	1,200.	
		Never hinged	1,900.	
81a	A32	7c	600.	
82a	A32	8c	1,200.	
		Never hinged	1,900.	
83a	A32	10c	1,200.	
		Never hinged	1,900.	
84a	A32	20c	4,500.	

Nos. 77e, 77e, 81a and 84a were made only without gum. No. 80a was made only with gum. Others either with or without gum and of these those without gum sell for about ⅔ of the values shown for unused hinged. Specialists can distinguish printings made with and without gum by shade and paper quality.

Imperial Penny Postage Issue

Map of British Empire on Mercator Projection A33

No. 86

1898, Dec. 7 — Engr. & Typo.

85	A33	2c black, lav & car	45.00	7.50
		Never hinged	90.00	
a.		Imperf., pair	550.00	
86	A33	2c black, bl & car	40.00	7.00
		Never hinged	80.00	
a.		Imperf., pair	550.00	
		Never hinged	77.50	

Imperfs. are without gum.

Nos. 69 and 78 Surcharged in

1899, July

87	A31	2c on 3c carmine	17.50	7.50
		Never hinged	45.00	
88	A32	2c on 3c carmine	27.50	6.00
		Never hinged	70.00	

No. 78 Surcharged in Blue or Violet

A32a   A32b

1899, Jan. 5

88B	A32a	1(c) on ⅓ of 3c, on cover (Bl)	7,750.
88C	A32b	2(c) on ⅔ of 3c, on cover (V)	7,750.

Nos. 88B-88C were prepared and used at Port Hood, Nova Scotia, without official authorization.

King Edward VII — A34

1903-08 — Engr.

89	A34	1c green	35.00	.20
		Never hinged	87.50	
90	A34	2c carmine	37.50	.20
		Never hinged	95.00	
b.		Booklet pane of 6	1,600.	1,250.
		Never hinged	2,750.	
91	A34	5c blue, *blue*	220.00	4.00
		Never hinged	550.00	
92	A34	7c olive bister	225.00	4.00
		Never hinged	550.00	
93	A34	10c brown lilac	400.00	10.00
		Never hinged	1,000.	
94	A34	20c olive green ('04)	675.00	50.00
		Never hinged	1,700.	

95	A34	50c purple ('08)	850.00	175.00
		Never hinged	2,100.	
		Nos. 89-95 (7)	2,442.	243.40
		Nos. 89-95, never hinged	6,020.	

Values for Nos. 94 and 95 used are for examples with contemporaneous circular datestamps. Stamps with heavy cancellations or parcel cancellations sell for much less.
Issued: 1c-10c, 7/1/03; 20c, 9/27/04; 50c, 11/19/08.

Imperf., Pairs

89a	A34	1c	725.00	
90a	A34	2c	45.00	45.00
		Never hinged	95.00	
c.		As No. 90b, imperf, 2 panes tete beche	14,500.	
91a	A34	5c	1,200.	
92a	A34	7c	800.	
93a	A34	10c	1,200.	

All imperfs except No. 90a were made without gum.
No. 90a issued to the public with gum; also made without gum from different plates distinguishable by experts. Value without gum, $350 with certificate of authenticity.

Quebec Tercentenary Issue

Prince and Princess of Wales, 1908 — A35

Jacques Cartier and Samuel de Champlain A36

Queen
Alexandra
and King
Edward
A37

Champlain's
Home in
Quebec
A38

Generals
Montcalm
and
Wolfe — A39

View of
Quebec in
1700 — A40

Champlain's
Departure for
the
West — A41

Arrival of
Cartier at
Quebec
A42

1908, July 16

96	A35	½c black brown	6.00	5.00
		Never hinged	15.00	
97	A36	1c blue green	22.50	4.50
		Never hinged	55.00	
98	A37	2c carmine	32.50	2.00
		Never hinged	82.50	
99	A38	5c dark blue	75.00	50.00
		Never hinged	190.00	
100	A39	7c olive green	150.00	100.00
		Never hinged	375.00	
101	A40	10c dark violet	200.00	125.00
		Never hinged	500.00	
102	A41	15c red orange	225.00	125.00
		Never hinged	550.00	
103	A42	20c yellow brown	250.00	175.00
		Never hinged	625.00	
		Nos. 96-103 (8)	961.00	586.50

Nos. 96-103, never hinged 2,367.

Imperf., Pairs

96a	A35	½c	650.00
		Never hinged	1,150.
97a	A36	1c	650.00
		Never hinged	1,150.
98a	A37	2c	650.00
		Never hinged	1,150.
99a	A38	5c	650.00
		Never hinged	1,150.
100a	A39	7c	650.00
		Never hinged	1,150.
101a	A40	10c	650.00
		Never hinged	1,150.
102a	A41	15c	650.00
		Never hinged	1,150.
103a	A42	20c	650.00
		Never hinged	1,150.

100 pairs of imperfs made, 50 with gum and 50 without. Due to demand, pairs without gum generally sell for 90-95% of the unused hinged price.

King George V — A43

Two dies of 1c.
Die I — The "N" of "ONE" is separated from the oval above it.
Die II — The "N" of "ONE" almost touches the oval above it.

Two dies of 3c carmine.

Die I — The "R" of "THREE" is separated from the oval above it. The bottom line of the vignette does not touch the heavy diagonal stroke at right.
Die II — The "R" of "THREE" almost touches the oval above it. The bottom horizontal line of the vignette touches the heavy diagonal stroke at right.

1911-25

104	A43	1c green	17.50	.20
		Never hinged	42.50	
a.		Booklet pane of 6	32.50	35.00
		Never hinged	65.00	
105	A43	1c org yellow (I) ('22)	17.50	.20
		Never hinged	42.50	
a.		Booklet pane of 4 + 2 labels	55.00	55.00
		Never hinged	110.00	
b.		Booklet pane of 6	62.50	62.50
		Never hinged	125.00	
d.		1c org yellow (II)	15.00	.20
		Never hinged	37.50	
106	A43	2c carmine	17.50	.20
		Never hinged	42.50	
a.		Booklet pane of 6	40.00	40.00
		Never hinged	80.00	
b.		2c pink	150.00	18.00
		Never hinged	350.00	
c.		2c rose carmine	17.50	.20
		Never hinged	42.50	
d.		As "c," booklet pane of 6	160.00	160.00
		Never hinged	320.00	
107	A43	2c yel green ('22)	15.00	.20
		Never hinged	37.50	
a.		Thin paper ('24)	15.00	2.50
		Never hinged	37.50	
b.		Booklet pane of 4 + 2 labels ('22)	65.00	70.00
		Never hinged	130.00	
c.		Booklet pane of 6 ('22)	300.00	325.00
		Never hinged	550.00	
108	A43	3c brown ('18)	15.00	.20
		Never hinged	37.50	
a.		Booklet pane of 4 + 2 labels	90.00	95.00
		Never hinged	180.00	
109	A43	3c car (I) ('23)	15.00	.20
		Never hinged	37.50	
a.		Booklet pane of 4 + 2 labels	70.00	75.00
		Never hinged	140.00	
c.		Die II ('24)	32.50	.20
		Never hinged	82.50	
110	A43	4c ol bis ('22)	47.50	3.00
		Never hinged	120.00	
111	A43	5c dark blue ('12)	125.00	.85
		Never hinged	320.00	
112	A43	5c violet ('22)	32.50	.70
		Never hinged	80.00	
a.		Thin paper ('24)	27.50	7.50
		Never hinged	67.50	
113	A43	7c yel ocher ('12)	45.00	3.00
		Never hinged	110.00	
114	A43	7c red brown ('24)	20.00	10.00
		Never hinged	50.00	
115	A43	8c blue ('25)	32.50	10.00
		Never hinged	80.00	
116	A43	10c plum ('12)	260.00	2.75
		Never hinged	650.00	
117	A43	10c blue ('22)	45.00	2.00
		Never hinged	110.00	
118	A43	10c bis brn ('25)	40.00	2.00
		Never hinged	95.00	
119	A43	20c ol grn ('25)	100.00	1.75
		Never hinged	250.00	
120	A43	50c blk brn ('25)	80.00	2.75
		Never hinged	200.00	
a.		50c black ('12)	225.00	9.00
		Never hinged	550.00	
122	A43	$1 orange ('23)	95.00	10.00
		Never hinged	240.00	
		Nos. 104-122 (18)	1,020.	50.00

Nos. 104-122, never hinged 2,545.

For type A43 perforated 12x8 see No. 184.
For surcharges see Nos. 139-140.
Issued: #104, #106, 12/22/11; #105, 6/7/22; #108, 8/6/18; #109, 12/18/23; 4c, 7/7/22; #111, 1/17/12; #112, 2/2/22; #113, 116, 1/12/12; #114, 12/12/24; 8c, 9/1/25; #117, 2/20/22; #118, 8/1/25; 20c, 1/23/12; 50c, 1/26/12; $1, 7/22/23.

Imperf., Panes

105c		As No. 105b, imperf, 2 panes tete beche	12,500.
107d		As No. 107c, imperf, 2 panes tete beche	12,500.
109b		As No. 109a, imperf, 2 panes tete beche	12,500.

Imperf., Pairs

110a	A43	4c	2,000.
		Never hinged	3,600.
112b	A43	5c	2,000.
		Never hinged	3,600.
114a	A43	7c	2,000.
		Never hinged	3,600.
115a	A43	8c	2,000.
		Never hinged	3,600.
118a	A43	10c	2,000.
		Never hinged	3,600.
119a	A43	20c	2,000.
		Never hinged	3,600.
120b	A43	50c	2,400.
		Never hinged	4,250.
122a	A43	$1	2,000.
		Never hinged	3,600.

Nos. 105c and 109b made without gum, others with gum. About half of the No. 120b pairs have creases; value thus $500.

Coil Stamps

1913 **Perf. 8 Horizontally**

123	A43	1c dark green	100.00	60.00
		Never hinged	250.00	
124	A43	2c carmine	100.00	60.00
		Never hinged	250.00	

1912-24 **Perf. 8 Vertically**

125	A43	1c green	25.00	2.00
		Never hinged	50.00	
126	A43	1c org yellow (II) ('23)	12.00	7.50
		Never hinged	24.00	
a.		As #126, block of 4 (II)	60.00	50.00
		Never hinged	90.00	
b.		1c org yellow (I)	25.00	11.00
		Never hinged	50.00	
c.		As "b," block of 4 (I)	450.00	
		Never hinged	750.00	
127	A43	2c carmine	35.00	2.00
		Never hinged	70.00	
128	A43	2c green ('22)	16.00	1.10
		Never hinged	32.50	
a.		Block of 4	60.00	60.00
		Never hinged	90.00	
129	A43	3c brown ('18)	27.50	1.30
		Never hinged	55.00	
130	A43	3c carmine (I) ('24)	70.00	9.00
		Never hinged	140.00	
a.		Block of 4 (I)	950.00	750.00
		Never hinged	1,500.	
b.		Die II	85.00	10.00
		Never hinged	170.00	
		Nos. 125-130 (6)	185.50	22.90

Nos. 125-130, never hinged 399.00

Nos. 126a and 128a were issued to the public. Nos. 126c and 130a were issued "by favor" as were the various other imperf and part-perfs of this era.
Beware of fakes of No. 130a made from No. 138.

1915-24 **Perf. 12 Horizontally**

131	A43	1c dark green	7.50	6.50
		Never hinged	15.00	
132	A43	2c carmine	27.50	8.00
		Never hinged	55.00	
133	A43	2c yellow grn ('24)	75.00	60.00
		Never hinged	150.00	

134	A43	3c brown ('21)	11.00	6.50
		Never hinged	22.00	
		Nos. 131-134 (4)	121.00	81.00
		#131-134, never hinged	242.00	

"The Fathers of Confederation" — A44

1917, Sept. 15 **Perf. 12**

135	A44	3c brown	47.50	1.25
		Never hinged	120.00	
a.		Imperf., pair	600.00	

50th anniv. of the Canadian Confederation. Imperfs. are without gum.

1924 **Imperf.**

136	A43	1c orange yellow	35.00	35.00
		Never hinged	65.00	
		Pair	87.50	87.50
		Never hinged	160.00	
137	A43	2c green	35.00	35.00
		Never hinged	65.00	
		Pair	87.50	87.50
		Never hinged	160.00	
138	A43	3c carmine (I)	17.50	17.50
		Never hinged	32.50	
		Pair	42.50	42.50
		Never hinged	77.50	
		Nos. 136-138 (3)	87.50	87.50

Nos. 136-138, never hinged 110.00

No. 109 Surcharged:

a

b

1926   **Perf. 12**

139	A43(a)	2c on 3c carmine		
		(I)	55.00	55.00
		Never hinged	90.00	
a.		Pair, one without surcharge	350.00	
b.		Double surcharge	225.00	
		Never hinged	350.00	
c.		Die II	700.00	
		Never hinged	1,150.	
140	A43(b)	2c on 3c carmine	25.00	22.50
		Never hinged	42.50	
a.		Double surcharge	250.00	
		Never hinged	400.00	
b.		Triple surcharge	250.00	
		Never hinged	400.00	
c.		Double surch., one invtd.	375.00	
		Never hinged	550.00	

Sir John A.
Macdonald
A45

Sir Wilfrid
Laurier
A48

"The Fathers of Confederation" — A46

Parliament
Building at
Ottawa
A47

Map of
Canada
A49

1927, June 29

141	A45	1c orange	3.50	1.30
		Never hinged	6.50	
142	A46	2c green	1.90	.20
		Never hinged	3.50	
143	A47	3c brown carmine	10.00	6.50
		Never hinged	18.00	
144	A48	5c violet	4.50	3.50
		Never hinged	8.25	
145	A49	12c dark blue	25.00	6.50
		Never hinged	45.00	
		Nos. 141-145 (5)	44.90	18.00
		#141-145, never hinged	81.25	

60th year of the Canadian Confederation.
Nos. 141-145 exist partly perforated.

Imperf., Pairs

141a	A45	1c	125.00
		Never hinged	180.00
142a	A46	2c	125.00
		Never hinged	180.00
143a	A47	3c	125.00
		Never hinged	180.00
144a	A48	5c	125.00
		Never hinged	180.00
145a	A49	12c	125.00
		Never hinged	180.00

Thomas d'Arcy
McGee — A50

Laurier and
Macdonald
A51

Robert
Baldwin and
Sir Louis
Hypolyte
Lafontaine
A52

1927, June 29

146	A50	5c violet	4.00	3.00
		Never hinged	7.25	
147	A51	12c green	10.00	5.50
		Never hinged	18.00	
148	A52	20c brown carmine	27.50	6.50
		Never hinged	50.00	
		Nos. 146-148 (3)	41.50	15.00
		#146-148, never hinged	75.25	

Nos. 146-148 were to have been issued in
July, 1926, as a commemorative series, but
were withheld and issued June 29, 1927.

Imperf., Pairs

146a	A50	5c	125.00
		Never hinged	180.00
147a	A51	12c	125.00
		Never hinged	180.00
148a	A52	20c	125.00
		Never hinged	180.00

King George V — A53

Mt. Hurd from Bell-Smith's Painting
"The Ice-crowned Monarch of the
Rockies"
A54

Quebec
Bridge
A55

Harvesting
Wheat
A56

Schooner
"Bluenose"
A57

Parliament
Building
A58

1928-29

149	A53	1c orange	3.50	.35
		Never hinged	6.50	
a.		Booklet pane of 6	25.00	20.00
		Never hinged	35.00	
150	A53	2c green	1.90	.20
		Never hinged	3.50	
a.		Booklet pane of 6	25.00	20.00
		Never hinged	35.00	
151	A53	3c dk carmine	30.00	12.50
		Never hinged	55.00	
152	A53	4c bister ('29)	27.50	6.00
		Never hinged	50.00	
153	A53	5c dp violet	16.00	3.00
		Never hinged	30.00	
a.		Booklet pane of 6	200.00	140.00
		Never hinged	280.00	
154	A53	8c blue	19.00	7.50
		Never hinged	35.00	
155	A54	10c green	22.50	2.50
		Never hinged	42.50	
156	A55	12c gray ('29)	45.00	7.50
		Never hinged	85.00	
157	A56	20c dk car ('29)	60.00	12.00
		Never hinged	110.00	
158	A57	50c dk blue		
		('29)	220.00	65.00
		Never hinged	440.00	
159	A58	$1 olive grn		
		('29)	300.00	80.00
		Never hinged	600.00	
		Nos. 149-159 (11)	745.40	196.55
		Nos. 149-159, never hinged	1,463.	

Imperf., Panes

149c	As No. 149a, imperf,		
	2 panes tete beche	1,050.	
	Never hinged	1,550.	
150c	As No. 150a, imperf,		
	2 panes tete beche	1,050.	
	Never hinged	1,550.	
153c	As No. 153a, imperf,		
	2 panes tete beche	1,050.	
	Never hinged	1,550.	

Imperf., Pairs

149b	A53	1c	100.00
		Never hinged	140.00
150b	A53	2c	100.00
		Never hinged	140.00
151a	A53	3c	120.00
		Never hinged	170.00
152a	A53	4c	120.00
		Never hinged	170.00
153b	A53	5c	100.00
		Never hinged	140.00
154a	A53	8c	120.00
		Never hinged	170.00
155a	A54	10c	200.00
		Never hinged	280.00
156a	A55	12c	200.00
		Never hinged	280.00
157a	A56	20c	200.00
		Never hinged	280.00
158a	A57	50c	800.00
		Never hinged	1,150.
159a	A58	$1	725.00
		Never hinged	1,050.

Coil Stamps

1929   **Perf. 8 Vertically**

160	A53	1c orange	40.00	22.50
		Never hinged	75.00	
		Precanceled		22.50
161	A53	2c green	35.00	3.50
		Never hinged	65.00	

King George
V
A59

Library of
Parliament
A60

The Citadel
at Quebec
A61

Harvesting
Wheat
A62

Museum at
Grand Pré
and
Monument to
Evangeline
A63

Mt. Edith
Cavell
A64

Two dies of 1c.
Die I — Three thick and one thin colored
lines between "P" at right and ornament above
it.
Die II — Four thick colored lines. Curved
line in ball of ornament at right is longer than in
die I.

Two dies of 2c.
Die I — The top of the letter "P" encloses a
tiny dot of color.
Die II — The top of the "P" encloses a larger
spot of color than in die I. The "P" appears
almost like a "D."

1930-31   **Perf. 11**

162	A59	1c orange	1.25	.60
		Never hinged	2.50	
163	A59	1c deep green		
		(II)	2.00	.25
		Never hinged	4.00	
a.		Booklet pane of 4 + 2 labels (II)	120.00	110.00
		Never hinged	180.00	
b.		Die I	2.00	.20
		Never hinged	4.00	
c.		Booklet pane of 6 (I)	22.50	20.00
		Never hinged	35.00	
164	A59	2c dull green (I)	1.25	.20
		Never hinged	2.50	
a.		Booklet pane of 6	32.50	32.50
		Never hinged	47.50	
165	A59	2c deep red (I)	1.75	.20
		Never hinged	3.50	
a.		Die II	2.10	.20
		Never hinged	4.20	
b.		Booklet pane of 6 (I)	25.00	25.00
		Never hinged	37.50	
166	A59	2c dk brn (II)		
		('31)	2.00	.20
		Never hinged	4.00	
a.		Booklet pane of 4 + 2 labels (II)	130.00	130.00
		Never hinged	200.00	
b.		Die I	5.00	4.25
		Never hinged	10.00	
c.		Booklet pane of 6 (I)	57.50	57.50
		Never hinged	87.50	
167	A59	3c deep red ('31)	3.25	.20
		Never hinged	6.50	
a.		Booklet pane of 4 + 2 labels	40.00	40.00
		Never hinged	60.00	
168	A59	4c yel bister	14.00	7.50
		Never hinged	28.00	
169	A59	5c dull violet	7.50	5.00
		Never hinged	15.00	

170	A59	5c dull blue	5.50	1.25
		Never hinged	11.00	
171	A59	8c dark blue	27.50	13.50
		Never hinged	55.00	
172	A59	8c red orange	6.50	5.50
		Never hinged	13.00	
173	A60	10c olive green	12.50	1.30
		Never hinged	25.00	
174	A61	12c gray black	27.50	6.50
		Never hinged	55.00	
175	A62	20c brown red	42.50	1.40
		Never hinged	85.00	
176	A63	50c dull blue	175.00	14.00
		Never hinged	350.00	
177	A64	$1 dk of green	175.00	27.50
		Never hinged	350.00	
		Nos. 162-177 (16)	505.00	85.15
		Nos. 162-177, never hinged	1,108.	

No. 169 rotary printing is distinguished unused from No. 169a flat plate printing by the former having gum ridges about 5mm apart.
See No. 201. For surcharge see No. 191. For overprint see No. 203.

Imperf., Pairs

163d	A59	1c (II)	1,600.
		Never hinged	2,400.
173a	A60	10c	1,600.
		Never hinged	2,400.
174a	A61	12c	725.
		Never hinged	1,050.
175a	A62	20c	725.
		Never hinged	1,050.
176a	A63	50c	1,000.
		Never hinged	1,500.
177a	A64	$1	1,000.
		Never hinged	1,500.

Coil Stamps

1930-31   Perf. 8½ Vertically

178	A59	1c orange	15.00	9.00
		Never hinged	30.00	
179	A59	1c deep green	9.00	5.75
		Never hinged	18.00	
180	A59	2c dull green	6.00	3.00
		Never hinged	12.00	
181	A59	2c deep red	25.00	2.50
		Never hinged	50.00	
182	A59	2c dark brown ('31)	12.00	.70
		Never hinged	24.00	
183	A59	3c deep red ('31)	18.00	.70
		Never hinged	36.00	
		Nos. 178-183 (6)	85.00	21.65
		Nos. 178-183, never hinged	170.00	

George V Type of 1912-25

1931, June 24   Perf. 12x8

184	A43	3c carmine	8.00	4.50
		Never hinged	20.00	

Sir Georges Etienne Cartier — A65

1931, Sept. 30   Perf. 11

190	A65	10c dark green	14.00	.20
		Never hinged	30.00	
a.		Imperf., pair	500.00	
		Never hinged	750.00	

Nos. 165, 165a Surcharged

1932, June 21

191	A59	3c on 2c dp red (II)	1.40	.20
		Never hinged	2.25	
a.		Die I	2.75	1.90
		Never hinged	4.50	

King George V — A66

Edward, Prince of Wales — A67

Allegory of British Empire A68

1932, July 12

192	A66	3c deep red	1.25	.20
		Never hinged	2.50	
193	A67	5c dull blue	7.00	3.00
		Never hinged	14.00	
194	A68	13c deep green	10.00	7.00
		Never hinged	20.00	
		Nos. 192-194 (3)	18.25	10.20
		Nos. 192-194, never hinged	36.50	

Imperial Economic Conference, Ottawa.

Type of 1930 and

King George V — A69

Two dies of 3c.
Die I — Upper left tip of "3" level with horizontal line to its left.
Die II — Raised "3"; upper left tip of "3" is above horizontal line.

1932, Dec. 1

195	A69	1c dk green	1.25	.20
		Never hinged	2.50	
a.		Booklet pane of 4 + 2 labels ('33)	80.00	80.00
		Never hinged	120.00	
b.		Booklet pane of 6 ('33)	47.50	47.50
		Never hinged	72.50	
196	A69	2c black brown	1.40	.20
		Never hinged	2.80	
a.		Booklet pane of 4 + 2 labels ('33)	110.00	110.00
		Never hinged	165.00	
b.		Booklet pane of 6 ('33)	70.00	70.00
		Never hinged	105.00	
197	A69	3c deep red (I)	1.40	.20
		Never hinged	2.80	
c.		Die II	1.40	.20
		Never hinged	15.00	
d.		Booklet pane of 4 + 2 labels, die II ('33)	37.50	37.50
		Never hinged	75.00	
198	A69	4c ocher	50.00	7.00
		Never hinged	100.00	
199	A69	5c dark blue	14.00	.50
		Never hinged	28.00	
a.		Horiz. pair, imperf. vert.	1,600.	
		Never hinged	2,250.	
200	A69	8c red orange	45.00	3.50
		Never hinged	90.00	
201	A61	13c dull violet	42.50	3.50
		Never hinged	85.00	
		Nos. 195-201 (7)	155.55	15.10
		Nos. 195-201, never hinged	311.40	

Type A66 has at the foot of the stamp "OTTAWA-CONFERENCE 1932". This inscription does not appear on the stamps of type A69.

Imperf., Pairs

195c	A69	1c	240.00
		Never hinged	360.00
196c	A69	2c	240.00
		Never hinged	360.00
197b	A69	3c (I)	240.00
		Never hinged	360.00
197e	A69	3c (II)	2,000.
198a	A69	4c	240.00
		Never hinged	360.00
199b	A69	5c	240.00
		Never hinged	360.00
200a	A69	8c	240.00
		Never hinged	360.00
201a	A69	13c	800.00
		Never hinged	1,200.

No. 197e exists as one unused block of 4.

Government Buildings, Ottawa — A70

1933, May 18   Perf. 11

202	A70	5c dark blue	10.00	3.75
		Never hinged	18.50	
a.		Imperf., pair	625.00	
		Never hinged	950.00	

Meeting of the Executive Committee of the UPU at Ottawa, May and June, 1933.

No. 175 Overprinted in Blue

1933, July 24

203	A62	20c brown red	45.00	14.00
		Never hinged	80.00	
a.		Imperf., pair	625.00	
		Never hinged	950.00	

World's Grain Exhibition and Conference at Regina.

Steamship Royal William — A71

1933, Aug. 17

204	A71	5c dark blue	10.00	3.75
		Never hinged	18.50	
a.		Imperf., pair	625.00	
		Never hinged	950.00	

Centenary of the linking by steam of the Dominion, then a colony, with Great Britain, the mother country. The Royal William's 1833 voyage was the first Trans-Atlantic passage under steam all the way.

George V Type of 1932
Coil Stamps

1933   Perf. 8½ Vertically

205	A69	1c dark green	15.00	3.00
		Never hinged	26.00	
206	A69	2c black brown	19.00	1.10
		Never hinged	32.50	
207	A69	3c deep red	16.00	.40
		Never hinged	27.50	
		Nos. 205-207 (3)	50.00	4.50
		Nos. 205-207, never hinged	86.00	

Cartier's Arrival at Quebec — A72

1934, July 1   Perf. 11

208	A72	3c blue	4.50	1.40
		Never hinged	9.00	
a.		Imperf., pair	625.00	
		Never hinged	950.00	

Landing of Jacques Cartier, 400th anniv.

Group from Loyalists Monument, Hamilton, Ontario A73

1934, July 1

209	A73	10c olive green	28.00	7.50
		Never hinged	52.50	
a.		Imperf., pair	1,400.	
		Never hinged	2,100.	

Emigration of the United Empire Loyalists from the US to Canada, 150th anniv.

Seal of New Brunswick — A74

1934, Aug. 16

210	A74	2c red brown	3.25	2.25
		Never hinged	6.00	
a.		Imperf., pair	675.00	
		Never hinged	1,100.	

150th anniv. of the founding of the Province of New Brunswick.

Princess Elizabeth A75

Duke of York A76

King George V and Queen Mary — A77

Prince of Wales — A78

Windsor Castle A79

Royal Yacht Britannia A80

1935, May 4   Perf. 12

211	A75	1c green	.75	.35
		Never hinged	1.10	
212	A76	2c brown	1.00	.20
		Never hinged	1.50	
213	A77	3c carmine	2.00	.20
		Never hinged	3.25	
214	A78	5c blue	5.25	3.00
		Never hinged	8.50	
215	A79	10c green	8.00	3.00
		Never hinged	13.00	
216	A80	13c dark blue	9.00	6.50
		Never hinged	15.00	
		Nos. 211-216 (6)	26.00	13.25
		Nos. 211-216, never hinged	42.35	

25th anniv. of the accession to the throne of George V.

Imperf., Pairs

211a	A75	1c	275.00
		Never hinged	425.00
212a	A76	2c	275.00
		Never hinged	425.00
213a	A77	3c	275.00
		Never hinged	425.00
214a	A78	5c	275.00
		Never hinged	425.00
215a	A79	10c	275.00
		Never hinged	425.00
216b	A80	13c	275.00
		Never hinged	425.00

King George V — A81

Royal Canadian Mounted Police — A82

Confederation Conference at Charlottetown, 1864 — A83

Niagara
Falls — A84

Parliament
Buildings,
Victoria,
B.C. — A85

Champlain
Monument,
Quebec
A86

1935, June 1   **Perf. 12**

217	A81	1c green	.30	.20
		Never hinged	.40	
a.		Bklt. pane of 4 + 2 labels	70.00	70.00
		Never hinged	105.00	
b.		Booklet pane of 6	55.00	55.00
		Never hinged	82.50	
218	A81	2c brown	.45	.20
		Never hinged	.65	
a.		Bklt. pane of 4 + 2 labels	70.00	70.00
		Never hinged	105.00	
b.		Booklet pane of 6	55.00	55.00
		Never hinged	60.00	
219	A81	3c dk carmine	.60	.20
		Never hinged	.90	
a.		Bklt. pane of 4 + 2 labels	40.00	40.00
		Never hinged	60.00	
c.		Printed on gummed side	475.00	
220	A81	4c yellowish orange	2.50	.55
		Never hinged	3.75	
221	A81	5c blue	3.25	.35
		Never hinged	5.00	
a.		Horiz. pair, imperf. vert.	225.00	
		Never hinged	340.00	
222	A81	8c dp orange	3.00	2.25
		Never hinged	4.50	

223	A82	10c car rose	7.00	.20
		Never hinged	10.50	
224	A83	13c violet	7.50	.75
		Never hinged	11.00	
225	A84	20c olive green	17.50	.75
		Never hinged	25.00	
226	A85	50c dull violet	27.50	6.00
		Never hinged	40.00	
227	A86	$1 deep blue	62.50	11.00
		Never hinged	95.00	
		Nos. 217-227 (11)	132.10	22.45
		Nos. 217-227, never hinged	212.70	

No. 219c is valued in the grade of fine. Very fine examples are rare and sell for much more.

Imperf., Pairs

217c	A81	1c	150.00	
		Never hinged	220.00	
218c	A81	2c	150.00	
		Never hinged	220.00	
219b	A81	3c	150.00	
		Never hinged	220.00	
220a	A81	4c	150.00	
		Never hinged	220.00	
221b	A81	5c	150.00	
		Never hinged	220.00	
222a	A81	8c	150.00	
		Never hinged	220.00	
223a	A82	10c	225.00	
		Never hinged	340.00	
224a	A83	13c	225.00	
		Never hinged	340.00	
225a	A84	20c	225.00	
		Never hinged	340.00	
226a	A85	50c	225.00	
		Never hinged	340.00	
227a	A86	$1	300.00	
		Never hinged	450.00	

Coil Stamps

1935   **Perf. 8 Vertically**

228	A81	1c green	15.00	3.25
		Never hinged	22.50	
229	A81	2c brown	19.00	1.00
		Never hinged	28.00	
230	A81	3c dark carmine	16.00	.60
		Never hinged	24.00	
		Nos. 228-230 (3)	50.00	4.85
		Nos. 228-230, never hinged	74.50	

George VI — A87

George VI
and Queen
Elizabeth
A88

1937   **Perf. 12**

231	A87	1c green	.25	.20
		Never hinged	.40	
a.		Booklet pane of 4 + 2 labels	20.00	25.00
		Never hinged	30.00	
b.		Booklet pane of 6	7.50	20.00
		Never hinged	11.50	
232	A87	2c brown	.60	.20
		Never hinged	.90	
a.		Booklet pane of 4 + 2 labels	20.00	22.50
		Never hinged	30.00	
b.		Booklet pane of 6	12.00	15.00
		Never hinged	18.00	
233	A87	3c carmine	.65	.20
		Never hinged	1.00	
a.		Booklet pane of 4 + 2 labels	7.00	14.00
		Never hinged	10.50	
234	A87	4c yellow	2.75	.20
		Never hinged	4.00	
235	A87	5c blue	3.50	.20
		Never hinged	5.00	
236	A87	8c orange	2.75	.45
		Never hinged	4.00	
		Nos. 231-236 (6)	10.50	1.45
		Nos. 231-236, never hinged	15.40	

Imperf., Pairs

231c	A87	1c	300.00	
		Never hinged	450.00	
232c	A87	2c	300.00	
		Never hinged	450.00	
233b	A87	3c	300.00	
		Never hinged	450.00	
234a	A87	4c	300.00	
		Never hinged	450.00	
235a	A87	5c	300.00	
		Never hinged	450.00	
236a	A87	8c	300.00	
		Never hinged	450.00	

1937, May 10

237	A88	3c carmine	.25	.20
		Never hinged	.35	
a.		Imperf., pair	625.00	
		Never hinged	950.00	

Coronation of King George VI and Queen Elizabeth.

George VI Types of 1937
Coil Stamps

1937   **Perf. 8 Vertically**

238	A87	1c green	2.30	1.10
		Never hinged	3.50	
239	A87	2c brown	3.75	.40
		Never hinged	6.00	
240	A87	3c carmine	7.50	.20
		Never hinged	12.00	
		Nos. 238-240 (3)	13.55	1.70
		Nos. 238-240, never hinged	21.85	

Memorial Chamber,
Parliament Building,
Ottawa — A89

Entrance to
Halifax
Harbor
A90

Fort Garry Gate, Winnipeg A91

Vancouver Harbor A92

Chateau de Ramezay, Montreal A93

1938   *Perf. 12*

241	A89	10c dk carmine	9.00	.20
		Never hinged	13.50	
a.		10c carmine rose	9.00	.20
		Never hinged	13.50	
242	A90	13c deep blue	12.00	.60
		Never hinged	18.00	
243	A91	20c red brown	16.00	.45
		Never hinged	24.00	
244	A92	50c green	37.50	6.00
		Never hinged	55.00	
245	A93	$1 dull violet	80.00	7.75
		Never hinged	120.00	
a.		Vert. pair, imperf., horiz.	4,750.	
		Nos. 241-245 (5)	154.50	15.00

Nos. 241-245, never hinged 235.50

Imperf., Pairs

241b	A89	10c dark carmine	450.00	
		Never hinged	675.00	
241c	A89	10c carmine rose	450.00	
		Never hinged	675.00	
242a	A90	13c	450.00	
		Never hinged	675.00	
243a	A91	20c	450.00	
		Never hinged	675.00	
244a	A92	50c	450.00	
		Never hinged	675.00	
245b	A93	$1	600.00	
		Never hinged	900.00	

Princess Elizabeth and Princess Margaret Rose — A94

War Memorial, Ottawa — A95

King George VI and Queen Elizabeth A96

Unwmk.

1939, May 15   **Engr.**   *Perf. 12*

246	A94	1c green & black	.25	.20
		Never hinged	.30	
247	A95	2c brown & black	.25	.20
		Never hinged	.30	
248	A96	3c dk car & black	.25	.20
		Never hinged	.30	
		Nos. 246-248 (3)	.75	.60

Nos. 246-248, never hinged .90

Visit of George VI and Queen Elizabeth to Canada and the US.

Imperf., Pairs

246a	A94	1c	550.00	
		Never hinged	800.00	
247a	A95	2c	550.00	
		Never hinged	800.00	
248a	A96	3c	550.00	
		Never hinged	800.00	

A97

A98

King George VI — A99

Grain Elevators A100

Farm Scene A101

Parliament Buildings — A102

"Ram" Tank — A103

Corvette A104

Munitions Factory A105

Destroyer A106

1942-43   **Engr.**   *Perf. 12*

249	A97	1c green	.30	.20
		Never hinged	.40	
a.		Booklet pane of 4 + 2 labels	3.50	3.75
		Never hinged	5.25	
b.		Booklet pane of 6	5.00	5.50
		Never hinged	7.50	
c.		Booklet pane of 3 ('43)	2.50	5.00
		Never hinged	3.75	
250	A98	2c brown	.40	.20
		Never hinged	.60	
a.		Booklet pane of 4 + 2 labels ('43)	7.00	8.00
		Never hinged	10.50	
b.		Booklet pane of 6	10.50	11.50
		Never hinged	16.00	
d.		Vert. strip of 3, imperf. horiz.	5,000.	
251	A99	3c dk carmine	.60	.20
		Never hinged	.90	
a.		Booklet pane of 4 + 2 labels	4.25	5.25
		Never hinged	6.50	
252	A99	3c rose violet ('43)	.40	.20
		Never hinged	.60	
a.		Booklet pane of 4 + 2 labels	3.25	4.50
		Never hinged	5.00	
b.		Booklet pane of 3	3.25	4.50
		Never hinged	4.75	
c.		Booklet pane of 6 ('47)	3.50	4.00
		Never hinged	5.25	
253	A100	4c greenish black	1.25	.60
		Never hinged	1.90	

254	A98	4c dk car ('43)	.60	.20
		Never hinged	.90	
a.		Booklet pane of 6	5.25	10.00
		Never hinged	8.00	
b.		Booklet pane of 3	3.25	4.50
		Never hinged	4.75	
255	A97	5c deep blue	1.20	.20
		Never hinged	1.80	
256	A101	8c red brown	1.60	.50
		Never hinged	2.40	
257	A102	10c brown	4.50	.20
		Never hinged	6.75	
258	A103	13c dull green	5.00	3.60
		Never hinged	7.50	
259	A103	14c dull grn ('43)	7.00	.35
		Never hinged	10.50	
260	A104	20c chocolate	9.00	.20
		Never hinged	13.50	
261	A105	50c violet	30.00	1.75
		Never hinged	45.00	
262	A106	$1 deep blue	65.00	7.50
		Never hinged	100.00	
		Nos. 249-262 (14)	126.85	15.90

Nos. 249-262, never hinged 192.75

Canada's contribution to the war effort of the Allied Nations.

No. 250d totally imperf horiz. is unique. Beware of strips with blind perfs; these sell for much less.

For overprints see Nos. O1-O4.

Imperf., Pairs

249d	A97	1c	300.00	
		Never hinged	450.00	
250c	A98	2c	300.00	
		Never hinged	450.00	
251b	A99	3c	300.00	
		Never hinged	450.00	
252d	A99	3c	300.00	
		Never hinged	450.00	
253a	A100	4c	300.00	
		Never hinged	450.00	
254c	A98	4c	300.00	
		Never hinged	450.00	
255a	A97	5c	300.00	
		Never hinged	450.00	
256a	A100	8c	300.00	
		Never hinged	450.00	
257a	A102	10c	450.00	
		Never hinged	675.00	
258a	A103	13c	450.00	
		Never hinged	675.00	
259a	A103	14c	450.00	
		Never hinged	675.00	
260a	A104	20c	450.00	
		Never hinged	675.00	
261a	A105	50c	450.00	
		Never hinged	675.00	
262a	A106	$1	450.00	
		Never hinged	675.00	

Types of 1942 Coil Stamps

1942-43   *Perf. 8 Vertically*

263	A97	1c green ('43)	1.40	.55
		Never hinged	2.10	
264	A98	2c brown	2.00	1.10
		Never hinged	3.00	
265	A99	3c dark carmine	2.00	1.10
		Never hinged	3.00	
266	A99	3c rose violet ('43)	3.40	.40
		Never hinged	5.25	
267	A98	4c dk carmine ('43)	5.50	.30
		Never hinged	8.25	
		Nos. 263-267 (5)	14.30	3.45

Nos. 263-267, never hinged 21.60

See Nos. 278-281.

Catalogue values for unused stamps in this section, from this point to the end of the section, are for Never Hinged items.

Farm Scene, Ontario A107

Great Bear Lake, Mackenzie A108

Hydroelectric Station, Saint Maurice River A109

Combine A110

Logging, British Columbia A111

Train Ferry, Prince Edward Island A112

1946, Sept. 16   **Engr.**   *Perf. 12*

268	A107	8c red brown	2.00	.60
269	A108	10c olive	2.75	.20
270	A109	14c black brown	4.25	.20
271	A110	20c slate black	5.00	.20
272	A111	50c dk blue green	22.50	1.50
273	A112	$1 red violet	45.00	3.00
		Nos. 268-273 (6)	81.50	5.70

For overprints see Nos. O6-O10, O21-O23, O25.

Alexander Graham Bell — A113

Citizen of Canada — A114

1947, Mar. 3

274	A113	4c deep blue	.30	.20

Birth centenary of Alexander Graham Bell.

1947, July 1

275	A114	4c deep blue	.30	.20

Issued on the 80th anniv. of the Canadian Confederation, to mark the advent of Canadian Citizenship.

Princess Elizabeth — A115

1948, Feb. 16

276	A115	4c deep blue	.25	.20

Marriage of Princess Elizabeth to Lieut. Philip Mountbatten, R. N., on Nov. 20, 1947.

Parliament Buildings Ottawa A116

1948, Oct. 1

277	A116	4c gray	.25	.20

Centenary of Responsible Government.

George VI Types of 1942 Coil Stamps

1948   *Perf. 9½ Vertically*

278	A97	1c green	6.50	2.00
279	A98	2c brown	20.00	8.50
280	A99	3c rose violet	12.50	2.00
281	A98	4c dark carmine	17.50	2.25
		Nos. 278-281 (4)	56.50	14.75

John Cabot's
Ship
"Matthew"
A117

1949, Apr. 1   Engr.   Perf. 12
282 A117 4c deep green   .25   .20

Entry of Newfoundland into confederation with Canada.

"Founding of
Halifax,
1749"
A118

1949, June 21   Unwmk.
283 A118 4c purple   .25   .20

200th anniv. of the founding of Halifax, Nova Scotia.

 A119   A120

 A121

 A122   A123

1949, Nov. 15
284 A119 1c green   .25   .20
  a. Booklet pane of 3 ('50)   .60   1.25
285 A120 2c sepia   .30   .20
286 A121 3c rose violet   .35   .20
  a. Booklet pane of 3 ('50)   2.50   6.50
  b. Booklet pane of 4 + 2 labels ('50)   3.25   3.75
287 A122 4c dk carmine   .60   .20
  a. Booklet pane of 3 ('50)   12.50   12.50
  b. Booklet pane of 6 ('50)   18.00   18.00
288 A123 5c deep blue   1.25   .30
    Nos. 284-288 (5)   2.75   1.10

Stamps from booklet panes of 3 are imperf. on 2 or 3 sides.

"POSTES POSTAGE" Omitted
1950, Jan. 19
289 A119 1c green   .25   .20
290 A120 2c sepia   .30   .20
291 A121 3c rose violet   .30   .20
292 A122 4c dark carmine   .30   .20
293 A123 5c deep blue   1.40   1.00
    Nos. 289-293 (5)   2.55   1.80

See Nos. 295-300, 305-306, 309-310. For overprints see Nos. O12-O20.

Oil Wells,
Alberta
A124

1950, Mar. 1   Engr.   Perf. 12
294 A124 50c dull green   9.00   1.40

Development of oil wells in Canada. For overprints see Nos. O11, O24.

Types of 1949
"POSTES POSTAGE" Omitted
Coil Stamps
1950   Perf. 9½ Vertically
295 A119 1c green   .70   .30
296 A121 3c rose violet   1.10   .60

With "POSTES POSTAGE"
Perf. 9½ Vertically
297 A119 1c green   .45   .20
298 A120 2c sepia   3.50   1.30
299 A121 3c rose violet   2.25   .20
300 A122 4c dark carmine   17.50   .70
    Nos. 297-300 (4)   23.70   2.40

See note after No. 288.

Indians
Drying Skins
on Stretchers
A125

1950, Oct. 2   Perf. 12
301 A125 10c black brown   .90   .20

Canada's fur resources. For overprint see No. O26.

Fishing
A126

1951, Feb. 1   Unwmk.
302 A126 $1 bright ultra   45.00   10.00

Canada's fish resources. For overprint see No. O27.

Sir Robert
Laird Borden
A127

William L.
Mackenzie
King
A128

1951, June 25   Perf. 12
303 A127 3c turquoise green   .25   .20
304 A128 4c rose pink   .30   .20

George VI Types of 1949
1951   Perf. 12
305 A120 2c olive green   .20   .20
306 A122 4c orange vermilion   .25   .20
  a. Booklet pane of 3   5.25   2.75
  b. Booklet pane of 6   5.00   5.00

For overprints see Nos. O28-O29.

Coil Stamps
Perf. 9½ Vertically
309 A120 2c olive green   1.50   .60
310 A122 4c orange vermilion   3.00   .70

Trains of
1851 and
1951 — A129

"Threepenny Beaver"
of 1851 — A130

Designs: 5c, Steamships City of Toronto and Prince George. 7c, Stagecoach and Plane.

1951, Sept. 24   Unwmk.   Perf. 12
311 A129 4c dark gray   .60   .20
312 A129 5c purple   1.80   1.25
313 A129 7c deep blue   1.10   .30
314 A130 15c bright red   1.20   .30
    Nos. 311-314 (4)   4.70   2.05

Centenary of British North American postal administration.

Princess
Elizabeth
and Duke of
Edinburgh
A131

1951, Oct. 26   Engr.
315 A131 4c violet   .20   .20

Visit of Princess Elizabeth, Duchess of Edinburgh and the Duke of Edinburgh to Canada and the US.

Symbols of
Newsprint
Paper
Production
A132

1952, Apr. 1   Unwmk.   Perf. 12
316 A132 20c gray   1.70   .20

Canada's paper production. For overprint see No. O30.

Red Cross
on
Sun — A133

1952, July 26   Engr. and Litho.
317 A133 4c blue & red   .20   .20

18th Intl. Red Cross Conf., Toronto, July 1952.

Sir John J. C.
Abbott
A134

Alexander
Mackenzie
A135

1952, Nov. 3   Engr.
318 A134 3c rose lilac   .20   .20
319 A135 4c orange vermilion   .25   .20

Canada
Goose
A136

1952, Nov. 3
320 A136 7c blue   .40   .20

For overprint see No. O31.

Pacific Coast Indian
House and Totem
Pole — A137

1953, Feb. 2
321 A137 $1 gray   7.00   .90

For overprint see No. O32.

Natl. Wildlife
Week — A138

1953, Apr. 1
322 A138 2c Polar bear   .20   .20
323 A138 3c Moose   .25   .20
324 A138 4c Bighorn sheep   .25   .20
    Nos. 322-324 (3)   .70   .60

Elizabeth II — A139

1953, May 1
325 A139 1c violet brown   .20   .20
  a. Booklet pane of 3   1.40   1.40
326 A139 2c green   .20   .20
327 A139 3c carmine rose   .20   .20
  a. Booklet pane of 3   1.90   1.50
  b. Booklet pane of 4 + 2 labels   1.40   1.75
328 A139 4c violet   .25   .20
  a. Booklet pane of 3   1.90   1.75
  b. Booklet pane of 6   1.60   1.60
329 A139 5c ultramarine   .25   .20
    Nos. 325-329 (5)   1.10   1.00

Stamps from booklet panes of 3 are imperf. on 2 or 3 sides.
See Nos. 331-333. For overprints see Nos. O33-O37.

Coronation Issue

Queen
Elizabeth II — A140

1953, June 1
330 A140 4c violet   .20 .20

Coil Stamps

1953   *Perf. 9½ Vertically*
331 A139 2c green   1.50 .90
332 A139 3c carmine rose   1.50 .90
333 A139 4c violet   3.50 1.40
   Nos. 331-333 (3)   6.50 3.20

See note after No. 329.
Issued: 2c, 7/30; 3c, 7/27; 4c, 9/3.

Bobbin, Cloth
and Spinning
Wheel
A141

1953, Nov. 2   *Perf. 12*
334 A141 50c light green   3.25 .25

For overprint see No. O38.

Walrus   Beaver
A142   A143

1954, Apr. 1
335 A142 4c gray   .30 .20
336 A143 5c ultramarine   .35 .20
  a.   Booklet pane of 5 + label   1.75 1.50

National Wildlife Week, 1954.

Elizabeth II   Gannet
A144   A145

1954-61
337 A144 1c violet brn   .20 .20
  a.   Booklet pane of 5 + label
     ('56)   1.10 1.10
338 A144 2c green   .20 .20
  a.   Pane of 25 ('61)   3.75 3.75
339 A144 3c carmine rose   .20 .20
  a.   Horiz. pair, imperf. vert.   1,500.
340 A144 4c violet   .25 .20
  a.   Booklet pane of 5 + label
     ('56)   1.50 1.50
  b.   Booklet pane of 6 ('55)   3.00 3.00
341 A144 5c bright blue   .25 .20
  a.   Booklet pane of 5 + label   1.20 1.20
  b.   Pane of 20 (5 x 4) ('61)   7.00 7.00
  c.   Horiz. pair, imperf. vert.   6,000.
342 A144 6c orange   .50 .20
343 A145 15c gray   1.50 .20
   Nos. 337-343 (7)   3.10 1.40

Panes of 20 and 25 are imperf. on 4 sides.
Issued: 5c, 15c, 4/1; others, 6/10.
For overprints see Nos. O40-O44.

___

Luminescence

The overprinting of regular stamps
with vertical luminescent bands began
experimentally in 1962 when Nos.
337p-341p were released at Winnipeg.
The bands are of varying number, position and chemical content.

Tagged varieties of stamps which
were issued both untagged and with
luminescent overprint are listed with
suffix letter "p".

Tagged

1962, Jan. 13
337p A144 1c violet brown   1.30 .95
338p A144 2c green   1.30 .95
339p A144 3c carmine rose   1.30 .95
340p A144 4c violet   3.75 3.25
341p A144 5c bright blue   4.25 2.25
   Nos. 337p-341p (5)   11.90 8.35

Coil Stamps

1954   *Perf. 9½ Vertically*
345 A144 2c green   .55 .20
347 A144 4c violet   1.60 .25
348 A144 5c bright blue   2.25 .20
   Nos. 345-348 (3)   4.40 .65

Issued: 2c, 9/9; 3c, 8/23; 4c, 7/6.

Sir John   Sir Mackenzie
Sparrow   Bowell
David   A147
Thompson
A146

1954, Nov. 1   *Perf. 12*
349 A146 4c violet   .35 .20
350 A147 5c bright blue   .35 .20

Eskimo and
Kayak
A148

1955, Feb. 21
351 A148 10c violet brown   .40 .20

For overprint see No. O39.

Musk Ox — A149

Whooping
Cranes
A150

1955, Apr. 4
352 A149 4c purple   .35 .20
353 A150 5c blue   .40 .20

National Wildlife Week, April 10-16.

Torch, Dove and
Maple
Leaves — A151

1955, June 1   *Unwmk.*
354 A151 5c light blue   .40 .20

ICAO, 10th anniversary.

Pioneer
Settlers
A152

1955, June 30   *Perf. 12*
355 A152 5c ultramarine   .40 .20

50th anniv. of the founding of the provinces
of Alberta and Saskatchewan.

Globe and
Scout
Emblem
A153

1955, Aug. 20   *Engr.*
356 A153 5c green & org brown   .40 .20

8th Boy Scout World Jamboree, Niagara-on-
the-Lake, Ont.

Richard   Sir Charles
Bedford   Tupper
Bennett   A155
A154

1955, Nov. 8
357 A154 4c violet   .35 .20
358 A155 5c ultramarine   .35 .20

Ice Hockey
Players
A156

1956, Jan. 23
359 A156 5c ultramarine   .35 .20

Issued to publicize Canada's most popular
winter sport.

Caribou   Mountain
A157   Goat
             A158

1956, Apr. 12
360 A157 4c deep violet   .40 .20
361 A158 5c ultramarine   .40 .20

National Wildlife Week, 1956.

"Paper
Industry"
A159

"Chemical
Industry" — A160

1956, June 7   *Engr.*
362 A159 20c green   1.40 .20
363 A160 25c red   1.50 .20

For overprint see No. O45.

House on Fire — A161

1956, Oct. 9   *Unwmk.*   *Perf. 12*
364 A161 5c gray & red   .35 .20

Issued to emphasize the needless waste
caused by preventable fires.

Canada's
Outdoor
Recreation
Facilities
A162

1957, Mar. 7
365 A162 5c Fishing   .40 .20
366 A162 5c Swimming   .40 .20
367 A162 5c Hunter and dog   .40 .20
368 A162 5c Skiing   .40 .20
  a.   Block of 4, #365-368   1.60 1.10

All four designs are printed alternating in
sheet of 50, with various combinations
possible.

Loon — A163

1957, Apr. 10   *Perf. 12*
369 A163 5c black   .35 .20

David
Thompson
and Map of
Western
Canada
A164

1957, June 5   *Unwmk.*
370 A164 5c ultramarine   .35 .20

David Thompson (1770-1857), explorer and
geographer.

Parliament Building,
Ottawa — A165

Post Horn
and Globe
A166

1957, Aug. 14   *Perf. 12*
371 A165 5c dark blue   .35 .20
372 A166 15c dark blue   2.10 1.90

UPU, 14th Congress, Ottawa, Aug. 1957.

Miner With Pneumatic
Drill — A167

1957, Sept. 5
373 A167 5c black   .30 .20

Canada's mining industry; 6th Commonwealth Mining and Metallurgical Congress,
Vancouver, Sept. 8-Oct. 8.

Elizabeth II and Prince Philip — A168

1957, Oct. 10 Unwmk.
374 A168 5c black .30 .20
Visit of Queen Elizabeth II and Prince Philip to Canada, Oct. 12-16.

Newspapers and Symbols of Industry A169

1958, Jan. 22 Engr.
375 A169 5c black .35 .20
Canadian press; the importance of a free press.

Microscope and Globe — A170

1958, Mar. 5 Perf. 12
376 A170 5c blue .35 .20
Intl. Geophysical Year, 1957-1958.

Miner Panning Gold — A171

1958, May 8
377 A171 5c bluish green .35 .20
Province of British Columbia, cent.

La Verendrye A172

1958, June 4
378 A172 5c bright ultra .35 .20
Pierre Gaultier de Varenne, Sieur de la Verendrye, 18th century French explorer of Western Canada.

Champlain and View of Quebec A173

1958, June 26
379 A173 5c dk green & bis brn .35 .20
Founding of Quebec, 350th anniv.

Nurse — A174

1958, July 30 Engr.
380 A174 5c rose lilac .35 .20
Importance of health, both to the individual and to the nation.

Kerosene Lamp and Refinery — A175

1958, Sept. 10 Perf. 12
381 A175 5c olive & red .35 .20
Centennial of Canada's oil industry.

Speaker's Chair and Mace A176

1958, Oct. 2
382 A176 5c slate blue .35 .20
Bicentennial of the meeting of the first House of Representatives in Canada, Halifax, Oct. 2, 1758.

"Silver Dart" and Delta Wing Planes A177

1959, Feb. 23
383 A177 5c blue & black .35 .20
50th anniv. of the 1st airplane flight in Canada near Baddeck, N. S., with J. A. D. McCurdy as pilot.

Globe and Dove — A178

1959, Apr. 2
384 A178 5c violet blue .35 .20
NATO, 10th anniversary.

Woman Tending Tree — A179

1959, May 13
385 A179 5c apple green & blk .35 .20
Associated Country Women of the World.

Elizabeth II — A180

1959, June 18
386 A180 5c dark carmine .35 .20
Visit of Queen Elizabeth and Prince Philip to Canada, June 18-Aug. 1.

Great Lakes, Maple Leaf and Eagle Emblems A181

1959, June 26 Engr.
387 A181 5c red & blue .35 .20
  a.   Center inverted 12,000. 10,000.
Opening of the St. Lawrence Seaway, June 26, 1959.
See United States No. 1131.

British Lion, Fleur-de-Lis and Maple Leaves A182

1959, Sept. 10 Perf. 12
388 A182 5c crim rose & dk green .35 .20
Bicentenary of the Battle of the Plains of Abraham.

Girl Guide Emblem — A183

1960, Apr. 20 Unwmk.
389 A183 5c brown org & ultra .35 .20
Canadian Girl Guides Assoc., 50th anniv.

Dollard des Ormeaux and Battle Scene — A184

1960, May 19
390 A184 5c ultra & bis brown .35 .20
Battle of the Long Sault, 300th anniv.

Compass Rose, Earth Mover and Surveyor A185

Emily Pauline Johnson A186

1961, Feb. 8 Engr.
391 A185 5c green & vermilion .35 .20
Development of Canada's Northland.

1961, Mar. 10
392 A186 5c green & red .35 .20
Emily Pauline Johnson (1861-1913), Mohawk princess and poet.

Arthur Meighen — A187

1961, Apr. 19
393 A187 5c ultramarine .35 .20
Arthur Meighen, Prime Minister of Canada, (1920-21, 1926).

Power Plant and Men Holding Blueprint A188

1961, June 28 Unwmk.
394 A188 5c lt red brn & blue .35 .20
10th anniv. of the Colombo Plan, initiated to assist underdeveloped countries by providing trained manpower and resources.

Natural Resources and Hands Holding Cogwheel — A189

1961, Oct. 12   Engr.
395 A189 5c brown & blue grn   .35 .20

Canada's "Resources for Tomorrow Program" and to publicize the close link between industry and the country's renewable natural resources.

Young Adults and Education Symbols — A190

1962, Feb. 28
396 A190 5c black & lt red brn   .35 .20
   a.   Light red brown (symbols) omitted

Issued to stimulate public awareness of the importance of education.

Scottish Settler and Lord Selkirk A191

1962, May 3
397 A191 5c lt green & vio brn   .35 .20

150th anniv. of the Red River Settlement in Western Canada (Prairie Provinces).

Jean Talon Presenting Gifts to Young Farm Couple — A192

1962, June 13   Unwmk.
398 A192 5c dark blue   .35 .20

Jean Talon, administrator of New France (Canada), 1665-1668.

British Columbia Legislative Building and Stamp of 1860 — A193

1962, Aug. 22   Engr.
399 A193 5c black & rose   .35 .20

Centenary of Victoria as incorporated city.

Arms of the Provinces A194

1962, Aug. 31
400 A194 5c brown orange & black   .35 .20

Official opening of the Trans-Canada Highway, Rogers Pass, Glacier National Park, Sept. 4.

Queen Elizabeth II and Wheat — A195

Designs (Symbol in upper left corner): 1c, Mineral crystals. 2c, Tree. 3c, Fish. 4c, Electric high tension tower.

1962-63   Engr.   *Perf. 12*
401 A195 1c dp brn ('63)   .20 .20
   a.   Booklet pane of 5 + label ('63)   3.00 3.00
402 A195 2c green ('63)   .20 .20
   a.   Pane of 25 ('63)   8.00 8.00
403 A195 3c purple ('63)   .20 .20
404 A195 4c carmine ('63)   .20 .20
   a.   Booklet pane of 5 + label ('63)   3.00 3.00
   b.   Pane of 25 ('63)   12.00 12.00
405 A195 5c violet blue   .25 .20
   a.   Booklet pane of 5 + label ('63)   3.00 3.00
   b.   Pane of 20 ('63)   14.00 14.00
   c.   Imperf., pair (#405b)   3,500.
   d.   Vert. pair, imperf. horiz.   4,000. 575.00
   Nos. 401-405 (5)   1.05 1.00

Nos. 402a, 404b, and 405b are imperf. on four sides.

Used examples of No. 405d are canceled "Gonor, MB." Beware of examples with traces of blind perfs; a certificate of authenticity is recommended.

Issued: 5c, 10/3; 1c, 4c, 2/4/63; 2c, 3c, 5/2/63.

For overprints see Nos. O46-O49.

Tagged

1963
401p A195 1c deep brown   .20 .20
402p A195 2c green   .20 .20
403p A195 3c purple   .25 .20
404p A195 4c carmine   .80 .50
405p A195 5c violet blue   .50 .25
   q.   Pane of 20   42.50 42.50
   Nos. 401p-405p (5)   1.95 1.35

See note after No. 343.

Coil Stamps

1962-63   *Perf. 9½ Horiz.*
406 A195 2c green   4.75 2.25
407 A195 3c purple   3.50 1.75
408 A195 4c carmine   4.75 2.25
   a.   Pair, imperf between   3,000.
409 A195 5c violet blue   4.75 1.00
   Nos. 406-409 (4)   17.75 7.25

No. 408a is valued in the grade of fine. Beware of dangerous fakes; a certificate of authenticity is necessary.

Issued: 5c, 10/3; 4c, 2/4/63; 2c, 3c, 5/2/63.

Sir Casimir Stanislaus Gzowski (1813-98), Engineer, Soldier and Educator — A196

1963, Mar. 5   Unwmk.   *Perf. 12*
410 A196 5c rose lilac   .30 .20

Export Crate and Mercator Map — A197

1963, June 14
411 A197 $1 rose carmine   10.00 2.25

Sir Martin Frobisher (1535-1594), Explorer and Discoverer of Frobisher Bay — A198

1963, Aug. 21
412 A198 5c ultramarine   .30 .20

Postrider and First Land Mail Routes A199

1963, Sept. 25
413 A199 5c green & red brn   .30 .20

Bicentennial of the 1st regular postal service between Quebec, Three Rivers & Montreal.

Jet at Ottawa Airport — A200   Canada Geese — A201

1963-64
414 A200 7c blue ('64)   .50 .40
415 A201 15c deep ultra   1.80 .20

See No. 436. For surcharge see No. 430.

"Peace on Earth" — A202

1964, Apr. 8   Engr. & Litho.
416 A202 5c grnsh blue, Prus bl & ocher   .30 .20

Issued to promote world peace.

Three-Maple-Leaf Emblem (Canadian Unity) — A203

White Trillium and Arms of Ontario A204

#419, White garden lily and arms of Quebec. #420, Mayflower (trailing arbutus) and arms of Nova Scotia. #421, Purple violet and arms of New Brunswick. #422, Prairie crocus and arms of Manitoba. #423, Dogwood and arms of British Columbia. #424, Lady's slipper and arms of Prince Edward Island. #425, Prairie lily and arms of Saskatchewan. #426, Wild rose and arms of Alberta. #427, Pitcher plant and arms of Newfoundland. #428, Fireweed and arms of Yukon. #429, Mountain avens and arms of Northwest Territories. #429A, Maple leaf and arms of Canada.

1964-66   Engr. & Litho.   *Perf. 12*
417 A203 5c lt blue & dk car   .25 .20
418 A204 5c red brn, buff & green   .25 .20
419 A204 5c grn, yel & org   .25 .20
420 A204 5c blue, pink & grn   .25 .20
421 A204 5c car, green & vio   .25 .20
422 A204 5c red brn, lil & dl grn   .25 .20
423 A204 5c lilac, grn & bis   .25 .20
424 A204 5c vio, grn & dp rose   .25 .20
425 A204 5c sepia, org & grn   .25 .20
426 A204 5c dl grn, yel & car   .25 .20
427 A204 5c black, grn & car   .25 .20
428 A204 5c dk bl, rose & grn   .25 .20
429 A204 5c ol, yel & green   .25 .20
429A A204 5c dk blue & dp red   .25 .20
   Nos. 417-429A (14)   3.50 2.80

Issued: #417, 5/14/64; #418-419, 6/30/64; #420-421, 2/3/65; #422-423, 4/28/65; #424, 7/21/65; #425-426, 1/19/66; #427, 2/23/66; #428-429, 3/23/66; #429A, 6/30/66.

No. 414 Surcharged

1964, July 15   Engr
430 A200 8c on 7c blue   .45 .2
   a.   Pair, one without surcharge   12,000.
   b.   Surcharge on reverse, inverted   4,000.

Nos. 430a and 430b are each unique.

Fathers of Confederation Memorial, Charlottetown — A205

1964, July 29
431 A205 5c black   .30 .2

Centenary of the Charlottetown, P.E.I., Conference, Sept. 1-9, 1864, which led to the creation of the Canadian nation in 1867.

Maple Leaf and Hand Holding Quill Pen — A206

1964, Sept. 9
432 A206 5c dark brown & rose   .30 .2

Centenary of the Quebec Conference, Oct 10-27, 1864, which led to the creation of the Canadian nation.

Elizabeth II A207   Family and Star of Bethlehem A208

1964, Oct. 5
433 A207 5c claret   .25 .2

Queen Elizabeth's visit, Oct. 6-13.

1964, Oct. 14   *Perf. 12*
434 A208 3c red   .20 .2
   a.   Pane of 25   8.00 8.0
   p.   Tagged   .70 .3
   q.   As "a," tagged   12.50 12.5
435 A208 5c blue   .25 .2
   p.   Tagged   1.20 .4

Panes of 25 are imperf. on four sides.

Jet Type of 1964

1964, Nov. 18   Unwmk
436 A200 8c blue   .40 .2

Maple Leaf and ICY Emblem A209

1965, Mar. 3
437 A209 5c slate green   .25 .2

International Cooperation Year.

Sir Wilfred Grenfell at Wheel of Hospital Ship Strathcona II A210

1965, June 9
438 A210 5c Prussian blue .25 .20

Sir Wilfred Grenfell, author, medical missionary and founder of the Grenfell Mission, birth cent.

Canada's Maple Leaf Flag, 1965 A211

1965, June 30
439 A211 5c blue & red .25 .20

Winston Churchill — A212

1965, Aug. 12   Litho.   Perf. 12
440 A212 5c brown .25 .20

Sir Winston Spencer Churchill (1874-1965).

Peace Tower, Ottawa — A213

1965, Sept. 8   Engr.
441 A213 5c slate green .25 .20

Meeting of the Inter-Parliamentary Union, Ottawa, Sept. 8-17.

Parliament and Ottawa River A214

1965, Sept. 8
442 A214 5c brown .25 .20

Centenary of the final selection of Ottawa as national capital.

Gifts of the Wise Men — A215

1965, Oct. 13
443 A215 3c olive .20 .20
  a. Pane of 25 6.50 6.50
  p. Tagged .25 .20
  q. As "a," tagged 8.75 8.75
444 A215 5c violet blue .20 .20
  p. Tagged .35 .20

Christmas. Panes of 25 are imperf. on four sides.

Alouette II Orbiting Globe — A216

1966, Jan. 5
445 A216 5c dark violet blue .25 .20

Launching (in California) of the Canadian satellite Alouette II, Nov. 28, 1965, as part of the Canadian-American program of space research.

La Salle, Map of 17th Century Canada, Ship, Canoe, Spyglass and Compass — A217

1966, Apr. 13
446 A217 5c blue green .25 .20

Tercentenary of the arrival in Canada of Rene Robert Cavelier, Sieur de La Salle (1643-1687).

Traffic Signs — A218

1966, May 2
447 A218 5c black, blue & yel .25 .20

Issued to publicize traffic safety.

House of Commons, Thames River and Canadian Delegates A219

1966, May 26
448 A219 5c brown .25 .20

Centenary of the London Conf., Dec. 4, 1866, which resulted in the British North America Act.

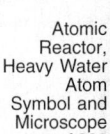

Atomic Reactor, Heavy Water Atom Symbol and Microscope A220

1966, July 27
449 A220 5c deep ultra .25 .20

Peaceful uses of atomic power. The design shows a stylized view of the Douglas Point Nuclear Power Station, Lake Huron, Ontario.

Parliamentary Library, Ottawa — A221

Praying Hands, by Albrecht Dürer — A222

1966, Sept. 8
450 A221 5c plum .25 .20

12th General Conf. of the Commonwealth Parliamentary Assoc., Ottawa, Sept. 8-Oct. 5.

1966, Oct. 12
451 A222 3c carmine rose .20 .20
  a. Pane of 25 4.00 4.00
  p. Tagged .20 .20
  q. As "a," tagged 5.00 5.00
452 A222 5c orange .20 .20
  p. Tagged .45 .25

Christmas. Panes of 25 are imperf. on four sides.

Canadian Flag over Globe and Centennial Emblem — A223

1967, Jan. 11
453 A223 5c blue & red .25 .20
  p. Tagged .35 .30

Canada's centenary as a nation.

Northern Lights and Dog Team — A224

"Alaska Highway" by A. Y. Jackson A225

Two types of 6c black:

Type I   Type II

Designs: 2c, Totem pole (Pacific Area). 3c, Combine and oil rig (Prairie Region). 4c, Ship in lock (Central Canada). 5c, Lobster traps and boat (Atlantic Provinces). 6c, Transportation means. 10c, "The Jack Pine" by Tom Thomson. 15c, "Bylot Island" by Lawren Harris. 20c, "The Ferry, Quebec" by James Wilson Morrice. 25c, "The Solemn Land" by J. E. H. MacDonald. 50c, "Summer's Stores" by John Ensor (grain elevators). $1, Oilfield near Edmonton, by H. G. Glyde.

1967-72   Engr.   Perf. 12
454 A224 1c brown .20 .20
  a. Booklet pane of 5 + label .45 .45
  b. Bklt. pane, 1 #454d, 4 #459 + label, perf. 10 ('68) 3.00 2.50
  c. Bklt. pane 5 #454d + 5 #457d, perf. 10 ('68) 1.75 1.75
  d. Perf. 10 ('68) .25 .20
  e. Perf. 12½x12 ('71) .20 .20
  f. Printed on gummed side 925.00
455 A224 2c green .20 .20
  a. Bklt. pane, 4 #455, 4 #456 with gutter btwn. ('70) 1.60 1.60
456 A224 3c dull purple .20 .20
  a. Perf. 12½x12 ('71) .75 .30
457 A224 4c car rose .20 .20
  a. Booklet pane of 5 + label 1.10 1.10
  b. Pane of 25 (5x5) 25.00 22.50
  c. Booklet pane of 25 + 2 labels, perf. 10 ('68) 8.00 7.50
  d. Perf. 10 .50 .50
458 A224 5c blue .20 .20
  a. Booklet pane of 5 + label 5.25 5.25
  b. Pane of 20 35.00 32.50
  c. Bklt. pane of 20, perf. 10 ('68) 8.00 8.00
  d. Perf. 10 .60 .60
459 A224 6c org, perf. 10 .25 .20
  a. Bklt. pane of 25 + 2 labels, perf. 10 ('68) 8.00 8.00
  b. Perf. 12½x12 ('69) .25 .20
460 A224 6c black (I), perf. 12½x12 .20 .20
  a. Bklt. pane of 25 + 2 labels (I), perf. 10 ('70) 12.00 8.00
  b. As "a," perf. 12½x12 16.00 13.00
  c. Type II, 12½x12 .40 .20
  d. As "c," booklet pane of 4 3.50 3.25
  e. As "d," perf. 10 ('70) 11.00 6.50
  f. Type II, perf. 12 ('72) .40 .20
  g. Type I, perf. 10 1.60 .30
  h. Type II, perf. 10 2.00 .65
  i. As "f," printed on gummed side 20.00
461 A225 8c violet brown .25 .20
462 A225 10c olive green .25 .20
463 A225 15c dull purple .50 .20
464 A225 20c dark blue .55 .20
465 A225 25c slate green 1.60 .20

465A A225 50c brown org 3.75 .20
465B A225 $1 carmine rose 6.00 .75
  Nos. 454-465B (14) 14.35 3.35

Nos. 454d, 454e, 456a, 457d, 458d, 460c, 460g and 460h are from booklet panes.
  Issued: #459, 11/1/68; #460, 1/7/70; others, 2/8/67.
  See Nos. 543-544, 549-550.

Tagged
454p A224 1c brown .25 .20
  ep. Perf. 12½x12 ('71) .30 .20
455p A224 2c green .25 .20
456p A224 3c dull purple .20 .20
457p A224 4c car rose .60 .20
458p A224 5c blue .60 .20
  bp. Pane of 20 60.00 50.00
459p A224 6c org, perf. 10 .60 .20
  bp. Perf. 12½x12 ('69) .75 .30
460p A224 6c black (I), perf. 12½x12 .35 .20
  cp. Type II ('70) .45 .50
  fp. As "cp," perf. 12 ('72) .25 .20
462p A225 10c olive green .90 .35
463p A225 15c dull purple .90 .35
464p A225 20c dark blue 1.60 .55
465p A225 25c slate green 7.00 2.00
  Nos. 454p-465p (11) 13.25 4.65

Nos. 454ep and 460cp are from booklet panes Nos. 544q-544s.
  Issued: 1c-5c, 2/8/67; #459p, 11/1/68; #460p, 1/7/70; others, 12/9/69.
  See note after No. 343.

Coil Stamps
1967-70   Perf. 9½ Horiz.
466 A224 3c dull purple 3.75 .85
467 A224 4c carmine rose 1.10 .50
468 A224 5c blue 2.25 .65

Perf. 10 Horiz.
468A A224 6c orange .50 .20
  c. Imperf., pair 325.00
468B A224 6c black, die II .45 .20
  d. Imperf., pair 2,750.
  Nos. 466-468B (5) 8.05 2.40

Horizontal pairs or blocks of Nos. 468A and 468B may be found with a fine vertical score line between the stamps. These sell for little more than vertical pairs or strips.
  Issued: #468A, 1/69; #468B, 8/70; others, 2/8/67.

EXPO '67 Emblem and Canadian Pavilion A226

1967, Apr. 28   Engr.   Perf. 12
469 A226 5c blue & red .25 .20

EXPO '67, Intl. Exhib., Montreal, Apr. 28-Oct. 27.

Symbolic Woman and Ballot — A227

1967, May 24   Litho.
470 A227 5c black & rose lilac .25 .20

50th anniversary of woman suffrage.

Elizabeth II — A228

1967, June 30   Engr.
471 A228 5c deep org & purple .25 .20

Centennial Year visit of Queen Elizabeth II and the Duke of Edinburgh.

Runner
A229

1967, July 19
472 A229 5c red .25 .20
Pan-American Games, Winnipeg, Manitoba, July 22-Aug. 7.

Globe and Flash A230

1967, Aug. 31
473 A230 5c deep ultra .25 .20
50th anniv. of the Canadian Press, news gathering and distributing service.

Georges Philias Vanier A231

1967, Sept. 15 **Engr. & Litho.**
474 A231 5c black .25 .20
Georges Philias Vanier (1888-1967), Governor General of Canada, 1959-1967.

Toronto in 1967 and Citizens of 1867 — A232

1967, Sept. 28
475 A232 5c sl grn & sal pink .25 .20
Centenary of Toronto as capital of Ontario.

Singing Children and Peace Tower, Ottawa — A233

1967, Oct. 11
476 A233 3c carmine .20 .20
a. Pane of 25 4.00 4.00
p. Tagged .20 .20
q. As "a" tagged 4.50 4.50
477 A233 5c green .20 .20
p. Tagged .30 .20
Christmas. Panes of 25 are imperf. on four sides.

Gray Jays — A234

1968, Feb. 15 **Litho.**
478 A234 5c green, blk & red .45 .20

Weather Map and Composite of Instruments A235

1968, Mar. 13 **Perf. 11**
479 A235 5c dk & lt blue, yel & red .25 .20
200th anniv. of Canada's first long-term fixed point weather observations at Fort Prince of Wales, Churchill, by William Wales and Joseph Dymond.

Male Narwhal A236

1968, Apr. 10
480 A236 5c multicolored .30 .20

Weighing Rain Gauge, World Map and Maple Leaf A237

1968, May 8
481 A237 5c multicolored .25 .20
Intl. Hydrological Decade, 1965-74.

The Nonsuch A238

Photo. & Engr.
1968, June 5 **Perf. 10**
482 A238 5c dk blue & multi .25 .20
300th anniv. of the voyage of the Nonsuch which opened the way to Canada's West through the fur trade.

Contemporary and Indian Lacrosse Players — A239

1968, July 3
483 A239 5c yel, black & red .25 .20

George Brown, "Globe" Front Page and Legislature, Prince Edward Island A240

1968, Aug. 21
484 A240 5c multicolored .25 .20
George Brown (1818-1880), founder of Toronto "Globe" and political leader.

Henri Bourassa and Newspaper Page — A241

Canadian Memorial, Near Vimy, France — A242

Litho. & Engr.
1968, Sept. 4 **Perf. 12**
485 A241 5c ver, buff & black .25 .20
Henri Bourassa (1868-1952), jounalist and statesman.

1968, Oct. 15 **Engr.**
486 A242 15c slate 2.00 1.25
50th anniv. of the Armistice which ended WWI. The stamp shows "The Defenders and the Breaking of the Sword," a detail from the memorial designed by W. S. Allward.

John McCrae and "Flanders Fields" A243

1968, Oct. 15 **Litho. & Engr.**
487 A243 5c multicolored .25 .20
50th death anniv. of Lt. Col. John McCrae (1872-1918), author of "In Flanders Fields."

Eskimo Family, Carving — A244

1968, Nov. **Photo.**
Eskimo soapstone carving: 6c, Mother and infant, by Munamee of Cape Dorset.
488 A244 5c brt blue & black .20 .20
a. Booklet pane of 10 3.25 3.25
p. Tagged .20 .20
q. As "a," tagged 4.00 4.00
489 A244 6c dp bister & black .20 .20
p. Tagged .25 .20
Christmas. Issued: 5c, Nov. 1; 6c, Nov. 15.

Curling A245

Photo. & Engr.
1969, Jan. 15 **Perf. 10**
490 A245 6c black, brt blue & car .20 .20

Vincent Massey — A246

Litho. & Engr.
1969, Feb. 20 **Perf. 12**
491 A246 6c yel olive & dk brn .25 .20
Vincent Massey (1887-1967), 1st Canadian-born Gov. General of Canada, 1952-59.

Return from the Harvest Field, by Aurele de Foy Suzor-Cote A247

1969, Mar. 14 **Photo.**
492 A247 50c multicolored 3.50 2.50
Aurele de Foy Suzor-Cote (1869-1937), painter.

Globe and Tools of Various Trades A248

1969, May 21 **Engr.** **Perf. 12x12½**
493 A248 6c dk olive green .25 .20
50th anniv. of the ILO.

Vickers Vimy, 1919, and Map of the Atlantic A249

1969, June 13 **Photo. and Engr.**
494 A249 15c red brn, yel grn & lt ultra 1.75 1.50
50th anniv. of the first non-stop Atlantic flight from Newfoundland to Ireland of Capt. John Alcock and Lt. Arthur Whitten Brown.

Sir William Osler — A250

Ipswich Sparrow A251

1969, June 23 **Perf. 12½x12**
495 A250 6c dk blue & lt red brn .25 .20
Osler (1849-1919), physician, professor of physiology and pathology in Canada, US and England.

1969, July 23 **Litho.** **Perf. 12**
Birds: 6c, White-throated sparrows, vert. 25c, Hermit thrush.
496 A251 6c multicolored .35 .20
497 A251 10c ultra & multi .70 .40
498 A251 25c black & multi 1.75 1.50
Nos. 496-498 (3) 2.80 2.10

Map of Prince Edward Island A252

Photo. & Engr.
1969, Aug. 15 **Perf. 12x12½**
499 A252 6c ultra, org brn & black .25 .20
Bicentenary of Charlottetown as capital of Prince Edward Island.

Flags of Summer and Winter Canada Games — A253

Litho. & Engr.
1969, Aug. 15 *Perf. 12*
500 A253 6c ultra, brt green & red .25 .20
1st Canada Summer Games, Halifax and Dartmouth, N.S., Aug. 16-24.

Sir Isaac Brock and Memorial Queenston Heights — A254

1969, Sept. 12
501 A254 6c yel brown, brn & pale sal .25 .20
Major General Sir Isaac Brock (1769-1812), administrator of Upper Canada and leader in the war of 1812.

Children of Various Races — A255

1969, Oct. 8 **Litho.**
502 A255 5c blue & multi .20 .20
a. Booklet pane of 10 3.00 3.00
p. Tagged .25 .20
q. As "a" tagged 4.00
503 A255 6c red & multi .20 .20
a. Black (inscriptions & frame line) omitted 2,250. 1,750.
p. Tagged .25 .20
Christmas.

Stephen Leacock, Comedy Mask and Mariposa View A256

Photo. & Engr.
1969, Nov. 12 *Perf. 12x12½*
504 A256 6c multicolored .25 .20
Stephen Butler Leacock (1869-1944), humorist, historian and economist.

Manitoba, Crossroads of Canada A257

1970, Jan. 27 **Litho.** *Perf. 12*
505 A257 6c violet blue & multi .25 .20
p. Tagged .35 .20
Centenary of the province of Manitoba.

Enchanted Owl, by Kenojuak — A258

1970, Jan. 27 **Engr.**
506 A258 6c dark red & black .25 .20
Centenary of Nortwest Territories.

Microscopic View of Inside of Leaf A259

1970, Feb. 18 **Photo. & Engr.**
507 A259 6c green, lt org & blue .25 .20
Canada's participation in the Intl. Biological Program, 1967-1972.

Emblems of EXPO '67 and '70 — A260

EXPO '70 Emblem and Dogwood, British Columbia A261

Designs: No. 510, EXPO '70 emblem and white garden lily, Quebec. No. 511, EXPO '70 emblem and white trillium, Ontario.

1970, Mar. 18 **Litho.**
508 A260 25c red emblem 2.00 2.00
p. Tagged 2.25 2.25
509 A261 25c violet emblem 2.00 2.00
p. Tagged 2.25 2.25
510 A261 25c green emblem 2.00 2.00
p. Tagged 2.25 2.25
511 A261 25c blue emblem 2.00 2.00
p. Tagged 2.25 2.25
a. Block of 4, #508-511 8.00 8.00
b. As "a" tagged 10.00 10.00
Nos. 508-511 (4) 8.00 8.00

EXPO '70 Intl. Exhibition, Osaka, Japan, Mar. 15-Sept. 13. Nos. 508-511 printed setenant in panes of 50 (5x10), with various combinations possible.

Henry Kelsey A262

Photo. & Engr.
1970, Apr. 15 *Perf. 12x12½*
512 A262 6c multicolored .25 .20
300th birth anniv. of Henry Kelsey, explorer of Canada's western plains.

"A Divided World, with Energy Focused on Unification..." — A263

1970, May 13 **Litho.** *Perf. 11*
513 A263 10c blue .70 .55
p. Tagged .85 .85
514 A263 15c lilac & dk red 1.10 .70
p. Tagged 1.50 1.50
25th anniversary of the United Nations.

Louis Riel A264

Mackenzie Rock, Dean Channel A265

1970, June 19 Photo. *Perf. 12½x12*
515 A264 6c red & brt blue .25 .20
Louis Riel (1844-1885), Metis leader who became president of the Council of Assiniboin in 1870.

1970, June 25 Engr. *Perf. 12*
516 A265 6c brown .25 .20
Sir Alexander Mackenzie (1764-1820), Scottish explorer who in 1793 completed the first crossing of the North American continent north of Mexico.

Sir Oliver Mowat and Parliament, Ottawa A266

Photo. & Engr.
1970, Aug. 12 *Perf. 12x12½*
517 A266 6c red & black .25 .20
Sir Oliver Mowat (1820-1903), government leader and a Father of Confederation.

Isle of Spruce, by Arthur Lismer A267

1970, Sept. 18 **Litho.** *Perf. 11*
518 A267 6c multicolored .25 .20
50th anniv. of "The Group of Seven," Canadian landscape artists.

Santa Claus — A268

Christ Child — A269

Child in the Manger and Star-studded Sky — A270

Christmas: Designs by Canadian School Children.

1970, Oct. 7 **Litho.** *Perf. 12*
519 A268 5c Santa Claus .30 .20
520 A268 5c Horse-drawn Sleigh .30 .20
521 A268 5c Nativity .30 .20
522 A268 5c Children Skiing .30 .20
523 A268 5c Snowmen and Christmas Tree .30 .20
a. Strip of 5, #519-523 2.75 2.25

524 A269 6c Christ Child .40 .20
525 A269 6c Christmas Tree and Children .40 .20
526 A269 6c Toy Store .40 .20
527 A269 6c Santa Claus .40 .20
528 A269 6c Church .40 .20
a. Strip of 5, #524-528 3.25 2.50
529 A270 10c Christ Child .40 .35
530 A270 15c Snowmobile and Trees .90 .90
Nos. 519-530 (12) 4.80 3.25

Tagged
519p A268 5c multicolored .35 .25
520p A268 5c multicolored .35 .25
521p A268 5c multicolored .35 .25
522p A268 5c multicolored .35 .25
523p A268 5c multicolored .35 .25
ap. Strip of 5, #519p-523p 3.25 2.75
524p A269 6c multicolored .40 .25
525p A269 6c multicolored .40 .25
526p A269 6c multicolored .40 .25
527p A269 6c multicolored .40 .25
528p A269 6c multicolored .40 .25
ap. Strip of 5, #524p-528p 4.50 3.00
529p A270 10c multicolored .50 .50
530p A270 15c multicolored 1.10 1.10
Nos. 519p-530p (12) 5.35 4.10

Christmas.
The sheets of 100 of both 5c and 6c contain all 5 designs, generally alternating, and arranged to permit vertical and horizontal pairs of each design in the two center vertical and horizontal rows. The center block of 4 is entirely of No. 522 (5c) and 525 (6c). The sheet may also be broken to provide 20 strips of 5, each stamp of different design.

Sir Donald Alexander Smith — A271

1970, Nov. 4
531 A271 6c dk grn, yel & black .25 .20
Smith (1820-1914), railroad builder and Canadian High Commissioner, 1896-1914.

Big Raven, by Emily Carr — A272

1971, Feb. 12
532 A272 6c multicolored .25 .20
Emily Carr (1871-1945), painter and writer.

Laboratory Equipment Used for Insulin Discovery — A273

1971, Mar. 3 *Perf. 11*
533 A273 6c multicolored .25 .20
Discovery of insulin by Dr. Frederick G. Banting and Dr. Charles H. Best, 50th anniversary.

A274

1971, Mar. 24
534 A274 6c red, org & black .25 .20
Sir Ernest Rutherford (1871-1937), physicist, developer of theory of spontaneous disintegration of the atom.

Spring, Winged
Maple Seed
A275

Louis Joseph
Papineau
A276

1971
535	A275	6c shown	.25	.20
a.		Imperf., pair	950.00	
536	A275	6c Summer	.25	.20
537	A275	7c Autumn	.25	.20
538	A275	7c Winter	.25	.20
		Nos. 535-538 (4)	1.00	.80

Issue dates: No. 535, Apr. 14; No. 536, June 16; No. 537, Sept. 3; No. 538, Nov. 19.

Litho. & Engr.
1971, May 7   **Perf. 12½x12**
539	A275	6c multicolored	.25	.20

Louis Joseph Papineau (1786-1871), member of Legislative Assembly and leader of French Canadian Patriote party.

Map of
Copper
Mine River
Basin
A277

1971, May 7   **Perf. 12x12½**
540	A277	6c buff, red & brown	.25	.20

Bicentenary of Samuel Hearne's expedition to the Copper Mine River.

Maple
Leaves
A278

1971, June 1
541	A278	15c blk, red org & yel	1.60	1.10
p.		Tagged	2.25	2.25

Inauguration of new transmitters for Radio Canada International.

Computer Tape
and
Reels — A279

1971, June 1
542	A279	6c black, ultra & red	.25	.20

Centenary of measured progress through census.

Migrating Phosphor
Canada's "Ottawa/General" tagging of engraved stamps printed March-October, 1972, used a phosphor which migrates onto or through other stamps, booklet covers and album pages. It fluoresces yellow under ultraviolet light.

This bleeding, contaminating "OP4" phosphor can be somewhat contained in mounts or envelopes of acetate, glassine or polyethylene, but it may leak or penetrate.

The migrating phosphor is found on all examples of Nos. 560p-561p, and on some of Nos. 544p, 544q, 544r, 544s, 562p-565p and 594-598.

Transportation
Means — A280

Design: 8c, Library of Parliament.

1971-72   **Engr.**   **Perf. 12½x12**
543	A280	7c slate green	.35	.20
a.		Booklet pane of 5 + label (#454e, #456a + 3#543)	4.25	2.25
b.		Booklet pane of 20 (4 #454e, 4 #456a, 12 #543)	8.00	7.00
p.		Tagged	.60	.25
544	A280	8c slate	.25	.20
a.		Booklet pane of 6 (3 #454e, 1 #460c, 2 #544)	1.75	.80
b.		Booklet pane of 18 (6 #454e, 1 #460c, 11 #544)	5.25	3.50
c.		Booklet pane of 10 (4 #454e, 5 #544 ('72)	2.25	2.25
p.		Tagged	.35	.20
q.		As "a," tagged	2.00	2.00
r.		As "b," tagged	4.00	4.00
s.		As "c," tagged	2.00	2.00

Coil Stamps
1971   **Perf. 10 Horiz.**
549	A280	7c slate green	.40	.20
a.		Imperf., pair	1,200.	
550	A280	8c slate	.35	.20
a.		Imperf., pair	600.00	
p.		Tagged	.50	.20
q.		As "p," imperf, pair	1,100.	

See note below No. 468B.
Issued: 7c, 6/30/71; 8c, 12/30/71.

Abstract
"BC"
A282

1971, July 20   **Litho.**   **Perf. 12**
552	A282	7c multicolored	.25	.20

Centenary of British Columbia's entry into Canadian Confederation.

Indian Encampment on Lake Huron,
by Kane — A283

1971, Aug. 11   **Perf. 12½**
553	A283	7c multicolored	.40	.20

Paul Kane (1810-1971), painter.

Snowflake
A284

Pierre Laporte
A285

1971, Oct. 6   **Engr.**   **Perf. 12**
Size: 24x30mm
554	A284	6c dark blue	.20	.20
p.		Tagged	.20	.20
a.		All color omitted (from foldover)	2,000.	
b.		Printed on gummed side (from foldover)	1,100.	
555	A284	7c bright green	.20	.20
p.		Tagged	.30	.20

Litho. and Engr.
Size: 30x30mm
556	A284	10c dp car & silver	.35	.30
p.		Tagged	.45	.30
557	A284	15c lt ultra, dp car & silver	.70	.65
p.		Tagged	.90	.75
		Nos. 554-557 (4)	1.45	1.35

Christmas.

1971, Oct. 20   **Perf. 12½x12**
558	A285	7c black	.25	.20

Pierre Laporte (1921-1970), Minister of Labor, kidnapped and killed.

Figure
Skating — A286

1972, Mar. 1   **Litho.**   **Perf. 12**
559	A286	8c deep red lilac	.25	.20

World Figure Skating Championships, Calgary, Alberta, Mar. 6-12.

"Your Heart
is your
Health"
A287

1972, Apr. 7   **Engr.**   **Perf. 12x12½**
560	A287	8c red	.30	.20
p.		Tagged	.55	.35

World Health Day, Apr. 7.

Frontenac,
by Philippe
Hébert and
Fort Saint
Louis,
Quebec
A288

1972, May 17   **Photo. and Engr.**
561	A288	8c red brown & multi	.25	.20
p.		Tagged	.65	.55

Tercentenary of the appointment of Louis de Buade, Count of Frontenac and Palluau (1622-1698), as Governor of New France.

Indians of Canada

Buffalo
Chase, by
George Catlin
A289

Thunderbird,
Assiniboin
Pattern — A290

In Nos. 562-581, the first two and last two stamps of each annual set are printed checkerwise in same sheet of 50.

1972   **Litho.**   **Perf. 12x12½**
562	A289	8c shown	.40	.20
p.		Tagged	.55	.30
563	A289	8c Plains Indian artifacts	.40	.20
p.		Tagged	.55	.30
a.		Pair, #562-563	.80	.50
b.		As "a," tagged	1.10	.75

Perf. 12½x12
Photo. & Engr.
564	A290	8c shown	.40	.20
p.		Tagged	.55	.30
565	A290	8c Ceremonial sun dance costume	.40	.20
p.		Tagged	.55	.30
a.		Pair, #564-565	.80	.50
b.		As "a," tagged	1.10	.75

Plains Indians of Canada.
Issued: #562-563, July 6; #564-565, Oct. 4.

Tagged (Nos. 566-581)
1973   **Litho.**   **Perf. 12x12½**
566	A289	8c Algonkian artifacts	.35	.20
567	A289	8c "Micmac Indians"	.35	.20
a.		Pair, #566-567	.70	.50

Perf. 12½x12
Photo. & Engr.
568	A290	8c Thunderbird and belt	.35	.20
569	A290	8c Algonkian man and woman	.35	.20
a.		Pair, #568-569	.70	.50

Algonkian-speaking Indians of Canada (Malecite, Micmac, Montagnais, Algonquin and Ojibwa).
Issued: #566-567, 2/21; #568-569, 11/28.

1974   **Litho.**   **Perf. 12x12½**
570	A289	8c Nootka Sound, house, inside	.35	.20
571	A289	8c Artifacts	.35	.20
a.		Pair, #570-571	.70	.50

Perf. 12½x12
Photo. & Engr.
572	A290	8c Chief wearing Chilkat blanket	.35	.20
573	A290	8c Thunderbird from Kwakiutl house	.35	.20
a.		Pair, #572-573	.70	.50

Pacific Coast Indians of Canada (Haida, Salish, Tsimshian, Chilkat and Kwakiutl).
Issued: #570-571, 1/16; #572-573, 2/22.

1975, Apr. 4   **Litho.**   **Perf. 13½**
574	A289	8c Montagnais-Naskapi artifacts	.25	.20
575	A289	8c Dance of the Kutcha-Kutchin	.25	.20
a.		Pair, #574-575	.50	.50
b.		As "a," imperf. between	900.00	

Perf. 12½
576	A290	8c Kutchin ceremonial costume	.25	.20

Litho. and Embossed
577	A290	8c Ojibwa thunderbird and Naskapi pattern	.25	.20
a.		Pair, #576-577	.50	.50

Subarctic Indians.

1976, Sept. 17   **Litho.**   **Perf. 13½**
578	A289	10c Cornhusk mask, artifacts	.25	.20
579	A289	10c Iroquoian Encampment, by George Heriot	.25	.20
a.		Pair, #578-579	.50	.50

Perf. 12½
Litho. & Embossed
580	A290	10c Iroquoian thunderbird	.25	.20

Litho.
581	A290	10c Iroquoian man, woman	.25	.20
a.		Pair, #580-581	.50	.50
		Nos. 562-581 (20)	6.40	4.00

Iroquois (Mohawk, Cayuga, Seneca, Oneida, Onondaga and Tuscarora).

Geological
Fault — A291

1972, Aug. 2   **Perf. 12**
582	A291	15c shown	1.80	1.60
p.		Tagged	2.50	2.50
583	A291	15c Bird's eye view of town	1.80	1.60
p.		Tagged	2.50	2.50
584	A291	15c Aerial map photography	1.80	1.60
p.		Tagged	2.50	2.50
585	A291	15c Contour lines	1.80	1.60
p.		Tagged	2.50	2.50
a.		Block of 4, #582-585	7.25	7.25
b.		As "a," tagged	10.00	10.00
		Nos. 582-585 (4)	7.20	6.40

Earth sciences: 24th Intl. Geological Cong. (#582); 22nd Intl. Geographical Cong. (#583); 12th Cong. of Intl. Soc. of Photogrammetry (#584); 6th Cong. of Intl. Cartographic Assoc. (#585).

Sir John A.
Macdonald
A292

Elizabeth II
A292a

Forest, Central
Canada — A293

Vancouver, B.C. — A294

Designs: 2c, Sir Wilfrid Laurier. 3c, Sir Robert L. Borden. 4c, William Lyon Mackenzie King. 5c Richard Bedford Bennett. 6c, Lester B. Pearson. 7c, Louis St. Laurent. 15c, Mountain sheep, Western Canada. 20c, Grain fields, Prairie. 25c, Polar bears, North. 50c, Seashore. $2, Quebec.

1972-76   Engr.   Perf. 12x12½
Tagged

586	A292	1c orange ('73)	.20	.20
a.		Booklet pane, 3 #586, 1 #591, 2 #593 ('74)	1.20	1.00
b.		Bklt. pane, 6 #586, 1 #591, 11 #593 ('75)	1.60	1.60
c.		Bklt. pane, 2 #586, 4 #587, 4 #593Ac ('76)	1.20	1.00
d.		Printed on gummed side	600.00	
587	A292	2c green ('73)	.20	.20
588	A292	3c brown ('73)	.20	.20
589	A292	4c black ('73)	.20	.20
590	A292	5c lilac ('73)	.20	.20
591	A292	6c dk red ('73)	.20	.20
a.		Printed on gummed side	200.00	
592	A292	7c dk brn ('74)	.20	.20
593	A292a	8c ultra ('73)	.20	.20
b.		Perf. 13x13½ ('76)	.65	.20

Perf. 13x13½

593A	A292a	10c dk car ('76)	.20	.20
c.		Perf. 12x12½	.35	.20

Perf. 12½x12
Photo. & Engr.

594	A293	10c multicolored	.30	.20
595	A293	15c multicolored	.45	.20
596	A293	20c multicolored	.45	.20
597	A293	25c multicolored	.50	.20
598	A293	50c multicolored	1.10	.20
599	A294	$1 multi ('73)	2.50	.50

Perf. 11
Litho. & Engraved

600	A294	$1 multicolored	6.00	1.60
601	A294	$2 multicolored	4.50	2.25
		Nos. 586-601 (17)	17.60	7.15

No. 599 has engraved shading added in some areas.

Plates 1 and 2 of the scenic 10c differ in impression and colors. Plate 1 has distinct crosshatching of "Canada" background. On plate 2, released in 1974, this area appears solidly inked.

A 1976 printing of the 15c shows the blue trees on the hillside as solid color, while the 1972 printing shows clear detail on the trees.

A 1974 printing of the 50c has darker shading and a deeper tone for the dark blue areas of the photogravure impression.

Nos. 600 and 601 are untagged.

1976-77   Photo. & Engr.   Perf. 13½

594a	A293	10c multicolored	.30	.20
595a	A293	15c multicolored	.45	.20
596a	A293	20c multicolored	.60	.20
597a	A293	25c multicolored	.65	.20
598a	A293	50c multicolored	1.75	.20
599a	A294	$1 multi ('77)	2.50	.30
		Nos. 594a-599a (6)	6.25	1.30

Coil Stamps

1974-76   Engr.   Perf. 10 Vert.

604	A292a	8c ultramarine	.25	.20
a.		Imperf., horiz. pair	160.00	
605	A292a	10c dk carmine ('76)	.35	.20
a.		Imperf., horiz. pair	175.00	

See note below No. 468B. No. 604 also exists in vertical multiples without score line.

Candles — A295

Candles
and Fruit
A296

Christmas: 8c, Like 6c. 15c, Candles, 15th century prayer book, boxes and brass vase.

1972, Nov. 1   Litho.   Perf. 12½x12

606	A295	6c red & multi	.20	.20
p.		Tagged	.30	.25
607	A295	8c vio blue & multi	.20	.20
p.		Tagged	.35	.25

Perf. 11

608	A296	10c green & multi	.45	.35
p.		Tagged	.65	.55
609	A296	15c yel bister & multi	.65	.65
p.		Tagged	1.20	1.20
		Nos. 606-609 (4)	1.50	1.40

"The Blacksmith's Shop," by
Krieghoff — A297

1972, Nov. 29   Perf. 12½

610	A297	8c multicolored	.30	.20
p.		Tagged	.35	.20

Cornelius Krieghoff (1815-1872), painter.

Tagged
From No. 611 onward, all stamps are tagged unless otherwise noted.

Monsignor de
Laval — A298

1973, Jan. 31   Perf. 11

611	A298	8c silver, ultra & gold	.20	.20

François-Xavier de Montmorency-Laval de Montigny (1623-1708), 1st Bishop of Quebec and founder of many educational institutions; one of the builders of New France.

Commissioner G. A. French and Map
of 1874 Trek — A299

10c, Spectrograph. 15c, R.C.M.P. Musical Ride.

1973, Mar. 9

612	A299	8c dk brn, org & red	.20	.20
613	A299	10c dk blue & multi	.35	.30
614	A299	15c yel grn & multi	.75	.50
a.		Imperf., pair	500.00	
		Nos. 612-614 (3)	1.30	1.00

Royal Canadian Mounted Police, cent. Imperfs of No. 614 with a double impression and examples with 15c printed on 10c are from printer's waste.

Jeanne
Mance
A300

1973, Apr. 18

615	A300	8c multicolored	.20	.20

Jeanne Mance (1606-1673), first secular nurse in North America and founder of first hospital, the Hôtel-Dieu in Montreal settlement.

Joseph Howe — A301

1973, May 16

616	A301	8c gold & black	.20	.20

Joseph Howe (1804-1873), journalist, poet and Lieutenant-Governor of Nova Scotia.

Mist Fantasy, by
James
MacDonald
A302

1973, June 8   Perf. 12½

617	A302	15c multicolored	.55	.50

Centenary of the birth of James E. H. MacDonald (1873-1932), painter.

Oaks on
Shore
A303

Photo. & Engr.
1973, June 22   Perf. 12x12½

618	A303	8c orange & red brn	.20	.20

Centenary of Prince Edward Island's entry into Confederation.

Scottish
Settlers and
"Hector"
A304

1973, July 20

619	A304	8c multicolored	.20	.20

Bicentenary of arrival of Scottish settlers at Pictou, N.S.

Queen
Elizabeth
II — A305

1973, Aug. 2   Photo. and Engr.

620	A305	8c silver & multi	.20	.20
621	A305	15c gold & multi	.70	.60

Visit to Ottawa of Elizabeth II and the Duke of Edinburgh, July 31-Aug. 4, and meeting of Commonwealth Heads of Government, Ottawa, Aug. 2-10.

Nellie
McClung — A306

1973, Aug. 29   Litho.   Perf. 10½x11

622	A306	8c multicolored	.20	.20

Nellie McClung (1873-1951), leader of women's suffrage movement, social reformer and writer.

Montreal Olympic
Games — A307

1973, Sept. 20   Perf. 12x12½
Size: 26x44mm

623	A307	8c silver & multi	.20	.20
624	A307	15c gold & multi	.60	.50

21st Olympic Games, Montreal, 1976.
See Nos. B1-B3.

Ice
Skate — A308

Santa
Claus — A309

1973, Nov. 7   Perf. 12½x12

625	A308	6c shown	.20	.20
626	A308	8c Dove	.20	.20

Perf. 10½

627	A309	10c shown	.25	.25
628	A309	15c Shepherd and star	.55	.55
		Nos. 625-628 (4)	1.20	1.20

Christmas.

Children Diving
from
Dock — A310

1974, Mar. 22   Engr.   Perf. 12

629	A310	8c shown	.40	.20
630	A310	8c Joggers	.40	.20
631	A310	8c Bicycling family	.40	.20
632	A310	8c Hikers	.40	.20
a.		Block of 4, #629-632	1.60	.85

"Keep Fit." 21st Summer Olympic Games, Montreal, 1976. When stamps are observed at an angle the Montreal Olympic Games' emblem can be seen.

Main St. and Portage Ave., Winnipeg, 1872 — A311

Litho. & Engr.

1974, May 3   **Perf. 12x12½**
633 A311 8c multicolored   .20 .20

Winnipeg's incorporation as a city, cent.

Postmaster A312

1974, June 11 Litho. Perf. 13½x13
634 A312 8c shown   .35 .30
635 A312 8c Mail collector and
          truck   .35 .30
636 A312 8c Mail handler   .35 .30
637 A312 8c Mail sorters   .35 .30
638 A312 8c Mailman   .35 .30
639 A312 8c Rural mail delivery   .35 .30
  a.   Block of 6, #634-639   2.25 2.25

Centenary of letter carrier delivery service. Printed in sheets of 50 (5x10).

Agricultural Education A313

1974, July 12   **Perf. 12½x12**
640 A313 8c multicolored   .20 .20

Ontario Agricultural College centenary.

Pedestal, Gallows Frame and Contempra Telephones A314

1974, July 26   **Perf. 12½**
641 A314 8c multicolored   .20 .20
  a.   Imperf., pair   1,600.

Centenary of the idea for the telephone by Alexander Graham Bell while visiting Brantford, Canada.

Bicycle Wheel and Cycling Emblem A315

Photo. & Engr.
1974, Aug. 7   **Perf. 12x12½**
642 A315 8c black, red & silver   .20 .20

World Cycling Championships, Montreal, Aug. 14-25.

Mennonite Settlers A316

1974, Aug. 28 Litho. Perf. 12x12½
643 A316 8c multicolored   .20 .20

Centenary of arrival of Mennonite settlers in Manitoba.

Snowshoeing A317

1974, Sept. 23 Engr.   Perf. 13½
644 A317 8c shown   .35 .20
645 A317 8c Skiing   .35 .20
646 A317 8c Skating   .35 .20
647 A317 8c Curling   .35 .20
  a.   Block of 4, #644-647   1.40 1.40
  b.   Block or strip of 4, printed
       on gummed side   3,000.

"Keep Fit." 1976 Winter Olympic Games. When the stamps are observed at an angle the Montreal Olympic Games' emblem can be seen.
Warning: No. 647b must show each design; blocks exist that contain 2 No. 645 but no example of No. 647.

Mercury with Winged Horses, UPU Emblem A318

Photo. & Engr.
1974, Oct. 9   **Perf. 12x12½**
648 A318 8c violet, red & blue   .20 .20
649 A318 15c violet, red & blue   .90 .75

Centenary of Universal Postal Union.

Nativity, by Jean Paul Lemieux A319

Skaters at Hull, by Henri Masson — A320

Christmas (Paintings): 10c, The Ice Cone, Montmorency Falls, by Robert C. Todd. 15c, Village in the Laurentian Mountains, by Clarence A. Gagnon.

1974, Nov. 1   Litho.   Perf. 13½
650 A319 6c multicolored   .20 .20
651 A320 8c multicolored   .20 .20
652 A319 10c multicolored   .35 .30
653 A319 15c multicolored   .65 .55
       Nos. 650-653 (4)   1.40 1.25

Marconi and St. John's, Newfoundland, from Signal Hill — A321

1974, Nov. 15   **Perf. 13**
654 A321 8c multicolored   .20 .20

Guglielmo Marconi (1874-1937), Italian electrical engineer and inventor.

Merritt and Welland Canal A322

Litho. & Engr.
1974, Nov. 29   **Perf. 13x13½**
655 A322 8c multicolored   .20 .20

Sesquicentennial of the start of construction of the Welland Canal between Lakes Ontario and Erie, a project conceived and supervised by William Hamilton Merritt (1793-1862). Portrait by Robert Whale.

The Sprinter — A323

The Plunger — A324

Designs: Sculptures by Robert Tait McKenzie, M.D. (1867-1938), and Montreal Olympic Games' emblem.

Perf. 12½x12, 12x12½
1975, Mar. 14   Litho.; Embossed
656 A323 $1 multicolored   2.50 2.50
657 A324 $2 multicolored   4.75 3.75

21st Olympic Games, Montreal, July 17-Aug. 1, 1976.

A325

No. 658, Anne of Green Gables. No. 659, Maria Chapdelaine.

1975, May 15   Litho.   Perf. 13
658   8c blue & multi   .20 .20
659   8c brown & multi   .20 .20
  a.   A325 Pair, #658-659   .40 .40

Birth centenary of Lucy Maud Montgomery (1874-1942), writer and author of "Anne of Green Gables"; Louis Hémon (1880-1913), writer and author of "Maria Chapdelaine." Nos. 658-659 printed checkerwise.

Marguerite Bourgeoys A327

Alphonse Desjardins A328

1975, May 30   Litho.   Perf. 12½x12
660 A327 8c red & multi   .20 .20
661 A328 8c red & multi   .20 .20

Marguerite Bourgeoys (1620-1700), founder of the Congrégation de Notre-Dame, Montreal, first girls' school in New France; Alphonse

Desjardins (1854-1920), journalist, founder of first credit union in North America.

A329

No. 662, Samuel Dwight Chown (1853-1933), Methodist minister, leader of temperance movement, founder of United Church. No. 663, Dr. John Cook (1805-92), 1st Moderator of the United Presbyterian Church in Canada.
Nos. 662-663 printed checkerwise.

Photo. & Engr.
1975, May 30   **Perf. 12x12½**
662   8c dk brown, yel & buff   .20 .20
663   8c dk brown, yel & buff   .20 .20
  a.   A329 Pair, #662-663   .40 .40

Pole Vaulting — A331

Hurdling — A332

Design: 25c, Marathon running and Montreal Olympic Games' emblem.

1975, June 11 Litho. Perf. 12x12½
664 A331 20c dk blue & multi   .60 .45
665 A331 25c maroon & multi   .75 .50
666 A332 50c green & multi   1.50 1.00
       Nos. 664-666 (3)   2.85 1.95

21st Olympic Games, Montreal, July 17-Aug. 1, 1976.

"Untamed" (Wild Horse Race) A333

1975, July 3
667 A333 8c gray & multi   .20 .20

Centenary of the founding of Calgary.

Female Symbol
A334

"Justice," by
Walter S.
Allward
A335

Photo. & Engr.

1975, July 14   *Perf. 13*
668 A334 8c dp yel, gray & black   .20   .20
    International Women's Year.

1975, Sept. 2   **Litho.**   *Perf. 12½*
669 A335 8c multicolored   .20   .20
    Supreme Court of Canada, centenary.

"Wm. D.
Lawrence"
A336

Photo. & Engr.

1975, Sept. 24   *Perf. 13*
670 A336 8c shown   .35   .30
671 A336 8c "Beaver"   .35   .30
672 A336 8c "Neptune"   .35   .30
673 A336 8c "Quadra"   .35   .30
   a.   Block of 4, #670-673   1.40   1.40
    Coastal ships.

Santa
Claus — A337

Child — A338

Trees — A339

    Designs by Canadian School Children:
"What Christmas Means to Me."

1975, Oct. 22   **Litho.**   *Perf. 13½*
674 A337 6c shown   .20   .20
675 A337 6c Skater   .20   .20
   a.   Pair, #674-675   .40   .30
676 A338 8c shown   .20   .20
677 A338 8c Family and Christ-
        mas tree   .20   .20
   a.   Pair, #676-677   .40   .35
678 A338 10c Gift box   .25   .20
679 A339 15c shown   .45   .45
    Nos. 674-679 (6)   1.50   1.45
    Christmas. Stamps of same denomination
printed checkerwise.

Legion
Emblem
and Bugle
A340

Photo. & Engr.

1975, Nov. 10   *Perf. 13*
680 A340 8c gray & multi   .20   .20
    Royal Canadian Legion, 50th anniversary.

Olympic Torch
Ignited by
Satellite in
Canada
A341

Communication
Arts — A342

High-rise Tower, Notre Dame Church,
Montreal, and Games'
Emblem — A343

Snowflake, Winter
Olympics'
Emblem — A344

    Montreal Olympic Games' Emblem and:
20c, Canadian athletes carrying Olympic flag.
25c, Women athletes receiving Olympic
medals.

1976, June 18   **Litho.**   *Perf. 13*
681 A341 8c black & multi   .20   .20
682 A341 20c black & multi   .70   .55
683 A341 25c black & multi   .90   .60
    Nos. 681-683 (3)   1.80   1.35
    1976 Olympic Games ceremonies.

1976, Feb. 6   **Photo.**   *Perf. 12x12½*
    25c, Handicraft tools. 50c, Performing arts.
684 A342 20c gray & multi   1.25   .60
685 A342 25c ocher & multi   1.60   .75
686 A342 50c blue & multi   2.25   1.25
    Nos. 684-686 (3)   5.10   2.60
    Olympic Fine Arts and Cultural Program.

Photo. & Engr.

1976, Mar. 12   *Perf. 13*
    Design: $2, Olympic Stadium, Velodrome,
flags and emblem.
687 A343 $1 silver & multi   3.25   2.25
688 A343 $2 gold & multi   5.50   4.50
    Nos. 681-688 were issued in commemora-
tion of, or in connection with the 21st Olympic
Games, Montreal, July 17-Aug. 1. Nos. 687-
688 were issued in panes of 8.

Photo. and Embossed

1976, Feb. 6   *Perf. 12½*
689 A344 20c multicolored   .90   .65
    12th Winter Olympic Games, Innsbruck,
Austria, Feb. 4-15.

Flower
Growing from
City — A345

1976, May 12   **Litho.**   *Perf. 12x12½*
690 A345 20c multicolored   .60   .45
    Habitat, UN Conference on Human Settle-
ments, Vancouver, May 31-June 11.

Franklin
and Map of
North
America,
1776
A346

Litho. & Engr.

1976, June 1   *Perf. 13*
691 A346 10c multicolored   .35   .20
    American Bicentennial; Benjamin Franklin
(1706-1790), deputy postmaster general for
the colonies (1753-1774).
    See US No. 1690.

Royal Military College, Kingston, Ont.,
Cent. — A347

    No. 692, Color Parade, Memorial Arch. No.
693, Wing Parade, Mackenzie Building.

1976, June 1   **Litho.**   *Perf. 12*
692   8c red & multi   .20   .20
693   8c red & multi   .20   .20
   a.   A347 Pair, #692-693   .40   .30
   b.   As "a," imperf.   2,250
   c.   Block of 4, imperf. horiz.   650.00
   d.   As "a," double impression   3,750.

    A few used singles exist of Nos. 692-693
with double impression. Very rare.

Archer in
Wheelchair
A349

1976, Aug. 3   *Perf. 12x12½*
694 A349 20c green & multi   .60   .50
    Olympiad for the Physically Disabled (25th
Stoke Mandeville Games), Toronto, Aug. 3-11.

A350

    No. 695, The Cremation of Sam McGee.
No. 696, The Outlander.

1976, Aug. 17   *Perf. 13½*
695   8c multicolored   .20   .20
696   8c multicolored   .20   .20
   a.   A350 Pair, #695-696   .40   .30
    Robert W. Service (1874-1958), author of
poem "The Cremation of Sam McGee"; Germaine Guevremont, author of "Le Survenant"
(The Outlander).

Nativity, St.
Michael's,
Toronto — A352

    Stained-glass windows: 10c, Nativity, St.
Jude, London, Ontario. 20c, Nativity, by
Yvonne Williams.

1976, Nov. 3   *Perf. 13½*
697 A352 8c multicolored   .20   .20
698 A352 10c multicolored   .20   .20
699 A352 20c multicolored   .40   .40
    Nos. 697-699 (3)   .80   .80
    Christmas.

Inland
Vessels
A353

Litho. & Engr.

1976, Nov. 19   *Perf. 12*
700 A353 10c Northcote   .35   .30
701 A353 10c Passport   .35   .30
702 A353 10c Chicora   .35   .30
703 A353 10c Athabasca   .35   .30
   a.   Block of 4, #700-703   1.40   1.25

Elizabeth II
A354

Litho. and Typo.

1977, Feb. 4   *Perf. 12½x12*
704 A354 25c silver & multi   .65   .50
    25th anniv. of the reign of Elizabeth II.

Bottle
Gentian
A355

Elizabeth II
A356

Parliament,
Ottawa
A357

Trembling
Aspen
A358

Main Street,
Prairie
Town — A359

Fundy National Park — A359a

Designs: 2c, Western columbine. 3c, Canada lily. 4c, Hepatica. 5c, Shooting star. 10c, Franklin's lady's-slipper. No. 712, Jewelweed. No. 715, Parliament, Ottawa. No. 716, Queen Elizabeth II. 20c, Douglas fir. 25c, Maple. 30c, Red oak. 35c, White pine. 60c, Street scene, Ontario City. 75c, Old houses, eastern City street. 80c, Street leading to the sea, Eastern Maritime Provinces. $2 Kluane National Park.

Litho. & Engr.

1977-82   *Perf. 12x12½*

705	A355	1c multicolored	.20	.20
a.	Printed on gummed side, precanceled		950.00	
707	A355	2c multicolored	.20	.20
a.	Printed on gummed side		950.00	
708	A355	3c multicolored	.20	.20
709	A355	4c multicolored	.20	.20
a.	Printed on gummed side		300.00	
710	A355	5c multicolored	.20	.20
711	A355	10c multicolored	.20	.20
a.	Perf. 13x13½ ('78)		.20	.20

Photo. & Engr.
Perf. 13x13½

712	A355	12c multi ('78)	.30	.20
713	A356	12c blue & multi	.25	.20
a.	Perf. 12x12½		.35	.20

Engraved
Perf. 13x13½

714	A357	12c blue	.25	
a.	Printed on gummed side		300.00	
715	A357	14c red ('78)	.30	.20
a.	Printed on gummed side		37.50	
b.	All color omitted		400.00	

Photo. & Engr.
Perf. 13x13½

716	A356	14c red & blk ('78)	.30	.20
a.	Perf. 12x12½ ('78)		.30	.20
b.	As "a," booklet pane of 25 + 2 labels ('78)		6.00	
c.	Red omitted		1,500.	

Perf. 13½

717	A358	15c multi	.40	.20
718	A358	20c multi	.40	.20
719	A358	25c multi	.50	.20
720	A358	30c multi ('78)	.60	.20
721	A358	35c multi ('79)	.70	.20
723	A359	50c multi ('78)	1.10	.20
723A	A359	50c multi, litho. & engr. ('78)	1.00	.20
b.	Brown (all inscriptions, etc.) omitted		2,250.	
723C	A359	60c multi, litho. ('82)	1.20	.20
724	A359	75c multi ('78)	1.50	.25
725	A359	80c multi ('78)	1.60	.35

Lithographed and Engraved

726	A359a	$1 multi ('79)	2.00	.55
a.	Untagged		2.75	.65
b.	As "a," blk inscriptions omitted		750.00	600.00
727	A359a	$2 multi ('79)	4.00	1.40
a.	Silver inscriptions omitted		525.00	
	Nos. 705-727 (23)		17.60	6.35

On No. 715b, a strong embossed impression from the plate, without color, is evident.
On No. 723A license plate on yellow car reads "1978."
See Nos. 781-806, 934-937, 1084.

Coil Stamps

1977-78   **Engr.**   *Perf. 10 Vert.*

729	A357	12c blue	.25	.20
a.	Imperf., pair		160.00	
730	A357	14c red ('78)	.30	.20
a.	Imperf., pair		175.00	

See note below No. 468B.

Eastern Cougar A360

1977, Mar. 30   **Litho.**   *Perf. 12½*

732 A360 12c multicolored   .25 .20

Wildlife protection.

April in Algonquin Park, by Thomson — A361

#734, Autumn Birches, by Tom Thomson.

1977, May 26   *Perf. 12*

733	A361	12c black & multi	.25	.20
734	A361	12c ocher & multi	.25	.20
a.	Pair, #733-734		.50	.40

Tom Thomson (1877-1917), landscape painter, birth centenary. Nos. 733-734 printed checkerwise.

Names of Governors General and Standard A362

1977, June 30   *Perf. 12½*

735 A362 12c vio blue & multi   .25 .20

Honoring Canadian-born Governors General: Vincent Massey, Georges Philias Vanier, Daniel Roland Michener and Jules Léger.

Order of Canada A363

Litho. & Embossed
1977, June 30

736 A363 12c multicolored   .25 .20

Order of Canada, 10th anniversary.

Peace Bridge, Canadian, US and UN Flags A364

1977, Aug. 4   737 A364 12c blue & multi   **Litho.**

50th anniversary of the Peace Bridge, connecting Fort Erie, Ontario, with Buffalo, N.Y.

Joseph E. Bernier, CGS Arctic A365

Sandford Fleming, Railroad Bridge A366

1977, Sept. 16   **Engr.**   *Perf. 13*

738	A365	12c dark blue	.25	.20
739	A366	12c brown	.25	.20
a.	Pair, #738-739		.50	.40

Joseph-Elzéar Bernier (1852-1934), explorer; Sandford Fleming (1827-1915), mapped route for Intercolonial Railway and designed Canada's first stamp.
Nos. 738-739 printed checkerwise.

Peace Tower, Parliament, Ottawa A367

1977, Sept. 19   **Litho.**   *Perf. 12½*

740 A367 25c multicolored   .75 .65

23rd Commonwealth Parliamentary Conference, Ottawa, Sept. 19-25.

Hunters Following Star — A368

Christmas: 12c, Angelic choir in northern light. 25c, Christ Child in Ring of Glory blessing chiefs from afar. Illustrations for Canada's first Christmas carol, written by Father Brébeuf, 1649.

1977, Oct. 26   *Perf. 13½*

741	A368	10c multicolored	.20	.20
a.	Horiz. pair, imperf between		1,250.	
b.	Printed on gummed side		700.00	
742	A368	12c multicolored	.20	.20
a.	Left margin block of 4, left vert. pair imperf, right pair part perf		1,900.	
743	A368	25c multicolored	.50	.35
	Nos. 741-743 (3)		.90	.75

Pinky A369

Designs: Canadian sailing ships.

Litho. and Engr.

1977, Nov. 18   *Perf. 12x12½*

744	A369	12c shown	.25	.20
745	A369	12c Tern schooner	.25	.20
746	A369	12c 5-masted schooner	.25	.20
747	A369	12c Mackinaw boat	.25	.20
a.	Block of 4, #744-747		1.00	.90
b.	As "a," #745, 747 imperf, #744, 746 part perf		3,500.	

See Nos. 776-779.

Seal Hunter, Soapstone Sculpture A370

Disguised Caribou Hunter, Print — A371

Inuit Art: #749, Spear fishing. #751, Walrus hunt. #749-751 are after stonecut prints.

1977, Nov. 18   **Litho.**

748	A370	12c multicolored	.25	.20
749	A371	12c multicolored	.25	.20
a.	Pair, #748-749		.50	.40
b.	As "a," gray (inscriptions) omitted on No. 749		2,400.	
750	A371	12c multicolored	.25	.20
751	A371	12c multicolored	.25	.20
a.	Pair, #750-751		.50	.40
	Nos. 748-751 (4)		1.00	.80

Inuit hunting. Nos. 748-749 and Nos. 750-751 printed se-tenant checkerwise.

Peregrine Falcon A372

1978, Jan. 18

752 A372 12c multicolored   .25 .20

Endangered wildlife.

Canada No. 3, 1851 — A373

1978   **Photo. & Engr.**   *Perf. 13½*

753	A373	12c shown	.25	.20
754	A373	14c No. 7	.25	.20
755	A373	30c No. 8	.55	.30

756	A373	$1.25 No. 2	2.40	1.00
a.	Souvenir sheet of 3		3.50	
	Nos. 753-756 (4)		3.45	1.70

CAPEX '78, Canadian Intl. Phil. Exhib., Toronto, June 9-18 (cent. of Canada's admission to UPU).
No. 756a contains one each of Nos. 754-756 ($1.25 untagged). Value of No. 756 untagged, $2.75.
Issue dates: 12c, Jan. 18; others, June 10.

Games' Emblem A374

Stadium A375

Design: 30c, Badminton.

1978, Mar. 31   **Litho.**   *Perf. 12½*

757	A374	14c silver & multi	.30	.20
758	A374	30c silver & multi	.60	.45

1978, Aug. 3

No. 760, Running. No. 761, Alberta Legislature building, Edmonton. No. 762, Lawn bowling.

759	A375	14c silver & multi	.30	.20
760	A375	14c silver & multi	.30	.20
a.	Pair, #759-760		.60	.40
761	A375	30c silver & multi	.60	.50
762	A375	30c silver & multi	.60	.50
a.	Pair, #761-762		1.20	1.10
	Nos. 759-762 (4)		1.80	1.40

Nos. 757-762 commemorate 11th Commonwealth Games, Edmonton, Aug. 3-12.
Nos. 760a, 762a printed checkerwise.

A376

No. 763, Capt. Cook, by Nathaniel Dance. No. 764, Nootka Sound, by John Webber.

1978, Apr. 26   *Perf. 13*

763		14c multicolored	.30	.20
764		14c multicolored	.30	.20
a.	A376 Pair, #763-764		.60	.60

Capt. James Cook (1728-1779), explorer of Canada's East and West Coasts and bicentenary of his anchorage near Anchorage, June 1, 1778. Nos. 763-764 printed checkerwise.

Silver Mine, Cobalt Lake A378

Stripmining, Athabasca Tar Sands A379

1978, May 19   *Perf. 12½*

765	A378	14c multicolored	.30	.20
766	A379	14c multicolored	.30	.20
a.	Pair, #765-766		.60	.60

Development of national resources. Nos. 765-766 printed checkerwise.

Prince's Gate A380

1978, Aug. 16
767 A380 14c multicolored   .30 .20
Canadian National Exhibition, centenary.

Mère d'Youville and Miracle of Food — A381

1978, Sept. 21   *Perf. 13x13½*
768 A381 14c multicolored   .30 .20
Marguerite d'Youville (1701-1771), founder of the Gray Nuns, beatified 1959.

Woman Walking, by Pitseolak A382

Migration, Soapstone by Joe Talurinili A383

Works by Eskimo Artists: No. 771, Plane over village, stonecut and stencil print by Pudlo. No. 772, Dogteam and sled, ivory sculpture by Abraham Kingmeatook.

1978, Sept. 27   *Perf. 13½*
769 A382 14c multicolored   .30 .20
770 A383 14c multicolored   .30 .20
  a.   Pair, #769-770   .60 .40
771 A382 14c multicolored   .30 .20
772 A383 14c multicolored   .30 .20
  a.   Pair, #771-772   .60 .40
     Nos. 769-772 (4)   1.20 .80

Travels of the Inuit. Printed checkerwise.

Madonna of the Flowering Pea, Cologne School — A384

Renaissance Paintings in National Gallery of Canada: 14c, Virgin and Child, by Hans Memling. 30c, Virgin and Child, by Jacopo Di Cione.

1978, Oct. 20   *Perf. 12½*
773 A384 12c multicolored   .25 .20
774 A384 14c multicolored   .30 .20
  a.   Black omitted   1,200.
775 A384 30c multicolored   .60 .25
     Nos. 773-775 (3)   1.15 .65

Christmas.

Sailing Ships Type of 1977
Litho. & Engr.

1978, Nov. 15   *Perf. 13*
776 A369 14c "Chief Justice
      Robinson," 1842   .30 .25
777 A369 14c "St. Roch," 1928   .30 .25
778 A369 14c "Northern Light,"
      1928   .30 .25
779 A369 14c "Labrador," 1954   .30 .25
  a.   Block of 4, #776-779   1.25 1.10

Ice vessels.

Quebec Carnival — A386

1979, Feb. 1   **Litho.**   *Perf. 13½*
780 A386 14c multicolored   .30 .20

Flower, Queen & Parliament Types

1c, Bottle gentian. 2c, Western columbine. 3c, Canada lily. 4c, Hepatica. 5c, Shooting star. 10c, Franklin's lady's-slipper. 15c, Canada violet. No. 789, Elizabeth II. No. 790, Parliament, Ottawa.

Photo. & Engr., Engr. (#790)
1977-83   *Perf. 13x13½*
781 A355 1c multi ('79)   .20 .20
  a.   Perf. 12x12½ ('77)   .20 .20
  b.   Bkt. pane, 2 #781a, 4
      #713a   1.50
782 A355 2c multi ('79)   .20 .20
  a.   Bkt. pane, 4 #782b, 3
      #716a + label   1.00
  b.   Perf. 12x12½ ('78)   .20 .20
783 A355 3c multi ('79)   .20 .20
784 A355 4c multi ('79)   .20 .20
785 A355 5c multi ('79)   .20 .20
786 A355 10c multi ('79)   .20 .20
787 A355 15c multi ('79)   .30 .20
789 A356 17c green & blk
      ('79)   .35 .20
  a.   Perf. 12x12½   .35 .20
  b.   Bkt. pane of 25 #789a + 2
      labels   8.75
  c.   Horiz. pair, imperf. btwn.
      and at left and bottom   2,000.
  d.   Black inscriptions omitted   1,000.
790 A357 17c slate green
      ('79)   .35 .20
  a.   Printed on gummed side   37.50
791 A356 30c multi ('82)   .60 .20
792 A356 32c multi ('83)   .65 .20
     Nos. 781-792 (11)   3.45 2.20

Nos. 781a, 782b, 789a are from booklet panes. No. 782b has one straight edge, others one or two.
No. 789d also shows the horiz. perfs. shifted.

Parliament Type of 1977
Booklet Stamps

1979, Mar. 28   **Engr.**   *Perf. 12x12½*
797 A357 1c slate blue   .50 .20
  a.   Bkt. pane, 1 #797, 3 #800, 2
      #789a   1.40
800 A357 5c violet brown   .25 .20

#797 has one straight edge, #800 has one or two.

Coil Stamps

1979, Mar. 8   *Perf. 10 Vert.*
806 A357 17c slate green   .35 .20
  a.   Imperf., pair   150.00

Endangered Wildlife A392

1979, Apr. 10   **Litho.**   *Perf. 12½*
813 A392 17c Soft-shelled turtle   .35 .20
814 A392 35c Bowhead whale   .70 .35

Ribbon Around Woman's Finger — A393

No. 816, String around man's finger.

1979, Apr. 10
815 A393 17c multicolored   .35 .20
816 A393 17c multicolored   .35 .20
  a.   Pair, #815-816   .70 .65

Use postal code. Printed checkerwise.

Fruits of the Earth, by F. P. Grove A394

The Golden Vessel, by Emile Nelligan A395

1979, May 3   *Perf. 13x13½*
817 A394 17c multicolored   .30 .20
818 A395 17c multicolored   .30 .20
  a.   Pair, #817-818   .60 .55
  c.   As "a," left margin block of
      4, left vert. pair imperf,
      right pair part perf   2,000. —

Frederick Philip Grove (1879-1948), teacher and writer; Emile Nelligan (1879-1941), French-Canadian poet. Nos. 817-818 printed checkerwise.
Warning: horizontal pairs exist of No. 818a that appear to be imperforate. These actually are pairs made from No. 818c with normal perforations trimmed off the right edge.

A396

1979, May 11   *Perf. 13½*
819   17c De Salaberry   .35 .20
820   17c John By   .35 .20
  a.   A396 Pair, #819-820   .70 .65

Charles-Michel d'Irumberry de Salaberry (1778-1829), and John By (1779-1836), Canadian colonels. Printed checkerwise.

Flag of Ontario A398

Designs: Provincial and Territorial flags.

1979, June 15   *Perf. 13½*
821 A398 17c shown   .35 .25
822 A398 17c Quebec   .35 .25
823 A398 17c Nova Scotia   .35 .25
824 A398 17c New Brunswick   .35 .25
825 A398 17c Manitoba   .35 .25
826 A398 17c British Columbia   .35 .25
827 A398 17c Prince Edward Is-
      land   .35 .25
828 A398 17c Saskatchewan   .35 .25
829 A398 17c Alberta   .35 .25
830 A398 17c Newfoundland   .35 .25
831 A398 17c Northwest Territo-
      ries   .35 .25
832 A398 17c Yukon Territory   .35 .25
  a.   Pane of 12, #821-832   4.50 4.00

White Water Kayak Race A399

1979, July 3   *Perf. 12½*
833 A399 17c multicolored   .35 .20

Canoe-Kayak (Slalom and Wild Water) World Championships, Jonquière and Desbiens, Quebec, June 30-July 8.

Women's Field Hockey A400

1979, Aug. 16
834 A400 17c multicolored   .35 .20

Women's Field Hockey Championship, Vancouver, B.C., Aug. 16-30.

Summer Tent, Print by Kiakshuk A401

Eskimos Building Igloo, by Abraham of Povungnituk A402

Works by Eskimo Artists: No. 837, The Dance, print by Kalvak of Holman Island. No. 838, Two soapstone figures from Repulse Bay, by Madeleine Isserkut and Jean Mapsalak.

1979, Sept. 13   *Perf. 13½*
835 A401 17c multicolored   .35 .20
836 A402 17c multicolored   .35 .20
  a.   Pair, #835-836   .70 .65
837 A401 17c multicolored   .35 .20
838 A402 17c multicolored   .35 .20
  a.   Pair, #837-838   .70 .65
     Nos. 835-838 (4)   1.40 .80

Inuit shelters and community. Printed checkerwise.

Painted Wooden Train A403

Antique Toys: 17c, Horse, pull toy. 35c, Knitted doll, vert.

1979, Oct. 17   *Perf. 13*
839 A403 15c multicolored   .30 .20
840 A403 17c multicolored   .35 .20
841 A403 35c multicolored   .70 .30
  a.   Gold (and tagging) omitted   1,400.
     Nos. 839-841 (3)   1.35 .70

Christmas.

Girl Watering Tree of Life — A404

1979, Oct. 24
842 A404 17c multicolored   .35 .20

International Year of the Child.

Curtiss HS-2L A405

1979, Nov. 15   *Perf. 12½*
843 A405 17c shown   .35 .20
844 A405 17c Canadair CL-215   .35 .20
  a.   Pair, #843-844   .70 .55
845 A405 35c Vickers Vedette   .70 .55
846 A405 35c Consolidated
      Canso   .70 .55
  a.   Pair, #845-846   1.40 1.25
     Nos. 843-846 (4)   2.10 1.50

Map of Canada Showing Arctic Islands A406

1980, Jan. 23   **Perf. 13½**
847 A406 17c multicolored   .35   .20

Acquisition of the Arctic Islands, centenary.

Downhill Skiing A407

1980, Jan. 23
848 A407 35c multicolored   .80   .40

13th Winter Olympic Games, Lake Placid, NY, Feb. 12-24.

Meeting of the School Trustees, by Robert Harris A408

Royal Canadian Academy of Arts Centenary: No. 850, Inspiration, bronze sculpture, by Louis-Philippe Hebert (1850-1917). No. 851, Parliament Buildings, by Thomas Fuller (1822-1919). No. 852, Sunrise on the Saguenay, by Lucius O'Brien (1832-99).

1980, Mar. 6
849 A408 17c multicolored   .35   .20
850 A408 17c multicolored   .35   .20
  a.   Pair, #849-850   .70   .55
851 A408 35c multicolored   .70   .55
852 A408 35c multicolored   .70   .55
  a.   Pair, #851-852   1.40   1.25
     Nos. 849-852 (4)   2.10   1.50

Printed checkerwise.

Atlantic Whitefish A409

Endangered wildlife. No. 854, Greater prairie chicken.

1980, May 6   **Perf. 12½**
853 A409 17c multicolored   .40   .20
854 A409 17c multicolored   .40   .20

Garden — A410

1980, May 29   **Perf. 13½**
855 A410 17c multicolored   .35   .20

Intl. Flower Show, Montreal, May 17-Sept. 1.

Helping Hands — A411

Litho. & Embossed
1980, May 29   **Perf. 12½**
856 A411 17c ultra & gold   .35   .20

14th World Congress of Rehabilitation International, Winnipeg, June 22-27.

"O Canada" Opening Bars A412

Composers Lavallee, Routhier, Weir A413

1980, June 6   **Litho.**
857 A412 17c multicolored   .35   .20
858 A413 17c multicolored   .35   .20
  a.   Pair, #857-858   .70   .65

"O Canada" centenary. Printed checkerwise in sheets of 16.

John George Diefenbaker (1895-1979), Prime Minister, 1956-63 — A414

1980, June 20   **Engr.**   **Perf. 13½**
859 A414 17c dark blue   .35   .20

Emma Albani (1847-1930), Soprano — A415

No. 861, Healey Willan (1880-1968), organist, composer. Printed checkerwise.

1980, July 4   **Litho.**
860 A415 17c multicolored   .35   .20
861 A415 17c multicolored   .35   .20
  a.   Pair, #860-861   .70   .65

Ned Hanlan (1855-1908), Oarsman A416

1980, July 4
862 A416 17c multicolored   .35   .20

Wheat Fields, Saskatchewan A417

No. 864, Strip mining and town, Alberta.

1980, Aug. 27
863 A417 17c multicolored   .35   .20
864 A417 17c multicolored   .35   .20

75th anniversary of Saskatchewan's and Alberta's creation as Provinces.

Uraninite Molecular Structure A418

1980, Sept. 3
865 A418 35c multicolored   .70   .50
  a.   Printed on gummed side   850.00

Discovery of uranium in Canada, 80th anniversary.

Sedna, by Ashoona Kiawak A419

Return of the Sun, Print by Kenojouak A420

Works by Eskimo Artists: No. 868, Bird Spirit, by Doris Hagiolok. No. 869, Shaman, print by Simon Tookoome.

1980, Sept. 25
866 A419 17c multicolored   .35   .20
867 A420 17c multicolored   .35   .20
  a.   Pair, #866-867   .70   .65
868 A419 35c multicolored   .70   .55
869 A420 35c multicolored   .70   .55
  a.   Pair, #868-869   1.40   1.30
     Nos. 866-869 (4)   2.10   1.50

Inuit spirits. Printed checkerwise.

Christmas Morning, by Frank Charles Hennessey — A421

Christmas (Greeting Cards, 1931): 17c, Sleigh Ride, by Joseph Sydney Hallam. 35c, McGill Cab Stand, by Kathleen Morris.

1980, Oct. 22   **Perf. 12½x12**
870 A421 15c multicolored   .30   .20
871 A421 17c multicolored   .35   .20
872 A421 35c multicolored   .70   .35
     Nos. 870-872 (3)   1.35   .75

Avro Canada CF-100, 1950 A422

Military Aircraft: No. 874, Avro Lancaster, 1941. No. 875, Curtiss JN-4 Canuck. No. 876, Hawker Hurricane, 1935.

1980, Nov. 10   **Perf. 13x13½**
873 A422 17c multicolored   .35   .20
874 A422 17c multicolored   .35   .20
  a.   Pair, #873-874   .70   .55
875 A422 35c multicolored   .70   .55
876 A422 35c multicolored   .70   .55
  a.   Pair, #875-876   1.40   1.25
     Nos. 873-876 (4)   2.10   1.50

Printed checkerwise.

Emmanuel-Persillier Lachapelle, Caduceus — A423

1980, Dec. 5   **Perf. 13½**
877 A423 17c multicolored   .35   .20

Lachapelle (1845-1918), physician, founded Notre Dame Hospital, Montreal, 1880.

Mandora, 18th Century A424

1981, Jan. 19   **Perf. 12½**
878 A424 17c multicolored   .35   .20

"The Look of Music" rare musical instrument exhibition, Vancouver, Nov. 2, 1980-Apr. 5, 1981.

No. 878 exists printed on gummed side with gold color and tagging omitted, from printer's waste.

Emily Stowe (1831-1903) and Toronto General Hospital — A425

Designs: No. 880, Louise McKinney, (1868-1931) Alberta legislative building. No. 881, Idola Saint-Jean, (1875-1945) Quebec legislative building. No. 882, Henrietta Edwards, (1849-1931) clubwomen.

1981, Mar. 4   **Perf. 13x13½**
879 A425 17c multicolored   .40   .20
880 A425 17c multicolored   .40   .20
881 A425 17c multicolored   .40   .20
882 A425 17c multicolored   .40   .20
  a.   Block of 4, #879-882   1.60   1.60

Vancouver Island Marmot, by Michael Dumas A426

Endangered Wildlife: 35c, Wood bison, by Robert Bateman.

1981, Apr. 6
883 A426 17c multicolored   .35   .20
884 A426 35c multicolored   .70   .60

Kateri Tekakwitha ("Lily of the Mohawks"), by Emile Brunet — A427

Brunet Sculpture: #886, Marie de L'Incarnation.

1981, Apr. 24   **Perf. 12½**
885 A427 17c brown & pale grn   .35   .20
886 A427 17c lt blue & ultra   .35   .20
  a.   Pair, #885-886   .70   .55

Beatification of Kateri Tekakwitha (1656-1680), first North American Indian saint, and Marie De L'Incarnation (1599-1672), founder of Ursuline Order.

At Baie Saint-Paul, by Marc-Aurele
Fortin (1888-1970) — A428

Paintings: No. 888, Self-portrait, by Frederick H. Varley (1881-1969). 35c, Untitled No. 6, by Paul-Emile Borduas (1905-60).

1981, May 22

887	A428	17c multi	.35	.20
888	A428	17c multi, vert.	.35	.20
a.		Imperf., pair	1,600.	

Photo.
Perf. 13

889	A428	35c multi, vert.	.70	.60
		Nos. 887-889 (3)	1.40	1.00

Map of Canada Showing Provincial Boundaries, 1867 — A429

1981, June 30   Litho.   Perf. 13½

890	A429	17c shown	.35	.20
891	A429	17c 1873	.35	.20
892	A429	17c 1905	.35	.20
893	A429	17c 1949	.35	.20
a.		Strip of 4, #890-893	1.40	1.40

Canada Day.

Frere Marie-Victorin (1885-1944) Botanist — A430

Botanists: #895, John Macoun (1831-1920).

1981, July 22   Perf. 12½

894	A430	17c multicolored	.35	.20
895	A430	17c multicolored	.35	.20
a.		Pair, #894-895	.70	.50

Montreal Rose — A431

1981, July 22   Perf. 13½

896	A431	17c multicolored	.35	.20

A432

1981, July 31   Photo. & Engr.

897	A432	17c multicolored	.35	.20

Niagara-on-the-Lake (1st capital of Upper Canada).

A433

1981, Aug. 14   Litho.

898	A433	17c multicolored	.35	.20

Acadian Congress centenary.

A434

1981, Sept. 8

899	A434	17c multicolored	.35	.20

Aaron Mosher (1881-1959), Labor Congress founder.

A435

1981, Nov. 16   Litho.

900	A435	15c 1781	.30	.20
901	A435	15c 1881	.30	.20
902	A435	15c 1981	.30	.20
		Nos. 900-902 (3)	.90	.60

Christmas; bicentenary of 1st illuminated Christmas tree in Canada.

Canadair CL-41 Tutor A436

1981, Nov. 24   Perf. 12½

903	A436	17c shown	.35	.20
904	A436	17c de Havilland Tiger Moth	.35	.20
a.		Pair, #903-904	.70	.55
905	A436	35c Avro Canada C-102	.70	.55
906	A436	35c de Havilland Canada Dash-7	.70	.55
a.		Pair, #905-906	1.40	1.25
		Nos. 903-906 (4)	2.10	1.50

A437

1981, Dec. 29   Engr.   Perf. 13x13½

907	A437	(30c) red	.90	.20
a.		Printed on gummed side	800.00	

Coil Stamp
Perf. 10 Vert.

908	A437	(30c) red	.85	.20
a.		Imperf., pair	400.00	

See Nos. 923-924, 940, 943-946, 950-951.

CANADA '82 Intl. Philatelic Youth Exhibition, Toronto, May 20-24 — A438

1982   Litho.   Perf. 13½

909	A438	30c No. 1	.60	.20
910	A438	30c No. 102	.60	.20
911	A438	35c No. 223	.70	.50
912	A438	35c No. 155	.70	.50
913	A438	60c No. 158	1.20	.75
a.		Souvenir sheet of 5, #909-913	4.25	4.25
		Nos. 909-913 (5)	3.80	2.15

Issued: #909, 911, 3/11; others, 5/20.

Jules Leger (1913-1980), 26th Governor General — A439

1982, Apr. 2

914	A439	30c multicolored	.60	.20

Terry Fox (1958-1981), Marathon of Hope — A440

1982, Apr. 13   Perf. 12½

915	A440	30c multicolored	.60	.20

1982 Constitution — A441

1982, Apr. 16   Perf. 12x12½

916	A441	30c multicolored	.60	.20

Types of 1979-81 and

Decoy
A442

Parliament (Library)
A443

Parliament (West Block) — A444

Parliament (East Block) — A445

Elizabeth II — A446

Designs: Artifacts, 18th and 19th cent.

1982-87   Litho.   Perf. 14x13½

917	A442	1c shown	.20	.20
a.		Perf. 13x13½ ('85)	.20	.20
918	A442	2c Fishing spear	.20	.20
a.		Perf. 13x13½ ('84)	.20	.20
b.		Bottom margin block of 4, bottom pair imperf, top pair part perf	2,100.	
c.		As "a," printed on gummed side	60.00	
919	A442	3c Stable lantern	.20	.20
a.		Perf. 13x13½ ('85)	.20	.20
920	A442	5c Bucket	.20	.20
a.		Perf. 13x13½ ('85)	.20	.20
921	A442	10c Weathercock	.20	.20
a.		Perf. 13x13½ ('85)	.30	.20
922	A442	20c Ice skates	.40	.20
a.		Brown omitted	400.00	

Photo. & Engr.
Perf. 13x13½

923	A437	30c lt blue, bl, & red	.60	.20
a.		Bklt. pane of 20, perf. 12x12½	16.00	
b.		Perf. 12x12½	.80	.20
924	A437	32c beige, red & brn	.60	.20
a.		Bklt. pane of 25, perf. 12x12½	16.00	
b.		Perf. 12x12½	.80	.20
c.		As #924, beige (and tagging) omitted	1,200.	

Litho.
Perf. 13½x13

925	A443	34c multi	.65	.20
a.		Booklet pane of 25	13.00	
b.		Perf. 13½x14 ('86)	.65	.20
c.		Bklt. pane of 25, perf. 13½x14	13.00	

Photo. & Engr.
Perf. 13x13½

926	A446	34c lt bl & int bl	.70	.20
926A	A446	36c plum	3.50	2.50

Perf. 13½x13

926B	A443	36c multi	.70	.20
c.		Booklet pane of 10 #926Be	6.50	
d.		Booklet pane of 25 #926Be	19.00	
e.		Perf. 13½x14 ('87)	.80	.20
f.		Left margin block of 4, left vert. pair imperf, right pair part perf	1,600.	

Litho.   Perf. 12x12½
Size A442: 26x20mm

927	A442	37c Wooden plow	.75	.20
928	A442	39c Settle-bed	.80	.20
929	A442	48c Cradle	.95	.30
930	A442	50c Sleigh	1.00	.25
932	A442	64c Wood stove	1.25	.40
933	A442	68c Spinning wheel	1.35	.35

Litho. & Engr.
Perf. 13½

934	A359a	$1 Glacier Natl. Park	2.00	.45
a.		Blue inscriptions omitted	1,000.	
b.		Imperf., pair	3,000.	
935	A359a	$1.50 Waterton Lakes Natl. Park	3.75	.55
a.		Black omitted	2,400.	
936	A359a	$2 Moraine Lake, Banff Park	4.00	1.10
a.		Bluish green inscriptions omitted	1,200.	
937	A359a	$5 Point Pelee Natl. Park	10.00	2.25
		Nos. 917-937 (22)	34.00	10.75

Issued:1c-20c, 10/19; 30c, 5/11; $1.50, 6/18; $5, 1/10/83; 32c, 2/10/83; 37c, 48c, 64c, 4/8/83; $1, 8/15/84; #925, $2, 6/21/85; #926, 7/12/85; 39c, 50c, 68c, 8/1/85; #926B, 3/30/87; #926A, 10/1/87.
For former No. 931, see new No. 723C.

Booklet Stamps
Perf. 12x12½ (A437), 12½x12
Engr.

938	A445	1c sage green ('87)	.20	.20
939	A444	2c myrtle grn ('85)	.20	.20
a.		2c slate green ('89)	.20	.20
940	A437	5c deep claret	.20	.20
941	A445	5c dp brown ('85)	.25	.20
942	A444	6c henna brn ('87)	.20	.20
943	A437	8c dk blue ('83)	.50	.25
944	A437	10c dark green	.40	.25
945	A437	30c red	.75	.30
a.		Bklt. pane of 4 + 2 labels (2 #940, 944, 945)	1.20	1.40
946	A437	32c brown ('83)	.65	.20
b.		Bklt. pane of 4 + 2 labels (2 #940, 944, 946)	1.20	1.40
947	A443	34c dp slate bl ('85)	1.15	.55
a.		Bklt. pane of 6 (3 #939, 2 #941, #947)	1.75	1.25

948 A443 36c dark lil rose ('87) 1.50 .55
 a. Bklt. pane of 5 + label (2 #938, 2 #942, #948) 2.00 1.25

Issued: #940, 10c, 30c, 3/1; 8c, 32c, 2/15/83; #941, 30c, 6/21/85; 1c, 6c, 36c, 3/30/87.

Coil Stamps
Engr.   Perf. 10 Vert.
950 A437 30c red 1.10 .20
 a. Imperf., pair 350.00
951 A437 32c brown ('83) .85 .20
 a. Imperf., pair 175.00

Perf. 10 Horiz.
952 A443 34c dull red brn ('85) .80 .20
 a. Imperf., pair 160.00
953 A443 36c dark red ('87) .85 .20
 a. Imperf., pair 300.00

Issued: 30c, 5/11; 32c, 2/10/83; 34c, 8/1/85; 36c, 5/19/87.

See #1080-1083, 1186-1188, 1194-1194A.

Centenary of Salvation Army in Canada A457

1982, June 25   Litho.   Perf. 13
954 A457 30c multicolored .60 .20

Canada Day A458

Paintings: No. 955, The Highway near Kluana Lake, by A.Y. Jackson. No. 956, Montreal Street Scene, by Adrien Hebert. No. 957, Breakwater, by Christopher Pratt. No. 958, Along Great Slave Lake, by Rene Richard. No. 959, Tea Hill, by Molly Lamb. No. 960, Family and Rainstorm, by Alex Colville. No. 961, Brown Shadows, by Dorothy Knowles. No. 962, The Red Brick House, by David Milne. No. 963, Campus Gates, by Bruno Bobak. No. 964, Prairie Town—Early Morning, by Illingworth Kerr. No. 965, Totems at Ninstints, by Joe Plaskett. No. 966, Doc Snider's House, by Lionel LeMoine FitzGerald.

1982, June 30   Perf. 12½x12
955 A458 30c multicolored .75 .75
956 A458 30c multicolored .75 .75
957 A458 30c multicolored .75 .75
958 A458 30c multicolored .75 .75
959 A458 30c multicolored .75 .75
960 A458 30c multicolored .75 .75
961 A458 30c multicolored .75 .75
962 A458 30c multicolored .75 .75
963 A458 30c multicolored .75 .75
964 A458 30c multicolored .75 .75
965 A458 30c multicolored .75 .75
966 A458 30c multicolored .75 .75
 a. Min. pane of 12, #955-966 9.50 9.50

Regina Centenary A459

1982, Aug. 3   Perf. 13½x13
967 A459 30c multicolored .60 .20

Centenary of Royal Canadian Henley Regatta, St. Catharines, Aug. 4-8 — A460

1982, Aug. 4
968 A460 30c multicolored .60 .20

Fairchild FC-2W1 A461

1982, Oct. 5   Litho.   Perf. 12½
969 A461 30c shown .80 .20
970 A461 30c De Havilland Canada Beaver .80 .20
 a. Pair, #969-970 1.60 1.25
971 A461 60c Noorduyn Norseman 1.25 .80
972 A461 60c Fokker Super Universal 1.25 .80
 a. Pair, #971-972 2.50 2.00
   Nos. 969-972 (4) 4.10 2.00

Christmas A462

Designs: Creche figures.

1982, Nov. 3   Perf. 13½
973 A462 30c Holy Family .60 .20
 a. All colors except black omitted 12,000.
 b. Printed on gummed side, black omitted 12,000.
974 A462 35c Shepherds .70 .45
975 A462 60c Three Kings 1.30 .75
   Nos. 973-975 (3) 2.60 1.40

Nos. 973a and 973b are each unique and were caused by a paper foldover.

World Communications Year — A463

1983, Mar. 10   Litho.   Perf. 12x12½
976 A463 32c multicolored .65 .20

Commonwealth Day — A464

1983, Mar. 14
977 A464 $2 multicolored 9.50 3.75

Scene from Angeline de Montbrun, by Laure Conan (1845-1924), Painted by Rene Milot — A465

Design: No. 979, Sea Gulls, by Edwin John Pratt (1882-1966), woodcut by Claire Pratt.

1983, Apr. 22   Litho.   Perf. 13½
978 A465 32c multicolored .65 .20
979 A465 32c multicolored .65 .20
 a. Pair, #978-979 1.30 1.10
 b. As "a," all color missing 4,000.

No. 979b resulted from an extraneous piece of paper receiving the colors. After removal, the issued pane shows two vertical pairs without color plus six other stamps with only partial color.

St. John Ambulance Centenary A466

1983, June 3   Perf. 13½
980 A466 32c Emblem .65 .20

World University Games, Edmonton, July 1-11 — A467

1983, June 28   Perf. 13½
981 A467 32c multicolored .65 .20
 a. Printed on gummed side 1,000.
982 A467 64c multicolored 1.30 .75

Canada Day — A468

#983, Fort Henry, Ontario. #984, Fort William, Ontario. #985, Fort Rodd Hill, British Columbia. #986, Fort Wellington, Ontario. #987, Fort Prince of Wales, Manitoba. #988, Halifax Citadel, Nova Scotia. #989, Fort Chambly, Quebec. #990, Fort No. 1, Point Levis, Quebec. #991, Fort at Coteau-du-Lac, Quebec. #992, Fort Beausejour, New Brunswick. Sizes: #983, 988: 44x22mm; #984-985, 989-990, 36x22mm; #986-987, 991-992, 28x22mm.

Booklet Stamps
1983, June 30   Perf. 12½x13
983 A468 32c multicolored .85 .75
984 A468 32c multicolored .85 .75
985 A468 32c multicolored .85 .75
986 A468 32c multicolored .85 .75
987 A468 32c multicolored .85 .75
988 A468 32c multicolored .85 .75
989 A468 32c multicolored .85 .75
990 A468 32c multicolored .85 .75
991 A468 32c multicolored .85 .75
992 A468 32c multicolored .85 .75
 a. Booklet pane of 10, #983-992 8.50 8.50

Scouting Year — A469

1983, July 6   Perf. 13½
993 A469 32c multicolored .65 .20

Church Council Emblem — A470

1983, July 22   Litho.
994 A470 32c tan & green .65 .20
 6th World Council of Churches Assembly, Vancouver, July 24-Aug. 10.

Humphrey Gilbert — A471

1983, Aug. 3   Litho.
995 A471 32c multicolored .65 .20
 400th anniv. of discovery of Newfoundland by Sir Humphrey Gilbert (1537-1583).

Centenary of Discovery of Nickel, Sudbury, Ontario A472

Litho. & Typo.
1983, Aug. 12   Perf. 13
996 A472 32c multicolored .70 .20
 a. Silver (and tagging) omitted 850.00

 Beware of forgeries of No. 996a. A certificate of authenticity is mandatory.

Josiah Henson (1789-1883), Preacher — A473

1983, Sept. 16   Litho.   Perf. 13x13½
997 A473 32c multicolored .65 .20

Antoine Labelle (1833-1891), Deputy Minister for Settlement A474

1983, Sept. 16   Perf. 13½
998 A474 32c multicolored .65 .20

Locomotives — A475

1983, Oct. 3   Perf. 12½x13
999 A475 32c Toronto 4-4-0, 1853 .65 .30
1000 A475 32c Dorchester 0-4-0, 1836 .65 .30
 a. Pair, #999-1000 1.30 .90
1001 A475 37c Samson 0-6-0, 1838 .80 .60
1002 A475 64c Adam Brown 4-4-0, 1860 1.30 1.10
   Nos. 999-1002 (4) 3.40 2.30

Dalhousie Law School Centenary A476

1983, Oct. 28   Perf. 13
1003 A476 32c Arms .65 .20

Christmas
A477

1983, Nov. 3
1004 A477 32c Urban church .65 .20
1005 A477 37c Family going to
church .75 .45
1006 A477 64c Rural church 1.25 .75
Nos. 1004-1006 (3) 2.65 1.40

Army Regiments,
Centenaries
A478

19th Cent. Uniforms: No. 1007, Royal Canadian Regiment, British Columbia Regiment. No. 1008, Royal Winnipeg Rifles, Royal Canadian Dragoons.

1983, Nov. 10   Perf. 13½x13
1007 A478 32c shown .65 .20
1008 A478 32c multicolored .65 .20
a. Pair, #1007-1008 1.30 1.00

Yellowknife, 50th
Anniv. — A479

1984, Mar. 15   Perf. 13½
1009 A479 32c Gold mine .65 .20

50th Anniv.
of Montreal
Symphony
Orchestra
A480

1984, Mar. 24   Perf. 12½
1010 A480 32c multicolored .65 .20

450th
Anniv. of
Cartier's
Landing in
Quebec
A481

1984, Apr. 20   Photo. & Engr.
1011 A481 32c multicolored .65 .20
See France No. 1923.

Voyage of Tall
Ships, Saint-Malo,
France, to
Quebec
City — A482

1984, May 18   Litho.   Perf. 12x12½
1012 A482 32c multicolored .65 .20
450th anniv. of Cartier's landing in Quebec.

Canadian Red
Cross Society,
75th
Anniv. — A483

1984, May 28   Perf. 13
1013 A483 32c Meritorious Service Medal .65 .20

New Brunswick,
Bicentenary
A484

1984, June 18   Photo. & Engr.
1014 A484 32c Galleys .65 .20

St. Lawrence Seaway, 25th
Anniv. — A485

1984, June 26   Litho.
1015 A485 32c Seaway, Lake
Superior .65 .20

Canada
Day
A486

Provincial Landscapes by Jean Paul Lemieux (b. 1904).

1984, June 29
1016 A486 32c New Brunswick .70 .45
1017 A486 32c British Columbia .70 .45
1018 A486 32c Yukon Territory .70 .45
1019 A486 32c Quebec .70 .45
1020 A486 32c Manitoba .70 .45
1021 A486 32c Alberta .70 .45
1022 A486 32c Prince Edward Island .70 .45
1023 A486 32c Saskatchewan .70 .45
1024 A486 32c Nova Scotia, vert. .70 .45
1025 A486 32c Northwest Territories .70 .45
1026 A486 32c Newfoundland .70 .45
1027 A486 32c Ontario, vert. .70 .45
a. Min. pane of 12, #1016-1027 8.50 8.00

Nos. 1018 and 1025 incorrectly inscribed. No. 1018 shows Northwest Territories landscape; No. 1025, Yukon Territory church.

Loyalists, British Flag (1606-
1801) — A487

1984, July 3
1028 A487 32c multicolored .65 .20

United Empire Loyalists, American colonists who remained loyal to British throne and emigrated to Canada during American Revolution.

Roman Catholic
Church in
Newfoundland
A488

1984, Aug. 17   Perf. 13½
1029 A488 32c St. John's Basilica .65 .20

Papal Visit
A489

1984, Aug. 31   Perf. 12½
1030 A489 32c multicolored .65 .20
1031 A489 64c multicolored 1.30 .70

Lighthouses — A490

1984, Sept. 21
1032 A490 32c Louisbourg, 1734 .70 .25
1033 A490 32c Fisgard, 1860 .70 .25
1034 A490 32c Ile Verte, 1809 .70 .25
1035 A490 32c Gibraltar Point,
1808 .70 .25
a. Block of 4, #1032-1035 2.80 1.40

Steam Locomotives — A491

1984, Oct. 25   Perf. 12½x13
1036 A491 32c Scotia .65 .20
1037 A491 32c Countess of Dufferin .65 .20
a. Pair, #1036-1037 1.30 1.00
1038 A491 37c Grand Trunk
Class E3 .90 .70
1039 A491 64c Canadian Pacific
D10a 1.60 1.10
a. Souvenir sheet 4.00 4.00
Nos. 1036-1039 (4) 3.80 2.20

#1039a contains #1036-1039 in changed colors.
See #1071-1074, 1118-1121.

Christmas
A492

Paintings: 32c, The Annunciation, by Jean Dallaire. 37c, The Three Kings, by Simone Mary Bouchard. 64c, Snow in Bethlehem, by David Milne.

1984, Nov. 2   Perf. 13
1040 A492 32c multicolored .65 .20
1041 A492 37c multicolored .75 .55
1042 A492 64c multicolored 1.30 .75
Nos. 1040-1042 (3) 2.70 1.50

Royal Canadian
Air Force — A493

1984, Nov. 9   Perf. 12x12½
1043 A493 32c Pilots .65 .20

Cent. of La
Presse — A494

1984, Nov. 16   Perf. 13x13½
1044 A494 32c Treffle
Berthiaume .65 .20

International Youth Year — A495

1985, Feb. 8   Perf. 12½
1045 A495 32c Heart, arrow,
jeans .65 .20

Canadians in
Space — A496

1985, Mar. 15   Perf. 13½
1046 A496 32c Astronaut .70 .20

Therese
Casgrain
(1896-1981),
Suffragist
A497

Emily Murphy
(1868-1933),
Writer
A498

1985, Apr. 17
1047 A497 32c multicolored .65 .20
1048 A498 32c multicolored .65 .20
a. Pair, #1047-1048 1.30 1.10

Gabriel Dumont (1837-1906), Metis
Leader — A499

1985, May 6   Perf. 13
1049 A499 32c multicolored .65 .20
Centenary of the Northwest Rebellion.

Canada Day — A500

#1050, Lower Ft. Garry, Manitoba. #1051, Ft. Anne, Nova Scotia. #1052, Ft. York, Ontario. #1053, Castle Hill, Newfoundland. #1054, Ft. Whoop Up, Alberta. #1055, Ft. Erie, Ontario. #1056, Ft. Walsh, Saskatchewan. #1057, Ft. Lennox, Quebec. #1058, York Redoubt, Nova Scotia. #1059, Ft. Frederick, Ontario. Sizes: #1050, 1055: 48x26mm. #1051-1052, 1056-1057: 40x26mm. #1053-1054, 1058-1059, 32x26mm.

Booklet Stamps

1985, June 28				**Perf. 12½x13**	
1050	A500	34c	multicolored	1.10	.75
1051	A500	34c	multicolored	1.10	.75
1052	A500	34c	multicolored	1.10	.75
1053	A500	34c	multicolored	1.10	.75
1054	A500	34c	multicolored	1.10	.75
1055	A500	34c	multicolored	1.10	.75
1056	A500	34c	multicolored	1.10	.75
1057	A500	34c	multicolored	1.10	.75
1058	A500	34c	multicolored	1.10	.75
1059	A500	34c	multicolored	1.10	.75
a.		Bkt. pane of 10, #1050-1059		11.00	12.00

Intl. Pharmaceutical Federation Congress — A501

Design: Louis Hebert (1575-1627), 1st French Apothecary in North America.

1985, Aug. 30				**Perf. 12½**	
1060	A501	34c	multicolored	.65	.20

Interparliamentary Union '85, Ottawa — A502

1985, Sept. 3				**Perf. 13½**	
1061	A502	34c	multicolored	.65	.20

A503

1985, Sept. 12 Photo.				**Perf. 13½x13**	
1062	A503	34c	Guide, brownie saluting	.65	.20

Natl. Girl Guides movement, cent.

Lighthouses A504

1985, Oct. 3	**Litho.**			**Perf. 13½**	
1063	A504	34c	Sisters Islets	.90	.30
1064	A504	34c	Pelee Passage	.90	.30
1065	A504	34c	Haut-fond Prince	.90	.30

1066	A504	34c	Rose Blanche	.90	.30
a.		Block of 4, #1063-1066		3.60	2.75
b.		Souv. sheet of 4, #1063-1066		5.50	5.00

Santa Claus Parade A505

Paintings by Barbara Carroll.

1985, Oct. 23					
1067	A505	34c	Santa Claus	.65	.20
1068	A505	39c	Horse-drawn coach	.85	.60
1069	A505	68c	Christmas tree	1.60	1.10
		Perf. 13½ on 3 Sides			
1070	A505	32c	Polar float	1.25	.50
a.		Booklet pane of 10		12.50	
		Nos. 1067-1070 (4)		4.35	2.40

No. 1070 printed in booklets only.

Locomotives Type of 1984

1985, Nov. 7				**Perf. 12½x13**	
1071	A491	34c	Grand Trunk K2	.85	.25
1072	A491	34c	Canadian Pacific P2a	.85	.25
a.		Pair, #1071-1072		1.70	1.25
1073	A491	39c	Canadian Northern O10a	.90	.80
1074	A491	68c	Canadian Govt. Railways H4D	1.75	1.25
		Nos. 1071-1074 (4)		4.35	2.55

1910 Gunner's Mate, World War II Officer, 1985 Woman Recruit — A507

1985, Nov. 8				**Perf. 13½x13**	
1075	A507	34c	multicolored	.65	.20

Royal Canadian Navy, 75th anniv.

Old Holton House, Sherbrooke Street, Montreal, by James Wilson Morrice (1865-1924) A508

1985, Nov. 15				**Perf. 13½**	
1076	A508	34c	multicolored	.65	.20

Montreal Museum of Fine Arts, 120th anniv.

Southwestern Alberta, Computer Design Map — A509

1986, Feb. 13	**Litho.**			**Perf. 12½x13**	
1077	A509	34c	multicolored	.65	.20

1988 Winter Olympics, Calgary, Alberta, Feb. 13-28.

EXPO '86, Vancouver, May 2-Oct. 13 — A510

1986, Mar. 7		**Photo. & Engr.**			
1078	A510	34c	Canada Pavilion	.65	.20
1079	A510	39c	Communications	.85	.65

Heritage Artifacts Type of 1982

1987, May 6	**Litho.**			**Perf. 14x13½**	
1080	A442	25c	Butter stamp	.65	.30
		Size: 20x26mm			
		Perf. 12x12½			
1081	A442	42c	Linen chest	1.25	.20
1082	A442	55c	Iron kettle	1.75	.30
1083	A442	72c	Hand-drawn cart	2.00	.40
		Nos. 1080-1083 (4)		5.65	1.20

Park Type of 1979

		Litho. & Engr.			
1986, Mar. 14				**Perf. 13½**	
1084	A359a	$5	La Mauricie Natl. Park	10.00	2.25
a.		Dark blue inscriptions omitted		2,750.	1,600.

No. 1084a is valued in the grade of fine as all known examples are centered thus.

Philippe Aubert de Gaspe (1786-1871), Novelist A511

Molly Brant (1736-1796), Iroquois Leader and Loyalist A512

1986, Apr. 14	**Litho.**			**Perf. 12½**	
1090	A511	34c	multicolored	.65	.20
		Perf. 13½			
1091	A512	34c	multicolored	.65	.20

EXPO '86 — A513

		Photo. & Engr.			
1986, Apr. 28				**Perf. 13x13½**	
1092	A513	34c	Expo Center, Vancouver	.65	.20
1093	A513	68c	Transportation, horiz.	1.40	.75

Canadian Forces Postal Service, 75th Anniv. A514

1986, May 9	**Litho.**			**Perf. 13½**	
1094	A514	34c	multicolored	.65	.20

Indigenous Birds — A515

1986, May 22					
1095	A515	34c	Great blue heron	.80	.35
1096	A515	34c	Snow goose	.80	.35
1097	A515	34c	Great horned owl	.80	.35
1098	A515	34c	Spruce grouse	.80	.35
a.		Block of 4, #1095-1098		3.20	2.50

19th Intl. Ornithological Congress, Ottawa, June 22-29.

Canada Day — A516

Invention blueprints.

1986, June 27					
1099	A516	34c	Rotary snowplow, 1869	.90	.30
1100	A516	34c	Canadarm, 1986	.90	.30
1101	A516	34c	Anti-gravity flight suit, 1938	.90	.30
1102	A516	34c	Variable pitch propeller, 1923	.90	.30
a.		Block of 4, #1099-1102		3.60	2.75

Canadian Broadcasting Corp., 50th Anniv. — A517

1986, July 23				**Perf. 12½**	
1103	A517	34c	Emblem, map	.65	.20

Exploration of Canada A518

#1104, Siberian Indians discover and inhabit America, 10,000 B.C. #1105, Viking settlement, A.D. 1000. #1106, John Cabot lands, 1498. #1107, Henry Hudson pioneers Hudson Strait and Bay, 1610.

1986, Aug. 29				**Perf. 12½x13**	
1104	A518	34c	multicolored	.65	.30
1105	A518	34c	multicolored	.65	.30
1106	A518	34c	multicolored	.65	.30
1107	A518	34c	multicolored	.65	.30
a.		Block of 4, #1104-1107		2.60	2.25
b.		Souv. sheet of 4, #1104-1107		3.25	2.75

No. 1107b issued Oct. 1 for CAPEX '87. See #1126-1129, 1199-1202, 1233-1236.

Peacemakers of the Frontier, 1870s — A519

Designs: No. 1108, Crowfoot (1830-1890), Blackfoot Indian chief. No. 1109, James F. Macleod (1836-1894), asst. commissioner of Northwest Mounted Police.

1986, Sept. 5				**Perf. 13x13½**	
1108	A519	34c	scar, gray & ind	.65	.25
1109	A519	34c	ind, gray & scar	.65	.25
a.		Pair, #1108-1109		1.30	1.10

Intl. Peace Year — A520

		Litho. & Embossed			
1986, Sept. 16				**Perf. 13½**	
1110	A520	34c	multicolored	.65	.20

1988 Calgary Winter Olympics — A521

1986, Oct. 15   *Perf. 13½x13*
1111	A521	34c Ice hockey	.65	.20
1112	A521	34c Biathlon	.65	.20
a.		Pair, #1111-1112	1.30	1.00

See #1130-1131, 1152-1153, 1195-1198.

Christmas Angels — A522

1986, Oct. 29   *Perf. 12½*
1113	A522	34c multicolored	.65	.20
1114	A522	39c multicolored	.80	.65
1115	A522	68c multicolored	1.40	1.00

Booklet Stamps
Size: 72x26mm
Perf. 13½ Horiz.
1116	A522	29c multicolored	1.50	1.10
a.		Booklet pane of 10	15.00	14.00
b.		Perf. 12½ horiz.	8.50	3.25
c.		Bklt. pane of 10, #1116b	85.00	75.00
		Nos. 1113-1116 (4)	4.35	2.95

No. 1116 has bar code at left, for use on covers with printed postal code matrix.

John Molson (1763-1836), Entrepreneur — A523

1986, Nov. 4
1117	A523	34c multicolored	.65	.20

Locomotives Type of 1984

Locomotives, 1925-1945.

1986, Nov. 21   *Perf. 12½x13*
1118	A491	34c CN V1a	.85	.30
1119	A491	34c CP T1a	.85	.30
a.		Pair, #1118-1119	1.70	1.25
1120	A491	39c CN U2a	1.05	.85
1121	A491	68c CP H1c	1.60	1.30
		Nos. 1118-1121 (4)	4.35	2.75

CAPEX '87 — A524

1987   *Litho. & Engr.*   *Perf. 13x13½*
1122	A524	34c 1st Toronto P.O.	.65	.20
1123	A524	36c Nelson-Miramichi P.O.	.75	.25
1124	A524	42c Saint Ours P.O.	.90	.75
1125	A524	72c Battleford P.O.	1.60	1.25
		Nos. 1122-1125 (4)	3.90	2.45

Souvenir Sheet
Yellow Green Inscription
1125A		Sheet of 4	4.00	4.00
b.	A524	36c like #1122	.75	.70
c.	A524	36c like #1123	.75	.70
d.	A524	42c like #1124	.90	.85
e.	A524	72c like #1125	1.40	1.30

Issue dates: 34c, Feb. 16; others, June 12.

Exploration Type of 1986

Pioneers of New France: #1126, Etienne Brule (c. 1592-1633), 1st European to see the Great Lakes. #1127, Pierre Esprit Radisson (c. 1636-1710) & Medard Chouart des Groseilliers (1625-98), British expedition to Hudson Bay, 1668. #1128, Louis Jolliet (1645-1700) & Fr. Jacques Marquette (1637-75) discovering

the Mississippi River, 1673. #1129, Recollet wilderness mission, 1615.

1987, Mar. 13   *Litho.*   *Perf. 12½x13*
1126	A518	34c multicolored	.70	.30
1127	A518	34c multicolored	.70	.30
1128	A518	34c multicolored	.70	.30
1129	A518	34c multicolored	.70	.30
a.		Block of 4, #1126-1129	2.80	2.40

Olympics Type of 1986

1987, Apr. 3   *Perf. 13½x13*
1130	A521	36c Speed skating	.75	.20
1131	A521	42c Bobsledding	.90	.75

Volunteers Week — A525

1987, Apr. 13   *Perf. 12½x13*
1132	A525	36c multicolored	.75	.20

Law Day — A526

1987, Apr. 15   *Perf. 14x13½*
1133	A526	36c Coat of arms	.75	.20
a.		Imperf., pair	1,600.	

Canadian Charter of Rights and Freedoms, 5th anniv.

Engineering Institute of Canada, Cent. — A527

1987, May 19   *Perf. 12½x13*
1134	A527	36c multicolored	.75	.20

Canada Day — A528

Inventors & communications innovations: #1135, Reginald Aubrey Fessenden (1866-1932), AM radio, 1900. #1136, Charles Fenerty, newsprint, 1838. #1137, Georges-Edouard Desbarats and William Leggo, half-tone engraving, 1869. #1138, Frederick Newton Gisborne, No. America's 1st undersea cable, 1852, New Brunswick-Prince Edward Island.

1987, June 25   *Perf. 13½*
1135	A528	36c multicolored	.75	.30
1136	A528	36c multicolored	.75	.30
1137	A528	36c multicolored	.75	.30
1138	A528	36c multicolored	.75	.30
a.		Block of 4, #1135-1138	3.00	2.50

Steamships A529

1987, July 20   *Perf. 13½x13*
1139	A529	36c Segwun, 1887	.75	.30

51x22mm
1140	A529	36c Princess Marguerite, 1948	.75	.30
a.		Pair, #1139-1140	1.50	1.25

Shipwrecks A530

1987, Aug. 7
1141	A530	36c Hamilton & Scourge, 1813	.75	.30
1142	A530	36c San Juan, 1565	.75	.30
1143	A530	36c Breadalbane, 1853	.75	.30
1144	A530	36c Ericsson, 1892	.75	.30
a.		Block of 4, #1141-1144	3.00	2.50

Air Canada, 50th Anniv. — A531

1987, Sept. 1   *Perf. 13½*
1145	A531	36c multicolored	.75	.20

2nd Intl. Francophone Summit, Quebec, 9/2-4 — A532

1987, Sept. 2   *Perf. 13x12½*
1146	A532	36c multicolored	.75	.20

9th Commonwealth Meeting, Vancouver, Oct. 13-17 — A533

1987, Oct. 13
1147	A533	36c multicolored	.75	.20

Christmas A534

1987, Nov. 2   *Litho.*   *Perf. 13½*
1148	A534	36c Poinsettia	.75	.20
1149	A534	42c Holly wreath	.90	.80
1150	A534	72c Mistletoe, Christmas tree	1.50	1.10

Size: 39x25mm
1151	A534	31c Gifts, Christmas tree	.90	.80
a.		Booklet pane of 10	9.00	11.00
		Nos. 1148-1151 (4)	4.05	2.90

No. 1151 has bar code at left, for use on covers with printed postal code matrix. Issued in booklets only.

Olympics Type of 1986

1987, Nov. 13   *Perf. 13½x13*
1152	A521	36c Cross-country skiing	.75	.30
1153	A521	36c Ski jumping	.75	.30
a.		Pair, #1152-1153	1.50	1.10

75th Grey Cup, Vancouver, Nov. 29 — A535

1987, Nov. 20   *Perf. 12½*
1154	A535	36c multicolored	.75	.20

Types of 1982 and

Elizabeth II A536   Mammals A538

Parliament (Center Block)
A537   A539

Architecture — A540

Flag and Clouds A541   Flag A542

Natl. Flag, Deciduous Forest A543   Flag and Mountains A544

Sizes Vary on A536, A538

1987-91   *Litho.*   *Perf. 13x13½*
1155	A538	1c Flying squirrel	.20	.20
a.		Perf. 13x12½	4.00	.85
1156	A538	2c Prickly porcupine	.20	.20
1157	A538	3c Muskrat	.20	.20
1158	A538	5c Varying hare	.20	.20
a.		Imperf., pair	1,600.	
1159	A538	6c Red fox	.20	.20
a.		Horiz. pair, imperf	2,400.	
1160	A538	10c Skunk	.20	.20
a.		Perf. 13x12½	4.00	.40
1161	A538	25c Beaver	.50	.20

Perf. 13½x13
1162	A536	37c multicolored	.85	.20
1163	A537	37c multicolored	.85	.20
a.		Bklt. pane of 10, #1163c	8.50	8.50
b.		Bklt. pane of 25, #1163c	27.50	20.00
c.		Perf. 13½x14	.85	.25

Perf. 13x12½
1164	A536	38c multicolored	.85	.20
a.		Perf. 13x13½	.85	.25
b.		As "a," bklt. pane of 10 + 2 labels	8.50	
c.		Vert. block of 10, middle pair imperf, 2nd and 4th pairs part perf	1,200.	
d.		As "a," horiz. pair, imperf btwn.	1,000.	

e.	Bottom margin horiz. pair, imperf	—	

Perf. 13x13½ on 3 or 4 Sides

1165	A539	38c multicolored	.85	.20
a.		Bklt. pane of 10 + 2 labels	8.50	
b.		Bklt. pane of 25 + 2 labels	22.50	
c.		Printed on gummed side	120.00	
d.		Double impression of all litho colors except black	275.00	

Perf. 13½x13

1166	A541	39c multicolored	.85	.20
a.		Bklt. pane of 10 + 2 labels	8.50	
b.		Bklt. pane of 25 + 2 labels	22.50	
c.		Perf. 12½x13	17.50	.85

Perf. 13x13½

1167	A536	39c multicolored	.85	.20
a.		Bklt. pane of 10 + 2 labels	8.50	
b.		Perf. 13	11.00	.85
1168	A536	40c multicolored	.85	.20
a.		Bklt. pane of 10 + 2 labels	8.50	

Perf. 13½x13

1169	A544	40c multicolored	.85	.20
a.		Bklt. pane of 25 + 2 labels	27.50	
b.		Bklt. pane of 10 + 2 labels	8.50	

Perf. 12x12½

1170	A538	43c Lynx	1.25	.40

Perf. 14½x14

1171	A538	44c Walrus	1.75	.20
a.		Perf. 12½x13	3.25	1.75
b.		As "a," bklt. pane of 5 + label	16.50	15.00
c.		Perf. 13½x13	475.00	50.00
1172	A538	45c Pronghorn	1.00	.25
b.		As "f," bklt. pane of 5 + label	15.00	14.00
d.		Perf. 13	22.50	1.20
f.		Perf. 12½x13	3.00	.50
h.		Imperf., pair	950.00	

Perf. 13

1172A	A538	46c Wolverine	1.10	.25
c.		Perf. 12½x13	1.50	.55
e.		As "c," bklt. pane of 5 + label	7.50	6.50
g.		Perf. 14½x14	6.00	.45

Perf. 12x12½

1173	A538	57c Killer whale	1.30	.35

Perf. 14½x14

1174	A538	59c Musk-ox	1.50	.35
a.		Perf. 13	13.00	7.75
1175	A538	61c Timber wolf	1.25	.40
a.		Perf. 13	85.00	6.75
1176	A538	63c Harbor porpoise	3.25	.40
a.		Perf. 13	12.50	5.00

Perf. 12x12½

1177	A538	74c Wapiti	2.20	.85

Perf. 14½x14

1178	A538	76c Grizzly bear	2.20	.65
a.		Perf. 12½x13	3.50	3.00
b.		As "a," bklt. pane of 5 + label	17.50	17.50
c.		Perf. 13	42.50	16.00
1179	A538	78c Beluga whale	2.50	.75
a.		As "c," bklt. pane of 5	17.50	17.50
b.		Perf. 12½x13	37.50	6.75
c.		Perf. 13	3.50	2.25
d.		Imperf, pair	950.00	

Perf. 13

1180	A538	80c Peary caribou	2.25	.85
a.		Perf. 12½x13	3.25	1.25
b.		As "a," bklt. pane of 5 + label	16.50	16.50
c.		Perf. 14½x14	6.50	2.50

Perf. 13½

Litho. & Engr.

1181	A540	$1 Runnymede Library, Toronto	2.00	.60
a.		Engr. inscriptions inverted	13,500.	
b.		Imperf, pair	1,600.	
1182	A540	$2 McAdam Railway Station	4.00	1.00
a.		Imperf., pair	1,200.	
1183	A540	$5 Bonsecours Market, Montreal	10.00	2.50
		Nos. 1155-1183 (30)	*46.05*	*12.80*

A later printing of No. 1182 has more intense and clearly defined green shading on the roofline and the deep orange background extends closer to the roofline.

Imperfs exist of Nos. 1155-1157 and 1160, from printer's waste.

Issued: 1c, 2c, 3c, 5c, 6c, 10c, 25c, 10/3/88; 37c, 12/30/87; 38c, 12/29/88; 43c, 57c, 74c, 1/18/88; 44c, 59c, 76c, 1/18/89; $1, $2, 5/5/89; #1166, 12/28/89; 45c, 61c, 78c, #1167, 1/12/90; $5, 5/28/90; 40c, 46c, 63c, 80c, 12/28/90.

Booklet Stamps

Perf. 13½x14 on 3 Sides

Litho.

1184	A542	1c shown	.25	.20
a.		Perf. 12½x13	12.50	12.50
1185	A542	5c multi	.20	.20
a.		Perf. 12½x13	8.50	8.50

Perf. 12½x12 on 2 or 3 sides

Engr.

1186	A445	6c dark purple	.75	.30
1187	A443	37c dark blue	1.10	.80
a.		Bklt. pane of 4 + 2 labels (#938, 2 #942, #1187)	1.50	1.50
1188	A443	38c dark blue	1.00	.40
a.		Bklt. pane of 5 (3 #939a, #1186, #1188)	2.00	2.00

Perf. 13½x14 on 3 Sides

Litho.

1189	A542	39c multi	1.00	.40
a.		Bklt. pane of 4 (#1184, 2 #1185, #1189)	1.20	1.20
b.		Perf. 12½x13	17.50	17.50
c.		Bklt. pane of 4 (#1184a, 2 #1185a, 1189b)	47.50	47.50
1190	A542	40c multi	1.75	.65
a.		Bklt. pane of 4 (2 #1184, #1185, #1190)	2.50	1.40
b.		As "a," imperf	1,600.	

Nos. 1190a, 1190c sold for 50c.
Issued: #1187, 2/3/88; #1188, 1/18/89; #1186, 1989; #1184-1185, 1189, 1/12/90; #1190, 12/28/90.

Self-Adhesives

Die Cut

Booklet Stamps

1191	A543	38c multicolored	1.75	.85
a.		Booklet of 12	19.00	
b.		Blue omitted	2,000.	
c.		Yellow omitted	1,000.	
1192	A543	39c Flag, field	1.50	.85
a.		Booklet of 12	18.00	
1193	A543	40c Flag, seacoast	1.50	.85
a.		Booklet of 12	18.00	

Issued: 38c, 6/30/89; 39c, 2/8/90; 40c, 1/11/91.
Issued on peelable paper backing serving as booklet cover. Nos. 1191a, 1192a sold for $5, No. 1193a for $5.25.

Coil Stamps

Perf. 10 Horiz.

Engr.

1194	A443	37c dark blue	.80	.20
d.		Imperf., pair	175.00	
1194A	A443	38c dark green	1.20	.20
e.		Imperf., pair	500.00	
1194B	A542	39c violet	.85	.20
f.		Imperf., pair	200.00	
1194C	A542	40c blue gray	.85	.20
g.		Imperf., pair	300.00	

Issued: 37c, 2/22/88; 38c, 2/1/89; 39c, 2/8/90; 40c, 12/28/90.
See #1356-1362, 1375-1376, 1388, 1394-1396, 1682-1683, 1687, 1695, 1698.

Olympics Type of 1986

1988, Feb. 12   Litho.   Perf. 12x12½

1195	A521	37c Alpine skiing	.75	.30
1196	A521	37c Curling	.75	.30
a.		Pair, #1195-1196	1.50	1.10
1197	A521	43c Figure skating	.85	.75
1198	A521	74c Luge	1.50	1.10
		Nos. 1195-1198 (4)	*3.85*	*2.45*

Exploration Type of 1986

18th Cent. explorers of the western territories: No. 1199, Anthony Henday, who traveled the Prairies in 1754 from the Hayes River to Red Deer, Alberta. No. 1200, George Vancouver (1757-1798), who circumnavigated Vancouver Is. and explored the Pacific Coast, 1792-94. No. 1201, Simon Fraser (1776-1862), fur trader who discovered and navigated the Fraser River. No. 1202, John Palliser (1807-1887), geographer who determined the topographical boundary between Canada and the US from Lake Superior to the Pacific Coast.

1988, Mar. 17   Litho.   Perf. 12½x13

1199	A518	37c multicolored	.75	.40
1200	A518	37c multicolored	.75	.40
1201	A518	37c multicolored	.75	.40
1202	A518	37c multicolored	.75	.40
a.		Block of 4, #1199-1202	3.00	2.75

The Young Reader, by Ozias Leduc A546

Photo. & Engr. with Foil Application

1988, May 20   Perf. 13x13½

1203	A546	50c multicolored	1.20	1.00

Masterpieces of Canadian art. Printed in sheets of 16.
See Nos. 1241, 1271, 1310, 1419, 1466, 1516, 1545, 1602, 1635, 1754, 1800, 1863, 1916, 1945.

Wildlife and Habitat Conservation A547

1988, June 1   Litho.   Perf. 13x13½

1204	A547	37c Duck landing	.75	.35
1205	A547	37c Moose at water hole	.75	.35
a.		Pair, #1204-1205	1.50	1.10

Grey Owl, born Archibald Belaney, (b. 1888), conservationist; Ducks Unlimited Canada, 50th anniv.

Science and Technology — A548

Inventions: No. 1206, Kerosene, invented by Abraham Gesner (1797-1864), patented in 1854. No. 1207, Marquis wheat, developed in 1908 by Charles Saunders. No. 1208, Electron microscope, developed in 1938 at the University of Toronto by James Hillier and Albert Prebus under the supervision of Eli Burton. No. 1209, Cobalt cancer therapy, introduced by Dr. Harold Johns and Atomic Energy of Canada, Ltd., in 1951.

1988, June 17   Perf. 12½x13

1206	A548	37c multicolored	.75	.35
1207	A548	37c multicolored	.75	.35
1208	A548	37c multicolored	.75	.35
1209	A548	37c multicolored	.75	.35
a.		Block of 4, #1206-1209	3.00	2.75

Intl. Entomology Congress, Vancouver A549

1988, July 4   Perf. 12

1210	A549	37c Short-tailed swallowtail	.75	.35
1211	A549	37c Northern blue	.75	.35
1212	A549	37c Macoun's Arctic	.75	.35
1213	A549	37c Canadian tiger swallowtail	.75	.35
a.		Block of 4, #1210-1213	3.00	2.75

St. John's, Newfoundland, Cent. of Incorporation — A550

1988, July 22   Perf. 13½x13

1214	A550	37c Harbor entrance, skyline	.75	.20

Canadian 4-H Council, 75th Anniv. A551

1988, Aug. 5

1215	A551	37c Motto, farm, young scientists	.75	.20

Les Forges Du St. Maurice (1738-1883), Canada's 1st Industrial Complex — A552

Litho. & Engr.

1988, Aug. 19   Perf. 13½

1216	A552	37c multicolored	.75	.20

Canadian Kennel Club, Cent. A553

1988, Aug. 26   Perf. 12½x12

1217	A553	37c Tahltan bear dog	1.10	.40
1218	A553	37c Nova Scotia duck-tolling retriever	1.10	.40
1219	A553	37c Canadian Eskimo dog	1.10	.40
1220	A553	37c Newfoundland dog	1.10	.40
a.		Block of 4, #1217-1220	4.40	3.25

A554

1988, Sept. 14   Litho.   Perf. 13½x13

1221	A554	37c multicolored	.75	.20

Sesquicentennial of the 1st baseball game played in Canada, June 4, 1838 at Beachville, Upper Canada.

A555

1988, Oct. 27   Perf. 13½

Christmas (Icons of the Eastern Church): 32c, Nativity. 37c, Conception. 43c, Virgin and Child. 74c, Virgin and Child, diff.

1222	A555	37c multicolored	.75	.20
1223	A555	43c multicolored	.85	.65

1224 A555 74c multicolored 1.60 1.10

Booklet Stamp
Size: 35½x21mm
Perf. 12½x13½

1225 A555 32c multicolored 1.10 .80
  a. Booklet pane of 10 11.00 11.00
  Nos. 1222-1225 (4) 4.30 2.75

Millennium of Christianity in the Ukraine. No. 1225 has bar code at left; for use on covers with printed postal code matrix.

Inglis and Anglican Church A556

1988, Nov. 1   **Perf. 12½x12**
1226 A556 37c multicolored .75 .25

Charles Inglis (1734-1816), Canada's 1st Anglican bishop and founder of the Kings-Edgehill School, Nova Scotia, and the University of King's College at Halifax, bicent.

Hopkins and *Canoe Manned by Voyageurs* A557

1988, Nov. 18   **Perf. 13½x13**
1227 A557 37c multicolored .75 .25

Frances Ann Hopkins (1838-1918), painter.

The Bluenose and Capt. Walters — A558

1988, Nov. 18   **Perf. 13½**
1228 A558 37c multicolored .75 .25

Angus Walters (1882-1968), mariner.

Small Craft A559

1989, Feb. 1   **Perf. 13½x13**
1229 A559 38c Chipewyan canoe .75 .35
1230 A559 38c Haida canoe .75 .35
1231 A559 38c Inuit kayak .75 .35
1232 A559 38c Micmac canoe .75 .35
  a. Block of 4, #1229-1232 3.00 2.40

See Nos. 1266-1269, 1317-1320.

Exploration Type of 1986

Explorers of the North: No. 1233, Matonabbee (c. 1737-1782), Indian guide who led 1st overland European expedition to the Arctic Ocean. No. 1234, Relics of expedition led by Sir John Franklin (1786-1847) that proved the existence of the Northwest Passage. No. 1235, Relics of the discovery of the Alberta fossil bed by geologist Joseph Burr Tyrrell (1858-1957). No. 1236, Vilhjalmur Stefansson (1879-1962), American ethnologist who discovered the last uncharted islands in the Arctic Archipelago.

1989, Mar. 22   **Perf. 12½x13**
1233 A518 38c multicolored .75 .35
1234 A518 38c multicolored .75 .35
1235 A518 38c multicolored .75 .35
1236 A518 38c multicolored .75 .35
  a. Block of 4, #1233-1236 3.00 2.40

Photography in Canada, Sesquicentennial — A560

Photographers and their work: No. 1237, William Notman (1826-1891). No. 1238, W. Hanson Boorne (1859-1945). No. 1239, Alexander Henderson (1831-1913). No. 1240, Jules-Ernest Livernois (1851-1933).

1989, June 23   **Perf. 12½x12**
1237 A560 38c multicolored .75 .35
1238 A560 38c multicolored .75 .35
1239 A560 38c multicolored .75 .35
1240 A560 38c multicolored .75 .35
  a. Block of 4, #1237-1240 3.00 2.40

Art Type of 1988

Ceremonial Frontlet (headpiece) Worn by Tsimshian Indian Chiefs, Early 20th Cent.

Litho. with Foil Application
1989, June 29   **Perf. 12½x13**
1241 A546 50c multicolored 1.25 1.00

Masterpieces of Canadian Art and opening of the Museum of Civilization.

Poets — A562

1989, July 7   **Litho.**   **Perf. 13½**
1243 A562 38c Louis Frechette (1839-1908) .75 .35
1244 A562 38c Archibald Lampman (1861-1899) .75 .35
  a. Pair, #1243-1244 1.50 1.00

Mushrooms A563

1989, Aug. 4
1245 A563 38c *Clavulinopsis fusiformis* .75 .35
1246 A563 38c *Boletus mirabilis* .75 .35
1247 A563 38c *Cantharellus cinnabarinus* .75 .35
1248 A563 38c *Morchella esculenta* .75 .35
  a. Block of 4, #1245-1248 3.00 2.60

Infantry Regiments, 75th Annivs. A564

#1249, Princess Patricia's Canadian Light Infantry. #1250, Royal 22nd Regiment.

Litho. & Engr.
1989, Sept. 8   **Perf. 13**
1249 A564 38c multicolored .80 .40
1250 A564 38c multicolored .80 .40
  a. Pair, #1249-1250 1.60 1.50

Intl. Trade A565

1989, Oct. 2   **Litho.**   **Perf. 13½x13**
1251 A565 38c multicolored .75 .30

Performing Arts — A566

1989, Oct. 4   **Perf. 13x13½**
1252 A566 38c Dancers .75 .35
1253 A566 38c Musicians .75 .35
1254 A566 38c Camera, director .75 .35
1255 A566 38c Youth and adult entertainers .75 .35
  a. Block of 4, #1252-1255 3.00 2.40

Royal Winnipeg Ballet 50th anniv. (No. 1252), Vancouver Opera 30th anniv. (No. 1253), Natl. Film Board 50th anniv. (No. 1254), and Confederation Center of the Arts, Charlottetown, P.E.I., 25th anniv. (No. 1255).

A566a

A567

Winter landscapes: 33c, *Champ-de-Mars, Winter,* 1892, by William Brymner (1855-1925). 38c, *Bend in the Gosselin River, Arthabaska,* c. 1906, by Marc-Aurele de Foy Suzor-Cote (1869-1937). 44c, *Snow II,* 1915, by Lawren S. Harris (1885-1970). 76c, *Ste. Agnes,* c. 1925-30, by Albert H. Robinson (1881-1956). Nos. 1256-1258 vert.

1989, Oct. 26
Size of 44c, 76c: 25x31mm
1256 A566a 38c multicolored .75 .25
  a. Bklt. pane of 10, #1256b 50.00 50.00
  b. Perf. 13x12½ 5.00 5.00

Perf. 13½
1257 A566a 44c multicolored .90 .65
  a. Booklet pane of 5 + label 16.00 16.00
1258 A566a 76c multicolored 1.50 1.00
  a. Booklet pane of 5 + label 30.00 30.00

Booklet Stamp
Size: 35x21mm
Perf. 12½x13½
1259 A567 33c shown 1.50 1.50
  a. Booklet pane of 10 15.00
  b. Horiz. pair, imperf btwn. *2,400.*
  Nos. 1256-1259 (4) 4.65 3.40

Christmas. No. 1259 has bar code at left; for use on covers with printed postal code matrix. Booklet panes separate easily.

Declaration of War, 1939 — A568

Political and military actions taken by Canada at the outbreak of World War II.

1989, Nov. 10   **Perf. 13½**
1260 A568 38c shown .85 .60
1261 A568 38c Army mobilization .85 .60
1262 A568 38c Navy convoy system .85 .60
1263 A568 38c Commonwealth Air Training Plan .85 .60
  a. Block of 4, #1260-1263 3.40 3.00

See Nos. 1298-1301, 1345-1348, 1448-1451, 1503-1506, 1537-1544.

Norman Bethune (1890-1939), Surgeon — A569

Litho. & Engr.
1990, Mar. 2   **Perf. 13x13½**
1264 A569 39c In Canada 1.10 .40
1265 A569 39c In China 1.10 .40
  a. Pair, #1264-1265 2.20 1.25

See People's Republic of China Nos. 2263-2264.

Small Craft Type of 1989
1990, Mar. 15   **Litho.**   **Perf. 13½x13**
1266 A559 39c Dory .80 .35
1267 A559 39c Pointer .80 .35
1268 A559 39c York boat .80 .35
1269 A559 39c North canoe .80 .35
  a. Block of 4, #1266-1269 3.20 2.75

Multicultural Heritage of Canada A570

Litho. & Engr.
1990, Apr. 5   **Perf. 13**
1270 A570 39c multicolored .80 .20
  a. Black (inscriptions) omitted *1,200.*

Art Type of 1988
Painting: *The West Wind,* by Tom Thomson.

Litho. with Foil Application
1990, May 3   **Perf. 12½x13**
1271 A546 50c multicolored 1.25 1.10

Masterpieces of Canadian Art.

Mail Trucks
A571   A572

1990, May 3   **Litho.**   **Perf. 13½**
Booklet Stamps
1272 A571 39c multicolored .90 .60
1273 A572 39c multicolored .90 .60
  a. Bklt. pane of 8+printed margin (4 each #1272-1273) 7.25
  b. Bklt. pane of 9+3 labels, printed margin (5 #1272, 4 #1273) 12.50

Dolls A573

1990, June 8   **Perf. 12½x12**
1274 A573 39c Native .80 .35
1275 A573 39c Settlers .80 .35
1276 A573 39c 4 Commercial .80 .35
1277 A573 39c 5 Commercial .80 .35
  a. Block of 4, #1274-1277 3.20 2.75

Natl. Flag, 25th Anniv. — A574

1990, June 29 — Perf. 13x12½

1278 A574 39c Flag, fire-works — .80 .20
a. Silver (inscriptions) omitted — 2,000.

Printed in sheets of 16.

Prehistoric Life A575

Litho. & Engr.
1990, July 12 — Perf. 13x13½
1279 A575 39c Trilobite — .80 .35
1280 A575 39c Sea scorpion — .80 .35
1281 A575 39c Fossil algae — .80 .35
1282 A575 39c Soft invertebrate — .80 .35
a. Block of 4, #1279-1282 — 3.20 2.75

See Nos. 1306-1309.

Canadian Forests A576

1990, Aug. 7 Litho. — Perf. 12½x13
1283 A576 39c Acadian — .80 .30
a. Pane of 4 — 10.00 8.00
1284 A576 39c Great Lakes-St. Lawrence — .80 .30
a. Pane of 4 — 10.00 8.00
1285 A576 39c Coast — .80 .30
a. Pane of 4 — 10.00 8.00
1286 A576 39c Boreal — .80 .30
a. Block of 4, #1283-1286 — 3.20 2.75
b. Pane of 4 — 10.00 8.00

Panes of four sold for $1 each through Petro-Canada gas stations, and for full face value through the philatelic bureau. Issue date: Sept. 7.

Weather Observations in Canada, 150th Anniv. — A577

1990, Sept. 5 — Perf. 12½x13½
1287 A577 39c multicolored — .80 .20

The left and right margin singles of No. 1287 differ slightly in design from stamps from columns 2-4, due to the nature of the continuous cloud design across the pane.

Intl. Literacy Year — A578

1990, Sept. 7 — Perf. 13½x13
1288 A578 39c multicolored — .80 .20

Legendary Creatures A579

1990, Oct. 1 — Perf. 12½x13½
1289 A579 39c Sasquatch — .90 .75
1290 A579 39c Kraken — .90 .75
1291 A579 39c Werewolf — .90 .75

1292 A579 39c Ogopogo — .90 .75
a. Block of 4, #1289-1292 — 3.60 3.00
b. As "a," imperf. — 2,000.

Perf. 12½x12
1289a	A579	39c	12.50	4.00
1290a	A579	39c	12.50	4.00
1291a	A579	39c	12.50	4.00
1292c	A579	39c	12.50	4.00
d.	Block of 4, #1289a-1292c		50.00	30.00

Agnes Campbell Macphail (1890-1954), First Woman Member of Parliament — A580

1990, Oct. 9 — Perf. 13x13½
1293 A580 39c multicolored — .80 .20

Virgin Mary with Christ Child and St. John the Baptist by Norval Morrisseau A581

Rebirth by Jackson Beardy A582

Indian Art: 45c, Sculpture of Mother and Child by an Inuit artist. 78c, Children of the Raven by Bill Reid.

1990, Oct. 25 — Perf. 13½
1294 A581 39c multicolored — .85 .20
a. Booklet pane of 10 — 8.50
1295 A581 45c multicolored — 1.00 .70
a. Bklt. pane of 5 + label — 5.00 5.00
1296 A581 78c multicolored — 1.75 1.10
a. Bklt. pane of 5 + label — 8.75 7.75

Booklet Stamp
Perf. 12½x13 on 2 or 3 Sides
1297 A582 34c multicolored — .85 .40
a. Booklet pane of 10 — 8.50
Nos. 1294-1297 (4) — 4.45 2.40

Christmas. No. 1297 has bar code at left; for use on covers with printed postal code matrix.

World War II Type of 1989
1990, Nov. 9 — Perf. 12½x12
1298 A568 39c Home front — .90 .60
1299 A568 39c Communal war efforts — .90 .60
1300 A568 39c Food production — .90 .60
1301 A568 39c Science and war — .90 .60
a. Block of 4, #1298-1301 — 3.60 3.25

A583

Physicians: No. 1302, Jennie Trout (1841-1921), first licensed Canadian woman physician. No. 1303, Wilder Penfield (1891-1976), neurosurgeon. No. 1304, Sir Frederick Banting (1891-1941), discoverer of insulin. No. 1305, Harold Griffith (1894-1985), anesthesiologist.

1991, Mar. 15 — Perf. 13½
1302 A583 40c multicolored — .80 .35
1303 A583 40c multicolored — .80 .35
1304 A583 40c multicolored — .80 .35
1305 A583 40c multicolored — .80 .35
a. Block of 4, #1302-1305 — 3.20 2.75

Prehistoric Life Type of 1990
1991, Apr. 5 — Perf. 12½x13½
1306 A575 40c Microfossils — .80 .35
1307 A575 40c Early tree — .80 .35
1308 A575 40c Early fish — .80 .35
1309 A575 40c Land reptile — .80 .35
a. Block of 4, #1306-1309 — 3.20 2.75

Art Type of 1988
Forest, British Columbia by Emily Carr.

Litho. with Foil Application
1991, May 7 — Perf. 12½x13
1310 A546 50c multicolored — 1.25 1.10

Masterpieces of Canadian Art.

A584

Public Gardens: #1311, Butchart Gardens, Victoria, B.C. #1312, Intl. Peace Garden, Boissevain, Manitoba. #1313, Royal Botanical Gardens, Hamilton, Ontario. #1314, Montreal Botanical Gardens. #1315, Halifax Public Gardens, Nova Scotia.

Booklet Stamps
1991, May 22 Litho. — Perf. 13x12½
1311 A584 40c multicolored — .90 .40
1312 A584 40c multicolored — .90 .40
1313 A584 40c multicolored — .90 .40
1314 A584 40c multicolored — .90 .40
1315 A584 40c multicolored — .90 .40
a. Strip of 5, #1311-1315 — 4.50 3.75
b. Bklt. pane, 2 each #1311-1315 — 9.00

Canada Day — A585

1991, June 28 — Perf. 13½x13
1316 A585 40c multicolored — .80 .20

Small Craft Type of 1989
1991, July 18
1317 A559 40c Verchere rowboat — .80 .35
1318 A559 40c Touring kayak — .80 .35
1319 A559 40c Sailing dinghy — .80 .35
1320 A559 40c Cedar strip canoe — .80 .35
a. Block of 4, #1317-1320 — 3.20 2.75

Canadian Rivers — A586

Booklet Stamps
1991, Aug. 20 — Perf. 13x12½
1321 A586 40c South Nahanni — .85 .35
1322 A586 40c Athabasca — .85 .35
1323 A586 40c Boundary Waters-Voyageur Waterway — .85 .35
1324 A586 40c Jacques Cartier — .85 .35
1325 A586 40c Main — .85 .35
a. Strip of 5, #1321-1325 — 4.25 3.25
b. Bklt. pane, 2 each #1321-1325 — 8.50

See #1408-1412, 1485-1489, 1511-1515.

Arrival of Ukrainians, Cent. — A587

Paintings by William Kurelek.

1991, Aug. 29 — Perf. 13½x13
1326 A587 40c Leaving homeland — .80 .35
1327 A587 40c Winter in Canada — .80 .35
1328 A587 40c Clearing land — .80 .35
1329 A587 40c Growing wheat — .80 .35
a. Block of 4, #1326-1329 — 3.20 2.75

Dangerous Public Service Occupations A588

1991, Sept. 23 — Perf. 13½
1330 A588 40c Ski Patrol — 1.25 .35
1331 A588 40c Police — 1.25 .35
1332 A588 40c Fire fighters — 1.25 .35
1333 A588 40c Search & Rescue — 1.25 .35
a. Block of 4, #1330-1333 — 5.00 2.75

Folktales A589

1991, Oct. 1 Litho. — Perf. 13½x12½
1334 A589 40c Witched Canoe — .85 .35
1335 A589 40c Orphan Boy — .85 .35
1336 A589 40c Chinook Wind — .85 .35
1337 A589 40c Buried Treasure — .85 .35
a. Block of 4, #1334-1337 — 3.40 2.75

Queen's University, Kingston, Ont., Sesqui. — A590

1991, Oct. 16
1338 A590 40c multicolored — .80 .55
a. Bklt. pane of 10 + 2 labels — 8.00

A591

Santa Claus A592

1991, Oct. 23 — Perf. 13½
1339 A591 40c At fireplace — .80 .20
a. Booklet pane of 10 — 8.00
1340 A591 46c With white horse, tree — .90 .50
a. Bklt. pane of 5 + label — 4.50 3.50
1341 A591 80c Sinterklaas, girl — 1.60 1.00
a. Bklt. pane of 5 + label — 8.00 8.00

Booklet Stamp
Perf. 12½x13 on 2 or 3 Sides

1342	A592	35c With punchbowl	.80	.25
a.		Booklet pane of 10	8.00	
		Nos. 1339-1342 (4)	4.10	1.95

Christmas. No. 1342 has bar code at left; for use on covers with printed postal code matrix.

Basketball, Cent. — A593

1991, Oct. 25 — Perf. 13x13½

1343	A593	40c multicolored	.80	.20

Souvenir Sheet

1344		Pane of 3	5.75	5.75
a.	A593	40c like #1343	1.30	1.30
b.	A593	46c Player shooting, diff.	1.75	1.75
c.	A593	80c Player dribbling	2.60	2.60

No. 1344a has 3-line inscription.

World War II Type of 1989
1991, Nov. 8 — Perf. 13½

1345	A568	40c Women's Armed Forces	.80	.55
1346	A568	40c War industry	.80	.55
1347	A568	40c Cadets and veterans	.80	.55
1348	A568	40c Defense of Hong Kong	.80	.55
a.		Block or strip of 4, #1345-1348	3.20	2.75

Types of 1987-91 and

Edible Berries — A594

Hills — A595

Prairie A596

Building A597

Trees — A598

Flag — A599

1991-98 — Litho. — Perf. 13x13½

1349	A594	1c Blueberry	.20	.20
1350	A594	2c Wild strawberry	.20	.20
1351	A594	3c Black crowberry	.20	.20
1352	A594	5c Rose hip	.20	.20
1353	A594	6c Black raspberry	.20	.20
1354	A594	10c Kinnikinnick	.20	.20
a.		Horiz. pair, imperf at sides and bottom	1,250.	
1355	A594	25c Saskatoon berry	.45	.20

Perf. 13½x13

1356	A595	42c multicolored	.85	.20
a.		Booklet pane of 10	8.50	
b.		Bklt. pane of 50 + 2 labels	95.00	80.00
c.		Bklt. pane of 25 + 2 labels	21.00	16.00
d.		Vert. pair, imperf between	1,000.	

Perf. 13x13½

1357	A536	42c multicolored	.85	.20
a.		Booklet pane of 10	8.50	7.50

1358	A536	43c multicolored	1.00	.20
a.		Booklet pane of 10	10.00	9.00

Perf. 13½x13

1359	A596	43c multicolored	1.00	.20
a.		Booklet pane of 10	10.00	7.50
b.		Bklt. pane of 25 + 2 labels	25.00	
c.		Perf. 14½	1.25	.20
d.		As "c," bklt. pane of 10	12.50	9.00
e.		As "c," bklt. pane of 25 + 2 labels	32.50	25.00
f.		Vert. pair, imperf between (from #1359e)	900.00	

Perf. 13x13½

1360	A536	45c multicolored	.90	.20
a.		Booklet pane of 10	9.00	7.50
		Complete booklet, #1360a	9.00	

Perf. 14½

1361	A597	45c multicolored	.90	.20
a.		Booklet pane of 10	9.00	
		Complete booklet, #1361a	9.00	
b.		Bklt. pane of 25 + 2 labels	30.00	
		Complete booklet, #1361b	30.00	
c.		Perf. 13½x13	.90	.20
d.		As "c," bklt. pane of 10	9.00	
		Complete booklet, #1361d	9.00	
e.		As "c," bklt. pane of 25 + 2 labels	22.50	
		Complete booklet, #1361e	22.50	

Perf. 13x13½
Size: 16x20mm

1362	A597	45c multicolored	.90	.30
a.		Booklet pane of 10	9.00	
		Complete booklet, #1362a	9.00	
b.		Booklet pane of 30	27.50	
		Complete booklet, #1362b	27.50	

No. 1361 is 17x21mm.

Perf. 13

1363	A598	48c McIntosh apple	1.00	.25
a.		Perf. 14½x14 on 3 sides	1.75	.40
b.		As "a," bklt. pane of 5 + label	8.75	7.00
1364	A598	49c Delicious apple	1.00	.25
a.		Perf. 14½x14	3.00	.35
b.		As "a," bklt. pane of 5 + 1 label	15.00	6.50
c.		Booklet pane of 5 + label	14.00	11.00
1365	A598	50c Snow apple	1.00	.30
a.		Booklet pane of 5 + label	7.00	5.75
b.		Perf. 14½x14	2.50	.45
c.		As "b," bklt. pane of 5 + label	14.00	12.50
1366	A598	52c Gravenstein apple	1.60	.40
a.		Booklet pane of 5 + label	8.00	6.00
		Complete booklet, #1366a	8.50	
b.		Perf. 14½x14	2.50	.60
c.		As "b," bklt. pane of 5 + label	12.50	11.00
		Complete booklet, #1366c	13.00	
1367	A598	65c Black walnut	1.30	.40
1368	A598	67c Beaked hazelnut	1.35	.40
1369	A598	69c Shagbark hickory	1.40	.35
1370	A598	71c American chestnut	1.40	.35
a.		Perf. 14½x14	60.00	3.75
1371	A598	84c Stanley plum	1.70	.40
a.		Perf. 14½x14 on 3 sides	2.50	.60
b.		As "a," bklt. pane of 5 + label	12.50	10.00
1372	A598	86c Bartlett pear	1.90	.60
a.		Perf. 14½x14	3.25	1.50
b.		As "a," bklt. pane of 5 + 1 label	16.00	12.50
c.		Booklet pane of 5 + label	19.00	16.00
1373	A598	88c Westcot apricot	1.75	.55
a.		Booklet pane of 5 + label	12.00	8.00
b.		Perf. 14½x14	5.00	2.25
c.		As "b," bklt. pane of 5 + label	25.00	15.00
1374	A598	90c Elberta peach	1.80	.60
a.		Booklet pane of 5 + label	10.00	8.00
		Complete booklet, #1374a	10.50	
b.		Perf. 14½x14	4.50	1.60
c.		As "b," bklt. pane of 5+label	22.50	14.00
		Complete booklet, #1374c	23.50	

Size: 48x40mm
Litho. & Engr.
Perf. 14½x14

1375	A540	$1 Court House, Yorkton	2.00	.60
a.		Dk bl (inscriptions) omitted	1,500.	
b.		Perf 13½x13	2.00	.60
c.		As "b," dk bl (inscriptions) omitted	1,500.	
1376	A540	$2 Provincial Normal School, Truro	4.00	1.10
a.		Dk grn (inscriptions) omitted	1,200.	
b.		Engr. inscriptions inverted	10,500.	
c.		Perf. 13½x13	4.50	1.10

d.		As "c," dk grn (inscriptions) omitted	1,600.	

Perf. 13½x13

1378	A540	$5 Carnegie Public Library, Victoria	10.00	2.50
		Nos. 1349-1378 (29)	41.25	11.80

Self-Adhesive
Die Cut
Imperf
Booklet Stamps

1388	A543	42c Flag, mountains	1.20	.80
a.		Booklet of 12	16.00	
1389	A543	43c Flag, estuary shore	1.20	.60
a.		Booklet of 12	16.00	

Nos. 1388a, 1389a issued on peelable paper backing serving as booklet cover and sold for $5.25.

Coil Stamps
Perf. 10 Horiz.
Engr.

1394	A599	42c red	.85	.20
a.		Imperf., pair	180.00	
1395	A599	43c olive green	.85	.20
a.		Imperf., pair	160.00	
1396	A599	45c blue green	.90	.20
a.		Imperf., pair	160.00	
		Nos. 1394-1396 (3)	2.60	.60

Nos. 1349-1363 are known imperf from printer's waste. Items exist imperf in wrong colors and with wrong denominations. These may be essays or printer's waste.

Issued: 1c-25c, 8/5/92; #1356-1357, 1394, 48c, 65c, 84c, 12/27/91; #1388, 1/28/92; #1358-1359, 1364, 1368, 1372, 1395, 12/30/92; #1389, 2/15/93; #1359c-1359e, 1/18/94; #1364c, 1372c, 1/7/94; 50c, 69c, 88c, 2/25/94; $1, $2, 2/21/94; #1375b, 1376c, 2/20/95; #1365c, 1373c, 3/27/95; #1360-1361, 1396, 52c, 71c, 90c, 7/31/95; $5, 2/29/96; #1362, 2/2/98.

1992 Winter Olympics, Albertville A601

Booklet Stamps
1992, Feb. 7 — Litho. — Perf. 12½x13

1399	A601	42c Ski jumping	.85	.40
1400	A601	42c Pairs figure skating	.85	.40
1401	A601	42c Hockey	.85	.40
1402	A601	42c Bobsledding	.85	.40
1403	A601	42c Alpine skiing	.85	.40
a.		Strip of 5, #1399-1403	4.25	3.75
b.		Bklt. pane of 2 each #1399-1403	8.50	8.50

See Nos. 1414-1418.

City of Montreal, 350th Anniv. — A602

Designs: No. 1404, City of Montreal, modern times. No. 1405, Early settlement of Montreal (Ville-Marie). 48c, Jacques Cartier's chart of Canada, snowshoe, ship's mast. 84c, World map, nocturnal and Aztec calendar stone.

1992, Mar. 25 — Perf. 13½

1404	A602	42c multicolored	.85	.35
1405	A602	42c multicolored	.85	.35
a.		Pair, #1404-1405	1.70	.90
1406	A602	48c multicolored	.95	.75
1407	A602	84c multicolored	1.70	1.00
a.		Souvenir sheet of 4, #1404-1407	4.50	4.50
		Nos. 1404-1407 (4)	4.35	2.45

Discovery of America, 500th anniv. (#1407). Nos. 1404-1405 printed checkerwise. No. 1407a with engraved signatures in margin was produced in limited quantities for World Philatelic Youth Exhibition catalogue which sold for $12.

Canadian Rivers Type of 1991
Booklet Stamps
1992, Apr. 22 — Perf. 12½

1408	A586	42c Margaree	.90	.40
1409	A586	42c West (Eliot)	.90	.40
1410	A586	42c Ottawa	.90	.40

1411	A586	42c Niagara	.90	.40
1412	A586	42c South Saskatchewan	.90	.40
a.		Strip of 5 #1408-1412	4.50	4.00
b.		Bklt. pane, 2 each #1408-1412	9.00	

Nos. 1408-1412 are horiz.

Alaska Highway, 50th Anniv. — A603

1992, May 15 — Perf. 13½

1413	A603	42c multicolored	.85	.25

1992 Olympic Games Type
1992, June 15 — Perf. 12½x13

1414	A601	42c Gymnastics	.85	.40
1415	A601	42c Running	.85	.40
1416	A601	42c Diving	.85	.40
1417	A601	42c Cycling	.85	.40
1418	A601	42c Swimming	.85	.40
a.		Strip of 5, #1414-1418	4.25	4.25
b.		Bklt. pane, 2 each #1414-1418	8.50	

1992 Summer Olympics, Barcelona. Stamps in bottom row of #1418b are in different sequence than those in #1418a.

Art Type of 1988

Painting: Red Nasturtiums, by David Milne.

Litho. with Foil Application
1992, June 29

1419	A546	50c multicolored	1.10	.85

Masterpieces in Canadian Art.

Miniature Sheet

Canada Day A604

1992, June 29

1420	A604	42c Nova Scotia	1.75	1.75
1421	A604	42c Ontario	1.75	1.75
1422	A604	42c Prince Edward Island	1.75	1.75
1423	A604	42c New Brunswick	1.75	1.75
1424	A604	42c Quebec	1.75	1.75
1425	A604	42c Saskatchewan	1.75	1.75
1426	A604	42c Manitoba	1.75	1.75
1427	A604	42c Northwest Territories	1.75	1.75
1428	A604	42c Alberta	1.75	1.75
1429	A604	42c British Columbia	1.75	1.75
1430	A604	42c Yukon	1.75	1.75
1431	A604	42c Newfoundland	1.75	1.75
a.		Pane of 12, #1420-1431 + 13 labels	21.00	21.00

Canadian Folklore — A605

Legendary heroes: No. 1432, Jerry Potts, guide, interpreter. No. 1433, Captain William Jackman, rescuer. No. 1434, Laura Secord, patriot. No. 1435, Jos Monferrand, lumberjack.

1992, Sept. 8 — Perf. 12½

1432	A605	42c multicolored	.85	.35
1433	A605	42c multicolored	.85	.35
1434	A605	42c multicolored	.85	.35
1435	A605	42c multicolored	.85	.35
a.		Block of 4, #1432-1435	3.50	2.75

Minerals
A606

1992, Sept. 21

1436	A606 42c Copper	1.10	.40
1437	A606 42c Sodalite	1.10	.40
1438	A606 42c Gold	1.10	.40
1439	A606 42c Galena	1.10	.40
1440	A606 42c Grossular	1.10	.40
a.	Strip of 5, #1436-1440	5.50	4.75
b.	Bklt. pane, 2 each #1436-1440	11.00	

Canada in Space
A607

1992, Oct. 1   *Perf. 13*

1441	A607 42c Anik E2 satellite	.85	.85
a.	Silver omitted	3,000.	2,000.

Size: 32x26mm

1442	A607 42c Earth, space shuttle	1.25	1.25
a.	Pair, #1441-1442	2.10	2.10
b.	As "a," hologram omitted on #1442	2,000.	

No. 1442 has a holographic image. Soaking in water may affect the hologram.

Natl. Hockey League, 75th Anniv. A608

Designs: No. 1443, Skates, stick, puck, photograph from the early years (1917-1942). No. 1444, Photograph, team emblems from the six-team years (1942-1967). No. 1445, Goalie's mask, gloves, photograph from the expansion years (1967-1992).

Booklet Stamps

1992, Oct. 9   *Perf. 13x12½*

1443	A608 42c multicolored	.85	.25
a.	Bklt. pane of 8 + 4 labels	7.00	
1444	A608 42c multicolored	.85	.25
a.	Bklt. pane of 8 + 4 labels	7.00	
1445	A608 42c multicolored	.85	.25
a.	Bklt. pane of 9 + 3 labels	7.75	
	Nos. 1443-1445 (3)	2.55	.75

A609

No. 1446, Order of Canada, 25th anniv. No. 1447, Daniel Roland Michener (1900-1991), Governor General.

1992, Oct. 21   *Perf. 12½*

1446	42c multicolored	.85	.25
1447	42c multicolored	.85	.35
a.	A609 Pair, #1446-1447	1.70	1.25

Nos. 1446-1447 printed in panes of 25 containing 16 #1446 and 9 #1447.

World War II Type of 1989

1992, Nov. 10   *Perf. 13½*

1448	A568 42c War reporting	.85	.45
1449	A568 42c Newfoundland air bases	.85	.45
1450	A568 42c Raid on Dieppe	.85	.45
1451	A568 42c U-boats offshore	.85	.45
a.	Block or strip of 4, #1448-1451	3.40	2.75

Santa Claus
A612

A611

1992, Nov. 13   *Perf. 12½*

1452	A611 42c Jouluvana	.85	.20
a.	Perf. 13½	1.00	.25
b.	As "a," booklet pane of 10	10.00	6.00

Perf. 13½

1453	A611 48c La Befana	1.20	.80
a.	Booklet pane of 5 + label	6.00	5.25
1454	A611 84c Weihnachtsmann	1.70	.75
a.	Booklet pane of 5 + label	8.50	6.50

Booklet Stamp
Perf. 12½x13

1455	A612 37c Santa Claus	.85	.85
a.	Booklet pane of 10	8.50	
	Nos. 1452-1455 (4)	4.60	2.60

Christmas. No. 1455 has bar code at left; for use on covers with printed postal code matrix.

A613

Canadian Women: No. 1456, Adelaide Sophia Hoodless (1857-1910), founder of Victorian Order of Nurses. No. 1457, Marie-Josephine Gerin-Lajoie (1890-1971), founder of Notre-Dame du Bon Conseil Institute. No. 1458, Pitseolak Ashoona (c. 1904-83), Inuit graphic artist. No. 1459, Helen Alice Kinnear (1894-1970), first woman appointed King's Counsel and first federally appointed woman judge.

1993, Mar. 8   *Perf. 12½*

1456	A613 43c multicolored	.85	.35
1457	A613 43c multicolored	.85	.35
1458	A613 43c multicolored	.85	.35
1459	A613 43c multicolored	.85	.35
a.	Block or strip of 4, #1456-1459	3.40	2.75

Natl. Council of Women of Canada (NCWC), and Natl. office of YWCA, cent.

Stanley Cup, Cent. — A614

1993, Apr. 16   *Perf. 13½*

1460	A614 43c multicolored	.85	.25

Handcrafted Textiles — A615

#1461, Coverlet, New Brunswick. #1462, Pieced quilt, Ontario. #1463, Doukhobor bedcover, Saskatchewan. #1464,

Kwakwaka'wakw ceremonial robe, British Columbia. #1465, Boutonne coverlet, Quebec.

Booklet Stamps
Perf. 13x12½ on 3 Sides

1993, Apr. 30

1461	A615 43c multicolored	.85	.40
1462	A615 43c multicolored	.85	.40
1463	A615 43c multicolored	.85	.40
1464	A615 43c multicolored	.85	.40
1465	A615 43c multicolored	.85	.40
a.	Strip of 5, #1461-1465	4.25	3.50
b.	Bklt. pane, 2 ea #1461-1465	8.50	

Stamps in bottom row of #1465b are in different sequence than those in #1465a.

Art Type of 1988

Painting: Drawing for The Owl, by Kenojuak Ashevak.

Litho. with Foil Application

1993, May 17   *Perf. 12½x13½*

1466	A546 86c multicolored	1.75	1.10

Intl. Year of Indigenous People.

Historic Canadian Pacific Railway Hotels
A616

#1467, Empress, Victoria, B.C. #1468, Banff Springs, Banff, Alberta. #1469, Royal York, Toronto, Ont. #1470, Chateau Frontenac, Quebec. #1471, Algonquin, St. Andrews, N.B.

Booklet Stamps

1993, June 14   *Perf. 13½ on 3 Sides*

1467	A616 43c multicolored	1.00	.65
1468	A616 43c multicolored	1.00	.65
1469	A616 43c multicolored	1.00	.65
1470	A616 43c multicolored	1.00	.65
1471	A616 43c multicolored	1.00	.65
a.	Strip of 5, #1467-1471	5.00	4.00
b.	Booklet pane, 2 #1471a	10.00	

Opening of Chateau Frontenac, cent.

Miniature Sheet

Canada Day
A617

Provincial and Territorial Parks: No. 1472, Algonquin, Ontario. No. 1473, De la Gaspesie, Quebec. No. 1474, Cedar Dunes, Prince Edward Island. No. 1475, Cape St. Mary's Seabird Ecological Reserve, Newfoundland. No. 1476, Mount Robson, British Columbia. No. 1477, Writing-On-Stone, Alberta. No. 1478, Spruce Woods, Manitoba. No. 1479, Herschel Island, Yukon. No. 1480, Cypress Hills, Saskatchewan. No. 1481, The Rocks, New Brunswick. No. 1482, Blomidon, Nova Scotia. No. 1483, Katannilik, Northwest Territories.

1993, June 30   *Perf. 13*

1472	A617 43c multicolored	1.10	1.00
1473	A617 43c multicolored	1.10	1.00
1474	A617 43c multicolored	1.10	1.00
1475	A617 43c multicolored	1.10	1.00
1476	A617 43c multicolored	1.10	1.00
1477	A617 43c multicolored	1.10	1.00
1478	A617 43c multicolored	1.10	1.00
1479	A617 43c multicolored	1.10	1.00
1480	A617 43c multicolored	1.10	1.00
1481	A617 43c multicolored	1.10	1.00
1482	A617 43c multicolored	1.10	1.00
1483	A617 43c multicolored	1.10	1.00
a.	Pane of 12, #1472-1483	13.50	13.50

Algonquin Park, centennial.

City of Toronto, Bicent. — A618

1993, Aug. 6   *Perf. 13½x13*

1484	A618 43c multicolored	.85	.25

Canadian Rivers Type of 1991
Booklet Stamps

1993, Aug. 10   *Perf. 13x12½*

1485	A586 43c Fraser	.85	.40
1486	A586 43c Yukon	.85	.40
1487	A586 43c Red	.85	.40
1488	A586 43c St. Lawrence	.85	.40
1489	A586 43c St. John	.85	.40
a.	Strip of 5, #1485-1489	4.25	4.00
b.	Bklt. pane, 2 each #1485-1489	8.50	

Miniature Sheet

Historic Automobiles — A619

a, 1867 H.S. Taylor Steam Buggy. b, 1908 Russell Model L Touring Car. c, 1914 Ford Model T Open Touring Car. d, 1950 Studebaker Champion Deluxe Starlight Coupe. e, 1928 McLaughlin-Buick Model 28-496 Special Car. f, 1923-24 Gray-Dort 25-SM Luxury Sedan.

1993, Aug. 23   *Perf. 12½x13*

1490	A619 Pane of 6	8.00	8.00
a.-b.	43c any single, 35x22mm	.90	.90
c.-d.	49c any single, 43x22mm	1.10	1.10
e.-f.	86c any single, 51x22mm	1.75	1.75

See Nos. 1527, 1552, 1604-1605.

Folk Songs
A620

Designs: No. 1491, The Alberta Homesteader, Alberta. No. 1492, Les Raftmans, Quebec. No. 1493, I'se the B'y That Builds the Boat, Newfoundland. No. 1494, Onkwa:ri tenhanonniahkwe, Kanien'kehaka (Mohawk).

1993, Sept. 7   *Perf. 12½*

1491	A620 43c multicolored	.85	.35
1492	A620 43c multicolored	.85	.35
1493	A620 43c multicolored	.85	.35
1494	A620 43c multicolored	.85	.35
a.	Block of 4, #1491-1494	3.40	2.75

Dinosaurs — A621

1993, Oct. 1   *Perf. 13½*

1495	A621 43c Massospondylus	.85	.35
1496	A621 43c Styracosaurus	.85	.35
1497	A621 43c Albertosaurus	.85	.35
1498	A621 43c Platecarpus	.85	.35
a.	Block or strip of 4, #1495-1498	3.40	2.75

See Nos. 1529-1532.

Santa Claus
A623

1993, Nov. 4

1499	A622	43c	Swięty Mikolaj	.85	.20
a.			Booklet pane of 10	8.50	5.75
b.			Horiz. pair, imperf between	*1,500.*	
1500	A622	49c	Ded Moroz	1.00	.45
a.			Booklet pane of 5 + label	5.00	4.50
1501	A622	86c	Father Christmas, Australia	1.75	.55
a.			Booklet pane of 5 + label	8.75	7.50

Booklet Stamp
Perf. 13

1502	A623	38c	Santa Claus	.80	.60
a.			Booklet pane of 10	8.00	
			Nos. 1499-1502 (4)	4.40	1.80

Christmas. No. 1502 has bar code at left; for use on covers with printed postal code matrix.

World War II Type of 1989
1993, Nov. 8 — *Perf. 13½*

1503	A568	43c	Aid to Allies	.85	.50
1504	A568	43c	Bomber forces	.85	.50
1505	A568	43c	Battle of the Atlantic	.85	.50
1506	A568	43c	Italian campaign	.85	.50
a.			Block or strip of 4, #1503-1506	3.40	3.00

Greetings — A624

Design: No. 1508, "Canada" at right.

1994, Jan. 28 — *Die Cut*

1507	A624	43c	multicolored	1.10	.75
1508	A624	43c	multicolored	1.10	.75
a.			Bklt pane, 5 ea #1507-1508	11.00	

No. 1508a also contains 35 self-adhesive greetings labels in seven designs that complete the design when placed in the central circle of Nos. 1507-1508.
See Nos. 1568-1569, 1600-1601.

Jeanne Sauvé (1922-93), Governor General — A625

1994, Mar. 8 — *Perf. 12½x13*

1509	A625	43c + label, multi	.85	.30
a.		Block or horiz. strip of 4 + 4 labels	3.40	2.75

No. 1509 issued se-tenant with label in sheets of 20 + 20 labels in four designs. In alternating rows, labels appear on left or right side of stamp.

T. Eaton Company, 125th Anniv. — A626

1994, Mar. 17 — *Perf. 13½x13*

1510	A626	43c	multicolored	.85	.30
a.			Booklet pane of 10 + 2 labels	8.50	

Canadian Rivers Type of 1991
Booklet Stamps
1994, Apr. 22 — *Perf. 13½*

1511	A586	43c	Saguenay	1.10	.50
1512	A586	43c	French	1.10	.50
1513	A586	43c	Mackenzie	1.10	.50
1514	A586	43c	Churchill	1.10	.50
1515	A586	43c	Columbia	1.10	.50
a.			Strip of 5, #1511-1515	5.50	4.00
b.			Bklt. pane, 2 ea #1511-1515	11.00	10.00

Art Type of 1988
Vera, by Frederick H. Varley (1881-1969).

Litho. with Foil Application
1994, May 6 — *Perf. 14x14½*

1516	A546	88c	multicolored	1.75	1.20

XV Commonwealth Games, Victoria, BC — A627

1994 — **Litho.** — *Perf. 14*

1517	A627	43c	Lawn bowls	.85	.25
1518	A627	43c	Lacrosse	.85	.25
a.			Pair, #1517-1518	1.70	1.20
1519	A627	43c	Wheelchair marathon	.85	.25
1520	A627	43c	High jump	.85	.25
a.			Pair, #1519-1520	1.70	1.20
1521	A627	50c	Diving	1.00	.75
a.			Gold ("CANADA 50") omitted	*1,600.*	
1522	A627	88c	Cycling	1.75	1.00
a.			Gold ("CANADA 88") omitted	*2,000.*	
			Nos. 1517-1522 (6)	6.15	2.75

Certificates of authenticity recommended for Nos. 1521a and 1522a.
Issued: #1517-1518, 5/20; #1519-1522, 8/5.

Souvenir Sheet

Intl. Year of the Family — A628

Designs: a, Mother and infant. b, Adults, children playing. c, Elderly woman, child. d, Adults, children in class. e, Judge, health care worker, child.

1994, June 2

1523	A628	Pane of 5	4.25	4.25
a.-e.		43c any single	.85	.55

Canada Day
A629

Maple trees: a, Big leaf. b, Sugar. c, Silver. d, Striped. e, Norway. f, Manitoba. g, Black. h, Douglas. i, Mountain. j, Vine. k, Hedge. l, Red.

1994, June 30 — *Perf. 13x13½*

1524	A629	Pane of 12	10.50	10.50
a.-l.		43c any single	.85	.85

Billy Bishop (1894-1956), Fighter Ace — A630

Design: No. 1526, Mary Travers, "La Bolduc" (1894-1941), folk singer.

1994, Aug. 12 — *Perf. 13*

1525	A630	43c	multicolored	.85	.35
1526	A630	43c	multicolored	.85	.35
a.			Pair, #1525-1526	1.70	1.20

Historic Vehicles Type of 1993
Miniature Sheet

Designs: a, 1942 Ford F60L-AMB military ambulance. b, 1925 REO Speed Wagon Police Wagon. c, 1927 Sicard Snow Remover/Snowblower. d, 1936 Bickle Chieftain Fire Engine. e, 1894 Ottawa Car Company Streetcar. f, 1950 Motor Coach Industries Courier 50 Skyview bus.

1994, Aug. 19 — *Perf. 12½x13*

1527		Pane of 6	8.00	8.00
a.-b.	A619	43c any single	.85	.85
c.-d.	A619	50c any single	1.00	1.00
e.-f.	A619	88c any single	1.90	1.90

ICAO, 50th Anniv.
A632

1994, Sept. 16 — *Perf. 13*

1528	A632	43c	multicolored	1.10	.25

Dinosaur Type of 1993

Prehistoric animals: No. 1529, Coryphodon. No. 1530, Megacerops. No. 1531, Short-faced bear. No. 1532, Woolly mammoth.

1994, Sept. 26

1529	A621	43c	multicolored	.85	.30
1530	A621	43c	multicolored	.85	.30
1531	A621	43c	multicolored	.85	.30
1532	A621	43c	multicolored	.85	.30
a.			Block or strip of 4, #1529-1532	3.40	2.75

Family Singing Carols
A633

Soloist
A634

1994, Nov. 3 — *Perf. 13½*

1533	A633	43c	multicolored	.85	.20
a.			Booklet pane of 10	8.50	7.50
1534	A633	50c	Choir, vert.	1.00	.55
a.			Booklet pane of 5 + label	5.00	4.50
1535	A633	88c	Caroling, vert.	1.75	1.00
a.			Booklet pane of 5 + label	8.75	7.50

Booklet Stamp
Perf. 13

1536	A634	38c	multicolored	.80	.45
			Nos. 1533-1536 (4)	4.40	2.20

Christmas. No. 1536 has bar code at left; for use on covers with printed postal code matrix.

Examples exist of 52c and 90c denominations with the same designs as Nos. 1534 (52c) and 1535 (90c). These were prepared in advance in anticipation of a rate increase that was not approved. Virtually all were destroyed, but a small quantity are known in private hands. None were regularly issued or sold at post offices.

World War II Type of 1989
1994, Nov. 7 — *Perf. 13½*

1537	A568	43c	D-Day beachhead	1.00	.35
1538	A568	43c	Artillery-Normandy	1.00	.35
1539	A568	43c	Tactical Air Forces	1.00	.35
1540	A568	43c	Walcheren and the Scheldt	1.00	.35
a.			Block or strip of 4, #1537-1540	4.00	2.50

1995, Mar. 20

1541	A568	43c	Veterans return home	1.00	.35
1542	A568	43c	Freeing the POW	1.00	.35
1543	A568	43c	Liberation of civilians	1.00	.35
1544	A568	43c	Crossing the Rhine	1.00	.35
a.			Block or strip of 4, #1541-1544	4.00	2.50

Art Type of 1988
Painting: Floraison, by Alfred Pellan (1906-88).

Litho. with Foil Application
1995, Apr. 21 — *Perf. 13*

1545	A546	88c	multicolored	1.90	1.20
a.			Gold foil omitted	*1,600.*	

Flag Over Lake — A635

1995, May 1 — **Litho.** — *Perf. 13½x13*

1546	A635	(43c)	multicolored	.90	.25

No. 1546 was valued at the first class domestic letter rate on day of issue.

Fortress of Louisbourg, 275th Anniv. — A636

#1547, Louisbourg Harbor, ships near Dauphin Gate. #1548, Walls, streets, buildings of Louisbourg. #1549, Museum behind King's Bastion. #1550, Drawing of King's Garden, Convent, Hospital and barracks. #1551, Partially eroded fortifications.

1995, May 5 — *Perf. 12½x13*

1547	A636	(43c)	48x32mm	.85	.40
1548	A636	(43c)	32x32mm	.85	.40
1549	A636	(43c)	40x32mm	.85	.40
1550	A636	(43c)	56x32mm	.85	.40
1551	A636	(43c)	48x32mm	.85	.40
a.			Strip of 5, #1547-1551	4.25	3.75
b.			Booklet pane, 2 #1551a	8.50	
			Complete booklet, #1551b	8.75	

Nos. 1547-1551 were valued at the first class domestic letter rate on day of issue. No. 1551a is a continuous design.

Historic Vehicles Type of 1993
Miniature Sheet

Farm, frontier vehicles: a, 1950 Cockshutt "30" farm tractor. b, 1970 Bombardier Ski-Doo Olympique 335 snowmobile. c, 1948 Bombardier B-12 CS multi-passenger snowmobile. d, 1924 Gotfredson model 20 farm truck. e, 1962 Robin-Nodwell RN 110 tracked carrier. f, 1942 Massey-Harris No. 21 self-propelled combine.

1995, May 26

1552		Pane of 6	8.00	8.00
a.-b.	A619	43c any single, 35x22mm	.85	.85
c.-d.	A619	50c any single, 43x22mm	1.00	1.00
e.-f.	A619	88c any single, 43x22mm	1.90	1.90

Golf in Canada
A637

Designs: No. 1553, Banff Springs Golf Club. No. 1554, Riverside Country Club. No. 1555, Glen Abbey Golf Club. No. 1556, Victoria Golf Club. No. 1557, Royal Montreal Golf Club.

Booklet Stamps
Perf. 13½x13 on 3 Sides
1995, June 6
1553	A637	43c multicolored	1.00	.40
1554	A637	43c multicolored	1.00	.40
1555	A637	43c multicolored	1.00	.40
1556	A637	43c multicolored	1.00	.40
1557	A637	43c multicolored	1.00	.40
a.		Strip of 5, #1553-1557	5.00	4.00
b.		Booklet pane, 2 #1557a	10.00	
		Complete booklet, #1557b	10.50	

Nat. Golf Week. Canadian Amateur Golf Championship, cent. Royal Canadian Golf Assoc., cent.

Lunenburg Academy, Cent. — A638

1995, June 29   *Perf. 13*
1558	A638	43c multicolored	.85	.25

Souvenir Sheets

Group of Seven — A639

Painting, original members: No. 1559a, October Gold, by Franklin Carmichael. b, From the North Shore, Lake Superior, by Lawren Harris. c, Evening, Les Eboulements, Quebec, by A.Y. Jackson.

No. 1560a, Serenity, Lake of the Woods, by Frank H. Johnston. b, A September Gale, Georgian Bay, by Arthur Lismer. c, Falls, Montreal River, by J.E.H. MacDonald. d, Open Window, by Frederick Horsman Varley.

Painting, new members: No. 1561a, Mill Houses, by Alfred J. Casson. b, Pembina Valley, by Lionel LeMoine FitzGerald. c, The Lumberjack, by Edwin Headley Holgate.

1995, June 29
1559	A639	Pane of 3	3.30	3.30
a.-c.		43c any single	1.10	1.10
1560	A639	Pane of 4	4.40	4.40
a.-d.		43c any single	1.10	1.10
1561	A639	Pane of 3	3.30	3.30
a.-c.		43c any single	1.10	1.10

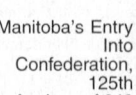

Manitoba's Entry Into Confederation, 125th Anniv. — A640

1995, July 14   *Perf. 13½x13*
1562	A640	43c multicolored	.85	.30

Migratory Wildlife — A641

1995, Aug. 15   *Perf. 13x12½*
1563	A641	45c Monarch butterfly	.90	.25
1564	A641	45c Belted kingfisher	.90	.40
1565	A641	45c Northern pintail	.90	.25
1566	A641	45c Hoary bat	.90	.25
a.		Block or strip of 4, #1563-1566	3.60	2.75

No. 1564 with Revised Inscription
1995, Sept. 26
1567	A641	45c like #1564	1.10	.90
a.		Block or strip of 4, #1563, 1565-1567	4.00	4.00

#1564 inscribed "aune," #1567 "Faune." See Mexico #1924.

Greetings Type of 1994
Designs: No. 1568, "Canada" at left. No. 1569, "Canada" at right.

Self-Adhesive
Size: 46x22mm
1995, Sept. 1   *Die Cut*
1568	A624	45c green & multi	1.00	.75
1569	A624	45c green & multi	1.00	.75
a.		Bklt. pane, 5 ea #1568-1569	10.00	

By its nature, No. 1569a is a complete booklet. The peelable backing serves as a booklet cover.

No. 1569a also contains 15 self-adhesive greetings labels in four designs that complete the design when placed in the central circle of Nos. 1568-1569.

No. 1569a exists with special cover and labels commemorating the Canadian Memorial Chiropractic College, Toronto, 50th anniv.

Bridges A642

#1570, Quebec Bridge, Quebec. #1571, Highway 403-401-410 interchange, Ontario. #1572, Hartland Covered Wooden Bridge, New Brunswick. #1573, Alex Fraser Bridge, British Columbia.

1995, Sept. 1   *Perf. 12½x13*
1570	A642	45c multicolored	.90	.30
1571	A642	45c multicolored	.90	.30
1572	A642	45c multicolored	.90	.30
1573	A642	45c multicolored	.90	.30
a.		Block or strip of 4, #1570-1573	3.60	2.75

Canadian Arctic A643

#1574, Polar bear, caribou. #1575, Arctic poppy, cargo canoe. #1576, Inuk man, igloo, sled dogs. #1577, Dog-sled team, ski plane. No. 1578, Children.

Booklet Stamps
1995, Sept. 15   *Perf. 13x12½*
1574	A643	45c multicolored	.90	.30
1575	A643	45c multicolored	.90	.30
1576	A643	45c multicolored	.90	.30
1577	A643	45c multicolored	.90	.30
1578	A643	45c multicolored	.90	.30
a.		Strip of 5, #1574-1578	4.50	3.50
b.		Bklt. pane, 2 #1578a	9.00	
		Complete booklet, #1578b	9.00	

Stamps in bottom row of #1578b are in different sequence.

Comic Book Characters A644

Booklet Stamps
1995, Oct. 2   *Perf. 13x12½*
1579	A644	45c Superman	1.25	.40
1580	A644	45c Johnny Canuck	1.25	.40
1581	A644	45c Nelvana	1.25	.40
1582	A644	45c Captain Canuck	1.25	.40
1583	A644	45c Fleur de Lys	1.25	.40
a.		Strip of 5, #1579-1583	6.25	5.00
b.		Booklet pane, 2 #1583a	12.50	
		Complete booklet, #1583b	13.00	

Stamps in the bottom row of No. 1583b are in different sequence.

UN, 50th Anniv. A645

1995, Oct. 24   *Perf. 13½*
1584	A645	45c blue & multi	1.25	.25

No. 1584 printed in panes of 10 with top label equal to 10 stamps. Label shows details of Canadian participation in UN activities. UN emblem on No. 1584 is stamped in blue foil.

Capital Sculptures, by Emile Brunet (1893-1977), Sainte-Anne-de-Beaupre Basilica — A646

Holly A647

1995, Nov. 2
1585	A646	45c The Nativity	.90	.20
a.		Booklet pane of 10	9.00	
		Complete booklet, #1585a	9.50	
1586	A646	52c The Annunciation	1.05	.55
a.		Booklet pane of 5 + label	5.25	5.00
		Complete booklet, #1586a	5.50	
1587	A646	90c Flight to Egypt	1.80	.65
a.		Booklet pane of 5 + label	9.00	8.00
		Complete booklet, #1587a	9.50	

Booklet Stamp
Perf. 12½x13
1588	A647	40c multicolored	.85	.85
a.		Booklet pane of 10	8.50	10.50
		Complete booklet, #1588a	8.75	
		Nos. 1585-1588 (4)	4.60	2.25

Christmas. No. 1588 has bar code at left; for use on covers with printed postal code matrix.

La Francophonie's Agency for Cultural and Technical Cooperation, 25th Anniv. — A648

1995, Nov. 6   *Perf. 13x13½*
1589	A648	45c multicolored	.90	.25

End of the Holocaust, 50th Anniv. — A649

1995, Nov. 9   *Perf. 12½x13*
1590	A649	45c multicolored	.90	.25

Birds A650

#1591, American kestrel. #1592, Atlantic puffin. #1593, Pileated woodpecker. #1594, Ruby-throated hummingbird.

1996, Jan. 9   *Perf. 13½*
1591	A650	45c multicolored	.90	.30
1592	A650	45c multicolored	.90	.30
1593	A650	45c multicolored	.90	.30
1594	A650	45c multicolored	.90	.30
a.		Strip of 4, Nos. 1591-1594	3.60	3.00

Issued in panes of 12 stamps, printed checkerwise, and in uncut sheets of 5 panes. See Nos. 1631-1634, 1710-1713, 1770-1777, 1839-1846, 1886-1889.

High Technology Industries — A651

Designs: No. 1595, Ocean technology. No. 1596, Aerospace technology. No. 1597, Information technology. No. 1598, Biotechnology.

Booklet Stamps
1996, Feb. 15   *Perf. 13½ on 3 Sides*
1595	A651	45c multicolored	1.00	.35
1596	A651	45c multicolored	1.00	.35
1597	A651	45c multicolored	1.00	.35
1598	A651	45c multicolored	1.00	.35
a.		Booklet pane of 12, 3 each Nos. 1595-1598	12.00	8.00
		Complete booklet, No. 1598a	12.50	
		Nos. 1595-1598 (4)	4.00	1.40

Greetings Type of 1994
"Canada": No. 1600, at L. #1601, at R.

Self-Adhesive
Size: 51x25mm
1996, Jan. 15   *Die Cut*
1600	A624	45c green & multi	1.75	1.25
1601	A624	45c green & multi	1.75	1.25
a.		Booklet pane, 5 ea #1600-1601	17.50	
b.		As "a," die cutting omitted	3,250.	

By its nature No. 1601a is a complete booklet. The peelable backing serves as a booklet cover.

No. 1601a also contains 35 self-adhesive greetings labels in seven designs that complete the design when placed in the central circle of Nos. 1600-1601.

Art Type of 1988
Sculpture: The Spirit of Haida Gwaii, by Bill Reid.

Litho. with Foil Application
1996, Apr. 30   *Perf. 12½x13*
1602	A546	90c multicolored	1.80	1.20

AIDS Awareness — A652

1996, May 8   Litho.   *Perf. 13½*
1603	A652	45c multicolored	.90	.20

Historic Vehicles Type of 1993
#1604: a, 1899 Still Motor Co. Ltd. Electric Van. b. 1914 Waterous Engine Works Road Roller. c, 1938 International D-35 Delivery Truck. d, 1936 Champion Road Grader. e, 1947 White Model WA 122 Tractor Trailer. f, 1975 Hayes HDX 45-115 Logging Truck.

#1605: a, like #1490a. b, like #1490b. c, like #1527a. d, like #1527b. e, like #1552b. f, like #1604a. g, like #1604b. h, like #1552a. i, like #1604c. j, like 1604d. k, like #1527e. l, like #1527f. m, like #1604e. n, like #1604f. o, like #1490c. p, like #1490d. q, like #1527d. r, like #1490e. s, like #1490f. t, like #1527c. u, like #1552c. v, like #1552d. w, like #1552e. x, like #1552f. y, 1975 Bricklin SV-1 Sports car.

1996   *Perf. 12½x13*
1604	A619	Pane of 6	8.00	8.00
a.-b.		45c any single	1.00	1.00
c.-d.		52c any single	1.10	1.10
e.-f.		90c any single	1.80	1.80

1605 A619 Pane of 25   9.00 9.00
  a.-j.   5c any single   .20 .20
  k.-n.   10c any single   .35 .35
  o.-x.   20c any single   .45 .45
  y.   45c multicolored   1.00 1.00

Nos. 1604e-1604f, 1605k-1605n, 1605y are 51x22mm. Nos. 1605o-1605x are 43x21mm.

Yukon Gold Rush, Cent. A653

Designs: a, "Skookum" Jim Mason's discovery on Rabbit (Bonanza) Creek, 1896. b, Miners trekking to gold fields, boats on Lake Laberge. c, Supr. Sam Steele, North West Mounted Police, Alaska-Yukon border. d, Dawson, boom town, city of entertainment. e, Klondike gold fields.

1996, June 13   *Perf. 13½*
1606   Strip of 5   6.25 5.50
  a.-e. A653 45c any single   1.25 .65

CAPEX '96. #1606 was issued in panes of 10 stamps.

Canada Day — A654

Self-Adhesive
1996, June 28   *Die Cut*
1607 A654 45c multicolored   .90 .25
  a.   Pane of 12   11.00

Canadian Olympic Gold Medalists A655

#1608, Ethel Catherwood, high jump, 1928. #1609, Etienne Desmarteau, 56 lb. weight throw, 1904. #1610, Fanny Rosenfeld, 100m, 400m relay, 1928. #1611, Gerald Ouellette, smallbore rifle, prone, 1956. #1612, Percy Williams, 100m, 200m, 1928.

Booklet Stamps
Litho. & Typo.
1996, July 8   *Perf. 13x12½*
1608 A655 45c gold, sep & silver   1.20 .60
1609 A655 45c gold, sep & silver   1.20 .60
1610 A655 45c gold, sep & silver   1.20 .60
1611 A655 45c gold, sep & silver   1.20 .60
1612 A655 45c gold, sep & silver   1.20 .60
  a.   Strip of 5, #1608-1612   6.00 4.50
  b.   Booklet pane, 2 #1612a   12.00
     Complete booklet, #1612b   12.50

British Columbia's Entry Into Confederation, 125th Anniv. — A656

1996, July 19
1613 A656 45c multicolored   .90 .25

A657

1996, Aug. 19   Litho.   *Perf. 12½x12*
1614 A657 45c Canadian Heraldry   .90 .25

Motion Pictures, Cent. — A658

Film strips from motion pictures: No. 1615a, L'arrivée d'un train en gare, Lumière cinematography, 1896. b, Back to God's Country, Nell & Ernest Shipman, 1919. c, Hen Hop, Norman McLaren, 1942. d, Pour la suite du monde, Pierre Perrault, Michel Brault, 1963. e, Goin' Down the Road, Don Shebib, 1970.
No. 1616a, Mon oncle Antoine, Claude Jutra, 1971. b, The Apprenticeship of Duddy Kravitz, Ted Kotcheff, 1974. c, Les Ordres, Michel Brault, 1974. d, Les Bons Débarras, Francis Mankiewiez, 1980. e, The Grey Fox, Philip Borsos, 1982.

Self-Adhesive
1996, Aug. 22   *Die Cut*
1615 A658   Pane of 5   4.50 4.50
  a.-e.   45c Any single   .90 .90
1616 A658   Pane of 5   4.50 4.50
  a.-e.   45c Any single   .90 .90

Edouard Montpetit (1881-1954), Educator A659

1996, Sept. 26   *Perf. 12½*
1617 A659 45c multicolored   .90 .25

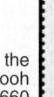

Winnie the Pooh A660

Designs: No. 1618, Winnie, Lt. Colebourne, 1914. No. 1619, Winnie, Christopher Robin, 1925. No. 1620, Milne and Shepard's Winnie the Pooh, 1926. No. 1621, Winnie the Pooh at Walt Disney World, 1996.

1996, Oct. 1   *Perf. 12½x13*
1618 A660 45c multicolored   .90 .40
1619 A660 45c multicolored   .90 .40
1620 A660 45c multicolored   .90 .40
1621 A660 45c multicolored   .90 .40
  a.   Block of 4, #1618-1621   3.60 2.75
  b.   Souv. sheet of 4, #1618-1621   8.50 8.00
  c.   Booklet pane of 16, 4 each
       #1618-1621   14.50
       Complete booklet, #1621c   15.00

No. 1621c was issued with the halves of the booklet pane printed tete-beche. The booklet pane of 16 was used as a cover for a souvenir story booklet.
Walt Disney World, 25th anniv.

Margaret Laurence   45   Authors — A661

1926-1987

#1622, Margaret Laurence (1926-87). #1623, Donald G. Creighton (1902-79). #1624, Gabrielle Roy (1909-83). #1625, Felix-Antoine Savard (1896-1982). #1626, Thomas C. Haliburton (1796-1865).

Booklet Stamps
Perf. 13½x13 on 3 Sides
1996, Oct. 10   **Litho. & Engr.**
1622 A661 45c multicolored   1.20 .40
1623 A661 45c multicolored   1.20 .40
1624 A661 45c multicolored   1.20 .40
1625 A661 45c multicolored   1.20 .40
1626 A661 45c multicolored   1.20 .40
  a.   Strip of 5, #1622-1626   6.00 5.00
  b.   Booklet pane, 2 #1626a   12.00 12.00
     Complete booklet, #1626b   12.50

A662

Christmas: 45c, Children on snowshoes, sled. 52c, Santa Claus skiing. 90c, Children skating.

Perf. 13½ (#1627, 1629a), 12¾x12¼ (#1628, 1629), 13½x13 (#1627a, 1628a)
1996, Nov. 1   **Litho.**
1627 A662 45c multicolored   .90 .20
  a.   Booklet pane of 10   9.00 8.50
     Complete booklet, #1627a
1628 A662 52c multicolored   1.05 .25
  a.   Booklet pane of 5 + label   5.25 5.25
     Complete booklet, #1628a   5.50
1629 A662 90c multicolored   1.80 .55
  a.   Booklet pane of 5 + label   9.00 9.00
     Complete booklet, #1629a   9.50

UNICEF, 50th anniv.

New Year 1997 (Year of the Ox) — A663

1997, Jan. 7   *Perf. 13x12½*
1630 A663 45c multicolored   1.10 .25
  a.   Souvenir sheet of 2   3.00 3.00
  b.   As No. 1630, gold omitted   4,000.

No. 1630a is fan shaped.
No. 1630a with Hong Kong 97 overprint was sold as a limited edition only at the show. Value $8.

Bird Type of 1996

#1631, Mountain bluebird. #1632, Western grebe. #1633, Northern gannet. #1634, Scarlet tanager.

1997, Jan. 10   *Perf. 12½x13*
1631 A650 45c multicolored   .90 .30
1632 A650 45c multicolored   .90 .30
1633 A650 45c multicolored   .90 .30
1634 A650 45c multicolored   .90 .30
  a.   Block or strip of 4, #1631-1634   3.60 2.75

Nos. 1631-1634 were issued in panes of 20, 5 each, printed checkerwise to contain 4 complete blocks or 5 strips.

Art Type of 1988

Painting: York Boat on Lake Winnipeg, by Walter J. Phillips.

Litho. with Foil Application
1997, Feb. 17
1635 A546 90c gold & multi   2.10 1.20

Canadian Tire, 75th Anniv. A664

1997, Mar. 3   Litho.   *Perf. 13x13½*
1636 A664 45c multicolored   .90 .25

Father Charles-Emile Gadbois (1906-81), Musicologist A665

1997, Mar. 20   *Perf. 13½x13*
1637 A665 45c multicolored   .90 .25

Québec en Fleurs 97, Intl. Horticultural Exhibition A666

Booklet Stamps
Perf. 13x12½ on 3 Sides
1997, Apr. 4
1638 A666 45c Blue poppy   .90 .25
  a.   Booklet pane of 12   11.00 11.00
     Complete booklet, #1638a   11.50

Victorian Order of Nurses for Canada, Cent. A667

1997, May 12   *Perf. 12½x13*
1639 A667 45c multicolored   .90 .25

Law Society of Upper Canada, Bicent. — A668

1997, May 23   *Perf. 13½x13*
1640 A668 45c multicolored   .90 .25

Salt Water Fish A669

#1641, Great white shark. #1642, Pacific halibut. #1643, Atlantic sturgeon. #1644, Bluefin tuna.

1997, May 30   *Perf. 12½x13*
1641 A669 45c multicolored   .90 .30
1642 A669 45c multicolored   .90 .30
1643 A669 45c multicolored   .90 .30
1644 A669 45c multicolored   .90 .30
  a.   Block or strip of 4, #1641-1644   3.60 2.75

Opening of the Confederation Bridge — A670

1997, May 31
1645 A670 45c Lighthouse, bridge   .90 .25
1646 A670 45c Bridge, bird   .90 .25
  a.   Pair, #1645-1646 + label   1.80 1.20

Gilles Villeneuve (1950-82), Formula
One Race Car Driver — A671

45c, Villeneuve winning race in Ferrari T-4.
90c, Close-up, racing in Number 12 Ferrari T-3.

1997, June 12
1647	A671	45c multicolored	.90	.25
1648	A671	90c multicolored	1.80	1.10
a.		Pair, #1647-1648	2.70	2.70
b.		Pane of 4 #1648a	11.00	10.50

John Cabot's Voyage to Canada,
500th Anniv.
A672

1997, June 24
1649	A672	45c multicolored	.90	.25

See Italy No. 2162.

Scenic Canadian Highways — A673

Designs: No. 1650, Sea to Sky Highway,
British Columbia. No. 1651, The Cabot Trail,
Nova Scotia. No. 1652, The Wine Route, start-
ing in Ontario. No. 1653, The Big Muddy,
Saskatchewan.

1997, June 30
1650	A673	45c multicolored	.90	.45
1651	A673	45c multicolored	.90	.45
1652	A673	45c multicolored	.90	.45
1653	A673	45c multicolored	.90	.45
a.		Block or strip of 4, #1650-1653	3.60	2.75

See Nos. 1739-1742, 1780-1783.

Canadian Industrial Design — A674

1997, July 23
1654	A674	45c multicolored	.90	.25

No. 1654 was issued with se-tenant label in
panes of 24 + 24 labels. The 12 different
labels each appear twice in different colors. In
alternating rows, labels appear on left or right
side of stamp.
Association of Canadian Industrial Designers, 50th anniv. and 20th Intl. Congress of Intl.
Council of Societies of Industrial Design.

Highland Games, Maxville,
Ontario — A675

1997, Aug. 1
1655	A675	45c multicolored	.90	.25

Knights of Columbus
in Canada,
Cent. — A676

1997, Aug. 5   *Perf. 13*
1656	A676	45c multicolored	.90	.25

28th World Congress of Postal,
Telegraph and Telephone Intl. Labor
Union, Montreal
A677

1997, Aug. 18
1657	A677	45c multicolored	.90	.25

Asia
Pacific
Year
A678

1997, Aug. 25   *Perf. 13½*
1658	A678	45c multicolored	.90	.25

Canada-USSR Ice Hockey "Series of
the Century," 25th Anniv. — A679

Designs: No. 1659, Canadian players, Paul
Henderson, Yvan Cournoyer (No. 12), after
scoring winning goal in final game. No. 1660,
Canadian team members celebrating victory.

Booklet Stamps

1997, Sept. 20   *Perf. 14x13*
1659	A679	45c multicolored	.90	.30
1660	A679	45c multicolored	.90	.30
a.		Bklt. pane, 5 ea #1659-1660	9.00	9.00
		Complete booklet, #1660a	9.50	

Famous
Politicians
A680

#1661, Martha Black (1866-1957). #1662,
Lionel Chevrier (1903-87). #1663, Judy
LaMarsh (1924-80). #1664, Réal Caouette
(1917-76).

1997, Sept. 26   *Perf. 13½x13*
1661	A680	45c multicolored	.90	.35
1662	A680	45c multicolored	.90	.35
1663	A680	45c multicolored	.90	.35
1664	A680	45c multicolored	.90	.35
a.		Block or strip of 4, #1661-1664	3.60	2.75

Supernatural — A681

1997, Oct. 1   *Perf. 13x12½*
1665	A681	45c Vampire	.90	.35
1666	A681	45c Werewolf	.90	.35
1667	A681	45c Ghost	.90	.35
1668	A681	45c Goblin	.90	.35
a.		Block of 4, #1665-1668	3.60	2.75

Christmas — A682

Stained glass windows: 45c, "Our Lady of
the Rosary," Holy Rosary Cathedral, Vancou-
ver. 52c, "Nativity Scene," United Church,
Leith, Ontario. 90c, Madonna and Child, St.
Stephen's Ukrainian Byzantine Rite Roman
Catholic Church, Calgary.

1997, Nov. 3   *Perf. 12½x13*
1669	A682	45c multicolored	.90	.20
a.		Booklet pane of 10	9.00	9.00
		Complete booklet, #1669a	9.50	
1670	A682	52c multicolored	1.05	.35
a.		Booklet pane of 5	5.25	5.25
		Complete booklet, #1670a	5.50	
1671	A682	90c multicolored	1.80	.55
a.		Booklet pane of 5	9.00	9.00
		Complete booklet, #1671a	9.50	
		Nos. 1669-1671 (3)	3.75	1.10

75th Royal
Agriculture
Winter Fair,
Toronto
A683

1997, Nov. 6
1672	A683	45c multicolored	.90	.25

Types of 1987-98 and:

Traditional
Handiwork
A684

Maple Leaf
A685

Moose — A687

Flag and
Inukshuk — A688

1997-2005   **Litho.**   *Perf. 13¼*
1673	A684	1c Bookbinding	.20	.20
1674	A684	2c Ironwork	.20	.20
1675	A684	3c Glass blowing	.20	.20
1676	A684	4c Oyster farmer	.20	.20
1677	A684	5c Weaving	.20	.20
1678	A684	9c Quilting	.20	.20
1679	A684	10c Artistic wood-working	.20	.20
a.		Imperf, single	—	
b.		Block of 4, top two stamps imperf (cut between)	—	
1680	A684	25c Leatherwork-ing	.50	.20

      Perf. 13¼x13
1681	A536	46c Queen Eliza-beth II	.90	.20

      Perf. 13x13¼
1682	A541	46c Flag over Ice-bergs	.90	.20
a.		Booklet pane of 10	9.00	9.00
		Complete booklet, #1682a	9.50	

      Perf. 13¼x13
1683	A536	47c multi	.95	.20
a.		Imperf, pair	725.00	

      Perf. 13x13¼
1684	A685	55c multicolored	1.10	.25
a.		Booklet pane of 5 + label	5.50	5.00
		Complete booklet, #1684a	5.75	
1685	A685	73c multicolored	1.50	.50
1686	A685	95c multicolored	1.90	.60
a.		Booklet pane of 5 + label	9.50	9.00
		Complete booklet, #1686a	10.00	

     Litho. & Engr.
      Perf. 13¼x13
1687	A686	$1 Loon	2.00	.60

      Perf. 12½x13
1688	A686	$1 White-tailed deer ('05)	2.00	.60
1689	A686	$1 Atlantic wal-rus ('05)	2.00	.60
a.		Pair, #1688-1689	4.00	2.75
b.		Souvenir sheet, 2 each #1688-1689	8.00	8.00

      Perf. 13¼x13
1690	A686	$2 Polar bear	4.00	1.10

      Perf. 12½x13
1691	A686	$2 Peregrine fal-cons ('05)	4.00	1.00
1692	A686	$2 Sable Island horses ('05)	4.00	1.00
a.		Pair, #1691-1692	8.00	6.00
b.		Souvenir sheet, 2 each #1691-1692	16.00	16.00

     Size 63x48mm
1693	A687	$5 Moose	10.00	2.00
a.		Engraved colors (Moose, etc.) omitted	6,000.	
1694	A687	$8 Grizzly bear	15.00	4.50
		Nos. 1673-1694 (22)	52.15	14.95

     Coil Stamp
     Engr.
     Perf. 10 Horiz.
1695	A599	46c red	.90	.30
a.		Imperf, pair	175.00	

     Photo.
     Booklet Stamp
     Self-Adhesive
     Die Cut
1696	A685	45c multicolored	1.50	1.50
a.		Booklet pane of 18	27.50	

     Typo. & Embossed
     Die Cut Perf. 13
     Coil Stamp
1697	A685	45c multicolored	1.20	.75

Loon
A686

Litho.
Booklet Stamps
Die Cut

1698	A541	46c Flag over Icebergs	.95	.65
a.		Booklet pane of 30	28.50	
b.		Imperf, pair	325.00	

Photo.

1699	A685	46c multicolored	2.75	2.25
a.		Booklet pane of 18	50.00	

Litho.

1700	A688	47c multi	.95	.20
a.		Booklet of 10	9.50	
b.		Booklet of 30	28.50	

Nos. 1698a-1699a are complete booklets. The peelable backing serves as a booklet cover.

Issued: #1681, 1682, 1685-1687, 1695, 1698-1699, 12/28/98; $8, 10/15/97; Nos. 1690-1691, 4/14/98. No. 1688, $2, 10/27/98; 1c-25c, 4/29/99; 47c, 12/28/00; Nos. 1689-1690, 10/20/05; Nos. 1692-1693, 12/19/05.

The peelable paper backing of No. 1696a serves as a booklet cover.

No. 1697 does not have the "POSTAGE / POSTES" and copyright inscriptions found in No. 1696. The gold on No. 1697 is embossed and brighter than that on No. 1696.

See Nos. 1928-1930.

New Year 1998 (Year of the Tiger) A690

1998, Jan. 8   Litho.   *Perf. 13x12½*

1708	A690	45c multicolored	.90	.25
a.		Souvenir sheet of 2	1.80	1.60

No. 1708a overprinted exists. Value $3.

Provincial Leaders A691

Designs: a, John P. Robarts (1917-82), Ontario. b, Jean Lesage (1912-80), Quebec. c, John B. McNair (1889-1968), New Brunswick. d, Tommy Douglas (1904-86), Saskatchewan. e, Joseph R. Smallwood (1900-91), Newfoundland. f, Angus L. MacDonald (1890-1954), Nova Scotia. g, W.A.C. Bennett (1900-79), British Columbia. h, Ernest C. Manning (1908-95), Alberta. i, John Bracken (1883-1969), Manitoba. j, J. Walter Jones (1878-1954), Prince Edward Island.

1998, Feb. 18   *Perf. 13½*

1709	A691	Sheet of 10	12.00	9.00
a.-j.		45c any single	1.20	.65

Bird Type of 1996

#1710, Hairy woodpecker. #1711, Great crested flycatcher. #1712, Eastern screech owl. #1713, Gray-crowned rosy-finch.

1998, Mar. 13   *Perf. 13x13½*

1710	A650	45c multicolored	.90	.30
1711	A650	45c multicolored	.90	.30
1712	A650	45c multicolored	.90	.30
1713	A650	45c multicolored	.90	.30
a.		Block or strip of 4, #1710-1713	3.60	2.75

Nos. 1710-1713 were issued in panes of 20, 5 each, printed checkerwise to contain 4 complete blocks or 5 strips.

Fly Fishing in Canada — A693

Lure, type of fish: No. 1715, Coquihalla orange, steelhead trout. No. 1716, Steelhead bee, steelhead trout. No. 1717, Dark Montreal, brook trout. No. 1718, Lady Amherst, Atlantic salmon. No. 1719, Coho blue, coho salmon. No. 1720, Cosseboom special, Atlantic salmon.

1998, Apr. 16   *Perf. 12½x13*

1715	A693	45c multicolored	1.00	.50
1716	A693	45c multicolored	1.00	.50
1717	A693	45c multicolored	1.00	.50
1718	A693	45c multicolored	1.00	.50
1719	A693	45c multicolored	1.00	.50
1720	A693	45c multicolored	1.00	.50
a.		Vertical strip of 6, #1715-1720	6.00	5.00
b.		Bklt. pane, 2 ea #1715-1720	12.00	
		Complete booklet, #1720a	12.50	

Canadian Institute of Mining, Metallurgy and Petroleum, Cent. — A694

1998, May 4   *Perf. 12½*

1721	A694	45c multicolored	.90	.25

Imperial Penny Post, Cent. A695

St. Edward's Crown, #86, Sir William Mulock.

1998, May 29   *Perf. 12½x13*

1722	A695	45c multicolored	.90	.25

No. 1722 was issued in panes of 14 + 1 label.

Sumo Wrestling Tournament, Vancouver — A696

Rising sun, mapleleaf and: No. 1723, Two wrestlers. No. 1724, Sumo champion performing bow twirling ceremony.

1998, June 5   Litho. & Embossed

1723	A696	45c multicolored	.90	.25
1724	A696	45c multicolored	.90	.25
a.		Horiz. or Vert. Pair, #1723-1724 + 4 labels	1.80	1.50
b.		Souvenir sheet, #1723-1724	4.50	4.50

Nos. 1723-1724 were printed checkerwise in panes of 20, 10 each + 40 labels.

Canals of Canada — A697

#1725, St. Peters Canal, Nova Scotia. #1726, St. Ours Canal, Quebec. #1727, Port Carling Lock, Ontario. #1728, Locks, Rideau Canal, Ontario. #1729, Peterborough lift lock, Trent-Severn Waterway, Ontario. #1730, Chambly Canal, Quebec. #1731, Lachine Canal, Quebec. #1732, Ice skating on Rideau Canal, Ottawa. #1733, Boat on Big Chute Marine Railway, Trent-Severn Waterway. #1734, Sault Ste. Marie Canal, Ontario.

Booklet Stamps
1998, June 17   Litho.   *Perf. 12½*

1725	A697	45c multicolored	1.20	.75
1726	A697	45c multicolored	1.20	.75
1727	A697	45c multicolored	1.20	.75
1728	A697	45c multicolored	1.20	.75
1729	A697	45c multicolored	1.20	.75
1730	A697	45c multicolored	1.20	.75
1731	A697	45c multicolored	1.20	.75
1732	A697	45c multicolored	1.20	.75
1733	A697	45c multicolored	1.20	.75

1734	A697	45c multicolored	1.20	.75
a.		Bklt. pane, #1725-1734 + 10 labels	16.00	
		Complete booklet, #1734a	17.00	

Health Professionals A698

Litho. & Embossed with Foil Application
1998, June 25

1735	A698	45c multicolored	.90	.25

Royal Canadian Mounted Police, 125th Anniv. — A699

#1736, Male mountie, native, horse. #1737, Female mountie, helicopter, cityscape.

1998, July 3   *Perf. 12½x13*

1736	A699	45c multicolored	.90	.25
1737	A699	45c multicolored	.90	.25
a.		Pair, #1736-1737 + 2 labels	1.80	1.25
b.		Souvenir sheet, #1736-1737 + 1 label	1.80	1.60
c.		As "b," with signature	3.50	3.25
d.		As "b," with Portugal 98 emblem	4.00	4.00
e.		As "b," with Italia 98 emblem	4.00	4.00
f.		As "d," gold embossed emblem omitted	800.00	

#1737c-1737e have added inscriptions in gold. Issued: #1737c, 7/3; #1737d, 9/4; #1737e, 10/23.

William James Roué (1879-1970), Naval Architect — A700

Litho. & Engr.
1998, July 24   *Perf. 13*

1738	A700	45c multicolored	.90	.25

Scenic Highway Type of 1997

Designs: No. 1739, Dempster Highway, Yukon. No. 1740, Dinosaur Trail, Alberta. No. 1741, River Valley Scenic Drive, New Brunswick. No. 1742, Blue Heron Route, Prince Edward Island.

1998, July 28   Litho.   *Perf. 12½x13*

1739	A673	45c multicolored	.90	.35
1740	A673	45c multicolored	.90	.35
1741	A673	45c multicolored	.90	.35
1742	A673	45c multicolored	.90	.35
a.		Block or strip of 4, #1739-1742	3.60	2.75

Publication of "Refus Global" by The Automatistes, 50th Anniv. — A701

Painting, artist: No. 1743, "Peinture," Jean-Paul Riopelle. No. 1744, "La dernière campagne de Napoléon," Fernand Leduc. No. 1745, "Jet fuligineux sur noir torturé," Jean-Paul Mousseau. No. 1746, "Le fond du garde-

robe," Pierre Gauvreau. No. 1747, "Joie lacustre," Paul-Emile Borduas. No. 1748, "Syndicat des gens de mer," Marcelle Ferron. No. 1749, "Le tumulte á la machoire crispée," Marcel Barbeau.

Self-Adhesive
Booklet Stamps
1998, Aug. 7   *Die Cut*

1743	A701	45c multicolored	1.20	1.20
1744	A701	45c multicolored	1.20	1.20
1745	A701	45c multicolored	1.20	1.20
1746	A701	45c multicolored	1.20	1.20
1747	A701	45c multicolored	1.20	1.20
1748	A701	45c multicolored	1.20	1.20
1749	A701	45c multicolored	1.20	1.20
a.		Booklet pane, #1743-1749	8.50	

No. 1746 is 34x48mm. No. 1749a is a complete booklet. The peelable paper backing serves as a booklet cover.

Legendary Canadians A702

#1750, Napoléon-Alexandre Comeau (1848-1923), outdoorsman, "King of the North Shore." #1751, Phyllis Munday (1894-1990), mountaineer, community service worker. #1752, Bill Mason (1929-88), film maker, canoe enthusiast. #1753, Harry "Red" Foster (1905-1985), founder of Canadian Special Olympics, sports enthusiast.

1998, Aug. 15   *Perf. 13½*

1750	A702	45c multicolored	.90	.30
1751	A702	45c multicolored	.90	.30
1752	A702	45c multicolored	.90	.30
1753	A702	45c multicolored	.90	.30
a.		Block or strip of 4, #1750-1753	3.60	2.75

Art Type of 1988

Painting: The Farmer's Family (detail), by Bruno Bobak.

Litho. with Foil Application
1998, Sept. 8   *Perf. 12½x13*

1754	A546	90c gold & multi	1.80	1.20

Housing in Canada A703

a, Native peoples. b, Settler. c, Regional. d, Heritage preservation. e, Multiple unit. f, Prefabricated. g, Veterans. h, Planned community. i, Innovative.

1998, Sept. 23   Litho.

1755		Pane of 9	12.00	12.00
a.-i.		A703 45c Any single	1.20	1.20

University of Ottawa, 150th Anniv. — A704

1998, Sept. 25   *Perf. 13*

1756	A704	45c multicolored	.90	.25

The Circus — A705

Various circus clowns and: No. 1757, Elephant, bear performing tricks. No. 1758, Woman standing on horse, aerial act. No. 1759, Lion tamer. No. 1760, Contortionists, acrobats.

Booklet Stamps

1998, Oct. 1   *Perf. 13 on 3 Sides*

1757	A705	45c multicolored	.90	.30
1758	A705	45c multicolored	.90	.30
1759	A705	45c multicolored	.90	.30
1760	A705	45c multicolored	.90	.30
a.		Bklt. pane, 3 ea #1757-1760	11.00	11.00
		Complete booklet, #1760a	11.50	
b.		Souvenir sheet, #1757-1760	5.25	4.50

Stamps in No. 1760b are perforated on all four sides.

John Peters Humphrey (1905-95), Author of Universal Declaration of Human Rights
A706

1998, Oct. 7   *Perf. 13*

1761	A706	45c multicolored	.90	.25

Canadian Naval Reserve, 75th Anniv. — A707

1998, Nov. 4   *Perf. 12½x13*

1762	A707	45c HMCS Sackville	.90	.25
1763	A707	45c HMCS Shawinigan	.90	.25
a.		Pair, #1762-1763	1.80	1.50

Christmas — A708

Sculpted wooden angels: 45c, "Angel of Last Judgment" blowing trumpet. 52c, "Adoring Angel" raising hand. 90c, "Adoring Angel, Kneeling," by Thomas Baillairgé.

1998, Nov. 6   *Perf. 13*

1764	A708	45c multicolored	.90	.25
a.		Booklet pane of 10	35.00	35.00
		Complete booklet, #1764a	37.50	
b.		Perf 13x13½	425.00	16.00
c.		As "b," booklet pane of 10	15.00	
		Complete booklet, #1764c	16.00	

The values for No. 1764b are for singles perfed on all four sides from sheet format. These are extremely scarce. Single stamps from booklet No. 1764c have a straight edge on one side. Value, booklet single, unused $1.60, used $.30.

    Perf. 13x13½

1765	A708	52c multicolored	1.05	.30
a.		Booklet pane of 5 + label	20.00	17.50
		Complete booklet, #1765a	21.00	
b.		Perf 13	1.25	.50
c.		As "b," booklet pane of 5 + label	6.25	5.50
		Complete booklet, #1765c	6.75	

1766	A708	90c multicolored	1.80	.70
a.		Booklet pane of 5 + label	32.50	27.50
		Complete booklet, #1766a	35.00	
b.		Perf 13	1.75	.90
c.		As "b," booklet pane of 5 + label	8.75	7.00
		Complete booklet, #1766c	9.25	
		Nos. 1764-1766 (3)	3.75	1.25

New Year 1999 (Year of the Rabbit)
A709

1999, Jan. 8   *Perf. 13½*

1767	A709	46c multicolored	.90	.25

Souvenir Sheet
    Perf. 12½x13

1768	A709	95c Pane of 1	2.50	2.25
a.		Single stamp	1.80	1.25

No. 1768 with China 99 overprint was sold only at the show. Value same as unoverprinted pane.

Le Theatre du Rideau Vert, 50th Anniv. — A710

1999, Feb. 17   *Perf. 13x12½*

1769	A710	46c multicolored	.90	.30

Bird Type of 1996

Designs: No. 1770, Northern goshawk. No. 1771, Red-winged blackbird. No. 1772, American goldfinch. No. 1773, Sandhill crane.

1999, Feb. 24   *Perf. 12½x13*

1770	A650	46c multicolored	.90	.30
1771	A650	46c multicolored	.90	.30
1772	A650	46c multicolored	.90	.30
1773	A650	46c multicolored	.90	.30
a.		Block or strip of 4, #1770-1773	3.60	1.75

Booklet Stamps
Self-Adhesive
Die Cut Perf. 11½

1774	A650	46c like #1770	1.10	.35
1775	A650	46c like #1771	1.10	.35
1776	A650	46c like #1772	1.10	.35
1777	A650	46c like #1773	1.10	.35
a.		Booklet pane, 2 each #1774-1775, 1 each #1776-1777	6.00	
b.		Booklet pane, 2 each #1776-1777, 1 each #1774-1775	6.00	
		Complete booklet, #1777a, #1777b	12.00	

Nos. 1770-1773 were issued in panes of 20, 5 each, printed checkerwise to contain 4 complete blocks or strips.
The peelable paper backing of Nos. 1777a, 1777b serves as the booklet cover.

Univ. of British Columbia's Museum of Anthropology, 50th Anniv. — A711

1999, Mar. 9   *Perf. 13½*

1778	A711	46c multicolored	.90	.25

Sailing Ship Marco Polo — A712

1999, Mar. 19   *Perf. 13x12½*

1779	A712	46c multicolored	.90	.25
a.		Pane of 2, #1779b, Australia #1631 perf. 13½	3.25	3.25
b.		Perf 13 (from No. 1779a)	1.75	1.75

Australia '99 World Stamp Expo. See Australia #1631a.

Scenic Highway Type of 1997

#1780, Gaspé Peninsula, Highway 132, Quebec. #1781, Yellowhead Highway (PTH 16), Manitoba. #1782, Dempster Highway 8, Northwest Territories. #1783, Discovery Trail, Route 230N, Newfoundland.

1999, Mar. 31   *Perf. 12½x13*

1780	A673	46c multicolored	.90	.35
1781	A673	46c multicolored	.90	.35
1782	A673	46c multicolored	.90	.35
1783	A673	46c multicolored	.90	.35
a.		Block or strip of 4, #1780-1783	3.60	2.75

Creation of the Nunavut Territory — A713

1999, Apr. 1

1784	A713	46c multicolored	.90	.25

Intl. Year of Older Persons — A714

1999, Apr. 12   *Perf. 13½*

1785	A714	46c multicolored	.90	.25

A715

1999, Apr. 19   *Perf. 13*

1786	A715	46c multicolored	1.10	.35

Baisakhi, Religious Holiday of Sikh Canadians, 300th Anniv.

A716

Paintings (Canadian Orchids): No. 1787, Arethusa bulbosa, by Poon-Kuen Chow. No. 1788, Amerorchis rotundifolia, by Yakman Lai. No. 1789, Platanthera psycodes, by Lai. No. 1790, Cypripedium pubescens, by Chow.

Booklet Stamps

1999, Apr. 27   *Perf. 13x12½*

1787	A716	46c multicolored	1.10	.30
1788	A716	46c multicolored	1.10	.30
1789	A716	46c multicolored	1.10	.30
1790	A716	46c multicolored	1.10	.30
a.		Bklt. pane, 3 ea #1787-1790	13.50	
		Complete booklet, #1790a	14.00	
b.		Souvenir sheet, #1787-1790	4.00	4.00

China '99 World Philatelic Exhibition, Beijing. Designs of some stamps contained in No. 1790a extend into selvage of booklet pane. Issued: No. 1790b, 8/21/99.

Horses A717

#1791, Northern Dancer, thoroughbred race horse. #1792, Kingsway Skoal, bucking horse. #1793, Big Ben, show horse. #1794, Armbro Flight, harness race horse.

1999, June 2   *Perf. 13x13½*

1791	A717	46c multicolored	1.10	.35
1792	A717	46c multicolored	1.10	.35
1793	A717	46c multicolored	1.10	.35
1794	A717	46c multicolored	1.10	.35
a.		Block or strip of 4, #1791-1794	4.40	3.50

Booklet Stamps
Self-Adhesive
Serpentine Die Cut 11½

1795	A717	46c like #1791	1.25	.35
1796	A717	46c like #1792	1.25	.35
1797	A717	46c like #1793	1.25	.35
1798	A717	46c like #1794	1.25	.35
a.		Block of 4, #1795-1798	5.00	
b.		Complete booklet, 3 each #1795-1798	15.00	

Nos. 1791-1794 were issued in panes of 16, 4 each, printed checkerwise to contain 4 complete blocks or strips.

Quebec Bar Assoc., 150th Anniv. — A718

1999, June 3   *Perf. 13½*

1799	A718	46c multicolored	.90	.25

Art Type of 1988

Coq Licorne, by Jean Dallaire (1916-65).

Litho. with Foil Application

1999, July 3   *Perf. 12½x13¼*

1800	A546	95c multicolored	1.80	1.10
a.		Silver omitted	1,350.	

1999 Pan American Games, Winnipeg
A719

Designs: No. 1801, Track & field. No. 1802, Cycling, weight lifting, gymnastics. No. 1803, Swimming, sailboarding, kayaking. No. 1804, Soccer, tennis, medal winners.

1999, July 12   Litho.   *Perf. 13¼*

1801	A719	46c multicolored	.90	.35
1802	A719	46c multicolored	.90	.35
1803	A719	46c multicolored	.90	.35
1804	A719	46c multicolored	.90	.35
a.		Block of 4, #1801-1804	3.60	2.75

Issued in panes of 16 stamps.

23rd World Rowing Championships,
St. Catherines, Ont. — A720

1999, Aug. 22   *Perf. 12½x13*
1805 A720 46c multicolored   .90 .25

UPU, 125th Anniv. — A721

1999, Aug. 26
1806 A721 46c multicolored   .90 .25

Airplanes — A722

No. 1807: a, Fokker DR-1, CT-114 Tutors. b, Tutors, H101 Salto sailplane. c, De Havilland DH100 Vampire MKIII. d, Stearman A-75.

No. 1808: a, De Havilland Mosquito FBVI. b, Sopwith F1 Camel. c, De Havilland Canada DHC-3 Otter. d, De Havilland Canada CC-108 Caribou. e, Canadair CL-28 Argus MK 2. f, North American F-86 Sabre 6. g, McDonnell Douglas CF-18 Hornet. h, Sopwith SF-1 Dolphin. i, Armstrong Whitworth Siskin IIIA. j, Canadian Vickers (Northrop) Delta II. k, Sikorsky CH-124A Sea King helicopter. l, Vickers-Armstrong Wellington MKII. m, Avro Anson MKI. n, Canadair (Lockheed) CF-104G Starfighter. o, Burgess-Dunne seaplane. p, Avro 504K.
Illustration reduced.

1999, Sept. 4
1807 A722 Pane of 4   5.00 5.00
 a.-d. 46c any single   1.25 1.00
1808 A722 Pane of 16   18.00 18.00
 a.-p. 46c any single   1.10 1.10

Canadian Intl. Air Show, 50th anniv. (#1807). Royal Canadian Air Force, 75th anniv. (#1808). Nos. 1808a-1808p are each 56x28mm.

NATO, 50th Anniv. — A723

1999, Sept. 21
1809 A723 46c multicolored   .90 .25

Frontier College, 100th Anniv. A724

1999, Sept. 24   *Perf. 13x13½*
1810 A724 46c multicolored   .90 .25

Kites
A725

Designs: a, Master Control, sport kite by Lam Hoac (triagular). b, Indian Garden Flying Carpet, edo kite by Skye Morrison (trapezoidal). c, Gibson Girl, manufactured box kite (rectangular). d, Dragon centipede kite by Zhang tian Wei (oval).

Self-Adhesive
Die cut in various patterns
1999, Oct. 1
1811   Complete booklet, 2
     each #a.-d.   9.00
 a.-d. A725 46c any single   1.10 .35

A726

A727

Millennium
A728

Self-Adhesive (46c)
1999, Oct. 12 Holography   *Die Cut*
1812 A726 46c silver   1.40 .40
   Pane of 4   4.40 4.40

Litho.
Perf. 13¼
1813 A727 55c multicolored   1.10 .90
   Pane of 4   4.40 4.40

Engr.
Perf. 12¾
1814 A728 95c brown   2.00 1.70
   Pane of 4   8.00 8.00
   Nos. 1812-1814 (3)   4.50 3.00

Nos. 1812-1814 each exist in souvenir sheets of 1 with decorative border.

Christmas — A729

1999, Nov. 4   **Litho.**   *Perf. 13¼*
1815 A729 46c Angel, drum   .90 .25
 a. Booklet pane of 10   9.00 9.00
   Complete booklet   9.50
1816 A729 55c Angel, toys   1.10 .35
 a. Booklet pane of 5 + label   5.50 5.50
   Complete booklet   6.00
1817 A729 95c Angel, candle   1.90 .75
 a. Booklet pane of 5 + label   9.50 9.50
   Complete booklet   10.00
   Nos. 1815-1817 (3)   3.90 1.35

Souvenir Sheets

Millennium — A730

No. 1818 — Media Technologies: a, IMAX movies. b, Softimage animation software. c, Ted Rogers, Sr. (1900-39) and radio tube. d, Invention of radio facsimile device for transmission of photographs for publishing by Sir William Stephenson (1896-1989).

No. 1819 — Canadian Entertainment: a, Calgary Stampede. b, Performers from Cirque du Soleil. c, Hockey Night in Canada. d, La Soiree du Hockey.

No. 1820 — Entertainers: a, Portia White (1911-68), singer. b, Glenn Gould (1932-82), pianist. c, Guy Lombardo (1902-77), band leader. d, Félix Leclerc (1914-88), singer, guitarist.

No. 1821 — Fostering Canadian Talent: a, Royal Canadian Academy of Arts (men viewing painting). b, Canada Council (sky, musical staff, "A"). c, National Film Board of Canada. d, Canadian Broadcasting Corporation.

No. 1822 — Medical Innovators: a, Sir Frederick Banting (1891-1941), co-discoverer of insulin, syringe and dog. b, Dr. Armand Frappier (1904-91), microbiologist, holding flask. c, Dr. Hans Selye (1907-82), endocrinologist, and molecular diagram. d, Maude Abbott (1869-1940), pathologist, and roses.

No. 1823 — Social Progress: a, Nun, doctor, hospital. b, Statue of woman holding decree. c, Alphonse Desjardins (1854-1920) and wife Dorimène (1858-1932), credit union founders, and credit union emblem. d, Father Moses Coady (1882-1959), educator of adults.

No. 1824 — Charity: a, Canadian International Development Agency (hands and tools). b, Dr. Lucille Teasdale (1929-96), hospital administrator in Uganda. c, Marathon of Hope inspired by Terry Fox (1958-81). d, Meals on Wheels program.

No. 1825 — Humanitarians and Peacekeepers: a, Raoul Dandurand (1861-1942), b, Pauline Vanier (1898-1991), Red Cross volunteer, and Elizabeth Smellie (1884-1968), head of various nursing services. c, Lester B. Pearson (1897-1972), prime minister, and Nobel Peace Prize winner, and dove. d, Amputee and shadow (Ottawa Convention on Land Mines).

No. 1826 — Canada's First People: a, Chief Pontiac (c. 1720-69). b, Tom Longboat (1887-1949), marathon runner. c, Inuit sculpture of shaman. d, Medicine man.

No. 1827 — Canada's Cultural Fabric: a, Norse boat, L'Anse aux Meadows. b, Immigrants on Halifax's Pier 21. c, Neptune Theater, Halifax (head of Neptune). d, Stratford Festival (actor and theater).

No. 1828 — Literary Legends: a, W. O. Mitchell (1914-98), novelist, and prairie scene. b, Gratien Gélinas (1909-99), actor and playwright, and stars. c, Le Cercle du Livre de France book club. d, Harlequin paperback books.

No. 1829 — Great Thinkers: a, Marshall McLuhan (1911-80), philosopher, and television set. b, Northrop Frye (1912-91), literary critic, and word "code." c, Roger Lemelin (1919-92), novelist, and cast of "The Plouffe Family" TV series. d, Hilda Marion Neatby (1904-75), historian, and farm scene.

No. 1830 — A Tradition of Generosity: a, Hart Massey (1823-96), Hart House, University of Toronto. b, Dorothy (1899-1965) and Izaak Killam (1885-1955), philantropists, and molecular model. c, Eric Lafferty Harvie (1892-1975), philantropist, and mountain scene. d, Macdonald Stewart Foundation.

No. 1831 — Engineering and Technological Marvels: a, Map of Rogers Pass, locomotive, tunnel diggers. b, Manic Dams. c, Canadian satellites, Remote Manipulator Arm. d, CN Tower.

No. 1832 — Fathers of Invention: a, George Klein (1904-92), gearwheels. b, Abraham Gesner (1797-1864), beaker of kerosene and lamp. c, Alexander Graham Bell (1847-1922), passenger-carrying kite, hydrofoil. d, Joseph-Armand Bombardier (1907-64), snowmobile.

No. 1833 — Food: a, Sir Charles Saunders (1867-1937), Marquis wheat. b, Pablum. c, Dr. Archibald Gowanlock Huntsman (1883-1973), marketer of frozen fish. d, Products of McCain Foods, Ltd., tractor.

No. 1834 — Enterprising Giants: a, Hudson's Bay Company (Colonist, Indian, canoe). b, Bell Canada Enterprises (earth, satellite, string of binary digits). c, Vachon Co. snack cakes. d, George Weston Limited (Baked goods, eggs).

		Perf. 13¼
1999-2000	**Litho.**	
1818 A730 Pane of 4	6.50	6.50
a.-d. 46c any single	1.60	.80
1819 A730 Pane of 4	6.50	6.50
a.-d. 46c any single	1.60	.80
1820 A730 Pane of 4	6.50	6.50
a.-d. 46c any single	1.60	.80
1821 A730 Pane of 4	6.50	6.50
a.-d. 46c any single	1.60	.80
1822 A730 Pane of 4	6.50	6.50
a.-d. 46c any single	1.60	.80
1823 A730 Pane of 4	6.50	6.50
a.-d. 46c any single	1.60	.80
1824 A730 Pane of 4	6.50	6.50
a.-d. 46c any single	1.60	.80
1825 A730 Pane of 4	6.50	6.50
a.-d. 46c any single	1.60	.80
1826 A730 Pane of 4	6.50	6.50
a.-d. 46c any single	1.60	.80
1827 A730 Pane of 4	6.50	6.50
a.-d. 46c any single	1.60	.80
1828 A730 Pane of 4	6.50	6.50
a.-d. 46c any single	1.60	.80
1829 A730 Pane of 4	6.50	6.50
a.-d. 46c any single	1.60	.80
1830 A730 Pane of 4	6.50	6.50
a.-d. 46c any single	1.60	.80
1831 A730 Pane of 4	6.50	6.50
a.-d. 46c any single	1.60	.80
1832 A730 Pane of 4	6.50	6.50
a.-d. 46c any single	1.60	.80
1833 A730 Pane of 4	6.50	6.50
a.-d. 46c any single	1.60	.80
1834 A730 Pane of 4	6.50	6.50
a.-d. 46c any single	1.60	.80
Nos. 1818-1834 (17)	110.50	110.50

Issued: #1818-1821, 12/17; #1822-1825, 1/17/00; #1826-1830, 2/17/00; #1831-1834, 3/17/00.

Stamps similar to these were printed in a hardcover book produced by Canada Post Sept. 15, 1999 that sold for $59.99. Stamps from souvenir panes show a distinct upward turn of the tails of the nines in the small 1999 date at upper left. The tails of the nines on stamps from the book are flat.

Millennium — A731

2000, Jan. 1   *Perf. 13x12½*
1835 A731 46c multicolored   .90 .25

New Year 2000 (Year of the Dragon) — A732

Litho. & Embossed
2000, Jan. 5   *Perf. 12½x12¾*
1836 A732 46c multicolored   .90 .25
Souvenir Sheet
Perf. 13¾x13¼
1837 A732 95c multicolored   2.00 2.00
 a. Orange and tagging omitted   *1,600.*

No. 1837 has rounded corners and contains one 56x29mm stamp.

50th National Hockey League All-Star Game A733

Famous NHL players: a, Wayne Gretzky (Oilers jersey No. 99). b, Gordie Howe (Red Wings jersey No. 9). c, Maurice Richard (red, white and blue Canadiens jersey No. 9). d, Doug Harvey (Canadiens jersey No. 2). e,

Bobby Orr (Bruins jersey No. 4). f, Jacques Plante (Canadiens jersey No. 1).

2000, Feb. 5		**Litho.**	**Perf. 12¾**
1838	A733 Pane of 6	5.50	5.50
a.-f.	46c any single	.90	.60

Bird Type of 1996

Designs: Nos. 1839, 1843, Canada warbler. Nos. 1840, 1844, Osprey. Nos. 1841, 1845, Pacific loon. Nos. 1842, 1846, Blue jay.

2000, Mar. 1	**Litho.**	**Perf. 12½x13¼**	
1839	A650 46c multi	1.10	.35
1840	A650 46c multi	1.10	.35
1841	A650 46c multi	1.10	.35
1842	A650 46c multi	1.10	.35
a.	Block or strip of 4	4.50	2.75

Booklet Stamps
Self-Adhesive
Die Cut 11½x11¼

1843	A650 46c multi	1.10	.35
1844	A650 46c multi	1.10	.35
1845	A650 46c multi	1.10	.35
1846	A650 46c multi	1.10	.35
a.	Booklet pane, 2 each #1843-1844, 1 each #1845-1846	6.75	
b.	Booklet pane, 2 each #1845-1846, 1 each #1843-1844	6.75	
	Complete bklt., #1846a, 1846b	13.50	

Nos. 1839-1842 were issued in panes of 20, 5 each printed checkerwise to contain 4 complete blocks or strips.

Supreme Court, 125th Anniv. A734

2000, Apr. 10		**Perf. 12½x13¼**	
1847	A734 46c multi	.90	.25

Ritual of the Calling of an Engineer, 75th Anniv. — A735

2000, Apr. 25			
1848	A735 46c multi	.90	.25
a.	Tete-beche pair	1.80	1.25
b.	Silver ("CANADA 46") omitted	2,400.	

Decorated Rural Mailboxes — A736

Mailboxes with: No. 1849, Ship, fish, house designs. No. 1850, Flower, cow and church designs. No. 1851, Tractor design. No. 1852, Goose head, house designs.

Booklet Stamps
Perf. 12½x13¼ on 3 sides

2000, Apr. 28			
1849	A736 46c multi	1.10	.30
1850	A736 46c multi	1.10	.30
1851	A736 46c multi	1.10	.30
1852	A736 46c multi	1.10	.30
a.	Block of 4, #1849-1852	4.50	3.75
b.	Bklt. pane, 3 ea #1849-1852	13.50	
	Complete booklet, #1852a	14.00	

Picture Frame A737

Self-Adhesive
Serpentine Die Cut 11½

2000, Apr. 28			
1853	A737 46c multi	1.10	.30
a.	Booklet pane of 5 + 5 different labels	5.50	
	Complete booklet, #1853a	6.00	
b.	Pane of 25	45.00	

No. 1853b sold for $24.95 each for one or two panes, and $22.95 for three to ten panes. Twenty-five self-adhesive, die cut address labels and reproductions of a photo sent in by the customer are on the reverse of No. 1853b. These panes were not available at post offices or through the philatelic bureau, but special orders from the printer, Ashton-Potter. The front cover of the booklet containing No. 1853a served as the order blank for No. 1853b.

See No. 1882.

A738

A739

A740

A741

A742

A743

A744

A745

A746

Fresh Waters — A747

Self-Adhesive
Serpentine Die Cut 2½ Horiz.

2000, Feb. 23			
1854	Complete booklet, #a.-e.	8.50	
a.	A738 55c multi	1.70	1.10
b.	A739 55c multi	1.70	1.10
c.	A740 55c multi	1.70	1.10
d.	A741 55c multi	1.70	1.10
e.	A742 55c multi	1.70	1.10
1855	Complete booklet, #a.-e.	11.00	
a.	A743 95c multi	2.20	1.60
b.	A744 95c multi	2.20	1.60
c.	A745 95c multi	2.20	1.60
d.	A746 95c multi	2.20	1.60
e.	A747 95c multi	2.20	1.60

Queen Mother (b. 1900) A748

2000, May 23		**Perf. 13x13¼**	
1856	A748 95c multi	1.90	1.00

Boys and Girls Clubs of Canada, Cent. — A749

2000, June 1		**Perf. 13**	
1857	A749 46c multi	.90	.25

World Session of Seventh Day Adventist Church, Toronto A750

2000, June 29		**Perf. 13½x13¼**	
1858	A750 46c multi	.90	.25

Stampin' the Future Children's Stamp Design Contest Winners A751

Designs: No. 1859, Rainbow, space vehicle, astronauts, flag, by Rosalie Anne Nardelli. No. 1860, Three children in space vehicle, three children on ground, by Sarah Lutgen. No. 1861, Children and map of Canada, by Christine Weera. No. 1862, Two astronauts in space vehicle, planets, by Andrew Wright.

2000, July 1		**Perf. 13¼**	
1859	A751 46c multi	.90	.35
1860	A751 46c multi	.90	.35
1861	A751 46c multi	.90	.35
1862	A751 46c multi	.90	.35
a.	Block or strip, #1859-1862	3.60	3.00
b.	Souvenir sheet, #1859-1862	3.60	3.60

Art Type of 1988

The Artist at Niagara, by Cornelius Krieghoff.

Litho. with Foil Application

2000, July 7		**Perf. 12½x13¼**	
1863	A546 95c multi	1.90	.85

Tall Ships in Halifax Harbor — A752

Various ships: No. 1864, Denomination at L. No. 1865, Denomination at R.

Self-Adhesive
Booklet Stamps
Serpentine Die Cut 4¾x5

2000, July 19		**Litho.**	
1864	A752 46c multi	1.10	.40
1865	A752 46c multi	1.10	.40
a.	Pair, #1864-1865	2.20	
b.	Booklet, 5 #1864a	11.00	

Dept. of Labor, Cent. — A753

2000, Sept. 1		**Perf. 12½x13¼**	
1866	A753 46c multi	.90	.30

Petro-Canada, 25th Anniv. — A754

Self-Adhesive
Booklet Stamp

2000, Sept. 13		**Die Cut**	
1867	A754 46c multi	1.10	.40
a.	Booklet pane of 12	13.50	
	Booklet, #1867a	14.00	
b.	Die cutting inverted (2 points jut at T, L)	9.00	9.00

No. 1867a is the cover of an informational booklet about Petro-Canada. No. 1867b was issued in collector packs.

Cetaceans — A755

#1868, Monodon monoceros. #1869, Balaenoptera musculus. #1870, Balaena mysticetus. #1871, Delphinapterus leucas.

2000, Oct. 2		**Perf. 12½x13**	
1868	A755 46c multi	.90	.30
1869	A755 46c multi	.90	.30
1870	A755 46c multi	.90	.30
1871	A755 46c multi	.90	.30
a.	Block of 4, #1868-1871	3.60	2.75

Christmas A756

Self-Adhesive
Booklet Stamp
Serpentine Die Cut 11¾

2000, Oct. 5
1872 A756 46c multi   1.10 .80
   a.   Booklet pane of 5 + 5 labels   5.50
    Booklet, #1872a   6.00

See No. 1882e.

Christmas
A757

Designs: 46c, Adoration of the shepherds. 55c, Creche. 95c Flight into Egypt.

2000, Nov. 3   *Perf. 13¼*
1873 A757 46c multi   .90 .25
   a.   Booklet pane of 10   9.00 9.00
    Booklet, #1873a   9.50
1874 A757 55c multi   1.10 .35
   a.   Booklet pane of 6   6.75 6.75
    Booklet, #1874a   7.25
1875 A757 95c multi   1.90 .70
   a.   Booklet pane of 6   11.50 11.50
    Booklet, #1875a   12.00
    Nos. 1873-1875 (3)   3.90 1.30

Regiments
A758

No. 1876, Lord Strathcona's Horse Regiment. No. 1877, Les Voltigeurs de Quebec.

2000, Nov. 11   *Perf. 13¼x13*
1876 A758 46c multi   .90 .30
1877 A758 46c multi   .90 .30
   a.   Pair, #1876-1877   1.80 1.10

Maple Leaves
A759

Animals
A760

Self-Adhesive
Coil Stamps
Serpentine Die Cut 8½ Horiz.

2000, Dec. 28
1878 A759   47c multi   .95 .20
   a.   Blue inscriptions omitted   725.00
1879 A760   60c Red fox   1.20 .35
   a.   Booklet pane of 6   11.50
1880 A760   75c Gray wolf   1.50 .50
1881 A760 $1.05 White-tailed deer   2.10 .75
   a.   Booklet pane of 6   13.00
    Nos. 1878-1881 (4)   5.75 1.80

Nos. 1879a and 1881a are complete booklets. See No. 1927.

Frame Type of 2000

No. 1882: a, Silver. b, Like #1853. c, Mahogany. d, Love (roses). e, Christmas.

Self-Adhesive
Booklet Stamps
Serpentine Die Cut 11¾

2000, Dec. 28
1882   Bklt. pane of 5+5 labels   5.50
   a.-e.   A737 47c Any single   1.10 1.10
    Booklet, #1882   6.00

New Year 2001 (Year of the Snake)
A761

Litho. & Embossed

2001, Jan. 5   *Perf. 13¼*
1883 A761   47c green & multi   .95 .25
   a.   Gold omitted   1,600.

Souvenir Sheet
1884 A761 $1.05 brown & multi   2.50 2.50

National Hockey League Stars
A762

No. 1885: a, Jean Beliveau (Montreal Canadiens jersey No. 4). b, Terry Sawchuk (goalie in Detroit Red Wings uniform). c, Eddie Shore (Boston Bruins jersey No. 2). d, Denis Potvin (Islanders jersey No. 5). e, Bobby Hull (Chicago Black Hawks jersey No. 9). f, Syl Apps, Sr. (Toronto Maple Leafs jersey).

Perf. 12½x13 on 3 sides
2001, Jan. 18   Litho.
1885   Sheet of 6 + 3 labels   5.75 5.75
   a.-f.   A762 47c Any single   .95 .50

Bird Type of 1996

Designs: Nos. 1886, 1890, Golden eagle. Nos. 1887, 1891, Arctic tern. Nos. 1888, 1892, Rock ptarmigan. Nos. 1889, 1893, Lapland longspur.

2001, Feb. 1   *Perf. 12½x13*
1886 A650 47c multi   .95 .30
1887 A650 47c multi   .95 .30
1888 A650 47c multi   .95 .30
1889 A650 47c multi   .95 .30
   a.   Block or strip of 4, #1886-1889   3.80 2.75

Booklet Stamps
Self-Adhesive
Die Cut Perf 11½x11¼

1890 A650 47c multi   1.10 .35
1891 A650 47c multi   1.10 .35
1892 A650 47c multi   1.10 .35
1893 A650 47c multi   1.10 .35
   a.   Booklet pane, 2 each #1890-1891, 1 each #1892-1893   6.75
   b.   Booklet pane, 2 each #1892-1893, 1 each #1890-1891   6.75
    Booklet, #1893a, 1893b   13.50

Nos. 1886-1889 were issued in panes of 20, 5 each printed checkerwise to contain 4 complete blocks or strips.

Games of La Francophonie, Ottawa and Hull — A763

2001, Feb. 28   *Perf. 13¼*
1894 A763 47c High jumper   .95 .30
1895 A763 47c Dancer   .95 .30
   a.   Horiz. pair, #1894-1895   1.90 1.10

World Figure Skating Championships, Vancouver — A764

Designs: No. 1896, Pairs. No. 1897, Ice dancing. No. 1898, Men's singles. No. 1899, Women's singles.

2001, Mar. 19   *Perf. 13x12½*
1896 A764 47c shown   .95 .30
1897 A764 47c multi   .95 .30
1898 A764 47c multi   .95 .30
1899 A764 47c multi   .95 .30
   a.   Block of 4, #1896-1899   3.80 2.75

First Canadian Postage Stamps, 150th Anniv. — A765

Litho. & Engr.
2001, Apr. 6   *Perf. 13*
1900 A765 47c multi   .95 .30

Toronto Blue Jays Baseball Team, 25th Anniv. A766

Self-Adhesive
2001, Apr. 9   Litho.   *Die Cut*
1901 A766 47c multi   1.10 .30
   a.   Booklet pane of 8   9.00

No. 1901a is a complete booklet.

Summit of the Americas, Quebec — A767

2001, Apr. 20   *Perf. 13¼x13*
1902 A767 47c multi   .95 .30

Tourist Attractions — A768

No. 1903: a, Butchart Gardens, British Columbia. b, Apple Blossom Festival, Nova Scotia. c, White Pass and Yukon Route. d, Sugar bushes, Quebec. e, Niagara-on-the-Lake, Ontario.
No. 1904: a, The Forks, Manitoba. b, Barkerville, British Columbia. c, Canadian Tulip Festival, Ontario. d, Auyuittuq National Park, Nunavut. e, Signal Hill National Historic Site, Newfoundland.

Self-Adhesive
2001, May 11   *Die Cut Perf. 11x11¼*
1903   Booklet of 5   5.50
   a.-e.   A768 60c Any single   1.10 .75
1904   Booklet of 5   10.00
   a.-e.   A768 $1.05 Any single   2.00 1.25

See Nos. 1952-1953, 1989-1990.

Armenian Church, 1,700th Anniv. — A769

2001, May 16   *Perf. 13x12½*
1905 A769 47c multi   .95 .30

Royal Military College of Canada, 125th Anniv. — A770

2001, June 1   *Perf. 12½x13*
1906 A770 47c multi   .95 .30

Eighth Intl. Amateur Athletic Federation World Championships, Edmonton
A771

2001, June 25   *Perf. 12¾x12½*
1907 A771 47c Pole vault   .95 .30
1908 A771 47c Runner   .95 .30
   a.   Pair, #1907-1908   1.90 1.10

Pierre Elliott Trudeau (1919-2000), Prime Minister — A772

2001, July 1   *Perf. 13x12½*
1909 A772 47c multi   .95 .30
   a.   Souvenir sheet of 4   3.80 3.80

Roses — A773

Designs: Nos. 1910a, 1911, Morden Centennial. Nos. 1910b, 1912, Agnes. Nos. 1910c, 1913, Champlain. Nos. 1910d, 1914, Canadian White Star.
Illustration reduced.

Souvenir Sheet

2001, Aug. 1   **Perf. 12½x13**
1910   Pane of 4   5.00 5.00
a.-d. A773 47c Any single   1.25 .75

Booklet Stamps
Die Cut
1911 A773 47c multi   .95 .30
1912 A773 47c multi   .95 .30
1913 A773 47c multi   .95 .30
1914 A773 47c multi   .95 .30
   a.   Booklet pane, #1911-1914   3.80
    Booklet, 3 #1914a   11.50

Phila Nippon '01, Japan (No. 1910). Die cutting on Nos. 1911-1914 has "thorn" at the center of each side, pointing outward at top and left and toward the design at bottom and right.

Great Peace of Montreal, 300th Anniv. — A774

2001, Aug. 3   **Perf. 12½x13**
1915 A774 47c multi   .95 .30

Art Type of 1988
Design: The Space Between Columns #21 (Italian), by Jack Shadbolt.

Litho. with Foil Application
2001, Aug. 24   **Perf. 13x13¼**
1916 A546 $1.05 multi   2.00 1.10

Shriners — A775

2001, Sept. 19   Litho.   Perf. 13¼x13
1917 A775 47c multi   .95 .30

Frame Type of 2000 Inscribed "Domestic Lettermail / Poste-lettres du régime intérieur"
No. 1918: a, Like #1882a. b, Like #1882b. c, Baby toys and flowers. d, Like #1882d. e, Like #1882e.

Self-Adhesive
Serpentine Die Cut 11¾
2001, Sept. 21
1918   Bklt. pane of 5 + 5 labels   5.50
   a.-e. A737 (47c) Any single   1.10 1.10
    Booklet, #1918   6.00

Theater Anniversaries — A776

Designs: No. 1919, Théatre du Nouveau Monde, Montreal, 50th anniv. No. 1920, Grand Theater, London, Ont., cent.

2001, Sept. 28   **Perf. 12½x12¾**
1919 A776 47c multi   .95 .30
1920 A776 47c multi   .95 .30
   a.   Horiz. pair, #1919-1920   1.90 1.10

Hot Air Balloons A777

Background colors: a, Green. b, Blue violet. c, Red violet. d, Olive.

Self-Adhesive
2001, Oct. 1   *Die Cut*
1921   Booklet, 2 each #a-d   8.75
   a.-d. A777 47c Any single   1.10 .40

Christmas A778

Illuminated trees and: 47c, Horse-drawn sleigh. 60c, Skaters. $1.05, Children making snowman.

2001, Nov. 1   **Perf. 12½x13¼**
1922 A778   47c multi   .95 .25
   a.   Booklet pane of 10   9.50
    Booklet, #1922a   10.00
1923 A778   60c multi   1.20 .40
   a.   Booklet pane of 6   7.25
    Booklet, #1923a   7.75
1924 A778 $1.05 multi   2.10 .65
   a.   Booklet pane of 6   12.75
    Booklet, #1924a   13.25

YMCA in Canada, 150th Anniv. — A779

2001, Nov. 8   **Perf. 13¼**
1925 A779 47c multi   .95 .30

Royal Canadian Legion, 75th Anniv. — A780

2001, Nov. 11   **Perf. 12½x13**
1926 A780 47c multi   .95 .30

Maple Leaves Type of 2000, Traditional Handiwork Type of 1999 and

Flag and Canada Post Headquarters, Ottawa — A781

Designs: 65c, Jewelry making, horiz. 77c, Basket weaving, horiz. $1.25, Sculpture, horiz.

Self-Adhesive Coil Stamps
Serpentine Die Cut 8½ Horiz.
2002, Jan. 2
1927 A759   48c multi   .95 .20
1928 A684   65c multi   1.30 .40
   a.   Booklet of 6   8.00
1929 A684   77c multi   1.55 .40
1930 A684 $1.25 multi   2.50 .65
   a.   Booklet of 6   15.00

Booklet Stamp
Serpentine Die Cut 8½
1931 A781   48c multi   .95 .20
   a.   Booklet of 10   9.50
   b.   Booklet of 30   29.00
    Nos. 1927-1931 (5)   7.25 1.85

By separating the booklet along the columns of rouletting, No. 1931b could be broken up into three separately obtainable examples of No. 1931a. See No. 1991.

Reign of Queen Elizabeth II, 50th Anniv. A782

2002, Jan. 2   **Perf. 13¼x12½**
1932 A782 48c multi   .95 .30
   a.   Imperf, pair   1,500.

New Year 2002 (Year of the Horse) — A783

Horse and: 48c, Bamboo leaves. $1.25, Peach blossoms.

Litho. & Embossed With Foil Application
2002, Jan. 3   **Perf. 13¼**
1933 A783   48c multi   .95 .30

Souvenir Sheet
1934 A783 $1.25 multi   2.50 2.50

National Hockey League Stars A784

No. 1935: a, Tim Horton (Toronto Maple Leafs jersey No. 7). b, Guy Lafleur (Montreal Canadiens jersey No. 10). c, Howie Morenz (Canadiens jersey, with brown gloves). d, Glenn Hall (Chicago Black Hawks jersey No. 1). e, Red Kelly (Maple Leafs jersey No. 4). f, Phil Esposito (Boston Bruins jersey no. 7).

Perf. 12½x13 on 3 Sides
2002, Jan. 12
1935   Pane of 6 + 3 labels   6.00 6.00
   a.-f. A784 48c Any single   1.00 .65

2002 Winter Olympics, Salt Lake City — A785

Designs: No. 1936, Short track speed skating. No. 1937, Curling. No. 1938, Freestyle aerial skiing. No. 1939, Women's hockey.

2002, Jan. 25   **Perf. 13¼x13**
1936 A785 48c multi   .95 .35
1937 A785 48c multi   .95 .35
1938 A785 48c multi   .95 .35
1939 A785 48c multi   .95 .35
   a.   Block or strip of 4, #1936-1939   3.80 3.20

Appointment of First Canadian Governor General, 50th Anniv. A786

2002, Feb. 1   **Perf. 13¼x12½**
1940 A786 48c multi   .95 .30

Universities — A787

Design: No. 1941, University of Manitoba, 125th anniv. No. 1942, Laval University, 150th anniv. No. 1943, University of Trinity College, 150th anniv. No. 1944, Saint Mary's University, Halifax, 200th anniv.

Booklet Stamp
2002   **Perf. 13½**
1941 A787 48c multi   .95 .30
   a.   Booklet pane of 8   7.50
    Booklet, #1941a   8.00
1942 A787 48c multi   .95 .30
   a.   Booklet pane of 8   7.50
    Booklet, #1942a   8.00
1943 A787 48c multi   .95 .30
   a.   Booklet pane of 8   7.50
    Booklet, #1943a   8.00
1944 A787 48c multi   .95 .30
   a.   Booklet pane of 8   7.50
    Booklet, #1944a   8.00
    Nos. 1941-1944 (4)   3.80 1.20

Issued: No. 1941, 2/28. No. 1942, 4/4. No. 1943, 4/30. No. 1944, 5/27.

Art Type of 1988
Design: Church and Horse, by Alex Colville.

Litho. with Foil Application
2002, Mar. 22   **Perf. 12½x13**
1945 A546 $1.25 multi   2.50 1.25
   a.   Foil only (all other colors and tagging omitted)   1,600.
   b.   Imperf, pair   1,500.

Tulips — A788

Tulip varieties: a, City of Vancouver. b, Monte Carlo. c, Ottawa. d, The Bishop.
No. 1947: a, Like #1946a. b, Like #1946b. c, Like #1946c. d, Like #1946d.

Self-Adhesive
2002, May 3   Litho.   Die Cut
1946   Booklet pane of 4   3.80
   a.-d. A788 48c Any single   .95 .30
    Booklet, 2 #1946   7.75

Souvenir Sheet
Perf. 13x12½
1947   Pane of 4   3.80 3.80
   a.-d. A788 48c Any single   .95 .85

Issued: No. 1946, 5/3; No. 1947, 8/30.

Dendronepthea Giagantea and Dendronepthea Corals — A789

Tubastrea and Echinogorgia Corals — A790

North Atlantic Pink Tree, Pacific Orange Cup and North Pacific Horn Corals
A791

North Atlantic Giant Orange Tree and Black Corals
A792

2002, May 19   *Perf. 12½x13*
1948	A789 48c multi	.95	.35
1949	A790 48c multi	.95	.35
1950	A791 48c multi	.95	.35
1951	A792 48c multi	.95	.35
a.	Block of 4, #1948-1951	3.80	3.00
b.	Souvenir sheet, #1948-1951, perf. 13¼x13	3.80	3.80

See Hong Kong Nos. 979-982.

Tourist Attractions Type of 2001

No. 1952: a, Yukon Quest, Yukon Territory. b, Icefields Parkway, Alberta. c, Agawa Canyon, Ontario. d, Old Port of Montreal, Quebec. e, Kings Landing, New Brunswick.
No. 1953: a, Northern Lights, Northwest Territories. b, Stanley Park, Vancouver, British Columbia. c, Head-Smashed-In Buffalo Jump, Alberta. d, Saguenay Fjord, Quebec. e, Peggy's Cove, Nova Scotia.

Self-Adhesive
2002, June 1   *Die Cut Perf. 11x11¼*
1952	Booklet of 5	6.25	
a.-e.	A768 65c Any single	1.25	.85
1953	Booklet of 5	12.50	
a.-e.	A768 $1.25 Any single	2.50	1.20

Sculpture — A793

Designs: No. 1954, Embacle, by Charles Daudelin. No. 1955, Lumberjacks, by Leo Mol.

2002, June 10   *Perf. 13¼*
1954	A793 48c multi	.95	.30
1955	A793 48c multi	.95	.30
a.	Horiz. or vert. pair, #1954-1955	1.90	1.00

Canadian Postmasters and Assistants Association, Cent. — A794

2002, July 5   *Perf. 13¼x12½*
1956	A794 48c multi	.95	.30

Printed in panes of 16 stamps + 12 labels.

17th World Youth Day, Toronto — A795

Self-Adhesive
Booklet Stamp
2002, July 23   *Die Cut*
1957	A795 48c multi	.95	.30
a.	Booklet of 8	7.75	

Public Services International World Congress, Ottawa — A796

2002, Sept. 4   *Perf. 12½x13*
1958	A796 48c multi	.95	.30

Public Pensions, 75th Anniv. — A797

2002, Sept. 10   *Perf. 13¼*
1959	A797 48c multi	.95	.30

Souvenir Sheet

Intl. Year of Mountains — A798

No. 1960: a, Mt. Logan, Canada. b, Mt. Elbrus, Russia. c, Puncak Jaya, Indonesia. d, Mt. Everest, Nepal and China. e, Mt. Kilimanjaro, Tanzania. f, Vinson Massif, Antarctica. g, Mt. Aconcagua, Argentina. h, Mt. McKinley, Alaska.

Self-Adhesive
2002, Oct. 1   *Die Cut*
1960	A798 Pane of 8 + 8 labels	9.00	9.00
a.-h.	48c Any single	1.10	1.10

World Teachers' Day — A799

2002, Oct. 4   *Perf. 12½x13*
1961	A799 48c multi	.95	.30

Toronto Stock Exchange, 150th Anniv. — A800

2002, Oct. 24
1962	A800 48c multi	.95	.30

Communication Technology Centenaries — A801

Part of map of North America and: No. 1963, Sir Sandford Fleming (1827-1915), cable-laying ship . No. 1964, Guglielmo Marconi (1874-1937), radio and transmission towers.

2002, Oct. 31   *Perf. 13x12½*
1963	48c multi	.95	.30
1964	48c multi	.95	.30
a.	A801 Horiz. pair, #1963-1964	1.90	1.20

Cent. of first telegraph message sent over transpacific cable (#1963); first transatlantic radio message (#1964).

Christmas A802

Art by aboriginals: 48c, Genesis, by Daphne Odjig. 65c, Winter Travel, by Cecil Youngfox. $1.25, Mary and Child, sculpture by Irene Katak Angutitaq.

2002, Nov. 4   *Perf. 12½x13*
1965	A802 48c multi	.95	.25
a.	Booklet pane of 10	9.50	
	Booklet, #1965a	10.00	
1966	A802 65c multi	1.30	.40
a.	Booklet pane of 6	8.00	
	Booklet, #1966a	8.50	
1967	A802 $1.25 multi	2.50	.80
a.	Booklet pane of 6	15.00	
	Booklet, #1967a	15.50	
	Nos. 1965-1967 (3)	4.75	1.45

Quebec Symphony Orchestra, Cent. A803

2002, Nov. 7
1968	A803 48c multi	.95	.30

New Year 2003 (Year of the Ram) — A804

Litho. & Embossed with Foil Application
2003, Jan. 3   *Perf. 13*
1969	A804 48c shown	.95	.30
a.	Gold omitted	400.00	

Souvenir Sheet
Perf. 13¼
1970	A804 $1.25 Ram, diff.	2.50	2.50

No. 1970 contains one 33x58mm stamp. Slits replace perforations on the vertical sides of the stamps between the point of the acute angle made with the curving perforations and the point perpendicular to where the perforations on the opposite side form the obtuse angle with the curving perforations.

National Hockey League Stars A805

Designs: Nos. 1971a, 1972a, Frank Mahovlich (orange panel). Nos. 1971b, 1972b, Raymond Bourque (lilac panel). Nos. 1971c, 1972c, Serge Savard (blue panel). Nos. 1971d, 1972d, Stan Mikita (red violet panel). Nos. 1971e, 1972e, Mike Bossy (bright pink panel). Nos. 1971f, 1972f, Bill Durnan (green panel).

Perf. 12½x13¼ on 3 Sides
2003, Jan. 18
1971	Pane of 6 + 3 labels	16.00	—
a.-f.	A805 48c Any single	2.50	2.00

Self-Adhseive
Die Cut
1972	Pane of 6	62.50	
a.-f.	A805 48c Any single	7.00	2.00

Universities A806

Design: No. 1973, Bishop's University, Lennoxville, Quebec, 150th anniv. No. 1974, University of Western Ontario, London, Ont., 125th anniv. No. 1975, St. Francis Xavier University, Antigonish, N. S., 150th Anniv. No. 1976, Macdonald Institute, Guelph, Ont., cent. No. 1977, University of Montreal, 125th anniv.

Booklet Stamps
2003   *Perf. 13¼x13½*
1973	A806 48c multi	.95	.30
a.	Booklet pane of 8	7.75	—
	Booklet, #1973a	8.25	
1974	A806 48c multi	.95	.30
a.	Booklet pane of 8	7.75	—
	Booklet, #1974a	8.25	
1975	A806 48c multi	.95	.30
a.	Booklet pane of 8	7.75	—
	Complete booklet, #1975a	8.25	
1976	A806 48c multi	.95	.30
a.	Booklet pane of 8	7.75	—
	Booklet, #1976a	8.25	
1977	A806 48c multi	.95	.30
a.	Booklet pane of 8	7.75	—
	Complete booklet, #1977a	8.25	

Issued: No. 1973, 1/28. No. 1975, 4/4. No. 1976, 6/20. No. 1977, 9/4. No. 1974, 3/19.
See Nos. 2033-2034, 2089, 2172, 2209-2210.

Bird Paintings by John James Audubon — A807

Designs: No. 1979, Leach's storm petrel. No. 1980, Brant. No. 1981, Great cormorant. No. 1982, Common murre. 65c, Gyrfalcon, vert.

2003, Feb. 21   *Perf. 13¼x12½*
1979	A807 48c multi	.95	.35
1980	A807 48c multi	.95	.35
1981	A807 48c multi	.95	.35
1982	A807 48c multi	.95	.35
a.	Block of 4, #1979-1982	3.80	2.75

Booklet Stamp
Self-Adhesive
Die Cut
1983	A807 65c multi	1.30	.75
a.	Booklet pane of 6	8.00	
	Nos. 1979-1983 (5)	5.10	2.15

Canadian Rangers — A808

2003, Mar. 3   *Perf. 12½x13¼*
1984 A808 48c multi   .95 .30

American Hellenic Educational Progressive Association In Canada, 75th Anniv. — A809

2003, Mar. 25
1985 A809 48c multi   .95 .30

Volunteer Firefighters A810

2003, May 30   *Perf. 13¼*
1986 A810 48c multi   .95 .30

Coronation of Queen Elizabeth II, 50th Anniv. A811

2003, June 2   *Perf. 13x12½*
1987 A811 48c multi   .95 .30

Quebec City, Seal of Sovereign Council of New France, Signature of Pedro da Silva — A812

2003, June 6   *Perf. 13*
1988 A812 48c multi   .95 .30

Pedro da Silva, first courier in New France, 50th anniv. of Portuguese immigration to Canada.

Tourist Attractions Type of 2001

No. 1989: a, Wilberforce Falls, Nunavut. b, Inside Passage, B. C. c, Royal Canadian Mounted Police Depot Division, Regina, Sask. d, Casa Loma, Toronto, Ont. e, Gatineau Park, Que.

No. 1990: a, Dragon boat races, Vancouver, B. C. b, Polar bear watching, Man. c, Niagara Falls, Ont. d, Magdalen Islands, Que. e, Charlottestown, P. E. I.

Self-Adhesive

2003, June 12   *Die Cut Perf. 11¼*
1989   Booklet of 5   6.50
   a.-e.   A768 65c Any single   1.30 .70
1990   Booklet of 5   12.50
   a.-e.   A768 $1.25 Any single   2.50 1.20

"Vancouver 2010" Added in Red

Self-Adhesive
Booklet Stamp
Serpentine Die Cut 8½

2003, July 11   Litho.
1991 A781 48c multi   1.75 1.20
  a.   Booklet of 10   17.50
  b.   Booklet of 30   52.50
  c.   Die cutting omitted, pair   *800.00*

Selection of Vancouver as site of 2010 Winter Olympics. By separating the booklet along the columns of rouletting, No. 1991b could be broken up into three separately obtainable examples of No. 1991a.

Canada-Alaska Cruise Scenes — A813

Mountains and: No. 1991C, Totem pole. No. 1991D, Whale's tail.

Self-Adhesive

2003, July 19   *Die Cut*
1991C A813 ($1.25) multi   8.25 8.25
1991D A813 ($1.25) multi   8.25 8.25
  e.   Horiz. pair, #1991C-1991D   16.50

Nos. 1991C-1991D were printed in panes of 10 containing five of each stamp. The blank spaces in each stamp and the three stamp-like vignettes at the left of the pane that lack die cutting and "Postage Paid / Port Payé" inscription could be personalized on cruise ships. Personalized panes sold for $19.95 in US currency, while unpersonalized panes sold for $12.50. Value, unpersonalized complete pane $80.

Lutheran World Federation, 10th Assembly, Winnipeg A814

2003, July 21   *Perf. 12½x13*
1992 A814 48c multi   .95 .30

Korean War Armistice Agreement, 50th Anniv. — A815

2003, July 25   *Perf. 12¾*
1993 A815 48c multi   .95 .30

Authors A816

Designs: No. 1994, Anne Hébert (1916-2000). No. 1995, Hector de Saint-Denys Garneau (1912-43). No. 1996, Morley Callaghan (1903-90). No. 1997, Susanna Moodie (1803-85), and Catharine Parr Traill (1802-99).

Booklet Stamps

2003, Sept. 8   *Perf. 13¼x12½*
1994 A816 48c multi   .95 .35
1995 A816 48c multi   .95 .35
1996 A816 48c multi   .95 .35
1997 A816 48c multi   .95 .35
  a.   Block of 4, #1994-1997   3.80 2.75
  b.   Booklet pane, 2 #1997a   7.75
    Complete booklet, #1997b   8.25

2003 Road Cycling World Championships, Hamilton, Ont. — A817

Booklet Stamp

2003, Sept. 10   *Perf. 12½x13*
1998 A817 48c multi   .95 .55
  a.   Booklet pane of 8   7.75
    Complete booklet, #1998a   8.25

Canadian Astronauts A818

No. 1999: a, Marc Garneau. b, Roberta Bondar. c, Steve MacLean. d, Chris Hadfield. e, Robert Thirsk. f, Bjarni Tryggvason. g, Dave Williams. h, Julie Payette.

Self-Adhesive
Litho. With Foil Application

2003, Oct. 1   *Die Cut*
1999   Pane of 8   10.00
  a.-h.   A818 48c Any single   .95 .75

Trees of Canada and Thailand — A819

Designs: No. 2000, Acer saccharum leaves (Canada). No. 2001, Cassia fistula (Thailand).

2003, Oct. 4   Litho.   *Perf. 12¾x12½*
2000 A819 48c multi   .95 .30
2001 A819 48c multi   .95 .30
  a.   Pair, #2000-2001   1.90 1.25
  b.   Souvenir sheet, #2000-2001   5.00 5.00
  c.   As "a," imperf   *1,000.*
  d.   As "b," imperf   *1,600.*

Bangkok 2003 Intl. Philatelic Exhibition (#2001b).
See Thailand No. 2090.

L'Hommage à Rosa Luxemburg, by Jean-Paul Riopelle — A820

Painting details — No. 2002; a, Red and blue dots between birds at LR. b, Bird with yellow beak at center. c, Three birds in circle at R. d, Sun at UR. e, Birds with purple outlines at L. f, Bird with red outline in circle at R. $1.25, Pink bird in red circle at R.

2003, Oct. 7   *Perf. 12½x13*
2002 A820   Pane of 6   8.50 8.50
  a.-f.   48c Any single   1.40 1.00

Souvenir Sheet
Perf. 12¾

2003 A820 $1.25 multi   3.25 3.25

Christmas A821

Gift boxes and: 48c, Ice skates. 65c, Teddy bear. $1.25, Toy duck.

Self-Adhesive
Booklet Stamps

2003, Nov. 4   *Die Cut*
2004 A821   48c multi   .95 .30
  a.   Booklet pane of 6   5.75
    Complete booklet, 2 #2004a   11.50
  b.   Pair, die cutting omitted   400.00
2005 A821   65c multi   1.30 .60
  a.   Booklet pane of 6   7.75
  b.   As "a," die cutting omitted   1,600.
2006 A821 $1.25 multi   2.50 1.00
  a.   Booklet pane of 6   15.00
  b.   Die cutting omitted, pair   500.00
    Nos. 2004-2006 (3)   4.75 1.90

Maple Leaf and Samara A822   Maple Leaf on Twig A823

Flag Over Edmonton, Alberta A824   Queen Elizabeth II A825

Coil Stamps
Self-Adhesive

2003, Dec. 19
Serpentine Die Cut 8½ Horiz.
2008 A822 49c multi   1.00 .20

Serpentine Die Cut 8½ Vert.
2009 A823 80c red & multi   1.60 .40
2010 A823 $1.40 grn & multi   2.80 .60

Booklet Stamps
Die Cut

2011 A824 49c multi   1.00 .20
  a.   Booklet pane of 10   10.00
  b.   Die cutting omitted, pair   160.00
2012 A825 49c multi   1.00 .20
  a.   Booklet pane of 10   10.00
2013 A823 80c red & multi   1.60 .35
  a.   Booklet pane of 6   9.50
2014 A823 $1.40 grn & multi   2.80 .65
  a.   Booklet pane of 6   17.00
    Nos. 2008-2014 (7)   11.80 2.60

See Nos. 2053-2055, 2075.

New Year 2004 (Year of the Monkey) — A826

Scenes from Chinese story *Journey to the West*: 49c, Monkey King. $1.40, Monkey King, Xuan Zang, Sandy, Pigsy and horse.

Litho. & Embossed with Foil Application

2004, Jan. 8   *Perf. 13x12½*
2015 A826 49c multi   1.00 .30

Souvenir Sheet

2016 A826 $1.40 multi   3.25 3.25
  a.   As No. 2016, with 2004 Hong Kong Stamp Expo ovpt. in margin   4.00 4.00

No. 2016 has rouletted tab at right showing bar code.

National Hockey League Stars
A827

Designs: Nos. 2017a, 2018a, Larry Robinson (blue background). Nos. 2017b, 2018b, Marcel Dionne (orange background). Nos. 2017c, 2018c, Ted Lindsay (red background). Nos. 2017d, 2018d, Johnny Bower (green background). Nos. 2017e, 2018e, Brad Park (brown background). Nos. 2017f, 2018f, Milt Schmidt (purple background).

Perf. 12½x13¼ on 3 Sides

2004, Jan. 24   **Litho.**
2017   Pane of 6 + 3 labels   6.75 6.75
  a.-f. A827 49c Any single   1.00 .60

Self-Adhesive
Die Cut

2018   Pane of 6   6.75
  a.-f. A827 49c Any single   1.00 .55

Tourist Attractions Type of 2001

Design: No. 2019, Quebec Winter Carnival; No. 2020, St. Joseph's Oratory, Montreal, Quebec; No. 2021, International Jazz Festival, Montreal. No. 2022, Traversée Internationale du Lac St. Jean Swimming Marathon, Quebec; No. 2023, Canadian National Exhibition, Toronto.

Self-Adhesive
Booklet Stamp

2004, Jan. 29   *Die Cut*
2019 A768 49c multi   1.00 .35
  a.   Booklet of 6   6.00
2020 A768 49c multi   1.00 .35
  a.   Booklet of 6   6.00
2021 A768 49c multi   1.00 .35
  a.   Booklet of 6   6.00
2022 A768 49c multi   1.00 .35
  a.   Booklet of 6   6.00
2023 A768 49c multi   1.00 .35
  a.   Booklet of 6   6.00

Issued: No. 2019, 1/29; No. 2020, 4/2; No. 2021, 6/1; No. 2022, 6/18; No. 2023, 7/19.

Governor General Ramon John Hnatyshyn (1934-2002) — A828

2004, Mar. 16   *Perf. 12½x13*
2024 A828 49c multi   1.00 .25

Royal Canadian Army Cadets, 125th Anniv. A829

Self-Adhesive
Booklet Stamp

2004, Mar. 26   *Die Cut*
2025 A829 49c multi   1.00 .30
  a.   Booklet pane of 4   4.00
       Complete booklet, 2 #2025a   8.00

The Fram, Ship of Otto Sverdrup (1854-1930), Arctic Explorer — A830

Litho. & Engr.

2004, Mar. 26   *Perf. 13¼*
2026 A830 49c multi   1.00 .30

Souvenir Sheet

2027 A830 $1.40 multi + 2 labels   3.25 3.25

See Greenland No. 426, Norway Nos. 1398-1399.

Urban Transit and Light Rail Systems — A831

Train cars, station names and system emblems of: No. 2028, Toronto Transit Commission. No. 2029, TransLink SkyTrain, Vancouver. No. 2030, Société de Transport de Montreal. No. 2031, Calgary Transit Light Rail.

2004, Mar. 30   Litho.   *Perf. 12½x13*
2028 A831 49c multi   1.00 .30
2029 A831 49c multi   1.00 .30
2030 A831 49c multi   1.00 .30
2031 A831 49c multi   1.00 .30
  a.   Vert. strip of 4, #2028-2031   4.00 2.75

Home Hardware, 40th Anniv. — A832

Self-Adhesive
Booklet Stamp

2004, Apr. 19   *Die Cut Perf. 11*
2032 A832 49c multi   1.00 .20
  a.   Booklet pane of 10 + label   10.00
       Complete booklet, #2032a   10.50

No. 2032a is the inside front cover of the complete booklet. Fifteen self-adhesive seals are on the inside back cover of the complete booklet.

Universities Type of 2003

Designs: No. 2033, Sherbrooke University, Sherbrooke, Quebec, 50th anniv. No. 2034, University of Prince Edward Island, Charlottetown, bicent.

Booklet Stamps

2004   *Perf. 13¼x13½*
2033 A806 49c multi   1.00 .30
  a.   Booklet pane of 8   8.00
       Complete booklet, #2033a   8.50
2034 A806 49c multi   1.00 .30
  a.   Booklet pane of 8   8.00
       Complete booklet, #2034a   8.50

Issued: No. 2033, 5/4; No. 2034, 5/8.

Montreal Children's Hospital, Cent. — A833

Self-Adhesive
Booklet Stamp

2004, May 6   *Die Cut Perf. 9½x10¾*
2035 A833 49c multi   1.00 .35
  a.   Booklet pane of 4   4.00
       Complete booklet, 2 #2035a   8.00

Bird Paintings by John James Audubon A834

Designs: No. 2036, Ruby-crowned kinglet. No. 2037, White-winged crossbill. No. 2038, Bohemian waxwing. No. 2039, Boreal chickadee. 80c, Lincoln's sparrow.

2004, May 14   *Perf. 12½x13*
2036 A834 49c multi   1.00 .35
2037 A834 49c multi   1.00 .35
2038 A834 49c multi   1.00 .35
2039 A834 49c multi   1.00 .35
  a.   Block of 4, #2036-2039   4.00 3.00

Self-Adhesive
Booklet Stamp
Die Cut

2040 A834 80c multi   1.60 .65
  a.   Booklet pane of 6   9.50
     Nos. 2036-2040 (5)   5.60 2.05

Pioneers of Transatlantic Mail Service — A835

Designs: No. 2041, Sir Samuel Cunard (1787-1865). No. 2042, Sir Hugh Allan (1810-82).

Self-Adhesive

2004, May 28   *Perf. 13¼x12½*
2041 A835 49c multi   1.00 .30
2042 A835 49c multi   1.00 .30
  a.   Horiz. pair, #2041-2042   2.00 1.20

D-Day, 60th Anniv. A836

2004, June 6   *Perf. 13x12½*
2043 A836 49c multi   1.00 .30

Pierre Dugua de Mons, Leader of First French Settlement in Acadia, and Ship A837

2004, June 26   **Litho. & Engr.**
2044 A837 49c multi   1.00 .30

See France No. 3032.

Butterfly and Flower A838

Children on Beach A839

Rose A840

Dog A841

Self-Adhesive
Booklet Stamps

Serpentine Die Cut 11¾

2004, June   **Litho.**
2045 A838 (49c) multi   10.00 *15.00*
  a.   Booklet pane of 2   20.00
       Complete booklet, #2045a + phonecard in greeting card   26.00
2046 A839 (49c) multi   10.00 *15.00*
  a.   Booklet pane of 2   20.00
       Complete booklet, #2046a + phonecard in greeting card   26.00
2047 A840 (49c) multi   10.00 *15.00*
  a.   Booklet pane of 2   20.00
       Complete booklet, #2047a + phonecard in greeting card   26.00
2048 A841 (49c) multi   10.00 *15.00*
  a.   Booklet pane of 2   20.00
       Complete booklet, #2048a + phonecard in greeting card   26.00
     Nos. 2045-2048 (4)   40.00 60.00

Nos. 2045-2048, have a frame like No. 1918a, and are similarly inscribed "Domestic Lettermail" and "Poste-lettres du régime intérieur," but Nos. 2045-2048 have the vignettes printed on the stamps, while any vignettes found on No. 1918a are affixed stickers. Nos. 2045a-2048a are affixed to the insides of greeting cards that contain detachable phonecards valid for 15 minutes calling time on any touchtone phone in Canada or the United States. The stamps were available only in the greeting card, which sold for $5.99 along with a blank envelope for sending the greeting card.

2004 Summer Olympics, Athens — A842

Olympic rings and: No. 2049, Spyros Louis, 1896 Marathon gold medalist, diagram of track, "Athens" in Greek, and stylized runner. No. 2050, Soccer net inscribed "Canada," girls playing soccer.

2004, July 28   *Perf. 12½x13¼*
2049 A842 49c multi   1.00 .30
2050 A842 49c multi   1.00 .30
  a.   Horiz. pair, #2049-2050   2.00 1.25

Canadian Open Golf Championship, Cent. — A843

Crowd, trophy and golfer: No. 2051, Finishing swing. No. 2052, Ready to putt.

Self-Adhesive

Litho. & Embossed With Foil Application

2004, Aug. 12			*Serpentine Die Cut*	
2051	A843	49c multi	1.00	.30
2052	A843	49c multi	1.00	.30

Nos. 2051-2052 were issued in a sheet containing four of each stamp.

Maple Leaf Types of 2003
Self-Adhesive　Coil Stamps

2004, Aug. 18		Litho.	*Die Cut*	
2053	A822	49c multi	1.00	.20

Serpentine Die Cut 8¼ Horiz.

2054	A823	80c red & multi	1.90	.55
2055	A823	$1.40 grn & multi	3.25	.85
a.	Die cutting omitted, pair			
	Nos. 2053-2055 (3)		6.15	1.60

Die cut gauges on Nos. 2054-2055 vary widely within the roll, from 8¼-8¾. Gauge 8¼ is the most common.

Montreal Heart Institute, 50th Anniv. — A844

Self-Adhesive
Booklet Stamp

2004, Sept. 15			*Die Cut Perf. 13½*	
2056	A844	49c multi	1.00	.30
a.	Booklet pane of 4		4.00	
	Complete booklet, 2 #2056		8.00	

Pets A845

Self-Adhesive
Booklet Stamps

2004, Oct. 1			*Die Cut*	
2057	A845	49c Fish	1.00	.35
2058	A845	49c Cats	1.00	.35
2059	A845	49c Rabbit	1.00	.35
2060	A845	49c Dog	1.00	.35
a.	Booklet pane, #2057-2060		4.00	
	Complete booklet, 2 #2060a		8.00	

Nobel Laureates in Chemistry — A846

Designs: No. 2061, Gerhard Herzberg, 1971 laureate, and molecular structures. No. 2062, Michael Smith, 1993 laureate, and DNA double helix.

2004, Oct. 4			*Perf. 12½x13*	
2061	A846	49c multi	1.00	.30
2062	A846	49c multi	1.00	.30
a.	Pair, #2061-2062		2.00	1.20

Ribbon Frame A847

Picture Album Frame A848

Self-Adhesive

Serpentine Die Cut 12¾x13

2004, Oct. 8				
2063	A847	(49c) multi	1.00	.75
2064	A848	(49c) multi	1.00	.75

Nos. 2063 and 2064 were each printed in panes of 21 that sold for $9.80. These panes were split by a row of rouletting in the center, with 20 stamps on one side and one on the other side. Panes of 21 with vignettes that could be personalized by the customer were available for $24.95. Panes of 40 stamps with personalized vignettes were also available for $39.95.

Victoria Cross, 150th Anniv. — A849

Designs: No. 2065, Victoria Cross. No. 2066, Design for Canadian Victoria Cross, approved with Queen Elizabeth II's signature.

Litho. & Embossed

2004, Oct. 21			*Perf. 13x12½*	
2065	A849	49c multi	1.00	.30

Litho.

2066	A849	49c multi	1.00	.30
a.	Pair, #2065-2066		2.00	1.20

Paintings by Jean Paul Lemieux — A850

Designs: 49c, Self-portrait. 80c, A June Wedding, horiz. (53x35mm). $1.40, Summer, horiz. (64x31mm).

2004, Oct. 22			*Perf. 13x13¼*	
2067	A850	49c multi	1.00	.35
a.	Perf. 13		1.75	1.60

Souvenir Sheet
Perf. 13

2068		Sheet, #2067a, 2068a,		
		2068b	6.00	6.00
a.	A850 80c multi		1.60	1.60
b.	A850 $1.40 multi		2.60	2.60

Christmas — A851

Santa Claus and: 49c, Sleigh. 80c, Automobile. $1.40, Train.

Self-Adhesive
Booklet Stamps
Serpentine Die Cut 7¼ Horiz.

2004, Nov. 2				
2069	A851	49c multi	1.00	.20
a.	Booklet pane of 6		6.00	
	Complete booklet, 2 #2069a		12.50	

2070	A851	80c multi	1.60	.50
a.	Booklet pane of 6		9.50	
2071	A851	$1.40 multi	2.80	.80
a.	Booklet pane of 6		16.75	

Queen Type of 2003 and

Red Calla Lilies A852

Flag and Saskatoon, Saskatchewan A853

Flag and Durrell, Newfoundland A854

Flag and Shannon Falls, British Columbia A855

Flag and Mont-Saint-Hilaire, Quebec — A856

Flag and Toronto — A857

Designs: 85c, Yellow calla lily. $1.45, Dutch iris.

Self-Adhesive
Coil Stamps

Serpentine Die Cut 6½-8¾ Horiz.

2004-05				
2072	A852	50c multi	1.00	.20
a.	Serpentine die cut 6¾ horiz. ('05)		1.00	.20
2073	A852	85c multi	1.70	.30
a.	Serpentine die cut 6¾ horiz. ('05)		1.80	.30
2074	A852	$1.45 multi	2.90	.65
a.	Serpentine die cut 6¾ horiz. ('05)		4.25	1.60

The die cutting gauge on Nos. 2072-2074a will vary between stamps on a roll and between stamps on one roll and other rolls. Issued: Nos. 2072, 2073, 2074, 12/20/04. Nos. 2072a, 2073a, 2074a, 2/2005. Die cuttings on these issues are variable.

Booklet Stamps
Die Cut

2075	A825	50c multi	1.00	.20
a.	Booklet pane of 10		10.00	
2076	A853	50c multi	1.00	.20
2077	A854	50c multi	1.00	.20
2078	A855	50c multi	1.00	.20
2079	A856	50c multi	1.00	.20
2080	A857	50c multi	1.00	.20
a.	Booklet pane, 2 each #2076-2080		10.00	
2081	A852	85c multi	1.90	.40
a.	Booklet pane of 6		11.50	
b.	As "a," black inscriptions omitted		5,000.	
2082	A852	$1.45 multi	2.90	.60
a.	Booklet pane of 6		17.50	
	Nos. 2072-2082 (11)		16.40	3.35

New Year 2005 (Year of the Cock) — A858

Rooster with: 50c, Red tail feathers. $1.45, Gold tail feathers.

Litho. & Embossed with Foil Application

2005, Jan. 7			*Perf. 13¼*	
2083	A858	50c multi	1.00	.30
a.	Red omitted		1,600.	

Souvenir Sheet
Perf. 12½x13

2084	A858	$1.45 multi	2.90	2.90
a.	With dates, Canadian and Chinese flags added in sheet margin		4.00	4.00

Canada — People's Republic of China diplomatic relations, 35th anniv. (#2084a). No. 2084 contains one 40x40mm stamp.

National Hockey League Stars A859

Designs: Nos. 2085a, 2086a, Henri Richard (blue background). Nos. 2085b, 2086b, Grant Fuhr (orange background). Nos. 2085c, 2086c, Allan Stanley (red background). Nos. 2085d, 2086d, Pierre Pilote (green background). Nos. 2085e, 2086e, Bryan Trottier (purple background). Nos. 2085f, 2086f, John Bucyk (yellow background).

Perf. 12½x13¼ on 3 Sides

2005, Jan. 29			Litho.	
2085		Pane of 6 + 3 labels	6.00	6.00
a.-f.	A859 50c Any single		1.00	.55

Self-Adhesive
Die Cut

2086		Pane of 6	6.00	
a.-f.	A859 50c Any single		1.00	.50

Fishing Flies — A860

Designs: Nos. 2087a, 2088a, Alevin. Nos. 2087b, 2088b, Jock Scott. Nos. 2087c, 2088d, P. E. I. Fly. Nos. 2087d, 2088c, Mickey Finn.

2005, Feb. 4			*Perf. 12½x13¼*	
2087	A860	Pane of 4	6.00	6.00
a.-d.	50c Any single		1.50	1.20

Self-Adhesive
Serpentine Die Cut 10 Syncopated

2088	A860	Booklet pane of 4	4.00	
a.-d.	50c Any single		1.00	.35
	Complete booklet, 2 #2088		8.00	

Universities Type of 2003

Design: Nova Scotia Agricultural College, cent.

Self-Adhesive
Booklet Stamp
Die Cut Perf. 12¾x13¼

2005, Feb. 14				
2089	A806	50c multi	1.00	.35
a.	Booklet pane of 4		4.00	
	Complete booklet, 2 #2089a		8.00	

Expo 2005, Aichi, Japan — A861

2005, Mar. 4			*Perf. 13½*	
2090	A861	50c multi	1.00	.35

Daffodils
A862

Designs: Nos. 2091a, 2092, Yellow daffodils, green and yellow background. Nos.
2091b, 2093, White daffodils, red orange and
yellow background.

Souvenir Sheet

2005, Mar. 10		**Perf. 13x13¼**	
2091	Pane of 2	2.50	2.50
a.-b.	A862 50c Either single	1.25	.80

Booklet Stamps
Self-Adhesive
Die Cut Perf. 10

2092	A862 50c multi	1.00	.35
2093	A862 50c multi	1.00	.35
a.	Booklet pane, 5 each #2092-2093 + 10 stickers	10.00	

Pacific Explore 2005 World Stamp Expo,
Sydney, Australia (#2091).

TD Bank
Financial Group,
150th
Anniv. — A863

Self-Adhesive
Booklet Stamp

2005, Mar. 18		**Die Cut Perf. 11¼**	
2094	A863 50c multi	1.00	.35
a.	Booklet pane of 10	10.00	
	Complete booklet, #2094a	13.50	

The booklet pane of 10 is the inside front
cover of the booklet. Fifteen stickers are on
inside back cover.

Bird Paintings by John James
Audubon — A864

Designs: No. 2095, Horned lark. No. 2096,
Piping plover. No. 2097, Stilt sandpiper. No.
2098, Willow ptarmigan. 85c, Double-crested
cormorant.

2005, Mar. 23		**Perf. 12½x13¼**	
2095	A864 50c multi	1.00	.35
2096	A864 50c multi	1.00	.35
2097	A864 50c multi	1.00	.35
2098	A864 50c multi	1.00	.35
a.	Block of 4, #2095-2098	4.00	3.00

Booklet Stamp
Self-Adhesive
Size: 48x39mm
Die Cut

2099	A864 85c multi	1.70	.50
a.	Booklet pane of 6	10.00	

Bridges — A865

Designs: No. 2100, Jacques Cartier Bridge,
Quebec. No. 2101, Souris Swinging Bridge,
Manitoba. No. 2102, Angus L. Macdonald
Bridge, Nova Scotia. No. 2103, Canso Cause-
way, Nova Scotia.

Self-Adhesive

2005, Apr. 2		**Perf. 12½x13**	
2100	A865 50c multi	1.00	.45
2101	A865 50c multi	1.00	.45

2102	A865 50c multi	1.00	.45
2103	A865 50c multi	1.00	.45
a.	Block or strip of 4, #2100-2103	4.00	3.00

Maclean's
Magazine,
Cent.
A866

2005, Apr. 12			
2104	A866 50c multi	1.00	.30

Biosphere Reserves in Canada and
Ireland — A867

Designs: No. 2105, Saskatoon berries,
Waterton Lakes National Park, Canada. No.
2106, Deer, Killarney National Park, Ireland.

2005, Apr. 22			
2105	A867 50c multi	1.00	.30
2106	A867 50c multi	1.00	.30
a.	Pair, #2105-2106	2.00	1.25
b.	Souvenir sheet, #2105-2106	2.50	2.50

See Ireland Nos. 1611-1612.

Battle of the Atlantic, World War
II — A868

2005, Apr. 29			
2107	A868 50c multi	1.00	.35

Opening of Canadian War Museum,
Ottawa — A869

Self-Adhesive
Booklet Stamp

Serpentine Die Cut 8x8½
Syncopated

2005, May 6			
2108	A869 50c multi	1.00	.35
a.	Booklet pane of 4	4.00	
	Complete booklet, 2 #2108a	8.00	

Paintings by Homer Watson (1855-
1936) — A870

Designs: 50c, Down in the Laurentides. 85c,
The Flood Gate (54x40mm)

2005, May 27		**Perf. 13¼x13**	
2109	A870 50c multi	1.00	.35
a.	Perf. 13½x13	1.75	1.75

Souvenir Sheet
Perf. 13½x13

2110	Pane of 2, Nos. 2109a, 2110a	5.50	5.50
a.	A870 85c multi	3.40	3.40

Miniature Sheet

Search and Rescue — A871

No. 2111: a, Rescuer and dog at plane
crash. b, Rescuers at shipwreck. c, Helicopter,
airplane and rescuers. d, Mountainside
rescuers.

2005, June 13		**Perf. 13x13¼**	
2111	A871 Pane of 8, 2 each #a-d	8.00	7.50
a.-d.	50c Any single	1.00	.50

No. 2111 contains two horizontal strips, one
of which is inverted, so that a tete-beche pair
of No. 2111c and two tete-beche pairs containing Nos. 2111b and 2111d can be created.

Ellen Fairclough
(1905-2004), First
Female Cabinet
Minister — A872

2005, June 21		**Perf. 13x12½**	
2112	A872 50c multi	1.00	.35

Diver	Swimmer
A873	A874

2005, July 5		**Perf. 13¼**	
2113	A873 50c multi	1.00	.40
2114	A874 50c multi	1.00	.40
a.	Horiz. pair, #2113-2114		

9th FINA World Championships, Montreal.
In No. 2114a, the denomination for one stamp
is on the opposite side of the pair from that of
the other stamp.

Founding of
Port-Royal,
Nova
Scotia,
400th
Anniv.
A875

Litho. & Engr.

2005, July 16		**Perf. 13x12½**	
2115	A875 50c multi	1.00	.35

Province of
Alberta,
Cent. — A876

Self-Adhesive

2005, July 21	Litho.	**Perf. 12½x13**	
2116	A876 50c multi	1.00	.35

Printed in panes of 8 with each stamp having a different design on the backing.

Province of Saskatchewan,
Cent. — A877

2005, Aug. 2		**Perf. 13x12½**	
2117	A877 50c multi	1.00	.35

Oscar Peterson,
Pianist, 80th
Birthday — A878

2005, Aug. 15			
2118	A878 50c multi	1.00	.35
a.	Souvenir sheet of 4	4.00	4.00

No. 176
and
Acadian
Flag
A879

2005, Aug. 15			
2119	A879 50c multi	1.00	.35

Acadian Deportation, 250th anniv.

Children Playing and Leg
Braces — A880

2005, Sept. 2		**Perf. 12½x13**	
2120	A880 50c multi	1.00	.35

Mass polio vaccinations in Canada, 50th
anniv.

Youth
Sports — A881

No. 2121: a, Wall climbing. b, Skateboarding. c, Mountain biking. d, Snowboarding.

Self-Adhesive

2005, Oct. 1		*Die Cut*	
2121	Complete booket, 2		
	each #a-d	8.00	
a.-d.	A881 50c Any single	1.00	.35

Wild Cats
A882

Designs: No. 2122, Puma concolor. No.
2123, Panthera pardus orientalis.

Perf. 13½x13¼ Syncopated

2005, Oct. 13			
2122	A882 50c multi	1.00	.35
2123	A882 50c multi	1.00	.35
a.	Horiz. pair, #2122-2123	2.00	1.00
b.	Souvenir sheet, #2123a	2.20	2.10

Diplomatic relations with People's Republic
of China, 35th anniv. (#2123b). The perforation column between the two stamps, which
gauges perf. 13½, has a maple leaf shaped
syncopation.
See People's Republic of China Nos. 3458-
3459.

Snowman — A883

Litho. with Hologram Applied
Serpentine Die Cut 8¼ Horiz.

2005, Nov. 1			
Booklet Stamp			
Self-Adhesive			
2124	A883 50c multi	1.00	.35
a.	Booklet pane of 6	6.00	
	Complete booklet, 2 #2124a	12.00	

A884   A885

Creche Figures, St.
Joseph's Oratory,
Montreal — A886

Self-Adhesive
Booklet Stamps

Serpentine Die Cut 6¾ Horiz.

2005, Nov. 2			
2125	A884 50c multi	1.00	.35
a.	Booklet pane of 6	6.00	

| | Complete booklet, 2 #2125a | 12.00 | |

Serpentine Die Cut 6½ Horiz.

2126	A885 85c multi	1.70	.50
a.	Booklet pane of 6	10.25	

Serpentine Die Cut 6¾ Horiz.

2127	A886 $1.45 multi	2.90	1.20
a.	Booklet pane of 6	17.25	

Flowers — A887

Designs: 51c, Red bergamot. 89c, Yellow
lady's slipper. $1.05, Pink fairy slipper. $1.49,
Himalayan blue poppy.

Self-Adhesive
Coil Stamps

Serpentine Die Cut 7 to 9¼ Horiz.

2005, Dec. 19			
2128	A887 51c multi	1.00	.20
2129	A887 89c multi	1.80	.45
2130	A887 $1.05 multi	2.10	.60
2131	A887 $1.49 multi	3.00	.90

Booklet Stamps
Die Cut

2132	A887 89c multi	1.80	.40
a.	Booklet pane of 6	10.75	
2133	A887 $1.05 multi	2.10	.65
a.	Booklet pane of 6	12.50	
2134	A887 $1.49 multi	3.00	.90
a.	Booklet pane of 6	18.00	
	Nos. 2128-2134 (7)	14.80	4.10

Flag and
Houses, New
Glasgow,
Prince
Edward
Island
A888

Flag and
Bridge,
Bouctouche,
New
Brunswick
A889

Flag and
Windmills,
Pincher
Creek,
Alberta
A890

Flag and
Lower Fort
Garry,
Manitoba
A891

Flag and Dogsled,
Yukon Territory — A892

Self-Adhesive
Booklet Stamps

2005, Dec. 19		*Die Cut*	
2135	A888 51c multi	1.00	.20
2136	A889 51c multi	1.00	.20
2137	A890 51c multi	1.00	.20
2138	A891 51c multi	1.00	.20
2139	A892 51c multi	1.00	.20
a.	Booklet pane, 2 each #2135-2139	10.00	
a.	As "a," die cutting omitted	1,600.	
	Nos. 2135-2139 (5)	5.00	1.00

New Year 2006
(Year of the
Dog) — A893

**Litho. & Embossed With Foil
Application**

2006, Jan. 6		*Perf. 13¼*	
2140	A893 51c shown	1.00	.35
Souvenir Sheet			
2141	A893 $1.49 Dog and pup	3.00	3.00

Queen
Elizabeth II,
80th Birthday
A894

Self-Adhesive
Booklet Stamp

Serpentine Die Cut 10

2006, Jan. 12		*Litho.*	
2142	A894 51c multi	1.00	.30
a.	Booklet pane of 10	10.00	
	See No. 2150.		

2006
Winter
Olympics,
Turin, Italy
A895

Designs: No. 2143, Team pursuit speed
skating. No. 2144, Skeleton.

2006, Feb. 3		*Perf. 12½x13*	
2143	A895 51c multi	1.00	.30
2144	A895 51c multi	1.00	.30
a.	Horiz. pair, #2143-2144	2.00	1.00

Gardens — A896

No. 2145: a, Shade garden and black-
throated blue warbler. b, Flower garden and
American painted lady butterfly. c, Water garden and green darner dragonfly. d, Rock garden and blue-spotted salamander.

Self-Adhesive

2006, Mar. 8	*Serpentine Die Cut 10*		
2145	Complete booklet, 2		
	each #a-d	8.00	
a.-d.	A896 51c Any single	1.00	.45

Party
Balloons
A897

Self-Adhesive
Booklet Stamp

Serpentine Die Cut 6¾ Horiz.

2006, Apr. 3			
2146	A897 51c multi	1.00	.35
a.	Booklet pane of 6	6.00	

Paintings by Dorothy Knowles — A898

Designs: 51c, The Field of Rapeseed. 89c,
North Saskatchewan River, vert. (42x51mm).

2006, Apr. 7		*Perf. 13¼x12½*	
2147	A898 51c multi	1.00	.35
a.	Perf. 12¾x12½	1.80	1.80
Souvenir Sheet			
Perf. 13			
2148	Pane, Nos. 2147a, 2148a	4.50	4.50
a.	A898 89c multi	2.60	2.60

Canadian Labor
Congress, 50th
Anniv. — A899

2006, Apr. 20		*Perf. 13½x13¼*	
2149	A899 51c multi	1.00	.35

**Queen Elizabeth II, 80th Birthday
Type of 2006
Souvenir Sheet**

2006, Apr. 21		*Perf. 12½x13*	
2150	Pane of 2, No. 2150a	6.00	6.00
a.	A894 149c multi, 36x28mm	3.00	3.00

McClelland &
Stewart Publishing
House,
Cent. — A900

Self-Adhesive
Booklet Stamp

2006, Apr. 26	*Die Cut Perf. 11¼x11*		
2151	A900 51c slate grn & sil	1.00	.35
a.	Booklet pane of 4 + 4 stickers	4.00	
	Complete booklet, 2 #2151a	8.00	

Northwest Coast Transformation Mask
and Northwest Coast Exhibit — A901

Self-Adhesive
Booklet Stamp

*Serpentine Die Cut 8 Horiz.
Syncopated*

2006, May 11			
2152	A901 89c multi	1.80	.80
a.	Booklet pane of 4	7.25	
	Complete booklet, 2 #2152a	14.50	

Canadian Museum of Civilization, 150th
anniv.

Canadians in
Hollywood
A903

Actors and actresses: Nos. 2153a, 2154a,
John Candy (1950-94). Nos. 2153b, 2154c,
Fay Wray (1907-2004). Nos. 2153c, 2154d,
Lorne Greene (1915-87). Nos. 2153d, 2154b,
Mary Pickford (1893-1979).

2006, May 26   **Perf. 13x12½**
2153   Souvenir sheet of 4   5.00 5.00
   a.-d.   A903 51c Any single   1.25 1.25

Self-Adhesive
Serpentine Die Cut 9¾x10
2154   Booklet pane of 4 + 4
     stickers   4.00
   a.-d.   A903 51c Any single   1.00 .40
     Complete booklet, 2 #2154   8.00

Complete booklets were issued with four different covers depicting the featured actors or actresses.
See Nos. 2279-2280.

A904

Exploration of Eastern Coast by Samuel de Champlain, 400th Anniv. — A905

Litho. & Engr.
2006, May 28   **Perf. 13x12½**
2155 A904 51c multi   1.00 .35

Souvenir Sheet
Perf. 11
2156 A905   Pane of 2 #2156a,
     2 US #4074a   8.00 8.00
   a.   A904 51c multi   2.00 2.00

Washington 2006 World Philatelic Exhibition (#2156). No. 2156, sold only by Canada Post for $2, has bar code in pane margin at lower left. United States No. 4074, sold only by the United States Postal Service, lacks this bar code.

Vancouver Aquarium, 50th Anniv. — A906

Self-Adhesive
Booklet Stamp
Serpentine Die Cut 9½   **Litho.**
2006, June 15
2157 A906 51c multi   1.00 .35
   a.   Booklet pane of 5   5.00
     Complete booklet, 2 #2157a   10.00

Canadian Forces Snowbirds Aerobatics Team — A907

Designs: No. 2158, Pilot in cockpit, two airplanes. No. 2159, Three airplanes.

2006, June 28   **Perf. 12½x13¼**
2158 A907 51c multi   1.00 .35
2159 A907 51c multi   1.00 .35
   a.   Horiz. pair, #2158-2159   2.00 1.25
   b.   Souvenir sheet, #2159a   2.75 2.75

James White, Dividers and Map of Canada — A908

2006, June 30   **Perf. 13¼x12½**
2160 A908 51c multi   1.00 .35
Atlas of Canada, cent. Printed in panes of 16 + 4 labels.

World Lacrosse Championships, London, Ontario — A909

Self-Adhesive
Booklet Stamp
Serpentine Die Cut 11¾ Horiz.
2006, July 6
2161 A909 51c multi   1.00 .35
   a.   Booklet pane of 8   8.00

Alpine Club of Canada, Cent. — A910

Self-Adhesive
Booklet Stamp
2006, July 19   **Die Cut Perf. 12½x13**
2162 A910 51c multi   1.00 .35
   a.   Booklet pane of 8   8.00

Ducks and Duck Decoys A911

Designs: No. 2163, Barrow's goldeneyes. No. 2164, Mallards. No. 2165, American black ducks. No. 2166, Redbreasted mergansers.

2006, Aug. 3   **Perf. 13¼x12½**
2163 A911 51c blue & multi   1.00 .40
2164 A911 51c yel & multi   1.00 .40
2165 A911 51c red & multi   1.00 .40
2166 A911 51c grn & multi   1.00 .40
   a.   Block of 4, #2163-2166   4.00 2.50
   b.   Souvenir sheet, #2163-2166   4.50 4.50

Society of Graphic Designers of Canada, 50th Anniv. — A912

2006, Aug. 16   **Perf. 12½x13**
2167 A912 51c multi   1.00 .35

Canadian Wines A913

Canadian Cheeses A914

Designs: No. 2168, Three glasses of wine. No. 2169, Wine taster, barrels. No. 2170, Various cheeses. No. 2171, Woman with tray of cheeses and fruit.

Self-Adhesive
Booklet Stamps
2006, Aug. 23   **Die Cut**
2168 A913 51c multi   1.00 .45
2169 A913 51c multi   1.00 .45
2170 A914 51c multi   1.00 .45
2171 A914 51c multi   1.00 .45
   a.   Booklet pane, 2 each #2168-2171   8.00
     Nos. 2168-2171 (4)   4.00 1.80

Universities Type of 2003
Design: Macdonald College, Sainte-Anne-de-Bellevue, Quebec, cent.

Self-Adhesive
Booklet Stamp
Die Cut Perf. 12¾x13¼
2006, Sept. 26
2172 A806 51c multi   1.00 .35
   a.   Booklet pane of 4   4.00
     Complete booklet, 2 #2172a   8.00

Endangered Animals — A915

Designs: Nos. 2173a, 2174, Newfoundland marten. Nos. 2173b, 2175, Blotched tiger salamander. Nos. 2173c, 2176, Blue racer snake. Nos. 2173d, 2177, Swift fox.

2006, Sept. 29   **Perf. 13¼**
2173   Pane of 4 + 4 labels   4.40 4.40
   a.-d.   A915 51c Any single   1.10 1.10

Booklet Stamps
Self-Adhesive
Size: 47x24mm
Die Cut
2174 A915 51c multi   1.00 .40
2175 A915 51c multi   1.00 .40
2176 A915 51c multi   1.00 .40
2177 A915 51c multi   1.00 .40
   a.   Block of 4, #2174-2177   4.00
   b.   Booklet pane, 2, #2177a   8.00

See Nos. 2229-2233, 2285-2289.

Opera Singers — A916

Designs: No. 2178, Maureen Forrester. No. 2179, Raoul Jobin (1906-74). No. 2180, Léopold Simoneau (1916-2006) and Pierrette Alarie. No. 2181, Jon Vickers. No. 2182, Edward Johnson (1878-1959).

2006, Oct. 17   **Perf. 13½x13**
2178 A916 51c multi   1.00 .40
2179 A916 51c multi   1.00 .40
2180 A916 51c multi   1.00 .40
2181 A916 51c multi   1.00 .40
2182 A916 51c multi   1.00 .40
   a.   Vert. strip of 5, #2178-2182   5.00 5.00

Madonna and Child, by Antoine-Sébastien Falardeau A917

Christmas Card Art A918

Designs: No. 2184, Snowman, by Yvonne McKague Housser. 89c, Winter Joys, by J. E. Sampson. $1.49, Contemplation, by Edwin Holgate.

Self-Adhesive
Booklet Stamp
2006, Nov. 1   **Die Cut**
2183 A917 51c multi   1.00 .25
   a.   Booklet pane of 12   12.00

Serpentine Die Cut 13¼ Horiz.
2184 A918   51c multi   1.00 .25
   a.   Booklet pane of 12   12.00
2185 A918   89c multi   1.80 .55
   a.   Booklet pane of 6   10.75
2186 A918 $1.49 multi   3.00 1.00
   a.   Booklet pane of 6   18.00
     Nos. 2183-2186 (4)   6.80 2.05

Spotted Coralroot A919

Queen Elizabeth II A920

Flag and Sirmilik Natl. Park, Nunavut A921

Flag and Cliff Near Chemainus, British Columbia A922

Flag and Polar Bears Near Churchill, Manitoba A923

Flag and Bras d'Or Lake, Nova Scotia A924

Flag and Tuktut Nogait Natl. Park, Northwest Territories — A925

Self-Adhesive
Coil Stamp
Serpentine Die Cut 7½-9 Horiz.
2006, Nov. 16   **Litho.**
2187 A919 P multi   1.25 .20

Booklet Stamps
Die Cut
2188 A920 P multi   1.00 .20
   a.   Booklet pane of 10   10.00
2189 A921 P multi   1.00 .20
2190 A922 P multi   1.00 .20
2191 A923 P multi   1.00 .20
2192 A924 P multi   1.00 .20
2193 A925 P multi   1.00 .20
   a.   Booklet pane, 2 each #2189-2193   10.00

b. Booklet pane, 6 each #2189-
2193   30.00
Nos. 2187-2193 (7)   7.25 1.40

Nos. 2187-2193 each sold for 51c on day of issue. On Nos. 2188a, 2193a and 2193b, adjacent stamps that are on both sides of the booklet fold have rouletting rather than die-cutting between them. No. 2193b is sold folded into thirds. Each of the thirds has selvage surrounding the ten stamps on it, unlike No. 2193a.

Spotted Coralroot Type of 2006 and

Flat-leaved
Bladderwort — A926

Designs: $1.10, Marsh skullcap. $1.55, Little larkspur.

2006, Dec. 19   **Perf. 13¼x13**
2194   Souvenir sheet of 4   8.25 8.25
a. A919 P multi   1.00 .70
b. A926 93c multi   1.85 1.25
c. A926 $1.10 multi   2.20 1.50
d. A926 $1.55 multi   3.10 2.25

Self-Adhesive
Coil Stamps
Serpentine Die Cut 7½-9

2195 A926 93c multi   1.85 .40
2196 A926 $1.10 multi   2.20 .60
2197 A926 $1.55 multi   3.10 .65

Booklet Stamps
Die Cut

2198 A926 93c multi   1.85 .50
a. Booklet pane of 6   11.00
2199 A926 $1.10 multi   2.20 .75
a. Booklet pane of 6   13.25
2200 A926 $1.55 multi   3.10 1.00
a. Booklet pane of 6   18.50
Nos. 2195-2200 (6) 14.30 3.90

No. 2194a sold for 51c on day of issue.
See Nos. 2243, 2245-2247, 2254-2256.

New Year 2007 (Year of the Pig) A927

Pig facing: 52c, Left. $1.55, Right.

Litho. & Embossed with Foil Application
2007, Jan. 5   **Perf. 13½x13**
2201 A927 52c red & multi   1.00 .35
a. Gold foil omitted   —

Souvenir Sheet
2202 A927 $1.55 grn & multi   3.10 3.10

Confetti and Streamers A928

Self-Adhesive
Booklet Stamp
Serpentine Die Cut 6¾ Horiz.
2007, Jan. 15   **Litho.**
2203 A928 52c multi   1.00 .35
a. Booklet pane of 6   6.00

International Polar Year — A929

Designs: No. 2204, Somateria spectabilis. No. 2205, Crossota millsaeare.

Perf. 13½ Syncopated
2007, Feb. 12
2204 A929 52c multi   1.00 .35
2205 A929 52c multi   1.00 .35
a. Horiz. pair, #2204-2205   2.00 1.00
b. Souvenir sheet, #2205a   2.50 2.50

Lilacs — A930

Color of lilacs: Nos. 2206a, 2207, White. Nos. 2206b, 2208, Purple.

Souvenir Sheet
2007, Mar. 1   **Perf. 12¾**
2206 A930 Pane of 2   2.50 2.50
a.-b. 52c Either single   1.25 .75

Booklet Stamps
Self-Adhesive
Die Cut
2207 A930 52c multi   1.00 .35
2208 A930 52c multi   1.00 .35
a. Booklet pane of 10, 5 each
#2207-2208   10.00

Universities Type of 2003
Design: No. 2209, HEC Montreal, cent. No. 2210, University of Saskatchewan, cent.

Self-Adhesive
Booklet Stamp
2007   *Die Cut Perf. 12¾x13¼*
2209 A806 52c multi   1.00 .35
a. Booklet pane of 4   4.00
   Complete booklet, 2 #2209a   8.00
2210 A806 52c multi   1.00 .35
a. Booklet pane of 4   4.00
   Complete booklet, 2 #2210a   8.00

Issued: No. 2209, 3/12. No. 2210, 4/3.

Art by Mary Pratt — A931

Designs: 52c, Jelly Shelf. $1.55 Iceberg in the North Atlantic (58x36mm).

2007, Mar. 15   **Perf. 13x12½**
2211 A931 52c multi   1.00 .35

Souvenir Sheet
2212 Pane, #2211, 2212a   4.00 4.00
a. A931 $1.55 multi   3.00 3.00

Selection of Ottawa as National Capital, 150th Anniv. — A932

Litho., Litho & Embossed with Foil Application (#2213b)
2007, May 3   **Perf. 13¼**
2213 Pane of 2, #2213a,
2213b   4.25 4.25
a. A932 52c multi   1.25 1.25
b. A932 $1.55 multi   3.00 3.00

Booklet Stamp
Self-Adhesive
Serpentine Die Cut 7¼ Horiz.
2214 A932 52c multi   1.00 4.00
a. Booklet pane of 4   4.00
   Complete booklet, 2 #2214a   8.00

Royal Architectural Institute of Canada, Cent. — A933

Buildings: No. 2215, University of Lethbridge, by Arthur Erickson. No. 2216, St. Mary's Church, by Douglas Cardinal. No. 2217, Ontario Science Centre, by Raymond Moriyama. No. 2218, National Gallery of Canada, by Moshe Safdie.

2007, May 9   **Litho.**   **Perf. 13**
2215 A933 52c multi + label   1.00 .45
2216 A933 52c multi + label   1.00 .45
2217 A933 52c multi + label   1.00 .45
2218 A933 52c multi + label   1.00 .45
a. Vert. strip of 4, #2215-2218, +
4 labels   4.00 2.50

Nos. 2215-2218 were printed in panes containing two of each stamp. Labels flank the stamps, with labels on the left showing drawings of the buildings and the labels on the right showing the architect.

Capt. George Vancouver (1757-98), Explorer — A934

Litho. & Embossed
2007, June 22   **Perf. 13x12½**
2219 A934 $1.55 multi   3.00 1.20
a. Souvenir sheet of 1, perf. 13   3.00 2.90

FIFA Under-20 World Soccer Championships, Canada — A935

2007, June 26   **Litho.**   **Perf. 12½x13**
2220 A935 52c multi   1.00 .35

Popular Singers — A936

Designs: Nos. 2221a, 2222a, Gordon Lightfoot. Nos. 2221b, 2222b, Joni Mitchell. Nos. 2221c, 2222c, Anne Murray. Nos. 2221d, 2222d, Paul Anka.

2007, June 29   **Perf. 12½x13**
2221 A936 Pane of 4   4.00 4.00
a.-d. 52c Any single   1.00 .90

Self-Adhesive
Serpentine Die Cut 13½
2222 A936 Booklet pane of 4   4.00
a.-d. 52c Any single   .45
   Complete booklet, 2 #2222   8.00

Complete booklets were issued with four different covers depicting the featured singers.

National Parks — A937

Designs: No. 2223, Terra Nova National Park, Newfoundland, 50th anniv. No. 2224, Jasper National Park, Alberta, cent.

Self-Adhesive
Booklet Stamps
2007   *Serpentine Die Cut 13½*
2223 A937 52c multi   1.00 .35
a. Booklet pane of 5   5.00
   Complete booklet, 2 #2223a   10.00
2224 A937 52c multi   1.00 .35
a. Booklet pane of 5   5.00
   Complete booklet, 2 #2224a   10.00
b. Gutter pane, 5 each #2223-
2224   12.50

Issued: No. 2223, 7/6; No. 2224, 7/20.

Scouting, Cent. A938

Self-Adhesive
Booklet Stamp
2007, July 25
2225 A938 52c multi   1.00 .35
a. Booklet pane of 4 + 4 labels   4.00
   Complete booklet, 2 #2225a   8.00

Henri Membertou, Grand Chief of Mi'kmaq Tribe — A939

2007, June 26   **Engr.**   **Perf. 13x12½**
2226 A939 52c multi   1.00 .35

Law Society of Saskatchewan, Cent. — A940

2007, Sept. 13   **Litho.**   **Perf. 13**
2227 A940 52c multi   1.00 .35

Printed in panes of 8 + 8 labels.

Law Society of Alberta, Cent. A941

2007, Sept. 13   **Perf. 12½x13**
2228 A941 52c multi   1.00 .35

Endangered Animals Type of 2006
Designs: Nos. 2229a, 2230, North Atlantic right whale. Nos. 2229b, 2231, Northern cricket frog. Nos. 2229c, 2232, White sturgeon. Nos. 2229d, 2233, Leatherback turtle.

2007, Oct. 1   *Perf. 13¼*
2229	Pane of 4 + 4 labels	4.00	4.00
a.-d.	A915 52c Any single	1.00	.90

Booklet Stamps
Self-Adhesive
Size: 47x24mm
Die Cut

2230	A915 52c multi	1.00	.35
2231	A915 52c multi	1.00	.35
2232	A915 52c multi	1.00	.35
2233	A915 52c multi	1.00	.35
a.	Block of 4, #2230-2233	4.00	
b.	Booklet pane, 2 #2233a	8.00	

Beneficial
Insects — A942

Designs: 1c, Convergent lady beetle (Hippodamia convergens). 3c, Golden-eyed lacewing (Chrysopa oculata). 5c, Northern bumblebee (Bombus polaris). 10c, Canada darner (Aeshna canadensis). 25c, Cecropia moth (Hyalophora cecropia).

 No. 2235

No. 2235a

2007, Oct. 12   *Perf. 13¼x13*
2234	A942 1c multi	.20	.20
2235	A942 3c multi	.20	.20
a.	"Canada" shifted to right, touching "Oculata" (pos. 11-14)	.45	.25
2236	A942 5c multi	.20	.20
2237	A942 10c multi	.20	.20
2238	A942 25c multi	.50	.20
a.	Souvenir sheet, #2234-2238	.95	.95
	Nos. 2234-2238 (5)	1.30	1.00

No. 2235a occurs four times on each pane of 50. Panes printed in 2010 correct the errors. See Nos. 2328, 2406-2410.

Christmas
A943   A944

Designs: No. 2239, Reindeer and snowflakes. No. 2240, Holy Family. 93c, Angel over town. $1.55, Dove.

Self-Adhesive
Booklet Stamps

Litho. With Hologram Affixed
Serpentine Die Cut 8¼ Horiz.
2007, Nov. 1
2239	A943 (52c) multi	1.00	.20
a.	Booklet pane of 6	6.00	
	Complete booklet, 2 #2239a	12.00	
b.	Die cutting omitted, pair	650.00	

Litho.
Serpentine Die Cut 13½
2007, Nov. 1
2240	A944 (52c) multi	1.00	.20
a.	Booklet pane of 6	6.00	
	Complete booklet, 2 #2240a	12.00	
2241	A944 93c multi	1.80	.45
a.	Booklet pane of 6	10.75	
2242	A944 $1.55 multi	3.00	.60
a.	Booklet pane of 6	18.00	
	Nos. 2239-2242 (4)	6.80	1.45

Flowers Type of 2006 and

Odontioda   Queen
Island Red   Elizabeth
Orchid — A945   II — A946

Flag and
Sambro Island
Lighthouse,
Nova Scotia
A947

Flag and Point
Clark
Lighthouse,
Ontario
A948

Flag and Cap-des-
Rosiers Lighthouse,
Quebec — A949

Flag and
Warren
Landing
Lighthouse,
Manitoba
A950

Flag and
Pachena Point
Lighthouse,
British
Columbia
A951

Flag and Pachena
Point Lighthouse,
British Columbia —
A951a

Designs: 96c, Potinara Janet Elizabeth "Fire Dancer" orchid. $1.15, Laeliocattleya Memoria Evelyn Light orchid. $1.60, Masdevallia Kaleidoscope "Conni" orchid.

2007, Dec. 27   **Litho.**   *Perf. 13¼x13*
2243	Pane of 4	8.50	8.50
a.	A945 P multi	1.00	.65
b.	A926 96c multi	1.90	1.20
c.	A926 $1.15 multi	2.30	1.40
d.	A926 $1.60 multi	3.20	2.00

Self-Adhesive
Coil Stamps
Serpentine Die Cut 8-9½ Horiz.
2244	A945 P multi	1.00	.20

Serpentine Die Cut 9.2 Horiz.
2244A	A945 P multi	1.25	.85

Serpentine Die Cut 8-9½
2245	A926 96c multi	1.90	.30
2246	A926 $1.15 multi	2.25	.50
2247	A926 $1.60 multi	3.20	.65
	Nos. 2244-2247 (5)	9.60	2.50

Die cutting is irregular across the stamp (saw tooth tips) on Nos. 2244 and 2245-2247 compared to being consistent across the stamp (rounded tips) on No. 2244A. On No. 2244, stamps are vertically contiguous on the backing paper, while on No. 2244A the stamps are separated on horizontal backing paper that is taller than the stamp.

Booklet Stamps *Serpentine Die Cut 13¼*
2248	A946 P multi	1.00	.20
a.	Booklet pane of 10	10.00	
2249	A947 P multi	1.00	.20
2250	A948 P multi	1.00	.20
2251	A949 P multi	1.00	.20
2252	A950 P multi	1.00	.20
2253	A951 P multi	1.00	.20
a.	Booklet pane of 10, 2 each #2249-2253	10.00	

Serpentine Die Cut 13¼
2253B	A951a P multi	1.00	.55
c.	Booklet pane of 10, 2 each #2249-2252, 2253B	10.00	
d.	Booklet pane of 30, 6 each #2249-2252, 2253B	30.00	

Die Cut
2254	A926 96c multi	1.90	.30
a.	Booklet pane of 6	11.50	
2255	A926 $1.15 multi	2.25	.45
a.	Booklet pane of 6	13.50	
2256	A926 $1.60 multi	3.20	.65
a.	Booklet pane of 6	19.00	
	Nos. 2248-2256 (10)	14.35	3.15

Nos. 2243a, 2244, 2248-2253 each sold for 52c on day of issue.
No. 2244A issued 2/21/08. No. 2253Bd was separated into thirds by two rows of rouletting. The separated thirds of this booklet have the

same contents as No. 2253Bc, but have different selvage markings.

New Year 2008
(Year of the
Rat) — A952

Designs: 52c, Rat with umbrella. $1.60, Rat with fan.

Litho. & Embossed With Foil Application
2008, Jan. 8   *Perf. 13*
2257	A952 52c multi	1.00	.30

Souvenir Sheet
2258	A952 $1.60 multi	3.20	3.20

No. 2257 printed in panes of 25 + 20 labels.

Fireworks
A953

Self-Adhesive
Booklet Stamp
Serpentine Die Cut 13½ Horiz.
2008, Jan. 15   **Litho.**
2259	A953 P multi	1.00	.30
a.	Booklet pane of 6	6.00	

No. 2259 sold for 52c on day of issue.

Peonies
A954

Peony color: Nos. 2260a, 2261, Pink. Nos. 2260b, 2262, Red.

2008, Mar. 3   **Litho.**   *Perf. 13¼*
2260	Pane of 2	2.50	2.50
a.-b.	A954 52c Either single	1.25	1.00

Booklet Stamps
Self-Adhesive
Serpentine Die Cut 13¼
2261	A954 52c multi	1.00	.35
2262	A954 52c multi	1.00	.35
a.	Pair, #2261-2262	2.00	
b.	Booklet pane, 5 each #2261-2262, + 10 stickers	10.00	

The country name and denomination are closer to the flowers on Nos. 2261-2262 than on Nos. 2260a-2260b.

Universities
A955

Designs: No. 2263, University of Alberta, cent. No. 2264, University of British Columbia, cent.

Self-Adhesive
Booklet Stamps
Serpentine Die Cut 13¼
2008, Mar. 7
2263	A955 52c multi	1.00	.30
a.	Booklet pane of 8	8.00	
2264	A955 52c multi	1.00	.30
a.	Booklet pane of 8	8.00	
b.	Gutter pane, 4 each #2263-2264	8.00	

2008 Intl. Ice Hockey Federation
Championships, Halifax and
Quebec — A956

Self-Adhesive
Booklet Stamp
Serpentine Die Cut 13½
2008, Apr. 3
2265	A956 52c multi	1.00	.30
a.	Booklet pane of 10	10.00	

No. 2265a was printed with two different booklet covers.

Guide Dog
A957

Self-Adhesive
Booklet Stamp
Serpentine Die Cut 13½x13
2008, Apr. 21   **Litho. & Embossed**
2266	A957 52c multi	1.00	.30
a.	Booklet pane of 10	10.00	

Montreal Association for the Blind, cent.

Oil and Gas Anniversaries — A958

Designs: No. 2267, Welder welding Trans-Canada Pipeline. No. 2268, James M. Williams, Charles Tripp, Oil Springs, Ontario oil field.

Self-Adhesive
Booklet Stamps
Serpentine Die Cut 13¼
2008, May 2 Litho.
2267	A958	52c multi	1.00	.30
2268	A958	52c multi	1.00	.30
a.	Booklet pane of 10, 5 each #2267-2268			10.00

Trans-Canada Pipeline, 50th anniv., First commercial oil well in Canada, 150th anniv.

Quebec City, 400th Anniv. A959

Litho. & Engr.
2008, May 16 **Perf. 13x12½**
2269	A959	52c multi	1.00 .35

See France No. 3437. A souvenir sheet containing No. 2269 and France No. 3437 sold for $4.99.

Photographic Portraits by Yousuf Karsh (1908-2008) A960

Designs: 52c, Self-portrait, 1952. 96c, Audrey Hepburn, 1956. $1.60, Sir Winston Churchill, 1941.

2008, May 21 Litho. **Perf. 13x12½**
2270	A960	52c multi	1.00 .35

Souvenir Sheet
2271	Pane of 3, #2270, 2271a, 2271b		6.25 6.25
a.	A960 96c multi		1.90 1.30
b.	A960 $1.60 multi		3.20 3.00

Booklet Stamps
Self-Adhesive
2272	A960	96c multi	1.90 .65
a.	Booklet pane of 4		7.50 —
	Complete booklet, 2 #2272a		15.00
2273	A960	$1.60 multi	3.20 1.00
a.	Booklet pane of 4		12.75 —
	Complete booklet, 2 #2273a		26.00
b.	Gutter pane, #2273a, 2273a		19.00

No. 2270 printed in panes of 16 + 4 labels.

1908 Fifty-cent Coin — A961

Litho. & Embossed
2008, June 4 **Perf. 13x13¼**
2274	A961	52c multi	1.00 .35

Royal Canadian Mint, cent. Printed in panes of 16 + 4 labels.

Canadian Nurses Association, Cent. — A962

Self-Adhesive
Booklet Stamp
Serpentine Die Cut 13¼
2008, June 16 Litho.
2275	A962	52c multi	1.00	.35
a.	Booklet pane of 10			10.00

Publication of *Anne of Green Gables*, by Lucy Maud Montgomery, Cent. — A963

Designs: Nos. 2276a, 2277, Anne holding buttercups. Nos. 2276b, 2278, Green Gables House.

Perf. 13½ Syncopated
2008, June 20
Souvenir Sheet
2276	A963	Pane of 2	2.40 2.40
a.-b.	52c Either single		1.20 .80

Booklet Stamps
Self-Adhesive
Serpentine Die Cut 13¼x13
2277	A963	52c multi	1.00	.35
2278	A963	52c multi	1.00	.35
a.	Booklet pane of 10, 5 each #2277-2278 + 10 stickers			10.00

See Japan No. 3028.

Canadians in Hollywood Type of 2006

Actors and actresses: Nos. 2279a, 2280c, Norma Shearer (1902?-83). Nos. 2279b, 2280b, Chief Dan George (1899-1981). Nos. 2279c, 2280a, Marie Dressler (1868-1934). Nos. 2279d, 2280d, Raymond Burr (1917-93).

2008, June 30 **Perf. 13x12½**
2279	Souvenir sheet of 4		4.75 4.75
a.-d.	A903 52c Any single		1.20 .85

Self-Adhesive
Serpentine Die Cut 13½x13¼
2280	Booklet pane of 4 + 4 stickers		4.00
a.-d.	A903 52c Any single		1.00 .30
	Complete booklet, 2 #2280		8.00

Complete booklets were issued with four different covers depicting the featured actors or actresses. The order of the stamps and labels in the booklet pane differed in the four booklets.

2008 Summer Olympics, Beijing — A964

Self-Adhesive
Booklet Stamp
Serpentine Die Cut 13½
2008, July 18
2281	A964	52c multi	1.00	.30
a.	Booklet pane of 10			10.00

Lifesaving Society, Cent. A965

Self-Adhesive
Booklet Stamp
Serpentine Die Cut 13¼x12¾
2008, July 25
2282	A965	52c multi	1.00	.30
a.	Booklet pane of 10			10.00

British Columbia, 150th Anniv. — A966

Self-Adhesive
2008, Aug. 1 **Perf. 12½x13**
2283	A966	52c multi	1.00 .35

R. Samuel McLaughlin (1871-1972), Automobile Manufacturer, and Buick Automobile — A967

2008, Sept. 8 **Perf. 12½x13**
2284	A967	52c multi	1.00 .35

Endangered Animals Type of 2006

Designs: Nos. 2285a, 2286, Prothonotary warbler. Nos. 2285b, 2287, Taylor's checkerspot butterfly. Nos. 2285c, 2288, Roseate tern. Nos. 2285d, 2289, Burrowing owl.

2008, Oct. 1 **Perf. 13¼**
2285	Pane of 4 + 4 labels		4.00 4.00
a.-d.	A915 52c Any single		1.00 .75

Booklet Stamps
Self-Adhesive
Size: 48x24mm
Die Cut
2286	A915	52c multi	1.00	.35
2287	A915	52c multi	1.00	.35
2288	A915	52c multi	1.00	.35
2289	A915	52c multi	1.00	.35
a.	Block of 4, #2286-2289			4.00
b.	Booklet pane, 2 #2289a			8.00

12th Francophone Summit, Quebec — A968

2008, Oct. 15 **Perf. 12½x13¼**
2290	A968	52c multi	1.00 .35

A969

Christmas — A970

Child: Nos. 2291a, 2293, Making snow angel. Nos. 2291b, 2294, Skiing. Nos. 2291c, 2295, Tobogganing.

Souvenir Sheet
2008, Nov. 3 **Perf. 13½**
2291	Pane of 3		6.00 6.00
a.	A969 P multi		1.00 .75
b.	A969 96c multi		1.90 1.75
c.	A969 $1.60 multi		3.20 3.00

Booklet Stamps
Self-Adhesive
Serpentine Die Cut 13¼
2292	A970	P multi	1.00 .25
a.	Booklet pane of 6		6.00
	Complete booklet, 2 #2292a		12.00

Serpentine Die Cut 13¾
2293	A969	P multi	1.00 .25
a.	Booklet pane of 6		6.00
	Complete booklet, 2 #2293a		12.00
2294	A969	96c multi	1.90 .65
a.	Booklet pane of 6		11.50
2295	A969	$1.60 multi	3.20 1.10
a.	Booklet pane of 6		19.00
b.	Gutter pane, #2294a, 2295a		27.50
	Nos. 2292-2295 (4)		7.10 2.25

Nos. 2291a, 2292 and 2293 each sold for 52c on day of issue.
See No. 2243.

A971

New Year 2009 (Year of the Ox) A972

Litho. & Embossed With Foil Application
2009, Jan. 8 **Perf. 12½**
2296	A971	P multi	1.00 .30

Souvenir Sheet
2297	A972	$1.65 multi	3.25 3.25
a.	With China 2009 emblem overprinted in gold in pane margin		3.25 3.25

No. 2296 sold for 54c on day of issue.

Queen Elizabeth II — A973

Self-Adhesive
Booklet Stamp
Serpentine Die Cut 13½x13¼

2009, Jan. 12   Litho.
2298	A973		1.00	.20
a.	Booklet pane of 10		10.00

No. 2298 sold for 54c on day of issue.

Sports of the Winter Olympics and Paralympics
A974   A975

Designs: Nos. 2299a, 2303, Curling. Nos. 2299b, 2302, Bobsledding. Nos. 2299c, 2304, Snowboarding. Nos. 2299d, 2300, Freestyle skiing. Nos. 2299e, 2301, Ice-sled hockey.

2009, Jan. 12   *Perf. 13¼x13*
2299	Pane of 5	5.00	4.50
a.-d.	A974 P Any single	1.00	.75
e.	A975 P multi	1.00	.75
f.	As No. 2299, with "Vancouver / 2010" overprinted in sheet margin in silver	5.00	5.00

Booklet Stamps
Self-Adhesive
Serpentine Die Cut 13¼x13½
2300	A974 P multi	1.00	.20
2301	A975 P multi	1.00	.20
2302	A974 P multi	1.00	.20
2303	A974 P multi	1.00	.20
2304	A974 P multi	1.00	.20
a.	Booklet pane of 10, 2 each #2300-2304	10.00
b.	Booklet pane of 30, 6 each #2300-2304	27.00

On day of issue, Nos. 2299a-2299e, 2300-2304 each sold for 54c.
No. 2299f was originally sold with a set of coins in 2009. It was made available in 2010 in a set of 3 sheets, Nos. 2299f, 2305f, and 2366c that sold for $8.73.

2010 Vancouver Winter Olympics Emblem A976   2010 Vancouver Winter Paralympics Emblem A977

Miga, Winter Olympics Mascot — A978   Sumi, Paralympics Mascot — A979

Quatchi, Winter Olympics Mascot — A980

2009   *Perf. 13¼x13*
2305	Pane of 5	9.75	9.75
a.	A976 P multi	1.00	.65
b.	A977 P multi	1.00	.65
c.	A978 98c multi	2.00	1.25
d.	A979 $1.18 multi	2.40	1.75
e.	A980 $1.65 multi	3.30	2.50
f.	As No. 2305, with "Vancouver / 2010" overprinted in sheet margin in bronze	10.50	10.50

Self-Adhesive
Coil Stamps
Serpentine Die Cut 9¼ (Rounded Tips)
2306	A976 P multi	1.10	.60
2307	A977 P multi	1.10	.60

Serpentine Die Cut 7¾-9½ (Sawtooth Tips)
2307A	A976 P multi	1.00	.30
2307B	A977 P multi	1.00	.30
c.	Vert. pair, #2307A-2307B	2.00
2308	A978 98c multi	2.00	.30
2309	A979 $1.18 multi	2.40	.50
2310	A980 $1.65 multi	3.30	.70

Booklet Stamps
Serpentine Die Cut 9¼ (Rounded Tips)
2311	A978 98c multi	2.00	.30
a.	Booklet pane of 6	12.00
2312	A979 $1.18 multi	2.40	.50
a.	Booklet pane of 6	14.00
2313	A980 $1.65 multi	3.30	.70
a.	Booklet pane of 6	19.50
	Nos. 2306-2313 (10)	19.60	4.80

Issued: Nos. 2305, 2309, 2312, 2/12; Nos. 2306-2308, 2310-2311, 2313, 1/12. On day of issue, Nos. 2305a, 2305b, 2306-2307B each sold for 54c. Rolls of Nos. 2306 and 2307 have horizontal pairs of the same stamp that do not abut each other. Stamps from rolls containing Nos. 2307A and 2307B have pairs of different stamps that abut each other vertically.
No. 2305f was originally sold with a set of coins in 2009. It was made available in 2010 in a set of 3 sheets, Nos. 2299f, 2305f, and 2366c that sold for $8.73.

Celebration A981

Self-Adhesive
Booklet Stamp
Serpentine Die Cut 13½ Horiz.

2009, Feb. 2
2314	A981 P multi	1.00	.30
a.	Booklet pane of 6	5.50

No. 2314 sold for 54c on day of issue.

Rosemary Brown (1930-2003) — A982

Abraham Doras Shadd (1801-82) A983

2009, Feb. 2   *Perf. 13x12½*
2315	A982 54c multi	1.00	.30
2316	A983 54c multi	1.00	.30
a.	Pair, #2315-2316	2.00	.60

Black History Month. Brown and Shadd were the first black woman and man elected to public office in Canada.

First Airplane Flight in Canada, Cent. — A984

Self-Adhesive

2009, Feb. 23   *Perf. 12½x13*
2317	A984 P multi	1.00	.40

No. 2317 sold for 54c on day of issue.

Rhododendrons — A985

Color of rhododendrons: Nos. 2318a, 2319, White and pink. Nos. 2318b, 2320, Pink.

2009, Mar. 13   *Perf. 13¼*
2318	A985 Pane of 2	2.00	2.00
a.-b.	54c Either single	1.00	.40

Booklet Stamps
Self-Adhesive
Serpentine Die Cut 13½x12¾
2319	A985 54c multi	1.00	.40
2320	A985 54c multi	1.00	.40
a.	Booklet pane of 10, 5 each #2319-2320	10.00

Paintings by Jack Bush (1909-77) A986

Designs: 54c, Striped Column. $1.65, Chopsticks, horiz. (57x23mm).

2009, Mar. 20   *Perf. 13¼*
2321	A986 54c multi	1.00	.45
a.	Perf. 12½x13¼	1.40	1.25

Souvenir Sheet
Perf. 12½x13¼
2322	Pane, #2321a, 2322a	4.75	4.75
a.	A986 $1.65 multi	3.25	3.25

Souvenir Sheet

Intl. Year of Astronomy — A987

Designs: Nos. 2323a, 2324, Dominion Astrophysical Observatory, Saanich, British Columbia, and Horsehead Nebula. Nos. 2323b, 2325, Canada-France-Hawaii Telescope, Hawaii, and Eagle Nebula.

2009, Apr. 2   *Perf. 13¼x13*
2323	A987 Pane of 2	2.00	2.00
a.-b.	54c Either single	1.00	.90
c.	As #2323, with buff background behind product code	2.00	2.00

Booklet Stamps
Size: 24x34mm
Self-Adhesive
Serpentine Die Cut 13½
2324	A987 54c multi	1.00	.45
2325	A987 54c multi	1.00	.45
a.	Booklet pane, 5 each #2324-2325	10.00

The product code on No. 2323 is "063491072031," and on No. 2323c, "063491072024." The background behind the product code on No. 2323 is white. No. 2323c also has a fluorescent overprint in the margin, not found on No. 2323. Nos. 2323a and 2323b are 27x36mm.

Preservation of Polar Regions and Glaciers — A988

2009, Apr. 9   *Perf. 13x12¾*
2326	A988 54c Polar bear	1.00	.45
2327	A988 54c Arctic tern	1.00	.45
a.	Pair, #2326-2327	2.00	1.00
b.	Souvenir sheet, #2326-2327	2.00	2.00

Beneficial Insects Type of 2007

Design: Danaus plexippus caterpillar.

2009, Apr. 22   *Perf. 13¼x13*
2328	A942 2c multi	.20	.20

Horses A989

Designs: No. 2329, Canadian horse. No. 2330, Newfoundland pony.

Self-Adhesive
Booklet Stamps
Serpentine Die Cut 13¼

2009, May 15
2329	A989 54c multi	1.00	.45
2330	A989 54c multi	1.00	.45
a.	Booklet pane of 10, 5 each #2329-2330	10.00

Department of Foreign Affairs and International Trade, Cent. A990

2009, June 1   *Perf. 13¼x13*
2331	A990 54c multi	1.00	.50

Boundary Waters Treaty, Cent. A991

2009, June 12   *Perf. 13¼*
2332	A991 54c multi	1.00	.50

Popular Singers — A992

Designs: Nos. 2333a, 2334d, Robert Charlebois. Nos. 2333b, 2334c, Edith Butler. Nos. 2333c, 2334b, Stompin' Tom Connors. Nos. 2333d, 2334a, Bryan Adams.

2009, July 2   *Perf. 12½x13¼*
2333	A992 Pane of 4	4.00	4.00
a.-d.	54c Any single	1.00	.50

Self-Adhesive
Serpentine Die Cut 13½

2334	A992	Booklet pane of 4	4.00	
a.-d.		54c Any single	1.00	.50
		Complete booklet, 2 #2334	8.00	

Complete booklets were issued with four different covers depicting the featured singers.

Roadside Attractions — A993

Designs: Nos. 2335a, 2336a, Mr. PG, Prince George, British Columbia. Nos. 2335b, 2336b, Sign Post Forest, Watson Lake, Yukon Territory. Nos. 2335c, 2336c, Inukshuk, Hay River, Northwest Territories. Nos. 2335d, 2336d, Pysanka, Vegreville, Alberta.

2009, July 6   **Perf. 13**

2335	A993	Pane of 4	4.00	4.00
a.-d.		54c Any single	1.00	.50

Self-Adhesive
Serpentine Die Cut 13½

2336	A993	Booklet pane of 4	4.00	
a.-d.		54c Any single	1.00	.50
		Complete booklet, 2 #2336	8.00	

Captain Robert Abram Bartlett (1875-1946), Arctic Explorer — A994

2009, July 10   **Perf. 13**

2337	A994	54c multi	1.00	.45

Sports Invented By Canadians — A995

No. 2338: a, Five-pin bowling. b, Ringette. c, Lacrosse. d, Basketball.

Serpentine Die Cut 13¼
2009, Aug. 10

2338		Booklet pane of 4	4.00	
a.-d.	A995	54c Any single	1.00	.50
		Complete booklet, 2 #2338	8.00	

Montreal Canadiens Hockey Jersey — A996

500-Goal Scorers of the Montreal Canadiens — A997

No. 2340 — 500th goal of: a, Maurice Richard. b, Jean Béliveau. c, Guy Lafleur.

Self-Adhesive
Booklet Stamp
Serpentine Die Cut 13½x13¼
2009, Oct. 17

2339	A996	P multi	1.00	.50
a.		Booklet pane of 10	10.00	

Souvenir Sheet
Litho. With Three-Dimensional Plastic Affixed
Serpentine Die Cut 13x13¼
Self-Adhesive

2340	A997	Sheet of 3	17.00	8.50
a.-c.		$3 Any single	5.50	2.75

Montreal Canadiens hockey team, cent. No. 2339 sold for 54c on day of issue.

National War Memorial, Ottawa, and Poppy — A998

2009, Oct. 19   **Litho.**   **Perf. 12½**

2341	A998	P multi	1.00	.50
a.		Souvenir sheet of 2	2.00	1.00

Booklet Stamp
Self-Adhesive
Serpentine Die Cut 13¼

2342	A998	P multi	1.00	.50
a.		Booklet pane of 10	10.00	

End of World War I, 91st anniv. On day of issue, Nos. 2341-2342 each sold for 54c. No. 2341 was issued only in the souvenir sheet of 2.

Christmas Type of 2008 and

Christmas
A999   A1000

Designs: Nos. 2343b, 2345, Madonna and child. 98c, Magus. $1.65, Shepherd and lamb.

2009, Nov. 2   **Perf. 13x12½**

2343		Pane of 4 + 6 labels	7.25	3.75
a.	A970	P multi	1.00	.50
b.	A999	P multi	1.00	.50
c.	A999	98c multi	1.90	.95
d.	A999	$1.65 multi	3.25	1.60

Booklet Stamps
Self-Adhesive
Litho. With Hologram Affixed
Serpentine Die Cut 8¼ Horiz.

2344	A1000	P multi	1.00	.50
a.		Booklet pane of 6	6.00	
		Complete booklet, 2 #2344a	12.00	

Litho.
Serpentine Die Cut 13½

2345	A999	P multi	1.00	.50
a.		Booklet pane of 6	6.00	
		Complete booklet, 2 #2345	12.00	
2346	A999	98c multi	1.90	.95
a.		Booklet pane of 6	11.50	

2347	A999	$1.65 multi	3.25	1.60
a.		Booklet pane of 6	19.50	
b.		Booklet pane of 12, 6 each #2346-2347	31.00	
		Nos. 2344-2347 (4)	7.15	3.55

On day of issue, Nos. 2343a, 2343b, 2344, and 2345 each sold for 54c. No. 2347b is Nos. 2346a and 2347a unseparated but with horizontal slits cut in margin between the panes.

New Year 2010 (Year of the Tiger) — A1001

Designs: P, Seal impression of tiger in circle. $1.70, Sculpted tiger seal.

Litho. & Embossed With Foil Application
2010, Jan. 8   **Perf. 12½**

2348	A1001	P multi	1.10	.55

Souvenir Sheet

2349	A1001	$1.70 multi	3.25	1.60

No. 2348 sold for 57c on day of issue.

Flag Over Watson's Mill, Manotick, Ont. A1002

Flag Over Keremeos Grist Mill, Keremeos, B.C. A1003

Flag Over Old Stone Mill Natl. Historic Site, Delta, Ont. — A1004

Flag Over Riordon Grist Mill, Caraquet, N. B. — A1005

Flag Over Cornell Mill, Stanbridge East, Que. — A1006

2010, Jan. 11   **Litho.**   **Perf. 13x13¼**

2350		Souvenir sheet of 5	5.50	5.50
a.	A1002	P multi	1.10	.55
b.	A1003	P multi	1.10	.55
c.	A1004	P multi	1.10	.55
d.	A1005	P multi	1.10	.55
e.	A1006	P multi	1.10	.55

Booklet Stamps
Self-Adhesive
Serpentine Die Cut 13¼

2351	A1002	P multi	1.10	.55
2352	A1003	P multi	1.10	.55
2353	A1004	P multi	1.10	.55
2354	A1005	P multi	1.10	.55
2355	A1006	P multi	1.10	.55
a.		Booklet pane of 10, 2 each #2351-2355	11.00	
b.		Booklet pane of 30, 6 each #2351-2355	33.00	
		Nos. 2351-2355 (5)	5.50	2.75

On day of issue, Nos. 2350a-2350e and 2351-2355 each sold for 57c.

Striped Coralroot Orchid — A1007

Giant Helleborine Orchid — A1008

Rose Pogonia Orchid — A1009

Grass Pink Orchid — A1010

2010, Jan. 11   **Perf. 13¼x13¼**

2356		Souvenir sheet of 4	8.75	8.75
a.	A1007	P multi	1.10	.55
b.	A1008	$1 multi	2.00	.95
c.	A1009	$1.22 multi	2.40	1.25
d.	A1010	$1.70 multi	3.40	1.60

Coil Stamps
Self-Adhesive
Serpentine Die Cut 8 to 9½ (Sawtooth Tips)

2357	A1007	P multi	1.10	.55
2358	A1008	$1 multi	2.00	.95
2359	A1009	$1.22 multi	2.40	1.25
2360	A1010	$1.70 multi	3.40	1.60

Serpentine Die Cut 9¼ (Rounded Tips)

2361	A1007	P multi	1.10	.55
		Nos. 2357-2361 (5)	10.00	4.90

Booklet Stamps

2362	A1008	$1 multi	2.00	.95
a.		Booklet pane of 6	12.00	
2363	A1009	$1.22 multi	2.40	1.25
a.		Booklet pane of 6	14.50	
2364	A1010	$1.70 multi	3.40	1.60
a.		Booklet pane of 6	20.00	
		Nos. 2362-2364 (3)	7.80	3.80

On day of issue, Nos. 2356a and 2357 each sold for 57c. No. 2357 was printed in vertical rolls with stamps that are adjacent. No. 2361 was printed in horizontal rolls with stamps that are separated.

Queen Elizabeth II — A1011

Serpentine Die Cut 13¼
2010, Jan. 11
Booklet Stamp
Self-Adhesive

2365	A1011	P multi	1.10	.55
a.		Booklet pane of 10	11.00	

No. 2365 sold for 57c on day of issue.

Venues of the 2010 Winter Olympics — A1012

Designs: Nos. 2366a, 2367, Whistler, B.C. Nos. 2366b, 2368, Vancouver.

2010, Jan. 12   **Perf. 13½x13¼**

2366	A1012	Souvenir sheet of 2	2.25	2.25
a.-b.		57c Either single	1.10	.55
c.		As No. 2366, with "Vancouver / 2010" overprinted in sheet margin in gold	2.25	2.25

Booklet Stamps
Self-Adhesive
Serpentine Die Cut 13¼

2367	A1012	57c multi	1.10	.55
2368	A1012	57c multi	1.10	.55
a.		Booklet pane of 10, 5 each #2367-2368, + 10 stickers	11.00	

No. 2366c was sold in a package of 3 sheets that also contained Nos. 2299f and 2305f.

William Hall (1827-1904), First Black
Recipient of Victoria Cross — A1013

2010, Feb. 1   Perf. 12¾x12½
2369 A1013 57c multi   1.10   .55

Roméo LeBlanc (1927-2009),
Governor-General — A1014

2010, Feb. 8   Perf. 12½
2370 A1014 57c multi   1.10   .55

Gold Medal
From Vancouver
Winter Olympics
A1015

2010, Feb. 15   Perf. 12½
2371   Sheet of 2 #2371a   2.25 2.25
a.   A1015 57c Single stamp   1.10   .55

First day cancels have a Feb. 14 date, which
was the date on which the first gold medal was
awarded to a Canadian athlete on home soil,
but which also was a Sunday. Post offices in
Vancouver had the stamp available for sale on
Feb. 15.

Booklet Stamp
Self-Adhesive
Serpentine Die Cut 13½

2372 A1015 57c multi   1.10   .55
a.   Booklet pane of 10   11.00

Awarding of first gold medal to a Canadian
on home soil.

Spirit of the Winter Olympics — A1016

Winter Olympic athletes and: Nos. 2373a,
2374, Woman with painted face at left. Nos.
2373b, 2375, Woman with painted face at
right.

2010, Feb. 22   Perf. 13
2373 A1016   Souvenir sheet
                   of 2   2.25 2.25
a.-b.   57c Either single   1.10   .55
Booklet Stamps
Self-Adhesive
Serpentine Die Cut 13¼

2374 A1016 57c multi   1.10   .55
2375 A1016 57c multi   1.10   .55
a.   Booklet pane of 10, 5 each
       #2374-2375   11.00

African Violet Hybrids — A1017

Flower colors: Nos. 2376a, 2377, Red
(Descelles' Avalanche). Nos. 2376b, 2378,
Purple (Picasso).

2010, Mar. 3   Litho.   Perf. 13
2376 A1017   Souvenir sheet
                   of 2   2.25 2.25
a.-b.   P Either single   1.10   .55
Booklet Stamps
Self-Adhesive
Serpentine Die Cut 13½

2377 A1017 P multi   1.10   .55
2378 A1017 P multi   1.10   .55
a.   Booklet pane of 10, 5 each
       #2377-2378   11.00

On day of issue, Nos. 2376a, 2376b, 2377
and 2378 each sold for 57c.

Friendship
Between
Canada
and Israel,
60th Anniv.
A1018

Serpentine Die Cut 13¼
2010, Apr. 14   Litho.
Booklet Stamp
Self-Adhesive

2379 A1018 $1.70 multi   3.50 1.75
a.   Booklet pane of 3 + label 10.50
       Complete booklet, 2 #2379a 21.00

See Israel No. 1812.

Indian
Kings — A1019

Portraits by John Verelst of: No. 2380, Tee
Yee Neen Ho Ga Row. No. 2381, Sa Ga Yeath
Qua Pieth Tow. No. 2382, Ho Nee Yeath Taw
No Row. No. 2383, Etow Oh Koam.

2010, Apr. 19   Litho.   Perf. 12½
2380 A1019 57c multi   1.10   .55
2381 A1019 57c multi   1.10   .55
2382 A1019 57c multi   1.10   .55
2383 A1019 57c multi   1.10   .55
a.   Block or strip of 4, #2380-
       2383   4.40 2.20
b.   Souvenir sheet of 4, #2380-
       2383   4.40 2.20
c.   As "b," with London 2010 em-
       blem on sheet margin   4.40 2.20
       Nos. 2380-2383 (4)   4.40 2.20

Meeting of the four Indian Kings and Queen
Anne in London, 300th anniv.

Canadian Navy, Cent. — A1020

Designs: Nos. 2384a, 2385, Male sailor,
HMCS Niobe. Nos. 2384b, 2386, Female
sailor, HMCS Halifax.

2010, May 4   Litho.   Perf. 12½
2384 A1020   Sheet of 2   2.25 2.25
a.-b.   Either single   1.10   .55
Booklet Stamps
Self-Adhesive
Serpentine Die Cut 13¼x13¼

2385 A1020 57c multi   1.10   .55
2386 A1020 57c multi   1.10   .55
a.   Booklet pane of 10, 5 each
       #2385-2386   11.00

Sea Mammals — A1021

Designs: No. 2387a, Harbor porpoise. No.
2387b, Sea otter.

Perf. 13x12¼x13x13 Syncopated
(#2387a), 13x13x13x12¼
Syncopated (#2387b)
2010, May 13   Litho. & Engr.
2387 A1021   Sheet of 2   2.25 2.25
a.-b.   57c Either single   1.10   .55
c.   As "a," perf. 13x12¾ synco-
       pated   1.10   .55
d.   As "b," perf. 13x12¾ synco-
       pated   1.10   .55
e.   Booklet pane of 8, 4 each
       #2387c-2387d   9.00   —
       Complete booklet, #2387e 9.00

Nos. 2387a and 2387b have syncopation on
left and right side, with the syncopation
between the stamps in the shape of a maple
leaf. Nos. 2387c and 2387d have syncopation
on one side only, with the syncopation
between pairs of stamps in the shape of con-
joined ovals.
See Sweden No. 2368.

Canadian Geographic's Wildlife
Photography of the Year — A1022

Designs: Nos. 2388a, 2393, Ardia herodias,
by Martin Cooper. Nos. 2388b, 2392, Vulpes
vulpes, by Ben Boulter. Nos. 2388c, 2391, Tet-
tigoniidae, by Julie Bazinet. Nos. 2388d, 2390,
Tachycineta bicolor, by Mark Bradley. Nos.
2388e, 2389, Selaphorus rufus, by Wing Yan
Tam.

2010, May 22 Litho. Perf. 12½x13
2388 A1022   Sheet of 5   5.50 5.50
a.-e.   57c Any single   1.10   .55
Booklet Stamps
Self-Adhesive
Serpentine Die Cut 13¼

2389 A1022 57c multi   1.10   .55
2390 A1022 57c multi   1.10   .55
2391 A1022 57c multi   1.10   .55
2392 A1022 57c multi   1.10   .55
2393 A1022 57c multi   1.10   .55
a.   Booklet pane of 10, 2 each
       #2389-2393   11.00
       Nos. 2389-2393 (5)   5.50 2.75

Rotary
International
in Canada,
Cent.
A1023

Serpentine Die Cut 13½x12¾
2010, June 18   Litho.
Booklet Stamp
Self-Adhesive

2394 A1023 57c multi   1.10   .55
a.   Booklet pane of 8   9.00

Paintings by
Prudence
Heward (1896-
1947)
A1024

Designs: 57c, Rollande. $1.70, At the Thea-
tre, horiz. (42x40mm).

2010, July 2   Perf. 13¼x13
2395 A1024 57c multi   1.10   .55
Souvenir Sheet
2396   Sheet of 2, #2395,
          2396a   4.50 4.50
a.   A1024 $1.70 multi   3.25 1.60

Roadside Attractions — A1025

Designs: Nos. 2397a, 2398, Coffee Pot,
Davidson, Saskatchewan. Nos. 2397b, 2399,
Happy Rock, Gladstone, Manitoba. Nos.
2397c, 2400, Wawa Goose, Wawa, Ontario.
Nos. 2397d, 2401, Puffin, Longue-Pointe-de-
Mingan, Quebec.

2010, July 5   Perf. 13
2397 A1025   Sheet of 4   4.40 4.40
a.-d.   P Any single   1.10   .55
Booklet Stamps
Self-Adhesive
Serpentine Die Cut 13½

2398 A1025 P multi   1.10   .55
2399 A1025 P multi   1.10   .55
2400 A1025 P multi   1.10   .55
2401 A1025 P multi   1.10   .55
a.   Booklet pane of 4, #2398-
       2401   4.40
       Complete booklet, 2 #2401a 8.80

On day of issue, Nos. 2397a-2397d, 2398-
2401 each sold for 57c.

Girl Guides,
Cent. — A1026

Serpentine Die Cut 13¾
2010, July 8
Booklet Stamp
Self-Adhesive

2402 A1026 P multi   1.10   .55
a.   Booklet pane of 10   11.00

No. 2402 sold for 57c on day of issue.

Founding of Cupids, Newfoundland
Settlement, 400th Anniv. — A1027

2010, Aug. 17   Perf. 12½
2403 A1027 57c multi   1.10   .55

Year of
British
Home
Children
A1028

2010, Sept. 1
2404 A1028 57c multi .... 1.10 .55

Blue Whale — A1029

Litho., Engr. & Silk-screened
2010, Oct. 4 *Perf. 12½x13*
2405 A1029 $10 multi 20.00 10.00
Printed in sheets of 2.

Beneficial Insects Type of 2007
Designs: 4c, Paper wasp (Polistes fuscatus). 6c, Assassin bug (Zelus luridus). 7c, Large milkweed bug (Oncopeltus fasciatus). 8c, Margined leatherwing (Chauliognathus marginatus). 9c, Dogbane beetle (Chrysochus auratus).

2010, Oct. 19 Litho. *Perf. 13¼x13*
2406 A942 4c multi .... .20 .20
2407 A942 6c multi .... .20 .20
2408 A942 7c multi .... .20 .20
2409 A942 8c multi .... .20 .20
2410 A942 9c multi .... .20 .20
   a. Souvenir sheet, #2406-2410 .70 .70
   Nos. 2406-2410 (5) 1.00 1.00

Christmas
Ornaments
A1030

Madonna and Child,
Sculpture by Antonio
Caruso — A1031

Designs: Nos. 2411a, 2413, Three red ornaments, greenish blue background. $1, Two blue ornaments, purple background. $1.70, Three red ornaments, dull blue background.

2010, Nov. 1 Litho. *Perf. 12½*
2411 Souvenir sheet of 3 6.75 6.75
  a. A1030 P multi 1.25 .60
  b. A1030 $1 multi 2.00 1.00
  c. A1030 $1.70 multi 3.50 1.75

Booklet Stamps
Self-Adhesive
Serpentine Die Cut 13¼
2412 A1031 P multi 1.25 .60
  a. Booklet pane of 6 7.50
  Complete booklet, 2 #2412a 15.00

Serpentine Die Cut 13½
2413 A1030 P multi 1.25 .60
  a. Booklet pane of 6 7.50
  Complete booklet, 2 #2413a 15.00
2414 A1030 $1 multi 2.00 1.00
  a. Booklet pane of 6 12.00
2415 A1030 $1.70 multi 3.50 1.75
  a. Booklet pane of 6 21.00
  b. Gutter pane, #2414a, 2415a 33.00
  Nos. 2412-2415 (4) 8.00 3.95

Nos. 2411a, 2412 and 2413 each sold for 57c on day of issue.

New Year 2011
(Year of the
Rabbit)
A1032

Design: $1.75, Two rabbits in circle.

Litho. & Embossed With Foil Application
2011, Jan. 7 *Perf. 12½*
2416 A1032 P shown 1.25 .60
Souvenir Sheet
2417 A1032 $1.75 multi 3.50 1.75
No. 2416 sold for 59c on day of issue.

SEMI-POSTAL STAMPS

Catalogue values for unused stamps in this section are for Never Hinged items.

Olympic Type of 1973 and

SP1

SP2

1974, Apr. 17 Litho. *Perf. 12½*
Size: 20x36mm
B1 A307 8c + 2c multi .40 .40
B2 A307 10c + 5c multi .60 .60
B3 A307 15c + 5c multi .80 .80
  Nos. B1-B3 (3) 1.80 1.80

1975, Feb. 5 *Perf. 13*
B4 SP1 8c + 2c Swimming .40 .40
B5 SP1 10c + 5c Rowing .60 .60
B6 SP1 15c + 5c Sailing .80 .80
  Nos. B4-B6 (3) 1.80 1.80

1975, Aug. 6
B7 SP2 8c + 2c Fencing .40 .40
B8 SP2 10c + 5c Boxing .60 .60
B9 SP2 15c + 5c Judo .80 .80
  Nos. B7-B9 (3) 1.80 1.80

1976, Jan. 7
B10 SP2 8c + 2c Basketball .40 .40
B11 SP2 10c + 5c Vaulting .60 .60
B12 SP2 20c + 5c Soccer 1.00 1.00
  Nos. B10-B12 (3) 2.00 2.00

21st Olympic Games, Montreal, July 17-Aug. 1. The surtax was for the Canadian Olympic Committee.

Literacy — SP3

1996, Sept. 9 Litho. *Perf. 13x12½*
B13 SP3 45c +5c multi 1.00 .35
  a. Booklet pane of 10 10.00
  Complete booklet 11.50

No. B13 has die cut opening in center to represent missing puzzle piece.

Surcharge donated to ABC CANADA literacy organization.

Mental
Health — SP4

Self-Adhesive
Booklet Stamp
Serpentine Die Cut 13¼
2008, Oct. 6 Litho.
B14 SP4 P +10c multi 1.00 .35
  a. Booklet pane of 10 10.00

No. B14 had a franking value of 52c on day of issue. Surtax for Canada Post Foundation for Mental Health.

Mental
Health — SP5

Self-Adhesive
Booklet Stamp
Serpentine Die Cut 13¼
2009, Sept. 14 Litho.
B15 SP5 P +10c multi 1.25 1.25
  a. Booklet pane of 10 12.50

No. B15 had a franking value of 54c on day of issue. Surtax for Canada Post Foundation for Mental Health.

Mental
Health — SP6

Serpentine Die Cut 13¼
2010, Sept. 7 Litho.
Booklet Stamp
Self-Adhesive
B16 SP6 P +10c multi 1.40 1.40
  a. Booklet pane of 10 14.00

No. B16 had a franking value of 57c on day of issue. Surtax for Canada Post Foundation for Mental Health.

AIR POST STAMPS

Allegory of
Flight — AP1

Unwmk.
1928, Sept. 21 Engr. *Perf. 12*
C1 AP1 5c brown olive 15.00 5.00
  Never hinged 27.50
  a. Imperf., pair 275.00
  Never hinged 375.00

No. C1 is known imperforate horizontally and imperforate vertically.
For surcharge see No. C3.

For information on imperforate and part-perforate varieties, see note following No. 47a.

Allegory-Air
Mail Circles
Globe
AP2

1930, Dec. 4 *Perf. 11*
C2 AP2 5c olive brown 85.00 27.50
  Never hinged 140.00
For surcharge see No. C4.

No. C1 Surcharged

1932, Feb. 22 *Perf. 12*
C3 AP1 6c on 5c brown olive 12.50 4.00
  Never hinged 22.00
  a. Inverted surcharge 200.00
  Never hinged 280.00
  b. Double surcharge 675.00
  Never hinged 950.00
  c. Triple surcharge 400.00
  Never hinged 550.00
  d. Pair, one without surcharge 950.00
  Never hinged 1,350.

Counterfeit surcharges exist.
No. C3b is valued in the grade of fine.

No. C2 Surcharged in Dark Blue

1932, July 12 *Perf. 11*
C4 AP2 6c on 5c olive brown 40.00 12.50
  Never hinged 70.00

Daedalus
AP3

1935, June 1 *Perf. 12*
C5 AP3 6c red brown 4.25 1.25
  Never hinged 6.00
  a. Horiz. pair, imperf. vert. 6,000.
  b. Imperf., pair 650.00
  Never hinged 1,000.

No. C5a is believed to be unique and is the result of a pre-perforating paper foldover.

Mackenzie
River
Steamer and
Seaplane
AP4

1938, June 15
C6 AP4 6c blue 3.75 .40
  Never hinged 5.25
  a. Imperf., pair 650.00
  Never hinged 950.00

Planes and
Student
Flyers
AP5

1942-43
C7 AP5 6c deep blue 5.25 1.20
  Never hinged 7.50
  a. Imperf., pair 650.00
  Never hinged 950.00

C8 AP5 7c deep blue ('43)   1.00 .20
   Never hinged   1.40
  a. Imperf., pair   650.00
   Never hinged   950.00

Canada's contribution to the war effort of the Allied Nations.

> Catalogue values for unused stamps in this section, from this point to the end of the section, are for Never Hinged items.

Canada Geese in Flight — AP6

1946, Sept. 16
C9 AP6 7c deep blue   1.25 .20
  a. Booklet pane of 4 3.50 3.25

For overprints see Nos. CO1, CO2.

AIR POST SPECIAL DELIVERY STAMPS

Trans-Canada Airplane and Aerial View of a City — APSD1

1942-43 Unwmk. Engr. *Perf. 12*
CE1 APSD1 16c bright ultra 2.50 2.00
   Never hinged   3.50
  a. Imperf., pair   750.00
   Never hinged   1,100.
CE2 APSD1 17c brt ultra   3.25 3.00
   ('43)
   Never hinged   4.75
  a. Imperf., pair   650.00
   Never hinged   950.00

Canada's contribution to the war effort of the Allied Nations.

> Catalogue values for unused stamps in this section, from this point to the end of the section, are for Never Hinged items.

DC-4 Transatlantic Mail Plane Over Quebec — APSD2

1946, Sept. 16
CE3 APSD2 17c bright ultra 6.50 4.25

Circumflex accent on second "E" of "EXPRES."

Corrected Die
1947, Dec. 3
CE4 APSD2 17c bright ultra 6.50 4.25

Grave accent on the 2nd "E" of "EXPRES."

AIR POST OFFICIAL STAMPS

> Catalogue values for unused stamps in this section are for Never Hinged items.

No. C9 Overprinted in Black

1949 Unwmk. *Perf. 12*
CO1 AP6 7c deep blue 12.00 4.75
  a. No period after "S" 110.00 60.00

Same Overprinted

1950
CO2 AP6 7c deep blue 17.50 15.00

SPECIAL DELIVERY STAMPS

SD1

Unwmk.
1898, June 28 Engr. *Perf. 12*
E1 SD1 10c blue green 110.00 11.00
   Never hinged   300.00

SD2

1922, Aug. 21
E2 SD2 20c carmine 100.00 9.00
   Never hinged   220.00

Five Stages of Mail Transportation SD3

1927, June 29
E3 SD3 20c orange 30.00 17.50
   Never hinged   60.00
  a. Imperf., pair 200.00
   Never hinged   275.00

No. E3 forms part of the Confederation Commemorative issue. It is known imperforate vertically and imperforate horizontally.

SD4

1930, Sept. 2   *Perf. 11*
E4 SD4 20c henna brown 65.00 15.00
   Never hinged   125.00

SD5

1932, Dec. 24
E5 SD5 20c henna brown 60.00 16.00
   Never hinged   115.00
  a. Imperf., pair   650.00
   Never hinged   950.00

Allegory of Progress — SD6

1935, June 1   *Perf. 12*
E6 SD6 20c dark carmine 14.00 7.50
   Never hinged   22.50
  a. Imperf., pair   650.00
   Never hinged   950.00

Arms of Canada — SD7

1938-39
E7 SD7 10c dk green 7.00 3.25
   (4/1/39)
   Never hinged   11.00
  a. Imperf., pair   650.00
   Never hinged   950.00
E8 SD7 20c dark carmine 30.00 25.00
   (6/15/38)
   Never hinged   50.00
  a. Imperf., pair   650.00
   Never hinged   950.00

No. E8 Surcharged in Black

1939, Mar. 1
E9 SD7 10c on 20c dk car 8.00 6.50
   Never hinged   12.00

Coat of Arms and Flags SD8

1942, July 1
E10 SD8 10c green 3.25 2.00
   Never hinged   4.50
  a. Imperf., pair   650.00
   Never hinged   950.00

Canada's contribution to the war effort of the Allied Nations.

> Catalogue values for unused stamps in this section, from this point to the end of the section, are for Never Hinged items.

Arms of Canada — SD9

1946, Sept. 16
E11 SD9 10c green 4.25 1.10

The laurel and olive branches symbolize Victory and Peace.
For overprints see Nos. EO1, EO2.

SPECIAL DELIVERY OFFICIAL STAMPS

> Catalogue values for unused stamps in this section are for Never Hinged items.

No. E11 Overprinted in Black

1950 Unwmk. *Perf. 12*
EO1 SD9 10c green 17.50 15.00

Same Overprinted

EO2 SD9 10c green 25.00 20.00

REGISTRATION STAMPS

R1

	1875-88 Unwmk.	Engr.	*Perf. 12*
F1	R1 2c orange	115.00	5.75
	Never hinged	225.00	
a.	2c vermilion	170.00	15.00
	Never hinged	290.00	
b.	2c rose carmine	340.00	110.00
	Never hinged	625.00	
c.	As "a," imperf., pair	—	
d.	Perf. 12x11½	525.00	100.00
	Never hinged	950.00	
F2	R1 5c dark green	150.00	6.00
	Never hinged	300.00	
a.	5c blue green ('88)	160.00	6.00
	Never hinged	325.00	
b.	5c yellow green	240.00	7.50
	Never hinged	475.00	
c.	Imperf., pair	1,200.	
	Never hinged	1,700.	
d.	Perf. 12x11½	1,300.	240.00
	Never hinged	2,500.	
F3	R1 8c dull blue ('76)	500.00	350.00
	Never hinged	1,000.	
	Nos. F1-F3 (3)	765.00	361.75

The used No. F1c is unique (fine centering).

POSTAGE DUE STAMPS

D1   D2

1906-28   Unwmk.   Engr.   Perf. 12

J1	D1	1c violet	25.00	4.75
		Never hinged	40.00	
a.		Thin paper ('24)	45.00	7.50
		Never hinged	80.00	
b.		Imperf., pair	400.00	
J2	D1	2c violet	25.00	1.00
		Never hinged	40.00	
a.		Thin paper ('24)	45.00	11.00
		Never hinged	80.00	
b.		Imperf., pair	400.00	
J3	D1	4c violet ('28)	65.00	22.50
		Never hinged	110.00	
J4	D1	5c violet	25.00	2.00
		Never hinged	40.00	
a.		As "c," thin paper	20.00	7.50
		Never hinged	35.00	
b.		Imperf., pair	400.00	
J5	D1	10c violet ('28)	85.00	14.00
		Never hinged	160.00	
		Nos. J1-J5 (5)	225.00	44.25
		#J1-J5, never hinged	390.00	

In 1924 there was a printing of Nos. J1, J2 and J4 on thin semi-transparent paper. Imperf pairs are without gum.

1930-32   Perf. 11

J6	D2	1c dark violet	12.50	4.25
		Never hinged	22.50	
J7	D2	2c dark violet	7.00	1.10
		Never hinged	12.50	
J8	D2	4c dark violet	20.00	5.50
		Never hinged	35.00	
J9	D2	5c dark violet	25.00	6.50
		Never hinged	42.50	
J10	D2	10c dark violet ('32)	110.00	10.00
		Never hinged	200.00	
a.		Vert. pair, imperf. horiz.	2,000.	—
		Never hinged	3,000.	
		Nos. J6-J10 (5)	174.50	27.35
		#J6-J10, never hinged	312.50	

No. J10a is valued in the grade of fine.

D3   D4

1933-34

J11	D3	1c dark violet ('34)	15.00	6.50
		Never hinged	27.50	
a.		Imperf., pair	400.00	
		Never hinged	575.00	
J12	D3	2c dark violet	7.50	1.25
		Never hinged	13.00	
J13	D3	4c dark violet	13.00	8.00
		Never hinged	22.50	
J14	D3	10c dark violet	32.50	6.50
		Never hinged	52.50	
		Nos. J11-J14 (4)	68.00	22.25
		Nos. J11-J14, never hinged 115.50		

> Catalogue values for unused stamps in this section, from this point to the end of the section, are for Never Hinged items.

1935-65   Perf. 12

J15	D4	1c dark violet	.30	.20
a.		Imperf., pair	200.00	
J16	D4	2c dark violet	.30	.20
a.		Imperf., pair	200.00	
J16B	D4	3c dark vio ('65)	2.00	1.50
J17	D4	4c dark violet	.35	.20
a.		Imperf., pair	200.00	
J18	D4	5c dark vio ('48)	.40	.35
J19	D4	6c dark vio ('57)	2.25	1.75
J20	D4	10c dark violet	.40	.20
a.		Imperf., pair	200.00	
		Nos. J15-J20 (7)	6.00	4.40

D5

1967, Feb. 8   Litho.   Perf. 12
Size: 20x17mm

J21	D5	1c carmine rose	.20	.20
J22	D5	2c carmine rose	.20	.25
J23	D5	3c carmine rose	.20	.20
J24	D5	4c carmine rose	.25	.25
J25	D5	5c carmine rose	1.50	1.50

J26	D5	6c carmine rose	.25	.25
J27	D5	10c carmine rose	.40	.30
		Nos. J21-J27 (7)	3.00	3.00

1969-78   Perf. 12
Size: 20x15¾mm

J28	D5	1c car rose ('70)	.45	.30
a.		Perf. 12½x12 ('77)	.20	.20
J29	D5	2c car rose ('72)	.25	.20
J30	D5	3c car rose ('74)	.25	.20
J31	D5	4c carmine rose	.40	.30
a.		Perf. 12½x12 ('77)	.20	.20
J32	D5	5c car rose, perf. 12½x12 ('77)	.20	.20
a.		Perf. 12	16.00	12.50
J33	D5	6c carmine rose ('72)	.20	.20
J34	D5	8c carmine rose ('78)	.40	.30
J35	D5	10c carmine rose	.55	.20
a.		Perf. 12½x12 ('77)	.25	.20
J36	D5	12c carmine rose	.75	.60
a.		Perf. 12½x12 ('77)	1.50	.70
J37	D5	16c carmine rose ('74)	.40	.25

Perf. 12½x12

J38	D5	20c carmine rose ('77)	.55	.40
J39	D5	24c carmine rose ('77)	.65	.40
J40	D5	50c carmine rose ('77)	1.00	.75
		Nos. J28-J40 (13)	5.85	4.20

WAR TAX STAMPS

WT1   WT2

Unwmk.
1915, Mar. 25   Engr.   Perf. 12

MR1	WT1	1c green	25.00	.20
		Never hinged	60.00	
MR2	WT1	2c carmine	25.00	.25
		Never hinged	60.00	

In 1915 postage stamps of 5, 20 and 50 cents were overprinted "WAR TAX" in two lines. These stamps were intended for fiscal use, the war tax on postal matter being 1 cent. A few of these stamps were used to pay postage.

1916

TWO DIES:
Die I — There is a colored line between two white lines below the large letter "T."
Die II — The right half of the colored line is replaced by two short diagonal lines and five small dots.

MR3	WT2	2c + 1c car (I)	35.00	.20
		Never hinged	87.50	
a.		2c + 1c carmine (II)	175.00	4.50
		Never hinged	400.00	
b.		2c + 1c rose red (I)	42.50	.40
		Never hinged	85.00	
MR4	WT2	2c + 1c brn (II)	20.00	.20
		Never hinged	50.00	
a.		2c + 1c brown (I)	600.00	10.00
		Never hinged	1,100.	
b.		Imperf., pair (I)	200.00	
c.		Imperf., pair (II)	1,600.	

Nos. MR4b and MR4c were made without gum.

Perf. 12x8

MR5	WT2	2c + 1c car (I)	65.00	30.00
		Never hinged	140.00	

Coil Stamps
Perf. 8 Vertically

MR6	WT2	2c + 1c car (I)	150.00	9.00
		Never hinged	320.00	
MR7	WT2	2c + 1c brn (II)	35.00	1.10
		Never hinged	75.00	
a.		2c + 1c brown (I)	175.00	7.50
		Never hinged	400.00	

OVERPRINTED OFFICIAL STAMPS

> Catalogue values for unused stamps in this section are for Never Hinged items.

With Perforated Initials O H M S
On March 28, 1939 the Treasury Board ruled that on and after June 30, 1939 all stamps used by government departments throughout the country should be perforated O H M S (On His Majesty's Service) and that "the Post Office Department is to make arrangements required to provide that all stamps sold to Government Departments are perforated with the letters O H M S." The sale of such perforated stamps was discontinued in 1948.

For listings see the *Scott Classic Specialized Catalogue*.

Nos. 249, 250, 252 and 254 Overprinted in Black

1949-50   Unwmk.   Perf. 12

O1	A97	1c green	2.00	1.75
a.		No period after "S"	150.00	65.00
O2	A98	2c brown	10.00	7.50
a.		No period after "S"	150.00	65.00
O3	A99	3c rose violet	2.25	1.25
O4	A98	4c dark carmine	2.75	.75

Nos. 269 to 273 Overprinted in Black

O6	A108	10c olive	3.50	.60
a.		No period after "S"	85.00	60.00
O7	A109	14c black brown	4.00	2.25
a.		No period after "S"	125.00	75.00
O8	A110	20c slate black	16.00	3.25
a.		No period after "S"	150.00	75.00
O9	A111	50c dk blue grn	200.00	110.00
a.		No period after "S"	1,000.	500.00
O10	A112	$1 red violet	70.00	35.00
a.		No period after "S"	2,500.	1,750.
		Nos. O1-O4,O6-O10 (9)	310.50	162.35

It is recommended that a certificate of authenticity be acquired for No. O10a.

Same Overprint on No. 294

1950

O11	A124	50c dull green	40.00	25.00

Nos. 284 to 288 Overprinted in Black

1950

O12	A119	1c green	.40	.30
O13	A120	2c sepia	1.10	.75
O14	A121	3c rose violet	1.10	.60
O15	A122	4c dark carmine	1.10	.20
b.		No period after "S"	85.00	55.00
O15A	A123	5c deep blue	2.25	1.50
c.		No period after "S"	85.00	55.00
		Nos. O12-O15A (5)	5.95	3.25

Stamps of 1946-50 Overprinted in Black

a

b

c

1950

O16	A119(a)	1c grn (#284)	.50	.20
O17	A120(a)	2c sep (#285)	1.30	.90
O18	A121(a)	3c rose vio (#286)	1.30	.90
O19	A122(a)	4c dk car (#287)	1.30	.20
O20	A123(a)	5c dp bl (#288)	1.60	.90
O21	A108(b)	10c olive	2.50	.50
O22	A109(b)	14c black brn	6.50	2.00
O23	A110(b)	20c slate blk	14.00	1.00
O24	A124(b)	50c dull green	10.00	5.50
O25	A112(b)	$1 red violet	105.00	80.00
		Nos. O16-O25 (10)	144.00	91.40

Nos. 301-302 Overprinted Type "b"
1950-51

O26	A125	10c black brown	1.30	.20
a.		One, without "G"	775.00	650.00
O27	A126	$1 brt ultra ('51)	100.00	90.00

It is recommended that a certificate of authenticity be acquired for No. O26a.

Nos. 305-306 Overprinted Type "a"
1951-52   Unwmk.   Perf. 12

O28	A120	2c olive green	.60	.20
O29	A122	4c orange ver ('52)	.95	.20

No. 316 Overprinted Type "b"
1952

O30	A132	20c gray	2.25	.20

Nos. 320-321 Overprinted Type "b"
1952-53

O31	A136	7c blue	4.00	1.25
O32	A137	$1 gray ('53)	15.00	8.00

Same Overprints on #325-329, 334
1953-61

O33	A139(a)	1c violet brown	.35	.20
O34	A139(a)	2c green	.35	.20
O35	A139(a)	3c carmine rose	.35	.20
O36	A139(a)	4c violet	.45	.20
O37	A139(a)	5c ultramarine	.45	.20
O38	A141(b)	50c light green	5.00	1.20
a.		Overprinted type "c" ('61)	5.00	2.00
		Nos. O33-O38 (6)	6.95	2.20

No. 351 Overprinted Type "b"
1955-62

O39	A148	10c violet brown	.90	.20
a.		Overprinted type "c" ('62)	1.90	1.25

#337-338, 340-341 Ovptd. Type "a"
1955-56

O40	A144	1c vio brown ('56)	.35	.30
O41	A144	2c green ('56)	.35	.20
O43	A144	4c violet ('56)	1.00	.20
O44	A144	5c bright blue	.60	.20
		Nos. O40-O44 (4)	2.30	.90

No. 362 Overprinted Type "b"
1956-62

O45	A159	20c green	1.75	.20
a.		Overprinted type "c" ('62)	7.00	.50

#401-402, 404-405 Ovptd. Type "a"
1963, May 15   Engr.   Perf. 12

O46	A195	1c deep brown	.75	.70
a.		Double overprint	850.00	
O47	A195	2c green	.75	.70
a.		Pair, one without "G"	1,000.	
O48	A195	4c carmine	.80	.70
O49	A195	5c violet blue	.50	.50
		Nos. O46-O49 (4)	2.80	2.60

CAPE JUBY

'kāp 'jü-bē

LOCATION — Northwest coast of Africa in Spanish Sahara
GOVT. — Spanish administration
AREA — 12,700 sq. mi.
POP. — 9,836
CAPITAL — Villa Bens (Cape Juby)

By agreement with France, Spain's Sahara possessions were extended to include Cape Juby and in 1916 Spanish troops occupied the territory. It was attached for administrative purposes to Spanish Sahara.

100 Centimos = 1 Peseta

Stamps of Rio de Oro, 1914 Surcharged in Violet, Red, Green or Blue

1916		Unwmk.	Perf. 13	
1	A6	5c on 4p rose (V)	175.00	19.00
a.		Inverted surcharge	250.00	30.00
d.		Double surcharge	325.00	50.00
2	A6	10c on 10p dl vio (R)	40.00	19.00
a.		Inverted surcharge	55.00	30.00
b.		Double surcharge	75.00	50.00
2E	A6	10c on 10p dl vio (V)	125.00	72.50
f.		Double surcharge (R, V)	150.00	90.00
2G	A6	10c on 10p dl vio (R)	125.00	72.50
3	A6	15c on 50c dk brn (G)	52.50	30.00
a.		Inverted surcharge	57.50	30.00
4	A6	15c on 50c dk brn (R)	37.50	19.00
a.		Inverted surcharge	75.00	37.50
5	A6	40c on 1p red vio (G)	77.50	35.00
a.		Inverted surcharge	75.00	37.50
6	A6	40c on 1p red vio (R)	65.00	26.00
a.		Inverted surcharge	75.00	42.50
		Nos. 1-6 (8)	697.50	293.00
		Set, never hinged	1,200.	

Very fine examples of Nos. 1-6 will be somewhat off center. Well centered examples are uncommon and will sell for more.

Stamps of Spain, 1876-1917, Overprinted in Red or Black

1919			Imperf.	
7	A21	¼c bl grn (R)	.30	.30
		Perf. 13x12½, 14		
8	A46	2c dk brn (Bk)	.30	.30
a.		Double overprint	19.00	16.00
b.		Double overprint (Bk + R)	60.00	52.50
9	A46	5c dk brn (Bk)	.65	.60
a.		Double overprint	19.00	16.00
b.		Inverted overprint	30.00	47.50
10	A46	10c car (Bk)	.75	.70
a.		Double overprint (Bk + R)	60.00	52.50
b.		Double overprint (R)	22.50	22.50
11	A46	15c ocher (Bk)	3.25	3.00
b.		Double overprint	19.00	16.00
c.		Red control #	6.50	3.75
d.		As "c," inverted overprint	13.00	
12	A46	20c ol grn (R)	17.00	16.00
13	A46	25c dp bl (R)	3.25	3.00
a.		Double overprint	19.00	16.00
14	A46	30c bl grn (R)	3.25	3.00
15	A46	40c rose (Bk)	3.50	3.25
16	A46	50c sl bl (R)	3.75	3.50
17	A46	1p lake (Bk)	10.50	8.75
18	A46	4p dp vio (R)	40.00	34.00
19	A46	10p blk (R)	55.00	45.00
		Nos. 7-19 (13)	141.50	121.40
		Set, never hinged	260.00	

Nos. 8-19 have blue control number on back. For imperfs, see the Scott Classic Catalogue.

Same on Stamps of Spain, 1920-21

1922			Imperf.	
20	A47	1c blue green (R)	25.00	14.00
		Never hinged	45.00	

	Engr.	Perf. 13x12½		
	Blue Control Number on Back			
23	A46	20c violet	145.00	42.50

A 2c and a 15c exist, values $400 and $10, respectively, for unused, hinged examples, $600 and $15 for never hinged.

Same on Stamps of Spain, 1922-23

1925			Perf. 13½x13	
25	A49	5c red vio	5.25	3.50
26	A49	10c bl grn	13.00	3.50
28	A49	20c violet	27.50	10.00
		Nos. 25-28 (3)	45.75	17.00
		Set, never hinged	72.50	

Exists on Spain No. 331, 2c olive green. Value $350 unused hinged and $600 never hinged.

Seville-Barcelona Exposition Issue

CABO JUBY

Stamps of Spain, 1929, Overprinted in Red or Blue

1929			Perf. 11	
29	A52	5c rose lake (Bl)	.45	.45
30	A53	10c green (R)	.45	.45
31	A53	15c Prus bl (R)	.45	.45
32	A51	20c pur (R)	.45	.45
33	A50	25c brt rose (Bl)	.45	.45
34	A50	30c blk brn (Bl)	.45	.45
35	A53	40c dk bl (R)	.45	.45
36	A51	50c dp org (Bl)	.60	.60
37	A52	1p bl blk (R)	21.00	21.00
38	A53	4p dp rose (Bl)	27.50	27.50
39	A53	10p brn (Bl)	27.50	27.50
		Nos. 29-39 (11)	79.75	79.75
		Set, never hinged	130.00	

Stamps of Spanish Morocco, 1928-33, Overprinted in Black or Red

1934			Perf. 14	
40	A7	1c brt rose (Bk)	.50	.50
41	A2	2c dk vio (R)	4.50	4.50
42	A2	5c dp bl (R)	5.00	5.00
43	A2	10c dk grn (Bk)	10.00	10.00
43A	A10	10c dk grn (R)	3.00	3.00
44	A2	15c org brn (Bk)	25.00	25.00
45	A7	20c sl grn (R)	8.75	8.75
46	A3	25c cop red (Bk)	4.75	4.75
47	A10	30c red brn (Bk)	8.75	8.75
48	A13	40c dp bl (R)	32.50	32.50
49	A13	50c red org (Bk)	60.00	60.00
50	A4	1p yel grn (R)	50.00	50.00
51	A25	2p red vio (Bk)	100.00	100.00
52	A6	4p ultra (R)	125.00	125.00

No. 43A and 1c, 20c, 30c, 40c, 50c, with control numbers.

Same Overprint in Black on Stamp of Spanish Morocco, 1932

53	A2	1c car rose ("Ct")	2.10	2.10
		Nos. 40-53 (15)	439.85	439.85
		Set, never hinged	825.00	

Stamps of Spanish Morocco, 1933-35, Overprinted in Black, Blue or Red

1935-36				
54	A8	2c grn (R)	.95	.95
55	A9	5c mag (Bk)	3.00	3.00
55A	A10	10c dk grn (R) ('36)	19.00	19.00
56	A11	15c yel (Bl)	7.50	7.50
57	A12	25c crim (Bk)	85.00	85.00
58	A8	1p sl blk (R)	11.50	11.50
59	A9	2.50p brn (Bl)	45.00	45.00
60	A11	4p yel grn (R)	77.50	77.50
61	A12	5p blk (R)	65.00	65.00
		Nos. 54-61 (9)	314.45	314.45
		Set, never hinged	525.00	

Same Overprint in Black or Red on Stamps of Spanish Morocco, 1935

1935			Perf. 13½	
62	A14	25c vio (R)	4.00	4.00
63	A15	30c crim (Bk)	4.00	4.00
64	A14	40c org (Bk)	5.25	5.25
65	A15	50c brt bl (R)	9.50	9.50
66	A14	60c dk bl grn (R)	11.50	11.50
67	A15	2p brn ink (R)	62.50	62.50

Same Overprint on Stamps of Spanish Morocco, 1933

			Perf. 13½, 14	
68	A7	1c brt rose (Bk)	.30	.30

			Perf. 14	
69	A7	20c slate grn (R)	4.50	4.50
		Nos. 62-69 (8)	101.55	101.55
		Set, never hinged	160.00	160.00

Same Overprint on Stamps of Spanish Morocco, 1937

1937			Perf. 13½	
70	A21	1c dk bl (Bk)	.45	.45
71	A21	2c org brn (Bk)	.45	.45
72	A21	5c cer (Bk)	.45	.45
73	A21	10c emer (Bk)	.45	.45
74	A21	15c brt bl (Bk)	.45	.45
75	A21	20c red brn (Bk)	.45	.45
76	A21	25c mag (Bk)	.45	.45
77	A21	30c red org (Bk)	.45	.45
78	A21	40c org (Bk)	1.25	1.25
79	A21	50c ultra (R)	1.25	1.25
80	A21	60c vio blk (R)	1.25	1.25
81	A21	1p bl vio (Bk)	1.25	1.25
82	A21	2p Prus bl (Bk)	75.00	75.00
83	A21	2.50p gray blk (R)	75.00	75.00
84	A21	4p dk brn (Bk)	75.00	75.00
85	A22	10p vio blk (R)	75.00	75.00
		Nos. 70-85 (16)	308.60	308.60
		Set, never hinged	500.00	

1st Year of the Revolution.

Same Overprint in Black on Types of Spanish Morocco, 1939

Designs: 5c, Spanish quarter. 10c, Moroccan quarter. 15c, Street scene, Larache. 20c, Tetuan.

1939		Photo.	Perf. 13½	
86	A25	5c vermilion	.50	.50
87	A25	10c deep green	.50	.50
88	A25	15c brown lake	.50	.50
89	A25	20c bright blue	.50	.50
		Nos. 86-89 (4)	2.00	2.00
		Set, never hinged	2.75	

Same Overprint in Black or Red on Stamps of Spanish Morocco, 1940

1940			Perf. 11½x11	
90	A26	1c dk brn (Bk)	.25	.25
91	A27	2c ol grn (R)	.25	.25
92	A28	5c dk bl (R)	.25	.25
93	A29	10c dk red lil (Bk)	.25	.25
94	A30	15c dk grn (R)	.25	.25
95	A31	20c pur (R)	.25	.25
96	A32	25c blk brn (R)	.25	.25
97	A33	30c grn (Bk)	.30	.30
98	A34	40c slate grn (R)	.60	.60
99	A35	45c org ver (Bk)	.60	.60
100	A36	50c brn org (Bk)	.65	.65
101	A37	70c saph (R)	1.90	1.90
102	A38	1p ind & brn (Bk)	4.00	4.00
103	A39	2.50p choc & dk grn (Bk)	10.00	10.00
104	A40	5p dk cer & sep (Bk)	10.50	10.50
105	A41	10p dk ol grn & brn org (Bk)	26.00	26.00
		Nos. 90-105 (16)	56.30	56.30
		Set, never hinged	95.00	

Imperfs exist. Value, set $275.

Stamps of Spanish Morocco, 1944. Overprinted in Black or Red

1944, Oct. 2		Unwmk.	Perf. 12½	
106	A47	1c choc & lt bl	.25	.25
107	A48	2c slate grn & lt grn	.25	.25
108	A49	5c choc & grnsh blk (R)	.25	.25
109	A50	10c brt ultra & red org	.25	.25
110	A51	15c sl grn & lt grn	.25	.25
111	A52	20c dp cl & blk (R)	.25	.25
112	A53	25c lt bl & choc	.25	.25
113	A47	30c yel grn & brt ultra (R)	.25	.25
114	A48	40c choc & red vio	.25	.25
115	A49	50c brt ultra, & red grn	.25	.25
116	A50	75c yel grn & brt ultra (R)	1.25	1.25
117	A51	1p brt ultra & choc	1.40	1.40
118	A52	2.50p blk & brt ultra (R)	3.25	3.25
119	A53	10p sal & gray blk (R)	25.00	25.00
		Nos. 106-119 (14)	33.40	33.40
		Set, never hinged	52.50	

Same Overprint on Stamps of Spanish Morocco, 1946

1946, Mar.			Perf. 10½x10	
120	A54	1c pur & brn	.25	.25
121	A55	2c dk Prus grn & vio blk (R)	.25	.25
122	A54	10c dp org vio bl	.25	.25
123	A55	15c dk bl & bl grn	.25	.25
124	A54	25c yel grn & ultra	.25	.25
125	A56	40c dk bl & brn (R)	.30	.30
126	A55	45c blk & rose	.45	.45
127	A57	1p dk Prus grn & dp bl	1.60	1.60
128	A58	2.50p dp org & grnsh gray (R)	4.75	4.75
129	A59	10p dk bl & gray (R)	13.50	13.50
		Nos. 120-129 (10)	21.85	21.85
		Set, never hinged		

Same Overprint in Carmine, Black or Brown on Stamps of Spanish Morocco, 1948

1948, Jan. 1			Perf. 10, 10x10½	
130	A64	2c pur & brn	.40	1.00
131	A65	5c dp claret & vio	.25	.25
132	A66	15c brt ultra & bl grn (Bk)	.25	.25
133	A67	25c blk & Prus grn	.25	.25
134	A65	35c brt ultra & gray blk	.25	.25
135	A68	50c red & vio (Br)	.25	.25
136	A66	70c dk gray grn & ultra (R)	.25	.25
137	A67	90c cer & dk gray grn (Bk)	.30	.30
138	A68	1p brt ultra & vio (Br)	.45	.45
139	A64	2.50p vio brn & sl grn	1.60	1.60
140	A69	10p blk & dp ultra	3.00	3.00
		Nos. 130-140 (11)	7.25	7.85
		Set, never hinged	12.00	

SEMI-POSTAL STAMPS

Types of Semi-Postal Stamps of Spain, 1926, Overprinted

1926		Unwmk.	Perf. 12½, 13	
B1	SP1	1c orange	12.50	12.50
B2	SP2	2c rose	12.50	12.50
B3	SP3	5c blk brn	3.50	3.50
B4	SP4	10c pink	1.60	1.60
B5	SP1	15c dk vio	1.10	1.10
B6	SP4	20c vio brn	1.10	1.10
B7	SP5	25c dp car	1.10	1.10
B8	SP1	30c ol grn	1.10	1.10
B9	SP3	40c ultra	.45	.45
B10	SP2	50c red brn	.45	.45
B11	SP4	1p vermilion	.45	.45
B12	SP3	4p bister	1.60	1.60
B13	SP5	10p lt vio	3.50	3.50
		Nos. B1-B13 (13)	40.95	40.95
		Set, never hinged	65.00	

Nos. B12-B13 surcharged "Alfonso XIII" and new value are listed as Spain Nos. B68-B69. See Spain No. B6a.

AIR POST STAMPS

Spanish Morocco, Nos. C1 to C10 Overprinted "CABO JUBY" as on #54-61

1938, June 1		Unwmk.	Perf. 13½	
C1	AP1	5c brown	.25	.25
C2	AP1	10c brt grn	.25	.25
C3	AP1	25c crimson	.25	.25
C4	AP1	40c light blue	2.10	2.10
C5	AP2	50c brt mag	.25	.25
C6	AP2	75c dk bl	.25	.25
C7	AP1	1p sepia	.25	.25
C8	AP1	1.50p dp vio	1.90	1.90
C9	AP1	2p dp red brn	2.75	2.75
C10	AP1	3p brn blk	7.25	7.25
		Nos. C1-C10 (10)	15.50	15.50
		Set, never hinged	25.00	

Moroccan Views — AP3

Designs: 5c, Ketama landscape. 10c, Mosque, Tangier. 15c, Velez. 90c, Sanjurjo. 5p, Strait of Gibraltar

1942, Apr. 1　Photo.　Perf. 12½

C11	AP3	5c deep blue	.25	.25
C12	AP3	10c org brn	.25	.25
C13	AP3	15c grnsh blk	.25	.25
C14	AP3	90c dk rose	.50	.50
C15	AP3	5p black	1.75	1.75
	Nos. C11-C15 (5)		3.00	3.00
	Set, never hinged		4.00	

SPECIAL DELIVERY STAMPS

Special Delivery Stamp of Spain Ovptd. "CABO JUBY" as on #7-28

1919　　Unwmk.　　Perf. 14

E1	SD1	20c red (Bk)	3.25	3.25
b.		Double overprint	27.50	13.00

Spanish Morocco #E4 Overprinted "CABO JUBY" as on #40-52 in Red

1934

E2	SD2	20c black	10.00	10.00

Spanish Morocco No. E5 Overprinted "CABO JUBY" as on Nos. 54-61

1935

E3	SD3	20c vermilion	3.50	3.50

Same Ovpt. on Spanish Morocco #E6

1937　　　　　　Perf. 13½

E4	SD4	20c bright carmine	1.10	1.10

1st Year of the Revolution.

Same Ovpt. on Spanish Morocco #E8

1940　　　　　　Perf. 11½x11

E5	SD5	25c scarlet	.55	.55

SEMI-POSTAL SPECIAL DELIVERY STAMP

Type of Semi-Postal Special Delivery Stamp of Spain, 1926, Overprinted "CABO-JUBY" as on Nos. B1-B13

1926　　Unwmk.　　Perf. 12½, 13

EB1	SPSD1	20c ultra & black	3.50	3.50

CAPE OF GOOD HOPE

ˈkāp əv ˈgud ˈhōp

LOCATION — In the extreme southern part of South Africa.
GOVT. — Former British Colony
AREA — 276,995 sq mi. (1911)
POP. — 2,564,965 (1911)
CAPITAL — Cape Town

Cape of Good Hope joined with Natal, the Transvaal and the Orange River Colony in 1910, forming the Union of South Africa.

12 Pence = 1 Shilling

Watermarks

Wmk. 15 —　　　Wmk. 16 —
Anchor　　　　　Anchor

"Hope"
Seated
A1

Printed by Perkins, Bacon & Co.
Wmk. 15

1853, Sept. 1　Engr.　Imperf.

1	A1	1p brick red, bluish paper	3,500.	250.00
a.		1p pale brick red, deeply blued paper	*4,500.*	*350.00*
b.		1p deep brick red, deeply blued paper	*10,500.*	*390.00*
2	A1	4p deep blue, lightly blued paper	1,750.	130.00
a.		4p deep blue, deeply blued paper	*3,500.*	*190.00*
b.		4p blue, bluish paper	*3,250.*	*175.00*

Counterfeits exist.

1855-58

White Paper

3	A1	1p rose ('57)	600.00	240.00
a.		1p dull red	*825.00*	*300.00*
b.		1p brick red	*6,000.*	*1,050.*
4	A1	4p blue	600.00	65.00
a.		Half used as 2p on cover		*42,000.*
b.		4p deep blue	*825.00*	*65.00*
c.		4p bright blue	*825.00*	*65.00*
5	A1	6p pale lilac ('58)	950.00	240.00
a.		6p rose lilac	*2,500.*	*350.00*
b.		6p grayish lilac on bluish paper	*5,000.*	*540.00*
c.		6p slate purple on bluish paper	*4,150.*	*1,200.*
d.		Half used as 3p on cover		—
6	A1	1sh yellow grn ('58)	*3,250.*	225.00
a.		1sh dark green	*350.00*	*600.00*
b.		Half used as 6p on cover		—

Nos. 3-6 are known rouletted unofficially. Counterfeits exist.
No. 4 was reproduced by the collotype process in an unwatermarked souvenir sheet distributed at the London Intl. Stamp Exhib. 1950.

A2

Printed by Saul Solomon & Co.

1861　Laid Paper　Unwmk.　Typo.

7	A2	1p vermilion	16,500.	2,650.
a.		1p carmine	*42,500.*	*4,000.*
b.		1p red	*45,000.*	*5,000.*
c.		1p milky blue (error)	*175,000.*	*32,500.*
d.		1p pale blue (error)		*36,000.*
9	A2	4p milky blue	40,000.	3,000.
a.		4p pale blue	*42,500.*	*3,250.*
b.		4p blue	*45,000.*	*3,500.*
c.		4p dark blue	*112,500.*	*5,750.*
d.		As #9, right corner retouched		*7,750.*
e.		As #9a, right corner retouched		*7,750.*
f.		4p vermilion (error)	*177,500.*	*65,000.*
g.		4p carmine (error)		*112,500.*

Nos. 7 and 9 are usually called Wood Blocks. The plates were made locally and composed of clichés mounted on wood. The errors were caused by a cliché of each value being mounted in the plate of the other value.
In 1883 plate proofs of both values on white paper, usually called "reprints," were made. The 1p is in dull orange red; the 4p in dark blue. These are known canceled, as a few were misused as stamps. The proofs do not include the errors.
Counterfeits exist.

Printed by De La Rue & Co.

1863-64　　Wmk. 15　　Engr.

12	A1	1p dark carmine	210.00	270.00
a.		1p reddish brown	*450.00*	*300.00*
b.		1p brownish red	*450.00*	*275.00*
13	A1	4p dark blue	200.00	80.00
a.		4p slate blue	*2,400.*	*600.00*
14	A1	6p purple	300.00	540.00
15	A1	1sh emerald	475.00	540.00
a.		1sh pale emerald	*1,200.*	—

Nos. 12-15 can be distinguished from Nos. 3-6 not only by colors but because Nos. 12-15 often appear in a granular ink or with the background lightly printed in whole or part.
No. 12a, Wmk. 1, is believed to be a proof. Value, $29,000.
Counterfeits exist.

"Hope" and Symbols of Colony

A3　　　　　　　　A6
Frame Line Around Stamp

1864-65　Typo.　Wmk. 1　Perf. 14

16	A3	1p rose ('65)	100.00	30.00
17	A3	4p blue ('65)	140.00	4.25
a.		4p pale blue	*140.00*	*4.25*
b.		4p dull ultramarine	*325.00*	*65.00*
c.		4p deep blue ('72)	*200.00*	*4.50*
18	A3	6p bright violet	175.00	1.75
a.		6p dull violet	*275.00*	*8.25*
b.		6p pale lilac ('84)	*150.00*	*26.00*
19	A3	1sh yellow green	150.00	4.50
a.		1sh blue green	*165.00*	*5.75*
	Nos. 16-19 (4)		565.00	40.50

Imperf. stamps are believed to be proofs.
For surcharges see Nos. 20-21, N3.
For types A3 and A6 with manuscript surcharge of 1d or overprints "G. W." or "G," see Griqualand West listings.

Stamps of 1864 Surcharged in Red or Black:

a　　　　　　　　b

1868-74　　　　　Red Surcharge

20	A3(a)	4p on 6p	350.00	19.00
a.		"Peuce" for "Pence"	*2,150.*	*900.00*
b.		"Fonr" for "Four"		*850.00*
21	A3(b)	1p on 6p ('74)	600.00	115.00
a.		"E" of "PENNY" omitted		*1,300.*

Space between words and bars varies from 12½-16mm on #20, and 16½-18mm on #21.

1876　　　　　　Black Surcharge

22	A3 (b)	1p on 1sh green	110.00	65.00

Without Frame Line Around Stamp

1871-81　　　　　　Perf. 14

23	A6	½p gray black ('75)	27.50	10.50
24	A6	1p rose ('72)	45.00	.75
25	A6	3p lilac rose ('80)	250.00	31.00
26	A6	3p claret ('81)	145.00	3.50
27	A6	4p blue ('76)	130.00	.90
a.		4p ultramarine	*275.00*	*60.00*
28	A6	5sh orange	425.00	20.00
	Nos. 23-28 (6)		1,022.	66.65

For surcharges see Nos. 29-32, 39, 55.

No. 27 Surcharged in Red

1879

29	A6	3p on 4p blue	130.00	2.40
a.		"THE.EE"	*2,750.*	*350.00*
b.		"PENCB"	*2,250.*	*275.00*
c.		Double surcharge	*11,000.*	*3,900.*
d.		As "a," double surcharge		

Type of 1871 Surcharged in Black

1880

30	A6	3p on 4p lilac rose	90.00	2.75

No. 25 Surcharged in Black

e　　　　　　　　f

31	A6(e)	3p on 3p lilac rose	275.00	9.00
a.		Inverted surcharge	*10,000.*	*1,200.*
32	A6(f)	3p on 3p lilac rose	100.00	2.10
a.		Inverted surcharge	*1,200.*	*47.50*

1882-83　　　　　　Wmk. 2

33	A6	½p gray black	32.50	3.25
34	A6	1p rose	72.50	2.50
35	A6	2p bister	120.00	1.50
36	A6	3p claret	9.25	1.50
37	A3	6p bright violet	110.00	1.00
38	A6	5sh orange ('83)	950.00	275.00

For overprint see Rhodesia No. 49.

Nos. 26 and 36 Surcharged in Black

1882　　　　　　Wmk. 1

39	A6	½p on 3p claret	7,000.	150.00
a.		Hyphen omitted		*3,750.*

**　　　　　　Wmk. 2**

40	A6	½p on 3p claret	45.00	5.00
a.		"ENNY"	*2,400.*	*825.00*
b.		"PENN"	*1,300.*	*725.00*
c.		Hyphen omitted	*825.00*	*425.00*

1884-98　　　　　　Wmk. 16

41	A6	½p gray black ('86)	7.25	.20
42	A6	½p yel green ('96)	1.80	.60
43	A6	1p rose ('85)	9.00	.20
44	A6	2p bister	10.00	.20
45	A6	2p choc brown ('97)	2.35	1.75
46	A6	3p red violet ('98)	13.50	1.20
47	A6	4p blue ('90)	17.00	.60
48	A6	4p pale ol grn ('97)	7.00	.20
49	A3	6p violet	14.00	.25
50	A3	1sh dull bluish grn ('89)	130.00	.60

51	A6	1sh blue grn ('94)	82.50	6.50
52	A6	1sh yel buff ('96)	14.00	2.50
53	A6	5sh orange ('87)	120.00	7.75
54	A6	5sh brown org ('96)	92.50	5.00
		Nos. 41-54 (14)	520.90	30.60

For surcharges see Nos. 58, 162, 165-166.
For overprints see Rhodesia Nos. 43, 45-48.

Type of 1871
Surcharged in Black

1891, Mar.

| 55 | A6 | 2½p on 3p deep magenta | 5.25 | .25 |
| a. | | "1" of "½" has straight serif | 70.00 | 37.50 |

Hope Seated — A13

1892-96

| 56 | A13 | 2½p sage green | 17.50 | .20 |
| 57 | A13 | 2½p ultra ('96) | 8.00 | .20 |

For surcharge see No. N4. For overprint see Orange River Colony No. 55.

No. 44 Surcharged in Black

1893, Mar.

58	A6	1p on 2p bister	4.75	.60
a.		Double surcharge		500.00
b.		No period after "PENNY"	82.50	20.00

Hope Standing A15 · Table Mountain and Bay; Coat of Arms A16

1893-1902

59	A15	½p green ('98)	5.00	.20
60	A15	1p rose	2.00	.20
61	A15	3p red violet ('02)	5.25	2.00
		Nos. 59-61 (3)	12.25	2.40

For surcharges see Nos. 163-164, N2. For overprints see Orange River Colony #54, 56, Rhodesia #44, Transvaal #236-236A.

1900, Jan.

| 62 | A16 | 1p carmine rose | 5.00 | .25 |

King Edward VII — A17

Various frames.

1902-04 Wmk. 16

63	A17	½p emerald	2.75	.20
64	A17	1p car rose	2.40	.20
65	A17	2p brown ('04)	16.50	.95
66	A17	2½p ultra ('04)	3.25	8.25
67	A17	3p red violet ('03)	11.00	1.40
68	A17	4p ol green ('03)	14.50	.80
69	A17	6p violet ('03)	22.00	.60
70	A17	1sh bister	17.50	1.10
71	A17	5sh brown org ('03)	120.00	25.00
		Nos. 63-71 (9)	209.90	38.50

Imperf. stamps are proofs.

Cape of Good Hope stamps were replaced by those of Union of South Africa.

ISSUED IN MAFEKING

Excellent forgeries of Nos. 162-180 are known.

Stamps of Cape of Good Hope Surcharged

1900, Mar. 24

162	A6	1p on ½p grn	275.	77.50
163	A15	1p on ½p grn	325.	92.50
164	A15	3p on 1p rose	275.	60.00
165	A6	6p on 3p red vio	42,500.	300.00
166	A6	1sh on 4p pale ol green	8,000.	425.00

Stamps of Bechuanaland Protectorate Surcharged

1900 Wmk. 30

167	A54	1p on ½p ver	275.	77.50
a.		Inverted surcharge		7,000.
168	A40	3p on 1p lilac	1,000.	110.
a.		Double surcharge		30,000.
169	A56	6p on 2p grn & car	2,250.	90.
170	A58	6p on 3p vio, yel	16,500.	325.
a.		Inverted surcharge	—	36,000.
b.		Double surcharge		

The lettering of "Mafeking Besieged" shows varying breaks in various letters, and may have either a period or no punctuation after "Mafeking."

On Stamps of Bechuanaland
Wmk. 29

| 171 | A1 | 6p on 3p violet & black | 475. | 82.50 |

Wmk. 30

172	A59	1sh on 4p brn & grn	1,650.	95.
a.		Double surch., one inverted	—	27,500.
b.		Triple surcharge	—	25,000.
c.		Inverted surcharge	—	25,000.
d.		Double surcharge	—	25,000.

Stamps of Bechuanaland Protectorate Surcharged

173	A40	3p on 1p lilac	1,050.	90.
a.		Double surcharge	—	10,750.
174	A56	6p on 2p grn & car	1,300.	90.
175	A62	1sh on 6p vio, rose	7,250.	105.

On Stamps of Bechuanaland

| 176 | A62 | 1sh on 6p vio, rose | 55,000. | 900. |
| 177 | A65 | 2sh on 1sh green | 14,500. | 500. |

Sgt. Major Goodyear M1 · Gen. Robert S. S. Baden-Powell M2

Wmk. OCEANA FINE
Photographic Print

1900, Apr. Perf. 12
Laid Paper

| 178 | M1 | 1p blue, blue | 1,000. | 425.00 |
| a. | | Imperf., pair | | 21,500. |

179	M2	3p blue, blue, 18½mm wide	1,400.	425.00
a.		Horiz. pair, imperf btwn.	—	77,500.
b.		Double impression	—	20,000.
c.		Reversed design	77,500.	45,000.
180	M2	3p blue, blue, 21mm wide	10,750.	1,500.

The color of the paper varies from pale to deep blue.
OCEANA FINE is a sheet watermark and does not appear on every stamp.
Imperfs of No. 178 are proofs.
There is one used pair of No. 179a privately owned. There are 2 unused and 6 used examples of No. 179c privately owned.
Issued: #179, Apr. 6; #178, 180, Apr. 10.

ISSUED IN VRYBURG

Under Boer Occupation

Cape of Good Hope Stamps of 1884-96 Surcharged

Two Types of Surcharge:
Type I — Surcharge 10mm high. Space between lines 5½mm.
Type II — Surcharge 12mm high. Space between lines 7½mm.

1899, Nov. Wmk. 16 Perf. 14

N1	A6	½p on ½p emer (I)	240.	95.
a.		Type II	2,000.	825.
N2	A15	1p on 1p rose (I)	275.	120.
a.		Double surcharge	2,250.	950.
b.		Type II		
N3	A3	2p on 6p vio (II)	2,500.	600.
N4	A13	2½p on 2½p ultra (I)	2,000.	500.
a.		Type II	12,000.	5,000.

"Z.A.R." stands for Zuid Afrikaansche Republiek (South African Republic).

Under British Occupation

Transvaal Stamps of 1895-96 Handstamped

1900 Unwmk. Perf. 12½

N5	A13	½p green	—	3,250.
N6	A13	1p rose & grn	10,750.	5,000.
N7	A13	2p brown & grn	—	36,000.
N8	A13	2½p ultra & grn	—	36,000.

CAPE VERDE

ˈkāp ˈvərd

LOCATION — A group of 10 islands and five islets in the Atlantic Ocean, about 500 miles due west of Senegal.
GOVT. — Republic
AREA — 1,557 sq. mi.
POP. — 405,748 (1999 est.)
CAPITAL — Praia

The Portuguese territory of Cape Verde became independent on July 5, 1975.

1000 Reis = 1 Milreis
100 Centavos = 1 Escudo (1913)

Catalogue values for unused stamps in this country are for Never Hinged items, beginning with Scott 268 in the regular postage section, Scott J31 in the postage due section, and Scott RA6 in the postal tax section.

Crown of Portugal — A1 · King Luiz — A2

1877 Unwmk. Typo. Perf. 12½

1	A1	5r black	3.50	2.00
2	A1	10r yellow	40.00	11.00
3	A1	20r bister	3.00	1.40
4	A1	25r rose	2.50	1.40
5	A1	40r blue	82.50	50.00
b.		Cliche of Mozambique in Cape Verde plate, in pair with #5	2,000.	1,400.
6	A1	50r green	150.00	72.50
7	A1	100r lilac	8.25	3.50
8	A1	200r orange	5.00	3.75
9	A1	300r brown	6.00	5.25
		Nos. 1-9 (9)	300.75	150.80

For expanded treatment of Nos. 1-9, see the Scott Classic Catalogue.

1881-85 Perf. 12½

10	A1	10r green	2.75	2.10
11	A1	20r carmine ('85)	5.50	3.75
12	A1	25r violet ('85)	4.00	3.00
13	A1	40r yellow buff	2.40	1.75
a.		Imperf.		
b.		Cliche of Mozambique in Cape Verde plate, in pair with #13	110.00	110.00
c.		As "b," imperf.		
14	A1	50r blue	6.75	4.25
		Nos. 10-14 (5)	21.40	14.85

Reprints of the 1877-85 issues are on smooth white chalky paper, ungummed, and on thin white paper with shiny white gum. They are perf 13½.
For expanded treatment of nos. 10-14, see the Scott Classic Catalogue.

1886 Embossed Perf. 12½, 13½
Chalk-Surfaced Paper

15	A2	5r black	4.50	3.00
16	A2	10r green	6.75	3.00
17	A2	20r carmine	8.25	5.25
18	A2	25r violet	8.25	5.50
19	A2	40r chocolate	8.25	3.50
20	A2	50r blue	8.25	3.50
21	A2	100r yel brown	8.25	4.50
22	A2	200r gray lilac	18.00	10.50
23	A2	300r orange	21.00	4.25
		Nos. 15-23 (9)	91.50	43.00

The 25r, 50r and 100r have been reprinted in aniline colors with clean-cut Perf. 13½.
For expanded treatment of nos. 15-19, see the Scott Classic Catalogue.
For surcharges see Nos. 59-67, 184-187.

King Carlos
A3 · A4

1894-95 Typo. Perf. 11½, 12½, 13½

24	A3	5r orange	1.60	1.25
25	A3	10r redsh violet	1.60	1.25
26	A3	15r chocolate	4.00	2.60
a.		Perf. 12½	150.00	120.00
27	A3	20r lavender	4.00	2.60
28	A3	25r dp green	3.50	2.25
a.		Perf. 12½	4.00	3.25
29	A3	50r lt blue	3.50	2.25
a.		Perf. 13 1/2	14.00	4.50
30	A3	75r carmine ('95)	11.50	5.75
a.		Perf. 13½	55.00	42.00
31	A3	80r yel grn ('95)	12.00	6.50
a.		Perf. 13½	45.00	35.00
32	A3	100r brn, buff ('95)	9.00	5.25
a.		Perf. 12½	100.00	55.00
33	A3	150r car, rose ('95)	32.00	27.00
a.		Perf. 12½	400.00	300.00
b.		Perf. 11½	70.00	45.00
34	A3	200r dk blue, lt blue ('95)	32.00	27.00
a.		Perf. 12½	150.00	120.00
35	A3	300r dk blue, sal ('95)	36.00	17.00
		Nos. 24-35 (12)	150.70	100.70

For surcharges see Nos. 68-78, 137, 189-193, 201-205.

1898-1903   *Perf. 11½*
Name and Value in Black except 500r

36	A4	2½r gray	.40	.30
37	A4	5r orange	.50	.30
38	A4	10r lt green	.55	.30
39	A4	15r brown	5.50	2.00
40	A4	15r gray green ('03)	1.90	1.25
41	A4	20r gray violet	1.60	1.00
42	A4	25r sea green	3.50	1.25
a.		Perf 12½	300.00	180.00
43	A4	25r carmine ('03)	1.00	.40
44	A4	50r dark blue	3.50	1.50
45	A4	50r brown ('03)	3.75	2.40
46	A4	65r slate blue ('03)	40.00	30.00
47	A4	75r rose	8.50	3.50
48	A4	75r lilac ('03)	3.50	2.25
49	A4	80r violet	8.50	3.50
50	A4	100r dk blue, *blue*	3.50	2.00
51	A4	115r org brn, *pink* ('03)	15.00	13.50
52	A4	130r brown, *straw* ('03)	15.00	13.50
53	A4	150r brown, *straw*	8.50	6.75
54	A4	200r red vio, *pnksh*	4.00	3.00
55	A4	300r dk blue, *rose*	10.00	5.00
56	A4	300r dull blue, *straw* ('03)	16.00	10.50
57	A4	500r blk & red, *blue* ('01)	10.00	5.00
58	A4	700r violet, *yelsh* ('01)	28.00	17.50
		Nos. 36-58 (23)	192.70	126.70

For overprints and suecharges see Nos. 80-99, 139, 200.

Regular Issues Surcharged in Red or Black

Two spacing types of surcharge. See note above Angola No. 61.

On Issue of 1886

1902, Dec. 1   *Perf. 12½, 13½*

59	A2	65r on 5r black (R)	5.75	3.75
60	A2	65r on 200r gray lilac	5.75	3.75
61	A2	65r on 300r orange	5.75	3.75
62	A2	115r on 10r green	5.75	3.75
63	A2	115r on 20r rose	5.75	3.75
a.		Perf 13½	50.00	35.00
64	A2	130r on 50r blue	5.75	3.75
65	A2	130r on 100r brown	5.75	3.75
66	A2	400r on 25r violet	2.75	2.60
67	A2	400r on 40r choc	6.75	3.75
a.		Perf 13½	50.00	35.00

On Issue of 1894
Perf. 11½, 12½, 13½

68	A3	65r on 10r red violet	6.75	3.75
69	A3	65r on 20r lavender	6.75	3.75
70	A3	65r on 100r brown, *buff*	8.50	5.25
a.		Perf 12½	26.00	24.00
71	A3	115r on 5r orange	4.00	3.00
a.		Inverted surcharge	60.00	60.00
72	A3	115r on 25r blue grn	3.00	2.10
a.		Perf 11½	55.00	55.00
73	A3	115r on 150r car, *rose*	8.25	6.50
a.		Perf 13½	55.00	25.00
74	A3	130r on 75r car	4.00	3.00
a.		Perf 12½	250.00	200.00
75	A3	130r on 80r yel grn	3.50	2.00
76	A3	130r on 200r dk blue, *blue*	3.75	2.60
77	A3	400r on 50r lt blue	5.50	3.00
a.		Inverted surcharge	65.00	55.00
b.		Perf 13½	300.00	300.00
78	A3	400r on 300r dk blue, *sal*	2.50	1.75

On Newspaper Stamp of 1893

79	N1	400r on 2½r brown	1.60	1.50
a.		Inverted surcharge	27.50	
b.		Perf 12½	225.00	200.00
		Nos. 59-79 (21)	107.85	70.80

Reprints of Nos. 59, 66, 67, and 77 have shiny white gum and clean-cut perforation 13½.

For overprint and surcharge see #137, 205-206.

Overprinted in Black
On Nos. 39, 42, 44, 47

1902-03   *Perf. 11½*

80	A4	15r brown	2.00	1.25
81	A4	25r sea green	2.00	1.25
82	A4	50r blue ('03)	2.00	1.25
83	A4	75r rose ('03)	3.75	2.75
a.		Inverted overprint	42.50	42.50
		Nos. 80-83 (4)	9.75	6.50

For overprint see No. 139.

No. 46 Surcharged in Black

1905, July 1

84	A4	50r on 65r slate blue	4.00	3.00

Stamps of 1898-1903 Overprinted in Carmine or Green

1911, Aug. 20

85	A4	2½r gray	.25	.25
86	A4	5r orange	.25	.25
87	A4	10r lt green	1.00	.80
88	A4	15r gray green	.90	.45
89	A4	20r gray violet	1.50	.80
90	A4	25r carmine (G)	.90	.45
91	A4	50r brown	8.50	6.00
92	A4	75r red lilac	1.40	.80
93	A4	100r dk blue, *blue*	1.40	.80
94	A4	115r org brn, *pink*	1.40	.80
95	A4	130r brown, *straw*	1.40	.80
96	A4	200r red vio, *pnksh*	6.50	4.00
97	A4	400r dull bl, *straw*	3.50	1.25
98	A4	500r blk & red, *bl*	3.50	1.25
99	A4	700r violet, *straw*	3.50	1.40
		Nos. 85-99 (15)	35.90	20.10

King Manuel II — A5

Overprinted in Carmine or Green

1912   *Perf. 11½x12*

100	A5	2½r violet	.25	.25
101	A5	5r black	.25	.25
102	A5	10r gray grn	.45	.40
103	A5	20r carmine (G)	2.40	1.40
104	A5	25r vio brown	.45	.25
105	A5	50r dk blue	5.00	3.50
106	A5	75r bister brn	1.10	1.00
107	A5	100r brown, *lt grn*	1.10	1.00
108	A5	200r dk green, *sal*	1.75	1.10
109	A5	300r black, *azure*	1.75	1.10

Perf. 14½x15

110	A5	400r black & blue	3.75	3.00
111	A5	500r ol grn & vio brn	3.75	3.00
		Nos. 100-111 (12)	22.00	16.25

Common Design Types pictured following the introduction.

Vasco da Gama Issue of Various Portuguese Colonies

Common Design Types CD20-CD27 Surcharged

On Stamps of Macao

1913, Feb. 13   *Perf. 12½ to 16*

112		¼c on ½a blue grn	1.40	.85
113		½c on 1a red	1.40	.85
114		1c on 2a red violet	1.40	.85
115		2½c on 4a yel grn	1.40	.85
116		5c on 8a dk blue	7.00	6.00
117		7½c on 12a vio brn	5.75	2.40
118		10c on 16a bister brn	2.10	1.60
119		15c on 24a bister	5.75	3.50
		Nos. 112-119 (8)	26.20	16.90

On Stamps of Portuguese Africa
Perf. 14 to 15

120		¼c on 2½r bl grn	1.40	.60
121		½c on 5r red	1.40	.60
122		1c on 10r red vio	1.40	.60
123		2½c on 25r yel grn	1.40	.60
124		5c on 50r dk blue	2.00	1.50
125		7½c on 75r vio brn	3.75	3.00
126		10c on 100r bis brn	2.00	1.90
127		15c on 150r bister	2.50	2.50
		Nos. 120-127 (8)	15.85	11.30

On Stamps of Timor

128		¼c on ½a bl grn	1.40	.85
129		½c on 1a red	1.40	.85
130		1c on 2a red vio	1.40	.85
131		2½c on 4a yel grn	1.40	.85
132		5c on 8a dk blue	7.00	5.50
133		7½c On 12a vio brn	5.50	3.00
134		10c on 16a bis brn	2.25	1.90
135		15c on 24a bister	4.50	2.40
		Nos. 128-135 (8)	24.85	16.20
		Nos. 112-135 (24)	66.90	44.40

For surcharges see Nos. 197-198.

No. 75 Overprinted in Red

1913   *Perf. 11½, 12½, 13½*

137	A3	130r on 80r yel grn	5.00	3.75

Nos. 73 and 76 overprinted but not issued. Values, $15, $20.

Same Overprint on No. 83 in Green

1914   *Perf. 12*

139	A4	75r rose	5.50	3.75
a.		"PROVISORIO" double (G and R)	70.00	57.50

Ceres — A6

Perf. 11½, 12x11½, 15x14
1914-26   Typo.
Name and Value in Black

144	A6	¼c olive brn	.20	.20
a.		Imperf.		
145	A6	½c black	.20	.20
146	A6	1c blue grn	.85	.75
147	A6	1c yel grn ('22)	.20	.20
148	A6	1½c lilac brown	.20	.20
149	A6	2c carmine	.20	.20
150	A6	2c gray ('26)	.25	.50
151	A6	2½c lt violet	.20	.20
152	A6	3c org ('22)	.30	.25
153	A6	4c rose ('22)	.20	.50
154	A6	4½c gray ('22)	.20	.50
155	A6	5c deep blue	.75	.45
156	A6	5c brt blue ('22)	.20	.20
157	A6	6c lilac ('22)	.20	.50
158	A6	7c ultra ('22)	.20	.50
159	A6	7½c yel brn	.20	.50
160	A6	8c slate	.40	.30
161	A6	10c orange brn	.20	.20
162	A6	12c blue grn ('22)	.35	.25
163	A6	15c plum	.90	.75
164	A6	15c brn rose ('22)	.25	.20
165	A6	20c yel grn	.20	.20
166	A6	24c ultra ('26)	1.50	1.40
167	A6	25c choc ('26)	1.50	1.40
168	A6	30c brown, *grn*	3.00	3.00
169	A6	30c gray grn ('22)	.75	.25
170	A6	40c brown, *pink*	3.00	3.00
171	A6	40c turq blue ('22)	1.75	.25
172	A6	50c orange, *sal*	3.00	3.00
173	A6	50c violet ('26)	1.75	.30
174	A6	60c dk blue ('22)	1.75	.45
175	A6	60c rose ('26)	1.75	.45
176	A6	80c brt rose ('22)	2.00	1.10
177	A6	1e green, *blue*	3.00	3.00
178	A6	1e rose ('22)	7.00	2.25
179	A6	1e dp blue ('26)	9.00	1.50
180	A6	2e dk violet ('22)	10.00	4.00
181	A6	5e buff ('26)	25.00	12.00
182	A6	10e pink ('26)	75.00	30.00
183	A6	20e pale turq ('26)	100.00	50.00
		Nos. 144-183 (40)	257.60	125.10

For surcharge see No. 214.

Provisional Issue of 1902 Overprinted in Carmine

1915   *Perf. 11½, 12½, 13½*

184	A2	115r on 10r green	2.50	2.00
a.		Perf. 13½	100.00	100.00
185	A2	115r on 20r rose	2.75	1.75
a.		Perf. 13½	30.00	30.00
186	A2	130r on 50r blue	2.50	1.25
187	A2	130r on 100r brown	1.60	1.00
188	A3	115r on 5r orange	1.40	.75
a.		Inverted overprint	45.00	
189	A3	115r on 25r blue grn	2.50	1.75
a.		Perf. 11½	70.00	70.00
190	A3	115r on 150r car, *rose*	1.00	.75
191	A3	130r on 75r carmine	2.50	1.00
192	A3	130r on 80r yel grn	2.50	1.00
a.		Inverted overprint	50.00	
193	A3	130r on 200r bl, *bl*	1.00	1.00
a.		Perf. 12½	90.00	80.00
		Nos. 184-193 (10)	21.25	12.25

War Tax Stamps of Portuguese Africa Surcharged

1921, Feb. 3   *Perf. 15x14, 11½*

194	WT1	¼c on 1c green	.60	.40
195	WT1	½c on 1c green	.70	.50
a.		"1/2" instead of "½" as shown	10.00	10.00
196	WT1	1c green	.65	.50

Nos. 127 and 126 Surcharged

Perf. 14 to 15

197	CD27	2c on 15c on 150r	2.25	1.50
198	CD26	4c on 10c on 100r	2.75	2.60
a.		On No. 118 (error)		

The 4c surcharge also exists on No. 134. Value, $500.

No. 50 Surcharged

Perf. 12

200	A4	6c on 100r dk bl, *bl*	2.75	2.10
a.		No accent on "U" of surcharge	17.50	15.00
		Nos. 194-200 (6)	9.70	7.60

No. 200 has an accent on the "U" of the surcharge.

Stamps of 1913-15 Surcharged

1922, Apr.   *Perf. 11½, 12½, 13½*
On No. 137

201	A3	4c on 130r on 80r	1.25	1.25

On Nos. 191-193

202	A3	4c on 130r on 75r	1.60	1.60
203	A3	4c on 130r on 80r	1.25	1.25
204	A3	4c on 130r on 200r	1.00	.80
a.		Perf. 12½	15.00	15.00
		Nos. 201-204 (4)	5.10	4.90

Surcharge of Nos. 201-204 with smaller $ occurs once in sheet of 28. Value eight times normal.

Nos. 78-79
Surcharged

1925 Perf. 13½, 11½
205 A3 40c on 400r on 300r 1.00 .80
206 N1 40c on 400r on 2½r 1.00 .75

No. 176 Surcharged

1931, Nov. Perf. 12x11½
214 A6 70c on 80c brt rose 3.75 2.50

Ceres — A7

1934, May 1 Wmk. 232
215 A7 1c bister .20 .20
216 A7 5c olive brown .20 .20
217 A7 10c violet .20 .20
218 A7 15c black .25 .25
219 A7 20c gray .25 .25
220 A7 30c dk green .25 .25
221 A7 40c red org .25 .25
222 A7 45c brt blue 2.00 .85
223 A7 50c brown .90 .55
224 A7 60c olive grn .90 .55
225 A7 70c brown org .90 .55
226 A7 80c emerald .90 .55
227 A7 85c deep rose 4.00 2.60
228 A7 1e maroon 2.75 .50
229 A7 1.40e dk blue 3.75 3.00
230 A7 2e dk violet 4.50 2.60
231 A7 5e apple green 21.00 5.00
232 A7 10e olive bister 32.50 18.00
233 A7 20e orange 60.00 24.00
  Nos. 215-233 (19) 135.70 60.35

For surcharge see No. 256.

Vasco da Gama Issue
Common Design Types

1938 Unwmk. Perf. 13½x13
Name and Value in Black
234 CD34 1c gray green .20 .20
235 CD34 5c orange brn .20 .20
236 CD34 10c dk carmine .20 .20
237 CD34 15c dk vio brn 1.00 .85
238 CD34 20c slate .50 .25
239 CD35 30c rose vio .50 .25
240 CD35 35c brt green .50 .25
241 CD35 40c brown .50 .25
242 CD35 50c brt red vio .50 .25
243 CD36 60c gray blk .50 .25
244 CD36 70c brown vio .50 .25
245 CD36 80c orange .45 .25
246 CD36 1e red .60 .25
247 CD37 1.75e blue 1.90 .70
248 CD37 2e dk blue grn 3.50 2.00
249 CD37 5e ol grn 8.00 2.00
250 CD38 10e blue vio 13.00 2.60
251 CD38 20e red brown 37.50 5.00
  Nos. 234-251 (18) 70.05 16.00

For surcharges see Nos. 255, 271-276, 288-292.

Outline Map of
Africa — A8

1939, June 23 Litho. Perf. 11½x12
252 A8 80c vio, pale rose 5.00 3.50
253 A8 1.75e blue, pale bl 40.00 30.00
254 A8 20e brown, buff 85.00 26.00
  Nos. 252-254 (3) 130.00 59.50

Visit of the President of Portugal in 1939.

Nos. 239 and 221 Surcharged with
New Value and Bars in Black

1948 Unwmk. Perf. 13½x13
255 CD35 10c on 30c rose violet 2.00 1.25

Perf. 12x11½
Wmk. 232
256 A7 25c on 40c red orange 2.00 1.25

Machado Pt., Sao
Vicente — A9

Brava Creek,
Sao
Nicoláo — A10

Designs: 10c, Ribeira Grande. 1e, Harbor, Sao Vicente. 1.75e, Mindelo, distant view. 2e, Joao de Evora Beach. 5e, Mindelo. 10e, Volcano, Fire Island. 20e, Mt. Paul.

Perf. 14½
1948, Oct. 1 Litho. Unwmk.
257 A9 5c vio brn & bis .35 .30
258 A9 10c ol grn & pale
  grn .35 .30
259 A10 50c mag & lil rose .65 .30
260 A10 1e brn vio & rose
  lil 2.00 1.25
261 A10 1.75e ultra & grnsh
  bl 3.00 2.25
262 A10 2e dk brn & buff 6.00 2.00
263 A10 5e ol grn & yel 12.00 5.00
264 A10 10e red & cream 22.50 16.00
265 A10 20e dk vio & bis 50.00 32.00
  Nos. 257-265 (9) 96.85 59.40

Lady of Fatima Issue
Common Design Type

1948, Dec.
266 CD40 50c dark blue 8.50 4.50

UPU Symbols —
A10a

1949, Oct. Perf. 14
267 A10a 1e red vio & pink 7.00 3.00
UPU, 75th anniversary.

Catalogue values for unused stamps in this section, from this point to the end of the section, are for Never Hinged items.

Holy Year Issue
Common Design Types

1950, May Perf. 13x13½
268 CD41 1e orange brown 1.00 .45
269 CD42 2e slate 3.75 1.75

Holy Year Conclusion Issue
Common Design Type

1951, Oct. Unwmk. Perf. 14
270 CD43 2e purple & lilac + label 1.50 1.25
Stamps without labels sell for less.

Nos. 240, 244-245, 247, 250
Surcharged with New Value and Bars
Perf. 13½x13

1951, May 21 Unwmk.
271 CD35 10c on 35c .70 .55
272 CD36 20c on 70c .90 .65
273 CD36 40c on 70c 1.10 .65
274 CD36 50c on 80c 1.10 .65
275 CD37 1e on 1.75e 1.25 .65
276 CD38 2e on 10e 5.75 2.00
  a. 1e on 10e 200.00 125.00
  Nos. 271-276 (6) 10.80 5.15

Map of
Cape
Verde
Islands,
1502
A11

Vicente
Dias and
Gonçalo de
Cintra
A12

Portraits: 30c, Diogo Alfonso and Alvaro Fernandes. 50c, Lançarote and Soeiro da Costa. 1e, Diogo Gomes and Antonio da Nola. 2e, Prince Fernando and Prince Henry the Navigator. 3e, Antao Gonçalves and Dinis Dias. 5e, Alfonso Goncalves Baldaia and Joao Fernandes. 10e, Dinis Eanes da Gra and Alvaro de Freitas. 20e, Map of Cape Verde Islands, 1502.

1952, Feb. 24 Perf. 14
277 A11 5c multicolored .20 .20
278 A12 10c multicolored .20 .20
279 A12 30c multicolored .20 .20
280 A12 50c multicolored .20 .20
281 A12 1e multicolored .20 .20
282 A12 2e multicolored 1.50 .20
283 A12 3e multicolored 11.50 1.50
284 A12 5e multicolored 4.00 .70
285 A12 10e multicolored 8.00 1.75
286 A11 20e multicolored 14.00 2.40
  Nos. 277-286 (10) 40.00 7.55

Medical Congress Issue
Common Design Type
Design: Hypodermic Injection.

1952, June Perf. 13½
287 CD44 20c ol grn & dk brn .70 .50

No. 247 Surcharged with New Values
and "X" in Black

1952, Jan. 25 Perf. 13½x13
288 CD37 10c on 1.75e 2.00 1.10
289 CD37 20c on 1.75e 2.00 1.10
290 CD37 50c on 1.75e 8.00 5.00
291 CD37 1e on 1.75e 1.00 .25
292 CD37 1.50e on 1.75e 1.00 .25
  Nos. 288-292 (5) 14.00 7.70

Facade of
Jeronymos
Convent
A13

Perf. 13½
1953, Jan. Unwmk. Litho.
293 A13 10c brown & pale olive .20 .20
294 A13 50c purple & fawn .90 .40
295 A13 1e dark green & fawn 2.10 1.10
  Nos. 293-295 (3) 3.20 1.70

Exhibition of Sacred Missionary Art held at Lisbon in 1951.

Stamp of Portugal
and Arms of
Colonies — A13a

1953 Photo.
296 A13a 50c multicolored 1.75 1.10
Centenary of Portuguese stamps.

Sao Paulo Issue
Common Design Type

1954 Litho. Perf. 13½
297 CD46 1e green, cream & gray .70 .60

Belem Tower,
Lisbon, and
Colonial
Arms — A14

Arms of
Praia — A15

1955, May 15 Litho. Perf. 13½
298 A14 1e multicolored .50 .25
299 A14 1.60e buff & multi .75 .60
Visit of Pres. Francisco H. C. Lopes.

1958, June 14 Perf. 12x11½
300 A15 1e multicolored .65 .45
301 A15 2.50e pink & multi 1.10 .90
Centenary of city of Praia.

Fair Emblem,
Globe and
Arms — A15a

1958 Perf. 12x11½
302 A15a 2e multicolored .90 .40
World's Fair, Brussels, Apr. 17-Oct. 19.

Tropical Medicine Congress Issue
Common Design Type

1958, Sept. 5 Perf. 13½
303 CD47 3e Aloe vera 5.50 2.10

Prince
Henry — A16

Antonio da
Nola — A17

1960, June 25 Litho. Perf. 13½
304 A16 2e multicolored .50 .25
500th anniv. of the death of Prince Henry the Navigator.

1960, Oct. Unwmk. Perf. 14½
Design: 2.50e, Diogo Gomes.
305 A17 1e multicolored .75 .45
306 A17 2.50e multicolored 2.50 1.00
Discovery of Cape Verde, 500th anniv.

School
Children
A18

1960
307 A18 2.50e multicolored 1.25 .65
10th anniv. of the Commission for Technical Cooperation in Africa South of the Sahara (C.C.T.A.).

Arms of
Praia — A19

Arms of various cities & towns of Cape Verde.

1961, July Litho. Perf. 13½
308 A19	5c shown	.25	.20
309 A19	15c Nova Sintra	.25	.20
310 A19	20c Ribeira Brava	.25	.20
311 A19	30c Assomada	.25	.20
312 A19	1e Maio	.65	.20
313 A19	2e Mindelo	.65	.20
314 A19	2.50e Santa Maria	1.00	.20
315 A19	3e Pombas	1.60	.50
316 A19	5e Sal-Rei	1.60	.50
317 A19	7.50e Tarrafal	1.75	.90
318 A19	15e Maria Pia	2.40	.90
319 A19	30e San Felipe	6.50	2.50
	Nos. 308-319 (12)	17.15	6.70

Sports Issue
Common Design Type

Sports: 50c, Javelin. 1e, Discus. 1.50e, Cricket. 2.50e, Boxing. 4.50e, Hurdling. 12.50e, Golf.

1962, Jan. 18 Perf. 13½
320 CD48	50c lt brown	.25	.20
321 CD48	1e lt green	.75	.25
322 CD48	1.50e lt blue grn	7.00	2.00
323 CD48	2.50e pale vio bl	.75	.35
324 CD48	4.50e orange	1.10	.75
325 CD48	12.50e beige	2.40	1.60
	Nos. 320-325 (6)	12.25	5.15

Anti-Malaria Issue
Common Design Type

Design: Anopheles pretoriensis.

1962 Litho. Perf. 13½
326 CD49	2.50e multicolored	1.40	.90

Airline Anniversary Issue
Common Design Type

1963, Oct. Unwmk. Perf. 14½
327 CD50	2.50e gray & multi	1.10	.70

National Overseas Bank Issue
Common Design Type

Design: 1.50e, Jose da Silva Mendes Leal.

1964, May 16 Perf. 13½
328 CD51	1.50e multicolored	1.10	.75

ITU Issue
Common Design Type

1965, May 17 Litho. Perf. 14½
329 CD52	2.50e buff & multi	2.10	1.40

Militia Drummer, 1806 — A20

Designs: 1e, Soldier, Militia, 1806. 1.50e, Grenadier officer, 1833. 2.50e, Grenadier, 1833. 3e, Cavalry officer, 1834. 4e, Grenadier, 1835. 5e, Artillery officer, 1848. 10e, Drum major, infantry, 1856.

1965, Dec. 1 Litho. Perf. 14½
330 A20	50c multicolored	.25	.25
331 A20	1e multicolored	.45	.25
332 A20	1.50e multicolored	.45	.40
333 A20	2.50e multicolored	1.25	.35
334 A20	3e multicolored	2.50	.55
335 A20	4e multicolored	1.10	.55
336 A20	5e multicolored	1.25	.55
337 A20	10e multicolored	2.75	1.75
	Nos. 330-337 (8)	10.00	4.65

National Revolution Issue
Common Design Type

1e, Dr. Adriano Moreira School & Health Center.

1966, May 28 Litho. Perf. 12
338 CD53	1e multicolored	.60	.45

Navy Club Issue
Common Design Type

Designs: 1e, Capt. Fontoura da Costa and gunboat Mandovy. 1.50e, Capt. Carvalho Araujo and minesweeper Augusto Castilho.

1967, Jan. 31 Litho. Perf. 13
339 CD54	1e multicolored	.75	.50
340 CD54	1.50e multicolored	1.25	.90

Virgin Mary Statue — A21

Pres. Rodrigues Thomaz — A22

1967, May 13 Litho. Perf. 12½x13
341 A21	1e multicolored	.35	.25

50th anniv. of the apparition of the Virgin Mary to 3 shepherd children at Fatima.

1968, Feb. 9 Litho. Perf. 13½
342 A22	1e multicolored	.35	.25

Issued to commemorate the 1968 visit of Pres. Americo de Deus Rodrigues Thomaz.

Cabral Issue

Pedro Alvares Cabral — A23

1e, Cantino's world map, 1502, horiz.

1968, Apr. 22 Litho. Perf. 14
343 A23	1e multicolored	.85	.70
344 A23	1.50e multicolored	1.40	.75

See note after Angola No. 545.
For overprint see No. 365.

Sao Vicente Harbor — A24

Physic Nut — A25

Designs: 1.50e, Peanut plant. 2.50e, Castor-oil plant. 3.50e, Yams. 4e, Date palm. 4.50e, Guavas. 5e, Tamarind. 10e, Bitter cassava. 30e, Woman carrying fruit baskets.

1968, Oct. 15 Litho. Perf. 14
345 A24	50c multicolored	.25	.20
346 A25	1e multicolored	.40	.25
347 A25	1.50e multicolored	.40	.25
348 A25	2.50e multicolored	.40	.25
349 A25	3.50e multicolored	.45	.25
350 A25	4e multicolored	.45	.25
351 A25	4.50e multicolored	.70	.25
352 A25	5 multicolored	1.00	.30
353 A25	10e multicolored	1.25	.60
354 A25	30e multicolored	3.00	2.50
	Nos. 345-354 (10)	8.30	5.10

For overprint see No. 372.

Admiral Coutinho Issue
Common Design Type

Adm. Coutinho & map showing route of 1st flight from Lisbon to Rio de Janeiro.

1969, Feb. 17 Litho. Perf. 14
355 CD55	30c multi, vert.	.35	.25

For surcharge see No. 388.

Vasco da Gama — A26

King Manuel I — A27

Vasco da Gama Issue
1969, Aug. 29 Litho. Perf. 14
356 A26	1.50e multicolored	.35	.25

Vasco da Gama (1469-1524), navigator.

Administration Reform Issue
Common Design Type

1969, Sept. 25 Litho. Perf. 14
357 CD56	2e multicolored	.35	.25

King Manuel I Issue
1969, Dec. 1 Litho. Perf. 14
358 A27	3e multicolored	.55	.35

500th anniv. of the birth of King Manuel I.

Marshal Carmona Issue
Common Design Type

Design: 2.50e, Antonio Oscar Carmona in marshal's uniform.

1970, Nov. 15 Litho. Perf. 14
359 CD57	2.50e multi	.55	.35

Galleons on Sanaga River — A28

1972, May 25 Litho. Perf. 13
360 A28	5e lilac rose & multi	.65	.30

4th centenary of the publication of The Lusiads by Luiz Camoens.

Olympic Games Issue
Common Design Type

4e, Basketball & boxing, Olympic emblem.

1972, June 20 Perf. 14x13½
361 CD59	4e multicolored	.65	.30

For surcharge see No. 371.

Lisbon-Rio de Janeiro Flight Issue
Common Design Type

Design: "Lusitania" landing at San Vicente.

1972, Sept. 20 Litho. Perf. 13½
362 CD60	3.50e multi	.65	.30

WMO Centenary Issue
Common Design Type

1973, Dec. 15 Litho. Perf. 13
363 CD61	2.50e ultra & multi	.65	.30

For overprint see No. 387.

Mindelo Desalination Plant — A29

1974 Litho. Perf. 13½
364 A29	4e multicolored	1.25	.85

Opening of the Mindelo desalination plant.
For surcharge see No. 371A.

Republic
No. 343 Overprinted:
"INDEPENDENCIA / 5-Julho-75"

1975, Dec. 19 Litho. Perf. 14
365 A23	1e multicolored	.35	.25

Proclamation of Independence.

Amilcar Cabral, Flag and Crowd — A30

1976, Jan. 20
366 A30	5e multicolored	.55	.25

3rd anniv. of the assassination of Amilcar Cabral (1924-73), revolutionary leader.

Rising Sun, Coat of Arms, Liberated People — A31

1976, July 5 Litho. Perf. 14
367 A31	50c multicolored	.25	.20
368 A31	3e multicolored	.90	.20
369 A31	15e multicolored	2.00	.35
370 A31	50e multicolored	6.25	1.25
a.	Miniature sheet, #367-370	16.00	16.00
	Nos. 367-370 (4)	9.40	2.00

First anniversary of independence.

Nos. 351, 361, 364 Overprinted with Row of Stars and: "REPUBLICA / DE"

1976 Litho. Perf. 14
371 CD59	4e multi	—	
371A A29	4e multi	37.50	27.50
372 A25	4.50e multi	4.25	2.25

Amilcar Cabral, Map and Flag of Cape Verde A32

1976, Sept. 19 Perf. 14
373 A32	1e multicolored	.45	.25

Party of Intl. Action (PAICC), 20th anniv.

Electronic Tree and ITU Emblem — A33

Ashtray — A34

1977, May 17   Litho.   *Perf. 13½x13*
374 A33 5.50e multi   .45   .25
World Telecommunications Day.

1977, July 5   Litho.   *Perf. 14*
Carved Coconut Shells: 30c, Bell on stand.
50c, Lamp with Adam and Eve. 1e, Hollow
shell with Nativity. 1.50e, Desk lamp. 5e, Jar.
10e, Jar with hinged cover. 20e, Tobacco jar
with palms. 30e, Stringed instrument.
375 A34 20c lilac & multi   .25   .20
376 A34 30c rose & multi   .25   .20
377 A34 50c salmon & multi   .25   .20
378 A34 1e lt green & multi   .35   .25
379 A34 1.50e orange yel & multi   .35   .25
380 A34 5e gray & multi   .75   .35
381 A34 10e lt blue & multi   1.25   .55
382 A34 20e yellow & multi   2.00 1.25
383 A34 30e rose lilac & multi   3.25 1.40
     Nos. 375-383 (9)   8.70 4.65

Cape Verde No. 1
and Coat of
Arms — A35

Congress
Emblem — A36

1977, Sept. 12   Litho.   *Perf. 13½*
384 A35 4e blue & multi   .40   .25
385 A35 8e lilac & multi   .80   .35
Centenary of Cape Verde stamps.

1977, Nov. 15   *Perf. 14*
386 A36 3.50e multi   .60   .25
African Party of Independence of Guinea-
Bissau and Cape Verde (PAIGC), 3rd cong.,
Nov. 15-20.

No. 363 Overprinted

1978, May 1   *Perf. 12*
387 CD61 2.50e ultra & multi   .60   .25

No. 355 Surcharged with New Value
and Bars

1978, May 1   *Perf. 14*
388 CD55 3e on 30c multi   2.25   .35

Antenna and ITU Emblem — A37

1978, May 17   Litho.   *Perf. 14*
389 A37 3.50e silver & multi   .55   .25
10th World Telecommunications Day.

Freighter Cabo Verde — A38

1978, June 25   Litho.   *Perf. 14*
391 A38 1e multicolored   .70   .20
First ship of Cape Verde merchant marine.

Map of Africa
and Equality
Emblem — A39

1978, June 21
392 A39 4.50e multi   .55   .25
Anti-Apartheid Year.

Human Rights
Emblem — A40

1978, Dec. 10   Litho.   *Perf. 14*
393 A40 1.50e multicolored   .35   .25
394 A40 2e multicolored   .55   .35
Universal Declaration of Human Rights,
30th anniversary.

Children and Balloons, IYC
Emblem — A41

IYC Emblem and Child's Drawing: 3.50e,
Children and flowers.

1979, June 1   Litho.   *Perf. 14*
395 A41 1.50e multi   .65   .25
396 A41 3.50e multi   1.10   .35
International Year of the Child.

Pindjiguiti
Massacre
Monument — A42

Natl. Youth Week
— A42a

1979, Aug. 3   *Perf. 13*
397 A42 4.50e multi   2.10   .25
Massacre of Pindjiguiti, 20th anniversary.

1979, Sept. 1   Litho.   *Perf. 14*
397A A42a 3.50e Poster   1.10   .25

Flag of Cape   Stylized Bird,
Verde — A44   "V" — A45

1980   Litho.   *Perf. 12½*
399 A44 4e multicolored   1.25   .25
400 A45 4e multicolored   .45   .25
401 A45 7e multicolored   .80   .35
402 A45 11e multicolored   1.10   .45
     Nos. 399-402 (4)   3.60 1.30
5th anniversary of independence.
Issued: No. 399, June 1; others July 5.

Centenary of Mindelo — A43

1980, Apr. 23   Litho.   *Perf. 12½*
398 A43 4e multicolored   .70   .25

A45a

A46

1980, May 13
402A A45a 3.50e multi   .55   .25
402B A45a 4.50e multi   .70   .25
1980 Natl. census.

1980, June 6
403 A46 1e Running   .20   .20
404 A46 2.50e Boxing   .25   .20
405 A46 3e Basketball   .35   .25
406 A46 4e Volleyball   .50   .30
407 A46 20e Swimming   1.40   .90
408 A46 50e Tennis   4.00 1.75
     Nos. 403-408 (6)   6.70 3.60

Souvenir Sheet
Perf. 13
409 A46 30e Soccer, horiz. *18.00 18.00*
22nd Summer Olympic Games, Moscow,
July 19-Aug. 3.

Thunnus
Alalunga
A47

1980, Nov. 11   Litho.   *Perf. 13*
410 A47 50c shown   .25   .20
411 A47 4.50e Trachurus
                 trachurus   .40   .20
412 A47 8e Muraena helena   .65   .25
413 A47 10e Corvina nigra   .75   .35
414 A47 12e Katsuwonus pe-
                 lamis   1.10   .60
415 A47 50e Prionace glauca   4.00 1.90
     Nos. 410-415 (6)   7.15 3.50

Lochnera
Rosea — A48

1980, Dec. 29
416 A48 50c shown   .25   .20
417 A48 4.50e Poinciana regia-
                 bojer   .30   .25
418 A48 8e Mirabilis jalapa   .75   .35
419 A48 10e Nerium oleander   .95   .45
420 A48 12e Bougainvillia
                 litoralis   1.10   .55
421 A48 30e Hibiscus   2.60 1.50
     Nos. 416-421 (6)   5.95 3.30

WHO Anti-smoking Campaign — A48a

1980, Sept. 19   Perf. 12½
421A A48a 4e multicolored   .50 .25
421B A48a 7e multicolored   1.10 .35

Arca Verde A49

1980, Nov. 30   Litho.   Perf. 12½x12
422 A49   3e shown   .30 .20
423 A49 5.50e Ilha do Maio   .50 .25
424 A49 7.50e Ilha de Komo   .95 .55
425 A49   9e Boa Vista   1.25 .75
426 A49   12e Santo Antao   1.40 .55
427 A49   30e Santiago   3.25 1.40
    Nos. 422-427 (6)   7.65 3.70

Hand-woven Bag, Map — A49a

Various hand-woven articles. 10e, vert.

1978, May 21   Litho.   Perf. 14
427A A49a   50c multi   .25 .20
427B A49a 1.50e multi   .25 .20
427C A49a   2e multi   .55 .25
427D A49a   3e multi   .55 .30
427E A49a   10e multi   1.40 .70
    Nos. 427A-427E (5)   3.00 1.65

Desert Erosion Prevention Campaign — A50

1981, Mar. 30   Litho.   Perf. 13
428 A50   4.50e multi   .60 .25
429 A50 10.50e multi   1.25 .50

6th Anniv. of Constitution A51

1981, Apr. 15
430 A51 4.50e multicolored   .60 .25

Souvenir Sheet

Austria No. B336 A52

1981, May 18
431 A52 50e multicolored   6.50 6.50
   WIPA '81 Philatelic Exhibition, Vienna, Austria, May 22-31.

Antenna — A53

1981, Aug. 25   Litho.   Perf. 12½
432 A53 4.50e shown   .65 .25
433 A53   8e Dish antenna   .95 .40
434 A53   20e Dish antenna, diff. 2.00 .95
    Nos. 432-434 (3)   3.60 1.60

Intl. Year of the Disabled A54

1981, Dec. 25   Litho.   Perf. 12½
435 A54 4.50e multicolored   .65 .35

Purple Gallinule A55

1981, Dec. 30
436 A55   1e Egret, vert.   .60 .20
437 A55 4.50e Barn owl, vert.   1.25 .40
438 A55   8e Passerine, vert.   2.75 .55
439 A55   10e shown   3.00 .65
440 A55   12e Guinea fowl   3.75 .75
    Nos. 436-440 (5)   11.35 2.55

Souvenir Sheet
Perf. 13
441 A55   50e Razo Isld. lark   9.50 9.50
   No. 441 contains 31x39mm one stamp.

CILSS Congress, Praia, Jan. 17 — A56

1982, Jan. 17   Perf. 13x12½
442 A56 11.50e multicolored   1.40 .65

Amilcar Cabral Soccer Championship — A57

Designs: Soccer players and flags.

1982, Feb. 10   Litho.   Perf. 12½
443 A57   4.50e multicolored   .55 .25
444 A57   7.50e multicolored   .85 .40
445 A57 11.50e multicolored   1.40 .70
    Nos. 443-445 (3)   2.80 1.35

1982 World Cup — A58

Designs: Soccer players and ball.

1982, Apr. 25
446 A58   1.50e multi   .25 .20
447 A58   4.50e multi   .50 .25
448 A58   8e multi   .85 .35
449 A58 10.50e multi   1.00 .45
450 A58   12e multi   1.25 .55
451 A58   20e multi   2.25 .90
    Nos. 446-451 (6)   6.10 2.70

Souvenir Sheet
452 A58   50e multi   6.25 6.25

First Anniv. of Women's Organization — A59

1982, Apr. 15   Litho.   Perf. 12½x12
453 A59 4.50e Marching   .55 .25
454 A59   8e Farming   1.10 .40
455 A59   12e Child care   1.60 .70
    Nos. 453-455 (3)   3.25 1.35

Estaleiros Navais Port, St. Vincent A59a

1982, July 5   Litho.   Perf. 13x12½
455A A59a 10.50e multi   1.75 .60
   Natl. independence, 7th anniv.

Return of Barque Morrissey-Ernestina — A60

1982, July 5   Litho.   Perf. 13
456 A60 12e multi   1.40 .80

Butterflies — A61

1982, July 27   Litho.
457 A61   2e Hypolimnas misippus   .35 .20
458 A61   4.50e Melanitis lede   .70 .25
459 A61   8e Catopsilia florella 1.10 .25
460 A61 10.50e Colias electo   1.50 .40
461 A61 11.50e Danaus chrysippus   1.60 .60
462 A61   12e Papilio demodecus   2.75 .70
    Nos. 457-462 (6)   8.00 2.40

Francisco Xavier da Cruz (1905-1958), Composer — A62

14e, Eugenio Tavares (1867-1930), poet.

1983, Feb. 20   Litho.   Perf. 13
463 A62   7e multi   .45 .30
464 A62 14e multi   1.90 .80

World Communications Year — A63

1983, Oct. 10   Litho.
465 A63 13e multicolored   1.60 .80

Local Seashells — A64

1983, Nov. 30   Perf. 13½
466 A64 50c Conus ateralbus   .25 .20
467 A64   1e Conus decoratus   .25 .20
468 A64   3e Conus salreiensis   .35 .20
469 A64   10e Conus verdensis   1.50 .55
470 A64   50e Conus cuneolus   5.00 2.75
    Nos. 466-470 (5)   7.35 3.90

40th Anniv. of Intl. Civil Aviation Org. A65

Airplanes: 50c, Ogma-Auster D5/160, 1966. 2e, De Havilland DH-104 Dove, 1945. 10e, Hawker Siddeley 748-200, 1972. 13e, De Havilland Dragon Rapide, 1945. 20e, De Havilland Twin Otter, 1977. 50e, Britten-Norman Islander, 1971.

1984, Feb. 15   **Litho.**

471	A65	50c multicolored	.25 .20
472	A65	2e multicolored	.30 .25
473	A65	10e multicolored	1.10 .50
474	A65	13e multicolored	1.25 .85
475	A65	20e multicolored	1.90 1.25
476	A65	50e multicolored	4.50 2.50
		Nos. 471-476 (6)	9.30 5.55

Amilcar Cabral — A66

A67

1983, Jan. 17   **Litho.**   **Perf. 14½**

477	A66	7e multi	1.00 .50
478	A66	10.50e multi	1.50 .90
a.		Souvenir sheet of 2, #477-478	30.00 30.00

Amilcar Cabral Symposium, Jan. 17-20. No. 478a sold for 30e.

1983, Dec. 10   **Photo.**   **Perf. 14½**

479	A67	7e Cross overshadowing islands	1.10 .50

Christianity in Cape Verde, 450th anniv.

Natl. Solidarity Campaign A68

1984, Sept. 12   **Perf. 13½**

480	A68	6.50e multi	1.10 .25
481	A68	13.50e multi	2.10 .85

2nd Conference of Natl. Women's Orgs., Mar. 23-27 — A69

1985, Mar. 27   **Litho.**   **Perf. 13½**

482	A69	8e multicolored	1.10 .55

Miniature Sheet

483	A69	30e multicolored	100.00 100.00

Natl. Independence, 10th Anniv. — A70

1985, July 5   **Litho.**   **Perf. 14**

484	A70	8c multicolored	1.25 .55
485	A70	12e multicolored	1.90 .80

Intl. Youth Year — A71

1985, Sept. 12   **Litho.**   **Perf. 14**

486	A71	12e multicolored	2.50 .90

Vapor, by Hundertwasser A72

Photogravure and Engraved

1986, Apr. 25   **Perf. 14**

Black Surcharge

487	A72	30e on 10e multi	22.50 4.00

Souvenir Sheets

Background Color

488		Sheet of 4	150.00
a.		A72 50e yellow & multi	17.50 17.50
489		Sheet of 4	150.00
a.		A72 50e red & multi	17.50 17.50
490		Sheet of 4	150.00
a.		A72 50e green & multi	17.50 17.50

No. 487 exists without surcharge. Value $27.50.

World Wildlife Fund — A73

Perf. 13½x14½

1986, June 15   **Litho.**

491	A73	8e Mabuya vaillanti	6.50 2.50
492	A73	10e Tarentola gigas brancoensis	8.00 3.25
493	A73	15e Tarentola gigas gigas	12.00 4.00
494	A73	30e Hemidactylus bouvieri	24.00 5.00
		Nos. 491-494 (4)	50.50 14.75

Souvenir Sheet

495		Sheet of 2	30.00 22.50
a.		A73 50e Mabuya vaillanti	14.00 10.00
b.		A73 50e Hemidactylus bouvieri	14.00 10.00

No. 495 printed with center label picturing progress union emblem. Nos. 495a-495b printed without WWF emblem.

World Food Day — A74

Intl. Peace Year — A75

1986, June 20   **Perf. 14**

496	A74	8e Cauldron	.50 .25
497	A74	12e Mortar & pestle	.80 .35
498	A74	15e Quern stone	1.40 .50
		Nos. 496-498 (3)	2.70 1.10

1986, Dec. 24   **Litho.**   **Perf. 14**

499	A75	12e multicolored	.60 .25
500	A75	30e multicolored	2.10 1.40

Natl. Child Survival Campaign A76

1987, Mar. 27   **Litho.**   **Perf. 14**

501	A76	8e multicolored	.45 .20
502	A76	10e multicolored	.55 .25
503	A76	12e multicolored	.65 .35
504	A76	16e multicolored	.95 .50
505	A76	100e multicolored	4.50 2.75
		Nos. 501-505 (5)	7.10 4.05

Tourism A77

1987, May 17

506	A77	1e Bay, Mindelo	.20 .20
507	A77	2.50e Hill country	.20 .20
508	A77	5e Mountain peak	.25 .25
509	A77	8e Monument	.45 .25
510	A77	10e Mountain peaks	.65 .30
511	A77	12e Beached boats	.85 .40
512	A77	100e Harbor	5.25 3.00
		Nos. 506-512 (7)	7.85 4.60

For surcharge see No. 710.

Ships — A78

1987, Aug. 3   **Perf. 13½x14½**

513	A78	12e Carvalho, 1937	.75 .25
514	A78	16e Nauta, 1943	1.25 .25
515	A78	50e Maria Sony, 1911	3.75 1.25
		Nos. 513-515 (3)	5.75 1.75

Souvenir Sheet

516		Sheet of 2	9.00 9.00
a.		A78 60e Madalan, 1928	4.00 4.00

Crop Protection A80

1988, May 9   **Litho.**   **Perf. 13½**

518	A80	50c Identification of insect plague	.20 .20
519	A80	2e Use of insecticides	.20 .20
520	A80	9e Import of parasites	.50 .25
521	A80	13e Import of predators	.60 .25
522	A80	16e Locust	1.00 .40
523	A80	19e Estimation of crop loss	1.25 .60
		Nos. 518-523 (6)	3.75 1.90

Souvenir Sheet

524	A80	50e Agricultural Research Institute	5.00 5.00

Maps — A81

1988, July 5   **Litho.**   **Perf. 14**

525	A81	1e Dutch, 17th cent.	.20 .20
526	A81	2.50e Belgian, 18th cent.	.20 .20
527	A81	4.50e French, 18th cent.	.30 .20
528	A81	9.50e English, 18th cent.	.60 .25
529	A81	19.50e English, 19th cent.	1.25 .55
530	A81	20e French, 18th cent., vert.	1.40 .65
		Nos. 525-530 (6)	3.95 2.05

Churches A82

5e, St. Amaro Abade, Tarrafal, Santiago Is. 8e, Our Lady of the Light, Maio Is. 10e, Nazarene, Praia, Santiago Is. 12e, Our Lady of Rosa'rio, Sao Nicolau Is. 15e, Nazarene, Mindelo, Sao Vicente Is. 20e, Our Lady of Grace, Praia, Santiago Is.

1988, Aug. 15   **Perf. 13½x14½**

531	A82	5e multicolored	.20 .20
532	A82	8e multicolored	.45 .20
533	A82	10e multicolored	.55 .25
534	A82	12e multicolored	.60 .25
535	A82	15e multicolored	.85 .35
536	A82	20e multicolored	1.25 .45
		Nos. 531-536 (6)	3.90 1.70

Water Conservation — A83

1988, Sept. 26   **Litho.**   **Perf. 14**

537	A83	12e multicolored	.75 .35

Intl. Red Cross, 125th Anniv. — A84

1988, Oct. 20

538	A84	7e multi	.45 .25

3rd Communist Party (PAICV) Congress — A85

Portrait of Pres. Pereira, PAICV secretary-general, and: 7e, S. Jorginho Vocational Training Center. 10.50e, UN Secretary-General Perez de Cuellar. 30e, 100e, Star and text.

Perf. 14½x13½
1988, Nov. 25 — Litho.
539 A85	7e multi	.40	.25
540 A85	10.50e multi	.60	.25
541 A85	30e multi	1.75	.75
	Nos. 539-541 (3)	2.75	1.25

Souvenir Sheet
542 A85	100e multi	6.25	6.25

1988 Summer Olympics, Seoul — A86

1988, Dec. 26
543 A86	12e shown	.60	.25
544 A86	15e Tennis	.90	.35
545 A86	20e Soccer	1.25	.50
546 A86	30e Boxing	1.75	.90
	Nos. 543-546 (4)	4.50	2.00

Souvenir Sheet
547 A86	50e Long jump	4.00	4.00

Roberto Duarte Silva (1837-89), Chemist A86a

1989, May 2 — Litho. — Perf. 14¼x14
547A A86a	12.50e multi	.45	.25

2nd JAAC-CV Congress, Sept. 7-12 — A87

1989, Apr. 7 — Litho. — Perf. 14
548 A87	30e Hot air balloon	1.10	.75

Liberty Guiding the People — A88

Relief, Arc de Triomphe — A89

1989, July 7 — Litho. — Perf. 14
549 A88	20e multicolored	.85	.45
550 A88	24e multicolored	1.10	.55
551 A88	25e multicolored	1.25	.65
	Nos. 549-551 (3)	3.20	1.65

Souvenir Sheet
Perf. 14½x13½
552 A89	100e multicolored	5.50	5.50

French revolution, bicent.

Interparliamentary Union, Cent. — A90

1989, Sept. 18 — Litho. — Perf. 14
553 A90	2e shown	.20	.20
554 A90	4e Dove	.25	.20
555 A90	13e Natl. Assembly Bldg.	.45	.20
	Nos. 553-555 (3)	.90	.60

Traditional Ceramics A91

1989, Nov. 13 — Litho. — Perf. 13½
Panel Colors
556 A91	13e lilac	.50	.25
557 A91	20e red, vert.	.70	.40
558 A91	24e brown	.90	.50
559 A91	25e orange, vert.	1.00	.55
	Nos. 556-559 (4)	3.10	1.70

Outdoor Toys — A92

1989, Dec. 23
560 A92	1e Yellow truck	.20	.20
561 A92	6e Car	.20	.20
562 A92	8e White truck	.35	.20
563 A92	11.50e Trucks	.45	.25
564 A92	18e Scooter	.75	.45
565 A92	100e Boat	4.00	2.25
	Nos. 560-565 (6)	5.95	3.55

Visit of Pope John Paul II — A93

1990, Jan. 25
566 A93	13e blue & multi	.40	.25
567 A93	20e purple & multi	.75	.40

Souvenir Sheet
568 A93	200e multi, diff.	8.00	8.00

Turtles A94

1990, May 17 — Litho. — Perf. 13½
569 A94	50c Chelonia mydas	.20	.20
570 A94	1e Dermochelys coriacea	.20	.20
571 A94	5e Lepidochelys olivacea	.35	.20
572 A94	10e Caretta caretta	.60	.25
573 A94	42e Eretmochelys imbricata	2.75	.90
	Nos. 569-573 (5)	4.10	1.75

Women's Congress A95

1990, Aug. 13
574 A95	9e multicolored	.35	.20

A96

A97

Various drawings of soccer players in action.

1990, Aug. 7
575 A96	4e multicolored	.20	.20
576 A96	7.50e multicolored	.25	.20
577 A96	8e multicolored	.25	.20
578 A96	100e multicolored	3.50	2.10
	Nos. 575-578 (4)	4.20	2.70

Souvenir Sheet
579 A96	100e multi, diff.	4.50	4.50

World Cup Soccer Championships, Italy. For surcharges see Nos. 711-712.

1990, Oct. 15 — Perf. 11½

Vaccinations: 5e, Emile Roux (1853-1933), diphtheria. 13e, Robert Koch (1843-1910), tuberculosis. 20e, Gaston Ramon (1886-1963), tetanus. 24e, Jonas Salk (1914-95), polio.

Granite Paper
580 A97	5e multicolored	.35	.20
581 A97	13e multicolored	1.00	.25
582 A97	20e multicolored	1.40	.40
583 A97	24e multicolored	1.75	.50
	Nos. 580-583 (4)	4.50	1.35

Intl. Literacy Year — A98

Designs: 3e, Adult literacy class. 15e, Teacher holding flash card, children. 19e, Teacher, student at blackboard.

1990, Sept. 28
Granite Paper
584 A98	2e shown	.20	.20
585 A98	3e multicolored	.20	.20
586 A98	15e multicolored	.50	.25
587 A98	19e multicolored	.75	.30
	Nos. 584-587 (4)	1.65	.95

Traditional Fairy Tales A99

1990, Dec. 20 — Litho. — Perf. 12½
588 A99	50c shown	.20	.20
589 A99	2.50e Man catching mermaid	.25	.20
590 A99	12e Woman, snake	.50	.45
591 A99	25e Man, eggs, woman	1.00	.40
	Nos. 588-591 (4)	1.95	1.30

Fight Against AIDS A100

1991, Feb. 20 — Litho. — Perf. 14
Granite Paper
592 A100	13e multicolored	.75	.30
593 A100	24e multi, diff.	1.25	.75

Fishing — A101

24e, Man removing hook from fish. 25e, Fishing boats. 50e, Two men long-line fishing.

1991, Apr. 23 — Litho. — Perf. 11½
594 A101	10e multicolored	.35	.25
595 A101	24e multicolored	1.10	.60
596 A101	25e multicolored	1.25	.65
597 A101	50e multicolored	2.40	1.50
	Nos. 594-597 (4)	5.10	3.00

Medicinal Plants — A102

10e, Lavandula rotundifolia. 15e, Micromeria forbesii. 21e, Sarcostemma daltonii. 24e, Periploca chevalieri. 30e, Echium hypertropicum. 35e, Erysimum caboverdeanum.

1991, July 5 — Litho. — Perf. 11½
598 A102	10e multicolored	.30	.20
599 A102	15e multicolored	.55	.25
600 A102	21e multicolored	.70	.30
601 A102	24e multicolored	.90	.35
602 A102	30e multicolored	1.10	.45
603 A102	35e multicolored	1.40	.55
	Nos. 598-603 (6)	4.95	2.10

Landmarks in Old Ribeira Grande on Santiago Island A103

12.50e, Church of Our Lady of the Rosary, 1495. 15e, Ruins of the Cathedral, 1556. 20e, Fortress of San Felipe, 1587. 30e, Ruins of the Convent of St. Francis, 1642. 100e, Pillory, 1520, vert.

1991, June 25 — Litho. — Perf. 11½
604 A103	12.50e multicolored	.45	.25
605 A103	15e multicolored	.55	.25
606 A103	20e multicolored	.75	.45
607 A103	30e multicolored	1.10	.75
	Nos. 604-607 (4)	2.85	1.70

Souvenir Sheet
608 A103	100e multicolored	4.00	4.00

Musical Instruments — A104

1991, Oct. 9 — Litho. — Perf. 11½
609 A104	10e 6-string guitar	.35	.20
610 A104	20e Violin	.85	.55
611 A104	29e 5-string guitar	1.40	.65
612 A104	47e Cimba	2.00	1.25
	Nos. 609-612 (4)	4.60	2.65

Souvenir Sheet
613 A104	60e Accordion, horiz.	3.00	3.00

Christmas A105

1991, Dec. 20 — Litho. — Perf. 11½
614 A105	31e Nativity scene	1.10	.50
615 A105	50e Nativity scene, diff.	1.75	.90

Discovery of America, 500th Anniv. A106

1992, Mar. 31   Litho.   Perf. 11½
616 A106 40e shown   2.00 1.10
617 A106 40e Columbus on ship 2.00 1.10
 a.   Pair, #616-617   4.50 4.50

Souvenir Sheet
618 A106   Sheet of 2   8.00 8.00

Stamps in No. 618 are smaller, without white border and "Luis Duran" and "Courvoisier" inscriptions. No. 618 was printed in continuous design and sold for 150e.

Souvenir Sheet

Granada '92 — A107

Illustration reduced.

1992, Apr.24   Perf. 11½
619 A107 50e multicolored   8.00 8.00

No. 619 sold for 150e.

Tropical Fruits A108

1992, Feb. 29   Perf. 12x11½
620 A108 16e Syzygium jambos .65   .30
621 A108 25e Mangifera indica 1.10 .50
622 A108 31e Anacardium oc-
             cidentale   1.40 .65
623 A108 32e Persea americana 1.60 .75
     Nos. 620-623 (4)   4.75 2.20

1992 Summer Olympics, Barcelona A109

1992, June 30   Litho.   Perf. 13½
624 A109 16e Women's javelin .60   .25
625 A109 20e Weight lifting   .75   .30
626 A109 32e Women's pole
             vault   1.40 .65
627 A109 40e Women's shot
             put   1.60 .85
     Nos. 624-627 (4)   4.35 2.05

Souvenir Sheet
628 A109 100e Women's gym-
              nastics   4.25 4.25

Sugar Cane Production — A110

Designs: 19e, Oxen, sugar cane. 20e, Oxen yoked to press. 37e, Man placing cane inside press. 38e, Refining process.

1992, Nov.   Litho.   Perf. 11
629 A110 19e multicolored   .65   .30
630 A110 20e multicolored   .65   .30
631 A110 37e multicolored   1.25 .60
632 A110 38e multicolored   1.40 .60
     Nos. 629-632 (4)   3.95 1.80

Domestic Animals A111

1992, Nov.   Perf. 13½
633 A111 16e Cat   .65   .40
634 A111 31e Chickens   1.10 .80
635 A111 32e Dog, vert.   1.25 .90
636 A111 50e Horse   2.00 1.25
     Nos. 633-636 (4)   5.00 3.35

Corals A112

1993, Apr. 29   Litho.   Perf. 11½
637 A112 5e Tubastrea aurea   .20   .20
638 A112 31e Corallium rubrum 1.25 .80
639 A112 37e Porites porites 1.50 1.10
640 A112 50e Millepora alcicornis 2.00 1.25
     Nos. 637-640 (4)   4.95 3.25

Treaty of Tordesillas, 500th Anniv. (in 1994) A113

Designs: No. 641, King Ferdinand, Queen Isabella of Spain, Pope Alexander VI. No. 642, Pope Julius II, King John II of Portugal. No. 643, Astrolabe, treaty signing. No. 644, Compass rose, map.

1993, Aug. 1   Litho.   Perf. 12x11½
641 A113 37e multicolored   1.50 .65
642 A113 37e multicolored   1.50 .65
 a.   Pair, #641-642   3.50 3.25
643 A113 38e multicolored   1.50 .65
644 A113 38e multicolored   1.50 .65
 a.   Pair, #643-644   3.50 3.25
     Nos. 641-644 (4)   6.00 2.60

Souvenir Sheet

Santiago Island, 1806 — A114

1993, July 30   Perf. 13½
645 A114 100e multicolored   4.25 4.25

Brasiliana '93.

Lobsters — A115

1993, Sept. 29   Litho.   Perf. 11½
646 A115 2e Palinurus
            charlestoni   .35   .20
647 A115 10e Panulirus
            echinatus   .70   .25
648 A115 17e Panulirus regius 1.25 .50
649 A115 38e Scyllarides latus 2.75 1.00
     Nos. 646-649 (4)   5.05 1.95

Souvenir Sheet

Birds A116

650 A115 100e Panulirus regius,
              diff.   6.50 6.50

No. 650 contains one 51x36mm stamp.

1993, Oct. 29   Litho.   Perf. 12x11½
651 A116 10e Calonectris ed-
             wardsii   .75   .25
652 A116 30e Sula leuco-
             gaster   2.25 .85
653 A116 40e Fregata
             magnificens   3.00 1.10
 a.   Souvenir sheet of 1   11.00 11.00
654 A116 41e Phaeton aether-
             eus   3.25 1.10
     Nos. 651-654 (4)   9.25 3.30

Hong Kong '94 (#653a).
No. 653a sold for 150e.

Flowers A117

1993, Dec. 16   Litho.   Perf. 12x11½
655 A117 5e Rosa alexandra   .20   .20
656 A117 30e Strelitzia reginae 1.10 .80
657 A117 37e Dianthus barbatus 1.50 1.00
 a.   Souvenir sheet of 1   7.50 7.50
658 A117 50e Dahlia   1.90 1.25
     Nos. 655-658 (4)   4.70 3.25

Singapore '95 (#657a). Issued 9/1/95.
No. 657a sold for 150e.

1994 World Cup Soccer Championships, US — A118

Players, US flag, and: 1e, Giant's Stadium, New Jersey. 20e, Rose Bowl Stadium, Pasadena. 37e, Foxboro Stadium, Boston. 38e, Silverdome, Pontiac. 100e, RFK Stadium, Washington DC.

1994, May 31   Litho.   Perf. 11½
659 A118 1e multicolored   .20   .20
660 A118 20e multicolored   .85   .50
661 A118 37e multicolored   1.50 1.00
662 A118 38e multicolored   1.60 1.10
     Nos. 659-662 (4)   4.15 2.80

Souvenir Sheet
663 A118 100e multicolored   5.50 5.50

Prince Henry the Navigator (1394-1460) — A119

Illustration reduced.

1994, Mar. 4   Litho.   Perf. 12
664 A119 37e multicolored   3.00 1.00

See Brazil #2463, Macao #719, Portugal #1987.

Sharks A120

1994, June 27   Litho.   Perf. 12x11½
665 A120 21e Eugomphodus tau-
             rus   1.00 .60
666 A120 27e Carcharhinus
             limbatus   1.25 .75
667 A120 37e Rhiniodon typus 1.75 1.25
668 A120 38e Etmopterus spinax 2.00 1.40
     Nos. 665-668 (4)   6.00 4.00

Bananas A121

1994, Aug. 16   Litho.   Perf. 11½
669 A121 12e Prata, vert.   .50   .25
670 A121 16e Pao   .75   .40
671 A121 30e Ana roberta, vert. 1.50 .85
672 A121 40e Roxa, vert.   2.00 1.10
     Nos. 669-672 (4)   4.75 2.60

Souvenir Sheet
673 A121 100e Prata, diff., vert. 9.00 9.00

PHILAKOREA '94, SINGPEX '94 (#673).
No. 673 sold for 150e.

Lighthouses — A122

1994, Oct. 17   Perf. 12
674 A122 2e Fontes Pereira de
            Melo   .25   .20
675 A122 37e Morro Negro   1.75 1.00
676 A122 38e Amelia, vert.   1.75 1.10
677 A122 50e Maria Pia, vert. 2.25 1.40
     Nos. 674-677 (4)   6.00 3.70

Wilhelm Roentgen (1845-1923), Discovery of the X-Ray, Cent. — A123

1995, Mar. 31   Litho.   Perf. 12
678 A123 20e yellow & multi   .80   .50
679 A123 37e blue & multi   1.50 1.00
 a.   Souvenir sheet of 2, #678-679 4.50 4.50

No. 679a sold for 100e.

A124

FAO, 50th Anniv. — A125

1995, May 17   Litho.   Perf. 12
680 A124 37e multicolored   1.50 .90
681 A125 38e multicolored   1.50 .90

Dogs
A126

Dog, scene depicting story of dogs: 1e, Fox terrier, Two foxhounds and fox terrier, by John Emms. 10e, Cavalier King Charles, Shooting over Dogs, by Richard Ansdell. 40e, Rough collie, German shepherd. 50e, Braco, Hounds at Full Cry, by Thomas Blinks.

1995, June 16   Litho.   Perf. 12x11½
682	A126	1e multicolored	.25 .20
683	A126	10e multicolored	.55 .25
684	A126	40e multicolored	2.25 1.25
685	A126	50e multicolored	2.75 1.10
		Nos. 682-685 (4)	5.80 2.80

Independence, 20th Anniv. — A127

1995, July 20   Litho.   Perf. 12
686	A127	37e multicolored	1.90 1.25

Traditional Festival
A128

Designs: 2e, Horse race. 10e, Horseman leading parade. 37e, People singing, playing drums. 40e, Playing game on horseback.

1995, Oct. 9   Perf. 12x11½
687	A128	2e multicolored	.20 .20
688	A128	10e multicolored	.45 .25
689	A128	37e multicolored	1.50 .85
690	A128	40e multicolored	1.75 1.00
		Nos. 687-690 (4)	3.90 2.30

Children's Stories
A130

Designs: 10e, The cicadas making music, ants. 25e, Cicada being exposed to light. 38e, Cicada with guitar, ants working. 45e, Ants at table making fun of cicada.

1995, Dec. 15   Litho.   Perf. 11½
692	A130	10e multicolored	.40 .55
693	A130	25e multicolored	.85 .85
694	A130	38e multicolored	1.40 1.10
695	A130	45e multicolored	1.60 1.00
		Nos. 692-695 (4)	4.25 3.50

Endangered Plants — A131

20e, Sonchus daltonii. 37e, Echium vulcanorum. 38e, Nauplius smithii. 50e, Campanula jacobaea.

1996, Apr. 24   Litho.   Perf. 11½
696	A131	20e multicolored	.65 .40
697	A131	37e multicolored	1.20 .75
698	A131	38e multicolored	1.20 .75
699	A131	50e multicolored	1.60 1.10
		Nos. 696-699 (4)	4.65 3.00

1996 Summer Olympic Games, Atlanta
A132

1996, June 30   Litho.   Perf. 11½
700	A132	1e Tennis	.20 .20
701	A132	37e Gymnastics	1.10 .75
702	A132	100e Athletics	3.25 2.10
		Nos. 700-702 (3)	4.55 3.05

UNICEF, 50th Anniv. — A133

Cabo Verde 1996

Water Sports — A134

1996, Aug. 1   Litho.   Perf. 12
703	A133	20e Young girl	.90 .40
704	A133	40e Mother, child	1.75 .85

1996, Oct. 9   Litho.   Perf. 12
Designs: 2.50e, Fishing. 10e, Windsurfing. 22e, Jet skiing. No. 708, Surfing, horiz. No. 709, Diver's hand, pufferfish, horiz.

705	A134	2.50e multicolored	.20 .20
706	A134	10e multicolored	.35 .20
707	A134	22e multicolored	.70 .45
708	A134	100e multicolored	3.25 2.10
		Nos. 705-708 (4)	4.50 2.95

Souvenir Sheet
709	A134	100e multicolored	4.50 4.50

No. 709 contains one 80x61mm stamp.

Nos. 507, 575-576 Surcharged

a   3$00

b   37$

1997   Litho.   Perf. 14
710	A77(a)	3e on 2.50e #507	.20 .20

Perf. 13½
711	A96(b)	37e on 4e #575	1.25 .75
712	A96(a)	38e on 7.50e #576	1.25 .75
		Nos. 710-712 (3)	2.70 1.70

Natl. Symbols
A135

1997   Perf. 12
713	A135	25e Arms	.80 .50
714	A135	37e Anthem	1.10 .75
715	A135	50e Flag	1.60 1.00
		Nos. 713-715 (3)	3.50 2.25

World Wildlife Fund
A136

Pristis pectinata: a, On seabed. b, Swimming, school of small fish. c, Swimming along seabed, small fish. d, Two near seabed.

1997   Litho.   Perf. 11½
716	A136	15e Strip of 4, #a.-d.	10.00 10.00

Legends of the Sea — A137

a, Fish, dolphins. b, Merman, mermaid. c, Fish swimming through portal, moray eel.

1997   Litho.   Perf. 11½
717	A137	45e Strip of 3, #a.-c.	4.00 4.00

Fish
A138

Designs: 13e, Thunnus albacares. 21e, Thunnus obesus. 41e, Euthynnus alletteratus. 45e, Katsuwonus pelamis.

1997   Perf. 12
718	A138	13e multicolored	.35 .30
719	A138	21e multicolored	.65 .60
720	A138	41e multicolored	1.40 1.25
721	A138	45e multicolored	1.60 1.50
		Nos. 718-721 (4)	4.00 3.65

1998 World Cup Soccer Championships, France — A139

Designs: 30e, Soccer ball in net, vert. 45e, Soccer player, ball, vert. 50e, Globe, ball, World Cup trophy, fans in stadium.

1998   Litho.   Perf. 12x11½, 11½x12
722	A139	10e shown	.30 .25
723	A139	30e multicolored	.80 .80
724	A139	45e multicolored	1.25 1.25
725	A139	50e multicolored	1.50 1.40
		Nos. 722-725 (4)	3.85 3.70

Traditional Cuisine
A140

5e, Boiled fish. 25e, Xerém com friginato. 35e, Cachupa. 40e, Molho de Saint-Nicholas.

1998   Litho.   Perf. 12x11½
726	A140	5e multicolored	.20 .20
727	A140	25e multicolored	.65 .65
728	A140	35e multicolored	1.00 1.00
729	A140	40e multicolored	1.10 1.10
		Nos. 726-729 (4)	2.95 2.95

Early Exploration
A141

a, Quotation from Lusiadas, two men looking at maps. b, Man with sword, man & woman. c, Compass, map, sailing ship, buildings on cliff.

1998   Perf. 11½
730	A141	50e Strip of 3, #a.-c.	6.00 6.00

Women's Traditional Costumes — A142

1998   Litho.   Perf. 12
731	A142	10e Brava	.25 .25
732	A142	18e Fogo	.50 .50
733	A142	30e Boa Vista	.80 .80
734	A142	50e Santiago	1.40 1.40
		Nos. 731-734 (4)	2.95 2.95

Butterflies and Moths
A143

Designs: 5e, Byblia ilithyia. 10e, Aganais speciosa. 20e, Utetheisia pulchella. 30e, Vanessa cardui. 50e, Trichoplusia ni. 100e, Grammodes congenita.

1999, Mar. 16   Litho.   Perf. 11¾
735	A143	5e multi	.20 .20
736	A143	10e multi	.25 .25
737	A143	20e multi	.50 .50
738	A143	30e multi	.80 .80
a.		Souvenir sheet, #737-738	4.00 4.00
739	A143	50e multi	1.25 1.25
740	A143	100e multi	2.60 2.60
		Nos. 735-740 (6)	5.60 5.60

No. 738a sold for 100e.

First Concorde Flight, 30th Anniv. A144

Concorde: 30e, In flight. 50e, On ground.

1999, June 14   Litho.   Perf. 12
741-742	A144	Set of 2	2.75 2.75

Famous People — A145

Design: 30e, Alain Gerbault (1893-1941), sailor, boats at dock. 50e, Roberto Duarte Silva (1837-89), chemist, Eiffel Tower.

1999, July 2   Litho.   Perf. 14½
743	A145	30e multi	2.00 2.00
744	A145	50e multi	3.25 3.25
a.		Souvenir sheet #743-744	6.50 6.50

Philex France 99 (#744a).

A146

UPU,
125th
Anniv.
A147

1999, Sept. 15   *Perf. 12x11¾*
745 A146 30e shown   20.00 20.00
746 A147 50e shown   20.00 20.00
With Country Name Added
747 A146 30e multi   .65 .65
748 A147 50e multi   1.10 1.10
     Nos. 745-748 (4)   41.75 41.75

Dance
A148

Designs: 10e, Colá Sanjon, vert. 30e, Contradança, vert. 50e, Desfile de tabanca. 100e, Batuque.

     Perf. 11¾x12, 12x11¾
1999, Nov. 5   Litho.
749-752 A148   Set of 4   5.00 5.00

Millennium — A149

Designs: 40e, Globe, hourglass and open antique book inscribed "2000," vert. 50e, "2000 Milenio."

2000, Jan. 31 Litho.   *Perf. 11¾x11½*
753-754 A149   Set of 2   2.50 2.50

SOS
Children's
Villages
A150

Emblem and child: 50e, Seated, vert. 100e, With arms outstretched.

     Perf. 11¾x12, 12x11¾
2000, Apr. 28   Litho.
755-756 A150   Set of 2   4.00 4.00

Independence, 25th Anniv. — A151

2000, July 5   *Perf. 11¾*
757 A151 50e multi   2.00 1.25

2000
Summer
Olympics,
Sydney
A152

Designs: 10e, Women's gymnastics. 40e, Taekwondo. 50e, Women's hurdles.

2000, Sept. 15   Litho.   *Perf. 11¾*
758-760 A152   Set of 3   2.60 2.60
 760a   Souvenir sheet of 3, #758-
        760   2.75 2.75

Dragoeiro
Tree — A153

2000, Oct. 9 Litho.   *Perf. 11¾x11½*
761 A153   5e green   .20 .20
762 A153 40e red   1.00 1.00
763 A153 60e brown   1.60 1.60

Sao Nicolau Seminary and
School — A154

No. 764: a, Seminarians and students (denomination at LR, 27x26mm). b, Seminarians and students (denomination at LL, 29x26mm). c, José Alves Feijo, Dr. Julio Dias and Canon António Bouças (56x26mm). Illustration reduced.

2000, Dec. 15   Litho.   *Perf. 14½*
764 A154 60e Horiz. strip of 3,
        #a-c   5.00 5.00

Fish
A155

Designs: 10e, Diplodus sargus lineatus. 22e, Diplodus prayensis. 28e, Lithognathus mormyrus. 48e, Diplodus fasciatus. 60e, Diplodus puntazzo.

2001, Apr. 24   *Perf. 12x11¾*
765-769 A155   Set of 5   5.00 5.00

Spiders
A156

Designs: 13e, Thomisus onustus. 16e, Scytodes velutina. 40e, Hersiliola simoni. 100e, Loxosceles rufescens.

2001, May 28
770-773 A156   Set of 4   5.00 5.00

Trees — A156a

Designs: 50e, Acacia albida. 60e, Ficus sycomorus.

2001, June 9 Litho.   *Perf. 11¾x11½*
773A-773B A156a   Set of 2   2.75 2.75

Souvenir Sheet

Belgica 2001 Intl. Stamp Exhibition,
Brussels — A157

     Perf. 11¾x11½
2001, June 9   Photo.
774 A157 100e multi   2.75 2.75

Medicinal
Plants — A157a

Designs: 20e, Artimisia gorgonum. 27e, Globularia amygdalifolia. 47.50e, Sidereoxylon marginata, horiz. 50e, Umbilicus schmidtii, horiz. 60e, Verbascum cystolithicum. 100e, Limonium lobinii.

     Perf. 11¾x12, 12x11¾
2001, Sept. 27   Litho.
774A-774F A157a   Set of 6   8.00 8.00

Year of Dialogue
Among
Civilizations — A158

2001, Oct. 9 Litho.   *Perf. 11¾x12*
775 A158 60e multi   1.60 1.60

António Aurélio Gonçalves (1901-84),
Writer — A159

2001, Dec. 20   *Perf. 12¼*
776 A159 100e multi   2.75 2.75

Medicinal
Plants
A160

Designs: 10e, Euphorbia tuckeyna. 50e, Limonium sunding, vert. 60e, Aeonium gorgoneum, vert. 100e, Polycarpaea gayi, vert.

     Perf. 12x11¾, 11¾x12
2002, Apr. 26   Litho.
777-780 A160   Set of 4   5.75 5.75

2002 World Cup Soccer
Championships, Japan and
Korea — A161

Designs: 60e, Player heading ball towards goal. 100e, Player kicking ball towards goal.

2002, July 22   *Perf. 12x11¾*
781-782 A161   Set of 2   4.00 4.00

Caretta
Caretta
A162

Designs: 10e, Pair mating. 20e, Female laying eggs, vert. 30e, Eggs hatching. 60e, Hatchlings heading for sea, vert. No. 787, 100e, Turtle swimming underwater.
No. 788, 100e, Turtle on beach.

2002, Sept. 9   *Perf. 12x11¾, 11¾x12*
783-787 A162   Set of 5   6.50 6.50
     Souvenir Sheet
788 A162 100e multi   3.00 3.00
   No. 788 contains one 80x60mm stamp.

Basketry
A163

Baskets and basket weavers from: 20e, Sao Nicolau Island. 33e, Santo Antao Island. 60e, Santiago Island, 100e, Boa Vista Island.

2002, Oct. 29   *Perf. 12x11¾*
789-792 A163   Set of 4   6.50 6.50

Composers
and Poets
A164

Designs: 12e, Katcháss (1951-88), composer. 20e, Jorge Monteiro (1913-98), composer. 32e, Luis Rendall (1898-1986), composer. 47.50e, Jorge Barbosa (1902-71), poet. 60e, Januário Leite (1865-1930), poet. 100e, José Lopes (1872-1962), poet.

2003, Feb. 24
793-798 A164   Set of 6   7.50 7.50

Birds — A165

Designs: 10e, Ardea bournei. 27e, Ardea cinerea. 42e, Bubulcus ibis. 60e, Egretta garzeta.

2003, July 9   *Perf. 14x13¾*
799-802 A165   Set of 4   4.00 4.00

Cesaria
Evora,
Singer
A166

Designs: 60e, Evora at left. 100e, Evora at right.
200e, Feet of Evora.

2003, May 26 Perf. 13¾x14
803-804 A166 Set of 2   4.50 4.50
Souvenir Sheet
Perf. 12¼x12
805 A166 200e multi + label   6.00 6.00
No. 805 contains one 50x38mm stamp.

[image 1]
Scouting in Cape Verde A167

Emblem and scout of: 60e, Scouts Association of Cape Verde. 100e, Cape Verde Scouts Corps.

2003, Oct. 24 Litho. Perf. 13¾x14
806-807 A167 Set of 2   4.50 4.50

[image 2]
Whales A168

Designs: 10e, Balaenoptera musculus. 20e, Physeter macrocephalus. 50e, Megaptera novaeangliae. 60e, Globicephala macrorhynchus.

2003, Nov. 25 Perf. 12
808-811 A168 Set of 4   6.00 6.00

[image 3]
First Dakar — Praia Seaplane Flight of Europe — Africa — South America Airmail Service, 75th Anniv. — A169

Seaplane and: 10e, Crew. 42e, Pilot Paulin Paris, map of South America — Africa route. 60e, Map of entire route. 100e, Like 10e.

2003, Dec. 11 Perf. 14
812-814 A169 Set of 3   3.25 3.25
Souvenir Sheet
815 A169 100e multi   3.00 3.00

[image 4]
Election of Pope John Paul II, 25th Anniv. — A170

Pope John Paul II and: 30e, Girl. 60e, Boats, horiz. 100e, Censer and crucifix.

2003, Dec. 29 Perf. 14x13¾, 13¾x14
816-817 A170 Set of 2   2.40 2.40
Souvenir Sheet
818 A170 100e multi   3.00 3.00

[image 5] Trees A171
[image 6] Windmill A172

Designs: 20e, Khaya senegalensis. 27e, Acacia nilotica. 60e, Ceiba pentandra. 100e, Phoenix atlantica.

2004, Jan. 25 Perf. 14x13¾
819-822 A171 Set of 4   5.50 5.50

2004, June 3 Perf. 13¼x13
Colors: 20e, Blue. 60e, Red. 100e, Green.
823-825 A172 Set of 3   4.75 4.75

[image 7]
2004 Summer Olympics, Athens — A173

Designs: 10e, Taekwondo. 60e, Rhythmic gymnastics. 100e, Boxing, horiz.

Perf. 13¼x13, 13x13¼
2004, Aug. 13 Litho.
826-828 A173 Set of 3   4.75 4.75

[image 8]
Lighthouses A174

Designs: 10e, Ponta do Barril Lighthouse, Sao Nicolau Island. 30e, Ponta Jalunga Lighthouse, Brava Island. 40e, D. Luis Lighthouse, Passaros Islands, horiz. 50e, Ponta Preta Lighthouse, Santiago Island, horiz.

2004, Sept. 7
829-832 A174 Set of 4   4.00 4.00

[image 9]
Houses on Fogo Island A175

Various houses: 20e, 40e, 50e, 60e.

2004, Oct. 9 Perf. 13x13¼
833-836 A175 Set of 4   4.75 4.75

[image 10]
Telephones — A176

Old telephones and: 10e, Switchboard. 40e, Operator. 60e, Telephone directory. 100e, Truck and telephone poles.

2004, Nov. 12
837-840 A176 Set of 4   5.50 5.50

[image 11]
Oral Stories and Legends A177

Designs: 10e, Stória Stória. 20e, Era um Vez! 30e, Sapatinha Ribera Baxu. 60e, Quem ki Sabi Mas, Conta Midjor!, vert.

Perf. 13x13¼, 13¼x13
2005, Feb. 21 Litho.
841-844 A177 Set of 4   3.50 3.50

[image 12]
Amilcar Cabral (1924-73), Revolutionary Leader — A178

2005, June 30 Litho. Perf. 13¼x13
845 A178 60e multi   1.60 1.60
Independence, 30th anniv.

[image 13]
Shells A179

Designs: 30e, Conus evorai. 40e, Harpa doris. 50e, Strombus lotus. 60e, Phyllonotus duplex.

2005, July 18 Perf. 13x13¼
846-849 A179 Set of 4   5.00 5.00

[image 14]
Birds — A180

Designs: 19e, Passer iagoensis. 42e, Estrilda astrild. 44e, Passer domesticus. 55e, Acrocephalus brevipennis.

2005, Aug. 8 Perf. 13¼x13
850-853 A180 Set of 4   4.25 4.25

[image 15]
World Summit on the Information Society, Tunis A181

2005, Nov. 16 Litho. Perf. 13x13¼
854 A181 60e multi   1.60 1.60

Artifacts of the Slave Trade A182

Designs: 5e, Pipe. 10e, Telescope. 30e, Cannon. 60e, Nautical instrument.

100e, Shackles.

2006, Jan. 31
855-858 A182 Set of 4   3.00 3.00
Souvenir Sheet
859 A182 100e multi   3.00 3.00
No. 859 contains one 80x60mm stamp.

[image 16]
Community of Portuguese-Speaking Nations, 10th Anniv. — A186

2006, Nov. 2
872 A186 60e multi   2.40 2.40

[image 17]
Sir Francis Drake (c. 1540-96), Explorer — A187

Drake and: 5e, Sextant.

2006, Nov. 27 Perf. 13¼x13
873 A187 5e multi   —
Three additional stamps were issued in this set. The editors would like to examine any examples.

[image 18]
Writers — A189

Designs: No. 882, 60e, Manuel Lopes (1907-2005). No. 883, 60e, Baltasar Lopes da Silva (Osvaldo Alcantara) (1907-89).

2007 Perf. 13¼
882-883 A189 Set of 2   4.75 4.75

[image 19]

Designs: 60e, Evora at left. 100e, Evora at right.
200e, Feet of Evora.

2003, May 26 Perf. 13¾x14
803-804 A166 Set of 2   4.50 4.50
Souvenir Sheet
Perf. 12¼x12
805 A166 200e multi + label   6.00 6.00
No. 805 contains one 50x38mm stamp.

Scouting in Cape Verde A167

Emblem and scout of: 60e, Scouts Association of Cape Verde. 100e, Cape Verde Scouts Corps.

2003, Oct. 24 Litho. Perf. 13¾x14
806-807 A167 Set of 2   4.50 4.50

Whales A168

Designs: 10e, Balaenoptera musculus. 20e, Physeter macrocephalus. 50e, Megaptera novaeangliae. 60e, Globicephala macrorhynchus.

2003, Nov. 25 Perf. 12
808-811 A168 Set of 4   6.00 6.00

First Dakar — Praia Seaplane Flight of Europe — Africa — South America Airmail Service, 75th Anniv. — A169

Seaplane and: 10e, Crew. 42e, Pilot Paulin Paris, map of South America — Africa route. 60e, Map of entire route. 100e, Like 10e.

2003, Dec. 11 Perf. 14
812-814 A169 Set of 3   3.25 3.25
Souvenir Sheet
815 A169 100e multi   3.00 3.00

Election of Pope John Paul II, 25th Anniv. — A170

Pope John Paul II and: 30e, Girl. 60e, Boats, horiz. 100e, Censer and crucifix.

2003, Dec. 29 Perf. 14x13¾, 13¾x14
816-817 A170 Set of 2   2.40 2.40
Souvenir Sheet
818 A170 100e multi   3.00 3.00

Trees A171

Windmill A172

Designs: 20e, Khaya senegalensis. 27e, Acacia nilotica. 60e, Ceiba pentandra. 100e, Phoenix atlantica.

2004, Jan. 25 Perf. 14x13¾
819-822 A171 Set of 4   5.50 5.50

2004, June 3 Perf. 13¼x13
Colors: 20e, Blue. 60e, Red. 100e, Green.
823-825 A172 Set of 3   4.75 4.75

2004 Summer Olympics, Athens — A173

Designs: 10e, Taekwondo. 60e, Rhythmic gymnastics. 100e, Boxing, horiz.

Perf. 13¼x13, 13x13¼
2004, Aug. 13 Litho.
826-828 A173 Set of 3   4.75 4.75

Lighthouses A174

Designs: 10e, Ponta do Barril Lighthouse, Sao Nicolau Island. 30e, Ponta Jalunga Lighthouse, Brava Island. 40e, D. Luis Lighthouse, Passaros Islands, horiz. 50e, Ponta Preta Lighthouse, Santiago Island, horiz.

2004, Sept. 7
829-832 A174 Set of 4   4.00 4.00

Houses on Fogo Island A175

Various houses: 20e, 40e, 50e, 60e.

2004, Oct. 9 Perf. 13x13¼
833-836 A175 Set of 4   4.75 4.75

Telephones — A176

Old telephones and: 10e, Switchboard. 40e, Operator. 60e, Telephone directory. 100e, Truck and telephone poles.

2004, Nov. 12
837-840 A176 Set of 4   5.50 5.50

Oral Stories and Legends A177

Designs: 10e, Stória Stória. 20e, Era um Vez! 30e, Sapatinha Ribera Baxu. 60e, Quem ki Sabi Mas, Conta Midjor!, vert.

Perf. 13x13¼, 13¼x13
2005, Feb. 21 Litho.
841-844 A177 Set of 4   3.50 3.50

Amilcar Cabral (1924-73), Revolutionary Leader — A178

2005, June 30 Litho. Perf. 13¼x13
845 A178 60e multi   1.60 1.60
Independence, 30th anniv.

Shells A179

Designs: 30e, Conus evorai. 40e, Harpa doris. 50e, Strombus lotus. 60e, Phyllonotus duplex.

2005, July 18 Perf. 13x13¼
846-849 A179 Set of 4   5.00 5.00

Birds — A180

Designs: 19e, Passer iagoensis. 42e, Estrilda astrild. 44e, Passer domesticus. 55e, Acrocephalus brevipennis.

2005, Aug. 8 Perf. 13¼x13
850-853 A180 Set of 4   4.25 4.25

World Summit on the Information Society, Tunis A181

2005, Nov. 16 Litho. Perf. 13x13¼
854 A181 60e multi   1.60 1.60

Artifacts of the Slave Trade A182

Designs: 5e, Pipe. 10e, Telescope. 30e, Cannon. 60e, Nautical instrument.

100e, Shackles.

2006, Jan. 31
855-858 A182 Set of 4   3.00 3.00
Souvenir Sheet
859 A182 100e multi   3.00 3.00
No. 859 contains one 80x60mm stamp.

Community of Portuguese-Speaking Nations, 10th Anniv. — A186

2006, Nov. 2
872 A186 60e multi   2.40 2.40

Sir Francis Drake (c. 1540-96), Explorer — A187

Drake and: 5e, Sextant.

2006, Nov. 27 Perf. 13¼x13
873 A187 5e multi   —
Three additional stamps were issued in this set. The editors would like to examine any examples.

Writers — A189

Designs: No. 882, 60e, Manuel Lopes (1907-2005). No. 883, 60e, Baltasar Lopes da Silva (Osvaldo Alcantara) (1907-89).

2007 Perf. 13¼
882-883 A189 Set of 2   4.75 4.75

Pico do Fogo Volcano A190

Various depictions of erupting volcano: 10e, 50e, 55e, 60e. 50e and 55e are vert.

2007 Perf. 13x13¼, 13¼x13
884-887 A190 Set of 4   7.00 7.00

Luís de Cadamosto Type of 2007
Designs: 16e, Cadamosto and ship. 44e, Ship and compass rose. 60e, Cadamosto.

2007 Perf. 13¼x13
888 A191 16e multi   — —
889 A191 44e multi   — —
890 A191 60e multi   — —

Luis de Cadamosto (1432-88), Discoverer of Cape Verde Islands — A191

Designs: 100e, Cadamosto, ship and astrolabe.

2007 *Perf. 13¼x13*
891 A191 100e multi — —

Three additional stamps exist in this set. The editors would like to examine any examples.

Aviation A193

Designs: 10e, Airplane, map of South America, Cape Verde, and Africa. 50e, Concorde. 60e, Airplane, map of Africa and Asia. 100e, Airplane over airport.

2007 *Perf. 13x13¼*
896-899 A193 Set of 4 6.00 6.00

Local Cuisine A194

Designs: 10e, Cozido (stew). 20e, Cuscus com mel (couscous with honey), vert. 60e, Trotxida. 100e, Xerem (cornmeal puree).

2008 *Perf. 13¼x13, 13¼x13*
900-903 A194 Set of 4 9.75 9.75

Occupations A195

Designs: 30e, Engraxador (shoe polisher). 40e, Vendedeira de pao (bread seller). 50e, Vendedeira de leite (milk seller), horiz. 100e, Vendedeira de peixe (fish seller).

2008 *Perf. 13¼x13, 13x13¼*
904-907 A195 Set of 4 10.50 10.50

Souvenir Sheet

Praia, 150th Anniv. — A196

2008 *Perf. 13¼x13*
908 A196 200e multi 9.75 9.75

Peace Corps in Cape Verde, 20th Anniv. — A197

2008
909 A197 60e multi 3.00 3.00

Birds of Prey — A198

Designs: 5e, Buteo bannermani. 20e, Falco tinnunculus. 40e, Pandion haliaetus. 60e, Falco peregrinus madeus.

2008
910-913 A198 Set of 4 4.75 4.75

Louis Braille (1809-52), Educator of the Blind A199

Designs: No. 914, 60e, Hands reading Braille text. No. 915, 60e, Blind man with cane. No. 916, 60e, Blind children. No. 917, 60e, Blind man with seeing-eye dog, vert.

2009 *Perf. 13x13¼, 13¼x13*
Granite Paper
914-917 A199 Set of 4 7.50 7.50

Charles Darwin (1809-82), Naturalist — A200

No. 918 — Map of Darwin's voyages and: a, Darwin, skulls. b, Skull, ship, Darwin's legs. c, Darwin and octopus.

2009 *Perf. 13½x13¼*
918 Horiz. strip of 3 8.25 8.25
a. A200 60e Any single 2.75 2.75

Red Cross, 150th Anniv. A201

2009 *Litho. Perf. 13x13¼*
Granite Paper
919 A201 100e multi 2.75 2.75

Flora and Fauna A202

Designs: 5e, Chioninia delalandii. 10e, Tornabenea annua. 20e, Tarentola darwini. 30e, Satureja forbesii, vert. 40e, Campylnatus glaber glaber, vert. 60e, Chioninia vailanti.

2009 *Perf. 13x13¼, 13¼x13*
Granite Paper
920-925 A202 Set of 6 4.50 4.50

Souvenir Sheet

Serra Malagueta Protected Areas — A203

No. 926 — Various views of Serra Malagueta: a, 50e. b, 100e.

2009 *Perf. 13¼*
Granite Paper
926 A203 Sheet of 2, #a-b 4.25 4.25

Discovery of Cape Verde Islands, 550th Anniv. — A204

No. 927: a, Two ships. b, Map of Cape Verde and Africa, compass rose, birds, "14." c, Ship, rowboat, map of Africa and Asia, compass rose, "60."

2010 *Perf. 13½x13¼*
Granite Paper
927 Horiz. strip of 3 4.50 4.50
a.-c. A204 60e Any single 1.50 1.50

Monte Gordo Protected Areas — A205

Flora and birds of Monte Gordo Protected Areas: 5e, Diplotaxis gracilis. 20e, Theresia. 30e, Verbascum capitis-viridis. 40e, Coturnix coturnix, horiz. 50e, Corvus ruficollis, horiz. 60e, Columba livia, horiz. 100e, Monte Gordo, horiz.

2010 *Perf. 13¼x13, 13x13¼*
928-933 A205 Set of 6 5.25 5.25
Souvenir Sheet
934 A205 100e multi 2.50 2.50

2010 World Cup Soccer Championships, South Africa — A206

Designs: 40e, Mascot, silhouettes of players. 50e, Emblem, players, vert. 60e, Mascot, players. 100e, World Cup, silhouettes of players.

2010 *Perf. 13x13¼, 13¼x13*
935-938 A206 Set of 4 6.25 6.25

AIR POST STAMPS

Common Design Type
Name and Value in Black
Perf. 13½x13

			Unwmk.	
1938, July 26				
C1	CD39	10c red orange	.60	.50
C2	CD39	20c purple	.60	.50
C3	CD39	50c orange	.60	.50
C4	CD39	1e ultra	.60	.50
C5	CD39	2e lilac brown	1.40	.80
C6	CD39	3e dk green	1.75	1.40
C7	CD39	5e red brown	5.50	2.10
C8	CD39	9e rose carmine	9.00	3.75
C9	CD39	10e magenta	9.75	5.00
Nos. C1-C9 (9)			29.80	15.05
Set, never hinged			50.00	

No. C7 exists with overprint "Exposicao Internacional de Nova York, 1939-1940" and Trylon and Perisphere.

POSTAGE DUE STAMPS

D1 D2

1904		Unwmk. Typo.	*Perf. 12*	
J1	D1	5r yellow grn	.40	.25
J2	D1	10r slate	.40	.25
J3	D1	20r yellow brn	.50	.40
J4	D1	30r red orange	1.25	.40
J5	D1	50r gray brown	.50	.35
J6	D1	60r red brown	9.25	4.25
J7	D1	100r lilac	1.75	1.25
J8	D1	130r dull blue	1.90	1.25
J9	D1	200r carmine	1.60	1.60
J10	D1	500r dull violet	5.00	3.00
Nos. J1-J10 (10)			22.55	13.00

Overprinted in Carmine or Green

1911				
J11	D1	5r yellow grn	.30	.20
J12	D1	10r slate	.30	.20
J13	D1	20r yellow brn	.35	.20
J14	D1	30r orange	.35	.20
J15	D1	50r gray brown	.65	.40
J16	D1	60r red brown	.65	.40
J17	D1	100r lilac	.65	.40
J18	D1	130r dull blue	.75	.65
J19	D1	200r carmine (G)	2.00	1.50
J20	D1	500r dull violet	2.50	1.75
Nos. J11-J20 (10)			8.50	5.90

1921			*Perf. 11½*	
J21	D2	½c yellow grn	.30	.20
J22	D2	1c slate	.30	.20
J23	D2	2c red brown	.30	.20
J24	D2	3c orange	.30	.20
J25	D2	5c gray brown	.30	.20
J26	D2	6c lt brown	.30	.20
J27	D2	10c red violet	.30	.20
J28	D2	13c dull blue	.55	.40

J29	D2	20c carmine	.60	.50
J30	D2	50c gray	1.75	1.10
		Nos. J21-J30 (10)	5.00	3.40

> Catalogue values for unused stamps in this section, from this point to the end of the section, are for Never Hinged items.

Common Design Type
Photogravure and Typographed

1952		Unwmk.	Perf. 14	

Numeral in Red, Frame Multicolored

J31	CD45	10c chocolate	.30	.25
J32	CD45	30c black brown	.30	.25
J33	CD45	50c dark blue	.30	.25
J34	CD45	1e dark blue	.40	.25
J35	CD45	2e red brown	.40	.30
J36	CD45	5e olive green	1.10	1.00
		Nos. J31-J36 (6)	2.80	2.30

NEWSPAPER STAMP

N1

1893		Typo.	Unwmk.	Perf. 11½	
P1	N1	2½r brown		1.50	1.00
a.		Perf. 12½		3.00	1.50
b.		Perf. 13½		6.50	3.00

For surcharges see Nos. 79, 206.

POSTAL TAX STAMPS

Pombal Issue
Common Design Types

1925		Unwmk.	Engr.	Perf. 12½	
RA1	CD28	15c dull vio & blk		1.25	1.10
RA2	CD29	15c dull vio & blk		1.25	1.10
RA3	CD30	15c dull vio & blk		1.25	1.10
		Nos. RA1-RA3 (3)		3.75	3.30

St. Isabel — PT1

PT2

1948		Litho.	Perf. 11	
RA4	PT1	50c dark green	3.75	2.40
RA5	PT1	1e henna brown	7.50	3.00

> Catalogue values for unused stamps in this section, from this point to the end of the section, are for Never Hinged items.

No. RA5 Surcharged with New Value and Bars

1959

RA6	PT1	50c on 1e henna brown	1.40	1.10

Perf. 14

RA7	PT1	50c carmine rose	2.10	1.00
RA8	PT1	1e blue	2.10	1.00

St. Isabel Type Redrawn

1967-73		Litho.	Perf. 14	
RA9	PT1	30c (blue panel)	.40	.40
RA9A	PT1	30c (orange panel)	.40	.40
RA10	PT1	50c (lilac rose panel)	.85	.85
RA11	PT1	50c (red panel) ('72)	.45	.45
RA12	PT1	1e (brn panel)	.90	.90
RA13	PT1	1e (red lilac panel) ('72)	.90	.90
		Nos. RA9-RA13 (6)	3.90	3.90

Nos. RA9-RA13 are inscribed "ASSIS-TENCIA" in large letters in bottom panel and "PORTUGAL" and "CABO VERDE" in small letters in upper left corner.

Revenue Stamps Surcharged in Green, Blue or Black

1967-72		Typo.	Perf. 12	

Black "CABO VERDE" & Value
Pale Green Burelage

RA14	PT2	50c on 1c org (Bl) ('71)	1.40	.90
a.		Black surcharge ('68?)	15.00	14.50
RA15	PT2	50c on 2c org (Bk) ('69)	15.00	14.50
c.		Inverted surcharge	50.00	35.00
RA16	PT2	50c on 3c org (G) ('72)	1.10	.60
RA17	PT2	50c on 5c org (G) ('72)	1.10	.60
RA18	PT2	50c on 10c org (G) ('71)	1.25	1.00
RA19	PT2	1e on 1c org (Bk)	2.75	2.10
RA20	PT2	1e on 2c org (G) ('71)	1.90	1.75
a.		Blue surcharge ('71)	2.00	1.10
b.		Black surcharge	2.10	2.10
		Nos. RA14-RA20 (7)	24.50	21.45

POSTAL TAX DUE STAMPS

Pombal Issue
Common Design Types

1925		Unwmk.	Perf. 12½	
RAJ1	CD28	30c dull vio & blk	.75	.70
RAJ2	CD29	30c dull vio & blk	.75	.70
RAJ3	CD30	30c dull vio & blk	.75	.70
		Nos. RAJ1-RAJ3 (3)	2.25	2.10

CARIBBEAN NETHERLANDS

ˈkar-ē-bbe-ə-n ˈne-thər-lənˌdz

LOCATION — The islands of Bonaire (north of Venezuela), Saint Eustatius and Saba (south of Anguilla)
AREA — 125 sq. mi.
POP. — 18,012 (2010)
CAPITAL — Kralendijk, Bonaire; Oranjestad, Saint Eustatius; The Bottom, Saba

On Oct. 10, 2010, Caribbean Netherlands, formerly part of Netherlands Antilles, became special municipalities within the Kingdom of the Netherlands.

100 Cents = 1 Gulden

> Catalogue values for all unused stamps in this country are for Never Hinged items.

Map of Islands and West Indies, Arms, Queen Beatrix — A1

Perf. 13¾

2010, Oct. 10		Litho.	Unwmk.	
1	A1	111c multi	1.25	1.25

CAROLINE ISLANDS

ˈkar-ə-ˌlīn ˈī-lənds

LOCATION — A group of about 549 small islands in the West Pacific Ocean, north of the Equator.
GOVT. — German colony
AREA — 550 sq. mi.
POP. — 40,000 (approx. 1915)

100 Pfennig = 1 Mark

Watermark

Wmk. 125 — Lozenges

Stamps of Germany 1889-90 Overprinted in Black

#1-6

#1a-6a

Overprinted at 56 degree Angle

1900		Unwmk.	Perf. 13½x14½	
1	A9	3pf dk brown	13.00	14.00
2	A9	5pf green	18.00	18.00
3	A10	10pf carmine	19.00	19.00
4	A10	20pf ultra	24.00	30.00
5	A10	25pf orange	55.00	65.00
6	A10	50pf red brown	55.00	65.00
		Nos. 1-6 (6)	184.00	211.00

1899
Overprinted at 48 degree Angle

1a	A9	3pf light brown	625.00	750.00
2a	A9	5pf green	650.00	650.00
3a	A10	10pf carmine	65.00	150.00
4a	A10	20pf ultra	65.00	150.00
5a	A10	25pf orange	1,650.	3,100.
6a	A10	50pf red brown	900.00	1,600.

A3

Kaiser's Yacht "Hohenzollern" — A4

1901, Jan.		Typo.	Perf. 14	
7	A3	3pf brown	1.10	1.75
8	A3	5pf green	1.10	2.10
9	A3	10pf carmine	1.10	5.00
a.		Half used as 5pf on cover, back-stamped in Jaluit ('05)		120.00
10	A3	20pf ultra	1.25	9.00
a.		Half used as 10pf on cover ('10)		8,500.
11	A3	25pf org & blk, *yel*	1.60	14.50
12	A3	30pf org & blk, *sal*	1.60	14.50
13	A3	40pf lake & blk	1.60	16.50
14	A3	50pf pur & blk, *sal*	2.00	22.50
15	A3	80pf lake & blk, *rose*	3.00	25.00

		Engr.	Perf. 14½x14	
16	A4	1m carmine	4.50	62.50
17	A4	2m blue	7.25	87.50
18	A4	3m black violet	10.00	150.00
19	A4	5m slate & carmine	160.00	550.00
		Nos. 7-19 (13)	196.10	960.85

No. 9a is known as the "typhoon provisional" the stock of 5pf stamps having been destroyed during a typhoon. Covers (cards) without backstamp, value about $72.50.
Forged cancellations are found on #7-19.

No. 7 Handstamp Surcharged
5 Pf

1910, July 12

20	A3	5pf on 3pf brown	5,500.
a.		Inverted surcharge	7,750.
b.		Double surcharge	11,000.

Values are for stamps tied to cover. Stamps on piece sell for about 40% less.

1915-19		Wmk. 125	Typo.	
21	A3	3pf brown ('19)	.90	
22	A3	5pf green	12.50	

Engr.

23	A4	5m slate & carmine	35.00
		Nos. 21-23 (3)	48.40

Nos. 21-23 were not placed in use.

CASTELLORIZO

ˌkäs-tə-ˈlor-ə-ˌzō

(Castelrosso)

LOCATION — A Mediterranean island in the Dodecanese group lying close to the coast of Asia Minor and about 60 miles east of Rhodes.
GOVT. — Former Italian Colony
AREA — 4 sq. mi.
POP. — 2,238 (1936)

Formerly a Turkish possession, Castellorizo was occupied by the French in 1915 and ceded to Italy after World War I. In 1945 it became part of Greece.

25 Centimes = 1 Piaster
100 Centimes = 1 Franc

> Used values in italics are for postally used copies. Stamps with CTO cancels sell for about the same as hinged, unused stamps.

Issued under French Occupation

Stamps of French Offices in Turkey Overprinted
B. N. F. CASTELLORIZO

1920		Unwmk.	Perf. 14x13½	
1	A2	1c gray	55.00	62.50
a.		Inverted overprint	240.00	240.00
b.		Double overprint	400.00	440.00
2	A2	2c vio brn	60.00	67.50
a.		Double overprint	350.00	450.00
3	A2	3c red org	55.00	62.50
a.		Inverted overprint	225.00	225.00
4	A2	5c green	85.00	85.00
a.		Inverted overprint	275.00	275.00
5	A3	10c rose	97.50	97.50
6	A3	15c pale red	135.00	135.00
a.		Inverted overprint	450.00	450.00
7	A3	20c brn vio	135.00	135.00
8	A5	1pi on 25c blue	125.00	125.00
a.		Pair, one without overprint	800.00	800.00
9	A3	30c lilac	150.00	150.00

Overprint Reading Down

10	A4	40c red & pale bl (down)	225.00	225.00
a.		Inverted ovpt (reading up)	925.00	925.00
11	A6	2pi on 50c bis brn & lav (down)	250.00	275.00
a.		Inverted ovpt (reading up)	975.00	975.00
b.		Double overprint	1,350.	1,350.
12	A6	4pi on 1fr cl & ol grn (down)	300.00	350.00
a.		Double overprint	1,350.	1,350.
b.		Inverted ovpt (reading up)	1,050.	1,050.
13	A6	20pi on 5fr dk bl & buff	675.00	750.00
a.		Double overprint	1,900.	1,900.
		Nos. 1-13 (13)	2,347.	2,520.

Nos. 1-9 were overprinted in blocks of 25. Position 4 had "CASTELLORIZO" inverted and Positions 8 and 18 had "CASTELLORISO." The later variety also occurred in the setting of the form for Nos. 10-13.
"B. N. F." are the initials of "Base Navale Francaise".

Overprinted in Black or Red
O. N. F. Castellorizo

1920
On Stamps of French Offices in Turkey

14	A2	1c gray	37.50	42.50
15	A2	2c vio brn	42.50	50.00
16	A2	3c red org	72.50	77.50
17	A3	5c green (R)	37.50	37.50
19	A3	10c rose	47.50	47.50
20	A3	15c pale red	77.50	77.50
21	A3	20c brn vio	120.00	120.00
22	A5	1pi on 25c bl (R)	72.50	72.50
23	A3	30c lilac (R)	85.00	92.50
24	A4	40c red & pale bl	77.50	77.50
25	A6	2pi on 50c bis brn & lav	72.50	72.50
26	A6	4pi on 1fr claret & ol grn	125.00	140.00
28	A6	20pi on 5fr dk bl & buff	400.00	450.00
		Nos. 14-28 (13)	1,267.	1,357.

On Nos. 25, 26 and 28 the two lines of the overprint are set wider apart than on the lower values.

"O.N.F." are the initials of "Occupation Navale Francaise."

"Casetllorizo" and "astellorizo" varieties are known on Nos. 14-23.

Overprint on 5c in black and on 8pi on 2fr (#37) were prepared but not issued. Values: 5c, $1,100; 8pi on 2fr, $1,200.

On Stamps of France

30	A22	10c red	50.00	50.00
a.		Inverted overprint	240.00	240.00
31	A22	25c blue (R)	50.00	50.00
a.		Inverted overprint	240.00	240.00

This overprint exists on 8 other 1900-1907 denominations of France (5c, 15c, 20c, 30c, 40c, 50c, 1fr, 5fr). These are believed not to have been issued or postally used. Values: 5c, $775; 15c, $775; 20c, $825; 30c, $1,250; 40c, $1,250; 50c, $1,250; 1fr, $1,350; 5fr, $12,500.

Stamps of France, 1900-1907, Handstamped in Black or Violet

1920

33	A22	5c green	190.00	190.00
34	A22	10c red	190.00	190.00
35	A22	20c vio brn	190.00	190.00
a.		Overprint inverted (reading up)	1,500.	
b.		Double overprint (V)		725.00
36	A22	25c blue	190.00	190.00
37	A18	50c bis brn & lav	1,000.	1,150.
		Double overprint	1,700.	
38	A18	1fr cl & ol grn	1,000.	1,150.
		Nos. 33-38 (6)	2,760.	3,060.

Nos. 1-38 are considered speculative.

Forgeries of overprints on Nos. 1-38 exist. They abound of Nos. 33-38.

French Offices in Turkey Nos. 25//38 were hand-stamped "Occupation Francaise Castellorizo" locally by the officers in charge of the French Navy postal facilities but were not issued. Values: 5c, 10c, 15c, 20c, 1pi on 25c, each $1,050; 40c, 2pi on 50c, each $2,000; 4pi on 1fr, $2,350; 20pi on 5fr, $9,250.

Issued under Italian Dominion
100 Centesimi = 1 Lira

Italian Stamps of 1906-20 Overprinted

1922   Wmk. 140   Perf. 14

51	A48	5c green	6.50	25.00
52	A48	10c claret	3.50	25.00
53	A48	15c slate	4.25	25.00
54	A50	20c brn org	3.50	25.00
a.		Double overprint	450.00	
b.		Vertical pair, one without overprint	2,000.	
55	A49	25c blue	3.50	25.00
56	A49	40c brown	52.50	34.00
57	A49	50c violet	52.50	34.00
58	A49	60c carmine	52.50	50.00
a.		Diagonal overprint	725.00	
59	A49	85c chocolate	7.25	60.00
		Nos. 51-59 (9)	186.00	303.00
		Set, never hinged	450.00	

Map of Castellorizo; Flag of Italy — A1

1923

60	A1	5c gray green	6.50	34.00
61	A1	10c dull rose	6.50	34.00
62	A1	25c dull blue	6.50	34.00
63	A1	50c gray lilac	6.50	34.00
64	A1	1 l brown	6.50	34.00
		Nos. 60-64 (5)	32.50	170.00
		Set, never hinged	72.00	

Italian Stamps of 1901-20 Overprinted

1924

65	A48	5c green	2.75	32.50
66	A48	10c claret	2.75	32.50
67	A48	15c slate	2.75	42.50
68	A50	20c brn orange	2.75	42.50
a.		Double overprint	150.00	
69	A49	25c blue	2.75	32.50
70	A49	40c brown	2.75	32.50
71	A49	50c violet	2.75	42.50
72	A49	60c carmine	2.75	50.00
a.		Double overprint	475.00	
73	A49	85c red brown	2.75	60.00
74	A46	1 l brn & green	2.75	60.00
		Nos. 65-74 (10)	27.50	427.50
		Set, never hinged	52.50	

Ferrucci Issue
Types of Italian Stamps of 1930, Overprinted in Red or Blue

1930   Wmk. Crowns (140)

75	A102	20c violet	10.00	10.00
76	A103	25c dark green	10.00	24.00
77	A103	50c black	10.00	10.00
78	A103	1.25 l deep blue	10.00	24.00
79	A104	5 l + 2 l dp car (Bl)	32.50	85.00
		Nos. 75-79 (5)	72.50	153.00
		Set, never hinged	180.00	

Garibaldi Issue
Types of Italian Stamps of 1932, Overprinted like Nos. 75-79 in Red or Blue

1932

80	A138	10c brown	25.00	50.00
81	A138	20c red brn (Bl)	25.00	50.00
82	A138	25c dp grn	25.00	50.00
83	A138	30c bluish slate	25.00	50.00
84	A138	50c red vio (Bl)	25.00	50.00
85	A141	75c cop red (Bl)	25.00	50.00
86	A141	1.25 l dull blue	25.00	50.00
87	A141	1.75 l + 25c brn	25.00	50.00
88	A144	2.55 l + 50c org (Bl)	25.00	50.00
89	A145	5 l + 1 l dl vio	25.00	50.00
		Nos. 80-89 (10)	250.00	500.00
		Set, never hinged	625.00	

CAYMAN ISLANDS
ˌkā-ˈman ˈī-lənds

LOCATION — Three islands in the Caribbean Sea, about 200 miles northwest of Jamaica
GOVT. — British Crown Colony, formerly a dependency of Jamaica
AREA — 100 sq. mi.
POP. — 39,335 (1999 est.)
CAPITAL — George Town, located on Grand Cayman

12 Pence = 1 Shilling
20 Shilling = 1 Pound
100 Cents = 1 Dollar (1969)

Watermark

Wmk. 362 — Basotho Hat Multiple

> Catalogue values for unused stamps in this country are for Never Hinged items, beginning with Scott 112.

Victoria A1   Edward VII A2

1900   Typo.   Wmk. 2   Perf. 14

1	A1	½p pale green	7.00	22.50
2	A1	1p carmine rose	7.00	3.75

1901-03

3	A2	½p green ('02)	6.00	32.50
4	A2	1p car rose ('03)	13.00	11.50
5	A2	2½p ultramarine	13.00	11.50
6	A2	6p chocolate	40.00	77.50
7	A2	1sh brown orange	80.00	140.00
		Nos. 3-7 (5)	152.00	277.50

1905   Wmk. 3

8	A2	½p green	8.50	11.50
9	A2	1p carmine rose	17.00	22.50
10	A2	2½p ultramarine	8.50	4.25
11	A2	6p chocolate	20.00	50.00
12	A2	1sh brown orange	40.00	62.50
		Nos. 8-12 (5)	94.00	150.75

For surcharge see No. 17.

1907, Mar. 13

13	A2	4p brown & blue	40.00	75.00
14	A2	6p ol green & rose	40.00	87.50
15	A2	1sh violet & green	70.00	110.00
16	A2	5sh ver & green	240.00	375.00
		Nos. 13-16 (4)	390.00	647.50

Numerals of 4p, 1sh and 5sh of type A2 are in color on colorless tablet.
For surcharges see Nos. 18-20.

Nos. 9, 16, 13 Handstamped

No. 17   No. 18

No. 19   No. 20

1907-08

17	A2	½p on 1p	60.00	100.00
18	A2	½p on 5sh	350.00	575.00
a.		Inverted surcharge	57,500.	
b.		Double surcharge	12,750.	12,750.
c.		Double surcharge, one inverted		
d.		Pair, one without surcharge	75,000.	
19	A2	1p on 5sh	375.00	575.00
a.		Double surcharge	22,500.	20,000.
b.		Double surcharge, inverted	150,000.	
20	A2	2½p on 4p ('08)	2,000.	3,750.
a.		Double surcharge	45,000.	24,000.

No. 19b is unique. It exists on the upper left stamp in an upper left corner margin plate no. 1 block of four that is lightly hinged in the top margin only.

The 1p on 4p is a revenue stamp not authorized for postal use, although postally used examples exist. Value for unused is about $300.

A3   A4

1907-09   Perf. 14

21	A3	½p green	3.50	5.50
22	A3	1p carmine rose	2.10	1.10
23	A3	2½p ultramarine	4.75	5.25

Chalky Paper

24	A3	3p violet, yellow	4.50	9.75
25	A3	4p blk & red, yel	67.50	100.00
26	A3	6p purple & br pur	13.50	52.50
27	A3	1sh black, grn	11.00	32.50
28	A3	5sh grn & red, yel	52.50	90.00
		Nos. 21-28 (8)	159.35	296.60

Issued: ½p, 1p, 12/27/07; 2½p, 3p, 4p, 5sh, 3/30/08; 6d, 10/2/08; 1sh, 4/5/09.
Forged cancellations are found on No. 28.

1908, Mar. 30   Wmk. 2

29	A3	1sh black, green	85.00	125.00
30	A3	10sh grn & red, grn	225.00	400.00

Numerals of 3p, 4p, 1sh and 5sh of type A3 are in color on plain tablet.
Forged cancellations are found on No. 30.

1908   Wmk. 3
Ordinary Paper

31	A4	¼p brown	6.00	1.00

King George V
A5   A6

1912-20

32	A5	¼p brown ('13)	1.25	.50
33	A5	½p green	3.25	6.00
34	A5	1p carmine ('13)	4.00	3.00
35	A5	2p gray	1.25	12.50
36	A5	2½p ultra ('14)	8.50	13.50

Chalky Paper

37	A5	3p vio, yel ('13)	3.00	22.50
38	A5	4p blk & red, yel ('13)	1.25	12.50
39	A5	6p vio & red vio ('13)	4.50	9.00
40	A5	1sh blk, grn ('13)	4.25	32.50
41	A5	2sh vio & ultra, bl	14.50	57.50
42	A5	3sh green & vio	22.50	77.50
43	A5	5sh grn & red, yel ('14)	90.00	190.00
44	A5	10sh grn & red, bl grn, olive back ('18)	125.00	225.00
a.		10sh green & red, grn ('13)	100.00	175.00
		Nos. 32-44 (13)	283.25	662.00

The first printings of the 3p, 1sh and 10sh have a white back.
For surcharges, see Nos. MR1-MR7.

1913, Nov. 19
Surface-colored Paper

45	A5	3p violet, yel	4.25	9.50
46	A5	1sh black, green	4.25	4.25
47	A5	10sh grn & red, grn	100.00	175.00
		Nos. 45-47 (3)	108.50	188.75

Numeral of ¼p, 2p, 3p, 4p, 1sh, 2sh, 3sh and 5sh of type A5 are in color on plain tablet.

1921-26   Wmk. 4   Perf. 14

50	A6	¼p yel brown	.60	1.75
51	A6	½p gray green	.60	.35
52	A6	1p rose red	1.75	1.00
53	A6	1½p orange brn	2.10	.35
54	A6	2p gray	2.10	4.75
55	A6	2½p ultramarine ('22)	.60	.60
56	A6	3p violet, yel	1.25	4.75
57	A6	4½p olive grn	2.75	3.75
58	A6	6p claret	6.50	37.50
59	A6	1sh black, grn ('25)	11.50	37.50
60	A6	2sh violet, blue	17.00	29.00
61	A6	3sh violet	27.50	19.00
62	A6	5sh green, yel	29.00	25.00
63	A6	10sh car, green	72.50	100.00
		Nos. 50-63 (14)	175.75	295.30

Issued: 1½p, 4/4/21; ¼p, ½p, 1p, 2p, 2½p, 6p, 2sh, 3sh, 4/1/22; 3p, 4½p, 6/29/23; 5sh, 2/15/25; 1sh, 5/15/25; 10sh, 9/5/26.

1921-22   Wmk. 3

64	A6	3p violet, org	1.75	9.50
65	A6	4p red, yel	1.25	4.75
66	A6	1sh black, green	1.50	11.50
67	A6	5sh green, yel	19.00	85.00
68	A6	10sh car, green	72.50	125.00
		Nos. 64-68 (5)	96.00	235.75

Issued: 4p, 4/1/22; others, 4/4/21.

King William IV, King George V A7

Perf. 12½
1932, Dec. 5   Wmk. 4   Engr.

69	A7	¼p brown	1.90	1.40
70	A7	½p green	3.25	10.50
71	A7	1p carmine	3.25	10.50
72	A7	1½p orange	3.25	3.75
73	A7	2p gray	3.25	4.75
74	A7	2½p ultramarine	3.25	2.00
75	A7	3p olive green	4.00	6.75
76	A7	6p red violet	11.50	30.00
77	A7	1sh brn & black	20.00	42.50
78	A7	2sh ultra & blk	55.00	100.00
79	A7	5sh green & blk	100.00	160.00
80	A7	10sh car & black	350.00	475.00
		Nos. 69-80 (12)	558.65	847.15
		Set, never hinged		1,225.

Centenary of the formation of the Cayman Islands Assembly.

Common Design Types pictured following the introduction.

Silver Jubilee Issue
Common Design Type
1935, May 6   Perf. 13½x14

81	CD301	½p green & black	.35	1.50
82	CD301	2½p blue & brown	1.60	1.50
83	CD301	6p ol grn & lt bl	1.60	4.75
84	CD301	1sh brt vio & ind	11.00	10.00
		Nos. 81-84 (4)	14.55	17.75
		Set, never hinged		22.50

King George V A8

Catboat A9

Red-footed Boobies A10

Conches and Coconut Palms — A11

Hawksbill Turtles A12

1935-36   Perf. 12½

85	A8	¼p brown & blk	.60	1.25
86	A9	½p yel grn & ultra	1.25	1.25
87	A10	1p car & ultra	5.00	3.00
88	A11	1½p org & black	1.75	2.40
89	A9	2p brown vio & ultra	4.50	1.50
90	A12	2½p dp blue & blk	4.00	1.60
91	A8	3p ol grn & blk	3.00	3.75
92	A12	6p red vio & blk	10.50	6.00
93	A9	1sh org & black	7.25	9.25
94	A10	2sh black & ultra	55.00	50.00
95	A12	5sh green & blk	60.00	70.00
96	A11	10sh car & black	125.00	140.00
		Nos. 85-96 (12)	277.85	290.00
		Set, never hinged		525.00

Issued: #86, 2½p, 6p, 1sh, 1/1/36; others, 5/1/35.

Coronation Issue
Common Design Type
1937, May 13   Perf. 11x11½

97	CD302	½p deep green	.20	1.50
98	CD302	1p dark carmine	.25	.25
99	CD302	2½p deep ultra	.55	.55
		Nos. 97-99 (3)	1.00	2.30
		Set, never hinged		2.25

Beach View, Grand Cayman A13

Dolphin — A14

Hawksbill Turtles — A16

Map of the Islands A15

Cayman Schooner A17

Perf. 12½; 11½x13 or 13x11½ (A14, #111); 14 (#104, 107)
1938-43   Engr.

100	A13	¼p red orange	.55	.75
a.		Perf. 13½x12½ ('43)	.20	.85
101	A14	½p yel green	.85	.75
a.		Perf. 14 ('43)	1.10	1.75
102	A15	1p carmine	.20	1.00
103	A13	1½p black	.20	.20
104	A16	2p dp violet ('43)	.50	.35
a.		Perf. 11½x13	2.50	.30
105	A17	2½p ultra	.30	.20
106	A15	3p orange	.30	.20
107	A16	6p dk ol grn ('43)	2.50	2.50
a.		Perf. 11½x13	7.25	5.25
108	A14	1sh reddish brown	5.75	2.00
a.		Perf. 14 ('43)	3.75	2.50
109	A13	2sh green	24.00	18.00
110	A17	5sh deep rose	27.50	19.00
111	A16	10sh dark brown	19.00	12.00
a.		Perf. 14 ('43)	19.00	12.00
		Nos. 100-111 (12)	81.65	56.95
		Set, never hinged		135.00

See Nos. 114-115.

Catalogue values for unused stamps in this section, from this point to the end of the section, are for Never Hinged items.

Peace Issue
Common Design Type
1946, Aug. 26   Wmk. 4   Perf. 13½

112	CD303	1½p black	.25	.20
113	CD303	3p orange	.25	.20

Types of 1938
1947, Aug. 25   Perf. 12½

114	A17	2½p orange	3.50	.65
115	A15	3p ultramarine	3.50	.45

Silver Wedding Issue
Common Design Types
1948, Nov. 29   Photo.   Perf. 14x14½

116	CD304	½p dark green	.25	.90

Perf. 11½x11
Engr.; Name Typo.

117	CD305	10sh blue violet	25.00	25.00

UPU Issue
Common Design Types
Engr.; Name Typo. on #119, 120
1949, Oct. 10   Perf. 13½, 11x11½

118	CD306	2½p orange	.40	1.00
119	CD307	3p indigo	1.90	2.50
120	CD308	6p olive	.85	2.50
121	CD309	1sh red brown	.85	.40
		Nos. 118-121 (4)	4.00	6.40

Catboat A18

Designs: ½p, Coconut grove. 1p, Green turtle. 1½p, Thatch rope industry. 2p, Caymanian seamen. 2½p, Map. 3p, Parrot fish. 6p, Bluff, Cayman Brac. 9p, George Town harbor. 1sh, Turtle "crawl". 2sh, Cayman schooner. 5sh, Boat-building. 10sh, Government offices.

Perf. 11½x11
1950, Oct. 2   Wmk. 4   Engr.

122	A18	¼p rose red & blue	.20	.80
123	A18	½p bl grn & red violet	.20	1.75
124	A18	1p dp blue & olive	.75	1.00
125	A18	1½p choc & bl grn	.45	1.00
126	A18	2p rose car & vio	1.75	2.00
127	A18	2½p sepia & aqua	1.75	.85
128	A18	3p bl & blue grn	2.10	2.00
129	A18	6p dp bl & org brn	2.50	1.75
130	A18	9p dk grn & rose red	10.50	2.50
131	A18	1sh red org & brn	4.50	3.75
132	A18	2sh red vio & vio	11.50	14.50
133	A18	5sh vio & olive	17.00	9.50
134	A18	10sh rose red & blk	22.50	10.00
		Nos. 122-134 (13)	75.70	60.40

Types of 1950 with Portrait of Queen Elizabeth II and

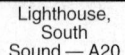

Lighthouse, South Sound — A20

Elizabeth II and Turtles — A21

Perf. 11½x11, 11x11½
1953-59   Engr.

135	A18	¼p rose red & bl	1.40	.80
136	A18	½p bl grn & red vio	1.10	.75
137	A18	1p dp bl & olive	1.00	.70
138	A18	1½p choc & bl grn	.75	.35
139	A18	2p rose car & vio	3.50	1.40
140	A18	2½p black & aqua	4.25	1.25
141	A18	3p blue & bl grn	5.25	1.00
142	A20	4p dp blue & black	2.50	.70
143	A18	6p dp bl & red brn	2.10	.30
144	A18	9p dk green & rose red	8.50	.40
145	A18	1sh red org & brn	4.75	.40
146	A18	2sh red vio & vio	16.00	11.50
147	A18	5sh violet & olive	17.50	10.00

148	A18	10sh rose red & blk	19.00	11.50
149	A21	£1 bright blue	37.50	16.00
		Nos. 135-149 (15)	125.10	57.05

Issued: 4p, 3/2; 2p, 2½p, 9p, 6/2/54; ½p, 1p, 1½p, 6p, 7/7/54; ¼p, 3p, 1sh-10sh, 2/21/55; £1, 1/6/59.

Coronation Issue
Common Design Type
1953, June 2   Perf. 13½x13

150	CD312	1p brt green & black	.40	1.00

Arms of Cayman Islands A22

Perf. 12
1959, July 4   Wmk. 4   Photo.

151	A22	2½p dull blue & blk	.70	1.25
152	A22	1sh red orange & blk	.80	.50

Granting of a new constitution.

Cayman Parrot — A23

Catboat A24

1½p, Orchid. 2p, Map of Islands. 2½p, Fisherman casting net. 3p, West Bay Beach. 4p, Green turtle. 6p, Cayman schooner. 9p, Angler with kingfish. 1sh, Iguana. 1sh3p, Swimming pool, Cayman Brac. 1sh9p, Girl and sailboat. 5sh, Fort George. 10sh, Coat of Arms. £1, Queen Elizabeth II.

Perf. 11x11½, 11½x11
1962, Nov. 28   Wmk. 314   Engr.

153	A23	¼p rose red & ember	1.00	1.50
154	A24	1p olive & black	.85	.40
155	A24	1½p purple & yel	4.25	1.25
156	A24	2p sepia & blue	1.10	.50
157	A24	2½p green & vio	.85	1.50
158	A24	3p car & blue	.40	.40
159	A24	4p pur & green	1.40	.95
160	A24	6p sepia & green	3.25	.55
161	A24	9p pur & vio bl	2.25	.85
162	A24	1sh rose & sepia	.85	.20
163	A24	1sh3p brn org & lt grn	3.75	3.50
164	A24	1sh9p vio & bl grn	15.00	2.25
165	A24	5sh grn & dl pur	11.50	9.50
166	A23	10sh blue & olive	21.00	13.00
167	A23	£1 blk & car rose	21.00	24.00
		Revenue cancel		.80
		Nos. 153-167 (15)	88.45	60.35

Freedom from Hunger Issue
Common Design Type
1963, June 4   Photo.   Perf. 14x14½

168	CD314	1sh9p car rose	.65	.30

Red Cross Centenary Issue
Common Design Type
Wmk. 314
1963, Sept. 2   Litho.   Perf. 13

169	CD315	1p black & red	.25	.20
170	CD315	1sh9p ultra & red	1.25	.90

Shakespeare Issue
Common Design Type
1964, Apr. 23   Photo.   Perf. 14x14½

171	CD316	6p deep lilac rose	.45	.30

ITU Issue
Common Design Type
1965, May 17   Litho.   Wmk. 314

172	CD317	1p ultra & red lil	.20	.20
173	CD317	1sh3p rose lil & grn	.90	.75

Intl. Cooperation Year Issue
Common Design Type
1965, Oct. 25   Wmk. 314   Perf. 14½
174 CD318 1p blue grn & claret   .30 .20
175 CD318 1sh lt vio & green   .70 .70

Churchill Memorial Issue
Common Design Type
1966, Jan. 24   Photo.   Perf. 14
Design in Black, Gold and Carmine Rose
176 CD319 ¼p bright blue   .35 1.50
177 CD319 1p green   .60 .50
178 CD319 1sh brown   1.10 .65
179 CD319 1sh9p violet   2.00 .90
    Nos. 176-179 (4)   4.05 3.55

Royal Visit Issue
Common Design Type
1966, Feb. 4   Litho.   Perf. 11x12
180 CD320 1p violet blue   .85 .30
181 CD320 1sh9p dk car rose 3.50 1.50

World Cup Soccer Issue
Common Design Type
1966, July 1   Litho.   Perf. 14
182 CD321 1½p multicolored   .20 .20
183 CD321 1sh9p multicolored .65 .65

WHO Headquarters Issue
Common Design Type
1966, Sept. 20   Litho.   Perf. 14
184 CD322 2p multicolored   .80 .30
185 CD322 1sh3p multicolored 1.90 1.10

UNESCO Anniversary Issue
Common Design Type
1966, Dec. 1   Litho.   Perf. 14
186 CD323 1p "Education"   .20 .20
187 CD323 1sh9p "Science"   1.10 .35
188 CD323 5sh "Culture"   2.25 1.10
    Nos. 186-188 (3)   3.55 1.65

Telephone and Map of Caymans — A25

Perf. 14½x14
1966, Dec. 5   Litho.   Wmk. 314
189 A25 4p multicolored   .20 .20
190 A25 9p multicolored   .30 .30
Linking of the Cayman telephone system with the intl. system.

BAC 1-11 Jet Liner over Schooner — A26

1966, Dec. 17
191 A26 1sh blue, ol & black .40 .40
192 A26 1sh9p ultra, grn & sepia .85 .85
Opening of the Grand Cayman Airport jet service.

Water Skiing and ITY Emblem A27

ITY Emblem and: 6p, Skin diving. 1sh, Sport fishing. 1sh9p, Sailing.

Perf. 14½x14
1967, Dec. 1   Photo.   Wmk. 314
193 A27 4p multi & gold   .45 .20
a.   Gold omitted   250.00 225.00

194 A27 6p multi & gold   .45 .25
195 A27 1sh multi & gold   .45 .40
196 A27 1sh9p multi & gold .65 .75
    Nos. 193-196 (4)   2.00 1.60
International Tourist Year.

Human Rights Flame and Freed Slaves A28

1968, June 3   Photo.   Wmk. 314
197 A28 3p slate bl, grn & gold .20 .20
198 A28 9p lt brn, grn & gold .20 .20
199 A28 5sh ultra, grn & gold .70 .70
    Nos. 197-199 (3)   1.10 1.10
International Human Rights Year.

Long Jump A29

1sh3p, High jump. 2sh, Pole vault, vert.

1968, Oct. 1   Litho.   Perf. 13½
200 A29 1sh multicolored   .20 .20
201 A29 1sh3p multicolored .25 .25
202 A29 2sh yellow & multi .40 .40
    Nos. 200-202 (3)   .85 .85
19th Olympic Games, Mexico City, 10/12-27.

Adoration of Shepherds, by Carel Fabritius — A30

Christmas: 1p, 8p, 2sh, Adoration of the Shepherds, by Rembrandt.

Perf. 14x14½
1968, Nov. 18   Photo.   Wmk. 314
203 A30 ¼p brown & multi   .20 .20
a.   Gold omitted   250.00
204 A30 1p violet & multi   .20 .20
205 A30 6p multicolored   .20 .20
206 A30 8p car & multi   .20 .20
207 A30 1sh3p multicolored .30 .30
208 A30 2sh gray & multi   .45 .45
    Nos. 203-208 (6)   1.55 1.55

1969, Jan. 8   Unwmk.
209 A30 ¼p red lilac & multi .75 .35

Grand Cayman Thrush A31

1p, Brahman cattle. 2p, Blowholes on coast. 2½p, Map of Grand Cayman. 3p, Town scene in George Town. 4p, Royal poinciana. 6p, Map of Cayman Brac and Little Cayman. 8p, Motor vessels at berth. 1sh, Basket making. 1sh3p, Beach scene. 1sh6p, Rope making. 2sh, Barracudas. 4sh, Government House. 10sh, Coat of arms. £1, Queen Elizabeth II.

Unwmk.
1969, June 5   Litho.   Perf. 14
210 A31 ¼p multi   .20 .90
211 A31 1p multi   .20 .20
212 A31 2p multi   .20 .20
213 A31 2½p multi .20 .20
214 A31 3p multi   .20 .20
215 A31 4p multi   .20 .20
216 A31 6p multi   .20 .20
217 A31 8p multi   .20 .20
218 A31 1sh multi   .25 .20
219 A31 1sh3p multi .30 1.90
220 A31 1sh6p multi .40 1.90
221 A31 2sh multi   1.50 1.40
222 A31 4sh multi   .70 1.40

223 A31 10sh multi, vert. 1.50 2.50
224 A31 £1 multi, vert.   3.50 3.50
    Nos. 210-224 (15)   9.75 15.10
See #262-276. For surcharges see #227-241.

1969, Aug. 11   Wmk. 314 Sideways
225 A31 ¼p multicolored   .70 .70

Type of 1969 Surcharged

1969, Sept. 8   Wmk. 314   Perf. 14
227 A31 ¼c on ¼p multi   .20 .85
228 A31 1c on 1p multi   .20 .25
229 A31 2c on 2p multi   .20 .25
230 A31 3c on 4p multi   .20 .25
231 A31 4c on 2½p multi .20 .25
232 A31 5c on 6p multi   .20 .25
233 A31 7c on 8p multi   .20 .25
234 A31 8c on 3p multi   .20 .25
235 A31 10c on 1s multi .35 .25
236 A31 12c on 1sh3p multi .50 1.90
237 A31 15c on 1sh6p multi .65 1.25
238 A31 20c on 2sh multi 2.25 2.10
239 A31 40c on 4sh multi .65 1.25
240 A31 $1 on 10sh multi 1.60 3.75
241 A31 $2 on £1 multi   2.50 4.50
    Nos. 227-241 (15)   10.10 17.60
The surcharge is arranged differently on various denominations.

Madonna and Child, by Alvise Vivarini — A32

1969, Nov. 4   Photo.   Perf. 14
242 A32 ¼c blue & multi   .20 .20
243 A32 ¼c emer & multi   .20 .20
244 A32 ¼c red org & multi .20 .20
245 A32 ¼c brt pink & multi .20 .20
246 A32 1c vio blue & multi .20 .20
247 A32 5c red org & multi .20 .20
248 A32 7c dk green & multi .20 .20
249 A32 12c emer & multi   .20 .20
250 A32 20c multicolored   .20 .20
    Nos. 242-250 (9)   1.80 1.80

"Noli me Tangere," by Titian — A33

Christmas: 1c, 7c, 20c, The Adoration of the Kings, by Jan Gossaert.

1970, Mar. 23   Litho.   Unwmk.
251 A33 ¼c dull grn & multi .20 .20
252 A33 ¼c dk car & multi .20 .20
253 A33 ¼c violet & multi   .20 .20
254 A33 ¼c bister & multi .20 .20
255 A33 10c vio blue & multi .20 .20
256 A33 12c red brn & multi .25 .25
257 A33 40c brn vio & multi .60 .60
    Nos. 251-257 (7)   1.85 1.85
Easter.

Barnaby from "Barnaby Rudge" by Dickens (1812-70), English Novelist — A34

Characters from Charles Dickens: 12c, Sairey Gamp, from "Martin Chuzzlewit." 20c, Mr. Micawber and David, from "David Copperfield." 40c, The Marchioness from "The Old Curiosity Shop."

1970, June 17   Photo.   Perf. 14½x14
258 A34 1c ol green, yel & blk .20 .20
259 A34 12c red brn, brick red & black .20 .20
260 A34 20c dk ol bister, gold & black .35 .35
261 A34 40c dp ultra, lt bl & blk .75 .75
    Nos. 258-261 (4)   1.50 1.50

Type of Regular Issue 1969 Values in Cents and Dollars

Designs: ¼c, Grand Cayman thrush. 1c, Brahman cattle. 2c, Blowholes on coast. 3c, Royal poinciana. 4c, Map of Grand Cayman. 5c, Map of Cayman Brac and Little Cayman. 7c, Motor vessels at berth. 8c, Town scene in George Town. 10c, Basket making. 12c, Beach scene. 15c, Rope making. 20c, Barracudas. 40c, Government House. $1, Coat of arms, vert. $2, Queen Elizabeth II, vert.

Wmk. 314
1970, Sept. 8   Litho.   Perf. 14
262 A31 ¼c multicolored   .60 .30
263 A31 1c multicolored   .20 .20
264 A31 2c multicolored   .20 .20
265 A31 3c multicolored   .25 .20
266 A31 4c multicolored   .25 .20
267 A31 5c multicolored   .45 .20
268 A31 7c multicolored   .40 .20
269 A31 8c multicolored   .40 .20
270 A31 10c multicolored   .40 .20
271 A31 12c multicolored   1.40 1.10
272 A31 15c multicolored   1.60 3.50
273 A31 20c multicolored   3.75 1.75
274 A31 40c multicolored   1.25 1.25
275 A31 $1 multicolored   1.60 5.75
276 A31 $2 multicolored   2.40 5.75
    Nos. 262-276 (15)   15.15 21.00

The Three Wise Men A35

Christmas: 1c, 10c, 20c, Nativity and globe.

1970, Oct. 8   Litho.   Perf. 14
277 A35 ¼c brt grn & yel grn .20 .20
278 A35 1c bl grn, yel grn & blk .20 .20
279 A35 5c dp claret & org .20 .20
280 A35 10c red org, yel & blk .20 .20
281 A35 12c ultra & lt grnsh bl .20 .20
282 A35 20c grn, yel grn & blk .25 .25
    Nos. 277-282 (6)   1.25 1.25

Grand Cayman Terrapin A36

Cayman Islands Turtles: 7c, Green turtle. 12c, Hawksbill turtle. 20c, Turtle farm.

1971, Jan. 28   Perf. 14x14½
283 A36 5c multicolored   .85 .50
284 A36 7c multicolored   1.10 .50
285 A36 12c multicolored   2.25 .60
286 A36 20c multicolored   3.75 3.50
    Nos. 283-286 (4)   7.95 5.10

Dendrophylax Fawcetii — A37

Adoration of the Kings, 15th Century — A38

Wild Orchids of West Indies: 2c, Schomburgkia thomsoniana. 10c, Vanilla claviculata. 40c, Oncidium variegatum.

1971, Apr. 7   Wmk. 314   Perf. 14
287	A37	¼c brown & multi	.35	1.60
288	A37	2c ol green & multi	1.00	1.25
289	A37	10c gray bl & multi	3.75	1.00
290	A37	40c lt violet & multi	7.00	5.00
		Nos. 287-290 (4)	12.10	8.85

1971, Sept. 27   Perf. 14

Christmas: 1c, 15c, Nativity (detail), Paris, 14th cent. 5c, 20c, Adoration of the Kings (detail), Burgundian, 15th cent.

291	A38	¼c gold & multi	.20	.20
292	A38	1c gold & multi	.20	.20
293	A38	5c gold & multi	.20	.20
294	A38	12c gold & multi	.20	.20
295	A38	15c gold & multi	.30	.30
296	A38	20c gold & multi	.40	.40
a.		Souvenir sheet of 6, #291-296	4.75	4.75
		Nos. 291-296 (6)	1.50	1.50

Underwater Cable, Turtle and Telephone — A39

1972, Jan. 10
297	A39	5c multicolored	.25	.25
298	A39	10c multicolored	.25	.25
299	A39	40c multicolored	1.25	1.25
		Nos. 297-299 (3)	1.75	1.75

Coaxial cable for world communications.

Courthouse — A40

Designs: 15c, 40c, Legislative Assembly Building, George Town.

1972, Aug. 15   Perf. 13½x14
300	A40	5c dp car & multi	.20	.20
301	A40	15c lilac rose & multi	.20	.20
302	A40	25c dull grn & multi	.30	.30
303	A40	40c dk blue & multi	.50	.50
a.		Souvenir sheet of 4, #300-303	1.25	1.25
		Nos. 300-303 (4)	1.20	1.20

New Cayman Islands government buildings.

Silver Wedding Issue, 1972
Common Design Type

Design: Queen Elizabeth II, Prince Philip, hawksbill turtle and conch.

1972, Nov. 20   Photo.   Perf. 14x14½
304	CD324	12c vio black & multi	.40	.40
305	CD324	30c olive & multi	.75	.75

$1 Note and 1c Coin A41

6c, $5 note and 5c coin. 15c, $10 note and 10c coin. 25c, $25 note and 25c coin.

1973, Jan. 15
306	A41	3c emerald & multi	.20	.20
307	A41	6c yellow & multi	.30	.60
308	A41	15c lilac & multi	.75	.50
309	A41	25c orange & multi	1.50	.90
a.		Souvenir sheet of 4, #306-309	5.25	5.25
		Nos. 306-309 (4)	2.75	2.20

First Cayman Islands coinage and bank notes, May 1, 1972.

Last Supper A42

Stained Glass Windows: 10c, Christ Carrying Cross, vert. 12c, Resurrection, vert. 30c, Crucifixion.

Perf. 14½x14, 14x14½
1973, Apr. 11   Litho.
310	A42	10c pink & multi	.20	.20
311	A42	12c yel green & multi	.20	.20
312	A42	15c lt blue & multi	.30	.30
313	A42	30c yellow & multi	.40	.40
a.		Souvenir sheet of 4	1.60	1.60
		Nos. 310-313 (4)	1.10	1.10

Easter. No. 313a contains 4 stamps similar to Nos. 310-313 with simulated perforations.

Nativity — A43

White-winged Dove — A44

Christmas: 5c, 12c, 25c, Adoration of the Magi, from Breviary of Queen Isabella. 9c, 15c, Like 3c, Nativity from Sforza Book of Hours.

1973, Oct. 2   Perf. 14½
314	A43	3c dull green & multi	.20	.20
315	A43	5c dull pur & multi	.20	.20
316	A43	9c sepia & multi	.20	.20
317	A43	12c dk blue & multi	.20	.20
318	A43	15c dp rose & multi	.20	.20
319	A43	25c black & multi	.40	.40
		Nos. 314-319 (6)	1.40	1.40

Princess Anne's Wedding Issue
Common Design Type

1973, Nov. 14   Wmk. 314   Perf. 14
320	CD325	10c brt green & multi	.20	.20
321	CD325	30c lilac & multi	.30	.30

1974, Jan. 2   Litho.   Perf. 14x14½
322	A44	3c shown	2.75	.40
323	A44	10c Vitelline warblers	3.50	.40
324	A44	12c Greater Antillean grackles	3.50	.40
325	A44	20c West Indian red-bellied woodpecker	5.75	1.00
326	A44	30c Stripe-headed tanagers	7.25	2.25
327	A44	50c Yucatan vireos	9.75	6.25
		Nos. 322-327 (6)	32.50	10.70

See Nos. 354-359.

One-room Schoolhouse — A45

Designs: 20c, New comprehensive school. 30c, Creative Arts Center, Mona, Jamaica.

1974, May 1   Perf. 14
328	A45	12c multicolored	.20	.20
329	A45	20c multicolored	.20	.20
330	A45	30c multicolored	.30	.30
		Nos. 328-330 (3)	.70	.70

25th anniv. of the University College of the West Indies.

Hermit Crab and Pirate Gold A46

Coat of Arms — A47

Elizabeth II — A48

Designs: 3c, Pirate, treasure chest and lion's paw. 4c, Spotted scorpionfish and crown. 5c, Flint-lock pistol and brain coral. 6c, Blackbeard on Grand Cayman and green turtle. 8c, 9c, Jeweled pomander and porkfish. 10c, Spiny lobster and gold coins. 12c, Jeweled sword, dagger and sea fan. 15c, Cabrit's murex and jeweled necklace. 20c, Queen conch, pistol and gold cup. 25c, Hogfish and pirate chest. 40c, Gold chalice and sea whip.

Wmk. 314 Upright, Sideways (#331-332, 336, 344-345)
1974-75   Litho.   Perf. 14
331	A46	1c multi ('75)	5.00	1.75
a.		Wmk. upright	4.25	1.75
332	A46	3c multicolored	5.00	1.00
a.		Wmk. upright	5.50	1.00
333	A46	4c multicolored	.70	.95
334	A46	5c multicolored	4.25	1.00
335	A46	6c multicolored	.50	3.25
336	A46	8c multicolored	3.50	11.50
337	A46	9c multicolored	5.25	12.50
338	A46	10c multicolored	6.25	1.10
339	A46	12c multicolored	.50	2.25
340	A46	15c multicolored	.65	1.75
341	A46	20c multicolored	5.00	4.00
342	A46	25c multicolored	.65	.95
343	A46	40c multicolored	5.75	1.75
344	A47	$1 multicolored	4.00	4.50
345	A48	$2 multicolored	10.50	9.00
		Nos. 331-345 (15)	57.50	57.25

Issued: #332, 11/12; 8c, 12/16; #331, 9/29; others, 8/1.

1976-77   Wmk. 373
332b	A46	3c multicolored	1.40	5.50
333a	A46	4c multi ('77)	1.75	6.50
334a	A46	5c multi ('77)	9.00	8.25
336b	A46	8c multicolored	10.50	7.25
338b	A46	10c multicolored	4.00	5.50
341b	A46	20c multicolored	4.50	4.25
344a	A47	$1 multi ('77)	9.00	13.50
345b	A48	$2 multi ('77)	10.00	9.25
		Nos. 332b-345b (8)	50.15	60.00

Issued: 3c, 8c, 10c, 20c, $2, 9/3; 4c, 5c, $1, 10/19.

Design Smaller
Size: 40x25mm
Wmk. 373 (Sideways on 1c-40c)
1978-80
346	A46	1c multicolored	1.50	2.25
346A	A46	3c multicolored	1.25	.85
346B	A46	5c multi ('79)	3.25	4.75
347	A46	10c multicolored	2.50	1.25
347A	A46	20c multicolored	5.25	2.25
347B	A46	40c multi ('79)	21.00	30.00
347C	A47	$1 multi ('80)	26.00	11.00
348	A48	$2 multi ('80)	9.50	29.00
		Nos. 346-348 (8)	70.25	81.35

Issued: 1c, 3c, 3/16; 10c, 20c, 5/25; 5c, 12/11; $2, 4/3; $1, 7/30.

Sea Captain and Ship — A49

1974, Oct. 7   Wmk. 314   Perf. 14
349	A49	8c shown	.20	.20
350	A49	12c Thatch weaver	.25	.20
351	A49	55c Farmer	.55	.50
a.		Miniature sheet of 3, #349-351	2.00	2.50
		Nos. 349-351 (3)	1.00	.90

Arms of Cinque Ports and Lord Warden's Flag — A50

Churchill Coat of Arms — A51

1974, Nov. 30
352	A50	12c multicolored	.20	.20
353	A51	50c multicolored	.70	.70
a.		Souvenir sheet of 2, #352-353	1.10	1.25

Sir Winston Churchill (1874-1965).

Bird Type of 1974
Wmk. 314
1975, Jan. 1   Litho.   Perf. 14
354	A44	3c Yellow-shafted flicker	.80	.45
355	A44	10c West Indian tree duck	1.50	.45
356	A44	12c Yellow warblers	1.90	.70
357	A44	20c White-bellied dove	3.25	3.00
358	A44	30c Magnificent frigate bird	5.25	5.00
359	A44	50c Cayman amazon	6.25	11.50
a.		Wmk. 362 (Lesotho)	650.00	
		Nos. 354-359 (6)	18.95	21.10

Ivory Crosier with Crucifixion — A52

Design: 35c, Crucifixion, ivory and gilt. Designs show heads of 14th century French pastoral staffs.

Wmk. 314
1975, Mar. 24   Litho.   Perf. 14
360	A52	15c plum & multi	.20	.20
361	A52	35c gray & multi	.65	.65
a.		Souvenir sheet of 2, #360-361	1.10	1.10

Easter. No. 361a exists imperf.
See Nos. 366-367.

Israel Hands A53

Designs: Pirates and various scenes.

1975, July 25   Wmk. 314
362	A53	10c shown	.65	.20
363	A53	12c John Fenn	.65	.20
364	A53	20c Thomas Anstis	1.00	.45
365	A53	30c Edward Low	1.25	1.90
		Nos. 362-365 (4)	3.55	2.75

Easter Type of 1975

Designs after ivory carved pastoral staffs showing Virgin and Child with angels, French, 14th century.

Wmk. 373
1975, Oct. 31   Litho.   Perf. 14

366	A52	12c dk green & multi	.20 .20
367	A52	50c multicolored	.70 .70
a.		Souvenir sheet of 2, #366-367	1.50 1.90

Christmas.

Registered Letter with Nos. 1-2; Cayman Brac Government House and Sub Post Office — A54

Cayman Islands 1st postage stamps, 75th anniv.: 20c, Cayman Islands #1 and cancelation used 1890-94; 30c, #2, 20; 50c, #1-2.

1976, Mar. 12   Litho.   Perf. 13½x14

368	A54	10c lt blue & multi	.20 .20
369	A54	20c pink & multi	.25 .25
370	A54	30c multicolored	.40 .40
371	A54	50c yellow & multi	.60 .60
a.		Souvenir sheet of 4, #368-371	4.50 4.50
		Nos. 368-371 (4)	1.45 1.45

Seals of Georgia, Delaware and New Hampshire — A55

15c, Seals of SC, NJ, MD. 20c, Seals of VA, RI, MA. 25c, Seals of NY, CT, NC. 30c, Seal of PA, Liberty Bell and Great Seal of the US.

Wmk. 373
1976, May 29   Litho.   Perf. 14

372	A55	10c olive & multi	.40 .20
373	A55	15c blue & multi	.50 .20
374	A55	20c multicolored	.70 .30
375	A55	25c blue grn & multi	1.00 .60
376	A55	30c red brn & multi	1.25 .85
a.		Souvenir sheet of 5 + label	7.50 7.50
		Nos. 372-376 (5)	3.85 2.15

American Bicentennial. Nos. 372-376 printed in sheets of 5. No. 376a contains one each of Nos. 372-376 and corner label inscribed "USA 200."

French Class 470 Racing Dinghies — A56

Queen Elizabeth II — A57

Design: 50c, One racing dinghy.

1976, Aug. 16   Litho.   Perf. 14

377	A56	20c multicolored	.70 .45
378	A56	50c multicolored	1.25 1.25

21st Olympic Games, Montreal, Canada, July 17-Aug. 1.

Perf. 14x13½, 13½x14
1977, Feb. 7   Litho.   Wmk. 373

8c, Prince Charles, 1973 visit. 50c, Preparation for anointing ceremony, horiz.

379	A57	8c multicolored	.20 .20
380	A57	30c multicolored	.35 .30
381	A57	50c multicolored	.55 .50
		Nos. 379-381 (3)	1.10 1.00

25th anniv. of the reign of Elizabeth II.

Scuba Diving A58

10c, Divers examining underwater wreck. 20c, Fairy basslets (fish). 25c, Sergeant majors (fish).

1977, July 25   Perf. 13½

382	A58	5c multicolored	.25 .25
383	A58	10c multicolored	.30 .30
384	A58	20c multicolored	.60 .60
385	A58	25c multicolored	.80 .75
a.		Souvenir sheet of 4	4.00 4.00
		Nos. 382-385 (4)	1.95 1.90

Tourist publicity. No. 385a contains one each of Nos. 382-385, perf. 14½.

Composia Fidelissima — A59

Butterflies: 8c, Heliconius charitonius. 10c, Danaus gilippus. 15c, Agraulis vanillae. 20c, Junonia evarete. 30c, Anartia jatrophae.

1977, Dec. 2   Wmk. 373   Perf. 14x13

386	A59	5c multicolored	1.40 .20
387	A59	8c multicolored	1.50 .30
388	A59	10c multicolored	1.60 .35
389	A59	15c multicolored	2.10 .55
390	A59	20c multicolored	2.40 .60
391	A59	30c multicolored	2.75 1.10
		Nos. 386-391 (6)	11.75 3.10

Cruise Ship "Southward" A60

Designs: 5c, "Renaissance." 30c, New harbor, vert. 50c, "Daphne," vert.

1978, Jan. 23   Litho.   Perf. 14

392	A60	3c multicolored	.45 .20
393	A60	5c multicolored	.45 .20
394	A60	30c multicolored	1.40 .65
395	A60	50c multicolored	1.90 .95
		Nos. 392-395 (4)	4.20 2.00

New harbor and cruise ships.

Crucifixion, by Dürer — A61

Explorers, Singing Game — A62

Etchings by Dürer: 15c, Christ at Emmaus. 20c, Entry into Jerusalem. 30c, Christ washing Peter's feet.

1978, Mar. 20   Litho.   Perf. 12

396	A61	10c multicolored	.35 .20
397	A61	15c multicolored	.50 .30
398	A61	20c multicolored	.65 .40
399	A61	30c multicolored	.75 .55
a.		Souvenir sheet of 4, #396-399	7.00 7.00
		Nos. 396-399 (4)	2.25 1.45

Easter; Albrecht Dürer (1471-1528). Nos. 396-399 issued in sheets of 6.

1978, Apr. 25   Litho.   Perf. 14

10c, Girls' Brigade presenting flag. 20c, Guides studying Bible, playing guitar, tennis and volleyball. 50c, Guides setting table.

400	A62	3c multicolored	.20 .20
401	A62	10c multicolored	.45 .40
402	A62	20c multicolored	.75 .70
403	A62	50c multicolored	1.60 1.60
		Nos. 400-403 (4)	3.00 2.90

3rd Intl. Council Meeting of Girls' Brigade.

Elizabeth II Coronation Anniversary Issue
Common Design Types
Souvenir Sheet

1978, June 2   Unwmk.   Perf. 15

404		Sheet of 6	3.00 3.50
a.		CD326 30c Yale of Beaufort	.45 .45
b.		CD327 30c Elizabeth II	.45 .45
c.		CD328 30c Screech owl	.45 .45

No. 404 contains 2 se-tenant strips of Nos. 404a-404c, separated by horizontal gutter with commemorative and descriptive inscriptions.

A63

A63a

A63: 1c, Trumpetfish. 3c, Nassau grouper. 5c, French angelfish. 10c, Schoolmaster snappers. 20c, Banded butterflyfish. 50c, Black-bar soldierfish.

A63a: 3c, Four-eyed butterflyfish. 5c, Grey angel fish. 10c, Squirrelfish. 15c, Parrotfish. 20c, Spanish hogfish. 30c, Queen angelfish.

1978-79   Wmk. 373   Litho.   Perf. 14

405	A63	1c multicolored	.25 .20
406	A63	3c multicolored	.45 .20
407	A63a	3c multicolored	.40 .20
408	A63a	5c multicolored	.45 .20
409	A63	5c multicolored	.40 .20
412	A63a	10c multicolored	.75 .20
413	A63	10c multicolored	.75 .20
414	A63a	15c multicolored	.85 .35
415	A63	20c multicolored	1.10 .45
416	A63	20c multicolored	1.40 .45
417	A63a	30c multicolored	2.25 .70
418	A63	50c multicolored	3.50 1.10
		Nos. 405-418 (12)	12.55 4.45

Issued: design A63, 4/20/79; design A63a, 8/28/78.

Lockheed Lodestar — A64

Aircraft: 5c, Consolidated PBY. 10c, Vickers Viking. 15c, BAC1-11. 20c, Piper Cheyenne, HS 125 and Bell 47. 30c, BAC1-11.

1979, Feb. 5   Perf. 14½

420	A64	3c multicolored	.40 .20
421	A64	5c multicolored	.40 .20
422	A64	10c multicolored	.55 .20
423	A64	15c multicolored	1.00 .20
424	A64	20c multicolored	1.25 .45
425	A64	30c multicolored	1.75 .55
		Nos. 420-425 (6)	5.35 2.00

Opening of Owen Roberts Airport, 25th anniv.

Rowland Hill and No. 2 — A65

Sir Rowland Hill (1795-1879), originator of penny postage, and: 10c, Great Britain #132. 20c, Cayman Islands #149. 50c, Cayman Islands #20.

Perf. 13½x14½

1979, Aug. 15   Litho.

426	A65	5c multicolored	.20 .20
427	A65	10c multicolored	.20 .20
428	A65	20c multicolored	.60 .60
		Nos. 426-428 (3)	1.00 1.00

Souvenir Sheet

429	A65	50c multicolored	1.50 1.50

Flight into Egypt A66

Christmas: 20c, Shepherds, Star of Bethlehem. 30c, Nativity. 40c, Three Kings, Star of Bethlehem.

1979, Nov. 20   Litho.   Perf. 13½

430	A66	10c multicolored	.20 .20
431	A66	20c multicolored	.25 .20
432	A66	30c multicolored	.40 .20
433	A66	40c multicolored	.70 .30
		Nos. 430-433 (4)	1.55 .95

Bonaventure House, Rotary Emblem — A67

Perf. 14x13½, 13½x14

1980, Feb. 14   Litho.   Wmk. 373

434	A67	20c shown	.30 .20
435	A67	30c Paul P. Harris, vert.	.50 .25
436	A67	50c Anniversary emblem, vert.	.80 .50
		Nos. 434-436 (3)	1.60 .95

Rotary International, 75th anniversary.

Mailman, London 1980 Emblem A68

1980, May 6   Litho.   Perf. 14
437 A68 5c shown .20 .20
438 A68 10c Cat boat .20 .20
439 A68 15c Mounted mailman .25 .25
440 A68 30c Mail wagon .50 .35
441 A68 40c Mailman on bicycle .60 .45
442 A68 $1 Mail truck 1.25 .90
　Nos. 437-442 (6) 3.00 2.35

London '80 Intl. Stamp Exhib., May 6-14.

Queen Mother Elizabeth Birthday Issue
Common Design Type

1980, Aug. 4   Litho.   Perf. 14
443 CD330 20c multicolored .45 .45

Spondylus
Americanus
A69

1980, Aug. 12   Perf. 14½x14
444 A69 5c shown .95 .20
445 A69 10c Murex brevifrons .95 .30
446 A69 30c Cymatium femorale 1.90 .65
447 A69 50c Vasum muricatum 2.10 1.25
　Nos. 444-447 (4) 5.90 2.40

See Nos. 502-505, 518-521.

Lantana — A70

1980, Oct. 21   Litho.   Perf. 14
448 A70 5c shown .20 .20
449 A70 15c Bauhinia .35 .20
450 A70 30c Hibiscus .70 .30
451 A70 $1 Milk and wine lily 1.75 1.40
　Nos. 448-451 (4) 3.00 2.10

See Nos. 478-481.

Juvenile Tarpon
and Fire
Sponges — A71

1980, Dec. 9   Litho.   Perf. 13½x13
Without Imprint
452 A71 3c shown 1.40 2.25
453 A71 5c Mangrove root oysters 1.60 1.10
　d.　Wmk. 384 8.00 8.00
　e.　Wmk. 384, perf. 14 6.75 7.00
454 A71 10c Mangrove crab .65 1.10
　d.　Wmk. 384, perf. 14 10.00 9.75
455 A71 15c Lizard, crescent spot butterfly 1.40 2.25
456 A71 20c Tricolored heron 1.90 2.75
457 A71 30c Red mangrove flower .90 1.40
458 A71 40c Red mangrove seeds .95 1.60
459 A71 50c Waterhouse's leaf-nosed bat 1.60 2.25
460 A71 $1 Black-crowned night heron 7.00 7.50
461 A71 $2 Cayman Isls. arms 2.75 5.50
462 A71 $4 Queen Elizabeth II 5.25 7.25
　Nos. 452-462 (11) 25.40 34.95

Nos. 453d, 453e and 454d inscribed "1986" below design. Issued: #453d, 4/86; #453e, 454fa, 6/86.
Issued: #453a, 4/86; #453b, 454a, 6/86.

1982, June 14
Inscribed "1982"
452a A71 3c shown 5.00 4.00
453a A71 5c Mangrove root oysters 1.25 .90
454a A71 10c Mangrove crab 1.25 .90

455a A71 15c Lizard, crescent spot butterfly 4.50 2.00
456a A71 20c Tricolored heron 2.50 2.25
457a A71 30c Red mangrove flower 1.50 1.50
458a A71 40c Red mangrove seeds 1.50 1.50
459a A71 50c Waterhouse's leaf-nosed bat 2.00 2.00
460a A71 $1 Black-crowned night heron 6.00 5.00
461a A71 $2 Cayman Isls. arms 4.00 4.00
462a A71 $4 Queen Elizabeth II 9.00 9.00
　Nos. 452a-462a (11) 38.50 33.05

1984
Inscribed "1984"
453b A71 5c Mangrove root oysters 2.50 2.50

1985
Inscribed "1985"
453c A71 5c Mangrove root oysters 1.25 1.25
454c A71 10c Mangrove crab 1.25 1.25
455c A71 15c Lizard, crescent spot butterfly 4.50 4.50
456c A71 20c Tricolored heron 2.50 2.50
457c A71 30c Red mangrove flower 1.50 1.50
458c A71 40c Red mangrove seeds 1.50 1.50
459c A71 50c Waterhouse's leaf-nosed bat 2.00 2.00
460c A71 $1 Black-crowned night heron 6.00 5.00
461c A71 $2 Cayman Isls. arms 5.00 5.00
　Nos. 453c-461c (9) 25.50 24.50

Bread and
Wine — A72

1981, Mar. 17   Wmk. 373   Perf. 14
463 A72 3c shown .20 .20
464 A72 10c Crown of thorns .20 .20
465 A72 20c Crucifix .35 .35
466 A72 $1 Christ 1.00 1.10
　Nos. 463-466 (4) 1.75 1.85

Easter.

Wood
Slave
A73

1981, June 16   Litho.   Perf. 13½
467 A73 20c shown .45 .45
468 A73 30c Cayman iguana .70 .70
469 A73 40c Lion lizard .95 .95
470 A73 50c Freshwater turtle 1.10 1.10
　Nos. 467-470 (4) 3.20 3.20

Royal Wedding Issue
Common Design Type

1981, July 22   Litho.   Perf. 14
471 CD331 20c Bouquet .25 .25
472 CD331 30c Charles .40 .40
473 CD331 $1 Couple 1.00 1.00
　Nos. 471-473 (3) 1.65 1.65

Intl. Year
of the
Disabled
A74

1981, Sept. 29   Litho.   Perf. 14
474 A74 5c Scuba divers .20 .20
475 A74 15c Old School for Handicapped .25 .25
476 A74 20c New School for Handicapped .35 .35
477 A74 $1 Beach scene 1.75 1.75
　Nos. 474-477 (4) 2.55 2.55

Flower Type of 1980

1981, Oct. 20   Litho.   Perf. 14
478 A70 3c Bougainvillea .25 .20
479 A70 10c Morning glory .25 .20
480 A70 20c Wild amaryllis .55 .55
481 A70 $1 Cordia 3.00 3.00
　Nos. 478-481 (4) 4.05 3.95

TB Bacillus Centenary — A75

1982, Mar. 24   Litho.   Perf. 14½
482 A75 15c Koch, horizontal microscope .35 .35
483 A75 30c Koch, vert. .75 .75
484 A75 40c Microscope, vert. .90 .90
485 A75 50c Koch, diff., vert. 1.25 1.25
　Nos. 482-485 (4) 3.25 3.25

Princess Diana Issue
Common Design Type

1982, July 1   Litho.   Perf. 13
486 CD333 20c Arms .65 .40
487 CD333 30c Diana 1.10 .75
488 CD333 40c Wedding 1.25 .75
489 CD333 50c Portrait 4.00 1.50
　Nos. 486-489 (4) 7.00 3.40

Scouting
Year
A76

1982, Aug. 24   Wmk. 373   Perf. 14
490 A76 3c Pitching tent .30 .20
491 A76 20c Cooking .75 .75
492 A76 30c Troop 1.25 1.25
493 A76 50c Boating skills 1.75 1.75
　Nos. 490-493 (4) 4.05 3.95

Christmas
1982 — A77

Virgin and Child Paintings by Raphael.

1982, Oct. 26   Perf. 14½
494 A77 3c multicolored .20 .20
495 A77 10c multicolored .35 .35
496 A77 20c multicolored .70 .70
497 A77 30c multicolored 1.00 1.00
　Nos. 494-497 (4) 2.25 2.25

Representative Govt.
Sesquicentennial — A78

1982, Nov. 9   Litho.   Wmk. 373
498 A78 3c Mace .20 .20
499 A78 10c Old Courthouse .20 .20
500 A78 20c Commonwealth Parliamentary Assoc. arms .45 .45
501 A78 30c Legislative Assembly building .75 .75
　Nos. 498-501 (4) 1.60 1.60

Shell Type of 1980

1983, Jan. 11   Litho.   Perf. 13½
502 A69 5c Natica canrena .30 .30
503 A69 10c Cassis tuberosa .50 .50
504 A69 20c Strombus gallus 1.10 1.10
505 A69 $1 Cypraecassis testiculus 4.50 4.50
　Nos. 502-505 (4) 6.40 6.40

Visit of
Queen
Elizabeth
II and
Prince
Philip
A79

1983, Feb. 15   Litho.   Perf. 1
506 A79 20c Legislative Building, Cayman Brac .60 .6
507 A79 30c Leg. Bldg., Grand Cayman 1.00 .9
508 A79 50c Prince Philip 1.75 1.5
509 A79 $1 Queen Elizabeth II 3.00 3.0
　a.　Souvenir sheet of 4, #506-509 7.50 7.5
　Nos. 506-509 (4) 6.35 6.0

A80

1983, Mar. 14
510 A80 3c Globe .30 .2
511 A80 15c Flags .70 .6
512 A80 20c Fisherman .80 .7
513 A80 40c Elizabeth II 1.25 .9
　Nos. 510-513 (4) 3.05 2.4

Commonwealth Day.

Manned Flight Bicentenary and
Mosquito Research and Control
Unit — A81

Airplanes.

1983, Oct. 10   Litho.   Perf. 14½
514 A81 3c MRCU Cessna 1.10 .7
515 A81 10c Consolidated Catalina PBY 1.25 .7
516 A81 20c Boeing 727 2.10 2.1
517 A81 40c Hawker Siddeley HS-748 3.00 3.7
　Nos. 514-517 (4) 7.45 7.2

Shell Type of 1980

1984, Jan. 18   Perf. 14x14½
518 A69 3c Natica floridana 1.50 .4
519 A69 10c Conus austini 1.75 .4
520 A69 30c Colubrania obscura 5.00 5.0
521 A69 50c Turbo cailletii 5.25 5.2
　Nos. 518-521 (4) 13.50 11.0

Lloyd's List Issue
Common Design Type

1984, May 16   Litho.   Perf. 1
522 CD335 5c Cruise ship .75 .2
523 CD335 10c The Old Harbor .85 .3
524 CD335 25c Ridgefield 1.60 1.6
525 CD335 50c Goldfield 3.25 3.2
　Nos. 522-525 (4) 6.45 5.3

Souvenir Sheet
526 CD335 $1 Goldfield, diff. 4.00 4.00

No. 525 Overprinted:
"U.P.U. CONGRESS
HAMBURG 1984"

1984, June 18
527 CD335 50c multicolored 1.50 1.60

Local
Birds — A82

Perf. 14x14½

1984, Aug. 15   Litho.   Wmk. 373
528	A82	5c Snowy egret	1.40	.65
529	A82	10c Bananaquit	1.40	.65
530	A82	35c Kingfisher	4.75	3.25
531	A82	$1 Brown booby	8.50	9.50
		Nos. 528-531 (4)	16.05	14.05

Christmas — A83   Orchids — A84

#532a-532d, evening beach scenes. #533a-533d, daytime boating and beach scenes.

1984, Oct. 17   Litho.   Perf. 14
532		Strip of 4	5.00	5.00
a.-d.	A83	5c Any single	1.25	1.25
533		Strip of 4	6.00	5.00
a.-d.	A83	25c Any single	1.50	1.25

Souvenir Sheet
| 534 | A83 | $1 Bonfire, diff. | 6.75 | 6.75 |

No. 534 contains one stamp 29x48mm.

1985, Mar. 13   Litho.   Perf. 14x13½
535	A84	5c Schomburgkia thomsoniana var.	1.75	.55
536	A84	10c Schomburgkia thomsoniana	1.75	.55
537	A84	25c Encyclia plicata	4.25	1.60
538	A84	50c Dendrophylax fawcetti	6.25	4.25
		Nos. 535-538 (4)	14.00	6.95

Shipwrecks A85

Unspecified shipwrecks found in Cayman waters.

1985, May 22   Perf. 14
539	A85	5c multicolored	1.50	.55
540	A85	25c multicolored	4.75	2.10
541	A85	35c multicolored	5.50	4.25
542	A85	40c multicolored	5.75	5.75
		Nos. 539-542 (4)	17.50	12.65

Intl. Youth Year — A86

5c, Natl. Athletic Assoc. track competition. 15c, High school students studying in Grand Cayman Campus Library. 25c, Amateur League Competition Football. 50c, Natl. Netball Assoc. competition.

1985, Aug. 14   Perf. 14½
543	A86	5c multicolored	.30	.25
544	A86	15c multicolored	.50	.40
545	A86	35c multicolored	1.10	.85
546	A86	50c multicolored	2.10	2.10
		Nos. 543-546 (4)	4.00	3.60

Telecommunications, 50th Anniv. — A87

Designs: 5c, Morse Code transmitter, 1935. 10c, Hand-cranked telephone, 1935. 25c, Tropospheric scatter dish, 1966. 50c, Earth dish receiver, 1979.

1985, Oct. 25   Perf. 14
547	A87	5c multicolored	.65	.65
548	A87	10c multicolored	.70	.70
549	A87	25c multicolored	1.90	1.10
550	A87	50c multicolored	3.25	4.00
		Nos. 547-550 (4)	6.50	6.45

Birds A88

1986, Mar. 20   Litho.   Wmk. 384
551	A88	10c Magnificent frigatebird	2.50	1.10
552	A88	25c West Indian whistling duck	3.25	1.75
553	A88	35c La Sagra's flycatcher	3.75	3.75
554	A88	40c Yellow-faced grassquit	4.50	4.50
		Nos. 551-554 (4)	14.00	11.10

Nos. 552-553 vert.

Queen Elizabeth II 60th Birthday
Common Design Type

Designs: 5c, As bridesmaid at wedding of Lady Mary Cambridge, 1931. 10c, Royal visit to Norway, 1955. 25c, Inspecting West Indian troop, royal tour, 1985. 50c, Gulf tour, 1979. $1, Visiting Crown Agents' offices, 1983.

1986, Apr. 21   Perf. 14x14½
555	CD337	5c scar, blk & sil	.20	.20
556	CD337	10c ultra, blk & sil	.25	.25
557	CD337	25c grn & multi	2.00	.95
558	CD337	50c vio & multi	1.00	1.10
559	CD337	$1 rose vio & multi	1.60	1.90
		Nos. 555-559 (5)	5.05	4.40

Royal Wedding Issue, 1986
Common Design Type

Designs: 5c, Informal portrait. 50c, Andrew in uniform, helicopter.

Perf. 14½x14
1986, July 23   Litho.   Wmk. 384
| 560 | CD338 | 5c multicolored | .35 | .25 |
| 561 | CD338 | 50c multicolored | 1.50 | 1.90 |

Marine Life — A89

Perf. 13½x13
1986, Sept. 15   Wmk. 373
Inscribed "1986"
562	A89	5c Rhynchocinetes rigeus	.80	.65
563	A89	10c Nemaster rubiginosa	.80	.65
a.		Wmk. 384, inscribed "1990"	2.75	3.00
564	A89	15c Calcinus tibicen	.70	.75
565	A89	20c Rhodactis sanctithomae	.70	.95
566	A89	25c Spirobranchus gigantea	.45	3.00
567	A89	35c Diodon holacanthus	.70	3.25
568	A89	50c Pseudocorynactis aribbeorum	.80	5.00
569	A89	60c Astrophyton muricatum	3.50	9.50
570	A89	75c Cyphoma gibbosum	9.50	12.00
571	A89	$1 Conolylactis gigantea	2.25	3.25
572	A89	$2 Malacoctenus boehlkei	5.00	5.25
573	A89	$4 Lima scabra	10.00	8.25
		Nos. 562-573 (12)	35.20	52.50

1987
Inscribed "1987"
562a	A89	5c multicolored	.80	1.60
563a	A89	10c multicolored	.80	1.25
564a	A89	15c multicolored	.70	1.50
565a	A89	20c multicolored	.70	2.00
571a	A89	$1 multicolored	2.25	6.50
572a	A89	$2 multicolored	5.00	10.50
573a	A89	$4 multicolored	10.00	17.50
		Nos. 562a-573a (7)	20.25	40.85

1990
Inscribed "1990"
562b	A89	5c multicolored	2.75	5.00
563b	A89	10c multicolored	2.75	4.00
564b	A89	15c multicolored	2.50	5.00
565b	A89	20c multicolored	2.50	7.00
566b	A89	25c multicolored	1.50	10.00
571b	A89	$1 multicolored	8.00	10.00
572b	A89	$2 multicolored	17.50	17.50
		Nos. 562b-573b (7)	37.50	58.50

Tourism A90

Perf. 13x13½
1987, Jan. 26   Wmk. 384
574	A90	10c Golfing	3.00	1.00
575	A90	15c Sailing	3.25	1.00
576	A90	25c Snorkeling	3.25	1.50
577	A90	35c Parasailing	3.25	2.00
578	A90	$1 Fishing	7.25	9.75
		Nos. 574-578 (5)	20.00	15.25

Fruit — A91

1987, May 20   Perf. 14½
579	A91	5c Akee	1.00	1.00
580	A91	25c Breadfruit	2.25	.75
581	A91	35c Papaya	2.25	1.00
582	A91	$1 Soursop	6.00	7.00
		Nos. 579-582 (4)	11.50	9.75

Lizards — A92

1987, Aug. 26   Litho.   Perf. 14
583	A92	10c Lion lizard	2.40	1.00
584	A92	50c Iguana	6.00	4.50
585	A92	$1 Anole	7.25	8.75
		Nos. 583-585 (3)	15.65	14.25

Flowers — A93   Herons — A95

Butterflies A94

1987, Nov. 18   Perf. 14½x14
586	A93	5c Poinsettia	1.25	.55
587	A93	25c Periwinkle	3.00	.90
588	A93	35c Yellow allamanda	3.00	1.25
589	A93	75c Blood lily	5.25	6.00
		Nos. 586-589 (4)	12.50	8.70

1988, Mar. 29   Wmk. 384   Perf. 14

Designs: 5c, Hemiargus ammon erembis and Strymon martialis. 25c, Phocides pigmalion batabano. 50c, Anaea troglodyta cubana. $1, Papilio andraemon andraemon.
590	A94	5c multicolored	2.00	.65
591	A94	25c multicolored	4.25	1.40
592	A94	50c multicolored	6.50	5.25
593	A94	$1 multicolored	8.25	8.25
		Nos. 590-593 (4)	21.00	15.55

1988, Jan. 26   Litho.   Perf. 14
594	A95	5c Butorides striatus	2.75	.65
595	A95	25c Egretta tricolor	5.25	.90
596	A95	50c Nycticorax violaceus	6.50	6.00
597	A95	$1 Egretta caerulea	7.00	6.50
		Nos. 594-597 (4)	21.50	14.05

1988 Summer Olympics, Seoul — A96

1988, Sept. 21   Perf. 14½
598	A96	5c Cycling	2.25	.65
599	A96	50c Natl. team, passenger jet	3.75	2.75
600	A96	$1 Yachting	4.00	4.00
		Nos. 598-600 (3)	10.00	7.40

Souvenir Sheet
Wmk. 373
| 601 | A96 | $1 Tennis | 7.25 | 7.25 |

No. 601 commemorates the 75th anniv. of the Intl. Tennis Federation.

Visit of Princess Alexandra A97

1988, Nov. 1   Wmk. 373   Perf. 15
| 602 | A97 | 5c Portrait | 2.75 | 1.25 |
| 603 | A97 | $1 Seated in garden | 9.75 | 7.50 |

Cayman Islands P.O., Cent. — A98

Designs: 5c, P.O., Georgetown, 1889, and Jamaica #24, canceled. 25c, S.S. Orinoco and Cayman Isls. #1. 35c, Grand Cayman G.P.O. and #442. $1, Cayman Airways mail plane and #191.

1989, Apr. 12   Wmk. 384   Perf. 14½
604	A98	5c multicolored	1.25	1.25
605	A98	25c multicolored	2.75	1.50
606	A98	35c multicolored	3.00	1.75
607	A98	$1 multicolored	11.00	11.00
		Nos. 604-607 (4)	18.00	15.50

A99   A100

Mutiny on the Bounty: a, Capt. Bligh. b, HMS Providence, two crewmen. c, HMS Assistant, transplanted breadfruit. d, Moving breadfruit on land, in longboat. e, Midshipman among casks and crates.

1989, May 24   *Perf. 14*
608		Strip of 5	32.50	32.50
a.-e.		A99 50c any single	6.50	6.50

Perf. 14½x14
1989, Oct. 18   **Litho.**   **Wmk. 373**
609	A100	5c Panton House	1.00	1.00
610	A100	10c Town Hall	1.00	1.00
611	A100	25c Old Courts House	2.25	.90
612	A100	35c Elmslie Memorial Church	2.25	1.25
613	A100	$1 Post office	5.50	5.75
		Nos. 609-613 (5)	12.00	9.90

Natl. Trust emblem & architecture, George Town.

Island Surveys
A101

Maps or survey ships: 5c, Navigational instruments and George Gauld's map of 1773. 25c, Instruments and map created by surveyors aboard HMS *Vidal*, 1956. 50c, *Mutine*, 1914. $1, HMS *Vidal*.

1989, Nov. 15
614	A101	5c multicolored	1.75	1.40
615	A101	25c multicolored	4.50	1.75
616	A101	50c multicolored	7.00	5.25
617	A101	$1 multicolored	11.00	11.00
		Nos. 614-617 (4)	24.25	19.40

Angelfish
A102

1990, Apr. 25   **Wmk. 384**   *Perf. 14*
618	A102	10c French	2.10	.65
619	A102	25c Gray	3.75	1.40
620	A102	50c Queen	5.50	5.50
621	A102	$1 Rock beauty	9.00	9.00
		Nos. 618-621 (4)	20.35	16.55

Queen Mother, 90th Birthday
Common Design Types
1990, Aug. 4   **Wmk. 384**   *Perf. 14x15*
622	CD343	50c King, Queen Elizabeth, 1948	1.75	2.50

Perf. 14½
623	CD344	$1 King, Queen with Churchill, 1940	3.75	4.25

Butterflies
A103

1990, Oct. 24   *Perf. 14½x14*
624	A103	5c Soldier	1.60	1.25
625	A103	25c Pygmy blue	3.50	2.40
626	A103	35c Cayman crescent spot	4.50	2.75
627	A103	$1 Gulf fritillary	10.50	10.50
		Nos. 624-627 (4)	20.10	16.90

Expo '90, International Garden and Greenery Exposition, Osaka, Japan.

Hurricane Awareness — A104

Designs: 5c, Goes weather satellite. 30c, Meteorologist tracks storm. 40c, Hurricane

damage. $1, Lockheed WP-3D Orion flying in hurricane's eye.

1991, Aug. 8   *Perf. 14*
628	A104	5c multicolored	1.60	1.50
629	A104	30c multicolored	3.75	1.75
630	A104	40c multicolored	4.00	2.10
631	A104	$1 multicolored	9.50	9.50
		Nos. 628-631 (4)	18.85	14.85

Christmas
A105

Local flowers and Christmas scenes: 5c, Angel's trumpet, angels with trumpets. 30c, Golden trumpet, Mary on donkey led by Joseph. 40c, Christmas flower, Adoration of the Magi. 60c, Tree of life, nativity scene.

1991, Nov. 6   **Wmk. 373**
632	A105	5c multicolored	1.00	1.00
633	A105	30c multicolored	3.00	.85
634	A105	40c multicolored	3.25	1.40
635	A105	60c multicolored	3.75	5.00
		Nos. 632-635 (4)	11.00	8.25

Island Scenes
A106

Perf. 12½x13, 13x12½
1991, Dec. 11   **Litho.**   **Wmk. 373**
636	A106	5c Coconut tree, vert.	.75	.55
a.		Inscribed "1994"	1.00	.75
637	A106	15c Beach scene	1.60	.55
638	A106	20c Poincianas in bloom	.85	.70
639	A106	30c Blowholes	2.25	.90
640	A106	40c Police band	3.75	2.25
641	A106	50c Downtown scene, vert.	3.00	2.25
642	A106	60c The Bluff, Cayman Brac	2.50	3.50
643	A106	80c Coat of arms, vert.	2.25	3.75
644	A106	90c View of Hell	2.25	3.75
645	A106	$1 Sportfishing	4.50	3.75
646	A106	$2 Harbor scene, vert.	9.50	9.00
647	A106	$8 Queen Elizabeth II, vert.	22.50	25.00
		Nos. 636-647 (12)	55.70	55.95

Queen Elizabeth II's Accession to the Throne, 40th Anniv.
Common Design Type
Wmk. 373, 384 (40c)
1992, Feb. 6   **Litho.**   *Perf. 14*
648	CD349	5c multicolored	.45	.45
649	CD349	20c multicolored	1.60	.50
650	CD349	30c multicolored	1.75	.75
651	CD349	40c multicolored	1.75	1.40
652	CD349	$1 multicolored	3.25	4.00
		Nos. 648-652 (5)	8.80	7.10

1992 Summer Olympics, Barcelona
A107

1992, Aug. 5   **Wmk. 373**
653	A107	15c Cyclist	2.25	.55
654	A107	40c Two cyclists	3.75	1.50
655	A107	60c Feet, pedals	4.50	4.50
656	A107	$1 Two cyclists, diff.	5.50	5.50
		Nos. 653-656 (4)	16.00	12.05

Island Heritage — A108

1992, Oct. 21
657	A108	5c Lady with donkey	.70	.70
658	A108	30c Making fish nets	1.75	1.00
659	A108	40c Maypole dancing	3.00	1.60
660	A108	60c Basket making	3.50	3.50
661	A108	$1 Cooking on caboose	4.25	4.25
		Nos. 657-661 (5)	13.20	11.05

Rays
A109

Perf. 13½x14
1993, June 16   **Litho.**   **Wmk. 373**
662	A109	5c Yellow stingray	1.10	.85
663	A109	30c Southern stingray	2.75	1.60
664	A109	40c Spotted eagle ray	3.25	1.90
665	A109	$1 Manta ray	7.00	7.00
		Nos. 662-665 (4)	14.10	11.35

A110

A111

Tourism: No. 666a, Turtle, sailboats. b, Diver, coral boats. c, Golf. d, Beach, tennis. e, Pirates, sailing ship.
No. 667: a, Cruise ship, boat, sailboat. b, City street scene. c, Submarines. d, Cyclist, scooters. e, Jet planes.

Perf. 14x13½
1993, Sept. 30   **Litho.**   **Wmk. 373**
666	A110	15c Strip of 5, #a.-e.	11.50	11.50
667	A110	30c Strip of 5, #a.-e.	12.50	12.50
f.		Booklet pane of 10, #666-667	32.50	

1993, Oct. 29   *Perf. 14*

Various views of Grand Cayman Parrot.

668	A111	5c green & multi	1.40	1.40
669	A111	5c red & multi	1.40	1.40
670	A111	30c yellow & multi	3.50	3.50
671	A111	30c blue & multi	3.50	3.50
		Nos. 668-671 (4)	9.80	9.80

Christmas
A112

Christmas scenes, orchids: 5c, Manger, Ionopsis utricularioides. 40c, Shepherd, lamb, Encyclia cochleata. 60c, Magi, Vanilla pompona. $1, Virgin in prayer, Oncidium caymanense.

Perf. 13½x14
1993, Dec. 6   **Litho.**   **Wmk. 38[4]**
672	A112	5c multicolored	1.40	.7[?]
673	A112	40c multicolored	3.75	1.[?]
674	A112	40c multicolored	4.75	4.7[?]
675	A112	$1 multicolored	6.25	6.2[?]
		Nos. 672-675 (4)	16.15	12.7[?]

Souvenir Sheet

Reef Life — A113

Designs: a, Holocanthus ciliaris. b, Bod[i]anus pulchellus, anisotremus virginicus. c, Holocanthus tricolor, gramma loreto. d, Poma[-]canthus paru, chaeton striatus.

Perf. 14½x13
1994, Feb. 18   **Wmk. 37[3]**
676	A113	60c Sheet of 4, #a.-d.	15.00	15.0[0]

Hong Kong '94.

Royal Visit — A114

Designs: 5c, Cayman Islands, United King[-]dom flags. 15c, Royal yacht Britannia. 30c, Queen Elizabeth II. $2, Queen, Prince Philip.

1994, Feb. 22   *Perf. 14[?]*
677	A114	5c multicolored	2.00	.9[?]
678	A114	15c multicolored	3.75	1.6[?]
679	A114	30c multicolored	3.75	1.7[?]
680	A114	$2 multicolored	10.50	10.5[?]
		Nos. 677-680 (4)	20.00	14.8[?]

West Indian Whistling Duck
A115

5c, One standing. 15c, Landing in wate[r]. 20c, Four ducks, various activities. 80c, One [?] raising wings. $1, Adult, chick.

Wmk. 373
1994, Apr. 21   *Perf. 1[?]*
681	A115	5c multi, vert.	1.75	.9[?]
682	A115	15c multi	2.50	.9[?]
683	A115	20c multi	2.50	1.0[?]
684	A115	80c multi, vert.	5.50	6.0[?]
685	A115	$1 multi, vert.	6.25	6.5[?]
a.		Souvenir sheet of 1	13.00	13.0[?]
		Nos. 681-685 (5)	18.50	15.3[?]

No. 685a has a continuous design and con[-]tains Cayman Islands Natl. Trust emblem.

Butterflies
A116

No. 686: a, Fulvous hairstreak. b, Atal[a] butterfly.
No. 687: a, Barred sulphur. b, Dorante[s] skipper.

Wmk. 373
1994, Aug. 16   **Litho.**   *Perf. 13[?]*
686	A116	10c Pair, #a.-b.	3.00	3.2[?]
687	A116	$1 Pair, #a.-b.	14.50	14.5[?]

Wreck of the Ten Sail, Bicent. — A117

Perf. 13½x14
1994, Oct. 12   Litho.   Wmk. 373

688	A117	10c shown	.75	.75
689	A117	10c multicolored	.75	.75
690	A117	15c multicolored	1.25	.60
691	A117	20c multicolored	1.50	.70
692	A117	$2 multicolored	7.75	7.75
		Nos. 688-692 (5)	12.00	10.55

Sea Turtles A118

Wmk. 384
1995, Feb. 28   Litho.   Perf. 14

693	A118	10c Green	.85	.45
694	A118	20c Kemp's ridley	1.25	.55
695	A118	25c Hawksbill	1.40	.65
696	A118	30c Leatherback	1.60	.75
697	A118	$1.30 Loggerhead	5.75	5.75
698	A118	$2 Pacific ridley	7.25	7.25
a.		Souvenir sheet, #693-698	19.00	19.00
		Nos. 693-698 (6)	18.10	15.40

1995 CARIFTA & IAAF Games A119

1995, Apr. 15   Litho.   Perf. 14

699	A119	10c Running	1.00	.55
700	A119	20c Pole vault	1.50	1.10
701	A119	30c Javelin	2.10	1.10
702	A119	$1.30 Sailing	7.25	7.25
		Nos. 699-702 (4)	11.85	10.15

Souvenir Sheet
703	A119	$2 Medal winners	11.00	11.00

End of World War II, 50th Anniv.
Common Design Type
10c, Two soldiers, Cayman Home Guard. 25c, Freighter Comayagua torpedoed off Caymans, 5/14/42. 40c, Type IXc U-Boat U-125. $1, Navy airship L-3 used for U-boat patrol. $1.30, Reverse of War Medal 1939-45.

Wmk. 373
1995, May 8   Litho.   Perf. 13½

704	CD351	10c multicolored	1.50	.55
705	CD351	25c multicolored	3.00	.90
706	CD351	40c multicolored	3.50	2.25
707	CD351	$1 multicolored	6.50	6.50
		Nos. 704-707 (4)	14.50	10.20

Souvenir Sheet
Perf. 14
708	CD352	$1.30 multicolored	6.25	6.25

Souvenir Sheet

Queen Mother, 95th Birthday — A120

1995, Aug. 25   Perf. 14½

709	A120	$4 multicolored	13.50	13.50

Singapore '95.

A121

A122

Animals of the Nativity.

1995, Nov. 1   Perf. 14

710	A121	10c Ox	1.00	.30
711	A121	20c Sheep, lamb	1.50	.50
712	A121	30c Donkey	2.50	.60
713	A121	$2 Camels	9.00	10.50
a.		Souvenir sheet of 4, #710-713	15.00	15.00
		Nos. 710-713 (4)	14.00	11.90

1996, Mar. 21   Wmk. 384
Litho.   Perf. 14

Wild fruit.

714	A122	10c Sea grape	.70	.50
715	A122	25c Guava	1.50	.70
716	A122	40c West Indian cherry	2.25	1.25
717	A122	$1 Tamarind	4.50	5.75
		Nos. 714-717 (4)	8.95	8.20

Modern Olympic Games, Cent. — A123

Perf. 14x13½
1996, June 19   Litho.   Wmk. 384

718	A123	10c Sailing	.65	.45
719	A123	20c Sailboarding	1.25	.55
720	A123	30c Sailing, diff.	1.60	.80
721	A123	$2 Running	6.50	6.50
		Nos. 718-721 (4)	10.00	8.30

Symbols of National Identity — A124

Designs: 10c, Guitar, music, natl. song. 20c, Boeing 737. 25c, Queen Elizabeth II opening Legislative Assembly. 30c, Seven Mile Beach. 40c, Scuba diver, stingrays. 60c, School children, Cayman Turtle Farm. 80c, Cayman parrot, natl. bird. 90c, Silver thatch palm, natl. tree. $1, Natl. flag. $2, Wild banana orchid, natl. flower. $4, Natl. arms. $6, Natl. currency.

Wmk. 373
1996, Sept. 26   Litho.   Perf. 14
Inscribed "1996"

722	A124	10c multicolored	.50	.45
		Complete booklet, 10 #722	5.25	
a.		Inscribed "1997"	.50	.45
723	A124	20c multicolored	1.10	.85
724	A124	25c multicolored	1.25	.80
725	A124	30c multicolored	1.25	.80
		Complete booklet, 10 #725	13.00	
726	A124	40c multicolored	1.60	1.25
		Complete booklet, 10 #726	17.00	
727	A124	60c multicolored	2.25	1.60
728	A124	80c multicolored	3.75	3.00
a.		Souvenir sheet of 1	4.25	4.25
729	A124	90c multicolored	2.50	3.00
730	A124	$1 multicolored	4.00	3.25
731	A124	$2 multicolored	7.25	7.00
732	A124	$4 multicolored	13.00	16.00
733	A124	$6 multicolored	17.00	20.00
		Nos. 722-733 (12)	55.45	58.00

No. 728a for Hong Kong '97. Issued 2/3/97.

1999, Feb. 5   Wmk. 373 Sideways

723a	A124	20c multicolored	1.10	.85
725a	A124	30c multicolored	1.25	.80
727a	A124	60c multicolored	2.25	1.60
		Nos. 723a-727a (3)	4.60	3.25

Christmas A125

Designs: 10c, Christmas time on North Church Street. 25c, Santa "Gone Fishing." 30c, "Claus Encounters." $2, "Caymanian Christmas."

Wmk. 373
1996, Nov. 12   Litho.   Perf. 14

734	A125	10c multicolored	.65	.35
735	A125	25c multicolored	1.60	.90
736	A125	30c multicolored	2.00	1.25
737	A125	$2 multicolored	4.50	4.50
		Nos. 734-737 (4)	8.75	7.00

Queen Elizabeth II and Prince Philip, 50th Wedding Anniv. — A126

#738, Queen. #739, Royal Guard. #740, Young Prince riding horse. #741, Queen in blue, Prince in military attire in open carriage. #742 Prince holding horse's reins. #743, Queen looking at horses.
$1, Queen, Prince in open carriage.

Perf. 14x13½
1997, July 10   Litho.   Wmk. 373

738	A126	10c multicolored	1.25	1.25
739	A126	10c multicolored	1.25	1.25
a.		Pair, #738-739	2.50	2.50
740	A126	30c multicolored	2.00	2.00
741	A126	30c multicolored	2.00	2.00
a.		Pair, #740-741	4.00	4.00
742	A126	40c multicolored	2.40	2.40
743	A126	40c multicolored	2.40	2.40
a.		Pair, #742-743	5.00	5.00
		Nos. 738-743 (6)	11.30	11.30

Souvenir Sheet
744	A126	$1 multicolored	7.25	7.25

Telecommunications — A127

Designs: 10c, Children using the Internet. 25c, Cable and wireless ship. 30c, Children wearing numbers of new area code, "345." 60c, Cable and wireless satellite communications.

Perf. 14x14½
1997, Oct. 10   Litho.   Wmk. 384

745	A127	10c multicolored	.45	.30
746	A127	25c multicolored	1.25	.80
747	A127	30c multicolored	1.40	.95
748	A127	60c multicolored	2.25	2.25
		Nos. 745-748 (4)	5.35	4.30

Christmas A128

Santa Claus: 10c, Relaxing in hammock, Little Cayman. 30c, With children on bluff, Cayman Brac. 40c, Playing golf. $1, Diving with stingrays.

Wmk. 373
1997, Dec. 3   Litho.   Perf. 13

749	A128	10c multicolored	.40	.25
750	A128	30c multicolored	.85	.45
751	A128	40c multicolored	2.00	.80
752	A128	$1 multicolored	3.25	3.50
		Nos. 749-752 (4)	6.50	5.00

Diana, Princess of Wales (1961-97)
Common Design Type
Portraits: a, 10c. b, 20c. c, 40c. d, $1.

Perf. 14½x14
1998   Litho.   Wmk. 373

752A	CD355	10c Like #753a	1.00	1.00
752B	CD355	20c Like #753b	2.00	2.00

Sheet of 4
753	CD355	#a.-d.	6.50	6.50

No. 753 sold for $1.70 + 30c, with surtax from international sales being donated to the Princess Diana Memorial Fund and surtax from national sales being donated to designated local charity.

Royal Air Force, 80th Anniv.
Common Design Type of 1993 Re-Inscribed
Designs: 10c, Hawker Horsley. 20c, Fairey Hendon. 25c, Hawker Siddeley Gnat. 30c, Hawker Siddeley Dominie.
No. 758: a, 40c, Airco DH-9. b, 60c, Spad 13 Scout. c, 80c, Airspeed Oxford. d, $1, Martin Baltimore.

Wmk. 373
1998, Apr. 1   Litho.   Perf. 14

754	CD350	10c multicolored	1.25	1.25
755	CD350	20c multicolored	1.60	1.60
756	CD350	25c multicolored	1.90	1.90
757	CD350	30c multicolored	2.25	2.25
		Nos. 754-757 (4)	7.00	7.00

Souvenir Sheet
758	CD350	Sheet of 4, #a.-d.	11.00	11.00

Birds — A129

Designs: 10c, West Indian whistling duck. 20c, Magnificent frigatebird. 60c, Red footed booby. $1, Grand Cayman parrot.

1998 Litho. Wmk. 373 *Perf. 13½*

759	A129	10c multicolored	1.10	.60
760	A129	20c multicolored	2.00	.60
761	A129	60c multicolored	3.50	3.50
762	A129	$1 multicolored	4.25	4.25
		Nos. 759-762 (4)	10.85	8.95

Christmas
A130

Santa at various island locations: 10c, At Blowholes. 30c, Diving on wreck of MV Capt. Keith Tibbetts. 40c, Visiting Pedro Castle. 60c, Arriving at Little Cayman.

1998 *Perf. 14x14½*

763	A130	10c multicolored	.40	.40
764	A130	30c multicolored	1.10	.85
765	A130	40c multicolored	1.50	1.10
766	A130	60c multicolored	3.00	3.00
		Nos. 763-766 (4)	6.00	5.35

Easter
A131

Artworks by Miss Lassie (Gladwyn Bush): 10c, "They Rolled the Stone Away." 20c, "Ascension," vert. 30c, "The World Praying for Peace." 40c, "Calvary," vert.

Wmk. 373
1999, Mar. 26 Litho. *Perf. 13*

767	A131	10c multicolored	.50	.50
768	A131	20c multicolored	.90	.90
769	A131	30c multicolored	1.40	1.40
770	A131	40c multicolored	1.50	1.50
		Nos. 767-770 (4)	4.30	4.30

Vision 2008
A132

Children's drawings: 10c, "Cayman House." 30c, "Coral Reef." 40c, "Fisherman on North Sound." $2, "Three Fish and A Turtle."

1999, June *Perf. 13½*

771	A132	10c multicolored	.35	.35
772	A132	30c multicolored	1.25	1.25
773	A132	40c multicolored	1.40	1.40
774	A132	$2 multicolored	7.00	7.00
		Nos. 771-774 (4)	10.00	10.00

Wedding of Prince Edward and Sophie Rhys-Jones
Common Design Type
Perf. 13¾x14

1999, June 16 Litho. Wmk. 384

775	CD356	10c Separate portraits	.50	.50
776	CD356	$2 Couple	5.50	5.50

1st Manned Moon Landing, 30th Anniv.
Common Design Type

Designs: 10c, Coast Guard during launch. 25c, 3rd stage fires and puts rocket in orbit. 30c, Aldrin descends to lunar surface. 60c, Lander module sent back to moon. $1.50, Looking at earth from moon.

1999, July 20 *Perf. 14x13¾*

777	CD357	10c multicolored	.45	.45
778	CD357	25c multicolored	1.10	1.10
779	CD357	30c multicolored	1.25	1.25
780	CD357	60c multicolored	2.50	2.50
		Nos. 777-780 (4)	5.30	5.30

Souvenir Sheet
Perf. 14

781	CD357	$1.50 multicolored	5.50	5.50

No. 781 contains one circular stamp 40mm in diameter.

Queen Mother's Century
Common Design Type

Queen Mother: 10c, Looking at London's defenses, 1940. 20c, At Clarence House, 94th birthday. 30c, With Princes Charles and William. 40c, Reviewing the Chelsea Pensioners, 1986.
$1.50, At her wedding.

Wmk. 384
1999, Aug. 18 Litho. *Perf. 13¼*

782	CD358	10c multicolored	.45	.45
783	CD358	20c multicolored	.80	.80
784	CD358	30c multicolored	1.40	1.40
785	CD358	40c multicolored	1.75	1.75
		Nos. 782-785 (4)	4.40	4.40

Souvenir Sheet

786	CD358	$1.50 multicolored	4.75	4.75

Christmas — A133

Wmk. 373
1999, Nov. 17 Litho. *Perf. 13¼*

787	A133	10c #242, vert.	.40	.35
788	A133	30c #532d, vert.	1.10	.90
789	A133	40c #749, vert.	1.50	1.25
790	A133	$1 #431	3.00	3.00
a.		Souv. sheet, #787-790, perf. 12	6.00	6.00
		Nos. 787-790 (4)	6.00	5.50

British Monarchs — A134

No. 792: a, Henry VIII. b, Mary I. c, Charles II. d, Anne. e, George IV. f, George V.

Wmk. 373
2000, Feb. 29 Litho. *Perf. 14*

791	A134	10c Henry VII	.70	.70

Sheet of 6

792	A134	40c #a.-f.	9.00	9.00

The Stamp Show 2000, London.

Sesame Street — A135

Designs: 10c, Ernie. 30c, Big Bird.
No. 795: a, Grover. b, Zoe. c, Oscar the Grouch. d, The Count. e, Like 30c. f, Cookie Monster. g, Like 10c. h, Bert. i, Elmo in pond.
No. 796, Elmo collecting stamps.

Perf. 14½x14¾
2000, Mar. 15 Litho. Wmk. 373

793	A135	10c multi	.40	.40
794	A135	30c multi	1.10	1.10
795	A135	20c Sheet of 9, #a-i	6.25	6.25

Souvenir Sheet

796	A135	20c multi	1.90	1.90

Prince William, 18th Birthday
Common Design Type

10c, In checked shirt and in sweater and checked shirt. 20c, In white shirt and black bow tie. 30c, In blue casual shirt, vert. 40c, As child, with beret, vert. $1, As infant.

Perf. 14¼x13¾, 13¾x14¼
2000, June 21 Litho. Wmk. 373
Stamps With White Border

797	CD359	10c multi	.50	.40
798	CD359	20c multi	1.00	.95
799	CD359	30c multi	1.40	1.25
800	CD359	40c multi	1.90	1.90
		Nos. 797-800 (4)	4.80	4.50

Souvenir Sheet
Stamps Without White Border
Perf. 14¼

801		Sheet of 5	8.25	8.25
a.		CD359 10c multi	.35	.35
b.		CD359 20c multi	.75	.75
c.		CD359 30c multi	1.00	1.00
d.		CD359 40c multi	1.40	1.40
e.		CD359 $1 multi	4.00	4.00

Marine Life
A136

10c, Green turtle. 20c, Queen angelfish. 30c, Parrotfish. $1, Green moray eel.

Wmk. 384
2000, Aug. 25 Litho. *Perf. 14*

802-805	A136	Set of 4	8.75	8.75

National Drug Council
A137

Various children's drawings. Denominations, 10c, 15c, 30c, $2.

2000, Aug. 25

806-809	A137	Set of 4	12.00	12.00

Christmas
A138

10c, Backing sand. 30c, Christmas dinner. 40c, Yard dance. 60c, Conch shell border.

Perf. 14½x14¼
2000, Nov. 14 Wmk. 373

810-813	A138	Set of 4	9.00	9.00

UN Women's Human Rights Campaign — A139

Wmk. 373
2001, Mar. 8 Litho. *Perf. 14*

814	A139	10c multi	.90	.90

Cayman Brac
A140

Designs: 15c, Red mangrove. 20c, Peter's Cave, vert. 25c, Bight Road stairway, vert.

30c, Westerly Pond. 40c, Aerial view. 60c, Marshes.

2001, Apr. 21

815-820	A140	Set of 6	11.00	11.00

Non-profit Organizations — A141

Designs: Nos. 821, 826a, 15c, National Council of Voluntary Organizations. Nos. 822, 826b, 20c, Cayman Humane Society. Nos. 823, 826c, 25c, Red Cross/Red Crescent. Nos. 824, 826d, 30c, Cayman Islands Cancer Society, vert. Nos. 825, 826e, 40c, Lions Club of Tropical Gardens, vert.

Wmk. 373
2001, Aug. 15 Litho. *Perf. 14*
Stamps With White Margins

821-825	A141	Set of 5	8.50	8.50

Souvenir Sheet
Stamps With Pink Margins

826	A141	Sheet of 5, #a-e	8.50	8.50

No. 826 sold for $1.80, 50c of which went to the various organizations honored.

Transportation — A142

Designs: No. 827, Walking home. No. 828, Boy on donkey. 20c, Bananas by canoe. 25c, Horse and buggy. 30c, Catboats. 40c, Schooner. 60c, Police bicycle, vert. 80c, Lady drivers. 90c, Launcing Cimboco, vert. $1, Seaplane. $4, Freighter. $10, Boeing 767.

Perf. 14¼x14½, 14½x14¼
2001, Sept. 29 Litho. Wmk. 373

827	A142	15c multi	.40	.40
828	A142	15c multi	.40	.40
829	A142	20c multi	.55	.55
830	A142	25c multi	.70	.70
831	A142	30c multi	.80	.80
832	A142	40c multi	1.10	1.10
833	A142	60c multi	1.60	1.60
834	A142	80c multi	2.25	2.25
835	A142	90c multi	2.50	2.50
836	A142	$1 multi	2.75	2.75
837	A142	$4 multi	11.00	11.00
838	A142	$10 multi	26.00	26.00
		Nos. 827-838 (12)	50.05	50.05

Christmas
A143

Santa Claus: 15c, With children on dock. 30c, On eagle ray. 40c, In catboat. 60c, Parasailing.

Perf. 14¼x14½
2001, Nov. 21 Litho. Wmk. 373

839-842	A143	Set of 4	6.50	6.50

In Remembrance of Sept. 11, 2001 Terrorist Attacks — A144

Perf. 14x14¾
2002, Jan. 22 Litho. Wmk. 373

843	A144	$1 multi	4.75	4.75

Reign Of Queen Elizabeth II, 50th Anniv. Issue
Common Design Type

Designs: Nos. 844, 848a, 15c, Princess Elizabeth as child. Nos. 845, 848b, 20c, In 1976. Nos. 846, 848c, 30c, With Princess Margaret, 1942. Nos. 847, 848d, 80c, In 1996. No. 848e, $1, 1955 portrait by Annigoni (38x50mm).

Perf. 14¼x14½, 13¾ (#848e)
2002, Feb. 6   Litho.   Wmk. 373
With Gold Frames

844-847 CD360 Set of 4   4.25 4.25

Souvenir Sheet
Without Gold Frames

848 CD360 Sheet of 5, #a-e   10.50 10.50

Peanuts Comic Strip Characters
A145

Designs: 15c, Snoopy painting Woodstock at Cayman Brac Bluff. 20c, Charlie Brown and Sally at Hell Post Office. 25c, Peppermint Patty and Marcie at Little Cayman beach. 30c, Snoopy and Boeing 737-200. 40c, Linus and Snoopy at Point of Sand. 60c, Charlie Brown at Links Golf Course.

Wmk. 373
2002, Mar. 9   Litho.   Perf. 14
849-854 A145 Set of 6   9.50 9.50
854a   Souvenir sheet, #849-854   9.50 9.50

2002 World Cup Soccer Championships, Japan and Korea — A146

Denominations: 30c, 40c.

2002, Apr. 30   Perf. 13¾
855-856 A146 Set of 2   4.75 4.75

Queen Mother Elizabeth (1900-2002)
Common Design Type

Designs: 15c, Wearing hat (sepia photograph). 30c, Wearing dark blue hat. Nos. 859, 861a, 40c, Wearing hat (black and white photograph). Nos. 860, 861b, $1, Wearing tiara.

Perf. 13¾x14¼, 14¼ (#859-860)
2002, Aug. 5   Litho.   Wmk. 373
With Purple Frames
857-860 CD361 Set of 4   8.75 8.75

Souvenir Sheet
Without Purple Frames
Perf. 14½x14¼
861 CD361 Sheet of 2, #a-b   8.75 8.75

Christmas
A147

Designs: 15c, Hail Mary. 20c, Journey to Bethlehem. 30c, Her firstborn Son. 40c, I bring good tidings. 60c Star in the east.

Wmk. 373
2002, Oct. 18   Litho.   Perf. 14
Stamps + labels
862-866 A147 Set of 5   6.25 6.25
866a   Souvenir sheet of 5, #862-866 + 5 labels   7.00 7.00

Aviation in the Cayman Islands, 50th Anniv.
A148

Designs: 15c, PBY Catalina Flying Boat. 20c, First landing at Grand Cayman Airport, 1952. 25c, Cayman Brac Airways AC 50. 30c, Cayman Airways B-737. 40c, Concorde at original airport, 1984. $1.30, Island Air DHC6.

2002, Nov. 8
867-872 A148 Set of 6   12.00 12.00

Children's Games
A149

Designs: 15c, Rope skipping. 20c, Maypole dancing. 25c, Gig. 30c, Hopscotch. $1, Marbles.

Wmk. 373
2003, May 27   Litho.   Perf. 13¾
873-877 A149 Set of 5   9.00 9.00

Head of Queen Elizabeth II
Common Design Type

Wmk. 373
2003, June 2   Litho.   Perf. 13¾
878 CD362 $4 multi   20.00 20.00

Coronation of Queen Elizabeth II, 50th Anniv.
Common Design Type

Designs: Nos. 879, 15c, 881a, 20c, Queen wearing crown. Nos. 880, $2, 881b, $4, Queen holding symbols of office.

Perf. 14¼x14½
2003, June 2   Litho.   Wmk. 373
Vignettes Framed, Red Background
879-880 CD363 Set of 2   8.75 8.75

Souvenir Sheet
Vignettes Without Frame, Purple Panel
881 CD363 Sheet of 2, #a-b   14.50 14.50

Prince William, 21st Birthday
Common Design Type

Color photographs: 15c, William with backpack at right. 40c, William in suit and tie at left
No. 884: a, William with hand on chin at right. b, William with white bow tie at left.

Wmk. 373
2003, June 21   Litho.   Perf. 14¼
882 CD364 15c multi   .50 .50
883 CD364 40c multi   1.40 1.40
884   Horiz. pair   5.75 5.75
  a.   CD364 80c multi   2.50 2.50
  b.   CD364 $1 multi   3.25 3.25
    Nos. 882-884 (3)   7.65 7.65

Discovery of the Cayman Islands, 500th Anniv.
A150

Designs: 15c, Turtle hatchlings. No. 886, 20c, Old waterfront. No. 887, 20c, Turtle and ship of Christopher Columbus. 25c, Nassau grouper. 30c, Cayman Brac schooner "Kirk-B." 40c, George Town harbor. 60c, Musical instruments. 80c, Smokewood tree. 90c, Little Cayman Baptist Church. $1, Thatch rope. $1.30, Children's dance troupe. $2, Parliament in session.

Wmk. 373
2003, July 24   Litho.   Perf. 13¾
885-896 A150 Set of 12   29.00 29.00
896a   Souvenir sheet, #885-896   29.00 29.00

Holiday Greetings
A151

Various Christmas decorations and inscriptions of: 15c, Merry Christmas. 20c, Celebrate With Family. 30c, Happy New Year. 40c, Happy Holidays. 60c, Seasons Greetings.

Wmk. 373
2003, Nov. 4   Litho.   Perf. 13¼
897-901 A151 Set of 5   9.00 9.00

Worldwide Fund for Nature (WWF)
A152

Short-finned pilot whale: 15c, Adult and calf. 20c, Pod of four whales. 30c, Two whales at surface. 40c, One adult.

2003, Nov. 26   Perf. 14
902-905 A152 Set of 4   7.50 7.50
905a   Sheet, 4 each #902-905   32.50 32.50

Shipping Registry, Cent. — A153

Ships: 15c, Lady Slater. 20c, Seanostrum. 30c, Kirk Pride. $1, Boadicea.

Perf. 14x14¾
2004, Jan. 29   Litho.   Wmk. 373
906-909 A153 Set of 4   11.00 11.00

Easter — A154

Designs: 15c, Jesus Carrying His Cross. 30c, The Ascension.

2004, Mar. 16   Perf. 14¾x14
910-911 A154 Set of 2   3.25 3.25

2004 Summer Olympics, Athens — A155

Designs: 15c, Swimmer. 40c, Runner. 60c, Long jumper. 80c, Swimmers.

Perf. 13½x13¼
2004, Aug. 23   Litho.   Wmk. 373
912-915 A155 Set of 4   8.00 8.00

Blue Iguana
A156

Designs: 15c, Adult on rocks. 20c, Eggs. 25c, Four juveniles. 30c, Juvenile on finger. 40c, Adult with open mouth. 90c, Eye.
No. 922: a, 60c, On rock facing right. b, 80c, On rock facing left.

2004, Oct. 26   Litho.   Perf. 13¾
916-921 A156 Set of 6   8.50 8.50

Souvenir Sheet
922 A156 Sheet of 2, #a-b   7.00 7.00
No. 922 sold for $1.90.

Battle of Trafalgar, Bicent. — A157

Designs: 15c, HMS Victory. 20c, HMS Tonnant tangles into the bow of the Algesiras. 25c, Flint cannon lock and linstock. No. 926, 60c, Royal Navy boatswain's mate. $1, Adm. Horatio Nelson, vert. No. 928, $2, HMS Orion in action against the Intrepide.
No. 929, vert.: a, 60c, French gunship Pluton. b, $2, HMS Tonnant.

Wmk. 373, Unwmkd. (15c)
2005, June 8   Litho.   Perf. 13¼
923-928 A157 Set of 6   14.00 14.00
Souvenir Sheet
929 A157 Sheet of 2, #a-b   8.00 8.00
No. 923 has particles of wood from the HMS Victory embedded in the areas covered by a thermographic process that produces a raised, shiny effect.

Rotary International, Cent. — A158

Designs: 15c, Centennial emblem. 30c, PolioPlus emblem.

2005, June 30   Wmk. 373   Perf. 13¾
930-931 A158 Set of 2   2.50 2.50

Orchids
A159

Designs: 15c, Myrmecophila albopurpurea. 20c, Prosthechea boothiana. 30c, Tolumnia calochila, vert. 40c, Encyclia phoenicia. 80c, Prosthechea cochleata, vert. $1.50, Encyclia kingsii.

2005, July 28   Perf. 14
932-936 A159 Set of 5   8.50 8.50
Souvenir Sheet
937 A159 $1.50 multi   7.00 7.00

Pope John Paul II
(1920-2005)
A160

2005, Aug. 18
938   A160   30c multi   1.75   1.75

A161

Butterflies
A162

Designs: 15c, Queen. 20c, Mexican fritillary. 25c, Malachite. 30c, Cayman crescent spot. 40c, Cloudless sulphur. 90c, Swallowtail.

Wmk. 373
2005, Sept. 21   Litho.   *Perf. 14*
939	A161	15c multi	.60	.60
940	A161	20c multi	.75	.75
941	A161	25c multi	.85	.85
942	A161	30c multi	1.10	1.10
943	A161	40c multi	1.60	1.60
944	A161	90c multi	3.25	3.25
		Nos. 939-944 (6)	8.15	8.15

Booklet Stamps
Self-Adhesive
Unwmk.
Serpentine Die Cut 9½x9
945	A162	15c multi	.60	.60
a.		Booklet pane of 10	6.00	
946	A162	20c multi	.70	.70
a.		Booklet pane of 6	4.20	
947	A162	30c multi	1.00	1.00
a.		Booklet pane of 10	10.00	
		Nos. 945-947 (3)	2.30	2.30

Christmas
A163

Designs: 15c, Angels. 30c, Magi, horiz. 40c, Holy Family. 60c, Shepherds, horiz.

Perf. 14x14¾, 14¾x14
2005, Oct. 26   **Wmk. 373**
948-951	A163	Set of 4	4.00	4.00
951a		Souvenir sheet, #948-951, perf. 14¾	4.00	4.00

Trees and
Blossoms — A164

Designs: 15c, Wash wood. 20c, Red mangrove. 30c, Ironwood. 60c, West Indian cedar. $2, Spanish elm.

Wmk. 373
2006, Feb. 23   Litho.   *Perf. 13¼*
Stamp + Label
952-956   A164   Set of 5   8.00   8.00

Queen Elizabeth II, 80th Birthday
A165

Designs: 15c, As child. 40c, Wearing uniform and cap. $1, Wearing tiara. $2, Wearing sunglasses.
No. 961: a, 40c, Like #958. b, $1, Like #959.

2006, Apr. 21   *Perf. 14*
With White Frames
957-960   A165   Set of 4   8.75   8.75
Souvenir Sheet
Without White Frames
961   A165   Sheet of 2, #a-b   3.50   3.50

A166

Marine Life — A167

Designs: Nos. 962, 967a, 968, Hawksbill turtle. Nos. 963, 967b, 969, Gray angelfish. Nos. 964, 967c, 970, Queen angelfish. Nos. 965, 967c, 971, Diamond blenny. Nos. 966, 967e, Juvenile spotted drum, vert. Nos. 964 and 967c are vert.

Wmk. 373
2006, July 18   Litho.   *Perf. 14*
With White Margins
962	A166	25c multi	.60	.60
963	A166	25c multi	.60	.60
964	A166	60c multi	1.50	1.50
965	A166	75c multi	1.90	1.90
966	A166	$1 multi	2.50	2.50
		Nos. 962-966 (5)	7.10	7.10

Souvenir Sheet
Without White Margin
967   A166   Sheet of 5, #a-e   7.25   7.25

Booklet Stamps
Self-Adhesive
Serpentine Die Cut 9½x9
Unwmk.
968	A167	25c multi	.60	.60
a.		Booklet pane of 10	6.00	
969	A167	25c multi	.60	.60
a.		Booklet pane of 10	6.00	
970	A167	60c multi	1.50	1.50
a.		Booklet pane of 10	15.00	
971	A167	75c multi	1.90	1.90
a.		Booklet pane of 10	19.00	
		Nos. 968-971 (4)	4.60	4.60

Birds
A168

Designs: 25c, Bananaquit. 50c, Vitelline warbler. 75c, Grand Cayman parrot. 80c, Caribbean dove. $1, Caribbean elaenia. $1.50, West Indian woodpecker. $1.60, Thick-billed vireo. $2, Northern flicker. $4, Cuban bullfinch. $5, Western spindalis. $10, Loggerhead kingbird. $20, Red-legged thrush.

Perf. 13½x13¾
2006, Oct. 9   Litho.   **Wmk. 373**
972	A168	25c multi	.60	.60
973	A168	50c multi	1.25	1.25
974	A168	75c multi	1.90	1.90
975	A168	80c multi	2.00	2.00
976	A168	$1 multi	2.50	2.50
977	A168	$1.50 multi	3.75	3.75
978	A168	$1.60 multi	4.00	4.00
979	A168	$2 multi	5.00	5.00
980	A168	$4 multi	9.75	9.75
981	A168	$5 multi	12.00	12.00
982	A168	$10 multi	24.00	24.00
983	A168	$20 multi	50.00	50.00
		Nos. 972-983 (12)	116.75	116.75

Booklet Stamps
Self-Adhesive
Unwmk.
Serpentine Die Cut 10x9½
Size:29x24mm
983A	A168	25c multi	.60	.60
d.		Booklet pane of 10	6.00	
983B	A168	75c multi	1.90	1.90
e.		Booklet pane of 10	19.00	
983C	A168	80c multi	2.00	2.00
f.		Booklet pane of 10	20.00	
		Nos. 983A-983C (3)	4.50	4.50

Christmas
A169

Designs: 25c, "Faith," Magi. 75c, "Hope," Prophet with scroll. 80c, "Joy," angel. $1, "Love," Madonna and Child.

Perf. 12½x13¼
2006, Oct. 26   Litho.   **Wmk. 373**
984-987   A169   Set of 4   7.00   7.00

Island Scenes
A170

Designs: 20c, Brac Reed dock. 25c, Waterfront buildings, Hog Sty Bay. 30c, East End blowholes, vert. 40c, Man in hammock, vert. 75c, Poinciana blooms. $1, Driftwood on Little Cayman.

Wmk. 373
2007, June 26   Litho.   *Perf. 13¾*
988-993   A170   Set of 6   7.25   7.25

Scouting, Cent.
A171

Designs: 25c, Wolf Cubs and leaders, hands lashing rope. 75c, Cub Scouts and leaders, hands with trumpet. 80c, Scouts camping, hand with compass. $1, Scout Drill Team, poppies.
No. 998, vert.: a, 50c, Scouts marching. b, $1.50, Lord Robert Baden-Powell and dog.

2007, July 9
994-997   A171   Set of 4   7.00   7.00
Souvenir Sheet
998   A171   Sheet of 2, #a-b   5.00   5.00

Wedding of Queen Elizabeth II and Prince Philip, 60th Anniv. — A172

Designs: 50c, Couple and wedding coach. 75c, Elizabeth wearing bridal veil. 80c, Princess Elizabeth, Philip, Queen Mother Elizabeth, King George VI, Princess Margaret. $1, Wedding procession, Westminster Abbey. $2, Couple.

Wmk. 373
2007, Sept. 12   Litho.   *Perf. 13¾*
999-1002   A172   Set of 4   7.50   7.50
Souvenir Sheet
Perf. 14
1003   A172 $2 multi   5.00   5.00
No. 1003 contains one 42x57mm stamp.

Christmas
A173

Stained-glass windows from local churches: 25c, Nativity, Wesleyan Holiness Church. 50c, Jesus Praying, Elmslie Memorial Church. 75c, Jesus Calling First Disciples, St. George's Anglican Church. 80c, Dove, East End Adventist Church. $1, Orb, First Baptist Church of Grand Cayman. $1.50, Shepherd, Frank Sound Church of God.

2007, Oct. 22   *Perf. 15x14*
1004-1009   A173   Set of 6   12.00   12.00

A174

Greetings
A175

Nos. 1010-1015: a, Hello. b, Good Luck. c, Congratulations. d, You're Invited. e, Best Wishes. f, Love.
No. 1016, Hello. No. 1017, Congratulations. No. 1018, You're Invited. No. 1019, Love.

Wmk. 373
2008, Feb. 5   Litho.   *Perf. 14¼*
1010	A174	20c Sheet of 6, #a-f	3.00	3.00
1011	A174	25c Sheet of 6, #a-f	3.75	3.75
1012	A174	50c Sheet of 6, #a-f	7.50	7.50
1013	A174	75c Sheet of 6, #a-f	11.00	11.00
1014	A174	80c Sheet of 6, #a-f	12.00	12.00
1015	A174	$1 Sheet of 6, #a-f	15.00	15.00
		Nos. 1010-1015 (6)	52.25	52.25

Booklet Stamps
Self-Adhesive
Serpentine Die Cut 9½x9
Unwmk.
1016	A175	20c multi	.50	.50
a.		Booklet pane of 10	5.00	
1017	A175	25c multi	.60	.60
a.		Booklet pane of 10	6.00	
1018	A175	25c multi	.60	.60
a.		Booklet pane of 10	6.00	
1019	A175	25c multi	.60	.60
a.		Booklet pane of 10	6.00	
		Nos. 1016-1019 (4)	2.30	2.30

Darwin Initiative A176

Fauna: 20c, Land crab. 25c, Needlecase. 75c, Little Cayman green anole, vert. 80c, Cayman Brac ground boa. $1, White-shouldered bat.
$2, Caribbean reef squid, vert.

Wmk. 373
2008, July 9   Litho.   Perf. 14
1020-1024 A176   Set of 5   7.50 7.50
Souvenir Sheet
1025 A176 $2 multi   5.00 5.00

2008 Olympic Games, Beijing A177

Designs: 20c, Lanterns, swimming. 25c, Fish, swimming. 50c, Bamboo, running. 75c, Dragon, hurdles.

Wmk. 373
2008, Aug. 8   Litho.   Perf. 13¼
1026-1029 A177   Set of 4   4.25 4.25

Water Authority, 25th Anniv. A178

Children's art: 25c, Stop Water Pollution. 75c, Water droplets. $2, Splash of Life.

Wmk. 373
2008, Oct. 16   Litho.   Perf. 13¼
1030-1032 A178   Set of 3   7.50 7.50

Christmas A179

Santa Claus and: 25c, Ship. 75c, Horse-drawn carriage. 80c, Helicopter. $1, Race car.

2008, Nov. 12   Perf. 13¾
1033-1036 A179   Set of 4   7.00 7.00

Silver Thatch A180

No. 1037: a, Silver thatch plant. b, People making rope strands. c, Man cobbing rope. d, Thatch products. e, Traditional home.

Wmk. 406
2009, Jan. 28   Litho.   Perf. 13¾
1037   Horiz. strip of 5   3.00 3.00
a.-e. A180 25c Any single   .60 .60
        Complete booklet, 2 #1037   6.00

Island Scenes A181

Designs: 20c, Hammock, palm trees, boat. 25c, House. 75c, Hammock under shelter at beach, palm trees, vert. 80c, Three cruise liners. $1, Direction signs near bus depot, vert. $1.50, Limestone pinnacles, Hell.
$2, Iguana.

2009, Apr. 9   Perf. 12½
1038-1043 A181   Set of 6   11.50 11.50
Souvenir Sheet
Perf. 13
1044 A181 $2 multi   5.00 5.00

Space Exploration A182

Designs: 20c, Mars Rover, 2004. 25c, Space Shuttle STS-71 launch, 1995. 75c, Hubble Space Telescope. $1, Apollo 11 launch, 1969. $1.50, International Space Station.
$2, Lunar Rover on Moon, painting by Capt. Alan Bean, vert.

Wmk. 406
2009, July 20   Litho.   Perf. 13¼
1045-1049 A182   Set of 5   9.00 9.00
Souvenir Sheet
Perf. 13x13¼
1050 A182 $2 multi   5.00 5.00
No. 1050 contains one 40x60mm stamp. Nos. 1045-1049 each were printed in sheets of 6.

Equality Through Democracy A183

Designs: No. 1051, 25c, Hands holding pens signing voting rolls. No. 1052, 25c, George Town Town Hall. 50c, Woman casting ballot.

Wmk. 406
2009, Sept. 23   Litho.   Perf. 13¾
1051-1053 A183   Set of 3   2.50 2.50
1053a   Sheet of 3,
        #1051-1053   2.50 2.50
Woman suffrage and Cayman Islands constitution, 50th anniv.

Christmas — A184

Images of Christmas stamps of 1997: 25c, Cayman Islands #749. 75c, Cayman Islands #750. 80c, Cayman Islands #751. $1, Cayman Islands #752.

Wmk. 406
2009, Oct. 22   Litho.   Perf. 14
1054-1057 A184   Set of 4   7.00 7.00

Shells A185

Designs: 20c, Hawk-wing conch. 25c, Ornate scallop. 60c, Chestnut turban. 75c, Beautiful mitre. 80c, Four-toothed nerite. $1.60, White-spotted marginella.
$3, Queen conch.

Wmk. 406
2010, June 30   Litho.   Perf. 13¼
1058-1063 A185   Set of 6   10.50 10.50
Souvenir Sheet
1064 A185 $3 multi   7.50 7.50

Shells — A186

Designs: 25c, Ornate scallop. 75c, Beautiful mitre.

Serpentine Die Cut 9½x9
2010, June 30   Unwmk.
Booklet Stamps
Self-Adhesive
1065 A186 25c multi   .65 .65
a.   Booklet pane of 10   6.50
1066 A186 75c multi   1.90 1.90
a.   Booklet pane of 10   19.00

WAR TAX STAMPS

No. 36 Surcharged:

a   b

1917, Feb. 26   Wmk. 3   Perf. 14
MR1 A5(a)   1½p on 2½p   11.00 13.50
a.   Fraction bar omitted   150.00 210.00
MR2 A5(b)   1½p on 2½p   2.10 7.25
a.   Fraction bar omitted   85.00 150.00
No. 1 exists with missing period. On No. 1 the distance between "WAR STAMP" and "1 ½" varies.

Surcharged

1917, Sept. 4
MR3 A5 1½p on 2½p ultra   1,000. 2,500.

Surcharged

1917, Sept. 4
MR4 A5 1½p on 2½p ultra   .30 .65

No. 33 Overprinted

1919, Feb. 4
MR5 A5 ½p green   .70 3.00
The "brownish paper" variety comes from the interleaving used for shipment from England.

Type of 1912-16 Surcharged

1919, Feb. 4
MR6 A5 1½p on 2½p orange   .95 1.50

No. 35 Surcharged

1920, Mar. 10
MR7 A5 1½p on 2p gray   1.90 8.50
The "rose-tinted paper" variety comes from the interleaving used for shipment from England.
A surcharge in red was not issued.

CENTRAL AFRICAN REPUBLIC

'sen-trəl 'a-fri-kən ri-'pə-blik

LOCATION — Western Africa, north of equator
GOVT. — Republic
AREA — 241,243 sq. mi.
POP. — 3,444,951 (1999 est.)
CAPITAL — Bangui

The former French colony of Ubangi-Shari, a unit in French Equatorial Africa, proclaimed itself the Central African Republic Dec. 1, 1958. It became the Central African Empire Dec. 4, 1976. It became the Central African Republic again in 1979.

100 Centimes = 1 Franc

Catalogue values for all unused stamps in this country are for Never Hinged items.

Watermark

TOR C
CARTE
TOR C
CARTE

Wmk. 385

Premier Barthélemy Boganda and Flag — A1

Design: 25fr, Boganda and flag, horiz.

Unwmk.

1959, Dec. 1		**Engr.**	**Perf. 13**	
1	A1	15fr multi	.40	.20
2	A1	25fr multi	.60	.20

1st anniv. of the Republic and honoring Premier Barthélemy Boganda (1910-59).
For overprints & surcharge see #12, 59, M1-M2.

Imperforates
Many stamps of Central African Republic exist imperforate in issued and trial colors, and also in small presentation sheets in issued colors.

Common Design Types pictured following the introduction.

C.C.T.A. Issue
Common Design Type

1960, May 21	**Unwmk.**	**Perf. 13**	
3	CD106	50fr lt grn & dk bl	1.90 .65

Dactyloceras Widenmanni — A2

Designs: Various butterflies.

1960-61				
4	A2	50c bl grn & dk red	.20	.20
5	A2	1fr multi	.20	.20
6	A2	2fr dk grn & brn	.20	.20
7	A2	3fr yel grn & dk red	.30	.20
8	A2	5fr multi	.35	.20
9	A2	10fr multi	.85	.35
10	A2	20fr multi	2.00	.50
11	A2	85fr multi	8.00	1.60
		Nos. 4-11 (8)	12.10	3.45

Issued: 50c-3fr, 6/10/61; others, 9/3/60.

No. 2 Overprinted:
"FETE NATIONALE 1-12-1960"

1960, Dec. 1			
12	A1	25fr multi	1.60 1.60

National Holiday, Dec. 1, 1960.

Louis Pasteur and Pasteur Institute, Bangui A3

1961, Feb. 25	**Unwmk.**	**Perf. 13**	
13	A3	20fr multi	1.25 .80

Opening of Pasteur Institute at Bangui.

Flag, Map, and UN Emblem A4

1961, Mar. 4			**Engr.**	
14	A4	15fr multi	.50	.30
15	A4	25fr multi	.60	.30
16	A4	85fr multi	1.75	1.00
		Nos. 14-16 (3)	2.85	1.60

Admission to the UN.

No. 15 Overprinted in Green: "FETE NATIONALE 1-12-61" and Star

1961, Dec. 1			
17	A4	25fr multi	2.25 2.25

National Holiday, Dec. 1.

No. 16 Surcharged in Red Brown:
"U.A.M. CONFERENCE DE BANGUI 25-27 Mars 1962"

1962, Mar. 25			
18	A4	50fr on 85fr multi	1.90 1.90

Conf. of the African and Malgache Union at Bangui, Mar. 25-27.

Abidjan Games Issue
Common Design Type

1962, July 21	**Photo.**	**Perf. 12½x12**	
19	CD109	20fr Hurdling	.55 .30
20	CD109	50fr Bicycling	1.40 .80
		Nos. 19-20,C6 (3)	4.45 2.60

African-Malgache Union Issue
Common Design Type

1962, Sept. 8		**Unwmk.**	
21	CD110	30fr multi	1.40 1.40

African and Malgache Union, 1st anniv.

Pres. David Dacko — A5

Soldiers with Flag — A6

1962		**Perf. 12**	
22	A5	20fr multi	.40 .20
23	A5	25fr multi	.60 .20

For surcharge see No. 60.

1963, Aug. 13		**Photo.**	
24	A6	20fr blk & multi	.75 .35

National Army, third anniversary.

Waves Around Globe A6a

Design: 100fr, Orbit patterns around globe.

1963, Sept. 19	**Unwmk.**	**Perf. 12½**	
25	A6a	25fr plum & grn	.75 .55
26	A6a	100fr org, bl & grn	1.90 1.50

Issued to publicize space communications.

Young Pioneers A7

1963, Oct. 14	**Engr.**	**Perf. 12½**	
27	A7	50fr grnsh bl, vio bl & brn	1.00 .55

Issued to honor Young Pioneers.

Boali Falls — A8

1963, Oct. 28		**Perf. 13**	
28	A8	30fr bl, grn & red brn	1.00 .45

Colotis Evippe A9

Designs: Various butterflies.			

1963, Nov. 18	**Photo.**	**Perf. 12½x13**	
29	A9	1fr multi	.35 .20
30	A9	3fr multi	.85 .30
31	A9	4fr multi	1.25 .45
32	A9	60fr multi	6.75 3.25
		Nos. 29-32 (4)	9.20 4.20

For surcharge see No. 58.

UNESCO Emblem, Scales and Tree — A9a

1963, Dec. 10		**Perf. 13**	
33	A9a	25fr grn, ol & red brn	1.00 .55

15th anniversary of the Universal Declaration of Human Rights.

Leaves and IQSY Emblem A10

1964, Apr. 20	**Engr.**	**Perf. 13**	
34	A10	25fr org, Prus grn & bis	1.40 .80

International Quiet Sun Year, 1964-65.

Child — A11

"All Men Are Men" — A12

Designs: Heads of Children.

1964, Aug. 13		**Unwmk.**	**Perf. 13**	
35	A11	20fr multi	.40	.20
36	A11	25fr multi	.50	.30
37	A11	40fr multi	.65	.45
38	A11	50fr multi	.90	.45
a.	Miniature sheet of 4, #35-38		3.75	3.75
	Nos. 35-38 (4)		2.45	1.40

Cooperation Issue
Common Design Type

1964, Nov. 7		**Engr.**	
39	CD119	25fr grn, mag & dk brn	1.00 .55

1964, Dec. 1	**Litho.**	**Perf. 13x12½**	
40	A12	25fr multi	1.00 .45

Issued to publicize National Unity.

Putting Yoke on Oxen A13

Designs: 50fr, Ox pulling harrow. 85fr, Team of oxen in field. 100fr, Hay wagon.

1965, Apr. 28		**Engr.**	**Perf. 13**	
41	A13	25fr sl grn, sep & rose	.60	.30
42	A13	50fr sl grn, lt bl & brn	1.00	.45
43	A13	85fr bl, grn & red brn	1.40	.70
44	A13	100fr multi	1.90	.90
		Nos. 41-44 (4)	4.90	2.35

For surcharges see Nos. 63-64.

Telegraph Receiver by Pouget-Maisonneuve — A14

ITU cent.: 30fr, Chappe telegraph, vert. 50fr, Doignon regulator, vert. 85fr, Pouillet telegraph transcriber.

1965, May 17		**Unwmk.**	
45	A14	25fr red, grn & ultra	.60 .40
46	A14	30fr lake & grn	.65 .40
47	A14	50fr car & vio	1.00 .60
48	A14	85fr red lil & slate	1.90 1.00
		Nos. 45-48 (4)	4.15 2.40

"Health" A15

25fr, "Clothes;" shuttle, cloth & women. 60fr, "Teaching;" student & school. 85fr, "Food;" mother feeding child, tractor in wheat field.

1965, June 10   Engr.   Perf. 13
49 A15 25fr ultra, brt grn & brn .50 .30
50 A15 50fr ultra, brn & grn .90 .45
51 A15 60fr grn, ultra & brn 1.00 .60
52 A15 85fr multi 1.40 .70
Nos. 49-52 (4) 3.80 2.05

Issued to publicize the slogans and aims of "M.E.S.A.N." (Mouvement d'Evolution Sociale de l'Afrique Noire). See No. C30.

Caterpillars and Moth on Coffee Branch — A16

Designs: 3fr, Hawk moth and caterpillar on coffee leaves, horiz. 30fr, Platyedra moth and larvae on cotton plant.

1965, Aug. 25   Engr.   Perf. 13
53 A16 2fr dk pur, dp org & sl grn .45 .20
54 A16 3fr blk, sl grn & red 1.25 .25
55 A16 30fr red lil, red & sl grn 7.25 .90
Nos. 53-55 (3) 8.95 1.35

Issued to publicize plant protection.

Boy Scout, Tents and Animals A17

Design: 25fr, Campfire and Scout emblem.

1965, Sept. 27   Unwmk.   Perf. 13
56 A17 25fr red org, bl & red lil 1.00 .25
57 A17 50fr brn & Prus bl 1.40 .60

Issued to honor the Boy Scouts.

Nos. 30, 1 and 22 Surcharged in Black or Brown

Engraved; Photogravure
Perf. 13, 12, 12½x13
1965, Aug. 26   Unwmk.
58 A9 2fr on 3fr multi 5.75 5.75
59 A1 5fr on 15fr multi 4.50 4.50
60 A5 10fr on 20fr multi (Br) 6.25 6.25
Nos. 58-60 (3) 16.50 16.50

The surcharges are adjusted to shape of stamps.

UN Emblem and Wheat A18

1965, Oct. 16   Engr.   Perf. 13
61 A18 50fr ocher, sl grn & brt bl 1.25 .70

FAO "Freedom from Hunger Campaign."

Diamond Cutter A19

1966, Mar. 14   Engr.   Perf. 13
62 A19 25fr car rose, dk pur & brn 1.40 .45

Nos. 43-44 Surcharged

1966, Feb.
63 A13 5fr on 85fr multi .40 .40
64 A13 10fr on 100fr multi .60 .60

Issue dates: 5fr, Feb. 17; 10fr, Feb. 15.

Statue of Mbaka Woman Porter — A20

WHO Headquarters, Geneva — A21

1966, Apr. 9   Photo.   Perf. 13x12½
65 A20 25fr multi 1.00 .45

Intl. Negro Arts Festival, Dakar, Senegal, Apr. 1-24.

1966, May 3   Photo.   Unwmk.
66 A21 25fr pur, bl & yel 1.00 .45

Inauguration of the WHO Headquarters, Geneva.

Eulophia Cucullata — A22

Orchids: 5fr, Lissochilus horsfalii. 10fr, Tridactyle bicaudata. 15fr, Polystachya. 20fr, Eulophia alta. 25fr, Microcelia macrorrhynchium.

1966, May 16   Photo.   Perf. 12x12½
Orchids in Natural Colors
67 A22 2fr dk red .40 .20
68 A22 5fr brn org & vio .95 .25
69 A22 10fr bl grn & blk 1.25 .40
70 A22 15fr lt grn & dk brn 1.75 .65
71 A22 20fr dk grn 2.75 1.00
72 A22 25fr lt ultra & brn 4.00 1.25
Nos. 67-72 (6) 11.10 3.75

For surcharge see No. 78.

Congo Forest Mouse A23

Rodents: 10fr, One-stripe mouse. 20fr, Dollman's tree mouse, vert.

1966, Sept. 15   Photo.   Perf. 12½x12
73 A23 5fr yel & multi .70 .30
74 A23 10fr tan & multi 1.25 .45
75 A23 20fr lt grn & multi 2.40 .80
Nos. 73-75 (3) 4.35 1.55

UNESCO Emblem — A24

Pres. Jean Bedel Bokassa — A25

1966, Dec. 5   Photo.   Perf. 13
76 A24 30fr multi .75 .35

20th anniv. of UNESCO.

1967, Jan. 1   Perf. 12x12½
77 A25 30fr yel grn, blk & bis brn .75 .35

No. 72 Surcharged with New Value and "XX"

1967, May 8   Photo.   Perf. 12x12½
78 A22 10fr on 25fr multi .55 .25

See No. C43.

Central Market, Bangui A26

1967, Aug. 8   Photo.   Perf. 12½x13
79 A26 30fr multi 1.00 .40

Safari Hotel, Bangui A27

1967, Sept. 26   Photo.   Perf. 12½x13
80 A27 30fr multi 1.00 .40

Leucocoprinus Africanus — A28

Various Mushrooms

1967, Oct. 3   Photo.   Perf. 13
81 A28 5fr dk brn, ol & ocher 10.00 .80
82 A28 10fr dk brn, ultra & yel 15.00 1.25
83 A28 15fr dk brn, sl grn & yel 17.50 1.40
84 A28 30fr multi 50.00 4.00
85 A28 50fr multi 75.00 6.00
Nos. 81-85 (5) 167.50 13.45

Map, Radio Tower, Projector and People A29

1967, Oct. 31   Engr.
86 A29 30fr emer, ocher & indigo 1.00 .45

Radiovision service.

African Hair Style — A30

Various African Hair Styles.

1967, Nov. 7   Engr.   Perf. 13
87 A30 5fr ultra, dk brn & bis brn .30 .20
88 A30 10fr car, dk brn & bis brn .50 .25
89 A30 15fr dp grn, dk brn & bis brn .75 .40
90 A30 20fr org, dk brn & bis brn .75 .40
91 A30 30fr red lil, dk brn & bis brn 1.40 .55
Nos. 87-91 (5) 3.70 1.80

Nurse Vaccinating Children A31

1967, Nov. 14
92 A31 30fr dk red brn & brt grn 1.00 .55

Vaccination campaign, 1967-70.

Douglas DC-3 A32

1967, Nov. 24
93 A32 1fr shown .20 .20
94 A32 2fr Beechcraft Baron .20 .20
95 A32 5fr Douglas DC-4 .20 .20
Nos. 93-95,C47-C49 (6) 22.60 7.40

Pierced Stone, Kwe Tribe — A33

Designs: 30fr, Primitive dwelling at Toulou, horiz. 100fr, Megaliths, Bouar. 130fr, Rock painting (people), Toulou, horiz.

1967, Dec. 26   Engr.   Perf. 13
96 A33 30fr crim, ind & mar .75 .20
97 A33 50fr ol brn, ocher & dk grn 1.50 .50
98 A33 100fr dk brn, brt bl & brn 3.00 .65
99 A33 130fr dk red, brn & dk grn 3.25 .65
Nos. 96-99 (4) 8.50 2.00

6th Pan-African Prehistoric Cong., Dakar.

Tanker, Refinery and Map of Area Served — A33a

1968, July 30   Photo.   Perf. 12½
100 A33a 30fr multi 1.00 .30

Issued to commemorate the opening of the Port Gentil (Gabon) Refinery, June 12, 1968.

Bulldozer Clearing Land — A34

Designs: 10fr, Baoule cattle. 20fr, 15,000-spindle spinning machine. No. 104, Automatic Diederichs looms. No. 105, Bulldozer.

1968, Oct. 1   **Engr.**   **Perf. 13**
101 A34   5fr blk, grn & dk brn   .40   .20
102 A34   10fr blk, pale grn & bis brn   .55   .30
103 A34   20fr grn, red brn & yel   .90   .30
104 A34   30fr brn, ol & ultra   1.40   .55
105 A34   30fr ind, red brn & sl grn   1.40   .55
    Nos. 101-105 (5)   4.65 1.90

Issued to publicize "Operation Bokassa."

Bangui Mosque A35

1968, Oct. 14
106 A35   30fr grn, bl & ocher   .90   .40

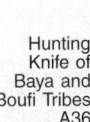

Hunting Knife of Baya and Boufi Tribes A36

20fr, Hunting knife of Nzakara tribe. 30fr, Crossbow of Babinga & Babenzele (pygmy) tribes.

1968, Nov. 19   **Engr.**   **Perf. 13**
107 A36   10fr lem, Prus bl & ultra   .55   .25
108 A36   20fr ultra, dk ol & sl grn   .70   .30
109 A36   30fr sl grn, ultra & brn org   1.60   .40
    Nos. 107-109 (3)   2.85   .95

"Ville de Bangui," 1958 — A37

River Boats: 30fr, "J. B. Gouandjia," 1968. 50fr, "Lamblin," 1944.

1968, Dec. 10   **Engr.**   **Perf. 13**
    Size: 36x22mm
110 A37   10fr mag, brt grn & vio bl   .65   .40
111 A37   30fr bl, grn & brn   1.10   .45
112 A37   50fr brn, sl & ol grn   1.90   .55
    Nos. 110-112,C62-C63 (5)   9.15 3.65

Woman Javelin Thrower — A38

1969, Mar. 18   **Photo.**   **Perf. 13x12½**
113 A38   5fr shown   .30   .20
114 A38   10fr Women runners   .30   .20
115 A38   15fr Soccer   .50   .25
    Nos. 113-115,C71-C72 (5)   4.45 1.55

BIT and ILO Emblems and Worker A39

1969, May 20   **Photo.**   **Perf. 12½x13**
116 A39   30fr dp bl, grn & ol brn   1.10   .40
117 A39   50fr dp car, grn & ol brn   1.60   .55
    50th anniv. of the ILO.

Pres. Bokassa — A40   Garayah — A41

1969, Dec. 1   **Litho.**   **Perf. 13x13½**
118 A40   30fr vermilion & multi   .65   .30

ASECNA Issue
Common Design Type

1969, Dec. 12   **Engr.**   **Perf. 13**
119 CD132   100fr dp bl   2.25   .80

1970, Jan. 6   **Engr.**   **Perf. 13**
    Musical Instuments: 15fr, Ngombi (harp) horiz. 30fr, Xylophone, horiz. 50fr, Ndala (lute) horiz. 130fr, Gatta and babyon (drums).
120 A41   10fr yel grn, dk grn & ocher   .65   .25
121 A41   15fr bl grn, ocher & dk brn   .65   .25
122 A41   30fr mar, ocher & dk brn   1.10   .45
123 A41   50fr rose car & ind   1.60   .55
124 A41   130fr brt bl, brn & ol   5.25   .95
    Nos. 120-124 (5)   9.25 2.45

UPU Headquarters Issue
Common Design Type

1970, May 20   **Engr.**   **Perf. 13**
125 CD133   100fr ultra, ver & red brn   1.90   .70

Loading Platform and Flour Storage Bins A42

50fr, Flour milling machinery. 100fr, View of mill.

1970, Feb. 24   **Litho.**   **Perf. 14**
126 A42   25fr sl & multi   11.00   .70
127 A42   50fr lil & multi   26.50 1.50
128 A42   100fr red & multi   37.50 2.50
    Nos. 126-128 (3)   75.00 4.70

    Inauguration of SICPAD (Société Industrielle Centrafricaine des Produits Alimentaires et Dérivés), a part of Operation Bokassa, 2/22/68.

Pres. Bokassa — A43

1970, Aug. 13   **Litho.**   **Perf. 14**
129 A43   30fr multi   5.75 3.50
130 A43   40fr multi   7.50 4.25

Cheese Factory, Sarki — A44

Silk Worm — A45

10fr, M'Bali Ranch. 20fr, Zebu, vert.

    Perf. 13x13½, 13½x13
1970, Sept. 15
131 A44   5fr red & multi   .55   .30
132 A44   10fr red & multi   6.50 4.25
133 A44   20fr red & multi   1.40   .55
134 A45   40fr red & multi   3.00   .95
    Nos. 131-134,C83 (5)   15.95 7.15

    Issued to publicize Operation Bokassa, a national development plan.
    Nos. 131-134 exist perf 10.

Gnathonemus Monteiri — A46

    River Fish: 20fr, Mormyrus proboscirostris. 30fr, Marcusenius wilverthi. 40fr, Gnathonemus elephas. 50fr, Gnathonemus curvirostris.

1971, Apr. 6   **Photo.**   **Perf. 12½**
135 A46   10fr multi   .40   .25
136 A46   20fr multi   .75   .30
137 A46   30fr multi   1.10   .60
138 A46   40fr multi   2.50   .70
139 A46   50fr multi   2.75 1.10
    Nos. 135-139 (5)   7.50 2.95

Berberati Cathedral A47

1971, July 20   **Litho.**   **Perf. 13½**
140 A47   5fr grn & multi   .55   .25
    New Roman Catholic Cathedral at Berberati.

Charles de Gaulle — A48

Gray Galago — A49

1971, Aug. 20   **Perf. 13½x13**
141 A48   100fr brt bl & multi   3.25 1.75
    In memory of Gen. Charles de Gaulle (1890-1970), president of France.

1971, Oct. 25   **Photo.**   **Perf. 13**
    Designs: 40fr, Elegant galago. 100fr, Calabar potto, horiz. 150fr, Bosman's potto, horiz. 200fr, Oustalet's colobo, horiz.
142 A49   30fr pink & multi   .80   .60
143 A49   40fr lt bl & multi   1.10   .70
144 A49   100fr multi   3.25 1.50
145 A49   150fr multi   5.50 2.40
146 A49   200fr multi   6.75 3.00
    Nos. 142-146 (5)   17.40 8.20

Alan B. Shepard — A50

    #148, Yuri Gagarin. #149, Edwin E. Aldrin, Jr. #150, Alexei Leonov. #151, Neil A. Armstrong on moon. #152, Lunokhod I on moon.

1971, Nov. 19   **Litho.**   **Perf. 14**
147 A50   40fr vio & multi   .55   .30
148 A50   40fr vio & multi   .55   .30
149 A50   100fr multi   1.40   .45
150 A50   100fr multi   1.40   .45
151 A50   200fr red & multi   2.75 1.10
152 A50   200fr red & multi   2.75 1.10
    Nos. 147-152 (6)   9.40 3.70

    Space achievements of US and Russia.

"Operation Bokassa" and Pres. Bokassa A51

1971, Dec. 1   **Photo.**   **Perf. 13**
153 A51   40fr red & multi   .90   .45
    12th anniversary of independence.

Racial Equality Emblem A52

1971, Dec. 6   **Litho.**
154 A52   50fr multi   .90   .45
    Intl. Year Against Racial Discrimination.

Bokassa School Emblem and Cadets — A53

Book Year Emblem — A54

1972, Jan. 1   Photo.
155 A53 30fr gold & multi   .90 .45
J. B. Bokassa Military School.

1972, Mar. 11   Photo.   Perf. 12½x13
156 A54 100fr red brn, gold & org   3.50 1.50
International Book Year 1972.

"Your Heart is your Health" A55

1972, Apr. 7   Photo.   Perf. 13x12½
157 A55 100fr yel, blk & car   1.90 .95
World Health Day.

Red Cross Workers in Village — A56

1972, May 8   Perf. 13
158 A56 150fr multi   3.50 1.60
25th World Red Cross Day.

Globe A57

1972, May 17   Litho.
159 A57 50fr yel, blk & dp org   .90 .55
4th World Telecommunications Day.

Pres. and Mrs. Bokassa and Family — A58

1972, May 28   Perf. 14
160 A58 30fr yel & multi   .65 .30
Mother's Day. Mothers' gold medal awarded to Catherine Bokassa.

Pres. Bokassa Planting Cotton, Map of Africa — A59

1972, June 5   Photo.   Perf. 13
161 A59 40fr yel & multi   .65 .40
Operation Bokassa, a natl. development plan.

Postal Checking and Savings Center A60

1972, June 21
162 A60 30fr yel org & multi   .65 .40

Irrigated Rice Fields — A61

"Le Pacifique" Apartment House A62

25fr, Plowing rice field. #166, Swimming pool, Hotel St. Sylvestre. #167, Entrance, Hotel St. Sylvestre. #168, J. B. Bokassa University.

1972   Litho.   Perf. 13x13½
163 A61 5fr multi   1.25 .25
164 A61 25fr multi   2.10 .30
**   Engr.   Perf. 13**
165 A62 30fr multi   .40 .25
166 A62 30fr multi   .50 .30
167 A62 40fr multi   .60 .40
168 A62 40fr multi   .65 .40
     Nos. 163-168 (6)   5.50 1.90
Operation Bokassa. Issued: 5fr, 25fr, 11/10; #165, 6/27; #166-167, 12/9; #168, 8/26.

Bull Chasing Woman on Clock Face — A63

Scenes Painted on Clock Faces: 10fr, Men & open cooking fire. 20fr, Fishermen. 30fr, Palms, monkeys & giraffe. 40fr, Warriors.

1972, July 31   Photo.   Perf. 12½
169 A63 5fr dk red & multi   .30 .30
170 A63 10fr brt bl & multi   .30 .30
171 A63 20fr grn & multi   .60 .30
172 A63 30fr yel & multi   .85 .45
173 A63 40fr vio & multi   1.25 .60
     Nos. 169-173 (5)   3.30 1.95
HORCEN Central African clock and watch factory.

Protestant Youth Center — A64

10fr, Postal runner carrying mail in cleft stick.

1972, Aug. 12   Perf. 13
174 A64 10fr multi, vert.   .30 .30
175 A64 20fr multi   .50 .30
     Nos. 174-175,C95-C98 (6)   8.35 5.10
Centraphilex 1972, Central African Philatelic Exhibition, Bangui.

Mail Truck A65

1972, Oct. 23   Photo.   Perf. 13
176 A65 100fr ocher & multi   1.90 .70
Universal Postal Union Day.

Mother Teaching Child to Write — A66

Central African Mothers: 10fr, Caring for infant. 15fr, Combing child's hair. 20fr, Teaching to read. 180fr, Nursing. 190fr, Teaching to walk.

1972, Dec. 27   Perf. 13½x13
177 A66 5fr multi   .20 .20
178 A66 10fr lil & multi   .30 .20
179 A66 15fr dl org & multi   .30 .20
180 A66 20fr yel grn & multi   .50 .25
181 A66 180fr multi   2.75 1.25
182 A66 190fr pink & multi   2.75 1.25
     Nos. 177-182 (6)   6.80 3.35

Farmer Carrying Sheaf — A67

1973, May 30   Photo.   Perf. 13
183 A67 50fr vio bl & multi   .90 .45
10th anniv. of the World Food Program.

Garcinia Punctata A68

African Flora: 20fr, Bertiera racemosa. 30fr, Corynanthe pachyceras. 40fr, Combretoden-dron africanum. 50fr, Xylopia Villosa, vert.

1973, June 8
184 A68 10fr pale bl & multi   .55 .25
185 A68 20fr multi   .90 .30
186 A68 30fr lt gray & multi   1.10 .45
187 A68 40fr multi   1.75 .60
188 A68 50fr multi   2.25 .80
     Nos. 184-188 (5)   6.55 2.40
For surcharge see No. 193.

Pygmy Chameleon A69

1973, June 26   Photo.   Perf. 13
189 A69 15fr multi   1.50 .40

Caterpillar — A70

Designs: Various caterpillars.

1973, Aug. 6   Photo.   Perf. 13
190 A70 3fr multi   1.50 .30
191 A70 5fr multi   2.25 .40
192 A70 25fr multi   4.75 .60
     Nos. 190-192 (3)   8.50 1.30
For surcharge see No. 259.

No. 184 Surcharged with New Value, 2 Bars, and Overprinted in Red: "SECHERESSE SOLIDARITE AFRICAINE"

1973, Aug. 16
193 A68 100fr on 10fr multi   1.75 1.00
African solidarity in drought emergency.

African Postal Union Issue
Common Design Type

1973, Sept. 12   Engr.   Perf. 13
194 CD137 100fr dk brn, red org & ol   1.10 .55

Pres. Bokassa and CAR Flag — A71

1973, Nov. 30   Photo.   Perf. 12½
195 A71 1fr brn & multi   .20 .20
196 A71 2fr pur & multi   .20 .20
197 A71 3fr vio bl & multi   .20 .20
198 A71 5fr ocher & multi   .20 .20
199 A71 10fr multi   .40 .20
200 A71 15fr org & multi   .40 .25
201 A71 20fr multi   .50 .25
202 A71 30fr dk grn & multi   .50 .30
203 A71 40fr dk brn & multi   .65 .40
     Nos. 195-203,C117-C118 (11)   5.40 3.30

INTERPOL Emblem A72

1973, Dec. 20   *Perf. 13x12½*
204 A72 50fr yellow & multi   .90 .45
Intl. Criminal Police Organization, 50th anniv.

Catherine Bokassa Center A73

40fr, Ambulance in front of Catherine Bokassa Center.

1974, Jan. 24   **Engr.**   *Perf. 13*
205 A73 30fr multi   .40 .25
206 A73 40fr multi   .50 .30
Catherine Bokassa Center for Mothers and Children.

Cigarette-making Machine — A74

10fr, Cigarette in ashtray, & factory. 30fr, Hand lighting cigarette, & Administration Building.

1974, Jan. 29
207 A74 5fr slate grn & multi   .20 .20
208 A74 10fr slate grn & multi   .40 .25
209 A74 30fr slate grn & multi   .50 .25
     Nos. 207-209 (3)   1.10 .70
Publicity for Centra cigarettes.

"Communications" A75

1974, June 8   **Photo.**   *Perf. 12½x13*
210 A75 100fr multi   1.75 .85
World Telecommunications Day.
For surcharge see No. 280.

People and WPY Emblem A76

1974, June 20   **Engr.**   *Perf. 13*
211 A76 100fr red, slate grn & brn 1.10 .55
World Population Year.
For surcharge see No. 281.

Mother, Child, WHO Emblem — A77

1974, July 10
212 A77 100fr multi   1.75 .70
26th anniv. of WHO.
For surcharge see No. 282.

Hoeing — A78

Veterans' activities: 10fr, Battle scene ("yesterday"). 15fr, Pastoral scene ("today"). 20fr, Rice planting. 25fr, Storehouse. 40fr, Veterans Headquarters. Borders show tanks and tractors.

1974, Nov. 15   **Litho.**   *Perf. 13*
213 A78 10fr multi   .20 .20
214 A78 15fr multi   .30 .20
215 A78 20fr multi   .30 .20
216 A78 25fr multi   .40 .25
217 A78 30fr multi   .40 .25
218 A78 40fr multi   .60 .25
     Nos. 213-218 (6)   2.20 1.35
For surcharges see Nos. 260, 265, 267.

Presidents and Flags of Cameroun, CAR, Congo, Gabon and Meeting Center — A79

1974, Dec. 8   **Photo.**   *Perf. 13*
219 A79 40fr gold & multi   .65 .40
See #C126 and note after Cameroun #595.
For surcharge see No. 272.

House in OCAM City — A80

Scenes in housing development, OCAM City.

1975, Feb. 1   **Photo.**   *Perf. 13*
220 A80 30fr multi   .40 .25
221 A80 40fr multi   .50 .30
222 A80 50fr multi   .60 .30
223 A80 100fr multi   1.00 .55
     Nos. 220-223 (4)   2.50 1.40
For surcharges see Nos. 269, 273.

1975, Feb. 22
Cottage scenes in J. B. Bokassa "pilot village."
224 A80 25fr multi   .30 .20
225 A80 30fr multi   .40 .25
226 A80 40fr multi   .50 .30
     Nos. 224-226 (3)   1.20 .75
For surcharges see Nos. 268, 270, 274.

Foreign Ministry A81

Television Station A82

1975, Feb. 28   *Perf. 13x12½*
227 A81 40fr multi   .65 .40
     Perf. 13
228 A82 40fr multi   .65 .40
Public buildings, Bangui.
For surcharges see Nos. 275-276.

Bokassa's Saber — A83

Design: 40fr, Bokassa's baton.

1975, Feb. 22   **Photo.**   *Perf. 13*
229 A83 30fr dp bl & multi   .55 .30
230 A83 40fr vio bl & multi   .55 .30
Jean Bedel Bokassa, President for Life and Marshal of the Republic. See Nos. C127-C128. For surcharge see No. 286.

Traffic Signs A84

1975, Mar. 20
231 A84 5fr Do Not Enter   .20 .20
232 A84 10fr Stop   .20 .20
233 A84 20fr No parking   .30 .20
234 A84 30fr School   .50 .25
235 A84 40fr Intersection   .75 .30
     Nos. 231-235 (5)   1.95 1.15
For surcharges see Nos. 261, 277.

Buffon's Kob — A85

1975, June 24   **Photo.**   *Perf. 13*
236 A85 10fr shown   .60 .30
237 A85 15fr Wart hog   1.40 .30
238 A85 20fr Waterbuck   2.00 .30
239 A85 30fr Lion   2.00 .45
     Nos. 236-239 (4)   6.00 1.35
For surcharges see Nos. 262-263, 266, 271.

Crane Lifting Log onto Truck A86

Designs: 10fr, Forest, vert. 15fr, Tree felling, vert. 100fr, Log pile. 150fr, Logs transported by raft. 200fr, Lumberyard.

1975, Nov. 28   **Engr.**   *Perf. 13*
240 A86 10fr multi   .20 .20
241 A86 15fr multi   .30 .20
242 A86 50fr multi   .55 .20
243 A86 100fr multi   1.50 .55
244 A86 150fr multi   1.75 1.00
245 A86 200fr multi   2.25 1.10
     Nos. 240-245 (6)   6.55 3.25
Promotion of Central African wood.
For surcharges see Nos. 264, 279.

Women's Heads and Various Occupations — A87

1975, Dec. 10   **Photo.**
246 A87 40fr multi   .50 .25
247 A87 100fr multi   1.40 .55
International Women's Year 1975.

Alexander Graham Bell — A88

1976, Mar. 25   **Litho.**   *Perf. 12½x13*
248 A88 100fr yel & blk   2.25 1.00
Centenary of first telephone call by Alexander Graham Bell, Mar. 10, 1876.
For surcharge see No. 283.

Satellite and ITU Emblem — A89

#250, UPU emblem, various forms of mail transport.

1976   **Engr.**   *Perf. 13*
249 A89 100fr vio bl, claret & grn 1.90 1.00
250 A89 100fr car, grn & ocher 1.60 .80
World Telecommunications Day (No. 249); Universal Postal Union Day (No. 250).
For surcharges see Nos. 284-285.

Soyuz on Launching Pad — A90

Design: 50fr, Apollo rocket.

1976, June 14   **Litho.**   *Perf. 14x13½*
251 A90 40fr multi   .65 .25
252 A90 50fr multi   1.00 .25
     Nos. 251-252,C135-C137 (5)   8.10 2.25
Apollo Soyuz space test project, Russo-American cooperation, launched July 15, link-up July 17, 1975.
For surcharges see Nos. 287, 290, C161, C168, C173, C177.

Drurya Antimachus — A91

Butterfly: 40fr, Argema mittrei, vert.

1976, Sept. 20   Litho.   Perf. 12½
253 A91 30fr ocher & multi   9.00 1.25
254 A91 40fr ultra & multi   12.50 1.50
   Nos. 253-254,C145-C146 (4)   48.50 6.25

For surcharge see #278.

Slalom, Piero Gros — A92

60fr, Karl Schnabel and Toni Innauer.

1976, Sept. 23   Perf. 13½
255 A92 40fr multi   .65 .25
256 A92 60fr multi   1.00 .30
   Nos. 255-256,C147-C149 (5)   8.05 2.45

12th Winter Olympic Games winners,
Innsbruck.
For surcharges see Nos. 288, 291, C164,
C170, C174, C178.

Viking Components A93

Design: 60fr, Viking take-off.

1976, Dec.
257 A93 40fr multi   .65 .25
258 A93 60fr multi   1.00 .30
   Nos. 257-258,C151-C153 (5)   8.05 2.40

Viking Mars project.
For surcharges and overprints see Nos.
289, 292, 391-392, C165, C171, C175, C179.

Central African Empire
Stamps of 1973-76 Overprinted with
Bars and "EMPIRE CENTRAFRICAIN"
in Black, Green, Violet Blue, Silver,
Carmine, Brown or Red

Printing and Perforations as Before
1977, Mar.
259 A70   3fr (#190; B)   .30 .30
260 A78   10fr (#213;B)   .30 .30
261 A84   10fr (#232;VB)   .30 .30
262 A85   10fr (#236;C)   .30 .30
263 A85   15fr (#237;C)   .50 .50
264 A86   15fr (#241;B)   .30 .30
265 A78   20fr (#215;B)   .40 .40
266 A85   20fr (#238;C)   .50 .50
267 A78   25fr (#216;B)   .40 .40
268 A80   25fr (#224;B)   .40 .40
269 A80   30fr (#225;VB)   .50 .50
270 A80   30fr (#220;B)   .50 .50
271 A85   30fr (#239;C)   .60 .60
272 A79   40fr (#219;B)   .70 .70
273 A80   40fr (#221;VB)   .75 .75
274 A80   40fr (#226;B)   .70 .70
275 A81   40fr (#227;B & S)   .70 .70
276 A82   40fr (#228;B)   .75 .75
277 A84   40fr (#235;VB)   .75 .75
278 A91   40fr (#254;B)   .75 .75
279 A86   50fr (#242;Br)   1.00 1.00
280 A75 100fr (#210;B)   1.90 1.90
281 A76 100fr (#211;B)   1.90 1.90
282 A77 100fr (#212;G)   1.90 1.90
283 A88 100fr (#248;B)   1.90 1.90
284 A89 100fr (#249;B)   2.25 2.25
285 A89 100fr (#250;B)   2.50 2.50
   Nos. 259-285 (27)   23.75 23.75

Stamps of 1975-76 Overprinted
"EMPIRE CENTRAFRICAIN" in Black
on Silver Panel

1977, Apr. 1
286 A83 40fr multi (#230)   .90 .90
287 A90 40fr multi (#251)   .70 .70
288 A92 40fr multi (#255)   .70 .70
289 A93 40fr multi (#257)   .70 .70
290 A90 50fr multi (#252)   1.00 1.00
291 A92 60fr multi (#256)   .90 .90
292 A93 60fr multi (#258)   .90 .90
   Nos. 286-292 (7)   5.80 5.80

Pierre and Marie Curie — A94

Design: 60fr, Wilhelm C. Roentgen.

1977, Apr. 1   Litho.   Perf. 13½
293 A94 40fr multi   1.00 .30
294 A94 60fr multi   1.00 .40
   Nos. 293-294,C180-C182 (5)   14.25 2.75

Nobel Prize winners.

Italy No. C42 and Faustine Temple,
Rome — A95

60fr, Russia #C12 & St. Basil's Cathedral,
Moscow.

1977, Apr. 11   Litho.   Perf. 11
295 A95 40fr multi   1.00 .25
296 A95 60fr multi   1.10 .40
   Nos. 295-296,C184-C186 (5)   9.75 2.55

75th anniversary of the Zeppelin.

Lindbergh over Paris — A96

Designs: 60fr, Santos Dumont and "14 bis."
100fr, Bleriot and monoplane. 200fr, Roald
Amundsen and "N24." 300fr, Concorde. 500fr,
Lindbergh and Spirit of St. Louis.

1977, Sept. 30   Litho.   Perf. 13½
297 A96 50fr multi   .65 .20
298 A96 60fr multi   1.00 .25
299 A96 100fr multi   1.75 .40
300 A96 200fr multi   2.50 .55
301 A96 300fr multi   5.00 1.25
   Nos. 297-301 (5)   10.90 2.65

Souvenir Sheet
302 A96 500fr multi   6.00 2.00

History of aviation, famous fliers.

Shot on Goal A97

Designs: 60fr, Heading ball in net. 100fr,
Backfield defense. 200fr, Argentina '78
poster. 300fr, Mario Zagalo and stadium.
500fr, Ferenc Puskas.

1977, Nov. 18   Litho.   Perf. 13½
303 A97 50fr multi   .50 .20
304 A97 60fr multi   .65 .25
305 A97 100fr multi   1.25 .30
306 A97 200fr multi   2.10 .55
307 A97 300fr multi   3.50 .90
   Nos. 303-307 (5)   8.00 2.20

Souvenir Sheet
308 A97 500fr multi   5.50 1.75

World Soccer Championships, Argentina,
June 1-25, 1978.
For overprints see Nos. 370-375.

Emperor Bokassa I, Central African Flag — A98

1977, Dec. 4   Litho.   Perf. 13½
309 A98 40fr multi   .40 .20
310 A98 60fr multi   .55 .25
311 A98 100fr multi   1.00 .45
312 A98 150fr multi   1.40 .60
   Nos. 309-312,C188-C189 (6)   8.00 3.55

Coronation of Emperor Bokassa I, Dec. 4.

Lilium — A99   Electronic Tree,
                   ITU
                   Emblem — A100

1977   Litho.   Perf. 13½x14
313 A99 5fr shown   .55 .30
314 A99 10fr Hibiscus   1.10 .55

For overprints see Nos. 408-409.

1977
315 A100 100fr blk, org & brn   3.00 1.60

World Telecommunications Day.

Bible and People A101

1977   Litho.   Perf. 14x13½
316 A101 40fr multi   9.00 1.50

Bible Week.

People and Rotary Emblem A102

1977
317 A102 60fr multi   4.50 2.00

Rotary Club of Bangui, 20th anniversary.

Holy Family, by Rubens A103

Rubens Paintings: 150fr, Marie de Medicis.
200fr, Son of artist. 300fr, Neptune. 500fr,
Marie de Medicis, diff.

1978, Jan. 26
318 A103 60fr multi   .60 .20
319 A103 150fr multi   1.50 .40
320 A103 200fr multi   2.40 .60
321 A103 300fr multi   3.50 .80
   Nos. 318-321 (4)   8.00 2.00

Souvenir Sheet
322 A103 500fr gold & multi   6.00 2.00

Peter Paul Rubens (1577-1640).

Rhinoceros — A104

Endangered Animals and Wildlife Fund
Emblem: 50fr, Slender-nosed crocodile. 60fr,
Leopard, vert. 100fr, Giraffe, vert. 200fr, Ele-
phant. 300fr, Gorilla, vert.

1978, Feb. 21   Litho.   Perf. 13½
323 A104 40fr multi   1.75 .30
324 A104 50fr multi   2.50 .35
325 A104 60fr multi   2.75 .55
326 A104 100fr multi   4.75 .90
327 A104 200fr multi   12.00 1.25
328 A104 300fr multi   14.00 2.00
   Nos. 323-328 (6)   37.75 5.35

Bokassa Sports Palace A105

Design: 60fr, Sports Palace, side view.

1978   Perf. 14
329 A105 40fr multi   .50 .25
330 A105 60fr multi   .65 .40

Automatic Telephone Exchange, Bangui A106

1978
331 A106 40fr multi   .50 .25
332 A106 60fr multi   .65 .40

Diligence and Satellite — A107

Designs (UPU Emblem and): 50fr, Steam
locomotive and communications via satellite.
60fr, Paddle-wheel steamer and ship-to-shore

communication via satellite. 80fr, Old mail truck and satellite.

1978, May 17   *Perf. 13½*
333 A107 40fr multi   .20   .20
334 A107 50fr multi   3.00 1.25
335 A107 60fr multi   .30   .20
336 A107 80fr multi   .40   .20
    Nos. 333-336,C191-C192 (6) 6.10 2.40
    Posts and telecommunications, cent. of progress.

Mask — A108

Capt. Cook on "Endeavour" A109

Designs: 30fr, Mask. 60fr, Women dancers, horiz. 100fr, Men dancers, horiz.

Perf. 13½x14, 14x13½

1978, July 11   *Litho.*
337 A108 20fr blk & yel   .75   .30
338 A108 30fr blk & brt bl   .75   .30
339 A108 60fr blk & multi   1.90   .60
340 A108 100fr blk & multi   3.25   .95
    Nos. 337-340 (4)   6.65 2.15

Black-African World Arts Festival, Lagos. For overprints see Nos. 411-412.

1978, Aug. 30   *Perf. 14½*
    60fr, Resolution off Hawaii. 200fr, Hawaiians welcoming Capt. Cook. 350fr, Masked rowers in Hawaiian boat.
341 A109 60fr multi, horiz.   .75   .20
342 A109 80fr multi   1.25   .25
343 A109 200fr multi, horiz.   2.50   .70
344 A109 350fr multi, horiz.   4.50 1.25
    Nos. 341-344 (4)   9.00 2.40
    Capt. James Cook (1728-1779), explorer.

Dürer, Self-portrait A110

Dürer Paintings: 80fr, The Four Apostles. 200fr, Virgin and Child. 350fr, Emperor Maximilian I.

**1978, Oct. 24   Litho.   *Perf. 13½*
345 A110 60fr multi   .65   .25
346 A110 80fr multi   1.10   .25
347 A110 200fr multi   2.50   .85
348 A110 350fr multi   4.75 1.40
    Nos. 345-348 (4)   9.00 2.75

Albrecht Dürer (1471-1528), German painter.

Tutankhamen's Gold Mask — A111

Treasures of Tutankhamen: 60fr, King and Queen, gold back panel of throne. 80fr, Gilt folding chair. 100fr, King wearing crowns of Upper and Lower Egypt, painted wood sculpture. 120fr, Lion's head. 150fr, Tutankhamen, wood stature. 180fr, Gold throne. 250fr, Gold miniature coffin.

1978, Nov. 22
349 A111 40fr multi   .85   .30
350 A111 60fr multi   1.40   .40
351 A111 80fr multi   1.90   .55
352 A111 100fr multi   2.10   .55
353 A111 120fr multi   3.00   .60
354 A111 150fr multi   4.00   .70
355 A111 180fr multi   4.75   .85
356 A111 250fr multi   6.00 1.10
    Nos. 349-356 (8)   24.00 5.05

Tutankhamen, c. 1358 B.C., King of Egypt.

Lenin at Smolny Institute — A112

Soviet Union, 60th anniv.: 60fr, 200fr, 300fr, Various Lenin portraits. 100fr, Ulyanov family, horiz. 150fr, Lenin, Cruiser "Aurora" and flag, horiz. 500fr, "Aurora" and star.

1978, Nov.   *Perf. 14*
357 A112 40fr multi   .50   .30
358 A112 60fr multi   .60   .40
359 A112 100fr blk & gold   1.00   .45
360 A112 150fr blk, gold & red 1.90   .70
361 A112 200fr multi   3.00 1.00
362 A112 300fr multi   4.00 1.40
    Nos. 357-362 (6)   11.00 4.25

Souvenir Sheet
363 A112 500fr multi   6.00 4.00

Catherine Bokassa A113

Design: 60fr, Emperor Bokassa.

**1978, Dec. 4   Litho.   *Perf. 13*
364 A113 40fr multi   .65   .25
365 A113 60fr multi   .90   .30

1st anniv. of coronation. See No. C202.

Rowland Hill, Letter Scale and G.B. No. 1 — A114

Rowland Hill and: 50fr, US #1, mailman on bicycle. 60fr, Austria #P4, 19th cent. mailman. 80fr, Switzerland #2L1, postilion and mailcoach.

**1978, Dec. 9   Litho.   *Perf. 13½*
366 A114 40fr multi   .40   .20
367 A114 50fr multi   .50   .25
368 A114 60fr multi   .50   .30
369 A114 80fr multi   .65   .25
    Nos. 366-369,C203-C204 (6) 7.80 3.05
    Sir Rowland Hill (1795-1879), originator of penny postage.

Nos. 303-307 Overprinted in Silver: "VAINQUEUR: ARGENTINE"

1978, Dec. 27
370 A97 50fr multi   .55   .25
371 A97 60fr multi   .65   .30
372 A97 100fr multi   1.00   .55
373 A97 200fr multi   2.25 1.00
374 A97 300fr multi   3.25 1.40
    Nos. 370-374 (5)   7.70 3.50

Souvenir Sheet
No. 308 Overprinted in Silver:
"ARGENTINE-PAYS BAS 3-1 / 25 juin 1978"
375 A97 500fr multi   5.00 5.00
    Argentina's victory in World Cup Soccer Championship 1978.

Children Painting and Dutch Portrait — A115

UNICEF, Eagle Emblems and: 50fr, Eskimo children skiing, ski jump. 60fr, Children with toy racing car, Carl Benz with early car model. 80fr, Children launching rocket, Intelsat.

**1979, Mar. 6   Litho.   *Perf. 13½*
376 A115 40fr multi   .65   .20
377 A115 50fr multi   .75   .20
378 A115 60fr multi   .90   .20
379 A115 80fr multi   1.25   .30
    Nos. 376-379,C206-C207 (6) 7.70 1.95

International Year of the Child.

High Jump, Moscow '80 Emblem and "M" — A116

Designs (Moscow '80 Emblem, Various Sports and): 50fr, Bicycling and "O." 60fr, Weight lifting and "C." 80fr, Judo and "K."

**1979, Mar. 16   Litho.   *Perf. 13*
380 A116 40fr multi   .55   .20
381 A116 50fr multi   .65   .20
382 A116 60fr multi   .75   .20
383 A116 80fr multi   1.10   .30
    Nos. 380-383,C209-C210 (6) 6.25 1.90

22nd Olympic Games, Moscow, July 19-Aug. 3, 1980. Background letters on Nos. 380-383, C209-C210 spell "Mockba." A 1500fr gold embossed stamp showing emblems and Discobolus exists.

Memorial, Bangui, Butterfly, Hibiscus — A117

Design: 150fr, Canoe, truck and letters.

**1979, June 8   Litho.   *Perf. 12x12½*
384 A117 60fr multi   2.00   .80
385 A117 150fr multi   4.50 2.00

Philexafrique II, Libreville, Gabon, June 8-17. Nos. 384, 385 each printed in sheets of 10 with 5 labels showing exhibition emblem.

Schoolgirl A118

**1979, July 25   Litho.   *Perf. 12½x12*
386 A118 70fr multi   .95   .40

Intl. Bureau of Education, Geneva, 50th anniv.

Chicken A119

1979, Aug.   *Perf. 13*
387 A119 10fr shown   1.90 1.10
388 A119 20fr Bull   1.90 1.10
389 A119 40fr Sheep   4.00 2.10
    Nos. 387-389,C211 (4)   13.55 6.30

National Husbandry Assoc.

Souvenir Sheet

Virgin and Child, by Dürer — A120

1979, Aug.   *Perf. 13½*
390 A120 500fr lt grn & dl red 5.50 1.60

Albrecht Dürer (1471-1528), German engraver and printer.

Central African Republic
Nos. 257-258 Overprinted
"ALUNISSAGE/APOLLO XI/
JUILLET/1969" and Emblem

1979, Nov. 11   Litho.   Perf. 13½
391 A93 40fr multi   .65 .30
392 A93 60fr multi   .75 .40
    Nos. 391-392,C212-C214 (5)   7.05 3.35

Apollo 11 moon landing, 10th anniversary.

Girl and Rose A121

1979, Dec. 15
393 A121 30fr Butterfly and girl,
            vert.   .30 .20
394 A121 40fr shown   .50 .20
395 A121 60fr Hansel and
            Gretel, vert.   .55 .25
396 A121 200fr Cinderella   2.25 .70
397 A121 250fr Mermaid, vert. 2.75 .80
    Nos. 393-397 (5)   6.35 2.15

International Year of the Child.

Locomotive, U.S. Type A27, Hill — A122

Locomotives, Hill and Stamps: 100fr, France #1. 150fr, Germany type A11. 250fr, Great Britain #32. 500fr, CAR #2.

1979, Dec. 20
398 A122 60fr multi   .55 .20
399 A122 100fr multi   1.10 .30
400 A122 150fr multi   1.75 .45
401 A122 250fr multi   3.00 .95
    Nos. 398-401 (4)   6.40 1.90

Souvenir Sheet
402 A122 500fr multi   5.75 2.00

Sir Rowland Hill (1795-1879), originator of penny postage.

Basketball, Moscow '80 Emblem — A123

Pre-Olympic Year: Men's or women's basketball.

1979, Dec. 28   Litho.   Perf. 14½
403 A123 50fr multi   .50 .20
404 A123 125fr multi   1.10 .35
405 A123 200fr multi   1.90 .55
406 A123 300fr multi   3.25 .80
407 A123 500fr multi   5.00 1.40
    Nos. 403-407 (5)   11.75 3.30

For overprints see Nos. 425-429.

Nos. 313-314, 337-338 Overprinted
"REPUBLIQUE CENTRAFRICAINE" in
Black on Silver Panel and

Balambo Chair A124

Perf. 13½x14, 14x13½
1980, Mar. 20   Litho.
408 A99 5fr multi   .20 .20
409 A99 10fr multi   .20 .20
410 A124 20fr multi   .30 .20
411 A108 20fr multi   .30 .20
412 A108 30fr multi   .50 .25
    Nos. 408-412 (5)   1.50 1.05

Apollo-Soyuz — A125

1980, Apr. 8   Perf. 13½
413 A125 40fr Viking Satellite .55 .20
414 A125 50fr Apollo-Soyuz   .65 .20
415 A125 60fr Voyager   .75 .20
416 A125 100fr European Space
            Agency emblem,
            flags   1.25 .30
    Nos. 413-416,C221-C222 (6)   6.70 1.85

Walking, Olympic Medal, Moscow '80 Emblem — A126

1980, July 25   Litho.   Perf. 13½
417 A126 30fr shown   .50 .20
418 A126 40fr Relay race   .55 .20
419 A126 70fr Running   .75 .20
420 A126 80fr High jump   .90 .25
    Nos. 417-420,C231-C232 (6)   5.30 1.50

For overprints see #462-465, C248-C250.

Fruit — A126a

1980, Aug. 1   Litho.   Perf. 13½
420A A126a 40fr multicolored — —
420B A126a 70fr green & multi — —

Agricultural Development A127

1980, Nov. 4   Litho.   Perf. 13½
421 A127 30fr shown   .30 .20
422 A127 40fr Telecommunica-
            tions   .50 .20
423 A127 70fr Engineering   .90 .25
424 A127 100fr Civil engineering 1.10 .40
    Nos. 421-424,C234-C235 (6)   6.20 2.15

Europe-Africa cooperation.

Nos. 403-407 Overprinted with Medal and Country

1980, Nov. 12   Perf. 14½
425 A123 50fr multi   .55 .20
426 A123 125fr multi   1.10 .40
427 A123 200fr multi   1.90 .55

428 A123 300fr multi   3.60 .90
429 A123 500fr multi   5.00 1.60
    Nos. 425-429 (5)   12.15 3.65

Virgin and Child, by Raphael — A128

African Postal Union, 5th Anniversary A129

Christmas: Virgin & Child paintings by Raphael.

1980, Dec. 20   Perf. 12½
430 A128 60fr multi   .65 .20
431 A128 150fr multi   1.60 .60
432 A128 250fr multi   3.00 1.10
    Nos. 430-432 (3)   5.25 1.95

1980, Dec. 24   Photo.   Perf. 13½
433 A129 70fr multi   .75 .40

Peruvian Soccer Team, Soccer Cup — A130

1981, Jan. 13   Litho.   Perf. 13½
434 A130 10fr shown   .20 .20
435 A130 15fr Scotland   .20 .20
436 A130 20fr Mexico   .30 .20
437 A130 25fr Sweden   .30 .20
438 A130 30fr Austria   .40 .20
439 A130 40fr Poland   .50 .20
440 A130 50fr France   .55 .20
441 A130 60fr Italy   .65 .20
442 A130 70fr Germany   .75 .25
443 A130 80fr Brazil   .90 .25
    Nos. 434-443,C237-C238 (12)   7.25 2.90

ESPANA '82 World Cup Soccer Championship.

13th World Telecommunications Day — A131

1981, May 17   Litho.   Perf. 12½
444 A131 150fr multi   1.40 .70

Apollo 15 Crew on Moon — A132

Space Exploration: Columbia space shuttle.

1981, June 10   Litho.   Perf. 14
445 A132 100fr multi   .90 .30
446 A132 150fr multi   1.50 .40
447 A132 200fr multi   2.10 .60
448 A132 300fr multi   3.50 1.00
    Nos. 445-448 (4)   8.00 2.30

Souvenir Sheet
449 A132 500fr multi   5.00 1.60

Family of Acrobats with Monkey, by Picasso A133

Picasso Birth Cent.: 50fr, The Balcony. 80fr, The Artist's Son as Pierrot. 100fr, The Three Dancers.

1981, June 30   Perf. 13½
450 A133 40fr multi   .50 .20
451 A133 50fr multi   .65 .25
452 A133 80fr multi   1.10 .25
453 A133 100fr multi   1.40 .40
    Nos. 450-453,C245-C246 (6)   8.40 2.15

First Anniv. of Zimbabwe's Independence — A134

1981, July 9   Litho.   Perf. 12½
454 A134 100fr multi   1.10 .45
455 A134 150fr multi   1.50 .55
456 A134 200fr multi   2.25 .70
    Nos. 454-456 (3)   4.85 1.70

Prince Charles and Lady Diana — A135

1981, July, 24   Perf. 14
457 A135 75fr Charles   .60 .25
458 A135 100fr Diana   .90 .30
459 A135 150fr St. Paul's Cathe-
            dral   1.50 .45
460 A135 175fr shown   1.90 .50
    Nos. 457-460 (4)   4.90 1.50

Souvenir Sheet
461 A135 500fr Couple   5.00 1.40

Royal Wedding.
For overprints see Nos. 529-533.

Nos. 417-420 Overprinted with Event, Winner and Country in Gold

1981		Litho.		Perf. 13½
462	A126	30fr multi	.30	.20
463	A126	40fr multi	.40	.20
464	A126	70fr multi	.65	.30
465	A126	80fr multi	.75	.40
		Nos. 462-465,C248-C249 (6)	4.50	1.75

Prince Charles and Lady
Diana — A136

1981, Aug. 20		Litho.		Perf. 13½
466	A136	40fr shown	.50	.20
467	A136	50fr Crowned Prince of Wales	.50	.25
468	A136	80fr Diana	.85	.30
469	A136	100fr Naval training	1.10	.40
		Nos. 466-469,C251-C252 (6)	6.65	2.10

Royal wedding.

1906 Renault — A137

1981, Sept. 22		Litho.		Perf. 12½
470	A137	20fr shown	.30	.20
471	A137	40fr Mercedes-Benz, 1937	.65	.20
472	A137	50fr Matra-Ford, 1969	.75	.20
473	A137	110fr Tazio Nuvolari, 1927	1.50	.40
474	A137	150fr Jackie Stewart, 1965	2.25	.55
		Nos. 470-474 (5)	5.45	1.55

Souvenir Sheet
Perf. 10

475	A137	450fr Finish line, 1914	6.00	6.00

Grand Prix of France, 75th anniv.

World Food
Day
A138

1981, Oct. 16

476	A138	90fr multi	.95	.30
477	A138	110fr multi	1.10	.40

Navigators and their Ships — A139

1981, Sept. 4		Litho.		Perf. 13½
478	A139	40fr C.V. Rietschoten	.50	.30
479	A139	50fr M. Pajot	.55	.45
480	A139	60fr K. Jaworski	.75	.55
481	A139	80fr M. Birch	1.00	.60
		Nos. 478-481,C254-C255 (6)	6.30	4.00

Downfall
of Empire
A140

1981, Oct. 6

482	A140	5fr Bayonet through crown	.20	.20
483	A140	10fr like #482	.20	.20
484	A140	25fr Victory holding map	.30	.20
485	A140	60fr like #484	.75	.25
486	A140	90fr Toppled Bokassa statue	1.10	.40
487	A140	500fr like #486	4.75	2.00
		Nos. 482-487 (6)	7.30	3.25

Komba — A141

1981, Nov. 17

488	A141	50fr shown	.65	.20
489	A141	90fr Dodoro, horiz.	1.60	.25
490	A141	140fr Kaya, horiz.	2.75	.40
		Nos. 488-490 (3)	5.00	.85

Central
African
States
Bank
A142

1981, Dec. 12		Litho.		Perf. 12½x13
491	A142	90fr multi	1.00	.30
492	A142	110fr multi	1.10	.40

Christmas
1981 — A143

Virgin and Child Paintings.

1981, Dec. 24

493	A143	50fr Fra Angelico, 1430	1.00	.30
494	A143	60fr Cosimo Tura, 1484	1.10	.40
495	A143	90fr Bramantino	1.75	.45
496	A143	110fr Memling	2.25	.70
		Nos. 493-496,C260-C261 (6)	13.10	3.00

Scouting Year — A144

1982, Jan. 13				Perf. 12½
497	A144	100fr Hiking	1.25	.40
498	A144	150fr Scouts, horiz.	1.90	.55
499	A144	200fr Hiking	2.75	.80
500	A144	300fr Salute, flag, vert.	3.75	1.25
		Nos. 497-500 (4)	9.65	3.00

Souvenir Sheet
Perf. 13

501	A144	500fr Scout, Baden-Powell, vert.	6.25	1.60

Elephant
A145

1982, Jan. 22				Perf. 13½
502	A145	60fr shown	.90	.20
503	A145	90fr Giraffes	1.10	.30
504	A145	100fr Addaxes	1.25	.30
505	A145	110fr Okapi	1.50	.45
		Nos. 502-505,C263-C264 (6)	13.50	3.30

Norman
Rockwell
Illustrations
A146

1982, Feb. 17				Perf. 13½x14
506	A146	30fr Grandfather snowman	.30	.20
507	A146	60fr Croquet players	.55	.25
508	A146	110fr Women talking	1.25	.30
509	A146	150fr Searching	1.75	.55
		Nos. 506-509 (4)	3.85	1.40

AT 16
Dirigible
A147

1982, Feb. 27		Litho.		Perf. 13½
510	A147	5fr shown	.20	.20
511	A147	10fr Beyer-Garrat locomotive	.20	.20
512	A147	20fr Bugatti 24 "Royale," 1924	.30	.20
513	A147	110fr Vickers "Valentia," 1928	1.40	.40
		Nos. 510-513,C266-C267 (6)	11.10	3.05

Bellvue Garden, by Edouard
Manet — A148

Anniversaries: 400fr, Goethe, vert. #519-520, Princess Diana, 21st birthday, July 1, vert. 300fr, George Washington, vert.

1982, Apr. 6		Litho.		Perf. 13
517	A148	200fr multi	3.00	.60
517A	A148	300fr multi	3.00	.95
518	A148	400fr multi	4.00	1.25
519	A148	500fr multi	5.00	2.00
		Nos. 517-519 (4)	15.00	4.80

Souvenir Sheet

520	A148	500fr multi	5.50	1.40

23rd Olympic Games, Los Angeles,
1984 — A149

1982, July 24		Litho.		Perf. 13½
521	A149	5fr Soccer	.20	.20
522	A149	10fr Boxing	.20	.20
523	A149	20fr Running	.30	.20
524	A149	110fr Long jump	1.00	.30
		Nos. 521-524,C269-C270 (6)	9.70	3.10

21st Birthday of Princess
Diana — A150

Portraits.

1982, July 20		Litho.		Perf. 13½
525	A150	5fr multi	.20	.20
526	A150	10fr multi	.20	.20
527	A150	20fr multi	.30	.20
528	A150	110fr multi	1.40	.30
		Nos. 525-528,C272-C273 (6)	10.85	3.10

Nos. 457-461 Overprinted in Blue:
"NAISSANCE ROYALE 1982"

1982, Aug. 20				Perf. 14
529	A135	75fr multi	.55	.25
530	A135	110fr multi	.75	.40
531	A135	150fr multi	1.40	.55
532	A135	175fr multi	2.25	.80
		Nos. 529-532 (4)	4.95	2.00

Souvenir Sheet

533	A135	500fr multi	5.00	3.75

Birth of Prince William of Wales, June 21.

2nd UN
Conference
on Peaceful
Uses of Outer
Space,
Vienna, Aug.
9-21 — A151

Various satellites and space scenes.

1982, Aug. 15		Litho.		Perf. 13½
534	A151	5fr multi	.20	.20
535	A151	10fr multi	.20	.20
536	A151	20fr multi	.30	.20
537	A151	110fr multi	1.00	.30
		Nos. 534-537,C277-C278 (6)	9.70	3.10

Sakpa
Basket
A152

Baskets and bowls.

1982, Sept. 2   *Perf. 13*
538	A152	5fr shown	.20	.20
539	A152	10fr like 5fr	.20	.20
540	A152	25fr Ngbenda gourd, vert.	.30	.20
541	A152	60fr like 25fr	.75	.20
542	A152	120fr Ta ti ngou jugs	1.60	.40
543	A152	175fr Kangu bowls	2.25	.60
544	A152	300fr Kolongo bowls, vert.	4.50	1.25
		Nos. 538-544 (7)	9.80	3.05

For surcharges see #792A-792B.

1982 World Cup Soccer Championships, Spain — A152a

Various soccer plays.

1982, Sept.   **Litho.**   *Perf. 13½x13*
Overprinted in Silver or Gold
545	A152a	60fr Italy, 1st, 2nd	.90	.25
546	A152a	150fr Poland, 3rd	1.75	.55
547	A152a	300fr France, 4th	3.75	1.25
		Nos. 545-547 (3)	6.40	2.05

Souvenir Sheet
548	A152a	500fr Italy, 1st (G)	5.25	1.40

Not issued without overprint.

13th World UPU Day — A153

1982, Oct. 9
549	A153	60fr multi	.55	.25
550	A153	120fr multi	1.25	.45

Comb and Hairpins A154

1982, Oct. 20   *Perf. 13x12½*
551	A154	20fr multi	.20	.20
552	A154	30fr multi	.40	.25
553	A154	60fr multi	.75	.30
554	A154	80fr multi	1.10	.45
555	A154	120fr multi	1.50	.45
		Nos. 551-555 (5)	3.95	1.60

Artist Pierre Ndarata and No.69 A155

1982, Oct.   *Perf. 13*
556	A155	40fr Jean Tubind at easel, vert.	.20	.20
557	A155	70fr shown	.45	.20
558	A155	90fr like 70fr	.55	.25
559	A155	140fr like 40fr	1.00	.35
		Nos. 556-559 (4)	2.20	1.00

TB Bacillus Centenary A156

1982, Nov. 30   *Perf. 13½x13*
560	A156	100fr vio & blk	1.10	.30
561	A156	120fr red org & blk	1.40	.45
562	A156	175fr bl & blk	2.25	.80
		Nos. 560-562 (3)	4.75	1.55

10th Anniv. of UN Conference on Human Environment A157

1982, Dec. 8
563	A157	120fr multi	1.10	.40
564	A157	150fr multi	1.40	.55
565	A157	300fr multi	3.00	1.00
		Nos. 563-565 (3)	5.50	1.95

Granary A158

1982, Dec. 15   *Perf. 13*
566	A158	60fr multi	.55	.25
567	A158	90fr multi	.90	.40
568	A158	120fr multi	1.10	.55
569	A158	200fr multi	2.25	.90
		Nos. 566-569 (4)	4.80	2.10

A159   A160

1982, Dec.
570	A159	100fr multi	1.00	.40
571	A159	120fr multi	1.40	.45

ITU Plenipotentiaries Conf., Nairobi, Sept.

1983, Jan. 31   **Litho.**   *Perf. 13½x13*
572	A160	5fr Modes of communication	.20	.20
573	A160	60fr like 5fr	.55	.20
574	A160	120fr Map, jet	1.40	.40
575	A160	175fr like 120fr	1.75	.55
		Nos. 572-575 (4)	3.90	1.35

UN Decade for African Transportation and Communication, 1978-88.

Chess Champions — A161

Men and Chess Pieces: 5fr, Steinitz, first world champion, 1886. 10fr, Aaron Niemzovitch, castle. 20fr, Alexander Alekhine, knights. 110fr, Botvinnik. 300fr, Boris Spassky, glass pieces. 500fr, Bobby Fischer, king, knight. 600fr, Korchnoi, Karpov, pawn. No. 582A, Bobby Fischer. No. 582B, Reti, Larsen, Petrossian, and Mecking, horiz.

1983, Jan. 15
576	A161	5fr multi	.20	.20
577	A161	10fr multi	.20	.20
578	A161	20fr multi	.20	.20
579	A161	110fr multi	1.40	.20
580	A161	300fr multi	3.25	.55
581	A161	500fr multi	5.50	1.40
		Nos. 576-581 (6)	10.75	2.75

Souvenir Sheet
582	A161	600fr multi	5.75	1.60

Litho. & Embossed
Perf. 13½
Size: 35x60mm
582A	A161	1500fr gold & multi	42.50	3.50

Souvenir Sheet
582B	A161	1500fr gold & multi	10.00	10.00

No. 582 contains one 56x33mm stamp, No. 582B one 35x60mm stamp. 300fr, 500fr, 600fr, Nos. 582A and 582B are airmail.

Marshal Tito (1892-1980) A162

1983, Jan. 22
583	A162	20fr George Washington	.20	.20
a.		Souvenir sheet	5.50	
584	A162	110fr shown	1.25	.30
a.		Souvenir sheet	5.50	

1982 World Cup Soccer Championships, Spain — A162a

Trophy, flags, scores, players: 5fr, Hamilton, Pezzey. 10fr, Borovski, Boniek. 20fr, Littbarski, Zamora. 110fr, Zico, Passarella. 300fr, Rossi, Smolarek. 500fr, Rummenigge, Giresse. 600fr, Rossi, Rummenigge. No. 584I, Platini. No. 584J, Rossi.

1983, Feb. 8   **Litho.**   *Perf. 13½*
584B	A162a	5fr multi	.20	.20
584C	A162a	10fr multi	.20	.20
584D	A162a	20fr multi	.20	.20
584E	A162a	110fr multi	1.25	.30
584F	A162a	300fr multi	3.25	.70
584G	A162a	500fr multi	5.50	1.40
		Nos. 584B-584G (6)	10.60	3.00

Souvenir Sheet
584H	A162a	600fr multicolored	5.50	4.25

Litho. & Embossed
584I	A162a	1500fr gold & multi	35.00	6.50

Souvenir Sheet
584J	A162a	1500fr gold & multi	10.00	10.00

Nos. 584F-584J are airmail.

Easter 1983 A163

Rembrandt Paintings.

1983, Apr. 16
585	A163	100fr Entombment	1.00	.40
586	A163	300fr Crucifixion	2.50	1.25
587	A163	400fr Descent from the Cross	3.50	1.60
		Nos. 585-587 (3)	7.00	3.25

Vintage Cars and their Makers A164

A164a

Designs: 10fr, Emile Levassor, Rene Panhard, 1895 car. 20fr, Henry Ford, 1896 car. 30fr, Louis Renault, 1899 car. 80fr, Ettore Bugatti, type 37, 1925. 400fr, Enzo Ferrari, 815 sport, 1940. 500fr, Ferdinand Porsche, 356 coupe, 1951. 600fr, Karl Benz, velocipede, 1886. No. 594A, F.H. Royce and C.S. Rolls, 1911 Rolls-Royce Silver Ghost. No. 594B, G. Daimler, 1900 Mercedes 35CV.

1983, June 3   **Litho.**   *Perf. 13½*
588	A164	10fr multi	.20	.20
589	A164	20fr multi	.20	.20
590	A164	30fr multi	.30	.20
591	A164	80fr multi	1.00	.30
592	A164	400fr multi	4.50	1.10
593	A164	500fr multi	5.50	1.40
		Nos. 588-593 (6)	11.70	3.40

Souvenir Sheet
594	A164	600fr multi	5.75	1.60

Litho. & Embossed
594A	A164a	1500fr gold & multi	25.00	4.00

Souvenir Sheet
594B	A164a	1500fr gold & multi	10.00	6.00

Nos. 592-594B are airmail.

25th Anniv. of Intl. Maritime Org. — A165

1983, July 8   **Litho.**   *Perf. 12½x13*
595	A165	40fr multi	.50	.20
596	A165	100fr multi	1.00	.40

World Communications Year — A166

1983, July 22
597	A166	50fr multi	.50	.25
598	A166	130fr multi	1.40	.45

Pre-Olympics, Los Angeles A167

1984 Summer Olympics, Los Angeles A167a

1983, Aug. 3   Litho.   Perf. 13
599	A167	5fr Gymnast	.20	.20
600	A167	40fr Javelin throwing	.40	.20
601	A167	60fr Pole vault	.65	.25
602	A167	120fr Fencing	1.40	.30
603	A167	200fr Cycling	2.25	.40
604	A167	300fr Sailing	3.25	.80
		Nos. 599-604 (6)	8.15	2.15

Souvenir Sheet
605	A167	600fr Handball	5.00	1.60

**Litho. & Embossed
Perf. 13½**
605A	A167a	1500fr Shot put	35.00	3.50

Souvenir Sheet
605B	A167a	1500fr Dressage, horiz.	10.00	10.00

Nos. 603-605B are airmail.

Namibia Day — A168

1983, Sept. 16   Litho.   Perf. 13
606	A168	100fr multi	1.10	.40
607	A168	200fr multi	1.90	.80

Manned Flight Bicentenary — A169

A169a

Designs: 50fr, J. Montgolfier and his balloon, 1783. 100fr, J.P. Blanchard, English Channel crossing, 1785. 200fr, L.-J. Gay-Lussac, 4000-meter balloon ascent, 1804. 300fr, Giffard and his dirigible, 1852. 400fr, Santos Dumont, dirigible, Eiffel Tower. 500fr, A. Laquot, captive observation balloon, 1914. 600fr, J.A. Charles, first gas balloon; G. Tissandier, dirigible, 1883. No. 614, Marquis d'Arlandes and Jean Francois Pilatre de Rozier, Montgolfier balloon. No. 614B, Ferdinand von Zeppelin, Graf Zeppelin, horiz.

1983, Sept. 30   Litho.   Perf. 13½
608	A169	50fr multi	.50	.20
609	A169	100fr multi	1.10	.40
610	A169	200fr multi	2.50	.80
611	A169	300fr multi	3.25	1.10
612	A169	400fr multi	4.25	1.50
613	A169	500fr multi	5.75	1.90
		Nos. 608-613 (6)	17.35	5.90

Souvenir Sheet
614	A169	600fr multi	5.50	1.40

Litho. & Embossed
614A	A169a	1500fr gold & multi	37.50	4.00

Souvenir Sheet
614B	A169a	1500fr gold & multi	10.00	10.00

Nos. 612-614B are airmail.

Black Rhinoceros and World Wildlife Emblem — A170

Various black rhinoceroses.

1983, Nov. 14
615	A170	10fr multi	1.25	.50
616	A170	40fr multi	1.50	.75
617	A170	70fr multi	2.25	1.00
618	A170	180fr multi	6.75	2.00
		Nos. 615-618 (4)	11.75	4.25

Nos. 615-618 were issued in support of the World Wildlife Fund.
See Nos. C291A-C293.

UPU Day, World Communications Year — A171

1983, Nov. 2   Litho.   Perf. 13
619	A171	205fr multi	1.90	.90

2nd Anniv. of the Natl. Military Committee A172

Gen. Andre Kolingba, head of state.

1983, Sept. 1   Perf. 12½
620	A172	65fr sil & multi	.55	.25
621	A172	130fr gold & multi	1.40	.45

Earth Satellite Receiving Station, Bangui M'Poko — A173

1983   Perf. 13
622	A173	130fr multi	1.40	.55

Natl. Day of the Handicapped and the Elderly — A174

1983, Dec. 20   Engr.   Perf. 13x12½
623	A174	65fr vio & org	.55	.30
624	A174	130fr ultra & org	1.10	.45
625	A174	205fr dk grn & org	1.75	.80
		Nos. 623-625 (3)	3.40	1.55

Fishing Resources A175

1983, Dec. 31   Litho.   Perf. 12½
626	A175	25fr Breeding tank	.20	.20
627	A175	65fr Net fishing	1.10	.25
628	A175	100fr Dam fishing	1.25	.40
629	A175	130fr Still life with fish	2.50	.70
630	A175	205fr Basket trap	2.75	.70
		Nos. 626-630 (5)	7.80	2.25

Wildlife Protection — A176

1984, Jan. 25   Perf. 13
631	A176	30fr Forest fire	3.50	.40
632	A176	130fr Hunters	5.00	1.10

CC-1500 Locomotive — A177

1984, July 16   Litho.   Perf. 12½
633	A177	110fr CC-1500 locomotive	1.40	.30
634	A177	240fr PLM series 210, 1868	3.00	.85
635	A177	350fr 231-726 locomotive, 1937	4.25	1.10
636	A177	440fr Pacific S3/6, 1908	5.75	1.25
637	A177	500fr Henschel 151 series 45, 1937	6.75	1.60
		Nos. 633-637 (5)	21.15	5.10

For overprints see Nos. 702, 704.

Packet Ship Pericles — A177a

1984, July 23   Litho.   Perf. 12½
638	A177a	65fr shown	.90	.30
639	A177a	120fr Three-master Pereire	1.40	.55
640	A177a	250fr Admella	3.00	1.10
641	A177a	400fr Royal William	5.50	1.90
642	A177a	500fr Great Britain	6.25	2.40
		Nos. 638-642 (5)	17.05	6.25

For overprints see Nos. 701, 703.

J. W. Goethe, Scene from Faust A178

Designs: 100fr, Henri Dunant, Red Cross Founder, Battle of Solferino, 125th anniv.

200fr, Alfred Nobel, Nobel Foundation headquarters. 300fr, Lord Baden-Powell, World Scouting Jamboree, Alberta, 1983. 400fr, John F. Kennedy, first man on the Moon, 1969. 500fr, 600fr, wedding of Prince and Princess of Wales.

1984, Feb. 25   Litho.   Perf. 13½
643	A178	50fr multi	.55	.20
644	A178	100fr multi	1.10	.40
645	A178	200fr multi	2.50	.55
646	A178	300fr multi	3.25	1.10
647	A178	400fr multi	4.50	1.10
648	A178	500fr multi	5.50	1.10
		Nos. 643-648 (6)	17.40	4.45

Souvenir Sheet
649	A178	600fr multi	5.00	1.40

Nos. 647-649 are airmail.

Old Masters A179

Paintings: 50fr, Madonna and Child, by Raphael. 100fr, Madonna with Pear, by Durer. 200fr, Aldobrandini Madonna, by Raphael. 300fr, Madonna with Carnation, by Durer. 400fr, Virgin and Child, by Correggio. 500fr, La Bohemienne, by Modigliani. 600fr, Madonna and Child on the Throne, by Raphael.

1984, Mar. 30   Litho.   Perf. 13½
650	A179	50fr multi	.60	.20
651	A179	100fr multi	1.10	.25
652	A179	200fr multi	2.50	.45
653	A179	300fr multi	3.50	.85
654	A179	400fr multi	4.75	1.90
655	A179	500fr multi	5.75	2.50
		Nos. 650-655 (6)	18.20	6.15

Miniature Sheet
656	A179	600fr multi	5.50	1.40

No. 656 contains 1 stamp, size 30x59mm.
Nos. 654-656 are airmail.

Space — A180

1984, Aug. 6   Litho.   Perf. 13½
657	A180	20fr Galileo, Ariane rocket	.30	.20
658	A180	70fr Piccard, X-15, balloon	.65	.25
659	A180	150fr Oberth, satellite	1.40	.45
660	A180	205fr Einstein, satellites	1.90	.55
661	A180	300fr Curie, Viking vehicle	3.25	.80
662	A180	500fr Merbold, Spacelab	5.00	1.00
		Nos. 657-662 (6)	12.50	3.25

Miniature Sheet
663	A180	600fr Armstrong, Apollo 11, horiz.	4.50	1.40

No. 663 contains 1 stamp, size: 42x36mm.
300fr, 500fr and 600fr are airmail.

Forestry Resources A181

UNICEF — A182

1984, Oct. 9   Litho.   Perf. 13x12½
664 A181 70fr Forest   1.00 .30
665 A181 130fr Logging   2.00 .55

1984, Oct. 27   Litho.   Perf. 13x12½
666 A182 10fr Weighing child   .20   .20
667 A182 30fr Vaccinating child   .40   .25
668 A182 65fr Giving liquids   .55   .30
669 A182 100fr Balancing diet   1.25   .55
   Nos. 666-669 (4)   2.40 1.30

Fishing Traps A183

1984, Nov. 6   Litho.   Perf. 13
670 A183 50fr Bangui-Kette   .75   .30
671 A183 80fr Mbres   1.10   .55
672 A183 150fr Bangui-Kette   1.90   .55
   Nos. 670-672 (3)   3.75 1.40

Mushrooms A184

1984, Nov. 15   Litho.   Perf. 13½
673 A184 5fr Leptoporus
           lignosus   .20   .20
674 A184 10fr Phlebopus
           sudanicus   .20   .20
675 A184 40fr Termitomyces
           letestui   .65   .20
676 A184 130fr Lepiota es-
           culenta   1.60   .30
677 A184 300fr Termitomyces
           aurantiacus   3.50   .80
678 A184 500fr Termitomyces
           robustus   6.25 1.25
   Nos. 673-678 (6)   12.40 2.95

Souvenir Sheet
679 A184 600fr Tricholoma-
           lobayensis   6.25 1.40

   Nos. 677-679 are airmail.

1984 Winter Olympics, Sarajevo A184a

Gold medalists, communications satellite and events: 30fr, Gaetan Boucher, Canada, 1000 and 1500-meter speed skating. 90fr, W. Hoppe, R. Wetzig, D. Schauerhammer and A. Kirchner, German Democratic Republic, 4-man bobsled. 140fr, Paoletta Magoni, Italy, women's slalom. 200fr, Jayne Torvill and Christopher Dean, Great Britain, ice dancing. 400fr, Matti Nykaenen, Finland, 90-meter ski jumping. 500fr, USSR, ice hockey. 600fr, Bill Johnson, US, men's downhill.

1984, Nov. 30   Litho.   Perf. 13½
679A A184a 30fr multi   .30   .20
679B A184a 90fr multi   1.00   .30
679C A184a 140fr multi   1.50   .40
679D A184a 200fr multi   2.25   .55
679E A184a 400fr multi   4.00 1.00
679F A184a 500fr multi   5.25 1.25
   Nos. 679A-679F (6)   14.30 3.70

Souvenir Sheet
679G A184a 600fr multi   5.00 1.40

   Nos. 679E-679G are airmail.

Flowers — A185

1984, Nov. 22   Litho.   Perf. 13½
680 A185 65fr Hibiscus   1.10   .40
681 A185 130fr Canna Indica   1.90   .50
682 A185 205fr Eichlornia Cras-
           sipes   3.00 1.00
   Nos. 680-682 (3)   6.00 1.90

Economic Campaign — A186

1984, Dec. 3   Litho.   Perf. 13½
683 A186 25fr Cotton planting   .40   .25
684 A186 40fr Selling cotton
           crop   .65   .40
685 A186 130fr Cotton market   1.70   .55
   Nos. 683-685 (3)   2.75 1.20

World Food Day A187

1984, Dec. 10   Litho.   Perf. 13½
686 A187 205fr Picking corn   2.50   .90

OLYMPHILEX '85 — A188

Publicity posters from previous Games and host city landmarks.

1985, Mar 18   Litho.   Perf. 13½
687 A188 5fr Stockholm,
           1912   .20   .20
688 A188 10fr Paris, 1924   .20   .20
689 A188 20fr London, 1948   .20   .20
690 A188 100fr Tokyo, 1964   5.25 1.00
691 A188 400fr Mexico   2.25   .45
692 A188 500fr Munich, 1972   2.75   .55
   Nos. 687-692 (6)   10.85 2.60

Souvenir Sheet
693 A188 600fr Athens, 1896,
           Baron Pierre
           de Coubertin   5.50 1.50

   Nos. 691-693 are airmail. No. 693 contains one 60x30mm stamp.

Anniversaries and Events — A189

Queen Mother, 85th Birthday — A189a

Famous men: 50fr, Abraham Lincoln, American Civil War soldiers. 90fr, Auguste Piccard (1884-1962), inventor, bathyscaphe Trieste. 120fr, Gottlieb Daimler (1834-1900), 1938 Mercedes Type 540. 200fr, Louis Bleriot (1872-1936), inventor, plane. 350fr, Anatoly Karpov, world chess champion. 400fr, Jean Henri Dunant (1828-1910), Red Cross founder, worker caring for wounded soldier.

1984, Dec. 22   Litho.   Perf. 13½
694 A189 50fr multi   .55   .20
695 A189 90fr multi   1.00   .30
696 A189 120fr multi   1.60   .40
697 A189 200fr multi   2.50   .55
698 A189 350fr multi   3.75   .80
698A A189 400fr multi   3.75   .90
   Nos. 694-698A (6)   13.15 3.15

   Nos. 698-698A are airmail.

Souvenir Sheet
1984   Litho.   Perf. 13½
698B A189a 600fr multi   5.00 1.40

Bangui Rotary Club and Water — A190

1984, Dec. 29
699 A190 130fr multi   1.90   .45
700 A190 205fr multi   2.75   .80

   Nos. 635//641, C302A Overprinted with Exhibitions in Red

1985, Mar. 13   Litho.   Perf. 12½
701 A177 250fr Argentina
           '85, Buenos
           Aires
           (#640)   2.50 1.25
702 A177a 350fr Tsukuba Ex-
           po '85
           (#635)   3.50 1.60
703 A177 400fr Italia '85,
           Rome
           (#641)   4.50 2.00
704 A177a 440fr Mophila '85,
           Hamburg
           (#636)   5.50 2.40
   Nos. 701-704 (4)   16.00 7.25

Souvenir Sheet
Perf.   13½x13
705 AP89 500fr Olymphilex
           '85, Lau-
           sanne   5.00 5.00

   500fr airmail.

Beetles — A191

1985, Mar.   Litho.   Perf. 13½
706 A191 15fr Chelorrhina poly-
           phemus   1.75   .20
707 A191 20fr Fornasinius rus-
           sus   2.25   .20
708 A191 25fr Goliathus gi-
           ganteus   2.50   .20
709 A191 65fr Goliathus
           meleagris   6.50   .30
   Nos. 706-709 (4)   13.00   .90

Audubon Birth Bicentenary — A192

Illustrations of North American bird species by John Audubon.

1985, Mar. 25   Litho.   Perf. 13½
710 A192 40fr Cyanocitta cris-
           tata   .90   .20
711 A192 80fr Caprimulgus
           carolinensis   1.25   .20
712 A192 130fr Campephilus
           principalis   2.40   .25
713 A192 250fr Calocitta formo-
           sa   3.25   .55
714 A192 300fr Coccizus minor,
           horiz.   3.50   .60
715 A192 500fr Hirundo rustica,
           horiz.   5.75 1.10
   Nos. 710-715 (6)   17.05 2.90

Souvenir Sheet
716 A192 600fr Dryocopus
           pileatus, horiz.   7.75 2.50

   Nos. 714-716 are airmail.

Intl. Youth Year A193

Famous children's book authors and scenes from their best-known novels: 100fr, The Jungle Book, 1894, by Kipling, vert. 200fr, Les Cavaliers, 1967, by Joseph Kessel (1898-1979). 300fr, Twenty-Thousand Leagues Under the Sea, 1873, by Verne. 400fr, The Adventures of Tom Sawyer, 1876, by Twain.

1985, Apr.   Litho.   Perf. 13
718 A193 100fr multi   1.10   .45
719 A193 200fr multi   2.40   .85
720 A193 300fr multi   3.00 1.25
721 A193 400fr multi   4.50 2.10
   Nos. 718-721 (4)   11.00 4.65

Philexafrica '85, Lome — A194

#722, UPU emblem, Postmen unloading parcel post van. #723, Exhibition emblem, scout troop.

1985, May 15   Perf. 13x12½
722 A194 200fr multi   2.50   .90
723 A194 200fr multi   2.50   .90
   a. Pair, #722-723 + label   5.25 4.50

Rabies Vaccine Cent., Louis Pasteur
(1822-95), Chemist,
Microbiologist — A195

Anniversaries and events: 200fr, Battle of
Solferino, founding of the Red Cross, 125th
Anniv., founder Jean-Henri Dunant (1828-
1910), horiz. 300fr, Girl Guides, 75th anniv.
450fr, Elizabeth, the Queen Mother, 85th birthday. 500fr, Statue of Liberty, cent.

1985, June   **Perf. 13**
724	A195	150fr multi	1.60	.70
725	A195	200fr multi	1.90	.90
726	A195	300fr multi	2.25	1.40
727	A195	450fr multi	3.75	2.25
728	A195	500fr multi	5.00	2.50
	Nos. 724-728 (5)		14.50	7.75

1986 World Cup Soccer
Championships, Mexico — A196

Famous soccer players and match scenes.

1985, July 24   **Litho.**   **Perf. 13½**
730	A196	5fr Pele	.20	.20
731	A196	10fr Tony Schu-macher	.20	.20
732	A196	20fr Paolo Rossi	.20	.20
733	A196	350fr Kevin Keegan	3.50	.90
734	A196	400fr Michel Platini	4.00	.90
735	A196	500fr Karl Heinz Rummenigge	5.00	1.10
	Nos. 730-735 (6)		13.10	3.50

Souvenir Sheet
736	A196	600fr Diego Armando Maradona	5.00	1.40

Nos. 734-736 are airmail.

Kotto
Waterfalls
A197

1985, July 27   **Litho.**   **Perf. 13½**
737	A197	65fr multi	1.00	.30
738	A197	90fr multi	1.10	.40
739	A197	130fr multi	1.75	.60
	Nos. 737-739 (3)		3.85	1.30

State Visit of
Pope John
Paul II — A198

Portraits.

1985, Aug. 14
740	A198	65fr multi	1.25	.40
741	A198	130fr multi	2.50	.80

Natl. Economic Development
Campaign — A199

Designs: 5fr, Troops plowing. 60fr, Soldier
preparing field for planting, vert. 130fr, Planting cotton seeds, vert.

1985, Sept. 1   **Perf. 13**
742	A199	5fr multi	.20	.20
743	A199	60fr multi	.75	.30
744	A199	130fr multi	1.50	.45
	Nos. 742-744 (3)		2.45	.95

Queen Mother, 85th Birthday — A200

1985, Sept. 16   **Litho.**   **Perf. 13½**
745	A200	100fr Age 4, with brother	.90	.25
746	A200	200fr Duchess of York, 1923	2.10	.35
747	A200	300fr Reviewing Irish Guards, 1928	3.25	.70
748	A200	350fr Family portrait, 1936	3.50	.75
749	A200	400fr George VI coronation, 1937	4.25	.90
750	A200	500fr Wedding anniv., 1948	5.50	1.00
	Nos. 745-750 (6)		19.50	3.95

Souvenir Sheet
751	A200	600fr Christening Prince Charles, 1948	4.50	1.40

Nos. 749-751 are airmail.

Dr. Rene Labusquiere (1919-1977),
Promoter of Preventive
Medicine — A201

1985, Sept. 22   **Litho.**   **Perf. 13½**
752	A201	10fr multi	.20	.20
753	A201	45fr multi	.50	.20
754	A201	110fr multi	.75	.45
	Nos. 752-754 (3)		1.45	.85

Natl. Postal Service — A202

1985, Oct. 9   **Perf. 12½**
755	A202	15fr Loading mail van	.20	.20
756	A202	60fr Bangui P.O., van	.65	.25
757	A202	150fr Hdqtrs, Bangui, and vans	1.60	.80
	Nos. 755-757 (3)		2.45	1.25

Space Research — A203

Designs: 40fr, Yuri Gagarin, Soviet cosmonaut, and Sergei Korolev, rocket engineer.
110fr, Nicolaus Copernicus, Cassini probe.
240fr, Galileo, Viking orbiter. 300fr, Theodor
von Karman (1881-1963), American aeronau-
tical engineer, and space shuttle recovering
Palapa B satellite. 450fr, Percival Lowell
(1855-1916), American astronomer, and
Viking probe. 500fr, Dr. U. Merbold and orbiting space station project Colombo. 600fr,
Apollo 11 Project, first step on Moon by Neil
Armstrong.

1985, Oct. 31   **Litho.**   **Perf. 13½**
758	A203	40fr multi	.25	.20
759	A203	110fr multi	1.00	.30
760	A203	240fr multi	2.75	.55
761	A203	300fr multi	3.50	.80
762	A203	450fr multi	5.50	1.00
763	A203	500fr multi	6.00	1.10
	Nos. 758-763 (6)		19.00	3.95

Souvenir Sheet
Imperf
764	A203	600fr multi	5.00	1.40

Nos. 762-764 are airmail.

Solar
Energy
Apparatus,
Damara
A204

1985, Nov. 4   **Litho.**   **Perf. 13½**
765	A204	65fr multi	.65	.30
766	A204	130fr multi	1.40	.55

Girl Guides Nature Study — A205

1985, Nov. 16   **Perf. 13**
767	A205	250fr shown	3.50	1.40
768	A205	250fr Quaka Sugar Refinery	3.50	1.40
a.		Pair, #767-768 + label	10.00	6.50

PHILEXAFRICA '85, Lome, Togo, 11/16-24.

State Visit of Pres. Mitterand of
France, Dec. 12-13 — A206

1985-86   **Litho.**   **Perf. 13x12½**
769	A206	65fr multi	.75	.25
770	A206	130fr multi	1.50	.55
770A	A206	160fr multi ('86)	2.10	.80
	Nos. 769-770A (3)		4.35	1.60

Issued: #769-770, Dec. 12.

UN 40th Anniv.,
Central Africa
Admission, 25th
Anniv. — A207

1985, Dec. 18   **Perf. 13½**
771	A207	140fr multi	1.40	.55

Intl. Youth
Year
A208

Designs: 40fr, David, by Andrea del Ver-
rocchio; Madonna with the Carnation, 1470,
by Leonardo da Vinci. 80fr, Johann Sebastian
Bach. 100fr, St. John at Patmos, 1619, by
Velazquez. 250fr, The Erl King score, by
Franz Schubert. 400fr, Portrait of Vicente
Osorio de Moscoso, by Goya. 500fr, The
Young Mozart Playing in Paris, 1764. 600fr,
Woman in a Plumed Hat, 1901, by Picasso.

1985, Dec. 28
772	A208	40fr multi	.40	.20
773	A208	80fr multi	.90	.25
774	A208	100fr multi	1.25	.25
775	A208	250fr multi	2.50	.55
776	A208	400fr multi	4.50	.90
777	A208	500fr multi	5.00	1.10
	Nos. 772-777 (6)		14.55	3.25

Souvenir Sheet
778	A208	600fr multi	5.25	1.40

Nos. 776-778 are airmail.

Halley's
Comet
A209

100fr, Edmond Halley, British astronomer.
200fr, Sir Isaac Newton's telescope & comet
sighting. 300fr, Halley & Newton observing
comet. 350fr, US probe. 400fr, Soviet probe
plotting comet's perihelion. 500fr, Isodensity
photograph of comet. 600fr, Comet, Earth,
Sun & probe.

1985, Dec. 31
779	A209	100fr multi	.75	.25
780	A209	200fr multi	1.90	.40
781	A209	300fr multi	2.75	.45
782	A209	350fr multi	3.25	.80
783	A209	400fr multi	3.75	.85
784	A209	500fr multi	5.00	1.00
	Nos. 779-784 (6)		17.40	3.75

Souvenir Sheet
785	A209	600fr multi	6.00	1.75

Nos. 783-785 are airmail.

Christopher Columbus — A210

Various events leading to the discovery of
America and beyond.

1986
786	A210	90fr Plotting course	.90	.25
787	A210	110fr Receiving blessing	1.10	.25
788	A210	240fr Fleet in port	2.50	1.25

789	A210	300fr	Trade with na-tives	3.25 .55
790	A210	400fr	Storm at sea	4.50 2.00
791	A210	500fr	Fleet at sea	5.50 2.40
			Nos. 779-784 (6)	17.40 3.75

Souvenir Sheet

792	A210	600fr	Portrait	6.50 1.75

Nos. 790-792 are airmail.

Nos. 543-544 Surcharged

1986, Apr. 1   Litho.   Perf. 13

792A	A152	30fr on 175fr Kangu bowls		
792B	A152	65fr on 300fr Kolongo bowls		

Hairstyles
A211

France- Central
Africa
Week — A212

1986, May 21   Litho.   Perf. 12½

793	A211	20fr multi		.45 .20
794	A211	30fr multi		.55 .25
795	A211	65fr multi		.80 .40
796	A211	160fr multi		2.75 .70
		Nos. 793-796 (4)		4.55 1.55

1986, May 26

797	A212	40fr	Communications, horiz.	.40 .20
798	A212	60fr	Youth, horiz.	.55 .25
799	A212	100fr	Basket maker	.75 .40
800	A212	130fr	Bicycling	1.60 .55
			Nos. 797-800 (4)	3.30 1.40

Centrapalm
Palm
Oil — A213

25fr, 65fr, Refinery, Bossongo, and palm tree. 120fr, 160fr, Refinery and palm tree.

1986, Aug. 12   Litho.   Perf. 13½

801	A213	25fr multi		.30 .25
802	A213	65fr multi		.75 .40
803	A213	120fr multi, vert.		1.40 .80
804	A213	160fr multi, vert.		1.90 .60
		Nos. 801-804 (4)		4.35 2.05

Dogs
and
Cats
A214

1986, Sept. 9

805	A214	10fr	Pointer	.25 .20
806	A214	20fr	Egyptian mau	.50 .20
807	A214	200fr	Newfoundland	3.00 .55

808	A214	300fr	Borzoi	3.75 .60
809	A214	400fr	Persian red	5.50 .85
			Nos. 805-809 (5)	13.00 2.40

Souvenir Sheet

810	A214	500fr	Spaniel, Bur-mese-Malayan	7.00 1.75

Nos. 808-810 are airmail.

African Coffee Producers
Organization, 25th Anniv. — A215

1986, Sept. 25   Litho.   Perf. 13

811	A215	160fr multi		1.60 .55

1986 World Cup Soccer
Championships, Mexico — A216

Satellites, final scores, World Cup and ath-letes: 30fr, Muller, Socrates. 110fr, Scifo, Ceulemans. 160fr, Stopyra, Platini. 350fr, Brehme, Schumacher. 450fr, Maradona. 500fr, Schumacher, Burruchaga.

1986, Nov. 12   Perf. 13½

812	A216	30fr multi		.30 .20
813	A216	110fr multi		1.00 .25
814	A216	160fr multi		1.40 .30
815	A216	350fr multi		3.25 .80
816	A216	450fr multi		4.50 1.10
		Nos. 812-816 (5)		10.45 2.65

Souvenir Sheet

817	A216	500fr multi		5.50 1.40

Nos. 816-817 are airmail.

US
Anniversaries
and Events
A217

15fr, Judith Resnik. 25fr, Frederic Auguste Bartholdi. 70fr, Elvis Presley. 300fr, Ronald McNair. 450fr, Christa McAuliffe. 500fr, Chal-lenger Astronauts: McAuliffe, Scobee, Smith, Resnik, Onizuka, McNair, Jarvis.

1986, Nov. 19

818	A217	15fr multi		.20 .20
819	A217	25fr multi		.40 .20
820	A217	70fr multi		1.90 .20
821	A217	300fr multi		3.00 .60
822	A217	450fr multi		4.50 1.10
		Nos. 818-822 (5)		10.00 2.30

Souvenir Sheet

823	A217	500fr multi		6.25 1.50

US space shuttle Challenger explosion; Statue of Liberty, cent. #822-823 are airmail. For surcharges & overprint see #851-851B.

Flora and
Fauna
A218

1986, May 30   Litho.   Perf. 13½

824	A218	25fr	Allamanda neri-ifolia	.25 .20
825	A218	65fr	Taurotragus eurycerus	.90 .20
826	A218	160fr	Plumieria acuminata	2.10 .30
827	A218	300fr	Acinonyx jubatus	4.50 .80
828	A218	400fr	Eulophia erthoplata	4.75 .90
829	A218	500fr	Leopard	6.50 1.10
			Nos. 824-829 (6)	19.00 3.50

Souvenir Sheet

830	A218	600fr	Derby's eland, eulophia cucu-lata	5.75 1.75

#824, 826, 828 vert. #828-830 are airmail. #830 contains one 51x30mm stamp.

Intl. Peace
Year — A219

1986, Nov. 29

831	A219	160fr multi		1.60 .55

Air Africa, 25th
Anniv. — A220

1986, Dec. 15

832	A220	200fr multi		1.90 .80

UNICEF, 40th
Anniv. — A221

1986, Dec. 24

833	A221	15fr shown		.20 .20
834	A221	130fr	Child immunization	1.10 .55
835	A221	160fr	Youth, food, map	1.25 .70
			Nos. 833-835 (3)	2.55 1.45

German Railways
Sesquicentenary — A222

Inventors and locomotives: 40fr, Alfred de Glehn, Prussian Railways DH2 Green Ele-phant. 70fr, Rudolf Diesel, S3/6 No. 1829 Rhe-ingold. 160fr, Carl Golsdorf, Trans-Europe Express train Type 103. 300fr, Wilhelm Schmidt, Beyer Garratt locomotive. 400fr,

Monsieur Du Bousquet, Series 3500 com-pound locomotive. 500fr, Werner von Sie-mens, 1980s electric locomotive.

1986, Dec. 31

836	A222	40fr multi		.55 .20
837	A222	70fr multi		1.00 .20
838	A222	160fr multi		2.25 .40
839	A222	300fr multi		3.75 .60
840	A222	400fr multi		4.50 1.10
		Nos. 836-840 (5)		12.05 2.50

Souvenir Sheet

841	A222	500fr multi		5.00 1.40

Nos. 840-841 are airmail. No. 841 contains one 42x36mm stamp.

Agriculture
Radio Project
A223

1986, Dec. 27   Litho.   Perf. 13½

842	A223	170fr shown		2.25 .90
843	A223	265fr	Satellite commu-nication	3.25 1.40

Pan-African Telecommunications Union congress, Dec. 7, 1986.
No. 842 exists in souvenir sheet of one.

Space
A224

Scientists and inventions: 25fr, Sir William Herschel (1738-1822), British astronomer, and Mariner Mark II. 65fr, Wernher von Braun (1912-1977), American engineer, and Mars rover. 160fr, Rudolf Hanel, Mariner Mark II and Titan. 300fr, Patrick Baudry, Hermes shuttle and Eureka platform. 400fr, U. Keller, Halley's Comet and Giotto probe. 500fr, Wubbo Ock-els, Ulf Merbold and Columbus European Space Station. 600fr, Wilhelm Obers (1758-1840) and Mariner Mark II surveying aster-oids. No. 850 horiz.

1987, Jan. 27

844	A224	25fr multi		.35 .20
845	A224	65fr multi		.75 .20
846	A224	160fr multi		1.75 .30
847	A224	300fr multi		3.00 .75
848	A224	400fr multi		3.25 .90
849	A224	500fr multi		4.00 1.25
		Nos. 844-849 (6)		13.10 3.60

Souvenir Sheet

850	A224	600fr multi		6.25 1.75

Nos. 848-850 are airmail.

No. 820 Surcharged

1987, Feb. 20   Litho.   Perf. 13½

851	A217	485fr on 70fr Elvis Presley		7.75 2.00

Nos. 820 and 851 Ovptd. "Elvis PRESLEY / 1977-1987" in Black

1987, Feb. 20   Litho.   Perf. 13½

851A	A217	70fr multi		1.40 .40
851B	A217	485fr on 70fr multi		6.50 2.00

Overprint in red exists.

1992 Barcelona Olympics A225

Athletes and landmarks or sights: 30fr, Soccer player, Lady with Umbrella fountain. 150fr, Judo, Barcelona Cathedral. 265fr, Cyclist, Church of the Holy Family, by Gaudi. 350fr, Gymnast, Tomb of Columbus. 495fr, Runner, human tower. 500fr, Swimmer, Statue of Columbus.

1987, June 4
852	A225	30fr multi	.40	.20
853	A225	150fr multi	1.40	.45
854	A225	265fr multi	2.50	.80
855	A225	350fr multi	3.50	1.00
856	A225	495fr multi	5.50	1.40
	Nos. 852-856 (5)		13.30	3.85

Souvenir Sheet
857	A225	500fr multi	4.50	1.40

Nos. 855-857 are airmail.

A226

1988 Winter Olympics, Calgary A227

1987, June 26
858	A226	20fr Two-man luge	.30	.20
859	A226	140fr Cross-country skiing	1.40	.45
860	A226	250fr Women's figure skating	2.25	.80
861	A226	300fr Hockey	3.00	.90
862	A226	400fr Men's slalom	3.75	1.10
	Nos. 858-862 (5)		10.70	3.45

Souvenir Sheet
863	A227	500fr Downhill skiing	4.50	1.40

Nos. 861-863 are airmail.

Intl. Peace Year — A228

1987, July 20
864	A228	50fr dull ultra, sepia & blk	.50	.25
865	A228	160fr lt ol grn, sep & blk	1.40	.60

Intl. Decade of Drinkable Water — A228a

Designs: 5fr, Woman at village pump; 10fr, Two women at village pump; 200fr, Three women at village pump.

1987, Sept. 22   Litho.   Perf. 13½
865A	A228a	5fr multi	32.50	—
865B	A228a	10fr multi	32.50	—
865C	A228a	200fr multi	37.50	—
	Nos. 865A-865C (3)		102.50	

Butterflies A229

1987, Oct. 5   Litho.   Perf. 13½
866	A229	100fr Charaxes candiope	2.00	.85
867	A229	120fr Graphium leonidas	2.75	.90
868	A229	130fr Charaxes brutus	3.00	.90
869	A229	160fr Salamis aetiops	3.25	1.10
	Nos. 866-869 (4)		11.00	3.75

Pygmy Soccer Team from Nola — A230

1987, Nov. 30   Litho.   Perf. 13
870	A230	90fr multi	1.10	.60
871	A230	160fr multi	1.75	.90

Integration of the pygmy people into Central African society.

Dinosaurs — A231

Perf. 14x13½, 13½x14
1988, Mar. 19   Litho.
872	A231	50fr Brontosaurus	.45	.20
873	A231	65fr Triceratops	.80	.25
874	A231	100fr Ankylosaurus	1.10	.40
875	A231	160fr Stegosaurus	1.90	.60
876	A231	200fr Tyrannosaurus rex	2.00	.80
877	A231	240fr Corythosaurus	3.00	.90
878	A231	300fr Allosaurus	3.50	1.25
879	A231	350fr Brachiosaurus	4.25	1.50
	Nos. 872-879 (8)		17.00	5.90

Nos. 876-879 vert.

Anniversaries and Events A232

Designs: 40fr, Pres. James Madison and "We the People..." from the US Constitution. 160fr, Elizabeth II and Duke of Edinburgh . 200fr, Steffi Graf, tennis champion. 300fr, Garri Kasparov of Russia, 1985 world chess champion. 400fr, Boris Becker, 1985-86 Wimbledon champion. 500fr, Christoph Willibald Gluck (1714-87), composer. Nos. 880-884 vert.

1988, Feb. 15   Perf. 13½
880	A232	40fr multi	.40	.20
881	A232	160fr multi	1.50	.25
882	A232	200fr multi	1.90	.45
883	A232	300fr multi	3.00	.80
884	A232	400fr multi	3.50	1.25
	Nos. 880-884 (5)		10.30	2.95

Souvenir Sheet
885	A232	500fr multi	6.25	1.75

US Constitution bicentennial (40fr); 40th wedding anniv. of Elizabeth II and Prince Philip (160fr). Nos. 883-885 are airmail.

World Health Organization, 40th Anniv. — A233

1988, Apr. 7   Litho.   Perf. 13½
886	A233	70fr multi	.65	.40
887	A233	120fr multi	1.00	.55

Scout Ornithological Activities A234

Scouts and: 25fr, *Merops nubicus.* 170fr, *Euplectes hordeacea.* 300fr, *Ceryle rudis.* 400fr, *Estrilda bengala.* 450fr, *Kaupifalco monogrammicus.* 500fr, *Lamprotornis splendidus.*

1988, July 1   Litho.   Perf. 13½
888	A234	25fr multi	.20	.20
889	A234	170fr multi	1.50	.70
890	A234	300fr multi	3.00	2.00
891	A234	400fr multi	4.25	2.00
892	A234	450fr multi	5.00	2.40
	Nos. 888-892 (5)		13.95	7.30

Souvenir Sheet
893	A234	500fr multi	6.25	1.75

Nos. 891-893 are airmail.
For surcharges see Nos. 921-924.

1988 Summer Olympics, Seoul A235

1988, Sept. 30
894	A235	150fr Running, vert.	1.25	.25
895	A235	300fr Judo, vert.	2.75	.70
896	A235	400fr Soccer, vert.	3.00	1.00
897	A235	450fr Tennis, vert.	3.50	1.10
	Nos. 894-897 (4)		10.50	3.05

Souvenir Sheet
898	A235	500fr Boxing	5.00	1.50

Nos. 896-898 are airmail.

1988 Winter Olympics, Calgary — A236

1988, Sept. 30   Litho.   Perf. 13½
899	A236	170fr Cross-country skiing	1.40	.30
900	A236	350fr Ice hockey	2.25	.60
901	A236	400fr Downhill skiing	3.00	.90
902	A236	450fr Freestyle	3.25	1.00
	Nos. 899-902 (4)		9.90	2.80

Souvenir Sheet
903	A236	500fr shown	5.50	1.50

Nos. 899-902 vert. Nos. 901-903 are airmail.

Natl. Arbor Day — A237

1988, July 16   Litho.   Perf. 13½
904	A237	50fr Students planting trees	.50	.25
905	A237	100fr like 50fr	1.00	.55
906	A237	130fr Forest (before and after)	1.40	.60
	Nos. 904-906 (3)		2.90	1.40

L'Amitie Hospital, 1st Anniv. A238

1988, Nov. 30
907	A238	5fr shown	.20	.20
908	A238	60fr Aerial view	.65	.40
909	A238	160fr Front gate	1.40	.80
	Nos. 907-909 (3)		2.25	1.40

Proclamation of Central African Republic, 30th Anniv. A238a

Design: 65fr, 160fr, Dove, map, flag, people. 240fr, Government buildings, horiz.

1988 (?)   Litho.   Perf. 13½
909A	A238a	65fr multi	52.50	—
909B	A238b	160fr multi	52.50	—
909C	A238a	240fr multi	52.50	—

A239

A240

Olympic Medalists, Seoul, 1988: 150fr, Kristine Otto, DDR, swimming. 240fr, Matt Biondi, US, swimming. 300fr, Florence Griffith-Joyner, US, running. 450fr, Pierre Durand, France, equestrian. 600fr, Carl Lewis, US, running.

1989, Apr. 1
910	A239	150fr multi	2.25	.55
911	A239	240fr multi	3.50	.80
912	A239	300fr multi	4.50	1.10
913	A239	450fr multi	7.50	1.75
a.		Souv. sheet of 4, #910-913	17.50	
		Nos. 910-913 (4)	17.75	4.20

Souvenir Sheet
914	A239	600fr multi	5.75	2.00

Nos. 913-914 airmail. No. 914 contains one 37x43mm stamp.

1989, Apr. 10   Litho.   Perf. 13½

Transportation Innovations, Inventors: 20fr, Hebmuller and 1953 Volkswagen Beetle. 205fr, Werner von Siemens (1816-1892) and 1879 Locomotive B. 300fr, Dennis Conner, skipper of *Stars and Stripes*, winner of the 1988 America's Cup. 400fr, Andre Citroen (1878-1935) and 1955 Citroen-15 SIX. 450fr, Marc Seguin (1786-1875) and 1895 Decauville-Mallet 020-020. 750fr, Frederick S. Duesenberg (1876-1932), brother August, US flag and 1929 J Phaeton.

915	A240	20fr multi	.20	.20
916	A240	205fr multi	1.90	.55
917	A240	300fr multi	2.50	.60
918	A240	400fr multi	3.50	1.10
919	A240	450fr multi	4.50	1.25
		Nos. 915-919 (5)	12.60	3.70

Souvenir Sheet
920	A240	750fr multi	6.25	1.50

Nos. 919-920 airmail. No. 920 contains one 43x74mm stamp.
#915-919 exist in souvenir sheets of 1.

Nos. 889-892 Surcharged in Black or Silver

1988, Oct. 7   Litho.   Perf. 13½
921	A234	30fr on 170fr (B)	.40	.20
922	A234	70fr on 300fr	1.10	.55
923	A234	160fr on 400fr	1.90	.85
924	A234	200fr on 450fr	2.50	1.10
		Nos. 921-924 (4)	5.90	2.70

Nos. 923-924 are airmail.

PHILEXFRANCE '89, French Revolution Bicent. — A241

Designs: 200fr, Allegory in Honor of Liberty. 300fr, Declaration of Human Rights and Citizenship. 500fr, The Bastille, horiz.

1989, July 7   Litho.   Perf. 13
925	A241	200fr multi	1.90	.80
926	A241	300fr multi	4.00	1.25
a.		Pair, #925-926 + label	6.50	6.50

Souvenir Sheet
927	A241	500fr multi	6.25	3.75

Souvenir Sheet

Statue of Liberty — A242

Designs: a, Crown and torch observatories lit at night. b, Working on statue's coiffure. c, Face and scaffolding. d, Workman sanding copper sheeting around the crown observatory. e, Re-opening ceremony, 1986. f, Crown observatory at night.

Wmk. 385

1989, July   Litho.   Perf. 13
928		Sheet of 6	11.00	11.00
a.-c.	A242	150fr any single	1.60	.60
d.-f.	A242	200fr any single	1.75	1.00

Statue of Liberty cent. (in 1986). Photograph of the statue is reversed.

M. Champagnat (1789-1840), Founder of the Marist Order — A243

1989   Litho.   Perf. 13½
929	A243	15fr Madonna and child, map	.20	.20
930	A243	50fr Cross, Earth	.45	.25
931	A243	160fr shown	1.40	.80
		Nos. 929-931 (3)	2.05	1.25

Nos. 929-930 vert.

Harvest Feast, Bambari A244

1989, Oct. 15
932	A244	100fr Produce	1.00	.55
933	A244	160fr Ox plow	1.50	.60

World Food Day A245

1989, Oct. 16
934	A245	60fr Domestic animals	.55	.30
935	A245	240fr Arresting ivory poachers	2.25	1.00

French Revolution, Bicent. — A246

Battle scenes and leaders: 160fr, Brig.-Gen. Francois-Christophe Kellermann (1735-1820), Battle of Valmy, Sept. 22, 1792. 200fr, Minister of War Charles-Francois du Perier Dumouriez (1739-1823), Battle of Jemappes, Nov. 7, 1792. 500fr, Gen. Jean-Charles Pichegru (1761-1804), capture of the Dutch fleet, Jan. 22, 1795. 600fr, Gen. Louis-Lazare Hoche (1768-97), Battle of Quiberon Bay, July 21, 1795. 1000fr, Napoleon at the Battle of Rivoli Veronese, Jan. 15, 1797. 1500fr, General Jean-Baptiste Jourdan.

1989, Dec. 5   Litho.   Perf. 13½
936	A246	160fr multicolored	1.40	.40
937	A246	200fr multicolored	1.75	.55
938	A246	500fr multicolored	5.50	1.10
939	A246	600fr multicolored	5.00	1.00
a.		Souvenir sheet of 4, #936-939	15.00	15.00
		Nos. 936-939 (4)	13.65	3.05

Souvenir Sheet
940	A246	1000fr multicolored	10.00	3.00

Litho. & Embossed
940A	A246	1500fr gold & multi		

PHILEXFRANCE '89. Nos. 938-940A are airmail.
No. 936 is incorrectly inscribed "Francois-Etienne." Jemappes is incorrectly spelled on No. 937. No. 940 is incorrectly inscribed "January 14."

1990 World Cup Soccer Championships, Italy — A247

Various athletes and Italian landmarks: 20fr, Bell tower, Palermo Cathedral. 120fr, Trinity of the Mount, Rome. 160fr, St. Francis Church apse, Bologna. 200fr, Palace, Florence. 1000fr, Milan Cathedral.

1989, Dec. 23
941	A247	20fr multicolored	.20	.20
942	A247	120fr multicolored	1.25	.40
943	A247	160fr multicolored	1.40	.40
944	A247	200fr multicolored	1.60	.55
		Nos. 941-944 (4)	4.45	1.55

Souvenir Sheet
945	A247	1000fr multicolored	9.25	2.00

Nos. 942 and 945 are airmail.

Save the Forests A247a

1989   Litho.   Perf. 13½
945A	A247a	160fr multicolored	1.40	.60

Town of Bangui, Cent. A247b

Designs: 100fr, Governor's Palace, 1906. 160fr, Outpost. 200fr, A. Dolisie, founder of Bangui, vert. 1000fr, Signing of peace treaty between Michel Dolisie and Chief Gbembo, 1889, vert.

1989   Litho.   Perf. 13½
945B	A247b	100fr multi	1.25	.40
945C	A247b	160fr multi	1.75	1.00
945D	A247b	200fr multi	2.50	.95
945E	A247b	1000fr multi	10.50	4.25
		Nos. 945B-945E (4)	16.00	6.60

Championship Team from Central Africa, 1987 — A248

1990, Feb. 23   Litho.   Perf. 13½
946	A248	160fr Flag, players, trophy	1.40	.60
947	A248	240fr shown	2.25	.85
948	A248	500fr like 160fr	4.50	1.75
		Nos. 946-948 (3)	8.15	3.20

African Basketball Championships. Dated 1988. Nos. 946 and 948 vert.

A249

A250

1990, Feb. 23   Litho.   Perf. 13½
949	A249	100fr multicolored	1.00	.40
950	A249	130fr multicolored	1.10	.55

Central Africa, winner of the 1987 African Basketball Cup Championships, Tunis. Dated 1989.

1990, Mar. 12   Litho.   Perf. 13½

1992 Winter Olympics, Albertville: No. 955A, Slalom skier. No. 955B, Pairs figure skating.

951	A250	10fr Speed skating	.20	.20
952	A250	60fr Cross-country skiing	.55	.25
953	A250	500fr Slalom	4.50	1.00
954	A250	750fr Figure skating	6.25	1.40
		Nos. 951-954 (4)	11.50	2.85

Souvenir Sheet
955	A250	1000fr Downhill skiing	8.75	2.00

Litho. & Embossed
955A	A250	1500fr gold & multi	12.00	3.50

Souvenir Sheet
955B	A250	1500fr gold & multi	30.00	30.00

Nos. 953-955B are airmail. No. 955 contains one 36x42mm stamp. Nos. 951-954 exist in souvenir sheets of one.

Scout, *Euphaera eusemoides* — A251

Boy scouts and butterflies: 65fr, *Cymothoe beckeri.* 160fr, *Pseudacraea clarki.* 250fr, *Charaxes castor.*300fr, *Euphaedra gausape.* 500fr, *Graphium ridleyanus.* 1000fr, *Euphaedra edwardsi.* No. 962A, Antanartia delius. No. 962B, Spotted flycatcher. No. 962C, Cymothoe sangaris.

1990, Mar. 26
956	A251	25fr multicolored	.30	.20
957	A251	65fr multicolored	.55	.20
958	A251	160fr multicolored	1.25	.25
959	A251	250fr multicolored	2.25	.55
960	A251	300fr multicolored	2.75	.60
961	A251	500fr multicolored	4.75	1.00
	Nos. 956-961 (6)	11.85	2.80

Souvenir Sheet
|962|A251|1000fr multicolored|11.00|2.25|

Litho. & Embossed
Perf. 12½
|962A|A251|1500fr gold & multi|13.75|4.00|
Perf. 13½
|962B|A251|1500fr gold & multi|45.00|4.00|

Souvenir Sheet
|962C|A251|1500fr gold & multi|12.00|12.00|

Nos. 962A-962C are airmail. No. 962A exists in a souvenir sheet of 1.

1992 Summer Olympics, Barcelona A252

1990, Apr. 1 Litho. Perf. 13½
963	A252	10fr Javelin	.20	.20
964	A252	40fr Runner	.40	.20
965	A252	130fr Tennis	1.10	.25
966	A252	240fr Hurdles	2.00	.55
967	A252	400fr Yachting	3.50	1.00
968	A252	500fr Soccer	4.50	1.10
	Nos. 963-968 (6)	11.70	3.30

Souvenir Sheet
|969|A252|1000fr Boxing|9.75|2.00|

Nos. 963-965 vert. Nos. 967-969 are airmail.

Pres. Gorbachev, Pres. Bush — A253

Pres. Gorbachev, Pope John Paul II — A254

1990, July 27 Litho. Perf. 13½
|970|A253|120fr multicolored|.95|.25|
|971|A254|200fr multicolored|1.50|.30|

Pope John Paul II-Gorbachev meeting Dec. 2, 1989. Bush-Gorbachev Summit Meeting Dec. 3, 1989. Nos. 970-971 exist in souvenir sheets of 1. Value, each $20.

Great Britain No. 1, Sir Rowland Hill (1795-1879) — A255

1990, July 27
|972|A255|130fr multicolored|1.00|.25|

No. 972 exists in a souvenir sheet of 1.

Events and Anniversaries — A256

Designs: 160fr, Galileo Probe to Jupiter. 240fr, Neil Armstrong, 1st man on moon. 250fr, Concorde, rapid-transit train, Rotary Intl. emblem.

1990, July 27 Litho. Perf. 13½
973	A256	160fr multicolored	1.10	.40
974	A256	240fr multicolored	1.75	.50
975	A256	250fr multicolored	3.75	.50
	Nos. 973-975 (3)	6.60	1.40

Wildlife Protection A258

100fr, Declining elephant population, vert.

1991, Jan. 25 Litho. Perf. 13½
976	A258	15fr gold & multi	.60	.20
977	A258	60fr multicolored	1.90	.40
978	A258	100fr multicolored	3.00	.55
	Nos. 976-978 (3)	5.50	1.15

Eutropius A259

Design: 240fr, Distichodus.

1991, Jan. 26
979	A259	50fr multicolored	.55	.25
980	A259	160fr gold & multi	2.10	.75
981	A259	240fr multicolored	3.50	1.50
	Nos. 979-981 (3)	6.15	2.50

Fight Against AIDS A260

Design: 120fr, Class speaker, vert.

1991, Jan. 24
982	A260	5fr gold & multi	.45	.20
983	A260	70fr multicolored	1.40	.55
984	A260	120fr multicolored	1.90	.80
	Nos. 982-984 (3)	3.75	1.55

Central African Diamonds A260a

Designs: 65fr, Woman polishing diamond, 160fr, Map, diamond.

1991, Feb. 14 Litho. Perf. 11½
Granite Paper
|984A|A260a|65fr multicolored|—|
|984B|A260a|160fr multicolored|—|

Assumption of Power by Pres. Andre Kolingba, 10th Anniv. (in 1991) — A261

1992, Sept. 1 Litho. Perf. 13x13½
|985|A261|160fr multicolored|1.60|.60|

Anniversaries and Events — A262

Designs: 80fr, Maybach Zeppelin, zeppelin airship, Count Ferdinand Zeppelin. 140fr, Child being comforted, Jean-Henri Dunant. 160fr, Benetton-Ford B 192, Michael Schumacher. 350fr, Konrad Adenauer signing Constitution of German Republic. 500fr, Pope John Paul II, mother and child, map. 600fr, Wolfgang Amadeus Mozart. 1000fr, Columbus at La Rabida, sailing ship, and building in Seville, Spain.

1992, Sept. 22 Litho. Perf. 13½
986	A262	80fr multicolored	.65	.20
987	A262	140fr multicolored	1.60	.25
988	A262	160fr multicolored	1.90	.40
989	A262	350fr multicolored	4.50	1.10
990	A262	500fr multicolored	6.25	1.40
991	A262	600fr multicolored	8.25	1.50
	Nos. 986-991 (6)	23.15	4.85

Souvenir Sheet
|992|A262|1000fr multicolored|8.25|2.00|

Count Zeppelin, 75th anniv. of death (#986). Jean-Henri Dunant, first recipient of Nobel Peace Prize, 90th anniv. (in 1991) (#987). Grand Prix of Monaco (#988). Brandenburg Gate, bicent. (#989). Visit of Pope John Paul II to Africa (#990). Wolfgang Amadeus Mozart, bicent. of death (in 1991) (#991). Discovery of America, 500th anniv. and Expo '92, Seville (#992).
Nos. 990-992 are airmail. Nos. 986-991 exist in souvenir sheets of 1.
For overprint see No. 1073.

A264

Elvis Presley (1935-1977) — A264a

Portrait of Presley, song or movie: 200fr, Heartbreak Hotel, 1956. 300fr, Love Me Tender, 1957. 400fr, Jailhouse Rock, 1957. 600fr, Harem Scarum, 1965.
1000fr, With guitar, at microphone. No. 1001A, Holding microphone. No. 1001B, Playing guitar.

1993, July 12 Litho. Perf. 13½
997	A264	200fr multi	2.40	.25
998	A264	300fr multi	3.50	.50
999	A264	400fr multi	4.25	.60
1000	A264	600fr multi	6.00	1.00
	Nos. 997-1000 (4)	16.15	2.35

Souvenir Sheet
|1001|A264|1000fr multi|9.50|2.40|

Litho. & Embossed
|1001A|A264a|1500fr gold & multi|20.00|7.50|

Souvenir Sheet
|1001B|A264a|1500fr gold & multi|13.00|8.00|

Nos. 1000-1001B are airmail. Nos. 997-1000, 1001A exist imperf. and in souvenir sheets of one. Nos. 1001, 1001B exist imperf.

A265

Wedding of Japan's Crown Prince Naruhito and Masako Owada — A265a

Designs: 50fr, Princess Masako, parents. 65fr, Crown Prince Naruhito, parents. 160fr, Princess Masako, Harvard University 450fr, Crown Prince Naruhito, Oxford University. 750fr, Crown Prince, Princess.

1993, July 12 Litho. Perf. 13½
1002	A265	50fr multi	.30	.20
1003	A265	65fr multi	.65	.25
1004	A265	160fr multi	1.75	.25
1005	A265	450fr multi	4.50	1.00
	Nos. 1002-1005 (4)	7.20	1.70

Souvenir Sheet
|1006|A265|750fr multi|7.75|3.00|

Litho. & Embossed
|1006A|A265a|1500fr gold & multi|26.00|4.00|

Nos. 1005-1006A are airmail. Nos. 1002-1005, 1006A exist imperf. and in souvenir sheets of one. No. 1006 exists imperf.

A266

1994 World Cup Soccer
Championships, US — A266a

Designs show winning team, scenes from:
40fr, Amsterdam, 1928; Montevideo, 1930.
50fr, Rome, 1934; Paris, 1938. 60fr, Rio,
1950; Berne, 1954. 80fr, Stockholm, 1958;
Santiago, 1962. 160fr, London, 1966; Mexico
City, 1970. 200fr, Munich, 1974; Buenos
Aires, 1978. 400fr, Madrid, 1982; Mexico City,
1986. 500fr, Rome, 1990; emblem for US
competition, 1994.
1000fr, 1990 German team; 1994 US team.
No. 1015A, Pele, Brazil. No. 1015B, Gerd
Muller, Germany.

1993, Oct. 9		Litho.		Perf. 13½	
1007	A266	40fr multi		.40	.20
1008	A266	50fr multi		.40	.20
1009	A266	60fr multi		.50	.20
1010	A266	80fr multi		.65	.20
1011	A266	160fr multi		1.40	.40
1012	A266	200fr multi		1.90	.70
1013	A266	400fr multi		3.50	.70
1014	A266	500fr multi		5.00	1.00
	Nos. 1007-1014 (8)			13.75	3.60

Souvenir Sheet

1015	A266	1000fr multi	10.00	2.75

Litho. & Embossed

1015A	A266a	1500fr gold &		
		multi	26.00	

Souvenir Sheet

1015B	A266a	1500fr gold &		
		multi	13.50	

#1015 contains one 60x30mm stamp.
#1007-1014 exist in souvenir sheets of one.
Nos. 1015A-1015B are airmail.

Miniature Sheets

Modern Olympic Games, Cent. (in
1996) — A267

No. 1016: a, Ancient olympian. b, Baron de
Coubertin, 1896. c, Charles Bennett, 1900. d,
Etienne Desmarteau, 1904. e, Harry Porter,
1908. f, Patrick MacDonald, 1912. g, No
games, 1916. h, Frank Loomis, 1920. i, Albert
White, 1924.
No. 1017: a, El Ouafi, 1928. b, Eddie Tolan,
1932. c, Jesse Owens, 1936. d, No games,
1940. e, No games, 1944. f, Tapio Rautavaara,
1948. g, Jean Boiteux, 1952. h, Petrus Kas-
terman, 1956. i, Sante Gaiardoni, 1960.

No. 1018: a, Anton Geesink, 1964. b, Bob
Beamon, 1968. c, Mark Spitz, 1972. d, Nadia
Comaneci, 1976. e, Aleksandre Dityatin, 1980.
f, J.F. Lamour, 1984. g, Pierre Durand, 1988.
h, Michael Jordan, 1992. i, Soccer player,
1996.

1993		Litho.		Perf. 13½	
1016	A267	90fr Sheet of 9,			
		#a.-i.		7.50	3.25
1017	A267	100fr Sheet of 9,			
		#a.-i.		8.25	3.75
1018	A267	160fr Sheet of 9,			
		#a.-i.		13.00	5.75

Miniature Sheet

Dinosaurs — A268

Designs: No. 1019a, 25fr, Saltoposuchus. b,
25fr, Rhamphorhynchus. c, 25fr,
Dimorphodon. d, 25fr, Archaeopteryx. e, 30fr,
Compsognathus longipes. f, 30fr, Cryptocle-
idus oxoniensis. g, 30fr, Stegosaurus. h, 30fr,
Cetiosaurus. i, 50fr, Brontosaurus. j, 50fr,
Corythosaurus casuarius. k, 50fr,
Styracosaurus. l, 50fr, Gorgosaurus. m, 500fr,
Scolosaurus. n, 500fr, Trachodon. o, 500fr,
Struthiomimus. p, 500fr, Tarbosaurus.
No. 1020, Tylosaur.

1993, Dec. 3					
1019	A268	Sheet of 16, #a.-p.	26.00	26.00	

Souvenir Sheet

1020	A268	1000fr multicolored	10.50	2.75

No. 1020 is airmail and contains one
51x60mm stamp.

Biodiversity
A269

Various fauna surrounding: 100fr, Man
planting tree. 130fr, Man with local fauna, vert.

1993, Oct. 20		Litho.		Perf. 13½	
1021	A269	100fr multicolored		1.25	.50
1022	A269	130fr multicolored		1.75	.80

M'Bali
Dam — A270

1993, Jan. 14		Litho.		Perf. 13	
1023	A270	160fr shown		1.60	.30
1024	A270	200fr Women, men			
		with fish		2.25	.40

Cooperation Council, 40th
Anniv. — A271

1993, Jan. 26

1025	A271	240fr multicolored	2.50	.50

Intl. Conference
on Nutrition,
Rome — A272

1993, Apr. 1

1026	A272	90fr shown	.75	.20
1027	A272	140fr Fresh foods	1.40	.30

University
of Bangui
A273

1993, Apr. 8

1028	A273	100fr multicolored	1.00	.25

Dated 1992.

Environmental
Development
A274

Designs: 160fr, Woman with vegetables,
fruit. 240fr, Woman cooking food.

1993, Oct. 27		Litho.		Perf. 13½	
1029	A274	160fr multicolored		1.75	.80
1030	A274	240fr multicolored		2.50	.95

Miniature Sheets

1994 Winter Olympics,
Lillehammer — A275

Past Winter Olympic champions: 1031a, Th.
Haug, Nordic combined skiing, Chamonix,
1924. b, J. Heaton, 1-man sled, St. Moritz,
1928. c, B. Ruud, ski jumping, Lake Placid,
1932. d, I. Ballangrud, speed skating,
Garmisch-Partenkirchen, 1936. e, G. Fraser,
women's slalom skiing, St. Moritz, 1948. f,
German 4-man bobsled, Oslo, 1952. g, USSR
hockey team, Cortina D'Ampezzo, 1956. h, J.
Vuarnet, downhill skiing, Squaw Valley, 1960.

No. 1032a, M. Goitschel, giant slalom, Innsbruck, 1964. b, Jean-Claude Killy, slalom skiing, Grenoble, 1968. c, U. Wehling, Nordic
combined, Sapporo, 1972. d, Rodnina & Zait-
sev, pairs figure skating, Innsbruck, 1976. e,
E. Heiden, speed skating, Lake Placid, 1980.
f, K. Witt, figure skating, Sarajevo, 1984. g, J.
Mueller, luge, Calgary, 1988. h, E. Grospiron,
freestyle skiing, Albertville, 1992. i, Speed skiing, Lillehammer, 1994.

1994, Jan. 14		Litho.		Perf. 13½	
1031	A275	100fr Sheet of 8,			
		#a.-h. + la-			
		bel		6.50	6.50
1032	A275	200fr Sheet of 9,			
		#a.-i.		15.00	15.00

1994 Winter Olympics,
Lillehammer — A276

Design: 1500fr, Women figure skaters.

1994		Litho. & Embossed		Perf. 13½	
1033	A276	1500fr gold & multi		12.00	

#1033 is airmail & exists in a souvenir sheet
of 1. Value $24.

Flowers,
Vegetables,
Fruit, &
Mushrooms
A277

Flowers: No. 1034a, 25fr, Ansellia africana.
b, 60fr, Polystachia bella. c, 90fr, Aerangis
rhodosticta. d, 500fr, Angraecum eburneum.
Vegetables: No. 1035a, 30fr, Yams. b, 65fr,
Manioc. c, 100fr, Corn. d, 400fr, Sweet potato.
Fruits: No. 1036a, 40fr, Orange. b, 70fr,
Banana. c, 160fr, Mango. d, 300fr, Coffee.
Mushrooms: No. 1037a, 50fr, Termitomyces
schimperi. b, 80fr, Sympodia arborescens. c,
200fr, Phlebopus sudanicus. d, 600fr,
Leucocoprinus africanus.

1994, Jan. 21		Litho.		Perf. 13½	
1034	A277	Strip of 4, #a.-d.		5.50	2.50
1035	A277	Strip of 4, #a.-d.		5.00	2.25
1036	A277	Strip of 4, #a.-d.		4.50	2.00
1037	A277	Strip of 4, #a.-d.		8.75	3.75
e.		Sheet of 16, #1034-1037		26.00	12.00

Catholic
Church in
Africa,
Cent. — A278

Designs: 130fr, Monsignor Augouard,
founder of mission, St. Paul of the Rapids.
160fr, Monsignor Grandin, Abbe Boganda,
first sacred ordainment, 1938. 240fr, Father
Louis Godart, House of Charity, Bangui.

1994, June 2		Litho.		Perf. 13½	
1038	A278	130fr multicolored		.55	.25
1039	A278	160fr multicolored		.70	.30
1040	A278	240fr multicolored		1.00	.45
	Nos. 1038-1040 (3)			2.25	1.00

Relics from Early Civilizations,
Landmarks — A279

Designs: 10fr, Cabin-shaped cinerary urn,
Rome. 25fr, Face of the secret denunciation,
Venice, vert. 30fr, Statue of the Tetrarchs, Venice, vert. 50fr, Little cube-shaped building,
Palermo, vert. 65fr, Frieze, The Alhambra,
Granada, vert. 90fr, Grand Chateau, Bellinzona. 100fr, Museum D'Orsay, Paris, vert.
130fr, Granary, Galicia. 140fr, Mural, by Diego
Rivera, Mexico, vert. 160fr, Guacamaya mask,
Mexico, vert. 200fr, Ivory mask, Western
Africa, vert. 240fr, La Sagrada Familia, Barcelona, vert. 260fr, Casbah of Amerhidil. 300fr,
Gold aureus of Sulla, Rome, 82 BC. 400fr,
Chimborazo volcano.

1994, June 2   **Perf. 13**
1041-1055 A279 Set of 15   10.50 4.50

D-Day, 50th Anniv. — A280

Pegasus Bridge, June 6: No. 1056a, British
troops crossing bridge, piper. b, Glider, British
and German soldiers. c, German soldiers.
  Operation COBRA, July 24: a, Tank, monument, soldiers. b, Bombers, soldiers, gun barrel. c, Tank, soldiers up close.

1994, Oct. 25   **Litho.**   **Perf. 13½**
1056 A280 600fr Strip of 3, #a.-
      c.   10.00 3.75
1057 A280 600fr Strip of 3, #a.-
      c.   10.00 3.75
  Nos. 1056b, 1057b are 30x46mm. Nos.
1056-1057 are continuous designs. See No.
C359.

Anniversaries & Events — A281

No. 1058, 600fr — Characters from "Star
Wars:" a, Han Solo, Chewbaca. b, Darth
Vader, Princess Leia, Luke Skywalker, R2D2,
C3PO. c, Obi Wan Kenobi.
  No. 1059 — First manned moon landing,
25th anniv.: a, 400fr, Buzz Aldrin. b, 500fr, Neil
Armstrong, Apollo 11 liftoff. c, 600fr, Michael
Collins.
  No. 1060: a, 400fr, Theodor von Karman. b,
500fr, Apollo 11 command module, Wernher
von Braun. c, 600fr, Hermes Rocket, Hermann
Oberth.

1994, Oct. 25   **Litho.**   **Perf. 13½**
1058 A281   Strip of 3, #a.-c.   8.00 3.50
1059 A281   Strip of 3, #a.-c.   7.50 3.00
1060 A281   Strip of 3, #a.-c.   7.50 3.00

  Motion Pictures, cent. (#1058).
  Nos. 1058b, 1059b, 1060b are 60x51mm.
Nos. 1058-1060 are continuous design and
exist in a souvenir sheet of 1.

Natl.
Assembly
A282

1994, Dec. 8
1061 A282   65fr blue & multi   .35   .20
1062 A282 430fr yel brn & multi   1.90   .90

Antoine de Saint-Exupery (1900-44),
Aviator, Author — A283

1994, Dec 16
1063 A283   80fr Airplane   .35   .20
1064 A283 235fr Portrait, vert.   1.00   .50

Inauguration of
Pres. Ange-Felix
Patasse, 1st
Anniv. — A284

1994, Oct. 22
1065 A284   65fr blue & multi   .40   .20
1066 A284 300fr yellow & multi   1.60   .60
1067 A284 385fr green & multi   2.00   .75
    Nos. 1065-1067 (3)   4.00 1.55

A285

Intl. Olympic Committee,
Cent. — A286

1994, Oct. 25
1068 A285   60fr bl grn & multi   .35   .20
1069 A285 405fr yel grn & multi   1.75   .80
     Souvenir Sheet
1070 A286 675fr Pierre de
          Coubertin   3.00 1.40
  No. 1070 is airmail.

Nos. 1031-1032 Ovptd. with Medalist
& Country Name in Gold

  Overprints on No. 1031: No. 1071a, "F.B.
LUNDBERG / NORVEGE." b, "G. HACKL /
ALLEMAGNE." c, "B. DAEHLIE / NORVEGE."
d, "J.O. KOSS / NORVEGE." e, "V. SCHNEIDER / SUISSE." f, "MEDAILLE D'OR /
ALLEMAGNE." g, "MEDAILLE D'OR /
SUEDE." h, "T. MOE / U.S.A."
  Overprints on No. 1032: No. 1072a, "M.
WASMEIER / ALLEMAGNE." b, "T. STANGASSINGER / AUTRICHE." c, "MEDAILLE
D'OR / PAR EQUIPES / JAPON." d, "Y.
GORDEYEVA / S. GRINKOV / RUSSIE." e, "D.
JANSEN / U.S.A." f, "O. BAYUL / UKRAINE."
g, "G. HACKL / ALLEMAGNE." h, "J.-L. BRASSARO / CANADA." i, "K. SEIZINGER /
ALLEMAGNE."

1994
1071 A275 100fr Sheet of 8,
         #a.-h. + label   6.50 3.00
1072 A275 200fr Sheet of 9,
         #a.-i.   15.00 7.00

No. 988 Overprinted in Silver
**MICHAEL SCHUMACHER
CHAMPION DU MONDE
FORMULE I   1994**

1994, Dec. 28   **Litho.**   **Perf. 13½**
1073 A262 160fr multicolored   10.00 4.50
  No. 1073 also exists in souvenir sheet of 1.

1995 Boy Scout
Jamboree,
Holland — A287

  Scout with mushrooms or butterflies: 300fr,
Armillariela mellea. 385fr, Charaxes pleione.
405fr, Charaxes candiope. 430fr, Charaxes
pollux. 500fr, Volvaria esculenta. 1000fr,
Cortinarius.
  2000fr, Euphaedra medon.

1995, May 24
1074-1079 A287   Set of 6   15.00 7.00
 1077a   Sheet, #1075-1077   10.00 2.75
 1079a   Sheet, #1074, #1078-1079   14.50 4.00
     Souvenir Sheet
1080 A287 2000fr multicolored   18.00 4.25
  Nos. 1074-1079 exist in souvenir sheets of
1. No. 1080 is airmail and contains one
39x57mm stamp.

1994 World Cup Soccer
Championships, US — A288

  Stadium: 300fr, Citrus Bowl, Orlando. 385fr,
RFK Stadium, Washington, DC. 405fr, Soldier
Field, Chicago. 430fr, Cotton Bowl, Dallas.
500fr, Giants Stadium, East Rutherford, NJ.
1000fr, Foxboro Stadium, Foxboro, MA.
  2000fr, Rose Bowl, vert.

1995, July 14   **Litho.**   **Perf. 13½**
1081-1086 A288   Set of 6   14.00 6.50
     Souvenir Sheet
1087 A288 2000fr multicolored   12.50 5.75
  No. 1087 is airmail.

African
Development
Bank, 30th
Anniv. — A289

1995, June 29
1088 A289   70fr multicolored   .35   .20
1089 A289 200fr multicolored   1.00   .45
  Nos. 1088-1089 also exist in souvenir sheet
of 1.

Fish
A290

  Designs, 25fr, 300fr, Auchenoglanis. 30fr,
50fr, Chrisicntys.

1995, June 22
1090-1093 A290 Set of 4   2.75   .90

Entertainers
A291

  Designs: 300fr, Freddie Mercury (Queen).
385fr, Jimi Hendrix. 430fr, Marilyn Monroe.
500fr, Michael Jackson. 600fr, Jerry Garcia
(Grateful Dead). 800fr, Elvis Presley.
  1500fr, Charlton Heston in "Planet of the
Apes." 2000fr, Marilyn Monroe, diff.

1995, July 21
1094-1099 A291 Set of 6   15.00 6.50
     Souvenir Sheets
1099B A291 1500fr multicolored   8.25 3.25
1100   A291 2000fr multicolored   10.50 4.25
  Nos. 1094-1099 exist in souvenir sheets of
1. No. 1100 is airmail. No. 1099B contains one
51x60mm airmail stamp.

Volleyball,
Cent. — A292

1995, Oct. 3   **Litho.**   **Perf. 13½**
1101 A292 300fr multicolored   1.40   .65
  No. 1101 exists in a souvenir sheet of 1.
Value $10.

Sports
Figures
A293

  400fr, Andre Agassi, tennis. 500fr, Boris
Becker, tennis. 700fr, Ayrton Senna (1960-94)
race car driver. 800fr, Michael Schumacher, F-1 world driving champion.
  2000fr, Michael Schumacher, diff.

1996, June 20   **Litho.**   **Perf. 13½**
1102-1105 A293 Set of 4   12.00 5.50
     Souvenir Sheet
1106 A293 2000fr multicolored   10.00 4.50
  #1102-1105 exist in souvenir sheets of 1.
Value $30.

1996 Summer Olympic Games, Atlanta A294

Olympic athletes, sites in Atlanta: 170fr, Atlanta-Fulton County Stadium. 300fr, Martin Luther King Memorial. 350fr, Alexander H. Stephens Monument. 600fr, High Museum of Art.
2000fr, Pierre de Coubertin, runner.

1996, June 20
1107-1110 A294 Set of 4   7.50 3.25
Souvenir Sheet
1110A A294 2000fr multicolored   9.50 4.00
No. 1110A contains one 42x51mm stamp.

UN, 50th Anniv. (in 1995) A295

1996, July 15   **Perf. 14**
1111 A295 5fr "50," emblem, vert.   .20 .20
1112 A295 430fr shown   1.90 .90
#1111-1112 exist in souvenir sheets of 1.

1996 Summer Olympic Games, Atlanta A296

1900 Summer Olympics, Paris: 235fr, Alvin Kraenzlein, vert. 300fr, Paris Stadium. 385fr, Irving Baxter. 430fr, British soccer team.
Past Olympic medalists: No. 1117a, Miruts Yifter, 5,000-meters, 1980. b, Germany, team dressage, 1976. c, Bruce Jenner, decathlon, 1976. d, Mark Gorski, 1000-meter match sprint, 1984. e, Randy Williams, long jump, 1972. f, Shinodu Sekine, judo, 1972. g, Kiyomi Kato, wrestling, 1972. h, Mitsuo Tsukahama, gymnastics, 1976. i, Hartwig Steenken, Germany, 1972.
Each 1000fr: No. 1118, Betty Cuthbert, 100-meters, 1956. No. 1119, Gerhard Stock, javelin, 1936.

1996, July 19
1113-1116 A296 Set of 4   6.00 2.75
1117 A296 200fr Sheet of 9, #a.-i.   8.00 3.50
Souvenir Sheets
1118-1119 A296 Set of 2   8.75 4.00
Olymphilex '96 (#1113-1116, 1118-1119).

Francophonie, 25th Anniv. (in 1995) — A297

300fr, "25 ANS" surrounded by "1970-1995."

1996, July 22
1120 A297 235fr multicolored   1.00 .50
1121 A297 300fr multicolored   1.40 .60
#1120-1121 exist in souvenir sheets of 1.

FAO, 50th Anniv. (in 1995) A298

Designs: 10fr, Fish being lifted in net, vert. 385fr, Boy drinking water.

1996
1122 A298 10fr multicolored   .20 .20
1123 A298 385fr multicolored   1.60 .75
#1122-1123 exist in souvenir sheets of 1.

Queen Elizabeth II, 70th Birthday A299

a, Formal portrait. b, In blue suit. c, In red hat. 1000fr, Balmoral Castle.

1996, July 24   **Perf. 13½x14**
1124 A299 300fr Strip of 3, #a.-c.   3.75 1.75
Souvenir Sheet
1125 A299 1000fr multicolored   4.50 2.00
Nos. 1124 was issued in sheets of 9 stamps.

Pets — A300

1996   **Litho.**   **Perf. 13½**
1126 A300 250fr Dog   1.25 .60
1127 A300 600fr Cat   3.00 1.40
#1126-1127 exist in souvenir sheets of 1.

1998 World Cup Soccer Championships, France — A301

Winning country, year, player: No. 1128a, Uruguay 1930, Pedro Cea (Argentina), Italy 1934. b, Italy 1938, Piola (Italy), Uruguay 1950. c, Germany 1954, Brazil 1958, Walter, (Germany). d, Amarildo, (Brazil), Brazil 1962, England 1966.
No. 1129: a, Brazil 1970, Pele (Brazil), Germany 1974. b, Kempes (Argentina), Argentina 1978, Italy 1982. c, Argentina 1986, Mattaus (Germany), Germany 1990. d, Platini (France), Brazil 1994.

1996   **Litho.**   **Perf. 13½**
1128 A301 375fr Sheet of 4, #a.-d.   7.25 3.25
1129 A301 425fr Sheet of 4, #a.-d.   8.25 3.75

Dinosaur Eggs — A302

Denomination at: a, LR. b, LL.

1996, Apr. 28
1130 A302 140fr Pair, #a.-b.   2.10 .65
   c.   Souv. Sheet, #1130a-1130b   3.00 .65
CHINA '96 (#1130c).

Scouting A303

Raptors, butterflies, mushrooms: 175fr, Buzzard. 200fr, H. misippus. 300fr, Lepiota aspera. 350fr, Raptor with feathers ruffled. 450fr, Amanita caesarea. 500fr, Morpho portis-nymphalidae.

1996   **Litho.**   **Perf. 13½**
1131-1136 A303 Set of 6   10.00 4.50
Nos. 1132-1133, 1135-1136 exist in souvenir sheets of 1.

Horses A304

Great Nebula, Andromeda A305

No. 1137, 235fr: a, Appaloosa. b, Arabian. c, Quarter horse. d, Belgian. e, Pure blood English. f, Mustang. g, Haflinger. h, Welsh pony.
No. 1138, 235fr: a, Pinto. b, Palomino. c, Welara. d, Morgan. e, Standard American. f, Norwegian fjord. g, Shetland. h, Shire.
1000fr, Saddlebred.

1996, Nov. 20   **Perf. 14**
Sheets of 8, #a-h
1137-1138 A304 235fr Set of 2   16.00 7.50
Souvenir Sheet
1139 A304 1000fr multicolored   4.50 2.25

1996, Nov. 22
Designs: b, Halley's Comet. c, Jupiter. d, Saturn. e, Moon. f, Mars.
1140 A305 300fr Sheet of 6, #a.-f.   8.00 3.50

Wildlife — A306

Flowers: a, Bomax costatum. b, Clappertonia flcifolia. c, Canarina abyssinica. d,

---

Kigelia africana. e, Adenium obesum. f, Oncoba spinosa. g, Orinum ornatum. h, Gloriosa simplex. i, Strophanthus gratus.
Bird: 1500fr, Sagittarius serpentarius.

1997, Feb. 6   **Litho.**   **Perf. 14**
1141 A306 205fr Sheet of 9, #a.-i.   8.25 3.75
Souvenir Sheet
1142 A306 1500fr multicolored   8.25 3.00

Intl. Express Mail Service A307

300fr, Globe, international express mail routes. 405fr, Emblem of hand holding letter.

1996   **Litho.**   **Perf. 13½**
1143 A307 300fr multicolored   1.40 .65
1144 A307 405fr multicolored   1.90 .90
No. 1144 exists in a souvenir sheet of 1.

Human Rights Advocates A308

Designs: a, Dalai Lama. b, Martin Luther King. c, John F. Kennedy. d, Nelson Mandela. e, Mother Teresa. f, Mahatma Gandhi.

1996
1145 A308 175fr Sheet of 6, #a.-f. + 2 labels   5.00 2.25

Red Cross and Red Crescent Societies — A309

Designs: a, Doctor with patient. b, Man sifting grain. c, Using stethoscope on patient. d, Wounded man. e, Bandaging patient. f, Aiding infant.

1996
1146 A309 250fr Sheet of 6, #a.-f. + 2 labels   7.25 3.25

Boy Scouts — A310

Boy scout: a, With dog. b, Riding horse. c, Holding cat. d, Holding butterfly. e, On bicycle. f, Playing game.
Butterfly: 2000fr, Saturnidae, horiz.

1996   Litho.   Perf. 13½
1147 A310 300fr Sheet of 6,
    #a.-f. + 2 labels   9.00 4.00

Souvenir Sheet
1148 A310 2000fr multicolored   10.00 4.50

No. 1148 contains one 42x36mm stamp.

Lions Intl., Rotary Intl. — A311

Designs: a, Child drinking from cup. b, Child carrying sack. c, Girl holding sheaves of grain. d, Man breaking bread. e, Woman cooking over fire. f, Boy, corn stalk.

1996
1149 A311 500fr Sheet of 6,
    #a.-f. + 2 labels   14.00 6.50

Flora and Fauna
A312

15fr, Cucumis sativus, vert. 20fr, Phyllochistis citrella. 40fr, Cetonia aurata. 65fr, Nomadacris septemfasciata. 100fr, Crocodilus vulgaris. 140fr, Athyrium filix, vert. 405fr, Rhopalo ceres.

1996
1150-1156 A312 Set of 7   5.00 1.75

#1151, 1156 exist in sourvenir sheets of 1.

UN, UNICEF, 50th Anniv. — A313

Designs: a, Futuristic space vehicle. b, MIR space station. c, US space shuttle, space station. d, Woman carrying food. e, Child receiving vaccination. f, Baby being weighed.

1996
1157 A313 350fr Sheet of 6,
    #a.-f. + 2 labels   10.00 4.50

Elizabeth Taylor, Actress — A314   Princess Diana — A315

Various portraits.

1997, Apr. 10   Litho.   Perf. 14
1158 A314 300fr Sheet of 6,
    #a.-f.   8.00 3.50
1159 A315 300fr Sheet of 6,
    #a.-f.   8.00 3.50

Souvenir Sheets
1160 A314 1500fr multicolored   6.50 3.00
1161 A315 1500fr multicolored   6.50 3.00

For overprints see Nos. 1181-1182.

UNESCO, 50th Anniv. A316

No. 1162, 235fr: a, Fortress ruins, Ethiopia. b, Victoria Falls, Zambia. c, River during dry season, Zimbabwe. d, Nature Reserve, Niger. e, Pelican, Natl. Park, Mauritania. f, Native huts in village, Niokolo-Kobo Natl. Park, Senegal. g, M'Zab Valley, Algeria. h, Mosque, Morocco.
No. 1163, 235fr: a, c, Ruins of Roman Amphitheater, France. b, Split, Croatia. d, e, Quedlinberg, Germany. f, h, Tower of London, England. g, Olympic Natl. Park, US.
No. 1164, 235fr: a, Horyu-Ji, Japan. b, Waterfalls, Amazon River, Los Katios Natl. Park, Colombia. c, Abu Mena Church, Egypt. d, Boat on river, Fortress of Suomenlinna, Finland. e, Venice, Italy. f, Mural, Potala Palace, Lhasa, Tibet, China. g, Cathedral, town of Olinda, Brazil. h, Monastery, Mystras, Greece.
No. 1165, 1000fr, Jiuzhaigou Valley, China. No. 1166, 1000fr, Interior, Pilgrimage Church of Wies, Germany. No. 1167, 1000fr Ruins of Fountains Abbey, Studley Park, England.

1997, Apr. 30   Perf. 13½x14
Sheets of 8, #a-h + Label
1162-1164 A316 Set of 3   25.00 12.00

Souvenir Sheets
1165-1167 A316 Set of 3   13.00 6.00

UNICEF, 50th Anniv. — A317

No. 1168: a, 200fr, UN headquarters building. b, 250fr, Baby. c, 500fr, Danny Kaye seated inside vehicle.
1500fr, Child.

1997, Apr. 30   Perf. 14
1168 A317 Sheet of 3, #a.-c.   4.00 1.90

Souvenir Sheet
1169 A317 1500fr multicolored   6.50 3.00

US Pres. Bill Clinton and His Cat, "Socks" — A318

Designs: a, b, c, e, g, h, i, Socks in various poses. d, f, Clinton, Socks.

1996
1170 A318 200fr Sheet of 9, #a.-i.   8.50 3.75

Conquest of Space — A319

Events in 1977: No. 1171: a, Voyager 1, US. b, Space Shuttle Enterprise, US. c, Meteosat 1, US. d, Salyut 6 Space Station, USSR.
Events in 1982: No. 1172: a, Salyut 7 Space Station, USSR. b, Landsat 4 Satellite, US. c, Venera 13, USSR. d, IRAS Infrared Telescope, US.
Events of 1967: No. 1173: a, Cosmos 186 & 188. b, Molnya satellite. c, Surveyor 3. d, Mariner 5.
Events in 1972: No. 1174: a, Copernicus probe, US. b, Pioneer 10, US. c, Apollo 16, US. d, Apollo 17, John F. Kennedy.
Events of 1962: No. 1175: a, Mariner 2, US. b, OSO 1, US. c, John Glenn. d, Mars 1, USSR.
Events of 1957: No. 1176: a, Vostok 1, Yuri Gagarin, USSR. b, Sputnik 2, USSR. c, Sputnik 1, USSR. d, Bell X15, US.
2000fr, Voyager, Pioneer 10, Apollo 11, US.

1997   Perf. 13½
1171 A319 250fr Sheet of 4, #a.-d.   4.50 2.00
1172 A319 350fr Sheet of 4, #a.-d.   6.25 3.00
1173 A319 450fr Sheet of 4, #a.-d.   8.00 3.75
1174 A319 500fr Sheet of 4, #a.-d.   9.00 4.00
1175 A319 600fr Sheet of 4, #a.-d.   10.50 5.00
1176 A319 800fr Sheet of 4, #a.-d.   14.50 6.50

Souvenir Sheet
1177 A319 2000fr multicolored   9.00 4.00

No. 1177 contains one 60x30mm stamp.
No. 1173 exists imperf.

Marilyn Monroe (1926-62) — A320

Various portraits.

1997
1178 A320 375fr Sheet of 9, #a.-i.   14.00 6.50

John F. Kennedy (1917-63) — A321

Various portraits.

1997
1179 A321 300fr Sheet of 9, #a.-i.   11.00 5.00

Bruce Lee (1940-73), Actor — A322

Various portraits.

1997   Litho.   Perf. 13½
1180 A322 200fr Sheet of 9, #a.-i.   7.50 3.25

Nos. 1159, 1161 Ovptd. "In Memoriam"

1997   Perf. 14
1181 A315 300fr Sheet of 6, #a.-f.   8.00 3.50

Souvenir Sheet
1182 A315 1500fr multicolored   6.50 3.00

Nos. 1181-1182 each contain "Diana, Princess of Wales (1961-1997) IN MEMORIAM" in sheet margin and on each stamp in No. 1181.

Dogs & Cats — A323

Dogs: No. 1183: a, Chinese crested. b, King Charles spaniel. c, Dachshund. d, Borzoi. e, Chow chow. f, Welsh springer. g, Rottweiler. h, Keeshond.
Cats: No. 1184: a, Birman. b, Black and white Persian. c, Siamese kitten. d, Red and black. e, American curl. f, Cornish rex. g, Silver shaded. h, White-footed cat.
1500fr, Pekingese. 2000fr, Somali.

1997   Litho.   Perf. 13½
1183 A323 175fr Sheet of 8, #a.-h.   6.00 2.00
1184 A323 250fr Sheet of 8, #a.-h.   8.25 3.75

Souvenir Sheets

| 1185 | A323 | 1500fr multicolored | 7.00 | 2.75 |
| 1186 | A323 | 2000fr multicolored | 9.25 | 3.75 |

Nos. 1185-1186 each contain one 42x51mm stamp.

Return of Hong Kong to China — A324

No. 1187: a, Tung Chee-Hwa, taking down British flag. b, Raising Chinese flag, Chris Patten, British flag. c, Jiang Zemin, skyline at night. d, City lights, Queen Elizabeth II. 600fr, Tung Chee-Hwa.

1997

| 1187 | A324 | 175fr Sheet of 4, #a.-d. | 2.75 | 1.25 |

Souvenir Sheet

| 1188 | A324 | 600fr multicolored | 2.50 | 1.25 |

No. 1188 contains one 38x42mm stamp.

Paintings by Hiroshige (1797-1858) A325

No. 1189: a, Minami-Shinagawa and Samezu Coast. b, Plum Garden, Kamata. c, The Kawaguchi Ferry and Zenkoji Temple. d, Armor-Hanging Pine, Hakkeizaka. e, Robe-Hanging Pine, Senzoku Pond. f, Benten Shrine, Inokashira Pond.

No. 1190: a, A Little Brown Owl on a Pine Branch with a Crescent Moon Behind. b, Sparrows and Camellia in snow. c, Three Wild Geese Flying Downward across the Moon. d, A Blue Bird on a Yellow-flowered Hibiscus. e, Five Swallows in flight.

No. 1191: a, Sparrows and Wild Rose. b, Peonies. c, Morning Glory and Cricket. d, Blossoming Plum Tree. e, Kingfisher above a Yellow-flowered Water Plant.

No. 1192, 1500fr, Haneda Ferry and Benten Shrine. No. 1193, 1500fr, A Bird Clinging to a Tendril of Wisteria. No. 1194, 1500fr, Butterfly and Peony.

1998, Feb. 20 Litho. Perf. 14

1189	A325	300fr Sheet of 6, #a.-f.	6.75	3.00
1190	A325	430fr Sheet of 5, #a.-e.	8.25	3.75
1191	A325	500fr Sheet of 5, #a.-e.	9.25	4.25

Souvenir Sheets

| 1192-1194 | A325 | Set of 3 | 18.00 | 7.50 |

Nos. 1190-1191 each contain five 26x72mm stamps. Nos. 1192-1194 each contain one 26x72mm stamp.

Chinese Lunar New Year A326

Animals representing lunar year: a, Rat. b, Ox. c, Tiger. d, Hare. e, Dragon. f, Snake. g, Horse. h, Sheep. i, Monkey. j, Rooster. k, Dog. l, Boar. 1000fr, Tiger, diff.

1998 Litho. & Typo. Perf. 14

| 1195 | A326 | 150fr Sheet of 12, #a.-l. | 8.00 | 3.75 |

Souvenir Sheet

| 1196 | A326 | 1000fr gold & multi | 3.75 | 1.75 |

Intl. Scouting, 90th Anniv. A327

Insects: No. 1196A: b, Apis mellifica. c, Lucanus cervus. d, Oryctes nasicornis. e, Pseudacraea boisduvalii. f, Helictopleurus quadripunctatus, euchroea spininasuta. g, Bombus terrestris. h, Charaxes smaragdalis. i, Euchroea coelestis, mantis religiosa.

Wildlife — No. 1197: a, Coracias caudata, Otocyon megalotis. b, Gnu. c, Milvus aegyptus, pelecanus onocrotalus. d, Panthera leo. e, Loxodonta africana. f, Buffalo. g, Hippopotamus amphibius. h, Acinonyx jubatus.

Raptors — No. 1198: a, Buteo rufinus. b, Circus aeruginosus. c, Aquila verreauxii. d, Circaetus gallicus. e, Terathopius ecaudatus. f, Haliaeetus vocifer. g, Milvus milvus. h, Accipiter badius.

1997(?) Litho. Perf. 13

1196A	A327	200fr Sheet of 8, #b.-i.	7.00	3.00
1197	A327	300fr Sheet of 8, #a.-h.	10.00	4.50
1198	A327	350fr Sheet of 8, #a.-h.	13.00	5.25

1998 World Cup Soccer Championships, France — A328

Player, country, vert: No. 1199, 300fr, Moore, England. No. 1200, 300fr, Rahn, Germany. No. 1201, 300fr, Paulao, Angola. No. 1202, 300fr, Shearer, England.

No. 1203: a, Seaman, England. b, Schillaci, Italy. c, Romario, Brazil. d, McCoist, Scotland. e, Makanaky, Angola. f, Moore, England. g, Muller, Germany. h, Schmeichel, Denmark.

No. 1204, 1500fr, Moore, England, diff. No. 1205, 1500fr, Pele, Brazil.

1998, June 2 Perf. 13½x14, 14x13½

| 1199-1202 | A328 | Set of 4 | 4.50 | 2.00 |
| 1203 | A328 | 205fr Sheet of 8, #a-h, + label | 7.00 | 7.00 |

Souvenir Sheets

| 1204-1205 | A328 | Set of 2 | 12.00 | 12.00 |

Diana, Princess of Wales (1961-97) A329

Various portraits.

1998 Perf. 13½

| 1206 | A329 | 200fr Sheet of 9, #a.-i. | 7.00 | 3.25 |
| 1207 | A329 | 250fr Sheet of 9, #a.-i. | 9.00 | 4.00 |

Diana, Princess of Wales (1961-97) — A330

Diana wearing gowns in one of four seasons: No. 1208, White gown, spring. No. 1209, Blue gown, summer. No. 1210, Bridal gown, fall. No. 1211, High-collared white gown, winter.

1998 Litho. Perf. 13½

Souvenir Sheets

1208	A330	1500fr multicolored	5.75	2.50
1209	A330	1500fr multicolored	5.75	2.50
1210	A330	2000fr multicolored	8.00	3.50
1211	A330	2000fr multicolored	8.00	3.50

Nos. 1208-1211 each contain one 50x60mm stamp.

Jacqueline Kennedy Onassis (1929-94) A331

Various portraits.

1997 Litho. Perf. 13½

| 1212 | A331 | 250fr Sheet of 9, #a.-i. | 10.50 | 4.25 |

1998 Winter Olympic Games, Nagano — A332

Mirror images of vignette with different backgrounds, denomination at — No. 1213: a, Bobsled, LR. b, Slalom skier, CL. c, Ski jumper, CL. d, Bobsled, LL. e, Slalom skier, CR. f, Ski jumper, CR.

No. 1214: a, Ice hockey, LR. b, Cross-country skier, CR. c, Speed skater, LR. d, Ice hockey, LL. e, Cross-country skier, CL. f, Speed skater, LL.

No. 1215: a, Snow boarding, UR. b, Downhill skier, CR. c, Pairs figure skating, CR. d, Snow boarding, UL. e, Downhill skier, CL. f, Pairs figure skating, CL.

No. 1216, Cross-country, freestyle skiers.

1998

1213	A332	180fr Sheet of 6, #a.-f.	4.00	1.75
1214	A332	300fr Sheet of 6, #a.-f.	7.00	3.00
1215	A332	350fr Sheet of 6, #a.-f.	8.25	3.75

Souvenir Sheet

| 1216 | A332 | 2000fr multicolored | 9.25 | 3.50 |

Sports A333

No. 1217 — Cyclists: a, Woman wearing helmet. b, Woman in pink, white & black outfit. c, Man in black & white outfit. d, Man in yellow & black outfit.

No. 1218 — Female tennis players: a, Holding racket above head. b, Wearing black head band. c, Wearing white head band. d, Wearing dreadlocks.

No. 1219 — Male tennis players: a, Holding racket with his right hand. b, In blue shirt, shorts. c, Holding racket behind head. d, Wearing cap backwards.

No. 1220 — Golfers: a, Completing swing. b, Hitting ball in sand trap. c, In orange knickers, argyle socks. d, Lining up putt.

1998 Litho. Perf. 13½

1217	A333	350fr Sheet of 4, #a.-d.	5.25	2.25
1218	A333	375fr Sheet of 4, #a.-d.	5.75	2.50
1219	A333	450fr Sheet of 4, #a.-d.	7.25	3.25
1220	A333	500fr Sheet of 4, #a.-d.	8.00	3.50

Mickey Mouse, 70th Birthday A334

Scenes from various Disney films drawn by Floyd Gottfredson.

No. 1221: a, 10/78. b, 11/78. c, 3/79. d, 7/79. e, 9/79.

No. 1222: a, 10/79. b, 2/80. c, 4/80. d, 6/80. e, 7/80.

No. 1223: a, 11/80. b, 3/81. c, 6/81. d, 9/81. e, 3/82.

No. 1224: a, 5/82. b, 7/82. c, 10/82. d, 3/83. e, 5/83.

No. 1225, 1500fr, Mickey with camera, flashlight. No. 1226, 1500fr, Mickey with pearl in box. No. 1227, 2000fr, Mickey and magic lamp. No. 1228, 2000fr, Floyd Gottfredson.

Perf. 13½x14, 14x13½

1999, Feb. 10 Litho.

1221	A334	280fr Sheet of 5, #a.-e., + label	5.25	2.25
1222	A334	365fr Sheet of 5, #a.-e., + label	7.00	3.00
1223	A334	390fr Sheet of 5, #a.-e., + label	7.50	3.25
1224	A334	440fr Sheet of 5, #a.-e., + label	8.25	3.75

Souvenir Sheets

| 1225-1226 | A334 | 1500fr Set of 2 | 11.00 | 5.00 |
| 1227-1228 | A334 | 2000fr Set of 2 | 15.00 | 6.50 |

Birds of Africa — A335   World Wildlife Fund — A336

Designs: No. 1229, 500fr, Pandion haliaetus. No. 1230, 500fr, Chaetops frenatus. No. 1231, 500fr, Tachymarptis melba. No. 1232, 500fr, Ceratogymna bucinator. No. 1233, 500fr, Laniarius atrococcineus. No. 1234, 500fr, Coturnix coturnix.

No. 1235: a, Lamprotornis superbus. b, Agapornis personatus. c, Coracias spatulata.

d, Euplectes jacksoni. e, Nectarinia violacea. f, Emberiza schoeniclus. g, Pica pica. h, Tauraco erythrolophus. i, Sitta europaea.

No. 1236: a, Merops apiaster. b, Coracias garrulus. c, Cuculus canorus. d, Hirundo rustica. e, Motacilla flava. f, Ardea cinerea. g, Falco tinnunculus. h, Tyto alba. i, Charadrius hiaticula.

1500fr, Eremophila alpestris. 2000fr, Delichon urbica.

1999, Mar. 10		**Litho.**	**Perf. 14**		
1229-1234	A335	Set of 6		11.00	5.00
1235	A335	280fr Sheet of 9,			
		#a.-i.		9.25	4.25
1236	A335	490fr Sheet of 9,			
		#a.-i.		16.00	7.50

Souvenir Sheets

1237	A335	1500fr multicolored	5.50	2.50
1238	A335	2000fr multicolored	7.50	3.50

1999

Balaeniceps rex: a, Eating fish. b, Up close. c, Standing. d, One in flight, one up close.

1239	A336	200fr Strip of 4, #a.-d.	5.00	4.00

No. 1239 was issued in sheets of 16 stamps.

Trains
A337

No. 1240: a, 40fr, 2-4-0 Steam locomotive. b, 50fr, German Mallat. c, 60fr, Shunting locomotive. d, 260fr, Rhodesian 14A 2-6-2+2-6-2 Garrat. e, 280fr, Steam train. f, 390fr, Engine No. 7, 0-6-0 Baldwin, 1920. g, 440fr, Amtrak passenger train. h, 460fr, German TEE diesel. i, 490fr, "Sir Nigel Gresley."

No. 1241: a, 40fr, Steam train. b, 50fr, 4-4-0, LNWR, 1897. c, 60fr, 2-4-0 locomotive, Midland. d, 260fr, Class XC. e, 280fr, 2-6-0T Sernada and Aveiro, 1910. f, 390fr, East Daggafontein Mines train, Great Britain. g, 440fr, Union Pacific. h, 460fr, Engine No. 6, Baldwin. i, 490fr, 4-4-2 aerodynamic train, Belgium, 1939.

No. 1242, 2000fr, Fairlie, Snake and Auckland, New Zealand, 1874. No. 1243, 2000fr, Steam train arriving at the London-Brighton Depot.

1999, Mar. 11

Sheets of 9

1240-1241	A337	Set of 2	22.50	8.50

Souvenir Sheets

1242-1243	A337	Set of 2	17.00	6.50

Prehistoric Animals
A338

No. 1244: a, Archaeopteryx. b, Stegosaurus. c, Placerias. d, Rutiodon. e, Tyrannosaurus rex. f, Lystrosaurus.

No. 1245: a, Spinosaurus. b, Cynognathus. c, Kuehneosaurus. c, Compsognathus. d, Compsognathus. e, Triceratops. f, Euoplocephalus.

2000fr, Desmatosuchus.

1998		**Litho.**		**Perf. 13½**	
1244	A338	250fr Sheet of 6,			
		#a.-f.		6.25	2.75
1245	A338	300fr Sheet of 6,			
		#a.-f.		7.50	3.25

Souvenir Sheet

1246	A338	2000fr multicolored	8.50	3.75

No. 1246 contains one 51x36mm stamp.

Transportation
A339

No. 1247 — Antique automobiles: a, 1899 Fiat. b, First Chevrolet. c, Serpollet steam carriage. d, 130HP Fiat.

No. 1248 — Cyclists: a, Swiss rider. b, US rider. c, Miguel Indurain (riding to right). d, Jan. Ullrich (riding to left).

No. 1249 — Sports cars: a, Porsche Boxster. b, Corvette. c, Jaguar S-type. d, Maserati 3200 GT.

No. 1250 — High-speed trains: a, TGV Atlantique. b, Shin Kansen. c, ETR X-500. d, Advanced passenger train.

No. 1251 — Trains: a, Cornish Riviera Express. b, Lancashire and Yorkshire Railway. c, Type 230. d, Pacific Mallard.

No. 1252 — Fire trucks: a, 1916 Seagrave. b, 1927 Ahrens-Fox Model JS-2. c, 1992 Diesel. d, 1958 Mack Bulldog, Type B-95.

No. 1253 — Space flight of John Glenn: a, Portrait in business suit. b, In Project Mercury spacesuit. c, In shuttle launch suit, 1998. d, Orbiting earth, Space Shuttle.

No. 1254 — Supersonic airplanes: a, Boeing 2707. b, Transatmospheric prototype. c, Tupolev 144. d, Project of European Supersonic ESRP.

1998

1247	A339	300fr Sheet of 4,		
		#a.-d.	5.00	2.25
1248	A339	350fr Sheet of 4,		
		#a.-d.	5.75	2.50
1249	A339	400fr Sheet of 4,		
		#a.-d.	6.75	3.00
1250	A339	450fr Sheet of 4,		
		#a.-d.	7.50	3.25
1251	A339	500fr Sheet of 4,		
		#a.-d.	8.25	3.75
1252	A339	600fr Sheet of 4,		
		#a.-d.	10.00	4.50
1253	A339	800fr Sheet of 4,		
		#a.-d.	13.00	6.00
1254	A339	1000fr Sheet of 4,		
		#a.-d.	16.00	7.50

Scouting
A340

No. 1255 — Scouts with flowers: a, Vanilla planifolia. b, Flamboyant. c, Angraecum sesquipedale.

No. 1256 — Scouts with butterflies or bird: a, Hesperie a bande. b, Philepitte souimanga. c, Dryope.

No. 1257 — Scouts with dogs, cats, and their young: a, Basenji. b, Egyptian mau cat. c, White dog.

No. 1258 — Scouts with minerals: a, Tourmaline. b, Jasper. c, Madgascar corundum.

No. 1259 — Scouts administrering Red Cross aid: a, Girl Scout wiping child's tears. b, Scout bandaging child. c, Scout kneeling to help child.

No. 1260 — Scouts in leisure activities: a, Playing table tennis. b, Playing chess. c, Riding horse.

1998		**Litho.**		**Perf. 13½**	
1255	A340	400fr Sheet of 3,			
		#a.-c.		5.00	2.25
1256	A340	475fr Sheet of 3,			
		#a.-c.		6.50	2.50
1257	A340	500fr Sheet of 3,			
		#a.-c.		6.75	2.75
1258	A340	600fr Sheet of 3,			
		#a.-c.		7.50	3.25
1259	A340	700fr Sheet of 3,			
		#a.-c.		8.50	3.75
1260	A340	800fr Sheet of 3,			
		#a.-c.		10.00	4.50

Minerals
A341

No. 1261: a, Hematite (red). b, Challophyllite. c, Fer natif. d, Sylvanite. e, Hematite (specularite). f, Spodumene.

No. 1262: a, Amber. b, Opal. c, Struvite. d, Rhodochrosite. e, Polybasite. f, Silver.

1998		**Litho.**		**Perf. 13½**	
1261	A341	400fr Sheet of 6,			
		#a.-f.		10.00	4.50
1262	A341	600fr Sheet of 6,			
		#a.-f.		14.50	6.75

A number has been reserved for a souvenir sheet to go with this set.

Mushrooms
A342

40fr, Jelly babies. 50fr, Herald of winter. 65fr, Dentate elf cup. 280fr, Pink wax cap. 345fr, Tripe fungus. 465fr, Funnel tooth. 485fr, Common white saddle. 600fr, False morel.

No. 1272: a, Parrot wax cap. b, Orange naval cap. c, Amethyst deceiver. d, Plums and custard. e, Blue legs. f, Tawny funnel cap. g, Goblet. h, Spindle-shank. i, Buttery tough shank.

No. 1273: a, Fetid mummy cap. b, Stainer. c, Lilac bonnet. d, Firm-fleshed brittle gill. e, Fly agaric. f, Arched bonnet. g, King bolete. h, Orange birch bolete. i, Dog stinkhorn.

1500fr, Hedgehog puffball. 2000fr, Striated earth star.

1999, June 11		**Litho.**		**Perf. 14**	
1264-1271	A342	Set of 8		9.50	4.25
1272	A342	390fr Sheet of 9,			
		#a.-i.		14.00	6.50
1273	A342	440fr Sheet of 9,			
		#a.-i.		15.00	6.75

Souvenir Sheets

1274	A342	1500fr multicolored	5.75	2.50
1275	A342	2000fr multicolored	8.25	3.75

Birds
A343

No. 1276: a, Psittacula himalayama. b, Anodorhynchus hyacinthinus. c, Trichoglossus haematodus. d, Xipholena punicea. e, Chloebia gouldiae. f, Ramphastos tucanus.

No. 1277: a, Falco sparverius. b, Polyborus plancus. c, Terathopius ecaudatus. d, Tyto alba. e, Glaucidium passerinum. f, Speotyto cunicularia.

1999		**Litho.**		**Perf. 13½**	
1276	A343	350fr Sheet of 6,			
		#a.-f.		8.25	3.75
1277	A343	500fr Sheet of 6,			
		#a.-f.		11.50	5.25

Dogs, Cats, & Horses
A344

Designs: 60fr, Doberman, vert. 280fr, Domestic cat, vert. No. 1280, 390fr, Korat, vert. No. 1281, 390fr, Hanoverian, vert. 440fr, Ardennais. 490fr, Lhasa apso.

Dogs — No. 1284: a, Alaskan malamute. b, Musterlander. c, German shepherd. d, Borzoi. e, Afghan hound. f, Irish terrier. g, Komondor. h, Finnish spitz.

Cats — No. 1285: a, American bobtail. b, American curl. c, Singapura. d, Burmese. e, Tortoise shell. f, Scottish fold. g, British shorthair blue. h, Turkish van.

Horses — No. 1286: a, Shire. b, Clydesdale. c, Arabian. d, Soviet work horse. e, Finnish work horse. f, Percheron. g, Draco. h, North Swedish.

No. 1287, 2000fr, Beagle. No. 1288, 2000fr, Havana. No. 1289, 2000fr, Hanoverian.

1999, July 9		**Litho.**		**Perf. 14**	
1278-1283	A344	Set of 6		9.75	3.50
1284	A344	465fr Sheet of 8,			
		#a.-h.		14.50	6.50
1285	A344	485fr Sheet of 8,			
		#a.-h.		15.00	6.75
1286	A344	515fr Sheet of 8,			
		#a.-h.		15.00	7.00

Souvenir Sheets

1287-1289	A344	Set of 3	30.00	10.50

Nos. 1287-1289 each contain one 44x56mm stamp.

Butterflies
A345

Designs: 40fr, Heliconius melpomene. 65fr, Large oak blue. 280fr, Danaus chrysippus. 345fr, Aricia agestis. 485fr, Danis danis. 600fr, Plebejus argus.

No. 1296: a, Delias mysis. b, Ornithoptera priamus. c, Phoebis philea. d, Heliconius doris. e, Thecla coronata f, Lycaena dispar. g, Bematistes aganise. h, Pereute leucodrosime.

No. 1297: a, Colotis danae. b, Eueides isabella. c, Papilio cresphontes. d, Mimacraea marshalli. e, Parathyma nefte. f, Appias nero. g, Uraneis ucubis. h, Eurema brigitta.

No. 1298: a, Heliconius melpomene, diff. b, Mylothris chloris. c, Catopsilia florella. d, Hebomoia glaucippe. e, Palla ussheri. f, Papilio glaucus. g, Colias erytheme. h, Euploea corus.

No. 1299, 1500fr, Unnamed. No. 1300, 1500fr, Papilio, glaucus, vert.

1999, Dec.		**Litho.**		**Perf. 14**	
1290-1295	A345	Set of 6		9.00	3.25
1296	A345	280fr Sheet of 8,			
		#a.-h.		12.00	4.00
1297	A345	390fr Sheet of 8,			
		#a.-h.		16.00	5.50
1298	A345	465fr Sheet of 8,			
		#a.-h.		19.00	6.50

Souvenir Sheets

1299-1300	A345	Set of 2	15.00	6.00

Trains
A346

Designs: No. 1301, 280fr, Le Capitole, France. No. 1302, 390fr, Montreaux-Bern Line, Switzerland. No. 1303, 485fr, Zugspitzbahn, Switzerland. No. 1304, 485fr, Rhatische Bahn, Swizerland.

No. 1305: a, Schwebebahn, Germany. b, Reichsbahn Class 44, Germany. c, Rembrandt, Germany. d, Trans-Europe Express, Germany. e, Inter-city, Germany. f, Steam locomotive, Germany.

No. 1306: a, ETR300, Italy. b, Mistral, France. c, ER200, Russia. d, Pendoline, Italy. e, Class 1100, Netherlands. f, Rheingold Express, Germany.

No. 1307, 1500fr, TGV, France. No. 1308, 1500fr, Austrian train.

2000, Jan. 25					
1301-1304	A346	Set of 4		8.50	3.00
1305	A346	280fr Sheet of 6,			
		#a.-f.		9.00	3.00
1306	A346	390fr Sheet of 6,			
		#a.-f.		12.00	4.25

Souvenir Sheets

1307-1308	A346	Set of 2	17.50	5.00

Flowers — A347

No. 1309: a, Orchid. b, Water crinum. c, Flame lily. d, Narcissus poeticus. e, Belladonna lily. f, Table Mountain orchid. g, Upland cotton. h, Narcissus jonquilla.

No. 1310: a, Moore's crinum. b, Cyrtanthus brachyscyphus. c, Namaqualand daisy. d, "Narcissus poeticus," diff. e, Painted homeria. f, Helen O'Connor. g, Pink oxalis. h, Pink oxalis and pink arum.

No. 1311: a, Yellow wild iris. b, White arum lily (mountains in background). c, Blue tulip. d, Osteospermum. e, Table Mountain orchid, diff. f, White arum lily (with stems and leaves). g, Daisy. h, Meadow saffron.

No. 1312, 1500fr, Amaryllis belladonna, horiz. No. 1313, 1500fr, African tulip tree, horiz. No. 1314, 1500fr, Bird of paradise, horiz.

2000, Feb. 24
1309 A347 280fr Sheet of 8,
    #a.-h.   12.00 3.50
1310 A347 390fr Sheet of 8,
    #a.-h.   16.00 4.75
1311 A347 515fr Sheet of 8,
    #a.-h.   20.00 6.00
Souvenir Sheets
1312-1314 A347 Set of 3   22.50 8.00
    Inscription on No. 1310d is incorrect.

Birds
A348

Designs: 100fr, Dendrocygna bicolor, vert. 150fr, Tockis flavirostris, vert. 200fr, Treron calva. 300fr, Ardeola ralloides. 450fr, Passer melanus, vert. 750fr, Sturnus vulgaris, vert.
No. 1321, vert.: a, Trachyphonus vaillantii. b, Polyhierax semitorquatus. c, Tockus nasutus. d, Estrilda astrild. e, Merops persicus. f, Amandava subflava. g, Guttera pucherani. h, Oriolus oriolus. i, Bycanistes brevis.
No. 1322: a, Butoides striatus. b, Limnocorax flavirostra. c, Terathopius ecaudatus. d, Mycteria ibis. e, Actophilornis africanus. f, Poicephalus rueppellii. g, Alopochen aegyptiacus. h, Morus capensis. i, Sagittarius serpentarius.
No. 1323: a, Gyps africanus. b, Tyto alba. c, Pelecanus onocrotalus. d, Ephippiorhynchus senegalensis. e, Ardea goliath. f, Sylvia communis. g, Buteo rufofuscus. h, Parus caeruleus. i, Dromas ardeola.
No. 1324, 2000fr, Buphagus africanus. No. 1325, 2000fr, Haliaeetus vocifer. No. 1326, 2000fr, Erythropgia coryphaeus, vert.

2000, Feb. 25
1315-1320 A348 Set of 6   8.50 3.00
1321 A348 390fr Sheet of 9,
    #a.-i.   16.00 5.25
1322 A348 440fr Sheet of 9,
    #a.-i.   18.00 6.00
1323 A348 485fr Sheet of 9,
    #a.-i.   18.00 6.50
Souvenir Sheets
1324-1326 A348 Set of 3   27.50 10.00

Aviation
A349

Designs: 280fr, Spirit of St. Louis. 345fr, Hindenburg. 465fr, Flight at Kitty Hawk. 485fr, AH-1 Cobra.
No. 1331: a, Fokker triplane. b, Spad XIII. c, Blériot XI. d, Nieuport 12. e, Sopwith Camel. f, 1920s US Mail plane. g, Otto Lilienthal's hang glider. h, Hydrogen-filled balloon of J. A. C. Charles.
No. 1332: a, Mitchell-B25. b, P-38E Lightning. c, Vought F-4U Corsair. d, Mitsubishi Zero. e, B-17 Flying Fortress. f, P-51 Mustang. g, Flying Tiger plane. h, Messerschmitt Bf-109.
No. 1333: a, X-1. b, B-52C. c, Boeing 707. d, F-16C. e, Sabre jet. f, MiG-15. g, F-4 Phantom. h, F-117A Stealth.
No. 1334, 1500fr, Concorde. No. 1335, 1500fr, Space shuttle "Enterprise."

2000, Feb. 28
1327-1330 A349 Set of 4   7.50 2.40
1331 A349 345fr Sheet of 8,
    #a.-h.   13.00 4.25
1332 A349 390fr Sheet of 8,
    #a.-h.   14.50 4.75
1333 A349 515fr Sheet of 8,
    #a.-h.   19.00 6.25
Souvenir Sheets
1334-1335 A349 1500fr Set of 2 13.00 5.00

Chess Players — A350

No. 1336, 280fr: a, Otto IV of Brandenburg. b, Mme. de Verzu and Chevalier de Bourgogne. c, Chess Players by Estienne Porcher. d, Fresco by F. Pella.
No. 1337, 300fr: a, Two Nobles. b, Depiction from book of Jean Wauquelin. c, Girolamo de Cremona. d, Ashtapada.
No. 1338, 390fr: a, Ulysses and Palamedes. b, Christian cavalier and Muslim. c, Two Moorish women. d, Burzurgmikhr and Kannuja.
No. 1339, 465fr: a, Two men, 18th Cent. b, Napoleon and Cornwallis. c, Adolf Andersen and Wilhelm Steinitz. d, Queen Victoria.
No. 1340, 485fr: a, Two women. b, Chess on an enlarged board. c, Xerxes. d, King Evil-Merodach.
No. 1341, 515fr: a, King Henry VIII of England. b, Queen Elizabeth I of England. c, King Charles I of England. d, Russian czarevitch.
Illustration reduced.

1999   Litho.   *Perf. 13½*
Sheets of 4, #a-d
1336-1341 A350 Set of 6   37.50 15.00

Cosmonauts and Astronauts — A351

No. 1342, 485fr: a, Vladimir Soloviev. b, Georgi Beregovoy. c, Alexei Leonov. d, Pavel Popovich. e, Yuri Gagarin. f, Valentina Tereshkova. g, Helena Kondakova. h, Gherman Titov. i, Alexander Volkov.
No. 1343, 515fr: a, Neil Armstrong. b, Edwin Aldrin. c, Michale Collins. d, Alan Bean. e, James Lovell. f, Alan Shepard. g, David Scott. h, John Young. i, Eugene Cernan.
2000fr, Armstrong and Gagarin, horiz.
Illustration reduced.

1999
Sheets of 9, #a-i
1342-1343 A351 Set of 2   35.00 14.00
Souvenir Sheet
1344 A351 2000fr multi   9.00 3.25
    No. 1344 contains one 60x51mm stamp.

Millennium — A352

2000, Mar. 31   *Perf. 14*
1345 A352 515fr multicolored   2.50 1.00
    Issued in sheets of six.

2000 Summer Olympics,
Sydney — A353

No. 1346, 300fr: a, Individual dressage. b, Rhythmic gymnastics. c, Women's 100-meter hurdles. d, Cycling.
No. 1347, 485fr: a, Tennis. b, Diving. c, Soccer. d, Pole vault.
No. 1348, 750fr: a, Long jump. b, Judo. c, Basketball. d, Show jumping.
No. 1349, 800fr: a, Boxing. b, Table tennis. c, Women's 200-meter sprint. d, Individual three-day equestrian event.
Illustration reduced.

2000   *Perf. 13½*
Sheets of 4, #a-d
1346-1349 A353 Set of 4   35.00 15.00

2002 Winter Olympics, Salt Lake
City — A354

No. 1350, 280fr: a, Freestyle skiing. b, Cross-country skiing. c, Bobsled. d, Men's slalom.
No. 1351, 390fr: a, Luge. b, Women's ski relay. c, Downhill skiing. d, Short track skating.
No. 1352, 465fr: a, Women's figure skating. b, Hockey. c, Ski jumping. d, Biathlon.
No. 1353, 515fr, a, Pairs figure skating. b, Women's giant slalom. c, Speed skating. d, Nordic combined.
Illustration reduced.

2000
Sheets of 4, #a-d
1350-1353 A354 Set of 4   26.00 10.50

UPU, 125th Anniv. — A355

UPU emblem and various men: 280fr, 300fr, 390fr, 465fr, 485fr, 515fr, 750fr, 800fr.

2000, Sept. 8   Litho.   *Perf. 13¼*
1354-1361 A355 Set of 8   16.00 5.25

Millennium — A356

No. 1362: a, Roald Amundsen, first polar exploration by dirigible, 1926. b, Vladimir Zworykin, inventor of television camera, 1928. c, Sir Alexander Fleming, discoverer of penicillin, 1928.
No. 1363: a, Henri Dunant, 1901 Nobel Peace prize winner. b, Wilbur and Orville Wright, first airplane, 1903. c, Enrico Caruso, opera singer.
No. 1364: a, Theodore Roosevelt, opening of Panama Canal, 1914. b, Albert Einstein, theory of general relativity, 1916. c, Battle of Verdun, 1916.
No. 1365: a, Auguste Piccard, flight to stratosphere in balloon, 1931. b, Robert Goddard, rocketry pioneer, 1935. c, Ferdinand von Zeppelin and Graf Zeppelin, 1928-37.
No. 1366: a, Felix Eboue, governor of Chad, 1940. b, Mahatma Gandhi, independence of India, 1947. c, Marilyn Monroe (1926-62), actress.
No. 1367: a, Juan Manuel Fangio, race car driver. b, James Dean (1931-55), actor. c, Sputnik 1, 1957.
No. 1368: a, Charles De Gaulle (1890-1970), French general and political leader. b, Yuri Gagarin (1934-68), Soviet Cosmonaut. c, Neil Armstrong (1930-), American Astronaut.
No. 1369: a, Elvis Presley (1935-77), American entertainer. b, Muhammed Ali (1942-), American boxer. c, John Young (1930-), American Astronaut.
No. 1370: a, John Young, Space Shuttle, 1981. b, Mikhail Gorbachev, fall of the Berlin Wall, 1989. c, Dalai Lama, 1989 Nobel Peace prize winner.
No. 1371: a, Nelson Mandela, 1993 Nobel Peace prize winner. b, Galileo probe reaches Jupiter, 1995. c, Mars Pathfinder, 1998.

2000, Sept. 28   *Perf. 13¼*
1362 A356 100fr Sheet of 3,
    #a-c   1.25 .60
1363 A356 280fr Sheet of 3,
    #a-c   3.50 1.25
1364 A356 300fr Sheet of 3,
    #a-c   4.25 1.50
1365 A356 390fr Sheet of 3,
    #a-c   5.00 2.00
1366 A356 465fr Sheet of 3,
    #a-c   6.00 2.25
1367 A356 485fr Sheet of 3,
    #a-c   6.50 2.50
1368 A356 515fr Sheet of 3,
    #a-c   6.00 3.00
1369 A356 750fr Sheet of 3,
    #a-c   9.00 4.50
1370 A356 800fr Sheet of 3,
    #a-c   10.50 3.75
1371 A356 1000fr Sheet of 3,
    #a-c   12.50 4.75
    Nos. 1362-1371 (10)   64.50 26.10
    Numbers have been reserved for two additional sheets.

Flora, Dinosaurs and
Mushrooms — A357

No. 1372 — Butterflies: a, Cymothoe lurida. b, Charaxes lasti. c, Charaxes lactetinctus. d, Charaxes opinatus. e, Charaxes subornatus. f, Coelides hanno.

No. 1373 — Butterflies: a, Charaxes cithaeron. b, Charaxes anticlea. c, Bebearia plistonax. d, Charaxes jahlusa. e, Charaxes acraeoides. f, Bebearia oxione.

No. 1374 — Dinosaurs: a, Compsognathus. b, Kritosaurus. c, Nodosaurus. d, Tuojiangosaurus. e, Homalocephalus. f, Tsintaosaurus.

No. 1375 — Birds: a, Veuve royale. b, Travailleur cardinal. c, Gonolek a ventre rouge. d, Touraco de Schalow. e, Touraco Pauline. f, Souimanga orange.

No. 1376 — Dinosaurs: a, Monoclonius. b, Dryosaurus. c, Anatosaurus. d, Styracosaurus. e, Pinacosaurus. f, Kentrosaurus.

No. 1377 — Birds: a, Bateleur de savanes. b, Corbeau a nuque blanche. c, Corvinelle pie. d, Cordon-bleu violace. e, Fauvette passerinette. f, Crombec a face rousse.

No. 1378 — Mushrooms: a, Lentinus sajorcaju. b, Lentinus velutinus. c, Pleurotus luteoalbus. d, Pluteus congolensis. e, Lentinus crinitus. f, Leucoagaricus ferruginosus.

No. 1379 — Mushrooms: a, Lentinus squarrosulus. b, Phlebopus colossus. c, Lentinus tuberregium. d, Phlebopus sudanicus. e, Phlebopus silvaticus. f, Volvariella congolensis.

No. 1380 — Dogs: a, Briard. b, Pyrenees shepherd. c, Chow chow. d, Cocker spaniel. e, Puli. f, Yorkshire terrier.

No. 1381 — Cats: a, American wirehair. b, California spangled cat. c, Chinchilla. d, Exotic shorthair. e, Selkirk Rex. f, Oriental.

No. 1382 — Dogs: a, Greenland dog. b, Alaskan malamute. c, Samoyed. d, Siberian husky.

2001, May 28		**Litho.**	**Perf. 13¼**	
1372	A357	280fr Sheet of 6, #a-f	7.25	2.25
1373	A357	300fr Sheet of 6, #a-f	7.75	2.40
1374	A357	300fr Sheet of 6, #a-f	7.75	2.40
1375	A357	350fr Sheet of 6, #a-f	9.50	2.75
1376	A357	390fr Sheet of 6, #a-f	9.50	3.25
1377	A357	390fr Sheet of 6, #a-f	9.50	3.25
1378	A357	390fr Sheet of 6, #a-f	9.50	3.25
1379	A357	465fr Sheet of 6, #a-f	11.50	3.75
1380	A357	465fr Sheet of 6, #a-f	11.00	3.75
1381	A357	485fr Sheet of 6, #a-f	12.00	4.00
1382	A357	600fr Sheet of 4, #a-d	10.00	3.25
		Nos. 1372-1382 (11)	105.25	34.30

Fauna and Fish A358

Designs: 280fr, Salamandra salamandra. No. 1384, 300fr, Epiplatys annulatus. No. 1385, 350fr, Pseudotropheus zebra. 400fr, Trichechus senegalensis. 450fr, Pelomedusa subrufa. 500fr, Xenomystus nigri.

No. 1389, vert.: a, Damaliscus dorcas. b, Manis temmincki. c, Hyaena brunnea. d, Lycaon pictus. e, Diceros bicornis. f, Osteolaemis tetraspis. g, Cercocebus torquatus. h, Bunologus monticularis. i, Myosciurus pumilia.

No. 1390: a, Plotosus lineatus. b, Protopterus dolloi. c, Calamoichthys calabaricus. d, Malapterurus electricus. e, Discoglossus pictus. f, Dugong dugon.

No. 1391, 1500fr, Julidochromis ornatus, vert. No. 1392, 1500fr, Hippopotamus amphibius, vert. No. 1393, 1500fr, Afropavo congensis, vert.

Perf. 13¼x13½, 13½x13¼				
2001, July 12				
1383-1388	A358	Set of 6	10.00	3.00
1389	A358	300fr Sheet of 9, #a-i	12.50	3.50
1390	A358	350fr Sheet of 6, #a-f	9.50	2.75
Souvenir Sheets				
1391-1393	A358	Set of 3	21.00	7.50

Reptiles and Amphibians — A359

No. 1394, 350fr: a, Boa arc-en-ciel. b, Crapaud marine. c, Basilic vert. d, Grenouille taureau. e, Tortue happante. f, Pseudoeurycea leprosa.

No. 1395, 350fr: a, Trionix epinelix. b, Iguane rhinoceros. c, Boa constrictor. d, Boa canin. e, Tortue d'etang. f, Dermophis mexicanus.

No. 1396, 1500fr, Serpent des arbres. No. 1397, 1500fr, Grenouille poison.

2001, July 12		**Perf. 13¼x13½**		
Sheets of 6, #a-f				
1394-1395	A359	Set of 2	20.00	5.50
Souvenir Sheets				
1396-1397	A359	Set of 2	14.00	6.00

Butterflies — A360

No. 1398, 350fr, vert.: a, Papilio garamus. b, Eunica orphise. c, Parides lysander. d, Julia dryas iulia. e, Adelpha mythra. f, Thecla coronata.

No. 1399, 350fr, vert.: a, Battus polydamas. b, Mesene phareus. c, Anartia jatrophae. d, Siproeta epaphus. e, Uraneis ucubis. f, Pereute leucodrosime.

No. 1400, 1500fr, Prepona meander. No. 1401, 1500fr, Morpho peleides. No. 1402, 1500fr, Pieris rapae. No. 1403, 1500fr, Helconius melpomene.

2001, July 12		**Perf. 13½x13¼**		
Sheets of 6, #a-f				
1398-1399	A360	Set of 2	20.00	6.00
Souvenir Sheets				
1400-1403	A360	Set of 4	27.50	10.00

Nos. 1398-1399 each contain six 28x42mm stamps.

A361

Birds — A362

Designs: 50fr, Macareux moine. 75fr, Harfang des neiges, vert. 100fr, Manchots, vert. 150fr, Fou à pieds bleus.

No. 1408, 325fr: a, Perruche soleil. b, Toucan de cuviée. c, Colibri. d, Ara hyacinthe. e, Pione à tete bleue. f, Perruche flavéolée. g, Pelican. h, Flamant rose. i, Toucan toco.

No. 1409, 325fr: a, Touraco à gros bec. b, Martin-chaseuse à poitrine bleue. c, Faucon lanier. d, Inséparable masqué. e, Loriquet à tete bleue. f, Perroquet jaco. g, Perenoptere d'Egypte. h, Grue grise couronnée. i, Marabou.

No. 1410, 350fr: a, Colibri caraibe. b, Jaseur des cèdres. c, Colibri d'abeille. d, Bruant indigo. e, Tourterelle pleureuse. f, Talève pourprée.

No. 1411, 350fr, horiz.: a, Gros-bec bleu. b, Fauvette à gorge orangée. c, Pic flamboyant. d, Passerin nonpareil. e, Fauvette à capuchon. f, Bananaquit.

No. 1412, 1500fr, Cygne, vert. No. 1413, 1500fr, Pygargue à tete blanche, vert. No. 1414, 1500fr, shown. No. 1415, 1500fr, Balbuzard.

Perf. 13¼x13½, 13½x13¼				
2001, July 19				
1404-1407	A361	Set of 4	3.75	1.50
Sheets of 9, #a-i				
1408-1409	A361	Set of 2	26.50	8.25
Sheets of 6, #a-f				
Perf. 13¼x13, 13x13¼				
1410-1411	A362	Set of 2	20.00	6.00
Souvenir Sheets				
Perf. 13½x13¼				
1412-1413	A361	Set of 2	14.00	5.00
Perf. 13¼				
1414-1415	A362	Set of 2	14.00	5.00

No. 1410 contains six 30x40mm stamps; No. 1411 contains six 40x30mm stamps.

Mushrooms A363

Designs: 550fr, Coltricia montagnei. 600fr, Inocybe fuscodisca. 650fr, Hydnum imbricatum. 700fr, Hygrophorus miniatus.

No. 1420: a, Coprinus picaceus. b, Crinipellis zonata. c, Naematoloma fasciculare. d, Cortinarius caerulescens. e, Amanita muscaria. f, Cortinarius obtusus. g, Entoloma serrulatum. h, Strobilomyces floccopus.

1500fr, Sarcosphaera crassa, horiz.

Perf. 13½x13¼, 13¼x13½				
2001, July 26				
1416-1419	A363	Set of 4	12.00	3.50
1420	A363	350fr Sheet of 8, #a-h	13.00	4.00
Souvenir Sheet				
1421	A363	1500fr multi	7.00	2.50

Prehistoric Animals — A364

Designs: 50fr, Anatasaurus. 100fr, Apatosaurus. 150fr, Allosaurus. 200fr, Velociraptor.

No. 1426, 240fr: a, Rhamphorhynchus. b, Pteranodon. c, Tyrannosaurus rex. d, Deinonychus antirrhopus. e, Parasaurolophus. f, Corythosaurus. g, Patagosaurus. h, Triceratops. i, Brachylophosaurus. j, Europlocephalus. k, Dimetrodon. l, Leptoceratops.

No. 1427, 240fr: a, Perosaur. b, Albertosaurus. c, Dryptosaurus. d, Archaeopteryx. e, Ouranosaurus. f, Myahuera. g, Camptosaurus. h, Ichthyosaurus. i, Geosaurus. j, Trilobita. k, Plesiosaurus. l, Lewisiceras.

No. 1428, 1500fr, Herrerasaurus. No. 1429, 1500fr, Stegosaurus.

2001, July 31		**Perf. 12½**		
1422-1425	A364	Set of 4	2.50	.70
Sheets of 12, #a-l, + 8 labels				
1426-1427	A364	Set of 2	27.50	8.25
Souvenir Sheets				
1428-1429	A364	Set of 2	14.00	4.25

Dinosaurs A365

Designs: 250fr, Apatosaurus. 300fr, Baryonyx. 325fr, Albertosaurus. 375fr, Dimetrodon.

No. 1434, 350fr: a, Triceratops. b, Ornithocherius. c, Brachiosaurus. d, Utahraptor. e, Tyrannosaurus rex. f, Stegosaurus.

No. 1435, 350fr: a, Diplodicus. b, Pachycephalosaurus. c, Archaeopteryx. d, Pteranodon. e, Herrerasaurus. f, Struthiomimus.

No. 1436, 1500fr, Rhamphorhynchus. No. 1437, 1500fr, Proleratops and Deinonychus.

2001, July 31		**Perf. 13¼x13½**		
1430-1433	A365	Set of 4	6.00	1.75
Sheets of 6, #a-f				
1434-1435	A365	Set of 2	20.00	6.00
Souvenir Sheets				
1436-1437	A365	Set of 2	12.00	5.00

Belgica 2001 Intl. Stamp Exhibition, Brussels (#1434-1437).

2001 Catastrophes — A366

No. 1438: a, Jan. 26 earthquake, India. b, Sept. 11 terrorist attacks, US. c, Dec. 26 fires, Australia. d, Hurricane Michelle, Cuba, Oct. 27. e, July 4 tornado, Canada. f, July 24 eruption of Mt. Etna, Italy.

2002, July 23		**Perf. 13¼**		
1438	A366	390fr Sheet of 6, #a-f	9.00	4.00

Each stamp in sheet exists in a souvenir sheet of 1.

Painters and Paintings — A367

No. 1439, 390fr: a, Claude Monet. b, Woman with an Umbrella, by Monet. c, Argenteuil, by Edouard Manet. d, Manet. e, Joseph Mallord William Turner. b, Mornings Amongst the Conniston Falls, Cumberland, by Turner.

No. 1440, 390fr: a, Girl with a Mandolin, by Pablo Picasso. b, Picasso. c, Georges Braque. d, The Musician, by Braque. e, Woman in Blue, by Fernand Leger. f, Leger.

2002, July 23
Sheets of 6, #a-f
1439-1440 A367 Set of 2   15.00 7.00

Chess — A368

No. 1441: a, Board from match between Garry Kasparov and Viswanathan Anand. b, Kasparov. c, Anand. d, Board from match between Anand and Shirov. e, Board from match between Ruslan Ponomariov and Vassily Ivanchuk. f, Ponomariov.

2002, July 23
1441 A368 605fr Sheet of 6, #a-
           f   13.00 5.50
Each horizontal pair in the sheet exists in a souvenir sheet of 2 stamps.

Cosmonauts — A369

No. 1442: a, Yuri Gagarin, Vostok 1. b, Pavel Vinogradov, Mir 24. c, Valentina Tereshkova, Vostok 6. d, Valeri Kubasov, Apollo-Soyuz. e, Alexei Leonov, Voskhod 2. f, Sergei Treschev, Intl. Space Station.

2002, July 23
1442 A369 605fr Sheet of 6, #a-
           f   13.00 5.50

Zeppelin NT and Concorde — A370

No. 1443: a, Zeppelin NT over Friedrichshafen, Germany. b, Concorde over Rio de Janeiro. c, Concorde over Alaska. d, Zeppelin NT over Lake Constance. e, Zeppelin NT over Orly Airport, Paris. f, Concorde over New York.

2002, July 23
1443 A370 665fr Sheet of 6, #a-
           f   15.00 6.00
Each stamp in sheet exists in a souvenir sheet of 1.

Famous People — A371

No. 1444: a, Paul Harris, founder of Rotary International. b, Princess Diana, Intl. Red Cross Ambassador against land mines. c, Pope John Paul II. d, Sir Alexander Fleming. e, Mother Teresa. f, Melvin Jones, founder of Lions Club International.

2002, July 23
1444 A371 665fr Sheet of 6, #a-
           f   15.00 6.00
Each stamp in sheet exists in a souvenir sheet of 1.

Rotary and Lions Emblems and Animals — A372

No. 1445, 390fr — Turtles: a, Eretmochelys imbricata. b, Lepidochelys olivacea. c, Natator depressa.
No. 1446, 600fr — Dinosaurs: a, Sauropelta. b, Chasmosaurus. c, Herrerasaurus.

2002, Dec. 23
Sheets of 3, #a-c
1445-1446 A372 Set of 2   11.00 4.75

Scouts — A373

No. 1447, 605fr — Orchids: a, Dactylorhiza markusii. b, Cephalanthera rubra. c, Neotinea maculata.
No. 1448, 665fr — Mushrooms: a, Agaricus ostreatus. b, Russula virescens. c, Lactarius deliciosus.
No. 1449, 815fr — Dinosaurs: a, Brachiosaurus. b, Sarcosuchus. c, Gigantosaurus carolinii.
No. 1450, 840fr — Minerals: a, Guilleminite. b, Torbernite. c, Bornite.
Nos. 1451-1452A (each 3000fr), Scout playing: Nos. 1451, 1451A, Chess. Nos. 1452, 1452A, Table tennis.

2002, Dec. 23
Sheets of 3, #a-c
1447-1450 A373 Set of 4   32.50 14.00

A373a

Litho. & Embossed
Perf. 13½
1451   A373a   gold & multi   9.50 9.50
1451A A373a   sil & multi   9.50 9.50
1452   A373a   gold & multi   9.50 9.50
1452A A373a   sil & multi   9.50 9.50
  Nos. 1451-1452A (4)   38.00 38.00
Each stamp in each sheet and Nos. 4151-4152A exists in a souvenir sheet of 1.

Famous People A374

Designs: No. 1453, 485fr, Christopher Columbus (1450-1506), explorer. No. 1454, 485fr, Admiral Horatio Nelson (1758-1805). No. 1455, 605fr, Jacques Cartier (1491-1557), explorer. No. 1456, 605fr, Vladimir Yourkevitch (1885-1964), naval designer. No. 1457, 665fr, Columbus, diff. No. 1458, 665fr, Sir Francis Drake (1540-96), explorer. No. 1459, 815fr, Jean-François Champollion (1790-1832), Egyptologist. No. 1460, 815fr, Queen Mother Elizabeth of England (1900-2002). No. 1461, 840fr, Marilyn Monroe (1926-62), actress. No. 1462, 840fr, Elvis Presley (1935-77), singer. No. 1463, 1000fr, Pres. John F. Kennedy (1917-63). No. 1464, 1000fr, French President Charles de Gaulle (1890-1970).

2003, May 15   Litho.   Perf. 13½
1453-1464 A374 Set of 12   40.00 16.00
Dated 2002. Each stamp also exists in souvenir sheet of 1.

2004 Summer Olympics, Athens A375

Designs: 390fr, Boxing. 485fr, Basketball. 605fr, Equestrian. 655fr, Tennis. 815fr, Table tennis.

2004, Mar. 3   Litho.   Perf. 13½
1465-1469 A375 Set of 5   14.00 5.75
Dated 2003. Each stamp also exists in souvenir sheet of 1.

2006 World Cup Soccer Championships, Germany — A376

Various soccer players and stadia: 160fr, 390fr, 485fr, 605fr, 815fr.

2004, Mar. 3   Litho.   Perf. 13½
1470-1474 A376 Set of 5   9.25 9.25
1474a   Horiz. strip of 5, #1470-
           1474   9.25 9.25
Each stamp also exists in a souvenir sheet of 1.

2004
Summer
Olympics,
Athens —
A376a

Designs: Nos. 1475, 1476, Table tennis.
Nos. 1477, 1478, Tennis.

Litho. & Embossed
2004, Mar. 3   **Perf. 13½**
1475 A376a 3000fr gold & mul-
           ti   11.00 11.00
1476 A376a 3000fr sil & multi   11.00 11.00
1477 A376a 3000fr gold & mul-
           ti   11.00 11.00
1478 A376a 3000fr sil & multi   11.00 11.00
       Nos. 1475-1478 (4)   44.00 44.00

Europa Stamps,
50th Anniv. (in
2006) — A377

Top stamp: 5fr, Netherlands #387. 20fr, Italy
#810. 100fr, San Marino #1065. 150fr, Greece
#718. 300fr, Italy #1039. 390fr, Italy #916.
465fr, Liechtenstein #368. 485fr, Germany
#996. 515fr, Spain #941. 750fr, Finland #419.
800fr, Italy #979. 1500fr, Belgium #840.

2005, Apr. 10   Litho.   Perf. 13½
1479-1490 A377   Set of 12   22.00 22.00

Gen. François
Bozizé, President
of Central
Africa — A378

2005 ?   Litho.   Perf. 13¼
Frame Color
1498 A378 100fr blue   —
1501 A378 300fr red   —
1504 A378 515fr bister   —

Dated 2004. Eleven additional stamps were
issued in this set. The editors would like to
examine any examples.

Pope John Paul II (1920-
2005) — A379

Various portraits of Pope John Paul II: 280fr,
1000fr.

2007, Aug. 24   Litho.   Perf. 13¼
1505-1506 A379   Set of 2   5.50 2.75

Each stamp also exists in a souvenir sheet
of 1.

2008 Summer Olympics,
Beijing — A380

Designs: 300fr, Chinese female athlete,
swimmer. 390fr, Chinese soccer players, stadium. 1000fr, Chinese table tennis players,
building.

2007, Apr. 24
1507-1509 A380   Set of 3   7.00 3.50

Each stamp also exists in a souvenir sheet
of 1.

Princess Diana (1961-97) — A381

Princess Diana with: No. 1510, 390fr,
Mother Teresa. No. 1511, 390fr, Pope John
Paul II.

2007, Aug. 24   Litho.   Perf. 13¼
1510-1511 A381   Set of 2   3.25 3.25

Nos. 1510 and 1511 each exist in souvenir
sheets of 1.

Worldwide Fund For Nature
(WWF) — A382

Civettictis civetta: 390fr, Standing in grass.
485fr, Adult and juvenile at den. 515fr, Head.
750fr, On branch.

2007, Aug. 24
1512-1515 A382   Set of 4   9.00 9.00

Nos. 1512-1515 exist with printer's inscription at lower left in a souvenir sheet of 4.

SEMI-POSTAL STAMPS

Anti-Malaria Issue
Common Design Type
Perf. 12½x12
1962, Apr. 7   Engr.   Unwmk.
B1 CD108 25fr + 5fr slate   1.40 1.40
WHO drive to eradicate malaria.

Freedom from Hunger Issue
Common Design Type
1963, Mar. 21   Perf. 13
B2 CD112 25fr + 5fr multi   1.25 1.25

Guinea
Fowl and
Partridge
SP1

Designs: 10fr+5fr, Yellow-backed duiker
and snail. 20fr+5fr, Elephant, tortoise and hippopotamus playing tug-of-war. 30fr+10fr,
Cuckoo and tortoise. 50fr+20fr, Patas monkey
and leopard.

1971, Feb. 9   Photo.   Perf. 12½x12
B3 SP1 5fr + 5fr multi   4.50 2.00
B4 SP1 10fr + 5fr multi   5.75 2.50
B5 SP1 20fr + 5fr multi   7.50 2.75

B6 SP1 30fr + 10fr multi   10.00   7.00
B7 SP1 50fr + 20fr multi   16.00 12.00
       Nos. B3-B7 (5)   43.75 26.25

Lengué
Dancer — SP2

Dancers: 40fr+10fr, Le Lengué. 100fr+40fr,
Teke. 140fr+40fr, Englabolo.

1971   Litho.   Perf. 13
B8   SP2 20fr + 5fr multi   .65   .25
B9   SP2 40fr + 10fr multi   1.10   .40
B10 SP2 100fr + 40fr multi 2.50 1.25
B11 SP2 140fr + 40fr multi 3.25 1.50
       Nos. B8-B11 (4)   7.50 3.40

AIR POST STAMPS

Abyssinian Roller — AP1

Birds: 200fr, Gold Coast touraco. 500fr,
African fish eagle.

Unwmk.
1960, Sept. 3   Engr.   Perf. 13
C1 AP1 100fr vio bl, org brn &
        emer   2.50   .70
C2 AP1 200fr multi   4.75 2.00
C3 AP1 500fr Prus bl, emer &
        red brn   14.75 4.75
       Nos. C1-C3 (3)   22.00 7.45

French Equatorial Africa No. C37
Surcharged in Red

1960, Dec. 15   Perf. 13
C4 AP8 250fr on 500fr grnsh
        blk, blk & slate   8.25 8.25
17th Olympic Games, Rome, 8/25-9/11.

Air Afrique Issue
Common Design Type
1962, Feb. 17   Unwmk.   Perf. 13
C5 CD107 50fr vio, lt grn & red
        brn   1.00   .55
Founding of Air Afrique airline.

Pole
Vault — AP1a

1962, July 21   Photo.   Perf. 12x12½
C6 AP1a 100fr grn, yel, brn &
         blk   2.50 1.50
Abidjan games.

Red-faced Lovebirds — AP2

1962-63   Engr.   Perf. 13
C7 AP2 50fr Great blue touraco 2.50   .55
C8 AP2 250fr shown ('63)   7.50 2.50
Issued: 50fr, Nov. 15; 250fr, Mar. 11, 1963.

Runner with
Torch and Palm
Branch — AP3

1962, Dec. 24
C9 AP3 100fr gray grn, brn &
        car   2.75 1.50
Tropics Cup Games, Bangui, Dec. 24-31.

African Postal Union Issue
Common Design Type
1963, Sept. 8   Photo.   Perf. 12½
C10 CD114 85fr emer, ocher &
         red   1.90   .85

Sun Shining on Africa — AP4

1963, Nov. 9   Perf. 13x12
C11 AP4 25fr bl, yel & vio bl   .75   .40
Issued for African unity.

Europafrica Issue
Common Design Type
1963, Nov. 30   Perf. 12x13
C12 CD116 50fr ultra, yel & dk
         brn   2.75 2.00

Diesel Engine — AP5

Various Locomotives; 25fr, 50fr, vertical.

1963, Dec. 1   Engr.   Perf. 13
C13 AP5 20fr brn, cl & dk grn   .75   .75
C14 AP5 25fr brn, bl & choc   .90   .90
C15 AP5 50fr brn, red lil &
         vio   3.00 3.00
C16 AP5 100fr brn, grn & dl
         red brn   4.00 4.00
  a. Min. sheet of 4, #C13-C16 13.50 13.50
       Nos. C13-C16 (4)   8.65 8.65
Bangui-Douala railroad project.

Bangui Cathedral — AP6

1964, Jan. 21   Unwmk.   Perf. 13
C17 AP6 100fr yel grn, org brn &
bl   2.25 1.10

Radar Tracking Station and WMO
Emblem — AP7

1964, Mar. 23   Engr.   Perf. 13
C18 AP7 50fr org brn, bl & pur 1.25 1.25
World Meteorological Day.

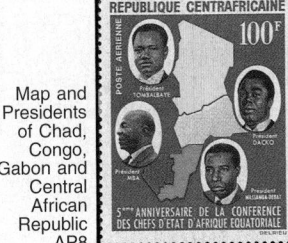

Map and
Presidents
of Chad,
Congo,
Gabon and
Central
African
Republic
AP8

1964, June 23   Photo.   Perf. 12½
C19 AP8 100fr multi   1.75 .80
5th anniversary of the Conference of Chiefs
of State of Equatorial Africa.

Javelin Throwers — AP9

Designs: 50fr, Basketball game. 100fr,
Four runners. 250fr, Swimmers, one in water.

1964, June 23   Engr.   Perf. 13
C20 AP9 25fr grn, dk brn & lt
vio bl   .55   .30
C21 AP9 50fr blk, car & grn   1.10   .45
C22 AP9 100fr grn, vio bl & dk
brn   2.50   .95
C23 AP9 250fr grn, blk & car 6.75 2.50
a.   Min. sheet of 4, #C20-C23 18.00 18.00
Nos. C20-C23 (4)   10.90 4.20
18th Olympic Games, Tokyo, 10/10-25/64.

John F.
Kennedy — AP10

1964, July 4   Photo.   Perf. 12½
C24 AP10 100fr lil, brn & blk 3.00 1.75
a.   Min. sheet of 4   12.00 12.00

Industrial Symbols, Maps of Africa and
Europe — AP11

1964, Dec. 19   Unwmk.   Perf. 13x12
C25 AP11 50fr yel, org & grn 1.50 .85
See note after Cameroun No. 402.

International Cooperation Year
Emblem — AP12

1965, Jan. 2   Perf. 13
C26 AP12 100fr red brn, yel & bl 1.90 .80
International Cooperation Year.

Nimbus Weather Satellite — AP13

1965, Mar. 23   Engr.   Perf. 13
C27 AP13 100fr org brn, ultra &
blk   1.90 .80
Fifth World Meteorological Day.

Lincoln and Statue of Liberty — AP14

1965, Apr. 15   Photo.   Perf. 13
C28 AP14 100fr bluish grn, ind &
bis   1.90 .80
Centenary of death of Abraham Lincoln.

ITU Emblem and Relay
Satellite — AP15

1965, May 17   Engr.   Perf. 13
C29 AP15 100fr dk grn vio bl &
brn   2.10 1.25
Centenary of the ITU.

"Housing," New Home in
Village — AP16

1965, June 10   Unwmk.
C30 AP16 100fr ultra, brn & sl grn 1.40 .80
See note after No. 52.

Europafrica Issue

Tractor, Cotton
Picker, Cotton,
Sun and
Emblem — AP17

1965, Nov. 7   Photo.   Perf. 12x13
C31 AP17 50fr multi   1.10 .80
See note after Chad No. C11.

Mercury by
Antoine
Coysevox
AP18

1965, Dec. 5   Engr.   Perf. 13
C32 AP18 100fr red brn, bl & blk 2.75 1.10
5th anniv. of Central African Republic's
admission to the UPU.

1965, Dec. 12
Design: 100fr, Mother and child.

Father Holding
Sick
Child — AP19

C33 AP19 50fr dk bl, car & blk 1.25 .45
C34 AP19 100fr red brn, red &
brt grn   2.75 1.10
Issued to honor the Red Cross.

Air Afrique Issue
Common Design Type
1966, Aug. 31   Photo.   Perf. 13
C35 CD123 25fr bl, blk & lem 1.00 .40
For surcharge see No. C43.

Surveyor Spacecraft on Moon — AP20

Designs: No. C37, Luna 9 on Moon and
Earth. 200fr, Rocket take-off, Jules Verne's
"From the Earth to the Moon."

1966, Oct. 24   Photo.   Perf. 12x12½
C36 AP20 130fr multi   1.60 .95
C37 AP20 130fr multi   1.60 .95
C38 AP20 200fr multi   3.00 1.75
a.   Souv. sheet of 3, #C36-C38 9.00 9.00
Nos. C36-C38 (3)   6.20 3.65
Conquest of the Moon.
For surcharges see Nos. C58, C61.

Eugene A.
Cernan, Gemini
9 and Agena
Rocket — AP21

No. C40, Pavel R. Popovich and rocket.

1966, Nov. 14   Photo.   Perf. 13
C39 AP21 50fr multi   1.25 .55
C40 AP21 50fr multi   1.25 .55
American and Russian astronauts.

Diamant Rocket, D-1 Satellite and
Globe with Map of Africa — AP22

1966, Nov. 14   Engr.
C41 AP22 100fr brt rose lil & brn 1.90 .95
Issued to commemorate the launching of
France's first satellite, Nov. 26, 1965, and the
launching of the D-1 satellite, Feb. 17, 1966.

Exchange of
Agricultural and
Industrial
Products between
Africa and
Europe — AP23

1966, Dec. 5   Photo.   Perf. 12x13
C42 AP23 50fr multi   1.40 .95
See note after Gabon No. C46.

No. C35 Surcharged

1967, May 8 **Perf. 13**
C43 CD123 5fr on 25fr multi .55 .30

The surcharge obliterates the "2" of the original 25fr denomination.

DC-8F Over M'Poko Airport, Bangui — AP24

1967, July 3 **Engr.** **Perf. 13**
C44 AP24 100fr sl, dk grn & brn 2.50 1.00

View of EXPO '67, Montreal — AP25

1967, July 17
C45 AP25 100fr vio bl, dk red brn & dk grn 2.25 .80

International Exposition. EXPO '67, Montreal, Apr. 28-Oct. 27.

African Postal Union Issue, 1967
Common Design Type

1967, Sept. 9 **Engr.** **Perf. 13**
C46 CD124 100fr brt grn, dk car rose & plum 2.25 .85

Potez 25 TOE — AP26

1967, Nov. 24 **Engr.** **Perf. 13**
C47 AP26 100fr shown 2.50 .80
C48 AP26 200fr Junkers 52 5.50 1.75
C49 AP26 500fr Caravelle 11R 14.00 4.25
    Nos. C47-C49 (3) 22.00 6.80

For surcharges see Nos. C59-C60.

Presidents Boganda and Bokassa — AP27

1967, Dec. 1 **Photo.** **Perf. 12½**
C50 AP27 130fr org, red, lt bl & blk 2.50 1.25

9th anniversary of the republic.

Pres. Jean Bedel Bokassa AP28

1968, Jan. 1 **Perf. 12½x12**
C51 AP28 30fr multi 1.00 .45

Human Rights Flame, Men and Globe — AP29

1968, Mar. 26 **Photo.** **Perf. 13**
C52 AP29 200fr brt grn, vio & ver 3.75 1.60

International Human Rights Year.

Man, WHO Emblem and Tsetse Fly — AP30

1968, Apr. 8 **Engr.**
C53 AP30 200fr multi 4.00 2.00

20th anniv. of WHO.

Javelin Thrower — AP31

Space Probe Landing on Venus — AP32

1968, Apr. 16 **Engr.** **Perf. 13**
C54 AP31 200fr shown 5.50 3.25
C55 AP31 200fr Downhill skier 5.50 3.25

The 1968 Olympic Games.

1968, Apr. 23
C56 AP32 100fr ultra, dk & brt grn 1.75 .95

Venus exploration by Venus IV, 10/18/67.

Marie Curie and "Cancer Destroyed" — AP33

1968, Apr. 30
C57 AP33 100fr vio, brt bl & brn 2.75 1.10

Marie Curie (1867-1934), scientist.

Nos. C36-C37 and C47-C48 Surcharged with New Value

Photogravure; Engraved
1968, Sept. 16 **Perf. 12x12½, 13**
C58 AP20 5fr on 130fr multi .20 .20
C59 AP26 10fr on 100fr multi .30 .20
C60 AP26 20fr on 200fr multi .50 .30
C61 AP20 50fr on 130fr multi 1.10 .55
    Nos. C58-C61 (4) 2.10 1.25

On No. C58 the old denomination has been obliterated with "XIX," on No. C61 the obliteration is a rectangular bar. On Nos. C59-C60 the last zero of the old denomination has been obliterated with a black square.

River Boat Type of Regular Issue

Craft: 100fr, "Pie X," Bangui, 1894. 130fr, "Ballay," Bangui, 1891.

1968, Dec. 10 **Engr.** **Perf. 13**
Size: 48x27mm
C62 A37 100fr bl, dk brn & ol 2.50 1.00
C63 A37 130fr brt pink, sl grn & slate 3.00 1.25

PHILEXAFRIQUE Issue

Mme. de Sévigné, French School, 17th Century AP34

1968, Dec. 17 **Photo.** **Perf. 12½**
C64 AP34 100fr brn & multi 3.25 2.40

Issued to publicize PHILEXAFRIQUE, Philatelic Exhibition in Abidjan, Feb. 14-23. Printed with alternating brown label.

2nd PHILEXAFRIQUE Issue
Common Design Type

Design: 50fr, Ubangi-Shari No. J16, cotton field and Pres. Bokassa.

1969, Feb. 14 **Engr.** **Perf. 13**
C65 CD128 50fr bis brn, blk & dk grn 1.90 1.90

Holocerina Angulata Aur. — AP35

Butterflies and Moths: 20fr, Nudaurelia dione fabr. 30fr, Eustera troglophylla hamp., vert. 50fr, Aurivillius aratus west. 100fr, Epiphora albida druce.

1969, Feb. 25 **Photo.**
C66 AP35 10fr yel & multi 1.10 .35
C67 AP35 20fr vio & multi 1.60 .55
C68 AP35 30fr multi 3.75 1.00
C69 AP35 50fr multi 5.25 2.25
C70 AP35 100fr multi 9.00 3.25
    Nos. C66-C70 (5) 20.70 7.40

Boxing — AP36

1969, Mar. 18 **Photo.** **Perf. 13**
C71 AP36 50fr shown 1.10 .30
C72 AP36 100fr Basketball 2.25 .60

Apollo 8 over Moonscape — AP37

1969, May 27 **Photo.** **Perf. 13**
C73 AP37 200fr dp bl, gray & yel 3.75 1.75

US Apollo 8 mission, the 1st men in orbit around the moon, Dec. 21-27, 1968.
For overprint see No. C81.

Market Cross, Nuremberg, and Toys — AP38

1969, June 3
C74 AP38 100fr blk, brt rose lil & emer 2.25 .95

Intl. Toy Fair in Nuremberg, Germany.

Napoleon as First Consul, by Anne-Louis Girodet-Trioson — AP39

Designs: 130fr, Napoleon meeting Emperor Francis II, by Antoine Jean Gros, horiz. 200fr, The Wedding of Napoleon and Marie-Louise, by Georges Rouget, horiz.

1969, Nov. 4 **Photo.** **Perf. 12½**
C75 AP39 100fr multi 2.25 1.25
C76 AP39 130fr brn & multi 3.25 1.50
C77 AP39 200fr multi 5.50 2.75
    Nos. C75-C77 (3) 11.00 5.50

Napoleon Bonaparte (1769-1821).

Pres. Bokassa, Map of Africa and Flag — AP40

Franklin Delano Roosevelt — AP41

1970, Jan. 1 *Die-cut; Perf. 10½*
Embossed on Gold Foil
C78 AP40 2000fr gold   40.00 40.00

1970   Litho.   Perf. 13½x14
C79 AP41 100fr shown   2.25 1.00
C80 AP41 100fr Lenin   3.50 1.25
Roosevelt, 25th death anniv., Lenin, birth cent.
Issue dates: #C79, Apr. 29; #C80. Apr. 22.

No. C73 Overprinted in Red:

1970, June 1   Photo.   Perf. 13
C81 AP37 200fr multi   17.00 9.50
Moon landing mission of Apollo 12, 11/14-24/69.

AP42

1970, Sept. 15   Litho.   Perf. 10
C82 AP42   Pair + label   4.50 3.00
  a.   100fr Dancer   1.90 .55
  b.   100fr Still life   1.90 .55
Knokphila 70, 6th Intl. Phil. Exhib. at Knokke, Belgium, July 4-10. Imperf. between stamps and label.

Sericulture Type of Regular Issue
1970, Sept. 15   Perf. 10
C83 A45 140fr multi   4.50 1.10

C.A.R. Flag, EXPO Emblem and Pavilion AP43

1970, Dec. 18   Litho.   Perf. 13½x13
C84 AP43 200fr red & multi   4.25 1.75
Intl. Exposition EXPO '70, Osaka, Japan.

Soccer — AP44

1970, Dec. 8   Perf. 13x13½
C85 AP44 200fr multi   4.00 1.60
World Soccer Championships, Mexico, May 30-June 21, 1970.

Dove — AP45

1970, Dec. 31
C86 AP45 200fr bl, yel & blk   4.00 1.60
25th anniversary of the United Nations.

Presidents Mobutu, Bokassa, and Tombalbaye — AP46

1971, Jan. 10
C87 AP46 140fr multi   3.25 1.10
Return of Central African Republic to the United States of Central Africa which also includes Congo Democratic Republic and Chad.

Satellite over Globe — AP47

1971, May 17   Photo.   Perf. 12½
C88 AP47 100fr multi   2.25 .85
3rd World Telecommunications Day.

African Postal Union Issue, 1971
Common Design Type
Design: 100fr, Carved head and UAMPT building, Brazzaville, Congo.

1971, Nov. 13   Photo.   Perf. 13x13½
C89 CD135 100fr bl & multi   2.25 .85

Child and Education Year Emblem — AP48

1971, Nov. 11   Litho.   Perf. 13x13½
C90 AP48 140fr multi   2.25 .80
25th anniv. of UNESCO.

Fight Against Cancer — AP49

Gamal Abdel Nasser — AP50

1971, Nov. 20   Photo.   Perf. 12½
C91 AP49 100fr grn & multi   2.75 1.10

1972, Jan. 15
C92 AP50 100fr dk red, blk & bister   2.25 .85
In memory of Gamal Abdel Nasser (1918-1970), president of Egypt.

Olympic Rings and Boxing — AP51

No. C94, Track and Olympic rings, vert.

1972, May 26   Engr.   Perf. 13
C93 AP51 100fr brn org & sepia   1.75 .80
C94 AP51 100fr green & violet   1.75 1.10
  a.   Miniature sheet of 2   5.00 5.00
20th Olympic Games, Munich, Aug. 26-Sept. 10. No. C94a contains 2 stamps similar to Nos. C93-C94, but in changed colors. The boxing stamp is red lilac and green, the track stamp ocher and red lilac.
For overprints see Nos. C100-C101.

Tiling's Mail Rocket, 1931, and Mailman — AP52

Designs: 50fr, DC-3 and mailman riding camel, vert. 150fr, Sirio satellite and rocket, vert. 200fr, Intelsat 4 and rocket.

1972, Aug. 12
C95 AP52 40fr bl, org & indigo   .65 .45
C96 AP52 50fr bl, brn & org   .90 .55
C97 AP52 150fr brn, org & gray   2.50 1.25
C98 AP52 200fr brn, bl & org   3.50 2.25
  a.   Souv. sheet of 4, #C95-C98   9.25 9.25
         Nos. C95-C98 (4)   7.55 4.50
Centraphilex 1972, Central African Philatelic Exhibition, Bangui.

Europafrica Issue

Arrows with Symbols of Agriculture and Industry — AP53

1972, Nov. 17   Litho.   Perf. 13
C99 AP53 100fr multi   1.75 .80

Nos. C93-C94, C94a Overprinted

(a)

(b)

1972, Nov. 24   Engr.
C100 AP51 (a) 100fr   1.75 .95
C101 AP51 (b) 100fr   1.75 .95
  a.   Miniature sheet of 2   3.75 3.75
Gold Medal Winners in 20th Olympic Games: Viatscheslav Lemechev, USSR, middleweight boxing; Randy Williams, US, broad jump.

Lunar Rover and Module — AP54

1972, Dec. 18   Engr.   Perf. 13
C102 AP54 100fr slate grn, bl & gray   1.75 .80
Apollo 16 US moon mission, 4/15-27/72.

Virgin and Child, by Francesco Pesellino AP55

Christmas: 150fr, Adoration of the Child with St. John the Baptist and St. Romuald, by Fra Filippo Lippi.

1972, Dec. 25   Photo.
C103 AP55 100fr gold & multi   1.60 .85
C104 AP55 150fr gold & multi   2.75 1.25

Parthenon, Athens, Spyridon Louis, Marathon, 1896 — AP56

Olympic Rings and: 40fr, Arc de Triomphe, Paris, H. Barrelet, single scull, 1900. 50fr, Old Courthouse and Western Arch, St. Louis, Myer Prinstein, triple jump, 1904. 100fr, Tower, London, Henry Taylor, swimming, 1908. 150fr, City Hall, Stockholm, Greco-Roman wrestling, 1912.

1972, Dec. 28   **Engr.**

C105 AP56 30fr brt grn, mag & brn   .40 .25
C106 AP56 40fr vio bl, emer & brn   .50 .25
C107 AP56 50fr car rose, vio bl & Prus bl   .55 .40
C108 AP56 100fr sl, red lil & brn   1.10 .45
C109 AP56 150fr red lil, blk & Prus bl   1.75 1.10
Nos. C105-C109 (5)   4.30 2.45
Olympic Games 1896-1912.

WHO Emblem, Surgeon and Nurse — AP57

1973, Apr. 7   **Photo.**   **Perf. 13**
C110 AP57 100fr multi   1.75 .80
WHO, 25th anniv.

AP58

AP58a

1973, May 17   **Litho.**   **Perf. 12½**
C111 AP58 200fr World map, arrows, waves   2.75 1.10
5th International Telecommunications Day.

1973, Sept. 17   **Engr.**   **Perf. 13**
Head and City Hall, Brussels.
C112 AP58a 100fr pur, ocher & brn   1.40 .70
African Weeks, Brussels, Sept. 15-30, 1973.

Europafrica Issue

Map of Central African Republic with Industry and Agriculture, Young Man — AP59

1973, Sept. 28   **Engr.**   **Perf. 13**
C113 AP59 100fr sepia, grn & org   1.75 .80

Carrier Pigeon with Letter and UPU Emblem — AP60

1973, Oct. 9   **Photo.**
C114 AP60 200fr multi   2.50 1.10
Universal Postal Union Day.

WMO Emblem, Weather Map — AP61

1973, Oct. 20   **Engr.**   **Perf. 13**
C115 AP61 150fr brt ultra & sl grn   2.75 1.00
Cent. of intl. meteorological cooperation.

Copernicus, Heliocentric System — AP62

1973, Nov. 2   **Photo.**
C116 AP62 100fr gold & multi   3.00 1.75
Copernicus (1473-1543), Polish astronomer.

Pres. Bokassa AP63

Pres. Bokassa — AP64

Rocket Launch and Apollo 17 Badge — AP65

1973, Nov. 30   **Photo.**   **Perf. 12½**
C117 AP63 50fr multi   .75 .40
C118 AP64 100fr multi   1.40 .70

1973, Dec. 15   **Engr.**   **Perf. 13**
65fr, Capsule over moonscape, horiz. 100fr, Moon landing, horiz. 150fr, Astronauts on moon. 200fr, Splashdown with parachutes and badge.

C119 AP65 50fr ver, gray grn & brn   .55 .30
C120 AP65 65fr dk brn, brn red & sl grn   .75 .40
C121 AP65 100fr ver, slate & choc   1.10 .55
C122 AP65 150fr brn, ol & sl grn   1.75 .80
C123 AP65 200fr red, bl & sl grn   2.25 1.10
Nos. C119-C123 (5)   6.40 3.15
Apollo 17 US moon mission, 12/7-19/72.

St. Teresa — AP66

UPU Emblem, Letter — AP67

1973, Dec. 25
C124 AP66 500fr vio bl & grnsh bl   6.75 3.50
St. Teresa of the Infant Jesus, the Little Flower (1873-1897), Carmelite nun.

1974, Oct. 9   **Engr.**   **Perf. 13**
C125 AP67 500fr multi   7.50 4.00
Centenary of Universal Postal Union.
For surcharge see No. C159.

Presidents and Flags of Cameroun, CAR, Gabon and Congo — AP68

1974, Dec. 8   **Photo.**   **Perf. 13**
C126 AP68 100fr gold & multi   1.40 .80
See note after Cameroun No. 595.
For surcharge see No. C155.

Marshal Bokassa AP69

100fr, Bokassa in Marshal's uniform with cape.

1975, Feb. 22   **Photo.**   **Perf. 13**
C127 AP69 50fr tan & multi   .65 .40
C128 AP69 100fr tan & multi   1.40 .45
Jean Bedel Bokassa, President for Life and Marshal of the Republic.

Mask, Map of Africa, Arphila Emblem — AP70

Albert Schweitzer and Dugout, Lambarene AP71

1975, Aug. 25   **Engr.**   **Perf. 13**
C129 AP70 100fr brt bl, red brn & red   1.40 .60
ARPHILA 75 International Philatelic Exhibition, Paris, June 6-16.
For surcharge see No. C156.

1975, Sept. 30   **Engr.**   **Perf. 13**
C130 AP71 200fr blk, ultra & ol   3.50 1.75
Dr. Albert Schweitzer (1875-1965), medical missionary and musician.
For surcharge see No. C158.

Pres. Bokassa's Houseboat, Bow — AP72

40fr, Pres. Bokassa's houseboat, stern.

1976, Feb. 22   **Litho.**   **Perf. 13**
C131 AP72 30fr multi   .65 .30
C132 AP72 40fr multi   .85 .45

Monument to Franco-CAR Cooperation AP73

Presidents
and Flags
of France
and CAR
AP74

1976, Mar. 5
C133 AP73 100fr multi 1.40 .80
C134 AP74 200fr multi 2.50 1.25

Official visit of Pres. Valery Giscard
d'Estaing to Central African Republic, 3/5-8.
For surcharge see No. C157.

Apollo Soyuz Type, 1976

Designs: 100fr, Soyuz space ship. 200fr,
Apollo space ship. 300fr, Astronauts and cosmonauts in cabin. 500fr, Apollo and Soyuz
after link-up.

1976, June 14   Litho.   Perf. 14x13½
C135 A90 100fr multi 1.10 .25
C136 A90 200fr multi 2.10 .55
C137 A90 300fr multi 3.25 .95
    Nos. C135-C137 (3) 6.45 1.75
Souvenir Sheet
C138 A90 500fr multi 5.00 1.75

For surcharges see #C161, C168, C173,
C177.

French
Hussar
AP75

Uniforms: 125fr, Scottish "Black Watch."
150fr, German dragoon. 200fr, British grenadier. 250fr, American ranger. 450fr, American
dragoon.

1976, July 4   Perf. 13½
C139 AP75 100fr multi .90 .30
C140 AP75 125fr multi 1.00 .45
C141 AP75 150fr multi 1.25 .45
C142 AP75 200fr multi 1.90 .55
C143 AP75 250fr multi 2.50 .95
    Nos. C139-C143 (5) 7.55 2.70
Souvenir Sheet
C144 AP75 450fr multi 7.50 2.00

American Bicentennial.
For surcharges see Nos. C162, C166-C167,
C169, C172, C176.

Acherontia Atropos — AP76

100fr, Papilio nireus & niocha marnois.

1976, Sept. 20   Litho.   Perf. 12½
C145 AP76 50fr multi 9.00 1.50
C146 AP76 100fr multi 18.00 2.00

For surcharges see Nos. C160, C163.

Olympic Winners Type, 1976

Designs: 100fr, Women's figure skating,
Dorothy Hamill, vert. 200fr, Ice skating, Alexander Gorshkov and Ludmilla Pakhomova.
300fr, Men's figure skating, John Curry, vert.
500fr, Downhill skiing, Rosi Mittermaier, vert.

1976, Sept. 23   Litho.   Perf. 13½
C147 A92 100fr multi .75 .30
C148 A92 200fr multi 2.40 .60
C149 A92 300fr multi 3.25 1.00
    Nos. C147-C149 (3) 6.40 1.90
Souvenir Sheet
C150 A92 500fr multi 6.00 1.75

For surcharges see #C164, C170, C174,
C178.

Viking Mars Type, 1976

Designs: 100fr, Phases of Mars landing.
200fr, Viking descending on Mars, horiz.
300fr, Viking probe. 500fr, Viking flight to
Mars, horiz.

1976, Dec.
C151 A93 100fr multi 1.00 .30
C152 A93 200fr multi 2.40 .60
C153 A93 300fr multi 3.00 .95
    Nos. C151-C153 (3) 6.40 1.85
Souvenir Sheet
C154 A93 500fr multi 5.50 1.75

For surcharges and overprints see Nos.
C165, C171, C175, C179, C212-C215.

Central African Empire
Stamps of 1973-76 Overprinted with
Bars and "EMPIRE CENTRAFICAIN"
in Black, Violet Blue or Gold
Printing and Perforations as Before
1977, Mar.
C155 AP68 100fr (#C126;B) 1.10 1.10
C156 AP70 100fr (#C129;VB) 1.10 1.10
C157 AP73 100fr (#C133;G) 1.10 1.10
C158 AP71 200fr (#C130;B) 3.25 1.50
C159 AP67 500fr (#C125;B) 10.00 10.00
    Nos. C155-C159 (5) 16.55 14.80

No bar on No. C159.

Stamps of 1976 Overprinted "EMPIRE
CENTRAFRICAIN" in Black on Silver
Panel
1977, Apr. 1
C160 AP76 50fr (#C145) .55 .55
C161 A90 100fr (#C135) 1.10 1.10
C162 AP75 100fr (#C139) 1.10 1.10
C163 AP76 100fr (#C146) 1.10 1.10
C164 A92 100fr (#C147) 1.10 1.10
C165 A93 100fr (#C151) 1.10 1.10
C166 AP75 125fr (#C140) 1.40 1.40
C167 AP75 150fr (#C141) 1.60 1.60
C168 A90 200fr (#C136) 2.75 2.75
C169 AP75 200fr (#C142) 2.50 2.50
C170 A92 200fr (#C148) 2.25 2.25
C171 A93 200fr (#C152) 2.25 2.25
C172 AP75 250fr (#C143) 2.75 2.75
C173 A90 300fr (#C137) 3.50 3.50
C174 A92 300fr (#C149) 3.50 3.50
C175 A93 300fr (#C153) 3.50 3.50
    Nos. C160-C175 (16) 32.05 32.05
Souvenir Sheets
C176 AP75 450fr (#C144) 5.50 5.50
C177 A90 500fr (#C138) 8.00 8.00
C178 A92 500fr (#C150) 5.50 5.50
C179 A93 500fr (#C154) 5.50 5.50

Overprint on type AP75 is in upper and
lower case letters.

Nobel Prize Type, 1977

Designs: 100fr, Rudyard Kipling. 200fr,
Ernest Hemingway. 300fr, Luigi Pirandello.
500fr, Rabindranath Tagore.

1977, Apr. 1   Perf. 13½
C180 A94 100fr multi 2.00 .40
C181 A94 200fr multi 4.00 .70
C182 A94 300fr multi 6.25 .95
    Nos. C180-C182 (3) 12.25 2.05
Souvenir Sheet
C183 A94 500fr multi 6.00 1.75

Zeppelin Type of 1977

100fr, Germany #C42 and North Pole.
200fr, Germany #C44 and Science and Industry Building, Chicago. 300fr, Germany #C35
and Brandenburg Gate, Berlin. 500fr, US
#C14 and US Capitol.

1977, Apr. 11   Litho.   Perf. 11
C184 A95 100fr multi 1.40 .30
C185 A95 200fr multi 2.75 .60
C186 A95 300fr multi 3.50 1.00
    Nos. C184-C186 (3) 7.65 1.90
Souvenir Sheet
C187 A95 500fr multi 5.50 2.00

75th anniversary of Zeppelin.

Bokassa Type of 1977

1977, Dec. 4   Litho.   Perf. 13½
C188 A98 200fr multi 1.90 .80
C189 A98 300fr multi 2.75 1.25
    a. Souvenir sheet, 500fr 6.00 2.50

Coronation of Emperor Bokassa I, Dec. 4.
No. C189a contains a horizontal stamp in similar design. A 2500fr gold embossed horizontal
stamp in similar design exists. Value $25.

Vaccination
AP77

1977   Litho.   Perf. 14x13½
C190 AP77 150fr multi 4.00 1.25

World Health Day.

Communications Type of 1978

Designs: 100fr, Balloon and spaceships
docking in space. 200fr, Hydrofoil and Concorde. 500fr, Tom-tom and Zeppelin. No.
C193A, Early postman and rider, UPU
emblem, Concorde. No. C193B, Mail coach,
dove, satellites.

1978, May 17   Litho.   Perf. 13½
C191 A107 100fr multi 1.10 .25
C192 A107 200fr multi 1.10 .30
Souvenir Sheet
C193 A107 500fr multi 5.75 2.25

Cent. of progress of posts and telecommunications. No. C193 contains one 53x35mm
stamp.

1978, Mar. 21   Litho. & Embossed
Size: 57x39mm
C193A A107 1500fr gold & mul-
    ti 55.00 4.00
Souvenir Sheet
C193B A107 1500fr gold & mul-
    ti 15.00 4.75

Nos. C193A-C193B exist imperf. No. C193A
exists in a souvenir sheet of one. No. C193B
contains one 57x39mm stamp.

Clement Ader and his Plane — AP78

Designs: 50fr, Wilbur and Orville Wright and
plane. 60fr, John W. Alcock, Arthur W. Brown
and plane. 100fr, Alan Cobham and plane
150fr, Claude Dornier and hydroplane. 500fr,
Wilbur and Orville Wright and plane.

1978, Sept. 19   Perf. 14
C194 AP78 40fr multi .55 .20
C195 AP78 50fr multi .55 .20
C196 AP78 60fr multi .65 .25
C197 AP78 100fr multi 1.25 .40
C198 AP78 150fr multi 1.90 .60
    Nos. C194-C198 (5) 4.90 1.65
Souvenir Sheet
C199 AP78 500fr multi 6.00 1.75

History of aviation.

Philexafrique II-Essen Issue
Common Design Types
#C200, Crocodile, #C3. #C201, Birds,
Mecklenburg-Schwerin #1.

1978, Nov. 1   Litho.   Perf. 12½
C200 CD138 100fr multi 1.90 1.10
C201 CD139 100fr multi 1.90 1.10
    a. Pair, #C200-C201 + label 7.50 7.50

Bokassa Type of 1978

150fr, Catherine & Jean Bedel Bokassa.

1978, Dec. 4   Litho.   Perf. 13
C202 A113 150fr multi, horiz. 1.90 .70

First anniv. of coronation. A 1000fr gold
embossed souvenir sheet showing Emperor
Bokassa exists. Value $9.

Rowland Hill Type of 1978

Designs (Rowland Hill and): 100fr, Mailman
and Tuscany No. 23. 200fr, Balloon and
France No. 1. 500fr, Central Africa Nos. 1-2.

1978, Dec. 27
C203 A114 100fr multi 4.00 1.40
C204 A114 200fr multi 1.75 .65
Souvenir Sheet
C205 A114 500fr multi 5.50 1.75

Sir Rowland Hill (1795-1879), originator of
penny postage. No. C205 contains one
37½x39mm stamp. 1500fr gold embossed
stamp and souvenir sheet exist.

IYC Type of 1979

Designs (UNICEF, Eagle Emblems and):
100fr, Chinese girl flying kites and German
Do-X flying boat, 1929. 200fr, Boys playing
leapfrog, hurdler and Olympic emblem. 500fr,
Child with abacus and Albert Einstein with his
equation.

1979, Mar. 6   Perf. 13½
C206 A115 100fr multi 1.40 .40
C207 A115 200fr multi 2.75 .65
Souvenir Sheet
C208 A115 500fr multi 5.50 1.75

International Year of the Child. No. C208
contains one 56x33mm stamp. 1500fr gold
embossed stamp and souvenir sheet exist.

Olympic Type of 1979

Moscow '80 Emblem, various Sports and:
100fr, Hurdles & "B." 200fr, Broad jump & "A."

1979, Mar. 16   Litho.   Perf. 13
C209 A116 100fr multi 1.10 .35
C210 A116 200fr multi 2.10 .65

22nd Olympic Games, Moscow, July 19-
Aug. 3, 1980. A 1500fr gold embossed souvenir sheet exists showing diver, runner and
javelin.

National Husbandry Association Type

1979, Aug.   Litho.   Perf. 13
C211 A119 60fr Horse 5.75 2.00

Central African Republic
Nos. C151-C154 Overprinted
"ALUNISSAGE/APOLLO XI/ JUILLET
1969" and Emblem in Black or Silver

1979, Oct.   Litho.   Perf. 14x13½
C212 A93 100fr multi 1.00 .55
C213 A93 200fr multi 1.90 .85
C214 A93 300fr multi 2.75 1.25
    Nos. C212-C214 (3) 5.65 2.65
Souvenir Sheet
C215 A93 500fr multi (S) 5.50 5.50

Apollo 11 moon landing, 10th anniversary.

Ski Jump, Lake Placid '80
Emblem — AP79

1979, Nov. 11   Litho.   Perf. 13½
C216 AP79 60fr shown .65 .20
C217 AP79 100fr Downhill skiing 1.10 .40
C218 AP79 200fr Hockey 2.25 .85
C219 AP79 300fr Bobsledding 3.25 1.25
    Nos. C216-C219 (4) 7.25 2.70
Souvenir Sheet
C220 AP79 500fr multi 5.50 1.75

13th Winter Olympics Games, Lake Placid,
NY, Feb. 12-24, 1980.
For overprints see Nos. C224-C228.

Space Type of 1980

1980, Apr. 8   Litho.   Perf. 13½
C221 A125 150fr Early satel-
    lites 1.60 .40
C222 A125 200fr Space
    shuttle 1.90 .55
Souvenir Sheet
C223 A125 500fr Apollo 11,
    Armstrong 5.50 1.40

Litho. & Embossed
Size: 51x57mm

C223A A125 1500fr Armstrong,
Apollo 11 50.00 3.00
Souvenir Sheet
C223B A125 1500fr Space
shuttle,
horiz. 10.00

C223A-C223B exist imperf. No. C223A exists in a souvenir sheet of one. Value $40. No. C223B contains one 57x51mm stamp.

Nos. C216-C220 Overprinted:

a

1980, May 12 Litho. Perf. 13½
C224 AP79 (a) 60fr multi .50 .20
C225 AP79 (b) 100fr multi .75 .40
C226 AP79 (c) 200fr multi 1.90 .85
C227 AP79 (d) 300fr multi 2.75 1.25
Nos. C224-C227 (4) 5.90 2.70
Souvenir Sheet
C228 AP79 (e) 500fr multi 5.00 5.00

World Telecommunications
Day — AP80

1980, June 26 Litho. Perf. 12½
C229 AP80 100fr multi 1.10 .55
C230 AP80 150fr multi, vert. 1.40 .80

Olympic Type of 1980

1980, July 25 Litho. Perf. 13½
C231 A126 100fr Boxing 1.00 .25
C232 A126 150fr Hurdles 1.60 .40
Souvenir Sheet
C233 A126 250fr Long jump 3.00 .65
Litho. & Embossed
C233A A126 1500fr Relay race,
diff. 35.00 4.00
Souvenir Sheet
C233B A126 1500fr Basketball,
vert. 11.00 4.75

22nd Summer Olympic Games, Moscow, July 19-Aug. 3. #C233 contains one 39x36mm stamp.
For overprints see Nos. C248-C250B.

Europe-Africa Type of 1980

1980, Nov. 4 Litho. Perf. 13½
C234 A127 150fr Meteorolo-
gy 1.50 .50
C235 A127 200fr Aviation 1.90 .60
Souvenir Sheet
C236 A127 500fr Concorde
jet 5.50 1.60

No. C236 contains one 41½x29mm stamp.

Litho. & Embossed
Size: 42x39mm
C236A A127 1500fr Boy Scouts 15.00 4.00
Souvenir Sheet
C236B A127 1500fr Concorde 12.00 4.75

Nos. C236A-C236B exist imperf. No. C236B contains one 42x39mm stamp.
No. C236A exists in a souvenir sheet of one. Value $30.

Soccer Type of 1981

1981, Jan. 13 Litho. Perf. 13½
C237 A130 100fr Nether-
lands 1.00 .25
C238 A130 200fr Spain 1.50 .55
Souvenir Sheet
C239 A130 500fr Argentina 6.25 1.75

Litho. & Embossed
Size: 57x39mm
C239A A130 1500fr Players,
trophy 24.00 5.50
Souvenir Sheet
C239B A130 1500fr Players,
trophy,
diff. 10.00 4.00

No. C239A exists with tabs for either Philex-afrique II or Essen 78.
Nos. C239A-C239B exist imperf. No. C239A exists in a souvenir sheet of one. Value $38. No. C239B contains one 36x60mm stamp.

Jacob Wrestling with the Angel, by Rembrandt AP81

Rembrandt Paintings: 90fr, Christ during the Storm. 150fr, Jeremiah Mourning the Destruction of Jerusalem. 250fr, Tobit Accusing Anne of Theft of a Goat. 500fr, Belshazzar's Feast, horiz.

1981, Feb. 20 Perf. 12½
C240 AP81 60fr multi .55 .20
C241 AP81 90fr multi .90 .25
C242 AP81 150fr multi 1.40 .55
C243 AP81 250fr multi 2.50 .65
Nos. C240-C243 (4) 5.35 1.65
Souvenir Sheet
C244 AP81 500fr multi 5.50 1.75

Picasso Type of 1981

Paintings: 150fr, Woman in Mirror with Self-portrait. 200fr, Woman Sleeping, The Dream. 500fr, Portrait of Maia (the Artist's Daughter). No. C247A, Two Women and Glasses, Picasso. No. C247B, Woman with Handbag, statue of standing woman, vert.

1981, June 30 Litho. Perf. 13½
C245 A133 150fr multi 2.25 .45
C246 A133 200fr multi 2.50 .60
Souvenir Sheet
C247 A133 500fr multi 5.75 1.40

No. C247 contains one 42x46mm stamp.

Litho. & Embossed
Size: 57x39mm
C247A A133 1500fr gold & mul-
ti 15.00 4.00
Souvenir Sheet
C247B A133 1500fr gold & mul-
ti 12.00

Nos. C247A-C247B exist imperf. No. C247A exists in a souvenir sheet of one. Value $30. No. C247B contains one 39x58mm stamp.

Nos. C231-C233B Overprinted with
Event, Winner and Country in Gold

1981 Litho. Perf. 13½
C248 A126 100fr multi 1.00 .25
C249 A126 150fr multi 1.40 .40
Souvenir Sheet
C250 A126 250fr multi 3.00 .65
Litho. & Embossed
C250A A126 1500fr on #C233A 14.00
Souvenir Sheet
C250B A126 1500fr on #C233B 15.00

No. C250A exists in a souvenir sheet of 1. Value $35.

Royal Wedding Type of 1981
1981, Aug. 20 Litho. Perf. 13½
C251 A136 150fr Prince of
Wales
arms 1.60 .40
C252 A136 200fr Palace 2.10 .55
Souvenir Sheet
C253 A136 500fr St. Paul's
Cathedral 4.75 1.40

No. C253 contains one 60x32mm stamp.

Litho. & Embossed
Size: 51x42mm
C253A A136 1500fr Diana,
Charles 15.00 4.00
Souvenir Sheet
C253B A136 1500fr Charles,
Diana,
ship 12.00

Nos. C253A-C253B exist imperf. No. C253A exists in a souvenir sheet of one. Value $21. No. C253B contains one 51x42mm stamp.

Navigator Type of 1981

1981, Sept. 4 Litho. Perf. 13½
C254 A139 100fr O. Ker-
sauson 1.10 .70
C255 A139 200fr Chichester 2.40 1.40
Souvenir Sheet
C256 A139 500fr A. Colas 6.50 1.40
Litho. & Embossed
Size: 51x42mm
C256A A139 1500fr Riguidel 16.00 4.50
Souvenir Sheet
C256B A139 1500fr Tabarly 13.00

Nos. C256A-C256B exist imperf. No. C256A exists in a souvenir sheet of one. Value $40. No. C256B contains one 51x42mm stamp.

Lizard
AP82

1981, Oct. 30 Perf. 12½x13
C257 AP82 30fr shown 1.00 .25
C258 AP82 60fr Snake 1.25 .30
C259 AP82 110fr Crocodile 2.50 .45
Nos. C257-C259 (3) 4.75 1.00

Christmas Type of 1981

1981, Dec. 24 Litho. Perf. 13½
C260 A143 140fr Correggio 2.50 .45
C261 A143 200fr Gentiles-
chi, 1610 4.50 .70
Souvenir Sheet
C262 A143 500fr Holy Fami-
ly, by
Cranach 6.75 1.75

No. C262 contains one 41x50mm stamp.

Litho. & Embossed
Size: 30x60mm
C262A A143 1500fr 15.00 4.50
Souvenir Sheet
C262B A143 1500fr Fra Angeli-
co, 1438 11.00

Nos. C262A-C262B exist imperf. No. C262A exists in a souvenir sheet of one. Value $25. No. C262B contains one 30x60mm stamp.

Animal Type of 1982
1982, Jan. 22 Litho. Perf. 13½
C263 A145 300fr Mandrill 3.25 .65
C264 A145 500fr Lion 5.50 1.40
Souvenir Sheet
C265 A145 600fr Nile croco-
diles 6.75 1.60

No. C265 contains one 47x38mm stamp.

Litho. & Embossed
Size: 51x57mm
C265A A145 1500fr Leopard,
Rotary
emblem 15.00 4.00
Souvenir Sheet
C265B A145 1500fr Emblem,
eagle,
horiz. 13.00

Nos. C265A-C265B exist imperf. No. C265A exists in a souvenir sheet of one. Value $42.50. No. C265B contains one 57x51mm stamp.

Transportation Type of 1982 and

AP82a

Designs: 300fr, Savannah cargo ship. 500fr, Columbia space shuttle. 600fr, Spirit of Loco-motion emblem. No. C268A, Space shuttle launch, horiz. No. C268B, Shuttle, space telescope.

1982, Feb. 27 Litho. Perf. 13½
C266 A147 300fr mul-
ticolored 3.50 .65
C267 A147 500fr mul-
ticolored 5.50 1.40
Souvenir Sheet
C268 A147 600fr mul-
ticolored 5.50 1.60
Litho. & Embossed
C268A AP82a 1500fr gold &
multi 15.00 4.50
Souvenir Sheet
C268B AP82a 1500fr gold &
multi 11.50

No. C268 contains one 39x43mm stamp.
No. C268B contains one 51x42mm stamp.
No. C268A exists in a souvenir sheet of 1. Value $50.

Olympic Type of 1982
1982, July 24 Litho. Perf. 13½
C269 A149 300fr Diving 3.00 .80
C270 A149 500fr Equestrian 5.00 1.40
Souvenir Sheet
C271 A149 600fr Basketball 5.50 1.60

No. C271 contains one 38x56mm stamp.

Diana Type of 1982

1982, July 20 Litho. Perf. 13½
C272 A150 300fr multi 3.25 .80
C273 A150 500fr multi 5.50 1.40
Souvenir Sheet
C274 A150 600fr multi 5.75 1.60

No. C274 contains one 56x32mm stamp.

Christmas
1982
AP83

Raphael Paintings.

1982, Dec. Perf. 13
C275 AP83 150fr Beautiful Gar-
dener 1.75 .40
C276 AP83 500fr Holy Family 5.50 1.40

Space Type of 1982

Designs: Various satellites and space scenes. No. C279A, European communications satellite, controller. No. C279B, Viking on Mars, vert.

1982, Aug. 15 Litho. Perf. 13½
C277 A151 300fr multi 3.00 .80
C278 A151 500fr multi 5.00 1.40
Souvenir Sheet
C279 A151 600fr multi 5.00 1.60
Litho. & Embossed
Size: 60x36mm
C279A A151 1500fr gold &
multi 15.00 4.50

Souvenir Sheet

C279B A151 1500fr gold & multi 12.00

Nos. C279A-C279B exist imperf. No. C279A exists in a souvenir sheet of one. Value $55. No. C279B contains one 36x60mm stamp.

Birth of Prince William of Wales, June 21, 1982 — AP84

Designs: No. C281, Diana, William, Charles. No. 281B, Diana, William, vert.

1983, Jan. 22

C280 AP84 500fr Diana, William 5.50 1.40

Souvenir Sheet

C281 AP84 600fr Family 5.50 4.00

Litho. & Embossed

C281A AP84 1500fr gold & multi 15.00 3.50

Souvenir Sheet

C281B AP84 1500fr gold & multi 10.00

No. C281A exists in a souvenir sheet of 1. Value $40.

Manned Flight Bicentenary AP85

1983, Apr.

C282 AP85 65fr Robert's & Hullin's balloon 1.00 .20
C283 AP85 130fr John Wise's, 1859 1.50 .35
C284 AP85 350fr Mail balloon, 1870 3.25 .90
C285 AP85 400fr Dirigible Underberg 4.25 1.10
Nos. C282-C285 (4) 10.00 2.55

Souvenir Sheet

C286 AP85 500fr Montgolfiere, 1783 5.75 1.40

Pre-Olympics — AP86

Various equestrian events.

1983, July Litho. Perf. 13

C287 AP86 100fr multi 1.00 .40
C288 AP86 200fr multi 2.10 .60
C289 AP86 300fr multi 2.75 .80
C290 AP86 400fr multi 3.50 1.10
Nos. C287-C290 (4) 9.35 2.90

Souvenir Sheet

C291 AP86 500fr multi 5.75 1.40

Animal Type of 1983

Endangered Animals, Rotary Emblem

1983, Nov. 14 Litho. Perf. 13½

C291A A170 400fr Black rhinoceros, parrot, zebra, scouts 10.00 3.00

C292 A170 500fr Lions, parrot, antelope, elephant, flag, Rotary Int'l emblem 12.00 3.50

Souvenir Sheet

C293 A170 600fr Leopard 16.00 4.00

15th World Scout Jamboree, Alberta (400fr). No. C293 contains one 47x32mm stamp.

Christmas 1983 AP88

Paintings: 130fr, Annunciation, by da Vinci. 205fr, Virgin of the Rocks, by da Vinci. 350fr, Adoration of the Shepherds, by Rubens. 500fr, Virgin and Child with Donor, by Rubens.

1984, Jan. 3 Litho. Perf. 13

C294 AP88 130fr multi 1.00 .25
C295 AP88 205fr multi 1.60 .35
C296 AP88 350fr multi 2.75 .80
C297 AP88 500fr multi 4.50 1.00
Nos. C294-C297 (4) 9.85 2.40

1984 Summer Olympics — AP89

Various gymnastic and rhythmic gymnastic events. 65fr, 100fr, 205fr, 350fr vert.

1984, Mar. 13 Litho. Perf. 13

C298 AP89 65fr multi .55 .20
C299 AP89 100fr multi 1.10 .25
C300 AP89 130fr multi 1.40 .30
C301 AP89 205fr multi 2.10 .45
C302 AP89 350fr multi 3.50 .85
Nos. C298-C302 (5) 8.65 2.05

Souvenir Sheet

Perf. 13½x13

C302A AP89 500fr Rhythmic formation 5.00 1.25

For overprint see No. 705.

Summer Olympics Winners AP90

1985, Jan. 7 Litho. Perf. 14

C303 AP90 60fr 400 meter relay .55 .25
C304 AP90 140fr 400 meter hurdles 1.40 .30
C305 AP90 300fr 5000 meter race 3.25 .80
C306 AP90 440fr Decathlon 4.50 1.00
Nos. C303-C306 (4) 9.70 2.35

Souvenir Sheet

C307 AP90 500fr 800 meter race, horiz. 5.00 4.50

Christmas 1984 — AP91

Paintings by Titian: 130fr, Virgin and Infant Jesus. 350fr, Virgin with Rabbit. 400fr, Virgin and Child.

1985, Jan. 17 Litho. Perf. 13

C308 AP91 130fr multi 1.25 .55
C309 AP91 350fr multi 2.75 1.10
C310 AP91 400fr multi 3.75 1.25
Nos. C308-C310 (3) 7.75 2.90

Audubon Bicentenary — AP92

1985, Jan. 25 Litho. Perf. 13

C311 AP92 60fr Otus asio .80 .25
C312 AP92 110fr Coccizus minor, vert. 1.25 .45
C313 AP92 200fr Zenaidura macroura, vert. 2.10 1.00
C314 AP92 500fr Aix sponsa 5.25 2.50
Nos. C311-C314 (4) 9.40 4.20

Christmas 1985 AP93

Religious paintings: 100fr, Virgin with Angels, by the Master of Burgo de Osma. 200fr, Nativity, by Louis Le Nain (1593-1648). 400fr, Virgin and Child with Dove, by Piero de Cosimo (1462-1521).

1985, Dec. 24 Litho. Perf. 13

C315 AP93 100fr multi 1.10 .40
C316 AP93 200fr multi 2.50 .85
C317 AP93 400fr multi 4.75 1.90
Nos. C315-C317 (3) 8.35 3.15

Halley's Comet — AP94

1986, Mar. 8

C318 AP94 110fr Edmond Halley 1.00 .25
C319 AP94 130fr Giotto probe 1.40 .25
C320 AP94 200fr Comet, planet 1.90 .45
C321 AP94 300fr Vega probe 2.75 .60
C322 AP94 400fr Space shuttle 4.50 1.00
Nos. C318-C322 (5) 11.55 2.55

Christmas AP95

Painting details: 250fr, Nativity, by Giotto. 440fr, Adoration of the Magi, by Botticelli, vert. 500fr, Nativity, by Giotto, diff.

1986, Dec. 24 Litho. Perf. 13½

C323 AP95 250fr multi 2.50 1.10
C324 AP95 440fr multi 4.25 1.75
C325 AP95 500fr multi 5.25 2.10
Nos. C323-C325 (3) 12.00 4.95

Tennis at the 1988 Olympics — AP96

Various plays.

1986, Dec. 31 Perf. 12½

C326 AP96 150fr multi 1.60 .60
C327 AP96 250fr multi, vert. 3.00 .70
C328 AP96 440fr multi, vert. 3.75 1.25
C329 AP96 600fr multi 6.25 1.40
Nos. C326-C329 (4) 14.60 3.95

1988 Summer Olympics, Seoul — AP97

1987, June 15 Litho. Perf. 13

C330 AP97 100fr Triple jump, vert. .90 .40
C331 AP97 200fr High jump 1.75 .80
C332 AP97 300fr Long jump 2.50 1.10
C333 AP97 400fr Pole vault, vert. 3.25 1.60
Nos. C330-C333 (4) 8.40 3.90

Souvenir Sheet

C334 AP97 500fr High jump, diff. 4.50 3.25

1988 Summer Olympics, Seoul — AP98

Stamps on stamps and gymnasts: 90fr, No. C94, balance beam, vert. 200fr, No. C21, balance beam, diff. 300fr, No. C22, pommel horse. 400fr, No. C23, parallel bars. 500fr, No. C93, rings.

1988, July 26 Litho. Perf. 13

C335 AP98 90fr multi .65 .40
C336 AP98 200fr multi 1.40 .80
C337 AP98 300fr multi 2.10 1.10
C338 AP98 400fr multi 3.00 1.60
Nos. C335-C338 (4) 7.15 3.90

Souvenir Sheet

C339 AP98 500fr multi 3.75 2.75

1st Moon Landing, 20th Anniv. AP99

1989, Aug. 4   Litho.   Perf. 13
C340 AP99   40fr Apollo 11   .35   .25
C341 AP99   80fr Apollo 15   .65   .30
C342 AP99   130fr Apollo 16   1.25 .55
C343 AP99   1000fr Apollo 17   10.00 2.75
Nos. C340-C343 (4)   12.25 3.85

World Cup Soccer Championships, Italy — AP100

1990, July 7   Litho.   Perf. 13
C344 AP100   5fr multicolored   .20   .20
C345 AP100   30fr multi, diff.   .30   .20
C346 AP100   500fr multi, diff.   4.25 1.00
C347 AP100   1000fr multi, diff.   9.25 1.60
Nos. C344-C347 (4)   14.00 3.00

Charles de Gaulle (1890-1979) — AP101

1990, July 27   Perf. 13½
C348 AP101   500fr multicolored   3.75 .90

No. C348 exists in a souvenir sheet of 1.
For overprint see No. C360.

Don Mattingly, Baseball Player — AP102

Saturn V Rocket, Apollo 11 Astronauts — AP103

Charles de Gaulle, Birth Cent. AP104

No. C352, De Gaulle and Cross of Lorraine.

1990, July 27   Litho.   Perf. 13½
C349 AP102   300fr multicolored   2.50 .80
Souvenir Sheet
C350 AP103   1000fr multicolored   8.25 1.75
Litho. & Embossed
C351 AP104   1500fr gold & multi   14.00 3.50
Souvenir Sheet
C352 AP104   1500fr gold & multi   11.00

No. C351 exists in souvenir sheet of 1.
Value $14.
For overprints see Nos. C355-C356.

Visit of Pope John Paul II to Africa AP105

Pope John Paul II and: No. C353, Mother Theresa, portrait. No. C354, Papal arms, globe.

1993 Litho. & Embossed Perf. 13½
C353 AP105   1500fr gold & multi   11.50 2.75
Souvenir Sheet
C354 AP105   1500fr gold & multi   20.00

No. C353 exists in a souvenir sheet of 1.
Value $20.

No. C351 Ovptd. "6 JUIN / 1944"
Litho. & Embossed
1994, June 6   Perf. 13½
C355 AP105   1500fr gold & multi   10.50 9.00
No. C352 Ovptd. in Silver in Sheet Margin
Souvenir Sheet
C356 AP104   1500fr gold & multi   10.50 9.00

Overprint on No. C356 contains map, soldiers and "50 eme ANNIVERSAIRE DU /DEBARQUEMENT."
No. C355 exists in souvenir sheet of 1.
Value $12.

Souvenir Sheets

Japanese Exploration of Antarctica — AP106

1994, Oct. 25
C357 AP106   1200fr Nobu Shirase   4.75 4.75
C358 AP106   1200fr Schooner Kainman Maru, horiz. 4.75 4.75

D-Day, 50th Anniv. (in 1994) — AP107

Designs: a, Gliders over Pegasus Bridge, Sword beach. b, Fighter planes over Juno, Gold and Omaha beaches. c, Planes over Utah beach, St. Mere Eglise.

Litho. & Embossed
1995, Oct. 25   Perf. 13½
C359 AP107   1000fr Strip of 3,
                #a.-c.   13.00 13.00

No. C359b is 60x45mm.

No. C348 Overprinted Souvenir Sheet

1995, Oct. 10   Litho.   Perf. 13½
C360 AP101   500fr multicolored   11.50 11.50

AIR POST SEMI-POSTAL STAMPS

Isis of Kalabsha SPAP1

Unwmk.
1964, Mar. 7   Engr.   Perf. 13
CB1 SPAP1   25fr + 10fr multi   1.40 1.40
CB2 SPAP1   50fr + 10fr multi   2.25 2.25
CB3 SPAP1   100fr + 10fr multi   3.50 3.50
Nos. CB1-CB3 (3)   7.15 7.15

UNESCO world campaign to save historic monuments in Nubia.

African Infants and Globe — SPAP2

1971, Dec. 11   Litho.   Perf. 13x13½
CB4 SPAP2   140fr + 50fr multi   3.25 1.75
25th anniv. of UNICEF, and Children's Day.

POSTAGE DUE STAMPS

Sternotomis Virescens — D1

Beetles: #J2, Sternotomis gama. #J3, Augosoma centaurus. #J4, Phosphorus virescens, ceroplesis carabarica. #J5, Cetoine scaraboidae. #J6, Ceroplesis S.P. #J7, Macrorhina S.P. #J8, Cetoine scaraboidae. #J9, Phryneta leprosa. #J10, Taurina longiceps. #J11, Monohamus griseoplagiatus. #J12, Jambonus trifasciatus.

Unwmk.
1962, Oct. 15   Engr.   Perf. 11
J1 D1 50c grn & dp org   .20   .20
J2 D1 50c grn & dp org   .20   .20
a.   Pair, #J1-J2   .45
J3 D1 1fr blk, brn & lt grn   .30   .30
J4 D1 1fr blk, brn & lt grn   .30   .30
a.   Pair, #J3-J4   .75
J5 D1 2fr blk, org & yel grn .40   .40
J6 D1 2fr blk & red org   .40   .40
a.   Pair, #J5-J6   .85
J7 D1 5fr brn, org & grn   .55   .55
J8 D1 5fr brn, org, grn & red .55   .55
a.   Pair, #J7-J8   1.25
J9 D1 10fr blk, grn & brn   1.00 1.00
J10 D1 10fr blk, brn & grn   1.00 1.00
a.   Pair, #J9-J10   2.25
J11 D1 25fr blk, bl grn & brn 3.00 2.40
J12 D1 25fr blk, brn & bl grn 3.00 2.40
a.   Pair, #J11-J12   6.50
    Nos. J1-J12 (12)   10.90 9.70

Pairs se-tenant at the base.

Giant Anteater — D2

1985, Jan. 25   Litho.   Perf. 12½
J13 D2 5fr multi   .50   .50
J14 D2 20fr multi   .90   .90
J15 D2 30fr multi   1.10 1.10
    Nos. J13-J15 (3)   2.50 2.50

MILITARY STAMPS

No. 1 Overprinted

Unwmk.
1962, Jan. 1 Engr. *Perf. 13*
M1 A1 bl, car, grn & yel 15.00 —

No. 1 Overprinted

1963
M2 A1 bl, car, grn & yel 16.00 —

OFFICIAL STAMPS

Coat of Arms — O1

Imprint: "d'après G. RICHER SO.GE.IM."
Perf. 13x12½
1965-69 Litho. Unwmk.
Arms in Original Colors

O1	O1	1fr blk & brn org	.20	.20
O2	O1	2fr blk & violet	.20	.20
O3	O1	5fr blk & gray	.20	.20
O4	O1	10fr blk & green	.25	.20
O5	O1	20fr blk & red brn	.55	.25
O6	O1	30fr blk & emer ('69)	1.10	.55
O7	O1	50fr blk & dk bl	1.25	.70
O8	O1	100fr blk & bister	2.75	1.10
O9	O1	130fr blk & ver ('69)	4.25	2.25
O10	O1	200fr blk & claret	6.25	2.75
		Nos. O1-O10 (10)	17.00	8.40

Redrawn
Imprint: "d'après G. RICHER DELRIEU"
1971 Photo. *Perf. 12x12½*
Arms in Original Colors

O11	O1	5fr blk & gray	.20	.20
O12	O1	30fr blk & emer	.50	.25
O13	O1	40fr blk & dp claret	.65	.30
O14	O1	100fr blk & bister	1.50	.55
O15	O1	140fr blk & lt bl	2.75	.85
O16	O1	200fr blk & claret	3.25	1.40
		Nos. O11-O16 (6)	8.85	3.55

Empire
Nos. O11, O13-O16 Overprinted with Bar and "EMPIRE CENTRAFRICAIN"
1977 Litho. *Perf. 12x12½*

O17	O1	5fr multi	.20	.20
O18	O1	40fr multi	.40	.20
O19	O1	100fr multi	1.10	.45
O20	O1	140fr multi	1.50	.70
O21	O1	200fr multi	2.50	1.00
		Nos. O17-O21 (5)	5.70	2.55

Type of 1965 Inscribed: "EMPIRE CENTRAFRICAIN"
1978, July Litho. *Perf. 12½*

O22	O1	1fr multi	.20	.20
O23	O1	2fr multi	.20	.20
O24	O1	5fr multi	.20	.20
O25	O1	10fr multi	.20	.20
O26	O1	15fr multi	.20	.20
O27	O1	20fr multi	.20	.20
O28	O1	30fr multi	.30	.25
O29	O1	40fr multi	.40	.25
O30	O1	50fr multi	.55	.30
O31	O1	60fr multi	.75	.40
O32	O1	100fr multi	1.00	.55
O33	O1	140fr multi	1.60	.95
O34	O1	140fr multi	1.75	.95
O35	O1	200fr multi	3.50	1.25
		Nos. O22-O35 (14)	11.05	6.10

CENTRAL LITHUANIA
ˈsen-trəl ˌli-thə-ˈwā-nē-ə

LOCATION — North of Poland and east of Lithuania
CAPITAL — Vilnius

At one time Central Lithuania was a grand duchy of Lithuania but at the end of the 18th Century it fell under Russian rule. After World War I, Lithuania regained her sovereignty but certain areas were occupied by Poland. During the Russo-Polish war this territory was seized by Lithuania whose claim was promptly recognized by the Soviet Government. Under the leadership of the Polish General Zeligowski the territory was recaptured and it was during this occupation the stamps of Central Lithuania came into being. Subsequently the territory became a part of Poland.

100 Fennigi = 1 Markka

Coat of Arms — A1

Perf. 11½, Imperf.
1920-21 Typo. Unwmk.

1	A1	25f red	.35	.50
2	A1	25f dark grn ('21)	.35	.50
3	A1	1m blue	.35	.50
4	A1	1m dark brn ('21)	.35	.50
5	A1	2m violet	.35	.50
6	A1	2m orange ('21)	.35	.50
		Nos. 1-6 (6)	2.10	3.00

For surcharges see Nos. B1-B5.

Lithuanian Stamps of 1919 Surcharged in Blue or Black

Perf. 11½x12, 12½x11½, 14
1920, Nov. 23 Wmk. 145

13	A5	2m on 15sk lil	40.00	40.00
a.		Inverted surcharge	125.00	700.00
14	A5	4m on 10sk red	40.00	40.00
a.		Inverted surcharge	125.00	
15	A5	4m on 20sk dl bl (Bk)	40.00	40.00
a.		Inverted surcharge	125.00	
16	A5	4m on 30sk buff	40.00	40.00
a.		Inverted surcharge	125.00	
17	A6	6m on 50sk lt grn	40.00	40.00
a.		4m on 50sk (error)	125.00	
b.		10m on 50sk (error)	125.00	
c.		Surcharge inverted		—
18	A6	6m on 60sk vio & red	40.00	50.00
a.		4m on 60sk (error)	125.00	
b.		10m on 60sk (error)	125.00	
19	A6	6m on 75sk bis & red	40.00	50.00
a.		4m on 75sk (error)	125.00	
b.		10m on 75sk (error)	125.00	
20	A8	10m on 1auk gray & red	80.00	80.00
a.		Inverted surcharge	190.00	
21	A8	10m on 3auk lt brn & red	1,200.	1,200.
22	A8	10m on 5auk bl grn & red	1,200.	1,200.
		Nos. 13-20 (8)	360.00	380.00
		Nos. 13-22 (10)	2,760.	2,780.

The overprint on Nos. 17-19 is down-reading, i.e., the top of the overprint is at the right of the original design, the bottom at the left. The inverted overprint on No. 17c is up-reading.
Reprints of Nos. 17a, 17b, 18a, 18b, 19a, 19b. Value, each $45.
Counterfeits of Nos. 21-22 exist.

Lithuanian Girl — A2

Warrior — A3

Holy Gate of Vilnius — A4

Tower and Cathedral, Vilnius — A5

Rector's Insignia — A6

Gen. Lucien Zeligowski — A7

Perf. 11½, Imperf.
1920 Litho. Unwmk.

23	A2	25f gray	.20	.75
24	A3	1m orange	.20	.75
25	A4	2m claret	.40	1.00
26	A5	4m gray grn & buff	.70	1.50
27	A6	6m rose & gray	2.00	3.25
28	A7	10m brown & yellow	2.75	4.75
		Nos. 23-28 (6)	6.25	12.00

For surcharges see Nos. B13-B14, B17-B19.

St. Anne's Church, Vilnius — A8

St. Stanislas Cathedral, Vilnius — A9

White Eagle, White Knight Vytis — A10

Queen Hedwig and King Ladislas II Jagello — A11

Coat of Arms of Vilnius — A12

Poczobut Astronomical Observatory A13

Union of Lithuania and Poland — A14

Tadeusz Kosciuszko and Adam Mickiewicz A15

1921 *Perf. 14, Imperf.*

35	A8	1m dk gray & yel	.60	1.00
36	A9	2m rose & green	.60	1.00
37	A10	3m dark green	.75	1.25
38	A11	4m brown & buff	.75	1.25
39	A12	5m red brown	.75	1.25
40	A13	6m slate & buff	.75	1.50
41	A14	10m red vio & buff	1.00	2.50
42	A15	20m blk brn & buff	1.00	2.50
		Nos. 35-42 (8)	6.20	12.25

Set, perf. 13½, $150.

Peasant Girl Sowing — A16

White Eagle and Vytis — A17

Great Theater at Vilnius — A18

Allegory: Peace and Industry — A19

Gen. Zeligowski Entering Vilnius — A20

Gen. Zeligowski — A21

1921-22 *Perf. 11½, Imperf.*

53	A16	10m brown ('22)	3.25	6.25
54	A17	25m red & yel ('22)	3.50	8.00
55	A18	50m dk blue ('22)	5.00	12.00
56	A19	75m violet ('22)	6.00	22.50
57	A20	100m bl & bister	2.50	5.25
58	A21	150m ol grn & brn	3.50	6.75
		Nos. 53-58 (6)	23.75	60.75

Opening of the Natl. Parliament, Nos. 53-56; anniv. of the entry of General Zeligowski into Vilnius, Nos. 57-58.

SEMI-POSTAL STAMPS

Nos. 1-6 Surcharged in Black or Red

1921 Unwmk. *Perf. 11½, Imperf.*

B1	A1	25f + 2m red (Bk)	1.00	2.25
B2	A1	25f + 2m dk green	1.00	2.25
B3	A1	1m + 2m blue	1.25	2.25
B4	A1	1m + 2m dk brown	1.25	2.25

Column 1 (Central Lithuania)

B5	A1	2m + 2m violet	1.50	2.25
B6	A1	2m + 2m orange	1.50	2.25
		Nos. B1-B6 (6)	7.50	13.50

The surcharge means "For Silesia 2 marks." The stamps were intended to provide a fund to assist the plebiscite in Upper Silesia.

Nos. 25, 26 Surcharged:

a   b

Perf. 11½, Imperf.

B13	A4 (a)	2m + 1(m) claret	1.00	2.00
B14	A5 (b)	4m + 1m gray green & buff	1.00	2.00

Nos. 25-26, 28 with inset

Perf. 11½, Imperf.

B17	A4	2m + 1m claret	.65	1.25
B18	A5	4m + 1m gray green & buff	.65	1.25
B19	A7	10m + 2m brn & yel	.90	1.25
		Nos. B13-B19 (5)	4.20	7.75

POSTAGE DUE STAMPS

University, Vilnius D1   Castle Hill, Vilnius D2

Castle Ruins, Troki — D3   Holy Gate, Vilnius — D4

St. Stanislas Cathedral D5   St. Anne's Church, Vilnius D6

1920-21   Unwmk.   Perf. 11½, Imperf.

J1	D1	50f red violet	.40	1.00
J2	D2	1m green	.40	1.00
J3	D3	2m red violet	.50	1.00
J4	D4	3m red violet	.80	1.50
J5	D5	5m red violet	.95	2.50
J6	D6	20m scarlet	2.00	3.25
		Nos. J1-J6 (6)	5.05	10.25

CEYLON

si-ˈlän

Column 2 (Ceylon intro)

LOCATION — An island in the Indian Ocean separated from India by the Gulf of Manaar

GOVT. — Independent republic within the British Commonwealth

AREA — 25,332 sq. mi.

POP. — 12,670,000 (est. 1971)

CAPITAL — Colombo

Ceylon changed its name to Republic of Sri Lanka on May 22, 1972.

12 Pence = 1 Shilling

100 Cents = 1 Rupee (1872)

Values for unused stamps are for examples with original gum as defined in the catalogue introduction except for Nos. 2, 5, 8-9 which seldom have any remaining trace of their original gum. Many unused stamps of Ceylon, especially between Nos. 59 and 274, have toned gum or tropical stains. Values quoted are for stamps with fresh gum. Toned stamps have lower values, and common stamps with toned gum are worth very little.

Very fine examples of Nos. 1-15 will be cut square, will have small margins, but will show an intact design. Inferior examples with the design partly cut away will sell for much less, and examples with large margins will command higher prices. Very fine examples of Nos. 17-58b will have perforations just cutting into the design on one or more sides due to the narrow spacing of the stamps on the plates and to imperfect perforating methods. Stamps with perfs clear on all four sides are extremely scarce and will command substantially higher prices.

Catalogue values for unused stamps in this country are for Never Hinged items, beginning with Scott 290 in the regular postage section and Scott B1 in the semi-postal section.

Watermarks

Wmk. 1a — 22½mm high, Oval Letters   Wmk. 1b — 21mm high, Round Letters

Wmk. 6 — Large Star

Wmk. 290 — Lotus and "Sri" Multiple

Column 3 (Ceylon)

Queen Victoria

A1   A2

1857   Engr.   Wmk. 6   Imperf.

Blued Paper

1	A1	1p blue	—	260.
2	A1	6p plum	15,000.	525.

1857-59

White Paper

3	A1	1p dp turq	1,000.	42.50
4	A1	2p deep grn	190.00	72.50
a.		2p yellow green	600.00	105.00
5	A2	4p dl rose ('59)	75,000.	5,250.
6	A1	5p org brown	1,750.	175.00
6A	A1	6p plum	2,400.	160.00
7	A1	6p brown	7,750.	550.00
8	A2	8p brown ('59)	30,000.	1,750.
9	A2	9p lil brn ('59)	60,000.	1,050.
10	A1	10p vermilion	950.00	350.00
11	A1	1sh violet	5,500.	240.00
12	A2	1sh9p green ('59)	950.00	950.00
a.		1sh9p yellow green	5,000.	3,500.
13	A2	2sh blue ('59)	6,500.	1,400.

Stamps of type A2 frequently have repaired corners.

Nos. 3-4 exist unofficially rouletted. See the *Scott Classic Specialized Catalogue of Stamps & Covers* for listings.

Beware of Nos. 17-57 trimmed to resemble Nos. 3-13. Values are for stamps with clear margins on all sides.

No. 5 was reproduced by the collotype process in a souvenir sheet distributed at the London International Stamp Exhibition 1950. The paper is unwatermarked.

A3

1857-58   Typo.   Unwmk.

14	A3	½p lilac ('58)	210.	260.
15	A3	½p lilac, bluish	4,200.	600.

No. 14 exists unofficially rouletted.

Nos. 14-15, 38 are printed on surface-glazed paper. Values are for stamps without cracking of the surface, and examples showing cracking should be discounted.

Clean-Cut Perf. 14 to 15½

1861   Wmk. 6   Engr.

17	A1	1p blue	190.00	18.00
18	A1	2p yel grn	240.00	29.00
b.		Vert. pair, imperf between		—
19	A2	4p dull rose	2,400.	350.00
20	A1	5p org brown	110.00	10.00
20A	A1	6p brown	3,000.	140.00
b.		6p bister brown	2,250.	215.00
21	A2	8p brown	2,400.	600.00
22	A2	9p lilac brown	14,000.	275.00
23	A1	1sh violet	130.00	17.50
24	A2	2sh blue	4,000.	775.00

Rough Perf. 14 to 15½

25	A1	1p blue	150.00	11.00
b.		Blued paper	800.00	25.00
26	A1	2p yel green	500.00	95.00
27	A2	4p rose red	540.00	110.00
28	A1	6p olive brown	1,000.	120.00
a.		6p deep brown	1,100.	115.00
b.		6p bister brown	1,800.	160.00
29	A2	8p brown	1,775.	650.00
30	A2	8p yel brown	1,800.	400.00
31	A2	9p olive brown	750.00	80.00
32	A2	9p deep brown	110.00	90.00
33	A1	10p vermilion	300.00	26.00
a.		Imperf. vert., pair		

Column 4 (Ceylon)

34	A1	1sh violet	300.00	17.50
35	A2	1sh9p green	825.00	
36	A2	2sh blue	800.00	160.00

The 1sh9p green was never placed in use.

1863   Perf. 12½

37	A1	10p vermilion	275.00	20.00

1864   Typo.   Unwmk.

38	A3	½p lilac	260.00	210.00

See note following No. 15.

1863   Engr.   Perf. 13

39	A1	1p blue	160.00	7.00
40	A1	5p car brown	1,900.	175.00
41	A1	6p deep brown	210.00	32.50
42	A2	9p brown	1,400.	110.00
43	A1	1sh grayish violet	2,100.	95.00

Parts of the papermaker's sheet watermark, "T. H. SAUNDERS 1862," may be found on some examples of Nos. 39-43.

Perf. 12

44	A1	1p blue	1,700.	150.00
a.		Horiz. pair, imperf. btwn.		16,000.

Two Types of Watermark Crown and CC (1)

1863-67   Typo.   Wmk. 1a   Perf. 12½

45	A3	½p lilac	65.00	45.00
a.		½p reddish lilac	77.50	55.00

Engr.

46	A1	1p blue	150.00	8.00
a.		1p dark blue	150.00	8.00
c.		Perf. 11½	3,500.	375.00
47	A1	2p gray green	90.00	14.00
48	A1	2p emerald	175.00	115.00
48A	A1	2p yel green	10,000.	475.00
48B	A1	2p bottle green		4,000.
49	A1	2p olive	300.00	260.00
50	A2	4p rose	525.00	110.00
a.		4p carmine rose	825.00	200.00
51	A1	5p car brown	240.00	90.00
52	A1	5p olive green	875.00	275.00
e.		5p deep sage green	2,100.	450.00
53	A1	6p choc brown	190.00	7.50
a.		Perf. 13	2,500.	225.00
b.		6p black brown	225.00	12.00
c.		As "b," double impression		4,250.
d.		6p reddish brown	275.00	14.00
54	A2	8p red brown	130.00	60.00
55	A2	9p brown	350.00	52.50
c.		Perf. 13	5,000.	950.00
56	A1	10p vermilion	3,750.	70.00
a.		10p orange	5,500.	500.00
58	A2	2sh blue	325.00	45.00

The ½p, 1p blue, 2p olive, 4p and 5p green exist imperf.

Wmk. 1b

46d	A1	1p blue	225.00	15.00
e.		1p dark blue	200.00	12.00
49d	A1	2p orange yellow	110.00	7.00
e.		2p olive yellow	175.00	24.00
f.		2p olive green	175.00	30.00
50b	A2	4p rose	300.00	65.00
c.		4p carmine rose	125.00	40.00
52b	A1	5p myrtle green	130.00	19.00
c.		5p olive green	130.00	19.00
d.		5p bronze green	47.50	60.00
53e	A1	6p chocolate brown	47.50	42.50
f.		6p brown	110.00	12.00
54a	A2	8p red brown	100.00	72.50
55a	A2	9p dark brown	65.00	7.00
b.		9p bister brown	850.00	37.50
56b	A1	10p orange	120.00	15.00
c.		10p orange red	75.00	18.00
d.		10p vermilion	4,500.	160.00
57	A1	1sh purple	120.00	10.00
a.		1sh reddish lilac	325.00	32.50
58a	A2	2sh deep blue	160.00	15.00
b.		2sh indigo	300.00	22.50

The 1p blue and 6p brown exist imperf. For overprints see Nos. O2, O4-O7.

A4   A5

1866   Typo.   Wmk. 1   Perf. 12½

59	A5	3p rose	275.00	100.00
a.		Imperf., pair	900.00	

For overprint see No. O3.

1868   Perf. 14

61	A4	1p blue	30.00	11.00
62	A5	3p rose	95.00	55.00

For overprint see No. O1.

A6

A7

A8

A9

A10

A11

A12

A13

A14

A15

A16

1872-80   Perf. 14

63	A6	2c brown	26.00	4.00
64	A7	4c gray	47.50	1.75
65	A7	4c lil rose ('80)	72.50	1.75
66	A8	8c orange	47.50	6.50
a.		8c orange yellow	37.50	7.00
67	A9	16c violet	110.00	3.25
68	A10	24c green	72.50	2.40
69	A11	32c slate bl ('77)	175.00	17.50
70	A12	36c blue	190.00	26.00
71	A13	48c rose	95.00	8.50
72	A14	64c red brn ('77)	350.00	85.00
73	A15	96c olive gray	275.00	30.00
		Nos. 63-73 (11)	1,461.	186.65

For surcharges see #83-84, 94A-110, 112-114. For types surcharged see #124-129.

1872   Perf. 12½

74	A6	2c brown	3,500.	225.00
75	A7	4c gray	2,250.	325.00

1879   Perf. 14x12½

77	A6	2c brown	425.00	77.50
78	A7	4c gray	2,000.	35.00
79	A8	8c orange	450.00	57.50

Perf. 12½x14

82	A16	2r50c claret	700.00	375.00

The 32c and 64c are known perf. 14x12½, but were not regularly issued.
No. 82, perf. 12½, was not regularly issued.

See Nos. 142, 158. For surcharges see Nos. 111, 115, 130. For types surcharged see Nos. 160-161.

Nos. 68, 72 Surcharged

SIXTEEN
16
CENTS

1882   Perf. 14

83	A10	16c on 24c green	32.50	8.00
a.		Inverted surcharge		
84	A14	20c on 64c red brn	13.00	8.00
a.		Double surcharge		1,500.

1883-99   Wmk. 2

85	A6	2c pale brown	72.50	3.00
86	A6	2c green ('84)	3.00	.20
a.		Perf. 12	6,000.	
87	A6	2c org brn ('99)	4.00	.40
88	A7	4c lilac rose	4.50	.35
89	A7	4c rose ('84)	7.50	14.00
a.		Perf. 12	6,000.	
90	A7	4c brt rose ('98)	10.00	10.50
91	A7	4c yellow ('99)	3.50	3.25
92	A8	8c orange	6.00	11.00
93	A9	16c violet	2,000.	190.00
94	A10	24c purple brown	1,650.	
b.		Perf. 12	6,500.	

Nos. 86a, 89a, 94 and 94b were never placed in use. A 48c brown, perf. 12, was prepared but not issued.
For surcharges and overprints see Nos. 116-123, 143-151D, 155-156. O8-O9.

Issues of 1872-82 Surcharged:

Postage &
FIVE
CENTS
Revenue

a

CEYLON POSTAGE
TEN
CENTS
SIXTY FOUR CENTS

b

Twenty-
five
Cents

c

CEYLON POSTAGE
One Rupee
Twelve
Cents

d

1885   Wmk. 1   Perf. 14

94A	A9 (a)	5c on 16c		3,500.
95	A10 (a)	5c on 24c	5,000.	130.00
96	A11 (a)	5c on 32c	77.50	20.00
a.		Inverted surcharge		2,250.
97	A12 (a)	5c on 36c	350.00	14.00
a.		Inverted surcharge		3,000.
98	A13 (a)	5c on 48c	2,000.	72.50
99	A14 (a)	5c on 64c	130.00	10.00
a.		Double surcharge		2,500.
100	A15 (a)	5c on 96c	600.00	85.00
101	A9 (b)	10c on 16c	9,000.	3,000.
102	A10 (b)	10c on 24c	540.00	140.00
103	A12 (b)	10c on 36c	450.00	225.00
104	A14 (b)	10c on 64c	500.00	225.00
105	A10 (b)	20c on 24c	72.50	22.50
106	A11 (c)	20c on 32c	90.00	72.50
107	A11 (c)	25c on 32c	21.00	6.00
108	A13 (c)	28c on 48c	47.50	9.00
a.		Double surcharge		2,250.
109	A12 (b)	30c on 36c	19.00	14.00
a.		Inverted surcharge	300.00	130.00
110	A15 (b)	56c on 96c	30.00	25.00

Perf. 12½

111	A16 (d)	1r12c on 2r50c	700.00	120.00

Perf. 14x12½

112	A11 (a)	5c on 32c	900.00	60.00
113	A14 (a)	5c on 64c	950.00	52.50
114	A14 (b)	10c on 64c	82.50	150.00
a.		Vert. pair, imperf. btwn.		4,500.

Perf. 12½x14

115	A16 (d)	1r12c on 2r50c	130.00	52.50

Perf. 14
Wmk. 2

117	A7 (a)	5c on 4c rose	27.50	5.00
a.		Inverted surcharge		350.00
118	A8 (a)	5c on 8c org	95.00	10.00
a.		Inverted surcharge		3,250.
b.		Double surcharge		2,750.
119	A9 (a)	5c on 16c vio	140.00	15.00
a.		Inverted surcharge		260.00
120	A10 (a)	5c on 24c pur brn	—	600.00
121	A9 (b)	10c on 16c vio	10,000.	1,750.
122	A10 (b)	10c on 24c pur brn	17.50	9.00
123	A9 (b)	15c on 16c vio	14.00	10.00

A 5c on 4c lilac rose and a 5c on 24c green are known to exist and are considered to be a forgeries.

Types of 1872-80 Surcharged

REVENUE AND POSTAGE
5 CENTS

e

f

10 CENTS

g

CEYLON POSTAGE
1 R. 12 C.

1885-87

124	A 8 (e)	5c on 8c lilac	25.00	1.75
125	A10 (f)	10c on 24c pur brn	13.00	9.50
126	A 9 (f)	15c on 16c org	72.50	14.00
127	A11 (f)	28c on 32c sl bl	30.00	3.00
128	A12 (f)	30c on 36c ol grn	32.50	16.00
129	A15 (f)	56c on 96c ol gray	60.00	17.50

Wmk. 1 Sideways

130	A16 (g)	1r12c on 2r50c cl	60.00	120.00
		Nos. 124-130 (7)	293.00	181.75

A23

15c
A24

FIVE CENTS

Type I — Thin lines in background. Hair and curl clear.
Type II — Thicker lines in background. Heavier shading under chin.

1886   Wmk. 2

131	A23	5c lilac, type I	3.25	.20
a.		Type II	8.00	.20

For overprint see No. O12.

1886-1900

132	A24	3c org brn & green ('93)	5.00	.50
133	A24	3c green ('00)	4.00	.65
134	A24	6c rose & blk ('99)	2.00	.55
135	A24	12c ol grn & car ('00)	4.75	8.50
136	A24	15c olive green	8.00	2.00
137	A24	15c ultra ('00)	7.00	1.50
138	A24	25c brown	5.25	1.50
a.		25c brown, value in ol yel	140.00	90.00
139	A24	28c slate	26.00	1.60
140	A24	30c vio & org brown ('93)	5.00	1.50
141	A24	75c blk & org brown	8.50	8.50
		Nos. 132-141 (10)	75.50	28.30

Numeral tablet of 3c, 12c and 75c has lined background with colorless value and "c."
For surcharges & overprints see #152-154, 157, 159, O10-O11, O13-O17.

1887   Wmk. 1

142	A16	1r12c claret	32.50	27.50

For overprint see No. O18.

Issue of 1883-84
Surcharged

TWO CENTS

1888-90   Wmk. 2

143	A7	2c on 4c lilac rose	1.60	.95
a.		Inverted surcharge	25.00	24.00
b.		Double surcharge, one invtd.		325.00
144	A7	2c on 4c rose	2.50	.35
a.		Inverted surcharge	18.00	19.00
b.		Double surcharge		350.00

Surcharged

Two CENTS

145	A7	2c on 4c lilac rose	.90	.35
a.		Inverted surcharge	37.50	37.50
b.		Double surcharge	95.00	95.00
c.		Double surcharge, one invtd.	77.50	77.50
146	A7	2c on 4c rose	7.50	.20
a.		Double surcharge, one invtd.	105.00	110.00
b.		Double surcharge	100.00	110.00
c.		Inverted surcharge	375.00	

Surcharged

2 Cents

147	A7	2c on 4c lilac rose	82.50	35.00
a.		Inverted surcharge	150.00	47.50
b.		Double surcharge, one inverted	190.00	
148	A7	2c on 4c rose	3.25	.90
a.		Inverted surcharge	17.50	10.00
b.		Double surcharge, one inverted	9.50	14.00
c.		Double surcharge	190.00	160.00

Surcharged

149 A7	2c on 4c lilac rose	65.00	27.50
a.	Inverted surcharge	190.00	35.00
150 A7	2c on 4c rose	3.00	1.25
a.	Inverted surcharge	17.50	7.00
b.	Double surcharge	140.00	130.00
c.	Double surcharge, one inverted	17.50	9.50

Surcharged

151 A7	2c on 4c rose	13.00	1.20
a.	Inverted surcharge	24.00	6.50
b.	Double surcharge	120.00	120.00
c.	Double surch., one invtd.	26.00	12.00
i.	"S" of "Cents" inverted	475.00	300.00
151D A7	2c on 4c lilac rose	65.00	35.00
e.	Inverted surcharge	95.00	47.50
f.	Double surcharge		375.00
g.	Double surch., one invtd.	120.00	120.00
h.	"S" of "Cents" inverted		600.00

Counterfeit errors of surcharges of Nos. 143 to 151D are prevalent.

No. 136 Surcharged

POSTAGE / Five Cents / REVENUE

1890

152 A24	5c on 15c ol green	3.75	2.50
a.	"Five" instead of "Five"	140.00	100.00
b.	"REVENUE" omitted	200.00	190.00
c.	Inverted surcharge	60.00	65.00
d.	Double surcharge	120.00	140.00
e.	As "a," inverted surcharge	—	1,600.
f.	Inverted "s" in "Cents"	95.00	100.00
g.	As "f," inverted surcharge	2,000.	
h.	As "b," invtd. "s" in "Cents"		1,500.

Nos. 138-139 Surcharged

FIFTEEN CENTS

1891

153 A24	15c on 25c brown	17.00	16.00
154 A24	15c on 28c slate	19.00	10.00

Nos. 88, 89 and 139 Surcharged

3 Cents

1892

155 A7	3c on 4c lilac rose	1.20	3.75
156 A7	3c on 4c rose	6.50	10.00
a.	Double surcharge, one invtd.		
157 A24	3c on 28c slate	5.50	5.00
a.	Double surcharge	175.00	
	Nos. 155-157 (3)	13.20	18.75

Type of 1879

1898

158 A16	2r50c violet, *red*	35.00	62.50

No. 136 Surcharged in Black

Six Cents

1899

159 A24	6c on 15c olive green	1.25	.85

Surcharged Type "g" in Black

1899   **Wmk. 1**

160 A16	1r50c on 2r50c gray	24.00	52.50
161 A16	2r25c on 2r50c yel	42.50	95.00

A35

1900   **Wmk. 1**

162 A35	1r50c car rose	29.00	47.50
163 A35	2r25c dull blue	42.50	47.50

King Edward VII

A36   A37

A38   A39

A40

1903-05   **Wmk. 2**

166 A36	2c org brown	2.40	.20
167 A37	3c green	2.40	1.20
168 A37	4c yel & blue	2.40	4.50
169 A38	5c dull lilac	1.75	.70
170 A39	6c car rose	11.00	1.75
171 A37	12c ol grn & car	6.00	13.00
172 A40	15c ultra	7.75	3.50
173 A40	25c bister	4.75	9.50
174 A40	30c vio & green	3.75	4.75
175 A37	75c bl & org ('05)	3.50	24.00
176 A40	1r50c gray ('04)	75.00	62.50
177 A40	2r25c brn & grn ('04)	85.00	60.00
	Nos. 166-177 (12)	205.70	185.60
	Set, never hinged	400.00	

For overprints see Nos. O19-O24.

1904-10   **Wmk. 3**

178 A36	2c orange brown	1.75	.20
a.	2c orange	1.75	.60
179 A37	3c green	1.75	.20
180 A37	4c yel & blue	2.75	1.75
181 A38	5c dull lilac	3.00	1.50
a.	Booklet pane of 12		
182 A39	6c car rose	3.50	.20
183 A40	10c org grn & vio ('10)	3.00	3.00
184 A37	12c ol grn & car	1.75	2.00
185 A40	15c ultra	3.25	.70
186 A40	25c bister ('05)	7.25	4.50
187 A40	25c slate ('10)	3.00	2.50
188 A40	30c vio & grn ('05)	3.00	3.50
189 A40	50c brown ('10)	4.75	9.00
190 A37	75c bl & org ('05)	6.25	9.50
191 A40	1r vio, *yel* ('10)	9.00	12.00
192 A40	1r50c gray ('05)	32.50	12.00
193 A40	2r scar, *yel* ('10)	17.50	32.50
194 A40	2r25c brn & grn	26.00	35.00
195 A40	5r blk, *grn* ('10)	45.00	85.00
196 A40	10r blk, *red* ('10)	105.00	210.00
	Nos. 178-196 (19)	280.00	425.05
	Set, never hinged	600.00	

No. 181 exists on ordinary and chalky paper.

A41   A42

1908

197 A41	5c deep red violet	4.50	.20
a.	Booklet pane of 12		
198 A42	6c carmine rose	1.75	.20

1911, July 5

199 A40	3c green	1.10	.85

A44   King George V — A45

3 AND 6 CENTS

Type I — Small "c" after value, 2¼mm wide and 2mm high.
Type II — Large "c" after value, 2½mm wide and 2¼mm high.
1, 5 AND 9 CENTS are Type II, other denominations Type I.

Die I

For description of dies I and II see "Dies of British Colonial Stamps" in the Table of Contents.

1912-25   **Wmk. 3**

200 A44	1c dp brn (Die Ib) ('20)	1.20	.20
201 A44	2c brown org	.40	.20
202 A44	3c dp grn (Die Ia, type II)	4.50	.50
a.	3c deep green, die I, type I	6.50	2.25
203 A44	5c red violet	1.20	.70
204 A44	6c car (Die Ib, type II)	1.50	1.00
a.	6c carmine, die I, type I	18.00	1.25
b.	As "a," bklt. pane of 6		
205 A44	10c olive green	3.50	2.00
206 A44	15c ultra	2.10	1.50

Chalky Paper

207 A44	25c yel & ultra	2.10	2.10
208 A44	30c green & vio	4.75	3.75
209 A44	50c black & scar	1.75	2.10
210 A44	1r violet, *yel*	5.00	4.25
211 A44	2r blk & red, *yel*	3.75	15.00
212 A44	5r blk, *green*	20.00	35.00
a.	5r black, *bl grn,* olive back	22.50	45.00
b.	5r blk, *emer* (Die II) ('20)	52.50	120.00
213 A44	10r vio & blk, *red*	85.00	105.00
a.	Die II ('20)	95.00	165.00
214 A44	20r blk & red, *bl*	165.00	175.00
215 A45	50r dull violet	500.00	
216 A45	100r gray black	2,750.	
217 A45	500r gray green	7,250.	
218 A45	1000r vio, *red* ('25)	26,000.	
	Nos. 200-214 (15)	301.75	348.30
	Set, never hinged	600.00	

Although Nos. 217 and 218 were theoretically available for postage it is not probable that they were ever used for other than fiscal purposes.

The 1r through 100r with revenue cancellations sell for minimal prices.

For surcharge & overprints see #223, MR1-MR3.

Die I
Surface-colored Paper

1913-14

220 A44	1r violet, *yellow*	5.00	5.75
221 A44	2r black & red, *yel*	3.25	15.00
222 A44	5r black, *green*	26.00	37.50
	Nos. 220-222 (3)	34.25	58.25

No. 203 Surcharged

ONE CENT

1918

223 A44	1c on 5c red violet	.20	.30

For overprint see No. MR4.

Die I

1921-33   **Wmk. 4**
Ordinary Paper

225 A44	1c dp brn (Die Ib) ('27)	1.20	.40
226 A44	2c brn org (Die II)	.85	.30
227 A44	3c green (Die Ia, type II)	4.25	.90
228 A44	3c slate (Die Ia, type II) ('22)	.90	.20
229 A44	5c red vio (Die I)	.70	.20

---

230 A44	6c carmine (Die Ib, type II)	2.60	.90
231 A44	6c vio (Die Ib, type II) ('22)	2.00	.20
232 A44	9c red, *yel* (Die II) ('26)	2.00	.35
233 A44	10c olive green	1.60	.45
a.	Die II	2.10	.70
234 A44	12c scarlet, Die II	1.20	7.50
a.	Die II ('25)	6.00	12.50
235 A44	15c ultramarine	3.75	15.00
236 A44	15c green, *yel,* Die II	4.00	1.20
237 A44	20c ultra, Die II ('24)	4.25	.50
a.	Die I ('22)	4.75	7.25
238 A44	25c yel & blue	2.40	2.25
a.	Die I	4.50	1.50

For surcharges see Nos. 248-249.

Chalky Paper

239 A44	30c green & violet (Die II)	1.90	4.25
a.	Die II	5.00	1.50
240 A44	50c blk & scar (Die II)	1.90	.95
a.	Die I	65.00	90.00
241 A44	1r vio, *yel,* Die II	22.50	32.50
a.	Die I	15.00	35.00
242 A44	2r blk & red, *yel* (Die I)	8.50	10.00
243 A44	5r blk, *emer,* (Die II)	45.00	75.00
244 A44	20r blk & red, *bl,* (Die II)	225.00	300.00
245 A45	50r dull vio	600.00	1,050.
246 A45	100r gray black	2,750.	
247 A45	100r ultra & dl vio ('27)	2,500.	
	Nos. 225-244 (20)	336.50	453.05
	Set, never hinged	625.00	

Nos. 228, 231 Surcharged

2 Cents.

1926

248 A44	2c on 3c slate	1.75	1.20
a.	Double surcharge	85.00	
b.	Bar omitted	90.00	100.00
249 A44	5c on 6c violet	.60	.45
a.	Double surcharge		

A46

1927-29   **Chalky Paper**   **Wmk. 4**

254 A46	1r red vio & dl vio ('28)	3.00	1.50
255 A46	2r car & green ('29)	4.50	3.25
256 A46	5r brn vio & grn ('28)	16.00	24.00
257 A46	10r org & green	47.50	100.00
258 A46	20r ultra & dl vio	160.00	300.00
	Nos. 254-258 (5)	231.00	428.75
	Set, never hinged	450.00	

Common Design Types pictured following the introduction.

Silver Jubilee Issue
Common Design Type

1935, May 6   **Engr.**   **Perf. 13½x14**

260 CD301	6c gray blk & ultra	.75	.35
261 CD301	9c indigo & green	.80	2.75
262 CD301	20c blue & brown	5.00	3.25
263 CD301	50c brt vio & ind	6.00	8.00
	Nos. 260-263 (4)	12.55	14.35
	Set, never hinged	22.50	

Tapping Rubber Tree — A47   Colombo Harbor — A49

Adam's
Peak — A48

Picking
Tea — A50

Coconut
Palms — A53

Rice
Terraces
A51

River Scene
A52

Temple of
the Tooth,
Kandy
A54

Ancient
Reservoir
A55

Wild
Elephants
A56

View of
Trincomalee
A57

**Perf. 11x11½, 11½x11; 11½x13,
13x11½ (A47, A48, A53); 14 (A56)**

1935-36			**Wmk. 4**
264 A47	2c car rose & blk	.45	.55
a.	Perf. 14	12.00	.55
265 A48	3c olive & black	.50	.55
a.	Perf. 14	35.00	3.00
266 A49	6c blue & black	.45	.40
267 A50	9c org red & ol grn	1.50	.90
268 A51	10c dk vio & blk	1.75	3.00
269 A52	15c grn & org brn	1.50	.70
270 A53	20c ultra & black	2.25	3.50
271 A54	25c choc & dk ultra	2.00	1.75
272 A55	30c green & lake	3.00	3.50
273 A56	50c dk vio & blk	14.00	2.50
274 A57	1r brown & vio	30.00	21.00
	Nos. 264-274 (11)	57.40	38.35
	Set, never hinged	97.50	

Issued: 2c, 15c, 25c, 5/1/35; 10c, 6/1/35; 1r, 7/1/35; 30c, 8/1/35; 3c, 10/1/35; 6c, 9c, 20c, 50c, 1/1/36.

Coronation Issue
Common Design Type

1937, May 12		**Perf. 11x11½**	
275 CD302	6c dark carmine	.75	.20
a.	Booklet pane of 10		

276 CD302	9c deep green	3.00	6.00
a.	Booklet pane of 10	300.00	
277 CD302	20c deep ultra	4.25	8.25
	Nos. 275-277 (3)	8.00	14.45
	Set, never hinged	16.00	

**Types of 1935 with
"Postage & Revenue Removed"
and Picturing George VI and:**

Ancient Guard
Stone — A68

George
VI — A69

Sigiriya (Lion
Rock) — A61

Perf. 11x11½, 11½x11; 12 (#286)

1938-52	**Engr.**		**Wmk. 4**
278 A47	2c car rose & blk ('44)	.45	1.00
a.	Perf. 13½x13 ('38)	100.00	2.00
b.	Perf. 13½ ('38)	2.00	.20
c.	Perf. 12 ('49)	1.25	4.00
d.	Perf. 11½x13 ('38)	9.00	2.25
279 A48	3c dk grn & blk ('42)	.50	.20
a.	Perf. 13x13½ ('38)	225.00	12.00
b.	Perf. 14 ('41)	100.00	1.10
c.	Perf. 13½ ('38)	3.50	.20
d.	Perf. 12 ('46)	.70	.95
e.	Perf. 13x11½	8.00	2.00
280 A49	6c blue & black	.20	.20
281 A61	10c blue & black	1.60	.20
282 A52	15c red brn & grn	1.25	.20
283 A50	20c dull bl & blk	2.25	.20
284 A54	25c choc & dk ultra	3.25	.30
285 A55	30c dk grn & rose car	8.00	3.25
286 A56	50c dk vio & blk ('46)	2.75	.20
a.	Perf. 14 ('42)	90.00	29.00
b.	Perf. 13x11½ ('38)	140.00	47.50
c.	Perf. 13x13½ ('38)	300.00	3.00
d.	Perf. 13½ ('38)	15.00	.35
e.	Perf. 11½x11 ('42)	4.00	4.00
287 A57	1r dk brn & bl vio	10.50	1.50
288 A68	2r dark car & blk	9.25	3.50

**Perf. 14
Typo.**

289 A69	5r brn vio & grn	27.50	11.00
289A A69	10r yel org & dl grn ('52)	90.00	45.00
	Nos. 278-289A (13)	157.50	66.75
	Set, never hinged	300.00	

No. 289A differs from type A69 in having "REVENUE" inscribed vertically at either side of the frame. This revenue 10r was valid for postage Dec. 1, 1952-Mar. 14, 1954.
See #292, 295. For surcharges see #290-291.

Catalogue values for unused stamps in this section, from this point to the end of the section, are for Never Hinged items.

No. 283 Surcharged
in Black

1940, Nov. 5		**Perf. 11x11½**	
290 A50	3c on 20c dull bl & blk	4.00	2.50

No. 280 Surcharged with New Value and Bars

1941, May 10			
291 A49	3c on 6c blue & black	.65	.25

Coconut
Palms — A70

1943-47 Wmk. 4 Engr. Perf. 12			
292 A70	5c red org & ol grn ('47)	2.00	.35
a.	Perf. 13½ ('43)	.35	.20

Peace Issue
Common Design Type

1946, Dec. 10		**Perf. 13½x14**	
293 CD303	6c deep blue	.30	.35
294 CD303	15c brown	.30	1.75

Guard Stone Type of 1938

1947, Mar. 15		**Perf. 11x11½**	
295 A68	2r violet & black	2.40	2.75

Parliament Building, Colombo — A71

Adam's Peak
A72

Dagoba at
Anuradhapura
A74

Temple of
the Tooth,
Kandy
A73

1947, Nov. 25		**Perf. 11x12, 12x11**	
296 A71	6c deep ultra & black	.20	.20
297 A72	10c car, orange & black	.25	.40
298 A73	15c red vio & grnsh blk	.25	.80
299 A74	25c brt green & bister	.25	1.75
	Nos. 296-299 (4)	.95	3.15

New constitution of 1947.

National Flag
A75

D. S.
Senanayake
A76

**Engr., Flag Typo. (A75); Engr. (A76)
Perf. 12½x12, 12x12½, 13x12½**

1949			**Wmk. 4**
300 A75	4c org brn, car & yel	.20	.20
301 A76	5c dark green & brn	.20	.20
			Wmk. 290
302 A75	15c red org, car & yel	1.00	.40
303 A76	25c dp blue & brown	.20	1.00
	Nos. 300-303 (4)	1.60	1.80

Size of No. 302: 28x22¼mm.
1st anniv. of Ceylon's independence.
Issued: #300-301, Feb. 4; #302-303, Apr. 5.

A77

A78

Design: 15c, Lion Rock and UPU symbols.

Wmk. 290

1949, Oct. 10	**Engr.**		**Perf. 12**
304 A77	5c dk green & brown	.85	.20
305 A77	15c dark car & black	1.25	2.75
306 A78	25c ultra & black	1.25	1.25
	Nos. 304-306 (3)	3.35	4.20

75th anniv. of the UPU.

Kandyan
Dancer
A79

Kiri Vehera,
Polonnaruwa
A80

Vesak
Orchid — A81

Sigiriya — A82

Ratmalana,
Plane — A83

Vatadage
Ruins at
Madirigiriya
A84

1950, Feb. 4		**Perf. 12x12½**	
307 A79	4c bright red & choc	.20	.20
308 A80	5c green	.20	.20
309 A81	15c pur & blue green	2.75	.50
310 A82	30c carmine & yel	.40	.70

Perf. 11x11½, 11½x11

311 A83	75c red org & blue	8.50	.20
312 A84	1r red brn & dp blue	2.50	.45
	Nos. 307-312 (6)	14.55	2.25

See Nos. 340-345.

Coconut
Palms — A85

Star
Orchid — A86

1951-52 Unwmk. Photo. *Perf. 11½*
313 A85 10c gray & dark green   1.25 .75
314 A86 35c dk grn & rose brn
          ('52)   1.90 1.75
  a. Corrected inscription ('54)   7.00 .70

On No. 314a a dot has been added above the third character in the second line of the Tamil inscription.
  Issue dates: 10c, Aug. 1; 35c, Feb. 1.
  See No. 351.

Mace and Symbols of Industry
A87

Perf. 12½x14
1952, Feb. 23   Wmk. 290
315 A87 5c green   .20 .30
316 A87 15c brt ultramarine   .40 .60

Colombo Plan Exhibition, February 1952.

Coronation Issue

Queen
Elizabeth II — A88

1953, June 2 Engr. *Perf. 12x12½*
317 A88 5c green   1.25 .20

Royal Procession
A89

1954, Apr. 10   *Perf. 13x12½*
318 A89 10c deep blue   .75 .20

Visit of Queen Elizabeth II and the Duke of Edinburgh, 1954.

Sambar in Ruhuna National Park — A90

Rubber Trees — A91

Designs: 3c, Ancient guard stone. 6c and 10r, Harvesting rice. 25c, Sigiriya fresco. 50c, Outrigger fishing canoe. 85c, Tea Picker. 2r, Gal Oya dam. 5r, Bas-relief, "The Lovers."

1954 Unwmk. Photo. *Perf. 11½*
Size: 21x25½mm
319 A90 2c green & brown   .20 1.25
320 A90 3c violet & black   .20 1.00
321 A90 6c yel grn & blk brn   .20 .30
322 A90 25c vio bl, bl & brn
          orange   .20 .20
Size: 25½x21mm
323 A91 40c black brown   5.50 1.25
324 A91 50c indigo   .45 .20
Size: 23x32½mm, 32½x23mm
325 A90 85c dk grn & gray   1.50 .40
326 A91 2r blk & blk brn   9.25 1.40
327 A90 5r dp org & blk brn   8.00 1.50
328 A90 10r brown   60.00 20.00
      Nos. 319-328 (10)   85.50 27.50

      See Nos. 346-356.
  Issued: 25c, 50c, 5r, 10r, 3/15; others, 5/15.
  Nos. 327-328 with revenue cancellations sell for minimal prices.

King Coconuts — A92

Symbols of Agriculture
A93

1954, Dec. 1
329 A92 10c brown & orange   .30 .20
      See No. 349.

Perf. 14x14½
1955, Dec. 10   Wmk. 290
330 A93 10c orange & brown   .30 .20

Royal Agricultural and Food Exhibition.

House of Representatives — A94

1956, Mar. 26 Unwmk. *Perf. 11½*
Granite Paper
331 A94 10c deep green   .20 .20

  25th anniv. of Prime Minister Sir John Kotelawala's entry into the Ceylon Legislature.

Arrival of Vijaya in Ceylon — A95

Dharmachakra Encircling Globe — A96

1956, May 23   Granite Paper
332 A95 3c dull vio gray & saph   .20 .20
333 A96 15c ultramarine   .80 .20

Birth of Buddha, 2500th anniv. See #B1-B2.

Methods of Transportation — A97

  35c, 85c, Ceylon's 1st stamp & coat of arms.

1957, Apr. 1 Photo. *Perf. 12½x13*
334 A97 4c blue green & ver   .80 .50
335 A97 10c blue & vermilion   .80 .20

Perf. 11½
Granite Paper
336 A97 35c blue, yel & brown   .40 .55
337 A97 85c dull grn, yel & brn   .85 1.60
      Nos. 334-337 (4)   2.85 2.85

  Ceylon's 1st postage stamps, cent.

Nos. B1-B2 Overprinted with Black Bars and Squares
1958, Jan. 15   Unwmk.
Granite Paper
338 SP1 4c dp blue & lt yel   .20 .20
  a. Inverted overprint   15.00 22.50
  b. Double overprint   22.50 29.00
339 SP1 10c dk gray, yel & brt
          pink   .20 .20
  a. Inverted overprint   15.00 17.00

  The overprint obliterates the surtax and inscription at right.

Types of 1950-54 Redrawn
Perf. 12x12½
1958-59   Engr.   Wmk. 290
340 A79 4c brt red & choco-
          late   .20 .20
341 A80 5c green   .20 1.60
342 A81 15c purple & blue grn   4.50 1.10
343 A82 30c car & yel ('59)   .20 1.50
Perf. 11½x11
344 A83 75c red org & bl   11.50 3.25
Perf. 11x11½
345 A84 1r red brn & dp blue   .85 .20
      Nos. 340-345 (6)   17.45 7.85
  Issued: 4c, 5/14; 5c, 15c, 1r, 10/1; 30c, 75c, 5/1.
  For surcharge see No. 368.

1958-59 Unwmk. Photo. *Perf. 11½*
Granite Paper
346 A90 2c green & brown   .20 .50
347 A90 3c violet & black   .20 .70
348 A90 6c yel grn & blk brn   .20 .65
349 A92 10c brown & orange   .20 .20
350 A90 25c vio bl, bl & brn
          orange   .20 .20
351 A86 35c dk grn & rose brn   7.75 .40
352 A91 50c indigo   .25 .40
353 A90 85c dark green &
          gray   4.50 8.50
354 A91 2r blue & blk brn   2.00 .30
355 A90 5r dp org & blk brn   10.00 .40
356 A90 10r brown   12.00 1.40
      Nos. 346-356 (11)   37.50 13.45

  Designs and sizes of Nos. 340-356 remain as before, but wording has been changed to be predominantly Singhalese. "Ceylon" appears in small letters only in English and Tamil.
  Nos. 355-356 with revenue cancellations sell for minimal prices.
  Issue dates: 35c, 50c, July 15; 10c, Oct. 1; 85c, May 1, 1959; others, May 14, 1958.
  For surcharges, see Sri Lanka Nos. 1572, 1577.

Hands Reaching for UN Symbol
A98

Perf. 13x12½
1958, Dec. 10 Photo.   Unwmk.
357 A98 10c red brown & red   .20 .20
358 A98 85c Prus green & red   .55 .55

  10th anniv. of the signing of the Universal Declaration of Human Rights.

Pirivena Universities and Founders
A99

1959, Dec. 31
359 A99 10c brt ultra & dp org   .30 .30

  Institution of Pirivena Universities; founders Hikkaduwe Sri Sumangala Nayaka Thero and Ratmalane Sri Dharmaloka Nayake Thero.

Uprooted Oak Emblem
A100

Prime Minister Bandaranaike
A101

1960, Apr. 7 Photo. *Perf. 11½*
Granite Paper
360 A100 4c chocolate & gold   .20 .85
361 A100 25c vio blue & gold   .20 .20

  World Refugee Year, 7/1/59-6/30/60.

1961, Jan. 8   Granite Paper
  Two types:
  I — Gray hair at temple.
  II — Dark hair at temple (redrawn).

362 A101 10c vio bl & gray bl (I)   .40 .60
  a. Type II   .90 .20

  Solomon West Ridgeway Dias Bandaranaike, assassinated Sept. 26, 1959.

Badge of Singhalese Scouts — A102

Malaria Eradication Emblem — A103

1962, Feb. 26 Unwmk. *Perf. 11½*
Granite Paper
363 A102 35c dark blue & ocher   .35 .20

  Boy Scouts of Ceylon, 50th anniv.

Perf. 14½x14
1962, Apr. 7 Photo.   Wmk. 290
364 A103 25c lt sep, red org &
           brn   .40 .40

  WHO drive to eradicate malaria.

Monoplane 1938, and De Havilland Comet IV — A104

1963, Feb. 28 Unwmk. *Perf. 11½*
Granite Paper
365 A104 50c lt grnsh blue & blk   .60 .60

  25th anniv. of Ceylonese airmail service.

Stylized Vase and Wheat Emblem
A105

1963, Mar. 21
Granite Paper
366 A105 5c blue & orange ver   .75 2.50
367 A105 25c olive & brown   3.00 .50

  FAO "Freedom from Hunger" campaign.

No. 340 Surcharged

Perf. 12x12½
1963, June 1   Engr.   Wmk. 290
368 A79 2c on 4c brt red & choc   .40   .40
a.   Inverted surcharge   20.00
b.   Double surcharge   40.00

Rural Life — A106

1963, July 5   Photo.   Perf. 14x14½
369 A106 60c dull red & black   2.00   .75
50th anniv. of the Cooperative Movement.

Landscape and Elephant A107

1963, Dec. 2   Wmk. 290
370 A107 5c blue & black   .80   .45
National Conservation Week.

S.W.R.D. Bandaranaike A108

Anagarika Dharmapala A109

Perf. 11½
1963, Sept. 26   Unwmk.   Engr.
Granite Paper
371 A108 10c blue   .30   .30

Redrawn
1964, July 1   Photo.
Granite Paper
372 A108 10c grnsh gray & bl vio   .30   .30
Frame redrawn on No. 372; inscription in bottom panel replaced by ornament.
For surcharge see No. 389.

1964, Sept. 16   Unwmk.   Perf. 11½
Granite Paper
373 A109 25c gray brn & dull yel   .30   .30
Anagarika Dharmapala, Buddhist missionary, birth cent.

Ceylon Jungle Fowl — A110

Vatadage Ruins at Madirigiriya A111

Tea Picker — A112

Designs: 5c, Hill myna. 15c, Blue peafowl. 75c, Asiatic black-headed oriole. 5r, Girls, working in rice field. 10r, Map of Ceylon on

scroll, showing agricultural development stations.

Wmk. 290, Unwmkd. (20c)
1964-69   Photo.   Perf. 14, 11½ (20c)
374 A110 5c brt bl, blk, yel & grn   2.00   1.40
375 A110 15c yel, grn, blk, brt bl & rose   3.75   .30
376 A111 20c dk red brn, *buff*   .20   .25
377 A110 60c yel & multi   4.25   1.10
a.   Blue omitted   50.00
b.   Red omitted   50.00
378 A110 75c ol, blk, org & brn   3.00   .75
a.   Souvenir sheet of 4   10.00   14.00
b.   As "a," overprinted   10.00
379 A112 1r brown & grn   1.00   .25
c.   Brown omitted   750.00
379A A111 5r multicolored   7.50   7.50
379B A112 10r brown & multi   22.50   3.50
Nos. 374-379B (8)   44.20   15.05

No. 378a contains four imperf. stamps with simulated perforations similar to Nos. 374-375 and 377-378.
No. 378b is overprinted "First National Stamp Exhibition 1967" in two lines of black capitals.
No. 376 is on granite paper.
Issued: 20c, 1r, 10/1; 5c, 15c, 60c, 75c, 2/5/66; 5r, 8/15/69; 10r, 10/1/69.
See No. 325.

Exhibition Buildings, Cogwheels — A113

1964, Dec. 1   Unwmk.   Perf. 11
"Industrial Exhibition" in Singhalese and English
380 A113 5c multicolored   .20   .75
"Industrial Exhibition" in Singhalese and Tamil
381 A113 5c multicolored   .20   .75
a.   Pair, #380-381   .35   2.50
1965 Industrial Exhibition.

Railroad Trains, 1864-1964 A114

Wmk. 290
1964, Dec. 21   Photo.   Perf. 14
"Railway Centenary" in Singhalese and English
382 A114 60c lil rose, bl & yel grn   3.25   .55
"Railway Centenary" in Singhalese and Tamil
383 A114 60c lil rose, bl & yel grn   3.25   .55
a.   Vertical pair, #382-383   7.75   7.75
Centenary of Ceylonese railroads.

ITU Emblem, Old and New Communication Equipment — A115

1965, May 17   Perf. 14
384 A115 2c ultra & red   1.75   1.40
385 A115 30c brown & red   4.75   .55
ITU, centenary.

ICY Emblem A116

1965, June 26   Unwmk.   Perf. 11½
Granite Paper
386 A116 3c rose car & dk bl   1.50   1.25
387 A116 50c gold, rose car & blk   4.00   .60
International Cooperation Year.

Municipal Council Building A117

1965, Oct. 29   Photo.   Perf. 11½
Granite Paper
388 A117 25c gray & green   .30   .30
Centenary of Colombo Municipal Council.

No. 372 Surcharged

1965, Dec. 18   Photo.   Perf. 11½
389 A108 5c on 10c   .30   1.25

D. S. Senanayake — A118

View and Arms of Kandy — A119

1966, Mar. 22   Unwmk.   Perf. 11½
Granite Paper
390 A118 10c bright green   .85   .20
D. S. Senanayake, first prime minister of Ceylon, 14th death anniv. See No. 418.

Perf. 14x13½
1966, June 15   Photo.   Wmk. 290
391 A119 25c multicolored   .30   .30
Centenary of Kandy Municipal Council.

Opening of WHO Headquarters, Geneva A120

Unwmk.
1966, Oct. 8   Litho.   Perf. 14
392 A120 4c multicolored   2.50   3.00
393 A120 1r multicolored   8.00   1.60

Rice, Map of Ceylon, FAO Emblem — A121

UNESCO Emblem A122

Design: 30c, Rice and globe.

1966, Oct. 25   Photo.   Perf. 11½
Granite Paper
394 A121 6c dk green, org & brn   .20   .75
395 A121 30c brt blue, org & brn   .50   .20
Intl. Rice Year under sponsorship of the FAO.

1966, Nov. 3   Litho.   Perf. 12
396 A122 3c tan & multi   4.00   4.00
397 A122 50c brt green & multi   7.75   1.00
20th anniv. of UNESCO.
For surcharge, see Sri Lanka No. 1578.

Map of Ceylon and UNESCO Emblem — A123

Worshippers at Buddhist Shrine A124

1966, Dec. 1   Unwmk.   Perf. 14
398 A123 2c yel brn, yel & blue   .45   1.00
399 A123 2r multicolored   1.75   2.25
Intl. Hydrological Decade (UNESCO), 1965-74.

1967, Jan. 2   Photo.   Perf. 12
Designs: 20c, Muhintale Rock. 35c, Sacred Bo Tree. 60c, Adam's Peak.
400 A124 5c multicolored   .20   .60
401 A124 20c multicolored   .20   .20
402 A124 35c multicolored   .20   .20
403 A124 60c multicolored   .20   .20
Nos. 400-403 (4)   .80   1.20
1st anniv. of the Poya Holiday System, Buddhist holiday replacing Sunday.
For surcharge, see Sri Lanka No. 1573.

Dutch Ramparts, Clock Tower and Arms of Galle A125

1967, Jan. 5   Litho.   Perf. 14x13½
404 A125 25c dk green & multi   .80   .20
Centenary of Galle Municipal Council.

Tea Research A126

40c, Tea tasting (cup & loose tea). 50c, Tea picking. 1r, Tea export (crate & freighter).

1967, Aug. 1   Unwmk.   Perf. 13½
405 A126 4c multicolored   .70   .70
406 A126 40c multicolored   2.10   1.60
407 A126 50c multicolored   2.10   .40
408 A126 1r multicolored   2.10   .20
Nos. 405-408 (4)   7.00   2.90
Centenary of the Ceylonese tea industry.

Elephant and ITY Emblem A127

1967, Aug. 15 **Litho.**
409 A127 45c multicolored 3.00 .85
Intl. Tourist Year.

Girl Guide, Jubilee Emblem and Flag — A128

1967, Sept. 19 **Perf. 12x12½**
410 A128 3c green & multi .60 .20
411 A128 25c org yel & multi .90 .20
Ceylon Girl Guide Assoc., 50th anniv.

Henry S. Olcott and Buddhist Flag A129

Perf. 13½
1967, Dec. 12 **Unwmk.** **Litho.**
412 A129 15c multicolored .40 .20
Colonel Henry S. Olcott (1832-1907), an American who reorganized the Buddhist hierarchy and school system in Ceylon and was the first president of the Theosophical Society.

Independence Memorial, Colombo A130

Design: 1r, Flag of Ceylon and mace.

1968, Feb. 4 **Wmk. 290** **Perf. 14**
413 A130 5c multicolored .20 .55
414 A130 1r multicolored .60 .20
20th anniversary of independence.

D. B. Jayatilaka — A131

1968, Feb. 14 **Photo.**
415 A131 25c brown .30 .30
Sir Don Baron Jayatilaka (1868-1944), Buddhist leader and scholar.

Hygiene Institute, Kalutara A132

Perf. 11½x12
1968, Apr. 4 **Litho.** **Wmk. 290**
416 A132 50c multicolored .30 .30
WHO, 20th anniversary.

Jet over Colombo Terminal A133

1968, Aug. 5 **Perf. 13½**
417 A133 60c org brn, dk bl & org 1.00 .20
Opening of Colombo Airport.

D. S. Senanayake — A134

1968, Sept. 23 **Photo.** **Perf. 14**
418 A134 10c deep green .20 .20
See No. 390.

Open Koran A135

1968, Oct. 14 **Photo.** **Perf. 14**
419 A135 25c org brn, blk, blue & emerald .30 .30
1,400th anniversary of the Koran.

Human Rights Flame A136

Perf. 12½x13½
1968, Dec. 10 **Unwmk.**
420 A136 2c multicolored .20 .30
421 A136 20c multicolored .20 .20
422 A136 40c multicolored .20 .20
423 A136 2r multicolored .90 4.00
Nos. 420-423 (4) 1.50 4.70
International Human Rights Year.

Ceylon Buddhist Headquarters, Colombo — A137

1968, Dec. 19 **Litho.** **Perf. 13½**
424 A137 5c multicolored .40 .60
All-Ceylon Buddhist Cong., 50th anniv.
A multicolored 50c showing the Sri Padmaya (Sacred Footprint) on Adam's Peak was prepared but the issuance order was countermanded on Dec. 18. Some were sold in ignorance of the withdrawal order. Value $65.

E. W. Perera — A138

"Strength in Saving" — A139

1969, Feb. 17 **Photo.** **Perf. 14**
425 A138 60c brown .30 .50
E. W. Perera, member of Legislative Council.

1969, Mar. 20
426 A139 3c blue, yel & black .30 .40
National Savings Movement, 25th anniv.

A140 A141

4c, Seat of Enlightenment under Bodhi Tree. 6c, Buduresmala (disk symbolic of six-fold Buddha rays).

Wmk. 290
1969, Apr. 10 **Litho.** **Perf. 15**
427 A140 4c orange & multi .20 .50
428 A140 6c gold & multi .20 .50
429 A140 35c scarlet & multi .20 .20
Nos. 427-429 (3) .60 1.20
Vesak Day, which commemorates the birth, enlightenment and death of Buddha. For surcharges see Nos. 463, 466.

1969, Apr. 29 **Photo.** **Perf. 14x14½**
430 A141 15c org yel & multi .30 .30
Alexander Ekanayake Goonesingha (1891-1967), trade unionist, political leader and diplomat.

ILO, 50th Anniv. A142

1969, May 4 **Perf. 14½x14**
431 A142 5c grnsh bl & black .20 .20
432 A142 25c car rose & black .20 .20

Convocation Hall, University of Ceylon A143

Elephant Lamp (Ath Pana) — A144

35c, "Lamp of Education," globe & flags. 50c, Uranium atom diagram. 60c, Symbols of science education. 1r, Aerial view of Sigiriya rock fortress.

Unwmk.
1969, Aug. 1 **Litho.** **Perf. 14**
Inscribed: "SIYAWASA"
433 A143 4c yellow & multi .20 .80
434 A144 6c multicolored .40 1.50
435 A143 35c multicolored .20 .20
436 A144 50c red & multi .20 .20
437 A143 60c blue & multi .30 .20
438 A144 1r yel & multi .40 .20
Nos. 433-438 (6) 1.70 3.10
Centenary of public education and archaeological research.
For surcharges see Nos. 464-467.

Wild Water Buffalo A145

15c, Slender loris. 50c, Axis deer. 1r, Leopard.

Perf. 14x13½
1970, May 11 **Litho.** **Unwmk.**
439 A145 5c lt blue & multi 1.25 1.40
440 A145 15c buff & multi 2.00 1.00
441 A145 50c salmon & multi 1.50 1.40
442 A145 1r gray & multi 1.50 1.90
Nos. 439-442 (4) 6.25 5.70

Symbols of Agriculture and Industry A146

1970, June 17
443 A146 60c multicolored .30 .30
Asian Productivity Year.

Inauguration of UPU Headquarters, Bern — A147

1970, Aug. 14 **Litho.** **Unwmk.**
444 A147 50c org, black & blue .75 .20
445 A147 1.10r red, black & blue 4.75 .60

Caduceus and Oil Lamp — A148

1970, Sept. 1 **Perf. 13½x14**
446 A148 5c multicolored 1.00 1.40
447 A148 45c gray & multi 1.00 1.10
Centenary of the Ceylon Medical School.

Victory March and S.W.R.D. Bandaranaike A149

1970, Sept. 25 **Perf. 14**
448 A149 10c red & multi .20 .20
For surcharge see No. 465.

UN Emblem and Dove — A150

Keppetipola
Dissawe — A151

1970, Oct. 24   Photo.   Perf. 12½x14
449 A150 2r dp orange & multi   3.00 3.50
25th anniversary of the United Nations.

1970, Nov. 26   Litho.   Perf. 14x14½
450 A151 25c multicolored   .30 .20
The 152nd anniversary of the execution of Keppetipola Dissawe, leader of the Great Rebellion of 1817-18.

Ola Leaf Manuscript and Education
Year Emblem — A152

1970, Dec. 21   Photo.   Perf. 13
451 A152 15c brown & multi   3.25 1.75
International Education Year.

Charles Henry   Edward Henry
de   Pedris — A154
Soysa — A153

1971, Mar. 3   Litho.   Perf. 14x13½
452 A153 20c orange & multi   .40 .50
de Soysa (1836-90), philanthropist who founded hospitals and schools.

1971, July 8   Litho.   Perf. 14x14½
453 A154 25c blue & multi   .40 .40
Edward Henry Pedris (1888-1925), patriot.

A 5c stamp for the 10th Conf. of World Fellowship of Buddhists, Ceylon, May 9-13, was supposedly not issued without "1972" overprint. See Sri Lanka No. 471.

Lenin (1870-   Cumaratunga
1924)   Munidasa
A156   A157

1971, Aug. 31   Perf. 14½
455 A156 40c dp car & multi   .70 .70

1971, Oct. 29   Perf. 14
Poets and Philosophers: #457, Ananda Coomaraswamy (1887-1947). #458, Rev. S. Mahinda Thero (1905-51). #459, Ananda Rajakaruna (1885-1957). #460, Arumuga Navalar (1822-78).

456 A157 5c brown   .20 .20
457 A157 5c slate   .20 .20
458 A157 5c deep orange   .20 .20
459 A157 5c dp vio blue   .20 .20
460 A157 5c brown red   .20 .20
       Nos. 456-460 (5)   1.00 1.00

CARE
Package
A158

1971, Dec. 28   Perf. 14x13
461 A158 50c purple, blue & pink   .55 .35
25th anniv. of CARE, a US-Canadian Co-operative for American Relief Everywhere.

Map of
Ceylon,
Colombo
Plan
Emblem
A159

1971, Dec. 28   Litho.   Perf. 14x14½
462 A159 20c multicolored   .40 .40
20th anniversary of the Colombo Plan.

Issues of 1969-70 Surcharged

a

b

c

d

e

Wmk. 290, Unwmkd.
1971, Dec. 5   Perf. 15, 14
463 A140 (a) 5c on 4c (#427)   7.50 2.50
464 A143 (b) 5c on 4c (#433)   .20 1.90
465 A149 (c) 15c on 10c (#448)   .20   .50
466 A140 (d) 25c on 6c (#428)   .80   .95
467 A144 (e) 25c on 6c (#434)   .80 3.25
       Nos. 463-467 (5)   9.50 9.10
Nos. 463-466 exist with surcharge inverted.

WHO Emblem
and
Heart — A160

1972, May 2   Unwmk.   Perf. 13x13½
468 A160 25c multicolored   3.25 .90
"Your heart is your health," World Health Day.

UN
Emblem,
Map
Showing
Asian
Highway
A161

1972, May 2   Perf. 13x12½
469 A161 85c lt blue & multi   6.50 3.25
Economic Commission for Asia and the Far East (ECAFE), 25th anniversary.

SEMI-POSTAL STAMPS

> Catalogue values for unused stamps in this section are for Never Hinged items.

Lamp and
Dharmachakra
SP1

Design: 10c+5c, Hand of Peace.

Perf. 11½
1956, May 10   Unwmk.   Photo.
Granite Paper
B1 SP1 4c + 2c dp bl & lt yel   .35 .75
B2 SP1 10c + 5c dk gray, yel & brt pink .50 1.00
2500th anniv. of the birth of Buddha. The surtax went to the Buddha Jayanti Fund. For overprints, see Nos. 338-339.

WAR TAX STAMPS

Nos. 201, 202, 202a
and 203 Overprinted

WAR
STAMP

Die I
1918   Wmk. 3   Perf. 14
MR1 A44 2c brown orange   .25 .45
   a.   Double overprint   35.00 47.50
   b.   Inverted overprint   65.00 75.00
MR2 A44 3c dp grn (Die Ia, type II) 3.00 .45
   a.   3c dp green (Die I, type I)   .25 .60
   b.   Double overprint (Die I)   95.00 110.00
MR3 A44 5c red violet   .60 .35
   a.   Double overprint   60.00 70.00
   b.   Inverted overprint   120.00
Same Overprint on No. 223
MR4 A44 1c on 5c red violet   .20 .30
   a.   Double overprint   210.00
       Nos. MR1-MR4 (4)   4.05 1.55

OFFICIAL STAMPS

Regular Issues
Overprinted

SERVICE

1869   Wmk. 1   Perf. 12½, 14
Black Overprint
O1 A4 1p blue   85.00
O2 A1 2p yellow   85.00
O3 A5 3p rose   150.00
O4 A2 8p red brown   85.00
O5 A1 1sh gray lilac   190.00
Red Overprint
O6 A1 6p brown   85.00
O7 A2 2sh blue   140.00
   a.   Imperf.   1,000.
       Nos. O1-O7 (7)   820.00
Nos. O1-O7 were never placed in use. The overprint measures 15mm on #O1, O3.

Regular Issues
Overprinted in Black or
Red

On
Service

1895-1900   Wmk. 2   Perf. 14
O8   A6   2c green   15.00 .70
O9   A6   2c org brn ('00) 10.00 .70
O10 A24 3c org brn & grn 12.00 2.00
O11 A24 3c green ('00)   12.00 4.00
O12 A23 5c lilac   4.75 .40
O13 A24 15c olive green   18.00 .60
O14 A24 15c ultra ('00)   24.00 .70
O15 A24 25c brown   13.00 2.00
O16 A24 30c vio & org brn 15.00 .70
O17 A24 75c blk & org brn (R) ('99) 7.00 7.50
       Wmk. 1
O18 A16 1r12c claret   100.00 65.00
       Nos. O8-O18 (11)   230.75 84.30

1903-04   Wmk. 2
O19 A36 2c orange brown   18.00 1.20
O20 A37 3c green   12.00 2.40
O21 A38 5c dull lilac   26.00 1.75
O22 A40 15c ultramarine   37.50 3.25
O23 A40 25c bister   30.00 21.00
O24 A40 30c violet & green 18.00 1.75
       Nos. O19-O24 (6)   141.50 31.35

CHAD

'chad

(Tchad)

LOCATION — Central Africa, south of Libya
GOVT. — Republic
AREA — 495,572 sq. mi.
POP. — 7,557,436 (1999 est.)
CAPITAL — N'Djamena

A former dependency of Ubangi-Shari, Chad became a separate French colony in 1920. In 1934, the colonies of Chad, Gabon, Middle Congo and Ubangi-Shari were grouped in a single administrative unit known as French Equatorial Africa, with the capital at Brazzaville. The Republic of Chad was proclaimed November 28, 1958.

100 Centimes = 1 Franc

Catalogue values for unused stamps in this country are for Never Hinged items, beginning with Scott 64 in the regular postage section, Scott B1 in the semipostal section, Scott C1 in the air post section, Scott CB1 in the air post semi-postal section, Scott J23 in the postage due section, Scott M1 in the military stamp section, and Scott O1 in the officials section.

See French Equatorial Africa No. 190 for stamp inscribed "Tchad."

Types of Middle Congo, 1907-17, Overprinted

Perf. 14x13½, 13½x14

			Unwmk.	
1922				
1	A1	1c red & violet	.40	.55
a.		Overprint omitted	225.00	
2	A1	2c ol brn & salmon	.50	.70
a.		Overprint omitted	260.00	
3	A1	4c ind & vio	1.10	1.50
4	A1	5c choc & grn	1.25	1.60
5	A1	10c dp grn & gray grn	2.40	2.75
6	A1	15c vio & red	2.50	2.75
7	A1	20c grn & vio	4.00	4.75
8	A2	25c ol brn & brn	9.50	11.00
9	A2	30c rose & pale rose	1.60	2.00
10	A2	35c dl bl & dl rose	2.75	3.25
11	A2	40c choc & grn	3.25	4.00
12	A2	45c vio & grn	2.40	2.75
13	A2	50c dk bl & pale bl	2.75	3.50
14	A2	60c on 75c vio, pnksh	4.00	4.75
a.		"TCHAD" omitted	300.00	
b.		"60" omitted	300.00	
15	A1	75c red & violet	3.25	4.00
16	A3	1fr indigo & salmon	13.00	13.00
17	A3	2fr indigo & violet	21.00	24.00
18	A3	5fr ind & olive brn	21.00	24.00
		Nos. 1-18 (18)	96.65	110.85

See Nos. 26a, 32a, 38a, 55a.

Stamps of 1922 Overprinted in Various Colors:

Nos. 19-28

Nos. 29-50

1924-33				
19	A1	1c red & vio	.30	.50
a.		"TCHAD" omitted	225.00	250.00
b.		Double overprint	300.00	
c.		Violet overprint	300.00	
20	A1	2c ol brn & sal	.30	.50
a.		"TCHAD" omitted	225.00	
b.		Double overprint	240.00	
21	A1	4c ind & vio	.30	.50
a.		"TCHAD" omitted	950.00	
22	A1	5c choc & grn (Bl)	1.60	2.00
a.		"TCHAD" omitted	200.00	
23	A1	5c choc & grn	.50	.70
a.		"TCHAD" omitted	225.00	
24	A1	10c dp grn & gray grn (Bl)	1.20	1.40
25	A1	10c dp grn & gray grn	1.20	1.40
26	A1	10c red org & blk ('25)	.55	.80
a.		"Afrique Equatoriale Francaise" omitted	225.00	250.00
b.		"Afrique Equatoriale Francaise" doubled	240.00	260.00
27	A1	15c vio & red	.65	.85
28	A1	20c grn & vio	.80	.80
a.		"TCHAD" omitted	225.00	
b.		"Afrique Equatoriale Francaise" doubled	340.00	
29	A2	25c ol brn & brn	.65	.85
a.		"Afrique Equatoriale Francaise" omitted	160.00	
30	A2	30c rose & pale rose	.80	1.10
31	A2	30c gray & bl (R) ('25)	.55	.80
32	A2	30c dk grn & grn ('27)	1.20	1.60
a.		"Afrique Equatoriale Francaise" omitted	340.00	
33	A2	35c indigo & dl rose	.65	.85
34	A2	40c choc & grn	1.25	1.60
a.		Double overprint (R + Bk)	275.00	
35	A2	45c vio & grn	.95	1.40
a.		Double overprint (R + Bk)	275.00	
36	A2	50c dk bl & pale bl	1.60	1.90
a.		Inverted overprint	160.00	
37	A2	50c grn & vio ('25)	2.00	2.00
38	A2	65c org brn & bl ('28)	2.00	2.40
a.		"Afrique Equatoriale Francaise" omitted	260.00	
39	A2	75c red & vio	1.60	1.90
40	A2	75c dp bl & lt bl (R) ('25)	.90	1.20
a.		"TCHAD" omitted	260.00	
41	A2	75c rose & dk brn ('28)	2.75	3.25
42	A2	90c brn red & pink ('30)	7.25	8.75
43	A3	1fr ind & salmon	2.00	2.50
44	A3	1.10fr dl grn & bl ('28)	3.25	4.00
45	A3	1.25fr org brn & lt bl ('33)	8.00	9.50
46	A3	1.50fr ultra & bl ('30)	7.25	8.75
47	A3	1.75fr ol brn & vio ('33)	40.00	45.00
48	A3	2fr ind & vio	2.75	3.50
a.		Double impression of frame	550.00	
49	A3	3fr red vio ('30)	10.50	12.00
50	A3	5fr ind & ol brn	3.50	4.75
		Nos. 19-50 (32)	108.80	129.05

See No. 58a.

Types of 1922 Overprinted like Nos. 29-50 and Surcharged with New Values

1924-27				
51	A2	60c on 75c dk vio, pnksh	.95	1.20
a.		"60" omitted	200.00	
52	A3	65c on 1fr brn & ol grn ('25)	1.60	2.00
53	A3	85c on 1fr brn & ol grn ('25)	1.60	2.00
54	A2	90c on 75c brn red & rose red ('27)	1.60	2.00
55	A3	1.25fr on 1fr dk bl & ultra (R) ('26)	.70	.80
a.		"Afrique Equatoriale Francaise" omitted	175.00	
56	A3	1.50fr on 1fr ultra & bl ('27)	1.60	2.00
57	A3	3fr on 5fr org brn & dl red ('27)	5.00	6.00
58	A3	10fr on 5fr ol grn & cer ('27)	13.00	14.50
a.		"10fr" omitted	400.00	400.00
59	A3	20fr on 5fr vio & ver ('27)	18.00	21.00
		Nos. 51-59 (9)	44.05	51.50

Common Design Types pictured following the introduction.

Colonial Exposition Issue
Common Design Types

1931		**Engr.**	**Perf. 12½**	
		Name of Country in Black		
60	CD70	40c deep green	5.50	5.50
61	CD71	50c violet	5.50	5.50
62	CD72	90c red orange	5.50	5.50
63	CD73	1.50fr dull blue	5.50	5.50
		Nos. 60-63 (4)	22.00	22.00

Catalogue values for unused stamps in this section, from this point to the end of the section, are for Never Hinged items.

Republic

"Birth of the Republic" A1

"Solidarity of the Community" A2

1959	**Unwmk.**	**Engr.**	**Perf. 13**	
64	A1	15fr ultra, grn & maroon	.80	.20
65	A2	25fr dk grn & dp claret	1.00	.20

1st anniv. of the proclamation of the Republic.

Imperforates

Most Chad stamps from 1959 onward exist imperforate in issued and trial colors, and also in small presentation sheets in issued colors.

C.C.T.A. Issue
Common Design Type

1960				
66	CD106	50fr rose lil & dk pur	1.75	.35

Flag and Map of Chad and UN Emblem — A3

		Unwmk.		
1961, Jan. 11		**Engr.**	**Perf. 13**	
	Flag in blue, yellow and carmine			
67	A3	15fr brn & dk bl	.60	.20
68	A3	25fr org brn & dk bl	.90	.20
69	A3	85fr slate grn & dk bl	2.50	.40
		Nos. 67-69 (3)	4.00	.80

Admission of Chad to United Nations.

Chari Bridge and Hippopotamus — A4

Abtouyoua Mountain and Ox — A5

Designs: 50c, Biltine and dorcas gazelle. 1fr, Logone and elephant. 2fr, Batha and lion. 3fr, Salamat and buffalo. 4fr, Ouaddai and Kudu. 15fr, Bessada and giant kudu. 20fr, Tibesti mountains and mouflon. 25fr, Rocherg and antelope. 30fr, Kanem and cheetah. 60fr, Borkou and oryx. 85fr, Gorge of Archet and addax.

Perf. 13½x14, 14x13½

1961-62			**Typo.**	
70	A5	50c yel grn & dk grn ('62)	.20	.20
71	A5	1fr bl grn & dk bl grn ('62)	.20	.20
72	A5	2fr dk red brn & blk ('62)	.20	.20
73	A5	3fr ocher & dl grn ('62)	.20	.20
74	A5	4fr dk crim & blk ('62)	.20	.20
75	A4	5fr yellow & blk	.20	.20
76	A5	10fr pink & blk	.35	.20
77	A5	15fr lilac & blk ('62)	.70	.20
78	A5	20fr red & blk	.85	.20
79	A5	25fr blue & blk ('62)	.90	.20
80	A5	30fr ultra & blk ('62)	1.00	.20
81	A5	60fr yel & ol grn ('62)	2.25	.20
82	A5	85fr org & blk	2.75	.25
		Nos. 70-82 (13)	10.00	2.65

First anniversary of Independence.
For overprint see No. M1.

Abidjan Games Issue
Common Design Type

1962, July 21		**Photo.**	**Perf. 12½x12**	
83	CD109	20fr Relay race	.80	.20
84	CD109	50fr High jump	2.00	.30
		Nos. 83-84,C8 (3)	6.30	1.25

African-Malgache Union Issue
Common Design Type

1962, Sept. 8			**Unwmk.**	
85	CD110	30fr dk bl, bluish grn, red & gold	1.25	.20

Pres. Ngarta Tombalbaye — A7

1963, Apr. 22			**Perf. 12x12½**	
86	A7	20fr multi	.65	.20
87	A7	85fr multi	1.75	.30

For surcharge, see No. 125.

Space Communcations Issue

Waves Around Globe — A8

Design: 100fr, Orbit patterns around globe.

		Perf. 12½		
1963, Sept. 19		**Unwmk.**	**Photo.**	
88	A8	25fr grn & pur	1.00	.20
89	A8	100fr pink & ultra	3.00	.60

Ancestral Mask — A9

Excavated Sao Art: 5fr, Clay weight. 25fr, Ancestral clay statuette. 60fr, Gazelle, bronze. 80fr, Bronze pectoral.

1963, Dec. 2		**Engr.**	**Perf. 13**	
90	A9	5fr brt grn & red brn	.20	.20
91	A9	15fr gray, dl cl & red	.45	.20
92	A9	25fr dk bl & org brn	1.10	.20

93	A9 60fr org brn & slate grn 2.75 .35
94	A9 80fr org red & olive 3.00 .40
	Nos. 90-94 (5) 7.50 1.40

UNESCO Emblem, Scales and Tree — A10

1963, Dec. 10
95 A10 25fr green & maroon 1.00 .20
15th anniv. of the Universal Declaration of Human Rights.

Potter A11

Perf. 12½
1964, Feb. 5 Unwmk. Engr.
96 A11 10fr shown .35 .20
97 A11 30fr Boatmaker .90 .20
98 A11 50fr Weaver 1.50 .25
99 A11 85fr Smiths 2.25 .35
Nos. 96-99 (4) 5.00 1.00

Barograph and WMO Emblem A12

1964, Mar. 23 Perf. 13
100 A12 50fr red lil, pur & ultra 1.40 .25
Fourth World Meteorological Day.

Cotton A13

1964, Apr. 6 Photo. Perf. 12½x13
101 A13 20fr shown 1.75 .35
102 A13 25fr Royal poinciana 2.00 .40

Co-operation Issue
Common Design Type
1964, Nov. 7 Engr. Perf. 13
103 CD119 25fr ver, dk bl & dk brn 1.00 .25

National Guard and Map of Chad A14

Design: 25fr, Infantry, flag and map, vert.

Perf. 12½x13, 13x12½
1964, Dec. 11 Photo.
104 A14 20fr multi .85 .20
105 A14 25fr lt bl & multi .95 .20
Issued to honor the army of Chad.

Aoudad or Barbary Sheep A15

10fr, Addax. 20fr, Oryx. 25fr, Derby's eland, vert. 30fr, Giraffe, buffalo & lion, Zakouma Park, vert. 85fr, Great kudu at water hole, vert.

Perf. 12½x12, 12x12½
1965, Jan. 11 Unwmk.
106 A15 5fr dk brn, ultra & yel .50 .20
107 A15 10fr ultra, org & blk .75 .20
108 A15 20fr multi 1.50 .20
109 A15 25fr multi 1.75 .25
110 A15 30fr multi 2.50 .40
111 A15 85fr multi 5.00 .75
Nos. 106-111 (6) 12.00 2.00

Olsen Perforator A16

Designs: 60fr, Mildé telephone, vert. 100fr, Distributor of Baudot telegraph.

1965, May 17 Engr. Perf. 13
112 A16 30fr multi .75 .20
113 A16 60fr multi 1.25 .45
114 A16 100fr multi 2.00 .60
Nos. 112-114 (3) 4.00 1.25
Cent. of the ITU.

Motorized Police A17

Perf. 12½x12
1965, June 22 Photo. Unwmk.
115 A17 25fr ol, dk grn, gold & brn .75 .25
Issued to honor the national police.

Guitar A18

Musical Instruments from National Museum: 1fr, Drum and stool, vert. 3fr, Shoulder drums, vert. 15fr, Viol. 60fr, Harp, vert.

1965, Oct. 26 Engr. Perf. 13
Size: 22x36mm, 36x22mm
116 A18 1fr car, emer & brn .20 .20
117 A18 2fr red, brt lil & brn .20 .20
118 A18 3fr red & sepia .20 .20
119 A18 15fr red, ocher & sl grn .75 .20
120 A18 60fr maroon & slate grn 1.75 .60
Nos. 116-120,C23 (6) 5.85 2.25

Head and Bowl — A19 / WHO Headquarters, Geneva — A20

Sao Art: 20fr, Head. 60fr, Head with crown. 80fr, Circlet with human head. From excavations at Bouta Kebira and Gawi.

1966, Apr. 1 Engr. Perf. 13
121 A19 15fr ol, choc & ultra .40 .20
122 A19 20fr dk red, brn & bl grn .75 .20
123 A19 60fr brt bl, choc & ver 1.75 .50
124 A19 80fr brn org, grn & pur 2.50 .60
Nos. 121-124 (4) 5.40 1.50
Issued to publicize the International Negro Arts Festival, Dakar, Senegal, Apr. 1-24.

No. 86 Surcharged with New Value and Two Bars in Orange
1966, Apr. 15 Photo. Perf. 12½x12
125 A7 25fr on 20fr multi .75 .30

1966, May 3
126 A20 25fr car, lt ultra & yel .60 .20
127 A20 32fr emer, ultra & yel .75 .20
New WHO Headquarters, Geneva.

Staff of Mercury and Map of Africa A21

1966, May 24 Perf. 12½x12
128 A21 30fr multi .75 .25
Central African Customs and Economic Union (Union Douaniere et Economique de l'Afrique Centrale, UDEAC).

Soccer Player — A22

Design: 60fr, Soccer player facing left.

1966, July 12 Engr. Perf. 13
129 A22 30fr grn, bl grn & mar .75 .25
130 A22 60fr dk bl, gray & car 1.40 .30
8th World Cup Soccer Championship, Wembley, England, July 11-30.

Young Men, Flag and Emblem A23

1966, Aug. 11 Photo. Perf. 12½x13
131 A23 25fr dk bl & multi .75 .20
Chad Youth Movement.

Greek Columns and UNESCO Emblem — A24

1966, Aug. 23 Engr. Perf. 13
132 A24 32fr sl bl, vio & car rose .75 .20
20th anniv. of UNESCO.

Reconstructed Skull of Chadanthropus — A25

1966, Sept. 20 Engr. Perf. 13
133 A25 30fr gray, red & ocher 1.90 .50
Yves Coppens' discovery of Lake Chad man.

Stone Axe — A26

Prehistoric Tools: 30fr, Flint arrow head. 85fr, Bone harpoon. 100fr, Sandstone millstone with grinder.

1966, Dec. 11 Engr. Perf. 13
134 A26 25fr dp bl, red & dk brn .55 .20
135 A26 30fr brn, dp bl & blk .80 .20
136 A26 85fr dk red, brt bl & brn 2.40 .50
137 A26 100fr Prus grn, dk brn & bis brn 2.75 .65
a. Miniature sheet of 4, #134-137 15.00 5.00
Nos. 134-137 (4) 6.50 1.55

Map of Chad and Various Sports — A27

1967, Apr. 10 Photo. Perf. 12x12½
138 A27 25fr multi .75 .30
Issued for Sports Day, Apr. 10, 1967.

Colotis Protomedia A28

Various Butterflies.

1967, May 23 Photo. Perf. 12½x12
139 A28 5fr blue & multi 1.75 .30
140 A28 10fr emerald & multi 4.25 .75
141 A28 20fr orange & multi 8.50 1.50
142 A28 130fr red & multi 17.50 2.50
Nos. 139-142 (4) 32.00 5.05

WHO Headquarters, Brazzaville — A29

1967, Sept. 23 Photo. Perf. 12½x13
143 A29 30fr vio bl & multi .75 .25
Opening of the Regional Office of the WHO, Brazzaville.

Jamboree Emblem and Boy Scouts A30

32fr, Jamboree emblem and Boy Scout.

1967, Oct. 17 Photo. Perf. 12½x13
144 A30 25fr multi .80 .20
145 A30 32fr multi .90 .20
12th Boy Scout World Jamboree, Farragut State Park, Idaho, Aug. 1-9.

Great Mills of Chad A31

30fr, Lake reclamation project, grain fields.

1967, Nov. 14 Engr. Perf. 13
146 A31 25fr brt bl, ind & sep .70 .20
147 A31 30fr ultra, emer & ol brn .90 .20
Economic development of Chad.

Woman and Harp Player A32

Rock Paintings: 30fr, Giraffes. 50fr, Camel rider hunting ostrich.

1967, Dec. 19   Engr.   *Perf. 13*
Size: 36x22mm

148	A32	15fr bl, sal & mar	2.00	.20
149	A32	30fr grnsh bl, sal & mar	4.00	.40
150	A32	50fr emer, sal & mar	5.50	.55
		Nos. 148-150,C38-C39 (5)	28.50	3.60

Balloud expedition in the Ennedi Mountains. See Nos. 163-166.

Rotary Emblem — A33

Map of Chad, WHO Emblem, Well, Physicians, Mother and Child — A34

1968, Jan. 9   Photo.   *Perf. 13x12½*

151	A33	50fr multi	1.40	.40

Rotary Club of Chad, 10th anniversary.

1968, Apr. 6   *Perf. 13x12½*

152	A34	25fr multi	.70	.20
153	A34	32fr multi	.90	.20

20th anniv. of WHO.

"Water" Aiding Agriculture and Industry A35

1968, Apr. 23   Engr.   *Perf. 13*

154	A35	50fr grnsh bl, brn & brt grn	1.10	.25

Hydrological Decade (UNESCO), 1965-74.

National Administration School — A36

1968, Aug. 20   Engr.   *Perf. 13*

155	A36	25fr slate, brn red & rose vio	.70	.20

Boy Learning to Write A37

1968, Sept. 10

156	A37	60fr dk bl, dk brn & blk	1.10	.30

Issued for National Literacy Day.

Cotton Harvest A38

Loom, Fort Archambault Factory — A39

Tiger Moth — A40

1968, Sept. 24   Engr.   *Perf. 13*

157	A38	25fr Prus bl, choc & dk grn	.80	.20
158	A39	30fr brt grn, ol & ultra	.90	.20

Issued to publicize the cotton industry.

1968, Oct. 1   Photo.

Moths: 30fr, Owlet. 50fr, Saturnid (Gynanisa maja). 100fr, Saturnid (Epiphora bauhiniae).

159	A40	25fr multi	5.25	.60
160	A40	30fr multi	6.25	.75
161	A40	50fr multi	9.50	.85
162	A40	100fr multi	11.00	1.50
		Nos. 159-162 (4)	32.00	3.70

Rock Paintings Type of 1967

Rock Paintings: 2fr, Archers. 10fr, Costumes (4 women, 1 man). 20fr, Funeral vigil. 25fr, Dispute.

1968, Nov. 19   Engr.   *Perf. 13*
Size: 36x22mm

163	A32	2fr scar, salmon & brn	.65	.20
164	A32	10fr pur, salmon & dk red	1.60	.20
165	A32	20fr grn, salmon & mar	3.25	.50
166	A32	25fr bl, salmon & maroon	3.50	.60
		Nos. 163-166 (4)	9.00	1.50

Man and Human Rights Flame — A41

St. Paul — A42

1968, Dec. 10   Engr.   *Perf. 13*

167	A41	32fr grn, brt bl & red	.75	.20

International Human Rights Year.

1969, May 6   Litho.   *Perf. 12½x13*

Apostles: 1fr, St. Peter. 2fr, St. Thomas. 5fr, St. John the Evangelist. 10fr, St. Bartholomew. 20fr, St. Matthew. 25fr, St. James the Less. 30fr, St. Andrew. 40fr, St. Jude. 50fr, St. James the Greater. 85fr, St. Philip. 100fr, St. Simon.

168	A42	50c multi	.20	.20
169	A42	1fr multi	.20	.20
170	A42	2fr multi	.20	.20
171	A42	5fr multi	.20	.20
172	A42	10fr multi	.20	.20
173	A42	20fr multi	.30	.20
174	A42	25fr multi	.40	.20
175	A42	30fr multi	.50	.20
176	A42	40fr multi	.60	.20
177	A42	50fr multi	.70	.20
178	A42	85fr multi	1.10	.40
179	A42	100fr multi	1.25	.40
a.		Sheet of 12, #168-179	6.00	1.75

Jubilee Year of the Catholic Church in Chad.

Tractors and Trucks — A43

1969, June 19   Engr.   *Perf. 13*

180	A43	32fr grn, red brn & ind	.75	.20

50th anniv. of the ILO.

Deborah Meyer, US, 200 Meter Freestyle A44

Woman with Flowers, by Veneto — A45

Winners of 1968 Olympic Games: #182, Roland Matthes, East Germany, 100m backstroke. #183, Klaus DiBiasi, Italy, springboard diving. #184, Bruno Cipolla, Primo Baran and Renzo Sambo, Italy, pair with coxswain. #185, Annemarie Zimmermann and Rosewitha Esser, West Germany, women's kayak tandem. #186, Sailing, G.B. #187, Pierre Trentin, France, 1000 meter bicycling. #188, Pier Franco Vianelli, Italy, 196k bicycle road race. #189, Daniel Morelon and Pierre Trentin, France, tandem.

#190, Daniel R. Rebillard, France, 4000m pursuit (bicycle). #191, Ingrid Becker, West Germany, pentathlon. #192, Jean J. Guyon, France, equestrian. #193, Olympic dressage team, West Germany. #194, Bernd Klinger, West Germany, small bore rifle. #195, Manfred Wolke, East Germany, welterweight. #196, Randy Matson, US, shot put. #197, Colette Besson, France, 400m run. #198, Mohammed Gammoudi, Tunisia, 5,000m run. #199, Tommie Smith, US, 200m run.

#200, David Hemery, G.B., 200m hurdles. #201, Willie Davenport, US, 110m hurdles. #202, Bob Beamon, US, long jump. #203, Sawao Kato, Japan, all around gymnastics. #204, Dick Fosbury, US, high jump.

Paintings: #206, Holy Family, by Murillo, horiz. #207, Adoration of the Magi, by Rubens. #208, Portrait of an African Woman, by Bezombes. #209, Three Black Men, by Rubens. #210, Mother and Child, by Gauguin.

1969, June 30   Litho.   *Perf. 12½x13*

181-204	A44 1fr set of 24	8.00	8.00

**   *Perf. 12½x13, 13x12½***

205-210	A45 1fr set of 6	1.90	1.90

Issued to stress the brotherhood of mankind.
For overprints see Nos. 244A-244F, 245A-245X.

Cochlospermum Tinctorium — A46

Flowers: 4fr, Parkia biglobosa. 10fr, Pancratium trianthum. 15fr, Morning glory.

1969, July 8   Photo.   *Perf. 12½x13*

211	A46	1fr pink, yel & blk	.60	.20
212	A46	4fr dk grn, yel & red	.90	.20
213	A46	10fr dk grn, yel & gray	1.10	.20
214	A46	15fr vio bl & multi	1.90	.20
		Nos. 211-214 (4)	4.50	.80

Meat Freezer, Farcha A47

30fr, Cattle at Farcha slaughterhouse.

1969, Aug. 19   Engr.   *Perf. 13*

215	A47	25fr sl grn, ocher & red brn	.60	.20
216	A47	30fr red brn, sl grn & gray	.75	.20

Economic development in Chad.

Development Bank Issue
Common Design Type
1969, Sept. 10

217	CD130 30fr dl red, grn & ocher	.70	.20

Tilapia Nilotica A48

Fish: 3fr, Citharinus latus. 5fr, Tetraodon fahaka strigosus. 20fr, Hydrocyon forskali.

1969, Nov. 25   Engr.   *Perf. 13*

218	A48	2fr choc, grn & gray	.55	.20
219	A48	3fr gray, red & bl	1.10	.20
220	A48	5fr ocher, blk & yel	1.75	.25
221	A48	20fr blk, red & grn	4.75	.60
		Nos. 218-221 (4)	8.15	1.25

ASECNA Issue
Common Design Type
1969, Dec. 12   Engr.   *Perf. 13*

222	CD132 30fr orange	.75	.25

Pres. François Tombalbaye A49

Lenin — A50

1970, Jan. 11   Litho.   *Perf. 14*

223	A49	25fr multi	.70	.20

1970, Apr. 22   Photo.   *Perf. 11½*

224	A50	150fr gold, blk & buff	3.25	1.10

Lenin (1870-1924), Russian communist leader.

UPU Headquarters Issue
Common Design Type
1970, May 20   Engr.   *Perf. 13*

225	CD133 30fr dk red, pur & brn	.75	.25

During the 1970-73 period three different agents had entered into contracts to produce stamps with various officials of the Chad government, apparently including Pres. Tombalbaye.

In June 1973, Tombalbaye declared that some of the stamps produced by these agents were not recognized by the Chad government but might be put on sale at a later date, and that other stamps produced and shipped to Chad were refused by the government.

In July 1973, the Chad government announced that the stamps that were not recognized would be put on sale by the end of the year. We have no evidence that this actually happened.

Apollo Program A50a

Designs: 15fr, Apollo 11 in Lunar orbit. 25fr, Apollo 12 astronaut deploying lunar research equipment. 40fr, Astronaut, lunar module on moon. 50fr, Astronauts Conrad and Bean in life raft after splashdown, horiz.

1970, June 12   Litho.   Perf. 12x12½
225A A50a Strip of 3, #b-d   6.00   —
Souvenir Sheet
Perf. 13½x13
225E A50a 50fr multicolored   10.00   —
No. 225E contains one 66x44mm stamp. 15fr, 25fr are airmail.

Expo '70, Japan — A50b

Japanese prints of women: 50c, by Kiyonaga. 1fr, by Utamaro. 2fr, from Heian period.

1970, June 12   Litho.   Perf. 12x12½
225F A50b Strip of 3, #a-c   13.50   —
For overprint see No. 239C.

Adult Education Class and UN Emblem — A52

1970, June 16   Litho.   Perf. 14
226 A52 100fr blue & multi   1.75 .50
International Education Year.

Bull's Head, Symbols of Weather and Agriculture — A53

1970, July 22   Engr.   Perf. 13
227 A53 50fr org, gray & grn   1.00 .20
Issued for World Meteorological Day.

1970 World Cup Soccer Championships, Mexico City — A53a

Designs: 1fr, Three players, Italian flag. 4fr, Franz Beckenbauer, German flag. Nos. 227C, 227E, English players receiving World Cup trophy, 1966. No. 227D, Three players, Brazilian flag. No. 227F, Four players, "1970."

1970-71   Litho.   Perf. 12
227A A53a 1fr multicolored
227B A53a 4fr multicolored
227C A53a 5fr multicolored
227D A53a 5fr multicolored
  Nos. 227A-227D (4)   3.75   —
Embossed
Die Cut Perf 13
227E A53a 5fr gold   17.50   —
Souvenir Sheet
Litho.
Perf. 13½x13
227F A53a 15fr multicolored   6.25   —
No. 227F contains one 66x44mm stamp. Nos. 227D, 227F are airmail.
Issued: #227A-227D, 227F, 7/2; #227E, 11/1/71.
For overprints see Nos. 267A-267E.

Christmas A53b

Virgin and Child by: 3fr, Solario. 25fr, Durer. 32fr, Fouquet.

1970, Aug. 19   Litho.   Perf. 12x12½
227G A53b 3fr multicolored
227H A53b 25fr multicolored
227I A53b 32fr multicolored
  Nos. 227G-227I (3)   13.50   —
No. 227I is airmail.

Ahmed Mangue, Minister of Education — A54

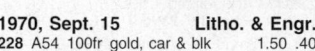

1970, Sept. 15   Litho. & Engr.
228 A54 100fr gold, car & blk   1.50 .40

1972 Summer Olympics, Munich — A54a

Designs: No. 228A, 3fr, Horses pulling chariot. 8fr, Men running. 10fr, No. 228C, Woman hurdling. No. 228B, 20fr, Equestrian. 35fr, Woman diving. No. 228D, Woman diver in tuck position.

1970   Litho.   Perf. 12½x12
228A A54a Strip of 3, #a-c   4.00   —
Perf. 12x12½
228B A54a Pair, #a-b + label   4.00   —
Embossed
Die Cut Perf 13
228C A54a 10fr gold   17.50
Souvenir Sheet
Litho.
Perf. 13½x13
228D A54a 40fr multicolored   10.00
10fr, 35fr, Nos. 228C-228D are airmail. No. 228D contains one 66x43mm stamp.
Issued: #228A-228B, 228D, Sept; #228C, 10/14.
For overprints see Nos. 239D-239F.

Tanner A55

Designs: 2fr, Cloth dyer, vert. 3fr, Camel turning oil press. 4fr, Water carrier. 5fr, Copper worker.

1970, Oct. 10   Engr.   Perf. 13
229   A55 1fr ol brn, bl & brn   .20 .20
229A A55 2fr dk brn, ol & ind   .20 .20
229B A55 3fr pur, ol brn & rose car .30 .20
229C A55 4fr choc, lem & bl grn .40 .20
229D A55 5fr red, choc & sl grn .50 .20
  Nos. 229-229D (5)   1.60 1.00

UN Emblem, Grain and Dove — A56

1970, Oct. 24   Photo.   Perf. 12x12½
230 A56 32fr dk bl & multi   .75 .25
25th anniversary of United Nations.

OCAM Headquarters, Map of Africa, Stars — A57

1971, Jan. 23   Photo.   Perf. 12½x12
231 A57 30fr dk grn & multi   .75 .20
OCAM (Organisation Commune Africaine, Malgache et Mauricienne) Summit Conference, N'djamena, Jan. 22-30.

Space Exploration — A57a

Illustration reduced.

1971, Feb. 16   Litho.   Perf. 13x13½
231A A57a 8fr shown   .60
231B A57a 10fr Apollo 11   .90
231C A57a 35fr Soviet space station 6.25
  Nos. 231A-231C (3)   7.75
Embossed
Die Cut Perf 13
231D A57a 8fr gold, like #231A   8.25   —
  f. Sheet of 1, Imperf.
Souvenir Sheet
Perf. 13½x13
231E A57a 40fr John F. Kennedy, Apollo spacecraft, vert. 10.00   —
Nos. 231C, 231E are airmail. No. 231Df contains one 73x45mm stamp with same size design as No. 231D. No. 231E contains one 33x50mm stamp.
Nos. 231D, 231Df probably were not available in Chad.

1972 Winter Olympics, Sapporo A57b

Paintings by Kiyonaga: 50c, Cherry Trees in Bloom, Tokyo. 1fr, Snowy Morning. 2fr, Sake Party.

1971   Litho.   Perf. 12x12½
231G A57b 50c multicolored   .80
231H A57b 1fr multicolored   1.40
231I A57b 2fr multicolored   2.25
  Nos. 231G-231I (3)   4.45
Embossed
Die Cut Perf 13
231J A57b 2fr gold, like #231I 17.50
  k. Sheet of 1, Imperf.   35.00
Issued: #231G-231I, 2/16; #231J-231Jk, 11/1. #231Jk contains one 43x54mm stamp with same size design as #231I.
For overprints see Nos. 246A-246C.
Nos. 231J-231Jk probably were not available in Chad.

Portraits of French Royalty — A57c

Designs: No. 232A, 25fr, The Dauphin (Louis XVII), by J.M. Vien the Younger. 32fr, Marie Antoinette, by E. Vigee-Lebrun. 60fr, Louis XVI, by J.S. Duplessis.

No. 232B, 25fr, Comtesse du Barry, by E. Vigee-Lebrun. 40fr, Louis XV, by M.Q. Delatour.

No. 232C, 40fr, Marie Antoinette, by Charpentier. 50fr, Louis XVI (Dauphin), by Michel Van Loo.

No. 232D, 35fr, Madame de Pompadour (detail), by Delatour. 70fr, Louis XV by Delatour.

No. 232E, 30fr, Madame de Pompadour (entire), by Delatour. 60fr, Marie Leszczynska, by Jean Marc Nattier. 80fr, Louis XV, by Van Loo.

No. 232F, 40fr, Duc D'Orleans as Regent, by 19th cent. French school. 200fr, Louis XIV, by H. Rigaud.

No. 232G, 100fr, Madame de Montespan, by Henry Gascard. 100fr, Madame de Maintenon, by Pierre Mignard.

No. 232H, 50fr, Colbert, by Claude Lefebvre. 200fr, Louis XIV, by J. Garnier.

No. 232J, 50fr, Marie Therese, by Mignard. 200fr, Louis XIV, by Marot.

No. 232K, 50fr, Marie de la Valliere, by English school. 200fr, Louis XIV, by French school.

No. 232L, 100fr, Giulio Cardinal Mazarin, by Mignard. 100fr, Anne of Austria, by Rubens.

No. 232M, 50fr, Vicomte de Turenne, by Champaigne. 200fr, Louis XIV as a Boy, by Mignard.

No. 232N, 100fr, Marquis de Cinq-Mars, by M. le Nain. 150fr, Cardinal Richelieu, by Champaigne.

No. 232P, 150fr, Anne of Austria, by Rubens. 250fr, Louis XIII (detail), by Simon Vouet.

No. 232Q, 150fr, Marriage of Marie de Medicis (looking right), by Rubens. 150fr, Mirror image.

No. 232R, 150fr, Duke of Sully, by Quesnel. 150fr, Mirror image.

No. 232S, 150fr, Henry IV, by Rubens. 150fr, Marie de Medicis, by Rubens.

No. 232T, 200fr, Gabrielle d'Estrees, by unknown artist. 250fr, Henry IV, by French school, c. 1595.

No. 232U, 150fr, Jeanne d'Albret, by Francois Clouet. 200fr, Marie de Medicis as a Girl, by Angelo Bronzino.

No. 232V, 200fr, Henry III, by Clouet. 250fr, Ambroise Pare, by 16th century French school.

No. 232W, 150fr, Catherine de Medicis, by Clouet. 250fr, Henry II, by Clouet.

No. 233A, 200fr, Elizabeth of Austria, by Clouet. 250fr, Charles IX, by Clouet.

No. 233B, 200fr, Mary Stuart, by 16th cent. Scottish school. 300fr, Diane of Poitiers, by Fontainbleu school.

No. 233C, 200fr, Elizabeth of Valois, by Alonso S. Coello. 250fr, Francis, Duke of Alencon, by Clouet.

No. 233D, 150fr, Marguerite d'Angouleme, by Clouet. 300fr, Francis I, by Clouet.

No. 233E, 200fr, Francis I, by Titian. 300fr, Francis I as Dauphin, by Corneille of Lyon.

No. 233F, 100fr, Anne of Austria, by Coello. 250fr, Louis XIII, by Champaigne.

No. 233G, 200fr, Marie de Medicis, by Rubens. 200fr, Marie de Medicis, Louis XIII, by Rubens.

No. 233H, 150fr, The Exchange of Princess Elizabeth of France and Princess Anne of Austria on the Andaye River, by Rubens. 250fr, Louis XIII of France and Navarre, by Vouet.

No. 233J, 250fr, Marie de Medicis, by Rubens. 250fr, Henry IV, by Rubens.

No. 233K, Louis XV and the Dauphin at Battle of Fontenoy. No. 233L, The Grand Dauphin and his Family, by Mignard. No. 233M, Madame de Montespan, horiz. No. 233N, Madame de la Valliere and her Children. No. 233P, The Birth of Louis XIII at Fontainebleau, by Rubens. No. 233Q, Reconciliation of the Queen and Louis XIII, by Rubens. No. 233R, Henry IV Entrusting Regency to Marie de Medici, by Rubens. No. 233S, The Majority of Louis XIII, by Rubens. No. 233T, The Apotheosis of Henry IV and the Proclamation of Regency, by Rubens. No. 233U, Felicity of the Regency, by Rubens.

Small numbers appear at the lower right on Nos. 232A-233J. To ease identication, these numbers are shown in parentheses after each listing.

1971-73		Litho.	Perf. 12½x13
232A	A57c	Strip of 3, #aa-ac (58-60)	2.50
232B	A57c	Pair, #aa-ab (53-54)	1.50
232C	A57c	Pair, #aa-ab (56-57)	1.50
232D	A57c	Pair, #aa-ab (51-52)	1.90
232E	A57c	Strip of 3, #aa-ac (48-50)	3.75
232F	A57c	Pair, #aa-ab (45, 47)	3.75
232G	A57c	Pair, #aa-ab (44, 45B)	2.50
232H	A57c	Pair, #aa-ab (42-43)	3.75
232J	A57c	Pair, #aa-ab (40-41)	3.75
232K	A57c	Pair, #aa-ab (38-39)	3.75
232L	A57c	Pair, #aa-ab (36-37)	2.50
232M	A57c	Pair, #aa-ab (34-35)	3.75
232N	A57c	Pair, #aa-ab (32-33)	3.75
232P	A57c	Pair, #aa-ab (30-31)	6.00
232Q	A57c	Pair, #aa-ab (22-23)	4.00
232R	A57c	Pair, #aa-ab (22A-22B)	4.50
232S	A57c	Pair, #aa-ab (26, 27A)	4.50
232T	A57c	Pair, #aa-ab (18-19)	7.50
232U	A57c	Pair, #aa-ab (16-17)	5.50
232V	A57c	Pair, #aa-ab (16-16A)	7.50
232W	A57c	Pair, #aa-ab (14-15)	7.50
233A	A57c	Pair, #aa-ab (13-13A)	7.50
233B	A57c	Pair, #aa-ab (11-12)	8.00
233C	A57c	Pair, #aa-ab (10, 11A)	6.50
233D	A57c	Pair, #aa-ab (8-9)	7.50
233E	A57c	Pair, #aa-ab (7, 8A)	8.00
233F	A57c	Pair, #aa-ab (29, 32B)	6.00
233G	A57c	Pair, #aa-ab (24-25)	6.00
233H	A57c	Pair, #aa-ab (27-28)	6.00
233J	A57c	Pair, #aa-ab (20-21)	7.50
		Nos. 232A-233J (30)	148.65

Souvenir Sheets
Perf. 13x13½, 13½x13, 13½

233K	A57c	75fr multi	6.25
233L	A57c	100fr multi	5.50
233M	A57c	200fr multi	5.00
233N	A57c	300fr multi	5.00
233P	A57c	350fr multi	12.00
233Q	A57c	400fr multi	16.00
233R	A57c	400fr multi	10.00
233S	A57c	400fr multi	10.00
233T	A57c	400fr multi	6.00
233U	A57c	500fr multi	13.50
		Nos. 233K-233U (10)	89.25

Nos. 232A 60fr, 232B 40fr, 232C 50fr, 232D 70fr, 232E 80fr, 232F 200fr, 232G, 232H 200fr, 232J 200fr, 232K, 232L, 232M 200fr, 232N-233U are airmail.

Issued: 1971 — #232A, 2/24; #232B, 3/30; #232C, 3/4; #232D, 233K, 3/15; #232E, 4/12; #232F, 233L, 4/26; #232G, 8/10; #232H, 9/6; #232J, 9/23; #232K, 10/6; #232L, 10/26; #232M, 11/16; #232N, 11/20.

1972 — #232P, 233P, Jan.; #232Q, 233M-233N, Feb.; #233Q-233R, May; #232R, 233S, 6/15; #232S, 233T, 6/26; #232T, 8/8; #232U, 8/17; #232V, 8/30; #232W, 233U, 12/11; #233A, 12/18; #233B, 12/28.

1973 — #233C-233J.

Nos. 233K-233L, 233T-233U each contain one 37x62mm stamp. Nos. 233N, 233P each contain one 32x50mm stamp. No. 233M contains one 45x65mm stamp. Nos. 233Q-233R, 233U each contain one 65x45mm stamp.

Nos. 232Q-232V, 233G, 233J, 233R-233U and possibly 232P, 232W-233F, 233H probably were not available in Chad.

Symbolic Tree — A58

1971, Mar. 21   Engr.   Perf. 13
236   A58   40fr bl grn, dk red & grn   1.00   .20
Intl. year against racial discrimination.

Paintings of Flowers A58a

Designs: 1fr, The Three Graces (detail), by Rubens. 4fr, Imperial Bouquet, by Van Os. 5fr, Bouquet, by Jan Brueghel.

1971, Apr. 28   Litho.   Perf. 12x12½
236A   A58a   Strip of 3, #a-c   5.50
For overprint see No. 278A.

Summer Olympic Games — A58b

15fr, Swimming. 20fr, Women's relay races. 25fr, Swimming, medals. 50fr, Running.

Perf. 12x12½, 12x12

1971, Apr. 28			Litho.
236B	A58b	15fr multi, vert.	1.75
236C	A58b	20fr multi, vert.	2.75
236D	A58b	25fr multi	3.50
		Nos. 236B-236D (3)	8.00

Embossed
Perf. 13
236E   A58b   25fr gold, like No. 236D   17.50

Souvenir Sheet
Litho.
Die Cut Perf 13
236F   A58b   50fr multicolored   10.00

Nos. 236D-236F are airmail. No. 236F contains one 62x36mm stamp.

Issued: #236B-236D, 236F, 4/28; #236E, 11/1.

For overprints see Nos. 251A-251D.

No. 236E probably was not available in Chad.

Map of Africa, Radar Antenna A59

Map of Africa and: 40fr, Communications tower. 50fr, Communications satellite.

1971, May 17   Engr.   Perf. 13
237   A59   5fr ultra, org & dk red   .20   .20
238   A59   40fr pur, emer & brn   .75   .20
239   A59   50fr dk red, blk & brn   1.00   .20
       Nos. 237-239 (3)   1.95   .60
3rd World Telecommunications Day.

Apollo 11 — A59a

1971, July 5   Embossed   Perf. 13
239A   A59a   10fr gold   22.50
   b.   Sheet of 1, Imperf.   37.50

No. 239Ab contains one 73x45mm stamp with same size design as No. 239A.
Nos. 239A-239Ab probably were not available in Chad.

No. 225F Overprinted in Gold

1971, July 17   Litho.   Perf. 12x12½
239C   A50b   Strip of 3, #a-c   6.00
1972 Winter Olympics, Sapporo.

Nos. 228A-228B, 228D Ovptd. with "MUNICH 72" and Olympic Rings in Gold

Perf. 12½x12, 12x12½
1971, Nov. 1			Litho.
239D	A54a	Strip of 3, #a-c	10.00
239E	A54a	Pair, #a-b + label	6.00

Souvenir Sheet
Perf. 13½x13
239F   A54a   40fr on #228D   20.00

UNICEF Emblem and Children — A60

1971, Dec. 11   Engr.   Perf. 13
240   A60   50fr Prus bl, emer & brt pink   1.10   .20
25th anniv. of UNICEF.

Gorane Nangara Dancers A61

Dancers: 15fr, Girls' initiation dance, Yondo. 30fr, Women of M'Boum, vert. 40fr, Men of Sara Kaba, vert.

1971, Dec. 18   Litho.   Perf. 13
241   A61   10fr blk & multi   .75   .20
242   A61   15fr brn org & multi   1.10   .20
243   A61   30fr bl & multi   1.50   .20
244   A61   40fr yel grn & multi   1.90   .20
       Nos. 241-244 (4)   5.25   .80

Nos. 205-210 Ovptd. in Gold

1971 Litho. Perf. 12½x13, 13x12½
244A-244F A45 1fr on #205-210 4.50
Nos. 244A-244F probably were not available in Chad.

Presidents Pompidou and Tombalbaye,
Map with Paris and Fort Lamy — A62

1972, Jan. 25 Photo. Perf. 13
245 A62 40fr blue & multi 1.75 .20
Visit of Pres. Georges Pompidou of France,
Jan. 1972.

Nos. 181-204 Ovptd. with "MUNICH
72" and Olympic Rings in Gold

1972, Feb. 7 Litho. Perf. 12½x13
245A-245X A44 1fr on #181-204 16.00
Nos. 245A-245X probably were not available in Chad.

Nos. 231G-231I Ovptd. in Gold

a

b

1972, Feb. Litho. Perf. 12x12½
246A A57b 50c Pair, #d.-e. 1.50
246B A57b 1fr Pair, #f.-g. 2.25
246C A57b 2fr Pair, #h.-i. 2.75
Nos. 246A-246C probably were not available in Chad.

President Tombalbaye — A63

1972, Apr. 13 Litho. Perf. 13
247 A63 30fr multi .40 .20
247A A63 40fr multi .60 .20
Nos. 247-247A,C112-C113 (4) 3.00 .80

Downhill Skiing — A64

75fr, Women's figure skating. 150fr, Luge.

1972, Apr. 13 Perf. 13½
248 A64 25fr multi .30 .20
249 A64 75fr multi .75 .25
250 A64 150fr multi 1.50 .45
Nos. 248-250,C114-C115 (5) 6.45 1.95
11th Winter Olympic Games, Sapporo,
Japan.

Heart — A65 Gorrizia Dubiosa — A66

1972, Apr. 25 Engr. Perf. 13
251 A65 100fr purple, bl & car 1.75 .20
"Your heart is your health," World Health
Month.

Nos. 236B-236D, 236F Ovptd. with
"MUNICH 72" and Olympic Rings in
Gold

1972 Litho. Perf. 12x12½, 12½x12
251A A58b 15fr multicolored 3.25
251B A58b 20fr multicolored 5.00
251C A58b 25fr multicolored 7.75
Nos. 251A-251C (3) 16.00

Souvenir Sheet
Die Cut Perf 13
251D A58b 50fr multicolored 47.50
Nos. 251C-251D are airmail.

1972, May 6 Photo.
Insects and Spiders: 2fr, Spider (argiope
sector). 3fr, Silk spider (nephila senegalense).
4fr, Beetle (oryctes boas). 5fr, Dragonfly
(hemistigma albipunctata).
252 A66 1fr green & multi 1.40 .20
253 A66 2fr blue & multi 2.25 .25
254 A66 3fr car rose & multi 2.50 .30

255 A66 4fr yellow grn & multi 4.50 .40
256 A66 5fr dp green & multi 5.00 .60
Nos. 252-256 (5) 15.65 1.75

Trains — A66a

1972 Litho. Perf. 12
256A A66a 10fr Orient Express 1.00
256B A66a 40fr Osaka Express 2.25
256C A66a 50fr St. Germain 2.50
256D A66a 150fr Blue train 5.00
256E A66a 200fr Trans-Europe Express 9.25
Nos. 256A-256E (5) 20.00

Souvenir Sheet
256F A66a 300fr Rogers "Madison," 1855 14.00
No. 256F contains one 60x40mm stamp.
See note before No. 225A.

Scout Greeting — A67

70fr, Mountain climbing. 80fr, Canoeing.

1972, May 15 Photo.
257 A67 30fr multi .75 .20
258 A67 70fr multi 1.40 .20
259 A67 80fr multi 1.75 .20
Nos. 257-259,C118-C119 (5) 8.40 1.30
Scout Jamboree.

Hurdles, Motion and Olympic Emblems A68

Motion and Olympic Emblems and: 130fr,
Gymnast on rings. 150fr, Swimming. 300fr,
Bicycling.

1972, June 9 Litho. Perf. 13½
260 A68 50fr blk & multi .75 .20
261 A68 130fr blk & multi 1.90 .25
262 A68 150fr blk & multi 2.25 .30
Nos. 260-262 (3) 4.90 .75

Souvenir Sheet
263 A68 300fr blk & multi 5.00 2.00
20th Olympic Games, Munich, Aug. 26-
Sept. 10.

Ski Jump, Kasaya, Japan — A69

Designs: 75fr, Cross-country skiing, P.
Tyldum, Sweden. 100fr, Figure-skating, pairs,

L. Rodnina and A. Ulanov, USSR. 130fr,
Men's speed skating, A. Schenk, Netherlands.

1972, June 15 Perf. 14½
264 A69 25fr gold & multi .40 .20
265 A69 75fr gold & multi 1.00 .25
266 A69 100fr gold & multi 1.50 .40
267 A69 130fr gold & multi 1.90 .50
Nos. 264-267,C130-C131 (6) 11.55 3.10
11th Winter Olympic Games, gold-medal
winners. Nos. 264-267 exist se-tenant with
label showing earth satellite.

Nos. 227A-227D, 227F Overprinted
With Soccer Ball, "MUNICH 72" and
Olympic Rings in Gold

1972 Litho. Perf. 12
267A A53a 1fr multicolored .95
267B A53a 4fr multicolored 1.20
267C A53a 5fr multicolored 1.90
267D A53a 5fr multicolored 1.90
Nos. 267A-267D (4) 5.95

Souvenir Sheet
Perf. 13½x13
267E A53a 15fr multicolored 9.00
Nos. 267D-267E are airmail.
Nos. 267A-267E probably were not available in Chad.

TV Tower and Weight-lifting — A70

Designs (TV Tower, Munich and): 40fr,
Woman sprinter. 60fr, Soccer goalkeeper.

1972, Aug. 15 Litho. Perf. 14½
268 A70 20fr gold & multi .65 .20
269 A70 40fr gold & multi .80 .20
270 A70 60fr gold & multi 1.40 .20
Nos. 268-270,C135-C137 (6) 10.70 2.50
20th Summer Olympic Games, Munich.
Nos. 268-270 exist se-tenant with label showing arms of Munich.

Domestic Animals A71

1972, Aug. 29 Engr. Perf. 13
271 A71 25fr Dromedary 1.75 .20
272 A71 30fr Horse 2.25 .20
273 A71 40fr Dog 3.25 .30
274 A71 45fr Goat 3.75 .40
Nos. 271-274 (4) 11.00 1.10
For surcharge see No. 293.

Tobacco Cultivation A72

1972, Oct. 24 Engr. Perf. 13
275 A72 40fr shown .75 .20
276 A72 50fr Plowing 1.25 .20

Massa Warrior — A73

Design: 20fr, Moundang warrior.

1972, Nov. 15   Photo.   _Perf. 14x13_
277   A73   15fr orange & multi   .75   .20
278   A73   20fr yellow & multi   1.00   .20

No. 236A Overprinted "Noel 1972" in gold

1972   Litho.   _Perf. 12x12½_
278A   A58a   Strip of 3, #a-c   5.50

No. 278A probably was not available in Chad.

King Faisal and Pres.
Tombalbaye — A74

1972, Nov. 17   Litho.   _Perf. 13_
279   A74   100fr gold & multi   2.50   .40

Visit of King Faisal of Saudi Arabia. See No. C143.

Gen. Gowon and Pres.
Tombalbaye — A75

1972, Dec. 7
280   A75   70fr multi   1.00   .20

Visit of Gen. Yakubu Gowon of Nigeria.

Olympic Emblem and 100-meter
Sprint, Valeri Borzov, USSR — A76

Designs (Olympic Emblem and): 20fr, Shotput, Komar, Poland. 40fr, Hammer throw, Bondartchuk, USSR. 60fr, Discus, Danek, Czechoslovakia.

1972, Dec. 22   _Perf. 11_
281   A76   10fr multi   .55   .20
282   A76   20fr multi   .55   .20
283   A76   40fr multi   .70   .20
284   A76   60fr multi   1.10   .30
    Nos. 281-284,C148-C149 (6)   10.15   2.25

20th Summer Olympic Games, winners.

Olympic Emblem and Fencing, Woyda,
Poland — A77

Olympic Emblem and: 30fr, 3-day equestrian event, Richard Meade, Gt. Britain. 50fr,

Two-man sculls, Brietzke-Mager, East Germany.

1972, Dec. 22
285   A77   20fr gold & multi   .65   .20
286   A77   30fr gold & multi   .65   .20
287   A77   50fr gold & multi   1.00   .25
    Nos. 285-287,C151-C152 (5)   10.55   2.40

20th Summer Olympic Games, winners.

1972 Summer Olympics Gold
Medalists — A77a

20fr, Teofilo Stevenson, boxing, Cuba. 25fr, Yugoslavia, team handball. 30fr, M. Peters, pentathlon, Great Britain. 40fr, basketball, USSR. No. 287E, W. Ruska, judo, Netherlands. No. 287F, Women's gymnastics, Ludmila Touristcheva, USSR. 75fr, Men's volleyball, Japan. No. 287H, A. Scalzone, shooting, Italy. No. 287I, Soccer, Poland. 130fr, J. Williams, archery, US. No. 287K, A. Nakayama, men's rings, Japan. No. 287L, Field hockey, West Germany. 200fr, Vassily Alexeiev, weight lifting, USSR. 250fr, D. Morelon, cycling, France.

1972, Dec. 22   Litho.   _Perf. 11½_
287A   A77a   20fr multicolored
287B   A77a   25fr multicolored
287C   A77a   30fr multicolored
287D   A77a   40fr multicolored
287E   A77a   50fr multicolored
287F   A77a   50fr multicolored
287G   A77a   75fr multicolored
287H   A77a   100fr multicolored
287I   A77a   100fr multicolored
287J   A77a   130fr multicolored
287K   A77a   150fr multicolored
287L   A77a   150fr multicolored
    Nos. 287A-287L (12)   19.00

Souvenir Sheets
Perf. 15
287M   A77a   200fr multicolored   13.50
287N   A77a   250fr multicolored   13.50

Nos. 287G-287N are airmail.

Soviet Flag
and
Shield — A78

1972, Dec. 30   Litho.   _Perf. 12_
288   A78   150fr red & multi   1.90   .40

50th anniversary of the Soviet Union.

High
Jump — A79

Designs (Games Emblem and): 125fr, Running. 200fr, Shot put. 250fr, Discus.

1973, Jan. 17   Litho.   _Perf. 13½x13_
289   A79   50fr vio bl & multi   .75   .20
290   A79   125fr olive & multi   1.60   .40
291   A79   200fr lilac & multi   3.00   .65
    Nos. 289-291 (3)   5.35   1.25

Souvenir Sheet
292   A79   250fr brn & multi   3.75   2.25

2nd African Games, Lagos, Nigeria, 1/7-18.

Paintings with Musical
Instruments — A79a

Details from Paintings: 30fr, Madeleine Playing her Lute, by unknown artist. 70fr, A Concert, by Lorenzo Costa. 100fr, Bass and Sheet Music, by Jean-Baptiste Oudry, horiz. 125fr, St. Cecilia and Angel, by Carlo Saraceni. 150fr, Woman Listening to Violinist, by Gabriel Metsu. 300fr, Still Life with Musical Instruments, by Pieter Claesz, horiz.

1973, Apr.   Litho.   _Perf. 11½_
292A   A79a   30fr multicolored
292B   A79a   70fr multicolored
292C   A79a   100fr multicolored
292D   A79a   125fr multicolored
292E   A79a   150fr multicolored
    Nos. 292A-292E (5)   13.50

Souvenir Sheet
Perf. 15
292F   A79a   300fr multicolored   13.50

Nos. 292D-292F are airmail.

No. 271 Surcharged with New Value, 2 Bars, and Overprinted in Red: "SECHERESSE SOLIDARITE AFRICAINE"

1973, Aug. 16   Engr.   _Perf. 13_
293   A71   100fr on 25fr multi   2.25   .50

African solidarity in drought emergency.

African Postal Union Issue
Common Design Type

1973, Sept. 17   Engr.   _Perf. 13_
294   CD137   100fr multicolored   1.75   .40

Easter
A79b

Details from paintings: 40fr, Christ on the Cross, by Lucas Cranach. 60fr, Supper in Emmaus, by Titian, horiz. 120fr, The Crucifixion, by Durer. 150fr, The Tribute, by Titian. 250fr, The Pieta, by Botticelli. 400fr, Entombment of Christ, by Gaspard Isenmann, horiz.

1973   Litho.   _Perf. 11½_
294A   A79b   40fr multicolored
294B   A79b   60fr multicolored
294C   A79b   120fr multicolored
294D   A79b   150fr multicolored
294E   A79b   250fr multicolored
    Nos. 294A-294E (5)   13.50

Souvenir Sheet
Perf. 15
294F   A79b   400fr multicolored   13.50

Nos. 294A, 294D-294F are airmail.

Animals
A79c

1973   Litho.   _Perf. 13½_
294G   A79c   20fr Sheep
294H   A79c   30fr Camels
294J   A79c   100fr Cats
294K   A79c   130fr Dogs
294L   A79c   150fr Horses
    Nos. 294G-294L (5)   13.50

Nos. 294J-294L are airmail.
See note before No. 225A.

Christmas — A79d

30fr, The Virgin & Infant Surrounded by Saints, by Lorenzo Lotto. 40fr, Madonna and Child with St. Peter and a Martyred Saint, by Paolo Veronese (not Tintoretto), vert. 55fr, Nativity Scene, by Martin Schongauer, vert. 60fr, Nativity Scene, by Federico Barocci, vert. 250fr, Adoration of the Magi, by Stephan Lochner, vert. 400fr, Epiphany, by Hans Memling.

1973   Litho.   _Perf. 11½_
294M   A79d   30fr multicolored
294N   A79d   40fr multicolored
294P   A79d   55fr multicolored
294Q   A79d   60fr multicolored
294R   A79d   250fr multicolored
    Nos. 294M-294R (5)   13.50

Souvenir Sheet
Perf. 15
294S   A79d   400fr multicolored   13.50

Nos. 294Q-294S are airmail.
See note before No. 225A.

Dinothrombium   Rotary Emblem
Tinctorium   A81
A80

1974, Sept. 3   Photo.   _Perf. 13_
295   A80   25fr _shown_   1.50   .20
296   A80   30fr Bupreste
           sternocera   2.25   .20
297   A80   40fr Diptere hyper-
           echia   2.75   .25
298   A80   50fr Chrysis   3.25   .35
299   A80   100fr Longicorn beetle   4.75   .65
300   A80   130fr Spider   7.50   .95
    Nos. 295-300 (6)   22.00   2.60

1975, Apr. 11   Typo.   _Perf. 13_
301   A81   50fr multi   1.00   .20

Rotary International, 70th anniversary.

Craterostigma Plantagineum — A82

Flowers: 10fr, Tapinanthus globiferus. 15fr, Commelina forskalaei, vert. 20fr, Adenium obesum. 25fr, Yellow hibiscus. 30fr, Red hibiscus. 40fr, Kigelia africana.

1975, Sept. 25   Photo.   Perf. 13
302 A82 5fr org & multi   .40 .20
303 A82 10fr gray bl & multi   .60 .20
304 A82 15fr yel grn & multi   .75 .20
305 A82 20fr lt brn & multi   1.00 .20
306 A82 25fr lil & multi   1.75 .25
307 A82 30fr bis & multi   1.90 .35
308 A82 40fr ultra & multi   3.00 .50
      Nos. 302-308 (7)   9.40 1.90

A. G. Bell, Satellite and Waves — A83

1976, June 10   Litho.   Perf. 12½
309 A83 100fr bl, brn & ocher   1.40 .40
310 A83 125fr lt grn, brn & ocher   1.90 .60
      Centenary of first telephone call by Alexander Graham Bell, Mar. 10, 1876.

Ice Hockey, USSR — A84

90fr, Ski jump, Karl Schnabl, Austria.

1976, June 21   Perf. 14
311 A84 60fr multi   .75 .20
312 A84 90fr multi   1.25 .25
      Nos. 311-312,C178-C179 (4)   8.25 2.05
      12th Winter Olympic Games, winners. See No. C180.

High Hurdles A85

1976, July 12   Litho.   Perf. 13½
313 A85 45fr multi   .70 .20
      Nos. 313,C187-C189 (4)   8.70 1.65
      21st Summer Olympic Games, Montreal, Canada. See No. C190.

Mars Landing and Viking Rocket A86

Mars Landing and: 90fr, Viking trajectory, Earth to Mars.

1976, July 23   Perf. 14
314 A86 45fr multi   .50 .20
315 A86 90fr multi   1.00 .20
      Nos. 314-315,C191-C193 (5)   7.35 2.05
      Viking Mars project. For overprints see Nos. 379-380.

Robert Koch, Medicine — A87

Design: 90fr, Anatole France, literature.

1976, Dec. 15
316 A87 45fr multi   .75 .20
317 A87 90fr multi   1.50 .25
      Nos. 316-317,C196-C198 (5)   9.75 2.00
      Nobel Prize winners.

Map and Flag of Chad, Clasped Hands A88

120fr, Map of Chad, people & occupations.

1976, Sept. 15   Litho.   Perf. 12½x13
318 A88 30fr multi   .60 .20
319 A88 60fr orange & multi   1.10 .30
320 A88 120fr brown & multi   2.25 .50
      Nos. 318-320 (3)   3.95 1.00
      National reconciliation.

Freed Political Prisoners — A89

Designs: 60fr, Parade of cadets.

1976, Sept. 25   Litho.   Perf. 12½
321 A89 30fr blue & multi   .30 .20
322 A89 60fr black & multi   .75 .20
323 A89 120fr red & multi   1.40 .20
      Nos. 321-323 (3)   2.45 .65
      Revolution of Apr. 13, 1975, 1st anniv.

Decorated Calabashes — A90

Designs: Various pyrographed calabashes.

1976, Nov.   Litho.   Perf. 12½x13
324 A90 30fr multi   .40 .20
325 A90 60fr multi   .90 .20
326 A90 120fr multi   1.75 .25
      Nos. 324-326 (3)   3.05 .65

Germany No. C57 and Friedrichshafen, Germany — A91

1977, Mar. 30   Perf. 14
327 A91 100fr multi   1.40 .25
      Nos. 327,C206-C209 (5)   11.55 2.10
      75th anniversary of the Zeppelin.

Elizabeth II in Coronation Regalia and Clergy — A92

Design: 450fr, Elizabeth II and Prince Philip.

1977, June 15   Litho.   Perf. 14x13½
328 A92 250fr multi   3.25 .75
      Souvenir Sheet
329 A92 450fr multi   5.75 2.50
      25th anniv. of the reign of Elizabeth II. Nos. 328-329 exist imperf. For overprints see Nos. 347-348.

Simon Bolivar A93

Famous Personalities: 175fr, Joseph J. Roberts. No. 332, Queen Wihelmina of Netherlands. No. 333, Charles de Gaulle. 325fr, King Baudouin and Queen Fabiola of Belgium.

1977, June 15   Perf. 13½x14
330 A93 150fr multi   1.50 .30
331 A93 175fr multi   2.25 .45
332 A93 200fr multi   3.00 .65
333 A93 200fr multi   3.00 .75
334 A93 325fr multi   4.00 1.00
      Nos. 330-334 (5)   13.75 3.15

Post and Telecommunications Emblem — A94

Map of Chad and Waves — A95

Society Emblem — A96

1977, Aug. 15   Litho.   Perf. 13
335 A94 30fr yel & blk   .50 .20
      Perf. 12½
336 A95 60fr multi   .75 .20
      Perf. 13½x13
337 A96 120fr multi   1.60 .50
      Nos. 335-337 (3)   2.85 .90
      Telecommunications (30fr); Natl. Telecomunications School, 10th anniv. (60fr); Intl. Telecommunication Soc. of Chad (120fr).

WHO Emblem and Man (Back Pain) — A97

World Rheumatism Year (WHO Emblem and): 60fr, Woman's head (neck pain), horiz. 120fr, Leg (knee pain).

Perf. 12½x13, 13x12½
1977, Nov. 10   Engr.
338 A97 30fr multi   .50 .20
339 A97 60fr multi   1.00 .20
340 A97 120fr multi   1.40 .40
      Nos. 338-340 (3)   2.90 .80

World Cup Emblems and Saving a Goal — A98

Designs (Argentina '78, World Cup Emblems and): 60fr, Heading the ball. 100fr, Referee whistling a goal. 200fr, World Cup poster. 300fr, Pelé. 500fr, Helmut Schoen and Munich stadium.

1977, Nov. 25   Litho.   Perf. 13½
341 A98 40fr multi   .50 .20
342 A98 60fr multi   .75 .20
343 A98 100fr multi   1.10 .25

344	A98 200fr multi	2.50	.50
345	A98 300fr multi	3.75	.75
	Nos. 341-345 (5)	8.60	1.90

Souvenir Sheet

346	A98 500fr multi	5.75	3.00

World Cup Soccer Championship, Argentina '78.

For overprints see Nos. 359-364.

Nos. 328-329 Overprinted in Silver: "ANNIVERSAIRE DU COURONNEMENT 1953-1978"

1978, Sept. 13   Perf. 14x13½

347	A92 250fr multi	3.00	1.00

Souvenir Sheet

348	A92 450fr multi	5.50	4.50

25th anniv. of coronation of Elizabeth II.

Abraham and Melchisedek, by Rubens — A99

Rubens Paintings: 120fr, Helene Fourment, vert. 200fr, David and the Elders of Israel. 300fr, Anne of Austria, vert. 500fr, Marie de Medicis, vert.

1978, Nov. 23   Litho.   Perf. 13½

349	A99 60fr multi	.75	.20
350	A99 120fr multi	1.75	.35
351	A99 200fr multi	3.00	.75
352	A99 300fr multi	4.50	1.25
	Nos. 349-352 (4)	10.00	2.55

Souvenir Sheet

353	A99 500fr multi	6.75	3.00

Peter Paul Rubens (1577-1640).

Dürer Portrait A100

Dürer Paintings: 150fr, Jacob Muffel. 250fr, Young Woman. 350fr, Oswolt Krel.

1978, Nov. 23

354	A100 60fr multi	.60	.20
355	A100 150fr multi	1.75	.50
356	A100 250fr multi	3.00	.80
357	A100 350fr multi	4.50	1.25
	Nos. 354-357 (4)	9.85	2.75

Head, Village and Fly — A101

1978, Nov. 28   Perf. 13

358	A101 60f multi	.75	.20

National Health Day.

Nos. 341-346 Overprinted in Silver:
a. 1962 BRESIL-TCHECOSLOVA-QUIE / 3-1
b. 1966 / GRANDE BRETAGNE / - ALLEMAGNE (RFA) / 4-2
c. 1970 BRESIL-ITALIE 4-1
d. 1974 ALLEMAGNE (RFA)- / PAYS BAS 2-1

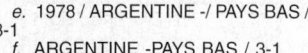

e. 1978 / ARGENTINE -/ PAYS BAS / 3-1
f. ARGENTINE -PAYS BAS / 3-1

1978, Dec. 30   Litho.   Perf. 13½

359	A98(a) 40fr multi	.50	.20
360	A98(b) 60fr multi	.75	.20
361	A98(c) 100fr multi	1.40	.40
362	A98(d) 200fr multi	2.50	.75
363	A98(e) 300fr multi	3.50	1.25
	Nos. 359-363 (5)	8.65	2.80

Souvenir Sheet

364	A98(f) 500fr multi	5.75	5.00

World Soccer Championship winners.

UPU Emblems, Camel Caravan, Satellites — A102

Design: 150fr, Obus woman and houses, Massa Territory, hibiscus.

1979, June 8   Litho.   Perf. 12x12½

365	A102 60fr multi	3.00	.20
366	A102 150fr multi	5.00	.40

Philexafrique II, Libreville, Gabon, June 8-17. Nos. 365, 366 each printed in sheets of 10 with 5 labels showing exhibition emblem.

Wildlife Fund Emblem and Gazelle — A103

Protected Animals.

1979, Sept. 15   Litho.   Perf. 14½

367	A103 40fr shown	2.00	.30
368	A103 50fr Addax	2.25	.50
369	A103 60fr Oryx antelope	2.75	.75
370	A103 100fr Cheetah	4.25	1.40
371	A103 150fr Zebra	5.75	1.90
372	A103 300fr Rhinoceros	11.50	3.00
	Nos. 367-372 (6)	28.50	7.85

Souvenir Sheet

Holy Family, by Dürer — A104

1979, Sept. 1   Perf. 13½

373	A104 500fr brown & dull red	6.75	2.50

Boy and Handpainted Doors — A105

IYC Emblem and: 75fr, Oriental girl. 100fr, Caucasian girl, doves. 150fr, African boys. 250fr, Pencil and outlines of child's hands.

1979, Sept. 19   Litho.   Perf. 13½

374	A105 65fr multi	.60	.20
375	A105 75fr multi	.75	.20
376	A105 100fr multi	1.00	.25
377	A105 150fr multi	1.50	.40
	Nos. 374-377 (4)	3.85	1.05

Souvenir Sheet

378	A105 250fr multi	3.00	1.50

Nos. 314-315 Overprinted "ALUNISSAGE/APOLLO XI/JUILLET 1969" and Emblem

1979, Nov. 26   Litho.   Perf. 13½x14

379	A86 45fr multi	.60	.20
380	A86 90fr multi	1.00	.30
	Nos. 379-380,C240-C242 (5)	7.45	2.50

Apollo 11 moon landing, 10th anniversary.

Ski Jump, Lake Placid '80 Emblem — A106

Lake Placid '80 Emblem and: 20fr, Slalom, vert. 40fr, Biathlon, vert. 150fr, Women's slalom, vert. 350fr, Cross-country skiing. 500fr, Downhill skiing.

1979, Dec. 18   Perf. 14½

381	A106 20fr multi	.30	.20
382	A106 40fr multi	.65	.20
383	A106 60fr multi	.80	.20
384	A106 150fr multi	1.75	.50
385	A106 350fr multi	3.00	1.40
386	A106 500fr multi	4.50	1.90
	Nos. 381-386 (6)	11.00	4.40

13th Winter Olympic Games, Lake Placid, NY, Feb. 12-24, 1980.

Jet over Map of Africa A107

1980, Feb. 20   Litho.   Perf. 12½

387	A107 15fr yellow & multi	.20	.20
388	A107 30fr blue & multi	.40	.20
389	A107 60fr red & multi	.60	.20
	Nos. 387-389 (3)	1.20	.60

ASECNA (Air Safety Board), 20th anniv.

1982 World Cup Soccer Championships, Spain — A108

1982   Litho.   Perf. 13½

390	A108 30fr Hungary	.30	.20
391	A108 40fr Italy	.40	.20
392	A108 50fr Algeria	.50	.20
393	A108 60fr Argentina	.60	.20
	Nos. 390-393,C258-C259 (6)	5.80	1.50

21st Birthday of Princess Diana A109

1982, July 2   Litho.   Perf. 13½

395	A109 30fr 1961	.30	.20
396	A109 40fr 1965	.40	.20
397	A109 50fr 1967	.50	.20
398	A109 60fr 1975	.60	.20
	Nos. 395-398,C260-C261 (6)	5.80	2.00

For overprints see Nos. 413-419B.

A110

1984 Summer Olympics, Los Angeles — A110a

#405A, Runner. #405B, Long jumper, vert.

1982, Aug. 2   Litho.   Perf. 13½

399	A110 30fr Gymnast	.30	.20
400	A110 40fr Equestrian	.40	.20
401	A110 50fr Judo	.50	.20
402	A110 60fr High jump	.60	.20
403	A110 80fr Hurdles	1.00	.25
404	A110 300fr Woman gymnast	3.00	.95
	Nos. 399-404 (6)	5.80	2.00

Souvenir Sheet

405	A110 500fr Relay race	5.50	1.50

For surcharge see No. C302.

1982, July 31   Litho. & Embossed

405A	A110a 1500fr gold & multi	16.00	

Souvenir Sheet

405B	A110a 1500fr gold & multi	12.00	

No. 405 contains one 56x39mm stamp. Nos. 403-405B airmail.
No. 405A exists in a souvenir sheet of 1. Value $47.50.

Scouting Year — A111

Boy Scouts, 75th Anniv. A111a

Scouts from various countries. No. 412A, Lord Robert Baden-Powell. No. 412B, Scouts at campsite, Baden-Powell, horiz.

1982, July 15
406	A111	30fr West Germany	.30	.20
407	A111	40fr Upper Volta	.40	.20
408	A111	50fr Mali	.50	.20
409	A111	60fr Scotland	.60	.20
410	A111	80fr Kuwait	1.00	.25
411	A111	300fr Chad	3.00	.95
		Nos. 406-411 (6)	5.80	2.00

Souvenir Sheet
412	A111	500fr Chad, diff.	5.50	2.00

Litho. & Embossed
412A	A111a	1500fr gold & multi	17.00

Souvenir Sheet
412B	A111a	1500fr gold & multi	17.00

No. 412 contains one 53x35mm stamp. Nos. 410-412B airmail.
No. 412A exists in a souvenir sheet of 1. Value $40.
For overprints see Nos. 466-472B.

Nos. 395-398, C260-C262B Overprinted: "21 JUIN 1982 / WILLIAM ARTHUR PHILIP LOUIS/ PRINCE DE GALLES"

1982, Oct. 4   Litho.   Perf. 13½
413	A109	30fr multi	.30	.20
414	A109	40fr multi	.40	.20
415	A109	50fr multi	.50	.20
416	A109	60fr multi	.60	.20
417	A109	80fr multi	1.00	.25
418	A109	300fr multi	3.00	.95
		Nos. 413-418 (6)	5.80	2.00

Souvenir Sheet
419	A109	500fr multi	5.50	1.60

Litho. & Embossed
419A	AP71b	1500fr on #C262A	16.00

Souvenir Sheet
419B	AP71b	1500fr on #C262B	13.50

Birth of Prince William of Wales, June 21. Nos. 417-419B airmail.
No. 419A exists in a souvenir sheet of 1. Value $42.50.

A112

1982 World Cup Soccer Championships, Spain — A112a

Various players and flags. No. 426A, Dino Zoff, Italy, holding World Cup trophy. No.

426B, Paolo Rossi, Italy, two players, trophy, horiz.

1982, Nov. 30
420	A112	30fr multi	.30	.20
421	A112	40fr multi	.40	.20
422	A112	50fr multi	.50	.20
423	A112	60fr multi	.60	.20
424	A112	80fr multi	1.00	.25
425	A112	300fr multi	3.00	.95
		Nos. 420-425 (6)	5.80	2.00

Souvenir Sheet
426	A112	500fr multi	5.50	2.00

Litho. & Embossed
426A	A112a	1500fr gold & multi	16.00

Souvenir Sheet
426B	A112a	1500fr gold & multi	16.00

No. 426 contains one 56x32mm stamp. Nos. 424-426B airmail.
No. 426A exists in a souvenir sheet of 1. Value $42.50.
For surcharge see No. C306.

A113

Chess Champions — A113a

#433A, Bobby Fischer. #433B, William Steinitz.

1982, Dec. 24
427	A113	30fr Philidor	1.00	.20
428	A113	40fr Paul Morphy	1.10	.20
429	A113	50fr Howard Staunton	1.25	.20
430	A113	60fr Capablanca	1.40	.20
431	A113	80fr Boris Spassky	2.10	.25
432	A113	300fr Anatoly Karpov	3.75	.75
		Nos. 427-432 (6)	10.60	1.80

Souvenir Sheet
433	A113	500fr Victor Korchnoi	9.00	3.00

Litho. & Embossed
433A	A113a	1500fr gold & multi	17.50

Souvenir Sheet
433B	A113a	1500fr gold & multi	12.00

No. 433 contains one 53x35mm stamp. Nos. 431-433B airmail.
No. 433A exists in a souvenir sheet of 1. Value $50.
For overprints see Nos. 459-465.

2nd UN Conference on Peaceful Uses of Outer Space, Vienna, Aug. 9-21 — A114

A114a

Inventors and Satellites: 30fr, K.E. Tsiolkovsky, Soyuz. 40fr, R.H. Goddard, space telescope design. 50fr, Korolev, ultraviolet telescope. 60fr, von Braun, Columbia space shuttle. 80fr, Esnault Pelterie, Ariana rocket. 300fr, H. Oberth, orbital space station. 500fr, Pres. Kennedy, Apollo 11 badge, lunar rover. No. 440A, Sir Bernard Lovell, Viking I & II. No. 440B, Sir Isaac Newton, satellite TDF 1.

1983, Feb. 1   Litho.   Perf. 13½
434	A114	30fr multi	.30	.20
435	A114	40fr multi	.40	.20
436	A114	50fr multi	.50	.20
437	A114	60fr multi	.60	.20
438	A114	80fr multi	1.00	.25
439	A114	300fr multi	3.00	.95
		Nos. 434-439 (6)	5.80	2.00

Souvenir Sheet
440	A114	500fr multi	5.50	2.50

Litho. & Embossed
440A	A114a	1500fr gold & multi	16.00

Souvenir Sheet
440B	A114a	1500fr gold & multi	12.00

No. 440 contains one 42x50mm stamp. Nos. 438-440B airmail.
No. 440A exists in a souvenir sheet of 1. Value $50.

Bobsledding — A115

Woman Figure Skater A115a

Design: No. 447B, Slalom skier, horiz.

1983, Apr. 25   Litho.   Perf. 13½
441	A115	30fr shown	.30	.20
442	A115	40fr Speed skating	.40	.20
443	A115	50fr Cross-country skiing	.50	.20
444	A115	60fr Hockey	.60	.25
445	A115	80fr Ski jumping	1.00	.30
446	A115	300fr Downhill skiing	3.00	1.10
		Nos. 441-446 (6)	5.80	2.25

Souvenir Sheet
447	A115	500fr Figure skating	5.50	1.60

Litho. & Embossed
447A	A115a	1500fr gold & multi	16.00

Souvenir Sheet
447B	A115a	1500fr gold & multi	12.00

14th Winter Olympic Games, Sarajevo, Yugoslavia, Feb. 8-19, 1984. Nos. 445-447B airmail.
No. 447A exists in a souvenir sheet of 1. Value $45.
For surcharge see No. C298.

First Manned Balloon Flight, 200th Anniv. A116

Designs: 25fr, Hot air balloon, Montgolfier Brothers. 45fr, Captive balloon, Pilatre De Rozier. 50fr, First parachute descent, Jacques Garnerin. 60fr, Chelsea balloon, J.P. Blanchard.

1983, May 30   Litho.   Perf. 13½
448	A116	25fr multi	.30	.20
449	A116	45fr multi	.40	.20
450	A116	50fr multi	.50	.20
451	A116	60fr multi	.60	.20
		Nos. 448-451,C268-C269 (6)	5.80	1.45

Automobiles — A116a

Automobiles and their builders: 25fr, 1927 Mercedes Type S, Gottlieb Daimler and Karl Benz. 45fr, 1913 Torpedo Martini Type GC 32-2, 6L, Friedrich Martini. 50fr, 1926 Chrysler "70," Walter P. Chrysler. 60fr, 1929 Alfa Romeo 6C 1750 Grand Sport, Nicola Romeo. 80fr, 1934 Phantom II Continental, Stewart Rolls and Henry Royce. 250fr, 1948 Talbot Lago, Lord Shrewsbury and Talbot.

1983, July 15   Litho.   Perf. 13½
451A	A116a	25fr multicolored		
451B	A116a	45fr multicolored		
451C	A116a	50fr multicolored		
451D	A116a	60fr multicolored		
451E	A116a	80fr multicolored		
451F	A116a	250fr multicolored		
		Nos. 451A-451F (6)	6.75	1.60

Nos. 451E-451F are airmail.

1984 Summer Olympics, Los Angeles A117

A117a

1983, Nov. 15   Litho.   Perf. 13½
452	A117	25fr Kayak	.30	.20
453	A117	45fr Long jump	.60	.20
454	A117	50fr Boxing	.70	.20
455	A117	60fr Discus	.75	.20
456	A117	80fr Running	1.00	.25
457	A117	350fr Equestrian	3.50	.75
		Nos. 452-457 (6)	6.85	1.80

Souvenir Sheet
458	A117	500fr Gymnastics	5.50	2.50

Litho. & Embossed
458A	A117a	1500fr Hurdles	16.00

Souvenir Sheet
458B	A117a	1500fr Equestrian, vert.	12.00

Nos. 456-458B are airmail.
No. 458A exists in a souvenir sheet of 1. Value $47.50.

Pres. Hissein
Habre — A117b

Designs: Nos. 458D, 458H, Sources of food.
Nos. 458E, 458I, Dove of peace, different tribal groups, country map.

1983, Dec. 26   Litho.   Perf. 13½
458C	A117b	50fr multicolored	.60	.20
458D	A117b	50fr multicolored	.60	.20
458E	A117b	50fr multicolored	.60	.20
458F	A117b	60fr multicolored	.70	.20
458G	A117b	80fr multicolored	.90	.25
458H	A117b	80fr multicolored	.90	.25
458I	A117b	80fr multicolored	.90	.25
458J	A117b	100fr multicolored	1.10	.35

See Nos. C276-C279.

Nos. 427-433 Overprinted: "60e
ANNIVERSAIRE FEDERATION /
MONDIALE D'ECHECS 1924-1984"

1983, Dec. 27   Litho.   Perf. 13½
459	A113	30fr multi	.90	.20
460	A113	40fr multi	1.10	.20
461	A113	50fr multi	1.40	.20
462	A113	60fr multi	1.75	.20
463	A113	80fr multi	2.25	.30
464	A113	300fr multi	4.50	.75
	Nos. 459-464 (6)		*11.90*	*1.85*

Souvenir Sheet
465	A113	500fr multi	4.50	2.50

World Chess Fedn., 60th anniv.

Nos. 406-412B Ovptd. with Emblem
for the 15th World Scout Jamboree,
Alberta, Canada, 1983

1983, Dec. 27   Litho.   Perf. 13½
466	A111	30fr multi	.30	.20
467	A111	40fr multi	.40	.20
468	A111	50fr multi	.50	.20
469	A111	60fr multi	.60	.20
470	A111	80fr multi	.70	.20
471	A111	300fr multi	3.00	.50
	Nos. 466-471 (6)		*5.50*	*1.50*

Souvenir Sheet
472	A111	500fr multi	6.00	2.50

Litho. & Embossed
472A	A111a	1500fr on #412A	16.00

Souvenir Sheet
472B	A111a	1500fr on #412B	12.00

Locomotive "Lady," 1879 — A118

1984, Mar. 15
473	A118	50fr shown	.60	.20
474	A118	200fr Sailboat, Lake Chad	2.40	.60
475	A118	300fr Graf Zeppelin	3.25	.90
476	A118	350fr Renault desert transport, 1930	4.00	1.10
477	A118	400fr Bloch 120 monoplane	4.25	1.25
478	A118	500fr Air Africa DC-8	5.50	1.50
	Nos. 473-478 (6)		*20.00*	*5.55*

Souvenir Sheet
479	A118	600fr Intelsat V satellite	5.75	5.00

Nos. 477-479 airmail. For surcharge see
No. 579.

Liberation, 2nd
Anniv. — A119

Pres. Hissein
Habre — A120

1984, June 6   Perf. 12½
480	A119	50fr multi	.60	.20

1984, June 18   Perf. 12½x13
481	A120	125fr multi	1.50	.40

Anniversaries and Events — A121

Designs: 50fr, Pres. Habre, civil war martyrs. 200fr, Paul Harris, Rotary Intl. headquarters, Illinois. 300fr, Alfred Nobel, will establishing fund for Prizes. 350fr, Raphael, detail from Virgin with Child and St. John the Baptist. 400fr, Rembrandt, detail from The Holy Family. 500fr, J.W. Goethe, scene from Faust. 600fr, Rubens, detail from Helene Fourment and Her Two Children.

1984, Jan. 16   Litho.   Perf. 13½
482	A121	50fr multi	.50	.20
483	A121	200fr multi	1.90	.30
484	A121	300fr multi	3.00	.45
485	A121	350fr multi	3.75	.55
486	A121	400fr multi	4.50	.60
487	A121	500fr multi	5.75	.70
	Nos. 482-487 (6)		*19.40*	*2.80*

Souvenir Sheet
488	A121	600fr multi	6.75	2.50

Nos. 486-488 are airmail.

Homage to Our
Martyred
Dead — A122

1984, Feb. 22   Litho.   Perf. 13½
500	A122	50fr multi	.50	.20
501	A122	80fr multi	.75	.20
502	A122	120fr multi	1.10	.20
503	A122	200fr multi	1.90	.40
504	A122	250fr multi	2.50	.50
	Nos. 500-504 (5)		*6.75*	*1.50*

#503-504 airmail. For surcharge see #C303.

World Communications Year — A123

1984, Feb. 29   Litho.   Perf. 13½
505	A123	50fr sil & multi	.50	.20
506	A123	60fr sil & multi	.60	.20
507	A123	70fr sil & multi	.75	.20
508	A123	125fr sil & multi	1.10	.20
509	A123	250fr sil & multi	2.50	.50
	Nos. 505-509 (5)		*5.45*	*1.30*

#508-509 airmail. For surcharge see #C304.

Anniversaries and Events — A123a

50fr, Durer, detail from Madonna of the Rosary. 200fr, Henri Dunant, Red Cross founder, Battle of Solferino. 300fr, Early telephone, Goonhilly Downs Satellite Station, Britain. 350fr, J.F. Kennedy, Neil Armstrong's 1st step on Moon, 1969. 400fr, Europe-Africa Satellite infrared photograph. 500fr, Prince Charles & Lady Diana. 600fr, Wedding photograph of Prince Charles & Lady Diana.

1984
510	A123a	50fr multi	.50	.20
511	A123a	200fr multi	2.10	.30
512	A123a	300fr multi	3.00	.45
513	A123a	350fr multi	3.50	.50
514	A123a	400fr multi	3.75	.55
515	A123a	500fr multi	5.00	.80
	Nos. 510-515 (6)		*17.85*	*2.80*

Souvenir Sheet
516	A121	600fr multicolored		5.25

A souvenir sheet of 6 containing #510-515
exists. Nos. 514-516 are airmail.
For surcharge see No. 578.

Development of
Communications — A123b

Ships and locomotives.

1984, Aug. 1   Litho.   Perf. 12½
517	A123b	90fr Indiaman, East India Co.	1.10	.20
518	A123b	100fr Nord 701, 1885	1.10	.20
519	A123b	125fr Vera Cruz	1.75	.20
520	A123b	150fr Columbia, 1888	1.75	.20
521	A123b	200fr Carlisle Castle	2.50	.25
522	A123b	250fr Rete Mediterranea, 1900	3.00	.30
523	A123b	300fr Britannia	3.25	.35
524	A123b	350fr Mav 114	3.75	.50
	Nos. 517-524 (8)		*18.20*	*2.20*

Christmas — A124

1984, Dec. 28   Litho.   Perf. 13
525	A124	50fr lt bl & org brn	.50	.20
526	A124	60fr ver & org brn	.60	.20
527	A124	80fr emer & org brn	.75	.20
528	A124	85fr rose lil & org brn	.75	.20

529	A124	100fr org yel & org brn	1.00	.30
530	A124	135fr dp bl vio & org brn	1.25	.40
	Nos. 525-530 (6)		*4.85*	*1.50*

European Music
Year — A125

Instruments.

1985, Apr. 30   Litho.   Perf. 12x12½
531	A125	20fr Guitar	.20	.20
532	A125	25fr Harp	.30	.20
533	A125	30fr Xylophone	.40	.20
534	A125	50fr Shoulder drum	.50	.20
535	A125	70fr like #534	.70	.25
536	A125	80fr like #532	.75	.30
537	A125	100fr like #531	1.00	.40
538	A125	250fr like #533	2.50	.80
	Nos. 531-538 (8)		*6.35*	*2.55*

Mushrooms
A126

1985, May 15   Litho.   Perf. 12½
539	A126	25fr Chlorophyllum molybdites	.60	.20
540	A126	30fr Tulostoma volvulatum	.70	.20
541	A126	50fr Lentinus tuberregium	1.00	.20
542	A126	70fr like #541	1.40	.20
543	A126	80fr Podaxis pistillaris	1.60	.20
544	A126	100fr like #539	2.50	.35
	Nos. 539-544 (6)		*7.80*	*1.35*

Anniversaries and Events — A127

Designs: 25fr, Abraham Lincoln. 45fr, Henri Dunant, Geneva birthplace and red cross. 50fr, Gottlieb Daimler, 1887 Motor Carriage. 60fr, Louis Bleriot, Bleriot XI monoplane, 1909. 80fr, Paul Harris, Chicago site of Rotary Intl. founding. 350fr, Auguste Piccard, bathyscaphe Trieste, 1953. 600fr, Anatoly Karpov, 1981 world chess champion. 1500fr, Paul Harris.

1985, May 25   Litho.   Perf. 13½
545	A127	25fr multi	.30	.20
546	A127	45fr multi	.60	.20
547	A127	50fr multi	.75	.20
548	A127	60fr multi	1.00	.25
549	A127	80fr multi	1.10	.35
550	A127	350fr multi	4.00	1.25
	Nos. 545-550 (6)		*7.75*	*2.45*

Souvenir Sheets
551	A127	600fr multi	6.75	5.00

Litho. & Embossed
551A	A127	1500fr Paul Harris on Medal	14.50

No. 551A contains one 130x90mm stamp.
Nos. 548-551A are airmail.
Souvenir sheets of 1 exist for #545-551.

Intl. Youth
Year — A128

1985, May 30   Litho.   Perf. 13
552 A128 70fr Development
              levels, vert.   .70 .20
553 A128 200fr Globe   1.75 .50

A129

3rd Anniv.
of the
Republic
A130

Perf. 13, 12½x13
1985, June 7   Litho.
554 A129 70fr Hand, claw   .70 .20
555 A129 70fr Hands, map   .70 .20
556 A130 70fr Pres. Hissein
              Habre   .70 .20
557 A129 110fr like #554   1.10 .40
558 A129 110fr like #555   1.25 .40
559 A130 110fr like #556   1.25 .40
      Nos. 554-559 (6)   5.70 1.80

Audubon Birth
Bicent. — A131

1985, July 20   Engr.   Perf. 13
560 A131 70fr Stork   1.10 .30
561 A131 110fr Ostrich   1.60 .40
562 A131 150fr Marabou   2.25 .65
563 A131 200fr Snake eagle   3.00 .90
      Nos. 560-563 (4)   7.95 2.25
Souvenir Sheet
564 A131 500fr like 200fr   6.75 5.00

Mammals
A132

1985, Aug. 25
565 A132 50fr Waterbuck   .75 .25
566 A132 70fr Kudus, horiz.   1.00 .40
567 A132 250fr Shaggy mouflon 3.25 1.25
      Nos. 565-567 (3)   5.00 1.90
Souvenir Sheet
568 A132 500fr White rhinoceros 5.75 5.00

UN, 40th Anniv. — A133

1985, Nov. 24
569 A133 200fr brt bl, red & brn 2.25 .75

Chad Admission
to UN, 25th
Anniv. — A134

1985, Nov. 24
570 A134 300fr red, brt bl & yel 3.25 1.00

President's
Visit to the
Nation's
Interior
A135

1986, June 7   Litho.   Perf. 12½x13
571 A135 100fr multi   1.10 .20
572 A135 170fr multi   2.25 .35
573 A135 200fr multi   2.50 .45
      Nos. 571-573 (3)   5.85 1.00

Lions Club Intl. — A135a

1987   Litho.   Perf. 14
573A A135a 30fr Like #573C
573C A135a 100fr Sick child
573E A135a 170fr Three chil-
                dren, horiz.
573F A135a 200fr Eye exam,
                horiz.
    There are two additional stamps in this. The
editors would like to examine them.

World Wildlife Fund — A136

Various mouflons, *Ammotragus lervia*.

1988, Nov. 10   Litho.   Perf. 13
574 A136 25fr shown   2.50 .50
575 A136 45fr Adult, young   3.25 .75
576 A136 70fr Two adults, diff. 4.25 1.25
577 A136 100fr Adults, young 6.00 1.75
      Nos. 574-577 (4)   16.00 4.25

Nos. 512 and 475 Surcharged
1989   Litho.   Perf. 13½
578 A123a 170fr on 300fr #512
579 A118 240fr on 300fr #475

Liberation — A137

1989   Perf. 11½x12
580 A137 20fr multi   .20 .20
581 A137 25fr multi   .30 .20
582 A137 40fr multi   .50 .20
583 A137 100fr multi   1.10 .30
584 A137 170fr multi   1.75 .50
      Nos. 580-584 (5)   3.85 1.40

World Post Day —
A137a

1989, Oct. 9   Photo.   Perf. 12
Granite Paper
584A A137a 100fr grn bl & mul-
                ti
584B A137a 120fr red & multi
584C A137a 170fr purple &
                multi
584D A137a 250fr olive & multi
      Nos. 584A-584D (4)   160.00

Visit of Pope John Paul II — A138

    Cathedral in Chad and: 20fr, 100fr, Pope
holding crosier. 80fr, 170fr, Pope, diff.

1989, Dec. 20   Litho.   Perf. 13
585 A138 20fr multicolored   .35 .20
586 A138 80fr multicolored   1.10 .40
587 A138 100fr multicolored 1.40 .50
588 A138 170fr multicolored 2.25 1.10
      Nos. 585-588 (4)   5.10 2.20

Traditional Hair
Styles — A139

1989, Oct. 9   Photo.   Perf. 12
Granite Paper
589 A139 100fr apple grn &
                multi
590 A139 120fr purple & multi
591 A139 170fr pink & multi
592 A139 250fr org yel & multi
      Nos. 589-592 (4)   160.00

Vaccinations
A140

1991, Dec. 1   Photo.   Perf. 11½
Granite Paper
593 A140 30fr brown & multi   .30 .20
594 A140 100fr green & multi 1.00 .45
595 A140 170fr vio & multi   1.60 .75
596 A140 180fr blue & multi 1.75 .80
597 A140 200fr red & multi   1.90 .90
      Nos. 593-597 (5)   6.55 3.10

Liberty and
Democracy Day —
A141

1991, Dec. 1   Litho.
598 A141 10fr green & multi   .20 .20
599 A141 20fr lilac & multi   .20 .20
600 A141 40fr yellow & multi .40 .20
601 A141 70fr blue & multi   .65 .30
602 A141 130fr tan & multi   1.25 .75
603 A141 200fr pink & multi 1.90 1.00
      Nos. 598-603 (6)   4.60 2.65

Fight Against
Insect Pests —
A141a

1992, Sept. 1   Photo.   Perf. 12
603A A141a 25fr multicolored
603B A141a 45fr multicolored
603C A141a 100fr multicolored
603D A141a 150fr multicolored
603E A141a 170fr multicolored
      Nos. 603A-603E (5)   160.00

A142

1992, Nov. 15   Litho.   Perf. 11½
604 A142 20fr bright yel & multi .20 .20
605 A142 45fr golden yel & mul-
                ti   .40 .20
606 A142 85fr pink & multi   .75 .35
607 A142 170fr blue & multi   1.50 .70
608 A142 300fr gray & multi   3.00 1.40
      Nos. 604-608 (5)   5.85 2.85
    Doctors Without Borders, 20th anniv.

Campaign Against Illiteracy A143

1992, Nov. 30
609	A143	25fr yel grn & multi	.20	.20
610	A143	40fr golden yel & multi	.40	.20
611	A143	70fr pink & multi	.60	.30
612	A143	100fr lilac & multi	.75	.40
613	A143	180fr blue & multi	1.60	.60
614	A143	200fr gray & multi	1.75	.70
		Nos. 609-614 (6)	5.30	2.40

Intl. Conference on Nutrition, Rome — A144

1992, Dec. 15
615	A144	10fr yellow & multi	.20	.20
616	A144	60fr pink & multi	1.00	.25
617	A144	120fr yel grn & multi	1.75	.40
618	A144	500fr blue & multi	4.50	1.60
		Nos. 615-618 (4)	7.45	2.45

Palace of the People A145

1993, Apr. 15   Litho.   Perf. 11½
619	A145	80fr multi		
620	A145	100fr multi		
621	A145	130fr multi	—	—
622	A145	400fr multi		
		Nos. 619-622 (4)	*160.00*	

Natl. Conference A146   OAU, 30th Anniv. A147

1993, Dec. 1   Litho.   Perf. 11¾
Granite paper
623	A146	55fr multi	.50	.35
624	A146	70fr multi	.70	.45
625	A146	110fr multi	1.10	.80
626	A146	125fr multi	1.10	.90
		Nos. 623-626 (4)	3.40	2.50

1993, Dec. 4   Litho.   Perf. 11½x11¾
627	A147	15fr multi	.20	.20
628	A147	30fr multi	.30	.20
629	A147	110fr multi	1.10	.80
630	A147	190fr multi	1.90	1.50
		Nos. 627-630 (4)	3.50	2.70

Victor Schoelcher (1804-93), Abolitionist A148

Perf. 11¾x11½
1993, Dec. 26   Litho.
631	A148	55fr multi	.40	.40
632	A148	105fr multi	1.10	.75
633	A148	125fr multi	1.40	1.10
634	A148	300fr multi	2.75	2.00

Tourism A149

Perf. 11¾x11½
1993, Dec. 27   Litho.
635	A149	15fr multi	37.50	20.00
636	A149	95fr multi	37.50	20.00
637	A149	100fr multi	37.50	20.00
638	A149	190fr multi	—	—

Bank of Central African States A150

1994, June 22   Litho.   Perf. 11½
639	A150	20fr multicolored	.20	.20
640	A150	30fr pink & multi	.20	.20
641	A150	105fr blue & multi	.70	.30
642	A150	190fr lilac & multi	1.25	.90

Huts for Storing Grain A151

Designs: 75fr, Arabe, kim. 150fr, Sara, moundang. 300fr, Boulala, kotoko. 450fr, Ouaddai, kenga.

1995, Oct. 15   Litho.   Perf. 14
643	A151	75fr multicolored	.45	.20
644	A151	150fr multicolored	.80	.30
645	A151	300fr multicolored	1.50	.75
646	A151	450fr multicolored	2.50	1.00

Souvenir Sheet

Chinese Post, Cent. — A151a

1996   Litho.   Perf. 13¼
646A	A151a	270fr multi	1.60	1.50

1996 Olympic Games, Atlanta A151b

No. 646B: e, Tennis. f, Equestrian. g, Soccer. h, Boxing.
No. 646C: i, Judo. j, Running. k, Cycling. l, Table tennis.
1500fr, Hurdler.

1996   Litho.   Perf. 13¼
646B	A151b	250fr Sheet of 4, #e-h	4.00	4.00
646C	A151b	300fr Sheet of 4, #i-l	5.00	5.00

Souvenir Sheet
646D	A151b	1500fr multi	6.25	6.25

No. 646D contains one 39x57mm stamp.

1995 Boy Scout Jamboree, Holland — A152

Mushrooms: 150fr, Amanita phalloides. 170fr, Phallus impudicus. 200fr, Lyloperdon perlatum. 350fr, Hydne commun. 450fr, Agaricus bisporus. 800fr, Cortinarius orellanus.
1500fr, Pleurotus ostreatus.

1996, Apr. 15   Litho.   Perf. 13½
647-652	A152	Set of 6	9.25	4.75
	a.	Souvenir sheet, #647-652	9.25	4.75

Souvenir Sheet
653	A152	1500fr multicolored	6.50	3.25

Nos. 647-652 exist in souvenir sheets of 1.

Butterflies, Mushrooms and Minerals A152a

No. 653A: g, Papilio zalmoxis. h, Anacridium melanorhodon. i, Otidea leporina. j, Haliaetus vocifer.
No. 653B: k, Amanita phalloides, Papilio dardanus. l, Papilio antimachus, Cortinarius praestans. m, Phallus impudicus, Chrysidia croesus. n, Papilio dardanus, Lycoperon perlatum.
No. 653C: o, Charaxes brutus. p, Epiphora albida. q, Euchloron megaera. r, Salamis duprei.
No. 653D: s, Disthene. t, Olivine. u, Sphene. v, Hemimorphite.
No. 653E, Argema mittrei. No. 653F, Zoisite.

1996   Litho.   Perf. 13¼
653A	A152a	350fr Sheet of 4, #g-j	5.75	5.75
653B	A152a	400fr Sheet of 4, #k-n	6.50	6.50
653C	A152a	650fr Sheet of 4, #o-r	10.50	10.50
653D	A152a	800fr Sheet of 4, #s-v	13.00	13.00
		Nos. 653B-653D (3)	30.00	30.00

Souvenir Sheets
653E	A152a	2000fr multi	8.25	8.25
653F	A152a	2000fr multi	8.25	8.25

A number has been reserved for an additional sheet in this set. Nos. 653E-653F each contain one 42x36mm stamp.

Greenpeace, 25th Anniv. — A153

No. 654: a, 170fr, Green coral, school of small fish. b, 200fr, Yellow & orange coral. c, 300fr, Red orange coral. d, 350fr, White coral. 1500fr, Diver, coral, vert.

1996, July 16
654	A153	Block of 4, #a.-d.	5.00	5.00

Souvenir Sheet
655	A153	1500fr multicolored	6.50	6.50

Entertainers A154

Designs: No. 656, 170fr, Bob Marley. No. 657, 170fr, Marilyn Monroe. No. 658, 200fr, Elvis Presley. No. 659, 200fr, Monroe. No. 660, 300fr, Monroe. No. 661, 350fr, Stevie Wonder. No. 662, 350fr, Presley. No. 663, 400fr, John Lennon. No. 664, 500fr, Presley. No. 665, 600fr, Lennon. No. 666, 700fr, Madonna. No. 667, 800fr, Presley. No. 668, 1000fr, Monroe.
No. 669, 1500fr, Tina Turner. No. 670, 1500fr, Clint Eastwood. No. 670A, 1500fr, Presley.

1996, May 15
656-668	A154	Set of 13	25.00	12.50
665a		Sheet of 2, #663, 665	4.50	2.25
667a		Sheet of 4, #658, 662, 664, 667	8.00	3.75
668a		Sheet of 4, #657, 659-660, 668	7.00	3.50

Souvenir Sheets
669-670A	A154	Set of 3	20.00	10.00

Nos. 656-668 exist in souvenir sheets of 1.
No. 670A contains one 51x90mm stamp.
See No. 674.

Pres. Bill Clinton — A155

No. 671: a, Shown. b, Elvis Presley in white jumpsuit.
No. 672: a, Pres. Richard Nixon. b, Presley in white shirt, black jacket.

1996, Dec. 17   Litho.   Perf. 13½
671	A155	1500fr Sheet of 2, #a.-b.	16.00	8.00
672	A155	1500fr Sheet of 2, #a.-b.	16.00	8.00

Giant Panda A156

No. 673: a, Holding branch, left claw out. b, Holding branch. c, Lying on back. d, Holding branch in mouth.

1996, Oct. 15
673	A156	100fr Sheet of 4, #a.-d.	1.90	1.25

Entertainers Type of 1996

1996   **Litho.**   **Perf. 13½**
674 A154 500fr Jerry Garcia   2.50 1.25
No. 674 exists in a souvenir sheet of 1.

1998 World Cup Soccer
Championships, France — A157

1998 World Cup Soccer
Championships, France — A157a

Unidentified players, stadium: No. 675, 150fr, The Beaujoire, Nantes. No. 676, 200fr, Lescure Park, Bordeaux. No. 676A, 300fr, Municipal Stadium, Toulouse. No. 676B, 600fr, Felix Bollaert, Lens.
No. 677A: b, Player in white shirt. c, Player in red shirt.

1996, Dec. 17
675-676B A157 Set of 4   6.00 3.00
Souvenir Sheet
677 A157a 1500fr George
Weah   7.50 3.50
677A A157a 3000fr Sheet of 2,
#b-c   — —

Dinosaurs, Dog & Cats, Butterflies &
Insects — A158

No. 678 — Dinosaurs: a, Heterodontosaurus. b, Ornitholestes. c, Dromaeosaurus. d, Pinacosaurus.
No. 679 — Dinosaurs: a, Corythosaurus. b, Ankylosaurides. c, Ornithomimus. d, Styracosaurus.
No. 680 — Dogs & cats: a, Artois. b, Bengal. c, Persian. d, Vendeen.
No. 681 — Butterflies & insects: a, Euphaedra zaddachi. b, Pseudacraea dolomena. c, Cicindela barbara. d, Goliath.

1996, Oct. 15
678 A158 150fr Sheet of 4, #a.-d. 3.00 1.50
679 A158 200fr Sheet of 4, #a.-d. 3.75 1.90
680 A158 250fr Sheet of 4, #a.-d. 5.00 2.50
681 A158 300fr Sheet of 4, #a.-d. 6.00 3.00

Ovptd. in Gold in Sheet Margin

1997   **Litho.**   **Perf. 13½**
678e   Sheet of 4   2.50 1.25
679e   Sheet of 4   3.25 1.60
680e   Sheet of 4   4.75 2.25

Gold overprints on Nos. 678e-680e contain two-line inscription in Chinese and Hong Kong '97 exhibition emblem.

UNICEF, UN, 50th Anniv., Lions
Intl. — A159

No. 682 — UNICEF, 50th anniv.: a, 150fr, Girl, boy turtles. b, 400fr, Feeding small child.
No. 683 — UN, 50th anniv.: a, 170fr, Huygens probe, starving child. b, 500fr, Man with plant, Marsnet probe.
No. 684 — Lions Intl.: a, 200fr, Man carrying sack of grain. b, 800fr, Men examining plants, native man stirring kettle over fire.

1996, Oct. 15   **Litho.**   **Perf. 13½**
682 A159 Pair, #a.-b. + label   2.75 1.40
683 A159 Pair, #a.-b. + label   3.25 1.60
684 A159 Pair, #a.-b. + label   5.00 2.50

Nos. 682-684 exist as souvenir sheets with colored margins.

1996 European Soccer
Championships — A160

No. 685: a, Oliver Bierhoff holding trophy. b, Two players. c, Two players, referee. d, Queen Elizabeth II, player holding trophy.

1996, Dec. 17
685 A160 350fr Sheet of 4, #a.-d. 6.75 3.25

Michael Schumacher, 1995 World
Driving Champion — A161

No. 686: a, Ferrari Formula-1 race car. b, Schumacher close-up. c, Schumacher in Benetton uniform. d, Benetton Formula-1 race car.
No. 687, Schumacher with arms raised. No. 687A, Winner of 1996 Italian Grand Prix.

1997, June 16
686 A161 700fr Sheet of 4, #a.-d. 13.50 6.75
Souvenir Sheets
687 A161 2000fr multicolored   10.00 5.00
687A A161 2000fr multicolored   10.00 5.00

No. 687 contains one 36x51mm stamp.

1998 Winter
Olympic
Games,
Nagano,
Japan
A162

Designs: 100fr, Women's figure skating. 170fr, Hockey. 350fr, Downhill skiing. 750fr, Speed skating.
1500fr, Slalom skiing.

1996, Dec. 17
688-691 A162 Set of 4   6.75 3.25
Souvenir Sheet
692 A162 1500fr multicolored   7.50 3.50

World Wildlife
Fund — A163

No. 693 — Struthio camelus rothschildi: a, Female. b, Male. c, Chicks. d, Male, female up close.

1996, Dec. 17   **Litho.**   **Perf. 13½**
693 A163 200fr Block of 4, #a.-
d.   15.50 3.25

Jacqueline Kennedy Onassis (1929-
94) — A164

Various portraits.

1996, Dec. 17
694 A164 200fr Sheet of 9, #a.-i. 9.00 4.50

Intl. Red Cross, Rotary Intl.,
Scouts — A165

No. 695 — Intl. Red Cross: a, 100fr, Woman, airplane. b, 350fr, Man, train.
No. 696 — Rotary Intl.: a, 300fr, Boy, water coming through pipes. b, 700fr, Native boy and man, volunteers.
No. 697 — Scouts: a, 250fr, Boy scout holding book, hyena. b, 1000fr, Garry Kasparov, chess player, scout.

1996, Oct. 15   **Litho.**   **Perf. 13½**
695 A165 Pair, #a.-b. + label   2.25 1.10
696 A165 Pair, #a.-b. + label   5.00 2.50
697 A165 Pair, #a.-b. + label   6.00 3.00

Nos. 695-697 exist in souvenir sheets with colored margins.

Japanese
Sumo
Wrestling
A166

Various wrestlers in ring.

1996, Dec. 17   **Litho.**   **Perf. 13½**
698 A166 400fr Sheet of 4, #a.-d. 8.00 3.75

China '96 — A168

Various paintings showing mountains and trees.

1996
704 A168 100fr Sheet of 9, #a.-i. 4.50 2.25

Marilyn Monroe — A168a

Various portraits.

1997   **Litho.**   **Perf. 13¼**
704J A168a 500fr Sheet of 9,
#k-s   16.00 16.00

History of Space Travel — A169

No. 705: a, Lunar N1 rocket, USSR, Saturn 1, US, Apollo 1 crew, Grissom, White, Chaffee. b, Launch of Soyuz, USSR, V.M. Komarov. c, US Lunar Orbiter 4. d, Neil Armstrong, US, Molnya 1, USSR. e, Venera 4, USSR, Mariner, US. f, Surveyor 3, US.
No. 706: a, Ariane 1, Landsat 4, US. b, Spacelab & space shuttle, NASA, ESA, Thomas Mattingly, US. c, L-Sat Telecom Satelite, ESA. d, J.L. Chretien, Soviet Salyut 7, US Space Shuttle. e, Venera 13, USSR. f, Intelsat 6, US.
No. 707: a, John Glenn, Atlas rocket, Mercury capsule. b, Mariner 2, US. c, Scott Carpenter, US. d, Telstar, Tiros 6, US. e, Vostok capsule, USSR, Bell X15 airplane, US. f, Mars 1, USSR.
No. 708: a, "Sounds of Earth" record, Voyager 1 & 2, US. b, Himawari 1, MU-3H, Japan, Atlas Centaur, US. c, Soviet Salyut 6, Proton rocket, Galileo (1564-1642). d, Meteosat, SMS Geos, Atlas EF, US. e, Boeing 747, space shuttle, US. f, ISEE, US.
No. 709: a, Saturn 5, US, OAO 3 Copernicus. b, Pioneer 10, US. c, Luna 20, USSR, John F. Kennedy. d, Landsat 1, US. e, Apollo 16, US astronauts Mattingly, Duke, Young. f, Lunar Rover, US Apollo 17 astronauts Schmitt, Evans, Cernan.
No. 710: a, RD 107 rocket, USSR, Vanguard rocket, US, Vanguard I, US. b, Aerobee, Goddard rockets, Robert H. Goddard. c, Laika, 1st dog in space, USSR. d, Theodor von Karman, V2A, Gird 09 rockets, USSR. e, Sputnik 1, USSR, Korolev airplane, US. f, Sanger, Bell X1 airplanes, US, Eugene Sanger.
No. 711, US Astronauts, Neil Armstrong, Michael Collins, Edwin E. Aldrin, Jr., USSR animals in space, Laika, Felix the cat.
Illustration reduced.

1997		**Litho.**	**Perf. 13½**	
705	A169	150fr Sheet of 6,		
		#a.-f.	3.50	1.75
706	A169	250fr Sheet of 6,		
		#a.-f.	6.00	3.00
707	A169	300fr Sheet of 6,		
		#a.-f.	7.50	3.75
708	A169	450fr Sheet of 6,		
		#a.-f.	11.00	5.50
709	A169	475fr Sheet of 6,		
		#a.-f.	11.50	5.75
710	A169	800fr Sheet of 6,		
		#a.-f.	19.00	10.00

Souvenir Sheet

711	A169	2000fr multicolored	8.25	4.00

No. 711 contains one 80x85mm stamp.

Elvis Presley — A169a

Various portraits.

1997		**Litho.**	**Perf. 13¼**	
711A	A169a	300fr Sheet of 9,		
		#b-j	12.00	12.00

Jacqueline Kennedy Onassis (1929-94) — A170

Various portraits.

1997, July 15		**Litho.**	**Perf. 13½**	
712	A170	150fr Sheet of 9, #a.-i.	5.75	2.75

Pres. John F. Kennedy — A170a

No. 712J: k, Standing, looking right. l, With family. m, Looking left. n, With statue of George Washington. o, Seated, with Great Seal of the United States. p, Facing forward, with stars and arrows. q, In chair. r, With statue of Lincoln. s, Behind podium, with flag and Capitol.

1997		**Litho.**	**Perf. 13¼**	
712J	A170a	250fr Sheet of 9,		
		#k-s	8.25	8.25

Diana, Princess of Wales (1961-97) — A171

Various portraits.

1997				
713	A171	300fr Sheet of 9,		
		#a.-i.	11.00	5.50
714	A171	450fr Sheet of 9,		
		#a.-i.	16.00	8.25

Souvenir Sheet

715	A171	2000fr multicolored	8.25	4.00

No. 715 contains one 42x60mm stamp.

Deng Xiaoping and Bruce Lee — A171a

No. 715A — Deng and: c, Child. d, Chinese flag. e, Dancer. f, Boats in water. g, Farmers. h, Cityscape.
No. 715B — Lee and movie titles: i, Operation Dragon. j, La Fureur du Dragon. k, La Fureur de Vaincre. l, La Flute Silencieuse. m, Le Jeu de la Mort. n, Le Retour du Dragon. 1000fr, Deng and stars.

1997		**Litho.**	**Perf. 13¼**	
715A	A171a	75fr Sheet of 6,		
		#c-h	1.60	1.60
715B	A171a	125fr Sheet of 6,		
		#i-n	2.75	2.75

Souvenir Sheet

715O	A171a	1000fr multi	—	—

No. 715O contains one 36x41mm stamp.

Mahatma Gandhi (1869-1948), Mother Teresa (1910-97) — A172

No. 716: a, Gandhi seated, dendrobium speciosum. b, Mother Teresa with Indian people. c, Bulbophyllum umbellatum, Gandhi with 2 women.

1998, Feb. 5		**Litho.**	**Perf. 13½**	
716	A172	150fr Sheet of 3, #a.-c.	1.90	.95

Famous Men — A173

Designs: 300fr, Nelson Mandela, Pres. of South Africa, diamond. 450fr, Albert Einstein (1879-1955), physicist, satellite. 800fr, Robert Barany (1876-1936), physician, Felix the space cat.
2000fr, Alfred Nobel (1833-96).

1998, Feb. 5				
717-719	A173	Set of 3	6.50	3.25

Souvenir Sheet

720	A173	2000fr multicolored	8.25	4.00

Nos. 717-719 exist in souvenir sheets of 1. No. 720 contains one 41x60mm stamp. See Nos. 729-734.

The Beatles — A174

No. 721: a-i, Various portraits of John Lennon.
No. 722 — The Beatles: a, Paul McCartney. b, Silhouettes. c, John Lennon. d, George Harrison, Lennon. e, Four faces. f, McCartney, Ringo Starr. g, Starr. h, Four in Sgt. Pepper's costumes. i, Harrison.
No. 723 — Life of John Lennon: a, Yoko Ono. b, With McCartney. c, In profile. d, Wearing suit. e, Wearing white shirt, tie. f, With mother. g, Wearing dark glasses. h, With guru. i, In white suit.
No. 724: Various portraits of Lennon, McCartney, Harrison, Starr.
No. 724J, Beatles in suits and ties. No. 724K, Beatles in Sgt. Pepper uniforms.

1996		**Litho.**	**Perf. 13½**	
721	A174	100fr Sheet of 9,		
		#a-f	3.25	3.25
722	A174	170fr Sheet of 9,		
		#a.-i.	5.50	2.75
723	A174	200fr Sheet of 9,		
		#a.-i.	6.75	3.50
724	A174	300fr Sheet of 9,		
		#a.-i.	10.50	5.25

Souvenir Sheets

724J	A174	1500fr multi	5.50	5.50
724K	A174	1500fr multi	5.50	5.50

Rotary Intl. — A175

Antelopes: a, 170fr, Damaliscus dorcas. b, 350fr, Oryx gazella. c, 500fr, Addax nasomaculatus. d, 600fr, Aepyceros melampus.

1996, Dec. 17				
725	A175	Block of 4, #a.-d.	7.00	3.50

#725a-725d exist in souvenir sheets of 1.

No. 725 Overprinted in Gold

1996				
726	A175	Block of 4, #a.-d.	7.00	3.50

#726a-726d exist in souvenir sheets of 1.

Marilyn Monroe (1926-1962) — A176

Various portraits.

1996				
727	A176	250fr Sheet of 9,		
		#a.-i.	10.50	6.50

Souvenir Sheet

728	A176	1500fr multicolored	5.75	2.75

No. 728 contains one 51x90mm stamp.

Famous People Type of 1997

Nobel Prize winners: 100fr, Mother Teresa (1910-97), humanitarian. 150fr, Martin Luther King, Jr. (1929-68), civil rights leader. 475fr, Otto Hahn (1879-1968), chemist, nuclear powered ship. 500fr, Ivan Pavlov (1849-1936), physiologist, Russian space dog, Laika. 600fr, Johannes van der Waals (1837-1923), physicist. 1000fr, Sir Edward Appleton (1892-1965), physicist, Concorde jet.

1998, Feb. 5				
729-734	A173	Set of 6	14.50	7.00

Nos. 729-734 exist in souvenir sheets of 1.

Scouting A177

Wild animals: No. 735: a, Hyena. b, Mongoose.
No. 736: a, Wildcat. b, Addax nasomaculatus.
No. 737: a, Fennec. b, Hyena, diff.

1998, Feb. 6

735	A177	150fr Pair, #a.-b.	2.00	.75
736	A177	550fr Pair, #a.-b.	5.75	3.00
737	A177	600fr Pair, #a.-b.	7.00	4.00

Cats and Dogs — A178

No. 738: a, Maine coon. b. Singapore.
No. 739: a, Siberian husky. b, Malamute.
No. 740: a, Spitz. b, Eskimo.
No. 741: a, Siamese. b, Common cat.
No. 742, 1500fr, Abyssinian. No. 743, 1500fr, Samoyed.

1998, Feb. 6

738	A178	300fr Pair, #a.-b.	2.50	1.25
739	A178	450fr Pair, #a.-b.	3.75	1.90
740	A178	475fr Pair, #a.-b.	3.75	1.90
741	A178	500fr Pair, #a.-b.	4.00	2.00

Souvenir Sheets

| 742-743 | A178 | Set of 2 | 12.50 | 6.50 |

Nos. 742-743 each contain one 42x60mm stamp.

Airplanes, Ships, & Trains A179

No. 743A — Early aircraft: b, Latecoere 28, France. c, D'Equeuilly, France. d, Liore et Olivier Leo-213, France. e, Louis Bleriot monoplane. f, Graf Zeppelin LZ 127. g, Caproni CA 133, Italy.
No. 744 — Airplanes: a, Sikorsky VS-44A. b, Short S25/V Sandringham 4. c, Bristol 167 Brabazon 1. d, Savoia S13 Bis. e, Curtiss CR-3. f, Curtiss R3C-2.
No. 745 — Ships: a, Normandy, 1935. b, Persia, 1856. c, Queen Elizabeth II, 1968. d, Christian Radich, 1937. e, Amerigo Vespucci, 1933. f, Tovarich, 1933.
No. 745G — Classic sports cars: h, 1963-65 Porsche 356 SC. i, 1961-66 AC Cobra. j, 1960-61 Maserati Tipo 63 Birdcage. k, 1962-63 Austin Healey 3000 MK11. l, 1959-62 Ferrari 250 GT Berlinetta SWB. m, 1958 Aston Martin DB4.
No. 746 — Trains: a, BRB cog steam train. b, AE 4/7 10969. c, Crocodile of Saint-Gothard BE 6/8 111. d, RAE 2/4 1001. e, Steam train, Spain. f, RE 6/6 11612 express.
No. 746G — High speed trains: h, ETR 470, Italy. i, TGV Metro, France. j, Hikari, Japan. k, TGV 001 turbotrain. l, Eurostar 3203/3204 Metro train, France, Germany, Great Britain. m, 990 ICE train, Germany.
1500fr, Steam locomotive, C5/6 2978. 2000fr, TGV, France.

1998, Feb. 4

743A	A179	150fr Sheet of 6, #b.-g.	3.75	1.90
744	A179	200fr Sheet of 6, #a.-f.	5.00	2.50
745	A179	250fr Sheet of 6, #a.-f.	6.25	3.25
745G	A179	300fr Sheet of 6, #h.-m.	7.50	3.75
746	A179	350fr Sheet of 6, #a.-f.	9.00	4.50
746G	A179	400fr Sheet of 6, #h.-m.	10.00	5.00

Souvenir Sheets

| 747 | A179 | 1500fr multicolored | 6.25 | 3.25 |
| 748 | A179 | 2000fr multicolored | 8.25 | 4.00 |

Nos. 747-748 contain one 36x42mm stamp. Swiss rail service, 150th anniv. (#746-747). Issued: #745G, 2/6.
See No. 758.

Diana, Princess of Wales (1961-97) A180

Various portraits.
2000fr, Portrait wearing high lace collar.

1997 **Litho.** **Perf. 13½**

| 749 | A180 | 250fr Sheet of 9, #a.-i. | 9.00 | 4.50 |

Souvenir Sheet

| 749J | A180 | 2000fr multicolored | 8.50 | 4.50 |

Literacy Campaign A181

Kellou Dahalob — A182

1997, June 16

750	A181	150fr olive & multi	.55	.25
751	A181	300fr buff & multi	1.10	.50
752	A181	475fr salmon & multi	1.75	.80
		Nos. 750-752 (3)	3.40	1.55

1998, Apr. 8

753	A182	50fr pink & multi	.20	.20
754	A182	100fr blue & multi	.40	.20
755	A182	150fr green & multi	.65	.30
756	A182	300fr lilac & multi	1.10	.50
757	A182	400fr yellow & multi	1.50	.70
		Nos. 753-757 (5)	3.85	1.90

Transportation Type of 1997

No. 758 — Modern aircraft: a, SAT, France, Germany. b, BAC/Aerospatiale Concorde. c, X001, Japan. d, Bell X-2, US. e, Douglas X-3, US. f, Aerospatiale STS 2000, France.

1998, Feb. 4 **Litho.** **Perf. 13½**

| 758 | A179 | 475fr Sheet of 6, #a.-f. | 12.00 | 6.25 |

Women — A183

Women: 50fr, 100fr, 150fr, Using grindstone. 300fr, 450fr, 500fr, Kneeling.

1997, June 16

759	A183	50fr vio & multi, vert.	.20	.20
760	A183	100fr grn & multi, vert.	.40	.20
761	A183	150fr yel & multi, vert.	.55	.25
762	A183	300fr vio & multi	1.10	.50
763	A183	450fr grn & multi	1.75	.80
764	A183	500fr yel & multi	1.90	.85
		Nos. 759-764 (6)	5.90	2.80

Protect the Ozone Layer — A184

1998, June 20 **Litho.** **Perf. 13½**

765	A184	150fr blue & multi	.60	.25
766	A184	300fr green & multi	1.25	.55
767	A184	475fr pink & multi	1.90	.85
768	A184	500fr blue green & multi	1.90	.85
		Nos. 765-768 (4)	5.65	2.50

Fauna — A185

No. 769 — Bats: a, Holding mouse, tree branch. b, Drinking. c, One in flight, bottom of mouse. d, One flying left. e, One flying right. f, Mouse on rock, bat landing.
No. 769G — Horses: h, Gray Arabian. i, Brown Arabian. j, Przewalski's. k, Australian brumbies. l, Camargue. m, Zebras.
No. 769N — Sea mammals: o-t, Various portraits of Trichechus senegalensis.
No. 770 — Gorillas & chimpanzees: a, Chimpanzee scratching head. b, Gorilla walking on all fours. c, Gorilla seated. d, Chimpanzee swinging from branch. e, Chimpanzee using stick. f, Two gorillas.
No. 771 — Raptors: a, Terathopius ecaudatus. b, Buteo buteo. c, Sagittarius serpentarius. d, Polemaetus belligosus. e, Circaetus allicus. f, Aquila chrysaetos.
No. 771G — Reptiles: h, Crocodylus niloticus. i, Drendroaspis angusticeps. j, Bitis nasicornis. k, Chamaeleo johnstoni. l, Naja nigricolis. m, Meroles cuneirostris.
No. 771N — Mushrooms: o, Coprinus atramentarius. p, Romaria botrytis. q, Aleuria aurantia. r, Amanita muscaria. s, Macrolepiota rhacodes. t, Helvella crispa.
No. 771U — Mushrooms: v, Morchella vulgaris. w, Tuber aestiuum. x, Tuber melanosporum. y, Mitrophora hybrida. z, Morchella conica. aa, Choeromyces meandriformis.
No. 772 — Butterflies: a, Charaxes jasius. b, Hamanumidia daedalus. c, Charaxes bohemani. d, Hallimoides rumia, denomination LL. e, Hallimoides rumia, denomination LR. f, Pseudacraea boisduuali.
1500fr, Coelogyne ovalis, palla ussheri. 2000fr, Baleniceps, Neurophyllum clauatum.

1998, June 20

769	A185	150fr Sheet of 6, #a.-f.	4.00	2.10
769G	A185	250fr Sheet of 6, #h.-m.	5.50	2.75
769N	A185	300fr Sheet of 6, #o.-t.	6.50	6.50
770	A185	300fr Sheet of 6, #a.-f.	8.00	4.00
771	A185	350fr Sheet of 6, #a.-f.	9.25	4.50
771G	A185	450fr Sheet of 6, #h.-m.	10.00	10.00
771N	A185	475fr Sheet of 6, #o.-t.	10.50	10.50
771U	A185	500fr Sheet of 6, #v.-aa.	11.00	11.00
772	A185	600fr Sheet of 6, #a.-f.	16.00	8.00

Souvenir Sheets

| 773 | A185 | 1500fr multicolored | 6.50 | 3.25 |
| 773A | A185 | 2000fr multicolored | 7.50 | 3.75 |

Nos. 773-773A contain one 51x42mm stamp.

Bela Lugosi as Dracula — A185a

Lugosi in various poses.

1998, Dec. 11 **Litho.** **Perf. 13½**

| 773B | A185a | 250fr Sheet of 9, #d.-l. | 8.50 | 8.50 |

Souvenir Sheet

| 773C | A185a | 1500fr multi, horiz. | 5.75 | 5.75 |

Diana, Princess of Wales — A186

No. 774 — Various portraits: a, 200fr. b, 250fr. c, 300fr. d, 400fr. e, 475fr. f, 500fr. g, 800fr. h, 900fr. i, 1000fr.

1999, Jan. 10 **Litho.** **Perf. 12½**

| 774 | A186 | Sheet of 9, #a.-i. | 17.50 | 9.00 |

Birds — A187

Designs: 75fr, Ibis ibis. 150fr, Ephippi-orhynchus senegalensis. 200fr, Phoen-icopterus ruber. 300fr, Leptoptilus crumeniferus. 400fr, Scopus umbretta. 475fr, Platalea alba. 1000fr, Balaeniceps rex.

1999, Jan. 15   Litho.   Perf. 12¾
775-780 A187   Set of 6   5.75 2.75
Souvenir Sheet
781 A187 1000fr multicolored   3.50 1.75
No. 781 contains one 32x40mm stamp.

Fire Trucks A188

Designs: 50fr, 1840 model. 150fr, 1920 Fiat. 200fr, 1915 Mack. 300fr, 1930 Renault. 400fr, Pegaso M 1090. 500fr, 1960 Jet Fire Power. 700fr, 1720 King George III Fire Company.

1998, Dec. 30
782-787 A188   Set of 6   5.75 2.75
Souvenir Sheet
788 A188 700fr multicolored   2.50 1.25
No. 788 contains one 35x28mm stamp.

Minerals — A188a

No. 788A: a, Opal. b, Cyanite. c, Chalcopy-rite. d, Apatite. e, Celestite. f, Scorodite.
No. 788B: a, Agate. b, Wulfenite. c, Bary-tine. d, Tanzanite. e, Amazonite. f, Malachite.

1998, Nov. 12   Litho.   Perf. 13½
788A A188a 475fr Sheet of 6,
    #a.-f.   11.00 5.50
788B A188a 500fr Sheet of 6,
    #a.-f.   11.50 5.75

Dinosaurs — A188b

No. 788C: a, Dilophosaurus. b, Argenti-nosaurus. c, Kritosaurus. d, Scutellosaurus. e, Ornithomimosaurus. f, Bactrosaurus.
No. 788D: a, Coelophysis. b, Kan-nemeyeria. c, Apatosaurus. d, Scipionyx. e, Lystrosaurus. f, Kentrosaurus.
No. 788E, Giganotosaurus, vert.

1998, Nov. 12   Litho.   Perf. 13¼
Sheets of 6
788C A188b 400fr #a.-f.   9.25 4.75
788D A188b 450fr #a.-f.   10.50 5.25
Souvenir Sheet
788E A188b 2000fr multi   7.50 3.75

US Pres. Ronald Reagan — A189

No. 789: a, Family portrait as young boy. b, In front of family home. c, In football uniform, as radio announcer. d, Riding horse. e, Up close portrait. f, With Nancy, greeting Pope John Paul II. g, Making speech at podium. h, Being sworn in as president. i, At desk in Oval Office.
2000fr, At desk, White House.

1999, Feb. 2   Litho.   Perf. 13½
789 A189   450fr Sheet of 9,
    #a.-i.   16.00 8.00
Souvenir Sheet
790 A189 2000fr multicolored   8.00 3.75

American Railroads — A190

No. 791 — Train, railroad pioneer: a, "Alco" Santa Fe, 1945, Cyrus Holliday. b, Rio Grande, 1961, J.F. Stevens. c, Amtrak, 1976, Thomas Dehone Judah. d, 250 Gobernador, 1884, Mark Hopkins. e, Meeting of Central Pacific and Union Pacific at Promontory Point, 1869, Leland Stanford, Thomas Durant. f, Great Northern W1, 1947, Jim Hill. g, Union Pacific Railroad, 1951, G.M. Dodge. h, Penn-sylvania GG1, 1934, S.M. Vauclain. i, 151 Santa Fe U.P. 1917, S. Barstow Strong.

1999, Feb. 2
791 A190 200fr Sheet of 9, #a.-i. 7.00 3.50

Fossils and Cave Paintings — A191

No. 792: a, Harlania enigmatica. b, Spirophyton. c, Fossils, dunes of Djourab. d, Chain of people, oxen, Bardai. e, Man of Gonoa. f, Oxen, Kozen, Borkou.

1998, Dec. 11
792 A191 150fr Sheet of 6, #a.-f. 3.50 1.75

Frank Sinatra — A191a

No. 792G — Sinatra with: h, Blonde actress. i, Green jacket. j, Ava Gardner. k, Striped suit. l, Actor. m, Gun. n, Dark green hat. o, Oscar statuette. p, Military cap.

1998, Dec. 30   Litho.   Perf. 13½
792G A191a 300fr Sheet of 9,
    #h.-p.   11.00 5.50

James Dean (1931-55), Actor — A192

Various portraits.

1999, Feb. 2
793 A192 200fr Sheet of 9, #a.-i. 7.00 3.50

Pope John Paul II — A193

Various portraits.

1999, Feb. 2
794 A193 300fr Sheet of 9,
    #a.-i.   10.50 5.25
Souvenir Sheet
795 A193 1500fr multicolored   6.00 3.00
No. 795 contains one 58x51mm stamp.

John Glenn's Return to Space — A194

Various portraits.

1999, Feb. 11   Litho.   Perf. 13½
796 A194   500fr Sheet of 9,
    #a.-i.   17.50 9.00
Souvenir Sheet
797 A194 2000fr multicolored   8.00 3.75
No. 797 contains one 57x51mm stamp.

Kofi Annan, UN Secretary-General — A195

Various portraits.

1999, Feb. 11
798 A195 150fr Sheet of 9, #a.-i. 5.25 2.75

Chess — A196

No. 798J: k, Paul Morphy. l, Chess board, Morphy-Anderssen, 1858. m, Adolf Anders-sen. n, Emanuel Lasker. o, Chess board, Lasker-Capablanca, 1914. p, José Raul Capablanca. q, David Bronstein. r, Chess

board, Bronstein-Botvinnik, 1951. s, Mikhail Botvinnik.
a, Bobby Fischer. b, Chess board, Fischer-Tal, 1961. c, Mikhail Tal. d, Boris Spassky. e, Chess board, Spassky-Petrosian, 1969. f, Tigran Petrosian. g, Garry Kasparov. h, Chess board, Kasparov-Karpov, 1960. i, Anatoly Karpov.
No. 800, Margrave Othon IV of Brandenburg.
No. 800A, King Louis XVI playing chess, horiz.

1999, Feb. 20
798J A196 375fr Sheet of 9,
#k.-s. 13.00 6.50
799 A196 500fr Sheet of 9,
#a.-i. 17.50 9.00

Souvenir Sheets
800 A196 2000fr multi 7.75 3.75
800A A196 2000fr multi

Dated 1998. No. 800 contains one 58x51mm stamp. No. 800A contains one 58x51mm stamp. Sheets of 3 stamps, containing Nos. 798Jk-798Jm, 798Jn-798Jp, 798Jq-798Js, 799a-799c, 799d-799f, or 799g-799i exist.

Souvenir Sheets

France, 1998 World Cup Champions — A197

No. 801: a, Bikente Lizarazu. b, Christian Karembeu. c, Frank Leboeuf. d, Emmanuel Petit.
No. 802: a, Fabien Barthez. b, Marcel Desailly. c, Didier Deschamps. d, Christophe Dugarry.
No. 803: Youri Djorkaeff. b, Aime Jacquet. c, Lilian Thuram. d, Zinedine Zidane.
2000fr, Deschamps holding World Cup.

1999, Feb. 20   Litho.   Perf. 13½
801 A197 300fr Sheet of 4,
#a.-d. 4.50 2.25
802 A197 400fr Sheet of 4,
#a.-d. 6.25 3.00
803 A197 500fr Sheet of 4,
#a.-d. 8.00 3.75
Perf. 13¼
804 A197 2000fr multicolored 8.00 3.75
No. 804 contains one 57x51mm stamp.

Hokusai Paintings A198

Designs: a, Voyagers Crossing the Oi River. b, Bird. c, On Totomi Mountain. d, Evening at Ueno. e, Higashimachi-matsuri-yatai-tenjou. f, Evening shower at Yoshiwara. g. Woman with Umbrella. h, Cascade. i, Courtesan.

1999, Sept. 10   Litho.   Perf. 13½
805 A198 475fr Sheet of 9,
#a.-i. 17.50 9.00
Japex '99.

Millennium — A199

No. 806 — Highlights of 1000-1899: a, Commercial routes in West Africa. b, Crusades. c, Notre Dame Cathedral. d, Ming dynasty tombs. e, Discovery of America. f, Albrecht Dürer. g, Sir Isaac Newton. h, American Independence. i, Napoleon.
No. 807 — 1900-24: a, Return of Halley's Comet. b, Lord Baden-Powell founds Scouting movement. c, Sinking of the Titanic. d, 1st film in Technicolor. e, Marconi sends 1st message across Atlantic, birth of radio. f, Harry Houdini. g, Capablanca-Lasker chess matches. h, Pierre & Marie Curie win Nobel Prize. i, Theft of the Mona Lisa.
No. 808 — 1925-49: a, Birth of Marilyn Monroe. b, Discovery of Pluto. c, Laurel and Hardy. d, Independence of India. e, Alexander Fleming discovers penicillin. f, Introduction of Volkswagen Beetle & Vespa motor scooter. g, Opening of film "Dracula." h, World War II. i, Discovery of Lascaux cave drawings.
No. 809 — 1950-74: a, 1st flight of the Concorde, 7 original astronauts. b, Death of Buddy Holly. c, 1st Super Bowl. d, Death of Eva Peron. e, Art by Andy Warhol. f, The Beatles. g, Cultural Revolution in China. h, Assassination of Pres. John F. Kennedy. i, Cuban Revolution.
No. 810 — 1975-99: a, Death of Princess Diana. b, Death of Enzo Ferrari. c, Akira. d, Argentina, 1986 World Cup Soccer champions. e, B. Lara breaks cricket records. f, France, 1998 World Cup Soccer champions. g, Explosion of the Space Shuttle Challenger. h, Pope John Paul II meets Lech Walesa. i, Deaths of Frank Sinatra, Freddie Mercury.

1999, Sept. 10
806 A199 150fr Sheet of 9,
#a.-i. 5.25 2.50
807 A199 300fr Sheet of 9,
#a.-i. 10.00 5.25
808 A199 450fr Sheet of 9,
#a.-i. 15.00 7.75
809 A199 475fr Sheet of 9,
#a.-i. 16.00 8.00
810 A199 500fr Sheet of 9,
#a.-i. 16.00 8.25
Nos. 806-810 (5) 62.25 31.75

Souvenir Sheet

PhilexFrance '99 — A200

Illustration reduced.

1999, Sept. 10
811 A200 1500fr multi 6.00 3.00

I Love Lucy — A201

No. 812: a, Lucy leaning against tree, Ricky. b, Lucy, Ricky kissing. c, Lucy pointing gun. d, Ricky falling to ground. e, Lucy in apartment. f, Ricky holding animal. g, Ricky drinking from canteen. h, Lucy, Ricky talking. i, Lucy behind bush.
No. 813, Lucy in grape vat. No. 814, Lucy, Ricky in bed.

1999, Feb. 20   Litho.   Perf. 13¼
812 A201 450fr Sheet of 9,
#a.-i. 18.00 9.00

Souvenir Sheets
813 A201 1500fr multi 6.75 3.25
814 A201 2000fr multi 9.00 4.50
Dated 1998.
See Nos. 865-867.

Betty Boop — A202

No. 815: a, With cat and dog. b, In flowered dress. c, Looking back over shoulder. d, With hammer, dresser. e, As majorette. f, In red dress with fur collar. g, Holding paper. h, Holding blue dress. i, Holding telephone.
No. 816, With feathered hat. No. 817, In leopard-spotted blouse.

1999, Feb. 20   Litho.   Perf. 13¼
815 A202 450fr Sheet of 9,
#a.-i. 18.00 9.00

Souvenir Sheets
816 A202 1500fr multi 6.75 3.25
817 A202 2000fr multi 9.00 4.50
Dated 1998.
See Nos. 856-858.

Antique Automobiles — A203

150fr, 1900 F.N. 300fr, 1906 Bianchi. 400fr, 1906 Renault. 500fr, 1919 Pierce-Arrow. 700fr, 1919 Citroen 5CV. 900fr, 1928 Ford. 1000fr, 1898 Renault.

1999   Litho.   Perf. 13x12¾
818-823 A203 Set of 6 14.00 6.75
Souvenir Sheet
Perf. 13x13¼
824 A203 1000fr multi 5.00 2.50
No. 824 contains one 40x31mm stamp.

Locomotives — A204

Designs: 150fr, 0-4-4-0. 300fr, Red 0-4-0. 400fr, Green 0-6-0. 500fr, Brown 0-4-0. 700fr, Blue 0-4-0. 900fr, Blue 0-6-0. 1000fr, Electric locomotive.

1999   Perf. 12¾
825-830 A204 Set of 6 14.00 6.50
Souvenir Sheet
Perf. 13x13¼
831 A204 1000fr multi 5.00 2.50
No. 831 contains one 36x28mm stamp.

Wonders of Forgotten Cultures — A205

Designs: 50fr, Easter Island. 150fr, Stonehenge. 300fr, Jericho. 400fr, Machu Picchu. 500fr, Valley of Statues. 700fr, Chichén Itzá. 900fr, Persepolis.

1999   Perf. 12¾
832-838 A205 Set of 7 15.00 7.00

Chad postal officials have declared the following items to be "not authorized:"
Set of six stamps of various denominations: New Year 2000 (Year of the Dragon)
Sheet of nine stamps of various denominations: Orchids
Sheet of nine 150fr stamps: Spanish Impressionist paintings
Sheet of nine 300fr stamps: Millennium (Composers), Van Gogh paintings
Sheet of nine 450fr stamps: Millennium (Marilyn Monroe), French Impressionist paintings
Sheet of nine 475fr stamps: Impressionist paintings
Sheet of nine 500fr stamps: Renoir nudes, Elvis Presley, Olympics
Souvenir sheets of one: Millennium (three 300fr, two 450fr, one 475fr, three 500fr, one 1500fr), New Year 2000 (1000fr), Palace of Versailles (1500fr, 2000fr), Hiroshige paintings (1500fr, 2000fr).

Minerals A206

Designs: 150fr, Wulfenite. 200fr, Argentite. 400fr, Siderite. 500fr, Dolomite and quartz. 700fr, Azurite. 900fr, Spinel and calcite. 1000fr, Cassiterite.

2000, Jan. 15   Litho.   Perf. 12¾
839-844 A206 Set of 6 14.00 14.00
Souvenir Sheet
845 A206 1000fr multi 5.00 5.00
Dated 1999.

Dogs — A206a

Designs: 150fr, Caucasian Mountain dog (Berger caucasique). 500fr, Kuvasz.

2000, Jan. 15   Litho.   Perf. 13
845A A206a 150fr multi —
845D A206a 500fr multi —

Four additional stamps were issued in this set. The editors would like to examine any examples.

Elvis Presley — A207

No. 846: a, Playing guitar, wearing red jacket. b, Holding microphone and guitar, wearing red jacket. c, Holding guitar, wearing gold jacket. d, Playing guitar wearing black leather jacket. e, Playing guitar, wearing black jacket. f, Playing guitar, wearing blue jacket. g, Holding microphone, wearing blue shirt. h, Singing, wearing brown jacket. i, Holding microphone, wearing striped yellow jacket.

2000, Mar. 10   Perf. 13¼
846 A207 300fr Sheet of 9, #a-
i   12.00 12.00
Dated 1999.

Carl Benz and Mercedes-Benz Automobiles — A208

No. 847: a, 1934 W-25. b, 1934 500 K. c, 1964 230 SL. d, 1935 150. e, 1954 300 SL. f, 1971 280 SE.
2000fr, 1934 500 K, diff.

2000, Mar. 10
847 A208 250fr Sheet of 6, #a-f 7.00 7.00
Souvenir Sheet
848 A208 2000fr multi   9.00 9.00
No. 847 contains six 30x30mm stamps. Dated 1999.

Trains — A209

No. 849: a, FES 3228, European Union flag. b, TGV Duplex, French flag. c, 500 Series Unit W1, Japanese flag. d, AVE Class 100, Spanish flag. e, ICE3, German flag. f, ETR 500, Italian flag.
2000fr, TGC 001 V56, TGV Duplex, Etienne Chambron.

2000, Mar. 10
849 A209 600fr Sheet of 6,
#a-f   11.50 11.50
Souvenir Sheet
850 A209 2000fr multi   6.50 6.50
No. 849 contains six 30x30mm stamps. Dated 1999.

French Rulers — A210

No. 851, 150fr: a, Charlemagne. b, King Charles VIII. c, King Francis I. d, King Henry II. e, Catherine de Medici. f, King Henry III.
No. 852, 200fr: a, King Louis XII. b, King Louis XIII. c, King Louis XIV. d, King Louis XV. e, King Louis XVI. f, King Louis XVIII.
No. 853, 300fr — Napoleon Bonaparte: a, Standing, wearing red cape. b, On horseback, wearing red cape. c, On horseback, with soldier at right. d, On horseback, with crowd at right. e, Standing with opter people. f, On white horse, leading battle.

2000, Mar. 10
Sheets of 6, #a-f
851-853 A210 Set of 3   17.50 17.50
Dated 1999.

Pope John Paul II — A211

No. 854 — Pope John Paul II and: a, Dalai Lama. b, Fidel Castro. c, King Hassan II of Morocco. d, Grand Rabbi Elio Toaff. e, Patriarch Bartholomew I. f, Mother Teresa.

2000, Mar. 10
854 A211 475fr Sheet of 6, #a-
f   13.00 13.00
Dated 1999.

Space — A212

No. 855: a, Sputnik, dog Laika. b, Yuri Gagarin, Vostok 1. c, Konstantin Feoktistov, Vladimir Komarov, Boris Yegorov, Voskhod 1. d, Luna 1, chimpanzee Ham. e, Neil Armstrong, Michael Collis, Edwin Aldrin, Apollo 11. f, Aldrin, splashdown of capsule.

2000, Mar. 10
855 A212 500fr Sheet of 6, #a-
f   13.00 13.00
Dated 1999.

Betty Boop Type of 1999
No. 856: a, Wearing red and violet striped leotard, kicking leg up. b, As cheerleader. c, At football field, holding pennant. d, At ice cream shop. e, Wearing yellow and green striped leotard. f, Wearing baseball cap and orange shorts. g, Wearing baseball cap and checked shirt. h, Seated, drinking beverage. i, Wearing cut-off shorts.
No. 857, 1500fr, Riding bicycle. No. 858, 2000fr, Wearing glasses, elbow and knee pads.

2000, Mar. 30
856 A202 250fr Sheet of 9, #a-
i   10.00 10.00
Souvenir Sheets
857-858 A202 Set of 2   16.00 16.00

The Three Stooges — A213

No. 859, 250fr, horiz.: a, Larry, in surgeon's gown, and Curly. b, Curly, Moe, Larry around barrel. c, Moe, Larry and Curly on horse. d, Larry attacking man. e, Moe getting hair pulled. f, Moe with mallet. g, Curly, Moe and Larry in western outfits, outdoors. h, Larry, Curly and Moe in white doctor's jackets. i, Man looking at Moe.
No. 860, 300fr, horiz.: a, Larry grabbing Moe's chin. b, Moe and Larry holding scrolls. c, Moe, yellow background. d, Larry, blue background. e, Moe, Shemp and Larry. f, Shemp, blue background. g, Shemp, yellow background. h, Shemp pointing bellows at Larry. i, Moe and Larry in white.
No. 861, 1500fr, Moe in surgeon's gown. No. 862, 1500fr, Moe wearing hat. No. 863, 2000fr, Curly, Moe and Larry in western outfits, outdoors. No. 864, 2000fr, Larry with violin.

2000
Sheets of 9, #a-i
859-860 A213 Set of 2   22.50 22.50
Souvenir Sheets
861-864 A213 Set of 4   32.50 32.50
Issued: Nos. 859, 861, 863, 3/30; Nos. 860, 862, 864, 5/29.

I Love Lucy Type of 1999
No. 865: a, Lucy dancing, man in background. b, Lucy dancing, with knees bent and arms extended. c, Lucy in doorway. d, Lucy dancing behind sofa. e, Lucy kicking out leg. f, Lucy being caught by two men. g, Lucy with one arm extended. h, Lugy being sprayed with seltzer water. i, Lucy with leg on dance rail.
No. 866, 1500fr, Lucy looking at clown, horiz. No. 867, 2000fr, Lucy with clown costume and arms extended.

2000, May 29
865 A201 225fr Sheet of 9, #a-
i   9.00 9.00
Souvenir Sheets
866-867 A201 Set of 2   16.00 16.00

N'Djamena, Cent. A213a

Background colors: 150fr, Blue. 300fr, Red. 475fr, Green.

2000, May 29   Litho.   Perf. 13¼
867A-867C A213a Set of 3 —

Chadian Political History — A214

No. 868, 150fr: a, Louis Léon César Faidherbe. b, François Joseph Lamy. c, Henri Eugène Gouraud. d, Gustav Nachtigal. e, Head of Rabah on spike. f, Fernand Foureau.
No. 869, 300fr: a, Pierre Savorgnan de Brazza. b, Philippe Marie de Hautecloque Leclerc. c, Emile Gentil. d, Gabriel Lisette. e, Charles de Gaulle. f, Felix Eboué.

2000, May 29   Perf. 13½
Sheets of 6, #a-f
868-869 A214 Set of 2   18.00 18.00

Wildlife, Map of Chad, Scouting Emblem — A215

No. 870, 150fr — Giraffa camelopardalis: a, Pair, one with head lowered. b, Pair, both with heads extended. c, Pair near forest. d, Trio.
No. 871, 200fr: a, Pair of Gazella granti in field. b, Gazella cuiveri. c, Gazella dorcas. d, Pair of Gazella granti at waterhole.
No. 872, 250fr — Addax nasomaculatus: a, View of head. b, Lying in grass. c, Standing. d, Grazing.
No. 873, 300fr — Ammotragus lervia: a, Pair. b, View of head. c, Standing on mountain ledge. d, Standing, with purple mountain in background
No. 874, 375fr — Diceros bicornis: a, View of head. b, Facing right, line of dark green foliage in background. c, Facing left. d, Facing right, with trees in background.
No. 875, 400fr — Panthera pardus: a, On tree branch. b, Lying in grass. c, Standing. d, View of head.
No. 876, 450fr: a, Head of Theropithecus gelada. b, Cercopithecus aethiops. c, Papio anubis. d, Adult and juvenile Thereopithecus gelada.
No. 877, 450fr — Hippopotamus amphibius: a, Pair laying in mud. b, With open mouth. c, Standing. d, Herd.
No. 878, 475fr — Oryx dammah: a, Facing right, green foliage in background. b, View of head. c, Pair. d, Grazing, mountain in background.
No. 879, 500fr — Panthera leo: a, Male on female. b, Females at waterhole. c, Female and cub. d, Female and male.
No. 880, 600fr — Loxodonta africana: a, With tree at right. b, Facing right. c, View of head. With tree and mountain in background.
No. 881, 750fr — Syncerus caffer: a, Juvenile, adult grazing. b, Adult in field. c, Pair lying on ground. d, With grass in mouth.

No. 882, 1000fr, Pair of Diceros bicornis. No. 883, 1000fr, Pair of Hippopotamus amphibius fighting. No. 884, 1500fr, Panthera leo with kill.

Illustration reduced.

2000, Aug. 1   *Perf. 13¼*
Horiz. Strips of 4, #a-d
870-881   A215   Set of 12   90.00 90.00
Souvenir Sheets
882-884   A215   Set of 3   16.00 16.00

Nos. 882-884 each contain one 36x51mm stamp.

Miniature Sheet

Baseball Player — A216

2000, Oct. 11   Litho. & Embossed
885   A216   3000fr gold & multi   10.00 10.00

Exists with silver background.

High-five of Teenagers — A217

No. 886: a, Moon Hee-jun and Lee Jae-won. b, Jang Woo-hyuk and ear of Tony An. c, Tony an and Kang Ta. d, Jang Woo-hyuk. e, Entire group. f, Kang Ta. g, Moon Hee-jun. h, Lee Jae-won. i, Tony An.

2000   **Litho.**
886   A217   150fr Sheet of 9, #a-i   4.50 4.50

Sports and Chess — A218

No. 887, 30fr — Dogs involved in sport activities: a, Sled dogs. b, Dog racing. c, Hunting dogs. d, Dogs and skier.
No. 888, 70fr — Various sports: a, Petanque. b, Rugby. c, Archery. d, Jai alai.
No. 889, 250fr — 2000 Summer Olympics, Sydney: a, Fencing. b, Judo. c, Tennis. d, Boxing.

No. 890, 300fr — 2000 Summer Olympics, Sydney: a, Cycling. b, Basketball. c, Beach volleyball. d, Baseball.
No. 891, 400fr — Soccer players: a, Zinedine Zidane. b, Lilian Thuram. c, Yuri Djorkaeff. d, Nicolas Anelka.
No. 892, 475fr — 2000 Summer Olympics, Sydney: a, Table tennis. b, Equestrian. c, Swimming. d, Kayaking.
No. 893, 500fr — Golf: a, Man with white pants swinging club. b, Golfer analyzing putt. c, Man with black pants swinging club. d, Woman golfer.
No. 894, 750fr — Formula I race drivers: a, Michael Schumacher. b, Mikka Hakkinen. c, Ralf Schumacher. d, David Coulthard.
No. 895, 1000fr — Chess: a, Knight with shield. b, Knight with attendant. d, Horses and wheeled castle.
2000fr, Venus Williams.

2001, Jan. 31   *Perf. 13¼*
Sheets of 4, #a-d
887-895   A218   Set of 9   85.00 85.00
Souvenir Sheet
896   A218   2000fr multi   9.00   9.00

2000 Summer Olympics, Sydney (No. 896). No. 896 contains one 36x51mm stamp.

Trains — A219

No. 897, 200fr: a, Mallard, 1935. b, P8 Prussian, 1908. c, F2A, 1936. b, 240 P, 1940.
No. 898, 300fr: a, NSB No. 3641. b, New Zealand Railways Sereis EW. c, Series 277, Renfe. d, Series DF4 Vent d'Est IV Co-Co.
No. 899, 400fr: a, SNCF Series 9100 2-D-2, 1950. b, SNCF Series 72000 C-C, 1967. c, CC 21000, 1969. d, VL-80, 1963.
No. 900, 475fr: a, GNER Eurostar. b, Electric EMU ETR 500. c, DER OBB 1016 001. d, GNER train.
No. 901, 500fr: a, OL-49, 1951. b, Pacific Series 16E, 1935. c, Andaluces 030, 1877. d, Franco-Crosti Gr. 743, 1937.
No. 902, 500fr: a, JR West 8-car unit E4. b, TGV KTX. c, 300 Series unit J3. d, E3 Series unit R6.
No. 903, 600fr: a, 2D2 PO, 1926. b, Metropolitan BB Vickers, 1920. c, DB ET 491, 1935. d, Series D, 1925.
No. 904, 600fr: a, Electric EMU 490. b, Acela, 2001. c, CFF-FFS Electric EMU RABe 500. d, ICE-T Bavereihe 41.
No. 905, 750fr: a, Single Driver, 1870. b, Great Western Railway Castle, 1923. c, Schools Class, 1930. d, 230 Besa, 1905.
No. 906, 750fr: a, TGV Thalys. b, TGV Duplex. c, TGV La Poste. d, TGV Atlantique. 1500fr, SAR Series 26 2-D-2. 2000fr, TGV Sud-est.

2001, June 22   **Litho.**
Sheets of 4, #a-d
897-906   A219   Set of 10   90.00 90.00
Souvenir Sheets
907-908   A219   Set of 2   16.00 16.00

Nos. 907-908 each contain one 51x36mm stamp.

British Royalty — A220

No. 909, 300fr — Queen Mother: a, With King George VI. b, With young daughter. c, With Prince Charles. d, Waving. e, Wearing tiara and yellow dress. f, Wearing pink dress and hat. g, Wearing green dress and hat. h, Holding flowers. i, With dogs.
No. 910, 300fr — Prince William wearing: a, Black suit with lapel handkerchief. b, Suit with red and blue vest. c, Suit with gold vest. d, Sweater, looking right. e, Black suit and dark blue tie. f, Sweater, facing forward. g, Blue shirt with button. h, Dark blue shirt without button. i, Light blue suit.

2001, July 22   *Perf. 13¼*
Sheets of 9, #a-i
909-910   A220   Set of 2   24.00 24.00

No. 910 contains nine 36x51mm stamps.

French Rulers — A221

No. 911, 300fr: a, King Francis I. b, King Louis XIII. c, Elizabeth of Austria, consort of King Charles IX. d, King John II the Good.
No. 912, 375fr: a, King Louis XIV. b, King Francis I, diff. c, King Louis XVI. d, King Louis XVIII.
No. 913, 475fr: a, King Louis XV as child. b, King Louis XV as adult. c, Queen Marie Antoinette. d, King Charles VII.
No. 914, 500fr — Napoleon Bonaparte wearing: a, White tunic. b, Black jacket. c, Emperor's robes. d, Red tunic.

2001, July 22
Sheets of 4, #a-d
911-914   A221   Set of 4   30.00 30.00

Stamps of Nos. 911-913 exist in souvenir sheets of 1. Value, set $70.

Pope John Paul II — A222

No. 915, 800fr: a, Standing in room, looking left. b, Waving, c, Holding flowers. d, With blue sky background.
No. 916, 1000fr: a, Wearing red hat. b, Wearing miter, waving. c, Bending to kiss ground. d, Wearing miter, holding crucifix. 4000fr, Wearing zucchetto.

2001   **Litho.**   *Perf. 13¼*
Sheets of 4, #a-d
915-916   A222   Set of 2   32.50 32.50
Miniature Sheet
Litho. & Embossed
917   A222   4000fr gold & multi   22.50 22.50

Issued: Nos. 915-916, 7/22; No. 917, 7/23. No. 917 contains one 60x90mm stamp and exists with a silver background. Stamps of Nos. 915-916 exist in souvenir sheets of 1. Value, set $60.

Famous Men — A223

Designs: 200fr, Charles Darwin (1809-82), naturalist. 250fr, Christopher Columbus (1451-1506), explorer. 300fr, Jacques-Yves Cousteau (1910-97), marine scientist. 350fr, Albert Schweitzer (1875-1965), missionary. 400fr, Juan Manuel Fangio (1911-95), race car driver. 450fr, Nicolaus Copernicus (1473-1543), astronomer. 500fr, Robert Stephenson (1803-59), engineer. 550fr, Etienne Chambron, high speed rail pioneer. 600fr, Garry Kasparov, chess player. 750fr, Lord Robert Baden-Powell (1857-1941), founder of scouting. 800fr, Neil Armstrong, astronaut. 1000fr, Sir Alexander Fleming (1881-1955), bacteriologist.

2001, Oct. 30   **Litho.**
918-929   A223   Set of 12   29.00 29.00

Nos. 918-929 exist in souvenir sheets of 1. Value, set $115.

Fossils, Dinosaurs, Meteorites and Minerals — A224

No. 930, 300fr — Fossils: a, Stenosaurus bollensis. b, Rhamphorhynchus. c, Archaeopteryx lithographica. d, Keichousaurus hui.
No. 931, 375fr — Dinosaurs: a, Mesadactylus. b, Pteranodon. c, Tropeognathus. d, Quetzalcoatlus.
No. 932, 400fr — Meteorites found in: a, India. b, Nigeria. c, US. d, Australia.
No. 933, 500fr — Dinosaurs: a, Deinonychus. b, Seismosaurus. c, Pleurocoelus, Acrocanthosaur. d, Styracosaurus.
No. 934, 500fr — Minerals: a, Fluorite. b, Pyrite. c, Wulfenite. d, Merovingian scoria.
No. 935, 550fr — Meteorites found in: a, Antarctica. b, Libya. c, USSR. d, China.
No. 936, 600fr — Minerals: a, Magnetite. b, Kunzite. c, Apophyllite, Stilbite. d, Fluorite, diff.
No. 937, 750fr — Minerals: a, Quartz. b, Merovingian scoria, diff. c, Epidote. d, Amethyst, agate.
3000fr, Tyrannosaurus rex, vert.

2001, Dec. 27   **Litho.**
Sheets of 4, #a-d
930-937   A224   Set of 8   77.50 77.50
Miniature Sheet
Litho. & Embossed
938   A224   3000fr gold & multi   17.00 17.00

No. 938 contains one 60x90mm stamp and exists with silver background.

French Kings — A225

Designs: No. 939, 3000fr, Louis IX. No. 940, 3000fr, Francis I. No. 941, 3000fr, Henry IV. No. 942, 3000fr, Louis XIII. No. 943, 3000fr, Louis XV.

2002, Apr. 10   Litho. & Embossed
Gold & Multicolored
939-943 A225   Set of 5   50.00 50.00
Nos. 939-943 exist with silver background.

Egyptian Treasures A225a

Designs: No. 943A, 3000fr, Painted wooden box. No. 943B, 3000fr, Nekhbet vulture. No. 943C, 3000fr, Oushebti of Tutankhamen, vert. No. 943D, 3000fr, Pair of royal scepters, vert. No. 943E, 3000fr, Diadem, vert. No. 943F, 3000fr, Gold-plated throne, vert. No. 943G, 3000fr, Cynocephalic pectoral, vert. No. 943H, 3000fr, Coffin of Tutankhamen, vert. No. 943I, 3000fr, Statue of Ka, vert. No. 943J, 3000fr, Duck earring, vert. No. 943K, 3000fr, Lion-shaped vase, vert. No. 943L, 3000fr, Canopic dais and chapel, vert.

Embossed on Gold Paper
2002, Apr. 10   Perf. 13¼
943A-943L A225a Set of 12   140.00 140.00

Artists and Their Paintings — A226

On Nos. 944-957, painting titles (in French) and artist's birth and death dates are in margins adjacent to each stamp. On Nos. 958-962 painting titles are not shown, but artist's name is in sheet margin
No. 944, 150fr: a, Berthe Morisot (1841-95). b, Cache-cache. c, Le Berceau. d, Au bal. e, Jeune femme se poudrant. f, Paule Gobillard peignant.
No. 945, 200fr: a, Marc Chagall (1887-1985). b, Nature morte. c, Le violoniste vert. d, La maison bleue. e, Mariage. f, Le soldat ivre.
No. 946, 250fr: a, Camille Pissarro (1830-1903). b, Les chataigniers a Osny. c, Le verger. d, Le repos des glaneuses. e, Jeune paysanne prenant son cafe. f, Le bergere.
No. 947, 300fr: a, Alfred Sisley (1839-99). b, Le pont de Villeneuve la Garenne. c, Allee de jardin a Louveciennes. d, Meule de foin bord du Loing. e, Moret sur Loing. f, Moulin a Moret.
No. 948, 325fr: a, Paul Delvaux (1897-1994). b, La voix publique. c, Nocturnes. d, Balgnade des Nymphes. e, Pygmalion. f, Jeunes femmes revant.
No. 949, 350fr: a, Edouard Manet (1832-83). b, Le Déjeuner sur l'herbe. c, Olympia. d, Le fifre. e, La serveuse de bocks. f, Le balcon.
No. 950, 375fr: a, Vincent van Gogh (1853-90). b, Champ de blé avec cypres. c, Rue a Auvers. d, La sieste. e, Chambre jaune a Arles. f, Rue de village.
No. 951, 400fr: a, Salvador Dali (1904-89). b, Cannibalisme en automne. c, Corpus Hypercubicus. d, Le sommeil. e, Le tentation de St. Antoine. f, Meditation sur harpe.
No. 952, 425fr: a, Paul Cézanne (1839-1906). b, Les baigneurs. c, Les grandes baigneuses (light blue background). d, Les grandes baigneuses, diff. (dark blue background). e, Les baigneueses. f, Les baigneurs au repos.

No. 953, 450fr: a, Pablo Picasso (1881-1973). b, Femme a l'eventail. c, Femme a l'eventail. d, La danse. e, La vie. f, La mere et son fils.
No. 954, 475fr: a, Amadeo Modigliani (1884-1920). b, Nu souche sur un divan. c, Nu debout. d, Cariatide debout. e, Nu allongé. f, Nu assis de dos.
No. 955, 500fr: a, Auguste Renoir (1841-1919). b, Diane chasseresse. c, Nu allongé. d, Baigneuses. e, Baigneuse assise. f, Nymphe au printemps.
No. 956, 550fr: a, Edgar Degas (1834-1917). b, Femme se coiffant. c, Aprés le bain (view of front of seated woman). d, Femme se peignant. e, Aprés le bain (view of back of woman). f, Aprés le bain (woman dressing).
No. 957, 600fr: a, Henri Matisse (1869-1954). b, Le nu bleu. c, Le genou levé. d, Nu assis sur un fauteuil. e, Odalisques. f, Nu allongé.
No. 958, 1500fr, Gustave Caillebotte. No. 959, 1500fr, Picasso, diff. No. 960, 1500fr, Auguste Renoir, diff. No. 961, 2000fr, Pablo Picasso, diff. No. 962, 2000fr, Van Gogh, diff.

2002, Apr. 10   Perf. 12¾x13¼
Sheets of 6, #a-f
944-957 A226 Set of 14   140.00 140.00
Souvenir Sheets
Perf. 13¼x12¾
958-962 A226 Set of 5   27.50 27.50
Nos. 944a-955a and 957a exist in souvenir sheets of 1 that are perf. 13¼x12¾. Value, set $92.50.

Miniature Sheet

Zeppelin NT — A227

No. 963: a, 475fr, Over Lake Constance. b, 500fr, Over Frankfurt. c, 600fr, Over Nürburgring, Germany. d, 750fr, At 2001 Salon du Bourget.

2002, Oct. 30   Perf. 13¼
963 A227   Sheet of 4, #a-d   11.00 11.00
Nos. 963a-963d exist in souvenir sheets of 1. Value, set $45.

Fauna and Mushrooms — A228

No. 964, 150fr: a, Hemichromis lifalili. b, Trichechus senegalensis. c, Synodontis nigriventris. d, Gnathonemus petersii. e, Ctenopoma ansorgii. f, Pseudocrenilabrus multicolor.
No. 965, 300fr, vert.: a, Nectarina venusta. b, Lamprotornis splendidus. c, Poicephalus meyeri. d, Halcyon leucocephala. e, Quelea quelea. f, Merops pusillus.
No. 966, 350fr, vert.: a, Terathopius ecaudatus. b, Gymnogyps californianus. c, Buteo jamaicensis. d, Lophaetus occipitalis. e, Aquila rapax. f, Melierax metabates.
No. 967, 375fr, vert.: a, Elanus caeruleus. b, Harpia harpyja. c, Gyps rueppellii. d, Milvus migrans. e, Torgos tracheliotus. f, Aquila chrysaetos.
No. 968, 550fr: a, Kallimoides rumia. b, Zophopetes dysmephila. c, Megalopalpus zymna. d, Coeliades forestan. e, Catopsilia florella. f, Anaphaesis aurota.
No. 969, 600fr: a, Amanita muscaria. b, Amanita rubescens. c, Cortinarius orellanus. d, Hygrophorus hypothejus. e, Leccinum piceinum. f, Strobilomyces strobilaceus.

2003, June 2   Litho.
Sheets of 6, #a-f
964-969 A228 Set of 6   55.00 55.00
Stamps of Nos. 965-969 exist in a set of twelve souvenir sheets of two, with each souvenir sheet of two containing adjacent stamps found in the sheet of six. Value, set $160.

Chad - Taiwan Cooperation — A229

Flags and: 50fr, Grain. 100fr, Surgeon's hands, Red Cross. 150fr, Bridge. 300fr, Handshake, maps.

2003, Dec. 1
970-973 A229   Set of 4   2.50 2.50
973a   Booklet pane, 2 each #970-973   5.00 —
      Complete booklet, #973a   5.00
973b   Souvenir sheet, #970-973   2.50 2.50

AIDS Prevention A230

Red ribbon and: 50fr, People under umbrella. 100fr, Man and woman. 150fr, Doctor. 300fr, "Prudence, Abstinence, Fidelité."

2004, July 7   Litho.   Perf. 13x12¾
974-977 A230   Set of 4   2.50 2.50

Opening of Petroleum Refinery, 1st Anniv. A231

Pres. Idriss Deby opening pipeline and: 150fr, Storage tank. 350fr, Storage tanks. 400fr, Refinery. 500fr, Tower, vert.

2004, Oct. 10   Perf. 12¾x13, 13x12¾
978-981 A231   Set of 4   6.50 6.50

Women's Hairstyles A232

Designs: 150fr, Figuerier. 350fr, Sakkindjala. 550fr, Kileskou. 575fr, Dabbou.

2005, Mar. 8   Perf. 13
982-985 A232   Set of 4   8.00 8.00

Toumai Skull A233

Color of skull: 25fr, Purple. 50fr, Green. 100fr, Gray. 150fr, Red. 1500fr, Gray.

2005, July 19   Litho.   Perf. 12¾x13
986-989 A233   Set of 4   1.40 1.40
Souvenir Sheet
990 A233 1500fr multi   5.75 5.75

SEMI-POSTAL STAMPS

Catalogue values for unused stamps in this section are for Never Hinged items.

Anti-Malaria Issue
Common Design Type
Perf. 12½x12
1962, Apr. 7   Engr.   Unwmk.
B1 CD108 25fr + 5fr orange   1.00 .45

Freedom from Hunger Issue
Common Design Type
1963, Mar. 21   Perf. 13
B2 CD112 25fr + 5fr dk grn, dk
           bl & brn   1.00 .45

Red Cross, Mother and Children — SP1

1974, Oct. 2   Photo.   Perf. 12½x13
B3 SP1 30fr + 10fr multi   1.00 .20
Red Cross of Chad, first anniversary.

AIR POST STAMPS

Catalogue values for unused stamps in this section are for Never Hinged items.

Olympic Games Issue
French Equatorial Africa No. C37 Surcharged in Red

Unwmk.
1960, Dec. 15   Engr.   Perf. 13
C1 AP8 250fr on 500fr grnsh
        blk, blk & slate   12.00 5.00
17th Olympic Games, Rome, Aug. 25-Sept. 11. Surcharge 46mm wide; illustration reduced.

Red Bishops — AP1

Discus
Thrower — AP2

Birds in pairs: 100fr, Scarlet-chested sunbird. 200fr, African paradise flycatcher. 250fr,
Malachite kingfisher. 500fr, Nubian carmine
bee-eater.

1961-63   Unwmk.   Engr.   Perf. 13
C2 AP1 50fr dk grn, mag &
          blk   1.25   .35
C3 AP1 100fr multi   3.75   1.25
C4 AP1 200fr multi   6.50   1.90
C5 AP1 250fr dk bl, grn & dp
          org ('63)   10.00   3.00
C6 AP1 500fr multi   22.50   9.50
      Nos. C2-C6 (5)   44.00 16.00

Air Afrique Issue
Common Design Type
1962, Feb. 17   Unwmk.   Perf. 13
C7 CD107 25fr lt bl, org brn &
            blk   1.00   .20

Abidjan Games Issue
1962, July 21   Photo.   Perf. 12x12½
C8 AP2 100fr brn, lt grn & blk   3.50   .75

African Postal Union Issue
Common Design Type
1963, Sept. 8   Unwmk.   Perf. 12½
C9 CD114 85fr dk bl, ocher &
            red   2.40   .40

Air Afrique Issue, 1963
Common Design Type
1963, Nov. 19   Perf. 13x12
C10 CD115 50fr multi   2.40   .40

Europafrica Issue
Common Design Type
1963, Nov. 30   Photo.   Perf. 12x13
C11 CD116 50fr dp grn, yel & dk
             brn   1.75   .40

Mail Truck and Broussard
Plane — AP4

Unwmk.
1963, Dec. 16   Engr.   Perf. 13
C12 AP4 100fr sl grn, ultra & red
            brn   4.00   .20

Chiefs of State Issue

Map and
Presidents
of Chad,
Congo,
Gabon and
Central
African
Republic
AP4a

1964, June 23   Photo.   Perf. 12½
C13 AP4a 100fr multi   2.40   .20
   See note after Central African Republic No.
C19.

Europafrica Issue, 1964

Globe and Emblems of Industry and
Agriculture — AP5

1964, July 20   Perf. 13x12
C14 AP5 50fr brn, pur & dp org   1.75   .30
   See note after Cameroun No. 402.

Soccer — AP6

   Designs: 50fr, Javelin throw, vert. 100fr,
High jump, vert. 200fr, Runners.

1964, Aug. 12   Engr.   Perf. 13
C15 AP6 25fr yel grn, sl grn &
           org brn   .75   .20
C16 AP6 50fr org brn, ind &
           brt bl   1.75   .30
C17 AP6 100fr blk, red & brt grn   3.50   .50
C18 AP6 200fr bis, blk & car   6.00   1.10
  a.   Min. sheet of 4, #C15-C18   18.00   6.50
      Nos. C15-C18 (4)   12.00   2.10
   18th Olympic Games, Tokyo, 10/10-25/64.

Communications Symbols — AP7

1964, Nov. 2   Litho.   Perf. 12½x13
C19 AP7 25fr lil, dk brn & lt red
            brn   1.00   .20
   Pan-African and Malagasy Posts and Tele-
communications Cong., Cairo, Oct. 24-Nov. 6.

President John F.
Kennedy (1917-
63) — AP8

1964, Nov. 3   Photo.   Perf. 12½
C20 AP8 100fr multi   2.40   .70
  a.   Souvenir sheet of 4   12.00   6.00

ICY Emblem — AP9

1965, July 5   Photo.   Perf. 13
C21 AP9 100fr multi   1.50   .25
   International Cooperation Year, 1965.

Abraham Lincoln — AP10

1965, Sept. 7   Unwmk.   Perf. 13
C22 AP10 100fr multi   2.25   .35
   Centenary of death of Abraham Lincoln.

Musical Instrument Type
Design: 100fr, Xylophone (marimba).
1965, Oct. 26   Engr.   Perf. 13
Size: 48x27mm
C23 A18 100fr ocher, brt bl & vio
            bl   2.75   .85

Sir Winston
Spencer
Churchill (1874-
1965)
AP11

1965, Nov. 23   Engr.   Perf. 13
C24 AP11 50fr dk grn & blk   1.40   .20

Dr. Albert Schweitzer and
Outstretched Hands — AP12

1966, Feb. 15   Photo.   Perf. 12½
C25 AP12 100fr multi   2.75   .50
   Dr. Albert Schweitzer (1875-1965), medical
missionary, theologian and musician.

Air Afrique Issue, 1966
Common Design Type
1966, Aug. 31   Photo.   Perf. 13
C26 CD123 30fr yel grn, blk &
             gray   .75   .20

White-throated Bee-eater — AP13

   Birds: 50fr, Blue-eared glossy starling.
200fr, African pygmy kingfisher. 250fr, Red-
throated bee-eater. 500fr, Little green bee-
eater.

1966-67   Photo.   Perf. 13x12½
C27 AP13 50fr gold & multi   1.25   .40
C28 AP13 100fr bluish gray &
            multi   3.50   1.00
C29 AP13 200fr grnsh gray &
            multi   6.75   1.75
C30 AP13 250fr pale bl & multi   7.50   1.75
C31 AP13 500fr pale sal & multi   14.00   3.25
      Nos. C27-C31 (5)   33.00   8.15
   Issued: 100fr, 200fr, 500fr, 8/18/66; others,
3/21/67.
   For surcharges see Nos. C67-C69.

Congress Hall — AP14

1967, Jan. 5   Photo.   Perf. 12½
C32 AP14 25fr multi   .75   .20
   Opening of the new Congress Hall.

Breguet 19 Biplane — AP15

   Planes: 30fr, Latécoère 631 hydroplane.
50fr, Douglas DC-3. 100fr, Piper Cherokee 6.

1967, Aug. 1   Engr.   Perf. 13
C33 AP15 25fr sky bl, sl grn & lt
            brn   .75   .25
C34 AP15 30fr sky bl, indigo &
            grn   1.00   .30
C35 AP15 50fr sky bl, ol bis &
            sl grn   1.75   .50
C36 AP15 100fr dk bl, sl grn &
            dk red   3.50   .75
      Nos. C33-C36 (4)   7.00   1.80
   First anniversary of Air Chad.

African Postal Union Issue, 1967
Common Design Type
1967, Sept. 9   Engr.   Perf. 13
C37 CD124 100fr ol, brt pink &
             red brn   1.90   .40

Rock Painting Type of Regular Issue
1967, Dec. 19   Engr.   Perf. 13
Size: 48x27mm
C38 A32 100fr Masked dancers   8.00   .95
C39 A32 125fr Rabbit hunt   9.00   1.50

Downhill Skiing — AP16

1968, Feb. 5   Engr.   Perf. 13
C40 AP16 30fr shown   1.25   .20
C41 AP16 100fr Ski jump, vert.   3.25   .50
   10th Winter Olympic Games, Grenoble,
France, Feb. 6-18.

Konrad Adenauer
(1876-1967),
Chancellor of
West Germany
(1949-63)
AP17

1968, Mar. 19   Photo.   Perf. 12½
C42 AP17 52fr grn, dk brn & lt lil 1.40 .30
  a.   Souvenir sheet of 4 6.00 2.40

The Snake Charmer, by Henri
Rousseau — AP18

Design: 130fr, "War" by Henri Rousseau.

1968, May 14   Photo.   Perf. 13½
Size: 41x41mm
C43 AP18 100fr ultra & multi 3.50 .30
Size: 48x35mm
Perf. 12½
C44 AP18 130fr brn & multi 5.50 .40

Hurdlers — AP19

1968, Oct. 16   Engr.   Perf. 13
C45 AP19 32fr shown 1.00 .20
C46 AP19 80fr Relay race 2.75 .20

19th Olympic Games, Mexico City, 10/12-27.

PHILEXAFRIQUE Issue

The Actor
Wolf
(Bernard),
by Jacques
L. David
AP20

1969, Jan. 15   Photo.   Perf. 12½
C47 AP20 100fr multi 3.75 1.75

PHILEXAFRIQUE, Philatelic Exhib. in
Abidjan, Feb. 14-23. Printed with alternating
label.

2nd PHILEXAFRIQUE Issue
Common Design Type
50fr, Chad #J12 and Moundang Dancers.

1969, Feb. 14   Engr.   Perf. 13
C48 CD128 50fr red, brt bl, brn &
      grn 2.25 1.25

Gustav Nachtigal and Tibesti Gorge,
1869 — AP21

#C50, Heinrich Barth & Lake Chad, 1851.

1969, Feb. 17
C49 AP21 100fr vio bl, dk brn &
      brn 2.40 .50
C50 AP21 100fr grn, pur & bl 2.40 .50

German explorers Gustav Nachtigal (1834-
85) and Heinrich Barth (1821-65), and state
visit of the Pres. of West Germany Heinrich
Lubke.

Apollo 8, Earth and Moon — AP22

1969, Apr. 10   Photo.   Perf. 13
C51 AP22 100fr multi 2.10 .60

US Apollo 8 mission, the 1st men in orbit
around the moon, Dec. 21-27, 1968.

Mahatma
Gandhi — AP23

#C53, John F. Kennedy. #C54, Dr. Martin
Luther King, Jr. #C55, Robert F. Kennedy.

1969, May 20   Photo.   Perf. 12½
C52 AP23 50fr blk & lt grn 1.25 .40
C53 AP23 50fr blk & tan 1.25 .40
C54 AP23 50fr blk & pink 1.25 .40
C55 AP23 50fr blk & lt vio bl 1.25 .40
  a.   Souvenir sheet of 4, #C52-C55 6.00 6.00
    Nos. C52-C55 (4) 5.00 1.60

Issued to honor exponents of non-violence.

Presidents Tombalbaye and Mobutu,
Map and Flags of Chad and
Congo — AP24

Embossed on Gold Foil
1969   Die-cut Perf. 13½
C56 AP24 1000fr gold, dk bl &
      red 27.50 27.50

1st anniv. of the establishment of the Union
of Central African States, comprising Chad,
Congo Democratic Republic and Central African Republic.

Napoleon Visiting Hospital, by
Alexandre Veron-Bellecourt — AP25

Paintings: 85fr, Battle of Wagram, by Horace Vernet. 130fr, Battle of Austerlitz, by Francois Pascal Gerard.

1969, July 23   Photo.   Perf. 12x12½
C57 AP25 30fr multi 1.10 .25
C58 AP25 85fr multi 2.40 .65
C59 AP25 130fr multi 4.25 1.25
    Nos. C57-C59 (3) 7.75 2.15

Bicentenary of birth of Napoleon I.

Apollo 11 Issue

Astronaut on Moon — AP26

Embossed on Gold Foil
1969, Oct. 17   Die-cut Perf. 13½
C60 AP26 1000fr gold 27.50 19.00

See note after Algeria No. 427.

Village Life, by Goto Narcisse — AP27

No. 62, Women at the Market, by Iba
N'Diaye. No. 63, Woman with Flowers, by Iba
N'Diaye, vert.

1970   Photo.   Perf. 12x12½, 12½x12
C61 AP27 100fr multi 3.25 .20
C62 AP27 250fr grn & multi 5.00 .35
C63 AP27 250fr brn & multi 5.00 .35
    Nos. C61-C63 (3) 13.25 .90

Issued: 100fr, Mar. 17; #C62-C63, Aug. 28.

Napoleon — AP27a

Designs: Nos. C63A, C63E, Napoleon II,
Duke of Reichstadt, vert.
  No. C63B: g, 10fr, Crossing the Grand St.
Bernard, by David. h, 25fr, Emperor Napoleon,
by Gerard. i, 32fr, Marriage of Napoleon and
Marie Louise, by Rouget.
  40fr, Napoleon after return from Elba, vert.

Perf. 12x12½, 12½x12
1970-71   Litho.
C63A AP27a 10fr multicolored 4.00 —
C63B AP27a Strip of 3,
        #g.-i. 13.50 —
Embossed
Perf. 13
C63C AP27a 10fr gold 20.00 —
  f.   Sheet of 1, Imperf. 37.50 —
Souvenir Sheets
Litho.
Perf. 13x13½
C63D AP27a 40fr multicolored 10.00 —
Embossed
Imperf
C63E AP27a 10fr gold, like
        #C63A 37.50 —

#C63A is printed se-tenant with label.
#C63D contains one 43x67mm stamp.
#C63Cf contains one 53x42mm stamp with
same size design as #C63Bg. #C63E contains
one 43x104mm stamp with same size design
as #C63A.
  No. C63E probably was not available in
Chad.
  Issued: #C63B, 6/12; #C63A, C63D-C63E,
4/1971; #C63C, 11/1/71.

EXPO Emblem
and Osaka
Print — AP28

EXPO Emblem and: 100fr, Tower of the
Sun. 125fr, Osaka print, diff.

1970, June 30   Engr.   Perf. 13
C64 AP28 50fr bl, red brn & sl
      grn .70 .20
C65 AP28 100fr red, yel grn &
      Prus bl 1.40 .20
C66 AP28 125fr blk, dk red & bis 1.90 .25
    Nos. C64-C66 (3) 4.00 .65

Issued to publicize EXPO '70 International
Exhibition, Osaka, Japan, Mar. 15-Sept. 13.

1968 Summer Olympics, 1970 World
Cup Soccer Championships, Mexico
AP28a

1970, July 1   Litho.   Perf. 12½x12½
C66A AP28a 5fr Flags, soccer
        players 1.40
Souvenir Sheet
Perf. 13½x13
C66C AP28a 15fr Olympic
        torch, soccer
        player 6.25

No. C66A printed in sheets of 2 + 2 labels.
No. C66C contains one 66x43mm stamp.
For overprints see Nos. C88A-C88B.

Nos. C28-C30 Surcharged in Carmine
with New Value and Bars and
Overprinted:
  a. "APOLLO XI / 1er débarquement
  · sur la lune/20 juillet 1969"
  b. "APOLLO XII / Exploration de la
  lune / 19 Novembre 1969"
  c. "APOLLO XIII / Exploit spatial / 11-
  17 avril 1970"

1970, July 9   Photo.   Perf. 13x12½
C67 AP13 (a) 50fr on 100fr 1.90 .25
C68 AP13 (b) 100fr on 200fr 3.25 .45
C69 AP13 (c) 125fr on 250fr 4.75 .55
    Nos. C67-C69 (3) 9.90 1.25

Space missions of Apollo 11, 12 and 13.

DC-8 "Fort Lamy" over Airport — AP29

1970, Aug. 5   Perf. 12½
C70 AP29 30fr dk sl grn & multi 1.10 .20

Souvenir Sheet

Apollo 12 — AP29a

1970, Sept.   Embossed   Imperf.
C70A AP29a 25fr gold   35.00
 No. C70A probably was not available in Chad.

The Visitation, Venetian School, 15th Century AP30

Paintings, Venetian School: 25fr, Nativity, 15th century. 30fr, Virgin and Child, c. 1350.

1970, Dec. 15 Photo.   Perf. 12½x12
C71 AP30 20fr gold & multi   .75   .20
C72 AP30 25fr gold & multi   1.10   .20
C73 AP30 30fr gold & multi   1.25   .20
   Nos. C71-C73 (3)   3.10   .60
 Christmas 1970. See Nos. C144-C147.

Post Office Mauritius and Emblem AP31

1971, Jan. 23   Engr.   Perf. 13
C74 AP31 10fr shown   .20   .20
C75 AP31 20fr Tuscany #23   .40   .20
C76 AP31 30fr France #8   .60   .20
C77 AP31 60fr US #2   1.10   .25
C78 AP31 80fr Japan #8   1.50   .30
C79 AP31 100fr Saxony #1   1.90   .40
  a.   Souvenir sheet of 6, #C74-C79   8.00 5.00
   Nos. C74-C79 (6)   5.70 1.55
 Publicity for PHILEXOCAM, philatelic exhibition, Fort Lamy, Jan. 23-30.

Gamal Abdel Nasser — AP32

1971, Feb. 16   Photo.   Perf. 12½
C80 AP32 75fr multi   1.10   .20
 In memory of Gamal Abdel Nasser (1918-1970), President of Egypt.

Presidents Mobutu, Bokassa and Tombalbaye — AP33

1971, Apr. 28   Photo.   Perf. 13
C81 AP33 100fr multi   1.75   .20
 Return of Central African Republic to the United States of Central Africa which also includes Congo Democratic Republic and Chad.

Map of Africa, Communications Network and Symbols — AP34

1971, May 17   Engr.   Perf. 13
C82 AP34 125fr ultra, sl grn &
           brn red   2.25   .20
 Pan-African telecommunications system.

Boys Around Campfire, Torii AP35

1971, Aug. 24   Photo.   Perf. 12½
C83 AP35 250fr multi   5.50   .40
 13th Boy Scout World Jamboree, Asagiri Plain, Japan, Aug. 2-10.

White Egret — AP36

1971, Sept. 28 Photo. Perf. 13x12½
C84 AP36 1000fr blk, dk bl &
           ocher   75.00 6.75

Greek Marathon Runners — AP37

45fr, Ancient Olympic Stadium. 75fr, Greek wrestlers. 130fr, Olympic Stadium, Athens, 1896.

1971, Oct. 5   Perf. 12½
C85 AP37 40fr multi   .75   .20
C86 AP37 45fr multi   1.00   .20
C87 AP37 75fr multi   1.75   .20
C88 AP37 130fr multi   1.90   .35
   Nos. C85-C88 (4)   5.40 1.00
 75th anniv. of modern Olympic Games.

Nos. C66A, C66C Ovptd. in Gold

1971   Litho.   Perf. 12½x12
C88A AP28a 5fr multi   2.50
   Souvenir Sheet
       Perf. 13½x13
C88B AP28a 15fr multi   5.50
 Overprint on No. C88B is 36mm long.

Duke Ellington — AP38

Charles de Gaulle — AP39

50fr, Sidney Bechet. 100fr, Louis Armstrong.

1971, Oct. 20   Litho.   Perf. 13
C89 AP38 50fr multi   2.00   .50
C90 AP38 75fr lt bl & multi 3.00   .70
C91 AP38 100fr multi   5.00   .85
   Nos. C89-C91 (3)   10.00 2.05
 Famous American jazz musicians.

Lithographed and Embossed
1971, Nov. 9   Perf. 12½
 Design: No. C93, Félix Eboué.
C92 AP39 200fr grn, yel grn &
           gold   8.00 4.00
C93 AP39 200fr bl, lt bl & gold 8.00 4.00
  a.   Souv. sheet, #C92-C93 + label 20.00 20.00
 Charles de Gaulle (1890-1970), pres. of France.

African Postal Union Issue, 1971
Common Design Type
 Design: 100fr, Sao antelope head and UAMPT building, Brazzaville, Congo.

1971, Nov. 13   Photo.   Perf. 13x13½
C94 CD135 100fr bl & multi 1.50   .20

Apollo 15 Rocket AP40

80fr, Apollo 15 capsule, horiz. 150fr, Lunar module on Moon, horiz. 250fr, Astronaut making tests. 300fr, Moon-buggy. #C100, Successful splashdown, horiz. #C101, Apollo 15 insignia.

1972, Jan. 5   Litho.   Perf. 13½
C95   AP40 40fr multi   .50   .20
C96   AP40 80fr multi   .90   .20
C97   AP40 150fr multi   1.50   .30
C98   AP40 250fr multi   2.50   .45
C99   AP40 300fr multi   3.00   .60
C100 AP40 500fr multi   5.50 1.40
   Nos. C95-C100 (6)   13.90 3.15
   Souvenir Sheet
C101 AP40 500fr multi   8.00 1.25
 Apollo 15 moon landing.

Soyuz 11 Link-up — AP41

 Designs: 30fr, Soyuz 11 on launching pad, vert. 50fr, No. C108, Cosmonauts in uniform. 200fr, V. I. Patsayev. No. C106, V. N. Volkov. 400fr, G. L. Dobrovolsky. No. C109, Three cosmonauts.

1972, Jan. 5   Perf. 13½x13
C102 AP41 30fr multi   .25   .20
C103 AP41 50fr multi   .45   .20
C104 AP41 100fr multi   .80   .25
C105 AP41 200fr multi   2.00   .50
C106 AP41 300fr multi   3.25   .75
C107 AP41 400fr multi   4.25 1.10
   Nos. C102-C107 (6)   11.00 3.00
   Souvenir Sheets
C108 AP41 300fr multi   3.50 1.00
C109 AP41 400fr multi   4.00 1.40
 Soyuz 11 link-up project.

Bobsledding — AP42

 Design: 100fr, Slalom.

1972, Feb. 24   Engr.   Perf. 13
C110 AP42 50fr Prus bl & rose
            red   1.00   .20
C111 AP42 100fr red lil & slate
            grn   1.90   .20
 11th Winter Olympic Games, Sapporo, Japan, Feb. 3-13.

Pres. Tombalbaye Type, 1972
1972, Apr. 13   Litho.   Perf. 13
C112 A63 70fr multi   .90   .20
C113 A63 80fr multi   1.10   .20

11th Winter Olympic Type, 1972
 130fr, Speed skating. #C115, Ice hockey. #C116, Ski jumping. 250fr, 4-man bobsled.

1972, Apr. 13   Perf. 13½
C114 A64 130fr multi   1.40   .45
C115 A64 200fr multi   2.50   .60
   Souvenir Sheets
C116 A64 200fr multi   3.25   .75
C117 A64 250fr multi   4.25 1.10

Scout Jamboree Type, 1972
 Designs: 100fr, Cooking preparation. 120fr, Lord Baden Powell. 250fr, Hiking.

1972, May 15
C118 A67 100fr multi   2.10   .30
C119 A67 120fr multi   2.40   .40
   Souvenir Sheet
C120 A67 250fr multi   8.50   .75

Zebras — AP43

African wild animals: 30fr, Mandrills. 100fr,
African elephants. 130fr, Gazelles. 150fr, Hip-
popotamuses. 200fr, Lion cub.

1972, May 15   Litho.   Perf. 13
C121 AP43 20fr multi   .35   .20
C122 AP43 30fr multi   .50   .20
C123 AP43 100fr multi   1.40   .35
C124 AP43 130fr multi   2.25   .50
C125 AP43 150fr multi   3.50   .75
    Nos. C121-C125 (5)   8.00 2.00
Souvenir Sheet
C126 AP43 200fr multi   35.00 25.00

View of Venice, by Caffi — AP44

Paintings by Ippolito Caffi: 40fr, Sailing ship
and Doge's Palace, vert. 140fr, Grand Canal,
vert.

1972, May 23   Photo.
C127 AP44 40fr gold & multi   1.10   .20
C128 AP44 45fr gold & multi   1.90   .20
C129 AP44 140fr gold & multi   3.50   .60
    Nos. C127-C129 (3)   6.50 1.00

UNESCO campaign to save Venice.

11th Winter Olympic Winners Type,
1972

Designs: 150fr, Slalom, B. Cochran, US.
200fr, Women's figure skating, B. Schuba,
Austria. 250fr, Ice hockey, USSR. 300fr, 2-
man bobsled. W. Zimmerer and P.
Utzschneider, West Germany.

1972, June 15   Perf. 14½
C130 A69 150fr gold & multi   3.00   .75
C131 A69 200fr gold & multi   3.75 1.00
Souvenir Sheets
C132 A69 250fr gold & multi   3.25 2.75
C133 A69 300fr gold & multi   3.75 3.00

Nos. C130-C131 exist se-tenant with label
showing earth satellite.

Daudet, "Tartarin de Tarascon," Book
Year Emblem — AP45

1972, July 22   Engr.   Perf. 13
C134 AP45 100fr dk red, lil & dk
            brn   1.90   .20

Intl. Book Year, 1972, and to honor
Alphonse Daudet (1840-1897), French writer.

20th Summer Olympics Type, 1972

Designs (TV Tower, Munich and): 100fr,
Gymnast. 120fr, Pole vault. 150fr, Fencing.
250fr, Hammer throw. 300fr, Boxing.

1972, Aug. 15
C135 A70 100fr gold & multi   2.10   .50
C136 A70 120fr gold & multi   2.50   .60
C137 A70 150fr gold & multi   3.25   .80
    Nos. C135-C137 (3)   7.85 1.90

Souvenir Sheets
C138 A70 250fr gold & multi   3.50 2.75
C139 A70 300fr gold & multi   4.00 3.00

Nos. C135-C137 exist se-tenant with label
showing arms of Munich.

Lunokhod on Moon — AP46

Russian moon missions: 100fr, Luna 16 on
moon and rocket in flight, vert.

1972, Sept. 19
C140 AP46 100fr dk bl, pur & bis 1.90   .50
C141 AP46 150fr slate, brn & lil 2.50   .75

Farcha Laboratory, Cattle,
Scientist — AP47

1972, Nov. 11   Photo.   Perf. 13
C142 AP47 75fr yellow & multi   1.40   .30

20th anniversary of the Farcha Laboratory
for veterinary research.

King Faisal and Holy Kaaba,
Mecca — AP48

1972, Nov. 17
C143 AP48 75fr multi   1.40   .25

Visit of King Faisal of Saudi Arabia.

Christmas Type of 1970

Christmas: 40fr, Virgin and Child, by Giovanni Bellini. 75fr, Virgin and Child, by
Dall'Occhio. 80fr, Nativity, by Fra Angelico,
horiz. 95fr, Adoration of the Kings, by Il
Perugino.

1972, Dec. 15   Photo.   Perf. 13
C144 AP30 40fr gold & multi   .20   .20
C145 AP30 75fr gold & multi   1.75   .30
C146 AP30 80fr gold & multi   2.00   .40
C147 AP30 95fr gold & multi   2.00   .50
    Nos. C144-C147 (4)   5.95 1.40

Summer Olympic Winners Type, 1972

Olympic Emblems and: 150fr, Pole vault,
Nordwig, East Germany. 250fr, Hurdles, Mil-
burn, US. 300fr, Javelin, Wolfermann, West
Germany.

1972, Dec. 22
C148 A76 150fr multi   3.00   .60
C149 A76 250fr multi   4.25   .75
Souvenir Sheet
C150 A76 300fr multi   15.00 3.00

Summer Olympic Winners Type, 1972

Olympic Emblem and: 150fr, Dressage,
Mancinelli, Italy. #C152, Finn class sailing,
Serge Maury, France. #C153, Swimming,
Mark Spitz.

1972, Dec. 22   Litho.   Perf. 11
C151 A77 150fr gold & multi   3.25   .75
C152 A77 250fr gold & multi   5.00 1.00
Souvenir Sheet
C153 A77 250fr multi   15.00 3.00

Copernicus and Solar System — AP49

1973, Mar. 31   Engr.   Perf. 13
C154 AP49 250fr gray, mag &
            brn   5.25 1.25

500th anniversary of the birth of Nicolaus
Copernicus (1473-1543), Polish astronomer.

Horses — AP49a

Details from paintings: 20fr, A Horse Fright-
ened by Lightning, by Theordore Gericault.
60fr, The White Horse, by Paul Potter. 100fr,
Mares and Foals, by George Stubbs. 150fr,
Horse Head, by Theordore Gericault, vert.
500fr, The Carriage, by Vernet.

1973   Litho.   Perf. 11½
C154A AP49a 20fr multi
C154B AP49a 60fr multi
C154C AP49a 100fr multi
C154D AP49a 150fr multi
    Nos. C154A-C154D (4)   14.00
Souvenir Sheet
        Perf. 15
C154E AP49a 500fr mul-
            ticolored   15.00

See note before No. 225A.

Airplanes — AP49b

1973   Litho.   Perf. 12
C154F AP49b   5fr Fokker F
                  VII/3M
C154G AP49b 25fr DH 89A
                  Rapide
C154H AP49b 70fr Viscount
C154J AP49b 150fr Boeing
                  747
C154K AP49b 200fr Concorde
    Nos. C154F-C154K (5)   14.00
Souvenir Sheet
        Perf. 12
C154L AP49b 350fr Concorde,
            diff.   14.00

Nos. C154L contains one 60x40mm stamp.
See note before No. 225A.

Skylab over Africa — AP50

1974, Aug. 6   Engr.   Perf. 13
C155 AP50 100fr shown   1.50   .25
C156 AP50 150fr Skylab   2.50   .35

Exploits of Skylab, US manned space
station.

Soccer — AP51

125fr, 150fr, Soccer players; 125fr, vert.

1974, Oct. 22   Engr.   Perf. 13
C157 AP51 50fr dl red & choc   .75   .25
C158 AP51 125fr red & dp grn   1.75   .50
C159 AP51 150fr grn & rose red   2.50   .75
    Nos. C157-C159 (3)   5.00 1.50

World Cup Soccer Championship, Munich,
June 13-July 7.

Family and WPY
Emblem — AP52

1974, Nov. 11
C160 AP52 250fr multi   3.75 1.25

World Population Year.

Mail Delivery by Canoe — AP53

UPU Cent.: 40fr, Diesel train. 100fr, Jet.
150fr, Spacecraft.

1974, Dec. 20   Engr.   Perf. 13
C161 AP53 30fr car & multi   .60   .20
C162 AP53 40fr ultra & blk   1.00   .20
C163 AP53 100fr brn, ultra & blk 1.90   .40
C164 AP53 150fr grn, lil & ol   2.40   .55
    Nos. C161-C164 (4)   5.90 1.35

Women of Different Races, IWY
Emblem — AP54

1975, June 25   Photo.   Perf. 13
C165 AP54 250fr bl & multi   4.50 1.25

International Women's Year 1975.

Apollo and Soyuz Before Link-
up — AP55

130fr, Apollo and Soyuz after link-up.

1975, July 15   Engr.   Perf. 13

C166	AP55	100fr ultra, choc & grn	1.50 .40
C167	AP55	130fr vio bl, brn & grn	2.00 .50

Apollo Soyuz space test project (Russo-American space cooperation), launching 7/15; link-up 7/17.
For overprints see Nos. C171-C172.

Soccer Player, View of Montreal — AP56

Olympic Rings, Montreal Skyline: 100fr, Discus thrower. 125fr, Runner.

1975, Oct. 14   Engr.   Perf. 13

C168	AP56	75fr car & slate grn	1.00 .25
C169	AP56	100fr car, choc & bl grn	1.40 .40
C170	AP56	125fr brn, bl & car	1.90 .75
		Nos. C168-C170 (3)	4.30 1.40

Pre-Olympic Year 1975.

Nos. C166-C167 Overprinted: "JONCTION / 17 JUILLET 1975"

1975, Nov. 4   Engr.   Perf. 13

C171	AP55	100fr multi	1.75 .25
C172	AP55	130fr multi	2.10 .35

Apollo-Soyuz link-up in space, July 17.

Stylized British and American Flags, "200" — AP57

1975, Dec. 5   Engr.   Perf. 13

C173	AP57	150fr vio bl, car & ol bis	2.25 .75

American Bicentennial.

Adoration of the Shepherds, by Murillo — AP58

Christmas (Paintings): 75fr, Adoration of the Shepherds, by Georges de La Tour. 80fr, Virgin and Child with Bible, by Rogier van der Weyden, vert. 100fr, Holy Family, by Raphael, vert.

1975, Dec. 15   Litho.   Perf. 13x12½

C174	AP58	40fr yel & multi	.75 .25
C175	AP58	75fr yel & multi	1.25 .35
C176	AP58	80fr yel & multi	1.75 .40
C177	AP58	100fr yel & multi	2.75 .75
		Nos. C174-C177 (4)	6.50 1.75

12th Winter Olympic Winners Type, 1976

250fr, 4-man bobsled, West Germany. 300fr, Speed skating, J. E. Storholt, Norway. 500fr, Downhill skiing, F. Klammer, Austria.

1976, June 21   Perf. 14

C178	A84	250fr multi	2.75 .60
C179	A84	300fr multi	3.50 1.00

Souvenir Sheet

C180	A84	500fr multi	6.00 3.00

Paul Revere's Ride and Portrait by Copley — AP59

American Bicentennial: 125fr, Washington crossing Delaware. 150fr, Lafayette offering his services to America. 200fr, Rochambeau at Yorktown with Washington. 250fr, Franklin presenting Declaration of Independence. 400fr, Count de Grasse's victory at Cape Charles.

1976, July 4   Litho.   Perf. 14

C181	AP59	100fr multi	1.10 .30
C182	AP59	125fr multi	1.25 .35
C183	AP59	150fr multi	1.90 .40
C184	AP59	200fr multi	2.25 .50
C185	AP59	250fr multi	3.00 .55
		Nos. C181-C185 (5)	9.50 2.10

Souvenir Sheet

C186	AP59	400fr multi	6.00 3.00

Summer Olympics Type, 1976

1976, July 12

C187	A85	100fr Boxing	1.50 .30
C188	A85	200fr Pole vault	2.50 .50
C189	A85	300fr muShot put	4.00 .65
		Nos. C187-C189 (3)	8.00 1.45

Souvenir Sheet

C190	A85	500fr Sprint	6.00 3.00

Viking Mars Project Type, 1976

Mars Lander and: 100fr, Viking landing on Mars. 200fr, Capsule over Mars. 250fr, Lander over Mars. 450fr, Lander and probe.

1976, July 23   Litho.   Perf. 14

C191	A86	100fr multi	1.10 .30
C192	A86	200fr multi	2.25 .55
C193	A86	250fr multi	2.50 .75
		Nos. C191-C193 (3)	5.85 1.60

Souvenir Sheet

C194	A86	450fr multi	7.50 3.00

For overprints see Nos. C240-C243.

Concorde — AP60

1976, Oct. 15   Litho.   Perf. 12½

C195	AP60	250fr bl, blk & ver	6.00 1.75

First commercial flight of supersonic jet Concorde, Jan. 21.

Nobel Prize Type, 1976

100fr, Albert Einstein, physics. 200fr, Dag Hammarskjold, peace. 300fr, Shinichiro Tomanaga, physics. 500fr, Alexander Fleming, medicine.

1976, Dec. 15

C196	A87	150fr multi	1.50 .30
C197	A87	200fr multi	2.50 .55
C198	A87	300fr multi	3.50 .70
		Nos. C196-C198 (3)	7.50 1.55

Souvenir Sheet

C199	A87	500fr multi	8.00 3.50

Adoration of the Shepherds, by Gerard van Honthorst — AP61

Christmas (Paintings): 30fr, Nativity, by Albrecht Altdorfer, vert. 60fr, Nativity, by Hans Holbein, vert. 150fr, Adoration of the Kings, by Gerard David.

1976, Dec. 22   Litho.   Perf. 12½

C200	AP61	30fr gold & multi	.50 .20
C201	AP61	60fr gold & multi	.75 .20
C202	AP61	120fr gold & blk	1.50 .50
C203	AP61	150fr gold & blk	2.25 .75
		Nos. C200-C203 (4)	5.00 1.65

Lesdiguières Bridge, by Jongkind — AP62

Design: 120fr, Sailing Ship and Boats, by Johan Barthold Jongkind (1819-1891).

1976, Dec. 27   Photo.   Perf. 13

C204	AP62	100fr multi	1.75 .55
C205	AP62	120fr multi	2.25 .60

Centenary of impressionism.

Zeppelin Type of 1977

125fr, Germany #C40, North Pole. 150fr, Germany #C45, Chicago department store. 175fr, Germany #C38 and scenes of NYC and London. 200fr, 500fr, US #C15, NYC.

1977, Mar. 30   Perf. 11

C206	A91	125fr multi	1.90 .35
C207	A91	150fr multi	2.25 .40
C208	A91	175fr multi	2.75 .50
C209	A91	200fr multi	3.25 .60
		Nos. C206-C209 (4)	10.15 1.85

Souvenir Sheet

C210	A91	500fr multi	8.00 3.00

Sassenage Castle, Grenoble — AP63

1977, May 21   Litho.   Perf. 12½

C211	AP63	100fr multi	1.00 .30

Intl. French Language Council, 10th Anniv.

Lafayette and Ships — AP64

American Bicentennial: 120fr, Abraham Lincoln, eagle and flags, vert. 150fr, James Madison and family.

1977, July 30   Engr.   Perf. 13

C212	AP64	100fr multi	1.40 .35
C213	AP64	120fr multi	1.75 .40
C214	AP64	150fr multi	2.25 .50
		Nos. C212-C214 (3)	5.40 1.25

Lindbergh and Spirit of St. Louis — AP65

100fr, Concorde. 150fr, 200fr, 300fr, Various Lindbergh portraits & Spirit of St. Louis.

1977, Sept. 27

C215	AP65	100fr multi	1.25 .30
C216	AP65	120fr multi	1.25 .40
C217	AP65	150fr multi	1.40 .55
C218	AP65	200fr multi	2.25 .65
C219	AP65	300fr multi	3.00 .90
		Nos. C215-C219 (5)	9.15 2.80

Charles A. Lindbergh's solo transatlantic flight from NY to Paris, 50th anniv., and 1st supersonic transatlantic flight of Concorde.
For overprint see No. C227.

Mariner 10 — AP66

Spacecraft: 200fr, Lunokhod on moon, Luna 21. 300fr, Viking on Mars.

1977, Oct. 10   Engr.   Perf. 13

C220	AP66	100fr multi	1.25 .40
C221	AP66	200fr multi	2.00 .70
C222	AP66	300fr multi	2.75 .90
		Nos. C220-C222 (3)	6.00 2.00

Running — AP67

1977, Oct. 24   Engr.   Perf. 13

C223	AP67	30fr shown	.40 .20
C224	AP67	60fr Volleyball	.85 .20
C225	AP67	120fr Soccer	1.50 .40
C226	AP67	125fr Basketball	1.25 .50
		Nos. C223-C226 (4)	4.00 1.35

No. C215 Overprinted: "PARIS NEW-YORK / 22.11.77"

1977, Nov. 22

C227	AP65	100fr multi	3.25 .20

Concorde, 1st commercial flight Paris-NYC.

Virgin and Child, by Rubens AP68

Rubens Paintings: 60fr, Virgin and Child and Two Donors. 100fr, Adoration of the Shepherds. 125fr, Adoration of the Kings.

1977, Dec. 20   Litho.   Perf. 12½x12

C228	AP68	30fr multi	.75 .20
C229	AP68	60fr multi	1.10 .30
C230	AP68	100fr multi	1.50 .40
C231	AP68	125fr multi	1.90 .60
		Nos. C228-C231 (4)	5.25 1.50

Christmas 1977.

Antoine de Saint-Exupéry — AP69

50fr, Wilbur & Orville Wright & Flyer. 80fr, Hugo Junkers & his plane. 100fr, Gen. Italo Balbo & his plane. 120fr, Concorde. 500fr, Wilbur & Orville Wright & Flyer.

1978, Oct. 25	Litho.		Perf. 13½	
C232	AP69	40fr multi	.60	.20
C233	AP69	50fr multi	.75	.20
C234	AP69	80fr multi	1.10	.30
C235	AP69	100fr multi	1.50	.40
C236	AP69	120fr multi	1.75	.50
	Nos. C232-C236 (5)		5.70	1.60

Souvenir Sheet

C237	AP69	500fr multi	6.75	2.00

History of aviation and 75th anniversary of 1st powered flight.

Philexafrique II-Essen Issue
Common Design Types

#C238, Rhinoceros & Chad #C6. #C239, Kingfisher & Mecklenburg-Strelitz #1.

1978, Nov. 1			Perf. 12½	
C238	CD138	100fr multi	3.00	1.00
C239	CD139	100fr multi	3.00	1.00
a.	Pair, #C238-C239 + label		8.00	4.00

Nos. C191-C194 Overprinted
"ALUNISSAGE/APOLLO XI/ JUILLET 1969"

1979, Nov. 26	Litho.		Perf. 13½x14	
C240	A86	100fr multi	1.10	.35
C241	A86	200fr multi	2.25	.65
C242	A86	250fr multi	2.50	1.00
	Nos. C240-C242 (3)		5.85	2.00

Souvenir Sheet

C243	A86	450fr multi	5.50	4.50

Apollo 11 moon landing, 10th anniversary.

Hurdles, Moscow '80 Emblem — AP70

Emblem and: 30fr, Field hockey. 250fr, Swimming. 350fr, Running. 500fr, Yachting.

1979, Nov. 30			Perf. 13½	
C244	AP70	15fr multi	.20	.20
C245	AP70	30fr multi	.30	.20
C246	AP70	250fr multi	1.90	.60
C247	AP70	350fr multi	3.00	1.10
	Nos. C244-C247 (4)		5.40	2.10

Souvenir Sheet

C248	AP70	500fr multi	5.75	3.00

Pre-Olympic Year.
For overprints see Nos. C254-C255.

Austria Jubilee Issue of 1910, Canoe,
Hill — AP71

Hill, Stamps & Vessels: 100fr, US design A97, dhow. 200fr, France #21, Sidewheeler. 300fr, Holstein #16, ocean liner. 500fr, Chad #J13, ocean liner.

1979, Dec. 3			Perf. 14x13½	
C249	AP71	65fr multi	.60	.20
C250	AP71	100fr multi	1.40	.25
C251	AP71	200fr multi	2.25	.45
C252	AP71	200fr multi	2.75	.70
	Nos. C249-C252 (4)		7.00	1.60

Souvenir Sheet

C253	AP71	500fr multi	5.75	3.00

Sir Rowland Hill (1795-1879), originator of penny postage.
For overprints see Nos. C256-C257.

Nos. C244-C245, C249-C250
Overprinted: "POSTES 1981" in Red or Overprinted and Surcharged Silver on Red

Perf. 13½, 14x13½

1981, Nov. 15			Litho.	
C254	AP70	30fr on 15fr multi	1.25	.40
C255	AP70	30fr multi	1.25	.40
C256	AP71	60fr on 65fr multi	2.25	.70
C257	AP71	60fr on 100fr multi	2.25	.70
	Nos. C254-C257 (4)		7.00	2.20

Soccer Type of 1982 and

1982 World Cup Soccer
Championships, Spain — AP71a

#C259C, Soccer players, ball, & trophy, vert.

1982	Litho.		Perf. 13½	
C258	A108	80fr Brazil	1.00	.20
C259	A108	300fr W. Germany	3.00	.50

Souvenir Sheet

C259A	A108	500fr like 300fr	6.00	2.00

Litho. & Embossed

C259B	AP71a	1500fr gold & multi	16.00

Souvenir Sheet

C259C	AP71a	1500fr gold & multi	14.00

No. C259A contains one 42x51mm stamp.
No. C259B exists in a souvenir sheet of 1. Value $42.50.
For surcharge see No. C305.

Diana Type of 1982 and

Princess Diana, 21st Birthday —
AP71b

Design: No. C262A, Portrait, horiz.

1982, July 2	Litho.		Perf. 13½	
C260	A109	80fr 1977	1.00	.25
C261	A109	300fr 1980	3.00	.95

Souvenir Sheet

C262	A109	500fr 1981	5.50	2.00

Litho. & Embossed

C262A	AP71b	1500fr gold & multi	16.00

Souvenir Sheet

C262B	AP71b	1500fr gold & multi	16.00

No. C262A exists in a souvenir sheet of 1.
Value $42.50.
For overprints see Nos. 419A-419B.

Manned Flight Bicentenary AP72

Balloons: 100fr, Charles' & Roberts', 1783. 200fr, J.P. Blanchard, Berlin, 1788. 300fr, Charles Green, London, 1837. 400fr, Modern blimp. 500fr, Montgolfiere, 1783.

1983, Apr.	Litho.		Perf. 13	
C263	AP72	100fr multi, vert.	1.25	.25
C264	AP72	200fr multi, vert.	2.50	.40
C265	AP72	300fr multi, vert.	3.50	.60
C266	AP72	400fr multi, vert.	4.75	.75
	Nos. C263-C266 (4)		12.00	2.00

Souvenir Sheet

C267	AP72	500fr multi, vert.	5.75	2.50

Balloon Type and

First Balloon Ascension,
Bicent. — AP72a

80fr, Steam Powered Airship, H. Giffard. 250fr, Graf Zeppelin; Airship L-1, 1st flight. 300fr, 1st Balloon Flight, Montgolfier & Rozier. #C270A, Airship Hindenburg, Count Ferdinand von Zeppelin. #C270B, Jean-Francois Pilatre de Rozier & Marquis d'Arlandes, 1st balloon ascension.

1983, May 30	Litho.		Perf. 13	
C268	A116	80fr multi	1.00	.25
C269	A116	250fr multi	3.00	.40

Souvenir Sheet

C270	A116	300fr multi	3.75	2.50

Litho. & Embossed

Perf. 13½

C270A	AP72a	1500fr gold & multi	16.00

Souvenir Sheet

C270B	AP72a	1500fr gold & multi	12.00

No. C270A exists in a souvenir sheet of 1. Value $25.
For surcharge see No. C299.

1984 Summer Olympics — AP73

Various kayak scenes.

1984, Mar. 1	Litho.		Perf. 13	
C271	AP73	100fr multi	1.00	.20
C272	AP73	200fr multi	2.00	.25
C273	AP73	300fr multi	3.00	.50
C274	AP73	400fr multi	4.00	.60
	Nos. C271-C274 (4)		10.00	1.55

Souvenir Sheet

C275	AP73	500fr multi	5.00	3.50

Natl. Goals
AP73a

#C276, C278, Peace & reconciliation. #C277, C279, Self-sufficiency in food production.

1983, Dec. 26	Litho.		Perf. 13½	
C276	AP73a	150fr multi	1.50	.40
C277	AP73a	150fr multi	1.50	.40
C278	AP73a	200fr multi	2.25	.55
C279	AP73a	200fr multi	2.25	.55
	Nos. C276-C279 (4)		7.50	1.90

For surcharges see Nos. C300-C301.

Souvenir Sheet

Paul P. Harris (1868-1947), Founder
of Rotary Intl. — AP73b

Litho. & Embossed

1984, Jan. 16			Perf. 13½	
C279B	AP73b	1500fr gold & multi	12.00

IYY, PHILEXAFRICA '85 — AP74

1985, May 2	Litho.		Perf. 13	
C280	AP74	200fr Boy scout, tree	3.00	1.50
C281	AP74	200fr Air Chad Fokker 27	3.00	1.50
a.	Pair, #C280-C281 + label		6.75	5.00

IYY, PHILEXAFRICA Type of 1985

1985, Nov. 1	Litho.		Perf. 13x12½	
C283	AP74	250fr Girl, Scout ceremony	3.00	1.50
C284	AP74	250fr Communications and transportation	3.00	1.50
a.	Pair, #C283-C284 + label		6.75	5.00

ASCENA Airlines, 25th Anniv. — AP75

1985, Aug. 25			Perf. 12½	
C285	AP75	70fr bl & multi	.60	.20
C286	AP75	110fr org & multi	1.00	.20
C287	AP75	250fr yel & multi	2.25	.80
	Nos. C285-C287 (3)		3.85	1.20

Victor Hugo (1802-1885), French Novelist — AP76

Scene from Les Miserables.

1985, Nov. 24   Engr.   Perf. 13
C288 AP76 70fr org brn, chkly bl & dp brn   .75   .20
C289 AP76 110fr lake, dk brn & dk grn   1.00   .30
C290 AP76 250fr brt org, blk & dk red   2.50   .80
C291 AP76 300fr dk red, cl & sl bl   2.75   .90
      Nos. C288-C291 (4)   7.00 2.20

Christmas 1985 — AP77

1985, Dec. 22   Litho.   Perf. 13½
C292 250fr Adoration of the Ma-gi   2.25   .60

1988 Summer Olympics, Seoul — AP78

1988, June 1   Litho.   Perf. 13
C293 AP78 100fr 400-Meter hurdles, vert.   1.10   .30
C294 AP78 170fr 5000-Meter race   1.75   .55
C295 AP78 200fr Long jump   2.25   .65
C296 AP78 600fr Triple jump, vert.   5.75 2.00
      Nos. C293-C296 (4)   10.85 3.50

Souvenir Sheet
C297 AP78 750fr 10,000-Meter race, vert.   8.00 6.00

Stamps of 1982-84 Surcharged
1989   Perfs. as Before
C298 A115 100 on 300fr #446
C299 A116 100 on 250fr #C269
C300 AP73a 100 on 200fr #C278
C301 AP73a 100 on 200fr #C279
C302 A110 170 on 300fr #404
C303 A122 170 on 200fr #503
C304 A123 170 on 250fr #509
C305 A108 170 on 300fr #C259
C306 A112 240 on 300fr #425

AIR POST SEMI-POSTAL STAMPS

> Catalogue values for unused stamps in this section are for Never Hinged items.

Ramses II Battling the Hittites (from Abu Simbel) — SPAP1

1964, Mar. 9   Unwmk.   Engr.   Perf. 13
CB1 SPAP1 10fr + 5fr multi   .60   .20
CB2 SPAP1 25fr + 5fr multi   1.10   .20
CB3 SPAP1 50fr + 5fr multi   2.25   .50
      Nos. CB1-CB3 (3)   3.95   .90

UNESCO world campaign to save historic monuments in Nubia.

Lions Emblem SPAP2

1967, July 5   Photo.   Perf. 13
CB4 SPAP2 50fr + 10fr multi   1.50   .20

50th anniv. of Lions Intl. and to publicize the Lions work for the blind.

POSTAGE DUE STAMPS

Postage Due Stamps of France Overprinted

1928   Unwmk.   Perf. 14x13½
J1   D2   5c light blue   .40   .50
J2   D2   10c gray brown   .40   .50
J3   D2   20c olive green   .55   .75
J4   D2   25c bright rose   .85 1.10
J5   D2   30c light red   .85 1.10
J6   D2   45c blue green   1.50 1.90
J7   D2   50c brown violet   2.00 2.50
J8   D2   60c yellow brown   2.00 2.50
J9   D2   1fr red brown   2.10 2.75
J10 D2   2fr orange red   4.75 6.50
J11 D2   3fr bright violet   4.00 5.50
      Nos. J1-J11 (11)   19.40 25.60

Huts — D3

Canoe — D4

1930   Typo.   Perf. 14x13½, 13½x14
J12 D3   5c dp bl & olive   .50   .40
J13 D3   10c dk red & brn   .50   .40
J14 D3   20c grn & brn   .80   .65
J15 D3   25c lt bl & brn   1.10   .90
J16 D3   30c bis brn & Prus bl   1.10   .90
J17 D3   45c Prus bl & olive   1.50 1.50
J18 D3   50c red vio & brn   2.25 3.25
J19 D3   60c gray lil & bl blk   3.00 4.25
J20 D4   1fr bis brn & bl blk   3.00 4.25
J21 D4   2fr vio & brn   6.25 8.50
J22 D4   3fr dp red & brn   35.00 60.00
      Nos. J12-J22 (11)   55.00 75.00

In 1934 stamps of Chad were superseded by those of French Equatorial Africa.

> Catalogue values for unused stamps in this section, from this point to the end of the section, are for Never Hinged items.

Rhinoceros — D5

Tibesti Pictographs: #J24, Kudu. #J25, 2 antelopes. #J26, 3 antelopes. #J27, Ostrich. #J28, Horned bull. #J29, Bull. #J30, Wild swine. #J31, Elephant. #J32, Rhinoceros. #J33, Warrior with spear and shield. #J34, Masked archer.

Unwmk.
1962, Apr. 20   Engr.   Perf. 13
J23 D5   50c olive bister   .30   .20
J24 D5   50c brown red   .30   .20
  a. Pair, #J23-J24   .55
J25 D5   1fr blue   .40   .20
J26 D5   1fr green   .40   .20
  a. Pair, #J25-J26   .75
J27 D5   2fr vermilion   .50   .20
J28 D5   2fr maroon   .50   .20
  a. Pair, #J27-J28   1.00
J29 D5   5fr slate green   .75   .20
J30 D5   5fr violet blue   .75   .20
  a. Pair, #J29-J30   1.50
J31 D5   10fr brown   1.40   .30
J32 D5   10fr orange brown   1.40   .30
  a. Pair, #J31-J32   2.75
J33 D5   25fr carmine rose   3.25   .75
J34 D5   25fr violet   3.25   .75
  a. Pair, #J33-J34   6.50
      Nos. J23-J34 (12)   13.20 3.70

Dolls — D6

1969, Sept. 19   Engr.   Perf. 14x13
J35 D6   1fr Kanem   .20   .20
J36 D6   2fr Kotoko   .20   .20
J37 D6   5fr Leather   .20   .20
J38 D6   10fr Kotoko   .40   .20
J39 D6   25fr Guera   .40   .20
      Nos. J35-J39 (5)   1.40 1.00

MILITARY STAMPS

> Catalogue values for unused stamps in this section are for Never Hinged items.

No. 78 Overprinted "F.M."
1965   Typo.   Perf. 14x13½
M1   A5   20fr red & black   300.00 250.00

Flag Bearer and Map of Chad — M1   1st Regiment Emblem — M2

1968 Unwmk. Litho.   Perf. 13x12½
M2   M1   tan & multi   1.75   .50

1972, Jan. 21   Photo.   Perf. 13
M3   M2   blue & multi   1.00   .25

OFFICIAL STAMPS

> Catalogue values for unused stamps in this section are for Never Hinged items.

Flag and Map of Chad — O1

Perf. 13½x14
1966-71   Typo.   Unwmk.
Flag in blue, yellow and carmine
O1   O1   1fr light blue   .20   .20
O2   O1   2fr gray   .20   .20
O3   O1   5fr black   .20   .20
O4   O1   10fr violet blue   .20   .20
O5   O1   25fr orange   .30   .20
O6   O1   30fr bright green   .50   .20
O7   O1   40fr carmine ('71)   .75   .20
O8   O1   50fr red lilac   .75   .20
O9   O1   85fr green   1.10   .30
O10 O1   100fr brown   1.75   .35
O11 O1   200fr red   3.00   .50
      Nos. O1-O11 (11)   8.95 2.75

Flag and Map Type of 1966-71 Redrawn with "N'Djamena" as Capital on Map
Perf. 13½x13¼, 11¾ (100fr)
1993-2000 ?   Litho.
Center Flag Stripe in Yellow Frame Color
O13 O1   100fr brown   —   —
O14 O1   200fr red   —   —

Nos. O13 and O14 have a large "F" in denomination, "POSTES" without serifs, and has printer's inscription of "COURVOISIER."

Center Flag Stripe in Orange Frame Color
O17 O1   50fr green   —   —
O18 O1   85fr orange   —   —
O19 O1   100fr red orange   —   —
O20 O1   150fr blue green   —   —
O21 O1   200fr green   —   —
O22 O1   250fr lilac   —   —
O23 O1   300fr blue   —   —
O24 O1   500fr red   —   —
O25 O1   1000fr dark green   —   —

Additional stamps may have been issued in this set. The editors would like to examine any examples. Numbers may change.

CHILE

'chi-lē

LOCATION — Southwest corner of South America
GOVT. — Republic
AREA — 284,520 sq. mi.
POP. — 14,973,843 (1999 est.)
CAPITAL — Santiago

100 Centavos = 1 Peso
1000 Milésimos = 100 Centésimos = 1 Escudo (1960)
100 Centavos = 1 Peso (1975)

Catalogue values for unused stamps in this country are for Never Hinged items, beginning with Scott 257 in the regular postage section, Scott B3 in the semipostal section, Scott C125 in the airpost section, and Scott CB1 in the airpost semi-postal section.

Issues of the Republic

Unused values for Nos. 1-14 are for stamps without gum. Examples with original gum are very scarce and are worth considerably more.

Pen cancellations are common on the 1862-67 issues. Such stamps sell for much less than the quoted values which are for those with handstamped postal cancellations.

Watermarks

a   *b*   *c*   *d*

e   *f*   *g*

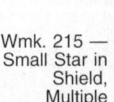

Wmk. 215 —
Small Star in
Shield,
Multiple

Christopher
Columbus — A1

London Prints

1853		Wmk. b	Engr.	*Imperf.*
Blued Paper				
1	A1	5c brown red	650.00	150.00
a.		White paper		250.00
		Wmk. e		
		White Paper		
2	A1	10c dp brt bl	1,000.	175.00
a.		Blued paper		225.00
b.		Diag. half used as 5c on cover		550.00
c.		Horiz. half used as 5c on cover		550.00
d.		Vert. half used as 5c on cover		550.00

Santiago Prints
Impressions Fine and Clear

1854			Wmk. b and e
		White Paper	
3	A1	5c pale red brn	600.00	67.50
a.		5c deep red brown	650.00	67.50
b.		5c chestnut	1,000.	200.00
e.		Double impression		275.00
4	A1	5c burnt sienna	1,800.	300.00
a.		5c dull chocolate	3,500.	2,000.
5	A1	10c deep blue	1,500.	200.00
a.		10c slate blue		200.00
b.		10c greenish blue		475.00
d.		Diag. half used as 5c on cover		450.00
e.		Horiz. half used as 5c on cover		450.00
f.		Vert. half used as 5c on cover		450.00
6	A1	10c lt dl bl	1,000.	190.00
a.		10c pale blue		190.00
b.		Diag. half used as 5c on cover		425.00
c.		Horiz. half used as 5c on cover		425.00
d.		Vert. half used as 5c on cover		425.00

Litho.

7	A1	5c pale brown	2,000.	325.00

London Print

1855	**Blued Paper**	**Wmk. c**	**Engr.**
8	A1	5c brown red	220.00	16.00
		Fiscal cancellation		2.75

Santiago Prints
Impressions Worn and Blurred

1856-62			Wmk. b and e
		White Paper	
9	A1	5c rose red ('58)	40.00	7.00
		Fiscal cancellation		1.40
a.		5c carmine red ('62)	90.00	20.00
b.		5c orange red ('61)	225.00	100.00
c.		5c dull redsh brn ('57)	250.00	27.50
f.		Printed on both sides	450.00	250.00
g.		Double impression	450.00	140.00
10	A1	10c sky blue ('57)	125.00	27.50
		Fiscal cancellation		1.40
a.		10c deep blue	125.00	27.50
b.		10c light blue ('59)	150.00	27.50
c.		10c indigo blue ('60)	175.00	50.00
k.		Printed on both sides		350.00
n.		As "j," half used as 5c on cover		165.00
o.		Any shade, horiz. half used as 5c on cover		200.00
p.		Any shade, vert. half used as 5c on cover		200.00

London Prints

1862			Wmk. a, f and g
11	A1	1c lemon yellow	67.50	40.00
		Fiscal cancellation		1.50
a.		Double impression, one inverted		200.00
12	A1	10c bright blue	40.00	15.00
		Fiscally used		1.50
a.		10c deep blue	32.50	21.00
b.		Blued paper		17.50
c.		Wmkd. "20" (error)	5,000.	5,200.
d.		Diag. half used as 5c on cover		110.00
e.		Horiz. half used as 5c on cover		125.00
f.		Vert. half used as 5c on cover		125.00
13	A1	20c green	160.00	67.50
		Fiscally used		6.75
		Nos. 11-13 (3)	267.50	122.50

No. 11a is only known fiscally used.

Santiago Print

1865			Wmk. d
14	A1	5c rose red	55.00	13.50
		Fiscally used		1.50
a.		5c carmine red	55.00	13.50
b.		Printed on both sides	375.00	200.00
c.		Laid paper	—	90.00
d.		Double impression, entire stamp	825.00	160.00

The 5c rose red (shades) on unwatermaked paper, either wove or ribbed, and on paper watermarked Chilean arms in the sheet are reprints made about 1870.

No. 13 has been reprinted in the color of issue and in fancy colors, both from the original engraved plate and from lithographic transfers. The reprints are on paper without watermark or with watermark CHILE and Star.

A2

A3

1867		**Unwmk.**		*Perf. 12*
15	A2	1c orange	28.00	22.00
		Pen cancellation		.50
16	A2	2c black	35.00	44.00
		Pen cancellation		.65
17	A2	5c red	25.00	2.50
		Pen cancellation		.20

18	A2	10c blue	25.00	7.50
		Pen cancellation		.35
19	A2	20c green	36.00	4.00
		Pen cancellation		.45
		Nos. 15-19 (5)	149.00	80.00

Unused values for Nos. 15-19 are for stamps with original gum.

1877			**Rouletted**
20	A3	1c gray	3.00	1.75
21	A3	2c orange	17.00	5.00
22	A3	5c dull lake	20.00	1.10
23	A3	10c blue	18.00	2.75
a.		Diagonal half used as 5c on cover		
24	A3	20c green	20.00	4.50
		Nos. 20-24 (5)	78.00	15.10

The panel inscribed "CENTAVO" is straight on No. 22.

A4

A5

Columbus — A6

1878-99			**Rouletted**
25	A4	1c green ('81)	1.00	.20
26	A4	2c rose ('81)	1.00	.20
27	A5	5c dull lake ('78)	7.25	.90
28	A5	5c ultra ('83)	1.90	.50
29	A5	10c orange ('85)	2.75	.35
a.		10c yellow	9.00	1.90
30	A5	15c dk grn ('92)	3.00	.55
31	A5	20c gray ('86)	3.00	.55
32	A5	25c org brn ('92)	3.00	.55
33	A5	30c rose car ('99)	7.25	3.75
34	A5	50c lilac ('78)	45.00	27.50
35	A5	50c violet ('85)	3.00	2.00
36	A6	1p dk brn & blk ('92)	19.00	2.75
a.		Imperf. horiz. or vert., pair	75.00	
		Nos. 25-36 (12)	97.15	39.80

For surcharge and overprint see Nos. 50, O16.

A7

A8

Columbus

1894			**Re-engraved**
37	A7	1c blue green	.90	.25
38	A7	2c carmine lake	.90	.25

In type A4 there is a small colorless ornament at each side of the base of the numeral, above the "E" and "V" of "CENTAVO." In type A7 these ornaments are missing, the figure "1" is broader than in type A4 and the head of the figure "2" is formed by a curved line instead of a ball.

1900-01

Type I — There is a heavy shading of short horzontal lines below "Chile" and the adjacent ornaments.

Type II — There is practically no shading below "Chile" and the ornaments.

		Type I		
39	A8	1c yel grn	.80	.20
40	A8	2c brn rose	1.25	.20
41	A8	5c dp bl	6.50	.35
42	A8	10c violet	6.50	.70
43	A8	20c gray	6.50	2.50
44	A8	30c dp org ('01)	6.50	2.50
45	A8	50c red brn	7.50	2.50
		Nos. 39-45 (7)	35.55	8.95

		Type II		
46	A8	1c yel grn ('01)	.85	.20
47	A8	2c rose ('01)	.85	.30
48	A8	5c dull blue ('01)	5.00	.25
a.		Printed on both sides		
49	A8	10c vio ('01)	6.00	.85
		Nos. 46-49 (4)	12.70	1.60

For surcharge see No. 57.

No. 33 Surcharged in Black

1900

	Black Surcharge		
50	A5	5c on 30c rose car	1.25	.35
a.		Inverted surcharge	32.50	24.00
b.		Double surcharge	90.00	60.00
c.		Double surcharge, both invtd.	90.00	60.00
d.		Double surcharge, one invtd.	90.00	60.00

Columbus — A10

1901-02			*Perf. 12*
51	A10	1c green	.50	.30
52	A10	2c carmine	.65	.20
53	A10	5c ultra	1.50	.20
54	A10	10c red & blk	2.25	.35
55	A10	30c vio & blk	6.75	.85
56	A10	50c red org & blk	7.25	2.25
		Nos. 51-56 (6)	18.90	4.15

No. 44 Surcharged in Dark Blue

1903			*Rouletted*
57	A8	10c on 30c orange	1.90	.75
a.		Inverted surcharge	18.00	12.00
b.		Double surcharge	25.00	15.00
c.		Double surch., one inverted	25.00	15.00
d.		Double surch., both invtd.	25.00	15.00
e.		Stamp design printed on both sides		

Pedro de
Valdivia — A11

Coat of
Arms — A12

A13

Telegraph Stamps Surcharged or Overprinted in Black

Type I — Animal at left has neither mane nor tail.

Type II — Animal at left has mane and tail.

1904			*Perf. 12*
58	A11	1c on 20c ultra	.40	.30
a.		Imperf. horiz., pair	40.00	40.00
b.		Inverted surcharge	50.00	50.00
59	A13	2c yel brn, I	.35	.20
a.		Inverted overprint	20.00	20.00
b.		Pair, one without overprint	50.00	50.00
60	A13	5c red, I	.55	.20
a.		Inverted overprint	20.00	20.00
b.		Pair, one without overprint	50.00	50.00
61	A13	10c ol grn, I	1.50	.50
a.		Inverted overprint	50.00	50.00
		Nos. 58-61 (4)	2.80	1.20

	Perf. 12½ to 16		
62	A13	2c yel, brn, II	5.25	4.50
63	A11	3c on 5c brn red	37.50	32.50
64	A12	3c on 1p brn, II	.45	.30
a.		Double surcharge	50.00	50.00

65	A13	5c red, II	6.25	5.50
66	A13	10c ol grn, II	14.50	10.00
67	A13	12c on 5c brn red	1.00	.45
a.		Inverted overprint		
a.		No star at left of "Centavos"	3.00	2.50
b.		Inverted surcharge	40.00	40.00
c.		Double surcharge	50.00	50.00
		Nos. 62-67 (6)	64.95	53.25

Counterfeits exist of the overprint and surcharge varieties of Nos. 57-67.
For overprint see No. O12.

A14

A15

Columbus — A16

1905-09   *Perf. 12*

68	A14	1c green	.25	.20
69	A14	2c carmine	.30	.20
70	A14	3c yel brn	.65	.30
71	A14	5c ultra	.70	.20
72	A15	10c gray & blk	1.10	.20
73	A15	12c lake & blk	5.50	2.25
74	A15	15c vio & blk	1.25	.20
75	A15	20c org brn & blk	2.25	.20
76	A15	30c bl grn & blk	3.50	.35
77	A15	50c ultra & blk	3.50	.40
78	A16	1p gold, grn & gray	16.00	11.00
		Nos. 68-78 (11)	35.00	15.50

A 20c dull red and black, type A15, was prepared but not issued. Value $125. "Specimen" examples of Nos. 74, 76-78 exist, punched to prevent postal use.
For surcharges and overprints see Nos. 79-82, O9, O11-O15.

Nos. 73, 78 Surcharged in Blue or Red

a

b

1910

79	A15 (a)	5c on 12c (Bl)	.50	.25
80	A16 (b)	10c on 1p (R)	1.10	.30
81	A16 (b)	20c on 1p (R)	1.60	.60
82	A16 (b)	1p (R)	3.00	1.10
		Nos. 79-82 (4)	6.20	2.25

The 1p is overprinted "ISLAS DE JUAN FERNANDEZ" only. The use of these stamps throughout Chile was authorized.

Independence Centenary Issue

Oath of Independence — A17

 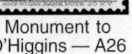
Monument to O'Higgins — A26

Adm. Lord Thomas Cochrane — A29

Designs: 2c, Battle of Chacabuco. 3c, Battle of Roble. 5c, Battle of Maipu. 10c, Naval Engagement of "Lautaro" and "Esmeralda." 12c, Capturing the "Maria Isabel." 15c, First Sortie of Liberating Forces. 20c, Abdication of O'Higgins. 25c, Chile's First Congress. 50c, Monument to José M. Carrera. 1p, Monument to San Martin. 2p, Gen. Manuel Blanco Encalada. 5p, Gen. José Ignacio Zenteno.

1910

Center in Black

83	A17	1c dk green	.20	.25
a.		Center inverted	7,000.	
84	A17	2c lake	1.10	.75
85	A17	3c red brown	.80	.45
86	A17	5c dp blue	.45	.20
87	A17	10c gray brn	1.20	.30
88	A17	12c vermilion	2.50	1.00
89	A17	15c slate	1.90	.55
90	A17	20c red orange	2.50	.85
91	A17	25c ultra	3.25	2.00
92	A26	30c violet	3.25	1.40
93	A26	50c olive grn	6.75	2.25
94	A26	1p yel org	14.00	5.25
95	A29	2p red	14.00	5.25
96	A29	5p yel grn	37.50	17.50
97	A29	10p dk violet	35.00	16.00
		Nos. 83-97 (15)	124.40	54.00

Columbus A32

De Valdivia A33

Mateo de Toro Zambrano A34

Bernardo O'Higgins A35

Ramón Freire — A36

F. A. Pinto — A37

Joaquín Prieto — A38

Manuel Bulnes — A39

Manuel Montt — A40

José Joaquín Pérez — A41

Federico Errázuriz Zanartu — A42

José de Balmaceda — A43

Designs: 1p, Anibal Pinto, 2p, Domingo Santa María. 10p, Federico Errázuriz Echaurren.

Outer backgrounds consist of horizontal and diagonal lines

1911   **Engr.**   *Perf. 12*

98	A32	1c dp green	.25	.20
99	A33	2c scarlet	.25	.20
100	A34	3c sepia	.75	.25
101	A35	5c dk blue	.25	.20
102	A36	10c gray & blk	.75	.20
a.		Center inverted	800.00	600.00
103	A37	12c carmine & blk	1.00	.20
104	A38	15c violet & blk	.90	.20
a.		Center inverted	1,000.	
105	A39	20c org red & blk	1.75	.20
a.		Center inverted	50.00	50.00
106	A40	25c lt blue & blk	2.75	.60
107	A41	30c bis brn & blk	4.00	.30
108	A42	50c myr grn & blk	5.00	.30
109	A43	1p green & blk	9.00	.40
110	A43	2p ver & blk	17.50	1.75
111	A43	5p ol grn & blk	50.00	9.50
112	A43	10p org yel & blk	50.00	8.50
		Nos. 98-112 (15)	139.15	23.00

See Nos. 117, 121, 123, 127-128, 133-141, 143, 155A, 157-161, 165-169,171-172 and designs A47-A55, A57. For overprints see Nos. C6, C6B-C6D, C7-C8, C10-C11, C13-C21, O19-O22, O24-O27, O30-O34, O40.

Columbus A47

Toro Zambrano A48

Freire A49

O'Higgins A50

1912-13   **Engr.**   *Perf. 12*

113	A47	2c scarlet	.20	.20
114	A48	4c black brn	.30	.20
115	A49	8c gray	1.00	.20
116	A50	10c blue & blk	1.00	.20
a.		Center inverted	500.00	400.00
b.		Imperf. horiz. or vert., pair	50.00	
117	A37	14c car & blk	1.50	.20
121	A38	40c violet & blk	5.75	.60
123	A40	60c lt blue & blk	14.00	1.75
		Nos. 113-123 (7)	23.75	3.35

See Nos. 125-126, 131, 164, 170, 173. For overprints see Nos. C6E, O18, O23, O28, O29.

Cochrane — A52

Columbus — A53

1915   **Engr.**   *Perf. 13½x14*

124	A52	5c slate blue	.60	.35
a.		Imperf., pair	11.50	

See Nos. 155, 162-163. For overprints see Nos. O17, O37.

1918

125	A49	8c slate	17.50	.80

No. 125 is from a plate made in Chile to resemble No. 115. The top of the head is further from the oval, the spots of color enclosed in the figures "8" are oval instead of round, and there are many small differences in the design.

1921

Worn Plate

126	A49	8c gray	20.00	5.00

No. 126 differs from No. 125 in not having diagonal lines in the frame and only a few

diagonal lines above the shoulders (due to wear), while No. 125 has diagonal lines in the oval up to the level of the forehead.

1915-25   **Typo.**   *Perf. 13½ to 14½*

127	A32	1c gray green	.20	.20
128	A33	2c red	.20	.20
129	A53	4c brown ('18)	.25	.20

Frame Litho.; Head Engr.

131	A50	10c bl & blk	1.25	.20
a.		10c dark blue & black	1.25	.20
b.		Imperf., pair	110.00	
c.		Center inverted	325.00	
133	A38	15c vio & blk	.90	.20
134	A39	20c org red & blk	1.40	.20
a.		20c brown orange & blk	1.75	
135	A40	25c dl bl & blk	.55	.20
136	A41	30c bis brn & blk	1.75	.20
137	A42	50c dp grn & blk	1.75	.20

Perf. 14

138	A43	1p grn & blk	8.00	.20
139	A43	2p red & blk	9.75	.20
a.		2p vermilion & black	32.50	.60
140	A43	5p ol grn & blk ('20)	24.00	.60
141	A43	10p org & blk ('25)	25.00	1.75
		Nos. 127-141 (13)	75.00	4.55

The frames have crosshatching on the 15c, 20c, 30c, 2p, 5p and 10p. They have no crosshatching on the 10c, 25c, 50c and 1p.
Nos. 131a and 134a are printed from new head plates which give blacker and heavier impressions. No. 131a exists with; (a) frame litho., head engr.; (b) frame typo., head engr.; (c) frame typo., head litho. No. 134a is with frame typo., head engr.
A 4c stamp with portrait of Balmaceda and a 14c with portrait of Manuel de Salas were prepared but not placed in use. Both stamps were sent to the paper mill at Puente Alto for destruction. They were not all destroyed as some were privately preserved and sold.

Columbus A54

Manuel Rengifo A55

Types of 1915-20 Redrawn

1918-20   *Perf. 13½x14½*

143	A32	1c gray grn ('20)	.30	.20
144	A54	4c brown	.50	.20

No. 143 has all the lines much finer and clearer than No. 127. The white shirt front is also much less shaded.

1921

145	A55	40c dk vio & blk	2.00	.40

For overprints see Nos. C6A, C9.

Pan-American Congress Building — A56

Adm. Juan José Latorre — A57

1923, Apr. 25   **Typo.**   *Perf. 14½x14*

146	A56	2c red	.20	.20
147	A56	4c brown	.20	.20

Typo.; Center Engr.

148	A56	10c blue & blk	.20	.20
149	A56	20c orange & blk	.75	.25
150	A56	40c dl vio & blk	1.00	.30
151	A56	1p green & blk	1.25	.50
152	A56	2p red & blk	2.90	.80
153	A56	5p dk grn & blk	17.00	4.50
		Nos. 146-153 (8)	25.60	6.75

Fifth Pan-American Congress.

Typographed; Head Engraved

1927   *Perf. 13½x14½*

154	A57	80c dk brn & blk	2.00	.60

Types of 1915-25 Issues
Inscribed: "Chile Correos"
Perf. 13½x14½

1928-31		Engr.		Wmk. 215	
155	A52	5c slate blue		1.40	.20

Frame Typo.; Center Engr.

155A	A38	15c violet & blk		2,200.	
156	A55	40c dk vio & blk		.60	.20
157	A42	50c dp grn & blk		2.50	.20

Perf. 14

158	A43	1p green & blk		1.00	.20
159	A43	2p red & blk		5.00	.20
160	A43	5p ol grn & blk		9.75	.45
161	A43	10p orange & blk		9.75	1.90
		Nos. 155,156-161 (7)		30.00	3.35

Paper of #155-161 varies from thin to thick.

Types of 1915-25 Issues
Inscribed: "Correos de Chile"

1928		Engr.	Perf. 13½x14½	
162	A52	5c deep blue	.35	.20

1929			Litho.	
163	A52	5c light green	.50	.20

Frame Litho.; Center Engr.

164	A50	10c blue & blk	2.00	.20
165	A38	15c violet & blk	2.40	.20
166	A39	20c org red & blk	5.75	.20
167	A40	25c blue & blk	.95	.20
168	A41	30c brown & blk	.75	.20
169	A42	50c dp grn & blk	.65	.20
		Nos. 163-169 (7)	13.00	1.40

Redrawn

1929		Frame Typo.; Center Litho.		
170	A50	10c blue & blk	3.00	.20
171	A38	15c violet & blk	2.75	.20
172	A39	20c org red & blk	4.25	.20
		Nos. 170-172 (3)	10.00	.60

1931			Unwmk.	
173	A50	10c blue & blk	.70	.20

In the redrawn stamps the lines behind the portraits are heavier and completely fill the ovals. There are strong diagonal lines above the shoulders. On #170 the head is larger than on #164, 173.

A58

Prosperity of Saltpeter Trade
A59   A60

Perf. 13½x14

1930, July 21		Litho.	Wmk. 215	
		Size: 20x25mm		
175	A58	5c yellow grn	.60	.40
176	A58	10c red brown	.60	.30
177	A58	15c violet	.60	.30
178	A59	25c deep gray	1.90	.60
179	A60	70c dark blue	4.50	1.50

Perf. 14
Size: 24½x30mm

| 180 | A60 | 1p dk gray grn | 3.75 | .75 |
| | | *Nos. 175-180 (6)* | 11.95 | 3.85 |

Cent. of the 1st shipment of saltpeter from Chile, July 21, 1830.

Manuel Bulnes
A61

Bernardo O'Higgins
A62

1931			Perf. 13½, 14	
181	A61	20c dark brown	1.00	.30

For overprints see Nos. O35, O39.

1932				
182	A62	10c deep blue	1.50	.45

For overprints see Nos. O36, O38.

Mariano Egana — A63

Joaquin Tocornal — A64

1934			Perf. 13½x14	
183	A63	30c magenta	.60	.20

Perf. 14

| 184 | A64 | 1.20p bright blue | 1.00 | .20 |

Centenary of the constitution.

José Joaquín Pérez — A65

1934			Perf. 13½x14	
185	A65	30c bright pink	1.60	.35

Atacama Desert — A66

Designs: 10c, Fishing boats. 20c, Coquito palms. 25c, Sheep. 30c, Mining. 40c, Lonquimay forest. 50c, Colliery at Port Lota. 1p, Shipping at Valparaiso. 1.20p, Puntiagudo volcano. 2p, Diego de Almagro. 5p, Cattle. 10p, Mining saltpeter.

Wmk. 215

1936, Mar. 1		Litho.	Perf. 14	
186	A66	5c vermilion	.60	.30
187	A66	10c violet	.30	.25
188	A66	20c magenta	.40	.25
189	A66	25c grnsh blue	3.00	.80
190	A66	30c lt green	.30	.25
191	A66	40c blk, *cream*	3.00	.85
192	A66	50c bl, *bluish*	1.50	.30

Engr.

193	A66	1p dk green	1.60	.50
194	A66	1.20p dp blue	1.75	.70
195	A66	2p dk brown	2.00	.80
196	A66	5p copper red	5.00	2.25
197	A66	10p dk violet	12.00	8.00
		Nos. 186-197 (12)	31.45	15.25

400th anniv. of the discovery of Chile by Diego de Almagro.

Laja Waterfall — A78

Fishing in Chiloé — A84

Designs: 10c, Agriculture. 15c, Boldo tree. 20c, Nitrate Industry. 30c, Mineral spas. 40c, Copper mine. 50c, Mining. 1.80p, Osorno Volcano. 2p, Mercantile marine. 5p, Lake Villarrica. 10p, State railways.

Perf. 13½x14

1938-40		Litho.	Wmk. 215	
198	A78	5c brn car ('39)	.20	.20
199	A78	10c sal pink ('39)	.20	.20
200	A78	15c brn org ('40)	.20	.20
201	A78	20c light blue	.20	.20
202	A78	30c brt pink	.20	.20
203	A78	40c lt grn ('39)	.20	.20
204	A78	50c violet	.20	.20

		Engr.	Perf. 14	
205	A84	1p orange brn	.20	.20
206	A84	1.80p deep blue	.45	.40
207	A84	2p car lake	.20	.20
208	A84	5p dk slate grn	.35	.20
209	A84	10p rose vio ('40)	.90	.20
		Nos. 198-209 (12)	3.50	2.60

See Nos. 217-227. For surcharge and overprints see Nos. 253, O41-O66, O70-O71.

Map of the Americas — A89

Unwmk.

1940, Sept. 11			Perf. 14	
210	A89	40c dl grn & yel grn	.35	.20

Pan American Union, 50th anniversary.

Camilo Henríquez — A90

Founding of Santiago — A93

Designs: 40c, Pedro de Valdivia. 1.10p, Benjamin Vicuna Mackenna. 3.60p, Diego Barros Arana.

Perf. 14½x14, 14½

1941, Jan. 23		Engr.	Wmk. 215	
211	A90	10c carmine lake	.20	.20
212	A90	40c green	.35	.20
213	A90	1.10p red	1.25	.70
214	A93	1.80p blue	1.25	.70
215	A90	3.60p indigo	3.75	2.75
		Nos. 211-215 (5)	6.80	4.55

400th anniversary of Santiago.

Types of 1938
Perf. 13½x14

1942-46			Unwmk.	Litho.
217	A78	10c sal pink ('43)	.20	.20
218	A78	15c brown org ('43)	.20	.20
219	A78	20c lt blue ('43)	.20	.20
220	A78	30c brt pink ('43)	.20	.20
221	A78	40c yellow grn	.80	.20
222	A78	50c violet ('43)	.20	.20

		Engr.	Perf. 14	
223	A84	1p brown orange	1.50	.20
225	A84	2p car lake ('43)	.20	.20
226	A84	5p dk sl grn ('43)	.50	.20
227	A84	10p rose violet ('46)	.90	.20
		Nos. 217-227 (10)	4.90	2.00

Valentin Letelier — A95

University of Chile — A98

Designs: 40c, Andrés Bello. 90c, Manuel Bulnes. 1.80p, Manuel Montt.

1942, Nov. 1		Perf. 14x14½, 14 (1p)		
228	A95	30c rose red	.20	.20
229	A95	40c deep green	.20	.20
230	A95	90c rose violet	1.90	1.50
231	A98	1p deep brown	1.10	.90
232	A95	1.80p dark blue	3.50	3.00
		Nos. 228-232 (5)	6.90	5.80

University of Chile cent. See No. C89.

Manuel Bulnes — A100

Map Showing Strait of Magellan — A104

Designs: 30c, Juan Williams Wilson. 40c, Diego Duble Almeida. 1p, José Mardones.

1944, Mar. 2		Litho.	Perf. 14	
233	A100	15c black	.20	.20
234	A100	30c deep rose	.20	.20
235	A100	40c yellow green	.20	.20
236	A100	1p brown carmine	.95	.20
237	A104	1.80p ultra	1.40	.95
		Nos. 233-237 (5)	2.95	1.75

100th anniversary of the occupation of the Strait of Magellan.

Red Cross and Lamp of Life — A105

Serpent and Cup — A106

1944, Oct. 18			Unwmk.	
238	A105	40c green, red & blk	.30	.20
239	A106	1.80p ultra & red	.90	.45

80th anniv. of the Intl. Red Cross Soc.

Bernardo O'Higgins — A107

"Embrace of Maipú" (O'Higgins Joining San Martin) — A108

Designs: 40c, Abdication of O'Higgins. 1.80p, Battle of Rancagua.

1945   Engr.   Perf. 14 (15c), 14½
Center in Black

240	A107	15c carmine	.30 .20
241	A108	30c brown	.30 .20
242	A108	40c deep green	.30 .20
243	A108	1.80p dark blue	1.40 .90
		Nos. 240-243 (4)	2.30 1.50

Death of Bernardo O'Higgins in 1842, cent.

A111

A112

Proposed Columbus lighthouse.

Wmk. 215
1945, Sept. 10   Litho.   Perf. 14
244 A111 40c light green   .50 .20

Issued in honor of the discovery of America by Columbus and the Memorial Lighthouse to be erected in his memory.

1946   Engr.
245 A112 40c dark green   .20 .20
246 A112 1.80p dark blue   .20 .20

80th anniv. of the death of Andrés Bello, poet and educator.

Map Showing Chile's Claims of Antarctic Territory A113

1947, May 12   Litho.   Perf. 14½
247 A113 40c carmine   .60 .30
248 A113 2.50p deep blue   1.60 .50

Eusebio Lillo and Ramon Carnicer A114

1947, Sept. 18   Engr.
249 A114 40c dark green   .20 .20

Centenary of national anthem.

Miguel de Cervantes Saavedra A115

1947, Oct. 11   Wmk. 215
250 A115 40c dk carmine   .20 .20

400th anniv. of the birth of Cervantes, novelist, playwright and poet.

Arturo Prat Chacón and Iquique Naval Battle A116

1948, Dec. 24   Perf. 14½
251 A116 40c deep blue   .20 .20

Centenary of the birth of Arturo Prat Chacon, Chilean naval hero.

Bernardo O'Higgins — A117

Perf. 13½x14
1948   Wmk. 215   Litho.
252 A117 60c black   .20 .20

See #262. For surcharges see #266-267.

No. 203 Surcharged in Black

1948
253 A78 20c on 40c lt grn   .20 .20

Chilean Pigeons — A118

FAUNA: a, Chilean Otter. c, Chilean pigeons. d, American skunk. f, Southern sea lions. g, Sugar-cane borer moth. h, Emperor penguins. i, Bat. j, Chinchilla. k, Grant's stag beetle. l, Trevally (fish). m, Chilean slender lizard. o, Crested caracara. q, Red-gartered coot. r, Chilean guemal (deer). s, Spiny rock lobster. u, Tilefish. v, Praying mantis. x, Torrent duck. y, Red conger.
FLORA: b, Araucarian pine (monkey puzzle tree). e, Evening primrose. n, Chilean red bell flower. p, Loxodon (flower). t, Boldo tree. w, Coquito palm trees.

Wmk. 215
1948, Dec. 6   Litho.   Perf. 14
254	A118	60c Block of 25	22.50
a.-y.		any single	1.25 .80
255	A118	2.60p Block of 25	37.50
a.-y.		any single	2.50 .95

Issued in panes of 100.

Cent. (in 1944) of the publication of the 1st volume of Claudio Gay's Natural History of Chile. See No. C124.

> **Catalogue values for unused stamps in this section, from this point to the end of the section, are for Never Hinged items.**

Benjamin Vicuna Mackenna — A121

1949, Mar. 22   Engr.   Perf. 13½x14
257 A121 60c deep blue   .30 .20

See No. C126.

Symbols of Arts and Crafts Education — A122

Heinrich von Stephan — A123

Design: 2.60p, Badge and book.

Unwmk.
1949, Nov. 11   Litho.   Perf. 14
258 A122 60c lilac rose   .20 .20
259 A122 2.60p violet blue   .40 .30
   Nos. 258-259,C127-C128 (4) 2.85 1.50

Cent. of the foundation of Chile's School of Arts and Crafts.

1950, Jan. 6   Engr.
260 A123 60c deep carmine   .20 .20
261 A123 2.50p deep blue   .70 .50
   Nos. 260-261,C129-C130 (4) 2.50 1.50
                    UPU, 75th anniv.

O'Higgins Type of 1948
1950   Litho.   Perf. 13x14
262 A117 60c black   .20 .20

For surcharge see No. 266.

San Martín — A124

Isabella I — A125

Wmk. 215
1951, Mar. 16   Engr.   Perf. 14
263 A124 60c deep blue   .40 .20

Cent. of the death of Gen. José de San Martin. See No. C165.

1952, Mar. 20
264 A125 60c brt blue   .35 .20

500th anniv. of the birth of Queen Isabella I of Spain. See No. C166.

Bernardo O'Higgins A126   Mateo de Toro Zambrano A127

1952 Unwmk. Litho. Perf. 13½x14
265 A126 1p dk blue grn   .30 .20

See No. 275. For overprints see Nos. O67-O69.

#262, 252 Surcharged "40 Ctvs." in Red
1952, Sept.
266 A117 40c on 60c black   .35 .20

Wmk. 215
267 A117 40c on 60c black   .35 .20

1953, Mar. 13   Wmk. 215
268 A127 80c green   .20 .20

See No. 285.

Valdivia Arms — A128

Old Fort — A129

3p, Modern Valdivia. 5p, Street in ancient Valdivia.

1953, May   Perf. 14
269 A128 1p brt ultra   .40 .20
270 A129 2p dull rose vio   .40 .20
271 A129 3p blue green   .50 .20
272 A129 5p deep brown   .50 .20
   Nos. 269-272,C167 (5)   4.05 1.25

4th centenary of the founding of Valdivia, capital of Valdivia province.

José Toribio Medina (1852-1930), Historian and Bibliographer A130

1953, June   Engr.   Perf. 14½
273 A130 1p brown   .35 .20
274 A130 2.50p deep blue   .45 .20

O'Higgins Type of 1952
Perf. 13½x14
1953, Oct.   Wmk. 215   Litho.
275 A126 1p dk blue green   .35 .20

For overprint see No. O69.

A131

A132

1953, Oct. 15　Engr.　Perf. 14½
276　A131　1p Stamp of 1853　　　.50　.20
　　Centenary of Chile's first postage stamps.
　　Souvenir sheet including No. 276 is noted below No. C168.

1953, Nov. 5　Litho.　Perf. 13½x14
　　Census chart and map.
277　A132　1p blue green　　　.30　.20
278　A132　2.50p violet blue　　　.30　.20
279　A132　3p chocolate　　　.50　.20
280　A132　4p carmine　　　.50　.20
　　　Nos. 277-280 (4)　　　1.60　.80
　　12th general census of population and housing.

Arms of Angol — A133

Ignacio Domeyko — A134

1954, May 28　Unwmk.　Perf. 14
281　A133　2p deep carmine　　　.35　.20
　　400th anniversary of the founding of Angol, capital of Malleco province.

1954, Aug. 16　Engr.　Perf. 13½x14
282　A134　1p greenish blue　　　.35　.20
　　150th anniversary of the birth of Ignacio Domeyko (1802-89), mineralogist and educator. See No. C171.

Early Steam Locomotive — A135

1954, Sept. 10　Wmk. 215　Perf. 14½
283　A135　1p red　　　.60　.30
　　Centenary (in 1951) of the first South American railroad. See No. C172.

Adm. Arturo Prat Chacón — A136

Arms of Viña del Mar — A137

1954　Unwmk.　Litho.　Perf. 14
284　A136　2p dk violet blue　　　.35　.20
　　75th anniv. of the naval Battle of Iquique.

Toro Zambrano Type of 1953
1954, Nov. 6　　　　Perf. 13½x14
285　A127　80c green　　　.30　.20

1955, Mar. 5　Wmk. 215　Perf. 14
　　Design: 2p, Arms of Valparaiso.
286　A137　1p violet blue　　　.35　.20
287　A137　2p carmine　　　.35　.20
　　1st Intl. Phil. Exhib., Valparaiso, Mar. 1955.

Dr. Alejandro del Rio — A138

1955, May 24　　　　Perf. 13½x14
288　A138　2p violet blue　　　.40　.20
　　14th Pan-American Sanitary Conference.

Christ of the Andes, Emblems of Chile, Argentina A139

1955, Aug. 31　Unwmk.　Perf. 14½
289　A139　1p violet blue　　　.35　.20
　　Reciprocal visits of Presidents Juan D. Peron and Carlos Ibanez del Campo. See No. C173.

Manuel Rengifo — A140

　　5p, Mariano Egana. 50p, Diego Portales.
1955-56　Unwmk.　Perf. 14x14½
290　A140　3p violet blue　　　.35　.20
291　A140　5p dk car rose　　　.35　.20
292　A140　50p rose lilac ('56)　1.90　.45
　　　Nos. 290-292 (3)　　　2.60　.85
　　Joaquin Prieto (1786-1854), soldier and political leader; president, 1831-41. See No. QRA1.

Jose M. Carrera A141

Ramón Freire A142

　　Portraits: 5p, Manuel Bulnes. 10p, Pres. Francisco A. Pinto. 50p, Manuel Montt.

Perf. 14x14½
1956-58　Unwmk.　　　Litho.
293　A141　2p purple　　　.30　.20
293A　A142　3p lt violet blue　　　.25　.20
294　A141　5p redsh brn
　　　　　　(19½x23mm)　　　.30　.20
　a.　Size 19x22mm　　　.30　.20
295　A142　10p vio (19x22¼mm)　.30　.20
　a.　Perf. 13½x14 (19¼x22½mm)
　　　　　('58)　　　.55　.25
296　A141　50p rose red　　　.50　.20
　　　Nos. 293-296 (5)　　　1.65　1.00
Wmk. 215
297　A141　2p dull purple　　　.30　.20
298　A142　3p violet blue　　　.30　.20
　　#294 has yellow gum; #294a, white gum.
　　For overprints see Nos. O72-O76.

Federico Santa Maria — A143

Gabriela Mistral — A144

Unwmk.
1957, Jan. 31　Engr.　Perf. 14
299　A143　5p dk red brown　　　.30　.20
　　25th anniv. of the Federico Santa Maria Technical University. See Nos. C190-C191.
　　Souvenir sheet including No. 299 is noted below No. C191.

1958, Jan. 10
300　A144　10p red brown　　　.45　.20
　　Issued in honor of Gabriela Mistral, poet and educator. See No. C192.

Arms of Osorno — A145

Arms of Santiago — A146

　　Design: 50p, Garcia Hdo. de Mendoza.
1958, Mar. 23　Litho.　Perf. 14
301　A145　10p carmine　　　.20　.20
Engr.
302　A145　50p green　　　.40　.20
　　400th anniversary of the founding of the city of Osorno, capital of Osorno province.

　　Souvenir sheet including No. 302 in red brown is noted below No. C193.

1958, Oct. 18　Unwmk.　Perf. 14
303　A146　10p dark violet　　　.30　.20
　　Natl. Philatelic Exposition, Santiago, Oct. 18-26.
　　Souvenir sheet including No. 303 in deep red is noted below No. C194.

Symbolical Savings Bank — A147

Modern Map of Antarctica — A148

1958, Dec. 18
304　A147　10p dark blue　　　.40　.20
　　Savings Bank for Public Employees, cent.
　　Souvenir sheet including No. 304 in violet is noted below No. C195.

1958, Aug. 28　Unwmk.　Perf. 14
305　A148　40p rose carmine　　　.60　.60
　　IGY, 1957-1958. See No. C214.

Antarctic Map and "La Araucana" A149

Map of Strait of Magellan, 1588 — A150

1958　Litho.　Perf. 14
310　A149　10p violet blue　　　.75　.20
Engr.
311　A150　200p dull purple　　2.75　1.75
　　　Nos. 310-311,C199-C200 (4)　7.75　3.90
　　For overprint see No. O77.

Valdivia River Bridge — A153

1959, Feb. 9　Engr.　Perf. 14
319　A153　40p green　　　.45　.20
　　Cent. of the German School in Valdivia and to publicize the Valdivia Phil. Exhib., 2/9-18.
　　Souvenir sheet including No. 319 is noted below No. C213.

Strait of
Magellan, Map
by Pedro
Sarmiento de
Gamboa, c.
1582 — A154

1959, Aug. 27   **Litho.**
320 A154 10p dull purple   .45 .20

Juan Ladrillero expedition to explore the
Strait of Magellan, 1557-58, 400th anniv. See
#C215.

Diego Barros
Arana — A155

Henri
Dunant — A156

1959, Aug. 27
321 A155 40p ultra   .45 .20

50th anniv. of the death of Diego Barros
Arana (1830-1907), historian. See No. C216.

1959, Oct. 6   **Unwmk.**   **Perf. 14**
322 A156 20p red & red brn   .45 .20

Cent. of the Red Cross idea. See No. C217.

Manuel
Bulnes — A157

Francisco A.
Pinto — A158

Choshuenco
Volcano
A159

#326, Choshuenco volcano, redrawn. 5c,
Manuel Montt. 10c, Maule River Valley. 20c,
1e, Inca Lake.

1960-67   **Litho.**   **Perf. 13x14**
323 A157 5m bluish grn   .20 .20
324 A158 1c carmine   .20 .20
     Perf. 14
     Size: 29x25mm
325 A159 2c ultra ('61)   .20 .20
     Perf. 14x13
     Size: 23½x18mm
326 A159 2c ultra ('62)   .20 .20
     Perf. 13x14
327 A157 5c blue   .20 .20
     Perf. 14
     Size: 29x25mm
328 A159 10c green ('62)   .20 .20
329 A159 20c Prus blue ('62)   .35 .20
329A A159 1e bluish grn ('67)   .65 .25
    Nos. 323-329A (8)   2.20 1.65

On No. 325 "Volcan Choshuenco" is at
upper left, below "Correos." On No. 326, it is at
bottom, above "Centesimos."
For overprint and surcharge see #O79,
RA1.

Refugee
Family
A160

1960, Apr. 7   **Perf. 14½**
330 A160 1c green   .30 .20

WRY, July 1, 1959-June 30, 1960. A souvenir sheet is noted below No. C218.

Type of Air Post Issue, 1962, and

Arms of
Chile
A161

José M.
Carrera
A162

#332, Palace of Justice. 5c, Natl. Memorial.
10c, Manuel de Toro y Zambrano and Martinez de Rozas. 20c, Manuel de Salas and Juan
Egana. 50c, Manuel Rodriguez and Juan
Mackenna.

   Wmk. 215 (#331, 1e); Unwmk.
1960-65   **Engr.**   **Perf. 14½**
331 A161 1c maroon & sepia   .20 .20
332 A161 1c brn & claret ('62)   .20 .20
333 A162 5c grn & Prus grn
       ('61)   .20 .20
334 AP54 10c brn & vio brn
       ('64)   .40 .25
334A AP54 20c ind & bl grn ('65)   .40 .25
335 AP54 50c red brn & mar
       ('65)   .70 .25
336 A162 1e gray ol & brn   1.25 .40
    Nos. 331-336,C218A-C220D (14)   6.60 3.45

150th anniv. of the formation of the 1st Natl.
Government. A souvenir sheet is noted below
No. C220B. See No. C285.

Family — A163

Design: 10c, Various buildings.

     Unwmk.
1960, Jan. 18   **Litho.**   **Perf. 14**
337 A163 5c green   .25 .20
338 A163 10c brt violet   .25 .20

13th population census (No. 337) and 2nd
housing census (No. 338).

Chamber
of
Deputies
A164

1961, Aug. 14   **Unwmk.**   **Perf. 14½**
339 A164 2c red brown   .65 .20

150th anniv. of the 1st National Congress.
See No. C245.

Soccer
Players
and
Globe
A165

Design: 5c, Goalkeeper and stadium, vert.

1962, May 30   **Engr.**   **Perf. 14½**
340 A165 2c blue   .40 .20
341 A165 5c green   .55 .20

World Soccer Championship, Chile, May 30-
June 17. Note on souvenir sheet follows No.
C247.

Mother and
Child — A166

Centenary
Emblem — A167

1963, Mar. 21   **Litho.**   **Perf. 14**
342 A166 3c maroon   .35 .20

FAO "Freedom from Hunger" campaign.
See No. C248.

1963, Aug. 23   **Unwmk.**   **Perf. 14**
343 A167 3c red & gray   .35 .20

Cent. of the Intl. Red Cross. See #C249.

Fireman Carrying
Woman — A168

Enrique
Molina — A169

1963, Dec. 20   **Unwmk.**   **Perf. 14**
344 A168 3c violet   .45 .20

Centenary of the Santiago Fire Brigade.
See No. C250.

1964, Nov. 14   **Litho.**   **Perf. 14**
Design: No. 346, Magr. Carlos Casanueva.
345 A169 4c bister brown   .35 .20
346 A169 4c rose claret   .35 .20
    Nos. 345-346,C257-C258 (4)   1.30 .80

Enrique Molina, founder of the University of
Concepcion, and Msgr. Carlos Casanueva,
rector of the Catholic University, 1920-53.

Easter Island
Statue — A170

Copihue, National
Flower — A171

Design: 30c, Robinson Crusoe.

1965-69   **Litho.**   **Perf. 14x14½**
347 A170 6c rose lilac   .95 .20
347A A170 10c rose pink ('68)   .30 .20
     Perf. 14
348 A171 15c yel grn & rose
       red   .75 .20
348A A171 20c yel grn & rose
       red ('69)   .35 .20
     Perf. 14x14½
349 A170 30c rose claret   .55 .20
    Nos. 347-349 (5)   2.90 1.00

For surcharge see No. RA2.

Skier — A172

Lorenzo
Sazie — A173

1965, Aug. 30   **Perf. 14**
350 A172 4c blue green   .40 .20

World Skiing Championships, Chile, 1966.

1966, Feb. 9   **Litho.**   **Perf. 14x14½**
351 A173 1e green   .95 .20

Cent. of the death of Dr. Lorenzo Sazie,
dean of the Faculty of Medicine, University of
Santiago.

German Riesco,
President in 1901-
1906 — A174

Portrait: 30c, Jorge Montt (1847-1922),
president in 1891-1896.

1966   **Unwmk.**   **Perf. 13x14**
354 A174 30c violet   .30 .20
355 A174 50c dull brown   .35 .20

For surcharge see No. 450.

William Wheelwright and S.S.
Chile — A175

1966, Aug. 2   **Perf. 14½**
358 A175 10c ultra & lt bl   .35 .20

125th anniv. (in 1965) of the arrival of the
paddle steamers "Chile" and "Peru." See No.
C268.

Learning to Read — A176

1966, Aug. 13   Litho.   Perf. 14
359 A176 10c red brown   .35 .20
Literacy campaign.

UN and ICY Emblems A177

1966, Oct. 28   Unwmk.   Perf. 14½
360 A177 1e green & brown   1.40 .25
Intl. Cooperation Year, 1965. See No. C269.

Capt. Luis Pardo and Ship in Antarctica — A178

1967, Jan.   Litho.   Perf. 14½
361 A178 20c turquoise blue   .45 .25
Rescue of the Shackleton South Pole expedition by Capt. Luis Pardo of Chile, 50th anniv. See #C271.

Family — A179

Trees and Mountains A180

1967, Apr. 13   Unwmk.   Perf. 14
362 A179 10c magenta & blk   .35 .20
8th Intl. Conf. for Family Planning, Santiago, Apr. 1967. See No. C272.

1967, June 9   Litho.   Perf. 14½
363 A180 10c blue grn & lt bl   .35 .20
Reforestation Campaign. See No. C274.

Lions Emblem — A181

1967, July 12   Litho.   Perf. 14
364 A181 20c Prus blue & yel   .35 .25
Nos. 364,C275-C276 (3)   1.85 .80
50th anniv. of Lions Intl.

Chilean Flag A182

1967, Oct. 20   Unwmk.   Perf. 14½
365 A182 80c crimson & ultra   .60 .25
Natl. flag, 150th anniv. See No. C277.

José Maria Cardinal Caro — A183

1967, Dec. 4   Engr.   Perf. 14½
366 A183 20c deep carmine   .75 .35
Cent. of the birth of José Maria Cardinal Caro, the first Chilean cardinal. See #C279.

San Martin and O'Higgins — A184

1968, Apr. 23   Litho.   Unwmk.
367 A184 3e blue   .65 .25
Sesquicentennial of the Battles of Chacabuco and Maipu. See No. C280.

Farm Couple — A185

1968, June 18   Perf. 14½
368 A185 20c black, org & grn   .40 .25
Agrarian reforms. See No. C281.

Juan I. Molina A186

1968, Aug. 27   Litho.   Perf. 14½
369 A186 2e red lilac   .60 .25
Issued to honor Juan I. Molina, educator and scientist. See No. C282.

Hand Holding Cogwheel — A187

1968, Sept.   Perf. 14x14½
370 A187 30c deep carmine   .30 .25
Fourth census of manufacturers.

Map of Chiloé Province, Sailing Ship and Coastal Vessel A188

1968, Oct. 7   Perf. 14½
371 A188 30c ultra   .40 .25
Anniversaries of the founding of five towns in Chiloé Province. See No. C283.

Automobile Club Emblem A189

1968, Nov. 10   Engr.   Perf. 14½x14
372 A189 1e carmine rose   .35 .25
40th anniversary of the Automobile Club of Chile. See No. C284.

Francisco Garcia Huidobro A190

Design: 5e, King Philip V of Spain.

1968, Dec. 31   Litho.   Perf. 14½
373 A190 2e pale rose & ultra   .40 .20
374 A190 5e brown & yel grn   .40 .20
Nos. 373-374,C288-C289 (4)   1.40 .80
225th anniv. of the founding of the State Mint (Casa de Moneda de Chile).

Satellite and Radar Station A191

1969, May 20   Litho.   Perf. 14½
375 A191 30c blue   .40 .25
Inauguration of ENTEL-Chile, the 1st commercial satellite communications ground station, Longovilo.
See #C290. For surcharges see #397, C308.

Red Cross, Crescent and Lion and Sun Emblems A192

1969, Sept.   Litho.   Perf. 14½
376 A192 2e violet blue & red   .40 .25
50th anniversary of the League of Red Cross Societies. See No. C291.

Rapel Hydroelectric Plant — A193

1969, Nov. 18   Litho.   Perf. 14½
377 A193 40c green   .30 .25
See No. C292.

Col. Rodriguez Monument — A194

1969, Nov. 24
378 A194 2e rose claret   .40 .25
150th anniversary of the death of Col. Manuel Rodriguez. See No. C293.

EXPO '70 Emblem — A195

1969, Dec. 2   Litho.   Perf. 14
379 A195 3e blue   .55 .25
EXPO '70 Intl. Exhibition, Osaka, Japan, Mar. 15-Sept. 13, 1970. See No. C294.

Open Book A196

1969, Dec. 3   Perf. 14½
380 A196 40c red brown   .40 .25
Translation of the Bible into Spanish by Casiodoro de Reina, 400th anniv. See No. C295.

Globes and ILO Emblem A197

1969, Dec. 17   Perf. 14½
381 A197 1e green & blk   .35 .25
ILO, 50th anniv. See No. C296.

Human Rights Flame A198

1969, Dec. 18
382 A198 4e blue & red   .60 .25
Human Rights Year, 1968. See No. C297.

Policarpo Toro and Easter Island A199

1970, Jan. 26 **Perf. 14½**
383 A199 5e lilac .90 .25
80th anniversary of the acquisition of Easter Island. See No. C298.

Sailing Ship and Arms of Valdivia A200

1970, Feb. 4 **Litho.** **Perf. 14½**
384 A200 40c dk carmine .60 .25
150th anniv. of the capture of Valdivia during Chile's war of independence by Thomas Cochrane (1775-1860), naval commander. See No. C299.

Paul Harris and Rotary Emblem — A201

1970, Mar. 18 **Litho.** **Perf. 14**
385 A201 10e violet blue 1.10 .25
Cent. of the birth of Paul Harris (1868-1947), founder of Rotary Intl. See No. C300.

Mahatma Gandhi — A202

1970, Apr. 1 **Litho.** **Perf. 14½**
386 A202 40c blue green 3.50 .30
Mohandas K. Gandhi (1869-1948), leader in India's fight for independence, birth cent. See #C301. For surcharge see #449.

Santo Domingo Church, Santiago, Chile — A203

1970, Apr. 30 **Engr.**
Designs: 2e, Casa de Moneda de Chile, horiz. 3e, Pedro de Valdivia. 5e, Bridge, horiz. 10e, Ambrosio O'Higgins.

387 A203	2e violet brown	.40	.20
388 A203	3e dark red	.40	.20
389 A203	4e dark blue	.30	.20
390 A203	5e brown	.30	.20
391 A203	10e green	.30	.20
	Nos. 387-391 (5)	1.70	1.00

Exploration and development of Chile by Spanish explorers.
A sheet containing imperf examples of Nos. 388, 390 and 391 exists. It was not valid for postage.

Education Year Emblem — A204

1970, July 17 **Litho.** **Perf. 14½**
392 A204 2e claret .35 .25
International Education Year. See No. C302.

Virgin and Child — A205

1970, July 28
393 A205 40c green .30 .25
O'Higgins National Shrine at Maipu. See No. C303. For surcharge see No. 454.

Torch and Snake — A206

1970, Aug. 11
394 A206 40c claret & light blue .50 .25
International Cancer Congress, Houston, Texas, May 22-29. See No. C304.

Copper Symbol, Chile Arms — A207

1970, Oct. 21 **Litho.** **Perf. 14½**
395 A207 40c car & lt red brn .35 .25
Nationalization of the copper industry. See No. C305. For surcharge see No. 459.

Dove and World Map A208

1970, Oct. 22
396 A208 3e rose magenta & pur .40 .25
25th anniv. of the UN. See No. C306.

No. 375 Surcharged in Red
1970, Dec. 24 **Litho.** **Perf. 14½**
397 A191 52c on 30c blue .45 .25

Freighter and Ship's Wheel — A209

1971, Jan. 18 **Litho.** **Perf. 14**
398 A209 52c deep carmine .35 .20
Natl. Maritime Commission. See #C307.

Bernardo O'Higgins and Ship A210

1971, Feb. 3 **Perf. 14½**
399 A210 5e grnsh bl & grn .55 .20
150th anniv. of the expedition to liberate Peru from Spanish rule. See No. C309.

Youth, Girl and UN Emblem A211

1971, Feb. 11 **Litho.** **Perf. 14½**
400 A211 52c dk blue & brn .35 .20
1st meeting in Latin America of the Executive Council of UNICEF, Santiago, May 20-31, 1969. See No. C310.

Chilean Boy Scout Emblem — A212

1971, Feb. 10 **Perf. 14**
401 A212 1e green & brn .45 .20
Founding of Chilean Boy Scouts, 60th anniversary. See No. C311.

Satellite and Radar Station A213

1971, May 25 **Litho.** **Perf. 14½**
402 A213 40c dull green .50 .20
First commercial Chilean satellite communications ground station, Longovilo. See No. C312.

Diver with Harpoon Gun A214

1971, Sept. 1
403 A214 1.15e lt & dk green 1.10 .25
404 A214 2.35e vio bl & dp vio bl .40 .25
10th World Championship of Underwater Fishing.

Ferdinand Magellan and Sailing Ship — A215

1971, Nov. 3
405 A215 35c lt vio & brn vio .35 .25
450th anniv. of 1st trip through and discovery of the Strait of Magellan, Oct. 21-Nov. 28, 1520.

Dagoberto Godoy and Plane over Andes — A216

1971, Nov. 4
406 A216 1.15e blue & grn .40 .20
First trans-Andean flight, Dec. 12, 1918.

Virgin of San Cristobal — A217

Chilean Flag and Congress Emblem A218

Congress Emblem and: 4.35e, Church of San Francisco. 9.35e, Central post office, horiz. 18.35e, La Posada (Inn) del Corregidor, horiz.

1971
407 A217	1.15e dk blue	.60	.30
408 A218	2.35e ultra & car	.60	.30
409 A217	4.35e brown red	.60	.30
410 A217	9.35e violet	.60	.30
411 A217	18.35e lilac rose	1.25	.30
	Nos. 407-411 (5)	3.65	1.50

10th Cong. of the Postal Union of the Americas and Spain, Santiago.
An imperf souvenir sheet containing #407-411 was not valid for postage. Value $11.
Issued: 2.35e, 4.35e, Nov. 5; 1.15e, Nov. 11; 9.35e, Nov. 18; 18.35e, Nov. 19.

Observation Dome, Cerro el Tololo Observatory — A219

1971, Dec. 18
412 A219 1.95e lt & dk blue .35 .20

Boeing 707 over Easter Island A220

1971, Dec. 18
413 A220 2.35e dk brn & yel   .45   .20
Inauguration of regular flights: Santiago, Easter Island, Tahiti.

Alonso de Ercilla y Zuniga — A221

1972, Mar. 20   Engr.   Perf. 14
414 A221 1e dark red   .40   .20
4th centenary (in 1969) of "La Araucana," by Alonso de Ercilla y Zuniga (1533-1596), Spanish author. See No. C313.

Map of Antarctica and Dog Sled — A222

1972, Mar. 20   Litho.   Perf. 14½x15
415 A222 1.15e vio bl & blk   .65   .30
416 A222 3.50e blue grn & grn   1.10   .30
10th anniversary (in 1971) of the Antarctic Treaty pledging peaceful uses of and scientific cooperation in Antarctica.
For surcharge see No. 630.

"Your Heart is your Health" — A223

1972, Apr. 2   Litho.   Perf. 14½
417 A223 1.15e black & car   .40   .25
World Health Month.
For surcharge see No. 631.

People and Statement by Pres. Allende — A224

Conference Hall and UN Emblem — A225

1972, Apr. 13   Litho.   Perf. 14½
418 A224 35c dl grn & buff   .35   .25
419 A225 1.15e ultra & pur   .40   .20
420 A224   4e dk pur & pale
              rose   .60   .35
421 A225   6e orange & vio bl   .50   .20
      Nos. 418-421 (4)   1.85 1.00
3rd UN Conf. on Trade and Development (UNCTAD III), Santiago, Apr.-May 1972. Design A224 is perf. horiz. in the middle.

Soldier, 1822, Andes, Military College Emblem A226

1972, June 9
422 A226 1.15e blue & yel   .35   .25
Sesquicentennial of Bernardo O'Higgins Military College.

Miner Holding Copper Ingot, Chilean Flag — A227

Sailing Ship — A228

1972, July 11   Litho.   Perf. 15x14½
423 A227 1.15e blue & rose red   .35   .20
424 A227   5e blue, blk & rose
              red   .45   .20
Nationalization of copper industry.

1972, Aug. 4
425 A228 1.15e violet brown   .55   .25
Arturo Pratt Naval Training School, sesqui.

Mt. Calan Observatory — A229

1972, Aug. 31   Litho.   Perf. 14½
426 A229 50c ultra   .40   .25
University of Chile Mt. Calan Observatory.

Carrier Pigeon — A230

1972, Oct. 9   Litho.   Perf. 14½
427 A230 1.15e red lilac & vio   .40   .25
Intl. Letter Writing Week, Oct. 9-15.

René Schneider and Army Flag — A231

1972, Oct. 25   Perf. 14
428 A231 2.30e multi   .40   .30
2nd anniv. of the death of Gen. René Schneider. No. 428 is perforated vertically in the middle.

Book and Young People A232

1972, Oct. 31   Perf. 14½
429 A232 50c black & dp org   .40   .25
International Book Year 1972.

Guitar and Earthen Jar A233

Designs: 2.65e, Fish and produce. 3.50e, Stove, pots and rug, vert.

1972, Nov. 20   Litho.   Perf. 14½
430 A233 1.15e red & blk   .30   .20
431 A233 2.65e ultra & rose lake   .40   .20
432 A233 3.50e red & red brn   .40   .20
      Nos. 430-432 (3)   1.10   .60
Tourism Year of the Americas.

José M. Carrera Before Execution A234

Map of Antarctica, Flag at Base — A235

1973, Feb. 1   Litho.   Perf. 14½
433 A234 2.30e lt ultra   .40   .25
Sesquicentennial of the death of José Miguel Carrera (1785-1821), Chilean revolutionist and dictator.

1973, Feb. 8
434 A235 10e ultra & red   .90   .20
Bernardo O'Higgins Antarctic Base, 25th anniv.

Naval Air Service Emblem, Destroyer A236

La Silla Observatory A237

1973, Mar. 16   Litho.   Perf. 14½
435 A236 20e brt bl & ocher   .45   .25
Chilean Naval Aviation, 50th anniversary.

1973, Apr. 25   Litho.   Perf. 14½
436 A237 2.30e ultra & blk   .40   .25

INTERPOL Emblem A238

Designs: 50e, Fingerprint over globe.

1973, Sept. 23   Litho.   Perf. 14½
437 A238 30e bister & ultra   .65   .30
438 A238 50e black & red   .85   .30
50th anniversary of International Criminal Police Organization.

Grapes — A239

Chilean wine export: 100e, Globe inscribed "Chile Exporta Vino."

1973, Dec. 10   Litho.   Perf. 14½
439 A239 20e buff & lilac   .45 .20
440 A239 100e blue & claret   1.00 .25

UPU Headquarters, Bern — A240

1974, Apr. 4
441 A240 500e on 45c green   .75 .25
UPU cent. No. 441 was not issued without dark green surcharge and overprint.

Bernardo O'Higgins, Armed Forces Emblems — A241

1974, Apr. 11   Litho.   Perf. 14½
442 A241 30e shown   .30 .20
443 A241 30e Soldiers with mortar   .30 .20
444 A241 30e Navy anti-aircraft gunners   .30 .20
445 A241 30e Pilot in cockpit   .30 .20
446 A241 30e Mounted policeman   .30 .20
    Nos. 442-446 (5)   1.50 1.00
Honoring the Armed Forces.

Soccer Ball and Globe — A242

Traffic Police — A243

1000e, Soccer ball and stadium, horiz.

1974   Litho.   Perf. 14
447 A242 500e dk red & org   .60 .25
448 A242 1000e bl & indigo   1.25 .30
World Cup Soccer Championship, Munich, June 13-July 7.

A souvenir sheet contains 2 imperf. stamps similar to Nos. 447-448, with blue marginal inscription. Printed on thin card. Size: 90x119mm. Value, $15.

Nos. 386, 355 Surcharged
1974, June   Litho.   Perf. 14½
449 A202 100e on 40c bl grn   .35 .25
Perf. 13x14
450 A174 300e on 50c dl brn   .40 .20

1974, June 20   Perf. 14½
451 A243 30e red brn & grn   .40 .20
Traffic safety.

Santiago-Australia Air Service — A244

1974, Sept. 5   Litho.   Perf. 14½x14
452 A244 Block of 4   4.75 3.00
  a. 200e Easter Island turtle   .70 .30
  b. 200e Polynesian dancer   .70 .30
  c. 200e Map of Fiji Islands   .70 .30
  d. 200e Kangaroo   .70 .30
Inauguration of air service by LAN (Chile's national airline) from Santiago to Easter Island, Tahiti, Fiji, Australia.

Globe Cut to Show Mantle and Core — A245

1974, Sept. 9   Perf. 14x14½
453 A245 500e red brn & org   1.00 .20
International Volcanology Congress, Santiago, Sept. 9-14.

No. 393 Surcharged in Brown

1974, Oct. 24   Litho.   Perf. 14½
454 A205 100e on 40c green   .40 .25
Inauguration of the O'Higgins National Shrine at Maipu, Oct. 24, 1974.

Juan Fernandez Archipelago — A246

1974, Nov. 22   Litho.   Perf. 14½x14
455 A246 Block of 4   3.50 2.00
  a. 200e Robinson Crusoe Island   .75 .35
  b. 200e Chonta palms   .75 .35
  c. 200e Mountain goat   .75 .35
  d. 200e Spiny rock lobster   .75 .35
400th anniversary of discovery of Juan Fernandez Archipelago.

O'Higgins and Bolivar A247

1974, Dec. 9   Perf. 14½
456 A247 100e red brn & buff   .30 .25
Sesquicentennial of the Battles of Junin and Ayacucho.

F. Vidal Gormaz and Institute Seal A248

Albert Schweitzer A249

1975, Jan. 22   Litho.   Perf. 14½
457 A248 100e rose claret & bl   .35 .25
Centenary of the Naval Hydrographic Institute; F. Vidal Gormaz was first commandant.

1975, Apr. 7   Litho.   Perf. 14x14½
458 A249 500e yel & red brn   .70 .25
Dr. Albert Schweitzer (1875-1965), medical missionary, birth centenary.

No. 395 Surcharged in Red

1975, Apr. 7   Perf. 14½
459 A207 70e on 40c car & lt red brn   .35 .25

Volunteer Lifeboat Service — A250

1975, Apr. 15   Litho.   Perf. 14½x14
460 A250 Block of 4   6.00 3.75
  a. 150e Lighthouse   .85 .30
  b. 150e Shipwreck   .85 .30
  c. 150e Lifeboat   .85 .30
  d. 150e Sailor reaching for life preserver   .85 .30
Valparaiso Volunteer Lifeboat service, 50th anniversary.

Note: souvenir cards were issued by Chile starting in 1975 for various issues. They were printed on thin card. These are not souvenir sheets.

Frigate Lautaro A251

1975, May 21   Photo. & Engr.
461 A251 500e shown   .75 .30
462 A251 500e Corvette Baquedano   .75 .30
463 A251 500e Cruiser Chacabuco   .75 .30
464 A251 500e Brigantine Goleta Esmeralda   .75 .30
  a. Block of 4, #461-464   6.50 6.50
465 A251 800e like #461   1.00 .35
466 A251 800e like #462   1.00 .35
467 A251 800e like #463   1.00 .35

468 A251 800e like #464   1.00 .35
  a. Block of 4, #465-468   8.50 8.50
469 A251 1000e like #461   1.50 .50
470 A251 1000e like #462   1.50 .50
471 A251 1000e like #463   1.50 .50
472 A251 1000e like #464   1.50 .50
  a. Block of 4, #469-472   11.00 11.00
    Nos. 461-472 (12)   13.00 4.60
Shipwreck of training frigate Lautaro, 30th anniversary. Se-tenant in sheets of 25 (5x5) with 7 Lautaro stamps and 6 each of the others.

Happy Mother, by Alfredo Valenzuela P. — A252

Diego Portales, Finance Minister — A253

Paintings: No. 474, Young Girl, by Francisco Javier Mandiola. No. 475, Lucia Guzman, by Pedro Lira Rencoret. No. 476, Woman, by Magdalena Mira Mena.

1975, Oct. 13   Litho.   Perf. 14½
473 A252 50c multicolored   .80 .25
474 A252 50c multicolored   .80 .25
475 A252 50c multicolored   .80 .25
476 A252 50c multicolored   .80 .25
    Nos. 473-476 (4)   3.20 1.00
International Women's Year 1975. Gray inscription on back, printed beneath gum, gives details about painting shown.

Inscribed D. Portales
1975-78   Litho.   Perf. 13x14
477 A253 10c gray grn   .30 .20
478 A253 20c violet ('76)   .30 .20
479 A253 30c orange ('76)   .30 .20
480 A253 50c lt brown   .30 .20
481 A253 1p blue   .30 .20
482 A253 1.50p ocher ('76)   .30 .20
483 A253 2p gray ('77)   .30 .20
483A A253 2.50p citron ('78)   .30 .20
483B A253 3.50p pnksh rose ('78)   .35 .20
484 A253 5p rose claret   .35 .20
    Nos. 477-484 (10)   3.10 2.00
See #635-639. For surcharge see #533.

Cochrane and Liberating Squadron, 1820 — A254

#486, Capture of Valdivia, 1820. #487, Capture of Three-master Esmeralda, 1820. #488, Cruiser Cochrane, 1874. #489, Destroyer Cochrane, 1962.

1976, Jan. 6   Perf. 14½
485 A254 1p multicolored   .70 .25
486 A254 1p multicolored   .70 .25
487 A254 1p multicolored   .70 .25
488 A254 1p multicolored   .70 .25
489 A254 1p multicolored   .70 .25
  a. Strip of 5, #485-489   3.50 3.50
Lord Thomas Cochrane, first commander of Chilean Navy, birth bicentenary.

Flags of Chile and Bolivia
A255

1976, May 25   Litho.   Perf. 14½
490 A255 1.50p multicolored   1.50   .25
Sesquicentennial of Bolivia's independence.

Lake of the Inca, OAS Emblem
A256

1976, June 11
491 A256 1.50p multicolored   1.25   .25
6th General Assembly of the Organization of American States.

George Washington
A257

1976, July 3
492 A257 5p multicolored   .80   .25
American Bicentennial.

Minerva and Academy Emblem
A258

1976, July
493 A258 2.50p multicolored   1.50   .25
Polytechnic Military Academy, 50th anniv.

Araucan Indian — A259

Designs: 2p, Condor with broken chain. 3p, Winged woman, symbolizing rebirth.

1976, Sept. 20   Litho.   Perf. 14½
494 A259 1p blue & multi   .30   .20
495 A259 2p blue & multi   1.50   .75
496 A259 3p yellow & multi   .60   .25
 a.   Strip of 3, #494-496   2.75 2.00
3rd anniversary of the Military Junta.

View, Antarctica — A260

1977, Feb. 10   Litho.   Perf. 14½
497 A260 2p multicolored   9.00   .50
Visit of President Augusto Pinochet to Antarctica.

School Emblem, Planted Field — A261

Justice — A262

1977, Mar. 10   Perf. 14½
498 A261 2p multicolored   1.40   .30
Cent. of advanced agricultural education.

1977, Mar. 30   Litho.   Perf. 14½
499 A262 2p brown & slate   1.60   .35
Supreme Court of Justice, sesquicentennial.

Eye with Globe, Caduceus — A263

1977, Mar. 30   Litho.   Perf. 14½
500 A263 2p multicolored   2.00   .55
11th Pan-American Ophthalmological Cong.

Mounted Policeman
A264

Designs: No. 502, Policewoman with children. No. 503, Paine Peaks and Osorno Volcano, crossed rifle emblem. No. 504, Crossed rifle emblem, mounted and motorcycle policemen, helicopter and automobile, horiz.

1977, Apr. 27
501 A264 2p multicolored   .45   .25
502 A264 2p multicolored   .45   .25
503 A264 2p multicolored   .45   .25
504 A264 2p multicolored   .45   .25
 Nos. 501-504 (4)   1.80 1.00
Chilean police organization, 50th anniv.

Intelsat Satellite over Globe — A265

1977, May 17   Litho.   Perf. 14½
505 A265 2p multi   .90   .35
World Telecommunications Day.

El Mercurio's First Front Page, Press and Ship — A266

1977, July 5   Litho.   Perf. 14½
506 A266 2p multi   .40   .20
El Mercurio de Valparaiso, first Chilean newspaper, 150th anniversary.

St. Francis, Birds and Cross — A267

Science and Technology
A268

1977, July 26   Litho.   Perf. 14½
507 A267 5p multi   1.75   .30
St. Francis of Assisi, 750th death anniv.

1977, Aug. 26   Litho.   Perf. 14½
508 A268 4p multi   .55   .25

Young Mother Weaving — A269

Diego de Almagro — A270

#510, Handicapped boy in wheelchair & nurse. #511, Children dancing in circle. #512, Old man & home.

1977, Sept. 13   Litho.   Perf. 14½
509 A269 5p multi   .60   .20
510 A269 5p multi   .60   .20
511 A269 10p multi, horiz.   1.25   .25
512 A269 10p multi, horiz.   1.25   .25
 Nos. 509-512 (4)   3.70   .90
4th anniversary of Government Junta and social services of armed forces.

1977, Oct. 31   Engr.   Perf. 14½
513 A270 5p rose & carmine   .40   .25
Diego de Almagro (1475-1538), leader of Spanish expedition to Chile.

Bell, Letters, Dove and Child
A271

1977, Dec. 12   Litho.   Perf. 14½
514 A271 2.50p multi   .40   .20
Christmas 1977.

Loading Timber
A272

1978   Litho.   Perf. 15
515 A272 10p multi   1.25   .25
516 A272 20p multi   1.50   .35
No. 516 inscribed "CORREOS," ship is flying Chilean flag.

Papal Arms and Globe
A273

University — A274

1978   Litho.   Perf. 14½
521 A273 10p multi   1.00   .30
522 A274 25p multi   2.25   .75
World Peace Day (10p); Catholic University of Valparaiso, 50th anniversary (25p). Issue dates: 10p, July 28; 25p, July 31.

O'Higgins, by Gil de Castro — A275

1978, Aug. 20   Litho.   Perf. 15
523 A275 10p multi   .90   .30
Bernardo O'Higgins (1778-1842), soldier and statesman.

Chacabuco Victory Monument A276

1978, Sept. 11
524 A276 10p multi .90 .30

160th anniv. of O'Higgins victory at Chacabuco, and 5th anniv. of military government.

Teacher Writing on Blackboard — A277

1978, Sept. 21
525 A277 15p multi 1.00 .25

10th anniversary and 9th Reunion of Interamerican Council for Education, Science and Culture (C.I.E.C.C.), Sept. 21-29.

First National Fleet, by Thomas Somerscales — A278

Design: 30p, Last Moments of Rancagua Battle, by Pedro Subercaseaux.

1978 **Litho.** **Perf. 15**
526 A278 20p multi 2.25 .55
527 A278 30p multi 2.50 .90

Bernardo O'Higgins (1778-1842), soldier and statesman.
Issue dates: 20p, Oct. 9; 30p, Oct. 2.

San Martin-O'Higgins Medal, by Rene Thenot, 1942 — A279

1978, Oct. 20
528 A279 7p multi .50 .25

José de San Martin and Bernardo O'Higgins, 200th birth anniversaries.

Council Emblem — A280

1978, Nov. 27 **Litho.** **Perf. 14½**
529 A280 50p multi 5.25 2.10

Intl. Council of Military Sports, 30th anniv.

Three Kings — A281

Virgin and Child — A282

1978, Dec. 14 **Litho.** **Perf. 14½**
530 A281 3p multi .75 .20
531 A282 11p multi 1.40 .40

Christmas 1978.

Philippi Brothers A283

1978, Dec. 29 **Litho.** **Perf. 14½x15**
532 A283 3.50p multi .40 .20

Bernardo E. Philippi (1811-1852) and Rodulfo A. Philippi (1808-1904), scientists and travelers.

No. 477 Surcharged in Bright Green
1979 **Litho.** **Perf. 13x14**
533 A253 3.50p on 10c gray grn .25 .20

Flags of Chile and Salvation Army — A284

1979, Mar. 17 **Litho.** **Perf. 14½**
534 A284 10p multi 1.25 .65

Salvation Army in Chile, 70th anniversary.

Pope Paul VI (1897-1978) — A285

1979, Mar. 30
535 A285 11p multi 1.50 .90

Battle of Maipu Monument — A286

1979, Apr. 17 **Litho.** **Perf. 14½**
536 A286 8.50p multi 1.40 .50

Bernardo O'Higgins (1778-1842), Liberator of Chile.

Naval Battles A287

1979, May 21 **Litho.** **Perf. 14½**
537 A287 3.50p Angamos .80 .30
538 A287 3.50p Iquique .80 .30
539 A287 3.50p Punta Gruesa .80 .30
   Nos. 537-539 (3) 2.40 .90

Centenary of victorious naval battles against Peru.

1903 Ambulance and Red Cross — A288

1979, June 29 **Litho.** **Perf. 14½**
540 A288 25p multi 4.00 1.10

75th anniversary of Chilean Red Cross.

Diego Portales — A289

1979-86 **Litho.** **Perf. 13½**
542 A289 1.50p ocher .25 .20
543 A289 2p gray ('81) .25 .20
544 A289 3.50p red .30 .20
545 A289 4.50p bl grn ('81) .40 .20
546 A289 5p rose claret .50 .20
547 A289 6p emerald .60 .30
548 A289 7p yellow ('82) .55 .30
549 A289 10p blue ('82) .80 .30
550 A289 12p orange ('86) .35 .20
   Nos. 542-550 (9) 4.00 2.10

1.50p, 3.50p, 5p and 6p inscribed "D. Portales."

People and Flag — A290

1979, Aug. 28 **Litho.** **Perf. 14½**
551 A290 10p multi .90 .60

Yugoslavian immigration, centenary.

Coat of Arms and Mt. Castillo A290a

1979, Oct. 12 **Litho.** **Perf. 14½**
552 A290a 20p multi 2.00 1.00

Coyhaique 50th anniv.

IYC Emblem, Playground — A291

IYC Emblem, Children's Drawings: 11p, Girl and shadow, vert. 12p, Dancing.

1979, Oct. 9 **Perf. 14½**
553 A291 9.50p multi .95 .60
554 A291 11p multi 1.10 .75
555 A291 12p multi 1.60 .85
   Nos. 553-555 (3) 3.65 2.20

International Year of the Child.

Telecom 79 A292

1979, Oct. 26 **Litho.** **Perf. 14½**
556 A292 15p multi 1.50 .75

3rd World Telecommunications Exhibition, Geneva, Sept. 20-26.

Puerto Williams, 25th Anniversary — A293

1979, Nov. 21
557 A293 3.50p multi .60 .20

Adoration of the Kings A294

1979, Dec. 4 **Litho.** **Perf. 15**
558 A294 3.50p multi .60 .25

Christmas 1979.

Rafael Sotomayor, Minister of War — A295

Military heroes.

1979, Dec. 29   *Perf. 13½*
559 A295 3.50p ocher & brn   .50 .25
560 A295 3.50p Erasmo Escala   .50 .25
561 A295 3.50p Emilio
    Sotomayor   .50 .25
562 A295 3.50p Eleuterio Rami-
    rez   .50 .25
   a. Block of 4, #559-562   2.00 2.00

Bell UH-1 Rescue Helicopter at
Tinguiririca Volcano, by S.O.
Mococain — A296

Air Force, 50th Anniversary: No. 564, Flying
boat Catalina Skua over Antarctic, by E.F.
Alvarez. No. 565, F5-E Tiger II over Andes, by
M.M. Barria.

1980, Mar. 21   Litho.   *Perf. 13½*
563 A296 3.50p shown   .50 .25
564 A296 3.50p Jet   .50 .25
565 A296 3.50p Sea plane   .50 .25
    Nos. 563-565 (3)   1.50 .75

The Death of
Bueras, by Pedro
Leon
Carmona — A297

1980, Apr. 14   Litho.   *Perf. 13½*
566 A297 12p multi   1.00 .50

Charge of Bueras, Battle of Maipo, 1818.

Rotary International, 75th
Anniversary — A298

1980, Apr. 15
567 A298 10p multi   1.25 .45

Gen. Manuel
Baquedano,
by Pedro
Subercaseaux
A299

Gen. Pedro Lagos, Battle Scene, by
Subercaseaux — A300

Battle of Morro de Arica Centenary (Subercaseaux Paintings): No. 570, Commander
Juan J. San Martin, battle scene.

1980, June 7   Litho.   *Perf. 13½*
568 A299 3.50p multi   .40 .20
569 A300 3.50p multi   .40 .20
570 A300 3.50p multi   .40 .20
    Nos. 568-570 (3)   1.20 .60

Score and Perez's Silhouette — A301

1980, June 27   Litho.   *Perf. 13½*
571 A301 6p multi   .60 .30
Osman Perez Freire (1880-1930), composer, and fragment from his song "Ay, Ay,
Ay."

Mt. Gasherbrum II, Chilean Flag, Ice
Pick — A302

1980, July 9
572 A302 15p multi   1.40 .60

Chilean Himalayan expedition, June 1979.

"Charity,"
Stained-glass
Window
A303

1980, July 18
573 A303 10p multi   1.50 .35

Daughters of Charity, 125th anniv. in Chile.

Condor, Colors of Chile — A304

1980, Sept. 11   Litho.   *Perf. 13½*
574 A304 3.50p multi   .40 .25

17th anniversary of constitution.

Inca Child
Mummy
A305

Pablo Burchard, by
Pedro Lira
A306

1980, Sept. 14
575 A305 5p shown   .60 .20
576 A305 5p Claudio Gay   .60 .20
   a. Pair, #575-576 + label   1.40 1.25

Natl. Museum of Natural History (founded
by Claudio Gay, 1800-73) sesqui.

1980, Sept. 27   Litho.   *Perf. 13½*
577 A306 3.50p multi   .40 .20

Museum of Fine Art centenary (directed by
Burchard, 1932).

Santiago
International
Fair — A307

1980, Oct. 30
578 A307 3.50p multi   .40 .20

Nativity — A308

Christmas 1980: 3.50p, Family, vert.

1980, Nov. 25   Litho.   *Perf. 13½*
579 A308 3.50p multi   .80 .30
580 A308 10.50p multi   1.60 .55

Infantryman   Congress
1879 — A309   Emblem — A310

Pacific War period uniforms, 1879.

1980, Nov. 27
581 A309 3.50p shown   .75 .20
582 A309 3.50p Cavalry officer   .75 .20
583 A309 3.50p Artillery officer   .75 .20
584 A309 3.50p Engineer colonel   .75 .20
   a. Block of 4, #581-584   4.00 4.00

    See Nos. 606-609.

1980, Dec. 1
585 A310 11.50p multi   1.25 .60

23rd Intl. Cong. of Military Medicine &
Pharmacy.

Eradication of
Hoof and
Mouth
Disease
A311

1981, Jan. 16   Litho.   *Perf. 13½*
586 A311 9.50p multi   .90 .25

Moai Statues, Easter Island — A312

1981, Jan. 28   Litho.   *Perf. 13½*
587 A312 3.50p shown   .45 .35
588 A312 3.50p Robinson Cru-
    soe Island   .80 .35
589 A312 10.50p Penguins,
    Antarctic Terri-
    tory   3.50 1.00
    Nos. 587-589 (3)   4.75 1.70

National Heroine Javiera Carrera, by
O.M. Pizarro, Birth
Bicentenary — A313

1981, Mar. 20
590 A313 3.50p multi   .40 .20

UPU
Membership
Centenary
A314

1981, Apr. 1
591 A314 3.50p multi   .40 .25

C130 Hercules Air Force Transport
Plane Unloading Cargo — A315

1981, Apr. 21
592 A315 3.50p multi   1.25 .40

Lieutenant Marsh Air Force Base, 1st anniv.

13th World Telecommunications
Day — A316

1981, May 17   Litho.   *Perf. 13½*
593 A316 3.50p multi   .40 .20

Arturo Prat Naval Base A317

1981, June 23   Litho.   Perf. 13½
594 A317 3.50p multi   .75 .25

Capt. Jose Luis Araneda A318

1981, June 26
595 A318 3.50p multi   .40 .20
Battle of Sangrar centenary.

Philatelic Society of Chile, 90th Anniv. A319

1981, July 29   Litho.   Perf. 13½
596 A319 4.50p multi   .40 .20

Minister Recabarren and Chief Conuepan Giving Speeches, by Hector Robles Acuna — A320

1981, Aug. 7
597 A320 4.50p multi   .90 .25
Temuco city centenary.

Exports A321

1981, Aug. 31   Litho.   Perf. 13½
598 A321 14p multi   .80 .35

Presidential Palace — A322

1981, Sept. 11
599 A322 4.50p multi   .80 .20
Natl. liberation, 8th anniv.

St. Vincent de Paul, 400th Birth Anniv. A323

1981, Sept. 27   Litho.   Perf. 13½
600 A323 4.50p multi   .50 .25

Andres Bello, Poet and Sholar, Birth Bicentenary A324

1981, Sept. 29
601 A324 4.50p Coin   .40 .25
602 A324 9.50p Bust, books   .60 .30
603 A324 11.50p Statue, arms   1.00 .40
    Nos. 601-603 (3)   2.00 .95

2nd Congress of South American Uniformed Police A325

1981, Oct. 15
604 A325 4.50p multi   .50 .20

World Food Day A326

1981, Oct. 16
605 A326 5.50p multi   .50 .25

Uniform Type of 1980
1879 Parade Uniforms.

1981, Nov. 6   Perf. 13½
606 A309 5.50p Infantry private   .80 .25
607 A309 5.50p Cadet   .80 .25
608 A309 5.50p Cavalryman   .80 .25
609 A309 5.50p Artilleryman   .80 .25
    a.   Block of 4, #606-609   4.00 3.00

Intl. Year of the Disabled A327

1981, Nov. 11
610 A327 5.50p multi   1.00 .30

Christmas 1981 — A328

1981, Nov. 25
611 A328 5.50p Nativity   .50 .25
612 A328 11.50p Three Kings   1.00 .40

50th Anniv. of Federico Santa Maria Technical University — A329

1981, Dec 1   Litho.   Perf. 13½
613 A329 5.50p multi   .40 .25

Dario Salas (1881-1941), Educator — A330

1981, Dec. 4
614 A330 5.50p multi   .45 .25

FIDA '82, 2nd Natl. Air Force Fair — A331

1982, Mar. 6   Litho.   Perf. 13½
615 A331 4.50p multi   .50 .20

1980 Constitution — A332

1982, Mar. 11
616 A332 4.50p Cardinal Caro,
                family   .50 .25
617 A332 11p Diego Portales   1.50 .40
618 A332 30p Bernardo
                O'Higgins   2.50 .90
    Nos. 616-618 (3)   4.50 1.55

Panamerican Institute of Geography and History, 12th General Assembly A333

1982, Mar. 22   Litho.   Perf. 13½
619 A333 4.50p multi   .50 .25

American Air Forces Cooperation System — A334

1982, Apr. 12
620 A334 4.50p multi   .45 .20

Pedro Montt — A335   Fish Exports — A336

1982, Mar. 27
621 A335 4.50p light vio   .50 .20

1982, May 3   Litho.   Perf. 13½
622 A336 20p multi   2.00 .75

Scouting Year — A337

#623b, Robert Baden-Powell.

1982, May 21   Litho.   Perf. 13
623   Pair   40.00 32.50
    a.-b.   A337 4.50p, either single 15.00 8.00

Battle of Concepcion Centenary A338

Chacabuco Regiment officers killed in battle.

1982, June 18 Litho. Perf. 13½

624		Block of 4	2.50	2.50
a.	A338	4.50p I. Carrera Pinto	.50	.20
b.	A338	4.50p A. Perez Canto	.50	.20
c.	A338	4.50p J. Montt Salamanca	.50	.20
d.	A338	4.50p L. Cruz Martinez	.50	.20

UN World Assembly on Aging, July 26-Aug. 6 — A339

1982, Aug. 5

625	A339	4.50p multi	.40	.25

TB Bacillus Centenary A340

1982, Aug. 31

626	A340	4.50p multi	.40	.20

9th Anniv. of National Liberation — A341

1982, Sept. 11 Litho. Perf. 13½

627	A341	4.50p multi	.40	.20

Christmas 1982 — A342

Children's drawings.

1982, Nov. 2

628	A342	10p multi	1.00	.25
629	A342	25p multi, vert.	1.50	.60

Nos. 416-417 Surcharged in Green or Black

1982, Nov. Perf. 14½x15, 14½

630	A222	1p on 3.50p bl grn & grn (G)	.20	.20
631	A223	2p on 1.15p blk & car	.20	.20

Marist Alumni, 9th World Congress A342a

Virgin Mary & Marcellus Champagnat (founder of Marist Brotherhood), stained glass window, Church of the Sacred Heart of Jesus, Barcelona.

1982, Nov. 11 Litho. Perf. 13½

631A	A342a	7p multi	1.40	.40

El Sur Newspaper Centenary A342b

1982, Nov. 15

631B	A342b	7p Wooden hand-press, masthead	.50	.25

110th Anniv. of South American Steamship Co. — A342c

1982, Dec. 20

631C	A342c	7p Steamer Copiapo	1.00	.35

60th Anniv. of Radio Club of Chile — A342d

1982, Dec. 29

631D	A342d	7p multi	.50	.25

First Anniv. of Postal Agreement with Order of Malta — A343

1983, Mar. 30 Litho. Perf. 13½

632		25p Arms of Order of Malta	2.00	.40
633		50p Chile	4.00	.80
a.		Pair, #632-633	8.00	6.50

D.D. No. 20
This and similar inscriptions indicate that the stamps would be sold at a discount if purchased in large quantities.

D. Portales Type of 1975 Inscribed Diego Portales and:

Ramon Barros Luco A344

Juan Luis Sanfuentes A344a

1983-88 Litho. Perf. 13½

634	A344	1p grnsh bl	.20	.20
635	A344	1p chalky bl	.20	.20
636	A253	1.50p ocher	.20	.20
637	A344	2p dl vio ('84)	.20	.20
638	A253	2p ol gray	.20	.20
639	A253	2.50p lemon	.20	.20
640	A253	5p red lilac	.35	.25
641	A344	5p crim rose	.20	.20
642	A344a	5p red ('84)	.20	.20
643	A344	7p ultra	.30	.20
644	A344a	9p brn ('84)	.25	.20

645	A344a	9p grn ('84)	.25	.20
646	A344	10p black	.25	.20
646A	A344a	10p gray ('84)	.25	.20
647	A344a	15p ultra ('87)	.20	.20
a.		Booklet pane of 10	1.50	
648	A344a	20p yel ('88)	.20	.20
b.		Booklet pane of 10	2.00	

Nos. 644, 647, 648 inscribed "D.S. No. 20."
Issued: No. 640, 8/85.
For surcharge see No. 779.

50th Anniv. of Bureau of Investigation A345

1983, June 19 Litho. Perf. 13½

649	A345	20p multi	1.25	.50

Antonio Cardinal Samore (1905-1983) — A346

1983, June 26

650	A346	30p multi	2.00	.60

Centenary of Cliff Elevators in Valparaiso A347

1983, Aug. 19 Litho. Perf. 13½

651	A347	40p multi	4.00	.45

Pucara de Quitor Settlement Ruins, San Pedro de Atacama — A348

No. 653, Llamas, rock painting, Rio Ibanez, Aisen. No. 654, Duck-shaped jug with human head, Diaguita cultures. No. 655, Puoko Tangata carved stone head, Easter Isld.

1983, Aug. 26

652	A348	7p multi	1.10	.40
653	A348	7p multi	1.10	.40
654	A348	7p multi	1.10	.40
655	A348	7p multi, vert.	.20	.20
		Nos. 652-655 (4)	3.50	1.40

10th Anniv. of National Liberation — A349

1983, Sept. 11 Litho. Perf. 13½

656	A349	7p Angel with broken chains	.60	.25
657	A349	7p Couple, flag	.60	.25
658	A349	10p Family, torch	.60	.25
659	A349	40p Coat of arms, "10"	2.00	.75
a.		Strip of 4, #656-659	5.00	3.50

For surcharges see Nos. 669-670.

Famous Hondurans A350

#660, Francisco Morazan (1792-1842), Advocate of United Central America. #661, Jose Cecilio Del Valle (1777-1834), Scholar and Leader of Pan Americanism.

1983, Oct. 3 Litho. Perf. 13½

660	A350	7p multi	.40	.20
661	A350	7p multi	.40	.20
a.		Pair, #660-661	.80	.80

World Communications Year — A351

1983, Oct. 13 Litho. Perf. 13½

662		7p Central P.O.	.85	.25
663		7p Challenger spaceship	.85	.25
a.	A351	Pair, #662-663	1.75	1.75

Christmas 1983 — A353

Childrens' Drawings: 10p Chilean Peasant, Hanny Chacon. 30p, Holy Family. Lucrecia Cardenas, vert.

1983, Nov. 14 Litho. Perf. 13

664	A353	10p multi	.50	.20
665	A353	30p multi	1.50	.40

Design descriptions printed on back on top of gum.

State Railways Centenary — A354

Train Cars: a, Presidential coach, 1911. b, Service coach, 1910; tender, 1929. c, Locomotive Type 80, 1929.

1984, Jan. 4 Litho. Perf. 13½

666		Strip of 3	10.00	8.75
a.-c.	A354	9p, any single	2.40	.45

3rd Intl. Air Fair, Santiago, Mar. 3-11 — A355

1984, Jan. 31   Litho.   Perf. 13½
667 A355 9p Flags, plane   .90 .20

20th Anniv. of Nuclear Energy Commission — A356

1984, Apr. 16   Litho.   Perf. 13
668 A356 9p multi   .50 .25

Nos. 656-657 Surcharged in Purple
1984, June 11   Litho.   Perf. 13½
669 A349 9p on 7p #656   .45 .25
670 A349 9p on 7p #657   .45 .25
a.   Pair, #669-670   1.25 .95

Antarctic Colonization — A357

1984, June 18
671 A357 15p Women's expedition   .75 .35
672 A357 15p Villa las Estrellas Station   .75 .35
673 A357 15p Scouts, flag, Air Force base   .75 .35
a.   Strip of 3, #671-673   5.75 5.50

10th Anniv. of Regionalization — A358

Designs: a, Parinacota Church, Tarapaca. b, El Tatio geyser, Antofagasta. c, Copper mining, Atacama. d, Tololo Observatory, Coquimbo. e, Valparaiso Harbor, Valparaiso. f, Ahu Akivi head sculptures, Easter Isld. g, St. Francis Church, Santiago. h, El Hunique House, O'Higgins. i, Colburn Machicura Dam and Hydroelectric Power Station, Maule. j, Sta. Juana de Guadalcazar Fort, Bio-Bio. k, Indian woman, Araucania. l, Guar Isld. Church, Los Lagos. m, Main road, Gen. del Campo. n, Shepherds' Monument, Magellanes and Antarctic. o, Family, Villa las Estrellas Station, Antarctic.

1984, July 11
674   Sheet of 15   15.00 15.00
a.-o. A358 9p multi, any single   .75 .40

Capt. Pedro Sarmiento de Gamboa, Map, 1584 — A359

1984, July 31   Litho.   Perf. 13
675 A359 100p multi   5.25 1.10

400th anniv. of Spanish presence in Straits of Magellan.

State Bank of Chile Centenary — A360

1984, Sept. 6   Litho.   Perf. 13½
676 A360 35p Founder Antonio Varas de la Barra, coin   1.25 .55

11th Anniv. of Liberation — A361

1984, Sept. 11
677 A361 20p Monument to O'Higgins   1.10 .30

Circus Centenary — A362

1984, Sept. 28   Litho.   Perf. 13½
678 A362 45p Clown   1.50 .70

Endangered Species, World Wildlife Emblem — A363

1985, July   Litho.   Perf. 13½
679 A363 9p Chinchilla   9.00 2.50
680 A363 9p Blue whale   9.00 2.50
681 A363 9p Sea lions   9.00 2.50
682 A363 9p Chilean huemuls   9.00 2.50
a.   Block of 4, #679-682   48.00 25.00

Christmas 1984 — A364

Children's drawings.

1984, Nov. 20   Litho.   Perf. 13½
683 A364 9p Shepherds   .40 .20
684 A364 40p Bethlehem   1.50 .40

Santiago University Planetarium Opening — A365

1984, Dec. 29
685 A365 10p multi   .70 .40

Flora and Fauna — A366

Wildlife: a, Conepatus chinga. b, Leucocoryne purpurea. c, Himantopus himantopus. d, Lutra felina. e, Balbisia peduncularis. f, Psittacus cyanalysias. g, Pudu pudu. h, Fuschia magellanica. i, Diuca diuca. j, Dusicyon griseus. k, Alstroemeria sierrae. l, Glaucidium nanum.

1985, Feb.
686   Block of 12   15.00 10.00
a.-l. A366 10p, Any single   .75 .40

American Airforces Cooperation System, 25th Anniv. A367

1985, Mar. 26
687 A367 45p Emblem, flags   2.00 1.10

Chile-Argentina Peace Treaty — A368

1985, May 2   Litho.   Perf. 13½
688 A368 20p Papal arms, flags   3.00 .60

Fr. Joseph Kentenich (1885-1968), Founder, Intl. Schonstatt Movement of Catholic Laymen A369

1985, May 19   Litho.   Perf. 13½
689 A369 40p Portrait, La Florida Sanctuary, Santiago   .70 .40

Antarctic Treaty, 25th Anniv. — A370

Resources, research: 15p, Krill, pack ice, map. 20p, Seismological Station, O'Higgins' Base. 35p, Georeception Station, dish receiver.

1985, June 21
690 A370 15p multi   .65 .35
691 A370 20p multi   .85 .50
692 A370 35p multi   1.50 .75
    Nos. 690-692 (3)   3.00 1.60

Canis Fulvipes — A371

Endangered wildlife: b, Phoenicoparrus jamesi. c, Fulica gigantea. d, Lutra provocax.

1985, Aug. 9   Litho.   Perf. 13½
693   Block of 4   13.00 4.50
a.-d. A371 20p, any single   1.75 .35

Intl. Youth Year A372

UN, 40th Anniv. A373

1985, Aug. 31
694 A372 15p multi   .50 .25
695 A373 15p multi   .50 .25
a.   Pair, #694-695   1.50 1.50

Gen. Jose Miguel Carrera Verdugo (1785-1821) — A374

1985, Oct. 8   Litho.   Perf. 13½
696 A374 40p multi   .90 .55

Farmer and Ox-drawn Hay Cart — A375

Folklore: b, Street photographer, wet plate camera. c, One-man band. d, Basket maker.

1985, Oct.
697   Block of 4   1.25 .90
a.-d. A375 10p, any single   .25 .20

For surcharges see Nos. 770-771.

Christmas
1985 — A376

Holy
Family — A376a

Winning children's drawings, 7th natl.
design contest.

1985, Nov. 4
698 A376 15p Nativity .55 .20
699 A376 100p Father Christmas,
vert. 3.75 1.00

Nos. 698-699 inscribed in black on gummed
side with child's name, age, school and region.

1985 Litho. Perf. 13½
699A A376a 10p buff & brn .30 .20

For surcharge see No. 768.

16th Armed Forces
Conference — A377

20p, Cavalryman, Directorial Escort, 1818.
35p, Officer, Grand Guard, 1813.

1985, Nov. 15 Litho. Perf. 13½
700 A377 20p multicolored .75 .25
701 A377 35p multicolored 1.00 .35

Halley's Comet — A378

1985, Nov. 29 Litho. Perf. 13½
702 A378 45p multicolored .75 .25
a. Souvenir sheet 20.00 20.00

No. 702a exists imperf. Value $30.

Natl. Solidarity Campaign — A379

1985
703 A379 5p red & blue .50 .50

Campaign for
Prevention of
Forest
Fires — A380

1985, Dec. 27
704 A380 40p Forest .75 .40
705 A380 40p Fire destruction .75 .40
a. Pair, #704-705 2.75 1.50

No. 705a has continuous design.

Dungeness Point Lighthouse, Straits of
Magellan — A381

1986, Jan. 26
706 A381 45p shown 1.40 .45
707 A381 45p Evangelistas Lighthouse 1.40 .45
a. Pair, #706-707 4.00 2.50

No. 707a continuous design.

View of Santiago, Mackenna — A382

1986, Jan. 28
708 A382 30p multi .45 .20

Benjamin Vicuna Mackenna (d. 1886),
municipal superintendent of Santiago, 1872-
1875.

Diego Portales, Natl. Crest,
Text — A382a

1986, Feb. Litho. Perf. 13½
708A A382a 12p on 3.50p multi .45 .20

No. 708A not issued without surcharge.

1986 World Cup Soccer
Championships, Mexico — A383

Host stadiums: 15p, Natl. Stadium, Chile,
1962. 20p, Aztec Stadium, Mexico, 1970.
35p, Maracana Stadium, Brazil, 1950. 50p,
Wembley Stadium, Great Britain, 1966.

1986, Feb. 18
709 A383 15p multi .40 .25
710 A383 20p multi .55 .25
711 A383 35p multi .80 .35
712 A383 50p multi 1.25 .50
Nos. 709-712 (4) 3.00 1.35

Environmental Conservation — A384

1986, Feb. 28
713 A384 20p Water .75 .20
714 A384 20p Air .75 .20
715 A384 20p Soil .75 .20
Nos. 713-715 (3) 2.25 .60

Sailing Ship
Santiaguillo,
Flags — A385

1986, Mar. 20
716 A385 40p multi 1.00 .55

Discovery of Valparaiso Bay, 450th anniv.

A386

A387

1986, Apr. 9
717 A386 45p multi 1.00 .45

Interamerican Development Bank, 25th
anniv.

1986, Apr. 30 Litho. Perf. 13½
718 A387 15p multi .65 .25

St. Rosa de Lima (1586-1617), sanctuary at
Pelequen.

Moai Statues,
Easter
Is. — A388

1986, May 15
719 A388 60p Raraku Volcano 1.75 .60
a. Souvenir sheet 12.50 12.50
720 A388 100p Tongariki Ruins 3.25 1.00
a. Souvenir sheet 19.00 19.00

AMERIPEX '86 — A389

1986, May 23
721 A389 100p multi 2.50 1.10

Historic Naval Ships — A390

1986, May 30
722 A390 35p Schooner Ancud,
1843 1.25 .60
723 A390 35p Armed merchantman Aguilar,
1830 1.25 .60
724 A390 35p Corvette Esmeralda, 1856 1.25 .60
725 A390 35p Frigate O'Higgins,
1834 1.25 .60
a. Block of 4, #722-725 6.50 6.50

See Nos. 752-753.

Paintings by
Juan
Francisco
Gonzalez
(1853-1933)
A391

1986, June 24
726 A391 30p Rush and Chrysanthemums 1.00 .35
727 A391 30p Gate of La Serena 1.00 .35
a. Pair, #726-727 2.50 1.75

Exports — A392

Designs: a, Saltpeter. b, Iron. c, Copper. d,
Molybdenum.

1986 Litho. Perf. 13½
728 A392 Block of 4 1.60 1.25
a.-d. 12p, any single .25 .20

Antarctic Fauna — A393

a, Sterna vittata. b, Phalacrocorax atriceps.
c, Aptenodytes forsteri. d, Catharacta
lonnberg.

1986, July 16 Litho. Perf. 13½
729 Block of 4 9.00 5.50
a.-d. A393 40p, any single 1.75 .70

Writers — A394

No. 730, Pedro de Ona (1570-1643). No. 731, Vicente Huidobro (1893-1948).

1986, Aug. 19

730	A394	20p multi	.65 .40
731	A394	20p multi	.65 .40
a.		Pair, #730-731	1.75 1.00

Has continuous design.

Military Academy, Cent. — A395

1986, Sept. 8   Litho.   Perf. 13½

732	A395	45p Major-General, 1878	.75 .40
733	A395	45p Major, 1950	.75 .40
a.		Pair, #732-733	1.75 1.10

Art A396

1986, Oct. 17   Perf. 13½

734	A396	30p Diaguita urn, duck jug	.65 .40
735	A396	30p Mapuche silver ornament, embroidery	.65 .40
a.		Pair, #734-735	2.25 1.60

Christmas — A397

8th Natl. design contest-winning children's drawings.

1986, Nov. 19   Litho.   Perf. 13½

736	A397	15p multi	.65 .20
737	A397	105p multi	2.75 .70

Nos. 736-737 inscribed in black on gummed side with child's name, age, school and region.

Christmas A397a

Design: Shepherds see star, Bethlehem.

1986, Nov.   Litho.   Perf. 13½

737A	A397a	12p multi	.35 .20

Intl. Peace Year — A398

1986, Nov. 26

738	A398	85p multi	1.50 .60

Natl. Women Volunteers — A399

1986, Dec. 15   Litho.   Perf. 13½

739	A399	15p multi	.45 .20

Crowning of Our Lady of Mt. Carmel, Patron of Chile, by Pius XI, 60th Anniv. — A400

1986, Dec. 19

740	A400	25p multi	.70 .25

Andean Railways Kitson-Meyer No. 59, 1907, Designed by Robert Sterling — A401

1987, Jan. 27   Litho.   Perf. 13½

741	A401	95p multi	3.00 1.25

Arturo Prat Naval Base, Greenwich Island, the Antarctic, 40th Anniv. — A402

Illustration reduced.

1987, Feb. 6

742		100p Storage and power supplies	4.50 2.00
743		100p Working and living quarters	4.50 2.00
a.	A402	Pair, #742-743	10.00 7.75

State Visit of Pope John Paul II, Apr. 1-6, 1987 A403

Pope John Paul II and: 20p, Christ the Redeemer statue. 25p, Votive Church, Maipu. 90p, Cross of the Seas, Straits of Magellan. 115p, Virgin of the Hill.

1987   Litho.   Perf. 13½

744	A403	20p multi	.30 .20
745	A403	25p multi	.40 .20
746	A403	90p multi	1.40 .60
747	A403	115p multi	1.90 .95
a.		Souv. sheet of one	5.25 5.25
747B	A403	115p multi	2.00 1.00
		Nos. 744-747B (5)	6.00 2.95

No. 747a sold for 250p.
No. 747B differs from No. 747 in that the Statue of the Virgin has a halo and Pope John Paul II is smiling.
Issue date: Nos. 744-747a, Apr. 6.

Los Carabineros (Natl. Guard), 60th Anniv. — A404

World Youth Soccer Championships A405

1987, Apr. 21

748	A404	50p Cavalry showmanship	.80 .35
749	A404	50p Air-sea rescue	.80 .35
a.		Pair, #748-749	2.40 2.00

1987, May 28

b, Concepcion Stadium, kick play. c, Antofagasta Stadium, dribbling the ball. d, Valparaiso Stadium, heading the ball.

750		Block of 4	4.50 4.50
a.-d.		A405 45p any single	1.10 .60

Souvenir Sheet

751	A405	45p Four players	5.00 5.00

No. 751 sold for 150p.

Naval Ships Type of 1986

1987, May 29

752	A390	60p Battleship Almirante Latorre, 1913	1.00 .60
753	A390	60p Cruiser O'Higgins, 1936	1.00 .60
a.		Pair, #752-753	3.75 2.25

Diego Portales (1793-1837), Finance Minister — A406

1987, June 16

754	A406	30p multi	.50 .25

Public Works Ministry, Cent. — A407

1987, June 26

755	A407	25p multi	.55 .30

Infantry School, Cent. — A408

1987, July 9

756	A408	50p Entrance	.50 .25
757	A408	100p Soldiers, natl. flag	1.00 .50

Miniature Sheet

Flora and Fauna — A409

Designs: a, Chiasognathus granti. b, Calidris alba. c, Hippocamelus antisensis. d, Jubaea chilensis. e, Colias vauthieri. f, Pandion haliaetus. g, Cephalorhynchus commersonii. h, Austrocedrus chilensis. i, Jasus frontalis. j, Stephanoides fernandensis. k, Vicugna vicugna. l, Thyrsopteris elegans. m, Lithodes antarctica. n, Pterocnemia pennata. o, Lagidium viscacia. p, Cereus atacamensis.

1987, July 30

758		Sheet of 16	15.00 15.00
a.-p.		A409 25p any single	.55 .30

Intl. Year of Shelter for the Homeless A410

The Guitarist of Quinchamali A411

1987, Aug. 6

759	A410	40p multi	.60 .30

1987, July   Litho.   Perf. 13½

Legends and folk tales: b, El Caleuche. c, El Pihuychen. d, La Lola.

760		Block of 4	1.60 1.00
a.-d.		A411 15p any single	.20 .20

Nos. 760a-760d exist ovptd. "D.S. No 20." in golden brown on back. Value $2.50.
For surcharges see Nos. 812, 1104.

FISA '87, Santiago — A412

1987, Oct. 16   Litho.   Perf. 13½

761	A412	20p multi	.40 .20

25th Intl. agriculture and exports exhibition.

Rear Admiral Carlos Condell de la Haza (1843-1887), Naval Hero at the Battle of the Pacific — A413

1987, Nov. 7
762 A413 50p multi   1.50 .90

Christmas 1987 — A414

COBRE '87, Intl. Conf. on Copper — A415

Children's drawings: 30p, Holy Family. 100p, Star Over Bethlehem, horiz.

1987, Nov. 13
763 A414 30p multi   .75 .30
764 A414 100p multi   3.00 .95

1987, Nov. 23
765 A415 40p Foundry   2.10 .60
a.   Souv. sheet of one   2.50 2.50
       No. 765 sold for 150p.

Natl. Antarctic Exploration Commission, 25th Anniv. — A415a

1987, Dec. 11   Litho.   Perf. 13½
765B A415a 45p multi   1.25 .55

Ramon Freire Serrano (1787-1851), Chief of State A416

To Smoke Is To Contaminate A417

1987, Dec. 29   Perf. 13x13½
766 A416 20p pale lil & rose claret   .40 .30

1987, Dec.   Litho.   Perf. 13½
767 A417 15p blue & ver   .40 .20
Natl. Commission for the Control of Smoking.

No. 699A Surcharged in Green

1987   Litho.   Perf. 13½
768 A376a 12p on 10p buff & brn   .30 .20

Christmas 1987 — A418

1987, Dec.
769 A418 15p ultra, org yel & blk   .30 .20
a.   Bklt. pane of 10   4.00
No. 769a exists ovptd. "D.S. No 20." on back.

No. 697 Surcharged with New Value and 6 Bars in Rose Red and Black

1987, Dec.
770   Block of 4   1.10 .80
a.-d. A375 12p on 10p, #697a-697d   .25 .20
771   Block of 4   1.10 .80
a.-d. A375 15p on 10p, #697a-697d   .25 .20

St. John Bosco (1815-1888), Educator Canonized in 1934 — A419

1988, Jan. 29
772 A419 40p multi   .75 .30

20th Music Week, Frutillar — A420

1988, Jan. 27
773 A420 30p multi   .50 .25

FIDA '88, 5th Intl. Aviation Fair — A421

1988, Mar. 4   Litho.   Perf. 13½
774 A421 60p dark blue & blue   .90 .60

1988 Summer Olympics, Seoul — A422

Flags of Chile and Korea, events: 50p, Shot put, pole vault, javelin. 100p, Swimming, cycling, running.

1988, Mar. 18   Perf. 13½
775 A422 50p multi   1.25 .60
776 A422 100p multi   2.50 1.00
a.   Souv. sheet of 2, #775-776   5.25 5.25
No. 776a sold for 250p.

Natl. Agricultural Soc., 150th Anniv. — A423

1988, Apr. 8
777 A423 45p multi   1.40 .35

Intl. Red Cross and Red Crescent Organizations, 125th Annivs. — A424

1988, May 10
778 A424 150p multi   2.10 .65

No. 645 Surcharged

1988   Litho.   Perf. 13½
779 A344a 20p on 9p green   .25 .20

Easter Island Folk Art — A425

Designs: Nos. 780, 782, Carved wooden head from Kava Kava. Nos. 781, 783, Bird man stone carving from Tangata Manu.

1988, Apr. 1   Litho.   Perf. 13½
780 A425 20p brick red & blk   .30 .20
781 A425 20p brick red & blk   .30 .20
a.   Bklt. pane, 6 #780, 4 #781   3.50
b.   Pair, #780-781   2.00 2.00
782 A425 20p yel & blk   .30 .20
783 A425 20p yel & blk   .30 .20
a.   Bklt. pane, 6 #782, 4 #783   3.50
b.   Pair, #782-783   2.00 2.00
       Nos. 780-783 (4)   1.20 .80

Nos. 782-783 inscribed "D.S. No 20."
For surcharges see Nos. 813-816, 955-956.

Merino, Biplane, Jet Passenger Plane and Supersonic Fighter Plane — A426

1988, May 17   Litho.   Perf. 13½
784 A426 35p multi   .90 .25
Commodore Arturo Merino Benitez (b. 1888), aviation pioneer.

Naval Tradition — A427

Designs: No. 785, Training ship *Esmeralda.* No. 786, Capt. Arturo Pratt, a stained-glass window in the Naval Museum, Valparaiso.

1988, May 23
785 50p multi   .90 .50
786 50p multi   .90 .50
a.   A427 Pair, #785-786   2.25 1.75

Pontifical Catholic University of Chile, Santiago, Cent. — A429

1988, June 21
787 A429 40p Papal & university arms   .90 .25

Locomotives — A430

1988, July 22   Litho.   Perf. 13½
788 A430 60p Esslingen No. 3331   1.00 .70
789 A430 60p North British No. 45   1.00 .70
a.   Souv. sheet, #788-789, imperf   7.00 7.00
b.   Pair, #788-789   2.40 2.40

Arica-La Paz Railway, 75th anniv. (#788); Antofagasta Bolivia Railway, cent. (#789).

Jose Miguel Carrera Natl. Institute, 175th Anniv. — A431

1988, Aug. 10   Litho.   Perf. 13½
790 A431 45p multi   .70 .35

Annexation of Easter Is., Cent. — A432

1988, Sept. 9
791 A432 50p Ship, officer   1.00 .40
792 A432 50p Map, globe   1.00 .40
a.   Pair, #791-792   2.50 1.50
793 A432 100p Easter Is. folk dancers   1.50 .75
794 A432 100p Stone ruins   1.50 .75
a.   Souv. sheet of 4, #791-794, imperf.   7.00 6.50
b.   Pair, #793-794   5.00 3.00
       Nos. 791-794 (4)   5.00 2.30

Miniature Sheet

Flowers — A433

Designs: a, *Chloraea chrysantha*. b, *Lapageria rosea*. c, *Nolana paradoxa*. d, *Rhodophiala advena*. e, *Schizanthus hookeri*. f, *Acacia caven*. g, *Cordia decandra*. h, *Leontochir ovallei*. i, *Alstroemeria pelegrina*. j, *Copiapoa cinerea*. k, *Salpiglossis sinuata*. l, *Leucocoryne coquimbensis*. m, *Eucryphia glutinosa*. n, *Calandrinia longiscapa*. o, *Desfontainia spinosa*. p, *Sophora macrocarpa*.

1988, Aug. 23	**Litho.**	**Perf. 13½**	
795	Sheet of 16	20.00	20.00
a.-p.	A433 30p any single	.85	.40

First Domestic Airmail Route, 1919 — A434

1988, Oct. 11			
796	A434 150p Clodomiro Figueroa Ponce's aircraft	2.25	1.10

Christmas 1988
A435   A436

Children's drawings: 35p, Nativity, by Paulette Thiers, age 8. 100p, Going to church, by Jose M. Lamas, age 9, horiz.

1988, Nov. 17			
797	A435 20p rose lake & org yel	.45	.20
a.	Bklt. pane of 10	6.00	
798	A435 20p rose lake & org yel	.45	.20
a.	Bklt. pane of 10	6.00	
799	A436 35p multi	.65	.20
800	A436 100p multi	1.10	.40
	Nos. 797-800 (4)	2.65	1.00

No. 798 inscribed "D.S. No 20."

Artisans — A437

1988, Oct. 25	**Litho.**	**Perf. 13½**	
801	A437 25p Potter	.70	.20
802	A437 25p Weaver	.70	.20
a.	Pair, #801-802	1.60	1.25

No. 802a has continuous design.

Natl. Philatelic Soc., Cent. — A438

1988, Nov. 24			
803	A438 40p No. 38, cancellation	.60	.20

School Crossing Guards — A439

1988, Oct. 26			
804	A439 45p multi	.60	.25

A440

Battle scenes and: #805, 807, Commanders. #806, 808, Servicemen.

1989, Jan. 12	**Litho.**	**Perf. 13½**	
805	50p Manuel Bulnes (1799-1866)	.85	.40
806	50p Cavalryman	.85	.40
a.	A440 Pair, #805-806	3.00	1.00
807	100p Roberto Simpson	1.60	.85
808	100p Seaman	1.60	.85
a.	A440 Pair, #807-808	3.50	2.10
	Nos. 805-808 (4)	4.90	2.50

Battles of 1839: Yungay (50p) and Casma (100p). Nos. 806a, 808a have continuous designs.

Municipal Annivs. A442

Municipal coats of arms and: 30p, San Ambrosio Church. 35p, Craftsman sculpting marble. 45p, Laja Spring and falls.

1989, Jan. 20			
809	A442 30p multi	.30	.20
810	A442 35p multi	.45	.20
811	A442 45p multi	.50	.20
	Nos. 809-811 (3)	1.25	.60

Founding of Vallenar, 200th anniv. (30p); founding of Combarbala, 200th anniv. (35p); founding of Los Angeles, 250th anniv. (45p).

Nos. 760a-760d and 780-783
Surcharged

a

b

1989, Mar. 20	**Litho.**	**Perf. 13½**	
812	Block of 4	1.25	.75
a.-d.	A411(a) 25p on 15p #760a-760d, any single	.25	.20
813	A425(b) 25p on 20p #780	.25	.20
814	A425(b) 25p on 20p #781	.25	.20
815	A425(b) 25p on 20p #782	.20	.20
816	A425(b) 25p on 20p #783	.20	.20
	Nos. 812-816 (5)	2.15	1.55

Surcharge differs on Nos. 814, 816.
Issued: #812-814, 3/20. #815-816, 11/30.

Women
Beatified — A443

A444

1989, Mar. 21	**Litho.**	**Perf. 13½**	
818	A443 40p Sr. Teresa de Los Andes	.75	.35
819	A443 40p Laura Vicuna	.75	.35
a.	Pair, #818-819	1.75	1.10

No. 819a has continuous design.

1989, Mar. 31			
820	A444 100p Christopher Columbus	1.75	.80
821	A444 100p Galleons	1.75	.80
a.	Pair, #820-821	4.00	3.25
b.	Souvenir sheet of 2, #820-821	7.00	5.25
c.	Souvenir sheet of 2, #820-821	10.50	6.25

EXFINA '89, Santiago. No. 821a has continuous design. No. 821b margin pictures Columbus's coat of arms and the Order of the Great Admiralty, No. 821c margin Nos. 55, 69, 18, 76, 37, 1, 20 and 98.

CORFO Development Corp., 50th Anniv. — A445

1989, Apr. 4			
822	A445 60p Shipping	.60	.30
823	A445 60p Lumber	.60	.30
824	A445 60p Communication	.60	.30
825	A445 60p Coal	.60	.30
a.	Block of 4, #822-825	3.00	2.50

Gabriela Mistral (1889-1957), Poet — A446

1989, Apr. 7	**Litho.**	**Perf. 13½**	
826	A446 30p Poet, steeple	.50	.20
827	A446 30p Poet, children	.50	.20
828	A446 30p Poet working	.50	.20
829	A446 30p Receiving Nobel Prize, 1945	.50	.20
a.	Block of 4, #826-829	3.25	2.00

Exports — A447

#830, 832, Grapes. #831, 833, Apple.

1989, Apr. 19			
830	A447 25p indigo & brt yel grn	.45	.20
831	A447 25p ver & brt yel grn	.45	.20
a.	Bklt. pane, 5 each #830-831	3.50	
b.	Pair, #830-831	2.00	1.00
832	A447 25p indigo & pale yel org	.45	.20
833	A447 25p ver & pale yel org	.45	.20
a.	Bklt. pane, 5 each #832-833	3.50	
b.	Pair, #832-833	2.00	1.00
	Nos. 830-833 (4)	1.80	.80

Nos. 832-833 inscribed "D.S. No 20." See Nos. 861-864, 943-946. For surcharges see Nos. 956B-956C, 1085-1088.

Military Justice Department, 150th Anniv. — A448

1989, Apr. 24	**Litho.**	**Perf. 13½**	
834	A448 50p multicolored	.60	.25

Monument to the Martyrs of Carabineros de Chile — A449

1989, Apr. 26			
835	A449 35p multicolored	.50	.20

Surveyor and Penguins — A450

1989, May 29			
836	A450 150p multi	2.75	1.00

Antarctic Research Institute expeditions, 25th anniv.

Naval Engineers, Cent. — A451

#837, Naval school. #838, Seamen in boiler room. #839, Ship, helicopter, submarine. #840, *Aquiles* launch, Asmar-Talcahuano.

1989, May 31			
837	A451 45p multicolored	.75	.25
838	A451 45p multicolored	.75	.25
839	A451 45p multicolored	.75	.25
840	A451 45p multicolored	.75	.25
a.	Block of 4, #837-840	3.50	3.50

Horse-drawn
Carriage (Victoria),
Vina del Mar — A452

Early transportation: 35p, Launch off Chiloe
Is., vert. 40p, Cart, Cautin. 45p, Ferry, Rio
Palena. 50p, Car transport, Lake Gral, Car-
retta. 60p, Incline railroad, Valparaiso. 100p,
Cable car (funicular), Santiago.

1989-92   Litho.   Perf. 13½
841 A452 30p black & orange   .55   .20
842 A452 60p black & lemon   1.00   .45
843 A452 60p like No. 842   .85   .20
844 A452 100p black & brt yel
                    grn   1.75   .85

1989-91
845 A452 35p black & brt blue   .55   .20
846 A452 40p black & olive   .65   .20
847 A452 45p blk & pale blue
                    grn   .65   .20
  a.   Inscribed "1991"   .65   .20
848 A452 45p black & lt ol grn   .35   .20
849 A452 50p black & scarlet   .45   .20
  a.   Inscribed "1992"   .45   .20
       Nos. 841-849 (9)   6.80 2.70

     Nos. 843, 848 inscribed DS No. 20.
Issued: #841-842, 844, 4/22/89; #848,
2/1/91; #843, 1992; others, 8/1989.
For surcharge see No. 1002.

Export Type of 1989

#861, 863, Grapes. #862, 864, Apple.

1989, May 22
861 A447 5p dark blue & gray   .40   .40
862 A447 5p brt red, dark blue
                    & gray   .40   .40
  a.   Pair, #861-862   .90   .90
863 A447 10p dark blue & gray   .40   .40
864 A447 10p brt red, dark blue
                    & gray   .40   .40
  a.   Pair, #863-864   .90   .90

A453

A454

1989, Aug. 25   Litho.   Perf. 13½
865 A453 250p multicolored   3.50 1.40
  a.   Souvenir sheet of 1   8.00 8.00
     World Stamp Expo '89.

1989, Oct. 12
UPAE emblem and pre-Columbian peoples:
30p, Atacamena potter. 150p, Selk'nam-onas
bow hunter.

866 A454 30p multicolored   .50   .20
867 A454 150p multicolored   2.75   .95

Drawing by Christina Lopez — A455

1989, Nov. 20   Litho.   Perf. 13½
868 A455 100p multicolored   1.40   .45
     Christmas.

Christmas
Ornaments — A456

Nos. 869, 871, Balls. Nos. 870, 872, Bells.

1989
869 A456 25p dull green & org   .45   .20
870 A456 25p dull green & org   .45   .20
  a.   Bklt. pane, 5 each Nos. 869-870 4.50
  b.   Pair, #869-870   1.00   .70
871 A456 25p dull green & ver   .45   .20
872 A456 25p dull green & ver   .45   .20
  a.   Bklt. pane, 5 each Nos. 871-872 4.50
  b.   Pair, #871-872   1.00   .70
       Nos. 869-872 (4)   1.80   .80

Nos. 871-872 inscribed "D.S. No 20."

Miniature Sheet

Wildlife, Natl.
Parks — A457

Designs: a, Vicuna, Lauca Park. b, Chilean
flamingos, Salar de Surire. c, Cactus, La
Chimba Reserve. d, Guanaco, Pan de Azucar
Park. e, Song bird, Father Jorge Park. f, Terns,
Rapa Nui Park. g, Ferret, La Campana Park.
h, Duck, Rio Clarillo Park. i, Cypress tree, Rio
de Los Cipreses Reserve. j, Black-headed
swan, Laguna de Torca Reserve. k, Puma,
Laguna del Laja Park. l, Araucaria tree, Villar-
rica Park. m, Flower, Vicente Perez Rosales
Park. n, Lenga tree, Dos Lagunas. o, Sea lion,
Laguna San Rafael Park. p, Rhea, Torres del
Paine Park.

1990, Jan. 25
873 Sheet of 16   18.00 13.00
  a.-p. A457 35p any single   .65   .20

1990 World Cup Soccer
Championships, Italy — A458

1990, Feb. 23
874 A458 50p Cleated shoe   .60   .25
875 A458 50p Hand   .60   .25
876 A458 50p Soccer ball   .60   .25
877 A458 50p Athlete   .60   .25
  a.   Block of 4, #874-877   3.00 2.40

Natl.
Air
Force
A459

Various aircraft: No. 878, Vickers Wibault.
No. 879, Curtiss O1E Falcon. No. 880, Pitts
S2A. No. 881, Extra 300.

1990, Mar. 16   Litho.   Perf. 13½
878 A459 40p multicolored   .70   .20
879 A459 40p multicolored   .70   .20
880 A459 40p multicolored   .70   .20
881 A459 40p multicolored   .70   .20
  a.   Souvenir sheet of 4, #878-881 3.50 2.00
       Nos. 878-881 (4)   2.80   .80
                 FIDAE '90.

Discovery of America 500th Anniv. (in
1992) — A460

Maps and 16th cent. men: No. 882, Incan.
No. 883, Spanish infantryman.

1990, Apr. 20   Litho.   Perf. 13½
882 60p multicolored   1.00   .20
883 60p multicolored   1.00   .20
  a.   A460 Pair, #882-883   4.00 3.00

Port
Cities
A462

1990, Apr. 27
884 A462 40p Valparaiso   .60   .20
885 A462 40p San Vicente   .60   .20
  a.   Pair, #884-885   1.60 1.25

Democracy — A463

1990, June 8   Litho.   Perf. 13½
886 A463 20p Sunrise   .20   .20
887 A463 30p Peace dove   .55   .20
888 A463 60p Pleasure   .90   .40
889 A463 100p Star   1.60   .75
  a.   Souvenir sheet of 4, #886-889 6.25 6.25
       Nos. 886-889 (4)   3.25 1.55

Equality — A464

1990, June 8
890 A464 45p multicolored   .60   .30
  a.   Souvenir sheet   2.50 2.50
     No. 890a margin continues the design.

Naval Tradition — A465

#891, Transport ship Piloto Pardo. #892,
Oceanographic research ship Yelcho.

1990, May 30   Litho.   Perf. 13½
891 A465 50p multicolored   .60   .20
892 A465 50p multicolored   .60   .20
  a.   Pair, #891-892   1.40 1.00

A466

A467

1990, June 12
893 A466 250p Sir Rowland Hill   3.50 1.25
  a.   Souvenir sheet of 1   6.00 4.50
     Penny Black, 150th anniv.
No. 893a margin continues the design.

1990, June 21
894 A467 150p multicolored   1.75   .75
Organization of American States, cent.

Marine Resources — A468

Designs: a, Scallop. b, Clam. c, Swordfish.
d, Crab. e, Fish. f, Baiting, processing.

1990, July 27   Litho.   Perf. 13½
895 Block of 6   4.00 3.00
  a.-f. A468 40p any single   .40   .20

Curimon
Convent
A469

1990, Aug. 1
896 A469 50p multicolored   .60   .20
     250th anniversary of San Felipe.

Environmental
Protection — A470

1990, Sept. 1   Litho.   Perf. 13½
897 A470 35p Aerosol propel-
                    lants   .35   .20
898 A470 35p Deforestation   .35   .20
899 A470 35p Smokestacks   .35   .20
900 A470 35p Oil slick, shore   .35   .20
901 A470 35p Forest fire   .35   .20
  a.   Strip of 5, #897-901   2.25 1.25
  b.   Bklt. pane, 2 each #897-901 7.25

     Inscribed "D.S. No 20"

902 A470 35p Aerosol propel-
                    lants   .35   .20
903 A470 35p Deforestation   .35   .20
904 A470 35p Smokestacks   .35   .20
905 A470 35p Oil slick, shore   .35   .20
906 A470 35p Forest fire   .35   .20
  a.   Strip of 5, #902-906   2.25 1.25
  b.   Bklt. pane, 2 each #902-906 7.25
       Nos. 897-906 (10)   3.50 2.00

     See Nos. 988-997.

Presidents of Chile — A471

1990, Sept. 4

912	A471	35p Salvador Allende	.35	.20
913	A471	35p Eduardo Frei	.35	.20
914	A471	40p Jorge Alessandri	.50	.20
a.		Inscribed "1992"	.50	.20
915	A471	45p Gabriel Gonzalez V	.55	.20
916	A471	50p Juan Antonio Rios	.65	.35
917	A471	60p Pedro Aguirre Cerda	.70	.40
918	A471	70p Juan E. Montero	.85	.40
a.		Inscribed "1992"	.85	.40
919	A471	80p Carlos Ibanez	1.00	.50
920	A471	90p Emiliano Figueroa	1.10	.55
a.		Inscribed "1992"	1.10	.55
921	A471	100p Arturo Alessandri	1.25	.65
a.		Inscribed "1992"	1.75	.90
		Nos. 912-921 (10)	7.30	3.65

Rodeos — A472

Designs: a, Rodeo ring. b, Men on horses. c, Man stopping horse. d, Men, horses, bull.

1990, Sept. 24

926		Block of 4	2.75	2.00
a.-d.	A472 45p any single	.45	.20

Discovery of America, 500th Anniv. (in 1992) — A473

1990, Oct. 12   Litho.   Perf. 13½

927	A473	30p Phoenicopterus chilensis	.75	.20
928	A473	150p Arctocephalus australis	3.75	.85

King and Queen of Spain's Visit — A474

#930, Arms of King Juan Carlos I, Chilean Arms.

1990, Oct. 18

929	A474	100p shown	1.25	.60
930	A474	100p Denomination at LR	1.25	.60
a.		Pair, #929-930	3.25	2.25

Malleco Bridge, Cent. — A475

Design: #932, Boy waving at train on bridge.

1990, Oct. 26   Litho.   Perf. 13½

931	A475	60p multicolored	1.25	.55
932	A475	60p multicolored	1.25	.55
a.		Pair, #931-932	3.00	2.10

Chilean Antarctic Territorial Claims, 50th Anniv. — A476

Design: #934, Penguins, helicopter, camp.

1990, Nov. 6   Perf. 13½

933	A476	250p multicolored	2.75	1.40
934	A476	250p multicolored	2.75	1.40
a.		Souvenir sheet of 2, #933-934	12.00	12.00

A477

Christmas — A478

1990, Nov. 20   Litho.   Perf. 13½

935	A477	35p lt green & bl grn	.45	.20
a.		Booklet pane of 10	3.50	
936	A477	35p dull org & bl grn	.30	.20
a.		Booklet pane of 10	3.50	
937	A478	35p shown	.65	.20
938	A478	150p Underwater dwelling	2.75	1.50
		Nos. 935-938 (4)	4.15	2.10

No. 936 inscribed "D.S. No.20."

National Congress — A479

1990, Dec. 21   Litho.   Perf. 13½

939	A479	100p Congress chamber	1.25	.55
940	A479	100p Early congressional session	1.25	.55
a.		Pair, #939-940	2.75	1.75

City of Santiago, 450th Anniv. — A480

1991, Feb. 7

941	A480	100p Colorado House	1.25	.55
942	A480	100p Skyline	1.25	.55
a.		Pair, #941-942	4.00	2.50
b.		Souvenir sheet of 2, #941-942	5.00	5.00

Exports Type of 1989

Nos. 943, 945, Grapes. Nos. 944, 946, Apple.

1991, Feb. 8   Perf. 13½ on 3 Sides

943	A447	45p indigo & brt pink	.50	.20
944	A447	45p ver & brt pink	.50	.20
a.		Bklt. pane, 5 each #943-944	8.25	
945	A447	45p indigo & yel	.50	.20
946	A447	45p ver & yel	.50	.20
a.		Bklt. pane, 5 each #945-946	8.25	
		Nos. 943-946 (4)	2.00	.80

Nos. 945-946 inscribed "D.S. No.20." For surcharges see Nos. 1085-1088.

Historical Aircraft — A481

Designs: a, Voisin. b, S.E. 5a. c, Morane Saulnier MS 35. d, Consolidated PBY-5A/OA-10 Catalina. Illustration reduced.

1991, Mar. 21   Litho.   Perf. 13½

947	A481	150p Block of 4, #a.-d.	7.25	4.50

American Soccer Cup, Chile — A482

1991, Apr. 12   Litho.   Perf. 13½

948	A482	100p shown	1.10	.40
949	A482	100p Ball, goalie	1.10	.40
a.		Pair, #948-949	2.25	1.00

Coal Mining A483

Design: #951, Miners dumping cart of coal.

1991, Apr. 18

950	A483	200p shown	2.00	.95
951	A483	200p multicolored	2.00	.95
a.		Pair, #950-951	4.50	3.00

Cultural Art — A484

Design: #953, Small sculptures, spurs, dish.

1991, Apr. 29

952	A484	90p shown	1.00	.50
953	A484	90p multicolored	1.00	.50
a.		Pair, #952-953	2.25	1.40

Chilean Scientific Society, Cent. — A485

1991, Apr. 29

954	A485	45p blue grn & blk	.50	.20

Nos. 782-783 Surcharged

a

b

1991, Apr. 30

955	A425(a)	45p on 20p, #782	.30	.20
956	A425(b)	45p on 20p, #783	.30	.20
a.		Pair, #955-956	1.00	.75

Nos. 832-833 Surcharged

1991, May 6   Litho.   Perf. 13½

956B	A447	45p on 25p, #832	.70	.20
956C	A447	45p on 25p, #833	.70	.20
d.		Pair, #956B-956C	1.60	1.10

Santiago Cathedral A486

1991, May 9   Litho & Engr.

957	A486	300p red brn, sal & blk	3.75	1.75

World Telecommunications Day — A487

1991, May 17   Litho.

958	A487	90p multicolored	1.00	.30

A488   A489

1991, May 23

959	A488	100p Pope Leo XIII	1.00	.40

Rerum Novarum Encyclical, cent.

1991, May 28   Litho.   Perf. 13½

Rescue of Shackleton Expedition, 75th anniv.: a, Lt. Luis Pardo, Sir Ernest Shackleton. b, Rescue ship, Yelcho. c, Sailor pointing to survivors. d, Shackleton's ship, Endurance.

960	A489	50p Block of 4, #a.-d.	2.00	1.50
e.		Miniature sheet, #960	2.50	2.50

21st General Assembly of Organization of American States, Santiago — A490

1991, June 5

961	A490	70p multicolored	.70	.25

New Carabinero School — A491

1991, June 12
962 A491 50p multicolored   .60   .20

Natl. Merchant Marine Day — A492

1991, June 26
963 A492 45p black & red   .60   .20

11th Pan American Games, Havana — A493

1991, July 23
964 A493 100p Runners, torch, flags   .90   .35
965 A493 100p Cycling, running, basketball   .90   .35
a.   Pair, #964-965   2.25 1.60

Founding of the City of Los Andes, Bicent. — A494

1991, July 29
966 A494 100p multicolored   1.25   .40

Miniature Sheet

Marine Life — A495

Designs: No. 967a, Octopus vulgaris. b, Durvillaea antarctica. c, Paralichthys adspersus. d, Austromegabalanus psittacus. e, Concholepas concholepas. f, Cancer setosus. g, Lessonia nigrescens. h, Loxechinus albus. i, Homalaspis plana. j, Porphyra columbina. k, Oplegnathus insignis. l, Chorus giganteus. m, Rhynchocinetes typus. n, Engraulis ringens. o, Gracilaria spp. p, Pyura chilensis.

1991, Aug. 20   Litho.   Perf. 13½
967   Sheet of 16   16.00 7.50
a.-p.   A495 50p any single   .90   .20

1891 Revolution, Cent. — A496

Jose M. Balmaceda (1840-1891) and: No. 968, Machinery. No. 969, Teacher, students at Valentin Letelier School of Medicine.

1991, Aug. 29
968 A496 100p multicolored   1.00   .45
969 A496 100p multicolored   1.00   .45
a.   Pair, #968-969   2.25 1.25

Chilean Art — A497

Paintings: 50p, Woman in Red, by Pedro Reszka. 70p, The Traveler, by Camilo Mori. 200p, Head of Child, by Benito Rebolledo. 300p, Boy Wearing a Fez, by A. Valenzuela Puelma.

1991, Sept. 26
970 A497 50p multicolored   .60   .20
971 A497 70p multicolored   .60   .30
972 A497 200p multicolored   2.40   .85
973 A497 300p multicolored   3.50 1.25
      Nos. 970-973 (4)   7.10 2.60

Antarctic Treaty, 30th Anniv. — A498

1991, Oct. 7   Litho.   Perf. 13½
974 A498 80p shown   1.75   .70
975 A498 80p Birds, sea life   1.75   .70
a.   Pair, #974-975   4.50 1.60

Intl. Letter Writing Week A499

1991, Oct. 9
976 A499 45p shown   .45   .20
977 A499 70p Envelope filled with people   .70   .30

America Issue — A500

UPAEP emblem, sailing ships and: 150p, Navigator.

1991, Oct. 14
978 A500 50p multicolored   .75   .20
979 A500 150p multicolored   2.10   .75

A501

A502

1991, Oct. 21
980 A501 45p blue hat   .45   .20
981 A501 45p red hat   .45   .20
a.   Pair, #980-981   1.50   .75
b.   Souvenir sheet of 2, #980-981   2.75 2.75

Pablo Neruda, (1904-1973), Nobel Prize winner for literature, 1971. Nos. 981a has a continuous design.

1991, Nov. 4
982 A502 45p Boy with stars   .50   .20
983 A502 100p Girl with stars   1.00   .50
      Christmas.

Christmas
A503   A504

1991, Nov. 18   Litho.   Perf. 13½
984 A503 45p violet & brt pink   .45   .20
985 A504 45p violet & brt pink   .45   .20
a.   Pair, #984-985   1.10   .20
b.   Bklt. pane of 5 #985a   7.00
986 A503 45p violet & brt pink   .45   .20
987 A504 45p violet & brt pink   .45   .20
a.   Pair, #986-987   1.10   .20
b.   Bklt. pane of 5 #987a   7.00
      Nos. 984-987 (4)   1.80   .80

Nos. 986-987 inscribed "D.S. No. 20." For surcharges see Nos. 1016-1019.

Environmental Protection Type of 1990
1992, Jan. 28   Litho.   Perf. 13½
Lemon & Black
988 A470 60p like #897   .55   .20
989 A470 60p like #898   .55   .20
990 A470 60p like #899   .55   .20
991 A470 60p like #900   .55   .20
992 A470 60p like #901   .55   .20
a.   Strip of 5, #988-992   4.00 2.50
b.   Bklt. pane, 2 each #988-992   8.00

Inscribed "D.S. No. 20"
Orange & Dark Green
993 A470 60p like #902   .55   .20
994 A470 60p like #903   .55   .20
995 A470 60p like #904   .55   .20
996 A470 60p like #905   .55   .20
997 A470 60p like #906   .55   .20
a.   Strip of 5, #993-997   4.00 2.50
b.   Bklt. pane, 2 each #993-997   8.00
      Nos. 988-997 (10)   5.50 2.00

Wolfgang Amadeus Mozart, Death Bicent. (in 1991) — A505

1992, Jan. 31
998 A505 60p shown   .60   .20
999 A505 200p Hands at piano   1.75   .90
a.   Sheet of 2, #998-999   4.00 4.00

FIDAE '92, Intl. Air and Space Fair — A506

1992, Mar. 5   Litho.   Perf. 13½
1000 A506 60p multicolored   .60   .20

16th Population and Housing Census A507

1992, Mar.
1001 A507 60p multicolored   .60   .20

No. 847 Surcharged in Red Brown

1992, Mar.
1002 A452 60p on 45p   .60   .20

Chilean Cities — A508

Cities' coat of arms and: 80p, Church of San Jose de Maipo. 90p, People making pottery. 100p, Lircunlauta House. 150p, Wine and lumber industries. 250p, Huilquilemu cultural center. Illustration reduced.

1992, Apr. 10   Litho.   Perf. 13½
1003 A508 80p multicolored   .65   .25
1004 A508 90p multicolored   .75   .35
1005 A508 100p multicolored   .95   .35
1006 A508 150p multicolored   1.50   .50
1007 A508 250p multicolored   2.40   .80
      Nos. 1003-1007 (5)   6.25 2.15

80p, San Jose de Maipo, 200th anniv. 90p, Melipilla, 250th anniv. 100p, San Fernando, 250th anniv. 150p, Cauquenes, 250th anniv. 250p, Talca, 250th anniv.

Expo '92, Seville A509

1992, Apr. 23
1008 A509 150p Pavilion   1.40   .50
1009 A509 200p Iceberg   2.00   .65
a.   Sheet of 2, #1008-1009   4.50 4.50

A510

Easter Island — A511

Marine life: No. 1010a, Morula praecipua, Strombus maculatus, Cypraea caputdraconis. b, Codium pocockiae. c, Myripristis tiki. d, Sargassum skottsbergii. e, Pseudolabrus fuentesi. f, Pocillopora danae. g, Panulirus pascuensis. h, Tripneustes gratilla.
No. 1011b, Natives, airplane, petroglyph.

1992, June 9   Litho.   Perf. 13½
1010 A510 60p Sheet of 8,
     #a.-h.   5.00 2.75
1011 A511 200p Pair, #a.-b.   4.00 1.50

Natl. Council of the Disabled — A512

Military Chiefs of Staff, 50th Anniv. — A513

1992, June 23
1012 A512 60p multicolored   .60   .20

1992, July 3
1013 A513 60p multicolored   .60   .20

Submarine Forces, 75th Anniv. — A514

Coat of arms and: 250p, Officer using periscope, control room.

1992, July 4
1014 A514 150p multicolored   1.50 .50
1015 A514 250p multicolored   2.25 .90

Nos. 984-987 Surcharged
1992, Aug. 11   Litho.   Perf. 13½
1016 A503 60p on 45p No. 984   .45   .20
1017 A504 60p on 45p No. 985   .45   .20
   a.   Pair, #1016-1017   1.90 .90
1018 A503 60p on 45p No. 986   .45   .20
1019 A504 60p on 45p No. 987   .45   .20
   a.   Pair, #1018-1019   1.90 .90
        Nos. 1016-1019 (4)   1.80 .80

Nos. 1018-1019 inscribed "D.S. No. 20."

Emperor Penguins — A515

1992, Sept. 28   Litho.   Perf. 13½
1020 A515 200p shown   1.00 .75
1021 A515 250p Adults with
             young   2.40 1.00
   a.   Souv. sheet of 2, #1020-1021 6.25 6.25

Central Post Office, Santiago, 1772 — A516

1992, Oct. 9
1022 A516 200p multicolored   1.75 .70

Discovery of America, 500th Anniv. — A517

UPAEP emblem and: 200p, Calendar stone, astrolabe, Columbus. 250p, Church, map of Central and South America, sailing ship.

1992, Oct. 20
1023 A517 200p multicolored   1.75 .65
1024 A517 250p multicolored   2.25 .75

Radio Chile, 75th Anniv. — A518

Bernardo O'Higgins (1778-1842) A519

1992, Oct. 22
1025 A518 250p multicolored   2.00 .80

1992, Oct. 23
1026 A519 60p multicolored   .60   .20

Claudio Arrau, Pianist — A520

1992, Nov. 12   Litho.   Perf. 13½
1027 A520 150p As child   1.25 .55
1028 A520 200p As adult   1.60 .75
   a.   Souv. sheet of 2, #1027-1028 3.50 3.50

Natl. Human Rights Day — A521

1992, Dec. 10
1029 A521 100p multicolored   .80   .40
   a.   Souvenir sheet of 1   1.50 1.50

Christmas — A522

Designs: Nos. 1030, 1032, Denomination at LR. Nos. 1031, 1033, Denomination at LL.

1992, Dec. 12   Litho.   Perf. 13½
1030 A522 60p buff & brown   .45   .20
1031 A522 60p buff & brown   .45   .20
   a.   Pair, #1030-1031   1.00 .45
   b.   Booklet pane of 5 #1031a 4.50 4.50
1032 A522 60p buff & red   .45   .20
1033 A522 60p buff & red   .45   .20
   a.   Pair, #1032-1033   1.00 .45
   b.   Booklet pane of 5 #1033a 4.50
        Nos. 1030-1033 (4)   1.80 .80

Nos. 1032-1033 inscribed "DS/20."

A523

A524

University of Chile, 150th Anniv.: a, Statue. b, Coat of arms, facade of building.

1992, Nov. 19   Litho.   Perf. 13½
1034 A523 200p Pair, #a.-b.   3.00 1.25
   c.   Souvenir sheet of 1, #1034 4.00 4.00

Nos. 1034a-1034b have a continuous design.

1992, Dec. 12
1035 A524 70p black & yellow   .60   .25

23rd meeting of Latin American Energy Ministers.

Churches of Chiloe — A525

#1036, 1038, Achao. #1037, 1039, Castro.

1993, Mar. 1   Litho.   Perf. 13½
1036 A525 70p black & pink   .70   .55
1037 A525 70p black & pink   .70   .55
   a.   Pair #1036-1037   1.50 1.50
   b.   Booklet pane of 5 #1037a 7.50

        Inscribed "DS/20"
1038 A525 70p black & yellow   .70   .55
1039 A525 70p black & yellow   .70   .55
   a.   Pair, #1038-1039   1.50 1.50
   b.   Booklet pane of 5 #1039a 7.50
        Nos. 1036-1039 (4)   2.80 2.20

See Nos. 1053-1060, 1093-1098.
For surcharges see Nos. 1129-1130.

Arrival of the Jesuits, 400th Anniv. — A526

Canonization of St. Teresa of the Andes, 1993 — A527

1993   Litho.   Perf. 13½
1040 A526 200p St. Ignatius of
             Loyola   1.50 .60
   a.   Souvenir sheet of 1   2.50 2.50
1041 A527 300p St. Teresa of the
             Andes   2.50 1.00

Issue dates: 200p, Mar. 15; 300p, Mar. 31. No. 1040a sold for 250p.

World Festival of Theatre of the Nations — A528

Second Space Conference of the Americas — A529

Clotario Blest
(1899-1990),
Syndicalist
A530

1993, Apr. 22
1042 A528 250p multicolored 2.00 .75

1993, Apr. 26
1043 A529 150p multicolored 1.50 .75
  a. Souvenir sheet of 1 3.25 3.25

No. 1043a sold for 350p.

1993, Apr. 30
1044 A530 70p multicolored .60 .20

Intl. Labor Day.

Vicente Huidobro,
Poet (1893-1948)
A531

1993, May 19 Litho. Perf. 13½
1045 A531 100p shown .80 .40
1046 A531 100p Portrait, seated .80 .40
  a. Pair, #1045-1046 1.75 1.10

Antique Fire Engines — A532

#1047, 1902 Watterous Engineering Co.
Ltd., Canada. #1048, 1872 Merryweather,
England.

1993, June 30 Litho. Perf. 13½
1047 A532 100p multicolored 1.10 .40
1048 A532 100p multicolored 1.10 .40
  a. Souv. sheet of 2, #1047-1048 3.50 3.50

No. 1048a sold for 400p.

Aircraft — A533

Designs: No. 1049, Douglas B-26 Invader.
No. 1050, Mirage M50 Panther. No. 1051,
Sanchez Besa. No. 1052, Bell 47D1
helicopter.

1993, July 13
1049 A533 100p multicolored .65 .35
1050 A533 100p multicolored .65 .35
1051 A533 100p multicolored .65 .35
1052 A533 100p multicolored .65 .35
  a. Block of 4, #1049-1052 3.50 3.00

Church Type of 1993

Designs: 10p, Chonchi. 20p, Vilupulli. 30p,
Llau-llao. 40p, Dalcahue. 50p, Tenaun. 80p,
Quinchao. 90p, Quehui. 100p, Nercon.

1993, July Litho. Perf. 13½
1053 A525 10p green & black .20 .20
1054 A525 20p black & brown .20 .20
1055 A525 30p black & vermilion .20 .20
1056 A525 40p black & blue .30 .30
1057 A525 50p black & green
  blue .35 .35

1058 A525 80p black & buff .55 .55
  a. Booklet pane of 10 8.25
  b. Inscribed "1994" .60 .60
1059 A525 90p olive & black .60 .60
  a. Booklet pane of 10 8.25
  Complete booklet, #1059a 8.25
1060 A525 100p gray vio & blk .65 .65
  a. Booklet pane of 10 8.25
  Nos. 1053-1060 (8) 3.05 3.05

Issued: #1058a, 1/1/94; #1059a, 1995;
#1060a, 2/1/96.
See No. 1093 for 80p black and violet.

Natl. Dance, "La
Cueca" — A534

Paintings — A535

1993, Sept. 15 Litho. Perf. 13½
1061 A534 70p Cueca chilota .60 .20
1062 A534 70p Cueca central .60 .20
1063 A534 70p Cueca nortina .60 .20
  Nos. 1061-1063 (3) 1.80 .60

1993, Sept. 28

Designs: 80p, Tarde Amanecer, by Mario
Carreno, horiz. 90p, Summer, by Gracia Bar-
rios, horiz. 150p, Figura Protegida, by Roser
Bru. 200p, Tangueria-Valparaiso, by Nemesio
Antunez, horiz.

1064 A535 80p multicolored .55 .25
1065 A535 90p multicolored .60 .25
1066 A535 150p multicolored 1.00 .40
1067 A535 200p multicolored 1.40 .55
  Nos. 1064-1067 (4) 3.55 1.45

Chilean Mint,
250th Anniv.
A536

1993, Oct. 7 Litho. & Engr.
1068 A536 250p multicolored 2.40 .95
  a. Souvenir sheet of 1 3.50 3.50

A537

A538

1993, Oct. 19 Litho.
1069 A537 80p multicolored .70 .25
Urban transportation system, 25th anniv.

1993, Oct. 12 Litho. Perf. 13½
1070 A538 150p Cyanoliseus
  patagonus 1.40 .55
1071 A538 200p Hippocamelus
  bisulcus 2.00 .75
America issue.

Chilean Possession of Straits of
Magellan, 150th Anniv. — A539

1993, Oct. 21
1072 A539 100p multicolored 3.50 .35

Naval Anniversaries — A540

1993, Oct. 27
1073 A540 80p Sailing ships .75 .30
1074 A540 80p Schooner .75 .30
1075 A540 80p Assault ship .75 .30
1076 A540 80p Patrol boat .75 .30
  Nos. 1073-1076 (4) 3.00 1.20

Sailing of first naval squadron (#1073),
Arturo Prat Naval Academy (#1074), Marine
Corps (#1075), 175th anniversaries. Alejandro
Navarette School for Cadets (#1076), 125th
anniv.

Intl. Year of Indigenous
Peoples — A541

1993, Nov. 24
1077 A541 100p multicolored .90 .40

Christmas
A542

Pygoscelis Adelie
A543

1993, Dec. 1 Litho. Perf. 13½
1078 A542 70p tan & violet .55 .20
  a. Booklet pane of 10 6.00
1079 A542 70p green & blue .65 .20
  a. Booklet pane of 10 7.00

No. 1079 inscribed "DS/20."
For surcharge see No. 1131.

1993, Dec. 3
1080 A543 200p Nesting 1.60 .60
1081 A543 250p Adult, chicks 2.00 .80
  a. Souv. sheet of 2, #1080-1081,
  imperf. 4.75 4.75

Chilean Antarctica.
No. 1081a has simulated perfs.

Chilean Cities — A544

1993, Dec. 15
1082 A544 80p Rancagua .70 .20
1083 A544 80p Curico .70 .20
1084 A544 80p Ancud .70 .20
  Nos. 1082-1084 (3) 2.10 .60

Rancagua and Curico, 250th anniv. Ancud,
225th anniv.

Nos. 943-946
Surcharged

1993 Litho. Perf. 13½ on 3 Sides
1085 A447 60p on 45p, #943 .35 .20
1086 A447 60p on 45p, #944 .35 .20
  a. Bklt. pane, 5 each #1085-1086 3.50
1087 A447 60p on 45p, #945 .35 .20
1088 A447 60p on 45p, #946 .35 .20
  a. Bklt. pane, 5 each #1087-1088 3.50
  Nos. 1085-1088 (4) 1.40 .80

Nos. 1087-1088 inscribed "D.S. No. 20."

Intl. Year of the
Family — A545

1994, Jan. 17 Litho. Perf. 13½
1089 A545 100p multicolored .70 .25

Musical Instruments — A546

Designs: a, Violin. b, Cello.

1994, Jan. 27 Litho. Perf. 13½
1091 A546 150p Pair, #a.-b. 3.25 3.25

No. 1091 has a continuous design.

Church Type of 1993

Designs: 80p, Quinchao. 90p, Quehui.
#1097, 1098, Nercon.

1994-96 Litho. Perf. 13½
1093 A525 80p black & violet .50 .25
1095 A525 90p red & black .50 .25
  a. Booklet pane of 10 4.75
  Complete booklet, #1095a 4.75
1097 A525 100p yellow & black .55 .30
  a. Booklet pane of 10 6.00
  Complete booklet, #1097a 6.00

1098	A525 100p gray vio & blk	.60	.30
a.	Booklet pane of 10	6.50	
	Complete booklet, #1098a	6.50	
	Nos. 1093-1098 (4)	2.15	1.10

Issued: 80p, 1/1/94; 90p, 1995; #1097-1098, 2/1/96.
Nos. 1093, 1095, 1097 inscribed "DS/20."
This is an expanding set. Numbers may change.

Souvenir Sheet

Natl. Aviation Museum, 50th
Anniv. — A547

Aircraft: a, Sukhoi SU-30 Flanker. b, Vought-Sikorsky OS-2U3 Kingfisher. c, Lockheed F-117A Nighthawk. d, Northrop F-5E Tiger III.

1994, Mar. 17   Litho.   Perf. 13

1102	A547 300p Sheet of 4, #a.-d. + 2 labels	9.00	5.50

Intl. Air and Space Fair, FIDAE '94.
See No. 1159.

College of
Agronomy, 50th
Anniv. — A548

1994, Apr. 28   Litho.   Perf. 13

1103	A548 220p multicolored	1.50	.75

No. 760 Surcharged

1994, May 1   Litho.   Perf. 13½

1104	Block of 4	2.75	1.50
a.-d.	A411 80p on 15p any single	.60	.20

Concepcion University, 75th
Anniv. — A549

Sections of mural, by Jorge Gonzalez Camarena: No. 1105, Cactus plant, skeletons. No. 1106, Flags, pillars, nude woman, faces. No. 1107, Flags, bodies, woman, soldier in armor. No. 1108, Women's faces, pipelines.

1994, May 14   Litho.   Perf. 13

1105	A549 250p multicolored	1.75	.75
1106	A549 250p multicolored	1.75	.75
1107	A549 250p multicolored	1.75	.75
1108	A549 250p multicolored	1.75	.75
a.	Strip of 4, #1105-1108 + label	7.50	5.00

No. 1108a is a continuous design.

Chilean Antarctic Institute, 30th
Anniv. — A550

Designs: No. 1109, Penguins, buildings. No. 1110, Buildings, coastal waters.

1994, May 31   Perf. 13

1109	A550 300p multicolored	2.00	1.10
1110	A550 300p multicolored	2.00	1.10
a.	Pair, #1109-1110	4.50	2.50

No. 1110a is a continuous design.

Antique Fire Engines — A551

#1111, Merryweather steam pumper, England, 1869. #1112, Western lever pumper, US, 1863. #1113, Mieusset steam pumper, France, 1905. #1114, Merryweather pumper, England, 1903.

1994, July 19   Litho.   Perf. 13

1111	A551 150p multicolored	.90	.50
1112	A551 150p multicolored	.90	.50
1113	A551 150p multicolored	.90	.50
1114	A551 150p multicolored	.90	.50
a.	Block of 4, #1111-1114	4.50	3.50

Javiera Carrera Girls' School,
Cent. — A552

1994, Aug. 10

1115	A552 200p multicolored	1.25	.60

Arms, Sights from Chilean
Cities — A553

Designs: 90p, Porvenir, cent. 100p, Villa Alemana, cent. 150p, Constitucion, bicent. 200p, Linares, bicent. 250p, Copiapo, 250th anniv. 300p, La Serena, 450th anniv.

1994, Aug. 26

1116	A553 90p multicolored	.50	.20
1117	A553 100p multicolored	.60	.30
1118	A553 150p multicolored	.95	.40
1119	A553 200p multicolored	1.40	.55
1120	A553 250p multicolored	1.75	.65
1121	A553 300p multicolored	2.00	.85
	Nos. 1116-1121 (6)	7.20	2.95

Miniature Sheet of 8

Butterflies — A554

Designs: a, Vanessa terpsichore. b, Hypsochila wagenknechti. c, Battus polydamas. d, Polythysana apollina. e, Satyridae. f,

Tetraphloebia stellygera. g, Eroessa chilensis. h, Phoebis sennae.

1994, June 24   Litho.   Perf. 13

1122	A554 100p #a.-h.	9.00	9.00

20th Intl.
Conference on
Data
Bases — A555

1994, Sept. 21   Litho.   Perf. 13½

1123	A555 100p multicolored	.60	.30

America Issue — A556

Early postal transport vehicles: 80p, Van. 220p, DH-60-G, Gypsy Moth.

1994, Oct. 12

1124	A556 80p multicolored	.65	.30
1125	A556 220p multicolored	1.60	.70

A557

1994, Oct. 31   Litho. & Engr.

1126	A557 300p multicolored	2.00	1.00

Beatification of Father Alberto Hurtado.

1994   Litho.   Perf. 13½

1127	A558 80p multicolored	.60	.25
a.	Booklet pane of 10	6.00	
	Complete booklet, #1127a	6.00	

Inscribed "DS/20"

1128	A558 80p multicolored	.60	.25
a.	Booklet pane of 10	7.00	
	Complete booklet, #1128a	7.00	

Christmas.

Nos. 1036-1037, 1079 Surcharged

Perf. 13½ on 3 Sides

1994, Nov. 4   Litho.

1129	A525 80p on 70p #1036	.45	.25
1130	A525 80p on 70p #1037	.45	.25
a.	Pair, #1129-1130	.90	.50
b.	Booklet pane, 5 #1130a	7.00	
	Complete booklet, #1130b	7.00	

A558

1131	A542 80p on 70p #1079	.45	.25
a.	Booklet pane, 10 #1131	7.00	
	Complete booklet, #1131a	7.00	

Size and location of surcharge varies.

Miniature Sheet

Intl. Women's Day — A559

Designs: a, Star, "Women enriching the future." b, Moon, sun, "Women bringing harmony." c, Bird, "Women bringing peace." d, Earth, "Women changing the world."

1995, Mar. 8   Litho.   Perf. 13½

1132	A559 90p Sheet of 4, #a.-d.	5.00	2.50

Ancud Seminary
of Conciliation,
150th
Anniv. — A560

1995, Apr. 27

1133	A560 200p multicolored	1.25	.60

Destroyer
Admiral
Williams
A561

1995, Apr. 21

1134	A561 100p multicolored	.70	.30

World Conference
on Social
Development
A562

1995, Apr. 25

1135	A562 150p multicolored	1.00	.45

Order of St. Augustine in Chile, 400th
Anniv. — A563

Stained glass, Cathedral of Santiago.

1995, Apr. 28

1136	A563 250p multicolored	1.60	.75

Petroglyphs — A564

Designs: a, Ceremonial mask, Buitre, Limari Province. b, Lamas, Taira Sector, El Loa Province. c, Harpooned whale, El Medano, Taltal Province. d, Two masks, Encanto, Ovalle.

1995, June 16   Litho.   Perf. 13½
1137 A564 150p Block of 4, #a.-
      d.   6.25 6.25

Miniature Sheet

Motion Pictures, Cent. — A565

Posters: a, Director's chair, camera. b, Charlie Chaplin in "The Kid." c, Lumiere brothers' 1895 Cinematographe. d, "Valparaiso, My Love", with Aldo Francia.

1995, June 21
1138 A565 100p Sheet of 4, #a.-
      d.   6.25 3.00

City of Parral, Bicent. A566

1995, June 30   Litho.   Perf. 13½
1139 A566 200p multicolored   1.60 .85

Miniature Sheet

Insects and Cacti — A567

a, Cheloderus childreni. b, Eulychnia acida. c, Chiasognathus grantii. d, Browningia candelaris. e, Copiapoa dealbata. f, Acanthinodera cummingi. g, Neoporteria subgibbosa. h, Semiotus luteipennis.

1995, Aug. 10   Litho.   Perf. 13½
1140 A567 100p Sheet of 8,
      #a.-h.   10.00 7.50

2nd World Congress of Police, Santiago — A568

1995, Oct. 2
1141 A568 200p multicolored   1.60 .80

Ministry of Housing and Urban Development, 30th Anniv. — A569

Design: Tower of Babel V, by Mario Toral.

1995, Oct. 5   Litho.   Perf. 13½
1142 A569 200p multicolored   1.60 .85

Andres Bello (1781-1865), Scholar, Author A570

1995, Oct. 9   Litho. & Engr.
1143 A570 250p dk brn & blk   1.75 .85
Andres Bello Convenant, 25th anniv.

UNESCO, UN, FAO, 50th Anniv. — A571

Designs: a, Hands holding book, UNESCO emblem. b, Hands clasped between two globes, UN emblem. c, Hand holding seedling, FAO emblem.

1995, Oct. 10   Litho.   Perf. 13½
1144 A571 100p Strip of 3, #a.-c. 2.75 1.40
No. 1144 is a continuous design.

America Issue — A572

Children's drawings of environmental protection: 100p, Family in garden, trees, vert. 250p, Three people working with trees.

1995, Oct. 12   Litho.   Perf. 13½
1145 A572 100p multicolored   .90 .45
1146 A572 250p multicolored   2.40 1.10

A573

A574

Chilean Soccer, Cent.: a, Carlos Dittborn. b, Hugo Lepe. c, Eladio Rojas. d, Honorino Landa.

1995, Nov. 13   Litho.   Perf. 13½
1147 A573 100p Sheet of 4, #a.-
      d.   3.00 1.40

1995, Oct. 24   Litho.   Perf. 13½
1148 A574 250p multicolored   1.60 .95
51st World Congress of Cape Horn captains.

Gabriela Mistral (1889-1957), 50th Anniv. of Receiving Nobel Prize for Literature A575

Litho. & Engr.
1995, Nov. 15   Perf. 13½
1149 A575 300p blue black & blk 2.00 1.00

Eudyptes Chrysolophus A576

1995, Nov. 22   Litho.   Perf. 13½
1150 A576 100p shown   1.25 .45
1151 A576 250p Penguins, diff.   2.25 1.10
   a. Souv. sheet, #1150-1151   5.00 5.00
No. 1151a sold for 600p.

Chilean Export Assoc., 60th Anniv. — A577

Cargo ship and: a, Kiwi fruit. b, Grapes. c, Peaches. d, Apples.
Jet plane and: e, Various berries.

1995, Dec. 1
1152 A577 100p Strip of 5, #a.-e. 3.50 3.50

Christmas
A578   A579

Booklet Stamps
1153 A578 90p brt blue & blue   .60 .30
1154 A579 90p brt blue & blue   .60 .30
   a. Bklt. pane, 5 ea #1153-1154 6.50
       Complete booklet, #1154a 6.75
1155 A578 90p brt grn & brown   .60 .30
1156 A579 90p brt grn & brown   .60 .30
   a. Bklt. pane, 5 ea #1155-1156 6.50
       Complete booklet, #1156a 6.75
Nos. 1155-1156 inscribed "DS/20."

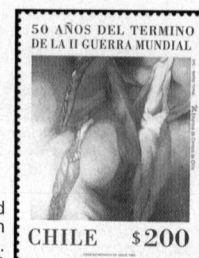

End of World War II, 50th Anniv. A580

1995, Dec. 20   Litho.   Perf. 13½
1157 A580 200p multicolored   1.50 .75

Petroleum Production in Chile, 50th Anniv. — A581

Designs: a, Off-shore oil derrick, one main tower. b, Refinery, road trees, building. c, Refinery, up close. d, Off-shore oil derrick, four towers.

1995, Dec. 29
1158 A581 100p Block of 4, #a.-
      d.   3.00 3.00

Aviation Type of 1994

Designs: a, Embraer EMB-145. b, Mirage M5M Elkan. c, DHC-6 Twin Otter Series 300. d, SAAB JAS 39, Gripen.

1996, Mar. 9   Litho.   Perf. 13½
1159 A547 400p Sheet of 4,
      #a.-d.   13.00 8.50
Intl. Air and Space Fair, FIDAE '96.

Men's High School, La Serena, 175th Anniv. — A582

1996, Apr. 12
1160 A582 100p multicolored   .70 .35

Espamer '96, World Philatelic Exhibition — A583

Designs: No. 1161, Old Train Station, Cordoba. No. 1162, Lope de Vega Theater.

1996, Apr. 25
1161 A583 200p multicolored   1.25 .70
1162 A583 200p multicolored   1.25 .70
   a. Pair, #1161-1162   3.00 3.00

Accident
Prevention
A584

Traffic safety: No. 1163a, Cross street at crosswalk. b, Respect traffic police. c, Obey traffic signals. d, Wait for ride on sidewalk. e, Don't cross street between parked cars. f, Never ride on side of bus. g, Walk beside road facing oncoming traffic. h, Pay attention to where you are walking. i, Don't play on streets. j, Obey traffic rules while riding a bicycle.

Safety in the home: No. 1164a, Extinguish matches after using. b, Be careful with boiling water. c, Curb sharp objects. d, Protect electrical outlets. e, Don't improvise electrical connections. f, Don't play radio or TV too loudly. g, Check all gas connections. h, Don't overload electrical outlets. i, Keep flammable materials away from furnace. j, Keep toys off floor.

Recreational safety: No. 1165a, Swim only in designated areas. b, Keep hands, head inside the car. c, Don't get a sunburn. d, Don't contaminate water with detergents. e, Don't litter. f, Extinguish camp fires. g, Don't bother others when swimming. h, Check car safety features. i, Keep kites away from electrical wires. j, Don't run in swimming pool area.

Safety in the workplace: No. 1166a, Use protective gear. b, Use only safe tools. c, Keep you mind on your work. d, Use proper tools. e, Avoid work accidents. f, Keep stairs free of objects. g, Don't carry objects that obstruct your view. h, Check ladder before using. i, Keep area clean, organized. j, Be aware of protruding nails.

Proper use of drugs and alcohol: No. 1167a, Don't drink and drive. b, Don't drink if you are pregnant. c, Don't encourage friends to drink. d, Alcohol and work don't mix. e, Drinking could destroy your family. f, Drugs can't make you happy. g, Drugs don't make you successful. h, Be happy without drugs. i, For your family say "no" to drugs. j, Drug free, happy and confident.

Safety in schools: No. 1168a, Keep calm in case of fire. b, Don't run along sides of buildings. c, Don't play dangerous jokes. d, Don't sit or stand in high dangerous places. e, Don't run on stairs. f, Don't walk and drink at the same time. g, Don't rock on chairs. h, Don't play with sharp objects. i, Don't open doors abruptly. j, Don't talk to strangers outside the school.

1996, May 2
1163 A584 50p Block of 10, #a.-j. 4.75 2.25
1164 A584 50p Block of 10, #a.-j. 4.75 2.25
1165 A584 50p Block of 10, #a.-j. 4.75 2.25
1166 A584 50p Block of 10, #a.-j. 4.75 2.25
1167 A584 50p Block of 10, #a.-j. 4.75 2.25
1168 A584 50p Block of 10, #a.-j. 4.75 2.25

No. 1 Dry Dock, Talcahuano,
Cent. — A585

1996, May 20
1169 A585 200p multicolored 1.40 .70

Sculptures — A586

#1170, Mariner's Compass, by Ricardo Mesa, vert. #1171, Friendship, by Francisca Cerda, vert. #1172, Andes Winds, by Benito Rojo. #1173, Memory, by Fernando Undurraga.

1996, June 20 Litho. Perf. 13½
1170 A586 150p multicolored 1.75 .90
1171 A586 150p multicolored 1.75 .90
  a. Pair, #1170-1171 4.75 4.75
1172 A586 200p multicolored 2.25 .90
1173 A586 200p multicolored 2.25 .90
  a. Pair, #1172-1173 6.00 6.00
  Nos. 1170-1173 (4) 8.00 3.60

Intl. Day Against Use of Illegal Drugs
and Drug Trafficking — A587

1996, June 26
1174 A587 250p multicolored 2.00 1.25

1996 Summer Olympic Games,
Atlanta — A588

Designs: a, Boxer's glove. b, Runner's shoe. c, Roller blade. d, Ball.

1996, July 3
1175 A588 450p Block of 4,
  #a.-d. 13.50 11.00

Order of Mother of God, 50th Anniv. of
Presence in Chile — A589

1996, Aug. Litho. Perf. 13½
1176 A589 200p multicolored 1.50 .75

Lyceum of San Fernando, 150th
Anniv. — A590

1996, Aug. 2
1177 A590 200p multicolored 1.50 .75

4th Intl. Congress
of Earth
Sciences — A591

Globe showing portions of continents, and: a, Forest fire. b, Smoke stacks creating air pollution. c, Cutting down trees. d, Surveying equipment, desert.

1996, Aug. 5 Litho. Perf. 13½
1178 A591 200p Block of 4, #a.-
  d. 6.75 6.75

Minerals — A592

a, Kroehnkita. b, Lapis lazuli. c, Bornite. d, Azurite.

1996, Aug. 9
1179 A592 150p Block of 4, #a.-
  d. 5.00 4.25

German Immigration, 150th
Anniv. — A593

Designs: 250p, House, lake, mountain. 300p, Monument showing arrival on boat.

1996, Aug. 22
1180 A593 250p multicolored 1.90 .90
1181 A593 300p multicolored 2.10 1.00

Aptenodytes
Patagonica
A594

1996, Sept. 9 Litho. Perf. 13½
1182 A594 250p shown 2.00 1.00
1183 A594 300p Molting 2.10 1.10
  a. Souvenir sheet, #1182-1183 5.75 5.75

Castro
Fire
Dept.,
Cent.
A595

Designs: a, 1937 Italian pumper. b, 1940 Ford fire truck. c, Gorlitz G.A. Fischer manual 4-speed pumper. d, 1907 pumper.

1996, Sept. 14
1184 A595 200p Block of 4, #a.-
  d. 6.00 6.00

Ecotourism in National Parks — A596

Designs: a, River rafting. b, Horseback riding. c, Snow skiing. d, Hiking around cacti.

1996, Sept. 27
1185 A596 100p Sheet of 4, #a.-
  d. 3.25 3.25

Juan José Latorre
Benavente (1846-
1912),
Admiral — A597

1996, Oct. 8
1186 A597 200p multicolored 1.50 .75

Historical Costumes — A598

America issue: No. 1187, Two women, child, dog, vert. No. 1188, Two men with horse, vert. 250p, Two men on horseback.

1996, Oct. 23
1187 A598 100p multicolored .95 .50
1188 A598 100p multicolored .95 .50
  a. Pair, #1187-1188 2.00 2.00
1189 A598 250p multicolored 1.75 1.10

Church, City of Arica — A599

150p, Fauna, mountains, Parinacota Park.

1996, Nov. 18 Litho. Perf. 13½
1190 A599 100p multicolored .65 .35
1191 A599 150p multicolored .85 .45

Christmas — A600

1996, Nov. 25
1192 A600 100p black & multi .70 .30
  a. Booklet pane of 10 7.50
    Complete booklet, #1192a 8.00
1193 A600 100p orange & multi .70 .30
  a. Booklet pane of 10 7.50
    Complete booklet, #1193a 8.00
  No. 1193 is inscribed DS/20.

Mythology
A601 A602

1997, Feb. 12 Litho. Perf. 13½
1194 A601 40p black & blue .25 .25
1195 A602 110p black & green .80 .40
  a Booklet pane of 10 8.00
    Complete booklet, #1195a 8.50
1196 A602 110p black & orange .80 .40
  a. Booklet pane of 10 8.00
    Complete booklet, #1196a 8.50
  No. 1195 inscribed DS/20.

Sixth Summit of Spanish-Americana Heads of State and Government — A603

Mural, Visual Memory of the Nation, by Mario Toral: No. 1198, Left half. No. 1199, Right half.

1996, Nov. 6
1198 A603 110p multicolored .90 .45
1199 A603 110p multicolored .90 .45
a. Pair, #1198-1199 2.00 .95
No. 1199a is a continuous design.

State Visit of King Carl XVI Gustaf, Queen Silvia of Sweden — A604

Design: Nobel Laureates Pablo Neruda, Gabriela Mistral, Nobel medal.

1996, Dec. 3
1200 A604 300p multicolored 2.25 1.10

UNICEF, 50th Anniv. — A605

1996, Dec. 11
1201 A605 200p multicolored 1.50 .75

Frontier Region, Cent. — A606

#1202, Christian Alliance & Missionary Church, cent. #1203, Lonquimay municipality, cent.

1997
1202 A606 110p multicolored .80 .40
1203 A606 110p multicolored .90 .45
Issued: #1202, 1/19; #1203, 1/25.

Arturo Prat Antarctic Naval Base, 50th Anniv. — A607

1997, Feb. 6   Litho.   Perf. 13½
1204 A607 250p Aerial view, vert. 1.90 .95
1205 A607 300p shown 2.40 1.10

Controller General of the Republic, 70th Anniv. — A608

1997, Mar. 26
1206 A608 110p multicolored 2.00 .40

Opening of Metro Line 5 — A609

1997, Apr. 2
1207 A609 200p multicolored 1.50 .75

Interamerican Masonic Confederation, 50th Anniv. — A610

1200p, Emblems, compass, square, book.

1997, Apr. 8
1208 A610 250p shown 2.00 1.00
Souvenir Sheet
1209 A610 1200p multicolored 9.00 9.00
No. 1209 contains one 48x60mm stamp.

Heinrich von Stephan (1831-97) A611

1997, Apr. 15
1210 A611 250p multicolored 2.00 1.00

World Book and Copyright Day — A612

1997, Apr. 23
1211 A612 110p multicolored .80 .45

Details from "Death to the Invader," by David Alfaro Siqueiros (1896-1974), Muralist — A613

1997, June 26   Litho.   Perf. 13½
1212 A613 150p shown 1.50 .40
1213 A613 200p Detail, diff. 1.75 .60
Souvenir Sheets
1214 A613 1000p like #1212 6.25 6.25
1215 A613 1000p like #1213 6.25 6.25
#1214-1215 each contain one 48x36mm stamp.

Providencia, Cent. — A614

1997, July 17
1216 A614 250p multicolored 1.60 .90

A615   A616

1997, Sept. 1
1217 A615 300p multicolored 2.00 1.10
Diplomatic relations between Chile and Japan, cent. See Japan No. 2578.

1997, Oct. 1   Litho.   Perf. 13½
1218 A616 110p Quality .80 .40

1st Radio Broadcast in Chile, 75th Anniv. — A617

1997   Litho.   Perf. 13½
1219 A617 110p multicolored .80 .50

Chilean Opera Singers A618

Singer, opera: 120p, Carlo Morelli, "Rigoletto." 200p, Pedro Navia, "La Bohéme." 250p, Renato Zanelli, "Faust." 300p, Rayèn Quitral, "The Magic Flute." 500p, Ramón Vinay, "Othello."

1997, Oct. 15
1220 A618 120p multicolored 1.00 .55
1221 A618 200p multicolored 1.75 .85
1222 A618 250p multicolored 2.25 1.10
1223 A618 300p multicolored 2.50 1.25
1224 A618 500p multicolored 4.25 2.25
Nos. 1220-1224 (5) 11.75 6.00

America Issue — A619

Life of a postman: 110p, Delivering mail on bicycle. 250p, Delivering mail on horseback.

1997, Oct. 12   Litho.   Perf. 13½
1225 A619 110p multicolored .90 .45
1226 A619 250p multicolored 2.10 1.00

Christmas — A620

1997   Litho.   Perf. 13½
1227 A620 110p multicolored .80 .40
a. Booklet pane of 10 8.00
Complete booklet, #1227a 8.50
1228 A620 110p multicolored .80 .40
a. Booklet pane of 10 8.00
Complete booklet, #1228a 8.50
No. 1228 is inscribed D/S20 and was only issued in booklets.

Chilean Post, 250th Anniv. A621

Designs: 120p, Postman canceling letters. 300p, Man depositing letter into postbox.

1997, Dec. 22
| 1229 | A621 | 120p multicolored | .75 | .40 |
| 1230 | A621 | 300p multicolored | 1.90 | .95 |

Dogs
A622   A623

1998 **Litho.** **Perf. 13½**
1231	A622	120p Great Dane	.60	.20
1232	A623	120p Dalmatian	.60	.20
a.		Pair, #1231-1232	1.25	1.00
b.		Booklet pane, 5 #1232a	7.00	
		Complete booklet, #1232b	7.00	
1233	A622	120p Great Dane	.60	.20
1234	A623	120p Dalmatian	.60	.20
a.		Pair, #1233-1234	1.25	1.00
b.		Booklet pane, 5 #1234a	7.00	
		Complete booklet, #1234b	7.00	

Nos. 1233-1234 are inscribed DS/20.

2nd Summit of the Americas, Santiago — A624

1998, Apr. 17 **Litho.** **Perf. 13½**
| 1235 | A624 | 150p multicolored | .85 | .40 |
| 1236 | A624 | 1000p Logo, diff. | 10.00 | 10.00 |

No. 1236 contains one 26x42mm stamp.

Paintings — A625

350p, "Los Zambos de Calama," by Mauricio Moran. 400p, "Sandia Calada," by Roser Bru.

1998, May 14 **Litho.** **Perf. 13½**
| 1237 | A625 | 350p multicolored | 2.10 | 1.25 |
| 1238 | A625 | 400p multicolored | 2.40 | 1.50 |

Capuchin Order in Chile, 150th Anniv. — A626

Designs: 150p, Native village, friar writing in book. 250p, Friar aiding injured man.

1998, May 18
| 1239 | A626 | 150p multicolored | .90 | .50 |
| 1240 | A626 | 250p multicolored | 1.40 | .70 |

1998 World Cup Soccer Championships, France — A627

Players and: 250p, Crowd. 350p, World Cup Trophy. 500p, Map of France. 700p, Chilean flag.
1500p, Player, vert.

1998, May 23
1241	A627	250p multicolored	1.50	.70
1242	A627	350p multicolored	2.00	1.00
1243	A627	500p multicolored	3.00	1.50
1244	A627	700p multicolored	4.25	2.00
		Nos. 1241-1244 (4)	10.75	5.20

Souvenir Sheet
| 1245 | A627 | 1500p multicolored | 9.00 | 9.00 |

A628

A629

Antarctic Research: 250p, Scientific Committee on Antarctic Research, 25th meeting. 350p, Natl. Administrators of Antarctic Programs, 10th meeting.

1998, July 22
| 1246 | A628 | 250p Logo, penguin | 1.50 | .75 |
| 1247 | A628 | 350p Penguins, map, logo | 2.25 | 1.10 |

1998, Apr. 3
| 1248 | A629 | 120p multicolored | .80 | .40 |

Captain Arturo Prat Chacon, 150th birth anniv.

Army Veterinarian Service, Cent. — A630

350p, Veterinarian listening to horse's heartbeat.

1998, Apr. 20
| 1249 | A630 | 250p multicolored | 1.50 | .75 |
| 1250 | A630 | 350p multicolored | 2.25 | 1.10 |

Merchant Marine's Director General of Maritime Territory, 150th Anniv. — A631

1998, Aug. 31 **Litho.** **Perf. 13½**
| 1251 | A631 | 500p multicolored | 3.25 | 1.40 |

Intl. Year of the Ocean.

Intl. Year of the Ocean A632

#1252, Nautical cartography. #1253, Iceberg. 500p, Silhouette of stone head, Easter Island.

1998, Sept. 10
1252	A632	400p multicolored	2.50	1.25
1253	A632	400p multicolored	2.50	1.25
1254	A632	500p multicolored	3.25	1.50
		Nos. 1252-1254 (3)	8.25	4.00

Folk Singers and Composers — A633

Designs: 200p, Clara Solovera Cortes (1909-92). 250p, Francisco Flores del Campo (1908-93). 300p, Victor Jara Martinez (1932-73). 350p, Violeta Parra Sandoval (1917-67).

1998, Sept. 14
1255	A633	200p multicolored	1.00	.50
1256	A633	250p multicolored	1.40	.60
1257	A633	300p multicolored	1.50	.70
1258	A633	350p multicolored	1.90	.80
		Nos. 1255-1258 (4)	5.80	2.60

World Stamp Day A634

1998, Oct. 9 **Litho.** **Perf. 13½**
| 1259 | A634 | 250p multicolored | 1.25 | .60 |

Francisco Bilbao (1823-65), Writer — A635

Litho. & Engr.
1998, Oct. 29 **Perf. 13½**
| 1260 | A635 | 250p multicolored | 1.75 | .85 |

Chilean Painters — A636

Designs: 300p, Self-portrait, by Augusto Eguiluz (1894-1969), vert. 450p, Landscape, by Agustin Abarca (1882-1953).
1500p, "Two Nudes," by Henriette Petit (1894-1983).

1998, Nov. 3 **Litho.**
| 1261 | A636 | 300p multi | 1.50 | .80 |
| 1262 | A636 | 450p multi | 2.25 | 1.10 |

Souvenir Sheet
| 1262A | A636 | 1500p multicolored | 8.00 | 8.00 |

No. 1262A contains one 36x47mm stamp.

Catholic University of Valparaiso, 70th Anniv. — A637

1998, Nov. 18 **Litho.** **Perf. 13½**
| 1263 | A637 | 130p multicolored | .70 | .35 |

Prominent Women from the University of Chile — A638

America Issue: 120p, Amanda Labarca, educator. 250p, Marta Brunet, writer.

1998, Nov. 19 **Litho.** **Perf. 13½**
| 1264 | A638 | 120p multicolored | .80 | .45 |
| 1265 | A638 | 250p multicolored | 1.60 | .85 |

1999 World Scout Jamboree, Chile — A639

Scouting emblems and: 120p, Children of two races, stylized tents. 200p, Robert Baden-Powell. 250p, Stylized doves. 300p, Scout, stylized tents. 1000p, Scouts, leaders seated in semi-circle, vert.
3000p, Jamboree emblem over drawing of Jamboree site at Picarquin, emblems of past jamborees, Intl. Scouting Emblem.

1998, Dec. 27
1266	A639	120p multicolored	.75	.35
1267	A639	200p multicolored	1.10	.55
1268	A639	250p multicolored	1.40	.70
1269	A639	300p multicolored	1.50	.80
1270	A639	1000p multicolored	5.25	2.75
		Nos. 1266-1270 (5)	10.00	5.15

Imperf
Size: 126x104mm
| 1270A | A639 | 3000p multicolored | 17.00 | 17.00 |

Birds — A640

Designs: 10p, Zonotrichia capensis. 20p, Curaeus curaeus.

1998, Nov. 29
1271	A640 10p multicolored	.80	.20
a.	Inscribed "2000"	.80	.20
1272	A640 20p multicolored	.80	.20
a.	Inscribed "2000"	.80	.20

See Nos. 1313-1314, 1385-1386.

World Equestrian High Jump Record, 50th Anniv. — A641

Captain Alberto Larraguibel and Huaso.

1999, Feb. 5   Litho.   Perf. 13½
| 1273 | A641 200p multicolored | 1.10 | .65 |

Temuco Fire Dept., Cent. — A642

Designs: 140p, 1900 pumper. 200p, 1929 Ford. 300p, 1955 Ford K tanker. 350p, 1967 Mercedes Benz hook and ladder truck. 1500p, Firefighter rescuing victim, vert.

1999, Feb. 18   Litho.   Perf. 13½
1274	A642 140p multicolored	.65	.30
1275	A642 200p multicolored	.95	.40
1276	A642 300p multicolored	1.50	.60
1277	A642 350p multicolored	1.75	.70
	Nos. 1274-1277 (4)	4.85	2.00

Souvenir Sheet
| 1278 | A642 1500p multicolored | 8.50 | 8.50 |

Chilean Chamber of Deputies, 1000th Session — A643

1999, Mar. 3   Perf. 13½
| 1279 | A643 140p multicolored | .70 | .50 |

Sacred Heart College, 150th Anniv. — A644

1999, Mar. 15
| 1280 | A644 250p multicolored | 1.25 | .85 |

Economic Development Corporation (CORFO), 60th Anniv. — A645

Pedro Aguirre Cerda, former president of Chile.

1999, Apr. 29   Perf. 13½
| 1281 | A645 140p multicolored | .80 | .50 |

Chilean Insurance Assoc., Cent. — A646

1999, May 18   Litho.   Perf. 13½
| 1282 | A646 140p multicolored | .65 | .50 |

Chilean Antarctica A647

Designs: 360p, Leptonychotes weddellii. 450p, Pygoscelis antarctica. 1500p, Arctocephalus gazella, penguins.

1999, June 15
| 1283 | A647 360p multicolored | 1.75 | .90 |
| 1284 | A647 450p multicolored | 3.25 | 1.25 |

Souvenir Sheet
| 1285 | A647 1500p multicolored | 8.50 | 8.50 |

No. 1285 contains one 35x48mm stamp.

Easter Island A648

1999, June 25
| 1286 | A648 360p multicolored | 2.00 | 2.00 |

Souvenir Sheet

Barcelona Soccer Club, Cent. — A649

1999
| 1287 | A649 1000p multicolored | 5.00 | 5.00 |

University of Santiago, 150th Anniv. — A650

Designs: 140p, Monument, students in training room, School of Arts and Sciences, 1849. 250p, Technical equipment, building on campus, State Technical University, 1947. 300p, Student looking into microscope, computer, modern building, 1999.

1999, July 6   Litho.   Perf. 13½
1288	A650 140p multicolored	.75	.35
1289	A650 250p multicolored	1.25	.60
1290	A650 300p multicolored	1.60	.75
	Nos. 1288-1290 (3)	3.60	1.70

Alexander von Humboldt (1769-1859), 200th Anniv. of Scientific Research in Latin America — A651

Face from monument and: 300p, Bust of Humboldt, wildlife, mountains. 360p, Portrait of Humboldt, penguins, sea.

1999, July 16
| 1291 | A651 300p multicolored | 1.75 | .75 |
| 1292 | A651 360p multicolored | 1.90 | .95 |

China '99, World Philatelic Exhibition, Beijing — A652

Chinese, Chilean flags and: 140p, Pagoda. 450p, Chinese junk. 1500p, Great Wall of China, Gate of Heavenly Peace.

1999, Aug. 10
| 1293 | A652 140p multicolored | .75 | .35 |
| 1294 | A652 450p multicolored | 2.10 | 1.10 |

Souvenir Sheet
| 1295 | A652 1500p multicolored | 8.00 | 5.00 |

No. 1295 contains one 60x48mm stamp.

City of Quilpue, Cent. — A653

1999, Aug. 20
| 1296 | A653 250p multicolored | 1.60 | .80 |

A654   A655

140p, Raúl Cardinal Silva Henriquez (1907-99). 200p, Walking in street clothes, administering sacrament, face of Christ.

1999, Aug. 9
| 1297 | A654 140p shown | .80 | .40 |
| 1298 | A654 200p multicolored | 1.00 | .50 |

Holy Year 2000.

1999, Sept. 23   Litho.   Perf. 13½
| 1299 | A655 140p multicolored | .70 | .35 |

Red Cross blood donation campaign.

2000 World Congress of Authors & Composers, Santiago — A656

1999, Oct. 5
| 1300 | A656 170p multicolored | .90 | .45 |

Intl. Year of Older Persons — A657

1999, Oct. 6
| 1301 | A657 250p multicolored | 1.25 | .60 |

UPU, 125th Anniv. A658

1999, Oct. 9
1302	A658 300p Red mailbox	2.75	.90
1303	A658 360p Gold mailbox	2.75	1.10
a.	Pair, #1302-1303 + label	6.75	5.25

Nos. 1302-1303 printed in sheets of 16 pairs, with label in central column.

America Issue, A New Millennium Without Arms — A659

1999, Oct. 12
| 1304 | A659 140p shown | 1.00 | .30 |
| 1305 | A659 320p Broken bomb | 1.50 | .65 |

Labor Management, 75th Anniv. — A660

1999, Aug. 23
1306 A660 320p multicolored   1.50 .75

Interamerican Development Bank, 40th Anniv. — A661

1999, Oct. 29   Litho.   Perf. 13½
1307 A661 360p multicolored   1.75 .85

A662

A663

1999, Dec. 1
1308 A662 450p multicolored   2.10 1.10
        Holy Year 2000.

1999, Dec. 1
1309 A663 170p multicolored   .90 .45
    Inscribed "D.S. 20"
1310 A663 170p multicolored   .90 .45
  a.   Booklet pane of 10   9.50
        Complete booklet, #1310a   10.00
  b.   Booklet pane of 5   5.00
        Complete booklet, #1310b   5.50

Nos. 1309-1310 each were issued se-tenant with two labels that served as a lottery ticket and stub.

Union Leaders — A664

#1311, Luis Emilio Recabarren Serrano (1876-1924), Clotario Leopoldo Blest Riffo (1899-1990). #1312, Tucapel Jiménez Alfaro (1921-82), Manuel Bustos Huerta (1943-99).

1999, Dec. 29   Litho.   Perf. 13½
1311 A664 200p multi   .90 .50
1312 A664 200p multi   .90 .50
  a.   Pair, #1311-1312 + label   4.00 3.00

Bird Type of 1998
Designs: 50p, Campephilus magellanicus, vert. 100p, Falco peregrinus cassini, vert.

2000, Feb.   Perf. 13½
1313 A640 50p multi   .20 .20
1314 A640 100p multi   .90 .20

Discovery of Juan Fernández, Archipelago, 425th Anniv. — A665

a, Más Afuera (Alejandro Selkirk) Island, Santa Clara Island, tip of Más a Tierra (Robinson Crusoe) Island. b, Más a Tierra Island. c, Dendroseris litoralis. d, Rhaphythamnus venustus. e, Lobster. f, Lobster's antenna, boat. g, Boat, Gavilea insularis. h, Gavilea insularis.

2000, Feb. 29   Perf. 13¼
1315 A665 360p Sheet of 8,
        #a.-h.   16.00 16.00

Condorito, Cartoon Character by Rene Rios Boettiger Pepo — A666

Condorito: 150p, Celebrating millennium. 260p, As soccer player. 480p, As fire fighter. 980p, On horse.
2000p, With people.

2000, Mar. 20   Perf. 13½
1316 A666 150p multi   .75 .30
1317 A666 260p multi   1.50 .50
1318 A666 480p multi   2.50 .95
1319 A666 980p multi   5.25 2.00
    Nos. 1316-1319 (4)   10.00 3.75
    Souvenir Sheet
1320 A666 2000p multi   11.00 11.00

Easter Island — A667

Designs: 200p, Dancer, stone weapon. 260p, Stone statue and carvings. 340p, Island native, stone statue. 480p, Female dancer, inscribed tablet, map of island.

2000, Apr. 27   Litho.   Perf. 13¼
1321 A667 200p multi   1.10 .60
1322 A667 260p multi   1.50 .70
1323 A667 340p multi   2.00 1.00
1324 A667 480p multi   2.75 1.40
    Nos. 1321-1324 (4)   7.35 3.70

Town of Carahue, Cent. (in 1998) — A668

Bridge and: No. 1325, Locomotive, pottery. No. 1326, Potatoes.

2000, May 5
1325 A668 220p multi   1.10 .55
1326 A668 220p multi   1.10 .55
  a.   Pair, #1325-1326   2.50 2.00

El Mercurio Newspaper, Cent. — A669

2000, June 1
1327 A669 370p multi   2.00 1.00

4th Natl. Masonic Convention — A670

2000, June 23
1328 A670 460p multi   2.50 1.25

Medicinal Plants — A671

Designs: 200p, Quillaja saponaria. 360p, Fabiana imbricata.

2000, July 3
1329 A671 200p multi   1.25 .60
1330 A671 360p multi   3.00 1.50

Discovery of Brazil, 500th Anniv. — A672

Designs: 260p, Map of Brazil, butterfly, girl. 1500p, Monkey, parrots, boy.

2000, July 10
1331 A672 260p multi   1.50 .75
    Souvenir Sheet
1332 A672 1500p multi   8.50 8.50
    No. 1332 contains one 48x36mm stamp.

Folklore A673

Religious festivals: 150p, Dancer in devil costume, La Tirana. 200p, Festival of San Pedro de Atacama. 370p, Candlemas Festival, Copiapo. 460p, Chinese dancers, Andacollo.

2000, July 13
1333 A673 150p multi   .80 .40
1334 A673 200p multi   1.10 .55
1335 A673 370p multi   2.00 1.00
1336 A673 460p multi   2.50 1.25
    Nos. 1333-1336 (4)   6.40 3.20

Prehistoric Animals — A674

No. 1337: a, Milodon. b, Titanosaurus. c, Plesiosaurus. d, Iguanodon.

2000
1337 A674 150p Block of 4, #a-d   2.75 1.40

José de San Martín (1778-1850) — A675

2000, Aug. 25   Litho.   Perf. 13½
1338 A675 320p multi   1.60 .80

World Meteorological Organization, 50th Anniv. — A676

2000, Aug. 28
1339 A676 320p multi   1.60 .80

Antarctic Fauna — A677

450p, Sphenis magellanicus, vert. 650p, Megaptera novaeangliae. 940p, Orcinus orca.

2000, Sept. 15
1340-1342 A677 Set of 3   19.00 19.00
    Souvenir Sheet
1343 A677 2000p Mirounga leonina, vert. 18.00 18.00

No. 1343 contains one 36x48mm stamp.

2000 Summer Olympics, Sydney — A678

Sydney Opera House, Olympic flag and: a, 290p, Chilean flag, tennis player, soccer player, sprinter. b, 290p, Australian flag, archer, high jumper, cyclist.

2000, Sept. 20
1344 A678 Pair, #a-b   4.50 2.25

City of Concepcion, 450th
Anniv. — A679

Mural by Gregorio De la Fuente: a, Indian
holding stick. b, Soldier on white horse. c, Finger pointing upward. d, Seated figure, arms,
horse-drawn carriage. e, Horse, statue, train. f,
People and rainbow.

2000, Oct. 2
1345　　Horiz. strip of 6　　　10.00 10.00
a.-f. A679 250p Any single　　　1.50　.75

America Issue,
World AIDS
Day — A680

Designs: 150p, Heart, clasped hands of
adult and child. 220p, Clasped hands.

2000, Oct. 12
1346-1347 A680 Set of 2　　　3.00 1.50

Penal Reform — A681

Designs: 150p, Flag, court proceedings.
2000p, People, doors of Justice Ministry.

2000, Nov. 16
1348 A681 150p multi　　　　　.80　.40
Souvenir Sheet
1349 A681 2000p multi　　　11.50 11.50

Christmas — A682

Designs: a, Star of Bethlehem. b, Santa
Claus flying over town. c, Three Magi on camels. d, Star on top of Christmas tree. e, Boy at
mailbox. f, Sleeping child. g, Two Magi, cow. h,
Baby Jesus, cow. i, Mary, Joseph. j, Girl putting ornaments on tree.

2000, Nov. 20　　　　Perf. 13½
1350　　Block of 10　　　8.00 8.00
a.-j. A682 150p Any single　　　.75　.40
Inscribed "DS/20"
Perf. 13½ on 3 sides
1351　　Booklet pane of 10　　9.00
a.-j. A682 150p Any single　　　.90　.45
　　　Booklet, #1351　　　9.00

National Zoo, 75th Anniv. — A683

Various animals and birds, denomination in:
a, LL. b, LR. c, UL. d, UR.

2001, Jan. 13　　Litho.　　Perf. 13½
1352 A683 160p Block of 4, #a-d　5.50 5.50

San Sebastian Festival,
Yumbel — A684

2001, Jan. 18
1353 A684 210p multi　　　　1.50　.75

Father
Alberto
Hurtado
(1901-52)
A685

Hurtado and: 160p, Truck. 340p, Children.

2001, Jan. 20
1354-1355 A685　Set of 2　　　2.50 1.25

Bird Type of 1998

No. 1356, vert.: a, Sephanoides fernandensis. b, Mimus thenca. c, Pteroptochos
megapodius. d, Enicognathus leptorhynchus.
Size of Nos. 1356a-1356d: 24x29mm.

2001, Jan. 29
1356 A640 160p Block of 4, #a-d　4.50 4.50

Assembly of Governors of Inter-
American Development Bank and
Investment Corporation — A686

2001, Mar. 16
1357 A686 230p multi　　　　1.10　.55

Souvenir Sheet

Air Force Anniversaries — A687

No. 1358: a, Lockheed C-130 Hercules,
map of Antarctica. b, Flugzeugbau Extra-300,
acrobatic squadron. c, North American AT-6
Texan. d, Consolidated PBY-5A/OA-10 Catalina, map of Easter Island.

2001, Mar. 29
1358 A687 260p Sheet of 4, #a-d　5.50 5.50

Air Force presence in Antarctica, 50th anniv.
(No. 1358a); Halcones acrobatic squadron,
20th anniv. (No. 1358b); Aviation Group No. 1,
75th anniv. (No. 1358c); First flight ot Easter
Island, 50th anniv. (No. 1358d).

Nationalization of Copper Industry,
30th Anniv. — A688

Design: 2000p, Miner and equipment.

2001, Apr. 26　　Litho.　　Perf. 13¼
1359 A688 400p multi　　　　2.25 1.10
Souvenir Sheet
1359A A688 2000p multi　　　12.50 12.50

Organ Donation — A689

2001, May 3
1360 A689 160p multi　　　　1.10　.45

Easter Island — A690

Designs: No. 1361, Stone carvings, map of
island and: a, Compass rose. b, Bird and
native. No. 1361C, Artifact and map of island.

2001, June 25
1361 A690 260p Horiz. pair,
　　　#a-b　　　　　　　3.25 3.25
Souvenir Sheet
1361C A690 2000p multi　　　11.50 11.50

Lynchailurus
Colocolo — A691

2001
1362 A691 100p multi　　　　.60　.30
Endangered species.

Valparaiso Firefighting Corps, 150th
Anniv. — A692

Firefighters and: 160p, Manuel Blanco
Encalada. 260p, Old pumper, building on fire,
modern fire truck. 350p, Flags, building. 490p,
Helicopter, rail tank car.
　2000p, Helicopter, modern fire truck.

2001, June 28　　Litho.　　Perf. 13¼
1363-1366 A692　Set of 4　　　6.75 3.25
Souvenir Sheet
1367 A692 2000p multi　　　11.50 11.50

Mushrooms
A693

Designs: 300p, Macrolepiota rhacodes.
400p, Laccata ohiensis.

2001, July 25　　Litho.　　Perf. 13¼
1368-1369 A693　Set of 2　　　4.50 2.75

24th Conference of American Armies,
Santiago — A694

2001, Aug. 13
1370 A694 350p multi　　　　2.00　.95

Bernardo O'Higgins (1778-1842),
Soldier and Statesman — A695

2001, Aug. 17
1371 A695 260p multi　　　　1.50　.70

Chilean Antarctic Research — A696

Designs: 350p, Researcher, Leptonychotes
weddellii. 700p, Researchers, Macronectes
giganteus. 2000p, Chionis alba.

2001, Aug. 29
1372-1373 A696　Set of 2　　　5.75 2.75
Souvenir Sheet
1374 A696 2000p multicolored 11.50 11.50

America Issue —
UNESCO World
Heritage — A697

World Heritage Sites and stamps: 160p,
Quinchao Church, #1058. 230p, Tenaun
Church, #1057.

2001, Oct. 9　　Litho.　　Perf. 13¼
1375-1376 A697　Set of 2　　　8.00 2.50

Cape Horn A698

2001, Nov. 22
1377 A698 220p multi   1.25 .60

El Indice del Indice, by Roberto Matta (1911-2002) — A699

2001, Nov. 5   Litho.   Perf. 13¼
1378 A699 300p multi   1.75 .85

Railroads in Chile, 150th Anniv. — A700

No. 1379 (50x29mm): a, Caldera Station, train cars. b, Locomotive and Copiapó Station. 220p, Train on bridge.

2001, Nov. 20
1379 A700 200p Horiz. pair, #a-b 3.00 1.50
1380 A700 220p multi   1.50 .85

Christmas — A701

Designs: a, Heads of three shepherds. b, Shepherd and cow. c, Joseph and Mary. d, Donkey and Magus. e, Cow and two Magi. f, Head of shepherd. g, Two sheep. h, Infant Jesus. i, Shepherd with staff. j, One sheep.

2001, Nov.
1381 A701 160p Block of 10,
        #a-j   8.00 8.00
    Inscribed "DS/20"
1382 A701 160p Block of 10,
        #a-j   9.00 9.00
 k. Booklet pane, #1382 with
        straight edge at right   10.00   —
     Complete booklet, #1382k   10.00

Rotary Intl. Emblem, Map of Chile, Globe, Tropic of Capricorn Monument — A702

2001, Dec. 21
1383 A702 240p multi   1.40 .70

Antofagasta Rotary Club, 75th anniv.

Taxation Department, Cent. — A703

2002, Jan. 14
1384 A703 180p multi   .80 .40

Bird Type of 1998

Designs: 10p, Turdus falcklandii. 20p, Sturnella loyca.

2002, Jan. 25
1385 A640 10p multi   .55 .20
1386 A640 20p multi   .55 .20

City of Valdivia, 450th Anniv. — A704

2002, Feb. 9
1387 A704 260p multi   1.25 .65

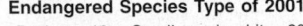

Carabinero Force, 75th Anniv. — A705

2002, Apr. 8
1388 A705 250p multi   1.25 .65

Ignacy Domeyko (1802-89), Mineralogist — A706

2002, Apr. 11
1389 A706 290p multi   1.75 .85

See Poland No. 3645.

City of Villarrica, 450th Anniv. — A707

2002, Apr. 26
1390 A707 290p multi   1.50 .75

Town of Calbuco, 400th Anniv. — A708

2002, May 2
1391 A708 230p multi   1.25 .60

Barros Arana Natl. Boarding School — A709

2002, May 20
1392 A709 250p multi   1.25 .65

Abolition of Death Penalty, 1st Anniv. — A710

2002, May 29
1393 A710 240p multi   1.25 .65

Endangered Species Type of 2001

Designs: 10p, Oreailurus jacobita. 20p, Oncifelis geoffrovi.

2002, June 5
1394 A691 10p multi   .55 .20
1395 A691 20p multi   .55 .20

Easter Island A711

Map of Easter Island and: 250p, Toromiro sophora, moai. 450p, Bird, row of moai statues, native in traditional costume.
2000p, Toromiro sophora and bird.

2002, July 1
1396-1397 A711 Set of 2   3.50 1.75
        Souvenir Sheet
1398 A711 2000p multi   10.50 10.50

No. 1398 contains one 47x47mm stamp.

World Heritage Sites — A712

Churches and stamps: 230p, Achao, #1036. 290p, Dalcahue, #1056.

2002, July 27
1399-1400 A712 Set of 2   2.25 1.10

America Issue — Youth, Education, and Literacy — A713

Designs: 230p, Adult students. 450p, Woman reading to child, teacher, boy at computer.

2002, Sept. 9
1401-1402 A713 Set of 2   3.25 1.60

Children's Toys — A714

Designs: 290p, Pinwheel. 380p, Kite, vert.

2002, Sept. 16
1403-1404 A714 Set of 2   3.00 1.50

Observatories — A715

Designs: 450p, Cerro-Tololo. 550p, Paranal. 2000p, Cerro-Tololo, diff.

2002, Sept. 27
1405-1406 A715 Set of 2   4.00 2.00
        Souvenir Sheet
1407 A715 2000p multi   8.50 8.50

No. 1407 contains one 47x47mm stamp.

University of Chile Clinical Hospital, 50th Anniv. — A716

2002, Oct. 17
1408 A716 250p multi   1.10 .55

Forestry Education, 50th Anniv. — A717

2002, Oct. 22
1409 A717 250p multi   1.10 .55

12th Convention on International Trade in Endangered Species Conference — A718

Designs: 300p, Phoenicoparrus andinus. 450p, Vicugna vicugna. 2000p, Chinchilla lanigera.

2002, Oct. 29
1410-1411 A718 Set of 2   4.00 2.00
        Souvenir Sheet
1412 A718 2000p multi   10.00 10.00

No. 1412 contains one 47x47mm stamp.

Protected Whales — A719

Designs: 250p, Eubalaena australis. 500p, Balaenoptera acutorostrata.
2000p, Physeter macrocephalus.

2002, Nov. 2
1413-1414 A719 Set of 2   3.50 1.50
Souvenir Sheet
1415 A719 2000p multi   10.00 10.00

Violence Against Women Prevention Day — A720

2002, Nov. 22
1416 A720 230p multi   1.00   .50

Town of Puerto Varas, 150th Anniv. A721

2002, Nov. 29
1417 A721 190p multi   1.00   .50

Bird Type of 1998
Designs: 500p, Campephilus magellanicus, vert. 1000p, Falco peregrinus cassini, vert.

2003, Jan. 15   Litho.   Perf. 13¼
1418 A640 500p multi   2.10   .75
1419 A640 1000p multi   4.00 1.75

Puerto Montt, 150th Anniv. A722

2003, Feb. 13
1420 A722 240p multi   1.00   .45

Claudio Arrau (1903-91), Pianist — A723

2003, June 9   Litho.   Perf. 13¼
1421 A723 200p multi   .85   .30

First Chilean Postage Stamps, 150th Anniv. — A724

No. 1422 — Mailbox, building and: a, #1. b, #2.
2000p, Building, #1 and various other stamps.

2003, July 1
1422 A724 300p Horiz. pair,
                     #a-b   2.50 1.25
Souvenir Sheet
1423 A724 2000p multi   8.00 3.00

America Issue — Flora and Fauna — A725

Designs: 240p, Trees, flowers, cactus. 300p, Frog, fox, butterfly, pudu, parrot.

2003, Oct. 12   Litho.   Perf. 13¼
1424-1425 A725 Set of 2   2.00 1.00

Supreme Court, 180th Anniv. — A726

2003, Nov. 5
1426 A726 200p multi   .85   .35

Chilean Red Cross, Cent. A727

2003, Nov. 18
1427 A727 200p black & red   .85   .35

Christmas — A728

2003, Nov. 28
1428 A728 190p multi   .80   .30
Inscribed "DS-20"
1429 A728 190p multi   .80   .30

Powered Flight, Cent. — A729

2003, Dec. 11
1430 A729 200p multi   .85   .35

Cristo Redentor Statue, Cent. A730

2004, Apr. 22   Litho.
1431 A730 200p multi   .85   .30

Seventh World Conference of Grand Masonic Lodges — A731

2004, May 5   Perf. 13¼
1432 A731 190p multi   .80   .30

Pablo Neruda (1904-73), Poet — A732

2004, June 11
1433 A732 300p multi   1.25   .45

Social Security, 80th Anniv. — A733

2004, Aug. 18
1434 A733 190p multi   .80   .30

America Issue — Environmental Protection — A734

Designs: 100p, Burnt forest, logs, field of flowers, puma, flower. 600p, Flower, wildlife, tanker truck, smokestacks.

2004, Sept. 27
1435-1436 A734 Set of 2   2.60 1.50

German Institute, Osorno, 150th Anniv. — A735

2004, Oct. 6
1437 A735 250p multi   1.75   .60

Tematica 2004 National Philatelic Exhibition A736

2004, Oct. 19
1438 A736 310p multi   1.25   .55

Naval Telecommunications, Cent. — A737

2004, Nov. 5
1439 A737 400p multi   1.75   .80

Electricity and Fuel Superintendency, Cent. — A738

2004, Dec. 7
1440 A738 240p multi   1.00   .40

Chilean Air Force, 75th Anniv. — A739

2005, Mar. 15   Litho.   Perf. 13¼
1441 A739 230p multi   1.00   .40

Law No. 20,000 — A740

2005, May 4
1442 A740 220p multi   .95   .40

Pope John Paul II (1920-2005) — A741

Pope John Paul II and: a, Child, condor, mountain. b, Crucifix, Chilean flag, mountain. c, Church, Chilean flag.

2005, May 13
1443   Horiz. strip of 3   3.25 1.75
a.-c. A741 230p Any single   1.00   .50

Rotary International, Cent. — A742

2005, June 30   Litho.   Perf. 13¼
1444 A742 230p multi   1.00   .40

Treasury Building, Bicent. — A743

2005, June 30
1445 A743 230p multi   1.00   .40

Publication of Don Quixote, 400th Anniv. A744

No. 1446: a, Don Quixote on horseback. b, Windmill. c, Windmills. d, Miguel de Cervantes, author.

2005, July 14
1446   Horiz. strip of 4   .25   .20
a.-b. A744 10p Either single   .20   .20
c.-d. A744 20p Either single   .20   .20

El Teniente Copper Mine, Cent. — A745

2005, Aug. 3
1447 A745 390p multi   1.75   .75

Undersecretariat of Aviation, 75th Anniv. — A746

2005, Aug. 19
1448 A746 400p multi   1.75 1.00

Valparaiso Customs House, 150th Anniv. — A747

2005, Sept. 1
1449 A747 390p multi   1.75   .75

Bicentennial Fountain, Santiago — A748

2005, Sept. 5
1450 A748 230p multi   1.00   .45

America Issue — Fight Against Poverty — A749

No. 1451: a, Denomination at right. b, Denomination at left.

2005, Oct. 3   Litho.   Perf. 13¼
1451 A749 250p Horiz. pair, #a-b   2.25   .95

Canonization of Father Alberto Hurtado (1901-52) — A750

2005, Oct. 13   Litho.   Perf. 13¼
1452 A750 390p multi   1.75   .75

Expo Austral 2005 Philatelic Exhibition, Punta Arenas — A751

2005, Oct. 22
1453 A751 390p multi   1.75   .75

New Civil Matrimony Law — A752

2005, Nov. 18   Litho.   Perf. 13¼
1454 A752 260p multi   1.40   .60

German Clinic, Cent. — A753

2005, Nov. 23
1455 A753 230p multi   1.25   .55

Restoration of Central Post Office, Santiago A754

2005, Nov. 30
1456 A754 230p multi   1.25   .55

Political Constitution A755

2005, Dec. 1
1457 A755 230p multi   1.25   .55

Department of Physical Education, Sports and Recreation, Cent. — A756

2006, Mar. 6   Litho.   Perf. 13¼
1458 A756 230p multi   1.25   .55

Intl. Women's Day — A757

2006, Mar. 7
1459 A757 390p multi   1.75   .75

Wulff Castle, Cent. — A758

No. 1460 — Castle, arms of Vina del Mar and: a, Birds. b, Windmill.

2006, Mar. 21
1460   Horiz. pair   3.00 1.50
a. A758 230p multi   1.00   .55
b. A758 390p multi   1.75   .85

Tourism — A759

No. 1461: a, Morro de Arica. b, Moais, Easter Island. c, Palafittes, Castro. d, Torres del Paine. e, Penguins, Chilean Antarctic Territory.

2006, May 19
1461   Horiz. strip of 5   6.25 3.00
a.-e. A759 230p Any single   1.10   .55

Don Quixote Type of 2005

No. 1462: a, Building. b, Windmills. c, Windmill, country name at LR. d, Don Quixote and Sancho Panza.

2006, May 31
1462   Horiz. strip of 4   .20   .20
a.-d. A744 10p Any single   .20   .20

Catholic University of the North, 50th Anniv. — A760

No. 1463: a, Students using computers, denomination at UR. b, Students, denomination at LL.

2006, June 9
1463   Horiz. pair   2.50 1.25
a.-b.   A760 230p Either single   1.10 .55

Citizenship Plaza, Santiago — A761

2006, July 7
1464 A761 390p multi   1.75 .85

World Quality Forum — A762

No. 1465: a, Building. b, Building and flags.

2006, Aug. 29   Litho.   Perf. 13¼
1465 A762 230p Horiz. pair, #a-b 2.50 1.25

America Issue, Energy Conservation — A763

No. 1466: a, River and mountains. b, Clouds. c, Oil rigs in water. d, Windmill.

2006, Sept. 29
1466 A763 390p Block of 4, #a-d 7.25 3.50

Adventist University of Chile, Cent. — A764

No. 1467 — University emblem and: a, Building, 1906. b, Family and building, 1922. c, Building, 1960-70. d, Building, 2006.

2006, Oct. 20
1467   Horiz. strip of 4 + central label   4.50 2.25
a.-d.   A764 250p Any single   1.10 .55

Antarctic Wildlife — A765

No. 1468 — Chilean and Estonian flags and: a, Balaenoptera acutorostrata. b, Aptenodytes forsteri.

2006, Oct. 25   Perf. 13½
1468 A765 500p Horiz. pair, #a-b 4.50 2.25
   See Estonia No. 555.

Anniversaries — A766

No. 1469: a, Colonization of the Straits of Magellan area, 160th anniv. b, Fort Bulnes, 160th anniv.

2006, Dec. 7   Perf. 13¼
1469 A766 250p Horiz. pair, #a-b 2.25 2.10

Gasco, 150th Anniv. — A767

No. 1470: a, San Borja facility. b, Gasco headquarters.

2006, Dec. 14
1470 A767 250p Horiz. pair, #a-b 2.25 1.10

Federico Santa Maria Technical University, 75th Anniv. — A768

2006, Dec. 20
1471 A768 250p multi   1.10 .50

Carabineros, 80th Anniv. — A769

No. 1472: a, Carabineros and mountains. b, Carabineros on horseback.

2007, Apr. 10   Litho.   Perf. 13¼
1472 A769 250p Pair, #a-b   2.25 1.10

Tourism — A770

No. 1473: a, Valley of the Moon, Antofagasta Region. b, Easter Island, Valparaiso Region. c, Tourism emblem. d, Villarrica-Pucón Volcano, Araucania Region. e, Penguin in Chilean Antarctic.

2007, May 9
1473   Horiz. strip of 5   9.00 4.50
a.-e.   A770 390p Any single   1.75 .90

Church Centenaries — A771

No. 1474: a, Parinacota Church. b, San Pedro de Atacama Church.

Litho. With Foil Application
2007, June 29
1474 A771 250p Pair, #a-b   2.25 1.10

Raul Cardinal Silva Henríquez (1907-99) — A772

No. 1475 — Color of portrait and panel: a, Blue violet. b, Red violet. c, Red orange. d, Green.

2007, Aug. 21   Litho.
1475   Horiz. strip of 4 + central label   4.50 2.25
a.-d.   A772 250p Any single   1.10 .55

 A773

 A774

 A775

Sculptures by Marta Colvin (1907-95) — A776

2007, Aug. 24   Perf. 13¼
1476   Horiz. strip of 4 + central label   4.50 2.25
a. A773 250p multi   1.10 .55
b. A774 250p multi   1.10 .55
c. A775 250p multi   1.10 .55
d. A776 250p multi   1.10 .55

Las Condes, 106th Anniv. — A777

2007, Aug. 28
1477 A777 330p multi   1.50 .75

Museums in Santiago A778

Designs: 10p, Artequin Museum. 20p, National Museum of Fine Arts. 30p, National Museum of Natural History. 50p, Museum of Santiago.

2007, Aug. 31   Engr.
1478 A778 10p green   .20 .20
1479 A778 20p black   .20 .20
1480 A778 30p purple   .20 .20
1481 A778 50p red   .20 .20
   Nos. 1478-1481 (4) .80 .80

Los Rios Region — A779

No. 1482: a, Lake Ranco. b, Huilo Huilo Waterfall. c, Bridge, Valdivia. d, Choshuenco Volcano.

2007, Oct. 2   Litho.
1482   Horiz strip of 4 + central label   7.25 3.75
a.-d.   A779 390p Any single   1.75 .90

Arica and Parinacota Region — A780

No. 1483: a, Morro de Arica. b, Parinacota Volcano. c, Anzota Caves. d, Vicunas.

2007, Oct. 8
1483   Horiz strip of 4 + central label   4.50 2.25
a.-d.   A780 250p Any single   1.10 .55

Chilean Postal Service, 260th Anniv. — A781

No. 1484: a, Half of original General Post Office, Santiago (denomination at UR). b, Half of modern General Post Office, Santiago (denomination at UL). c, Original and modern General Post Offices.
3000p, Statue of postal carrier on bicycle.

Litho. With Foil Application
2007, Oct. 9
1484 A781 390p Horiz. strip of
3, #a-c   5.50 2.75
Souvenir Sheet
1485 A781 3000p multi   13.50 6.75

Comptroller of the Navy, 80th
Anniv. — A782

Arms of Chilean Navy and: a, Chilean Navy
Building, denomination at UL. b, Naval and
Maritime Museum, denomination at UR.

2007, Oct. 11   Litho.   Perf. 13¼
1486 A782 390p Horiz. pair, #a-b 3.50 1.75

America Issue, Education For
All — A783

No. 1487: a, Children at computer. b, Boy
watching chemistry experiment. c, Children
running. d, Children playing musical instruments. e, Boy pointing to globe.

2007, Nov. 5
1487   Horiz. strip of 5   5.75 2.75
  a.-e.   A783 250p Any single   1.10 .55

Christmas — A784

No. 1488 — Santa Claus: a, In chimney. b,
In automobile. c, Near sleigh. d, In front of fan.

Litho. With Foil Application
2007, Nov. 16
1488 A784 250p Block of 4, #a-d 4.50 2.25

Malleco National Reserve,
Cent. — A785

No. 1489: a, Tree, flower. b, Tree, puma. c,
Waterfall, flowers. d, Forest, fox.

2007, Nov. 20   Litho.
1489   Horiz. strip of 4 + central label   4.50 2.25
  a.-d.   A785 250p Any single   1.00 .50

La Nación Newspaper, 90th
Anniv. — A786

No. 1490 — Newspaper's office building,
Chilean flag and: a, Newspapers at end of
production line. b, Newspaper pages.
Illustration reduced.

2007, Dec. 7
1490 A786 250p Horiz. pair, #a-b 2.25 1.10

Santa María de Iquique Massacre,
Cent. — A787

No. 1491: a, People, ships. b, Man raising
shovel. c, School, dead on ground. d, Wagon,
people weeping. e, People hugging, woman
weeping.
3000p, Family, vert.

2007, Dec. 19
1491   Horiz. strip of 5   5.75 2.75
  a.-e.   A787 250p Any single   1.10 .55
Souvenir Sheet
1492 A787 3000p multi   14.00 7.00

Miniature Sheet

Easter Island — A788

No. 1493 — Natives in traditional garb and:
a, Ahu Koteriku moais overlooking water. b,
Motu Nui, Motu Iti and Motu Kaokao Islets. c,
Rock painting. d, Petroglyphs. e, Orongo stone
houses. f, Ahu Tahai moai. g, Anakena Beach.
h, Rano Kau Volcanic Lake.
No. 1494, vert.: a, Native male. b, Native
female.

2008, Jan. 18
1493 A788 390p Sheet of 8,
  #a-h   15.00 7.50
Souvenir Sheet
1494 A788 1500p Sheet of 2,
  #a-b   15.00 7.50

Miniature Sheet

Intl. Polar Year — A789

No. 1495: a, Antarctic base, penguins. b,
Ship and icebergs. c, Helicopter and direction
signs. d, Cargo airplane and snow vehicle. e,
Man directing small airplane. f, People on
snowmobiles.

2008, Jan. 29   Perf. 13¼
1495 A789 250p Sheet of 6, #a-f 7.50 3.75

Occupations — A790

No. 1496, 20p: a, Knife grinder. b, Street
sweeper.
No. 1497, 30p: a, Photographer. b, Peanut
vendor.
No. 1498, 50p: a, Ice cream vendor. b,
Shoeshine man.
No. 1499, 100p: a, Laundry worker. b,
Organ grinder.
No. 1500, 500p: a, Street musician. b,
Newspaper vendor.

2008, Feb. 25   Litho.
Pairs, #a-b
1496-1500 A790   Set of 5   7.50 3.75

Visit to Chile of Italian Pres. Giorgio
Napolitano — A791

No. 1501 — Chilean poet Pablo Neruda
and: a, His house on Isla Negra, Chile, Chil-
ean flag. b, His house on Isle of Capri, Italy,
Italian flag. c, His house on Isla Negra, flags of
Chile and Italy. d, Rocks off Capri, flags of
Chile and Italy.
Illustration reduced.

2008, Mar. 17
1501 A791 280p Block of 4, #a-d 5.25 2.10

Miniature Sheets

Ensenar la Eternidad, by Roberto
Matta — A792

Foyer du Moi, by Matta — A793

Espejo de Cronos, by Matta — A794

Nos. 1502-1504 — Portion of painting: a,
Upper left. b, Top center. c, Upper right. d, Left

center. e, Center. f, Right center. g, Lower left.
h, Bottom center. i, Lower right.

2008, Mar. 25   Perf. 13¼
1502 A792 280p Sheet of 9,
  #a-i   12.00 6.00
1503 A793 410p Sheet of 9,
  #a-i   17.00 8.50
1504 A794 410p Sheet of 9,
  #a-i   17.00 8.50
  Nos. 1502-1504 (3)   46.00 23.00

Pres. Salvador Allende (1908-
73) — A795

2008, June 26   Litho.   Perf. 13¼
1505 A795 410p multi   2.00 1.00

Taltal,
150th
Anniv.
A796

2008, July 18
1506 A796 280p multi   1.40 .70

Women's Under-20 Soccer World
Championships, Chillán — A797

No. 1507 — Quarter of soccer ball and stadium and: a, Cross. b, Group of people. c,
Fruits and vegetables. d, Pottery.

2008, July 31
1507 A797 280p Block of 4, #a-d 5.50 2.75

Chilean Accountancy Association, 50th
Anniv. — A798

No. 1508 — Emblem and: a, Accountants,
building. b, Map of Western hemisphere.

2008, Aug. 14
1508 A798 280p Horiz. pair, #a-b 2.75 1.25

Bishop Francisco Valdés
Subercaseaux (1908-82) — A799

No. 1509 — Bishop Valdés Subercaseaux and: a, Christ of Tromen. b, Osorno Cathedral.

2008, Sept. 5   **Litho.**   *Perf. 13¼*
1509 A799 280p Horiz. pair, #a-b   2.25   1.10

Miniature Sheet

La Vida Allende la Muerte, by Roberto Matta — A800

No. 1510 — Section of painting: a, Upper left. b, Top center. c, Upper right. d, Left center. e, Center. f, Right center. g, Lower left. h, Bottom center. i, Lower right.

2008, Sept. 15
1510 A800 410p Sheet of 9,
     #a-i   13.00   6.50

America Issue, National Festivals — A801

Designs; 10p, Cuasimodo. 200p, La Vendimia. 1000p, La Tirana. 2000p, Fiestas Patrias. 5000p, El Rodeo.

2008, Oct. 30
1511 A801	10p multi	.20	.20
1512 A801	200p multi	.60	.30
1513 A801	1000p multi	3.00	1.50
1514 A801	2000p multi	6.00	3.00
1515 A801	5000p multi	15.00	7.50
Nos. 1511-1515 (5)		24.80	12.50

Miniature Sheet

Torres del Paine National Park, 50th Anniv. — A802

No. 1516: a, Fox, Torres del Paine. b, Puma, Grey Glacier. c, Condor (at right), Paine Grande. d, Condor (at left), Cuernos del Paine. e, Guanaco, Cuernos del Paine. f, Guemal, Macizo Paine and Cordillera Paine.

2008, Nov. 21
1516 A802 500p Sheet of 6, #a-f   9.00   4.50

Telethon, 30th Anniv. — A803

2008, Nov. 25
1517 A803 280p multi   .85   .40

Christmas — A804

No. 1518 — Children's art: a, Drawing by Antonia Retamal Figueroa. b, Drawing by Lucas Bastidas Escobar. c, Drawing by Oscar Maya Lazo. d, Drawing of girl, Christmas tree, mountains, Santa Claus. e, Drawing of Christmas tree, cross and handprints.

2008, Nov. 26
1518	Horiz. strip of 5	4.25	2.10
a.-e.	A804 280p Any single	.85	.40

Osorno, 450th Anniv. — A805

2008, Nov. 28
1519 A805 280p multi   .85   .40

General Carlos Ibáñez del Campo Carabineros School, Cent. — A806

No. 1520: a, Carabineros, old school building (sepia photograph). b, Carabineros, new school building (color photograph).

2008, Dec. 10
1520 A806 310p Horiz. pair, #a-b 1.90   .95

Expo Antarctica Chile 2009 Philatelic Exhibition, Pres. Eduardo Frei Montalva Antarctic Base — A807

Designs: 470p, Map of Antarctica, Pres. Eduardo Frei Montalva Antarctic Base. 3000p, Villa Las Estrellas, horiz.

2009, Mar. 12
1521 A807 470p multi   1.75   .85
     Souvenir Sheet
1522 A807 3000p multi   10.50   5.25

Antarctic Treaty, 50th anniv. No. 1522 contains one 48x30mm stamp.

Preservation of Polar Regions and Glaciers — A808

Nos. 1523, 1524 — Emblem and map of: a, Arctic area. b, Antarctic area. No. 1524 has vert. stamps.

   Litho. with Foil Application
2009, Mar. 18   *Perf. 13¼*
1523 A808 470p Vert. pair,
     #a-b   3.25   1.60
   Souvenir Sheet
1524 A808 1500p Sheet of 2,
     #a-b   10.50   5.25

Miniature Sheets

Independence, Bicent. — A809

No. 1525: a, Chile #92. b, Chile #93. c, Chile #94. d, Chile #95. e, Chile #96. f, Chile #97.
No. 1526, horiz.: a, Chile #83. b, Chile #84. c, Chile #85. d, Chile #86. e, Chile #87. f, Chile #88. g, Chile #89. h, Chile #90. i, Chile #91. j, Bicentennial emblem.

2009, Apr. 20   **Litho.**
1525 A809 310p Sheet of 6,
     #a-f   6.50   3.25
1526 A809 310p Sheet of
     10, #a-j   10.50   5.25

University of Concepción, 90th Anniv. — A810

No. 1527: a, Homage to the Founders, sculpture by Samuel Román. b, Campanile.

2009, May 14
1527 A810 310p Horiz. pair, #a-b 2.25   1.10

Santa María de Los Angeles Diocese, 50th Anniv. — A811

No. 1528: a, Virgin Mary, Jesus and angels. b, Los Angeles Cathedral.

2009, June 10
1528 A811 470p Horiz. pair, #a-b 3.50   1.75

Protected Birds — A812

Designs: 10p, Condor. 20p Triachue parrot. 50p, Chilean flamingo. 100p, Humboldt penguin. 500p, Black-necked swan.

2009, July 15   **Litho.**   *Perf. 13¼*
1529 A812	10p black	.20	.20
1530 A812	20p black	.20	.20
1531 A812	50p black	.20	.20
1532 A812	100p black	.40	.20
1533 A812	500p black	1.90	.95
Nos. 1529-1533 (5)		2.90	1.75

21st UPAEP Congress, Santiago — A813

2009, Aug. 17   **Litho.**   *Perf. 13¼*
1534 A813 500p multi   1.90   .95

Mutual de Seguros Insurance Company, 90th Anniv. — A814

No. 1535: a, Old building, emblem with black gear. b, Modern building, emblem with blue gray gear.

   Litho. With Foil Application
2009, Oct. 14   *Perf. 13¼*
1535 A814 310p Horiz. pair, #a-b 2.40   1.25

A815

Winning Art in Bicentennial Stamp Design Contest — A816

No. 1536: a, Flag with mountains and city, by Andrea Barreda, elementary school competition. b, City, by Javiera Monreal Arcil, middle school competition.
No. 1537: a, People in various costumes, by Patricio Díaz Donay, visual arts competition. b, Pepper, by Joshua Arévalo Carreño, university and technical school competition.

2009, Oct. 15   Litho.   Perf. 13¼
1536 A815 310p Vert. pair, #a-b   2.40 1.25
1537 A816 310p Horiz. pair, #a-b   2.40 1.25

America Issue, Traditional Games — A817

Designs: 310p, Spinning top. 470p, Girl flying kite.

2009, Oct. 30
1538-1539 A817   Set of 2   3.00 1.50

Christmas — A818

No. 1540 — Children: a, Painting nativity scene. b, Drawing pictures of Santa Claus. c, Opening presents under Christmas tree. d, Looking out of window.

2009, Nov. 26
1540 A818 310p Block of 4, #a-d   5.00 2.50

Gabriela Mistral (1889-1957), 1945 Nobel Laureate in Literature — A819

No. 1451: a, Mistral at left, mountain at right. b, Church at left, Mistral at right. c, Mistral at left, church at right. d, Mountain at left, Mistral at right.

2009, Dec. 18
1541 A819 500p Block of 4, #a-d   8.00 4.00

Chile Philatelic Society, 120th Anniv. — A820

2009, Dec. 30
1542 A820 500p multi   2.00 1.00

Bicentennial Art by National Art Prize Winners — A821

No. 1543 — Works of art by: a, José Balmes. b, Eugenio Dittborn. c, Guillermo Núñez.

2010, Mar. 3
1543   Horiz. strip of 3   6.75 3.50
a.-c.   A821 290p Any single   2.25 1.10

Bicentenary Regatta — A822

No. 1544 — Flags and: a, Ships. b, Map of South America, ship.

2010, Apr. 15   Litho.   Perf. 13¼
1544 A822 430p Horiz. pair, #a-b   3.50 1.75

Miniature Sheet

Pres. Eduardo Frei Montalva Antarctic Air Base, 40th Anniv. — A823

No. 1545: a, People near cargo airplane. b, Hangar. c, Airplane over base. d, Helicopter. e, Small airplane. f, Penguin, people, base.

2010, May 4
1545 A823 500p Sheet of 6, #a-
f   11.50 5.75

Bauer Tower, Vicuña, 105th Anniv. — A824

Designs: 500p, Tower. 3000p, Tower, diff.

2010, May 7
1546 A824 500p multi   1.90 .95
Souvenir Sheet
1547 A824 3000p multi   11.50 5.75

2010 World Cup Soccer Championships, South Africa — A825

No. 1548 — Flags of Chile and South Africa, emblem of Chile Soccer Federation and: a, Soccer ball and players. b, Map of Africa, leopard skin.

2010, June 25
1548 A825 500p Vert. pair, #a-b   3.75 1.90

Inauguration of Mini University of Tokyo Atacama Observatory Telescope, Mt. Chajnantor — A826

2010, July 7   Litho.   Perf. 13¼
1549 A826 430p multi   1.60 .80
Souvenir Sheet
1550 A826 3000p multi   11.00 5.50

Valparaiso, UNESCO World Heritage Site — A827

No. 1551: a, British Arch. b, Heroes of Iquique Monument.
No. 1552, horiz.: a, Palacio Polanco. b, Palacio Lyon.
No. 1553: a, Polanco Funicular. b, Artillería Funicular.
No. 1554, horiz.: a, Trolley bus with doors closed. b, Trolley bus with front doors open.

2010, July 12   Litho.   Perf. 13¼
1551 A827 10p Horiz. pair, #a-b   .20 .20
1552 A827 20p Horiz. pair, #a-b   .20 .20
1553 A827 50p Horiz. pair, #a-b   .40 .20
1554 A827 100p Horiz. pair, #a-b   .75 .40
       Nos. 1551-1554 (4)   1.55 1.00

Independence of Latin America, Bicent. — A828

2010, Sept. 10
1555 A828 430p multi   1.75 .85

La Serena — A829

No. 1556: a, Monumental Lighthouse. b, Plaza de Armas Fountain.

2010, Sept. 15
1556 A829 420p Pair, #a-b   3.50 1.75

Bicentennial Naval Review — A830

No. 1557: a, Steamship from 1910 naval review. b, Ships and sailing vessel with flags hoisted from 1910 naval review. c, Ships from 2010, denomination at UR. d, Ships from 2010, denomination at UL.

2010, Sept. 20
1557 A830 430p Block of 4, #a-d   7.25 3.75

Miniature Sheet

Antofagasta — A831

No. 1558: a, La Portada. b, Fishing terminal. c, Costanera Avenue. d, Historic District. e, Huanchaca Ruins. f, Antofagasta at night.

2010, Sept. 24
1558 A831 500p Sheet of 6, #a-
f   12.50 6.25

Arica — A832

No. 1559: a, Fountain, Morro de Arica. b, Fuerza del Sol Carnival.

2010, Sept. 30   Litho.   *Perf. 13¼*
1559 A832 420p Horiz. pair, #a-b 3.50 1.75

SEMI-POSTAL STAMPS

S. S. Abtao and Captain Policarpo Toro SP1

S. S. Abtao and Brother Eugenio Eyraud SP2

Perf. 14½x15
1940, Mar. 1   Engr.   Unwmk.
B1 SP1 80c + 2.20p dk grn
         & lake   2.50 2.00
B2 SP2 3.60p + 6.40p lake &
         dk grn   2.50 2.00
  a. Pair, #B1-B2   10.00 8.00
     Set, never hinged   8.00

50th anniv. of Chilean ownership of Easter Is. Surtax used for charitable institutions. Sheets containing 15 of each value, with 9 se-tenant pairs.

> Catalogue values for unused stamps in this section, from this point to the end of the section, are for Never Hinged items.

Pedro de Valdivia — SP3

Portraits: 10c+10c, Jose Toribio Medina.

1961, Apr. 29   Photo.   *Perf. 13x12½*
B3 SP3 5c + 5c pale brn & sl
         grn   1.40 .45
B4 SP3 10c +10c buff & vio blk 1.00 .35

Printed without charge by the Spanish Mint as a gift to Chile. The surtax was to aid the 1960 earthquake victims and to increase teachers' salaries. See Nos. CB1-CB2.

No. 402 Surcharged in Dark Green

1974, Mar. 25   Litho.   *Perf. 14½*
B5 A213 27e + 3e on 40c dl grn   .50 .25

Cent. of intl. meteorological cooperation. The 3e surtax of Nos. B5-B10 was for modernization of the postal system.

No. 412 Surcharged in Dark Blue

1974, Apr. 25   Litho.   *Perf. 14½*
B6 A219 27e + 3e on 1.95e   .50 .25

500th anniversary of the birth of Nicolaus Copernicus (1473-1534), Polish astronomer.

No. 329A Surcharged

1974, May 2   Litho.   *Perf. 14*
B7 A159 27e + 3e on 1e bluish
         grn   .40 .25

Centenary of the city of Vina del Mar.

#377 Surcharged in Blk, #395, 380 in Red

1974   Litho.   *Perf. 14½*
B8 A193 47e + 3e on 40c grn   .35 .25
B9 A207 67e + 3e on 40c multi   .40 .25
B10 A196 97e + 3e on 40c red
          brn   .35 .25
     Nos. B8-B10 (3)   1.10 .75

Issued: #B8, 6/7; #B9, 7/9; #B10, 6/20.

AIR POST STAMPS

Black Surcharge
Lithographed; Center Engraved
1927   Unwmk.   *Perf. 13½x14*
Black Brown & Blue

C1 40c on 10c   400.00 50.00
C2 80c on 10c   400.00 65.00
C3 1.20p on 10c   400.00 75.00
C4 1.60p on 10c   400.00 75.00
C5 2p on 10c   400.00 75.00
   Nos. C1-C5 (5)   2,000. 340.00

Issued for air post service between Santiago and Valparaiso. The stamps picture Bernardo O'Higgins and are not known without surcharge.

Regular Issues of 1915-28 Overprinted or Surcharged in Black, Red or Blue

Inscribed: "Chile Correos"
1928-29   *Perf. 13½x14, 14*
C6 A39 20c brn org & blk
          (Bk)   .30   .25
C6A A55 40c dk vio & blk (R)   .30   .20
C6B A43 1p grn & blk (Bl)   1.50   .50
C6C A43 2p red & blk (Bl)   2.00   .30
   f. 2p ver & blk (Bl)   65.00 15.00
C6D A43 5p ol grn & blk (Bl)   2.40   .75
C6E A50 6p on 10c dp bl &
          blk (R)   40.00 22.50
C7 A43 10p org & blk (Bk)
          ('29)   9.50 3.00
C8 A43 10p org & blk (Bl)   40.00 25.00
   Nos. C6-C8 (8)   96.00 52.50

On Nos. C6B to C6D, C7 and C8 the overprint is larger than on the other stamps of the issue.

Same Overprint or Surcharge on Nos. 155, 156, 158-161
Inscribed: "Chile Correos"
1928-32   Wmk. 215
C9 A55 40c vio & blk (R)   .55   .30
C10 A43 1p grn & blk (Bl)   1.50   .45
C11 A43 2p red & blk (Bl)   7.00 1.50
C12 A52 3p on 5c sl bl (R)   50.00 40.00
C13 A43 5p ol grn & blk (Bl)   6.00 1.50
C14 A43 10p org & blk (Bk)   27.50 7.25
   Nos. C9-C14 (6)   92.55 51.00

Same Overprint on Nos. 166-169, 172 and 158 in Black or Red
Inscribed: "Correos de Chile"
1928-30
C15 A39 20c (#166) ('29)   .75   .50
C16 A39 20c (#172) ('30)   .35   .20
C17 A40 25c bl & blk (R)   .45   .20
C18 A41 30c brn & blk   .20   .20
   a. Double ovpt., one inverted 250.00 250.00
C19 A42 50c dp grn & blk
          (R)   .25   .20
   Nos. C15-C19 (5)   2.00 1.30

Inscribed: "Chile Correos"
1932   *Perf. 13½x14, 14*
C21 A43 1p yel grn & blk (Bk)   2.75 1.50

Condor on Andes — AP1a

Airplane Crossing Andes — AP3

Los Cerrillos Airport — AP2

1931   Litho.   *Perf. 13½x14, 14½x14*
C22 AP1a 5c yellow grn   .25 .20
C23 AP1a 10c yellow brn   .25 .20
C24 AP1a 20c rose   .25 .20
C25 AP2 50c dark blue   1.50 .50
C26 AP3 50c black brn   .75 .20
C27 AP3 1p purple   .60 .20
C28 AP3 2p blue blk   .90 .30
   a. 2p bluish slate   1.00 .45
C29 AP2 5p lt red   3.00 .30
   Nos. C22-C29 (8)   7.50 2.10

For surcharges see Nos. C51-C53.

Airplane over City — AP4

Two Airplanes over Globe — AP9

Designs: 30c, 40c, 50c, Wings over Chile. 60c, Condor. 70c, Airplane and Star of Chile. 80c, Condor and Statue of Canpolican. 3p, 4p, 5p, Seaplane. 6p, 8p, 10p, Airplane. 20p, 30p, Airplane and Southern Cross. 40p, 50p, Airplane and symbols of space.

Perf. 13½x14
1934-39   Engr.   Wmk. 215
C30 AP4 10c yel grn ('35)   .30 .20
C31 AP4 15c dk grn ('35)   .45 .20
C32 AP4 20c dp bl ('36)   .20 .20
C33 AP4 30c blk brn ('35)   .20 .20
C34 AP4 40c indigo ('38)   .20 .20
C35 AP4 50c dk brn ('35)   .20 .20
C36 AP4 60c vio blk ('35)   .20 .20
C37 AP4 70c blue ('35)   .45 .20
C38 AP4 80c ol blk ('35)   .20 .20

Perf. 14
C39 AP9 1p slate blk   .20 .20
C40 AP9 2p grnsh bl   .20 .20
C41 AP9 3p org brn ('35)   .30 .20
C42 AP9 4p brn ('35)   .30 .20
C43 AP9 5p org red   .30 .20
C44 AP9 6p yel brn ('35)   .45 .20
   a. 6p brown ('39)   2.75 1.90
C45 AP9 8p grn ('35)   .40 .20
C46 AP9 10p brn lake   .45 .20
C47 AP9 20p olive   .45 .20
C48 AP9 30p gray blk   .50 .20
C49 AP9 40p gray vio   1.40 .70
C50 AP9 50p brn vio   1.60 .70
   Nos. C30-C50 (21)   8.95 5.20

Nos. C30-C50 have been re-issued in slightly different colors, with white gum. The first printings are considerably scarcer. See Nos. C90-C107B, C148-C154.

Types of 1931 Surcharged in Black or Red

Perf. 13½x14, 14½x14
1940   Wmk. 215
C51 AP1a 80c on 20c lt rose .65 .20
C52 AP2 1.60p on 5p lt red 4.50 .75
C53 AP3 5.10p on 2p sl bl (R) 2.10 1.25
   Nos. C51-C53 (3)   7.25 2.20

The surcharge on #C52 measures 21½mm.

Plane and Weather Vane — AP14

Plane and Caravel — AP23

Designs (Plane and): 20c, Globe. 30c, Chilean flag. 40c, Star of Chile and Southern Cross. 50c, Mountains. 60c, Tree. 70c, Lakes. 80c, Shore. 90c, Sunrise. 2p, Compass. 3p, Telegraph lines. 4p, Rainbow. 5p, Factory. 10p, Snow-capped mountain.

1941-42   Wmk. 215   Litho.   Perf. 14

C54	AP14	10c ol gray	.20	.20
C55	AP14	20c dp rose	.20	.20
C56	AP14	30c blue vio	.20	.20
C57	AP14	40c dl red brn	.20	.20
C58	AP14	50c red org ('42)	.35	.20
C59	AP14	60c dp green	.20	.20
C60	AP14	70c rose	.30	.25
C61	AP14	80c ultra ('42)	1.50	.45
C62	AP14	90c dk brown	.45	.25
C63	AP23	1p brt blue	.30	.20
C64	AP23	2p rose lake	.45	.20
C65	AP23	3p dk bl grn & yel grn	.65	.50
C66	AP23	4p bl vio & buff	1.00	.65
C67	AP23	5p dk org red ('42)	9.00	4.50
C68	AP23	10p gray grn & bl grn	5.00	3.50
		Nos. C54-C68 (15)	20.00	11.80

The 1p, dated "1541-1941", commemorates the 400th anniversary of Santiago.

1942-46   Unwmk.

C69	AP14	10c ultra ('43)	.20	.20
C70	AP14	10c rose lil ('45)	.20	.20
C71	AP14	20c dull grn ('43)	.20	.20
C72	AP14	20c cop brn ('45)	.20	.20
C73	AP14	30c dull vio ('44)	.20	.20
C74	AP14	30c ol blk ('45)	.20	.20
C75	AP14	40c red brn ('44)	.30	.20
C76	AP14	40c ultra ('45)	.20	.20
C77	AP14	50c rose ('45)	.20	.20
C78	AP14	50c org red ('45)	.20	.20
C79	AP14	60c orange	.20	.20
C79B	AP14	60c dp grn ('46)	.20	.20
C80	AP14	70c rose ('45)	.45	.35
C81	AP14	80c slate grn	.20	.20
C82	AP14	90c brown ('45)	.45	.35
C83	AP23	1p gray grn & lt bl ('43)	.25	.20
C84	AP23	2p org red ('43)	.45	.20
C85	AP23	3p dk pur & pale org ('43)	.45	.20
C86	AP23	4p bl grn & yel grn	.45	.35
C87	AP23	5p dk rose car ('43)	.35	.20
a.		5p dk car rose ('44)	.20	.20
C88	AP23	10p sapphire ('43)	.45	.35
		Nos. C69-C88 (21)	6.00	4.80

No. C83 is without dates "1541-1941." See Nos. C109-C123. For surcharges see Nos. C145-C147.

Coat of Arms and Plane AP29

1942, Nov. 5   Engr.   Perf. 14½

C89	AP29	100p car lake	25.00	20.00

University of Chile centenary.

Types of 1934-39
Perf. 13½x14

1944-55   Unwmk.   Engr.

C90	AP4	10c yel grn ('55)	.25	.20
C91	AP4	20c deep blue	.20	.20
C92	AP4	30c black brn	.20	.20
C93	AP4	40c indigo	.20	.20
C94	AP4	50c dk brn ('47)	.20	.20
C95	AP4	60c slate vio	.20	.20
C96	AP4	70c blue ('48)	.20	.20
C97	AP4	80c olive blk	.20	.20

Perf. 14

C98	AP9	1p slate blk	.20	.20
C99	AP9	2p grnsh bl	.25	.20
C100	AP9	3p org brn ('45)	.20	.20
C101	AP9	4p brown	.20	.20
C102	AP9	5p org red	.35	.20
C103	AP9	6p yel brn ('46)	.40	.20
C104	AP9	8p green	.40	.20
C105	AP9	10p brn lake	1.10	.20
C106	AP9	20p ol gray ('45)	.75	.20
C107				
a.		Imperf. pair	70.00	
C107B	AP9	50p rose vio ('50)	17.50	2.50
		Nos. C90-C107B (18)	23.00	5.90

Plane and Radio Tower — AP30

1945   Unwmk.   Litho.   Perf. 14

C108	AP30	1.60p brt violet	.55	.25

See Nos. C118-C119.

Types of 1941-45

1946-48   Wmk. 215

C109	AP14	10c rose lil ('47)	.20	.20
C110	AP14	20c dk red brn ('48)	.20	.20
C111	AP14	20c dull grn ('48)	1.50	.30
C112	AP14	30c black ('48)	.20	.20
C113	AP14	40c ultra ('48)	.20	.20
C114	AP14	60c ol grn ('48)	.20	.20
C115	AP14	80c ol blk ('48)	.20	.20
C116	AP14	90c choc ('48)	.20	.20
C117	AP23	1p gray grn & lt bl ('48)	.20	.20
C118	AP30	1.60p brt violet	.20	.20
C119	AP30	1.80p brt vio ('48)	.20	.20
C119A	AP23	2p org red	.40	.20
C120	AP23	3p dk pur & pale org ('47)	1.50	.30
C121	AP23	4p bl grn & yel grn ('48)	1.10	.45
C122	AP23	5p rose car ('47)	.80	.20
C123	AP23	10p sapphire ('47)	1.00	.20
		Nos. C109-C123 (16)	8.30	3.65

No. C117 is without dates "1541-1941." For surcharges see Nos. C145, C147.

Flora and Fauna Type of 1948

1948

C124	A118	3p Block of 25	50.00	
		Never hinged	60.00	
a.-y.		any single	1.40	1.40

Catalogue values for unused stamps in this section, from this point to the end of the section, are for Never Hinged items.

Air Line Emblem and Planes — AP32

1949   Wmk. 215   Litho.   Perf. 14

C125	AP32	2p ultra	.45	.25

20th anniversary of the establishment of Chile's National Air Line.

Benjamin Vicuna Mackenna AP33

Factory, Badge and Book AP34

1949, Mar. 22   Engr.   Perf. 13½x14

C126	AP33	3p dk car rose	.30	.20

Unwmk.

1949, Nov. 11   Litho.   Perf. 14

Design: 10p, Column and cogwheel.

C127	AP34	5p green	.85	.45
C128	AP34	10p red brown	1.40	.55

Centenary of the founding of Chile's School of Arts and Crafts.

Plane and Globe — AP35

1950, Jan.   Engr.

C129	AP35	5p green	.60	.20
C130	AP35	10p red brown	1.00	.60

75th anniv. of the UPU.

Plane over Snow-capped Mountain AP36

Araucarian Pine and Plane — AP38

Plane and: 40c, Coast and Sunrise. 60c, Over fishing boat. 2p, Chilean flag. 3p, Dock crane. 4p, Above river. 5p, Blast furnace. 10p, Mountain lake. 20p, Cable cars.

Imprint: "Especies Valoradas-Chile"

1950-54   Wmk. 215   Litho.   Perf. 14

C135	AP36	20c yel brn ('54)	.35	.20
C136	AP36	40c purple ('52)	.35	.20
C137	AP36	60c lt bl ('53)	1.60	.90
C138	AP38	1p dull green	.35	.20
C139	AP38	2p brown red	.35	.20
C140	AP38	3p violet bl	.35	.20
C141	AP38	4p red org ('54)	.35	.20
C142	AP38	5p violet	.35	.20
C143	AP38	10p yel brn ('53)	.35	.20
C144	AP38	20p red brn ('54)	.60	.20
		Nos. C135-C144 (10)	5.00	2.70

See Nos. C155-C164, C207-C212.

Nos. C115, C81 and C116 Surcharged with New Value in Carmine or Black

1951-52   Wmk. 215

C145	AP14	40c on 80c ol blk (C) ('52)	.25	.20

Unwmk.

C146	AP14	40c on 80c sl grn (C) ('52)	5.50	3.50

Wmk. 215

C147	AP14	1p on 90c choc	.25	.20
		Nos. C145-C147 (3)	6.00	3.90

Types of 1934-39

1951-53   Unwmk.   Engr.   Perf. 14

C148	AP9	1p deep blue	.20	.20
C149	AP9	2p blue	.35	.20
C150	AP9	6p bis brn ('52)	.45	.20
C151	AP9	30p dk gray ('53)	4.00	.60
C152	AP9	40p dk pur brn	12.00	1.60
C153	AP9	50p dark purple	20.00	6.50
		Nos. C148-C153 (6)	37.00	9.30

Wmk. 215

C154	AP9	50p dk pur ('52)	.80	.40

Types of 1950-54
Designs as Before
Imprint: "Especies Valoradas-Chile"

1951-55   Unwmk.   Litho.   Perf. 14

C155	AP36	20c yel brn ('54)	.20	.20
C156	AP36	40c purple	.20	.20
C157	AP36	60c lt blue ('53)	.25	.20
C158	AP38	1p dk bl grn ('55)	.20	.20
C159	AP38	2p brown red	.20	.20
C160	AP38	3p violet bl	.20	.20
C161	AP38	4p red org ('52)	.30	.20
C162	AP38	5p violet	.30	.20
C163	AP38	10p emerald	.30	.20
C164	AP38	20p brown	.40	.20
		Nos. C155-C164 (10)	2.55	2.00

San Martin Crossing Andes AP40

Wmk. 215

1951, Mar. 16   Engr.   Perf. 14½

C165	AP40	5p red violet	.90	.50

Gen. José de San Martín, death cent.

Isabella Type of Regular Issue, 1952.

1952, Mar. 21   Perf. 14

C166	A125	10p carmine	.70	.40

A souvenir card without franking value was issued for the Hispano-Chilean Philatelic Exhibition at Santiago, Oct. 12, 1969. It contains 2 imperf. stamps similar to Nos. 264 and C166-60c green and 10p rose red. Size: 115x137½mm.

Ancient Fortress AP42

1953, Apr. 28

C167	AP42	10p brown car	2.25	.45

4th centenary of the founding of Valdivia.

Stamp Centenary Type of 1953

1953, Oct. 15   Engr.   Perf. 14½

C168	A131	100p dp grnsh bl	2.75	1.00

An imperf. souvenir sheet contains one each of Nos. 276 and C168, with inscriptions in black at top and bottom center. Sheet measures 178x229mm. It is stated that this sheet was not valid for postage.

Early Plane and Stylized Modern Version — AP44

Unwmk.

1954, May 26   Engr.   Perf. 14

C170	AP44	3p deep blue	.30	.20

25th anniversary of the founding of Chile's National Air Line.

Domeyko Type of Regular Issue, 1954.

1954, Aug. 16   Perf. 13½x14

C171	A134	5p orange brown	.30	.20

Railroad Type of Regular Issue, 1954

1954, Sept. 10   Wmk. 215   Perf. 14½

C172	A135	10p dk purple	1.00	.20

An imperforate souvenir sheet contains one each of Nos. 283 and C172. Size: 174x232mm. Value, $200.

Presidential Visits Type of 1955

1955, May 24

C173	A139	100p red	1.50	1.25

Jet Plane in Clouds — AP48

Comet Air
Liner — AP49

Designs: 2p, Helicopter over bridge. 10p, Oil derricks and plane. 50p, Control tower and plane. 200p, Beechcraft monoplane. 500p, Douglas DC-6.

Perf. 14½x14, 14x13½ (AP49)

1955-56		Engr.	Wmk. 215	
C174	AP48	1p dp red lil ('56)	.20	.20
C175	AP48	2p pale brn ('56)	.20	.20
C176	AP48	10p bluish grn ('56)	.20	.20
C177	AP48	50p rose ('56)	.60	.25
C178	AP49	100p green	1.00	.20
C179	AP49	200p dp ultra	6.50	.90
C180	AP49	500p dk carmine	7.50	.90
		Nos. C174-C180 (7)	16.20	2.85

Stamps similar to type AP49, but inscribed in escudo currency, are listed as type AP58.

1956-58 Unwmk.

Designs: 5p, Train and plane. 20p, Jet plane and Easter Island statue.

C183	AP48	5p violet	.20	.20
C184	AP48	10p grn ('57)	.20	.20
C185	AP48	20p ultra	.20	.20
C186	AP48	50p rose ('57)	.20	.20
C187	AP49	100p bl grn ('57)	.55	.20
a.		Lithographed ('60)	.55	.20
C188	AP49	200p dp ultra ('57)	.65	.20
C189	AP49	500p car ('58)	.85	.20
		Nos. C183-C189 (7)	2.85	1.40

Symbols of University
Departments — AP50

Design: 100p, View of the University.

1956, Dec. 15	Unwmk.		Perf. 14½
C190	AP50	20p green	.35	.20
C191	AP50	100p dk vio bl	1.40	.80

25th anniversary of the Federico Santa Maria Technical University, Valparaiso.
A souvenir sheet contains one each of Nos. 299, C190-C191, imperf. It was not issued for postal use, though some served postally. Size: 127x160mm. Value, $125.

Mistral Type of Regular Issue, 1958

1958, Jan. 10	Engr.		Perf. 14
C192	A144	100p green	.25	.20

Ambrosio
O'Higgins — AP51

1958, Mar. 23

C193	AP51	100p lt blue	.40	.20

Founding of the city of Osorno, 500th anniv.
A souvenir sheet contains one each of Nos. 302 and C193, imperf. and printed in red brown. It was not issued for postal use, though some served postally. Size: 155x138mm. Value, $70.

Exhibition Type of Regular Issue

1958, Oct. 18 Unwmk.

C194	A146	50p dull green	.45	.45

A souvenir sheet contains one each of Nos. 303 and C194, imperf. and printed in deep red. It was not issued for postal use, though some served postally. Size: 188x220mm. Value, $55.

Bank Type of Regular Issue, 1958.

1958, Dec. 18	Engr.		Perf. 14
C195	A147	50p redsh brown	.25	.25

A souvenir sheet contains one each of Nos. 304 and C195, printed in dull violet, imperf. It was not issued for postal use, though some served postally. Value, $190.

Antarctic Types of Regular Issue

1958	Litho.		Perf. 14
C199	A149	20p violet	.50	.20
	Engr.		
C200	A150	500p dark blue	3.75	1.75

Symbols of
Various
Religions
AP52

Perf. 14½

1959, Jan. 23	Unwmk.		Engr.
C206	AP52	50p dk car rose	.30	.20

10th anniversary of the Universal Declaration of Human Rights.

Types of 1950-54.

Imprint: "Casa de Moneda de Chile."

Designs: 50p, Plane silhouette over shore. 100p, Plane over map of Antarctica. 200p, Plane over natural arch rock.

1959		Litho.	Perf. 14
C207	AP38	1p dk blue grn	.85	.50
a.		Wmk. 215	30.00	
C208	AP38	10p emerald	.55	.20
C209	AP38	20p red brown	.35	.20
C210	AP38	50p yellow grn	.35	.20
C211	AP38	100p car rose	.35	.20
C212	AP38	200p brt blue	.55	.20
		Nos. C207-C212 (6)	3.00	1.50

Carlos Anwandter
AP53

1959, June 18	Engr.		Perf. 14
C213	AP53	20p rose carmine	.25	.25

Centenary of the German School in Valdivia, founded by Carlos Anwandter.
A souvenir sheet contains one each of Nos. 319 and C213, imperf. It was not issued for postal use, though some served postally. Value, $75.

IGY Type of Regular Issue, 1958.

1959, Aug. 28	Unwmk.		Perf. 14
C214	A148	50p green	.70	.20

Ladrillero Type of Regular Issue

1959, Aug. 28			Litho.
C215	A154	50p green	.50	.20

Barros Arana Type of Regular Issue

1959, Aug. 28

C216	A155	100p purple	.50	.20

Red Cross Type of Regular Issue

1959, Oct. 6

C217	A156	50p red & blk	.60	.20

WRY Type of Regular Issue, 1960.

1960, Apr. 7	Unwmk.		Perf. 14½
C218	A160	10c violet	.35	.20

A souvenir sheet contains two stamps similar to Nos. 330 and C218, the 1c printed in blue, the 10c airmail in maroon. The sheet is imperf., printed on thin cardboard. Size: 160x204mm. Value, $125.

Type of Regular Issue, 1960-62, and

José Agustin Eyzaguirre and José
Miguel Infante — AP54

Designs: 2c, Palace of Justice. 5c, National memorial. No. C220, Arms of Chile. No. C220A, José Gaspar Marin and J. Gregorio Argomedo. 50c, Archbishop J. I. Cienfuegos and Brother Camilo Henriquez. 1e, Bernardo O'Higgins.

1960-65	Unwmk.	Engr.	Perf. 14½
C218A	AP54	2c mar & gray vio ('62)	.20	.20
C219	A162	5c vio bl & dl pur ('61)	.20	.20
	Wmk. 215		
C220	A161	10c dk brn & red brn	.20	.20
	Unwmk.		
C220A	AP54	10c vio brn & brn ('64)	.40	.25
C220B	AP54	20c dk bl & dl pur ('64)	.25	.20
C220C	AP54	50c bl grn & ind ('65)	1.00	.25
C220D	A162	1e dk red & red brn ('63)	1.00	.40
		Nos. C218A-C220D (7)	3.25	1.70

150th anniv. of the formation of the 1st Natl. Government.
A souvenir sheet contains two airmail stamps: a 5c brown similar to No. C219 (National Memorial) and a 10c green, type A161. The sheet is imperf., printed on heavy paper with papermaker's watermark. Size: 120x168mm. Value, $85.

Map and Rotary
Emblem — AP55

Unwmk.

1960, Dec. 1	Litho.		Perf. 14
C221	AP55	10c blue	.50	.20

South American Rotary Regional Conference, Santiago, 1960.
A souvenir sheet contains one 10c maroon, type AP55, with brown marginal inscription. Size: 118x158mm. Value, $65.
The souvenir sheet was overprinted in green "El Mundo Unida Contra la Malaria" and the outline of a mosquito, and released in October, 1962. Value, $110.

Araucan pine
and
plane — AP56

Designs: 2m, Chilean flag and plane. 3m, Plane and dock crane. 4m, Plane above river (vignette like AP39). 5m, Blast furnace. 1c, Plane over mountain lake. 2c, Plane over cable cars. 5c, Plane silhouette over shore. 10c, Plane over map of Antarctica. 20c, Plane over natural arch rock.

Imprint: "Casa de Moneda de Chile."

1960-62		Litho.	Perf. 14
C222	AP56	1m orange	.20	.20
C223	AP56	2m yellow grn	.20	.20
C224	AP56	3m violet	.20	.20
C225	AP56	4m gray olive	.20	.20
C226	AP56	5m brt bl grn	.20	.20
C227	AP56	1c ultra	.20	.20
C228	AP56	2c red brn ('61)	.35	.20
C229	AP56	5c yel grn ('61)	1.75	.20
C230	AP56	10c car rose ('62)	.45	.20
C231	AP56	20c brt bl ('62)	.50	.20
		Nos. C222-C231 (10)	4.25	2.00

Oil Derricks and
Douglas DC-
6 — AP57

Beechcraft
Monoplane
AP58

5m, Train and plane. 2c, Jet plane & Easter Island statue. 5c, Control tower & plane. 10c, Comet airliner. 50c, Douglas DC-6.

Perf. 14x13½

1960-67		Unwmk.	Litho.
C234	AP57	5m red brown	.35	.35
C235	AP57	1c dull blue	.35	.35
C236	AP57	2c ultra ('62)	.35	.35
C237	AP57	5c rose red ('64)	.35	.35
C238	AP58	10c ultra ('67)	.35	.35
C239	AP58	20c car ('62)	.35	.35
C240	AP58	50c green ('63)	.35	.35
		Nos. C234-C240 (7)	2.45	2.45

Stamps similar to type AP58, but inscribed in peso ($) currency, are listed as type AP49.

Congress Type of Regular Issue.

1961, Oct. 5			Perf. 14½
C245	A164	10c gray green	.95	.60

Soccer Type of Regular Issue, 1962.

Designs: 5c, Goalkeeper and stadium, vert. 10c, Soccer players and globe.

1962, May 30	Unwmk.		Engr.
C246	A165	5c rose lilac	.20	.20
C247	A165	10c dk carmine	.25	.20

A souvenir sheet of four contains one each of Nos. 340-341, C246-C247, imperf., with light brown marginal inscriptions. Size: 123x194mm. Sold for 7.50 escudos (face value, 22 centavos). Value $12.

Hunger Type of Regular Issue.

20c, Mother with empty bowl, horiz.

1963, Mar. 21	Litho.		Perf. 14
C248	A166	20c green	.25	.20

Red Cross Type of Regular Issue.

Design: 20c, Centenary emblem and plane silhouette, horiz.

1963, Sept. 6	Unwmk.		Perf. 14
C249	A167	20c gray & red	.25	.20

Fire
Engine of
1860's
AP59

1963, Dec. 20	Litho.		Perf. 14½
C250	AP59	30c red	.50	.20

Centenary of the Santiago Fire Brigade.

Western
Hemisphere
AP60

1964, Apr. 9	Unwmk.		Perf. 14½
C254	AP60	4c ultra	.40	.20

Issued in memory of President John F. Kennedy and to honor the Alliance for Progress.

Battle of Rancagua — AP61

1965, May 7   Engr.   Perf. 14½
C255 AP61 5c dull grn & sepia   .40   .20
Battle of Rancagua, 10/7/14, 150th anniv.

ITU Emblem, Old and New Communication Equipment AP62

1965, May 7   Litho.   Perf. 14½x14
C256 AP62 40c red & maroon   .40   .20
ITU centenary.

Portrait Type of 1964
Portraits: No. C257, Enrique Molina. No. C258, Msgr. Carlos Casanueva.

1965, June   Litho.   Perf. 14
C257 A169 60c brt violet   .30   .20
C258 A169 60c green   .30   .20
See note after No. 346.

Skier Type of Regular Issue 1965
Design: 20c, Skier, horiz.

1965, Aug. 30   Unwmk.   Perf. 14
C259 A172 20c ultra   .30   .20

Fishing Boats, Angelmo Harbor AP63   Aviators' Monument AP64

1965
C260 AP63 40c brown   .30   .20
Perf. 14x14½
C262 AP64 1e car rose   .30   .20

Andrés Bello (1780?-1865), Venezuela-born Writer and Educator — AP65

1965, Nov. 29   Engr.   Unwmk.
C263 AP65 10c dk car rose   .35   .35

Skiers — AP66

Basketball AP67

1966, Apr. 6   Litho.   Perf. 14
C264 AP66 4e dk bl & red brn   1.25   .20
World Skiing Championships, Partillo, Aug. 1966.

1966, Apr. 28
C265 AP67 13c rose carmine   .40   .20
International Basketball Championships.

Slalom AP68

Perf. 14½x15
1966, July 20   Litho.   Unwmk.
C266 AP68 75c rose car & lil   .40   .20
C267 AP68 3e ultra & lt bl   .40   .20
Intl. Skiing Championships, Partillo, August 1966. A souvenir sheet of 2 contains imperf. stamps similar to Nos. C266-C267. No gum. Size: 109x140mm. Value $36.

Ship Type of Regular Issue
1966   Litho.   Perf. 14½
C268 A175 70c Prus grn & yel grn   .35   .20
See note below No. 358.

ICY Type of Regular Issue
1966, Oct. 28   Unwmk.   Perf. 14½
C269 A177 3e blue & carmine   .50   .25
A souvenir sheet of 2 contains imperf. stamps similar to Nos. 360 and C269. No gum. Size: 111x140mm. Value $7.50.

Chilean Flag and Ships — AP69

1966, Nov. 21   Litho.   Perf. 14
C270 AP69 13c dull red brn   .40   .20
Centenary of the city of Antofagasta.

Pardo Type of Regular Issue
40c, Pardo & map of Chile's claim to Antarctica.

1967, Jan. 6   Unwmk.   Perf. 14½
C271 A178 40c ultra   .50   .20
See note below No. 361.

Family Type of Regular Issue
1967, Apr. 13   Litho.   Perf. 14
C272 A179 80c brt bl & blk   .35   .20

Ruben Dario and Title Page of "Azul" AP70

1967, May 15   Engr.   Perf. 14½
C273 AP70 10c dark blue   .30   .20
Ruben Dario (pen name of Felix Ruben Garcia Sarmiento, 1867-1916), Nicaraguan poet, newspaper correspondent and diplomat.

Tree Type of Regular Issue
1967, June 9
C274 A180 75c grn & pale rose   .35   .20

Lions Type of Regular Issue
1967   Litho.   Perf. 14
C275 A181 1e purple & yel   .40   .25
C276 A181 5e blue & yel   1.10   .30
A souvenir sheet without franking value contains 3 imperf. stamps, 20c, 1e and 5e, in violet blue and yellow. Size: 110x140mm. Value, $13.50.
Issue dates: 1e, July 12; 5e, Aug. 11.

Flag Type of Regular Issue
1967, Oct. 20   Unwmk.   Perf. 14½
C277 A182 50c ultra & crimson   .35   .20

ITY Emblem AP71

1967, Nov. 22   Litho.   Perf. 14½
C278 AP71 30c lt vio bl & blk   .35   .20
Issued for International Tourist Year, 1967.

Caro Type of Regular Issue, 1967.
1967, Dec. 4   Engr.   Perf. 14½
C279 A183 40c violet   .70   .35

Type of Regular Issue, 1968
1968, Apr. 23   Litho.   Perf. 14½
C280 A184 2e brt violet   .60   .25
Sesquicentennial of the Battles of Chacabuco and Maipu. A souvenir sheet of 2 contains imperf. stamps similar to Nos. 367 and C280. Value, $12. A second sheet exists with the 2e in green and the 3e in brown. Size: 139½x100mm. Value, $12.

Farm Type of Regular Issue
1968, June 18   Unwmk.
C281 A185 50c blk, org & grn   .35   .20

Juan I. Molina, Educator and Scientist AP72

1968, Aug. 27   Litho.   Perf. 14½
C282 AP72 1e bright green   .30   .20

Map of Chiloé Province — AP73

Perf. 14½
1968, Oct. 7   Unwmk.   Litho.
C283 AP73 1e rose claret   .35   .35
Anniversaries of the founding of five towns in Chiloé Province.

Auto Club Type of Regular Issue
1968, Nov. 10   Engr.   Perf. 14½x14
C284 A189 5e ultra   .35   .20

British Crown and Map of Chile — AP74

1968, Nov. 12   Litho.   Perf. 14½
50c, Chilean coat of arms (horiz.; similar to type A161). 3e, British coat of arms, horiz.
C285 AP74 50c green & brn   .25   .20
C286 AP74 3e bl & org brn   .40   .20
Engr.
C287 AP74 5e purple & mag   .60   .20
Nos. C285-C287 (3)   1.25   .60
Visit of Queen Elizabeth II of Great Britain, Nov. 11-18. A souvenir sheet of 3 contains imperf., lithographed stamps similar to Nos. C285-C287. Size: 124½x190mm. The souvenir sheet also publicizes the British-Chilean Philatelic Exhibition. Value, $20.

First Coin Minted in Chile and Coin Press AP75

Design: 1e, Chile No. 128.

1968, Dec. 31   Litho.   Perf. 14½
C288 AP75 50c ocher & vio brn   .30   .20
C289 AP75 1e lt bl & dp org   .30   .20
225th anniversary of the founding of the State Mint (Casa de Moneda de Chile). A souvenir sheet of 4 contains imperf. stamps similar to Nos. 373-374, C288-C289. Size: 150x119mm. Value, $10.

Satellite Type of Regular Issue
1969, May 20   Litho.   Perf. 14½
C290 A191 2e rose lilac   .30   .20

Red Cross Type of Regular Issue
1969, Sept.   Litho.   Perf. 14½
C291 A192 5e black & red   .50   .20
A souvenir card contains 2 imperf. stamps similar to Nos. 376 and C291, with red marginal inscription. Size: 109x140mm. Value $5.

Dam Type of Regular Issue
1969, Nov. 18   Litho.   Perf. 14½
C292 A193 3e blue   .50   .20

Rodriguez Type of Regular Issue
1969, Nov. 24
C293 A194 30c brown   .35   .20

EXPO '70 Type of Regular Issue
1969, Dec. 1   Litho.   Perf. 14
C294 A195 5e red   .35   .20

Bible Type of 1969
1969, Dec. 2   Perf. 14½
C295 A196 1e green   .30   .20

ILO Type of Regular Issue
1969, Dec. 17   Perf. 14½
C296 A197 2e rose lil & blk   .35   .20

Human Rights Year Type of 1969
1969, Dec. 18
C297 A198 4e brown & red   .35   .35
A souvenir sheet of 2 contains imperf. stamps similar to Nos. 382 and C297. Size: 110x140mm. Value, $9.

Easter Island Type of 1970
1970, Jan. 26
C298 A199 50c dull grnsh bl   .70   .20

Ship Type of Regular Issue
1970, Feb. 4   Litho.   Perf. 14½
C299 A200 2e deep ultra   .40   .20

Rotary Type of Regular Issue

1970, Mar. 18   **Litho.**   *Perf. 14*
C300 A201 1e rose claret   .35 .25

Gandhi Type of Regular Issue

1970, Apr. 1   **Litho.**   *Perf. 14½*
C301 A202 1e red brown   .40 .20

Education Year Type of 1970

1970, July 17   **Litho.**   *Perf. 14½*
C302 A204 4e red brown   .30 .25

National Shrine Type of 1970

1970, July 28   **Litho.**   *Perf. 14½*
C303 A205 1e ultra   .35 .20

Cancer Type of Regular Issue

1970, Aug. 11
C304 A206 2e brn & lt olive   .40 .20

A few stampss are known inscribed "Correos de Chile" instead of "Correos Aereo Chile." Value $350.

Copper Type of Regular Issue

1970, Oct. 21   **Litho.**   *Perf. 14½*
C305 A207 3e grn & lt red brn   .50 .20

United Nations Type of 1970

1970, Oct. 22
C306 A208 5e dk car & grn   .50 .20

Freighter Type of Regular Issue

1971, Jan. 18   **Litho.**   *Perf. 14*
C307 A209 5e lt red brown   .50 .20

No. C290 Surcharged in Red

1971, Jan. 21   **Litho.**   *Perf. 14½*
C308 A191 52c on 2e rose lil   .40 .20

Liberation Type of Regular Issue

1971, Feb. 3   *Perf. 14½*
C309 A210 1e gray bl & brn   .40 .20

UNICEF Type of Regular Issue

1971, Feb. 11   **Litho.**   *Perf. 14½*
C310 A211 2e blue & grn   .30 .20

Boy Scout Type of Regular Issue

1971, Feb. 10   *Perf. 14*
C311 A212 5c dk car & ol   .40 .20

Satellite Type of Regular Issue

1971, May 25   **Litho.**   *Perf. 14½*
C312 A213 2e brown   .40 .20

De Ercilla Type of Regular Issue

1972, Mar. 20   **Engr.**   *Perf. 14*
C313 A221 2e Prussian blue   .30 .20

A souvenir card contains impressions of Nos. 414 and C313 with black marginal inscription commemorating España 75 Philatelic Exhibition. Size: 165x220mm. Value $19.

AIR POST SEMI-POSTAL STAMPS

> Catalogue values for unused stamps in this section are for Never Hinged items.

Type of Semi-Postal Stamps, 1961

Portraits: 10c+10c, Alonso de Ercilla. 20c+20c, Gabriela Mistral.

Perf. 13x12½
1961, Apr. 29   **Photo.**   **Unwmk.**
CB1 SP3 10c + 10c salmon & choc   1.00 .30
CB2 SP3 20c + 20c gray & dp cl   1.00 .30

Printed without charge by the Spanish Mint as a gift to Chile. The surtax was to aid the 1960 earthquake victims and to increase teachers' salaries.

ACKNOWLEDGMENT OF RECEIPT STAMPS

AR1

1894   **Unwmk.**   *Perf. 11½*
H1 AR1 5c brown   .75 .50
   a. Imperf., pair   3.00

The black stamp of design similar to AR1 inscribed "Avis de Paiement" was prepared for use on notices of payment of funds but was not regularly issued.

POSTAGE DUE STAMPS

D1   D2

Handstamped

1894   **Unwmk.**   *Perf. 13*
J1 D1 2c black, *straw*   11.00 5.00
J2 D1 4c black, *straw*   11.00 5.00
J3 D1 6c black, *straw*   11.00 5.00
J4 D1 8c black, *straw*   11.00 5.00
J5 D2 10c black, *straw*   11.00 5.00
J6 D1 16c black, *straw*   11.00 5.00
J7 D1 20c black, *straw*   11.00 5.00
J8 D1 30c black, *straw*   11.00 5.00
J9 D1 40c black, *straw*   11.00 5.00
   Nos. J1-J9 (9)   99.00 45.00

J1a D1 2c black, *yellow*   45.00 42.50
J2a D1 4c black, *yellow*   37.50 30.00
J3a D1 6c black, *yellow*   27.50 25.00
J4a D1 8c black, *yellow*   11.00 9.00
J5a D2 10c black, *yellow*   11.00 9.00
J6a D1 16c black, *yellow*   11.00 9.00
J7a D1 20c black, *yellow*   11.00 9.00
J8a D1 30c black, *yellow*   11.00 9.00
J9a D1 40c black, *yellow*   11.00 9.00
   Nos. J1a-J9a (9)   176.00 151.50

Counterfeits exist.

D3

1895   **Litho.**   *Perf. 11*
J19 D3 1c red, *yellow*   5.00 2.00
J20 D3 2c red, *yellow*   5.00 2.00
J21 D3 4c red, *yellow*   4.25 2.00
J22 D3 6c red, *yellow*   5.00 2.00
J23 D3 8c red, *yellow*   3.25 2.00
J24 D3 10c red, *yellow*   3.25 3.00
J25 D3 20c red, *yellow*   3.25 1.50
J26 D3 40c red, *yellow*   3.25 2.00
J27 D3 50c red, *yellow*   3.25 2.00
J28 D3 60c red, *yellow*   6.50 3.00
J29 D3 80c red, *yellow*   6.50 4.25
J30 D3 1p red, *yellow*   6.50 4.25
   Nos. J19-J30 (12)   55.00 30.00

Nos. J19-J30 were printed in sheets of 100 (10x10) containing all 12 denominations. Counterfeits of Nos. J19-J42 exist.

1896   *Perf. 13½*
J31 D3 1c red, *straw*   .75 .35
J32 D3 2c red, *straw*   .75 .35
J33 D3 4c red, *straw*   1.00 .35
J34 D3 6c red, *straw*   2.00 .75
J35 D3 8c red, *straw*   1.00 .40
J36 D3 10c red, *straw*   .75 .40
J37 D3 20c red, *straw*   .75 .40
J38 D3 40c red, *straw*   12.00 10.00
J39 D3 50c red, *straw*   12.00 10.00
J40 D3 60c red, *straw*   12.00 10.00
J41 D3 80c red, *straw*   12.00 10.00
J42 D3 100c red, *straw*   25.00 21.00
   Nos. J31-J42 (12)   80.00 64.00

D4   D5

1898   *Perf. 13*
J43 D4 1c scarlet   .35 .30
J44 D4 2c scarlet   .90 .60
J45 D4 4c scarlet   .35 .30
J46 D4 10c scarlet   .35 .30
J47 D4 20c scarlet   .35 .30
   Nos. J43-J47 (5)   2.30 1.80

1924   *Perf. 11½, 12½*
J48 D5 2c blue & red   .75 .60
J49 D5 4c blue & red   .75 .60
J50 D5 8c blue & red   .75 .60
J51 D5 10c blue & red   .75 .60
J52 D5 20c blue & red   .75 .35
J53 D5 40c blue & red   .75 .60
J54 D5 60c blue & red   .75 .60
J55 D5 80c blue & red   .75 .60
J56 D5 1p blue & red   1.00 .75
J57 D5 2p blue & red   1.75 1.25
J58 D5 5p blue & red   1.75 1.25
   Nos. J48-J58 (11)   10.50 7.80

Nos. J48-J58 were printed in sheets of 150 containing all 11 denominations, and in sheets of 50 containing the five lower denominations, providing various se-tenants.

All values of this issue exist imperforate, also with center inverted, but are not believed to have been regularly issued. Those with inverted centers sell for about 10 times normal stamps.

OFFICIAL STAMPS

For Domestic Postage

O1

Single-lined frame
Control number in violet

1907   **Unwmk.**   **Imperf.**
O1 O1 dl bl, "CARTA" org   22.50 17.50
O2 O1 red, "OFICIO" bl   22.50 17.50
O3 O1 vio, "PAQUETE" red   22.50 17.50
O4 O1 org, *bl,* "EP" vio   22.50 17.50
   Nos. O1-O4 (4)   90.00 70.00

The diagonal inscription in differing color indicates type of usage: CARTA for letters of ordinary weight; OFICIO, heavy letters to 100 grams; PAQUETE, parcels to 100 grams; E P (Encomienda Postal), heavier parcels; C (Certificado), as on No. O8, registration including postage.

Varieties include CARTA, PAQUETE and E P inverted, OFICIO omitted, etc.

Double-lined frame

Large control number in black

Perf. 11
O5 O1 bl, "CARTA" yel   8.00 7.00
O6 O1 red, "OFICIO" bl   8.00 5.25
O7 O1 brn, "PAQUETE" grn   8.00 5.25
O8 O1 grn, "C" red   110.00 82.50
   Nos. O5-O8 (4)   134.00 100.00

Nos. O5-O8 exist in tête bêche pairs; with CARTA, OFICIO or PAQUETE double or inverted, and other varieties.
Counterfeits of Nos. O1-O8 exist.

For Foreign Postage

Regular Issues of
1892-1909
Overprinted in Red —
a

On Stamps of 1904-09
1907   *Perf. 12*
O9 A14 1c green   7.50 7.50
   a. Inverted overprint   17.50
O10 A12 3c on 1p brn   14.00 13.00
   a. Inverted overprint   52.50

O11 A14 5c ultra   10.00 9.50
   a. Inverted overprint   35.00
O12 A15 10c gray & blk   10.50 10.50
O13 A15 15c vio & blk   14.00 13.00
O14 A15 20c org brn & blk   14.00 14.00
O15 A15 50c ultra & blk   45.00 45.00

On Stamp of 1892
Rouletted
O16 A6 1p dk brn & blk   110.00 87.50
   Nos. O9-O16 (8)   225.00 200.00

Counterfeits of Nos. O9-O16 exist.

Regular Issues of
1915-25 Overprinted
in Red or Blue — **b**

1926   *Perf. 13½x14, 14*
O17 A52 5c slate bl (R)   2.50 .50
O18 A50 10c bl & blk (R)   4.00 .75
O19 A39 20c org red & blk (Bl)   2.00 .40
O20 A42 50c dp grn & blk (Bl)   2.00 .40
O21 A43 1p grn & blk (R)   2.75 .40
O22 A43 2p ver & blk (Bl)   4.00 1.00
   Nos. O17-O22 (6)   17.25 3.75

Nos. O21 and O22 are overprinted vertically at each side.
Nos. O17 to O22 were for the use of the Biblioteca Nacional.

Regular Issue of
1915-25 Overprinted
in Red — **c**

1928   *Perf. 13½x14, 14*
O23 A50 10c bl & blk   6.50 2.00
O24 A39 20c brn org & blk   3.00 1.00
O25 A40 25c dl bl & blk   7.50 1.00
O26 A42 50c dp grn & blk   4.00 1.00
O27 A43 1p grn & blk   5.00 1.50
   Nos. O23-O27 (5)   26.00 6.50

The overprint on Nos. O23 to O26 is 16½mm high; on No. O27 it is 20mm.

Regular Issues of
1928-30 Overprinted
in Red — **d**

On Stamp Inscribed: "Correos de Chile"

1930-31
O28 A50 10c bl & blk   3.00 1.50

Wmk. 215
On Stamps Inscribed: "Correos de Chile"
O29 A50 10c bl & blk   6.00 3.00
O30 A39 20c org red & blk   .75 .50
O31 A40 25c bl & blk   .75 .50
O32 A42 50c dp grn & blk   1.00 .75

On Stamps Inscribed: "Chile Correos"
O33 A42 50c dp grn & blk   1.50 .75
O34 A43 1p grn & blk   1.50 .75
   Nos. O28-O34 (7)   15.00 7.75

Same Overprint on No. 181
1933   *Perf. 13½x14*
O35 A61 20c dk brn   .75 .25

Same Overprint in Red on No. 182
1935   **Wmk. 215**
O36 A62 10c deep blue   .75 .50

No. 163 Ovptd. Type "b" in Red
Inscribed: "Correos de Chile"
1934
O37 A52 5c lt grn   .60 .50

Overprint "b" on No. 182
1935
O38 A62 10c dp bl   .50 .50

Same Overprint in Black on No. 181
1936 **Wmk. 215** *Perf. 13½x14*
O39 A61 20c dk brn 10.00 .50

Overprint "b" in Red on No. 158
1938 *Perf. 14*
O40 A43 1p grn & blk 2.50 1.00

Nos. 204 and 205 Overprinted Type "d" in Black
1939 *Perf. 13½x14, 14*
O41 A78 50c violet 4.00 2.50
O42 A84 1p org brn 5.00 4.00

Stamps of 1938-40 Overprinted Type "b" in Black, Red or Blue
1940-46 *Perf. 13½x14, 14*
O43 A78 10c sal pink ('45) 2.00 1.75
O44 A78 15c brn org 1.00 .40
O45 A78 20c lt bl (R) ('42) 1.50 .60
O46 A78 30c brn pink (Bl) .75 .40
O47 A78 40c lt grn .75 .40
O48 A78 50c vio ('45) 4.00 .75
O49 A84 1p org brn ('42) 2.50 .75
O50 A84 1.80p dp bl (R) ('45) 10.00 6.00
O51 A84 2p car lake ('42) 2.00 1.25
Nos. O43-O51 (9) 24.50 12.30

Overprint "b" in Black on Nos. 223, 225
Unwmk.
O58 A84 1p brn org 2.50 1.50
O59 A84 2p car lake ('46) 5.00 2.00

Regular Issues of 1938-43 Overprinted Diagonally in Carmine, Black or Blue — e

Wmk. 215, Unwmkd.
1948-54 *Perf. 13½x14, 14*
O60 A78 20c lt bl, #219 (C) .75 .35
O61 A78 30c brt pink, #202 (Bl) ('54) 1.50 .50
O62 A78 40c brt grn, #203 ('54) 2.50 1.25
O63 A78 50c vio #222 ('49) .75 .40
O64 A84 1p org brn, #205 2.50 1.00
O65 A84 2p car lake, #207 ('54) 1.00 .50
O66 A84 5p dk sl grn, #208 (C) ('51) 1.75 1.00
Nos. O60-O66 (7) 10.75 5.00

Overprint "e" Diagonally on Nos. 265 and 275 in Red or Black
Wmk. 215, Unwmkd.
1953-55 *Perf. 13½x14, 13x14*
O67 A126 1p dk bl grn, #265 (R) 1.00 .50
O68 A126 1p dk bl grn, #265 (Bk) ('55) .75 .50
O69 A126 1p dk bl grn, #275 (R) ('55) .75 .50
Nos. O67-O69 (3) 2.50 1.50

Overprint "e" Horizontally on Nos. 207, 209 in Black or Blue
1955-56 **Wmk. 215** *Perf. 14*
O70 A84 2p car lake ('56) 1.75 .75
O71 A84 10p rose vio (Bl) 2.75 1.75

Overprint "e" Horizontally on Nos. 293-295 and Types of 1956 Regular Issue in Black or Red
1956 **Unwmk.** *Perf. 14x14½*
O72 A141 2p purple 1.00 .60
O73 A142 3p lt vio bl (R) 3.00 2.00
O74 A141 5p redsh brn .75 .35
O75 A142 10p vio (19x22¼mm) (R) 3.00 1.75
a. Perf. 13½x14 (19½x22¼mm) ('58) .50 .40
O76 A141 50p rose red 2.50 1.00

No. 310 Overprinted in Red Vertically, Reading Down, Similar to Type "e"
Size of Overprint: 21x2½mm
1958 **Litho.** *Perf. 14*
O77 A149 10p vio blue 200.00 30.00

Overprint "e" Horizontally on No. 327 in Red
1960 **Unwmk.** *Perf. 13x14*
O79 A157 5c blue 1.75 .70

POSTAL TAX STAMPS

Talca Issue.
A 10c blue postal tax stamp, inscribed "Bicentenario de Talca" and picturing a coat of arms, was issued in 1942. It was sold only in Talca and was required for a time on all domestic letters sent from that city. The tax helped pay for Talca's bicentenary celebration. Value 20 cents.

Nos. 326 and 347 Surcharged

1970 Unwmk. Litho. *Perf. 14x13*
RA1 A159 10c on 2c ultra .25 .20
Perf. 14x14½
RA2 A170 10c on 6c rose lil .25 .20

Chilean Arms — PT1

Perf. 14½x14
1970, Apr. 23 **Litho.** **Unwmk.**
RA3 PT1 10c blue .25 .20
See No. RA6.

No. RA3 Surcharged in Red

a b

1971-72
RA4 PT1 (a) 15c on 10c bl .25 .20
RA5 PT1 (b) 15c on 10c bl ('72) .25 .20

Type of 1970
1972, July **Litho.** *Perf. 14½x14*
RA6 PT1 15c rose red .25 .20

No. RA6 Surcharged in Ultramarine

1972-73
RA7 PT1 20c on 15c rose red .25 .20
RA8 PT1 50c on 15c rose red ('73) .25 .20
No. RA8 has 9 bars instead of 8.
The surtax on Nos. RA1-RA8 was for modernization of postal system. Compulsory on all inland mail.

PARCEL POST POSTAL TAX STAMP

Pres. J. J. Prieto V. — PPT1

Unwmk.
1957, Apr. 8 **Litho.** *Perf. 14*
QRA1 PPT1 15p green .35 .30
The surtax aided the Prieto Foundation. No. QRA1 was required on parcel post entering or leaving Chile.

CHINA

ˈchī-nə

LOCATION — Eastern Asia
GOVT. — Republic
AREA — 2,903,475 sq. mi.
POP. — 462,798,093 (1948)

10 Candareen = 1 Mace
10 Mace = 1 Tael
100 Cents = 1 Dollar (Yuan) (1897)

Watermarks

Wmk. 103 —
Yin-Yang Symbol

Wmk. 261 —
Character Yu
(Post) Multiple

Issues of the Imperial Maritime Customs Post

Imperial Dragon — A1

1878   Unwmk.   Typo.   Perf. 12½
Thin Paper
Stamps printed 2½-3¼mm apart

1	A1 1c green	600.00	475.00
a.	1c dark green	725.00	525.00
2	A1 3c brown red	725.00	400.00
a.	3c vermilion	825.00	450.00
3	A1 5c orange	825.00	400.00
a.	5c bister orange	1,100.	525.00

Imperforate essays of Nos. 1-3 have an extra circle near the dragon's lower left foot. Examples with the circle completely or mostly removed are proofs or unfinished stamps.

1882

Thin or Pelure Paper
Stamps printed 4½mm apart

4	A1 1c green	700.00	375.00
a.	1c dark green	775.00	425.00
5	A1 3c brown red	1,200.	350.00
6	A1 5c orange yellow	14,500.	1,600.

1883   Rough to smooth Perf. 12½
Medium to Thick Opaque Paper
Stamps printed 2½ to 3¼mm apart

7	A1 1c green	700.00	475.00
a.	1c dark green	800.00	550.00
b.	1c light green	850.00	575.00
c.	Vert. pair, imperf. between	160,000.	
8	A1 3c brown red	1,200.	400.00
a.	3c vermilion	1,500.	
b.	Vert. pair, imperf. between		60,000.
9	A1 5c yellow	2,000.	650.00
a.	5c chrome yellow	2,250.	850.00
b.	Horiz. pair, imperf. btwn.		60,000.

Nos. 1-9 were printed from plates of 25, 20 or 15 individual copper dies, but only No. 5 exists in the 15-die setting. Many different printings and plate settings exist. All values occur in a wide variety of shades and papers. The effect of climate on certain papers has produced the varieties on so-called toned papers in Nos. 1-15.
Value for No. 8b is for a damaged example.
Counterfeits, frequently with forged cancellations, occur in all early Chinese issues.

Imperial Dragon — A2

1885   Wmk. 103   Perf. 12½

10	A2 1c green	200.00	90.00
a.	Vert. pair, imperf. btwn.	20,000.	17,500.
b.	Horiz. pair, imperf. btwn.		
11	A2 3c lilac	450.00	125.00
a.	Vert. pair, imperf. btwn.	22,000.	17,500.
b.	Horiz. pair, imperf. btwn.		24,000.
12	A2 5c grnsh yellow	400.00	125.00
a.	5c bister brown	650.00	150.00
b.	Vert. pair, imperf. btwn.	24,000.	24,000.
c.	Horiz. pair, imperf. btwn.		24,000.
	Nos. 10-12 (3)	1,050.	340.00

1888   Perf. 11½-12

13	A2 1c green	90.00	50.00
14	A2 3c lilac	225.00	80.00
b.	Double impression		975.00
15	A2 5c grnsh yellow	400.00	125.00
b.	Horiz. pair, imperf. vert.		—
c.	Double impression	1,000.	1,000.
	Nos. 13-15 (3)	715.00	255.00

Nos. 10-15 were printed from plates made of 40 individual copper dies, arranged in two panes of 20 each. Several different settings exist of all values.
Imperforates of Nos. 13-15 are considered proofs by most authorities.
Stamps overprinted "Formosa" in English or Chinese are proofs.
For surcharges see Nos. 25-27, 75-77.

"Shou" and "Wu Fu" — A3   Dragon and Hydrangea Leaves — A4

"Pa Kua" Signs in Corners — A5   Dragon and Peony — A6

Carp, the Messenger Fish — A7

Dragon, "Pa Kua" and Immortelle A8

Dragons and "Shou" A9

Dragons and Giant Peony — A10

Junk on the Yangtse A11

1894   Lithographed in Shanghai

16	A3	1c orange red	60.00	42.50
a.		Vert. pair, imperf. btwn.	2,250.	2,100.
b.		Horiz. pair, imperf. btwn.	17,500.	12,000.
c.		Horiz. pair, imperf. horiz.	3,250.	3,250.
17	A4	2c green	62.50	40.00
a.		Horiz. pair, imperf. btwn.	3,750.	3,500.
18	A5	3c orange	55.00	32.50
a.		Vert. pair, imperf. btwn.	3,350.	3,500.
b.		Horiz. pair, imperf. btwn.	5,000.	3,800.
19	A6	4c rose pink	200.00	225.00
a.		Vert. pair, imperf. btwn.	14,000.	
20	A7	5c dull orange	400.00	450.00
a.		Vert. pair, imperf. btwn.	18,000.	18,000.
21	A8	6c dark brown	175.00	55.00
a.		Vert. pair, imperf. btwn.	24,000.	
b.		Horiz. pair, imperf. btwn.	12,500.	
22	A9	9c dark green	275.00	110.00
a.		Imperf., pair	2,250.	
b.		Horiz. pair, imperf. vert.	4,250.	3,750.
c.		Horiz. pair, imperf. horiz.	4,250.	
d.		Vert. pair, imperf. btwn.	4,750.	4,250.
e.		Tete beche pair, vert.	1,650.	1,400.
f.		Tete beche pair, imperf. horiz.	5,500.	
g.		Tete beche pair, imperf. vert.	5,500.	4,750.
h.		Vert. strip of 3, imperf. btwn.	5,500.	
i.		Tete beche pair, horiz.	1,500.	1,300.
23	A10	12c orange	575.00	275.00
24	A11	24c carmine	800.00	225.00
a.		Vert. pair, imperf. btwn.	30,000.	
		Nos. 16-24 (9)	2,602.	1,455.

60th birthday of Tsz'e Hsi, the Empress Dowager. All values exist in several distinct shades.
On Mar. 20, 1896, the Customs Post was changed, by Imperial Edict, effective Jan. 1, 1897, to a National Post and the dollar was adopted as the unit of currency.

Time was required to work out details of the Imperial Post and design new stamps. As a provisional measure, stocks of Nos. 16-24 were ordered surcharged with new values in dollars and cents. It is believed that only the

Shanghai office stock of Nos. 16-24 (plus any reserve stock at the printers) was surcharged with small figures of value. Other post offices throughout China were instructed to return all unoverprinted stocks on receipt of the new surcharges.
Early in the year it was apparent that all stamps would be exhausted before the new issues were ready (Nos. 86-97), and since the stones from which Nos. 16-24 had been printed no longer existed, new stones were made from the original transfers. A printing from the new stones was made early in 1897 and surcharged with large figures of value spaced 2½mm below the Chinese characters. During the surcharging, sheets from the 1894 (original) printing were received from outlying post offices and surcharged as they arrived. A small quantity of the 1897 printing reached the public without surcharge (Nos. 16n-24n).
Additional stamps were still required and another printing was made from the new stones and surcharged with large figures, but in a new setting with 1½mm between the Chinese characters and the value. Additional sheets of the 1894 printing were received from the most distant post offices and were also surcharged with the 1½mm setting. Thus there are four different sets of the large-figure surcharges. All these stamps were regularly issued but no attempt was made by the post office to separate printings. Some values are difficult to distinguish as to printing, particularly in used condition.
See No. 73. For surcharges see Nos. 28-72, 74.

1897   Lithographed in Shanghai

16n	A3	1c pink	725.00
17n	A4	2c olive green	1,200.
18n	A5	3c chrome yellow	725.00
p.		3c yellow buff	1,000.
19n	A6	4c pale rose	875.00
20n	A7	5c yellow	875.00
21n	A8	6c red brown	1,000.
22n	A9	9c yellowish green	3,750.
p.		9c emerald green	—
23n	A10	12c yellowish orange	3,750.
24n	A11	24c purplish red	2,200.

The colors of the 1897 printings are pale or dull; the gum is thin and white. The 1894 printing has a thicker, yellowish gum.
The set of 9 values on thick unwatermarked paper is a special printing of 5,000 sets ordered by P. G. von Mollendorf, a Customs official, for presentation purposes. Value, set $2,400.
For surcharges see Nos. 47-55, 65-72.

Issues of the Chinese Government Post

Preceding Issues Surcharged in Black

Small Numerals 2½mm Below Chinese Characters
Surcharged on Nos. 13-15

1897, Jan. 2   Perf. 11½-12

25	A2	1c on 1c	65.00	77.50
26	A2	2c on 3c	300.00	110.00
a.		Double surcharge		
27	A2	5c on 5c	95.00	52.50
		Nos. 25-27 (3)	460.00	240.00

Surcharged on Nos. 16-24

28	A5	½c on 3c	45.00	32.50
a.		"1" instead of "½"	350.00	350.00
b.		Horiz. pair, imperf. btwn.	5,000.	
c.		Vert. pair, imperf. horiz.	5,000.	3,000.
d.		Double surcharge	12,000.	11,000.
e.		Vert. pair, imperf. btwn.	5,000.	
29	A3	1c on 1c	27.50	25.00
a.		Inverted surcharge	25,000.	5,250.
30	A4	2c on 2c	32.50	22.50
a.		Horiz. pair, imperf. vert.	4,000.	
b.		Vert. pair, imperf. btwn.	4,000.	
c.		Double surcharge	14,000.	
d.		Inverted surcharge	—	15,000.
e.		Horiz. pair, imperf. btwn.	2,000.	
31	A6	4c on 4c	35.00	27.50
a.		Double surcharge	30,000.	20,000.
b.		Vert. pair, imperf. btwn.	5,000.	5,000.
c.		Horiz. pair, imperf. btwn.	5,000.	5,000.
32	A7	5c on 5c	42.50	19.00
a.		Vert. pair, imperf. btwn.	15,000.	10,000.
33	A8	8c on 6c	50.00	30.00
a.		Vert. pair, imperf. btwn.	2,750.	2,250.
b.		Vert. strip of 3, imperf. btwn.	4,200.	2,500.
c.		Horiz. pair, imperf. btwn.	2,500.	2,500.
34	A8	10c on 6c	80.00	65.00
a.		Vert. pair, imperf. btwn.	7,500.	2,500.
b.		Vert. pair, imperf. horiz.	2,400.	2,400.
35	A9	10c on 9c	425.00	175.00
a.		Double surcharge	40,000.	40,000.
b.		Inverted surcharge	15,000.	15,000.
36	A10	10c on 12c	375.00	175.00
a.		Vert. pair, imperf. horiz.	2,000.	
b.		Vert. pair, imperf. btwn.	2,200.	2,200.
37	A11	30c on 24c	525.00	225.00
a.		Vert. pair, imperf. btwn.	7,500.	
		Nos. 28-37 (10)	1,637.	796.50

Small Numerals 4mm Below Chinese Characters

25a	A2	1c on 1c green	75.00	85.00
28f	A4	½c on 3c orange	60.00	60.00
29b	A3	1c on 1c vermilion	75.00	75.00
30f	A4	2c on 2c dark green	55.00	55.00
31d	A6	4c on 4c dark pink	55.00	55.00
32b	A7	5c on 5c dull orange	55.00	55.00
33d	A8	8c on 6c brown	55.00	37.50
35c	A9	10c on 9c dark red	425.00	350.00
37b	A11	30c on 24c dark red	500.00	500.00

Preceding Issues Surcharged in Black

Large Numerals
Numerals 2½mm below Chinese characters

1897, Mar.
Surcharged on Nos. 16-24

38	A5	½c on 3c	2,500.	850.00
b.		Inverted surcharge		10,000.
39	A3	1c on 1c	700.00	200.00
40	A4	2c on 2c	375.00	350.00
41	A6	4c on 4c	475.00	375.00
b.		Horiz. pair, imperf. btwn.		11,000.
42	A7	5c on 5c	225.00	200.00
43	A8	8c on 6c	2,250.	1,750.
44	A9	10c on 9c	800.00	375.00
45	A10	10c on 12c	35,000.	2,750.
46	A11	30c on 24c	1,200.	1,300.
b.		2mm spacing between "30" and "cents."		15,000.

Same Surcharge on Nos. 16n-24n

47	A5	½c on 3c	32.50	40.00
a.		"cen" for "cent"	850.00	850.00
b.		Vert. pair, imperf.		
c.		Vert. pair, imperf. horiz.	2,100.	2,100.
			1,750.	1,250.
d.		As "a" and "c"	9,500.	9,500.
e.		As "a" and "b"	7,500.	7,500.
f.		Horiz. pair, imperf. btwn.	1,900.	1,900.
48	A3	1c on 1c	27.50	22.50
a.		Horiz. pair, imperf. btwn.		2,500.
49	A4	2c on 2c	25.00	17.50
50	A6	4c on 4c	35.00	25.00
a.		Horiz. pair, imperf. btwn.	3,250.	3,250.
b.		Vert. pair, imperf. btwn.		4,000.
51	A7	5c on 5c	47.50	27.50
52	A8	8c on 6c	500.00	275.00
53	A9	10c on 9c	200.00	80.00
a.		10c on 9c emerald	210.00	82.50
b.		Pair, one without surcharge	1,100.	
54	A10	10c on 12c	350.00	82.50
55	A11	30c on 24c	700.00	325.00
a.		2mm spacing btwn "30" and "cents"	1,250.	750.00
b.		Vert. pair, imperf. btwn.	6,250.	

All recorded unused examples of #45 are flawed.

Numerals 1½mm below Chinese characters

1897, May
Surcharged on Nos. 16-24

56	A5	½c on 3c org yel	500.00	425.00
57	A3	1c on 1c	350.00	275.00
58	A4	2c on 2c	—	3,500.
59	A6	4c on 4c	275.00	225.00
60	A7	5c on 5c	175.00	160.00
61	A8	8c on 6c	1,600.	1,350.
62	A9	10c on 9c	350.00	250.00
63	A10	10c on 12c	1,500.	1,100.
64	A11	30c on 24c	60,000.	

Same Surcharge on Nos. 16n-24n

65	A5	½c on 3c	25.00	27.50
a.		Inverted surcharge	3,000.	3,000.
b.		½mm spacing	1,500.	1,200.
66	A3	1c on 1c	27.50	22.50
67	A4	2c on 2c	30.00	25.00
a.		Inverted surcharge	25,500.	8,750.
b.		Horiz. pair, imperf. btwn.		8,500.
68	A6	4c on 4c	300.00	160.00
a.		Inverted surcharge	2,500.	1,500.
69	A7	5c on 5c	300.00	140.00
70	A9	10c on 9c	210.00	95.00
a.		Inverted surcharge	1,350.	1,100.
71	A10	10c on 12c	375.00	110.00
72	A11	30c on 24c	13,000.	2,600.

Same Surcharge (1½mm Spacing) on Type A12, and

    A12   A12a

Redrawn Designs
Printed from New Stones

1897

73	A12	½c on 3c yel	250.00	200.00
a.		½mm spacing	7,000.	5,000.
74	A12a	2c on 2c yel grn	60.00	45.00
a.		Horiz. pair, imperf. btwn.	6,000.	

Nos. 73 and 74 were surcharged on stamps printed from new stones, which differ slightly from the originals. On No. 73 the numeral "3" and symbols in the four corner panels have been enlarged and strengthened. On No. 74, the numeral "2" has a thick, flat base.

Surcharged on Nos. 13-15

75	A2	1c on 1c green	450.00	575.00
76	A2	2c on 3c lilac	925.00	925.00
77	A2	5c on 5c grnsh yel	300.00	450.00

Revenue Stamps Surcharged in Black:

    A13   a

    b   c

    d   e

    f   g

1897   Unwmk.   Perf. 12 to 15

78	A13 (a)	1c on 3c red	425.00	275.00
a.		No period after "cent"	475.00	325.00
b.		Central character with large "box"	500.00	475.00
79	A13 (b)	2c on 3c red	725.00	400.00
a.		Inverted surcharge	25,000.	12,000.
b.		Inverted "S" in "CENTS"	800.00	525.00
c.		No period after "CENTS"	800.00	525.00
d.		Comma after "CENTS"	775.00	450.00
e.		Double surcharge	25,000.	25,000.
f.		Dbl. surch., both inverted	50,000	
g.		Double surch. (blk & grn)	52,500.	
80	A13 (c)	2c on 3c red	500.00	350.00
81	A13 (d)	4c on 3c red	40,000.	40,000.
a.		Double surcharge (blk & vio)	250,000.	250,000.
82	A13 (e)	4c on 3c red	1,500.	500.00
83	A13 (f)	$1 on 3c red	725,000.	—
a.		No period after "r"		
84	A13 (g)	$1 on 3c red	6,750.	2,500.
85	A13 (g)	$1 on 3c red	75,000.	30,000.
a.		Inverted surcharge	110,000.	35,000.

A few examples of the 3c red exist without surcharge; one canceled. No. 79 with green surcharge is a trial printing. Value for faulty upper left corner block is $190,000.

No. 79g is unique. The only canceled example of #83 is in a museum.

Dragon — A14   Carp — A15

Wild Goose — A16

"Imperial Chinese Post"
Lithographed in Japan
Perf. 11, 11½, 12

1897, Aug. 16   Wmk. 103

86	A14	½c purple brn	5.50	4.50
a.		Horiz. pair, imperf. btwn.	650.00	
87	A14	1c yellow	6.50	4.00
88	A14	2c orange	5.75	3.75
89	A14	4c brown	10.50	3.75
a.		Horiz. pair, imperf. btwn.	1,000.	
90	A14	5c rose red	12.00	3.75
91	A14	10c dk green	40.00	3.75
92	A15	20c maroon	85.00	17.50
93	A15	30c red	140.00	32.50
94	A15	50c yellow grn	100.00	45.00
a.		50c black green	1,150.	
b.		50c blue green	1,300.	
95	A16	$1 car & rose	300.00	200.00
a.		Horiz. pair, imperf. vert.		
96	A16	$2 orange & yel	2,100.	1,200.
a.		Horiz. pair, imperf. btwn.		
97	A16	$5 yel grn & pink	1,600.	1,000.

The inner circular frames and outer frames of Nos. 86-91 differ for each denomination.

No. 97 imperforate was not regularly issued. **Examples have been privately perforated and offered as No. 97.** Shades occur in most values of this issue.

    A17   A18

    A19

"Chinese Imperial Post"
Engraved in London

1898   Wmk. 103   Perf. 12 to 16

98	A17	½c chocolate	6.00	2.75
a.		Vert. pair, imperf. btwn.	850.00	475.00
b.		Vert. pair, imperf. horiz.	850.00	475.00
99	A17	1c ocher	6.50	2.75
a.		Horiz. pair, imperf. btwn.	300.00	250.00
b.		Vert. pair, imperf. btwn.	400.00	350.00
100	A17	2c scarlet	7.25	2.75
a.		Vert. pair, imperf. btwn.	400.00	200.00
b.		Horiz. pair, imperf. vert.	400.00	300.00
101	A17	4c orange brn	7.50	2.75
a.		Vert. pair, imperf. btwn.	575.00	
b.		Vert. pair, imperf. btwn.	400.00	300.00
c.		Horiz. pair, imperf. btwn.	700.00	600.00
d.		Horiz. strip of 3, imperf. btwn.	2,250.	1,500.
102	A17	5c salmon	11.00	4.75
a.		Horiz. pair, imperf. btwn.	400.00	300.00
b.		Horiz. pair, imperf. btwn.	775.00	500.00
c.		Horiz. pair, imperf. horiz.	600.00	500.00
d.		5c pale reddish orange	16.00	5.50
e.		As "d", vert pair, imperf. btwn	600.00	300.00
103	A17	10c dk blue grn	17.50	3.00
a.		Vert. or horiz. pair, imperf. btwn		
104	A18	20c claret	70.00	9.00
a.		Horiz. pair, imperf. btwn.	850.00	750.00
b.		Horiz. pair, imperf. btwn.	850.00	750.00
c.		Horiz. pair, imperf. btwn.	900.00	800.00
105	A18	30c dull rose	60.00	14.00
a.		Horiz. pair, imperf. btwn.	2,000.	
b.			1,750.	
c.			1,750.	
106	A18	50c lt green	85.00	19.00
a.		Vert. pair, imperf. btwn.	2,250.	
107	A18	$1 red & pale rose	350.00	40.00
108	A19	$2 brn & red & yel	550.00	85.00
109	A19	$5 dp grn & sal	900.00	300.00
a.		Vert. pair, imperf. btwn.	8,000.	
b.		Vert. pair, imperf. btwn.	8,500.	

Nos. 98-109 (12)   2,070.   485.75

No. 98 surcharged "B. R. A.-5-Five Cents" in three lines in black or green, was surcharged

---

by British military authorities shortly after the Boxer riots for use from military posts in an occupied area along the Peking-Mukden railway. Usually canceled in violet.

See note following No. 122.

1900(?)-06   Unwmk.   Perf. 12 to 16

110	A17	½c brown	4.00	2.75
a.		Horiz. pair, imperf. btwn.	400.00	400.00
b.		Vert. pair, imperf. btwn.	400.00	400.00
111	A17	1c ocher	4.00	2.75
a.		Horiz. pair, imperf. btwn.	350.00	350.00
b.		Vert. pair, imperf. btwn.	350.00	350.00
c.		Horiz. pair, imperf. horiz.	350.00	350.00
112	A17	2c scarlet	5.25	2.75
a.		Horiz. pair, imperf. btwn.	300.00	325.00
b.		Vert. pair, imperf. btwn.	300.00	300.00
c.		Horiz. pair, imperf. horiz.	300.00	300.00
d.		Vert. pair, imperf. vert.	300.00	300.00
e.		Vert. strip of 3, imperf.	1,250.	750.00
113	A17	4c orange brn	5.75	2.75
a.		Horiz. pair, imperf. btwn.	300.00	300.00
b.		Vert. pair, imperf. btwn.	300.00	300.00
114	A17	5c rose red	30.00	4.25
a.		Vert. pair, imperf. btwn.	300.00	300.00
b.		Horiz. pair, imperf. horiz.	275.00	275.00
115	A17	5c orange	27.50	4.75
		5c yellow	200.00	27.50
a.		Horiz. pair, imperf. btwn.	475.00	475.00
b.		Vert. pair, imperf. btwn.	475.00	475.00
116	A17	10c green	20.00	2.75
a.		Horiz. pair, imperf. btwn.	425.00	
b.		Horiz. pair, imperf. btwn.	725.00	
c.		Vert. pair, imperf. btwn.	425.00	
d.		Vert. strip of 3, imperf.		
			700.00	
117	A18	20c red brown	30.00	2.75
a.		Horiz. pair, imperf. btwn.	600.00	
b.		Horiz. pair, imperf. btwn.	500.00	
c.		Vert. pair, imperf. btwn.	500.00	
118	A18	30c dull red	30.00	2.75
a.		Horiz. pair, imperf. btwn.	850.00	
119	A18	50c yellow grn	55.00	2.75
a.		Horiz. pair, imperf. btwn.	1,000.	
120	A19	$1 red & pale rose ('06)	175.00	27.50
121	A19	$2 brn red & yel ('06)	400.00	60.00
122	A19	$5 dp grn & sal	650.00	200.00
		Nos. 110-122 (13)	1,436.	368.50

See #124-130. For surcharges and overprints see #123, 134-177, J1-J6, Offices in Tibet 1-11.

Diagonal Half of No. 112 Surcharged on Stamp and Envelope

1903

123	A17	1c on half of 2c scarlet, on cover		1,600.

Used Oct. 22 to Oct. 24. Value is for cover mailed to post office other than sending office (Foochow) and bearing backstamp showing arrival date. Locally addressed or unaddressed covers without backstamps properly used are worth approximately $1,000. Others are worth less.

Forgeries are plentiful, particularly on pieces of cover. Certificates of authenticity are mandatory.

1905-10

124	A17	2c green ('08)	3.00	2.50
a.		Horiz. pair, imperf. btwn.	325.00	325.00
b.		Vert. pair, imperf. btwn.	325.00	325.00
c.		Vert. pair, imperf. vert.	325.00	325.00
d.		Horiz. strip of 4, imperf. btwn.	725.00	725.00
125	A17	3c slate grn ('10)	5.00	2.50
a.		Horiz. pair, imperf. btwn.	250.00	
b.		Vert. pair, imperf. btwn.	250.00	
126	A17	4c vermilion ('09)	6.00	2.25
127	A17	5c violet	7.50	2.50
a.		5c lilac	8.50	
b.		Horiz. pair, imperf. btwn.	450.00	
c.		Vert. pair, imperf. btwn.	1,000.	
d.		Vert. pair, imperf. horiz.	500.00	
128	A17	7c maroon ('10)	16.00	8.75
129	A17	10c ultra ('08)	21.00	2.75
a.		Horiz. pair, imperf. btwn.	400.00	
b.		Vert. pair, imperf. btwn.	400.00	
c.		Vert. pair, imperf. horiz.	400.00	400.00
130	A18	16c olive grn ('07)	60.00	17.50
		Nos. 124-130 (7)	118.50	38.75

Temple of Heaven, Peking — A20

909 — Perf. 14

31	A20	2c orange & green	6.00	8.00
32	A20	3c orange & blue	9.00	21.00
33	A20	7c orange & brn vio	13.50	12.00
		Nos. 131-133 (3)	28.50	41.00

1st year of the reign of Hsuan T'ung, who later became Henry Pu-yi and then Emperor Kang Teh of Manchukuo.

Stamps of 1902-10 Overprinted with Chinese Characters

Foochow Issue

Overprinted in Red or Black

1912 — Perf. 12 to 16

134	A17	3c slate grn (R)	275.	150.
135	A19	$1 red & pale rose	2,900.	2,500.
136	A19	$2 brn red & yel	4,400.	3,500.
137	A19	$5 dp grn & sal	5,750.	4,000.

The overprint "Ling Shih Chung Li" or "Provisional Neutrality," signified that the P.O. was conducted neutrally by agreement between the Manchu and opposing forces.

Nanking Issue

Overprinted in Red or Black

138	A17	1c ocher (R)	275.	160.
139	A17	3c slate grn (R)	250.	150.
140	A17	7c maroon	525.	350.
141	A18	16c olive grn (R)	2,750.	2,500.
142	A18	50c yellow grn (R)	3,500.	2,250.
143	A19	$1 red & pale rose	3,750.	1,800.
144	A19	$2 brn red & yel	5,500.	4,400.
145	A19	$5 dp green & sal	12,750.	10,000.

Vertical overprint reads: "Chung Hwa Min Kuo" (Republic of China).

Stamps of this issue were also used in Shanghai and Hankow.

Additional values were overprinted but not issued. Excellent forgeries of the overprints of Nos. 134-145 exist.

Issues of the Republic

Overprinted in Black or Red

Overprinted by the Maritime Customs Statistical Department, Shanghai

146	A17	½c brown	1.50	1.25
a.		Inverted overprint	50.00	50.00
b.		Double overprint	100.00	
147	A17	1c ocher (R)	2.25	1.25
a.		Vert. pair, imperf. horiz.	200.00	200.00
b.		Inverted overprint	175.00	125.00
c.		Double overprint	200.00	175.00
d.		Horiz. pair, imperf. btwn.	300.00	250.00
e.		Horiz. pair, imperf. vert.	175.00	
f.		Pair, one without overprint	175.00	
148	A17	2c green (R)	2.50	1.75
a.		Vert. pair, imperf. btwn.	350.00	300.00
149	A17	3c slate grn (R)	3.00	1.50
a.		Inverted overprint	125.00	75.00
b.		Horiz.. pair, imperf. btwn.	300.00	300.00
c.		Vert. pair, imperf btwn.	300.00	300.00
d.		Horiz. pair, imperf. vert.	125.00	
e.		Horiz. strip of 3, imperf btwn.	450.00	
f.		Horiz. strip of 5, imperf btwn.	975.00	
150	A17	4c vermilion	4.75	1.75
a.		Vert. pair, imperf. btwn.	800.00	
151	A17	5c violet (R)	6.25	1.75
a.		Horiz. pair, imperf. btwn.		
152	A17	7c maroon	8.25	3.50
153	A17	10c ultra (R)	8.50	1.75
a.		Double overprint	250.00	
b.		Pair, one without overprint	900.00	
c.		Brownish red overprint	22.50	9.00
d.		Inverted overprint	275.00	275.00
154	A18	16c olive grn (R)	22.50	8.50

155	A18	20c red brown	19.00	5.00
156	A18	30c rose red	24.00	6.00
157	A18	50c yel grn (R)	40.00	6.00
158	A19	$1 red & pale rose	375.00	30.00
a.		Inverted overprint		27,500.
159	A19	$2 brn red & yel	275.00	60.00
a.		Inverted overprint	600.00	600.00
160	A19	$5 dp grn & sal	650.00	475.00
		Nos. 146-160 (15)	1,442.	605.00

Stamps with blue overprint similar to the preceding were not an official issue but were privately made by a printer in Tientsin.

Overprinted in Red

Overprinted by the Commercial Press, Shanghai

This type differs in that the top character is shifted slightly to right and the bottom character is larger and has small "legs".

161	A17	1c ocher	6.00	1.25
a.		Inverted overprint	375.00	375.00
b.		Vert. pair, imperf. btwn.	450.00	
c.		Double overprint	450.00	
162	A17	2c green	34.00	2.25
a.		Inverted overprint	1,100.	900.00
b.		Vert. pair, imperf. btwn.	260.00	
c.		Horiz. pair, imperf. btwn.	300.00	
d.		Horiz. strip of 3, imperf. btwn.	475.00	

Overprinted in Blue, Carmine or Black

Overprinted by Waterlow & Sons, London

163	A17	½c brown (Bl)	1.75	1.25
a.		Vert. pair, imperf. btwn.	1,400.	1,275.
164	A17	1c ocher (C)	1.75	1.25
a.		Horiz. pair, imperf. btwn.	825.00	
165	A17	2c green (C)	3.25	1.40
166	A17	3c slate grn (C)	3.75	1.50
a.		Inverted overprint		1,750.
167	A17	4c vermilion (Bk)	5.00	1.75
168	A17	5c violet (C)	11.00	1.60
169	A17	7c maroon (Bk)	35.00	37.50
170	A17	10c ultra (C)	17.50	2.75
a.		Vert. pair, imperf. btwn.	1,500.	2,600.
171	A18	16c olive grn (R)	50.00	19.00
172	A18	20c red brn (Bk)	32.50	3.50
173	A18	30c dull red (Bk)	100.00	6.75
174	A18	50c yellow grn (R)	150.00	15.00
175	A19	$1 red & pale rose (Bk)	225.00	18.50
176	A19	$2 brn red & yel (Bk)	475.00	200.00
177	A19	$5 dp grn & sal (C)	750.00	525.00
		Nos. 163-177 (15)	1,861.	836.75

Due to instructions issued to postmasters throughout China at the time of the Revolution, a number of them prepared unauthorized overprints using the same characters as the overprints prepared by the government. While many were made in good faith, some, like the blue overprints from Tientsin, were bogus, and the status of certain others is extremely dubious.

Dr. Sun Yat-sen — A21

1912, Dec. 14 — Perf. 14½

178	A21	1c orange	4.75	3.25
179	A21	2c yellow grn	4.75	3.25
180	A21	3c slate grn	4.75	3.25
181	A21	5c rose lilac	9.50	3.25
182	A21	8c dp brown	9.50	5.00
183	A21	10c dull blue	9.50	5.00
184	A21	16c olive grn	27.50	17.50
185	A21	20c maroon	37.50	10.00
186	A21	50c dk green	100.00	40.00
187	A21	$1 brown red	260.00	50.00
188	A21	$2 yellow brn	750.00	300.00
189	A21	$5 gray	275.00	225.00
		Nos. 178-189 (12)	1,492.	665.50

Honoring the leader of the Revolution.

President Yuan Shih-kai — A22

1912, Dec. 14

190	A22	1c orange	2.75	1.75
191	A22	2c yellow green	2.75	1.75
192	A22	3c slate green	2.75	1.75
193	A22	5c rose lilac	3.75	2.00
194	A22	8c deep brown	11.50	4.00
195	A22	10c dull blue	9.50	2.50
196	A22	16c olive green	10.00	12.00
197	A22	20c maroon	9.00	10.00
198	A22	50c dark green	55.00	35.00
199	A22	$1 brown red	160.00	52.50
200	A22	$2 yellow brown	200.00	50.00
201	A22	$5 gray	600.00	290.00
		Nos. 190-201 (12)	1,067.	463.25

Honoring the 1st pres. of the Republic.

Junk — A24

Reaping Rice — A25

Gateway, Hall of Classics, Peking — A26

DESIGN A24
London Printing: Vertical shading lines under top panel fine, junk with clear diagonal shading lines on sails, right pennant of junk usually long, lines in water weak except directly under junk.
Peking Printing: Vertical shading lines under top panel and inner vertical frame line much heavier, water and sails of junk more evenly and strongly colored, white wave over "H" of "CHINA" pointed upward, touching the junk.

DESIGN A25
London: Front hat brim thick and nearly straight, left foot touches shadow.
Peking: Front hat brim thin and strongly upturned, left foot and sickle clearly outlined in white, shadow of middle tree lighter than those of the right and left trees.

DESIGN A26
London: Light colored walk clearly defined almost to the doorway, figure in right doorway "T" shaped with strong horizontal cross-bar, white panel in base of central tower rectangular, vertical stroke in top left character uniformly thick at its base, tree to right of doorway ends in minute dots.
Peking: Walk more heavily shaded near doorway, especially at right; figure in right doorway more like a "Y", white panel at base of central tower is a long oval, right vertical stroke in top left character incurved near its

base, tree at right has five prominent dots at top.
London Printing: By Waterlow & Sons, London, perf. 14 to 15.
Peking Printing: By the Chinese Bureau of Engraving and Printing, Peking, perf. 14.

London Printing

1913, May 5 — Perf. 14-15

202	A24	½c black brn	.75	.40
a.		Horiz. or vert. pair, imperf. btwn.	200.00	
203	A24	1c orange	.75	.40
a.		Horiz. pair, imperf. btwn.	250.00	
b.		Vert. pair, imperf. btwn.	175.00	
c.		Horiz. strip of 5, imperf. btwn	650.00	
204	A24	2c yellow grn	2.75	.40
a.		Horiz. pair, imperf. btwn.	400.00	
205	A24	3c blue grn	6.75	.45
a.		Horiz. pair, imperf. btwn.	200.00	
b.		Vert. pair, imperf. btwn.		400.00
206	A24	4c scarlet	9.50	.70
207	A24	5c rose lilac	30.00	.60
208	A24	6c gray	5.00	.90
209	A24	7c violet	22.50	8.75
210	A24	8c brown org	42.50	2.50
211	A24	10c dk blue	37.50	1.10
a.		Horiz. pair, imperf. btwn.	375.00	375.00
b.		Vert. pair, imperf. btwn.	400.00	300.00
212	A25	15c brown	32.50	5.75
213	A25	16c olive grn	17.50	2.25
214	A25	20c brown red	30.00	2.75
215	A25	30c brown vio	32.50	2.00
a.		Horiz. pair, imperf. btwn.	400.00	400.00
216	A25	50c green	60.00	3.50
217	A26	$1 ocher & blk	150.00	4.75
218	A26	$2 blue & blk	275.00	15.50
219	A26	$5 scarlet & blk	425.00	110.00
220	A26	$10 yel grn & blk	1,375.	925.00
		Nos. 202-220 (19)	2,555.	1,087.

First Peking Printing

1915 — Perf. 14

221	A24	½c black brn	.80	.35
222	A24	1c orange	.80	.35
223	A24	2c yellow grn	1.60	.35
224	A24	3c blue grn	1.75	.35
225	A24	4c scarlet	20.00	.35
226	A24	5c rose lilac	8.50	.35
a.		Booklet pane of 4	140.00	
227	A24	6c gray	16.00	.35
228	A24	7c violet	25.00	4.50
229	A24	8c brown org	14.00	.40
230	A24	10c dk blue	15.00	.70
a.		Booklet pane of 4	140.00	
231	A25	15c brown	42.50	4.50
232	A25	16c olive grn	17.50	.70
233	A25	20c brown red	18.50	.70
234	A25	30c brown vio	17.50	.70
235	A25	50c green	42.50	.80
236	A26	$1 ocher & blk	140.00	.85
237	A26	$2 blue & blk	350.00	3.50
a.		Center inverted	125,000.	
238	A26	$5 scarlet & blk	800.00	30.00
239	A26	$10 yel grn & blk	1,300.	250.00
		Nos. 221-239 (19)	2,831.	299.80

1919

240	A24	1½c violet	3.75	.60
241	A25	13c brown	9.50	.70
242	A26	$20 yellow & blk	4,900.	3,250.

Nos. 226 and 230 overprinted in red with five characters in vertical column were for postal savings use.

The higher values of the 1913-19 issues are often overprinted with Chinese characters, which are the names of various postal districts. Stamps were frequently stolen while in transit to post offices. The overprints served to protect them, since the stamps could only be used in the districts for which they were overprinted.

Compare designs A24-A26 with designs A29-A31. For surcharges and overprints see Nos. 247, 288, B1-B3, Sinkiang 1-38.

Yeh Kung-cho, Hsu Shi-chang and Chin Yun-peng
A27

1921, Oct. 10

243	A27	1c orange	6.00	1.75
244	A27	3c blue green	6.50	1.50
245	A27	6c gray	7.50	5.00
246	A27	10c blue	8.50	4.00
		Nos. 243-246 (4)	28.50	12.25

National Post Office, 25th anniversary. For overprints see Sinkiang Nos. 39-42.

No. 224 Surcharged in Red

1922

247	A24	2c on 3c blue green	3.50	.70
a.		Inverted surcharge	172,500.	

Second Peking Printing

A29

A30

A31

Types of 1913-19 Issues Re-engraved

Type A29: Most of the whitecaps in front of the junk have been removed and the water made darker. The shading lines have been removed from the arabesques and pearls above the top inscription. The inner shadings at the top and sides of the picture have been cut away.

Type A30: The heads of rice in the side panels have a background of crossed lines instead of horizontal lines. The Temple of Heaven is strongly shaded and has a door. There are rows of pearls below the Chinese characters in the upper corners. The arabesques above the top inscription have been altered and are without shading lines.

Type A31: The curved line under the inscription at top is single instead of double. There are four vertical lines, instead of eight, at each side of the picture. The trees at the sides of the temple had foliage in the 1913-19 issues, but now the branches are bare. There are numerous other alterations in the design.

1923   **Perf. 14**

248	A29	½c black brown	1.75	.30
a.		Horiz. pair, imperf. btwn.	175.00	175.00
b.		Horiz. pair, imperf. vert.	150.00	150.00
249	A29	1c orange	1.00	.30
a.		Imperf., pair	125.00	
b.		Horiz. pair, imperf. vert.	125.00	
c.		Booklet pane of 6	90.00	
d.		Booklet pane of 4	45.00	
250	A29	1½c violet	3.50	.90
251	A29	2c yellow grn	2.00	.30
252	A29	3c blue green	6.00	.30
a.		Booklet pane of 6	80.00	
253	A29	4c gray	27.50	.80
254	A29	5c claret	4.00	.50
a.		Booklet pane of 4	100.00	
255	A29	6c scarlet	8.50	.50
256	A29	7c violet	8.50	.50
257	A29	8c orange	17.50	.50

258	A29	10c blue	14.50	.30
a.		Booklet pane of 6	120.00	
b.		Booklet pane of 2	150.00	
259	A30	13c brown	32.50	.60
260	A30	15c dp blue	10.00	.60
261	A30	16c olive grn	11.00	.60
262	A30	20c brown red	8.50	.40
263	A30	30c purple	32.50	.40
264	A30	50c dp green	60.00	.55
265	A31	$1 org brn & sep	65.00	.65
266	A31	$2 blue & red brn	85.00	1.00
267	A31	$5 red & slate	140.00	4.25
268	A31	$10 green & claret	675.00	60.00
269	A31	$20 plum & blue	1,300.	150.00
		Nos. 248-269 (22)	2,514.	224.25

Nos. 249 and 275 exist with webbing watermark from experimental printing.

To prevent speculation and theft, the dollar denominations were overprinted with single characters in red for use in Kwangsi ($1-$20) and Kweichow ($1-$5).

See Nos. 275, 324. For surcharges and overprints see Nos. 274, 289, 311, 325, 330, 339-340, Szechwan 1-3, Yunnan 1-20, Manchuria 1-20, Sinkiang 47-69, 114, C1-C4.

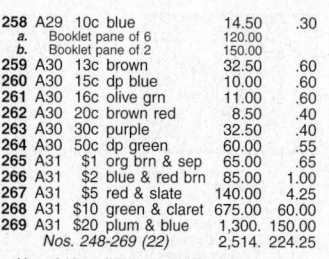

Temple of Heaven, Peking — A32

1923, Oct. 17   **Perf. 14**

270	A32	1c orange	5.00	1.00
271	A32	3c blue green	5.50	2.25
272	A32	4c red	10.50	2.50
273	A32	10c blue	16.50	3.50
		Nos. 270-273 (4)	37.50	9.25

Adoption of Constitution, October, 1923. For overprints see Sinkiang Nos. 43-46.

No. 253 Surcharged in Red

1925

274	A29	3c on 4c gray	3.50	.35
a.		Inverted surcharge	300,000.	275,000.
b.		Vert. pair, imperf. btwn.		

Junk Type of 1923

1926

275	A29	4c olive green	1.60	.25
a.		Horiz. pair, imperf. vert.	200.00	
b.		Horiz. pair, imperf. btwn.	200.00	
c.		Horiz. strip of 3, imperf. btwn.	250.00	

Marshal Chang Tso-lin — A34

President Chiang Kai-shek — A35

1928, Mar. 1   **Perf. 14**

276	A34	1c brown orange	1.50	1.50
277	A34	4c olive green	3.00	3.00
278	A34	10c dull blue	7.50	5.00
279	A34	$1 red	60.00	65.00
		Nos. 276-279 (4)	72.00	75.00

Assumption of office by Marshal Chang Tso-lin. The stamps of this issue were only available for postage in the Provinces of Chihli and Shantung and at the Offices in Manchuria and Sinkiang.

For overprints see Manchuria Nos. 21-24, Sinkiang 70-73.

1929, May

280	A35	1c brown orange	1.00	.40
281	A35	4c olive green	1.50	.75
282	A35	10c dark blue	12.50	1.50
283	A35	$1 dark red	75.00	55.00
		Nos. 280-283 (4)	90.00	57.65

Unification of China. For overprints see Yunnan Nos. 21-24, Manchuria 25-28, Sinkiang 74-77.

Sun Yat-sen Mausoleum, Nanking — A36

1929, May 30   **Perf. 14**

284	A36	1c brown orange	1.25	.75
285	A36	4c olive green	1.00	1.25
286	A36	10c dark blue	7.00	2.50
287	A36	$1 dark red	70.00	35.00
		Nos. 284-287 (4)	79.25	39.50

The transfer of Dr. Sun Yat-sen's remains from Peiping to the mausoleum at Nanking.

For overprints see Yunnan Nos. 25-28, Manchuria 29-32, Sinkiang 78-81.

Nos. 224 and 252 Surcharged in Red

1930

288	A24	1c on 3c blue green	1.25	2.25
289	A29	1c on 3c blue green	1.00	.40
a.		No period after "Ct"	18.00	18.00

See Nos. 311, 325, 330.

Dr. Sun Yat-sen — A37

Type I — Double-lined circle in the sun.
Type II — Heavy, single-lined circle in the sun.

Printed by De la Rue & Co., Ltd., London

Perf. 11½x12½, 12½x13, 12½, 13½

1931, Nov. 12   **Engr.**

Type I

290	A37	1c orange	.55	.30
291	A37	2c olive green	.65	.40
292	A37	4c green	1.10	.30
293	A37	20c ultra	1.40	.30
294	A37	$1 org brn & dk brn	12.00	.50
295	A37	$2 blue & org brn	32.50	3.00
296	A37	$5 dull red & blk	47.50	5.00
		Nos. 290-296 (7)	95.70	9.80

1931-37

Type II

297	A37	2c olive grn	.45	.20
298	A37	4c green	.65	.20
299	A37	5c green ('33)	.40	.20
300	A37	15c dk green	4.25	1.25
301	A37	15c scarlet ('34)	.45	.20
302	A37	20c ultra ('37)	.85	.20
303	A37	25c ultra	.45	.65
304	A37	$1 org brn & dk brn	14.00	.50
305	A37	$2 blue & org brn	25.00	1.25
306	A37	$5 dull red & blk	47.50	5.00
		Nos. 297-306 (10)	94.00	9.65

Stamps issued prior to 1933 were printed by a wet-paper process, and owing to shrinkage such stamps are 1-1½mm narrower than the later dry-printed stamps.

Early printings are perf. 12½x13. Nos. 304, 305 and 306 were later perf. 11½x12½.

See #631-635. For surcharges and overprints see #341, 343, 678, 682, 684-685, 689-691, 768, 843, 1N1, 2N1-2N5, 2N57-2N59, 2N83-2N84, 2N101-2N106, 2N116, 2N124-2N126, 3N1-3N5, 4N1-4N5, 5N1-5N4, 6N1-6N5, 7N1-7N4, 7N54, 8N2-8N3, 8N43-8N44, 8N54, 8N57, 8N69-8N71, 8N85, 9N1-9N5, Taiwan 19, 21-22, Northeastern Provinces 44, Szechwan 4-11, Yunnan 29-44, Sinkiang 82-97.

"Nomads in the Desert" — A38

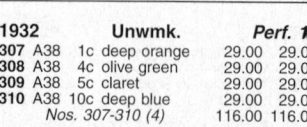

1932   **Unwmk.**   **Perf. 1**

307	A38	1c deep orange	29.00	29.0
308	A38	4c olive green	29.00	29.0
309	A38	5c claret	29.00	29.0
310	A38	10c deep blue	29.00	29.0
		Nos. 307-310 (4)	116.00	116.0

Northwest Scientific Expedition of Sve Hedin. A small quantity of this issue was sol at face at Peking and several other cities. The bulk of the issue was furnished to Hedin an sold at $5 (Chinese) a set for funds to financ the expedition.

#252 Surcharged in Black Like #288

1932

311	A29	1c on 3c blue green	2.50	1.1

Martyrs Issue

Teng Keng
A39

Ch'en Ying-shi
A40

Chu Chih-hsin
A45

Sung Chiao-jen
A46

Huang Hsing
A47

Liao Chung-kai
A48

1932-34   **Perf. 1**

312	A39	½c black brown	.25	.25
313	A40	1c orange ('34)	.25	.25
314	A39	2½c rose lilac ('33)	.25	.25
315	A48	3c dp brown ('33)	.25	.25
316	A45	8c brown orange	.50	.30
317	A46	10c dull violet	.60	.30
318	A45	13c blue green	.65	.30
319	A46	17c brown olive	.55	.30
320	A47	20c brown red	1.10	.30
321	A48	30c brown violet	1.50	.30
322	A47	40c orange	1.40	.35
323	A40	50c green ('34)	5.00	.50
		Nos. 312-323 (12)	12.30	3.6

Perfs. 12 to 13 and compound and with secret marks are listed as Nos. 402-439. No 316 re-drawn is No. 485.

For overprints and surcharge see Nos. 342 472, 474, 478-479, 486-487, 490, 531-536 539-541, 544-549, 616, 619, 622-624, 647 659, 662-663, 665, 669, 672, 698, 704, 711 713-715, 720-721, 831, 846-847, 867, 870 872, 881-882, J120-J121, 1N14-1N15, 1N59 2N6-2N9, 2N32-2N56, 2N60, 2N76-2N82 2N85, 2N87-2N90, 2N107-2N115, 2N118 2N121-2N123, 3N6-3N10, 3N34-3N55, 3N59 4N6-4N9, 4N39-4N64, 4N69, 5N5-5N8, 5N34 5N60, 5N65, 6N6-6N8, 6N35-6N61, 6N66 7N5-7N7, 7N30-7N53, 7N55, 7N59, 8N1, 8N4 8N28-8N42, 8N45, 8N47-8N50, 8N60-8N61 8N68, 8N73, 8N76-8N79, 8N89, 8N97, 8N99-8N100, 8N103-8N104, 9N72-9N77, Taiwan 14-17, 20, 28A, 74, Northeastern Provinces 6 8, 11, Szechwan 12-23, Yunnan 49-60, Sinki ang 102-113, 140-161, 197.

Junk Type of 1923 Issue

1933   **Perf. 14**

324	A29	6c brown	20.00	1.25

#275 Surcharged in Red Like #288

1933

325	A29	1c on 4c olive green	1.75	.35
a.		No period after "Ct"	21.00	21.00

Tan Yuan-chang — A49

1933, Jan. 9
326	A49	2c olive green	2.50	1.25
327	A49	5c green	4.00	.40
328	A49	25c ultra	10.00	1.75
329	A49	$1 red	72.50	35.00
		Nos. 326-329 (4)	89.00	38.40

Tan Yuan-chang, more commonly known as Tan Yen-kai, a prominent statesman in China since the revolution of 1912 and Pres. of the Executive Dept. of the Natl. Government. Placed on sale Jan. 9, 1933, the date of the ceremony in celebration of the completion of the Tan Yuan-chang Memorial Hall and Tomb at Mukden.

For overprints see Yunnan Nos. 45-48, Sinkiang 98-101.

#251 Surcharged in Red Like #288
1935 ***Perf. 14***
330	A29	1c on 2c yellow grn	2.50	.25

Emblem of New Life Movement A50

Four Virtues of New Life A51

Lighthouse — A52

1936, Jan. 1
331	A50	2c olive green	1.75	.75
332	A50	5c green	2.00	.25
333	A51	20c dark blue	6.00	.70
334	A52	$1 rose red	40.00	11.00
		Nos. 331-334 (4)	49.75	12.70

"New Life" movement.

Methods of Mail Transportation A53

Maritime Scene — A54

Shanghai General Post Office — A55

Ministry of Communications, Nanking — A56

1936, Oct. 10
335	A53	2c orange	3.00	.70
336	A54	5c green	1.50	.20
337	A55	25c blue	4.75	.45
338	A56	$1 dk carmine	27.50	8.50
		Nos. 335-338 (4)	36.75	9.85

Founding of the Chinese PO, 40th anniv.

Nos. 260 and 261 Surcharged in Red

1936, Oct. 11
339	A30	5c on 15c dp blue	1.75	.50
340	A30	5c on 16c olive grn	3.00	1.00

No. 298 Surcharged in Red

1937
341	A37	1c on 4c green, type II	1.25	.50
a.		Upper left character missing		

Nos. 322 and 303 Surcharged in Black or Red

1938 ***Perf. 12½, 14***
342	A47	8c on 40c orange (Bk)	2.00	.75
343	A37	10c on 25c ultra (R)	1.75	.30

Dr. Sun Yat-sen — A57

Type I — Coat button half circle. Six lines of shading above head. Top frame partially shaded with vertical lines.
Type II — Coat button complete circle. Nine lines of shading above head. Top frame partially shaded with vertical lines.
Type III — Coat button complete circle. Nine lines of shading above head. Top frame line fully shaded with vertical lines.

Printed by the Chung Hwa Book Co.
1938 Unwmk. Engr. Perf. 12½
Type I
344	A57	$1 henna & dk brn	85.00	12.00
345	A57	$2 dp blue & org brn	17.50	4.25
346	A57	$5 red & grnsh blk	150.00	19.00
		Nos. 344-346 (3)	252.50	35.25

1939
Type II
347	A57	$1 henna & dk brn	16.00	1.00
348	A57	$2 dp blue & org brn	18.00	4.00

1939-43
Type III
349	A57	2c olive green	.25	.25
350	A57	3c dull claret	.25	.25
351	A57	5c green	.25	.25
352	A57	5c olive green	.25	.25
353	A57	8c olive green	.25	.25
354	A57	10c green	.25	.25
355	A57	15c scarlet	1.25	2.25
356	A57	15c dk vio brn ('43)	17.50	32.50
357	A57	16c olive gray	1.75	.45
358	A57	25c dk blue	.35	.75
359	A57	$1 henna & dk brn	2.00	.75
360	A57	$2 dp blue & org brn	4.50	.55
a.		Imperf., pair	275.00	
361	A57	$5 red & grnsh blk	2.75	.50
362	A57	$10 dk green & dull pur	17.50	2.00
363	A57	$20 rose lake & dk blue	60.00	50.00
		Nos. 349-363 (15)	109.10	91.50

Several values exist imperforate, but these were not regularly issued. No. 361 imperforate is printer's waste.

See Nos. 368-401, 506-524. For surcharges and overprints see Nos. 440-448, 473, 475-477, 480-481, 482-484, 489, 537-538, 615, 618, 620, 660-661, 664, 666-668, 673-676, 680-681, 686, 688, 699-703, 707-709, 717, 719, 830, J67-J68, M2, M11-M12, 1N2-1N13, 1N23-1N42, 1N57-1N58, 2N10-2N31, 2N61-2N75, 2N86, 2N91-2N93, 2N117, 2N119-2N120, 3N11-3N33, 3N56-3N58, 3N60-3N61, 4N10-4N38, 4N65-4N68, 4N70-4N71, 5N9-5N33, 5N61-5N64, 5N66-5N68, 6N9-6N34, 6N62-6N65, 6N67-6N69, 7N8-7N29, 7N56-7N58, 7N60-7N61, 8N5-8N27, 8N46, 8N51-8N53, 8N55-8N56, 8N58-8N59, 8N62-8N67, 8N72, 8N74-8N75, 8N80-8N84, 8N86-8N88, 8N90, 8N95-8N96, 8N98, 8N101-8N102, 8N105-8N106, 9N6-9N71, 9N97, 9N99, Taiwan 78, 84, Northeastern Provinces 9-10, Sinkiang 115-139, 174-188, 196, 198.

Chinese and American Flags and Map of China — A58

Printed by American Bank Note Co.
Frame Engr., Center Litho.
1939, July 4 Unwmk. Perf. 12
Flag in Deep Rose and Ultramarine
364	A58	5c dark green	1.75	.50
365	A58	25c deep blue	1.75	.90
366	A58	50c brown	4.00	1.10
367	A58	$1 rose carmine	6.50	2.25
		Nos. 364-367 (4)	14.00	4.75

150th anniv. of the US Constitution.

Type of 1939-41 Issue
Re-engraved

2c, 1939-41   Re-engraved

8c, 1939-41   Re-engraved

1940 Perf. 12½
368	A57	2c olive green	.20	.20
369	A57	8c olive green	.20	.20

Type of 1938-41 Issue
1940 Unwmk. Perf. 14
Type III
370	A57	2c olive green	2.50	1.00
371	A57	5c green	5.00	2.10
372	A57	$1 henna & dk brn	110.00	19.00
373	A57	$2 dp blue & org brn	21.00	5.00
374	A57	$5 red & grnsh blk	26.00	16.50
375	A57	$10 dk grn & dull pur	72.50	12.50
		Nos. 370-375 (6)	237.00	56.10

See surcharge note following No. 363.

Type of 1939-41
1940 Wmk. 261 Perf. 12½
Type III
376	A57	$1 henna & dk brn	7.00	9.00
377	A57	$2 dp blue & org brn	9.00	9.00
378	A57	$5 red & grnsh blk	10.00	18.00
379	A57	$10 dk green & dull pur	15.00	30.00
380	A57	$20 rose lake & dp blue	19.00	30.00
		Nos. 376-380 (5)	60.00	96.00

See surcharge note following No. 363.

Printed by the Dah Tung Book Co.
Type III with Secret Marks
Five Cent

Type III — Characters joined

Secret Mark — Characters not joined

Eight Cent

Type III — Characters not joined

Secret Mark — Characters joined

Ten Cent

Type III — Characters sharp and well shaped

Secret Mark — Characters coarse and varying in thickness

Dollar Values

Type III

Secret Mark

1940		Unwmk.	Perf. 14	
381	A57	5c green	.20	.20
382	A57	5c olive green	.20	.20
383	A57	8c olive green	.40	.20
a.		Without "star" in uniform button	1.50	2.50
384	A57	10c green	.20	.20
385	A57	30c scarlet	.35	.20
386	A57	50c dk blue	.45	.20
387	A57	$1 org brn & sepia	2.50	.20
388	A57	$2 dp blue & yel brn	1.00	.35
389	A57	$5 red & slate grn	1.00	.45
390	A57	$10 dk grn & dull pur	4.00	2.25
391	A57	$20 rose lake & dk blue	12.00	3.50
		Nos. 381-391 (11)	22.30	7.95

Type III with Secret Marks

1940		Wmk. 261	Perf. 14	
392	A57	5c green	.20	.20
393	A57	5c olive green	.20	.20
394	A57	10c green	.35	.20
395	A57	30c scarlet	.20	.20
396	A57	50c dk blue	.55	.20
397	A57	$1 org brn & sepia	4.50	2.75
398	A57	$2 dp blue & yel brn	12.50	13.00
399	A57	$5 red & slate grn	11.50	12.00
400	A57	$10 dk grn & dull pur	16.00	17.00
401	A57	$20 rose lake & dk blue	25.00	20.00
		Nos. 392-401 (10)	71.00	65.75

Nos. 383, 384, 385, 397, 400 and 401 exist perf. 12½, but were not issued with this perforation.

See surcharge note following No. 363.

Types of 1932-34 Martyrs Issue with Secret Mark

1932-34 Issue. In the left Chinese character in bottom row, the two parts are not joined.

Secret Mark, 1940-41 Issue. The two parts are joined.

Perf. 12½, 13 and Compound				
1940-41			Wmk. 261	
402	A39	½c olive blk	.25	.20
403	A40	1c orange	.25	.20
404	A46	2c dp blue ('41)	.25	.20
405	A39	2½c rose lilac	.25	.20
406	A39	3c dp yellow brn	.30	.20
407	A39	4c pale vio ('41)	.30	.20
408	A48	5c dull red org ('41)	.30	.20
409	A45	8c dp orange	.25	.20
410	A46	10c dull violet	.25	.20
411	A45	13c dp yellow grn	.35	.20
412	A48	15c brown car	.25	.20
413	A46	17c brown olive	.25	.20
414	A47	20c lt blue	.20	.20
415	A45	21c olive brn ('41)	1.10	1.25
416	A40	25c red vio ('41)	.25	.20
417	A48	28c olive ('41)	.30	.20
418	A48	30c brown car	.45	.20
a.		Vert. pair, imperf. btwn.	125.00	
419	A47	40c orange	.30	.20
420	A40	50c green	.30	.20
		Unwmk.		
421	A39	½c olive black	.20	.20
422	A40	1c orange	.20	.20
a.		Without secret mark	2.75	2.75
b.		Horiz. pair, imperf. vert.	110.00	
423	A46	2c dp blue	.20	.20
a.		Vert. pair, imperf. horiz.	100.00	
b.		Horiz. pair, imperf. between	160.00	
424	A39	2½c rose lilac	.20	.20
425	A39	3c dp yellow brn	.20	.20
426	A39	4c pale violet	.20	.20
427	A48	5c dull red org	.25	.20
428	A45	8c dp orange	.25	.20
429	A46	10c dull violet	3.25	.40
430	A45	13c dp yel grn	.20	.65
431	A48	15c brown car	.35	.60
432	A46	17c brn olive	.40	.20
433	A47	20c lt blue	.30	.20
a.		Vert. pair, imperf. vert.	125.00	
b.		Horiz. pair, imperf. vert.	125.00	
434	A45	21c olive brn	.50	.35
435	A40	25c rose vio	.35	.50
436	A46	28c olive	.70	.50
437	A48	30c brown car	2.50	2.50

438	A47	40c orange	.35	.35
439	A40	50c green	3.50	.40
		Nos. 402-439 (38)	20.35	13.10

Several values exist imperforate, but they were not regularly issued.

Used values are for favor cancels. Postally used examples sell for more.

See surcharge note following No. 323.

Regional Surcharges.

The regional surcharges, Nos. 440-448, 482-484, 486-491, 525-549, have been listed according to the basic stamps, with black or red surcharges. The surcharges of the individual provinces, plus Hong Kong and Shanghai, are noted in small type. The numeral following each letter is the surcharge denomination. These surcharges are identified by the following letters:

a — Hong Kong		i — Kwangsi	
b — Shanghai		j — Kwangtung	
bx — Anhwei		k — Western Szechwan	
c — Hunan		l — Yunnan	
d — Kansu		m — Honan	
e — Kiangsi		n — Shensi	
f — Eastern Szechwan		o — Kweichow	
g — Chekiang		p — Hupeh	
h — Fukien			

Regional Surcharges on Stamps of 1939-40:

Hong Kong — a4

Shanghai — b3

Hunan — c3

Kansu — d3

Kiangsi — e3

Eastern Szechwan — f3

Chekiang — g3

1940-41		Unwmk.	Perf. 12½, 14	
		Carmine Surcharge		
440	A57	4c on 5c grn (#382)	.60	.60
r.		Lower right character duplicated at left	30.00	32.50
		Black Surcharge		
441	A57	3c on 5c grn (#351) (b3)	1.25	1.40
442	A57	3c on 5c ol grn (#352) (c3, d3)	.65	2.00
443	A57	3c on 5c grn (#381) (b3)	.60	1.25
444	A57	3c on 5c ol grn (#382) (e3)	.70	1.00
r.		Lower left character duplicated at right (Kiangsi)	42.50	42.50
		(b3) Shanghai	.65	1.40
		(f3) Eastern Szechwan	.65	1.60

The Kansu surcharges of #442 are of 6 types. Differences include formation of top part of fen character (at left of "3"), fen with low right hook, height of "3" (5-4mm), space between upper and lower characters (6-9mm), etc.

1940-41		Wmk. 261	Perf. 14	
445	A57	3c on 5c grn (#392) (e3)	.60	1.40
r.		Lower left character duplicated at right (Kiangsi)	35.00	35.00
		(b3, c3) Shanghai, Hunan	.60	1.60
446	A57	3c on 5c ol grn (#393) (f3)	.70	1.75
		(b3) Shanghai	.95	1.75
r.		Lower left character duplicated at right (f3)	60.00	65.00
		Red Surcharge		
447	A57	3c on 5c grn (#392) (g3)	1.25	3.25
448	A57	3c on 5c ol grn (#393) (g3)	6.00	6.00

Dr. Sun Yat-sen — A59

Printed by American Bank Note Co.

1941		Unwmk.	Engr.	Perf. 12	
449	A59	½c sepia		.20	.30
450	A59	1c orange		.25	.25
451	A59	2c brt ultra		.25	.25
452	A59	5c green		.25	.25
453	A59	8c red orange		.60	.70
454	A59	8c turq green		.30	.20
455	A59	10c brt green		.20	.20
456	A59	17c olive		4.50	12.00
457	A59	25c rose violet		.30	1.00
458	A59	30c scarlet		.35	.25
459	A59	50c dk blue		.50	.20
460	A59	$1 brown & blk		.60	.20
461	A59	$2 blue & blk		.75	.25
a.		Center inverted		120,000.	
462	A59	$5 scarlet & blk		1.75	.65
463	A59	$10 green & blk		5.00	2.75
464	A59	$20 rose vio & blk		4.00	6.00
		Nos. 449-464 (16)		19.75	25.45

For surcharges see Nos. 488, 491, 542-543, 617, 621, 670, 677, 687, 705-706, 712, 716, 718, M1, M3-M4, 1N16-1N22, 1N43-1N56, 9N78-9N96, 9N98, 9N100.

Industry and Agriculture — A60

1941, June 21			Perf. 12½	
465	A60	8c green	.50	.50
466	A60	21c red brown	.65	.65
467	A60	28c dk olive grn	.85	.85
468	A60	33c vermilion	1.10	1.50
469	A60	50c dp ultra	1.25	1.25
470	A60	$1 dk violet	1.75	1.75
		Nos. 465-470 (6)	6.10	6.50

		Souvenir Sheet		
		Imperf		
		Typo.		
471		Sheet of 6	70.00	70.00
a.		A60 8c dull green	6.50	6.50
b.		A60 21c dark orange brown	6.50	6.50
c.		A60 28c dull yellow green	6.50	6.50
d.		A60 33c red	6.50	6.50
e.		A60 50c dull blue	6.50	6.50
f.		A60 $1 dark violet	6.50	6.50

The Thrift Movement and its aim to "Save for Reconstruction."

Issued in sheets measuring 155x171mm, without gum.

This sheet exists with additional blue marginal overprints in Russian, French and Chinese reading "Souvenir of the Exhibition of the Russian Philatelic Society in China, Shanghai, China, Feb. 28, 1943." Value, $80.

The overprinting was applied by the society, and when so overprinted this sheet had no franking power.

Stamps of 1939-41 Overprinted in Carmine or Blue

1941, Oct. 10			Perf. 12½, 14, 13	
472	A40	1c dull orange	.25	.60
473	A57	2c olive grn (C)	.25	.60
474	A39	4c pale violet (C)	.25	.60
475	A57	8c ol grn (#369) (C)	.25	.60
476	A57	10c green (#354) (C)	.25	.60
477	A57	16c ol gray (#357) (C)	.25	.60
478	A45	21c olive brn (C)	.25	.60

479	A46	28c olive (C)	.60	1.65
480	A57	30c scarlet	1.00	3.25
481	A57	$1 hn & dk brn (#359)	4.00	4.00
		Nos. 472-481 (10)	7.35	13.10

Chinese Republic, 30th anniversary.

Kiangsi — e7

Eastern Szechwan — f7

Chekiang — g7

Fukien — h7

1941		Unwmk.	Perf. 12½, 14	
482	A57	7c on 8c (#353) (g7, h7)	1.00	1.10
483	A57	7c on 8c (#369) (f7)	1.00	.55
484	A57	7c on 8c (#383) (h7)	1.00	.90
		(e7) Kiangsi	1.00	.90
		(g7) Chekiang	1.00	1.10
r.		Without "star" in uniform button	70.00	

Type of 1932-34 Re-engraved

1941		Unwmk.	Perf. 14	
485	A45	8c deep orange	13.00	57.50

The original stamps are 19½mm wide, the re-engraved 21mm.

Eleven other values of the Martyrs Issue and types A37 and A57 exist re-engraved, but were not issued.

Hunan — c1

Kiangsi — e1

Fukien — h1

Kwangsi — i1

Kwangtung — j1

1942

Red Surcharge

486	A39	1c on ½c blk brn (#312) (i1)	1.00	1.75
		(c1) Hunan	2.00	2.75
487	A39	1c on ½c ol blk (#421) (e1)	.75	1.60
		(c1) Hunan	.85	2.00
		(i1) Kwangsi	1.65	2.50
		(h1) Fukien	6.00	9.50
488	A59	1c on ½c sepia (#449) (j1)	1.00	1.60
		(c1) Hunan	1.25	2.50

Hunan — c40

Eastern Szechwan — f40

Western Szechwan — k40 | Yunnan — l40

Red Surcharge

489	A57	40c on 50c dk bl		
		(#386) (f40)	.75	1.25
	(k40)	Western Szechwan	4.25	6.00
	(l40)	Yunnan	3.75	5.50
r.		Inverted surcharge (Yunnan)	110.00	

Wmk. 261

490	A40	40c on 50c grn		
		(#420) (c40)	1.75	6.50

Unwmk.

491	A59	40c on 50c dk bl		
		(#459) (c40)	3.25	8.25

Dr. Sun Yat-sen — A62

Central Trust Printing
Perf. 10½-11, 11½-12½, 13 and Compounds

1942-43					Typo.

Without Gum

492	A62	10c dp green		
		('43)	.25	1.50
493	A62	16c dull ol brn	13.50	47.50
a.		Perf 10½	550.00	550.00
494	A62	20c dk ol grn		
		('43)	.25	1.50
a.		Perf. 11	13.50	11.00
495	A62	25c brown vio	.25	1.00
496	A62	30c dull ver	.25	1.00
a.		Perf. 11	3.00	5.00
497	A62	40c dk red brn		
		('43)	.25	1.00
a.		Perf. 11x13	85.00	
b.		Perf. 11	14.00	14.00
498	A62	50c sage green	.25	.25
a.		Perf. 11	7.00	13.50
499	A62	$1 rose lake	.35	.25
a.		Perf. 11	40.00	40.00
500	A62	$1 dull grn ('43)	.35	.35
501	A62	$1.50 dp blue ('43)	.35	.45
a.		Perf. 11	290.00	290.00
502	A62	$2 dk blue grn	.35	.35
503	A62	$3 dk yel ('43)	.35	.35
504	A62	$4 red brown	.40	.45
505	A62	$5 cerise ('43)	.35	.35
		Nos. 492-505 (14)	17.50	56.30

Many shades and part-perforate varieties exist.

See Nos. 550 to 563 for other stamps of type A62 with secret mark and new values and colors. For surcharges and overprints see Nos. 525-530, 671, 683, 692-694, 696, 771, 773, 807-809, 811-820, 824-827, 832, 834-834A, 836, 848-850, 852-854, 857, 860-863, 876, 879, M5-M10, Taiwan 55, 86, 99, Kwangsi 6-7, Sinkiang 162-173, 194-195.

Type of 1938
Thin Paper Without Gum

1942-44		Unwmk.	Engr.	Imperf.
506	A57	$10 red brown	1.75	1.25
507	A57	$20 blue grn	1.75	1.00
508	A57	$20 rose red ('44)	17.00	11.00
509	A57	$30 dull vio ('43)	1.25	1.00
510	A57	$40 rose red ('43)	1.40	1.00
511	A57	$50 blue	2.00	1.25
512	A57	$100 org brn ('43)	8.00	5.00

Rouletted

513	A57	$5 lilac gray ('44)	14.00	14.00
a.		Rouletted x perf. 12½	25.00	30.00
514	A57	$10 red brown	6.75	5.00
515	A57	$50 blue	7.25	6.00
a.		Rouletted x imperf.		
		Nos. 506-515 (10)	61.15	46.50

1942-45			Perf. 12½ to 15
516	A57	$4 dp blue ('43)	.80	1.25
517	A57	$5 lil gray ('43)	1.75	1.25
518	A57	$10 red brown	1.75	1.25
519	A57	$20 blue grn ('43)	1.75	1.00
520	A57	$20 rose red ('45)	100.00	125.00
521	A57	$30 dull vio ('43)	1.25	1.00
522	A57	$40 rose red ('43)	1.25	1.00
523	A57	$50 blue	5.50	2.50
524	A57	$100 org brn ('45)	110.00	125.00
		Nos. 516-524 (9)	224.05	259.25

Beware of Nos. 508 and 512 with faked perforations that are offered as Nos. 520 and 524. See surcharge note following No. 363.

No. 493 Overprinted in Black or Red

1942

525	A62	(i) 16c (Bk)	85.00	100.00
	(c)	Hunan	500.00	
	(k)	Western Szechwan	190.00	190.00
	(m)	Honan	850.00	850.00
	(n)	Shensi	250.00	260.00
r.		Perf. 10½ (Kwangsi)	550.00	
s.		Inverted ovpt. (Shensi)	300.00	
526	A62	(d) 16c (R)	60.00	50.00
	(bx)	Anhwei	550.00	550.00
	(e)	Kiangsi	77.50	60.00
	(f)	Eastern Szechwan	120.00	75.00
	(h)	Fukien	300.00	225.00
	(j)	Kwangtung	675.00	675.00
	(l)	Yunnan	60.00	50.00
	(o)	Kweichow	275.00	200.00
	(p)	Hupeh, perf. 10½	925.00	850.00
r.		Perf. 10½ (E. Szechwan)	500.00	
s.		Horiz. pair, imperf. btwn (Yunnan)	650.00	—
t.		Perf. 13 (Hupeh)	—	—

This overprint means "Domestic Ordinary Letter Surcharge Paid." It was applied in various sizes and types by 14 districts, 9 using red ink, 5 using black. (The Anhwei overprint comes in two types.) These overprinted stamps were briefly sold for $1.16 before the government ordered their sale suspended. The vertical bars and 50c surcharge of Nos. 527-528 were then applied.

Anhwei — bx

Hunan — c

Kansu — d

Kiangsi — e

Eastern Szechwan — f

Fukien — h

Kwangsi — i

Kwangtung — j

Western Szechwan — k

Yunnan — l

Honan — m

Shensi — n

Kweichow — o | Hupeh — p

Nos. 525-526 Surcharged "50 cents" and 2 Vertical Bars in Black or Red

1942				Unwmk.
527	A62	50c on 16c (Bk)	3.25	3.00
	(c,f)			
	(i)	Kwangsi	6.00	6.00
	(k)	Western Szechwan	11.00	8.50
	(m)	Honan	11.50	10.00
	(n)	Shensi	4.25	5.00
r.		Inverted surch. (W. Szech.)	250.00	
s.		"k" surcharge on #493	350.00	
528	A62	50c on 16c (R) (p)	5.00	5.00
	(bx)	Anhwei	95.00	300.00
	(d)	Kansu	3.25	5.00
	(e)	Kiangsi	5.50	10.00
	(h)	Fukien	6.50	8.50
	(j)	Kwangtung	6.50	6.00
	(l)	Yunnan	6.50	8.00
	(o)	Kweichow	4.00	7.00
r.		"o" surcharge inverted	300.00	
s.		"p" surch. on #526(f)	100.00	47.50

Many varieties of Nos. 527-528 exist, including narrow or wide spacing between the two top characters, or between the vertical bars, or both.

Surcharges on stamps perf. 10½ (basic No. 493a) usually sell at much higher prices.

General Issue

Hunan — c50

Eastern Szechwan — f50

Chekiang — g50

Kwangsi — i50

Kwangtung — j50

Fukien — h

Western Szechwan — k50 | Honan — m50

Shensi — n50 | Kweichow — o50

No. 493 Surcharged in Black, Red or Carmine

1943				Unwmk.
529	A62	50c on 16c (Bk)		
	(m50)		11.00	11.00
	(n50)	Shensi	11.00	11.00
r.		Perf. 11x13 (Shensi)	95.00	
530	A62	50c on 16c (C)	1.00	2.00
	(c50)	Hunan	3.00	6.00
	(f50)	Eastern Szechwan	3.75	2.75
	(g50)	Chekiang	42.50	50.00
	(i50)	Kwangsi	6.50	7.50
	(j50)	Kwangtung	5.00	7.00
	(k50)	Western Szechwan	6.50	6.50
	(m50)	Honan	8.50	9.50

	(o50)	Kweichow	11.00	13.00
r.		Inverted surch. (Hunan)	65.00	
s.		"05" instead of "50" (Kweichow)	450.00	

Many varieties of Nos. 529-530 exist, such as narrow or wide spacing horizontally or vertically between the overprinted Chinese characters.

Surcharges on No. 493a (perf. 10½) usually sell at much higher prices.

The General Issue type, No. 530, was distributed to all head offices, which in turn supplied the post offices under their direction. It is surcharged in carmine; the other stamps listed under No. 530 are surcharged in red or carmine.

Hunan — c20

Kansu — d20

Kiangsi — e20 | Eastern Szechwan — f20

Fukien — h20

Kwangsi — i20

Kwangtung — j20

Western Szechwan — k20

Yunnan — l20

Honan — m20

Shensi — n20

Kweichow — o20

Hupeh — p20

1943		Wmk. 261, Unwmkd.

On No. 318

531	A45	20c on 13c (k20)	2.25	5.00
	(d20)	Kansu	2.25	6.00
	(n20)	Shensi	3.50	5.50
532	A45	20c on 13c (i20;R)	1.00	2.75
	(c20)	Hunan	1,100.	
	(e20)	Kiangsi	275.00	
	(j20)	Kwangtung	85.00	95.00
	(p20)	Hupeh	2.00	4.00

On No. 411

533	A45	20c on 13c (n20)	2.25	4.25
	(d20)	Kansu	2.75	7.50
	(k20)	Western Szechwan	2.00	7.50
	(l20)	Yunnan	21.00	35.00
	(m20)	Honan	350.00	
534	A45	20c on 13c (p20;R)	1.75	5.25
	(c20)	Hunan	2.50	1.75
	(e20)	Kiangsi	9.00	2.10

(f20)	Eastern Szechwan	2.50	2.75
(h20)	Fukien	9.50	11.00
(i20)	Kwangsi	2.00	2.75
(j20)	Kwangtung	22.00	22.00
(o20)	Kweichow	3.75	3.25

On No. 430

535	A45	20c on 13c (l20)	2.25	4.75
	(d20)	Kansu	2.25	2.75
	(k20)	Western Szechwan	35.00	42.50
	(m20)	Honan	9.50	9.25
	(n20)	Shensi	3.50	5.50
536	A45	20c on 13c		
		(f20;i20;R)	2.25	3.50
	(c20)	Hunan	11.00	9.75
	(e20)	Kiangsi	4.50	4.00
	(j20)	Kwangtung	2.25	2.75
	(o20)	Kweichow	2.25	10.00
	(p20)	Hupeh	2.25	4.00

On No. 357

537	A57	20c on 16c (k20)	2.25	2.75
	(c20)	Hunan	3.50	13.50
	(d20)	Kansu	3.50	13.50
	(m20)	Honan	11.00	17.50
	(n20)	Shensi	3.50	13.50
538	A57	20c on 16c (e20, o20; R)	2.25	13.50
	(c20)	Hunan	11.00	17.50
	(i20)	Kwangsi	11.00	13.50
	(j20)	Kwangtung	52.50	55.00

On No. 413

539	A46	20c on 17c (c20;R)	2.75	4.25
	(i20)	Kwangsi	2.25	2.75
	(j20)	Kwangtung	30.00	42.50

On No. 432

540	A46	20c on 17c (k20)	3.50	5.50
	(d20)	Kansu	3.50	6.50
	(m20)	Honan	40.00	47.50
541	A46	20c on 17c (e20;R)	2.25	5.50
	(j20)	Kwangtung	3.75	15.00
	(o20)	Kweichow	2.50	6.75

On No. 456

542	A59	20c on 17c (m20)	210.00	275.00
543	A59	20c on 17c (c20;R)	18.00	30.00

On No. 415

544	A45	20c on 21c (e20;R)	11.00	12.00

On No. 434

545	A45	20c on 21c (c20, k20)	2.25	4.00
	(d20)	Kansu	2.50	6.75
	(l20)	Yunnan	2.50	4.00
	(m20)	Honan	2.50	9.25
546	A45	20c on 21c (f20;R)	1.75	4.25
	(e20)	Kiangsi	1.75	5.50
	(h20)	Fukien	2.50	4.75
	(i20)	Kwangsi	2.75	4.00
	(j20)	Kwangtung	3.75	5.00
	(o20)	Kweichow	2.50	2.75
	(p20)	Hupeh	2.50	5.50

On No. 417

547	A46	20c on 28c (e20;R)	775.00	725.00

On No. 436

548	A46	20c on 28c (l20)	3.50	6.25
	(d20)	Kansu	17.50	24.00
	(k20)	Western Szechwan	25.00	65.00
	(m20)	Honan	40.00	47.50
549	A46	20c on 28c (e20;R)	1.75	3.25
	(c20)	Hunan	1.90	4.75
	(h20)	Fukien	3.50	4.75
	(i20)	Kwangsi	4.75	4.75
	(j20)	Kwangtung	4.25	6.25
	(o20)	Kweichow	4.75	4.75

Many varieties of Nos. 531-549 exist, such as narrow or wide spacing between the overprinted Chinese characters, and "20" higher or lower than illustrated.

Type of 1942-43 Pacheng Printing

1944-46   Unwmk.   Perf. 12
Without Gum

550	A62	30c chocolate	.40	13.00
551	A62	$1 green	4.00	5.00
552	A62	$2 dk vio brn	.25	.25
a.		Imperf., pair	30.00	25.00
553	A62	$2 dk bl grn	.25	.25
a.		Perf. 10½	47.50	35.00
554	A62	$2 deep blue	1.75	6.00
555	A62	$3 lt yellow	1.60	.80
556	A62	$4 violet brn	.25	.25
a.		Imperf., pair	60.00	
557	A62	$5 car ('46)	.25	.25
a.		Perf. 10½	75.00	75.00
558	A62	$6 gray vio ('45)	.25	.40
559	A62	$10 red brn ('45)	.25	.25
a.		Imperf., pair	60.00	
560	A62	$20 dp ultra ('46)	.25	.25
561	A62	$50 dk green ('46)	4.00	.25
562	A62	$70 lilac ('46)	5.00	.25
563	A62	$100 lt brown ('46)	.30	.25
		Nos. 550-563 (14)	18.80	27.45

In the Pacheng printing of the Central Trust type stamps, the secret mark "C" has been added below the lower left foliate ornament beneath the sun emblem. On the $3, it is below the right ornament. New values also include a "P" at right of sun emblem on the $6 and $10, and at right of necktie on the $20. Some values of Pacheng printing exist on paper with elephant watermark in sheet.
See surcharge note following No. 505.

Dr. Sun Yat-sen
A63

Allegory of Savings
A64

1944-46   Unwmk.   Typo.   Perf. 12½
Without Gum

565	A63	40c brown red	.35	.35
566	A63	$2 gray brown	.35	.35
567	A63	$3 red	.35	.35
a.		$3 orange red	4.00	4.00
568	A63	$3 lt red brown ('45)	.95	.75
569	A63	$6 pale lilac gray ('45)	.35	.45
570	A63	$10 dull lake ('45)	.35	.35
571	A63	$20 rose ('45)	.35	.35
a.		Perf. 16	375.00	375.00
572	A63	$50 lt brown ('46)	.45	.55
573	A63	$70 rose violet ('46)	.55	.55
		Nos. 565-573 (9)	4.05	4.05

For surcharges see Nos. 772, 774, 828, 833, 835, 836A, 839, 842, 851, 864, 868, 873-875, 877, 880. Taiwan 81, 98, Sinkiang 200-201.

1944-45   Engr.   Perf. 13
Without Gum

574	A64	$40 indigo ('45)	.35	.90
575	A64	$50 yellow grn ('45)	.35	.35
576	A64	$100 yellow brn	.35	.35
577	A64	$200 dk green ('45)	.35	.35
		Nos. 574-577 (4)	1.40	1.95

All four values were printed on thick paper; the first three were also printed on thin paper.
For surcharges see Szechwan Nos. F1, F3.

A65

Dr. Sun Yat-sen — A66

1944, Dec. 25   Litho.
Without Gum

578	A65	$2 deep green	.70	2.00
579	A65	$5 fawn	.70	2.00
580	A65	$6 dull rose vio	1.40	3.50
581	A65	$10 violet blue	2.75	7.00
582	A65	$20 carmine	5.25	9.00
		Nos. 578-582 (5)	10.80	23.50

50th anniversary of the Kuomintang.

1945, Mar. 12
Without Gum

583	A66	$2 gray green	.45	1.75
584	A66	$5 red brown	.55	1.75
585	A66	$6 dk vio blue	.65	2.25
586	A66	$10 lt blue	1.00	1.75
587	A66	$20 rose	1.25	4.00
588	A66	$30 buff	2.00	6.00
		Nos. 583-588 (6)	5.90	17.50

Death of Dr. Sun Yat-sen, 20th anniv.

Dr. Sun Yat-sen — A67

1945-46   Without Gum   Perf. 12½

589	A67	$2 green	.25	.35
590	A67	$5 dull green	.25	.35
591	A67	$10 dk blue	.25	.35
a.		Imperf., pair	75.00	
592	A67	$20 carmine ('46)	.25	.35
a.		Imperf., pair	75.00	
		Nos. 589-592 (4)	1.00	1.40

For surcharges see Nos. 695, 697, 837, 855, Taiwan 58, 82, 87-88.

Statue of Liberty, Map of China, Flags of Great Britain, China and United States, and Chiang Kai-shek
A68

Unwmk.
1945, July 7   Engr.   Perf. 12
Flags in Dark Blue and Red

593	A68	$1 deep blue	.50	.50
594	A68	$2 dull green	.50	1.00
595	A68	$5 olive gray	.50	1.00
596	A68	$6 brown	1.00	1.25
597	A68	$10 rose lilac	5.00	7.00
598	A68	$20 carmine rose	5.00	9.50
		Nos. 593-598 (6)	12.50	20.25

Signing of a Treaty in 1943 between Great Britain, the US and China.

Pres. Lin Sen (1864-1943)   Pres. Chiang Kai-shek
A69   A70

1945, Aug.   Unwmk.   Perf. 12

599	A69	$1 dp ultra & blk	.65	2.00
600	A69	$2 myrtle grn & blk	.65	2.00
601	A69	$5 red & blk	.65	2.00
602	A69	$6 purple & blk	.90	2.00
603	A69	$10 choc & blk	4.00	4.00
604	A69	$20 olive grn & blk	4.25	6.00
		Nos. 599-604 (6)	11.10	18.00

1945, Oct. 10
Flag in Rose Red and Violet Blue

605	A70	$2 green	.45	1.00
606	A70	$4 dark blue	.50	1.00
607	A70	$5 olive gray	.50	1.50
608	A70	$6 bister brown	1.50	2.25
609	A70	$10 gray	4.00	7.00
610	A70	$20 red violet	5.00	7.00
		Nos. 605-610 (6)	11.95	19.75

Inauguration of Chiang Kai-shek as president, Oct. 10, 1943.

President Chiang Kai-shek — A71

1945, Oct. 10   Typo.   Perf. 13
Without Gum
Flag in Carmine and Blue

611	A71	$20 green & blue	.25	.25
612	A71	$50 bister brn & bl	.50	.50
613	A71	$100 blue	.50	.40
614	A71	$300 rose red & blue	.50	.40
		Nos. 611-614 (4)	1.75	1.55

Victory of the Allied Nations over Japan.

C. N. C. Surcharges

The green surcharges on Nos. 615 to 621, and the surcharges on Nos. 647 to 721, and 768 to 774 represent Chinese National Currency and were applied at Shanghai.

Stamps of 1938-41 Surcharged in Black with Chinese Characters and

New Value in Checkered Rectangle at Bottom, Resurcharged in Green

1945   Perf. 12, 12½

615	A57	10c on $20 on 3c (#350)	.20	1.00
616	A46	15c on $30 on 2c (#423)	.20	1.00
a.		Horiz. pair, imperf. between	90.00	
b.		Vert. pair, imperf. between	85.00	
617	A59	25c on $50 on 1c (#450)	.20	.90
618	A57	50c on $100 on 3c (#350)	.20	.50
619	A40	$1 on $200 on 1c (#422)	.20	.25
620	A57	$2 on $400 on 3c (#350)	.20	.30
621	A59	$5 on $1000 on 1c (#450)	.20	.20
		Nos. 615-621 (7)	1.40	4.10

The black (first) surcharges on Nos. 615 to 621 represent Nanking puppet government currency.
In the green surcharge, the characters at the left express the new value and are either two or four in number.

Types of 1932-34, Re-engraved, and Surcharged in Green with Horizontal Bar and Four or Five Chinese Characters and Overprinted in Black:

Perf. 14

622	A47	$10 on 20c brown red	8.00	12.00
623	A47	$20 on 40c orange	25.00	29.00
a.		Green surcharge inverted	60.00	
624	A48	$50 on 30c violet brn	18.50	22.00
		Nos. 622-624 (3)	51.50	63.00

These provisional surcharges were applied in Honan in National currency to stamps of the Hwa Pei (North China) government. The black overprint reads: "Hwa Pei."
The two-character "Hwa Pei" overprint was applied to various stamps in 1941-43 by the North China puppet government. See Nos. 8N1-8N53, 8N60-8N84.

Dr. Sun Yat-sen
A72   A73

1945, Dec.   Typo.   Perf. 12
Without Gum

625	A72	$20 dp carmine	.25	.25
626	A72	$30 dp blue	.25	.25
627	A72	$40 orange	.60	1.25
628	A72	$50 green	1.00	.35
629	A72	$100 dk brown	.25	.25
630	A72	$200 brown violet	.25	.25
		Nos. 625-630 (6)	2.60	2.60

For surcharges see Nos. 810, 829, 838, 865, J110-J119, Taiwan 75, Kwangsi F2, Szechwan F2, F4, Yunnan 66-67, 71.

Type of 1931-37

Perf. 12½, 13x12½, 13½

1946   Unwmk.

631	A37	$1 dk violet	.30	1.50
632	A37	$2 olive green	.30	3.00
633	A37	$20 brt yellow grn	.30	.55
634	A37	$30 chocolate	.30	.50
635	A37	$50 red orange	.30	.50
		Nos. 631-635 (5)	1.50	6.05

$4 blue and $5 red values were prepared but not issued. Value $400.
For surcharges see Nos. 678, 684, 689-690, 768, 843.

1946-47   Engr.   Perf. 14
Without Gum

636	A73	$20 carmine	6.25	.25
637	A73	$30 dk blue ('47)	.35	.25
638	A73	$50 purple	.25	.20
639	A73	$70 red org ('47)	17.50	2.50
640	A73	$100 dk carmine	.20	.20
641	A73	$200 olive grn ('47)	.20	.20
642	A73	$500 brt bl grn ('47)	.35	.20
643	A73	$700 red brown ('47)	.20	.20
644	A73	$1000 rose lake	.35	

645 A73 $3000 blue 1.00 .40
646 A73 $5000 dp green & ver 1.00 .40
Nos. 636-646 (11) 27.65 5.15

For surcharges see Nos. 679, 769, 775, 823, 837A, 844-845, 856, 866, 875A, 878, Taiwan 18, 23-28, 54, 76-77, 100, Northeastern Provinces 41-43, Fukien 5-6, Hunan 1, E1, F1, Kwangsi 11, F2, Szechwan F5-F8, Sinkiang 202-204, People's Republic of China 3L53, 3L67-3L68, 6L28.

Stamps of 1932-41 Surcharged in Black

Perf. 12½, 13, 13x12, 14
Wmk. 261

647 A45 $20 on 8c
(#409) .20 .65
648 A39 $30 on ½c
(#402) 2,000.
649 A45 $50 on 21c
(#415) .20 .20
650 A45 $70 on 13c
(#411) .20 .20
651 A46 $100 on 28c
(#417) .20 .65

Unwmk.
652 A39 $3 on 2½c
(#424) 7.50 6.25
653 A48 $10 on 15c
(#431) .20 .20
654 A45 $20 on 8c
(#428) .20 .20
655 A47 $20 on 20c
(#433) .35 .35
656 A39 $30 on ½c
(#421) .20 .20
657 A45 $50 on 21c
(#434) .40 .55
657A A45 $70 on 13c
(#318) 210.00 210.00
658 A45 $70 on 13c
(#430) .40 .55
659 A46 $100 on 28c
(#436) .40 .40

Forgeries of No. 648 exist.

Stamps and Types of 1931-1946 Surcharged in Black or Carmine

Perf. 12½, 13, 14
1946-47   Wmk. 261

660 A57 $50 on 5c green
(#392) .35 .85
661 A57 $50 on 5c ol grn
(#393) 21.00 20.00
662 A48 $50 on 5c dl red org
(#408) .20 1.25
663 A40 $100 on 1c org
(#403) .20 1.10

Perf. 12, 12½, 12½x13, 13, 14
1946-47   Unwmk.

664 A57 $20 on 3c (#350) .20 .35
665 A57 $20 on 8c (#428) .20 .20
666 A57 $50 on 3c (#350) .20 .20
667 A57 $50 on 5c (#352) .20 .20
668 A57 $50 on 5c (#382) .95 1.75
669 A48 $50 on 5c (#427) .20 .20
670 A59 $50 on 5c (#452) .20 .20
671 A62 $50 on $1 (#500) .20 .20
672 A40 $100 on 1c (#422) .20 .20
a. Without secret mark
(#422a) 67.50 67.50
673 A57 $100 on 3c (#350) .20 .20
674 A57 $100 on 8c (#353) 14.00 14.00
675 A57 $100 on 8c (#369) 2.00 .35
676 A57 $100 on 8c (#383) .35 .35
a. Without "star" in uniform
button (No. 383a) 25.00 16.00
677 A59 $100 on 8c (#454) .20 .20
678 A37 $100 on $1 (#631) .20 .20
679 A73 $100 on $20
(#636) .35 .35
680 A57 $200 on 10c
(#354) .75 .25
681 A57 $200 on 10c
(#384) .40 1.10
682 A37 $200 on $4 dl bl .50 .20
a. Double surcharge 16.00
683 A62 $250 on $1.50
(#501) .30 2.50
a. Perf. 11 250.00 250.00
684 A37 $250 on $2 (#632) .50 .20
685 A37 $250 on $5 car .50 .20
686 A57 $300 on 10c
(#354) .20 .20
687 A59 $300 on 10c
(#455) .20 .20

688 A57 $500 on 3c (#350) .50 .20
689 A37 $500 on $20
(#633) .20 .20
690 A37 $800 on $30
(#634) .30 .20
691 A37 $1000 on 2c (#297) .65 .35
692 A62 $1000 on $2 (#552) .30 .20
a. Imperf., pair 30.00 20.00
693 A62 $1000 on $2 (#553) .20 .25
694 A62 $1000 on $2 (#554) .25 .55
695 A67 $1000 on $2 (#589) .20 .20
696 A62 $2000 on $5 (#557) .30 .20
697 A67 $2000 on $5 dl grn
(C) (#590) .20 .20
Nos. 664-697 (34) 26.30 26.55

Nos. 682 and 685 were not issued without surcharge. No. 682 is perf. 13x13½; No. 685, perf. 12x12½.

The characters at the left express the new value and vary in number.

Stamps of 1938-41 Surcharged in Black

Perf. 12, 12½, 13, 14
1946   Wmk. 261

698 A45 $20 on 8c (#409) 200.00 175.00
699 A57 $50 on 5c (#392) .20 .65
700 A57 $50 on 5c (#393) .50 1.25

1946-48   Unwmk.
700A A57 $20 on 5c (#381) 1,050.
701 A57 $20 on 8c (#353) .20 .35
702 A57 $20 on 8c (#369) .35 .35
703 A57 $20 on 8c (#383) .20 .50
a. Without "star" in uniform
button (No. 383a) 4.50 4.50
b. Inverted surcharge 20.00
c. Dbl. surch., one on back 32.50 32.50
d. Double surcharge 32.50
704 A45 $20 on 8c (#428) .20 .20
a. Double surcharge 22.50
705 A59 $20 on 8c (#453) .20 .20
706 A59 $20 on 8c (#454) .20 .20
a. Inverted surcharge 13.00
b. Double surcharge 13.00
707 A57 $50 on 5c (#351) 7.25 6.75
708 A57 $50 on 5c (#352) .20 .20
a. Inverted surcharge 27.50
709 A57 $50 on 5c (#381) .70 .70
710 A57 $50 on 5c (#382) .50 .35
711 A48 $50 on 5c (#427) .20 .20
a. Inverted surcharge 27.50
712 A59 $50 on 5c (#452) .50 .20
a. Double surcharge 16.00

Stamps of 1939-41 Surcharged in Blue or Red

1946   Wmk. 261   Perf. 12½

713 A40 $10 on 1c org
(#403) .20 .20
a. Inverted surcharge 40.00
714 A48 $20 on 3c dp yel
brn (#406) 800.00 800.00

Forgeries of No. 714 exist.

1946   Unwmk.   Perf. 12, 12½, 13

715 A40 $10 on 1c org (#422) .20 .20
a. Without secret mark (#422a) 10.00 12.00
b. Inverted surcharge 8.00 10.00
716 A59 $10 on 1c org (#450) .20 .20
a. Double surcharge 27.50
717 A57 $20 on 2c ol grn (R)
(#368) .20 .20
718 A59 $20 on 2c brt ultra
(R) (#451) .20 .20
a. Inverted surcharge 20.00
b. Double surcharge 16.00
719 A57 $20 on 3c dl cl (#350) .20 .20
a. Double surcharge 22.50
720 A48 $20 on 3c dp yel brn
(#425) .20 .35
721 A39 $30 on 4c pale vio
(R) (#426) .20 .25
a. Inverted surcharge 9.00
Nos. 715-721 (7) 1.40 1.60

President Chiang Kai-shek — A74

Perf. 10½-11½
1946, Oct. 31   Engr.   Unwmk.

722 A74 $20 carmine .50 .55
723 A74 $30 green .50 .75
724 A74 $50 vermilion .50 .50
725 A74 $100 yellow grn .60 1.10
726 A74 $200 yellow org .95 1.00
727 A74 $300 magenta .95 .65
Nos. 722-727 (6) 4.00 4.70

60th birthday of Chiang Kai-shek.
Printed by Dah Yeh Printing Co.; the earlier ones are gumless, the later ones gummed.
See Taiwan Nos. 29-34, Northeastern Provinces 30-35.

Printed by Dah Tung Book Co.
Without Gum
Perf. 14

722a A74 $20 carmine 1.10 1.50
723a A74 $30 green 1.10 1.50
724a A74 $50 vermilion 1.10 1.50
725a A74 $100 yellow green 3.00 3.00
726a A74 $200 yellow orange 2.00 2.00
727a A74 $300 magenta 2.50 2.50
Nos. 722a-727a (6) 10.80 12.00

Assembly House, Nanking A75

1946, Nov. 15   Litho.   Perf. 14
Without Gum

728 A75 $20 green .75 .40
729 A75 $30 blue .75 .40
730 A75 $50 dk brown .75 .40
731 A75 $100 carmine .75 .40
a. Horiz. pair, imperf. between 70.00 70.00
Nos. 728-731 (4) 3.00 1.60

Convening of National Assembly.
For surcharges see Taiwan Nos. 10-13, Northeastern Provinces 26-29.

Entrance to Dr. Sun Yat-sen Mausoleum — A76   **Dr. Sun Yat-sen — A77**

1947, May 5   Engr.

732 A76 $100 dp green .35 .35
733 A76 $200 deep blue .35 .35
734 A76 $250 carmine .35 .35
735 A76 $350 lt brown .35 .35
736 A76 $400 dp claret .35 .35
Nos. 732-736 (5) 1.75 1.75

First anniversary of return of Chinese National Government to Nanking.
See Taiwan Nos. 35-39, Northeastern Provinces 36-40.

1947   Perf. 12½, 11½x12½

737 A77 $500 olive green .25 .20
738 A77 $1000 green & car .25 .20
739 A77 $2000 dp blue & red brn .30 .20
740 A77 $5000 org red & blk .30 .20
Nos. 737-740 (4) 1.10 .80

For surcharge see Szechwan No. 50.

Confucius A78   **Confucius' Lecturing School A79**

Tomb of Confucius A80

Temple of Confucius A81

1947, Aug. 27   Litho.   Perf. 14
Without Gum

741 A78 $500 carmine rose .60 .65

Engr.
742 A79 $800 yellow brown .50 .80
743 A80 $1250 blue green .50 1.25
744 A81 $1800 blue .50 1.90
Nos. 741-744 (4) 2.10 4.60

Sun Yat-sen and Plum Blossoms A82   **Chinese Flag and Map of Taiwan A83**

1947-48   Engr.   Perf. 14
Without Gum

745 A82 $150 dk blue .25 .25
746 A82 $250 dp lilac .35 .20
747 A82 $500 blue grn .25 .20
748 A82 $1000 red .25 .20
749 A82 $2000 vermilion .25 .20
750 A82 $3000 blue .25 .20
751 A82 $4000 gray ('48) .25 .25
752 A82 $5000 dk brown .25 .20
753 A82 $6000 rose lilac
('48) .25 .25
754 A82 $7000 lt red brn
('48) .25 .25
755 A82 $10,000 dp blue & car 1.10 .20
756 A82 $20,000 car & yel grn .35 .20
757 A82 $50,000 grn & dk bl 1.25 .20
758 A82 $100,000 dl yel & ol
grn ('48) 1.80 .20
759 A82 $200,000 vio brn & dp
bl ('48) 2.25 .45
760 A82 $300,000 sep & org
brn ('48) 2.25 .55
761 A82 $500,000 dk Prus grn
& sep ('48) 3.00 .55
Nos. 745-761 (17) 14.60 4.55

See Nos. 788-799. For similar type see Formosa A1. For surcharges see Nos. 770, 804-806, 821-822, 840-841, 858-859, 869, 871, 880A-880B, 885A-885E, 1025-1036, Taiwan 56-57, 59, 89, Fukien 1-4, 7-12, 19-23, Hunan 2-5, C1, Kiangsi 1-3, C1, E1, F1-F2, Kwangsi 8-10, 12-17, Shensi 1-2, C1, E1, Szechwan 24-49, Yunnan 61-62, 69, 205-207, People's Republic of China 3L69-3L70, 3L76, 4L63-4L64, 6L22, 6L27, 6L29, 6L32.

1947, Oct. 25
With Gum

762 A83 $500 carmine .35 1.00
763 A83 $1250 deep green .35 1.00
Restoration of Taiwan to China, 2nd anniv.

Mobile Post Office — A84

Street-Corner Branch Post Office — A85

1947, Nov. 5

764 A84 $500 carmine .25 .50
765 A85 $1000 lilac .25 .50
766 A85 $1250 green .25 .85
767 A84 $1800 deep blue .25 1.10
Nos. 764-767 (4) 1.00 2.95

Stamps and Type of 1943-47 Surcharged in Black or Green

1947-48 Unwmk. Perf. 12½, 13, 14
768	A37	$500 on $20 brt yel grn (#633)	.25	.20
769	A73	$1250 on $70 red org (#639)	.25	.20
770	A82	$1800 on $350 yel org	.25	.20
771	A62	$2000 on $3 dk yel ('48) (#503)	.50	.20
772	A63	$2000 on $3 red (#567)	.25	.20
a.		On #567a	6.50	2.25
773	A62	$3000 on $3 lt yel ('48) (#555)	.25	.20
774	A63	$3000 on $3 lt red brn (G) ('48) (#568)	.25	.20
		Nos. 768-774 (7)	2.00	1.40

The characters at the left express the new value and vary in number.

No. 640 Surcharged

1948, Aug. Perf. 14
775	A73	$5000 on $100 dk car	7.00	70.00

No. 775 received its surcharge in Kwangsi for use in that province.

Map of China and Mail-carrying Vehicles A86

Rural Mail Delivery — A87

Early and Modern Mail Transportation A88

1947, Dec. 16 Engr. Perf. 12
776	A86	$100 violet	.25	1.00
777	A87	$200 brt green	.25	1.00
778	A87	$300 red brown	.25	1.00
779	A88	$400 scarlet	.25	1.00
780	A88	$500 brt vio blue	.25	1.00
		Nos. 776-780 (5)	1.25	5.00

Chinese Postal Administration, 50th anniv.

National Assembly Building and New Constitution A89

1947, Dec. 25 Perf. 14
Without Gum
781	A89	$2000 brt red	.50	.60
782	A89	$3000 blue	.50	.60
783	A89	$5000 deep green	.50	.60
		Nos. 781-783 (3)	1.50	1.80

1st anniv. of the adoption of China's new constitution, Dec. 25, 1946.

Chinese Stamps of 1947 and 1912 — A90

Perf. 14, Imperf.
1948, Mar. 20 Litho.
Without Gum
784	A90	$5000 dk car rose	1.00	4.00
a.		Vert. pair, imperf. btwn	40.00	
785	A90	$5000 dk green	1.00	4.00
a.		Vert. pair, imperf. btwn	40.00	

Stamp exhibitions at Nanking, Mar. 20 (No. 784), and at Shanghai, May 19 (No. 785).

Sun Yat-sen Memorial Hall, Taipei — A91

1948, Apr. 28 Engr. Perf. 14
786	A91	$5000 violet	.30	1.25
787	A91	$10000 red	.30	1.25

Restoration of Formosa to China, 3rd anniv.

Sun Yat-sen Type of 1947-48
1948
Without Gum
788	A82	$20000 rose pink	.50	.35
789	A82	$30000 chocolate	.25	.25
790	A82	$40000 green	.25	.25
791	A82	$50000 dp blue	.25	.25
792	A82	$100000 dull grn	.25	.25
793	A82	$200000 brn vio	.75	.25
794	A82	$300000 yel grn	2.75	1.00
795	A82	$500000 lil rose	1.25	.25
796	A82	$1000000 claret	.75	.25
797	A82	$2000000 vermilion	1.50	.25
798	A82	$3000000 ol bis	3.00	.55
799	A82	$5000000 ultra	6.00	.90
		Nos. 788-799 (12)	17.50	4.80

Zeros for "cents" omitted.
For surcharges see Nos. 841, 871, 880A-880B, 885A-885E, 1025-1028, 1031-1036.

Early Ship and Modern Hai Tien — A92

Passenger Ship Kiang Ya — A93

1948, Aug. 16
Without Gum
800	A92	$20000 blue	.60	1.75
801	A92	$30000 rose lilac	.60	1.75
802	A93	$40000 yel brown	.60	2.75
803	A93	$60000 vermilion	.60	2.75
		Nos. 800-803 (4)	2.40	9.00

75th anniversary of the China Merchants' Steam Navigation Company.

Type of 1947-48 Surcharged in Black

1948 Unwmk. Perf. 14
804	A82	$4000 on $100 car	.25	25.00
805	A82	$5000 on $100 car	.25	.25
806	A82	$8000 on $700 red brn	.35	.90
		Nos. 804-806 (3)	.85	26.15

Stamps of 1942-46 Surcharged in Black or Red

1948 Perf. 12½, 13
807	A62	$5000 on $1 (#500)	.25	.25
808	A62	$5000 on $1 (#551)	20.00	20.00
809	A62	$5000 on $2 (#502)	.25	.25
810	A72	$10000 on $20 (#625)	.25	.25
811	A62	$20000 on 10c (#492)	.25	.25
812	A62	$20000 on 50c (#498;R)	.25	.50
813	A62	$30000 on 30c (#496)	.25	.50
a.		Perf. 10½	22.00	22.00
		Nos. 807-813 (7)	21.50	22.00

Nos. 492, 556 and 558 Surcharged in Black or Carmine

1948
814	A62	$15,000 on 10c dp grn	.20	.20
815	A62	$15,000 on $4 vio brn	.20	.20
816	A62	$15,000 on $6 gray vio (C)	.20	.20
		Nos. 814-816 (3)	.60	.60

No. 498, 494 and 504 Surcharged in Black

1948 Unwmk. Perf. 11½, 13
817	A62	$15,000 on 50c, perf. 13	.25	.50
a.		Perf. 11½	10.00	10.00
818	A62	$40,000 on 20c dk ol grn	.25	.90
a.		Perf. 11	10.00	7.50
819	A62	$60,000 on $4 red brn	.45	.50
		Nos. 817-819 (3)	.95	1.90

Gold Yuan Surcharges
(Nos. 820-885E)

Stamps of 1942-47 Surcharged in Black, Carmine or Red

1948 Perf. 14, 13, 11
820	A62	½c on 30c (#496)	.25	5.00
821	A82	½c on $500 (Bk) (#747)	.25	.25
822	A82	½c on $500 (C) (#747)	.25	.90
823	A73	1c on $20 (#636)	.25	2.25
824	A62	2c on $1.50 (R) (#501)	.25	3.25
825	A62	3c on $5 (#505)	.25	3.25
826	A62	4c on $1 (#499)	.25	3.25
827	A62	5c on 50c (#498)	.25	.45
a.		Perf. 11	6.50	6.50
		Nos. 820-827 (8)	2.00	18.60

On No. 820-827, the position of the surcharged denomination and "Gold Yuan" characters varies, the aim being to obliterate the original denomination.

Stamps of 1940-48 Surcharged in Black, Violet, Carmine, Blue or Green

Perf. 12, 12½, 13, 14, 12½x13
1948-49
828	A63	5c on $20 (#571)	.25	1.10
829	A72	5c on $30 (C) (#626)	.25	1.40
a.		Double surcharge	17.50	
830	A57	10c on 2c (#368)	.25	1.75
831	A39	10c on 2½c (#424)	.25	1.10

832	A62	10c on 25c (V) (#495)	.25	1.25
833	A63	10c on 40c (#565)	.25	1.40
834	A62	10c on $1 (#500)	.25	.35
834A	A62	10c on $1 (#551)	275.00	225.00
835	A63	10c on $2 (#566)	.25	.25
836	A62	10c on $20 (C) (#560)	.25	.25
836A	A63	10c on $20 (#571)	300.00	300.00
837	A67	10c on $20 (#592)	.25	.25
837A	A73	10c on $20 (#636)	1.00	3.50
838	A72	10c on $30 (C) (#626)	.25	1.50
839	A63	10c on $70 (#573)	.25	1.50
a.		Double surcharge	15.00	
840	A82	10c on $7000 (#754)	1.00	1.00
841	A82	10c on $20,000 (#788)	.25	4.75
842	A63	20c on $6 (#569)	.25	.35
843	A37	20c on $30 (#634)	.45	4.75
844	A73	20c on $30 (C) (#637)	.65	3.75
845	A73	20c on $100 (#640)	.25	3.00
a.		Inverted surcharge	22.00	
b.		Double surcharge	16.00	
846	A39	50c on ½c (#312)	75.00	75.00
847	A39	50c on ½c (#421)	.25	.65
a.		Inverted surcharge	30.00	
848	A62	50c on 20c (#494)	.25	.50
849	A62	50c on 30c (Bl) (#496)	.25	1.40
850	A62	50c on 40c (V) (#497)	.25	.90
a.		Perf. 11	9.00	10.00
851	A63	50c on 40c (V) (#565)	.25	1.00
852	A62	50c on $4 (#556)	1.00	3.50
853	A62	50c on $4 (Bl) (#556)	.25	2.00
854	A62	50c on $20 (C) (#560)	.25	.25
855	A67	50c on $20 (V) (#592)	.50	1.50
856	A73	50c on $20 (#636)	.25	1.25
857	A62	50c on $70 (C) (#562)	.30	.30
858	A82	50c on $6000 (#753)	2.00	3.50
859	A82	50c on $6000 (Bl) (#753)	.25	1.50
860	A62	$1 on 30c (#550)	.25	.25
a.		Perf. 11	22.00	22.00
861	A62	$1 on 40c (#497)	.25	.25
a.		Perf. 11	4.00	4.00
862	A62	$1 on $1 (#499)	.55	2.00
863	A62	$1 on $5 (#557)	.70	.40
864	A63	$2 on $2 (R) (#566)	.25	.25
865	A72	$2 on $20 (#625)	.25	.25
866	A73	$2 on $100 (#640)	.25	.25
867	A46	$5 on 17c (#432)	.90	.90
868	A63	$5 on $2 (#566)	.25	.25
869	A82	$5 on $3000 (C) (#750)	.25	1.50
870	A47	$8 on 20c (#433)	.50	.50
871	A82	$8 on $30,000 (C) (#789)	.25	2.50
872	A47	$10 on 40c (#438)	1.25	1.00
873	A63	$10 on $2 (G) (#566)	.25	.35
874	A63	$10 on $2 (C) (#566)	.25	.20
875	A63	$20 on $2 (#566)	.25	.20
875A	A73	$20 on $20 (#636)	4.75	3.00
876	A62	$50 on 30c (#496)	.25	.30
877	A63	$50 on $2 (Bl) (#566)	.30	.25
878	A73	$80 on $20 (#636)	.25	1.00
879	A62	$100 on $1 (#551)	.25	1.00
a.		Perf. 11	60.00	60.00
880	A63	$100 on $2 (C) (#566)	.35	.35
880A	A82	$50,000 on $20,000 (#788)	1.40	.40

880B A82 $100,000 on
$30,000
(V)
(#789) 2.75 .90

Wmk. 261

881 A39 10c on 2½c (#405) .40 4.00
882 A39 50c on ½c (#402) .20 .85
Nos. 828-882 (61) 680.45 673.55

Characters at left express the new value.
Style of characters and numerals varies.

Nos. Q7 to Q9
Surcharged in Black or
Carmine

1948 **Unwmk.** **Perf. 12½**

883 PP2 $200 on $3000 red org .70 .50
884 PP2 $500 on $5000 dk bl
(C) .70 .45
885 PP2 $1000 on $10,000 vio .70 .50
Nos. 883-885 (3) 2.10 1.45

Nos. 788-791
Surcharged in Gold
Yuan in Red (Nos.
885A, 885D-885E) or
Black (Nos. 885B-
885C) at Foochow

1949, Apr. 30 **Unwmk.** **Perf. 14**

885A $20,000 on $40,000 15.00 21.00
885B $50,000 on $30,000 15.00 21.00
885C $100,000 on $20,000 15.00 21.00
885D $200,000 on $40,000 15.00 21.00
885E $200,000 on $20,000 15.00 21.00
Nos. 885A-885E (5) 75.00 105.00

Issued in Fukien Postal District.

Dr. Sun Yat-sen — A94

1949 **Unwmk.** **Engr.** **Perf. 14**
Without Gum

886 A94 $1 orange .45 .65
887 A94 $10 green .50 .65
888 A94 $20 vio brown .45 .65
889 A94 $50 dk Prus grn .45 .65
890 A94 $100 org brn .45 .65
891 A94 $200 red org .45 .65
892 A94 $500 rose lilac .45 .65
893 A94 $800 car rose .45 2.50
894 A94 $1000 blue .45 .65

Redrawn
Engr.
Perf. 12½

895 A94 $10 green .45 5.00
a. Perf. 14 4.00 8.00
b. Perf. 13 .45 5.50
896 A94 $20 violet brn .45 .55
a. Perf. 14 1.10 4.50
b. Perf. 13 .45 .90
Nos. 886-896 (11) 5.00 13.25

Small "T" at left of necktie on #895-896a.

Redrawn
1949 **Litho.** **Perf. 12½**
Without Gum

897 A94 $50 grnsh gray .30 2.75
898 A94 $100 dk org brn .30 .50
899 A94 $200 orange red .60 3.00
900 A94 $500 rose lilac .30 .50
901 A94 $1000 deep blue .30 .50
902 A94 $2000 violet .30 1.50
903 A94 $5000 light blue .30 .45
904 A94 $10,000 sepia .30 .45
905 A94 $20,000 apple grn .30 1.50
906 A94 $50,000 rose pink .30 .45
907 A94 $80,000 brn red .70 4.50
908 A94 $100,000 bl grn .45 .45
Nos. 897-908 (12) 4.45 16.55

Diagonal lines have been added to the
background of the redrawn design.
Zeros for "cents" omitted on No. 908.
See Nos. 973-981. For surcharges see Nos.
991-1006, 1057-1060, Fukien 13-17,
Szechwan 51, Tsingtau 1-4, Yunnan 63-65,
68, 70, People's Republic of China 4L34-4L44,
4L48-4L60, 5L43-5L50, 5L54-5L59, 5L91-
5L95, 6L1-6L16, 6L23-6L26, 6L30-6L31, 7L6-
7L8, 7L13-7L16, 8L12-8L13, 8L48-8L51.

Gold Yuan Surcharge in Black or
Other
Colors on Revenue Stamps

Plane, Train and
Ship — A95

Two types, 50c on $20:
I — Thick numerals in "20." Vertical stroke in
lower right corner of vignette. (Dah Tung Book
Co.)
II — Thin "20." No vertical stroke in corner.
(Central Trust.)

Two types, $2 on $50, $10 on $30, $100 on
$50 and $300 on $50:
III — "Y" in lower right corner of vignette.
(Dah Yeh Printing Co.)
IV — No "Y" in corner. (Dah Tung, Central
Trust or Chung Ming.)

Two types, $50 on $300 and $1000 on $100:
V — Projection on left frame column below
foliate ornament. (Dah Yeh Printing Co.)
VI — No projection. (Dah Tung Book Co.)

Litho.; Nos. 923, 933, 935-936 Engr.
1949 **Perf. 12½, 13, 14**
Without Gum

913 A95 50c on $20 red
brn, I .25 .50
a. 50c on $20 brown, II .25 .50
914 A95 $1 on $15 red
org .25 9.00
915 A95 $2 on $50 dk
bl, IV (C) .25 1.00
a. Type III .40 1.25
916 A95 $3 on $50 dk bl
(Bl) .25 1.00
917 A95 $3 on $50 dk bl .25 1.00
918 A95 $5 on $500 brn .25 .90
919 A95 $10 on $30 dk
vio, III (Bl) .25 .45
a. Type III .70 1.75
b. Double surcharge, IV
920 A95 $15 on $20 org
brn (Bl) .25 .45
921 A95 $25 on $20 org
brn (G) .25 .45
922 A95 $50 on $50 dk bl
(R O) .25 .45
923 A95 $50 on $300 grn,
VI (C) .25 .60
a. $50 on $300 yel grn, V (C) .25 .50
924 A95 $80 on $50 dk
(Dk Br) .25 1.25
925 A95 $100 on $50 dk
bl, IV 1.00 .60
a. Type III 5.00 17.50
926 A95 $200 on $50 dk bl .90 .90
927 A95 $200 on $500 brn
(Bl) .60 .70
928 A95 $300 on $50 dk
bl, III (C) 1.25 1.25
a. Type IV 1.75 2.00
929 A95 $300 on $50 dk bl
(Br) 2.00 2.00
930 A95 $500 on $15 red
org (Bl) 1.50 4.25
931 A95 $500 on $30 dk
vio .75 3.00
932 A95 $1000 on $50 dk bl
(C) 9.00 9.00
933 A95 $1000 on $100 ol
grn, V 3.00 4.50
a. Type VI 14.00 15.00
934 A95 $1500 on $50 dk bl
(Bl) 2.50 3.00
935 A95 $2000 on $300 grn
(Bl) .45 .65
a. Horiz. pair, imperf. between
936 A95 $5000 on $100 ol
grn 350.00
Nos. 913-936 (24) 375.95
Nos. 913-935 (23) 25.95 46.90

No. 936 was officially authorized, but never
issued.

Key pattern of overprinted border
inverted and in 2 or 3 detached
sections at top and bottom in Blue,
Black or Green

1949 **Hankow Prints** **Litho.**
Without Gum
Type A95

937 A95 $50 on
$10
(Bk) 9.50 11.00
938 A95 $100 on
$10 11.00 14.00
939 A95 $500 on
$10
(Bk) 9.00 6.50
940 A95 $1000 on
$10 7.00 7.00
941 A95 $5000 on
$20 29.00 25.00

---

942 A95 $10,000 on
$20
(Bk) 17.50 14.00
943 A95 $50,000 on
$20 20.00 25.00
944 A95 $100,000 on
$20
(Bk) 25.00 25.00
945 A95 $500,000 on
$20 350.00 250.00
946 A95 $2,000,000 on
$20
(G) 900.00 375.00
947 A95 $5,000,000 on
$20 1,600. 750.00
Nos. 937-944 (8) 128.00 127.50

The $10 stamp is slate green, the $20 red
brown.
The basic revenue stamps of Nos. 915-947
were the work of several printers. There are
three main types, differing in the bottom label.
Nos. 922 and 925 are in a second type: Nos.
923 and 930 in a third. Varieties of paper, color
and overprint exist.
Counterfeits exist of Nos. 945-947.
For surcharges and overprints see Nos.
960-970, C63, E13, F3, J122-J126, Hupeh 1-
2, People's Republic of China 5L51-5L53,
6L17-6L21.

Redrawn Coarse Impression

1949 **Litho.**
Without Gum
Size: 18¼x20¾mm

951 A94 $50 green .40 40.00
952 A94 $1000 dp blue .50 2.00
953 A94 $5000 carmine .65 2.00
954 A94 $10,000 brown 4.00 7.50
955 A94 $20,000 orange 1.25 2.00
956 A94 $50,000 blue 3.00 3.50
957 A94 $50,000 violet 5.00 3.75
958 A94 $500,000 vio brn 6.00 3.00
Nos. 951-958 (8) 20.80 63.75

Zeros for "cents" omitted on Nos. 957-958.
See surcharge note following No. 900.

Locomotive and
Ship — A96

1949, May 1 **Litho.** **Perf. 12½**
Without Gum

959 A96 orange 5.00 2.50
a. Rouletted 13.50 10.00

Nos. 959, C62, E12 and F2 were printed
without denomination and sold at the daily rate
of the gold yuan. This was necessitated by the
gold yuan inflation.
For surcharges and overprints see Nos.
1130, 1213, Taiwan 97, Fukien 18, Kansu 1,
People's Republic of China 24-29, 101-104,
4L31-4L33, 4L45-4L47, 4L61-4L62, 7L9-7L12,
8L52-8L54.

Revenue Stamps
Overprinted in Black

1949, May **Perf. 12½, 13, 14**
Without Gum

960 A95 $30 dark violet 125.00 120.00

Engr.

961 A95 $200 violet brown 15.00 12.00
962 A95 $500 dark green 20.00 20.00
Nos. 960-962 (3) 160.00 152.00

A similar overprint appears on #C63, E13,
F3, differing in 2nd and 3rd characters of bottom row.

Silver Yuan
Surcharge in Black
or Other Colors

1949 **Litho.**

963 A95 1c on $5000 brn
(G) 8.50 5.50
964 A95 4c on $100 ol grn
(Bl) 6.00 3.75
965 A95 4c on $3000 org) 6.00 2.00
966 A95 10c on $50 dk bl
(RV) 8.50 2.75

---

967 A95 10c on $1000 car 8.50 3.25
a. Inverted surcharge 60.00
968 A95 20c on $1000 red
(V) 8.50 5.00
b. Inverted surcharge
968A A95 50c on $30 dk vio
(C) 47.50 6.00
969 A95 50c on $50 dk bl
(C) 21.00 2.75
970 A95 $1 on $50 dk bl 25.00 35.00
Nos. 963-970 (9) 139.50 66.00

Nos. 963-965 and 967 are engraved.

Sun Type of 1949 Redrawn
Coarse Impression

1949 **Perf. 12½, 13 or Compound**

973 A94 1c apple green 29.00 11.00
974 A94 2c orange 9.00 17.50
975 A94 4c blue green .35 2.00
976 A94 10c deep lilac .35 2.00
977 A94 16c orange red .75 17.50
978 A94 20c blue .45 5.50
979 A94 50c dk brown 2.40 48.00
980 A94 100c deep blue 475.00 475.00
981 A94 500c scarlet 500.00 525.00
Nos. 973-981 (9) 1,017. 1,103.

For surcharges see Nos. 1057-1060.

 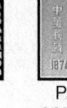

Flying Geese   Pigeons, Globe
Over   and Wreath — A98
Globe — A97

1949, May **Litho.** **Perf. 12½**
Without Gum

984 A97 $1 brown org 12.00 14.00
985 A97 $2 blue 65.00 24.00
986 A97 $5 car rose 65.00 27.50
987 A97 $10 blue grn 65.00 62.50
Nos. 984-987 (4) 207.00 128.00

Five other denominations — 10c, 16c, 50c,
$20 and $50 — were also printed at Shanghai,
but were not issued.
For surcharges see Nos. 1007-1011, 1042-
1045, 1061-1063, People's Republic of China
49-56, 5LQ17-5LQ26, 7L17-7L18, 8L14-8L16.

Engraved and Typographed
1949, Aug. 1 **Without Gum** **Imperf.**

988 A98 $1 org red & blk 12.00 17.50

75th anniv. of the UPU.
Exists with black denomination omitted.

Summer Palace,
Peiping — A99

Bronze Bull
and Kunming
Lake — A100

Engraved and Typographed
1949, Aug. **Rouletted**
Without Gum

989 A99 15c org brn & grn 8.00 9.50
990 A100 40c dl grn & car 9.25 9.50
a. 2nd and 3rd characters at
top transposed 160.00 200.00

Silver Yuan Surcharge
in Black on 1949 Sun
Yat-sen Issues

1949 **Perf. 12½, 14**

991 A94 1c on $100 org
brn (890) 15.00 10.00
992 A94 1c on $100 dk
org brn (898) 15.00 10.00

993	A94	2½c on $500 rose lil (892)	19.00	11.00
a.		Inverted surcharge	60.00	
994	A94	2½c on $500 rose lil (900)	21.00	12.00
995	A94	15c on $10 grn (887)	30.00	40.00
a.		Inverted surcharge	67.50	
996	A94	15c on $20 vio brn (896)	42.50	65.00
		Nos. 991-996 (6)	142.50	148.00

Silver Yuan Surcharge in Black or Carmine

997	A94	2½c on $50 grn (951)	2.75	3.75
998	A94	2½c on $50,000 bl (956)	7.50	3.75
999	A94	5c on $1000 dp bl (952) (C)	6.00	3.75
1000	A94	5c on $20,000 org (955)	4.00	3.25
1001	A94	5c on $200,000 vio (957) (C)	5.50	3.25
1002	A94	5c on $500,000 vio brn (958)	5.50	3.25
1003	A94	10c on $5000 car (953)	11.00	8.00
1004	A94	10c on $10,000 brn (954)	11.00	8.00
1005	A94	15c on $200 red org (891)	13.50	16.00
1006	A94	25c on $100 dk org brn (896)	27.50	30.00
		Nos. 997-1006 (10)	94.25	83.00

REPUBLIC OF CHINA

ri-ˈpə-blik of ˈchī-nə

(Taiwan)

LOCATION — Taiwan (since 1949) (Formosa)
GOVT. — Republic
AREA — 13,970 sq. mi.
POP. — 22,113,250 (1999 est.)
CAPITAL — Taipei

Stamps issued and used in Taiwan after Communist forces occupied the Chinese mainland include Taiwan Nos. 91-96, 101-103, J10-J17.

Catalogue values for unused stamps in this country are for Never Hinged items, beginning with Scott 1124 in the regular postage section, Scott B17 in the semi-postal section, Scott C69 in the airpost section, and Scott J142 in the postage due section.

Watermarks

Wmk. 281 — Wavy Lines

Wmk. 323 — Seal Character (found with "Yu" in various arrangements)

Wmk. 368 — JEZ Multiple

Wmk. 370 — Geometrical Design

Type of 1949 with Value Omitted Surcharged in Various Colors

1950, Jan. 1   Unwmk.   Perf. 12½

1007	A97	$1 green (Bk)	200.00	9.00
1008	A97	$2 green (C)	250.00	20.00
1009	A97	$5 green (V)	2,500.	100.00
1010	A97	$10 green (Br)	3,500.	275.00
1011	A97	$20 green (Dk Bl)	6,000.	1,000.
		Nos. 1007-1011 (5)	12,450.	1,404.

Two printings of the $1 and $2 show minor differences.

Cheng Ch'eng-kung (Koxinga) — A101

1950, June 26   Typo.   Rouletted
Without Gum

1012	A101	3c dk gray grn	4.00	1.10
1013	A101	10c orange brn	3.00	.30
1014	A101	15c orange yel	14.25	3.25
1015	A101	20c emerald	4.00	.25
1016	A101	30c claret	55.00	16.00
1017	A101	40c red orange	4.50	.30
1018	A101	50c chocolate	7.50	1.10
1019	A101	80c carmine	22.00	3.75
1020	A101	$1 ultra	18.50	1.10
1021	A101	$1.50 green	60.00	10.75
1022	A101	$1.60 blue	50.00	1.40
1023	A101	$2 red violet	23.00	1.10
1024	A101	$5 aqua	135.00	24.50
		Nos. 1012-1024 (13)	400.75	64.90

Part perf pairs exist of the 10c, 20c, 80c.
The 10c and 20c were reprinted from new plates. There are slight differences.
For surcharges see Nos. 1070-1072, 1105-1108, 1118-1119.

Nos. 751, 753, 788-791, 793, 795-799 Surcharged in Carmine or Black

1950   Engr.   Perf. 14

1025	A82	3c on $30,000	3.75	2.25
1026	A82	3c on $40,000 (C)	3.25	2.25
1027	A82	3c on $50,000 (C)	3.25	3.00
1028	A82	5c on $200,000	3.75	2.50
1029	A82	10c on $4000	32.50	4.00
1030	A82	10c on $6000	24.00	4.00
1031	A82	10c on $20,000	24.00	4.00
1032	A82	10c on $2,000,000	24.00	4.00
1033	A82	20c on $500,000	35.00	4.00
1034	A82	20c on $1,000,000	60.00	8.00
1035	A82	30c on $3,000,000	90.00	10.00
1036	A82	50c on $5,000,000 (C)	150.00	10.00
		Nos. 1025-1036 (12)	453.50	58.00

Issued: #1025-1027, 3/6; #1028, 3/25; #1031, 6/10:#1029-1030, 1032, 1035-1036, 8/1; #1033-1034, 8/25.
Forgeries exist.

Inverted Surcharge

1029a	A82	10c on $4000	160.00
1030a	A82	10c on $6000	350.00
1031a	A82	10c on $20,000	200.00
1032a	A82	10c on $2,000,000	210.00
1033a	A82	20c on $500,000	275.00
1034a	A82	20c on $1,000,000	275.00

Allegory of Election A102

Perf. 12x12½, Imperf.
1951, Mar. 20   Engr.   Unwmk.
Without Gum

1037	A102	40c carmine	14.00	1.00
a.		Horiz. pair, imperf. btwn.	85.00	
1038	A102	$1 dp blue	30.00	2.75
1039	A102	$1.60 purple	55.00	4.00
1040	A102	$2 brown	80.00	4.00
		Nos. 1037-1040 (4)	179.00	11.75

Souvenir Sheet
Imperf

1041	A102	$2 dp blue grn	575.00	400.00

Adoption of local self-government in Taiwan.

Design A97 Surcharged A103

Farmer and Scroll Announcing Tax Reduction A104

Surcharge in Various Colors

1951, July 19   Perf. 12½
Without Gum

1042	A103	$5 green (R Br)	100.00	11.00
1043	A103	$10 green (Bk)	200.00	12.00
1044	A103	$20 green (R)	900.00	30.00
1045	A103	$50 green (P)	1,500.	95.00
		Nos. 1042-1045 (4)	2,700.	148.00

1952, Jan. 1   Perf. 14
Without Gum

1046	A104	20c red orange	11.00	1.50
1047	A104	40c dk green	15.00	2.75
1048	A104	$1 brown	25.00	6.50
1049	A104	$1.40 dp blue	40.00	4.50

1050	A104	$2 dk gray	110.00	40.00
1051	A104	$5 brown car	150.00	16.00
		Nos. 1046-1051 (6)	351.00	71.25

Land tax reduction of 37.5% in Taiwan.
Value, imperf. set, $1,100.

Pres. Chiang Kai-shek, Flag and Followers A105

1952, Mar. 1   Unwmk.   Perf. 14
Without Gum

Flag in Violet Blue and Carmine

1052	A105	40c rose car	16.00	.50
a.		Vert. pair, imperf. btwn.	150.00	
1053	A105	$1 dp green	30.00	2.25
1054	A105	$1.60 brown org	60.00	1.10
a.		Horiz. pair, imperf. btwn.	320.00	
1055	A105	$2 brt blue	120.00	19.00
1056	A105	$5 violet brn	135.00	5.00
		Nos. 1052-1056 (5)	361.00	27.85

2nd anniv. of Chiang Kai-shek's return to the presidency.
Value, imperf. set, $495.
See Nos. 1064-1069.

Nos. 975-976, 978-979 Surcharged in Black

1952, Aug. 1   Perf. 12½

1057	A94	3c on 4c bl grn	6.25	5.25
1058	A94	3c on 10c dp lil	6.25	5.25
a.		Inverted surcharge		
1059	A94	3c on 20c blue	8.75	7.50
1060	A94	3c on 50c dk brn	10.00	8.75
		Nos. 1057-1060 (4)	31.25	26.75

Forgeries exist.

Geese Type of 1949 with Value Omitted Surcharged

1952, Dec. 8

1061	A97	$10 green (P)	100.00	16.00
1062	A97	$20 green (R)	290.00	27.50
1063	A97	$50 green (Bk)	2,750.	750.00
		Nos. 1061-1063 (3)	3,140.	793.50

Chiang Type of 1952 Redrawn
Perf. 12½
1953, Mar. 1   Engr.   Unwmk.
Without Gum

Flag in Dark Blue & Carmine

1064	A105	10c red orange	5.00	1.50
1065	A105	20c green	1.05	1.50
1066	A105	40c rose pink	15.00	2.00
1067	A105	$1.40 blue	45.00	3.25
1068	A105	$2 brown	11.00	6.00
1069	A105	$5 rose violet	175.00	16.00
		Nos. 1064-1069 (6)	351.05	30.25

Chiang Kai-shek's return to presidency, 3rd anniv.
Many differences in redrawn design. Value, imperf. set, $495.

Nos. 1020, 1014, 1016 and 1022 Surcharged in Various Colors

1953   Rouletted

1070	A101	3c on $1 ultra (C)	2.00	.50
1070A	A101	10c on 15c org yel (G) ('54)	7.50	1.05
1071	A101	10c on 30c cl (Bl)	4.00	1.40
1072	A101	20c on $1.60 bl (Bk)	4.50	1.50
		Nos. 1070-1072 (4)	18.00	4.45

Chinese characters and ornamental device at bottom differ on each value.

Issued: #1071, 2/1; #1070, 5/25; #1072, 6/13; #1070A, 7/16.

Nurse & Patients — A106
Chiang Kai-shek — A107

1953, July 1   Litho.   Perf. 12½
Without Gum
Cross in Red, Burelage Color in Italics

1073	A106	40c brown, *buff*	14.50	1.50
1074	A106	$1.60 blue, *bl*	35.00	1.40
1075	A106	$2 green, *yel*	55.00	2.25
1076	A106	$5 red org, *org*	95.00	10.00
	Nos. 1073-1076 (4)	199.50	15.15

Chinese Anti-Tuberculosis Association.

1953, Oct. 31   Engr.
Without Gum

1077	A107	10c dk brown	5.75	.25
1078	A107	20c lilac	5.75	.25
1079	A107	40c dp green	5.75	.25
1080	A107	50c dp pink	8.00	.25
1081	A107	80c brown bis	22.00	2.00
1082	A107	$1 dp olive grn	10.00	.25
1083	A107	$1.40 dp blue	10.00	.25
1084	A107	$1.60 dp carmine	10.00	.25
1085	A107	$1.70 apple grn	10.00	1.10
1086	A107	$2 brown	12.00	.25
1087	A107	$3 dark blue	190.00	7.00
1088	A107	$4 aqua	12.00	.70
1089	A107	$5 red orange	18.00	.70
1090	A107	$10 dk green	80.00	3.25
1091	A107	$20 dk brn lake	100.00	10.00
a.	Souvenir folder	600.00
	Nos. 1077-1091 (15)	499.25	26.95

67th birthday of Pres. Chiang Kai-shek.
#1091a contains #1077-1091 imperf, arranged in 3 sheets of 5 stamps each.

Silo Highway Bridge — A108

Forest of Evergreens — A109

$1.60 and $5, Silo bridge, side view.

1954, Jan. 28   Unwmk.   Perf. 12½
Without Gum
Various Frames

1092	A108	40c vermilion	20.00	1.00
1093	A108	$1.60 blue violet	92.50	1.75
1094	A108	$3.60 sepia	60.00	5.00
1095	A108	$5 magenta	145.00	9.00
a.	Souvenir folder	2,100.
	Nos. 1092-1095 (4)	317.50	16.75

Opening of Silo bridge, 1st anniversary. No. 1095a contains one sheet of 4 containing Nos. 1092-1095 imperforate. Beware of stapled folders.

1954, Mar. 12   Perf. 12x12½
Without Gum

1096	A109	40c shown	17.00	1.50
1097	A109	$10 Nursery	126.50	10.00

Issued to publicize forest conservation.

Runner — A110

Globe, Bridge and Ship — A111

1954, Mar. 29
Without Gum

1098	A110	40c dp ultra	14.00	2.00
1099	A110	$5 carmine	100.00	10.00

11th Youth Day, Mar. 29, 1954.

1954, Oct. 21   Perf. 12
Without Gum

1100	A111	40c red orange	15.00	1.00
1101	A111	$5 deep blue	17.50	4.50

2nd Overseas Chinese Day, Oct. 21, 1954.

Ex-Prisoner with Broken Chains — A112

Designs: $1, Ex-prisoner with torch and flag, UN emblem. $1.60, Torch and date.

1955, Jan. 23

1102	A112	40c blue green	2.50	.65
a.	Vert. pair, imperf. btwn.	150.00
1103	A112	$1 sepia	18.50	5.00
1104	A112	$1.60 lake	18.50	4.25
	Nos. 1102-1104 (3)	39.50	9.90

Honoring Chinese who fought on the side of the North Korean army, who, when released January 23, 1954, chose to return to the Republic of China.

Nos. 1019-1021, 1017 Surcharged in Brown, Blue or Green:

a   b

c

1955   Rouletted

1105	A101(a)	3c on $1 (Br)	2.75	.50
1106	A101(b)	10c on 80c (Bl)	3.75	.50
1107	A101(b)	10c on $1.50 (Bl)	3.75	.50
1108	A101(c)	20c on 40c (G)	4.50	.85
	Nos. 1105-1108 (4)	14.75	2.35

Issued: #1105, 1108, 2/18; #1106-1107, 8/1.

Hand Planting Evergreen Tree — A113

Chiang Kai-shek, Flags, Building A114

Design: $50, Seedling and map of Taiwan.

1955, Apr. 1   Perf. 12
Without Gum

1109	A113	$20 dp carmine	32.50	1.25
1110	A113	$50 blue	80.00	5.75

Issued to publicize forest conservation.

1955, May 20   Engr.   Perf. 12
Without Gum

1111	A114	20c olive	4.50	.40
1112	A114	40c blue green	4.00	.40
1113	A114	$2 car rose	10.75	1.25
1114	A114	$7 dp ultra	17.00	2.00
a.	Souv. sheet of 4, #1111-1114, imperf.	350.00	210.00
	Nos. 1111-1114 (4)	36.25	4.05

First anniversary of Pres. Chiang Kai-shek's re-election.
No. 1114a is perf. 12 at right edge of sheet. Value is for sheet with right selvage.

Armed Forces Emblem — A115

1955, Sept. 3
Without Gum

1115	A115	40c dk blue	4.75	.50
1116	A115	$2 org ver	17.00	1.50
1117	A115	$7 bl grn	27.50	1.75
a.	Sheet of 3, #1115-1117, imperf.	800.00	500.00
	Nos. 1115-1117 (3)	49.25	3.75

Armed Forces Day, Sept. 3.
No. 1117a is perf. 12 at right edge of sheet. Value is for sheet with right selvage.

Nos. 1017, 1018 and C64 Surcharged in Magenta

1955, Sept. 16   Typo.   Rouletted

1118	A101	20c on 40c red org	5.00	.40
1119	A101	20c on 50c choc	5.00	.40
1120	AP6	20c on 60c dp blue	7.00	.50
	Nos. 1118-1120 (3)	17.00	1.30

Flags of UN and China A116

1955, Oct. 24   Engr.   Perf. 11½
Without Gum

1121	A116	40c dk blue	3.50	.55
1122	A116	$2 dk car rose	6.75	1.10
1123	A116	$7 slate green	11.50	1.90
	Nos. 1121-1123 (3)	21.75	3.55

10th anniv. of the UN, Oct. 24, 1955.

> **Catalogue values for unused stamps in this section, from this point to the end of the section, are for Never Hinged items.**

Pres. Chiang Kai-shek A117
Birthplace of Sun Yat-sen A118

1955, Oct. 31   Photo.   Perf. 13½

1124	A117	40c dk bl, red & brn	6.00	.60
1125	A117	$2 grn, red & dk bl	12.75	2.00
1126	A117	$7 brn, red & grn	19.00	3.00
a.	Souv. sheet of 3, #1124-1126, imperf.	180.00	180.00
	Nos. 1124-1126 (3)	37.75	5.60

69th birthday of Pres. Chiang Kai-shek.
No. 1126a is perf. 12 at right edge of sheet. Value is for sheet with right selvage.

1955, Nov. 12   Engr.   Perf. 12
Without Gum

1127	A118	40c blue	3.25	.45
1128	A118	$2 red brown	8.00	1.00
1129	A118	$7 rose lake	10.00	2.00
	Nos. 1127-1129 (3)	21.25	3.45

90th anniversary, birth of Sun Yat-sen.

No. 959a Surcharged in Bright Green

1956, Feb. 10   Litho.   Rouletted

1130	A96	20c on orange	.60	.20

See No. 1213.

China Map and Transportation Methods — A119

Wmk. 281
1956, Mar. 20   Engr.   Perf. 12
Without Gum

1131	A119	40c dk carmine	2.00	.25
1132	A119	$1 intense blk	4.00	.65
1133	A119	$1.60 chocolate	5.50	.45
1134	A119	$2 dk green	8.75	1.00
	Nos. 1131-1134 (4)	20.25	2.35

60th anniv. of the founding of modern Chinese postal system.

Souvenir Sheets
Imperf

1135	A119	$2 magenta	60.00	30.00
1136	A119	$2 red	60.00	30.00

Exhib. for the 60th anniv. of the modern Chinese postal system, Mar. 20, 1956.

Children at Play — A120

Early and Modern Locomotives A121

1956, Apr. 4   Unwmk.   Perf. 12
Without Gum

1137	A120	40c emerald	1.75	.25
1138	A120	$1.60 dk blue	3.50	.50
1139	A120	$2 dk carmine	5.75	1.00
	Nos. 1137-1139 (3)	11.00	1.75

Children's Day, Apr. 4, 1956.

1956, June 9   Wmk. 281 Vert.
Without Gum

1140	A121	40c rose car	4.25	.40
1141	A121	$2 blue	6.00	.65
1142	A121	$8 green	10.00	1.75
	Nos. 1140-1142 (3)	20.25	2.80

75th anniversary of Chinese Railroads.

Pres. Chiang Kai-shek
A122   A123

A124

Various Portraits of Chiang
Perf. 14½x13½, 14½ (A123), 13½x14½

1956, Oct. 31   Photo.   Unwmk.
1143 A122   20c red orange   4.50   .20
1144 A122   40c carmine rose 6.75   .20
1145 A123 $1 brt ultra   9.00   .30
1146 A123 $1.60 red lilac   11.50 .20
1147 A124 $2 red brown   16.00 .50
1148 A124 $8 brt grnsh
              blue   35.00 .85
  Nos. 1143-1148 (6)   82.75 2.25

70th birthday of Pres. Chiang Kai-shek.

Types of Special Delivery, Air Post and
Registration Stamps of 1949
Surcharged in Black or Maroon

a   b

c

1956 Unwmk. Litho. *Rouletted*
Without Gum
1150 SD2(a) 3c red violet   1.25   .20
  a.   Perf. 12½   3.50   .30
1151 AP5(b) 3c blue green (M) 1.25   .20
1152 R2(c)   10c bright red   1.25   .20
  Nos. 1150-1152 (3)   3.75   .60

Issued: #1150, 4/25; #1151, 11/11; #1152, 12/25.

Telecommunications
Emblem and Radio
Tower — A125

Wmk. 281
1956, Dec. 28 Engr. *Perf. 12*
Without Gum
1153 A125   40c deep ultra   1.60   .20
1154 A125 $1.40 carmine   2.25   .20
1155 A125 $1.60 dark green 3.25   .20
1156 A125 $2 chocolate   4.25   .40
  Nos. 1153-1156 (4)   11.35 1.00

Chinese telegraph service, 75th anniv.

Map of China
A126

Mother
Instructing
Mencius
A127

Pin Perf., Perf. 12x12½
1957 Litho. Wmk. 281
Without Gum
1157 A126   3c brt blue   .90   .20
1158 A126   10c violet   1.40   .20
1159 A126   20c red orange   .90   .20
1160 A126   40c rose red   1.75   .20
Unwmk.
1161 A126 $1 orange brown 2.50   .20
1162 A126 $1.60 green   3.75   .25
  Nos. 1157-1162 (6)   11.20 1.25

Map inscription reads: "Recovery of Mainland."
See Nos. 1177-1182.

Unwmk.
1957, May 12 Engr. *Perf. 12*
Design: $3, Mother tattooing Yueh Fei.
Without Gum
1163 A127   40c green   1.50   .20
1164 A127 $3 redsh brown   2.75   .40

Issued to honor Mother's Day, 1957.

Badge of Chinese Boy Scouts — A128

1957, Aug. 11
Without Gum
1165 A128   40c lilac   .80   .20
1166 A128 $1 green   1.75   .50
1167 A128 $1.60 dk blue   2.50   .25
  Nos. 1165-1167 (3)   5.05   .95

Cent. of the birth of Lord Baden-Powell and to publicize the World Scout Jubilee Jamboree, England, Aug. 1-12.

Globe, Radio
Tower and
Microphone
A129

1957, Sept. 16
Without Gum
1168 A129   40c vermilion   .60   .20
1169 A129   50c brt rose lilac 1.00 .20
1170 A129 $3.50 dark blue 1.75   .55
  Nos. 1168-1170 (3)   3.35   .95

30th anniv. of Chinese broadcasting.

Map of
Taiwan — A130

1957, Oct. 26
Without Gum
1171 A130   40c blue green   3.25   .40
1172 A130 $1.40 lt ultra   6.25 1.75
1173 A130 $2 gray   8.50 1.90
  Nos. 1171-1173 (3)   18.00 4.05

Start of construction on the Cross Island Highway, Taiwan.

Freighter "Hai Min" and River Boat
"Kiang Foo" — A131

1957, Dec. 16 Engr. *Perf. 12*
Without Gum
1174 A131   40c deep ultra   .75   .25
1175 A131   80c rose lake   1.50   .95
1176 A131 $2.80 vermilion 2.25 1.40
  Nos. 1174-1176 (3)   4.50 2.60

85th anniv. of the establishment of the China Merchants Steam Navigation Co.

Type of 1957
Pin Perf., Perf. 12x12½
1957, Dec. 25 Typo. Unwmk.
Without Gum
Dark Blue Frames
1177 A126   3c brt blue   .30   .20
1178 A126   10c violet   .55   .20
1179 A126   20c brick red   .85   .20
1180 A126   40c rose red   1.00   .20
1181 A126 $1 dp org brn   3.25   .25
1182 A126 $1.60 dp green 4.00   .30
  Nos. 1177-1182 (6)   9.95 1.35

Stamps with bars obliterating the face value are specimens.

Butterfly   Mme. Chiang
A132   Kai-shek Orchid
                A133

Perf. 13½
1958, Mar. 20 Unwmk. Photo.
Various Insects in Natural Colors
1183 A132 10c pale grn, grn
              & blk   1.25   .50
1184 A132 40c lem, pink, grn
              & blk   1.25   .50
1185 A132 $1 yel grn & mar 2.25   .60
1186 A132 $1.40 yel, org & blk 3.25 .75
1187 A132 $1.60 pale brn & dk
              pur   4.75   .90
1188 A132 $2 brt yel, org &
              blk   5.75 1.25
  Nos. 1183-1188 (6)   18.50 4.50

1958, Mar. 20
Orchids: 20c, Formosan Wilson, horiz. $1.40, Klotzsch. $3, Fitzgerald, horiz.

Orchids in Natural Colors
1189 A133 20c chocolate   2.25   .40
1190 A133 40c purple   2.50   .40
1191 A133 $1.40 dk vio brn 4.50   .60
1192 A133 $3 dark blue   6.25 1.10
  Nos. 1189-1192 (4)   15.50 2.50

World Health Organization
Emblem — A134

President's Mansion,
Taipei — A135

1958, May 28 Engr. *Perf. 12*
Without Gum
1193 A134   40c dark blue   .50   .20
1194 A134 $1.60 brick red .65   .20
1195 A134 $2 deep red lilac .85 .40
  Nos. 1193-1195 (3)   2.00   .80

10th anniv. of the WHO.

Wmk. 323
1958, Sept. 20 Engr. *Perf. 12*
Without Gum
1196 A135 $10 blue green   16.00   .30
  a.   Granite paper   12.00   .30
1197 A135 $20 car rose   24.00   .50
  a.   Granite paper   20.00   .50
1198 A135 $50 red brown   60.00 2.00
1199 A135 $100 dk blue   90.00 5.00
  Nos. 1196-1199 (4)   190.00 7.80

Issued: #1196a, 1197a, 5/24/63.
See #1349-1351. For surcharge see #J131.

Taiwan
Farm
Scene
A136

1958, Oct. 1 Unwmk.
Without Gum
1200 A136   20c emerald   1.25   .20
1201 A136   40c black   1.50   .20
1202 A136 $1.40 brt magenta 2.75 .25
1203 A136 $3 ultra   4.50   .75
  Nos. 1200-1203 (4)   10.00 1.40

10th anniversary of the Joint Commission on Rural Reconstruction.

Pres. Chiang
Kai-shek
A137

1958, Oct. 31 Photo. *Perf. 13½*
1204 A137 40c multicolored 1.25   .45

Pres. Chiang Kai-shek on his 72nd birthday.

UNESCO
Building,
Paris
A138

1958, Nov. 3 Engr. *Perf. 12*
Without Gum
1205 A138   20c dark blue   .35   .25
1206 A138   40c green   .50   .25
1207 A138 $1.40 orange ver .70   .40
1208 A138 $3 red lilac   1.25   .55
  Nos. 1205-1208 (4)   2.80 1.45

UNESCO Headquarters in Paris opening, Nov. 3.

Flame from Liberty
Torch Encircling
Globe — A139

1958, Dec. 10 Unwmk.
Without Gum
1209 A139 40c green .20 .20
1210 A139 60c gray brown .30 .20
1211 A139 $1 carmine .50 .20
1212 A139 $3 ultra .75 .40
Nos. 1209-1212 (4) 1.75 1.00

10th anniversary of the signing of the Universal Declaration of Human Rights.

No. 959a Surcharged
in Bright Green

Rouletted
1958, Dec. 11 Litho. Unwmk.
Without Gum
1213 A96 20c on orange .55 .20

Ballot Box, Scales and
Constitution — A140

1958, Dec. 25 Engr. *Perf. 12*
Without Gum
1214 A140 40c green 1.25 .20
1215 A140 50c dull purple 1.75 .20
1216 A140 $1.40 car rose 2.00 .25
1217 A140 $3.50 dk blue 3.50 .75
Nos. 1214-1217 (4) 8.50 1.40

Adoption of the constitution, 10th anniv.

Chu Kwang Tower,
Quemoy — A141

1959-60 Wmk. 323 Litho. *Perf. 12*
Without Gum
1218 A141 3c orange .50 .20
1218A A141 5c lt yel grn
('60) .60 .20
1219 A141 10c lilac .70 .20
1220 A141 20c ultra .90 .20
1221 A141 40c brown 1.10 .20
1222 A141 50c bluish grn 1.40 .20
1223 A141 $1 rose red 1.50 .20
1224 A141 $1.40 yel grn 2.10 .20
1225 A141 $2 gray grn 2.75 .20
1226 A141 $2.80 rose pink 4.00 .25
1227 A141 $3 slate blue 4.25 .25
Nos. 1218-1227 (11) 19.80 2.30

See Nos. 1270-1283.

ILO Emblem and Headquarters,
Geneva — A142

1959, June 15 Engr. *Perf. 12*
Without Gum
1228 A142 40c blue .40 .20
1229 A142 $1.60 dk brown .50 .20
1230 A142 $3 brt blue grn .75 .20
1231 A142 $5 orange ver 1.25 .50
Nos. 1228-1231 (4) 2.90 1.10

40th anniversary of the ILO.

Bugler
and Tents
A143

1959, July 8 Unwmk.
Without Gum
1232 A143 40c carmine .95 .20
1233 A143 50c dark blue 1.10 .25
1234 A143 $5 green 1.90 .55
Nos. 1232-1234 (3) 3.95 1.00

10th World Boy Scout Jamboree, Makiling National Park, Philippines, July 17-26.

Inscribed Stone,
Mt. Tai-wu,
Quemoy — A144

Map of
Taiwan
Straits
A145

1959, Sept. 3 Engr. *Perf. 12*
Without Gum
1235 A144 40c brown .90 .20
1236 A145 $1.40 ultra 1.00 .20
1237 A145 $2 green 1.75 .20
1238 A145 $3 dark blue 2.10 .30
Nos. 1235-1238 (4) 5.75 .90

Defense of Quemoy and Matsu islands.
For overprints see Nos. 1258-1259.

Pigeons
Circling
Globe
A146

1959, Oct. 4
Without Gum
1239 A146 40c blue .45 .20
1240 A146 $1 rose carmine .80 .20
1241 A146 $2 gray brown 1.10 .20
1242 A146 $3.50 red orange 1.40 .50
Nos. 1239-1242 (4) 3.75 1.10

Intl. Letter Writing Week, Oct. 4-10.

National Taiwan
Science Hall,
Taipei — A147

1959, Nov. 12 Photo. *Perf. 13x13½*
1243 A147 40c shown 1.40 .20
1244 A147 $3 Front view 2.75 .70

Emblem
A148

1959, Dec. 7 Engr. *Perf. 12*
Without Gum
1245 A148 40c blue green .40 .25
1246 A148 $1.60 red lilac .70 .25
1247 A148 $3 orange 1.10 .60
Nos. 1245-1247 (3) 2.20 1.10

Intl. Confederation of Free Trade Unions, 10th anniv.

Sun Yat-
sen,
Lincoln
and
Flags
A149

Perf. 13½, 12
1959, Dec. 25 Photo. Unwmk.
1248 A149 40c multicolored .50 .25
1249 A149 $3 multicolored 1.25 .60

Issued to honor Sun Yat-sen and Abraham Lincoln as "Leaders of Democracy."

Mailman on Motorcycle Delivering
Night Mail — A150

Postal
Launch
A151

1960, Mar. 20 Engr. *Perf. 11½*
Without Gum
1250 A150 $1.40 dk violet brn 1.50 .25
1251 A151 $1.60 ultra 1.50 .25

Issued to publicize the Prompt Delivery Service.

WRY Uprooted
Oak
Emblem — A152

1960, Apr. 7 Photo. *Perf. 13*
1252 A152 40c blk, red brn & emer .75 .20
1253 A152 $3 blk, red org & grn 1.40 .35

World Refugee Year, 7/1/59-6/30/60.

Cross Island Highway, Taiwan — A153

Design: $1, $2, Road through tunnel, vert.

Perf. 11½
1960, May 9 Engr. Unwmk.
Without Gum
1254 A153 40c green 1.25 .20
1255 A153 $1 dk blue 2.50 .30
1256 A153 $2 brown vio 2.50 .30
1257 A153 $3 brown 3.75 .40
a. Souv. sheet of 2, #1255,
1257, wmk. 323, im-
perf. 230.00 125.00
Nos. 1254-1257 (4) 10.00 1.20

Opening of the Cross Island Highway, Taiwan.

Red Overprint on Nos. 1237-1238
Chinese and English: "Welcome U.S.
President Dwight D. Eisenhower 1960"
1960, June 18 Unwmk. *Perf. 12*
1258 A145 $2 green 1.40 .30
a. Inverted overprint 2,250. 2,250.
1259 A144 $3 dk blue 1.75 .45

Eisenhower's visit to China, June 18, 1960.

Phonopost — A154

1960, June 27
Without Gum
1260 A154 $2 red orange 1.75 .40

Phonopost Service of the Chinese armed forces.

Two Horses and Groom, by Han
Kan — A155

Paintings from Palace Museum, Taichung:
$1, Two Riders, by Wei Yen. $1.60, Flowers
and Birds by Hsiao Yung, vert. $2, Pair of Man-
darin Ducks by Monk Hui Ch'ung.

1960, Aug. 4 Photo. *Perf. 13*
1261 A155 $1 ol gray, blk &
brn 4.00 .55
1262 A155 $1.40 bis brn, blk &
fawn 8.00 1.00
1263 A155 $1.60 multicolored 9.00 1.75
1264 A155 $2 beige, blk &
gray grn 14.00 3.25
Nos. 1261-1264 (4) 35.00 6.55

Chinese paintings, 7th-11th centuries.
For other painting types with large straight
numerals in the upper corners and large Chinese characters on the side see A186, A241
and A285.

Youth Corps
Flag and
Summer
Activities
A156

Reforestation
A157

Design: $3, similar to 50c, horiz.

1960, Aug. 20 Engr. *Perf. 12*
Without Gum
1265 A156 50c slate green .50 .20
1266 A156 $3 copper brown 1.10 .45

Summer activities of China Youth Corps.

1960, Aug. 29　Photo.　Perf. 13½x13

$2, Protection of forest. $3, Timber industry.

1267	A157	$1 multicolored	1.60	.20
1268	A157	$2 multicolored	2.25	.80
1269	A157	$3 multicolored	3.25	.60
a.		Souvenir sheet of 3	27.50	20.00
		Nos. 1267-1269 (3)	7.10	1.60

Fifth World Forestry Congress, Seattle, Washington, Aug. 29-Sept. 10.

No. 1269a contains Nos. 1267-1269 assembled as a triptych, 65½x40mm and imperf., but with simulated black perforations.

Chu Kwang Tower, Quemoy — A158

Sports — A159

1960-61　Wmk. 323　Litho.　Perf. 12
Without Gum

1270	A158	3c lt red brown	.50	.20
1271	A158	40c pale violet	.50	.20
1272	A158	50c orange ('61)	.80	.20
1273	A158	60c rose lilac	1.00	.20
1274	A158	80c pale green	1.10	.20
1275	A158	$1 gray grn ('61)	1.25	.20
1276	A158	$1.20 gray olive	1.25	.20
1277	A158	$1.50 ultra	1.50	.25
1278	A158	$2 car rose ('61)	1.75	.20
1279	A158	$2.50 pale blue	1.90	.25
1280	A158	$3 bluish green	2.00	.25
1281	A158	$3.20 lt red brown	1.75	.20
1282	A158	$3.60 vio blue ('61)	3.75	.30
1283	A158	$4.50 vermilion	7.00	.35
		Nos. 1270-1283 (14)	26.05	3.20

For surcharges see Nos. J132-J134.

1962-64

Granite Paper
Without Gum

1270a	A158	3c light red brown	.75	.20
1270B	A158	10c emerald ('63)	2.25	.20
1271a	A158	40c pale violet	.75	.20
1274a	A158	80c pale green	.75	.20
1275a	A158	$1 gray grn ('63)	12.00	.20
1278a	A158	$2 carmine rose	6.00	.20
1281a	A158	$3.20 red brn ('64)	15.00	.20
1282A	A158	$4 brt blue grn	15.00	.20
1283a	A158	$4.50 vermilion	21.00	.50
		Nos. 1270a-1283a (9)	73.50	2.10

Two types of No. 1271a: I. Seven lines in "0" of "40." II. Eight lines in "0."

Perf. 12½
1960, Oct. 25　Photo.　Unwmk.

1284	A159	50c Diving	1.25	.25
1285	A159	80c Discus thrower	1.00	.25
1286	A159	$2 Basketball	2.50	.30
1287	A159	$2.50 Soccer	2.75	.55
1288	A159	$3 Hurdling	4.00	.75
1289	A159	$3.20 Runner	5.25	.80
		Nos. 1284-1289 (6)	16.75	2.90

Bronze Wine Container, 1751-1111 B.C. — A160

Flat Bowl, 1111-771 B.C. — A161

Ancient Chinese Art Treasures: $1, Cauldron, 1111-771 B.C. $1.20, Porcelain vase, 960-1126 A.D. $1.50, Perforated tube, 1111-771 B.C. $2, Jug in shape of monk's cap, 1368-1661 A.D. $2.50, Jade flower vase, 1368-1661, A.D.

1961　Photo.　Perf. 13

1290	A160	80c lt ol, blk & dk vio	3.00	.20
1291	A160	$1 sal, bl & blk	5.75	.35
1292	A160	$1.20 yel, brn & ultra	9.00	.50
1293	A160	$1.50 lil, bl & sep	7.00	1.10
1294	A160	$2 pale grn, dk grn & red	10.00	.70
1295	A160	$2.50 grnsh bl & dk vio	15.00	1.25
		Nos. 1290-1295 (6)	49.75	4.10

Issue dates: Nos. 1290, 1292, 1295, Feb. 1. Nos. 1291, 1293-1294, May 1.

1961

80c, Palace perfumer, 1662-1911. $1, Corn vase, 770-221 B.C. $2, Jade tankard, 960-1126 A.D. $4, Glazed washer, 1127-1279 A.D. $4.50, Jade chimera, 8 B.C.-206 A.D.

1296	A160	80c pink, brn, bl & yel	2.25	.30
1297	A160	$1 cit, blk & brn	6.00	.60
1298	A161	$1.50 sal & ind	7.00	1.25
1299	A160	$2 bl, blk & rose	14.50	.75
1300	A161	$4 red, blk & bluish gray	17.00	1.25
1301	A161	$4.50 grnsh bl, blk & brn	35.00	3.00
		Nos. 1296-1301 (6)	81.75	7.15

Issued: #1296-1298, 8/15; #1299-1301, 9/15.

1962

Designs: 80c, Topaz twin wine vessels, 1662-1911 A.D. $1, Squat pouring vase, 1751-1111 B.C. $2.40, Vase, 1368-1661 A.D. $3, Wine vase, 1751-1111 B.C. $3.20, Covered porcelain jar, 1662-1911 A.D. $3.60, Perforated disc, 206 B.C.-8 A.D.

1302	A160	80c crim, blk & ocher	2.00	.25
1303	A160	$1 blue & vio blk	2.50	.25
1304	A160	$2.40 hn brn, blk & bl	20.00	1.00
1305	A160	$3 blue, blk & pink	22.50	.90
1306	A160	$3.20 ultra, lt grn & red	20.00	.90
1307	A160	$3.60 yel, blk & brn	35.00	1.25
		Nos. 1302-1307 (6)	102.00	4.55

Issue dates: Nos. 1303-1304, 1307, Jan. 15. Nos. 1302, 1305-1306, Feb. 15.

Farmer with Mechanized Plow — A162

Madame Chiang Kai-shek and League Emblem — A163

1961, Feb. 4　Engr.　Perf. 12
Without Gum

1308	A162	80c rose violet	1.40	.20
1309	A162	$2 green	3.25	.50
1310	A162	$3.20 vermilion	5.00	.35
		Nos. 1308-1310 (3)	9.65	1.05

1961 agricultural census.

Unwmk.
1961, Mar. 8　Photo.　Perf. 13
Portrait in Black

1311	A163	80c lt grn & car rose	2.10	.30
1312	A163	$1 yel grn & car rose	4.00	.60
1313	A163	$2 org brn & car rose	4.00	.70
1314	A163	$3.20 lil & car rose	6.50	1.40
		Nos. 1311-1314 (4)	16.60	3.00

10th anniversary of the Chinese Women's Anti-Aggression League.

Spiny Lobster and Mail Order Service Emblem — A164

Jeme Tien-yow and Pataling Tunnel — A165

1961, Mar. 20　Engr.　Perf. 11½
Without Gum

1315	A164	$3 slate green	5.50	.40

Issued to publicize the mail order service for consumer goods.

1961, Apr. 26　Perf. 11½
Without Gum

$2, Jeme Tien-yow & 1909 locomotive.

1316	A165	80c lilac	1.50	.20
1317	A165	$2 black, horiz.	3.50	.60

Centenary of the birth of Jeme Tien-yow, builder of the Peking-Kalgan railroad.

Map of China inscribed: "Recovery of the Mainland" — A166

Pres. Chiang Kai-shek — A167

1961, May 20　Photo.　Perf. 13½

1318	A166	80c multicolored	2.50	.25
1319	A167	$2 multicolored	5.00	1.25
a.		Souvenir sheet of 2	20.00	20.00

1st anniversary of Pres. Chiang Kai-shek's 3rd term inauguration.

No. 1319a contains one each of Nos. 1318-1319, imperf. with simulated perforations. Without gum.

Convair 880-M, Biplane of 1921 and Flag — A168

1961, July 1　Perf. 13x12½

1320	A168	$10 multicolored	4.50	1.40

40th anniversary of civil air service.

Sun Yat-sen and Chiang Kai-shek — A169

Flag and Map of China — A170

Perf. 13½
1961, Oct. 10　Unwmk.　Photo.

1321	A169	80c gray, lt brn & sl	1.60	.20
1322	A170	$5 gray, ultra, red & beige	4.25	1.60
a.		Souvenir sheet of 2	16.00	16.00

50th anniv. of the Republic of China. No. 1322a contains one each of Nos. 1321-1322, imperf. with simulated perforations. No gum.

Green Lake A171

Oil Refinery A173

Lotus Pond A172

Taiwan Scenery: $2, Sun-Moon Lake. $3.20, Wulai waterfalls.

Perf. 13½x14, 14x13½
1961, Oct. 31　Unwmk.

1323	A171	80c multicolored	4.00	.20
1324	A172	$1 multicolored	9.00	.90
1325	A172	$2 multicolored	12.00	.70
1326	A171	$3.20 multicolored	16.00	1.25
		Nos. 1323-1326 (4)	41.00	3.05

1961, Nov. 14　Perf. 11½

Designs: $1.50, Steel works. $2.50, Aluminum plant. $3.20, Fertilizer plant, horiz.

1327	A173	80c multicolored	2.00	.25
1328	A173	$1.50 multicolored	3.50	.80
1329	A173	$2.50 multicolored	5.00	.70
1330	A173	$3.20 multicolored	7.25	.65
		Nos. 1327-1330 (4)	17.75	2.40

Chinese industrial development and the Golden Jubilee Convention of the Chinese Institute of Engineers, Nov. 13-16.

Atomic Reactor, Tsing-Hwa University A174

Atomic Reactor in Operation A175

Design: $3.20, Atomic symbol and laboratory, Tsing-Hwa, horiz.

1961-62　Photo.　Perf. 12½

1331	A174	80c multicolored	2.25	.20
1332	A175	$2 multicolored	5.00	1.40
1333	A175	$3.20 multicolored	5.50	1.25
		Nos. 1331-1333 (3)	12.75	2.85

Inauguration on Apr. 13, 1961, of the 1st Chinese atomic reactor at the National Tsing-Hwa University Institute of Nuclear Science. Issued: 80c, 12/2; $2, $3.20, 3/20/62.

Microwave Reflector and Telegraph Wires — A176

Design: $3.20, Microwave parabolic antenna and mountains, horiz.

1961, Dec. 28   *Perf. 12½*
1334 A176   80c multicolored   1.50   .20
1335 A176 $3.20 multicolored   3.00   .80

80th anniv. of Chinese telecommunications.

Mechanical Postal Equipment and Twine Tying Machine — A176a

Wmk. 323
1962, Mar. 20   **Engr.**   *Perf. 11½*
Without Gum
1336 A176a 80c chocolate   1.50 .45

Yu Shan Observatory A177

Observation Balloon, Earth and Cumulus Clouds A178

Design: $1, Map showing route of typhoon Pamela, Sept. 1961, horiz.

1962
Without Gum
1337 A177   80c brown   .95   .20
1338 A178 $1 bluish black   1.90   .30
1339 A178 $2 green   2.50   .65
    Nos. 1337-1339 (3)   5.35 1.15

Issue dates: 80c, $2, Mar. 23; $1, May 7. World Meteorological Day, Mar. 23.

Child Receiving Milk, UN Emblem A179

1962, Apr. 4
Without Gum
1340 A179   80c rose red   .85   .20
1341 A179 $3.20 green   2.50   .50
   a.   Souvenir sheet of 2   16.00 4.50

15th anniv. of UNICEF. No. 1341a contains one each of Nos. 1340-1341 imperf. with simulated perforations.

Malaria Eradication Emblem — A180

Unwmk.
1962, Apr. 7   **Photo.**   *Perf. 13*
1342 A180   80c dk bl, red & lt grn   .60   .20
1343 A180 $3.60 brn, pink & grn   1.60 1.00

WHO drive to eradicate malaria.

Yu Yu-jen — A181

Cheng Ch'eng-kung (Koxinga) — A182

1962, Apr. 24   *Perf. 13*
1344 A181 80c gray, blk & pink   2.00 .25

Issued to honor Yu Yu-jen, newspaper reporter, revolutionary leader and co-worker of Sun Yat-sen, on his 84th birthday.

1962, Apr. 29
1345 A182 80c deep claret   2.00 .20
1346 A182 $2 dark green   3.50 .55

300th anniversary (in 1961) of the recovery of Taiwan from the Dutch by Koxinga.

Emblem of Intl. Cooperative Alliance — A183

Clasped Hands Across Globe — A184

Wmk. 323
1962, July 7   **Engr.**   *Perf. 12*
Without Gum
1347 A183 80c brown   .90 .20
1348 A184 $2 violet   2.00 .45

Intl. Cooperative Movement and 40th Intl. Cooperative Day, July 7, 1962.

Mansion Type of 1958

1962, July 20
Without Gum
1349 A135 $5 gray green   2.75   .20
1350 A135 $5.60 violet   3.75   .20
1351 A135 $6 orange   3.50   .20
    Nos. 1349-1351 (3)   10.00   .60

1963
Granite Paper
1349a A135 $5 gray green   3.50   .20
1350a A135 $5.60 violet   4.00   .20
1351a A135 $6 orange   5.50   .20
    Nos. 1349a-1351a (3)   13.00   .60

"Art and Science" — A185

$2, "Education," book and UNESCO emblem, horiz. $3.20, "Communications," globes, horiz.

1962, Aug. 28   **Wmk. 323**   *Perf. 12*
Without Gum
1352 A185   80c lilac rose   .60   .20
1353 A185 $2 rose claret   1.50   .40
1354 A185 $3.20 yellow green   1.75   .30
    Nos. 1352-1354 (3)   3.85   .90

UNESCO activities in China.

Emperor T'ai Tsung, T'ang Dynasty, 627-649 A186

Emperors: $2, T'ai Tsu, Sung dynasty, 960-975. $3.20, T'ai Tsu, Yuan dynasty (Genghis Khan), 1206-27. $4, T'ai Tsu, Ming dynasty, 1368-98.

1962, Sept. 20   **Photo.**   **Unwmk.**
1355 A186   80c multicolored   25.00   2.25
1356 A186 $2 multicolored   90.00   7.00
1357 A186 $3.20 multicolored   150.00   7.50
1358 A186 $4 multicolored   250.00   19.50
    Nos. 1355-1358 (4)   515.00 36.25

Lions International Emblem A187

1962, Oct. 8   *Perf. 13½*
1359 A187   80c multicolored   1.25   .20
1360 A187 $3.60 multicolored   2.50   .80
   a.   Souvenir sheet of 2   18.00 9.00

45th anniv. of Lions Intl. No. 1360a contains one each of Nos. 1359-1360, imperf. with simulated perforations.

Pole Vaulting — A188

Shooting A189

1962, Oct. 25   **Unwmk.**   *Perf. 13*
1361 A188   80c multicolored   1.00 .20
1362 A189 $3.20 multicolored   2.25 .40

Sports meet.

Young Farmers and 4-H Emblem — A190

Flag, Liner of China Merchants' Steam Navigation Co. — A191

Design: $3.20, 4-H emblem and rice.

Wmk. 323
1962, Dec. 7   **Engr.**   *Perf. 12*
Without Gum
1363 A190   80c carmine   .75   .20
1364 A190 $3.20 green   2.25   .65
   a.   Souvenir sheet of 2   18.00 11.00

10th anniv. of the 4-H Club in China. No. 1364a contains one each of Nos. 1363-1364, imperf. with simulated perforations.

Perf. 13½
1962, Dec. 16   **Unwmk.**   **Photo.**
Design: $3.60, Company's Pacific navigation chart and freighter, horiz.

1365 A191   80c multicolored   1.60   .20
1366 A191 $3.60 multicolored   4.25 1.00

90th anniversary of the China Merchants' Steam Navigation Co., Ltd.

Farm Woman, Tractor and Plane Dropping Food over Mainland — A192

Perf. 12½
1963, Mar. 21   **Unwmk.**   **Photo.**
1367 A192 $10 multicolored   4.00 1.00

FAO "Freedom from Hunger" campaign.

Torch, Young Couple and Martyrs' Monument, Canton A193

Wmk. 323
1963, Mar. 29   **Engr.**   *Perf. 11½*
Without Gum
1368 A193   80c purple   1.00   .20
1369 A193 $3.20 green   2.00   .40

Issued for the 20th Youth Day.

Swallows, Pagoda and AOPU Emblem — A194

Designs: $2, Northern gannet, horiz. $6, Japanese crane and pine.

Unwmk.
1963, Apr. 1   **Photo.**   *Perf. 13*
1370 A194   80c multicolored   5.00   .75
1371 A194 $2 multicolored   7.00   .65
1372 A194 $6 multicolored   10.50 2.10
    Nos. 1370-1372 (3)   22.50 3.50

1st anniversary of the formation of the Asian-Oceanic Postal Union, AOPU.

Refugee Girl (Li Ying) and Map of China — A195

Refugees Fleeing Mainland A196

Wmk. 323
1963, June 27   **Engr.**   **Perf. 11½**
Without Gum
1373 A195   80c bluish black   1.40   .20
1374 A196 $3.20 dp claret   3.00   .30

1st anniv. of the evacuation of Chinese mainland refugees from Hong Kong to Taiwan. Designs from photographs of refugees.

Nurse and Red Cross A197

Design: $10, Globe and Red Cross.

Perf. 12½
1963, Sept. 1   **Unwmk.**   **Photo.**
1375 A197   80c black & carmine   6.50   .30
1376 A197 $10 slate, gray & car   7.75   2.75

Centenary of International Red Cross.

Basketball Player, Stadium and Asian Cup — A198

$2, Hands reaching for ball and Asian cup.

Wmk. 323
1963, Nov. 20   **Engr.**   **Perf. 12**
Without Gum
1377 A198   80c lilac rose   1.25   .25
1378 A198 $2 violet   2.40   .80

The 2nd Asian Basketball Championship, Taipei, Nov. 20.

UN Emblem, Torch and Men — A199

Scales and Men of Various Races A200

1963, Dec. 10   **Wmk. 323**   **Perf. 11½**
Without Gum
1379 A199   80c brt green   .80   .30
1380 A200 $3.20 maroon   1.50   .65

Universal Declaration of Human Rights, 15th anniversary.

Village and Orchids A201

"Kindle the Fire of Conscience" A202

Perf. 13½x13
1963, Dec. 17   **Photo.**   **Unwmk.**
1381 A201   40c multicolored   3.50   .40
1382 A202 $4.50 multicolored   5.50   2.25

Contribution of the Good-People-Good-Deeds campaign to improve ethical standards.

Sun Yat-sen and Book, "Three Principles of the People" A203

1963, Dec. 25   **Perf. 13**
1383 A203 $5 blue & multi   10.00   1.50

"Land-to-the-Tillers" program, 10th anniv. An 80c was prepared but not issued.

Torch — A204

Hands Unchained — A205

Wmk. 323
1964, Jan. 23   **Engr.**   **Perf. 11½**
Without Gum
1384 A204   80c red orange   .60   .20
1385 A205 $3.20 indigo   2.75   .35

Liberty Day, 10th anniversary.

Broadleaf Cactus A206

Wu Chih-hwei A207

Designs: $1, Crab cactus. $3.20, Nopalxochia. $5, Grizzly bear cactus.

Perf. 12½
1964, Feb. 27   **Unwmk.**   **Photo.**
Plants in Original Colors
1386 A206   80c dp plum & fawn   4.50   .20
1387 A206 $1 dk blue & car   7.75   .90
1388 A206 $3.20 green   11.50   .20
1389 A206 $5 lilac & yellow   12.50   1.10
    Nos. 1386-1389 (4)   36.25   2.40

Wmk. 323
1964, Mar. 25   **Engr.**   **Perf. 11½**
Without Gum
1390 A207   80c black brown   1.75   .20

Centenary of the birth of Wu Chih-hwei (1865-1953), politician and leader of the Kuomintang.

Chu Kwang Tower, Quemoy — A208

Perf. 13x12½
1964-66   **Wmk. 323**   **Litho.**
Granite Paper; Without Gum
1391 A208   3c sepia   .25   .20
1392 A208   5c brt yel grn ('65)   .25   .20
1393 A208   10c yellow grn   .25   .20
1394 A208   20c slate grn ('65)   .25   .20
1395 A208   40c rose red   .25   .20
1396 A208   50c brown   .25   .20
1397 A208   80c orange ('65)   .25   .20
1398 A208 $1 violet ('65)   .25   .20

1399 A208 $1.50 brt lilac ('66)   2.50   .25
1400 A208 $2 lilac rose   .25   .20
1401 A208 $2.50 ultra ('65)   2.50   .25
1402 A208 $3 slate   2.50   .30
1403 A208 $3.20 brt blue   5.00   .25
1404 A208 $4 brt green   5.75   .25
    Nos. 1391-1404 (14)   20.50   3.05

Nurses Holding Candles A209

Florence Nightingale and Student Nurse — A210

1964, May 12   **Engr.**   **Perf. 11½**
Without Gum
1406 A209   80c violet blue   1.40   .25
1407 A210 $4 red   3.50   .50

Issued for Nurses Day.

Shihmen Reservoir A211

Designs: $1, Irrigation system. $3.20, Main dam and power plant. $5, Spillway.

Perf. 12½
1964, June 14   **Unwmk.**   **Photo.**
1408 A211   80c multicolored   2.25   .25
1409 A211 $1 multicolored   3.75   .45
1410 A211 $3.20 multicolored   7.00   .55
1411 A211 $5 multicolored   10.00   1.40
    Nos. 1408-1411 (4)   23.00   2.65

Completion of Shihmen Reservoir.

15th Century Ship, Modern Liner — A212

Wmk. 323
1964, July 11   **Engr.**   **Perf. 11½**
Without Gum
1412 A212 $2 orange   1.25   .20
1413 A212 $3.60 brt green   1.90   .35

China's 10th Navigation Day.

Bananas A213

Unwmk.
1964, July 25   **Photo.**   **Perf. 14**
1414 A213   80c shown   10.00   1.00
1415 A213 $1 Oranges   20.00   2.00
1416 A213 $3.20 Pineapple   23.50   2.00
1417 A213 $4 Watermelon   37.50   5.00
    Nos. 1414-1417 (4)   91.00   10.00

Artillery, Warships, Jet Fighters A214

Wmk. 323
1964, Sept. 3   **Engr.**   **Perf. 11½**
Without Gum
1418 A214   80c dk blue   1.60   .20
1419 A214 $6 violet brown   4.25   .60

Issued for the 10th Armed Forces Day.

Unisphere, Flags of China and U.S. — A215

Chinese Pavilion, NY World's Fair — A216

1964, Sept. 10   **Photo.**   **Unwmk.**
1420 A215   80c violet & multi   2.75   .25
1421 A216 $5 blue & multi   6.25   .90

NY World's Fair, 1964-65. See #1450-1451.

Cowboy Carrying Calf, and Ranch — A217

Bicycling — A218

Wmk. 323
1964, Sept. 24   **Engr.**   **Perf. 11½**
Without Gum
1422 A217 $2 brown lake   1.60   .20
1423 A217 $4 dark violet blue   3.25   .80

Animal Protection Week, Sept. 24-30.

1964, Oct. 10   **Without Gum**

Sports: $1, Runner. $3.20, Gymnast on rings. $10, High jump.

1424 A218   80c violet blue   1.05   .25
1425 A218 $1 rose red   1.75   .25
1426 A218 $3.20 dull blue grn   2.25   .40
1427 A218 $10 lilac   4.00   2.00
    Nos. 1424-1427 (4)   9.05   2.90

18th Olympic Games, Tokyo, Oct. 10-25.

Hsü Kuang-chi A219

Pharmaceutical Industry A220

Textile Industry A221

1964, Nov. 8   **Engr.**   **Perf. 11½**
Without Gum
1428 A219   80c indigo   2.75   .25

Issued to honor Hsü Kuang-chi (1562-1633), scholar and statesman.

1964, Nov. 11   Photo.   Unwmk.

$2, Chemical industry. $3.60, Cement industry.

1429	A220	40c multi	2.75 .20
1430	A221	$1.50 multi	3.50 .70
1431	A220	$2 multi	5.50 .50
1432	A221	$3.60 multi	6.25 1.10
		Nos. 1429-1432 (4)	18.00 2.50

Dr. Sun Yat-sen — A222

Eleanor Roosevelt and Scales of Justice — A223

1964, Nov. 24   Engr.   Wmk. 323
Without Gum

1433	A222	80c green	2.00 .30
1434	A222	$3.60 purple	5.25 1.00

Founding of the Kuomintang by Sun Yat-sen, 70th anniversary.

Unwmk.
1964, Dec. 10   Photo.   Perf. 13

1435	A223	$10 violet & brown	2.10 .40

Issued to honor Eleanor Roosevelt (1884-1962) on the 16th anniversary of the Universal Declaration of Human Rights.

Scales, Code Book and Plum Blossom A224

Rotary Emblem and Mainspring A225

Wmk. 323
1965, Jan. 11   Engr.   Perf. 11½
Without Gum

1436	A224	80c carmine rose	.55 .20
1437	A224	$3.20 dull slate grn	1.10 .65

The 20th Judicial Day.

1965, Feb. 23   Wmk. 323   Perf. 11½
Without Gum

1438	A225	$1.50 vermilion	.75 .25
1439	A225	$2 emerald	.90 .25
1440	A225	$2.50 blue	1.25 .40
		Nos. 1438-1440 (3)	2.90 .90

Rotary International, 60th anniversary.

Double Carp Design A226

Madame Chiang Kai-shek A227

Wmk. 323
1965, Mar. 29   Engr.   Perf. 11½
Granite Paper; Without Gum

1441	A226	$5 purple	12.50 1.25
1442	A226	$5.60 dp blue	21.00 2.00
1443	A226	$6 brown	19.00 1.25
1444	A226	$10 lilac rose	32.00 1.25
1445	A226	$20 rose car	35.00 2.00
1446	A226	$50 green	42.50 4.50
1447	A226	$100 crim rose	52.50 7.50
		Nos. 1441-1447 (7)	214.50 19.75

New dies used to reprint #1444-1447, 8/20/67. Remainders of #1441-1447 issued with gum, 11/1/71.

1965, Apr. 17   Photo.   Unwmk.

1448	A227	$2 multicolored	18.00 1.00
1449	A227	$6 salmon & multi	32.50 4.00

Chinese Women's Anti-Aggression League, 15th anniversary.

Unisphere and Chinese Pavilion — A228

"100 Birds Paying Homage to Queen Phoenix" and Unisphere — A229

1965, May 8

1450	A228	$2 blue & multi	30.00 1.50
1451	A229	$10 red, ocher & bis	35.00 3.00

New York World's Fair, 1964-65.

ITU Emblem, Old and New Communication Equipment A230

Design: $5, similar to 80c, vert.

Perf. 13½x13, 13x13½
1965, May 17   Photo.   Unwmk.

1452	A230	80c multicolored	.80 .20
1453	A230	$5 multicolored	2.40 .75

Centenary of the ITU.

Red Sea Bream A231

Fish: 80c, White pomfret. $2, Skipjack, vert. $4, Moonfish.

1965, July 1   Perf. 13

1454	A231	40c multicolored	2.25 .25
1455	A231	80c multicolored	3.50 .40
1456	A231	$2 multicolored	7.75 1.40
1457	A231	$4 multicolored	13.50 2.00
		Nos. 1454-1457 (4)	27.00 4.05

Issued for Fishermen's Day.

Confucius A232

ICY Emblem A233

Portraits: $2.50, Yueh Fei. $3.50, Wen Tien-hsiang. $3.60, Mencius.

Wmk. 323
1965-66   Engr.   Perf. 11½
Without Gum

1458	A232	$1 deep carmine	4.50 .35
1459	A232	$2.50 black brown	3.00 .35
1460	A232	$3.50 dark red	6.50 .75
1461	A232	$3.60 dark blue	7.75 .90
		Nos. 1458-1461 (4)	21.75 2.35

The $2.50 and $3.50 have colored background.
Forgeries of #1461 exist.
Issued: #1458, 1461, 9/28/65; #1459-1460, 9/3/66.

See Nos. 1507-1508, design A251.

Unwmk.
1965, Oct. 24   Photo.   Perf. 13

Design: $6, ICY emblem, horiz.

1462	A233	$2 brn, blk & gold	1.60 .25
1463	A233	$6 brt grn, red & gold	3.75 1.40

International Cooperation Year, 1965.

Street Crossing, Traffic Light A234

Sun Yat-sen A235

Wmk. 323
1965, Nov. 1   Engr.   Perf. 11½
Without Gum

1464	A234	$1 brown violet	1.50 .55
1465	A234	$4 crimson rose	3.00 1.10

Issued to publicize traffic safety.

Perf. 13½
1965, Nov. 12   Unwmk.   Photo.

Designs: $4, Dr. Sun Yat-sen, portrait at right. $5, Sun Yat-sen and flags, horiz.

1466	A235	$1 multicolored	3.50 .25
1467	A235	$4 multicolored	1.10 1.00
1468	A235	$5 multicolored	13.00 2.50
		Nos. 1466-1468 (3)	17.60 3.75

Children with New Year's Firecrackers A236

Dragon Dance, "Dragon Playing Ball" A237

1965, Dec. 1   Photo.   Perf. 13

1469	A236	$1 multi	5.50 .30
1470	A237	$4.50 multi	12.50 1.10

Lien Po from "Marshal and Prime Minister Reconciled" — A238

Facial Paintings for Chinese Operas: $3, Kuan Yü from "Reunion at Ku City." $4, Gen. Chang Fei from "The Battle of Chang Pan Hill." $6, Buddha from "The Flower-Scattering Angel."

1966, Feb. 15   Unwmk.   Perf. 11½

1471	A238	$1 olive & multi	10.75 1.00
1472	A238	$3 multicolored	20.00 2.00
1473	A238	$4 multicolored	38.00 4.00
1474	A238	$6 ver & multi	40.00 6.00
		Nos. 1471-1474 (4)	108.75 13.00

Labels with a similar appearance to these stamps exist. These labels have the numbers 1 to 20 in the upper right corner, but lack the "00."

Postal Service Emblem Held by Carrier Pigeon — A239

Stone, Mt. Tai-wu, Quemoy, and Mailman A240

postal service emblem and: $3, Postal Museum. $4, Mailman climbing symbolic slope.

1966, Mar. 20   Photo.   Perf. 12½

1475	A239	$1 green & multi	1.75 .25
1476	A240	$2 multicolored	3.50 .30
1477	A240	$3 multicolored	4.25 .40
1478	A239	$4 multicolored	8.75 2.25
		Nos. 1475-1478 (4)	18.25 3.20

China postal service, 70th anniversary.

Fishing on a Snowy Day, "Five Dynasties" (907-960) A241

Paintings from Palace Museum: $3.50, Calves on the Plain, Sung artist (960-1126). $4.50, Winter landscape, Sung artist (960-1126). $5, Magpies, by Lin Ch'un, Southern Sung dynasty (1127-1279).

1966, May 20   Photo.   Perf. 13

1479	A241	$2.50 blk, brn & red	11.50 .50
1480	A241	$3.50 bis brn, blk & gray	30.00 .75
1481	A241	$4.50 blk, buff & sl	42.50 1.90
1482	A241	$5 multicolored	55.00 2.75
		Nos. 1479-1482 (4)	139.00 5.90

Inauguration of Pres. Chiang Kai-shek for a 4th term.

Dragon Boat Race A242

Lion Dance — A243

$4, Lady Chang O flying to the Moon.

1966   Unwmk.

1483	A242	$2.50 multi	5.50 .40
1484	A242	$4 multi	10.00 .50
1485	A243	$6 multi	20.00 1.00
		Nos. 1483-1485 (3)	35.50 1.90

Dragon Boat, Mid-Autumn and Lunar New Year Festivals. Issued: $2.50, 6/23; $4, 9/29; $6, 11/26.

Flags of China
and Argentina
A244

1966, July 9   **Photo.**   *Perf. 13*
1486 A244 $10 multicolored   4.25   .60

Argentina's Independence. 150th anniv.

Lin Sen — A245   Flying
Geese — A246

Wmk. 323
1966, Aug. 1   **Engr.**   *Perf. 11½*
Without Gum
1487 A245 $1 dk brown   2.00   .20

Centenary of the birth of Lin Sen (1867-1943), Chairman of the Nationalist Government of China (1931-43).

1966-67   *Perf. 11½ Rough*
Granite Paper; Without Gum
1496 A246 $3.50 brown   1.10   .40
1497 A246 $4 vermilion   1.05   .40
1498 A246 $4.50 brt green   1.90   .45
1499 A246 $5 rose lilac   1.10   .40
1500 A246 $5.50 yel grn ('67)   2.25   .40
1501 A246 $6 brt blue   2.50   .50
1502 A246 $6.50 violet   2.25   .45
1503 A246 $7 black   1.25   .40
1504 A246 $8 car rose ('67)   1.90   .40
    Nos. 1496-1504 (9)   15.30 3.80

The $4.50, $5, $6, $7 and $8 were reissued with gum in 1970-71.

Pres. Chiang Kai-shek in Chung San Robe — A247

$5, Chiang Kai-shek in marshal's uniform.

Unwmk.
1966, Oct. 31   **Photo.**   *Perf. 13*
1505 A247 $1 multicolored   1.90   .30
1506 A247 $5 multicolored   6.25 1.60

Chiang Kai-shek's inauguration for a fourth term as president, May 20, 1966.

Famous Men Type of 1965-66 with Frame Line

Portraits: No. 1507, Tsai Yuan-pei (1868-1940), educator. No. 1508, Chiu Ching (1875-1907), woman educator and revolutionist.

1967   **Wmk. 323**   **Engr.**   *Perf. 11½*
Without Gum
1507 A232 $1 violet blue   2.25   .25
1508 A232 $1 black   2.25   .25

Issue dates: #1507, Jan. 11. #1508, July 15. No. 1507 is on granite paper.

Motorized Mailman
and Microwave
Station — A248

"Transportation" and Radar Weather
Station — A249

Unwmk.
1967, Mar. 15   **Photo.**   *Perf. 13*
1511 A248 $1 multicolored   1.40   .25
1512 A249 $5 multicolored   2.50   .90

Issued to publicize the progress in communication and transportation services.

Pres. Chiang Kai-shek and Chinese
Flag — A250   Chu Yuan, 332-295 B.C. — A251

Design: $4, Different frame.

1967, May 20   **Litho.**   *Perf. 13*
1513 A250 $1 multicolored   1.90   .20
1514 A250 $4 multicolored   3.00   .90

First anniversary of President Chiang Kai-shek's 4th-term inauguration.

Wmk. 323
1967, June 12   **Engr.**   *Perf. 11½*
Portraits: $2, Li Po (705-760). $2.50, Tu Fu (712-770). $3, Po Chu-i (772-846).

Granite Paper; Without Gum
1515 A251 $1 black   1.10   .20
1516 A251 $2 brown   3.50   .25
1517 A251 $2.50 brown blk   4.75   .45
1518 A251 $3 grnsh black   7.00   .45
    Nos. 1515-1518 (4)   16.35 1.35

Issued for Poets' Day.
See design A232.

Hotei, Wood
Carving — A252

World
Map — A253

Handicrafts: $2.50, Vase and plate. $3, Dolls. $5, Palace lanterns.

Perf. 11½
1967, Aug. 12   **Unwmk.**   **Photo.**
1519 A252 $1 gray & multi   3.00   .65
1520 A252 $2.50 multi   4.00 1.00
1521 A252 $3 multi   5.00 1.65
1522 A252 $5 multi   6.75 3.50
    Nos. 1519-1522 (4)   18.75 6.80

Taiwan handicraft industry.

Wmk. 323
1967, Sept. 25   **Engr.**   *Perf. 11½*
Granite Paper; Without Gum
1523 A253 $1 vermilion   .45   .20
1524 A253 $5 blue   1.10   .50

1st Conference of the World Anti-Communist League, WACL, Taipei, Sept. 25-29.

Players on
Stilts: "The
Fisherman
and the
Woodcutter"
A254

Unwmk.
1967, Oct. 10   **Photo.**   *Perf. 13*
1525 A254 $4.50 multi   1.90   .45

Issued for the 56th National Day.

Maroon Oriole — A255

Formosan Birds: $1, Formosan barbet, vert. $2.50, Formosan green pigeon. $3, Formosan blue magpie. $5, Crested serpent eagle, vert. $8, Mikado pheasants.

1967, Nov. 25   **Photo.**   *Perf. 11*
Granite Paper
1526 A255 $1 multi   4.00   .25
1527 A255 $1 multi   5.50   .40
1528 A255 $2.50 multi   6.75   .50
1529 A255 $3 multi   8.00   .60
1530 A255 $5 multi   9.50   .70
1531 A255 $8 multi   11.50 1.25
    Nos. 1526-1531 (6)   45.25 3.70

Chung Hsing
Pagoda — A256

Buddha,
Changhua
A257

Designs: $2.50, Seashore, Yeh Liu Park. $5, National Palace Museum, Taipei.

Unwmk.
1967, Dec. 10   **Photo.**   *Perf. 13*
1532 A256 $1 multi   1.50   .25
1533 A257 $2.50 multi   4.00   .50
1534 A257 $4 multi   5.00   .60
1535 A257 $5 multi   5.75   .90
    Nos. 1532-1535 (4)   16.25 2.25

Issued for International Tourist Year 1967.

China Park,
Manila, and
Flags — A258

1967, Dec. 30   *Perf. 13½*
1536 A258 $1 multicolored   .65   .20
1537 A258 $5 multicolored   2.25   .65

Sino-Philippine Friendship Year 1966-67.

Sun Yat-sen Building,
Yangmingshan
A259   A259a

Perf. 13x12½
1968-75   **Litho.**   **Wmk. 323**
Granite Paper
1538 A259 5c lt brown   .60   .20
1539 A259 10c grnsh black   .60   .20
1540 A259 50c brt rose lilac   .60   .20
1541 A259 $1 vermilion   .60   .20
1542 A259 $1.50 emerald   1.10   .70
1543 A259 $2 plum   1.05   .20
1544 A259 $2.50 blue   1.25   .20
1545 A259 $3 grnsh blue   1.40   .25
    Nos. 1538-1545 (8)   7.20 2.15

See Nos. 1702-1709. For overprints see Nos. 1723-1725.

Coil Stamps
Perf. 13 Horiz.
   Photo.   **Unwmk.**
1546 A259a $1 carmine rose   .55   .25
1547 A259a $1 vermilion   .55   .25

Issued: 50c, $1, $2.50, 1/23/68; #1546, 3/20/70; #1547, 1/28/75; others 7/11/68.
Inscription on No. 1546 is in color with white background. On No. 1547 it is white with colored background.

Harvesting
Sugar Cane
A260   Jade Cabbage,
1662-1911
A261

Unwmk.
1968, Mar. 1   **Photo.**   *Perf. 13*
1548 A260 $1 olive & multi   1.75   .20
1549 A260 $4 multicolored   3.00   .45

1968, Mar. 29   **Unwmk.**   *Perf. 13*
Ancient Art Treasures: $1.50, Jade battle axe. $2, Porcelain flower bowl, 960-1126 A.D., horiz. $2.50, Cloisonné enamel vase, 1723-1736 A.D. $4, Agate flower holder in shape of finger citrus, 1662-1911 A.D., horiz. $5, Sacrificial kettle, 1111-771 B.C.

1550 A261 $1 rose & multi   2.25   .20
1551 A261 $1.50 blue & multi   3.25   .25
1552 A261 $2 blue & multi   3.50   .20
1553 A261 $2.50 dull rose &
       multi   4.25   .50
1554 A261 $4 pink & multi   5.50   .60
1555 A261 $5 blue & multi   6.50   .70
    Nos. 1550-1555 (6)   25.25 2.70

For similar artifact designs inscribed "Republic of China," with single-color denominations in slanted numerals and the cents underlined, see types A276, A291, A323, A336, A384, A395, A411.

Artifact designs with denominations in outlined numerals begin with type A439.

View of City in Cathay (1) — A262

Views: No. 1557, City and wall of Forbidden City (2). No. 1558, Wall at right, bridge at left (3). No. 1559, Queen's ship landing at left (4). No. 1560, Palace (5). $5, City wall and gate. $8, Suburb around Great Bridge. Design from scroll "A City in Cathay," painted 1736.

1968, June 18   **Photo.**   *Perf. 13½*
Size: 50x29mm
1556 A262 $1 multicolored   2.25   .40
1557 A262 $1 multicolored   2.25   .40
1558 A262 $1 multicolored   2.25   .40
1559 A262 $1 multicolored   2.25   .40
1560 A262 $1 multicolored   2.25   .40
   a.   Strip of 5, #1556-1560   10.00 10.00

Size: 60x31mm
Perf. 13x13½

1561	A262	$5 multicolored	12.00	2.10
1562	A262	$8 multicolored	21.00	2.75
		Nos. 1556-1562 (7)	44.25	6.85

See Nos. 1610-1614. For similar designs see types A281, A299, A326, A343.

Entrance Gate, Taroko Gorge A263

$8, Sun Yat-sen Building, Yangmingshan.

1968, Feb. 12   Photo.   Perf. 13

1563	A263	$5 multicolored	1.75	.35
1564	A263	$8 multicolored	3.00	.40

The 17th Annual Conference of the Pacific Area Travel Association.

Vice President Chen Cheng — A264

Flying Geese — A265

1968, Mar. 5

1565	A264	$1 brown & multi	1.60	.25

Vice President Chen Cheng (1898-1965).

Wmk. 323
1968, Mar. 20   Litho.   Perf. 12
Granite Paper

1566	A265	$1 vermilion	9.00	.20

Souvenir Sheet
Imperf

1567	A265	$3 green	11.00	3.50

90th anniv. of Chinese postage stamps. No. 1567 contains one stamp with simulated perforations.

WHO Emblem and "20" — A266

Symbolic Water Cycle — A267

1968, Apr. 7   Engr.   Perf. 12
Granite Paper

1568	A266	$1 green	.45	.20
1569	A266	$5 scarlet	1.25	.65

20th anniv. of WHO.

Wmk. 323
1968, June 6   Litho.   Perf. 11½
Granite Paper

1570	A267	$1 green & org	.45	.20
1571	A267	$4 brt blue & org	1.40	.20

Hydrological Decade (UNESCO) 1965-74.

Broadcasting to Mainland China — A268

Dual Carriers for FM Broadcasting A269

Wmk. 323
1968, Aug. 1   Litho.   Perf. 12
Granite Paper

1572	A268	$1 bl, vio bl & gray	.55	.20
1573	A269	$4 lt ultra & ver	1.25	.25

40th anniv. of the Broadcasting Corp. of China, and the inauguration of frequency modulation broadcasting.

Human Rights Flame — A270

Crop Improvement and Extension Work — A271

1968, Sept. 3
Granite Paper

1574	A270	$1 multicolored	.60	.20
1575	A270	$5 multicolored	1.50	.20

International Human Rights Year 1968.

Wmk. 323
1968, Sept. 30   Litho.   Perf. 12
Granite Paper

1576	A271	$1 yel, bister & dk brn	.45	.20
1577	A271	$5 yel, emer & dk grn	1.75	.50

Joint Commission on Rural Reconstruction, 20th anniversary.

Javelin — A272

Designs: $2.50, Weight lifting. $5, Pole vault, horiz. $8, Woman hurdling, horiz.

Unwmk.
1968, Oct. 12   Photo.   Perf. 13

1578	A272	$1 multi	.55	.20
1579	A272	$2.50 multi	.80	.20
1580	A272	$5 multi	1.25	.25
1581	A272	$8 pink & multi	1.90	.35
		Nos. 1578-1581 (4)	4.50	1.00

19th Olympic Games, Mexico City, 10/12-27.

Pres. Chiang Kai-shek and Whampoa Military Academy — A273

Designs: $2, Pres. Chiang Kai-shek reviewing forces of the Northern Expedition. $2.50, Suppression of bandits, reconstruction work and New Life Movement emblem. $3.50, Marco Polo Bridge near Peking and victory parade, Nanking. $4, Original copy of Constitution of Republic of China. $5, Nationalist Chinese flag flying over mainland China.

1968, Oct. 31   Perf. 11½x12

1582	A273	$1 multi	.75	.30
1583	A273	$2 multi	1.00	.30
1584	A273	$2.50 multi	1.40	.45
1585	A273	$3.50 multi	1.75	.60
1586	A273	$4 multi	2.25	1.00
1587	A273	$5 multi	3.75	1.25
		Nos. 1582-1587 (6)	10.90	3.90

Chiang Kai-shek's achievements for China.

Cock — A274

Flag — A275

1968, Nov. 12   Litho.   Perf. 12
Granite Paper

1588	A274	$1 pink & multi	17.00	1.00
1589	A274	$4.50 lilac & multi	40.00	6.00

Issued for use on New Year's greetings.

1968, Dec. 25   Wmk. 323   Perf. 12½
Granite Paper

1590	A275	$1 multicolored	.70	.20
1591	A275	$5 lt blue & multi	1.00	.75

Constitution of the Republic of China, 20th anniversary.

Jade Belt Buckle, 1662-1911 A276

Ancient Art Treasures: $1.50, Yellow jade vase, 960-1126 A.D., vert. $2, Cloisonne enamel square teapot, 1662-1911 A.D. $2.50, Kuei, sacrificial bronze vessel, 722-481 B.C. $4, Heavenly ball vase, 1368-1661 A.D., vert. $5, Gourd-shaped vase, 1662-1911 A.D., vert.

Unwmk.
1969, Jan. 15   Photo.   Perf. 13

1592	A276	$1 dl rose & multi	1.10	.20
1593	A276	$1.50 rose & multi	2.00	.25
1594	A276	$2 brt rose & multi	2.50	.20
1595	A276	$2.50 lt blue & multi	2.75	.60
1596	A276	$4 tan & multi	3.00	.80
1597	A276	$5 pale blue & multi	3.00	1.00
		Nos. 1592-1597 (6)	14.35	3.05

Servicemen and Savings Emblem A277

Wmk. 323
1969, Feb. 1   Engr.   Perf. 12
Granite Paper

1598	A277	$1 dull red brown	.35	.20
1599	A277	$4 deep blue	1.00	.55

Military Savings Program, 10th anniv.

Ti (Flute) A278

Musical Instruments: $2.50, Sheng (13 bamboo pipes connected at the base). $4, P'i p'a (lute). $5, Cheng (zither).

Unwmk.
1969, Mar. 16   Photo.   Perf. 13

1600	A278	$1 buff & multi	.55	.30
1601	A278	$2.50 lt ap grn & multi	1.25	.40

1602	A278	$4 pink & multi	1.60	.45
1603	A278	$5 lt grnsh bl & multi	2.25	.60
		Nos. 1600-1603 (4)	5.65	1.75

Sun Yat-sen Building and Kuomintang Emblem A279

Double Carp Design — A280

1969, Mar. 29   Litho.   Perf. 13½

1604	A279	$1 multicolored	.70	.20

10th Natl. Cong. of the Chinese Nationalist Party (Kuomintang), Mar. 29. A $2.50 stamp portraying Sun Yat-sen and Chiang Kai-shek was prepared but not issued.

Perf. 13½x12½
1974   Engr.   Wmk. 323
Granite Paper

1606	A280	$10 dark blue	2.50	.40
1607	A280	$20 dark brown	5.25	.40
1608	A280	$50 green	8.50	.75
1609	A280	$100 bright red	10.75	1.40
		Nos. 1606-1609 (4)	27.00	2.95

1969
Perf. 11½

1606a	A280	$10	3.25	.35
1607a	A280	$20	4.25	.35
1608a	A280	$50	11.00	.45
1609a	A280	$100	17.00	.90
		Nos. 1606a-1609a (4)	35.50	2.05

The 1969 issue is 27mm high; 1974, 28mm. See No. 1980.

Bridal Procession — A281

Designs: No. 1610, Musicians and standard bearer from bridal procession. $2.50, Emigrant farm family in oxcart. $5, Art gallery. $8, Roadside food stands. Designs from scroll "A City in Cathay," painted in 1736.

Perf. 13½
1969, May 20   Unwmk.   Photo.

1610	A281	$1 multi	1.25	.35
1611	A281	$1 multi	1.25	.35
a.		Pair, #1610-1611	2.75	2.75
1612	A281	$2.50 multi	4.00	1.00
1613	A281	$5 multi	4.25	.75
1614	A281	$8 multi	7.25	1.25
		Nos. 1610-1614 (5)	18.00	3.70

ILO Emblem A282

Wmk. 323
1969, June 15   Engr.   Perf. 11½
Granite Paper

1615	A282	$1 dark blue	.70	.20
1616	A282	$8 dark carmine	1.50	.55

ILO, 50th anniversary.

Family at Dinner Table and Dressing A283

Pupils in Laboratory and Playing — A284

Designs: $2.50, Housecleaning and obeying traffic rules. $4, Recreation (music, fishing, basketball) and education.

Wmk. 323

1969, July 15		**Engr.**	**Perf. 11½**	
1617	A283	$1 brick red	.25	.20
1618	A283	$2.50 blue	.70	.35
1619	A283	$4 green	.80	.45
		Nos. 1617-1619 (3)	1.75	1.00

Model Citizen's Life Movement.

1969, Sept. 1   Wmk. 323   Perf. 11½

Design: $1, $5, Pupils with book and various school activities, horiz.

Granite Paper

1620	A284	$1 brt red	.25	.20
1621	A284	$2.50 brt green	.75	.30
1622	A284	$4 dk blue	1.00	.30
1623	A284	$5 brown	1.40	.55
		Nos. 1620-1623 (4)	3.40	1.35

Free 9-year education system, 1st anniv.

Wild Flowers and Pheasants, by Lu Chih (Ming) A285

Paintings: $2.50, Bamboo and birds, Sung dynasty. $5, Flowers and Birds, Sung dynasty. $8, Cranes and Flowers, by G. Castiglione, S.J. (1688-1766).

1969, Oct. 9		**Photo.**	**Perf. 13½**	
1624	A285	$1 multi	1.40	.20
1625	A285	$2.50 multi	3.50	.45
1626	A285	$5 multi	8.50	.75
1627	A285	$8 multi	11.50	1.10
		Nos. 1624-1627 (4)	24.90	2.65

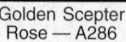

Golden Scepter Rose — A286

Rocket and Radar Station — A287

Roses: $1, "Charles Mollerin," called black rose. $5, Peace. $8, Josephine Bruce.

1969, Oct. 31		**Litho.**	**Perf. 14**	
1628	A286	$1 lt vio & multi	1.25	.20
1629	A286	$2.50 lt bl & multi	3.75	.20
1630	A286	$5 dl org & multi	4.75	.35
1631	A286	$8 ap grn & multi	4.50	.70
		Nos. 1628-1631 (4)	14.25	1.45

Wmk. 323

1969, Nov. 21		**Engr.**	**Perf. 11½**	
1632	A287	$1 rose claret	1.50	.25

The 30th Air Defense Day.

Symbol of International Cooperation A288

Pekingese — A289

1969, Nov. 25				
1633	A288	$1 rose claret	.35	.20
1634	A288	$5 green	1.10	.35

5th General Assembly of the Asian Parliamentary Union, Taipei, Nov. 24-28.

1969, Dec. 1		**Litho.**	**Perf. 12**	
Granite Paper				
1635	A289	50c red & multi	2.00	.50
1636	A289	$4.50 green & multi	10.00	2.00

Issued for use on New Year's greetings.

Satellite, Earth Station and Map of Taiwan A290

Unwmk.

1969, Dec. 28		**Photo.**	**Perf. 13**	
1637	A290	$1 brown & multi	.45	.20
1638	A290	$5 vio blue & multi	1.60	.35
1639	A290	$8 purple & multi	2.25	.65
		Nos. 1637-1639 (3)	4.30	1.20

Inauguration of the Communication Satellite Earth Station at Chin-Shan-Li, Dec. 28.

Agate Grinding Stone, 1662-1911 A291

Ancient Art Treasures: $1, Carved lacquer ware vase, 1662-1911, vert. $2, White jade Chin-li-chih melons, 1662-1911. $2.50, Black jade shepherd and ram, 206 B.C.-220 A.D. $4, Chien-lung twin porcelain vase, 1736-1796, vert. $5, Ju porcelain vase with 3 bulls, 960-1126, vert.

1970, Jan. 23				
1640	A291	$1 lt grnsh bl & multi	.75	.20
1641	A291	$1.50 pale bl & multi	1.40	.20
1642	A291	$2 green & multi	1.60	.20
1643	A291	$2.50 pink & multi	2.75	.35
1644	A291	$4 ol bis & multi	3.00	.45
1645	A291	$5 ultra & multi	4.00	.80
		Nos. 1640-1645 (6)	13.50	2.20

Hsuan Chuang — A292

Chu Hsi — A293

Design: $2.50, Hua To.

1970	**Wmk. 323**	**Engr.**	**Perf. 11½**	
Granite Paper				
1646	A292	$1 car rose	.70	.20
1647	A293	$2.50 blue grn	1.10	.35
1648	A293	$4 blue	1.75	.45
		Nos. 1646-1648 (3)	3.55	.90

Issued in memory of Hsuan Chuang (602-664), who propagated Buddhism in China;

Chu Hsi (1130-1200), who developed Neo-Confucianism, and Hua To (3rd century A.D.) physician and surgeon.
  Issued: $2.50, 3/17; others, 2/20.

EXPO '70 Pavilion, Emblem and Flags of Participants A294

Design: $5, Chinese pavilion, EXPO '70 emblem, exhibition and Chinese flags.

Unwmk.

1970, Mar. 13		**Photo.**	**Perf. 13**	
1649	A294	$5 org red & multi	.70	.25
1650	A294	$8 lt blue & multi	1.75	.70

EXPO '70 International Exhibition, Osaka, Japan, Mar. 15-Sept. 13.

Nimbus III and WMO Emblem A295

Design: $1, Agricultural meteorological station and tropical landscape, vert.

Perf. 14x13½, 13½x14

1970, Mar. 23	**Litho.**		**Wmk. 323**	
Granite Paper				
1651	A295	$1 green & multi	.55	.20
1652	A295	$8 blue & multi	1.00	.65

10th Annual World Meteorological Day.

Martyrs' Shrine, Taipei A296

Shrine's Gate A297

Unwmk.

1970, Mar. 29		**Photo.**	**Perf. 13**	
1653	A296	$1 multicolored	.70	.20
1654	A297	$8 multicolored	1.75	.65

Completion of the Martyrs' Shrine in Northern Taipei, dedicated to the memory of 72 young revolutionaries who died Mar. 29, 1911.

Yueh Fei Fighting for Lost Territories A298

Characters from Chinese Operas: $2.50, Emperor Shun and stepmother. $5, The Lady Warrior Chin Liang-yu. $8, Kuan Yu and groom.

1970, May 4		**Unwmk.**	**Perf. 13½**	
1655	A298	$1 multi	1.10	.25
1656	A298	$2.50 multi	2.75	.55
1657	A298	$5 multi	3.75	.65
1658	A298	$8 multi	5.75	.80
		Nos. 1655-1658 (4)	13.35	2.25

— A299

Three Horses Playing — A300

Horses: #1659, Barren tree at right. #1660, Horse standing in river. #1661, Tree trunk in lower left corner. #1662, Trees in left background. #1663, shown. $8, Groom roping horses. Designs from scroll "One Hundred Horses" by Lang Shih-ning (Giuseppe Castiglione, 1688-1766).

Perf. 13½

1970, June 18	**Unwmk.**		**Photo.**	
1659	A299	$1 multi	1.00	.25
1660	A299	$1 multi	1.00	.25
1661	A299	$1 multi	1.00	.25
1662	A299	$1 multi	1.00	.25
1663	A299	$1 multi	1.00	.25
a.		Strip of 5, #1659-1663	8.00	8.00
1664	A300	$5 bister & multi	9.75	2.00
1665	A300	$8 dl yel & multi	11.50	3.00
		Nos. 1659-1665 (7)	26.25	6.25

Lai-tsu Amusing his Old Parents — A301

Chinese Fairy Tales: #1667, Man disguised as deer, and hunters. #1668, Boy cooling his father's bed. #1669, Boy fishing through ice. #1670, Son reunited with old mother. #1671, Emperor tasting mother's medicine. #1672, Boy saving oranges for mother. #1673, Boy saving father from tiger.

Wmk. 323

1970, July 10	**Litho.**		**Perf. 13½**	
Granite Paper				
1666	A301	10c red & multi	.20	.20
1667	A301	10c car rose & multi	.20	.20
1668	A301	10c lt vio & multi	.20	.20
1669	A301	10c gray & multi	.20	.20
1670	A301	10c emerald & multi	.20	.20
1671	A301	50c bister & multi	.45	.25
1672	A301	$1 sky blue & multi	.65	.35
1673	A301	$1 dp blue & multi	.55	.45
		Nos. 1666-1673 (8)	2.65	2.05

See Nos. 1726-1733.

Man's First Step onto Moon — A302

$1, Pres. Chiang Kai-shek's message brought to the moon. $5, Neil A. Armstrong, Michael Collins, Edwin E. Aldrin, Jr., and moon, horiz.

Perf. 13½x13, 13x13½
1970, July 21   **Photo.**   **Unwmk.**
1674 A302 $1 yellow & multi   1.00   .20
1675 A302 $5 lt yel grn & multi   1.60   .45
1676 A302 $8 blue & multi   2.75   .70
    Nos. 1674-1676 (3)   5.35 1.35

1st anniv. of man's 1st landing on the moon.

Asian Productivity Year Symbol A303

Wmk. 323
1970, Aug. 18   **Litho.**   *Perf. 13½*
Granite Paper
1677 A303 $1 emerald & multi   .65 .20
1678 A303 $5 blue & multi   1.25 .40

Issued to publicize Asian Productivity Year.

Flags of China and UN — A304

1970, Sept. 19   **Wmk. 323**   *Perf. 12*
Granite Paper
1679 A304 $5 blue, car & blk   1.75 .65

25th anniversary of the United Nations.

Postal Zone Map — A305

Postal Code Emblem A306

1970, Oct. 8   **Litho.**
1680 A305 $1 lt blue & multi   .90 .20
1681 A306 $2.50 green & multi   1.10 .40

Issued to publicize the postal code system.

Eleventh Month Scroll — A307

Designs: A scroll series, "Activities of the 12 Months," painted on silk by a group of painters of the Ch'ien Lung court (1736-1796). Chinese number in parenthesis at right of denomination tells month.

Jan., Feb., Mar.
（一）（二）（三）

Perf. 13½x13
1970-71   **Photo.**   **Unwmk.**
1682 A307 $1 multi   2.25 .40
1683 A307 $2.50 multi   5.00 1.00
1684 A307 $5 multi   8.50 1.40

Apr., May, June
（四）（五）（六）

1685 A307 $1 multi   2.25 .40
1686 A307 $2.50 multi   5.00 1.00
1687 A307 $5 multi   8.50 1.40

July, Aug., Sept.
（七）（八）（九）

1688 A307 $1 multi   2.25 .40
1689 A307 $2.50 multi   5.00 1.00
1690 A307 $5 multi   8.50 1.40

Oct., Nov., Dec.
（十）（一十）（二十）

1691 A307 $1 multi   2.25 .40
1692 A307 $2.50 multi   5.00 1.00
1693 A307 $5 multi   8.50 1.40
    Nos. 1682-1693 (12)   63.00 11.20

Issued: #1691-1693, 10/21/70; #1682-1684, 1/14/71; #1685-1687, 4/26/71; #1688-1690, 8/27/71.

Family at Home A308

Piggy Bank — A309

$4, Family of 5 going on an excursion, vert.

Perf. 13½x14, 14x13½
1970, Nov. 11   **Litho.**   **Wmk. 323**
Granite Paper
1694 A308 $1 multicolored   .70 .20
1695 A308 $4 yel grn & multi   1.50 .35

Issued to publicize family planning.

1970, Dec. 1   *Perf. 12½x12*
Granite Paper
1696 A309 50c multi   3.25 .25
1697 A309 $4.50 blue & multi   5.00 .90

Issued for use on New Year's greetings.

Tibia Fusus Shells A310

Rare Taiwan Shells: $2.50, Harpeola kurodai. $5, Conus stupa kuroda. $8, Entemnotrochus rumphii.

1971, Feb. 25   *Perf. 13x13½*
1698 A310 $1 vio & multi   .50 .20
1699 A310 $2.50 multi   1.90 .25
1700 A310 $5 org & multi   2.40 .45
1701 A310 $8 grn & multi   3.25 .65
    Nos. 1698-1701 (4)   8.05 1.55

Sun Yat-sen Building, Yangmingshan A311

Passbook and Postal Savings Certificate A312

1971   **Litho.**   **Wmk. 323**
Granite Paper
1702 A311 5c brown   .25 .20
1703 A311 10c dk gray   .25 .20
1704 A311 50c brt rose lilac   .95 .20
1705 A311 $1 vermilion   1.00 .20
1706 A311 $1.50 ultra   1.10 .25
1707 A311 $2 plum   1.25 .20
1708 A311 $2.50 emerald   1.40 .20
1709 A311 $3 aqua   1.90 .30
    Nos. 1702-1709 (8)   8.10 1.75

Perf. 13½x14
1971, Mar. 20   **Litho.**   **Wmk. 323**
$4, People and hand dropping coin into bank.
1712 A312 $1 yel grn & multi   .65 .20
1713 A312 $4 ver & multi   1.50 .30

Publicizing Chinese Postal Savings Service.

Cooperation Emblem, Farmers — A313

Rock Monkey — A314

Design: $8, Chinese teaching rice farming to Africans, horiz.

Unwmk.
1971, May 20   **Photo.**   *Perf. 13*
1714 A313 $1 multicolored   .65 .20
1715 A313 $8 multicolored   1.40 .70

Sino-African Technical Cooperation Committee, 10th anniversary.

1971, June 25   *Perf. 11½*
Taiwan Animals: $2, White-face flying squirrel. $3, Chinese pangolin. $5, Formosan sika deer. $2, $3, $5 are horiz.
1716 A314 $1 gold & multi   .40 .20
1717 A314 $2 gold & multi   1.25 .20
1718 A314 $3 gold & multi   1.75 .30
1719 A314 $5 gold & multi   2.50 .50
    Nos. 1716-1719 (4)   5.90 1.20

Pitcher — A315

Designs: $2.50, Players at base, horiz. $4, Batter and catcher.

1971, July 29   **Photo.**   *Perf. 13*
1720 A315 $1 multi   .30 .20
1721 A315 $2.50 multi   .50 .20
1722 A315 $4 multi   .90 .25
    Nos. 1720-1722 (3)   1.70 .65

Pacific Regional competition for the 1971 Little League World Series.

Nos. 1541, 1544-1545 Overprinted in Magenta or Red

Perf. 13x12½
1971, Sept. 9   **Litho.**   **Wmk. 323**
Granite Paper
1723 A259 $1 vermilion (M)   .30 .20
1724 A259 $2.50 blue (R)   .60 .20
1725 A259 $3 grnsh blue (R)   .60 .25
    Nos. 1723-1725 (3)   1.50 .65

Chinese victory in 1971 Little League World Series, Williamsport, Pa., Aug. 24.

Fairy Tale Type of 1970
Chinese Fairy Tales (Filial Piety): No. 1726, Birds and elephant helping in rice field. No. 1727, Son gathering mulberries for mother. No. 1728, Son gathering firewood. No. 1729, Son, mother and bandits. No. 1730, Son carrying heavy burden. 50c, Son digging for bamboo shoots in winter. No. 1732, Man and wife working as slaves. No. 1733, Father, son and carriage.

1971, Sept. 22   *Perf. 13½*
Granite Paper
1726 A301 10c dp org & multi   .20 .20
1727 A301 10c lilac & multi   .20 .20
1728 A301 10c ocher & multi   .20 .20
1729 A301 10c dp car & multi   .20 .20
1730 A301 10c lt ultra & multi   .20 .20
1731 A301 50c multicolored   .30 .20
1732 A301 $1 emerald & multi   .80 .20
1733 A301 $1 lt red brn & multi   .80 .20
    Nos. 1726-1733 (8)   2.90 1.60

Flag of China, "Double Ten" Anniversary Emblems A316

Designs (Flag of China and): $2.50, National anthem. $5, Gen. Chiang Kai-shek. $8, Sun Yat-sen.

1971, Oct. 10   **Photo.**   *Perf. 13*
1734 A316 $1 orange & multi   .40 .20
1735 A316 $2.50 multi   1.05 .20
1736 A316 $5 green & multi   1.25 .30
1737 A316 $8 olive & multi   1.25 .35
    Nos. 1734-1737 (4)   3.95 1.05

60th National Day.

Bird in Flight (AOPU Emblem) A317

Perf. 13½x14
1971, Nov. 8   **Wmk. 323**
1738 A317 $2.50 yellow & multi   .70 .20
1739 A317 $5 orange & multi   .90 .25

Asian-Oceanic Postal Union Executive Committee Session, Taipei, Nov. 8-15.

"White Frost Hawk," by Lang Shih-ning A318

Dog Series I
Designs: $2, "Star-Glancing Wolf." $2.50, "Golden-Winged Face." $5, "Young Black Dragon." $8, "Young Gray Dragon."
Designs from painting series "Ten Prized Dogs," by Lang Shih-ning (Giuseppe Castiglione, 1688-1766).

Perf. 13½x13
1971, Nov. 16   **Litho.**   **Unwmk.**
1740 A318 $1 Facing left   .70 .20
1741 A318 $2 Lying down   1.00 .20
1742 A318 $2.50 Scratching   1.25 .30
1743 A318 $5 Facing right   3.00 .50
1744 A318 $8 Looking back   5.00 1.00
    Nos. 1740-1744 (5)   10.95 2.20

Dog Series II

Designs: $1, "Black with Snow-white Paws." $2, "Yellow Leopard." $2.50, "Flying Magpie." $5, "Heavenly Lion." $8, "Mottled Tiger."

1972, Jan. 12

1745	A318	$1 Facing right	2.00	.20
1746	A318	$2 Walking	3.50	.20
1747	A318	$2.50 Sleeping	5.00	.30
1748	A318	$5 Facing left	10.00	.50
1749	A318	$8 Sitting	22.50	1.00
		Nos. 1745-1749 (5)	43.00	2.20

Squirrels — A319

Perf. 13½x12½

1971, Dec. 1　　　**Wmk. 323**

1750	A319	Block of 4	5.00	3.50
a.		50c in UL corner	.90	.25
b.		50c in UR corner	.90	.25
c.		50c in LL corner	.90	.25
d.		50c in LR corner	.90	.25
1751	A319	Block of 4	20.00	5.00
a.		$4.50 in UL corner	4.50	.60
b.		$4.50 in UR corner	4.50	.60
c.		$4.50 in LL corner	4.50	.60
d.		$4.50 in LR corner	4.50	.60

New Year 1972.

Flags of China and Jordan A320

1971, Dec. 16　　　**Perf. 13½**

Granite Paper

1752	A320	$5 multicolored	1.60	.25

50th anniversary of the founding of the Hashemite Kingdom of Jordan.

Cargo Ship "Hai King" — A321

$7, Ocean liner & map of Pacific Ocean, vert.

1971, Dec. 16　　　**Perf. 12½**

1753	A321	$4 grn, dk bl & red	.70	.45
1754	A321	$7 ocher & multi	1.10	.55

China Merchants Steam Navigation Co., cent.

Downhill Skiing, Olympic Rings A322

$5, Cross-country skiing. $8, Giant slalom.

1972, Feb. 3　　　**Perf. 13½**

1755	A322	$1 org, blk & bl	.30	.20
1756	A322	$5 yel grn, dp org & blk	.70	.20
1757	A322	$8 red, gray & blk	.80	.25
		Nos. 1755-1757 (3)	1.80	.65

11th Winter Olympic Games, Sapporo, Japan, Feb. 3-13.

Vase, 18th Century — A323

Porcelain Series I

Porcelain Masterworks of Ching Dynasty: $2, Covered jar. $2.50, Pitcher. $5, Vase with 5 openings and dragon design. $8, Covered jar with children design.

1972, Mar. 20　　**Photo.**　　**Unwmk.**

1758	A323	$1 violet & multi	.70	.20
1759	A323	$2 plum & blue	1.50	.20
1760	A323	$2.50 org ver & bl	2.25	.25
1761	A323	$5 bis brn & bl	2.50	.45
1762	A323	$8 sl grn & multi	3.75	.45
		Nos. 1758-1762 (5)	10.70	1.55

See Nos. 1812-1821, 1864-1868.

Nine Flying Doves A324

Perf. 13½x14

1972, Apr. 1　　**Litho.**　　**Wmk. 323**

1763	A324	$1 lt blue & blk	.55	.20
1764	A324	$5 lt violet & blk	1.60	.30

Asian-Oceanic Postal Union, 10th anniv.

"Dignity with Self-reliance" — A325

Perf. 13½x12½

1972-75　　**Litho.**　　**Wmk. 323**

1765	A325	5c brown & yel	.20	.20
1766	A325	10c blue & org	.20	.20
1767	A325	20c cl & yel grn ('75)	.20	.20
1768	A325	50c lil & lil rose	.20	.20
1769	A325	$1 red & brt bl	.30	.20
1770	A325	$1.50 yel & dk bl	.40	.20
1771	A325	$2 maroon & org	.60	.20
1772	A325	$2.50 emer & ver	1.50	.20
1773	A325	$3 red & lt grn	1.10	.20
		Nos. 1765-1773 (9)	4.70	1.80

Souvenir Sheet

Imperf

1775	A325	Sheet of 2	5.00	2.25

No. 1775 commemorates ROCPEX '72 Philatelic Exhibition, Taipei, Oct. 24-Nov. 2. It contains 2 stamps similar to Nos. 1771 and 1773 with simulated perforations.

Issued: $1, $1.50, $2, $3, 5/20/72; 5c, 10c, 50c, $2.50, #1775, 10/24/72; 20c, 1975.

For overprints see Nos. 1787-1790.

Emperor Shih-tsung's Procession — A326

Messengers on Horseback — A327

Designs from scrolls depicting Emperor Shih-tsung's (reigned 1522-1566) journey to and from tombs at Cheng-tien. No. 1776 shows land journey departure and is designed from right to left. No. 1779 shows return trip by boat and is designed from left to right. The 5 stamps of Nos. 1776 and 1780 are numbered 1 to 5 in Chinese (see illustrations with Nos. 1682-1686 for numerals).

1972　**Photo.**　**Unwmk.**　**Perf. 13½**

1776		Strip of 5	3.50	3.00
a.	A326	$1 shown (1)	.55	.35
b.	A326	$1 Seven carriages (2)	.55	.35
c.	A326	$1 Carriage drawn by 23 horses (3)	.55	.35
d.	A326	$1 Procession (4)	.55	.35
e.	A326	$1 Emperor under 2 canopies (5)	.55	.35
1777	A327	$2.50 shown	2.25	.50
1778	A327	$5 Guards with flags, fans & spears	3.00	.50
1779	A327	$8 Sedan chair carried by 28 men	6.00	.60
1780		Strip of 5	3.50	3.00
a.	A326	$1 Three barges (1)	.55	.35
b.	A326	$1 Procession, sedan chairs (2)	.55	.35
c.	A326	$1 Two barges with trunks (3)	.55	.35
d.	A326	$1 Procession on land (4)	.55	.35
e.	A326	$1 Procession, 2 sedan chairs (5)	.55	.35
1781	A326	$2.50 Courtiers at city welcoming Emperor	2.25	.40
1782	A327	$5 Orchestra on horseback	3.00	.40
1783	A326	$8 Barges	3.75	.50
		Nos. 1776-1783 (8)	27.25	8.90

Issue dates: No. 1776-1779, June 14; Nos. 1780-1783, July 12.

First Day Covers — A328

Magnifying Glass, Tongs, Gauge — A329

Design: $2.50, Sun Yat-sen stamp of 1971 (type A311) under magnifying glass.

Wmk. 323

1972, Aug. 9　**Engr.**　**Perf. 12**

1784	A328	$1 dk vio blue	.20	.20
1785	A328	$2.50 brt green	.25	.20
1786	A329	$8 scarlet	.55	.25
		Nos. 1784-1786 (3)	1.00	.65

Promotion of philately. Printed in sheets of 40. Each sheet contains 4 blocks of 10 stamps surrounded by margins with inscriptions.

Nos. 1768-1770, 1772 Overprinted in Dark Blue or Red

Perf. 13½x12½

1972, Sept. 9　**Litho.**　**Wmk. 323**

1787	A325	$1 red & brt bl (DB)	.25	.20
1788	A325	$1.50 yel & dk bl (R)	.40	.20
1789	A325	$2 mar & org (R)	.55	.20
1790	A325	$3 red & lt grn (DB)	.60	.20
		Nos. 1787-1790 (4)	1.80	.80

China's championship victories in the Little League World Series, Gary, Ind., and in the Senior League World Series, Williamsport, Pa., Aug. 1972.

Emperor Yao (2357-2258 B.C.) — A330

Mountain Climbing — A331

Rulers: $4, Emperor Shun (ruled 2255-2208 B.C.). $4.50, Yu, the Great (ruled 2205-2198 B.C.). $5, King T'ang (ruled 1783-1754 B.C.). $5.50, King Wen (ruled 1171-1122 B.C.). $6, King Wu (ruled 1121-1114 B.C.). $7, Chou Kung (died 1105 B.C.). $8, Confucius (551-479 B.C.).

1972-73　**Engr.**　**Perf. 12**

Granite Paper

1791	A330	$3.50 dk blue	.40	.20
1792	A330	$4 rose red	.60	.20
1793	A330	$4.50 bluish lil	.80	.20
1794	A330	$5 brt green	.40	.20
1795	A330	$5.50 dp claret ('73)	1.25	.25
1796	A330	$6 dp org ('73)	1.10	.20
a.		Perf. 13½x12½ ('76)	1.10	.30
1797	A330	$7 sepia ('73)	1.10	.20
a.		Perf. 13½x12½ ('76)	1.10	.30
1798	A330	$8 indigo ('73)	1.25	.20
a.		gray, perf. 13½x12½ ('76)	1.25	.30
		Nos. 1791-1798 (8)	6.90	1.65

In the first printing, Nos. 1791-1794, 1796-1798 measure 32mm high. In a 1974 reissue they are 33mm.

Unwmk.

1972, Oct. 31　**Photo.**　**Perf. 12**

Designs (China Youth Corps emblem and): $2.50, Skiing (skiers forming circle). $4, Diving. $8, Parachute jumping.

1800	A331	$1 green & multi	.25	.20
1801	A331	$2.50 blue & multi	.50	.20
1802	A331	$4 orange & multi	.75	.20
1803	A331	$8 multicolored	1.25	.25
		Nos. 1800-1803 (4)	2.75	.85

China Youth Corps, 20th anniversary.

JCI Emblem A332

1972, Nov. 12　**Litho.**　**Wmk. 323**

1804	A332	$1 multicolored	.20	.20
1805	A332	$5 orange & multi	.40	.20
1806	A332	$8 multicolored	.70	.40
		Nos. 1804-1806 (3)	1.30	.80

27th Junior Chamber International (JCI) World Congress, Taipei, Nov. 12-19.

Electronic Mail Sorter — A333

Plane, Ship and Pier — A334

Progress of Communications System on Taiwan: $5, Highway overpass over railroad.

Wmk. 323

1972, Nov. 12　**Engr.**　**Perf. 11½**

1807	A333	$1 red	.20	.20
1808	A334	$2.50 blue	.50	.20
1809	A334	$5 dk violet brn	1.10	.35
		Nos. 1807-1809 (3)	1.80	.75

Cow and Calf (Parental Love) — A335

1972, Dec. 1   Litho.   Perf. 12
| 1810 | A335 | 50c red & blk | 2.75 | .30 |
| 1811 | A335 | $4.50 yel, red & brn | 4.25 | .90 |

New Year 1973. Printed in sheets of 80, divided into 4 panes of 20, separated by vertical and horizontal gutters 2 rows wide. 20 red chops meaning "Happy New Year" are printed in the gutters.

Porcelain Type of 1972 and

Stem Bowl with Dragons A336

Porcelain Series II

Porcelain Masterworks of Ming Dynasty: $1, Covered vase with fruits and flowers. $2, Vase with ornamental and floral design. $2.50, Vase imitating ancient bronze. $5, Flask with flowers of 4 seasons. $8, Garlic head vase.

1973   Photo.   Perf. 11½
1812	A323	$1 gray & multi	1.10	.20
1813	A323	$2 lt brn & multi	1.60	.20
1814	A323	$2.50 brt grn & multi	2.25	.20
1815	A323	$5 ultra & multi	2.40	.35
1816	A323	$8 olive & multi	3.50	.60
	Nos. 1812-1816 (5)		10.85	1.55

Porcelain Series III

Ming Porcelain: $2, Refuse container with dragons. $2.50, Covered jar with lotus. $5, Covered jar with horses. $8, Bowl with figures of immortals.

1817	A336	$1 gray & multi	1.10	.20
1818	A336	$2 lt vio & multi	1.60	.20
1819	A336	$2.50 dk red & multi	2.25	.20
1820	A336	$5 blue & multi	2.40	.35
1821	A336	$8 dp org & multi	3.50	.60
	Nos. 1817-1821 (5)		10.85	1.55

Issued: #1812-1816, 1/10; #1817-1821, 3/24.
See Nos. 1864-1868.

Oyster Fairy and Fisherman's Dance — A337

1973, Feb. 7   Photo.   Perf. 11½
Granite Paper
1822	A337	$1 Kicking shut-tlecock, vert.	.70	.20
1823	A337	$4 Shown	1.10	.20
1824	A337	$5 Rowing boat over land	1.25	.25
1825	A337	$8 Old man carrying young lady, vert.	1.40	.40
	Nos. 1822-1825 (4)		4.45	1.05

Chinese folklore popular entertainment.

Bamboo Boat A338

Taiwanese Handicrafts: $2.50, Painted marble vase, vert. $5, Painted glass plate. $8, Doll, bridegroom carrying bride on back, vert.

Perf. 13½x14½, 14½x13½
1973, Mar. 9   Photo.
1826	A338	$1 multi	.25	.20
1827	A338	$2.50 multi	.85	.20
1828	A338	$5 multi	1.25	.25
1829	A338	$8 multi	1.75	.40
	Nos. 1826-1829 (4)		4.10	1.05

Federation Emblem, Cargo Hook, Crane — A339

Emblem, Tractor, New Buildings A340

Wmk. 323
1973, Apr. 2   Litho.   Perf. 12½
| 1830 | A339 | $1 salmon & multi | .40 | .20 |
| 1831 | A340 | $5 blue & blk | .75 | .25 |

12th convention of International Federation of Asian and Western Pacific Contractors Association, Taipei, Apr. 2-10.

Pres. Chiang Kai-shek, Flag of China — A341

Lin Tse-hsü — A342

Design: $4, like $1 with different border.

Unwmk.
1973, May 20   Photo.   Perf. 12
| 1832 | A341 | $1 yellow & multi | .75 | .25 |
| 1833 | A341 | $4 dk grn & multi | 1.10 | .50 |

First anniversary of Pres. Chiang Kai-shek's inauguration for a fifth term.

Wmk. 323
1973, June 3   Engr.   Perf. 12
| 1834 | A342 | $1 sepia | .75 | .20 |

Lin Tse-hsü (1785-1850), Governor of Hunan and Kwangtung, who destroyed large quantity of opium at Humen, Kwangtung, June 3, 1839.

Willows and Palace Gate in the Morning — A343

Lady Watering Peonies, Stone Ornament A344

Design from scroll "Spring Morning in the Han Palace," by Chiu Ying. The five stamps of No. 1835 are numbered 1 to 5 and the five stamps of No. 1838 are numbered 6-10 in Chinese (see illustrations with Nos. 1682-1691 for numerals). The stamps are numbered and listed from right to left.

1973   Photo.   Unwmk.   Perf. 11½
Granite Paper
1835		Strip of 5	3.00	3.00
a.	A343	$1 shown (1)	.40	.20
b.	A343	$1 Ladies feeding peacocks (2)	.40	.20
c.	A343	$1 Lady watering peonies (3)	.40	.20
d.	A343	$1 Pear tree in bloom (4)	.40	.20
e.	A343	$1 Lady musicians (5)	.40	.20
1836	A344	$5 shown	2.25	.60
1837	A344	$8 Lady musicians	3.50	1.00
1838		Strip of 5	3.00	3.00
a.	A343	$1 Ladies playing go (6)	.40	.20
b.	A343	$1 Various games (7)	.40	.20
c.	A343	$1 Talking and playing music (8)	.40	.20
d.	A343	$1 Artist painting portrait (9)	.40	.20
e.	A343	$1 Sentries guarding wall (10)	.40	.20
1839	A344	$5 Ladies playing go	2.25	.60
1840	A344	$8 Girl chasing butterfly	3.50	1.00
	Nos. 1835-1840 (6)		17.50	9.20

Issued: #1835-1837, 6/20; #1838-1840, 7/18.

Fan, Bamboo Design, by Hsiang Te-hsin — A345

Designs: Painted fans, Ming dynasty.

Perf. 12½x13
1973, Aug. 15   Photo.   Wmk. 368
1841	A345	$1 bister & multi	.50	.20
1842	A345	$2.50 bister & multi	.95	.25
1843	A345	$5 bister & multi	1.75	.35
1844	A345	$8 bister & multi	2.75	.50
	Nos. 1841-1844 (4)		5.95	1.30

See Nos. 1934-1937.

Little League Emblem — A346

INTERPOL Emblem — A347

Wmk. 370
1973, Sept. 9   Litho.   Perf. 13½
| 1845 | A346 | $1 yel, car & dk bl | .90 | .20 |
| 1846 | A346 | $4 yel, grn & dk bl | 1.60 | .35 |

Chinese victory in Little League Twin Championships, Gary, Ind., and Williamsport, Pa.

Wmk. 370
1973, Sept. 11   Litho.   Perf. 12
1847	A347	$1 blue & org	.25	.20
1848	A347	$5 green & org	.70	.25
1849	A347	$8 magenta & org	1.00	.40
	Nos. 1847-1849 (3)		1.95	.85

Intl. Criminal Police Organization, 50th anniv.

Ch'iu Feng-chia — A348

Wmk. 323
1973, Oct. 5   Engr.   Perf. 11½
| 1850 | A348 | $1 violet black | .70 | .25 |

2nd meeting of overseas Hakkas, Taipei, Oct. 5-7, and to honor Ch'iu Feng-chia (1864-1912), Hakka scholar, poet and revolutionist.

Tsengwen Reservoir A349

Tsengwen Dam — A350

Perf. 13½
1973, Oct. 31   Photo.   Unwmk.
1851		Strip of 3	.90	.70
a.	A349	$1 Upper shore	.25	.20
b.	A349	$1 shown	.25	.20
c.	A349	$1 Lower shore	.25	.20

Perf. 12x11½
1852	A350	$5 shown	.65	.30
1853	A350	$8 Spillway	1.00	.60
	Nos. 1851-1853 (3)		2.55	1.60

Inauguration of Tsengwen Reservoir. No. 1851 printed in sheets of 15.

Tiger — A351

Wmk. 370
1973, Dec. 1   Litho.   Perf. 12½
| 1854 | A351 | 50c multi | 1.10 | .20 |
| 1855 | A351 | $4.50 multi | 2.00 | .50 |

New Year 1974.

"Snow-dotted Eagle," by Lang Shih-ning — A352

#1857, "Comfortable Ride." #1858, "Red Flower Eagle." #1859, "Cloud-running Steed." #1860, "Sky-running steed." $2.50, "Red Jade Seat." $5, "Thunderclap Steed." $8, "Arabian Champion." Designs from painting series "Ten Prized Horses," by Lang Shih-ning (Giuseppe Castiglione, 1688-1766).

1973   Litho.   Unwmk.   Perf. 13
1856	A352	50c shown	.75	.20
1857	A352	$1 Pinto, blk tail	1.00	.35
1858	A352	$1 Facing left	1.00	.35
1859	A352	$1 Facing right	1.00	.35
1860	A352	$1 Pinto, white tail	1.00	.35
a.		Block of 4, #1857-1860	5.00	4.00
1861	A352	$2.50 Palomino	2.25	.60
1862	A352	$5 Grazing	3.75	1.00
a.		Souvenir sheet of 4	40.00	17.00
1863	A352	$8 Brown stallion	6.00	1.25
	Nos. 1856-1863 (8)		16.75	4.45

#1862a contains 4 stamps with simulated perforations similar to #1856-1857, 1861-1862.
Issued: 50c, $2.50, $5, 11/21; others 12/21.

Porcelain Types of 1972-73
Porcelain Series IV

Porcelain Masterworks of Sung Dynasty: $1, Vase. $2, Three-tiered vase. $2.50, Lotus-shaped bowl. $5, Incense burner. $8, Incense burner on stand.

1974, Jan. 16   Photo.   Perf. 11½
1864	A323	$1 ultra & multi	.60	.20
1865	A336	$2 multicolored	1.10	.20
1866	A336	$2.50 red & multi	1.40	.20
1867	A336	$5 lilac & multi	1.60	.25
1868	A336	$8 green & multi	1.60	.50
	Nos. 1864-1868 (5)		6.30	1.35

Juggler — A353

Taroko Gorge, Hualien — A354

Design: $8, Magician producing dishes from his robe, horiz.

1974, Feb. 6   Photo.   Perf. 11½
1869 A353 $1 yellow & multi   .70 .20
1870 A353 $8 yellow & multi   1.60 .20

1974, Mar. 22   Photo.   Perf. 12
Designs: $2.50, Luce Chapel, Tunghai University. $5, Tzu En Pagoda, Sun Moon Lake. $8, Goddess of Mercy, Keelung.

1871 A354 $1 multi   .50 .20
1872 A354 $2.50 multi   1.10 .20
1873 A354 $5 multi   1.40 .20
1874 A354 $8 multi   2.00 .25
      Nos. 1871-1874 (4)   5.00 .85
           Taiwan landmarks.

Fighting Cocks (Brass) A355

Designs: $2.50, Grapes and bowl with fruit (imitation jade). $5, Fisherman (wood carving), vert. $8, Basket with plastic roses, vert.

Perf. 13½x14½, 14½x13½
1974, Apr. 10
1875 A355 $1 bl grn & multi   .30 .20
1876 A355 $2.50 brown & multi   .70 .20
1877 A355 $5 crimson & multi   1.00 .25
1878 A355 $8 multicolored   2.10 .40
      Nos. 1875-1878 (4)   4.10 1.05
       Taiwanese handicraft products.

Sun Yat-sen Memorial Hall — A356

Taiwan landmarks: $2.50, Reaching-moon Tower, Cheng Ching Lake. $5, Orchid Island (boats). $8, Penghu Interisland Bridge.

1974, May 15   Photo.   Perf. 11½
Granite Paper
1879 A356 $1 blue & multi   .30 .20
1880 A356 $2.50 blue & multi   .70 .20
1881 A356 $5 blue & multi   .90 .20
1882 A356 $8 blue & multi   1.25 .20
      Nos. 1879-1882 (4)   3.15 .85

Pres. Chiang and Gate of Whampoa Military Academy A357

Marching Cadets and Entrance Gate — A358

Wmk. 323
1974, June 16   Engr.   Perf. 11½
1883 A357 $1 carmine rose   .45 .20
1884 A358 $14 violet blue   .90 .40
50th anniversary of the founding of the Whampoa Military Academy.

Long-distance Runner and Olympic Rings — A359

The Boy Wang Ch'i Fighting Invaders — A360

$8, Women's relay race, Olympic rings.

1974, June 23   Litho.   Perf. 12½
1885 A359 $1 blue, blk & red   .30 .20
1886 A359 $8 pink, blk & red   1.00 .40
     80th anniv. of Intl. Olympic Committee.

1974, July 15   Wmk. 370   Perf. 13½
Folk Tales: No. 1888, T'i Ying pleading for her father before the Emperor. No. 1889, Wen Yen-po flushing out ball caught in tree. No. 1890, Boy Wang Hua returning gold piece he found. No. 1891, Pu Shih, a rich sheep raiser and benefactor. No. 1892, K'ung Yung as a child choosing smallest pear. No. 1893, Tung Yu studying. No. 1894, Szu Ma-kuang saving playmate from drowning in water jar.

1887 A360 50c olive & multi   .30 .20
1888 A360 50c ultra & multi   .30 .20
1889 A360 50c ocher & multi   .30 .20
1890 A360 50c red brn & multi   .30 .20
   a.   Block of 4, #1887-1890   .80 .80
1891 A360 $1 green & multi   .70 .40
1892 A360 $1 lilac & multi   .70 .40
1893 A360 $1 blue & multi   .70 .40
1894 A360 $1 car & multi   .70 .40
   a.   Block of 4, #1891-1894   2.75 2.75
      Nos. 1887-1894 (8)   4.00 2.40
For similar designs see A380, A427, A456, A495.

Myrtle, by Wei Sheng — A361

Silk Fan Paintings, Sung Dynasty (960-1279 A.D.): $2.50, Cabbage and Insects, by Hsu Ti. $5, Hibiscus, Cat and Dog, by Li Ti. $8, Pomegranate and Birds, by Wu Ping. Fans from National Palace Museum.

Perf. 13x12½
1974, Aug. 14   Photo.   Wmk. 368
1895 A361 $1 multi   .25 .20
1896 A361 $2.50 multi   .85 .20
1897 A361 $5 multi   1.40 .20
1898 A361 $8 multi   2.00 .50
      Nos. 1895-1898 (4)   4.50 1.10
           See Nos. 1950-1953.

Battle at Marco Polo Bridge, July 7, 1937 A362

Wmk. 370
1974, Sept. 3   Litho.   Perf. 13½
1899 A362 $1 multicolored   .45 .20

Souvenir Sheet
Wmk. 323
Without Gum; Granite Paper
1900   Sheet of 8   9.00 9.00
   a.   A362 $1, single stamp   .80 .80
20th Armed Forces Day. No. 1900 commemorates Armed Forces Stamp Exhibition, Sun Yat-sen Memorial Hall, Sept. 3-9.

Chrysanthemum A363

Designs: Various chrysanthemums.

Unwmk.
1974, Sept. 30   Photo.   Perf. 12
Granite Paper
1901 A363 $1 lilac & multi   .25 .20
1902 A363 $2.50 multi   .70 .20
1903 A363 $5 orange & multi   .95 .25
1904 A363 $8 multi   1.60 .35
      Nos. 1901-1904 (4)   3.50 1.00

Rep. of China Pavilion, EXPO Emblem A364

Map of Fair Grounds, Chinese Flag A364a

Wmk. 370
1974, Oct. 10   Litho.   Perf. 13
1905 A364 $1 multi   .20 .20
1906 A364a $8 multi   .70 .40
EXPO '74, Spokane, Wash., May 4-Nov. 4. Theme, "Preserve the Environment."

Steel Mill, Kaohsiung A365

Taichung Harbor A366

Designs: $1, Taiwan North Link Railroad and map. $2, Oil refinery. $2.50, Electric train. $3.50, Taoyuan International Airport. $4, Taiwan North-South Highway and map. $4.50, Kaohsiung shipyard. $5, Su-ao Port.

Perf. 13x12½, 12½x13
1974, Oct. 31   Wmk. 323
1907 A365 50c lilac, yel & brn   .20 .20
1908 A365 $1 green & org   .20 .20
1909 A365 $2 blue & yel   .20 .20
1910 A365 $2.50 emer & org   .20 .20
1911 A366 $3 ocher & ultra   .20 .20
1912 A366 $3.50 sl grn & yel   .20 .20
1913 A366 $4 brown & yel   .20 .20
1914 A366 $4.50 ver & bl   .35 .20
1915 A366 $5 sepia & dk bl   .35 .20
      Nos. 1907-1915 (9)   2.10 1.80
         Major construction projects.
See Nos. 2009-2017, 2068-2076. For overprints see Nos. 2064-2065, 2112-2113.

Agaricus Bisporus A367

Edible Mushrooms: $2.50, Pleurotus ostreatus. $5, Dictyophora indusiata. $8, Flammulina velutipes.

Perf. 11½
1974, Nov. 15   Unwmk.   Photo.
1916 A367 $1 multi   .55 .20
1917 A367 $2.50 multi   .55 .20
1918 A367 $5 multi   1.00 .20
1919 A367 $8 multi   1.25 .30
      Nos. 1916-1919 (4)   3.35 .90
9th Intl. Scientific Congress on the Cultivation of Edible Fungi, Taipei, Nov. 1974.

Batters and World Map — A368

Pitcher and Championship Banners — A369

Wmk. 323
1974, Nov. 24   Litho.   Perf. 13½
1920 A368 $1 multicolored   .90 .20
1921 A369 $8 multicolored   .80 .35
China's victory in 1974 Little League Baseball World Series Triple Championships.

Rabbit — A370

Acrobat with Iron Rod — A371

Wmk. 323
1974, Dec. 10   Photo.   Perf. 12½
1922 A370 50c orange & multi   .60 .20
1923 A370 $4.50 brown & multi   2.10 .30
           New Year 1975.

1975, Jan. 15   Unwmk.   Perf. 11½
$5, Two acrobats spinning tops, horiz.

Granite Paper
1924 A371 $4 yellow & multi   .90 .40
1925 A371 $5 yellow & multi   1.40 .45

Children Watching Puppet Show — A372

Ceremonial New Year
Greetings — A373

Designs from scroll "Festivals for the New
Year," by Ting Kuan-p'eng. Nos. 1926a-1926e
are numbered 1-5 in Chinese.

1975, Feb. 25   Photo.   Perf. 11½
Granite Paper

1926		Strip of 5	3.75	2.50
a.	A372	$1 Ceremonial New Year Greetings (1)	.55	.20
b.	A372	$1 Man with trained monkey (2)	.55	.20
c.	A372	$1 Crowd and musicians (3)	.55	.20
d.	A372	$1 Picnic under a tree (4)	.55	.20
e.	A372	$1 shown (5)	.55	.20
1927	A373	$2.50 shown	2.50	.30
1928	A373	$5 Children buying firecrackers	3.00	.55
1929	A373	$8 Children and man with trained monkey	5.25	.90
		Nos. 1926-1929 (4)	14.50	4.25

Sun Yat-
sen
Memorial
Hall,
Taipei
A374

Sun Yat-sen's Handwriting — A375

Sun Yat-sen, Bronze
Statue in Memorial
Hall — A376

Sun Yat-sen Memorial
Hall, St. John's
University, NY
A377

Perf. 13½x14, 14x13½
1975, Mar. 12   Litho.

1930	A374	$1 green & multi	.25	.20
1931	A375	$4 yel grn & multi	.55	.20
1932	A376	$5 yellow & multi	.80	.20
1933	A377	$8 gray & multi	1.10	.30
		Nos. 1930-1933 (4)	2.70	.90

Dr. Sun Yat-sen (1866-1925), statesman
and revolutionary leader.

Fan Type of 1973 Inscribed
"Landscape" (1st Character, 2nd Row)

山水

Painted fans, Ming Dynasty. Second row of
inscription gives design description.

Perf. 12½x13
1975, Apr. 16   Photo.   Wmk. 368

1934	A345	$1 bister & multi	.30	.20
1935	A345	$2.50 bister & multi	.95	.20
1936	A345	$5 bister & multi	2.00	.35
1937	A345	$8 bister & multi	2.25	.55
		Nos. 1934-1937 (4)	5.50	1.30

Yuan-chin coin,
1122-221
B.C. — A378

Ancient Chinese Coins: $4, Pan-liang, 221-
207 B.C. $5, Five chu, 206 B.C.-220 A.D. $8,
Five chu, 502-557 A.D.

Wmk. 323
1975, May 20   Litho.   Perf. 13

1938	A378	$1 salmon & multi	.25	.20
1939	A378	$4 yellow & multi	.95	.20
1940	A378	$5 dl yel & multi	1.10	.20
1941	A378	$8 lt vio & multi	1.75	.25
		Nos. 1938-1941 (4)	4.05	.85

The Cloth-bag
Monk, by
Chang Hung
(1577-1668)
A379

Chinese Paintings: $4, Lao-tzu Riding Buf-
falo, by Chao Pu-chih (1053-1110). $5, Portrait
of Shih-te, by Wang Wen (1497-1576). $8,
Splashed-ink Immortal, by Liang K'ai (early
13th century).

Perf. 11½
1975, June 18   Photo.   Unwmk.
Granite Paper

1942	A379	$2 blk, buff & ver	.75	.20
1943	A379	$4 blk, gray & red	1.75	.25
1944	A379	$5 blk, yel & ver	2.75	.40
1945	A379	$8 tan, red & blk	3.75	.60
		Nos. 1942-1945 (4)	9.00	1.45

Chu Yin Reading
by the Light of
Fireflies — A380

Folk Tales: No. 1947, Hua Mu-lan going to
war for her father. No. 1948, King Kou Chien
tasting gall. $5, Chou Ch'u killing tiger.

Perf. 14x13½
1975, July 16   Litho.   Wmk. 368

1946	A380	$1 olive & multi	.25	.20
1947	A380	$2 bis brn & multi	.40	.20
1948	A380	$2 lt grn & multi	.60	.20
1949	A380	$5 blue & multi	1.40	.30
		Nos. 1946-1949 (4)	2.65	.90

See Nos. 2108-2111.

Cherry-Apple
Blossoms, by
Lin
Ch'un — A381

Silk Fan Paintings, Sung Dynasty: $2,
Spring Blossoms and Butterfly, by Ma K'uei.
$5, Monkeys and Deer, by I Yüan-chih. $8,
Tame Sparrow among Bamboo.

Perf. 13x12½
1975, Aug. 15   Litho.   Wmk. 323

1950	A381	$1 multicolored	.30	.20
1951	A381	$2 multicolored	1.10	.20
1952	A381	$5 multicolored	1.50	.40
1953	A381	$8 multicolored	3.00	.80
		Nos. 1950-1953 (4)	5.90	1.60

See Nos. 2001-2004.

Gen. Chang Tzu-
chung (1891-1940)
A382

#1955, Maj. Gen. Kao Chih-hong (1908-37).
#1956, Capt. Sha Shih-chiun (1896-1938).
#1957, Maj. Gen. Hsieh Chin-yuan (1905-41).
#1958, Lt. Yen Hai-wen (1916-37). #1959, Lt.
Gen. Tai An-lan (1905-42).

Wmk. 323
1975, Sept. 3   Engr.   Perf. 12

1954	A382	$2 carmine	.20	.20
1955	A382	$2 sepia	.20	.20
1956	A382	$2 dull green	.20	.20
1957	A382	$5 violet black	.30	.20
1958	A382	$5 violet blue	.30	.20
1959	A382	$5 dark blue	.30	.20
		Nos. 1954-1959 (6)	1.50	1.20

Martyrs of the resistance fight against Japan.

Lotus Pond with Willows, by Madame
Chiang — A383

Paintings by Madame Chiang Kai-shek: $5,
Sun Breaks through Mountain Clouds. $8, A
Pair of Pine Trees. $10, Fishing and Farming.

Perf. 13½
1975, Oct. 31   Litho.   Unwmk.

1960	A383	$2 multicolored	1.00	.20
1961	A383	$5 multicolored	2.25	.30
1962	A383	$8 multicolored	3.25	.40
1963	A383	$10 multicolored	4.50	.75
		Nos. 1960-1963 (4)	11.00	1.65

For similar design see type A404.

Cauldron
with
Phoenix
Handles,
481-221
B.C.
A384

Ancient Bronzes: $2, Rectangular cauldron,
1122-722 B.C., vert. $8, Flat jar, 481-221 B.C.
$10, 3-legged wine vessel, 1766-1122 B.C.,
vert.

1975, Nov. 12   Photo.   Perf. 12

1964	A384	$2 pink & multi	.25	.20
1965	A384	$5 lt blue & multi	.85	.20
1966	A384	$8 yellow & multi	1.10	.20
1967	A384	$10 lilac & multi	1.25	.30
		Nos. 1964-1967 (4)	3.45	.90

For similar design see type A395. No. 1964
has 7 Chinese characters at left, No. 2005 has
4. No. 1967 has 4 characters at left, No. 2008
has 5.

Dragon, Nine-
Dragon Wall,
Peihai — A385

Techi
Dam — A386

Wmk. 323
1975, Dec. 1   Litho.   Perf. 12½

1968	A385	$1 orange & multi	.75	.30
1969	A385	$5 green & multi	1.50	.90

New Year 1976.

1975, Dec. 17   Unwmk.   Perf. 13½

Design: $10, Panoramic view of Techi Dam.

1970	A386	$2 green & multi	.20	.20
1971	A386	$10 blue & multi	.55	.45

Completion of Techi Dam, Tachia River.

Biathlon and
Olympic
Rings — A387

Olympic Rings and: $5, Luge. $8, Skiing.

1976, Jan. 15   Litho.   Perf. 13½

1972	A387	$2 blue & multi	.35	.20
1973	A387	$5 blue & multi	.65	.20
1974	A387	$8 blue & multi	1.00	.25
		Nos. 1972-1974 (3)	2.00	.65

12th Winter Olympic Games, Innsbruck,
Austria, Feb. 4-15.

Chin, Oldest
Chinese
Instrument
A388

Musical Instruments: $5, Se, c. 2900 B.C.
$8, Standing kong-ho (harp). $10, Sleeping
kong-ho.

1976, Feb. 11   Unwmk.   Perf. 14

1975	A388	$2 yellow & multi	.35	.20
1976	A388	$5 orange & multi	.55	.20
1977	A388	$8 grnsh bl & multi	.80	.20
1978	A388	$10 multicolored	1.25	.30
		Nos. 1975-1978 (4)	2.95	.90

For similar design see Type A407.

Double Carp Type of 1969
Perf. 13½x12½
1976, Dec. 15   Engr.   Unwmk.

1980	A280	$14 carmine rose	2.25	.30

Mail
Collecting
A389

Mail
Sorting — A390

Postal Service, 80th Anniv.: $8, Mail trans-
port. $10, Mail delivery.

Wmk. 323

1976, Mar. 20   Litho.   Perf. 13½

1984	A389	$2 yellow & multi	.30	.20
1985	A390	$5 green & multi	.55	.30
1986	A390	$8 blue & multi	.80	.30
1987	A389	$10 orange & multi	1.00	.40
a.		Souv. sheet of 4, #1984-1987	12.50	9.00
		Nos. 1984-1987 (4)	2.65	1.20

Pres. Chiang Kai-shek A391

People Paying Homage — A392

#1990, Pres. Chiang lying in state. #1991, Hearse leaving funeral chapel. $5, People along funeral route. $8, Spirit tablet in Tzuhu Guest House. $10, Tzuhu Guest House, Pres. Chiang's burial place.

1976, Apr. 4

1988	A391	$2 gray & multi	.20	.20
1989	A392	$2 gray & multi	.20	.20
1990	A392	$2 gray & multi	.20	.20
1991	A392	$2 gray & multi	.20	.20
1992	A392	$5 gray & multi	.40	.20
1993	A392	$8 gray & multi	.40	.25
1994	A392	$10 gray & multi	.50	.35
		Nos. 1988-1994 (7)	2.10	1.60

Pres. Chiang Kai-shek (1887-1975), first death anniversary.

Flags of China and US — A393

Wmk. 323

1976, May 29   Litho.   Perf. 13½

1995	A393	$2 multicolored	.20	.20
1996	A393	$10 yellow & multi	.80	.40

American Bicentennial.

Coin, 12th Century B.C. — A394

Cauldron, Shang Dynasty — A395

Bronze Shovel Coins (pu): $5, Pointed-feet coin, 481-221 B.C. $8, Round-feet coin, 722-481 B.C. $10, Square-feet coin, 3rd-2nd centuries B.C.

1976, June 16

1997	A394	$2 salmon & multi	.25	.20
1998	A394	$5 lt blue & multi	.65	.20
1999	A394	$8 gray & multi	1.05	.30
2000	A394	$10 multicolored	1.60	.40
		Nos. 1997-2000 (4)	3.55	1.10

Fan Painting Type of 1975

Silk Fan Paintings, Sung Dynasty: $2, Hibiscus, by Li Tung. $5, Lilies, by Lin Ch'un. $8,

Deer and Pine, by Mou Chung-fu. $10, Quail and Wild Flowers, by Li An-chung.

Perf. 13x12½

1976, July 14   Litho.   Wmk. 323

2001	A381	$2 multicolored	.75	.20
2002	A381	$5 multicolored	1.75	.20
2003	A381	$8 multicolored	2.25	.30
2004	A381	$10 multicolored	3.50	.40
		Nos. 2001-2004 (4)	8.25	1.10

1976, Aug. 25   Photo.   Perf. 11½
Granite Paper

Ancient Bronzes: $5, 3-legged cauldron, Chou Dynasty (1122-722 B.C.). $8, Wine container, Chou Dynasty. $10, Wine vessel with spout, Shang Dynasty (1766-1122 B.C.).

2005	A395	$2 rose & multi	.25	.20
2006	A395	$5 lt blue & multi	.95	.20
2007	A395	$8 yellow & multi	1.40	.20
2008	A395	$10 lilac & multi	1.50	.30
		Nos. 2005-2008 (4)	4.10	.90

Construction Types of 1974

Designs: $1, Taiwan North Link railroad and map. $2, Railroad electrification. $3, Taichung Harbor. $4, Taiwan North-South Highway and map. $5, Steel Mill, Kaohsiung. $6, Taoyuan International Airport. $7, Kao-hsiung shipyard. $8, Oil refinery. $9, Su-ao Port.

Perf. 13½x12½, 12½x13½

1976   Litho.   Wmk. 323

2009	A365	$1 carmine & grn	.25	.20
2010	A365	$2 orange & multi	.25	.20
2011	A366	$3 violet & multi	.25	.20
2012	A366	$4 carmine & multi	.25	.20
2013	A365	$5 green & brn	.25	.20
2014	A366	$6 brown & multi	.40	.20
2015	A366	$7 brown & multi	.50	.20
2016	A365	$8 carmine & grn	.60	.20
2017	A366	$9 olive & blue	.70	.20
		Nos. 2009-2017 (9)	3.45	1.80

Chiang Kai-shek and Mother A396

Sun Yat-sen and Chiang Kai-shek at Canton Station — A397

Design: $5, Chiang Kai-shek, portrait.

1976, Oct. 31   Litho.   Perf. 13½

2023	A396	$2 multicolored	.35	.20
2024	A396	$5 multicolored	.80	.20
2025	A397	$10 multicolored	1.10	.40
		Nos. 2023-2025 (3)	2.25	.80

Pres. Chiang Kai-shek, 90th anniv. of birth.

Flags of Kuomintang and China A398

Sun Yat-sen and Chiang Kai-shek A399

1976, Nov. 12   Perf. 13½x14

2026	A398	$2 multicolored	.20	.20
2027	A399	$10 multicolored	.65	.45
a.		Souv. sheet of 2, #2026-2027	4.50	4.50

11th National Kuomintang Cong., Taipei.

Brazen Serpent — A400

1976, Dec. 15   Wmk. 323   Perf. 12½

2028	A400	$1 red, lilac & gold	.75	.20
2029	A400	$5 plum, yel & gold	1.75	.25

New Year 1977.

Bird and Plum Blossoms, by Ch'en Hung-shou A401

Chinese Paintings: $8, "Wintry Days" (pine), by Yang Wei-chen. $10, Rock and Bamboo, by Hsia Ch'ang.

Perf. 11½

1977, Jan. 12   Photo.   Unwmk.
Granite Paper

2030	A401	$2 multicolored	1.00	.20
2031	A401	$8 multicolored	3.00	.40
2032	A401	$10 multicolored	3.75	.40
		Nos. 2030-2032 (3)	7.75	.85

Black-naped Orioles — A402

Birds of Taiwan: $8, Common Kingfisher. $10, Chinese pheasant-tailed jacana.

1977, Feb. 16   Litho.

2033	A402	$2 multicolored	.55	.20
2034	A402	$8 multicolored	1.10	.20
2035	A402	$10 multicolored	2.00	.35
		Nos. 2033-2035 (3)	3.65	.75

See Nos. 2163-2165.

Census Emblem, Industry and Commerce A403

Perf. 13½

1977, Mar. 16   Litho.   Unwmk.

2036	A403	$2 red & multi	.20	.20
2037	A403	$10 purple & multi	.80	.40

Industry and Commerce Census.

Green Mountains Rising into Clouds, by Madame Chiang — A404

Landscapes, by Madame Chiang Kai-shek: $5, Boat in the Beauty of Spring. $8, Scholar beside Waterfall. $10, Water Rises to Meet the Bridge.

Perf. 11½

1977, Mar. 31   Unwmk.   Photo.
Granite Paper

2038	A404	$2 multi	.55	.20
2039	A404	$5 multi	2.25	.30
2040	A404	$8 multi	2.75	.50
2041	A404	$10 multi	3.00	.60
		Nos. 2038-2041 (4)	8.55	1.55

League Emblem — A405

Blood Donation — A406

1977, Apr. 18   Litho.   Perf. 12½

2042	A405	$2 carmine & multi	.25	.20
2043	A405	$10 green & multi	.80	.65

10th World Anti-Communist League Conference.

1977, May 5   Wmk. 323   Perf. 13½

Design: $2, Donating blood, horiz.

2044	A406	$2 red & black	.25	.20
2045	A406	$10 red & black	.80	.65

Blood donation movement.

San-hsien A407

Musical Instruments: $5, Tung-hsiao (bamboo flute). $8, Yang-chin (butterfly harpsichord). $10, Pai-hsiao (pipes). Background shows musician playing instrument.

Unwmk.

1977, June 21   Photo.   Perf. 14

2046	A407	$2 multicolored	.35	.20
2047	A407	$5 multicolored	.60	.20
2048	A407	$8 multicolored	.80	.20
2049	A407	$10 multicolored	1.00	.30
		Nos. 2046-2049 (4)	2.75	.90

Idea Leuconoe — A408

Protected Butterflies: $4, Hebomoia glaucippe formosana. $6, Stichophthalma howqua formosana. $10, Atrophaneura horishana.

1977, July 20   Litho.   Perf. 13½

2050	A408	$2 ver & multi	.40	.20
2051	A408	$4 lt grn & multi	.90	.25
2052	A408	$6 lt bl & multi	1.40	.40
2053	A408	$10 yellow & multi	1.75	.50
		Nos. 2050-2053 (4)	4.45	1.35

National Palace Museum A409

Temple — A410

Children's Drawings: $2, Sea Goddess Festival. $4, Boats on Shore of Lan-yu.

Wmk. 323

1977, Aug. 27	Litho.	Perf. 13½
2054 A409 $1 multicolored	.20	.20
2055 A409 $2 multicolored	.25	.20
2056 A409 $4 multicolored	.40	.20
2057 A410 $5 multicolored	.50	.25
Nos. 2054-2057 (4)	1.35	.85

8th Exhib. of World School Children's Art.

Carved Lacquer Plate, Wan-li Ware A411

Ancient Carved Lacquer Ware: $5, Bowl, Ching dynasty. $8, Round box, Ming dynasty. $10, Four-tiered box, Ching dynasty.

Perf. 13x14

1977, Sept. 28	Photo.	Wmk. 368
2058 A411 $2 multicolored	.40	.20
2059 A411 $5 multicolored	.85	.20
2060 A411 $8 multicolored	1.75	.20
2061 A411 $10 multicolored	1.50	.30
Nos. 2058-2061 (4)	4.50	.90

Lions International, Emblem and Activities — A412

Unwmk.

1977, Oct. 8	Litho.	Perf. 13
2062 A412 $2 multicolored	.20	.20
2063 A412 $10 multicolored	.55	.35

Intl. Association of Lions Clubs, 60th anniv.

Nos. 2069 and 2075 Overprinted in Claret

Perf. 13½x12½

1977, Sept. 9	Litho.	Unwmk.
2064 A365 $2 orange & multi	.20	.20
2065 A365 $8 carmine & grn	.60	.30

Little League baseball championship.

Chinese Quality Mark — A413

Perf. 13x12½

1977, Oct. 14	Litho.	Unwmk.
2066 A413 $2 red & multi	.50	.20
2067 A413 $10 blue & multi	2.00	.30

International Standardization Day.

Construction Types of 1974
Redrawn: Numerals Outlined

Designs as 1976 Issue.

Perf. 13½x12½, 12½x13½

1977	Litho.	Unwmk.
	Granite Paper	
2068 A365 $1 car & dp grn	.20	.20
2069 A365 $2 ver & multi	.20	.20
2070 A366 $3 violet & multi	.20	.20
2071 A366 $4 carmine & multi	.20	.20
2072 A365 $5 green & multi	.30	.20
2073 A366 $6 sepia & multi	.30	.20
2074 A366 $7 sepia & multi	.35	.20
2075 A365 $8 red lil & multi	.40	.20
2076 A366 $9 olive & multi	.40	.20
Nos. 2068-2076 (9)	2.55	1.80

Numerals are in solid color on #1907-1915, 2009-2017; in outline on #2068-2076.
For overprints see #2064-2065, 2112-2113.

Man and Heart — A414

White Stallion — A415

Perf. 13½x12½

1977, Nov. 12	Litho.	Wmk. 323
2077 A414 $2 multicolored	.20	.20
2078 A414 $10 multicolored	.80	.40

Physical health, cardiac care.

Perf. 12½

1977, Dec. 1	Unwmk.	Litho.

New Year 1978: $5, Two horses, horiz. Designs from painting "100 Horses," by Lang Shih-ning.

2079 A415 $1 red & multi	.50	.25
2080 A415 $5 emerald & multi	1.50	.55

First Page of Constitution A416

Pres. Chiang Accepting Constitution, 1946 — A417

1977, Dec. 25	Litho.	Perf. 13½
2081 A416 $2 multicolored	.20	.20
2082 A417 $10 multicolored	.80	.30

30th anniversary of the Constitution.

Knife Coin with 3 Characters, 403-221 B.C. — A418

Designs: Ancient knife coins.

1978, Jan. 18	Wmk. 323	Perf. 13½
2083 A418 $2 salmon & multi	.40	.20
2084 A418 $5 lt blue & blk	.90	.20
2085 A418 $8 lt gray & multi	1.00	.20
2086 A418 $10 tan & multi	1.25	.30
Nos. 2083-2086 (4)	3.55	.90

China No. 1 and Flag of China — A419

Designs: $5, No. 464 (Sun Yat-sen). $10, No. 1204 (Chiang Kai-shek).

1978, Feb. 21	Litho.	Perf. 13½
2087 A419 $2 brown & multi	.55	.20
2088 A419 $5 blue & multi	.70	.25
2089 A419 $10 orange & multi	1.00	.40
a. Souv. sheet of 3, #2087-2089	11.00	5.00
Nos. 2087-2089 (3)	2.25	.85

Centenary of Chinese postage stamps.

Sun Yat-Sen Memorial Hall A420

China Nos. 2079 and 2 — A421

Perf. 14x12½, 12½x14

1978, Mar. 20		Wmk. 323
2090 A420 $2 multicolored	.20	.20
2091 A421 $10 multicolored	.50	.35

ROCPEX '78 Phil. Exhib., Taipei, Mar. 20-29.

Chiang Kai-shek with Revolutionary Army — A422

Pres. Chiang Kai-shek (1887-1975); $2, as young man, 1912, vert. $8, Making speech at Mt. Lu, July 17, 1937. $10, Reviewing Armed Forces on National Day, 1956, and Chinese flags, vert.

1978, Apr. 5	Wmk. 323	Perf. 13½
2092 A422 $2 violet & multi	.30	.20
2093 A422 $5 green & multi	.50	.20
2094 A422 $8 blue & multi	.75	.40
2095 A422 $10 vio blue & multi	1.00	.40
Nos. 2092-2095 (4)	2.55	1.30

Nuclear Reactor and Plant — A423

Poem by Wen Cheng-ming (1470-1559) A424

Perf. 13½x12½

1978, Apr. 26		Unwmk.
2096 A423 $10 multicolored	.70	.20

First nuclear power plant on Taiwan.

1978, May 20	Wmk. 323	Perf. 13½

Chinese Calligraphy: $2, Letter by Wang Hsi-chih (307-365). $4, Eulogy by Chu Sui-liang (596-658). $8, From Autobiography of Huai-su, Tang Dynasty. $10, Poem by Ch'ang Piao, Sung Dynasty.

2097 A424 $2 multicolored	.85	.20
2098 A424 $4 multicolored	3.50	.20
2099 A424 $6 multicolored	3.50	.50
2100 A424 $8 multicolored	3.75	.30
2101 A424 $10 multicolored	5.00	.55
Nos. 2097-2101 (5)	16.60	1.75

Head and Dao Cancer Fund Emblem A425

Carved Lacquer Vase, Ming Dynasty A426

1978, June 15	Litho.	Perf. 13½
2102 A425 $2 red, org & ol	.20	.20
2103 A425 $10 dk & lt bl & grn	.70	.35

Cancer prevention.

1978, July 12

Ancient Carved Lacquer Ware: $2, Box with dragon and cloud design, Ch'ing dynasty, horiz. $5, Double box on legs, Ch'ing dynasty, horiz. $8, Round box with peonies, Ming dynasty, horiz.

2104 A426 $2 gray olive & multi	.40	.20
2105 A426 $5 gray olive & multi	.50	.20
2106 A426 $8 gray olive & multi	.75	.20
2107 A426 $10 gray olive & multi	1.05	.30
Nos. 2104-2107 (4)	2.70	.90

Tsu Ti Practicing with his Sword — A427

Folk Tales: No. 2109, Pan Ch'ao, diplomat and governor. No. 2110, Tien Tan's "Fire Bull Battle." $5, Liang Hung-yu, a general's wife, who served as drummer in battle.

Wmk. 323
1978, Aug. 16   Litho.   Perf. 13½

2108	A427	$1 multicolored	.25	.20
2109	A427	$2 bister & multi	.55	.20
2110	A427	$2 gray & multi	.90	.20
2111	A427	$5 multicolored	1.25	.25
		Nos. 2108-2111 (4)	2.95	.85

For similar designs see types A456, A495.

Nos. 2071 and 2073 Overprinted in Red

1978, Sept. 9   Perf. 12½x13

2112	A366	$4 multicolored	.30	.20
2113	A366	$6 multicolored	.75	.30

Triple championships won by Chinese teams in Little League World Series. "1978" overprint on $4 at left, on $6 at right.

Ixias Pyrene A428

Protected Butterflies: $4, Euploea sylvestor swinhoei. $6, Cyrestis thyodamas formosana. $10, Byasa polyeuctes termessus.

1978, Sept. 20

2114	A428	$2 multicolored	.55	.20
2115	A428	$4 multicolored	.70	.20
2116	A428	$6 multicolored	1.05	.30
2117	A428	$10 multicolored	2.75	.45
		Nos. 2114-2117 (4)	5.05	1.15

Scout Symbols — A429

Tropical Tomatoes — A430

1978, Oct. 5   Litho.   Perf. 13½

2118	A429	$2 multicolored	.40	.20
2119	A429	$10 multicolored	.65	.30

5th Chinese Boy Scout Jamboree, Cheng Ching Lake, Oct. 5-12.

1978, Oct. 23   Wmk. 323

Design: $10, Tropical tomatoes, horiz.

2120	A430	$2 multicolored	.30	.20
2121	A430	$10 multicolored	1.25	.40

International Symposium on Tropical Tomatoes, Taiwan, Oct. 23-28.

Sino-Saudi Bridge A431

Design: $6, Buttresses of bridge, flags of Taiwan and Saudi Arabia, horiz.

1978, Oct. 31

2122	A431	$2 multicolored	.35	.20
2123	A431	$6 multicolored	1.40	.30

Completion of Sino-Saudi Bridge over Cho-Shui River.

National Flag — A432

1978-80   Perf. 13½

2124	A432	$1 red & dk bl, I	.20	.20
a.		Bkt. pane of 16 ($5, $6, $8, $10, 3 $1, 9 $2)	7.75	
b.		Type II	.20	.20
2125	A432	$2 red & dk bl, I	.20	.20
a.		Bkt. pane of 15 + label	11.50	
b.		Type II	.20	.20
2126	A432	$3 yel grn & multi ('80)	.30	.20
2127	A432	$4 bis & multi ('80)	.35	.20
2128	A432	$5 dk grn & multi, I	.25	.20
a.		Type II	.25	
2129	A432	$6 brn org & multi	.30	.20
2130	A432	$7 dk brn & multi ('80)	.35	.20
2131	A432	$8 dk grn & multi, I	.45	.20
a.		Type II	.45	
2132	A432	$10 brt bl & multi ('79)	.60	.20
2133	A432	$12 brt rose lil & multi ('80)	.60	.25
		Nos. 2124-2133 (10)	3.60	2.05

Two types exist: I. Second line (red) below flag is same width as blue line. II. Second line is a hairline, notably thinner. The $3, $4, $7 and $12 were issued only in type II; $6, $10, Nos. 2134, 2124a, only in type I.

Nos. 2129-2133 have colorless inscriptions and denomination in a panel of solid color. Nos. 2124a, 2125a have selvage inscribed in blue. 1980 printings are in green or red.

Coil Stamp
1980, Jan. 15   Perf. 12 Horiz.

2134	A432	$2 multicolored	.25	.20

See Nos. 2288-2300. For overprints see Nos. 2540-2541.

Three Rams, by Emperor Hsuan-tsung A433

Taoyuan International Airport A434

Wmk. 323
1978, Dec. 1   Litho.   Perf. 12½

2135	A433	$1 multicolored	.30	.20
2136	A433	$5 multicolored	1.75	.40

New Year 1979.

1978, Dec. 31   Perf. 13½

$10, Passenger terminal, control tower.

2137	A434	$2 multi	.40	.20
2138	A434	$10 multi, horiz.	.70	.40

Completion of Taoyuan Intl. Airport.

Oracle Bones and Inscription, 1766-1123 B.C. — A435

Antiquities and Inscriptions: $5, Lehchi cauldron, 722-481 B.C. $8, Small seal (turtle), 206 B.C.-8 A.D. $10, Inscribed stone tablet, 175-183 A.D.

1979, Jan. 17

2139	A435	$2 multicolored	.60	.20
2140	A435	$5 multicolored	1.25	.30
2141	A435	$8 multicolored	2.25	.50
2142	A435	$10 multicolored	2.25	.65
		Nos. 2139-2142 (4)	6.35	1.65

Origin and development of Chinese characters.

Chihkan Tower, 1653 A436

Taiwan Scenery: $5, Shrine of Confucius, 1665. $8, Shrine of Koxinga, 1661. $10, Eternal Castle and moat.

1979, Feb. 11   Litho.   Perf. 13½

2143	A436	$2 multicolored	.40	.20
2144	A436	$5 multicolored	.85	.20
2145	A436	$8 multicolored	1.10	.20
2146	A436	$10 multicolored	2.10	.25
		Nos. 2143-2146 (4)	4.45	.85

Children Playing on Winter Day, Sung Dynasty — A437

1979, Mar. 8

2147	A437	Block of 4	14.00	9.25
a.		$5 in UL corner	3.50	.55
b.		$5 in UR corner	3.50	.55
c.		$5 in LL corner	3.50	.55
d.		$5 in LR corner	3.50	.55
e.		Souvenir sheet of 4, #2147, imperf.	27.50	16.00

No. 2147e has simulated perforations.

Lu Hao-tung — A438

Yellow Jade Brush Holder — A439

Perf. 13x12½
1979, Mar. 29   Engr.   Wmk. 323

2148	A438	$2 blue	.50	.20

Lu Hao-tung (1868-1895), revolutionist.

Unwmk.
1979, Apr. 12   Photo.   Perf. 12

Ancient Brush Washers: $5, White jade, Ming Dynasty. $8, Dark green jade, Ch'ing Dynasty. $10, Bluish jade, Ch'ing Dynasty. All horiz.

Granite Paper

2149	A439	$2 multicolored	.25	.20
2150	A439	$5 multicolored	1.10	.25
2151	A439	$8 multicolored	1.50	.35
2152	A439	$10 multicolored	2.10	.50
		Nos. 2149-2152 (4)	4.95	1.30

For similar artifacts designs with single-color background and denominations in outlined numerals with the cents, see types A453, A469, A489, A523, A547, A582.

A440   A440a

Plum Blossoms, Natl. Flower
Perf. 13½x12½
1979-92   Engr.   Wmk. 323
Granite Paper

2153	A440	$10 dk blue	1.60	.20
a.		Plain paper ('88)	2.50	.30
2154	A440	$20 brown	2.00	.20
b.		Plain paper ('87)	3.50	.60
2154A	A440	$40 brt car, plain paper ('85)	2.00	.20
2155	A440	$50 dull green	4.25	.25
e.		Plain paper ('87)	5.00	.55
2156	A440	$100 vermilion	6.00	.90
e.		Plain paper ('92)	6.00	3.25

Perf. 14x13½

2156A	A440a	$300 pur & red org ('83)	16.00	3.25
c.		Plain paper ('91)	18.00	3.25
2156B	A440a	$500 ver & brn ('82)	24.00	5.50
d.		Plain paper ('91)	26.00	5.50
		Nos. 2153-2156B (7)	55.85	10.50

Issued: #2156Ac, 2156Bd, May 1; #2156e, Jan. 7.

City Houses and Garden — A441

Design: $10, Rural landscape, horiz.

Perf. 13x12½, 12½x13
1979, June 5   Litho.

2157	A441	$2 multicolored	.20	.20
2158	A441	$10 multicolored	.75	.35

Protection of the Environment.

Bankbook and Computer Department A442

Designs: $2, Children at counter, vert. $5, People standing in line, vert. $10, Hand putting coin in savings bank, symbolic tree.

1979, July 1   Wmk. 323   Perf. 13½

2159	A442	$2 multicolored	.30	.20
2160	A442	$5 multicolored	.45	.20
2161	A442	$8 multicolored	.65	.20
2162	A442	$10 multicolored	.80	.25
		Nos. 2159-2162 (4)	2.20	.85

Postal savings, 60th anniversary.

Bird Type of 1977

Birds of Taiwan: $2, Swinoe's pheasant. $8, Steere's babbler. $10, Formosan yuhina.

1979, Aug. 8   Perf. 11½

2163	A402	$2 multicolored	.50	.20
2164	A402	$8 multicolored	1.25	.20
2165	A402	$10 multicolored	1.40	.35
		Nos. 2163-2165 (3)	3.15	.75

Rowland Hill, Penny Black A443

Perf. 13½x13
1979, Aug. 27   Litho.   Wmk. 323
2166 A443 $10 multicolored   1.25   .35
Sir Rowland Hill (1795-1879), originator of penny postage.

Jar with Rope Design, Shang Dynasty — A444

Ancient Chinese Pottery: $5, Two-handled jar, Shang dynasty. $8, Red jar with "ears," Han dynasty. $10, Green glazed jar, Han dynasty.

1979, Sept. 12   *Perf. 13½*
2167 A444 $2 multicolored   .45   .20
2168 A444 $5 multicolored   1.40   .20
2169 A444 $8 multicolored   2.50   .20
2170 A444 $10 multicolored   2.75   .30
      Nos. 2167-2170 (4)   7.10   .90

Children and IYC Emblem — A445

1979, Sept. 28   Litho.   *Perf. 13½*
2171 A445 $2 multicolored   .35   .20
2172 A445 $10 multicolored   .70   .35
International Year of the Child.

Trade Symbols, Competition Emblem A446

1979, Dec. 9   Litho.   *Perf. 13½*
2173 A446 $2 blue & multi   .25   .20
2174 A446 $10 green & multi   .80   .35
10th National Vocational Training Competition, Taichung, Dec. 9.

Trees on a Winter Plain, by Li Ch'eng A447

Paintings: $5, Bamboo, Wen T'ung. $8, Old tree, bamboo and rock, by Chao Meng-fu. $10, Twin Pines, by Li K'an.

1979, Nov. 21
2175 A447 $2 multicolored   .60   .20
2176 A447 $5 multicolored   1.25   .25
2177 A447 $8 multicolored   3.00   .40
2178 A447 $10 multicolored   4.25   .50
      Nos. 2175-2178 (4)   9.10   1.35

Monkey — A448

1979, Dec. 1   *Perf. 12½*
2179 A448 $1 yellow & multi   1.40   .20
2180 A448 $6 tan & multi   3.00   .50
      New Year 1980.

Rotary Emblem and "75" — A449

Rotary Intl., 75th Anniv.: $12, Anniv. emblem.

1980, Feb. 23   Litho.   *Perf. 13½*
2181 A449 $2 multicolored   .35   .20
2182 A449 $12 multi, vert.   .80   .35

Mt. Hohuan A450

Taiwan Landscapes (East-West Cross-Island Highway): $2, Tunnel of Nine Turns, vert. $12, Bridge, Tien Hsiang, vert.

1980, Mar. 1   **Wmk. 323**
2183 A450 $2 multicolored   .30   .20
2184 A450 $8 multicolored   1.00   .20
2185 A450 $12 multicolored   1.60   .35
      Nos. 2183-2185 (3)   2.90   .75

A451

A452

1980, Mar. 29   Engr.   *Perf. 13½x12½*
Granite Paper
2186 A451 $2 red brown   .55   .20
Shih Chien-Ju (1879-1900), revolutionist.

1980, Apr. 4   Litho.   *Perf. 13½*
2187 A452 $2 Chung-cheng Memorial Hall   .25   .20
2188 A452 $8 Quotation   .50   .20
2189 A452 $12 Bronze statue   .60   .50
      Nos. 2187-2189 (3)   1.35   .90
Chiang Kai-shek (1887-1975).

Melon-shaped Jade Brush Washer, Ming Dynasty — A453

Jade Pottery: $2, Jar with dragons, Sung dynasty, vert. $8, Monk's alms bowl, Ch'ing dynasty. $10, Yellow jade brush washer, Ch'ing dynasty.

1980, May 20   Photo.   *Perf. 12*
Granite Paper
2190 A453 $2 multicolored   .45   .20
2191 A453 $5 multicolored   .90   .20
2192 A453 $8 multicolored   1.60   .20
2193 A453 $10 multicolored   2.00   .30
      Nos. 2190-2193 (4)   4.95   .90

Energy Conservation A454

1980, July 15   Litho.   *Perf. 13½*
2194 A454 $2 multicolored   .25   .20
2195 A454 $12 multicolored   .80   .40

A455

A456

T'ang Dynasty pottery.

1980, Aug. 18   Litho.   *Perf. 13½*
2196 A455 $2 Soldier   .45   .20
2197 A455 $5 Roosters   1.40   .20
2198 A455 $8 Horse   1.90   .20
2199 A455 $10 Camel   2.25   .30
      Nos. 2196-2199 (4)   6.00   .90

Perf. 14x13½
1980, Sept. 23   Litho.   Wmk. 323
Folk Tales: $1, Grinding mortar into a needle. No. 2201, Confucius Returning Lost Article (shown). No. 2202, Wen Tien-hsiang in jail. $5, Sending coal in snow.

2200 A456 $1 multicolored   .20   .20
2201 A456 $2 multicolored   .30   .20
2202 A456 $2 multicolored   .80   .20
2203 A456 $5 multicolored   1.10   .30
      Nos. 2200-2203 (4)   2.40   .90

Railroad Electrification A457

1980, Oct. 10   *Perf. 13½x14*
2204 A457 $2 shown   .50   .20
2205 A457 $2 Taichung Harbor   .50   .20
2206 A457 $2 Chiang Kai-shek Airport   .50   .20
2207 A457 $2 Steel Mill   .50   .20
2208 A457 $2 Sun Yat-sen Freeway   .50   .20
2209 A457 $2 Nuclear power plant   .50   .20
2210 A457 $2 Petrochemical plants   .50   .20
2211 A457 $2 Su-ao Harbor   .50   .20
2212 A457 $2 Kaohsiung shipyard   .50   .20
2213 A457 $2 North link railroad   .50   .20
  a.   Souv. sheet of 10, #2204-2213   9.50   9.50
  b.   Block of 10, #2204-2213   4.50   4.50
      Nos. 2204-2213 (10)   5.00   2.00
Completion of major construction projects.

10th National Savings Day — A458

Wmk. 323
1980, Oct. 25   Litho.   *Perf. 13½*
2214 A458 $2 Ancient coin and coin banks   .55   .20
2215 A458 $12 shown   1.10   .40

Landscape, by Ch'iu Ying, Ming Dynasty — A459

1980, Nov. 12   Litho.   *Perf. 13½*
2216 A459 Block of 4   10.75   5.25
  a. $5 in UL corner   2.50   .40
  b. $5 in UR corner   2.50   .40
  c. $5 in LL corner   2.50   .40
  d. $5 in LR corner   2.50   .40
  e.   Souvenir sheet, imperf.   16.00   14.50
No. 2216e has simulated perforations.

Cock — A460

Faces, Flag, Census Form — A461

1980, Dec. 1   *Perf. 12½*
2217 A460 $1 multicolored   .90   .20
2218 A460 $6 multicolored   2.75   .35
  a.   Souv. sheet, 2 each #2217-2218   11.50   11.50
      New Year 1981.

1980, Dec. 13   *Perf. 13½*
2219 A461 $2 shown   .25   .20
2220 A461 $12 Buildings, horiz.   1.00   .40
1980 population and housing census.

TIROS-N Satellite — A462

Design: $10, Central weather bureau, horiz.

1981, Jan. 28　　Litho.　Perf. 13½
2221	A462	$2 multicolored	.35	.20
2222	A462	$10 multicolored	1.00	.40

Completion of meteorological satellite ground station, Taipei.

"Happiness" A463

New Year 1981 (Calligraphy): No. 2224, Wealth. No. 2225, Longevity. No. 2226, Joy.

1981, Feb. 3　　　　Perf. 13½x12½
2223	A463	$5 multi, 5 at B	1.00	.20
2224	A463	$5 multi, 5 at R	1.00	.20
2225	A463	$5 multi, 5 at L	1.00	.20
2226	A463	$5 multi, 5 at T	1.00	.20
a.		Block of 4, #2223-2226	4.50	1.75

International Year of the Disabled — A464

1981, Feb. 19　Litho.　Perf. 13½
2227	A464	$2 multicolored	.20	.20
2228	A464	$12 multicolored	.70	.25

Mt. Ali — A465

1981, Mar. 1
2229	A465	$2 shown	.30	.20
2230	A465	$7 Oluanpi Beach	1.00	.20
2231	A465	$12 Sun Moon Lake	1.60	.30
		Nos. 2229-2231 (3)	2.90	.70

A $2 multicolored stamp for the 12th National Kuomintang Congress at Taipei was prepared for release Mar. 29, 1981, but not issued. It showed Sun Yat-sen, Chiang Kai-shek, flags of China and the Kuomintang and a map of China.

Children in Forest A467

Children's Day: Drawings.

1981, Apr. 4
2233	A467	$1 multicolored	.20	.20
2234	A467	$2 multicolored	.20	.20
2235	A467	$5 multicolored	.25	.20
2236	A467	$7 multicolored	.30	.25
		Nos. 2233-2236 (4)	.95	.85

Chiang Kai-shek Memorial Hall — A468

1981, Apr. 5　　　Perf. 12½x13½
2237	A468	20c bluish lilac	.20	.20
a.		Photo. ('87)	.20	.20
2238	A468	40c crim rose	.20	.20
a.		Photo. ('87)	.20	.20

2239	A468	50c dull red brn	.20	.20
a.		Photo. ('88)	.20	.20
		Nos. 2237-2239 (3)	.60	.60

Chiang Kai-shek (1887-1975). See Nos. 2601-2603.

Cloisonne Enamel Brush Washer, 15th Cent. A469

Cloisonne Enamel: $5, Ritual vessel, 15th cent., vert. $8, Plate, 17th cent. $10, Vase, Ming Dynasty, vert.

1981, May 20　　Photo.　Perf. 12
Granite Paper
2240	A469	$2 multicolored	.50	.20
2241	A469	$5 multicolored	1.10	.20
2242	A469	$8 multicolored	1.25	.25
2243	A469	$10 multicolored	1.60	.30
		Nos. 2240-2243 (4)	4.45	.95

For similar enamelware stamps see Nos. 2318-2321, 2348-2351, 2410-2413.

Early & Modern Locomotives A470　　Linnaeus Crab A471

Wmk. 323
1981, June 9　Litho.　Perf. 12½
2244	A470	$2 shown	.45	.20
2245	A470	$14 Trains, horiz.	1.60	.40

Railroad service centenary.

1981, June 14　　　　Perf. 13½
2246	A471	$2 De Haan crab, horiz.	.30	.20
2247	A471	$5 shown	.60	.20
2248	A471	$8 Miers crab, horiz.	.95	.20
2249	A471	$14 Rathbun crab	1.75	.30
		Nos. 2246-2249 (4)	3.60	.90

Central Weather Bureau, 40th Anniv. — A472

1981, July 1　Litho.　Perf. 13½
2250	A472	$2 multicolored	.30	.20
2251	A472	$14 multicolored	1.25	.40

Scene from The Cowherd and the Weaving Maid — A473

Designs: Scenes from the Cowherd and the Weaving Maid.

1981, Aug. 6　Litho.　Perf. 13½x14
2252	A473	$2 multicolored	.50	.20
2253	A473	$4 multicolored	.80	.20
2254	A473	$8 multicolored	1.50	.20
2255	A473	$14 multicolored	2.25	.50
		Nos. 2252-2255 (4)	5.05	1.10

First Lasography Exhibition — A474

Lasography Designs.

1981, Aug. 15　　　Perf. 13½
2256	A474	$2 multicolored	.25	.20
2257	A474	$5 multicolored	.30	.20
2258	A474	$8 multicolored	.65	.20
2259	A474	$14 multicolored	1.10	.50
		Nos. 2256-2259 (4)	2.30	1.10

Soccer Players — A475

1981, Sept. 9　Litho.　Perf. 13½
2260		$5 multicolored	.50	.20
2261		$5 multicolored	.50	.20
a.	A475	Pair, #2260-2261	1.10	.65

Sports Day.

A477

70th Anniv. of Republic: No. 2263, Eastward Expedition (soldiers on Hill). No. 2264, Northward Expedition (Chiang on horse). No. 2265, Resistance War with Japan (Chiang, fist raised). No. 2266, Suppression of Communist Rebels (Battle scene). No. 2267, Counteroffensive and unification. $8, Chiang Kai-shek. $14, Sun Yat-sen.

1981, Oct. 10　　　　Perf. 13½
2262	A477	$2 multicolored	.20	.20
2263	A477	$2 multicolored	.20	.20
2264	A477	$2 multicolored	.20	.20
2265	A477	$2 multicolored	.20	.20
2266	A477	$3 multicolored	.20	.20
2267	A477	$3 multicolored	.20	.20
2268	A477	$8 multicolored	.45	.25
2269	A477	$14 multicolored	1.00	.45
a.		Souv. sheet of 8, #2262-2269	9.00	3.50
		Nos. 2262-2269 (8)	2.65	1.90

No. 2269a issued Oct. 25.

ROCPEX TAIPEI '81 Intl. Philatelic Exhibition, Taipei, Oct. 25-Nov. 2 A478

1981, Oct. 25
2270	A478	$2 multicolored	.20	.20
2271	A478	$14 multicolored	.50	.25

Nos. 2269a, 2270-2271 overprinted with four characters meaning "Best of Show" were not valid for postage. They were inserted in a special "ROCPEX" book, edition of 10,000. Value $25.

Boys Playing Games (#2272a) — A479

Designs: a.-j. "One Hundred Boys," Sung Dynasty scroll (each stamp is numbered from 1 to 10 in Chinese. See illustrations with Nos. 1682-1691 for numerals.) Two strips of 5 each in continuous design.

1981, Nov. 12
2272		Block of 10	16.50	16.50
a.-e.	A479	$2 single (top row)	1.50	.25
f.-j.	A479	$2 single (bottom row)	1.50	.25

New Year 1982 (Year of the Dog) — A480　　Information Week, Dec. 6-12 — A481

Wmk. 323
1981, Dec. 1　Litho.　Perf. 12½
2273	A480	$1 multicolored	1.25	.20
2274	A480	$10 multicolored	2.00	.40
a.		Souv. sheet, 2 ea #2273-2274	13.50	5.00

1981, Dec. 7　　　Perf. 14x13½
2275	A481	$2 multicolored	.55	.20

Telecommunications Centenary — A482

1981, Dec. 28　Perf. 14x13½, 13½x14
2276	A482	$2 Telephone, vert.	.20	.20
2277	A482	$3 Old, new phones	.25	.20
2278	A482	$8 Submarine cable	.40	.20
2279	A482	$18 Computers, vert.	.55	.30
		Nos. 2276-2279 (4)	1.40	.90

Floral Arrangement A483

Various floral arrangements in Ming vases.

Wmk. 323
1982, Jan. 23　Litho.　Perf. 13½
2280	A483	$2 multicolored	.25	.20
2281	A483	$3 multicolored	.35	.20
2282	A483	$8 multicolored	.75	.20
2283	A483	$18 multicolored	1.75	.50
		Nos. 2280-2283 (4)	3.10	1.10

Compare with designs A559, A584.

The Ku Cheng Reunion — A484

Designs: Opera scenes.

Wmk. 323

1982, Feb. 15	Litho.	*Perf. 13½*		
2284	A484	$2 multicolored	.55	.20
2285	A484	$3 multicolored	1.75	.20
2286	A484	$4 multicolored	1.90	.25
2287	A484	$18 multicolored	3.50	.60
		Nos. 2284-2287 (4)	7.70	1.25

Flag Type of 1978
Value Colorless in Colored Panel

1981		Litho.	*Perf. 13½*	
			Panel Color	
2288	A432	$1 dk blue	.30	.20
2289	A432	$1.50 lt olive	.30	.20
2290	A432	$2 dk olive bis	.30	.20
2291	A432	$3 red	.30	.20
2292	A432	$4 blue	.30	.20
2293	A432	$5 sepia	.30	.20
2294	A432	$6 orange	.40	.20
2295	A432	$7 green	.60	.20
2296	A432	$8 magenta	.75	.20
2297	A432	$9 olive grn	.95	.20
2298	A432	$10 dk purple	1.10	.20
2299	A432	$12 lilac	1.25	.25
2300	A432	$14 dk green	1.25	.30
		Nos. 2288-2300 (13)	8.10	2.75

Second line (red) below flag is a hairline, notably thinner.
For overprints see Nos. 2540-2541.

Robert Koch
A485

Cheng Shih-liang, Revolutionary
A486

Wmk. 323

1982, Mar. 24	Litho.	*Perf. 13½*		
2309	A485	$2 multicolored	.25	.20

Tubercle Bacillus centenary.

1982, Mar. 29	Engr.	*Perf. 13½x12½*		
		Granite Paper		
2310	A486	$2 carmine rose	.25	.20

Children's Day
A487

Designs: Various children's drawings.

1982, Apr. 4		Litho.		
2311	A487	$2 multi, vert.	.40	.20
2312	A487	$3 multicolored	.60	.20
2313	A487	$5 multicolored	.80	.20
2314	A487	$8 multicolored	.80	.20
		Nos. 2311-2314 (4)	2.60	.80

Dentists' Day
A488

1982, May 4	Litho.	*Perf. 13½*		
2315	A488	$2 Tooth, boy	.30	.20
2316	A488	$3 Flossing, brushing	.60	.20
2317	A488	$10 Examination	1.10	.30
		Nos. 2315-2317 (3)	2.00	.70

Champleve Enamel Cup and Saucer, 18th Cent. A489

Painted Enamelware: $5, Cloisonne gold-plated duck Ch'ien-lung period (1736-1795), vert. $8, Incense burner, K'ang-hsi period (1662-1722). $12, Cloisonne pitcher, Ch'ien-lung period, vert.

1982, May 20	Photo.	*Perf. 12*		
		Granite Paper		
2318	A489	$2 multicolored	.40	.20
2319	A489	$5 multicolored	.80	.20
2320	A489	$8 multicolored	2.00	.20
2321	A489	$12 multicolored	2.75	.25
		Nos. 2318-2321 (4)	5.95	.85

See Nos. 2348-2351.

Poets' Day — A490

Tang Dynasty Poetry Illustrations (618-906): $2, Spring Dawn, by Meng Hao-Jan. $3, On Looking for a Hermit and Not Finding Him, by Chia Tao. $5, Summer Dying, by Liu Yu-Hsi. $18, Looking at the Snow Drifts on South Mountain, by Tsu Yung. Chinese characters are to the left of the denominations on Nos. 2322-2325, Nos. 2396-2399 have no characters to the left of the denominations.

Wmk. 323

1982, June 25	Litho.	*Perf. 13½*		
2322	A490	$2 multicolored	2.25	.25
2323	A490	$3 multicolored	4.00	.35
2324	A490	$5 multicolored	6.25	.75
2325	A490	$18 multicolored	14.50	1.50
		Nos. 2322-2325 (4)	27.00	2.85

See Nos. 2352-2355.

5th World Women's Softball Championship, Taipei, July 1-12 — A491

1982, July 2				
2326	A491	$2 lt grn & multi	.65	.20
2327	A491	$18 tan & multi	1.25	.40

Scouting Year
A492

1982, July 18				
2328	A492	$2 Crossing bridge, Baden-Powell	.20	.20
2329	A492	$18 Emblem, camp	.70	.40

Stamp in Tongs
A493

1982, Aug. 9				
2330	A493	$2 shown	.65	.20
2331	A493	$18 Album stamps magnified	1.40	.40

Carved Lion, Tsu Shih Temple — A494

Hsun Kuan Saving Hsiang-cheng City — A495

Tsu Shih Temple of Sanhsia Architecture: $3, Lion brackets, horiz. $5, Sub-lintels, $18, Tiled roof, horiz.

1982, Sept. 1	Litho.	*Perf. 13½*		
2332	A494	$2 multicolored	.40	.20
2333	A494	$3 multicolored	.55	.20
2334	A494	$5 multicolored	1.25	.20
2335	A494	$18 multicolored	1.75	.40
		Nos. 2332-2335 (4)	3.95	1.00

1982, Oct. 15		*Perf. 14x13½*		

Designs: Scenes from The Thirty-Six Examples of Filial Piety, Folk Tale collection by Wu Yen-huan.

2336	A495	$1 multicolored	.20	.20
2337	A495	$2 multicolored	.50	.20
2338	A495	$3 multicolored	.70	.20
2339	A495	$5 multicolored	.80	.25
		Nos. 2336-2339 (4)	2.20	.85

30th Anniv. of China Youth Corps
A496

1982, Oct. 31				
2340	A496	$2 Riding	.20	.20
2341	A496	$3 Raising flag, vert.	.20	.20
2342	A496	$18 Mountain climbing	.60	.40
		Nos. 2340-2342 (3)	1.00	.80

Seated Lohan (Buddhist Saint) — A497

New Year 1983 (Year of the Boar) — A498

Paintings of Lohan, Hanging Scrolls by Liu Sung-nien, 13th cent.

Perf. 13x12½

1982, Nov. 12			**Wmk. 323**	
2343	A497	$2 multicolored	1.25	.20
2344	A497	$3 multicolored	3.00	.20
2345	A497	$18 multicolored	7.75	.85
a.		Souv. sheet, #2343-2345	27.50	13.00
		Nos. 2343-2345 (3)	12.00	1.25

No. 2345a comes overprinted in red in the sheet margins. Value, unused $18, Used $12.

1982, Dec. 1			*Perf. 12½*	
2346	A498	$1 multicolored	1.60	.20
2347	A498	$10 multicolored	2.75	.45
a.		Souv. sheet, 2 ea #2346-2347	14.50	6.50

Enamelware Type of 1982

Designs: $2, Square basin, Ch'ing Dynasty (1644-1911). $3, Vase, Ch'ien-lung period (1736-1795). $4, Tea pot, Ch'ien-lung period. $18, Elephant vase, Ch'ing Dynasty.

1983, Jan. 5	Photo.	*Perf. 12*		
		Granite Paper		
2348	A489	$2 multi	.50	.20
2349	A489	$3 multi, vert.	.70	.20
2350	A489	$4 multi, vert.	1.25	.20
2351	A489	$18 multi, vert.	2.00	.50
		Nos. 2348-2351 (4)	4.45	1.10

Poetry Illustration Type of 1982

Sung Dynasty Poetry: $2, Seeing the Flowers Fade Away. $3, River. $5, Freckled with Clouds is the Azure Sky. $11, Yielding Fine Fragrance in the Snow. Nos. 2352-2355 vert.

Wmk. 323

1983, Feb. 10	Litho.	*Perf. 13½*		
2352	A490	$2 multicolored	1.40	.25
2353	A490	$3 multicolored	5.25	.35
2354	A490	$5 multicolored	7.50	.50
2355	A490	$11 multicolored	11.00	.60
		Nos. 2352-2355 (4)	25.15	1.70

Mt. Jade, Taiwan — A499

1983, Mar. 1				
2356	A499	$2 Wawa Valley, vert.	.70	.20
2357	A499	$3 University Pond, vert.	1.10	.20
2358	A499	$18 shown	1.75	.50
		Nos. 2356-2358 (3)	3.55	.90

400th Anniv. of Arrival of Matteo Ricci (1552-1610), Italian Missionary A500

Perf. 14x13½

1983, Apr. 3	Litho.		**Wmk. 323**	
2359	A500	$2 Globe	.45	.20
2360	A500	$18 Great Wall	1.40	.35

Mandarin Phonetic Symbols, 70th Anniv. — A501

Scenes from Lady White Snake Fairytale — A502

Wmk. 323

1983, May 22 Litho. **Perf. 13½**
2361 A501 $2 Wu Ching-heng, inventor .45 .20
2362 A501 $18 Children writing 1.40 .30

1983, June 15 **Perf. 14x13½**
2363 A502 $2 multicolored .60 .20
2364 A502 $3 lt blue & multi 1.10 .20
2365 A502 $3 orange & multi 1.10 .20
2366 A502 $18 multicolored 1.25 .50
Nos. 2363-2366 (4) 4.05 1.10

A503

A504

Various bamboo carved objects. Nos. 2367-2369 Ch'ing dynasty.

Wmk. 323

1983, July 14 Litho. **Perf. 13½**
2367 A503 $2 Bamboo jug .75 .20
2368 A503 $3 Tao-t'ieh motif vase .90 .20
2369 A503 $4 Landscape sculpture 1.05 .20
2370 A503 $18 Brush holder, Ming dynasty 2.25 .40
Nos. 2367-2370 (4) 4.95 1.00

Wmk. 323

1983, Aug. 5 Litho. **Perf. 13½**
2371 A504 $2 Globe .55 .20
2372 A504 $18 Emblem .80 .35

World Communications Year.

Fishing Industry (Local Fish) A505

1983, Aug. 20
2373 A505 $2 Epinephelus tauvina .60 .20
2374 A505 $18 Saurida undosquamis 2.25 .35

40th Journalists' Day — A506

1983, Sept. 1
2375 A506 $2 multicolored .55 .20

Views of Mongolia and Tibet — A507

1983, Sept. 15
2376 A507 $2 Village .55 .20
2377 A507 $3 Potala Palace 1.00 .20
2378 A507 $5 Sheep grazing 1.10 .20
2379 A507 $11 Camel caravan 1.75 .40
Nos. 2376-2379 (4) 4.40 1.00

2nd East Asian Bird Protection Conference, Oct. — A508

1983, Oct. 8 Litho. **Perf. 13½**
2380 A508 $2 Lanius cristatus, vert. .65 .20
2381 A508 $18 Butastur indicus 2.50 .40

A509

A510

Plum Blossoms, photography by Hu Ch'unghsien.

1983, Oct. 31 Litho. **Perf. 14x13½**
2382 A509 $2 multicolored .35 .20
2383 A509 $3 multi, diff. .65 .20
2384 A509 $5 multi, diff. .70 .20
2385 A509 $11 multi, diff. 1.00 .30
Nos. 2382-2385 (4) 2.70 .90

1983, Nov. 6 **Perf. 13x13½, 13½x13**
2386 A510 $2 JCI and Congress emblems .25 .20
2387 A510 $18 Globe and emblems, horiz. .90 .40

Jaycees Intl., 38th World Congress, Taipei.

8th Asian-Pacific Cardiology Congress — A511

1983, Nov. 27 Litho. **Perf. 13½**
2388 A511 $2 shown .30 .20
2389 A511 $18 Electrocardiogram 1.10 .65

New Year 1984 (Year of the Rat) — A512

1983, Dec. 1 Litho. **Perf. 12½**
2390 A512 $1 multicolored 1.75 .70
2391 A512 $10 multicolored 4.00 .45
a. Souv. sheet, 2 each #2390-2391 30.00 9.00

Literacy Week A513

1983, Dec. 17 Litho. **Perf. 13½**
2392 A513 $2 shown .35 .20
2393 A513 $18 Modern family, vert. 1.10 .55

World Freedom Day A514

1984, Jan. 23 Litho. **Perf. 13½**
2394 A514 $2 Korean War Patriots .35 .20
2395 A514 $18 Intl. support 1.40 .35

Drama Day — A515

Yuan Dynasty Poetry Illustrations by Tien-shih Lin (Poems by): $2, Kuan Yun-shih. $3, Po Pu. $5, Chang Ko-chiu. $18, Shang Cheng-shu. (See note with Nos. 2322-2325.)

1984, Feb. 15 Litho. **Perf. 13½**
2396 A515 $2 multicolored 1.90 .35
2397 A515 $3 multicolored 3.75 .45
2398 A515 $5 multicolored 6.50 .55
2399 A515 $18 multicolored 10.00 1.40
Nos. 2396-2399 (4) 22.15 2.75

A516

A517

A518

Arbor Day — A519

1984, Mar. 12 Litho. **Perf. 13½x14**
2400 A516 $2 multicolored .90 .20
2401 A517 $2 multicolored .90 .20
2402 A518 $2 multicolored .90 .20
2403 A519 $2 multicolored .90 .20
a. Block of 4, #2400-2403 5.00 3.25

Lin Chueh-min A520

Central News Agency, 60th Anniv. A521

1984, Mar. 29 Engr. **Perf. 13x12½**
Granite Paper
2404 A520 $2 dark green .25 .20

Perf. 14x13½
1984, Apr. 1 Litho. **Wmk.**
2405 A521 $2 Emblem .20 .20
2406 A521 $10 Emblem, satellite, dish antenna .70 .45

God of Longevity — A522

Ch'ing Dynasty Enamelware A523

Paintings by Chang Ta-chien (1899-1983): $2, Five Auspicious Tokens. $18, Lotus Blossoms in Ink Splash.

Wmk. 323

1984, Apr. 20 Litho. **Perf. 11½**
2407 A522 $2 multicolored 1.50 .20
2408 A522 $5 multicolored 4.00 .20
2409 A522 $18 multicolored 6.00 .50
Nos. 2407-2409 (3) 11.50 .90

1984, May 20 Photo. **Perf. 12**
Granite Paper
2410 A523 $2 Cup, pot, plate, horiz. .40 .20
2411 A523 $3 Wine jug .80 .20
2412 A523 $4 Teapot 1.25 .20
2413 A523 $18 Candle holder 1.60 .45
Nos. 2410-2413 (4) 4.05 1.05

China Airlines World-wide Service Inauguration A524

1984, May 31 Litho. **Perf. 13½x14**
2414 A524 $2 Jet circling globe .25 .20
2415 A524 $7 Globe, jet .50 .20
2416 A524 $11 New York City .65 .30
2417 A524 $18 Amsterdam .85 .45
Nos. 2414-2417 (4) 2.25 1.15

30th
Navigation
Day
A525

Perf. 13½x13
1984, July 11   Litho.   Wmk. 323
2418 A525 $2 Container ship   1.10 .20
2419 A525 $18 Oil tanker   2.10 .35

1984 Summer
Olympics — A526

Alpine
Plants — A527

Perf. 13½x14, 14x13½
1984, June 23
2420 A526 $2 Judo, horiz.   .30 .20
2421 A526 $5 Archery   .50 .65
2422 A526 $18 Swimming, horiz. 1.00 .80
      Nos. 2420-2422 (3)   1.80 1.65

1984, Aug. 8   Perf. 13
$2, Gentiana arisanensis. $3, Epilobium
nankotaizanense. $5, Adenophora uehatae.
$18, Aconitum fukutomei.
2423 A527 $2 multi   .50 .20
2424 A527 $3 multi   1.00 .20
2425 A527 $5 multi   1.40 .20
2426 A527 $18 multi   2.00 .50
      Nos. 2423-2426 (4)   4.90 1.10

The Eighteen
Scholars,
Sung Dynasty
Hanging
Scroll — A528

Details.

Wmk. 323
1984, Aug. 20   Litho.   Perf. 13
2427 A528 $2 Playing instru-
        ments   2.40 .25
2428 A528 $3 Playing chess   4.75 .35
2429 A528 $5 Practicing callig-
        raphy   7.00 .50
2430 A528 $18 Painting   16.00 1.00
      Nos. 2427-2430 (4)   30.15 2.10

Athletics Day — A529

1984, Sept. 9
2431 $5 Two players   .90 .20
2432 $5 One player   .90 .20
  a. A529 Pair, #2431-2432   2.00 .90

A531   A532

1984, Sept. 9
2433 A531 $10 "20," map of Asia .70 .20
Asian-Pacific Parliamentarians' Union, 20th
anniv.

1984, Oct. 10   Litho.   Perf. 12½
2434 A532 $2 No. 1458   .25 .20
2435 A532 $5 No. 296   .60 .20
2436 A532 $18 Museum   .90 .50
  a. Souv. sheet of 3, #2434-2436 9.00 2.25
      Nos. 2434-2436 (3)   1.75 .90
Postal Museum opening.

Flag, Alliance
Emblem — A533

Veteran's
Assistance
A534

1984, Oct. 16   Perf. 13½
2437 A533 $2 multicolored   .45 .20
Grand Alliance for China's Reunification
Under the Three Principles of the People Convention, Taipei, Oct. 16-17.

1984, Nov. 1   Litho.   Perf. 13½
2438 A534 $2 Vignettes   .45 .20

Pine Tree
A535

Bamboo
A535a

Plum Tree — A535b

1984-88
2439 A535 $2 multicolored   .25 .20
2440 A535a $8 multicolored   .75 .20
2441 A535b $10 pale yellow bis-
        ter background .80 .20
  a. Grayish tan background .40 .20
      Nos. 2439-2441 (3)   1.80 .60
Issued: #2439-2440,   2441a, 11/12;
#2441,1/12/88.
See #2495-2503, 3303.

A536   A537

1984, Dec. 1   Perf. 12x12½
2442 A536 $1 multicolored   1.10 .20
2443 A536 $10 multicolored   3.00 .30
  a. Min. sheet, 2 ea #2442-2443 7.75 3.50
New Year 1985 (Year of the Ox).

1985, Jan. 11   Litho.   Perf. 13½
2444 A537 $5 Scales, legal
        codes   .65 .20
Judicial Day 1985.

Quemoy and
Matsu
Scenes
A538

1985, Jan. 23   Litho.   Perf. 13½x14
2445 A538 $2 Ku-kang Lake,
        Quemoy   .30 .20
2446 A538 $5 Kuang-hai Stone,
        Quemoy   .80 .20
2447 A538 $8 Sheng-li Reser-
        voir, Matsu   1.05 .20
2448 A538 $10 Tung-chu Light-
        house, Matsu   1.40 .25
      Nos. 2445-2448 (4)   3.55 .85

Sir Robert Hart
(1835-1911)
A539

1985, Feb. 15   Litho.   Perf. 14x13½
2449 A539 $2 No. 1   .45 .20
Inspector General of Chinese Customs,
1863-1908, and founder of the Chinese Postal
Service.

Lo Fu-hsing (1886-
1914)
A540

Tsou Jung (1882-
1905)
A541

1985, Feb. 24   Perf. 13x13½
2450 A540 $2 multicolored   .45 .20

1985, Mar. 29   Engr.   Perf. 13½x12½
Granite Paper
2451 A541 $3 green   .45 .20

Chung-cheng Memorial Hall Main
Gate — A542

1985, Apr. 5   Litho.   Perf. 13
2452 A542 $2 shown   .30 .20
2453 A542 $8 Tzuhu Memorial 1.10 .25
2454 A542 $10 Chiang Kai-shek,
        vert.   1.25 .30
      Nos. 2452-2454 (3)   2.65 .75
Tenth death anniv. of Chiang Kai-shek.

A543

A544

1985, May 8   Litho.   Perf. 13½
2455 A543 $2 Carnation   1.00 .20
2456 A543 $2 Day lily   1.00 .20
  a. Pair, #2455-2456   2.50 .80
Mother's Day.

1985, May 18
2457 A544 $5 Tunnel to Chi-chin Is-
        land   .70 .20
Kaohsiung Cross-Harbor Tunnel, 1st anniv.

Girl Scouts, 75th
Anniv. — A545

Wmk. 323
1985, June 1   Litho.   Perf. 13½
2458 A545 $2 multicolored   .25 .20
2459 A545 $18 multicolored   2.00 .30

The Book of
Odes,
Confucius
A545a

1985, June 22   Litho.   Wmk. 323
2460 A545a $2 Spring   1.25 .20
2461 A545a $5 Summer   2.40 .20
2462 A545a $8 Fall   4.75 .30
2463 A545a $10 Winter   6.00 .50
      Nos. 2460-2463 (4)   14.40 1.20

Fruit — A546

Perf. 13½x14

1985, July 5   Litho.   Wmk. 323
2464	A546	$2 Wax Jambo	.70	.20
2465	A546	$3 Guava	1.25	.20
2466	A546	$5 Carambola	1.40	.20
2467	A546	$8 Litchi nut	1.50	.30
		Nos. 2464-2467 (4)	4.85	.90

Ch'ing Dynasty (1644-1911) Ivory Carvings — A547

1985, July 18   Wmk. 323   Perf. 13½
2468	A547	$2 Dragon Boat	.25	.20
2469	A547	$3 Landscape	.60	.20
2470	A547	$5 Melon, water container	.90	.20
2471	A547	$18 Brush holder, vert.	1.10	.35
		Nos. 2468-2471 (4)	2.85	.95

T'ang Dynasty (618-907) Aristocrat — A548

Designs: $5, Sung Dynasty (960-1280) palace woman. $8, Yuan Dynasty (1280-1368) aristocrat. $11, Ming Dynasty (1368-1644) aristocrat.

1985, Aug. 1   Wmk. 323   Perf. 13½
2472	A548	$2 multicolored	.55	.20
2473	A548	$5 multicolored	1.75	.20
2474	A548	$8 multicolored	2.50	.20
2475	A548	$11 multicolored	3.00	.30
		Nos. 2472-2475 (4)	7.80	.90

4th Asian Conf. on Costume, Aug. 3.

In the 2 rows of Chinese characters above the denomination, the right row has 3 characters and a dot on #2472-2475, 4 characters and a dot on #2549-2552. #2605-2608, 2660-2663 have solid black numerals.

See #2549-2552, 2605-2608, 2660-2663, 2721-2724, 2794-2797.

Social Welfare Program A549

Perf. 13½x14

1985, Aug. 15   Wmk. 323
2476	A549	$2 Heart, bird feeding young	.45	.20

Historic Sites A550

Wmk. 323
1985, Sept. 3   Litho.   Perf. 13½
2477	A550	$2 Taipei North Gate	.25	.20
2478	A550	$5 San Domingo Fort, Tamsui	.65	.20
2479	A550	$8 Lung Shun Temple, Lukang	.85	.20
2480	A550	$10 Confucius Temple, Changhua	1.10	.25
		Nos. 2477-2480 (4)	2.85	.85

Bonsai — A551   Trade Shows — A552

Perf. 13½x14

1985, Sept. 22   Wmk. 323
2481	A551	$2 Oak	.35	.20
2482	A551	$5 Five-leaf pine	.75	.20
2483	A551	$8 Lohan pine	1.00	.25
2484	A551	$18 Banyan	1.50	.50
		Nos. 2481-2484 (4)	3.60	1.15

1985, Oct. 5   Perf. 13½

Taipei World Trade Center and show emblems: a, Sporting goods. b, Toys and gifts. c, Electronics. d, Machinery. Se-tenant in continuous design.
2485	Strip of 4	3.50	1.25
a.-d.	A552 $2 any single	.75	.20

Scenes of Modern Taiwan, Map, Flag A553

1985, Oct. 25
2486	A553	$2 shown	1.00	.20
2487	A553	$18 Chiang Kai-shek, Triumphal Arch	2.00	.70

Defeat of Japanese army, end of World War II, and return of Taiwan to control of the Republic, 40th anniv.

7th Asian Conference on Mental Retardation A554

Sun Yat-sen and Birthplace A555

1985, Nov. 8   Perf. 14x13½
2488	A554	$2 multicolored	.40	.20
2489	A554	$11 multicolored	1.50	.30

1985, Nov. 12   Perf. 13½
2490	A555	$2 multicolored	.40	.20
2491	A555	$18 multicolored	1.75	.40

Postal Life Insurance, 50th Anniv. — A556   New Year 1986 (Year of the Tiger) — A557

1985, Dec. 1
2492	A556	$2 multicolored	.45	.20

1985, Dec. 1   Perf. 12½
2493	A557	$1 multicolored	.60	.20
2494	A557	$10 multicolored	2.00	.35
a.	Min. sheet, 2 ea #2493-2494		11.00	3.25

Flora Types of 1984

1986, Jan. 10   Litho.   Perf. 13½
2495	A535	$1 multicolored	.20	.20
2496	A535a	$11 multicolored	.65	.20
2497	A535b	$18 multicolored	.90	.20

1988, Feb. 12
2498	A535	$1.50 multicolored	.20	.20
2499	A535a	$7.50 multicolored	.65	.20
2500	A535b	$16 multicolored	1.25	.30

#2500 has value expressed in dollars and cents.

1989, Feb. 24
2501	A535	$3 multicolored	.20	.20
2502	A535a	$16.50 multicolored	1.25	.30
2503	A535b	$21 multicolored	1.60	.35
		Nos. 2495-2503 (9)	6.90	2.15

Cultural Renaissance Movement — A558

Painting: Hermit Anglers on a Mountain Stream, Ming Dynasty, 1386-1644. Continuous design. (Each stamp is numbered from 1 to 5 in Chinese. See illustrations with Nos. 1682-1691 for numerals.)

1986, Jan. 28   Litho.   Perf. 13½
2507		Strip of 5	9.00	7.00
a.-e.	A558 $2 any single		1.50	.25

See No. 2604.

Floral Arrangements A559

Wmk. 323
1986, Feb. 20   Litho.   Perf. 13½
2517	A559	$2 denom. UL	.35	.20
2518	A559	$5 denom. UR	.75	.20
2519	A559	$8 shown	.85	.20
2520	A559	$10 denom. UL	1.25	.25
		Nos. 2517-2520 (4)	3.20	.85

Compare with designs A483, A584.

Natl. Postal Service, 90th Anniv. A560

$2, Unloading express mail at airport. $5, Motorcycle delivery. $8, Technological innovations. $10, Electronic sorting machine.

1986, Mar. 20
2521	A560	$2 multi	.25	.20
2522	A560	$5 multi, vert.	.35	.20
2523	A560	$8 multi, vert.	.55	.20
2524	A560	$10 multi	.65	.25
a.	Souv. sheet of 4, #2521-2524		5.75	2.55
		Nos. 2521-2524 (4)	1.80	.85

Chen Tien-hua (1875-1905), Revolutionary A561

1986, Mar. 29   Engr.   Perf. 13½x12½
Granite Paper
2525	A561	$2 violet	.55	.20

Yushan Natl. Park A562

1986, Apr. 10   Litho.   Perf. 13½
2526	A562	$2 multicolored	.50	.20
2527	A562	$5 multi, diff.	1.25	.20
2528	A562	$8 multi, diff.	1.60	.20
2529	A562	$10 multi, diff.	2.00	.30
		Nos. 2526-2529 (4)	5.35	.90

Power Plants A563

1986, Apr. 29
2530	A563	$2 Hydro-electric	.30	.20
2531	A563	$8 Thermo-electric	.80	.20
2532	A563	$10 Nuclear	1.10	.25
		Nos. 2530-2532 (3)	2.20	.65

Economic prosperity through energy development.

Paintings by P'u Hsin-yu (1896-1963) A564

1986, May 22   Perf. 11½
2533	A564	$2 Bird	1.75	.20
2534	A564	$8 Landscape	3.50	.30
2535	A564	$10 Woman in forest	5.50	.35
		Nos. 2533-2535 (3)	10.75	.85

Asian Productivity Org., 25th Anniv. — A565

1986, June 3   Perf. 13x13½
2536	A565	$2 multicolored	.20	.20
2537	A565	$11 multicolored	1.00	.30

Natl. Productivity Center, 30th anniv.

Coral-reef Fish
A566

Designs: a, Chrysiptera starcki. b, Chelmon rostratus. c, Chaetodon xanthurus. d, Chaetodon quadrimaculatus. e, Chaetodon meyeri. f, Genicanthus semifasciatus. g, Genicanthus semifasciatus. h, Pomacanthus annularis. i, Lienardella fasciata. j, Balistapus undulatus.

1986, June 27   **Perf. 13½**
2538   Block of 10   6.50 4.00
a.-j. A566 $2 any single   .60 .20

Protection of Intellectual Property Rights — A567

1986, June 12
2539 A567 $2 Macaw   1.40 .20

Nos. 2294, 2297 Surcharged

1986, July 9   **Litho.**   **Perf. 13½**
2540 A432 $2 on $6 multi   .20 .20
2541 A432 $8 on $9 multi   .55 .25
60th Anniv. of northward expedition by the national revolutionary army.

Bridges
A568

1986, July 30
2542 A568 $2 Tzu Mu, 1965   .45 .20
2543 A568 $5 Chang Hung, 1968   1.10 .20
2544 A568 $8 Kuan Fu, 1977   1.40 .20
2545 A568 $10 Kuan Tu, 1983   2.00 .25
Nos. 2542-2545 (4)   4.95 .85

Love between Liang Shanpo and Chu Yingtai, Folk Tale — A569

Cartoons by Huang Mu-ts'un: a, Yingtai disguised to go to school. b, Yingtai and Shanpo meet in class. c, The friends at pond. d, Yingtai summoned home for arranged marriage. e, Yingtai and Shanpo ascend to heaven as butterflies (each stamp is numbered from 1 to 5 in Chinese. See illustrations with Nos. 1682-1691 for numerals.)

1986, Aug. 12   **Perf. 12½**
2546   Strip of 5   4.00 2.00
a.-e. A569 $5 any single   .60 .20

Social Awareness Campaign
A570

Folk Costumes — A571

1986, Sept. 12   **Litho.**   **Perf. 13½**
2547 A570 $2 Rainbow, children   .30 .20
2548 A570 $8 Children, adults   .70 .25

Designs: $2, Shang Dynasty (1766-1122 B.C.) aristocrat. $5, Warring States (403-221 B.C.) aristocrat. $8, Later Han Dynasty (A.D. 25-221) empress. $10, Flying ribbons gown, Wei and Tsin Dynasties (A.D. 221-420) aristocrat.

1986, Sept. 23   **Litho.**   **Perf. 13½**
2549 A571 $2 multicolored   .85 .20
2550 A571 $5 multicolored   1.40 .20
2551 A571 $8 multicolored   1.75 .20
2552 A571 $10 multicolored   2.75 .20
Nos. 2549-2552 (4)   6.75 .80

Ch'ing Dynasty Ju-i Scepters
A572

1986, Oct. 10   **Photo.**   **Perf. 14x14½**
2553 A572 $2 White jade   .25 .20
2554 A572 $3 Red coral   .45 .20
2555 A572 $4 Redwood and gems   .60 .20
2556 A572 $18 Gilded wood   1.60 .40
Nos. 2553-2556 (4)   2.90 1.00
See Nos. 2582-2585.

Chiang Kai-shek
A573

Portrait and: $5, Map and flag. $8, Emblem. $10, Flags on globe.

1986, Oct. 31   **Litho.**   **Perf. 13½**
2557 A573 $2 multicolored   .25 .20
2558 A573 $5 multicolored   .85 .20
2559 A573 $8 multicolored   1.10 .20
2560 A573 $10 multicolored   1.40 .25
a.   Souv. sheet of 4, #2557-2560   9.00 2.50
Nos. 2557-2560 (4)   3.60 .85

Cultural Heritage
A574

Architecture: $2, Chin-Kuang Fu land development and defense fund building, 1826. $5, Erh-sha-wan Gun Emplacement, Keelung, 1841, restored 1979. $8, Fort Hsi T'ai, 1886. $10, Matsu Temple, Peng-hu, renovated 1563-1624.

1986, Nov. 14   **Litho.**   **Perf. 13½**
2561 A574 $2 multicolored   .40 .20
2562 A574 $5 multicolored   .95 .20
2563 A574 $8 multicolored   1.10 .25
2564 A574 $10 multicolored   1.40 .30
Nos. 2561-2564 (4)   3.85 .95

New Year 1987 (Year of the Hare) — A575

1986, Dec. 1   **Perf. 12½**
2565 A575 $1 dl pink & multi   .50 .20
2566 A575 $10 pale grn & multi   2.25 .30
a.   Souv. sheet, 2 each #2565-2566   14.50 3.50

Kenting, 1st Natl. Park
A576

1987, Jan. 8   **Litho.**   **Perf. 13½**
2567 A576 $2 Garden   .45 .20
2568 A576 $5 Shore rocks   1.10 .20
2569 A576 $8 Shore and hill   1.40 .20
2570 A576 $10 Shore and rocks, diff.   2.00 .30
Nos. 2567-2570 (4)   4.95 .90

Folk Art — A577

Puppets: $2, Hand puppet. $5, Marionette. $18, Shadow puppet.

1987, Feb. 12   **Litho.**   **Perf. 14x13½**
2571 A577 $2 multicolored   .35 .20
2572 A577 $5 multicolored   1.00 .20
2573 A577 $18 multicolored   1.75 .40
Nos. 2571-2573 (3)   3.10 .80

Speedpost
A578

Wu Yueh (1878-1905), Revolutionary
A579

1987, Mar. 20   **Litho.**   **Perf. 14x13½**
2574 A578 $2 multicolored   .35 .20
2575 A578 $18 multicolored   1.25 .40
Stamp Day.

1987, Mar. 29   **Engr.**   **Perf. 13½x12½**
2576 A579 $2 orange   1.10 .20

Landscapes Painted by Madame Chiang Kai-shek — A580

$2, Singing Creek with Bamboo Orchestra. $5, Mountains Draped in Clouds. $8, Vista of Tranquility. $10, Mountains after a Snowfall.

1987, Apr. 10   **Litho.**   **Perf. 13½**
2577 A580 $2 blk, buff & ver   .45 .20
2578 A580 $5 blk, buff & ver   1.25 .20
2579 A580 $8 blk, buff & ver   2.75 .30
2580 A580 $10 blk, buff & ver   3.75 .45
Nos. 2577-2580 (4)   8.20 1.15

Stone Sculptures — A581

Designs: a, Head of a Bodhisattva, sandstone, Northern Wei Dynasty (386-534). b, Standing Buddha, limestone, Northern Ch'i Dynasty (550-577). c, Head of a Bodhisattva, sandstone, T'ang Dynasty (618-907). d, Seated Buddha, alabaster, T'ang Dynasty.

1987, Apr. 23
2581   Strip of 4   3.50 2.25
a.-d. A581 $5 any single   .70 .30
No. 2581a shows seven Chinese characters at left; No. 2581c shows five.

Ju-i Scepters, Ch'ing Dynasty
A582

1987, May 7   **Photo.**   **Perf. 14x14½**
2582 A582 $2 Silver and gems   .55 .20
2583 A582 $3 Gold and gems   1.40 .20
2584 A582 $4 Gilded, jade and inlaid gems   2.10 .20
2585 A582 $18 Gilded, inlaid malachite   3.00 .45
Nos. 2582-2585 (4)   7.05 1.05

Feitsui Reservoir Inauguration
A583

1987, June 6   **Litho.**   **Perf. 13½x14**
2586 A583 $2 Reservoir   .45 .20
2587 A583 $18 Hsintien Stream, reservoir   1.75 .45

Flower Arrangements by Huang Yung-ch'uan
A584

Lions Club Intl. 70th Annual Convention, Taipei — A585

1987, June 19   **Perf. 13½**
2588 A584 $2 denom. LL   .25 .20
2589 A584 $5 denom. LL   .70 .20
2590 A584 $8 Flowers in brown vase   .90 .20
2591 A584 $10 denom. UR   1.00 .25
Nos. 2588-2591 (4)   2.85 .85
Compare with designs A483, A559.

1987, July 1
2592 A585 $2 multicolored   .30 .20
2593 A585 $18 multicolored   1.40 .50

Sino-Japanese War, 50th Anniv. — A586

1987, July 7   *Perf. 14x13½*
2594 A586 $1 Battle front .25 .20
2595 A586 $2 Chiang Kai-shek giving speech .40 .20
2596 A586 $5 Public donating funds .45 .20
2597 A586 $6 Troops marching .60 .20
2598 A586 $8 Signing of peace treaty .85 .25
2599 A586 $18 Parade 1.00 .40
Nos. 2594-2599 (6) 3.55 1.45

Wang Yun-wu (1888-1979), Lexicographer A587

1987, Aug. 14   *Perf. 13½*
2600 A587 $2 gray black .55 .20

Memorial Hall Type of 1981

1987, Sept. 24   *Perf. 12½x13½*   Photo.
2601 A468 10c lake .20 .20
2602 A468 30c brt green .20 .20
2603 A468 60c brt blue .20 .20
Nos. 2601-2603 (3) .60 .60

A588

Cultural Renaissance Movement — A589

Scroll, 1543, by Weng Chen-ming (1470-1559), a copy of Chao Po-su's *Red Cliff*. Nos. 2604a-2604e and 2604f-2604j are printed in continuous designs. (Each stamp is numbered from 1 to 10 in Chinese. See illustrations with Nos. 1682-1691 for numerals.)

1987, Sept. 22   Engr.   *Perf. 13½*
2604   Block of 10 13.50 13.50
a.-e. A588 $3 any single 1.00 .25
f.-j. A589 $3 any single 1.00 .25

Folk Costumes — A590

$1.50, Han woman, early Ch'ing Dynasty (1644-1911). $3, Wife of a Ch'ing Dynasty Manchu Bannerman. $7.50, Urban woman wearing Manchu ch'i-p'ao dress, c. 1912. $18, Short jacket over long skirt, c. 1920.

1987, Oct. 2   Litho.
2605 A590 $1.50 multicolored *1.25* .20
2606 A590 $3 multicolored *1.50* .20
2607 A590 $7.50 multicolored *1.75* .20
2608 A590 $18 multicolored *2.10* .50
Nos. 2605-2608 (4) 6.60 1.10

Nos. 2605-2608 have 3 groups of 2 smaller Chinese characters above denomination. Nos. 2660-2663 have 2 groups of 2 and 4 characters.

A591

A592

1987, Nov. 12   *Perf. 13½x14*
2609 A591 $3 Ta Chen Tian temple, Taichung .45 .25
2610 A591 $18 Confucius 1.75 1.10

Intl. Symposium on Confucianism, Taipei, Nov. 12-17.

1987, Dec. 1   *Perf. 12½*
2611 A592 $1.50 multicolored .60 .20
2612 A592 $12 multicolored 2.50 .45
a. Souv. sheet, 2 ea #2611-2612 11.00 2.50

New Year 1988 (Year of the Dragon).

Constitution, 40th Anniv. — A593

1987, Dec. 25   Litho.   *Perf. 13½*
2613 A593 $3 multicolored .20 .20
2614 A593 $16 multi, diff. 1.10 .55

Prevent Hypertension Campaign A594

1988, Jan. 8   *Perf. 12½x13½*
2615 A594 $3 multicolored .45 .20

Fruit Tree Blossoms — A595

Wmk. 323
1988, Feb. 4   Litho.   *Perf. 13½*
2616 A595 $3 Prunus mume 1.50 .20
2617 A595 $7.50 Prunus armeniaca 1.75 .30
2618 A595 $12 Prunus persica 2.25 .50
a. Min. sheet of 3, #2616-2618 22.50 22.50

Wmk. 323
1988, May 5   Litho.   *Perf. 13½*
2619 A595 $3 Paeonia suffruticosa .45 .20
2620 A595 $7.50 Punica granatum 1.40 .30

2621 A595 $12 Nelumbo nucifera 1.60 .50
a. Min. sheet of 3, #2619-2621 13.50 13.50

Wmk. 323
1988, Aug. 9   Litho.   *Perf. 13½*
2622 A595 $3 Impatiens balsamina .40 .20
2623 A595 $7.50 Osmanthus fragrans 1.25 .30
2624 A595 $12 Chrysanthemum morifolium 1.50 .50
a. Min. sheet of 3, #2622-2624 12.00 12.00

Wmk. 323
1988, Nov. 7   Litho.   *Perf. 13½*
2625 A595 $3 Hibiscus mutabilis .40 .20
2626 A595 $7.50 Camellia japonica 1.75 .30
2627 A595 $12 Narcissus tazetta 2.10 .50
a. Min. sheet of 3, #2625-2627 12.50 12.50
Nos. 2616-2627 (12) 16.35 4.00

Tourism Day — A596

Folk art: $3, Modeled dough figurines. $7.50, Blown sweet-malt sugar candy. $16, Sugar paintings.

Perf. 13½x14
1988, Mar. 2   Litho.   Wmk. 323
2628 A596 $3 multicolored .75 .30
2629 A596 $7.50 multicolored 1.50 .45
2630 A596 $16 multicolored 2.75 1.05
Nos. 2628-2630 (3) 5.00 1.80

A597   A598

Perf. 13½x12½
1988, Mar. 29   Engr.   Wmk. 323
2631 A597 $3 brown .40 .20

Hsu Hsi-lin (1873-1907), hero of the revolution.

1988   Litho.   *Perf. 13½*
2632 A598 $1.50 Biotechnology .25 .20
2633 A598 $3 Energy resources .30 .20
2634 A598 $7 Immunization .45 .25
2635 A598 $7.50 Automation .45 .25
2636 A598 $10 Telecommunications .60 .40
2637 A598 $12 Laser technology .65 .40
2638 A598 $16 Micro-optics .95 .65
2639 A598 $16.50 Agricultural research 1.25 .65
Nos. 2632-2639 (8) 4.90 3.00

Industrialization by technological development. Issued: $3, $7.50, $10, $16, Apr. 22; others, May 9.

Police Day A599

Wmk. 323
1988, June 15   Litho.   *Perf. 13½*
2640 A599 $3 Traffic control .25 .20
2641 A599 $12 Rescue operations .80 .40

Amphibians A600

1988, July 8   *Perf. 13½x14*
2642 A600 $1.50 Microhyla butleri 1.10 .20
2643 A600 $3 Rana taipehensis 1.75 .20
2644 A600 $7.50 Microhyla inornata 2.25 .35
2645 A600 $16 Rhacophorus smaragdinus 3.00 .75
Nos. 2642-2645 (4) 8.10 1.50

China Broadcasting Corp. (BBC), 60th Anniv. — A601

Wmk. 323
1988, Aug. 1   Litho.   *Perf. 13½*
2646 A601 $3 multicolored .45 .20

Victory at the Battle of Kinmen, 30th Anniv. A602

Designs: $1.50, Chiang Kai-shek and artillery commander. $3, With troops. $7.50, Cannon. $12, Tanks.

1988, Aug. 23
2647 A602 $1.50 multicolored .40 .20
2648 A602 $3 multicolored .50 .25
2649 A602 $7.50 multicolored .55 .25
2650 A602 $12 multicolored .80 .40
Nos. 2647-2650 (4) 2.25 1.05

Sports Promotion — A603

#2651-2652, Basketball. #2653-2654, Baseball.

1988, Sept. 9
2651 $5 Players .90 .25
2652 $5 Players .90 .25
a. A603 Pair, #2651-2652 1.90 1.10
2653 $5 Batter .90 .25
2654 $5 Catcher .90 .25
a. A603 Pair, #2653-2654 1.90 1.10
Nos. 2651-2654 (4) 3.60 1.00

#2652a, 2654a have continuous designs.

Yangmingshan Natl. Park — A604

1988, Sept. 16
2655 A604 $1.50 Volcanic crater .25 .20
2656 A604 $3 Lake .45 .20
2657 A604 $7.50 Tatun Volcanic Range .85 .25
2658 A604 $16 Dormant volcano 1.60 .55
Nos. 2655-2658 (4) 3.15 1.20

Lofty Mount Lu, a Hanging Scroll, 1467, By Shen Chou (1427-1509) — A605

Painting details: a, UL. b, UR. c, LL. d, LR.

Wmk. 323
1988, Oct. 19   **Litho.**   *Perf. 11½*
2659 A605   Block of 4   7.00 5.00
   a.-d. $5 any single   1.50 .35

Folk Costumes — A606

Designs: $2, Shang Dynasty (1766-1122 B.C.) nobleman. $3, Warring States (403-221 B.C.) ruler. $7.50, Wei-Chin Period (221-420) official. $12, Northern Dynasties (502-581) official.

Perf. 13½x14
1988, Nov. 23   **Litho.**   **Wmk. 323**
2660 A606 $2 multicolored   .50 .20
2661 A606 $3 multicolored   .85 .20
2662 A606 $7.50 multicolored   1.75 .35
2663 A606 $12 multicolored   2.40 .55
   Nos. 2660-2663 (4)   5.50 1.30

Nos. 2721-2724 have groups of 2 and 6 Chinese characters above denomination; Nos. 2660-2663 groups of 2 and 4; #2794-2797 groups of 1 and 5.

A607   A608

1988, Dec. 1   *Perf. 12½*
2664 A607 $2 multicolored   .55 .20
2665 A607 $13 multicolored   4.25 .60
   a.   Souv. sheet, 2 each #2664-2665   14.50 14.50

New Year 1989 (Year of the Snake).

Wmk. 323
1989, Jan. 4   **Litho.**   *Perf. 13½*
2666 A608 $3 black   .55 .20

Tai Ch'uan-hsien (1890-1949), party leader.

Pres. Chiang Ching-kuo (1910-88) A609

1989, Jan. 13
2667 A609 $3 shown   .25 .20
2668 A609 $6 Suffrage   .40 .20
2669 A609 $7.50 Industry   .60 .30
2670 A609 $16 Children   .95 .65
   Nos. 2667-2670 (4)   2.20 1.35

Ni Ying-tien (1884-1910), Revolution Leader — A610

Perf. 13½x12½
1989, Mar. 28   **Engr.**   **Wmk. 323**
2671 A610 $3 black   .45 .20

Stop Smoking A611   Lighthouses A612

Perf. 13½x12½
1989, Apr. 7   **Litho.**   **Wmk. 323**
2672 A611 $3 multicolored   .45 .20

1989-91   *Perf. 13½*
2673 A612 75c Mu Tou Yu   .40 .20
2674 A612 $1 Lu Tao   .40 .20
2675 A612 $2.25 Pen Chia Yu   .40 .20
2676 A612 $3 Pitou Chiao   .60 .20
2677 A612 $4.50 Tungyin Tao   .75 .20
2678 A612 $6 Chilai Pi   .80 .25
2679 A612 $7 Fukwei Chiao   .90 .35
2680 A612 $7.50 Hua Yu   .95 .35
2681 A612 $9 Oluan Pi   1.00 .25
2682 A612 $10 Kaohsiung   1.05 .45
2683 A612 $10.50 Yuweng Tao   1.10 .35
2683A A612 $12 Tungchu Tao   1.60 .55
2683B A612 $13 Yeh Liu   2.00 .45
2683C A612 $15 Tungchi Yu   2.10 .80
2684 A612 $16.50 Chimei Yu   2.40 .75
   Nos. 2673-2684 (15)   16.45 5.55

Issued: $7, $15, 5/19/90; $6, $12, 1/9/91; $2, $3, $7.50, $10, $16.50, 5/20/91; others, 1989.
See Nos. 2811-2823.

1st Natl. Wealth Survey A613

1989, May 18   **Litho.**   *Perf. 13½*
2685 A613 $3 multicolored   .30 .20

Ch'u Ts'u Collection of Poems, 722-481 B.C. — A614

Excerpts: $3, "I once tended nine fields of orchids; Also I had planted a hundred rods of melilotus" (Li Sao). $7.50, "No grief is greater than parting of the living; No joy is more than making new friends" (Chiu Ko, shao ssu ming). $12, "Since my heart is straight and good, Why should I be chagrined at living remote and neglected?" (Chiu Chang, she chiang). $16, "The steed will not gallop itself into servitude; The phoenix has no appetite for slave food." (Chiu Pien).

1989, June 7   **Photo.**   *Perf. 11½x12*
Granite Paper
2686 A614 $3 Man overlooking fields   .45 .20
2687 A614 $7.50 Man, woman on path   1.10 .45
2688 A614 $12 Man holding staff   2.10 .70
2689 A614 $16 Man, stallion, stone gate   2.50 1.00
   Nos. 2686-2689 (4)   6.15 2.35

Compare with types A629, A663. Nos. 2686-2689 have two Chinese characters near denomination. Nos. 2725-2728 have groups of 3 and 4 characters.

Taipei Subway Inauguration — A615

1989, June 27   **Litho.**   *Perf. 13½*
2690 A615 $3 Subway tunnel   .40 .20
2691 A615 $16 Entering underground   1.75 .90

A616

A616a

A616b

Butterflies A616c

$2, *Graphium sarpedon connectens.* $3, *Papilio memnon heronus.* $7.50, *Princeps demoleus libanius.* $9, *Pachliopa aristolochiae interpositas.*

Wmk. 323
1989, July 14   **Litho.**   *Perf. 13½*
2692 A616 $2 multicolored   .45 .25
2693 A616a $3 multicolored   .85 .30
2694 A616b $7.50 multicolored   2.00 .40
2695 A616c $9 multicolored   2.50 .50
   Nos. 2692-2695 (4)   5.80 1.45

Compare with design A627.

Ch'ing Dynasty Teapots from I-Hsing of Kiangsu, 1644-1911 A617

1989, July 28   *Perf. 13½x14*
2696 A617 $2 multicolored   .30 .20
2697 A617 $3 multi, diff.   .90 .20
2698 A617 $12 multi, diff.   2.25 .50
2699 A617 $16 multi, diff.   2.25 .70
   Nos. 2696-2699 (4)   5.70 1.60

For stamps with teapot designs and solid black denominations see Nos. 2760-2764.

Intl. Seminar on Fan Chung-yen (989-1052), Military Leader and Civil Service Reformer — A618

Perf. 14x13½
1989, Sept. 1   **Litho.**   **Wmk. 323**
2700 A618 $12 multicolored   1.25 .55

Autumn Colors on the Ch'iao and Hua Mountains, 14th Cent., by Ch'iao Meng-fu A619

a, Right side of mountain, trees. b, Trees, left side of mountain. c, House, trees. d, shown.

Wmk. 323
1989, Oct. 5   **Litho.**   *Perf. 13½*
2701   Strip of 4   10.00 4.75
   a.-d. A619 $7.50 any single   2.25 .55

Social Welfare A619a

1989, Nov. 3   **Litho.**   *Perf. 13½*
2701E A619a $3 multicolored   .45 .20

Taroko Natl. Park — A620   New Year 1990 (Year of the Horse) — A621

Designs: $2, Marble gorge, Liwu River. $3, Hohuan Mountain. $12, Waterfall, Cirque of Nanhu. $16, Chingshui Cliff.

Wmk. 323

1989, Nov. 28	Litho.	Perf. 13½	
2702	A620	$2 multicolored	.25	.25
2703	A620	$3 multicolored	.45	.35
2704	A620	$12 multicolored	1.00	.55
2705	A620	$16 multicolored	1.25	.70
		Nos. 2702-2705 (4)	2.95	1.85

1989, Dec. 1		Perf. 12½	
2706	A621	$2 multicolored	.45	.20
2707	A621	$13 multicolored	1.75	.80
a.		Souv. sheet, 2 ea #2706-2707	8.00	3.00

Yu Lu — A622

Men Shen, "guardian spirits" (likenesses of legendary beings placed on residence doors at the new year): No. 2708, Yu Lu. No. 2709, Shen Shu. No. 2710, Wei-ch'ih Ching-te. No. 2711, Ch'in Shu-pao.

Wmk. 323

1990, Jan. 19	Litho.	Perf. 13½	
2708	A622	$3 shown	1.25	.20
2709	A622	$3 "$3" at LR	1.25	.20
a.		Pair, #2708-2709	2.50	2.00
2710	A622	$7.50 "$7.50" at LL	3.00	.50
2711	A622	$7.50 "$7.50" at LR	3.00	.50
a.		Pair, #2710-2711	6.00	5.00
		Nos. 2708-2711 (4)	8.50	1.40

Nos. 2709a, 2711a have continuous designs.

A623

Scenery — A624

Designs: $2, Lishan House, Pear Mountain. $18, Tayu Pass, Tayuling, vert.

1990, Feb. 10	Litho.	Perf. 13½	
2712	A623	$2 multicolored	.50	.20
2713	A624	$18 multicolored	2.00	1.00

Labor Insurance System, 40th Anniv. — A625

1990, Mar. 1
2714 A625 $3 multicolored .60 .20

Liquefied Natural Gas A626

$3, Terminal, Yung-an Hsiang of Kaohsiung. $16, Container ship, map, refinery.

1990, Mar. 31	Litho.	Perf. 13½	
2715	A626	$3 multi	.50	.20
2716	A626	$16 multi, vert.	1.50	.65

A627

A627a

A627b

Butterflies A627c

1990, Apr. 20			
2717	A627	$2 Salatura genutia	.45	.20
2718	A627a	$3 Hypolimnas misippus	.45	.20
2719	A627b	$7.50 Pieris canidia	1.25	.35
2720	A627c	$9 Precis almana	1.75	.45
		Nos. 2717-2720 (4)	3.90	1.20

Compare with design A616.

Folk Costumes — A628

$2, Official, Sui & T'ang Dynasties (589-907). $3, Official, T'ang & Sung Dynasties (618-1280). $7.50, Royal guardsman, Chin & Yuan Dynasties (1115-1368). $12, Highest ranking civil official, Ming Dynasty (1368-1644).

1990, May 10	Litho.	Perf. 13½	
2721	A628	$2 multicolored	.35	.20
2722	A628	$3 multicolored	.75	.20
2723	A628	$7.50 multicolored	1.50	.30
2724	A628	$12 multicolored	1.60	.55
		Nos. 2721-2724 (4)	4.20	1.25

See note after No. 2663.

Yueh Fu Classical Poetry A629

Lyrics from Tzu-yeh folk songs, Six Dynasties (222-589): $3, Spring Song at Midnight. $7.50, Summer Song at Midnight. $12,

---

Autumn Song at Midnight. $16, Winter Song at Midnight.

Wmk. 323

1990, June 27	Litho.	Perf. 11½	
		Granite Paper		
2725	A629	$3 shown	.50	.20
2726	A629	$7.50 Couple, river	1.25	.35
2727	A629	$12 Washing clothes, river	3.00	.55
2728	A629	$16 River in winter	4.25	.80
		Nos. 2725-2728 (4)	9.00	1.90

Compare with designs A614 and A663.

Bonsai A630

Designs: $3, Pinus thunbergii parl. $6.50, Ehretia microphylla lamk. $12, Buxus harlandii hance. $16, Celtis sinensis pers.

1990, July 20	Litho.	Perf. 13½	
2729	A630	$3 multicolored	.30	.20
2730	A630	$6.50 multicolored	.70	.30
2731	A630	$12 multicolored	1.00	.70
2732	A630	$16 multicolored	1.50	.80
		Nos. 2729-2732 (4)	3.50	2.00

Snuff Bottles — A631

1990, Aug. 9
2733	A631	$3 Bamboo stem shaped	.40	.20
2734	A631	$6 Peony motif	.75	.30
2735	A631	$9 Amber	1.05	.45
2736	A631	$16 White jade	2.10	.80
		Nos. 2733-2736 (4)	4.30	1.75

Formosan Firecrest A632

1990, Aug. 20	Litho.	Perf. 13½	
2737	A632	$2 shown	.40	.20
2738	A632	$3 Laughing thrush	.40	.20
2739	A632	$7.50 White-eared sibia	1.00	.25
2740	A632	$16 Yellow tit	2.25	.60
		Nos. 2737-2740 (4)	4.05	1.25

Sports — A633

1990, Sept. 8	Litho.	Perf. 13½	
2741	A633	$2 Sprint	.30	.20
2742	A633	$3 Long jump	.30	.20
2743	A633	$7 Pole vault	1.10	.30
2744	A633	$16 High hurdle	1.50	.60
		Nos. 2741-2744 (4)	3.20	1.30

Flying Tigers, 50th Anniv. A634

1990, Sept. 26   Litho.   Perf. 13½
2745 A634 $3 multicolored 1.25 .20

Children's Drawings A635

1990, Oct. 9			
2746	A635	$2 Cat	.30	.20
2747	A635	$3 Peacocks	.30	.20
2748	A635	$7.50 Chickens	.90	.30
2749	A635	$12 Cattle	1.40	.50
		Nos. 2746-2749 (4)	2.90	1.20

National Theater A636

Photo. & Engr.

1990, Oct. 30		Perf. 13½	
2750	A636	$3 shown	.40	.20
2751	A636	$12 Natl. concert hall	1.60	.80

A637   A638

Ancient money.

1990, Nov. 5	Litho.	Perf. 13x13½	
2752	A637	$2 Shell	.40	.20
2753	A637	$3 Oyster	.40	.20
2754	A637	$6.50 Bone	.60	.35
2755	A637	$7.50 Jade	.80	.40
2756	A637	$9 Bronze	.90	.45
		Nos. 2752-2756 (5)	3.10	1.65

1990, Dec. 1		Perf. 12½	
2757	A638	$2 multicolored	.70	.20
2758	A638	$13 multicolored	2.75	.80
a.		Souv. sheet, 2 ea #2757-2758	9.50	2.50

New Year 1991 (Year of the Sheep).

Hu Shih (1891-1962), Educator — A639

Wmk. 323

1990, Dec. 17   Engr.   Perf. 13½
2759 A639 $3 purple .50 .20

Teapots, Natl. Palace Museum A640

Teapots: $2, Blue phoenix, Ming Dynasty. $3, Dragon handle and spout, Ming Dynasty. $9, Blue landscape, flowered top, Ch'ing Dynasty. $12, Rectangular, passion flower motif, Ch'ing Dynasty. $16, Rectangular, flower motif, Ch'ing Dynasty.

1991, Jan. 18   **Photo.**   *Perf. 12*
Granite Paper

2760	A640	$2 yel, blk & blue	.40	.20
2761	A640	$3 brt yel grn & blk	.60	.20
2762	A640	$9 pink & multi	1.00	.60
2763	A640	$12 violet & multi	1.40	.80
2764	A640	$16 lt blue & multi	1.60	1.20
		Nos. 2760-2764 (5)	5.00	3.20

God of Happiness
A641

God of Joy — A642

1991, Feb. 7   **Litho.**   *Perf. 13½*

2765	A641	$3 shown	.60	.20
2766	A641	$3 God of Wealth	.60	.20
2767	A642	$7.50 shown	1.40	.30
2768	A642	$7.50 God of Longevity	1.40	.30
		Nos. 2765-2768 (4)	4.00	1.00

Perf. 13½ Vert.

2765a	A641	$3	1.50	.20
2766a	A641	$3	1.50	.20
2767a	A642	$7.50	1.50	.20
2768a	A642	$7.50	1.50	.20
b.		Bkkt. pane of 8, 2 each #2765a-2768a + label	14.00	

Native Plants
A643

Designs: $2, Petasites formosanus. $3, Heloniopsis acutifolia. $7.50, Disporum shimadai. $9, Viola nagasawai.

1991, Mar. 12   **Litho.**   *Perf. 13½*

2769	A643	$2 multicolored	.40	.20
2770	A643	$3 multicolored	.50	.20
2771	A643	$7.50 multicolored	.80	.30
2772	A643	$9 multicolored	.90	.35

1991, June 12

Designs: $2, Gaultheria itoana. $3, Lysionotus montanus. $7.50, Leontopodium microphyllum. $9, Gentiana flavo-maculata.

2773	A643	$2 multicolored	.30	.20
2774	A643	$3 multicolored	.50	.20
2775	A643	$7.50 multicolored	1.25	.30
2776	A643	$9 multicolored	1.50	.35

1991, Sept. 12

Designs: $3.50, Rosa transmorrisonensis. $5, Impatiens devolii. $9, Impatiens uniflora. $12, Impatiens tayemonii.

2777	A643	$3.50 multicolored	.50	.20
2778	A643	$5 multicolored	.70	.20
2779	A643	$9 multicolored	1.25	.35
2780	A643	$12 multicolored	1.50	.45

1991, Dec. 12

Designs: $3.50, Kalanchoe garambiensis. $5, Pieris taiwanensis. $9, Pleione formosana. $12, Elaeagnus oldhamii.

2781	A643	$3.50 multicolored	.50	.20
2782	A643	$5 multicolored	.70	.20
2783	A643	$9 multicolored	.90	.60
2784	A643	$12 multicolored	1.25	.70
		Nos. 2769-2784 (16)	13.45	5.00

Hsiung Cheng-Chi (1887-1910), Revolutionary
A644

1991, Mar. 28   **Engr.**   *Perf. 13½x12½*
2785   A644 $3 blue   .50   .20

Republic of China, 80th Anniv.
A645

1991, Mar. 28   **Litho.**   *Perf. 13½*

2786	A645	$3 Agriculture	.40	.20
2787	A645	$7.50 Science & technology	.80	.40
2788	A645	$12 Cultural activities	1.40	.70
2789	A645	$16 Transportation	1.60	.90
		Nos. 2786-2789 (4)	4.20	2.20

Children's Toys
A646

Folk Costumes
A647

1991, Apr. 20   **Litho.**   *Perf. 13½*

2790	A646	$3 Bamboo pony	.50	.30
2791	A646	$3 Woven-grass grasshopper	.50	.30
2792	A646	$3 Top	.50	.30
2793	A646	$3 Pinwheels	.50	.30
a.		Souv. sheet of 4, #2790-2793	8.00	6.50
		Nos. 2790-2793 (4)	2.00	1.20

See Nos. 2840-2843. Compare with designs A676, A696.

Perf. 13½ Vert.

2790a	A646	$3	1.25	.30
2791a	A646	$3	1.25	.30
2792a	A646	$3	1.25	.30
2793b	A646	$3	1.25	.30
c.		Bklt. pane, 2 each #2790a-2793b + label	10.00	
		Nos. 2790a-2793b (4)	5.00	1.20

1991, June 29   **Litho.**   *Perf. 13½*

Ch'ing Dynasty (1644-1911): $2, Winter court hat, Mang robe. $3, Summer court hat, surcoat. $7.50, Winter overcoat. $12, Common hat, traveling robe.

2794	A647	$2 multicolored	.50	.20
2795	A647	$3 multicolored	.65	.20
2796	A647	$7.50 multicolored	1.60	.30
2797	A647	$12 multicolored	2.25	.45
		Nos. 2794-2797 (4)	5.00	1.15

See note after No. 2663.
Nos. 2794-2797 have groups of one and five Chinese characters.

Traffic Safety Year
A648

1991, July 17   **Litho.**   *Perf. 13½*

2798	A648	$3 shown	.30	.20
2799	A648	$7.50 Don't drink & drive	.90	.35

Cloisonne Enamel Lions, Ch'ing Dynasty (1644-1911)
A649   A649a

1991, July 20   **Litho.**   *Perf. 12½*

2800	A649	yel grn & multi	.70	.25
2801	A649a	violet & multi	2.75	.75
		Nos. 2800-2801 (2)	3.45	1.00

#2800 paid basic domestic rate, #2801 paid basic express mail rate on date of issue.

Fruits — A650

Birds — A651

1991, Aug. 10   **Litho.**   *Perf. 14x13½*

2802	A650	$3 Strawberry	.40	.20
2803	A650	$7.50 Grapes	.70	.50
2804	A650	$9 Mango	.90	.60
2805	A650	$16 Sugar apple	1.50	.90
		Nos. 2802-2805 (4)	3.50	2.20

1991, Aug. 24   *Perf. 13½*

Designs: a, Myiophoneus insularis. b, Cinclus pallasii. c, Aix galericulata. d, Nycticorax nycticorax. e, Egretta garzetta. f, Rhyacornis fuliginosus. g, Enicurus scouleri. h, Motacilla cinerea. i, Alcedo atthis. j, Motacilla alba.

2806		Block of 10	7.00	4.00
a.-j.		A651 $5 any single	.50	.30

Outdoor Activities
A652

Wmk. 323
1991, Sept. 27   **Litho.**   *Perf. 13½*

2807	A652	$2 Rock climbing	.30	.20
2808	A652	$3 Fishing	.40	.20
2809	A652	$7.50 Bird watching	.85	.35
2810	A652	$10 Playing in water	1.25	.50
		Nos. 2807-2810 (4)	2.80	1.25

Intl. Federation of Camping and Caravaning, 1991 Rally.

Lighthouse Type of 1989
Inscription Panel in Blue

1991-92   *Perf. 13½*

2811	A612	50c like #2683C	.30	.20
2812	A612	$1 like #2674	.40	.20
2813	A612	$3.50 like #2678	.50	.20
2814	A612	$5 like #2679	.60	.20
a.		Booklet pane of 10	7.00	
2815	A612	$7 like #2676	.60	.25
2816	A612	$9 like #2681	.90	.35
2817	A612	$10 like #2682	1.10	.40
2818	A612	$12 like #2683A	1.25	.50
a.		$12 Bklt. pane of 5 + label	7.00	
2819	A612	$13 like #2675	1.25	.50
2820	A612	$19 like #2680	1.90	.80
2821	A612	$20 like #2683B	2.00	.80
2822	A612	$26 like #2683	2.10	1.10
2823	A612	$28 like #2684	2.10	1.10
		Nos. 2811-2823 (13)	15.00	6.60

Issued: 50c, $3.50, $5, $12, 10/2; #2818a, 9/26/92; $1, $19, $20, 3/2/92; $26, $28, 5/20/92; $7, $9, $10, $13, 8/21/92.

Peacocks by Lan Shih-ning (Giuseppe Castiglione, 1688-1768)
A653

$20, Peacock spreading tail feathers.

Perf. 12x11½
1991, Oct. 30   **Photo.**   **Unwmk.**
Granite Paper

2826	A653	$5 multicolored	.80	.50
2827	A653	$20 multicolored	3.00	1.00
a.		Souvenir sheet of 1	6.00	5.00

New Year 1992 (Year of the Monkey) — A654

Wmk. 323
1991, Nov. 30   **Litho.**   *Perf. 12½*

2828	A654	$3.50 orange & multi	.40	.20
2829	A654	$13 tan & multi	1.50	.60
a.		Souv. sheet, 2 ea #2828-2829	6.00	2.00

Chinese Books
A655

Wmk. 323
1992, Jan. 17   **Litho.**   *Perf. 13½*

2830	A655	$3.50 Scroll	.30	.20
2831	A655	$5 Fold bindings	.50	.20
2832	A655	$9 Butterfly bindings	.90	.35
2833	A655	$15 String bindings	1.50	.65
		Nos. 2830-2833 (4)	3.20	1.40

Good Fortune and Satisfaction
A656

Five Blessings Upon the House — A657

Nienhwa paintings: No. 2835, Peace in the Wake of Firecrackers. No. 2837, An Abundance for Every Year.

1992, Jan. 27   **Litho.**   *Perf. 13½*

2834	A656	$5 multicolored	.40	.25
2835	A656	$5 multicolored	.40	.25
2836	A657	$12 multicolored	1.10	.60
2837	A657	$12 multicolored	1.10	.60
a.		Bklt. pane, 2 each #2834-2837 + label	10.00	
		Nos. 2834-2837 (4)	3.00	1.70

Lunar New Year.

A658

A659

Lunar New Year: a, like #2664. b, like #2611. c, like #2565. d, like #2493. e, like #2442. f, like #2390. g, like #2346. h, like #2273. i, like #2217. j, like #2828. k, like #2757. l, like #2706.

Wmk. 323

1992, Feb. 18   Litho.   Perf. 12½

2838   A658 $5 Block of 12, #a.-l.,
                    ver & multi   6.50   3.00
   m.   Sheet of 12, #2838a-2838 l   6.75   3.25

1992, Mar. 12   Perf. 13½

Trees: a, Chamaecyparis formosensis. b, Chamaecyparis taiwanensis. c, Calocedrus formosana. d, Cunninghamia konishii. e. Taiwania crypto- merioides.

2839   A659 $5 Strip of 5, #a.-e.   3.50   1.50

Children's Toys Type of 1991

1992, Apr. 29   Litho.   Perf. 13½

2840   A646 $5 Walking on iron
                    pots   .70   .25
2841   A646 $5 Chopstick gun   .70   .25
2842   A646 $5 Hoop rolling   .70   .25
2843   A646 $5 Grass fighting   .70   .25
   a.   Sheet of 4, #2840-2843   5.75   5.75
   b.   As "a," imperf. (simulated
              perfs), red inscription in
              sheet margin   11.50 11.50
   c.   Bklt. pane, 2 each #2840-
              2843 + label   5.75
          Nos. 2840-2843 (4)   2.80   1.00

          Issue date: No. 2843b, May 15.

A660

A661

Mother and son in: $3.50, Spring. $5, Summer. $9, Autumn. $10, Winter.

Wmk. 323

1992, May 9   Litho.   Perf. 13½

2844   A660 $3.50 multicolored   .35   .20
2845   A660 $5 multicolored   .70   .20
2846   A660 $9 multicolored   1.25   .40
2847   A660 $10 multicolored   1.40   .45
          Nos. 2844-2847 (4)   3.70   1.25

          Parent-child relationships.

Wmk. 323

1992, June 25   Litho.   Perf. 13½

Glassware Decorated with Enamel — Vases: $3.50, Faceted, decorated with bats and longevity characters. $5, Double-lobed, with children at play. $7, Flowered. $17, Tutoring scene.

Background colors

2848   A661 $3.50 pink   .30   .20
2849   A661 $5 green   .45   .20
2850   A661 $7 bister   .70   .30
2851   A661 $17 blue   2.00   .70
          Nos. 2848-2851 (4)   3.45   1.40

Stone Lion of Lugouqiao A662

Various stone lions.

Wmk. 323

1992, July 7   Engr.   Perf. 13½

2852   A662 $5 olive grn & pur   .60   .20
2853   A662 $5 blue & brown   .60   .20
2854   A662 $12 org & olive grn   1.40   .50
2855   A662 $12 purple & black   1.40   .50
          Nos. 2852-2855 (4)   4.00   1.40

     Compare with designs A614, A629, A663.

Ku Shih Classical Poetry — A663

Excerpts: $3.50, "Flesh and body are as closely linked as leaves to a tree." $5, "Once a man and woman get married, conjugal love will last forever without doubt." $9, "Man takes pains to uphold virtue." $15, "Tartar horses lean toward the northern wind."

1992, Aug. 8   Litho.

2856   A663 $3.50 Children playing
                    near tree   .30   .20
2857   A663 $5 Man & woman   .70   .20
2858   A663 $9 Couple near
                    stream   1.25   .35
2859   A663 $15 Horse, tree   1.75   .60
          Nos. 2856-2859 (4)   4.00   1.35

Life in the Countryside A664

Scenes of temple fair: a, Two women, man beating drum, crowd. b, Vendor with basket. c, People playing musical instruments. d, Man with food cart. e, Women with umbrella, basket.

Wmk. 323

1992, Sept. 22   Litho.   Perf. 11½

2860   A664 $5 Strip of 5, #a.-e.   5.00   3.50

Silk Tapestries A665

Ming Dynasty Silk Tapestry Drawing on Life: $5, Two Birds Perched on a Red Camellia Branch. $12, Two Birds Playing on a Peach Branch.

1992, Oct. 9   Litho.   Perf. 11½
Granite Paper

2861   A665 $5 multicolored   .70   .20
2862   A665 $12 multicolored   1.90   .60
   a.   Sheet of 2, #2861-2862   3.00   1.00

Chinese Opera A666

Actors, props: $3.50, Nin Hsiang-ju's carting to a party from "The General and Premier." $5, Hsao En rowing a boat from "The Lucky Pearl." $9, Wang Chao-chun making peace with the frontier from "Chao-chun Serves as an Envoy." $12, Scene with red sedan chair from "Escort to the Wedding."

Wmk. 323

1992, Oct. 21   Litho.   Perf. 13½

2863   A666 $3.50 multicolored   .30   .20
2864   A666 $5 multicolored   .65   .20
2865   A666 $9 multicolored   1.05   .40
2866   A666 $12 multicolored   1.00   .55
          Nos. 2863-2866 (4)   3.00   1.35

Alishan Forest Railway — A667

1992, Nov. 5   Perf. 11½

2867   A667 $5 Steam engine   .70   .20
2868   A667 $15 Diesel engine   1.50   .65

Endangered Mammals of Taiwan A668

Designs: a, Lutra lutra chinensis. b, Pteropus dasymallus formosus. c, Neofelis nebulosa brachyurus. d, Selenarctos thibetanus formosanus.

Perf. 11½x12

1992, Nov. 25   Photo.   Unwmk.
Granite Paper

2869   A668 $5 Block of 4, #a.-d.   3.50   1.50

New Year 1993 (Year of the Rooster) — A669

Design: $13, Rooster facing left.

Wmk. 323

1992, Dec. 1   Litho.   Perf. 12½

2870   A669 $3.50 red & multi   .50   .20
   a.   Perf. 13½ vert.   .50   .20
2871   A669 $13 pur & multi   1.25   .45
   a.   Souv. sheet, 2 ea #2870-
              2871   4.00   4.00
   b.   As "a" with added inscription
              in border   4.00   4.00
   c.   Bklt. pane, 5 ea #2870-2871   9.25
   d.   Perf. 13½ vert.   1.25   .50
   e.   Booklet pane, 6 each #2870a,
              2871d + label   10.75

Inscription on No. 2871b reads "Philippine Stamp Exhibition 1992-Taipei" in English and Chinese.

Johann Adam Schall von Bell (1592-1666), Astronomer and Missionary — A670

1992 Dec. 10   Perf. 11½

2872   A670 $5 multicolored   1.00   .20

Traditional Nienhwas of Window Frames — A671

Wmk. 323

1993, Jan. 7   Litho.   Perf. 11½
Background Color

2873   A671 $5 brt green   .25   .20
2874   A671 $5 red lilac   .25   .20
2875   A671 $12 yellow   .65   .40
2876   A671 $12 red   .65   .40
          Nos. 2873-2876 (4)   1.80   1.20

          Lunar New Year.

Perf. 13½ Vert.

2873a   A671 $5   1.00   .45
2874a   A671 $5   1.00   .45
2875a   A671 $12   1.00   .45
2876a   A671 $12   1.00   .45
   b.   Booklet pane, 2 each
              #2873a-2876a + label   9.00

          Nos. 2873a-2876a are 29x43mm.

Traditional Crafts A672

1993, Jan. 16

2877   A672 $3.50 Clip & paste
                    moldings   .30   .20
2878   A672 $5 Lanterns   .40   .20
2879   A672 $9 Pottery jars   .80   .40
2880   A672 $15 Oil paper um-
                    brella   1.25   .65
          Nos. 2877-2880 (4)   2.75   1.45

Chinese Creation Story — A673

Designs: $3.50, Pan Gu's creation of the universe, vert. $5, Pan Gu transmitted himself into all creatures. $9, Nu Wa created human beings with pestled earth. $19, Nu Wa mended sky with smelted stone, vert.

1993, Feb. 6   Perf. 12x11½, 11½x12

2881   A673 $3.50 multicolored   .30   .20
2882   A673 $5 multicolored   .50   .20
2883   A673 $9 multicolored   .90   .65
2884   A673 $19 multicolored   1.75   1.40
          Nos. 2881-2884 (4)   3.45   2.45

Lucky Animals
A674

Water Plants
A675

Wmk. 323

1993, Mar. 2   Litho.   Perf. 13½
2885	A674	$3.50 Mandarin duck	.30	.20
2886	A674	$5 Chinese uni-		
		corn	.45	.25
2887	A674	$10 Deer	.90	.50
2888	A674	$15 Crane	1.40	1.25
		Nos. 2885-2888 (4)	3.05	2.20

See Nos. 2920-2923.

1993, Mar. 12   Perf. 11½
2889	A675	$5 Nymphaea x		
		hybrida	.60	.20
2890	A675	$9 Nuphar shimadai	1.00	.40
2891	A675	$12 Eichhornia cras-		
		sipes	1.25	.50
		Nos. 2889-2891 (3)	2.85	1.10

A676

1993   Litho.   Wmk. 323   Perf. 11½
2892	A676	$5 Sandbag tossing	.50	.30
2893	A676	$5 Bamboo dragonfly		
		twisting	.50	.30
2894	A676	$5 Rubber band skip-		
		ping	.50	.30
2895	A676	$5 Waist-strength du-		
		eling	.50	.30
a.		Souv. sheet, #2892-2895	3.25	3.25
b.		As "a," with green & black in-		
		scriptions in border	3.25	3.25
c.		As "a," with red inscription in		
		border	3.25	3.25
		Nos. 2892-2895 (4)	2.00	1.20

Inscriptions on No. 2895b read "AUSTRA-
LIAN STAMP EXHIBITION 1993-TAIPEI" in
Chinese and English.
Inscription on No. 2895c reads "Chinese
Stamp Exhibition-Thailand" in Chinese.
Nos. 2895b-2895c each have perforations
extending into the margin at top (#2895c) or
bottom (#2895b).
Issue dates: Nos. 2892-2895, 2895a, Apr.
20; No. 2895b, Apr. 23; No. 2895c, Apr. 30.

Perf. 13½ Vert.
2892a	A676	$5	1.00	.30
2893a	A676	$5	1.00	.30
2894a	A676	$5	1.00	.30
2895d	A676	$5	1.00	.30
e.		Bklt. pane, 2 each #2892a-		
		2894a, 2895d + label	8.50	

A677

Yangtze
River
A678

Designs: No. 2896, Source on Ching-Kang-
Chang Plateau. No. 2897, Abrupt bend, Chin-
sha River. No. 2898, Narrow waterway, Roar-
ing Tiger Gorge, Chinsha River. No. 2899,
Sheer cliffs, Chuntang Gorge. $9, Three Small
Gorges (Dragon Gate, Pawu, and Titsui).

Perf. 13x13½

1993, May 15   Litho.   Wmk. 323
2896	A677	$3.50 shown	.30	.20
2897	A677	$3.50 multicolored	.30	.20
2898	A678	$5 shown	.55	.20

2899	A677	$5 multicolored	.55	.20
2900	A677	$9 multicolored	1.05	.40
		Nos. 2896-2900 (5)	2.75	1.20

Environmental Protection
A679   A680

Children's paintings: $5, No More Noise Pol-
lution, by Yen Chao-min. $17, Clothing My
Hometown with Green, by Hu Hui-chun.

Perf. 12½x13½, 13½x12½

1993, June 5
2901	A679	$5 multicolored	.50	.30
2902	A680	$17 multicolored	1.50	1.25

Ch'eng-hua
Porcelain, Natl.
Palace Museum
A681

Cups decorated in tou-ts'ai: $3.50, Human
figures. $5, Chickens. $7, Flowers and fruits.
$9, Dragon.

1993, June 30   Perf. 12
2903	A681	$3.50 multicolored	.30	.20
2904	A681	$5 multicolored	.55	.30
2905	A681	$7 multicolored	.75	.50
2906	A681	$9 multicolored	.90	.80
		Nos. 2903-2906 (4)	2.50	1.80

Vocational
Training
A682

Wmk. 323

1993, July 24   Litho.   Perf. 12½
2907	A682	$3.50 Graphic artist	.30	.20
2908	A682	$5 Computer oper-		
		ator	.40	.30
2909	A682	$9 Carpenter	.75	.60
2910	A682	$12 Welder	1.05	.90
		Nos. 2907-2910 (4)	2.50	2.00

Parent-Child
Relationship
A683

Silhouettes: $3.50, Adult carrying child on
shoulders. $5, Father playing flute for daugh-
ter. $9, Father teaching daughter. $10, Father,
adult son enjoying wildlife.

Wmk. 323

1993, Aug. 4   Litho.   Perf. 11½
Background Color
2911	A683	$3.50 tan	.30	.20
2912	A683	$5 green	.45	.30
2913	A683	$9 lilac	.95	.70
2914	A683	$10 red brown	1.10	.80
		Nos. 2911-2914 (4)	2.80	2.00

Souvenir Sheet

Taipei '93, Asian Intl. Philatelic
Exhibition — A684

Enjoying Antiques, by Tu Chin, 15th cent: a,
Man carrying stick. b, Man selecting antiques
from table. c, Man seated in chair. d, Two people at table.

Perf. 12x11½

1993, Aug. 14   Photo.   Unwmk.
Granite Paper
2915	A684	$5 Sheet of 4, #a.-d.	3.75	3.00

Persimmon   Loquat
A685   A686

1993, Sept. 10   Litho.   Perf. 12½
2916	A685	$5 shown	.50	.30
2917	A685	$5 Peach	.50	.30
2918	A686	$12 shown	1.25	.90
2919	A686	$12 Papaya	1.25	.90
		Nos. 2916-2919 (4)	3.50	2.40

Lucky Animals Type of 1993

Wmk. 323

1993, Sept. 29   Litho.   Perf. 13½
2920	A674	$1 Blue dragon	.30	.30
2921	A674	$2.50 White tiger	.30	.30
2922	A674	$9 Linnet	.85	.50
2923	A674	$19 Black tortoise	1.75	1.10
		Nos. 2920-2923 (4)	3.20	2.20

Taiwan Area   Stone
Games,   Lions — A688
Taoyuan — A687

Designs: a, Taekwondo. b, Pommel horse.

Wmk. 323

1993, Oct. 20   Litho.   Perf. 12½
2924	A687	$5 Pair, #a.-b.	1.25	.80

1993, Oct. 30

Stone lions from: $3.50, Taipei New Park.
$5, Hsinchu City Council. $9, Hsinchu City
God Temple. $12, Fort Providentia, Tainan.

2925	A688	$3.50 multicolored	.30	.30
2926	A688	$5 multicolored	.45	.30
2927	A688	$9 multicolored	.90	.55
2928	A688	$12 multicolored	1.25	.75
		Nos. 2925-2928 (4)	2.90	1.90

Syrmaticus
Mikado
A689

Designs: a, Hatchling. b, Mother with chicks.
c, Immature female, male. d, Adult female,
male (profile, showing plumage).

Perf. 11½

1993, Nov. 17   Photo.   Unwmk.
Granite Paper
2929	A689	$5 Strip of 4, #a.-d.	2.75	2.00

New Year 1994
(Year of the
Dog) — A690

Design: $13, Dog facing left.

Wmk. 323

1993, Dec. 1   Litho.   Perf. 12½
2930	A690	$3.50 red & multi	.30	.30
a.		Perf. 13½ vert.	.30	.30
b.		As "a," bklt. pane of 12 + label	2.75	
2931	A690	$13 green & multi	1.40	.70
a.		Souv. sheet, 2 ea #2930-2931	1.75	1.00
b.		As "a," overprinted in red	1.75	1.00

No. 2931b is inscribed in Chinese for Kaohsiung Kuo-kuang Stamp Exhibition-1993, and
has additional perforations extending into top
and bottom margins.

Asian
Vegetable
Research and
Development
Center, 20th
Anniv. — A691

1993, Dec. 7
2932	A691	$5 shown	.40	.30
2933	A691	$13 Researchers in		
		field	1.40	.90

Formation of
Constitutional
Court — A692

Wmk. 323

1994, Jan. 11   Litho.   Perf. 12½
2934	A692	$5 multicolored	.50	.30

Paper   Flowers — A694
Making — A693

Designs: No. 2935, Cutting bamboo. No.
2936, Cooking bamboo. No. 2937, Pouring
syrup into wooden panel. No. 2938, Stacking
panel. No. 2939, Drying paper.

1994, Jan. 24   Perf. 12x12½
2935	A693	$3.50 multicolored	.30	.20
2936	A693	$3.50 multicolored	.30	.20
2937	A693	$5 multicolored	.60	.20
2938	A693	$5 multicolored	.60	.20
2939	A693	$12 multicolored	1.25	.80
		Nos. 2935-2939 (5)	3.05	1.60

See Nos. 2993-2997, 3071-3075, 3098-
3102, 3174-3177.

1994, Feb. 17   Perf. 12½
2940	A694	$5 Clivia miniata	.40	.30
2941	A694	$12 Cymbidium		
		sinense	1.25	.80
2942	A694	$19 Primula mala-		
		coides	1.90	1.40
		Nos. 2940-2942 (3)	3.55	2.50

Kinmen Wind
Lion
Lords — A695

Various Wind Lion Lords.

1994, Mar. 18	Litho.	Perf. 12½
2943 A695 $5 green & multi	.50	.30
2944 A695 $9 yellow & multi	.80	.50
2945 A695 $12 org yel & multi	1.25	.70
2946 A695 $17 blue & multi	1.50	1.00
Nos. 2943-2946 (4)	4.05	2.50

Children at Play — A696

#2947, Playing with paper boat. #2948, Fighting with water gun. #2949, Throwing paper airplane. #2950, Playing "train" with rope.

Wmk. 323

1994, Apr. 2	Litho.	Perf. 12½
2947 A696 $5 multicolored	.50	.30
2948 A696 $5 multicolored	.50	.30
2949 A696 $5 multicolored	.50	.30
2950 A696 $5 multicolored	.50	.30
a. Souv. sheet, #2947-2950	2.75	1.50
Nos. 2947-2950 (4)	2.00	1.20

Perf. 13½ Vert.

2947a A696 $5		.50	.30
2948a A696 $5		.50	.30
2949a A696 $5		.50	.30
2950b A696 $5		.50	.30
c. Bklt. pane, 2 ea #2947a-2949a, 2950b + label		4.50	1.50
Nos. 2947a-2950b (4)		2.00	1.20

A697   A698

Life in the countryside: $5, Playing chess. $10, Playing musical instruments. $12, Telling stories. $19, Drinking tea.

Wmk. 323

1994, Apr. 25	Litho.	Perf. 12½
2951 A697 $5 multicolored	.40	.30
2952 A697 $10 multicolored	1.00	.60
2953 A697 $12 multicolored	1.25	.85
2954 A697 $19 multicolored	1.90	1.25
Nos. 2951-2954 (4)	4.55	3.00

1994, May 7

Mother, baby birds: $5, Malay bittern. $7, Little tern, horiz. $10, Common noddy, horiz. $12, Muller's barbet.

2955 A698 $5 multicolored	.40	.35
2956 A698 $7 multicolored	.70	.40
2957 A698 $10 multicolored	1.10	.70
2958 A698 $12 multicolored	1.25	.75
Nos. 2955-2958 (4)	3.45	2.20

A699   A700

Protection of Intellectual Property Rights: $5, Palm-shaped book. $15, Human head, computer disk.

Wmk. 323

1994, May 28	Litho.	Perf. 12½
2959 A699 $5 multicolored	.60	.30
2960 A699 $15 multicolored	1.60	.90

1994, June 11

Designs: $5, Care for Lost Children. $17, Care for the aged.

2961 A700 $5 multicolored	.30	.25
2962 A700 $17 multicolored	1.10	.75

Intl. Olympic Committee, Cent. — A701

1994, June 23

2963 A701 $5 shown	.50	.30
2964 A701 $15 Sporting events	1.50	.90

A702

A703

Shei-pa Natl. Park: $5, Tapachienshan. $7, Shei-san Landslide Scar. $10, Holy Ridge. $17, Shiah-tsuei Lake.

Wmk. 323

1994, July 1	Litho.	Perf. 12½
2965 A702 $5 multicolored	.55	.30
2966 A702 $7 multicolored	.70	.45
2967 A702 $10 multicolored	1.10	.60
2968 A702 $17 multicolored	1.75	1.10
Nos. 2965-2968 (4)	4.10	2.45

1994, July 30   **Perf. 11½x12**

$5, Portrait of Chien Mu (b. 1895), educator.

2969 A703 $5 multicolored	.50	.30

Intl. Year of the Family A704

$5, Rainbow, window. $15, Globe, house.

1994, Aug. 25		Perf. 11½
2970 A704 $5 multicolored	.50	.30
2971 A704 $15 yel & multi	1.50	.90

Invention Myths — A705

Designs: $5, Sueirenjy digging wood to obtain fire. $10, Fushijy drawing Pa-Kua. $12, Shennungjy making agricultural tools. $15, Tsang-jier creating written characters.

1994, Sept. 17	Photo.	Perf. 11½
	Granite Paper	
2972 A705 $5 multicolored	.50	.30
2973 A705 $10 multicolored	1.05	.65
2974 A705 $12 multicolored	1.25	.90
2975 A705 $15 multicolored	1.60	1.05
Nos. 2972-2975 (4)	4.40	2.90

A706

A707

Design: $5, Dr. Lin Yutang, linguist, writer, 100th birthday.

Wmk. 323

1994, Oct. 8	Litho.	Perf. 12½
2976 A706 $5 multicolored	.50	.30

1994, Oct. 17

$5, Cheng Ho's ship. $17, Chart, ship, Cheng Ho.

2977 A707 $5 multicolored	.50	.30
2978 A707 $17 multicolored	1.50	.90

World Trade Week.

Sun Yat-sen, Founding of Kuomintang, Cent. — A708

Design: $19, Democratic elections, factories, economic development.

Wmk. 323

1994, Nov. 24	Litho.	Perf. 12½
2979 A708 $5 multicolored	.50	.30
2980 A708 $19 multicolored	1.75	1.10

A709   A710

1994, Nov. 29

2981 A709 $3.50 Facing right	.40	.30
a. Perf. 13½ vert.	.40	.30
b. As "a," booklet pane of 6	2.50	
Complete booklet, 2 #2981b + label	5.00	
2982 A709 $13 Facing left	1.40	.90
a. Souv. sheet, 2 ea #2981-2982	3.50	2.40

New Year 1995 (Year of the Boar).

1994, Dec. 24	Litho.	Perf. 12½
2983 A710 $5 Portrait	.50	.30
2984 A710 $15 Greeting farm family	1.50	.90

Pres. Yen Chia-kan, 1st death anniv.

Traditional Architecture A711

Roof lines: #2985, Horse's back (shown). #2986, Swallow's tail. $12, Talisman (stove & bowl). $19, Cylinder-shaped brick.

1995, Jan. 10	Litho.	Perf. 12½x12
		Wmk. 323
2985 A711 $5 multicolored	.45	.30
2986 A711 $5 multicolored	.45	.30
2987 A711 $12 multicolored	1.25	.75
2988 A711 $19 multicolored	1.90	1.25
Nos. 2985-2988 (4)	4.05	2.60

See Nos. 3079-3082, 3113-3116, 3187-3190, 3235-3238.

Ancient Chinese Engravings — A712

Various floral designs.

1995, Jan. 24		Perf. 13½
	Denomination in Black	
2989 A712 $3.50 multicolored	.30	.20
2990 A712 $5 multicolored	.60	.30
2991 A712 $19 multicolored	1.75	1.25
2992 A712 $26 multicolored	2.75	1.75
Nos. 2989-2992 (4)	5.40	3.50

See Nos. 3018-3021, 3044-3047, 3076-3078, 3178-3181, 3221-3226, 3254-3256, 3299-3300.

Ancient Skills Type of 1994

Methods of irrigation: No. 2993, Water wheel. No. 2994, Gear-driven bucket lift. $5, Pedal-powered hoist. $12, Hand-cranked hoist. $13, Using pole with counter-weight to raise bucket.

	Perf. 12x11½	
1994, Feb. 14	Litho.	Wmk. 323
2993 A693 $3.50 multicolored	.30	.20
2994 A693 $3.50 multicolored	.30	.20
2995 A693 $5 multicolored	.50	.30
2996 A693 $12 multicolored	1.25	.85
2997 A693 $13 multicolored	1.40	.95
Nos. 2993-2997 (5)	3.75	2.50

Beauties on an Outing, by Lee Gong-lin — A713

a, Two riders. b, Rider on black horse, woman with child on horse. c, Three riders. d, One rider.

	Unwmk.	
1995, Mar. 3	Photo.	Perf. 12
	Granite Paper	
2998 A713 $9 Strip of 4, #a.-d.	4.00	2.50
e. Souv. sheet #2998b-2998c	2.00	1.25

No. 2998 is a continuous design.

Natl. Health Insurance Plan — A714

Flowers — A715

	Perf. 11½x12½	
1995, Mar. 1	Litho.	Wmk. 323
2999 A714 $12 multicolored	1.25	.80

1995, Mar. 20	Litho.	Perf. 12½
3000 A715 $5 Lilium speciosum	.40	.30
3001 A715 $12 Haemanthus multiflorus	.90	.75
3002 A715 $19 Hyacinthus orientalis	1.90	1.25
Nos. 3000-3002 (3)	3.20	2.30

Chinese Calligraphy A716

Cold Food Observance, poem by Su Shih, red inscriptions at: a, Lower left. b, Middle. c, Upper right. d, Right half of design.

1995, Apr. 6   *Perf. 13½*
3003		Strip of 4	4.00	2.50
a.-d.	A716	$5 any single	.50	.30

Paintings by Tsou I Kuei's — A717

1995, May 5   **Photo.**   *Die Cut*
Self-Adhesive
3004	A717	$5 Red peony	.60	.25
3005	A717	$5 Pink peony	.60	.25
a.		Bkt. pane, 9 ea #3004-3005	10.75	

By its nature, No. 3005a is a complete booklet. The peelable backing serves as a booklet cover.

Campaign Against Illegal Drugs — A718

Wmk. 323
1995, June 1   **Litho.**   *Perf. 12½*
3006	A718	$5 shown	.50	.30
3007	A718	$15 Arm, hypodermic needle	1.25	.90

Natl. Taiwan University Hospital, Cent. — A719

Designs: $5, Medical treatment, old hospital. $19, Medical research, new hospital.

1995, June 20
3008	A719	$5 multicolored	.70	.30
3009	A719	$19 multicolored	1.75	1.25

East Coast Scenes A720

Designs: No. 3010, Green hills above Chichi Bay. No. 3011, Rocky promontory, Shihyuesan. $12, Hsiaoyehlieu. $15, Changhong Bridge.

Wmk. 323
1995, July 1   **Litho.**   *Perf. 12½*
3010	A720	$5 multicolored	.50	.30
3011	A720	$5 multicolored	.50	.30
3012	A720	$12 multicolored	1.25	.80
3013	A720	$15 multicolored	1.75	1.10
		Nos. 3010-3013 (4)	4.00	2.50

Oncorhynchus Masou Formosanus A721

Designs: $5, Mating. $7, Female digging a spot to lay eggs. $10, Hatching of fry. $17, Fry swimming in river.

Perf. 14x14½
1995, July 27   **Litho.**   **Unwmk.**
3014	A721	$5 multicolored	.50	.30
3015	A721	$7 multicolored	.75	.50
3016	A721	$10 multicolored	.95	.75
3017	A721	$17 multicolored	1.75	1.25
		Nos. 3014-3017 (4)	3.95	2.80

Ancient Chinese Engraving Type
Various pictures of birds on tree branches.

Wmk. 323
1995, Aug. 18   **Litho.**   *Perf. 13½*
Denomination in Black
3018	A712	$2.50 multicolored	.35	.35
3019	A712	$7 multicolored	.80	.45
3020	A712	$13 multicolored	1.40	1.00
3021	A712	$28 multicolored	3.50	2.00
		Nos. 3018-3021 (4)	6.05	3.80

Marine Life — A722

Louis Pasteur (1822-95) — A723

#3022, Tubastraea aurea. #3023, Chromodoris elizabethina. $5, Spirobranchus gigateus. $17, Himerometra magnipinna.

Wmk. 323
1995, Sept. 7   **Litho.**   *Perf. 12½*
3022	A722	$3.50 multicolored	.35	.30
3023	A722	$3.50 multicolored	.35	.30
3024	A722	$5 multicolored	.65	.40
3025	A722	$17 multicolored	1.90	1.00
		Nos. 3022-3025 (4)	3.25	2.00

1995, Sept. 20
3026	A723	$17 multicolored	2.00	1.00

Natl. Palace Museum, 70th Anniv. A724

Designs: No. 3027, Painting, "Strange Peaks and Myriad Trees." No. 3028, Greenish blue porcelain vase, vert. $5, Bronze X Fu-K'uei Ting vessel, vert. $26, Calligraphy of quatrain in seven-character verse, "The Fragrance of Flowers."

Perf. 12x11½, 11½x12
1995, Oct. 9   **Photo.**   **Unwmk.**
3027	A724	$3.50 multicolored	.30	.20
3028	A724	$3.50 multicolored	.30	.20
3029	A724	$5 multicolored	.50	.20
3030	A724	$26 multicolored	2.40	1.50
		Nos. 3027-3030 (4)	3.50	2.10

A725   A726

End of World War II, 50th Anniv.: $5, Chinese soldiers in battle. $19, Flag, outline map of Taiwan, presidential mansion.

Perf. 11½x12
1995, Oct. 24   **Litho.**   **Wmk. 323**
3031	A725	$5 multicolored	.60	.20
3032	A725	$19 multicolored	1.90	.65
a.		Souvenir sheet, #3031-3032	2.50	.90

Wmk. 323
1995, Nov. 10   **Litho.**   *Perf. 12½*
Sea Turtles: No. 3033, Chelonia mydas. No. 3034, Caretta caretta. No. 3035, Lepidochelys olivacea. No. 3036, Eretmochelys imbricata.
3033	A726	$5 multicolored	.70	.20
3034	A726	$5 multicolored	.70	.20
3035	A726	$5 multicolored	.70	.20
3036	A726	$5 multicolored	.70	.20
		Nos. 3033-3036 (4)	2.80	.80

Taiwan Agricultural Research Institute, Cent. — A727

Perf. 12x11½
1995, Nov. 22   **Litho.**   **Wmk. 323**
3037	A727	$5 In rice field	.75	.20
3038	A727	$28 In anthurium field	2.50	.90

New Year 1996 (Year of the Rat) — A728

Designs: $3.50, $13, Different stylized rats.

Wmk. 323
1995, Dec. 1   **Litho.**   *Perf. 12½*
3039	A728	$3.50 pink & multi	.30	.20
a.		Perf. 13½ vert.	.30	.20
b.		As "a," booklet pane of 6	1.60	
		Complete booklet, 2 #3039b + gutter	3.25	
3040	A728	$13 olive & multi	.90	.45
a.		Souv. sheet, 2 ea #3039-3040	3.75	1.10

Traditional Wedding Ceremony A729

Designs: $5, Escorting bride. $12, Kowtowing Heaven, Earth, and ancestors. $19, Seated in bridal chamber.

1996, Jan. 10
3041	A729	$5 multicolored	.40	.20
3042	A729	$12 multicolored	1.25	.50
3043	A729	$19 multicolored	2.25	.75
		Nos. 3041-3043 (3)	3.90	1.45

Ancient Chinese Engraving Type of 1995
Various pictures of fruit.

Wmk. 323
1996, Jan. 25   **Litho.**   *Perf. 13½*
Denomination in Black
3044	A712	$9 multicolored	.90	.40
3045	A712	$12 multicolored	1.25	.65
3046	A712	$15 multicolored	1.50	.75
3047	A712	$17 multicolored	1.75	.85
		Nos. 3044-3047 (4)	5.40	2.65

Scenic Dwelling at Chü-Ch'ü, by Wang Meng, Yüan Dynasty — A730

Denominations: a, UL. b, UR. c, LL. d, LR. Illustration reduced.

Perf. 12½x12
1996, Feb. 15   **Litho.**   **Unwmk.**
3048	A730	Block of 4, #a.-d.	4.00	3.00
a.-d.		$5 any single	.85	.75

A731   A732

Flowers: $5, Bougainvillea spectabilis. $12, Wisteria sinensis. $19, Merremia tuberosa.

1996, Mar. 8   **Unwmk.**   *Perf. 12½*
3049	A731	$5 multicolored	.50	.20
3050	A731	$12 multicolored	1.25	.60

Wmk. 323
3051	A731	$19 multicolored	1.75	.90
		Nos. 3049-3051 (3)	3.50	1.70

Wmk. 323
1996, Mar. 20   **Litho.**   *Perf. 13½*
Chinese Postal Service, Cent.: $5, Mailboxes. $9, Instruments of measurement. $12, Methods of mail transport. $13, Computers, plastic card.
3052	A732	$5 multicolored	.55	.20
3053	A732	$9 multicolored	.90	.50
3054	A732	$12 multicolored	1.05	.60
3055	A732	$13 multicolored	1.25	.70
a.		Souvenir sheet, #3052-3055	3.75	1.90
		Nos. 3052-3055 (4)	3.75	2.00

Natl. Chiao Tung University, Cent. — A733

Wmk. 323
1996, Apr. 8   **Litho.**   *Perf. 12½*
3056	A733	$19 multicolored	1.75	.90

Penghu Natl. Scenic Areas — A734

#3057, Chimei Giant Lion. #3058, Chipei Beach. $12, Tungpan Yu. $17, Tingkou Yu.

1996, May 1
3057	A734	$5 multicolored	.40	.20
3058	A734	$5 multicolored	.40	.20
3059	A734	$12 multicolored	1.10	.45
3060	A734	$17 multicolored	1.60	.65
		Nos. 3057-3060 (4)	3.50	1.50

Tzu-Chi Buddhist Compassionate Relief Foundation — A735

Wmk. 323

1996, May 11   Litho.   Perf. 13
3061	A735	$5	Hand holding people	.50 .30
3062	A735	$19	Lotus blossom, sick person	2.75 1.00

First Democratic Presidential Election A736

New Pres., Vice Pres. and: $3.50, Natl. flag. $5, Presidential office building. $13, Development of Asia-Pacific Operations Hub project. $15, Greeting people at fair.

1996, May 20   Wmk. 323   Perf. 12½
3063	A736	$3.50	multicolored	.30 .20
3064	A736	$5	multicolored	.55 .20
3065	A736	$13	multicolored	1.25 .50
3066	A736	$15	multicolored	1.40 .55
a.			Souvenir sheet, #3063-3066	3.50 1.40
			Nos. 3063-3066 (4)	3.50 1.45

South China Sea Archipelago A737

Outline map of region, Interior Dept. monuments on: $5, Pratas Isl. $17, Itu Aba Isl.

1996, June 5   Wmk. 323   Perf. 12½
3067	A737	$5	multicolored	.50 .20
3068	A737	$17	multicolored	1.75 .65
a.			Souvenir sheet, #3067-3068	1.65 .85

Modern Olympic Games, Cent. — A738

Perf. 12½x12
1996, June 22   Litho.   Wmk. 323
3069	A738	$5	Gymnast, cyclist	.60 .20
3070	A738	$15	Early Greek athletes	1.60 .55

Ancient Skills Type of 1994

Manufacturing silk: #3071, Feeding silkworms. #3072, Picking out cocoons. $7, Reeling raw silk. $10, Degumming raw silk. $13, Weaving silk.

1996, July 5   Perf. 12
3071	A693	$5	multicolored	.50 .20
3072	A693	$5	multicolored	.50 .20
3073	A693	$7	multicolored	.60 .30
3074	A693	$10	multicolored	1.00 .40
3075	A693	$13	multicolored	1.40 .70
			Nos. 3071-3075 (5)	4.00 2.00

Ancient Chinese Engraving Type of 1995

1996, Aug. 5   Perf. 13½
Denomination in Black
3076	A712	$1	Bamboo	.50 .20
3077	A712	$10	Orchid	.90 .60
3078	A712	$20	Plum tree branch	2.00 1.00
			Nos. 3076-3078 (3)	3.40 1.80

Traditional Architecture Type of 1995
Parts of column and beam construction.

Perf. 12x11½
1996, Aug. 22   Litho.   Wmk. 323
3079	A711	$5	Tou-kung (lion)	.55 .30
3080	A711	$5	Chiue-ti	.55 .30
3081	A711	$10	Bu-tong	1.00 .50
3082	A711	$19	Dye-tou	1.90 .90
			Nos. 3079-3082 (4)	4.00 2.00

Motion Pictures, Cent. — A739

Chinese movies: No. 3083, Princess Iron Fan, first full-length animated film, 1941. No. 3084, Chin Shan Bi Xie, 1957. $5, Oyster Girl, 1964. $19, City of Sadness, 1989.

1996, Sept. 17   Litho.   Perf. 12½x12
3083	A739	$3.50	multicolored	.30 .20
3084	A739	$3.50	multicolored	.30 .20
3085	A739	$5	multicolored	.60 .20
3086	A739	$19	multicolored	1.75 .70
			Nos. 3083-3086 (4)	2.95 1.30

Winning Pictures from Children's Stamp Design Contest A740

Denomination triangle color, location: a, Red, LR. b, Red, LL. c, Green, LR. d, Green, LL. e, Pink, LL. f, Red, UR. g, Red, UL. h, Green, UR. i, Green, UL. j, Pink, UL. k, Purple, LR. l, Purple, LL. m, Tan, UR. n, Tan, LL. o, Pink, LR. p, Purple, UR. q, Purple, UL. r, Tan, UR. s, Tan, UL. t, Pink, UR.

Perf. 12½x12
1996, Oct. 9   Litho.   Unwmk.
3087	A740	$5	Sheet of 20, #a.-t.	15.00 6.00

A741   A742

Ancient Chinese paintings: $5, Autumn Scene with Wild Geese. $7, Reeds and Wild Geese. $13, Wild Geese Gathering on a Shore of Reeds. $15, Wild Geese on a Bank in Autumn.

1996, Oct. 21   Photo.   Perf. 12
Granite Paper
3088	A741	$5	multicolored	.55 .20
3089	A741	$7	multicolored	.70 .25
3090	A741	$13	multicolored	1.25 .50
3091	A741	$15	multicolored	1.50 .55
a.			Souv. sheet, #3088-3091	4.50 2.00
			Nos. 3088-3091 (4)	4.00 1.50

10th Asian Intl. Philatelic Exhib., Taipei '96.

Perf. 12½x12
1996, Nov. 1   Litho.   Wmk. 323

Designs: $5, Computerized letters, numbers, bar coding. $26, Globe, graph line.

3092	A742	$5	multicolored	.60 .30
3093	A742	$26	multicolored	2.75 1.40

Merchant's Day, 50th Anniv.

A743   A744

Caring for the Handicapped: $5, Woman in wheelchair working at computer. $19, Handicapped child painting picture.

Wmk. 323
1996, Nov. 15   Litho.   Perf. 12½
3094	A743	$5	multicolored	.70 .30
3095	A743	$19	multicolored	1.75 .90

1996, Dec. 2
3096	A744	$3.50	gray & multi	.40 .20
a.			Perf. 13½ vert.	.40
b.			As "a," booklet pane of 6	2.40
			Complete booklet, 2 #3096b + gutter	4.80
3097	A744	$13	blue & multi	1.60 .55
a.			Souv. sheet, 2 ea #3096-3097	4.00 1.50
b.			As "a," overprinted	4.00 1.50

New Year 1997 (Year of the Ox). No. 3097b overprinted in red lilac in sheet margin with Chinese inscription for Kaohsiung Intl. Stamp Exhibition for Chinese Postal Service cent.

Ancient Skills Type of 1994

Making porcelain: No. 3098, Pounding stone, looking at bottom of bowl. No. 3099, Painting, shaping. $7, Painting. $10, Glazing. $13, Firing.

Perf. 11½x12
1997, Jan. 15   Litho.   Wmk. 323
3098	A693	$5	multicolored	.50 .20
3099	A693	$5	multicolored	.50 .20
3100	A693	$7	multicolored	.80 .25
3101	A693	$10	multicolored	1.00 .40
3102	A693	$13	multicolored	1.25 .50
			Nos. 3098-3102 (5)	4.05 1.55

Carp Encircled By Dragons — A745

Perf. 13x12½
1997, Feb. 14   Engr.   Wmk. 323
3103	A745	$50	carmine	5.00 2.50
3104	A745	$60	dark blue	6.00 3.00
3105	A745	$70	red orange	7.00 3.50
3106	A745	$100	olive green	10.00 5.00
			Nos. 3103-3106 (4)	28.00 14.00

See Nos. 3131-3132, 3252-3253, 3369-3370, 3426, 3871.

Feb. 28, 1947 Rebellion, 50th Anniv. — A746

1997, Feb. 28   Litho.   Wmk. 323
3107	A746	$19	Memorial	1.75 .90

Woody Plants — A747

$5, Rhododendron x mucronatum. $12, Hibiscus rosa-sinensis. $19, Hydrangea macrophylla.

Wmk. 323
1997, Mar. 12   Litho.   Perf. 12½
3108	A747	$5	multicolored	.60 .30
3109	A747	$12	multicolored	1.40 .60
3110	A747	$19	multicolored	2.00 .90
			Nos. 3108-3110 (3)	4.00 1.80

Water Resource Protection
A748   A749

1997, Mar. 22   Perf. 12½
3111	A748	$5	multicolored	.60 .30
3112	A749	$19	multicolored	2.00 .90

Architecture Type of 1995
Perf. 12x12½
1997, Apr. 9   Litho.   Wmk. 323
3113	A711	$5	Door, vert.	.50 .30
3114	A711	$5	Gable wall, vert.	.50 .30
3115	A711	$10	Carved brick, vert.	1.25 .60
3116	A711	$19	Column dragon, vert.	1.75 .80
			Nos. 3113-3116 (4)	4.00 2.00

Insects — A750

Designs: $5, Dorcus formosanus. $7, Phyllophorina kotoshoensis. $10, Troides magellanus. $17, Megacrania tsudai.

1997, Apr. 25   Photo.   Perf. 11½
Granite Paper
3117	A750	$5	multicolored	.50 .30
3118	A750	$7	multicolored	.80 .40
3119	A750	$10	multicolored	1.10 .60
3120	A750	$17	multicolored	1.75 .90
			Nos. 3117-3120 (4)	4.15 2.20

Minerals A751

Wmk. 323
1997, May 8   Litho.   Perf. 13
3121	A751	$5	Aragonite	.50 .30
3122	A751	$5	Alunite	.50 .30
3123	A751	$12	Enargite	1.25 .60
3124	A751	$19	Hokutolite	1.75 .80
			Nos. 3121-3124 (4)	4.00 2.00

Nanyashan Outlook A752

1997, May 31   Perf. 12½
3125	A752	$5	shown	.55 .25
3126	A752	$5	Pitou coastline	.55 .25
3127	A752	$12	Stone pillars, Nanya	1.25 .60
3128	A752	$19	Tsaoling trail	1.25 .60
			Nos. 3125-3128 (4)	3.60 1.70

A753

Around-The-Island Railway System: $5, Cliffs at Chingshuei, Northern Loop Line. $28, Southbound train passing through tunnel, Central Mountain area.

Wmk. 323
1997, June 12   Litho.   Perf. 13½
3129	A753	$5	multicolored	.70 .30
3130	A753	$28	multicolored	2.40 .90

Carp Type
1997, July 3   Engr.   Perf. 13
3131	A745	$300	vio & dark blue	30.00 15.00
3132	A745	$500	dk red & mag	45.00 25.00

Electronic Industry's Use of Integrated Circuits
A754

$5, Integrated circuit for computer & telecommunications industry. $26, Wafer linked to portable computer, cellular phone, electronic synthesizer.

1997, July 16   Litho.   Perf. 12½x12

3133	A754	$5 multicolored	.60	.30
3134	A754	$26 multicolored	2.75	1.25

Chinese Martial Arts — A755

Various stances in martial arts.

Wmk. 323
1997, Aug. 8   Litho.   Perf. 13

3135	A755	$5 shown	.50	.30
3136	A755	$5 multi, vert.	.50	.30
3137	A755	$9 multicolored	.80	.40
3138	A755	$19 multi, vert.	1.75	.80
		Nos. 3135-3138 (4)	3.55	1.80

Chinese Classical (Yuan) Opera — A756

Designs: No. 3139, Chang Shen playing musical instrument, Tsuei Ying-ying listening outside, from "Hsi Hsiang Chi." No. 3140, Kuan Gung standing on ferry and holding large knife, enemies in distance, from "Dan Daw Huei." $12, Abduction of Wang Chao-juin on horseback, from "Han Guong Chiou." $15, Emperor Tang Ming Huang envisioning concubine, Makueibo, from "Wu Tong Yu."

1997, Aug. 22

3139	A756	$5 multicolored	.50	.30
3140	A756	$5 multicolored	.50	.30
3141	A756	$12 multicolored	1.00	.50
3142	A756	$15 multicolored	1.50	.70
		Nos. 3139-3142 (4)	3.50	1.80

Sports — A757

1997, Sept. 9   Perf. 12½

3143	A757	$5 Badminton	.50	.30
3144	A757	$12 Bowling	1.25	.60
3145	A757	$19 Tennis	1.60	.90
		Nos. 3143-3145 (3)	3.35	1.80

Ming Dynasty Novel "Journey to the West" — A758

Episodes from novel: No. 3146, "Palm of Buddha," man making inscription while holding pole. No. 3147, "The pilgrimage of T'ang Monk," characters traveling west, one on horse. $5, "The Flaming Mountain," people fighting, fire in background. $20, "The Cobweb Cave," man using pole to fight, spider in cobweb.

1997, Sept. 24   Photo.   Perf. 11½x12
Granite Paper

3146	A758	$3.50 multicolored	.50	.30
3147	A758	$3.50 multicolored	.50	.30
3148	A758	$5 multicolored	.60	.40
3149	A758	$20 multicolored	1.60	.80
		Nos. 3146-3149 (4)	3.20	1.80

Opening of Second Northern Freeway
A759

Designs: $5, Bitan Bridge crossing, Shindian River. $19, Hsinchu interchange.

Wmk. 323
1997, Aug. 26   Litho.   Perf. 13

3150	A759	$5 multicolored	.60	.20
3151	A759	$19 multicolored	1.75	.80

Illustrations from Ching Dynasty Bird Manual
A760

Various birds.

1997, Oct. 9   Photo.   Perf. 11½
Granite Paper

3152	A760	$5 Sheet of 20, #a.-t.	12.00	9.50

Compare with Nos. 3268-3269.

New Year 1998 (Year of the Tiger) — A761

Wmk. 323
1997, Dec. 1   Litho.   Perf. 12½

3153	A761	$3.50 pink & multi	.30	.20
a.		Perf. 14 vert.	.30	.20
b.		As "a," booklet pane of 6	1.90	
		Complete booklet, 2 #3153b + gutter	3.80	
3154	A761	$13 yellow & multi	1.00	.45
a.		Souv. sheet, 2 ea #3153-3154	2.60	1.10

Pres. Chiang Ching-kuo (1910-88)
A762

1998, Jan. 13   Engr.   Perf. 13½

3155	A762	$5 Portrait, vert.	.50	.30

Perf. 11½

3156	A762	$19 shown	1.25	.90

A763   A764

Common Chinese Expressions of Good Fortune, designs: No. 3157, "Happy Occasion of Abundance," fish, vase with pictures of sun and sea. No. 3158, "Harmonious Union as One," flower with two blooms. No. 3159, "Honor and Wealth," flowers growing in pot, vase of flowers. No. 3160, "All is Lucky," bowl of fruit, vase with branch of fruit blossoms.

Perf. 11½x12
1998, Jan. 23   Litho.   Wmk. 323
Background Color

3157	A763	$5 pink	.50	.20
3158	A763	$5 beige	.50	.20
a.		Pair, 3157-3158	1.00	.30
3159	A763	$12 light yellow	.90	.35
3160	A763	$12 tan	.90	.35
a.		Pair, #3159-3160	1.80	.70
		Nos. 3157-3160 (4)	2.80	1.10

Wmk. 323
1998, Mar. 1   Litho.   Perf. 12½

Herbaceous Flowers: $5, Gaillardia pulchella. $12, Kalanchoe blossfeldiana. $19, Portulaca oleracea.

3161	A764	$5 multicolored	.40	.20
3162	A764	$12 multicolored	.80	.50
3163	A764	$19 multicolored	1.75	.80
		Nos. 3161-3163 (3)	2.95	1.50

Emperor Shih-tzu, on Hunting Expedition, by Liu Kuan-tao
A765

$5, Horseman drawing bow. $19, Emperor Shih-tzu leading hunting party on horseback.

1998, Mar. 20   Photo.   Perf. 12
Granite Paper

3164	A765	$5 multicolored	1.00	.20

Size: 64x40mm

3165	A765	$19 multicolored	2.00	.60
a.		Souvenir sheet, #3164-3165	3.00	1.25

No. 3165a is a continuous design.

Children's Folk Rhymes
A766

#3166, "A Frog Has One Mouth." #3167, "A Little Mouse Climbs an Oil Lamp." $12, "Fireflies." $19, "Egrets."

Wmk. 323
1998, Apr. 4   Litho.   Perf. 11½

3166	A766	$5 multicolored	.50	.30
3167	A766	$5 multicolored	.50	.30
3168	A766	$12 multicolored	.75	.60
3169	A766	$19 multicolored	1.75	.80
		Nos. 3166-3169 (4)	3.50	2.00

Copyright Law in Taiwan, 70th Anniv.
A767

1998, Apr. 30

3170	A767	$19 multicolored	1.75	.80

A768

A769

Portraits of Mythological Character, Chung K'uei: $5, Making ghosts work for him, from Kung Kai's "Chung K'uei Moving," Song Dynasty. $20, Dancing beside small ghost, from "An Auspicious Occasion," Ming Dynasty.

1998, May 15   Photo.   Perf. 11½
Granite Paper

3171	A768	$5 multicolored	1.25	.20
3172	A768	$20 multicolored	2.25	.80

Wmk. 323
1998, May 25   Litho.   Perf. 11½

3173	A769	$15 multicolored	1.25	.60

Intl. Law Assoc., 125th anniv.

Ancient Skills Type of 1994

Ships and methods of transport, horiz.: $5, Grain barge. $7, Six-oared boat. $10, One-wheeled carriage. $13, Southern Chinese one-man push cart.

1998, June 10   Perf. 12x11½

3174	A693	$5 multicolored	.50	.20
3175	A693	$7 multicolored	.60	.20
3176	A693	$10 multicolored	.80	.30
3177	A693	$13 multicolored	1.00	.40
		Nos. 3174-3177 (4)	2.90	1.10

Ancient Chinese Engravings Type of 1995
Redrawn With Chinese Inscription Reading Left to Right

Various floral designs. Denominations do not include two zeros.

Wmk. 323
1998, July 8   Litho.   Perf. 13½
Denomination in Red

3178	A712	$7 like #2989	.55	.30
3179	A712	$19 like #2990	1.60	.75
3180	A712	$20 like #2991	1.75	.85
3181	A712	$26 like #2992	2.10	1.05
		Nos. 3178-3181 (4)	6.00	2.95

Novel, "Red Chamber Dream," by Tsao Hsueh-chin
A770

Scenes from love story: No. 3182, Chia Pao-yu visits the garden (with group of women). No. 3183, Lin Tai-yu buries flowers (with hoe). $5, Hsueh Pao-chai plays with butterflies. $20, Shih Hsiang-yun in a drunken sleep (on bench).

1998, July 16   Perf. 11x11½

3182	A770	$3.50 multicolored	.25	.25
3183	A770	$3.50 multicolored	.25	.25
3184	A770	$5 multicolored	.40	.25
3185	A770	$20 multicolored	1.60	.75
		Nos. 3182-3185 (4)	2.50	1.50

20th Asia Pacific Jamboree, 8th Taiwan Jamboree — A771

1998, Aug. 5   Litho.   Perf. 11

3186	A771	$5 Emblem	.30	.20
3186A	A771	$5 Tents	.30	.20
b.		Pair, #3186-3186A	1.00	.50

Traditional Architecture Type of 1995

Terraces set on raised platforms: #3187, Spirit way (carved stone ramp between two staircases). #3188, Octagonal base of a column. $10, Carved cornerstone. $19, Carved stone drainage spout.

Perf. 11½x12

1998, Aug. 26   Litho.   Wmk. 323

3187	A711	$5 multi, vert.	.50	.20
3188	A711	$5 multi, vert.	.50	.20
3189	A711	$10 multi, vert.	.80	.30
3190	A711	$19 multi, vert.	1.25	.55
		Nos. 3187-3190 (4)	3.05	1.25

Sports Stamps — A772

Table tennis: No. 3191, Player awaiting serve. No. 3192, Player serving.
Rugby: No. 3193, Two players. No. 3194, Three players.

Wmk. 323

1998, Sept. 9   Litho.   Perf. 11½

Denomination Color

3191		$5 green	.40	.20
3192		$5 red	.40	.20
a.		A772 Pair, #3191-3192	.80	.30
3193		$7 red	.50	.20
3194		$7 blue	.50	.20
a.		A772 Pair, #3193-3194	1.00	.40
		Nos. 3191-3194 (4)	1.80	.80

Chinese Fables A773

Designs: No. 3195, "A Frog in a Well." No. 3196, "The Fox Borrows the Tiger's Ferocity." $12, "Adding Legs to a Drawing of a Snake." $19, "The Snipe and the Clam are at a Deadlock."

Wmk. 323

1998, Sept. 25   Litho.   Perf. 11½

3195	A773	$5 multicolored	.50	.30
3196	A773	$5 multicolored	.50	.30
3197	A773	$12 multicolored	1.00	.50
3198	A773	$19 multicolored	1.50	.70
		Nos. 3195-3198 (4)	3.50	1.80

Kinmen National Park A774

#3199, Taiwushan mountain area. #3200, Kunningtou Cliff, beach. $12, Teyueh Tower, Huang Hui-huang's house, Shuitou village. $19, Putou Beach, Liehyu Coast.

1998, Oct. 16

3199	A774	$5 multicolored	.50	.30
3200	A774	$5 multicolored	.50	.30
3201	A774	$12 multicolored	1.10	.50
3202	A774	$19 multicolored	1.75	.70
		Nos. 3199-3202 (4)	3.85	1.80

Birds — A775

Spizaetus nipalensis: No. 3203, On tree branch. No. 3204, In flight.
Spilornis cheela: No. 3205, On tree branch. No. 3206, In flight.
Ictinaetus malayensis: No. 3207, On tree branch. No. 3208, In flight.
Milvus migrans: No. 3209, Perched on rock. No. 3210, In flight.

1998, Oct. 30   Litho.   Perf. 11½

3203		$5 multicolored	.40	.20
3204		$5 multicolored	.40	.20
a.		A775 Pair, #3203-3204	.80	.30
3205		$5 multicolored	.40	.20
3206		$5 multicolored	.40	.20
a.		A775 Pair, #3205-3206	.80	.30
3207		$10 multicolored	.80	.30
3208		$10 multicolored	.80	.30
a.		A775 Pair, #3207-3208	1.60	.60
3209		$10 multicolored	.80	.30
3210		$10 multicolored	.80	.30
a.		A775 Pair, #3209-3210	1.60	.60
		Nos. 3203-3210 (8)	4.80	2.00

Ancient Jade Carvings A776

#3211, 2 men mining jade on a mountain. #3212, Mountain with 2 pavilions, stream. $7, Figures washing an elephant. $26, Mountain, trees, men.

Perf. 11½x12, 12x11½

1998, Nov. 13   Photo.

Granite Paper

3211	A776	$5 multi	.40	.30
3212	A776	$5 multi, vert.	.40	.30
3213	A776	$7 multi	.60	.30
3214	A776	$26 multi, vert.	2.00	1.00
a.		Souvenir sheet, #3211-3214	4.50	2.00

New Year 1999 (Year of the Rabbit)
A777   A778

Wmk. 323

1998, Dec. 2   Perf. 12½

3215	A777	$3.50 multicolored	.40	.20
a.		Perf. 14 vert.	.40	.20
b.		As "a," booklet pane of 6	2.50	
		Complete bklt., 2 #3215b + gutter	5.00	
3216	A778	$13 multicolored	1.40	.40
a.		Souv. sheet, 2 ea #3215-3216	2.90	1.00
b.		As "a," ovptd. in margin, perf. 12½x11¾	2.90	1.00

No. 3216b was issued 1/30/99 and is inscribed in sheet margin, "ALLIANCE '99 INT'L. FAIR OF PRODUCTS & TRAVEL / Jan. 30-Feb. 1, 1999" and four lines of Chinese text.

Common Expressions of Good Fortune — A779

Expressions, designs: No. 3217, "To have prosperous descendants," gourd on a vine. No. 3218, "A good marriage that soon brings sons," pair of Mandarin ducks, lotus flowers, seeds. No. 3219, "Prosperity from start to finish," egret, flowers. No. 3220, "Reunion and abundance," fish surrounded by flowers.

Perf. 11½x12

1999, Jan. 6   Litho.   Wmk. 323

3217	A779	$5 multicolored	.50	.20
3218	A779	$5 multicolored	.50	.20
3219	A779	$12 multicolored	1.00	.50
3220	A779	$12 multicolored	1.00	.50
		Nos. 3217-3220 (4)	3.00	1.40

Ancient Chinese Engravings Type
Redrawn With Chinese Inscription
No Zeros
Reading Left to Right

Various pictures of birds on tree branches, bamboo and orchid.

1999, Jan. 20   Perf. 13½

Denomination in Red

3221	A712	$1 like #3018	.25	.20
3222	A712	$3.50 like #3019	.30	.25
3223	A712	$5 like #3020	.40	.25
3224	A712	$10 like #3021	.75	.35
3225	A712	$12 like #3076	1.00	.40
3226	A712	$28 like #3077	2.25	1.10
		Nos. 3221-3226 (6)	4.95	2.55

Indoor Potted Plants — A781

$5, Sinningia speciosa. $12, Saintpaulia x hybrida. $19, Anthurium scherzerianum.

Perf. 12½

1999, Feb. 10   Litho.   Unwmk.

3228	A781	$5 multicolored	.40	.20
3229	A781	$12 multicolored	.90	.40
3230	A781	$19 multicolored	1.60	.80
		Nos. 3228-3230 (3)	2.90	1.40

Ancient Chinese Painting, "Joy in Peacetime" A782

#3231, Woman holding child, boy with small elephant. #3232, Boy carrying lantern, crane on leash, people under tree. $7, Family, children playing with toy animals on wheels. $26, Women in front of steps, children playing with toys, boy on edge of balcony.

1999, Mar. 2   Photo.   Perf. 12

Granite Paper

3231	A782	$5 multicolored	.40	.20
3232	A782	$5 multicolored	.40	.20
3233	A782	$7 multicolored	.55	.20
3234	A782	$26 multicolored	1.75	.80
a.		Souvenir sheet, #3231-3234	2.00	1.75
		Nos. 3231-3234 (4)	3.10	1.40

Traditional Architecture Type of 1995

Decorative features, vert.: No. 3235, Hanging cylinder with carving of woman and deer. No. 3236, Taishi screen. $10, Xuanyu (decorative element on gable). $19, Wood carving.

1999, Mar. 20   Litho.   Wmk. 323

3235	A711	$5 multicolored	.40	.20
3236	A711	$5 multicolored	.40	.20
3237	A711	$10 multicolored	.75	.30
3238	A711	$19 multicolored	1.50	.60
		Nos. 3235-3238 (4)	3.05	1.30

Children's Folk Rhymes A783

Titles: No. 3239, "Baby Sleep." No. 3240, "Be Brave." $12, "Rock, Rock, Rock." $19, "Buggie Flies."

Perf. 11½x11

1999, Apr. 2   Litho.   Unwmk.

3239	A783	$5 multicolored	.50	.20
3240	A783	$5 multicolored	.50	.20
3241	A783	$12 multicolored	1.00	.35
3242	A783	$19 multicolored	1.40	.55
		Nos. 3239-3242 (4)	3.40	1.30

Taiwan's Aboriginal Culture A784

Celebrations wearing traditional costumes: a, Dancing in row, mountain in background, Atayal Ancestor Festival. b, People wearing hip bells, Saisiat Festival of the Dwarfs. c, Standing arm in arm in circle, Bunun eight-part contrapuntal vocals. d, Row of people standing inside building, Tsou Victory Festival. e, Group outside before large display board, Rukai Harvest Festival. f, Holding bamboo poles in air, Paiwan "Maleveq" Bamboo Festival. g, Men walking while holding millet leaves in air, Puyuma Harvest Ceremony. h, Women dancing in row, tree in background, Ami Harvest Ceremony. i, Holding boat in air, Yami Boat Ceremony.

1999, Apr. 22   Perf. 13

Block of 9

3243	A784	$5 #a.-i. + label	6.00	5.50

No. 3243 was issued in sheets of 2 blocks + 2 labels. The labels contain the upper and lower halves of Taiwan. The lower block of 9 is in reverse order.

Intl. Council of Nurses, Cent. A785

1999, May 12   Litho.   Perf. 11½

3244	A785	$5 shown	.50	.20
3245	A785	$17 Nurse, world map	1.40	.50

Chinese Classical Opera — A786

Legends of the Ming Dynasty: No. 3246, Fan Li watching Hsi-shih wash yarn, "Wuan Sha Chi.". No. 3247, Tsai Pochieh, Niu looking at moon, Chao Waniang with pipa (stringed instrument) on her back, "The Story of a Pipa." $12, Hung Funu surprising Li Ching, "The Story of Hung Fu." $15, Jueilan setting up incense table, "Paiyueh Pavilion."

1999, May 27   Perf. 13

3246	A786	$5 multicolored	.45	.20
3247	A786	$5 multicolored	.50	.20
3248	A786	$12 multicolored	1.10	.35
3249	A786	$15 multicolored	1.40	.45
a.		Souvenir sheet, #3246-3249	3.50	1.75
b.		As "a," imperf., with added inscription	3.50	1.75
		Nos. 3246-3249 (4)	3.45	1.20

No. 3249b was issued 7/23 and is inscribed in sheet margin with exhibition emblem, two lines of Chinese text and "TAIPEI INTERNATIONAL STAMP EXHIBITION 1999 (INVITATIONAL)."

New Taiwan Dollar, 50th Anniv. A787

1999, June 15   Perf. 11½

3250	A787	$5 Coins	.50	.20
3251	A787	$25 Currency	2.00	.75

Carp Encircled by Dragons Type of 1997 Redrawn With Denominations at Right

1999, July 1   Engr.   Perf. 13½x12½

3252	A745	$50 green	4.00	3.00
3253	A745	$100 brown	9.00	4.00

Ancient Chinese Engravings Type of 1995
Redrawn With Chinese Inscription Reading Left to Right
Perf. 13½

1999, July 15   Litho.   Unwmk.
Denomination in Red

3254	A712	50c like #3044	.20	.20
3255	A712	$6 like #3045	.50	.20
3256	A712	$25 like #3046	1.75	.75
		Nos. 3254-3256 (3)	2.45	1.15

Father's Day
A788

Designs: $5, Children with large present, silhouette of their father. $25, Father teaching son how to ride bicycle, girl.

1999, Aug. 8   Perf. 11½

3257	A788	$5 multicolored	.50	.30
3258	A788	$25 multicolored	2.00	1.25

Chinese Gourmet Food
A789

Dish, region: a, Peony lobster, Taiwan. b, "Buddha Jumps the Wall" steamed seafood (with blue & white teapot, bowl), Fukien. c, Hors d'oeuvres shaped as star, Canton. d, "Dongpo Pork" (on yellow plate, bowl), Kiangsu and Chekiang. e, "Stewed Fish Jaws" (surrounded by strawberries, pineapple), Shanghai. f, "Beggar's Chicken" (with napkin), Hunan. g, "Carp Jumping over Dragon's Gate," Szechwan. h, "Peking Duck" (in footed dish), Beijing.

Perf. 11½x11¼

1999, Aug 20   Litho.   Unwmk.

3259	A789	$5 Block of 8, #a.-h.	3.25	1.60

Outdoor Activities — A790

1999, Sept. 9   Perf. 11¼x11½

3260	A790	$5 Diving	.40	.30
3261	A790	$6 Rafting	.50	.40
3262	A790	$10 Surfing	.90	.50
3263	A790	$25 Windsurfing	2.25	.50
		Nos. 3260-3263 (4)	4.05	1.70

Taiwanese Opera
A791

1999, Oct. 15   Litho.   Perf. 11½x11¼

3264	A791	$5 Stage, audience	.40	.30
3265	A791	$6 Dressing room	.50	.40
3266	A791	$10 Actress, tents	.90	.50
3267	A791	$25 Actress as clown	2.25	.80
		Nos. 3264-3267 (4)	4.05	2.00

Illustrations from Ching Dynasty Bird Manual
A792

#3268, Yellow-headed parrot. #3269, Blue-winged parrotlet (4 characters at LL). $12, African gray parrot (5 characters at UL). $25, King parrot (5 characters at UL).

1999, Nov. 11   Litho.   Perf. 11½

3268	A792	$5 multicolored	.50	.30
3269	A792	$5 multicolored	.50	.30
3270	A792	$12 multicolored	1.25	.50
3271	A792	$25 multicolored	2.40	1.10
		Nos. 3268-3271 (4)	4.65	2.20

Compare with No. 3152.
See Nos. 3510-3512.

New Year 2000 (Year of the Dragon)
A793   A794

1999, Dec. 1   Litho.   Perf. 12½

3272	A793	$3.50 multicolored	.30	.20
a.		Perf. 13¼ vert.	.30	.20
b.		As "a," booklet pane of 6	1.60	
		Complete booklet, 2 #3272b + gutter	3.50	
3273	A794	$13 multicolored	1.00	.40
a.		Souv. sheet, 2 ea #3272-3273	2.50	1.50

Millennium
A795

#3274, ROCSAT-1. #3275, Deer. $12, Train. $15, Dove, St. Peter's Basilica.

1999, Dec. 31   Litho.   Perf. 11½

3274	A795	$5 multicolored	.50	.30
3275	A795	$5 multicolored	.50	.30
3276	A795	$12 multicolored	1.10	.50
3277	A795	$15 multicolored	1.40	.70
a.		Souvenir sheet of 4, #3274-3277, perf. 12	3.50	1.75
b.		Souvenir sheet of 4, #3274-3277, imperf.	3.50	1.75
		Nos. 3274-3277 (4)	3.50	1.80

Taipei 2000 Stamp Exhibition (No. 3277b). No. 3277b has simulated perforations.

Calligraphy Tools
A796

Designs: No. 3278, "Colored Cloud Dragon" writing brushes of Ming Emperor Chia-Ching. No. 3279, "Imperial Dragon Fragrance" ink stick of Ming Emperor Lung-Ching, vert. $7, "Clear Heart House" calligraphic work by Tsai Hsiang, Sung Dynasty, vert. $26, Celadon toad inkstone, Sung Dynasty.

2000, Jan. 12   Photo.   Perf. 11¾
Granite Paper

3278	A796	$5 multicolored	.40	.30
3279	A796	$5 multicolored	.50	.30
3280	A796	$7 multicolored	.65	.40
3281	A796	$26 multicolored	2.40	1.00
		Nos. 3278-3281 (4)	3.95	2.00

Opening of Second Southern Freeway
A797

Designs: $5, $25, Kaoping River bridge. $12, Interchange.

2000, Feb. 2   Litho.   Perf. 13x13¼

3282	A797	$5 multi	.60	.30
3283	A797	$12 multi	1.20	.60

Souvenir Sheet
Perf. 12

3284	A797	$25 multi	2.50	1.25

No. 3284 contains one 80x30mm stamp.

Seasons
A798

Spring — No. 3285: a, Buds on tree. b, Farmer plowing. c, Cranes. d, Farmers planting. e, Basket of offerings to dead ancestors. f, Farmer's clothing.

Summer — No. 3286: a, Rice seedlings. b, Water wheel. c, Ripened rice. d, Cicada on tree. e, Palm leaf fan. f, Watermelons.

Autumn — No. 3287: a, Farmers in field. b, Granary. c, Dew on grass. d, Reddened maple leaves. e, Leafless tree. f, Hoarfrost on leaves.

Winter — No. 3288: a, Jar on table. b, Snow-covered pine trees. c, Snow-covered mountains. d, Bowl of rice balls. e, Snow-covered plum blossoms. f, House and village.

2000, Feb. 3   Perf. 11¾

3285	A798	$5 Strip of 6, #a-f	3.00	1.75
3286	A798	$5 Strip of 6, #a-f	3.00	1.75
3287	A798	$5 Strip of 6, #a-f	3.00	1.75
3288	A798	$5 Strip of 6, #a-f	3.00	1.75
		Nos. 3285-3288 (4)	12.00	7.00

Issued: #3285, 2/3; #3286, 5/5; #3287, 8/4; #3288, 11/3.

Soochow University, Cent.
A799

Designs: $5 School gate. $25, Justice statue at Law School.

2000, Mar. 16   Perf. 13x13¼

3289	A799	$5 multi	.50	.30
3290	A799	$25 multi	2.40	1.25

Novel "The Romance of the Three Kingdoms"
A800

#3291, Gathering of Liu Bei, Guan Yu and Chang Fei. #3292, Guan Yu reading. $5, Three visits to the thatched cottage. $20, Filling boats with straw for making arrows.

2000, Apr. 12   Perf. 11½

3291	A800	$3.50 multi	.60	.30
3292	A800	$3.50 multi	.60	.30
3293	A800	$5 multi	.80	.40
3294	A800	$20 multi	1.75	.70
a.		Souv. sheet, #3291-3294, perf. 12	3.75	3.25
		Nos. 3291-3294 (4)	3.75	1.70

Inauguration of New President and Vice-president — A801

a, Pres. Chen Shui-bian, Vice-pres. Lu Hsiu-lien. b, Presidential Office Building. Illustration reduced.

2000, May 20   Litho.   Perf. 11¾

3295	A801	$5 Pair, #a-b	.75	.30
c.		Souvenir sheet, 2 #3295	2.50	1.00

Tropic of Cancer Monuments
A802

2000, June 21   Perf. 13

3296	A802	$5 Hsialiao	.40	.30
3297	A802	$12 Wuho	1.25	.60
3298	A802	$25 Chingpu	2.25	1.10
		Nos. 3296-3298 (3)	3.90	2.00

Ancient Chinese Engravings Type of 1995 Redrawn with Chinese Inscription Reading Left to Right

2000, July 5   Litho.   Perf. 13½
Denomination in Red

3299	A712	$32 like #3046	2.75	1.75
3300	A712	$34 like #3078	3.25	1.75

Sacred Trees — A803

Designs: $5, Taiwan Giant, Miaoli County. $39, Sleeping Moon, Chiayi County.

2000, July 20   Litho.   Perf. 11¼x11½

3301	A803	$5 multi	.40	.30
3302	A803	$39 multi	3.25	1.50

No. 2499 Surcharged in Red

2000, Aug. 24   Litho.   Perf. 13½

3303	A535a	$3.50 on $7.50 multi	.75	.30

Poisonous Plants — A804

Designs: No. 3304, $5, Lycoris radiata. No. 3305, $5, Cerbera manghas. $12, Abrus precatorius. $20, Nerium indicum.

2000, Sept. 8   Litho.   Perf. 13

3304-3307	A804	Set of 4	4.25	2.00

Sept. 21, 1999 Earthquake, 1st Anniv. — A805

Designs: $5, Map, seismograph reading. $12, Rescue workers. $25, Earthquake preparedness.

2000, Sept. 21   Perf. 11¼x11½

3308-3310	A805	Set of 3	4.25	2.00

Dragonflies
A806

Designs: Nos. 3311, 3315a, $5, Lamelligomphus formosanus. Nos. 3312, 3315b, $5, Anotogaster sieboldii, vert. Nos. 3313, 3315c,

$12, Trithemis festiva, vert. Nos. 3314, 3315d, $12, Neurothemis ramburii.

2000, Oct. 11   **Perf. 13**
3311-3314   A806   Set of 4   3.50   1.50

Souvenir Sheet
Stamps Without White Margins
Perf. 11¾
3315   A806   Sheet of 4, #a-d   3.50   1.50

Bird Manual Type of 1999

#3316, $5, Corn bunting (2 characters at UR). #3317, $5, Brambling (3 characters at UL). $12, Bali mynah (3 characters at LR). $25, Indian grackle (2 characters at LR).

2000, Oct. 26   **Perf. 11½**
3316-3319   A792   Set of 4   4.50   2.00
Compare No. 3317 with No. 3378.

Tamkang University, 50th Anniv. A807

$5, Palace Lamp Boulevard, classroom buildings. $25, Maritime Museum, Scroll Plaza.

2000, Nov. 8   **Perf. 13**
3320-3321   A807   Set of 2   3.00   1.50

A808   New Year 2001 (Year of the Snake) — A809

2000, Dec. 1   **Perf. 12½**
3322   A808 $3.50 multi   .50   .20
   a.   Perf. 13¼ vert.   .50   .20
   b.   As "a," booklet pane of 6   3.00
     Booklet, 2 #3322b + gutter   6.00
3323   A809 $13 multi   1.25   .40
   a.   Souv. sheet, 2 ea #3322-3323   3.50   1.50
   b.   As "a," with added marginal inscription in red   3.50   1.50

Added marginal inscription of No. 3323b reads in Chinese "Turn-of-the-Century Intl. Stamp Exhibition, Kaohsiung / Dec. 25, 2000-Jan. 3, 2001" in red.
Issued: No. 3323b, 12/25/00.

Establishment of Trade Links with People's Republic of China — A810

Ships in Taiwan Strait and: $9, Building. $25, Obelisk.

2001, Jan. 1   **Litho.**   **Perf. 11½**
3324-3325   A810   Set of 2   3.00   2.50

A811

Common Chinese expressions of good fortune: No. 3326, $5, "Marital bliss," twin lotus blossoms on one stalk (pink background). No. 3327, $5, "Success in one's career," longan, lichee and walnuts (light green background). No. 3328, $12, "Producing many offspring," split pomegranates (buff background). No.

3329, $12, "Growing old together with wealth and high position," bulbuls flying around peonies (light orange background).

2001, Jan. 2   **Perf. 11¾x12¼**
3326-3329   A811   Set of 4   3.00   2.50

Zodiac Signs A812

Designs: No. 3330, $5, Aquarius. No. 3331, $12, Gemini. No. 3332, $25, Libra. No. 3333, $5, Capricorn. No. 3334, $12, Taurus. No. 3335, $25, Virgo. No. 3336, $5, Aries. No. 3337, $12, Leo. No. 3338, $25, Sagittarius. No. 3339, $5, Pisces. No. 3340, $12, Cancer. No. 3341, $25, Scorpio.

2001   **Perf. 12**
3330-3341   A812   Set of 12   18.00   12.00
Values are for stamps with surrounding selvage.
Issued: Nos. 3330-3332, 2/14. Nos. 3333-3335, 4/20. Nos. 3336-3338, 7/25. Nos. 3339-3341, 11/8.

Fruit — A813

2001-05   **Litho.**   **Perf. 12½x13¼**
3342   A813 $1 Plums   .25   .25
3343   A813 $3.50 Tangerines   .35   .25
   a.   "Republic of China" 12½mm long ('05)   .35   .25
3344   A813 $5 Apples   .45   .25
3345   A813 $7 Pears   .65   .25
3346   A813 $12 Guavas   1.05   .65
3347   A813 $20 Longans   1.60   1.00
   a.   "Republic of China" 12½mm long ('05)   1.60   .85
3348   A813 $25 Cantaloupes   2.00   1.05
3349   A813 $40 Grapefruit   3.75   3.25
   Nos. 3342-3349 (8)   10.10   6.95

Issued: $5, $7, $12, $25, 2/23. $1, $3.50, $20, $40, 8/23. Nos. 3343a, 3347a, 5/16/05. "Republic of China" on Nos. 3343 and 3347 is 12mm long and is in taller letters.
See Nos. 3408-3411, 3472-3475.

Mount Jade A814

Designs: No. 3350, $5, Main peak (shown). No. 3351, $5, Western peak, flowers in foreground. $12, Northern peak. $25, Eastern peak.

2001, Mar. 8   **Litho.**   **Perf. 11½x11¼**
3350-3353   A814   Set of 4   4.50   3.75
Compare Type A814 with Types A834-A837, A855-A858.

Children's Rhymes A815

Designs: No. 3354, $5, Little Ball (blue background). No. 3355, $5, Point to the Water Vat (pink background). $12, Pangolin. $25, Shake and Stamp.

2001, Apr. 4
3354-3357   A815   Set of 4   4.50   3.75

Buddhist Statues — A816

Designs: $5, Sakyamuni Buddha, Northern Wei Dynasty. $9, Seated Buddha, Tang Dynasty. $12, Mahavairocana Buddha, Sung Dynasty.

2001, May 11   **Perf. 11¼x11½**
3358-3360   A816   Set of 3   2.50   2.00
3360a   Souvenir sheet, #3358-3360, perf. 12   2.50   2.50

Agricultural Implements — A817

Designs: $5, Rice wind drum. $7, Plow. $10, Bamboo rice baskets. $25, Coir rainwear.

2001, May 25   **Perf. 11½x11¼**
3361-3364   A817   Set of 4   4.50   3.75

Dr. George Leslie Mackay (1844-1901) A818

2001, June 1   **Perf. 11¼x11½**
3365   A818 $25 multi   2.25   2.00

2001 Kiwanis International Convention A819

Designs: $5, Girl, Earth. $25, Mother and child, map.

2001, June 22   **Perf. 13**
3366-3367   A819   Set of 2   2.50   2.00

Kites — A820

No. 3368: a, Dragon. b, Phoenix. c, Tiger. d, Fish.

2001, July 13   **Perf. 11¼x11½**
3368   Horiz. strip of 4   2.00   1.60
   a.-d.   A820 $5 Any single   .45   .80

Carp Encircled by Dragons Type of 1997 With Denominations at Right

2001, Aug. 3   **Engr.**   **Perf. 13**
Size: 25x33mm
3369   A745 $300 red vio & dk bl   20.00   10.00
3370   A745 $500 red & brown   45.00   20.00

Rapid Transit A821

Designs: $5, Train, transit system emblem. $12, Passengers in station, fare card. $25, Chientan Station.

2001, Aug. 14   **Litho.**   **Perf. 13**
3371-3372   A821   Set of 2   1.75   1.00

Souvenir Sheet
Perf. 11¾
3373   A821 $25 multi   2.75   1.50
No. 3373 contains one 85x42mm stamp.

Fables — A822

Designs: No. 3374, $5, Now Three, Now Four (man and monkeys). No. 3375, $5, Selling the All-Penetrating Sword and Unyielding Shield (men watching man with sword and shield). $12, Waiting by the Tree for the Rabbit. $25, An Old Fool Moves Mountains.

2001, Sept. 6   **Litho.**   **Perf. 11½**
3374-3377   A822   Set of 4   3.75   3.00

Bird Manual Type of 1999 and

Siberian Rubythroat A823

Designs: No. 3379, Waxwing (3 characters at UR). $12, White-rumped munia (2 characters at R). $25, Great barbet (3 characters at LL).

2001, Sept. 28   **Litho.**   **Perf. 11½**
3378   A823 $5 shown   .60   .40
3379   A792 $5 multi   .60   .40
3380   A792 $12 multi   1.10   .60
3381   A792 $25 multi   2.00   1.60
   Nos. 3378-3381 (4)   4.30   3.00

Republic of China, 90th Anniv. A824

Designs: No. 3382, $5, Terminal, Chiang Kai-shek Intl. Airport. No. 3383, $5, Electronic products made in Republic of China. $12, Dancers at National Theater. $15, Dolphins.

2001, Oct. 9   **Litho.**   **Perf. 11½**
3382-3385   A824   Set of 4   3.25   2.50

2001 National Games — A825

Athletes and: $5, Torch. $25, Map.

2001, Oct. 18   **Litho.**   **Perf. 12½**
3386-3387   A825   Set of 2   2.50   2.00

34th
Baseball
World Cup
A826

Emblem, map and: No. 3388, $5, Pitcher.
No. 3389, $5, Batter. $12, Catcher. $20, Run-
ner sliding.

2001, Oct. 30   **Perf. 11½**
3388-3391 A826   Set of 4   3.75   3.00
3391a   Souvenir sheet, #3388-3391,
    perf. 12   3.75   3.00

Puppet
Theater
A827

Designs: $5, Mozhaonu, from "Thunder
Storm." $6, Taiyangnu, from "Rising Winds,
Surging Clouds." $10, Kuangdao, from "Thun-
der Crazy Sword." $25, Chin Chia-chien, from
"Thunder Golden Light."

2001, Nov. 16   **Litho.**   **Perf. 11½**
3392-3395 A827   Set of 4   4.50   3.00

National
Defense
Medical
Center,
Cent. — A828

Designs: $5, Medical students, old medical
school building. $25, Doctors, new medical
school building.

2001, Nov. 23   **Perf. 13**
3396-3397 A828   Set of 2   2.50   2.00

New Year 2002 (Year
of the
Horse) — A829

Horse and: $3.50, Clouds. $13, Flowers.

2001, Dec. 3   **Litho.**   **Perf. 12½**
3398 A829 $3.50 multi   .50   .30
  a.   Perf. 13¾ vert.   .50   .30
  b.   Booklet pane, 12 #3398a   4.50
    Booklet, #3398b   5.00
3399 A829 $13 multi   1.50   1.00
  a.   Souvenir sheet, 2 each #3398-
    3399   4.00   2.50

Paul Cardinal Yu
Pin (1901-
78) — A830

2001, Dec. 7   **Perf. 11½**
3400 A830 $25 multi   2.25   .90
  a.   Souvenir sheet of 1, perf. 12   2.25   1.60

Greetings
A831

No. 3401: a, Pink chrysanthemums, red
background. b, White lilies, red background. c,

Pink flowers, yellow background. d, Red
orange flowers, yellow background. e, Pink
flowers, green background. f, Coral roses, blue
green background. g, Star and wreath, blue
background. h, Poinsettias, blue background.
i, Red violet flowers, purple background. j, Yellow flowers, purple background.

2001, Dec. 12   **Perf. 12½**
3401   Sheet of 10 + 10 labels   4.50   3.00
  a.-j.   A831 $5 Any single   .45   .30

Labels could be personalized for an additional fee.
Sheets with blank (unprinted) labels were
not released.

Fu Hsing
Kang
College,
50th Anniv.
A832

Designs: $5, Students with flags. $25,
Tower, administration building, statue of
students.

2002, Jan. 4   **Perf. 11½**
3402-3403 A832   Set of 2   2.50   2.00

Expressions of Good Fortune Type of 2001

Designs: No. 3404, $5, "Continuously pro-
duce good offspring," lotus and sweet
osmanthus flowers in a vase (gradiated pink
background). No. 3405, $5, "A high, moral
gentleman," orchid and sweet osmanthus in
containers (gradiated green background). No.
3406, $12, "A hall full of the rich and famous,"
flowering crabapple in a vase (gradiated
orange background). No. 3407, $12, "Safe and
peaceful in all seasons," roses in vase
(gradiated purple background).

2002, Jan. 16   **Perf. 11¾x12¼**
3404-3407 A811   Set of 4   3.50   2.00

Fruit Type of 2001

2002-05   **Litho.**   **Perf. 12½x13¼**
3408 A813 $6 Avocados   .45   .25
3409 A813 $10 Lichees   .90   .35
  a.   "Republic of China" 12½mm
    long ('05)   .75   .35
3410 A813 $17 Dates   1.50   .60
  a.   "Republic of China" 12½mm
    long ('05)   1.25   .65
3411 A813 $32 Passion fruit   2.75   1.05
  a.   "Republic of China" 12½mm
    long ('05)   2.50   1.25
   Nos. 3408-3411 (4)   5.60   2.25

Issued: Nos. 3408-3411, 2/8/02; 3409a,
3410a, 3411a, 5/16/05.
"Republic of China" on Nos. 3409-3411 is
12mm long and is in taller letters.

Folk Traditions
A833

Designs: No. 3412, $5, Release of sky lan-
terns (orange background). No. 3413, $5, Fire-
works display (blue background). $10, Matsu
procession (lilac background). $20, Dragon
boat race (pink background).

2002, Feb. 26   **Litho.**   **Perf. 12½**
3412-3415 A833   Set of 4   4.00   3.00

See Nos. 3440-3443.

Winter,
Mount
Hsueh
A834

North
Ridge,
Mount
Hsueh
A835

Autumn,
Mount
Hsueh
A836

Glacial
Cirques,
Mount
Hsueh
A837

2002, Mar. 20   **Perf. 11½**
3416 A834 $5 multi   .40   .40
3417 A835 $5 multi   .40   .40
3418 A836 $12 multi   1.00   .90
3419 A837 $25 multi   2.00   1.75
   Nos. 3416-3419 (4)   3.80   3.45
Compare with Types A814, A855-A858.

Novel "The
Romance of
the Three
Kingdoms"
A838

Designs: No. 3420, $3.50, Three heroes
battling Lu Bu (warriors on horseback). No.
3421, $3.50, To the rescue of his master's
family (one warrior on horseback). $5, Scrap-
ing away the poison from the bone (medicinal
bleeding). $20, Playing a lute to make the
enemy retreat (horseman and gate).

2002, Apr. 4
3420-3423 A838   Set of 4   5.00   2.10
  a.   Souvenir sheet, #3420-3423,
    perf. 12   5.00   5.00

Endangered Bird Thalasseus
Bernsteini — A839

No. 3424: a, Two birds in flight. b, Bird in
flight heading left. c, Bird landing on rock carrying fish. d, Bird on rock with beak open. e,
Adult feeding chick. f, Bird diving. g, Bird landing with bill open. h, Bird standing on rock,
looking left. i, Adult with chick. j, Adult on nest.
$25, Bird in flight.

2002, May 15   **Litho.**   **Perf. 11½**
3424 A839 $5 Sheet of 10, #a-j   5.00   4.00

Souvenir Sheet
Perf. 12
3425 A839 $25 multi   3.00   2.00
No. 3424 contains ten 40x30mm stamps.

Dragon & Carp Type of 1997 Redrawn With Denomination at Right

2002, June 5   **Engr.**   **Perf. 13¼x12½**
3426 A745 $80 brown   6.00   3.50

Porcelain
Bowls
A840

Ching Dynasty bowls depicting: No. 3427,
$5, Peacock (salmon background). No. 3428,
$5, Lotus flowers (blue green background). $7,
Peonies. $32, Sparrows and bamboo.

2002, June 21   **Litho.**   **Perf. 11½**
3427-3430 A840   Set of 4   4.25   3.75

Flowers — A841

Designs: $5, Matthiola incana. $12, Gardenia jasminoides. $25, Michelia figo.

2002, July 5   **Perf. 13**
3431-3433 A841   Set of 3   3.25   1.50

Cetaceans
A842

Designs: No. 3434, $5, Megaptera novaean-
gliae, whaling ship. No. 3435, $5, Tursiops
truncatus, people on shore attracting ceta-
cean. $10, Orcinus orca, boat following
cetaceans. $25, Grampus griseus, people res-
cuing beached dolphin.

2002, July 25   **Litho.**   **Perf. 11½x11¼**
3434-3437 A842   Set of 4   4.50   1.75
  a.   Souvenir sheet, #3434-3437,
    perf. 12   4.50   3.25

Intl. Paralympic Committee World
Table Tennis Championships — A843

Player: No. 3438, $5, On crutches. No.
3439, $5, In wheelchair.

2002, Aug. 13   **Perf. 11½x11¼**
3438-3439 A843   Set of 2   1.25   .80

Folk Traditions Type of 2002

Designs: No. 3440, $5, Launching of water
lanterns (green background). No. 3441, $5,
Snatching flags for good luck (yellow background). $10, Worship of the just (blue back-
ground). $20, Burning the Prince's boat (red
orange background).

2002, Aug. 22   **Perf. 12½**
3440-3443 A833   Set of 4   3.25   2.75

Republic of
China —
Vatican City
Diplomatic
Relations,
60th Anniv.
A844

Designs: $5, Chinese and Vatican flags,
Chinese Presidential building, St. Peter's
Basilica. $17, Flags, doves, Celso Cardinal
Costantini.

2002, Sept. 20   **Perf. 11½x11¼**
3444-3445 A844   Set of 2   2.00   1.25

Bird Manual Type of 1999 and

White-rumped Munia — A845

Designs: No. 3446, $5, Vernal hanging par-
rot (3 characters at LL). $12, White-headed
greenfinch (4 characters at LL). $25, Yunnan
greenfinch (2 characters at UL).

2002, Oct. 9

3446	A792	$5 multi	.50	.40
3447	A845	$5 multi	.50	.40
3448	A792	$12 multi	.90	.80
3449	A792	$25 multi	1.90	1.75
		Nos. 3446-3449 (4)	3.80	3.35

Taiwanese Opera
A846

Designs: $5, Liang Shan-po and Chu Ying-tai. $6, Hsueh Ting-shan and Fan Li-hua. $10, Hsueh Ping-kuei and Wang Pao-chuan. $25, The Living Buddha Chikung.

2002, Oct. 25

3450-3453	A846	Set of 4	3.50	1.50

Koalas — A847

Designs: No. 3454, $5, Adult with cub. No. 3455, $5, Adult on branch. $9, Adult with head on branch. $21, Adult with cub, diff.

2002, Nov. 15   Perf. 11¼x11½

3454-3457	A847	Set of 4	3.50	1.60
a.	Souvenir sheet, #3454-3457, perf. 12		3.50	2.75

Knots
A848

Nos. 3458-3459 — Various knots (Denomination location, denomination color and background color): a, UL, orange, light orange. b, UL, purple, yellow. c, UL, green, light green. d, UL, yellow, light blue. e, UL, blue, pink. f, UR, orange, light orange. g, UR, red violet, yellow. h, UR, blue, light green. i, UR, yellow, light blue. j, UR, red violet, pink.

No. 3460 (yellow denominations, olive green background): a, Like #3458a. b, Like #3458b. c, Like #3458c, d, #3458d, e, Like #3458e. f, Like #3458f. g, Like #3458g. h, Like #3458h. i, Like #3458i. j, Like #3458j.

2002, Nov. 22   Litho.   Perf. 12½

3458		Block of 10	2.25	1.20
a.-j.	A848 $3.50 Any single		.20	.20
k.	Sheet of 10 #3458f + 10 attached labels		12.00	12.00
l.	Sheet of 10 #3458g + 10 attached labels		12.00	12.00
m.	Sheet of 10 #3458h + 10 attached labels		12.00	12.00
n.	Sheet of 10 #3458i + 10 attached labels		12.00	12.00
o.	Sheet of 10 #3458j + 10 attached labels		12.00	12.00
p.	Sheet , #3458a-3458j + 10 attached labels		12.00	12.00
q.	Sheet, #3458a, 3458b, 3458d, 3458f, 3458g, 3458i + 6 attached labels ('04)		8.50	8.50
3459		Block of 10	3.50	1.75
a.-j.	A848 $5 Any single		.35	.20
k.	Sheet of 10 #3459a + 10 attached labels		12.50	12.50
l.	Sheet of 10 #3459b + 10 attached labels		12.50	12.50
m.	Sheet of 10 #3459c + 10 attached labels		12.50	12.50
n.	Sheet of 10 #3459d + 10 attached labels		12.50	12.50
o.	Sheet of 10 #3459e + 10 attached labels		12.50	12.50
p.	Sheet of 10 #3459f + 10 attached labels		12.50	12.50
q.	Sheet of 10 #3459g + 10 attached labels		12.50	12.50
r.	Sheet of 10 #3459h + 10 attached labels		12.50	12.50
s.	Sheet of 10 #3459i + 10 attached labels		12.50	12.50
t.	Sheet of 10 #3459j + 10 attached labels		12.50	12.50
3460		Block of 10	17.50	8.50
a.-j.	A848 $25 Any single		1.75	.80
k.	Sheet of 10 #3460a + 10 attached labels		24.00	24.00
l.	Sheet of 10 #3460b + 10 attached labels		24.00	24.00

---

m.	Sheet of 10 #3460c + 10 attached labels		24.00	24.00
n.	Sheet of 10 #3460d + 10 attached labels		24.00	24.00
o.	Sheet of 10 #3460e + 10 attached labels		24.00	24.00
p.	Sheet, #3460a-3460j + 10 attached labels		24.00	24.00
	Nos. 3458-3460 (3)		23.25	11.45

Nos. 3458k-3458p sold for $185 each; Nos. 3459k-3459u for $200 each; Nos. 3460k-3460p each. Labels, which were personalized, were separated from stamps on Nos. 3458k-3458p, 3459k-3459u, 3460k-3460p by vertical rows of simulated perforations.

No. 3458q sold for $141 and has labels, which could be personalized, that are separated from the stamps by simulated perforations. Issued 9/30/04.

New Year 2003 (Year of the Ram) — A849

Designs: $3.50, Yellow ram. $13, Red ram.

2002, Dec. 2   Litho.   Perf. 12¼

3461	A849	$3.50 multi	.40	.20
a.	Perf. 12¼ Vert.		.40	.20
b.	As "a," booklet pane of 6		2.25	
	Booklet, 2 #3461b		5.25	
3462	A849	$13 multi	1.10	.40
a.	Souvenir sheet, 2 each #3461-3462		3.00	1.50
b.	As "a," with Chinese text in red in L & R sheet margins		3.00	1.50

Issued: No. 3462b, 1/1/03. Chinese text in left and right sheet margins on No. 3462b commemorates the establishment of Chunghwa Post Co., Ltd.

Street Scene on a Summer Day, by Chen Cheng-po A850

Girl in the White Dress, by Li Mei-shu — A851

Courtyard with Banana Trees, by Liao Chi-chun — A852

Sunrise, by Kuo Po-chuan A853

Perf. 11½x11¼, 11¼x11½

2002, Dec. 6

3463	A850	$5 multi	.40	.20
3464	A851	$5 multi	.40	.20
3465	A852	$10 multi	.75	.30
3466	A853	$20 multi	1.60	.55
	Nos. 3463-3466 (4)		3.15	1.25

Admission to World Trade Organization, 1st Anniv. — A854

2003, Jan. 1   Litho.   Perf. 11½x11¼

3467	A854	$17 multi	2.75	1.10

Spring on Wuyen Peak A855

Glacial Cirques, Mt. Nanhu A856

Mt. Nanhu A857

Snow on Mt. Chungyang Chien A858

2003, Jan. 23

3468	A855	$5 multi	.40	.20
3469	A856	$5 multi	.40	.20
3470	A857	$12 multi	.90	.35
3471	A858	$25 multi	1.60	.70
	Nos. 3468-3471 (4)		3.30	1.45

Compare with Types A814, A834-A837.

Fruit Type of 2001

2003-05   Litho.   Perf. 12½x13¼

3472	A813	$9 Rose apples	.60	.25
a.	"Republic of China" 12½mm long ('05)		.60	.30
3473	A813	$13 Kumquats	.90	.40
3474	A813	$15 Lemons	1.10	.45
a.	"Republic of China" 12½mm long ('05)		.95	.50
3475	A813	$34 Coconuts	2.00	1.00

Issued: Nos. 3472-3475, 2/14/03; 3472a, 3474a, 5/16/05.
"Republic of China" on Nos. 3472 and 3474 is 12mm long and is in taller letters.

Love — A859

Hearts and: No. 3476, $5, Woman tending to man in wheelchair. No. 3477, $5, Family. $10, Landscape. $25, Girl and dogs.

2003, Mar. 20   Perf. 11¼x11½

3476-3479	A859	Set of 4	3.50	2.50

Puppet Theater A860

Designs: No. 3480, $5, Journey to the West performed on outdoor stage. No. 3481, $5, Puppets on television. $10, Mysteries of the Wolf Castle performed at the National Opera House. $25, Screening of movie, Legend of the Sacred Stone.

2003, Apr. 3   Perf. 11½x11¼

3480-3483	A860	Set of 4	3.50	2.50

Merops Philippinus A861

Designs: Nos. 3484, 3488a, $5, Foraging. Nos. 3485, 3488b, $5, Roosting. Nos. 3486, 3488c, $10, Bathing. Nos. 3487, 3488d, $20, Feeding chick.

2003, May 8   Perf. 12½

With White Frame

3484-3487	A861	Set of 4	3.00	2.25

Souvenir Sheet

Without White Frame

3488	A861	Sheet of 4, #a-d	3.00	2.25

No. 3488 contains four 33x25mm stamps.

Furniture — A862

Designs: No. 3489, $5, Wash basin stand. No. 3490, $5, Canopy bed. $12, Taishi chair. $20, Pahsien table.

2003, May 22   Perf. 11¼x11½

3489-3492	A862	Set of 4	3.25	1.50

Folktale "Eight Immortals Cross the Sea" — A863

Immortal: No. 3493, $5, Riding catfish. No. 3494, $5, On donkey. $10, Holding fan. $25, In brown robe.

2003, June 12

3493-3496	A863	Set of 4	3.50	1.50

Moths A864

Designs: No. 3497, $5, Antitrygodes divisaria perturbata. No. 3498, $5, Vamuna virilis. $12, Sinna extrema. $20, Thyas juno.

2003, June 26   Perf. 11½x11¼

3497-3500	A864	Set of 4	3.25	1.50

Dragonflies
A865

Designs: Nos. 3501, 3505a, $5, Acisoma panorpoides panorpoides. Nos. 3502, 3505b, $5, Sympetrum eroticu ardens, vert. Nos. 3503, 3505c, $10, Anax parthenope julius. Nos. 3504, 3505d, $17, Rhyothemis variegata arria, vert.

2003, July 25   **Perf. 12½**
With White Frames
3501-3504 A865   Set of 4   3.25 1.50
Souvenir Sheet
Without White Frames
3505 A865   Sheet of 4, #a-d   3.25 1.50

Stamp size: Nos. 3505a, 3505c, 33x25mm; Nos. 3505b, 3505d, 25x33mm.

Greetings
A866

No. 3506: a, Cranes. b, Wood carving and red plate. c, Fish and coin. d, Bamboo. e, Wood carving of bird.
No. 3507: a, Vase with tasseled rope. b, Like #3506a. c, Like #3506b. d, Three brown containers. e, Like #3508. f, Dragon. g, Like #3506c. h, Like #3506d. i, Horse and rider. j, Like #3506e.
No. 3508, Vase with flowers.

2003, Aug. 9   **Perf. 12½**
3506	Horiz. strip of 5	1.25	.65
a.-e.	A866 $3.50 Any single	.20	.20
f.	Sheet of 10 #3506a+ 10 attached labels	12.00	12.00
g.	Sheet of 10 #3506b+ 10 attached labels	12.00	12.00
h.	Sheet of 10 #3506c + 10 attached labels	12.00	12.00
i.	Sheet of 10 #3506d + 10 attached labels	12.00	12.00
j.	Sheet of 10 #3506e + 10 attached labels	12.00	12.00
k.	Sheet , 2 each #3506a-3506e + 10 attached labels	12.00	12.00
3507	Block of 10	3.50	1.75
a.-j.	A866 $5 Any single	.35	.20
k.	Sheet of 10 #3507a + 10 attached labels	12.50	12.50
l.	Sheet of 10 #3507b + 10 attached labels	12.50	12.50
m.	Sheet of 10 #3507c + 10 attached labels	12.50	12.50
n.	Sheet of 10 #3507d + 10 attached labels	12.50	12.50
o	Sheet of 10 #3507e + 10 attached labels	12.50	12.50
p.	Sheet of 10 #3507f + 10 attached labels	12.50	12.50
q.	Sheet of 10 #3507g + 10 attached labels	12.50	12.50
r.	Sheet of 10 #3507h + 10 attached labels	12.50	12.50
s.	Sheet of 10 #3507i + 10 attached labels	12.50	12.50
t.	Sheet of 10 #3507j + 10 attached labels	12.50	12.50
u.	Sheet, #3507a-3507j + 10 attached labels	12.50	12.50
v.	Sheet, #3507d, 3507e, 3507f, 3507g, 3507h, 3507j + 6 attached labels ('04)	9.00	9.00
3508	A866 $12 multi	.85	.45
a.	Sheet of 10 #3508 + 10 attached labels	17.00	17.00
	Nos. 3506-3508 (3)	5.60	2.85

Nos. 3506f-3506k sold for $185 each; Nos. 3507k-3507u for $200 each; No. 3508a for $270 each. Labels, which were personalized, were separated from stamps on Nos. 3506f-3506k, 3507k-3507u, 3508a by vertical rows of simulated perforations.
No. 3507v sold for $150 and has labels, which could be personalized, that are separated from the stamps by simulated perforations. Issued 5/30/04.

Bird Manual Type of 1999 and

White-throated Laughing
Thrush — A867

Designs: No. 3510, Great mynah (2 characters at LR). $12, Yellow-legged buttonquail (3 characters at UL). $25, Crested lark (4 characters at L).

    Perf. 11½x11¼
2003, Sept. 10   **Litho.**
3509	A867 $5 multi	.40	.20
3510	A792 $5 multi	.40	.20
3511	A792 $12 multi	.90	.35
3512	A792 $25 multi	1.75	.75
	Nos. 3509-3512 (4)	3.45	1.50

Chungshan Park, Taichung
A868

Tourist attractions: No. 3514, $5, Dongshan River Bridge, Ilan. $11, Badlands, Tianliao. $20, Sansiantai, Chenggong.

2003, Oct. 28   **Litho.**   **Perf. 11½**
3513-3516 A868   Set of 4   3.00 1.25
Chungshan Park, cent. (#3513).

Veterans Day, 25th Anniv.
A869

Veterans Affairs Commission insignia and: $5, Veterans building Central Cross-Island Highway. $25, Veterans, homes and hospital for veterans.

2003, Oct. 31
3517-3518 A869   Set of 2   2.00 .90

The Back Yard, by Lu Tie-jhou — A870

A Gold Mine Tower: Jioufen, by Lin Ke-gong — A871

Leisurely, by Chen Jin — A872

East Gate, by Li Ze-fan
A873

2003, Nov. 20
3519	A870 $5 multi	.40	.20
3520	A871 $5 multi	.40	.20
3521	A872 $10 multi	.75	.30
3522	A873 $20 multi	1.50	.60
	Nos. 3519-3522 (4)	3.05	1.30

New Year 2004 (Year of the Monkey) — A874

Monkey holding fruit: $3.50. With tail. $13, In hand.

2003, Dec. 1   **Perf. 12¼**
3523-3524	A874 Set of 2	1.40	.70
3523a	Perf. 12¼ vert.	.35	.20
3524a	Sheet, 2 each #3523-3524	2.50	1.60
3523b	Booklet pane, 12 #3523a	6.50	
	Complete booklet, #3523b	7.25	

Springs
A875

Designs: No. 3525, $5, Yangmingshan Hot Springs, fumaroles (light orange background). No. 3526, $5, Suao Cold Springs, Nanfangao Bridge (light blue background). $10, Guanziling Murky Hot Spring, Shuei Huo Tong Yuan. $25, Green Island Seabed Hot Springs, Green Island Lighthouse.

2003, Dec. 14   **Perf. 13**
3525-3528	A875 Set of 4	3.50	1.50
3528a	Souvenir sheet, #3525-3528	3.50	2.00

Completion of Highway 3 — A876

Designs: $5, Jhonggang Interchange. $25, Cingshuei Service Area. $20, Cingshuei Service Area, diff.

2004, Jan. 8   **Litho.**   **Perf. 12½**
3529-3530 A876   Set of 2   2.25 .90
Souvenir Sheet
Perf. 11½x11¼
3531 A876 $20 multi   1.50 1.25
No. 3531 contains one 80x30mm stamp.

Flowers — A877

Designs: No. 3532, $5, Lilium formosanum. No. 3533, $5, Hippeastrum x hybridum. $12, Fressia x hybrida.

2004, Jan. 17   **Perf. 12¼**
3532-3534	A877 Set of 3	1.75	.70
3534a	Souvenir sheet, #3532-3534, perf. 13	1.75	1.25
3534b	As "a," with Taiwan Flower Expo emblem and text added in margin	1.75	1.25

Eight Immortals Cross the Sea Type of 2003

Immortal: No. 3535, $5, With crane and flute. No. 3536, $5, With lotus flower. $10, Holding stick, wearing red robe. $25, Carrying flower basket.

2004, Feb. 25   **Perf. 11¼x11½**
3535-3538 A863   Set of 4   3.50 1.50

Red Cross Society, Cent. — A878

No. 3539: a, Heart, stylized people with arms raised. b, Heart, stylized people doing Red Cross activities.
Illustration reduced.

2004, Mar. 9   **Perf. 11¼x11½**
3539 A878 $5 Horiz. pair, #a-b   1.00 .50

A Young Girl From Lu Kai, by Yan Shui-long
A879

Old Street in Taipei, by Yang San-lang
A880

Happy Farmers, by Lee Shih-chiao
A881

Fish Shop, by Liu Chi-hsiang
A882

    Perf. 11¼x11½, 11½x11¼
2004, Mar. 25
3540	A879 $5 multi	.40	.20
3541	A880 $5 multi	.40	.20
3542	A881 $10 multi	.80	.30
3543	A882 $20 multi	1.40	.60
	Nos. 3540-3543 (4)	3.00	1.30

Butterflies
A883

Designs: No. 3544, $5, Parantica sita niphonica. No. 3545, $5, Choaspes benjaminii formosanus. $17, Junonia almana. $20, Artipe eryx horiliana.

2004, Apr. 21   **Perf. 11½x11¼**
3544-3547 A883   Set of 4   3.50 1.50

Yijhen Folk
Art
Performers
A884

Designs: No. 3548, $5, Eight Generals (buff background). No. 3549, $5, Song Jiang Battle Array (grayish blue background). $11, Drum Dance. $25, Stilt walkers.

2004, May 11
3548-3551 A884 Set of 4 3.50 1.50

Inauguration of Pres. Chen Shiu-bian
and Vice-President Hsiu-lien Annette
Lu — A885

No. 3552 — President, Vice-President and: a, Map of Taiwan, flag, crowd. b, Map of People's Republic of China and Taiwan, handshake, flowers. c, Buildings, crowd. d, Train, highway, buildings.
$12, President, Vice-President, buildings, train, highway.

2004, May 20   Perf. 12½
3552 Horiz. strip of 4 1.75 .70
a.-d. A885 $5 any single .40 .25

Souvenir Sheet
Perf. 12
3553 A885 $12 multi 1.50 1.25

No. 3553 contains one 80x30mm stamp.

Opening of Movie, *Harry Potter and
the Prisoner of Azkaban* — A886

No. 3554: a, $5, Harry, messenger owl, Hedwig, with letter. b, $5, Hedwig, rose background. c, $5, Harry riding Hippogriff. d, $5, Hippogriff, green background. e, $5, Harry, Monster Book of Monsters. f, $25, Crookshanks the Cat.
No. 3555: a, $5, Harry playing quidditch. b, $5, Harry playing quidditch, Dementors. c, $5, Harry and Hermoine riding Hippogriff. d, $5, Harry holding wand, Hogwarts. e, $5, Harry practicing Patronus Charm to repel Dementors. f, $25, Harry thrusting wand.

2004, June 4   Perf. 12
Sheets of 6, #a-f
3554-3555 A886 Set of 2 10.00 6.00

Nos. 3554-3555 were not sold directly to customers at foreign addresses but were made available abroad through Canada Post's philatelic agency.

Old Train
Stations
A887

Designs: No. 3556, $5, Keelung Station, rickshaws. No. 3557, $5, Taipei Station, automobile. $15, Hsinchu Station, ox and cart. $25, Taichung Station, wagons.

2004, June 9   Perf. 13½x13¾
3556-3559 A887 Set of 4 3.50 1.50
Compare Type A887 with Types A926-A929.

Iron Fort,
Nangan
Island
A888

Cinbi,
Beigan
Island
A889

Fujheng,
Tungchu
Island
A890

Lienyuyikeng, Tungyin Island — A891

2004, July 1 Litho. Perf. 11½x11¼
3560 A888 $5 multi .40 .20
3561 A889 $5 multi .40 .20
3562 A890 $9 multi .70 .25
3563 A891 $25 multi 1.90 .75
Nos. 3560-3563 (4) 3.40 1.40

Matsu National Scenic Area.

Crabs
A892

Designs: No. 3564, $3.50, Uca formosensis. No. 3565, $3.50, Uca borealis. $5, Uca arcuata. $25, Uca lactea.

2004, July 21
3564-3567 A892 Set of 4 2.50 1.10

Souvenir Sheet

Listening to the Lute, Attributed to Li
Sung — A893

No. 3568: a, $5, Lute player. b, $25, Scholar and woman.

2004, Aug. 6   Perf. 12
3568 A893 Sheet of 2, #a-b 2.50 2.50

Souvenir Sheet

Taipei 2005 Intl. Stamp
Exhibition — A894

No. 3569: a, $5, Sun Moon Lake. b, $25, Mt. Ali.

2004, Aug. 27   Perf. 11½x11¼
3569 A894 Sheet of 2, #a-b 3.00 3.00

Intl. Day of
Peace
A895

2004, Sept. 21   Perf. 12¼x11¾
3570 A895 $15 multi 1.25 .55

Souvenir Sheets

Hello Kitty — A896

No. 3571, oval stamps: a, $5, Dear Daniel, donuts. b, $15, Hello Kitty, Taipei 101 Building.
No. 3572, rectangular stamps: a, $5, Hello Kitty, bird, horiz. b, $15, Dear Daniel, Fisherman's Wharf, Danshuei.

2004, Sept. 24   Perf.
3571 A896 Sheet of 2, #a-b 1.75 1.25
Perf. 12
3572 A896 Sheet of 2, #a-b 1.75 1.25

**Sayings With Numbers Greeting
Stamps**

One Sea
of Smooth
Sailing
A897

Two Lions
Bring
Good
Fortune
A898

Three Goats of
Auspiciousness — A899

Safety in
All Four
Seasons
A900

Five
Blessings
at the
Door
A901

Six is Silky
Smooth
A902

Married for
Seven
Lives
A903

Eight
Immortals
Wish for
Your
Perfection
A904

Nine
Means
Success
A905

Ten is All
Around
Perfection
A906

2004, Oct. 10   Perf. 12½
3573 Block of 10 3.25 1.10
a. A897 $3.50 multi .30 .20
b. A898 $3.50 multi .30 .20
c. A899 $3.50 multi .30 .20

d.	A900 $3.50 multi	.30	.20
e.	A901 $3.50 multi	.30	.20
f.	A902 $3.50 multi	.30	.20
g.	A903 $3.50 multi	.30	.20
h.	A904 $3.50 multi	.30	.20
i.	A905 $3.50 multi	.30	.20
j.	A906 $3.50 multi	.30	.20

Changed Colors

3574	Block of 10	4.25	1.50
a.	A897 $5 multi	.40	.20
b.	A898 $5 multi	.40	.20
c.	A899 $5 multi	.40	.20
d.	A900 $5 multi	.40	.20
e.	A901 $5 multi	.40	.20
f.	A902 $5 multi	.40	.20
g.	A903 $5 multi	.40	.20
h.	A904 $5 multi	.40	.20
i.	A905 $5 multi	.40	.20
j.	A906 $5 multi	.40	.20
k.	Sheet, #3574a-3574j + 10 attached labels ('04)	11.00	11.00

No. 3574k sold for $170 and has labels, which could be personalized, that are separated from the stamps by simulated perforations. Issued 10/10/04.

Kaohsiung Medical University. 50th Anniv. A907

Designs: No. 3575, $5, University gate and buildings. No. 3576, $5, Building, researcher, beaker, mosquito and snake.

2004, Oct. 16   **Perf. 12½**
| 3575-3576 | A907 | Set of 2 | 1.00 | .50 |

Main Peak, Mt. Cilai A908

North Peak, Mt. Cilai A909

South Peak, Mt. Cilai A910

Grasslands, Mt. Cilai — A911

2004, Oct. 16   **Perf. 11½x11¼**
3577	A908	$5 multi	.35	.20
3578	A909	$5 multi	.35	.20
3579	A910	$12 multi	.95	.35
3580	A911	$25 multi	1.90	.75
	Nos. 3577-3580 (4)		3.55	1.50

Sports In Which Taiwanese Athletes Won Medals At 2004 Summer Olympics A912

Designs: No. 3581, $5, Women's Taekwondo. No. 3582, $5, Men's Taekwondo, vert. $9, Archery. $12, Athletes on winner's platform, vert.

Perf. 11¼x11½, 11½x11¼
2004, Oct. 22
| 3581-3584 | A912 | Set of 4 | 2.50 | 1.25 |

Platalea Minor A913

Designs: No. 3585, $2.50, Pair in flight. No. 3586, $2.50, Pair standing on one leg. $15, With wings spread. $25, Foraging for food. $20, Birds in water.

2004, Oct. 30   **Perf. 13¼x13¼**
| 3585-3588 | A913 | Set of 4 | 3.50 | 1.65 |

Souvenir Sheet
| 3589 | A913 | $20 multi | 2.25 | 1.00 |

No. 3589 contains one 80x30mm stamp.

Pres. Yen Chia-kan (1905-93) A914

2004, Nov. 5   **Perf. 13¼x13½**
| 3590 | A914 | $12 multi | 1.10 | .45 |

New Year 2005 (Year of the Cock) — A915

Designs: $3.50, Cock on lantern. $13, Lanterns, cock. $5, Cock, hen and chick, horiz.

2004, Nov. 10   **Perf. 12¼x11¾**
| 3591-3592 | A915 | Set of 2 | 1.25 | .90 |

Souvenir Sheet
Perf. 11¾x11¼
| 3593 | A915 | $5 multi | .60 | .45 |

No. 3593 contains one 46x26mm stamp.

Prefectural Hall, Chiayi A916

East Gate, Chiayi A917

2004, Nov. 20   **Perf. 13½x13¼**
| 3594 | A916 | $5 multi | .50 | .30 |
| 3595 | A917 | $5 multi | .50 | .30 |

Chiayi, 300th anniv.

Embroidered Squares for Ching Dynasty Civil Official Court Dresses — A918

Designs: No. 3596, $3.50, Manchurian crane (orange background). No. 3597, $3.50, Golden pheasant (green background). $5, Peacock. $25, Goose.

2005, Jan. 20 Litho.   **Perf. 11½x11¼**
| 3596-3599 | A918 | Set of 4 | 2.40 | 1.25 |

See Nos. 3727-3730.

Greetings A919

No. 3600 — Cartoon balloon with various keyboard characters creating faces and backgrounds with: a, Hands. b, Envelopes. c, Hearts. d, Flowers.

2005, Jan. 31   **Perf. 12½**
3600	Horiz. strip of 4	1.60	.85
a.-d.	A919 $5 Any single	.40	.25
e.	Sheet, #3600a-3600d + 4 attached labels	11.50	11.50

No. 3600e sold for $140 and has labels, which could be personalized, that are separated from the stamps by simulated perforations. Sheets exist with various arrangements of stamps and positions of labels respective to the stamps (at left, above or below).

Rotary International, Cent. — A920

Rotary emblem and: $5, Map of Taiwan. $12, Dove.

2005, Feb. 23   **Perf. 13½x13¼**
| 3601-3602 | A920 | Set of 2 | 1.25 | 1.00 |

Mangroves A921

Designs: No. 3603, $3.50, Kandelia obovata. No. 3604, $3.50, Rhizophora stylosa. No. 3605, $3.50, Avicennia marina. No. 3606, $5, Lumnitzera racemosa.

2005, Mar. 10   **Perf. 11½x11¼**
| 3603-3606 | A921 | Set of 4 | 1.25 | 1.00 |

Longshan Temple, Mengjia A922

Lin Ben Yuan Garden, Banciao A923

Designs: $13, Chaotain Temple, Beigang. $15, Fort Anping, Tainan.

2005, Mar. 18
3607	A922	$5 multi	.35	.20
3608	A923	$5 multi	.35	.20
3609	A923	$13 multi	.85	.40
3610	A923	$13 multi	.95	.45
	Nos. 3607-3610 (4)		2.50	1.25

Souvenir Sheet

Taipei 2005 Intl. Stamp Exhibition — A924

No. 3611 — a, $5, Wood carving, Mandarin Ducks Playing in a Lotus Pond. b, $25, Hand puppets, horiz.

2005, Apr. 19   **Perf. 12**
| 3611 | A924 | Sheet of 2, #a-b | 3.00 | 3.00 |

Coral Reef Fish A925

Designs: No. 3612, $5, Rhinomuraena quaesita. No. 3613, $5, Pomacanthus semicirculatus. $12, Forcipiger flavissimus. $25, Pterois volitans.

2005, May 16   **Perf. 11½x12**
| 3612-3615 | A925 | Set of 4 | 3.50 | 1.75 |
| a. | Sheet, 2 each #3612-3615 | 7.00 | 7.00 |

Changhua Train Station, 1918 A926

Chiayi Train Station, 1933 A927

Tainan Train Station, 1936
A928

Kaohsiung Train Station, 1941
A929

2005, June 9   **Perf. 13½x13¾**
3616 A926 $5 multi   .40 .20
3617 A927 $5 multi   .40 .20
3618 A928 $15 multi   1.10 .50
3619 A929 $25 multi   1.75 .80
   Nos. 3616-3619 (4)   3.65 1.70

Compare with type A887.

Novel "The Romance of the Three Kingdoms"
A930

Designs: No. 3620, $3.50, Mayhem in the Fengyi Pavilion (man and woman near pavilion railing). No. 3621, $3.50, Deterring the Enemy in Changban (horse and rider on bridge). $5, Releasing Tsao Tsao (rider on horse near flag). $20, A Trick in the Bag (man in bed holding bag).

2005, June 23   **Litho.**
Perf. 11½x11¼
3620-3623 A930 Set of 4   2.50 2.00
3623a   Souvenir sheet, #3620-3623   2.50 2.00

Lifeline Suicide Prevention Hotline — A931

2005, July 1   **Perf. 12x11½**
3624 A931 $12 multi   1.25 .90

Albert Einstein's Theory of Relativity, Cent. — A932

2005, July 1
3625 A932 $15 multi   1.25 .60

Souvenir Sheets

Mickey Mouse — A933

No. 3626: a, $5, At ship's wheel, in *Steamboat Willie*. b, $25. As wizard, in *Fantasia*.

No. 3627: a, $5, Holding sword, in *The Prince and the Pauper*. b, $25. With Pluto, in *Mickey's Twice Upon a Christmas*.

2005, Aug. 3   **Perf. 12**
Sheets of 2, #a-b
3626-3627 A933 Set of 2   4.00 2.00

Rooster-shaped Wine Vessel — A934

2005, Aug. 19   **Perf. 11¼x11½**
3628 A934 $15 multi   .95 .45
   a.   Sheet of 6, perf. 12   5.75 3.00

Taipei 2005 Intl. Stamp Exhibition.

Souvenir Sheets

A935

A936

A937

A938

A939

Taipei 2005 Intl. Stamp Exhibition — A940

No. 3629: a, $5, Green Island and shoreline. b, $25, Formosan rock monkey.

No. 3630: a, $5, Microscope. b, $25, DNA double helices, vert.

No. 3631: a, $5, Flowers. $25, Fruit.

No. 3632: a, $5, Ear Shooting Ceremony, vert. b, $25, Dragon boat in race.

No. 3633: a, $5, Bowl of food and ladle. b, $25, Rice cakes.

No. 3634: a, $5, Royal empress angelfish. b, $25, Red horny coral.

2005   **Perf.**
3629 A935 Sheet of 2, #a-b   2.50 .95
Perf. 13½x13, 13x13½
3630 A936 Sheet of 2, #a-b   2.50 .95
Perf. 13½
3631 A937 Sheet of 2, #a-b   2.50 .95
Perf. 13¼x13½, 13½x13¼
3632 A938 Sheet of 2, #a-b   2.50 .95
Perf. 12
3633 A939 Sheet of 2, #a-b   2.50 .95
Perf.
3634 A940 Sheet of 2, #a-b   2.50 .95
   Nos. 3629-3634 (6)   15.00 5.70

Issued: No. 3629, 8/19; No. 3630, 8/20; No. 3631, 8/21; No. 3632, 8/22; No. 3633, 8/23; No. 3634, 8/24. No. 3629 contains two 38mm diameter stamps. No. 3634 contains two 43x33mm oval stamps.

Novel, "Journey to the West" — A941

Designs: No. 3635, $3.50, Stone Monkey (monkeys at waterfall). No. 3636, $3.50, Buddhist Baby in the River. $5, Making a Pass at Chang E. $20, Taming the Monster of the River of Flowing Sands.

2005, Sept. 15   **Perf. 11¼x11½**
3635-3638 A941 Set of 4   2.40 1.90

Souvenir Sheet

Kaohsiung 2005 Intl. Stamp Exhibition — A942

No. 3639: a, $5, Loyalty and Filial Piety, by Cian Syuan, vert. b, Gilt scepter.

Perf. 13¼x13½, 13½x13¼

2005, Oct. 7
3639 A942   Sheet of 2, #a-b   2.00 2.00

Souvenir Sheets

A943

Opening of Movie, *Harry Potter and the Goblet of Fire* — A944

No. 3640: a, $5, Triwizard Cup. b, $5, Harry and Hungarian Horntail. c, $5, Golden Egg. d, $5, Harry swimming. e, $5, Harry summoning Firebolt with wand. f, $25, Harry and Triwizard Cup.
No. 3641: a, $5, Hungarian Horntail. b, $5, Harry on Firebolt. c, $5, Voldemort's snake, Nagini. d, $5, Grindylows. e, $5, Dumbledore's phoenix, Fawkes. f, $25, Merchieftainess.

2005, Nov. 18   **Perf. 12**
3640 A943   Sheet of 6, #a-f   5.00 2.50
3641 A944   Sheet of 6, #a-f   5.00 2.50

New Year 2006 (Year of the Dog) — A945

Designs: $3.50, Dog at left. $13, Dog at lower right.
$12, Three dogs, horiz.

2005, Dec. 1   **Perf. 12¼x11¾**
3642-3643 A945   Set of 2   1.25 1.00
Souvenir Sheet
Perf. 11¾x11¼
3644 A945 $12 multi   1.25 .70
No. 3644 contains one 46x26mm stamp.

Pets — A946

Designs: $3.50, Siberian husky. $5, Golden retriever. $12, Himalayan cat. $25, Scottish fold cat.

Perf. 13½x12½
2005, Dec. 22   **Litho.**
Country Name in Green
3645 A946 $3.50 multi   .30 .20
3646 A946 $5 multi   .40 .20
3647 A946 $12 multi   .80 .35
3648 A946 $25 multi   1.50 .75
     Nos. 3645-3648 (4)   3.00 1.50
See Nos. 3652-3655, 3685-3688 3712-3715.

Tea Ceremony A947

No. 3649: a, Preparation of tea set (dull orange panel). b, Placing of tea leaves in pot (lemon panel). c, Pouring hot water over pots and cups (light green panel). d, Drying of pot and pouring of tea (blue geen panel). e, Smelling and drinking of tea (gray blue panel).

2006, Jan. 26   **Perf. 13½**
3649   Horiz. strip of 5   2.00 1.00
a.-e.   A947 $5 Any single   .40   .25

Taipei 101 Building — A948

Designs: $5, In day. $12, At night.

2006, Feb. 23   **Perf. 12**
3650-3651 A948   Set of 2   1.25 .70

Pets Type of 2005
Designs: $2.50, Labrador retriever. $7, St. Bernard. $10, Siamese cat. $32, Persian cat.

2006, Mar. 8   **Perf. 13½x12½**
Country Name in Blue
3652 A946 $2.50 multi   .20 .20
3653 A946 $7 multi   .45 .20
3654 A946 $10 multi   .60 .30
3655 A946 $32 multi   2.00 1.00
     Nos. 3652-3655 (4)   3.25 1.70
See Nos. 3712-3715.

King Penguins A949

Aptenodytes patagonicus: No. 3656, $5, Adult and juvenile. No. 3657, $5, Courtship. $9, Swimming and diving, horiz. $12, Gliding and preening, horiz.
$15, Colony, horiz.

Perf. 11¼x11½, 11½x11¼
2006, Mar. 26
3656-3659 A949   Set of 4   2.40 2.00
Souvenir Sheet
Perf. 12
3660 A949 $15 multi   1.60 1.00
No. 3660 contains one 80x30mm stamp.

Miniature Sheet

Children's Art — A950

No. 3661 — Winning drawings in children's stamp design competition: a, Birds with black bills. b, People with red faces. c, Pheasants. d, Chinese celebration. e, Fishing boats and catch. f, People with large flowers and fruit. g, Man painting Chinese lantern. h, Bridge and ducks. i, Train. j, Bees and flowers. k, People with black faces. l, Boy on ladder. m, People and chickens. n, Ring of people around dancers and musicians. o, People and large lions. p, Two cats. q, People and cow. r, Whale and fish. s, People with white faces bending backwards. t, Bus.

2006, Apr. 4   **Perf. 11½**
3661 A950 $5 Sheet of 20, #a-t   6.50 3.50

Fireflies A951

Designs: No. 3662, $5, Pyrocoelia analis. No. 3663, $5, Diaphanes citrinus. No. 3664, $5, Diaphanes niveus. No. 3665, $5, Diaphanes formosus.

2006, May 25   **Perf. 13½x13¼**
3662-3665 A951   Set of 4   1.60 .75

Souvenir Sheet

Completion of Nangang to Suao Section of National Expressway 5 — A952

2006, June 16   **Litho.**   **Perf. 11½**
3666 A952 $12 multi   1.50 .80

Souvenir Sheets

Winnie the Pooh — A953

No. 3667: a, $5, Winnie the Pooh pushing Piglet in wheelbarrow. b, $25, Winnie the Pooh, Piglet and Tigger floating in inner tube.
No. 3668: a, $5, Winnie the Pooh and Piglet running in autumn. b, $25, Winnie the Pooh and Tigger ice fishing.

2006, June 21   **Perf. 12**
Sheets of 2, #a-b
3667-3668 A953   Set of 2   4.00 2.00

Tourism Greeting Stamps A954

Designs: Nos. 3669a, 3670a, Satchel and cliff. Nos. 3669b, 3670b, Camera and boat. Nos. 3669c, 3670c, Notebook, pen and bridge. No. 3669d, 3670d, Sailboat and rock. No. 3669e, 3670e, Heart and train.

2006, June 30   **Perf. 12½**
3669   Horiz. strip of 5   1.50 .55
a.-e.   A954 $3.50 Any single   .30 .20
f.   Sheet, 2 each #3669a-3669e, +
        5 labels   7.00   —
3670   Horiz. strip of 5   2.00 .80
a.-e.   A954 $5 Any single   .40 .20
f.   Sheet, 2 each #3670a-3670e, +
        5 labels   7.00   —
Nos. 3669f and 3670f each sold for $100.
Labels could be personalized.

Fish A955

Designs: No. 3671, $5, Amphiprion ocellaris. No. 3672, $5, Zanclus cornutus. No. 3673, $12, Coris gaimard. No. 3674, $12, Oxycirrhites typus.

2006, July 14   **Perf. 11½**
3671-3674 A955   Set of 4   2.40 2.00
3674a   Miniature sheet, 2 each
           #3671-3674, perf. 11½x12 4.75 4.75

A956

A957

Sung Dynasty Calligraphy and Painting — A957

Designs: $5, Poem by Huang T'ing-chien. $9, Calligraphy on silk, by Mi Fu. Nos. 3677, 3679a, $12, Detail of magpie in flight, from Magpies and Hare, by Ts'ui Po. Nos. 3678, 3679b, $15, Detail of magpie on branch, from Magpies and Hare.

2006, Aug. 4   *Perf. 11½*
Denominations in Black
3675-3678 A956   Set of 4   2.75 1.40
Souvenir Sheet
Denominations in Black and Orange
Perf. 12½
3679 A957   Sheet of 2, #a-b   2.25 1.10

Dragonflies
A958

Designs: Nos. 3680, 3684a, $5, Crocothemis servilia servilia. Nos. 3681, 3684b, $5, Orthetrum, pruinosum neglectum, vert. Nos. 3682, 3684c, $12, Diplacodes trivialis, vert. No. 3683, 3684d, $12, Orthetrum sabina sabina.

Perf. 13x13¼, 13¼x13
2006, Aug. 16
With White Frames
3680-3683 A958   Set of 4   2.40 2.00
Souvenir Sheet
Without White Frames
Perf. 11¾
3684 A958   Sheet of 4, #a-d   2.40 2.00

Pets Type of 2005
Designs: $1, Yorkshire terrier. $9, Pomeranian. $15, Abyssinian cat. $20, Norwegian Forest cat.

2006, Aug. 30   *Perf. 13½x12½*
Country Name in Blue
3685 A946 $1 multi   .20   .20
3686 A946 $9 multi   .55   .25
3687 A946 $15 multi   .90   .45
3688 A946 $20 multi   1.25   .60
   Nos. 3685-3688 (4)   2.90 1.50

Aerial
Activities — A959

Designs: No. 3689, $3.50, Paragliding. No. 3690, $3.50, Hang gliding, horiz. $12, Ultralight aircraft, horiz. $15, Parasailing.

2006, Sept. 15   *Perf. 13½*
3689-3692 A959   Set of 4   2.75 1.50

Pitta
Nympha — A960

Designs: Nos. 3693, 3697a, $5, On branch. Nos. 3694, 3697b, $5, In flight, horiz. Nos. 3695, 3697c, $10, With young at nest, horiz. Nos. 3696, 3697d, $10, With insect in beak.

Perf. 13¼x13, 13x13¼
2006, Sept. 30
With White Frames
3693-3696 A960   Set of 4   2.25 1.10
Souvenir Sheet
Without White Frames
Perf. 11¾
3697 A960   Sheet of 4, #a-d   2.25 1.10

Cetaceans
A961

Designs: No. 3698, $5, Stenella attenuata. No. 3699, $5, Stenella longirostris. $10, Feresa attenuata. $15, Physeter macrocephalus.

Perf. 13x12 Syncopated
2006, Oct. 18   Litho.
3698-3701 A961   Set of 4   2.50 1.50
3701a   Souvenir sheet, #3698-3701   2.50 1.50

Flowers
A962

Designs: No. 3702, $5, Ludwigia octovalvis. No. 3703, $5, Hygrophila pogonocalyx, vert. $12, Titanotrichum oldhamii, vert.

2006, Nov. 8   *Perf. 11½*
3702-3704 A962   Set of 3   1.60   .80

Scenic Areas — A963

Designs: No. 3705, $5, Jhongshan Building, Yangmingshan National Park. No. 3706, $5, Taroko Gorge, vert. $9, Queen's Head Rock, vert. $12, Sun Moon Lake.

2006, Nov. 11   *Perf. 12½*
3705-3708 A963   Set of 4   2.25 1.10

A964

New Year 2007 (Year of the Pig) — A965

Designs: $3.50, Pig on drum. $13, Pig and drums.

2006, Dec. 1   *Perf. 12¼x11¾*
3709-3710 A964   Set of 2   1.25   .60
Souvenir Sheet
Perf. 11½x11¼
3711 A965 $12 multi   1.25   .60

Pets Type of 2005
Designs: 50c, Border collie. $13, Beagle. $17, American Shorthair cat. $34, Maine Coon cat.

2006, Dec. 18   *Perf. 13½x12½*
Country Name in Green
3712 A946 50c multi   .20   .20
3713 A946 $13 multi   .80   .40
3714 A946 $17 multi   1.10   .55
3715 A946 $34 multi   2.10 1.10
   Nos. 3712-3715 (4)   4.20 2.25

Inauguration of High Speed Rail
Line — A966

No. 3716: a, 700T Series train. b, Hsinchu Station.
Illustration reduced.

2006, Dec. 25   *Perf. 11½*
3716 A966 $12 Horiz. pair, #a-b   1.50   .75

Orchids — A967

Designs: $3.50, Phaius tankervilleae. $5, Spiranthes sinensis. $12, Vanda x hybrida. $25, Cattleya sp.

2007, Jan. 10   Litho.   *Perf. 13½x12½*
3717 A967 $3.50 multi   .25   .20
3718 A967 $5 multi   .30   .20
3719 A967 $12 multi   .75   .35
3720 A967 $25 multi   1.50   .70
   Nos. 3717-3720 (4)   2.80 1.50
   See Nos. 3751-3754, 3768-3771.

Ching
Dynasty
Jewelry
A968

Designs: No. 3721, $5, Earrings. No. 3722, $5, Hairpin. $12, Fingernail guard. $25, Ring.

2007, Jan. 17   *Perf. 11½*
3721-3724 A968   Set of 4   3.00 1.50

Valentine's
Day — A969

Heart and faces in: $5, White. $20, Red.

2007, Feb. 6
3725-3726 A969   Set of 2   1.50   .75

Embroidered Squares Type of 2005
Embroidered squares for Ching Dynasty military officials: No. 3727, $3.50, Cilin (light green background). No. 3728, $3.50, Lion (light orange background). $5, Leopard (bright orange background). $25, Tiger (light blue background).

2007, Feb. 16   *Perf. 11½x11¼*
3727-3730 A918   Set of 4   2.25 1.10

Feb. 28,
1947
Massacre
Memorial
Museum
A970

2007, Feb. 28
3731 A970 $5 multi   4.00   .20

Bridges
A971

Designs: No. 3732, $5, Kanjin Bridge, Taoyuan (green panel). No. 3733, $5, Fusing Bridge, Luofu (purple panel). $12, MacArthur Second Bridge, Taipei. $15, Dajhih Bridge, Taipei.

2007, Apr. 12   Litho.   *Perf. 11½x12*
3732-3735 A971   Set of 4   2.25 1.10
   See Nos. 3808-3811.

Lesser
Panda
A972

Panda: No. 3736, $5, Eating bamboo. No. 3737, $5, Resting on rock. No. 3738, $10, Walking near tree, vert. No. 3739, $10, Scratching on rock, vert.
$12, Two pandas, vert.

Perf. 11½x11¼, 11¼x11½
2007, Apr. 25   Set of 4   1.90   .95
3736-3739 A972
Souvenir Sheet
Perf. 12
3740 A972 $12 multi   .75   .35
   No. 3740 contains one 40x50mm stamp.

Dharma Drum
Mountain Intl.
Buddhist
Educational
Complex — A973

Chung Tai Chan
Monastery
A974

Fo Guang Shan
Monastery
A975

Tzu Chi
Foundation
Building — A976

2007, May 24   *Perf. 13¼x13*
3741 A973 $5 multi   .30   .20
3742 A974 $5 multi   .30   .20
3743 A975 $5 multi   .30   .20
3744 A976 $5 multi   .30   .20
   Nos. 3741-3744 (4)   1.20   .80

Dahlia and Butterflies A977

Iris and Butterfly A978

Clematis and Ladybugs A979

Tung Blossom and Butterflies A980

Rose and Butterfly A981

Sunflower and Insects — A982

Bird-of-Paradise Flower and Butterfly A983

Lotus and Butterflies A984

English Daisies and Dragonfly A985

Balloon Flower and Dragonfly A986

2007, May 28   *Perf. 12½*
3745   Block of 10   2.10 1.10
a. A977 $3.50 multi .20 .20
b. A978 $3.50 multi .20 .20
c. A979 $3.50 multi .20 .20
d. A980 $3.50 multi .20 .20
e. A981 $3.50 multi .20 .20
f. A982 $3.50 multi .20 .20
g. A983 $3.50 multi .20 .20
h. A984 $3.50 multi .20 .20
i. A985 $3.50 multi .20 .20
j. A986 $3.50 multi .20 .20

Changed Colors
3746   Block of 10   3.00 1.50
a. A977 $5 multi .30 .30
b. A978 $5 multi .30 .30
c. A979 $5 multi .30 .30
d. A980 $5 multi .30 .30
e. A981 $5 multi .30 .30
f. A982 $5 multi .30 .30
g. A983 $5 multi .30 .30
h. A984 $5 multi .30 .30
i. A985 $5 multi .30 .30
j. A986 $5 multi .30 .30

Food Preparation Implements — A987

Designs: No. 3747, $5, Rice bucket and shelf (light blue background). No. 3748, $5, Steamer (green background). No. 3749, $12, Rice baskets (tan background). No. 3750, $12, Dinnerware (lilac background).

2007, June 28   *Perf. 11½x11¼*
3747-3750 A987 Set of 4   2.10 1.10

Orchids Type of 2007 Inscribed "Taiwan" Instead of "Republic of China"
Designs: $1, Paphiopedilum sp. $2.50, Phalaenopsis aphrodite. $10, Dendrobium sp. $32, Oncidium x hybridum.

2007, July 12   *Perf. 13½x12½*
3751 A967 $1 multi .20 .20
3752 A967 $2.50 multi .20 .20
3753 A967 $10 multi .60 .30
3754 A967 $32 multi 2.00 1.00
Nos. 3751-3754 (4) 3.00 1.70

End of Martial Law, 20th Anniv. — A988

2007, July 15   *Perf. 11¼x11½*
3755 A988 $12 multi .75 .35

Fish A989

Designs: No. 3756, $5, Nemateleotris magnifica. No. 3757, $5, Balistoides conspicillum. $12, Paracanthurus hepatus. $25, Cetoscarus bicolor.

2007, July 27   *Perf. 11½x11¼*
3756-3759 A989 Set of 4   5.50 1.60

Chiang Wei-shui (1890-1931), Political and Social Leader — A990

2007, Aug. 6 Engr.   *Perf. 11¼x11½*
3760 A990 $25 brown   1.50 .75

Taiwan - African Heads of State Summit, Taipei A991

2007, Sept. 9 Litho.   *Perf. 11½x11¼*
3761 A991 $12 multi   .90 .55

Miniature Sheet

Eighteen Scholars of T'ang, by Emperor Hui-tsung. — A992

No. 3762 — Various portions of painting numbered: a, (10-5), 36x30mm. b, (10-4), 51x30mm. c, (10-3), 43x30mm. d, (10-2), 45x30mm. e, (10-1), 43x30mm. f, (10-10), 43x30mm. g, (10-9), 51x30mm. h, (10-8), 43x30mm. i, (10-7), 45x30mm. j, (10-6), 36x30mm.

2007, Sept. 21   *Perf. 13¼*
3762 A992 Sheet of 10 3.00 1.50
a.-j. $5 Any single .30 .20

Doves — A993

2007, Sept. 28   *Perf. 11¼x11½*
3763 A993 $5 multi   .60 .30

Portions of the design were applied by a thermographic process producing a shiny, raised effect.

Shells A994

Designs: No. 3764, $5, Marchia loebbeckei. No. 3765, $5, Harpa major. No. 3766, $12, Epitonium scalare. No. 3767, $12, Cypraea aurantium.

2007, Oct. 11 Litho.   *Perf. 11½x11¼*
3764-3767 A994 Set of 4   2.10 1.10

Orchids Type of 2007 Inscribed "Taiwan" Instead of "Republic of China"
Designs: $7, Ascocentrum sp. $9, Arundina graminifolia. $15, Vanda teres. $20, Epidendrum sp.

2007, Oct. 24   *Perf. 13½x12½*
3768 A967 $7 multi .45 .20
3769 A967 $9 multi .55 .30
3770 A967 $15 multi .95 .45
3771 A967 $20 multi 1.25 .60
Nos. 3768-3771 (4) 3.20 1.55

Birds — A995

Designs: $3.50, Pericrocotus solaris. $5, Parus varius. $12, Luscinia calliope. $25, Phoenicurus auroreus.

2007, Nov. 3
3772 A995 $3.50 multi .25 .20
3773 A995 $5 multi .30 .20
3774 A995 $12 multi .75 .35
3775 A995 $25 multi 1.60 .80
Nos. 3772-3775 (4) 2.90 1.55

See Nos. 3792-3795, 3819-3822, 3845-3848.

Outdoor Activities — A996

Designs: No. 3776, $5, Speed walking. No. 3777, $5, Cycling. $12, Skateboarding. $25, Rollerblading.

2007, Nov. 9   *Perf. 11½*
3776-3779 A996 Set of 4   3.00 1.50

Scouting, Cent. — A997

2007, Nov. 28   *Perf. 12½*
3780 A997 $12 multi   .75 .35

A998

New Year 2008 (Year of the Rat) — A999

2007, Dec. 3   *Perf. 12½x11¾*
3781 A998 $3.50 Rat at left .30 .20
3782 A998 $13 Rat at right .90 .40

Souvenir Sheet
Perf. 12½

3783 A999 $12 multi   1.25 .60

Democracy
Movement
Leaders
A1000

Designs: No. 3784, Lei Chen (1897-1979),
publisher. No. 3785, Fu Jheng (1927-91), editor. No. 3786, Kuo Yu Shing (1908-85), politician. No. 3787, Huang Hsin Chieh (1928-99),
politician.

2007, Dec. 10   Engr.   Perf. 11½

3784 A1000 $5 brown   .30 .20
3785 A1000 $5 green   .30 .20
3786 A1000 $5 claret   .30 .20
3787 A1000 $5 brown black   .30 .20
      Nos. 3784-3787 (4)   1.20 .80

Liou Family Compound,
Shangfangliao — A1001

Lin Family Mansion, Banciao — A1002

Li Teng-fang Compound,
Dasi — A1003

Siao Family Compound,
Jiadong — A1004

2008, Jan. 23   Litho.   Perf. 12

3788 A1001 $5 multi   .30 .20
3789 A1002 $5 multi   .30 .20
3790 A1003 $5 multi   .30 .20
3791 A1004 $12 multi   .75 .40
      Nos. 3788-3791 (4)   1.65 1.00

Birds Type of 2007

Designs: $1, Dicrurus aeneus. $2.50,
Lanius schach. $10, Dendrocitta formosae.
$32, Pycnonotus sinensis.

2008, Jan. 30   Perf. 13½x12½

3792 A995 $1 multi   .20 .20
3793 A995 $2.50 multi   .20 .20
3794 A995 $10 multi   .65 .30
3795 A995 $32 multi   2.00 1.00
      Nos. 3792-3795 (4)   3.05 1.70

A1005

Puppet Theater — A1006

No. 3796: a, Mirror Man, denomination at
UL. b, Old Oddball, denomination at UR.
No. 3797: a, Shih Yan-wun, denomination at
UL. b, Dragon Lady of the Bitter Sea, denomi-
nation at UR.

2007, Feb. 4   Perf. 11½

3796 A1005 $5 Horiz. pair, #a-b   .65 .30
3797 A1006 $5 Horiz. pair, #a-b   .65 .30
   c. Souvenir sheet, #3796-3797,
        perf. 11½x11   1.30 .60

Syrmaticus Mikado — A1007

Litho. & Engr.
2008, Mar. 7   Perf. 12
3798 A1007 $25 multi   1.75 .85

Taipei 2008 Intl.
Stamp
Exhibition
A1008

Paintings: $5, Plum Blossoms and Solitary
Bird, by Pien Wen-chin. $9, Apricot Blossoms
and Peacocks, by Lu Chi. $13, Wild Duck by a
Brook, by Ch'en Lin. $15, Bamboo and Shrike,
by Li An-chung.

2008, Mar. 7   Litho.   Perf. 12½
3799-3802 A1008 Set of 4   2.75 1.40
3802a   Souvenir sheet, #3799-
          3802, perf. 12½ synco-
          pated   2.75 1.40

Miniature Sheets

A1009

Characters From Animated Film,
"Finding Nemo" — A1010

No. 3803: a, Turtles (32mm diameter). b,
Dory (26x34mm). c, Bubbles (32mm diame-
ter). d, Nemo (34x26mm). e, Pearl (32mm
diameter).
No. 3804 (all stamps 32mm diameter): a,
Sheldon. b, Squirt. c, Tad. d, Nemo. e, Peach.

Perf. 13x13½ (#3803b), 13½x13
(#3803d)

2008, Apr. 3
3803 A1009 $5 Sheet of 5, #a-e   1.75 .85
3804 A1010 $5 Sheet of 5, #a-e   1.75 .85

Cactus
Flowers — A1011

Designs: No. 3805, $5, Hylocerus undatus.
No. 3806, $5, Thelocactus bicolor. $12, Rhip-
salidopsis gaertneri.

2008, Apr. 30 Litho. Perf. 11¼x11½
3805-3807 A1011   Set of 3   1.50 .75

Bridges Type of 2007 Inscribed
"Taiwan"

Designs: No. 3808, $5, Wurih Bridge,
Taichung. No. 3809, $5, Jilu Bridge, Nantou, at
night. $12, Shueiyun Bridge, Shueili. $15,
Sindong Bridge, Miaoli.

2008, May 12   Perf. 11½x11¼
3808-3811 A971   Set of 4   2.50 1.25

A1012

A1013

A1014

Inauguration of President Ma Ying-
jeou and Vice-president Vincent C.
Siew — A1015

2008, May 20   Perf. 13½x13¼
3812 A1012 $5 multi   .35 .20
3813 A1013 $5 multi   .35 .20
3814 A1014 $13 multi   .85 .45
3815 A1015 $15 multi   1.00 .50
   a. Miniature sheet, #3812-3815,
        perf. 12   2.60 1.40
      Nos. 3812-3815 (4)   2.55 1.35

Yellow Tiger
Flag
A1016

Portrait of
Jheng
Cheng-gong
A1017

2008, May 29   Perf. 12½
Stamps With White Frames
3816 A1016 $5 multi   .35 .20
3817 A1017 $25 multi   1.75 .85
Souvenir Sheet
Perf. 13½
Stamps Without White Frames
3818   Sheet of 2   2.10 1.10
   a. A1016 $5 multi   .35 .20
   b. A1017 $25 multi   1.75 .85

National Taiwan Museum, cent.

Birds Type of 2007

Designs: $7, Streptopelia orientalis. $15,
Passer montanus. $20, Pica pica. $34, Zosterops japonicus.

2008, June 5   Perf. 13½x12½
3819 A995 $7 multi   .50 .25
3820 A995 $15 multi   1.00 .50
3821 A995 $20 multi   1.40 .70
3822 A995 $34 multi   2.25 1.10
      Nos. 3819-3822 (4)   5.15 2.55

Stag
Beetles — A1018

Designs: No. 3823, $5, Neolucanus
swinhoei. No. 3824, $5, Dorcus schenklingi.
$10, Lucanus datunensis. $12, Cyclommatus
asahinai.

2008, June 5   Perf. 12¼
3823-3826 A1018   Set of 4   2.10 1.10

Shells
A1019

Designs: No. 3827, $5, Murex troscheli. No.
3828, $5, Lambis chiragra. No. 3829, $12,
Spondylus regius. No. 3830, $12, Cymatium
pyrum.

2008, July 9   Litho.   Perf. 13½
3827-3830 A1019   Set of 4   2.25 1.10

Urocissa
Caerulea
A1020

Designs: Nos. 3831, 3835a, $5, Adults feed-
ing hatchlings in nest. Nos. 3832, 3835b, $5,

Bird holding snake in beak. Nos. 3833, 3835c, $12, Bird in flight. Nos. 3834, 3835d, $12, Bird on branch with spread wings.

2008, July 9   **Perf. 13x13¼**
Stamps With White Frames
3831-3834 A1020 Set of 4   2.25 1.10
Souvenir Sheet
Stamps Without White Frames
Perf. 11¾
3835 A1020 Sheet of 4, #a-d   2.25 1.10
No. 3835 contains four 34x25mm stamps.

Miniature Sheet

A Hundred Deers, by Ignace
Sichelbart — A1021

No. 3836 — Parts of painting numbered: a, 8-1 (45x38mm). b, 8-2 (55x38mm). c, 8-3 (45x38mm). d, 8-4 (43x38mm). e, 8-5 (37x38mm). f, 8-6 (43x38mm). g, 8-7 (43x38mm). h, 8-8 (65x38mm).

2008, July 16   **Perf. 13¼**
3836 A1021 Sheet of 8, #a-h   2.60 1.40
a.-h. $5 Any single   .30 .20

Items From
Aboriginal
Culture — A1022

Designs: $5, Paiwan earthenware pot. No. 3838, $12, Ami lover's bag (orange background). No. 3839, $12, Rukai men's headdress (green background). $25, Bunun men's neck ornament.

2008, Aug. 1   **Perf. 11¼x11½**
3837-3840 A1022 Set of 4   3.50 1.75

Miniature Sheet

Yimin Festival — A1023

No. 3841: a, Erection of lantern poles. b, Bowl of congee, spoon, flowers. c, Sinpu Yimin Temple, horiz. d, Pig competition, horiz.

2008, Aug. 20   **Litho.**   **Perf. 12½**
3841 A1023 $5 Sheet of 4, #a-d   1.25 .65

New Year 2009
(Year of the
Ox) — A1024

Designs: $3.50, Head of ox. $13, Ox. $12, Ox in water, horiz.

2008, Dec. 1   **Perf. 12¼x11¾**
3842-3843 A1024 Set of 2   1.00 .50
Souvenir Sheet
Perf. 11¾x11¼
3844 A1024 $12 multi   .75 .35
No. 3844 contains one 50x30mm stamp.

Birds Type of 2007 Inscribed
"Republic of China (Taiwan)"

Designs: 50c, Rostratula benghalensis. $9, Turdus poliocephalus. $13, Amaurornis phoenicurus. $17, Cettia acanthizoides.

2009, Jan. 15   **Perf. 13½x12½**
3845 A995 50c multi   .20 .20
3846 A995 $9 multi   .55 .25
3847 A995 $13 multi   .80 .40
3848 A995 $17 multi   1.00 .50
    Nos. 3845-3848 (4)   2.55 1.35

Giant
Pandas in
Taipei Zoo
A1025

Designs: $5, Tuan Tuan on log bridge. $9, Yuan Yuan eating.
$25, Tuan Tuan and Yuan Yuan.

2009, Jan. 20   **Perf. 11½x11¼**
3849-3850 A1025 Set of 2   .85 .40
Souvenir Sheet
Perf. 12
3851 A1025 $25 multi   1.50 1.00
No. 3851 contains one 50x40mm stamp.

Ceremonial
Objects
A1026

Designs: No. 3852, $5, Gift basket with handle, two women in background. No. 3853, $5, Wooden box, men carrying box in background. No. 3854, $12, Bridal sedan chair, wedding procession in background. No. 3855, $12, Candlesticks, bride and groom holding incense sticks in background.

2009, Feb. 10   **Perf. 11½x11¼**
3852-3855 A1026 Set of 4   2.25 1.10

Shells
A1027

Designs: No. 3856, $5, Strombus sinuatus. No. 3857, $5, Hydatina amplustre. No. 3858, $12, Cymatium hepaticum. No. 3859, $12, Mitra mitra.

2009, Feb. 26   **Perf. 13½**
3856-3859 A1027 Set of 4   2.25 1.10

Flowers — A1028

Designs: $3.50, Lantana camara. $5, Murraya paniculata. $12, Tabebuia chrysantha. $25, Hibiscus sabdariffa.

2009, Mar. 12   **Perf. 13½x12½**
3860 A1028 $3.50 multi   .20 .20
3861 A1028 $5 multi   .30 .20
3862 A1028 $12 multi   .75 .35
3863 A1028 $25 multi   1.50 .75
    Nos. 3860-3863 (4)   2.75 1.50
See Nos. 3890-3893, 3934-3937.

Opening of Red and Orange Lines of
Kaohsiung Mass Rapid Transit System
A1029

Train and: $5, Central Park Station. $25, World Games Station.

2009, Apr. 7   **Perf. 11½x11¼**
3864-3865 A1029 Set of 2   2.00 1.00

A1030

Pres. Chiang Ching-kuo (1910-
88) — A1031

Pres. Chiang: No. 3866, $5, Wearing hat (gray panel). No. 3877, $5, Wearing suit and tie (dull purple panel). $10, Holding cane (blue panel), horiz. $12, Holding baby (brown panel), horiz.

Perf. 11¼x11½, 11½x11¼
2009, Apr. 13
3866-3869 A1030 Set of 4   1.90 .95
Souvenir Sheet
3870 A1031 $25 shown   1.60 .75

Carp Encircled By Dragons Type of
1997 With Denominations at Lower
Right and Inscribed "Republic of
China (Taiwan)"

2009, May 20   **Engr.**   **Perf. 13¼x12½**
3871 A745 $50 blue   3.25 1.60

Miniature Sheet

Butterflies — A1032

No. 3872: a, $5, Papilio xuthus (butterfly cutout at LL). b, $5, Troides aeacus formosanus (butterfly cutout at LR). c, $12, Graphium agamemnon (butterfly cutout at UL). d, Papilio paris nakaharai (butterfly cutout at UR).

2009, June 25   **Litho.**   **Perf. 11½x12**
3872 A1032 Sheet of 4, #a-d   2.10 1.10

2009 World Games,
Kaohsiung — A1033

Designs: $5, Kaohsiung Arena and World Games mascots Kao Mei and Syong Ge. $12, Main Stadium and World Games emblem.

2009, July 16   **Perf. 12**
3873-3874 A1033 Set of 2   1.10 .55
3874a   Souvenir sheet, #3873-
3874   1.10 .55

Ancient Art
Treasures — A1034

Designs: No. 3875, $5, Two Qing Dynasty gold gourds. No. 3876, $5, Gold bowl used by Emperor Qianlong. No. 3877, $12, Mughal Empire inlaid round urn. No. 3878, $12, Qing Dynasty gilt ewer.

2009, July 20   **Perf. 12¼**
3875-3878 A1034 Set of 4   2.10 1.10
3878a   Souvenir sheet, #3875-
3878, perf. 12¼x11¾   2.10 1.10

Sites in Kinmen — A1035

Designs: $5, Guningtou. $9, Zhaishan Tunnel. No. 3881, $10, Interior of Qingtian Hall. No. 3882, $10, Lake Taihu.

2009, July 29   **Perf. 12½**
3879-3882 A1035 Set of 4   2.10 1.10

Paintings by Lin Yu-shan (1907-
2004) — A1036

No. 3883: a, $5, On the Way Home. b, $25, Two Heads of Cattle.
Illustration reduced.

2009, Aug. 7   **Litho.**   **Perf. 12½x12**
3883 A1036 Horiz. pair, #a-b, +
     central label   1.90 .95

Nursery
Rhymes — A1037

Designs: No. 3884, $5, Little Girl and Her Doll (blue denomination). No. 3885, $5, Kingdom of Dolls (king and soldier on horses, yellow denomination). No. 3886, $5, Train, horiz. (red denomination). No. 3887, $5, Thunder Shower, horiz. (fish, fireflies, lotus flower, denomination in orange).

2009, Aug. 26   **Perf. 12¼**
3884-3887 A1037 Set of 4   1.25 .60

21st Summer Deaflympics,
Taipei — A1038

Designs: $5, Badminton, running. $25,
Taekwondo, tennis.

2009, Sept. 5   **Perf. 11½**
3888-3889 A1038   Set of 2   1.90   .95

Flowers Type of 2009

Designs: $1, Calliandra emarginata. $2.50,
Bombax ceiba. $10, Delonix regia. $32,
Spathodea campanulata.

2009, Oct. 14   Litho.   Perf. 13½x12½
3890	A1028	$1 multi	.20	.20
3891	A1028	$2.50 multi	.20	.20
3892	A1028	$10 multi	.65	.30
3893	A1028	$32 multi	2.00	1.00
		Nos. 3890-3893 (4)	3.05	1.70

Greetings
A1039

No. 3894: a, Necklace (orange background).
b, Gift boxes (pink background). c, Bouquet of
roses (yellow background). d, Lollipop and
candy (light blue background). e, Balloons
(orange red background). f, Champagne flutes
(blue violet background). g, Hearts (yellow
green background). h, Cake and strawberry
(red background). i, Sparklers (red violet background). j, Four-leaf clover (green
background).

No. 3895: a, Necklace (orange red background). b, Gift boxes (yellow green background). c, Bouquet of roses (pink background). d, Lollipop and candy (yellow
background). e, Balloons (red background). f,
Champagne flutes (red violet background). g,
Hearts (orange background). h, Cake and
strawberry (green background). i, Sparklers
(blue background). j, Four-leaf clover (yellow
background).

2009, Nov. 12   **Perf. 12½**
3894	Block of 10	2.50	1.25
a.-j.	A1039 $3.50 Any single	.25	.20
3895	Block of 10	3.00	1.50
a.-j.	A1039 $5 Any single	.30	.20

Nos. 3894 and 3895 were each printed in
sheets containing two blocks + 5 labels.

Ferns — A1040

Designs: $5, Asplenium nidus. $9, Cyathea
spinulosa. $12, Cyathea lepifera. $25, Cibo-
tium taiwanense.

2009, Nov. 26   **Perf. 11¼x11½**
3896-3899	A1040	Set of 4	3.25	1.60
3899a		Souvenir sheet, #3896-3899	3.25	1.60

A1041

New Year 2010 (Year of the
Tiger) — A1042

Tiger at: $3.50, Left. $13, Right.

2009, Dec. 1   **Perf. 12¼x12½**
3900-3901 A1041   Set of 2   1.10   .55

Souvenir Sheet

Perf. 12½
3902 A1042 $12 multi   .75   .35

Anti-Corruption
Day — A1043

Background color: $5, Light blue. $25, Lilac.

2009, Dec. 9   **Litho.**   **Perf. 11½**
3903-3904 A1043   Set of 2   1.90   .95

Flowers Type of 2009

Designs: $7, Michelia champaca. $15,
Duranta repens. $20, Ixora chinensis. $34,
Lagerstroemia speciosa.

2010, Jan. 20   **Perf. 13½x12½**
3905	A1028	$7 multi	.45	.20
3906	A1028	$15 multi	.95	.45
3907	A1028	$20 multi	1.25	.65
3908	A1028	$34 multi	2.25	1.10
		Nos. 3905-3908 (4)	4.90	2.40

Lin An-tai Historical Home,
Taipei — A1044

Li Family Compound, Luzhou — A1045

Lin Family Compound,
Wufeng — A1046

Xiaoyun Villa, Shengang — A1047

2010, Feb. 9   **Perf. 13½x13¼**
3909	A1044	$5 multi	.35	.20
3910	A1045	$5 multi	.35	.20
3911	A1046	$5 multi	.35	.20
3912	A1047	$12 multi	.75	.35
		Nos. 3909-3912 (4)	1.80	.95

Little
Taiwan,
Qimei Islet
A1048

Whale
Arch,
Xiamoen
Islet
A1049

Scenery of Penghu Islands: No. 3914,
Basalt rocks, Xiamoen Islet. No. 3916, Heart-
shaped stone weir, Qimei Islet.

2010, Feb. 24   **Perf. 13½**
3913	A1048	$5 shown	.35	.20
3914	A1048	$5 multi	.35	.20
3915	A1049	$10 shown	.65	.30
3916	A1049	$10 multi	.65	.30
		Nos. 3913-3916 (4)	2.00	1.00

Bridges
A1050

Designs: No. 3917, $5, Jinde Bridge, Dong-
gang (shown). No. 3918, $5, Qigu River
Bridge, Tainan. No. 3919, $12, Anyi Bridge,
Tainan. No. 3920, $12, Wangyue Bridge, Tai-
nan (blue bridge at night).

2010, Mar. 10   **Perf. 11½**
3917-3920 A1050   Set of 4   2.25   1.10

Mushrooms
A1051

Designs: Nos. 3921, 3925a, $5, Dictyphora
multicolor. Nos. 3922, 3925b, $5, Pleurotus
salmoneostramineus. Nos. 3923, 3925c, $12,
Psuedocolus fusiformis. Nos. 3924, 3925d,
$12, Coprinus disseminatus.

2010, Mar. 25   **Perf. 13**
Stamps With White Frames
3921-3924 A1051   Set of 4   2.25   1.10
Miniature Sheet
Stamps Without White Frames
Perf. 11¾
3925 A1051   Sheet of 4, #a-d   2.25   1.10

Crabs
A1052

Designs: No. 3926, $5, Cardisoma carnifex.
No. 3927, $5, Scandarma lintou. $10,
Sesarmops intermedius. $25, Gecarcoidea
lalandii.

2010, Apr. 15   **Perf. 11½**
3926-3929 A1052   Set of 4   3.00   1.50

Scenes
From The
Romance
of the
Three
Kingdoms
A1053

Designs: No. 3930, $3.50, Shooting an
Arrow at the Halberd Beside the Gate of the
Camp (shown). No. 3931, $3.50, Commenting
on Heroes Over Wine. $5, Zhou Yu's Anger at
Being Tricked by Zhuge Liang Three Times.
$20, Holding Meng Huo Captive Seven Times.

2010, Apr. 29   **Perf. 11½**
3930-3933	A1053	Set of 4	2.10	1.10
3933a		Sheet of 4, #3930-3933, perf. 12	2.10	1.10

Flowers Type of 2009

Designs: 50c, Bauhinia variegata. $9,
Euphorobia milii. $13, Brunfelsia hopeana.
$17, Plumeria rubra.

2010, May 12   Litho.   Perf. 13½x12½
3934	A1028	50c multi	.20	.20
3935	A1028	$9 multi	.55	.30
3936	A1028	$13 multi	.80	.40
3937	A1028	$17 multi	1.10	.55
		Nos. 3934-3937 (4)	2.65	1.45

Long-horned
Beetles
A1054

Designs: 75c, Erythrus formosanus. $2.50,
Rosalia formosa conviva. $5, Aphrodisium
faldermannii yuagii. $25, Anoplophora hor-
sfieldi tonkinensis.

2010, May 21   **Perf. 12½x13½**
3938	A1054	75c multi	.20	.20
3939	A1054	$2.50 multi	.20	.20
3940	A1054	$5 multi	.30	.20
3941	A1054	$25 multi	1.60	.80
		Nos. 3938-3941 (4)	2.30	1.40

Girl Scouts, Cent. — A1055

Emblems and: $5, Two doves, stylized
globe. $25, Dove, ribbon hearts.

2010, June 1   **Perf. 12½**
3942-3943 A1055   Set of 2   1.90   .95

Souvenir Sheet

Water Buffaloes, Sculpture by Huang
Tu-shui (1895-1930) — A1056

Litho. & Embossed
2010, June 22   **Perf. 11½x11¼**
3944 A1056 $25 multi   1.60   .80

A1057

Scenes From Novel "Journey to the West" — A1058

Designs: No. 3945, Complete Enlightenment. No. 3946, Sun Wukong Wreaks Havoc in Heaven. No. 3946, \$12, Dreaming of Beheading the Jing River Dragon King. \$25, Stealing the Ginseng Fruits.

2010, July 7 Litho. Perf. 11¼x11½
3945	A1057	\$5 multi	.35	.20
3946	A1058	\$5 multi	.35	.20
3947	A1058	\$12 multi	.75	.35
3948	A1058	\$25 multi	1.60	.80
	Nos. 3945-3948 (4)		3.05	1.55

Lighthouses
A1059

Designs: No. 3949, \$5, Chilung Tao Lighthouse (denomination in yellow). No. 3950, \$5, Wenkan Tui Lighthouse (denomination in blue). \$10, Paisha Chia Lighthouse, horiz. \$25, Liuchiu Yu Lighthouse, horiz.

Perf. 11¼x11½, 11½x11¼
2010, July 28
3949-3952	A1059	Set of 4	3.00	1.50

Modern Taiwanese Paintings — A1060

No. 3953: a, \$5, Bamboo Grove in Early Summer, by Tsai Yun-yan. b, \$25, Pear Espalier, by Lu Yun-sheng.

2010, Aug. 9 Perf. 12x12½
3953	A1060	Horiz. pair, #a-b, + central label	1.90	.95

Souvenir Sheet

Nine Elders of Mt. Hsiang, by Unknown Painter — A1061

No. 3954: a, \$5, Servant and elders playing game (35mm diameter). b, \$25, Three elders and dancer (35mm diameter). c, \$25, Elders in bamboo grove (37x29mm oval stamp).

2010, Sept. 9 Perf.
3954	A1061	Sheet of 3, #a-c	3.50	1.75

Stamps Depicting Educators
A1062

Designs: \$5, Republic of China #293 (Chu Hsi). \$25, Republic of China #1798 (Confucius).

Perf. 11¼x11½
2010, Sept. 28 Litho.
3955-3956	A1062	Set of 2	1.90	.95

Shells
A1063

Designs: No. 3957, \$5, Thatcheria mirabilis. No. 3958, \$5, Tibia martinii. No. 3959, \$12, Stellaria solaris. No. 3960, \$12, Rapa rapa.

2010, Oct. 4 Perf. 11½x11¼
3957-3960	A1063	Set of 4	2.25	1.10

Bridges
A1064

Designs: No. 3961, \$5, Lizejian Bridge, Yilan (shown). No. 3962, \$5, Taroko Bridge, Hualien. \$12, Hongye Bridge, Taitung. \$15, Pudu Bridge, Hualien.

2010, Oct. 20
3961-3964	A1064	Set of 4	2.50	1.25

National Taipei University of Technology, Cent. — A1065

No. 3965: a, \$5, Building, old gate. b, \$25, Sixth Instructional Building, Technology Building, new gate.

2010, Nov. 1 Perf. 12½
3965	A1065	Horiz. pair, #a-b	2.00	1.00

SEMI-POSTAL STAMPS

SP1

Red or Blue Surcharge
1920, Dec. 1 Unwmk. Perf. 14, 15
B1	SP1	1c on 2c green	5.00	2.00
B2	SP1	3c on 4c scar (B)	8.00	3.00
B3	SP1	5c on 6c gray	12.00	5.00
	Nos. B1-B3 (3)		25.00	10.00

The surcharge represents the actual franking value. The extra cent helped victims of the 1919 Yellow River flood.

War Refugees SP2

Black Surcharge
1944, Oct. 10 Engr. Perf. 12
B4	\$2 +\$2 on 50c + 50c		2.00	2.00
B5	\$4 +\$4 on 8c + 8c		2.00	2.00
B6	\$5 +\$5 on 21c + 21c		2.00	2.00
B7	\$6 +\$6 on 28c + 28c		4.00	4.00
B8	\$10 +\$10 on 33c + 33c		5.00	5.00
B9	\$20 +\$20 on \$1 + \$1		6.00	6.00
a.	Sheet of 6, #B4-B9		45.00	45.00
	Nos. B4-B9 (6)		21.00	21.00

The borders of each stamp differ slightly in design. The surtax was for war refugees.
Nos. B4-B8 exist without surcharge, but were not regularly issued.

Great Wall of China — SP4   Chinese Refugee Family — SP5

1948, July 5 Litho. Perf. 14, Imperf.
Without Gum
Cross in Carmine
B11	SP4	\$5000 + \$2000 vio	.50	2.50
B12	SP4	\$10,000 + \$2000 brn	.50	2.50
B13	SP4	\$15,000 + \$2000 gray	.50	2.50
a.	Cross omitted			
	Nos. B11-B13 (3)		1.50	7.50

The surtax was for anti-tuberculosis work. Fakes of B13a exist with cross chemically removed. No genuine used copies are known.

Republic of China (Taiwan)
1954, Oct. 1 Engr. Perf. 12
Without Gum
B14	SP5	40c + 10c dp bl	25.00	5.00
B15	SP5	\$1.60 + 40c lil rose	67.50	26.00
B16	SP5	\$5 + \$1 red	125.00	110.00
	Nos. B14-B16 (3)		217.50	141.00

The surtax was used to aid in the evacuation of Chinese from North Viet Nam.

> **Catalogue values for unused stamps in this section, from this point to the end of the section, are for Never Hinged items.**

Sept. 21, 1999 Earthquake Relief — SP6

a, Damaged buildings, map, rescue workers. b, Hands, heart, earthquake fault.

1999, Nov. 1 Litho. Imperf.
Sheet of 2
B17	SP6	\$25 +\$25, #a.-b.	9.00	9.00

No. B17 has simulated perforations.

Souvenir Sheet

Typhoon Morakot Relief — SP7

No. B18: a, Map of Taiwan surrounded by clouds, rescuers and rafts. b, House, construction equipment and workers.

2009, Oct. 9 Litho. Imperf.
B18	SP7	\$25 +\$25 Sheet of 2, #a-b	7.00	7.00

No. B18 has simulated perforations.

AIR POST STAMPS

Curtiss "Jenny" over Great Wall (Bars of Republic flag on tail) — AP1

Unwmk.
1921, July 1 Engr. Perf. 14
C1	AP1	15c bl grn & blk	34.00	34.00
C2	AP1	30c scar & blk	34.00	34.00
C3	AP1	45c dull vio & blk	34.00	34.00
C4	AP1	60c dk blue & blk	40.00	40.00
C5	AP1	90c ol grn & blk	55.00	55.00
	Nos. C1-C5 (5)		197.00	197.00

(Nationalist sun emblem on tail) — AP2

1929, July 5
C6	AP2	15c blue grn & blk	5.00	1.00
C7	AP2	30c dk red & blk	9.00	3.00
C8	AP2	45c dk vio & blk	18.00	8.00
C9	AP2	60c dk blue & blk	20.00	11.00
C10	AP2	90c ol grn & blk	18.00	18.00
	Nos. C6-C10 (5)		70.00	41.00

Junkers F-13 over Great Wall AP3

1932-37
C11	AP3	15c gray grn	.45	.45
C12	AP3	25c orange ('33)	.55	.45
C13	AP3	30c red	7.00	.45
C14	AP3	45c brown vio	1.00	.45
C15	AP3	50c dk brown ('33)	1.00	.45
C16	AP3	60c dk blue	1.00	.45
C17	AP3	90c olive grn	1.00	.45
C18	AP3	\$1 yellow grn ('33)	1.25	.45
C19	AP3	\$2 brown ('37)	3.00	2.00
C20	AP3	\$5 brown car ('37)	5.00	4.00
	Nos. C11-C20 (10)		21.25	9.60

See #C21-C40. For surcharges and overprints see #C41-C52, C54-C60, 9N111-9N114, 9NC1-9NC7, Szechwan C1, C3-C6, Sinkiang C5-C19.

Type of 1932-37, with secret mark

1932-37 Issue. Lower part of left
character joined

Secret Mark, 1940-41 Issue.
Separated.

Perf. 12, 12½, 12½x13, 13
1940-41   **Wmk. 261**

C21	AP3	15c gray green	.50	.50
C22	AP3	25c yellow org	.50	.50
C23	AP3	30c red	.50	.50
a.		Vert. pair, imperf. between	200.00	
C24	AP3	45c dull rose vio ('41)	.50	.50
C25	AP3	50c brown	.50	.50
C26	AP3	60c dp blue ('41)	.50	.50
C27	AP3	90c olive ('41)	.50	.50
C28	AP3	$1 apple grn ('41)	.50	.50
C29	AP3	$2 lt brown ('41)	.50	.50
C30	AP3	$5 lake	1.25	1.25
		Nos. C21-C30 (10)	5.75	5.75

Unwmk.
Perf. 12½, 13, 13½

C31	AP3	15c gray green ('41)	.45	.30
C32	AP3	25c lt orange ('41)	.45	.30
C33	AP3	30c lt red ('41)	.45	.30
C34	AP3	45c dl rose vio ('41)	.45	.30
C35	AP3	50c brown	.45	.30
C36	AP3	60c blue ('41)	.45	.30
C37	AP3	90c lt olive ('41)	.45	.30
C38	AP3	$1 apple grn ('41)	.65	.65
C39	AP3	$2 lt brown ('41)	1.50	1.50
C40	AP3	$5 lake ('41)	1.25	1.25
		Nos. C31-C40 (10)	6.55	5.50

For surcharges see note following No. C20.

Nos. C11 and C12 Surcharged

1946, May 2   Unwmk.   Perf. 14

C41	AP3	$53 on 15c	1.25	3.50
C42	AP3	$73 on 25c	1,700.	1,700.

Forgeries of No. C42 exist.

On Nos. C23, C21, C22, C29 and C30
Perf. 13, 13x12, 12½
Wmk. 261

C43	AP3	$23 on 30c red	.50	.35
C44	AP3	$53 on 15c gray grn	19.00	25.00
C45	AP3	$73 on 25c yel org	.50	.35
C46	AP3	$100 on $2 lt brown	1.25	.50
C47	AP3	$200 on $5 lake	.50	.50
		Nos. C43-C47 (5)	21.75	26.70

On Nos. C33, C31, C32, C39 and C40
Perf. 13, 13x12, 13x12½, 12½
Unwmk.

C48	AP3	$23 on 30c lt red	.25	1.00
a.		Inverted surcharge	100.00	
b.		"2300" omitted	50.00	
c.		Last character (kuo) of surch. omitted	65.00	
C49	AP3	$53 on 15c gray grn	.25	1.00
a.		Horiz. pair, imperf. btwn.	675.00	
C50	AP3	$73 on 25c lt org	.25	1.50
a.		Inverted surcharge	525.00	
C51	AP3	$100 on $2 lt brn	.25	.40
C52	AP3	$200 on $5 lake	.25	.25
a.		Inverted surcharge	80.00	
		Nos. C48-C52 (5)	1.25	4.15

The surcharges on #C41-C52 represent
Chinese natl. currency and were applied at
Shanghai.

Douglas DC-4 over Sun Yat-sen
Mausoleum, Nanking — AP4

1946, Sept. 10   Litho.   Perf. 14
Without Gum

C53	AP4	$27 blue	.35	1.00

For surcharges see #C61, Szechwan C2.

No. C23 Surcharged in Black

Perf. 13x12
1948, May 18   Wmk. 261

C54	AP3	$10,000 on 30c red	.20	1.00

Same, in Black or Carmine, on Nos.
C33, C32, C37, C36, C18 and C38
Unwmk.
Perf. 12½, 13x12½, 14

C55	AP3	$10,000 on 30c lt red	.25	.75
C56	AP3	$20,000 on 25c lt org	.25	.75
C57	AP3	$30,000 on 90c lt ol (C)	.25	1.00
C58	AP3	$50,000 on 60c blue (C)	.25	1.00
C59	AP3	$50,000 on $1 yel grn (C) (#C18)	125.00	125.00
C60	AP3	$50,000 on $1 ap grn (C) (#C38)	.25	.90

No. C53 Surcharged in Black

Perf. 14

C61	AP4	$10,000 on $27 bl	.50	3.00
		Nos. C54-C61 (8)	126.95	133.40

Douglas DC-4 and
Arrow — AP5

Perf. 12½
1949, May 2   Unwmk.   Litho.
Without Gum

C62	AP5	blue green	5.00	5.50
a.		Rouletted	7.00	8.00

See note after No. 959.
For overprints see Taiwan #C1, Fukien #C1,
Kansu #C1, PRC #26, 102.

Revenue Stamp
Overprinted in Blue

1949, May   Engr.   Perf. 14

C63	A95	$100 olive green	40.00	40.00

See note after No. 962.

Republic of China (Taiwan)

Cheng Ch'eng-kung
(Koxinga) — AP6

Rouletted
1950, Sept. 26   Unwmk.   Typo.
Without Gum

C64	AP6	60c deep blue	14.00	7.00

For surcharge see No. 1120.

Plane over City
Gate,
Taipei — AP7

Jet Planes
above Chung
Shan
Bridge — AP8

Two Doves
Near Koxinga
Shrine — AP9

1954   Engr.   Perf. 11½
Without Gum

C65	AP7	$1 dk brown	11.00	1.00
a.		Vert. pair, imperf. btwn.		200.00
C66	AP8	$1.60 olive blk	14.00	.80
a.		Vert. pair, imperf. btwn.	140.00	
b.		Horiz. pair, imperf. btwn.	100.00	110.00
C67	AP9	$5 grnsh blue	20.00	1.75
		Nos. C65-C67 (3)	45.00	3.55

Issued: #C66, 8/14; #C65, C67, 9/1.

No. C67 Surcharged in Red
1958, Dec. 11
Without Gum

C68	AP9	$3.50 on $5 grnsh bl	4.00	1.50

> Catalogue values for unused
> stamps in this section, from this
> point to the end of the section, are
> for Never Hinged items.

Sea Gull
AP10

Sabre Jets in
Bomb Burst
Formation
AP11

1959, Mar. 20   Photo.   Perf. 13

C69	AP10	$8 blue, gray & blk	5.50	.40

1960, Feb. 29   Unwmk.   Perf. 13

Plane Formations: $2, Loop, horiz. $5, Diamond formation passing over grounded plane,
horiz.

C70	AP11	$1 multicolored	6.50	.50
C71	AP11	$2 multicolored	6.00	.50
C72	AP11	$5 multicolored	10.00	.60
		Nos. C70-C72 (3)	22.50	1.60

Issued to honor the Chinese Air Force and
the "Thunder Tiger" aerobatic team.

Jet Airliner
over Pitan
Bridge
AP12

Designs: $6, Jet over Tropic of Cancer mon-
ument, Kiai, vert. $10, Jet over Lion Head
mountain, Sinchu, vert.

1963, Aug. 14   Photo.   Perf. 13

C73	AP12	$2.50 multi	7.25	.20
C74	AP12	$6 multi	12.50	.40
C75	AP12	$10 multi	16.00	.65
		Nos. C73-C75 (3)	35.75	1.25

Boeing 727 over   Wild Geese
Chilin Pavilion,   Flying over
Grand Hotel   Mountains
AP13   AP14

Design: $8, Boeing 727 over National Pal-
ace Museum, Taipei.

1967, Apr. 1   Unwmk.   Perf. 13

C76	AP13	$5 multicolored	3.75	.25
C77	AP13	$8 multicolored	5.50	.50

1969, Aug. 14   Photo.   Perf. 13

Wild Geese flying over: $5, The sea. $8,
The land, horiz.

C78	AP14	$2.50 multicolored	3.00	.20
C79	AP14	$5 multicolored	4.75	.45
C80	AP14	$8 multicolored	5.75	.60
		Nos. C78-C80 (3)	13.50	1.25

Presidental
Palace and
Tzu-Ch'iang
Squadron
AP15

1980, June 18   Litho.   Perf. 13½

C81	AP15	$5 shown	.25	.20
C82	AP15	$7 China Airlines jet	.70	.30
C83	AP15	$12 China flag, jet	1.00	.50
		Nos. C81-C83 (3)	1.95	1.00

Civil Aeronautics Administration, 37th
Anniv. — AP16

Jet Airliners over: $7, Chiang Kai-shek Intl.
Airport, vert. $11, Chung Cheng Memorial
Hall. $18, Sun Yat-sen Memorial Hall.

Perf. 14x13½, 13½x14
1984, Jan. 20   Litho.

C84	AP16	$7 multicolored	.50	.20
C85	AP16	$11 multicolored	.80	.40
C86	AP16	$18 multicolored	1.00	.60
		Nos. C84-C86 (3)	2.30	1.20

Airplane
AP17

1987, Aug. 4   Litho.   Perf. 13½

C87	AP17	$9 multicolored	.60	.40
C88	AP17	$14 multicolored	.95	.55
C89	AP17	$18 multicolored	1.25	.65
		Nos. C87-C89 (3)	2.80	1.60

SPECIAL DELIVERY STAMPS

Used values of Nos. E1-E8 are for mailer's receipts. Complete unused strips of four are exceptionally scarce because the first section (#1) was to remain in the P.O. booklet.

The mailer received the righthand section (#4), usually canceled, as a receipt. The middle two sections were canceled and attached to the letter. Upon arrival at the destination P.O. they were canceled again, usually on the back, with the righthand copy (#3) retained by that P.O. The lefthand copy (#2) was signed by the recipient and returned to the original P.O. as evidence of delivery. Sections 2 and 3 usually are thin or badly damaged.

Unused strips of three (#2-4) can be found of Nos. E3-E8.

Design: Dragon in irregular oval. Stamp 8x2½ inches, divided into four parts by perforation or serrate rouletting.

"Chinese Imperial Post Office" in lines, repeated to form the background which is usually lighter in color than the rest of the design.

Dragon's head facing downward
Background with period after
"POSTOFFICE."
No Date

1905   Unwmk.   Perf. 11
E1   10c grass green   10,000. 475.00
Serrate Roulette in Black
E2   10c deep green   11,000. 350.00

Type, E3-E8

1907-10
Dragon's head facing forward
Background with no period after
"POSTOFFICE"
No Date

E3   10c light bluish green   1,700. 225.00

1909-11
Background with date at bottom
E4   10c green (Feby
                    1909)   1,300. 200.00
E5   10c bl grn (Jan.
                    1911)   200.00

1912
"IMPERIAL POST OFFICE" in
serifed letters repeated to form the
background.
No Date, No Border
Background of 30 or 28 lines
E6   10c green (30 lines)   90.00
   a.   28 lines   90.00
Background of 35 lines of sans-serif
letters
Colored Border
E8   10c green   175.00

On No. E8 the medallion in the third section has Chinese characters in the background instead of the usual English inscriptions. E6 and E8 occur with many types of four-character overprints reading "Republic of China," applied locally but unofficially at various post offices.

Type, E9, E10

1913
Design: Wild Goose. Stamp 7½x2¾ inches, divided
into five parts.
"CHINESE POST OFFICE" in sans-serif letters, repeated to form the background of 28 lines. With border.
Serrate Roulette in Black
E9   10c green   900.00 50.00

Unused values for Nos. E9-E10 are for complete strips of five parts. Used values are for single parts.

1914
"CHINESE POST OFFICE" in antique
letters, forming a background of
29 or 30 lines. No border.
Serrate Roulette in Green
E10   10c green   110.00 7.00

On No. E9 the background is in sans-serif capitals, the Chinese and English inscriptions are on white tablets and the serial numbers are in black.

On No. E10 the background is in antique capitals and extends under the inscriptions. The serial numbers are in green.

NOTE:
In February, 1916, the Special Delivery Stamps were demonetized and became merely receipts without franking value. To mark this, four of the five sections of the stamp had the letters A, B, C, D either handstamped or printed on them.

SD1

1941   Unwmk.   Typo.   Rouletted
Without Gum
E11   SD1 ($2) car & yel   35.00 32.50

Motorcycle
Messenger — SD2

1949, July   Litho.   Perf. 12½
Without Gum
E12   SD2   red violet   9.00 20.00
   a.   Rouletted   11.00 21.00
See note after No. 959.
For surcharge and overprints see Nos. 1150, Taiwan E1, Fukien E1.

Revenue Stamp
Overprinted in Purple
Brown

1949
Without Gum
E13   A95 $10 grnsh gray   22.00 22.00
See note after No. 962.

REGISTRATION STAMPS

R1

1941   Unwmk.   Typo.   Rouletted
Without Gum
F1   R1 ($1.50) green & buff   21.00 21.00

Mountain Scene — R2

1949, July   Litho.   Perf. 12½
Without Gum
F2   R2   carmine   10.00 13.00
   a.   Rouletted   12.00 18.00
See note after No. 959.
For surcharge and overprints see Nos. 1152, Taiwan F1, Fukien F1, PRC 103.

Revenue Stamp
Overprinted in
Carmine

1949
F3   A95 $50 dark blue   21.00 21.00
See note after No. 962.

POSTAGE DUE STAMPS

Regular Issue of 1902-03 Overprinted in Black

1904   **Unwmk.**   *Perf. 14 to 15*

J1	A17	½c chocolate	8.00	5.00
J2	A17	1c ocher	9.00	5.00
J3	A17	2c scarlet	10.00	6.00
J4	A17	4c red brn	18.00	7.00
J5	A17	5c salmon	20.00	12.00
J6	A17	10c dk blue grn	33.00	20.00
a.	Vert. pair, imperf. btwn.		475.00	
	Nos. J1-J6 (6)		98.00	55.00

D1

1904   *Engr.*

J7	D1	½c blue	2.75	1.00
a.	Horiz. pair, imperf. btwn.		350.00	325.00
J8	D1	1c blue	5.00	1.00
J9	D1	2c blue	3.50	1.60
a.	Horiz. pair, imperf. btwn.		400.00	350.00
J10	D1	4c blue	7.00	4.00
J11	D1	5c blue	9.00	4.00
J12	D1	10c blue	10.00	6.00
J13	D1	20c blue	27.50	6.00
J14	D1	30c blue	35.00	35.00
	Nos. J7-J14 (8)		99.75	58.60

Arabic numeral of value at left on #J12-J14.

1911

J15	D1	1c brown	8.00	5.00
J16	D1	2c brown	14.00	32.50

The ½c, 4c, 5c and 20c in brown exist but were not issued as they arrived in China after the downfall of the Ching dynasty.

Issue of 1904 Overprinted in Red

1912

J19	D1	½c blue	500.	450.
J20	D1	4c blue	565.	565.
J21	D1	5c blue	690.	690.
J22	D1	10c blue	1,050.	1,050.
J23	D1	20c blue	2,000.	2,000.
J24	D1	30c blue	2,000.	2,000.

Nos. J15-J16 exist with this overprint, but were not regularly issued.

Nos. J25-J33

Nos. J34-J42

1912

Overprinted in Red

J25	D1	½c blue	.30	.75
J26	D1	1c brown	.40	.70
a.	Horiz. pair, imperf. btwn.		550.00	
b.	Inverted overprint		225.00	
J27	D1	2c brown	.50	1.00
J28	D1	4c blue	3.50	3.00
J29	D1	5c blue	120.00	125.00
J30	D1	5c brown	2.00	2.75
a.	Inverted overprint		225.00	175.00
J31	D1	10c blue	6.00	4.50
J32	D1	20c blue	11.00	11.00
J33	D1	30c blue	14.00	19.00
	Nos. J25-J33 (9)		157.70	167.70

1912

Overprinted in Black

J34	D1	½c blue	8.75	5.00
J35	D1	½c brown	1.25	1.00
J36	D1	1c brown	1.25	1.00
a.	Inverted overprint		350.00	175.00
J37	D1	2c brown	3.25	5.00
J38	D1	4c blue	7.00	9.50
J39	D1	5c blue	12.00	14.00
a.	Horiz. pair, imperf. btwn.		700.00	
J40	D1	10c blue	12.50	27.50
J41	D1	20c brown	30.00	50.00
J42	D1	30c blue	65.00	65.00
	Nos. J34-J42 (9)		141.00	178.00

D4   D5   D6

Printed by Waterlow & Sons

1913, May   *Perf. 14, 15*

J43	D4	½c blue	.65	.40
a.	Horiz. pair, imperf. btwn.		200.00	
J44	D4	1c blue	1.25	.50
J45	D4	2c blue	2.75	3.00
J46	D4	4c blue	2.10	.90
J47	D4	5c blue	3.25	1.50
J48	D4	10c blue	6.50	7.25
J49	D4	20c blue	16.00	13.00
J50	D4	30c blue	20.00	11.00
	Nos. J43-J50 (8)		52.50	37.55

Printed by the Chinese Bureau of Engraving & Printing

1915   **Re-engraved**   *Perf. 14*

J51	D4	½c blue	.55	1.00
J52	D4	1c blue	1.40	.30
J53	D4	2c blue	1.40	.30
J54	D4	4c blue	1.40	.50
J55	D4	5c blue	2.75	.90
J56	D4	10c blue	3.25	1.25
J57	D4	20c blue	9.00	3.25
J58	D4	30c blue	35.00	12.00
	Nos. J51-J58 (8)		54.75	19.50

In the upper part of the stamps of type D4 there is an ornament of five marks like the letter "V". Below this is a curved label with an inscription in Chinese characters. On the 1913 stamps there are two complete background lines between the ornament and the label. The 1915 stamps show only one unbroken line at this place. There are other minute differences in the engraving of the two issues.

1932   *Perf. 14*

J59	D5	½c orange	.25	.30
J60	D5	1c orange	.25	.30
J61	D5	2c orange	.25	.30
J62	D5	4c orange	.40	.30
J63	D5	5c orange	.40	.30
J64	D5	10c orange	.90	.80
J65	D5	20c orange	1.25	1.00
J66	D5	30c orange	2.00	1.50
	Nos. J59-J66 (8)		5.70	4.80

See Nos. J69-J79. For surcharges see Nos. 1NJ1, 9NJ1-9NJ4.

Regular Stamps of 1939 Overprinted in Black or Red

1940

J67	A57	$1 henna & dk brn (Bk)	2.00	10.00
J68	A57	$2 dl bl & org brn (R)	2.00	10.00

Type of 1932
Printed by The Commercial Press, Ltd.
Perf. 12½, 12½x13, 13

1940-41   *Engr.*

J69	D5	½c yellow orange	.30	.55
J70	D5	1c yellow orange	.30	.55
J71	D5	2c yellow orange ('41)	.30	.55
J72	D5	4c yellow orange	.30	.55
J73	D5	5c yellow orange ('41)	1.00	.50
J74	D5	10c yellow orange ('41)	.30	.50
J75	D5	20c yellow orange ('41)	.30	.50
J76	D5	30c yellow orange	.30	.50
J77	D5	50c yellow orange	.50	.50
J78	D5	$1 yellow orange	.50	1.00
J79	D5	$2 yellow orange	.90	1.00
	Nos. J69-J79 (11)		5.00	6.70

For surcharge see No. 1NJ1.

Thin Paper Without Gum

1944   **Typo.**   *Perf. 13*

J80	D6	10c bluish green	.30	2.00
J81	D6	20c light chalky blue	.30	2.00
J82	D6	40c dull rose	.30	2.00
J83	D6	50c bluish green	.30	2.00
J84	D6	60c dull blue	.30	3.00
J85	D6	$1 dull rose	.30	2.00
J86	D6	$2 lilac brown	.30	2.00
	Nos. J80-J86 (7)		2.10	15.00

D7   D8

1945   **Without Gum**   **Unwmk.**

J87	D7	$2 rose carmine	.40	1.25
J88	D7	$6 rose carmine	.40	1.25
J89	D7	$8 rose carmine	.40	1.25
J90	D7	$10 rose carmine	.40	2.00
J91	D7	$20 rose carmine	.40	2.00
J92	D7	$30 rose carmine	.60	2.00
	Nos. J87-J92 (6)		2.60	9.75

For surcharges see Nos. J102-J109.

Thin Paper Without Gum

1947   **Litho.**   *Perf. 14*

J93	D8	$50 plum	.40	2.00
J94	D8	$80 plum	.40	2.00
J95	D8	$100 plum	.40	2.00
J96	D8	$160 plum	.40	2.00
J97	D8	$200 plum	.40	2.00
J98	D8	$400 violet brown	.40	2.00
J99	D8	$500 violet brown	.40	2.00
a.	Vert. pair, imperf. between		20.00	
J100	D8	$800 violet brown	.40	2.00
J101	D8	$2000 violet brown	.40	2.00
	Nos. J93-J101 (9)		3.60	18.00

Type of 1945, Redrawn
Surcharged with New Value in Black

1948   **Engr.**   *Perf. 13½x14*
Without Gum
Deep claret

J102	D7	$1000 on $20	.40	2.50
J103	D7	$2000 on $30	.40	2.50
J104	D7	$3000 on $50	.40	2.50
J105	D7	$4000 on $100	.40	2.00
J106	D7	$5000 on $200	.40	2.00
J107	D7	$10,000 on $300	.40	1.00
J108	D7	$20,000 on $500	.40	1.00
J109	D7	$30,000 on $1000	.40	.70
	Nos. J102-J109 (8)		3.20	14.20

There are many differences in the redrawn design.

No. 627 Surcharged in Black

1949   *Perf. 12*

J110	A72	1 (c) on $40 orange	.40	10.00
J111	A72	2 (c) on $40 orange	.40	10.00
J112	A72	5 (c) on $40 orange	.40	10.00
J113	A72	10 (c) on $40 orange	.40	10.00
J114	A72	20 (c) on $40 orange	.40	10.00
J115	A72	50 (c) on $40 orange	.40	10.00
J116	A72	$1 on $40 orange	.40	10.00
J117	A72	$2 on $40 orange	.40	10.00
J118	A72	$5 on $40 orange	.60	10.00
J119	A72	$10 on $40 orange	.70	5.00
	Nos. J110-J119 (10)		4.50	95.00

Republic of China (Taiwan)

No. 438 Surcharged in Green or Black

1951   **Unwmk.**   *Perf. 12½*

J120	A47	40c on 40c org (G)	18.00	24.00
J121	A47	80c on 40c org (Bk)	18.00	24.00

Revenue Stamps Surcharged in Various Colors

1953   **Unwmk.**   *Perf. 12½, 14*
Without Gum

J122	A95	10c on $50 dk bl (O)	18.00	4.50
J123	A95	20c on $100 ol grn (Dk Br)	18.00	4.50
J124	A95	40c on $20 org brn	20.00	1.50
J125	A95	80c on $500 sl grn (Dk Bl)	30.00	2.50
J126	A95	$1 on $30 dk vio (G)	30.00	8.25
	Nos. J122-J126 (5)		116.00	21.25

D9   D10

D11

1956   **Unwmk.**   **Litho.**   *Perf. 12½*
Without Gum

J127	D9	20c rose car, & lt bl	1.25	.20
J128	D9	40c green & buff	1.75	.20
J129	D9	80c brown & gray	3.50	.40
J130	D9	$1 ultra & pink	4.00	.40
	Nos. J127-J130 (4)		10.50	1.20

No. 1197 Surcharged in Dark Violet

Wmk. 323
1961, Dec. 28   **Engr.**   *Perf. 12*
Without Gum

J131	A135	$5 on $20 car rose	1.75	.50

Nos. 1274, 1282-1283 Surcharged in Black, Carmine Rose or Blue

1964-65   **Litho.**

J132	A158	10c on 80c pale grn	.20	.20
J133	A158	20c on $3.60 vio bl (CR) ('65)	.30	.20
J134	A158	40c on $4.50 ver (B) ('65)	.65	.40
	Nos. J132-J134 (3)		1.15	.60

1966-76   **Wmk. 323**   *Perf. 12½*
Granite Paper; Without Gum

J135	D10	10c dk brn & lil	.20	.20
J136	D10	20c blue & yel	.40	.20
J137	D10	50c vio bl & lt bl ('70)	.65	.20
J138	D10	$1 purple & sal	.50	.20
J139	D10	$2 grn & lt bl	.65	.20
J140	D10	$5 red & sal	1.25	.30
a.	$5 org red & pale yel		1.25	
J141	D10	$10 lil rose & pink ('76)	22.50	1.00
	Nos. J135-J141 (7)		26.15	2.30

The 50c, $10 and No. J140a are gummed. The $1 and $2 were reissued with gum in

1968 and 1973 respectively. No. J140a and the $10 are on ordinary paper.

Catalogue values for unused stamps in this section, from this point to the end of the section, are for Never Hinged items.

1984-88		**Litho.**	**Perf. 12½**	
J142	D11	$1 rose & violet	.20	.20
J143	D11	$2 yellow & blue	.20	.20
J144	D11	$3 pale grn & brt rose lil	.25	.20
J145	D11	$5 blue & yellow	.25	.20
J146	D11	$5.50 rose lil & brt blue	.40	.35
J147	D11	$7.50 bister yel & dp violet	.60	.45
J148	D11	$10 yel & lil rose	.50	.30
J149	D11	$20 sky blue & citron	1.60	1.25
		Nos. J142-J149 (8)	4.00	3.15

Issued: $3, $5.50, $7.50, $20, Apr. 1, 1988; others, Mar. 15, 1984.

D12

1998, Sept. 30		**Litho.**	**Perf. 12½**	
Background Color				
J150	D12	50c orange yellow	.25	.20
J151	D12	$1 pink	.25	.20
J152	D12	$2 deep pink	.25	.20
J153	D12	$5 yellow green	.40	.20
J154	D12	$10 blue	.75	.30
J155	D12	$20 green	1.60	.60
		Nos. J150-J155 (6)	3.50	1.70

Lotus Flower, Peach, Bats, Coins and Chinese Characters — D13

Perf. 12½x12¼

2008, Nov. 12			**Litho.**	
Denomination Color				
J156	D13	$1 dark red	.20	.20
J157	D13	$3 green	.20	.20
J158	D13	$5 olive green	.30	.20
J159	D13	$10 purple	.60	.30
J160	D13	$20 bister	1.25	.60
		Nos. J156-J160 (5)	2.55	1.50

PARCEL POST STAMPS

PP1

PP2

PP3

1945-48		**Unwmk. Engr.**	**Perf. 13**	
Without Gum				
Q1	PP1	$500 green	12.00	.25
Q2	PP1	$1000 blue	12.00	.25
Q3	PP1	$3000 rose red	22.50	.25
Q4	PP1	$5000 brown	120.00	18.00
Q5	PP1	$10,000 lil gray	195.00	25.00
Q6	PP1	$20,000 red org	2,000.	
		Nos. Q1-Q5 (5)	361.50	43.75

No. Q6 was prepared but not issued.
For surcharges see People's Republic of China Nos. 5LQ1-5LQ2, 5LQ27-5LQ28.

Perf. 12½

Q7	PP2	$3000 red org	18.00	2.00
Q8	PP2	$5000 dk blue	29.00	2.00
Q9	PP2	$10,000 violet	29.00	2.00
Q10	PP2	$20,000 dk red	29.00	2.00

			Perf. 13½	
Q11	PP3	$1000 org yel	6.00	1.00
Q12	PP3	$3000 bl grn	6.00	1.00
Q13	PP3	$5000 org red	6.00	1.00
Q14	PP3	$7000 dl blue	6.00	1.00
Q15	PP3	$10,000 car rose	7.00	1.00
Q16	PP3	$30,000 olive	7.00	1.00
Q17	PP3	$50,000 indigo	7.00	1.00
Q18	PP3	$70,000 org brn	10.00	1.00
Q19	PP3	$100,000 dp plum	10.00	1.00

Denomination Tablet Without Inner Frame

Q20	PP3	$200,000 dk grn	13.00	2.00
Q21	PP3	$300,000 pink	13.00	2.00
Q22	PP3	$500,000 vio brn	13.00	2.50
Q23	PP3	$3,000,000 sl bl	14.00	3.25
Q24	PP3	$5,000,000 lilac	14.00	3.25
Q25	PP3	$6,000,000 ol gray	16.00	4.00
Q26	PP3	$8,000,000 scar	16.00	4.25
Q27	PP3	$10,000,000 sage grn	19.00	5.25
		Nos. Q11-Q27 (17)	183.00	35.50

Zeros for "cents" omitted on Nos. Q23-Q27.
See Taiwan Nos. Q1-Q5. For surcharges see Nos. 883-885, Northeastern Provinces Q1, Szechwan Q1, People's Republic of China 3LQ1-3LQ9, 5LQ3-5LQ16, 5LQ29-5LQ30.

#Q11-Q15, Q23-Q24 Surcharged in Black or Carmine (#Q35)

1949		**Unwmk.**	**Perf. 13½**	
Q32	PP3	$10 on $3000	5.00	.20
Q33	PP3	$20 on $5000	5.00	.20
Q34	PP3	$50 on $10,000	5.00	.20
Q35	PP3	$100 on $3,000,000	6.00	.20
Q36	PP3	$200 on $5,000,000	12.00	.20
Q37	PP3	$500 on $1000	22.50	.20
Q38	PP3	$1000 on $7000	22.50	.30
		Nos. Q32-Q38 (7)	78.00	1.50

5 characters in each line on Nos. Q33-Q38.

MILITARY STAMPS

No. 454 Overprinted in Dull Red

1943-44		**Unwmk.**	**Perf. 12**	
M1	A59	8c turquoise green	2.50	4.25

Nos. 383, 453-454 Overprinted in Red or Black

6mm between characters
Perf. 14, 12½

M2	A57	8c olive green	2.75	4.50
a.		8mm between characters	2.75	4.25
M3	A59	8c red orange (B)	300.00	
M4	A59	8c turquoise green	6.00	5.25

Forgeries of No. M3 abound.

No. 493 Overprinted in Red

Perf. 13

M5	A62	16c dull olive brn	6.00	4.00
a.		Perf. 10½-11	110.00	

No. M5 overprinted in black is a proof.

Stamps of 1942-44 Overprinted in Carmine or Black

M6	A62	50c sage green (C)	2.00	3.50
M7	A62	$1 rose lake	3.00	4.25
M8	A62	$1 dull green	3.00	4.25
M9	A62	$2 dk blue grn (C)	5.00	7.50
M10	A62	$2 dk vio brn ('44)	80.00	80.00
		Nos. M6-M10 (5)	93.00	99.50

Nos. 383 and 357 Overprinted in Red

1944			**Perf. 12, 14**	
M11	A57	8c olive green	3.00	4.50
a.		Right character inverted	160.00	
M12	A57	16c olive gray	47.50	47.50

Anti-Aircraft Guns — M1

1945, Jan. 1	**Typo.**		**Perf. 12½**	
Thin Paper Without Gum				
M13	M1	rose	1.00	6.00

For overprints see Northeastern Provinces Nos. M2-M3.

TAIWAN

(Formosa)
100 Sen = 1 Yen
100 Cents = 1 Dollar

Stamps and Types of Japan (Taiwan) Overprinted in Black

Values in Sen and Yen
Black Overprint

1945		**Unwmk. Litho.**	**Imperf.**	
Stamps Divided by Lines of Colored Dashes				
1	A1	3s carmine	.60	.75
2	A1	5s blue grn	.65	.55
3	A1	10s pale blue	1.10	.55
a.		Inverted overprint	100.00	
b.		Double overprint	110.00	
4	A1	30s dk blue	3.75	5.00
5	A1	40s violet	3.50	4.00
6	A1	50s gray brn	3.75	3.75
7	A1	1y olive grn	4.50	4.75

Same Overprint on Types of Japan

8	A99	5y gray grn	18.00	18.00
9	A100	10y brown vio	26.00	26.00
a.		Inverted overprint	250.00	
		Nos. 1-9 (9)	61.85	63.35

The basic stamps of this issue were prepared by Japanese authorities for Taiwan use before the end of World War II when the island reverted to Chinese control. They are printed on crude buff or white wove paper. The overprint translates: "For Use in Taiwan, Chinese Republic."

A second overprinting of Nos. 2-3 was made with a different font.

China, Nos. 728-731, Surcharged in Black

1946			**Perf. 14**	
Without Gum				
10	A75	70s on $20 green	2.40	5.00
a.		Inverted surcharge	800.00	
11	A75	1y on $30 blue	3.25	5.50
12	A75	2y on $50 dk brn	3.00	5.75
13	A75	3y on $100 car	3.75	5.75
		Nos. 10-13 (4)	12.40	22.00

Convening of the Chinese Natl. Assembly.

China Issues and Types of 1940-1946 Surcharged in Black

a

Perf. 12½, 12½x13, 13, 13x12½, 14

1946-47				
14	A46	2s on 2c dp bl	.20	.50
15	A48	5s on 5c dl red org	.20	.50
16	A39	10s on 4c pale vio	.20	.35
17	A48	30s on 15c brn car	.20	.30
18	A73	50s on $20 car	.30	.25
19	A37	65s on $20 brt yel grn	.35	1.60
20	A47	1y on 20c lt bl	.20	1.10
a.		Inverted surcharge	375.00	
21	A37	1y on $30 choc	.35	1.10
22	A37	2y on $50 red org	.40	.45
23	A73	3y on $100 dk car	.20	.25
24	A73	5y on $200 ol grn	.20	.25
25	A73	10y on $500 brt bl grn	.25	.35
26	A73	20y on $700 red brn	.70	.60
27	A73	50y on $1000 rose lake	1.25	1.25
28	A73	100y on $3000 blue	2.75	.90
		Nos. 14-28 (15)	7.75	9.75

The bottom line of the surcharge expresses the new value and consists of 2, 3 or 4 characters.
Nos. 14, 18-19, 21-28 issued in 1947.

Same Surcharge on China No. 412

1947		**Wmk. 261**	**Perf. 13**	
28A	A48	30s on 15c brn car	110.00	150.00

Type of China, 1946, with additional inscription on both sides of head

1947		**Unwmk. Engr.**	**Perf. 11, 11½**	
29	A74	70c carmine	2.75	3.75
30	A74	$1 green	2.75	3.75
31	A74	$2 vermilion	2.75	3.75
32	A74	$3 yel grn	2.75	3.75
33	A74	$7 yel org	2.75	3.75
34	A74	$10 magenta	2.75	3.75
		Nos. 29-34 (6)	16.50	22.50

60th birthday of Chiang Kai-shek.

Type of China, 1947, with additional inscription above value

1947			**Perf. 14**	
35	A76	50c deep green	2.75	3.50
36	A76	$3 deep blue	2.75	3.50
37	A76	$7.50 carmine	2.75	3.50
38	A76	$10 light brown	2.75	3.50
39	A76	$20 deep claret	2.75	3.50
		Nos. 35-39 (5)	13.75	17.50

First anniversary of return of Chinese National Government to Nanking.

Dr. Sun Yat-sen — A3

1947, July 10				
Without Gum				
40	A3	$1 dk brown	3.00	.25
41	A3	$2 org brn	.85	.25
42	A3	$3 blue grn	.85	.25
43	A3	$5 vermilion	.85	.25
44	A3	$9 deep blue	.85	.25
45	A3	$10 brt rose car	.85	.25

46	A3	$20 deep green	.85	.30
47	A3	$50 rose lilac	.85	.25
48	A3	$100 blue	.85	.60
49	A3	$200 dark red	.85	.60
		Nos. 40-49 (10)	10.65	3.25

The 30c gray and $7.50 orange were not regularly issued without surcharge. Value for the two stamps, $450.

See #63-68. For overprint and surcharges see #51-53, 69-73, 101-103, J10-J17.

Type of 1947 Surcharged in Black

b

1948		**Unwmk.**	**Perf. 14**	
51	A3	$25 on $100 blue	1.60	2.50
52	A3	$500 on $7.50 org	1.60	.55
53	A3	$1000 on 30c gray	7.25	6.50
		Nos. 51-53 (3)	10.45	9.55

Stamps of China, 1943-48, Surcharged Type "a" in Black or Carmine

1948-49		**Perf. 12½, 14**		
54	A73	$5 on $70 red org	.65	2.50
55	A62	$10 on $3 dk yel	1.75	2.75
56	A82	$10 on $150 dk bl (C)	.45	.70
57	A82	$20 on $250 dp lil (C)	1.10	.85
58	A67	$100 on $20 car	650.00	650.00
59	A82	$1000 on $20,000 rose pink ('49)	2.25	1.75
		Nos. 54-59 (6)	656.20	658.55

The bottom line of the surcharge expresses the new value and consists of 2 or 3 characters.

Forgeries of No. 58 abound.

Type of 1947

1949		**Engr.**	**Perf. 14**	
63	A3	$25 olive grn	.70	.30
64	A3	$5000 ocher	7.25	.50
65	A3	$10,000 apple grn	8.50	2.00
66	A3	$20,000 ol bister	8.50	3.50
67	A3	$30,000 indigo	9.50	.70
68	A3	$40,000 violet brn	8.50	.60
		Nos. 63-68 (6)	42.95	7.60

For overprint and surcharges see #101, 103, J12.

No. 42 and Type of 1947 Surcharged Type "b" in Black, Carmine Violet or Red Violet

1949				
69	A3	$300 on $3 bl grn	.65	.30
70	A3	$1000 on $3 bl grn (C)	3.00	.55
71	A3	$3000 on $3 bl grn (V)	5.00	.55
72	A3	$3000 on $3 bl grn (RV)	3.75	1.10
73	A3	$3000 on $7.50 org	60.00	3.00
		Nos. 69-73 (5)	72.40	5.50

For overprints see Nos. J10-J11.

Stamps of China, 1940-47, Surcharged Type "a" in Black or Carmine

		Perf. 12½, 13x13½, 14		
74	A39	$2 on 2½c rose lil (#424)	.55	2.00
75	A72	$5 on $40 org (#627)	.70	1.10
76	A73	$5 on $50 pur (C) (#638)	.70	.25
77	A73	$5 on $100 dk car (#640)	.70	.50
78	A57	$20 on 2c ol grn (#368)	.75	.75
81	A63	$100 on $20 rose (#571)	1.10	.50
82	A67	$200 on $10 dk bl (C) (#591)	1.75	1.10
84	A57	$500 on $30 dl vio (#521)	6.00	2.10
86	A62	$800 on $4 red brn (#504)	5.25	4.25
87	A67	$5000 on $10 dk bl (#591)	6.00	4.00
88	A67	$10,000 on $20 car (#592)	9.50	3.25
89	A82	$200,000 on $3000 bl (C) (#750)	370.00	27.50
		Nos. 74-89 (12)	403.00	47.30

Northeastern Provinces No. 47, Surcharged in Green, Red Violet, Black or Blue

1949-50				
91	A2	2c on $44 (G)	62.50	6.00
92	A2	5c on $44 (RV) ('50)	57.50	7.00
a.		Violet surcharge	85.00	11.50
93	A2	10c on $44 (RV) ('50)	75.00	6.00
94	A2	20c on $44 (Bk) ('50)	100.00	7.00
a.		Double surcharge	200.00	
95	A2	30c on $44 (Bl) ('50)	110.00	14.00
96	A2	50c on $44 (Bl) ('50)	130.00	17.00
		Nos. 91-96 (6)	535.00	57.00

There were two printings of Nos. 91-93, with minor differences.

China 959a, Overprinted in Black

Overprint 15mm Wide

1949		**Unwmk.**	**Rouletted 9½**	
97	A96	orange	1.60	.20

China Nos. 567, 498 and 640 Surcharged Type "a" in Black

1948-49		**Unwmk.**	**Perf. 12½, 13, 14**	
98	A63	$20 on $3 red	2.25	1.40
99	A62	$50 on 50c sage grn	2.50	1.10
a.		Perf. 11	26.00	26.00
100	A73	$600 on $100 dk car	10.00	2.75
		Nos. 98-100 (3)	14.75	5.25

Bottom line of surcharge consists of 3 characters.

No. 99 has two settings of surcharge: I. Spacing 10mm between rows of characters. II. Spacing 12mm.

#67, 47 and 68 Surcharged in Violet (#101) or Black

1949			**Perf. 14**	
101	A3	2c on $30,000 ind	52.50	30.00
102	A3	10c on $50 rose lil	52.50	6.75
103	A3	10c on $40,000 vio brn	125.00	30.00
		Nos. 101-103 (3)	230.00	66.75

Numerals slightly larger on Nos. 101-103.
For similar surcharges on China type A82 see China Nos. 1025-1036.

AIR POST STAMP

China No. C62a, Overprinted in Black

Overprint 15mm Wide

1949		**Unwmk.**	**Rouletted 9½**	
C1	AP5	blue green	6.75	6.75

SPECIAL DELIVERY STAMP

China No. E12a, Overprinted in Black

Overprint 12½mm Wide

1950		**Unwmk.**	**Rouletted 9½**	
E1	SD2	red violet	4.50	4.50

REGISTRATION STAMP

China No. F2a Overprinted in Black

Overprint 12mm Wide

1950		**Unwmk.**	**Rouletted 9½**	
F1	R2	carmine	4.50	4.50

POSTAGE DUE STAMPS

D1

1948, Feb. 10		**Unwmk.** **Litho.**	**Perf. 14**	
		Without Gum		
J1	D1	$1 blue	1.40	5.00
J2	D1	$3 blue	1.40	5.75
J3	D1	$5 blue	1.40	5.75
J4	D1	$10 blue	1.40	7.75
J5	D1	$20 blue	1.40	4.75
		Nos. J1-J5 (5)	7.00	29.00

Nos. J1-J4 Surcharged in Carmine

1948, Dec. 4				
J6	D1	$50 on $1 blue	9.00	13.00
J7	D1	$100 on $3 blue	9.00	13.00
J8	D1	$300 on $5 blue	9.00	13.00
J9	D1	$500 on $10 blue	9.00	13.00
		Nos. J6-J9 (4)	36.00	52.00

Nos. 70, 72 and 64 Handstamped in Violet

1949, Aug. 5				
J10	A3	$1000 on $3 bl grn	19.00	19.00
J11	A3	$3000 on $3 bl grn	29.00	29.00
J12	A3	$5000 ocher	42.50	42.50
		Nos. J10-J12 (3)	90.50	90.50

No. 48 Surcharged in Various Colors

1950				
J13	A3	4c on $100 bl (Br)	12.00	10.00
J14	A3	10c on $100 bl (RV)	22.50	26.00
J15	A3	20c on $100 bl (Bk)	10.00	22.50
J16	A3	40c on $100 bl (C)	47.50	90.00
J17	A3	$1 on $100 bl (Bl)	35.00	47.50
		Nos. J13-J17 (5)	127.00	196.00

PARCEL POST STAMPS

Type of China, Parcel Post Stamps of 1945-48 With Added Inscription

1949		**Unwmk. Engr.**	**Perf. 14**	
Q1	PP3	$100 bluish grn	265.00	1.00
Q2	PP3	$300 rose car	265.00	1.00
Q3	PP3	$500 olive green	265.00	1.00
Q4	PP3	$1000 slate	265.00	1.00
Q5	PP3	$3000 deep plum	265.00	1.00
		Nos. Q1-Q5 (5)	1,325.	1.00

Chinese characters in lower corners have colorless background; denomination tablet in color.

OCCUPATION STAMPS

Issued Under Japanese Occupation

Unused values for Japanese occupation issues are for never hinged examples.

Canceled Stamps

Postally used stamps of the Japanese occupation generally have heavy, smudgy cancels.

Kwangtung

China No. 297 Overprinted in Black

1942		**Unwmk.**	**Perf. 12½**	
1N1	A37	2c olive green	8.00	8.00
a.		Inverted overprint	120.00	

Same Overprint in Red or Black on Stamps of China, 1939-41

		Perf. 12½, 14		
1N2	A57	3c dl cl (#350)	2.75	2.75
1N3	A57	8c ol grn (#383)	2.75	2.75
1N4	A57	10c grn (#354) (R)	2.50	2.75
1N5	A57	10c grn (#384) (R)	3.50	3.50
1N6	A57	16c ol gray (#357)	4.75	7.25
1N7	A57	30c scar (#385)	4.00	2.75
1N8	A57	50c dk bl (#386) (R)	4.00	8.00
1N9	A57	$1 org brn & sep (#387)	7.25	9.25
1N10	A57	$2 dp bl & yel brn (#388)	8.00	9.50
1N11	A57	$5 red & sl grn (#389)	7.00	8.75
1N12	A57	$10 dk grn & dl pur (#390)	16.00	20.00
1N13	A57	$20 rose lake & dk bl (#391)	7.00	9.50

Same Overprint on China Nos. 422 and 433

		Perf. 12½		
1N14	A40	1c orange	1.90	2.40
a.		Inverted overprint	80.00	80.00
1N15	A47	20c lt blue	3.50	4.00

Same Overprint on Stamps of China, 1941

		Perf. 12		
1N16	A59	1c orange	2.50	3.75
1N17	A59	5c green	2.50	3.75
1N18	A59	8c turq green	2.75	3.75
1N19	A59	10c brt green	3.25	3.75
1N20	A59	17c olive	3.25	3.75
1N21	A59	30c scarlet	3.25	3.75
1N22	A59	50c dark blue	3.25	3.75
		Nos. 1N1-1N22 (22)	103.65	127.40

Stamps of China, 1939-41 Overprinted in Black

1942   *Perf. 12½, 14*

1N23	A57	2c olive grn (#368)	.65	.80
1N24	A57	3c dl claret (#350)	.65	.95
1N25	A57	5c olive grn (#352)	.65	1.25
1N26	A57	8c olive grn (#353)	300.00	—
1N27	A57	8c olive grn (#369)	.80	1.00
1N28	A57	10c green (#354)	1.00	1.25
1N29	A57	16c ol gray (#357)	1.25	1.25
1N30	A57	25c dk bl (#358)	1.25	2.75
1N31	A57	30c scarlet (#385)	.80	2.40
1N32	A57	50c dk blue (#386)	2.25	2.75
1N33	A57	$1 org brn & sep (#387)	6.50	8.00
1N34	A57	$2 dp bl & yel brn (#388)	8.00	9.50
1N35	A57	$5 red & sl grn (#389)	10.00	12.00
1N36	A57	$10 dk grn & dl pur (#390)	16.00	20.00
1N37	A57	$20 rose lake & dk bl (#391)	14.00	20.00

Nos. 1N23-1N25,1N27-1N37 (14)   63.80   83.90

No. 1N26 is valued in fine condition.

Same Overprint on China Nos. 397-401

1942   *Wmk. 261*   *Perf. 14*

1N38	A57	$1 org brn & sep	9.00	9.00
1N39	A57	$2 dp bl & yel brn	8.00	8.25
1N40	A57	$5 red & sl grn	11.00	13.00
1N41	A57	$10 dk grn & dl bl	17.50	20.00
1N42	A57	$20 rose lake & dk bl	22.50	24.00

Nos. 1N38-1N42 (5)   68.00   74.25

Same Overprint on Stamps of China, 1941

1942   *Unwmk.*   *Perf. 12*

1N43	A59	2c brt ultra	.30	.50
1N44	A59	5c green	.30	.50
1N45	A59	8c red org	.35	.50
1N46	A59	8c turq grn	.35	.90
1N47	A59	10c brt green	.60	.65
1N48	A59	17c olive	.65	1.00
1N49	A59	25c rose vio	.65	1.00
1N50	A59	30c scarlet	.65	1.10
1N51	A59	50c dk blue	.65	1.10
1N52	A59	$1 brn & blk	4.75	8.00
1N53	A59	$2 bl & blk	6.00	8.75
1N54	A59	$5 scar & blk	4.75	4.75
1N55	A59	$10 grn & blk	9.00	13.00
1N56	A59	$20 rose vio & blk	11.00	20.00

Nos. 1N43-1N56 (14)   40.00   61.75

China Nos. 354 and 369 Surcharged in Black

1945   *Unwmk.*   *Perf. 12½*

1N57	A57	$200 on 10c grn	120.00	60.00
1N58	A57	$400 on 8c ol grn	120.00	60.00

China No. 422 Surcharged in Black

1945

1N59	A40	$400 on 1c org	750.00	600.00

Forgeries exist.

OCCUPATION POSTAGE DUE STAMPS

China, No. J79 Surcharged Diagonally with New Value Between Parallel Lines in Black

1945   *Unwmk.*   *Perf. 12½*

1NJ1	D5	$100 on $2 yel org	825.00	900.00
a.		Inverted surcharge	1,100.	1,100.

MENG CHIANG (Inner Mongolia)

Nos. 297-298, 301-303 Overprinted

Characters 4mm High — I   Characters 5mm High — II

1941   *Engr.*   *Unwmk.*

2N1	A37	2c #297, I	1.25	2.00
a.		Type II	1.60	2.00
2N2	A37	4c #298, II	45.00	—
a.		Type I	60.00	55.00
2N3	A37	15c #301, I	4.75	5.50
a.		Type II	4.50	6.00
2N4	A37	20c #302, II	8.75	8.75
a.		Type I	12.00	16.00
2N5	A37	25c #303, II	12.00	14.00
a.		Type I	92.50	92.50

Nos. 2N1-2N5 (5)   71.75   30.25

For surcharge see No. 2N116.

On Nos. 312, 314, 318, 321

1941   *Perf. 14*

2N6	A39	½c #312, I	14.00	17.50
a.		Type II	20.00	
2N7	A39	2½c #314, II	3.75	3.75
a.		Type I	7.25	8.75
2N8	A45	13c #318, I	1.25	1.10
a.		Type I	110.00	110.00
2N9	A48	30c #321, II	72.50	72.50

Nos. 2N6-2N9 (4)   91.50   94.85

On Stamps of 1939-41

1941   *Perf. 12½*

2N10	A57	2c #368, II	2.40	3.00
2N11	A57	3c #350, II	1.00	1.00
a.		Type I	1.25	1.25
2N12	A57	5c #352, II	2.10	2.50
a.		Type I	2.75	6.00
2N13	A57	8c #353, II	1.25	.85
a.		Type II	2.00	2.00
2N14	A57	8c #369, II	8.00	8.00
2N15	A57	10c #354, II	2.25	2.25
2N16	A57	16c #357, II	4.00	4.00
2N17	A57	$1 #359, II	9.50	9.50
a.		Type I	325.00	325.00
b.		#347, I	87.50	80.00
2N18	A57	$5 #361, II	65.00	65.00

Nos. 2N10-2N18 (9)   95.50   96.10

For surcharges see Nos. 2N117, 2N119.

On Stamps of 1940 with Secret Marks

1941   *Unwmk.*   *Perf. 14*

2N19	A57	5c #382, II	1.60	1.75
2N20	A57	8c #383, I	3.25	3.25
a.		Type II	55.00	
2N21	A57	10c #384, II	2.25	2.00
a.		Type I	4.00	4.00
2N22	A57	30c #385, I	2.75	2.75
a.		Type I	4.75	5.00
2N23	A57	50c #386, I	7.25	7.25
a.		Type II	7.25	7.25
2N24	A57	$1 #387, I	11.00	12.00
a.		Type II	20.00	20.00
2N25	A57	$2 #388, I	12.00	14.00
a.		Type II	27.50	27.50
2N26	A57	$5 #389, I	30.00	30.00
a.		Type II	67.50	—
2N27	A57	$10 #390, II	60.00	60.00
a.		Type I	70.00	70.00
2N28	A57	$20 #391, II	100.00	110.00
a.		Type I	100.00	110.00

Nos. 2N19-2N28 (10)   230.10   243.00

For surcharge see No. 2N120.

On Stamps of 1940 with Secret Marks

1941   *Wmk. 261*   *Perf. 14*

2N29	A57	10c #394, II	4.50	4.50
2N30	A57	30c #395, II	4.75	6.00
a.		Type I	65.00	65.00
2N31	A57	50c #396, II	4.00	4.75

Nos. 2N29-2N31 (3)   13.25   15.25

On Stamps of 1940-41 (Martyrs) with Secret Marks

Perf. 12½, 13 & Compound

1941   *Wmk. 261*

2N32	A39	½c #402, II	12.00	14.00
2N33	A40	1c #403, II	1.00	1.00
a.		Type I	3.50	3.50
2N34	A39	2½c #405, I	60.00	60.00
a.		Type II	80.00	80.00
2N35	A48	3c #406, II	3.50	3.50
2N36	A46	10c #410, I	12.50	12.50
2N37	A46	17c #413, II	47.50	
a.		Type I	80.00	80.00
2N38	A40	25c #416, II	3.50	3.50
2N39	A40	30c #418, II	60.00	60.00
a.		Type I	72.50	72.50
2N40	A47	40c #419, II	6.00	6.00
a.		Type I	8.00	8.00

2N41	A40	50c #420, I	12.00	12.00
a.		Type II	60.00	

Unwmk.

2N42	A39	½c #421, II	1.60	2.25
a.		Type I	5.00	5.00
2N43	A40	1c #422, I	1.60	1.40
a.		Type II	4.25	3.50
2N44	A39	2c #423, I	6.00	6.00
2N45	A48	3c #425, II	3.50	3.50
a.		Type I	4.00	4.00
2N46	A39	4c #426, II	2.00	1.75
2N47	A45	8c #428, II	16.00	
a.		Type I	80.00	
2N48	A46	10c #429, I	24.00	24.00
a.		Type II	72.50	
2N49	A45	13c #430, I	6.50	7.25
a.		Type II	24.00	
2N50	A48	15c #431, II	4.00	4.00
2N51	A46	17c #432, II	3.75	3.75
a.		Type I	4.75	4.75
2N52	A47	20c #433, II	2.25	3.00
a.		Type I	3.25	3.75
2N53	A45	21c #434, II	4.00	4.00
2N54	A40	25c #435, II	4.75	4.75
2N55	A46	28c #436, II	4.25	4.25
2N56	A40	50c #439, I	4.75	2.40
a.		Type II	7.75	7.75

Nos. 2N42-2N56 (15)   88.95   72.30

For surcharges see Nos. 2N114-2N115, 2N118, 2N121-2N122.

China Nos. 297-298, 302 Surcharged in Black

1942   *Unwmk.*   *Perf. 12½, 13*

2N57	A37	1c on 2c ol grn	24.00	24.00
2N58	A37	2c on 4c grn	14.00	14.00
2N59	A37	10c on 20c ultra	40.00	40.00

Nos. 2N57-2N59 (3)   78.00   78.00

Same, on China No. 313

Perf. 14

2N60	A40	½c on 1c org	20.00	20.00

Same, on Stamps of China, 1938-41

Perf. 12½

2N61	A57	1c on 2c (#368)	2.00	1.25
2N62	A57	4c on 8c (#353)	9.50	12.00
a.		Inverted surcharge	47.50	
2N63	A57	4c on 8c (#369)	1.25	1.25
2N64	A57	5c on 10c (#354)	1.00	.65
2N65	A57	8c on 16c (#357)	4.00	3.00
2N66	A57	50c on $1 (#359)	9.50	9.50
a.		On No. 347	47.50	47.50
b.		On No. 344	400.00	
2N67	A57	$1 on $2 (#360)	60.00	60.00

Nos. 2N61-2N67 (7)   87.25   87.65

No. 2N66b was issued without gum.

Same, on Stamps of China, 1940

Perf. 14

2N68	A57	4c on 8c (#383)	.65	.65
2N69	A57	15c on 30c (#385)	7.25	10.00
a.		Inverted surcharge	55.00	55.00
2N70	A57	25c on 50c (#386)	7.00	8.00
2N71	A57	50c on $1 (#387)	6.00	7.25
2N72	A57	$1 on $2 (#388)	12.00	12.00
2N73	A57	$5 on $10 (#390)	45.00	45.00
2N74	A57	$10 on $20 (#391)	72.50	80.00

Nos. 2N68-2N74 (7)   150.40   162.90

Same, on China No. 395

1942   *Wmk. 261*   *Perf. 14*

2N75	A57	15c on 30c scar	80.00	80.00

Same, on China Nos. 418 and 419

Perf. 12½, 13

2N76	A48	15c on 30c brn car	47.50	47.50
2N77	A47	20c on 40c org	9.50	11.00

Nos. 2N75-2N77 (3)   137.00   138.50

Same, on Stamps of China, 1940-41

1942   *Unwmk.*

2N78	A40	½c on 1c org	.25	.35
2N79	A39	2c on 4c pale vio	6.00	6.00
2N80	A47	10c on 20c lt bl	6.00	6.00
2N81	A47	20c on 40c org	14.50	14.50
2N82	A45	25c on 50c grn	24.00	24.00

Nos. 2N78-2N82 (5)   50.75   50.85

Same Surcharge on "New Peking" Prints

Perf. 14

2N83	A37	1c on 2c ol grn	14.50	25.00
2N84	A37	4c on 4c dl grn	.55	.65
2N85	A46	5c on 10c dl vio	5.00	9.00
2N86	A57	8c on 16c ol gray	2.00	2.75

2N87	A47	10c on 20c red brn	4.75	7.25
2N88	A48	15c on 30c brn car	2.10	3.50
2N89	A47	20c on 40c org	9.00	10.00
2N90	A47	25c on 50c grn	2.50	5.00
2N91	A57	50c on $1 org brn & sep	14.50	14.50
2N92	A57	$1 on $2 dp bl & org brn	35.00	45.00
2N93	A57	$5 on $10 dk grn & dl pur	80.00	80.00

Nos. 2N83-2N93 (11)   169.90   202.65

The "New Peking" printings were made by the Chinese Bureau of Engraving and Printing for use in Japanese controlled areas of North China. They are on thin, poor quality paper, with dull gum or without gum and there are slight alterations in the designs.

Dragon-Carved Pillar and Doves — A1   Mining Coal — A2

Wmk. Characters in Circle in Sheet

1943   *Engr.*   *Perf. 12xPin-perf. 12*

2N94	A1	4f deep orange	.60	1.00
2N95	A1	8f dark blue	.80	1.25

5th anniv. of the Inner Mongolia post and telegraph service.

The watermark, which is 40mm in diameter and covers four stamps, occurs three times in the sheet.

1943   *Unwmk.*   *Photo.*   *Perf. 12*

2N96	A2	4f Prus green	.60	1.00
2N97	A2	8f brown red	.80	1.25

2nd anniv. of the "Greater East Asia War."

Flying Horse — A3   Yun Wang — A4

1944   *Perf. 12½x12, 12x12½*

2N98	A3	4f rose	.60	1.00
2N99	A4	8f dull blue	.80	1.25

5th anniv. of the founding of the Federal Autonomous Government of Mongolia, Sept. 1, 1939.

Industrial Plant — A5

1944, Dec. 8   *Photo.*   *Perf. 12x12½*

2N100	A5	8f red brown	.60	1.60

3rd anniv. of the "Greater East Asia War" and to encourage production increase.

New Peking Printings of 1942 Overprinted in Black

1945   *Unwmk.*   *Engr.*   *Perf. 14*   *Without Gum*

2N101	A37	2c olive grn	12.00	—
2N102	A37	4c dull grn	20.00	—
2N103	A37	5c green	21.00	27.50
2N104	A57	$1 org brn & sep	3.50	4.25
2N105	A57	$2 dp bl & org brn	14.50	14.50
2N106	A57	$5 red & grnsh blk	50.00	50.00

Same Overprint on New Peking Printings of Martyrs Issue

2N107	A40	1c orange	1.00	1.00
2N108	A45	8c dp orange	.90	.90
2N109	A46	10c dl violet	.25	.35
2N110	A47	20c red brown	2.10	3.00
2N111	A48	30c brown car	.45	1.50
2N112	A47	40c orange	.45	.45
2N113	A40	50c green	7.25	8.00

For surcharges see Nos. 2N123-2N127.

Stamps of Meng Chiang, 1941, Surcharged in Red or Black

50c

10c

$1

1945

2N114	A39	10c on ½c ol blk (#2N42, II, R)	2.50	2.75
a.		On #2N42a, II	7.25	8.00
2N115	A40	10c on 1c org (#2N43a, II, R)	1.75	2.00
a.		Without secret mark (China #422a)	40.00	40.00
b.		On #2N43, I	3.00	3.50
2N116	A37	50c on 2c ol grn (#2N1a, II, B)	29.00	35.00
b.		On #2N1, I	29.00	35.00
2N117	A57	50c on 2c ol grn (#2N10, II, B)	1.40	1.75
2N118	A39	50c on 4c pale vio (#2N46, II, R)	1.00	1.25
2N119	A57	50c on 5c ol grn (#2N12, II, R)	.65	1.10
a.		On #2N12a, I	12.50	12.50
2N120	A57	50c on 5c ol grn (#2N19, II, R)	1.25	2.10
		Nos. 2N114-2N120 (7)	37.55	45.95

Same Surcharge on #2N32, 2N33

1945 — **Wmk. 261**

2N121	A39	10c on ½c ol blk, II (R)	29.00	35.00
2N122	A40	10c on 1c orange, II (R)	1.25	1.50
a.		On #2N33a, I	35.00	

Same Surcharge on Nos. 2N107, 2N101-2N103 and 2N108

1945 — **Unwmk.**

2N123	A40	10c on 1c org (R)	.65	.80
2N124	A37	50c on 2c ol grn (Bk)	3.50	3.50
2N125	A37	50c on 4c dl grn (R)	5.00	5.00
2N126	A37	50c on 5c green (R)	.40	.40
2N127	A45	$1 on 8c dp org (R)	.60	.60
		Nos. 2N123-2N127 (5)	10.15	10.30

NORTH CHINA
Honan
Nos. 297-298, 301-303 Overprinted

I

II

1941 — **Engr.** — **Unwmk.**

3N1	A37	2c #297, II	8.50	8.50
a.		Type I	21.00	21.00
3N2	A37	4c #298, I	8.50	8.50
		Type II	32.50	32.50
3N3	A37	15c #301, I	2.10	2.40
		Type II	2.75	2.40
3N4	A37	20c #302, I	8.00	8.00
3N5	A37	25c #303, II	24.00	24.00
		Nos. 3N1-3N5 (5)	51.10	50.15

1941 — **Perf. 14**

3N6	A39	½c #312, I	2.25	3.50
		Type II	40.00	
3N7	A39	2½c #314, I	1.50	2.10
		Type II	2.10	3.00
3N8	A45	13c #318, II	1.50	1.50
		Type I	100.00	100.00
3N9	A48	30c #321, II	18.00	18.00
3N10	A47	40c #322, II	100.00	100.00
		Nos. 3N6-3N10 (5)	123.25	125.10

On Stamps of 1939-41

1941 — **Perf. 12½**

3N11	A57	2c #368, II	1.50	1.50
3N12	A57	3c #350, I	.70	.70
		Type II	1.25	1.25
3N13	A57	5c #352, II	1.50	.80
		Type I	2.40	2.40
3N14	A57	8c #353, II	1.50	1.50
		Type I	1.50	1.50
3N15	A57	10c #354, II	3.00	4.25
3N16	A57	16c #357, II	1.75	3.00
3N17	A57	$1 #359, II	14.50	14.50
		Type I	325.00	325.00
b.		On #347, I	57.50	57.50
3N18	A57	$5 #361, II	80.00	80.00
		Nos. 3N11-3N18 (8)	104.45	106.25

For overprints see Nos. 3N56, 3N58, 3N61.

On Stamps of 1940 with Secret Marks

1941 — **Unwmk.** — **Perf. 14**

3N20	A57	5c #382, II	2.40	2.00
3N21	A57	8c #383, II	.65	.65
3N22	A57	10c #384, II	2.00	1.50
3N23	A57	30c #385, II	8.00	9.00
a.		Type I	11.00	11.00
3N24	A57	50c #386, II	4.00	3.50
a.		Type I	17.00	17.00
3N25	A57	$1 #387, II	8.00	8.00
a.		Type I	70.00	70.00
3N26	A57	$2 #388, II	14.50	17.00
a.		Type I	24.00	24.00
3N27	A57	$5 #389, II	40.00	29.00
a.		Type I	57.50	57.50
3N28	A57	$10 #390, II	50.00	50.00
a.		Type I	150.00	150.00
3N29	A57	$20 #391, II	125.00	140.00
a.		Type I	125.00	140.00
		Nos. 3N20-3N29 (10)	254.55	260.65

On Stamps of 1940 with Secret Marks

1941 — **Wmk. 261** — **Perf. 14**

3N30	A57	5c #392, II	24.00	14.50
3N31	A57	8c #393, II	12.00	7.25
3N32	A57	30c #395, II	24.00	24.00
a.		Type I	40.00	40.00
3N33	A57	50c #396, II	75.00	67.50
		Nos. 3N30-3N33 (4)	135.00	113.25

On Stamps of 1940-41 (Martyrs) with Secret Marks

Perf. 12½, 13 & Compound

1941 — **Wmk. 261**

3N34	A39	½c #402, II	2.75	3.50
3N35	A40	1c #403, II	.70	.45
a.		Type I	2.00	2.00
3N36	A39	2½c #405, II	13.50	17.00
3N37	A46	10c #410, II	15.00	18.50
a.		Type I	35.00	35.00
3N38	A45	13c #411, II	4.25	4.25
3N39	A46	17c #413, II	4.25	4.25
a.		Type I	10.00	10.00
3N40	A45	25c #416, II	3.00	3.00
3N41	A47	40c #419, II	5.00	5.00
a.		Type I	18.00	18.00
		Nos. 3N34-3N41 (8)	48.45	55.95

Unwmk.

3N42	A39	½c #421, II	2.00	2.00
a.		Type I	4.50	4.50
3N43	A40	1c #422, I	2.50	2.50
a.		Type II	4.50	4.50
3N44	A46	2c #423, I	15.00	15.00
3N45	A48	3c #425, I	1.50	2.50
3N46	A39	4c #426, II	.90	.90
3N47	A46	10c #429, I	45.00	45.00
3N48	A45	13c #430, II	3.50	3.50
a.		Type I	20.00	20.00
3N49	A48	15c #431, II	4.50	4.50
3N50	A46	17c #432, II	4.50	4.50
a.		Type I	17.50	17.50
3N51	A47	20c #433, II	2.00	2.00
a.		Type I	62.50	50.00
3N52	A45	21c #434, II	4.50	4.50
3N53	A40	25c #435, I	5.00	5.00
3N54	A46	28c #436, II	4.50	4.50
		Nos. 3N42-3N54 (13)	95.40	96.40

For overprints see Nos. 3N55, 3N59.

Overprinted in Red

1942

3N55	A39	4c #3N46	3.25	4.50
3N56	A57	8c #3N14	24.00	32.50
3N57	A57	8c #369, II	5.75	9.50
		Nos. 3N55-3N57 (3)	33.00	46.50

The fall of Singapore.

Overprinted in Red

1942

3N58	A57	2c #3N11	10.00	15.00
3N59	A39	4c #3N46	17.00	25.00
3N60	A57	8c #369, II	45.00	50.00
3N61	A57	8c #3N14	35.00	37.50
		Nos. 3N58-3N61 (4)	107.00	127.50

Formation of Manchukuo, 10th anniv.

Hopei
Nos. 297-298, 301-303 Overprinted

I

II

1941 — **Engr.** — **Unwmk.**

4N1	A37	2c #297, II	1.40	.80
a.		Type I	4.25	3.50
4N2	A37	4c #298, II	4.50	4.50
a.		Type II	85.00	—
4N3	A37	15c #301, II	3.00	3.00
a.		Type I	4.25	4.00
4N4	A37	20c #302, II	1.75	1.50
4N5	A37	25c #303, II	11.00	8.75
a.		Type I	95.00	90.00
		Nos. 4N1-4N5 (5)	21.65	18.55

On Nos. 312, 314, 318, 321

1941 — **Perf. 14**

4N6	A39	½c #312, II	.40	.70
a.		Type I	100.00	100.00
4N7	A39	2½c #314, II	.60	.40
a.		Type I	.55	.70
4N8	A45	13c #318, II	1.40	1.25
a.		Type I	2.50	2.50
4N9	A48	30c #321, II	5.50	6.75
		Nos. 4N6-4N9 (4)	7.90	9.10

On Stamps of 1939-41

1941 — **Perf. 12½**

4N10	A57	2c #368, II	1.25	.65
4N11	A57	2c #349, II	.80	1.00
4N12	A57	3c #350, II	.45	.45
a.		Type I	2.00	2.00
4N13	A57	5c #352, II	.80	.65
a.		Type I	2.25	2.00
4N14	A57	8c #353, II	.45	.45
a.		Type I	1.75	1.60
4N15	A57	8c #369, II	3.75	3.75
4N16	A57	10c #354, II	1.00	.80
4N17	A57	16c #357, II	2.50	1.00
4N18	A57	$1 #359, II	10.00	10.00
a.		On #347, I	250.00	
4N19	A57	$2 #360, II	12.50	12.50
a.		Type I	50.00	50.00
4N20	A57	$5 #361, I	50.00	50.00
a.		Type II	75.00	75.00
4N21	A57	$10 #362, II	200.00	200.00
4N22	A57	$20 #363, II	450.00	450.00
		Nos. 4N10-4N22 (13)	733.50	731.25

For overprints see Nos. 4N66-4N68, 4N70.

On Stamps of 1940 with Secret Marks

1941 — **Unwmk.** — **Perf. 14**

Type II

4N24	A57	5c #382	.60	.50
4N25	A57	8c #383	1.25	1.25
4N26	A57	10c #384	1.00	.30
4N27	A57	30c #385	1.00	1.00
4N28	A57	50c #386	2.00	2.00
4N29	A57	$1 #387	4.00	3.50
4N30	A57	$2 #388	14.00	9.50
4N31	A57	$5 #389	35.00	35.00
4N32	A57	$10 #390	40.00	40.00
4N33	A57	$20 #391	60.00	72.50
		Nos. 4N24-4N33 (10)	158.85	165.55

For overprints see Nos. 4N65, 4N71.

Type I

4N24a	A57	5c	1.00	1.00
4N25a	A57	8c	70.00	70.00
4N26a	A57	10c	2.40	2.40
4N28a	A57	50c	2.75	2.75
4N29a	A57	$1	8.25	5.50
4N30a	A57	$2	32.50	32.50
4N31a	A57	$5	55.00	55.00
4N32a	A57	$10	75.00	65.00
4N33a	A57	$20	110.00	110.00
		Nos. 4N24a-4N33a (9)	357.40	344.65

On Stamps of 1940 with Secret Marks

1941 — **Wmk. 261** — **Perf. 14**

4N34	A57	5c #392, II	.45	.45
4N35	A57	8c #393, II	1.50	1.50
4N36	A57	10c #394, II	1.25	.65
4N37	A57	30c #395, II	1.50	1.50
a.		Type I	3.50	3.50
4N38	A57	50c #396, II	5.00	5.00
		Nos. 4N34-4N38 (5)	9.70	9.10

On Stamps of 1940-41 (Martyrs) with Secret Marks

Perf. 12½, 13 & Compound

1941 — **Wmk. 261**

4N39	A39	½c #402, II	1.50	1.50
4N40	A40	1c #403, I	1.25	.90
a.		Type II	1.50	1.50
4N41	A46	2c #404, II	1.00	1.00
4N42	A39	2½c #405, II	1.25	1.75
4N43	A48	3c #406, II	2.00	3.00
4N44	A46	3c #410, II	3.00	3.00
a.		Type I	1.90	5.00
4N45	A45	13c #411, II	2.50	2.50
4N46	A46	17c #413, II	3.50	3.50
a.		Type I	4.25	4.25
4N47	A45	25c #416, II	3.25	3.25
4N48	A48	30c #418, II	12.50	12.50
a.		Type I	35.00	35.00
4N49	A47	40c #419, II	3.50	1.50
a.		Type I	5.75	5.75
		Nos. 4N39-4N49 (11)	35.25	34.40

Unwmk.

4N50	A39	½c #421, II	1.50	1.50
		Type I	2.25	2.25
4N51	A40	1c #422, II	2.25	1.50
		Type I	2.75	2.00
4N52	A46	2c #423	.50	.50
4N53	A48	3c #425, II	1.50	1.50
		Type II	3.50	4.25
4N54	A39	4c #426, II	1.25	1.25
4N55	A45	8c #428, II	1.50	1.90
		Type I	3.50	3.50
4N56	A46	10c #429, II	3.50	3.00
4N57	A45	13c #430, I	3.50	3.50
		Type II	4.50	4.50
4N58	A48	15c #431, II	5.75	5.75
4N59	A46	17c #432, II	3.50	3.50
		Type I	5.25	5.75
4N60	A47	20c #433, II	3.25	3.25
		Type I	4.00	4.00
4N61	A45	21c #434, II	5.00	5.00
4N62	A40	25c #435, I	5.00	5.00
		Type II	5.00	5.00
4N63	A46	28c #436, II	4.25	4.00
		Nos. 4N50-4N63 (14)	42.25	41.15

For overprints see Nos. 4N64, 4N69.

Honan Singapore Overprint in Red

1942

4N64	A57	4c #4N54	1.50	3.50
4N65	A57	8c #4N25	4.00	4.00
4N66	A57	8c #4N14	3.00	5.00
4N67	A57	8c #4N15	9.75	15.00
		Nos. 4N64-4N67 (4)	18.25	27.50

Honan Anniv. of Manchukuo Overprint in Red

1942

4N68	A57	2c #4N10	6.75	9.75
4N69	A39	4c #4N54	6.75	8.25
4N70	A57	8c #4N14	90.00	90.00
4N71	A57	8c #4N25	9.75	12.00
		Nos. 4N68-4N71 (4)	113.25	120.00

Shansi
Nos. 297-298, 301, 303 Overprinted

I

II

1941 — **Engr.** — **Unwmk.**

5N1	A37	2c #297, II	6.75	6.75
a.		Type I	6.75	6.75

5N2	A37	4c #298, I	62.50	62.50
a.		Type II	125.00	—
5N3	A37	15c #301, II	5.25	6.75
a.		Type I	9.00	11.00
5N4	A37	25c #303, II	9.00	13.50
a.		Type I	62.50	67.50
	Nos. 5N1-5N4 (4)		83.50	89.50

On Nos. 312, 314, 318, 321

1941   **Perf. 14**

5N5	A39	½c #312, II	1.25	1.50
a.		Type I	2.25	3.75
5N6	A39	2½c #314, II	1.50	1.75
5N7	A45	13c #318, I	2.50	2.50
a.		Type I	240.00	240.00
5N8	A48	30c #321, II	9.75	12.00
	Nos. 5N5-5N8 (4)		15.00	17.75

On Stamps of 1939-41

1941   **Perf. 12½**

5N9	A57	2c #368, II	.80	.80
5N10	A57	3c #350, II	1.25	1.25
a.		Type I	15.00	15.00
5N11	A57	5c #352, II	3.50	3.50
5N12	A57	8c #353, II	1.50	1.50
a.		Type I	3.50	3.50
5N13	A57	8c #369, II	42.50	25.00
5N14	A57	10c #354, II	3.75	5.00
5N15	A57	16c #357, II	5.00	5.00
5N16	A57	$1 #359, II	12.50	12.50
5N17	A57	$2 #360, II	50.00	50.00
5N18	A57	$5 #361, II	57.50	57.50
	Nos. 5N9-5N18 (10)		178.30	162.05

For overprints see Nos. 5N62-5N64, 5N66-5N67.

On Stamps of 1940 with Secret Marks

1941   **Unwmk.**   **Perf. 14**

5N19	A57	5c #382, II	.80	.75
5N20	A57	8c #383, II	1.75	1.75
5N21	A57	10c #384, II	1.25	1.75
a.		Type I	5.00	5.00
5N22	A57	30c #385, II	2.10	2.10
a.		Type I	3.00	3.00
5N23	A57	50c #386, I	4.25	4.25
a.		Type II	5.75	5.75
5N24	A57	$1 #387, I	11.50	11.50
a.		Type II	37.50	37.50
5N25	A57	$2 #388, II	17.00	25.00
a.		Type I	20.00	25.00
5N26	A57	$5 #389, I	32.50	32.50
a.		Type II	97.50	97.50
5N27	A57	$10 #390, II	70.00	70.00
a.		Type I	75.00	75.00
5N28	A57	$20 #391, II	70.00	70.00
a.		Type I	125.00	135.00
	Nos. 5N19-5N28 (10)		211.15	219.60

For overprints see Nos. 5N61, 5N68.

On Stamps of 1940 with Secret Marks

1941   **Wmk. 261**   **Perf. 14**

5N29	A57	5c #392, II	1.50	1.50
5N30	A57	5c #393, II	1.25	1.25
5N31	A57	10c #394, II	3.00	3.00
5N32	A57	30c #395, I	80.00	80.00
5N33	A57	50c #396, I	7.50	8.25
	Nos. 5N29-5N33 (5)		93.25	94.00

On Stamps of 1940-41 (Martyrs) with Secret Marks

Perf. 12½, 13 & Compound

1941   **Wmk. 261**

5N34	A39	½c #402, II	1.50	1.50
5N35	A40	1c #403, II	1.00	1.00
a.		Type I	1.50	1.50
5N36	A46	2c #404, II	3.00	3.00
5N37	A39	2½c #405, I	9.00	10.50
5N38	A45	10c #410, II	9.75	9.75
5N39	A45	13c #411, II	4.50	4.50
5N40	A40	17c #413, II	32.50	32.50
5N41	A40	25c #416, II	4.00	4.00
5N42	A48	30c #418, I	150.00	150.00
a.		Type II	150.00	150.00
5N43	A47	40c #419, I	5.50	5.50
a.		Type I	37.50	37.50
5N44	A40	50c #420, I	7.50	7.50
a.		Type I	42.50	42.50
	Nos. 5N34-5N44 (11)		228.25	229.75

Unwmk.

5N45	A39	½c #421, II	3.00	3.75
a.		Type I	5.25	5.75
5N46	A40	1c #422, II	3.00	3.00
a.		Type I	3.00	3.00
5N47	A46	2c #423, II	.75	.75
5N48	A48	3c #425, II	9.00	9.00
5N49	A39	4c #426, II	1.25	1.50
5N50	A45	8c #428, II	15.00	15.00
a.		Type I	17.50	17.50
5N51	A46	10c #429, II	50.00	50.00
a.		Type I	57.50	57.50
5N52	A45	13c #430, I	20.00	20.00
a.		Type II	20.00	20.00
5N53	A48	15c #431, II	6.75	6.75
5N54	A46	17c #432, II	4.25	4.25
a.		Type I	5.50	5.50
5N55	A47	20c #433, II	3.25	3.25
a.		Type I	4.00	4.00
5N56	A45	21c #434, II	4.25	4.25
5N57	A46	25c #435, I	3.25	3.50
5N58	A46	28c #436, II	5.75	5.75
5N59	A40	50c #439, II	15.00	15.00
	Nos. 5N45-5N59 (15)		144.50	145.50

For overprints see Nos. 5N60, 5N65.

Honan Singapore Overprint in Red

1942

5N60	A39	4c #5N49	2.75	3.50
5N61	A57	8c #5N20	4.50	4.50
5N62	A57	8c #5N12	6.75	17.00
5N63	A57	8c #5N13	14.00	20.00
	Nos. 5N60-5N63 (4)		28.00	39.00

Honan Anniv. of Manchukuo Overprint in Red

1942

5N64	A57	2c #5N9	11.50	17.00
5N65	A39	4c #5N49	13.50	17.00
5N66	A57	8c #5N12	50.00	60.00
5N67	A57	8c #5N13	72.50	85.00
5N68	A57	8c #5N20	40.00	40.00
	Nos. 5N64-5N68 (5)		187.50	219.00

Shantung

Nos. 297-298, 301-303 Overprinted

       I   II

1941   **Engr.**   **Unwmk.**

6N1	A37	2c #297, II	1.60	1.60
a.		Type I	4.25	4.25
6N2	A37	4c #298, II	8.00	7.25
a.		Type I	9.25	8.00
6N3	A37	15c #301, II	2.50	2.50
a.		Type I	3.50	3.50
6N4	A37	20c #302, II	5.00	5.00
6N5	A37	25c #303, II	7.25	7.25
a.		Type I	225.00	225.00
	Nos. 6N1-6N5 (5)		24.35	23.60

On Nos. 312, 314, 318

1941   **Perf. 14**

6N6	A39	½c #312, II	1.25	1.25
a.		Type I	2.50	1.50
6N7	A39	2½c #314, II	1.50	2.10
a.		Type I	1.50	2.00
6N8	A45	13c #318, II	1.50	1.40
a.		Type I	25.00	25.00
	Nos. 6N6-6N8 (3)		4.25	4.75

On Stamps of 1939-41

1941   **Perf. 12½**

6N9	A57	2c #349, II	.80	1.50
6N10	A57	2c #368, II	1.40	1.25
6N11	A57	3c #350, II	.75	.75
a.		Type I	1.50	1.50
6N12	A57	5c #352, II	1.40	1.40
a.		Type I	1.50	1.50
6N13	A57	8c #353, II	.80	.50
a.		Type I	.65	.65
6N14	A57	8c #369, II	1.10	.80
6N15	A57	10c #354, II	.90	.80
6N16	A57	16c #357, II	5.50	7.50
6N17	A57	$1 #359, II	13.50	12.50
a.		Type I	425.00	425.00
b.		On No. 347, I	57.50	57.50
6N18	A57	$5 #361, II	50.00	50.00
	Nos. 6N9-6N18 (10)		76.15	77.00

For overprints see Nos. 6N62, 6N64-6N65, 6N67-6N68.

On Stamps of 1940 with Secret Marks

1941   **Unwmk.**   **Perf. 14**

6N20	A57	5c #382, II	1.50	1.25
6N21	A57	8c #383, II	.35	.35
a.		Type I	1.50	1.50
6N22	A57	10c #384, II	1.50	1.25
6N23	A57	30c #385, II	2.00	1.50
a.		Type I	6.75	7.50
6N24	A57	50c #386, I	6.75	6.75
a.		Type II	9.00	8.00
6N25	A57	$1 #387, I	6.75	5.00
a.		Type II	17.00	17.00
6N26	A57	$2 #388, I	15.00	15.00
a.		Type I	24.50	24.50
6N27	A57	$5 #389, I	30.00	30.00
a.		Type I	40.00	40.00
6N28	A57	$10 #390, II	67.50	67.50
a.		Type I	72.50	72.50
6N29	A57	$20 #391, II	97.50	97.50
a.		Type I	97.50	110.00
	Nos. 6N20-6N29 (10)		228.85	226.10

For overprints see Nos. 6N63, 6N69.

On Stamps of 1940 with Secret Marks

1941   **Wmk. 261**   **Perf. 14**

6N30	A57	5c #392, II	1.25	1.25
6N31	A57	5c #393, II	1.25	1.25
6N32	A57	10c #394, II	8.00	8.00
6N33	A57	30c #395, II	5.00	4.00
a.		Type I	25.00	25.00

6N34	A57	50c #396, II	4.25	4.25
a.		Type I	9.75	11.50
	Nos. 6N30-6N34 (5)		19.75	18.75

On Stamps of 1940-41 (Martyrs) with Secret Marks

Perf. 12½, 13 & Compound

1941   **Wmk. 261**

6N35	A39	½c #402, II	3.00	3.00
6N36	A40	1c #403, II	2.10	2.00
a.		Type I	2.75	2.00
6N37	A39	2½c #405, I	9.00	11.50
6N38	A46	10c #410, I	4.00	4.00
6N39	A45	13c #411, II	4.00	4.00
6N40	A46	17c #413, II	4.25	4.25
a.		Type I	9.75	11.00
6N41	A40	25c #416, II	32.50	32.50
6N42	A48	30c #418, I	4.25	4.25
6N43	A47	40c #419, I	32.50	32.50
6N44	A40	50c #420, II	9.00	9.00
	Nos. 6N35-6N44 (10)		76.35	78.75

Unwmk.

6N45	A39	½c #421, II	2.00	2.00
a.		Type I	4.25	4.25
6N46	A40	1c #422, II	2.00	1.60
a.		Type I	3.25	3.25
b.		On No. 422a, II	97.50	97.50
6N48	A46	2c #423, II	2.00	2.00
6N49	A48	3c #425, I	4.25	5.00
a.		Type I	5.00	6.75
6N50	A39	4c #426, II	1.25	.60
6N51	A45	8c #428, II	3.50	3.50
a.		Type I	40.00	40.00
6N52	A46	10c #429, II	15.00	15.00
6N53	A45	13c #430, I	4.50	4.50
a.		Type I	4.50	4.50
6N54	A48	15c #431, II	5.00	5.00
6N55	A46	17c #432, II	3.50	3.50
a.		Type I	5.00	5.00
6N56	A47	20c #433, II	4.50	4.50
a.		Type I	6.75	6.75
6N57	A45	21c #434, II	5.00	5.00
6N58	A40	25c #435, I	5.75	5.75
6N59	A46	28c #436, II	5.00	5.00
6N60	A40	50c #439, II	11.50	11.50
	Nos. 6N45-6N60 (15)		74.75	73.45

For overprints see Nos. 6N61, 6N66.

Honan Singapore Overprint in Red

1942

6N61	A39	4c #6N50	2.50	3.50
6N62	A57	8c #6N13	24.50	30.00
6N63	A57	8c #6N21	24.50	24.50
6N64	A57	8c #6N14	4.00	6.75
	Nos. 6N61-6N64 (4)		55.50	64.75

Honan Anniv. of Manchukuo Overprint in Red

1942

6N65	A57	2c #6N10	3.50	5.00
6N66	A39	4c #6N50	5.00	5.25
6N67	A57	8c #6N13	19.50	24.50
6N68	A57	8c #6N14	50.00	57.50
6N69	A57	8c #6N21	4.00	5.00
	Nos. 6N65-6N69 (5)		82.00	97.25

Supeh

Nos. 297-298, 301-302 Overprinted

       I   II

1941   **Engr.**   **Unwmk.**

7N1	A37	2c #297, I	11.50	11.50
a.		Type II	15.00	15.00
7N2	A37	4c #298, I	57.50	57.50
a.		Type II	110.00	
7N3	A37	15c #301, II	3.50	3.50
a.		Type I	4.25	4.25
7N4	A37	20c #302, II	4.00	4.00
	Nos. 7N1-7N4 (4)		76.50	76.50

On Nos. 312, 314, 318

1941   **Perf. 14**

7N5	A39	½c #312, II	4.25	4.25
7N6	A39	2½c #314, II	1.50	1.50
a.		Type I	1.50	1.50
7N7	A45	13c #318, II	1.50	1.50
a.		Type I	110.00	110.00
	Nos. 7N5-7N7 (3)		7.25	7.25

On Stamps of 1939-41

1941   **Perf. 12½**

7N8	A57	2c #368, II	1.50	2.50
7N9	A57	3c #350, II	1.75	1.75
a.		Type I	24.50	24.50
7N10	A57	5c #352, II	1.50	2.10
a.		Type I	3.75	

7N11	A57	8c #353, I	2.50	2.50
a.		Type II	3.50	3.50
7N12	A57	8c #369, II	40.00	32.50
7N13	A57	10c #354, II	3.75	5.00
7N14	A57	16c #357, II	1.50	2.50
7N15	A57	$1 #359, II	16.00	16.00
a.		On No. 347, I	195.00	160.00
	Nos. 7N8-7N15 (8)		68.50	64.85

For overprints see Nos. 7N56-7N58, 7N60-7N61.

On Stamps of 1940 with Secret Marks

1941   **Unwmk.**   **Perf. 14**

7N17	A57	5c #382, II	1.50	1.50
7N18	A57	8c #383, II	1.50	1.50
7N19	A57	10c #384, I	4.25	4.25
a.		Type II		4.25
7N20	A57	30c #385, II	3.50	4.00
a.		Type I	8.00	9.00
7N21	A57	50c #386, II	4.50	5.50
a.		Type I	5.00	5.00
7N22	A57	$1 #387, I	24.50	30.00
a.		Type II	40.00	40.00
7N23	A57	$2 #388, I	24.50	24.50
a.		Type I	32.50	40.00
7N24	A57	$5 #389, I	30.00	30.00
a.		Type II	80.00	80.00
7N25	A57	$10 #390, I	80.00	80.00
a.		Type II	90.00	90.00
7N26	A57	$20 #391, II	100.00	100.00
a.		Type I	100.00	110.00
	Nos. 7N17-7N26 (10)		274.25	281.25

On Stamps of 1940 with Secret Marks

1941   **Wmk. 261**   **Perf. 14**

7N27	A57	10c #394, I	5.00	5.00
7N28	A57	30c #395, I	16.00	17.00
7N29	A57	50c #396, I	17.00	18.50
	Nos. 7N27-7N29 (3)		38.00	40.50

On Stamps of 1940-41 (Martyrs) with Secret Marks

Perf. 12½, 13 & Compound

1941   **Wmk. 261**

7N30	A39	½c #402, I	5.75	5.75
7N31	A40	1c #403, I	2.10	2.10
a.		Type II	3.50	3.50
7N32	A46	2c #404, II	2.00	2.00
7N33	A39	2½c #405, I	29.50	29.50
7N34	A46	10c #410, II	19.50	19.50
7N35	A45	13c #411, II	6.75	6.75
7N36	A46	17c #413, II	5.75	5.75
a.		Type I	100.00	100.00
7N37	A40	25c #416, I	5.75	5.75
7N38	A48	30c #418, I	14.50	14.50
7N39	A47	40c #419, I	5.75	5.75
7N40	A40	50c #420, I	9.00	9.00
	Nos. 7N30-7N40 (11)		197.35	197.35

Unwmk.

7N41	A39	½c #421, II	4.25	4.25
a.		Type I	5.75	5.75
7N42	A40	1c #422, II	2.00	2.00
7N43	A46	2c #423, I	14.50	14.50
7N44	A48	3c #425, I	4.25	4.25
7N45	A39	4c #426, II	1.25	1.25
7N46	A46	10c #429, II	50.00	50.00
7N47	A45	13c #430, I	6.75	7.50
7N48	A48	15c #431, II	7.50	7.00
7N49	A46	17c #432, II	4.50	4.50
a.		Type I	6.75	6.75
7N50	A47	20c #433, II	4.50	4.50
a.		Type I	6.75	6.75
7N51	A45	21c #434, II	5.00	5.00
7N52	A40	25c #435, I	6.50	6.50
a.		Type II	17.00	17.00
7N53	A46	28c #436, II	6.75	6.75
	Nos. 7N41-7N53 (13)		117.75	118.00

For overprints see Nos. 7N55, 7N59.

Honan Singapore Overprint in Red

1942

7N54	A37	4c #298, II	50.00	57.50
7N55	A39	4c #7N45	6.25	6.75
7N56	A57	8c #7N11a	16.00	21.00
7N57	A57	8c #7N12	15.00	20.00
	Nos. 7N54-7N57 (4)		87.25	105.25

Honan Anniv. of Manchukuo Overprint in Red

1942

7N58	A57	2c #7N8	17.00	24.50
7N59	A39	4c #7N45	16.00	17.00
7N60	A57	8c #7N11a	72.50	82.50
7N61	A57	8c #7N12	90.00	97.50
	Nos. 7N58-7N61 (4)		195.50	221.50

North China

For use in Honan, Hopei, Shansi, Shantung and Supeh (Northern Kiangsu)

Stamps of China, 1931-37 Surcharged North China (Hwa Pei) and Half of Original Value

1942		Unwmk.	Perf. 14, 12½	
8N1	A40	½c on 1c (#313)	2.00	2.50
8N2	A37	1c on 2c (#297)	.75	.45
8N3	A37	2c on 4c (#298)	1.50	1.25
8N4	A45	4c on 8c (#316)	150.00	

Same Surcharge on Stamps of 1938-41

Perf. 12½

8N5	A57	1c on 2c (#349)	5.00	7.50
8N6	A57	1c on 2c (#368)	.50	.30
8N7	A57	4c on 8c (#353)	2.10	1.25
8N8	A57	4c on 8c (#369)	.60	.35
8N9	A57	5c on 10c grn	.65	.50
8N10	A57	8c on 16c ol gray	2.00	.80
8N11	A57	50c on $1 (#359)	8.00	8.00
8N12	A57	50c on $1 (#344)	575.00	575.00
8N13	A57	50c on $1 (#347)	110.00	110.00
8N14	A57	$1 on $2 (#360)	12.50	12.50
8N15	A57	$1 on $2 (#345)	32.50	32.50
8N16	A57	$1 on $2 (#348)	155.00	155.00

No. 8N12 was issued without gum. For overprint see No. 8N58.

Same Surcharge on China Nos. 383-388, 390-391

Perf. 14

8N17	A57	4c on 8c ol grn	.65	.65
8N18	A57	5c on 10c grn	1.25	2.00
8N19	A57	15c on 30c scar	1.50	1.25
a.		Inverted surcharge	80.00	80.00
8N20	A57	25c on 50c dk bl	2.00	1.75
8N21	A57	50c on $1 org brn & sep	4.50	4.50
8N22	A57	$1 on $2 dp bl & yel brn	5.75	5.75
8N23	A57	$5 on $10 dk grn & dl pur	50.00	50.00
8N24	A57	$10 on $20 rose lake & dk bl	50.00	60.00
		Nos. 8N17-8N24 (8)	115.65	125.90

For overprint see No. 8N55.

Same Surcharge on China Nos. 394-396

Wmk. 261

8N25	A57	5c on 10c grn	.85	1.50
8N26	A57	15c on 30c scar	3.50	5.00
8N27	A57	25c on 50c dk bl	1.50	1.50
		Nos. 8N25-8N27 (3)	5.85	8.00

Same Surcharge on Stamps of 1940-41

1942		Wmk. 261	Perf. 12½, 13	
8N28	A40	½c on 1c org	.30	.25
8N29	A46	1c on 2c dp bl	2.50	2.50
8N30	A45	4c on 8c dp org	20.00	24.50
8N31	A45	5c on 10c dl vio	2.50	3.00
8N32	A48	15c on 30c brn car	9.75	9.75
8N33	A47	20c on 40c org	5.75	2.10
8N34	A40	25c on 50c grn	5.00	5.00
		Nos. 8N28-8N34 (7)	45.80	47.10

Unwmk.

8N35	A40	½c on 1c org (#422)	.30	.25
a.		½c on 1c org (#422a)	37.00	37.00
8N36	A46	1c on 2c dp bl	1.40	1.40
8N37	A39	2c on 4c pale vio	1.00	.85
8N38	A45	4c on 8c dp org	1.25	2.00
8N39	A46	5c on 10c dl vio	3.00	3.00
8N40	A47	10c on 20c lt bl	3.75	.75
8N41	A47	20c on 40c org	4.00	1.00
8N42	A40	25c on 50c grn	32.50	32.50
		Nos. 8N35-8N42 (8)	47.20	41.75

Same Surcharge on "New Peking" Prints

Perf. 14

8N43	A37	1c on 2c ol grn	.35	.25
8N44	A37	2c on 4c dl grn	.90	.25
a.		Inverted surcharge	42.50	
8N45	A45	4c on 8c dp org	.65	.25
8N46	A45	8c on 16c ol gray	.35	.25
8N47	A48	10c on 20c red brn	1.75	1.50
8N48	A48	15c on 30c brn car	.85	.85
8N49	A47	20c on 40c org	2.10	.30
a.		Inverted surcharge	55.00	
8N50	A40	25c on 50c grn	1.75	1.50
8N51	A57	50c on $1 org brn & sep	3.50	3.50
8N52	A57	$1 on $2 dp bl & org brn	5.75	3.50

8N53	A57	$5 on $10 dk grn & dl pur	24.50	24.50
		Nos. 8N43-8N53 (11)	42.45	36.65

See note after No. 2N93. For overprints see #8N54, 8N56-8N57, 8N59.

Nos. 8N44, 8N17 and 8N46 with Additional Overprint in Red

1943		Unwmk.	Perf. 14	
8N54	A37	2c on 4c dl grn	.30	1.00
8N55	A57	4c on 8c ol grn	1.50	1.75
8N56	A57	8c on 16c ol gray	1.50	2.00
		Nos. 8N54-8N56 (3)	3.30	4.75

Return of the Foreign Concessions to China.

Nos. 8N44, 8N8 and 8N46 with Additional Overprint in Red

1943, Aug. 15			Perf. 14, 12½	
8N57	A37	2c on 4c dl grn	.45	.85
8N58	A57	4c on 8c ol grn	.45	1.00
8N59	A57	8c on 16c ol gray	.50	.85
		Nos. 8N57-8N59 (3)	1.40	2.70

North China Postal Service, 5th anniv.

Stamps of China, 1934-41, Overprinted in Black

1943, Nov. 1				
8N60	A40	1c org (#313)	.85	.85
8N61	A40	1c org (#422)	.85	.75
8N62	A57	10c grn (#354)	.50	.45
8N63	A57	$2 dp bl & yel brn (#388)	30.00	30.00
8N64	A57	$5 red & grnsh blk (#361)	20.00	20.00
8N65	A57	$5 red & sl grn (#389)	9.75	9.75
8N66	A57	$10 dk grn & dl pur (#390)	14.50	14.50
8N67	A57	$20 rose lake & dk bl (#391)	90.00	110.00
		Nos. 8N60-8N67 (8)	166.45	186.30

Same Overprint on "New Peking" Prints

8N68	A40	1c orange	.30	.25
8N69	A37	2c olive grn	.30	.25
8N70	A37	4c dull green	.30	1.50
8N71	A37	5c green	.60	.75
8N72	A57	9c olive grn	.35	.60
8N73	A46	10c dl violet	.35	.75
8N74	A57	16c olive gray	.30	.45
8N75	A57	18c olive gray	.30	.45
8N76	A47	20c henna	.50	.60
8N77	A48	30c brown car	.45	.45
8N78	A47	40c brt orange	.45	.75
a.		Inverted overprint	42.50	42.50
8N79	A40	50c green	2.50	2.50
8N80	A57	$1 org brn & sep	4.25	1.25
8N81	A57	$2 bl & org brn	2.50	1.05
8N82	A57	$5 red & sl grn	5.00	7.50
8N83	A57	$10 dk grn & dl pur	9.00	9.00
8N84	A57	$20 rose lake & dk bl	10.00	12.50
		Nos. 8N68-8N84 (17)	37.45	41.10

See note after No. 2N93. For overprints see Nos. 8N85-8N90, 8N95-8N106.

Nos. 8N70 and 8N62 with Additional Overprint in Red

1944, Jan. 9				
8N85	A37	4c dull green	.35	1.05
8N86	A57	10c green	.35	.75

1st anniv. of the declaration of war against the Allies by North China.

Nos. 8N72, 8N75, 8N79 and 8N80 with Additional Overprint in Red

1944, Mar. 30				
8N87	A57	9c olive green	.55	1.50
8N88	A57	18c olive gray	1.00	3.00
8N89	A40	50c green	5.75	7.50
8N90	A57	$1 org brn & sepia	2.10	3.00
a.		Red overprint inverted	37.00	37.00
		Nos. 8N87-8N90 (4)	9.40	15.00

North China Political Council, 4th anniv.

Shanghai-Nanking Nos. 9N101-9N104 Surcharged North China (Hwa Pei) and New Value in Red or Black

a   b

c

d

1944		Perf. 12½x12, 12x12½		
8N91	OS1 (a)	9c on 50c org	1.40	1.75
8N92	OS1 (b)	18c on $1 grn (R)	1.50	2.10
a.		Double surcharge	37.00	37.00
8N93	OS2 (c)	36c on $2 dp bl (R)	1.75	2.10
8N94	OS2 (d)	90c on $5 car rose	2.10	2.50
		Nos. 8N91-8N94 (4)	6.75	8.45

Nos. 8N72, 8N75, 8N79 and 8N80 Overprinted in Red or Blue

1944, Aug. 15				
8N95	A57	9c olive grn	.90	1.50
8N96	A57	18c olive gray	.90	3.00
8N97	A40	50c green	1.50	2.10
8N98	A57	$1 org brn & sep (Bl)	3.50	4.00
		Nos. 8N95-8N98 (4)	6.80	10.60

6th anniv. of the General P.O. Dept. of North China.

North China Nos. 8N76, 8N79-8N81 Overprinted in Blue or Black

---

1944, Dec. 5				
8N99	A47	20c henna (Bl)	3.00	3.50
8N100	A40	50c green (Bl)	3.00	3.50
8N101	A57	$1 org brn & sep (Bl)	5.75	6.75
8N102	A57	$2 bl & org brn	1.75	1.75
		Nos. 8N99-8N102 (4)	13.50	15.50

Death of Wang Ching-wei, puppet ruler of China.

North China Nos. 8N76, 8N79-8N81 Overprinted in Red or Black

1945				
8N103	A47	20c henna	3.00	4.00
8N104	A40	50c green (R)	9.00	9.00
8N105	A57	$1 org brn & sep	3.25	3.50
8N106	A57	$2 bl & org brn	5.75	2.00
		Nos. 8N103-8N106 (4)	21.00	18.50

2nd anniv. of the declaration of war.

Shanghai-Nanking Nos. 9N105-9N106 Surcharged in Red

1945			Perf. 12x12½	
8N107	OS3	50c on $3 lt grn	.65	.85
8N108	OS3	$1 on $6 blue	.65	.85

Return of the foreign concessions in Shanghai.

Dragon Pillar   Dr. Sun Yat-
OS1   sen
          OS2

Designs: $2, Long Bridge and White Pagoda. $5, Tower in Imperial City. $10, Marble Boat, Summer Palace.

1945		Unwmk. Litho.	Perf. 14	
		Various Papers		
8N109	OS1	$1 dull yellow	1.50	1.50
8N110	OS1	$2 deep blue	.30	1.50
8N111	OS1	$5 carmine	1.05	.75
8N112	OS1	$10 dull green	.50	1.10
		Nos. 8N109-8N112 (4)	3.35	4.85

North China Political Council, 5th anniv.

1945

Without Gum; Various Papers

8N113	OS2	$1 bister	.30	.25
8N114	OS2	$2 dark blue	1.10	.25
8N115	OS2	$5 fawn	2.50	2.50
8N116	OS2	$10 sage green	2.50	.75
8N117	OS2	$20 dull violet	2.50	1.75
8N118	OS2	$50 brown	50.00	57.50
		Nos. 8N113-8N118 (6)	58.90	63.00

Nos. 8N113-8N118 without "Hwa Pei" overprint are proofs.

Wutai Mountain,
Shansi — OS3

Designs: $10, Kaifeng Iron Pagoda. $20, International Bridge, Tientsin. $30, Taishan Mountain, Shantung. $50, General Post Office, Peking.

1945, Aug. 15

Without Gum; Various Papers

8N119	OS3	$5 gray green	.30	1.05
8N120	OS3	$10 dull brown	.75	1.05
8N121	OS3	$20 dull purple	.55	1.05

8N122	OS3	$30 slate blue	1.10	1.50
8N123	OS3	$50 carmine	2.50	3.00
	Nos. 8N119-8N123 (5)	5.20	8.10

North China Postal Directorate, 7th anniv.

SHANGHAI AND NANKING

China Nos. 299-303 Surcharged

a   b

Overprinted Type "b"

			Unwmk.	Perf. 12½, 13½
1942-45				
9N1	A37	$6 on 5c green	.90	1.25
9N2	A37	$20 on 15c scar	.45	.90
9N3	A37	$500 on 15c dk grn	.30	
9N4	A37	$1000 on 20c ultra	3.50	3.50
9N5	A37	$1000 on 25c ultra	3.50	3.50
	Nos. 9N1-9N5 (5)		8.65	10.40

A $1000 on 20c ultramarine, No. 293, exists.

Surcharged Type "a"
(Nos. 9N6-9N10)
or Type "b" (Nos. 9N11-9N40)
on Type A57 Stamps of 1939-41
Perf. 12½

9N6	25c on 5c (#352)	2.50	4.00
9N7	30c on 2c (#368)	.25	.30
9N8	50c on 5c (#352)	.30	.35
9N9	50c on 5c (#352)	.30	.30
9N10	50c on 5c (#353)	.30	.45
9N11	$1 on 8c (#353)	.30	.25
9N12	$1 on 8c (#369)	14.50	14.50
9N13	$1 on 15c (#356)	.30	.25
9N14	$1.30 on 16c (#357)	.30	.50
9N15	$1.50 on 3c (#350)	.30	.50
9N16	$2 on 5c (#352)	1.40	1.40
9N17	$2 on 10c (#354)	.30	.35
9N18	$3 on 15c (#356)	.30	.35
9N19	$4 on 16c (#357)	.50	.30
9N20	$5 on 15c (#356)	.30	.30
9N21	$6 on 5c (#351)	.75	1.75
a.	Perf. 14 (#371)	62.50	62.50
9N22	$6 on 5c (#352)	.30	.35
9N23	$6 on 5c (#353)	.50	1.25
9N24	$6 on 8c (#369)	990.00	990.00
9N25	$6 on 10c (#354)	.30	.30
9N26	$10 on 10c (#354)	.30	.35
9N27	$10 on 16c (#357)	.60	.30
9N28	$20 on 3c (#350)	.30	.50
9N29	$20 on 15c (#355)	1.40	3.00
9N30	$20 on 15c (#356)	.50	.50
9N31	$20 on $2 (#360)	1.75	3.00
9N32	$100 on 3c (#350)	.60	.50
9N33	$500 on 8c (#353)	3.00	5.50
9N34	$500 on 8c (#369)	42.50	57.50
9N35	$500 on 10c (#354)	3.00	4.25
9N36	$500 on 15c (#355)	1.50	3.00
9N37	$500 on 15c (#356)	1.25	2.50
9N38	$500 on 16c (#357)	1.50	5.00
9N39	$1000 on 25c (#358)	1.50	3.00
9N40	$2000 on $5 (#361)	1.75	3.00
	Nos. 9N1-9N23,9N25-9N40 (39)	94.10	130.65

**Nos. 381-391 (Type A57) Surcharged
with Type "b"**
Perf. 14

9N41	$1 on 8c ol grn	.30	.35
9N42	$1.70 on 30c scar	.35	.75
a.	Perf. 12½	4.00	4.00
9N43	$2 on 5c ol grn	.50	1.50
9N44	$2 on $1 org brn & sep	1.25	3.00
9N45	$3 on 8c ol grn	.75	.75
a.	$3 on 8c olive green (#383a)	42.50	42.50
b.	"3" with flat top	.50	.50
9N46	$6 on 5c grn	.50	.60
9N47	$6 on 5c grn	.50	1.00
9N48	$6 on 8c ol grn	.45	.85
9N49	$10 on 10c grn	.50	2.50
a.	Perf. 12½	2.50	7.50
9N50	$20 on $2 dp bl & yel brn	1.50	1.50
9N51	$50 on 30c scar	.90	1.00
9N52	$50 on 50c dk grn	.80	.80
9N53	$50 on $5 red & sl grn	1.10	1.10
9N54	$50 on $20 rose lake & dk bl	2.50	3.00
9N55	$100 on 10 dk grn & dl pur	2.00	2.00
9N56	$200 on $20 rose lake & dk bl	.75	1.25
9N57	$500 on 8c ol grn	13.50	16.00
a.	$500 on 8c ol grn (#383a)	30.50	30.00
9N58	$500 on 10c grn	3.00	4.25
9N59	$1000 on 30c scar	2.50	3.50
9N60	$1000 on 50c dk bl	1.25	1.75

9N61	$1000 on $2 bl & yel brn	3.00	9.75
9N62	$2000 on $5 red & sl	1.50	2.00

China Nos. 392-395 and 399-401
(Type A57) Surcharged with Type "b"

		Wmk. 261	Perf. 14
1942-45			
9N63	$2 on $1 org brn & sep, perf. 12½	1.00	1.75
9N64	$6 on 5c grn	.50	1.05
9N65	$6 on 5c ol grn	1.40	2.00
9N66	$50 on $5 red & sl	.85	1.25
a.	Numeral tablet violet	1.00	1.25
9N67	$100 on 10 dk grn & dl pur	.50	.75
9N68	$200 on $20 rose lake & dk bl	.60	.75
9N69	$500 on 10c grn	2.50	3.00
9N70	$1000 on 30c scar	3.50	4.00
9N71	$5000 on $10 dl pur, perf. 12½	8.00	9.75
a.	Perf. 14	125.00	125.00
	Nos. 9N41-9N71 (31)	58.25	83.50

Nos. 9N63 and 9N71 were not issued without surcharge. A $50 on 30c scarlet exists.

Same Surch. on Stamps of 1940-41
Perf. 12½, 13
Wmk. 261

9N72	A46	$30 on 2c dp bl	150.00	150.00

A $7.50 on ½c and a $15 on 1c are known.

Unwmk.

9N73	A39	$7.50 on ½c ol blk	2.50	3.00
9N74	A40	$15 on 1c org	.35	1.50
a.	Without secret mark	62.50	62.50
9N75	A46	$30 on 2c dp bl	1.40	2.00
9N76	A40	$200 on 1c org	.30	.35
9N77	A45	$200 on 8c dp org	.85	1.25
	Nos. 9N73-9N77 (5)		5.40	8.10

**Surcharged Type "a" (Nos. 9N78-
9N81)
or Type "b" (Nos. 9N82-9N96) on
Type A59 Stamps of 1941**
Perf. 12

9N78	5c on ½c sepia	.25	.35
9N79	10c on 1c orange	.25	.35
9N80	20c on 1c orange	.25	.50
9N81	40c on 5c green	.25	.50
9N82	$5 on 5c green	.25	.35
9N83	$10 on 10c brt grn	.25	.35
9N84	$50 on ½c sepia	.25	.35
9N85	$50 on 1c orange	.45	.50
9N86	$50 on 17c olive	.45	.60
9N87	$200 on 5c green	.45	.60
9N88	$200 on 8c turq grn	.25	.30
9N89	$200 on 8c red org	.45	.75
9N90	$500 on $5 scar & blk	.50	.50
9N91	$1000 on 1c orange	.50	.65
9N92	$1000 on 25c rose vio	.50	.65
9N93	$1000 on 30c scarlet	1.25	.65
9N94	$1000 on $2 bl & blk	1.25	1.25
9N95	$1000 on $10 grn & blk	.50	.65
9N96	$2000 on $5 scar & blk	1.25	1.25
	Nos. 9N78-9N96 (19)	9.50	11.00

Stamps of China
1939-41 Surcharged in
Red or Blue

		Unwmk.	Perf. 12, 12½
1943			
9N97	A57	25c on 5c grn	.25	1.50
9N98	A59	50c on 8c red org (Bl)	.25	.60
9N99	A57	$1 on 16c ol gray	.25	1.75
9N100	A59	$2 on 50c dk bl	.25	.60
	Nos. 9N97-9N100 (4)		1.00	4.45

Return of the foreign concessions in Shanghai.

Wheat and
Cotton — OS1

Purple
Mountain,
Nanking
OS2

Perf. 12½x12, 12x12½

		Engr.	Unwmk.
1944			
9N101	OS1	50c orange	.90	1.10
9N102	OS1	$1 green	.90	1.10
9N103	OS2	$2 deep blue	.90	1.10
9N104	OS2	$5 carmine rose	.90	1.10
	Nos. 9N101-9N104 (4)	3.60	4.40

Puppet government at Nanking, 4th anniv.
For surcharges see Nos. 8N91-8N94,
9N107-9N110.

Map of Foreign
Concessions in
Shanghai — OS3

			Perf. 12x12½
1944			
9N105	OS3	$3 lt orange	.90	1.10
9N106	OS3	$6 blue	.90	1.10

1st anniversary of the return of the foreign concessions in Shanghai.
For surcharges see Nos. 8N107-8N108.

**Nos. 9N101-9N104 Surcharged in
Black with Type "b"**

1945, Mar. 30				
9N107	OS1	$15 on 50c orange	.90	1.10
9N108	OS1	$30 on $1 green	.90	1.10
9N109	OS2	$60 on $2 dp blue	.90	1.10
9N110	OS2	$200 on $5 car rose	.90	1.10
	Nos. 9N107-9N110 (4)	3.60	4.40

China Nos. C31, C32, C36 and C38
Surcharged in Red, Green, Orange
or Carmine

			Perf. 12½, 13
1945			
9N111	AP3	$150 on 15c (R)	.45	.90
9N112	AP3	$250 on 25c (G)	.45	.90
9N113	AP3	$600 on 60c (O)	.45	.90
9N114	AP3	$1,000 on $1 (C)	.45	.90
	Nos. 9N111-9N114 (4)	1.80	3.60

Issue as air raid precaution propaganda.

AIR POST STAMPS

China Nos. C35 and C38 Surcharged
in Black

The surcharges on Nos. 9NC1-9NC7 were in Japanese currency because all air mail then was carried by Japanese planes.

The surcharges translate: (10c) "Airmail fee for postcard within the nation has been paid." (20c) "Airmail fee for letter within the nation has been paid."

		Unwmk.	Perf. 12½
1941			
9NC1	AP3	10(s) on 50c brown	.55	.40
9NC2	AP3	20(s) on $1 apple grn	.90	.90

Two types of surcharge exist on No. 9NC1.

Similar Surcharge on No. C28

		Wmk. 261	Perf. 13
1941			
9NC3	AP3	20(s) on $1 ap grn	18.00	18.00

Nos. C37 and C39 Surcharged

The surcharges translate: (18c and 25c) "Airmail fee for postcard to Japan has been paid." (35c) "Airmail fee for letter to Japan has been paid."

		Unwmk.	Perf. 12½, 13
1941			
9NC4	AP3	18(s) on 90c lt olive	.55	.60
9NC5	AP3	25(s) on 90c lt olive	.45	.60
9NC6	AP3	35(s) on $2 lt brown	.45	.60
	Nos. 9NC4-9NC6 (3)	1.45	1.80

**No. 9NC6 with Additional Surcharge
in Red**
Perf. 12½

9NC7	AP3	60(s) on 35(s) on $2	.45	.55

POSTAGE DUE STAMPS

Postage Due Stamps of
China 1932 Surcharged
in Black

		Unwmk.	Perf. 14
1945			
9NJ1	D5	$1 on 2c org	.90	1.75
9NJ2	D5	$2 on 5c org	.90	1.75
9NJ3	D5	$5 on 10c org	.90	1.75
9NJ4	D5	$10 on 20c org	.90	3.00
	Nos. 9NJ1-9NJ4 (4)	3.60	8.25

Northeastern Provinces

With the end of World War II and the collapse of Manchukuo, the Northeastern Provinces reverted to China. In many Manchurian towns and cities, the Manchukuo stamps were locally hand-stamped in ideograms: "Republic of China," "China Postal Service" or "Temporary Use for China." A typical example is shown above.

Dr. Sun Yat-sen
A1   A2
Black Surcharge

			Unwmk. Typo.	Perf. 14
1946, Feb.				
1	A1	50c on $5 red	.35	1.40
2	A1	50c on $10 green	.90	2.10
3	A1	$1 on $5 green	.35	1.75
4	A1	$2 on $20 brown vio	.35	1.40
5	A1	$4 on $50 brown	.35	1.75
	Nos. 1-5 (5)	2.30	7.75

The two characters at left express the new value.

Stamps of China,
1938-41 Overprinted

1946, Apr.   Perf. 12½, 13, 13½, 14

6	A40	1c org (#422)	.35	3.75
7	A48	3c dp yel brn (#425)	.35	3.75
8	A48	5c dl red org (#427)	.35	4.75
9	A57	10c grn (#354)	.35	3.75
10	A57	10c grn (#384)	.35	3.75
11	A47	20c lt bl (#433)	.35	3.75
a.		Horiz. pair, imperf. btwn	100.00	
		Nos. 6-11 (6)	2.10	23.50

1946, July   Engr.   Perf. 14
Without Gum

12	A2	5c lake	.35	3.50
13	A2	10c orange	.35	3.50
14	A2	20c yel grn	.35	4.00
15	A2	25c blk brn	.35	3.50
16	A2	50c red org	.35	2.75
17	A2	$1 blue	.35	2.25
18	A2	$2 dk vio	.35	2.75
19	A2	$2.50 indigo	.35	3.50
20	A2	$3 brown	.35	2.75
21	A2	$4 org brn	.35	3.50
22	A2	$5 dk grn	.35	2.75
23	A2	$10 crimson	.35	1.75
24	A2	$20 olive	.35	1.40
25	A2	$50 blue vio	.40	1.00
		Nos. 12-25 (14)	4.95	38.90

Two types of $4, $10, $20 and $50: I- Character *kuo* directly left of sun emblem is open at upper and lower left corners of "box." Diagonal stroke from top center to lower right has no hook at bottom. II- Character is closed at left corners. Diagonal stroke has hook at bottom.

See Nos. 47-52, 61-63. For surcharges see Nos. M1, Taiwan 91-96, People's Republic of China 35-48, 3L37-3L52, 3L55-3L66, 3L71-3L75.

China Nos. 728-731 Surcharged in Black

1946

26	A75	$2 on $20 green	.35	3.25
27	A75	$3 on $30 blue	.35	3.25
28	A75	$5 on $50 dark brown	.35	3.25
29	A75	$10 on $100 carmine	.35	3.25
		Nos. 26-29 (4)	1.40	13.00

Convening of Chinese National Assembly.

Type of China, 1946, with added inscriptions on both sides of head:

1947   Engr.   Perf. 11, 11½

30	A74	$2 carmine	.65	4.00
31	A74	$3 green	1.10	4.00
32	A74	$5 vermilion	1.10	4.00
33	A74	$10 yel grn	1.10	4.00
34	A74	$20 yel org	1.40	4.00
35	A74	$30 magenta	1.40	4.00
		Nos. 30-35 (6)	6.75	24.00

60th birthday of Chiang Kai-shek.

Type of China, 1947, with additional inscription above value: 用貼北東

1947   Unwmk.   Engr.   Perf. 14

36	A76	$2 deep green	.65	2.00
37	A76	$4 deep blue	.65	2.00
38	A76	$6 carmine	.65	2.00
39	A76	$10 lt brown	.65	2.00
40	A76	$20 deep claret	.65	2.00
		Nos. 36-40 (5)	3.25	10.00

First anniversary of return of Chinese National Government to Nanking.

China Nos. 644 to 646 and 634 Surcharged in Black

1947   Perf. 12½, 14

41	A73	$100 on $1000 rose lake	1.10	4.25
42	A73	$300 on $3000 bl	1.10	4.25
43	A73	$500 on $5000 dp grn & ver	.55	5.00
44	A37	$500 on $30 choc	1.00	4.25
		Nos. 41-44 (4)	3.75	17.75

Type of 1946

1947   Engr.   Perf. 14
Without Gum

47	A2	$44 dk car rose	40.00	57.50
48	A2	$100 dp grn	.35	.70
49	A2	$200 rose brn	.35	1.40
50	A2	$300 bluish grn	.35	2.75
51	A2	$500 rose car	.35	.70
52	A2	$1000 dp orange	.35	.60
		Nos. 47-52 (6)	41.75	63.65

For surcharges see note following No. 25.

Stamps and Types of 1946-47 Surcharged in Black or Red

1948   Unwmk.   Perf. 14

53	A2	$1500 on 20c yel grn	.90	4.50
54	A2	$3000 on $1 blue	.45	5.00
55	A2	$4000 on 25c blk brn (R)	.45	4.00
56	A2	$8000 on 50c red org	.45	3.25
57	A2	$10,000 on 10c org	.55	3.25
58	A2	$50,000 on $109 dk grn (R)	1.00	6.25
59	A2	$100,000 on $65 dl grn	.90	6.25
60	A2	$500,000 on $22 gray (R)	1.50	6.25
		Nos. 53-60 (8)	6.20	38.75

Type of 1946

1947, Nov. 5
Without Gum

61	A2	$22 gray	80.00	85.00
62	A2	$65 dull green	80.00	100.00
63	A2	$109 dark green	85.00	100.00
		Nos. 61-63 (3)	245.00	285.00

For surcharges see note following No. 25.

POSTAGE DUE STAMPS

D1

1947   Unwmk.   Engr.   Perf. 14
Without Gum

J1	D1	10c dark blue	.55	7.75
J2	D1	20c dark blue	.55	7.75
J3	D1	50c dark blue	.55	5.75
J4	D1	$1 dark blue	.20	4.25
J5	D1	$2 dark blue	.20	5.50
J6	D1	$5 dark blue	.20	5.50
		Nos. J1-J6 (6)	2.25	36.50

Nos. J4-J6 are known on paper with the papermaker's watermark, "COSMOS BOND."

Nos. J1 to J3 Surcharged in Red

1948

J7	D1	$10 on 10c dark blue	.35	9.00
J8	D1	$20 on 20c dark blue	.35	9.00
J9	D1	$50 on 50c dark blue	.35	9.00
		Nos. J7-J9 (3)	1.05	27.00

The surcharge reads "Changed to . . . dollars." Characters at the left express the new value and vary on each denomination.

MILITARY STAMPS

No. 16 Surcharged in Black

1947   Unwmk.   Perf. 14

M1	A2	$44 on 50c red org	11.00	40.00

The surcharge reads: "Army Post. Temporarily for 44 dollars."

China No. M13 Overprinted in Black

Thin Paper Without Gum
Perf. 12½

M2	M1	rose	2.75	18.00

China No. M13 Overprinted in Black

M3	M1	rose	62.50	62.50

PARCEL POST STAMP

China No. Q25 Surcharged in Black

1948   Unwmk.   Engr.   Perf. 13½
Without Gum

Q1	PP3	$500,000 on $5,000,000 lil		180.00

Used value is for CTO.

The use of this handstamp from Anhwei has not been verified.

FUKIEN PROVINCE

Stamps of China, 1945-49, Surcharged

1949   Engr.   Perf. 14
Without Gum

1	A82	1c on $500 bl grn	10.00	6.25
2	A82	1c on $7000 lt red brn	15.00	22.50
3	A82	2c on $2,000,000 ver	5.00	6.75
4	A82	2½c on $50,000 dp bl	35.00	35.00
5	A73	4c on $100 dk car	4.50	4.50
6	A73	10c on $200 ol grn	7.25	9.00
7	A82	10c on $3000 bl	5.50	4.50
8	A82	10c on $4000 gray	7.25	10.75
9	A82	10c on $6000 rose lil	4.50	6.25
10	A82	10c on $100,000 dl grn	5.75	6.75
11	A82	10c on $1,000,000 cl	5.75	6.25
12	A82	40c on $200,000 brn vio	9.00	10.00
		Nos. 1-12 (12)	114.50	128.50

The surcharge on No. 2 is handstamped and in slightly larger characters.

Issue dates: No. 2, May 10; others, June.

China Nos. 973, 975-978 Overprinted

1949, June   Litho.   Perf. 12½, 13

13	A94	1c apple grn	18.00	5.50
14	A94	4c blue green	5.50	2.00
15	A94	10c deep lilac	55.00	27.50
16	A94	16c orange red	11.00	27.50
17	A94	20c blue	55.00	27.50
		Nos. 13-17 (5)	144.50	90.00

Same Overprint on China No. 959

1949, July   Litho.   Perf. 12½

18	A96	orange	72.50	72.50

Same Overprint on Fukien Nos. 1, 3-4, 8, 11 in Black or Red

1949, June   Engr.   Perf. 14

19	A82	1c on $500 bl grn	150.00	150.00
20	A82	2c on $2,000,000 ver	55.00	55.00
21	A82	2½c on $50,000 dp bl	90.00	90.00
22	A82	10c on $4000 gray	37.50	37.50
23	A82	10c on $1,000,000 cl	145.00	145.00
		Nos. 19-23 (5)	477.50	477.50

AIR POST STAMP

China #C62 Overprinted as #13-17

1949, July   Litho.   Perf. 12½

C1	AP5	blue green	72.50	37.50

SPECIAL DELIVERY STAMP

China #E12 Overprinted as #13-17

1949, July   Litho.   Perf. 12½

E1	SD2	red violet	50.00	35.00

REGISTRATION STAMP

China #F2 Overprinted as #13-17

1949, July   Litho.   Perf. 12½

F1	R2	carmine	50.00	35.00

HUNAN PROVINCE

China No. 640
Surcharged

1949, May   Engr.   Perf. 14

1	A73	on $100 dk car	14.50	8.50

The first printing of surcharge on No. 1 is in smaller characters.

China Nos. 797, 788, 750, 747
Surcharged

1949, May   Engr.   Perf. 14

2	A82	1c on $2,000,000 ver	27.50	27.50
3	A82	2c on $20,000 rose pink	27.50	27.50
4	A82	5c on $3000 blue	35.00	40.00
5	A82	10c on $500 blue grn	30.00	27.50
		Nos. 2-5 (4)	120.00	122.50

AIR POST STAMP

China No. 790
Surcharged

1949, May   Engr.   Perf. 14

C1	A82	On $40,000 green	22.50	24.00

SPECIAL DELIVERY STAMP

China No. 637 Surcharged as No. F1
in Red

1949, May   Engr.   Perf. 14

E1	A73	On $30 dark blue	27.50	27.50

REGISTRATION STAMP

China No. 754
Surcharged

1949, May   Engr.   Perf. 14

F1	A82	On $7000 lt red brn	27.50	27.50

HUPEH PROVINCE

China Type A95
Surcharged

1949, May   Litho.

1	A95	1c on $20 red brn	67.50	67.50
2	A95	10c on $20 red brn	67.50	67.50

KANSU PROVINCE

China No. 959
Handstamped in Purple

區書亭甘限
用貼

1949, Aug.   Litho.   Perf. 12½

1	A96	orange	1,100.

AIR POST STAMP

Same Handstamp Overprinted on
China No. C62 in Red

1949, Aug.   Litho.   Perf. 12½

C1	AP5	blue green	1,100.

Counterfeits exist.

KIANGSI PROVINCE

China Nos. 789-791
Surcharged

1949   Engr.   Perf. 14

1	A82	On $30,000 choc	57.50	55.00
2	A82	On $40,000 green	57.50	55.00
3	A82	On $50,000 dp bl	57.50	55.00
		Nos. 1-3 (3)	172.50	165.00

AIR POST STAMP

Similar Surcharge on China No. 754

1949   Engr.   Perf. 14

C1	A82	On $7000 lt red brn	62.50	62.50

Third and fourth characters in right column of surcharge read "Air Mail" in Chinese on No. C1, "Registered" on Nos. F1-F2.

SPECIAL DELIVERY STAMP

Similar Surcharge on China No. 750

1949   Engr.   Perf. 14

E1	A82	On $3000 blue	67.50	45.00

See note below No. C1.

REGISTRATION STAMPS

Similar Surcharge on China Nos. 747
and 754

1949   Engr.   Perf. 14

F1	A82	On $500 bl grn	67.50	45.00
F2	A82	On $7000 lt red brn	67.50	55.00

KWANGSI PROVINCE

China Nos. 811 and
818 Also Surcharged
in Red

1949, May 21   Typo.

6	A62	5c on $20,000 on 10c dp grn	30.00	30.00
7	A62	5c on $40,000 on 20c dk ol grn	67.50	67.50

China Stamps of 1946-48 Surcharged
in Black or Red

a   b

1949   Engr.   Perf. 14
Type "a" Surcharge

8	A82	½c on $500,000 lil rose	40.00	27.50
9	A82	1c on $200,000 brn vio	35.00	12.00
10	A82	2c on $300,000 yel grn	120.00	72.50
11	A73	5c on $3000 blue	35.00	20.00
12	A82	5c on $3000 blue	18.00	11.00
13	A82	5c on $40,000 grn	35.00	20.00

Type "b" Surcharge

14	A82	13c on $50,000 dp bl (R)	25.00	16.00
15	A82	13c on $50,000 dp bl	100.00	25.00
16	A82	17c on $7000 lt red brn	27.50	27.50
17	A82	21c on $100,000 dl grn	32.50	29.00
		Nos. 8-17 (10)	468.00	260.50

SHENSI PROVINCE

China Nos. 747, 750
Surcharged

1949, May   Engr.   Perf. 14

1	A82	On $500 bl grn	45.00	45.00
2	A82	On $3000 blue	45.00	45.00

AIR POST STAMP

Similar Surcharge on China No. 754

1949, May   Engr.   Perf. 14

C1	A82	On $7000 lt red brn	55.00	55.00

SPECIAL DELIVERY STAMP

Similar Surcharge on China No. 746 in
Red

1949, May   Engr.   Perf. 14

E1	A82	On $250 dp lil	62.50	62.50

REGISTRATION STAMPS

Similar Surcharge on China Nos. 626,
637 in Red

1949, May   Typo.   Perf. 12

F1	A72	on $30 dp bl	62.50	62.50
F2	A73	on $30 dk bl	55.00	55.00

SZECHWAN PROVINCE

Re-engraved Issue of
China, 1923,
Overprinted

1933   Unwmk.   Perf. 14

1	A29	1c orange	11.00	1.00
2	A29	5c claret	11.00	1.40
3	A30	50c deep green	32.50	6.75
		Nos. 1-3 (3)	54.50	9.15

The overprint reads "For use in Szechwan Province exclusively."

Same on Sun Yat-sen Issue of 1931-37
Type II

1933-34   Perf. 12½

4	A37	2c olive grn	2.00	1.00
5	A37	5c green	22.50	2.40
6	A37	15c dk green	7.75	3.50
7	A37	15c scar ('34)	9.00	12.00
8	A37	25c ultra	7.50	1.75
9	A37	$1 org brn & dk brn	22.50	4.00
10	A37	$2 bl & org brn	55.00	6.75
11	A37	$5 dl red & blk	125.00	37.50
		Nos. 4-11 (8)	251.25	68.90

Same on Martyrs Issue of 1932-34

1933   Perf. 14

12	A39	½c black brn	.80	.80
13	A40	1c orange	1.25	.55
14	A39	2½c rose lilac	3.50	3.75
15	A48	3c deep brown	3.00	3.00
16	A45	8c brown org	1.75	1.50
17	A46	10c dull violet	4.50	.55
18	A45	13c blue green	5.00	5.00
19	A46	17c brown olive	5.50	1.40
20	A47	20c brown red	8.50	1.00
21	A48	30c brown violet	6.75	1.00
22	A47	40c orange	18.00	1.40
23	A40	50c green	37.50	2.10
		Nos. 12-23 (12)	96.05	18.05

Stamps of China,
1947-48, Surcharged

1949   Engr.   Perf. 14

24	A82	on $150 dk bl	72.50	55.00
25	A82	on $250 dp lil	72.50	55.00
26	A82	on $500 bl grn	21.00	12.50
27	A82	on $1000 red	55.00	42.50
28	A82	on $2000 ver	21.00	9.50
29	A82	on $3000 blue	21.00	9.50
30	A82	on $4000 gray	21.00	9.50
31	A82	on $5000 dk brn	62.50	62.50
32	A82	on $6000 rose lil	21.00	21.00
33	A82	on $7000 lt red brn	55.00	45.00
34	A82	on $10,000 dk bl & car	30.50	16.00
35	A82	on $20,000 rose pink	22.50	16.00
36	A82	on $30,000 choc	29.00	22.50
37	A82	on $50,000 grn & dk bl	29.00	25.00
38	A82	on $50,000 dp bl	29.00	22.50
39	A82	on $100,000 dl yel & ol	29.00	22.50
40	A82	on $100,000 dl grn	29.00	25.00
41	A82	on $200,000 vio brn & dp bl	29.00	22.50
42	A82	on $200,000 brn vio	29.00	22.50
43	A82	on $300,000 sep & org brn	40.00	27.50
44	A82	on $300,000 yel grn	55.00	40.00
45	A82	on $500,000 dk Prus grn & sep	29.00	22.50
46	A82	on $1,000,000 claret	55.00	40.00
47	A82	on $2,000,000 ver	29.00	27.50
48	A82	on $3,000,000 ol bis	29.00	27.50
49	A82	on $5,000,000 ultra	110.00	67.50
		Nos. 24-49 (26)	1,025.	769.00

Several of Nos. 24-49 exist with inverted surcharge and a few with bottom character of left row repeated in right row, same position. Counterfeits exist.

China No. 737
Surcharged in Black

1949   Perf. 12½

50	A77	2c on $500 ol grn	40.00	55.00

China No. 975
Handstamp
Surcharged in Purple

1949 Litho.
51 A94 2½c on 4c bl grn 55.00 *40.00*

AIR POST STAMPS

China Nos. C55-C58, C60-C61
Surcharged

Perf. 12½, 13x12½, 14

1949, July Unwmk.
C1 AP3 On $10,000 on
30c 9.00 9.00
a. On #C54 500.00
C2 AP4 On $10,000 on
$27 14.50 20.00
a. Second surcharge inverted 250.00
b. On #C53 125.00
C3 AP3 On $20,000 on
25c 14.50 16.00
C4 AP3 On $30,000 on
90c 16.00 27.50
C5 AP3 On $50,000 on
60c 125.00 155.00
C6 AP3 On $50,000 on $1 17.00 24.00
Nos. C1-C6 (6) 196.00 251.50

REGISTRATION STAMPS

Stamps of China,
1944-47, Surcharged

Engraved; Typographed (A72)
1949 Perf. 12, 13, 14
F1 A64 On $100 yel brn 77.50
F2 A72 On $100 dk brn 77.50
F3 A64 On $200 dk grn 155.00
F4 A72 On $200 brn vio 72.50
F5 A73 On $200 ol grn 77.50
F6 A73 On $500 brt bl grn 155.00
F7 A73 On $700 red brn 275.00
F8 A73 On $5000 dp grn &
ver 120.00
Nos. F1-F8 (8) 1,010.

PARCEL POST STAMP

China No. Q10
Surcharged

1949 Engr. Perf. 12½
Q1 PP2 1c on $20,000 dk red — —

TSINGTAU PROVINCE

China Nos. 890, 903,
945, 894 Handstamp
Surcharged in Purple
(#1-2), Blue (#3) or
Red (#4)

Engraved; Lithographed
1949, May Perf. 14, 12½
1 A94 1c on $100 org
brn 100.00 90.00
2 A94 4c on $5000 lt bl 100.00 90.00
3 A94 6c on $500 rose lil 100.00 90.00
4 A94 10c on $1000 bl 100.00 90.00
Nos. 1-4 (4) 400.00 360.00

YUNNAN PROVINCE

Stamps of China,
1923-26, Overprinted

The overprint reads "For exclusive use in the
Province of Yunnan." It was applied to prevent
stamps being purchased in the depreciated
currency of Yunnan and used elsewhere.

1926 Unwmk. Perf. 14
1 A29 ½c blk brn 1.10 .35
2 A29 1c orange 1.75 .35
3 A29 1½c violet 3.75 4.25
4 A29 2c yellow grn 2.75 .50
5 A29 3c blue green 2.75 .35
6 A29 4c olive grn 3.50 .50
7 A29 5c claret 3.50 .50
8 A29 6c red 5.25 1.25
9 A29 7c violet 5.50 1.90
10 A29 8c brown org 4.75 1.40
11 A29 10c dark blue 3.00 .30
12 A30 13c brown 1.75 1.90
13 A30 15c dark blue 1.75 1.90
14 A30 16c olive grn 3.50 1.90
15 A30 20c brown red 8.50 3.25
16 A30 30c brown vio 5.25 5.75
17 A30 50c deep green 5.75 5.75
18 A31 $1 org brn & sep 20.50 14.00
19 A31 $2 blue & red brn 35.00 14.00
20 A31 $5 red & slate 240.00 260.00
Nos. 1-20 (20) 359.35 320.10

Unification Issue of
China, 1929,
Overprinted in Red

1929 Perf. 14
21 A35 1c brown org 2.25 2.25
22 A35 4c olive grn 3.75 5.75
23 A35 10c dark blue 12.00 9.00
24 A35 $1 dark red 120.00 90.00
Nos. 21-24 (4) 138.00 107.00

Similar Overprint in Black on Sun Yat-
sen Mausoleum Issue
Characters 15½-16mm apart
25 A36 1c brown orange 2.25 2.00
26 A36 4c olive green 2.25 3.75
27 A36 10c dark blue 9.00 8.50
28 A36 $1 dark red 77.50 67.50
Nos. 25-28 (4) 91.00 81.75

London Print Issue of
China, 1931-37,
Overprinted

1932-34 Unwmk. Perf. 12½
Type I (double circle)
29 A37 1c orange 4.00 2.75
30 A37 4c olive grn 5.00 5.50
31 A37 4c green 3.25 5.50

---

32 A37 20c ultra 3.25 3.00
33 A37 $1 org brn & dk
brn 50.00 55.00
34 A37 $2 bl & org brn 82.50 85.00
35 A37 $5 dl red & blk 250.00 295.00
Nos. 29-35 (7) 398.00 451.75
Type II (single circle)
36 A37 2c olive grn 26.00 26.00
37 A37 4c green 17.00 10.75
38 A37 5c green 15.00 10.00
39 A37 15c dk green 8.00 8.75
40 A37 15c scar ('34) 8.00 10.00
41 A37 25c ultra 11.00 11.50
42 A37 $1 org brn & dk
brn 67.50 67.50
43 A37 $2 bl & org brn 125.00 125.00
44 A37 $5 dl red & blk 260.00 260.00
Nos. 36-44 (9) 537.50 529.50

Nos. 36-39, 41-44 were overprinted in
London as well as in Peking. The London
overprints are 11mm in length; the Peking
overprints are 12mm in length. There are other
minor differences. Value of London overprints
is significantly more than the Peking overprints, which are valued above.

Tan Yuan-chang
Issue of China,
1933, Overprinted

1933 Perf. 14
45 A49 2c olive green 1.75 1.75
46 A49 5c green 3.00 2.40
47 A49 25c ultra 5.25 5.50
48 A49 $1 red 80.00 65.00
Nos. 45-48 (4) 90.00 74.65

Martyrs Issue of
China, 1932-34,
Overprinted

1933
49 A39 ½c blk brown 1.75 1.60
50 A40 1c orange 3.50 2.75
51 A39 2½c rose lilac 4.00 4.50
52 A48 3c deep brown 6.25 2.25
53 A45 8c brown org 2.75 2.75
54 A46 10c dull vio 4.00 4.50
55 A45 13c blue grn 2.50 1.10
56 A46 17c brn olive 12.50 12.50
57 A47 20c brown red 3.25 3.25
58 A48 30c brown vio 10.00 10.00
59 A47 40c orange 47.50 47.50
60 A40 50c green 47.50 47.50
Nos. 49-60 (12) 145.50 140.20

China No. 324 was overprinted with characters arranged vertically, like Sinkiang No. 114,
but was not issued.

China Stamps of
1945-49 Surcharged in
Black or Blue

**Engraved; Lithographed;
Typographed**
1949 Perf. 12, 12½, 14
61 A82 1c on $200,000
brn vio 19.00 19.00
62 A82 1.2c on $40,000
grn 19.00 21.00
63 A94 6c on $200 red
org 19.00 19.00
64 A94 10c on $20,000
org 19.00 21.00
65 A94 12c on $50 dk
Prus grn
(Bl) 19.00 19.00
66 A72 12c on $50 grnsh
gray (Bl) 19.00 19.00
67 A72 12c on $200 brn
vio (Bl) 19.00 21.00
68 A94 30c on $20 vio
brn 19.00 19.00
69 A82 $1.20 on $100,000
dl grn 30.00 35.00
Nos. 61-69 (9) 182.00 193.00

China No. 888 and
630 Surcharged

1949 Engr. Perf. 14
70 A94 4c on $20 vio brn 360.00 225.00

Typo. Perf. 12
71 A72 12c on $200 brn
vio 310.00 200.00

MANCHURIA

Kirin and Heilungkiang Issue
Stamps of China, 1923-26,
Overprinted

The overprint reads: "For use in Ki-Hei District" the two names being abbreviated.
The intention of the overprint was to prevent
the purchase of stamps in Manchuria, where
the currency was depreciated, and their resale
elsewhere.

1927 Unwmk. Perf. 14
1 A29 ½c black brn 1.90 .35
2 A29 1c orange 1.90 .35
3 A29 1½c violet 2.50 1.90
4 A29 2c yellow grn 2.50 1.90
5 A29 3c brown grn 1.75 .75
6 A29 4c olive grn .85 .35
7 A29 5c claret 1.75 .35
8 A29 6c red 2.50 1.90
9 A29 7c violet 5.25 1.90
10 A29 8c brown org 3.50 1.90
11 A29 10c dk blue 1.90 .50
12 A30 13c brown 4.00 3.00
13 A30 15c dk blue 4.00 3.00
14 A30 16c olive grn 4.00 2.75
15 A30 20c brown red 6.00 3.50
16 A30 30c brown vio 8.75 3.50
17 A30 50c dp green 12.00 4.25
18 A31 $1 org brn & sep 26.00 8.75
19 A31 $2 bl & red brn 70.00 19.00
20 A31 $5 red & slate 325.00 325.00
Nos. 1-20 (20) 486.05 384.90

Several values of this issue exist with
inverted overprint, double overprint and in
pairs with one overprint omitted. These
"errors" were not regularly issued. Forgeries
also exist.

Chang Tso-lin
Stamps of 1928
Overprinted in Red
or Blue

1928 Perf. 14
21 A34 1c brown org (R) 2.75 1.75
22 A34 4c olive grn (R) 1.75 1.75
23 A34 10c dull blue (R) 5.00 3.75
24 A34 $1 red (Bl) 50.00 45.00
Nos. 21-24 (4) 59.50 52.25

Unification Issue of China, 1929,
Overprinted in Red as in 1928

1929
25 A35 1c brown orange 2.00 2.00
26 A35 4c olive green 3.75 3.25
27 A35 10c dark blue 13.00 12.50
28 A35 $1 dark red 110.00 100.00
Nos. 25-28 (4) 128.75 117.75

Similar Overprint in Black on Sun Yat-sen Mausoleum Issue of China Characters 15-16mm apart

1929			Perf. 14	
29	A36	1c brown orange	2.25	2.50
30	A36	4c olive green	2.75	3.00
31	A36	10c dark blue	8.50	5.25
32	A36	$1 dark red	85.00	65.00
		Nos. 29-32 (4)	98.50	75.75

SINKIANG

Stamps of China, 1913-19, Overprinted in Black or Red

The first character of overprint is ½mm out of alignment, to the left, and the overprint measures 16mm.

1915		Unwmk.	Perf. 14	
1	A24	½c black brn	1.75	.95
2	A24	1c orange	1.75	.70
3	A24	2c yellow grn	2.40	1.25
4	A24	3c slate grn	2.40	.65
5	A24	4c scarlet	4.75	1.10
6	A24	5c rose lilac	3.50	.95
7	A24	6c gray	6.50	2.75
8	A24	7c violet	6.50	8.50
9	A24	8c brown orange	5.50	5.50
10	A24	10c dark blue	5.50	2.75
11	A25	15c brown	6.50	3.50
12	A25	16c olive grn	13.00	9.25
13	A25	20c brown red	13.00	7.25
14	A25	30c brown violet	14.50	11.00
15	A25	50c deep green	40.00	18.50
16	A26	$1 ocher & blk		
		(R)	145.00	62.50
a.		Second & third characters of overprint transposed	16,000.	
		Nos. 1-16 (16)	272.55	137.10

Stamps of China, 1913-19, Overprinted in Black or Red

The five characters of overprint are correctly aligned and measure 15½mm.

1916-19				
17	A24	½c black brn	2.00	2.40
18	A24	1c orange	3.25	1.75
19	A24	1½c violet	4.50	4.00
20	A24	2c yellow grn	3.25	1.75
21	A24	3c slate grn	5.50	.70
22	A24	4c scarlet	5.50	1.25
23	A24	5c rose lilac	5.50	.90
24	A24	6c gray	8.00	1.25
25	A24	7c violet	8.00	11.00
26	A24	8c brown org	8.75	8.50
27	A24	10c dark blue	8.75	1.25
28	A25	13c brown	4.75	8.00
29	A25	15c brown	6.00	8.50
30	A25	16c olive grn	5.50	4.00
31	A25	20c brown red	4.50	3.00
32	A25	30c brown vio	6.75	6.00
33	A25	50c deep green	9.25	5.50
34	A26	$1 ocher & blk		
		(R)	29.00	11.00
35	A26	$2 dk bl & blk (R)	57.50	12.00
36	A26	$5 scar & blk (R)	110.00	37.50
37	A26	$10 yel grn & blk		
		(R)	275.00	175.00
38	A26	$20 yel & blk (R)	1,435.	875.00
		Nos. 17-38 (22)	1,976.	1,180.

For overprint see No. C4.

China Nos. 243-246 Overprinted

1921			Perf. 14	
39	A27	1c orange	1.75	1.75
40	A27	3c blue green	3.50	3.50
41	A27	6c gray	13.50	13.50
42	A27	10c blue	80.00	80.00
		Nos. 39-42 (4)	98.75	98.75

Constitution Issue of China, 1923, Overprinted

1923				
43	A32	1c orange	1.55	1.55
44	A32	3c blue green	6.50	6.50
45	A32	4c red	9.75	9.75
46	A32	10c blue	27.50	27.50
		Nos. 43-46 (4)	45.30	45.30

Stamps of China, 1923-26, Overprinted as in 1916-19, in Black or Red

1924				
		Re-engraved		
47	A29	½c black brn	1.50	3.00
48	A29	1c orange	1.50	1.25
49	A29	1½c violet	2.75	5.00
50	A29	2c yellow grn	4.25	1.40
51	A29	3c blue grn	4.25	1.25
52	A29	4c gray	4.25	6.75
53	A29	5c claret	1.40	1.00
54	A29	6c red	7.50	2.75
55	A29	7c violet	8.50	7.50
56	A29	8c org brn	17.00	15.00
57	A29	10c dark blue	6.75	1.90
58	A30	13c red brown	6.00	8.50
59	A30	15c deep blue	8.75	6.75
60	A30	16c olive grn	10.00	9.75
61	A30	20c brown red	8.50	6.25
62	A30	30c brown vio	9.75	6.75
63	A30	50c deep green	10.00	6.75
64	A31	$1 org brn & sep		
		(R)	18.00	8.50
65	A31	$2 bl & red brn		
		(R)	40.00	12.00
66	A31	$5 red & slate (R)	95.00	19.00
67	A31	$10 grn & claret		
		(R)	300.00	170.00
68	A31	$20 plum & bl (R)	425.00	325.00
		Nos. 47-68 (22)	990.65	626.05

See #69, 114. For overprints see #C1-C3.

Same Overprint on China No. 275

1926				
69	A29	4c olive green	5.50	5.50

Chang Tso-lin Stamps of China, 1928, Overprinted in Red or Blue

1928			Perf. 14	
70	A34	1c brn org (R)	1.75	1.75
71	A34	4c ol grn (R)	2.75	2.75
72	A34	10c dull bl (R)	6.50	6.50
73	A34	$1 red (Bl)	55.00	55.00
		Nos. 70-73 (4)	66.00	66.00

Unification Issue of China, 1929, Overprinted in Red as in 1928

1929				
74	A35	1c brown org	2.75	2.75
75	A35	4c olive grn	4.75	4.75
76	A35	10c dk blue	11.50	11.50
77	A35	$1 dk red	90.00	90.00
		Nos. 74-77 (4)	109.00	109.00

Similar Overprint in Black on Sun Yat-sen Mausoleum Issue of China Characters 15mm apart

1929			Perf. 14	
78	A36	1c brown org	2.25	2.25
79	A36	4c olive grn	3.50	3.50
80	A36	10c dark blue	8.00	8.00
81	A36	$1 dark red	95.00	95.00
		Nos. 78-81 (4)	108.75	108.75

Stamps of Sun Yat-sen Issue of 1931-37 Overprinted

1932		Type I	Perf. 12½	
82	A37	1c orange	1.75	4.00
83	A37	2c olive grn	4.25	5.75
84	A37	4c green	2.50	6.50
85	A37	20c ultra	4.00	8.25
86	A37	$1 org brn & dk		
		brn	12.00	20.00
87	A37	$2 bl & org brn	35.00	42.50
88	A37	$5 dl red & blk	40.00	60.00
		Nos. 82-88 (7)	99.50	147.00

No. 83 was overprinted in Shanghai in 1938. The overprint differs in minor details.

1932-38				
		Type II		
89	A37	2c olive grn	.45	2.00
90	A37	4c green	1.25	4.00
91	A37	5c green	.80	4.00
92	A37	15c dk green	1.10	4.00
93	A37	15c scar ('34)	1.10	4.00
93A	A37	20c ultra ('38)	.80	2.75
94	A37	25c ultra	1.25	4.00
95	A37	$1 org brn & dk		
		brn	9.50	11.00
96	A37	$2 bl & org brn	20.00	32.50
97	A37	$5 dl red & blk	40.00	65.00
		Nos. 89-97 (10)	76.25	133.25

Nos. 89, 90 and 94 were overprinted in London, Peking and Shanghai. Nos. 92, 95-97 exist with London and Peking overprints. Nos. 91 and 93 exist with Peking and Shanghai overprints. No. 93A is a Shanghai overprint. The overprints differ in minor details.

Tan Yuan-chang Issue of China, 1933, Overprinted as in 1928

1933			Perf. 14	
98	A49	2c olive grn	3.75	3.75
99	A49	5c green	4.75	4.75
100	A49	25c ultra	15.00	15.00
101	A49	$1 red	75.00	65.00
		Nos. 98-101 (4)	98.50	88.50

Stamps of China Martyrs Issue of 1932-34 Overprinted

1933-34				
102	A39	½c black brown	.20	3.50
103	A40	1c orange	1.10	4.25
104	A39	2½c rose lilac	.25	3.25
105	A45	3c deep brown	.25	3.25
106	A45	8c brown orange	.75	3.50
107	A46	10c dull violet	.25	3.25
108	A46	13c blue green	.25	4.50
109	A46	17c brown olive	.25	2.50
110	A47	20c brown red	1.10	6.50
111	A48	30c brown violet	.40	4.50
112	A47	40c orange	.60	3.25
113	A40	50c green	.70	2.50
		Nos. 102-113 (12)	6.10	44.75

Nos. 102-113 were originally overprinted in Peking. In 1938, Nos. 103-105, 108-112 were overprinted in Shanghai. The two overprints differ in minor details. No. 105, Shanghai overprint, is scarce. Value $35.

China No. 324 Overprinted as in 1916-19

1936			Perf. 14	
114	A29	6c brown	20.00	20.00

Stamps of China, 1939-40 Overprinted in Black

1940-45		Unwmk.	Perf. 12½	
		Type III		
115	A57	2c olive green	.85	1.00
116	A57	3c dull claret ('41)	.20	1.50
117	A57	5c green	.20	1.50
118	A57	5c olive green	.20	1.50
119	A57	8c olive green ('41)	.20	.75
120	A57	10c green ('41)	.20	1.10
121	A57	15c scarlet	.55	2.50
122	A57	16c olive gray ('41)	.40	1.00
123	A57	25c dark blue	.55	2.75
124	A57	$1 hn & dk brn (type II)		
			6.25	11.00
125	A57	$2 dp bl & org brn (type I)		
			8.00	11.00
126	A57	$5 red & grnsh blk	26.00	32.50
		Nos. 115-126 (12)	40.10	68.10

		Perf. 14		
		With Secret Marks		
127	A57	8c ol grn (#383a)	1.10	1.65
a.		On #383	19.00	22.50
128	A57	10c green ('41)	10.00	13.00
129	A57	30c scarlet ('45)	.30	1.10
130	A57	50c dk blue ('45)	.55	1.75
131	A57	$1 org brn & sep	.55	2.25
132	A57	$2 dp bl & org brn	.55	2.25
133	A57	$5 red & sl grn	.65	3.75
134	A57	$10 dk grn & dl pur	1.90	2.75
135	A57	$20 rose lake & dk bl	3.50	5.50
		Nos. 127-135 (9)	19.10	34.00

Wmk. Character Yu (Post) (261)
Perf. 14

136	A57	5c olive green	.30	2.50
137	A57	10c green	.35	3.75
138	A57	30c scarlet	.35	5.00
139	A57	50c dark blue	.45	2.50
		Nos. 136-139 (4)	1.45	13.75

Martyrs Issue, 1940-41, Overprinted in Black

Perf. 12, 12½, 13, 13x12, 13½x13				
1941-45			Wmk. 261	
140	A40	1c orange	.35	2.40
141	A39	2½c rose lilac	.35	4.50
142	A46	8c dp org ('45)	5.75	12.00
143	A46	10c dull vio	.45	3.00
144	A46	13c dp yel grn	1.00	5.50
145	A46	17c brown olive	1.00	5.25
146	A46	25c red vio ('45)	2.00	7.25
147	A47	40c orange ('45)	3.50	9.25
		Nos. 140-147 (8)	14.40	49.15
		Unwmk.		
148	A39	½c olive blk	.35	3.25
149	A40	1c orange ('45)	.35	4.50
150	A46	2c dp blue ('45)	3.25	3.75
151	A48	3c dp yel brn	.35	4.50
152	A39	4c pale vio ('45)	.35	4.50
153	A46	8c dp orange	.35	5.50
154	A45	13c dp yel grn ('45)	.65	4.00
155	A48	15c brn car ('45)	.35	4.00
156	A46	17c brn ol ('45)	1.00	4.50
157	A47	20c lt blue ('45)	.35	3.25
158	A45	21c ol brn ('45)	1.25	4.50
159	A46	25c blue ('45)	1.45	5.50
160	A47	40c orange ('45)	3.00	14.00
161	A40	50c green ('45)	2.00	7.00
		Nos. 148-161 (14)	15.05	70.65

Stamps of China, 1942-43 Overprinted in Carmine, Black or Red

1944			Perf. 12½, 13	
		Without Gum		
162	A62	10c dp grn (C)	1.75	7.75
163	A62	20c dk ol grn (C)	2.00	7.75
164	A62	25c violet brn	.30	8.50
165	A62	30c dk orange	.95	9.00
166	A62	40c red brown	.30	8.50
167	A62	50c sage green	.30	5.00
a.		Perf. 11	16.00	24.00
168	A62	$1 rose lake	3.75	5.00
169	A62	$1 dull green	.30	8.50
170	A62	$1.50 dp bl (C)	.30	9.50
171	A62	$2 dk bl grn (R)	2.40	7.00
172	A62	$3 yellow	.30	12.00
173	A62	$5 cerise	2.40	11.00
		Nos. 162-173 (12)	15.05	99.50

For surcharges see Nos. 194-195.

Same Overprint on Stamps of China, 1942-43, in Black

1944-46			Imperf.	
174	A57	$10 red brown	140.00	125.00
175	A57	$20 rose red	6.75	17.00
176	A57	$30 dull vio	5.00	17.00
177	A57	$40 rose red	5.00	17.00
178	A57	$50 blue ('46)	1,080.	1,170.
179	A57	$100 orange brn	14.50	22.50
		Perf. 13½		
180	A57	$4 dp blue	2.00	13.50
181	A57	$5 lilac gray	3.50	13.50
182	A57	$10 red brn	3.50	13.50
183	A57	$20 blue grn	2.00	15.00
184	A57	$20 rose red	140.00	140.00
185	A57	$30 dull vio	4.00	17.00
186	A57	$40 rose	4.00	16.00
187	A57	$40 rose	4.50	17.00
188	A57	$100 orange brn	160.00	140.00
		Nos. 174-177,179-188 (14)	494.75	584.00

Beware of trimmed examples of Nos. 182 and 187 offered as Nos. 174 and 178.

Nos. 162 and 164
Surcharged in Black

1944, Aug. 1
194	A62	12c on 10c dp grn	9.00	27.50
195	A62	24c on 25c brn vio	9.00	27.50

Stamps of China,
1940-41, Overprinted
in Black at Chengtu,
Szechwan

1943
196	A57	10c green (#354)	25.00	30.00
197	A47	20c lt blue (#433)	25.00	30.00

	Wmk. 261		**Perf. 14**	
198	A57	50c dk blue (#396)	25.00	30.00

China Nos. 565 and
567 Overprinted in
Black

1945   Unwmk.   Perf. 12½
200	A63	40c brown red	.45	20.00
201	A63	$3 red	.45	18.00

China Nos. 640-642,
788, 751, 753
Surcharged in Black or
Red

1949   Engr.   Perf. 14
202	A73	1c on $100 dk car (R)	29.00	35.00
203	A73	3c on $200 ol grn (R)	29.00	35.00
204	A73	5c on $500 brt bl grn (R)	29.00	35.00
205	A82	10c on $20,000 rose pink	25.00	30.00
206	A82	50c on $4000 gray (R)	100.00	100.00
207	A82	$1 on $6000 rose lil	110.00	110.00
	Nos. 202-207 (6)		322.00	345.00

AIR POST STAMPS

Sinkiang Nos. 53, 57,
59, 32 Overprinted in
Red

1932-33   Unwmk.   Perf. 14
C1	A29	5c claret ('33)	400.00	290.00
C2	A29	10c dark blue ('33)	400.00	225.00
C3	A30	15c deep blue	2,700.	775.00
C4	A25	30c brown violet	1,170.	990.00

Counterfeits exist of Nos. C1-C19.

Air Post Stamps of China, 1932-37
Handstamped in Dull Red

1942
C5	AP3	15c gray green	7.25	9.00
C6	AP3	25c orange	425.00	350.00
C7	AP3	30c red	15.50	27.50
C8	AP3	45c brown vio	11.00	18.00
C9	AP3	50c dk brown	45.00	50.00

C10	AP3	60c dk blue	11.00	21.00
C11	AP3	90c olive grn	57.50	80.00
C12	AP3	$1 yellow grn	12.00	20.00
	Nos. C5-C12 (8)		584.25	600.50

Same Handstamped Overprint on Air
Post Stamps of China, 1940-41 in Dull
Red

1942   Wmk. 261   Perf. 12½, 13, 13½
C13	AP3	15c gray green	6.75	15.00
C14	AP3	25c yellow orange	6.75	17.00

1942   Unwmk.
C15	AP3	25c light orange	6.75	13.50
C16	AP3	30c light red	6.75	13.50
C17	AP3	50c brown	9.00	15.00
C18	AP3	$2 light brown	42.50	42.50
C19	AP3	$5 lake	42.50	42.50
	Nos. C15-C19 (5)		107.50	127.00

Twelve values exist with this overprint in
black. Their status has not been determined.
Inverted overprints exist in both red and black.

Official Perforated Characters

For use on official mail, various Sinkiang stamps were perforated with an
arrangement of four Chinese characters
("For Official Business Only"). These
include Nos. 1-38, 47-69, 114.

OFFICES IN TIBET

12 Pies = 1 Anna
16 Annas = 1 Rupee

Stamps of China,
Issues of 1902-10,
Surcharged

1911   Unwmk.   Perf. 12 to 16
1	A17	3p on 1c ocher	27.50	45.00
a.		Inverted surcharge	3,500.	
2	A17	½a on 2c grn	27.50	45.00
3	A17	1a on 4c ver	27.50	45.00
4	A17	2a on 7c mar	27.50	45.00
5	A17	2½a on 10c ultra	35.00	55.00
6	A18	3a on 16c ol grn	70.00	80.00
a.		Large "S" in "Annas"	1,250.	
7	A18	4a on 20c red brn	70.00	80.00
8	A18	6a on 30c rose red	125.00	140.00
9	A18	12a on 50c yel grn	325.00	400.00
10	A19	1r on $1 red & pale rose	900.00	900.00
11	A19	2r on $2 red & yel	1,620.	1,800.
	Nos. 1-11 (11)		3,255.	3,635.

Beware of fake overprints.

PEOPLE'S REPUBLIC OF CHINA

'pē-pəls ri-'pə-blik of 'chī-nə

LOCATION — Eastern Asia
GOVT. — Communist Republic
POP. — 1,246,871,951 (1999 est.)
CAPITAL — Beijing (Peking)

The communists completed their conquest of all mainland China in 1949.
They established the Central Government and General Postal Administration
in Peking. They ordered all but two
regions to stop selling regional issues
by June 30, 1950, extending validity
one year from that date. The Northeast
and Port Arthur-Dairen regions were
exempted because their currency had a
different value. These two regions
stopped using separate issues at the
end of 1950. Thereafter unified issues
were used throughout mainland China.
On July 1, 1997 Hong Kong returned
to Chinese control as an administrative
district. Hong Kong stamps issued
under Chinese rule will continue to be
listed under "Hong Kong."

Reprints

After currency revaluation Mar. 1,
1955, reprints were prepared and put
on sale by the Philatelic Agency in order
to supply stocks of exhausted issues for
collectors. Minor differences in design
or paper distinguish the reprints. They
are of commemorative and special
issues up to the gymnastics set of
1952. Reprints are less expensive. Values are for original issues. Reprint dis-
tinctions are footnoted.

Used Stamps

Most used stamps before 1970 exist
primarily canceled to order. Postally
used copies generally sell for ½ the
unused value.

Beginning in 1987 the PRC stopped
furnishing quantities of used stamps to
the philatelic market. When available,
used stamps of these issues sell for the
same or more than unused copies.

PRC Issue Numbers

Commemorative issues, beginning in
1949, and special issues, beginning in
1951, bear 4 numbers in lower margin:
1. Issue number. 2. Total of stamps in
set. 3. Position of stamp in set. 4.
Cumulative number of stamp (usually in
parenthesis). A fifth number, the year of
issue, was added in 1952.

The numbering system varies at
times, with all numbers omitted on Scott
938-1046.

In certain sets listings include
parenthetically the position-in-set number. During some periods these parentheses in listings hold the stamp's
cumulative number. Issue numbers are
noted when one or more designs are
not illustrated.

Gum

All stamps to the beginning of 1960
were issued without gum, except as
noted. After that date, most stamps
have gum, which is translucent and
almost invisible. All issues are
unwatermarked, unless otherwise
noted.

100 fen = 1 yuan ($)

> Catalogue values for unused
> stamps in this country are for
> Never Hinged items, beginning
> with Scott 487 in the regular post-
> age section, Scott B1 in the semi-
> postal section.

Syncopated Perforations

Type A (1st stamp #2880): On the two
shorter sides, an oval hole equal in width to
three holes is centered.

Lantern and Gate
of Heavenly
Peace — A1

Globe and Hand
Holding
Hammer — A2

1949, Oct. 8   Litho.   Perf. 12½
1	A1	$30 blue	5.00	2.00
2	A1	$50 rose red	5.00	2.00
3	A1	$100 green	8.00	2.00
4	A1	$200 maroon	8.00	2.00
	Nos. 1-4 (4)		26.00	8.00

1st session of Chinese People's Consultative Political Conference. See #1L121-1L124.

Original   Reprint

*Reprints have altered ornament on lantern
base. On originals, it is a full oval; in reprints,
only a partial circle. Value, set: unused $7;
used $1.50.*

1949, Nov. 16
5	A2	$100 carmine	11.50	9.00
6	A2	$300 slate green	11.50	9.00
7	A2	$500 dark blue	11.50	9.00
	Nos. 5-7 (3)		34.50	27.00

Asiatic and Australasian Congress of the
World Federation of Trade Unions, Peking.
The $100, imperf., is of dubious status.
See Nos. 1L133-1L135.

Original   Reprint

*Reprints show heavier shading on index fin-
ger and thumb. Value, set $7 unused or $2.40
used.*

Conference Hall,
Peking — A3

Mao Tse-
tung on
Rostrum
A4

1950, Feb. 1   Engr.   Perf. 14
8	A3	$50 red	4.00	4.00
9	A3	$100 blue	4.00	4.00
10	A4	$300 red brown	8.00	7.00
11	A4	$500 green	14.00	10.00
	Nos. 8-11 (4)		30.00	25.00

Chinese People's Consultative Political Conference. See Nos. 1L136-1L139.

Original   Reprint

*Nos. 8-9: First character in top inscription
shows a square, reprints an oblong.
Nos. 10-11: Originals have heavy crosshatching and lines which touch back of head
and top of rostrum. Reprints have lighter lines
which do not touch head or top of rostrum.
Reprints, value set $25 unused, $9 used.*

Gate of
Heavenly Peace
(actual
size) — A5

First Issue: Top line of shading broken at
right.

1950, Feb. 10   Litho.   Perf. 12½
12	A5	$200 green	13.00	2.00
13	A5	$300 brown red	.50	1.50
14	A5	$500 red	1.00	.50
15	A5	$800 orange	65.00	1.50
16	A5	$1000 dull violet	4.00	2.00
17	A5	$2000 olive	13.00	2.00
18	A5	$5000 brt pink	1.00	2.00
19	A5	$8000 blue	.50	20.00
20	A5	$10,000 brown	1.00	2.00
	Nos. 12-20 (9)		99.00	33.50

1950, June 9   Typo.

Second Issue: Top line of shading extends
to frame line at right.

21	A5	$1000 dull violet	2.00	1.75
22	A5	$3000 red brown	1.50	.90
23	A5	$10,000 brown	.75	1.10
	Nos. 21-23 (3)		4.25	3.75

Other Gate of Heavenly Peace issues are
illustrated where they are listed. See A10,
A13, A14 and A42 for similar designs.
For similar types with Chinese characters in
upper right corner see Northeast China A28,

A29, Port Arthur & Darien A11, North China A8.

China Nos. 959, C62, E12, F2 Surcharged in Blue, Black, Green or Red

Rouletted, Perf. 12½ (#27, 29)

1950, Mar.				Litho.
24	SD2	$100 on red vio (Bl)	.50	1.50
a.		Perf. 12½	7.50	3.00
25	R2	$200 on red (Bk)	4.00	1.50
a.		Perf. 12½	55.00	3.50
26	AP5	$300 on bl grn (Bk)	.50	1.00
a.		Perf. 12½	1.00	1.00
27	A96	$500 on org (Bk)	.60	.40
a.		Perf. 14	55.00	50.00
28	A96	$800 on org (R)	4.00	1.00
a.		Perf. 12½	32.50	4.00
b.		Perf. 14	900.00	70.00
29	A96	$1000 on org (Bk)	.40	.40
a.		Perf. 14	.80	.80
		Nos. 24-29 (6)	10.00	5.80

No. 27 exists with green surcharge.

Harvesters with Ox — A6

1950, May

30	A6	$20,000 on $10,000 red	750.00	125.00

No. 30 is surcharged on an unissued stamp of East China. Value, without surcharge (unissued) $1,000.

Flag, Mao Tse-tung, Gate of Heavenly Peace — A7

1950, July 1   Perf. 14
Yellow Stars

31	A7	$800 green & red	67.50	17.50
32	A7	$1000 brn & red	80.00	22.50
33	A7	$2000 dk brn & red	97.50	22.50
34	A7	$3000 dk blue & red	150.00	35.00
		Nos. 31-34 (4)	395.00	97.50

Inauguration of the People's Republic, Oct. 1, 1949. See Nos. 1L150-1L153.

Original	Reprint

Originals have a single curved line in jacket button, reprints have an extra dot in button. Value, set unused $42.50 used $16.

Sun Yat-sen Stamps of Northeastern Provinces Surcharged in Red, Black or Blue

1950, July 1   Engr.

35	A2	$50 on 20c yel grn	7.50	8.00
36	A2	$50 on 25c blk brn	7.50	5.50
37	A2	$50 on 50c red org (Bk)	2.00	3.00
38	A2	$100 on $2.50 ind	1.90	3.00
39	A2	$100 on $3 brn (Bk)	2.10	2.50
40	A2	$100 on $4 org brn, Type II (Bl)	5.00	10.00
a.		Type I	800.00	150.00

41	A2	$100 on $5 dk grn (Bk)	3.50	3.50
42	A2	$100 on $10 crim, Type II (Bl)	22.50	12.00
a.		Type I	7,500.	
43	A2	$100 on $20 ol, Type II (Bl)	50.00	50.00
a.		Type I	900.00	100.00
44	A2	$400 on $44 dk car rose (Bl)	1.25	9.00
45	A2	$400 on $65 dl grn	150.00	100.00
46	A2	$400 on $100 dp grn	32.50	12.00
47	A2	$400 on $200 rose brn (Bk)	80.00	20.00
48	A2	$400 on $300 bluish grn	80.00	25.00
		Nos. 35-48 (14)	445.75	263.50

Flying Geese Type of China Surcharged in Red, Blue, Green, Brown or Black

1950, Aug. 1   Perf. 12½, Imperf.

49	A97	$50 on 10c dk bl (R)	.30	.40
50	A97	$100 on 16c ol, imperf. (Bl)	.30	.40
51	A97	$100 on 50c dl grn, imperf. (Bl)	.30	.35
52	A97	$200 on $1 org (G)	.40	.25
53	A97	$200 on $2 bl (Br)	6.50	1.00
54	A97	$400 on $5 car rose (Bk)	.75	.75
55	A97	$400 on $10 bl grn (Bk)	.40	2.00
56	A97	$400 on $20 pur (Bk)	1.25	3.00
		Nos. 49-56 (8)	10.20	8.15

Dove of Peace, by Picasso — A8

1950, Aug. 1   Engr.   Perf. 14

57	A8	$400 brown	27.50	6.00
58	A8	$800 green	27.50	6.00
59	A8	$2000 blue	42.50	10.00
		Nos. 57-59 (3)	97.50	22.00

World Peace Campaign. See #1L154-1L156.
Paper of originals appears bright under ultraviolet lamp. That of reprints looks dull. Value, set unused $8.50 used $4.

Chinese Flag and "1" — A9

1950   Engr. & Litho.
Flag in Red & Yellow

60	A9	$100 purple	32.50	12.00
61	A9	$400 red brown	47.50	16.00
62	A9	$800 green	47.50	13.00
63	A9	$1000 lt olive	65.00	22.50
64	A9	$2000 blue	85.00	45.00
		Nos. 60-64 (5)	277.50	108.50

1st anniv. of the Chinese People's Republic. Size of $800: 38x46mm; others 26x32mm.
Issue dates: No. 62, Oct. 1; others Oct. 31. See Nos. 1L157-1L161.

$800

Original	Reprint

Reprints are a brighter red, leaves beside "1" are gray brown instead of reddish brown. On the $800 the arrangement of dots in background differs in relationship to large star. Value, set unused $13.50 used $10.

Gate of Heavenly Peace (actual size) — A10

Third Issue: Cloud almost touches character at upper left. Cloud breaks inner frame line at top.

1950				Litho.
65	A10	$100 lt grnsh bl	40.00	10.00
66	A10	$200 green	260.00	20.00
67	A10	$300 dk carmine	2.75	5.00
68	A10	$400 grnsh gray	1.00	3.00
69	A10	$500 carmine	.75	2.00
70	A10	$800 orange	7.00	1.00
71	A10	$2000 gray olive	1.50	1.00
		Nos. 65-71 (7)	313.00	42.00

Issued: $800, 10/8; $500, $2000, 12/1; others, 10/6.

"Communication" and Map of China — A11

1950, Nov. 1   Litho.

72	A11	$400 green & brn	25.00	8.00
73	A11	$800 carmine & grn	32.50	6.00

First All-China Postal Conference, Peking. See Nos. 1L162-1L163.

Original	Reprint

Originals have 3 lines below horizontal bar (2nd character); reprints have four. Value, set unused $2, used $1.50.

Stalin and Mao Tse-tung — A12

1950, Dec. 1   Engr.   Perf. 14

74	A12	$400 red	20.00	5.50
75	A12	$800 dp green	20.00	6.50
76	A12	$2000 dk blue	27.50	7.50
		Nos. 74-76 (3)	67.50	19.50

Signing of Sino-Soviet Treaty of Friendship, Alliance and Mutual Assistance. See Nos. 1L176-1L178.
Paper of originals appears bright under ultraviolet lamp. That of reprints looks dull. Value, set unused $13.50, used $7.

East China Issue of 1949 Surcharged in Red, Black, Brown or Blue

Train and Postal Runner — A12a

1950, Dec.			Litho.	Perf. 12½
77	A12a	$50 on $10 dp ultra (R)	.25	.25
78	A12a	$100 on $15 org ver (Bk)	.25	.25
a.		$100 on $15 red (Bk), perf. 14	.80	.80
79	A12a	$300 on $50 car (Bk)	.25	.25
80	A12a	$400 on $1600 vio bl (Br)	2.25	.80
81	A12a	$400 on $2000 brn vio (Bl)	.95	.50
		Nos. 77-81 (5)	3.95	2.05

East China Issue of 1949 Surcharged in Red or Black

Chairman Mao — A12b

1950, Dec.

82	A12b	$50 on $10 ultra (R)	.40	.20
83	A12b	$400 on $15 ver (Bk)	.40	.25
84	A12b	$400 on $2000 grn (Bk)	2.25	.80
		Nos. 82-84 (3)	3.05	1.25

(actual size) — A13

(actual size) — A14

Fourth Issue: Similar to 3rd issue, but large cloud does not break inner frame line at top.

1950-51   Litho.
85	A13	$100 lt blue	1.75	1.50
86	A13	$200 dull green	16.00	4.00
87	A13	$300 dull lilac	1.00	5.00
88	A13	$400 gray grn	13.00	1.25
89	A13	$500 carmine	1.00	1.50
90	A13	$800 orange	85.00	6.00
a.	Imperf., pair			
91	A13	$1000 violet	2.00	1.25
92	A13	$2000 olive	260.00	7.00
93	A13	$3000 brown	1.00	6.00
94	A13	$5000 pink	1.00	8.00
	Nos. 85-94 (10)		381.75	41.50

Issued: $200, $300, $500, $800, $2000, $5000, 12/22/50; others 6/8/51.

1951, Jan. 18   Engr.   Perf. 14

Fifth Issue: Colored network on surface in salmon.

95	A14	$10,000 brown	3.75	10.00
96	A14	$20,000 olive	9.50	8.25
97	A14	$30,000 green	65.00	95.00
98	A14	$50,000 violet	130.00	45.00
99	A14	$100,000 scarlet	2,500.	495.00
100	A14	$200,000 blue	3,500.	1,100.
	Nos. 95-100 (6)		6,208.	1,753.

Unit Issue of China Surcharged

1951, May 2   Litho.   Perf. 12½
101	SD2	$5 on rose lilac	3.50	3.00
102	AP5	$10 on brt grn	2.00	3.00
103	R2	$15 on red	1.25	1.50
104	A96	$25 on orange	1.25	1.50
	Nos. 101-104 (4)		8.00	9.00

Issued for use in Northeast China, but available for use throughout China. Nos. 101-104 rouletted were sold for philatelic purposes only. Value, set unused $10, used $8.

Chairman Mao Tse-tung — A15

1951, July 1   Engr.   Perf. 14
105	A15	$400 chestnut	10.00	6.00
106	A15	$500 deep green	10.00	6.00
107	A15	$800 crimson	12.50	6.00
	Nos. 105-107 (3)		32.50	18.00

Chinese Communist Party, 30th anniv.
Reprints are on whiter, thinner and harder paper. Value, set unused $18.50, used $12.

Picasso Dove — A16

1951, Aug. 15   Perf. 12½
108	A16	$400 orange brn	23.00	13.00
109	A16	$800 blue grn	23.00	13.00
110	A16	$1000 dull vio	23.00	13.00
	Nos. 108-110 (3)		69.00	39.00

Reprints are perf 14. Value, set unused $22.50, used $7.50.

Remittance Stamp of China Surcharged in Carmine or Black

(same size) — A17

Engraved, Commercial Press
1951, Sept.   Perf. 12½
111	A17	$50 on $2 bl grn (C)	1.50	1.00

Rouletted 9½
Typo., Kang Hwa Printing Co.
112	A17	$50 on $2 gray bl (C)	6.00	6.00
113	A17	$50 on $5 red org (Bk)	1.50	1.50
114	A17	$50 on $50 gray (C)	6.00	5.00

Perf. 13
Lithographed, Central Trust Co.
115	A17	$50 on $50 gray blk (C)	1.50	1.50

Perf. 11½x10
Lithographed, Chung Hwa Book Co.
116	A17	$50 on $50 gray (C)	3.00	1.50
a.	Perf. 11½		1.50	1.00
	Nos. 111-116 (6)		19.50	16.50

National Emblem — A18

Engraved; Background Network Lithographed in Yellow
1951, Oct. 1   Perf. 14
117	A18	$100 Prus blue	12.00	6.75
118	A18	$200 brown	12.00	6.75
119	A18	$400 orange	12.00	6.75
120	A18	$500 green	18.00	6.75
121	A18	$800 carmine	18.00	6.75
	Nos. 117-121 (5)		72.00	33.75

Reprints exist but are difficult to distinguish; paper whiter, and colors slightly brighter. Value, set unused or used $20.

Rough Perfs
Rough perforations are normal on many early issues. These include Nos. 122-123, 136-140, 155-176, 239-240, 299-300, 453-456, 467-482, 629-634, 684-707, 737-745 and probably others.

Lu Hsun and Quotation A19

1951, Oct. 19   Litho.   Perf. 12½
122	A19	$400 lilac	7.00	6.00
123	A19	$800 green	9.50	6.00

15th anniversary of the death of Lu Hsun (1881-1936), writer.

Original   Reprint

Reprints have dot in triangle at lower right; no dot in original. Value, set unused $6.50, used $2.25.

Peasant Uprising, Chintien — A20

Design: Nos. 126-127, Coin of Taiping Regime and decrees of peasant government.

1951, Dec. 15   Engr.   Perf. 14
124	A20	$400 green	12.00	7.50
125	A20	$800 scarlet	12.00	7.50
126	A20	$800 orange	18.00	7.50
127	A20	$1000 deep blue	22.00	7.50
	Nos. 124-127 (4)		64.00	30.00

Centenary of Taiping Peasant Rebellion.

Original   Reprint

Reprints of Nos. 124-125 have additional short stroke at upper left.

Original   Reprint

Reprints of Nos. 126-127 have two short strokes on scale near tail of right dragon on coin. Value, Nos. 124-127 unused $6.50, used $4.25.

Old and New Methods of Agriculture — A21

1952, Jan. 1
128	A21	$100 scarlet	9.50	5.75
129	A21	$200 bright blue	9.50	5.75
130	A21	$400 deep brown	9.50	5.75
131	A21	$800 green	9.50	5.75
	Nos. 128-131 (4)		38.00	23.00

Agrarian reform.

Original   Reprint

One short horizontal line between legs of plower; 2 lines in reprints. Value, set unused $7.50, used $4.

Potala Monastery, Lhasa — A22

Nos. 134-135, Farmer plowing with yaks.

1952, Mar. 15   Perf. 12½
132	A22	$400 vermilion	12.00	6.25
133	A22	$800 claret	12.00	6.25
134	A22	$800 blue grn	20.00	6.25
135	A22	$1000 dull vio	20.00	6.25
	Nos. 132-135 (4)		64.00	25.00

Liberation of Tibet.
Reprints, perf 14, have a small Chinese character at lower left of the vignette which is missing in the original. Value, set unused $16.50, used $7.

Children of Four Races A23   Hammer and Sickle on Numeral 1 A24

1952, Apr. 12   Litho.
136	A23	$400 dull grn	.60	.30
137	A23	$800 vio blue	.90	.35

Intl. Child Protection Conf., Vienna.

1952, May 1

Labor Day: #139, Dove rising from worker's hand. #140, Dove, hammer, wheat & chimneys.
138	A24	$800 scarlet	1.00	.20
139	A24	$800 blue grn	1.00	.20
140	A24	$800 orange brn	1.00	.20
	Nos. 138-140 (3)		3.00	.60

Physical Exercises — A25

Stamps printed in blocks of four for each color, each block representing a specific setting-up exercise; exercises coincided with a national radio program. Where exercise positions are identical within the block, the serial number (in parenthesis) is the only means of differentiation.

1952, June 20

141	A25	Block of 4	175.00	57.50
a.		$400 vermilion (1)	14.00	4.75
b.		$400 vermilion (2)	14.00	4.75
c.		$400 vermilion (3)	14.00	4.75
d.		$400 vermilion (4)	14.00	4.75
142	A25	Block of 4	175.00	57.50
a.		$400 blue (5)	14.00	4.75
b.		$400 blue (6)	14.00	4.75
c.		$400 blue (7)	14.00	4.75
d.		$400 blue (8)	14.00	4.75
143	A25	Block of 4	175.00	57.50
a.		$400 brown red (9)	14.00	4.75
b.		$400 brown red (10)	14.00	4.75
c.		$400 brown red (11)	14.00	4.75
d.		$400 brown red (12)	14.00	4.75
144	A25	Block of 4	175.00	57.50
a.		$400 yellow green (13)	14.00	4.75
b.		$400 yellow green (14)	14.00	4.75
c.		$400 yellow green (15)	14.00	4.75
d.		$400 yellow green (16)	14.00	4.75
145	A25	Block of 4	175.00	57.50
a.		$400 red orange (17)	14.00	4.75
b.		$400 red orange (18)	14.00	4.75
c.		$400 red orange (19)	14.00	4.75
d.		$400 red orange (20)	14.00	4.75
146	A25	Block of 4	175.00	57.50
a.		$400 dull blue (21)	14.00	4.75
b.		$400 dull blue (22)	14.00	4.75
c.		$400 dull blue (23)	14.00	4.75
d.		$400 dull blue (24)	14.00	4.75
147	A25	Block of 4	175.00	57.50
a.		$400 orange (25)	14.00	4.75
b.		$400 orange (26)	14.00	4.75
c.		$400 orange (27)	14.00	4.75
d.		$400 orange (28)	14.00	4.75
148	A25	Block of 4	175.00	57.50
a.		$400 dull purple (29)	14.00	4.75
b.		$400 dull purple (30)	14.00	4.75
c.		$400 dull purple (31)	14.00	4.75
d.		$400 dull purple (32)	14.00	4.75
149	A25	Block of 4	175.00	57.50
a.		$400 yellow bister (33)	14.00	4.75
b.		$400 yellow bister (34)	14.00	4.75
c.		$400 yellow bister (35)	14.00	4.75
d.		$400 yellow bister (36)	14.00	4.75
150	A25	Block of 4	175.00	57.50
a.		$400 sky blue (37)	14.00	4.75
b.		$400 sky blue (38)	14.00	4.75
c.		$400 sky blue (39)	14.00	4.75
d.		$400 sky blue (40)	14.00	4.75
		Nos. 141-150 (10)	1,750.	575.00

Originals are on thin gray paper, colors darker. Reprints on thicker white paper, colors brighter. Value, set of blocks unused $52.50, used $45.

Hunting, Wei Dynasty, A.D. 386-580 A26

Designs from Murals in Cave Temples at Tunhuang, Kansu Province: No. 152, Lady attendants, Sui Dynasty, 581-617 A.D. No. 153, Gandharvas (mythology), Tang Dynasty, 618-906. No. 154, Dragon, Tang Dynasty.

1952, July 1   **Engr.**

151	A26	$800 slate green (1)	1.50	.50
152	A26	$800 chocolate (2)	1.50	.50
153	A26	$800 indigo (3)	1.50	.50
154	A26	$800 dk vio (4)	1.50	.50
		Nos. 151-154 (4)	6.00	2.00

"Glorious Mother Country," 1st series.

Marco Polo Bridge, near Peking A27

Designs: No. 156, Cavalry passing through Great Wall. No. 157, Departure of New Fourth Army. No. 158, Mao Tse-tung and Gen. Chu Teh planning counter-attack.

1952, July 7   Litho.   Perf. 14

155	A27	$800 brt blue	1.50	.45
156	A27	$800 blue grn	1.50	.45
157	A27	$800 plum	1.50	.45
158	A27	$800 scarlet	1.75	.45
		Nos. 155-158 (4)	6.25	1.80

15th anniversary of war against Japan.

Huai River Sluice Dam A29

#164, Train on the Chengtu-Chungking Railway. #165, Oil refinery and derricks in the Northwest. #166, Mechanized state farm.

1952, Oct. 1   Perf. 14

163	A29	$800 dk violet	2.00	.35
164	A29	$800 red	2.00	.35
165	A29	$800 dk vio brn	2.00	.35
166	A29	$800 dp green	2.00	.35
		Nos. 163-166 (4)	8.00	1.40

"Glorious Mother Country," 2nd series.

Soldier and Tanks — A28

#159, Soldier, sailor & airman, vert. #161, Sailor & warships. #162, Airman & planes.

1952, Aug. 1   Engr.   Perf. 12½

159	A28	$800 carmine	2.00	.40
160	A28	$800 deep green	2.00	.40
161	A28	$800 purple	2.00	.40
162	A28	$800 orange brown	2.00	.40
		Nos. 159-162 (4)	8.00	1.60

25th anniv. of People's Liberation Army.

Doves and Globe A30

Designs: Nos. 167-168, Picasso dove over Pacific, vert. $2500, as No. 169.

1952, Oct. 2   Perf. 14

167	A30	$400 maroon	2.00	.30
168	A30	$800 red	2.00	.30
169	A30	$800 brown orange	2.00	.30
170	A30	$2500 deep green	2.00	.50
		Nos. 167-170 (4)	8.00	1.40

Peace Conf. of the Asian and Pacific Regions.

Volunteers on the March — A31

#172, Chinese peasants loading supplies.
#173, Volunteers attacking across river. #174,
Meeting of Chinese & Korean troops.

1952, Oct. 25
171	A31	$800 blue green (1)	2.25	.35
172	A31	$800 vermilion (2)	2.25	.35
173	A31	$800 violet (3)	2.25	.35
174	A31	$800 lake brown (4)	2.25	.35
		Nos. 171-174 (4)	9.00	1.40

2nd anniv. of Chinese Volunteers in Korea.

Woman Textile Worker A32

Design: No. 176, Farm woman with sickle.

1953, Mar. 10
175	A32	$800 carmine	2.00	.35
176	A32	$800 emerald	2.00	.35

International Women's Day.

Textile Worker — A33　Karl Marx — A34

$200, Shepherdess. $250, Stone lion. $800,
Lathe operator. $1600, Coal miners. $2000,
Corner tower of Forbidden City, Peking.

1953　Litho.　Perf. 14, 12½ ($250)
177	A33	$50 magenta	1.00	.25
178	A33	$200 emerald	1.75	.45
179	A33	$250 ultra	4.00	2.50
180	A33	$800 blue grn	1.00	.25
181	A33	$1600 gray	1.00	.45
182	A33	$2000 red org	2.75	.30
		Nos. 177-182 (6)	11.50	4.20

Issued: #177-181, Mar. 25; #182, May 23.

1953, May 20　Engr.　Perf. 14
183	A34	$400 dk brown	1.75	.30
184	A34	$800 slate grn	2.00	.35

135th anniv. of the birth of Karl Marx.

Workers and Banners — A35

1953, June 25
185	A35	$400 Prus blue	2.00	.35
186	A35	$800 carmine	2.00	.35

7th All-China Trade Union Congress.

Picasso Dove — A36

1953, July 25
187	A36	$250 blue grn	1.50	.35
188	A36	$400 orange brn	1.50	.35
189	A36	$800 purple	2.00	.50
		Nos. 187-189 (3)	5.00	1.20

World Peace.

Groom, Wei Dynasty, 386-580 A37

Scenes from Tunhuang Murals: No. 191,
Court Players, Wei Dynasty. No. 192, Battle
Scene, Sui Dynasty, 581-617. No. 193, Ox-
drawn palanquin, Tang Dynasty, 618-906.

1953, Sept. 1
190	A37	$800 dp green (1)	1.25	.35
191	A37	$800 red org (2)	1.25	.35
192	A37	$800 Prus blue (3)	1.25	.35
193	A37	$800 carmine (4)	1.25	.35
		Nos. 190-193 (4)	5.00	1.40

"Glorious Mother Country," 3rd series.

Stalin and Mao on Kremlin Terrace A38

Statue of Stalin at Volga-Don Canal — A39

Designs: No. 195, Lenin proclaiming Soviet
power. No. 197, Stalin as orator.

1953, Oct. 5
194	A38	$800 green (1)	2.50	.45
195	A38	$800 carmine (2)	2.50	.45
196	A39	$800 brt blue (3)	2.50	.45
197	A39	$800 org brn (4)	2.50	.45
		Nos. 194-197 (4)	10.00	1.80

Russian October Revolution, 35th anniv.
Stamps in same designs with two additional
characters meaning "Soviet" in the single-line
Chinese inscription, and in different colors,
were unofficially released at several small post
offices in Hunan, Fukien and Canton areas in
February, 1953, but were withdrawn after only
a small number had been sold. Value, set
$37,500. unused, $16,000 canceled.

Compass, 3rd Century B.C. A40

#199, Seismoscope, later Han Dynasty.
#200, Drum cart to measure distance, Chin
Dynasty. #201, Armillary sphere, Ming
Dynasty.

1953, Dec. 1
198	A40	$800 indigo (1)	1.00	.35
199	A40	$800 dk green (2)	1.00	.35
200	A40	$800 dk blue (3)	1.75	.35
201	A40	$800 choc (4)	1.50	.35
		Nos. 198-201 (4)	5.25	1.40

Major inventions by ancient and medieval
Chinese scientists.
"Glorious Mother Country," 4th series.

Francois Rabelais — A41　(same size) Gate of Heavenly Peace — A42

Designs: $400, Jose Marti, Cuban revolu-
tionary. $800, Chu Yuan (350-275 B.C.), phi-
losopher. $2200, Nicolaus Copernicus,
astronomer.

1953, Dec. 30
202	A41	$250 slate grn (3)	1.75	.35
203	A41	$400 brown blk (4)	1.75	.35
204	A41	$800 indigo (1)	1.75	.35
205	A41	$2200 choc (2)	1.75	.35
		Nos. 202-205 (4)	7.00	1.40

1954, Apr. 16　　　Litho.

Sixth Issue: Inscription at upper right.
206	A42	$50 carmine	.35	.25
207	A42	$100 lt blue	.35	.25
208	A42	$200 green	.35	.20
209	A42	$250 ultra	3.50	.75
210	A42	$400 gray grn	.75	.20
211	A42	$800 orange	.40	.20
212	A42	$1600 gray	.40	.65
213	A42	$2000 olive	1.25	.45
		Nos. 206-213 (8)	7.35	2.95

Textile Plant, Harbin — A43　Lenin — A44

Designs: $200, Tangku Harbor. $250, Tien-
shui-Lanchow railroad bridge, Kansu Province. $400, Heavy machine-building plant, Tai-
yuan, Shansi. No. 218, Automatic blast,
furnace, Anshan, Manchuria. No. 219, Fushun
open-cut coal mine. $2000, Automatic power
plant, Northeast. $3200, Prospecting in Tayeh
district, Hupeh.

1954, May 1　　　Engr.
214	A43	$100 brown olive	.65	.30
215	A43	$200 blue green	1.75	.55
216	A43	$250 violet	1.25	.55
217	A43	$400 black	.65	.30
218	A43	$800 claret	.55	.30
219	A43	$800 indigo	.55	.30
220	A43	$2000 red	2.00	.30
221	A43	$3200 dark brown	.65	.45
		Nos. 214-221 (8)	8.05	3.05

Economic progress.

1954, June 30　　　Engr.

$400, Lenin and Stalin Monument, Gorki,
horiz. $2000, Lenin proclaiming Soviet power.
222	A44	$400 deep green	2.50	.50
223	A44	$800 dark brown	1.75	.75
224	A44	$2000 deep carmine	3.25	1.00
		Nos. 222-224 (3)	7.50	2.25

30th anniversary of the death of Lenin.

Pottery Vessels, Neolithic Period, 2000 B.C. — A45

Archeological Treasures: No. 226, Stone
clime, Shang Dynasty, c. 1200 B.C. No. 227,
Kuo Chi Tsu-pai bronze basin, Middle Chou
Dynasty, 816 B.C. No. 228, Lacquered box
and wine cup, Warring States Period, 403-221
B.C.

1954, Aug. 25
225	A45	$800 brown	.90	.35
226	A45	$800 indigo	.90	.35
227	A45	$800 Prus bl	.90	.35
228	A45	$800 dk car	.90	.35
		Nos. 225-228 (4)	3.60	1.40

"Glorious Mother Country," 5th series.

Pipe Production, Anshan Steel Mill — A46　Stalin Statue, by Tomsky — A47

Design: $800, Rolling mill, Anshan.

1954, Oct. 1
229	A46	$400 Prus green	3.00	.55
230	A46	$800 vio brown	3.00	.55

1954, Oct. 15

Designs: $800, Stalin portrait. $2000, Stalin
viewing hydroelectric plant.

Size: 21x45mm
231	A47	$400 black	2.50	.65

Size: 26x37mm
232	A47	$800 black brown	2.50	.65

Size: 42x26mm
233	A47	$2000 deep red	4.00	.90
		Nos. 231-233 (3)	9.00	2.20

First anniversary of the death of Stalin.

Exhibition Building, Peking — A48

1954, Nov. 7
234	A48	$800 brown, cream	35.00	3.75
a.		Size: 53½x24mm	55.00	12.00

Russian Economic and Cultural Exhibition,
Peking. No. 234 measures 52½x24½mm.

Apprentices and Lathe — A49

Progress in Technology: $800, Heavy
machinery and workers.

1954, Dec. 15
235	A49	$400 dk olive grn	2.75	.45
236	A49	$800 bright red	2.75	.45

Woman Worker Voting — A50

People Celebrating Opening of Congress — A51

1954, Dec. 30
237 A50 $400 deep claret 1.50 .40
238 A51 $800 bright red 3.25 .50
First National Congress.

Flags, Worker and Woman Holding Constitution — A52

1954, Dec. 30
239 A52 $400 brown, *buff* 3.50 .40
240 A52 $800 brt red, *yel* 6.50 .60
Adoption of Constitution.

High-tension Pylon — A53

1955, Feb. 25
241 A53 $800 dk Prus bl 5.25 1.00
Development of electric power.

Factory Health Workers and Red Cross A54

1955, June 25 Engr.; Cross Typo.
242 A54 8f dp grn & red 15.00 2.25
50th anniversary of Chinese Red Cross.

Stalin and Mao in Kremlin A55

Soviet Specialist and Chinese Worker — A56

1955, July 25 Engr.
243 A55 8f brown red 25.00 .85
244 A56 20f olive blk 36.00 2.00
5th anniv. of Sino-Soviet Friendship Treaty.

Chang Heng (78-139), Astronomer — A57

Portraits of Scientists: No. 246, Tsu Chung-chih (429-500), mathematician. No. 247, Chang Sui (683-727), astronomer. No. 248, Li Shih-chen (1518-1593), physician and pharmacologist.

1955, Aug. 25 Perf. 14
245 A57 8f sepia, *buff* 8.00 .50
  a. Min. sheet, sepia, *white* 55.00 19.00
246 A57 8f dp grn, *buff* 8.00 .50
  a. Min. sheet, deep green, *white* 55.00 19.00
247 A57 8f black, *buff* 8.00 .50
  a. Min. sheet, blk, *white* 55.00 19.00
248 A57 8f claret, *buff* 8.00 .50
  a. Min. sheet, claret, *white* 55.00 19.00
  Nos. 245-248 (4) 32.00 2.00
Miniature sheets contain one imperf. stamp.

Steel Pouring Ladle A58

1955-56 Litho.
Position-in-set number in ( )
249 A58 8f shown (1) 3.00 .65
250 A58 8f High tension line (2) 3.00 .65
251 A58 8f Mechanized coal mining (3) 3.00 .65
252 A58 8f Tank cars and derricks (4) 3.00 .65
253 A58 8f Heavy machine shop (5) 3.00 .65
254 A58 8f Soldier on guard (6) 3.00 .65
255 A58 8f Spinning machine (7) 3.00 .65
256 A58 8f Workers discussing 5-year plan (8) 3.00 .65
257 A58 8f Combine harvester (9) 3.00 .65
258 A58 8f Milk production (10) 3.00 .65
259 A58 8f Dam (11) 3.00 .65
260 A58 8f Pottery industry (12) ('56) 3.00 .65
261 A58 8f Truck (13) 3.00 .65
262 A58 8f Ship at dock (14) 3.00 .65
263 A58 8f Geological survey (15) 3.00 .65
264 A58 8f Higher education (16) 3.00 .65
265 A58 8f Family (17) 3.00 .65
266 A58 8f Workers' rest home (18) ('56) 3.00 .65
  Nos. 249-266 (18) 54.00 11.70

1st 5 Year Plan. Issued: #249-257, 10/1; #258-259, 261-265, 12/15; #260, 266, 2/24/56.

Lenin — A59

Engels — A60

1955, Dec. 15 Engr. Perf. 14
267 A59 8f dk blue grn 25.00 .60
268 A59 20f dk rose car 25.00 2.25
85th anniversary of the birth of Lenin.

1955, Dec. 15
269 A60 8f deep orange 18.50 .60
270 A60 20f brown 18.50 2.25
135th anniversary of the birth of Friedrich Engels (1820-1895), German socialist.

Storming Lu Ting Bridge — A61

Crossing Great Snow Mountains A62

1955, Dec. 30
271 A61 8f dark red 14.00 .75
272 A62 8f dark blue 30.00 3.00
Long March of Chinese Communist army, 20th anniversary.

Miner — A63

Gate of Heavenly Peace — A64

Designs: 1f, Machinist. 2f, Airman. 2½f, Nurse. 4f, Soldier. 8f, Steel worker. 10f, Scientist. 20f, Farm woman. 50f, Sailor.

1955-56 Litho. Perf. 14
273 A63 ½f orange brn 2.00 .30
274 A63 1f purple 2.00 .30
275 A63 2f green 2.00 .30
276 A63 2½f blue ('56) 2.00 .30
277 A63 4f gray olive 2.00 .50
278 A63 8f red org (Peking printing) 2.00 .75
  a. Perf. 12½ (Shanghai printing) 450.00 17.50
279 A63 10f claret ('56) 26.00 .40
280 A63 20f dp blue 6.75 .50
281 A63 50f gray 6.75 .60
  Nos. 273-281 (9) 51.50 3.95

Engr.
282 A64 $1 claret ('56) 2.00 .30
283 A64 $2 sepia ('55) 3.00 .30
284 A64 $5 indigo ('56) 5.00 .60
285 A64 $10 dp org ('56) 10.00 5.50
286 A64 $20 gray vio ('56) 14.50 17.00
  Nos. 282-286 (5) 34.50 23.70

Nos. 282-286 are the 7th Gate Issue. Used values for Nos. 282-286 are for postally used examples.

Trucks, Mountains, Highway Map — A65

Suspension Bridge over Tatu River — A66

#289, 1st truck arriving in Lhasa, & the Potala.

1956, Mar. 10 Engr.
287 A65 4f dp blue 2.10 .45
288 A66 8f dk brown 2.10 .45
289 A65 8f carmine 2.10 .55
  Nos. 287-289 (3) 6.30 1.45

Completion of Sikang-Tibet and Chinghai-Tibet Highways.

Summer Palace and Marble Boat A67

Famous Views of Imperial Peking: No. 291, Peihai Park with Jade Belt Marble Bridge. No. 292, Gate of Heavenly Peace. No. 293, Temple of Heaven. No. 294, Great Throne Hall, Forbidden City.

1956-57
290	A67 4f car rose (1)	6.00	.45
291	A67 4f blue grn (2)	6.00	.45
292	A67 8f red org (3) ('57)	12.50	.45
293	A67 8f Prus blue (4)	6.00	.45
294	A67 8f yellow brn (5)	6.00	.45
	Nos. 290-294 (5)	36.50	2.25

Issued: #292, 2/20/57; others, 6/15/56.
No. 292 exists with sun rays in background.

Salt Making A68

Designs: No. 296, Dwelling of the Eastern Han period. No. 297, Duck hunting and harvesting. No. 298, Carriage crossing bridge.

1956, Oct. 1
295	A68 4f gray olive	.85	.30
296	A68 4f slate blue	.85	.30
297	A68 8f gray brown	.85	.30
298	A68 8f sepia	.85	.30
	Nos. 295-298 (4)	3.40	1.20

Murals, Tung Han Dynasty, 250 B.C.-220 A.D., found near Chengtu.

Ancient Coins and "Save" A69

1956, Oct. 1
299	A69 4f yellow brown	8.50	1.40
300	A69 8f rose red	12.50	1.40

Promotion of saving.

Gate of Heavenly Peace — A70   Sun Yat-sen — A71

1956, Nov. 10
301	A70 4f dk green	14.00	.50
302	A70 8f brt red	15.00	.75
303	A70 16f dk carmine	17.50	.85
	Nos. 301-303 (3)	46.50	2.10

8th National Congress of the Communist Party of China.

1956, Nov. 12
304	A71 4f brown, *cream*	27.50	.60
305	A71 8f dp blue, *cream*	30.00	1.75

90th anniversary of birth of Sun Yat-sen.

Weight Lifting — A72

1957, Mar. 20   Litho.   Perf. 12½
Hibiscus red and green; inscription brown
306	A72 4f Shot put (2)	2.25	.30
307	A72 4f shown (5)	2.25	.30
308	A72 8f Track (1)	2.25	.30
309	A72 8f Soccer (3)	2.25	.30
310	A72 8f Bicycling (4)	2.25	.30
	Nos. 306-310 (5)	11.25	1.50

First National Workers' Sports Meeting.

Truck Factory No. 1, Changchun — A73

China's truck industry: 8f, Trucks rolling off assembly line.

1957, May 1   Engr.   Perf. 14
311	A73 4f light brown	2.00	.40
312	A73 8f slate green	3.00	.60

Nanchang Uprising — A74

#314, Mao and Chu Teh at Chingkanshan. #315, Crossing Yellow River. #316, Liberation of Nanking, 4/23/49.

1957
313	A74 4f blk vio (1)	35.00	1.00
314	A74 4f slate grn (2)	35.00	1.25
315	A74 8f red brn (3)	35.00	1.00
316	A74 8f dp blue (4)	35.00	1.00
	Nos. 313-316 (4)	140.00	4.25

People's Liberation Army, 30th anniv. Issued: #313, 315, 8/10; #314, 8/30; #316, 12/30.

Congress Emblem — A75

1957, Sept. 30
317	A75 8f chocolate	12.00	.50
318	A75 22f indigo	10.00	.75

4th Intl. Trade Union Cong., Leipzig, 10/4-15.

Yangtze River Bridge A76

20f, Road leading to and over bridge.

1957, Oct. 1
319	A76 8f scarlet	1.75	.50
320	A76 20f slate blue	4.00	.50

Completion of Yangtze River Bridge at Wuhan.

Fireworks over Kremlin — A77

Designs: 8f, Hammer and sickle over globe and broken chain. 20f, Stylized dove and olive branch. 22f, Hands of three races holding book with Marx and Lenin. 32f, Star and pylon.

1957, Nov. 7
321	A77 4f brt red	15.00	.60
322	A77 8f chocolate	15.00	.60
323	A77 20f dp green	15.00	.60
324	A77 22f red brown	17.50	.60
325	A77 32f dp blue	17.50	1.25
	Nos. 321-325 (5)	80.00	3.65

40th anniv. of Russian October Revolution.

Map of Yellow River Basin A78

#327, Sanmen Gorge dam & powerhouse. #328, ocean liner on Yellow River. #329, Dam, irrigation canals & tree-bordered fields.

1957, Dec. 30
326	A78 4f deep orange (1)	22.50	1.25
327	A78 4f deep blue (2)	25.00	1.25
328	A78 8f deep lake (3)	32.50	1.50
329	A78 8f blue green (4)	40.00	1.75
	Nos. 326-329 (4)	120.00	5.75

Yellow River control plan.

Old Man and Young Drummer A79   Train on Bridge, Ship and Train A80

1957, Dec. 30   Litho.
330	A79 8f shown (1)	1.75	.25
331	A79 8f Plowman (2)	1.75	.25
332	A79 8f Woman planting tree (3)	1.75	.25
333	A79 8f Harvest (4)	1.75	.25
	Nos. 330-333 (4)	7.00	1.00

Agricultural cooperation.

1958, Jan. 30   Engr.

Designs (Congratulatory Banner and): 4f, Crane, dove and flowers. 8f, Crane with hot ingots, cotton bolls and wheat.
334	A80 4f emer, *cream*	1.75	.35
335	A80 8f red, *cream*	1.75	.35
336	A80 16f ultra, *cream*	1.75	.35
	Nos. 334-336 (3)	5.25	1.05

Fulfillment of First Five-Year Plan.

Sungyu Pagoda, Honan — A81

Trilobite, Kaoli — A82

Ancient Pagodas: No. 338, Chienhsun Pagoda, Yunnan. No. 339, Sakyamuni Pagoda, Shansi. No. 340, Flying Rainbow Pagoda, Shansi.

1958, Mar. 15   Engr.
337	A81 8f sepia (1)	2.75	.45
338	A81 8f Prus blue (2)	2.75	.45
339	A81 8f maroon (3)	2.75	.45
340	A81 8f dp green (4)	2.75	.50
	Nos. 337-340 (4)	11.00	1.85

1958, Apr. 15

Designs: 8f, Lufeng dinosaur. 16f, Choukoutien sino-megaceros.
341	A82 4f black	2.50	.35
342	A82 8f sepia	2.50	.35
343	A82 16f slate green	3.00	.35
	Nos. 341-343 (3)	8.00	1.05

Prehistoric animals of China.

Heroes Monument A83

1958, May 1
344	A83 8f scarlet	37.50	2.25
a.	Souvenir sheet, imperf.	300.00	90.00

Unveiling of People's Heroes Monument, Peking. No. 344a issued May 30.

Karl Marx — A84

Cogwheels and Factories — A85

Design: 22f, Marx Speaking to German Workers' Educational Association, London, painting by Zhukow.

1958, May 5
345	A84 8f chocolate	18.00	1.50
346	A84 22f dk green	18.00	2.25

Karl Marx (1818-83), 140th birth anniv.

1958, May 25
347	A85 4f brt grnsh bl	29.00	1.75
348	A85 8f red lilac	29.00	2.00

8th All-China Trade Union Cong., Peking.

Dove over Globe — A86   Mother and Child — A87

1958, June 1
349	A86 8f violet blue	15.00	.30
350	A86 20f blue green	22.00	3.50

4th Congress of the Intl. Democratic Women's Federation, Vienna, June 1958.

1958, June 1   Litho.

Children's Day: No. 352, Watering sunflowers. No. 353, Playing hide-and-seek. No. 354, Sailing toy boat.
351	A87 8f green & multi (1)	24.00	2.00
352	A87 8f green & multi (2)	24.00	2.00
353	A87 8f green & multi (3)	24.00	2.00
354	A87 8f green & multi (4)	24.00	2.00
	Nos. 351-354 (4)	96.00	8.00

Kuan Han-ching
A88

Designs (Operas): 4f, "Dream of Butterflies." 20f, "The Riverside Pavilion."

1958, June 20   Engr.
355 A88 4f indigo, *cr*   22.50   1.75
356 A88 8f brown, *cr*   35.00   5.00
357 A88 20f black, *cr*   40.00   1.75
  a.   Souvenir sheet of 3, ivory 650.00 150.00
      Nos. 355-357 (3)   97.50   8.50

700th anniversary of publication of works of Kuan Han-ching (1210-1280), dramatist. No. 357a contains 3 imperf. stamps similar to Nos. 355-357. Size: 130x100mm. Issued June 28.

Planetarium
A89

20f, Telescope and stars over Peking.

1958, June 25
358 A89 8f dk green   8.00   1.00
359 A89 20fr indigo   10.00   1.75

First Chinese planetarium, Peking.

Marx and
Engels — A90

Wild Goose and
Broadcasting
Tower — A91

8f, Cover of 1st edition of the Communist Manifesto.

1958, July 1
360 A90 4f dk red vio   22.50   3.00
361 A90 8f Prus blue   36.00   1.75

110th anniversary of publication of the Communist Manifesto.

1958, July 10
362 A91 4f ultra   21.00   2.25
363 A91 8f deep green   21.00   1.50

1st Conference of the Ministers of Posts and Telecommunications of Socialist Countries, Moscow, Dec. 3-17, 1957.

Peony and
Doves — A92

Bronze Weather
Vane — A93

8f, Olive branch with ribbon & clouds. 22f, Atomic energy symbol over factories.

1958, July 20
364 A92 4f red   22.50   2.00
365 A92 8f green   22.50   4.00
366 A92 22f red brown   17.50   4.00
      Nos. 364-366 (3)   62.50 10.00

Congress for Disarmament and International Cooperation, Stockholm, July 17-22.

1958, Aug. 25

Designs: No. 368, Weather balloon. No. 369, Typhoon tower and weather map of Asia.

367 A93 8f yel bis & blk (1)   3.25   .30
368 A93 8f blue & blk (2)   3.25   .30
369 A93 8f brt grn & blk (3)   3.25   .30
      Nos. 367-369 (3)   9.75   .90

Meteorological services in ancient and modern China.

"5" Encircling IUS
Emblem — A94

1958, Sept. 4
370 A94 8f rose lilac   35.00   .75
371 A94 22f dp blue grn   25.00 2.00

Intl. Union of Students, 5th Cong., Peking, 9/4-13.
Nos. 370-371 exist with incorrect inscription. Value, 8f used $5,250.

Telegraph
Building,
Peking
A95

1958, Sept. 29
372 A95 4f greenish black   5.00   .75
373 A95 8f rose red   5.00   .75

Opening of Telegraph Building, Peking.

Exhibition
Emblem and
Exhortation
A96

Designs: No. 375, Dragon over clouds signifying "aiming high." No. 376, Flying horses, signifying "great leap forward" in production.

1958, Oct. 1
374 A96 8f slate grn (1)   20.00   1.00
375 A96 8f rose car (2)   15.00   1.00
376 A96 8f red brown (3)   25.00   2.00
      Nos. 374-376 (3)   60.00   4.00

National Exhibition of Industry and Communications, Peking.

Worker and
Excavator
A97

Design: 8f, Completed dam and pylon.

1958, Oct. 25
377 A97 4f dark brown   3.00   .45
378 A97 8f deep Prussian blue 6.00 .45

13 Ming Tombs Reservoir completion.

Sputnik over Armillary Sphere — A98

Designs: 8f, Sputnik 3 in orbit. 10f, Trajectories of 3 Sputniks over earth.

1958, Oct. 30

379	A98	4f scarlet	4.50	.40
380	A98	8f dp violet bl	5.00	1.00
381	A98	10f dp green	5.50	2.25
		Nos. 379-381 (3)	15.00	3.65

Anniversary of first earth satellite launched by the USSR.

Chinese and North Korean Soldiers A99

Designs: No. 383, Chinese soldier embracing Korean woman. No. 384, Chinese girl presenting flowers to returning soldier.

1958, Nov. 20

382	A99	8f brt purple (1)	6.00	.50
383	A99	8f chestnut (2)	6.00	.50
384	A99	8f rose car (3)	6.00	.50
		Nos. 382-384 (3)	18.00	1.50

Return of the Chinese Volunteers from Korea.

Forest and Mountains — A100   Peony — A101

Afforestation: No. 386, Mounted forest patrol. No. 387, Mechanized lumbering, horiz. No. 388, Tree-planting: "Turning the Country Green," horiz.

1958, Dec. 15

385	A100	8f dp blue grn (1)	4.00	.80
386	A100	8f slate grn (2)	4.00	.80
387	A100	8f dk purple (3)	4.00	.80
388	A100	8f indigo (4)	4.00	.80
		Nos. 385-388 (4)	16.00	3.20

1958, Sept. 25   **Litho.**

Designs: 3f, Lotus. 5f, Chrysanthemums.

389	A101	1½f lilac rose	4.00	.75
390	A101	3f blue grn	8.50	2.00
391	A101	5f dp orange	5.00	.40
		Nos. 389-391 (3)	17.50	3.15

Atomic Reactor A102

1958, Dec. 30   **Engr.**

392	A102	8f shown	15.00	1.75
393	A102	20f Cyclotron	27.50	2.25

Inauguration of China's first atomic reactor and cyclotron, Peking.

Children Launching Model Planes — A103   Camel Carrying Load — A104

8f, Gliders over trees. 10f, Parachutists descending. 20f, Small monoplanes in mid-air.

1958, Dec. 30

394	A103	4f carmine	3.50	.35
395	A103	8f dp slate grn	3.50	.35
396	A103	10f dk brown	3.50	.35
397	A103	20f Prus blue	3.50	.35
		Nos. 394-397 (4)	14.00	1.40

Sports-aviation publicity.

1959, Jan. 1

Designs: No. 399, Pomegranates. No. 400, Rooster. No. 401, Theatrical figure.

398	A104	8f vio & blk (1)	15.00	.85
399	A104	8f dp bl grn & blk (2)	15.00	.85
400	A104	8f red & blk (3)	15.00	.85
401	A104	8f dp bl & blk (4)	15.00	.85
		Nos. 398-401 (4)	60.00	3.40

Paper cut-outs (folk art).

Red Flag, Mao and Workers — A105

1959

402	A105	4f brt red	23.50	1.75
403	A105	8f lake	23.50	1.75
404	A105	10f deep red	23.50	1.75
		Nos. 402-404 (3)	70.50	5.25

"Great Leap Forward" in steel production. Issue dates: 4f, 8f, Feb. 19; 10f, May 25.

Women Workers and Atomic Model — A106

Designs: 8f, Traditional and modern blast furnaces. 10f, Steel works and workers.

1959, Mar. 8

Design: 22f, Chinese and Soviet women holding banners dated "3.8."

405	A106	8f emerald, cr	4.75	.45
406	A106	22f magenta, cr	4.75	.25

International Women's Day.

Natural History Museum A107

1959, Apr. 1

407	A107	4f greenish blue	3.00	.45
408	A107	8f olive brown	3.00	.45

Opening of Museum of Natural History, Peking.

Wheat — A108

Designs on Chinese Flag: No. 410, Rice. No. 411, Cotton bolls. No. 412, Soybeans, rapeseed and peanuts.

1959, Apr. 25

409	A108	8f red (1)	2.25	.45
410	A108	8f red (2)	2.25	.45
411	A108	8f red (3)	2.25	.45
412	A108	8f red (4)	2.25	.45
a.		Block of 4, #409-412	14.00	4.00

Successful harvest, 1958.

A109

A110

Designs: 4f, Marx, Lenin and workers. 8f, Black, yellow and white fists holding banner. 22f, Steel workers parading with banners dated "5.1."

1959, May 1

413	A109	4f ultra	14.00	2.00
414	A109	8f red	17.50	1.50
415	A109	22f emerald	10.00	1.25
		Nos. 413-415 (3)	41.50	4.75

International Labor Day.

1959, June 20

8f, Peking airport. 10f, Plane loading on runway.

416	A110	8f lilac & blk	27.50	.50
417	A110	10f ol gray & blk	32.50	1.25

Opening of new Peking Airport.

Students with Marx-Lenin Banners A111

Design: 8f, Workers with banners of Mao.

1959, July 1   **Photo.**   **Perf. 11x11½**

418	A111	4f gray, red & dk brn	60.00	9.00
419	A111	8f bis, red & dk brn	80.00	7.50

40th anniv. of the May 4th students' uprising.

Frederick Joliot-Curie — A112

22f, Three races, dove and olive branch.

1959, July 25   **Engr.**   **Perf. 11½**

420	A112	8f violet brn	20.00	2.75
421	A112	22f dk violet	20.00	1.50

10th anniv. of the World Peace Movement.

Stamp Printing Plant, Peking A113

1959, Aug. 15   **Perf. 11x11½**

422   A113   8f dp blue grn   14.00   2.25

Sino-Czechoslovak cooperation in stamp production.

Table Tennis — A114

1959, Aug. 30   **Litho.**   **Perf. 14**

423	A114	4f black & blue	4.00	.50
424	A114	8f black & red	5.75	.70

25th World Table Tennis Championships, Dortmund, German Democratic Republic.

Soviet Space Rocket A115   Backyard Steel Production A116

1959, Sept. 10   Photo.   Perf. 11½

425   A115   8f Prus bl, red & blk   20.00   2.75

Launching of first Russian space rocket, Jan. 2, 1959.

1959, Sept. 25   **Engr.**

Designs: #426, Sun rising over "industry and agriculture." #428, Farming. #429, Trade. #430, Education. #431, Militia. #432, Communal dining. #433, Nursery. #434, Care for the aged. #435, Health services. #436, Flutist; culture and sports. #437, Flower symbolizing unity of industry, agriculture, trade, education and armed forces.

Position-in-set number in ( ).

426	A116	8f rose (1)	4.75	.50
427	A116	8f violet brn (2)	4.75	.50
428	A116	8f dp orange (3)	4.75	.50
429	A116	8f slate grn (4)	4.75	.50
430	A116	8f dp blue (5)	4.75	.50
431	A116	8f olive (6)	4.75	.50
432	A116	8f indigo (7)	4.75	.50
433	A116	8f lilac rose (8)	4.75	.50
434	A116	8f gray blk (9)	4.75	.50
435	A116	8f emerald (10)	4.75	.50
436	A116	8f dk violet (11)	4.75	.50
437	A116	8f red (12)	4.75	.50
		Nos. 426-437 (12)	57.00	6.00

First anniversary of Peoples' Communes.

Mao and Gate of Heavenly Peace — A117

National
Emblem
A118

Blast
Furnaces — A119

Celebration at Gate of Heavenly
Peace — A120

Mao Proclaiming Republic — A121

Designs: #439, Marx, Lenin and Kremlin.
22f, Dove over globe.

Perf. 11½ x 11

1959, Sept. 28			Photo.
With Gum			
438	A117	8f lt brown & red	60.00	6.00
439	A117	8f dull blue & red	29.00	2.00
440	A117	22f blue grn & red	29.00	5.50
		Nos. 438-440 (3)	118.00	13.50

1959, Oct. 1			Litho.	Perf. 14
441	A118	4f pale grn, red & gold	18.00	7.00
442	A118	8f gray, red & gold	25.00	2.00
443	A118	10f lt blue, red & gold	25.00	2.00
444	A118	20f pale brn, red & gold	25.00	5.00
		Nos. 441-444 (4)	93.00	16.00

Engraved and Photogravure

1959, Oct. 1   Perf. 11½ x 11

#446, Large coal mine. #447, Planer,
Wuhan heavy machinery plant. #448, Wuhan
Yangtze River Bridge. #449, Combine harvester. #450, Hsinankiang hydroelectric station. #451, Spinning machine. #452, Kirin
chemical fertilizer plant.

With Gum

445	A119	8f brown & rose red (1)	6.00	1.10
446	A119	8f brown & gray (2)	6.00	1.10
447	A119	8f brown & yel brn (3)	6.00	1.10
448	A119	8f brown & stl bl (4)	6.00	1.10
449	A119	8f brown & org (5)	6.00	1.10
450	A119	8f brown & ol (6)	6.00	1.10
451	A119	8f brown & bl grn (7)	6.00	1.10
452	A119	8f brown & vio (8)	6.00	1.10
		Nos. 445-452 (8)	48.00	8.80

1959, Oct. 1	Litho.	Perf. 14

Designs: 10f, Workers and factory, vert. 20f,
People rejoicing, vert.

453	A120	8f cream & multi	16.00	2.00
454	A120	10f cream & multi	20.00	2.00
455	A120	20f cream & multi	17.50	2.50
		Nos. 453-455 (3)	53.50	6.50

1959, Oct. 1		Engr.
456	A121 20f deep carmine	225.00	75.00

Nos. 438-456 commemorate 10th anniversary of the Proclamation of the People's
Republic of China.

A122   A123

Designs: No. 457, Pioneers' emblem. No.
458, Pioneer Bugler. No. 459, Schoolgirl. No.
460, Girl using rain gauge. No. 461, Boy planting tree. No. 462, Girl figure skater.

1959, Nov. 10		Photo.	Perf. 11½
457	A122	4f red yel & blk (1)	11.50	.70
458	A122	4f Prus bl & red (2)	11.50	.70
459	A122	8f brn & red (3)	11.50	.70
460	A122	8f dk bl & red (4)	11.50	.70
461	A122	8f red & grn (5)	11.50	.70
462	A122	8f mag & red (6)	11.50	.70
		Nos. 457-462 (6)	69.00	4.20

10th anniversary of the Young Pioneers.
Black inscription on No. 457 engraved.

1959, Dec. 1		Engr.

4f, Exhibition emblem, communications
symbols. 8f, Exhibition emblem & chimneys.

463	A123 4f dark blue	3.75	.50
464	A123 8f red	3.75	.50

Exhibition of Industry and Communications,
Peking.

Palace of
Nationalities
A124

Engraved, Frame Lithographed

1959, Dec. 10		Perf. 14
465	A124 4f red & blk	8.50	.85
466	A124 8f brt grn & blk	8.50	.85

Inauguration of the Cultural Palace of
Nationalities, Peking.

Athletes'
Monument and
Track — A125

#468, Parachuting. #469, Marksmanship.
#470, Diving. #471, Table tennis. #472, Weight
lifting. #473, High jump. #474, Rowing. #475,
Track. #476, Basketball. #477, Traditional Chinese fencing. #478, Motorcycling. #479, Gymnastics. #480, Bicycling. #481, Horsemanship.
#482, Soccer.

1959, Dec. 28			Litho.
467	A125	8f bis, blk & gray (1)	6.50	.90
468	A125	8f dl bl, blk & gray (2)	6.50	.90
469	A125	8f red brn & blk (3)	6.50	.90
470	A125	8f grn, blk & brn (4)	6.50	.90
471	A125	8f brt grn, blk, brn & gray (5)	6.50	.90
472	A125	8f gray, blk & brn (6)	6.50	.90
473	A125	8f dl bl, blk & brn (7)	6.50	.90
474	A125	8f Prus grn, blk & brn (8)	6.50	.90
475	A125	8f org, blk & brn (9)	6.50	.90
476	A125	8f dl vio, blk & brn (10)	6.50	.90
477	A125	8f lt ol, blk & brn (11)	6.50	.90
478	A125	8f bl, blk & gray (12)	6.50	.90
479	A125	8f gray bl, blk, grn, & bl (13)	6.50	.90
480	A125	8f gray, blk, brn, & vio (14)	6.50	.90
481	A125	8f red org, blk, brn, & gray (15)	6.50	.90
482	A125	8f lt gray, blk, brn, & red (16)	6.50	.90
		Nos. 467-482 (16)	104.00	14.40

First National Sports Meeting, Peking.

Wheat and
Main
Pavilion
A126

Designs (Pavilion and): 8f, Meteorological
symbols. 10f, Domestic animals. 20f, Fish.

1959, Jan. 20		Engr. & Litho.
Cream Background		
483	A126	4f black & org	2.00	.30
484	A126	8f black & dull bl	2.00	.30
485	A126	10f black & org brn	2.00	.30
486	A126	20f black & grnsh bl	2.00	.50
		Nos. 483-486 (4)	8.00	1.40

Opening of the National Agricultural Exhibition Halls, Peking.

With Gum

From No. 487 onward all stamps
were issued with gum except as noted.

**Catalogue values for unused
stamps in this section, from this
point to the end of the section, are
for Never Hinged items.**

Conference
Hall, Tsunyi
A127

Designs: 8f, Mao addressing conference.
10f, Crossing Chinsha River.

Engraved (4f, 10f); Photogravure (8f)

1960, Jan. 25		Perf. 11x11½
487	A127	4f violet & blue	65.00	4.00
488	A127	8f red & multi	85.00	7.50
489	A127	10f slate green	85.00	12.00
		Nos. 487-489 (3)	235.00	23.50

25th anniversary of the Communist Party
Conference at Tsunyl.

Clara Zetkin
(1857-1933)
A128

Chinese and
Russian
Workers — A129

8f, Mother, child and dove. 10f, Woman tractor driver. 22f, Women of three races.

1960, Mar. 8   Photo.   Perf. 11½x11
490 A128 4f black & multi   8.00 .40
491 A128 8f black & multi   8.00 .40
492 A128 10f black & multi   10.00 1.25
493 A128 22f black & multi   8.00 .65
        Nos. 490-493 (4)   34.00 2.70
50th anniv. of International Women's Day.

1960, Mar. 10

Designs: 8f, Chinese and Russian flags. 10f, Chinese and Russian soldiers.
494 A129 4f dk brown   30.00 3.00
495 A129 8f red, yel & blk 42.50 4.50
496 A129 10f dp blue   42.50 4.00
        Nos. 494-496 (3)   115.00 10.00
10th anniv. of Sino-Soviet Treaty of Friendship. Black inscription engraved on No. 495.

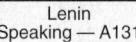

Flags of
Hungary
and China
A130

Design: 8f, Parliament Building, Budapest.

1960, Apr. 4   Perf. 11 x 11½
497 A130 8f yel, blk, red & grn 37.50 4.00
498 A130 8f blue, red & blk   37.50 10.00
15th anniv. of the liberation of Hungary.

Lenin
Speaking — A131

Lunik 2, Earth
and Russian
Arms — A132

Designs: 8f, Portrait of Lenin. 20f, Lenin talking with Smolny Palace guard.

**Engraved (4f, 20f); Engraved and
Photogravure (8f)**
1960, Apr. 22   Perf. 11½ x 11
499 A131 4f violet brn   30.00 1.25
500 A131 8f org red & blk   37.50 4.50
501 A131 20f dk brown   42.50 3.00
        Nos. 499-501 (3)   110.00 8.75
90th anniversary of the birth of Lenin.

1960, Apr. 30   Engr.   Perf. 11½

Design: 10f, Lunik 3 over earth.
502 A132 8f red   14.50 1.00
503 A132 10f green   17.50 1.00
        Russian space flights.

Pioneers and
Flags of
Czechoslovakia
and
China — A133

View of
Prague with
Charles
Bridge
A134

Perf. 11½x11; 11x11½
1960, May 9   Photo.
504 A133 8f yellow & multi 32.00 2.00
505 A134 8f deep green   32.00 5.00
Liberation of Czechoslovakia, 15th anniv.

Nostril
Bouquet
A135

Designs: Various goldfish.

1960, June 1   Perf. 11x11½
506 A135 4f shown (1)   47.50 5.75
507 A135 4f Black-back drag-
              on eye (2)   47.50 5.75
508 A135 8f Bubble eye (3)   5.00 5.75
509 A135 8f Red tiger head
              (4)   50.00 5.75
510 A135 8f Pearl scale (5) 85.00 5.75
511 A135 8f Blue dragon eye
              (6)   85.00 5.75
512 A135 8f Skyward eye (7) 50.00 5.75
513 A135 8f Red cap (8)   85.00 5.75
514 A135 8f Purple cap (9) 85.00 8.00
515 A135 8f Red head (10)   85.00 8.00
516 A135 8f Red and white
              dragon eye (11) 95.00 10.00
517 A135 8f Red dragon eye
              (12)   95.00 10.00
        Nos. 506-517 (12)   815.00 82.00

Sow with
Litter
A136

#519, Pig being inoculated. #520, Pigs. #521, Pig and mechanized feeding. #522, Pig and bales.

1960, June 15
518 A136 8f red & blk (1)   60.00 3.00
519 A136 8f dp grn & blk (2) 60.00 3.00
520 A136 8f lil rose & blk (3) 60.00 3.00
521 A136 8f lt yel grn & blk
              (4)   60.00 3.00
522 A136 8f org & blk (5)   60.00 12.00
        Nos. 518-522 (5)   300.00 24.00

Flag Inscribed
"Serving the
Workers" — A137

Flowers, Flags of
North Korea and
China — A138

Design: 8f, Inscribed stone seal.

1960, July 30   Photo.   Perf. 11½x11
523 A137 4f lt grn, red, pink &
              brn   40.00 2.00
Photogravure & Engraved
524 A137 8f pale bl, red & bis 52.50 3.50
3rd Natl. Cong. for Literature and Arts, Peking.

1960, Aug. 15   Photo.
Design: 8f, Flying horse of Korea.
525 A138 8f red & multi   42.50 4.00
526 A138 8f ultra, red & indigo 55.00 9.00
15th anniversary of the liberation of Korea.

Railroad Station, Peking — A139

Design: 10f, Train arriving at station.

1960, Aug. 30   Perf. 11½
527 A139 8f blue, cream & brn 45.00 6.50
528 A139 10f bluish grn, cr &
              ind   45.00 8.00
Opening of new Peking Railroad Station.

Girls and
Flags of
North Viet
Nam and
China
A140

Lake of the
Returning Sword,
Hanoi
A141

Worker and
Fresh-air
Installation
A142

1960, Sept. 2   Perf. 11x11½, 11½x11
529 A140 8f red & multi   16.00 2.50
530 A141 8f red, gray grn &
              gray   16.00 2.50
15th anniversary of the Democratic Republic of North Viet Nam.

1960, Sept. 10   Perf. 11½
Designs: No. 532, Exterminator. No. 533, Window cleaning. No. 534, Medical examination of child. No. 535, Physical exercise.
531 A142 8f black & orange (1) 11.50 .75
532 A142 8f indigo & slate (2) 11.50 .75
533 A142 8f brown & blue (3)   11.50 .75
534 A142 8f maroon & ocher (4) 11.50 .75
535 A142 8f indigo & brt grn (5) 11.50 .75
        Nos. 531-535 (5)   57.50 3.75
National health campaign.

Great Hall of the People — A143

Design: 10f, Inside view.

1960, Oct. 1
536 A143 8f yellow & multi 42.50 5.25
537 A143 10f brown & multi   50.00 6.00
Completion of the Great Hall of the People, Peking.

Dr. Norman
Bethune — A144

Engels
Addressing
Congress at The
Hague — A145

No. 539, Dr. Bethune operating on a soldier.

Photo. (No. 538); Engr. (No. 539)
1960, Nov. 20   Perf. 11½x11
538 A144 8f red & multi   13.00 2.50
539 A144 8f sepia   13.00 2.00
Dr. Norman Bethune (1890-1939), Canadian surgeon with 8th Army.

1960, Nov. 28   Engr.
540 A145 8f shown   25.00 .3.00
Photo.
541 A145 10f Portrait of Engels 32.50 8.00
140th anniversary of the birth of Friedrich Engels (1820-1895), German Socialist.

"Hwang Shi Ba"
A146

Freighter
A147

1960-61   Photo.
**Various Chrysanthemums in Natural
Colors**
542 A146 4f bl gray (1)   45.00 2.00
543 A146 4f pink (2)   87.50 2.00
544 A146 8f dk gray (3)   45.00 2.00
545 A146 8f dp blue (4)   45.00 2.00
546 A146 8f green (5)   45.00 2.00
547 A146 8f magenta (6)   45.00 2.00
548 A146 8f olive (7)   45.00 2.00
549 A146 8f grnsh bl (8)   110.00 2.50
550 A146 10f gray (9)   45.00 2.50
551 A146 10f choc (10)   45.00 3.00
552 A146 20f dp blue (11)   45.00 3.00
553 A146 20f brt red (12)   87.50 4.00
554 A146 22f olive bis (13) 65.00 12.00
555 A146 22f carmine (14)   87.50 14.00
556 A146 30f grnsh gray
              (15)   65.00 8.00
557 A146 30f brt pink (16)   65.00 10.00
558 A146 35f dp green (17)   45.00 10.00
559 A146 52f brt lilac rose
              (18)   65.00 17.50
        Nos. 542-559 (18) 1,082. 100.50
Issued: #548-550, 557-559, 12/10/60; #545-547, 554-556, 1/18/61; #542-544, 2/24/61.

1960, Dec. 15   Perf. 11½
Without Gum
560 A147 8f deep blue   12.00 1.50
1st 10,000-ton Chinese-built freighter, launching.

Pantheon, Paris — A148

Design: 8f, Proclamation of the Commune.

Engraved and Photogravure
1961, Mar. 18   **Perf. 11½x11**
561 A148 8f gray blk & red   30.00 12.00
562 A148 8f brown & red   30.00 12.00

90th anniversary of the Paris Commune.

Championship Symbol and Jasmine — A149

Designs: 10f, Table tennis racket and ball; Temple of Heaven. 20f, Table tennis match. 22f, Peking workers' gymnasium.

1961, Apr. 5   **Photo.**   **Perf. 11**
563 A149 8f multicolored   4.00 .75
564 A149 10f multicolored   4.00 .75
565 A149 20f multicolored   6.00 1.50
566 A149 22f multicolored   6.00 1.25
  a.   Souv. sheet, #563-566   2,000. 1,400.
    Nos. 563-566 (4)   20.00 4.25

26th World Table Tennis Championships, Peking.

Jeme Tien-yow — A150

Design: 10f, Train and tunnel, Peking-Changchow Railroad.

1961, June 20   **Perf. 11½x11**
567 A150 8f ol grn & blk   5.00 .75
568 A150 10f org brn & brn   20.00 2.25

Centenary of the birth of Jeme Tien-yow, railroad construction engineer.

Congress Building, Shanghai — A151

Designs: 8f, August 1st Building, Nanchang. 10f, Provisional Central Government Office, Juikin. 20f, Pagoda Hill, Yenan. 30f, Gate of Heavenly Peace, Peking.

1961, July 1   **Perf. 11½**
569 A151 4f gold, red & cl   50.00 3.00
570 A151 8f gold, red & bl grn   50.00 3.00
571 A151 10f gold, red & yel brn   50.00 10.00
572 A151 20f gold, red & ultra   100.00 6.00
573 A151 30f gold, red & org red   50.00 6.00
    Nos. 569-573 (5)   300.00 28.00

40th anniv. of the Chinese Communist Party.

August 1 Building, Nanchang — A152

3f, 4f, 5f, Trees & Sha Cho Pa Building, Juikin. 8f, 10f, 20f, Pagoda Hill, Yenan. 22f, 30f, 50f, Gate of Heavenly Peace, Peking.

1961-62   **Engr.**   **Perf. 11**
       Without Gum
       Size: 24x16mm
574 A152 1f vio blue   9.00 .45
575 A152 1½f maroon   25.00 .45
576 A152 2f indigo   10.00 1.50
577 A152 3f dull vio   37.50 2.00
578 A152 4f green   4.00 .60
579 A152 5f gray   3.50 .35
580 A152 8f sepia   3.50 .30
581 A152 10f brt lil rose   4.00 .30
582 A152 20f grnsh bl   6.00 .30
583 A152 22f brown   3.50 .30
584 A152 30f blue   3.50 .30
585 A152 50f vermilion   3.50 .30
    Nos. 574-585 (12)   113.00 7.15

Issued: 1f, 1½f, 5f, 7/20/62; others 7/20/61. See Nos. 647-654, 1059-1064.

Flowers, Flags of Mongolia and China A153

Design: 10f, Parliament, Ulan Bator, and statue of Sukhe Bator.

1961, July 11   **Photo.**   **Perf. 11x11½**
586 A153 8f crim, ultra & yel   150.00 4.00
587 A153 10f orange, blk & yel   160.00 22.50

40th anniv. of the Mongolian People's Republic.

Military Museum — A154

     Photo. & Engr.
1961, Aug. 1   **Perf. 11½**
588 A154 8f gray bl, brn & grn   92.50 2.00
  a.   Inscribed series "(229)" (error)   110.00 3.75
589 A154 10f gray, blk & grn   92.50 3.50

Opening of the People's Revolutionary Military Museum.

Uprising at Wuchang A155

Sun Yat-sen — A156

   Perf. 11x11½, 11½x11
1961, Oct. 10   **Photo.**
590 A155 8f gray & blk   57.50 2.75
591 A156 10f tan & black   57.50 1.50

50th anniversary of the 1911 Revolution.

Donkey — A157

Rejoicing Tibetans — A158

Designs: 8f, 10f, 20f, 22f, Horses; 30f, 50f, Camels. Ceramic statuettes from Tang Dynasty (618-906) graves.

1961, Nov. 10   **Perf. 11½x11**
   Statuettes in Original Colors
592 A157 4f dull blue   25.00 1.75
593 A157 8f gray green   25.00 1.75
594 A157 8f dp purple   25.00 1.75
595 A157 10f dp blue   25.00 2.50
596 A157 20f olive   37.50 2.50
597 A157 22f blue grn   25.00 3.50
598 A157 30f red brown   37.50 15.00
599 A157 50f slate   37.50 6.00
    Nos. 592-599 (8)   237.50 34.75

1961, Nov. 25

Designs: 8f, Woman sower. 10f, Celebration of bumper crop. 20f, People's representatives. 30f, Tibetan children.
600 A158 4f brn & ocher   25.00 2.00
601 A158 8f brn & lt bl grn   25.00 2.00
602 A158 10f brn & yel   45.00 4.00
603 A158 20f brn & rose   125.00 10.00
604 A158 30f brn & bluish gray   110.00 6.50
    Nos. 600-604 (5)   330.00 24.50

Rebirth of the Tibetan people.

Lu Hsun — A159

1962, Feb. 26
605 A159 8f red brown & blk   6.50 1.25

80th anniv. of the birth of Lu Hsun, writer.

An Chi Bridge, Chao Hsien — A160

Bridges of Ancient China: 8f, Pao Tai, Soochow. 10f, Chu Pu, Kwan Hsien. 20f, Chen Yang, San Kiang.

1962, May 15   **Perf. 11**
606 A160 4f dk gray blue   12.00 .30
607 A160 8f dp green   12.00 .30
608 A160 10f brown   12.00 1.00
609 A160 20f grnsh blue   12.00 2.75
    Nos. 606-609 (4)   48.00 4.35

Tu Fu — A161

Cranes and Bamboo — A162

4f, Tu Fu memorial pavilion, Chengtu.

1962, May 25   **Perf. 11½x11**
610 A161 4f ol bis & blk   62.50 1.50
611 A161 8f grnsh bl & blk   62.50 2.75

Poet Tu Fu, 1,250th anniversary of birth.

1962, June 10

10f, Two cranes in flight. 20f, Crane on rock.
612 A162 8f tan & multi   24.00 3.00
613 A162 10f blue & multi   45.00 4.00
614 A162 20f bister & multi   40.00 5.50
    Nos. 612-614 (3)   109.00 12.50

"The Sacred Crane," from paintings by Chen Chi-fo.

Cuban Soldier and Flag A163

Designs: 10f, Sugar cane worker. 22f, Militiaman and woman.

1962, July 10   **Perf. 11x11½**
615 A163 8f car, rose & blk   75.00 5.00
616 A163 10f green & blk   85.00 12.00
617 A163 22f ultra & blk   90.00 35.00
    Nos. 615-617 (3)   250.00 52.00

Support of Cuba.

Torch and Map of Algeria — A164

Mei Lan-fang — A165

Design: 22f, Algerian soldiers and flag.

1962, July 10   **Perf. 11½x11**
618 A164 8f dp brown & red org   4.00 .50
619 A164 22f ocher & dp brn   3.50 .90

Support of Algeria.

1962   **Perf. 11½x11, 11x11½**

Designs (Mei Lan-fang in Women's Roles): No. 621, Beating drum. No. 622, With fan. 10f, Lady Yu with swords. 20f, With bag. 22f, Heavenly Maiden, horiz. 50f, With spinning wheel, horiz. $3, Scene from opera "Drunken Beauty."
620 A165 4f tan & multi   650.00 45.00
621 A165 8f tan & multi   250.00 30.00
622 A165 8f gray & multi   250.00 30.00
623 A165 10f gray & multi   260.00 32.50
624 A165 20f lt grn & multi   275.00 40.00
625 A165 22f cream & multi   275.00 50.00
626 A165 30f lt blue & multi   275.00 70.00
627 A165 50f buff & multi   400.00 50.00
    Nos. 620-627 (8)   2,635. 347.50

Souvenir Sheet
Perf. 11

628 A165 $3 brown & multi   27,500. 12,500.

Stage art of Mei Lan-fang, actor. Issued: 4f, 8f, 10f, 8/8; $3, 9/15; others 9/1. Nos. 620-627 exist imperf. Value, set unused $15,000, used $2,800.

No. 628 contains one 48x58mm stamp and almost always has some faults. Value above is for fault-free examples. Value for No. 628 with small faults, unused $17,500. Excellent forgeries exist.

Flower Drum Dance, Han — A166

Folk Dances: 8f, Ordos, Mongolia. 10f, Catching shrimp, Chuang. 20f, Friend, Yi. 30f, Fiddle dance, Tibet. 50f, Tambourine dance, Uighur.
Cumulative numbers 246-251 at lower right.

1962, Oct. 15   Litho.   Perf. 12½
Without Gum
629	A166	4f cream & multi	2.50	.40
630	A166	8f cream & multi	2.50	.40
631	A166	10f cream & multi	3.50	.40
632	A166	20f cream & multi	6.00	.50
633	A166	30f cream & multi	6.00	.80
634	A166	50f cream & multi	7.00	1.50
		Nos. 629-634 (6)	27.50	4.00

See Nos. 696-707.

Soldiers Storming Winter Palace — A167

Design: 8f, Lenin leading soldiers, vert.

1962, Nov. 7   Photo.   Perf. 11½
635	A167	8f black & red	75.00	3.00
636	A167	20f slate grn & red	95.00	10.00

45th anniversary of the Russian Revolution.

Monument and Map of Albania — A168

Tsai Lun, Inventor of Papermaking A169

Design: 10f, Albanian flag and Girl Pioneer.

1962, Nov. 28   Perf. 11½x11
637	A168	8f Prus blue & sepia	7.50	1.25
638	A168	10f red, yel, & blk	7.50	1.25

50th anniversary of Albanian independence.

1962, Dec. 1   Perf. 11½x11

Designs: No. 640, Paper making. No. 641, Sun Szu-miao, physician. No. 642, Writing medical treatise. No. 643, Shen Ko, geologist. No. 644, Making field notes. No. 645, Kuo

Shou-chin, astronomer. No. 646, Astronomical instrument.
Cumulative numbers 297-304 at lower right.

639	A169	4f multicolored	12.00	4.00
640	A169	4f multicolored	12.00	4.00
641	A169	8f multicolored	12.00	4.00
642	A169	8f multicolored	12.00	4.50
643	A169	10f multicolored	12.00	4.50
644	A169	10f multicolored	14.00	4.50
645	A169	20f multicolored	16.00	12.00
646	A169	20f multicolored	16.00	12.00
		Nos. 639-646 (8)	106.00	49.50

Scientists of ancient China.
No. 639 exists with an extra character in the inscription. Value, unused $5,000, used $3,000.

Building Type of 1961

Designs: 1f, 2f, Building, Nanchang. 3f, 4f, Trees and Sha Cho Pa Building. 8f, 10f, 20f, Pagoda Hill, Yenan. 30f, Gate of Heavenly Peace, Peking.

1962, Jan.   Litho.   Rough Perf. 12½
Size: 21x16mm
Without Gum
647	A152	1f ultra	.80	.20
648	A152	2f greenish gray	.80	.20
649	A152	3f violet gray	.80	.20
650	A152	4f green	.80	.20
651	A152	8f dk olive, perf. 14	1.60	.20
b.		Perf. 11x11½	5.00	
652	A152	10f brt rose lilac	3.00	.20
653	A152	20f slate blue	3.00	.25
654	A152	30f dull blue	3.75	.30
		Nos. 647-654 (8)	14.55	1.75

Tank Monument, Havana A170

Crowd in Peking — A171

Designs: No. 656, Cuban revolutionaries. No. 657, Crowd in Havana. No. 659, Cuban soldier. No. 660, Castro and Cuban flag.

Perf. 11½, 11x11½
1963, Jan. 1   Photo.
655	A170	4f red & blk brn	75.00	2.50
656	A170	4f green & blk	75.00	2.50
657	A171	8f dull red & brn	100.00	5.00
658	A171	8f dull red & brn	150.00	35.00
659	A170	10f ocher & blk	125.00	40.00
660	A170	10f red, blue & blk	150.00	42.50
		Nos. 655-660 (6)	675.00	127.50

4th anniversary of the Cuban revolution.

Green Dragontail — A172

Karl Marx — A173

1963   Without Gum   Perf. 11
661	A172	4f Tibetan clouded yellow (1)	27.50	6.00
662	A172	4f Tritailed glory (2)	27.50	1.50
663	A172	4f Neumogeni jungle queen (3)	27.50	1.50
664	A172	4f Washan swordtail (4)	27.50	1.50
665	A172	4f Striped ringlet (5)	27.50	1.50
666	A172	8f shown (6)	30.00	1.50
667	A172	8f Dilunulated peacock (7)	30.00	1.50
668	A172	8f Yamfly (8)	30.00	1.50
669	A172	8f Golden kaiseri-hind (9)	30.00	1.50
670	A172	8f Mushaell hairstreak (10)	30.00	1.50
671	A172	10f Yellow orangetip (11)	30.00	2.50
672	A172	10f Great jay (12)	30.00	2.50
673	A172	10f Striped punch (13)	30.00	2.50
674	A172	10f Hainan violetbeak (14)	30.00	2.50
675	A172	10f Omeiskipper (15)	30.00	2.50
676	A172	20f Philippines birdwing (16)	30.00	4.00
677	A172	20f Richtofenis red apollo (17)	30.00	5.00
678	A172	22f Blue-banded king crow (18)	27.50	6.00
679	A172	30f Solskyi copper (19)	27.50	7.00
680	A172	50f Yunnan clipper (20)	75.00	10.00
		Nos. 661-680 (20)	627.50	65.50

Issued: #666-675, July 15; others Apr. 5.

1963, May 5   Perf. 11½

Designs: No. 682, "Workers of the World, Unite" on cover of first edition of Communist Manifesto. No. 683, Marx and Engels.

Without Gum
681	A173	8f black, gold & sal (1)	25.00	4.50
682	A173	8f gold & red (2)	27.50	4.50
683	A173	8f gold & choc (3)	27.50	4.50
		Nos. 681-683 (3)	80.00	13.50

145th anniversary of birth of Karl Marx (1818-1883), German political philosopher.

Child with Top — A174

Child: #685, eating berries. #686, as traffic policeman. #687, with windmill. #688, listening to caged cricket. #689, with sword. #690, embroidering. #691, with umbrella. #692, playing with sand. #693, playing table tennis. #694, learning to add. #695, with kite.

1963, June 1   Litho.   Perf. 12½
Without Gum
Multicolored Designs
684	A174	4f grnsh gray (1)	6.00	.40
685	A174	4f tan (2)	6.00	.40
686	A174	8f gray (3)	6.00	.40
687	A174	8f blue (4)	6.00	.40
688	A174	8f tan (5)	6.00	.40
689	A174	8f dp gray (6)	6.00	.40
690	A174	8f citron (7)	6.00	.40
691	A174	8f gray (8)	6.00	.40
692	A174	10f green (9)	6.00	1.00
693	A174	10f violet (10)	6.00	1.00
694	A174	20f bister (11)	12.00	2.50
695	A174	20f green (12)	12.00	2.50
		Nos. 684-695 (12)	84.00	10.20

Children's Day. Value, imperf set unused $475, used $250.

Dance Type of 1962

Folk Dances: 4f, Weavers' dance, Puyi. 8f, Kazakh. 10f, Olunchun. 20f, Labor dance, Kaochan. 30f, Reed pipe dance, Miao. 50f, Fan dance, Korea.
Cumulative numbers 261-266 at lower right.

1963, June 15   Perf. 12½
Without Gum
696	A166	4f cream & multi	3.00	.35
697	A166	8f cream & multi	3.00	.35
698	A166	10f cream & multi	3.00	.40
699	A166	20f cream & multi	4.00	.75
700	A166	30f cream & multi	3.50	.75
701	A166	50f cream & multi	7.00	.75
		Nos. 696-701 (6)	23.50	3.35

1963, June 30   Without Gum

Folk Dances: 4f, "Wedding Ceremony," Yu. 8f, "Encircling Mountain Forest," Pai. 10f, Long drum dance, Yao. 20f, Third day of the third month dance, Li. 30f, Knife dance, Kawa. 50f, Peacock dance, Thai.
Cumulative numbers 279-284 at lower right.

702	A166	4f cream & multi	2.00	.35
703	A166	8f cream & multi	2.00	.35
704	A166	10f cream & multi	3.50	.45
705	A166	20f cream & multi	3.50	1.00
706	A166	30f cream & multi	4.25	1.00
707	A166	50f cream & multi	7.50	1.10
		Nos. 702-707 (6)	22.75	4.25

Giant Panda Eating Apples — A175

Table Tennis Player — A176

Designs: No. 709, Giant panda eating bamboo shoots. 10f, Two pandas, horiz.

1963, Aug. 5   Photo.   Perf. 11½x11
Size: 28x38mm
708	A175	8f pale blue & blk	37.50	2.25
709	A175	8f pale blue & blk	37.50	6.50

Size: 50x29mm
Perf. 11½
710	A175	10f olive & blk	50.00	5.00
		Nos. 708-710 (3)	125.00	13.75

Value, imperf set unused $425, used $150.

1963, Sept. 10   Engr.   Perf. 11½

No. 712, Trophies won by Chinese team.
711	A176	8f dk olive grn	30.00	1.00
712	A176	8f brown	30.00	2.50

27th World Table Tennis Championships.

Snub-nosed Langur — A177

Jade-green Screen Mountain — A178

Designs: 10f, Two monkeys playing. 22f, Two monkeys grooming.

1963, Sept. 23 Photo.   Perf. 11½x11
713 A177 8f gray & multi   17.50 1.25
714 A177 10f gray & multi   17.50 1.25
715 A177 22f gray & multi   32.50 5.50
    Nos. 713-715 (3)   67.50 8.00
Value, imperf set unused $350, used $140.

Engraved and Photogravure
1963, Oct. 15   Perf. 11½
Hwang Shan Landscapes (Yellow Mountains), Anhwei Province. #724-731 horiz.

Design A178
716 4f shown (1)   27.50 5.00
717 4f "Guests Welcom-
        ing Pines" (2)   27.50 5.00
718 4f Pines and Rock
        Behind the Sea
        (3)   27.50 5.00
719 4f Terrace of Keep-
        ing Cool (4)   27.50 5.00
720 8f Mount of Heavenly
        Capital (5)   32.50 5.00
721 8f Mount of Scissors
        (6)   32.50 5.00
722 8f Forest of Ten
        Thousand Pines
        (7)   36.00 5.00
723 8f "Brush Blooming
        in Dream" (8)   36.00 5.00
724 10f Mount of Lotus
        Flower (9)   50.00 7.50
725 10f Cumulus Cloud
        over West Sea
        (10)   50.00 7.50
726 10f Old Pines of
        Hwang Shan (11)   60.00 7.50
727 10f "Watching the
        Clouds over
        West Sea" (12)   100.00 7.50
728 20f Mount of Stalag-
        mites (13)   120.00 11.00
729 22f "Stone Monkey
        Watching the
        Sea" (14)   120.00 12.00
730 30f Forest of Lions
        (15)   175.00 80.00
731 50f Three Fairy Tales
        of Pen Lai (16)   200.00 50.00
    Nos. 716-731 (16)   1,122. 223.00

Soccer Player — A179

Athletes and Banners — A180

#733, Discus, women's. #734, Diving, men's. #735, Gymnastics, women's.

Engraved and Photogravure
1963, Nov. 17   Perf. 11
732 A179 8f gray, red & blk
            (1)   30.00 2.00
733 A179 8f gray, ultra & blk
            (2)   30.00 2.00
734 A179 8f lt grn, brn & blk
            (3)   30.00 2.00
735 A179 8f gray, lil rose &
            blk (4)   30.00 2.00

Photo.
Perf. 11½
736 A180 10f red & multi (5)   45.00 9.00
    Nos. 732-736 (5)   165.00 17.00
Games of the Newly Emerging Forces, Djakarta.

Clay Rooster and Goat — A181

Chinese Folk Toys: No. 738, Cloth camel. No. 739, Cloth tigers. No. 740, Clay ox and rider. No. 741, Cloth rabbit, wooden doll, clay roosters. No. 742, Straw rooster. No. 743, Cloth donkey and bird. No. 744, Clay lion. No. 745, Cloth tiger and tumbler doll.

1963, Dec. 10   Litho.   Perf. 11½
Toys Multicolored; Without Gum
737 A181 4f bister (1)   2.75 .75
738 A181 4f gray (4)   2.75 .75
739 A181 4f lt blue (7)   2.75 .75
740 A181 8f bister (2)   2.75 .75
741 A181 8f gray (5)   2.75 .75
742 A181 8f lt blue (8)   2.75 .75
743 A181 10f bister (3)   2.75 .75
744 A181 10f gray (6)   2.75 .75
745 A181 10f lt blue (9)   2.75 .75
    Nos. 737-745 (9)   24.75 6.75

Armed Vietnamese Family — A182

Flags of Cuba and China — A183

Liberation of South Viet Nam: No. 747, Militia with Vietnamese flag.

1963, Dec. 20   Photo.   Perf. 11½x11
746 A182 8f tan, blk & red   11.00 1.75
747 A182 8f red & multi   11.00 3.50

1964, Jan. 1
Design: No. 749, Boy waving Cuban flag.
748 A183 8f red, yel, bl & ind 65.00 2.00
749 A183 8f multicolored   85.00 10.00
5th anniversary of the liberation of Cuba.

Woman Driving Tractor — A184

Woman of the People's Commune: No. 751, harvesting. No. 752, picking cotton. No. 753, picking fruit. No. 754, reading book. No. 755, on guard duty.

1964, Mar. 8
750 A184 8f ol, pink & brn (1) 3.50 1.25
751 A184 8f brn yel & org (2)   3.50 1.25
752 A184 8f gray & multi (3)   3.50 1.25
753 A184 8f black, org & bl (4) 3.50 1.25
754 A184 8f green & multi (5)   3.50 1.25
755 A184 8f lilac & multi (6)   3.50 1.25
    Nos. 750-755 (6)   21.00 7.50

Chinese and African Men A185

Design: No. 757, African drummer.
1964, Apr. 12   Photo.   Perf. 11
756 A185 8f red & multi   3.00 .50
757 A185 8f black & dk brn   3.00 .50
African Freedom Day.

Marx, Engels, Lenin and Stalin — A186

Design: No. 759, Banners and workers.
1964, May 1   Perf. 11½
758 A186 8f gold, red & blk   70.00 10.00
759 A186 8f gold, red & blk   40.00 3.50
Labor Day.

Orchard, Yenan A187

Yenan, Shrine of the Chinese Revolution: No. 761, Central Auditorium, Yang Chia Ling. No. 762, Mao's office and residence. No. 763, Auditorium, Wang Chia Ping. No. 764, Border Region Assembly Hall. No. 765, Pagoda Hill and Bridge.

1964, July 1   Photo.   Perf. 11x11½
760 A187 8f multicolored (1)   35.00 1.75
761 A187 8f multicolored (2)   27.50 1.75
762 A187 8f multicolored (3)   11.00 1.75
763 A187 8f multicolored (4)   20.00 1.75
764 A187 8f multicolored (5)   20.00 3.50
765 A187 52f multicolored (6)   47.50 12.00
    Nos. 760-765 (6)   161.00 22.50

Map and Flag of Viet Nam — A188

Alchemist's Glowing Crucible — A189

1964, July 20   Perf. 11½
766 A188 8f multicolored   26.00 5.00
Victory in South Viet Nam.

1964, Aug. 5   Perf. 11½x11
767 A189 4f shown (1)   37.50 2.50
768 A189 4f Night-shining
            jade (2)   37.50 2.50
769 A189 8f Purple Kuo's
            cap (3)   37.50 2.50
770 A189 8f Chao pink
            (4)   37.50 2.50
771 A189 8f Yao yellow
            (5)   37.50 2.50
772 A189 8f Twin beauty
            (6)   37.50 2.50
773 A189 8f Ice-veiled ru-
            by (7)   37.50 2.50

774 A189 10f Gold-sprin-
            kled Chi-
            nese ink (8)   37.50 4.00
775 A189 10f Cinnabar jar
            (9)   37.50 4.00
776 A189 10f Lan Tien
            jade (10)   37.50 4.00
777 A189 10f Imperial robe
            yellow (11)   37.50 4.00
778 A189 10f Hu red (12)   37.50 4.00
779 A189 20f Pea green
            (13)   70.00 10.00
780 A189 43f Wei purple
            (14)   80.00 25.00
781 A189 52f Intoxicated
            celestial
            peach (15)   110.00 30.00
    Nos. 767-781 (15)   710.00 102.50

Souvenir Sheet
Perf. 11½
Without Gum
782 A189 $2 Glorious
            crimson &
            great gold
            pink   5,500. 2,100.
No. 782 contains one 48x59mm stamp.

Wine Cup — A190

Grain Harvest — A191

Designs: Sacrificial bronze vessels of Yin dynasty, prior to 1050 B.C.

Engraved and Photogravure
1964, Aug. 25   Perf. 11½x11
783 A190 4f shown (1)   19.00 1.50
784 A190 4f Ku beaker (2)   19.00 1.50
785 A190 8f Kuang wine urn
            (3)   19.00 1.50
786 A190 8f Chia wine cup
            (4)   19.00 1.50
787 A190 10f Tsun wine ves-
            sel (5)   19.00 2.00
788 A190 10f Yu wine urn (6)   19.00 2.00
789 A190 20f Tsun wine ves-
            sel (7)   19.00 8.50
790 A190 20f Ceremonial
            cauldron (8)   19.00 8.50
    Nos. 783-790 (8)   152.00 27.00

1964, Sept. 26   Photo.
Designs: #792, Students planting trees. #793, Study period. #794, Scientific experimentation.
791 A191 8f multicolored (1)   4.75 .65
792 A191 8f multicolored (2)   4.75 .65
793 A191 8f multicolored (3)   4.75 .65
794 A191 8f multicolored (4)   4.75 .65
    Nos. 791-794 (4)   19.00 2.60
Youth helping in agriculture.

Marx, Engels, Trafalgar Square, London — A192

People with
Banners — A193

1964, Sept. 28   *Perf. 11½*
795 A192 8f red, gold & red
          brn   110.00 18.00
Centenary of the First International.

Gold Ink
Stamps with gold ink often show
some tarnishing. Values are for
untarnished gold color. Tarnished
stamps will sell for less.

1964, Oct. 1
No. 797, Gate of Heavenly Peace and Chinese flag. No. 798, People with banners, facing left.
796 A193 8f cream & multi
          (1)   45.00   5.00
797 A193 8f cream & multi
          (2)   45.00   5.00
798 A193 8f cream & multi
          (3)   45.00   5.00
   a.   Souvenir sheet of 3   7,500. 1,900.
   b.   Strip of 3, #796-798   275.00 60.00
   Nos. 796-798 (3)   135.00 15.00

15th anniv. of the People's Republic.
No. 798a contains No. 798b in continuous
design without separating perfs. No. 798a
almost always has disturbed gum, with interleaving paper sticking to it, or tarnished gilt.
Such examples sell for considerably less than
the very fine example valued above.
Values for No. 798b are for an unfolded
strip.

Oil
Derricks — A194

Oil industry: 4f, Geological surveyors and
truck, horiz. 8f, "Christmas tree" and extraction
accessories. 10f, Oil refinery. 20f, Tank cars,
horiz.

1964, Oct. 1
799 A194 4f lt blue & multi   100.00   8.00
800 A194 8f lt blue & multi   120.00   3.75
801 A194 8f lilac & multi   120.00   3.75
802 A194 10f slate & multi   120.00   8.50
803 A194 20f brown & multi   175.00 35.00
   Nos. 799-803 (5)   635.00 59.00

Albanian
and
Chinese
Flags
A195

10f, Enver Hoxha and Albanian coat of
arms.

1964, Nov. 29   *Perf. 11x11½*
804 A195 8f red & multi   30.00   7.50
805 A195 10f red, yel & blk   67.50 15.00
20th anniv. of the liberation of Albania.

Power Dam
Construction
A196

No. 807, Installation of turbogenerator rotor.
No. 808, Main dam. 20f, Pylon.

1964, Dec. 15   *Perf. 11½*
806 A196 4f multicolored   120.00   4.00
807 A196 8f multicolored   65.00   2.00
808 A196 8f multicolored   90.00   7.00
809 A196 20f multicolored   190.00 35.00
   Nos. 806-809 (4)   465.00 48.00

Hsin An Kiang Dam and hydroelectric power
station.

Fertilizer Industry — A197

Chemical Industry: #811, Plastics. #812,
Medicines. #813, Rubber. #814, Insecticides.
#815, Industrial acids. #816, Industrial alka-
loids. #817, Synthetic fibers.

1964, Dec. 30   **Photo. & Engr.**
810 A197 8f red & blk (1)   10.00   .75
811 A197 8f yel grn & blk (2)   10.00   .75
812 A197 8f brown & blk (3)   10.00   .75
813 A197 8f lilac rose & blk (4)   10.00   .75
814 A197 8f blue & blk (5)   10.00   .75
815 A197 8f orange & blk (6)   10.00   .75
816 A197 8f violet & blk (7)   10.00   .75
817 A197 8f brt green & blk (8)   10.00   .75
   Nos. 810-817 (8)   80.00   6.00

Mao Studying Map — A198

Mao Tse-
tung — A199

Design: No. 819, Victory at Lushan Pass.

1965, Jan. 31   **Photo.**   *Perf. 11*
818 A198 8f red & multi   80.00 20.00
819 A198 8f red & multi   95.00 20.00

               Perf. 11½x11½
820 A199 8f gold & multi   75.00 20.00
   Nos. 818-820 (3)   250.00 60.00

Tsunyi Conference, 30th anniversary.

Conference Hall,
Bandung — A200

Lenin — A201

#822, Asians and Africans applauding.

1965, Apr. 18   *Perf. 11½x11*
821 A200 8f cream & multi   5.00   .55
822 A200 8f cream & multi   5.00   .55

10th anniversary of the Bandung, Indonesia,
Conference, Apr. 1955.

1965, Apr. 25   *Perf. 11½*
823 A201 8f red, choc & salmon   27.50   5.50
95th anniversary of the birth of Lenin.

Chinese
Player — A202

1965, Apr. 25   *Perf. 11½*
824 A202 8f shown (1)   .50   .20
825 A202 8f European woman
          (2)   .50   .20
826 A202 8f Chinese woman
          (3)   .50   .20
827 A202 8f European man (4)   .50   .20
   a.   Block of 4, #824-827   7.50   3.50
28th World Table Tennis Championships,
Ljubljana, Yugoslavia, Apr. 15-25.

Climbers on Mt.
Minya
Konka — A203

Marx and
Lenin — A204

Mountain Climbers: No. 829, on Muztagh
Ata. No. 830, on Mt. Jolmo Lungma (Mt. Ever-
est). No. 831, Women camping on Kongur
Tiuble Tagh. No. 832, on Shisha Pangma.

1965, May 25   **Photo. & Engr.**
828 A203 8f blue, blk & ol (1)   15.00   1.50
829 A203 8f blue, blk & ol (2)   15.00   1.50
830 A203 8f ultra, blk & gray
          (3)   15.00   1.50
831 A203 8f lt bl, blk & yel
          gray (4)   15.00   1.50

832 A203 8f ultra, blk & gray
          (5)   15.00   5.00
   Nos. 828-832 (5)   75.00 11.00
Chinese mountaineering achievements,
1957-64.

1965, June 21 Photo.   *Perf. 11½x11*
833 A204 8f red, yel & blk   35.00   5.50
Postal Ministers' Congress, Peking.

Tseping
Valley
A205

Chingkang Mountains, Cradle of the Chinese Revolution.

1965, July 1   *Perf. 11x11½*
834 A205 4f shown (1)   35.00   4.00
835 A205 8f San Wan Tsun
          (2)   40.00   2.00
836 A205 8f Octagon Bldg.,
          Mao Ping (3)   65.00   3.00
837 A205 8f River and
          Bridge at Lung
          Shih (4)   65.00   3.00
838 A205 8f Ta Ching Tsun
          (5)   45.00   4.50
839 A205 10f Bridge across
          the Lung Yuan
          (6)   45.00   3.00
840 A205 10f Hwang Yang
          Mountain (7)   45.00 11.00
841 A205 52f Chingkang
          peaks (8)   35.00 10.00
   Nos. 834-841 (8)   375.00 40.50

Soldiers with Books — A206

1965, Aug. 1   *Perf. 11½*
          Without Gum
842 A206 8f shown (1)   60.00 10.00
843 A206 8f Soldiers reading
          Little Red
          Books (2)   60.00   7.00
844 A206 8f With shell and
          artillery (3)   50.00   5.00
845 A206 8f Rifle instruction
          (4)   55.00   5.00
846 A206 8f Sewing jacket (5)   50.00   5.00
847 A206 8f Bayonet charge
          (6)   50.00 10.00
848 A206 8f With Banner (7)   60.00 22.50
849 A206 8f Military band (8)   90.00 10.00
   Nos. 842-849 (8)   475.00 74.50

People's Liberation Army. Nos. 846-849
vertical.

"Welcome to
Peking" — A207

#851, Chinese and Japanese young men.
#852, Chinese and Japanese girls. #853,
Musical entertainment. #854, Emblem of
meeting.

1965, Aug. 25   *Perf. 11½x11*
850 A207 4f yellow & multi   4.25   .30
851 A207 8f pink & multi   4.25   .35
852 A207 8f multicolored   4.25   .40
853 A207 10f multicolored   4.25   .55
854 A207 22f lt blue & multi   4.25   1.10
   Nos. 850-854 (5)   21.25   2.70

Chinese-Japanese Youth Meeting, Peking.

North
Vietnamese
Soldier — A208

Peoples of the World — A209

Designs: No. 856, Soldier with guns. No. 857, Soldier giving victory salute.

1965, Sept. 2   *Perf. 11½x11*
855	A208	8f red & red brn (1)	5.00	.50
856	A208	8f red & blk (2)	5.00	.50
857	A208	8f red & vio brn (3)	5.00	.50

Perf. 11½
858	A209	8f black & red (4)	5.00	.50
		Nos. 855-858 (4)	20.00	2.00

Struggle of the people of Viet Nam.

Mao Tse-tung at His Desk — A210

Crossing
Yellow
River
A211

Victory Monument
A212

Design: No. 862, Recruits in cart.

1965, Sept. 3   *Perf. 11*
859	A210	8f red & multi (1)	65.00	12.00

Perf. 11x11½, 11½x11
860	A211	8f red & dk grn (2)	42.50	3.50
861	A212	8f red & dk brn (3)	42.50	5.00
862	A211	8f red & dk grn (4)	42.50	5.00
		Nos. 859-862 (4)	192.50	25.50

20th anniversary of victory over Japan.

2nd National
Games — A213

National Games Opening
Ceremonies — A214

Perf. 11½x11, 11 (A214)

1965, Sept. 28
863	A213	4f Soccer (1)	35.00	2.50
864	A213	4f Archery (2)	35.00	2.50
865	A213	8f Javelin (3)	40.00	2.50
866	A213	8f Gymnastics (4)	40.00	2.50
867	A213	8f Volleyball (5)	40.00	2.50
868	A214	10f shown (6)	110.00	6.00
869	A213	10f Bicyling (7)	135.00	4.00
870	A213	20f Diving (8)	135.00	8.00
871	A213	22f Hurdles (9)	40.00	7.50
872	A213	30f Weight lifting (10)	40.00	17.50
873	A213	43f Basketball (11)	40.00	12.50
		Nos. 863-873 (11)	690.00	68.00

Government
Building
A215

Textile Workers
A216

1½f, 5f, 22f, Gate of Heavenly Peace. 2f, 8f, 30f, People's Hall. 3f, 10f, 50f, Military Museum.

1965-66   *Perf. 11½x11*

Without Gum
874	A215	1f brown	.30	.25
875	A215	1½f red lilac	.30	.60
876	A215	2f green	.30	.25
877	A215	3f blue grn	.30	.25
878	A215	4f brt blue	.30	.25
879	A215	5f vio brn ('66)	.90	.25
880	A215	8f rose red	.90	.25
881	A215	10f gray olive	1.10	.25
882	A215	20f violet	1.10	.25
883	A215	22f orange	2.25	.25
884	A215	30f yellow grn	3.50	.35
885	A215	50f dp blue ('66)	9.00	3.50
		Nos. 874-885 (12)	20.25	6.70

1965, Nov. 30
886	A216	8f shown (1)	32.50	1.75
887	A216	8f Machine shop (2)	32.50	1.75
888	A216	8f Welder (3)	32.50	1.75
889	A216	8f Students (4)	32.50	1.75
890	A216	8f Militia (5)	32.50	3.00
		Nos. 886-890 (5)	162.50	10.00

Women workers.

Soccer — A217

Children's Sports: No. 892, Racing. No. 893, Tobogganing and skating. No. 894, Gymnastics. No. 895, Swimming. No. 896, Rifle practice. No. 897, Jumping rope. No. 898, Table tennis.

1966, Feb. 25   *Perf. 11*
891	A217	4f emerald & multi (1)	.90	.35
892	A217	4f yel brown & multi (2)	.90	.35
893	A217	8f blue & multi (3)	.90	.35
894	A217	8f yellow & multi (4)	.90	.35
895	A217	8f grnsh bl & multi (5)	1.25	.35
896	A217	8f green & multi (6)	1.25	.35
897	A217	10f orange & multi (7)	4.00	.75
898	A217	52f grnsh gray & multi (8)	10.00	2.00
		Nos. 891-898 (8)	20.10	4.85

Mobile
Transformer
A218

New Industrial Machinery: No. 900, Electron microscope, vert. No. 901, Lathe. No. 902, Vertical boring and turning machine, vert. No. 903, Gear-grinding machine. No. 904, Hydraulic press. No. 905, Milling machine. No. 906, Electron accelerator, vert.

Perf. 11x11½, 11½x11

1966, Mar. 30   **Photo. & Engr.**
899	A218	4f yellow & blk (1)	40.00	3.25
900	A218	8f blk & lt ultra (2)	40.00	3.25
901	A218	8f sal pink & blk (3)	40.00	3.25
902	A218	8f olive & blk (4)	40.00	3.25
903	A218	8f rose lil & blk (5)	40.00	3.25
904	A218	10f gray & blk (6)	40.00	3.50
905	A218	10f bl grn & blk (7)	40.00	4.00
906	A218	22f lilac & blk (8)	40.00	6.50
		Nos. 899-906 (8)	320.00	30.25

Military and
Civilian
Workers
A219

Women in Various Occupations: No. 908, Train conductor. No. 909, Red Cross worker. No. 910, Kindergarten teacher. No. 911, Road sweeper. No. 912, Hairdresser. No. 913, Bus conductor. No. 914, Traveling saleswoman. No. 915, Canteen worker. No. 916, Rural mail carrier.

1966, May 10   *Perf. 11x11½*
907	A219	8f red & multi (1)	3.00	.75
908	A219	8f pale grn & multi (2)	3.00	.75
909	A219	8f yellow & multi (3)	3.00	.75
910	A219	8f green & multi (4)	3.00	.75
911	A219	8f salmon & multi (5)	3.00	.75
912	A219	8f pale bl & bl (6)	3.00	.75
913	A219	8f yellow & multi (7)	3.00	.75
914	A219	8f tan & multi (8)	3.00	.75
915	A219	8f yel grn & multi (9)	3.00	.75
916	A219	8f green & multi (10)	3.00	.75
		Nos. 907-916 (10)	30.00	7.50

Statue "Thunderstorm" — A220

22f, Open book and association emblem.

1966, June 27   *Perf. 11*
917	A220	8f red & black	7.00	2.25
918	A220	22f red, gold & yel	12.00	4.75

Afro-Asian Writers' Assoc. Conf., Peking.

Sun Yat-
sen — A221

1966, Nov. 12   *Perf. 11½x11*
919	A221	8f sepia & lt buff	110.00	27.50

Birth centenary of Sun Yat-sen.

Athletes Holding Portrait of
Mao — A222

Two
Women
Athletes
with Little
Red Book
A223

#921, Athletes holding Little Red Books. #923, Athletes reading Mao texts.

1966, Dec. 31   *Perf. 11*
920	A222	8f red & multi (1)	75.00	11.00
921	A222	8f red & multi (2)	75.00	11.00

Perf. 11x11½
922	A223	8f blue & multi (3)	85.00	20.00
923	A223	8f blue & multi (4)	95.00	20.00
		Nos. 920-923 (4)	330.00	62.00

1st Athletic Games of the New Emerging Nations.

Appreciation of
Lu Hsun by
Mao — A224

"Be Resolute ...,"
by Mao Tse-
tung — A225

Designs: No. 925, Portrait of Lu Hsun. No. 926, Lu Hsun's handwriting (3 vert. rows).

Engr. & Photo.; Photo. (#925)
1966, Dec. 31   *Perf. 11½*
924	A224	8f red & black (1)	125.00	22.50
925	A224	8f red & multi (2)	95.00	20.00
926	A224	8f red & black (3)	85.00	22.50
		Nos. 924-926 (3)	305.00	65.00

Lu Hsun, Revolutionary writer (1881-1936).

Perf. 11½x11, 11½ (No. 928)
1967, Mar. 10   **Photo.**

Designs: No. 928, Drilling crew fighting natural gas fire, horiz. No. 929, Attempt to close fire-engulfed valve.

Sizes: Nos. 927, 929, 26x38mm; No. 928, 49x29mm

927	A225	8f red, gold & blk	50.00	15.00
928	A225	8f brick red & blk	50.00	17.50
929	A225	8f brick red & blk	72.50	32.50
		Nos. 927-929 (3)	172.50	65.00

Heroic oil well firefighters.

Liu Ying-chun
A226

1967, Mar. 25　　　**Perf. 11½x11**
930	A226	8f	shown (1)	60.00	16.00
931	A226	8f	With book by Mao (2)	65.00	16.00
932	A226	8f	Holding bridle of horse (3)	85.00	16.00
933	A226	8f	With film slide (4)	70.00	16.00
934	A226	8f	Lecturing (5)	70.00	19.00
935	A226	8f	Fatal attempt to stop runaway horse (6)	110.00	19.00
		Nos. 930-935 (6)		460.00	102.00

In memory of soldier Liu Ying-chun, hero.

Third 5-Year Plan — A227

Design: No. 936, Banners, 3 workers and male soldier facing right (industrial growth). No. 937, Banners, 3 workers and female militia member facing left (agricultural growth).

1967, Apr. 15　　　**Perf. 11**
936	A227	8f	red & multi	75.00	12.00
937	A227	8f	red & multi	75.00	17.50

Third Five-Year Plan.

Mao Tse-tung — A228

Thoughts of Mao — A229

1967, Apr. 20　　　**Perf. 11½**
938	A228	8f	red & multi	125.00	55.00

Red & Gold
939	A229	8f	39 characters	300.00	175.00
940	A229	8f	50 characters	300.00	175.00
941	A229	8f	39 characters in 6 lines	300.00	175.00
942	A229	8f	53 characters	300.00	175.00
943	A229	8f	46 characters	300.00	175.00
a.		Strip of 5, #939-943		5,000.	1,250.

Gold & Red
944	A229	8f	41 characters	400.00	250.00
945	A229	8f	49 characters	400.00	250.00
946	A229	8f	35 characters	400.00	250.00
947	A229	8f	22 characters	400.00	250.00
948	A229	8f	29 characters	400.00	250.00
a.		Strip of 5, #944-948		5,750.	1,600.
		Nos. 938-948 (11)		3,625.	2,180.

Thoughts of Mao Tse-tung.

Values for Nos. 943a and 948a are for unfolded strips without tarnishing.

No numbers appear below design on Nos. 938-1046.

Gate of Heavenly Peace and Text from C. C. P. Communique Praising Mao — A230

Mao and Lin Piao A231

#950, Mao and poem. #951, Mao among people of various races. #952, Mao facing left and Red Guards with books. #953, Mao with upraised right hand. #954, Mao leaning on rail, horiz. 10f, Mao and Lin Piao in discussion, horiz.

Engraved and Photogravure
1967　　　**Perf. 11x11½**
Size: 36x56mm
949	A230	4f	yel, red & mar	300.00	45.00

Photo.
950	A230	8f	yel, brn, & red	325.00	60.00
951	A230	8f	yel, red & multi	300.00	45.00
952	A230	8f	yel, red & multi	450.00	60.00

Size: 36x50mm, 50x36mm
953	A231	8f	black & multi	350.00	45.00
954	A231	8f	black & multi	650.00	125.00
955	A231	8f	lt blue & multi	350.00	45.00
956	A231	10f	black & multi	1,200.	225.00
		Nos. 949-956 (8)		3,925.	650.00

"Mao Tse-tung Our Great Teacher."
Issued: #949-953, 5/1; #954-956, 9/20.

Mao Text (4 lines) — A232

Parade of Supporters — A233

Design: No. 958, Mao text (5 lines).

Engraved and Photogravure
1967, May 23　　　**Perf. 11½**
957	A232	8f	black, red & yel	525.00	250.00
958	A232	8f	black, red & yel	600.00	250.00

Photo.
Perf. 11
959	A233	8f	multicolored	700.00	300.00
		Nos. 957-959 (3)		1,825.	800.00

25th anniversary of Mao Tse-tung's "Talks on Literature and Art" in Yenan.

A stamp was prepared in August 1967 for the 50th anniversary of the Autumn Harvest March. It was not issued, but a few examples have entered the marketplace. It depicts Mao Tse-tung on the left and Lin Piao on the right, against a blue sky. A cut example comprising the right half of the stamp was sold in a Jan. 2010 Hong Kong for auction for the equivalent of U.S. $285,000. Presumably, an intact example would sell for far more.

Mao Tse-tung — A234

1967　　　**Engr.**　　　**Perf. 11**
960	A234	4f	brown	90.00	30.00
961	A234	8f	carmine	240.00	40.00
962	A234	35f	dk brown	55.00	22.50
963	A234	43f	vermilion	55.00	22.50
964	A234	52f	carmine	55.00	22.50
		Nos. 960-964 (5)		495.00	137.50

46th anniv. of Chinese Communist Party. Issue dates: 8f, July 1; others Sept.

Mao, "Sun of the Revolution" — A235

No. 966, Mao and people of various races.

1967, Oct. 1　　　**Perf. 11½x11**
965	A235	8f	multicolored	75.00	22.50
966	A235	8f	multicolored	175.00	45.00

People's Republic of China, 18th anniv.

"September 9" — A236

"Huichang" A237

"Peitaiho" A238

Reply to Comrade Kuo Mo-jo — A239

Mao Tse-tung Writing Poems — A240

Poems by Mao: #967, "The Long March." #968, "Liupanshan." #969, shown. #970, "The Cave of the Fairies." #971, "Snow." #972, "Lushan Pass." #975, "Conquest of Nanking." #976, "The Yellow Crane Pavilion." #977, "Swimming." #979, "Changsha."

1967-68　　　**Photo.**　　　**Perf. 11**
Size: 79x18½mm
967	A236	4f	9 characters, UL panel	95.00	37.50
968	A236	4f	11 characters, UL panel	75.00	37.50

Size: 60x24mm
Perf. 11½
969	A236	8f	shown, 10 characters in UL panel	130.00	47.50
970	A236	8f	21 characters in UL panel	130.00	47.50
971	A236	8f	11 characters in UL panel	150.00	60.00
972	A236	8f	9 characters in UL panel	150.00	60.00

Size: 29x50mm
973	A237	8f	shown	650.00	250.00
974	A238	8f	shown	1,200.	225.00
975	A238	8f	3 rows in bottom panel	800.00	175.00
976	A238	8f	2 rows in bottom panel	800.00	175.00

Size: 52x38mm
Perf. 11
977	A239	8f	3 short vert. rows, at left of poem	550.00	250.00
978	A239	10f	shown	75.00	37.50
979	A239	10f	undivided text	75.00	37.50
980	A240	10f	red, yel & multi	75.00	37.50
		Nos. 967-980 (14)		4,955.	1,477.

Issued: #969-970, 980, 10/1; #973-974, 977, 5/20/68; others 7/20/68.

Lin Piao's Epigram on Mao Tsetung A241

1967, Dec. 26   Photo.   Perf. 11x11½
981   A241   8f red & gold   37.50   15.00

Mao and Parade of Artists — A242

"Raid on White Tiger Regiment" — A243

"Red Detachment of Women" — A244

1968   Perf. 11½x11; 11 (983, 990)
982   A242   8f shown
              (56x36mm)   250.00   55.00
983   A242   8f "The Red Lantern," vert.   250.00   55.00
984   A243   8f shown   250.00   55.00
985   A243   8f "Shachiapang"
              (women & soldier)   250.00   55.00
986   A243   8f "On the Dock"   250.00   55.00
987   A243   8f "Taking Bandits' Fort"   250.00   55.00
988   A244   8f shown   250.00   55.00
989   A244   8f "The White-
              haired Girl"   250.00   55.00
990   A242   8f Mao with
              Orchestra &
              Chorus
              (50x36mm)   250.00   55.00
Nos. 982-990 (9)   2,250.   495.00

Mao's direction for revolutionary literature and art. Issued: #982-987, Jan. 30; #988-990, May 1.

"Unite still more closely . . ." — A245

1968, May 31   Photo.   Perf. 11
991   A245   8f red, gold & red
              brn   375.00   125.00
Mao Tse-tung's statement of support of Afro-Americans.

Statement about Cultural Revolution A246

Directives of Chairman Mao: No. 993, Experiences of Revolutionary Committee. No. 994, Leadership role of Revolutionary Committee. No. 995, Basic principle of reform. No. 996, Purpose of Cultural Revolution.

1968, July 20   Photo.   Perf. 11½
No. of Lines Over Signature
992   A246   8f shown   550.00   375.00
993   A246   8f 5   550.00   375.00
994   A246   8f 4½   550.00   375.00
995   A246   8f 4   550.00   375.00
996   A246   8f 8   550.00   375.00
   a.   Strip of 5, #992-996   8,500.   4,250.
Nos. 992-996 (5)   2,750.   1,875.
Value for No. 996a is for an unfolded strip.

Lin Piao's Statement, July 26, 1965 — A247

1968, Aug. 1   Engr. & Photo.
997   A247   8f red, gold & blk   21.00   10.00
Chinese People's Liberation Army, 41st anniv.

Mao Tse-tung Going to An Yuan, 1921 A248

1968, Aug. 1   Perf. 11x11½
998   A248   8f multicolored   250.00   40.00
Shade varieties include varying amount of red in clouds.

A 8f stamp was prepared in Sept. 1968, showing black writing on a red background, regarding Chairman Mao's inscriptions to Japanese Labor Friends. It was not issued, but a few examples have reached the marketplace. Value, $175,000.

Directive of Chairman Mao — A249

1968, Nov. 30   Perf. 11½
999   A249   8f red & blk brn   350.00   85.00

China Map, Worker, Farmer and Soldier 999A

1968, Nov.   Photo.   Perf. 11½x11
999A   A249a   8f red, bl &
              bis   100,000.   100,000.

Map inscribed: "The entire nation is red." Issued in Canton and quickly withdrawn because Taiwan appears white instead of red. No. 999A most often is found repaired. Values are for sound, unrepaired examples. Counterfeits exist.

Two values were prepared to celebrate the Great Victory of the Cultural Revolution but were not issued, although a few examples have entered the marketplace. Values for sound stamps: 8f, Mao Tse-tung and Lin Piao, $300,000; 8f, map and workers, $475,000.

Woman, Miner and Soldier Holding Little Red Book A250

1968, Dec. 26   Perf. 11x11½
1000   A250   8f multicolored   67.50   10.00

Canceled-to-order
From about this point on stamps are valued postally used.

Yangtze Bridge, Nanking A251

Road across Bridge — A252

No. 1003, Side view. 10f, Aerial view.

Lithographed,
Perf. 11½x11 (A251);
Photogravure,
Perf. 11½ (A252)

1969
Without Gum
1001   A251   4f multicolored   8.00   2.25
1002   A252   8f multicolored   60.00   6.75
1003   A252   8f multicolored   14.00   6.75
1004   A251   10f multicolored   5.00   2.25
Nos. 1001-1004 (4)   87.00   18.00
Inauguration of Yangtze Bridge at Nanking on Dec. 29, 1968.

Singer and Pianist A253

(Piano Music from the Opera, "The Red Lantern"): #1006, Woman singer and pianist.

1969, Aug.   Photo.   Perf. 11x11½
Without Gum
1005   A253   8f multicolored   17.50   9.00
1006   A253   8f multicolored   115.00   15.00

Harvest A254

1969, Oct.
Without Gum
1007   A254   4f shown   16.00   4.50
   a.   Brown omitted   40.00   40.00
1008   A254   8f Two harvest-
              ers   16.00   4.50
1009   A254   8f Harvesters
              with Little
              Red Books   92.50   17.50
1010   A254   10f Red Cross
              Worker ex-
              amining baby   9.50   4.50
Nos. 1007-1010 (4)   134.00   31.00
Agriculture students.

Armed Forces and Slogan — A255

Guarding the Coast — A256

Designs: No. 1013, 43f, Snow patrol, vert.

1969, Oct.   Perf. 11½
Without Gum
1011   A255   8f red & multi   50.00   15.00
   a.   Bayonets omitted   300.00   85.00
1012   A256   8f blue & multi   10.00   5.00
1013   A256   8f blue & multi   10.00   5.00
1014   A256   35f black & multi   10.00   5.00
1015   A256   43f black & multi   10.00   5.00
Nos. 1011-1015 (5)   90.00   35.00
Defense of Chen Pao-tao (Damansky Islands) in Ussuri River.

Farm Woman A257

Designs: 8f, Foundry worker. 10f, Soldier.

1969, Dec.   Perf. 10; 11½
Without Gum

1016	A257	4f ver & dk pur	.75	.45
a.		Perf 11½	2.75	1.25
1017	A257	8f ver & dk brn	1.75	.65
a.		Perf 11½	2.50	1.25
1018	A257	10f ver & blk	2.50	1.40
a.		Perf 11½	—	900.00
		Nos. 1016-1018 (3)	5.00	2.50

Perforation
Nos. 1016-1018 and some succeeding issues bear two kinds of perforation: clean (Peking) and rough (Shanghai).

Building — A258

Communist Party Building, Shanghai A259

Agriculture Building, Canton — A260

Foundry Worker — A261

Two types of 8f Gate of Heavenly Peace:
I — Strong, definite halo around sun.
II — Halo missing, white shades gradually into red.

1969-72   Photo.   Perf. 10, 11½
Without Gum

1019	A258	1f shown	.20	.20
1020	A259	1½f shown	.80	.80
a.		Perf. 11½	5.50	4.00
1021	A260	2f shown	.20	.20
1022	A260	3f 1929 Party Day House, Pu Tien	.20	.20
1023	A260	4f Mao's Home and Office, Yunnan	.20	.20
1024	A261	5f Woman Tractor Driver	1.75	.75
1025	A260	8f Gate of Heavenly Peace, type II	.65	.35
a.		Type I	2.50	1.25
1026	A259	8f Heroes Monument	1.50	1.50
a.		Perf. 11½	4.50	3.50
1027	A260	8f Pagoda Hill, Yenan	2.25	4.00
1028	A260	8f Gate of Heavenly Peace (no sun)	.20	.20
1029	A260	10f Monument, Tsu Ping	.30	.20
1030	A259	20f Conference Hall, Tsunyi	4.00	1.75
a.		Perf. 11½	9.00	5.50
1031	A260	20f Highway ('72)	.90	.50
1032	A260	22f Shao Shan Village, Birthplace of Mao	.75	.50
1033	A260	35f Conference Hall	1.00	.50
1034	A260	43f Chingkang Peaks	1.50	.50
1035	A259	50f as 4f, different view	1.50	1.40
1036	A260	52f People's Hall, Peking	2.25	.50
1037	A261	$1 shown ('70)	5.00	2.75
		Nos. 1019-1037 (19)	25.15	17.00

Kin Hsün-hua A262

Mounted Patrol — A263

1970, Jan.   Without Gum   Perf. 11½
1045	A262	8f red & black	30.00	16.00
a.		8f red & gray brown	25.00	12.00

Death of Kin Hsün-hua in Kirin border flood.

1970, Aug. 1
Without Gum
1046	A263	8f yel grn & multi	17.50	7.50

People's Liberation Army, 43rd anniv.

Commemorative stamps from Nos. 1047 to 1142 and 1211-1214, carry a cumulative number in parentheses at lower left and the year at lower right. Where such numbers help to identify, they are quoted in parentheses.

Cpl. Yang Tse-jung — A264

Ensemble A265

1970, Aug. 1   Perf. 11½x11, 11x11½
Without Gum
1047	A264	8f shown (1)	60.00	10.00
1048	A264	8f Armed guards (2)	25.00	3.25
1049	A264	8f Yang leaping through forest (3)	35.00	7.50
1050	A265	8f shown (4)	90.00	13.00
1051	A265	8f Yang in folk costume (5)	25.00	3.25
1052	A265	8f Four actors (6)	35.00	10.00
		Nos. 1047-1052 (6)	270.00	47.00

Scenes from opera "Taking Tiger Mountain by Strategy." Nos. 1048, 1052, horizontal.

Frontier Guard A266

1971, Jan.   Litho.   Perf. 10
Without Gum
1053	A266	4f multicolored	3.00	1.75
a.		Perf. 11½	2.25	1.50
b.		Perf. 11½x10	3.50	2.75
c.		Perf. 10x11½	4.50	3.25

Banner of the Commune A267

Street Battle, Paris, 1871 A268

10f, Proclamation of the Commune. 22f, Rally.

Perf. 11½x11, 11x11½
1971, Mar. 18   Litho. & Engr.
Without Gum
1054	A267	4f sal & multi	90.00	25.00
1055	A268	8f ver, pink & brn	400.00	65.00
1056	A267	10f ver, pink & dk brn	35.00	14.00
1057	A268	22f ver, pink & dk brn	20.00	12.00
		Nos. 1054-1057 (4)	545.00	116.00

Centenary of the Paris Commune.

Redrawn Building Type of 1961
Designs: 2f, 3f, August 1 building, Nanchang. 4f, 52f, Gate of Heavenly Peace, Peking. 10f, 20f, Pagoda Hill, Yenan.

1971, July 1   Litho.   Perf. 11x11½
Size: 21x16mm
Without Gum
1059	A152	2f slate green	1.50	.75
1060	A152	3f sepia	1.50	1.25
1061	A152	4f brt pink	5.00	2.00
1062	A152	10f brt rose lil	1.50	1.25
1063	A152	20f dk blue grn	2.75	1.25
1064	A152	52f orange	1.50	1.50
		Nos. 1059-1064 (6)	13.75	8.00

Paper of Nos. 1059-1064 is white. That of Nos. 647-654 is toned.

Communist Party Building, Shanghai — A269

People and Factories — A270

Designs: No. 1068, Peasant Movement Training Institute. No. 1069, Ching Kang Peaks. No. 1070, Conference Building, Tsunyi. No. 1071, Pagoda Hill, Yenan. No. 1073, People and People's Hall, Peking. No. 1074, People and Pagoda Hill, Yenan. 22f, Gate of Heavenly Peace, Peking.

1971, July 1   Photo.   Perf. 11½
Red and Gold Frame
Without Gum
1067	A269	4f vermilion (12)	15.00	7.50
1068	A269	4f brt grn (13)	15.00	7.50
1069	A269	8f grnsh bl & red (14)	20.00	7.50
1070	A269	8f ol blk (15)	50.00	12.00
1071	A269	8f bis, grn & red (16)	30.00	10.00
1072	A270	8f yel, red & multi (18)	30.00	8.00
1073	A270	8f yel, red & multi (19)	30.00	8.00
1074	A270	8f yel, red & multi (20)	30.00	8.00
a.		Strip of 3, #1072-1074	500.00	125.00
1075	A269	22f red, gold & brn (17)	40.00	8.00
		Nos. 1067-1075 (9)	260.00	76.50

50th anniv. of the Chinese Communist Party. No. 1074a has a continuous design and is valued as an unfolded strip.

Chinese Welcome A271

Enver Hoxha — A272

#1077, Chinese & African players. #1078, Chinese & African girl players. 43f, Games' emblem.

1971, Nov. 3   Litho.   Perf. 11½
Without Gum
1076	A271	8f lil rose & multi	25.00	6.00
1077	A271	8f lt yellow & multi	25.00	6.00
1078	A271	8f dk grn & multi	25.00	6.00
1079	A271	43f grn, gold & org	120.00	20.00
		Nos. 1076-1079 (4)	195.00	38.00

Afro-Asian Table Tennis Games, Peking.

1971, Nov. 3   Photo.   Perf. 11
#1081, Party's birthplace. #1082, Albanian flag. 52f, Albanian partisans, horiz.

Without Gum
1080	A272	8f Prus blue & multi	17.50	5.75
1081	A272	8f buff & multi	10.00	3.50
1082	A272	8f red, yel & multi	10.00	3.50
1083	A272	52f lt blue & multi	32.50	8.00
		Nos. 1080-1083 (4)	70.00	20.75

30th anniversary of the founding of Albanian Communist Party.

Yenan Pagoda and 1942 Meeting House A273

1972, May 23   Photo.   Perf. 11
Without Gum
1084 A273 8f shown (33)   24.00   9.00
1085 A273 8f Uniformed choir
                (34)   24.00   9.00
1086 A273 8f "Brother & Sis-
                ter" (35)   24.00   9.00
1087 A273 8f Outdoor per-
                formance (36)   24.00   9.00
1088 A273 8f "The Red Sig-
                nal Lantern"
                (37)   24.00   9.00
1089 A273 8f Dancer from
                "The Red
                Company of
                Women" (38)   24.00   9.00
      Nos. 1084-1089 (6)   144.00 54.00

30th anniversary of the publication of the
Discussions on Literature and Art at the Yenan
Forum.

Various Ball Games — A274

Workers'
Gymnastics
A275

1972, June 10
1090 A274 8f shown (39)   50.00   6.00
1091 A275 8f shown (40)   30.00   6.00
1092 A275 8f Tug of war (41)   30.00   6.00
1093 A275 8f Mountain climb-
                ers and tents
                (42)   30.00   6.00
1094 A275 8f Children diving
                & swimming
                (43)   30.00   6.00
      Nos. 1090-1094 (5)   170.00 30.00

10th anniversary of Mao Tse-tung's edict on
physical culture.

Ocean Freighter Fenglei — A276

1972, July 10   Photo.   Perf. 11½
Without Gum
1095 A276 8f shown (29)   85.00 25.00
1096 A276 8f Tanker Taching
                No. 30 (30)   40.00   8.50
1097 A276 8f Cargo-passen-
                ger ship
                Changzeng
                (31)   40.00   8.50
1098 A276 8f Dredger
                Xienfeng (32)   70.00 17.50
      Nos. 1095-1098 (4)   235.00 59.50

Table
Tennis
Players'
Welcome
A277

1972, Sept. 2   Perf. 11½x11, 11x11½
Without Gum
1099 A277 8f Championship
                emblem, vert.
                (45)   27.50   5.25
1100 A277 8f shown (46)   27.50   5.25
1101 A277 8f Table tennis
                (47)   27.50   5.25

1102 A277 22f Women from
                 different
                 countries,
                 vert. (48)   27.50   5.25
      Nos. 1099-1102 (4)   110.00 21.00
First Asian table tennis championships.

Wang Chin-   Workers on Cliffs
hsi — A278   along
                   Canal — A279

Engraved and Photogravure
1972, Dec. 25   Perf. 11½x11
1103 A278 8f multicolored (44) 72.50   5.00
Wang Chin-hsi, the Iron Man, fighter for the
working class.

1972, Dec. 30
#1105, Canal flowing through tunnel. #1106,
Bridge. #1107, Canal along cliffs.
1104 A279 8f multicolored
                (49)   42.50 10.00
1105 A279 8f multicolored
                (50)   42.50 10.00
1106 A279 8f multicolored
                (51)   42.50 10.00
1107 A279 8f multicolored
                (52)   42.50 10.00
      Nos. 1104-1107 (4)   170.00 40.00
Construction of Red Flag Canal, Linhsien
county, Honan.

Giant
Panda — A280

Designs: Pandas in various positions. The
8f stamps are horizontal.

Perf. 11½x11, 11x11½
1973, Jan. 15   Photo.
Designs in Black and Red
1108 A280 4f lt yel grn (61)   12.50   6.00
1109 A280 8f buff (59)   12.50   6.00
1110 A280 8f lt tan (60)   12.50   6.00
1111 A280 10f pale green
                (58)   110.00 27.50
1112 A280 20f pale bl gray
                (57)   70.00 27.50
1113 A280 43f pale lilac (62)   27.50 12.00
      Nos. 1108-1113 (6)   245.00 85.00

1973, Mar. 8   Photo.   Perf. 11½x11
1114 A281 8f shown (63)   21.00   6.75
1115 A281 8f Committee mem-
                ber (64)   21.00   6.75
1116 A281 8f Telephone line
                worker (65)   21.00   6.75
      Nos. 1114-1116 (3)   63.00 20.25

Intl. Working Women's Day. Designs are
after paintings from an exhib. for 30th anniv. of
the Yenan Forum on Literature and Art.

Woman Coal
Miner — A281

Dancing
Girl — A282

1973, June 1   Photo.   Perf. 11
1117 A282 8f shown (86)   2.00   1.50
1118 A282 8f Musician, boy
                (87)   2.00   1.50
1119 A282 8f Girl with scarf
                (88)   2.00   1.50
1120 A282 8f Boy with tam-
                bourine (89)   2.00   1.50
1121 A282 8f Girl with drum
                (90)   2.00   1.50
  a. Strip of 5, #1117-1121   47.50 25.00
      Nos. 1117-1121 (5)   10.00   7.50
Values for No. 1121a are for an unfolded
strip.

Tournament
Emblem — A283

1973, Aug. 25   Photo.   Perf. 11½
#1123, Visitors from Asia, Africa and Latin
America arriving by plane. #1124, Woman
player. 22f, African, Asian & Latin American
women.
1122 A283 8f multicolored
                (91)   11.50   2.25
1123 A283 8f multicolored
                (92)   11.50   2.25
1124 A283 8f multicolored
                (93)   11.50   2.25
1125 A283 22f multicolored
                (94)   11.50   2.25
      Nos. 1122-1125 (4)   46.00   9.00

Asian, African and Latin American Table
Tennis Friendship Invitational Tournament.

The White-
haired
Girl — A284

Designs: Scenes from the ballet "The White-
haired Girl." Nos. 1126, 1129 vert.
1973, Sept. 25   Photo.   Perf. 11½
1126 A284 8f multicolored
                (53)   40.00   7.50
1127 A284 8f multicolored
                (54)   80.00 15.00
1128 A284 8f multicolored
                (55)   40.00   7.50
1129 A284 8f multicolored
                (56)   40.00   7.50
      Nos. 1126-1129 (4)   200.00 37.50

Fair Building, Canton — A285

1973, Oct. 15   Photo.   Perf. 11
1130 A285 8f multicolored (95) 21.00   3.50
Export Commodities Fall Fair, Canton.

Teapot with Blue
Phoenix
Design — A286

Excavated Works of Art: No. 1132, Silver
pot with horse design. No. 1133, Black pottery
horse. No. 1134, Woman, clay figurine. No.
1135, Carved stone pillar base. No. 1136, Galloping bronze horse. No. 1137, Bronze inkwell
(toad). No. 1138, Bronze lamp, Chang Hsin
Palace. No. 1139, Bronze tripod. No. 1140,
Square bronze pot. 20f, Bronze wine vessel.
52f, Painted red clay tripod.

1973, Nov. 20   Perf. 11½
1131 A286 4f ol bis & multi
                (66)   4.00   .70
1132 A286 4f ver & multi (67)   4.00   .70
1133 A286 8f yel grn & multi
                (68)   4.00   .70
1134 A286 8f brt rose & multi
                (69)   4.00   .70
1135 A286 8f lt vio & multi
                (70)   4.00   .70
1136 A286 8f yel bis & multi
                (71)   4.00   .70
1137 A286 8f lt bl & multi (72) 4.00   .70
1138 A286 8f gray & multi
                (73)   4.00   .70
1139 A286 10f yel bis & multi
                (74)   4.00   .70
1140 A286 10f dp org & multi
                (75)   4.00   .70
1141 A286 20f lil & multi (76)   5.00   1.40
1142 A286 52f grn & multi (77)   6.00   2.75
      Nos. 1131-1142 (12)   51.00 11.15

Marginal Markings

Marginal inscriptions on stamps of
1974-91 start at lower left with "J" for
commemoratives and "T" for "special
issues," followed by three numbers indicating (a) set sequence for the year, (b)
total of stamps in set, and (c) number of
stamp within set. At right appears the
year date. Listings include the "c" number parenthetically. The "a" number is
included only when it will help identify
stamps not illustrated.

Example: T26 (6-3), the 3rd stamp of
6 from the 26th special set. Set numbers and or positions will be shown only
when they help identify a stamp. An
illustrated single stamp set will not have
these numbers in the listings.

Woman
Gymnast — A287

Designs: No. 1144, Gymnast on rings. No.
1145, Aerial split over balance beam, woman.
No. 1146, Gymnast on parallel bars. No. 1147,
Uneven bars, woman. No. 1148, Gymnast on
horse. T.1.

1974, Jan. 1   Photo.   Perf. 11½x11
1143 A287 8f lt grn & multi (1) 11.50   3.75
1144 A287 8f lt vio & multi (2) 11.50   3.75
1145 A287 8f lt blue & multi (3) 11.50   3.75
1146 A287 8f sal & multi (4)   16.50   4.75
1147 A287 8f yel & multi (5)   11.50   4.75
1148 A287 8f lil rose & multi
                (6)   16.50   4.75
      Nos. 1143-1148 (6)   79.00 25.50

Girls Twirling Bamboo
Diabolos — A288

Designs: No. 1149, Lion Dance, vert. No.
1150, Handstand on chairs, vert. No. 1152,

Men balancing jar. No. 1153, Plate spinning, vert. No. 1154, Twirling umbrella, vert. T.2.

1974, Jan. 21   **Perf. 11**
1149	A288	8f brn & multi (1)	8.50 3.00
1150	A288	8f Prus bl & multi (2)	8.50 3.00
1151	A288	8f lilac & multi (3)	8.50 3.00
1152	A288	8f dull bl & multi (4)	8.50 3.00
1153	A288	8f ol grn & multi (5)	8.50 3.00
1154	A288	8f gray & multi (6)	8.50 3.00
		Nos. 1149-1154 (6)	51.00 18.00

Traditional acrobatics.

Shao Shan — A289

Transportation by Railroad — A290

1½f, Site of 1st National Communist Party Congress. 2f, Peasant Movement Institute, Kwangchow. 3f, Headquarters of Nanchang Uprising. 4f, Great Hall of the People, Peking. 5f, View of Wen Chia Shih. 8f, Tien An Men. 10f, Tzeping in Chingkang Mountains. 20f, Site of Kutien Meeting. 22f, Tsunyi Conference site. 35f, Yenan (bridge). 43f, Hsi Pai Ho, Communist Party meeting site. 50f, Fairy Cave, Lushan. 52f, Monument to People's Heroes. $2, Trucks on mountain road.

1973-74   **Litho.**   **Perf. 11**
Without Gum
1163	A289	1f sl grn & pale grn	.60 .30
1164	A289	1½f car & buff	.60 .30
1165	A289	2f dk blue & pale grn	.60 .30
1166	A289	3f dk ol & yel	.60 .30
1167	A289	4f red & yel	.60 .30
1168	A289	5f brn & lt yel	.60 .30
1169	A289	8f dull mag & buff	.60 .30
a.		Perf. 11½x12	10.00
1170	A289	10f blue & pink	.60 .30
1171	A289	20f dk red & buff	1.50 .30
1172	A289	22f vio & lt yel	2.10 .35
1173	A289	35f mar & lt yel	3.00 .95
1174	A289	43f red brn & buff	3.75 1.50
1175	A289	50f dk blue & pink	4.75 2.50
1176	A289	52f sepia & buff	5.50 3.00

Photogravure & Engraved
1177	A290	$1 multicolored ('73)	2.25 .40
1178	A290	$2 multicolored	3.25 .60
		Nos. 1163-1178 (16)	30.90 12.00

Capital Stadium — A290a

Design: 8f, Hotel Peking.

1974, Dec. 1   **Photo.**   **Perf. 11**
Without Gum
1179	A290a	4f black & yel grn	.35 .20
1180	A290a	8f black & ultra	.45 .20

"Veteran Secretary" — A291   Well Diggers — A292

Designs: Nos. 1183-1186 horizontal. T.3.

1974, Apr. 20   **Photo.**   **Perf. 11**
1181	A291	8f shown (1)	5.50 2.25
1182	A292	8f shown (2)	5.50 2.25
1183	A291	8f Spring hoeing (3)	5.50 2.25
1184	A291	8f Farmers (4)	5.50 2.25
1185	A292	8f Farm (5)	6.50 2.75
1186	A291	8f Bumper crops (6)	6.50 2.75
		Nos. 1181-1186 (6)	35.00 14.50

Paintings by farmers of Huhsien County, shown at exhibition in Peking.

Mailman on Motorcycle — A293

1974, May 15   **Photo.**   **Perf. 11**
1187	A293	8f shown (1)	8.00 3.75
1188	A293	8f People of the world (2)	8.00 3.75
1189	A293	8f Great Wall (3)	10.00 3.75
		Nos. 1187-1189 (3)	26.00 11.25

Centenary of the UPU. J.1.

Barefoot Doctor Inoculating Children A294

Designs (Barefoot Doctors): No. 1191, Crossing stream at night to reach patient, vert. No. 1192, Gathering herbs, vert. No. 1193, Acupuncture treatment for farmer in the field.

Perf. 11x11½, 11½x11
1974, June 26   **Photo.**
1190	A294	8f multicolored (82)	10.00 1.50
1191	A294	8f multicolored (83)	20.00 2.25
1192	A294	8f multicolored (84)	16.50 1.50
1193	A294	8f multicolored (85)	10.00 1.50
		Nos. 1190-1193 (4)	56.50 6.75

Steel Worker Wang Chin-hsi — A295

#1195, Workers studying Mao's writings around campfire. #1196, Drilling for oil in winter. #1197, Scientific industrial management. #1198, Oil derricks and farms. T.4.

1974, Sept. 30   **Photo.**   **Perf. 11**
1194	A295	8f multicolored (5-1)	5.25 1.10
1195	A295	8f multicolored (5-2)	5.25 1.10
1196	A295	8f multicolored (5-3)	5.25 1.10
1197	A295	8f multicolored (5-4)	6.00 1.10
1198	A295	8f multicolored (5-5)	6.00 1.10
		Nos. 1194-1198 (5)	27.75 5.50

Workers of Taching as examples of achievement.

Members of Tachai Commune — A296

#1200, Farmers leveling mountains and fields in winter. #1201, Scientific farming. #1202, Trucks carrying surplus harvest. #1203, Young workers with banner. T.5.

1974, Sept. 30
1199	A296	8f multi (5-1)	6.00 1.10
1200	A296	8f multi (5-2)	2.50 1.10
1201	A296	8f multi (5-3)	6.00 1.10
1202	A296	8f multi (5-4)	2.50 1.10
1203	A296	8f multi (5-5)	2.50 1.10
		Nos. 1199-1203 (5)	19.50 5.50

Farmers of Tachai as examples of achievement.

Arms of Republic and Members of Ethnic Groups — A297

1974, Oct. 1
1204	A297	8f multi (1-1)	14.00 3.75

Taching Steel Worker — A298

Designs: No. 1206, Tachai farm woman. No. 1207, Soldier, planes and ships. J.3.

1974, Oct. 1
1205	A298	8f multi (3-1)	3.75 1.75
1206	A298	8f multi (3-2)	3.75 1.75
1207	A298	8f multi (3-3)	3.75 1.75
a.		Strip of 3, #1205-1207	15.00 11.00

People's Republic of China, 25th anniv. Values for No. 1207a are for an unfolded strip.

Export Commodities Fair Building, Canton — A299

1974, Oct. 15
1208	A299	8f multicolored	9.50 1.75

Chinese Export Commodities Fair, Canton.

Guerrillas' Monument, Permet, Albania — A300

Albanian Patriots and Coat of Arms — A301

1974, Nov. 29   **Photo.**   **Perf. 11½x11**
1209	A300	8f multicolored	4.00 1.60
1210	A301	8f multicolored	4.00 1.60

Albania's liberation, 30th anniversary.

Water-cooled Generator — A302

Industrial Products: No. 1212, Motorized rice sprouts transplanter. No. 1213, Universal cylindrical grinding machine. No. 1214, Open-air rock drill, vert. All dated 1973.

Photogravure and Engraved
1974, Dec. 23   **Perf. 11**
1211	A302	8f vio & multi (78)	75.00 15.00
1212	A302	8f yel grn & multi (79)	90.00 30.00
1213	A302	8f ver & multi (80)	75.00 15.00
1214	A302	8f blue & multi (81)	100.00 30.00
		Nos. 1211-1214 (4)	340.00 90.00

Congress Delegates — A303

Designs: No. 1216, Red flags, constitution and flowers. No. 1217, Worker, farmer and soldier, agriculture and industry.

1975, Jan. 25   **Photo.**   **Perf. 11½**
1215	A303	8f gold & multi (3-1)	13.50 3.50
1216	A303	8f gold & multi (3-2)	13.50 3.50
1217	A303	8f gold & multi (3-3)	27.50 4.50
		Nos. 1215-1217 (3)	54.50 11.50

Fourth National People's Congress, Peking.

Teacher Studying Revolutionary Works — A304

#1219, Teacher, children and horse. #1220, Outdoors class. #1221, Class held in boat. T.9.

1975, Mar. 8   **Photo.**   **Perf. 11**
1218	A304	8f multi (4-1)	13.50 5.00
1219	A304	8f multi (4-2)	27.50 10.00
1220	A304	8f multi (4-3)	27.50 5.00
1221	A304	8f multi (4-4)	13.50 5.00
		Nos. 1218-1221 (4)	82.00 25.00

Rural women teachers and for International Working Women's Day.

"Broadsword," Encounter Position — A305

#1223, Exercise with 2 swords (woman). #1224, Graceful boxing (woman). #1225, Man leaping with spear. #1226, Woman holding fighting staff. 43f, 2 women with spears against man with 3-section staff.

1975, June 10   **Photo.**   **Perf. 11x11½**
Size: 39x29mm
1222	A305	8f (6-1)	6.50 3.00
1223	A305	8f (6-2)	6.50 3.00
1224	A305	8f (6-3)	6.50 3.00
1225	A305	8f (6-4)	6.50 3.00
1226	A305	8f (6-5)	6.50 3.00

Size: 59x29mm

1227 A305 43f red & multi (6-6) 6.50 6.00
Nos. 1222-1227 (6) 39.00 21.00

Wushu ("Kung Fu"), self-defense exercises. Tête bêche in sheets of 50 (5x10). Value, set of pairs $75.

Mass Judgment and Criticisms — A306

No. 1229, Brigade leader writing wall newspaper. No. 1230, Study and criticism on battlefield, horiz. No. 1231, Former "slave" led into battle by criticism of Lin Piao and Confucius, horiz. T.8.

Perf. 11½x11, 11x11½

1975, Aug. 20 **Photo.**
1228 A306 8f red & multi (4-1) 13.50 6.75
1229 A306 8f red & multi (4-2) 19.00 6.75
1230 A306 8f red & multi (4-3) 13.50 6.75
1231 A306 8f red & multi (4-4) 19.00 6.75
Nos. 1228-1231 (4) 65.00 27.00

Campaign to encourage criticism of Lin Piao and Confucius.

Athletes Studying Theory of Dictatorship of Proletariat — A307

3rd National Sports Meet: No. 1232, Women athletes leading parade, vert. No. 1234, Women volleyball players. No. 1235, Runner, soldier, farmer and worker, vert. No. 1236, Young athlete and various sports. No. 1237, Athletes of various races and horse race. 35f, Children and diving tower, vert. J.6.

1975, Sept. 12 **Photo.** **Perf. 11½**
1232 A307 8f multi (7-1) 3.50 .90
1233 A307 8f multi (7-2) 3.50 .90
1234 A307 8f multi (7-3) 3.50 .90
1235 A307 8f multi (7-4) 3.50 .90
1236 A307 8f multi (7-5) 3.50 .90
1237 A307 8f multi (7-6) 3.50 .90
1238 A307 35f multi (7-7) 4.75 4.25
Nos. 1232-1238 (7) 25.75 9.65

Mountaineers A308

Mt. Everest A309

Design: No. 1240, Mountaineers raising Chinese flag on summit, horiz. T.15.

1975 **Photo.** **Perf. 11½x11, 11x11½**
1239 A308 8f multi (3-2) 2.00 .90
1240 A308 8f multi (3-3) 1.25 .45
1241 A309 43f multi (3-1) 2.00 .90
Nos. 1239-1241 (3) 5.25 2.25

Chinese Mt. Everest expedition.

Agricultural Workers with Book — A310

#1243, Workers carrying load. #1244, Woman driving harvester combine. J.7.

1975, Oct. 1 **Perf. 11½**
1242 A310 8f multi (3-1) 8.00 1.50
1243 A310 8f multi (3-2) 8.00 1.50
1244 A310 8f multi (3-3) 15.00 1.75
Nos. 1242-1244 (3) 31.00 4.75

National Conference to promote learning from Tachai's achievements in agriculture.

Girl Giving Boy Red Scarf — A311

Designs (Children): No. 1246, Putting up wall posters criticizing Lin Piao and Confucius. No. 1247, Studying. No. 1248, Harvesting. 52f, Physical training. T.14.

1975, Dec. 1 **Photo.** **Perf. 11½**
1245 A311 8f multi (5-1) 3.75 1.25
1246 A311 8f multi (5-2) 3.75 1.25
1247 A311 8f multi (5-3) 3.75 1.25
1248 A311 8f multi (5-4) 3.75 1.25
1249 A311 52f multi (5-5) 6.50 3.75
Nos. 1245-1249 (5) 21.50 8.75

Moral, intellectual and physical progress of Chinese children.

Woman Plowing Rice Field A312

#1251, Mechanized rice planting. #1252, Drainage and irrigation. #1253, Woman spraying insecticide over cotton field. #1254, Combine. T.13.

1975, Dec. 15 **Perf. 11**
1250 A312 8f multi (5-1) 4.25 1.50
1251 A312 8f multi (5-2) 4.25 1.50
1252 A312 8f multi (5-3) 4.25 1.50
1253 A312 8f multi (5-4) 3.75 1.50
1254 A312 8f multi (5-5) 3.75 1.50
Nos. 1250-1254 (5) 20.25 7.50

Priority program of farm mechanization.

Farmland and Irrigation Canal — A313

Designs of Nos. 1255-1270 numbered J.8.

1976 **Photo.** **Perf. 11½**
1255 A313 8f shown (16-1) 8.50 2.50
1256 A313 8f Irrigation canal (16-2) 8.50 2.50
1257 A313 8f Fertilizer plant (16-3) 8.50 2.50
1258 A313 8f Textile plant (16-4) 8.50 2.50
1259 A313 8f Anshan Iron and Steel Co. (16-5) 8.50 2.50
1260 A313 8f Coal freight trains (16-6) 8.50 2.50
1261 A313 8f Hydroelectric station (16-7) 8.50 2.50
1262 A313 8f Ship building (16-8) 8.50 2.50

1263 A313 8f Oil industry (16-9) 8.50 2.50
1264 A313 8f Pipe line and port (16-10) 8.50 2.50
1265 A313 8f Train on viaduct (16-11) 8.50 2.50
1266 A313 8f Scientific research (16-12) 17.50 5.00
1267 A313 8f Classroom (16-13) 9.50 2.50
1268 A313 8f Health Center (16-14) 9.50 2.50
1269 A313 8f Apartment houses (16-15) 9.50 2.50
1270 A313 8f Department store (16-16) 17.50 5.00
Nos. 1255-1270 (16) 157.00 45.00

Nos. 1255-1270 commemorate fulfillment of 4th Five-year Plan. Issued: Nos. 1255-1259, 2/20; Nos. 1260-1264, 4/9; Nos. 1265-1270, 6/12.

Heart Surgery with Acupuncture Anesthesia — A314

Operating Room and: #1272, Man driving tractor with severed arm restored. #1273, Man exercising broken arm in cast. #1274, Patient threading needle after cataract operation. T.12.

1976, Apr. 9 **Photo.** **Perf. 11½**
1271 A314 8f brn & multi (4-1) 7.25 1.75
1272 A314 8f yel grn & multi (4-2) 15.00 2.75
1273 A314 8f bl grn & multi (4-3) 7.25 1.75
1274 A314 8f vio bl & multi (4-4) 7.25 1.75
Nos. 1271-1274 (4) 36.75 8.00

Achievements in medical and health services.

Students in May 7 School — A315

Designs: No. 1276, Students as farm workers. No. 1277, Production brigade. J.9.

1976, May 7 **Photo.** **Perf. 11½**
1275 A315 8f multi (3-1) 4.00 1.60
1276 A315 8f multi (3-2) 4.00 1.60
1277 A315 8f multi (3-3) 4.00 1.60
Nos. 1275-1277 (3) 12.00 4.80

Chairman Mao's May 7 Directive, 10th anniv.

Mass Training in Swimming — A316

No. 1279, Swimmers crossing Yangtze River. No. 1280, Swimmers walking into the surf. J.10.

1976, July 16 **Photo.** **Perf. 11½**
Size: 47x27mm
1278 A316 8f multi (3-1) 7.50 1.60
Size: 35x27mm
1279 A316 8f multi (3-2) 7.50 1.60
1280 A316 8f multi (3-3) 7.50 1.60
Nos. 1278-1280 (3) 22.50 4.80

Chairman Mao's swim in Yangtze River, 10th anniversary.

Workers, Peasants and Soldiers Going to College — A317

#1282, Classroom. #1283, Instruction on construction site. #1284, Computer room. #1285, Graduates returning home. T.18.

1976, Sept. 6 **Photo.** **Perf. 11½**
1281 A317 8f multi (5-1) 7.00 1.30
1282 A317 8f multi (5-2) 7.00 1.30
1283 A317 8f multi (5-3) 11.50 1.30
1284 A317 8f multi (5-4) 11.50 1.30
1285 A317 8f multi (5-5) 7.00 1.30
Nos. 1281-1285 (5) 44.00 6.50

Success of proletarian education system.

Power Line Repair by Woman — A318

#1287, Insulator repair. #1288, Cherry picker. #1289, Transformer repair. T.16.

1976, Sept. 15
1286 A318 8f multi (4-1) 7.50 2.00
1287 A318 8f multi (4-2) 14.50 2.50
1288 A318 8f multi (4-3) 3.75 1.75
1289 A318 8f multi (4-4) 3.75 1.75
Nos. 1286-1289 (4) 29.50 8.00

Maintenance of high power lines.

Lu Hsun A319

#1291, Lu Hsun sick, writing in bed. #1292, Lu Hsun with worker, soldier and peasant. J.11.

Photo. & Engr.
1976, Oct. 19 **Perf. 11x11½**
1290 A319 8f multi (3-1) 5.00 2.25
Photo.
1291 A319 8f multi (3-2) 14.00 3.00
1292 A319 8f multi (3-3) 6.00 2.25
Nos. 1290-1292 (3) 25.00 7.50

Lu Hsun (1881-1936), writer and revolutionary leader.

Old Farmer Tying Towel on Student's Head — A320

Designs: No. 1294, Student teaching farm woman, horiz. No. 1295, Students climbing mountain for new water resources. No. 1296, Student testing wheat, horiz. 10f, Student feeding lamb. 20f, Frontier guards, horiz. T.17.

1976, Dec. 22 **Photo.** **Perf. 11½**
1293 A320 4f multi (6-1) 3.50 .60
1294 A320 8f multi (6-2) 3.50 .60
1295 A320 8f multi (6-3) 3.50 .60
1296 A320 8f multi (6-4) 7.00 1.00
1297 A320 10f multi (6-5) 3.50 .60
1298 A320 20f multi (6-6) 7.00 2.25
Nos. 1293-1298 (6) 28.00 5.65

Students' efforts to help poor country people.

Mao's Home, Shaoshan — A321

Shaoshan, Mao's birthplace: No. 1300, School building. No. 1301, Farmers' Association building. 10f, Railroad station. T.11.

1976, Dec. 26				**Perf. 11**
1299	A321	4f multi (4-1)	2.00	1.25
1300	A321	8f multi (4-2)	3.00	1.25
1301	A321	8f multi (4-3)	3.00	1.25
1302	A321	10f multi (4-4)	3.00	1.75
		Nos. 1299-1302 (4)	11.00	5.50

Chou Enlai — A322

#1304, Chou giving report at 10th Party Congress. #1305, Chou with Wang Chin-hsi, famous oil worker, horiz. #1306, Chou with people of Tachai, 1973, horiz. J.13.

1977, Jan. 8		**Photo.**		**Perf. 11½**
1303	A322	8f multi (4-1)	1.50	.80
1304	A322	8f multi (4-2)	1.50	.80
1305	A322	8f multi (4-3)	1.50	.80
1306	A322	8f multi (4-4)	6.00	.80
		Nos. 1303-1306 (4)	10.50	3.20

Premier Chou En-lai (1898-1976), a founder of Chinese Communist Party, 1st death anniversary.

Liu Hu-lan, an Inspiration A323

Liu Hu-lan, Chinese heroine: No. 1307, Liu Hu-lan monument. No. 1308, Mao Tse-tung quotation: "A great life-a glorious death." J.12.

1977, Jan. 31				
1307	A323	8f multi (3-1)	16.00	3.75
1308	A323	8f multi (3-2)	6.00	2.00
1309	A323	8f multi (3-3)	5.00	2.00
		Nos. 1307-1309 (3)	27.00	7.75

Uprising in Taiwan A324

Design: 10f, Gate of Heavenly Peace, Peking; Sun Moon Lake, Taiwan, Taiwanese people holding PRC flag. J.14.

1977, Feb. 28		**Photo.**		**Perf. 11**
1310	A324	8f multi (2-1)	3.50	1.40
1311	A324	10f multi (2-2)	1.75	.70

Uprising of the people of Taiwan, 2/28/47.

Sharpshooters — A325

Militia Women: No. 1313, Women horseback riders. No. 1314, Underground defense tunnel. T.10.

1977, Mar. 8				**Perf. 11½**
1312	A325	8f multi (3-1)	5.50	3.00
1313	A325	8f multi (3-2)	5.50	3.00
1314	A325	8f multi (3-3)	11.00	4.00
		Nos. 1312-1314 (3)	22.00	10.00

Forestry — A326

Designs: 1f, Coal mining. 1½f, Sheepherding. 2f, Export (loading railroad car onto ship). 4f, Hydroelectric station. 5f, Fishery. 8f, Combine in field. 10f, Radio tower and mail truck. 20f, Steel production. 30f, Trucks on mountain road. 40f, Textiles. 50f, Tractor assembly line. 60f, Offshore oil rigs and birds, setting sun. 70f, Railroad bridge, Yangtze Gorge. No numbers.

1977		**Photo.**		**Perf. 11½**
1315	A326	1f yel grn, red & blk	.40	.25
1316	A326	1½f bl grn, yel grn & brn	.40	.25
1317	A326	2f org, bl & blk	.40	.25
1318	A326	3f ol & dk grn	.40	.25
1319	A326	4f lil, org & blk	.40	.25
1320	A326	5f lt ol & ultra	.40	.25
1321	A326	8f red & yel	.40	.25
1322	A326	10f lt grn, org & bl	.50	.25
1323	A326	20f org, yel & brn	.60	.25
1324	A326	30f bl, lt grn & blk	.60	.25
1325	A326	40f multicolored	.80	.30
1326	A326	50f cit, red & blk	1.00	.30
1327	A326	60f pur, yel & org	1.25	.40
1328	A326	70f blue & multi	2.00	.70
		Nos. 1315-1328 (14)	9.55	4.20

Address by Party Committee A327

Designs: No. 1330, Planting new rice fields. No. 1331, Farmers reading wall newspaper. No. 1332, Land reclamation. T.22.

1977, Apr. 9				**Perf. 11x11½**
1329	A327	8f multi (4-1)	2.00	.80
1330	A327	8f multi (4-2)	2.00	.80
1331	A327	8f multi (4-3)	2.00	.80
1332	A327	8f multi (4-4)	2.00	.80
		Nos. 1329-1332 (4)	8.00	3.20

Building Tachai-type communities throughout China.

Worker at Microphone — A328

Designs: No. 1334, Drilling for oil during snowstorm. No. 1335, Crowd advancing under Red banner. No. 1336, Workers, industrial complex, rocket blast-off. J.15.

1977, Apr. 25				**Perf. 11**
1333	A328	8f multi (4-1)	3.50	1.20
1334	A328	8f multi (4-2)	5.00	1.20
1335	A328	8f multi (4-3)	3.50	1.20
1336	A328	8f multi (4-4)	5.00	1.20
		Nos. 1333-1336 (4)	17.00	4.80

Conference on learning from Taching workers in industry.

Mongolians Hailing Anniversary A329

10f, Iron and steel complex, iron ore train. 20f, Cattle grazing in improved pasture. J.16.

1977, May 1				**Perf. 11x11½**
1337	A329	8f multi (3-1)	2.00	1.25
1338	A329	10f multi (3-2)	.60	.35
1339	A329	20f multi (3-3)	1.75	1.00
		Nos. 1337-1339 (3)	4.35	2.60

30th anniversary of Inner Mongolian Autonomous Region.

1877 Flag of Romania and Oak Leaves — A330

Mihai Viteazu Memorial (16th Century Hero) — A331

10f, Battle of Smirdan, by N. Grigorescu. J.17.

1977, May 9		**Photo.**		**Perf. 11**
1340	A330	8f multi (3-1)	2.50	1.25
1341	A331	10f multi (3-2)	.90	.65
1342	A331	20f multi (3-3)	.90	.90
		Nos. 1340-1342 (3)	4.30	2.80

Centenary of Romanian independence.

Yenan "Let 100 Flowers Bloom" A332

#1344, Hammer, sickle, gun & flowers; "Proletarian revolutionary literature will prosper." J.18.

1977, May, 23				
1343	A332	8f grn, red & gold	.95	.60
1344	A332	8f lt brn, red & gold	.95	.60

Yenan Forum on Literature & Art, 35th anniv.

Zhu De — A333

Designs: No. 1346, Zhu De, last address to Congress. No. 1347, Zhu De at his desk, horiz. No. 1348, Zhu De on horseback as commander of Red Army. J.19.

1977, July 6		**Photo.**		**Perf. 11½**
1345	A333	8f multi (4-1)	1.00	.40
1346	A333	8f multi (4-2)	1.00	.40
1347	A333	8f multi (4-3)	1.50	.50
1348	A333	8f multi (4-4)	1.50	.50
		Nos. 1345-1348 (4)	5.00	1.80

Zhu De (1886-1976), Commander of Red Army, Chairman of National People's Congress.

Military under Mao's Banner — A334

#1350, Red Flag, Soldiers, Chingkang Mountains. #1351, Guerrilla fighters returning to base. #1352, Guerrillas crossing Yangtze. #1353, National defense. J.20.

1977, Aug. 1				
1349	A334	8f multi (5-1)	5.50	1.40
1350	A334	8f multi (5-2)	3.50	1.40
1351	A334	8f multi (5-3)	4.00	1.40
1352	A334	8f multi (5-4)	4.00	1.40
1353	A334	8f multi (5-5)	3.50	1.40
		Nos. 1349-1353 (5)	20.50	7.00

Liberation Army Day, 50th anniversary of People's Army.

Gate of Heavenly Peace, People and Red Flags — A335

Designs: No. 1355, People marching under Red Flag with Mao's portrait. No. 1356, People marching under Red Flag with hammer and sickle. J.23.

1977, Aug. 22		**Photo.**	**Perf. 11½x11**
1354	A335	8f multi (3-1)	6.00 3.00
1355	A335	8f multi (3-2)	10.00 4.00
1356	A335	8f multi (3-3)	10.00 4.00
		Nos. 1354-1356 (3)	26.00 11.00

11th National Congress of the Communist Party of China.

Chairman Mao — A336

Designs (Mao Portraits): No. 1358, as young man in Shansi. No. 1359, addressing Communist Party in Plenary Session. No. 1360, Proclaiming People's Republic at Gate of Heavenly Peace. No. 1361, at airport with Chou En-lai and Zhu De, horiz. No. 1362, Reviewing Army as old man. J.21.

1977, Sept. 9		**Photo.**		**Perf. 11½**
1357	A336	8f multi (6-1)	5.75	1.25
1358	A336	8f multi (6-2)	5.75	1.25
1359	A336	8f multi (6-3)	5.75	1.25
1360	A336	8f multi (6-4)	5.75	1.25
1361	A336	8f multi (6-5)	5.75	1.25
1362	A336	8f multi (6-6)	5.75	1.25
		Nos. 1357-1362 (6)	34.50	7.50

Mao-Tse-tung (1893-1976), first death anniversary.

Mao Memorial Hall — A337

Completion of Mao Memorial Hall: No. 1364, Chairman Hua's inscription. J.22.

1977, Sept. 9

| 1363 | A337 | 8f lt ultra & multi | 2.75 | 1.75 |
| 1364 | A337 | 8f lt grn, tan & gold | 4.00 | 1.75 |

Tractors Moving Drilling Tower — A338

#1366, Shui Pow Tsi oil well and women workers. #1367, Construction of oil pipe line, Taching, and silos. #1368, Tung Fang Hung oil refinery, Peking. #1369, Taching oil loaded into tanker in harbor. 20f, Off-shore drilling platform "Pohai No. 1." T.19.

1978, Jan. 31   Photo.   Perf. 11

1365	A338	8f multi (6-1)	2.25	.60
1366	A338	8f multi (6-2)	2.25	.60
1367	A338	8f multi (6-3)	2.25	.60
1368	A338	8f multi (6-4)	3.50	.90
1369	A338	8f multi (6-5)	2.25	.60
1370	A338	20f multi (6-6)	3.50	.90
		Nos. 1365-1370 (6)	16.00	4.20

Development of Chinese oil industry.

"Army Teaching Militia" — A339

#1372, "Army helping with rice planting." T.23.

1978, Feb. 5   Photo.   Perf. 11

| 1371 | A339 | 8f multi (2-1) | 3.00 | 1.25 |
| 1372 | A339 | 8f multi (2-2) | 3.50 | 1.40 |

Army and people working as a family.

Red Flags, Mao Tse-tung — A340

Constitution and Red Flags — A341

#1375, Atom symbol over symbols of agriculture & industry. All designs include Great Hall of the People, Peking, & flowers. J.24.

1978, Feb. 26

1373	A340	8f multi (3-1)	4.25	.90
1374	A341	8f multi (3-2)	4.25	.90
1375	A340	8f multi (3-3)	4.25	.90
		Nos. 1373-1375 (3)	12.75	2.70

5th National People's Congress.

Mao's Eulogy for Lei Feng — A342

Lei Feng, Studying Mao's Works — A343

#1377, Chairman Hua's thoughts (5 lines). J.26.

1978, Mar. 5

1376	A342	8f gold & red (3-1)	8.50	1.50
1377	A342	8f gold & red (3-2)	8.50	1.50
1378	A343	8f multicolored (3-3)	4.00	1.50
		Nos. 1376-1378 (3)	21.00	4.50

Lei Feng (1940-1962), communist fighter; 15th anniversary of Chairman Mao's eulogy "Learn from Comrade Lei Feng."

Hsiang Ching-yu — A344

Yang Kai-hui — A345

1978, Mar. 8

| 1379 | A344 | 8f multi (2-1) | 2.50 | .85 |
| 1380 | A345 | 8f multi (2-2) | 2.50 | .85 |

Hsiang Ching-yu, pioneer of Women's Movement, executed 1928; Yang Kai-hui, communist fighter, executed 1930. J.27.

A346

A346a

A346b

#1381, Conference emblem. #1382, Banners symbolizing industry, agriculture, defense & science. #1383, Red flag, atom symbol & globe. J.25.

1978, Mar. 18   Litho.   Perf. 11½x11

1381	A346	8f gold & red (3-1)	1.60	.75
1382	A346a	8f multi (3-2)	1.60	.75
1383	A346b	8f multi (3-3)	1.60	.75
a.		Souvenir sheet of 3	675.00	275.00
		Nos. 1381-1383 (3)	4.80	2.25

Natl. Science Conf. #1383a contains #1381-1383 with simulated perforations. Sold for 50f.

Release of Weather Balloon A347

Weather Observations: No. 1385, Radar station, typhoon watch. No. 1386, Computer, weather maps. No. 1387, Local weather observers. No. 1388, Rockets intercepting hail clouds. T.24.

1978, Apr. 25   Photo.   Perf. 11x11½

1384	A347	8f multi (5-1)	1.25	.60
1385	A347	8f multi (5-2)	1.25	.60
1386	A347	8f multi (5-3)	1.25	.60
1387	A347	8f multi (5-4)	1.25	.60
1388	A347	8f multi (5-5)	1.25	.60
		Nos. 1384-1388 (5)	6.25	3.00

Galloping Horse — A348

Children Playing Soccer — A349

Designs: Galloping Horses, by Hsu Peihung (1895-1953). 40f, 50f, 60f, 70f, $5, horiz. T.28.

1978, May 5   Perf. 11½x11, 11x11½

1389	A348	4f multi (10-1)	3.50	.90
1390	A348	8f multi (10-2)	3.50	.90
1391	A348	8f multi (10-3)	3.50	.90
1392	A348	10f multi (10-4)	3.50	.90
1393	A348	20f multi (10-5)	4.75	.90
1394	A348	30f multi (10-6)	11.00	.90
1395	A348	40f multi (10-7)	4.75	1.60
1396	A348	50f multi (10-8)	18.00	4.50
1397	A348	60f multi (10-9)	11.00	3.00
1398	A348	70f multi (10-10)	6.00	4.25
		Nos. 1389-1398 (10)	69.50	18.75

Souvenir Sheet

| 1399 | A348 | $5 multicolored | 750.00 | 225.00 |

No. 1399 contains one stamp showing 4 horses, size: 89x39mm.

1978, June 1   Perf. 11½

Designs: No. 1401, Children on the beach. No. 1402, Little girls dancing. No. 1403, Children taking long walks. 20f, Children exercising for good health. T.21.

Size: 22x27mm

1400	A349	8f multi (5-2)	.55	.45
1401	A349	8f multi (5-3)	.55	.45
1402	A349	8f multi (5-4)	.55	.45
1403	A349	8f multi (5-5)	.55	.45

Size: 48x28mm

| 1404 | A349 | 20f multi (5-1) | 1.25 | .75 |
| | | Nos. 1400-1404 (5) | 3.45 | 2.55 |

Build up your health while young.

Synthetic Fiber Feeder A350

Designs: No. 1406, Drawing out threads. No. 1407, Weaving. No. 1408, Dyeing and printing. No. 1409, Finished products. T.25.

1978, June 15   Photo.   Perf. 11½

1405	A350	8f multi (5-1)	.70	.55
1406	A350	8f multi (5-2)	.70	.55
1407	A350	8f multi (5-3)	.70	.55
1408	A350	8f multi (5-4)	.70	.55
1409	A350	8f multi (5-5)	.70	.55
a.		Strip of 5, #1405-1409	11.50	11.50
		Nos. 1405-1409 (5)	3.50	2.75

Chemical fiber industry. No. 1409a has continuous design. No. 1409a is valued as an unfolded strip. Folded strips sell for less.

Conference Emblem A351

"Develop Economy and Ensure Supplies" A352

1978, June 20   Perf. 13

| 1410 | A351 | 8f multi (2-1) | 1.50 | .50 |
| 1411 | A352 | 8f multi (2-2) | 1.50 | .50 |

Natl. Conf. on Learning from Taching and Tachai in Finance and Trade. J.28.

New Pastures, Mongolia — A353

Designs: No. 1413, Kazakh shepherds selecting sheep for breeding. No. 1414, Mechanized shearing of sheep, Tibet. T.27.

1978, June 30   Photo.   Perf. 11½

1412	A353	8f multi (3-1)	2.75	.70
1413	A353	8f multi (3-2)	2.75	.70
1414	A353	8f multi (3-3)	2.75	.70
		Nos. 1412-1414 (3)	8.25	2.10

Learning from Tachai in developing animal husbandry and new pastoral areas.

Coke Oven — A354

Iron and Steel Industry: No. 1416, Iron furnace. No. 1417, Pouring steel. No. 1418, Steel rolling. No. 1419, Finished iron and steel products. T.26.

1978, July 22

1415	A354	8f multi (5-1)	2.25	.60
1416	A354	8f multi (5-2)	2.25	.60
1417	A354	8f multi (5-3)	2.25	.60
1418	A354	8f multi (5-4)	2.25	.60
1419	A354	8f multi (5-5)	2.25	.60
		Nos. 1415-1419 (5)	11.25	3.00

Iron Fist to Prevent Revisionism A355

Jug in Shape of Sheep — A356

#1421, "Carrying forward revolutionary tradition." #1422, "Strenuous training in military skills to wipe out enemy." T.32.

1978, Aug. 1   Photo.   Perf. 11½
1420	A355	8f multi (3-1)	2.50	.60
1421	A355	8f multi (3-2)	2.50	.60
1422	A355	8f multi (3-3)	2.50	.60
		Nos. 1420-1422 (3)	7.50	1.80

"Learn from Hard-boned 6th Company." (A military unit since 1939).

1978, Aug. 26
Arts and Crafts: 4f, Giant lion (toy; horiz.). No. 1425, Rhinoceros (lacquer ware; horiz.). 10f, Cat (embroidery). 20f, Bag (weaving; horiz.). 30f, Teapot in shape of peacock (cloisonné). 40f, Plate with lotus, and swan-shaped box (lacquer ware; horiz.). 50f, Dragon flying in sky (ivory). 60f, Sun rising (jade; horiz.). 70f, Flight to human world (ivory). $3, Flying fairies (arts and crafts; horiz.). T.29.

1423	A356	4f multi (10-1)	.90	.40
1424	A356	8f multi (10-2)	.90	.40
1425	A356	8f multi (10-3)	.90	.40
1426	A356	10f multi (10-4)	.90	.50
1427	A356	20f multi (10-5)	.90	.50
1428	A356	30f multi (10-6)	1.25	.75
1429	A356	40f multi (10-7)	2.50	1.00
1430	A356	50f multi (10-8)	5.00	2.50
1431	A356	60f multi (10-9)	5.00	2.50
1432	A356	70f multi (10-10)	3.00	1.50
		Nos. 1423-1432 (10)	21.25	10.45

Souvenir Sheet
1433	A356	$3 multi	625.00	200.00

No. 1433 contains one 85x36mm stamp.

Women, Atom Symbol, Rocket and Wheat A357

1978, Sept. 8   Photo.   Perf. 11
1434	A357	8f multicolored	1.50	1.00

4th National Women's Congress.

Ginseng — A358

Flag, Wheat, Cogwheel, Plane, Atom Symbols — A359

Medicinal Plants: No. 1436, Horn of plenty. No. 1437, Blackberry lily. No. 1438, Balloonflower. 55f, Rhododendron dauricum. T.30.

1978, Sept. 15
1435	A358	8f multi (5-1)	.75	.30
1436	A358	8f multi (5-2)	.75	.30
1437	A358	8f multi (5-3)	.75	.30
1438	A358	8f multi (5-4)	.75	.30
1439	A358	55f multi (5-5)	5.00	1.75
		Nos. 1435-1439 (5)	8.00	2.95

1978, Oct. 11   Photo.   Perf. 11
1440	A359	8f multicolored	2.50	1.90

9th National Trade Union Congress.

Youth League Emblem A360

1978, Oct. 16
1441	A360	8f multicolored	2.00	1.25

10th Natl. Communist Youth League Cong.

Chinese and Japanese Girls Exchanging Gifts A361

Great Wall and Mt. Fuji A362

1978, Oct. 22
1442	A361	8f multicolored	1.00	.50
1443	A362	55f multicolored	2.25	1.75

Signing of Sino-Japanese Peace and Friendship Treaty.

Moslem, Chinese and Mongolian People — A363

Chinsha River Bridge, West Szechuan A364

#1445, Loading coal at Holan Mountain. 10f, Irrigated rice fields & boxthorn. J.29.

1978, Oct. 25
1444	A363	8f multi (3-1)	2.00	1.00
1445	A363	8f multi (3-2)	1.00	1.00
1446	A363	10f multi (3-3)	1.00	1.00
		Nos. 1444-1446 (3)	4.00	3.00

20th anniversary of founding of Ningsia Moslem Autonomous Region.

1978, Nov. 1   Photo.   Perf. 11½x11
Highway Bridges: No. 1448, Hsinhong bridge, Wuhsi. No. 1449, Chiuhsikou bridge, Fengdu. No. 1450, Chinsha River bridge, West Szechuan. 60f, Shangyeh bridge, Sanmen. $2, Hsiang-kiang River bridge. T.31.

1447	A364	8f multi (5-1)	1.50	.40
1448	A364	8f multi (5-2)	1.50	.40
1449	A364	8f multi (5-3)	1.50	.40
1450	A364	8f multi (5-4)	1.50	.40
1451	A364	60f multi (5-5)	4.00	1.50
		Nos. 1447-1451 (5)	10.00	3.10

Souvenir Sheet
1452	A364	$2 multi	600.00	225.00

No. 1452 contains one 86x37mm stamp.

Mechanical Transplanting of Rice Seedlings A365

Paintings: No. 1454, Spraying fields. No. 1455, Seed selection. No. 1456, Trade. No. 1457, Delivery of public grain in city. T.34.

1978, Nov. 30   Perf. 11½
1453	A365	8f multi (5-1)	5.00	2.50
1454	A365	8f multi (5-2)	5.00	2.50
1455	A365	8f multi (5-3)	5.00	2.50
1456	A365	8f multi (5-4)	5.00	2.50
1457	A365	8f multi (5-5)	5.00	2.50
	a.	Strip of 5, #1453-1457	29.00	15.00

Agricultural progress. No. 1457a has a continuous design.

Dancers and Fireworks — A366

Designs: No. 1459, Industry, vert. 10f, Agriculture, vert. J.33.

1978, Dec. 11   Photo.   Perf. 11
1458	A366	8f multi (3-1)	4.00	2.00
1459	A366	8f multi (3-2)	3.00	1.50
1460	A366	10f multi (3-3)	1.25	1.00
		Nos. 1458-1460 (3)	8.25	4.50

20th anniversary of Kwangsi Chuang Autonomous Region.

Miners with Pneumatic Drill A367

Mine Development: 4f, Old Tibetan peasant reporting to surveyor. 10f, Open-cut mining with power shovel. 20f, Loaded electric train in pit. T.20.

1978, Dec. 29   Photo. & Engr.
1461	A367	4f multi (4-1)	1.75	.85
1462	A367	8f multi (4-2)	3.75	1.25
1463	A367	10f multi (4-3)	1.50	1.00
1464	A367	20f multi (4-4)	1.75	1.00
		Nos. 1461-1464 (4)	8.75	4.10

A368

A369

Golden Pheasants: 4f, Roosting on rock. 8f, In flight. 45f, Seeking food. T.35.

1979, Jan. 25   Photo.   Perf. 11½
1465	A368	4f multi (3-1)	2.00	1.25
1466	A368	8f multi (3-2)	4.50	2.00
1467	A368	45f multi (3-3)	3.25	2.00
		Nos. 1465-1467 (3)	9.75	5.25

1979, Mar. 14   Photo.   Perf. 11½x11
1468	A369	8f Albert Einstein, equation	2.25	1.75

Phoenix Battling Monster, Praying Woman A370

60f, Man riding dragon to heaven. Designs from silk paintings found in Changsha tomb, Warring States Period (475-221 B.C.). T.33.

1979, Mar. 29   Perf. 11
1469	A370	8f multi (2-1)	2.40	.85
1470	A370	60f multi (2-2)	1.60	1.60

Summer Palace — A371

Photo., Photo. & Engr. ($5)
1979-80   Perf. 13
1471	A371	$1 Pagoda ('80)	.75	.30
1472	A371	$2 Shown	1.40	.70
1473	A371	$5 Temple, Beihai Park	4.25	1.25
		Nos. 1471-1473 (3)	6.40	2.25

Issued: $2, June 16, 1979.

Hammer and Sickle "51" and Bars from "International" — A372

1979, May 1   Photo.   Perf. 11
1474	A372	8f multicolored	1.25	.90

International Labor Day, 90th anniv.

"Tradition of May 4th Movement" A373

Young Woman, Rocket, Antenna, Nuclear Reactor A374

1979, May 4
1475	A373	8f multicolored	1.25	.60
1476	A374	8f multicolored	1.25	.60

60th anniversary of May 4th Movement.

IYC Emblem, Children Holding Balloons — A375

Children of Three Races, IYC Emblem — A376

1979, May 25   *Perf. 11½*
1477 A375   8f multicolored   1.50   1.00
1478 A376   60f multicolored   10.00   6.00

International Year of the Child.

Great Wall in Spring A377

Designs (The Great Wall): No. 1480, in summer. No. 1481, in autumn. 60f, in winter. $2, Guard tower. T.38.

1979, June 25   **Photo.**   *Perf. 11*
1479 A377   8f multi (4-1)   1.50   .90
1480 A377   8f multi (4-2)   1.50   .90
1481 A377   8f multi (4-3)   1.50   .90
1482 A377   60f multi (4-4)   7.50   5.50
    Nos. 1479-1482 (4)   12.00   8.20

Souvenir Sheet
1483 A377 $2 multi   275.00   110.00

For overprint see No. 1492.

Roaring Tiger — A379

Manchurian Tiger: 8f, Two young tigers. 60f, Tiger at rest. T.40.

1979, July 20   *Perf. 11½x11*
1484 A379   4f multi (3-1)   1.75   1.25
1485 A379   8f multi (3-2)   3.25   1.75
1486 A379   60f multi (3-3)   3.25   1.75
    Nos. 1484-1486 (3)   8.25   4.75

Mechanical Harvesting — A380

Work of the Communes: No. 1488, Forestry. No. 1489, Raising ducks. No. 1490, Women weaving baskets. 10f, Fishing. T.39.

1979, Aug. 10   *Perf. 11½*
1487 A380   4f multi (5-1)   4.00   2.25
1488 A380   8f multi (5-2)   2.25   1.50
1489 A380   8f multi (5-3)   2.25   1.50

1490 A380   8f multi (5-4)   2.25   1.50
1491 A380   10f multi (5-5)   2.25   1.50
    Nos. 1487-1491 (5)   13.00   8.25

No. 1483 Overprinted with Gold Inscription and "1979"
Souvenir Sheet

1979, Aug. 25   **Photo.**   *Perf. 11*
1492 A377 $2 multicolored   *1,050.*   300.00

31st International Stamp Exhibition, Riccione, Italy. J41 (1-1).
Forged overprints exist.

Games Emblem, Sports — A381

#1494, Soccer, badminton, high jump, speed skating. #1495, Fencing, skiing, gymnastics, diving. #1496, Motorcycling, table tennis, basketball, archery. #1497, Emblem only. J.43.

1979, Sept. 15   *Perf. 11½x11*
1493 A381   8f multi (4-1)   2.10   .75
1494 A381   8f multi (4-2)   2.10   .75
1495 A381   8f multi (4-3)   2.10   .75
1496 A381   8f multi (4-4)   2.10   .75
  a.   Block of 4, #1493-1496   10.00   10.00

Souvenir Sheet
Perf. 11½
1497 A381 $2 multi, vert.   100.00   55.00

4th National Games. Size of stamp in No. 1497: 22x26mm.

Flag and Rainbow — A382

Design: No. 1499, Flag and mountains.

1979, Oct. 1   **Photo.**   *Perf. 11½*
1498 A382   8f multicolored   1.75   1.25
1499 A382   8f multicolored   2.75   1.75

National Emblem — A383   Dancers — A384

1979, Oct. 1   **Photo.**   *Perf. 11½*
1500 A383   8f multicolored   3.00   2.00

Souvenir Sheet
1501 A383 $1 multicolored   110.00   30.00

1979, Oct. 1   **Photo.**   *Perf. 11½*
Designs: #1503-1505, various dances. J.47.

1502 A384   8f multi (4-1)   .75   .35
1503 A384   8f multi (4-2)   .75   .35
1504 A384   8f multi (4-3)   .75   .35
1505 A384   8f multi (4-4)   .75   .35
  a.   Block of 4, #1502-1505   6.00   5.00

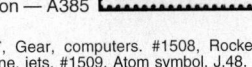

Tractor, Aerial Crop Spraying, Irrigation — A385

#1507, Gear, computers. #1508, Rocket, submarine, jets. #1509, Atom symbol. J.48.

1979, Oct. 1   **Photo.**   *Perf. 11½*
1506 A385   8f multi (4-1)   1.50   1.00
1507 A385   8f multi (4-2)   1.50   1.00
1508 A385   8f multi (4-3)   1.00   .75
1509 A385   8f multi (4-4)   1.00   .75
    Nos. 1506-1509 (4)   5.00   3.50

National Anthem A386

1979, Oct. 1   **Engr.**   *Perf. 11*
1510 A386   8f multicolored   5.00   3.00

Exhibition Emblem — A387   Children Flying Model Planes — A388

1979, Oct. 3
1511 A387   8f multicolored   1.00   .90

Junior National Scientific and Technological Exhibition.

1979, Oct. 3

#1513, Girls and microscope. #1514, Children and telescope. #1515, Boy catching butterflies. #1516, Girl taking meteorological readings. #1517, Boys sailing model boat. #1518, Girl with book. T.41.

1512 A388   8f multi (6-1)   1.25   .65
1513 A388   8f multi (6-2)   1.25   .65
1514 A388   8f multi (6-3)   1.25   .65
1515 A388   8f multi (6-4)   1.25   .65
1516 A388   8f multi (6-5)   1.25   .65
1517 A388   60f multi (6-6)   6.00   3.00
    Nos. 1512-1517 (6)   12.25   6.25

Souvenir Sheet
Perf. 11
1518 A388 $2 multi   *3,250.*   1,250.

Study Science from Childhood. No. 1518 contains one stamp, size: 90x40mm.

Yu Shan Mountain A389

Taiwan Landscapes: No. 1520, Sun and Moon Lake. No. 1521, Chihkan Tower. No. 1522, Suao-Hualien Highway. 55f, Tian Xiang Falls. 60f, Banping Mountain. T.42.

1979, Oct. 20   **Photo.**   *Perf. 11x11½*
1519 A389   8f multi (6-1)   1.75   .85
1520 A389   8f multi (6-2)   1.75   .85
1521 A389   8f multi (6-3)   1.75   .85
1522 A389   8f multi (6-4)   1.75   .85
1523 A389   55f multi (6-5)   5.00   2.50
1524 A389   60f multi (6-6)   6.75   3.00
    Nos. 1519-1524 (6)   18.75   8.90

Arts Symbols A390

8f, Seals and modernization symbols. J.39.

1979, Oct. 30
1525 A390   4f multicolored   .60   .50
1526 A390   8f multicolored   1.40   .75

4th Natl. Cong. of Literary and Art Workers.

Train in Tunnel A391

Railroads: No. 1528, Mountain bridge. No. 1529, Freight train. T.36.

1979, Oct. 30   **Photo. & Engr.**
1527 A391   8f multi (3-1)   2.50   1.00
1528 A391   8f multi (3-2)   2.50   1.00
1529 A391   8f multi (3-3)   2.50   1.00
    Nos. 1527-1529 (3)   7.50   3.00

Chrysanthemum Petal — A392

Camellias: No. 1531, Lion head. No. 1532, Camellia chryantha. 10f, Small osmanthus leaf. 20f, Baby face. 30f, Cornelian. 40f, Peony camellia. 50f, Purple gown. 60f, Dwarf rose. 70f, Willow leaf spinel pink. $2, Red jewelry. T.37.

1979, Nov. 10   **Photo.**   *Perf. 11x11½*
1530 A392   4f multi (10-1)   3.00   .60
1531 A392   8f multi (10-2)   1.50   .60
1532 A392   8f multi (10-3)   1.50   .60
1533 A392   10f multi (10-4)   1.50   .60
1534 A392   20f multi (10-5)   3.00   1.25
1535 A392   30f multi (10-6)   8.00   1.90
1536 A392   40f multi (10-7)   5.00   1.25
1537 A392   50f multi (10-8)   5.00   1.25
1538 A392   60f multi (10-9)   5.00   1.25
1539 A392   70f multi (10-10)   3.00   1.25
    Nos. 1530-1539 (10)   36.50   10.55

Souvenir Sheet
Perf. 11½x11
1540 A392 $2 multi   300.00   150.00

No. 1540 contains one 86x36mm stamp.

No. 1540 Overprinted and Numbered in Gold in Margin
Souvenir Sheet

1979, Nov. 10
1541 A392 $2 multicolored   700.00   160.00

People's Republic of China Phil. Exhib., Hong Kong, 1979. J.42 (1-1).
Forged overprints exist.

Norman Bethune Treating Soldier — A393

Design: 70f, Bethune statue.

1979, Nov. 12
1542 A393   8f multi (2-2)   .75   .40
1543 A393   70f multi (2-1)   3.00   1.75

Dr. Norman Bethune, 40th death anniv. J.50.

Central Archives Hall A394

Intl. Archives Weeks: No. 1545, Gold archive cabinet, vert. 60f, Pavilion. J.51.

Perf. 11x11½, 11½x11

1979, Nov. 26   Photo.
1544	A394	8f multi (3-1)	1.00 .40
1545	A394	8f multi (3-2)	1.00 .40
1546	A394	60f multi (3-3)	8.25 2.25
		Nos. 1544-1546 (3)	10.25 3.05

Monkey King in Waterfall Cave — A395

Monkey King, Scenes from Pilgrimage to the West (Novel): No. 1548, Fighting Necha, son of Prince Li. No. 1549, In Mother Queen's peach orchard. No. 1550, In the alchemy furnace. 10f, Subduing the white bone demon. 20f, With palm leaf fan. 60f, In cobweb cave. 70f, Walking on scripture-seeking route. T.43.

1979, Dec. 1   Perf. 11½x11
1547	A395	8f multi (8-1)	4.00 1.60
1548	A395	8f multi (8-2)	4.00 1.60
1549	A395	8f multi (8-3)	4.00 1.60
1550	A395	8f multi (8-4)	4.00 1.60
1551	A395	10f multi (8-5)	5.25 1.60
1552	A395	20f multi (8-6)	5.25 1.60
1553	A395	60f multi (8-7)	45.00 6.00
1554	A395	70f multi (8-8)	12.00 5.00
		Nos. 1547-1554 (8)	83.50 20.60

Stalin Delivering Speech A396

Joseph Stalin (1879-1953): No. 1555, Portrait of Stalin, vert. J.49.

Perf. 11x11½, 11½x11

1979, Dec. 21   Engr.
1555	A396	8f brown (2-1)	1.25 1.00
1556	A396	8f black (2-2)	1.25 1.00

A397   A398

1980   Photo.   Perf. 11½
1557	A397	4f Peony (16-1)	1.75 1.00
1558	A397	4f Squirrels and grapes (16-2)	1.75 1.00
1559	A397	8f Crabs candle and wine (16-3)	1.75 1.00
1560	A397	8f Tadpoles in mountain spring (16-4)	1.75 1.00
1561	A397	8f Chicks (16-5)	1.75 1.00
1562	A397	8f Lotus (16-6)	1.75 1.00
1563	A397	8f Red plum (16-7)	1.75 1.00
1564	A397	8f Kingfisher (16-8)	1.75 1.00
1565	A397	10f Bottle gourd (16-9)	3.50 1.25
1566	A397	20f Voice of autumn (16-10)	3.50 1.25
1567	A397	30f Wisteria (16-11)	3.50 1.50
1568	A397	40f Chrysanthemums (16-12)	12.00 1.50
1569	A397	50f Shrimp (16-13)	4.00 1.75
1570	A397	55f Litchi (16-14)	5.00 3.00

1571	A397	60f Cabbages, mushrooms (16-15)	17.50 9.00
1572	A397	70f Peaches (16-16)	8.50 4.50
		Nos. 1557-1572 (16)	71.50 31.75

Souvenir Sheet
1573	A397	$2 Hyacynth	400.00 150.00

Qi Baishi paintings. Issued: #1557-1560, 1569-1572, 1/15; others, 5/20. #1573 contains one 37½x61mm stamp. T. 44.

1980, Jan. 25   Perf. 11½x11

Opera Masks: No. 1574, Meng Liang Mask from Hongyang Cave Opera. No. 1575, Li Kui, from Black Whirlwind. No. 1576, Huang Gai, from Meeting of Heroes. No. 1577, 10f, Lu Zhishen, from Wild Boar Forest. 20f, Lian Po, from Reconciliation between the General and Minister. 60f, Zhang Fei, from Reed Marsh. 70f, Dou Erdun, from Stealing the Emperor's Horse, T. 45.

1574	A398	4f multi (8-1)	4.00 1.00
1575	A398	4f multi (8-2)	20.00 5.00
1576	A398	8f multi (8-3)	4.00 1.00
1577	A398	8f multi (8-4)	4.00 1.00
1578	A398	10f multi (8-5)	4.75 2.00
1579	A398	20f multi (8-6)	4.75 2.00
1580	A398	60f multi (8-7)	7.50 3.75
1581	A398	70f multi (8-8)	9.50 5.50
		Nos. 1574-1581 (8)	58.50 21.25

Speed Skating, Olympic Rings — A399   Monkey, New Year — A400

Olympic Rings and: No. 1582, Chinese flag. No. 1584, Figure skating. 60f, Downhill skiing. J.54.

1980, Feb. 13
1582	A399	8f multi (4-1)	1.75 .40
1583	A399	8f multi (4-2)	1.75 .40
1584	A399	8f multi (4-3)	1.75 .40
1585	A399	60f multi (4-4)	9.50 2.25
		Nos. 1582-1585 (4)	14.75 3.45

13th Winter Olympic Games, Lake Placid, NY, Feb. 12-24.

Engraved and Photogravure
1980, Feb. 15   Perf. 11½
1586	A400	8f multicolored	1,950. 750.00

Clara Zetkin — A401

Photogravure & Engraved
1980, Mar. 8   Perf. 11½x11
1587	A401	8f black & yellow	1.25 1.00

International Working Women's Day, 70th anniv., founded by Clara Zetkin (1857-1933).

Orchard A402

Afforestation: 8f, Trees lining highway. 10f, Aerial seeding. 20f, Trees surrounding factory. T.48.

1980, Mar. 12   Perf. 11x11½
1588	A402	4f multi (4-1)	.90 .50
1589	A402	8f multi (4-2)	.90 .50
1590	A402	10f multi (4-3)	.90 .50
1591	A402	20f multi (4-4)	.90 .50
		Nos. 1588-1591 (4)	3.60 2.00

Apsaras, Symbols of Modernization — A403

1980, Mar. 15   Photo.   Perf. 11½
1592	A403	8f multicolored	2.00 1.25

2nd National Conference of the Scientific and Technical Association of China.

Mail Transport (T.49) — A404

1980, Mar. 20   Perf. 11x11½
1593	A404	2f Ship (4-1)	1.50 1.40
1594	A404	4f Bus (4-2)	3.25 1.75
1595	A404	8f Train (4-3)	4.50 1.75
1596	A404	10f Jet (4-4)	3.75 2.25
		Nos. 1593-1596 (4)	13.00 7.15

Forgeries exist.

Lungs, Heart, Cigarette, WHO Emblem — A405

1980, Apr. 7   Perf. 11½x11
1597	A405	8f shown (2-1)	1.50 .55
1598	A405	60f Faces (2-2)	8.50 3.25

Fight against cigarette smoking. J.56.

Statue of Chien Chen (688-763) — A406

1980, Apr. 13   Perf. 11x11½, 11½x11

Loan to China by Japan of statue of Chien Chen (Jian Zhen), Buddhist missionary to Japan (754-763): No. 1600, Chien Chen Memorial Hall, Yangchou, horiz. 60f, Chien Chen's ship, horiz. His name in Japan is Ganjin. J.55.

1599	A406	8f multi (3-1)	3.50 1.00
1600	A406	8f multi (3-2)	3.50 1.00
1601	A406	60f multi (3-3)	22.50 7.00
		Nos. 1599-1601 (3)	29.50 9.00

Lenin's 110th Birthday — A407

Swallow Chick Kite — A408

Photogravure and Engraved
1980, Apr. 22   Perf. 11½x11
1602	A407	8f multicolored	2.00 1.00

1980, May 10   Photo.   Perf. 11½

Designs: Kites. T.50.
1603	A408	8f shown (4-1)	5.00 1.50
1604	A408	8f Slender-swallow (4-2)	5.00 1.50
1605	A408	8f Semi-slender swallow (4-3)	5.00 1.50
1606	A408	70f Dual swallows (4-4)	20.00 6.00
		Nos. 1603-1606 (4)	35.00 10.50

Hare Running from Fallen Papaya A409

1980, June 1   Photo.   Perf. 11x11½
1607		Strip of 4 + label	15.00 15.00
	a.	A409 8f shown (4-1)	1.75 1.50
	b.	A409 8f Hare fox, monkey running away (4-2)	1.75 1.50
	c.	A409 8f Lion instructing animals (4-3)	1.75 1.50
	d.	A409 8f Discovery of fallen papaya (4-4)	1.75 1.50
	e.	Bklt. pane, 2 #1607	975.00
		Complete booklet	975.00

Gu Dong fairy tale. T.51.

Terminal Building, Jets — A410

1980, June 20   Perf. 11½
1608	A410	8f Shown (2-1)	1.25 1.00
1609	A410	10f Runways, jets (2-2)	1.75 1.10

Peking Intl. Airport opening. T.47.

Sika Stag — A411

White Lotus — A412

1980, July 18   Photo.   Perf. 11½
1610	A411	4f Shown (3-1)	1.50 1.25
1611	A411	8f Doe and fawn (3-2)	1.50 1.25
1612	A411	60f Herd (3-3)	6.50 5.00
		Nos. 1610-1612 (3)	9.50 7.50

T.52.

1980, Aug. 4

1613	A412	8f Shown (4-1)	6.00	1.75
1614	A412	8f Rose-tipped snow (4-2)	6.00	1.75
1615	A412	8f Buddha's seat (4-3)	6.00	1.75
1616	A412	70f Variable charming face (4-4)	40.00	9.50
		Nos. 1613-1616 (4)	58.00	14.75

Souvenir Sheet

1617	A412	$1 Fresh lotus on rippling water	400.00	140.00

#1617 contains one 48x88mm stamp. T.54.

Pearl Cave, Sword-cut Stone Sculptures — A413

Guilin Landscapes: No. 1619, Three mountains, distant views. No. 1620, Nine-horse fresco hill. No. 1621, Egrets around aged banyan. No. 1622, Western hills at sunset, vert. No. 1623, Moonlight on Lijiang River, vert. 60f, Springhead, ancient ferry, vert. 70f, Scenic path, Yangshue, vert. T.53.

1980, Aug. 30   Photo.   Perf. 11½

1618	A413	8f multi (8-1)	2.00	.80
1619	A413	8f multi (8-2)	2.00	.80
1620	A413	8f multi (8-3)	2.00	.80
1621	A413	8f multi (8-4)	2.00	.80
1622	A413	8f multi (8-5)	2.00	.80
1623	A413	8f multi (8-6)	2.00	.80
1624	A413	60f multi (8-7)	15.00	6.00
1625	A413	70f multi (8-8)	13.50	5.00
		Nos. 1618-1625 (8)	40.50	15.80

Entrance Gate and Good Fairies A414

Great Wall, Symbols of Chicago, San Francisco and New York A415

1980, Sept. 13   Photo.   Perf. 11x11½

1626	A414	8f multicolored	1.50	.85
1627	A415	70f multicolored	9.00	3.50

Exhibitions of the People's Republic of China in San Francisco, Chicago and New York, Sept.-Dec. Sheets of 12 were sold only at the US exhibitions at increasing prices. Value, set of two sheets of 12, $1,500.

Romanian Flag, Warrior and Scroll — A416

1980, Sept. 20   Photo.   Perf. 11½x11

1628	A416	8f multicolored	2.00	1.40

2050th anniv. of Dacia, 1st independent Romanian state.

UNESCO Exhibition of Drawings and Paintings (J.60) — A417

1980, Oct. 8   Perf. 11½

1629	A417	8f Sea of Clouds, by Liu Haisu (3-1)	1.50	.75
1630	A417	8f Oriole and Magnolia, by Yu Feian, vert., (3-2)	1.50	.75
1631	A417	8f Camels, by Wu Zuoren (3-3)	1.50	.75
		Nos. 1629-1631 (3)	4.50	2.25

Scenes from Tarrying Garden (T.56) — A418

1980, Oct. 25   Photo.   Perf. 11½

1632	A418	8f Quxi Tower (4-1)	9.50	3.75
1633	A418	8f Yuancui Pavilion (4-2)	9.50	3.75
1634	A418	10f Hanbi Shanfang (4-3)	9.50	3.75
1635	A418	60f Guanyun Peak (4-4)	70.00	17.50
		Nos. 1632-1635 (4)	98.50	28.75

Xu Guangpi (1562-1633), Agronomist A419

Shooting, Olympic Rings — A420

Scientists of Ancient China: No. 1637, Li Bing, hydraulic engineer, 3rd century B.C. No. 1638, Jia Sixie, agronomist, 5th century. 60f, Huang Daopo, textile expert, 13th century. J.58.

Photogravure and Engraved

1980, Nov. 20   Perf. 11½x11

1636	A419	8f multi (4-1)	3.75	1.75
1637	A419	8f multi (4-2)	3.75	1.75
1638	A419	8f multi (4-3)	3.75	1.75
1639	A419	60f multi (4-4)	40.00	10.00
		Nos. 1636-1639 (4)	51.25	15.25

1980, Nov. 26   Photo.

1640	A420	4f shown (5-1)	1.40	.30
1641	A420	8f Gymnastics (5-2)	1.40	.35
1642	A420	8f Diving (5-3)	1.40	.35
1643	A420	10f Volleyball (5-4)	2.00	.75
1644	A420	60f Archery (5-5)	7.00	2.50
		Nos. 1640-1644 (5)	13.20	4.25

Return to International Olympic Committee, 1st anniversary. J.62.

Chinese River Dolphin A421

Photogravure & Engraved

1980, Dec. 25   Perf. 11x11½

1645	A421	8f shown (2-1)	1.50	.50
a.		Booklet pane of 6	45.00	
1646	A421	60f Dolphins (2-2)	5.50	1.75
a.		Booklet pane of 1	45.00	

Stamps from No. 1645a have straight edges on top or bottom.

Cock — A422

Photogravure & Engraved

1981, Jan. 5   Perf. 11½

1647	A422	8f multicolored	30.00	8.00
a.		Booklet pane of 12	360.00	
		Complete booklet	400.00	

New Year 1981.
Stamps from booklet pane have straight edges on top or bottom.

Early Morning in Xishuang Bana (T.55) A423

Perf. 11x11½, 11½x11

1981, Jan. 20   Photo.

1648	A423	4f shown (6-1)	4.50	1.25
1649	A423	4f Dai mountain village (6-2)	3.00	.70
1650	A423	8f Rainbow over Lanchang River (6-3)	3.00	.70
1651	A423	8f Ancient temple vert. (6-4)	3.00	.70
1652	A423	8f Moonlit night, vert. (6-5)	3.00	.70
1653	A423	60f Phoenix tree, vert. (6-6)	16.00	4.50
		Nos. 1648-1653 (6)	32.50	8.55

Flower Basket Palace Lantern — A424

Designs: Palace lanterns. T.60.

1981, Feb. 19   Photo.   Perf. 11½

1654	A424	4f multi (6-1)	2.25	1.00
1655	A424	8f multi (6-2)	2.25	1.00
1656	A424	8f multi (6-3)	2.25	1.00
1657	A424	8f multi (6-4)	2.25	1.00
1658	A424	20f multi (6-5)	4.25	3.75
1659	A424	60f multi (6-6)	12.50	8.00
		Nos. 1654-1659 (6)	25.75	15.75

Crossing River, Scene from Marking the Gunwale A425

Scenes from Marking the Gunwale fable. T.59.

1981, Mar. 10   Photo.   Perf. 11x11½

1660	A425	8f Text (5-1)	1.40	1.10
1661	A425	8f shown (5-2)	1.40	1.10
1662	A425	8f Dropping sword in water (5-3)	1.40	1.10
1663	A425	8f Marking gunwale (5-4)	1.40	1.10

1664	A425	8f Searching for sword (5-5)	1.40	1.10
a.		Bklt. pane, 2 each #1660-1664	50.00	
		Complete booklet, #1664a	55.00	
b.		Strip of 5, #1660-1664	9.00	7.50

Chinese Juniper A426

Designs: Miniature landscapes. T.61.

1981, Mar. 31   Perf. 11½

1665	A426	4f Chinese elm, vert. (6-1)	3.00	1.25
1666	A426	8f Juniper, vert. (6-2)	2.00	1.00
1667	A426	8f Maidenhair tree, vert. (6-3)	2.00	1.00
1668	A426	10f shown (6-4)	2.00	1.00
1669	A426	20f Persimmon (6-5)	2.00	1.25
1670	A426	60f Juniper (6-6)	12.00	4.00
		Nos. 1665-1670 (6)	23.00	9.50

Vase with Tiger-shaped Handles — A427

Cizhou Kiln Ceramic Pottery: 4f, Vase with 2 tigers, Song Dynasty. #1672, Black glazed jar, Jin Dynasty. #1673, Amphora. #1674, Jar with 2 phoenixes (Yuan Dynasty). 10f, Flat flask, Yuan Dynasty. T.62.

1981, Apr. 15   Photo.   Perf. 11½x11

1671	A427	4f multi, vert. (6-1)	1.25	.75
1672	A427	8f multi (6-2)	1.25	.75
1673	A427	8f multi, vert. (6-3)	1.25	.75
1674	A427	8f multi (6-4)	1.25	.75
1675	A427	10f multi (6-5)	1.25	.75
1676	A427	60f multi (6-6)	6.25	3.25
		Nos. 1671-1676 (6)	12.50	7.00

Panda and Colored Stamps — A428

1981, Apr. 29   Photo.   Perf. 11½x11

1677	A428	8f shown (2-1)	.40	.25
1678	A428	60f Boat, bird (2-2)	2.75	1.50
a.		Booklet pane (8 #1677, souv. sheet with 1677-1678)	20.00	
		Complete booklet, #1678a	22.50	

Qinchuan Steer A429

Cattle Breeds: #1680, Binhu buffalo. #1681, Yak. #1682, Black and white dairy cows. 10f, Pasture red cow. 55f, Simmental cross-breed. T.63.

1981, May 5   Perf. 11x11½

1679	A429	4f multi (6-1)	1.75	.90
1680	A429	8f multi (6-2)	1.75	.90
1681	A429	8f multi (6-3)	1.75	.90
1682	A429	8f multi (6-4)	1.75	.90
1683	A429	10f multi (6-5)	1.75	.90
1684	A429	55f multi (6-6)	2.75	.90
		Nos. 1679-1684 (6)	11.50	5.40

Mail Delivery
Slogan — A430

13th World Telecommunications
Day — A431

1981, May 9 Perf. 11
1685 A430 8f multicolored 1.00 .25

1981, May 17 Perf. 11½x11
1686 A431 8f multicolored 1.00 .25

Construction
Worker — A432

Telephone
Building,
Peking — A433

1981, May 20 Perf. 11½
1687 A432 8f shown (4-1) .65 .50
1688 A432 8f Miner (4-2) .65 .50
1689 A432 8f Children crossing
   street (4-3) .65 .50
1690 A432 8f Farm worker (4-4) .65 .50
   Nos. 1687-1690 (4) 2.60 2.00

National Safety Month. J.65.

1981, June 5 Engr. Perf. 11½x11
1691 A433 8f violet brown 1.00 .60

Swaythling Cup,
Men's Team Table
Tennis — A434

36th World Table Tennis Championships
Victory — #1692: a, St. Bride Vase, men's
singles (7-3). b, Iran Cup, men's doubles (7-4).
c, G. Geist Prize, women's singles (7-5). d,
W.J. Pope Trophy, women's doubles (7-6). e,
Heydusek Prize, mixed doubles (7-7). #1694,
Marcel Corbillon Cup, women's team. #1693-
1694 printed in sheets of 16 (8 each) + 2
labels. J.71.

1981, June 30 Photo. Perf. 11½x11
1692   Strip of 5 3.25 3.25
   a.-e. A434 8f multi .30 .20
1693 A434 20f multi (7-1) 1.00 .80
1694 A434 20f multi (7-2) 1.00 .80

Chinese
Communist
Party, 60th
Anniv.
A435

1981, July 1 Photo. Perf. 11x11½
1695 A435 8f multicolored 1.00 .40

Hanpo
Pass,
Lushan
Mountains
(T.67)
A436

Photogravure & Engraved
1981, July 20 Perf. 12½x12
1696 8f Five-veteran Peak,
   vert. (7-1) 1.50 .65
1697 8f shown (7-2) 1.50 .65
1698 8f Yellow Dragon Pool,
   vert. (7-3) 1.50 .65
1699 8f Sunlit Peak (7-4) 1.50 .65
1700 8f Three-layer Spring,
   vert. (7-5) 1.50 .65
1701 8f Stone and pines (7-
   6) 1.50 .65
1702 60f Dragon-head Cliff,
   vert. (7-7) 13.50 4.50
   Nos. 1696-1702 (7) 22.50 8.40

Tremella
Fuciformis
A437

Designs: Edible mushrooms. T.66.

1981, Aug. 6 Photo. Perf. 11½
1703 A437 4f shown (6-1) .75 .45
1704 A437 8f Dictyophora indusiata (6-2) .75 .45
1705 A437 8f Hericium er-
   inaceus (6-3) .75 .45
1706 A437 8f Russula rubra
   (6-4) .75 .45
1707 A437 10f Lentinus edodes
   (6-5) .75 .45
1708 A437 70f Agaricus
   bisporus (6-6) 6.50 2.00
   Nos. 1703-1708 (6) 10.25 4.25

Quality Month
(J.66) — A438

Lunan Stone
Forest,
Yunn — A439

1981, Sept. 1 Photo. Perf. 11½x11
1709 A438 8f Silver medal (2-1) .60 .45
1710 A438 8f Gold medal (2-2) .60 .45

1981, Sept. 18 Perf. 11½
Designs: Views of limestone formations,
Lunan Stone Forest. #1711-1713 horiz. T.64.
1711 A439 8f multi (5-1) .85 .55
1712 A439 8f multi (5-2) .85 .55
1713 A439 8f multi (5-3) .85 .55
1714 A439 10f multi (5-4) .85 .55
1715 A439 70f multi (5-5) 6.75 4.50
   Nos. 1711-1715 (5) 10.15 6.70

Lu Xun,
Writer, Birth
Centenary
(J.67)
A440

1981, Sept. 25
1716 A440 8f shown (2-1) 1.00 .45
1717 A440 20f Portrait (diff.) (2-2) 1.75 1.10

Sun Yat-
sen and
Text
A441

70th Anniv. of 1911 Revolution: No. 1719,
72 Martyrs Grave, Huang Hua Gang. No.
1720, Hubei Provincial Government Headquarters, 1911. J.68.

1981, Oct. 10 Photo. Perf. 11x11½
1718 A441 8f multi (3-1) .95 .40
1719 A441 8f multi (3-2) .95 .40
1720 A441 8f multi (3-3) .95 .40
   Nos. 1718-1720 (3) 2.85 1.20

Asian Conference of Parliamentarians
on Population and Development,
Peking, Oct. 27 (J.73) — A442

1981, Oct. 27 Perf. 11½x11, 11x11½
1721 A442 8f Tree, vert. (2-1) .25 .25
1722 A442 70f shown (2-2) .75 .65

Huang Guo Shu
Falls — A443

Cowrie Shell and
Shell-shaped
Coin — A444

Nos. 1731-1739 are horizontal.

Perf. 11¼, 13x13¼ (#1726, 1729),
13¼x13 (#1731)

1981-83 Engr.
1723 A443 1f Xishuang Ban-
   na .20 .20
1724 A443 1½f Mt. Hua .20 .20
1725 A443 2f Mt. Tai .20 .20
1726 A443 3f shown .20 .20
1727 A443 4f Hainan Isld. .20 .20
   b. Perf. 11½x11 10.00 10.00
1728 A443 5f Tiger Hill,
   Suzhou .20 .20
1729 A443 8f Great Wall .20 .20
1730 A443 10f Immense Forest .20 .20
1731 A443 20f Mt. Tian .25 .20
1732 A443 30f Grassland, Inner Mongolia .25 .20
1733 A443 40f Stone Forest .35 .20
1734 A443 50f Banping Mountain .45 .20
1735 A443 70f Mt. Qomo-
   langma .55 .40
1736 A443 80f Seven-Star
   Crag .65 .55

1737 A443 $1 Three Gorges,
   Changjiang
   River .80 .60
1738 A443 $2 Guilin land-
   scape 1.40 1.25
1739 A443 $5 Mt. Huangshan 3.25 2.25
   Nos. 1723-1739 (17) 9.55 7.50
   Issued: #1737-1739, 10/9/82; #1732, 1734-
1736 4/1/83.

Photo.
Perf. 11½
1726a A443 3f .20 .20
1727a A443 4f .20 .20
1729a A443 8f .30 .25
1730a A443 10f .50 .40
1731a A443 20f 1.00 .75
   Nos. 1726a-1731a (5) 2.20 1.80
   Nos. 1727a, 1729a, 1730a exist tagged.
Values 10-15% higher.

Photogravure and Engraved
1981, Oct. 29 Perf. 11½x11
Ancient Coins. T.65.
1740 A444 4f shown (8-1) .75 .35
1741 A444 4f Shovel (8-2) .75 .35
1742 A444 8f Shovel, diff. (8-3) .75 .35
1743 A444 8f Shovel, diff. (8-4) .90 .35
1744 A444 8f Knife (8-5) .90 .35
1745 A444 8f Knife (8-6) .90 .35
1746 A444 60f Knife, diff. (8-7) 5.00 2.00
1747 A444 70f Gong (8-8) 7.00 2.25
   Nos. 1740-1747 (8) 16.95 6.35
   See Nos. 1765-1772.

A445   A446

1981, Nov. 10 Photo. Perf. 11½x11
1748 A445 8f multicolored .60 .25
   Intl. Year of the Disabled.

1981-82 Photo. Perf. 11
Twelve Beauties, from The Dream of Red
Mansions, by Cao Xueqin.
1749 A446 4f Daiyu (12-1) 1.50 .85
1750 A446 4f Baochai (12-
   2) 1.50 .85
1751 A446 8f Yuanchun
   (12-3) 1.50 .85
1752 A446 8f Yingchun
   (12-4) 1.50 .90
1753 A446 8f Tanchun (12-
   5) 1.50 .90
1754 A446 8f Xichun (12-6) 1.50 .90
1755 A446 8f Xiangyuh
   (12-7) 1.50 .90
1756 A446 10f Liwan (12-8) 2.50 .90
1757 A446 20f Xifeng (12-9) 2.50 1.25
1758 A446 30f Sister Qiao
   (12-10) 3.50 1.50
1759 A446 40f Keqing (12-
   11) 15.00 4.50
1760 A446 80f Miaoyu (12-
   12) 15.00 4.50
   Nos. 1749-1760 (12) 49.00 18.80

Souvenir Sheet
1761 A446 $2 Baoyu, Daiyu 290.00 140.00
   No. 1761 contains one 59x39mm stamp.
Issued: #1749, 1751, 1753, 1755, 1757, 1759,
1761, 11/20/81; others, 4/24/82. T.69.

A447   A448

1981, Dec. 21 Photo.
1762 A447 8f Girl playing (2-1) .60 .25
1763 A447 20f Girl holding trophy
   (2-2) .90 .50
   Women's team victory in 3rd World Cup Volleyball Championship (J.76).

Photogravure & Engraved

1982, Jan. 5   *Perf. 11½*
1764	A448	8f multicolored	5.75	2.25
a.		Booklet pane of 10 + label	57.50	
		Complete booklet, #1764a	60.00	

New Year 1982 (Year of the Dog). Stamps from No. 1764a have straight edges at top or bottom.

Coin Type of 1981

1982, Feb. 12
1765	A444	4f Guilian mask (8-1)	1.00	.50
1766	A444	4f Shu shovel (8-2)	1.00	.50
1767	A444	8f Xia zhuan shovel (8-3)	1.00	.50
1768	A444	8f Han Dan shovel (8-4)	1.00	.50
1769	A444	8f Knife (8-5)	1.00	.50
1770	A444	8f Ming knife (8-6)	1.00	.65
1771	A444	70f Jin hua knife (8-7)	3.75	1.75
1772	A444	80f Yi Liu Hua coin (8-8)	4.25	2.25
		Nos. 1765-1772 (8)	14.00	7.15

T.71.

Nie Er (1912-1935), Natl. Anthem Composer — A449

1982, Feb. 15   *Perf. 11x11½*
1773	A449	8f multicolored	.70	.30

Intl. Drinking Water and Sanitation Decade, 1981-1990 A450

1982, Mar. 1   *Perf. 11½x11*
1774	A450	8f multicolored	.70	.30

TB Bacillus Centenary A451

1982, Mar. 24   *Perf. 11x11½*
1775	A451	8f multicolored	1.10	.35

Fire Control (T.76) — A452

1982, May 8   Photo.   *Perf. 11½x11*
1776	A452	8f Water hoses (2-1)	.75	.30
1777	A452	8f Chemical extinguisher (2-2)	.95	.30

Syzygy of the Nine Planets, Mar. 10 and May 16 — A453

1982, May 16   *Perf. 11½*
1778	A453	8f multicolored	1.00	.35

Medicinal Herbs — A454

Soong Ching Ling (1893-1981), Sun Yat-sen's Widow — A455

1982, May 20   *Perf. 11½x11*
1779	A454	4f Hemerocallis flava (6-1)	.55	.40
1780	A454	8f Fritillaria unibracteata (6-2)	.55	.40
1781	A454	8f Aconitum carmichaeli (6-3)	.55	.40
1782	A454	10f Lilium brownii (6-4)	1.00	.60
1783	A454	20f Arisaema (6-5)	1.00	.60
1784	A454	70f Paeonia lactiflora (6-6)	3.00	1.25
		Nos. 1779-1784 (6)	6.65	3.65

Souvenir Sheet
1785	A454	$2 Iris tectorum maxim	27.50	12.50

No. 1785 contains one 89x39mm stamp. Nos. 1779-1784 numbered T.72.

1982, May 29   *Perf. 11½*
1786	A455	8f Addressing Consultative Conf. (2-1)	.75	.40
1787	A455	20f Portrait (2-2)	1.50	1.25

J.82.

Sable (T.68) A456

1982, June 20   Photo.   *Perf. 11½*
1788	A456	8f shown (2-1)	.70	.50
1789	A456	80f Sable, diff. (2-2)	4.00	3.25
a.		Bklt. pane of 8, 6 8f plus sheetlet of 2 (8f, 80f)	37.50	
		Complete booklet, #1789a	42.50	

A457

A458

1982, June 30   *Perf. 11½x11*
1790	A457	8f multicolored	1.50	.30

Natl. census, July 1.

1982, July 25   Photo.   *Perf. 11½x11*
1791	A458	8f multicolored	1.00	.25

2nd UN Conference on Peaceful Uses of Outer Space, Vienna, Aug. 9-21.

Strolling in Autumn Woods, by Shen Zhou, Ming Dynasty — A459

Fan Paintings (Ming or Qing Dynasty): No. 1793, Jackdaw on Withered Tree, by Tang Yin. No. 1794 Bamboo and Sparrows, by Zhou Zhimian. 10f, Writing Poem under Pine, by Chen Hongshou and Bai Han. 20f, Chrysanthemums, by Yun Shouping, Qing. 70f, Birds, Crape Myrtle and Chinese Parasol, by Wang Wu, Qing. T.77.

1982, July 31   *Perf. 11½*
1792	A459	4f multi (6-1)	1.25	.75
1793	A459	8f multi (6-2)	1.00	.65
1794	A459	8f multi (6-3)	1.00	.65
1795	A459	10f multi (6-4)	1.00	.65
1796	A459	20f multi (6-5)	1.75	.75
1797	A459	70f multi (6-6)	3.50	2.00
		Nos. 1792-1797 (6)	9.50	5.45

A460

A461

1982, Aug. 25   *Perf. 11½x11*
1798	A460	8f multicolored	.40	.25

60th anniv. of Chinese Geological Society.

1982, Aug. 25   Photo.   *Perf. 11½x11*
1799	A461	4f Orpiment (4-1)	.40	.25
1800	A461	8f Stibnite (4-2)	1.00	.25
1801	A461	10f Cinnabar (4-3)	1.00	.25
1802	A461	20f Wolframite (4-4)	1.25	.50
		Nos. 1799-1802 (4)	3.05	1.25

T.73.

Souvenir Sheet

Messenger, Tomb Mural, Jiayu Pass, Wei-Jin Period — A462

1982, Aug. 25
1803	A462	$1 multicolored	20.00	10.00

All-China Philatelic Federation, 1st Cong.

12th Natl. Communist Party Congress A463

Hoopoe — A464

1982, Sept. 1   *Perf. 11½*
1804	A463	8f multicolored	1.00	.30

1982, Sept. 10   *Perf. 11½x11*
1805	A464	8f shown (5-1)	1.00	.35
1806	A464	8f Swallows (5-2)	1.00	.35
1807	A464	8f Oriole (5-3)	1.00	.35
1808	A464	20f Chickadees (5-4)	3.00	.75
1809	A464	70f Woodpecker (5-5)	8.75	3.00
		Nos. 1805-1809 (5)	14.75	4.80

Souvenir Sheet
1810	A464	$2 Cuckoos	47.50	20.00

#1810 contains one 56x36mm stamp. T.79.

Japan-China Relations Normalization, 10th Anniv. — A465

World Food Day — A466

Flower Paintings: 8f, Plum blossoms, by Guan Shanyue. 70f, Hibiscus, by Xiao Shufang. J.84.

1982, Sept. 29   *Perf. 11*
1811 A465 8f multi (2-1)   1.25   .30
1812 A465 70f multi (2-2)   2.50   .85

1982, Oct. 16   *Perf. 11½*
1813 A466 8f multicolored   .50   .25

Guo Morou (1892-1978), Acad. of Sciences Pres.
A467

Bodhisattva, 11th Cent. Sculpture
A468

Designs: Portraits. J.87.

1982, Nov. 16 Photo. Perf. 11½x11
1814 A467 8f multi (2-1)   .40   .25
1815 A467 20f multi (2-2)   .50   .30

1982, Nov. 19   *Perf. 11*
Liao Dynasty Buddha Sculptures, Lower Huayan Monastery. T.74.
1816 A468 8f multi (4-1)   .75   .35
1817 A468 8f multi (4-2)   .75   .35
1818 A468 8f multi (4-3)   1.00   .35
1819 A468 70f multi (4-4)   3.25 2.50
      Nos. 1816-1819 (4)   5.75 3.55

Souvenir Sheet
                                      Perf. 11x11½
1820 A468 $2 multicolored   40.00 18.00

No. 1820 contains one 36x55mm stamp.

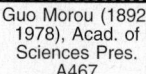

Dr. D.S. Kotnis, Indian Physician in 8th Army (J.83)
A469

Perf. 11½x11, 11x11½
1982, Dec. 9   *Photo.*
1821 A469 8f Portrait, vert. (2-1)   .50   .25
1822 A469 70f Riding horse (2-2)   1.90 1.40

11th Communist Youth League Natl. Congress
A470

1982, Dec. 20   *Perf. 11x11½*
1823 A470 8f multicolored   .75   .25

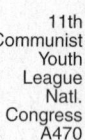

Bronze Wine Container — A471

Western Zhou Dynasty Bronze (1200-771 B.C.): No. 1825, Three-legged cooking pot. No. 1826, Food bowl. No. 1827, Three-legged cooking pot (diff.). No. 1828, Animal-shaped wine container. 10f, Wine container with lid.

20f, Round food bowl. 70f, Square wine container. T.75.

Photogravure & Engraved
1982, Dec. 25   *Perf. 11*
1824 A471 4f multi (8-1)   1.25   .60
1825 A471 4f multi (8-2)   1.25   .60
1826 A471 8f multi (8-3)   1.25   .60
1827 A471 8f multi (8-4)   1.25   .60
1828 A471 8f multi (8-5)   1.25   .60
1829 A471 10f multi (8-6)   2.00   .60
1830 A471 20f multi (8-7)   2.50 1.25
1831 A471 70f multi (8-8)   11.00 2.75
      Nos. 1824-1831 (8)   21.75 7.60

A472

1983, Jan. 5   *Perf. 11½*
1832 A472 8f multicolored   20.00 4.50
  a.   Booklet pane of 12   60.00 70.00
        Complete booklet, #1832a   110.00

New Year 1983 (Year of the Pig). Stamps from No. 1832a have straight edges at top or bottom and sell for less as singles than No. 1832.

A473

A474

Stringed Instruments (T.81).

1983, Jan. 20 Perf. 11½x11, 11x11½
1833 A473 4f Konghou (5-1)   2.50   .75
1834 A473 8f Ruan (5-2)   2.50   .75
1835 A473 8f Qin, horiz. (5-3)   2.50   .75
1836 A473 10f Piba (5-4)   3.00   .75
1837 A473 70f Sanxian (5-5)   19.00 4.00
      Nos. 1833-1837 (5)   29.50 7.00

1983, Feb. 7 Photo. Perf. 11½x11
1838 A474 8f Memorial Tower, Zhengzhou (2-1)   .80   .40
1839 A474 8f Monument, Jiangan (2-2)   1.00   .40

60th Anniv. of Peking-Hankow Railroad Workers' Strike (J.89).

The Western Chamber, Traditional Opera, by Wang Shifu (1271-1368)
A475

Scenes from the opera.

1983, Feb. 21 Photo. Perf. 11x11½
1840 A475 8f multi (4-1)   2.25   .85
1841 A475 8f multi (4-2)   2.25   .85
1842 A475 10f multi (4-3)   3.25 1.75
1843 A475 80f multi (4-4)   17.50 4.75
      Nos. 1840-1843 (4)   25.25 8.20

Souvenir Sheet
Photogravure and Engraved
                                      Perf. 12
1844 A475 $2 multicolored   150.00 40.00
#1844 contains one 27x48mm stamp. T.82.

Karl Marx (1818-1883) (J.90) — A476

Photogravure & Engraved
1983, Mar. 14   *Perf. 11½x11*
1845 A476 8f Portrait (2-1)   .50   .25
1846 A476 20f Making speech (2-2)   1.00   .35

Tomb of the Yellow Emperor (T.84)
A477

Photogravure & Engraved
1983, Apr. 5   *Perf. 11½*
1847 A477 8f Tomb, vert. (3-1)   1.25   .50
1848 A477 10f Hall of Founder of Chinese Culture (3-2)   1.75   .50
1849 A477 20f Cypress tree, vert. (3-3)   3.00   .90
      Nos. 1847-1849 (3)   6.00 1.90

World Communications Year — A478

1983, Apr. 28 Photo. Perf. 11½
1850 A478 8f multicolored   1.00   .25

Male Chinese Alligator (T.85) — A479

Photogravure & Engraved
1983, May 24   *Perf. 11*
1851 A479 8f shown (2-1)   1.00   .50
1852 A479 20f Female, hatching eggs (2-2)   1.75   .85

Kitten, by Tan Arxi — A480

Various children's drawings. T.86.

1983, June 1   *Perf. 11½x11*
1853 A480 8f multi (4-1)   .45   .25
1854 A480 8f multi (4-2)   .45   .25
1855 A480 8f multi (4-3)   .45   .25
1856 A480 8f multi (4-4)   .45   .25
      Nos. 1853-1856 (4)   1.80 1.00

6th Natl. People's Congress (J.94)
A481

1983, June 6   *Perf. 11x11½*
1857 A481 8f Hall (2-1)   .40   .25
1858 A481 20f Natl. anthem score (2-2) 1.10   .55

Terra Cotta Figures, Qin Dynasty (221-207 BC)
A482

1983, June 30
1859 A482 8f Soldiers (4-1)   1.00   .65
1860 A482 8f Heads (4-2)   1.00   .65
1861 A482 10f Soldiers, horses (4-3)   1.50   .75
1862 A482 70f Excavation site (4-4)   5.00 3.00
  a.   Bklt. pane of 8 (#1859, 3 #1860, 3 #1861, #1862)   50.00 35.00
      Nos. 1859-1862 (4)   8.50 5.05

Souvenir Sheet
1863 A482 $2 Soldier leading horse   52.50 35.00
  a.   Booklet pane of 1   55.00
        Complete booklet, #1862a, #1863a   140.00

#1863 contains one 59x39mm stamp. T.88.

A483

1983, July 20 Photo. Perf. 11
Design A483
1864   4f Sun Yujiao (8-1)   1.25   .40
1865   8f Chen Miaochang (8-2)   1.25   .40
1866   8f Bai Suzhen (8-3)   1.25   .40
1867   8f Sister Thirteen (8-4)   1.25   .40
1868   10f Qin Xianglian (8-5)   1.25   .40
1869   20f Yang Yuhuan (8-6)   2.50   .90
1870   50f Cui Yingying (8-7)   8.00 1.75
1871   80f Mu Guiying (8-8)   15.00 2.50
      Nos. 1864-1871 (8)   31.75 7.15

Female roles in Peking opera (T.87).

A484

1983, Aug. 10 Photo. Perf. 11½
Paintings by Liu Lingcang.
1872 A484 8f Li Bai (4-1)   1.25   .30
1873 A484 8f Du Fu (4-2)   1.25   .30
1874 A484 8f Han Yu (4-3)   1.25   .30
1875 A484 70f Liu Zongyuan (4-4)   11.00 2.75
      Nos. 1872-1875 (4)   14.75 3.65

Poets and philosophers of ancient China (J.92).

5th Natl. Women's Congress — A485

1983, Sept. 1   Photo.   Perf. 11½
1876 A485 8f multicolored   .70 .25

5th National Games (J.93) — A486

1983, Sept. 16   Photo.   Perf. 11½
1877 A486 4f Emblem (6-1)   .60 .30
1878 A486 8f Gymnast (6-2)   .60 .30
1879 A486 8f Badminton (6-3)   .60 .30
1880 A486 8f Diving (6-4)   .60 .30
1881 A486 20f High jump (6-5)   1.00 .75
1882 A486 70f Wind surfing (6-6) 5.25 2.00
   Nos. 1877-1882 (6)   8.65 3.95

Family Planning (T.91) A487

1983, Sept. 19   Perf. 11x11½
1883 A487 8f One child (2-1)   .30 .25
1884 A487 8f Cultivated land (2-2) .30 .25

10th Intl. Trade Union Congress — A488

1983, Oct. 18   Litho.   Perf. 11½
1885 A488 8f multicolored   .60 .25

Swans (T.83) A489

Perf. 11x11½ on 3 sides
1983, Nov. 18   Photo.
1886 A489 8f (4-1)   .35 .30
1887 A489 8f (4-2)   .35 .30
1888 A489 10f (4-3)   .60 .35
1889 A489 80f (4-4)   2.25 1.75
  a. Booklet pane, 7 #1886, 1
       each #1887-1889   27.50 15.00
      Complete booklet, #1889a 50.00
   Nos. 1886-1889 (4)   3.55 2.70

A490

A491

Various photos. J.96.

1983, Nov. 24   Photo.   Perf. 11½
1890 A490 8f multi (4-1)   .75 .40
1891 A490 8f multi (4-2)   .75 .40
1892 A490 8f multi (4-3)   .75 .40
1893 A490 8f multi (4-4)   .75 .40
   Nos. 1890-1893 (4)   3.00 1.60

85th birth anniv. of Liu Shaoqi, political leader.

1983, Nov. 29   Photo.   Perf. 11½
1894 A491 8f No. 117 (2-1)   .40 .25
1895 A491 20f No. 4L1 (2-2) .65 .35

CHINAPEX '83 Natl. Philatelic Exhibition (J.99).

A492   A493

Various portraits. J.97.

1983, Dec. 26   Photo.   Perf. 11½
1896 A492 8f 1925 (4-1)   .50 .30
1897 A492 8f 1945 (4-2)   .50 .30
1898 A492 10f 1952 (4-3) 2.00 .40
1899 A492 20f 1961 (4-4) 2.50 1.00
   Nos. 1896-1899 (4)   5.50 2.00

90th birth anniv. of Mao Tse-tung.

Photogravure and Engraved
1984, Jan. 5   Perf. 11½
1900 A493 8f multicolored   6.50 2.25
  a. Booklet pane of 12   80.00 27.00
      Complete booklet, #1900a 105.00

New Year 1984 (Year of the Rat). Stamps from No. 1900a have straight edge at top or bottom.

Beauties Wearing Flowers — A494

Portions of painting by Zhou Fang (Tang Dynasty). T.89.

1984, Mar. 24   Photo.   Perf. 11
1901 A494 8f multi (3-1)   1.00 .35
1902 A494 10f multi (3-2)   1.00 .40
1903 A494 70f multi (3-3)   6.25 2.50
   Nos. 1901-1903 (3)   8.25 3.25

Souvenir Sheet
1904 A494 $2 Entire painting 170.00 50.00

No. 1904 contains one 162x40mm stamp.

Chinese Roses (T.93) — A495

Ren Bishi (1904-50), Statesman A496

1984, Apr. 20   Photo.   Perf. 11½
1905 A495 4f Spring of Shang-
              hai (6-1)   .70 .25
1906 A495 8f Rosy Dawn of
              Pujiang River (6-2) .70 .25
1907 A495 8f Pearl (6-3)   .70 .25
1908 A495 10f Black whirlwind
              (6-4)   .70 .30
1909 A495 20f Yellow flower in
              battlefield (6-5) 1.25 .40
1910 A495 70f Blue Phoenix (6-6) 3.50 1.25
   Nos. 1905-1910 (6)   7.55 2.70

1984, Apr. 30   Perf. 11½x11
1911 A496 8f multicolored   .60 .25

Crested Ibis (T.94) A497

1984, May 15   Photo.   Perf. 11x11½
1912 A497 8f Flying (3-1)   .75 .25
1913 A497 8f Wading (3-2)   .75 .25
1914 A497 80f Perching (3-3)   2.25 1.50
   Nos. 1912-1914 (3)   3.75 2.00

Chinese Red Cross Society, 80th Anniv. — A498

1984, May 29   Perf. 11½
1915 A498 8f multicolored   .70 .25

Gezhou Dam, Yangtze River (T.95) — A499

1984, June 15   Photo.
1916 A499 8f Dam (3-1)   .40 .30
1917 A499 10f Bridge, vert. (3-2) .60 .35
1918 A499 20f Lock Gate #2 (3-
              3)   1.25 .65
   Nos. 1916-1918 (3)   2.25 1.30

Zhuo Zheng Garden, Suzhou (T.96) — A500

Photogravure & Engraved
1984, June 30   Perf. 11½x11
1919 A500 8f Inverted Image
              Tower (4-1)   .65 .40
1920 A500 8f Loquat Garden (4-2) .65 .40
1921 A500 10f Water Court, Xiao
              Cang Lang (4-3)   .70 .40
1922 A500 70f Yuanxiang Hall,
              Yiyu Study (4-4) 2.00 1.50
   Nos. 1919-1922 (4)   4.00 2.70

1984 Summer Olympics A501

1984, July 28   Photo.   Perf. 11½
1923 A501 4f Shooting (6-1)   .35 .25
1924 A501 8f High jump (6-2)   .35 .25
1925 A501 8f Weight lifting (6-3) .35 .25
1926 A501 10f Gymnastics (6-4) .40 .25
1927 A501 20f Volleyball (6-5) .45 .30
1928 A501 80f Diving (6-6)   1.25 .40
   Nos. 1923-1928 (6)   3.15 1.70

Souvenir Sheet
1929 A501 $2 Athletes, rings   10.00 4.50

#1929 contains one 61x38mm stamp. J.103.

Calligraphy A502

Luanhe River Water Diversion Project (T.97) A503

Artworks by Wu Changshuo. T.98.

1984, Aug. 27   Photo.   Perf. 11½
1930 A502 4f shown (8-1)   .50 .30
1931 A502 4f A Pair of
              Peaches (8-2)   .50 .30
1932 A502 8f Lotus (8-3)   .50 .30
1933 A502 8f Wisteria (8-4)   .50 .30
1934 A502 8f Peony (8-5)   1.00 .50
1935 A502 10f Chrysanthemum
              (8-6)   1.00 .50
1936 A502 20f Plum Blossom
              (8-7)   1.25 .50
1937 A502 70f Seal Cutting (8-8) 2.75 1.75
   Nos. 1930-1937 (8)   8.00 4.45

Perf. 11½x11, 11 (#1939)
1984, Sept. 11   Photo.
1938 A503 8f multi (3-1)   .35 .25
1939 A503 10f multi, horiz. (3-2) .35 .25
1940 A503 20f multi (3-3)   .50 .30
   Nos. 1938-1940 (3)   1.20 .80

Chinese-Japanese Youth
(J.104) — A504

1984, Sept. 24   Photo.   Perf. 11½
1941 A504 8f Neighbors (3-1)   .30   .25
1942 A504 20f Planting tree (3-2)   .50   .25
1943 A504 80f Dancing (3-3)   1.00   .65
Nos. 1941-1943 (3)   1.80 1.15

People's
Republic, 35th
Anniv.
(J.105) — A505

1984, Oct. 1   Photo.   Perf. 11½x11
Size: 26x35mm
1944 A505 8f Engineer (5-1)   .30   .25
1945 A505 8f Farm woman (5-2)   .30   .25
1946 A505 8f Scientist (5-4)   .30   .25
1947 A505 8f Soldier (5-5)   .30   .25
Size: 36x48mm
Perf. 11
1948 A505 20f Cranes (5-3)   .50   .30
Nos. 1944-1948 (5)   1.70 1.30

110th Birth
Anniv. of
Chen
Jiageng
(J.106)
A506

1984, Oct. 21   Photo.   Perf. 12½x12
1949 A506 8f Chen Jiageng (2-1)   .65   .25
1950 A506 80f Jimei School (2-2) 2.10 .40

The
Maiden's
Study
A507

Scenes from The Peony Pavilion, by Tang
Xianzu. T.99.

Photogravure & Engraved
1984, Oct. 30   Perf. 11
1951 A507 8f shown (4-1)   .50   .40
1952 A507 8f In the dream-
              land (4-2)   .50   .40
1953 A507 20f Du Liniang
              drawing self-
              portrait (4-3)   1.00   .75
1954 A507 70f Married to Liu
              Mengmai (4-4)   2.75 2.50
Nos. 1951-1954 (4)   4.75 4.05
Souvenir Sheet
Perf. 11½
1955 A507 $2 Playing in the
              garden   42.50 20.00
No. 1955 contains one 90x60mm stamp.

Emei Shan Mountain Scenery
(T.100) — A508

1984, Nov. 16   Perf. 11
1956 A508 4f Baoguo Temple
              (6-1)   .55   .30
1957 A508 8f Leiyin Temple (6-2)   .55   .35
1958 A508 8f Hongchun Lawn
              (6-3)   .35   .35
1959 A508 10f Elephant bath
              (6-4)   .75   .45
1960 A508 20f Woyun Temple
              (6-5)   1.50 1.00
1961 A508 80f Shining Cloud
              Sea at Jinding
              (6-6)   5.25 2.50
Nos. 1956-1961 (6)   8.95 4.95

A509   A510

Portraits.

1984, Dec. 15   Photo.   Perf. 11½x11
1962 A509 8f During the Long
              March (3-1)   .25   .25
1963 A509 10f At 7th Natl. Party
              Congress (3-2)   .35   .25
1964 A509 20f In motorcade (3-3)   .45   .25
Nos. 1962-1964 (3)   1.05   .75
Former party secretary Ren Bishi (1904-50).

1984, Dec. 25   Perf. 11
1965 A510 8f Flower arrange-
              ment   .50   .25
Chinese insurance industry.

New Year 1985
(Year of the
Ox) — A511

Photogravure & Engraved
1985, Jan. 5   Perf. 11½
1966 A511 8f T.102   2.00   .50
a.   Bklt. pane of 4 + 8 plus la-
       bel   24.00 12.00
       Complete booklet, #1966a   35.00
Stamps from No. 1966a have straight edge
at top or bottom.

Zunyi Meeting, 50th Anniv. — A512

Paintings: 8f, The Zunyi Meeting, by Liu
Xiangping. 20f, The Red Army Successfully
Arrived in Northern Shaanxi, by Zhao Yu.
J.107.

1985, Jan. 15   Photo.   Perf. 11x11½
1967 A512 8f multi (2-1)   .75   .30
1968 A512 20f multi (2-2)   1.25   .60

A513

A514

Lantern Folk Festival: No. 1969, Lotus of
Good Luck. No. 1970, Auspicious dragon and
phoenix. No. 1971, A hundred flowers blossoming. 70f, Prosperity and affluence. T.104.

1985, Feb. 28   Perf. 11½
1969 A513 8f multi (4-1)   .50   .50
1970 A513 8f multi (4-2)   .50   .50
1971 A513 8f multi (4-3)   .50   .50
1972 A513 70f multi (4-4)   2.25 1.25
Nos. 1969-1972 (4)   3.75 2.00

1985, Mar. 8
1973 A514 20f multicolored   .50   .25
UN Decade for Women (1976-85).

Mei (Prunus mume)
(T.103) — A515

1985, Apr. 5   Perf. 11
1974 A515 8f Green calyx (6-1)   .30   .25
1975 A515 8f Pendant mei (6-2)   .30   .25
1976 A515 8f Contorted drag-
              on (6-3)   .30   .25
1977 A515 10f Cinnabar (6-4)   .50   .25
1978 A515 20f Versicolor mei
              (6-5)   .60   .30
1979 A515 80f Apricot mei (6-6)   2.50 1.00
Nos. 1974-1979 (6)   4.50 2.30
Souvenir Sheet
Perf. 11½
1980 A515 $2 Duplicate and
              condensed
              fragrance mei   37.50 20.00
No. 1980 contains one 93x52mm stamp.

A516   A518

A517

1985, May 1   Photo.   Perf. 11
1981 A516 8f Huizo Guild Hall,
              Guangzhou   .50   .25
All-China Fed. of Trade Unions.

1985, May 4   Photo.
1982 A517 20f multicolored   .50   .25
Intl. Youth Year.

1985, May 24   Perf. 11½
Paintings of giant pandas: 8f, 20f, 50f, 80f,
by Han Meilin; $3, by Wu Zuoren. T.106.
1983 A518 8f multi (4-1), vert.   .30   .25
1984 A518 20f multi (4-2)   .30   .30
1985 A518 50f multi (4-3), vert.   .40   .25
1986 A518 80f multi (4-4)   .65   .50
Nos. 1983-1986 (4)   1.65 1.40
Souvenir Sheet
Perf. 11x11½
1987 A518 $3 multi, vert.   4.50 2.50
a.   Ovptd. in sheet margin   7.00
No. 1987 contains one 39x59mm stamp.
No. 1987a ovptd. in sheet margin with
panda hologram, PJZ-4 and horizontal Chinese inscription in gold. Issued 10/9/96.
No. 1987a was sold in a mount affixed to a
small card.

Xian Xinghai
(1905-1945),
Composer
A519

Agnes Smedley,
1892-1950 (3-
1) — A520

Design: Bust, by Cao Chongen and music
from The Yellow River Cantata.

1985, June 13   Photo.   Perf. 11½x11
1988 A519 8f multicolored   .65   .25

1985, June 25
American journalists: 20f, Anna Louise
Strong, 1885-1970 (3-2). 80f, Edgar Snow,
1905-1972 (3-3). J.112.
1989 A520 8f multicolored   .25   .25
1990 A520 20f multicolored   .35   .25
1991 A520 80f multicolored   .75   .40
Nos. 1989-1991 (3)   1.35   .90

Zheng He's West
Seas Expedition,
580th
Anniv. — A521

#1992, Portrait of the navigator. #1993,
Peace envoy. 20f, Trade, cultural exchange.
80f, Honored for navigational feats. J.113.

1985, July 11   **Perf. 11½**

1992	A521	8f multi (4-1)	.40	.25
1993	A521	8f multi (4-2)	.40	.25
1994	A521	20f multi (4-3)	.90	.35
1995	A521	80f multi (4-4)	2.25	.70
		Nos. 1992-1995 (4)	3.95	1.55

Xu Beihong, 1895-1953, Painter (J.114) A522

1985, July 19   **Perf. 11½x11, 11x11½**

1996	A522	8f Self-portrait (2-1), vert.	.30	.25
1997	A522	20f shown (2-2)	.75	.25

A523   A524

Designs: 8f, Lin Zexu, 1785-1850, statesman, patriot. 80f, Burning opium at Humen, bas-relief.

1985, Aug. 30   **Perf. 11**

1998	A523	8f multi (2-1)	.30	.25

Size: 51x22mm

1999	A523	80f multi (2-2)	.70	.30

Lin Zexu's ban of the opium trade catalyzed the Anglo-Chinese Opium Wars. J.115.

1985, Sept. 1   **Perf. 11½x11**

2000	A524	8f Prosperity (3-1)	.25	.20
2001	A524	10f Celebration (3-2)	.25	.25
2002	A524	20f Abundant Harvest (3-3)	.50	.45
		Nos. 2000-2002 (3)	1.05	.90

Tibet Autonomous Region, 20th anniv. (J.116).

End of World War II, 40th Anniv. A525

Woodcuts by Wu Biduan: 8f, The Chinese Army Rose Against the Japanese Agressors at Logouqiao (2-1). 80f, The Eighth Route Army and Militia Fought Around the Great Wall (2-2). J.117.

1985, Sept. 3   **Perf. 11**

2003	A525	8f multi	.30	.25
2004	A525	80f multi	.70	.25

2nd Natl. Worker's Games, Sept. 8-15, Beijing A526

Competitors from various events and: 8f, Men's bicycling (2-1). 20f, Women hurdlers (2-2). J.118.

1985, Sept. 8   **Perf. 11x11½**

2005	A526	8f multi	.65	.55
2006	A526	20f multi	.90	.80

Xinjiang Uygur Autonomous Region, 30th Anniv. (J.119) A527

1985, Oct. 1   **Photo.**   **Perf. 11½**

2007	A527	8f Oasis in the Gobi, woman (3-1)	.25	.25
2008	A527	10f Oil field, Lake Tianchi (3-2)	.30	.25
2009	A527	20f Tianshan pasture, woman (3-3)	.50	.25
		Nos. 2007-2009 (3)	1.05	.75

Size of No. 2008, 60x30mm.

1st Natl. Youth Games, Oct. 6-15, Zhengzhou (J.121) — A528

1985, Oct. 6   **Perf. 11½x11**

2010	A528	8f Girls' track & field (2-1)	.25	.25
2011	A528	20f Boys' basketball (2-2)	.35	.35

Forbidden City Main Buildings — A529

1985, Oct. 10   **Perf. 11½**

2012	A529	8f multi (4-1)	.25	.25
2013	A529	8f multi (4-2)	.25	.25
2014	A529	20f multi (4-3)	.25	.25
2015	A529	80f multi (4-4)	.50	.50
a.		Vert. strip of 4, #2012-2015	1.75	1.75

Palace Museum, 60th anniv. J.120.

Zou Taofen (1895-1935), Journalist (J.122) — A530

1985, Nov. 5   **Perf. 11½x11**

2016	A530	8f Portrait (2-1)	.25	.25
2017	A530	20f Epitaph by Zhou En-lai (2-2)	.25	.25
a.		Pair, #2016-2017	.60	.50

December 9th Revolution, 50th Anniv. — A531

1985, Dec. 9   **Perf. 11½**

2018	A531	8f Memorial Pavilion	.40	.25

New Year 1986 — A532   Natl. Space Industry — A533

Photogravure & Engraved

1986, Jan. 5   **Perf. 11½**

2019	A532	8f multicolored	1.00	.45
a.		Bkt. pane of 4 + 8 with label btwn	5.50	
		Complete booklet, #2019a	30.00	

1986, Feb. 1   **Photo.**

4f, 1st experimental satellite. #2021, Recoverable satellite. #2022, Underwater rocket launch. 10f, Rocket launch. 20f, Earth satellite receiver. 70f, Satellite trajectory diagram. T.108.

2020	A533	4f multi (6-1)	.40	.25
2021	A533	8f multi (6-2)	.40	.25
2022	A533	8f multi (6-3)	.40	.25
2023	A533	10f multi (6-4)	.50	.30
2024	A533	20f multi (6-5)	.50	.30
2025	A533	70f multi (6-6)	1.50	.50
		Nos. 2020-2025 (6)	3.70	1.85

Dong Biwu (1886-1975), Party Founder (J.123) — A534

Lin Boqu (1886-1960), Party Leader (J.124) — A535

Photogravure and Engraved

1986, Mar. 5   **Perf. 11½x11**

2026	A534	8f 1975 (2-1)	.30	.25
2027	A534	20f 1945 (2-2)	.40	.25

1986, Mar. 20

2028	A535	8f shown (2-1)	.30	.25
2029	A535	20f Lin standing (2-2)	.40	.25

Marshal He Long (1896-1969), Revolution Leader (J.126) — A536

1986, Mar. 22   **Perf. 11x11½**

2030	A536	8f shown (2-1)	.70	.25
2031	A536	20f On horseback (2-2)	.70	.25

Halley's Comet — A537

1986, Apr. 11   **Photo.**   **Perf. 11½**

2032	A537	20f dk bl & gray	.40	.25

White Crane (T.110) A538

1986, May 22   **Perf. 11x11½, 11½x11**

2033	A538	8f Two cranes (3-1)	.30	.25
2034	A538	10f One flying (3-2), vert.	.40	.25
2035	A538	70f Four cranes (3-3), vert.	.70	.30
		Nos. 2033-2035 (3)	1.40	.80

Souvenir Sheet

2036	A538	$2 Flock	7.00	4.00

No. 2036 contains one 116x25mm stamp.

Li Weihan (1896-1984), Party Leader (J.127) — A539

1986, June 2   **Perf. 11x11½**

2037	A539	8f Portrait (2-1)	.25	.25
2038	A539	20f Writing (2-2)	.30	.25

Intl. Peace Year A540

1986, June 16   **Perf. 11**

2039	A540	8f multi	.30	.25

Mao Dun (1896-1981), Writer (J.129) — A541

1986, July 4   **Perf. 11x11½**

2040	A541	8f Portrait (2-1)	.25	.25
2041	A541	20f Portrait, diff. (2-2)	.25	.25

Wang Jiaxiang (1906-1974), Party Leader (J.130) — A542

1986, Aug. 15   **Perf. 11½x11**

2042	A542	8f Portrait (2-1)	.25	.25
2043	A542	20f Portrait, diff. (2-2)	.25	.25

Teacher's Day A543

1986, Sept. 10   **Perf. 11**

2044	A543	8f multi	.35	.25

Magnolia Liliflora (T.111) A544

1986, Sept. 23   **Perf. 11x11½**

2045	A544	8f Blossom (3-1)	.40	.35
2046	A544	8f Two blossoms (3-2)	.40	.35
2047	A544	70f Blossom, diff. (3-3)	2.50	2.25
		Nos. 2045-2047 (3)	3.30	2.95

Souvenir Sheet

2048	A544	$2 Three blossoms	12.00	6.00

No. 2048 contains one 132x70mm stamp.

Folk Houses — A545

Perf. 13x13½, 11x11½, (1½f, 3f, #2057-2062)

				Photo.
1986, Apr. 1				**Photo.**
2049	A545	1f	Inner Mongolia	.25	.20
2050	A545	1½f	Tibet	.25	.20
2051	A545	2f	Northeastern China	.25	.20
2052	A545	3f	Hunan	.25	.20
2053	A545	4f	So. Yangtze River	.25	.20
2054	A545	8f	Beijing	.25	.20
2055	A545	10f	Yunnan	.25	.20
2056	A545	20f	Shanghai	.25	.20
2057	A545	30f	Anhui	.30	.20
2058	A545	40f	No. Shaanxi	.40	.30
2059	A545	50f	Sichuan	.60	.40
2060	A545	90f	Taiwan	.80	.55
2061	A545	$1	Fujian	.85	.65
2062	A545	$1.10	Zhejiang	.90	.75
		Nos. 2049-2062 (14)		5.85	4.45

Issue dates: 3f, Dec. 25; 4f, $1, Oct. 15; 20f, 50f, Sept. 10; 40f, Nov. 15; others, Apr. 1. Postal forgeries of No. 2056 exist.
See Nos. 2198-2204.

		Photo.
1989-90		**Photo.**
2055a	Perf. 11x11½ ('89)	1.00	1.00
2056a	Perf. 11x11½ ('89)	1.50	1.00
2057a	Perf. 13x13½ ('90)	.65	.35
2058a	Perf. 13x13½	9.00	4.50
2059a	Perf. 13x13½ ('89)	1.10	.60
2061a	Perf. 13x13½ ('90)	2.25	1.25
	Nos. 2055a-2061a (6)	15.50	8.70

Souvenir Sheet

All-China Philatelic Federation, 2nd Congress — A546

			Litho.	Perf. 11½
1986, Oct. 17		**Litho.**	**Perf. 11½**
2063	A546	$2 Jade lion	5.00	2.00

Leaders of the 1911 Revolution (J.132) A547

			Photo.	Perf. 11x11½
1986, Oct. 10		**Photo.**	**Perf. 11x11½**
2064	A547	8f Sun Yat-sen (3-1)	.35	.25
2065	A547	10f Huang Xing (3-2)	.60	.35
2066	A547	40f Zhang Taiyan (3-3)	1.25	1.00
		Nos. 2064-2066 (3)	2.20	1.60

Souvenir Sheet

Sun Yat-sen (1866-1925) — A548

				Perf. 11½
1986, Nov. 12			**Perf. 11½**
2067	A548	$2 multicolored	7.00	2.75

Marshal Zhu De (1886-1976) (J.134) — A549

Designs: 20f, Orating.

			Engr.	Perf. 11½x11
1986, Dec. 1		**Engr.**	**Perf. 11½x11**
2068	A549	8f sepia (2-1)	.25	.25
2069	A549	20f myrtle grn (2-2)	.45	.25

Sports of Ancient China A550

Stone carvings. T.113.

Perf. 11½x11, 11x11½

				Photo.
1986, Dec. 20				**Photo.**
2070	A550	8f Archery (4-1), vert.	.30	.25
2071	A550	8f Weiqi (4-2)	.30	.25
2072	A550	10f Golf (4-3)	.75	.35
2073	A550	50f Soccer (4-4), vert.	2.75	1.75
		Nos. 2070-2073 (4)	4.10	2.60

A551   A552

Photogravure & Engraved

				Perf. 11½
1987, Jan. 5				**Perf. 11½**
2074	A551	8f blk, dk pink & yel grn	1.00	.25
a.		Bklt. pane of 4 + 8 + label	12.00	—
		Complete booklet, #2074a	22.50	

New Year 1987 (Year of the Hare).

			Photo.	Perf. 11½
1987, Feb. 20		**Photo.**	**Perf. 11½**
2075	A552	8f Traveling (3-1)	.50	.30
2076	A552	20f Cave writing (3-2)	2.00	1.25
2077	A552	40f Mountain climbing (3-3)	3.50	2.00
		Nos. 2075-2077 (3)	6.00	3.55

Xu Xiake (1587-1621), Ming Dynasty geographer (J.136).

Birds of Prey (T.114) — A553

				Perf. 11½
1987, Mar. 20			
2078	A553	8f Kite (4-1)	.40	.30
2079	A553	8f Sea eagle (4-2), vert.	.40	.30
2080	A553	10f Vulture (4-3), vert.	.50	.30
2081	A553	90f Buzzard (4-4)	4.75	1.25
		Nos. 2078-2081 (4)	6.05	2.15

Liao Zhongkai (1877-1925), National Party Leader (J.137) — A554

				Perf. 11½x11
1987, Apr. 23				**Perf. 11½x11**
2082	A554	8f shown (2-1)	.35	.25
2083	A554	20f Liao, He Xiangning (2-2)	.45	.25

Kites (T.115) — A555

1987, Apr. 1			
2084	A555	8f Hawk (4-1)	.45	.25
2085	A555	8f Dragon (4-2)	.45	.25
a.		Pair, #2084-2085	1.00	1.00
2086	A555	30f Symbolic octagon (4-3)	1.60	.80
2087	A555	30f Phoenix (4-4)	1.60	.80
a.		Pair, #2086-2087	3.50	3.00
		Nos. 2084-2087 (4)	4.10	2.10

Nos. 2085a, 2087a have continuous designs.

A556

1987, Apr. 28

Portraits of Ye Jianying (1897-1986), central committee vice chairman (J.138).

2088	A556	8f multi (3-3)	.50	.30
2089	A556	10f multi (3-2)	.90	.40
2090	A556	30f multi (3-1)	2.50	1.75
		Nos. 2088-2090 (3)	3.90	2.45

Caves of the Thousand Buddhas, Dunhuang, Gansu Province — A557

Wall Paintings: 8f, Worshipping Bodhisattvas, Northern Liang Dynasty. 10f, Deer King Jatka, Northern Wei Dynasty. 20f, Heavenly Musicians, Northern Wei Dynasty. 40f, Flying Devata, Northern Wei Dynasty. $2, Mahasattva Jataka. T.116.

				Perf. 11½
1987, May 20				**Perf. 11½**
2091	A557	8f multi (4-1)	.45	.25
2092	A557	10f multi (4-2)	.55	.30
2093	A557	20f multi (4-3)	1.50	.75
2094	A557	40f multi (4-4)	2.50	1.25
		Nos. 2091-2094 (4)	5.00	2.55

Souvenir Sheet

2095	A557	$2 multi	24.00	13.00

No. 2095 contains one 92x73mm stamp.
See Nos. 2149-2152, 2283-2286, 2407-2411, 2505-2508, 2704-2707.

Children's Day Festival A558

Children's drawings: No. 2096, Happy Holiday, by Yan Qinghui, age 7. No. 2097, Peace and Happiness, by Liu Yuan, age 7. T.117.

				Perf. 12½x12
1987, June 1				**Perf. 12½x12**
2096	A558	8f shown (2-1)	.30	.25
2097	A558	8f multi, vert. (2-2)	.40	.25

Rural Development   Postal Savings
A559   Bank
                            Inauguration
                            A560

				Perf. 11½
1987, June 25				**Perf. 11½**
2098	A559	8f Village, southeast China (4-1)	.40	.40
2099	A559	8f Market (4-2)	.40	.40
2100	A559	10f Dairy industry (4-3)	.60	.55
2101	A559	20f Theater (4-4)	1.25	1.10
		Nos. 2098-2101 (4)	2.65	2.45

Nos. 2099-2100 horiz. T.118.

1987, July 1			
2102	A560	8f multicolored	.30	.20

Esperanto Language Movement, Cent. — A561

1987, July 26			
2103	A561	8f lt olive grn, blk & brt blue	.35	.25

People's Liberation Army, 60th Anniv. (J.140) A562

1987, Aug. 1 Perf. 11
2104 A562 8f Flag, Great Wall (4-1) .35 .25
2105 A562 8f Rocket launch, soldier, village (4-2) .35 .25
2106 A562 10f Submarine, sailor (4-3) .55 .30
2107 A562 30f Aircraft, pilot (4-4) 1.50 .50
Nos. 2104-2107 (4) 2.75 1.30

Intl. Year of Shelter for the Homeless A563

1987, Aug. 20 Perf. 11
2108 A563 8f gray, dk car rose & blk .45 .25

Chinese Art Festival, Sept. 5-25, Beijing — A564

1987, Sept. 5 Perf. 11
2109 A564 8f brt red, gold & blk .50 .25

1987, Sept. 25
4f, Pan Gu inventing the universe. #2111, Nu Wa creating man. #2112, Yi shooting nine suns. 10f, Chang'e flying to the moon. 20f, Kua Fu pursuing the sun. 90f, Jing Wei filling the sea. T.120.

2110 A565 4f multi (6-1) .25 .25
2111 A565 8f multi (6-2) .30 .25
2112 A565 8f multi (6-3) .30 .25
2113 A565 10f multi (6-4) .40 .25
2114 A565 20f multi (6-5) .65 .35
2115 A565 90f multi (6-6) 1.00 1.25
Nos. 2110-2115 (6) 2.90 2.60

Communist Party of China, 13th Natl. Congress A566

1987, Oct. 25 Perf. 11
2116 A566 8f multicolored .40 .25

Yellow Crane Tower (T.121) A567

1987, Oct. 30
2117 A567 8f shown (4-1) .40 .25
2118 A567 8f Yue Yang Tower (4-2) .40 .25

2119 A567 10f Teng Wang Pavilion (4-3) .50 .40
2120 A567 90f Peng Lai Pavilion (4-4) 3.50 3.25
a. Min. sheet of 4, #2117-2120 14.50 8.00
Nos. 2117-2120 (4) 4.80 4.15
No. 2120a sold for $1.50.

6th Natl. Games (J.144) — A568

1987, Nov. 20 Perf. 11½x11
2121 A568 8f Pole vault (4-1) .30 .25
2122 A568 8f Softball (4-2) .30 .25
2123 A568 30f Weight lifting (4-3) .55 .30
2124 A568 50f Diving (4-4) .95 .50
Nos. 2121-2124 (4) 2.10 1.30

Souvenir Sheet

Bronze Bells from the Tomb of Marquis Yi of the Zeng State (c. 433 B.C.), Hubei Province — A569

1987, Dec. 10 Litho. Imperf.
2125 A569 $3 multicolored 8.00 4.00

Classic Literature — A570

Outlaws of the Marsh: 8f, Shi Jin practicing martial arts. 10f, Sagacious Lu, the "Tattooed Monk," uprooting a willow tree. 30f, Lin Chong seeking shelter from snow storm at the Mountain Spirit Temple. 50f, Song Jiang helps Ward Chief Chao Gai flee. $2, Outlaws of the Marsh capture treasures. T.123.

1987, Dec. 20 Photo. Perf. 11
2126 A570 8f multi (4-1) .40 .25
2127 A570 10f multi (4-2) .50 .25
2128 A570 30f multi (4-3) 1.60 .50
2129 A570 50f multi (4-4) 2.25 1.00
Nos. 2126-2129 (4) 4.75 2.00

Souvenir Sheet
Perf. 11½x11
2130 A570 $2 multi 22.50 12.00
No. 2130 contains one 90x60mm stamp. See Nos. 2216-2219, 2373-2377, 2449-2452, 2822-2826, 2889-2893.

New Year 1988 (Year of the Dragon) — A571
Cai Yuanpei (1868-1940), Education Reformer ((J.145) — A572

Photo. & Engr.

1988, Jan. 5 Perf. 11½
2131 A571 8f multicolored 2.00 .35
a. Bklt. pane of 4 + 8 with label between 24.00 —
Complete booklet, #2131a 22.50

1988, Jan. 11 Photo. Perf. 11½x11
2132 A572 8f shown (2-1) .25 .25
2133 A572 20f Seated (2-2) .30 .25

Tao Zhu (1908-1969), Party Leader (J.146) — A573

1988, Jan. 16 Perf. 11x11½
2134 A573 8f shown (2-1) .35 .25
2135 A573 20f Tao, diff. (2-2) .45 .25

Folklore (T.125) A574

1988, Feb. 10
2136 A574 8f shown (4-1) .25 .25
2137 A574 10f multi, diff. (4-2) .25 .25
2138 A574 20f multi, diff. (4-3) .45 .30
2139 A574 30f multi, diff. (4-4) .75 .45
Nos. 2136-2139 (4) 1.70 1.25

A575

1988, Mar. 25 Photo. Perf. 11½
2140 A575 8f multicolored .40 .25
7th Natl. People's Congress.

1988, Apr. 20 Photo. Perf. 11½
2141 A576 8f Wuzhi Mountain (4-1) .25 .25
2142 A576 10f Wanquan River (4-2) .25 .25
2143 A576 30f "End of the Earth" (4-3) .25 .25
2144 A576 $1.10 "Deer Turning Its Head" (4-4) .60 .35
Nos. 2141-2144 (4) 1.35 1.10
Establishment of Hainan Province (J.148).

A576

Modern Scientists A577

Designs: 8f, Li Siguang, geologist. 10f, Zhu Kezhen, meteorologist and geographer. 20f, Wu Youxun, physicist. 30f, Hua Luogeng, mathematician. J.149.

1988, Apr. 28 Perf. 11x11½
2145 A577 8f multi (4-1) .25 .25
2146 A577 10f multi (4-2) .25 .25
2147 A577 20f multi (4-3) .30 .25
2148 A577 30f multi (4-4) .35 .30
Nos. 2145-2148 (4) 1.15 1.05

Wall Paintings Type of 1987

Caves of the Thousand Buddhas, Dunhuang, Gansu Province: No. 2149, Hunting, Western Wei Dynasty. No. 2150, Fishing, Western Wei Dynasty. 10f, Farming, Northern Zhou Dynasty. 90f, Building a Pagoda, Northern Zhou Dynasty. T.126.

1988, May 25 Perf. 11½x11
2149 A557 8f multi (4-1) .40 .25
2150 A557 8f multi (4-2) .50 .25
2151 A557 10f multi (4-3) .50 .25
2152 A557 90f multi (4-4) 2.00 .55
Nos. 2149-2152 (4) 3.30 1.30

Environmental Protection — A578

1988, June 5 Photo. Perf. 11
2153 A578 8f Soil (4-1) .25 .25
2154 A578 8f Air (4-2) .25 .25
2155 A578 8f Water (4-3) .25 .25
2156 A578 8f Prevent noise pollution (4-4) .25 .25
a. Block of 4, #2153-2156 1.25 1.00

Souvenir Sheet

China Nos. 1-3 — A579

Photo. & Engr.

1988, July 2 Perf. 13
2157 A579 $3 multicolored 4.75 3.00
Postage stamps of China, 110th anniv.

11th Asian Games (in 1990), Beijing (J.151) A580

1988, July 20   Photo.   Perf. 11x11½
2158	A580	8f Emblem (2-1)	.25	.25
2159	A580	30f Character trade-mark (2-2)	.30	.25

See No. 2300a.

Signing of the Sino-Japanese Peace Treaty, 10th Anniv. (J.152) — A581

1988, Aug. 12   Photo.   Perf. 11
2160	A581	8f Peony (2-1)	.25	.25
2161	A581	$1.60 Sakura (2-2)	.85	.45
a.		Pair, #2160-2161	1.25	1.00

Achievements in Construction — A582

Designs: 8f, Coal-loading wharf, Ch'in-huang-tao Port. 10f, Ethylene refinery, Qilu. 20f, Pao-shan steel plant, Shanghai. 30f, Central Television Broadcasting Station. T.128.

1988, Sept. 2   Photo.   Perf. 11
2162	A582	8f multi (4-1)	.25	.25
2163	A582	10f multi (4-2)	.25	.25
2164	A582	20f multi (4-3)	.30	.25
2165	A582	30f multi (4-4)	.35	.25
		Nos. 2162-2165 (4)	1.15	1.00

See #2221-2224, 2279-2282, 2354-2357.

Mt. T'ai Shan, Shantung Province (T.130) — A583

1988, Sept. 14   Photo. & Engr.
2166	A583	8f T'ai Shan Temple (4-1)	.30	.25
2167	A583	10f Ladder to Heaven (4-2)	.40	.30
2168	A583	20f Daguang peak (4-3)	.75	.35
2169	A583	90f Sun-watching peak (4-4)	3.00	1.00
		Nos. 2166-2169 (4)	4.45	1.90

Liao Chengzhi (1908-1983), Party Leader (J.153) — A584

1988, Sept. 25   Photo.   Perf. 11½x11½
2170	A584	8f shown (2-1)	.25	.25
2171	A584	20f Writing (2-2)	.35	.25

Marshal Peng Dehuai (1898-1974), Party Leader (J.155) — A585

1988, Oct. 24   Photo.   Perf. 11x11½
2172	A585	8f shown (2-1)	.25	.25
2173	A585	20f Peng in uniform (2-2)	.30	.25

1st Natl. Farmers' Games (J.154) A586

1988, Oct. 9   Photo.   Perf. 11½
2174	A586	8f Cycling (2-1)	.25	.25
2175	A586	20f Javelin (2-2)	.40	.25

Literary Masterpieces — A587

The Romance of the Three Kingdoms, by Luo Guanzhong, 14th cent.: No. 2176, Three heroes' sworn brotherhood (4-1). No. 2177, Battle between Lu Bu and the heroes, vert. (4-2). No. 2178, Struggle between man and woman at Fengyi Pavilion (4-3). No. 2179, Two noblemen, vert. (4-4). No. 2180, Guan Yu's battle through five passes. T.131.

Perf. 11½x11, 11x11½

1988, Nov. 25   Photo.
2176	A587	8f multicolored	.35	.25
2177	A587	8f multicolored	.35	.30
2178	A587	8f multicolored	.85	.60
2179	A587	50f multicolored	1.50	.85
		Nos. 2176-2179 (4)	3.05	2.00

Souvenir Sheet
Perf. 11
2180	A587	$3 multicolored	21.00	12.00

See #2310-2313, 2403-2406, 2539-2543.

A588   A589

1988, Dec. 5   Photo.   Perf. 11
2181	A588	20f multicolored	.35	.25

Intl Volunteers' Day.

1988, Dec. 20   Photo.   Perf. 11½x11

Milu, *Elaphurus davidianus* (T.132).
2182	A589	8f Buck (2-1)	.30	.25
2183	A589	40f Herd (2-2)	1.25	.75

Exist imperf. Value, pairs each $5.50.

Orchids (T.129) — A590

1988, Dec. 25   Perf. 12
2184	A590	8f Da yi pin (4-1)	.25	.25
2185	A590	10f Dragon (4-2)	.30	.30
2186	A590	20f Large phoenix tail (4-3)	.60	.35
2187	A590	50f Silver-edged black (4-4)	1.10	.45
a.		Strip of 4, #2184-2187	4.00	2.75
		Nos. 2184-2187 (4)	2.25	1.35

Souvenir Sheet
Perf. 11½x11
2188	A590	$2 Red lotus petal	14.00	5.50

No. 2188 contains one 55x37mm stamp.

A591   A592

Grotto Statuary: $2, Buddha. $5, Warrior, Longmen Grotto, Henan. $10, Goddess. $20, Woman and birds.

Photo. & Engr.

1988-89   Perf. 11½x11
2189	A591	$2 buff & reddish blk	.90	.30
2190	A591	$5 buff & grnh blk	1.75	.65
2191	A591	$10 buff & brn blk	2.75	1.25
a.		Souv. sheet of 1, buff & sep	19.00	
2192	A591	$20 buff & indigo	6.75	2.50
		Nos. 2189-2192 (4)	12.15	4.70

Issued: $2, 11/30; $5, 8/10; $10, 10/15; $20, 10/20.

No. 2191a released on Oct. 12, 1989, for the China Natl. Philatelic Exhibition and the 40th anniv. of the People's Republic.

Nos. 2189-2192, 2191a are almost always found with small ink spots on the stamps. Values are for stamps in this condition.

Photo. & Engr.

1989, Jan. 5   Perf. 11½
2193	A592	8f multicolored	1.50	.25
a.		Bklt. pane of 4+8 with label between	8.50	—
		Complete booklet, #2193a	13.00	

New Year 1989 (Year of the Snake). Stamps from No. 2193a have one or two straight edges and sell for less as singles than No. 2193.

Qu Qiubai (1899-1935), Party Leader (J.157) — A593

1989, Jan. 29   Photo.   Perf. 11x11½
2194	A593	8f multi (2-1)	.25	.25
2195	A593	20f multi, diff. (2-2)	.50	.25

Brown-eared Pheasant, *Crossoptilon mantchuricum* (T.134) — A594

1989, Feb. 21   Perf. 11½
2196	A594	8f multi (2-1)	.30	.25
2197	A594	50f multi, diff. (2-2)	.65	.25

Folk Houses Type of 1986

1989-91   Photo.   Perf. 13x13½
2198	A545	5f Shandong	.20	.20
2199	A545	15f Guangxi	.20	.20
2200	A545	25f Ningxia	.20	.20
2201	A545	80f Shanxi	.40	.25
2202	A545	$1.30 Qinghai	.50	.30
2203	A545	$1.60 Guizhou	.65	.35
2204	A545	$2 Jiangxi	.65	.35
		Nos. 2198-2204 (7)	2.80	1.85

Issued: 5f, 6/10/91; 15f, 11/25/90; 25f, 11/10/90; 80f, 9/20/90; $1.30, $1.60, 3/10/89; $2, 4/25/91.

Silk Painting Excavated from Han Tomb No. 1 at Mawangdui, Changsha (T.135) A595

1989, Mar. 25   Photo.   Perf. 11x11½
2208	A595	8f In the Heavens (3-1)	.30	.25
a.		Perf. 11½	5.00	5.00
2209	A595	20f On the Earth, vert. (3-2)	.30	.25
a.		Perf. 11½	5.00	5.00
2210	A595	30f In the Netherworld, vert. (3-3)	.30	.25
a.		Perf. 11½	5.00	5.00
		Nos. 2208-2210 (3)	.90	.75

Textured Paper, Without Gum
Size: 90x165mm
Imperf
2211	A595	$5 Entire painting	4.25	2.75

Prevention and Resistance of Cancer (T.136) — A596

1989, Apr. 7   Litho.   Perf. 12
2212	A596	8f shown (2-1)	.30	.25
2213	A596	20f Woman's thermogram (2-2)	.50	.25

May Fourth Movement, 70th Anniv. (J.158) A597

1989, May 4   Photo.   Perf. 11
2214	A597	8f Bas-relief	.50	.25

Interparliamentary Union, Cent. — A598

1989, June 29   Photo.   Perf. 11x11½
2215	A598	20f multi	.50	.25

Literature Type of 1987

Outlaws of the Marsh: 8f, Wu Song slaying a tiger on Jingyang Ridge. 10f, Qin Ming dodging arrows. 20f, Hua Rong shooting a wild goose on Mt. Liangshan. $1.30, Li Kui fighting Zhang Shun from a junk. T.138.

1989, July 25   Photo.   Perf. 11
2216	A570	8f multi (4-1)	.25	.25
2217	A570	10f multi (4-2)	.25	.25
2218	A570	20f multi (4-3)	.30	.25
2219	A570	$1.30 multi (4-4)	1.60	.35
		Nos. 2216-2219 (4)	2.40	1.10

Asia-Pacific Telecommunity, 10th Anniv. — A599

1989, Aug. 4   Litho.   Perf. 12
2220	A599	8f multi	.40	.25

Type of 1988

Achievements in Engineering and Construction: 8f, Beijing Intl. Telecommunications Building, vert. 10f, Xi Qu Coal Mine, Gu Jiao, Shanxi Province. 20f, Long Yang Gorge Hydroelectric Power Station, Qinghai Province. 30f, Da Yao Shan Tunnel of the Guangzhou-Heng Yang Railway. T.139.

1989, Aug. 10   Photo.   Perf. 11
2221	A582	8f multi (4-1)	.25	.25
2222	A582	10f multi (4-2)	.25	.25
2223	A582	20f multi (4-3)	.25	.25
2224	A582	30f multi (4-4)	.30	.25
		Nos. 2221-2224 (4)	1.05	1.00

Mt. Huashan — A601

Designs: 8f, Five prominent peaks. 10f, View from atop Huashan. 20f, 1000-foot precipice. 90f, Blue Dragon Ridge. T.140.

1989, Aug. 25   Photo. & Engr.
2225	A601	8f multi (4-1)	.30	.25
2226	A601	10f multi (4-2)	.30	.25
2227	A601	20f multi (4-3)	.40	.25
2228	A601	90f multi (4-4)	1.00	.35
		Nos. 2225-2228 (4)	2.00	1.10

Modern Art — A602

Paintings: 8f, *The Fable of the White Snake*, by Ye Qianyu. 20f, *Li River in Fine Rain*, by Li Keran. 50f, *Marching Together*, by Wu Zuoren. T.141.

1989, Sept. 1   Photo.
2229	A602	8f multi (3-1)	.25	.25
2230	A602	20f multi (3-2)	.30	.25
2231	A602	50f multi (3-3)	.65	.30
		Nos. 2229-2231 (3)	1.20	.80

People's Political Conference A603

1989, Sept. 21   Perf. 12
2232	A603	8f No. 2	.40	.25

A604

Confucius (551-479 B.C.) — A605

Designs: 8f, The lecture in the Apricot Temple, Qufu. $1.60, Confucius riding in an ox cart. J.162.

1989, Sept. 28   Photo.   Perf. 11
2233	A604	8f shown (2-1)	.25	.25
2234	A604	$1.60 multi (2-2)	.75	.35

Souvenir Sheet
Litho.   Imperf.
Without Gum
2235	A605	$3 multicolored	4.00	2.75

A606

Gate of Heavenly Peace — A607

1989, Oct. 1   Photo.   Perf. 11x11½
2236	A606	8f shown (4-1)	.25	.25
2237	A606	10f Flowers (4-2)	.25	.25
2238	A606	20f Five stars (4-3)	.25	.25
2239	A606	40f Construction (4-4)	.30	.25
		Nos. 2236-2239 (4)	1.05	1.00

Souvenir Sheet
Litho.   Imperf.
Without Gum
2240	A607	$3 shown	2.50	1.75

PRC, 40th anniv. J.163.

Photography, Sesquicentennial — A608

1989, Oct. 15   Photo.   Perf. 11
2241	A608	8f multicolored	.40	.25

Li Dazhao (1889-1927), Party Leader (J.164) — A609

1989, Oct. 29   Photo.   Perf. 11
2242	A609	8f Li, soldiers (2-1)	.35	.25
a.		Perf. 11½	5.50	5.50
2243	A609	20f Li, text (2-2)	.45	.25
a.		Perf. 11½	5.50	5.50

Nos. 2242-2243 exist perf. 11½. Value, set $11.

Positron Collider Produced in Beijing A610

1989, Nov. 1   Perf. 11
2244	A610	8f multicolored	.40	.25

Rocket Defense A611

Designs: 4f, Transporting 3 rockets. 8f, Disassembled rocket on transport. 10f, Launch, vert. 20f, Stage separation in space. T.143.

1989, Nov. 15   Litho.   Perf. 12
2245	A611	4f multicolored (4-1)	.25	.25
2246	A611	8f multicolored (4-2)	.25	.25
2247	A611	10f multicolored (4-3)	.25	.25
2248	A611	20f multicolored (4-4)	.30	.25
		Nos. 2245-2248 (4)	1.05	1.00

A612

Views of West Lake (T.144) — A613

1989, Nov. 25   Photo.   Perf. 11x11½
2249	A612	8f multi (4-1)	.25	.25
2250	A612	10f multi, diff. (4-2)	.25	.25
2251	A612	30f multi, diff. (4-3)	.30	.25
2252	A612	40f multi, diff. (4-4)	.40	.30
		Nos. 2249-2252 (4)	1.20	1.05

Souvenir Sheet
Perf. 11½x11
2253	A613	$5 multicolored	6.00	2.00

11th Asian Games A614

Various stadiums. J.165.

1989, Dec. 15   Perf. 11x11½
2254	A614	8f multi (4-1)	.25	.25
2255	A614	10f multi (4-2)	.25	.25
2256	A614	30f multi (4-3)	.25	.25
2257	A614	$1.60 multi (4-4)	.35	.30
		Nos. 2254-2257 (4)	1.10	1.05

See Nos. 2295-2300.

A615

Narcissus (T.147) — A616

Photo. & Engr.
1990, Jan. 5   Perf. 11½
2258	A615	8f multicolored	1.25	.30
a.		Bklt. pane of 12 + 4 labels	9.50	
		Complete booklet, #2258a	19.00	
b.		As. No. 2258, perf. 11½x11	15.00	15.00

New Year 1990 (Year of the Horse). Stamps from No. 2258a have straight edges at top or bottom and sell for less as singles than No. 2258.

1990, Feb. 10   Photo.   Perf. 11x11½
2259	A616	8f multi (4-1)	.25	.25
2260	A616	20f multi, diff. (4-2)	.25	.25
2261	A616	30f multi, diff. (4-3)	.25	.25
2262	A616	$1.60 multi, diff. (4-4)	.50	.30
		Nos. 2259-2262 (4)	1.25	1.05

Norman Bethune (1890-1939), Surgeon (J.166) — A617

Litho. & Engr.
1990, Mar. 3   Perf. 11x11½
2263	A617	8f In Canada (2-2)	.25	.25
2264	A617	$1.60 In China (2-1)	.55	.30
a.		Pair, #2263-2264	1.00	1.00

See Canada #1264-1265.

Intl. Women's Day — A618

1990, Mar. 8   Photo.   Perf. 11½x11
2265	A618	20f multicolored	.40	.25

Afforestation (T.148) — A619

1990, Mar. 12   Perf. 11
2266	A619	8f Bird, flora (4-1)	.25	.25
2267	A619	10f Buildings (4-2)	.25	.25
2268	A619	20f Great Wall, forest, (4-3)	.25	.25
2269	A619	30f Bushes, evergreens (4-4)	.30	.25
		Nos. 2266-2269 (4)	1.05	1.00

Pottery (T.149) — A620

1990, Apr. 10   **Litho.**   **Perf. 12**
2270	A620	8f multi (4-1)	.25 .25
2271	A620	20f multi (4-2)	.25 .25
2272	A620	30f multi (4-3)	.25 .25
2273	A620	50f multi (4-4)	.30 .25
		Nos. 2270-2273 (4)	1.05 1.00

Li Fuchun (1900-1975), Party Leader (J.168) — A621

1990, May 22   **Photo.**   **Perf. 11x11½**
2274	A621	8f shown	.35 .25
2275	A621	20f in uniform (2-2)	.45 .25

Bronze Head — A622

Bronze treasures from Emperor Qin Shi Huang Mausoleum: 50f, Horse head. $5, Chariots. T.151.

1990, June 20   **Photo.**   **Perf. 11½x11**
2276	A622	8f shown (2-1)	.30 .25
2277	A622	50f multicolored (2-2)	.30 .30

Miniature Sheet
Size: 141x79mm
2278	A622	$5 multicolored	6.50 3.25

Achievements Type of 1988

Designs: 8f, 2nd automobile factory. 10f, Yizheng Joint Corporation of Chemical Fiber Industry. 20f, Shengli Oil Field. 30f, Qinshan Nuclear Power Station. T.152.

1990, June 30   **Litho.**   **Perf. 12**
2279	A582	8f shown (4-1)	.25 .25
2280	A582	10f multicolored (4-2)	.25 .25
2281	A582	20f multicolored (4-3)	.30 .25
2282	A582	30f multicolored (4-4)	.30 .25
		Nos. 2279-2282 (4)	1.10 1.00

Wall Paintings Type of 1987

8f, Flying Devatas. 10f, Worshipping Bodhisatva. 30f, Savior Avolokitesvara. 50f, Indra. T.150.

1990, July 10   **Perf. 11½x11**
2283	A557	8f multi (4-1)	.25 .25
2284	A557	10f multi, vert. (4-2)	.25 .25
2285	A557	30f multi, vert. (4-3)	.45 .25
2286	A557	50f multi (4-4)	.75 .35
		Nos. 2283-2286 (4)	1.70 1.10

Snow Leopard (Uncia Uncia) (T.153) A624

1990, July 20   **Photo.**   **Perf. 11½**
2287	A624	8f multicolored (2-1)	.40 .25
2288	A624	50f multicolored (2-2)	.60 .30

Chinese Soviet Post Stamp of 1931 A625

Design: 20f, Chinese Red Post issue of West Fukien, 1929. J.169.

1990, Aug. 1   **Litho.**   **Perf. 12**
2289	A625	8f multi (2-1)	.35 .25
2290	A625	20f multi, diff. (2-2)	.55 .25

Zhang Wentian (1900-1990) (J.170) — A626

1990, Aug. 30   **Perf. 11x11½**
2291	A626	8f shown (2-1)	.30 .25
2292	A626	20f multi, diff. (2-2)	.60 .25

Intl. Literacy Year — A627   Chinese Films — A628

1990, Sept. 8   **Perf. 11½x11**
2293	A627	20f multicolored	.40 .25

1990, Sept. 21   **Litho.**   **Perf. 11**
2294	A628	20f multicolored	.50 .25

11th Asian Games, Beijing (J.172) A629

1990, Sept. 22   **Perf. 11x11½**
2295	A629	4f Running (6-1)	.25 .25
2296	A629	8f Gymnastics (6-2)	.25 .25
2297	A629	10f Karate (6-3)	.25 .25
2298	A629	20f Volleyball (6-4)	.25 .25
2299	A629	30f Swimming (6-5)	.35 .25
2300	A629	$1.60 Shooting (6-6)	.85 .60
a.		Souv. sheet of 12, #2158-2159, 2254-2257, 2295-2300	6.00 3.00
		Nos. 2295-2300 (6)	2.20 1.85

Souvenir Sheet

Sportphilex '90, Beijing — A629a

1990, Sept. 21   **Litho.**   **Perf. 11½**
2300B	A629a	$10 multicolored	20.00 10.00

No. 2300B exists imperf. Value, $700.

Modern Scientists A630

Designs: 8f, Lin Qiaozhi, obstetrician. 10f, Zhang Yuzhe, astronomer. 20f, Hou Debang, chemist. 30f, Ding Ying, agronomist. J.173.

1990, Oct. 10   **Litho.**   **Perf. 12**
2301	A630	8f multicolored (4-1)	.25 .25
2302	A630	10f multicolored (4-2)	.25 .25
2303	A630	20f multicolored (4-3)	.30 .25
2304	A630	30f multicolored (4-4)	.30 .25
		Nos. 2301-2304 (4)	1.10 1.00

Mt. Hengshan — A631

Designs: 8f, Towering Temple. 10f, South Sacred Mountain. 20f, Forested mountainside. 50f, Imposing Zhurong Peak. T.155.

Photo. & Engr.
1990, Nov. 5   **Perf. 11**
2305	A631	8f multicolored (4-1)	.25 .25
2306	A631	10f multicolored (4-2)	.25 .25
2307	A631	20f multicolored (4-3)	.30 .25
2308	A631	50f multicolored (4-4)	.45 .30
		Nos. 2305-2308 (4)	1.25 1.05

See Nos. 2342-2345. 2628-2631.

Souvenir Sheet

China Philatelic Federation, 3rd Congress — A632

1990, Nov. 28   **Perf. 11½x11**
2309	A632	$2 multicolored	5.00 2.50

Two types of No. 2309 exist. Either two or three of the horizontal bars in seventh character from top right are connected at left side. Value for No. 2309 is for the first type. Examples with three bars connected, value $7.

Literature Type of 1988

Romance of the Three Kingdoms by Luo Guanzhong: No. 2310, Night Attack on Wuchao. No. 2311, Making Three Calls at the Thatched Cottage. 30f, Rescuing the Master Single-handedly. 50f, Turning the Changban Bridge Upside Down. T.157.

1990, Dec. 10   **Photo.**   **Perf. 11½x11**
2310	A587	20f multicolored (4-1)	.25 .25
2311	A587	20f multi, vert. (4-2)	.25 .25
2312	A587	30f multi, vert. (4-3)	.30 .25
2313	A587	50f multi, vert. (4-4)	.50 .30
		Nos. 2310-2313 (4)	1.30 1.05

Han Xizai's Night Revels by Gu Hongzhong — A633

Designs: a, Guests enjoying food, music (5-1). b, Music and dance (5-2). c, Hand washing (5-3). d, Musicians (5-4). e, Guests departing (5-5). T.158. (Illustration reduced).

1990, Dec. 20   **Litho.**   **Perf. 12**
2314		Strip of 5	3.50 2.75
a.-e.		A633 50f any single	.60 .35

New Year 1991 (Year of the Sheep) — A634

Photo. & Engr.
1991, Jan. 5   **Perf. 11½**
2315	A634	20f multicolored	1.40 .30
a.		Bklt. pane of 12 + label	7.50
		Complete booklet, #2315a	13.00

Stamps from No. 2315a have straight edges at top or bottom and sell for less as singles than No. 2315.

Dujiangyan Irrigation Project — A635

Designs: 20f, Yuzui, flood control. 50f, Feishayan, drainage. 80f, Baopingkou, water volume control. T.156.

1991, Feb. 20   **Photo.**   **Perf. 11½x11**
2316	A635	20f multicolored	.25 .25
2317	A635	50f multicolored	.35 .25
2318	A635	80f multicolored	.55 .30
		Nos. 2316-2318 (3)	1.15 .80

A636

A637

1991, Mar. 18
2319	A636	20f multicolored	.40 .25

Paris Commune, 120th anniv.

1991, Apr. 20   **Photo.**   **Perf. 10**
2320	A637	20f multi (2-1)	.35 .25
a.		Perf. 11½x11	1.50 .90

    Perf. 11½x11
2321	A637	50f Child & adult hands (2-2)	.45 .25

Family planning (T.160).

Horned Animals (T.161) A638

1991, May 10   **Perf. 11x11½**
2322	A638	20f Saiga tatarica (4-1)	.25 .25
2323	A638	20f Budorcas taxicolor (4-2)	.25 .25
a.		Perf. 11	6.00 6.00
2324	A638	50f Ovis ammon (4-3)	.25 .25
a.		Perf. 11	15.00 15.00
2325	A638	$2 Capra ibex (4-4)	.55 .30
		Nos. 2322-2325 (4)	1.30 1.05

No. 2322 exists imperf. Value, pair $140.

A639

A640

1991, May 23   Photo.   Perf. 11
2326 A639 25f Song and dance
           (2-1)   .35 .25
2327 A639 50f Golden bridge (2-
           2)   .50 .25

Souvenir Sheet
2328 A639 $2 No. 132, cranes   4.50 2.00
Occupation of Tibet, 40th anniv. (J.176).

1991, June 22   Perf. 11½x11
2329 A640 20f multicolored   .40 .25

Antarctic Treaty, 30th anniv.

Rhododendrons — A641

Varieties of rhododendrons. T.162.

1991, June 25   Litho.   Perf. 12
2330 A641 10f Delavayi (8-1)   .25 .25
2331 A641 15f Molle (8-2)   .25 .25
2332 A641 20f Simsii (8-3)   .25 .25
2333 A641 20f Fictolacteum
           (8-4)   .25 .25
2334 A641 50f Agglutinatum,
           vert. (8-5)   .45 .25
2335 A641 80f Fortunei, vert.
           (8-6)   .70 .25
2336 A641 90f Giganteum,
           vert. (8-7)   .80 .30
2337 A641 $1.60 Rex, vert. (8-
           8)   1.40 .40
       Nos. 2330-2337 (8)   4.35 2.20

Souvenir Sheet
Perf. 11½
2338 A641 $5 Wardii   10.00 7.00
No. 2338 contains one 80x40mm stamp.

Chinese
Communist
Party, 70th
Anniv.
(J.178)
A642

1991, July 1   Photo.   Perf. 11x11½
2339 A642 20f shown (2-1)   .30 .25
2340 A642 50f Hammer and sick-
           le (2-2)   .95 .40

Peasant
Uprising,
209B.C.
A643

1991, July 7
2341 A643 20f brown   .40 .25

Mt. Hengshan Type of 1990
Designs: No. 2342, Monastery on mountainside. No. 2343, Snow-covered mountain top.
55f, Inscription carved into mountainside. 80f,
Hidden monastery. T.163.

Photo. & Engr.
1991, July 20   Perf. 11
2342 A631 20f multi (4-1)   .25 .25
2343 A631 20f multi (4-2)   .25 .25
2344 A631 55f multi (4-3)   .50 .25
2345 A631 80f multi (4-4)   .70 .35
       Nos. 2342-2345 (4)   1.70 1.10

Intl. Union
for
Quaternary
Research,
13th Conf.
A644

1991, Aug. 2   Photo.   Perf. 11x11½
2346 A644 20f multicolored   .50 .25
    a.   Perf. 11½   12.00 12.00

Chengde Mountain Resort — A645

Ch'ing Dynasty Royal Gardens: 15f, Pine
valleys. 20f, Mid-lake pavilion. 90f, Islet, maple
trees. $2, Chengde Royal Summer Resort.
T.164.

1991   Perf. 11½x11
2347 A645 15f multi (3-1)   .25 .25
2348 A645 20f multi (3-2)   .25 .25
2349 A645 90f multi (3-3)   .70 .30
       Nos. 2347-2349 (3)   1.20 .80

Souvenir Sheet
2350 A645 $2 multicolored   6.00 3.50
No. 2350 contains one 90x40mm stamp. Issue
dates: $2, Aug. 19; others, Aug. 10.

A646

Chen Yi, (b. 1901), party leader (J.181).

1991, Aug. 26   Photo.   Perf. 11½x11
2351 A646 20f shown (2-1)   .40 .25
2352 A646 50f Verse (2-2)   .85 .30

1991, Sept. 14
2353 A647 80f Disaster relief   .40 .25

A647

Achievements Type of 1988
20f, Luoyang glassworks. 25f, Urumchi
chemical fertilizer project. 55f, Dalian expressway, Shenyang. 80f, Xichang satellite launching center. T.165.

1991, Sept. 20   Litho.   Perf. 12
2354 A582 20f multi (4-1)   .25 .25
2355 A582 25f multi (4-2)   .25 .25
2356 A582 55f multi (4-3)   .25 .25
2357 A582 80f multi (4-4)   .35 .25
       Nos. 2354-2357 (4)   1.10 1.00

Revolutionary Heroes — A648

Designs: No. 2358, Xu Xilin (1873-1907).
No. 2359, Qiu Jin (1879-1907). No. 2360,
Song Jiaoren (1882-1913). J.182.

1991, Oct. 10   Photo.   Perf. 11x11½
2358 A648 20f multi (3-1)   5.00 1.25
    a.   Perf. 10   .30 .25
2359 A648 20f multi (3-2)   .30 .25
2360 A648 20f multi (3-3)   .30 .25

Jingdezhen
Chinaware
A649

Designs: 15f, Glazed wine pot and warming
bowl, Song Dynasty, vert. No. 2362, Porcelain
vase, Yuan Dynasty, vert. No. 2363, Jar, Ming
Dynasty. 25f, Porcelain vase, Ch'ing Dynasty,
vert. 50f, Modern underglazed plate, vert. $2,
Modern octagonal eggshell bowl. T.166.

**Perf. 11¼x11½, 11½x11¼ (#2363,
2366)**
1991, Oct. 11   Photo.
2361 A649 15f multi (6-1)   .25 .25
2362 A649 20f multi (6-2)   .25 .25
2363 A649 20f multi (6-3)   .25 .25
2364 A649 25f multi (6-4)   .25 .25
2365 A649 50f multi (6-5)   .25 .25
2366 A649 $2 multi (6-6)   .55 .25
       Nos. 2361-2366 (6)   1.80 1.50

**Perf. 11¼x11, 11x11¼ (#2363a,
2366a)**
1991
2361a A649 15f multi   .25 .25
2362a A649 20f multi   .25 .25
2363a A649 20f multi   .25 .25
2364a A649 25f multi   .25 .25
2365a A649 50f multi   .25 .25
2366a A649 $2 multi   .55 .25
       Nos. 2361a-2366a (6)   1.80 1.50

Tao Xingzhi,
Educator, Birth
Cent.
(J.183) — A650

1991, Oct. 18   Litho.   Perf. 12
2367 A650 20f shown (2-1)   .35 .25
2368 A650 50f Wearing robe (2-
           2)   .45 .30

Xu Xiangqian, Revolutionary Leader,
90th Birth Anniv. (J.184) — A651

1991, Nov. 8   Perf. 11x11½
2369 A651 20f shown (2-1)   .35 .25
2370 A651 50f In uniform (2-2)   .45 .30

1st Women's
Soccer World
Championships,
Guangdong
Province
(J.185) — A652

Designs: 50f, Woman kicking soccer ball.

1991, Nov. 16   Perf. 11½x11
2371 A652 20f red & multi (2-1)   .35 .25
2372 A652 50f grn & multi (2-2)   .45 .30

Literature Type of 1987
Outlaws of the Marsh: 20f, Dai Zong sends
a false letter from Liangshan Marsh. No. 2374,
Ten feet of steel alone captures Stumpy Tiger
Wang. No. 2375, Mistress Gu breaks open the
jail in Dengzhou to rescue the Xie Brothers.
90f, Sun Li offers a plan to attack Zhu Family

manor. $3, Mount Liangshan gallants raid the
execution grounds. T.167.

1991, Nov. 19   Perf. 11
2373 A570 20f multi (4-1)   .25 .25
2374 A570 25f multi (4-2)   .25 .25
2375 A570 25f multi (4-3)   .25 .25
2376 A570 90f multi (4-4)   1.00 .35
       Nos. 2373-2376 (4)   1.75 1.10

Souvenir Sheet
Perf. 11x11½
2377 A570 $3 multicolored   7.00 4.00
No. 2377 contains one 60x90mm stamp.

Beginning with No. 2378 stamps are
inscribed "CHINA" and are numbered
chronologically with the year followed
by the number of the set. Additional
numbers in parentheses indicate the
number and position of each stamp in a
set. We will note these only when help-
ful in identifying stamps.

New Year 1992, Year of the
Monkey

A653   A654

Photo. & Engr.
1992, Jan. 25   Perf. 11½
2378 A653 20f Monkey, peach   .35 .25
2379 A654 50f Magpies, plum
           branches   .65 .30

Storks — A655

Conifers — A656

1992, Feb. 20   Photo.   Perf. 11x11½
2380 A655 20f Ciconia nigra   .25 .25
2381 A655 $1.60 Ciconia ciconia   .75 .40

1992, Mar. 10   Litho.   Perf. 12½
Designs: 20f, Metasequoia glyptostro-
boides. 30f, Cathaya argyrophylla. 50f,
Taiwania flousiana. 80f, Abies beshanzuensis.

2382 A656 20f multicolored   .25 .25
2383 A656 30f multicolored   .25 .25
2384 A656 50f multicolored   .25 .25
2385 A656 80f multicolored   .35 .30
       Nos. 2382-2385 (4)   1.10 1.05

Marine Life
A660

1992, Apr. 15   Photo.   Perf. 11
2386 A660 20f Pagrosomus major   .25   .25
2387 A660 25f Penaeus chinesis   .25   .25
2388 A660 50f Chlamys farreri   .25   .25
2389 A660 80f Laminaria japonica   .30   .25
        Nos. 2386-2389 (4)   1.05 1.00

Publication of "Discussions on Literature and Art at the Yenan Forum," 50th Anniv. — A661

1992, May 23   Photo.   Perf. 11½x11
2390 A661 20f org, blk & red   .50   .25

A662

A663

1992, June 5   Litho.   Perf. 12
2392 A662 20f multicolored   .40   .25

UN Conf. on Human Development, 20th anniv.

1992, June 28

Insects: 20f, Coccinella septempunctata. 30f, Sympetrum croceolum. 50f, Chrysopa septempunctata. $2, Tenodera aridifolia sinensis.

2393 A663 20f multicolored   .25   .25
2394 A663 30f multicolored   .25   .25
2395 A663 50f multicolored   .30   .25
2396 A663 $2 multicolored   .85   .35
        Nos. 2393-2396 (4)   1.65 1.10

1992 Summer Olympics, Barcelona A664

1992, July 25   Photo.   Perf. 11
2397 A664 20f Basketball, vert.   .25   .25
2398 A664 25f Women's gymnastics   .25   .25
2399 A664 50f Women's diving   .30   .25
2400 A664 80f Weight lifting, vert.   .35   .30
        Nos. 2397-2400 (4)   1.15 1.05
              Souvenir Sheet
2401 A664 $5 Runners   2.75 2.25
No. 2401 contains one 54x40mm stamp.

Intl. Space Year — A665

1992, Aug. 18   Litho.   Perf. 12
2402 A665 20f multicolored   .45   .25

Literature Type of 1988

Romance of the Three Kingdoms by Luo Guanzhong: 20f, Verbal battle with scholars. 30f, Goading Sun Quan with sarcasm, vert. 50f, Jiang Gan stealing the letter. $1.60, Gathering arrows with straw-covered boats, vert.

      Perf. 11½x11, 11x11½

1992, Aug. 25   Photo.
2403 A587 20f multi   .25   .25
2404 A587 30f multi   .25   .25
2405 A587 50f multi   .25   .25
2406 A587 $1.60 multi   .45   .30
        Nos. 2403-2406 (4)   1.20 1.05

Wall Paintings Type of 1987

20f, Bodhisattva, vert. 25f, Musical performance, vert. 55f, Flight of a dragon. 80f, Envoy to the western regions. $5, Avalokitesvara-Bodhisattva, vert.

1992, Sept. 15   Perf. 11
2407 A557 20f multicolored   .25   .25
2408 A557 25f multicolored   .25   .25
2409 A557 55f multicolored   .30   .25
2410 A557 80f multicolored   .40   .30
        Nos. 2407-2410 (4)   1.20 1.05
            Souvenir Sheet
              Perf. 11½
2411 A557 $5 multicolored   3.00 2.00
No. 2411 contains one 52x70mm stamp.

Normalization of Diplomatic Relations Between China and Japan, 20th Anniv. — A666

20f, Cranes, Great Wall of China, Mt. Fuji. $2, Japanese, Chinese children, dove.

1992, Sept. 29   Photo.   Perf. 11x11½
2412 A666 20f multicolored   .25   .25
2413 A666 $2 multicolored   .80   .45

A667

A667a

Statue of Mazu, Chinese Goddess of the Sea.

1992, Oct. 4   Litho.   Perf. 12
2414 A667 20f multicolored   .45   .25

1992, Oct. 12   Photo.   Perf. 11½x11
2414A A667a 20f multicolored   .75   .25
14th Chinese Communist Party Congress.

Jiao Yulu (1922-1964), Communist Party Leader — A668

1992, Oct. 28   Litho.   Perf. 12
2415 A668 20f multicolored   .40   .25

Famous Men A669

Designs: 20f, Xiong Qinglai, mathematician. 30f, Tang Feifan, microbiologist. 50f, Zhang Xiaoqian, physician. $1, Liang Sicheng, architect.

1992, Nov. 20
2416 A669 20f multicolored   .25   .25
2417 A669 30f multicolored   .25   .25
2418 A669 50f multicolored   .25   .25
2419 A669 $1 multicolored   .30   .25
        Nos. 2416-2419 (4)   1.05 1.00

Luo Ronghuan, Leader of People's Army, 90th Anniv. of Birth A670

1992, Nov. 26   Photo.   Perf. 11x11½
2420 A670 20f In dress uniform   .35   .25
2421 A670 50f In field uniform   .45   .30

Constitution of the People's Republic of China, 10th Anniv. — A671

1992, Dec. 4   Perf. 11½x11
2422 A671 20f multicolored   .45   .25

Liu Bocheng, Leader of People's Army, Birth Cent. A672

Designs: 20f, In dress uniform. 50f, During period of Long March, vert.

1992, Dec. 4   Perf. 11x11½, 11½x11
2423 A672 20f multicolored   .35   .25
2424 A672 50f multicolored   .45   .30

Quingtian Stone Carvings — A673

1992, Dec. 15   Litho.   Perf. 12
2425 A673 10f Spring   .25   .25
2426 A673 20f Chinese sorghum   .25   .25
2427 A673 40f Harvest   .25   .25

2428 A673 $2 Blooming flowers, full moon   .45   .30
        Nos. 2425-2428 (4)   1.20 1.05

New Year 1993 (Year of the Rooster)
A674   A675

       Photo. & Engr.
1993, Jan. 5   Perf. 11½
2429 A674 20f red & black   .50   .25
2430 A675 50f red, white & blk   .50   .25

Madam Song Quingling, Chinese Communist Leader, Birth Cent. A676

1993, Jan. 20   Photo.   Perf. 11x11½
2431 A676 20f Portrait   .25   .25
  a.   Perf. 11   4.50 4.50
2432 A676 $1 With children   .40   .25
  a.   Perf. 11   4.50 4.50
No. 2431 exists imperf. Value, pair $140.

Camelus Bactrianus Ferus A677

1993, Feb. 20   Litho.   Perf. 12
2433 A677 20f shown   .25   .25
2434 A677 $1.60 Adult, young   .50   .25

8th Natl. People's Congress A678

1993, Mar. 15   Litho.   Perf. 12
2435 A678 20f multicolored   .50   .25

A679

A680

Game of Weiqi (Go): 20f, Painting of players of ancient times. $1.60, Game board showing Chinese-style position.

1993, Apr. 30   Litho.   Perf. 12
2436 A679 20f multi   .25   .25
2437 A679 $1.60 multi   .55   .35

1993, May 15   Litho.   Perf. 12
20th Cent. Revolutionaries: 20f, Li Jishen (1885-1959), horiz. 30f, Zhang Lan (1872-1955). 50f, Shen Junru (1875-1963). $1, Huang Yanpei (1878-1965), horiz.

2438	A680	20f multi	.25	.25
2439	A680	30f multi	.25	.25
2440	A680	50f multi	.25	.25
2441	A680	$1 multi	.30	.25
		Nos. 2438-2441 (4)	1.05	1.00

See Nos. 2483-2486.

A681

A682

1993, May 9   Photo.   Perf. 12
2442	A681	50f Runner (2-1)	.30	.25
2443	A681	50f Mascot (2-2)	.30	.25
a.		Pair, #2442-2443	.80	.70

First East Asian Games. No. 2443a printed in continuous design.

1993, June 15   Litho.   Perf. 12½
Bamboo: 20f, Phyllostachys nigra. 30f, Phyllostachys aureosulcata spectabilis. 40f, Bambusa ventricosa. $1, Pseudosasa amabilis. $5, Phyllostachys heterocycla pubescens, horiz.

2444	A682	20f multi	.25	.25
2445	A682	30f multi	.25	.25
2446	A682	40f multi	.25	.25
2447	A682	$1 multi	.35	.25
		Nos. 2444-2447 (4)	1.10	1.00

Souvenir Sheet
Photo.   Perf. 11
| 2448 | A682 | $5 multicolored | 3.00 | 2.25 |
| a. | | As #2448, added inscription | 4.25 | 3.75 |

No. 2448 contains one 54x40mm stamp.
No. 2448a is inscribed in sheet margin with hologram of panda at left, Chinese inscription for CHINA '96 and PJZ-3 at bottom, and flag and tagged security emblem at right. Soaking in water may affect the hologram. Issued: May 10, 1996.

Literature Type of 1987
Outlaws of the Marsh: 20f, Chai Jin is trapped in Gaotang. 30f, Shi Qian steals armor. 50f, Xu Ning teaches how to use barbed lance. $2, Shi Xiu leaps from building to rescue condemned man from execution.

1993, Aug. 20   Photo.   Perf. 11
2449	A570	20f multi	.25	.25
2450	A570	30f multi	.25	.25
2451	A570	50f multi	.25	.25
2452	A570	$2 multi	.65	.30
		Nos. 2449-2452 (4)	1.40	1.05

Changbai Mountains — A683

1993, Sept. 3   Perf. 11½x11
2453	A683	20f Tianchi	.25	.25
2454	A683	30f Alpine tundra	.25	.25
2455	A683	50f Waterfall	.25	.25
2456	A683	$1 Mixed forest	.35	.25
		Nos. 2453-2456 (4)	1.10	1.00

Seventh Natl. Games — A684

Longmen Grottoes — A685

1993, Sept. 4
2457 A684 20f multicolored   .45 .25

1993, Sept. 5   Litho.   Perf. 12
Designs: 20f, Rocana, Ancestor Worshipping Temple. 30f, Sakyamuni, Middle Binyang Cave, Northern Wei. 50f, Maharaja, devas treading on Yaksha. $1, Bodhisattva at the left side of Rocana, Guyang Cave, Northern Wei. $5, Ancestor Worshipping Temple.

2458	A685	20f multi	.25	.25
2459	A685	30f multi	.25	.25
2460	A685	50f multi	.25	.25
2461	A685	$1 multi	.35	.25
		Nos. 2458-2461 (4)	1.10	1.00

Souvenir Sheets
2462	A685	$5 multicolored	3.00	3.25
a.		Overprinted in gold	10.00	6.50
b.		Overprinted in silver	6.00	4.00

No. 2462 contains one 120x40mm stamp.
Overprint in margin of No. 2462a includes Chinese characters and "PJZ-1." Bangkok '95 (#2462a). No. 2462a sold for $6.
No. 2462a exists with serial number inscribed in sheet margin. The same number is inscribed on Thailand No. 1615b. These were sold as a set. Value for the two sheets with matching numbers, $26.50.
Sheet margin of No. 2462b contains silver lettering in Chinese for Thailand stamp exhibition and "PJZ-7." No. 2462b exists with serial number inscribed in sheet margin. Value: $11.50.
Issued: No. 2462a, 8/95; No. 2462b, 12/5/97.

Honey Bees A686

1993, Sept. 21   Photo.   Perf. 11½
2463	A686	10f Queen and two bees	.25	.25
a.		Perf. 11x11½	4.50	4.50
2464	A686	15f Extracting nectar	.25	.25
a.		Perf. 11x11½	4.50	4.50
2465	A686	20f Two Zhonghua bees	.25	.25
2466	A686	$2 Two bees in flight	.65	.40
		Nos. 2463-2466 (4)	1.40	1.15

Lacquerware — A687

Paintings, by Zheng Banqiao — A688

Designs: 10f, Bamboo, rock on fan. No. 2472, Orchard. No. 2473, Orchard, bamboo, rock on scroll, vert. 30f, Bamboo, rock on scroll, vert. 50f, Vase and chrysanthemums. $1.60, Chinese calligraphy on fan.

1993, Oct. 20   Photo.   Perf. 12
2467	A687	20f Bowl	.25	.25
2468	A687	30f Duck	.25	.25
2469	A687	50f Round tray	.25	.25
2470	A687	$1 Lidded box	.30	.25
		Nos. 2467-2470 (4)	1.05	1.00

1993, Nov. 22   Litho.   Perf. 12½
2471	A688	10f multi (6-1)	.25	.25
2472	A688	20f multi (6-2)	.25	.25
2473	A688	20f multi (6-3)	.25	.25
2474	A688	30f multi (6-4)	.35	.25
2475	A688	50f multi (6-5)	.35	.25
2476	A688	$1.60 multi (6-6)	.55	.30
		Nos. 2471-2476 (6)	2.00	1.55

No. 2476 exists imperf. Value, pair $240.

A689

1993, Nov. 26   Perf. 12
2477 A689 20f multicolored   .45 .25
Yang Hucheng, birth cent.

A690

1993   Photo.   Perf. 11½
Mao Tse-tung (1893-1976).
| 2478 | A690 | 20f shown | .75 | .30 |
| 2479 | A690 | $1 Portrait, seated | 1.75 | .50 |

Souvenir Sheet
| 2480 | A690 | $5 Standing by Great Wall | 2.75 | 2.25 |
| a. | | Overprinted in gold in margin | 3.50 | 2.25 |

No. 2480 contains one 48x58mm stamp. No. 2480a sold for $8.
No. 2478 exists imperf. Value, pair $350.
Issued: $5, 11/16; 20f, $1, 12/26; #2480a, 4/9/99.

New Year 1994 (Year of the Dog)
A691   A692

1994, Jan. 5   Photo.   Perf. 11½
| 2481 | A691 | 20f multi | .40 | .25 |
| 2482 | A692 | 50f yel, red & blk | .60 | .30 |

20th Cent. Revolutionaries Type
Designs: No. 2483, Chen Qiyou, horiz. No. 2484, Chen Shutong. No. 2485, Ma Xulun. No. 2486, Xu Deheng, horiz.

1994, Feb. 25   Litho.   Perf. 12
2483	A680	20f blk & brn (4-1)	.25	.25
2484	A680	30f blk & brn (4-2)	.25	.25
2485	A680	50f blk & brn (4-3)	.30	.25
2486	A680	50f blk & brn (4-4)	.30	.25
		Nos. 2483-2486 (4)	1.10	1.00

Sturgeon — A693

20f, Huso dauricus. 40f, Acipenser sinensis. 50f, Psephurus gladius. $1, Acipenser dabryanus.

1994, Mar. 18   Litho.   Perf. 12½
2487	A693	20f multi	.25	.25
2488	A693	40f multi	.25	.25
2489	A693	50f multi	.30	.25
2490	A693	$1 multi	.45	.30
		Nos. 2487-2490 (4)	1.25	1.05

Afforestation Campaign — A694

Designs: 15f, Sand dunes. 20f, Flowers on sand dune. 40f, Forest of poplars. 50f, Oasis.

1994, Apr. 21   Litho.   Perf. 12
2491	A694	15f multi	.25	.25
2492	A694	20f multi	.25	.25
2493	A694	40f multi	.25	.25
2494	A694	50f multi	.30	.25
		Nos. 2491-2494 (4)	1.05	1.00

Teapots — A695

Style of teapot: 20f, Round, three-legged. 30f, Square, four-legged. 50f, Eight diagrams. $1, Round-eared.

1994, May 5   Litho.   Perf. 12
2495	A695	20f multi	.25	.25
2496	A695	30f multi	.25	.25
2497	A695	50f multi	.25	.25
2498	A695	$1 multi	.35	.25
		Nos. 2495-2498 (4)	1.10	1.00

Huangpu Military School, 70th Anniv. A696

1994, June 16   Litho.   Perf. 12
2499 A696 20f multicolored   .60 .25

Intl. Olympic Committee, Cent. A697

1994, June 23
2500 A697 20f multicolored   .50 .25

Ancient Chinese
Writers — A698

Designs: 20f, Tao Yuanming holding basket of flowers. 30f, Cao Zhi holding sword at side. 50f, Si Maqian writing on scroll. $1, Qu Yuan walking away with sword under arm.

1994, June 25
2501	A698	20f multi	.25	.25
2502	A698	30f multi	.25	.25
2503	A698	50f multi	.30	.25
2504	A698	$1 multi	.35	.25
		Nos. 2501-2504 (4)	1.15	1.00

Wall paintings Type of 1987

10f, Flying Devata. 20f, Vimalakirti. 50f, Z. Yichao on the march. $1.60, Sorceresses.

1994, July 16   Photo.   Perf. 11
2505	A557	10f multi	.25	.25
2506	A557	20f multi	.25	.25
2507	A557	50f multi	.30	.25
2508	A557	$1.60 multi	.45	.25
		Nos. 2505-2508 (4)	1.25	1.00

Zhaojun's Marriage to
Xiongnu — A699

1994, Aug. 25   Photo.   Perf. 11½x11
2509	A699	20f Zhaojun	.30	.25
2510	A699	50f Leaving home	.50	.30

Souvenir Sheet
Perf. 11½
2511	A699	$3 Wedding	3.25	3.25

No. 2511 contains one 85x46mm stamp.

Sixth Far East
and South Pacific
Games for the
Disabled,
Beijing — A700

1994, Sept. 4   Litho.   Perf. 12
2512	A700	20f multicolored	.50	.25

Wulingyuan State Forest Park — A701

20f, South Gate to Heaven. 30f, Shentangwan. 50f, No. One Bridge. $1, Writing-brush Peak. $3, Picturesque corridor.

1994, Sept. 25   Litho.   Perf. 12
2513	A701	20f multi, vert.	.25	.25
2514	A701	30f multi, vert.	.25	.25
2515	A701	50f multi	.30	.25
2516	A701	$1 multi	.45	.30
		Nos. 2513-2516 (4)	1.25	1.05

Souvenir Sheet
Perf. 11½x12
2517	A701	$3 multicolored	3.25	2.75

No. 2517 contains one 50x36mm stamp.

Wuyi Mountains — A702

Designs: a, Jade-girl Peak (4-1). b, Nine-bend Brook (4-2). c, Guadun Village (4-3). d, Alpine Grassland (4-4).

1994, Sept. 30   Perf. 12
2518	Strip of 4	1.75	1.25
a.-d.	A702 50f any single	.35	.25

No. 2518 exists imperf. Value, $225.

Listening to the
Rapids, by Fu
Baoshi (1904-65)
A703

Paintings: No. 2520, Appreciating a Painting. No. 2521, Dadi's Thatched Hut. 40f, Playing the Ruan. 50f, At Hupao. $1, The Road to Shanyin.

1994, Oct. 5
2519	A703	10f multi (6-1)	.25	.25
2520	A703	20f multi (6-2)	.25	.25
2521	A703	20f multi (6-3)	.25	.25
2522	A703	40f multi (6-4)	.25	.25
2523	A703	50f multi (6-5)	.30	.25
2524	A703	$1 multi (6-6)	.35	.25
		Nos. 2519-2524 (6)	1.65	1.50

Cranes — A704

Photo. & Engr.
1994, Oct. 9   Perf. 11x11½
2528	A704	20f Whooping crane	.30	.25
2529	A704	$2 Black-necked crane	.60	.50

See US Nos. 2867-2868.

Souvenir Sheet

UPU, 120th Anniv. — A705

Illustration reduced.

1994, Oct. 9   Litho.   Perf. 12
2530	A705	$3 multicolored	3.00	2.00
a.		Ovptd. in sheet margin	3.75	2.75

No. 2530a ovptd. in sheet margin with UPU hologram, vertical Chinese inscription in gold. Issued: July 18, 1996.

Gorges of Yangtze River — A706

Designs: 10f, Baidicheng. No. 2532, Qutang Gorge. No. 2533, Wuxia Gorge. 30f, Goddess Peak. 50f, Xiling Gorge. $1, Qu Yuan Memorial Temple. $5, The Three Gorges.

1994, Nov. 4   Photo.   Perf. 12
2531	A706	10f multi (6-1)	.25	.25
2532	A706	20f multi (6-2)	.25	.25
2533	A706	20f multi (6-3)	.25	.25
2534	A706	30f multi (6-4)	.25	.25
2535	A706	50f multi (6-5)	.30	.25
2536	A706	$1 multi (6-6)	.25	.25
		Nos. 2531-2536 (6)	1.65	1.50

Souvenir Sheet
Perf. 11½x11
2537	A706	$5 multicolored	3.50	2.75

No. 2537 contains one 116x35mm stamp.

Souvenir Sheet

All-China Philatelic Federation, 4th
Congress — A707

Illustration reduced.

1994, Nov. 17   Litho.   Perf. 11
2538	A707	$3 multicolored	2.25	1.50

Literature Type of 1988

Romance of the Three Kingdoms by Luo Guanzhong: 20f, Composing a poem with a lance in hands. 30f, Liu Bei's marriage, vert. 50f, Overwhelming Xiaoyaojin with prowess. $1, Campsites burned, vert. $5, Fierce battle at Chibi.

Perf. 11½x11, 11x11½
1994, Nov. 24   Photo.
2539	A587	20f multicolored	.25	.25
2540	A587	30f multicolored	.25	.25
2541	A587	50f multicolored	.30	.25
2542	A587	$1 multicolored	.35	.25
		Nos. 2539-2542 (4)	1.15	1.05

Souvenir Sheet
Perf. 11
2543	A587	$5 multicolored	5.25	4.00

No. 2543 contains one 158x36mm stamp.

Special
Economic
Zones
A708

Designs: a, Shenzhen (5-1). b, Zhuhai (5-2). c, Shantou (5-3). d, Xiamen (5-4). e, Hainan (5-4).

1994, Dec. 10   Litho.   Perf. 12
2544	A708	50f Strip of 5, #a.-e.	1.10	1.00

Pagodas of
Ancient
China — A709

Designs: No. 2545, Dayan Pagoda, Cien Temple. No. 2546, Zhenguo Pagoda, Kaiyuan Temple. 50f, Liuhe Pagoda, Kaihua Temple. $2, Youguo Temple.

Photo. & Engr.
1994, Dec. 15   Perf. 11½x11
2545	A709	20f tan, brn & blk (4-1)	.25	.25
2546	A709	20f tan, brn & blk (4-2)	.25	.25
2547	A709	50f tan, brn & blk (4-3)	.25	.25
2548	A709	$2 tan, brn & blk (4-4)	.35	.30
a.		Souvenir sheet of 4, #2545-2548	8.00	5.00
		Nos. 2545-2548 (4)	1.10	1.05

No. 2548a sold for $5.

New Year 1995 (Year of the Boar)
A711   A712

Photo. & Engr.
1995, Jan. 5   Perf. 11½
2550	A711	20f multicolored	.70	.25
2551	A712	50f multicolored	.70	.25

Winter
Scenes
A713

Designs: 20f, Snow willows, Cold River. 50f, Ice & snow on jade trees, vert.

1995, Jan. 12   Litho.   Perf. 12
2552	A713	20f multicolored	.30	.25
2553	A713	50f multicolored	.50	.25

Mt. Dinghushan — A714

Designs: 15f, Topographical map. No. 2555, Stream flowing down from mountain. No. 2556, Buildings on mountain side. $2.30, Silver pheasants.

1995, Feb. 15   Litho.   Perf. 12½
2554	A714	15f multi (4-1)	.25	.25
2555	A714	20f multi (4-2)	.25	.25
2556	A714	20f multi (4-3)	.25	.25
2557	A714	$2.30 multi (4-4)	.70	.30
		Nos. 2554-2557 (4)	1.45	1.05

World Summit for Social Development,
Copenhagen — A715

1995, Mar. 6   Photo.   Perf. 11x11½
2558	A715	20f multicolored	2.00	.25

Owls — A716

1995, Mar. 22   Photo.   Perf. 11½
2559 A716 10f Eagle owl   .25   .25
2560 A716 20f Long-eared owl   .25   .25
2561 A716 50f Snowy owl   .30   .25
2562 A716 $1 Grass owl   .35   .25
    Nos. 2559-2562 (4)   1.15 1.00

Sweet
Osmanthus
A717

1995, Apr. 14   Litho.   Perf. 12
2563 A717 20f Thunbergii (4-1)   .25   .25
2564 A717 20f Latifolius (4-2)   .25   .25
2565 A717 50f Aurantiacus (4-3)   .30   .25
2566 A717 $1 Semperflorens (4-
                         4)   .35   .30
    Nos. 2563-2566 (4)   1.15 1.05

A souvenir sheet of 4, #2563-2566, exists, both perf and imperf. Value, perf $5., imperf. $75.

43rd World Table Tennis
Championships, Tianjin — A718

1995, May 1   Litho.   Perf. 12
2567 A718 20f Athlete   .30   .25
2568 A718 50f Arena   .50   .25
    a. Souv. sheet of 2, #2567-
        2568   20.00 14.00

No. 2568a sold for $7. Issued 8/14/95.

Spring Outing — A719

Designs: No. 2569, Group riding horses. No. 2570, Three riding horses.

1995, May 23   Litho.   Perf. 12
2569 A719 50f multi (2-1)   .30   .25
2570 A719 50f multi (2-2)   .30   .25
    a. Pair, #2569-2570   .80   .70

No. 2570a is a continuous design.

Shadow
Play — A720

Various costumed characters.

1995, June 8   Photo.   Perf. 12x12½
2571 A720 20f multi (4-1)   .25   .25
2572 A720 40f multi (4-2)   .25   .25
2573 A720 50f multi (4-3)   .30   .25
2574 A720 50f multi (4-4)   .35   .25
    Nos. 2571-2574 (4)   1.15 1.00

Highway Interchanges, Beijing — A721

1995, June 20   Photo.   Perf. 11½x11
2575 A721 20f Siyuan   .25   .25
2576 A721 30f Tianningsi   .25   .25
2577 A721 50f Yuting   .30   .25
2578 A721 $1 Anhui   .35   .25
    Nos. 2575-2578 (4)   1.15 1.00

Diplomatic Relations Between China &
Thailand, 20th Anniv. — A722

#2579, Elephants walking right into water. #2580, Elephants walking left into water.

1995, July 1
2579 A722 $1 multi (2-1)   .30   .25
2580 A722 $1 multi (2-2)   .30   .25
    a. Pair, #2579-2580   .80   .75

No. 2580a is a continuous design.

Taihu
Lake
A723

Lake scenes: No. 2581, Yellow trees. No. 2582, Structures on bank, boats, hills. No. 2583, Structures across inlet. No. 2584, Red trees, home. 230f, Winter scene. 500f, Houses on cliff, lighthouse.

1995, July 20   Photo.   Perf. 11½
2581 A723 20f multi (5-1)   .25   .25
2582 A723 20f multi (5-2)   .25   .25
2583 A723 50f multi (5-3)   .30   .25
2584 A723 50f multi (5-4)   .30   .25
2585 A723 230f multi (5-5)   .70   .35
    Nos. 2581-2585 (5)   1.80 1.35

Souvenir Sheet
Perf. 11
2586 A723 500f multicolored   3.50 2.75
    a. Ovptd. in sheet margin   8.50 6.00

No. 2586 contains one 90x60mm stamp with continuing design.
No. 2586a issued 3/24/97. Gold overprint in sheet margin contains an emblem, Chinese inscription saying "Hong Kong Returns to China" and "PJZ-5."

Posts of
Ancient
China
A724

1995, Aug. 17   Photo.   Perf. 12
2587 A724 20f Yucheng   .30   .25
2588 A724 50f Jimingshan   .50   .25

Shaolin
Temple,
1500th
Anniv.
A725

1995, Aug. 30
2589 A725 20f Entrance (4-1)   .25   .25
2590 A725 20f Pagoda Forest
                      (4-2)   .25   .25
2591 A725 50f Martial arts (4-3) .30   .25
2592 A725 100f Historical rescue
                      (4-4)   .35   .25
    Nos. 2589-2592 (4)   1.15 1.00

Cultural Relics of
Tibet — A726

1995, Sept. 1
2593 A726 20f Jar   .25   .25
2594 A726 30f Casque   .25   .25
2595 A726 50f Celestial motion
             chart   .30   .25
2596 A726 100f Pearl mandala   .35   .25
    Nos. 2593-2596 (4)   1.15 1.00

Wildlife
A727

1995, Sept. 1   Perf. 11x11½
2597 A727 20f Koalas   .25   .25
2598 A727 $2.90 Pandas   1.00   .75

See Australia No. 1459.

End of
World War
II, 50th
Anniv.
A728

10f, July 7th event. #2600, Victory at Taier village. #2601, Soldier, hundred-regiment battle. #2602, Guerrilla war. #2603, Troops on parade, joining forces at Mangyo. 60f, Aircraft donated by Chinese living abroad. #2605, Taiwan recovered. #2606, Japanese surrender aboard USS Missouri.

1995, Sept. 3
2599 A728 10f multi (8-1)   .25   .25
2600 A728 20f multi (8-2)   .25   .25
2601 A728 20f multi (8-3)   .25   .25
2602 A728 50f multi (8-4)   .25   .25
2603 A728 50f multi (8-5)   .25   .25
2604 A728 60f multi (8-6)   .30   .25
2605 A728 100f multi (8-7)   .35   .25
2606 A728 100f multi (8-8)   .35   .25
    Nos. 2599-2606 (8)   2.25 2.00

4th World
Conference
on Women,
Beijing
A729

Symbols of: 15f, Equality. 20f, Development. 50f, Peace. 60f, Friendship.

1995, Sept. 4   Perf. 12
2607 A729 15f multi   .25   .25
2608 A729 20f multi   .25   .25
2609 A729 50f multi   .25   .25
2610 A729 60f multi   .25   .25
    Nos. 2607-2610 (4)   1.00 1.00

The Great
Wall — A730

Jiuhua
Mountains — A731

1995, Oct. 5   Photo.   Perf. 12½
2611 A730 60f shown   .25   .20
2612 A730 230f Shanhaiguan
             Pass   .70   .30
2613 A730 290f Jinshanling   .90   .30
    Nos. 2611-2613 (3)   1.85   .75

See Nos. 2755, 2792-2795, 2907-2910, 2934-2941, 2952-2955.

1995, Oct. 9   Perf. 12

10f, Sunrise at Peak Terrace, horiz. #2615, Hall of Meditation. #2616, Temple of Bodhisattva, horiz. #2617, Sunset at Zhiyuan, horiz. #2618, Great Rock. #2619, Phoenix Pine, horiz.

2614 A731 10f multi (6-1)   .25   .25
2615 A731 20f multi (6-2)   .25   .25
2616 A731 20f multi (6-3)   .25   .25
2617 A731 50f multi (6-4)   .30   .25
2618 A731 50f multi (6-5)   .30   .25
2619 A731 290f multi (6-6)   .90   .30
    Nos. 2614-2619 (6)   2.25 1.55

Motion
Pictures,
Cent.
A732

Projector and: 20f, Black and white film. 50f, Color film.

1995, Oct. 13
2620 A732 20f blue & black   .25   .25
2621 A732 50f multicolored   .45   .25

UN, 50th
Anniv.
A733

Designs: 20f, UN flag, Headquarters. 50f, Stylized flags, UN emblem, "50."

1995, Oct. 24   Litho.
2622 A733 20f multi   .30   .25
2623 A733 50f multi   .50   .25

Sanqing Mountains — A734

#2624, Good Fortune Land. #2625, Sichun Goddess. 50f, Bodhisattva Enjoys Music. 100f, Huge Boa out of Mountain.

1995, Nov. 1   Photo.   Perf. 12
2624 A734 20f multi (4-1)   .25   .25
2625 A734 20f multi (4-2)   .30   .25
2626 A734 50f multi, vert. (4-3) .30   .25
2627 A734 100f multi, vert. (4-4) .35   .25
    Nos. 2624-2627 (4)   1.20 1.00

Mt. Hengshan Type of 1990

Songshan Mountains: 20f, Ancient Temple of Mount Song. 50f, Moon waiting at Songmen Gate. 60f, Shaolin Temple. $1, Panorama view of Mt. Song.

Photo. & Engr.

1995, Nov. 10   **Perf. 11**
2628 A631 20f multi .... .25 .25
2629 A631 50f multi .... .30 .25
2630 A631 60f multi .... .30 .25
2631 A631 $1 multi .... .35 .25
Nos. 2628-2631 (4) 1.20 1.00

Scenic Views of Hong Kong — A735

Designs: 20f, Victoria Harbor. 50f, Central Plaza at night. 60f, Hong Kong Cultural Center. 290f, Repulse Bay.

1995, Nov. 28   **Photo.**   **Perf. 12**
2632 A735 20f multi .... .25 .25
2633 A735 50f multi .... .25 .25
2634 A735 60f multi .... .30 .25
2635 A735 290f multi .... .90 .30
Nos. 2632-2635 (4) 1.70 1.05

No. 2635 exists imperf. Value, pair $140.

Sun Zi's Art of War — A736

Drawings depicting: No. 2637, Discussing strategy. 30f, Capturing Ying. 50f, Battle at Ailing. 100f, Meeting of sovereigns, Huangchi.

1995, Dec. 4   **Perf. 11x11½**
2636 A736 20f multi (5-1) ..... .25 .25
2637 A736 20f multi (5-2) ..... .25 .25
2638 A736 30f multi (5-3) ..... .25 .25
2639 A736 50f multi (5-4) ..... .30 .25
2640 A736 100f multi (5-5) .... .30 .25
Nos. 2636-2640 (5) 1.40 1.30

New Year 1996 (Year of the Rat)
A737   A738

Photo. & Engr.

1996, Jan. 5   **Perf. 11½**
2641 A737 20f multi .... .45 .25
2642 A738 50f multi .... .55 .30

3rd Asian Winter Games A739

#2643, Speed skating. #2644, Ice hockey. #2645, Figure skating. #2646, Skiing.

1996, Feb. 4   **Litho.**   **Perf. 12**
2643 A739 50f multi (4-1) ..... .25 .25
2644 A739 50f multi (4-2) ..... .25 .25
2645 A739 50f multi (4-3) ..... .25 .25
2646 A739 50f multi (4-4) ..... .25 .25
 a. Block of 4, #2643-2646 ... 1.10 .80

China/Korea Submarine Fiber Optic Cable System — A740

1996, Feb. 8   **Litho.**   **Perf. 12**
2647 A740 20f multicolored ..... .50 .25

First day covers are dated 12/15/95. See Korea No. 1863.

Shenyang Imperial Palace — A741

Designs: No. 2648, Buildings, denomination UL. No. 2649, Buildings, denomination LR.

1996, Mar. 18   **Photo.**   **Perf. 12**
2648 A741 50f multi (2-1) ..... .30 .25
2649 A741 50f multi (2-2) ..... .30 .25
 a. Pair, Nos. 2648-2649 ..... .80 .70

China Post, Cent. A742

Post Office buildings: 10f, Tianjin Posts Bureau. 20f, Beijing Postal Administration. 50f, Directorate of Posts of China. 100f, Beijing postal hub.
500f, China #78-85.

1996, Mar. 20   **Perf. 11½**
2650 A742 10f multi .... .25 .25
2651 A742 20f multi .... .25 .25
2652 A742 50f multi .... .30 .25
2653 A742 100f multi .... .35 .25
Nos. 2650-2653 (4) 1.15 1.00

Souvenir Sheet
Perf. 11
2654 A742 500f multicolored ... 5.50 4.75

No. 2654 contains one 89x59mm stamp.

Huang Binhong, Artist — A743

#2655, Calligraphy. #2656, Landscape. 40f, Qingcheng Mts. #2658, View from Xiing. #2659, Colored landscape. 230f, Flowers.

1996, Apr. 5   **Perf. 11½**
2655 A743 20f multi (6-1) ..... .25 .25
2656 A743 20f multi (6-2) ..... .25 .25
2657 A743 40f multi (6-3) ..... .45 .25
2658 A743 50f multi (6-4) ..... .55 .25
2659 A743 50f multi (6-5) ..... .55 .30
2660 A743 230f multi (6-6) ... 2.25 .50
Nos. 2655-2660 (6) 4.30 1.80

Aircraft — A744

1996, Apr. 17   **Perf. 12**
2661 A744 20f F-8 (4-1) ..... .25 .25
2662 A744 50f A-5 (4-2) ..... .35 .25
2663 A744 50f Yun-7 (4-3) ..... .35 .25
2664 A744 100f Yun-12 (4-4) ... .50 .25
Nos. 2661-2664 (4) 1.45 1.00

Potted Landscapes — A745

#2665-2666, Lijing & Divine Peak. #2667-2668, Melting Snow & Eagle Rock. #2668-2669, Manch & Rosy Clouds.

1996, Apr. 18
2665 A745 20f multi (6-1) ..... .25 .25
2666 A745 20f multi (6-2) ..... .25 .25
 a. Pair, #2665-2666 ..... .60 .50
2667 A745 50f multi (6-3) ..... .30 .25
2668 A745 50f multi (6-4) ..... .30 .25
 a. Pair, #2667-2668 ..... .75 .60
2669 A745 100f multi (6-5) .... .45 .40
2670 A745 100f multi (6-6) .... .45 .40
 a. Pair, #2669-2670 ..... 1.40 1.25
Nos. 2665-2670 (6) 2.00 1.80

Iron Trees — A746

#2671, Cycas revoluta. #2672, Cycas panzhihuaensis. 50f, Cycas pectinata. 230f, Cycas multipinnata.

1996, May 2   **Litho.**   **Perf. 12**
2671 A746 20f multi (4-1) ..... .25 .25
2672 A746 20f multi (4-2) ..... .25 .25
2673 A746 50f multi (4-3) ..... .30 .25
2674 A746 230f multi (4-4) ... .75 .35
Nos. 2671-2674 (4) 1.55 1.10

Nos. 2671-2674 exist imperf. Value, set of pairs $325.

China-San Marino Relations, 25th Anniv. A747

1996, May 6   **Photo.**   **Perf. 12**
2675 A747 100f Great Wall of China (2-1) ..... .35 .25
2676 A747 100f Mt. Titano (2-2) ..... .35 .25
 a. Pair, #2675-2676 ..... .80 .70

See San Marino Nos. 1356-1357.

Artifacts from Hemudu Ruins — A748

Designs: 20f, Agricultural tool. 50f, Pile to support building. 100f, Paddles for boats. 230f, Bird and sun carved in wood.

1996, May 12   **Litho.**   **Perf. 12**
2677 A748 20f multi .... .25 .25
2678 A748 50f multi .... .25 .25
2679 A748 100f multi .... .35 .25
2680 A748 230f multi .... .80 .30
Nos. 2677-2680 (4) 1.65 1.05

Souvenir Sheet

CHINA '96, 9th Asian Intl. Philatelic Exhibition — A749

1996, May 18   **Perf. 11½x12**
2681 A749 500f multicolored ... 6.25 4.25
 a. Overprinted in gold 8.50 6.00

No. 2681 exists imperf. Value, $18.
Overprint in margin of No. 2681a includes Chinese characters, Shanghai '97 exhibition emblem, and "PJZ-6." Issued in 1998.

Children's Activities A750

Designs: 20f, Singing, playing musical instruments. 30f, Pushing child in wheelchair, holding umbrella. 50f, Placing flag on South Pole, penguins. 100f, Planting tree.

1996, June 1   **Perf. 12**
2682 A750 20f multi .... .25 .25
2683 A750 30f multi .... .25 .25
2684 A750 50f multi .... .30 .25
2685 A750 100f multi .... .35 .25
Nos. 2682-2685 (4) 1.15 1.00

Modern Olympic Games, Cent. — A751

1996, June 23   **Photo.**   **Perf. 12**
2686 A751 20f multicolored ..... .80 .25

Protection of Land A752

Stylized designs representing: 20f, Making use of land. 50f, Protection of farmland.

1996, June 25   **Perf. 11x11½**
2687 A752 20f multi   .40 .25
2688 A752 50f multi   .60 .25

A753

Military Terraces — A754

1996, July 9   **Litho.**   **Perf. 12**
2689 A753 20f multi   .35 .25
2690 A754 50f multi   .45 .25

Vehicles — A755

#2691, Red Flag, 4-door limousine. #2692, Dongfeng, stake truck. 50f, Jiefang, 4-door truck. 100f, Beijing, canvas-topped jeep.

1996, July 15   **Photo.**   **Perf. 12**
2691 A755 20f multi (4-1)   .25 .25
2692 A755 20f multi (4-2)   .25 .25
2693 A755 50f multi (4-3)   .30 .25
2694 A755 100f multi (4-4)   .45 .30
   Nos. 2691-2694 (4)   1.25 1.05

New Tangshan Built Following 1976 Earthquake — A756

1996, July 28   **Perf. 11½**
2695 A756 20f Farm cottages (4-1)   .25 .25
2696 A756 50f Factory (4-2)   .30 .25
2697 A756 50f Street (4-3)   .30 .25
2698 A756 100f Port (4-4)   .35 .25
   Nos. 2695-2698 (4)   1.20 1.00

30th Intl. Geological Conference — A757

1996, Aug. 4   **Litho.**   **Perf. 12**
2699 A757 20f multicolored   .50 .25

Tianchi Lake, Tianshan Mountains — A758

20f, High mountain lake. #2701, Splendid Waterfalls. #2702, Snow-capped peaks. 100f, Lakeside scenery.

1996, Aug. 8
2700 A758 20f multi (4-1)   .25 .25
2701 A758 50f multi, vert. (4-2)   .30 .25
2702 A758 50f multi, vert. (4-3)   .30 .25
2703 A758 100f multi (4-4)   .45 .25
   Nos. 2700-2703 (4)   1.30 1.00

Wall Paintings Type of 1987

10f, Illustration of Mount Wutai. 20f, King of Khotan, vert. 50f, Savior Avalokitesvara. 100f, Worshipping Bodhisattvas. $5, Thousand Arm Avalokitesvara.

1996, Aug. 15   **Photo.**   **Perf. 11**
2704 A557 10f multi, vert.   .25 .25
2705 A557 20f multi   .25 .25
2706 A557 50f multi   .30 .25
2707 A557 100f multi   .35 .25
   Nos. 2704-2707 (4)   1.15 1.00

Souvenir Sheet

2708 A557 500f multicolored   6.25 4.00
No. 2708 contains one 46x102mm stamp.

Mausoleums of Western Xia — A759

Designs: No. 2709: Mausoleum terrace. No. 2710, Ornament on Divine Gate. 50f, Stele. 100f, Stele remnant, Shouling.

1996, Aug. 22   **Photo.**   **Perf. 11½**
2709 A759 20f multi (4-1)   .25 .25
2710 A759 20f multi (4-2)   .25 .25
2711 A759 50f multi (4-3)   .30 .25
2712 A759 100f multi (4-4)   .45 .25
   Nos. 2709-2712 (4)   1.25 1.00

Railways in China — A760

Designs: 15f, Datong-Quinhuangdao Railway. 20f, Lanzhou-Xinjiang Two-Track Railway. 50f, Beijing-Kowloon Railway. 100f, Beijing Western Railway Station

1996, Sept. 1
2713 A760 15f multi   .25 .25
2714 A760 20f multi   .30 .25
2715 A760 50f multi   .35 .25
2716 A760 100f multi   .50 .25
   Nos. 2713-2716 (4)   1.40 1.00

A761

A762

Chinese Archives: No. 2717, Archives on tortoise shells, Shang Dynasty. No. 2718, Archives on wood slips, Han Dynasty. 50f, Iron scrolls, Ming Dynasty. 100f, Books of Ch'ing Dynasty.

1996, Sept. 2   **Litho.**   **Perf. 12**
2717 A761 20f multi (4-1)   .25 .25
2718 A761 20f multi (4-2)   .30 .25
2719 A761 50f multi (4-3)   .35 .25
2720 A761 100f multi (4-4)   .45 .25
   Nos. 2717-2720 (4)   1.35 1.00

1996, Sept. 10   **Perf. 12**
2721 A762 20f Portrait   .35 .25
2722 A762 50f In uniform   .45 .25
Ye Ting (1896-1946), co-founder of Chinese People's Liberation Army.

96th Conference of Inter-Parliamentary Union — A763

1996, Sept. 16   **Perf. 11½**
2723 A763 20f multi   .80 .25

Shanghai — A764

Photo. & Engr.
1996, Sept. 21   **Perf. 11½**
2724 A764 10f Communication (6-1)   .25 .25
2725 A764 20f Lujiazui (6-2)   .25 .25
2726 A764 20f Jinqiao (6-3)   .25 .25
2727 A764 50f Zhanghiang (6-4)   .30 .25
2728 A764 60f Waigaoqiao (6-5)   .30 .25
2729 A764 100f Residential (6-6)   .40 .30
   Nos. 2724-2729 (6)   1.75 1.55

Souvenir Sheet
Perf. 11
2730 A764 500f Panoramic view   7.75 6.50
  a.   Margin ovptd.   18.00 10.00
No. 2730 contains one 90x45mm stamp. No. 2730a issued 10/20/01. It is inscribed in margin with multicolored emblems and gold "PJZ-14," "APEC CHINA 2001," and Chinese characters.

Space Navigation — A765

1996, Oct. 7   **Litho.**   **Perf. 12**
2731 A765 20f Rocket lift-off   .40 .25
2732 A765 100f Satellite in orbit   .60 .35

Singapore Waterfront — A766

Design: 290f, Panmen, Suzhou, China.

1996, Oct. 9   **Photo.**   **Perf. 11½**
2733 A766 20f multi   .25 .25
2734 A766 290f multi   .95 .30
See Singapore Nos. 768-769.

Victory of Long March, 60th Anniv. — A767

Designs: 20f, Red Army through Marshland. 50f, Reunion of Three Armies.

1996, Oct. 22   **Litho.**   **Perf. 12**
2735 A767 20f multi   .40 .30
2736 A767 50f multi   .80 .50

Colored Sculpture of Tianjin A768

Designs: 20f, The Two Immortals. No. 2738, Making Candy. No. 2739, Returning from Fishing. 100f, Xi Chun in Painting.

1996, Nov. 5   **Photo.**   **Perf. 11½**
2737 A768 20f multi (4-1)   .25 .25
2738 A768 50f multi (4-2)   .30 .25
2739 A768 50f multi (4-3)   .30 .25
2740 A768 100f multi (4-4)   .35 .25
   Nos. 2737-2740 (4)   1.20 1.00

Hong Kong A769

20f, Bank of China. 40f, Container Terminal. 60f, Kai Tak Airport. 290f, Stock Exchange.

1996, Dec. 19   **Litho.**   **Perf. 12**
2741 A769 20f multi (4-1)   .25 .25
2742 A769 40f multi (4-2)   .25 .25
2743 A769 60f multi (4-3)   .35 .25
2744 A769 290f multi (4-4)   1.10 .30
   Nos. 2741-2744 (4)   1.95 1.05

Nos. 2741-2744 exist imperf. Value, set of pairs $700.

A770   A771

1997, Jan. 1
2745 A770 50f Visit China   1.00 .25

1997, Jan. 1
2746 A771 50f multicolored   .80 .25
First natl. agricultural census.

New Year 1997 (Year of the Ox)
A772   A773

Photo. & Engr.
1997, Jan. 5   **Perf. 11½**
2747 A772 50f multi (2-2)   .45 .25
2748 A773 150f multi (2-1)   .85 .40

Paintings by Pan Tianshou (1897-1971)
A774

#2749, Pines on the Yellow Mountain. #2750, Rosy Clouds of Dawn. #2751, Clearing Up after Mould Rains. #2752, Chrysanthemum and Bamboo. #2753, Sleeping Cat. #2754, A Corner of Lingyan Brook.

1997, Mar. 14		Photo.	Perf. 11½	
2749	A774	50f multi (6-1)	.25	.25
2750	A774	50f multi (6-2)	.25	.25
2751	A774	100f multi (6-3)	.75	.30
2752	A774	100f multi (6-4)	.75	.30
2753	A774	150f multi (6-5)	1.40	.35
2754	A774	150f multi (6-6)	1.40	.35
	Nos. 2749-2754 (6)		4.80	1.80

Great Wall Type of 1995

1997, Apr. 1		Photo.	Perf. 13x12	
2755	A730	50f multicolored	.20	.20

A776

A777

Tea: No. 2756, People forming circle beside tea tree. No. 2757, Statue of tea sage. No. 2758, Tea utensils, horiz. No. 2759, Painting of tea party, horiz.

1997, Apr. 8		Litho.	Perf. 12	
2756	A776	50f multi (4-1)	.30	.25
2757	A776	50f multi (4-2)	.30	.25
2758	A776	150f multi (4-3)	.55	.25
2759	A776	150f multi (4-4)	.55	.25
	Nos. 2756-2759 (4)		1.70	1.00

1997, May 1		Photo.	Perf. 11½	

Stylized designs depicting: No. 2760, Celebration. No. 2761, Unity (group of people), horiz. 200f, Advance (horses running), horiz.

2760	A777	50f multi (3-1)	.30	.25
2761	A777	50f multi (3-2)	.30	.25
2762	A777	200f multi (3-3)	.90	.30
	Nos. 2760-2762 (3)		1.50	.80

Inner Mongolia Autonomous Region, 50th anniv.

Pheasants
A778

Designs: 50f, Chinese copper pheasant. 540f, Common pheasant.

Litho. & Engr.

1997, May 9			Perf. 11½x11	
2763	A778	50f multi (2-1)	.30	.25
2764	A778	540f multi (2-2)	2.00	.80

See Sweden Nos. 2225-2226.

Dong Architecture
A779

Maiji Grottoes — A780

#2765, Zengchong Drum Tower. #2766, Bai'er Drum Tower. #2767, Wind and Rain Bridge over the River, horiz. #2768, Wind and Rain Bridge in the Field, horiz.

1997, June 2		Litho.	Perf. 12	
2765	A779	50f multi (4-1)	.25	.25
2766	A779	50f multi (4-2)	.25	.25
a.		Pair, #2765-2766	.60	.55
2767	A779	150f multi (4-3)	.50	.25
2768	A779	150f multi (4-4)	.50	.25
a.		Pair, #2767-2768	1.10	1.00
	Nos. 2765-2768 (4)		1.50	1.00

1997, June 13

Statues: No. 2769, Buddha and Xieshi Bodhisattva. No. 2770, Xieshi Bodhisattva and his disciple. 100f, Maid. No. 2772, Buddha. No. 2773, Xieshi Bodhisattva. 200f, Provider.

2769	A780	50f multi (6-1)	.25	.25
2770	A780	50f multi (6-2)	.25	.25
2771	A780	100f multi (6-3)	.35	.25
2772	A780	150f multi (6-4)	.50	.25
2773	A780	150f multi (6-5)	.50	.25
2774	A780	200f multi (6-6)	.65	.30
	Nos. 2769-2774 (6)		2.50	1.55

A780a

A781

Texts surrounded by flowers: 50f, Sino-British Joint Declaration. 150f, Basic Law of the Hong Kong Special Adminstrative Region. 800f, Deng Xiaoping.

1997, July 1		Litho.	Perf. 12	
2774A	A780a	50f multi (2-1)	.35	.25
2774B	A780a	150f multi (2-2)	.90	.60

Souvenir Sheets

2774C	A781	800f multi	4.25	3.00
d.		Overprinted in sheet margin	7.00	4.50

Litho. (stamp) & Embossed (margin)
Perf. 13½

2775	A781	$50 gold & multi	45.00	45.00
a.		Overprinted in margin	47.50	47.50

Deng Xiaoping (1904-97), return of Hong Kong to China.

No. 2775 was released in special souvenir folder.

No. 2744C exists imperf. Value, $500.

No. 2774Cd contains gold Chinese inscription for Hong Kong's Return Exhibition Tour, emblem, and "PJZ-8" in sheet margin. Issued: 6/19/98.

Overprint in margin on No. 2775a is Chinese inscription, "2000-1" and "(2-1)J." Issued: 1/1/00.

Ancient Temples of Wutai Mountain — A782

Designs: 40f, Taihuai Township. No. 2777, Nanchan Temple. No. 2778, Foguang Temple. No. 2779, Xiantong Temple. No. 2780, Bodhisattva Summit. 200f, Zhenhai Temple.

1997, July 26		Litho.	Perf. 12	
2776	A782	40f multi (6-1)	.25	.25
2777	A782	50f multi (6-2)	.25	.25
2778	A782	50f multi (6-3)	.25	.25
2779	A782	150f multi (6-4)	.50	.25
2780	A782	150f multi (6-5)	.50	.25
2781	A782	200f multi (6-6)	.65	.30
	Nos. 2776-2781 (6)		2.40	1.55

Chinese People's Liberation Army, 70th Anniv. — A783

#2782, Land Force. #2783, Naval Force. #2784, Air Force. #2785, Strategic Missile Troops. 200f, Joint military maneuvers.

1997, Aug. 1

2782	A783	50f multi (5-1)	.25	.25
2783	A783	50f multi (5-2)	.25	.25
2784	A783	50f multi (5-3)	.25	.25
2785	A783	50f multi (5-4)	.25	.25
2786	A783	200f multi (5-5)	.65	.30
	Nos. 2782-2786 (5)		1.65	1.30

Shoushan Stone Carvings
A784

Designs: No. 2787, "Rhythm of Autumn," vert. No. 2788, "Rhinoceros under Sunshine,", vert. No. 2789, "Jade's Fragrance," (basket of fruit). No. 2790, "Drunken Joy." 800f, Qianlong's Chain Seals.

1997, Aug. 17		Litho.	Perf. 12	
2787	A784	50f multi (4-1)	.25	.25
2788	A784	50f multi (4-2)	.25	.25
2789	A784	150f multi (4-3)	.50	.25
2790	A784	150f multi (4-4)	.50	.25
	Nos. 2787-2790 (4)		1.50	1.00

Souvenir Sheet

2791	A784	800f multi	5.00	4.50

No. 2791 contains one 60x60mm stamp.

Great Wall Type of 1995

Gates: 30f, Huangyaguan. 100f, Badaling. 150f, Joyongguan. 200f, Zijingguan.

1997, Sept. 1		Photo.	Perf. 13x12	
2792	A730	30f yellow & black	.20	.20
2793	A730	100f vermilion & black	.35	.20
2794	A730	150f green & black	.50	.20
2795	A730	200f red & black	.65	.25
	Nos. 2792-2795 (4)		1.70	.85

Communist Party of China, 15th Natl. Congress
A785

1997, Sept. 12		Litho.	Perf. 12	
2796	A785	50f multicolored	1.00	.40

A786

#2797, China Rose. #2798, New Zealand Monthly Rose.

1997, Oct. 9		Photo.	Perf. 11½	
2797		150f multi (2-1)	.60	.25
2798		150f multi (2-2)	.60	.25
a.	A786	Pair, #2797-2798	1.75	1.25

See New Zealand Nos. 1469-1470.

Eighth Natl. Games
A788

1997, Oct. 12		Litho.	Perf. 12	
2799	A788	50f Athletes (2-1)	.25	.25
2800	A788	150f Stadium (2-2)	.55	.35
a.		Souv. sheet (#2799-2800)	5.25	4.00

No. 2800a sold for 300f.

Temple of Heaven, Beijing — A789

#2801, Hall of Prayers for Bumper Harvests. #2802, Imperial Vault of Heaven. #2803, Circular Mound Altar. #2804, Fasting Palace.

1997, Oct. 16		Litho.	Perf. 12	
2801	A789	50f multi (4-1)	.30	.25
2802	A789	50f multi (4-2)	.30	.25
a.		Pair, #2801-2802	.70	.60
2803	A789	150f multi (4-3)	.50	.25
2804	A789	150f multi (4-4)	.50	.25
a.		Pair, #2803-2804	1.20	.90
	Nos. 2801-2804 (4)		1.60	1.00

Mt. Huangshan — A790

a, Mt. Huangshan at sunrise (8-1). b, Xihai Peaks (8-2). c, Flying Rock in surging clouds (8-3). d, Beihai in drifting clouds (8-4). e, Yuping Peak (8-5). f, Mystical stone (8-6). g, Tiandu Peak over clouds (8-7). h, Fabled Abode of Immortals (8-8).

1997, Oct. 20		Photo.	Perf. 11½	
	Sheet of 8 + Label			
2805	A790	200f #a.-h.	12.00	8.50

Nos. 2805d, 2805e are each 36x46mm. 22nd UPU Congress, Beijing, 1999.

City Wall of Xi'an A791

Designs: No. 2806, Surrounding tower. No. 2807, Arrow Tower. No. 2808, Watch Tower. No. 2809, Corner Tower.

1997, Oct. 24   Litho.   Perf. 12

2806	A791	50f multi (4-1)	.25	.25
2807	A791	50f multi (4-2)	.25	.25
2808	A791	150f multi (4-3)	.50	.30
2809	A791	150f multi (4-4)	.50	.30
		Nos. 2806-2809 (4)	1.50	1.10

Three Gorges Dam Project on Yangtze River — A792

#2810, New channel being opened to navigation. #2811, Damming Yangtze River.

1997, Nov. 8   Photo.   Perf. 11½

2810	A792	50f multi (2-1)	.25	.25
2811	A792	50f multi (2-2)	.25	.25
a.		Pair, #2810-2811	.60	.55

Macao Landmarks — A793

50f, Ma Kok Temple. 100f, Lin Fong Temple. 150f, St. Paul's Ruins. 200f, Guia Lighthouse.

1997, Nov. 11   Litho.   Perf. 12

2812	A793	50f multi (4-1)	.25	.25
2813	A793	100f multi (4-2)	.35	.25
2814	A793	150f multi (4-3)	.50	.30
2815	A793	200f multi (4-4)	.65	.30
		Nos. 2812-2815 (4)	1.75	1.10

Steel Production Exceeds 100 Million Tons in 1996 A794

50f, Ancient method of producing steel. 150f, Modern mill, pouring steel from smelter.

1997, Nov. 25

2816	A794	50f multi (2-1)	.25	.25
2817	A794	150f multi (2-2)	.55	.30

Telecommunications — A795

Stylized designs: #2818, Digital transmissions. #2819, Computer, "X-changing" data. #2820, Computer receiving signals, Chinese landmarks. #2821, Cellular phone transmission, man's head.

1997, Dec. 10

2818	A795	50f multi (4-1)	.25	.25
2819	A795	50f multi (4-2)	.25	.25
2820	A795	150f multi (4-3)	.50	.30
2821	A795	150f multi (4-4)	.50	.30
		Nos. 2818-2821 (4)	1.50	1.10

Literature Type of 1987

Outlaws of the Marsh: 40f, Huyan Zhuo coaxes Guan Sheng in a moonlit night. No. 2823, Lu Junyi captures Shi Wengong. No. 2824, Yan Qing defeats sky supporting pillar. 150f, Thunderbolt defeats Imperial Army. 800f, Heroes of Mount Liangshan take seats in order of rank.

1997, Dec. 22   Photo.   Perf. 11

2822	A570	40f multi (4-1)	.25	.25
2823	A570	50f multi (4-2)	.30	.25
2824	A570	50f multi (4-3)	.30	.25
2825	A570	150f multi (4-4)	.70	.30
		Nos. 2822-2825 (4)	1.55	1.05

Souvenir Sheet

2826	A570	800f multicolored	3.50	3.25

No. 2826 contains one 60x90mm stamp.

New Year 1998 (Year of the Tiger) A796   A797

Photo. & Engr.

1998, Jan. 5   Perf. 11½

2827	A796	50f multi (2-1)	.30	.25
2828	A797	150f multi (2-2)	.70	.35

Gardens of Lingnan — A798

1998, Jan. 18   Litho.   Perf. 12

2829	A798	50f Keyuan (4-1)	.25	.25
2830	A798	50f Liangyuan (4-2)	.25	.25
2831	A798	100f Qinghui (4-3)	.35	.25
2832	A798	200f Yuyin Villa (4-4)	.65	.30
		Nos. 2829-2832 (4)	1.50	1.05

Deng Xiaoping (1904-97) — A799

#2833, At middle age. #2834, During Liberation War. #2835, With Mao Tse-tung. 100f, As Chairman of Central Military Commission. 150f, Making speech on 35th anniversary of People's Republic. 200f, Making speech, hand raised, 1992.

1998, Feb. 19   Photo.   Perf. 11½

2833	A799	50f multi (6-1)	.25	.25
2834	A799	50f multi (6-2)	.25	.25
2835	A799	50f multi (6-3)	.25	.25
2836	A799	100f multi (6-4)	.35	.25
2837	A799	150f multi (6-5)	.50	.30
2838	A799	200f multi (6-6)	.65	.35
		Nos. 2833-2838 (6)	2.25	1.65

Chinese People's Police — A800

Designs: 40f, Golden shield. No. 2840, Blitz operation. No. 2841, Cooperation between police and people. 100f, Traffic control. 150f, Fire police. 200f, Border guards.

1998, Feb. 28   Litho.   Perf. 12

2839	A800	40f multi (6-1)	.25	.25
2840	A800	50f multi (6-2)	.25	.25
2841	A800	50f multi (6-3)	.25	.25
2842	A800	100f multi (6-4)	.35	.25
2843	A800	150f multi (6-5)	.50	.25
2844	A800	200f multi (6-6)	.65	.30
		Nos. 2839-2844 (6)	2.25	1.55

A801

A802

1998, Mar. 5

2845	A801	50f multi (1-1)	1.00	.25

Ninth Natl. People's Congress, Beijing.

1998, Mar. 5   Photo.   Perf. 11½

Chou En-lai (1898-1976), Communist Party leader: No. 2846, In military uniform on horse. No. 2847, As First Premier, walking. No. 2848, As diplomat wearing lei. No. 2849, Standing and applauding.

2846	A802	50f multi (4-1)	.50	.25
2847	A802	50f multi (4-2)	.50	.25
2848	A802	150f multi (4-3)	1.25	.40
2849	A802	150f multi (4-4)	1.25	.40
		Nos. 2846-2849 (4)	3.50	1.30

Nine-Village Valley — A803

Designs: No. 2850, Fangcao Lake. No. 2851, Wuhua Lake. No. 2852, Shuzheng Waterfalls. No. 2853, Nuorilang Waterfalls.

1998, Mar. 26   Litho.   Perf. 12

2850	A803	50f multi (4-1)	.25	.25
2851	A803	50f multi (4-2)	.25	.25
2852	A803	150f multi (4-3)	.50	.30
2853	A803	150f multi (4-4)	.50	.30
		Nos. 2850-2853 (4)	1.50	1.10

Souvenir Sheet

2854	A803	800f Long Lake	3.25	3.00

No. 2854 contains one 93x52mm stamp.

Dai Architecture — A804

#2855, Building on stilts. #2856, Well. #2857, Pavilion. #2858, Pagoda.

1998, Apr. 12   Photo.   Perf. 11½

2855	A804	50f multi (4-1)	.25	.25
2856	A804	50f multi (4-2)	.25	.25
2857	A804	150f multi (4-3)	.50	.30
2858	A804	150f multi (4-4)	.50	.30
		Nos. 2855-2858 (4)	1.50	1.10

Construction, Hainan Special Economic Zone — A805

#2859, Urban construction, Haikou. #2860, Economic development zone, Yangpu. #2861, Phoenix Intl. Airport, Sanya. #2862, Natl. tourism and resort zone, Yalongwan.

1998, Apr. 13   Litho.   Perf. 12

2859	A805	50f multi (4-1)	.25	.25
2860	A805	50f multi (4-2)	.25	.25
a.		Pair, #2859-2860	.60	.55
2861	A805	150f multi (4-3)	.50	.30
2862	A805	150f multi (4-4)	.50	.30
a.		Pair, #2861-2862	1.10	.90
		Nos. 2859-2862 (4)	1.50	1.10

Ancient Academies — A806

Designs: No. 2863, Yingtian. No. 2864, Songyang. No. 2865, Yuelu. No. 2866, Bailu.

1998, Apr. 29

2863	A806	50f multi (4-1)	.25	.25
2864	A806	50f multi (4-2)	.25	.25
2865	A806	150f multi (4-3)	.50	.30
2866	A806	150f multi (4-4)	.50	.30
		Nos. 2863-2866 (4)	1.50	1.10

Beijing University, Cent. A807

1998, May 4   Litho.   Perf. 12

2867	A807	50f multicolored	.50	.25

22nd UPU Congress, Beijing A808

1998, May 15   Litho.   Perf. 12

2868	A808	50f Emblem (2-1)	.25	.25
2869	A808	540f Emblem, vert. (2-2)	1.75	.75

Shennongjia Nature Reserve — A809

#2870, Mountain peaks. #2871, River, gorge. #2872, Primitive forest. #2873, Grasslands.

1998, June 6

2870	A809	50f multi (4-1)	.25	.25
2871	A809	50f multi (4-2)	.25	.25
2872	A809	150f multi (4-3)	.50	.30
2873	A809	150f multi (4-4)	.50	.30
		Nos. 2870-2873 (4)	1.50	1.10

Chongqing — A810

1998, June 18   Litho.   Perf. 12
2874 A810 50f Great Hall (2-1)   .35   .25
2875 A810 150f Port (2-2)   .65   .40

Xilinguole Grassland — A811

Designs: No. 2876, Sheep grazing, sheep herders. No. 2877, Cattle grazing, flowers. 150f, Poplar and birch forest, deer. 800f, Xilinguole River Bend.

1998, June 24
2876 A811 50f multi (3-1)   .25   .25
2877 A811 50f multi (3-2)   .25   .25
2878 A811 150f multi (3-3)   .50   .30
        Nos. 2876-2878 (3)   1.00   .80
Souvenir Sheet
2879 A811 800f multicolored   3.00   2.75
No. 2879 contains one 56x36mm stamp.

Paintings, by He Xiangning (1878-1972) — A812

Perf. 12½ Syncopated Type A (2 Sides)
1998, June 27   Photo.
2880 A812 50f Tiger (3-1)   .30   .25
2881 A812 100f Lion, vert. (3-2)   .45   .30
2882 A812 150f Plum blossom, vert. (3-3)   .55   .35
        Nos. 2880-2882 (3)   1.30   .90

Jingpo Lake — A813

Views of lake: No. 2883, Bridge, houses on cliff, boat. No. 2884, Islands, boats at shore. No. 2885, Boat, island. No. 2886, Waterfalls.

1998, Aug. 15   Litho.   Perf. 12
2883 A813 50f multi (4-1)   .25   .25
2884 A813 50f multi (4-2)   .25   .25
2885 A813 50f multi (4-3)   .25   .25
2886 A813 50f multi (4-4)   .25   .25
  a.   Strip of 4, #2883-2886   1.20   1.10

Würzburg Palace — A814

Puning Temple, Chengde — A815

1998, Aug. 20   Litho.   Perf. 12
2887 A814 50f multi (2-1)   .35   .25
2888 A815 540f multi (2-2)   1.90   1.40
        See Germany Nos. 2012-2013.

Literature Type of 1987

Romance of the Three Kingdoms: No. 2889, Liu Bei finds a guardian for his heir at Baidi City. No. 2890, Zhuge Liang leads his army home, vert. 100f, Death of Zhuge Liang. 150f, Three Kingdoms united under the reign of Jin, vert. 800f, The Stratagem of Empty City.

1998, Aug. 26   Photo.   Perf. 11½
2889 A570 50f multi (4-1)   .25   .25
2890 A570 50f multi (4-2)   .25   .25
2891 A570 100f multi (4-3)   .35   .30
2892 A570 150f multi (4-4)   .55   .50
        Nos. 2889-2892 (4)   1.40   1.30
Souvenir Sheet
2893 A570 800f multicolored   7.25   4.25
No. 2893 contains one 158x37mm stamp.

Flood Victims Relief — A816

1998, Sept. 10   Photo.   Perf. 13x13½
2894 A816 50f + 50f label   .60   .35

The Louvre, France A817

Design: 200f, Hall of Heavenly Peace, Imperial Palace, China.

1998, Sept. 12   Photo.   Perf. 13x13½
2895 A817 50f multi (2-1)   .25   .25
2896 A817 200f multi (2-2)   .80   .55
        See France Nos. 2669-2670.

Cliff Paintings of Helan Mountains — A818

1998, Sept. 23   Litho.   Perf. 12
2897 A818 50f Human face (3-1)   .25   .25
2898 A818 100f Hunting (3-2)   .35   .30
2899 A818 150f Ox (3-3)   .50   .40
        Nos. 2897-2899 (3)   1.10   .95

Longquan Pottery and Porcelain — A819

Designs: No. 2900, Vase with five spouts. No. 2901, Vase with phoenix ears. No. 2902, Double gourd vase. 150f, Ewer.

1998, Oct. 13
2900 A819 50f multi (4-1)   .25   .25
2901 A819 50f multi (4-2)   .25   .25
2902 A819 50f multi (4-3)   .25   .25
2903 A819 150f multi (4-4)   .50   .45
        Nos. 2900-2903 (4)   1.25   1.20

Mausoleum of Yandi A820

Designs: 50f, Meridian Gate. 100f, Saluting Pavilion. 150f, Tomb.

1998, Oct. 28   Litho.   Perf. 12
2904 A820 50f multi (3-1)   .25   .25
2905 A820 100f multi (3-2)   .35   .30
2906 A820 150f multi (3-3)   .50   .40
  a.   Souvenir sheet, #2904-2906   2.40   2.00
        Nos. 2904-2906 (3)   1.10   .95

Great Wall Type of 1995

10f, Jiumenko Pass. 300f, Niagziguan Pass. 420f, Pianguan Pass. 500f, Bianjing Tower.

1998, Nov. 1   Photo.   Perf. 13x12
2907 A730 10f apple green & black   .20   .20
2908 A730 300f olive & black   1.00   .75
2909 A730 420f brn org & blk   1.40   1.00
2910 A730 500f blue, black & brown   1.60   1.25
        Nos. 2907-2910 (4)   4.20   3.20

Major Campaigns in Liberation War — A821

#2911, Making plans. #2912, Conquering Jinzhou. #2913, Battle in Huaihai. #2914, Liberating Beijing. 150f, People moving supplies.

1998, Nov. 14   Litho.   Perf. 12
2911 A821 50f red & multi (5-1)   .25   .25
2912 A821 50f gray & multi (5-2)   .25   .25
2913 A821 50f org yel & multi (5-3)   .25   .25
2914 A821 50f orange & multi (5-4)   .25   .25
2915 A821 150f brn org & multi (5-5)   .50   .40
        Nos. 2911-2915 (5)   1.50   1.40

Liu Shaoqi (1898-1969), Communist Party Leader — A822

Various portraits.

1998, Nov. 24   Photo.   Perf. 11½
2916 A822 50f multi (4-1), vert.   .30   .25
2917 A822 50f multi (4-2), vert.   .30   .25
2918 A822 50f shown (4-3)   .30   .25
2919 A822 150f multi (4-4)   .60   .40
        Nos. 2916-2919 (4)   1.50   1.15

Chillon Castle, Lake Geneva A823

Bridge 24, Slender West Lake, Yangzhou A824

1998, Nov. 25   Perf. 11x11½
2920 A823 50f multi (2-1)   .35   .25
2921 A824 540f multi (2-2)   1.90   1.40
        See Switzerland Nos. 1037-1039.

Lingqu Canal — A825

#2922, Dam. #2923, Bridge over canal, vert. 150f, Boat approaching lock, vert.

1998, Dec. 1   Litho.   Perf. 12
2922 A825 50f multi (3-1)   .25   .25
2923 A825 50f multi (3-2)   .25   .25
2924 A825 150f multi (3-3)   .50   .40
        Nos. 2922-2924 (3)   1.00   .90

Buildings in Macao — A826

Designs: 50f, Building complex, Nanwan. 100f, Friendship Bridge. 150f, Macao Stadium. 200f, Macao Intl. Airport.

1998, Dec. 12   Litho.   Perf. 12
2925 A826 50f multi (4-1)   .25   .25
2926 A826 100f multi (4-2)   .35   .30
2927 A826 150f multi (4-3)   .50   .40
2928 A826 200f multi (4-4)   .65   .60
        Nos. 2925-2928 (4)   1.75   1.55

11th Communist Party Congress, 20th Anniv. — A827

1998, Dec. 18
2929 A827 50f Deng Xiaoping (2-1)   .50   .25
2930 A827 150f Handbill, buildings (2-2)   1.50   .40

Fish of the Coral Reef A828

a, Pomacanthus imperator (8-1). b, Plectropomus maculatus (8-2). c, Chaetodon plebeius (8-3). d, Chaetodon chrysurus (8-4), vert. e, Heniochus acuminatus (8-5), vert. f, Lutjanus sebae (8-6). g, Balistoides conspicillum (8-7). h, Pygoplites diancanthus (8-8).

1998, Dec. 22   **Photo.**   **Perf. 11½**

Sheet of 8

2931	A828 200f #a.-h. + label	6.00	6.00
i.	As No. 2931, with margin ovptd. in gold	8.50	8.50

UPU, 22nd Congress, Beijing '99 World Philatelic Exhibition.

Nos. 2931d-2931e are each 40x49mm. No.2931i issued 7/15/00. No. 2931i inscribed in margin in gold "PJZ-12", "1997-1999" and Chinese characters. Inscription for best philatelic item from 1997-99.

New Year 1999 (Year of the Rabbit)

A829   A830

Photo. & Engr.

1999, Jan. 5   **Perf. 11½**

2932	A829 50f Stylized rabbit (2-1)	.60	.25
2933	A830 150f Symbol for rabbit (2-2)	1.25	.40

Great Wall Type of 1995

5f, Hushan Section. 20f, Shanhaiguan Pass. 40f, Jinshanling Section. 80f, Mutianyu Section. 270f, Pingxingguan Pass. 320f, Desheng Pass. 440f, Yanmen Pass. 540f, Zhenbei Tower.

1999, Mar. 1   **Photo.**   **Perf. 13x12**

2934	A730 5f bl, blk & bl grn	.20	.20
2935	A730 20f vio & blk	.20	.20
2936	A730 40f pink & blk	.20	.20
2937	A730 80f grn, blk & ol	.30	.20
2938	A730 270f grn, blk & brn	.90	.65
2939	A730 320f vio & bwn	1.10	.75
2940	A730 440f red brn, blk & bwn	1.50	1.10
2941	A730 540f blue & black	1.75	1.25
	Nos. 2934-2941 (8)	6.15	4.55

Stone Carvings of the Han Dynasty A831

#2942, Plowing fields with oxen. #2943, Group weaving. #2944, Three figures dancing in front of fire. #2945, Horses, carriage. #2946, Group in assassination attempt. #2947, Goddess Chang'e.

1999, Mar. 16   **Perf. 12**

2942	A831 50f dark green & blk	.25	.25
2943	A831 50f brown & blk	.25	.25
2944	A831 50f dark blue & blk	.25	.25
2945	A831 150f dark brown & blk	.50	.40
2946	A831 150f brown olive & blk	.50	.40
2947	A831 150f dark purple & blk	.50	.40
	Nos. 2942-2947 (6)	2.25	1.95

A832

A833

Chinese Ceramics (Porcelain from the Jun Kiln): 80f, Halberd-shaped cup. 100f, Cup. 150f, Dual-handled stove. 200f, Dual-handled vase with base.

1999, Apr. 8   **Photo.**   **Perf. 11½**

2948	A832 80f multi (4-1)	.25	.25
2949	A832 100f multi (4-2)	.35	.30
2950	A832 150f multi (4-3)	.50	.40
2951	A832 200f multi (4-4)	.65	.55
	Nos. 2948-2951 (4)	1.75	1.50

Great Wall Type of 1995

Designs: 60f, Huanghua Tower. $10, Huama section. $20, Sanguankou Pass. $50 Jiayuguan Pass.

1999, May 1   **Photo.**   **Perf. 13x12**

2952	A730 60f multicolored	.30	.30

Size: 28x22mm

Perf. 11½

Photo. & Engr.

2953	A730 $10 multicolored	3.00	3.00
2954	A730 $20 multicolored	6.00	5.75
2955	A730 $50 multicolored	15.00	14.50
	Nos. 2952-2955 (4)	24.30	23.55

1999, May 1   **Litho.**   **Perf. 12**

2956	A833 80f shown (2-1)	.30	.25
2957	A833 200f Tree (2-2)	.70	.50

Kunming World Horticultural Fair.

Red Deer A834

1999, May 18   **Litho.**   **Perf. 11x11½**

2958	A834 80f Bucks	.30	.25
2959	A834 80f Does	.30	.25
a.	Pair, #2958-2959	.65	.55

See Russia No. 6514.

Beauty of Putuo Mountain — A835

1999, June 3   **Litho.**   **Perf. 12**

2960	A835 30f Puji Temple (6-1)	.25	.25
2961	A835 60f Nantian Gate, vert. (6-2)	.25	.25
2962	A835 60f 100-step Sand (6-3)	.25	.25
2963	A835 80f Pantuo Rock (6-4)	.30	.25
2964	A835 80f Fanyin Cave, vert. (6-5)	.30	.25
2965	A835 280f Fayu Temple (6-6)	.90	.70
	Nos. 2960-2965 (6)	2.25	1.95

Fang Zhimin (1899-1935), Revolutionary — A836

1999, Aug. 21   **Photo.**   **Perf. 11¼**

2966	A836 80f Close-up (2-1)	.45	.30
2967	A836 80f Standing (2-2)	.45	.30

Souvenir Sheet

China 1999 World Philatelic Exhibition — A837

1999, Aug. 21   **Perf. 11½x11¼**

2968	A837 800f multicolored	4.50	4.00

Exists overprinted in upper corners in gold. Value, $10.

A838

22nd UPU Congress — A839

Congress sites: 80f, 1st, Bern. 540f, 22nd, Beijing.

800f, Inscription by Pres. Jiang Zemin.

1999, Aug. 23   **Litho.**   **Perf. 12**

2969	A838 80f multi (2-1)	.35	.25
2970	A838 540f multi (2-2)	1.90	1.40

Souvenir Sheet

Perf. 12¼

2971	A839 800f multicolored	5.50	5.00

UPU, 125th Anniv. — A840

Intl. Year of the Elderly — A841

1999, Sept. 7   **Litho.**   **Perf. 12**

2972	A840 80f multicolored	.60	.35

1999, Sept. 9

2973	A841 80f multicolored	.50	.25

Chinese People's Political Consultative Conference, 50th Anniv. — A842

1999, Sept. 21

2974	A842 60f Building (2-1)	.30	.25
2975	A842 80f Mao Zedong, vert. (2-2)	.70	.25

Ethnic Groups in China — A843

Designs (stamp number following "56-" at LR): a, Han (1). b, Mongols (2). c, Hui (3). d, Tibetans (4). e, Uygurs (5) f, Miao (6). g, Yi (7). h, Zhuang (8). i, Bouyei (9). j, Koreans (10). k, Manchu (11). l, Dongs (12). m, Yao (13). n, Bai (14). o, Tujia (15). p, Hani (16). q, Kazak (17). r, Dai (18). s, Li (19). t, Lisu (20). u, Va (21). v, She (22). w, Gaoshan (23). x, Lahu (24). y, Shui (25). z, Dongxiang (26). aa, Naxi (27). ab, Jingpo (28). ac, Kirgiz (29). ad, Tu (30). ae, Daur (31). af, Mulam (32). ag, Qiang (33). ah, Blang (34). ai, Salas (35). aj, Maonan (36). ak, Gelao (37). al, Xibe (38). am, Achang (39). an, Pumi (40). ao, Tajiks (41). ap, Nu (42). aq, Uzbeks (43). ar, Russians (44). as, Ewenki (45). at, De'ang (46). au, Bonan (47). av, Yugur (48). aw, Jing (49). ax, Tartars (50). ay, Drung (51). az, Oroqen (52). ba, Hezhe (53). bb, Moiba (54). bc, Lhoba (55). bd, Jino (56).

1999, Oct. 7   **Photo.**   **Perf. 13¼**

2976	A843 80f Sheet of 56, #a.-bd.	22.50	18.00

Mountains — A844

1999, Oct. 5   **Perf. 11½x11¼**

2977	A844 80f Lushan (2-1)	.50	.25
2978	A844 80f Kuryongyon (2-2)	.50	.25

Project Hope, 10th Anniv. — A845

Li Lisan (1899-1967), Minister of Labor — A847

Scientific and Technological
Achievements — A846

1999, Oct. 30   Photo.   Perf. 11½
2979 A845 80f multi   .60   .25

1999, Nov. 1   Litho.   Perf. 12
Designs: No. 2980, Cambrian era fossil. No.
2981, Underwater robot. No. 2982, Best result
of Goldbach conjecture, vert. No. 2983, 2.16m
telescope, vert.

2980 A846 80f multi (4-1)   .35   .25
2981 A846 80f multi (4-2)   .35   .25
  a.   Pair, #2980-2981   .90   .70
2982 A846 80f multi (4-3)   .35   .25
2983 A846 80f multi (4-4)   .35   .25
  a.   Pair, #2982-2983   .90   .70
      Nos. 2980-2983 (4)   1.40 1.00

1999, Nov. 19   Photo.   Perf. 11½
2984 A847 80f As young man (2-1)   .40   .25
2985 A847 80f Wearing glasses (2-
            2)   .40   .25

Return of Macao to China — A848

Designs: 80f, Sino-Portuguese declaration,
flower. 150f, Basic Law of Macao Special
Administrative Region, Great Wall.
800f, $50, Deng Xiaoping.

1999-2000   Photo.   Perf. 11¾x11½
2986 A848 80f multi (2-1)   .40   .25
2987 A848 150f multi (2-2)   .60   .40

Souvenir Sheets
Perf. 13
2988 A848 800f multi   4.25 3.75

Litho. (stamp) & Embossed (margin)
Perf. 12
2989 A848 $50 multi   24.00 24.00
  a.   Overprinted in margin   37.50 37.50
No. 2988 contains one 60x50mm stamp
with star-shaped perforations in the corners.
Overprint in margin on No. 2989a is Chinese inscription, "2000-1" and "(2-2)J."
Issued: No. 2989a, 1/1/00; others, 12/20/99.

Nie Rongzhen   New Year 2000
(1899-1992),   (Year of the
 Military   Dragon) — A851
 Leader — A849

Millennium — A850

1999, Dec. 29   Litho.   Perf. 12
2990 A849 80f In uniform (2-1)   .40   .25
2991 A849 80f Seated (2-2)   .40   .25

1999, Dec. 31   Litho.   Perf. 12
No. 2992, Sun Yat-sen, #590. No. 2993,
#2214. No. 2994, #2339. No. 2995, #2601.

No. 2996, Mao Zedong, #456. 200f, #2248.
260f, #2730. 280f, Deng Xiaoping, #2774C.

2992 A850 60f multi (8-1)   .25   .25
2993 A850 60f multi (8-2)   .25   .25
2994 A850 80f multi (8-3)   .30   .25
2995 A850 80f multi (8-4)   .30   .25
2996 A850 80f multi (8-5)   .30   .25
2997 A850 200f multi (8-6)   .65   .50
2998 A850 260f multi (8-7)   .85   .65
2999 A850 280f multi (8-8)   .90   .70
      Nos. 2992-2999 (8)   3.80 3.10

Photo. & Engr.
2000, Jan. 5   Perf. 11½x11¾
3000 A851 80f Dragon (2-1)   7.50   .40
3001 A851 $2.80 Rising sun (2-2)   7.50 1.00

A852

Spring Festival: No. 3002, Welcoming the
Spring Festival. No. 3003, Bidding farewell to
outgoing year. $2.80, Offering sacrifices to
god of land.
$8, Family reunion, horiz.

2000, Jan. 29   Photo.   Perf. 11¼
3002 A852 80f multi (3-1)   .30   .25
3003 A852 80f multi (3-2)   .30   .25
3004 A852 $2.80 multi (3-3)   .90   .70
      Nos. 3002-3004 (3)   1.50 1.20

Souvenir Sheet
Perf. 11¼x11
3005 A852 $8 multi   6.00 6.00
  a.   Ovptd. in sheet margin   8.50 8.50
No. 3005 contains one 90x60mm stamp.
No. 3005a contains gold Chinese inscription
for New Century Philatelic Exhibition, "2000,"
and "PJZ-11" in sheet margin. Issued: 4/28.

A853

2000, Feb. 25   Photo.   Perf. 13¼x13
Wildlife.
3006   Sheet of 10 + 2 labels   8.00 8.00
  a.   A853 30f Nipponia nippon   .25   .25
  b.   A853 60f Teinopalpus aureus   .25   .25
  c.   A853 80f Ailuropoda melanoleuca   .30   .25
  d.   A853 $1 Crossoptilon
             manichuricum   .35   .25
  e.   A853 $1.50 Acipenser sinensis   .50   .35
  f.   A853 $2 Rhinopithecus roxellanae   .65   .45
  g.   A853 $2.60 Lipotes vexillifer   .85   .60
  h.   A853 $2.80 Grus japonensis   .90   .65
  i.   A853 $3.70 Panthera tigris   1.25   .85
  j.   A853 $5.40 Alligator sinensis   1.90 1.40

Cultural
Relics — A854

Designs; 60f, Neolithic Age jade dragon. No.
3008, Dragon-shaped ornament. No. 3009,
Carved tile with dragon. No. 3010, Copper mirror with dragon. No. 3011, Bronze dragon.
$2.80, Dragon on sandalwood throne.

2000, Mar. 7   Litho.   Perf. 12
3007 A854 60f multi (6-1)   .55   .25
3008 A854 80f multi (6-2)   .55   .25
3009 A854 80f multi (6-3)   .55   .25
3010 A854 80f multi (6-4)   .55   .25
3011 A854 80f multi (6-5)   .55   .25
3012 A854 $2.80 multi (6-6)   1.25   .90
      Nos. 3007-3012 (6)   4.00 2.15

Yangtze River Highway
Bridges — A855

2000, Mar. 26   Litho.   Perf. 12
3013 A855 80f Wanxian (4-1)   .30   .25
3014 A855 80f Huangshi (4-2)   .30   .25
3015 A855 80f Tongling (4-3)   .30   .25
3016 A855 $2.80 Jiangyin (4-4)   .90   .65
      Nos. 3013-3016 (4)   1.80 1.40

Landscapes in Dali — A856

Designs: No. 3017, Cangshan Mountain
and Erhai Lake. No. 3018, Pagodas at Chong-
sheng Temple. No. 3019, Jizu Mountain.
$2.80, Shibao Mountain.

Perf. 11¾x11½
2000, Apr. 19   Photo.
3017 A856 80f multi (4-1)   .30   .25
3018 A856 80f multi (4-2)   .30   .25
3019 A856 80f multi (4-3)   .30   .25
3020 A856 $2.80 multi (4-4)   .90   .70
      Nos. 3017-3020 (4)   1.80 1.45

Legend of Mulan — A857

Mulan: No. 3021, Weaving cloth. No. 3022,
Joining army. No. 3023, On expedition. No.
3024, Returning home.

2000, Apr. 30   Litho.   Perf. 12
3021 A857 80f multi (4-1)   .30   .25
3022 A857 80f multi (4-2)   .30   .25
3023 A857 80f multi (4-3)   .30   .25
3024 A857 80f multi (4-4)   .30   .25
  a.   Strip, #3021-3024   2.25 2.25

Taer
Lamasery
A858

#3025, Good Luck Treasure Pagoda. #3026,
Big Golden Tile Palace. #3027, Big Scripture
Hall. $2.80, Banqen residence.

2000, May 5
3025 A858 80f multi (4-1)   .30   .25
3026 A858 80f multi (4-2)   .30   .25
3027 A858 80f multi (4-3)   .30   .25
3028 A858 $2.80 multi (4-4)   .90   .70
      Nos. 3025-3028 (4)   1.80 1.45

Cai Chang
and Li
Fuchun
A859

2000, May 22
3029 A859 80f multi   .80   .25

Stampin' the Future Children's Stamp
Design Contest Winners — A860

Various children's drawings: #3030, 30f, (8-
1). #3031, 60f, (8-2). #3032, 60f, (8-3). #3033,
80f, (8-4). #3034, 80f, (8-5). #3035, 80f, (8-6).
$2.60, (8-7). $2.80, (8-8).

Perf. 11½x11¼
2000, June 1   Photo.
3030-3037 A860 Set of 8   3.50 2.50

Chen Yun (1905-
95), Statesman
A861

#3038, 80f, As a young man (4-1). #3039,
80f, In uniform, vert. (4-2). #3040, 80f, In black
jacket, vert. (4-3). $2.80, As old man (4-4).

Perf. 13x13¼, 13¼x13
2000, June 13
3038-3041 A861 Set of 4   1.75 1.40

Pots
A862

Designs: No. 3042, 80f, Wine vessel (2-1).
No. 3042, 80f, Horse milk pot (2-2).

2000, June 28   Litho.   Perf. 12
3042-3043 A862 Set of 2   .90   .45
See Kazakhstan No. 305.

Laoshan Mountain — A863

#3044, 80f, Huge Peak (4-1). #3045, 80f,
Yangkou Bay (4-2). #3046, 80f, Beijiu Lake (4-
3). $2.80, Taiqing Palace (4-4).

Perf. 11½x11¼
2000, July 15   Photo.
3044-3047 A863 Set of 4   1.75 1.75
3047a   Souvenir sheet, #3044-3047   6.00 6.00

Souvenir Sheet

All-China Philatelic Federation, Fifth Congress — A864

Illustration reduced.

2000, July 18   Litho.   Perf. 12
3048 A864 $8 multi   6.00 5.50
a.   Margin ovptd. in gold   8.50 7.50

No. 3048a issued 9/21/01. It is inscribed in margin in gold "PJZ-13," "2001," with Chinese characters and Nanjing 2001 Philatelic Exhibition mascot.

Small Carp Leap Through Dragon Gate Legend — A865

No. 3049: a, Grandma Carp tells a story (5-1). b, Small Carp look for Dragon Gate (5-2). c, Help from Uncle Crab (5-3). d, Small Carp leap through Dragon Gate (5-4). e, Aunt Swallow passes on a letter (5-5).

2000, Aug. 8   Photo.   Perf. 11½
3049 A865 80f Horiz. strip of
      5, #a-e   2.25 2.25
f.   Booklet pane, #3049 + 2 la-
      bels, perf. 12   11.00
      Booklet, #3049f   12.50

Shenzhen Special Eonomic Zone — A866

No. 3050: a, 80f, Financial Center district (5-1). b, 80f, China Intl. Exhibition Center (5-2). c, 80f, Yantian Harbor area (5-3). d, 80f, Shenzhen Bay tourist area (5-4). e, $2.80, Shekou industrial district (5-5).

2000, Aug. 26   Litho.   Perf. 12
3050 A866 Horiz. strip of 5,
      #a-e   2.00 2.00

2000 Summer Olympics, Sydney — A867

Illustration reduced.

2000, Sept. 15   Photo.   Perf. 13¼x13
3051 A867 $8 multi   4.25 4.25
a.   Sheet of 2   50.00 50.00

No. 3051a issued 10/31/00.

Beaches — A868

---

a, Coconuts Bay, PRC (2-1). b, Varadero Beach, Cuba (2-2).

2000, Sept. 26   Litho.   Perf. 12
3052 A868 Pair   .80   .90
a.-b. 80f Any single   .30   .25

See Cuba Nos. 4108-4109.

Masks and Puppets A869

No. 3053, Tan background (2-1). No. 3054, Violet blue background (2-2).

2000, Oct. 9   Photo.   Perf. 13x13½
3053-3054 A869 80f Set of 2   .80   .50

See Brazil Nos. 2767-2768.

Relics from the Tomb of Prince Jing of Zhongshan — A870

#3055, 80f, Eternal Fidelity palace lamp (4-1). #3056, 80f, Bronze pot (4-2). #3057, 80f, Boshan incense burner (4-3). $2.80, Cup (4-4).

2000, Oct. 20   Perf. 13½x13¼
3055-3058 A870 Set of 4   2.00 1.40

Ancient Thinkers — A871

#3059, 60f, Confucius (6-1). #3060, 80f, Mencius (6-2). #3061, 80f, Lao Zi (6-3). #3062, 80f, Zhuang Zi (6-4). #3063, 80f, Mo Zi (6-5). $2.80, Xun Zi (6-6).

Photo. & Engr.
2000, Nov. 11   Perf. 11¼x11
3059-3064 A871 Set of 6   2.50 1.75

Test of Shenzhou Spacecraft, 1st Anniv. — A872

No. 3065: a, Launch (2-1). b, In orbit (2-2). Illustration reduced.

2000, Nov. 20   Photo.   Perf. 11½
3065 A872 Pair   3.00 3.00
a.-b. 80f Any single   .30   .25
c.   Sheet, 6 #3065   45.00 45.00

World Meteorological Organization, 50th Anniv. — A873

Designs: No. 3066, 80f, Weather satellite (4-1). No. 3067, 80f, Weather measuring equipment on Qinghai-Tibetan Plateau (4-2). No. 3068, 80f, Weather-predicting computer (4-3). $2.80, Airplane for cloud seeding (4-4).

2000, Nov. 22   Litho.   Perf. 12
3066-3069 A873 Set of 4   1.75 1.40

Flowers — A874

#3070, 80f, Scarlet kaffir lily (4-1). #3071, 80f, Noble clivia (4-2). #3072, 80f, Golden striated lily (4-3). $2.80, White kaffir lily (4-4).

Perf. 11¼x11½
2000, Dec. 12   Photo.
3070-3073 A874 Set of 4   2.00 1.40
3073a   Souv. sheet, #3070-3073   6.00 6.00

Ancient Bells — A875

#3074, 80f, Jingshu bell (4-1). #3075, 80f, Su chime bell (4-2). #3076, 80f, Jingyun bell (4-3). $2.80, Qianlong bell (4-4).

2000, Dec. 31   Perf. 11¼x11½
3074-3077 A875 Set of 4   1.90 1.40

Advent of New Millennium A876

Designs: 60f, Sun, moon, date, time, building (5-1). No. 3079, 80f, Dove, Earth (5-2). No. 3080, 80f, Map, leaf, infant's hands (5-3). No. 3081, 80f, Circuitboard, head, Earth, horiz. (5-4). $2.80, Moon, stars, sundial (5-5).

2001, Jan. 1   Litho.   Perf. 12
3078-3082 A876 Set of 5   2.25 1.50

New Year 2001 (Year of the Snake) — A877

Snake and: 80f, Flower (2-1). $2.80, Chinese character for snake (2-2).

Photo. & Engr.
2001, Jan. 5   Perf. 11½x11¾
3083 A877 80f multi   1.50   .50
a.   Sheet of 6   10.00 10.00
3084 A877 $2.80 multi   2.00 1.00
a.   Sheet of 6   24.00 24.00

Clown Roles in Peking Opera — A878

Designs: No. 3085, 80f, Tang Qin (6-1). No. 3086, 80f, Lin Lihua (6-2). No. 3087, 80f, Gao Lishi (6-3). No. 3088, 80f, Jiang Gan (6-4). No. 3089, 80f, Yang Xiangwu (6-5). $2.80, Shi Qian (6-6).

2001, Feb. 15   Photo.   Perf. 11½x11
3085-3090 A878 Set of 6   2.25 1.75

Wildlife — A879

2001, Mar. 16   Perf. 13¼x13
3091   Sheet of 10 + 2 labels   10.00 9.00
a. A879 30f Budorcas taxicolor   .20 .20
b. A879 60f Psephurus gladius   .40 .40
c. A879 60f Elaphurus davidianus   .40 .40
d. A879 80f Acipenser dabryanus   .50 .50
e. A879 80f Capra ibex   .50 .50
f. A879 80f Haliaeetus pelagicus   .50 .50
g. A879 80f Camelus bactrianus   .50 .50
h. A879 $1 Uncia uncia   .65 .65
i. A879 $2.60 Martes zibellina   1.75 1.75
j. A879 $5.40 Saiga tatarica   3.50 3.50

Ancient Towns — A880

Designs: No. 3092, 80f, Zhouzhuang, Kunshan (6-1). No. 3093, 80f, Tongli, Wujiang (6-2). No. 3094, 80f, Wuzhen, Tongxiang (6-3). No. 3095, 80f, Nanxun, Huzhou (6-4). No. 3096, 80f, Luzhi, Wuxian (6-5). $2.80, Xitang, Jiashan (6-6).

2001, Apr. 7   Photo.   Perf. 11½x11¼
3092-3097 A880 Set of 6   2.25 2.25
3097a   Booklet pane, #3092-
          3097 + 6 labels   9.00
          Booklet, #3097a   11.50

Strange Stories From a Chinese Studio, by Pu Songling A881

Designs: 60f, Ying Ning (4-1). No. 3099, 80f, A Bao (4-2). No. 3100, 80f, Mask of Evildoer (4-3). $2.80, Stealing Peach (4-4). $8, Taoist Priest from Laoshan.

2001, Apr. 21   Perf. 11½
3098-3101 A881 Set of 4   1.75 1.75

Souvenir Sheet
Perf. 13½x13
3102 A881 $8 multi   10.00 10.00

No. 3102 contains one 90x60mm stamp.

Yongle Temple Murals
A882

No. 3103: a, Lady Queen Mother (4-1). b, Jade Lady Presenting Treasure (4-2). c, Celestial Worthy of the East (4-3). d, Venus and Mercury (4-4).

2001, May 5   Litho.   Perf. 12
3103   Horiz. strip of 4   2.25   2.25
   a.   A882 60f multi   .25   .25
   b.-c.   A882 80f Any single   .30   .30
   d.   A882 $2.80 multi   1.00   .95

Mount Wudang — A883

Designs: 60f, Nanyan Hall (3-1). No. 3105, 80f, Zixiao Temple (3-2). No. 3106, 80f, Taizi Slope (3-3).
$8, Golden Crown in spring.

     Perf. 11¼x11½
2001, May 26   Photo.
3104-3106   Set of 3   1.10   .85

Souvenir Sheet
     Perf. 12¼x12½
3107   A883 $8 multi + label   7.00   7.00
No. 3107 contains one 47x71mm stamp.

Ancient Chinese Receptacles
A884

Designs: No. 3108, 80f, Earthenware vase. No. 3109, 80f, Porcelain coffee pot.

2001, June 12   Perf. 11¼x11½
3108-3109   A884   Set of 2   1.00   .60
See Belgium Nos. 1858-1859.

Dragon Boat Festival
A885

Designs: No. 3110, Dragon boat race (3-1). No. 3111, Making Zongzi (3-2). $2.80, Expelling five poisons (3-3).

2001, June 25   Photo.   Perf. 13x13½
3110   A885   80f multi   .40   .25
   a.   Sheet of 9   9.50
3111   A885   80f multi   .40   .25
   a.   Sheet of 9   9.50
3112   A885 $2.80 multi   1.00   .90
   a.   Sheet of 9   32.50
     Nos. 3110-3112 (3)   1.80   1.40
Nos. 3110-3112 each issued in sheets of 40.

Early Leaders of the Communist Party — A886

Designs: No. 3113, 80f, Wang Jinmei (5-1). No. 3114, 80f, Zhao Shiyan (5-2). No. 3115, 80f, Deng Enming (5-3). No. 3116, 80f, Cai Hesen (5-4). No. 3117, 80f, He Shuheng (5-5).

2001, June 28   Perf. 11¼x11
3113-3117   A886   Set of 5   2.00   1.50

Communist Party, 80th Anniv.
A887

2001, July 1   Photo.   Perf. 13x13¼
3118   A887 80f multi   1.00   .35
   a.   Sheet of 8   40.00
No. 3118 issued in sheets of 40.

Emblem of 2008 Summer Olympics, Beijing — A888

2001, July 14   Perf. 13x13¼
3119   A888 80f multi + label   .80   .50
   a.   Sheet of 36 + 39 labels   40.00
No. 3119 printed in sheets of 12 stamp + label pairs with one large central label. See Hong Kong No. 940, Macao No. 1067.
No. 3119a contains 12 each of No. 3119, Hong Kong No. 940 (with different adjacent label), and Macao No. 1067 (with different adjacent label).

Waterfalls
A889

Designs: No. 3120, 80f, Yinlianzhuitan (3-1). No. 3121, 80f, Doupotang, horiz. (3-2). No. 3122, 80f, Dishuitan (3-3).
$8, Huangguoshu.

     Perf. 12¼x12, 12x12¼
2001, July 22   Litho.
3120-3122   A889   Set of 3   1.00   .75

Souvenir Sheet
     Perf. 12
3123   A889 $8 multi   7.00   7.00
No. 3123 contains one 40x60mm stamp.

Beidaihe Beach — A890

Designs: 60f, Pigeon Nest (4-1). No. 3125, 80f, Zhonghai Beach (4-2). No. 3126, 80f, Lianfeng Hill (4-3). $2.80, Tiger Stone (4-4).

2001, Aug. 5   Litho.   Perf. 12
3124-3127   A890   Set of 4   1.75   1.50

21st Universiade
A891

Emblem, "2001" and: 60f, Concentric circles (3-1). 80f, Runners (3-2). $2.80, Hemispheres of globe (3-3).

2001, Aug. 22   Litho.
3128-3130   A891   Set of 3   1.50   1.25
3129a   Sheet of 20 +20 labels   22.50
No. 3129a exists with different margin designs.
Sheets of four No. 3129 plus four labels were not placed on sale but were included with 2001 year sets. Uncut sheets containing two of these sheets also exist.

Datong River Diversion Project — A892

Designs: No. 3131, 80f, Sluice gates (4-1). No. 3132, 80f, Xianming Gorge water pipeline (4-2). No. 3133, 80f, Tunnel (4-3). $2.80, Zhuanglang River Aqueduct (4-4).

2001, Aug. 26
3131-3134   A892   Set of 4   1.75   1.50

Wuhu Bridge — A893

View from: 80f, Shore (2-1). $2.80, Roadway (2-2).

Photo. & Engr.
2001, Sept. 20   Perf. 11½x11¼
3135-3136   A893   Set of 2   1.60   1.25

Orchids
A894

Designs: No. 3137, 80f, Paphiopedilum malipoense (4-1). No. 3138, 80f, Paphiopedilum dianthum (4-2). No. 3139, 80f, Paphiopedilum markianum (4-3). $2.80, Paphiopedilum appletonianum (4-4).

2001, Sept. 28   Photo.   Perf. 12½
3137-3140   A894   Set of 4   2.00   1.75
3140a   Souvenir sheet, #3137-3140   6.00

Ancient Gold Masks — A895

Designs: No. 3141, 80f, Mask of San Xing Dui (2-1). No. 3142, 80f, Funerary mask of King Tutankhamun, Egypt (2-2).

2001, Oct. 12   Perf. 11¾x11½
3141-3142   A895   Set of 2   1.00   .75
See Egypt Nos. 1807-1808.

People's Republic of China as 2001 Asia-Pacific Economic Cooperation Head
A896

2001, Oct. 20   Litho.   Perf. 12
3143   A896 80f multi   .80   .30

Souvenir Sheet

Ertan Hydroelectric Plant — A897

2001, Oct. 20   Litho.   Perf. 12¼
3144   A897 $8 multi   3.75   3.75

Horses, Zhaoling Mausoleum
A898

Horse: a, Facing right, galloping (6-1). b, Facing right, galloping, diff. (6-2). c, Facing right, walking (6-3). d, With attendant (6-4). e, Facing left, walking (6-5). f, Facing left, galloping (6-6).

2001, Oct. 28   Photo.   Perf. 12
Fawn Background
3145   Horiz. strip of 6   2.50   2.10
   a.   A898 60f multi   .25   .25
   b.-e.   A898 80f multi   .30   .25
   f.   A898 $2.80 multi   .90   .80
   g.   Sheet, 2 each #3145a-3145c, white background, photo. & embossed   16.00
   h.   Sheet, 2 each #3145d-3145f, white background, photo. & embossed   16.00

Sailing Ships — A899

No. 3146: a, Chinese junk, 13th cent. (2-1). b, Portuguese caravel, 15th cent. (2-2). Illustration reduced.

2001, Nov. 8   Perf. 13x13¼
3146   A899 80f Horiz. pair, #a-b   .80   .55
See Portugal No. 2454.

9th Natl. Games — A900

No. 3147: a, 80f, Diving (2-1). b, $2.80, Volleyball (2-2).

2001, Nov. 11 Litho. Perf. 12
3147 A900 Horiz. pair, #a-b 1.25 1.10
  c. Souvenir sheet, #3147 3.75 3.75

Liupan Shan Mountains — A901

Various landscapes: No. 3148, 80f (4-1). No. 3149, 80f (4-2). No. 3150, 80f (4-3). $2.80, (4-4).

Photo. & Engr.
2001, Nov. 24 Perf. 11¼x11½
3148-3151 A901 Set of 4 2.00 2.00

Xiu Xian and the White Snake — A902

Designs: No. 3152, Women, umbrella (4-1). No. 3153, Three men (4-2). No. 3154, Man with sword, man with bowl (4-3). $2.80, Women on bridge (4-4).

Perf. 11½, 11½x11 (#3153-3154)
2001, Dec. 5 Photo.
3152 A902 80f multi .30 .25
  a. Booklet pane of 1 1.10
3153 A902 80f multi .30 .25
  a. Booklet pane of 1 1.10
3154 A902 80f multi .30 .25
  a. Booklet pane of 1 1.10
3155 A902 $2.80 multi .90 .80
  a. Booklet pane of 1 4.00
    Booklet, #3152a-3155a 7.50
  Nos. 3152-3155 (4) 1.80 1.55

Admission to World Trade Organization A903

2001, Dec. 11 Photo. Perf. 13¼x13
3156 A903 80f multi 1.25 1.10

Koxinga's Recovery of Taiwan from the Dutch, 340th Anniv. — A904

Koxinga and: No. 3157, 80f, Warriors, ships (3-1). No. 3158, 80f, Warriors, horse (3-2). $2.80, People, trees (3-3).

Perf. 11½x11¼
2001, Dec. 13 Photo.
3157-3159 A904 Set of 3 1.75 1.75

Souvenir Sheet

Qinhai - Tibet Railway — A905

2001, Dec. 29 Perf. 13¼
3160 A905 $8 multi 5.00 5.00

New Year 2002 (Year of the Horse) — A906

Designs: 80f, Ceramic horse (2-1). $2.80, Flowers, Chinese symbol for horse (2-2).

Photo. & Engr.
2002, Jan. 5 Perf. 11½
3161-3162 A906 Set of 2 2.00 1.25
  Nos. 3161-3162 each exist in a miniature sheet of six. Value, each $45.

Art of Badashanren (1626-1705) A907

Designs: 60f, Two Eagles (6-1). No. 3164, 80f, Pine Tree (6-2). No. 3165, 80f, Lotus Flowers (6-3). No. 3166, 80f, Chysanthemum in Vase (6-4). $2.60, Two Magpies on a Rock (6-5). $2.80, Landscape After Dong Yuan (6-6).

Perf. 11¼x11½
2002, Jan. 20 Photo.
3163-3168 A907 Set of 6 2.75 2.75

Environmental Protection — A908

Designs: 5f, Keeping birth rate low. 10f, Forest conservation. 30f, Conservation of mineral resources. 60f, Preventing air pollution. 80f, Conservation of water. $1.50, Conservation of ocean resources.

Perf. 12¾x13¼ Syncopated
2002 Photo.
3169 A908 5f multi .20 .20
3170 A908 10f multi .20 .20
3171 A908 30f multi .25 .20
3172 A908 60f multi .25 .20
3173 A908 80f multi .25 .20
3174 A908 $1.50 multi .45 .40
  Nos. 3169-3174 (6) 1.60 1.40
  Issued: 10f, 60f, 2/1; others, 4/1. See Nos. 3334-3335.

Birds — A909

Designs: 80f, Yellow-bellied tragopan. $1, Biddulph's ground jay. $2, Taiwan blue magpies. $4.20, Alashan redstart. $5.40, Kozlov's bunting.

2002 Perf. 13¼
3175 A909 80f multi .25 .20
  a. Booklet pane of 10 +2 labels 2.50
    Booklet, #3175a 2.60
3176 A909 $1 multi .35 .30
3177 A909 $2 multi .65 .60
3178 A909 $4.20 multi 1.40 1.25
3179 A909 $5.40 multi 1.75 1.50
  Nos. 3175-3179 (5) 4.40 3.85
  Issued: 80f, $1, $2, 2/1; Nos. 3178, 3179, 4/1. No. 3175a, 12/7.
  See Nos. 3336-3337, 3547-3548.

Flowers — A910

No. 3180: a, Camellia nitidissima (2-1). b, Couroupita guianensis (2-2).

2002, Feb. 5 Perf. 13¼x13
3180 A910 80f Horiz. pair, #a-b 1.00 .60
  See Malaysia Nos. 861-864.

Musical Instruments A911

Designs: 60f, Yaqin (5-1). No. 3182, 80f, Erhu (5-2). No. 3183, 80f, Banhu (5-3). No. 3184, 80f, Satar (5-4). $2.80, Matouqin (5-5).

2002, Feb. 23 Litho. Perf. 12
3181-3185 A911 Set of 5 1.75 1.50

Souvenir Sheet

The Royal Carriage, by Yan Liben — A912

2002, Mar. 16 Photo.
3186 A912 $8 multi 6.50 3.50

Song Dynasty Pottery and Porcelain from Ruyao Kilns A913

Designs: 60f, Wine vessel (4-1). No. 3188, 80f, Three-legged basin (4-2). No. 3189, 80f, Bowl (4-3). $2.80, Dish (4-4).

2002, Mar. 30 Litho.
3187-3190 A913 Set of 4 2.00 1.75

Strange Stories from a Chinese Studio, by Pu Songling A914

No. 3191: a, 60f, Xi Fangping (4-1). b, 80f, Pianpian (4-2).
No. 3192: a, 80f, Tian Qilang (4-3). b, $2.80, Bai Qiulian (4-4).

2002, Apr. 21 Photo. Perf. 11½
3191 A914 Vert. pair, #a-b .55 .45
3192 A914 Horiz. pair, #a-b 1.25 1.00

Qianshan Mountain — A915

No. 3193: a, Wuliang Taoist Temple (4-1). b, Maitreya Peak (4-2). c, Longquan Temple (4-3). d, Terrace of Immortals (4-4).

2002, Apr. 26 Perf. 12
3193 Horiz. strip of 4 1.90 1.60
  a.-c. A915 80f Any single .30 .25
  d. A915 $2.80 multi .90 .70

Ancient City of Lijiang — A916

Designs: No. 3194, 80f, Sifang Street (3-1). No. 3195, 80f, Stream, vert. (3-2). $2.80, House of Naxi people (3-3).

2002, May 1 Perf. 11½
3194-3196 A916 Set of 3 1.50 1.25
  a. Souvenir sheet, #3194-3196 5.50 5.00
  No. 3196a sold for $6.60.

Ruyi (Good Luck Symbol) — A917

2002, May 10 Litho. Perf. 12
3197 A917 80f multi + label .40 .25
  Exists in miniature sheet of 4 + 4 vert. labels (value $6) and in sheet of 16 + 16 horiz. labels (value $20).

Stamps with Attached Labels

Starting with No. 3197, stamps listed as having attached labels are known to have been issued in dozens of different sheets having various margin and label designs, various numbers of stamps and labels in the sheets, and different stamp and label combinations. Little information has been made available about these sheets, and all seem to have been sold for prices significantly above face value. Labels on these sheets do not seem to have been personalizable with personal photos but have illustrations with approved designs.

2002 World Cup Soccer Championships, Japan and Korea — A918

No. 3198: a, 80f, Player (2-1). b, $2.80, Players (2-2).

2002, May 16   Photo.   Perf. 12¼
3198 A918 Horiz. pair, #a-b   1.00 .70

A souvenir sheet containing People's Republic of China No. 3198, Hong Kong Nos. 978a-978b and Macao 1091a-1091b exists, and sold for premium over face value. Value $8.

Lighthouses A919

Nautical charts and: No. 3199, 80f, Maota Pagoda Lighthouse (5-1). No. 3200, 80f, Jiangxin Pagoda Lighthouses (5-2). No. 3201, 80f, Huaniaoshan Lighthouse (5-3). No. 3202, 80f, Laotieshan Lighthouse (5-4). No. 3203, 80f, Lin'gao Lighthouse (5-5).

Photo. & Engr.
2002, May 18   Perf. 11½x11
3199-3203 A919 Set of 5   1.50 1.25

Yellow River Dams A920

Designs: No. 3204, 80f, Lijia Gorge (4-1). No. 3205, 80f, Liujia Gorge (4-2). No. 3206, 80f, Qingtong Gorge (4-3). No. 3207, 80f, Sanmen Gorge (4-4). $8, Xiaolangdi, vert.

2002, June 8   Photo.   Perf. 12
3204-3207 A920 Set of 4   1.25 1.10
Souvenir Sheet
Perf. 13x13¼
3208 A920 $8 multi   3.25 2.75

No. 3208 contains one 40x60mm stamp.

Dazu Stone Carvings — A921

Designs: No. 3209, 80f, Avalokitesvara of the Sun and Moon, North Mountain (4-1). No. 3210, 80f, Samantabhadra, North Mountain (4-2). No. 3211, 80f, Three Avatamasaka Sages, Holy Summit Mountain (4-3). No. 3212, 80f, Statue in Cave of the Three Emperors, Stone Gate Mountain (4-4). $8, Avalokitesvara of a Thousand Hands, Holy Summit Mountain.

2002, June 18   Litho.   Perf. 12
3209-3212 A921 Set of 4   1.25 .90
Souvenir Sheet
Photo.
Perf. 13x13¼
3213 A921 $8 multi   3.25 2.75

No. 3213 contains one 40x60mm stamp.

Desert Flowers A922

No. 3214: a, Ammopiptanthus mongolicus (4-1). b, Calligonum rubicandum (4-2). c, Hedysarum scoparium (4-3). d, Tamarix leptostachys (4-4).

2002, June 29 Photo. Perf. 13x13¼
3214   Vert. strip of 4   1.60 1.40
a.-c. A922 80f Any single   .30 .25
d.   A922 $2 multi   .65 .55

Antarctic Scenes A923

Designs: No. 3215, 80f, Penguins (3-1). No. 3216, 80f, Aurora Australis (3-2). $2, Bird, Grove Mountains (3-3).

2002, July 15   Litho.   Perf. 12
3215-3217 A923 Set of 3   1.75 1.25

Qinghai Lake — A924

Designs: No. 3218, 80f, Lake shore (3-1). No. 3219, 80f, Birds on rock (3-2). $2.80, View of lake and birds (3-3).

2002, July 20
3218-3220 A924 Set of 3   1.50 1.25

Early Communist Party Leaders — A925

Designs: No. 3221, 80f, Huang Gonglue (1898-1931) (5-1). No. 3222, 80f, Xu Jishen (1901-31) (5-2). No. 3223, 80f, Cai Shengxi (1906-32) (5-3). No. 3224, 80f, Wei Baqun (1894-1932) (5-4). No. 3225, 80f, Liu Zhidan (1903-36) (5-5).

2002, Aug. 1   Photo.
3221-3225 A925 Set of 5   1.50 1.25

Scientists of Ancient China — A926

Designs: No. 3226, 80f, Bian Que (4-1). No. 3227, 80f, Liu Hui (4-2). No. 3228, 80f, Su Song (4-3). No. 3229, 80f, Song Yingxing (4-4).

Photo. & Engr.
2002, Aug. 20   Perf. 11¼x11
3226-3229 A926 Set of 4   1.25 1.10

Yandangshan Mountain — A927

Designs: No. 3230, 80f, Xianshengmen Gate (4-1). No. 3231, 80f, Dalongqui Pond (4-2). No. 3232, 80f, Beidou Cave, horiz. (4-3). No. 3233, 80f, Guanyin Peak, horiz. (4-4).

2002, Sept. 7   Litho.   Perf. 12¾
3230-3233 A927 Set of 4   1.25 1.10

Mid-Autumn Festival — A928

Designs: No. 3234, 80f, Family reunion (3-1). No. 3235, 80f, People looking at Moon (3-2). $2, The Moon as a matchmaker (3-3).

2002, Sept. 21   Perf. 12
3234-3236 A928 Set of 3   1.50 1.25

Each printed in sheets of 20. Sheets of nine containing three of each stamp exist with a decorative border (value $25) and a border with Chinese text for the Beijing 2002 Stamp Exhibition (value $55).

Peng Zhen (1902-97) — A929

Designs: No. 3237, 80f, Head of Peng Zhen (2-1). No. 3238, 80f, Peng Zhen standing (2-2).

2002, Oct. 12   Perf. 11¾x12
3237-3238 A929 Set of 2   1.00 .60

Architecture in Slovakia and China — A930

No. 3239: a, Bojnice Castle, Slovakia (2-1). b, Handan Congtai Pavilion, China (2-2).

Photo. & Engr.
2002, Oct. 12   Perf. 11¼x11
3239 A930 80f Horiz. pair, #a-b   .60 .50

See Slovakia No. 410.

Dong Yong and Lady — A931

No. 3240: a, Dong Yong's filial love moves immortals (5-1). b, Dong Yong marries seventh immortal maiden (5-2). c, Immortal maiden weaving brocade (5-3). d, Dong Yong returns home (5-4). e, Everlasting love (5-5).

2002, Oct. 26   Litho.   Perf. 13¼x13
3240   Horiz. strip of 5   2.00 1.60
a.-d. A931 80f Any single   .30 .25
e.   A931 $2 multi   .65 .50

Nos. 3240a-3240e exist in booklet panes of one that made up a booklet that had limited distribution to people with standing order accounts.

Flower — A932

2002, Nov. 8   Litho.   Perf. 12
3241 A932 80f multi + label   .40 .30

Exists in a miniature sheet of 4 + 4 labels.

Souvenir Sheet

Hukou Waterfall — A933

Photo. (Margin Photo. & Embossed)
2002, Nov. 8   Perf. 13¼x13
3242 A933 $8 multi   10.00 4.00

Museums — A934

Designs: No. 3243, 80f, Shanxi History Museum (5-1). No. 3244, 80f, Shanghai Museum (5-2). No. 3245, 80f, Henan Museum (5-3). No. 3246, 80f, Tibet Museum (5-4). No. 3247, 80f, Tianjin Natural Museum.

2002, Nov. 9   Photo.   Perf. 12¾
3243-3247 A934 Set of 5   1.50 1.25

Martial Arts
A935

No. 3248: a, Kung Fu (2-1). b, Taekwondo (2-2).

2002, Nov. 20   Photo.   Perf. 12
3248 A935 80f Vert. pair, #a-b   1.00 .60
No. 3248 is a joint issue with South Korea No. 2109.

Gibbons — A936

Designs: No. 3249, 80f, Hylobates lar (4-1). No. 3250, 80f, Hylobates leucogenys (4-2). No. 3251, 80f, Hylobates concolor (4-3). $2, Hylobates hoolock (4-4).

Photo. & Engr.
2002, Dec. 7   Perf. 11¼x11
3249-3252 A936 Set of 4   1.50 1.25

New Year 2003 (Year of the Ram) — A937

Designs: 80f, Ram (2-1). $2, Chinese symbol (2-2).

Photo. & Engr.
2003, Jan. 5   Perf. 11½
3253-3254 A937 Set of 2   2.75 1.50
Sheets of 8 + central label of Nos. 3253-3254 exist. Value, each $22.50.

Yangliuqing New Year Woodprints A938

Designs: No. 3255, 80f, Five boys wrestling for a lotus (4-1). No. 3256, 80f, Zhong Kui, vert. (4-2). No. 3257, 80f, Steaing the herb of immortality (4-3). $2, Wealth in a jade hall (4-4).

2003, Jan. 25   Photo.   Perf. 12
3255-3258 A938 Set of 4   1.75 1.25
A sheet containing two each #3255-3258 exists. Value $22.50.

Seal Characters A939

Designs: No. 3259, 80f, 24 characters (2-1). No. 3260, 80f, 12 characters (2-2).

2003, Feb. 22   Litho.
3259-3260 A939 Set of 2   1.75 1.25
A sheet exists containing four each Nos. 3259-3260. Value $22.50.

Knot
A940

2003, Feb. 3
3261 A940 80f multi + label   1.00 .60
Exists in sheets of 4 stamps + 4 labels. Value $20.
Perf 12¾ examples come from a sheetlet containing four examples with labels below the stamps that also contain four #3375. The sheetlet sold for $15.

Lilies
A941

Designs: 60f, Lilium taliense (4-1). No. 3263, 80f, Lilium lankongense (4-2). No. 3264, 80f, Lilium distichum (4-3). $2, Lilium lophophorum (4-4).
$8, Lilium leucanthum.

2003, Mar. 5   Photo.   Perf. 13x13¼
3262-3265 A941 Set of 4   2.00 1.50
Souvenir Sheet
Perf. 13¼
3266 A941 $8 multi   4.25 3.50
Nos. 3262-3265 each exist in sheets of 10. Value, set of 4, $25.
No. 3266 contains one 75x53mm stamp.

Arch Bridges — A942

Designs: No. 3267, 80f, Maple Bridge (4-1). No. 3268, 80f, Xiaoshang Bridge (4-2). No. 3269, 80f, Lugouqiao Bridge (4-3). No. 3270, 80f, Double Dragon Bridge (4-4).

Photo. & Engr.
2003, Mar. 29   Perf. 11½
3267-3270 A942 Set of 4   1.50 1.10
A sheet of 8 exists for each of Nos. 3267-3270. Value, set of 2, $70.

Chinese and Iranian Buildings A943

Designs: No. 3271, 80f, Bell Tower, Xian, China (2-1). No. 3272, 80f, Mosque, Isfahan, Iran (2-2).

2003, Apr. 15   Photo.   Perf. 13x13¼
3271-3272 A943 Set of 2   1.00 1.00
See Iran No. 2856.
A sheet exists containing 4 each Nos. 3271-3272. Value $15.

Souvenir Sheet

Leshan Giant Buddha — A944

Photo. & Engr.
2003, Apr. 28   Perf. 12
3273 A944 $8 multi   3.25 3.00

Gulangyu Island — A945

No. 3274: a, Eight Diagram Building (3-1). b, Sunlight Rock (3-2). c, Shuzhuang Park (3-3).

2003, May 2   Photo.   Perf. 12
3274   Horiz. strip of 3   1.40 1.10
 a.-b. A945 80f Either single   .30 .25
 c.   A945 $2 multi   .65 .55
 d.   Souvenir sheet, #3274   3.00 2.25
A souvenir sheet exists containing 3 No. 3274. Value $45.

Campaign to Combat Epidemic of Severe Acute Respiratory Syndrome — A946

2003, May 19   Perf. 13¼x13
3275 A946 80f multi   45.00 15.00

Strange Stories from a Chinese Studio, by Pu Songling A947

Designs: 10f, Xiang Yu (6-1). 30f, Tiger of Zhaocheng (6-2). 60f, Huanniang (6-3). Ah Xiu (6-4). $1.50, Wang Gui'an (6-5). $2, Goddess (6-6).
$8, Princess of Dongting Lake, horiz.

2003, May 16   Perf. 12
3276-3281 A947 Set of 6   2.25 2.25
Souvenir Sheet
Perf. 13¼x13
3282 A947 $8 multi   5.00 5.00
No. 3282 contains one 90x60mm stamp.
Sheets exist containing 4 each of Nos. 3276-3277, 3278-3279 and 3280-3281. Value, set $18.

1976 Meteorite Shower Over Jilin — A948

Designs: No. 3283, 80f, Meteorites falling (3-1). No. 3284, 80f, Dispersal of meteorites (3-2). $2, Meteorite (3-3).

2003, June 21   Litho.
3283-3285 A948 Set of 3   1.25 1.10
A sheet exists containing 3 each of Nos. 3283-3285. Value $17.50.

Master-of-Nets Garden, Suzhou — A949

No. 3286: a, 80f, Late Spring Cottage (4-1). b, 80f, Pavilion Greeting the Moon and Breeze (4-2). c, 80f, Veranda of Bamboo (4-3). d, $2, Hall of Ten Thousand Volumes (4-4). Illustration reduced.

2003, June 29   Photo.   Perf. 12¾
3286 A949   Horiz. strip of 4, #a-d   1.60 1.40
A sheet exists containing 2 No. 3286. Value $16.

Tibetan Antelopes A950

Designs: 80f, Antelopes and mountain (2-1). $2, Antelope's head, adult with young (2-2).

Photo. & Engr.
2003, July 20   Perf. 11x11¼
3287-3288 A950 Set of 2   1.00 1.00
Sheets exist containing 3 each of Nos. 3287-3288. Value, set $12.

Kongtong Mountain — A951

No. 3289: a, 80f, Town of Huangcheng (4-1). b, 80f, Gorge of Playing the Zither (4-2). c, 80f, Pagoda Courtyard (4-3). d, $2, Peak of Thunder (4-4). Illustration reduced.

2003, July 26   Litho.   Perf. 12
3289 A951   Block of 4, #a-d   1.60 1.50
A sheet exists containing 2 No. 3289. Value, $20.

Sailing Ship — A952

2003, Aug. 5
3290 A952 80f multi + label   1.00 1.00
No. 3290 exists in sheets of 4 stamps + 4 labels. Value $7.

Powered Flight, Cent. — A953

Designs: 80f, Foreign airplanes (2-1). $2, Chinese airplanes (2-2).

2003, Aug. 9   Photo.   Perf. 12¾
3291-3292 A953   Set of 2   1.25 1.00

A sheet exists containing 6 each of Nos. 3291-3292. Value, $12.

Jinci Temple Painted Statues — A954

Designs: No. 3293, 80f, Ruyi maid (4-1). No. 3294, 80f, Maid holding a towel (4-2). No. 3295, 80f, Maid carrying a royal seal (4-3). $2, Maid singing and dancing (4-4).

2003, Aug. 16   Perf. 11¾x12
3293-3296 A954   Set of 4   1.75 1.40

Sheets exist containing four each of Nos. 3293-3294 and 3295-3296. Value, set of 2 sheets $20.

Three Gorges Project — A955

Designs: No. 3297, 80f, Dam and reservoir (3-1). No. 3298, 80f, Ship locks (3-2). $2, Power plant and high tension wire towers (3-3).

2003, Aug. 20   Litho.   Perf. 12
3297-3299 A955   Set of 3   1.50 1.25

A sheet exists containing 3 each of Nos. 3297-3299. Value, $11.

Traditional Sports of Ethnic Minorities A956

Designs: No. 3300, 80f, Wrestling (4-1). b, No. 3301, 80f, Archery (4-2). No. 3302, 80f, Horse racing (4-3). No. 3303, 80f, Swinging (4-4).

2003, Sept. 5   Photo.   Perf. 13x13½
3300-3303 A956   Set of 4   1.25 1.00
3303a   Souvenir sheet, #3300-
           3303   2.50 2.00

No. 3303a sold for $5. Sheets exist containing four each of No. 3300-3301 and 3302-3303. Value, set $16.

Tienanmen Gate, Beijing — A957

2003, Sept. 10   Litho.   Perf. 12
3304 A957 80f multi + label   .70 .40

Two different sheets each containing four examples of No. 3304 were included in a souvenir folder sold only at the International Stamp and Coin Expo in Beijing in 2004. Value, set of 2 $12. Two additional sheets of four stamps + four labels, perf. 12½, exist. Value, set of 2 $12.

General Yue Fei (1103-42) — A958

Designs: No. 3305, 80f, Mother tattooing "Loyalty to the Country" on Yue Fei's back (3-1). No. 3306, 80f, Yue Fei standing with sword (3-2). $2, Yue Fei seated (3-3).

2003, Sept. 25
3305-3307 A958   Set of 3   1.50 1.25

A sheet exists containing 3 each of Nos. 3305-3307. Value, $17.

Souvenir Sheet

Water Diversion Projects — A959

2003, Sept. 26   Photo.   Perf. 12¾
3308 A959 $8 multi   3.00 2.50

Book Printing — A960

Designs: No. 3309, 80f, Ritual of Zhou, China (2-1). No. 3310, 80f, Hungarian Illuminated Chronicle, 1473 (2-2).

2003, Sept. 30   Litho.   Perf. 12
3309-3310 A960   Set of 2   1.00 1.00

Nos. 3309-3310 have large perforation holes at the stamp corners. A sheet exists containing 4 each of Nos. 3309-3310 in se-tenant pairs. Value, $12.

See Hungary Nos. 3863-3864.

Double Ninth Festival — A961

Designs: No. 3311, 80f, Climbing mountain (3-1). No. 3312, 80f, Enjoying the beauty of chrysanthemums (3-2). $2, Playing chess and drinking wine (3-3).

2003, Oct. 4   Photo.   Perf. 11½
3311-3313 A961   Set of 3   1.25 1.10

A sheet exists containing 3 each of Nos. 3311-3313 in strips of 3. Value, $12.

Launch of First Manned Chinese Spacecraft A962

No. 3314: a, 80f, Astronaut, Shenzhou spacecraft (2-1). b, $2, Yang Liwei, flag (2-2).

2003, Oct. 16   Perf. 13x13¼
3314 A962 Pair, #a-b   5.50 5.50

A booklet containing No. 3314, Hong Kong No. 1062 and Macao No. 1128 exists. The booklet sold for a premium over face value. Value, $12.

Folktale of Liang Shanbo and Zhu Yingtai — A963

Designs: No. 3315, 80f, Zhu Yingtai, disguised as a man, and Liang Shanbo become sworn brothers at Caoqiao (5-1). No. 3316, 80f, Classmates for three years (5-2). No. 3317, 80f, Bidding farewell (5-3). No. 3318, 80f, Sad parting on the terrace (5-4). $2, Turning into butterflies (5-5).

2003, Oct. 18   Perf. 12
3315-3319 A963   Set of 5   1.75 1.50

A booklet containing booklet panes of 1 of each of Nos. 3315-3319 exists. Value, $14. A sheet exists containing 2 each of Nos. 3315-3319. Value, $15.

China 2003 Intl. Stamp Exhibition, Mianyang — A964

2003, Nov. 20   Photo.   Perf. 13¼
3320 A964 80f multi   1.00 .60

World AIDS Day — A965

2003, Dec. 1   Perf. 11¼x11
3321 A965 80f multi   1.50 .90

Mao Zedong (1893-1976) — A966

Mao: No. 3322, 80f, Seated in folding chair (4-1). No. 3323, 80f, Standing (4-2). No. 3324,

80f, Seated on bench (4-3). No. 3325, 80f, Seated at desk (4-4).

Litho. & Engr.
2003, Dec. 6   Perf. 12
3322-3325 A966   Set of 4   7.00 1.25

A sheet exists containing 2 each of Nos. 3322-3325 in se-tenant strips of 4. Value, $30.

Bronze Objects of Eastern Zhou Dyansty — A967

Designs: No. 3326, 60f, Square plate with turtle and fish patterns (8-1). No. 3327, 60f, Gui of the Duke of Qin (handled bowl with lid) (8-2). No. 3328, 80f, Iron-footed tripod of the King of Zhongshan (8-3). No. 3329, 80f, Gourd-shaped ladle of Yi, the Marquis of Zeng (8-4). No. 3330, 80f, Divine animal wine vessel (8-5). No. 3331, 80f, Wine vessel with phoenix pattern, vert. (8-6). $1, Square pot with lotus and cranes design, vert. (8-7). $2, Tripod with a dragon-shaped handle, vert. (8-8).

Perf. 11½x11¼, 11¼x11½
2003, Dec. 13   Photo. & Engr.
3326-3333 A967   Set of 8   2.75 2.50

A sheet of 8 No. 3328 exists. Value, $25.

Environmental Protection Type of 2002

Designs: 50f, Prevention and control of desertification. $4.50, Protection of biodiversity.

Perf. 12¾x13¼ Syncopated
2004, Jan. 1   Photo.
3334 A908 50f multi   .35 .35
3335 A908 $4.50 multi   1.50 1.40

Bird Type of 2002

Designs: $5, Yellow-bellied tit. $6, Yunnan nuthatch.

Perf. 13¼
2004, Jan. 1
3336 A909 $5 multi   1.75 1.60
3337 A909 $6 multi   2.00 1.90

New Year 2004 (Year of the Monkey) A968

2004, Jan. 5   Perf. 13 Syncopated
3338 A968 80f multi   1.00 1.00
a.   Booklet pane of 10   10.00
        Complete booklet, #3338a 10.50

Sheets of 4 and sheets of 6 exist. Value, set $35.

Taohuawu New Year Pictures — A969

Designs: No. 3339, 80f, Feelings of Pipa (4-1). No. 3340, 80f, Kylin Bringing a Son (4-2). No. 3341, 80f, Liu Hai Playing with the Golden Toad (4-3). $2, Ten Beauties Playing Football (4-4).

2004, Jan. 14   Litho.   Perf. 12
3339-3342 A969   Set of 4   1.50 1.25
3342a   Souvenir sheet, #3339-
           3342   5.00 5.00

A sheet of 2 each of Nos. 3339-3342 in se-tenant blocks of 4 exists. Value, $12.

Deng Yingchao (1904-92), Communist Party Leader — A970

No. 3343: a, Holding book. b, Portrait.

2004, Feb. 4 Litho. & Engr.
3343 A970 80f Vert. pair, #a-b 1.25 1.25

Suzhou Industrial Park, 10th Anniv. A971

2004, Mar. 1 Photo. Perf. 13x13¼
3344 A971 80f multi .80 .50

See Singapore No. 1084.

Red Cross Society, Cent. — A972

2004, Mar. 10 Perf. 11¼x11
3345 A972 80f multi .50 .35

Stories Explaining Chinese Idioms A973

Idioms: No. 3346, 80f, Trying to learn the Handan walk (4-1). No. 3347, 80f, Lord Ye's love for dragon (4-2). No. 3348, 80f, Filling a position in a Yu band (4-3). No. 3349, 80f, When the snipe and the clam grapple (4-4).

Perf. 12½x13¼ Syncopated
2004, Apr. 2
3346-3349 A973 Set of 4 1.25 1.25

A sheet of 2 each of Nos. 3346-3349 in se-tenant strips of 4 exists. Value, $15.

Peacocks — A974

Designs: No. 3350, 80f, Blue peacock (2-1). No. 3351, 80f, Albino peacock, vert. (2-2). $6, Green peacocks.

2004, Apr. 13 Perf. 12¾
3350-3351 A974 Set of 2 .65 .55

Souvenir Sheet
Perf. 13¼x13
3352 A974 $6 multi 3.75 3.25

No. 3352 contains one 60x40mm stamp

Nanxi River — A975

No. 3353: a, River and mountain (4-1). b, Tree and boat in foreground, mountains in background (4-2). c, Rocks, boat in river (4-3). d, Boat, spit of land with trees (4-4).

2004, Apr. 24 Photo. Perf. 12¾
3353 Horiz. strip of 4 1.75 1.50
a. A975 60f multi .30 .25
b.-c. A975 80f Either single .35 .30
d. A975 $2 multi .65 .55

Danxia Mountain — A976

Designs: 60f, Sengmao Peak (4-1). No. 3355, 80f, Xianlong Lake (4-2). No. 3356, 80f, Chahu Peak (4-3). $2, Jinjiang River (4-4).

2004, May 1 Litho. & Engr. Perf. 12
3354-3357 A976 Set of 4 1.60 1.40

Economic and Technological Development Zones, 20th Anniv. — A977

2004, May 4 Litho.
3358 A977 80f multi .80 .50

Exists in a sheet of 8 stamps + 8 labels. Value, $6.

Hometowns of Returned Chinese — A978

Designs: No. 3359, 80f, Xinglong Overseas Chinese Farm (4-1). No. 3360, 80f, Jinan University (4-2). No. 3361, 80f, Fuqing Rongqiao Development Zone (4-3). No. 3362, 80f, Kaiping (4-4).

2004, May 15 Photo. Perf. 11x11¼
3359-3362 A978 Set of 4 1.25 1.10

Sima Guang Breaking the Vat — A979

Designs: No. 3363, 80f, Sima Guang falling into water (3-1). No. 3362, 80f, Breaking vat (3-2). No. 3363, $2, Rescued (3-3).

2004, June 1 Perf. 12
3363-3365 A979 Set of 3 1.25 1.25

A sheet of 2 each of Nos. 3363-3365 exists. Value, $18.

Scenes of Villages of Southern Anhui Province A980

Designs: No. 3366, 80f, Archway (4-1). No. 3367, 80f, Old buildings (4-2). No. 3368, 80f, Buildings on South Lake (4-3). No. 3369, 80f, Moon Pond (4-4).

Photo. & Engr.
2004, June 25 Perf. 11x11¼
3366-3369 A980 Set of 4 1.25 1.25

Liu Yi Delivering a Letter — A981

Designs: No. 3370, 80f, Dragon Princess asking Liu Yi to deliver a letter (4-1). No. 3371, 80f, Delivering letter to Dongting Lake (4-2). No. 3372, 80f, Family reunion (4-3). $2, Couple embracing (4-4).

2004, July 17 Photo. Perf. 13¼x13
3370 A981 80f multi .30 .30
a. Booklet pane of 1 .35
3371 A981 80f multi .30 .30
a. Booklet pane of 1 .35
3372 A981 80f multi .30 .30
a. Booklet pane of 1 .35
3373 A981 $2 multi .60 .30
a. Booklet pane of 1 .35
Complete booklet, #3370a-3373a 2.00
Nos. 3370-3373 (4) 1.50 1.20

Complete booklet sold for $6.

Souvenir Sheet

Eight Immortals Crossing the Sea — A982

2004, July 30 Perf. 12 Syncopated
3374 A982 $6 multi 4.50 4.00

Peony — A983

2004, July 31 Litho. Perf. 12¾
3375 A983 80f multi + label .40 .35

Perf 12¾ examples come from a sheet containing four examples with labels below the stamps that also contain four #3261. The sheetlet sold for $15. Value, $17.50.

2004 Summer Olympics, Athens — A984

Olympic rings and: No. 3376, 80f, Parthenon, Athens (2-1). No. 3377, 80f, Hall of Good Harvest, Temple of Heaven, Beijing.

2004, Aug. 13 Photo. Perf. 12¾
3376-3377 A984 Set of 2 1.00 1.00

Perf. 12¾ examples come from a sheet containing four examples with labels below the stamps that also contain four #3261. The sheetlet sold for $15. Value, $17.50.
See Greece Nos. 2124-2125.

Deng Xiaoping (1904-97), Chinese Leader — A985

Designs: No. 3378, 80f, Walking (2-1). No. 3379, 80f, Saluting, horiz. (2-2). $6, Seated.

2004, Aug. 22 Perf. 12 Syncopated
3378-3379 A985 Set of 2 1.00 1.00

Souvenir Sheet
Perf. 13 Syncopated
3380 A985 $6 multi 3.25 3.00

No. 3380 contains one 47x57mm stamp.

South China Tiger A986

Designs: 80f, Head (2-1). $2, Adult and young (2-2).

2004, Aug. 23 Litho. Perf. 12
3381-3382 A986 Set of 2 1.00 1.00

A sheet of 4 each of Nos. 3381-3382 in se-tenant pairs exists. Value, $17.50.

People's Congress, 50th Anniv. — A987

Designs: No. 3383, 80f, Congress members arriving at Huairentang Hall of Zhongnanhai (2-1). No. 3384, 80f, Interior of Great Hall of the People (2-2).

2004, Sept. 15 Perf. 13¼
3383-3384 A987 Set of 2 1.00 1.00

A sheet containing 3 pairs of Nos. 3383-3384 exists. Value, $15.

Bloodstone
Seals
A988

No. 3385: a, 80f, Seal of Emperor Qianlong
(2-1). b, $2, Seal of Emperor Jiaqing (2-2).

Litho. & Embossed
2004, Sept. 17   Perf. 13x13¼
3385 A988   Pair, #a-b   1.00 1.00

Celery
Wormwood
A989

Designs: No. 3386, 80f, Purple flowers (4-
1). No. 3387, 80f, Blue flowers (4-2). No. 3388,
80f, Red flowers (4-3). $2, Yellow flowers (4-4).

2004, Sept. 19 Photo. Perf. 13¼x13
3386-3389 A989   Set of 4   1.50 1.50

A sheet containing 2 strips of 3386-3389
exists. Value, $10.

Chinese and
Romanian
Handicrafts
A990

Designs: No. 3390, 80f, Drum with tigers
and birds, China (2-1). No. 3391, 80f,
Cucuteni pottery jar, Romania (2-2).

2004, Sept. 22 Perf. 13 Syncopated
3390-3391 A990   Set of 2   1.00 1.00

A sheet containing 4 pairs of Nos. 3390-
3391 exists.
See Romania No. 4668.

National
Symbols
A991

Designs: No. 3392, 80f, Flag (2-1). No.
3393, 80f, Arms, vert. (2-2).

Perf. 13¼x13 Syncopated, 13x13¼
Syncopated
2004, Sept. 30
3392-3393 A991   Set of 2   2.00 2.00

A sheet of 4 self-adhesive examples of both
Nos. 3392 and 3393 was included in a souvenir folder sold only at the International Stamp
and Coin Expo in Beijing in 2004. Value, $35.

Landscapes of Chinese
Borderlands — A992

Designs: No. 3394, 80f, Forest, Xing'an
Mountains (12-1). No. 3395, 80f, Lake in Yalu
River Basin (12-2). No. 3396, 80f, Reefs in
Yellow Sea (12-3). No. 3397, 80f, Zhoushan
Archipelago (12-4). No. 3398, 80f, Coast of
Taiwan (12-5). No. 3399, 80f, Xisha Islands
(12-6). No. 3400, 80f, Karst landscape, South-
ern Guangxi (12-7). No. 3401, 80f, Rain forest,
Southern Yunnan (12-8). No. 3402, 80f, Mt.
Qomolangma (12-9). No. 3403, 80f, Pamirs
(12-10). No. 3404, 80f, Badain Jaran Desert
(12-11). No. 3405, 80f, Hulun Buir Steppe (12-
12).

2004, Oct. 1   Perf. 12¾
3394-3405 A992   Set of 12   3.50 3.00
3405a   Sheet of 12, #3394-3405
         + central label   10.00 7.50

Buildings in
China and
Spain — A993

Designs: No. 3406, 80f, Jinmao Tower,
China (2-1). No. 3407, 80f, Park Guell, Spain.

2004, Oct. 8   Perf. 13¼x13
3406-3407 A993   Set of 2   .90 .90
See Spain Nos. 3319-3320.

Miniature Sheet

The Festival of Pure Brightness on the
River, by Zhang Zeduan — A994

No. 3408 — Various details from painting: a,
60f, Trees (9-1). b, 80f, Trees, people on
horseback (9-2). c, 80f, Buildings, boats on
river (9-3). d, 80f, Buildings, boats on river,
diff. (9-4). e, 80f, Bridge (9-5). f, 80f, Buildings,
boats on river (9-6). g, 80f, Buildings (9-7). h,
$1, Tower (9-8). i, $2, Intersection (9-9).

Litho. & Engr.
2004, Oct. 18   Perf. 12
3408 A994   Sheet of 9, #a-i   18.00 15.00

Phoenix — A995

2004, Nov. 1 Litho. Perf. 12¾
3409 A995 80f multi + label   .40 .25

A sheet of 4 No. 3409 + label exists. Value,
$6.
A sheet of 10 serpentine die cut 12¼ self-
adhesive stamps like No. 3409 + 10 labels
depicting Snoopy for 25 yuan. Value, $15.

Pavilions — A996

Designs: No. 3410, 80f, Aiwan (4-1). No.
3411, 80f, Pipa (4-2). No. 3412, 80f, Lan (4-3).
No. 3413, 80f, Zuiweng (4-4).

2004, Nov. 6 Photo. Perf. 13¼x13
3410-3413 A996   Set of 4   1.25 .90
A sheet of 2 each of Nos. 3410-3413 exists.
Value, $13.

Ancient
Calligraphy
A997

Designs: No. 3414, 80f, Yiying stele (4-1).
No. 3415, 80f, Zhangqian stele (4-2). No.
3416, 80f, Caoquan stele (4-3). No. 3417, 80f,
Shimen song (4-4).

Photo. & Engr.
2004, Dec. 5   Perf. 11¼x11
3414-3417 A997   Set of 4   1.40 .90
A sheet of 2 each of Nos. 3414-3417 exists.
Value, $10.

New Year
2005 (Year of
the Rooster)
A998

Perf. 13 Syncopated
2005, Jan. 5   Photo.
3418 A998 80f multi   .50 .25
a.   Booklet pane of 10   5.00
      Complete booklet, #3418a   5.50

No. 3418 exists in sheets of 4 and 6. Value,
$12 each.

Tarim-Baihe Gas Pipeline — A999

No. 3419: a, 80f, Derrick (2-1). b, $3, Pipes
(2-2).

2005, Jan. 8 Litho. Perf. 12
3419 A999   Horiz. pair, #a-b   1.40 1.00

Historic
Structures
in Taiwan
A1000

No. 3420: a, North Gate, Taipei City Wall (5-
1). b, Confucian Temple (5-2). c, Longshan
Temple, Lugang (5-3). d, Erkunshen Cannon
Fort, Tainan (5-4). e, Matsu Temple, Penghu
(5-5).

Perf. 13 Syncopated
2005, Jan. 30   Litho. & Engr.
3420   Vert. strip of 5   2.00 1.50
a.-d. A1000 80f Any single   .30 .25
e.   A1000 $1.50 multi   .50 .45

Yangjiabu New
Year Woodprints
A1001

Designs: No. 3421, 80f, Door God (4-1). No.
3422, 80f, Abundance for year (4-2). No. 3423,
80f, Good news on New Year's Day (4-3). No.
3424, 80f, Goddess strewing flowers from
heaven (4-4).

2005, Feb. 1 Litho. Perf. 13¼x13
3421-3424 A1001   Set of 4   1.10 .80
3424a   Souvenir sheet, #3421-
         3424   4.50 2.50

No. 3424a sold for $4.80. A miniature sheet
containing 2 of each stamp exists. Value, $12.

Magnolias
A1002

Designs: No. 3425, 80f, Magnolia den-
nudata (4-1). No. 3426, 80f, Magnolia delavayi
(4-2). No. 3427, 80f, Magnolia grandiflora (4-
3). No. 3428, 80f, Magnolia liliflora (4-4).

2005, Mar. 5 Photo. Perf. 13x13¼
3425-3428 A1002   Set of 4   1.50 1.00

Great Wall of China — A1003

2005, Apr. 1 Litho. Perf. 12¾
3429 A1003 80f multi + label   .40 .25
See note following No. 3462.

Earth
Day — A1004

2005, Apr. 22 Photo. Perf. 13¼
3430 A1004 80f multi   .60 .25
A ring of syncopated perforations surrounds
the vignette.

Jigong
Mountains
A1005

No. 3431: a, Mountain at daybreak (4-1). b,
Garden in clouds (4-2). c, Moon Pond (4-3). d,
Black Dragon Waterfall (4-4).

Perf. 12½ Syncopated
2005, Apr. 28   Litho.
3431   Horiz. strip of 4   1.25 1.25
a.-d. A1005 80f Any single   .30 .25

All-China Federation of Trade Unions, 80th Anniv. — A1006

2005, May 1   *Perf. 12*
3432 A1006 80f multi   1.00 .25

Paintings of Flower Arrangements A1007

Designs: No. 3433, 80f, Magnolia Flowers, by Chen Hongshou (2-1). No. 3434, 80f, Flower Vase in a Window Niche, by Ambrosius Bosschaert the Elder (2-2).

Perf. 12½ Syncopated
2005, May 18   *Photo.*
3433-3434 A1007 Set of 2   1.00 .45
See Liechtenstein Nos. 1315-1316.

Dalian Bay Area Views — A1008

No. 3435: a, Tiger Beach (4-1). b, Bangchui Island (4-2). c, Golden Pebble Beach (4-3). d, Lushunkou (4-4).

2005, May 21 *Perf. 12¾ Syncopated*
3435   Horiz. strip of 4   1.25 1.25
a.-d. A1008 80f Any single   .30 .25

Fudan University, Cent. A1009

Litho., Engr. & Embossed
2005, May 27   *Perf. 12*
3436 A1009 80f multi   .40 .25

Hans Christian Andersen (1805-75), Author A1010

No. 3437 — Fairy tales by Andersen: a, The Emperor's New Clothes (5-1). b, The Little Mermaid (5-2). c, Thumbelina (5-3). d, The Little Match Girl (5-4). e, The Ugly Duckling (5-5).

Perf. 13¼ Syncopated
2005, June 1   *Photo.*
3437   Horiz. strip of 5   1.75 1.25
a.-e. A1010 80f Any single   .30 .25
f. Booklet pane of 1, #3437a   .55 —
g. Booklet pane of 1, #3437b   .55 —
h. Booklet pane of 1, #3437c   .55 —

---

i. Booklet pane of 1, #3437d   .55 —
j. Booklet pane of 1, #3437e   .55 —
Complete booklet, #3437f-3437j   5.50

The complete booklet sold for $6.
A sheet of ten serpentine die cut 10 self-adhesive stamps containing two of each of the designs of Nos. 3437a-3437e and ten labels exists. Value, $12.

Voyages of Admiral Zheng He, 600th Anniv. — A1011

No. 3438: a, Admiral Zheng He (3-1). b, Building, map of voyages (3-2). c, Compass, drawing of ship (3-3)
$6, Ship, horiz.

2005, June 28   *Litho.*
3438   Horiz. strip of 3   1.00 1.00
a.-c. A1011 80f Any single   .30 .25
Souvenir Sheet
3439 A1011 $6 multi   3.75 3.25
No. 3439 contains one 70x50mm stamp.

Nantong Museum — A1012

No. 3440: a, Southern Hall (2-1). b, Central Hall (2-2).
Illustration reduced.

Photo. & Engr.
2005, June 16   *Perf. 12½x12¾*
3440 A1012 80f Horiz. pair, #a-b   .80 .50

Xianghai National Nature Reserve — A1013

Designs: No. 3441, 80f, Red-crowned cranes in nest (4-1). No. 3442, 80f, Three birds in flight, trees (4-2). No. 3443, 80f, Birds at lake (4-3). No. 3444, 80f, Eagles flying above steppe (4-4).

2005, July 30 *Photo.* *Perf. 12¾*
3441-3444 A1013 Set of 4   1.25 .90

Miniature Sheet

People's Army Generals — A1014

No. 3445: a, Yang Jingyu (5-1). b, Zuo Quan (5-2). c, Peng Xuefeng (5-3). d, Luo Binghui (5-4). e, Guan Xiangying (5-5).

2005, Aug. 1   *Perf. 12*
3445 A1014 80f Sheet of 10, 2
          each #a-e   6.50 4.50

End of World War II, 60th Anniv. — A1015

No. 3446: a, Soldiers with machine guns (4-1). b, Bugler (4-2). c, Soldier holding gun, troops landing in Normandy (4-3). d, Conquering Berlin (4-4).
$6, Dove, vert.

Perf. 12¾ Syncopated
2005, Aug. 15   *Litho.*
3446 A1015 80f Block of 4, #a-d   1.25 .80
Souvenir Sheet
Photo.
Perf. 12¾
3447 A1015 $6 multi   3.00 2.00

Tibet Autonomous Region, 40th Anniv. — A1016

2005, Aug. 26 *Photo.* *Perf. 13¼*
3448 A1016 80f multi   .80 .25

Chinese Motion Pictures, Cent. — A1017

2005, Aug. 28 *Litho.* *Perf. 12¾x13*
3449 A1017 80f multi   .50 .25
Exists in a sheet of 8 stamps + 8 labels.

"Five Happinesses Arrive" — A1018

2005, Sept. 16   *Perf. 12¾*
3450 A1018 80f multi + label   1.00 .25
See note following No. 3462.

Fanjing Mountain Nature Reserve A1019

No. 3451: a, Golden Summit (4-1). b, Mushroom Rock (4-2). c, Forest (4-3). d, Heiwan River (4-4).

2005, Sept. 18 *Photo.* *Perf. 13x13¼*
3451   Horiz. strip of 4   1.50 1.25
a.-d. A1019 80f Any single   .35 .25

Farm Technology A1020

Sheep and: No. 3452, 80f, Chinese water wheel (2-1). No. 3453, 80f, Dutch windmill (2-2).

2005, Sept. 22   *Perf. 12*
3452-3453 A1020 Set of 2   1.00 .50
See Netherlands Nos. 1203-1204.

Miniature Sheet

People's Liberation Army Generals — A1021

No. 1021: a, Su Yu (10-1). b, Xu Haidong (10-2). c, Huang Kecheng (10-3). d, Chen Geng (10-4). e, Tan Zheng (10-5). f, Xiao Jinguang (10-6). g, Zhang Yunyi (10-7). h, Luo Ruiqing (10-8). i, Wang Shusheng (10-9). j, Xu Guangda (10-10).

Litho. & Engr.
2005, Sept. 27   *Perf. 13¼x13*
3454 A1021 80f Sheet of 10, #a-j   4.50 3.00

Miniature Sheet

Goddess of the River Luo, by Gu Kaizhi — A1022

Various painting details with width of: a, 50mm (10-1). b, 50mm (10-2). c, 60mm (10-3). d, 40mm (10-4). e, 60mm (10-5). f, 60mm (10-6). g, 60mm (10-7). h, 50mm (10-8). i, 40mm (10-9). j, 50mm (10-10).

2005, Sept. 28   *Perf. 12*
3455 A1022 80f Sheet of 10,
          #a-j   12.00 8.50

Xinjiang Uygur Autonomous Region, 50th Anniv. — A1023

No. 3456: a, Male dancers and musicians (3-1). b, Male and female dancers (3-2). c, Women carrying plates of food (3-3).

Perf. 12x12½ Syncopated
2005, Oct. 1   *Litho.*
3456   Horiz. strip of 3   1.00 .90
a.-c. A1023 80f Any single   .30 .25

Souvenir Sheet

10th National Games, Jiangsu Province — A1024

2005, Oct. 12   Photo.   Perf. 12¾
3457 A1024 $6 multi   2.50 2.00

Wild Cats
A1025

Designs: No. 3458, 80f, Panthera pardus orientalis (2-1). No. 3459, 80f, Puma concolor (2-2).

2005, Oct. 13   Photo.   Perf. 13x13¼
3458-3459 A1025   Set of 2   .80 .45
See Canada Nos. 2122-2123.

"Be Safe Every Year" — A1026

Illustration reduced.

2005, Nov. 6   Litho.   Perf. 13¼
3460 A1026 80f red & blk + label 3.50 1.00
A serpentine die cut 10 self-adhesive stamp of type A1026 exists. Value, $22.50.

Relics From Chengtoushan Archaeological Site — A1027

2005, Nov. 6   Photo.   Perf. 12½
3461 A1027 80f multi   .60 .25

"Beam With Delight" — A1028

2005, Nov. 11   Litho.   Perf. 12¾
3462 A1028 80f multi + label   1.10 .25
A sheet of 2 each of Nos. 3429, 3450 and 3462 exists. Value, $6.

2008 Summer Olympics, Beijing — A1029

Designs: No. 3463, Beijing Olympics emblem, Olympic rings (6-1).
No. 3464 — Beijing Olympic mascots with emblem on chest: a, Beibei (6-2). b, Jingjing (6-3). c, Huanhuan (6-4). d, Yingying (6-5). e, Nini (6-6).
No. 3465: a, Like #3463. b, Like #3464a. c, Like #3464b. d, Like #3464c. e, Like #3464d. f, Like #3464e.

2005, Nov. 12   Photo.   Perf. 13¼x13
3463 A1029 80f multi   .50 .25
3464 A1029 80f Horiz. strip of
       5, #a-e   10.50 8.00

Self-Adhesive
Serpentine Die Cut 11¾
3465 A1029 80f Sheet, 2 each
                    #a-f   40.00 40.00
A sheet of 5 30x30mm stamps with the Beijing Olympics emblem and Olympic rings was issued in 2008. Value, $15.

New Year 2006 (Year of the Dog) A1030

Perf. 13 Syncopated
2006, Jan. 5   Photo.
3466 A1030 80f multi   .50 .25
  a.   Sheet of 6   7.00 6.00
  b.   Booklet pane of 10   5.00 —
           Complete booklet, #3466b 5.50
A sheet of 4 exists that was a giveaway for standing-order customers. Value, $9.

Wuqiang New Year Woodprints A1031

Designs: No. 3467, 80f, Being Safe All Year Round (4-1). No. 3468, 80f, Five Blessings Approach Your Door (4-2). No. 3469, 80f, Flower of Prosperity Blossoms (4-3). No. 3470, 80f, Lion Rolling the Embroidered Ball (4-4).

Litho. & Engr.
2006, Jan. 22   Perf. 12
3467-3470 A1031   Set of 4   1.50 1.00
3470a   Souvenir sheet, #3467-3470 3.50 2.50
3470b   Souvenir sheet, 2 each
          #3467-3470   9.00 6.00

Lanterns A1032

Designs: No. 3471, 80f, Fish lantern (5-1). No. 3472, 80f, Chinese white cabbage lantern (5-2). No. 3473, 80f, Lotus lantern (5-3). No. 3474, 80f, Dragon and phoenix lantern (5-4). $1.50, Butterfly lantern (5-5).

2006, Feb. 12   Photo.   Perf. 13¼x13
3471-3475 A1032   Set of 5   2.00 1.50
3475a   Sheet, 2 each #3471-3475 10.00 5.00

Abolition of Agricultural Tax — A1033

Perf. 13½ Syncopated
2006, Feb. 22
3476 A1033 80f multi   4.50 .50

Lijiang River — A1034

No. 3477: a, Yangdi (4-1). b, Langshi (4-2). c, Huangbu (4-3). d, Xingping (4-4).

2006, Feb. 25   Perf. 12¾
3477   Horiz. strip of 4   1.50 1.25
  a.-d.   A1034 80f Any single   .30 .25

Relic Plants — A1035

Designs: No. 3478, 80f, Ginkgo biloba (4-1). No. 3479, 80f, Glyptostrobus pensilis (4-2). No. 3480, 80f, Davidia involucrata (4-3). No. 3481, 80f, Liriodendron chinense (4-4).

Perf. 12x12¼ Syncopated
2006, Mar. 12   Set of 4   Litho.
3478-3481 A1035   Set of 4   1.50 .90

Dogs A1036

Designs: Nos. 3482, 3486a, 80f, Pekingese (4-1). Nos. 3483, 3486b, 80f, Pug, vert. (4-2). Nos. 3484, 3486c, 80f, Chow chow (4-3). Nos. 3485, 3486d, 80f, Tibetan mastiff, vert. (4-4).

Perf. 13¼ Syncopated
2006, Mar. 19   Litho. & Engr.
3482-3485 A1036   Set of 4   1.25 .90

Self-Adhesive
Serpentine Die Cut 11¾ on 2 Sides
3486 A1036 80f Sheet, 2 each
                    #3486a-3486d 11.00 7.00

Qingcheng Mountain A1037

Designs: 60f, Remote mountain gate (4-1). No. 3488, 80f, Winding path (4-2). No. 3489, 80f, Ancient temple (4-3). No. 3490, 80f, Spring (4-4).

2006, Apr. 12   Perf. 13¼ Syncopated
3487-3490 A1037   Set of 4   2.00 1.25

Statues in Yungang Grottoes — A1038

Designs: No. 3491, 80f, Sakyamuni (4-1). No. 3492, 80f, Bodhisattva (4-2). No. 3493, 80f, Head of Bodhisattva (4-3). No. 3494, 80f, Xieshi Bodhisattva (4-4). $6, Sakyamuni, diff.

Perf. 13¼x13½ Syncopated
2006, Apr. 13   Photo.
3491-3494 A1038   Set of 4   1.50 .90
Souvenir Sheet
Perf. 13 Syncopated
3495 A1038 $6 multi   3.25 2.25
No. 3495 contains one 40x60mm stamp.

Tianzhu Mountain — A1039

Designs: 60f, Green Dragon Mountain Stream (4-1). No. 3497, 80f, Taoist Practice Terrace (4-2). No. 3498, 80f, Sanzu Temple (4-3). No. 3499, 80f, Qingtian Peak (4-4).

2006, Apr. 22   Perf. 11½x11¼
3496-3499 A1039   Set of 4   2.00 1.00

Scientists A1040

Designs: No. 3500, 80f, Liang Xi (1883-1958), forester (4-1). No. 3501, 80f, Mao Yisheng (1896-1989), civil engineer (4-2). No. 3502, 80f, Yan Jici (1900-96), physicist (4-3). No. 3503, 80f, Zhou Peiyuan (1902-93), physicist (4-4).

Litho. & Engr.
2006, May 13   Perf. 12
3500-3503 A1040   Set of 4   2.00 1.00

Lighthouses
A1041

No. 3504: a, Dagu Lighthouse (4-1). b, Guishan Island Lighthouse (4-2). c, Wusongkou Lighthouse (4-3). d, Mulantou Lighthouse (4-4).

2006, May 22   Photo.   Perf. 12¾
3504   Horiz. strip of 4   2.50 2.00
a.-d.   A1041 80f Any single   .30   .25

Chinese Space Program, 50th Anniv. — A1042

No. 3505: a, Geospace Double Star Exploration (2-1). b, Shenzhou 6 (2-2).

Perf. 12x11¼ Syncopated
2006, June 8   Litho.
3505   A1042 80f Horiz. pair, #a-b   1.50 1.25

Silver and Gold Objects — A1043

Designs: No. 3506, 80f, Jeeweled Qing Dynasty cup, China (2-1). No. 3507, 80f, Tankard with Biblical designs, by Peter Rohde, Poland.

2006, June 20 Photo. Perf. 13¼x13
3506-3507 A1043 Set of 2   1.25 .65
        See Poland No. 3829.

Olympic Rings and Emblem of 2008 Summer Olympics, Beijing — A1043a

2006, June 23   Litho.   Perf. 12
3507A A1043a 80f multi + label 1.25 .35

Printed in sheets of 15 stamps + 15 labels, sheets of 5 stamps + 5 labels, sheets of 4 stamps + 4 labels to right of stamps, sheets of 4 stamps + 4 labels below stamps, and sheets of 8 stamps + 8 labels. Value, set of 5 sheets $50.

Early Communist Leaders A1044

Designs: No. 3508, 80f, Gao Junyu (1896-1925) (5-1). No. 3509, 80f, Wang Hebo (1882-1927) (5-2). No. 3510, 80f, Su Zhaozheng (1885-1929) (5-3). No. 3511, 80f, Peng Pai

(1896-1929) (5-4). No. 3512, 80f, Deng Xhongxia (1894-1933) (5-5).

2006, June 30   Litho. & Engr.
3508-3512 A1044 Set of 5   8.50 4.00

Opening of Qinghai-Tibet Railway — A1045

Designs: No. 3513, 80f, Bridge across Kekexili, antelopes (3-1). No. 3514, 80f, Train crossing Danggula Mountains, cattle (3-2). No. 3515, 80f, Lhasa Railway Station, birds (3-3).

Perf. 12½x12 Syncopated
2006, July 1   Litho.
3513-3515 A1045 Set of 3   3.50 2.00

Kanasi Nature Reserve — A1046

Designs: No. 3516, 80f, Kanasi Lake (4-1). No. 3517, 80f, Crouching Dragon Bend (4-2). No. 3518, 80f, Celestial Bend (4-3). No. 3519, 80f, Moon Bend (4-4).

2006, July 8   Photo.   Perf. 12¾
3516-3519 A1046 Set of 4   2.00 1.00

Earthquake Protection and Damage Mitigation A1047

2006, July 26   Perf. 13½x13
3520 A1047 80f multi   4.00 .35

2008 Summer Olympics, Beijing — A1048

Designs: Nos. 3521, 3525a, 60f, Basketball (4-1). Nos. 3522, 3525b, 80f, Fencing (4-2). Nos. 3523, 3525c, Sailing (4-3). Nos. 3524, 3525d, $3, Gymnastics (4-4).

2006, Aug. 8   Photo.   Perf. 13¼x13
3521-3524 A1048 Set of 4   3.00 2.00
Self-Adhesive
Serpentine Die Cut 11¾
3525   A1048   Sheet of 8, 2
        each #a-d   16.00 11.00

Portions of the designs of Nos. 3525a-3525d were applied by a thermographic process, producing a shiny, raised effect.

Treasures of the Study — A1049

Designs: No. 3526, 80f, Brushes (4-1). No. 3527, 80f, Ink (4-2). No. 3528, 80f, Paper (4-3). No. 3529, 80f, Ink stone (4-4).

Perf. 12x12½ Syncopated
2006, Sept. 10   Litho.
3526-3529 A1049 Set of 4   4.50 1.00
A sheet of 2 each of Nos. 3526-3529 exists. Value, $60.

All-China Federation of Returned Overseas Chinese, 50th Anniv. A1050

Perf. 12½x12 Syncopated
2006, Sept. 25
3530   A1050 80f multi   1.00 .30

Musical Instruments — A1051

Designs: No. 3531, 80f, Seven-stringed qin, China (2-1). No. 3532, 80f, Bösendorfer piano, Austria (2-2).

Perf. 13x12½ Syncopated
2006, Sept. 26   Litho.
3531-3532 A1051 Set of 2   1.25 .45
        See Austria Nos. 2066-2067.

Chinese Export Commodities Fair — A1052

Perf. 13½x13¼ Syncopated
2006, Oct. 15   Photo.
3533   A1052 80f multi   1.00 .25

Long March, 70th Anniv. — A1053

Designs: No. 3534, 80f, Setting Out (4-1). No. 3535, 80f, Zunyi Conference (4-2). No. 3536, 80f, Speedily Occupy the Luding Bridge (4-3). No. 3537, 80f, The Red Army Through the Marshland (4-4).
$6, Reunion.

2006, Oct. 22   Perf. 13x13¼
3534-3537 A1053 Set of 4   2.00 1.00
Souvenir Sheet
3538 A1053 $6 multi   3.75 3.00

No. 3538 contains one 80x50mm stamp.
No. 3538 exists imperf.

Dialogue With ASEAN, 15th Anniv. A1054

Perf. 12½x12 Syncopated
2006, Oct. 30   Litho.
3539 A1054 80f multi   1.50 .25

"Enjoying Prosperity Year After Year" A1055

"Happy New Year" — A1055a

Perf. 12¾ Syncopated
2006, Nov. 1   Photo.
3540 A1055 80f multi   .30   .25
3541 A1055a $3 multi   1.10 .85
A souvenir sheet containing Nos. 3540-3541 exists. Value, $12.
See note following No. 3628.

Beijing Summit of Forum on China-Africa Cooperation — A1056

2006, Nov. 3   Litho.   Perf. 13¼
3542 A1056 80f multi   1.00 .25

Buildings Associated With Dr. Sun Yat-sen (1826-1925) A1057

Designs: No. 3543, 80f, Sun Yat-sen Villa (4-1). No. 3544, 80f, Mausoleum (4-2). No. 3545, 80f, Sun Yat-sen Memorial Hall (4-3). No. 3546, 80f, Sun Yat-sen University (4-4).

Perf. 13¼ Syncopated
2006, Nov. 12   Litho. & Engr.
3543-3546 A1057 Set of 4   2.00 1.00

Birds Type of 2002

Designs: 40f, Chinese monal pheasant.
$1.20, Taiwan yuhinas.

Perf. 13½ Syncopated

2006, Nov. 15			Photo.	
3547	A909	40f multi	.20	.20
3548	A909	$1.20 multi	.35	.30

Heavenly Steed, Silk Roll
Painting — A1058

No. 3549: a, Horse and rider. b, People
looking at horse.
Illustration reduced.

2006, Dec. 3	Photo.		Perf. 12¾	
3549	A1058	$1.20 Horiz. pair,		
		#a-b	1.00	1.00

Wu Lanfu (1906-
88), Politician
A1059

2006, Dec. 23		Perf. 13¼x13	
3550	A1059	$1.20 multi	3.50	1.50

Trains — A1060

Designs: No. 3551, $1.20, Locomotive, blue
background (4-1). No. 3552, $1.20, Locomo-
tive, red brown background (4-2). No. 3553,
$1.20, Box car (4-3). No. 3554, $1.20, Log
cars and gateway (4-4).
$6, Locomotive and city skyline.

2006, Dec. 28		Perf. 13x13¼		
3551-3554	A1060	Set of 4	10.50	3.50

Souvenir Sheet
Perf. 13¼x13

3555	A1060	$6 multi	9.50	6.50

No. 3555 contains one 90x40mm stamp.

China Post, 110th Anniv. — A1061

Perf. 12x11½ Syncopated

2006, Dec. 30			Litho.	
3556	A1061	$1.20 multi	1.00	.40

A sheet containing 6 No. 3556 exists. Value,
$8.50.

New Year
2007 (Year of
the
Pig) — A1062

Perf. 13 Syncopated

2007, Jan. 5			Photo.	
3557	A1062	$1.20 multi	.60	.35
a.		Souvenir sheet of 6	11.00	6.00
b.		Booklet pane of 10	6.00	—
		Complete booklet, #3557b	6.25	

A sheet containing 4 No. 3557 exists. Value,
$12.50.

6th Asian Winter
Games — A1063

Perf. 12x12½ Syncopated

2007, Jan. 28			Litho.	
3558	A1063	$1.20 multi	1.10	.35

Shiwan Pottery
Figurines
A1064

Designs: No. 3559, $1.20, Ta Xue Xun Mei
(2-1). No. 3560, $1.20, Wang Zhaojun Chu Sai
(2-2).

2007, Feb. 3	Photo.		Perf. 13¼x13	
3559-3560	A1064	Set of 2	.80	.65
3560a		Miniature sheet, 4 each		
		#3559-3560	8.00	3.50

"Divine Birds of the Sun" — A1065

2007, Feb. 9	Litho.		Perf. 12	
3561	A1065	$1.20 multi + label	.65	.35

Printed in sheets of 6 + 6 labels (value,
$11), 8 + 8 labels and 15 + 15 labels (value,
$20).

Mianzhu New
Year Woodcuts
A1066

Designs: No. 3562, $1.20, Zuo Zuo Ti Dao
(4-1). No. 3563, $1.20, Mu Guiying (4-2). No.
3564, $1.20, Shuang Xi Tong Zi (4-3). No.
3565, $1.20, Zhang Xian She Gou (4-4).

Perf. 12x11½ Syncopated

2007, Feb. 10		Litho. & Engr.		
3562-3565	A1066	Set of 4	1.75	1.40
3565a		Souvenir sheet of 4, #3562-		
		3565	3.00	2.50
3565b		Miniature sheet of 8, 2 each		
		#3562-3565	11.00	8.00

A lithographed sheet similar to No. 3565b
on a textured silk-faced paper exists.

Beijing
Opera — A1067

Designs: 80f, Lin Xiangru (6-1). No. 3567,
$1.20, Song Shijie (6-2). No. 3568, $1.20,
Zhou Yu (6-3). No. 3569, $1.20, Xu Xian (6-4).
No. 3570, $1.20, Gao Chong (6-5). No. 3571,
$1.20, Ren Tanghui (6-6).

2007, Mar. 10	Photo.		Perf. 13¼x13	
3566-3571	A1067	Set of 6	2.50	1.90

Postal Savings Bank — A1068

2007, Mar. 20			Perf. 12¾	
3572	A1068	$1.20 multi	.60	.35
a.		Miniature sheet of 8	9.00	4.50

Writings of
Li Keran
A1069

Designs: No. 3573, $1.20, Man viewing
waterfall (6-1). No. 3574, $1.20, Mountains
with red-leaved trees (6-2). No. 3575, $1.20,
People looking at scroll (6-3). No. 3576, $1.20,
Crane flying above man under tent (6-4). No.
3577, $1.20, Cattle and driver in pond (6-5).
No. 3578, $1.20, Raining in Jiangnan (6-6).

Perf. 13x13¼ Syncopated

2007, Mar. 26				
3573-3578	A1069	Set of 6	2.50	2.25

Modern
Chinese
Drama,
Cent.
A1070

Perf. 13 Syncopated

2007, Apr. 6			Litho.	
3579	A1070	$1.20 multi	.50	.35

Yangzhou Garden — A1071

No. 3580: a, He Garden (3-1). b, Ge Garden
(3-2). c, Xu Garden (3-3).

Perf. 12x11½ Syncopated

2007, Apr. 8				
3580		Horiz. strip of 3	1.50	1.25
a.-c.		A1071 $1.20 Any single	.45	.35

Dances — A1072

Designs: No. 3581, $1.20, Dragon dance (2-
1). No. 3582, $1.20, Lion dance (2-2).

2007, Apr. 13	Litho.	Perf. 12¾x11	
3581-3582	A1072	Set of 2	.85	.70

See Indonesia No. 2100.

Torch Relay for 2008 Summer
Olympics, Beijing — A1073

2007, Apr. 27			Perf. 12	
3583	A1073	$1.20 multi + label	1.75	.55
a.		Sheet of 4 + 4 labels	.85	.70

Inner Mongolia Autonomous Region,
60th Anniv. — A1074

Designs: No. 3584, $1.20, Horsemen, wres-
tlers, archer (2-1). No. 3585, $1.20, Seven
women (2-2).

Perf. 12½x12 Syncopated

2007, May 1				
3584-3585	A1074	Set of 2	.85	.70
3585a		Souvenir sheet, #3584-3585	1.75	1.00

Mausoleums of
Qing Emperors
A1075

Designs: No. 3586, $1.20, Zhaoling Mauso-
leum (3-1). No. 3587, $1.20, Xiaoling Mauso-
leum (3-2). No. 3588, Tailing Mausoleum (3-3).

2007, May 12	Photo.		Perf. 12¾	
3586-3588	A1075	Set of 3	1.25	1.00

Tongji
University,
Cent.
A1076

2007, May 20		Perf. 12½ Syncopated	
3589	A1076	$1.20 multi	.50	.40

Kong Rong and Pears — A1077

Nos. 3590 and 3591: a, Denomination at LL (2-1). b, Denomination at LR (2-2).

2007, June 1   Perf. 13¼x13
3590 A1077 $1.20 Horiz. pair, #a-b   .90 .85

Self-Adhesive
Booklet Stamps
Serpentine Die Cut 11¾

3591 A1077 $1.20 Horiz. pair, #a-b   .75 .75
c.   Booklet pane, 4 #3591   5.00

Chongqing — A1078

No. 3592: a, City skyline (2-1). b, City and highway interchange (2-2). Illustration reduced.

Perf. 12x11½ Syncopated
2007, June 8   Litho.
3592 A1078 $1.20 Horiz. pair, #a-b   .90 .85

Wudalianchi Natl. Park — A1079

No. 3593: a, Heilong Mountain (3-1). b, Sanchi Pool (3-2). c, Sea of Rock (3-3).

2007, June 19 Photo.   Perf. 12¾
3593   Horiz. strip of 3   1.50 1.25
a.-c.   A1079 $1.20 Any single   .45 .35

Return of Hong Kong, 10th Anniv. A1080

Designs: No. 3594, $1.20, Flags of People's Republic of China and Hong Kong, doves, monument (3-1). No. 3595, $1.20, "CEPA" and stylized buildings (3-2). No. 3596, $1.20, Hong Kong buildings, bridge (3-3).

Perf. 13¼x12¾ Syncopated
2007, July 1
3594-3596 A1080   Set of 3   1.25 1.00

A souvenir sheet containing Nos. 3594-3596 and Hong Kong No. 1275 sold for $12.95 in Hong Kong currency. Value, $27.50.

Pres. Yang Shankun (1907-98) A1081

Designs: No. 3597, $1.20, Standing in uniform (2-1). No. 3598, $1.20, Seated at desk, horiz. (2-2).

Perf. 11½x11, 11x11½
2007, July 5   Photo. & Engr.
3597-3598 A1081   Set of 2   3.25 .85

Nanji Islands Marine Reserve — A1082

Shells and: No. 3599, $1.20, Sanpanwei (3-1). No. 3600, $1.20, Longchuanjiao (3-2). No. 3601, $1.20, Dashaao (3-3).

Perf. 12¾x12½ Syncopated
2007, July 10   Photo.
3599-3601 A1082   Set of 3   1.60 1.00

Emblem of People's Liberation Army — A1083

2007, July 15   Litho.   Perf. 12
3602 A1083 $1.20 multi + label   1.25 .45

Souvenir Sheet

All-China Philatelic Federation, 6th Congress — A1084

Perf. 12½ Syncopated
2007, July 28   Litho. & Engr.
3603 A1084 $6 multi   3.75 2.25

A sheet of 2 No. 3603 exists. Value, $9.

People's Liberation Army, 80th Anniv. — A1085

Designs: No. 3604, $1.20, Soldiers saluting (4-1). No. 3605, $1.20, Soldier carrying sack (4-2). No. 3606, $1.20, Soldier with rifle (4-3). No. 3607, $1.20, Soldiers wearing UN Peacekeeper berets (4-4).

Perf. 13¼x12½ Syncopated
2007, Aug. 1   Photo.
3604-3607 A1085   Set of 4   3.25 1.50

Olympic Sports — A1086

Designs: Nos. 3608, 3614a, $1.20, Diving (6-1). Nos. 3609, 3614b, $1.20, Shooting (6-2). Nos. 3610, 3614c, $1.20, Athletics (6-3). Nos. 3611, 3614d, $1.20, Volleyball (6-4). Nos. 3612, 3614e, $1.20, BMX bicycling (6-5). Nos. 3613, 3614f, $1.20, Weight lifting (6-6).

2007, Aug. 8 Photo.   Perf. 13¼x13
3608-3613 A1086   Set of 6   3.25 2.25
3613a   Sheet of 10, #3521-3524, 3608-3613, + label   12.00 12.00

Self-Adhesive
Serpentine Die Cut 11¾

3614   Miniature sheet of 12, 2 each #a-f   18.50
a.-f.   A1086 $1.20 Any single   .40 .30

No. 3613a sold for $18.60.

Tengchong Volcano Area — A1087

Designs: No. 3615, $1.20, Rehai (3-1). No. 3616, $1.20, Volcanoes, vert. (3-2). No. 3617, $1.20, Shenzhu Valley, vert. (3-3).

Perf. 12x12½ Syncopated, 12½x12 Syncopated
2007, Aug. 18
3615-3617 A1087   Set of 3   1.25 1.00

Nos. 3615-3617 were printed together in a sheet of 15 stamps + a horizontal label. The first row consists of the label and 2 #3615; the second row, 3 #3615; the third row, 5 #3616; and the fourth row, 5 #3617.

Jin Hu — A1088

No. 3618: a, Da Chibi (2-1). b, Maoer Mountain (2-2).

Perf. 12¾ Syncopated
2007, Sept. 2   Litho.
3618 A1088 $1.20 Horiz. pair, #a-b   1.00 .95

2007 Women's Soccer World Cup, People's Republic of China A1089

2007, Sept. 10   Photo.   Perf. 13¼
3619 A1089 $1.20 multi   1.10 .75

Values are for stamps with surrounding selvage.

2007 World Summer Special Olympics, Shanghai — A1090

2007, Oct. 2   Perf. 13¼
3620 A1090 $1.20 multi   .65 .40

Historic Sites in Three Gorges Reservoir Area — A1091

Designs: No. 3621, $1.20, Zhang Fei Temple (4-1). No. 3622, $1.20, Shibaozhai Village, vert. (4-2). No. 3623, $1.20, Ancient Dachang, vert. (4-3). No. 3624, $1.20, Quyuan's Grave (4-4).

Perf. 13¼ Syncopated
2007, Oct. 13   Litho. & Engr.
3621-3624 A1091   Set of 4   1.50 1.50

17th Natl. Communist Party Congress — A1092

Designs: No. 3625, $1.20, Memorial for First Natl. Communist Party Congress (2-1). No. 3626, $1.20, Site of Second Plenary Session of the Seventh Central Committee. $6, Dove and monument.

Perf. 13¼x13 Syncopated
2007, Oct. 15   Photo.
3625-3626 A1092   Set of 2   1.10 .70
Souvenir Sheet
Perf. 13¼x13
3627 A1092 $6 multi   3.00 2.25

No. 3627 contains one 60x40mm stamp.

"Happiness" A1093

Perf. 12¾ Syncopated
2007, Nov. 1   Photo.
3628 A1093 $1.20 multi   .45 .40

A sheet containing Nos. 3628, 3541 and four labels exists. Value, $14.

Ancient Calligraphy A1094

Designs: No. 3629, $1.20, Proclamation (6-1). No. 3630, $1.20, Zhang Menglong Stele (6-2). No. 3631, $1.20, Inscription for Sweet Spring at Jiucheng Palace (6-3). No. 3632, $1.20, Preface for Sacred Religion at Wild Goose Pagoda (6-4). No. 3633, $1.20, Yan Qinli Stele (6-5). No. 3634, $1.20, Mysterious Pagoda Stele (6-6).

Perf. 12x11½ Syncopated
2007, Nov. 5   Litho.
3629-3634 A1094   Set of 6   2.50 2.25

A sheet containing 2 each of lithographed and embossed examples of Nos. 3629-3634 exists. Value, $10.

Mountains — A1095

Designs: No. 3635, $1.20, Mount Gongga, People's Republic of China (2-1). No. 3636, $1.20, Popocatepetl, Mexico (2-2).

Perf. 12¾ Syncopated
2007, Nov. 22
3635-3636 A1095   Set of 2   2.25   .75
     See Mexico Nos. 2561-2562.

Launch of China's First Lunar Probe A1096

2007, Nov. 26   Litho. & Embossed
3637 A1096 $1.20 multi   3.00   .45

Emblem of Expo 2010, Shanghai A1097

Mascot of Expo 2010 — A1098

Perf. 11½ Syncopated
2007, Dec. 19   Litho.
3638 A1097 $1.20 multi   .45   .40
   a.   Booklet pane of 1   .50
3639 A1098 $1.20 multi   .45   .40
   a.   Booklet pane of 1   .50
   b.   Booklet pane of 10, 5 each
       #3638-3639   5.00   —
       Complete booklet, #3638a,
       3639a, 3639b   5.50

Venues at 2008 Summer Olympics, Beijing — A1099

Designs: 80f, China Agricultural University Gymnasium (6-1). No. 3641, $1.20, Laoshan Mountain Bike Course (6-2). No. 3642, $1.20, National Indoor Stadium (6-3). No. 3643, $1.20, Beijing University Gymnasium (6-4). No. 3644, $1.20, National Aquatics Center (6-5). No. 3645, $3, Qingdao Olympic Sailing Center (6-6).
$6, National Stadium.

2007, Dec. 20   Photo.   Perf. 13x13¼
3640-3645 A1099   Set of 6   3.00 2.40
Souvenir Sheet
Perf. 13
3646 A1099 $6 multi   5.75 1.75
     No. 3646 contains one pentagonal 65x62mm stamp.
     A self-adhesive sheet of 2 each of Nos. 3640-3645 exists. Value, $12.

New Year 2008 (Year of the Rat) A1100

Perf. 12¾ Syncopated
2008, Jan. 5   Photo.
3647 A1100 $1.20 multi   .80   .40
   a.   Booklet pane of 10   8.00
       Complete booklet, #3647a   8.00
     Miniature sheets containing 4 and 6 stamps exist. Value, each $9.

Zhuxian New Year Woodprints A1101

Designs: No. 3648, $1.20, Gate guardian (4-1). No. 3649, $1.20, Woman lecturing son (4-2). No. 3650, $1.20, Come back with fruitful result (4-3). No. 3651, $1.20, Chivalrous women (4-4).

2008, Jan. 15   Photo.   Perf. 13¼x13
3648-3651 A1101   Set of 4   1.75 1.50
3651a   Souvenir sheet of 4,
       #3648-3651   3.00 2.25
     No. 3651a sold for $7.20. A miniature sheet containing two each of #3648-3651 exists. Value, $7.50.

Beijing Opera Characters A1102

Designs: 80f, Zhang Fei (6-1). No. 3653, $1.20, Cao Cao (6-2). No. 3654, $1.20, Bao Zheng (6-3). No. 3655, $1.20, Lian Po (6-4). No. 3656, $1.20, Xu Yanzhao (6-5). No. 3657, $1.20, Yang Yansi (6-6).

Perf. 12x11½ Syncopated
2008, Feb. 23   Litho.
3652-3657 A1102   Set of 6   2.00 2.00

Miniature Sheet

Birds — A1103

No. 3658: a, Urocissa caerulea (6-1). b, Emberiza koslowi (6-2). c, Tragopan caboti (6-3). d, Garrulax sukatschewi (6-4). e, Chrysolophus pictus (6-5). f, Podoces biddulphi (6-6).

2008, Feb. 28   Photo.   Perf. 13¼x13
3658 A1103 $1.20 Sheet of 6,
       #a-f   4.25 2.75

11th National People's Congress — A1104

2008, Mar. 5
3659 A1104 $1.20 multi   .65   .40

Olympic Torch Relay — A1105

Designs: $1.20, Lighting of torch in Greece, mascot holding torch (2-1). $3, Torch, torch bearer, vert. (2-2).

2008, Mar. 5   Photo.   Perf. 13¼
3660-3661 A1105   Set of 2   2.00 1.25
3661a   Souvenir sheet, #3660-
       3661   9.00 4.50
     No. 3661a sold for $6.30. A sheet containing 4 self-adhesive examples each of Nos. 3660-3661 exists. Value, $15.

Suzhou-Nantong Yangtze River Bridge — A1106

No. 3662 — Denomination at: a, Left (2-1). b, Right (2-2).
Illustration reduced.

2008, Apr. 12   Perf. 13¼
3662 A1106 $1.20 Horiz. pair,
       #a-b   1.00   .75

Boao Forum For Asia — A1107

No. 3663: a, Dongyu Island (2-1). b, Forum venue (2-2).
Illustration reduced.

Perf. 12x11½ Syncopated
2008, Apr. 13   Litho.
3663 A1107 $1.20 Horiz. pair,
       #a-b   .90   .75

Qiandao Lake — A1108

No. 3664 — Islands with denomination at: a, Left (2-1). b, Right (2-2).
Illustration reduced.

2008, Apr. 16   Perf. 12¾ Syncopated
3664 A1108 $1.20 Horiz. pair,
       #a-b   .90   .75
   c.   Souvenir sheet, #3664   3.25 2.75
     No. 3664c sold for $3.60.

A1109

Olympic Expo, Beijing — A1110

2008, Apr. 30   Photo.   Perf. 11¼x11
3665 A1109 $1.20 multi   .75   .40
Litho.
Perf. 12½
3666 A1110 $1.20 multi   .75   .40
     A circle of perforations surrounds the circular design on No. 3665.

Summer Palace — A1111

Designs: No. 3667, $1.20, Shiqikong Bridge (6-1). No. 3668, $1.20, Corridor (6-2). No. 3669, $1.20, Boat (6-3). No. 3670, $1.20, Garden of Harmonious Pleasures (6-4). No. 3671, $1.20, Yudai Bridge (6-5). No. 3672, $1.20, Houhu Lake (6-6).
$6, Tower of the Fragrance of Buddha, vert.

Litho. & Engr.
2008, May 10   A1111   Set of 6   Perf. 12
3667-3672   2.50 2.10
Souvenir Sheet
Perf. 12x11¾
3673 A1111 $6 multi   3.00 2.00
     No. 3673 contains one 50x62mm stamp.

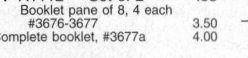

Cao Chong Weighs the Elephant A1112

Cao Chong: Nos. 3674, 3676, $1.20, Marking water level on boat carrying elephant (2-1). Nos. 3675, 3677, $1.20, Replacing elephant with weighable objects (2-2).

2008, June 1   Photo.   Perf. 13x13¼
3674-3675 A1112   Set of 2   .90   .75
Booklet Stamps
Self-Adhesive
Serpentine Die Cut 11¾
3676-3677 A1112   Set of 2   .85   —
3677a   Booklet pane of 8, 4 each
       #3676-3677   3.50   —
       Complete booklet, #3677a   4.00

Temples A1113

Designs: No. 3678, $1.20, White Horse Temple, China (2-1). No. 3679, $1.20, Maha Bodhi Temple, India (2-2).

2008, June 6   Perf. 13¼x13
3678-3679 A1113   Set of 2   .85   .75
     See India No. 2246.

Development on the Taiwan Strait — A1114

Designs: No. 3680, $1.20, Minjiang River development (4-1). No. 3681, $1.20, Port of Xiamen (4-2). No. 3682, $1.20, Exhibition Hall (4-3). No. 3683, $1.20, Fujian-Taiwan Kinship Museum (4-4).

2008, June 18   **Perf. 12¾**
3680-3683 A1114   Set of 4   1.75 1.50
A sheet containing 2 each of Nos. 3680-3683 + 1 label exists. Value, $7.

Second Land Survey — A1115

Designs: No. 3684, $1.20, Satellite, rural land survey (2-1). No. 3685, $1.20, Theodolite, urban land survey (2-2).

Perf. 12¾x12½   **Litho.**
2008, June 25
3684-3685 A1115   Set of 2   .85 .75

Qiuci Grotto Murals A1116

Designs: No. 3686, $1.20 Heavenly Kings (4-1). No. 3687, $1.20, Bodhisattva (4-2). No. 3688, $1.20, Flying Apsaras, horiz. (4-3). No. 3689, $1.20, Maitreya Preaching, horiz. (4-4).

2008, July 6   **Photo.**   **Perf. 13¼**
3686-3689 A1116   Set of 4   2.00 1.50

General Qi Jiguang (1528-88) A1117

Qi Jiguang: No. 3690, $1.20, Standing (2-1). No. 3691, $1.20, On horse (2-2).

Perf. 12x12½ Syncopated
2008, July 19   **Litho.**
3690-3691 A1117   Set of 2   .85 .75

Opening of 2008 Summer Olympics, Beijing — A1118

2008, Aug. 8   **Photo.**   **Perf. 13¼**
3692 A1118 $1.20 multi   2.25 .50
A sheet of 8 self-adhesive stamps similar to No. 3692 exists. Value, $11. A sheet of 8 stamps with a holographic background exists. Value, $22.50.

Olympex 2008 Philatelic Exhibition, Beijing — A1119

Designs: No. 3693, $1.20, Greece #127 (2-1). No. 3694, $1.20, Portugal #RA14 (2-2). $6, Greece #127, gold medal and mascots of 2004 Summer Olympics.

2008, Aug. 8   **Photo.**   **Perf. 13¼x13**
3693-3694 A1119   Set of 2   1.75 .85
Souvenir Sheet
    Litho.
    Perf.
3695 A1119 $6 multi   4.50 3.50
No. 3695 contains one 56mm diameter stamp.

2008 Summer Olympics Gold Medal — A1119a

2008, Aug. 9   **Litho.**   **Perf. 12**
3695A A1119a $1.20 multi + label   4.00 4.00
Labels could be personalized. No. 3695A was printed in sheets of various sizes, with many sheets having pre-printed labels depicting Olympic athletes.

Closing of 2008 Summer Olympics A1120

Designs: No. 3696, $1.20, National Stadium, Beijing (4-1). No. 3697, $1.20, Tower, Forbidden City, Beijing (4-2). No. 3698, $1.20, Millennium Wheel, London (4-3). No. 3699, $1.20, Tower of London (4-4).

2008, Aug. 24   **Photo.**   **Perf. 13¼**
3696-3699 A1120   Set of 4   3.00 1.75
A sheet containing 3 self-adhesive examples each of Nos. 3696-3699 exists. Value, $11.

China Central Television, 50th Anniv. A1121

Perf. 13½x13 Syncopated
2008, Sept. 2
3700 A1121 $1.20 multi   .85 .40

Emblem of 2008 Paralympic Games, Beijing — A1122

Paralympic Games Mascot — A1123

2008, Sept. 6   **Perf. 13¼x13**
3701 A1122 $1.20 multi   .75 .40
3702 A1123 $1.20 multi   .75 .40

University of Science and Technology, 50th Anniv. — A1124

Perf. 12x11¼ Syncopated
2008, Sept. 20   **Litho.**
3703 A1124 $1.20 multi   .60 .35

Ningxia Hui Autonomous Region, 50th Anniv. — A1125

No. 3704: a, Windmills (3-1). b, Trees and wildlife in desert (3-2). c, People holding flower bouquets (3-3).

Perf. 13¼x12¾ Syncopated
2008, Sept. 23   **Photo.**
3704   Horiz. strip of 3   1.25 1.25
  a.   A1125 80f multi   .25 .25
  b.-c.   A1125 $1.20 Either single   .45 .35

Airports — A1126

No. 3705: a, Beijing Capital International Airport (3-1). b, Shanghai Pudong International Airport (3-2). c, Guangzhou Baiyun International Airport (3-3).

2008, Sept. 28   **Perf. 12¾**
3705   Vert. strip of 3   1.50 1.50
  a.-c.   A1126 $1.20 Any single   .45 .35

Guangxi Zhuang Autonomous Region, 50th Anniv. — A1127

No. 3706: a, Dancers (3-1). b, Building (3-2). c, Port (3-3).

Perf. 12¾ Syncopated
2008, Oct. 18   **Litho.**
3706   Horiz. strip of 3   1.25 1.25
  a.   A1127 80f multi   .25 .25
  b.-c.   A1127 $1.20 Either single   .45 .35

Happy New Year Type of 2006 and

"Blossom of Fortune" A1128

Perf. 11¾ Syncopated
2008, Oct. 9   **Litho.**
3707 A1128 $1.20 multi   .35 .35
Souvenir Sheet
3708   Sheet of 2, #3707, 3708a   6.75 6.75
  a.   A1055a $3 gold & multi   6.25 6.25

Seventh Asia-Europe Meeting, Beijing — A1129

Perf. 12x11¼ Syncopated
2008, Oct. 24
3709 A1129 $1.20 multi   .40 .40
  a.   Miniature sheet of 12   6.75 6.75

"Harmony" — A1130

2008, Dec. 3   **Perf. 12**
3710 A1130 $1.20 multi + label   .50 .40

Expo 2010, Shanghai — A1131

Illustration reduced.

2008, Dec. 13   **Perf. 12**
3711 A1131 $1.20 multi + label   .60 .45
Compare with Type A1097.

A1132

Reform in China, 30th Anniv. — A1133

Perf. 12x11¼ Syncopated

2008, Dec. 18		**Litho.**	
3712	A1132 $1.20 multi	.60	.60
a.	Miniature sheet of 8	5.00	5.00

Souvenir Sheet

Photo.

Perf.

3713	A1133	$6 multi + label	3.75 3.75

A sheet containing 2 examples of No. 3713 exists. Value, $10.

New Year 2009 (Year of the Ox) — A1134

Perf. 13 Syncopated

2009, Jan. 5		**Photo.**	
3714	A1134 $1.20 multi	.80	.40
a.	Miniature sheet of 6	8.00	5.00
b.	Booklet pane of 10	8.00	—
	Complete booklet, #3714b	8.50	

A sheet of 4 No. 3714 exists. Value, $7.

Bo Yibo (1908-2007), Politician
A1135

Bo Yibo: No. 3715, $1.20, Standing (2-1). No. 3716, $1.20, Seated, horiz. (2-2).

2009, Jan. 15		**Perf. 13¼x13, 13x13¼**	
3715-3716	A1135	Set of 2	1.00 .90

Zhangzhou New Year Woodprints A1136

Designs: No. 3717, $1.20, Lion holding a sword in mouth (4-1). No. 3718, $1.20, The coming flood of wealth, vert. (4-2). No. 3719, $1.20, Goddess sending children, vert. (4-3). No. 3720, $1.20, Rat marrying off its daughter (4-4).

2009, Jan. 18		**Perf. 12**	
3717-3720	A1136	Set of 4	1.50 1.50
3720a	Souvenir sheet, #3717-3720 + label		2.50 2.50
3720b	Miniature sheet of 8, 2 each #3717-3720		4.50 4.50

A1137

24th Winter Universiade, Harbin — A1138

2009, Feb. 18		**Litho.**	**Perf. 12¾**
3721	A1137 $1.20 multi		.40 .40
3722	A1138 $1.20 multi		.40 .40

Electric Power Grid Construction — A1139

No. 3723: a, Power station (3-1). b, Transmission towers and power lines (3-2). c, Light bulb, city skyline (3-3).
Illustration reduced.

Perf. 12x12½ Syncopated

2009, Feb. 24			
3723	A1139 $1.20 Horiz. strip of 3, #a-c		1.25 1.25

Paintings by Shi Tao (1642-1707) A1140

No. 3724: a, Chaohu Lake (30x55mm) (6-1). b, Enjoying Fountain Sound (25x55mm) (6-2). c, Double Chrysanthemums (30x55mm) (6-3). d, Plum Blossoms and Bamboo (25x55mm) (6-4). e, Horse and its Owner (30x55mm) (6-5). f, Lotus (25x55mm) (6-6).

2009, Mar. 22		**Litho.**	**Perf. 12½x13**
3724	Horiz. strip of 6		2.25 2.25
a.	A1140 80f multi		.30 .25
b.-f.	A1140 $1.20 Any single		.40 .40

A1141

China 2009 World Stamp Exhibition, Luoyang — A1142

Designs: No. 3725, $1.20, Vase (2-1). No. 3726, $1.20, Jar with stopper (2-2). $6, National Beauty and Heavenly Fragrance.

Perf. 12¾ Syncopated

2009, Apr. 10		**Litho. & Embossed**	
3725-3726	A1141	Set of 2	.80 .80

Souvenir Sheet

Litho.

Perf. 13 Syncopated

3727	A1142 $6 multi		2.00 2.00

Nos. 3725 and 3726 both exist in sheets of 4. Value, set $6.50.
No. 3727 exists in a sheet of 2. Value, $16.

China at World Expos A1143

Scenes from Expos from: No. 3728, $1.20, 1904, 1915, 1926, 1933 (red panel) (4-1). No. 3729, $1.20, 1982, 1982 (brown panel) (4-2). No. 3730, $1.20, 1999 (green panel) (4-3). No. 3731, $1.20, 2010 (blue panel) (4-4).

Perf. 13¼x12¾ Syncopated

2009, May 1		**Photo.**	
3728-3731	A1143	Set of 4	2.00 2.00
3731a	Miniature sheet of 8, 2 each #3728-3731		7.00 7.00

Fenghuang — A1144

No. 3732: a, North Gate (3-1). b, Rainbow Bridge (3-2). c, Street (3-3).

Perf. 12¾ Syncopated

2009, May 23		**Litho.**	
3732	Horiz. strip of 3		1.25 1.25
a.-c.	A1144 $1.20 Any single		.40 .35

Children's Art — A1145

Designs: Nos. 3733, 3737, 80f, Love for the Motherland (yellow orange panel) (4-1). Nos. 3734, 3738, $1.20, Happy Life, horiz. (red panel) (4-2). Nos. 3735, 3739, $1.20, Peace Lovers (blue panel) (4-3). Nos. 3736, 3740, $1.20, Enthusiasm for Science, horiz. (green panel) (4-4).

Perf. 13¼x13, 13x13¼

2009, June 1		**Photo.**	
3733-3736	A1145	Set of 4	1.40 1.40

Booklet Stamps
Self-Adhesive
Serpentine Die Cut 12

3737-3740	A1145	Set of 4	1.40 1.40
3740a	Booklet pane of 8, 2 each #3737-3740		3.00

Hangzhou Bay Bridge — A1146

No. 3741: a, Bridge. b, Marine platform.
Illustration reduced.

2009, June 18		**Litho.**	**Perf. 12**
3741	A1146 $1.20 Horiz. pair, #a-b		.80 .80

Li Xiannian (1909-92), People's Republic of China President A1147

Designs: No. 3742, $1.20, Wearing army uniform and cap (3-1). No. 3743, $1.20, Wearing gray suit with collar buttoned (3-2). No. 3744, $1.20, Wearing gray suit and eyeglasses (3-3).

2009, June 23	**Photo.**	**Perf. 13¼x13**	
3742-3744	A1147	Set of 3	1.25 1.25

A1148

16th Asian Games, Guangzhou — A1149

2009, June 30	**Photo.**	**Perf. 13¼**	
3745	A1148 $1.20 multi		.50 .50
3746	A1149 $1.20 multi		.50 .50

A sheet containing four each of Nos. 3745-3746 exists.

Great Hall of the People — A1150

Designs: No. 3747, East Gate (2-1). No. 3748, Great Auditorium (2-2).

2009, July 18	**Litho.**	**Perf. 13¼x12½**	
3747	A1150 $1.20 multi		.40 .40
3748	A1150 $1.20 multi		.40 .40
a.	Booklet pane of 2, #3747-3748		.80

b. Booklet pane of 8, 4 each
#3747-3748 3.25 —
Complete booklet, #3748a,
3748b 4.25

Sanjiangyuan Nature
Reserve — A1151

No. 3749: a, Geladandong (3-1). b, Eling
Lake (3-2). c, Dza Chu (3-3).

Perf. 13¼x12½ Syncopated
2009, July 25 **Photo.**
3749 Horiz. strip of 3 1.25 1.25
a.-c. A1151 $1.20 Any single .40 .35

Flag, 60th Anniv. — A1152

Illustration reduced.

2009, Aug. 2 **Litho.** **Perf. 13¼**
3750 A1152 $1.20 multi + label .50 .50
A souvenir sheet of 4 No. 3750 + one label
exists.

Labrang
Lamasery
A1153

No. 3751: a, Grand Sutra Hall (2-1). b,
Gongtang Pagoda (2-2).

Perf. 13x12¾ Syncopated
2009, Aug. 2
3751 A1153 $1.20 Vert. pair, #a-
b .80 .80

Stork
Tower
A1154

Golden
Gate
A1155

2009, Aug. 14 **Photo.**
3752 A1154 $1.20 multi .40 .40
3753 A1155 $1.20 multi .40 .40

A1156

Huang Long Scenic Area — A1157

Designs: No. 3754, $1.20, Guest Welcome
Ponds (3-1). No. 3755, $1.20, Waterfall (3-2).
No. 3756, $1.20, Erdao Lake (3-3).
$6, Five-color Ponds.

2009, Aug. 27 **Perf. 12¾**
3754-3756 A1156 Set of 3 1.10 1.10
Souvenir Sheet
Perf. 13¼x12¾ Syncopated
3757 A1157 $6 multi 2.25 2.25
A miniature sheet containing 2 each of Nos.
3754-3756 exists. Value, $6.

National Library
of China — A1158

Books and: No. 3758, $1.20, Old building
(2-1). No. 3759, $1.20, Modern building (2-2).

2009, Sept. 9 Perf. 13¼ Syncopated
3758-3759 A1158 Set of 2 1.10 1.10

Miniature Sheet

Tang Poems — A1159

No. 3760: a, $1.20, Downstream to
Jiangling, by Li Bai (boat near rocks) (6-1). b,
$1.20, A View of Taishan Mountain, by Du Fu
(mountains) (6-2). c, $1.20, The Song of Pipa,
by Bai Juyi (musician) (6-3). d, $1.20, To One
Unnamed, by Li Shangyin (book) (6-4). e,
$1.50, Looking at the Moon and Thinking of
One Far Away, by Zhang Jiulin (Moon) (6-5). f,
$3, On the Stork Tower, by Wang Zhihuan
(Stork Tower) (6-6).

Litho., Engr. & Silk-screened
Perf. 12¾x13¼ Syncopated
2009, Sept. 13
3760 A1159 Sheet of 6, #a-f 6.50 6.50

Lanzhoui
University,
Cent.
A1160

Perf. 13x12½ Syncopated
2009, Sept. 17 **Litho.**
3761 A1160 $1.20 multi .50 .50

Chinese People's
Political
Consultative
Conference, 60th
Anniv. — A1161

Flowers and: No. 3762, $1.20, Conference
emblem (2-1). No. 3763, $1.20, Conference
venue, horiz. (2-2).

Perf. 13¼ Syncopated
2009, Sept. 17
3762-3763 A1161 Set of 2 1.10 1.10

A1162

Beijing-Hangzhou Grand
Canal — A1163

Designs: No. 3764, $1.20, Lantern Lighting
Pagoda (6-1). No. 3765, $1.20, Boats and
Tianhou Temple (6-2). No. 3766, $1.20, Shan-
shan Guild Hall (6-3). No. 3767, $1.20, Qingji-
ang Water Gate (6-4). No. 3768, $1.20, Boats
and Wenfeng Pagoda (6-5). No. 3769, $1.20,
Gongchen Bridge (6-6).
$6, Canal.

Perf. 13x13¼ Syncopated
2009, Sept. 26 **Photo.**
3764-3769 A1162 Set of 6 2.10 2.10
Souvenir Sheet
Perf. 13¼ Syncopated
3770 A1163 $6 multi 3.00 3.00

A1164

People's Republic of China, 60th
Anniv. — A1165

Designs: No. 3771, $1.20, Marchers (4-1).
No. 3772, $1.20, Tractors pulling floats bear-
ing Chinese symbols (4-2). No. 3773, $1.20,
Flag, emblems of Macao and Hong Kong (4-
3). No. 3774, $1.20, Olympic rings and torch
(4-4).
$6, Flag.

Perf. 13x12½ Syncopated
2009, Oct. 1
3771-3774 A1164 Set of 4 1.50 1.50
Souvenir Sheet
Perf. 13¼x13½ Syncopated
3775 A1165 $6 multi 3.25 3.25
A miniature sheet containing two each of
Nos. 3771-3774 exists.

National Day Parade — A1166

Designs: No. 3776, $1.20, Infantry Group
(red background) (4-1). No. 3777, $1.20, Army
and 2nd Artillery Group (green background)
(4-2). No. 3778, $1.20, Navy Equipment
Group (blue background) (4-3). No. 3779,
$1.20, Air Group (orange background) (4-4).

Perf. 13¼x12½ Syncopated
2009, Oct. 1
3776-3779 A1166 Set of 4 2.00 2.00
A miniature sheet containing two each of
Nos. 3776-3779 exists. Value, $9.

"Music" — A1167

2009, Sept. 29 **Litho.** **Perf. 12**
3780 A1167 $1.20 multi + label .35 .35
See Stamps With Attached Labels note
after No. 3197.

"Happiness With the Spring" — A1168

2009, Oct. 9 Perf. 13 Syncopated
3781 A1168 $1.20 multi .35 .35
A souvenir sheet containing Nos. 3781 and
3708a exists.

A1169

11th National
Games,
Shandong
A1170

Perf. 13¼x13 Syncopated

2009, Oct. 16
3782	A1169	$1.20 multi	.35	.35
3783	A1170	$1.20 multi	.35	.35
a.		Souvenir sheet, #3782-3783	1.10	1.10

No. 3783a sold for $3.60.

Ancient
Academies
A1171

Designs: No. 3784, $1.20, Stone Drum
Academy (4-1). No. 3785, $1.20, Anding
Academy (4-2). No. 3786, $1.20, Ehu Acad-
emy (4-3). No. 3787, $1.20, Dongpo Academy
(4-4).

Perf. 13¼ Syncopated

2009, Nov. 15   Photo.
3784-3787	A1171	Set of 4	1.40	1.40

A souvenir sheet containing two each of
Nos. 3784-3787 exists.

Guangji Bridge — A1172

No. 3788: a, Building at left on shore,
bridge, ships (3-1). b, Ships, central part of
bridge (3-2). c, Bridge, building at right on
shore (3-3).

Perf. 12¾ Syncopated

2009, Nov. 16   Litho.
3788		Horiz. strip of 3	1.10	1.10
a.-c.	A1172	$1.20 Any single	.35	.35

Ma Lianliang
(1901-66), Opera
Performer, in
Kong Ming
Borrows the East
Wing — A1173

Ma Lianliang in
Zhao the
Orphan — A1174

Perf. 13¼x13½ Syncopated

2009, Nov. 28   Photo.
3789	A1173	$1.20 multi	.35	.35
3790	A1174	$1.20 multi	.35	.35

Return of
Macao to
China,
10th
Anniv.
A1175

Doves and: No. 3791, $1.20, Golden Lotus
sculpture, flags of People's Republic of China
and Macao (3-1). No. 3792, $1.20, "CEPA,"
buildings (3-2). $1.50, Bridge, buildings (3-3).

Perf. 13¼x13 Syncopated

2009, Dec. 20
3791-3793	A1175	Set of 3	1.25	1.25
3793a		Souvenir sheet, #3791-3793, Macao #1302a-1302c	2.40	2.40

See Macao Nos. 1302-1303. No. 3793a was
not offered for sale in Macao.

16th Asian Games,
Guangzhou — A1176

2009, Dec. 25   Litho.   **Perf. 12**
3794	A1176	$1.20 multi + label	.35	.35

Compare with Type A1148. See Stamps
With Attached Labels note after No. 3197.

Gutian Conference, 80th
Anniv. — A1177

Perf. 13¼x13 Syncopated

2009, Dec. 28
3795	A1177	$1.20 multi	.35	.35

Ballet Dancers in
Red Detachment
of
Women — A1178

Designs: No. 3796, $1.20, Dancer in red (2-
1). No. 3797, $1.20, Dancers in blue (2-2).

2010, Jan. 1   Photo.   **Perf. 13¼**
3796-3797	A1178	Set of 2	.70	.70

New Year
2010 (Year of
the Tiger)
A1179

2010, Jan. 5   **Perf. 12¾ Syncopated**
3798	A1179	$1.20 multi	.35	.35
a.		Booklet pane of 10	3.50	—
		Complete booklet, #3798a	3.50	

No. 3798 exists in sheets of 4 and 6.

Gen. Song Renqiong (1909-
2005) — A1180

Designs: No. 3799, $1.20, Wearing cap (2-
1). No. 3800, $1.20, Reading book (2-2).

Perf. 13 Syncopated

2010, Jan. 8   Litho.
3799-3800	A1180	Set of 2	.70	.70

Expo 2010, Shanghai — A1181

Designs: 80f, Expo Center (4-1). No. 3802,
$1.20, China Pavilion (4-2). No. 3803, $1.20,
Expo Performance Center (4-3). $3, Theme
Pavilion (4-4).
$6, Shanghai Expo Park, vert.

Perf. 13¼x13 Syncopated

2010, Jan. 21   Photo.
3801-3804	A1181	Set of 4	1.90	1.90

Souvenir Sheet

Perf. 13x12¾ Syncopated
3805	A1181	$6 multi	1.75	1.75

No. 3805 contains one 30x75mm stamp. A
sheet containing two each of Nos. 3801-3804
exists.

Liangping New
Year Woodprints
A1182

Designs: No. 3806, $1.20, Gate god (4-1).
No. 3807, $1.20, Stealing the immortal grass
(4-2). No. 3808, $1.20, Peace leads to happi-
ness (4-3). No. 3809, $1.20, Exiting the pass
with a stolen token (4-4).

2010, Feb. 6   **Perf. 13¼x13**
3806-3809	A1182	Set of 4	1.40	1.40
3809a		Souvenir sheet, #3806-3809 + label	2.10	2.10

No. 3809a sold for $7.20.

Intl. Women's
Day,
Cent. — A1183

Perf. 13¼x13 Syncopated

2010, Mar. 8
3810	A1183	$1.20 multi	.35	.35

Dwelling in Fuchun Mountains,
Painting by Huang
Gongwang — A1184

No. 3811 — Various parts of painting with
inscription: a, (6-1). b, (6-2). c, (6-3). d, (6-4).
e, (6-5). f, (6-6).

2010, Mar. 20   **Perf. 13¼**
3811		Block of 6	2.75	2.75
a.-d.	A1184	$1.20 Any single	.35	.35
e.	A1184	$1.50 multi	.45	.45
f.	A1184	$3 multi	.90	.90

Tomb Sweeping
Festival — A1185

Designs: No. 3812, $1.20, Ancestor worship
(3-1). No. 3813, $1.20, Spring outing (3-2).
No. 3814, $1.20, Planting willows (3-3).

Perf. 13¼x13½ Syncopated

2010, Apr. 5   Litho.
3812-3814	A1185	Set of 3	1.10	1.10

A sheet containing three each of Nos. 3812-
3814 exists.

Idioms — A1186

Designs: No. 3815, $1.20, The foolish old
man removes the mountains (4-1). No. 3816,
$1.20, Sleeping on brushwood and tasting gall
(4-2). No. 3817, $1.20, Mao Sui recom-
mending himself (4-3). No. 3818, $1.20, Ris-
ing to practice swordplay upon hearing the
rooster crow (4-4).

Perf. 13¼x13½ Syncopated

2010, Apr. 18   Photo.
3815-3818	A1186	Set of 4	1.40	1.40

Opening of
Expo 2010,
Shanghai
A1187

2010, May 1   **Perf. 13¼ Syncopated**
3819	A1187	$1.20 multi	.35	.35

A sheet of six exists.

A1188

A1189

Ancient Calligraphy — A1190

No. 3820 — Preface to the Orchid Pavilion: a, Denomination at right (6-1). b, Denomination at left (6-2).
No. 3821 — Poems Composed During the Cold Food Festival in Huangzhou: a, Denomination at right (6-3). b, Denomination at left (6-4).
No. 3822 — Elegiac Lament for My Nephew: a, Denomination at right (6-5). b, Denomination at left (6-6).

2010, May 15   **Perf. 13x13¼**
3820	A1188 $1.20 Horiz. pair,		
	#a-b	.70	.70
3821	A1189 $1.20 Horiz. pair,		
	#a-b	.70	.70
3822	A1190 $1.20 Horiz. pair,		
	#a-b	.70	.70
	Nos. 3820-3822 (3)	2.10	2.10

A sheet containing two each #3820-3822 exists.

Tenth Global Travel and Tourism Summit, Beijing — A1191

2010, May 25   **Perf. 13¼ Syncopated**
3823	A1191 $1.20 multi	.35	.35

Wen Yanbo's Ball Goes Into Hole in Tree A1192

Wen Yanbo Retrieves Ball With Water A1193

2010, June 1   **Perf. 13 Syncopated**
3824	A1192 $1.20 multi	.35	.35
3825	A1193 $1.20 multi	.35	.35
a.	Booklet pane of 2, #3824-3825	.70	
b.	Booklet pane of 8, 4 each #3824-3825	3.00	—
	Complete booklet, #3825a, 3825b	3.75	

A1194

Environmental Protection A1195

Perf. 13¼x13½ Syncopated
2010, June 5
3826	A1194 $1.20 multi	.35	.35
3827	A1195 $1.20 multi	.35	.35

Kunqu Opera — A1196

Designs: No. 3828, $1.20, Washing the Silken Gauze (3-1). No. 3829, $1.20, The Peony Pavilion (3-2). No. 3830, $1.20, The Palace of Long Life (3-3).

Perf. 13¼ Syncopated
2010, June 12   A1196   **Photo.**
3828-3830	A1196 Set of 3	1.10	1.10

A miniature sheet containing 3 each of Nos. 3828-3830 exists.

Pearl River Scenes — A1197

Designs: No. 3831, $1.20, Five Goats Statue, Guangzhou (4-1). No. 3832, $1.20, Guangzhou Center for the Performing Arts (4-2). No. 3833, $1.20, Guangzhou skyline (4-3). No. 3834, $1.20, Guangzhou Intl. Convention and Exhibition Center (4-4).

Perf. 13¼x13 Syncopated
2010, June 28
3831-3834	A1197 Set of 4	1.40	1.40

A miniature sheet containing 2 each of Nos. 3831-3834 exists.

Loulan — A1198

Designs: No. 3835, $1.20, Ruins of Buddhist stupa (2-1). No. 3836, $1.20, Ruins of building (2-2).

2010, July 3   **Litho.**
3835-3836	A1198 Set of 2	.70	.70

Maritime Day — A1199

Perf. 13½x13 Syncopated
2010, July 11   **Photo.**
3837	A1199 $1.20 multi	.35	.35

Composers — A1200

Designs: No. 3838, $1.20, Johann Sebastian Bach (1685-1750) (4-1). No. 3839, $1.20, Joseph Haydn (1732-1809) (4-2). No. 3840, $1.20, Wolfgang Amadeus Mozart (1756-91) (4-3). $4.50, Ludwig van Beethoven (1770-1827) (4-4).

Perf. 13¼x12¾ Syncopated
2010, July 25   **Litho. & Engr.**
3838-3841	A1200 Set of 4	2.40	2.40

Legend of the Cowherd and the Weaving Maid — A1201

Designs: No. 3842, Dress-linked affection (4-1). No. 3843, Happy lovers (4-2). No. 3844, Carrying children to chase wife (4-3). No. 3845, Heavenly reunion (4-4).

Perf. 13¼x13¾ Syncopated
2010, Aug. 16   **Photo.**
3842	A1201 $1.20 multi	.35	.35
a.	Booklet pane of 1 + 5 labels	.60	—
3843	A1201 $1.20 multi	.35	.35
a.	Booklet pane of 1 + 5 labels	.60	—
3844	A1201 $1.20 multi	.35	.35
a.	Booklet pane of 1 + 5 labels	.60	—
3845	A1201 $1.20 multi	.35	.35
a.	Booklet pane of 1 + 5 labels	.60	—
	Complete booklet, #3842a-3845a	2.40	
	Nos. 3842-3845 (4)	1.40	1.40

Complete booklet sold for $8.

2010 Asian Para Games, Guangzhou — A1202

2010, Sept. 3   **Perf. 13**
3846	A1202 $1.20 multi	.35	.35

Values are for stamp with adjacent selvage.

A1203

Shangri-La (Zhongdian) — A1204

Designs: No. 3847, $1.20, Songzanlin Lamasery (4-1). No. 3848, $1.20, Napa Lake and grassland (4-2). No. 3849, $1.20, Pudacuo National Park (4-3). No. 3850, $1.20, Dukezong (4-4).

$6, Meili Snow Mountain.

Perf. 13¼x13 Syncopated
2010, Sept. 13
3847-3850	A1203 Set of 4	1.50	1.50

Souvenir Sheet
Perf. 13¼x13¾ Syncopated
3851	A1204 $6 multi	1.90	1.90

Confucius and Buildings — A1205

No. 3852: a, $1.20, Confucius and temple (3-1). b, $1.20, Family home of Confucius (3-2). c, $3, Cemetery of Confucius (3-3).

Perf. 13¼ Syncopated
2010, Sept. 28   **Litho.**
3852	A1205 Horiz. strip of 3,		
	#a-c	1.60	1.60
d.	Souvenir sheet, #3852a-3852c	1.60	1.60

Huai River Water Control Project — A1206

Designs: No. 3853, $1.20, Nanwan Reservoir (4-1). No. 3854, $1.20, Linhuaigang Water Control Project (4-2). No. 3855, $1.20, Huai River Outflow Project (4-3). No. 3856, $1.20, Nansi Lake Water Control Project (4-4).

Perf. 12¾x13 Syncopated
2010, Oct. 14
3853-3856	A1206 Set of 4	1.50	1.50

Flora — A1207

Drawings of: No. 3857, $1.20, Plum blossom (4-1). No. 3858, $1.20, Orchid (4-2). No. 3859, $1.20, Bamboo (4-3). No. 3860, $1.20, Chrysanthemums (4-4).

2010, Oct. 18   **Perf. 13¼ Syncopated**
3857-3860	A1207 Set of 4	1.50	1.50

Zhu Xi (Chu Hsi) (1130-1200), Philosopher A1208

Designs: No. 3861, $1.20, Portrait of Zhu Xi (2-1). No. 3862, $1.20, Zhu Xi, student and horse (2-2).

Perf. 13¼x13½ Syncopated
2010, Oct. 22   **Litho. & Engr.**
3861-3862	A1208 Set of 2	.75	.75

2010 Asian Games, Guangzhou A1209

Designs: 80f, Badminton (6-1). No. 3864, $1.20, Wushu (6-2). No. 3865, $1.20, Hurdles (6-3). No. 3866, $1.20, Equestrian (6-4). No. 3867, $1.20, Dragon boat racing (6-5). $3, Weiqi (6-6).

Perf. 13¼ Syncopated

2010, Nov. 12			Photo.
3863-3868	A1209	Set of 6	2.60 2.60

SEMI-POSTAL STAMPS

Catalogue values for unused stamps in this section are for Never Hinged items.

Girl Holding Ball — SP1

Hands Reading Braille — SP2

1984, Feb. 16	Photo.		Perf. 11½
B1	SP1	8f + 2f shown (2-1)	1.25 .30
B2	SP1	8f + 2f Boy, panda (2-2)	1.25 .30

Surtax for China Children's Fund. T.92.

1985, Mar. 15	Photo.		Perf. 11½
B3	SP2	8f + 2f shown (4-1)	1.00 .60
B4	SP2	8f + 2f Sign language, lip reading (4-2)	1.00 .60
B5	SP2	8f + 2f Artificial limb (4-3)	1.00 .60
B6	SP2	8f + 2f Handicapped person in wheelchair (4-4)	1.00 .60
		Nos. B3-B6 (4)	4.00 2.40

Surtax for China Welfare Fund. T.105.

Children (T.137) SP3

1989, June 1	Litho.		Perf. 12
B7	SP3	8f +4f Friends (4-1)	.25 .25
B8	SP3	8f +4f Penguins (4-2)	.25 .25
B9	SP3	8f +4f Bird, Moon, Sun (4-3)	.25 .25
B10	SP3	8f +4f Girl, boy playing ball (4-4)	.25 .25
a.		Strip of 4, #B7-B10	1.10 1.10

Intl Children's Day, 40th anniv., and 10th Intl. Year of the Child. Surtax for China Children's Fund.

Sichuan Earthquake Relief — SP4

2008, May 20	Photo.		Perf. 13x13¼
B11	SP4	$1.20 + $1 multi + label	10.00 1.25

AIR POST STAMPS

Mail Plane and Temple of Heaven — AP1

1951, May 1	Engr.		Perf. 12½
		Without Gum	
C1	AP1	$1000 carmine	.25 .25
C2	AP1	$3000 green	.50 .25
C3	AP1	$5000 orange	.25 .25
C4	AP1	$10,000 vio brn & grn	.35 .35
C5	AP1	$30,000 dk bl & brn	11.50 2.00
		Nos. C1-C5 (5)	12.85 3.10

Planes at Airport — AP2

Designs: 28f, Plane over winding mountain highway. 35f, Plane over railroad yard. 52f, Plane over ship.

1957-58			Perf. 14
		Without Gum	
C6	AP2	16f indigo	12.50 1.00
C7	AP2	28f olive black	12.50 1.00
C8	AP2	35f slate	12.50 5.00
C9	AP2	52f Prus blue ('58)	12.50 2.00
		Nos. C6-C9 (4)	50.00 9.00

POSTAGE DUE STAMPS

Grain and Cogwheel — D1

D2

1950, Sept. 1	Typo.		Perf. 12½
		Without Gum	
J1	D1	$100 steel blue	.20 .20
J2	D1	$200 steel blue	.20 .20
J3	D1	$500 steel blue	.20 .20
J4	D1	$800 steel blue	30.00 1.00
J5	D1	$1000 steel blue	.45 .40
J6	D1	$2000 steel blue	.45 .40
J7	D1	$5000 steel blue	.30 .60
J8	D1	$8000 steel blue	.30 1.00
J9	D1	$10,000 steel blue	1.00 2.00
		Nos. J1-J9 (9)	33.10 6.00

1954, Aug. 18	Litho.		Perf. 14
		Without Gum	
J10	D2	$100 red	2.00 .20
J11	D2	$200 red	.60 .20
J12	D2	$500 red	2.00 .20
J13	D2	$800 red	.20 .20
J14	D2	$1600 red	.20 .20
		Nos. J10-J14 (5)	5.00 1.00

MILITARY STAMP

Red Star, 8-1 in Center — M1

1953, Aug.	Litho.		Perf. 14
		Without Gum	
M1	M1	$800 yel, org & red	350.00 100.00

This stamp also was printed in deep purple, orange & red (value, $5,750), and blue, orange & red (value, $200,000). These were not issued.

While it has been assumed for many years that each color was for a separate branch of the armed forces (army, air force and navy), there is no documentation to support that theory. Quantities printed also do not correspond to the number of servicemen in each branch.

M2

1995	Litho.		Perf. 12
M4	M2	20f multicolored	6.50 2.00

NORTHEAST CHINA

The Northeast Liberation Area included the provinces of Liaoning, Kirin, Jehol and Heilungkiang, the area generally known as Manchuria under the Japanese. The first post war issues were local overprints on stamps of Manchukuo. In early 1946, a Ministry of Posts and Telegraphs served the areas already liberated, and in August, 1946, a Communications Committee of the Political Council was established. In June, 1947, these postal services were subordinated to the Harbin General Post Office, and this was extended to Changchun on Oct. 22, 1948, and to Mukden on Nov. 4, 1948. It was rapidly extended to cover all Manchuria.

Rough Perfs
Rough perforations are normal on most regional issues.

All Stamps Issued without Gum

Mao Tse-tung
A1   A2

1946, Feb.	Unwmk.	Litho.	Perf. 11
1L1	A1	$1 violet	22.50 12.00
1L2	A2	$2 vermilion	1.75 1.00
1L3	A2	$5 orange	2.00 1.00
a.		Booklet pane of 6	250.00
1L4	A2	$10 blue	2.25 1.25
a.		Booklet pane of 6	250.00
		Nos. 1L1-1L4 (4)	28.50 15.25

Value, imperf set $125.
For surcharges see Nos. 1L20-1L23, 1L49-1L50, 1L89, 1L91, 1L93.

Map of China, Lion, Hyena and Chiang Kai-shek — A3

1946, Dec. 12			Perf. 10½
1L5	A3	$1 violet	2.25 1.50
1L6	A3	$2 orange	2.25 1.50
1L7	A3	$5 org brn	7.50 7.00
1L8	A3	$10 lt grn	12.00 10.00
a.		Imperf., pair	60.00
		Nos. 1L5-1L8 (4)	24.00 20.00

10th anniversary of the capture of Chiang Kai-shek at Sian.

Railroad Workers, Chengchow A4

1947, Feb. 7			Perf. 10½
1L9	A4	$1 pink	2.00 2.00
1L10	A4	$2 dull grn	2.00 2.00
1L11	A4	$5 pink	3.50 2.25
1L12	A4	$10 dull grn	7.00 5.50
		Nos. 1L9-1L12 (4)	14.50 11.75

24th anniversary of the Chengchow railroad workers' strike and massacre.

Women (Worker, Soldier and Farmer) — A5

Wmk. Chinese Characters in Sheet
1947, Mar. 8   *Perf. 10½x11*
1L13	A5	$5 brick red	5.00	2.00
1L14	A5	$10 brown	5.00	2.00

International Women's Day, March 8. Exists imperf.

Same Overprinted in Green ("Northeast Postal Service")

1947, Mar. 18
1L15	A5	$5 brick red	6.50	6.00
1L16	A5	$10 brown	6.50	6.00

Exists imperf.

Children Carrying Banner — A6

1947, Apr. 4   *Perf. 11x10½*
Granite Paper
1L17	A6	$5 rose red	6.25	4.50
1L18	A6	$10 lt green	10.00	8.00
1L19	A6	$30 orange	15.00	10.00
		Nos. 1L17-1L19 (3)	31.25	23.00

Children's Day.

Nos. 1L1-1L2 Surcharged in Red, Brown, Black, Blue or Green

1947, Apr.   **Unwmk.**   *Perf. 11*
1L20	A1	$50 on $1 vio (R)	27.50	30.00
a.		Brown surcharge	27.50	30.00
1L21	A2	$50 on $2 ver	27.50	30.00
a.		Brown surcharge	27.50	30.00
1L22	A1	$100 on $1 vio	27.50	30.00
a.		Green surcharge	27.50	30.00
1L23	A2	$100 on $2 ver (Bl)	27.50	30.00
a.		Green surcharge	27.50	30.00
		Nos. 1L20-1L23 (4)	110.00	120.00

Farmer and Worker — A7   Ax Severing Chain — A8

Wmk. Chinese Characters in Sheet
1947, May 1   *Perf. 10½x11*
Granite Paper
1L24	A7	$10 orange red	5.50	5.50
1L25	A7	$30 ultra	6.00	6.00
1L26	A7	$50 gray green	10.00	10.00
		Nos. 1L24-1L26 (3)	21.50	21.50

Labor Day. Value, imperf. pairs, set $425.

1947, May 4   *Perf. 11*
1L27	A8	$10 brt green	8.00	8.00
1L28	A8	$30 brown	8.00	8.00
1L29	A8	$50 violet	10.00	10.00
		Nos. 1L27-1L29 (3)	26.00	26.00

28th anniversary of the students' revolt at Peking University against the 1918 peace treaty. Value, imperf. pairs, set $525.

Workers with Banner: "Oppose Imperialist Aggression" — A9

1947, May 30   *Perf. 10½x11*
Banner in Red
1L30	A9	$2 brt lilac	6.50	7.00
1L31	A9	$5 brt green	6.50	7.00
1L32	A9	$10 yellow	7.50	8.00
1L33	A9	$20 violet	7.00	7.50
1L34	A9	$30 red brown	7.00	7.50
1L35	A9	$50 dk blue	9.00	7.50
1L36	A9	$100 brown	12.00	7.50
a.		Souvenir sheet of 7	375.00	
		Nos. 1L30-1L36 (7)	55.50	52.00

22nd anniversary of the Shanghai-Nanking Road incident. No. 1L36a is on granite paper and contains 7 imperf. stamps similar to Nos. 1L30-1L36. Size: 215x158mm. Value, imperf. pairs, ordinary paper, set $1,300.

Mao and Communist Flag — A10

1947, July 1   *Perf. 10½x11*
1L37	A10	$10 red	20.00	22.50
1L38	A10	$30 brt lilac	20.00	22.50
1L39	A10	$50 rose brn	60.00	62.50
1L40	A10	$100 vermilion	70.00	75.00
		Nos. 1L37-1L40 (4)	170.00	182.50

26th anniversary of the founding of the Chinese Communist Party.

Hand Holding Rifle — A11

1947, July 7   *Perf. 10½*
1L41	A11	$10 orange	8.50	9.50
1L42	A11	$30 green	8.50	9.50
1L43	A11	$50 dull blue	11.50	11.50
1L44	A11	$100 brown	16.00	16.00
a.		Souvenir sheet of 4	350.00	400.00
		Nos. 1L41-1L44 (4)	44.50	46.50

10th anniversary of the start of Sino-Japanese War. No. 1L44a contains 4 imperf. stamps similar to Nos. 1L41-1L44. Size: 149x107mm. Exist imperf. Value, set of pairs $1,100.

White Mountain and Black Water, Northeast China — A12

Wmk. Zigzag Lines (141)
1947, Aug. 15   *Perf. 10½*
1L45	A12	$10 brown org	5.00	8.50
1L46	A12	$30 lt ol grn	5.00	8.50
1L47	A12	$50 blue grn	16.00	16.00
1L48	A12	$100 sepia	26.00	22.50
		Nos. 1L45-1L48 (4)	52.00	55.50

2nd anniversary of the reoccupation of Northeast China and the surrender of Japan. Exist imperf. Value, set of pairs $700.

Nos. 1L1-1L2 Surcharged in Black, Red, Green or Blue

1947, Aug. 29   **Unwmk.**   *Perf. 11*
1L49	A1	$5 on $1 vio	25.00	25.00
a.		Red surcharge	25.00	25.00
b.		Green surcharge	25.00	25.00
1L50	A2	$10 on $2 ver	25.00	25.00
a.		Blue surcharge	25.00	25.00
b.		Green surcharge	25.00	25.00

Map of Manchuria — A13

1947, Sept. 18   **Unwmk.**
White Paper
1L51	A13	$10 gray green	6.75	10.00
1L52	A13	$20 rose lilac	6.75	10.00
1L53	A13	$30 black brown	11.00	10.00
1L54	A13	$50 carmine	11.00	10.00
		Nos. 1L51-1L54 (4)	35.50	40.00

16th anniversary of Japanese attack on Mukden, Sept. 18, 1931.

Northeast Political Council Offices — A14

Mao Tse-tung (Value figures repeated) — A15

1947, Oct. 10   *Perf. 10½*
1L55	A14	$10 yel orange	42.50	42.50
1L56	A14	$20 rose red	42.50	42.50
1L57	A14	$100 brown	95.00	95.00
		Nos. 1L55-1L57 (3)	180.00	180.00

35th anniversary of the founding of the Chinese Republic.

1947, Oct. 10   **White Paper**   *Perf. 11*
1L58	A15	$1 brown	.35	1.50
1L59	A15	$5 gray green	2.25	1.50
1L60	A15	$10 brt green	12.00	9.00
1L61	A15	$15 bluish lilac	12.00	9.00
1L62	A15	$20 brt rose	.80	1.50
1L63	A15	$30 green	.80	2.00
1L64	A15	$50 black brown	22.50	13.50
1L65	A15	$90 blue	5.50	4.00
		Nos. 1L58-1L65 (8)	56.20	42.00

Newsprint
1L66	A15	$100 red	.70	
a.		White paper	7.50	5.00
1L67	A15	$500 red orange	32.50	17.50
a.		White paper	32.50	

Type A22 resembles A15, but has "YUAN" at upper right.
The $1, $90 were also printed on newsprint. See footnote following No. 1L72.
See Nos. 1L68-1L72. For surcharges see Nos. 1L84-1L88, 1L90, 1L92, 1L94.

1947, Nov.   **Redrawn**
White Paper
1L68	A15	$50 lt grn	1.00	1.50
1L69	A15	$150 red org, wmkd.	2.25	1.50
		Chinese characters		
a.		Unwatermarked	2.75	
1L70	A15	$250 bluish lil	.90	1.50
a.		Wmkd. Chinese characters	1.25	1.50

Nos. 1L69 and 1L69a exist in same sheet.

1947, Dec.   **Unwmk.**
Newsprint
1L71	A15	$300 green	52.50	27.50
1L72	A15	$1000 yellow	1.50	1.50
a.		White paper	1.50	1.50
		Nos. 1L68-1L72 (5)	58.15	33.50

Panel below portrait 8½x3mm on Nos. 1L68-1L70; 7x3mm on No. 1L58-1L67. Nos. 1L68-1L70 have different ornamental border. Nos. 1L71-1L72 without zeros for cents. For surcharges see Nos. 1L90, 1L92, 1L94.

Hand Holding Torch — A16

1947, Dec. 12   **Unwmk.**   *Perf. 11*
White Paper
1L73	A16	$30 rose red	14.00	16.00
1L74	A16	$90 dk bl	16.00	16.00
1L75	A16	$150 green	18.00	16.00
		Nos. 1L73-1L75 (3)	48.00	48.00

11th anniversary of the capture of Chiang Kai-shek at Sian.

Tomb of Gen. Li Chao-lin — A17

Globe and Banner — A18

1948, Mar. 9   **Unwmk.**   *Perf. 10½x11*
1L76	A17	$30 green	24.00	24.00
a.		Granite paper, wmkd.	24.00	24.00
1L77	A17	$150 vio gray	24.00	24.00
a.		Granite paper, wmkd.	24.00	24.00

2nd anniversary of the assassination of Gen. Li Chao-lin, Commander of 3rd Army.

Wmk. Chinese Characters in Sheet
1948, May 1   *Perf. 11x10½*
1L78	A18	$50 red	9.50	12.50
1L79	A18	$150 green	5.00	18.50
1L80	A18	$250 lilac	5.00	36.00
		Nos. 1L78-1L80 (3)	19.50	67.00

Labor Day.

Student, Torch and Banner — A19

1948, May 4   **Unwmk.**   *Perf. 10½x11*
Granite paper
1L81	A19	$50 green	21.00	19.50
1L82	A19	$150 brown	21.00	22.50
1L83	A19	$250 red	25.00	27.50
		Nos. 1L81-1L83 (3)	67.00	69.50

Youth Day, May 4.

Nos. 1L58, 1L61, 1L59, 1L63, 1L65, 1L2-1L4, 1L68-1L69, 1L71 Surcharged in Black, Blue, Red or Green

1948-49 — Perf. 11

1L84	A15	$100 on $1	75.00	90.00
a.		Blue surcharge	50.00	50.00
1L85	A15	$100 on $15	27.50	27.50
a.		Blue surcharge	50.00	50.00
1L86	A15	$300 on $5 (R)	55.00	25.00
1L87	A15	$300 on $30 (R)	20.00	20.00
1L88	A15	$300 on $90 (R)	15.00	15.00
1L89	A2	$500 on $2	12.00	12.00
1L90	A15	$500 on $50 (R, '49)	27.50	20.00
1L91	A2	$1500 on $5 (Bl)	12.00	10.00
1L92	A15	$1500 on $150 (G; '49)	25.00	20.00
a.		Blue surcharge	50.00	50.00
1L93	A2	$2500 on $10 (R)	15.00	12.00
1L94	A15	$2500 on $300 ('49)	20.00	17.50
	Nos. 1L84-1L94 (11)		304.00	269.00

Crane Operator — A20

Wmk. Chinese Characters in Sheet

1948, May — Perf. 11

1L95	A20	$100 red & pink	2.50	2.00
1L96	A20	$300 vio brn & yel	3.50	2.75
1L97	A20	$500 bl & grn	5.00	3.50
	Nos. 1L95-1L97 (3)		11.00	8.25

6th All-China Labor Conference, Harbin.

Farmer, Worker and Soldier Saluting — A21

Mao Tse-tung ("YUAN" at upper right) — A22

1948, Dec. 3 Unwmk. Perf. 11x10½
White paper

1L98	A21	$500 vermilion	18.00	18.00
1L99	A21	$1500 brt grn	21.00	21.00
1L100	A21	$2500 brown	32.50	32.50
	Nos. 1L98-1L100 (3)		71.50	71.50

Liberation of Northeast China.
Values for Nos. 1L98-1L100 are for fine stamps.

1949, Feb. — Perf. 11

1L101	A22	$300 olive	.75	1.25
1L102	A22	$500 orange	7.50	8.50
1L103	A22	$1500 bl grn	.75	1.25
1L104	A22	$4500 brown	.75	1.25
1L105	A22	$6500 dk bl	.75	1.25
	Nos. 1L101-1L105 (5)		10.50	13.50

See type A15. For surcharges see Nos. 1L126-1L129, 1L131-1L132.

Workers, Globe and Flag — A23

Fields and Factories — A24

1949, May 1 — Perf. 11½

1L106	A23	$1000 red & dl bl	.45	1.10
1L107	A23	$1500 red & pale bl	.45	1.10
1L108	A23	$4500 rose & ol brn	.65	1.10
1L109	A23	$6500 dl org & grn	.65	1.10
1L110	A23	$10,000 mar & ultra	3.50	3.50
	Nos. 1L106-1L110 (5)		5.70	7.90

Labor Day.

1949 — Perf. 10, 11

1L111	A24	$5000 Prus bl	7.50	5.25
1L112	A24	$10,000 org brn	.50	1.75
1L113	A24	$50,000 green	.75	2.50
1L114	A24	$100,000 violet	1.25	13.00
	Nos. 1L111-1L114 (4)		10.00	22.50

Production in agriculture and industry.

Workers with Flags — A25

Heroes' Monument, Harbin — A26

1949, July 1 — Perf. 11

1L115	A25	$1500 vio, lt bl & red	1.25	2.00
1L116	A25	$4500 dk brn, lt bl & ver	1.25	2.00
1L117	A25	$6500 gray, lt bl & rose red	2.75	5.00
	Nos. 1L115-1L117 (3)		5.25	9.00

28th anniversary of the founding of the Chinese Communist Party.

1949, Aug. 15 — Perf. 11½x11

1L118	A26	$1500 brick red	1.25	2.75
1L119	A26	$4500 yel grn	1.75	2.75
1L120	A26	$6500 lt blue	3.50	2.75
	Nos. 1L118-1L120 (3)		6.50	8.25

4th anniversary of the Reoccupation, and the surrender of Japan.

"Northeast Postal Service"

The following commemorative issues are similar to those of the People's Republic of China, with the 4 characters shown added in different sizes and various arrangements. Reprints were also issued similar to those of the PRC.

Chinese Lantern Type of PRC, 1949

1949, Sept. 12 Litho. Perf. 12½

1L121	A1	$1000 dp blue	35.00	11.00
1L122	A1	$1500 scarlet	35.00	13.00
1L123	A1	$3000 green	65.00	17.50
1L124	A1	$4500 maroon	65.00	17.50
	Nos. 1L121-1L124 (4)		200.00	59.00

Reprints exist. Value, set $6.

Factory — A27

1949, Oct. — Perf. 11x10½

1L125	A27	$1500 orange	1.00	1.75

For surcharge see No. 1L130.

Nos. 1L101, 1L103-1L105, 1L125 Surcharged in Black or Green

1949, Nov. 20

1L126	A22	$2000 on $300	25.00	4.25
1L127	A22	$2000 on $4500 (G)	50.00	35.00
1L128	A22	$2500 on $1500	.70	5.00
1L129	A22	$2500 on $6500	27.50	35.00
1L130	A27	$5000 on $1500	.60	1.75
1L131	A22	$20,000 on $4500	.40	5.00
1L132	A22	$35,000 on $300	.50	6.75
	Nos. 1L126-1L132 (7)		104.70	92.75

Globe and Hammer Type of PRC

1949, Nov. 15 — Perf. 12½

1L133	A2	$5000 crimson	625.00	225.00
1L134	A2	$20,000 dp green	950.00	250.00
1L135	A2	$35,000 vio blue	1,450.	300.00
	Nos. 1L133-1L135 (3)		3,025.	775.00

Reprints, value; #1L133-1L134, each $2; #1L135, $400.

Mao and Conference Hall Types of PRC

1950, Feb. 1 — Perf. 14

1L136	A3	$1000 vermilion	28.00	29.00
1L137	A3	$1500 dp blue	28.00	29.00
1L138	A4	$5000 dk vio brn	50.00	45.00
1L139	A4	$20,000 green	50.00	55.00
	Nos. 1L136-1L139 (4)		156.00	158.00

Reprints exist. Value, set $8.

Gate of Heavenly Peace — A28

1950 — Perf. 10½
Narrow horizontal shading

1L140	A28	$500 olive	1.75	.60
1L141	A28	$1000 orange	2.00	.60
1L142	A28	$1000 lil rose	4.50	.60
1L143	A28	$2000 gray grn	1.50	.35
1L144	A28	$2500 yellow	4.50	.35
1L145	A28	$5000 dp org	25.00	.35
1L146	A28	$10,000 brn org	2.50	.65
1L147	A28	$20,000 vio brn	1.50	.35
1L148	A28	$35,000 dp blue	1.50	.45
1L149	A28	$50,000 brt grn	25.00	1.00
	Nos. 1L140-1L149 (10)		69.75	5.30

See A29.

Flag and Mao Type of PRC

1950, July 1 — Perf. 14
Yellow Stars

1L150	A7	$5000 grn & red	175.00	90.00
1L151	A7	$10,000 brn & red	200.00	90.00
1L152	A7	$20,000 dk brn & red	200.00	90.00
1L153	A7	$30,000 dk vio bl & red	350.00	150.00
	Nos. 1L150-1L153 (4)		925.00	420.00

Reprints exist. Value, set $45.

Picasso Dove Type of PRC

1950, Aug. 1 Engr. Perf. 14

1L154	A8	$2500 brown	16.00	20.00
1L155	A8	$5000 green	21.00	20.00
1L156	A8	$20,000 blue	28.00	20.00
	Nos. 1L154-1L156 (3)		65.00	60.00

Reprints exist. Value, set $4.75.

Flag Type of PRC

1950, Oct. 1 Engr. & Litho.
Flag in Red & Yellow

1L157	A9	$1000 purple	175.00	40.00
1L158	A9	$2500 org brn	175.00	42.50
1L159	A9	$5000 dp grn	200.00	55.00
1L160	A9	$10,000 olive	210.00	57.50
1L161	A9	$20,000 blue	250.00	95.00
	Nos. 1L157-1L161 (5)		1,025.	290.00

Size of #1L159: 38x47mm, others 26x33mm.
Reprints exist. Value, set $30.

Postal Conference Type of PRC

1950, Nov. 1 — Litho.

1L162	A11	$2500 grn & dp org	40.00	20.00
1L163	A11	$5000 car & grn	40.00	20.00

Reprints exist. Value, set, $5.

Gate of Heavenly Peace — A29

1950-51 — Perf. 10½
Wide horizontal shading

1L164	A29	$5000 orange	10.00	11.00
1L165	A29	$30,000 scarlet	3.75	20.00
1L166	A29	$100,000 violet	16.00	21.00

Wmk. Zigzag Lines (141)

1L167	A29	$250 brown	1.50	2.00
1L168	A29	$500 olive	1.50	2.00
1L169	A29	$1000 lil rose	2.00	3.25
1L170	A29	$2000 dl grn ('51)	3.00	3.25
1L171	A29	$2500 yellow	1.50	3.25
1L172	A29	$5000 orange	3.75	3.25
1L173	A29	$10,000 brn org ('51)	2.50	3.25
1L174	A29	$12,500 maroon	1.50	3.25
1L175	A29	$20,000 dp brn ('51)	2.75	6.50
	Nos. 1L164-1L175 (12)		49.75	82.00

A $50,000 green was prepared, but not issued. Value $200.

Stalin and Mao Tse-tung Type of PRC
Unwmk.

1950, Dec. 1 Engr. Perf. 14

1L176	A12	$2500 red	24.00	17.50
1L177	A12	$5000 dp green	29.00	17.50
1L178	A12	$20,000 dk blue	29.00	17.50
	Nos. 1L176-1L178 (3)		82.00	52.50

Reprints exist. Value, set $9.50.

NORTHEAST CHINA PARCEL POST STAMPS

Locomotive — PP1

1951 Litho. Perf. 10½

1LQ1		$100,000 purple	200.00

Imperf.

1LQ2		$300,000 brown	500.00
1LQ3		$500,000 grnsh bl	800.00
1LQ4		$1,000,000 ver	1,300.

Value, Nos. 1LQ2-1LQ4 perf. 10½, $2,650. For similar type see North China PP1.

PORT ARTHUR AND DAIREN

The Liaoning Postal Administration was established on April 1, 1946, in accordance with the Sino-Soviet Treaty, but was renamed one week later the Port Arthur and Dairen Postal Administration. On Apr. 3, 1947, it was combined with telecommunications and renamed the Kwantung Post and Telegraph General Administration.

On May 1, 1949, the name was again changed to Port Arthur and Dairen Post and Telegraph Administration. Postal tariffs were based on local currency and both Manchukuo and Japanese stamps were overprinted for use.

Gum
#2L1-2L55 were issued with gum.

Manchukuo Nos. 162 and 94 Handstamp Surcharged in Violet ("Liaoning Post")

1946, Mar. 15

2L1	A19	20f on 30f buff	72.50	72.50
2L2	A18	1y on 12f org	37.50	37.50

Same Surcharge on Japan Nos. 260, 337, 195, 244, 263, 342 in Violet, Red or Black

1946, Apr. 1

2L3	A85	20f on 3s grn (V)	19.50	21.00
2L4	A151	1y on 17s gray vio (R)	16.00	18.00
2L5	A57	5y on 6s car	30.00	27.50
2L6	A57	5y on 6s crim	30.00	27.50

2L7 A88 5y on 6s org 22.00 20.00
2L8 A154 15y on 40s dk vio 110.00 *125.00*
Nos. 2L1-2L8 (8) 337.50 349.00

Surcharge sideways on Nos. 2L5-2L6.

Japan Nos. 260 and 263 Surcharged

1946, Apr.
2L9 A85 1y on 3s grn —
2L10 A88 5y on 6s org —

Sha Ho Kow (suburb of Dairen) issue. The status of this issue is in question.

Manchukuo Nos. 84, 88 and 98 Handstamp Surcharged in Green, Red or Black

1946, May 1
2L11 A16 1y on 1f red brn (G) 18.00 *24.00*
2L12 A18 5y on 4f lt ol grn (R) 24.00 *32.50*
2L13 A19 15y on 30f chnt brn 52.50 *62.50*
Nos. 2L11-2L13 (3) 94.50 119.00

Transfer of postal administration and Labor Day.

Manchukuo Nos. 159, 86 and 94 Surcharged in Green, Red or Black

1946, July 7
2L14 A17 1y on 6f crim rose (G) 11.50 *20.00*
2L15 A17 5y on 2f lt grn (R) 52.50 *85.00*
2L16 A18 15y on 12f dp org 110.00 110.00
Nos. 2L14-2L16 (3) 174.00 215.00

Outbreak of war with Japan, 9th anniv.

Manchukuo Nos. 94, 84 and 158 Surcharged in Black, Green or Red

1946, Aug. 15
2L17 A18 1y on 12f dp org 22.50 *27.50*
2L18 A16 5y on 1f red brn (G) 52.50 50.00
2L19 A10 15y on 5f gray blk (R) 110.00 100.00
Nos. 2L17-2L19 (3) 185.00 177.50

Surrender of Japan, first anniversary.

Manchukuo Nos. 159, 94 and 86 Surcharged in Green, Black or Red

1946, Oct. 10
2L20 A17 1y on 6f crim rose (G) 32.50 30.00
2L21 A18 5y on 12f dp org 57.50 55.00
2L22 A17 15y on 2f lt grn (R) 110.00 100.00
Nos. 2L20-2L22 (3) 200.00 185.00

35th anniversary of Chinese revolution.

Manchukuo Nos. 84, 159 and 94 Surcharged in Black, Green or Blue

1946, Oct. 19
2L23 A16 1y on 1f red brn 47.50 45.00
2L24 A17 5y on 6f crim rose (G) 87.50 85.00
2L25 A18 15y on 12f dp org (Bl) 125.00 125.00
Nos. 2L23-2L25 (3) 260.00 255.00

10th anniversary of the death of Lu Hsun (1881-1936), writer.

Manchukuo Nos. 86, 159 and 95 Surcharged in Red, Green or Black

1947, Feb. 20
2L26 A17 1y on 2f lt grn (R) 80.00 77.50
2L27 A17 5y on 6f crim rose (G) 160.00 150.00
2L28 A18 15y on 13f dk red brn 325.00 300.00
Nos. 2L26-2L28 (3) 565.00 527.50

29th anniversary of the Red (USSR) Army.

Manchukuo Nos. 86, 159 and 162 Surcharged in Red, Green or Black

1947, May 1
2L29 A17 1y on 2f lt grn (R) 24.00 24.00
2L30 A17 5y on 6f crim rose (G) 67.50 65.00
2L31 A19 15y on 30f buff 110.00 100.00
Nos. 2L29-2L31 (3) 201.50 189.00

Labor Day.

Manchukuo Nos. 86, 88, 98 and 162 Surcharged ("Kwantung Postal Service, China")

1947, Sept. 15
2L32 A17 5y on 2f lt grn 40.00 40.00
2L33 A18 15y on 4f lt ol grn 65.00 62.50
2L34 A19 20y on 30f red brn 100.00 95.00
2L35 A19 20y on 30f buff 110.00 100.00
Nos. 2L32-2L35 (4) 315.00 297.50

Manchukuo Nos. 86 and 159 Surcharged in Red and Green

Sacred Golden Kite (same size) — A1

1948, Feb. 20
2L36 A17 10y on 2f lt grn (R) 150.00 150.00
2L37 A17 20y on 6f crim rose (G) 190.00 190.00
2L38 A1 100y on bl & red brn 800.00 800.00

30th anniversary of the Red (USSR) Army. No. 2L38 is on an ungummed label for the 2600th anniv. of the Japanese Empire.

Japan No. 260 and Manchukuo Nos. 84, 86 and 88 Surcharged in Red, Blue or Black

1948, July
2L39 A85 5y on 3s grn (R) 125.00 125.00
2L40 A16 10y on 1f red brn (Bl) 225.00 250.00
2L41 A17 50y on 2f lt grn 500.00 475.00
2L42 A18 100y on 4f lt ol grn (R) 875.00 900.00

Smaller Characters on Bottom Line
2L43 A17 10y on 2f lt grn (R) 300.00 225.00
2L44 A16 50y on 1f red brn 350.00 300.00

Stamps of Manchukuo Nos. 84, 86 and 88 Surcharged in Blue, Red or Black

1948, Nov. 1
2L45 A16 10y on 1f red brn (Bl) 275.00 600.00
2L46 A17 50y on 2f lt grn (R) 450.00 600.00
2L47 A18 100y on 4f lt ol grn 1,100. 600.00

31st anniversary of the Russian Revolution.

Manchukuo Nos. 86 and 161 Surcharged in Red or Green

1948, Nov. 15
2L48 A17 10y on 2f lt grn 1,050. 1,050.
2L49 A17 50y on 20f brn (G) 1,200. 1,200.

Kwantung Agricultural and Industrial Exhibition.

Manchukuo Nos. 86, 88 and 161 Surcharged in Red, Black or Green

1949, Jan.
2L50 A17 20y on 2f lt grn (R) 500.00
2L51 A18 50y on 4f lt ol grn 700.00
2L52 A17 100y on 20f brn (G) 700.00

Without Gum
From No. 2L56 onward all stamps were issued without gum except as noted.

Farmer and Worker — A2

Train and Ship — A3

Ship at Dock (No. 2L55) — A4

(No. 2L56)

1949 Litho. Perf. 11, 11½
2L53 A2 5y pale grn 2.50 *5.00*
2L54 A3 10y orange 20.00 20.00
2L55 A4 50y vermilion 22.50 22.50
2L56 A4 50y red (redrawn) 24.00 24.00
Nos. 2L53-2L56 (4) 69.00 71.50

Issue dates: #2L56, July 7; others Apr. 1. For surcharges see Nos. 2L62-2L66.

Worker, Flag and Means of Transport A5

1949, May 1 Perf. 11
2L57 A5 10y rose pink 26.00 *30.00*
a. 10y vermilion 75.00 75.00

Labor Day. #2L57a is from a worn plate.

Mao Tse-tung and Red Flag — A6

Heroes Monument, Dairen — A7

1949, July 1
2L59 A6 50y red 45.00 45.00

28th anniversary of the founding of the Chinese Communist Party.

1949, Sept.
2L60 A7 10y red, bl & olive 35.00 35.00
a. 10y red, blue & pale blue 100.00 85.00

4th anniversary of victory over Japan and opening of the Dairen Industrial Fair.

Nos. 2L53-2L54 Surcharged in Red or Black

a b

c

1949, Sept. With Gum
2L62 A2(a) 7y on 5y (R) 40.00 35.00
2L63 A2(a) 7y on 5y 37.50 35.00
2L64 A2(b) 50y on 5y 95.00 85.00
2L65 A3(b) 100y on 10y 500.00 375.00
2L66 A3(c) 500y on 10y (R) 650.00 425.00
Nos. 2L62-2L66 (5) 1,322. 955.00

Size of surcharge on No. 2L63: 16x19mm. A 500y on 5y, red surcharge "c," and a 500y on 10y orange, surcharge "b" were prepared but not issued.

Stalin and Lenin — A8

1949, Nov. 7   *Perf. 11x11½*
2L68   A8   10y dl bl grn
     (shades)   100.00   50.00

32nd anniversary of the Russian Revolution.

Workers Saluting Mao, Star and Flag — A9

1949, Nov. 16   *Perf. 11*
2L69   A9   35y dk bl, red, & yel   75.00 75.00

Founding of the People's Republic of China.

Stalin — A10   Gate of Heavenly Peace — A11

1949, Dec. 20   *Perf. 11½*
2L70   A10   20y dull magenta   100.00 110.00
2L71   A10   35y rose red   100.00 110.00

70th birthday of Stalin.

1950, Mar. 10   Typo.   *Perf. 10½*
2L72   A11   10y Prus blue   400.00 400.00
2L73   A11   20y dull grn   150.00 150.00
2L74   A11   35y red   17.50 24.00
2L75   A11   50y deep pur   17.50 17.50
2L76   A11   100y lilac rose   55.00 55.00
    Nos. 2L72-2L76 (5)   640.00 646.50

NORTH CHINA

The North China Liberation Area included the provinces of Hopeh, Chahar, Shansi and Suiyuan. The original postal service, begun in the Shansi-Hopeh-Chahar Border Area in December, 1937, became the North China Postal and Telegraph Administration in May, 1949.

All Stamps Issued without Gum Except as Noted
Large Victory Issue

Cavalry Man Holding Nationalist Flag — A1

Wmk. Wavy Lines
1946, Mar.   *Perf. 10½*
Granite Paper
Size: 34½x42mm

3L1   A1 $1 red brown   4.50 4.50
   a.   Newsprint   10.00 12.00
3L2   A1 $2 gray grn   4.50 4.50
3L3   A1 $4 vermilion   5.00 5.00
3L4   A1 $5 vio brn   16.00 6.00
3L5   A1 $8 vio bl   16.00 6.00

3L6   A1 $10 dp car   5.00 5.00
3L7   A1 $12 yellow   15.00 15.00
3L8   A1 $20 lt green   34.00 34.00
    Nos. 3L1-3L8 (8)   100.00 80.00
    Defeat of Japan.

Small Victory Issue
Perf. 10½x10, 9½ rough
1946, May   Unwmk.
Granite paper
Size: 20x21mm

3L9   A1 $1 red org   1.60 2.25
3L10   A1 $2 green   2.50 2.25
3L11   A1 $3 lt lilac   4.75 8.50
3L12   A1 $5 dull pur   6.25 .40
3L13   A1 $8 dk blue   13.50 17.50
3L14   A1 $10 rose red   2.50 4.50
3L15   A1 $15 purple   77.50 67.50
3L16   A1 $20 green   4.75 6.25
3L17   A1 $30 brt grnsh bl   4.00 7.25
3L18   A1 $40 brt rose lilac   4.75 3.25
3L19   A1 $50 brown   36.00 .75
3L20   A1 $60 myrtle green   67.50 1.60

Wmk. Wavy Lines
3L21   A1 $100 orange   1.75 4.50
3L22   A1 $200 dull blue   1.75 4.50
3L23   A1 $500 rose   57.50 70.00
    Nos. 3L9-3L23 (15)   286.60 201.00

North China Postal and Telegraph Administration

Charging Infantrymen A2   Agriculture and Industry A3

1949, Jan.   Unwmk.   *Imperf.*
White Paper
3L24   A2   50c brown lake   3.50 3.50
3L25   A2 $1 Prussian blue   3.50 3.50
Newsprint
3L26   A2 $2 apple green   3.50 3.50
3L27   A2 $3 dull violet   3.50 3.50
3L28   A2 $5 brown   3.50 3.50
3L29   A3 $6 deep rose   3.50 3.50
   a.   White paper   3.50 3.50
3L30   A2 $10 blue grn   1.25 1.50
3L31   A2 $12 dp car   3.75 3.75
    Nos. 3L24-3L31 (8)   26.00 26.25

No. 3L29 issued in Peking, others in Tientsin.

Remittance Stamps of China Surcharged

A4

壹
$ 1

叁
$ 3

1949, Jan.   Engr.   *Perf. 13*
Small Central Characters
3L32   A4   50c on $50 brn blk   3.25 3.50
3L33   A4 $1 on $50 gray blk   2.25 2.75
3L34   A4 $3 on $50 gray   2.50 2.50
Large Central Characters
3L35   A4   50c on $50 blk   1.60 1.60
3L36   A4 $6 on $20 dk vio brn   1.60 1.60
    Nos. 3L32-3L36 (5)   11.20 11.95

Issued in Tientsin.
For surcharges see Nos. 3LQ10-3LQ21.

Sun Yat-sen Type A2 of Northeastern Provinces and China No. 640 Surcharged in Black, Red, Green or Blue

#3L37-3L45, 3L47-3L50, 3L52   #3L46, 3L51, 3L53

c

Type "b," bottom character of left vertical row (yuan) differs. Type "c," top character of right vertical row differs.

1949, Mar. 7   *Perf. 14*
3L37   A2   50c on 5c lake   .85 2.75
3L38   A2 $1 on 10c org   .85 2.25
3L39   A2 $2 on 20c yel grn   80.00 25.00
3L40   A2 $3 on 50c red org   .85 1.75
3L41   A2 $4 on $5 dk grn   9.50 2.25
3L42   A2 $6 on $10 crim   2.75 2.25
3L43   A2 $10 on $300 bluish grn   5.50 3.25
3L44   A2 $12 on $1 bl   2.50 3.25
3L45   A2 $18 on $3 brn   2.50 1.75
3L46   A2 $20 on 50c red org (Bl)   2.75 1.50
3L47   A2 $20 on $20 ol, II   5.50 4.50
   a.   Type I   20.00 13.50
3L48   A2 $30 on $2.50 ind (R)   5.50 4.00
3L49   A2 $40 on 25c blk brn (R)   8.50 6.25
3L50   A2 $50 on $109 dk grn (R)   17.50 9.00
3L51   A2 $80 on $1 bl (R)   22.50 4.50
3L52   A2 $100 on $65 dl grn (R)   30.00 9.00
3L53   A73 $100 on $100 dk car, surch. 16mm wide (Bl)   22.50 3.25
   a.   Surcharge 14mm wide   22.50 10.00

1949, Apr.
3L55   A2 (c) $2 on 20c yel grn   1.75 3.25
3L56   A2 (c) $3 on 50c red org   .85 2.25
3L57   A2 (c) $4 on $5 dk grn   7.00 4.25
3L58   A2 (c) $6 on $10 crim, I   4.50 4.25
   a.   Type II   15.00 10.00
3L59   A2 (c) $12 on $1 blue   1.75 1.75

d   e

1949, Apr.
Type "d"
3L60   A2 $1 on 25c blk grn (G)   .50 1.25
3L61   A2 $10 on $300 bluish grn (R)   11.00 5.75
3L62   A2 $20 on 50c red org (G)   21.00 25.00
3L63   A2 $20 on $20 ol (R)   7.00 4.25
3L64   A2 $40 on 25c blk brn (R)   7.00 5.00
3L65   A2 $50 on $109 dk grn, surch. 15mm wide (R)   11.00 13.00
   a.   Surcharge 13mm wide   30.00 30.00
3L66   A2 $80 on $1 bl (R)   8.00 6.50
Type "d" On Stamps on China
3L67   A73 $100 on $100 dk car (G)   60.00 35.00
3L68   A73 $300 on $700 red brn (Bl)   12.50 12.50
3L69   A82 $500 on $500 bl grn (R)   9.00 4.50
3L70   A82 $3000 on $3000 bl (R)   14.00 8.25
Type "e" On Stamps of Northeastern Provinces
1949, Aug.
3L71   A2 $10 on $10 crim, II (Bl)   8.00 3.50
   a.   Type I   12.50 12.00

3L72   A2 $30 on 20c yel grn (R)   8.00 2.25
3L73   A2 $50 on $44 dk car rose (Bl)   8.00 1.25
3L74   A2 $100 on $3 brn (Bl)   14.00 6.50
3L75   A2 $200 on $4 org brn, II (Bl)   40.00 24.00
   a.   Type I   1,100. 450.00
On China No. 754 in Blue
3L76   A82 $10 on $7000 lt red brn   12.50 8.50
    Nos. 3L37-3L76 (39)   487.40 269.25

Overprints on Nos. 3L71 and 3L76 have 2 characters in center row.

Farmer and Worker on Globe — A5

1949, May 1   Engr.   *Perf. 14*
3L77   A5 $20 crimson   9.50 9.50
3L78   A5 $40 dark blue   9.50 9.50
3L79   A5 $60 brown org   9.50 9.50
3L80   A5 $80 dk green   9.50 9.50
3L81   A5 $100 purple   9.50 9.50
    Nos. 3L77-3L81 (5)   47.50 47.50

Labor day. Exists imperf. Value, set $50. Also issued in blocks of 4, imperf between. Value, unused or used, $17.50.

Mao Tse-tung (Chinese Numeral) — A6

Mao Tse-tung (Arabic Numeral) — A7

1949, July 1   *Perf. 14*
3L82   A6 $10 red   4.00 5.00
3L83   A7 $20 dk blue   2.00 3.50
3L84   A6 $50 orange   13.00 5.50
3L85   A7 $80 dk green   4.00 5.00
3L86   A6 $100 purple   10.00 2.75
3L87   A7 $120 olive   2.00 5.00
3L88   A6 $140 vio brn   10.00 6.50
    Nos. 3L82-3L88 (7)   45.00 33.25

28th anniv. of the founding of the Chinese Communist Party. Value, imperf, set $150.

Gate of Heavenly Peace — A8   Farmers and Factory — A9

1949, Nov. 26   Litho.   *Perf. 12½*
3L89   A8 $50 orange   1.00 7.00
3L90   A8 $100 crimson   .50 2.00
3L91   A8 $200 green   2.00 2.00
3L92   A8 $300 rose brn   15.00 4.50
3L93   A8 $400 blue   15.00 4.50
3L94   A8 $500 brown   15.00 2.50
3L95   A8 $700 violet   8.00 7.00
    Nos. 3L89-3L95 (7)   56.50 29.50

1949, Dec.   Engr.   *Perf. 14*
3L96   A9 $1000 orange   18.00 6.00
3L97   A9 $3000 dark blue   1.00 1.50
3L98   A9 $5000 crimson   1.00 2.75
3L99   A9 $10,000 red brown   1.00 5.75
    Nos. 3L96-3L99 (4)   21.00 16.00

NORTH CHINA PARCEL POST STAMPS

Parcel Post Stamps of China Nos. Q23-Q27 (Type PP3) Surcharged in Red, Black (#3LQ6-3LQ9) or Blue (#3LQ2)

a   b

c

1949, June

Surcharged Type "a"

3LQ1	$300 on $6,000,000		55.00
3LQ2	$400 on $8,000,000		55.00
3LQ3	$500 on $10,000,000		55.00
3LQ4	$800 on $5,000,000		55.00
3LQ5	$1000 on $3,000,000		75.00

Surcharged Type "b"

3LQ6	$500 on $3,000,000		75.00
3LQ7	$1000 on $5,000,000		90.00

Surcharged Type "c"

3LQ8	$3000 on $8,000,000		225.00
3LQ9	$5000 on $10,000,000		300.00
Nos. 3LQ1-3LQ9 (9)			985.00

Nos. 3LQ8-3LQ9 have large numerals unboxed.

Remittance Stamps of China (like North China Type A4) Surcharged in Black or Red

a   b

Peking Surcharge "a"

		Litho.	Perf. 13	
3LQ10	$6 on $5 ver		11.00	3.50
3LQ11	$20 on $50 gray		11.00	3.50
3LQ12	$50 on $20 dk vio brn		11.00	3.50
3LQ13	$100 on $10 ol grn		11.00	7.00

Tientsin Surcharge "b"

		Engr.	Perf. 14	
3LQ14	$20 on $1 brn org		14.00	6.00
a. Perf. 12½			22.50	7.50
3LQ15	$30 on $2 dk grn		14.00	6.00
a. Red surcharge			22.50	11.00
3LQ16	$30 on $10 ol grn		125.00	42.50
3LQ17	$100 on $10 gray grn (R)		14.50	

Litho.
Perf. 13

3LQ18	$50 on $5 red		14.00	6.00

Engr.
Perf. 14

3LQ19	$20 on $1 org brn		40.00	17.00

Perf. 12½

3LQ20	$100 on $10 yel grn (R)		65.00	30.00

Typo.
Roulette 9½

3LQ21	$30 on $2 bl grn (R)		50.00	20.00

The surcharge on No. 3LQ19 is without first and last lines.
Nos. 3LQ14, 3LQ14a, 3LQ15, 3LQ15a, 3LQ16-3LQ17, 3LQ19-3LQ20 issued with gum.

Locomotive — PP1

1949, Nov.   Engr.   Perf. 14

3LQ22	PP1	$500 crimn	17.50	17.50
3LQ23	PP1	$1000 dp		
		bl	175.00	50.00
3LQ24	PP1	$2000 green	250.00	75.00
3LQ25	PP1	$5000 dp		
		ol	350.00	150.00
3LQ26	PP1	$10,000 orange	650.00	300.00
3LQ27	PP1	$20,000 red brn	1,400.	1,000.
3LQ28	PP1	$50,000 brn pur	3,000.	1,400.
Nos. 3LQ22-3LQ28 (7)			5,842.	2,992.

NORTHWEST CHINA

The Northwest China Liberation Area consisted of the provinces of Sinkiang, Tsinghai, Ningsia and the western part of Shensi. The area was first established as the Shensi-Kansu-Ningsia Border Area in October, 1936, after the Long March to Yenan. Remote Sinkiang was not included until late 1949.

All Stamps Issued without Gum

Pagoda on Yenan Hill — A1

1945, Mar.   Litho.   Imperf.

4L1	A1	$1 green	26.00
4L2	A1	$5 dk blue	150.00
4L3	A1	$10 rose red	25.00
4L4	A1	$50 dull pur	30.00
4L5	A1	$100 yel grn	55.00
Nos. 4L1-4L5 (5)			286.00

Rouletted 9

4L1a	A1	$1	95.00
4L2a	A1	$5	160.00
4L3a	A1	$10	100.00

First issue; denomination in Chinese and Arabic. Heavy shading at top of vignette. Columns at sides.
See types A2, A3 and A4. For surcharges see Nos. 4L6-4L10, 4L23.

Nos. 4L1-4L2 Surcharged in Red:

a   b

c   d

1946, Nov.

4L6	A1 (a) $30 on $1 grn		35.00
4L7	A1 (b) $30 on $1 grn		160.00
a. Rectangular lower left character			1,000.
4L8	A1 (c) $30 on $1 grn		20.00
4L9	A1 (b) $60 on $1 grn		2,500.
4L10	A1 (d) $90 on $5 dk bl		29.00

Surcharge on Nos. 4L7a is type "b" as illustrated. Surcharge on No. 4L7 differs from "b," having lower left character as in type "a."
Surcharge on No. 4L9 the upper left surcharge character differs from that shown in "b."

A2

Pagoda on Yenan Hill (same size) — A3

1948, June

4L11	A2	$100 buff	175.00
4L12	A2	$300 rose pink	8.00
4L13	A2	$500 red	8.00
4L14	A2	$1000 blue	8.00
4L15	A2	$2000 yel grn	24.00
4L16	A2	$5000 dull pur	22.50
Nos. 4L11-4L16 (6)			245.50

Second issue; denominations in Chinese only. Many shades and proofs exist. For surcharge see No. 4L24.

1948, Dec.

4L17	A3	10c yel grg	2.00
4L18	A3	20c lemon	2.00
4L19	A3	$1 dk blue	2.00
4L20	A3	$2 vermilion	2.00
4L21	A3	$5 pale bl grn	11.00
4L22	A3	$10 violet	18.00
Nos. 4L17-4L22 (6)			37.00

Third issue; ornamental border at sides. Many shades exist.

Nos. 4L2 and 4L13 Surcharged in Red or Black

1949, Jan.

4L23	A1	$1 on $5 dk bl	80.00	80.00
4L24	A2	$2 on $500 red	40.00	40.00

Pagoda on Yenan Hill — A4

1949, May 1

4L25	A4	50c yel to olive	.75	.50
4L26	A4	$1 dl bl to indigo	.75	.50
4L27	A4	$3 ol yel to org yel	.75	.50
4L28	A4	$5 blue green	2.25	.55
a. Upper left character as on #4L25				
4L29	A4	$10 vio to dp vio	5.00	5.75
4L30	A4	$20 pink to rose red	11.00	13.00
Nos. 4L25-4L30 (6)			20.50	20.80

Fourth issue; light shading at top of vignette, columns without ornaments at sides. Many shades exist.

China Nos. 959, F2 and E12 Overprinted ("People's Post, Shensi")

1949, June 13   Engr.   Perf. 12½

4L31	A96	orange	25.00	16.00
4L32	R2	carmine	35.00	35.00
4L33	SD2	red vio	35.00	35.00
Nos. 4L31-4L33 (3)			95.00	86.00

Stamps of China, Sun Yat-sen Type A94 of 1949, Overprinted in Black or Red ("People's Post, Shensi")

Lithographed; Engraved

1949, July 1   Perf. 14, 12½

4L34	$10 green (887)		1.25	1.25
4L35	$20 vio brn (888)		1.25	2.25
4L36	$20 vio brn (896)		1.25	1.25
4L37	$50 dk Prus grn (889; R)		6.00	5.25
4L38	$50 grn (951)		6.00	5.25
4L39	$100 org brn (890)		14.50	6.25
4L40	$500 ros lil (892)		20.00	6.25
4L41	$1000 dp bl (952; R)		27.50	15.00
4L42	$2000 vio (902; R)		30.00	18.00
4L43	$5000 car (953)		45.00	37.50
4L44	$10,000 brn (954)		80.00	75.00
Nos. 4L34-4L44 (11)			232.75	173.25

Kansu-Ningsia-Tsinghai Area, Lanchow Overprints

China Nos. 959a, F2 and E12 Overprinted ("People's Post, Kansu")

1949, Oct.   Engr.   Rouletted

4L45	A96	orange	22.50	22.50

Perf. 12½

4L46	R2	carmine	32.50	32.50
4L47	SD2	red vio	32.50	32.50
Nos. 4L45-4L47 (3)			87.50	87.50

Stamps of China, Sun Yat-sen Type A94 of 1949, Overprinted ("People's Post, Kansu")

Engraved; Lithographed

1949, Oct.   Perf. 14, 12½

4L48	$10 grn (887)		2.25	2.25
4L49	$20 vio brn (888)		2.25	3.25
4L50	$50 dk Prus grn (889)		5.25	8.25
4L51	$100 org brn (890)		3.50	3.25
4L52	$100 dk org brn (898)		5.25	6.00
4L53	$200 red org (891)		6.50	5.25
4L54	$500 rose lil (892)		6.50	5.25
4L55	$1000 blue (894)		3.50	3.25
4L56	$1000 dp bl (901)		6.50	7.50
4L57	$2000 vio (902)		11.00	15.00
4L58	$5000 lt bl (903)		22.00	27.50
4L59	$10,000 sepia (904)		30.00	37.50
4L60	$20,000 ap grn (905)		60.00	72.50
Nos. 4L48-4L60 (13)			164.50	196.75

No. 4L54-4L60 exist with wider spaced overprints.

China Nos. 959, F2 and 791-792 Surcharged in Black or Red ("People's Post, Sinkiang")

1949, Oct.

4L61	A96	$1 on org	12.00	13.50
4L62	R2	$3 on car	18.00	20.00
4L63	A82	10c on $50,000 dp bl (R)	40.00	40.00
4L64	A82	$1.50 on $100,000 dl grn (R)	80.00	80.00
Nos. 4L61-4L64 (4)			150.00	153.50

Northwest People's Post

Mao Tse-tung — A5 Great Wall — A6

1949, Oct. 15   Litho.   Imperf.

4L65	A5	$50 rose	3.00	3.75
a.	$200 cliche in $50 plate		200.00	
4L66	A5	$100 dark blue	1.75	2.00
4L67	A5	$200 orange	1.75	6.00
4L68	A6	$400 sepia	6.75	7.50
	Nos. 4L65-4L68 (4)		13.25	19.25

EAST CHINA

The East China Liberation Area included the provinces of Shantung, Kiangsu, Chekiang, Anhwei and Fukien. The original postal service established in Shantung in 1941, became the East China Posts and Telegraph General Office in July, 1948.

All Stamps Issued without Gum

Mao Tse-tung — A1

Transportation and Tower — A2

1948, Mar.   Litho.   Perf. 10½

5L1	A1	$50 yel org	2.00	1.75
5L2	A1	$100 dp rose	6.00	3.00
5L3	A1	$200 dk vio bl	6.00	3.00
5L4	A1	$300 brt grn	7.00	3.00
5L5	A1	$500 dp blue	2.50	3.00
5L6	A1	$800 vermilion	7.00	2.50
5L7	A1	$1000 dk blue	11.00	11.00
5L8	A1	$5000 rose	27.50	27.50
5L9	A1	$10,000 dp car	70.00	70.00
	Nos. 5L1-5L9 (9)		139.00	124.75

Many varieties, including unissued imperforates exist.

Perf. 9 to 11 and compound

1949, Apr.   Litho.

5L10	A2	$1 yel grn	.60	.25
5L11	A2	$2 blue grn	.60	.25
5L12	A2	$3 dull red	.60	.25
5L13	A2	$5 pale brn (ovpt. 4x4mm)	.60	.25
a.	Without overprint		65.00	65.00
b.	Overprint 3x3mm		1.25	1.00
c.	As "b," purple overprint		65.00	
5L14	A2	$10 ultra	.60	.25
5L15	A2	$13 brt vio	.60	.25
5L16	A2	$18 brt blue	.60	.25
5L17	A2	$21 vermilion	.60	.25
5L18	A2	$30 gray	.60	.60
5L19	A2	$50 crimson	1.50	1.50
5L20	A2	$100 olive	27.50	22.00
	Nos. 5L10-5L20 (11)		34.40	26.10

Seventh anniv. of Shantung Communist Postal Administration. The overprint on the $5, character "yu" meaning "Posts," obliterates Japanese flag on tower, erroneously included in design. Value, imperfs. of Nos. 5L10-5L12, 5L13c, 5L14-5L20 on different paper, set $150.

Train and Postal Runner (1949.2.7) — A3

Mao, Soldiers, Map — A4

1949, Apr.   Litho.   Perf. 8 to 11

5L21	A3	$1 brt emer	.25	1.00
5L22	A3	$2 blue grn	.25	1.00
5L23	A3	$3 dk red	.25	1.00
5L24	A3	$5 brown	.35	1.50
5L25	A3	$10 ultra	.60	1.75
5L26	A3	$13 brt vio	.35	1.50
5L27	A3	$18 brt blue	.35	1.50
5L28	A3	$21 vermilion	3.50	4.00
5L29	A3	$30 slate	.35	2.00
5L30	A3	$50 crimson	.45	2.00
5L31	A3	$100 olive	2.00	3.50
	Nos. 5L21-5L31 (11)		8.70	20.75

7th anniv. of Shantung P. O., Feb. 7. Imperf. sets were sold by the Philatelic Dept., Tientsin P.O. Value $40. See Nos. 5L69-5L76. For surcharges see People's Republic of China Nos. 77-81.

Perf. 9½ to 11 and comp.

1949, Apr.

5L32	A4	$1 brt emer	.25	.25
5L33	A4	$2 blue grn	.25	.25
5L34	A4	$3 dull red	.25	.25
5L35	A4	$5 brown	.25	.25
5L36	A4	$10 ultra	.40	.25
5L37	A4	$13 brt vio	.40	.40
5L38	A4	$18 brt blue	.40	.40
5L39	A4	$21 vermilion	.40	.40
5L40	A4	$30 gray	.60	.50
5L41	A4	$50 crimson	.60	.50
5L42	A4	$100 olive	6.75	5.00
	Nos. 5L32-5L42 (11)		10.55	8.45

Victory of Hwai-Hai (Hwaiying and Haichow). Imperf. sets were sold by the Philatelic Dept., Tientsin P.O. Value, set $100.

Stamps of China, Sun Yat-sen Type of 1949, Surcharged in Red or Black

(Nanking) — a   (Wuhu) — b

1949, May 4   Engr.   Perf. 12½

5L43	A94 (a)	$1 on $10 grn (895, R)	1.00	.75
a.	Perf. 13		3.25	3.00
5L44	A94 (a)	$3 on $20 vio brn (896)	2.25	1.50
a.	Perf. 13		2.50	4.50
b.	Perf. 14		5.75	5.50
c.	Surcharge inverted		200.00	

Sun Yat-sen Type A94 Surcharged Type "b"

Lithographed, Engraved

1949, May   Perf. 12½, 14

5L45	$30 on $1000 dp bl (901)	10.00	7.50
5L46	$30 on $1000 bl (894)	10.00	7.50
5L47	$50 on $200 org red (899)	10.00	7.50
5L48	$100 on $5000 lt bl (903, R)	22.50	20.00
5L49	$300 on $10,000 sep (904, R)	67.50	60.00
5L50	$500 on $200 org red (899)	100.00	85.00
	Nos. 5L45-5L50 (6)	220.00	187.50

Many varieties exist.

China Nos. 913a and 913 Surcharged in Blue, Green, Black or Red

(East China)

1949, May   Litho.   Perf. 12½

5L51	A95	$5 on 50c on $20 brn, II (B)	17.50	16.00
a.	Green surcharge		100.00	100.00
5L52	A95	$10 on 50c on $20 brn, II	17.50	16.00

5L53	A95	$20 on 50c on $20 red brn, II (R)	17.50	16.00
a.	Type I (R)		21.00	21.00
	Nos. 5L51-5L53 (3)		52.50	48.00

Stamps of China, Sun Yat-sen Type of 1949, Surcharged in Black or Red

(Hangchow)

Engr., Litho. (No. 5L57)

1949, June 25   Perf. 14, 12½

5L54	A94	$1 on $1 org (886)	3.50	3.50
5L55	A94	$3 on $20 vio brn (896, R)	1.75	1.75
5L56	A94	$5 on $100 org brn (890)	7.00	7.00
5L57	A94	$5 on $100 dk org brn (898)	4.50	4.50
5L58	A94	$10 on $50 dk Prus grn (889, R)	22.00	22.00
5L59	A94	$13 on $10 grn (895)	2.25	2.25
	Nos. 5L54-5L59 (6)		41.00	41.00

East China Liberation Area

Maps of Shanghai and Nanking — A5

1949, May 30   Litho.   Perf. 8½ to 11

5L60	A5	$1 orange ver	.20	3.00
5L61	A5	$2 blue green	.20	3.00
5L62	A5	$3 brt violet	.25	3.00
5L63	A5	$5 violet brn	.25	.50
5L64	A5	$10 ultra	.25	1.00
5L65	A5	$30 slate	.25	2.50
5L66	A5	$50 carmine	.25	2.50
5L67	A5	$100 olive	.25	1.00
5L68	A5	$500 orange	7.00	7.00
	Nos. 5L60-5L68 (9)		8.90	23.50

Liberation of Shanghai and Nanking. Many shades, paper and perforation varieties and imperfs. exist.

Train and Postal Runner Type Dated "1949"

1949, July-1950, Feb.   Perf. 12½, 14

5L69	A3	$10 dp ultra	.25	.25
5L70	A3	$15 orange ver	.25	.45
a.	$15 red, perf. 14		.50	.30
5L71	A3	$30 slate green	.25	.25
a.	Perf. 12½		.50	.30
5L72	A3	$50 carmine	.25	.50
5L73	A3	$60 bl grn, perf. 14	.25	1.50
5L74	A3	$100 ol, perf. 14	8.00	2.00
5L75	A3	$1600 vio bl ('50)	.90	4.00
5L76	A3	$2000 brn vio ('50)	1.00	4.00
	Nos. 5L69-5L76 (8)		11.15	12.95

Chu Teh, Mao, Troops with Flags — A7   Mao Tse-tung — A8

1949, Aug. 17   Perf. 12½

5L77	A7	$70 orange	.25	.35
5L78	A7	$270 crimson	.25	.35
5L79	A7	$370 emerald	.50	.50
5L80	A7	$470 vio brn	.70	.60
5L81	A7	$570 blue	.40	.50
	Nos. 5L77-5L81 (5)		2.10	2.30

22nd anniv. of the People's Liberation Army. For similar type see Southwest China A1.

1949, Oct.

5L82	A8	$10 dk blue	14.00	20.00
5L83	A8	$15 vermilion	20.00	27.50
5L84	A8	$70 brown	.50	.50
5L85	A8	$100 vio brn	.50	.50
5L86	A8	$150 orange	.50	.50
5L87	A8	$200 grnsh gray	.50	.50
5L88	A8	$500 gray bl	.50	.50
5L89	A8	$1000 rose	.50	.50
5L90	A8	$2000 emerald	.50	.50
	Nos. 5L82-5L90 (9)		37.50	51.00

For surcharges see People's Republic of China Nos. 82-84.

Stamps of China, Sun Yat-sen Type of 1949 Surcharged in Black or Red

1949, Nov.   Litho.   Perf. 12½

5L91	A94	$400 on $200 org red (899)	22.50	1.50
5L92	A94	$1000 on $50 grnsh gray (897, R)	2.25	.70
5L93	A94	$1200 on $100 dk org brn (898)	.30	1.50
5L94	A94	$1600 on $200 ap grn (905)	.30	3.00
5L95	A94	$2000 on $300 dp bl (952,R)	.30	.75
a.	Perf. 14		45.00	25.00
	Nos. 5L91-5L95 (5)		25.65	7.45

EAST CHINA PARCEL POST STAMPS

Parcel Post Stamps of China 1945-48 Surcharged

(Shantung)

1949, Aug. 1   Engr.   Perf. 13

5LQ1	PP1	$200 on $500 grn	8.00	8.00
5LQ2	PP1	$500 on $1000 bl	30.00	18.00

Type PP3   Perf. 13½

5LQ3	$200 on $200,000 dk grn	30.00	16.00
5LQ4	$200 on $10,000,000 sage grn	30.00	14.00
5LQ5	$500 on $7000 dl bl	65.00	40.00
5LQ6	$500 on $50,000 indigo	10.00	10.00
5LQ7	$1000 on $10,000 car rose	10.00	10.00
5LQ8	$1000 on $100,000 dk rose brn	30.00	18.00
5LQ9	$1000 on $300,000 pink	10.00	10.00
5LQ10	$1000 on $500,000 vio brn	85.00	45.00
5LQ11	$1000 on $8,000,000 org ver	12.00	10.00
5LQ12	$2000 on $5,000,000 dl vio	30.00	30.00
5LQ13	$2000 on $6,000,000 brn blk	55.00	35.00
5LQ14	$3000 on $30,000 ol	55.00	35.00
5LQ15	$3000 on $70,000 org brn	24.00	24.00
5LQ16	$5000 on $3,000,000 dl bl	85.00	52.50
	Nos. 5LQ1-5LQ16 (16)	569.00	377.50

China Type A97, No. 987 Surcharged

$200 $500
$1000 $2000
$5000 $10,000

1949, Sept. 7   Litho.   Perf. 12½

5LQ17	$200 on $10	35.00	15.00
5LQ18	$500 on $10	35.00	15.00
5LQ19	$1000 on $10	35.00	15.00
5LQ20	$2000 on $10	50.00	32.50
5LQ21	$5000 on $10	75.00	50.00
5LQ22	$10,000 on $10	150.00	75.00
	Nos. 5LQ17-5LQ22 (6)	380.00	202.50

Flying Geese Type of China, 1949, and China Nos. 984-986 Surcharged in Red or Black

1950, Jan. 28

5LQ23	A97	$5000 on 10c bl vio (R)	30.00 25.00
5LQ24	A97	$10,000 on $1 brn org	45.00 40.00
5LQ25	A97	$20,000 on $2 bl	75.00 70.00
5LQ26	A97	$50,000 on $5 car rose	130.00 130.00

Nos. 5LQ23-5LQ26 (4) 280.00 265.00

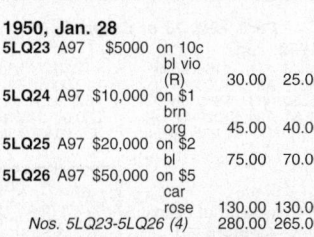

Parcel Post Stamps of China Type PP3, Nos. Q1-Q2, Q12-Q13 Surcharged in Red or Black

1950, Jan. 28   Engr.   Perf. 13, 13½

5LQ27		$5000 on $500 grn (R)	.75 15.00
5LQ28		$10,000 on $1000 bl (R)	80.00 65.00
5LQ29		$20,000 on $3000 bl grn	140.00 110.00
5LQ30		$50,000 on $5000 org red	7.50 75.00

Nos. 5LQ27-5LQ30 (4) 228.25 265.00

CENTRAL CHINA

The Central Chinese Liberation Area included the provinces of Honan, Hupeh, Hunan and Kiangsi. The area was established between August and September, 1949, following the occupation of Hankow by Red Army forces.

All Stamps Issued without Gum
Hupeh Postal and Telegraph Administration

Stamps of China, Sun Yat-sen Type A94 of 1949, Surcharged ("Chinese P.O., Temporary Use")

Engraved; Lithographed
1949, June 4   Perf. 14, 12½
Thin parallel lines

6L1	$1 on $200 red org (891)		3.50 4.00
6L2	$6 on $10,000 sep (904)		3.50 4.00
6L3	$15 on $1 org (886)		3.50 4.00
6L4	$30 on $100 org brn (890)		6.50 5.50
6L5	$30 on $100 dk org brn (898)		3.50 4.00
6L6	$50 on $20 vio brn (896)		25.00 14.00
6L7	$80 on $1000 dp bl (901)		4.75 4.00

Thick parallel lines

6L8	$1 on $200 red org (891)		5.25 5.25
6L9	$3 on $5000 lt bl (903)		3.50 4.00
6L10	$10 on $500 rose lil (892)		3.50 4.00
6L11	$10 on $500 rose lil (900)		4.75 4.00
6L12	$50 on $20 vio brn (888)		4.75 5.00
6L13	$50 on $20 vio brn (896)		4.00 5.00
6L14	$80 on $1000 bl (894)		6.50 5.00
6L15	$80 on $1000 dp bl (901)		27.00 16.00
6L16	$100 on $50 dk Prus grn (903)		5.00 6.00

Nos. 6L1-6L16 (16) 114.50 94.75

Kiangsi Postal and Telegraph Administration.
Central Trust Revenue Stamps of China Surcharged ("People's Post, Kiangsi")

(same size) — A1

$30 $60

1949, June 20   Engr.   Perf. 12½

6L17	A1	$3 on $30 pur	2.50 2.50
6L18	A1	$15 on $15 red org	2.50 2.50
6L19	A1	$30 on $50 dk bl	2.50 2.50
6L20	A1	$60 on $50 dk bl	2.50 2.50
6L21	A1	$130 on $15 red org	2.50 2.50

The $15 surcharge has 3 characters in left vertical row, the $130 surcharge has 5.

Same Surcharge on Sun Yat-sen Issues of China, 1945-49
Engraved, Lithographed
Perf. 14, 12½

6L22	A82	$1 on $250 dp lil (746)	6.50 6.50
6L23	A94	$5 on $1000 dp bl (901)	6.50 6.50
6L24	A94	$5 on $2000 vio (902)	6.50 6.50
6L25	A94	$5 on $5000 lt bl (903)	2.50 2.50
6L26	A94	$10 on $1000 bl (894)	6.50 6.50
6L27	A82	$20 on $4000 gray	2.50 2.50
6L28	A73	$20 on $100 dk car	6.50 6.50
6L29	A82	$30 on $20,000 rose pink	2.50 2.50
6L30	A94	$80 on $500 rose lil (900)	2.50 2.50
6L31	A94	$100 on $1000 dp bl (901)	2.50 2.50
6L32	A82	$200 on $250 dp lil	4.50 4.50

Nos. 6L17-6L32 (16) 62.00 62.00

Central China Posts and Telegraph Administration

Farmer, Soldier and Worker
A2   A3

I — Top white line of square character (yuan) at upper left does not touch left vertical stroke. No gap in shading between soldier's feet.
II — Top line connects with left vertical stroke. Gap in shading between feet.

Perf. 10 to 11½ & Comp.

1949   **Litho.**

6L33	A2	$1 orange	7.50 2.25
6L34	A2	$3 brn org	2.75 2.25
6L35	A2	$6 emerald	3.00 2.25
6L36	A3	$7 yel brn	.50 2.25
6L37	A2	$10 bl grn	.25 .35
6L38	A3	$14 org brn	27.50 25.00
6L39	A2	$15 ultra	.40 .50
6L40	A2	$30 grn, type I	.25 .40
a.		Type II	.80 .70
6L41	A3	$35 gray bl	17.50 20.00
6L42	A2	$50 rose vio	8.50 12.00
6L43	A2	$70 dp grn	.25 .25
6L44	A2	$80 pink	.55 .90
6L45	A3	$100 bl grn	.40 .95
6L46	A3	$220 rose red	3.50 .75

Nos. 6L33-6L46 (14) 72.85 70.10

Nos. 6L33 and 6L34 exist imperf. Value, each $13.50.
For surcharges & overprints see #6L63-6L65, 6L66-6L73, 6L75, 6L90-6L98, 6L100-6L108.

Star Enclosing Map of Hankow Area — A4

Two types of $500:
I — Thick numerals of "500." No period after "500."
II — Thin numerals and period.

Two types of $1000:
I — No period after "1000."
II — Period after "1000."

1949, July

6L48	A4	$110 org brn	.30 1.25
6L49	A4	$130 violet	4.00 2.00
6L50	A4	$200 dp org	.25 .50

6L51	A4	$290 brown	1.60 .50
6L52	A4	$370 dk bl	1.60 1.25
6L53	A4	$500 lt bl, I	4.00 .60
a.		$500 blue, II	18.00 7.00
6L54	A4	$1000 dull red, II	18.00 1.50
a.		$1000 dark red, I	25.00 8.00
6L55	A4	$5000 brown	.85 3.00
6L56	A4	$10,000 brt pink	1.75 6.00

Nos. 6L48-6L56 (9) 32.35 16.60

For surcharges and overprints see Nos. 6L74, 6L76-6L81, 6L99, 6L109.

Hankow River Customs Building
A5

River Wall, Wuchang — A6

Design: $290, $370, River scene, Hanyang.

1949, Aug. 16   Perf. 11

6L57	A5	$70 green	1.40 .90
6L58	A5	$220 crimson	1.40 1.25
6L59	A5	$290 brown	1.40 1.25
6L60	A6	$370 brt blue	1.40 1.25
6L61	A6	$500 purple	1.40 1.75
6L62	A6	$1000 vermilion	1.25 1.75

Nos. 6L57-6L62 (6) 8.25 8.15

Liberation of Hankow, Wuchang and Hanyang.
Exist imperf. About the same value.
For overprints see Nos. 6L82-6L87.

Nos. 6L35, 6L39 and 6L40 Surcharged in Red ("Honan Renminbi Currency")

1949, July

6L63	A2	$7 on $6 emer	3.00 4.00
6L64	A2	$14 on $15 ultra	4.50 6.00
6L65	A2	$70 on $30 grn	7.50 10.00

Nos. 6L63-6L65 (3) 15.00 20.00

Surcharge shown is for $70. The $7 has 5 characters in left column and no bottom line.

Issues of 1949 Overprinted ("Honan Renminbi Currency")

1949, Aug.

6L66	A2	$3 brn org	.95 .90
6L67	A3	$7 yel brn	.95 .90
6L68	A3	$10 bl grn	1.90 1.90
6L69	A3	$14 org brn	1.90 3.00
6L70	A3	$30 yel grn (6L40a)	2.00 3.00
6L71	A3	$35 gray bl	.95 5.00
6L72	A3	$50 rose vio	7.00 5.00
6L73	A3	$70 dp grn	2.00 3.75
6L74	A4	$110 org brn	7.00 7.00
6L75	A3	$220 rose red	6.00 6.00
6L76	A4	$290 brown	6.00 6.00
6L77	A4	$370 blue	10.00 10.00
6L78	A4	$500 bl, II	12.00 14.00
6L79	A4	$1000 dk red, I	25.00 30.00
6L80	A4	$5000 brown	100.00 110.00
6L81	A4	$10,000 brt pink	200.00 225.00

Nos. 6L66-6L81 (16) 383.65 431.45

Width of the overprint varies slightly.

Nos. 6L57-6L62 Overprinted ("Honan Renminbi Currency")

1949, Aug.   Perf. 11

6L82	A5	$70 green	2.00 2.50
6L83	A5	$220 crimson	3.50 3.75
6L84	A5	$290 brown	3.50 3.75
6L85	A5	$370 brt bl	5.50 6.00
6L86	A6	$500 purple	5.50 6.00
6L87	A6	$1000 vermilion	7.50 8.00

Nos. 6L82-6L87 (6) 27.50 30.00

Width of overprint on Nos. 6L82-6L85, 7mm; on Nos. 6L86-6L87, 12mm.
Exist imperf. About the same value.

Changchow Issue Surcharged in Red ("Honan Renminbi Currency")

(same size) Mao Tsetung — A7

1949, Sept.   Perf. 10

6L88	A7	$290 on $30 yel grn	27.50 30.00
6L89	A7	$370 on $30 yel grn	35.00 50.00

Issues of 1949 Surcharged

1950, Jan.

6L90	A2	$200 on $1	.55 1.75
6L91	A2	$200 on $3	3.00 1.60
6L92	A2	$200 on $6	.55 1.75
6L93	A3	$200 on $7	3.00 1.60
6L94	A3	$200 on $14	3.00 1.60
6L95	A3	$200 on $35	3.25 2.40
6L96	A3	$200 on $70	3.00 1.60
6L97	A3	$200 on $80	3.00 1.60
6L98	A3	$200 on $220	3.00 1.60
6L99	A4	$200 on $370	.50 1.75
6L100	A3	$300 on $70	.50 2.50
6L101	A3	$300 on $80	.50 1.75
6L102	A3	$300 on $220	.25 1.75
6L103	A2	$1200 on $3	32.50 32.50
6L104	A3	$1200 on $7	5.75 5.00
6L105	A3	$1500 on $14	8.25 6.75
6L106	A2	$2100 on $1	40.00 40.00
6L107	A2	$2100 on $6	40.00 40.00
6L108	A3	$2100 on $35	12.00 9.75
6L109	A4	$5000 on $370	5.00 5.00

Nos. 6L90-6L109 (20) 167.60 162.25

Two types of surcharge exist, differing in spacing of characters in top row.

CENTRAL CHINA PARCEL POST STAMPS

Star and Map of Hankow — PP1

1949, Nov.   Litho.   Perf. 11, 11½

6LQ1	PP1	$5000 brown	4.00 5.75
6LQ2	PP1	$10,000 scarlet	18.50 17.00
6LQ3	PP1	$20,000 dk sl grn	9.00 18.00
6LQ4	PP1	$50,000 vermilion	4.00 35.00

Nos. 6LQ1-6LQ4 (4) 35.50 75.75

SOUTH CHINA

The South China Liberation Area included the provinces of Kwangtung and Kwangsi and Hainan Island. The South China Postal and Telegraph Administration was organized on or about Nov. 4, 1949.

All Stamps Issued without Gum

Pearl River Bridge, Canton — A1

1949, Nov. 4   Litho.   Imperf.

7L1	A1	$10 green	.85	.50
7L2	A1	$20 sepia	.85	.50
7L3	A1	$30 violet	.85	.50
7L4	A1	$50 carmine	.85	.50
7L5	A1	$100 ultramarine	1.50	.50
		Nos. 7L1-7L5 (5)	4.90	2.50

For surcharges see Nos. 7L19-7L23.

China Nos. 993-995 With Additional Overprint in Red ("Liberation of Swatow")

1949, Nov. 9

7L6	A94	2½c on $500 rose lil (993)	32.50	32.50
a.		Handstamped	80.00	80.00
7L7	A94	2½c on $500 rose lil (994)	40.00	40.00
a.		Handstamped	95.00	95.00
7L8	A94	15c on $10 grn (995)	47.50	47.50
a.		Handstamped	175.00	175.00

On Unit Issues of China, 1949

7L9	A96	org (959)	19.00	12.50
7L10	AP5	bl grn (C62)	24.00	27.50
7L11	SD2	red vio (E12)	24.00	27.50
7L12	R2	car (F2)	20.00	27.50

On Sun Yat-sen and Flying Geese Issues of China

7L13	A94	2c org (974)	150.00	175.00
7L14	A94	4c bl grn (975)	300.00	375.00
7L15	A94	10c dp lil (976)	15.00	25.00
7L16	A94	20c bl (978)	30.00	32.50
7L17	A97	$1 brn org (984)	45.00	25.00
7L18	A97	$10 bl grn (987)	450.00	375.00
		Nos. 7L6-7L18 (13)	1,197.	1,217.

Forgeries exist of #7L13-7L14, 7L18.

Nos. 7L1-7L3 Surcharged in Red or Green

1950, Jan.

7L19	A1	$300 on $30 vio (R)	2.50	2.00
7L20	A1	$500 on $20 brn (R)	2.50	3.00
7L21	A1	$800 on $30 vio (G)	3.00	4.00
7L22	A1	$1000 on $10 gray grn (R)	3.50	3.00
7L23	A1	$1000 on $20 brn (R)	3.50	2.25
		Nos. 7L19-7L23 (5)	15.00	14.25

SOUTHWEST CHINA

The Southwest China Liberation Area included the provinces of Kweichow, Szechwan, Yunnan, Sikang and Tibet. The Southwest Postal and Telegraph Administration was organized on or about Nov. 15, 1949 after the liberation of Kweiyang, capital of Kweichow Province.

All Stamps Issued without Gum

Chu Teh, Mao and Troops — A1

1949, Dec.   Litho.   Perf. 12½

8L1	A1	$10 deep blue	2.50	3.75
8L2	A1	$20 rose claret	.40	1.25
8L3	A1	$30 dp org	.55	1.25
8L4	A1	$50 gray grn	.55	1.25
8L5	A1	$100 carmine	.90	.75
8L6	A1	$200 blue	1.25	1.00
8L7	A1	$300 bl vio	1.50	1.50

8L8	A1	$500 dk gray	2.75	2.25
8L9	A1	$1000 pale pur	7.50	6.00
8L10	A1	$2000 green	17.50	20.00
8L11	A1	$5000 orange	55.00	60.00
		Nos. 8L1-8L11 (11)	90.40	99.00

For surcharges and overprints see Nos. 8L21-8L29, 8L40-8L47, 8L55.

China Nos. 974-975, 984, 986-987 Surcharged ("Kweichow People's Post")

1949, Dec. 1   Perf. 12½

8L12	A94	$20 on 2c org	8.00	10.00
8L13	A94	$50 on 4c bl grn	12.00	12.00
8L14	A97	$100 on $1 brn org	20.00	15.00
8L15	A97	$400 on $5 car rose	40.00	45.00
8L16	A97	$2000 on $10 bl grn	140.00	95.00
		Nos. 8L12-8L16 (5)	220.00	177.00

Map of China, Flag Planted in Southwest A2

1950, Jan.   Litho.   Perf. 9 to 11½

8L17	A2	$20 dark blue	1.25	1.40
8L18	A2	$30 green	2.00	1.75
8L19	A2	$50 red	1.75	2.00
8L20	A2	$100 brown	2.00	2.00
		Nos. 8L17-8L20 (4)	7.00	7.15

Liberation of the Southwest.
For surcharges see #8L30-8L39, 8L56-8L59.

Nos. 8L5-8L6 Surcharged

Perf. 12½

8L21	A1	$300 on $100 car	3.50	4.00
8L22	A1	$500 on $100 car	3.50	4.00
8L23	A1	$1200 on $100 car	7.00	7.00
8L24	A1	$1500 on $200 bl	7.00	7.00
8L25	A1	$2000 on $200 bl	11.00	10.00
		Nos. 8L21-8L25 (5)	32.00	32.00

Nos. 8L5-8L6 Overprinted ("East Szechwan")

1950, Jan.

8L26	A1	$100 carmine	6.00	7.50
8L27	A1	$200 blue	6.00	7.50

Nos. 8L5-8L6 Handstamp Surcharged

1950, Jan.

8L28	A1	$1200 on $100 car	15.00	27.50
8L29	A1	$1500 on $200 bl	40.00	27.50

Many varieties, including wide and narrow settings, exist.

Nos. 8L17-8L20 Surcharged in Black or Red

叁仟圓 $3000   改作   伍仟圓 $5000

壹萬圓 $10,000   貳萬圓 $20,000   伍萬圓 $50,000

$60

$300

1950			**Perf. 9 to 11½**	
8L30	A2	$60 on $30	12.00	9.00
8L31	A2	$150 on $30	12.00	9.00
8L32	A2	$300 on $20 (R)	2.00	4.00
8L33	A2	$300 on $100	12.00	9.00
8L34	A2	$1500 on $100	72.50	22.50
8L35	A2	$3000 on $50	7.75	22.50
8L36	A2	$5000 on $50	3.50	22.50
8L37	A2	$10,000 on $50	120.00	42.50
8L38	A2	$20,000 on $50	4.00	42.50
8L39	A2	$50,000 on $50	5.75	60.00
		Nos. 8L30-8L39 (10)	251.50	243.50

Nos. 8L5-8L7 Overprinted ("West Szechwan")

1950, Jan.   Perf. 12½

8L40	A1	$100 carmine	22.50	24.00
8L41	A1	$200 pale blue	30.00	32.50
8L42	A1	$300 blue violet	40.00	42.50
		Nos. 8L40-8L42 (3)	92.50	99.00

Nos. 8L4-8L7 Surcharged

1950, Jan.

8L43	A1	$500 on $100	8.75	8.75
a.		Narrow spacing	70.00	60.00
8L44	A1	$800 on $100	8.75	8.75
8L45	A1	$1000 on $50	11.00	11.00
8L46	A1	$2000 on $200	22.50	27.50
8L47	A1	$3000 on $300	35.00	45.00
		Nos. 8L43-8L47 (5)	86.00	101.00

Two lines of surcharge 7mm apart on No. 8L43, 4mm on No. 8L43a.

China Nos. 975 and 977 Surcharged

Perf. 12½, 13 or Compound

1950, Jan.

8L48	A94	$100 on 4c	7.50	13.50
8L49	A94	$200 on 4c	12.00	22.50
8L50	A94	$800 on 16c	67.50	67.50
8L51	A94	$1000 on 16c	300.00	375.00
		Nos. 8L48-8L51 (4)	387.00	478.50

Unit Issue of China Overprinted ("Southwest People's Post")

1950, Jan.   Engr.   Rouletted

8L52	A96	orange	150.00	175.00
a.		Perf. 12½	225.00	250.00

Perf. 12½

8L53	SD2	red violet	225.00	250.00
8L54	R2	carmine	225.00	250.00
		Nos. 8L52-8L54 (3)	600.00	675.00

On No. 8L54, space between overprint columns is 3mm and right column is raised to height of left.

Nos. 8L3, 8L17-8L20 Surcharged in Black or Red

1950, Mar.   Perf. 12½, 9 to 11½

8L55	A1	$800 on $30	42.50	40.00
8L56	A2	$1000 on $50	9.00	12.00
8L57	A2	$2000 on $100	12.50	18.00
8L58	A2	$4000 on $20 (R)	35.00	37.50
8L59	A2	$5000 on $30	55.00	55.00
		Nos. 8L55-8L59 (5)	154.00	162.50

CHRISTMAS ISLAND

ˈkris-məs ˈī-lənd

LOCATION — In the Indian Ocean, 230 miles south of Java
GOVT. — A territory of Australia
AREA — 52 sq. mi.
POP. — 2,373 (1999 est.)

Australia took over Christmas Island from Singapore in 1958.

Catalogue values for all unused stamps in this country are for Never Hinged items.

Queen Elizabeth II — A1

Engr.; Name and Value Typo. in Black

1958, Oct. 15   Unwmk.   Perf. 14½

1	A1	2c yellow orange	1.00	2.10
2	A1	4c brown	1.00	.80
3	A1	5c lilac	1.00	.80
4	A1	6c dull blue	2.75	.80
5	A1	8c gray brown	5.50	1.40
6	A1	10c violet	3.75	.80
7	A1	12c carmine rose	5.75	4.75
8	A1	20c ultramarine	3.75	4.75
9	A1	50c yellow green	6.50	4.75
10	A1	$1 greenish blue	6.75	4.75
		Nos. 1-10 (10)	37.75	25.70
		Set, hinged	16.50	

Map of Island — A2   Island Scene — A3

4c, Moonflower. 5c, Robber crab. 8c, Phosphate train. 10c, Crane loading phosphate. 12c, Flying fish cove. 20c, Loading ship. 50c, Frigate bird. $1, Yellow-billed tropic bird.

Perf. 14x14½, 14½x14

1963, Aug. 28   Engr.

11	A2	2c orange	.90	.75
12	A2	4c red brown	.50	.35
13	A2	5c rose lilac	.50	.45
14	A3	6c slate	.45	.75
15	A2	8c black	2.75	.45
16	A2	10c violet	.45	.35
17	A3	12c dull red	.45	.55
18	A3	20c dark blue	1.00	.45
19	A3	50c green	1.40	.45

Size: 35x21mm

20	A3	$1 orange yellow	2.75	.75
		Nos. 11-20 (10)	11.15	5.60
		Set, hinged	6.50	

"Simpson and His Donkey" by Wallace Anderson — A3a

1965, Apr. 14   Photo.   Perf. 13½x13

21	A3a	10c brt grn, sepia & blk	.90	1.25

ANZAC issue. See note after Australia No. 387.

Moorish Goddess A4

Fish: 1c, Golden striped grouper. 3c, Forceps fish. 4c, Queen triggerfish. 5c, Regal angelfish. 9c, Surgeonfish. 10c, Turkeyfish. 15c, Saddleback butterflyfish. 20c, Clown butterflyfish. 30c, Ghost pipefish. 50c, Lined surgeonfish. $1, Meyer's butterflyfish.

1968-70   Photo.   Perf. 13½

22	A4	1c multicolored	.80	1.40
23	A4	2c multicolored	1.10	.60
24	A4	3c multicolored	1.10	.95
25	A4	4c multicolored	1.10	.60
26	A4	5c multicolored	1.10	.60
27	A4	9c multicolored	1.10	1.25
28	A4	10c multicolored	1.10	.60
29	A4	15c multicolored	16.00	7.75
30	A4	20c multicolored	3.00	1.75
31	A4	30c multicolored	16.00	7.75
32	A4	50c multicolored	3.75	4.75
33	A4	$1 multicolored	3.75	6.00
		Nos. 22-33 (12)	49.90	34.00
		Set, hinged	36.00	

Issued: 15c, 30c, 12/14/70; others, 5/6/68.

Christmas Issues

"Hark the Herald Angels Sing" — A5

1969, Nov. 10   Photo.   Perf. 13½

34	A5	5c dk blue, gold, buff & red	.45	.45

A6   A7

3c, The Ansidei Madonna, by Raphael. 5c, Virgin and Child, by Morando.

1970, Oct. 26   Photo.   Perf. 14x14½

35	A6	3c gold & multi	.20	.20
36	A6	5c silver & multi	.30	.30

1971, Oct. 4

5c, Adoration of the Shepherds, Seville School. 20c, Adoration of the Shepherds, by Guido Reni.

37	A7	6c black & multi	.90	.55
38	A7	20c dark blue & multi	1.90	1.40

"Flying Fish," 1887 — A8

Ships and Map of Christmas Island: 1c, "Eagle," 1714. 2c, "Redpole," 1890. 3c, "Hoi Houw", 1959. 4c, "Pigot," 1771. 5c, "Valetta," 1968. 7c, "Asia", 1805. 8c, "Islander," 1929-60. 9c, "Imperieuse," 1888 (incorrectly inscribed "Imperious"). 10c, "Egeria," 1887. 20c, "Thomas", 1615. 25c, "Gordon," 1864. 30c, "Cygnet," 1865. 35c, "Triadic," 1958. 50c, "Amethyst," 1857. $1, "Royal Mary," 1643.

1972-73   Photo.   Perf. 14½x13½

39	A8	1c yel green & multi	.35	.65
40	A8	2c lt red brn & multi	.40	.75
41	A8	3c dp rose & multi	.40	.75
42	A8	4c multicolored	.55	.80
43	A8	5c multicolored	.55	.80
44	A8	6c lilac & multi	.55	.80
45	A8	7c lt green & multi	.55	.80
46	A8	8c blue & multi	.55	.80
47	A8	9c org & multi	.85	.65
48	A8	10c lem & multi	.70	.75
49	A8	20c tan & multi	.95	1.00
50	A8	25c multicolored	1.00	1.60
51	A8	30c multicolored	1.00	1.00
52	A8	35c tan & multi	1.00	1.00
53	A8	50c ultra & multi	1.00	1.60
54	A8	$1 yellow & multi	1.40	1.90
		Nos. 39-54 (16)	11.80	15.65

Issued: 6c, 7c, 8c, 20c, 2/5/72; 1c, 2c, 3c, $1, 6/5/72; 4c, 5c, 9c, 50c, 2/6/73; 10c, 25c, 30c, 35c, 6/4/73.

A9 "Peace"   A9a "Joy"

1972, Oct. 2   Litho.   Perf. 14½

55	A9	3c black & multi	.70	.45
56	A9a	3c black & multi	.70	.45
a.		Pair, #55-56	1.50	1.50
57	A9	7c black & multi	.95	.80
58	A9a	7c black & multi	.95	.80
a.		Pair, #57-58	1.90	1.90
		Nos. 55-58 (4)	3.30	2.50

Mother and Child, Christmas Island Map — A10

1973, Oct. 2   Photo.   Perf. 14½x13½

59	A10	7c blue & multi	1.10	.65
60	A10	25c brt green & multi	3.25	2.50

Christmas.

Mother and Child with Star and Cross — A11

1974, Oct. 2   Photo.   Perf. 13½x14½

61	A11	7c black & lilac rose	.80	.65
62	A11	30c black & yellow	2.50	2.50

Christmas.

Flight into Egypt — A12

1975, Oct. 2   Photo.   Perf. 14½x13½

63	A12	10c gold, black & yel	.75	.45
64	A12	35c gold, vio blk & rose	1.50	1.75

Christmas.

Star of Bethlehem and Dove A13   A14

1976, Oct. 2   Photo.   Perf. 13½

65	A13	10c red & multi	.70	.45
66	A14	10c red & multi	.70	.45
a.		Pair, #65-66	1.50	1.50

67	A13	35c blue & multi	.95	.80
68	A14	35c blue & multi	.95	.80
a.		Pair, #67-68	1.90	1.90
		Nos. 65-68 (4)	3.30	2.50

Christmas.

Andrew Clunies-Ross (first settler) A15

Famous Visitors: 1c, William Dampier, explorer, buccaneer. 2c, Capt. Willem de Vlamingh, Dutch explorer. 3c, Vice Adm. John F. L. P. Maclear, Royal Navy. 4c, John Murray, oceanographer, scientist. 5c, Adm. Pelham Aldrich and crew collecting specimen. 7c, Joseph Jackson Lister, naturalist, and arenga listeri plant. 8c, Adm. William Henry May. 9c, Henry Nicholas Ridley, botanist. 10c, George Clunies-Ross, pioneer phosphate miner. 20c, Capt. Joshua Slocum. 45c, Charles William Andrews, zoologist, and frigate birds. 50c, Karl Richard Hanitsch, zoologist, and fruit pigeon. 75c, Victor W. W. Saunders Purcell, Sinologist. $1, Fam Choo Beng, educator. $2, Harold Spencer-Jones, astronomer.

1977-78   Photo.   Perf. 14x13½

69	A15	1c multicolored	.20	.90
70	A15	2c multicolored	.20	.90
71	A15	3c multicolored	.30	.90
72	A15	4c multicolored	.35	1.00
73	A15	5c multicolored	.35	.40
74	A15	6c multicolored	.35	.70
75	A15	7c multicolored	.35	.45
76	A15	8c multicolored	.40	.75
77	A15	9c multicolored	.45	2.25
78	A15	10c multicolored	.40	.65
79	A15	20c multicolored	.50	.80
80	A15	45c multicolored	.95	.50
81	A15	50c multicolored	1.10	2.25
82	A15	75c multicolored	1.00	1.75
83	A15	$1 multicolored	1.00	1.75
84	A15	$2 multicolored	1.60	2.75
		Nos. 69-84 (16)	9.50	18.70

Issued: 1c, 6c, 9c, $1, 4/30/77; 2c, 3c, 4c, $2, 2/22/78; 5c, 7c, 45c, 50c, 5/31/78; 8c, 10c, 20c, 75c, 9/1/78.

Australian Arms, Map of Christmas Island — A16

1977, June 2   Litho.   Perf. 14½x13½

85	A16	45c multicolored	.90	.90

25th anniv. of reign of Elizabeth II.

Souvenir Sheet

Partridge in a Pear Tree — A17

Twelve Days of Christmas: a, Partridge in a pear tree. b, 2 turtle doves. c, 3 French hens. d, 4 calling birds. e, 5 gold rings. f, 6 geese. g, 7 swans. h, 8 maids a-milking. i, 9 ladies dancing. j, 10 lords a-leaping. k, 11 pipers piping. l, 12 drummers drumming.

Unwmk.

1977, Oct. 20   Litho.   Perf. 14

86		Sheet of 12	2.10	2.50
a.-l.		A17 10c, single stamp	.20	.20
m.		Wmk. 373 ('78)	2.75	3.75

Christmas.

Common Design Types pictured following the introduction.

Elizabeth II Coronation Anniversary
Common Design Types
Souvenir Sheet

			Perf. 15	
1978, Apr. 21	**Litho.**			
87		Sheet of 6	4.75	4.75
a.	CD326	45c White swan of Bohun	.80	1.00
b.	CD327	45c Elizabeth II	.80	1.00
c.	CD328	45c Abbott's booby	.80	1.00

No. 87 contains 2 se-tenant strips of Nos. 87a-87c, separated by horizontal gutter with commemorative and descriptive inscriptions.

Souvenir Sheet

Christ Child — A18

Song of Christmas: a, Christ Child. b, Herald angels. c, Redeemer. d, Israel. e, Star. f, Three Wise Men. g, Manger. h. "All He stands for." i, "Shepherds came."

			Perf. 14	
1978, Oct. 2	**Litho.**			
88	A18	Sheet of 9	1.90	2.25
a.-i.		10c single stamp	.20	.20

Christmas. Each stamp design incorporates one letter of "Christmas."

IYC Emblem, Oriental Children — A19

Design: IYC emblem and children of different races holding hands, continuous design.

			Perf. 14	
1979, Apr. 20	**Litho.**			
89		Strip of 5	2.10	2.25
a.	A19 20c single stamp		.40	.40

International Year of the Child.

Rowland Hill and No. 25 A20

Sir Rowland Hill (1795-1879), originator of penny postage, and Christmas Island stamps: a, #1. b, #11. c, #21. d, #25. e, #34.

			Perf. 13½x13½	
1979, Aug. 27	**Litho.**			
90		Strip of 5	1.50	1.60
a.-e.	A20 20c any single		.20	.35

Three Kings Bearing Gifts — A21

Christmas: 55c, Virgin and Child, globe.

			Perf. 14x14½	
1979, Oct. 22	**Litho.**			
91	A21	20c multicolored	.30	.30
92	A21	55c multicolored	.65	.55

25 Years of Golf — A22

			Perf. 14½x14	
1980, Feb. 12	**Litho.**			
93	A22	20c shown	.55	.60
94	A22	55c Clubhouse	1.40	1.60

Surveyor, Phosphate Industry A23

			Perf. 14x14½	
1980-81	**Litho.**			
95	A23	15c shown	.35	.45
96	A23	22c Drilling for samples	.35	.45
97	A23	40c Sample analysis	.40	.50
98	A23	55c Mine planning	.60	.70
99	A23	15c Jungle clearing	.35	.35
100	A23	22c Overburden removal	.35	.35
101	A23	40c Open cut mining	.40	.40
102	A23	55c Restoration	.60	.60
103	A23	22c Screening and stockpiling	.40	.40
104	A23	28c Loading train	.50	.50
105	A23	40c Rail transport	.60	.60
106	A23	60c Drying	.70	.70
107	A23	22c Crushing	.40	.40
108	A23	28c Pipeline	.50	.50
109	A23	40c Bulk storage	.60	.60
110	A23	60c Loading ship	.70	.70
		Nos. 95-110 (16)	7.80	8.20

Issued: Nos. 96-98, 5/5/80; Nos. 99-102, 7/14/80; Nos. 103-106, 2/9/81; NOs. 107-110, 5/4/81.

Souvenir Sheet

Virgin and Child — A24

			Perf. 13½x13	
1980, Oct. 6	**Litho.**			
111		Sheet of 6	2.50	2.75
a.	A24 15c Angel		.20	.20
b.	A24 22c shown		.30	.35
c.	A24 60c Angel		.40	.40
d.	A24 15c Angel holding soldier		.20	.20
e.	A24 22c Kneeling woman and man		.30	.35
f.	A24 60c Chinese, Indian, European children		.40	.40

Christmas. No. 111 contains 2 strips of 3 (Nos. 111a-111c and 111d-111f) with gutter between.

Cryptoblepharus Egeriae — A25

Designs: Reptiles.

			Perf. 13½x13½	
1981, Aug. 10	**Litho.**			
112	A25	24c shown	.35	.35
113	A25	30c Emoia nativitata	.55	.55
114	A25	40c Lepidodactylus listeri	.65	.65
115	A25	60c Cyrtodactylus nov.	.80	.80
		Nos. 112-115 (4)	2.35	2.35

Souvenir Sheet

Nativity A26

			Perf. 14½x14	
1981, Oct. 19	**Litho.**			
116		Sheet of 4	1.90	2.10
a.	A26 18c Angels, star		.20	.20
b.	A26 24c shown		.30	.35
c.	A26 40c Children praying to Jesus		.55	.60
d.	A26 60c Children praying		.65	.75

Christmas.

Reef Heron A27

			Perf. 14	
1982-83	**Litho.**			
117	A27	1c shown	.75	.20
118	A27	2c Noddies	.75	.20
119	A27	3c Glossy swiftlet	.75	.75
120	A27	4c Imperial pigeon	.75	.75
121	A27	5c Christmas Isld. silvereyes	.95	.95
122	A27	10c Thrush	.75	.75
123	A27	25c Silver bosunbird	1.40	.75
124	A27	30c Christmas Isld. emerald doves	.80	.80
125	A27	40c Brown boobies	.80	.65
126	A27	50c Red-footed boobies	.80	.65
127	A27	65c Christmas Isld. frigatebird	.80	.65
128	A27	75c Golden bosunbirds	1.00	.90
129	A27	80c Nankeen kestrel, vert.	1.40	1.90
130	A27	$1 Christmas Isld. hawk owl, vert.	3.00	1.90
131	A27	$2 Goshawk, vert.	2.25	4.75
132	A27	$4 Abbott's boobies, vert.	3.50	3.50
		Nos. 117-132 (16)	20.45	20.05

Issued: 1c, 2c, 25c $4, 3/8; 3c, 4c, 10c, $2, 6/14; 40c, 50c, 65c, 75c, 8/23; 5c, 30c, 80c, $1, 2/21/83.

Christmas — A28   25th Anniv. of Boat Club — A29

Paper sculptures.

			Litho. & Embossed	
1982, Oct. 18				
135	A28	27c Joseph	.45	.45
136	A28	50c Angel	.60	.60
137	A28	75c Mary, Baby Jesus	.90	.70
a.	Strip of 3, #135-137		1.90	1.90

Perf. 14x14½, 14½x14

1983, May 2   **Litho.**

Designs: Various boating activities.

138	A29	27c multicolored	.55	.55
139	A29	35c multicolored	.55	.55
140	A29	50c multi, horiz.	.80	.80
141	A29	75c multi, horiz.	.80	.80
		Nos. 138-141 (4)	2.70	2.70

25th Anniv. of Australian Territory A30

			Perf. 14	
1983, Oct. 1	**Litho.**			
142	A30	24c Maps. golden bosun bird, kangaroo	.70	.45
143	A30	30c Map, flag	.80	.80
144	A30	85c Boeing 727, maps	1.60	1.60
		Nos. 142-144 (3)	3.10	2.85

Christmas — A31

Designs: Christmas candles.

			Perf. 13½x13	
1983, Oct. 31	**Litho.**			
145	A31	24c multicolored	.35	.35
146	A31	30c multicolored	.50	.50
147	A31	85c multicolored	1.25	1.50
		Nos. 145-147 (3)	2.10	2.40

Red Land Crab — A32

			Perf. 14x14½	
1984, Feb. 20	**Litho.**			
148	A32	30c Feeding	.75	.75
149	A32	40c Migration	.85	.85
150	A32	55c Developmental stages	.85	.85
151	A32	85c Adult female, young	1.40	1.40
		Nos. 148-151 (4)	3.85	3.85

Local Fungi — A33

			Perf. 13½x14½	
1984, Apr. 30				
152	A33	30c Leucocoprinus fragilissimus	.65	.65
153	A33	40c Microporus xanthopus	.80	.80
154	A33	45c Trogia anthidepas	1.00	1.00
155	A33	55c Haddowia longipes	1.10	1.10
156	A33	85c Phillipsia domingensis	1.40	1.40
		Nos. 152-156 (5)	4.95	4.95

Cricket on Christmas Isld., 25th Anniv. A34

			Perf. 14	
1984, July 23	**Litho.**			
157	A34	30c Runout	.75	.95
158	A34	40c Catch at point	.80	1.60
159	A34	55c Batsman	.90	1.60
160	A34	85c Batsman hitting	1.10	1.90
		Nos. 157-160 (4)	3.55	5.70

Souvenir Sheet

Christmas; Ausipex '84 A35

			Perf. 13½	
1984, Sept. 21	**Litho.**			
161		Sheet of 3 + 3 labels	3.25	3.25
a.	A35 30c Father Christmas arriving		.55	.55
b.	A35 55c Distributing gifts		1.10	1.10
c.	A35 85c Waving good-bye		1.50	1.50

Crabs A36

			Perf. 13½x13½	
1985	**Litho.**			
162	A36	30c Birgus latro	1.25	.90
163	A36	33c Cardiosoma hirtipes	1.25	.90
164	A36	33c Gecarcoidea natalis	1.40	1.00
165	A36	40c Ocypode ceratophthalma	1.40	1.00
166	A36	45c Ceonobita rugosa	1.40	1.25
167	A36	45c Metasesarma rousseauxi	1.60	1.50
168	A36	55c Coenobita brevimana	1.60	1.50
169	A36	60c Geograpsus stormi	2.10	1.90
170	A36	60c Grapsus tenuicrustatus	2.75	2.50
171	A36	85c Geograpsus grayi	3.00	2.75
172	A36	90c Ocypode cordimana	3.00	3.75
173	A36	90c Geograpsus crinipes	3.50	4.50
		Nos. 162-173 (12)	24.25	23.45

Issued: 30c, 40c, 55c, 85c, 1/30; #163, 166, 169, 172, 4/29; #164, 167, 170, 173, 7/22.

Once in Royal David's City — A37

Songs: 33c, While Shepherds Watched Their Flocks by Night. 45c, Away in a Manger. 60c, We Three Kings of Orient Are. 90c, Hark! The Herald Angels Sing.

1985, Oct. 28   Litho.   Perf. 14x14½
174	A37	27c multicolored	1.00	1.25
175	A37	33c multicolored	1.10	1.40
176	A37	45c multicolored	1.40	1.50
177	A37	60c multicolored	1.50	1.60
178	A37	90c multicolored	1.60	1.75
a.		Strip of 5, #174-178	8.25	9.00

Christmas.

Halley's Comet A38

1986, Apr. 30   Litho.   Perf. 14
179	A38	33c Over island	.65	.70
180	A38	45c Edmond Halley	.90	1.10
181	A38	60c Over phosphate shipping	1.25	2.10
182	A38	90c Over Flying Fish Cove	1.90	2.50
		Nos. 179-182 (4)	4.70	6.40

Indigenous Flowers — A39

1986, June 30   Litho.   Perf. 14
183	A39	33c Ridley's orchid	1.75	.60
184	A39	45c Hanging flower	1.10	1.00
185	A39	60c Hoya	1.10	1.75
186	A39	90c Sea hibiscus	1.50	2.50
		Nos. 183-186 (4)	5.45	5.85

Royal Wedding Issue, 1986
Common Design Type

Designs: 33c, Couple in Buckingham Palace garden. 90c, Andrew operating helicopter.

1986, July 23   Litho.   Perf. 14½x14
| 187 | CD338 | 33c multicolored | .65 | .55 |
| 188 | CD338 | 90c multicolored | 1.50 | 1.75 |

Christmas A40

Santa Claus at Christmas Island.

1986, Sept. 30   Litho.   Perf. 13x13½
189	A40	30c Speedboating	1.00	.75
190	A40	36c At the beach	1.10	.75
191	A40	55c Fishing	1.60	1.60
192	A40	70c Golfing	2.75	4.00
193	A40	$1 Sleeping in hammock	2.75	4.75
		Nos. 189-193 (5)	9.20	11.85

Visiting Ships, Cent. A41

1987, Jan. 21   Perf. 14½
| 194 | A41 | 36c Flying Fish | 1.40 | .80 |
| 195 | A41 | 90c Egeria | 2.50 | 2.50 |

Wildlife A42

1987-89   Litho.   Perf. 14
196	A42	1c Blind snake	.60	1.00
197	A42	2c Blue-tailed skink	.60	1.00
198	A42	3c Insectivorous bat	1.10	1.00
199	A42	5c Green cricket	1.10	1.00
200	A42	10c Christmas Is. fruit bat	1.10	1.00
201	A42	25c Gecko	1.40	1.10
202	A42	30c Praying mantis	1.60	1.40
203	A42	36c Hawk owl	3.50	2.25
204	A42	40c Bull-mouth helmet shell	2.25	1.90
204A	A42	41c Nudibranch ('89)	5.00	3.25
205	A42	50c Textile cone shell	2.50	2.25
206	A42	65c Brittle-stars	1.60	1.40
207	A42	75c Royal angelfish	1.60	1.90
208	A42	90c Christmas Is. white butterfly	5.00	4.50
209	A42	$1 Mimic butterfly	5.00	4.50
210	A42	$2 Shrew	5.00	8.25
211	A42	$5 Green turtle	6.00	8.75
a.		Sheet of 16, #196-204, 205-211	110.00	110.00
		Nos. 196-211 (17)	44.95	46.45

Issued: 1c, 2c, 25c, $5, 3/25; 3c, 10c, 36c, $2, 6/24; 40c, 50c, 65c, 75c, 8/26; 5c, 30c, 90c, $1, 3/1/88; 41c, 9/1/89.
Stamps contained in No. 211a inscribed "1988" at bottom.
For overprint see Nos. 246-247.

Souvenir Sheet

Santa Claus Delivering Presents — A43

Illustration reduced.

1987, Oct. 7   Litho.   Perf. 13½
212	A43	Sheet of 4	6.25	6.25
a.		30c multicolored	.65	.65
b.		37c multicolored	.70	.70
c.		90c multicolored	1.90	1.90
d.		$1 multicolored	2.10	2.10

Christmas. Nos. 212a-212d printed in a continuous design.

Australia Bicentennial A44

Designs: a, First Fleet sighted by 5 Aboriginals on land. b, Four Aboriginals on land, one in canoe. c, Ships entering bay, kangaroos. d, Europeans land. e, Flag raising.

1988, Jan. 26   Litho.   Perf. 13
| 213 | | Strip of 5 | 11.00 | 11.00 |
| a.-e. | A44 | 37c any single | 1.90 | 1.90 |

Nos. 213a-213e printed in a continuous design. See Cocos Islands No. 172.

Annexation of the Island, Cent. — A45

1988, June 8   Litho.   Perf. 14½
214	A45	37c Capt William Henry May	.80	.80
215	A45	53c Annexation ceremony	1.10	1.10
216	A45	95c HMS Imperieuse	1.90	1.90
217	A45	$1.50 Building cairn of stones	2.50	2.50
		Nos. 214-217 (4)	6.30	6.30

Settlement of Christmas Is., Cent. — A46

Transportation: 37c, Horse and cart, 1910. 55c, Phosphate mining, 1910. 70c, Steam locomotive, 1914. $1, Arrival of first aircraft, 1957.

1988, Aug. 24   Litho.   Perf. 14½
218	A46	37c multicolored	.95	.55
219	A46	55c multicolored	1.40	.75
220	A46	70c multicolored	1.40	1.00
221	A46	$1 multicolored	2.25	1.60
		Nos. 218-221 (4)	6.00	3.90

Christmas Presents — A47

1988, Nov. 15   Perf. 14x14½
222	A47	32c Bucket, shovel, boat	.70	.70
223	A47	39c Snorkeling equipment	.90	.90
224	A47	90c Toy soldier, doll, stuffed animals	1.90	1.90
225	A47	$1 Race car, truck, plane	2.25	2.25
		Nos. 222-225 (4)	5.75	5.75

Chinese New Year — A48

1989, Jan. 31   Perf. 14½
226	A48	39c Good harvest	.80	.70
227	A48	70c Prosperity	1.50	1.40
228	A48	90c Good fortune	2.00	1.60
229	A48	$1 Progress	2.25	1.90
		Nos. 226-229 (4)	6.55	5.60

Sir John Murray (1841-1914), Oceanographer — A49

1989, Mar. 16   Perf. 14½x14
230	A49	39c Portrait	.80	.80
231	A49	80c Murray Hill (map)	1.50	1.50
232	A49	$1 Murray's equipment	1.90	1.90
233	A49	$1.10 HMS Challenger	2.25	2.25
		Nos. 230-233 (4)	6.45	6.45

Malay-Hari Raya Folk Celebration — A50

1989, May 31   Perf. 14
234	A50	39c Children	.70	.65
235	A50	55c Tambourine player	1.10	.95
236	A50	80c Girl	1.60	1.40
237	A50	$1.10 Minaret	2.25	2.10
		Nos. 234-237 (4)	5.65	5.10

Ferns A51

Christmas A52

1989, Aug. 16
238	A51	41c Huperzia phlegmaria	1.00	1.00
239	A51	65c Asplenium polydon	1.40	1.40
240	A51	80c Davallia denticulata	1.60	1.40
241	A51	$1.10 Asplenium nidus	2.25	2.25
		Nos. 238-241 (4)	6.25	6.05

1989, Oct. 4   Litho.   Perf. 14½x15
Biblical scenes: 36c, Joseph. 41c, Manger. 80c, Shepherds see star. $1.10, Magi riding camels.
242	A52	36c multi	.75	.55
243	A52	41c multi	.80	.60
244	A52	80c multi	2.10	.90
245	A52	$1.10 multi	2.25	1.25
		Nos. 242-245 (4)	5.90	3.30

Nos. 204A and 209 Overprinted

1989, Oct. 18   Litho.   Perf. 14
| 246 | A42 | 41c multicolored | 1.40 | .60 |
| 247 | A42 | $1 multicolored | 4.75 | 1.40 |

STAMPSHOW '89, Melbourne.
No. 247 is dated "1989."

1st Sighting of Christmas Is., 375th Anniv. — A53

Sightings of the island: 41c, John Milward, master of the British East India ship *Thomas*, 1615. $1.10, William Mynors, captain of *Royal Mary*, 1643.

1990, Jan. 31   Litho.   Perf. 14x15
| 248 | A53 | 41c multicolored | 2.25 | .65 |
| 249 | A53 | $1.10 multicolored | 2.75 | 1.75 |

Transport Through the Ages — A55

Perf. 14x13½, 13½x14

				Unwmk.
1990		**Litho.**		
254	A55	1c	Phosphate transport	.30 .30
255	A55	2c	Phosphate train	.55 .55
256	A55	3c	Rail car, vert.	.40 .40
257	A55	5c	Road train	.60 .60
258	A55	10c	Trishaw, vert.	.50 .50
259	A55	15c	Terex	1.25 1.05
260	A55	25c	Long bus	.50 .50
261	A55	30c	Passenger rake, vert.	.50 .50
262	A55	40c	Passenger barge, vert.	.60 .50
263	A55	50c	Kolek canoe	.80 .60
264	A55	65c	Flying doctor, ambulance	5.50 2.25
265	A55	75c	Tradestore van	2.75 2.75
266	A55	90c	Vintage truck	2.75 2.75
267	A55	$1	Water tanker	3.00 2.75
268	A55	$2	Traction engine	3.75 3.75
269	A55	$5	Steam locomotive, flat car	5.25 6.75
		Nos. 254-269 (16)		29.00 26.50

Issued: 1c, 3c, 10c, 25c, 30c, 40c, 50c, $5, Apr. 18; others, Aug. 22.

World Wildlife Fund — A56

Abbott's boobies (*Sula abbotti*): 20c, Adult (facing left). 29c, Adult (facing right). No. 273, Adults, nest, hatchling. No. 274a, Adult landing on tree branch. No. 274b, Adult resting on branch. No. 274c, Adult, young in nest.

Perf. 14x14½

				Unwmk.
1990, June 6		**Litho.**		
270	A56	10c	shown	2.10 2.10
271	A56	20c	multicolored	2.75 2.75
272	A56	29c	multicolored	3.00 3.00
273	A56	41c	multicolored	3.75 3.75
		Nos. 270-273 (4)		11.60 11.60

Souvenir Sheet
Perf. 14½

274	Sheet of 3		14.50 14.50
a.-c.	A56 41c any single		4.75 4.75
d.	Overprinted in purple		22.00 22.00
e.	Overprinted in green		52.50 52.50

No. 274d overprint reads "WORLD STAMP EXHIBITION / AUCKLAND, NEW ZEALAND, 24 AUGUST-2 SEPTEMBER 1990."
No. 274e overprint reads "BIRDPEX '90 National Philatelic Exhibition / University of Canterbury Christchurch NZ 6-9 Dec 1990 / In Conjunction / With The 20th International Ornithological Congress" and Bird's head.
Issued: #274d, Aug. 24; #274e, Dec. 6.

Centenary of Visit by Botanist Henry Ridley — A57

1990, July 11		**Litho.**		**Perf. 14½**
275	A57	41c	No. 77	1.60 .90
276	A57	75c	Ridley, vert.	2.50 2.25

Christmas A58

Flowers.

1990, Oct. 3		**Litho.**		**Perf. 14½**
294	A58	38c	Corymborkus veratrifolia	1.10 1.00
295	A58	43c	Hoya aldrichii	1.40 1.10
296	A58	80c	Quisqualis indica	2.25 2.25
297	A58	$1.20	Barringtonia racemosa	3.25 3.75
		Nos. 294-297 (4)		8.00 8.10

1st Phosphate Mining Lease, Cent. — A59

1991, Feb. 13		**Litho.**		**Perf. 14½**
298	A59	43c	Freighter	1.40 1.40
299	A59	43c	Loading rail cars	1.40 1.40
300	A59	85c	Shay locomotive	1.60 1.60
301	A59	$1.20	Bucket shovel	2.25 2.25
302	A59	$1.70	Reforestation	2.75 2.75
a.	Strip of 5, #298-302			9.00 9.00

Island Police Force — A60

1991, Apr. 17		**Litho.**		**Perf. 14½**
303	A60	43c	Community relations	1.90 1.90
304	A60	43c	Traffic control	1.90 1.90
305	A60	90c	Customs and quarantine	2.75 2.75
306	A60	$1.20	Search and rescue	3.50 3.50
a.	Souvenir sheet of 4, #303-306			10.50 8.75
		Nos. 303-306 (4)		10.05 10.05

Maps — A61

1991, June 19		**Litho.**		**Perf. 14**
307	A61	43c	1991	1.40 1.40
308	A61	75c	Goos Atlas, 1666	2.50 2.25
309	A61	$1.10	Apres De Manevillette, 1745	3.00 3.00
310	A61	$1.20	Comberford, 1667	3.25 3.25
		Nos. 307-310 (4)		10.15 9.90

Trees A62

1991, Aug. 21		**Litho.**		**Perf. 14**
311	A62	43c	Bruguiera gymnorrhiza	1.60 1.60
312	A62	70c	Syzygium operculatum	2.25 2.25
313	A62	85c	Ficus microcarpa	2.50 2.50
314	A62	$1.20	Arenga listeri	2.75 2.75
		Nos. 311-314 (4)		9.10 9.10

Christmas A63

Drawings of "What Christmas Means to Me" by: No. 315a, S'ng Yen Luiw. b, Liew Ann Nee. c, Foo Pang Chuan. d, Too Lai Peng. e, Jesamine Wheeler. 43c, Ho Puay Ha. $1, Ng Hooi Hua. $1.20, Yani Kawi.

1991, Oct. 2	**Litho.**		**Perf. 14½**
315	Strip of 5		5.50 5.50
a.-e.	A63 38c any single		1.00 1.00

316	A63	43c	multicolored	1.10 .95
317	A63	$1	multicolored	2.50 2.50
318	A63	$1.20	multicolored	2.75 2.75
		Nos. 315-318 (4)		11.85 11.70

A64   Shells — A65

War Time Evacuation, 50th Anniv.: No. 319, Conference to decide upon evacuation. No. 320, Europeans awaiting barge. $1.05, Barge approaching waiting ship. $1.20, Remaining population waving to TSS Islander.

1992, Feb. 19		**Litho.**		**Perf. 14½**
319	A64	45c	multicolored	1.40 1.40
320	A64	45c	multicolored	1.40 1.40
321	A64	$1.05	multicolored	3.25 3.25
322	A64	$1.20	multicolored	3.50 3.50
		Nos. 319-322 (4)		9.55 9.55

1992		**Litho.**		**Perf. 15x14½**
326	A65	5c	Cypraea tigris	.70 1.00
327	A65	10c	Cypraea caputserpentis	1.05 1.00
328	A65	15c	Lambis scorpius	1.40 1.00
329	A65	20c	Chlamys pallium	1.40 1.00
330	A65	25c	Engina mendicaria	1.40 1.00
331	A65	30c	Drupa ricinus	1.40 1.00
332	A65	40c	Distorsio reticulata	1.40 1.00
333	A65	45c	Turbo petholatus	1.75 1.10
334	A65	50c	Cantharus pulcher	1.75 1.10
335	A65	60c	Conus capitaneus	2.25 1.40
336	A65	70c	Turbo lajonkairii	2.75 1.50
337	A65	80c	Lambis chiragra	2.75 1.75
338	A65	90c	Angaria delphinus	2.75 2.10
339	A65	$1	Vasum ceramicum	2.75 2.10
340	A65	$2	Tonna perdix	2.10 3.00
341	A65	$5	Drupa rubusidaea	5.25 5.00
		Nos. 326-341 (16)		32.85 26.05

Issued: 10c, 20c, 30c, 45c, 60c, 80c, $1, $2, 4/15; 5c, 15c, 25c, 40c, 50c, 70c, 90c, $5, 8/19.
For overprint see No. 348.

Sinking of Eidsvold and Nissa Maru, 50th Anniv. A66

Designs: 45c, Eidsvold hit by torpedo. 80c, Eidsvold sinking. $1.05, Nissa Maru hit by torpedo. $1.20, Nissa Maru sinking.

1992, June 17		**Litho.**		**Perf. 14x13½**
343	A66	45c	multicolored	1.90 1.40
344	A66	80c	multicolored	2.75 2.75
345	A66	$1.05	multicolored	3.25 3.25
346	A66	$1.20	multicolored	3.25 3.25
		Nos. 343-346 (4)		11.15 10.65

Christmas — A67

Coastline, booby birds: a, 40c, Plants on shore, birds. b, 40c, Birds, rocks offshore. c, 45c, Birds on shore. d, $1.05, Birds in flight, coastline. e, $1.20, Forest, rocky coastline.

1992, Oct. 7	**Litho.**		**Perf. 14½**
347	A67	Strip of 5, #a.-e.	10.00 10.00

No. 341 Ovptd. in Red Violet

1992, Sept. 1		**Litho.**		**Perf. 15x14½**
348	A65	$5	on #342	13.00 8.75

Kuala Lumpur Philatelic Exhibition.

Starting with No. 349, Christmas Island stamps are valid for postage on items mailed in Australia and Australian stamps are valid on items posted on Christmas Island.

Seabirds — A68

Designs: a, Abbott's booby. b, Christmas Island frigatebird. c, Common noddy. d, Golden bosunbird. e, Brown booby.

1993, Mar. 4		**Litho.**		**Perf. 14½x14**
349	A68	45c	Strip of 5, #a.-e.	4.75 5.00
f.	Souvenir sheet of 5, #a.-e.			5.50 5.50
g.	As "f," overprinted			16.50 16.50
h.	As "f," overprinted			14.50 14.50

No. 349g Ovptd. in Gold in sheet margin with Taipei '93 emblem and: "ASIAN INTERNATIONAL INVITATION STAMP EXHIBITION / TAIPEI '93" in Chinese and English.
No. 349h Ovptd. in Gold in Sheet Margin with "INDOPEX '93 / 6TH ASIAN INTERNATIONAL PHILATELIC EXHIBITION 1993 / PAMERAN INTERNASIONAL PENGUMPULAN / KEENAM DI ASIA TAHUN 1993" and show emblem.
Issued: #349g, 4/93; #349h, 5/29/93.

Scenic Views — A69

1993, June 1				**Perf. 14x14½**
350	A69	85c	Dolly Beach	1.90 1.90
351	A69	95c	Blow holes	2.25 2.25
352	A69	$1.05	Merrial Beach	2.50 2.50
353	A69	$1.20	Rain forest	2.75 2.75
		Nos. 350-353 (4)		9.40 9.40

Christmas — A70

1993, Sept. 2		**Litho.**		**Perf. 14½x14**
354	A70	40c	Turtle on beach	1.40 1.40
355	A70	45c	Crabs, wave	1.40 1.40
356	A70	$1	Frigatebird, rainforest	3.00 3.00
		Nos. 354-356 (3)		5.80 5.80

Naming of Christmas Island, 350th Anniv. — A71

1993, Dec. 1	**Litho.**		**Perf. 14x14½**
357	A71	$2	multicolored	4.50 4.50

New Year 1994 (Year of the Dog) — A72

1994, Jan. 20   Litho.   Perf. 14x14½
358 A72 45c shown   1.75   1.90
359 A72 45c Pekingese   1.75   1.90
a.   Pair, #358-359   3.25   4.00
b.   Souvenir sheet of 1, #359a   4.75   4.75
c.   As "b," overprinted   5.00   5.00
d.   As "b," overprinted   8.25   8.25
e.   As "b," overprinted   8.25   8.25
f.   As "b," overprinted   17.50 17.50

No. 359c Ovptd. in gold in sheet margin with dog and "Melbourne / STAMP & COIN SHOW / 11-13 February 1994;" No. 359d with "HONG KONG '94 STAMP EXHIBITION" and show emblem; No. 359e with "Canberra /Stamp Show '94 / 19-21 March / 1994" and show emblem; No. 359f with "QUEENSLAND STAMP & COIN SHOW 1994 / JUNE 11, 12, 13."

Issued: #359c, 2/11/94; #359d, 2/18/94; #359e, 3/19/94; #359f, 1995.

Christmas Island Railway Steam Locomotives A73

1994, May 19   Litho.   Perf. 14x14½
360 A73 85c Locomotive No. 4   2.25   1.90
361 A73 95c Locomotive No. 9   2.50   1.90
362 A73 $1.20 Locomotive No. 1   3.00   2.25
Nos. 360-362 (3)   7.75   6.05

Orchids — A74

a, Brachypeza archytas. b, Thelasis capitata. c, Corymborkis veratrifolia. d, Flickingeria nativitatis. e, Dendrobium crumenatum.

1994, Aug. 16   Litho.   Perf. 14½x14
363 A74 45c Strip of 5, #a.-e.   7.75   7.75

Christmas A75

1994, Sept. 8   Litho.   Perf. 14x14½
364 A75 40c Angel   1.25   .90
365 A75 45c Wise man   1.40   .90
366 A75 80c Bethlehem   1.90   1.60
Nos. 364-366 (3)   4.55   3.40

New Year 1995 (Year of the Boar) — A76

Design: 85c, Stylized boar, diff.

1995, Jan. 12   Litho.   Perf. 14x14½
367 A76 45c shown   1.00   .95
368 A76 85c multicolored   1.75   1.50
a.   Souvenir sheet, #367-368   3.50   3.50
b.   As "a," overprinted   8.75   8.75

No. 368b ovptd. in gold in sheet margin with outline of boar and: "STAMP & COIN FAIR / ROYAL EXHIBITION BUILDING / MELBOURNE VIC. 3000 . 10-12 FEB 1995."

Christmas Island Golf Course, 40th Anniv. — A77

1995, May 11   Litho.   Perf. 14
369 A77 $2.50 multicolored   8.25   8.25

Christmas A78

Santa Claus riding great frigatebird: 40c, Reading map. 45c, Dropping presents. 80c, Waving.

1995, Sept. 14   Litho.   Perf. 14x14½
370 A78 40c multicolored   1.10   .95
371 A78 45c multicolored   1.25   .95
372 A78 80c multicolored   1.90   1.50
Nos. 370-372 (3)   4.25   3.40

End of World War II, 50th Anniv. — A79

#373a, RAAF reconnaissance flight, 1945. #373b, Arrival of HMS Rother, 1945.

Litho. & Engr.
1995, Oct. 12   Perf. 14x14½
373   Pair   3.25   3.25
a.-b. A79 45c any single   1.50   1.50

Angelfish A80

1995, Oct. 12   Litho.
374 A80 75c Lemonpeel   1.75   1.75
375 A80 $1 Emperor   2.75   2.75

New Year 1996 (Year of the Rat) A81

1996, Jan. 9   Litho.   Perf. 14x14½
376 A81 45c Facing right   1.25   1.25
377 A81 45c Facing left   1.25   1.25
a.   Pair, #376-377   2.50   2.50
b.   Souvenir sheet, #377a   2.75   2.75
c.   As "b," overprinted   11.00 11.00

No. 377c overprinted in gold in sheet margin "STAMP AND COIN FAIR / MELBOURNE / 23-25 February 1996."

Fish — A82

1996-97   Litho.   Perf. 14x14½
381 A82 20c Pinktail triggerfish   .65   .65
382 A82 30c Longnose filefish   .80   .80
383 A82 45c Princess anthias   1.10   1.10

384 A82 85c Green moon wrasse   1.75   1.75
385 A82 90c Spotted boxfish   2.10   2.10
386 A82 95c Moorish idol   2.10   2.10
387 A82 $1.20 Glass bigeye   2.75   2.75
Nos. 381-387 (7)   11.25 11.25

Issued: 20c, 30c, 45c, 90c, 4/18/96; 85c, 95c, $1.20, 7/17/97.

Birds — A83

1996, July 11   Litho.   Perf. 14½x14
399 A83 45c White-eye   1.40   1.40
400 A83 85c Hawk-owl   2.25   2.25

Christmas A84

Sailing ships, words from Christmas carol: 40c, "I Saw Three Ships." 45c, "Come sailing in." 80c, "On Christmas day in the morning."

1996, Sept. 12   Litho.   Perf. 14
401 A84 40c multicolored   1.10   .75
402 A84 45c multicolored   1.25   .90
403 A84 80c multicolored   1.90   1.50
Nos. 401-403 (3)   4.25   3.15

Exploration of Australian Coast & Christmas Island by Willem de Vlamingh, 300th Anniv. — A85

"Portrait of a Dutch Navigator," by Jan Verkolje.

1996, Oct. 27   Litho.   Perf. 14
404 A85 45c multicolored   3.25   3.25

No. 404 was issued se-tenant with Australia No. 1571 (No. 1571a).

New Year 1997 (Year of the Ox) — A86

Constellation and: No. 405, Ox facing right. No. 406, Ox facing left.

1997, Jan. 6   Litho.   Perf. 14x14½
405 A86 45c multicolored   1.25   1.25
406 A86 45c multicolored   1.25   1.25
a.   Pair, #405-406   2.75   2.75
b.   Souvenir sheet, #405-406   3.25   3.25

Christmas A87

Santa on Christmas Island: 40c, Reading letters. 45c, Making toys. 80c, In sleigh.

1997, Sept. 11   Litho.   Perf. 14x14½
407 A87 40c multicolored   1.00   .95
408 A87 45c multicolored   1.05   1.00
409 A87 80c multicolored   2.25   1.90
Nos. 407-409 (3)   4.30   3.85

New Year 1998 (Year of the Tiger) — A88

1998, Jan. 5   Litho.   Perf. 14x14½
410 A88 45c shown   1.40   1.40
411 A88 45c Looking backward   1.40   1.40
a.   Pair, #410-411   3.00   3.00
b.   Souvenir sheet of 2, #410-411   3.75   3.75

Marine Life — A89

Designs: a, 5c, Frigatebird. b, 5c, Ambon chromis, denomination LR. c, 5c, Ambon chromis, denomination LL. d, 5c, Pink anemonefish, denomination, UR. e, 5c, Pink anemonefish, denomination LL. f, 10c, Eastern reef egret. g, 10c, Whitelined cod. h, 10c, Pyramid butterfly fish. i, 10c, Dusky parrotfish. j, 10c, Spotted garden eel. k, 25c, Sooty tern. l, 25c, Scissortail sergeant. m, 25c, Thicklip wrasse. n, 25c, Blackaxil chromis. o, 25c, Orange anthias. p, 45c, Brown booby. q, 45c, Green turtle. r, 45c, Pink anemonefish. s, 45c, Blue sea star. t, 45c, Kunie's chromodoris.

1998, Mar. 12   Litho.   Perf. 14
412 A89 Sheet of 20, #a.-t.   12.00 12.00

Tree Flowers of Christmas — A90

1998, Sept. 3   Litho.   Perf. 14½x14
413 A90 40c Orchid tree   .85   .85
414 A90 45c Flame tree   1.90   1.90
415 A90 95c Sea hibiscus   2.00   2.00
Nos. 413-415 (3)   4.75   4.75

New Year 1999 (Year of the Rabbit) A91

1999, Jan. 14   Litho.   Perf. 14x14½
416 A91 45c shown   1.50   1.50
417 A91 45c Rabbit looking left   1.50   1.50
a.   Pair, #416-417   3.25   3.25
b.   Souvenir sheet, #417a   3.50   3.50

Festivals on Christmas Island — A92

Children's drawings: No. 418, Carrying balloons in parade, by Fong Jason. No. 419, Giant crab, by Siti Zanariah Zainal. 85c, Children at night, by Tan Diana, vert. $1.20, Green mosque, tree, by Anwar Ramian, vert.

1999, July 15   Litho.   Perf. 14x14½
418 A92 45c multicolored   1.00   .90
419 A92 45c multicolored   1.00   .90
a.   Pair, #418-419   2.10   2.10

Perf. 14½x14
420 A92 85c multicolored   1.50   1.50
421 A92 $1.20 multicolored   2.25   2.25
Nos. 418-421 (4)   5.75   5.55

Christmas
A93

Designs: 40c, Santa Claus in hammock. 45c, Santa, birds, crab, lizard, cake. 95c, Santa, booby-drawn sleigh.

1999, Sept. 9   Litho.   Perf. 14x14½
422 A93 40c multicolored   1.05   .90
423 A93 45c multicolored   1.25 1.05
424 A93 95c multicolored   1.90 1.90
     Nos. 422-424 (3)   4.20 3.85

New Year 2000 (Year of the Dragon) A94

2000, Jan. 13   Litho.   Perf. 14x14½
425 A94 45c shown   1.40 1.40
426 A94 45c Dragon facing left   1.40 1.40
 a.   Pair, #425-426   3.00 3.00
 b.   Souvenir sheet, #426a   3.50 3.50

Faces of Christmas Island — A95

Ordinary people: a, Yeow Jian Min, without shirt. b, Ida Chin, with blue shirt. c, Ho Tak Wah, old man. d, Thomas Faul and James Neill. e, Siti Sanniah Kawi, with striped blouse.

2000, Apr. 13   Litho.   Perf. 14½x14
427 A95 45c Strip of 5, #a.-e.   5.50 6.00

Christmas — A96

No. 428: a, We three kings of Orient are. b, Bearing gifts we traverse afar. 45c, Star of wonder, star of night.

2000, Sept. 5   Litho.   Perf. 14½x14
428   Pair   1.75 1.75
 a.-b. A96 45c Any single   .90   .75
429 A96 45c multi   .90   .75

New Year 2001 (Year of the Snake) A97

Snake color: 45c, Green. $1.35, Silver.

Litho. with Foil Application
2001, Jan. 8   Perf. 14x14½
430-431 A97 Set of 2   3.25 3.25
 a.   Souvenir sheet, #430-431   4.50 5.00

Fungi — A98

Designs: $1, Chaetocalathus semisupinus. $1.50, Pycnoporus sanguineus.

2001, Oct. 25   Litho.   Perf. 14x14½
432-433 A98 Set of 2   4.50 4.75

New Year 2002 (Year of the Horse) — A99

Zodiac Animals and Their Chinese Characters A100

Designs: 45c, Purple horse. $1.35, Gold horse.
No. 436: a, Rat. b, Ox. c, Tiger. d, Rabbit. e, Dragon. f, Snake. g, Horse. h, Sheep. i, Monkey. j, Cock. k, Dog. l, Boar.

Litho. With Gold Foil Application
2002, Jan. 8   Perf. 14x14½
434-435 A99 Set of 2   3.50 3.50
 a.   Souvenir sheet, #434-435   4.50 4.50
436   Sheet of 14, #a-l,
          #435a   12.00 12.00
 a.-d. A100 5c Any single   .55   .55
 e.-h. A100 15c Any single, orange
          background   .60   .60
 i.-l. A100 25c Any single, orange
          background   .65   .65
See No. 442.

Worldwide Fund for Nature (WWF) — A101

Christmas Island birds - No. 437: a, Imperial pigeon. b, Hawk owl.
$1, Goshawk. $1.50, Thrush.

2002, May 1   Litho.   Perf. 14½x14
437 A101 45c Horiz. pair, #a-b   1.60 1.60
438 A101 $1 multi   1.60 1.60
439 A101 $1.50 multi   2.75 2.75
     Nos. 437-439 (3)   5.95 5.95

Zodiac Animals Type of 2002 and

New Year 2003 (Year of the Ram) A102

Designs: 50c, Yellow and orange ram. $1.50, Blue ram.
No. 442: a, Rat. b, Ox. c, Tiger. d, Rabbit. e, Dragon. f, Snake. g, Horse. h, Sheep. i, Monkey. j, Cock. k, Dog. l, Boar.

Litho. With Gold Foil Application
2003, Jan. 7   Perf. 14x14½
440-441 A102 Set of 2   3.75 3.75
 a.   Souvenir sheet, #440-441   4.50 4.50
442   Sheet of 14, #a-l,
          #441a   12.00 12.00
 a.-d. A100 10c Any single, red vio-
          let background   .50   .50
 e.-h. A100 15c Any single, red vio-
          let background   .60   .60
 i.-l. A100 25c Any single, red vio-
          let background   .70   .70

Christmas — A103

Designs: 45c, Arrival of Santa Claus on whale shark. 50c, Santa giving gifts to red crabs.

2003, Oct. 31   Litho.   Perf. 14½x14
443-444 A103 Set of 2   2.50 2.50

Zodiac Animals Type of 2002 and

New Year 2004 (Year of the Monkey) A104

Designs: 50c, Yellow and orange monkey. $1.45, Red orange monkey, lotus flower.
No. 447: a, Rat. b, Ox. c, Tiger. d, Rabbit. e, Dragon. f, Snake. g, Horse. h, Sheep. i, Monkey. j, Cock. k, Dog. l, Boar.

Litho. With Gold Foil Application
2004, Jan. 6   Set of 2   Perf. 14x14½
445-446 A104   4.75 4.75
446a   Souvenir sheet, #445-446 5.75 5.75
447   Sheet of 14, #a-l,
          #446a   12.00 12.00
 a.-d. A100 10c Any single, light and
          dark blue background   .50   .50
 e.-h. A100 15c Any single, light and
          dark blue background   .60   .60
 i.-l. A100 25c Any single, light and
          dark blue background   .70   .70
No. 446a exists with a 2004 Hong Kong Stamp Expo overprint in sheet margin in red. This sheet was sold at the show, but not on Christmas Island.

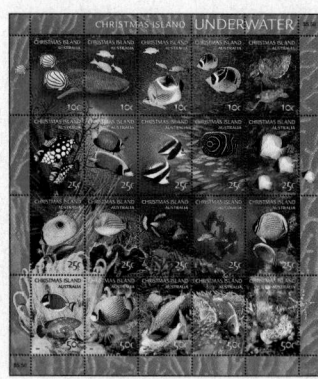

Marine Life — A105

No. 448: a, Two butterflyfish, rear of whale shark. b, Three striped fish, front of whale shark. c, Four fish. d, Two fish. e, Two green turtles. f, Two triggerfish (polka dots), red coral at LL. g, Two fish with thin horizontal stripes with yellow tails. h, Two fish with thick vertical stripes. i, Black and white fish. j, Three fish. k, Yellow fish with black spot, blue fish, red coral, yellow coral. l, Striped fish, clam. m, Black fish, small red fish. n Red fish, divers. o, Two striped fish, red coral under denomination. p, Blue and yellow fish, red and white spotted fish, yellow coral. q, Blue and yellow fish, yellow coral, sea anemones. r, Three blue fish with orange spots. s, Sea anemone and two anemonefish. t, Nudibranch, red coral and starfish.

2004, July 13   Litho.   Perf. 14½x14
448   Sheet of 20   10.50 10.50
 a.-e.   10c Any single   .20   .20
 f.-o.   25c Any single   .45   .45
 p.-t.   50c Any single   .95   .95

Zodiac Animals Type of 2002 and

New Year 2005 (Year of the Cock) A106

Designs: 50c, Cock, spirals at right. $1.45, Cock, spirals at right.
No. 451: a, Rat. b, Ox. c, Tiger. d, Rabbit. e, Dragon. f, Snake. g, Horse. h, Sheep. i, Monkey. j, Cock. k, Dog. l, Boar.

Litho. With Gold Foil Application
2005, Jan. 4   Perf. 14x14½
449-450 A106 Set of 2   4.50 4.50
450a   Souvenir sheet, #449-450 4.50 4.50
450b   As "a," with Taipei 2005 em-
          blem overprinted in margin 5.00 5.00
451   Sheet of 14, #a-l,
          #450a   12.00 12.00
 a.-d. A100 10c Any single, red and
          yellow background   .45   .45
 e.-h. A100 15c Any single, red and
          yellow background   .45   .45
 i.-l. A100 25c Any single, red and
          yellow background   .65   .65

Christmas
A107

Santa Claus, birds and: 45c, Palm tree, presents. 90c, Sleigh, crabs.

2005, Nov. 1   Litho.   Perf. 14¼x14
452 A107 45c multi   .80   .80
 a.   Booklet pane of 4   3.75
453 A107 90c multi   1.75 1.75
No. 452a exists with two different margins. These two panes were issued in a booklet that also contained three examples of Australia No. 2423a. The entire booklet sold for $9.95.

Zodiac Animals Type of 2002 and

New Year 2006 (Year of the Dog) A108

Designs: 50c, Purple dog. $1.45, Copper dog.
No. 456: a, Rat. b, Ox. c, Tiger. d, Rabbit. e, Dragon. f, Snake. g, Horse. h, Sheep. i, Monkey. j, Cock. k, Dog. l, Boar.

Litho. With Copper Foil Application
2006, Jan. 5   Perf. 14x14½
454-455 A106 Set of 2   3.25 3.25
455a   Souvenir sheet, #454-455 3.25 3.25
456   Sheet of 14, #a-l,
          #455a   6.50 6.50
 a.-d. A100 10c Any single, brown and
          yellow background   .20   .20
 e.-h. A100 15c Any single, brown and
          yellow background   .20   .20
 i.-l. A100 25c Any single, brown and
          yellow background   .40   .40

Buildings — A109

Designs: 50c, Mosque. $1.45, Tai Jin House.
No. 458: a, Tai Pak Kong Temple. b, Soon Tian Temple.

2006, June 13   Litho.   Perf. 14½x14
457 A109 50c multi   .80   .80
458 A109 $1 Horiz. pair, #a-b   3.25 3.25
459 A109 $1.45 multi   2.50 2.50
     Nos. 457-459 (3)   6.55 6.55

Zodiac Animals Types of 1996-2006 and

New Year 2007 (Year of the Boar) A110

Zodiac Animals A111

Designs: Nos. 460, 463l, 50c, Boar facing right. $1.45, Boar facing left.
No. 462: a, Rat. b, Ox. c, Tiger. d, Rabbit. e, Dragon. f, Snake. g, Horse. h, Sheep. i, Monkey. j, Cock. k, Dog. l, Boar.

Litho. With Copper Foil Application
2007, Jan. 9   Perf. 14x14½
460-461	A110	Set of 2	3.50	3.50
461a		Souvenir sheet, #460-461	3.50	3.50
462		Sheet of 14, #a-l,		
		#461a	7.25	7.25
a.-d.		A100 10c Any single, mul-		
		ticolored background	.20	.20
e.-h.		A100 15c Any single, mul-		
		ticolored background	.20	.20
i.-l.		A100 25c Any single, mul-		
		ticolored background	.45	.45

Self-Adhesive
Serpentine Die Cut 12¼ Syncopated (#463a-463l), Serpentine Die Cut (#463m)

463		Sheet of 13	19.00	
a.	A81 50c Like #376	1.10	1.10
b.	A86 50c Like #405	1.10	1.10
c.	A88 50c Like #410	1.10	1.10
d.	A91 50c Like #416	1.10	1.10
e.	A94 50c Like #425	1.10	1.10
f.	A97 50c Like #430	1.10	1.10
g.	A99 50c Like #434	1.10	1.10
h.	A102 50c Like #440	1.10	1.10
i.	A104 50c Like #445	1.10	1.10
j.	A106 50c Like #449	1.10	1.10
k.	A108 50c Like #454	1.10	1.10
l.	A110 50c Like #460	1.10	1.10
m.	A111 $1 multi	3.00	3.00
n.	Booklet pane, 2 each #463a-463b	4.00	
o.	Booklet pane, 2 each #463c-463f	4.00	
p.	Booklet pane, 2 each #463e-463f	4.00	
q.	Booklet pane, 2 each #463g-463h	4.00	
r.	Booklet pane, 2 each #463i-463j	4.00	
s.	Booklet pane, 2 each #463k-463l	4.00	
	Complete booklet, #463n-463s	25.00	

Complete booklet sold for $12.95.

Christmas A112

Santa Claus: 45c, In boat. 50c, Hoisted by crane. $1.10, On beach.

2007, Nov. 1   Litho.   Perf. 14x14½
464-466	A112	Set of 3	4.00	4.00

New Year 2008
(Year of the Rat) — A113

Designs: 50c, Rat. $1.45, Chinese character for "rat."
No. 469: a, Rat, diff. b, Ox. c, Dragon. d, Snake. e, Tiger. f, Rabbit. g, Horse. h, Pig. i, Goat. j, Monkey. k, Rooster. l, Dog.

Litho. With Foil Application
2008, Jan. 8   Perf. 14
467	A113	50c multi	1.00	1.00
a.		Perf. 14¾x14	1.00	1.00

Perf. 14¾x14
468	A113	$1.45 multi	2.75	2.75
a.		Souvenir sheet, #467a, 468	3.75	3.75
b.		As "a," with Olympex emblem in margin	3.75	3.75
469		Sheet of 14, #467a, 468, 469a-469l	7.75	7.75
a.-d.		A113 10c Any single	.20	.20
e.-h.		A113 15c Any single	.30	.30
i.-l.		A113 25c Any single	.45	.45
m.		Booklet pane of 4, #469a, 469b, 2 #468	6.75	—
n.		Booklet pane of 4, #469e, 469f, 2 #467a	2.75	—
o.		Booklet pane of 4, #469c, 469d, 2 #467a	2.75	—
p.		Booklet pane of 4, #469g, 469i, 2 #467a	3.00	—
q.		Booklet pane of 4, #469j, 469k, 2 #467a	3.25	—
r.		Booklet pane of 4, #469h, 469l, 2 #467a	3.00	—
		Complete booklet, #469m-469r	22.00	

Complete booklet sold for $10.95. Issued: No. 468b, 8/8.

Territorial Status of Christmas Island, 50th Anniv. A114

No. 470: a, Gecarcoidea natalis. b, Papasula abbotti. c, Asplenium listeri. $1.45, Seal of Union of Christmas Island Workers. $2.45, Christmas Island flag.

2008, June 10   Litho.   Perf. 14¼
470		Horiz. strip of 3	3.25	3.25
a.-c.		A114 50c Any single	1.10	1.10
471	A114	$1.45 multi	3.25	3.25
472	A114	$2.45 multi	5.25	5.25
		Nos. 470-472 (3)	11.75	11.75

Christmas — A115

Designs: Nos. 473, 475, 50c, Christmas tree, bird, crabs and shells. Nos. 474, 476, $1.20, Crabs with gifts and Christmas lights.

2008, Oct. 31   Litho.   Perf. 14½x14
473-474	A115	Set of 2	2.50	2.50

Serpentine Die Cut 11¼ Syncopated
Self-Adhesive
475	A115	50c multi	.70	.70
a.		Booklet pane of 20	14.50	

Booklet Stamp
476	A115	$1.20 multi	1.75	1.75
a.		Booklet pane of 5	8.75	

No. 475 was printed in sheets of 10.

Christmas With Personalized Picture — A116

Designs as before.

Serpentine Die Cut 11½x11¼ Syncopated
2008, Oct. 31   Litho.
Self-Adhesive
477	A116	50c multi	1.75	1.75
478	A116	$1.20 multi	2.75	2.75

Nos. 477-478 each were sold in sheets of 20 and have personalized pictures and a straight edge at right, and lack separations between the stamp and the personalized photo. Sheets of 20 of No. 477 sold for $23, and No. 478 sold for $37.

New Year 2009 (Year of the Ox) — A117

Designs: 55c, Rat. $1.65, Chinese character for "ox."
No. 481: a, Rat. b, Ox, diff. c, Dragon. d, Snake. e, Tiger. f, Rabbit. g, Horse. h, Pig. i, Goat. j, Monkey. k, Rooster. l, Dog.

Litho. With Foil Application
2009, Jan. 8   Perf. 14¾x14
479	A117	55c multi	.90	.90
480	A117	$1.65 multi	2.75	2.75
a.		Souvenir sheet, #479-480	3.50	3.50
481		Sheet of 14, #479-480, 481a-481l	7.25	7.25
a.-d.		A117 10c Any single	.20	.20
e.-h.		A117 20c Any single	.30	.30
i.-l.		A117 25c Any single	.40	.40
m.		Booklet pane of 4, #481b, 481e, 2 #480	6.50	—
n.		Booklet pane of 4, #481c, 481f, 2 #479	2.75	—
o.		Booklet pane of 4, #481d, 481g, 2 #479	2.75	—
p.		Booklet pane of 4, #481i, 481j, 2 #479	3.00	—
q.		Booklet pane of 4, #481k, 481l, 2 #479	3.00	—
r.		Booklet pane of 4, #481a, 481h, 2 #479	2.75	—
		Complete booklet, #481m-481r	21.00	

Complete booklet sold for $12.95.

Christmas — A118

2009, Nov. 2   Litho.   Perf. 14¾x14
482	A118	$1.25 multi	2.75	2.75

Booklet Stamp
Self-Adhesive
Serpentine Die Cut 11¼ Syncopated
483	A118	$1.25 multi	2.75	2.75
a.		Booklet pane of 5	13.00	

New Year 2010 (Year of the Tiger) — A119

Designs: 55c, Tiger. $1.65, Chinese character for "tiger."
No. 486: a, Rat. b, Ox. c, Dragon. d, Snake. e, Tiger. diff. f, Rabbit. g, Horse. h, Pigs. i, Goat. j, Monkey. k, Rooster. l, Dog.

Litho. With Foil Application
2010, Jan. 12   Perf. 14¾x14
484	A119	55c multi	1.00	1.00
485	A119	$1.65 multi	3.00	3.00
a.		Souvenir sheet, #484-485	4.00	4.00
486		Sheet of 14, #484-485, 486a-486l	8.00	8.00
a.-d.		A119 10c Any single	.20	.20
e.-h.		A119 20c Any single	.35	.35
i.-l.		A119 25c Any single	.45	.45
m.		Booklet pane of 4, #486e, 486f, 2 #485	7.75	—
n.		Booklet pane of 4, #486c, 486d, 2 #484	2.75	—
o.		Booklet pane of 4, #486g, 486i, 2 #484	3.25	—
p.		Booklet pane of 4, #486j, 486k, 2 #484	3.25	—
q.		Booklet pane of 4, #486h, 486l, 2 #484	3.25	—
r.		Booklet pane of 4, #486a, 486b, 2 #484	2.75	—
		Complete booklet, #486m-486r	23.00	

Complete booklet sold for $12.95. A sheet of 13 self-adhesive stamps containing a round $1 stamp depicting a flower and stamps similar to Nos. 467, 479, 484, 486c, 486d, 486f, 486g, 486h, 486i, 486j, 486k, 486l, sold for $9.95.
No. 484 was issued in a sheet of 9 + 9 labels that could not be personalized that sold for $15.95.

Worldwide Fund for Nature (WWF) — A120

No. 487 — Christmas Island frigatebird: a, Adult on nest. b, Adults and chick at nest.

No. 488 — Christmas Island frigatebird: a, Chick and adult at nest. b, Adult in flight.

2010, Aug. 17   Litho.   Perf. 14¼
487		Horiz. pair	2.25	2.25
a.-b.		A120 60c Either single	1.10	1.10
488		Horiz. pair	6.75	6.75
a.-b.		A120 $1.80 Either single	3.25	3.25
c.		Souvenir sheet, #487a-487b, 488a-488b	9.00	9.00

CILICIA
sə-'li-sh ē-ə

LOCATION — A territory of Turkey, in Southeastern Asia Minor
GOVT. — Former French occupation
AREA — 6,238 sq. mi.
POP. — 383,645
CAPITAL — Adana

British and French forces occupied Cilicia in 1918 and in 1919 its control was transferred to the French. Eventually part of Cilicia was assigned to the French Mandated Territory of Syria but by the Lausanne Treaty of 1923 which fixed the boundary between Syria and Turkey, Cilicia reverted to Turkey.

40 Paras = 1 Piaster

Issued under French Occupation

Numbers in parentheses are those of basic Turkish or French stamps.

Turkish Stamps of 1913-19 Handstamped

Perf. 11½, 12, 12½, 13½
1919   Unwmk.
On Pictorial Issue of 1913
2	A24	2pa red lilac (254)	8.00	8.00
a.		Inverted overprint	15.00	15.00
b.		Double overprint	15.00	15.00
3	A25	4pa dk brown (255)	7.25	7.25
a.		Inverted overprint	15.00	15.00
b.		Double overprint	15.00	15.00
4	A27	6pa dk blue (257)	27.50	20.00
a.		Inverted overprint	32.50	32.50
b.		Double overprint	32.50	32.50
5	A32	1¾pi slate & red brown (262)	8.75	8.75
a.		Inverted overprint	15.00	15.00
b.		Double overprint	15.00	15.00

On Issue of 1915
6	A17	1pi blue (300)	3.75	3.75
a.		Inverted overprint	8.00	8.00
b.		Double overprint	8.00	8.00
c.		In pair with unovptd. stamp	20.00	20.00
7	A21	20pa carmine rose (318)	13.50	12.00
a.		Inverted overprint	20.00	20.00
b.		Double overprint	20.00	20.00
9	A22	20pa carmine rose (330)	35.00	32.50
a.		Inverted overprint	40.00	40.00
b.		Double overprint	40.00	40.00

On Commemorative Issue of 1916
9A	A41	5pa green (345)	130.00	92.50
10	A41	20pa ultra (347)	7.25	7.25
a.		Double overprint	12.00	12.00
11	A41	1pi violet & black (348)	9.50	9.50
a.		Double overprint	12.00	12.00
b.		Perf 12½	6.50	6.50
c.		In pair with unovptd. stamp	16.00	16.00
12	A41	5pi yel brown & black (349)	3.75	3.75
a.		Double overprint	6.50	6.50

On Issue of 1916-18
13	A44	10pa grn (424)	8.75	8.75
a.		Perf 11½ (424a)	8.75	8.75
b.		Double overprint	13.50	3.50

14 A47 50pa ultra
           (428)   45.00   35.00
a.   Perf 11½ (428a)   45.00   35.00
b.   Double overprint   47.50   45.00
15 A51 25pi carmine,
           straw
           (434)   8.75   8.75
16 A52 50pi car (437)   8.75   8.75
17 A52 50pi ind (438)   32.50   32.50

On Issue of 1917

18 A53 5pi on 2pa
           Prus
           blue
           (547)   15.00   15.00
a.   Perf 11½ (547c)   15.00   15.00

On Issue of 1919

19 A47 50pa ultra
           (555)   40.00   32.50
a.   Perf 11½ (555a)   40.00   32.50
b.   Double overprint   47.50   40.00
20 A48 2pi org brown
           & indigo
           (556)   40.00   32.50
21 A49 5pi pale blue
           & black
           (557a)   40.00   32.50
a.   Perf 11½ (557)   40.00   32.50
b.   Perf 11½ (557b)   32.50   32.50
c.   Double overprint   47.50   40.00

On Newspaper Stamp of 1916

22 A10 5pa on 10pa
           gray
           green
           (P137)   4.75   4.75
d.   Inverted overprint   11.00   11.00
e.   Double overprint   14.00   14.00

On Semi-Postal Stamps of 1915

22A A21 20pa carmine
            rose
            (B8)   92.50   80.00
22B A21 1pi ultra (B9)   2,250.   1,700.
22C A21 1pi ultra
            (B13)   1,900.   1,200.

On Semi-Postal Stamps of 1916

23 A17 1pi bl (B19)   10.50   10.50
a.   Inverted overprint   16.00   16.00
b.   Double overprint   16.00   16.00
c.   Perf 13¼   10.50   10.50
24 A21 20pa carmine
           rose
           (B28)   3.75   3.75
a.   Inverted overprint   7.50   7.50
b.   Double overprint   7.50   7.50
25 A21 1pi ultra
           (B29)   8.75   8.75
a.   Inverted overprint   15.00   15.00
b.   Double overprint   15.00   15.00

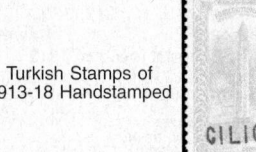

Turkish Stamps of
1913-18 Handstamped

1919

On Pictorial Issue of 1913

31 A24 2pa red lil (254)   4.00   4.00
a.   Inverted overprint   6.50   6.50
b.   Double overprint   6.50   6.50
c.   In pair with unovptd. stamp 16.00   16.00
32 A25 4pa dk brn (255)   15.00   15.00
a.   Inverted overprint   21.00   21.00
b.   Double overprint   21.00   21.00

On Issue of 1915

33 A17 1pi blue (300)   13.50   13.50
a.   Inverted overprint   20.00   20.00
b.   Double overprint   20.00   20.00
34 A22 20pa car rose
           (330)   4.75   4.75
a.   Inverted overprint   9.50   9.50
b.   Double overprint   9.50   9.50
c.   In pair with unovptd. stamp 20.00   20.00

On Commemorative Issue of 1916

35 A41 20pa ultra (347)   15.00   15.00
a.   Inverted overprint   21.00   21.00
b.   Perf 12½ (347a)   15.00   15.00
36 A41 1pi vio & blk
           (348)   3.25   3.25
a.   Inverted overprint   6.50   6.50
b.   Perf 12½ (348a)   3.25   3.25

On Issue of 1917

40 A53 5pi on 2pa Prus
           bl (547)   13.50   13.50
a.   Perf 11½ (547c)   13.50   13.50

On Newspaper Stamp of 1916

41 A10 5pa on 10pa gray
           grn (P137)   27.50   27.50
a.   Inverted overprint   37.50   37.50
b.   In pair with unovptd. stamp 60.00   60.00

On Semi-Postal Stamp of 1915

41A A21 20pa car rose (B8) 210.00 150.00

On Semi-Postal Stamps of 1916

42 A17 1pi blue (B19)   6.50   6.50
a.   Inverted overprint   12.00   12.00
b.   Double overprint   12.00   12.00

c.   Perf 12 (B19a)   12.00   12.00
d.   Perf 12x13¼ (B19b)   12.00   12.00
43 A21 20pa car rose
           (B28)   3.25   3.25
a.   Inverted overprint   7.50   *7.50*
b.   Double overprint   8.00   *8.00*
       Nos. 31-43 (11)   316.25   256.25

Turkish Stamps of
1913-19 Handstamped

1919

On Pictorial Issue of 1913

51 A24 2pa red lil (254)   11.00   11.00
a.   Inverted overprint   16.00   16.00
b.   Double overprint   16.00   16.00
c.   In pair with unovptd. stamp 32.50   32.50
52 A25 4pa dk brn (255)   3.75   3.75
a.   Inverted overprint   6.50   6.50
b.   Double overprint   6.50   6.50

On Issue of 1915

53 A17 1pi blue (300)   5.50   5.50
a.   Inverted overprint   9.50   9.50
b.   Double overprint   9.50   9.50
55 A22 5pa ocher (328)   40.00   35.00
a.   Double overprint   47.50   45.00
56 A22 20pa car rose
           (330)   4.00   4.00
a.   Inverted overprint   8.00   *8.00*
b.   Double overprint   8.00   *8.00*
c.   In pair with unovptd. stamp 16.00   16.00

On Commemorative Issue of 1916

57 A41 20pa ultra (347)   4.00   4.00
a.   Inverted overprint   8.00   *8.00*
b.   Double overprint   8.00   *8.00*
c.   Double overprint, one in-
         verted   9.50   9.50
d.   In pair with unovptd. stamp 16.00   16.00
58 A41 1pi vio & blk
           (348)   3.75   3.75
a.   Inverted overprint   6.50   6.50
b.   Double overprint   6.50   6.50
59 A41 5pi yel brn & blk
           (349)   12.00   12.00
a.   Inverted overprint   16.00   16.00
b.   Double overprint   16.00   16.00

On Issue of 1916

59A A17 1pi blue (372)   —   —

On Issue of 1916-18

60 A43 5pa org (421)   45.00   40.00
a.   Inverted overprint   52.50   52.50
b.   Perf 11½ (421a)   45.00   40.00
61 A46 1pi dl vio (426)   13.50   13.50
a.   Inverted overprint   21.00   21.00
b.   Double overprint   21.00   21.00
63 A52 50pi green, *straw*
           (439)   35.00   27.50

On Issue of 1917

64 A53 5pi on 2pa Prus
           bl (547)   32.50   27.50
a.   Double overprint   40.00   35.00
b.   Perf 11½ (421a)   32.50   27.50

On Newspaper Stamp of 1916

65 A10 5pa on 10pa gray
           grn (P137)   8.75   8.75
a.   Inverted overprint   13.50   13.50
b.   Double overprint   13.50   13.50

On Semi-Postal Stamp of 1915

65A A21 20pa car rose (B8) 1,200.   850.00

On Semi-Postal Stamps of 1916

66 A17 1pi blue (B19)   30.00   30.00
a.   Inverted overprint   35.00   35.00
67 A19 20pa car (B26)   13.50   13.50
a.   Inverted overprint   17.50   17.50
b.   Double overprint   17.50   17.50
68 A21 20pa car rose
           (B28)   180.00   92.50
69 A21 20pa car rose
           (B31)   8.00   8.00
a.   Inverted overprint   13.50   13.50
b.   Double overprint   13.50   13.50
69C A21 1pi ultra (401)   110.00   80.00
       Nos. 51-69C (20)   1,760.   1,270.

Turkey No. 424
Handstamped

1919

71 A44 10pa green (420)   9.50   9.50
a.   Inverted overprint   13.50   13.50
b.   Double overprint   13.50   13.50
c.   Perf 11½ (420a)   9.50   9.50

"T.E.O." stands for "Territoires Ennemis
Occupés."

Turkish
Stamps of
1913-19
Overprinted in
Black, Red or
Blue

In this setting there are various broken and
wrong font letters and the letter "i" is sometimes replaced by a "t."

1919   ### On Pictorial Issue of 1913

75 A30 1pi blue (R)
           (260)   4.75   4.75
a.   Inverted overprint   9.50   9.50
b.   Double overprint   9.50   9.50
c.   Double overprint, one in-
         verted   13.50   13.50

On Issue of 1915

76 A21 20pa carmine
           rose
           (318)   8.75   8.75

On Commemorative Issue of 1916

76A A41 5pa grn (345)   200.00   110.00
77 A41 20pa ultra (347)   13.50   13.50
a.   Inverted overprint   20.00   20.00
b.   Double overprint   20.00   20.00
c.   Perf 12½ (347a)   13.50   13.50
78 A41 1pi violet &
           black
           (348)   24.00   24.00
a.   Inverted overprint   27.50   27.50
b.   Double overprint   27.50   27.50
c.   Double overprint, one in-
         verted   32.50   32.50

On Issue of 1916-18

79 A43 5pa orange
           (Bl) (421)   4.75   4.75
a.   Inverted overprint   9.50   9.50
b.   Double overprint   9.50   9.50
c.   Double overprint, one in-
         verted   11.00   11.00
d.   Perf 11½ (421a)   4.75   4.75
80 A44 10pa grn (424)   8.75   8.75
a.   Double overprint   16.00   16.00
c.   Double overprint, one in-
         verted   20.00   20.00
d.   Perf 11½ (424a)   8.75   8.75
81 A45 20pa dp rose
           (Bk)
           (425)   27.50   27.50
a.   Double overprint   40.00   40.00
82 A45 20pa dp rose
           (Bl) (425)   1.00   1.00
a.   Inverted overprint   5.50   5.50
b.   Double overprint   5.50   5.50
c.   Double overprint, one in-
         verted   6.50   6.50
83 A48 2pi org brn &
           indigo
           (429)   1.60   1.60
a.   Double overprint   5.50   5.50
b.   Perf 11½ (429a)   1.60   1.60
83C A49 5pi pale blue
            & black
            (R) (430)   1.60   1.60
a.   Inverted overprint   9.50   9.50
b.   Double overprint   9.50   9.50
c.   Double overprint, one in-
         verted   12.00   12.00
d.   Perf 11½ (430a)   1.60   1.60
84 A51 25pi carmine,
           straw
           (434)   5.50   5.50
a.   Inverted overprint   12.00   12.00
b.   Double overprint   12.00   12.00
c.   Double overprint, one in-
         verted   13.50   13.50
85 A52 50pi green,
           straw
           (439)   92.50   87.50
a.   Inverted overprint   130.00   130.00
b.   Double overprint   130.00   130.00
c.   Double overprint, one in-
         verted   160.00   160.00

On Issue of 1917

85A A53 5pi on 2pa
            Prus bl
            (547)   —
86 A53 5pi on 2pa
           Prus bl
           (548)   13.50   13.50
a.   Perf 11½ (548c)   13.50   13.50

On Newspaper Stamps of 1916-19

87 A10 5pa on 10p
           gray
           green
           (P137)   1.75   1.75
a.   Inverted overprint   5.50   5.50
b.   Double overprint   5.50   5.50
c.   Double overprint, one in-
         verted   13.50   13.50
88 A21 5pa on 2pa ol
           green
           (P173)   1.00   1.00
a.   Inverted overprint   5.50   5.50
b.   Double overprint   5.50   5.50
c.   Double overprint, one in-
         verted   6.50   6.50

On Semi-Postal Stamps of 1915-17

90 A21 20pa carmine
           rose
           (B28)   8.75   8.75
b.   Double overprint   16.00   16.00
91 A41 10pa car (B42)   3.25   3.25
a.   Inverted overprint   7.25   7.25
b.   Double overprint   7.25   7.25

c.   Double overprint, one in-
         verted   12.00   12.00
d.   Perf 12½ (B42b)   3.25   3.25
92 A11 10pa on 20pa
           vio brn
           (B38)   3.25   3.25
a.   Inverted overprint   9.50   9.50
b.   Double overprint   9.50   9.50
c.   Double overprint, one in-
         verted   13.50   13.50
93 SP1 10pa red violet
           (B46)   2.00   2.00
a.   Overprint sideways   8.00   8.00

It is understood that the newspaper and
semi-postal stamps overprinted "Cilicie" were
used as ordinary postage stamps.

A1

1920   Blue Surcharge   *Perf. 11½*

98 A1 70pa on 5pa red   2.40   2.40
a.   Double surcharge   40.00   40.00
b.   Triple surcharge   240.00
c.   Inverted surcharge   35.00   35.00
d.   Double overprint, one inverted 45.00 45.00
e.   In pair with unovptd. stamp 45.00   45.00
99 A1 3½pi on 5pa red   2.40   2.40
a.   Se-tenant with No. 98, horiz.
         pair   120.00   120.00
b.   As "a." inverted surcharge 240.00   240.00
c.   Double surcharge   40.00   40.00
d.   Inverted surcharge   35.00   35.00
e.   Double surcharge, one invert-
         ed   45.00   45.00

Nos. 98-99 exist with a variety of surcharge
misspellings. For detailed listings, see the
Scott Classic Specialized Catalogue.

French Offices in Turkey
No. 26 Surcharged

1920   *Perf. 14x13½*

100 A3 20pa on 10c rose
            red (I)   1.25   1.25
a.   "PARAS" omitted   72.50   72.50

Three types of "20" exist on No. 100: I, "2"
bold; II "2" faint; III, "0" distinctly taller than "2."
See the *Scott Classic Specialized Catalogue
of Stamps and Covers* for detailed listings.

Stamps of France,
1900-17, Surcharged

1920

101 A16 5pa on 2c vio brn   1.60   1.60
102 A22 10pa on 5c green   2.00   2.00
103 A22 20pa on 10c red   4.00   4.00
104 A22 1pi on 25c blue   2.75   2.25
105 A20 2pi on 15c gray
            green   12.00   12.00
106 A18 5pi on 40c red &
            gray bl   25.00   25.00
107 A18 10pi on 50c bis
            brn & lav   32.50   32.50
108 A18 50pi on 1fr claret
            & ol grn   180.00   180.00
109 A18 100pi on 5fr dk bl &
            buff   900.00   900.00
       Nos. 101-109 (9)   1,159.   1,159.

Nos. 106 to 109 surcharged in four lines.
"O.M.F." stands for "Occupation Militaire
Francaise."

Stamps of France,
1917, Surcharged

1920

110	A16	5pa on 2c vio brn (109b)		12.00
111	A22	10pa on 5c grn (110b)		12.00
b.		Double surcharge		72.50
c.		On ordinary paper (110)		17.50
112	A22	20pa on 10c red (162)		8.75
a.		Inverted surcharge		72.50
b.		Double surcharge		65.00
113	A22	1pi on 25c bl (168d)		5.50
114	A20	2pi on 15c gray grn (139c)		25.00
115	A18	5pi on 40c red & gray bl (121)		47.50
116	A18	20pi on 1fr claret & ol grn (125)		175.00
a.		"O.M.F. Cilicie" omitted		600.00
b.		Double surcharge		600.00
		Nos. 110-116 (7)		285.75

On Nos. 115 and 116 "SAND. EST" is placed above the preceding issues. "Sand. Est" is an abbreviation of Sandjak de l'Est (Eastern County). Nos. 110-116 were prepared for use, but never issued.

Stamps of France, 1900-17, Surcharged

1920

117	A16	5pa on 2c vio brn	.95	.95
a.		Inverted surcharge	32.50	27.50
b.		"Cililie"	35.00	35.00
c.		Surcharge 5pi (error)	60.00	60.00
h.		Double surcharge	35.00	35.00
119	A22	10pa on 5c green	.90	.90
a.		Inverted surcharge	30.00	26.00
b.		Surch. 5pa (error), upright	55.00	55.00
c.		Surch. 5pa (error), invtd.	75.00	67.50
121	A22	20pa on 10c red	.95	.95
a.		Inverted surcharge	32.50	27.50
b.		Surch. 10pa (error), upright	60.00	60.00
c.		Surch. 10pa (error), invtd.	80.00	72.50
f.		Double surcharge	35.00	35.00
g.		Double surcharge, one inverted	47.50	47.50
122	A22	1pi on 25c blue	1.40	1.40
a.		Double surcharge	72.50	72.50
b.		Inverted surcharge	55.00	52.50
123	A20	2pi on 15c gray green	2.10	2.10
a.		Double surcharge	45.00	45.00
b.		Inverted surcharge	35.00	32.50
c.		Double surcharge, one inverted	55.00	55.00
124	A18	5pi on 40c red & gray blue	3.50	3.50
a.		Double surcharge	65.00	65.00
b.		Inverted surcharge	40.00	40.00
e.		"PIASRTES"	72.50	72.50
125	A18	10pi on 50c bis brn & lavender	12.50	12.50
a.		Double surcharge	60.00	60.00
b.		Inverted surcharge	55.00	47.50
c.		First "S" in "PIASTRES" inverted	110.00	110.00
		"PIASRTES"	72.50	72.50
126	A18	50pi on 1fr claret & ol grn	17.50	17.50
a.		Inverted surcharge	130.00	
b.		Double surcharge	180.00	
		"PIASRTES"	87.50	
127	A18	100pi on 5fr dk bl & buff	45.00	45.00
a.		Inverted surcharge	180.00	
d.		"PIASRTES"	925.00	
		Nos. 117-127 (9)	84.80	84.80

This surcharge has "O.M.F." in thicker letters than the preceding issues.

There were two printings of this surcharge, which may be distinguished by the spacing between "Cilicie" and figures of value. See the *Scott Classic Specialized Catalogue of Stamps and Covers* for detailed listings.

For overprints see Nos. C1-C2.

AIR POST STAMPS

Nos. 123 and 124 Handstamped

	Perf. 14x13½		
	1920, July 15		Unwmk.
C1	A20	2pi on 15c gray grn	9,250. 9,250.
C2	A18	5pi on 40c red & gray blue	9,500. 9,500.
a.	"PIASRTES"		

A very limited number of Nos. C1 and C2 were used on two air mail flights between Adana and Aleppo. At a later date impressions from a new handstamp were struck "to oblige" on stamps of the regular issue of 1920 (Nos. 123, 124, 125 and 126) that were in stock at the Adana Post Office. Counterfeits exist.

POSTAGE DUE STAMPS

Turkish Postage Due Stamps of 1914 Handstamped

Handstamped

1919		Unwmk.	Perf. 12	
J1	D1	5pa claret	21.00	21.00
a.		Inverted overprint	32.50	32.50
b.		Double surcharge	32.50	32.50
J2	D2	20pa red	22.50	22.50
a.		Inverted surcharge	32.50	32.50
b.		Double surcharge	32.50	32.50
J3	D3	1pi dark blue	35.00	35.00
a.		Inverted surcharge	45.00	45.00
J4	D4	2pi slate	40.00	40.00
a.		Inverted surcharge	60.00	60.00
		Nos. J1-J4 (4)	118.50	118.50

Handstamped

J5	D1	5pa claret	25.00	25.00
a.		Inverted overprint	40.00	40.00
b.		Double overprint	40.00	40.00
J6	D2	20pa red	30.00	30.00
a.		Inverted overprint	45.00	45.00
b.		Double overprint	45.00	45.00
J7	D3	1pi dark blue	35.00	35.00
a.		Inverted overprint	47.50	47.50
J8	D4	2pi slate	35.00	35.00
a.		Inverted overprint	47.50	47.50
		Nos. J5-J8 (4)	125.00	125.00

Handstamped

J9	D1	5pa claret	21.00	21.00
a.		Inverted overprint	32.50	32.50
b.		Double overprint	32.50	32.50
J10	D2	20pa red	22.50	22.50
a.		Inverted overprint	32.50	32.50
b.		Double overprint	35.00	35.00
J11	D3	1pi dark blue	32.50	32.50
a.		Inverted overprint	47.50	47.50
J12	D4	2pi slate	21.00	21.00
a.		Inverted overprint	32.50	32.50
		Nos. J9-J12 (4)	97.00	97.00

Postage Due Stamps of France Surcharged

1921				
J13	D2	1pi on 10c choc	11.00	11.00
a.		Inverted overprint	130.00	
J14	D2	2pi on 20c olive grn	11.00	11.00
a.		Inverted overprint	130.00	
J15	D2	3pi on 30c red	11.00	11.00
a.		Inverted overprint	92.50	
J16	D2	4pi on 50c vio brn	10.50	10.50
a.		Inverted overprint	92.50	
		Nos. J13-J16 (4)	43.50	43.50

COCHIN CHINA

'kō-chən 'chī-nə

LOCATION — The southernmost state of French Indo-China in the Cambodian Peninsula.
GOVT. — French Colony
AREA — 26,476 sq. mi.
POP. — 4,615,968
CAPITAL — Saigon

100 Centimes = 1 Franc

Values for unused stamps are for examples without gum, as most stamps were issued in that condition.

Surcharged in Black on Stamps of French Colonies:

a   b

c

1886-87		Unwmk.	Perf. 14x13½	
1	A9(a)	5c on 25c yel, *straw*	225.00	120.00
2	A9(b)	5c on 2c brn, *buff*	40.00	32.50
3	A9(b)	5c on 25c yel, *straw*	32.50	27.50
a.		A9(b) 5c on 25c yel, *straw*	275.00	275.00
4	A9(c)	5c on 25c blk, *rose ('87)*	60.00	47.50
a.		Double surch., one of type b	3,750.	2,750.
b.		Triple surch., two of type b	—	—
c.		Inverted surcharge	375.00	375.00
d.		Double surch., both type "a"	2,750.	3,250.
e.		Triple surch., types "a," "b" and "c"		8,750.
		Nos. 1-4 (4)	357.50	227.50

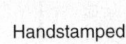

1888				
5	A9	15c on half of 30c brn, *bis*		72.50

No. 5 was prepared but not issued. The so-called Postage Due stamps were never issued. Stamps of Cochin China were superseded by those of Indo-China in 1892.

COCOS ISLANDS

'kō-kəs 'ī-lənds

(Keeling Islands)

LOCATION — Indian Ocean, 1,330 miles northwest of Australia, 580 miles southwest of Java
GOVT. — A territory of Australia
AREA — 6 sq. mi.
POP. — 670 (1994)

Of 27 small coral islands making up two atolls, two islands are inhabited.

Cocos Islands stamps are also valid within Australia.

12 Pence = 1 Shilling
100 Cents = 1 Dollar (1969)

Catalogue values for all unused stamps in this country are for Never Hinged items.

Copra Industry — A1

Super Constellation A2

Map of Islands — A3

Designs: 1sh, Coco palms. 2sh, Sailboat (dukong). 2sh3p, Fairy tern.

	Perf. 14½			
1963, June 11		Unwmk.		Engr.
1	A1	3p dk red brown	1.55	1.40
2	A2	5p vio blue	1.90	1.10
3	A3	8p red	4.00	1.90
4	A1	1sh green	4.00	1.10
5	A3	2sh dull purple	7.75	4.00
6	A2	2sh3p green	27.50	5.75
		Nos. 1-6 (6)	46.70	15.25
		Set, hinged	21.00	

"Simpson and His Donkey" by Wallace Anderson — A3a

1965, Apr. 14	Photo.	Perf. 13½x13		
7	A3a	5p brt grn, sepia & blk	1.10	.95

ANZAC issue. See note after Australia No. 387.

Turbo Lajonkairii — A4   Blenny — A5

Designs: 2c, Tridacna crocea (shell). 3c, Tridacna derasa (shell). 5c, Porites cocosensis (coral). 6c, Flyingfish. 10c, Banded rail (bird). 15c, Java sparrow. 20c, Red-tailed tropic bird. 30c, Sooty tern. 50c, Eastern reef heron. $1, Great frigate bird.

	Perf. 13½			
1969, July 9		Unwmk.		Photo.
	Size: 21½x27mm, 26½x22mm			
8	A4	1c multicolored	.30	.55
9	A4	2c multicolored	1.00	.20
10	A5	3c multicolored	.40	.20
11	A5	4c multicolored	.30	.45
12	A5	5c multicolored	.35	.30
13	A5	6c multicolored	.80	.75
14	A5	10c multicolored	1.25	.80
15	A5	15c multicolored	1.25	.60
16	A5	20c multicolored	1.25	.45
17	A5	30c multicolored	1.25	.50
18	A5	50c multicolored	1.25	.50

Size: 21½x34mm

19	A4	$1 multicolored	3.25	1.50
		Nos. 8-19 (12)	12.65	7.30

"Dragon" — A6

"Juno" — A7

Perf. 13½x13, 13x13½

1976, Mar. 29 Photo.

20	A6	1c shown	.45	.45
21	A7	2c shown	.45	.45
22	A7	5c "Beagle"	.45	.45
23	A7	10c "Sydney"	.50	.50
24	A7	15c "Emden"	.95	.95
25	A7	20c "Ayesha"	.95	.95
26	A6	25c "Islander"	.95	.95
27	A7	30c "Cheshire"	.95	.95
28	A7	35c "Jukung"	.95	.95
29	A7	40c "Scotia"	.95	.95
30	A6	50c "Orontes"	.95	.95
31	A6	$1 Royal Yacht "Gothic"	1.60	1.60
		Nos. 20-31 (12)	10.10	10.10

Historic ships.

Flag, Southern Cross, Islands' Map — A8

Council Emblem, Sailboat A9

1979, Sept. 3 Litho. **Perf. 15½**

32	A8	20c multicolored	.40	.35
33	A9	50c multicolored	.60	.75

Inauguration of Cocos Islands' postal service (20c), and establishment of Cocos Islands Council (50c).

Forcipiger Flavissimus A10

Fish: 2c, Chaetodon ornatissimus. 5c, Anthias. 10c, Meyer's coralfish. 15c, Halichoeres. 20c, Amphiprion clarkii. 22c, Balistapus undulatus. 25c, Maori wrasse. 28c, Macropharyngodon meleagris. 30c, Chaetodon madagascariensis. 35c, Centropyge colini. 40c, Bodianus axillaris. 50c, Corisgaimardi. 55c, Spotted wrasse. 60c, Epinepnelus tauvina. $1, Paracanthurus hepatus. $2, Striped butterflyfish.

1979-80 Litho. **Perf. 15½**

34	A10	1c multicolored	.20	1.00
35	A10	2c multicolored	.20	.35
36	A10	5c multicolored	.45	1.05
37	A10	10c multi ('80)	.20	1.00
38	A10	15c multicolored	.40	.35
39	A10	20c multicolored	.50	.35
40	A10	22c multi ('80)	.45	.35
41	A10	25c multi ('80)	.50	1.00
42	A10	28c multi ('80)	.45	.35
43	A10	30c multicolored	.60	.45
44	A10	35c multi ('80)	.70	1.50
45	A10	40c multicolored	.75	.55
46	A10	50c multicolored	1.05	.75
47	A10	55c multi ('80)	.95	1.25
48	A10	60c multi ('80)	.80	.75
49	A10	$1 multi ('80)	1.25	3.00
50	A10	$2 multi ('80)	2.50	3.25
		Nos. 34-50 (17)	11.95	17.30

Sailboats in Lagoon A11

Christmas: 25c, Yachts and seagulls, vert.

1979, Oct. 22 Litho. **Perf. 15½**

51	A11	25c multicolored	.40	.30
52	A11	55c multicolored	.60	.70

Star of Bethlehem, Map of Cocos Islands A12

Christmas (Map of Cocos Islands and): 28c, Three kings. 60c, Nativity.

1980, Oct. 22 Litho. **Perf. 13½x13**

53	A12	15c multicolored	.20	.20
54	A12	28c multicolored	.30	.30
55	A12	60c multicolored	.90	.90
		Nos. 53-55 (3)	1.40	1.40

Flag and Arms of Great Britain — A13

Australian Territory Status, 25th Anniv. (British Flag and Arms of Past Administrators): No. 57, Ceylon, 1878, 1942-1946. No. 58, Straits Settlements, 1886. No. 59, Singapore, 1946. No. 60, Australia (flag), 1955.

1980, Nov. 24 Litho. **Perf. 13½x13**

56	A13	22c multicolored	.35	.35
57	A13	22c multicolored	.35	.35
58	A13	22c multicolored	.35	.35
59	A13	22c multicolored	.35	.35
60	A13	22c multicolored	.35	.35
a.		Strip of 5, Nos. 56-60	1.75	1.75

Eye of the Wind, Map of Cocos Islands — A14

1980, Dec. 18 **Perf. 13x13½, 13½x13**

61	A14	22c shown	.50	.50
62	A14	28c Expedition routes, horiz.	.50	.50
63	A14	35c Francis Drake, Golden Hinde	.50	.50
64	A14	60c Prince Charles, Eye of the Wind	.80	.80
		Nos. 61-64 (4)	2.30	2.30

Operation Drake circumnavigation.

Livestock in Quarantine A15

1981, May 12 Litho. **Perf. 13½x13**

65	A15	22c Aerial view of station	.40	.40
66	A15	45c shown	.55	.55
67	A15	60c Livestock, diff.	.95	.95
		Nos. 65-67 (3)	1.90	1.90

West Island Quarantine Station opening.

Catalina Guba II A16

Inauguration of Air Service to Indian Ocean: No. 69, Avro Lancastrian. No. 70, Douglas DC4 Skymaster, Lockheed Constellation. No. 71, Lockheed Electra. No. 72, Boeing 727.

1981, June 23 Litho. **Perf. 13½x13**

68	A16	22c multicolored	.45	.45
69	A16	22c multicolored	.45	.45
70	A16	22c multicolored	.45	.45
71	A16	22c multicolored	.45	.45
72	A16	22c multicolored	.45	.45
a.		Strip of 5, #68-72	2.25	2.25

Prince Charles and Lady Diana — A17

1981, July 29 Litho. **Perf. 13½x13**

73	A17	24c multicolored	.40	.40
74	A17	60c multicolored	1.00	1.00

Royal Wedding.

Angels We Have Heard on High — A18

Christmas: Carols.

1981, Oct. 22 Photo. **Perf. 13½x13**

75	A18	18c shown	.40	.40
76	A18	30c Shepherds Why this Jubilee	.55	.55
77	A18	60c Come to Bethlehem and See Him	.75	.75
		Nos. 75-77 (3)	1.70	1.70

Sesquicentennial of Charles Darwin's Visit — A19

1981, Dec. 28 Litho. **Perf. 13½x13**

78	A19	24c Coral	.40	.40
79	A19	45c Darwin, coral	.55	.55
80	A19	60c Beagle, coral	.80	.80
		Nos. 78-80 (3)	1.75	1.75

Souvenir Sheet

81		Sheet of 2	1.40	1.40
a.		A19 24c Atoll	.65	.65
b.		A19 24c Atoll, diff.	.65	.65

125th Anniv. of Annexation to the British Dominions A20

1982, Mar. 31 Litho. **Perf. 13½x14**

82	A20	24c Queen Victoria	.45	.45
83	A20	45c British flag	.80	.80
84	A20	60c Capt. Fremantle	.95	.95
		Nos. 82-84 (3)	2.20	2.20

Scouting Year — A21

Perf. 13½x14, 14x13½

1982, July 21 Litho.

85	A21	27c Baden-Powell	.60	.60
86	A21	75c Emblem, map, vert.	1.25	1.25

Macroglossum Corythus — A22

1982, Sept. 6

87	A22	1c Presic villida, vert.	1.40	.75
88	A22	2c Cephonodes picus	.50	.50
89	A22	5c shown	2.00	.90
90	A22	10c Chasmina candida, vert.	.50	.50
91	A22	20c Nagia linteola	.50	.60
92	A22	25c Eublemma rivula, vert.	.50	.70
93	A22	30c Eurrhyparodes tricoloralis, vert.	.50	.60
94	A22	35c Hippotion boerhaviae	2.25	.90
95	A22	40c Euploea core corinna, vert.	.50	.75
96	A22	45c Psara hipponalis	.70	.75
97	A22	50c Danaus chrysippus	.75	1.40
98	A22	55c Hypolimas misippus, vert.	.75	.90
99	A22	60c Spodoptera litura, vert.	.80	1.90
100	A22	$1 Achaea janata, vert.	3.50	3.25
101	A22	$2 Hippotion velox	2.75	3.50
102	A22	$3 Utetheisa pulchelloides	4.00	3.50
		Nos. 87-102 (16)	21.90	21.40

Christmas A23

1982, Oct. 25 **Perf. 13x13½**

104	A23	21c Holy Family	.35	.20
105	A23	35c Angel	.50	.35
106	A23	75c Flight into Egypt	1.40	1.40
		Nos. 104-106 (3)	2.25	1.95

Christmas A24

Cocos-Malay Culture A25

The Birth of Christ: a, God Will Look After Us; b, Our Baby King Jesus; c, Your Saviour is Born; d, Wise Men Followed the Star; e, And Worship the Lord.

1983, Oct. 31 Litho. **Perf. 14x13½**

107		Strip of 5	1.90	1.90
a.-e.		A24 24c any single	.35	.35

1984, Jan. 27 Litho. **Perf. 14x13½**

Festive Occasions.

108	A25	45c Hari Raya	.70	.50
109	A25	75c Melenggok dance	1.10	.70
110	A25	85c Wedding	1.40	.80
		Nos. 108-110 (3)	3.20	2.00

75th Anniv. of Barrel Mail (1909-1955) A26

Designs: 35c, Mail distribution, Direction Isld. 55c, Jukongs retrieving barrels from ocean liner. 70c, Morea receiving outgoing barrel mail, 1909. $1, Barrel mail recovery.

1984, Apr. 20 Litho. Perf. 13½x14
111	A26	35c multicolored	.65	.65
112	A26	55c multicolored	1.10	1.10
113	A26	70c multicolored	1.25	1.25
		Nos. 111-113 (3)	3.00	3.00

Souvenir Sheet

114	A26	$1 multicolored	2.75	*2.75*

375th Anniv. of
Islands'
Discovery — A27

1984, July 10 Litho. Perf. 14x13½
115	A27	30c Capt. William Keeling	.80	.55
116	A27	65c The Hector	1.60	1.25
117	A27	95c Astrolabe	2.00	1.60
118	A27	$1.10 Map, 1666	2.25	1.90
		Nos. 115-118 (4)	6.65	5.30

AUSIPEX
'84 — A28

45c, Malay Settlement, Home Island. 55c, West Island Air Strip, settlement. $2, Jukong ships racing, Melbourne Exhibition Center.

1984, Sept. 21 Litho. Perf. 13½
119	A28	45c multicolored	.75	.55
120	A28	55c multicolored	.85	.70

Souvenir Sheet

121	A28	$2 multicolored	3.25	3.25

Christmas
A29

1984, Oct. 31 Litho. Perf. 13½
122	A29	24c Fish	.50	.50
123	A29	35c Butterfly	.75	.75
124	A29	55c Bird	1.25	1.25
		Nos. 122-124 (3)	2.50	2.50

Souvenir Sheet

Act of Self-Determination — A30

Integration with Australia: a, Australians welcoming Cocos islanders. b, Australian flag over the islands.

1984, Nov. 30 Litho. Perf. 13½x14
125		Sheet of 2	3.25	3.25
a.-b.	A30	30c any single	1.40	1.40

Crafts — A31

1985, Jan. 30 Perf. 14x13½
126	A31	30c Boat building	.65	.35
127	A31	45c Blacksmith	1.00	.50
128	A31	55c Woodcarving	1.40	.80
		Nos. 126-128 (3)	3.05	1.65

Cable-laying
Ships — A32

1985, Apr. 24 Perf. 13½x14
129	A32	33c Scotia	1.75	1.00
130	A32	65c Anglia	2.75	1.60
131	A32	80c Patrol	2.75	2.75
		Nos. 129-131 (3)	7.25	5.35

Birds
A33

1985, July 17 Perf. 13½
132	A33	33c Redfooted booby, vert.	3.00	3.00
133	A33	60c Nankeen night heron	3.50	3.50
134	A33	$1 Buff-banded rail	3.75	3.75
a.		"Block" of 3, #132-134	11.00	11.00

Nos. 132-134 printed in a continuous design.

Seashells
A34

1985-86 Litho. Perf. 13½x14
135	A34	1c Trochus maculatus	.75	*1.10*
136	A34	2c Smaragdia rangiana	.75	*1.10*
137	A34	3c Chama	.75	*1.10*
138	A34	4c Cypraea moneta	1.40	*1.10*
139	A34	5c Drupa morum	.75	*1.10*
140	A34	10c Conus miles	.90	*2.25*
141	A34	15c Terebra maculata	2.75	1.90
142	A34	20c Fragum fragum	2.75	2.25
143	A34	30c Turbo lajonkairii	2.75	2.25
144	A34	33c Mitra fissurata	2.75	2.25
145	A34	40c Lambis lambis	2.75	2.25
146	A34	50c Tridacna squamosa	2.75	3.00
147	A34	60c Cypraea histrio	2.75	3.25
148	A34	$1 Phillidia varicosa	4.00	*4.50*
149	A34	$2 Halgerda tessellata	4.50	*5.50*
150	A34	$3 Harminoea cymbalum	5.50	*6.50*
		Nos. 135-150 (16)	38.55	41.40

Issue dates: 1c, 5c, 33c, $1, Sept. 18. 2c, 3c, 10c, $3, Jan. 29, 1986. 15c-30c, 40c, Apr. 30, 1986. 4c, 50c, 60c, $2, July 30, 1986.
For surcharges see #225, 228-229, 231-233.

Souvenir Sheet

Christmas
A35

a, Star LR. b, Star LL. c, Star UR. d, Star UL.

1985, Oct. 30 Perf. 13½x14
151		Sheet of 4	3.25	3.25
a.-d.	A35	27c any single	.80	.80

Darwin's Visit to the
Islands — A36

1986, Apr. 1 Litho. Perf. 14x13½
152	A36	33c Charles Darwin	1.10	.80
153	A36	60c Map of voyage	1.90	*2.00*
154	A36	$1 HMS Beagle	2.75	*3.25*
		Nos. 152-154 (3)	5.75	*6.05*

Christmas
A37

1986, Oct. 20 Litho. Perf. 13½x14
155	A37	30c Coconut palm, holly	.80	.80
156	A37	90c Shell, ornament	3.00	*3.00*
157	A37	$1 Tropical fish, bell	3.00	*3.00*
		Nos. 155-157 (3)	6.80	*6.80*

Sailboats
A38

a, Jukong. b, Ocean racers. c, Sarimanok. d, Ayesha. #158 has a continuous design.

1987, Jan. 28
158		Strip of 4	6.50	6.50
a.-d.	A38	36c any single	1.25	1.25

Island
Views — A39

1987, Apr. 8
159	A39	70c Direction Is.	2.25	1.90
160	A39	90c West Is.	3.00	*3.25*
161	A39	$1 Golf course, Cocos	3.50	*3.75*
		Nos. 159-161 (3)	8.75	8.90

Communications — A40

1987, July 29 Litho. Perf. 13½x14
162	A40	70c Radio	1.50	1.50
163	A40	75c Air service	1.60	1.60
164	A40	90c Satellite	1.90	1.90
165	A40	$1 Airmail	2.25	2.25
		Nos. 162-165 (4)	7.25	7.25

Industries
A41

1987, Sept. 16
166	A41	45c Batik printing	1.50	1.50
167	A41	65c Boat building	2.00	2.00
168	A41	75c Copra production	2.50	2.50
		Nos. 166-168 (3)	6.00	6.00

Industrial activities of the Cocos Malay people.

Christmas — A42

1987, Oct. 28 Perf. 14x13½
169	A42	30c Peace on Earth	.60	.60
170	A42	90c Unity	1.60	1.60
171	A42	$1 Goodwill Towards All	2.25	2.25
		Nos. 169-171 (3)	4.45	4.45

Australia
Bicentennial
A43

Arrival of the First Fleet, Sydney Cove, Jan. 1788: a, Five aboriginals on shore. b, Four aboriginals on shore, one in canoe. c, Ships entering bay, kangaroos. d, Europeans land, white cranes. e, Flag raising.

1988, Jan. 26 Litho. Perf. 13
172		Strip of 5	11.00	11.00
a.-e.	A43	37c any single	1.40	1.40

No. 172 has a continuous design. See Christmas Is. No. 213.

Life Cycle of the
Coconut — A44

1988, Apr. 13 Litho. Perf. 14x13½
173	A44	37c Flower	.80	.75
174	A44	65c Small nut stage	1.50	1.50
175	A44	90c Mature nuts	1.75	*1.90*
176	A44	$1 Seedlings	2.25	*2.25*
a.		Souvenir sheet of 4, #173-176	9.00	9.00
		Nos. 173-176 (4)	6.30	6.40

For surcharge see No. O1.

Cocos
Postage
Stamps,
25th Anniv.
A45

Litho. & Engr.

1988, June 15 Perf. 15x14
177	A45	37c No. 1	1.40	1.00
178	A45	55c No. 4	1.75	1.40
179	A45	65c No. 2	1.90	1.90
180	A45	70c No. 3	2.25	2.25
181	A45	90c No. 5	2.50	3.00
182	A45	$1 No. 6	2.75	*3.25*
		Nos. 177-182 (6)	12.55	12.80

For overprint and surcharge see #216, 236.

Flowering
Plants — A46

1988-89 Litho. Perf. 14x13½
183	A46	1c Pisonia grandis	.75	*1.00*
184	A46	2c Cocos nucifera	.75	*1.00*
185	A46	5c Morinda citrifolia	1.50	1.10
186	A46	10c Cordia sub-cordata	1.00	*1.10*
189	A46	30c Argusia argentea	1.50	*1.60*
190	A46	37c Calophyllum inophyllum	2.25	1.40
191	A46	40c Barringtonia asiatica	1.50	*1.60*
192	A46	50c Caesalpinia bonduc	1.90	*3.50*
194	A46	90c Terminalia catappa	2.75	*5.25*
195	A46	$1 Pemphis acidula	2.75	*3.00*
197	A46	$2 Scaevola sericea	3.25	*4.75*
198	A46	$3 Hibiscus tiliaceus	3.25	*4.75*
		Nos. 183-198 (12)	25.15	28.55

Issued: 1c, 5c, 37c, $3, 7/29; 2c, 10c, 30c, $2, 1/18/89; 40c, 50c, 90c, $1, 4/19/89.

For self-adhesive sheet of 3 see No. 217.

Souvenir Sheet
1988, July 30
199 A46 $3 like No. 198   12.00 12.00
SYDPEX '88.

Christmas
A47

1988, Oct. 12   Litho.   Perf. 13½x14
200 A47 32c multicolored   1.10 1.10
201 A47 90c multicolored   2.50 2.50
202 A47 $1 multicolored   3.00 3.00
    Nos. 200-202 (3)   6.60 6.60

1st Aerial Survey of
the Indian Ocean Air
Route, 50th
Anniv. — A48

40c, P.G. Taylor, pilot. 70c, *Guba II* seaplane and crew. $1, *Guba II* landing off Direc-
tion Island. $1.10, Unissued 5sh stamp of Aus-
tralia, 1939.

1989, July 19   Litho.   Perf. 14x13½
203 A48 40c multicolored   1.10 1.10
204 A48 70c multicolored   1.75 1.75
205 A48 $1 multicolored   2.50 2.50
206 A48 $1.10 multicolored   2.75 2.75
    Nos. 203-206 (4)   8.10 8.10

Jukong, Traditional
Sailing Vessel of the
Cocos Malay
People — A49

1989, Oct. 18   Litho.   Perf. 14x13½
207 A49 35c multicolored   1.25 1.25
208 A49 80c multicolored   2.75 2.75
209 A49 $1.10 multicolored   4.00 4.00
    Nos. 207-209 (3)   8.00 8.00

Christmas.

Naval Engagement of the HMAS
Sydney and the German Raider SMS
Emden, 75th Anniv. — A50

Designs: 40c, HMAS *Sydney*. 70c, SMS
Emden. $1, Steam launch belonging to the
Emden. $1.10, HMAS *Sydney* and naval crest.

1989, Nov. 9   Litho.   Perf. 13½x14
210   Strip of 4 + label   8.00 8.25
  a. A50 40c multicolored   .70 .70
  b. A50 70c multicolored   1.40 1.40
  c. A50 $1 multicolored   1.90 1.90
  d. A50 $1.10 multicolored   2.10 2.10
  e. Souvenir sheet of 4, #210a-210d 11.00 11.00

Crabs — A52

1990, May 31   Litho.   Perf. 14½
212 A52 45c Xanthid   1.60 1.60
213 A52 75c Ghost   3.00 3.00
214 A52 $1 Red-backed
         mud crab   3.25 3.25
215 A52 $1.30 Coconut, vert.   4.00 4.00
    Nos. 212-215 (4)   11.85 11.85

No. 180 Overprinted in Red

Litho. & Engr.
1990, Aug. 24   Perf. 15x14
216 A45 70c gray, black & red   18.00 18.00

Flowering Plants Type of 1988
1990, Aug. 24   Photo.   Rouletted 9½
Self-Adhesive
217   Sheet of 3   15.50 15.50
  a. A46 10c like No. 186   .55 .55
  b. A46 90c like No. 194   3.50 3.50
  c. A46 $2 like No. 197   7.75 7.75

World Stamp Exhibition, New Zealand 1990.
Nos. 217a-217c inscribed 1990.

Explorers
and Their
Ships
A54

45c, Capt. Keeling, Hector, 1609. 75c, Capt.
Fitzroy, Beagle, 1836. $1, Capt. Belcher,
Samarang, 1846. $1.30, Capt. Fremantle,
Juno, 1857.

1990, Aug. 24   Litho.   Perf. 14½
218 A54 45c violet brown   1.90 1.75
219 A54 75c pale bl & vio
         brn   3.25 3.75
220 A54 $1 pale yel & vio
         brn   3.75 5.00
221 A54 $1.30 buff & vio brn   6.00 7.50
  a. Souv. sheet of 4, #218-221,
     imperf.   13.00 13.00
    Nos. 218-221 (4)   14.90 18.00

Christmas — A55

1990, Dec. 12   Litho.   Rouletted 5
222 A55 40c Star at left   1.75 1.75
  a. Bklt. pane of 10 + 2 labels 35.00
223 A55 70c Star in center   3.25 3.25
  a. Bklt. pane, 4 #222, 2 #223 + 6
     labels   45.00
224 A55 $1.30 Star at right   6.50 6.50
    Nos. 222-224 (3)   11.50 11.50

**Nos. 140, 141, 143, 146-147, 179
Surcharged
in Blue or Black**

Litho., Litho. & Engr.
1990-91   Perf. 13½x14, 15x14
225 A34   (1c) on 30c #143   27.50 14.00
228 A34   (43c) on 10c #140   100.00 100.00
229 A34   (43c) on 10c #140   30.00 27.50
231 A34   70c on 60c #147
           (bk)   19.00 14.00
232 A34   80c on 50c #146
           (bk)   19.00 14.00

233 A34 $1.20 on 15c #141
           (bk)   19.00 14.00
236 A45 $5 on 65c #179   100.00 50.00
    Nos. 225-236 (7)   314.50 233.50

Obliterator consists of diagonal lines on No.
228, crosshatched lines on No. 229.
Additional text in surcharges reads: "MAIN-
LAND / POSTAGE PAID" (Nos. 228-229),
"ZONE 1 / POSTAGE PAID" (No. 231), "ZONE
2 / POSTAGE PAID" (No. 232), "ZONE 5 /
POSTAGE PAID" (No. 233).
Issued: #236, 11/11; #228, 12/18; #225,
229, 231-233, 1/1991.

Beaded Sea
Star — A56

1991, Feb. 28   Litho.   Perf. 14½
237 A56 45c shown   1.40 1.40
238 A56 75c Feather star   1.90 1.90
239 A56 $1 Slate pencil
         urchin   2.75 2.75
240 A56 $1.30 Globose sea
         urchin   3.50 3.50
    Nos. 237-240 (4)   9.55 9.55

Hari
Raya — A57

1991, Mar.   Litho.   Perf. 14½
241 A57 45c multicolored   1.40 1.40
242 A57 75c multi, diff.   2.25 2.25
243 A57 $1.30 multi, diff.   4.00 4.00
    Nos. 241-243 (3)   7.65 7.65

Christmas — A58

1991, Nov. 6   Litho.   Perf. 15½
244 A58 38c Child praying   1.10 1.10
245 A58 43c Child sleeping   1.40 1.40
246 A58 $1 Child singing   2.75 2.75
247 A58 $1.20 Child in wonder   3.50 3.50
    Nos. 244-247 (4)   8.75 8.75

Souvenir Sheet
248   Sheet of 4   10.00 10.00
  a. A58 38c Two children   1.10 1.10
  b. A58 43c Three girls   1.25 1.25
  c. A58 $1 Boy, two girls   2.75 2.75
  d. A58 $1.20 Boy, girl   3.25 3.25

Nos. 248a-248d are in a continuous design
depicting a children's choir.

Crustaceans
A59

Designs: 5c, Lybia tessellata. 10c, Pilodius
areolatus. 20c, Trizopagurus strigatus. 30c,
Lophozozymus pulchellus. 40c, Thalamitoides
quadridens. 45c, Calcinus elegans, vert. 50c,
Clibarius humilis. 60c, Trapezia rufopunctata,
vert. 80c, Pylopaguropsis magnimanus, vert.
$1, Trapezia ferruginea, vert. $2, Trapezia gut-
tata, vert. $3, Trapezia cymodoce, vert.

1992   Litho.   Perf. 14½
249 A59 5c multicolored   1.40 1.75
250 A59 10c multicolored   1.40 1.75
251 A59 20c multicolored   1.40 1.75
252 A59 30c multicolored   1.50 3.00
253 A59 40c multicolored   1.60 3.00
254 A59 45c multicolored   1.75 3.00
255 A59 50c multicolored   1.75 4.00
256 A59 60c multicolored   2.00 4.00
257 A59 80c multicolored   2.50 4.00
258 A59 $1 multicolored   3.25 4.00

259 A59 $2 multicolored   6.50 6.50
260 A59 $3 multicolored   10.00 10.00
    Nos. 249-260 (12)   35.05 46.75

Issued: 10c, 30c, 50c, 80c, $1, $2, 8/11;
others, 2/28.

Discovery of
America, 500th
Anniv. — A60

1992, May 22   Litho.   Perf. 14½
261 A60 $1.05 multicolored   4.50 4.50

Buff-banded Rail — A61

No. 262: a, 10c, Bird looking for food. b, 15c,
Adult with chick. c, 30c, Two adults eating. d,
45c, Adult with eggs, hatchling.
No. 263: a, 45c, Two birds, one in water. b,
85c, Chick in nest. c, $1.20, Bird's head.

1992, June 18   Litho.   Perf. 14
262 A61 Strip of 4, #a.-d.   7.00 7.00

Souvenir Sheet
263 A61 Sheet of 3, #a.-c.   8.25 8.25

World Wildlife Fund (#262).

World War II,
50th
Anniv. — A62

45c, Royal Air Force Spitfire fighters. 85c,
Japanese bombing of Kampong. $1.20, Sun-
derland reconnaissance flying boat.

1992, Oct. 13   Litho.   Perf. 14½
264 A62 45c multicolored   1.90 1.90
265 A62 85c multicolored   3.50 3.50
266 A62 $1.20 multicolored   4.75 4.75
    Nos. 264-266 (3)   10.15 10.15

Festive   Corals — A64
Season — A63

40c, Storm waves on reef edge. 80c, Direction Island. $1, Moorish idols among coral.

1992, Nov. 10   Litho.   Perf. 15x14½
267 A63 40c multicolored   1.40 1.40
268 A63 80c multicolored   2.50 2.50
269 A63 $1 multicolored   3.25 3.25
    Nos. 267-269 (3)   7.15 7.15

1993, Jan. 28   Litho.   Perf. 14½
270 A64 45c Lobophyllia
         hemprichii   1.00 1.00
271 A64 85c Pocillopora
         eydouxi   1.75 1.75
272 A64 $1.05 Fungia scutaria   2.50 2.50
273 A64 $1.20 Sarcophyton
         sp.   3.00 3.00
    Nos. 270-273 (4)   8.25 8.25

A65

A66

Island Currency Tokens: 45c, 5r token, 1968. 85c, Island scene token, 1968. $1.05, 150r token, 1977. $1.20, Token, 1910.

1993, Mar. 30   Litho.   Perf. 15x14½

274	A65	45c multicolored	1.40	1.40
275	A65	85c multicolored	2.25	2.25
276	A65	$1.05 multicolored	3.00	3.00
277	A65	$1.20 multicolored	3.75	3.75
		Nos. 274-277 (4)	10.40	10.40

1993, June 1   Litho.   Perf. 14½

Education: 5c, Primary classroom activities. 45c, Secondary studies. 85c, Crafts, traditional basket weaving. $1.05, Office staff, higher education. $1.20, Marine officers, coxswain's training.

278	A66	5c multicolored	.95	.95
279	A66	45c multicolored	1.50	1.50
280	A66	85c multicolored	2.50	2.50
281	A66	$1.05 multicolored	2.75	2.75
282	A66	$1.20 multicolored	3.25	3.25
		Nos. 278-282 (5)	10.95	10.95

Air-Sea Rescue Service A67

45c, Men in lifeboat. 85c, Westwind Seascan. $1.05, R.J. Hawke inter-island ferry.

1993, Aug. 17   Litho.   Perf. 14½

283	A67	45c multicolored	1.90	1.90
284	A67	85c multicolored	2.75	2.75
285	A67	$1.05 multicolored	3.75	3.75
a.		Souvenir sheet of 3, #283-285	12.00	12.00
		Nos. 283-285 (3)	8.40	8.40

A limited printing exists of No. 285a with Taipei '95 overprint. Value, $110.

Festive Season — A68

1993, Oct. 24   Litho.   Perf. 14½

286	A68	40c pink & multi	1.40	1.40
287	A68	80c blue & multi	2.75	2.75
288	A68	$1 yellow & multi	3.75	3.75
		Nos. 286-288 (3)	7.90	7.90

Map and Reef Life — A69   Puppets — A70

Reef triggerfish — No. 289: a, Two fish, purple coral (b). b, Three fish. c, Two fish. d, Two fish, red coral (e). e, One fish.

Green turtles — No. 290: a, Eggs, turtles. b, Two turtles (c). c, Group of baby turtles. d, Baby turtle. e, Fish, large turtle.

Pyramid butterflyfish — No. 291: a, Three fish. b, Two small, one large fish, coral (c). c, One small, one large fish, coral (d). d, Three fish, coral (e). e, Coral, one fish.

Junkongs sailing craft — No. 292: a, One boat, red sail. b, Two boats, one blue & white sail, one red sail. c, One boat, yellow sail. d, Two boats sailing away. e, Two boats, one red sail, one white & blue sail.

1994, Feb. 17   Litho.   Perf. 14½x14

289	A69	5c Strip of 5, #a.-e.	1.40	1.75
290	A69	10c Strip of 5, #a.-e.	1.75	2.25
291	A69	20c Strip of 5, #a.-e.	2.25	3.00
292	A69	45c Strip of 5, #a.-e.	5.25	5.75
f.		Sheet of 20, #289-292	11.00	14.50

No. 292 also produced in sheets of 20.

1994, June 16   Litho.   Perf. 14½x14

293	A70	45c Prabu Abjasa	.95	.95
294	A70	90c Prabu Pandu	1.75	1.75
295	A70	$1 Judistra	1.90	1.90
296	A70	$1.35 Abimanju	2.50	2.50
		Nos. 293-296 (4)	7.10	7.10

Christmas A71

1994, Oct. 31   Litho.   Perf. 14x14½

297	A71	40c Angel	.80	.80
298	A71	45c Wise man	1.00	1.00
299	A71	80c Bethlehem	1.60	1.60
		Nos. 297-299 (3)	3.40	3.40

Seabirds A72

45c, White-tailed tropicbird, masked booby. 85c, Great frigatebird, white tern.

1995, Mar. 16   Litho.   Perf. 14x14½

300	A72	45c multicolored	.80	.80
301	A72	85c multicolored	1.60	1.60
a.		Souvenir sheet of 2, #300-301	3.00	3.00
b.		As "a," overprinted	7.75	7.75

No. 301b ovptd. in gold in sheet margin with Jakarta '95 exhibition emblem and: "8th Asian International Philatelic Exhibition / PAMERAN FILATELI INTERNASIONAL ASIA VIII."

No. 301b issued 8/19/95.

Insects — A73

#302a, Yellow crazy ant. b, Aedes mosquito. c, Hawk moth. d, Scarab beetle. e, Lauxaniid fly.

$1.20, Common eggfly butterfly.

1995, July 13   Litho.   Perf. 14½x14

302	A73	45c Strip of 5, #a.-e.	6.00	6.00
303	A73	$1.20 multicolored	2.75	2.75

Fish — A74

Designs: 5c, Redspot wrasse. 30c, Gilded triggerfish. 40c, Saddled butterflyfish. 45c, Ringeyed hawkfish. 75c, Orangespine unicornfish. 80c, Blue tang. 85c, Humpback wrasse. 90c, Threadfin butterflyfish. $1, Bluestripe snapper. $1.05, Longnosed butterflyfish. $1.20, Freckled hawkfish. $2, Powder blue surgeonfish.

1995-97   Litho.   Perf. 14x14½

304	A74	5c multicolored	.40	.40
305	A74	30c multicolored	.60	.60
306	A74	40c multicolored	.95	.95
307	A74	45c multicolored	1.10	1.10
308	A74	75c multicolored	1.60	1.60
309	A74	80c multicolored	1.75	1.75
310	A74	85c multicolored	1.75	1.75
311	A74	90c multicolored	2.00	2.00
312	A74	$1 multicolored	2.25	2.25
313	A74	$1.05 multicolored	2.25	2.25
314	A74	$1.20 multicolored	3.00	3.00
315	A74	$2 multicolored	5.25	5.25
		Nos. 304-315 (12)	22.90	22.90

Issued: 40c, 80c, $1.05, 11/1/95; 30c, 45c, 85c, $2, 8/8/96; 5c, 75c, 90c, $1, $1.20, 8/14/97.

See Nos. 327-329, 335.

Festive Season — A75

Designs: 45c, Greeting others, asking forgiveness. 75c, Drum beaters celebrate Hari Raya Puasa. 85c, Sharing food with friends.

1996, Feb. 19   Litho.   Perf. 14

316	A75	45c multicolored	.80	.80
317	A75	75c multicolored	1.90	1.90
318	A75	85c multicolored	2.25	2.25
		Nos. 316-318 (3)	4.95	4.95

Animals Imported Into Australia Through Cocos Islands Quarantine Station — A76

1996, June 13   Litho.   Perf. 14½x14

319	A76	45c Black rhinoceros	1.40	1.40
320	A76	50c Alpacas	1.60	1.60
321	A76	$1.05 Boran cattle	2.75	2.75
322	A76	$1.20 Ostrich	3.75	3.75
		Nos. 319-322 (4)	9.50	9.50

A77

A78

Festive Season: 45c, Tambourine, dancing on shore, bird. 75c, Woman clapping, sailboats racing. 85c, Fish, night scene on beach.

1997, Jan. 6   Litho.   Perf. 14x14½

323	A77	45c multicolored	.95	.95
324	A77	75c multicolored	1.50	1.50
325	A77	85c multicolored	1.90	1.90
		Nos. 323-325 (3)	4.35	4.35

1998, Jan. 22   Litho.   Perf. 14

Children's drawings: a, Gift package. b, Mosque. c, Cocos Malay woman. d, Island scene. e, Two dancers.

326	A78	45c Strip of 5, #a.-e.	5.25	5.25

Festive Season.

Fish Type of 1995

Designs: 70c, Crowned squirrelfish. 95c, Sixstripe wrasse. $5, Goldback anthias.

1998, Aug. 13   Litho.   Perf. 14x14½

327	A74	70c multicolored	1.25	1.25
328	A74	95c multicolored	1.50	1.50
329	A74	$5 multicolored	8.25	8.25
		Nos. 327-329 (3)	11.00	11.00

Jukong Boats, Hari Raya Festival — A79

a, Women placing items in leaves, people along beach. b, Two women, boats along beach. c, Flowers, man in boat. d, Palm trees, two men, man in boat. e, Two people in boat.

1999, Feb. 11   Litho.   Perf. 14½x14

330	A79	45c Strip of 5, #a.-e.	4.75	4.75

Flora and Fauna — A80

a, 45c, Two birds on tree branch. b, 25c, Bird in flight. c, 10c, Sailboat with sail down. d, 5c, Sailboat with red sails. e, 45c, Two birds in flight. f, 25c, Butterflies. g, 10c, School of fish. h, 5c, School of fish swimming left, coral. i, 45c, Red hibiscus flower. j, 25c, Three birds in flight. k, 10c, Two moorish idols. l, 5c, Turtles. m, 45c, Butterfly, flowers. n, 25c, Moth with wings folded, flowers. o, 10c, Two gold fish. p, 5c, Various fish swimming right. q, 45c, Yellow hibiscus. r, 25c, Butterfly on flowers. s, 10c, Two birds in flight. t, 5c, Large fish, coral.

1999, June 17   Litho.   Perf. 14x14½

331	A80	Sheet of 20, #a.-t.	17.00	17.00

Faces of Cocos Islands A81

Ordinary people: a, Ratma Anthoney, with white shirt. b, Nakia Haji Dolman, with multicolored head covering. c, Muller Eymin, with white head covering. d, Courtney Press, with flowered outfit. e, Mhd Abu-Yazid, with blue shirt with stripes.

2000, Apr. 13   Litho.   Perf. 14x14½

332	A81	45c Strip of 5, #a.-e.	5.00	5.00

Worldwide Fund for Nature — A82

#333: a, Purple crab. b, Little nipper crab. #334: a, Horn-eyed ghost crab. b, Smooth-banded ghost crab.

Illustration reduced.

2000, June 20   Litho.   Perf. 14x14¾

333	A82	5c Pair, #a-b	1.10	1.10
334	A82	45c Pair, #a-b	2.25	2.25

Fish Type of 1995

No. 335: a, Wideband fusilier. b, Striped surgeonfish. c, Orangeband surgeonfish. d, Indo-Pacific sergeant.

2001, Feb. 8   Litho.   Perf. 14x14½

335		Block of 4	7.00	7.00
a.-d.		A74 45c Any single	1.25	1.25

Turtles — A83

No. 336: a, Loggerhead. b, Hawksbill. c, Leatherback. d, Green. Illustration reduced.

2002, Oct. 1   Litho.   Perf. 14x14½
336	A83	Block of 4	5.50	5.50
a.-d.		45c Any single	1.00	1.00

Shore Birds — A84

No. 337: a, Eastern reef egret. b, Sooty tern. c, Ruddy turnstone. d, Whimbrel.

2003, June 17
337		Horiz. strip of 4	6.50	6.50
a.-d.		A84 50c Any single	1.25	1.25

Royal Visit, 50th Anniv. — A85

Queen Elizabeth II and: No. 338a, Cocos Malay musicians. No. 338b, Royal Yacht Gothic. #1, Clunies Ross (Oceania) House. $1.45, Dignitary presenting model of Malay jukong.

2004, Mar. 16
338	A85	50c Horiz. pair, #a-b	2.50	2.50
339	A85	$1 multi	2.50	2.50
340	A85	$1.45 multi	3.75	3.75
a.		Souvenir sheet, #338a, 338b, 339, 340	9.00	9.00
b.		As 'a,' with 2004 World Stamp Championship emblem ovptd. in gold in margin	10.00	10.00
		Nos. 338-340 (3)	8.75	8.75

No. 340b issued 8/28.

Worldwide Fund for Nature (WWF) A86

Designs: No. 341a, Blacktip reef shark. No. 341b, Gray reef sharks. #1, Blacktip reef sharks. $1.45, Gray reef shark.

2005, Jun 21   Perf. 14½x14
341	A86	50c Horiz. pair, #a-b	2.25	2.25
342	A86	$1 multi	2.25	2.25
343	A86	$1.45 multi	3.25	3.25
		Nos. 341-343 (3)	7.75	7.75

Wildlife — A87

No. 344: a-e, Various birds. f-t, Various fish and marine life.

2006, June 13   Perf. 14¾x14
344	A87	Sheet of 20	12.00	12.00
a.-e.		10c Any single	.30	.30
f.-o.		25c Any single	.45	.45
p.-t.		50c Any single	1.00	1.00

Mollusks A88

Designs: No. 345a, Oriental moonsnail. No. 345b, Perly nautilus. $1, Partridge tun. $1.45, Giant clam.

2007, Mar. 20   Perf. 14x14½
345	A88	50c Horiz. pair, #a-b	1.75	1.75
346	A88	$1 multi	1.75	1.75
347	A88	$1.45 multi	2.75	2.75
		Nos. 345-347 (3)	6.25	6.25

Birds — A89

No. 345, vert: a, Black-winged stilt. b, Chinese pond heron. $1, White-breasted waterhen. $1.45, Saunders' tern.

2008, Feb. 26   Perf. 14
348	A89	50c Horiz. pair, #a-b	2.10	2.10
349	A89	$1 multi	2.10	2.10
350	A89	$1.45 multi	3.00	3.00
		Nos. 348-350 (3)	7.20	7.20

History of Cocos Islands — A90

No. 351: a, Sighting of islands by Captain William Keeling, 1609. b, Visit of Charles Darwin, 1836.
$1.10, Control of islands by Clunies Ross family, 1827-1978. $1.65, Australian territory, 1955.

2009, Apr. 21   Perf. 14¼
351	A90	55c Horiz. pair, #a-b	1.75	1.75
352	A90	$1.10 multi	1.75	1.75
353	A90	$1.65 multi	2.75	2.75
		Nos. 351-353 (3)	6.25	6.25

Flowers — A91

No. 354: a, Ipomoea pes-caprae. b, Hibiscus tiliaceus.
No. 355: a, Suriana maritima. b, Morinda citrifolia.

2010, Sept. 15   Litho.   Perf. 14¾x14
354	A91	60c Horiz. pair, #a-b	2.40	2.40
355	A91	$1.20 Horiz. pair, #a-b	4.75	4.75

OFFICIAL STAMP

No. 175 Ovptd. and Surcharged in Dark Blue

1991, Jan. 25   Litho.   Perf. 14x13½
O1	A44	(43c) on 90c multi	130.00

No. O1 was not sold to the public unused. Used value is for a canceled-to-order example. Mint examples exist in the marketplace. Value, $250.

COLOMBIA

kə-'ləm-bē-ə

LOCATION — On the northwest coast of South America, bordering on the Caribbean Sea and the Pacific Ocean
GOVT. — Republic
AREA — 456,535 sq. mi.
POP. — 39,309,422 (1999 est.)
CAPITAL — Bogota

In 1810 the Spanish Viceroyalty of New Granada gained its independence and with Venezuela and Ecuador formed the State of Greater Colombia. In 1832 this state split into three independent units as Venezuela, Ecuador and the Republic of New Granada. The name of the country has been, successively, Granadine Confederation (1858-61), United States of New Granada (1861), United States of Colombia (1861-65), and the Republic of Colombia (1885 to date).

100 Centavos = 1 Peso

Catalogue values for unused stamps in this country are for Never Hinged items, beginning with Scott 594 in the regular postage section, Scott B1 in the semi-postal section, Scott C200 in the airpost section, Scott CE1 in the airpost special delivery section, Scott E2 in the special delivery section, and Scott RA33 in the postal tax section.

In the earlier days many towns did not have handstamps for canceling and stamps were canceled with pen and ink. Pen cancellations, therefore, do not indicate fiscal use. (Postage stamps were not used for revenue purposes.) Used values for Nos. 1-128 are for stamps with illegible manuscript cancels or handstamp cancels of Bogota or Medellin. Stamps with legible manuscript or other handstamped town-name cancels sell for more.

Fractions of many Colombian stamps of both early and late issues are found canceled, their use to pay postage having been tolerated even though forbidden by the postal laws and regulations. Many are known to have been made for philatelic purposes.

Watermarks

Wmk. 116 — Crosses and Circles

Wmk. 127 — Quatrefoils

Wmk. 194 — Multiple Curvilinear Triangles

Wmk. 229 — Wavy Lines

Wmk. 255 — Wavy Lines and C Multiple

Wmk. 331 — REPUBLICA DE COLOMBIA

Wmk. 334 — Rectangles

Wmk. 346 — Parallel Curved Lines

Stamps inscribed "Colombia" that show the Panama Canal area were used in Panama and can be found in Vol. 5.

Granadine Confederation

A1

A2
Coat of Arms

Type A1 — Asterisks in frame. Wavy lines in background.
Type A2 — Diamond-shaped ornaments in frame. Straight lines in background. Numerals larger.

1859　Unwmk.　Litho.　*Imperf.*
Wove Paper

1	A1	2½c green	120.00	120.00
a.		2½c yellow green	120.00	120.00
2	A1	5c blue	140.00	87.50
a.		Tête bêche pair	4,500.	7,250.
b.		"50" instead of "5"		7,500.
3	A1	5c violet	375.00	120.00
a.		Tête bêche pair	6,000.	6,000.
b.		"50" instead of "5"		15,000.
4	A1	10c red brown	140.00	80.00
a.		10c buff	140.00	80.00
6	A1	20c blue	120.00	67.50
a.		20c gray blue	120.00	67.50
b.		Se-tenant with 5c		
c.		Tête bêche pair	40,000.	32,500.

7	A1	1p carmine	72.50	*120.00*
a.		1p rose	110.00	150.00
8	A1	1p rose, *bluish*	350.00	

The 10c green is an essay.
Reprints of No. 7 are in brown rose or brown red. Wavy lines of background are much broken; no dividing lines between stamps.

1860
Laid Paper

9	A2	5c lilac	325.00	210.00

Wove Paper

10	A2	5c gray lilac	85.00	65.00
a.		5c lilac	85.00	65.00
11	A2	10c yellow buff	85.00	55.00
a.		Tête bêche pair	7,000.	7,000.
12	A2	20c blue	210.00	140.00

United States of New Granada

Arms of New Granada — A3

1861

13	A3	2½c black	1,450.	400.00
14	A3	5c yellow	350.00	175.00
a.		5c buff	350.00	175.00
16	A3	10c blue	1,250.	175.00
17	A3	20c red	500.00	475.00
18	A3	1p pink	1,250.	375.00

There are 54 varieties of the 5c, 20c, and 1 peso.
Forgeries exist of Nos. 13-18.

United States of Colombia

A4	A5	A6

Coat of Arms

1862

19	A4	10c blue	250.00	125.00
20	A4	20c red	4,500.	725.00
21	A4	50c green	250.00	175.00
22	A4	1p red lilac	600.00	175.00
23	A4	1p red lil, *bluish*	5,500.	1,750.

No. 23 is on a thinner, coarser wove paper than Nos. 19-22.

1863

24	A5	5c orange	100.00	65.00
a.		Star after "Cent"	110.00	72.50
25	A5	10c blue	175.00	24.00
a.		Period after "10"	200.00	30.00
26	A5	20c red	225.00	75.00
a.		Star after "Cent"	250.00	82.50
b.		Transfer of 50c in stone of 20c	18,500.	5,500.

Bluish Paper

28	A5	10c blue	175.00	32.50
a.		Period after "10"	190.00	35.00
29	A5	50c blue	210.00	75.00
a.		Star after "Cent"	210.00	77.50

Ten varieties of each.

1864
Wove Paper

30	A6	5c orange	60.00	37.50
a.		Tête bêche pair	475.00	400.00
31	A6	10c blue	55.00	15.00
a.		Period after 10	55.00	15.00
32	A6	20c scarlet	100.00	55.00
33	A6	50c green	85.00	55.00
34	A6	1p red violet	350.00	175.00

Two varieties of each.

Arms of Colombia
A7　　A9

A8

1865

35	A7	1c rose	10.00	10.00
a.		bluish pelure paper	30.00	21.00
36	A8	2½c black, *lilac*	21.00	14.00
37	A9	5c yellow	47.50	20.00
a.		5c orange	47.50	20.00
38	A9	10c violet	67.50	4.50
39	A9	20c blue	67.50	20.00
40	A9	50c green	120.00	52.50
41	A9	50c grn (small figures)	120.00	52.50
42	A9	1p vermilion	125.00	18.00
a.		1p rose red	125.00	18.00
b.		Period after "PESO"	150.00	20.00

Ten varieties of each of the 5c, 10c, 20c, and 50c, and six varieties of the 1 peso. No. 36 was used as a carrier stamp.

A10	A11	A12

A13	A14

A15	A16

1866
White Wove Paper

45	A10	5c orange	72.50	27.50
46	A11	10c lilac	17.00	5.25
a.		Pelure paper	21.00	11.50
47	A12	20c light blue	42.50	21.00
a.		Pelure paper	67.50	52.50
48	A13	50c green	17.00	13.00
49	A14	1p rose red, *bluish*	92.50	32.50
a.		1p vermilion	92.50	32.50
51	A15	5p blk, *green*	500.00	210.00
52	A16	10p blk, *vermilion*	350.00	200.00

There are several varieties of the 1 peso having the letters "U," "N," "S" and "O" smaller.

A17	A18

A19	A20

A21

TEN CENTAVOS:
Type I — "B" of "COLOMBIA" over "V" of "CENTAVOS".
Type II — "B" of "COLOMBIA" over "VO" of "CENTAVOS".
ONE PESO:
Type I — Long thin spear heads. Diagonal lines in lower part of shield.
Type II — Short thick spear heads. Horizontal and a few diagonal lines in lower part of shield.
Type III — Short thick spear heads. Crossed lines in lower part of shield. Ornaments at each side of circle are broken. (See No. 97.)

1868

53	A17	5c orange	67.50	52.50
54	A18	10c lilac (I)	4.25	1.10
a.		10c red violet (I)	4.25	1.10
b.		10c lilac (II)	4.25	1.10
c.		10c red violet (II)	4.25	1.10
d.		Printed on both sides	7.50	2.50
55	A19	20c blue	3.00	1.25
56	A20	50c yellow green	3.50	2.40
57	A21	1p ver (II)	4.25	2.10
a.		Tête bêche pair	140.00	100.00
b.		1p rose red (I)	60.00	27.50
c.		1p rose red (II)	4.00	2.10
		Nos. 53-57 (5)	82.50	59.35

See Nos. 83-84, 96-97.

Counterfeits or reprints.

10c — There is a large white dot at the upper left between the circle enclosing the "X" and the ornament above.

50c — There is a shading of dots instead of dashes below the ribbon with motto. There are crossed lines in the lowest section of the shield instead of diagonal or horizontal ones.

1p — The ornaments in the lettered circle are broken. There are crossed lines in the lowest section of the shield. These counterfeits, or reprints, are on white paper, wove and laid, on colored wove paper and in fancy colors.

A22

Two varieties

1869-70

Wove Paper

59	A22	2½c black, *violet*	4.75	2.50
a.		Laid paper ('70)	325.00	250.00
b.		Laid batonné paper ('70)	30.00	24.00

Nos. 59, 59a, 59b were used as carrier stamps.

Counterfeits, or reprints, are on magenta paper wove or ribbed.

A23	A24

1870

Wove Paper

62	A23	5c orange	2.00	1.25
a.		5c yellow	2.00	1.25
63	A24	25c black, *blue*	16.00	13.00

See No. 89.

In the counterfeits, or reprints, of No. 63, the top of the "2" of "25" does not touch the down stroke. The counterfeits are on paper of various colors.

A25	A26

5 pesos — The ornament at the left of the "C" of "Cinco" cuts into the "C," and the shading of the flag is formed of diagonal lines.

10 pesos — The stars have extra rays between the points, and the central part of the shield has some horizontal lines of shading at each end.

1870

Surface Colored, Chalky Paper

64	A25	5p blk, *green*	100.00	67.50
65	A26	10p blk, *vermilion*	120.00	67.50

See Nos. 77-79, 125-126.

A27	A28

A29

TEN CENTAVOS:
Type I — "S" of "CORREOS" 2½mm high.
First "N" of "NACIONALES" small.
Type II — "S" of "CORREOS" 2mm high.
First "N" of "NACIONALES" wide.

1871-74

Thin Porous Paper

66	A27	1c green ('72)	3.50	3.50
67	A27	1c rose ('73)	3.50	3.50
a.		1c carmine ('73)	3.50	3.50
68	A28	2c brown	1.60	1.60
a.		2c red brown	1.60	1.60
69	A29	10c vio (I) ('74)	2.50	2.50
a.		10c lilac (I) ('74)	2.50	2.50
b.		10c violet (II) ('74)	2.50	2.50
c.		10c lilac (II) ('74)	2.50	2.50
d.		As #69, laid paper ('72)	140.00	140.00
e.		As "b," laid paper ('72)	140.00	140.00
		Nos. 66-69 (4)	11.10	11.10

Counterfeits or reprints.

1c — The outer frame of the shield is broken near the upper left corner and the "A" of "Colombia" has no cross-bar.

2c — There are scratches across "DOS" and many white marks around the letters on the large "2." The counterfeits, or reprints, are on white wove and bluish white laid paper.

Condor — A30

Liberty Head
A31   A32

5 pesos, redrawn — The ornament at the left of the "C" only touches the "C," and the shading of the flag is formed of vertical and diagonal lines.

10 pesos, redrawn — The stars are distinctly five pointed, and there is no shading in the central part of the shield.

1877

Wove Paper

73	A30	5c purple	7.25	2.10
a.		5c lilac	7.25	2.10
74	A31	10c bister brown	3.50	.90
a.		10c red brown	3.50	.90
b.		10c violet brown	3.50	.90
75	A32	20c blue	4.25	1.40
a.		20c violet blue	25.00	3.50
77	A26	10p blk, *rose*	120.00	67.50
78	A25	5p blk, *lt grn*, redrawn	42.50	32.50
79	A26	10p blk, *rose*, redrawn	17.00	2.75
a.		10p blk, *dark rose*, redrawn	17.00	2.75
		Nos. 73-79 (6)	194.50	107.15

Stamps of the issues of 1871-77 are known with private perforations of various gauges, also with sewing machine perforation.

In the counterfeits, or reprints, of the 5 pesos the ornament at the left of the "C" of "Cinco" is separated from the "C" by a black line.

In the counterfeits, or reprints, of the 10 pesos the outer line of the double circle containing "10" is broken at the top, below "OS" of "Unidos," and the vertical lines of shading contained in the double circle are very indistinct. There is a colorless dash below the loop of the "P" of "Pesos."

1876-79

Laid Paper

80	A30	5c lilac	85.00	65.00
81	A31	10c brown	47.50	2.75
82	A32	20c blue	100.00	67.50
83	A20	50c green ('79)	97.50	65.00
84	A21	1p pale red (II) ('79)	62.50	15.00
		Nos. 80-84 (5)	392.50	215.25

1879

Wove Paper

89	A24	25c green	32.50	32.50

1881

Blue Wove Paper

93	A30	5c violet	20.00	13.00
a.		5c lilac	20.00	13.00
94	A31	10c brown	12.00	2.50
95	A32	20c blue	12.00	3.75
96	A20	50c yellow green	12.50	7.50
97	A21	1p ver (III)	17.00	7.50
		Nos. 93-97 (5)	73.50	34.25

For types of 1p, see note over No. 53.

Reprints of the 10c and 20c are much worn. On the 10c the letters "TAVOS" of "CENTA-VOS" often touch. On the 20c the letters "NT" of "VEINTE" touch and the left arm of the "T" is too long. Reprints of the 25c, 50c and 1p have the characteristics previously described. The reprints are on white wove or laid paper, on colored papers, and in fancy colors. Stamps on green paper exist only as reprints.

A34	A35

A36

1 centavo — The period before "UNION" is round and there are rays between the stars and the condors.

2 centavos — The "2's" and "C's" in the corners are placed upright.

5 centavos — The last star at the right almost touches the frame.

10 centavos — The letters of the inscription are thin; there are rays between the stars and the condor.

1881

White Wove Paper   *Imperf.*

103	A34	1c green	5.00	4.00
104	A35	2c vermilion	2.10	1.60
a.		2c rose	2.50	1.60
106	A34	5c blue	5.00	1.60
a.		Printed on both sides		
107	A36	10c violet	4.25	1.25
108	A34	20c black	4.75	2.00
		Nos. 103-108 (5)	21.10	10.45

The stamps of this issue are found with perforations of various gauges, also sewing machine perforation, all of which are unofficial.
See Nos. 112, 114-115.

Liberty
Head — A37   A37a

1881   *Imperf.*

109	A37	1c blk, *green*	3.50	5.00
110	A37	2c blk, *lilac rose*	3.50	5.00
111	A37	5c blk, *lilac*	8.50	1.75
		Nos. 109-111 (3)	15.50	11.75

Nos. 109 to 111 are found with regular or sewing machine perforation, unofficial.

Reprints:

1c — The top line of the stamp and the top frame extend to the left. 2c — There is a curved line over the scroll below the "AV" of "CENTAVOS."

5c — There are scratches across the "5" in the upper left corner. All three values were reprinted on the three colors of paper of the originals.

Redrawn

1 centavo — The period before "UNION" is square and the rays between the stars and the condor have been wholly or partly erased.

2 centavos — The "2's" and "C's" in the corners are placed diagonally.

5 centavos — The last star at the right touches the wing of the condor.

10 centavos — The inscription are thick; there are no rays under the stars; the last star at the right touches the wing of the condor and this wing touches the frame.

1883   *Imperf.*

112	A34	1c green	4.75	4.25
113	A37a	2c rose	2.10	1.75
114	A34	5c blue	4.00	1.00
a.		5c ultramarine	4.00	
b.		Printed on both sides, reverse ultra	25.00	20.00
115	A36	10c violet	5.00	1.00
		Nos. 112-115 (4)	15.85	8.40

The stamps of this issue are found with regular or sewing machine perforation, privately applied.

A38	A39

1883   *Perf. 10½, 12, 13½*

116	A38	1c gray grn, *grn*	1.00	1.00
a.		Imperf., pair	5.00	5.00
117	A39	2c red, *rose*	1.00	1.25
a.		2c org red, *rose*	1.00	1.40
b.		2c red, *buff*	12.00	12.00
c.		Imperf., pair (#117 or 117a)	7.75	7.75
d.		"DE LOS" in very small caps	15.00	15.00
118	A38	5c blue, *bluish*	2.50	1.50
a.		5c dk bl, *bluish*	2.50	1.00
b.		5c blue	3.25	2.50
c.		Imperf., pair (#118 or 118a)	7.75	7.75
d.		As "b," imperf., pair	12.00	12.00
119	A39	10c org, *yel*	1.25	1.40
a.		"DE LOS" in large caps	60.00	26.00
b.		Imperf., pair	16.00	16.00
120	A39	20c vio, *lilac*	1.40	1.40
a.		Imperf., pair	16.00	16.00
122	A38	50c brn, *buff*	3.00	3.25
a.		Perf. 12	3.00	3.25
123	A38	1p claret, *bluish*	5.50	1.90
a.		Imperf., pair	16.00	16.00
		Nos. 116-123 (7)	15.65	11.70

Redrawn Types of 1877

1883 (?)   *Perf. 10½, 12*

125	A25	5p orange brown	10.00	6.00
126	A26	10p black, *gray*	10.00	7.25

1886   *Perf. 10½, 11½, 12*

127	A38	5p brown, *straw*	10.00	5.50
a.		Imperf., pair	32.50	32.50
128	A38	10p black, *rose*	10.00	5.50
a.		Imperf., pair	32.50	32.50

Republic of Colombia

A40   Simón Bolívar — A41

Pres. Rafael Núñez — A42

1886   *Perf. 10½ and 13½*

129	A40	1c grn, *grn*	1.75	.70
a.		Imperf., pair	6.75	6.75
130	A41	5c blue, *bl*	1.75	.40
a.		5c ultra, *blue*	1.75	.40
b.		Imperf., pair (#130)	6.75	6.75
131	A42	10c orange	3.50	.70
a.		Imperf., pair	9.25	9.25
b.		Pelure paper	4.50	1.00
		Nos. 129-131 (3)	7.00	1.80

Gen. Antonio Jose de Sucre y Alcala — A43   Gen. Antonio Nariño — A44

1887

133	A43	2c org red, *rose*	2.25	1.00
a.		2c orange red, *yellowish*	6.00	6.00
b.		2c orange red	7.25	7.25
c.		Imperf., pair (#133)	10.00	10.00

134 A44	20c pur, *grysh*	3.00	1.10
a.	Imperf., pair	8.50	8.50
b.	Pelure paper	3.50	2.25

Impressions of No. 134 on white, blue or greenish blue paper were not regularly issued.

Arms — A45   Nariño — A46

1888

135 A45	50c brn, *buff*	1.75	*1.90*
a.	Imperf., pair	6.00	6.00
136 A45	1p claret, *bluish*	8.00	2.10
137 A45	1p claret	3.50	1.06
138 A45	5p org brn	8.50	6.50
139 A45	5p black	14.50	9.50
140 A45	10p black, *rose*	21.00	6.75
	Nos. 135-140 (6)	57.25	27.81

See Nos. 154, 156-157.

1889

141 A46	20c pur, *grayish*	1.90	1.25
a.	Imperf., pair	9.25	9.25

Impressions on white, blue or greenish blue paper were not regularly issued.

A47   A48

A49   A50

A51

1890-91   Perf. 10½, 13½, 11

142 A47	1c grn, *grn*	1.90	1.60
143 A48	2c org red, *rose*	.95	.95
144 A49	5c bl, *grnsh bl*	1.40	.40
a.	5c deep blue, *blue*	1.40	.40
b.	Imperf., pair	5.50	5.50
146 A50	10c brn, *yel*	1.00	.40
a.	10c brown, *buff*	1.00	.40
147 A51	20c vio, *pelure paper*	3.50	*3.50*
	Nos. 142-147 (5)	8.75	6.85

A52   A52a

A53   A53a

A54

Perf. 10½, 12, 13½, 14 to 15½
1892-99
Ordinary Paper

148 A47	1c red, *yel*	.85	.40
149 A52	2c red, *rose*	42.50	42.50
150 A52	2c green	.50	.30
a.	2c yellow green	.50	.30
151 A49	5c blk, *buff*	13.00	.35
152 A52a	5c org brn, *pale buff*	1.00	.30
a.	5c red brown, *salmon* ('97)	1.00	.30
153 A50	10c bis brn, *rose*	.75	.40
a.	10c brown, *brownish*	2.00	1.60
154 A53	20c brn, *bl*	.75	.40
a.	20c red brown, *blue*	.75	.40
b.	20c yel brn, *grnsh bl* ('97)	5.50	13.00
c.	20c brown, *buff* ('97)	19.00	13.00
155 A45	50c vio, *vio*	1.25	.75
156 A53a	50c red vio, *vio* ('99)	1.75	
157 A54	1p bl, *grnsh*	2.10	.90
a.	1p blue, *buff*	2.10	.90
158 A45	5p red, *pale rose*	8.50	3.25
159 A45	10p blue	16.00	3.25
a.	Thin, pale rose paper	27.50	7.25
	Nos. 148-159 (12)	88.95	
	Nos. 148-155,157-159 (11)	52.80	

Type A53a is a redrawing of type A45. The letters of the inscriptions are slightly larger and the numerals "50" slightly smaller than in type A45.

The 20c brown on white paper is believed to be a chemical changeling.
Nos. 148, 150-152a, 153-155, 157, 159 exist imperf. Value per pair, $6-9.

A56

1899

162 A56	1c red, *yellow*	.70	.35
163 A56	5c red brn, *sal*	.70	.35
164 A56	10c brn, *lil rose*	2.00	.90
165 A56	50c blue, *lilac*	1.40	1.25
	Nos. 162-165 (4)	4.80	2.90

Cartagena Issues

A57

1899   Blue Overprint   Imperf.

167 A57	5c red, *buff*	30.00	30.00
a.	Sewing machine perf.	30.00	30.00
168 A57	10c ultra, *buff*	30.00	30.00
a.	Sewing machine perf.	30.00	30.00

Nos. 168 and 168a differ slightly from the illustration.

Bolivar No. 55 Overprinted with 7 Parallel Wavy Lines and:

A58   A59

A60   A61

Perf. 14 (#169), Sewing Machine Perf.
1899   Purple Overprint

169 A18	1c black	60.00	60.00
170 A58	1c brn, *buff*	20.00	20.00
a.	Altered from 10c	30.00	30.00
171 A59	2c blk, *buff*	20.00	20.00
a.	Altered from 10c	30.00	30.00
172 A60	5c mar, *grnsh bl*	18.00	18.00
a.	Perf. 12	18.00	18.00
b.	Without overprint	10.50	10.50

173 A61	10c red, *sal*	18.00	18.00
a.	Perf. 12	18.00	18.00
	Nos. 169-173 (5)	136.00	136.00

Types A58 and A59 illustrate Nos. 170a and 171a, which were made from altered plates of the 10c (No. 168). Nos. 170 and 171 were made from altered plate of the 5c denomination (No. 167), show part of the top flag of the "5" and differ slightly from the illustrations.
Nos. 170-173 exist imperf. Values about same as perf.

A62

1900   Imperf.
Purple Overprint

174 A62	5c red	25.00	25.00
a.	Perf. 12	35.00	35.00

A63   A64

"Gobierno Provisorio" at Top
1900   Litho.   Perf. 12 Vertically

175 A63	1c (ctvo) blk, *bl grn*	47.50	8.00
a.	"cvo."	120.00	14.50
b.	"cvos."	47.50	8.00
c.	"centavo"	55.00	47.50
176 A63	2c black	26.00	6.00
177 A63	5c blk, *pink*	26.00	6.00
a.	Name at side (V)	62.50	9.00
178 A63	10c blk, *pink*	26.00	6.00
a.	Name at side (V)	62.50	9.00
179 A63	20c blk, *yellow*	47.50	8.00
a.	Name at side (G)	92.50	12.00
	Nos. 175-179 (5)	173.00	34.00

"Gobierno Provisional" at Top
Name at Side in Black or Green

180 A64	1c (ctvo.) blk, *bl grn*	47.50	8.00
a.	"centavo"	125.00	47.50
181 A64	2c blk, *bl grn*	30.00	5.00
182 A64	5c blk (G)	30.00	5.00
a.	"ctvos." smaller	47.50	9.00
183 A64	10c blk, *pink*	30.00	5.00
184 A64	20c blk, *yel* (G)	47.50	8.00
	Nos. 180-184 (5)	185.00	31.00

Issues of the rebel provisional government in Cucuta.

A65   A66

1901   Sewing Machine Perf.
Purple Overprint

185 A65	1c black	1.00	1.00
a.	Without overprint	2.25	2.25
b.	Double overprint	2.50	2.50
c.	Imperf., pair	2.50	2.50
d.	Inverted overprint	1.25	1.25
186 A66	2c blk, *rose*	1.00	1.00
a.	Imperf., pair	2.50	2.50
b.	Without overprint	2.25	2.25
c.	Double overprint	2.50	2.50

A67   A68

1901   Rose Overprint

187 A67	1c blue	1.00	1.00
a.	Imperf., pair	4.00	4.00

188 A68	2c brown	1.00	1.00
a.	Imperf., pair	4.00	4.00
b.	Without overprint	1.00	1.00

A69   A70

Sewing Machine or Regular Perf. 12, 12½
1902
Magenta Overprint

189 A69	5c violet	2.25	2.25
a.	Without overprint	2.25	2.25
b.	Double overprint	2.25	2.25
c.	Imperf., pair	4.75	4.75
190 A70	10c yel brn	2.25	2.25
a.	Double overprint	2.25	2.25
b.	Imperf., pair	4.75	4.75
c.	Without overprint	2.25	2.25
d.	Printed on both sides	3.25	3.25

A71   A72

1902
Magenta Overprint

191 A71	5c yel brn	2.25	2.25
a.	Without overprint	2.10	2.10
b.	Imperf., pair	6.00	6.00
192 A71	10c black	1.75	1.75
a.	Without overprint	1.50	1.50
b.	Imperf., pair	9.00	9.00
193 A72	20c maroon	5.50	4.50
b.	Imperf., pair	15.00	15.00
	Nos. 191-193 (3)	9.50	8.50

Nos. 191-193 exist tête bêche. Value of 10c and 20c, each $15.
Washed examples of Nos. 167-174, 185-193 are offered as "without overprint."

Barranquilla Issues

Magdalena River — A75   Iron Quay at Sabanilla — A76

La Popa Hill — A77

1902-03   Imperf.

194 A75	2c green	1.60	1.60
195 A75	2c dk bl	1.60	1.60
196 A75	2c rose	22.50	22.50
197 A76	10c scarlet	1.10	1.10
198 A76	10c orange	13.00	13.00
199 A76	10c rose	1.75	1.75
200 A76	10c maroon	1.90	1.90
201 A76	10c claret	1.90	1.90
202 A77	20c violet	3.50	3.50
a.	Laid paper		9.50
203 A77	20c dl bl	9.50	9.50
204 A77	20c dl bl, *pink*	125.00	125.00
205 A77	20c car rose	20.00	20.00
	Nos. 194-205 (12)	203.35	203.35

Sewing Machine Perf. and Perf. 12

194a A75	2c green	9.50	9.50
195a A75	2c dark blue	9.50	9.50
196a A75	2c carmine	47.50	47.50
197a A76	10c scarlet	4.75	4.75
198a A76	10c orange	35.00	35.00
199a A76	10c rose	6.50	6.50
200a A76	10c maroon	6.50	6.50
201a A76	10c claret	6.00	6.00
202b A77	20c purple	.70	.70
c.	20c lilac	.70	.70
203a A77	20c dull blue	9.50	9.50
204a A77	20c dull blue, *rose*	150.00	150.00
205b A77	20c carmine rose	72.50	72.50
	Nos. 194a-205b (12)	357.95	357.95

See Nos. 240-245.

Cruiser
"Cartagena" — A78

Bolívar — A79

General Próspero
Pinzón — A80

A81

A82

1903-04 — Imperf.

209	A78	5c blue	2.75	2.75
210	A78	5c bister	4.50	4.50
211	A79	50c yellow	3.75	3.75
212	A79	50c green	4.50	4.50
213	A79	50c scarlet	4.50	4.50
214	A79	50c carmine	4.50	4.50
a.		50c rose	4.50	4.50
215	A79	50c pale brown	4.50	4.50
216	A80	1p yellow brn	1.60	1.60
217	A80	1p rose	2.50	2.50
218	A80	1p blue	2.50	2.50
219	A80	1p violet	25.00	25.00
220	A81	5p claret	5.50	5.50
221	A81	5p pale brown	8.00	8.00
222	A81	5p blue green	7.50	7.50
223	A82	10p pale green	7.75	7.75
224	A82	10p claret	25.00	25.00
	Nos. 209-224 (16)		114.35	114.35

Nos. 216 and 217 measure 20½x26½mm and No. 218, 18x24mm. Stamps of this issue exist with forged perforations.

Perf. 12

209a	A78	5c blue	9.50	9.50
210a	A78	5c bister	9.50	9.50
211a	A79	50c yellow	25.00	25.00
b.		50c orange	25.00	25.00
212a	A79	50c green	25.00	25.00
213a	A79	50c scarlet	11.50	11.50
214b	A79	50c rose	11.50	11.50
215a	A79	50c pale brown	11.50	11.50
216a	A80	1p yellow brown	5.25	5.25
217a	A80	1p rose	7.50	7.50
218a	A80	1p blue	9.50	7.50
219a	A80	1p violet	62.50	62.50
220a	A81	5p claret	20.00	20.00
221a	A81	5p pale brown	22.50	22.50
222a	A81	5p blue green	22.50	22.50
223a	A82	10p pale green	30.00	30.00
224a	A82	10p claret	77.50	77.50
	Nos. 209-224a (16)		345.25	343.25

Laid Paper — Imperf.

240	A76	10c dk bl, *lil*	6.25	6.25
241	A76	10c dk bl, *bluish*	3.75	3.75
242	A76	10c dk bl, *brn*	3.75	3.75
243	A76	10c dk bl, *sal*	9.25	9.25
244	A76	10c dk bl, *grnsh bl*	5.00	5.00
245	A76	10c dk bl, *dp rose*	3.75	3.75
	Nos. 240-245 (6)		31.75	31.75

Perf. 12

240a	A76	10c dk bl, *lilac*	13.50	13.50
241a	A76	10c dk bl, *bluish*	9.25	9.25
242a	A76	10c dk bl, *brn*	9.25	9.25
243a	A76	10c dk bl, *salmon*	72.50	72.50
244a	A76	10c dk bl, *grnsh bl*	20.00	20.00
245a	A76	10c dk bl, *deep rose*	9.25	9.25
	Nos. 240a-245a (6)		133.75	133.75

Imperf., Sewing Machine Perf.
1902 — Typeset

255	A82a	10c black, *rose*	3.50	3.50
256	A82a	20c blk, *orange*	2.50	2.50

This issue was printed in either Cali or Popayan.

Medellin Issue

A83

1902

257	A83	1c grn, *straw*	.35	.50
258	A83	2c salmon, *rose*	.35	.50
259	A83	5c dp bl, *grnsh*	.35	.50
260	A83	10c pale brn, *straw*	.35	.50
261	A83	20c pur, *rose*	.45	.50
262	A83	50c dl rose, *grnsh*	2.25	3.00
263	A83	1p blk, *yellow*	4.50	6.75
264	A83	5p slate, *blue*	35.00	35.00
265	A83	10p dk brn, *rose*	22.50	22.50
	Nos. 257-265 (9)		66.10	69.75

For overprint see No. L8.

Imperf., Pairs

257a	A83	1c	11.00	11.00
258a	A83	2c	11.00	11.00
259a	A83	5c	11.00	11.00
260a	A83	10c	11.00	11.00
261a	A83	20c	11.00	11.00
262a	A83	50c	11.00	11.00
263a	A83	1p	27.50	27.50
264a	A83	5p	80.00	80.00
265a	A83	10p	50.00	50.00

Regular Issue

A84

A85

A86

A87

A88

A89

A90

A91

A92

1902 — Imperf.

266	A84	2c blk, *rose*	.20	.20
267	A85	4c red, *grn*	.20	.20
268	A86	5c grn, *bl*	.20	.20
269	A87	10c blk, *pink*	.20	.20
c.		10c blk, *rose*	1.10	1.10
270	A88	20c brn, *buff*	.20	.20
271	A89	50c dk grn, *rose*	1.40	1.40
272	A90	1p pur, *buff*	.60	.60
273	A91	5p grn, *bl*	4.25	4.25
274	A92	10p grn, *pale grn*	13.00	6.50
	Nos. 266-274 (9)		20.25	13.75

For overprint see No. H13.

Sewing Machine Perf.

266a	A84	2c blk, *rose*	1.90	1.90
267a	A85	4c red, *grn*	1.60	1.60
268a	A86	5c grn, *blue*	1.90	1.90
269a	A87	10c blk, *pink*	1.90	1.90
270a	A88	20c brn, *buff*	3.25	2.50
271a	A89	50c dk grn, *rose*	6.50	5.50
272a	A90	1p pur, *buff*	7.75	6.50
273a	A91	5p grn, *blue*	35.00	35.00
274a	A92	10p grn, *pale grn*	65.00	65.00
	Nos. 266a-274a (9)		124.80	121.55

1903 — Perf. 12

266b	A84	2c blk, *rose*	1.40	1.40
269b	A87	10c blk, *pink*	1.60	1.60
270b	A88	20c brn, *buff*	1.60	1.60
272b	A90	1p pur, *buff*	3.25	3.25
273b	A91	5p grn, *blue*	27.50	27.50
274b	A92	10p grn, *pale grn*	52.50	45.00
	Nos. 266b-274b (6)		87.85	80.25

1903 — Imperf.

284	A85	4c blue, *grn*	.35	.35
285	A86	5c blue, *blue*	.35	.35
286	A88	20c blue, *buff*	.35	.35
288	A89	50c blue, *rose*	1.75	1.75
	Nos. 284-288 (4)		2.80	2.80

Sewing Machine Perf.

284a	A85	4c blue, *grn*	2.25	1.75
285a	A86	5c blue, *blue*	2.25	1.75
286a	A88	20c blue, *buff*	3.25	2.50
288a	A89	50c blue, *rose*	6.50	5.75
	Nos. 284a-288a (4)		14.25	11.75

Perf. 12

284b	A85	4c blue, *grn*	2.50	2.50
285b	A86	5c blue, *blue*	2.50	2.50
286b	A88	20c blue, *buff*	3.50	3.50
288b	A89	50c blue, *rose*	9.75	9.75
	Nos. 284b-288b (4)		18.25	18.25

A93

1904 — Pelure Paper — Imperf.

303	A93	½c yellow brn	1.10	1.10
304	A90	1c blue green	1.10	1.10
a.		1c yellow green	1.10	1.10
306	A84	2c blue	.90	.65
307	A86	5c carmine	1.00	1.00
308	A87	10c violet	1.10	.90
	Nos. 303-308 (5)		5.20	4.75

For overprint see No. H13.

1904 — Perf. 13

303a	A93	½c yellow brown	4.25	4.25
304b	A90	1c blue green	5.50	5.00
c.		1c yellow green	7.50	7.00
306a	A84	2c blue	2.50	2.50

Perf. 12

307a	A86	5c carmine	2.25	2.25
308a	A87	10c violet	2.25	2.25
	Nos. 303a-308a (5)		16.75	16.25

A94

A95

Pres. José Manuel
Marroquín — A96

Imprint: "Lit. J.L.Arango Medellin. Col."

1904 — Wove Paper — Perf. 12

314	A94	½c yellow	.85	.25
315	A94	1c green	.85	.25
316	A94	2c rose	.85	.25
317	A94	5c blue	1.40	.25
318	A94	10c violet	1.75	.25
319	A94	20c black	1.75	.25
320	A95	1p brown	19.00	3.00
321	A96	5p red & blk, *yel*	60.00	60.00
322	A96	10p bl & blk, *grnsh*	60.00	60.00
	Nos. 314-322 (9)		146.45	124.50

Redrawn

314a	A94	½c	.85	.25
315a	A94	1c	.85	.25
316a	A94	2c	.85	.25
317a	A94	5c	1.40	.25
319a	A94	20c	1.75	.25
	Nos. 314a-319a (5)		5.70	1.25

Imperf., Pairs

314b	A94	½c	3.25	3.25
315b	A94	1c	2.50	2.50
316b	A94	2c	3.25	3.25
317b	A94	5c	3.25	3.25
318a	A94	10c	4.25	4.25
319b	A94	20c	7.75	7.75
320a	A95	1p	65.00	65.00
	Nos. 314b-320a (7)		89.25	89.25

On the redrawn types, the imprint is close to the base of the design instead of being spaced from it. On the redrawn 2c and 5c, the lower end of the vertical white line below "OR" of "CORREOS" forms a hook which turns to the right instead of to the left as in the originals.

See Nos. 325-330. For surcharges see Nos. 351-354, L1-L7, L9-L13, L15-L25.

A97

100p has different frame.

1903 — Imperf.

323	A97	50p org yel, *pale pink*	92.50	92.50
324	A97	100p dk bl, *dk rose*	77.50	77.50

Imprint: "Lit. Nacional"

Perf. 10, 13, 13½ and Compound
1908

325	A94	½c orange	.85	.20
a.		½c yellow	.85	.20
b.		Imperf., pair	2.50	1.90
c.		Without imprint	5.25	5.25
326	A94	1c yel grn	.75	.25
a.		Without imprint	.75	.25
d.		Imperf., pair	4.00	3.25
327	A94	2c red	.75	.25
a.		2c carmine	.75	.25
b.		Imperf., pair	4.00	3.25
328	A94	5c blue	.60	.25
a.		Imperf., pair	4.25	5.25
329	A94	10c violet	50.00	1.00
330	A94	20c gray blk	50.00	1.00
	Nos. 325-330 (6)		102.95	2.95

The above stamps may be easily distinguished from those of 1904 by the perforation, by the height of the design, 24mm instead of 23mm, and by the "Lit. Nacional" imprint.

Camilo Torres
A99

Policarpa
Salavarrieta
A100

Bolívar Demanding
Liberation of
Slaves — A105

Designs: 2c, Nariño. 5c, Bolívar. 10c, Francisco José de Caldas. 20c, Francisco de Paula Santander. 10p, Bolívar Resigning.

1910, Aug. — Engr. — Perf. 12

331	A99	½c violet & blk	.50	.30
a.		Center inverted	425.00	425.00
332	A100	1c deep green	.40	.25
333	A100	2c scarlet	.40	.25
334	A100	5c deep blue	1.25	.45
335	A100	10c plum	10.00	5.00
336	A100	20c black brn	15.00	5.00

337	A105	1p dk violet	85.00 25.00
338	A105	10p claret	325.00 250.00
		Nos. 331-338 (8)	437.55 286.75

Colombian independence centenary.

Caldas
A107

Monument to Battle of Boyacá
A113

View of Cartagena
A114

Coat of Arms
A118

Designs: 1c, Torres. 2c, Narino. 4c, Santander. 5c, Bolivar. 10c, Jose Maria Cordoba. 1p, Sucre. 2p, Rufino Cuervo. 5p, Antonio Ricaurte y Lozano.

1917 Engr. Perf. 14

339	A107	½c bister	.35 .20
340	A107	1c green	.30 .20
341	A107	2c car rose	.30 .20
342	A107	4c violet	.90 .30
343	A107	5c dull blue	3.00 .20
344	A107	10c gray	3.00 .20
345	A113	20c red	1.50 .20
346	A114	50c carmine	1.75 .20
347	A107	1p brt blue	12.00 1.00
348	A107	2p orange	13.50 .45
349	A107	5p gray	40.00 11.00
350	A107	10p dk brown	47.50 11.50
		Nos. 339-350 (12)	124.10 25.05

The 1c, 5c, 10c, 50c, 2p, 5p and 10p also exist perf. 11½ and 11½ compounded with 14. Litho. varieties of Nos. 343, 345 and 346 are counterfeits made to defraud the government. Imperforate examples of Nos. 339-350 are not known to have been regularly issued.
See Nos. 373-374, 400-405. For overprints and surcharges see Nos. 369-370, 377, 409-410, 440, C1, O3, O5-O9.

Nos. 318-319, 329-330
Surcharged in Red

1918
On Issue of 1904

351	A94	½c on 20c black	1.25 .35
352	A94	3c on 10c violet	3.00 .60

On Issue of 1908

353	A94	½c on 20c gray blk	10.00 6.25
354	A94	3c on 10c violet	15.00 5.00
		Nos. 351-354 (4)	29.25 12.20

Nos. 351-354 inclusive exist with surcharge reading up or down. On one stamp in each sheet the letter "S" in "Especie" is omitted. All denominations exist with a small zero before the decimal in the surcharge.

A119 A120

1918 Litho. Perf. 13½
358	A119	3c red	.95 .20
a.		Imperf., pair	5.00 5.00

1920 Engr. Perf. 14
359	A120	3c red, org	.40 .20
a.		Imperf., pair	3.75 3.75

See No. 371-372. For surcharge see No. 453.

A121 A122

A123

Perf. 10, 13½ and Compound
1920-21 Litho.

360	A121	½c yellow	1.40 .50
361	A121	1c green	.85 .20
362	A121	2c red	.65 .20
363	A122	3c green	.65 .20
a.		3c yellow green	.65 .20
364	A121	5c blue	1.25 .25
365	A121	10c violet	6.00 1.50
366	A121	20c deep green	6.75 4.00
367	A123	50c dark red	8.50 4.00
		Nos. 360-367 (8)	26.05 10.85

The tablet with "PROVISIONAL" was added separately to each design on the various lithographic stones and its position varies slightly on different stamps in the sheet. For some values there were two or more stones, on which the tablet was placed at various angles.
Nos. 360-366 exist imperf.
See No. 375.

No. 342 Surcharged in Red

a
PROVISIONAL $003

(15mm wide) — b

1921
369	A107 (a) 3c on 4c violet		.95 .25
a.	Double surcharge		15.00
370	A107 (b) 3c on 4c violet		3.75 2.00

See No. 377.

Types of 1917-21
1923-24 Engr. Perf. 13½
371	A120	1½c chocolate	1.25 .60
372	A120	3c blue	.50 .25
373	A107	5c claret ('24)	3.00 .25
374	A107	10c blue	9.25 .50

Litho.
375	A121	10c dark blue	12.50 7.25
		Nos. 371-375 (5)	26.50 8.85

No. 342 Surcharged in Red

(18mm wide)
PROVISIONAL $003

1924
377	A107	3c on 4c vio	3.75 1.50
a.	Double surcharge		15.00
b.	Double surch., one invtd.		15.00
c.	With added surch. "3cs." in red		

A124

1924-25 Litho. Perf. 10, 10x13½
379	A124	1c red	.85 .20
380	A124	3c dp blue ('25)	.85 .20

Exist imperf. Value, each pair $6.25.

A125 A126

Black, Red or Green Surch. & Ovpt.
Imprint of Waterlow & Sons
1925 Perf. 14, 14½
382	A125	1c on 3c bis brn	.70 .20
383	A126	4c violet (R)	.50 .20
a.	Inverted surcharge		8.75 8.75

Imprint of American Bank Note Co.
Perf. 12
384	A125	1c on 3c bis brn	7.50 6.25
a.	Inverted surcharge		19.00 19.00
385	A126	4c violet (G)	.50 .30
a.	Inverted overprint		9.50 9.50
		Nos. 382-385 (4)	9.20 6.95

Correos Provisional

Revenue stamps of basic types A125 and A126 were handstamped as above in violet or blue by the Cali post office in 1925, but were not authorized by the government. Denominations so overprinted are 1c, 2c, 3c, 4c and 5c.

A127 A128

Perf. 10, 13½x10
1926 Litho. Wmk. 194
395	A127	1c gray green	.50 .20
396	A128	4c deep blue	.55 .20

Exist imperf. Value, each pair $5.

Types of 1917 and

Sabana Station — A129

1926-29 Unwmk. Engr. Perf. 14
400	A107	4c deep blue	.50 .25
401	A118	8c dark blue	.60 .25
402	A107	30c olive bister	6.00 .70
403	A129	40c brn & yel brn	9.25 1.25
404	A107	5p violet	9.25 .90
a.	Perf. 11 ('29)		12.00 1.00
405	A118	10p green	15.00 2.50
a.	Perf. 11 ('29)		30.00 4.75
		Nos. 400-405 (6)	40.60 5.85

For surcharges & overprint see Nos. 409-410, O4.

Death of Bolívar
A130

1930, Dec. 17 Perf. 12½
408	A130	4c dk blue & blk	.60 .35

Cent. of the death of Simón Bolívar. See Nos. C80-C82.

Nos. 400 and 402 Surcharged in Red or Dark Blue

1932, Jan. 20 Perf. 14
409	A107	1c on 4c dp bl (R)	.30 .20
a.	Inverted surcharge		5.25 5.25
410	A107	20c on 30c ol bis	10.00 .70
a.	Inverted surcharge		21.00
b.	Double surcharge		21.00

Emerald Mine — A131
Oil Wells — A132

Coffee Cultivation
A133

Platinum Mine — A134
Gold Mining — A135

Christopher Columbus — A136

Imprint: "Waterlow & Sons Ltd. Londres"
1932 Wmk. 229 Perf. 12½
411	A131	1c green	.60 .25
412	A132	2c red	.60 .25
413	A133	5c brown	.70 .25
414	A134	8c blue blk	4.75 .60
415	A135	10c yellow	3.50 .25
416	A136	20c dk blue	10.00 .40
		Nos. 411-416 (6)	20.15 2.00

See Nos. 441-442, 464-466a, 517. For surcharges see Nos. 455, 527, O1, O10-O11, O13, RA30.

Pedro de Heredia — A137

Coffee Picking — A138

Perf. 11½
1934, Jan. 10 Unwmk. Litho.
417	A137	1c dark green	3.00 .80
418	A137	5c chocolate	3.75 .65
419	A137	8c dark blue	3.00 .80
		Nos. 417-419 (3)	9.75 2.25

Cartagena, 400th anniv. See Nos. C111-C114.

1934, Dec. Engr. Perf. 12
420	A138	5c brown	3.00 .20

Discus Thrower — A139

Condor — A145

Allegory of Olympic Games at Barranquilla — A140

Foot Race A141

Tennis A142

Pier at Puerto Colombia A143

View of the Bay A144

Designs: 2c, Soccer. 10c, Hurdling. 15c, Athlete in stadium. 18c, Baseball. 24c, Swimming. 50c, View of Barranquilla. 1p, Post and Telegraph Building. 2p, Monument to Flag. 5p, Coat of Arms.

1935, Jan. 26   Litho.   Perf. 11½

421	A139	2c bluish grn & buff	1.60	.50
422	A139	4c deep green	1.60	.50
423	A140	5c dk brn & yel	1.60	.50
a.		Horiz. pair, imperf. btwn.	240.00	
424	A141	7c dk carmine	3.00	1.75
425	A142	8c blk & pink	2.50	2.50
426	A141	10c brown & bl	3.50	1.75
427	A141	12c indigo	4.25	3.00
428	A141	15c bl & red brn	7.25	5.50
429	A141	18c dk vio & buff	10.00	8.25
430	A144	20c purple & grn	8.50	7.00
431	A144	24c bluish grn & ultra	8.50	6.75
432	A144	50c ultra & buff	13.00	10.00
433	A145	1p drab & blue	120.00	62.50
434	A145	2p dull grn & gray	140.00	110.00
435	A145	5p pur blk & bl	475.00	500.00
436	A145	10p black & gray	550.00	575.00
		Nos. 421-436 (16)	1,350.	1,295.

3rd Natl. Olympic Games, Barranquilla. Counterfeits of 10p exist.

Oil Wells — A155

Gold Mining — A157

Imprint: "American Bank Note Co."
1935, Mar.   Unwmk.   Engr.   Perf. 12

437	A155	2c carmine rose	.45	.25
439	A157	10c deep orange	25.00	.25

See Nos. 468, 470, 498, 516. For surcharge and overprints see Nos. 496, 596, O2.

No. 347 Surcharged in Black

1935, Aug.   Perf. 14

440	A107	12c on 1p brt bl	4.75	1.50

Types of 1932
Imprint: "Lit. Nacional Bogotá"
1935-36   Litho.   Perf. 11, 11½, 12½

441	A131	1c lt green	.25	.20
a.		Imperf., pair	4.25	
442	A133	5c brown ('36)	.70	.25
a.		Imperf., pair	4.75	4.00

For surcharge see No. 527.

Bolívar A159

Tequendama Falls A160

Wmk. Wavy Lines. (229)
1937   Engr.   Perf. 12½

443	A159	1c deep green	.20	.20
a.		Perf. 14	.20	.20
444	A160	12c deep blue	3.25	1.10

See No. 570. For surcharges and overprints see Nos. 454, 456, C231, C326, O12.

Soccer Player — A161

Runner — A163

Discus Thrower — A162

1937, Jan. 4   Photo.   Unwmk.

445	A161	3c lt green	1.40	.85
446	A162	10c carmine rose	3.75	1.75
447	A163	1p black	35.00	26.00
		Nos. 445-447 (3)	40.15	28.60

National Olympic Games, Manizales. For surcharge see No. 452.

Exposition Palace — A164

Stadium at Barranquilla A165

Monument to the Colors A166

1937, Jan. 4

448	A164	5c violet brown	2.75	.40
449	A165	15c blue	6.75	4.50
450	A166	50c orange brn	19.00	9.75
		Nos. 448-450 (3)	28.50	14.65

Barranquilla National Exposition.

Stamps of 1926-37 Surcharged in Black

1937-38   Unwmk.   Perf. 12½

452	A161	1c on 3c lt grn	1.00	1.00
a.		Inverted surcharge	2.25	2.25
453	A118	5c on 8c dk bl	.50	.45
a.		Inverted surcharge	2.25	2.25

Wmk. 229

454	A160	2c on 12c dp bl	.50	.40
455	A134	5c on 8c bl blk	.60	.65
a.		Invtd. surcharge	2.00	2.00
456	A160	10c on 12c dp bl ('38)	5.50	1.00
a.		Dbl. surcharge	11.00	11.00
		Nos. 452-456 (5)	8.10	3.50

Calle del Arco — A168

Entrance to Church of the Rosary — A169

Arms of Bogotá A170

Gonzálo Jiménez de Quesada A171

Bochica A172

Santo Domingo Convent A173

Mass of the Conquistadors — A174

1938, July 27   Unwmk.   Perf. 12½

457	A168	1c yellow green	.25	.20
458	A169	2c scarlet	.25	.20
459	A170	5c brown blk	.35	.25
460	A171	10c brown	.75	.40
461	A172	15c brt blue	3.75	1.60
462	A173	20c brt red vio	3.75	1.60
463	A174	1p red brown	50.00	29.00
		Nos. 457-463 (7)	59.10	33.25

Bogotá, 400th anniversary.

Types of 1932
Imprint: "Litografia Nacional Bogotá"
1938, Dec. 5   Litho.   Perf. 10½, 11

464	A132	2c rose	1.00	.35
465	A135	10c yellow	2.50	.35
466	A136	20c dull blue	10.00	1.25
a.		20c dark blue, perf. 12½ ('44)	62.50	6.25
		Nos. 464-466 (3)	13.50	1.95

Types of 1935 and

Bolívar A175

Coffee Picking A176

Arms of Colombia A177

Christopher Columbus A178

Caldas A179

Sabana Station A180

Imprint: "American Bank Note Co."
Wmk. 255
1939, Mar. 3   Engr.   Perf. 12

467	A175	1c green	.20	.20
468	A155	2c car rose	.20	.20
469	A176	5c dull brown	.20	.20
470	A157	10c deep orange	.50	.20
471	A177	15c dull blue	1.75	.20
472	A178	20c violet blk	19.00	.25
473	A179	30c olive bister	5.50	.35
474	A180	40c bister brn	17.00	3.75
		Nos. 467-474 (8)	44.35	5.35

See Nos. 497-499, 515, 518, 574. For surcharges and overprints see Nos. 506-507, 520-522, 596, RA26, RA47.

Gen. Santander A181

Allegory A182

Gen. Santander A183

Statue at Cúcuta A184

Birthplace of Santander A185

Church at Rosario A186

Paya — A187

Bridge at Boyacá — A188

Death of General
Santander
A189

Invasion of the
Liberators
A190

Perf. 13x13½, 13½x13
1940, May 6   Engr.   Wmk. 229
475 A181 1c olive green   .25   .25
476 A182 2c dk carmine   .50   .35
477 A183 5c sepia   .25   .25
478 A184 8c carmine   1.75 1.75
479 A185 10c orange yel   .85   .60
480 A186 15c dark blue   2.25 1.40
481 A187 20c green   3.00 2.10
482 A188 50c violet   6.75 6.25
483 A189 1p deep rose   21.00 21.00
484 A190 2p orange   72.50 72.50
    Nos. 475-484 (10)   109.10 106.45

Death of General Francisco Santander, cent.

Tobacco Plant
A194

Gen.
Santander
A195

Garcia
Rovira — A196

R.
Galan — A197

Antonio Sucre — A198

1940-43   Engr.   Wmk. 255   Perf. 12
488 A194 8c rose car & grn   1.25   .65
489 A195 15c dp blue ('43)   1.25   .25
490 A196 20c gray blk ('41) 4.75   .50
491 A197 40c brown bis ('41) 2.75   .50
492 A198 1p black   5.00 1.25
    Nos. 488-492 (5)   15.00 3.15

See #500, 554. For overprint see #RA28.

Arms of
Palmira — A199

Unwmk.
1942, July 4   Litho.   Perf. 11
493 A199 30c claret   5.50   .65

8th Natl. Agricultural Exposition, held at
Palmira.

Paradise of
Isaacs,
Palmira — A200

Signing Treaty of
the Wisconsin
A201

1942, July 4
494 A200 50c lt blue grn   5.50   .85

Issued in honor of the writer, Jorge Isaacs.

1942, Nov. 21   Perf. 10½
495 A201 10c dull orange   3.75   .50
  a. "2. XI.1902" instead of "21.
     XI. 1902"   22.50 25.00
  b. Perf. 12   6.00   6.00

40th anniv. of the signing of the Treaty of the
Wisconsin, Nov. 21, 1902.

No. 470 Surcharged
in Black

1944   Wmk. 255   Perf. 12
496 A157 5c on 10c dp org   .25   .20

Counterfeits exist of No. 496 with inverted or
double surcharge.

Types of 1935-41 and

National
Shrine — A202

San Pedro
Alejandrino
A203

Imprint: "Columbian Bank Note Co."
1944-45   Unwmk.   Engr.   Perf. 11
497 A175 1c green   .20   .20
498 A155 2c rose   .20   .20
499 A176 5c dull brown   .20   .20
500 A196 20c gray black   3.75   .75
501 A202 30c dl ol grn ('45) 2.25 1.25
502 A203 50c rose   2.25 1.25
    Nos. 497-502 (6)   8.85   3.85

No. 499
Surcharged in
Black

1944, Oct.
506 A176 1c on 5c dull brn .20   .20
507 A176 2c on 5c dull brn .20   .20

Nos. 506 and 507 exist with inverted or
double surcharge, created by favor.

Flag — A204

Arms — A205

Murillo Toro — A206

Hospital of
St. John of
God
A207

Virrey Solis
A208

1944, Oct. 10   Litho.
508 A204 2c ultra & bis   .30   .30
  a. Sheet of 18   15.00
  b. Imperf., pair   15.00
509 A205 5c ultra & bis   .45   .45
  a. Sheet of 22   18.00
  b. Imperf., pair   15.00
510 A206 20c blk & bluish
          grn   1.50 1.50
  a. Sheet of 8   16.00
  b. Imperf., pair   22.50
511 A207 40c blk & red   6.25 6.25
  a. Sheet of 4   26.00
512 A208 1p blk & red   14.00 14.00
  a. Sheet of 2   30.00
    Nos. 508-512 (5)   22.50 22.50

Souvenir Sheet
Perf. 11x11½ All Around, Stamps Imperf.
513 Sheet of 5, #508-512 35.00 40.00

75th anniv. of Gen. Benevolent Assoc. of
Cundinamarca.
Nos. 508-513 were printed in composite
sheets containing one each of Nos. 508a,
509a, 510a, 511a and 512a, and two of 513.
Fifty of these were presented to government
officials.

Murillo
Toro — A210

San Pedro
Alejandrino — A211

1944, Nov. 10   Perf. 11
514 A210 5c lt brown   .30   .20

Types of 1932-39 and A211
Imprint: "Litografia Nacional Bogota"
1944   Litho.   Perf. 12½
515 A175 1c dp green   .35   .20
  a. 1c olive green   .35   .20
  b. Imperf., pair   1.75 1.75
516 A155 2c dk carmine   .40   .20
  a. Imperf., pair   1.75 1.75
517 A135 10c yellow org   2.75   .45
518 A179 30c gray olive   10.00 3.50
  a. Imperf., pair   35.00
519 A211 50c rose   10.00 5.25
    Nos. 515-519 (5)   23.50 9.60

No. 469
Overprinted in
Green, Blue or
Red

Wmk. 255
1945, July 19   Engr.   Perf. 12
520 A176 5c dull brn (G)   .40   .25
521 A176 5c dull brn (R)   .40   .25
522 A176 5c dull brn (Bl)   .40   .25
    Nos. 520-522 (3)   1.20   .75

Portraits are Joseph Stalin, Franklin D.
Roosevelt and Winston Churchill.

Nos. 520-522 exist with overprint inverted.
Value, $20 each.

Clock Tower,
Cartagena — A212

1945, Nov. 15
523 A212 50c olive black   4.25 1.60

For overprints see Nos. 543-544.

Sierra
Nevada of
Santa Marta
A213

Designs: 30c, Seaplane Tolima. 50c, San
Sebastian Fort, Cartagena.

Unwmk.
1945, Dec. 14   Perf. 11
524 A213 20c light green   2.00 1.40
525 A213 30c pale blue   2.00 1.40
526 A213 50c salmon pink   2.00 1.40
    Nos. 524-526 (3)   6.00 4.20

25th anniv. of the 1st airmail service in
America, according to the inscription, but earlier services are known to have existed.

No. 442 Surcharged in Black

1946, Mar. 8   Perf. 11x11½, 12½
527 A133 1c on 5c brown   .20   .20
  a. Inverted surcharge   .90

Gen. Antonio Jose de
Sucre — A216

Wmk. 255
1946, Apr. 16   Engr.   Perf. 12
Size: 19x26½mm
528 A216 1c brn & turq grn .20   .20
529 A216 2c vio & rose car .20   .20
Size: 23x31mm
530 A216 5c sepia & blue   .20   .20
531 A216 9c dk grn & red   .85 1.60
532 A216 10c ultra & org   .65   .65
533 A216 20c blk & dp org   .65   .65
534 A216 30c brn red & grn .90   .35
535 A216 40c ol blk & red vio .90 .40
536 A216 50c dp brn & vio   .90   .40
    Nos. 528-536 (9)   5.45 4.65

Map of South
America
A217

National
Observatory
A218

Unwmk.
1946, June 7   Litho.   Perf. 11
537 A217 15c ultra   .50   .50
  a. Imperf., pair   4.00

1946, Aug.

| 538 | A218 | 5c fawn | .30 | .20 |
| a. | | Imperf., pair | 6.00 | |

See No. 565.

Andrés
Bello — A219

Joaquín de
Cayzedo y
Cuero — A220

Wmk. 255
1946, Sept. 3　　Engr.　　Perf. 12

539	A219	3c sepia	.25	.20
540	A219	10c orange	.60	.35
541	A219	15c slate black	.75	.35
		Nos. 539-541,C145 (4)	1.80	1.10

Bello (1781-1865), poet and educator.

1946, Sept. 20　Wmk. 229　Perf. 12½

| 542 | A220 | 2p bluish green | 4.50 | 1.40 |

See No. 568. For surcharge see No. 613.

Type of 1945,
Overprinted in
Black or Green

1946, Dec. 6　Wmk. 255　Perf. 12

543	A212	50c red (Bk)	4.00	2.75
a.		Double overprint	25.00	
544	A212	50c red (G)	4.00	2.75
a.		Double overprint	25.00	

5th Central American and Caribbean Championship Games.

Coffee — A221

Engraved and Lithographed
1947, Jan. 10　Wmk. 229　Perf. 12½

| 545 | A221 | 5c multicolored | .40 | .20 |

Colombian
Orchid:
Masdevallia
Nycterina
A222

Designs (Orchids): 2c, Miltonia vexillaria. No. 548, Cattleya chocoensis. No. 549, Odontoglossum crispum. No. 550, Cattleya dowiana aurea. 10c, Cattleya labiata trianae.

1947, Feb. 7　Wmk. 255　Perf. 12

546	A222	1c multicolored	.60	.20
547	A222	2c multicolored	.60	.20
548	A222	5c multicolored	1.75	.20
549	A222	5c multicolored	1.75	.20
550	A222	5c multicolored	1.75	.20
551	A222	10c multicolored	2.75	.35
		Nos. 546-551 (6)	9.20	1.35

Antonio
Nariño — A228

Alberto Urdaneta
y
Urdaneta — A229

Perf. 12½
1947, May 9　　Litho.　　Unwmk.

552	A228	5c blue, grnsh	.25	.20
553	A229	10c red brn, grnsh	.30	.20
		Nos. 552-553,C146-C147 (4)	1.40	1.05

4th Pan-American Press Congress, 1946.

Sucre Type of 1940
1947　Wmk. 255　Engr.　Perf. 12

| 554 | A198 | 1p violet | 2.75 | 1.25 |

José
Celestino
Mutis and
José
Jerónimo
Triana
A230

Miguel A. Caro
and Rufino J.
Cuervo — A231

1947　　Wmk. 229　　Perf. 12½

| 555 | A230 | 25c olive green | .75 | .40 |
| 556 | A231 | 3p dark purple | 4.50 | 3.75 |

See Nos. 567, 569. For surcharge see No. 610.

Metropolitan Cathedral, Plaza Bolívar,
Bogotá — A232

National
Capitol
A233

Ministry of
Foreign
Affairs
A234

33664

A235

1948, Apr. 2

557	A232	5c black brown	.20	.20
558	A233	10c orange	.55	.55
559	A234	15c dark blue	.55	.55
		Nos. 557-559,C148-C149 (5)	2.40	2.40

Miniature Sheet
Imperf

| 560 | A235 | 50c slate | 2.00 | 1.60 |

9th Pan-American Conf., Bogotá.

No. RA5A
Overprinted in
Black

1948　　Unwmk.　　Perf. 12½
Without Gum

| 561 | PT3 | 1c yellow orange | .20 | .20 |

The letter "C" is the initial of "CORREOS."

Nos. RA33, RA24
and RA25
Overprinted in Black

1948　　Wmk. 255　　Perf. 12.

562	PT6	1c olive	.20	.20
563	PT6	2c green	.20	.20
564	PT6	20c brown	.20	.20
		Nos. 562-564 (3)	.60	.60

Nos. 561-564 exist with inverted and double overprints.

Observatory Type of 1946
Unwmk.
1948, June 30　Litho.　Perf. 11

| 565 | A218 | 5c blue | .20 | .20 |

Simón
Bolívar — A236

Carlos Martinez
Silva — A237

Wmk. 255
1948, May 29　Engr.　Perf. 12

| 566 | A236 | 15c green | .40 | .20 |

Types of 1946-47

1948　　Unwmk.　　Perf. 12½

567	A230	25c green	.30	.20
568	A220	2p dp green	.55	.20
569	A231	3p dp red violet	.70	.20
		Nos. 567-569 (3)	1.55	.60

Falls Type of 1937

| 1948 | | | **Wmk. 229** | |
| 570 | A160 | 10c red | .20 | .20 |

For overprints see Nos. C231, C326.

Perf. 13½
1948, Dec. 21　Unwmk.　Litho.

| 571 | A237 | 40c carmine | .40 | .25 |

Juan de Dios
Carrasquilla
A238

1949, May 20　Wmk. 229　Perf. 12½

| 572 | A238 | 5c bister | .20 | .20 |

75th anniv. of the foundation of the Colombian Soc. of Agriculture.

Julio Garavito
Armero
A239

Arms of
Colombia
A240

Wmk. 229
1949, Apr. 24　Engr.　Perf. 12

| 573 | A239 | 4c green | .35 | .20 |

Issued to honor Julio Garavito Armero (1865-1920), mathematician.

Coffee Type of 1939.
Imprint: "American Bank Note Co."
1949, Aug. 4　　　Wmk. 255

| 574 | A176 | 5c blue | .20 | .20 |

1949, Oct. 7　Unwmk.　Perf. 13

| 575 | A240 | 15c blue | .20 | .20 |

Issued to honor the new Constitution. See Nos. C164-C165.

Shield and
Tree — A241

Francisco Javier
Cisneros — A242

1949, Oct. 13　Wmk. 229　Perf. 12½

| 576 | A241 | 5c olive | .20 | .20 |

4th anniv. of Colombia's 1st Forestry Cong. and propaganda for the government's reforestation program.

1949, Dec. 15　　Photo.　　Unwmk.

577	A242	50c red vio & yel	1.00	.60
578	A242	50c green & vio	1.00	.60
579	A242	50c brown & lt bl	1.00	.60
		Nos. 577-579 (3)	3.00	1.80

50th anniv. (in 1948) of the death of Francisco Javier Cisneros.

Masdevallia
Chimaera
A243

Odontoglossum Crispum — A244

Eastern Hemisphere — A245

Designs: 3c, Cattleya labiata trianae. 4c, Masdevallia nycterina. 5c, Cattleya dowiana aurea. 11c, Miltonia vexillaria. 18c, Santo Domingo post office.

1950, Aug. 22   Photo.   Perf. 13

580	A243	1c brown	.20 .20
581	A244	2c violet	.20 .20
582	A243	3c rose lilac	.25 .20
583	A243	4c emerald	.30 .20
584	A244	5c red orange	.75 .20
585	A244	11c red	1.75 1.50
586	A244	18c ultra	2.75 .50
		Nos. 580-586 (7)	6.20 3.00

Miniature Sheet
Imperf

587	A245	50c orange yel	1.50 1.50

75th anniv. (in 1949) of the UPU. See No. C199. For surcharge see No. C232.

Antonio
Baraya — A246

Perf. 12½

1950, Nov. 27   Unwmk.   Engr.

588	A246	2c red	.20 .20

Colombian
Farm
A247

1950, Dec. 28   Photo.   Perf. 11½

589	A247	5c dp car & buff	.20 .20
590	A247	5c bl grn & gray	.20 .20
591	A247	5c vio bl & gray	.20 .20
		Nos. 589-591 (3)	.60 .60

Issued to publicize rural life.

Arms of Bogotá   Arms of
A248   Colombia
A249

Perf. 12x12½

1950, Dec. 28   Engr.   Wmk. 255

592	A248	5p deep green	2.50 1.25
593	A249	10p red orange	7.50 1.75

Catalogue values for unused stamps in this section, from this point to the end of the section, are for Never Hinged items.

Map and Badge
A250

Guillermo
Valencia
A251

Perf. 12½x13

1951, Jan. 30   Photo.   Unwmk.

594	A250	20c red, yel & bl	.50 .25

60th anniversary (in 1947) of the formation of the Colombian Society of Engineers.

1951, Oct. 20   Engr.   Perf. 13x13½

595	A251	25c black	.90 .25

Issued to honor Guillermo Valencia (1873-1943), newspaper founder, governor of Cauca, presidential candidate, author.

No. 468 Overprinted
in Black

1951, Dec. 11   Wmk. 255   Perf. 12

596	A155	2c carmine rose	.30 .20

Issued to publicize the reversion of the Mares oil concession to Colombia.

Nicolas
Osorio — A252

No. 598, Pompilio Martinez. No. 599, Ezequiel Uricoechea. No. 600, Jose M. Lombana.

Perf. 11½

1952, Aug. 6   Unwmk.   Engr.
Various Frames

597	A252	1c deep blue	.25 .20
598	A252	1c deep blue	.25 .20
599	A252	1c deep blue	.25 .20
600	A252	1c deep blue	.25 .20
		Nos. 597-600 (4)	1.00 .80

Nos. 597-600 were printed in a single sheet containing four panes of twenty-five each, separated by double rows of ornamental tabs. Although inscribed "sobretasa," the stamps were for ordinary postage.

Types of Postal Tax Stamps of 1945-50 and

Communications Building
A253   A253a

1952   Perf. 12

601	A253	5c ultra	.35 .25

Wmk. 255

602	PT10	20c brown	10.00 4.50
603	PT6	25c dk gray	42.50 42.50
604	PT10	25c blue green	1.00 .25
605	A253a	50c orange yel	25.00 13.00
606	A253a	1p rose carmine	2.50 .30
607	A253a	2p lilac rose	25.00 9.75
608	A253a	2p violet	3.00 .65
		Nos. 601-608 (8)	109.35 71.20

Although inscribed "sobretasa," Nos. 601-608 were issued for ordinary postage. For surcharges see Nos. 612, RA48.

Cathedral of
Manizales — A254

Perf. 11½

1952, Oct. 10   Photo.   Unwmk.

609	A254	23c blue & gray blk	.45 .25

Centenary of city of Manizales.
For surcharge see No. 619.

No. 555 Surcharged in Blue

1952, Oct. 30   Wmk. 229   Perf. 12½

610	A230	15c on 25c olive green	.45 .25

Latin American Siderurgical Conf., 1952.
See No. C226.

Queen Isabella I
and Monument
A255

Perf. 12½

1953, Mar. 10   Unwmk.   Engr.

611	A255	23c blue & black	.95 .70

5th cent. of the birth of Queen Isabella I of Spain.
For surcharge see No. 693.

Nos. 606 and 568 Surcharged with
New Values in Dark Blue

1953, Oct. 19   Wmk. 255

612	A253a	40c on 1p rose car	1.60 .25
613	A220	50c on 2p dp green	1.60 .25

Manuel Ancizar
A256

Portraits: 23c, José Jeronimo Triana. 30c, Manuel Ponce de Leon. 1p, Agustin Codazzi.

Perf. 12½x13

1953, Nov.   Engr.   Unwmk.
Frames in Black

614	A256	14c rose red	.70 .65
615	A256	23c ultra	.60 .25
616	A256	30c chocolate	.45 .25
617	A256	1p emerald	.45 .25
		Nos. 614-617 (4)	2.20 1.40

Cent. (in 1950) of the establishment of the Chorographic Commission. For surcharges and overprint see Nos. 620, 687, 690, 692, C284.

Murillo Toro and
Map — A257

Engraved and Lithographed

1953, Dec. 12   Wmk. 255   Perf. 12
Black Surcharge

618	A257	5c on 5p multi	.40 .20

2nd Natl. Phil. Exhib., Bogotá, Dec. 1953. See No. C237.

Nos. 609 and 614 Surcharged with
New Value or New Value and
Ornaments

1953   Unwmk.   Perf. 11½, 12½x13

619	A254	5c on 23c (C)	.40 .20
620	A256	5c on 14c (Bk)	.40 .25

No. 614 surcharged "CINCO" in blue is listed as No. 687.

Symbolical of St.
Francis Receiving
Christ's
Wounds — A258

1954, Apr. 23   Photo.   Perf. 11½

621	A258	5c sepia & green	.40 .20

400th anniversary of the establishment of Colombia's first Franciscan community.

Soldier,
Map and
Arms
A259

1954, June 13   Engr.   Perf. 13

622	A259	5c dull blue	.25 .20

1st anniv. of the assumption of the presidency by Gen. Gustavo Rojas Pinilla. See Nos. C255, 637a.

Sports
Emblem — A260

Design: 10c, Stadium and athlete holding arms of Colombia.

1954, July 18   Unwmk.

623	A260	5c deep blue	.50 .20
624	A260	10c red	.85 .20
		Nos. 623-624,C256-C257 (4)	3.65 .95

7th Natl. Athletic Games, Cali, July 1954.

History Academy Seal — A261

1954, July 24
625 A261 5c ultra & green   .25 .20

50th anniversary (in 1952) of the Colombian Academy of History.

Convent and Cell of St. Peter Claver — A262

1954, Sept. 9
627 A262 5c dark green   .25 .20
a.   Souvenir sheet   5.50 7.50

300th anniv. of the death of St. Peter Claver. No. 627a contains one stamp similar to No. 627, but printed in greenish black. Sheet size: 121x129½mm. See Nos. C258-C258a.

Mercury — A263

1954, Oct. 29
628 A263 5c orange   .55 .25
Nos. 628,C259-C260 (3)   1.65 .75

1st Intl. Fair and Exhibition, Bogota, 1954.

Tapestry Madonna A264

College Cloister A265

Designs: 10c, Brother Cristobal de Torres. 20c, College chapel and arms.

Perf. 12½x11½, 11½x12½
1954, Dec. 6
629 A264 5c orange & blk   .40 .20
630 A264 10c blue   .40 .20
631 A265 15c violet brn   .40 .20
632 A265 20c black & brn   1.00 .35
a.   Souvenir sheet   8.50 10.00
Nos. 629-632,C263-C266 (8)   6.65 2.35

Founding of the Senior College of Our Lady of the Rosary, Bogota, 300th anniv. (in 1953). No. 632a contains four stamps similar to Nos. 629-632, but printed in different colors: 5c yellow and black, 10c green, 15c dull violet, 20c black and light-blue.

Steel Mill — A266

José Marti — A267

1954, Dec. 12   **Perf. 12½x13**
633 A266 5c ultra & blk   .25 .20

Issued to mark the opening of the Paz del Rio steel mill, October 1954. See No. C267.

1955, Jan. 28   **Perf. 13½x13**
634 A267 5c deep carmine   .25 .20

Centenary of the birth of José Marti (1853-1895), Cuban patriot. See No. C268.

Arms, Flags and Soldiers Building Bridge A268

1955, Mar. 23   **Perf. 12½**
635 A268 10c claret   .30 .20

Issued to honor Colombian soldiers who served in Korea, 1951-53. See Nos. 637a, C269.

Fleet Emblem — A269

M. S. City of Manizales and New York Skyline A270

1955, Apr. 12   **Unwmk.**
636 A269 15c deep green   .20 .20
637 A270 20c violet   .40 .20
a.   Souvenir sheet   7.50 9.50
Nos. 636-637,C270-C271 (4)   1.90 .95

Grand-Colombian Merchant Fleet. No. 637a contains four stamps similar to Nos. 622, 635-637, but printed in different colors: 5c blue, 10c dark carmine, 15c green, 20c purple.

Hotel Tequendama and Church of San Diego — A271

1955, May 16 Photo.   Perf. 11½x12
638 A271 5c blue   .25 .20

See No. C273.

Bolivar's Country Estate, Bogotá A272

1955, Sept. 28   Engr.   Perf. 12½
639 A272 5c deep ultra   .25 .20

50th anniv. of Rotary Intl. See No. C274.

Belalcazar, Jiménez de Quesada and Balboa A273

Caravels and Columbus A274

5c, San Martin, Bolivar and Washington.

Engraved and Photogravure
1955, Oct. 29   Perf. 13x12½
640 A273 2c yel grn & brn   .50 .25
641 A273 5c brt bl & brn   .50 .25
642 A274 23c lt ultra & blk   .55 .25
a.   Souvenir sheet   24.00 24.00
Nos. 640-642,C275-C280 (9)   29.45 14.90

7th Cong. of the Postal Union of the Americas and Spain, Bogota, Oct. 12-Nov. 9, 1955. No. 642a contains one each of Nos. 640-642, printed in slightly different shades.

José Eusebio Caro — A275

1955, Nov. 29   Engr.   Perf. 13½x13
643 A275 5c brown   .25 .20

José Eusebio Caro (1817-53), poet. See No. C281.

Departmental Issue

Map — A276

View of San Andres Harbor — A277

Cattle at Waterhole A278

Designs: 2c, Docks, Atlantico. 3c, "Industry," Antioquia. 4c, Cartagena Harbor, Bolivar. #647, Steel Mill, Boyaca. #648, Cattle, Cordoba. #649, Map. #650, San Andres Harbor. #651, Cacao picker, Cauca. 10c, Coffee picker, Caldas. 15c, Salt Mine Chapel, Zipaquira, Cundinamarca. 20c, Tropical plants and map, Choco. 23c, Harvester, Huila. 25c,

---

Banana Plantation, Magdalena. 30c, Gold mining, Nariño. 40c, Tobacco plantation, Santander. 50c, Oil wells, North Santander. 60c, Cotton plantation, Tolima. 1p, Sugar industry, Cauca. 3p, Amazon river at Leticia, Amazonas. 5p, Windmills and panoramic view, La Guajira. 10p, Rubber plantation, Vaupes.

Perf. 13½x13, 13x13½, 13
Engr.; Engr. & Litho.
1956   Unwmk.
Various Frames
644 A277 2c car & grn   .20 .20
645 A276 3c brn vio & blk   .20 .20
646 A277 4c grn & blk   .20 .20
647 A276 5c dk brn & bl   .20 .20
648 A277 5c ol & dk vio brn   .30 .20
649 A276 5c bl & blk   .25
650 A277 5c car & grnsh bl   .20 .20
651 A277 5c ol grn & red brn   .20 .20
652 A276 10c org & blk   .40 .20
653 A276 15c ultra & blk   .25 .20
654 A276 20c dk brn & bl   .25 .20
655 A277 23c ultra & ver   .30 .20
656 A277 25c ol grn & blk   .30 .20
657 A277 30c ultra & brn   .25 .20
658 A277 40c dl pur & red brn   .25 .20
659 A277 50c dk grn & blk   .25 .20
660 A277 60c pale brn & grn   .25 .20
661 A278 1p mag & grnsh bl   1.90 .20
662 A278 2p grn & red brn   2.75 .25
663 A278 3p car & blk   4.25 .50
664 A278 5p brn & lt ultra   7.50 1.00
665 A276 10p red brn & grn   20.00 6.00
Nos. 644-665 (22)   40.65 11.35

Nos. 645, 647, 649, 652-654 measure 27x32mm, No. 665 27x37mm. See Nos. 681-684, 685, 688-689. For surcharges and overprints see Nos. 685, 688-689, C289, C312.

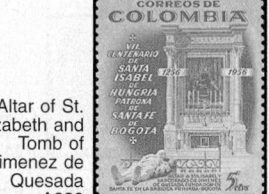

Columbus and Proposed Lighthouse A279

1956, Oct. 12   Photo.   Perf. 12
666 A279 3c gray black   .50 .25

Issued in honor of Christopher Columbus. See Nos. C285, C306.

Altar of St. Elizabeth and Tomb of Jimenez de Quesada A280

1956, Nov. 19   Unwmk.
667 A280 5c red lilac   .25 .20

7 cent. of St. Elizabeth of Hungary, patron saint of Sante Fé de Bogotá. See No. C286.

St. Ignatius of Loyola — A281

Javier Pereira — A282

1956, Nov. 26   Engr.   Perf. 12½x13
668 A281 5c blue   .25 .20
400th anniv. of the death of St. Ignatius of Loyola. See No. C287. For overprint see No. C324.

1956, Dec. 28   Unwmk.   Perf. 12
669 A282 5c blue   .25 .20
Issued to honor 167-year-old Javier Pereira. See No. C288.

Emblem and Dairy Farm A283

Designs: 2c, Emblem and tractor. 5c, Emblem, coffee and corn.

1957, Mar. 5   Photo.   Perf. 14x13½
670 A283 1c lt ol grn   .25 .20
671 A283 2c lt brn   .25 .20
672 A283 5c lt bl   .25 .20
  Nos. 670-672,C292-C296 (8)   2.85 1.80
Agrarian Savings Bank of Colombia, 25th anniv.
For overprint see No. C322.

Arms of Military Academy and Gen. Rafael Reyes A284

Design: 10c, Arms and Academy.

1957, July 20   Engr.   Perf. 12½
673 A284 5c blue   .25 .20
674 A284 10c orange   .40 .20
  a. Souv. sheet of 2   20.00 20.00
  Nos. 673-674,C299-C300 (4)   1.25 .85
50th anniv. of the Colombian Military Academy.
No. 674a contains one each of Nos. 673-674 in slightly different shades.
For overprints see Nos. C328, C312.

Statue of José Matias Delgado — A285

1957, Sept. 16   Photo.   Perf. 12
675 A285 2c rose brn   .25 .20
Issued in honor of Jose Matias Delgado, liberator of El Salvador. See No. C301.

Santo Michelena, Marcos y Crespo, P. Alcantara Herran and UPU Monument A286

1957, Oct. 10   Unwmk.
676 A286 5c green   .20 .20
677 A286 10c gray   .30 .20
  Nos. 676-677,C302-C303 (4)   1.20 .80
Intl. Letter Writing Week and 14th UPU Cong.

St. Vincent de Paul and Children — A287

1957, Oct. 18
678 A287 1c dark olive green   .25 .20
Colombian Society of St. Vincent de Paul, cent. See No. C304. For overprint see No. C323.

Fencer A288

1957, Nov. 22   Photo.   Perf. 12
679 A288 4c lilac   .25 .20
3rd South American Fencing Championship. See No. C305. For overprint see No. C332.

Francisco José de Caldas and Hypsometer — A289

1958, May 12   Unwmk.   Perf. 12
680 A289 10c black   .25 .20
  Nos. 680,C309-C310 (3)   1.40 .65
International Geophysical Year, 1957-58.

Departmental Issue
Type of 1956
Designs as before.

1958   Engr.   Perf. 13
681 A276 3c ultra & brn   .25 .20
682 A276 3c ol grn & pur   .25 .20
683 A276 10c grn & brn   .25 .20
684 A276 10c dk bl & brn   .25 .20
  Nos. 681-684 (4)   1.00 .80

Nos. 646, C291, 614, 653, 655, 616, C308, 615 and 611 Surcharged with New Value, and Old Value Obliterated, or Overprinted in Dark Blue or Green

Perf. 12½, 12½x13, 13

1958-59   Unwmk.
685 A277   2c on 4c grn & blk   .25 .20
686 AP48   5c dp plum & multi
            ('59)   .25 .20
687 A256   5c on 14c blk & rose
            red ("CINCO")
            ('59)   .30 .30
688 A276   5c on 15c ultra & blk   .25 .20
689 A277   5c on 23c ultra & ver
            (G)   .25 .20
690 A256   5c on 30c blk & choc
            ("CINCO")   .25 .20
691 AP40   10c on 25c rose vio   .25 .20
692 A256   20c on 23c blk & ultra
            (G) ("VENTE")
            ('59)   .30 .30
693 A255   20c on 23c bl & blk   .30 .20
  Nos. 685-693 (9)   2.40 1.90
On No. 686 the words "Correo Extra Rapido" are obliterated in dark blue.

Father Rafael Almanza and Church of San Diego, Bogota A290

1958, Oct. 23   Photo.   Perf. 14x13
695 A290 10c purple   .25 .20
  Nos. 695,C313-C314 (3)   .80 .65
For overprint see No. C336.

Msgr. R. M. Carrasquilla and Church A291

1959, Jan. 22   Perf. 14x13
696 A291 10c dk red brn   .25 .20
  Nos. 696,C315-C316 (3)   1.30 .65
Cent. of the birth of Msgr. R. M. Carrasquilla (1857-1930), rector of Our Lady of the Rosary Seminary, Bogotá. For overprints see Nos. C335, C341.

Miss Universe 1959 — A292   Jorge Eliecer Gaitan — A293

1959, June 26   Photo.   Perf. 11½
697 A292 10c multi   .80 .25
  Nos. 697,C317-C318 (3)   50.05 49.15
Luz Marina Zuluaga, Miss Universe, 1959.
For overprint see No. C342.

1959, July 28   Engr.   Perf. 12x13½
698 A293 10c on 3c gray bl (Bl)   .25 .20
699 A293 30c rose vio   .45 .25
  Nos. 698-699,C319-C320 (4)   4.20 3.45
Issued in honor of Jorge Eliecer Gaitan (1898-1948), lawyer and politician.
No. 698 exists without blue surcharge.

Gen. Francisco de Paula Santander — A294

Designs: Nos. 701, 703, Simon Bolivar.

1959   Litho.   Wmk. 331   Perf. 12½
700 A294 2c brown & yel   .25 .20
701 A294 5c ultra & bl   .25 .20
702 A294 10c gray & grn   .25 .20
703 A294 10c gray & red   .25 .20
  Nos. 700-703,C389 (5)   4.00 1.20

Capitol, Bogota A295

1959
704 A295 2c dk bl & red brn   .25 .20
705 A295 3c blk brn & lilac   .25 .20

Stamp of 1859 and Mail Transport by Mule — A296   Two-Toed Sloth — A297

Designs (various stamps of 1859 and): 10c, Mail boat on the Magdalena river. 15c, as 5c. 25c, Train.

Unwmk.
1959, Dec. 1   Photo.   Perf. 12
709 A296 5c org & grn   .20 .20
710 A296 10c rose cl & bl   .20 .20
711 A296 15c car rose & grn   .40 .40
712 A296 25c bl & red brn   .50 .50
  Nos. 709-712,C351-C354 (8)   5.75 4.00
Centenary of Colombian postage stamps.

1960, Feb. 12   Perf. 12
Designs: 10c, Alexander von Humboldt. 20c, Spider monkey.
713 A297 5c grnsh bl & brn   .30 .20
714 A297 10c blk & dp car   .40 .20
715 A297 20c cit & gray brn   .30 .20
  Nos. 713-715,C357-C359 (6)   6.65 4.30
Cent. of the death of Alexander von Humboldt (1769-1859), German naturalist and geographer.
For overprint and surcharge see Nos. C411, C413.

Anthurium Andreanum A298

Lincoln Statue, Washington A299

Flower: 20c, Espeletia grandiflora.

1960, May 10
716 A298 5c multi   .85 .25
717 A298 20c brn, yel & gray
           ol   .85 .25
  Nos. 716-717,C360-C370 (13)   14.45 15.20
See Nos. C420-C425. For overprint see No. C412.

Wmk. 331
1960, June 10   Litho.   Perf. 10½
718 A299 20c rose lil & blk   .35 .25
  Nos. 718,C375-C376 (3)   1.45 1.05

Florero House, Cradle of the Republic A300

Arms of Santa Cruz de Mompox — A301

Design: 5c, First coins of Republic.

Unwmk.
1960, July 19   Photo.   Perf. 12
719 A301 5c grn & ocher   .25 .20
720 A300 20c ol bis & mar   .25 .20
721 A301 20c multi   .25 .20
  Nos. 719-721,C377-C385 (12)   6.25 4.90
Colombia's independence, 150th anniv.

St. Isidore and Farm Animals — A302

Design: 20c, Nativity by Gregorio de Arce Vasquez y Ceballos.

1960, Sept. 26   *Perf. 12*
722 A302 10c multi   .25 .20
723 A302 20c multi   .25 .20
   Nos. 722-723,C387 (3)   .75 .60

St. Isidore the Farmer, patron saint of the rural people.
See Nos. 747, C388, C439-C440.

UN Headquarters and Emblem A303

Wmk. 331
1960, Oct. 24   Litho.   *Perf. 11*
724 A303 20c blk & pink   .25 .20
Souvenir Sheet
Imperf
725 A303 50c dk brn, brt grn & blk   4.00 4.00

15th anniversary of the United Nations.

Pan-American Highway through Colombia — A304

Alfonso Lopez — A305

1961, Mar. 7 Unwmk. Perf. 10½x11
726 A304 20c brn & grnsh bl   .75 .70
   Nos. 726,C390-C393 (5)   2.75 2.70

8th Pan-American Highway Congress, Bogota, May 20-29, 1960.

1961, Mar. 22 Photo. Perf. 12½
727 A305 10c brt rose & brn   .25 .20
728 A305 20c vio & brn   .25 .20
   Nos. 727-728,C394-C395 (4)   1.20 .80

Alfonso Lopez (1886-1959), President of Colombia. See No. C396.

Cauca River Bridge, Cali A306

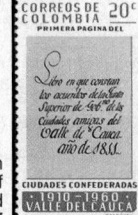

Page from Resolutions of Confederated Cities — A307

1961-62   *Perf. 12½x13, 13½x13*
729 A306 10c red brn, bl, grn & red ('62)   .25 .20
730 A307 20c pale brn & blk   .25 .20
   Nos. 729-730,C397-C401 (7)   3.00 2.05

50th anniversary (in 1960) of the Department of Valle del Cauca.

View of Cucuta and Arms A308

No. 732, Arms of Ocana and Pamplona.

1961, Aug. 29   *Perf. 13x13½*
731 A308 20c bl, blk, yel & red   .25 .20
732 A308 20c ocher, ultra & red   .25 .20
   Nos. 731-732,C402-C403 (4)   1.30 .80

50th anniv. (in 1960) of the Department of North Santander.

Arms of Popayan A309

Basketball A310

Designs: No. 734, Arms of Barranquilla. No. 735, Arms of Bucaramanga.

Perf. 12½x13
1961, Oct. 10   Unwmk.
Arms in Multicolor
733 A309 10c blue & silver   .25 .20
734 A309 20c blue & yellow   .25 .20
735 A309 20c blue & gold   .25 .20
   Nos. 733-735,C404-C408 (8)   2.75 1.60

Issued to honor Atlantico Department.

1961, Dec. 16   Litho.   *Perf. 13½x14*
736 A310 20c shown   .25 .20
737 A310 20c Runners   .25 .20
738 A310 20c Boxers   .40 .25
739 A310 25c Soccer   .25 .20
   Nos. 736-739,C414-C418 (9)   3.75 2.20

4th Bolivarian Games, Barranquilla, 1961.

Colombian Anti-Malaria Emblem — A311

Design: 50c, Malaria eradication emblem and mosquito in swamp.

1962, Apr. 12 Unwmk. Perf. 12
740 A311 20c lt bis & red   .25 .20
741 A311 50c bis & ultra   .30 .24
   Nos. 740-741,C426-C428 (5)   4.80 4.50

Engineers Society Emblem — A312

1962, June 12 Photo. Perf. 11½x12
742 A312 10c multi   .25 .25
   Nos. 742,C429-C432 (5)   2.40 2.35

Colombian Society of Engineers, 75th anniv.

Flags of American Nations A313

Woman Casting Ballot and Statue of Policarpa Salavarrieta A314

1962, June 28   *Perf. 13*
Flags in National Colors
743 A313 25c blk & org ver   .25 .20
Souvenir Sheet
744 A313 2.50p blk & yel   5.75 5.75

70th anniv. of the founding of the Organization of American States.
See No. C433.

Perf. 12x12½
1962, July 20 Litho. Wmk. 229
745 A314 10c lt bl, gray & blk   .25 .20

Issued to publicize women's political rights. See Nos. 752, C434, C448-C450.

Scouts at Campfire and Tents A315

Railroad Map of Colombia A316

Perf. 11½x12
1962, July 28 Photo. Unwmk.
746 A315 10c brt grnsh bl & brn   .35 .30
   Nos. 746,C435-C438 (5)   5.60 4.80

Colombian Boy Scouts, 30th anniv.

St. Isidore Type of 1960 Redrawn
1962, Aug. 28   *Perf. 12*
747 A302 10c pink & multi   .25 .20
   Nos. 747,C439-C440 (3)   4.20 3.90

The frame on No. 747 is solid color with white inscription similar to type AP82.

1962, Sept. 28   *Perf. 12½*
748 A316 10c blk, gray, grn & red   .25 .20
   Nos. 748,C441-C444 (5)   5.80 4.55

Progress of Colombian railroads and the completion of the Atlantic Line from Santa Marta to Bogota.

Post Horn — A317

Perf. 13½x14
1962, Oct. 18 Litho. Wmk. 346
749 A317 20c gold, dl gray vio & blk   .25 .20
   Nos. 749,C445-C446 (3)   .80 .60

50th anniv. of the founding of the Postal Union of the Americas and Spain, UPAE.

"Virgin of the Rock" A318

Red Cross Centenary Emblem A319

1963, Mar. 11   Wmk. 346
750 A318 60c multi   .25 .20

Vatican II, the 21st Ecumenical Council of the Roman Catholic Church. See No. C447.

1963, May 1   *Perf. 12x12½*
751 A319 5c olive bister & red   .25 .20

Centenary of International Red Cross.

Women's Rights Type of 1962
1963, July 11   Wmk. 346
752 A314 5c org, gray & blk   .25 .20
   Nos. 752,C448-C450 (4)   1.05 .80

Manuel Mejia J. and Flag of National Coffee Growers Assn. A320

Perf. 12½x13
1965, Feb. 10 Engr. Unwmk.
753 A320 25c rose & blk   .25 .20
   Nos. 753,C464-C466 (4)   4.60 .95

Manuel Mejia J. (1887-1958), banker and manager of the National Coffee Growers Association.

Julio Arboleda (1817-62), Writer, Soldier and Statesman A321

1966, Mar. 9 Litho. Perf. 14x13½
754 A321 5c lt brn, lt yel grn & blk   .30 .20

Spanish Galleon, 16th Century A322

History of Maritime Mail: 15c, Rio Hacha brigantine, 1850. 20c, Uraba canoe. 40c, Magdalena River steamship and barge, 1900. 50c, Modern motor ship and sea gull.

1966, June 16 Photo. Unwmk.
755 A322 5c org & multi   .35 .20
756 A322 15c car rose, blk & brn   .35 .20
757 A322 20c brt grn, org & blk   .35 .20
758 A322 40c dp bl & multi   .50 .20
759 A322 50c pale bl & multi   1.00 .40
   Nos. 755-759 (5)   2.55 1.20

Plumed Hogfish A323

Design: 10p, Bat ray and brittle starfish.

1966, Aug. 25 Photo. Perf. 12½x13
760 A323 80c multi   .25 .20
761 A323 10p multi   8.25 5.25
   Nos. 760-761,C481-C483 (5)   26.75 18.55

Arms of Venezuela, Colombia and Chile A324

1966, Oct. 11   Litho.   Perf. 14x13½
762 A324 40c yel & multi   .25 .20
   Nos. 762,C484-C485 (3)   .70 .60

Visits of Eduardo Frei and Raul Leoni, presidents of Chile and Venezuela.

Camilo Torres, 1766-1816, Lawyer — A325

Portraits: 60c, Jorge Tadeo Lozano (1771-1816), naturalist. 1p, Francisco Antonio Zea (1776-1822), naturalist and politician.

Perf. 13½x14
1967, Jan. 18   Litho.   Unwmk.
763 A325 25c vio & bis   .25 .20
764 A325 60c dk red brn & bis   .25 .20
765 A325 1p grn & bis   .35 .25
   Nos. 763-765,C486-C487 (5) 1.30 1.05

Issued to honor famous men of Colombia.

Map of South America and Arms A326

1967, Feb. 2   Litho.   Perf. 14x13½
766 A326 40c multi   .25 .20
767 A326 60c multi   .25 .20
   Nos. 766-767,C488 (3)   .85 .60

Declaration of Bogota for cooperation and world peace, signed by Colombia, Chile, Ecuador, Peru and Venezuela.

Monochaetum Orchid and Bee — A327

Orchid: 2p, Passiflora vitifolia and butterfly.

1967, May 23   Litho.   Perf. 14
768 A327 25c multi   .25 .20
769 A327 2p multi   4.25 2.75
   Nos. 768-769,C489-C491 (5) 14.70 4.40

1st Natl. Orchid Exhib. and the Topical Phil. Flora and Fauna Exhib., Medellin, Apr. 1967.

Lions Emblem — A328

SENA Emblem — A329

1967, July 12   Litho.   Perf. 13½x14
770 A328 10p multi   3.50 2.00

50th anniv. of Lions Intl. See No. C492.

Lithographed and Embossed
1967, Sept. 20   Unwmk.
771 A329 5p gold, brt grn & blk   1.50 .25

10th anniv. of Natl. Apprenticeship Service, SENA. See No. C494.

Gold Diadem in Calima Style — A330

Radar Installation A331

Pre-Columbian Art: 3p, Gold statuette, ornamental globe and bird, horiz.

Perf. 13½x14, 14x13½
1967, Oct. 13   Photo.
772 A330 1.60p brt rose lil,
         gold & brn   .95 .25
773 A330 3p dk bl, gold &
         brn   1.40 .40
   Nos. 772-773,C495-C497 (5) 20.45 11.35

Meeting of the UPU Committee of Postal Studies, Bogota, Oct., 1967.

1968, May 14   Litho.   Perf. 13½x14
1p, Map of communications network.
774 A331 50c brt yel grn, blk &
         org brn   .20 .20
775 A331 1p multi   .35 .20
   Nos. 774-775,C498-C499 (4) 1.05 .80

20th anniv. of the National Telecommunications Service (TELECOM).

The Eucharist — A332

St. Augustin, by Gregorio Vasquez — A333

1968, June 6   Litho.   Perf. 13½x14
776 A332 60c multi   .25 .20
   Nos. 776,C500-C501 (3)   .75

39th Eucharistic Cong., Bogotá, 8/18-25.

1968, Aug. 13   Photo.   Perf. 13
Designs: 60c, The Gathering of Manna, by Gregorio Vasquez. 1p, The Marriage of the Virgin, by Baltazar de Figueroa. 5p, Jeweled

monstrance, c. 1700. 10p, Pope Paul VI, painting by Roman Franciscan nuns.
777 A333 25c multicolored   .20 .20
778 A333 60c multicolored   .20 .20
779 A333 1p multicolored   .20 .20
780 A333 5p multicolored   .65 .20
781 A333 10p multicolored   1.25 .45
  a. Souvenir sheet of 2   4.00 4.00
   Nos. 777-781,C502-C506 (10) 7.95 4.05

39th Eucharistic Congress. Bogotá, Aug. 18-25. No. 781a contains two imperf. stamps similar to Nos. 780-781.

Pope Paul VI — A334

Arms of National University — A335

1968, Aug. 22   Litho.   Perf. 13½x14
782 A334 25c multi   .25 .20
   Nos. 782,C507-C509 (4)   .95 .80

Visit of Pope Paul VI to Colombia, 8/22-24.

1968, Oct. 29   Litho.   Perf. 13½x14
783 A335 80c multi   .35 .25

Centenary of the founding of the National University. See No. C510.

Stamp of Antioquia, 1868 — A336

Institute Emblem — A337

1968, Nov. 20   Litho.   Perf. 12x12½
784 A336 30c emer & bl   .30 .20
Souvenir Sheet
785 A336 5p lt olive & blue   5.50 5.50

Cent. of the 1st postage stamps of Antioquia and the 7th Natl. Phil. Exhib., Medellin, Nov. 20-29.

1969, Mar. 5   Litho.   Perf. 13½x14
786 A337 20c multi   .35 .25

25th anniv. (in 1967) of the Inter-American Agricultural Sciences Institute. See No. C511.

Battle of Boyaca (Detail), by José Maria Espinosa — A338

Design: 30c, Army of liberation crossing Pisba Pass, by Francisco Antonio Caro.

1969, July 24   Litho.   Perf. 13½x14
787 A338 20c gold & multi   .35 .25
788 A338 30c gold & multi   .35 .25
   Nos. 787-788,C517 (3)   1.70 .85

Fight for independence, sesquicentennial.

"Poverty" A339

1970, Mar. 1   Litho.   Perf. 14
789 A339 30c bl & multi   .35 .25

Colombian Institute for Family Welfare and 10th anniv. of the Children's Rights Law.

Greek Mask and Pre-Columbian Symbol of Literary Contest — A340

1970, Sept. 12   Litho.   Perf. 14x13½
790 A340 30c dk brn, red org &
         ocher   .25 .20

3rd Latin American Theatrical Festival of the Universities, Manizales, Sept. 12-20.

Colombian Stamps, Envelope and Emblem A341

1970, Sept. 24   Litho.   Perf. 14x13½
791 A341 2p brt bl & multi   .30 .25

Issued to publicize Philatelic Week.

Arms of Ibague and Discobolus A342

1970, Oct. 13
792 A342 80c buff, emer & sepia   .25 .20

9th National Games in Ibague.

St. Theresa, by Baltazar de Figueroa — A343

1970, Oct. 28   Litho.   Perf. 13½x14
793 A343 2p multi   .40 .25

Elevation of St. Theresa (1515-1582), to Doctor of the Church. See No. C568. For overprint see No. C568.

Casa Cural
A344

1971, May 20   Litho.   Perf. 14x13½
794 A344 1.10p multi   .30 .20
Fourth centenary (in 1970) of the founding of Guacari, Valle. See No. 809.

Dancers and Music, Currulao — A345

1p, Chicha Maya dancers and music.

1971   Litho.   Perf. 13½x14
795 A345 1p pink & multi   .35 .25
796 A345 1.10p lt bl & multi   .35 .25

Souvenir Sheets
Imperf
797   Sheet of 3   4.25 4.25
a.   A345 2.50p Napanga   .50   .50
b.   A345 2.50p Joropo   .50   .50
c.   A345 5p Guabina   1.00 1.00
798   Sheet of 3   4.25 4.25
a.   A345 4p Bambuco   .75   .75
b.   A345 4p Cumbia   .75   .75
c.   A345 4p Currulao   .75   .75

Issued: No. 795, 12/20; No. 796, 8/5; Nos. 797-798, 8/10.

Constitutional Assembly, by Delgado A346

1971, Oct. 2   Perf. 14
801 A346 80c multi   .25 .20
Sequicentennial of Gran Colombian Constitutional Assembly in Rosario del Cucuta. See No. C589. For overprint see No. C589.

Arrows Emblem — A347

1972, Feb. 24   Perf. 13½x14
802 A347 60c blk & gray   .30 .20
Inter-Governmental Committee on European Migration, 20th anniversary.

Student and World Map A348

1972, Mar. 15   Perf. 14x13½
803 A348 1.10p lt grn & brn .25 .20
20th anniv. of ICETEX, an organization which furnishes financial help for educational purposes and for technical studies abroad.

UN Emblem, Soldier and Frigate A349

1972, Apr. 7
804 A349 1.20p lt bl & multi .25 .20
Colombian Battalion in Korea, 20th anniv.

Mother Francisca Josefa del Castillo — A350

Handicraft A351

1972, Apr. 6   Perf. 13½x14
805 A350 1.20p brn & multi   .25 .20
Tercentenary (in 1971) of the birth of Mother Francisca Josefa del Castillo, Poor Clare abbess and writer.

1972, Apr. 11
806 A351 1.10p multi   .35 .20
   Nos. 806,C569-C571 (4)   1.55 .85
Colombian artisans.

Maxillaria Triloris — A352

1972, Apr. 20
807 A352 20p green & multi   7.25 .75
10th Natl. Phil. Exhib., Medellin.

Emeralds — A353

1972, June 16   Litho.   Perf. 13½x14
808 A353 1.10p multi   1.25 .20

Type of 1971
Design: Antonio Nariño House.

1972, June 17   Perf. 14x13½
809 A344 1.10p multi   .50 .25
4th centenary, town of Leyva.

San Andres and Providencia Islands — A354

1972, June 24   Perf. 13½x14
810 A354 60c bl & multi   .25 .20
Sesquicentennial of annexation by Colombia of San Andres and Providencia Islands.

Postal Service Emblem A355

1972, Nov. 15   Litho.   Perf. 12½x12
811 A355 1.10p emerald   .25 .20

Family A356

1972, Nov. 23
812 A356 60c orange   .25 .20
Social progress.

Radio League Emblem A357

Human Figure, Tamalameque A358

1973, Apr. 6   Litho.   Perf. 12x12½
813 A357 60c lt bl, ultra & red .25 .20
40th anniversary of the Colombian Radio Amateurs' League.

1973, June 15   Litho.   Perf. 13½x14
Excavated Ceramic Artifacts: 1p, Winged urn, Tairona. 1.10p, Jug, Muisca.
814 A358 60c lt bl & multi   .35 .25
815 A358 1p org & multi   .75 .25
816 A358 1.10p vio bl & multi .40 .25
   Nos. 814-816,C583-C586 (7) 4.65 2.50

Antonio Nariño, by José M. Espinosa — A359

Child — A360

1973, Dec. 13   Litho.   Perf. 13½x14
817 A359 60c multi   .25 .20
Sesquicentennial of the death of General Antonio Nariño (1765-1823).

1973, Dec. 17
818 A360 1.10p multi   .25 .20
National Campaign for Children's Welfare.

Symbols of Financial Controls A361

1973, Dec. 20   Litho.   Perf. 14x13½
819 A361 80c ultra, ocher & blk .25 .20
50th anniv. of Comptroller-general's Office.

Mother Laura Montoya — A362

1974, June 18   Litho.   Perf. 13½x14
820 A362 1p multi   .25 .20
Mother Laura Montoya (1874-1949), founder and Mother Superior of the Missionaries of Mary Immaculata and St. Catherine of Siena.

Runner and Games' Emblem A363

1974, July 18   Litho.   Perf. 14x13½
821 A363 2p ver, yel & brn   .35 .20
10th National Games, Pereira.

José Rivera A364

1974, Aug. 3   Litho.   Perf. 14x13½
822 A364 10p grn & multi   1.25 .20
50th anniv. of the publication of "La Voragine" (The Whirlpool) by José Eustasio Rivera.

Abstract Pattern — A365

Train Emerging from Tunnel — A366

1974, Oct. 24 Litho. Perf. 13½x14
823 A365 1.10p multi .25 .20
Cent. of Natl. Insurance Co. See No. C610.

1974, Nov. 27 Litho. Perf. 13½x14
824 A366 1.10p multi .25 .20
Centenary of the Antioquia railroad.

Boy, Puppy and Soccer Ball — A367

Christmas: 1p, Girl with racket and kitten.

1974, Dec. 9
825 A367 80c multi .25 .20
826 A367 1p multi .25 .20

A368

1975, Apr. 11 Litho. Perf. 14x13½
827 A368 80c Gold Animal .40 .25
828 A368 1.10p Gold necklace .40 .25
Nos. 827-828,C621-C622 (4) 6.45 1.30
Pre-Columbian Sinu culture artifacts.
For surcharge see No. 840.

Guglielmo Marconi — A369

Santa Marta Cathedral — A370

1975, June 2 Litho. Perf. 13½x14
829 A369 3p multi .30 .20
Birth centenary of Guglielmo Marconi (1874-1937), Italian electrical engineer and inventor.

1975, July 26
830 A370 80c multi .30 .20
400th anniv. of Santa Marta City. See No. C623.

Rafael Nuñez — A371

Arms of Medellin — A372

1975, Sept. 28 Litho. Perf. 13½x14
831 A371 1.10p multi .30 .20
Rafael Nunez (1825-1894), philosopher, poet, political leader, birth sesquicentenary. For surcharge see No. 848.

1975-79 Perf. 13½x14, 12 (1.20p)
832 A372 1p shown .40 .20
833 A372 1.20p Ibagué .35 .20
834 A372 1.20p Tunja .25 .20
835 A372 1.50p Cucuta .55 .20
836 A372 1.50p Cartagena .25 .20
836A A372 4p Sogamoso 1.00 .20
837 A372 5p Popayan .50 .20
838 A372 5p Barranquilla .55 .20
839 A372 10p San Gil 1.00 .20
839A A372 10p Socorro 1.00 .20
Nos. 832-839A (10) 5.85 2.00

1p for the tercentenary of Medellin; No. 835, the cent. of Cucuta's reconstruction.
Issued: 1p, 11/4; No. 835, 11/29; No. 836, 2/10/76; No. 833, 7/30/76; No. 834, 12/2076; No. 837, 8/30/77; No. 838, 9/20/77; 10p, 8/9/79; 4p, 9/14/79.
See Nos. 905-913, C818. For surcharge see No. 849.

No. 827 Surcharged

1975 Perf. 14x13½
840 A368 1.20p on 80c multi .25 .20

Purace Indians, Cauca — A373

1976, Nov. 10 Litho. Perf. 13½x14
841 A373 1.50p multi .25 .20

Callicore A374

5p, Morpho (butterfly). 20p, Anthurium.

1976, Nov. 17 Perf. 12
842 A374 3p multicolored .90 .25
843 A374 5p multicolored 1.50 .25
844 A374 20p multicolored 4.25 1.00
Nos. 842-844 (3) 6.65 1.50

Rotary Emblem — A375

1976, Dec. 3 Litho. Perf. 12
845 A375 1p multicolored .25 .20
Rotary Club of Colombia, 50th anniversary.

Declaration of Independence, by John Trumbull — A376

1976, Dec. 21 Litho. Perf. 12
846 A376 Strip of 3 10.00 11.50
a.-c. 30p any single 2.75 2.00
American Bicentennial. No. 846 printed in sheets of 4 triptychs.

Policeman with Dog — A377

1976, Dec. 29 Perf. 13½x14
847 A377 1.50p multicolored .25 .20
Honoring the National Police.
For surcharge see No. 850.

Nos. 831, 834, 847 Surcharged in Light Brown
1977, June Litho. Perf. 13½x14, 12
848 A371 2p on 1.10p multi .40 .20
849 A372 2p on 1.20p multi .20 .20
850 A377 2p on 1.50p multi .25 .20
Nos. 848-850 (3) .85 .60

Souvenir Sheet

Postal Museum, Bogota — A378

1977, July 27 Litho. Perf. 14
855 A378 25p multi 3.00 3.00
Postal Museum, Bogota.

Mother and Child — A379

1977-78 Litho. Perf. 12
856 A379 2p multi .25 .20
857 A379 2.50p multi ('78) 1.75 .20
National good nutrition plan.
Issue dates: 2p, Aug. 30; 2.50p, Jan. 26.

Jacana and Eichhornia A380

Fidel Cano, by Francisco Cano — A381

20p, Mayan cotinga and pyrostegia venusta.

1977, Sept. 6 Litho. Perf. 14
858 A380 10p multicolored 2.50 .25
859 A380 20p multicolored 4.00 .50
Nos. 858-859,C644-C647 (6) 10.20 1.55

1977, Sept. 16 Perf. 14
860 A381 4p multicolored .25 .20
90th anniversary of El Espectador, newspaper founded by Fidel Cano.

Abacus and Alphabet A382

Cattleya Triannae A383

1977, Sept. 16 Perf. 13½x14
861 A382 3p multicolored .25 .20
Popular education.

1978-79 Litho. Perf. 12
862 A383 2.50p multi .75 .20
863 A383 3p multi ('79) .75 .20
Issue dates: 2.50p, Apr. 18. 3p, May 10.

Sprinting and Games Emblem A384

Sports: a, sprinting. b, basketball. c, baseball. d, boxing. e. bicycling. f, fencing. g, soccer. h, gymnastics. i, judo. j, weight lifting. k, wrestling. l, swimming. m, tennis. n, target shooting. o, volleyball. p, water polo.

1978, June 27   Litho.   Perf. 14
868   Sheet of 16   29.00 29.00
a.-p. A384 10p, any single   1.25 .20
13th Central American and Caribbean Games, Medellin.

"Sigma 2" by Alvaro Herrán A385

1978, June 30
869 A385 8p multicolored   .55 .20
Chamber of Commerce, Bogota, centenary.

Gen. Tomás Cipriano de Mosquera (1778-1878), Statesman A386

1978, Oct. 6   Litho.   Perf. 12
870 A386 6p multicolored   .45 .20

Anthurium Narinenses — A387

1979, July 23   Perf. 12
871 A387 3p red & multi   .25 .20
872 A387 3p purple & multi   .25 .20
873 A387 3p rose & purple   .25 .20
874 A387 3p white & multi   .25 .20
a.   Block of 4, #871-874   1.75 1.75

Gen. Rafael Uribe, by Acevedo Bernal — A388

1979, Oct. 31   Litho.   Perf. 12
875 A388 8p multicolored   .40 .20
Gen. Uribe, statesman, 60th death anniv.

Village, by Leonor Alarcon — A389

1979, Nov. 22   Perf. 14
876 A389 15p multicolored   1.00 .35
Community Work Boards, 20th anniversary.

Introduction of Color Television A390

1980, Mar. 4   Litho.   Perf. 14
877 A390 5p multicolored   .50 .20

Bullfight, Arms of Cali A391

1980, Mar. 25
878 A391 5p multicolored   .70 .20
Cali Tourist Festival, 12/25/79-1/2/80.

"Learn to Write" — A392

a, shown. b, "a." c, "b." d, "c." e, "ch." f, "d." g, "e." h, "f." i, "g." j, "h." k, "i." l, "j." m, "k." n, "l." o, "ll." p, "m." q, "n." r, "ñ." s, "o." t, "p." u, "q." v, "r." w, "s." x, "t." y, "u." z, "v." aa, "w." ab, "x." ac, "y." ad, "z."

1980, Apr. 25   Litho.   Perf. 12½
879   Block of 30   27.50 27.50
a.-ad. A392 4p, any single   .75 .20
Each stamp shows letter of alphabet and corresponding animal or subject. Issued in sheets of 90 (10x9).

Villavicencio Festival — A393

Design: 9p, Vallenato festival.

1980   Litho.   Perf. 14
880 A393 5p multicolored   .45 .20
881 A393 9p multicolored   .45 .20
Issue dates: 5p, July 15; 9p, June 17.

Gustavo Uribe Ramirez and Tree A394

1980, Aug. 5   Litho.   Perf. 12
882 A394 10p multicolored   .90 .20
Gustavo Uribe Ramirez (1893-1968), ecologist.

Narino Palace (Former Presidential Residence) — A395

1980, Sept. 19   Litho.   Perf. 14
883 A395 5p multicolored   .60 .20

Monument to First Pioneers of 1819, Armenia A396

1980, Oct. 14
884 A396 5p multicolored   .50 .20

11th National Games, Neiva — A397

1980, Nov. 28   Perf. 13½x14
885 A397 5p multicolored   .45 .20

1980, Dec. 9
886 A398 10p multicolored   .40 .20

Fight against Cancer — A398

Xavier University Law Faculty, 50th Anniversary A399

1980, Dec. 16   Litho.   Perf. 14½
887 A399 20p multicolored   .60 .20

Death of Bolivar — A400

1980, Dec. 17   Perf. 12
888 A400 25p multicolored   1.00 .60
Simon Bolivar, death sesquicentennial. See No. C696.

José Maria Obando, President of Colombia A401

115th Anniv. of Constitution (Former Presidents): b, Jose Hilario Lopez. c, Manuel Murillo Toro. d, Santiago Perez. e, Rafael Reyes. f, Carlos E. Restrepo. g, Jose Vicente Concha. h, Miguel Abadia Mendez. i, Eduardo Santos. j, Mariano Ospina Perez.

1981, June 9   Litho.   Perf. 12
889   Strip of 10   6.00
a.-j. A401 5p multicolored   .50 .20

1981, Sept. 23   Litho.   Perf. 12
Designs: a, Rafael Nunez (1825-94). b, Marco Fidel Suarez (1855-1927). c, Pedro Nel Ospina (1858-1927). d, Enrique Olaya Herrera (1880-1937). e, Alfonso Lopez Pumarejo (1886-1959). f, Aquileo Parra (1825-1900). g, Santos Gutierrez (1820-72). h, Tomas Cipriano de Mosquera (1789-1878). i, Mariano Ospina Rodriguez. j, Pedro Alcantara Herran (1800-72).

890   Strip of 10   50.00
a.-j. A401 7p multicolored   3.50 .50

1981, Aug. 11   Litho.   Perf. 12
Designs like No. 889.
891   Strip of 10   55.00
a.-j. A401 7p multicolored   4.00 1.00

1981, Nov. 11   Litho.   Perf. 12
Designs: a, Manuel Maria Mallarino. b, Santos Acosta. c, Eustorgio Salgar. d, Julian Trujillo. e, Francisco Javier Zaldua. f, Guillermo Leon Valencia. g, Laureano Gomez. h, Manuel A. Sanclemente. i, Miguel Antonio Caro. j, Jose Eusebio Otalora.

892   Strip of 10   32.50
a.-j. A401 7p multicolored   2.50 .40

1981, Dec. 15   Litho.   Perf. 12
Designs: a, Ruben Piedrahita Arango. b, Jorge Holguin. c, Ramon Gonzalez Valencia. d, Jose Manuel Marroquin. e, Carlos Holguin. f, Bartolome Calvo. g, Sergio Camargo. h, Jose Maria Rojas Garrido. i, J.M. Campo Serrano. j, Eliseo Payan.

893   Strip of 10   25.00
a.-j. A401 7p multicolored   1.75 .30

1982, May 3   Perf. 12
Designs: a, Simon Bolivar. b, Francisco de Paula Santander. c, Joaquin Mosquera. d, Domingo Caicedo. e, Jose Ignacio de Marquez. f, Roberto Urdaneta Arbelaez. g, Carlos Lozano y Lozano. h, Guillermo Quintero Calderon. i, Jose de Obaldia. j, Juan de Dios Aranzazu.

894   Strip of 10   14.50
a.-j. A401 7p multicolored   1.40 .20
See No. 1110.

Jose Maria Villa and West Bridge over Cauca River A404

1981, Nov. 25   Litho.   Perf. 14x13½
895 A404 60p multicolored   1.40 .30

Agrarian, Mineral and Industrial Credit Bank, 50th Anniv. — A405

Los Nevados Park — A406

1981, Dec. 9   Litho.   Perf. 14
896 A405 15p multicolored   .35 .20

1981, Dec. 10   Litho.   Perf. 13½x14
897 A406 20p multicolored   .60 .20

Girl Sitting on Fence — A407

1982, Feb. 22   Litho.   Perf. 12½x12
898   Strip of 3   5.00 5.00
  a. A407 30p shown   1.10   .40
  b. A407 30p Girl, basket   1.10   .40
  c. A407 30p Boy, wheelbarrow 1.10   .40

Floral Bouquet — A408

Hipotecario Bank, 50th Anniv. — A409

Various floral arrangements (background): a, Flowers in vase (gray). b, Roses (red). c, Daisies (green). d, Roses (blue). e, Assorted (red). f, Yellow & orange flowers (green). g, Assorted (lilac). h, Roses (gray). i, Pink flowers (green). j, Flowers in basket (gray).

1982, July 28
900   Strip or block of 10   17.00 17.00
  a.-j. A408 7p, any single   1.75   .30

1982, July 29   Perf. 14
901 A409 9p black & green   .40 .20

St. Thomas Aquinas (1225-1274) A410

Paintings by Zurbaran.

1982   Litho.   Perf. 12
902 A410 5p multicolored   .40 .20
903 A410 5p St. Teresa of Avila   .40 .20
904 A410 5p St. Francis of Assisi .40 .20
    Nos. 902-904 (3)   1.20 .60

Issued: No. 902, 8/6; No. 903, 9/28; No. 904, 10/4.

Arms Type of 1975
1982-90   Litho.   Perf. 14, 12 (50p)
905 A372 10p Buga   .40 .20
906 A372 10p San Juan de
             Pasto   1.25 .20
907 A372 16p Rionegro   .70 .20
908 A372 20p Santa Fe de Bo-
             gota   1.00 .20
909 A372 20p Santiago de Cali   .30 .20
910 A372 23p Honda   .75 .25
911 A372 50p Cartago   .70 .20
912 A372 55p Antioquia ('86)   1.00 .25
    Nos. 905-912 (8)   6.10 1.70

Issued: 16p, 23p, No. 905, 12/7; No. 908, 3/1/83; No. 906, 4/12/83; No. 909, 7/25/86; 55p, 8/5/86; 50p, 5/30/90.
See No. C818.

Gabriel Marquez, 1982 Nobel Prize, Literature — A412

1982, Dec. 10   Perf. 13½x14
917 A412 7p gray & green   .25 .20
    See Nos. C731-C732.

Public Education Bicentenary (Society of Mary for Education) A413

1983, May 6
918 A413 9p gold & blk   .35 .20

José Maria Espinosa Prieto, Painter — A414

250th Anniv. of City of Cucuta — A415

1983, June 3   Perf. 12
919 A414 9p Self-portrait, 1860   .40 .20

1983, June 23   Litho.   Perf. 12
920 A415 9p multicolored   .35 .20

Porfirio Barba-Jacob (1883-1942), Poet — A416

1983, July 29   Litho.   Perf. 13½x14
921 A416 9p Portrait   .35 .20

Simon Bolivar, 200th Birth Anniv. A417

1983, July 24   Perf. 12
922 A417 9p multicolored   .30 .20
    See Nos. C736-C737.

Royal Spanish Botanical Expedition, 200th Anniv. — A418

1983, Aug. 18   Perf. 14
923 A418 9p Cinchona
             lancefolia   .25 .20
924 A418 9p Passiflora laurifolia .25 .20
925 A418 60p Cinchona
             cordiflora   1.75 .50
    Nos. 923-925,C738-C740 (6)   6.25 1.70

Dawn in the Andes, by Alejandro Obregon A420

1983, Oct. 5   Litho.   Perf. 12
928 A420 20p multicolored   .50 .20
    See No. C741.

Francisco de Paula Santander (1792-1840), General — A421

1984, Mar. 6   Litho.   Perf. 14½x14
929 A421 12p light olive green   .25 .20
930 A421 12p pale carmine   .25 .20
931 A421 12p light ultra   .25 .20
    Nos. 929-931 (3)   .75 .60

Admiral Jose Prudencio Padilla (1784-1831) — A423

1984, May 17   Litho.   Perf. 12
933 A423 10p multicolored   .35 .20

Luis Antonio Calvo (1882-1945) Composer — A424

1984, July 26
934 A424 18p multicolored   .35 .20

Diego Fallon (1834-1905), Educator, Musician, Poet — A425

1984, Aug. 31   Perf. 12
935 A425 20p multicolored   .45 .20

Candelario Obeso (1849-1884), Writer — A426

1984, Sept. 4   Perf. 14x13½
936 A426 20p multicolored   .45 .20

Site of Marandua, Future City A427

1984, Sept. 28   Perf. 12
937 A427 15p multicolored   .30 .20
    See No. C744.

Christmas 1984 A428

Nativity and Children Playing, by Jose Uriel Sierra, Age 7.

1984, Dec. 14
938 A428 12p multicolored   .30 .20
    See No. C746.

Dr. Luis Eduardo Lopez, Education Minister A429

1984, Dec. 21
939 A429 22p multicolored   .40 .20

Maria Concepcion Loperena de Fernandez de Castro, Independence War Heroine — A430

1985, Jan. 6
940 A430 12p multicolored   .35 .20

Gonzalo Mejia (1885-1956) — A431

1985, Feb. 25
941 A431 12p Portrait, biplane, camera   .40 .20

Aviation, motion picture and meat exporting industrialist.

Self-portrait with Wife — A432

1985, Feb. 25
942 A432 37p multicolored   .75 .30

Pedro Nel Gomez (1899-1984), painter. See No. C748.

Fauna A433

1985   **Perf. 14**
943 A433 12p Hydrochaeris hydrochaeris   .50 .30
        Perf. 13
944 A433 15p Felis pardalis   .50 .25
945 A433 15p Tremarctos ornatus, vert.   .50 .25
946 A433 20p Tapirus pinchaque   .85 .30
     Nos. 943-946,C758 (5)   3.85 1.35

Carlos Gardel (1890-1935), Entertainer A434

Camina Literacy Program — A435

1985, June 23   **Perf. 14**
947 A434 15p Portrait, Fokker F-31 Trimotor   .30 .20

1985, Nov. 25   **Perf. 13½x14**
948 A435 15p Tree, alphabet   .30 .20

Christmas 1985 A436

1985, Dec. 4   **Litho.**   **Perf. 13**
949 A436 15p multicolored   .40 .20

Rafael Pombo Children's Foundation. See No. C755.

Eduardo Carranza (b. 1913), Poet — A437

Colombian Free University, Cent. — A438

1986, Feb. 13
950 A437 18p multicolored   .30 .20

1986, Feb. 14
951 A438 18p multicolored   .30 .20

Gen. Antonio Ricaurte (b. 1786), Liberator A439

1986, May 7   **Litho.**   **Perf. 13**
952 A439 18p Leiva birthplace   .30 .20

Jose Asuncion Silva (1865-1896), Poet, and Scene from Nocturno — A440

1986, May 30   **Litho.**   **Perf. 12**
953 A440 18p multicolored   .30 .20

Fernando Gomez Martinez (1897-1985), Journalist — A441

1986, June 19
954 A441 24p multicolored   .30 .20

Santiago de Cali, 450th Anniv. A442

1986, July 25   **Litho.**   **Perf. 13**
955 A442 25p La Merced   .30 .20

A443

A444

Monsignor Jose Vicente Castro Silva (1885-1968), rector of the Mayor del Rosario School: portrait by Ricardo Gomez.

1986, Aug. 4   **Litho.**   **Perf. 12**
956 A443 20p multicolored   .30 .20

1986, Oct. 14   **Litho.**   **Perf. 12**
957 A444 40p Natl. University   .55 .20

Faculties: Fine Arts, cent., and Architecture, 50th anniv.

Rafael Maya (1897-1980), Poet, and Salamanca University Entrance — A445

1986, Oct. 15
958 A445 25p multicolored   .35 .20
    See No. C772.

Condor in Flight — A446

Inia goefrenis A446a

No. 962, Inia goeffrensis. No. 963, Procyon cancrivorus. No. 964, Monachus tropicalis. No. 965, Pteronura brasiliensis. No. 966, Trichechus manatus. No. 967, Odocoileus virginianus. No. 968, Trogon personatus personatus. Nos. 962-968 horiz.

1986-89   **Litho.**   **Perf. 12**
959 A446 20p ultra   .35 .25
960 A446 25p ultra ('87)   .50 .25
    Perf. 14½x14, 14x14½
961 A446a 30p grn ('87)   .50 .25
962 A446a 30p dull vio ('87)   .50 .25
    Engr.
    Wmk. 334
963 A446a 35p chest brn ('88)   .75 .25
964 A446a 35p dark grn ('88)   .75 .25
965 A446a 40p deep org ('88)   .75 .25
966 A446a 40p gray ('88)   .85 .25

---

967 A446a 40p tan ('89)   .85 .25
968 A446a 45p dark vio ('88)   .85 .25
    Nos. 959-968 (10)   6.65 2.50

Issued: 20p, 11/6; 25p, 5/25; No. 961, 6/8; No. 962, 12/24; No. 963, 8/6; No. 964, 9/20; No. 965, 9/20; No. 966, 11/29; No. 967, 4/29; No. 968, 12/16.
    See Nos. 996, 1000, C778-C781.

A447

A448

1987, Jan. 29   **Unwmk.**   **Perf. 12**
969 A447 25p multicolored   .50 .20

Pedro Uribe Mejia (1886-1972), pioneer of Colombian coffee industry.

1987, May 3   **Perf. 13½x13**
970 A448 500p Santa Barbara Church   5.50 1.75

Mompox, 450th anniv.

Writers A449

Portraits and scenes from works: 70p, Jorge Isaacs (1837-1895), novelist, and scene from *Maria.* 90p, Aurelio Martinez Mutis (1884-1954), poet, and scene from *La Epopeya del Condor.*

1987   **Perf. 12**
971 A449 70p multicolored   .90 .25
972 A449 90p multicolored   1.25 .40

Issue dates: 70p, July 28. 90p, Sept. 2.

A450

A451

Social Security & Communications.

1987   **Litho.**   **Perf. 13½x13**
973 A450 35p multicolored   .40 .20

1988, May 25 Litho. Perf. 12
Natl. Anthem, Cent.: Score, lyricist Rafael Nunez and composer Oreste Sindici. Dated 1987.

974 A451 70p multicolored .70 .25

Human Rights — A452

Perf. 14½x14, 14x14½
1988-89 Engr.
975 A452 30p Life .35 .25
976 A452 35p Suffrage .35 .25
977 A452 40p Association, horiz. .45 .25
978 A452 45p Culture, horiz. .35 .25
　Nos. 975-978 (4) 1.50 1.00
Issued: 30p, 35p, 5/12; 40p, 7/1; 45p, 10/27/89.
See Nos. C797, C807.

Pasto, 450th Anniv. A453

1988, May 20 Litho. Perf. 12
979 A453 60p Cathedral, Pasto .70 .35
Dated 1987.

Bogota Aqueduct and Sewage System, Cent. — A454

1988, May 20
980 A454 100p Waterfall 1.25 .35

Maria Currea de Aya (1888-1985), Women's Rights Activist — A455

1988, May 27
981 A455 80p multicolored .95 .25

A456

Sailfish, *Istiaophorus Americanus.*

Perf. 14x13½
1988, July 19 Engr. Wmk. 334
982 A456 (A) dark blue 4.25 2.25
983 A456 (B) Prus blue 1.25 .40
At the time of issue, No. 982 was sold for 400p and No. 983 for 100p. See type A486.

Unwmk.
1988, Aug. 10 Litho. Perf. 12
984 A457 120p multicolored 1.25 .35
San Bartolome College, founded in 1604.

Jorge Alvarez Lleras (1885-1952), Engineer and Director of the Natl. Astronomical Observatory — A458

1988, Aug. 17
985 A458 90p multicolored .85 .35

Pres. Eduardo Santos (1888-1974) A459

1988, Aug. 30
986 A459 80p multicolored .85 .25

Andres Bello Seminary A460

Unwmk.
1988, Dec. 27 Litho. Perf. 12
987 A460 115p multicolored 1.10 .20

Adpostal, 25th Anniv. A461

1989, May 3
988 A461 45p multicolored .40 .25

Military Leaders — A462

Bolivar and Santander at the Los Llanos Campaign — A463

1989 Litho. Perf. 12
989 A462 40p Santander .60 .25
990 A462 40p Bolivar .60 .25
991 A463 45p multicolored .60 .25
　Nos. 989-991 (3) 1.80 .75
Liberation campaign, 170th anniv.
Issued: No. 989, 8/25; No. 990, 7/25; 45p, 8/7.

From Boyaca to Santa Fe — A464

1989, Aug. 7 Litho. Perf. 12
992 45p multicolored 1.50 .45
993 45p multicolored 1.50 .45
　a. A464 Pair, #992-993 4.00 2.00
Liberation campaign, 170th anniv.

Liberation Campaign Triptych — A466

Designs: a, Gen. Santander, liberation force. b, Simon Bolivar riding mount. c, Insurgent cavalry.

Unwmk.
1989, Aug. 7 Litho. Perf. 13
994 A466 Strip of 3 4.50 1.75
　a.-c. 45p any single 1.25 .55
Liberation Campaign, 170th anniv.

Tunja, 450th Anniv. A467

1989, Aug. 8 Perf. 12
995 A467 45p multicolored .40 .25

Fauna Type of 1988
Designs: No. 996, Harpia harpyja, horiz. No. 997, Urocyon cinereoargenteus. No. 998, Dendrobates histrionicus. No. 1000, Phenacosaurus indenenae. No. 1001, Cebuella pygmaea. No. 1002, Eurypyga helias, horiz.

Perf. 14½x14, 14x14½
1989-90 Engr. Wmk. 334
996 A446a 45p black 1.00 .20
997 A446a 50p blue gray .60 .20
998 A446a 50p deep claret .40 .20
999 A446a 55p red brown .85 .20
1000 A446a 60p brown .60 .20
1001 A446a 60p org brown .60 .20
　Nos. 996-1001 (6) 4.05 1.20
Issued: 45p, 9/7; Nos. 997, 1000, 3/1/90; No. 998, 4/25; 55p, 8/18; No. 1001, 8/6.

A468

A469

1989, Aug. 30 Unwmk. Perf. 12
1011 A468 135p multicolored 1.25 .80
City of Armenia, cent.

1990, Mar. 28 Litho. Perf. 12
1012 A469 60p Espeletia hartwegiana .35 .25

Gen. Francisco De Paula Santander (1792-1840) — A470

1990, May 6 Perf. 14x13½
1013 A470 50p multicolored .40 .20
　Nos. 1013, C823-C827 (6) 3.80 2.50
See Nos. 1046-1047.

General Santander Police Academy, 50th Anniv. — A471

1990, May 16 Perf. 12
1014 A471 60p multicolored .40 .25

Department of La Guajira A473

1990, July 1 Perf. 12
1016 A473 60p multicolored .55 .20

Ceiba Pentandra A474

1990, July 15 Litho. Perf. 12
1017 A474 60p multicolored .40 .25

A475

A476

1990, Aug. 8   **Litho.**   *Perf. 12*
1018 A475 70p Tibouchina
     lepidota   .65   .25

Unwmk.
1990, Aug. 28   **Litho.**   *Perf. 14*
1019 A476 70p Ceroxylon
     quindiuense   .40   .20

A477

A478

1990, Sept. 28   *Perf. 12*
1020 A477 60p St. John Bosco   .50   .20
   Salesian Order in Colombia, cent.

1991, Mar. 28   **Litho.**   *Perf. 12*
1021 A478 70p multicolored   .40   .25
   Miraculous Christ, Pilgrimage Church of
Buga.

Moths and
Butterflies
A479

1991, Apr. 18   **Litho.**   *Perf. 14*
1022 A479 70p Callithea philo-
     tima   .75   .25
1023 A479 70p Anaea syene,
     vert.   .75   .25
1024 A479 80p Thecla
     coronata, vert.   .95   .25
1025 A479 80p Agrias amydon   1.00   .25
1026 A479 170p Morpho rhetenor   2.00   .35
1027 A479 190p Heliconius lon-
     garenus   2.25   .35
    Nos. 1022-1027 (6)   7.70   1.70
   Nos. 1025-1027 are airmail.

New
Constitution
A480

1991, July 4   **Litho.**   *Perf. 14*
1028 A480 70p multicolored   .40   .25

A481

A482

1991, July 19   *Perf. 12*
1029 A481 80p multicolored   .40   .30
   Pres. Dario Echandia Olaya (1897-1989).
See No. 1042.

1991, Aug. 7
1030 A482 70p multicolored   .35   .20
   Col. Antansaio Girardot (1791-1813).

A483

A484

1991, Aug. 15   **Litho.**   *Perf. 14*
1031 A483 80p multicolored   .50   .20
   Luis Carlos Galan Sarmiento (1943-1989),
political reformer.

1991, Aug. 24   *Perf. 12*
   Pre-Columbian Artifacts: 80p, Statue of cat
god. No. 1033, Pitcher from tomb of high official. No. 1034, Statue with two heads. 210p,
Flying fish, horiz.
1032 A484   80p multicolored   .65   .20
1033 A484   90p multicolored   .85   .20
1034 A484   90p multicolored   .85   .20
1035 A484 210p multicolored   1.90   .30
    Nos. 1032-1035 (4)   4.25   .90
   Nos. 1034-1035 are airmail.

Colonial
Architecture
A485

   80p, Cloister of St. Augustine, Tunja. No.
1037, Community Bridge, Chia. No. 1038,
Roadside Chapel, Pamplona. 190p, Church of
Immaculate Conception, Bogota.

1991   **Litho.**   *Perf. 12*
1036 A485   80p multi   .65   .20
1037 A485   90p multi   1.00   .20
1038 A485   90p multi, vert.   .85   .30
1039 A485 190p multi, vert.   1.60   .35
    Nos. 1036-1039 (4)   4.10   1.05
   Issue dates: No. 1037, Sept. 9; others, Sept.
27. Nos. 1038-1039 are airmail.

Istiaphorus
Americanus
A486

1991, Sept. 3   *Perf. 14*
1040 A486 830p multicolored   6.00   1.50

Colombian
Police
Force,
Cent.
A487

1991, Oct. 12   *Perf. 12*
1041 A487 80p multicolored   .50   .20

President Type of 1991
   Pres. Alberto Lleras Camargo (1906-1990)

1991, Nov. 5
1042 A481 80p multicolored   .40   .25

A489

A490

1991, Dec. 17   **Litho.**   *Perf. 12*
1043 A489 80p Sogamoso City
     Hall   .50   .20

1992   **Litho.**   *Perf. 14*
   Designs: No. 1044, Diana Turbay Quintero
(1950-91), journalist. No. 1045, Indalecio
Lievano Aguirre (1917-82), diplomat.
1044 A490 80p multicolored   .45   .25
1045 A490 80p multicolored   .45   .25
   Issued: No. 1044, Jan. 24; No. 1045, Apr.
21.

Santander Type of 1990 and

Battle of Boyaca — A491a

1992, Apr. 2   *Perf. 14*
    Size: 26x37mm
1046   A470   80p Monument   .40   .30
1047   A470   190p Portrait   1.00   .70
    Souvenir Sheet
     Perf. 13½x14
1047A A491a 950p multicolored   5.50   5.50
   Nos. 1047-1047A are airmail. Gen. Francisco de Paula Santander, bicent. of birth.

A492

A493

   Ministers of Justice: 100p, Enrique Low
Murtra (1939-91). 110p, Rodrigo Lara Bonilla
(1946-84).

1992, Apr. 30   **Litho.**   *Perf. 12*
1048 A492 100p multicolored   .40   .20
1049 A492 110p multicolored   .50   .20

1992, May 18   *Perf. 14*
1050 A493 110p multicolored   .60   .30
   15th natl. games, Barranquilla.

Wildlife — A494

1992, Apr. 14   **Litho.**   *Perf. 12*
1051 A494 (B) Oroaetus icidori   1.90   .80
1052 A494 (A) Tremarctos
     ornatus   8.75   3.25
   Nos. 1051-1052 had face values of 200p
and 950p respectively on date of issue.

Endangered
Species
A495

1992, Aug. 4
1053 A495 100p Crocodylus
     acatus   1.25   .40
1054 A495 100p Vultur gryphus,
     vert.   1.25   .40

A496

A497

1992, Aug. 24   Litho.   Perf. 14
1055 A496 100p multicolored   .50   .30
1056 A496 110p multicolored   .50   .30
Maria Lopez de Escobar, founder of the House of the Mother and Child. No. 1056 is airmail.

1992, Sept. 23   Litho.   Perf. 12
1057 A497 100p multicolored   .50   .30
Conference of First Ladies of the Americas and Caribbean, Cartagena.

Recycling — A498

1992, Oct. 9   Litho.   Perf. 12
1058 A498 100p multicolored   .50   .30

Discovery of America, 500th Anniv. — A499

Paintings: 100p, Zenaida, by Ana Mercedes Hoyos. No. 1060, Estudio Para 1/500, by Beatriz Gonzalez. No. 1061, Blue Eagle, by Alejandro Obregon. 230p, Cantileo, by Luis Luna. 260p, Corn, by Antonio Caro. 400p, Grand Curtain, by Luis Caballero. 440p, Homage to Guatavita, by Alejandro Obregon.

1992, Oct. 5   Litho.   Perf. 13½x14
1059 A499 100p multicolored   .50   .30
1060 A499 110p multicolored   .50   .30
1061 A499 110p multicolored   .50   .30
1062 A499 230p multicolored   1.10   .70
1063 A499 260p multicolored   1.25   .80
    Nos. 1059-1063 (5)   3.85 2.40
Souvenir Sheets
Perf. 12
1064 A499 400p multicolored   3.00 3.00
1065 A499 440p multicolored   3.00 3.00
Nos. 1061-1063 are airmail.

World Post Day — A500

1992, Oct. 19   Litho.   Perf. 12
1066 A500 (B) multicolored   .95   .65
No. 1066 had face value of 200p on day of issue.

Christmas — A501

Children's paintings of: 100p, Nativity scene. 110p, Adoration of the Magi.

1992, Nov. 20   Litho.   Perf. 12
1067 A501 100p multicolored   .50   .30
1068 A501 110p multicolored   .50   .30
No. 1068 is airmail.

Three Musicians, by Fernando Botero A502

1993, Feb. 5   Litho.   Perf. 12
1069 A502 (B) multicolored   1.25   .80
No. 1069 had a face value of 250p on day of issue.

Lions Intl. Campaign Against Amblyopia A503

1993, Mar. 26   Perf. 14
1070 A503 100p multicolored   .45   .30

Holy Week in Popayan A504

1993, Apr. 5   Perf. 14x13½
1071 A504 (B) multicolored   1.10   .80
No. 1071 had a face value of 250p on day of issue.

A505

A506

1993, Apr. 7   Perf. 12
1072 A505 (B) multicolored   1.25   .80
Pan American Health Org., 90th anniv. No. 1072 had a face value of 250p on day of issue.

1993, Apr. 14
1073 A506 (B) multicolored   1.25   .80
Franciscans of Mary Immaculate, cent. No. 1073 had a face value of 250p on day of issue.

A507

A508

1993, Apr. 22   Litho.   Perf. 14
1074 A507 (B) multicolored   .90   .60
EXFILBO '93, 18th Natl. Philatelic Exhibition. No. 1074 had a face value of 250p on day issue.

1993, July 2   Litho.   Perf. 12
1075 A508 250p Guillermo Cano,
                  writer   1.00   .65

Human Rights A509

Rights: a, 150p, Of prisoners. b, 150p, Of the elderly. c, 200p, Of the infirm. d, 200p, Of children. e, 220p, Of women. f, 220p, Of the poor. g, 460p, To clean environment. h, 520p, Of indigenous people.
Painting: 800p, Peace, Rights, and Freedom, by Alfredo Vivero, vert.

1993, June 10   Perf. 14
1076 A509 Block of 8, #a.-h.   12.00 7.50
Souvenir Sheet
1077 A509 800p multicolored   5.50 5.50
Nos. 1076e-1076h are airmail.

Amazon Region of Colombia — A510

No. 1078a, Parrot. No. 1078b, Anaconda. No. 1079a, Victoria regia. No. 1079b, Flor ipecacuana. 880p, Map, native, horiz.

1993   Litho.   Perf. 12
1078 A510 150p Pair, #a.-b.   1.25   .75
1079 A510 220p Pair, #a.-b.   1.75 1.00
Souvenir Sheet
1080 A510 880p multicolored   4.75 4.75
Nos. 1079-1080 are airmail.

Famous People — A511

Designs: a, 150p, Alberto Pumarejo (1893-1970). b, 150p, Lorencita Villegas de Santos (1892-1960). c, 200p, Meliton Rodriguez (1875-1942). d, 200p, Tomas Carrasquilla (1858-1940).

1993   Litho.   Perf. 14x13½
1081 A511 Block of 4, #a.-d.   3.25 2.25

Christmas — A512

1993, Nov. 30   Perf. 12
1082 A512 200p Holy Family   .95   .60
1083 A512 220p Shepherd   1.60 1.10
No. 1083 is airmail.

Tourism A513

Designs: No. 1084a, San Andres Providence. b, Cocuy Natl. Park. c, Lake Cocha. d, Waterfalls, Serrania de la Macarena. 250p, Lake Otun. No. 1086a, Chicamocha River. b, Sierra Nevada de Santa Marta mountains. 520p, Penol Reservoir.

1993, Dec. 1   Litho.   Perf. 12
1084 A513 220p Block of 4, #a.-
                  d.   4.50 3.00
1085 A513 250p multicolored   1.25   .75
1086 A513 460p Block, #a.-b.   4.75 3.00
1087 A513 520p multicolored   2.75 1.50
    Nos. 1084-1087 (4)   13.25 8.25
Nos. 1084, 1086-87 are airmail.

A514

A515

1993, Dec. 21   Litho.   Perf. 14
1088 A514 150p multicolored   .60   .40
Natl. Museum, 170th anniv.

1994, Jan. 25   Litho.   Perf. 14
1089 A515 300p Marie Poussepin 1.10   .70

A516

A517

Birds: 180p, Ognorhynchus icterotis. 240p, Rallus semiplumbeus. 270p, Semnornis ramphastinus. 560p, Anas cyanoptera.

1994, Mar. 4
1090 A516 180p multi   1.40   .40
1091 A516 240p multi   1.60   .55
1092 A516 270p multi, horiz.   2.00   .70
1093 A516 560p multi, horiz.   4.00   1.40
Nos. 1090-1093 (4)   9.00   3.05
Nos. 1092-1093 are airmail.

1994, Apr. 11   Litho.   Perf. 14
1094 A517 300p multicolored   1.25   .80
Air Force, 75th anniv.

Latin American Presidential Summit, Cartagena
A518

1994, June 14   Litho.   Perf. 14
1095 A518 300p shown   1.00   .65
1096 A518 630p Flags   2.10   1.60
No. 1096 is airmail.

1994 World Cup Soccer Championships, US — A519

World Cup Trophy and: 180p, Soccer player, Colombian flag. 270p, Two players with ball. 560p, Soccer ball, Colombian flag, vert.
1110p, Soccer player offering hand to another.

1994, May 26   Perf. 12
1097 A519 180p multicolored   .65   .40
1098 A519 270p multicolored   .95   .55
1099 A519 560p multicolored   2.10   1.40
Nos. 1097-1099 (3)   3.70   2.35
Souvenir Sheet
1100 A519 1110p multicolored   5.50   5.50
Nos. 1098-1099 are airmail.

Ricardo Rendon (1894-1931), Artist — A520

1993 Census — A521

1994, June 30   Litho.   Perf. 12
1101 A520 240p black   .90   .45

1994, Aug. 12   Perf. 14
1102 A521 240p multicolored   .80   .45

Ministry of Communications Inravision, 30th Anniv. — A522

1994, Aug. 3
1103 A522 180p multicolored   .65   .30

Intl. Year of the Family
A523

1994, Sept. 1   Litho.   Perf. 14
1104 A523 300p multicolored   1.00   .65

America Issue — A524

Methods of mail delivery: 270p, Horse, bicycle. 300p, Men holding stamps showing truck, ship, plane.

1994, Oct. 18   Litho.   Perf. 13
1105 A524 270p multicolored   1.60   .65
1106 A524 300p multicolored   2.40   .70
No. 1105 is airmail.

Colombian Society of Engineers, Cent.
A525

1994, Oct. 20   Litho.   Perf. 12
1107 A525 180p multicolored   .60   .40

Christmas
A526

1994, Nov. 22   Litho.   Perf. 13½x13
1108 A526 270p Magi   .95   .65
1109 A526 300p Holy family   1.10   .70
No. 1108 is airmail.

Former President Type of 1981
Miniature Sheet of 20

Designs: a, Jose Miguel Pey. b, Jorge Tadeo Lozano. c, Antonio Narino. d, Camilo Torres. e, Jose Fernandez Madrid. f, Jose Maria del Castillo y Rada. g, Custodio Garcia Rovira. h, Antonio Villavicencio. i, Liborio Mejia. j, Rafael Urdaneta. k, Juan Garcia del Rio. l, Jose Maria Melo. m, Tomas Herrera. n, Froilan Largacha. o, Salvador Camacho Roldan. p, Ezequiel Hurtado. q, Dario Echandia Olaya. r, Alberto Lleras Camargo. s, Gustavo Rojas Pinilla. t, Carlos Lleras Restrepo.

1995, Apr. 4   Litho.   Perf. 12
1110 A401 270p #a.-t.   35.00 35.00

World Offroad Bicycle Championships, Melgar — A527

1995, Mar. 30   Perf. 14
1111 A527 400p multicolored   1.40   .90

A528

A529

1995, Oct. 12   Litho.   Perf. 12
1112 A528 220p multicolored   .65   .30
Gen. Jose Maria Obando (1795-1861), President.

1995, Nov. 28   Perf. 14
1113 A529 400p Clean air   1.25   .75
1114 A529 400p Clean water   1.25   .75
Preserve the environment. America issue.

Christmas
A530

Stained glass windows: 220p, Flight into Egypt. 330p, Nativity.

1995, Dec. 18   Perf. 12
1115 A530 220p multicolored   .75   .40
1116 A530 330p multicolored   1.10   .65
No. 1116 is airmail.

Bogotá to Boyacá World Cycling Championship — A531

1995, Oct. 4   Litho.   Perf. 12
1117 A531 400p multicolored   1.40   .75

León De Greiff (1895-1976), Poet — A532

1996, May 2   Litho.   Perf. 12
1118 A532 400p black   1.40   .40

Mosquera Courtyard, Natl. Capitol
A533

1996, July 18   Litho.   Perf. 14
1119 A533 400p multicolored   1.10   .40

Medellin Rapid Transit System
A534

1996, July 2   Perf. 12
1120 A534 500p multicolored   1.75   .90

A535

A536

1996, June 20
1121 A535 500p multicolored   1.40 .50

Community of St. John of God in Colombia, 400th anniv.

1996, June 25

Arms: a, Santa Maria la Antigua del Darien. b, San Sebastian de Mariquita. c, Villa de la Marinilla. d, Villa of Santa Cruz of Mompox.

1122 A536 400p Block of 4, #a.-
         d.   4.75 3.25
  e.   As "d," inscribed AEREO   12.00
  f.   Block of 4, #1122a-1122c,
       1122e   15.00

Issued in sheets of 16 stamps.

1996 Summer Olympic Games, Atlanta — A537

1996, July 16
1123 A537 500p multicolored   1.50 .75

SAYCO (Colombian Authors and Composers Society), 50th Anniv. — A538

1996, Aug. 17   Litho.   Perf. 12
1124 A538 400p multicolored   1.25 .50

Exfilbo '96, 20th Natl. Philatelic Exhibition A539

Jewelry from Gold Museum, Bogotá.

1996, Oct. 19   Litho.   Perf. 12
1125 A539 400p multicolored   1.25 .50

Souvenir Sheet

Founders Theater, Manizales, 30th Anniv. — A540

Drop curtain: a, Eagle, people watching man drawing on ground, vert. b, People, animals on hillside.

1996, Oct. 28   Perf. 14
1126 A540 4000p #a.-b.   22.50 22.50

Christmas A541

Designs: No. 1127, Mailman handing woman letter. No. 1128, Woman reading letter, mailman holding bundle of mail.

1996, Nov. 22
1127 A541 400p multicolored   1.10 .40
1128 A541 400p multicolored   1.10 .40

No. 1128 is airmail.

America Issue — A542

1996, Nov. 29   Perf. 12
1129 A542 500p Men's costume   1.40 .50
1130 A542 500p Women's cos-
            tume   1.40 .50

Historical Landmarks — A543

a, Cemetery, Santa Cruz of Mompox. b, Carved face, San Agustin Archaeological Park. c, Entrance, Palace of the Inquisition, Cartagena de Indias. d, Inside ruins, Tierradentro Archaelogical Park.

1996, Dec. 6   Perf. 14
1131 A543 400p Block of 4,
            #a.-d.   10.00 10.00

Alvaro Gomez Hurtado (1919-95), Politician, Writer — A544

1997, Mar. 18   Litho.   Perf. 12
1132 A544 400p multicolored   1.00 .40

Bogotá Journalists Assoc., 50th Anniv. A545

1997, July 10   Litho.   Perf. 12
1133 A545 400p multicolored   1.00 .40

Natl. Festival of Porro — A546

1997, June 26   Perf. 13½x14
1134 A546 400p multicolored   1.00 .40

Pres. Virgilio Barco (1921-97) — A547

1997, Nov. 27   Litho.   Perf. 14
1135 A547 500p multicolored   1.25 .40

Colombia in Peace A548

1997, Dec. 30   Litho.   Perf. 12
1136 A548 500p Children play-
                ing   1.10 .40
1137 A548 1100p Children danc-
                ing   2.50 .90

No. 1137 is airmail.

America Issue A549

1997, Dec. 30
1138 A549 500p Postman by
                day   1.50 .50
1139 A549 1100p Postman by
                night   3.00 1.25

No. 1139 is airmail.

Jorge Eliecer Gaitan (1903-48), Politician — A550

1998, Apr. 24   Litho.   Perf. 14
1140 A550 500p multicolored   1.75 .80

Free University, 75th Anniv. A551

1998, July 1   Litho.   Perf. 14
1141 A551 500p black & red   2.25 .75

Santander Industrial University, 50th Anniv. — A552

1998, May 14   Perf. 12
1142 A552 500p multicolored   1.75 .80

City of Manizales, 150th Anniv. — A553

1998, July 24   Litho.   Perf. 12
1143 A553 500p multicolored   2.25 .75

A554

A555

Pre-Columbian art, agency: a, Tairona, Bank of the Republic. b, Malagana, Controller General. c, Quimbaya, Bank Superintendent.

1998, July 24
1144 A554 500p Strip of 3, #a.-c. 7.00 4.75

Natl. financial agencies, 70th anniv.

1998, Aug. 21   Perf. 14
1145 A555 500p multicolored   2.25 .80

Pres. Misael Pastrana Borrero (1923-97).

University
of the
Andes,
50th Anniv.
A556

1998, Sept. 28
1146 A556 500p multicolored   1.90   .80

Christmas
A557

Designs: 500p, Woman kneeling down to
get water with bowl, cherubs in sky. No.
1148a, Magi. No. 1148b, Nativity scene.

1998, Nov. 19   Litho.   Perf. 14
1147 A557 500p multicolored   1.25   .75
1148 A557 1000p Pair, #a.-b.   4.75 3.25

No. 1148 is airmail.

A558

Emblems of Colombian Academies: a, Language. b, Medicine. c, Law. d, History. e, Science. f, Ecomonics. g, Religion.

1998, Dec. 15   Perf. 12
Sheet of 7 + Label
1149 A558 500p #a.-g.   14.00 14.00

1999, Apr. 16   Perf. 14
1150 A559 1000p multicolored   1.75 1.00
Gen. José Hilario López.

A559

Famous
Women — A559a

America Issue: 600p, Soledad Román de
Nuñez. 1200p, Bertha Herández de Ospina.

1999, Mar. 25   Litho.   Perf. 12
1151 A559a 600p multicolored   1.50   .40
1152 A559a 1200p multicolored   2.75   .70

No. 1152 is airmail.

Turtles — A560

a, Chelonia mydas. b, Dermochelys
coriacea. c, Eretmochelys imbricata.

1999, Apr. 16   Perf. 14
1153 A560 1300p Strip of 3,
                #a.-c.   13.00 13.00

Dr. Eduardo
Zuleta Angel,
Diplomat (b.
1899) — A561

1999, Sept. 9   Litho.   Perf. 12
1154 A561 600p multicolored   1.40   .45

Pamplona,
450th
Anniv.
A562

1999   Litho.   Perf. 12
1155 A562 1000p multicolored   2.75   .75

Sovereign Military
Order of Malta,
900th
Anniv. — A563

1999, June 24   Perf. 14
1156 A563 1200p multicolored   4.00 1.25

Japanese Immigration to
Colombia — A564

Designs: a, Red at right. b, Red at left.

1999, May 12   Perf. 13½x14
1157 A564 1300p Pair, #a.-b.   5.25 5.25

Pan
American
Games,
Winnipeg,
Manitoba
A565

Designs: a, Flag, Olympic rings. b, Runner
facing right. c, Weight lifter facing left. d,
Cyclist facing right. e, Shooter facing left. f,
Roller skater facing right. g, Runner facing left.
h, Weight lifter facing right. i, Cyclist facing left.
j, Shooter facing right. k, Roller skater facing
left. l, Like "a," with lilac line under "12."

1999, July 23   Litho.   Perf. 14
1158 A565 1200p Sheet of 12,
                #a.-l.   30.00 30.00

Luis A. Robles (b.
1849) — A566

1999, Oct. 27
1159 A566 600p multi   .95   .40

Manufacture
of Aspirin,
Cent.
A567

1999, Dec. 1   Perf. 12¾
1160 A567 600p multi   .95   .40
Value is for stamp with surrounding selvage.

UPU,
125th
Anniv.
A568

1999, Oct. 29   Perf. 14¼
1161 A568 1000p "125"   1.75   .75
1162 A568 1300p "1874-1999"   2.75 1.00

Inter-American Development Bank,
40th Anniv. — A569

Abstract art: a, "Colombia" in yellow. b,
"Colombia" in red.

1999, Nov. 19   Perf. 14x14¼
1163 A569 1000p Pair, #a.-b.   3.25 1.40

America Issue, A New Millennium
Without Arms — A570

a, Stylized hands. b, Large flower at LR.

1999, Nov. 9   Perf. 14
1164 A570 1200p Pair, #a.-b.   4.25 1.90

Christmas — A571

a, Holy Family, animals. b, Angel, Magi.

1999, Nov. 29   Perf. 13½x14
1165 A571 600p Pair, #a.-b.   2.25   .90

Millennium — A572

Designs: a, Nude man, flag, dove. b, Globe,
rainbow, "2000."

2000, Jan. 3   Perf. 14
1166 A572 1000p Pair, #a.-b.   4.00 4.00

University
of Medellin,
50th Anniv.
A573

2000, Feb. 1   Litho.   Perf. 14
1167 A573 1000p multi   1.50   .65

Father José
Rafael Faría
Bermúdez (1896-
1979)
A574

2000, Mar. 6   Litho.   Perf. 14
1168 A574 1300p multi   1.75   .90

2000
Summer
Olympics,
Sydney
A575

2000, Apr. 21
1169 A575 1000p multi   1.75   .75

Popayán
Religious
Music
Festival
A576

2000, July 7
1170 A576 1000p multi   1.90   .65

America Issue, Campaign Against AIDS A577

2000, Sept. 19   Litho.   Perf. 14x13½
1171 A577 1000p multi   4.00 1.60

Radio Station HJCK, 50th Anniv. — A578

2000, Sept. 28   Litho.   Perf. 14
1172 A578 1000p multi   1.50 .65

Birth Registration A579

2000, Nov. 14   Litho.   Perf. 14¼
1173 A579 1000p multi   1.50 .60

Paintings A580

No. 1174: a, Archangel, by Fernando Botero. b, Gypsy Woman With Tamourine, by Jean-Baptiste-Camille Corot. c, Vera Sergine Renoir, by Renoir. d, Man on Horse, by Botero. e, Mother Superior, by Botero. f, A Town, by Botero. g, Flowers, by Botero. h, Cézanne, by Botero. i, Patio, by Botero. j, Absinthe Drinker in Grenelle, by Toulouse-Lautrec. k, A Little Valley, by Corot. l, The Studio, by Botero.

2001, Jan. 31   Perf. 12
1174   Sheet of 12   15.00 15.00
a.-l. A580 650p Any single   .95 .45

Children's Day — A581

2001, Mar. 15   Litho.   Perf. 14
1175 A581 1100p multi   3.75 1.40

Abolition of Slavery, 150th Anniv. — A582

2001, May 21   Litho.   Perf. 14¼x14
1176 A582 1100p multi   3.75 1.40

Discovery of Magdalena River, 500th Anniv. — A583

2001, June 13   Litho.   Perf. 14
1177 A583 1100p multi   3.75 1.40

Copa America Soccer Tournament A584

2001, July 18   Litho.   Perf. 12¾
1178 A584 1900p multi   4.00 1.75

Values are for examples with surrounding selvage.

America Issue — Los Katios Natl. Park, UNESCO World Heritage Site — A585

2001, Aug. 17   Perf. 13¾x14
1179 A585 2100p multi   7.50 3.00

Year of Dialogue Among Civilizations A586

2001, Oct. 9   Perf. 14
1180 A586 650p multi   2.50 .80

Reclining Woman, by Fernando Botero — A587

2001, Oct. 23   Perf. 14¼
1181 A587 1100p multi   4.00 1.40

Christmas A588

2001, Nov. 19   Perf. 14
1182 A588 1100p multi   4.00 1.40

National Beauty Pageant — A589

Flag, Miss Colombia Vanesa A. Mendoza Bustos and: a, Cartagena de Indias. b, St. Francis of Assisi Cathedral, Quibdo. Illustration reduced.

2002, Jan. 22   Perf. 14x14¼
1183 A589 800p Horiz. pair, #a-b 3.00 1.00

Natural Riches of Colombia — A590

Parts of map of Colombia, various wildlife and/or natives and: a, Bird and clouds at left. b, Turtle at upper left. c, Fish and whales at left. d, Man on horse at center. e, Volcano at upper left. f, Red and blue parrots at right. g, Flamingos at left. h, Snake at upper left.

2002, Feb. 1   Perf. 14¼x14
1184 A590 2300p Sheet of 8,
    #a-h   35.00 35.00

Children's Day — A591

2002, Feb. 18   Perf. 12
1185 A591 1400p multi   2.50 1.10

New Emblem of Adpostal — A592

2002, Mar. 7   Perf. 14
1186 A592 800p multi   1.60 .60

7th South American Games A593

2002, Jan. 7
1187 A593 2100p multi   3.00 1.25

Oxyura Jamaicensis A594

2002, Apr. 30   Litho.   Perf. 12
1188 A594 3900p multi   6.50 3.00

Souvenir Sheet

Frogs — A595

No. 1189: a, 7200p, Hyla crepitans. b, 7600p, Dendrobates histrionicus.

2002, Apr. 30   Perf. 13¾x14
1189 A595   Sheet of 2, #a-b   21.00 21.00

Souvenir Sheet

Butterflies — A596

No. 1190: a, Dryas iulia. b, Dryadula phaetusa, vert.

2002, Apr. 30   Perf. 12
1190 A596 13,700p Sheet of 2,
    #a-b   37.50 37.50

Foundation for Reconstructive Surgery, 25th Anniv. — A597

2002, May 24   Perf. 14
1191 A597 1000p multi   1.60 .60

Pre-Columbian Art — A598

No. 1192, 800p: a, Nariño pectoral. b, Nariño disc.
No. 1193, 1400p: a, Calima diadem. b, Calima pectoral.
No. 1194, 2100p: a, Anthropomorphic Tairona pectoral. b, Round Tairona pectoral. Illustration reduced.

2002, June 7   *Perf. 13½x14*
Horiz. Pairs, #a-b
1192-1194 A598   Set of 3   15.00   15.00

Surgical Society of Bogota San José Hospital, Cent. — A599

No. 1195: a, Early doctors and nurse. b, Hospital.

2002, July 22   *Perf. 14*
1195 A599 800p Horiz. pair, #a-b   2.75   2.75

Consuelo Araújo Noguera (1940-2001), Assassinated Former Minister of Culture — A600

2002, Aug. 1
1196 A600 1400p multi   2.50   1.00

Union Network International A601

2002, Aug. 12
1197 A601 1000p multi   1.60   .65

America Issue — Youth, Education and Literacy — A602

No. 1198: a, Person reading book. b, Letters amd words.

2002, Oct. 9
1198 A602 2500p Horiz. pair, #a-b   7.00   6.00

Christmas A603

2002, Nov. 6   *Litho.*   *Perf. 14x13¾*
1199 A603 800p multi   2.00   .65

Colombian History Academy, Cent. — A604

No. 1200: a, Mural scene with Simon Bolivar at UR. b, Mural scene with horsemen at top. c, Mural scene with man with outstretched arms at UL. d, Cafetal, 1956. e, Batalla de Palonegro, 1905. f, Tigre Cazando Sabanera, 1963. g, El Barqueo, 1936. h, Colombia Asesinada, 1902. i, Dos Mujeres, 1951. j, Bearded man at left, Plaza de Santander. k, Carriage, Plaza de Santander. l, Horse, man and woman, Plaza de Santander.

2002, Nov. 19   *Perf. 13¾x14*
1200 A604 800p Sheet of 12, #a-l   22.50   22.50

Peace Treaty Ending War of 1,000 Days, Cent. A605

2002, Nov. 21   *Perf. 14x13¾*
1201 A605 1600p multi   3.50   1.10

Carnival A606

No. 1202: a, shown. b, Participants holding masks on sticks. c, Participants on float.

2003, Jan. 4   *Perf. 14*
1202   Horiz. strip of 3   6.50   6.50
a.-b.   A606 1000p Either single   1.25   1.25
c.   A606 1200p multi   1.60   1.60

Printed in sheets of 3 horizontal strips and 2 horiz. strips of 3 labels.

Articulated Bus, Bogota A607

2003, Mar. 13   *Perf. 12*
1203 A607 1000p multi   1.60   .70

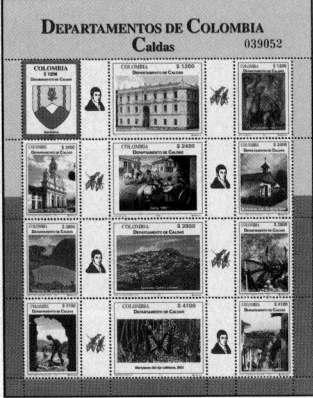

Departments — A608

No. 1204 — Caldas Department: a, 1200p, Arms. b, 1200p, Government office building, Manizales, horiz. c, 1200p, Campesinos, 1957. d, 2400p, Church, Salamina. e, 2400p, Neira, 1997, horiz. f, 2400p, Enea Chapel, Manizales. g, 2800p, Laguna Verde, Villamaria. h, 2800p, Aguadas, horiz. i, 2800p, Devil's carnival, Riosucio. j, 4100p, Miner, Marmato. k, 4100p, Mariposas del Eje Cafetero, 2001, horiz. l, 4100p, Pacora.
No. 1205, 1000p — Huila Department: a, Arms. b, Government office building, Neiva, horiz. c, La Gaitana. d, Bordones Waterfall, Isnos. e, San Agustín World Heritage Archaeological Park, horiz. f, Lavapatas Spring, San Agustín. g, La Tatacoa Desert, Villavieja. h, Liberty tree, Gigante, horiz. i, Sombrero maker, Suaza. j, Nuestra Señora de los Dolores Church, Aipe. k, Paisaje, horiz. l, Dancers.
No. 1206 — 2400p: a, Historic center of Barichara. b, Ophthalmologic Foundation of Santander, Bucaramanga, horiz. c, Girón. d, Santander Industrial University Intl. Piano Festival, 20th anniv. emblem. e, Petroleum Christ Statue, refinery, Barrancabermeja, horiz. f, Church, San Andrés. g, Gustavo Cote Uribe (1918-94), writer. h, Chamber of Commerce, Bucaramanga, horiz. i, Carnival of Eastern Colombia, Bucaramanga. j, Historic center of Albania. k, Chicamocha River Canyon, Cepitá, horiz. l, Entreguerras.

2003   *Perf. 12*
Sheets of 12, #a-l, + 8 labels
1204 A608 Caldas   42.50   42.50
1205 A608 Huila   17.50   17.50
1206 A608 Santander   27.50   27.50

Issued: No. 1204, Apr. 11. No. 1205, June 29. No. 1206, June 22. Size of horiz. stamps: 46x37mm.
See Nos. 1224-1226, 1246, 1265-1267, 1273, 1288-1289, 1316, 1335-1336.

Fish and Coral of the Rosario Islands — A609

2003, Jan. 16   *Litho.*   *Perf. 12*
1207 A609 1000p multi   3.25   .85

Hapalopsittaca Fuertesi — A610

2003, June 13
1208 A610 1000p multi   3.25   .85

Souvenir Sheets

Orchids — A611

No. 1209 — 2400p: a, Masdevallia ignea. b, Miltoniopsis vexillaria, horiz.
No. 1210 — 2800p: a, Odontoglossum crispum, horiz. b, Masdevallia macrura.
No. 1211 — 5000p: a, Cimbidium. b, Oncidium obryzatum.
No. 1212 — 7000p: a, Cattleya dowiana. b, Cattleya trianaei (49x49mm).

Perf. 14¼, 13¾x14 (#1212b)
2003, June 13
Sheets of 2, #a-b
1209-1212 A611   Set of 4   50.00   50.00

Tejo, National Sport A612

No. 1213: a, Players, tree in foreground (49x39mm). b, Players, light poles (49x39mm). c, Cacique Turmeque.

2003, July 25   *Perf. 12*
1213   Horiz. strip of 3   10.00   10.00
a.-c.   A612 2400p Any single   2.25   1.40

America Issue — A613

Flora and fauna: a, Denomination at UR. b, Denomination at LR.

2003, Oct. 9   *Litho.*   *Perf. 12*
1214 A613 1600p Vert. pair, #a-b 5.00 5.00

Printed in sheets of four pairs and four labels.

Souvenir Sheet

Colombia Libraries National Reading Plan — A614

No. 1215: a, 1200p, Building. b, 4100p, Building, diff.

2003, Oct. 30   Litho.   Perf. 12
1215 A614   Sheet of 2, #a-b   8.00 8.00

General Ramón Arturo Rincón Quiñones (1922-75) — A615

2003, Oct. 31
1216 A615 1000p multi   1.75 .50

Souvenir Sheet

Administrative Security Deparment, 50th Anniv. — A616

2003, Oct. 31
1217 A616 4100p multi   6.00 6.00

Armed Forces A617

No. 1218 — Arms and mottos (#a-d): a, General Command of Military Forces. b, National Army. c, National Navy. d, Air Force. e, Colombian Forces in Korea, 50th anniv.

2003, Nov. 7
1218   Vert. strip of 5   8.00 8.00
a.-e. A617 1200p Any single   1.10 .60

Christmas — A618

No. 1219: a, Good Shepherd, sheep. b, Tree, comet, airplane, rabbit. c, Rabbits, dog. d, Automobile, angel, reindeer, horse. e, Sheep, woman with basket, swan, house. f, Branch with leaves, horse and rider, duck, Indian with bow and arrow.

2003, Dec. 2   Litho.   Perf. 12
1219   Block of 6   9.00 9.00
a.-f. A618 1000p Any single   1.10 .65

Colombia and the Eldorado Legend — A619

No. 1220: a, Print of Eldorado ceremony, by Teodoro De Bry, 1595. b, Watercolor painting of Lake Guatavita, by M. María Paz, 1855. c, Watercolor painting of Lake Guatavita, by Gonzalo Ariza, 1984. d, Print of Lake Guatavita, by A. Humboldt Thibault and F. Schoell, 1813. e, Print of Lake Guatavita, by Fernando Urbina Rangel, 1983. f, Print of Lake Guatavita, by Eustacio Barreto, 1883.
No. 1221 — Muisca raft: a, 1700p, Front. b, 2000p, Back, vert.

2004, Mar. 10
1220 A619 2800p Sheet of 6, #a-f, + 3 labels   13.00 13.00

Souvenir Sheet
1221 A619   Sheet of 2, #a-b   3.00 3.00

Locomotives — A620

No. 1222, 1100p: a, 2-8-2. b, 4-8-0.
No. 1223, 1300p: a, 2-6-2. b, 4-6-2.
Illustration reduced.

2004, Mar. 19
Horiz. Pairs, #a-b
1222-1223 A620   Set of 2   13.50 13.50
Nos. 1222-1223 each printed in sheets of four pairs and two pairs of labels.

Departments Type of 2003

No. 1224, 1100p — Nariño Department: a, Galeras Volcano, San Juan de Pasto, horiz. b, Statue of Gen. Antonio Nariño. c, Nariño Government Building, San Juan de Pasto, horiz. d, Farm, Catambuco, horiz. e, Nuestra Señora de las Lajas Sanctuary, Ipiales. f, Sandoná city center, horiz. g, Gallery of Mirrors, horiz. h, Barnizadores de Pasto Chorography Commission. i, Golden palms, horiz. j, El Morro, Tumaco, horiz. k, Virgen de la Playa Sanctuary, San Pablo. l, Festival of Whites and Blacks, horiz.
No. 1225, 2000p — Tolima Department: a, Nevado del Tolima, horiz. b, Tolima arms. c, Ambalema, horiz. d, Bowls, La Chamba, horiz. e, Natural Bridge, Icononzo. f, Hermitage, Mariquita, horiz. g, Matachos, horiz. h, Prison, Ibagué. i, Alberto Castilla Conservatory Room, horiz. j, Fishermen, Magdalena River, horiz. k, Cacique Calarcá. l, Tolima Art Museum, Ibagué.
No. 1226, 3000p — Chocó Department: a, Coat of Arms. b, Quibdó skyline, horiz. c, Indian girls. d, San Pacho Fiesta. e, Carrasquilla College, Quibdó, horiz. f, Houses, Nóvita. g, Canoe on San Juan River. h, Women grinding corn meal, horiz. i, Nuestra Senora del Rosario Church, Condoto. j, Utría Bay. k, Bellavista Church, Bojayá, horiz. l, Goldsmith, Acandí.
Horiz. stamps are 46x37mm.

2004   Litho.   Perf. 13¾x14
Sheets of 12, #a-l, +8 labels
1224 A608   Nariño   10.50 10.50
1225 A608   Tolima   18.00 18.00
1226 A608   Chocó   30.00 30.00
    Nos. 1224-1226 (3)   58.50 58.50

Issued: No. 1224, 8/5; No. 1225, 4/16. No. 1226, 11/17.

Maloka Science and Technology Center A621

2004, July 6   Litho.   Perf. 12¾
1227 A621 1100p multi   1.25 1.25
Values are for stamps with surrounding selvage.

2004 Summer Olympics, Athens — A622

2004, Aug. 5   Perf. 13¾x14
1228 A622 4400p multi   3.75 3.75

Natl. Association of Contractors, 60th Anniv. A623

No. 1229: a, Denomination in white. b, Denomination in black.

2004, Aug. 5   Perf. 14x13¾
a.-b. A623 2800p Either single   2.25 2.25
Printed in sheets containing 6 pairs and one large central label.

FIFA (Fédération Internationale de Football Association), Cent. — A624

2004, Aug. 25   Perf. 13¼x14
1230 A624 3500p multi   3.00 3.00

Women's Citizenship, 50th Anniv. — A625

2004, Sept. 24   Perf. 14
1231 A625 15,000p multi   13.00 13.00

Fair and Expositions Corporation, 50th Anniv. — A626

2004, Oct. 14   Perf. 13½x13
1232 A626 1300p multi   1.25 1.25

Colombian Radio Announcers Association, 50th Anniv. — A627

2004, Oct. 21   Perf. 14
1233 A627 1700p multi   1.60 1.60

17th National Games — A628

Illustration reduced.

2004, Dec. 10   Litho.   Perf. 12¾
1234 A628 7000p multi + label   6.25 6.25
Printed in sheets of 4 + 5 labels.

America Issue — Environmental Conservation — A629

Designs: No. 1235, 5000p, Whale, Gorgona National Nature Park. No. 1236, 5000p, Hammerhead sharks, Malpelo Flora and Fauna Sanctuary.

2004, Dec. 14   Perf. 14
1235-1236 A629   Set of 2   9.00 9.00

Miniature Sheet

Christmas — A630

No. 1237 — Inscriptions: a, Jesús en la mansion de su padre. b, Eterna sumision a Dios. c, Jesús desciende al seno de su madre. d, Aceptacion de milagro divino. e, La ilusion de Maria. f, Voluntad divina en manos del emperador. g, Paciencia, expectativa y anhelo. h, Belén: Humilde hospedaje. i, Nacimiento, la faz de Dios encarnado.

2004, Dec. 15
1237 A630 2800p Sheet of 9, #a-i   22.00 22.00

Pre-Columbian Gold Artifacts From Gold Museum — A631

No. 1238, 1200p: a, Tumaco ear covering. b, Zenú nose ring.
No. 1239, 1800p: a, Cauma nose ring. b, Tierradentro bracelet.
Illustration reduced.

2005, Jan. 21   Perf. 12x12½
        Pairs, #a-b
1238-1239 A631 Set of 2   5.25 5.25
Issued: No. 1238, 1/21; No. 1239, 3/28.

Rotary International, Cent. — A632

2005, Feb. 23   Perf. 13½x14
1240 A632 3100p multi   2.75 2.75

Souvenir Sheet

Butterflies — A633

No. 1241: a, Protographium tyastes panamensis. b, Dismorphia zaela laura. c, Actinote ozomene.

2005, June 7   Litho.   Perf. 14¼
1241 A633 4600p Sheet of 3, #a-c   13.00 13.00

FENALCO (Natl. Federation of Retailers), 60th Anniv. A634

2005, June 10   Perf. 14
1242 A634 1200p multi   1.10 1.10

Souvenir Sheets

Department Centenaries — A635

No. 1243, 3100p: a, Map of Caldas Department. b, Map of Colombia highlighting Caldas.
No. 1244, 3700p: a, Map of Huila Department. b, Map of Colombia highlighting Huila.
No. 1245, 4200p: a, Map of Atlantico Department. b, Map of Colombia highlighting Atlantico.

2005, June   Perf. 14x13½
        Sheets of 2, #a-b
1243-1245 A635 Set of 3   21.00 21.00

Departments Type of 2003

No. 1246 — San Andrés y Providencia Department: a, Aerial view of San Andrés, horiz. b, Arms. c, Aerial view of Johnny Cay, horiz. d, Cayo Cangrejo, horiz. e, Artisan. f, Culture House, San Andrés, horiz. g, Morgan Head, Santa Catalina Island, horiz. h, Island view. i, Ensenada, San Andrés, horiz. j, Island architecture, horiz. k, Baptist Church, San Andrés. l, Aerial view of Providencia and Santa Catalina Islands.
Horiz. stamps are 46x37mm.

2005, July 20   Perf. 13¾x14
1246 A608 1200p Sheet of 12, #a-l   13.00 13.00

Bogota Botanical Gardens — A636

2005, Aug. 5   Perf. 14
1247 A636 1400p multi   1.25 1.25

15th Bolivarian Games — A637

2005, Aug. 11   Perf. 13¾x14
1248 A637 3500p multi   3.25 3.25

Association of Graduates of the University of the Andes, 50th Anniv. A638

2005, Sept. 14   Perf. 14
1249 A638 2000p multi   1.75 1.75

Intl. Day of Ozone Layer Protection A639

2005, Sept. 16
1250 A639 2000p multi   1.75 1.75

Souvenir Sheet

Publication of Don Quixote, 400th Anniv. — A640

No. 1251 — Paintings of Miguel de Cervantes by: a, Ricardo Rendón Bravo. b, Eduardo Ramírez Villamizar, vert. c, Santiago Martínez Delgado, vert.

Perf. 13½x14 (#1251a), 14x13½
2005, Oct. 25
1251 A640 1300p Sheet of 3, #a-c   3.50 3.50

Colpatria Bank, 50th Anniv. A641

2005, Nov. 2   Perf. 14x13½
1252 A641 1200p multi   1.10 1.10

Arms of City of Facatativá A642

2005, Oct. 30   Litho.   Perf. 14
1253 A642 1800p multi   1.75 1.75

Latin Union, 50th Anniv. — A643

2005, Dec. 1   Perf. 13½x14
1254 A643 5000p multi   4.75 4.75
    Printed in sheets of 4.

Souvenir Sheet

America Issue, Fight Against Poverty — A644

2005, Nov. 30   Perf. 14x13½
1255 A644   Sheet of 2 #1255a   9.50 9.50
a.   5000p Single stamp   4.75 4.75

Souvenir Sheet

Escuela de Lanceros (Military School), 50th Anniv. — A645

2005, Nov. 30   Perf. 14
1256 A645   Sheet of 2 #1256a   19.00 19.00
a.   10,000p Single stamp   9.50 9.50

Christmas A646

2005, Dec. 9   Perf. 14
1257 A646 3100p multi   3.00 3.00
    Printed in sheets of 7.

Colombian Journalism A647

2006, Feb. 9   Litho.
1258 A647 2000p multi   1.90 1.90

St. Francis Xavier (1506-52) A648

2006, Apr. 7
1259 A648 4500p multi   3.75 3.75

Pope John Paul II (1920-2005) A649

2006, Apr. 4
1260 A649 4800p multi   3.75 3.75

Souvenir Sheet

Frederic Chopin (1810-49), Composer A650

2006, May 25   *Perf. 13½x13*
1261 A650 5300p multi   5.00 5.00

Printed in sheets of 4.

Gold Artifacts Type of 2005

No. 1262: a, Quimbaya striated lime receptacle with handles. b, Quimbaya thin lime receptacle.

2006, Jan. 26   *Perf. 12x12½*
1262 A631 1500p Pair, #a-b   2.50 2.50

Italian Cultural Institute of Bogota, 50th Anniv. — A651

No. 1263: a, Lute at lower left. b, Violin at lower right.
Illustration reduced.

2006, Feb. 23   *Perf. 14*
1263 A651 1300p Horiz. pair, #a-b   2.25 2.25

Souvenir Sheet

Rayo Museum, 25th Anniv. — A652

No. 1264: a, Artwork in blue, white, red, yellow and black. b, Artwork in white, blue, tan and black.

2006, Jan. 21   *Perf. 13½x13*
1264 A652   Sheet, 2 each #a-b   4.50 4.50
  a.-b.   1300p Either single   1.10 1.10

Departments Type of 2003

No. 1265 — Valle del Cauca Department: a, Mapping Commission drawing of Cali, horiz. b, Arms of Valle del Cauca. c, Arms and panoramic view of Sevilla, horiz. d, Calima Lake, El Darién, horiz. e, La Ermita, Santiago de Cali. f, Port of Buenaventura, horiz. g, Railroad station, Palmira, horiz. h, Sugar cane. i, Salsa dancers, Cali, horiz. j, El Paraiso Museum, El Cerrito, horiz. k, Basilica, Buga. l, Aerial view of Valle del Cauca, horiz.
No. 1266 — Boyacá Department: a, Plaza de Bolivar, Tunja, horiz. b, Arms of Boyacá. c, Mapping Commission drawing of Campo de Boyacá, horiz. d, Bolivar Monument, Campo de Boyacá, horiz. e, Altar of the Virgin of Chiquinquirá. f, Panoramic view of Garagoa, horiz. g, Plaza de los Libertadores, Duitama, horiz. h, Emeralds. i, Plaza Mayor, Villa de Leyva, horiz. j, Sierra Nevada del Cocuy, horiz. k, Temple of the Sun, Sogamoso. l, El Salitre Farm, Paipa, horiz.
No. 1267 — Quindío Department: a, Quindío Pass, 1836, horiz. b, Quimbaya culture sculpture. c, Coffee plantation house, Quimbaya, horiz. d, Coffee bean picker, Pijao, horiz. e, Valle de Cocora, Salento. f, Botanical Gardens, Calarca, horiz. g, La Estación Metropolitan Cultural Center, Armenia, horiz. h, Monument and government building, Armenia. i, Free Cemetery, Circasia, horiz. j, Aerial view of Buenavista, horiz. k, San José Temple, Génova. l, Founding of Armenia, horiz.
Horizontal stamps are 46x37mm.

2006   *Perf. 13½x14*
Sheets of 12, #a-l, + 8 labels
1265 A608 1300p Valle del
       Cauca   13.00 13.00
1266 A608 2000p Boyacá   20.00 20.00
1267 A608 3300p Quindío   32.50 32.50
  Nos. 1265-1267 (3)   65.50 65.50

20th Central American and Caribbean Games A653

2006, July 15   *Litho.*   *Perf. 14*
1268 A653 2000p multi   1.75 1.75

Pres. Alberto Lleras Camargo (1906-90) — A654

Denominations: a, 1300p. b, 3300p.
Illustration reduced.

2006, Dec. 6   *Litho.*   *Perf. 14x13¾*
1269 A654   Horiz. pair, #a-b +
      alternating labels   4.25 4.25

Souvenir Sheet

America Issue, Energy Conservation — A655

No. 1270: a, Left hand. b, Right hand.

2006, Dec. 28   *Perf. 12*
1270 A655 5000p Sheet of 2, #a-
      b   9.50 9.50

Christmas — A656

Denominations: a, 1300p. b, 3300p.

2006, Dec. 13   *Perf. 13¾x14*
1271 A656   Vert. pair, #a-b   4.25 4.25

General José Maria Cordova Military School, Cent. — A657

2007, May 30   *Perf. 14*
1272 A657 10,000p multi   11.00 11.00

Departments Type of 2003

No. 1273 — Sucre Department: a, Coat of arms. b, St. Francis of Assisi Cathedral, Sincelejo, horiz. c, Palm trees, Tolú. d, Cattle, Sucre. e, Bull ring, Sincelejo, horiz. f, Church, Corozal. g, Musical score of "Fiesta en Corraleja." h, Painting of fandango dancers, horiz. i, Fisherman, Caimito. j, Palm trees, Sincelejo. k, Cane weaver, Sampués, horiz. l, Hammocks, Morroa.
Horizontal stamps are 46x37mm.

2007, May 30   *Perf. 12*
Sheet of 12, #a-l, + 8 Labels
1273 A608 3300p Sucre   42.50 42.50

Miniature Sheet

Scouting, Cent. — A658

No. 1274: a, International and Colombian Scouting emblems, Scouts with Lord Robert Baden-Powell. b, Emblem of 21st World Scout Jamboree, Colombian Scouting emblem, children's drawing of Colombian scout. c, Scouting emblem, Lord Robert Baden-Powell. d, International and Colombian Scouting emblems, animal track.

2007, June 26   *Perf. 14*
1274 A658 1500p Sheet of 8,
      2 each #a-
      d, + central
      label   12.50 12.50

Souvenir Sheet

El Espectador Newspaper, 120th Anniv. — A659

No. 1275: a, Newspaper from 1887. b, Paperboy, horiz.

2007, June 28   *Perf. 12*
1275 A659 4500p Sheet of 2, #a-
      b   9.25 9.25

Pan American Games, Rio de Janeiro — A660

2007, July 9   *Perf. 14*
1276 A660 3700p multi   3.75 3.75

Fourth Spanish Language Intl. Congress — A661

2007, June 25
1277 A661 5300p multi + label   5.25 5.25

Caja de Compensación Familiar, 50th Anniv. — A662

2007, Oct. 10   *Litho.*   *Perf. 14*
1278 A662 3500p multi   3.75 3.75

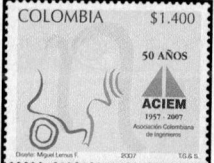

Colombian Association of Engineers, 50th Anniv. A663

2007, Oct. 17
1279 A663 1400p multi   1.40 1.40

Bogota Honors and Awards — A664

No. 1280: a, 2007 UNESCO World Book Capital. b, Venice Biennale Golden Lion Award

for Architecture. c, 2007 Latin American Cultural Capital.
Illustration reduced.

2007, Oct. 23
1280 A664 3700p Horiz. strip
of 3, #a-c   11.00 11.00

Minuto de
Dios, 50th
Anniv.
A665

2007, Nov. 22
1281 A665 1600p multi   1.60 1.60

Christmas
A666

2007, Nov. 27
1282 A666 3300p multi   3.25 3.25

America
Issue,
Education
For
All — A667

2007, Dec. 13
1283 A667 3500p multi   3.50 3.50

Pres. Carlos
Lleras Restrepo
(1908-94)
A668

2008, Apr. 8   Litho.   *Perf. 12*
1284 A668 1400p multi   1.60 1.60

Colombian
Friendship
With
Japan,
Cent.
A669

2008, May 22   *Perf. 14*
1285 A669 5200p multi   6.25 6.25

New Emblem of
Postal Network
of Colombia
A670

2008, May 28
1286 A670 2100p multi   2.50 2.50
Compare with Type A685.

National
Institute for
the Blind,
50th Anniv.
A671

Litho. & Embossed
2008, June 10
1287 A671 1400p multi   1.75 1.75

Departments Type of 2003

No. 1288 — Antioquia Department: a,
Medellín skyline, horiz. b, Arms of Antioquia.
c, Necoclí, horiz. d, Silleteros Parade, horiz. e,
Purse. f, Rafael Uribe Uribe Palace of Culture,
horiz. g, Molas, horiz. h, Lipaugus weberi. i,
Waterfall, Támesis, horiz. j, Coffee cups, horiz.
k, Santa Fé de Antioquia Church. l, Orquide-
orama, Medellín Botanical Gardens, horiz.

No. 1289 — Amazonas Department: a,
Departmental emblem. b, Monkey, Isla de los
Micos, horiz. c, Victoria Regia water lily. d,
Butterfly, Puerto Nariño. e, Indigenous child,
horiz. f, Caiman. g, Beaded mask. h, Dolphin,
horiz. i, Amazonas landscape. j, Flower. k,
Fisherman casting net, horiz. l, Fruits at Plaza
de Mercado, Puerto Leticia.
Horizontal stamps are 50x40mm.

2008   Litho.   *Perf. 13¾x14*
Sheets of 12, #a-l, + 8 labels
1288 A608 1500p Antioquia   15.00 15.00
                     Perf. 12
1289 A608 1600p Amazonas   22.00 22.00
Issued: No. 1288, 10/22; No. 1289, 7/18.

Battle of Maracaibo Lake, 185th
Anniv. — A672

2008, July 30   *Perf. 12*
1290 A672 3900p multi   4.50 4.50

Treaty of Amity
and Commerce
Between
Colombia and
Switzerland,
Cent. — A673

2008, July 31   *Perf. 14*
1291 A673 5200p multi   6.00 6.00

2008 Summer
Olympics,
Beijing — A674

2008, Aug. 1
1292 A674   5000p multi   5.75 5.75
Souvenir Sheet
1293 A674 10,000p multi   11.50 11.50

Aguadas,
Bicent. — A675

2008, Aug. 15
1294 A675 3500p multi   3.75 3.75

Accordion
Festival,
Villanueva
A676

2008, Sept. 25
1295 A676 5600p multi   5.25 5.25

Pres. Alfonso
López Michelsen
(1913-2007)
A677

2008, Oct. 8
1296 A677 5100p multi   4.50 4.50

Miniature Sheet

Ministry of Communications, 85th
Anniv. — A678

No. 1297 — Arms of Colombia and: a, Stylized person, emblem for Government Online
program. b, Children, emblem for Computers
for Education progam, vert. c, Girl with "@"
balloon, campaign for clean Internet. d,
Emblem for Compartel, vert.

2008, Oct. 29
1297 A678 1500p Sheet of 4,
#a-d   5.00 5.00

Episcopal
Conference of
Colombia,
Cent. — A679

2008, Nov. 6
1298 A679 1500p multi   1.40 1.40

18th
Carlos
Lleras
Restrepo
National
Games
A680

2008, Nov. 21
1299 A680 1500p multi   1.40 1.40

Natl.
Department
of Planning,
50th Anniv.
A681

2008, Dec. 9
1300 A681 1500p multi   1.40 1.40

Christmas
A682

Adoration of the Shepherds, by Gregorio
Vásquez de Arce y Ceballos: a, 1400p. b,
3500p.

2008, Dec. 12
1301 A682   Vert. pair, #a-b   4.50 4.50

Miniature Sheet

Luis Angel Arango Library, 50th
Anniv. — A683

No. 1302 — Open book with: a, Ship page
and "B." b, Sun page and "L." c, Dove page
and "a." d, Face page and "A."

2008, Dec. 16   *Perf. 13¾x14*
1302 A683 1300p Sheet of 4, #a-
d   4.75 4.75

America Issue, National
Festivals — A684

Paintings: No. 1303, 1400p, November 11, 1811, Absolute Independence of Cartagena, by Cecilia Porras. No. 1304, 1400p, Liberty Indian, by unknown artist, vert.

2008, Dec. 29   **Perf. 13¾x14, 14x13¾**
1303-1304 A684   Set of 2   2.50 2.50

4-72 Colombia Postal Network Emblem — A685

Designs: 200p, Emblem on blue background with red frame. 400p, Emblem against blue background, and three arrows against red, blue and yellow backgrounds. 500p, Emblem against white background with blue frame. 600p, Emblem and map of Colombia.

2009, Mar. 1   **Litho.**   **Perf. 14**
1305-1308 A685   Set of 4   1.40 1.40

Souvenir Sheet

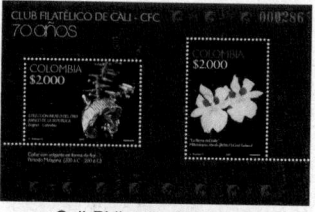

Cali Philatelic Club, 70th Anniv. — A686

No. 1309: a, Necklace with flower-shaped pendant. b, Miltoniopsis roezlii, vert.

2009, Mar. 12   **Perf. 12**
1309 A686 2000p Sheet of 2, #a-b   3.50 3.50

Inter-America Development Bank, 50th Anniv. — A687

2009, Mar. 27
1310 A687 3700p multi   3.25 3.25

President Julio César Turbay (1916-2005) — A688

2009, Apr. 1   **Perf. 14x13½**
1311 A688 1700p multi   1.40 1.40
Printed in sheets of 9 + 6 labels.

Naval School for Non-Commissioned Officers, Barranquilla, 75th Anniv. — A689

2009, Apr. 17   **Perf. 14**
1312 A689 4000p multi   3.50 3.50

Colombian War School, Cent. A690

2009, May 8   **Perf. 12**
1313 A690 5500p multi   5.50 5.50

President Guillermo León Valencia (1909-71) A691

2009, May 27
1314 A691 4200p multi   4.25 4.25

Fight of July 20, 1810, by Julián Rubiano Chávez A692

2009, June 25   **Perf. 12**
1315 A692 1700p multi   1.75 1.75

Departments Type of 2003
Miniature Sheet

No. 1316 — La Guajira Department: a, Arms of La Guajira. b, Francisco el Hombre, mural in La Guajira Cultural Center, horiz. c, Waterfall, Montes de Oca. d, Phoenicopterus ruber. e, Domingueka, Kogui village, horiz. f, Cape of La Vela. g, Majayuts (Wayuu women). h, Riohacha Cathedral, horiz. i, Cardinalis phoeniceus. j, Aloe vulgaris. k, Caesalpinia coriaria, horiz. l, Wayuu mochilas (bags). Horizontal stamps are 50x40mm.

2009, July 24   **Litho.**   **Perf. 12**
Sheet of 12, #a-l, + 8 Labels
1316 A608 1700p La Guajira   21.00 21.00

Miniature Sheet

Heliconia Varieties — A693

No. 1317: a, Heliconia stricta. b, Heliconia rostrata. c, Heliconia wagneriana. d, Heliconia orthotricha. e, Heliconia psittacorum.

2009, Aug. 14   **Litho.**   **Perf. 12**
1317 A693 2000p Sheet of 5, #a-e, + 5 labels   10.00 10.00

Miniature Sheet

First Colombian Postage Stamps, 150th Anniv. — A694

No. 1318: a, Colombia #1. b, Colombia #6. c, Colombia #4. d, Colombia #3. e, Colombia #7. f, Map of Colombia and text on gray background.
10,000p, Like No. 1318f with blue background.

2009, Aug. 25   **Perf. 12**
1318 A694 4000p Sheet of 6, #a-f   24.00 24.00
Souvenir Sheet
1319 A694 10,000p multi   10.00 10.00

America Issue, Traditional Games — A695

No. 1320 — Chaza player: a, Bare-handed. b, Holding racquet.

2009, Oct. 13   **Litho.**   **Perf. 14**
1320 A695 5000p Horiz. pair, #a-b   10.00 10.00

Rafael Uribe Uribe (1859-1914), General — A696

2009, Oct. 20
1321 A696 1500p multi   1.50 1.50

Madrid Town Hall A697

2009, Nov. 13
1322 A697 10,000p multi   10.50 10.50
Madrid, Cundinamarca Department, 450th anniv.

Miniature Sheet

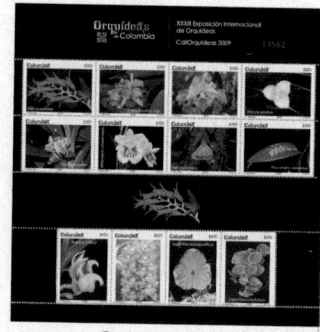

Orchids — A698

No. 1323: a, 500p, Ada aurantiaca (many flowers). b, 500p, Cattleya patinii cogn. c, 500p, Cattleya schroderae. d, 500p, Dracula amaliae. e, 500p, Huntleya gustavi. f, 500p, Miltoniopsis phalaenopsis. g, 500p, Ada aurantiaca (one flower). h, 500p, Pleurothallis casapensis. i, 600p, Anguloa cliftonii, vert. j, 600p, Cycnoche barthriorum, vert. k, 600p, Lepanthes telipogoniflora, vert. l, 600p, Lepanthes calodictyon, vert.

2009, Nov. 20
1323 A698   Sheet of 12, #a-l   6.50 6.50
33rd Intl. Orchid Exposition, Cali.

Miniature Sheet

Independence, Bicent. — A699

No. 1324: a, Bishop Andrés Rosillo y Meruelo (1758-1835). b, José Félix de Restrepo (1760-1832), statesman. c, Camilo Torres Tenorio (1766-1816), President of the Congress. d, Bishop Juan Fernández de Sotomayor (1777-1849). e, Antonio Villavicencio y Berástegui (1775-1816), President of the United Provinces of New Granada. f, Juan de Dios Morales (1767-1810), governmental minister and revolutionary. g, José María Carbonel (1778-1816), revolutionary agitator. h, Antonio Morales Galavís (1784-1852), military commander. i, José Ramón de Leyva (1747-1816), military commander. j, Nicolás Mauricio de Omaña, priest, lawyer.

2009, Nov. 24
1324 A699 6000p Sheet of 10, #a-j   60.00 60.00

Christmas
A700

2009, Nov. 27   *Perf. 12*
1325 A700 5000p multi   5.00 5.00

Souvenir Sheet

Campaign for a Mine-free
World — A701

2009, Dec. 3   *Perf. 14*
1326 A701 20,000p multi   20.00 20.00

Winning Designs in Stamp Design
Contest — A702

No. 1327: a, Abstract face, by Vito. b, Collage, by Caracha. c, People holding hands, by D. Bueno.

2009, Dec. 15
1327 A702 1800p Horiz. strip of
     3, #a-c   5.50 5.50

Miniature Sheet

Famous People — A703

No. 1328: a, Mercedes Abrego (1770-1813), spy. b, Gerardo Molina R. (1906-91), politician. c, Virginia Gutiérrez (1922-99), social anthropologist. d, María Mercedes Carranza (1945-2003), poet. e, Gonzalo Arango (1931-76), poet. f, Adolfo Mejía (1905-76), composer. g, General Benjamin Herrera (1853-1924). h, César Uribe Piedrahita (1896-1951), medical writer. i, Emilio Robledo (1875-1962), medical educator. j, Luis Duque Gómez (1916-2000), archaeologist. k, Enrique A. Becerra (1883-1954), jurist. l, Hugo Escobar Sierra (1927-2003), politician.

2010, Jan. 28   *Perf. 13½x14*
1328 A703 4000p Sheet of 12,
     #a-l   50.00 50.00

Presidents Type of 1981
Miniature Sheet

No. 1329 — Presidents, coup leaders and other leaders of Colombia: a, Virgilio Barco Vargas. b, Julio César Turbay Ayala. c, Alfonso López Michelsen. d, Misael Pastrana Borrero. e, Carlos Lemos Simmonds. f, Victor Mosquera Chaux. g, Indalecio Liévano Aguirre. h, Rafael Azuero Manchola. i, Gabriel París Gordillo. j, Deogracias Fonseca. k, Rafael Navas Pardo. l, Luis Ernesto Ordóñez. m, Diego Euclides de Angulo. n, Clímaco Calderón Reyes. o, Andrés Cerón Serrano. p, Ignacio Gutiérrez Vergara. q, Juan José Nieto Gil. r, Rufino Cuervo. s, Manuel Rodríguez Torices. t, José Joaquín Camacho.

2010, Jan. 28   *Perf. 14*
1329   Sheet of 20   40.00 40.00
   a.-t. A401 1900p Any single   2.00 2.00

Ninth South American Games,
Medellin — A704

2010, Feb. 18
1330 A704 5800p multi   6.00 6.00

Pope John Paul II
(1920-2005) — A705

2010, Feb. 19   *Perf. 13x13¼*
1331 A705 4400p multi   4.75 4.75

Miniature Sheet

Endangered Birds — A706

No. 1332: a, Crax alberti. b, Ognorhynchus icterotis. c, Hapalopsittaca fuertesi. d, Amazilia castaneiventris. e, Rallus semiplumbeus. f, Coeligena prunellei. g, Grallaria gigantea. h, Bangsia aureocincta. i, Hypopyrrhus pyrohypogaster.

2010, Apr. 6   *Perf. 13¼x13*
1332 A706 1900p Sheet of 9,
     #a-i   18.00 18.00

Souvenir Sheet

Expo 2010, Shanghai — A707

2010, May 7   *Perf. 13¾x14*
1333 A707 5000p multi   5.00 5.00

Miniature Sheet

Discovery of San Andrés, Providencia
and Santa Catalina Archipelago, 500th
Anniv. — A708

No. 1334: a, San Andrés Island. b, Providencia and Santa Catalina Islands. c, Quitasueño Keys. d, Bolivar Key. e, Roncador Keys. f, Bajo Nuevo Keys. g, Serranilla Keys. h, Serrana Keys. i, Alburquerque Keys.

2010, June 12   Litho.   *Perf. 14*
1334 A708 5900p Sheet of 9,
     #a-i, + 3 labels   57.50 57.50

Departments Type of 2003
No. 1335 — Guainía Department: a, Arms of Guainía. b, Princess Inírida Monument, horiz. c, Egretta alba. d, Cerro Mavicure. e, Canoe on Inírida River, horiz. f, Curripaco baskets. g, Guacamaya superba. h, Confluence of the Guaviare and Inírida Rivers, horiz. i, Remanso. j, Cualé Rapids. k, Children from Paujil, horiz. l, Coco Petroglyphs.
No. 1336 — Atlántico Department: a, Arms of Atlántico. b, Palacio de la Cultura, Barranquilla, horiz. c, Tubará rock paintings. d, Fluvicola pica. e, Julio Flórez Museum, Usiacurí, horiz. f, Tocagua Marsh, Luruaco. g, Bull's head carnival mask. h, San Antonio de Padua Church, Soledad, horiz. i, Tabebuya rosea. j, Iraca Palm handicrafts. k, Pier at Puerto Colombia, horiz. l, Customs House, Barranquilla.
Horiz. stamps are 50x40mm.

2010   *Perf. 12x12½*
Sheets of 12, #a-l, + 8 labels
1335 A608 600p Guainía   8.00 8.00
1336 A608 2000p Atlántico   26.00 26.00

Issued: No. 1335, 7/24; No. 1336, 6/15.

Gonzalo
Jiménez de
Quesada
Police
Academy
A709

2010, June 24   *Perf. 14*
1337 A709 2000p multi   2.10 2.10

Bambuco
National Pageant
and Folklore
Festival, Neiva,
50th
Anniv. — A710

2010, June 22   *Perf. 13¼x13*
1338 A710 4200p multi   4.50 4.50

Admiral
Padilla
Naval
Academy
A711

2010, July 3   *Perf. 14*
1339 A711 500p multi   .55 .55

Miniature Sheet

Norte de Santander Department,
Cent. — A712

No. 1340: a, Map of Norte de Santander Department. b, Government building. c, Estoraques Nature Area. d, Catatumbo River. e, Santa Ana de Ocaña Cathedral. f, Santa Clara de Pamplona Cathedral.

2010, July 14   Litho.
1340 A712 6000p Sheet of 6,
     #a-f   40.00 40.00

Teresa Pizarro de
Angulo (c. 1930-
2000), National
Beauty Pageant
Director — A713

2010, Aug. 3
1341 A713 5900p multi   6.50 6.50

SEMI-POSTAL STAMP

Catalogue values for unused stamps in this section are for Never Hinged items.

Girl Giving First
Aid — SP1

Perf. 13½x14

1966, Apr. 26   Litho.   Unwmk.
B1 SP1 5c + 5c multicolored   .25   .20
Issued for the Red Cross.

AIR POST STAMPS

No. 341 Overprinted

1919   Unwmk.   Perf. 14
C1 A107 2c car rose   3,500.   1,700.
  a. Numerals "1" with ser-
      ifs   7,250.   4,250.

Used for the first experimental flight from
Barranquilla to Puerto Colombia, 6/18/19.
Values are for faulty stamps.

Issued by Compania Colombiana de Navegacion Aerea

From 1920 to 1932 the internal airmail service of Colombia was handled
by the Compania Colombiana de Nave-
gacion Aerea (1920) and the Sociedad
Colombo-Alemana de Transportes Aér-
eos, known familiarly as "SCADTA"
(1920-1932).

These organizations, under government contracts, operated and maintained their own post offices and issued
stamps which were the only legal franking for airmail service during this period,
both in the internal and international
mails. All letters had to bear government stamps as well.

Woman and Boy Watching
Plane — AP1

Designs: No. C3, Clouds and small biplane
at top. No. C4, Tilted plane viewed close-up
from above. No. C5, Flier in plane watching
biplane. No. C6, Lighthouse. No. C7, Fuse-
lage and tail of biplane. No. C8, Condor on
cliff. No. C9, Plane at rest; pilot foreground.
No. C10, Ocean liner.

1920, Feb. Unwmk. Litho. Imperf.
Without Gum

C2   AP1 10c multi   3,000. 1,875.
C3   AP1 10c multi   3,800. 1,875.
C4   AP1 10c multi   4,600. 1,875.
C5   AP1 10c multi   3,500. 1,875.
C6   AP1 10c multi   3,000. 1,875.
C7   AP1 10c multi   11,000. 3,800.
C8   AP1 10c multi   6,000. 3,000.
C9   AP1 10c multi   3,500. 1,875.
C10 AP1 10c multi   4,600. 2,750.

Nos. C2-C10 were overprinted on the nine
lighter-colored varieties of a set of 18 publicity
labels produced by the Curtis Co. for inclusion
with packs of cigarettes. These labels were
printed setenant, in panes of 18 (3x6). Value
for the set of 18 values without overprint:
$4,000.

Flier in Plane Watching Biplane — AP2

1920, Mar.
C11 AP2 10c green   60.00   92.50

Four other 10c stamps, similar to No. C11,
have two designs showing plane, mountains
and water. They are printed in deep green or

---

light brown red. Some authorities state that
these four were not used regularly.

Issued by Sociedad Colombo-Alemana de Transportes Aereos (SCADTA)

Seaplane over Magdalena
River — AP3

1920-21   Litho.   Perf. 12
C12 AP3 10c yellow ('21)   60.00   47.50
C13 AP3 15c blue ('21)   65.00   52.50
C14 AP3 30c blk, rose   30.00   16.00
C15 AP3 30c rose ('21)   60.00   45.00
C16 AP3 50c pale green   60.00   47.50
  Nos. C12-C16 (5)   275.00 208.50

For surcharges see Nos. C17-C24, C36-C37.

No. C16 Handstamp Surcharged in
Violet or Black:

(Illustrations of types "a" to "e" are reduced
in size.)

VALOR 10 CENTAVOS
a

VALOR 10 CENTAVOS
b

Valor 10 Centavos
c

d

30¢   30¢
e

f

g

1921
C17 AP3 (a) 10c on 50c   1,250. 1,200.
C18 AP3 (b) 10c on 50c   1,250. 1,200.
C19 AP3 (c) 10c on 50c   1,250. 1,200.
C20 AP3 (b) 30c on 50c   925.   625.
C21 AP3 (d) 30c on 50c   925.   625.
C22 AP3 (e) 30c on 50c   1,850. 1,450.
C23 AP3 (f) 30c on 50c   1,850. 1,450.
C24 AP3 (g) 30c on 50c   1,850. 1,450.

Plane over
Magdalena
River — AP4

Plane over
Bogota
Cathedral
AP5

1921   Perf. 11½
C25 AP4   5c orange yellow   4.50   4.00
C26 AP4 10c slate green   2.10   1.50
C27 AP4 15c orange brown   2.10   1.60
C28 AP4 20c red brown   4.50   2.10
  a. Horiz. pair, imperf. vert. 210.00
C29 AP4 30c green   2.10   1.10
C30 AP4 50c blue   3.25   1.25
C31 AP4 60c vermilion   85.00   32.50
C32 AP5   1p gray black   22.50   5.00
C33 AP5   2p rose   42.50   20.00
C34 AP5   3p violet   125.00   72.50
C35 AP5   5p olive green   325.00 300.00
  Nos. C25-C35 (11)   618.55 441.55

Exist imperf.
For surcharge see No. C52.

Nos. C16 and C12 Handstamp
Surcharged
Illustration of type "h" is reduced in size.

VALOR 20 Ctvs.
h

30 cent.
i

1921-22   Perf. 12
C36 AP3 (h) 20c on 50c   3,750. 2,500.
C37 AP3 (i) 30c on 10c   850.   575.

Seaplane over
Magdalena
River — AP6

Plane over
Bogota
Cathedral
AP7

1923-28   Wmk. 116   Perf. 14x14½
C38 AP6   5c orange yellow   1.75   .25
C39 AP6 10c green   1.75   .25
C40 AP6 15c carmine   1.75   .25
C41 AP6 20c gray   1.75   .25
C42 AP6 30c blue   1.75   .25
C43 AP6 40c purple ('28)   12.50   8.00
C44 AP6 50c green   2.10   .25
C45 AP6 60c brown   3.25   .25
C46 AP6 80c olive grn ('28) 32.50   30.00
C47 AP7   1p black   14.50   3.25
C48 AP7   2p red orange   21.00   6.00
C49 AP7   3p violet   37.50   25.00
C50 AP7   5p olive green   67.50   32.50
  Nos. C38-C50 (13)   199.60 106.50

For surcharges and overprints see Nos.
C51, C53-C54, CF1.

Nos. C41 and C31 Surcharged in
Carmine and Dark Blue:

No. C51   No. C52

1923
C51 AP6 30c on 20c gray (C) 92.50   57.50
C52 AP4 30c on 60c ver   85.00   37.50

Nos. C41-C42
Overprinted in Black

1928   Wmk. 116   Perf. 14x14½
C53 AP6 20c gray   75.00   62.50
C54 AP6 30c blue   75.00   62.50

Goodwill flight of Lt. Benjamin Mendez from
New York to Bogota.

Magdalena   Columbus' Ship and
River and   Plane
Tolíma   AP9
Volcano
AP8

1929, June 1 Wmk. 127   Perf. 14
C55 AP8   5c yellow org   1.25   .20
C56 AP8 10c red brown   1.25   .20
C57 AP8 15c deep green   1.25   .20
C58 AP8 20c carmine   1.25   .20
C59 AP8 30c gray blue   1.25   .20
C60 AP8 40c dull violet   1.25   .25
C61 AP8 50c dk olive grn   2.50   .25
C62 AP8 60c orange brown   3.75   .25
C63 AP8 80c green   11.00   3.25
C64 AP9   1p blue   12.00   2.50
C65 AP9   2p brown orange   18.00   5.75
C66 AP9   3p pale rose vio   42.50   18.00
C67 AP9   5p olive green   100.00   37.50
  Nos. C55-C67 (13)   197.25   68.75

For surcharges and overprints see Nos.
C80-C95, CF2, CF4.

For International Airmail

AP10   AP11

1929, June 1   Wmk. 127   Perf. 14
C68 AP10   5c yellow org   6.25   7.25
C69 AP10 10c red brown   1.25   3.00
C70 AP10 15c deep green   1.25   3.00
C71 AP10 20c carmine   1.25   3.75
C72 AP10 25c violet blue   1.25   .85
C73 AP10 30c gray blue   1.25   .95
C74 AP10 50c dk olive grn   1.25   1.90
C75 AP10 60c brown   2.50   3.00
C76 AP11   1p blue   5.50   7.25
C77 AP11   2p red orange   8.50   10.00
C78 AP11   3p violet   100.00 100.00
C79 AP11   5p olive green   125.00 140.00
  Nos. C68-C79 (12)   255.25 280.95

This issue was sold abroad for use on correspondence to be flown from coastal to interior
points of Colombia. Cancellations are those of
the country of origin rather than Colombia.
For overprint see No. CF3.

Nos. C63, C66 and C64 Surcharged in
Black:

m

n

1930, Dec. 15
C80	AP8(m)	10c on 80c	7.25	7.25
C81	AP9(n)	20c on 3p	13.50	13.50
C82	AP9(n)	30c on 1p	17.00	13.50
	Nos. C80-C82 (3)		*37.75*	*34.25*

Simon Bolivar (1783-1830).

Colombian Government Issues
Nos. C55-C67 Overprinted in Black:

o

p

Wmk. 127

1932, Jan. 1   Typo.   Perf. 14
C83	AP8(o)	5c yellow org	10.00	10.00
C84	AP8(o)	10c red brown	2.25	.60
C85	AP8(o)	15c deep green	3.75	3.75
C86	AP8(o)	20c carmine	1.90	.35
C87	AP8(o)	30c gray blue	1.90	.60
C88	AP8(o)	40c dull violet	2.50	1.25
C89	AP8(o)	50c dk ol grn	5.00	3.75
C90	AP8(o)	60c orange brn	4.25	3.75
C91	AP8(o)	80c green	17.00	17.00
C92	AP9(p)	1p blue	14.50	12.00
C93	AP9(p)	2p brown org	37.50	35.00
C94	AP9(p)	3p pale rose vio	77.50	65.00
C95	AP9(p)	5p olive green	125.00	*140.00*
	Nos. C83-C95 (13)		303.05	293.05

Coffee
AP12

Gold
AP16

Designs: 10c, 50c, Cattle. 15c, 60c, Petroleum. 20c, 40c, Bananas. 3p, 5p, Emerald.

1932-39 Wmk. 127 Photo. Perf. 14
C96	AP12	5c org & blk brn	.90	.25
C97	AP12	10c lake & blk	1.00	.20
C98	AP12	15c bl grn & vio blk	.50	.20
C99	AP12	15c ver & vio blk ('39)	4.00	.25
C100	AP12	20c car & ol blk	.85	.20
C101	AP12	20c turq grn & ol blk ('39)	4.25	.35
C102	AP12	30c dk bl & blk brn	2.40	.20
C103	AP12	40c dk vio & ol bis	1.10	.20
C104	AP12	50c dk grn & brnsh blk	6.75	1.50
C105	AP12	60c brn & blk vio	1.40	.25
C106	AP12	80c grn & blk brn	9.50	2.00
C107	AP16	1p dk bl & ol bis	10.00	1.25
C108	AP16	2p org brn & ol bis	16.00	2.75
C109	AP16	3p dk vio & emer	26.00	7.25
C110	AP16	5p gray blk & emer	57.50	21.00
	Nos. C96-C110 (15)		142.15	37.85

For overprint see No. CF5.

Nos. C104, C106-C108 Surcharged:

a

b

1934, Jan. 5
C111	AP12(a)	10c on 50c	4.50	4.50
C112	AP12(a)	15c on 80c	6.25	6.25
C113	AP16(b)	20c on 1p	6.50	6.50
C114	AP16(b)	30c on 2p	7.25	7.25
	Nos. C111-C114 (4)		24.50	24.50

400th anniversary of Cartagena.

Nos. C100 and C103 Surcharged in Black or Carmine:

1939, Jan. 15
C115	AP12	5c on 20c (Bk)	.35	.35
C116	AP12	5c on 40c (C)	.35	.25
C117	AP12	15c on 20c (Bk)	1.50	.50
a.	Double surcharge		12.00	
b.	Pair, one with dbl. surch.		14.00	
c.	Inverted surcharge		12.00	12.00

No. CF5 Surcharged in Black
C118	AP12	5c on 20c	.70	.70
	Nos. C115-C118 (4)		2.90	1.80

Nos. C102-C103 Surcharged in Black or Red

1940, Oct. 20
C119	AP12	15c on 30c	1.25	.50
a.	Inverted surcharge		12.00	
C120	AP12	15c on 40c (R)	2.00	.75
a.	Double surcharge		12.00	

Pre-Columbian Monument — AP18

Proclamation of Independence — AP22

Designs: 10c, 40c, Symbol of Legend of El Dorado. 15c, 50c, Spanish Fortifications, Cartagena. 20c, 60c, Colonial Bogotá. 2p, 5p, National Library, Bogota.

Unwmk.

1941, Jan. 28   Engr.   Perf. 12
C121	AP18	5c gray black	.20	.20
C122	AP18	10c yellow org	.20	.20
C123	AP18	15c carmine rose	.20	.20
C124	AP18	20c yellow grn	.35	.20
a.	Horiz. pair, imperf. vert.		87.50	
C125	AP18	30c deep blue	.35	.20
C126	AP18	40c rose lake	.90	.20
C127	AP18	50c turq green	.90	.20
C128	AP18	60c sepia	.90	.20
C129	AP18	80c olive blk	2.40	.40

C130	AP22	1p blue & blk	4.00	.50
C131	AP22	2p red org & blk	6.50	2.00
C132	AP22	3p violet & blk	17.50	6.00
C133	AP22	5p lt green & blk	35.00	20.00
	Nos. C121-C133 (13)		69.40	30.50

See Nos. C151-C163, C217-C225. For overprints see Nos. C175-C198, C200-C216, C226, C290.

San Sebastian Fort, Cartagena — AP24

National Capitol, Bogotá AP27

Designs: 5c, 20c, 50c, San Sebastian Fort, Cartagena. 10c, 30c, 60c, Tequendama Waterfall. 15c, 40c, 80c, Bay of Santa Maria.

Unwmk.

1945, Nov. 3   Litho.   Perf. 11
C134	AP24	5c blue gray	.20	.20
C135	AP24	10c yellow org	.20	.20
C136	AP24	15c rose	.20	.20
C137	AP24	20c lt yel grn	.30	.20
C138	AP24	30c ultra	.30	.20
C139	AP24	40c claret	.50	.20
C140	AP24	50c bluish grn	.55	.20
C141	AP24	60c lt vio brn	2.25	.80
C142	AP24	80c dk slate grn	3.50	.80
C143	AP27	1p dk blue	5.00	.75
C144	AP27	2p red orange	7.00	2.50
	Nos. C134-C144 (11)		20.00	6.25

Part-perforate varieties exist for all denominations except 80c.

Imperf., Pairs
C134a	AP24	5c	8.50
C135a	AP24	10c	8.50
C136a	AP24	15c	8.50
C137a	AP24	20c	8.50
C138a	AP24	30c	8.50
C139a	AP24	40c	8.50
C140a	AP24	50c	8.50
C141a	AP24	60c	8.50
C142a	AP24	80c	10.50
C143a	AP27	1p	17.50
C144a	AP27	2p	60.00

Bello Type of Regular Issue, 1946
Wmk. 255

1946, Sept. 3   Engr.   Perf. 12
C145	A219	5c deep blue	.20	.20

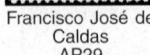

Francisco José de Caldas
AP29

Manuel del Socorro Rodriguez
AP30

Perf. 12½

1947, May 9   Litho.   Unwmk.
C146	AP29	5c dp bl, *grnsh*	.35	.20
C147	AP30	10c red org, *grnsh*	.50	.45

4th Pan-American Press Congress (1946).

Chancellery Patio — AP31

Capitol, Patio Rafael Nunez AP32

AP33

1948, Apr. 2   Engr.   Wmk. 229
C148	AP31	5c dark brown	.20	.20
C149	AP32	15c deep blue	.90	.90

Miniature Sheet
Imperf
C150	AP33	50c brown	1.90	1.90

9th Pan-American Conference, Bogotá.

Types of 1941

1948, July 21   Unwmk.   Perf. 12
C151	AP18	5c orange yel	.20	.20
C152	AP18	10c scarlet	.20	.20
C153	AP18	15c deep blue	.20	.20
C154	AP18	20c violet	.20	.20
C155	AP18	30c yellow grn	.35	.20
C156	AP18	40c gray	.40	.20
C157	AP18	50c rose lake	.40	.20
C158	AP18	60c olive gray	.70	.20
C159	AP18	80c red brn	.85	.20
C160	AP22	1p ol grn & vio brn	1.50	.30
C161	AP22	2p dp grn & brt bl	2.50	.65
C162	AP22	3p rose car & blk	5.50	3.75
C163	AP22	5p lt brn & turq grn	14.00	7.00
	Nos. C151-C163 (13)		27.00	13.50

"Air Week" 5c Blue
The War and Air Department issued a 5c blue stamp in May, 1949, to publicize Air Week (Semana de Aviacion). This stamp had no franking value and its use was optional during May 16-23.

Justice and Liberty
AP34

Wing
AP35

Design: 10c, Liberty holding tablet of laws.

1949, Oct. 7   Unwmk.   Perf. 13
C164	AP34	5c blue green	.20	.20
C165	AP34	10c orange	.20	.20

Issued to honor the new Constitution.

For Domestic Postage

1950, June 22 Litho. *Perf. 12*
C166	AP35	5c orange yellow	.25	.25
C167	AP35	10c brown red	.35	.30
C168	AP35	15c lt blue	.40	.30
C169	AP35	20c lt green	.60	.65
C170	AP35	30c lilac gray	1.50	2.00
C171	AP35	60c chocolate	1.90	2.50

With Network as in Parenthesis
C172	AP35	1p gray (buff)	14.00	16.00
C173	AP35	2p bl (pale grn)	14.00	16.00
C174	AP35	5p red brn (red brn)	40.00	45.00
Nos. C166-C174 (9)			73.00	83.00

No. C172 was issued both with and without network.

Nos. C151-C157 and C160-C163
Overprinted in Black

1950, July 18
C175	AP18	5c orange yel	.20	.20
C176	AP18	10c scarlet	.20	.20
C177	AP18	15c deep blue	.20	.20
C178	AP18	20c violet	.20	.20
C179	AP18	30c yellow green	.30	.20
C180	AP18	40c gray	.80	.25
C181	AP18	50c rose lake	.60	.25
C182	AP22	1p ol grn & vio brn	3.25	2.75
C183	AP22	2p dp grn & brt bl	6.00	5.50
C184	AP22	3p rose car & blk	11.00	11.00
C185	AP22	5p lt brn & turq grn	27.50	27.50
Nos. C175-C185 (11)			50.25	48.25

Nos. C151-C163
Overprinted in Black

1950, July 12
C186	AP18	5c orange yel	.20	.20
C187	AP18	10c scarlet	.20	.20
C188	AP18	15c deep blue	.20	.20
C189	AP18	20c violet	.20	.20
C190	AP18	30c yellow green	.20	.20
C191	AP18	40c gray	.45	.20
C192	AP18	50c rose lake	.45	.20
C193	AP18	60c olive gray	.70	.20
C194	AP18	80c red brown	1.00	.50
C195	AP22	1p ol grn & vio brn	1.25	.60
C196	AP22	2p dp grn & brt bl	3.50	2.40
C197	AP22	3p rose car & blk	8.00	7.25
C198	AP22	5p lt brn & turq grn	20.00	17.50
Nos. C186-C198 (13)			36.35	29.85

On Nos. C175-C198, "L" stands for LANSA, "A" for AVIANCA.

UPU Type
Miniature Sheet

Unwmk.

1950, Aug. 22 Photo. *Imperf.*
C199	A245	50c gray	2.00 2.00

75th anniv. (in 1949) of the UPU.

> Catalogue values for unused stamps in this section, from this point to the end of the section, are for Never Hinged items.

Types of 1941
Overprinted at Lower Right in Black

Unwmk.

1951, Sept. 15 Engr. *Perf. 12*
C200	AP18	40c orange yel	1.60	1.25
C201	AP18	50c ultra	2.10	1.40
C202	AP18	60c gray	1.60	1.25
C203	AP18	80c car rose	1.50	.95
C204	AP22	1p red org & red brn	6.00	5.00
C205	AP22	2p rose car & bl	7.25	6.00
C206	AP22	3p choc & emer	18.00	14.00
C207	AP22	5p org & gray	47.50	47.50
Nos. C200-C207 (8)			85.55	77.35

Types of 1941
Overprinted at Lower Right in Black

1951-54
C208	AP18	40c orange yel	5.50	.55
C209	AP18	50c ultra	6.00	.65
C210	AP18	60c gray	5.00	.55
a.		Overprint centered	5.00	.55
C211	AP18	80c car rose	1.00	.35
C212	AP22	1p red org & red brn	4.75	.50
C213	AP22	1p ol grn & vio brn ('54)	7.00	.95
C214	AP22	2p rose car & bl	4.75	.70
C215	AP22	3p choc & emer	8.75	2.10
C216	AP22	5p org & gray	15.00	2.25
Nos. C208-C216 (9)			57.75	8.60

All values except the 2p and 3p exist without overprint.

Types of 1941

1952, May 10 Engr.
C217	AP18	5c ultra	.50	.20
C218	AP18	10c ultra	.50	.25
C219	AP18	15c ultra	.50	.25
C220	AP18	20c ultra	.90	.40
C221	AP18	30c ultra	2.50	.80

Color Change
C222	AP18	5c car rose	.50	.20
C223	AP18	10c car rose	.50	.25
C224	AP18	20c car rose	.95	.25
C225	AP18	30c car rose	2.00	.50
Nos. C217-C225 (9)			8.85	3.10

Type of 1941
Surcharged in Blue

1952, Oct. 30
C226	AP18	70c on 80c car rose	1.75	.80

Latin American Siderurgical Conf., 1952.

Type of Postal Tax Stamps, 1948-50, Nos. 602 and 604 Surcharged or Overprinted in Black

1953 Wmk. 255 *Perf. 12*
C227	PT10	5c on 8c blue	.20	.20
C228	PT10	15c on 20c brown	.30	.20
C229	PT10	15c on 25c bl grn	1.60	.20
C230	PT10	25c blue green	.75	.20
Nos. C227-C230 (4)			2.85	.80

Many varieties of overprint or surcharge exist on Nos. C227-C231.

No. 570 Overprinted "AEREO" in Blue

1953, Aug. Wmk. 229 *Perf. 12½*
C231	A160	10c red	.25	.20

"Extra Rapido"
Stamps inscribed "Extra Rapido" are for use on domestic airmail carried by airlines other than AVIANCA.

No. 585 Surcharged and Overprinted "Extra Rapido" in Dark Blue

1953 Unwmk. *Perf. 13*
C232	A244	5c on 11c red	.50	.35

Capitol and Arms — AP37

Revenue Stamps Overprinted "Correo Extra-Rapido"
Gray Security Paper

1953 Wmk. 255 Engr. *Perf. 12*
C233	AP37	1c on 2c green	.25	.20
C234	AP37	50c red orange	.25	.20

AP38

Real Estate Tax Stamps Ovptd. "Correo Extra-Rapido" in Black or Carmine

1953
C235	AP38	5c red orange	.25	.20
C236	AP38	20c brown (C)	.30	.20

On 20c, overprint is at bottom of stamp and two lines of ornaments cover real estate tax inscription at top.

Castillo y Rada and Map — AP39

Real Estate Tax Stamp Surcharged "Correo Aereo, II Exposicion Filatelica Nacional, Bogota Dicbre 1953, 15 Centavos"

1953, Dec. 12 Engr. & Litho.
C237	AP39	15c on 10p multi	.50	.35

2nd Natl. Philatelic Exhib., Bogota, Dec. 1953.

No. RA45 Overprinted in Black

1953
C238	PT10	10c purple	.25	.20

Galeras Volcano — AP40

Retreat of San Diego — AP41

Designs: No. C241, Las Lajas Shrine, Narino. No. C242, 50c, Bolivar monument. 20c, 80c, Ruiz mountain, Manizales. 40c, George Isaacs monument, Cali. 60c, Monkey Fountain, Tunja. 1p, Stadium, Medellin. 2p, Pastelillo Fort, Cartagena. 3p, Santo Domingo University gate. 5p, Las Lajas Shrine. 10p, Map of Colombia.

Perf. 13½x13, 13
1954, Jan. 15 Engr. Unwmk.
C239	AP40	5c dp red vio	.20	.20
C240	AP41	10c black	.20	.20
C241	AP40	15c red orange	.20	.20
C242	AP40	15c car rose	.20	.20
C243	AP40	20c brown	.20	.20
C244	AP40	30c brown org	.25	.20
C245	AP40	40c blue	.25	.20
C246	AP40	50c dk violet brn	.35	.20
C247	AP40	60c dk brown	.40	.20
C248	AP40	80c red brown	.55	.20

Size: 37x27mm
Center in Black
C249	AP41	1p deep blue	3.25	.25
C250	AP41	2p dark green	4.75	.40
C251	AP41	3p carmine rose	11.00	1.40

Size: 38x32mm, 32x38mm
C252	AP41	5p dk grn & red brn	14.50	3.50
C253	AP40	10p gray grn & red org	7.00	7.50
Nos. C239-C253 (15)			56.30	15.05

See Nos. C307-C308. For surcharges and overprints see Nos. 691, C321, C325, C330, C333-C334, C343-C346.

Condor Carrying Shield
AP42

Inscribed: "Correo Extra-Rapido"
1954, Apr. 23 Litho. *Perf. 12½*
C254	AP42	5c lilac rose	.95	.40

For overprint see No. RA53.

Soldier-Map-Arms Type
1954, June 13 Engr. *Perf. 13*
C255	A259	15c carmine	.40	.20

See No. C271a.

Games Type
Design: 20c, Stadium and Athlete holding arms of Colombia.

1954, July 18
C256	A260	15c chocolate	.70	.20
C257	A260	20c deep blue green	1.60	.35

Church of St. Peter Claver, Cartagena
AP45

1954, Sept. 9
C258	AP45 15c brown	1.25	.20
a.	Souvenir sheet	8.00	12.00

St. Peter Claver, 300th death anniv.
No. C258a contains one stamp similar to No. C258, but printed in red brown.

Mercury Type

1954, Oct. 29
C259	A263 15c deep blue	.55	.25

Inscribed "Extra Rapido"
C260	A263 50c scarlet	.55	.25

Archbishop Manuel José Mosquera, Death Cent. — AP47

Inscribed: "Correo Extra Rapido"

1954, Nov. 17
C261	AP47 2c yellow green	.25	.20

Virgin of Chiquinquira — AP48

Inscribed: "Correo Extra Rapido"

1954, Dec. 4   Engr. & Litho.
C262	AP48 5c org brn & multi	.25	.20

See No. C291. For overprint see No. 686.

College Types

Designs: 20c, Brother Cristobal de Torres. 50c, College chapel and arms.

Perf. 12½x11½, 11½x12½

1954, Dec. 6   Engr.   Unwmk.
C263	A264 15c orange & blk	.50	.20
C264	A264 20c ultra	.85	.20
C265	A265 25c dark brown	.85	.20
C266	A265 50c black & car	2.25	.80
a.	Souvenir sheet	12.00	16.00
	Nos. C263-C266 (4)	4.45	1.40

No. C266a contains four stamps similar to Nos. C263-C266, but printed in different colors: 15c red and black, 20c pale purple, 25c brown, 50c black and olive green.

Steel Mill Type

1954, Dec. 12   Perf. 12½x13
C267	A266 20c green & blk	1.75	.60

Marti Type

1955, Jan. 28   Perf. 13½x13
C268	A267 15c deep green	.30	.20

Korean Veterans Type

1955, Mar. 23   Perf. 12½
C269	A268 20c dark green	.55	.20

Merchant Fleet Types

1955, Apr. 12   Perf. 12½
C270	A269 25c black	.40	.20
C271	A270 50c dark green	.90	.35
a.	Souvenir sheet	9.50	12.00

No. C271a contains 4 stamps similar to Nos. C255, C269-C271, but printed in different colors; 15c lilac red, 20c olive, 25c bluish black, 50c bluish green.

Marco Fidel Suarez (1855-1927), Pres. 1918-21 — AP56

Inscribed: "Correo Extra Rapido"

1955, April 23   Perf. 13
C272	AP56 10c deep blue	.25	.20

Hotel-Church Type

1955, May 16   Photo.   Perf. 11½x12
C273	A271 15c rose brown	.40	.20

Rotary Type
Unwmk.

1955, Oct. 17   Engr.   Perf. 13
C274	A272 15c dk carmine rose	.40	.20

Atahualpa, Tisquesuza and Montezuma AP59

Ferdinand the Catholic and Queen Isabella I AP60

Designs: 15c, O'Higgins, Santander and Sucre. 20c, Marti, Hidalgo and Petion. 1p, Artigas, Solano Lopez and Murillo. 2p, Abdon Calderon, Baron de Rio Branco and José de La Mar.

1955, Oct. 12   Engr. & Photo.
Inscribed: "Extra Rapido"
C275	AP59 2c dull brn & blk	.25	.20
C276	AP60 5c dk brn & yel	.25	.20

Regular Air Post
C277	AP59 15c rose car & blk	.55	.25
C278	AP59 20c pale brn & blk	.85	.25
a.	Souvenir sheet of 2	30.00	30.00

Inscribed: "Extra Rapido"
C279	AP60 1p ol gray & brn	15.00	7.50
C280	AP60 2p violet & blk	11.00	5.75
	Nos. C275-C280 (6)	27.90	14.15

7th Cong. of the Postal Union of the Americas and Spain, Bogota, Oct. 12-Nov. 9, 1955. No. C278a contains one each of Nos. C277-C278 printed in different shades.

Caro Type

1955, Nov. 29   Engr.   Perf. 13½x13
C281	A275 15c gray green	.40	.20

University of Salamanca AP62

Inscribed: "Extra Rapido"

1955, Nov. 29   Unwmk.   Perf. 13
C282	AP62 20c dark brown	.25	.20

University of Salamanca, 7th centenary.

Type of Postal Tax Stamp of 1948-50 Surcharged

1956   Wmk. 255   Engr.   Perf. 12
C283	PT10 2c on 8c blue	.25	.20

No. 617 Overprinted in Black

1956   Unwmk.   Perf. 12½x13
C284	A256 1p black & emerald	.40	.20

Columbus Type

1956, Oct. 11   Photo.   Perf. 12
C285	A279 15c intense blue	.65	.25

See No. C306.

St. Elizabeth Type

1956, Nov. 19
C286	A280 15c red brown	.50	.20

St. Ignatius Type

1956, Nov. 26   Engr.   Perf. 12½x13
C287	A281 5c brown	.25	.20

Javier Pereira — AP63

1956, Dec. 28   Unwmk.   Perf. 12
C288	AP63 20c rose carmine	.25	.20

Issued to honor 167-year-old Javier Pereira.

No. 649 and Type of 1941 Overprinted in Red "EXTRA RAPIDO"

1957   Perf. 13½x13
C289	A276 5c blue & black	7.50	3.25

Perf. 12
C290	AP22 5p orange & gray	11.00	7.50

The overprint measures 14mm.

Virgin Type of 1954
Engraved and Lithographed

1957, May 23   Unwmk.   Perf. 13
C291	AP48 5c dp plum & multi	.25	.20

Bank Type

No. C292, 20c, Emblem, cow, horse & herd. 10c, Emblem & tractor. 15c, Emblem, coffee & corn. No. C293, Emblem & dairy farm.

1957   Photo.   Perf. 14x13½
C292	A283 5c chocolate	.20	.20
C293	A283 5c orange	.20	.20
C294	A283 10c green	.55	.40
C295	A283 15c black	.35	.20
C296	A283 20c dull red	.80	.20
	Nos. C292-C296 (5)	2.10	1.20

No. C292 is inscribed "Extra Rapido." Issued: No. C292, 3/5; others 5/23.

Cyclist AP64

1957, July 6   Unwmk.   Perf. 12
C297	AP64 2c brown	.20	.20
C298	AP64 5c ultra	.25	.20

Seventh Bicycle Tour of Colombia.

Academy Type

Designs: 15c, Coat of arms and Gen. Rafael Reyes. 20c, Coat of arms and Academy.

1957, July 20   Engr.   Perf. 12½
C299	A284 15c rose carmine	.30	.20
C300	A284 20c brown	.30	.25

Delgado Type

1957, Sept. 15   Photo.   Perf. 12
C301	A285 10c slate blue	.25	.20

UPU Type

1957, Oct. 10
C302	A286 15c dark red brown	.30	.20
C303	A286 25c dark blue	.40	.20

St. Vincent de Paul Type

1957, Oct. 18
C304	A287 5c rose brown	.25	.20

Fencing Type

1957, Nov. 23   Perf. 12
C305	A288 20c dark red brown	.40	.30

Columbus Type Inscribed "Extra Rapido"

1958, Jan. 8   Unwmk.   Perf. 12
C306	A279 3c dark green	.25	.20

Scenic Type

Design: 25c, Las Lajas Shrine.

1958, June 20   Engr.   Perf. 13
C307	AP40 25c dark rose	.30	.20
C308	AP40 25c rose violet	.30	.20

IGY Type

1958, May 12   Photo.   Perf. 12
C309	A289 25c green	.50	.20

Inscribed "Extra Rapido"
C310	A289 1p purple	.65	.25

No. 659 Overprinted "AEREO" in Carmine

1958, Oct. 16   Engr.   Perf. 13
C312	A277 50c dk green & blk	.50	.20

Almanza Type

1958, Oct. 23   Photo.   Perf. 14x13
C313	A290 25c dark gray	.30	.25

Inscribed "Extra Rapido"
C314	A290 10c olive green	.25	.20

Carrasquilla Type

1959, Jan. 22   Photo.   Perf. 14x13
C315	A291 25c carmine rose	.25	.20
C316	A291 1p dark blue	.80	.25

Miss Universe Type

1959, June 26   Unwmk.   Perf. 11½
C317	A292 1.20p multicolored	1.75	1.40
C318	A292 5p multicolored	47.50	47.50

Gaitan Type Inscribed "Extra Rapido" and Surcharged in Black or Blue

1959, July 28   Engr.   Perf. 12x13½
C319	A293 2p on 1p black	1.75	1.50
C320	A293 2p on 1p black (Bl)	1.75	1.50

The 1p black, type A293, exists without surcharge.

No. C247 Surcharged with New Value in Dark Blue; Old Value Obliterated

1959, Aug. 24   Unwmk.   Perf. 13
C321	AP40 50c on 60c dk brown	1.75	.40

Regular and Air Post Issues of 1948-59 Overprinted in Black or Red

1959-60
C322	A283	5c orange	.35	.25
C323	A287	5c rose brn		
		('60)	.50	.50
C324	A281	5c brown (R)	.40	.30
C325	AP41	10c black	.25	.20
a.		Double overprint	2.50	2.50
C326	A160	10c red, #C231	.40	.20
a.		Double overprint	1.40	1.40
C328	A284	15c rose car	.25	.20
a.		Inverted overprint	3.00	3.00
C330	AP40	20c brown	.25	.20
a.		Double overprint	1.40	1.40
C331	A284	20c brown	.25	.20
C332	A288	20c dk red brn		
		('60)	.25	.20
C333	AP40	25c rose vio		
		('60)	.25	.20
C334	AP40	25c dark blue	.25	.20
C335	A291	25c car rose	.25	.20
C336	A290	25c dark gray	.25	.20
C338	AP40	30c brown org	.25	.20
C340	AP40	50c on 60c dk brn	.40	.20
C341	A291	1p dark blue	.95	.20
a.		Double overprint	2.50	2.50
C342	A292	1.20p brn, ultra, car & ol	1.50	.80
C343	AP41	2p dk grn & blk	2.00	.20
C344	AP41	3p car rose & blk	6.00	.50
a.		Double overprint	10.00	10.00
C345	AP41	5p dk grn & red brn	8.00	1.10
a.		Double overprint	10.00	10.00
b.		Inverted overprint	10.00	10.00

C346 AP40 10p gray grn & red org 10.00 2.25
Nos. C322-C346 (21) 33.00 8.50

Issued following agreement between the Colombian government and AVIANCA to unify the air postage used on all mail carried by AVIANCA.

Vertical overprint on Nos. C342 and C346.

Airmail Stamp of 1919 and Planes
AP66

60c, Nos. C349a, C350a, Planes of 1919 and 1959. Nos. C349b, C350b, Stamp of 1919 and Planes.

Unwmk.

1959, Dec. 5 Photo. Perf. 12
C347 AP66 35c lt bl, blk & red .65 .20
C348 AP66 60c yel grn & gray 1.10 .75

Souvenir Sheets
C349 Sheet of 2 10.00 10.00
a. AP66 1p orange & gray 2.00 1.50
b. AP66 1p lilac, gray & red 2.00 1.50

Inscribed "Extra Rapido"

1960, May 17
C350 Sheet of 2 10.00 10.00
a. AP66 1.50p red orange & gray 2.00 1.50
b. AP66 1.50p olive, gray & rose 2.00 1.50

Nos. C347-C350 for the 40th anniv. of air post service and of the AVIANCA company.

Type of Regular Issue and

1859 Stamp and Seaplane
AP67

Tête Bêche 5c Stamps of 1859 — AP68

Designs (various stamps of 1859 and): 10c, Map of Colombia. 25c, Pres. Mariano Ospina. 1.20p, Plane over mountains.

1959, Dec. 1 Photo. Perf. 12
C351 A296 25c choc & red .50 .35
C352 AP67 50c ver & ultra 1.25 .65
C353 AP67 1.20p yel grn & car 2.50 1.50

Inscribed "Extra Rapido"
C354 A296 10c lemon & vio .20 .20
Nos. C351-C354 (4) 4.45 2.70

Souvenir Sheet
Wmk. 331
1959, Dec. 23 Litho. Imperf.
C355 AP68 5p blue, *pink* 19.00 19.00

Cent. of Colombian postage stamps.
No. C355 exists with inscription "VALOR $5.10" instead of "VALOR $5."

Eldorado Airport, Bogota
AP69

1960, Jan. 5 Wmk. 331 Perf. 12½
C356 AP69 35c black & ocher .50 .20
C356A AP69 60c ver & gray .65 .35

Inscribed "Extra Rapido"
C356B AP69 1p Prus bl & gray .85 .50
Nos. C356-C356B (3) 2.00 1.05

Ant Bear
AP70

1.30p, Armadillo. 1.45p, Parrot fish.

Unwmk.

1960, Feb. 12 Photo. Perf. 12
C357 AP70 35c sepia 1.25 .20
C358 AP70 1.30p rose car & dk brn 2.40 2.25
C359 AP70 1.45p lt bl, bl & yel 2.00 1.25
Nos. C357-C359 (3) 5.65 3.70

Alexander von Humboldt, German naturalist and geographer (1769-1859).

Flower Type

Nos. C360, C362, C366, Passiflora mollissima. Nos. C361, C364, C367, Odontoglossum luteo purpureum. Nos. C363, C369, Anthurium andreanum. Nos. C365, C370, Stanhopea tigrina. No. C368, Espeletia grandiflora.

1960, May 10 Photo. Perf. 12
Flowers in Natural Colors
C360 A298 5c dark blue .20 .20
C361 A298 35c maroon .40 .20
C362 A298 60c dark blue .75 .55
C363 A298 1.45p dark brown 1.00 .85

Inscribed "Extra Rapido"
C364 A298 5c maroon .20 .20
C365 A298 10c brown .20 .20
C366 A298 1p dark blue 2.00 2.50
C367 A298 1p maroon 2.00 2.50
C368 A298 1p brown 2.00 2.50
C369 A298 1p brown 2.00 2.50
C370 A298 1p brown 2.00 2.50
Nos. C360-C370 (11) 12.75 14.70

See Nos. C420-C425.

Fleeing Family and Uprooted Oak Emblem
AP71

Perf. 10, 11
1960, May 24 Litho. Wmk. 331
C371 AP71 60c bl grn & gray .30 .20

World Refugee Year, 7/1/59-6/30/60.

Souvenir Sheet

Pan-American Highway Through Colombia — AP72

1960, May 28 Litho. Imperf.
C372 AP72 2.50p brn & aqua 5.00 5.00

8th Pan-American Highway Congress, Bogota, May 20-29.

Lincoln Type

1960, June 6 Perf. 10½
C375 A299 40c dl red brn & blk .85 .60
C376 A299 60c rose red & blk .25 .20

Type of Regular Issue and

Joaquin Camacho, Jorge Tadeo Lozano and Jose Miguel Pey
AP73

Flag, Coins and Arms of Mompox and Cartagena — AP74

No. C378, Arms of Cartagena. 35c, 1.45p, Colombian flag. 60c, Andres Rosillo, Antonio Villavicencio and Joaquin Caicedo. 1p, Manuel de Bernardo Alvarez and Joaquin Gutierrez. 1.20p, Jose Antonio Galan statue. 1.30p, Front page of newspaper La Bagatela, 1811. 1.65p, Antonia Santos, Jose Acevedo y Gomez and Liborio Mejia.

Unwmk.

1960, July 20 Photo. Perf. 12
C377 AP73 5c lilac & brn .20 .20
C378 A301 5c dp bl grn & multi .20 .20
C379 AP73 35c multicolored .20 .20
C380 AP73 60c red brn & grn .40 .20
C381 AP73 1p ver & sl grn .85 .60
C382 A301 1.20p ultra & ind .85 .60
C383 AP73 1.30p orange & blk .85 .60
C384 AP73 1.45p multicolored 1.10 .85
C385 AP73 1.65p green & brn .85 .85
Nos. C377-C385 (9) 5.50 4.30

Souvenir Sheet
Stamps Inscribed "Extra Rapido"
C386 AP74 Sheet of 4 4.00 4.00
a. 50c deep claret & multi .65 .65
b. 50c green & multi .65 .65
c. 1p brown olive, yel, blue & car .65 .65
d. 1p lilac & gray .65 .65

150th anniv. of Colombia's independence.

St. Isidore Type

Designs: 35c, No. C388a, St. Isidore and farm animals. No. C388b, Nativity.

Unwmk.

1960, Sept. 26 Photo. Perf. 12
C387 A302 35c multicolored .25 .20

Souvenir Sheet
Stamps Inscribed "Extra Rapido"
C388 A302 Sheet of 2 6.00 6.00
a. 1.50p multicolored 2.00 2.00
b. 1.50p multicolored 2.00 2.00

See Nos. C439-C440.

Type of Regular Issue, 1959
Wmk. 331
1960, Nov. 23 Litho. Perf. 12½
C389 A294 35c Bolivar 3.00 .40

Pan-American Highway Type
1961, Mar. 7 Unwmk. Perf. 10½x11
C390 A304 10c rose lil & emer .50 .50
C391 A304 20c ver & lt bl .50 .50
C392 A304 30c black & emer .50 .50

Inscribed "Extra Rapido"
C393 A304 10c dk blue & emer .50 .50
Nos. C390-C393 (4) 2.00 2.00

8th Pan-American Highway Congress, Bogota, May 20-29, 1960.

Lopez Type
1961, Mar. 22 Photo. Perf. 12½
C394 A305 35c blue & brown .50 .20

Inscribed "Extra Rapido"
C395 A305 10c emerald & brn .20 .20

Souvenir Sheet
C396 A305 1p lilac & brn 4.00 3.50

Brother Damian and San Francisco Church, Cali
AP75

Designs: 10c, View of Cali, vert. No. 398, Emblem of University del Valle. 1.30p, Fine Arts School, Cali. 1.45p, Agricultural College, Palmira.

Perf. 13x13½, 13½x13
1961, Aug. 17 Photo. Unwmk.
C397 AP75 35c vio brn & ol .30 .20
C398 AP75 35c olive & grn .30 .20
C399 AP75 1.30p sepia & pink .85 .45
C400 AP75 1.45p multicolored .85 .60

Inscribed "Extra Rapido"
C401 AP75 10c brn & yel grn .20 .20
Nos. C397-C401 (5) 2.50 1.65

50th anniv. (in 1960) of the department of Valle del Cauca.

View of Cucuta
AP76

10c, Church of the Rosary, Cucuta, vert.

1961, Aug. 29
C402 AP76 35c brn ol & grn .60 .20

Inscribed "Extra Rapido"
C403 AP76 10c dk brn & gray grn .20 .20

50th anniv. (in 1960) of the department of North Santander.

Old and New Ships of Barranquilla
AP77

Arms and View of San Gil — AP78

Hotel, Popayan
AP79

Statue of Christ in Procession
AP80

Design: 1.45p, View of Velez.

Perf. 12½x13, 13x12½
1961, Oct. 10 Photo. Unwmk.
C404 AP77 35c gold & bl .45 .20
C405 AP78 35c bl grn, yel & red .45 .20
C406 AP79 35c car & brn .45 .20
C407 AP78 1.45p brown & grn .45 .20

Inscribed: "Extra Rapido"
C408 AP80 10c brown & yel .20 .20
Nos. C404-C408 (5) 2.00 1.00

Types of Regular and Air Post
Souvenir Sheets

Designs, No. C409: 35c, Barranquilla arms. 40c, Popayan arms. c, Arms and view of San Gil. d, Holy Week in Popayan.
No. C410: a, Old and new ships at Barranquilla. b, Hotel, Popayan. c, Bucaramanga arms. d, Holy Week in Popayan.

C409 Sheet of 4 6.00 6.00
a. A309 35c gold & multi .55 .55
b. A309 40c gold & multi .55 .55
c. AP78 1p blue, yellow & red 1.10 1.10

d. AP80 1p car rose & yellow 1.10 1.10

Stamps Inscribed: "Extra Rapido"

C410		Sheet of 4	6.00	6.00
a.	AP77	50c gold & car rose	.85	.85
b.	AP79	50c gold & blue	.85	.85
c.	A309	50c pink & multi	.85	.85
d.	AP80	50c blue & yellow	.85	.85

Nos. C404-C408 are in honor of the Atlantico Department. Nos. C409-C410 are in honor of the Departments of Atlantico, Cauca and Santander.

Nos. 713, 716 and 715 Overprinted and Surcharged

1961, Sept.   Perf. 12

C411	A297	5c grnsh bl & brn	.20	.20
C412	A298	5c multicolored	.20	.20
C413	A297	10c on 20c cit & gray brn	.20	.20
		Nos. C411-C413 (3)	.60	.60

"Aereo" in script on No. C412.
See Nos. C420-C425.

Sports Type

Designs: No. C414, Women divers. No. C415, Tennis, mixed doubles. 1.45p, No. C419b, Baseball. No. C417, Torch bearer. Nos. C418, C419a, Bolivar statue and flags of six participating nations. No. C419c, Soccer. No. C419d, Basketball.

1961, Dec. 16   Litho.   Perf. 13½x14

C414	A310	35c ultra, yel & brn	.60	.20
C415	A310	35c car, yel & brn	.60	.20
C416	A310	1.45p Prus grn, yel & brn	1.00	.55

Inscribed: "Extra Rapido"

C417	A310	10c car lake, yel & brn	.20	.20
C418	A310	10c ol, yel, bl & red	.20	.20
		Nos. C414-C418 (5)	2.60	1.35

Souvenir Sheet
Stamps Inscribed: "Extra Rapido"
Imperf

C419		Sheet of 4	6.00	6.00
a.	A310	50c multi	.40	.40
b.	A310	50c multi	.40	.40
c.	A310	1p multi	.85	.85
d.	A310	1p multi	.85	.85

Flower Type of 1960

5c, Passiflora mollissima. 10c, Espeletia grandiflora. 20c, 2p, Odontoglossum luteo purpureum. 25c, Stanhopea tigrina. 60c, Anthurium Andreanum.

Unwmk.
1962, Jan. 30   Photo.   Perf. 12
Flowers in Natural Colors

C420	A298	5c gray	.20	.20
C421	A298	10c gray blue	.20	.20
C422	A298	20c rose lilac	.20	.20
C423	A298	25c citron	.30	.20
C424	A298	60c light brown	.30	.20

Inscribed "Extra Rapido"

C425	A298	2p salmon pink	2.75	1.25
		Nos. C420-C425 (6)	3.95	2.25

Anti-Malaria Type

Designs: 40c, Colombian anti-malaria emblem. 1p, 1.45p, Malaria eradication emblem and mosquito in swamp.

1962, Apr. 12   Litho.   Perf. 12

C426	A311	40c yellow & red	.25	.20
C427	A311	1.45p gray & ultra	.50	.40

Inscribed "Extra Rapido"

C428	A311	1p yel grn & ultra	3.50	3.50
		Nos. C426-C428 (3)	4.25	4.10

WHO drive to eradicate malaria.

Type of Regular Issue, 1962 and

Abelardo Ramos and Engineering School, Cauca — AP81

Designs: 10c, Miguel Triana, Andres A. Arroyo and Monserrate shrine with cable cars. 15c, Diodoro Sanchez and first meeting place of Engineers Society. 2p, Engineers Society emblem.

1962, June 12   Photo.   Perf. 11½x12

C429	AP81	5c blue & dp rose	.20	.20
C430	AP81	10c green & sepia	.20	.20
C431	AP81	15c lilac & sepia	.25	.20

Inscribed: "Extra Rapido"

C432	A312	2p blk, yel, red & bl	1.50	1.50
		Nos. C429-C432 (4)	2.15	2.10

75th anniv. of the founding of the Colombian Soc. of Engineers and 6th Natl. Cong. of Engineers.

American States Type
1962, June 28   Photo.   Perf. 13
Flags in National Colors

C433	A313	35c black & blue	.35	.20

Women's Rights Type
Perf. 12x12½
1962, July 20   Litho.   Wmk. 229

C434	A314	35c buff, gray & blk	.25	.20

See Nos. C448-C450.

Scout Type

Designs: 15c, No. C438, Scouts at campfire and tents. 40c and No. C437, Girl Scouts.

Perf. 11½x12
1962, July 26   Photo.   Unwmk.

C435	A315	15c brown & rose	.20	.20
C436	A315	40c dp cl & pink	.25	.20
C437	A315	1p blue & buff	.80	.35

Inscribed "Extra Rapido"

C438	A315	1p purple & yel	4.00	3.75
		Nos. C435-C438 (4)	5.25	4.50

Nos. C435 and C438 for 30th anniv. of the Colombian Boy Scouts. Nos. C436 and C437 for the 25th anniv. of the Girl Scouts.

Nativity by Gregorio Vasquez AP82

Design: 2p, St. Isidore, similar to type A302.

Inscribed "Extra Rapido"
Unwmk.
1962, Aug. 28   Photo.   Perf. 12

C439	AP82	10c gray & multi	.20	.20
C440	AP82	2p gray & multi	3.75	3.50

See Nos. C387-C388.

Type of Regular Issue, 1962 and

Pres. Aquileo Parra and Magdalena River Bridge AP83

Design: 5c, Locomotives of 1854 and 1961. 10c, Railroad map of Colombia.

1962, Sept. 28   Photo.   Perf. 12½

C441	AP83	5c sep & slate grn	.20	.20
C442	A316	10c multicolored	.20	.20

Engr.

C443	AP83	1p dull pur & brn	1.40	.20

Inscribed: "Extra Rapido."

C444	AP83	5p bl, brn & dl grn	3.75	3.75
		Nos. C441-C444 (4)	5.55	4.35

Progress of Colombian railroads and completion of the Atlantic Line from Santa Maria to Bogota.

UPAE Type

Designs: 50c, Map of Americas and carrier pigeon. 60c, Post horn.

Perf. 13½x14
1962, Oct. 18   Litho.   Wmk. 346

C445	A317	50c slate grn & gold	.30	.20
C446	A317	60c gold & plum	.25	.20

Pope John XXIII AP84

1963, Mar. 11

C447	AP84	60c gold, red brn, buff & red	.25	.20

Vatican II, the 21st Ecumenical Council of the Roman Catholic Church.

Women's Rights Type of 1962
1963-64   Perf. 12x12½

C448	A314	5c sal, gray & blk ('64)	.20	.20
C449	A314	45c pale grn, gray & blk	.30	.20
C450	A314	45c brt pink, gray & blk	.30	.20
		Nos. C448-C450 (3)	.80	.60

Games Emblem — AP85

1963, Aug. 12   Perf. 13x14

C451	AP85	20c gray & multi	.20	.20
C452	AP85	80c buff & multi	.25	.20

South American Athletic Championships (22nd for men, 12th for women), Cali, June 30-July 7.

Bolivar Statue by Arenas-Betancourt — AP86

Perf. 14x13½
1963, Aug. 30   Unwmk.

C453	AP86	1.90p olive bis & blue	.25	.20

Centenary of the city of Pereira.
For surcharge see No. C574.

Tennis Player — AP87

1963, Oct. 11   Perf. 13½x14

C454	AP87	55c multicolored	.25	.20

30th South American Tennis Championships, Medellin, Oct. 3-13.

Pres. John F. Kennedy and Alliance for Progress Emblem AP88

1963, Dec. 17   Litho.   Perf. 14x13½

C455	AP88	10c multicolored	.40	.20

President John F. Kennedy (1917-1963).

Church of the True Cross, National Pantheon, Bogota — AP89

2p, Christ of the Martyrs, bell and tomb.

Perf. 13½x14
1964, Mar. 10   Photo.   Unwmk.

C459	AP89	1p multicolored	.20	.20
C460	AP89	2p multicolored	.35	.20

View of Cartagena AP90

1964, Mar. 18   Litho.   Perf. 14x13½

C461	AP90	3p vio, bl, ocher & brn	1.40	.60

Cartagena's independence in 1811, Simon Bolivar's visit in 1812 and the siege of 1815.

Eleanor Roosevelt AP91

1964, Nov. 10   Photo.   Perf. 12

C462	AP91	20c ol & dl red brn	.25	.20

Eleanor Roosevelt (1884-1962).

Alberto Castilla and Score of "El Bunde" AP92

1964, Nov. 10   Unwmk.

C463	AP92	30c ol bis & Prus grn	.25	.20

Department of Tolima and Maestro Alberto Castilla (1878-1937) who in 1906 founded the Tolima Conservatory of Music in Ibague.

Mejia Type

Mejia portrait and: 45c, Women picking coffee. 5p, Mules carrying coffee bags. 10p, Loading coffee on freighter "Manuel Mejia."

1965, Feb. 10   Engr.   Perf. 12½x13

C464	A320	45c brown & blk	.20	.20
C465	A320	5p gray grn & blk	1.75	.25
C466	A320	10p ultra & blk	2.40	.30
	Nos. C464-C466 (3)		4.35	.75

ITU Emblem AP93

1965, Oct. 25   Photo.   Perf. 12

C467	AP93	80c Prus bl, lt bl & red	.25	.20

Cent. of the ITU.

Cattleya Truanae — AP94

1965, Oct. 3   Litho.   Perf. 13½x14

C468	AP94	20c yellow & multi	.25	.20

Fifth Philatelic Exhibition.

Cent. of the Telegraph in Colombia — AP95

1965, Nov. 1   Perf. 13½x14, 14x13½

No. C469, Pres. Manuel Murillo Toro statue, telegraph and orbits. No. C470, Telegraph and satellites over South America, horiz.

C469	AP95	60c multicolored	.25	.20
C470	AP95	60c multicolored	.25	.20

Junkers F-13 Seaplane, 1920 AP96

History of Colombian Aviation: 10c, Dornier Wal, 1924. 20c, Dornier Mercur, 1926. 50c, Trimotor Ford, 1932. 60c, De Havilland biplane, 1930. 1p, Douglas DC-4, 1947. 1.40p, Douglas DC-3, 1944. 2.80p, Superconstellation 1049, 1951. 3p, Boeing 720B jet, 1961.

Perf. 14x13½

1965-66   Photo.   Unwmk.

C471	AP96	5c multicolored	.20	.20
C472	AP96	10c multicolored	.20	.20
C473	AP96	20c multicolored	.20	.20
C474	AP96	50c multicolored	.20	.20
C475	AP96	60c multicolored	.40	.20
C476	AP96	1p multicolored	.75	.20
C477	AP96	1.40p multicolored	.90	.20
C478	AP96	2.80p multicolored	1.60	.60
C479	AP96	3p multicolored	2.40	.85
	Nos. C471-C479 (9)		6.85	2.85
	Nos. C471-C479,CE4 (10)		7.40	3.10

Issued: 5c, 60c, 3p, 12/13/65; 10c, 1p, 1.40p, 7/15/66; 20c, 50c, 2.80p, 12/14/66.

Automobile Club Emblem and Car on Road AP97

1966, Feb. 16   Litho.   Perf. 14x13½

C480	AP97	20c multicolored	.25	.20

25th anniv. (in 1965) of the Automobile Club of Colombia.

Fish Type

Fish: 2p, Flying fish. 2.80p, Queen angelfish. 20p, King mackerel.

1966, Aug. 25   Photo.   Perf. 12½x13

C481	A323	2p multicolored	.50	.20
C482	A323	2.80p multicolored	1.25	.90
C483	A323	20p multicolored	16.50	12.00
	Nos. C481-C483 (3)		18.25	13.10

Coat of Arms Type

1966, Oct. 11   Litho.   Perf. 14x13½

C484	A324	1p ultra & multi	.25	.20
C485	A324	1.40p red & multi	.20	.20

Portrait Type

80c, Father Felix Restrepo Mejia, S.J. (1887-1965), theologian, scholar. 1.70p, José Joaquin Casas (1866-1951), educator, diplomat.

Perf. 13½x14

1967, Jan. 18   Litho.   Unwmk.

C486	A325	80c dk bl & bis	.20	.20
C487	A325	1.70p blk & bis	.25	.20

Declaration of Bogota Type

1967, Feb. 2   Litho.   Perf. 14x13½

C488	A326	3p multicolored	.35	.20

See note after No. 767.

Orchid Type

Orchids: 1p, Cattleya dowiana aurea, vert. 1.20p, Masdevallia coccinea, vert. 5p, Catasetum macrocarpum and bee.

1967, May 23   Litho.   Perf. 14

C489	A327	1p multicolored	1.60	.30
C490	A327	1.20p multicolored	1.10	.25
C491	A327	5p multicolored	7.50	.90
a.	Souv. sheet of 3, #C489-C491		25.00	25.00
	Nos. C489-C491 (3)		10.20	1.45

Lions Type

1967, July 12   Litho.   Perf. 13½x14

C492	A328	25c multicolored	.25	.20

"First Caesarean Section" by Grau AP98

Perf. 14x13½

1967, Sept. 7   Litho.   Unwmk.

C493	AP98	80c multicolored	.25	.20

Issued to publicize the 6th Congress of Colombian Surgeons, Bogota, Sept. 25.

SENA Type

Lithographed and Embossed

1967, Sept. 20   Perf. 13½x14

C494	A329	2p gold, ver & blk	.50	.20

Pre-Columbian Art Type

Designs: 30c, Bird pectoral. 5p Ornamental pectoral. 20p, Pitcher.

1967, Oct. 13   Photo.   Perf. 13½x14

C495	A330	30c ver, gold & brn	.35	.20
C496	A330	5p red, gold & brn	3.25	.50
a.	Souvenir sheet of 2		10.00	10.00
C497	A330	20p vio, gold & brn	14.50	10.00
	Nos. C495-C497 (3)		18.10	10.70

No. C496a also commemorates the 6th Natl. Phil. Exhib. No. C496a contains 2 imperf. stamps in changed colors similar to Nos. C495-C496 (30c has green background and 5p maroon background).

Telecommunications Type

Designs: 50c, Signal lights. 1p, Early Bird satellite, Southern Cross and radar.

Perf. 13½x14

1968, May 14   Litho.   Unwmk.

C498	A331	50c blk, ver & emer	.20	.20
C499	A331	1p ultra, yel & gray	.30	.20

Eucharist Type

1968, June 6   Litho.   Perf. 13½x14

C500	A332	80c rose lil, red, yel & blk	.20	.20
C501	A332	3p bl, red, yel & blk	.30	.20

Eucharistic Congress Type

Designs: 80c, The Last Supper, by Gregorio Vasquez, horiz. 1p, St. Francis Xavier Preaching, by Gregorio Vasquez. 2p, The Dream of the Prophet Elias, by Gregorio Vasquez. 3p, Monstrance, c. 1700. 20p, Pope Paul VI, painting by Roman Franciscan nuns.

1968, Aug. 13   Photo.   Perf. 13

C502	A333	80c multicolored	.20	.20
C503	A333	1p multicolored	.25	.20
C504	A333	2p multicolored	.35	.20
C505	A333	3p lil & multi	.65	.20
C506	A333	20p gold & multi	4.00	2.00
	Nos. C502-C506 (5)		5.45	2.80

Shrine of the Eucharist, Bogotá AP99

1.20p, Pope Paul VI giving blessing and Papal arms. 1.80p, Cathedral of Bogota.

Perf. 14x13½, 13½x14

1968, Aug. 22   Litho.

C507	AP99	80c multi	.20	.20
C508	AP99	1.20p multi, vert.	.20	.20
C509	AP99	1.80p multi, vert.	.30	.20
	Nos. C507-C509 (3)		.70	.60

Visit of Pope Paul VI to Colombia.

Computer Symbols — AP100

1968, Oct. 29   Litho.   Perf. 13½x14

C510	AP100	20c buff, car & grn	.25	.20

Cent. of the Natl. University and the 1st Data Processing Cong. in 1967 at the University.

Agriculture Institute Type

1968, Mar. 5   Litho.   Perf. 13½x14

C511	A337	1p gray & multi	.25	.20

Microscope and Pen — AP101

1969, Mar. 24   Litho.   Perf. 14

C512	AP101	5p blk, yel, ver & pur	2.40	.35

20th anniv. (in 1968) of the University of the Andes.

Alexander von Humboldt and Andes AP102

1969, May 3   Litho.   Perf. 14x13½

C513	AP102	1p grn & brn	.65	.35

Alexander von Humboldt (1769-1859), German naturalist and traveler.

Map of Colombia, Amphibian Plane and Letter AP103

Design: 1.50p, No. C516b, Globe, letter, and jet of Avianca airlines.

1969, June 18   Litho.   Perf. 14x13½

C514	AP103	1p multi	.45	.20
C515	AP103	1.50p multi	.65	.25

Souvenir Sheet

Imperf

C516	Sheet of 2		7.50	7.50
a.	AP103 5p green & multi		1.00	1.00
b.	AP103 5p violet & multi		1.00	1.00

50th anniv. of the 1st air post flight in Colombia. No. C516 also for 8th Natl. Philatelic Exhibition, EXFILBA 69, Barranquilla, June 18-22. No. C516 contains 2 stamps in the designs of the 1p and 1.50p.

Independence Type

2.30p, Simon Bolivar, José Antonio Anzoategui, Francisco de Paula Santander and victorious army entering Bogotá, 9/18/1819; painting by Ignacio Castillo Cervantes.

1969, July 24   Litho.   Perf. 13½x14

C517	A338	2.30p gold & multi	1.00	.35

Social Security Emblem — AP104

Neurosurgeons' Congress Emblem — AP105

1969, Oct. 29   Litho.   Perf. 13½x14

C518	AP104	20c emer & blk	.25	.20

20th anniv. of the Colombian Institute of Social Security.

1969, Oct. 29

C519	AP105	70c vio, red & yel	.50	.30

Issued to publicize the 13th Congress of Latin-American Neurosurgeons, Bogotá.

Junkers F-13 AP106

Nos. C521, C522b, Globe with airlines from Bogota & Boeing jet. No. C522a, like No. C520.

1969, Nov. 28   Litho.   Perf. 14x13½
C520 AP106   2p grn & multi   .75   .25
C521 AP106   3.50p ultra & multi   1.40   .50

Souvenir Sheet
Imperf

C522   Sheet of 2   7.50   7.50
   a.   AP106 3.50p lt grn & multi   .75   .75
   b.   AP106 5p ultra & multi   1.00   1.00

50th anniv. of AVIANCA; No. C522 also publicizes the 1st Interamerican Phil. Exhib., Bogota, Nov. 28-Dec. 7.
No. C522 contains 2 imperf. stamps.

Child Mailing Letter — AP107

Christmas: 1.50p, Praying child and gifts.

1969, Dec. 16   Litho.   Perf. 13½x14
C523 AP107   60c ocher & multi   .80   .20
C524 AP107   1p multicolored   .85   .25
C525 AP107   1.50p multicolored   1.10   .25
   Nos. C523-C525 (3)   2.75   .70

Radar Station and Pre-Columbian Head — AP108

1970, Mar. 25   Litho.   Perf. 14x13½
C526 AP108 1p dl grn, blk & brick red   .30   .20

Issued to publicize the opening of the communications satellite earth station at Chocontá in Cundinamarca Province.

Emblem of Colombian Youth Sports Institute — AP109

Art Exhibition Emblem — AP110

2.30p, Games' emblem (dove and 3 rings).

1970, Apr. 6   Litho.   Perf. 13½x14
C527 AP109 1.50p dk ol grn, yel & blk   .30   .20
C528 AP109 2.30p red & multi   .40   .20

9th Natl. Youth Games, Ibague, July 10-20.

1970, Apr. 30   Litho.   Perf. 13½x14
C529 AP110 30c multicolored   .25   .20

2nd Biennial Art Exhib., Medellin, 6/1-7/14.

Eduardo Santos, Rural and Urban Buildings AP111

1970, June 18   Litho.   Perf. 14x13½
C530 AP111 1p grn, yel & blk   .25   .20

Issued to commemorate the founding (in 1939) of the Territorial Credit Institute.

UN Emblem, Scales and Dove — AP112

EXFILCA Emblem — AP113

1970, June 26   Perf. 13½x14
C531 AP112 1.50p dk bl, lt bl & yel   .25   .20

25th anniversary of United Nations.

1970, Nov.   Litho.   Perf. 13½x14
C532 AP113 10p bl, gold & blk   3.50   .25

EXFILCA 70, 2nd Interamerican Philatelic Exhib., Caracas, Venezuela, Nov. 27-Dec. 6.

Mother Juana Ruperta in Napanga Costume and Music by Efrain Orozco — AP114

Designs: 1p, Dancers from Eastern Plains and music by Alejandro Wills. No. C535, Guabina man, woman and folk song. No. C536, Bambuco man and woman, and music. No. C537, Man and woman dancing the Cumbia, and music.

1970-71   Litho.   Perf. 13½x14
C533 AP114   60c dp lil rose & multi   .50   .20
C534 AP114   1p ultra & multi   .40   .20
C535 AP114   1.30p bl & multi   .55   .20
C536 AP114   1.30p emer & multi ('71)   .60   .20
C537 AP114   1.30p lil & multi ('71)   .40   .20
   Nos. C533-C537 (5)   2.45   1.00

Athlete and Games Emblem — AP115

Design: 2p, Games emblem.

1971, Mar. 11
C542 AP115 1.50p multicolored   .90   .90
C543 AP115   2p blk, org & grn   .80   .55

6th Pan-American Games, Cali, 7/30-8/13.

Gilberto Alzate Avendano AP116

1971, Apr. 29   Litho.   Perf. 14x13½
C544 AP116 1p bl & multi   .40   .25

Avendano (1910-60), journalist, popular leader.

Commemorative Medal — AP117

Lithographed and Embossed
1971, June 21   Perf. 14x13½
C545 AP117 1p slate grn & gold   .55   .30

Centenary (in 1970) of the Bank of Bogota.

Olympic Center — AP118

Soccer — AP119

Designs (Games Emblem and): Nos. C546-C546C, Olympic Center. No. 547, Soccer. No. C548, Wrestling. No. C549, Bicycling. No. C550, Volleyball. No. C551, Diving (women). No. C552, Fencing. No. C553, Sailing. No. C554, Equestrian. No. C555, Jumping. No. C556, Rowing. No. C557, Cali emblem. No. C558, Basketball (women). No. C559, Stadium. No. C560, Baseball. No. C561, Hockey. No. C562, Weight lifting. No. C563, Medals. No. C564, Boxing. No. C565, Gymnastics (women). No. C566, Sharpshooting.

1971, July 16   Litho.   Perf. 13½x14
Multicolored and Emblem Color:
C546   AP118 1.30p yellow   1.25   .30
C546A   AP118 1.30p green   1.25   .30
C546B   AP118 1.30p blue   1.25   .30
C546C   AP118 1.30p carmine   1.25   .30
C547   AP119 1.30p emerald   1.25   .30
C548   AP119 1.30p lilac   1.25   .30
C549   AP119 1.30p blue   1.25   .30
C550   AP119 1.30p carmine   1.25   .30
C551   AP119 1.30p blue   1.25   .30
C552   AP119 1.30p carmine   1.25   .30
C553   AP119 1.30p blue   1.25   .30
C554   AP119 1.30p gray   1.25   .30
C555   AP119 1.30p green   1.25   .30
C556   AP119 1.30p blue   1.25   .30
C557   AP118 1.30p orange   1.25   .30
C558   AP119 1.30p carmine   1.25   .30
C559   AP118 1.30p light blue   1.25   .30
C560   AP119 1.30p plum   1.25   .30
C561   AP119 1.30p yel grn   1.25   .30
C562   AP119 1.30p pink   1.25   .30
C563   AP118 1.30p deep org   1.25   .30
C564   AP119 1.30p plum   1.25   .30
C565   AP119 1.30p lilac rose   1.25   .30
C566   AP119 1.30p green   1.25   .30
   a.   Sheet of 25, #C546-C566   35.00   35.00

6th Pan American Athletic Games, Cali. No. C546B appears twice in sheet.

Battle of Carabobo, by Martin Tovar y Tovar — AP120

1971, Nov. 25   Litho.   Perf. 13½x14
C567 AP120 1.50p multicolored   1.00   .20

Sesquicentennial of the Battle of Carabobo.

St. Theresa Type Overprinted "AEREO"
1972   Litho.   Perf. 13½x14
C568 A343 2p multicolored   .30   .20

See note after No. 793.

Vendor — AP121

Designs: 50c, Woman wearing shawl, and woven shawl. 3p, Fruit vendor (puppet).

1972, Apr. 11   Litho.   Perf. 13½x14
C569 AP121   50c multicolored   .35   .20
C570 AP121   1p multicolored   .35   .20
C571 AP121   3p multicolored   .50   .25
   Nos. C569-C571 (3)   1.20   .65

Colombian artisans.

Mormodes Rolfeanum AP122

1972, Apr. 20   Perf. 14x13½
C572 AP122 1.30p multicolored   .45   .20

7th World Orchidology Congress, Medellin.

Congo Grande Dancer — AP123

Laureano Gomez, by Ridriguez Cubillos — AP124

1972, June 21   Litho.   Perf. 13½x14
C573 AP123 1.30p multicolored   .50   .20

International Carnival of Barranquilla.

No. C453 Surcharged in Brown

1972, Oct. 5   Litho.   Perf. 14x13½
C574 AP86 1.30p on 1.90p   .55 .20

1972   Perf. 13½x14

1.30p (#C576), Guillermo Leòn Valencia Muñoz.

C575 AP124 1.30p multicolored   .25 .20
C576 AP124 1.30p multicolored   .25 .20

Laureano Gomez (1898-1966), Guillermo Leon Valencia Munoz (1909-71), Presidents of Colombia.
Issued: No. C575, 10/17; No. C576, 11/28.

Benito Juarez — AP125

1972, Dec. 12   Perf. 13½x14
C577 AP125 1.50p multicolored   .25 .20

Benito Juarez (1806-1872), revolutionary leader and president of Mexico.

Rebecca Fountain AP126

1972, Dec. 19   Litho.
C578 AP126 80c multicolored   .50 .45
C579 AP126 1p multicolored   .45 .20

"Bucaramanga" — AP127

1972, Dec. 22   Perf. 14x13½
C580 AP127 5p multicolored   .85 .20

Founding of Bucaramanga, 350th anniv.

Xavier University AP128

1973, May 8   Litho.   Perf. 14x13½
C581 AP128 1.30p lt grn & sep   .25 .20
C582 AP128 1.50p lt bl & sep   .25 .20

350th anniversary of the founding of Xavier University in Bogotá.

Ceramic Type

Excavated Ceramic Artifacts: 1p, Winged urn, Tairona. 1.30p, Woman and child, Sinu. 1.70p, Two-headed figure, Quimbaya. 3.50p, Man, Tumaco.

1973   Litho.   Perf. 13½x14
C583 A358 1p multicolored   1.00 1.00
C584 A358 1.30p multicolored   .50   .20
C585 A358 1.70p multicolored   .55   .25
C586 A358 3.50p multicolored 1.10   .30
     Nos. C583-C586 (4)   3.15 1.75

Issue dates: 1p, Oct. 11; others, June 15.

Battle of Maracaibo, by Manuel F. Rincon AP129

1973, July 24   Litho.   Perf. 14x13½
C587 AP129 10p bl & multi   2.00 .20

Battle of Maracaibo, sesquicentennial.

Bank Emblem AP130

1973, Oct. 1   Litho.   Perf. 14x13½
C588 AP130 2p multicolored   .25 .20

50th anniv. of the Bank of the Republic.

No. 801 Overprinted "AEREO"

1973, Oct. 11   Perf. 14
C589 A346 80c multicolored   .30 .20

Pres. Pedro Nel Ospina, by Coroleano Leudo — AP131

Arms of Toro — AP132

1973, Nov. 9   Perf. 13½x14
C590 AP131 1.50p multicolored   .25 .20

50th anniversary of the Ministry of Communications founded under Pres. Ospina.

1973, Dec. 1
C591 AP132 1p multicolored   .25 .20

Founding of Toro, Valle del Cauca, 4th cent.

Bolivar, Battle of Bombona AP133

1973, Dec. 7   Litho.   Perf. 14x13½
C592 AP133 1.30p multicolored   .25 .20

Sesquicentennial (in 1972) of the Battle of Bombona.

Nicolaus Copernicus AP134

Andes, Map of South America AP135

1974, Feb. 19   Litho.   Perf. 13½x14
C593 AP134 2.50p multicolored   .55 .20

500th anniversary of the birth of Nicolaus Copernicus (1473-1543), Polish astronomer.

1974, May 11   Litho.   Perf. 14
C594 AP135 2p multicolored   .50 .20

Meeting of Communications Ministers of Members of the Andean Group, Cali, May 7-11, 1974.

Television Set AP136

1974, July 16   Litho.   Perf. 14x13½
C595 AP136 1.30p org, blk & brn   .25 .20

20th anniversary of Colombian television and 10th anniversary of INRAVISION, the National Institute of Radio and Television.

Championship Emblem — AP137

1974, Aug. 5   Litho.   Perf. 14x13½
C596 AP137 4.50p multicolored   .30 .20

2nd World Swimming Championships, Cali.

Condor — AP138

1974, Aug. 28   Perf. 14
C597 AP138 1.50p multicolored   .25 .20

Bank of Colombia centenary.

UPU Envelope AP139

1974, Sept. 9   Litho.   Perf. 14
C598 AP139 20p multicolored   2.50 .30

Centenary of Universal Postal Union.

Symbol of Flight — AP140

1974, Sept.   Perf. 12x12½
C599 AP140 20c olive   .25 .20

Gen. José Maria Cordoba — AP141

White-tailed Trogon, Letter — AP142

1974, Oct. 14   Litho.   Perf. 13½x14
C609 AP141 1.30p multicolored   .25 .20

Sesquicentennial of the Battles of Junin and Ayacucho.

Insurance Type

Design: 3p, Abstract pattern.

1974, Oct. 24   Litho.   Perf. 13½x14
C610 A365 3p multicolored   .30 .20

Perf. 13½x14, 14x13½
1974, Nov. 14

Designs (UPU Letter and): 1.30p, Keelbilled Toucan, horiz. 2p, Peruvian cock-of-the-rock, horiz. 2.50p, Scarlet macaw.

C611 AP142 1p multicolored   .75 .20
C612 AP142 1.30p multicolored   .75 .20
C613 AP142 2p multicolored   1.00 .20
C614 AP142 2.50p multicolored   1.00 .20
     Nos. C611-C614 (4)   3.50 .80

Centenary of Universal Postal Union.
For surcharge see No. C656.

Forest No. 1, by Roman Roncancio — AP143

Boy with Thorn in Finger, by Gregorio Vazquez AP144

Paintings: 3p, Women Fruit Vendors, by Miguel Diaz Vargas (1886-1956). 5p, Annunciation, Santafereña School, 17th-18th cent.

Perf. 13½x14, 14x13½

1975, Mar. 12 Litho.
C615 AP143 2p multicolored .75 .20
C616 AP144 3p multicolored .50 .20
C617 AP144 4p multicolored .65 .20
C618 AP144 5p multicolored 1.10 .25
Nos. C615-C618 (4) 3.00 .85

Modern and Colonial Colombian paintings.

Trees and Lake AP145

Design: 6p, Victoria regia, Amazon River.

1975, Mar. 12 **Perf. 14x13½**
C619 AP145 1p yellow & multi .20 .20
C620 AP145 6p yellow & multi .60 .20

Nature conservation of trees and Amazon Region.

Gold Treasure Type

Designs: 2p, Nose pendant. 10p, Alligator-shaped staff ornament.

1975, Apr. 11 Litho. **Perf. 14x13½**
C621 A368 2p grn, gold & brn .90 .20
C622 A368 10p multicolored 4.75 .60

El Rodadero, Santa Maria AP146

1975, July 26 Litho. **Perf. 14x13½**
C623 AP146 2p multicolored .25 .20

400th anniversary of Santa Marta City.

AP147

AP148

1975, Aug. 31 Litho. **Perf. 13½x14**
C624 AP147 4p multicolored .25 .20

Intl. Women's Year 1975. Maria de Jesus Paramo de Collazos founded 1st normal school for women in Bucaramanga in 1875.

1976, Mar. 12 Litho. **Perf. 13½x14**
C625 AP148 5p "Sugar Cane" .85 .30

4th Congress of Latin-American and Caribbean sugar-exporting countries, Cali, 3/8-12.

View of Bogota — AP149

1976, July 2 Litho. **Perf. 12**
C626 AP149 10p shown 1.25 .90
C627 AP149 10p Barranquilla 1.25 .90
C628 AP149 10p Cali 1.25 .90
C629 AP149 10p Medellin 1.25 .90
a. Block of 4, #C626-C629 6.00 6.00

Habitat, UN Conf. on Human Settlements, Vancouver, Canada, May 31-June 11.

University Emblem and "90" — AP150

1976, Aug. 6 Litho. **Perf. 13½x14**
C630 AP150 5p lt blue & multi .50 .20

Univ. of Colombia day school, 90th anniv.

Miguel Samper — AP151

1976, Oct. 29 Litho. **Perf. 13½x14**
C631 AP151 2p multicolored .25 .20

Samper (1825-99), economist and writer.

Telephone, 1895 — AP152

1976, Nov. 2
C632 AP152 3p multicolored .25 .20

Centenary of first telephone call by Alexander Graham Bell, Mar. 10, 1876.

747 Jumbo Jet AP153

1976, Dec. 3 Litho. **Perf. 12**
C633 AP153 2p multicolored .25 .20

Inauguration of 747 jumbo jet service by Avianca.
For surcharge see No. C636.

Convent, Church and Plaza de San Francisco — AP154

1976, Dec. 29 Litho. **Perf. 14**
C634 AP154 6p multicolored .50 .20

150th anniv. of the Congress of Panama.

Souvenir Sheet

Bank of the Republic Emblem — AP155

1977, June 6 Litho. **Perf. 14**
C635 AP155 25p multicolored 11.00 11.00

Opening of Philatelic Museum of Medellin under auspices of Banco de la Republica.

No. C633 Surcharged in Light Brown

1977, June Litho. **Perf. 12**
C636 AP153 3p on 2p multi .25 .20

Coffee AP156

Coffee Grower, Pack Mule AP157

1977-78 Litho. **Perf. 12½**
C640 AP156 3p multi .50 .20
C641 AP156 3.50p multi ('78) .50 .20

Colombian coffee.

1977, Aug. 9 Litho. **Perf. 13½x14**
C642 AP157 10p multicolored .50 .20

National Federation of Coffee Growers, 50th anniversary.

Beethoven and 9th Symphony AP158

Games' Emblem AP159

1977, Aug. 17
C643 AP158 8p multicolored .75 .20

Sesquicentennial of the death of Ludwig van Beethoven (1770-1827).

Bird Type

Tropical Birds and Plants: No. C644, Woodpecker and Meriania. C645, Purple gallinule and water lilies. No. C646, Xipholaena punicea and Cochlospermum orinocense. No. C647, Crowned flycatcher and Jacaranda copaia.

1977, Sept. 6 Litho. **Perf. 14**
C644 A380 5p multicolored .75 .20
C645 A380 5p multicolored .75 .20
C646 A380 10p multicolored 1.10 .20
C647 A380 10p multicolored 1.10 .20
Nos. C644-C647 (4) 3.70 .80

1977, Sept. 9 **Perf. 12x12½**
C648 AP159 6p multicolored .25 .20

13th Central American and Caribbean Games, Medellin, 1978.

La Cayetana, by Enrique Grau AP160

No. C650, Water Nymphs, by Beatriz Gonzalez.

1977, Sept. 13 **Perf. 14x13½**
C649 AP160 8p multicolored .45 .20
C650 AP160 8p multicolored .45 .20

Women's suffrage, 20th anniversary.

Judge Francisco Antonio Moreno, by Joaquin Gutierrez AP161

Design: 25p, Viceroy Manuel de Guirior.

1977, Sept. 13 **Perf. 12**
C651 AP161 20p multicolored 1.25 .75
C652 AP161 25p multicolored 1.75 1.10

Bicentenary of National Library.

Federico Lleras Acosta — AP162

Cauca University Arms — AP163

1977, Sept. 27 **Litho.** *Perf. 14*
C653 AP162 5p multicolored .30 .20
Dr. Federico Lleras Acosta, veterinarian and bacteriologist; birth centenary.

1977, Oct. 14
C654 AP163 5p multicolored .30 .20
Sesquicentennial of the University of Cauca.

CUDECOM Building, Bogota AP164

1977, Oct. 14
C655 AP164 1.50p multicolored .25 .20
Colombian Society of Engineers, 90th anniv.

No. C612 Surcharged with New Value and Bars in Brown
1977, Dec. 3 **Litho.** *Perf. 14x13½*
C656 AP142 2p on 1.30p multi .30 .20

Lost City, Tayrona Culture AP165

Creator of Energy, by Arenas Betancourt AP166

1978, Apr. 18 **Litho.** *Perf. 12½*
C657 AP165 3.50p multicolored .25 .20

1978, Apr. 25 *Perf. 12*
C658 AP166 4p blue & multi .25 .20
Sesquicentennial of Antioquia University Law School.

Column of the Slaves — AP167

Statue of Catalina, Cartagena AP168

1978, May 9
C659 AP167 2.50p multicolored .25 .20
Sesquicentennial of Ocana Convention (meeting of various political groups).

1978, May 30 **Litho.** *Perf. 12*
C660 AP168 4p blk & lt bl .25 .20
Sesquicentennial of University of Cartagena.

Gold Pendant, Tolima — AP169

1978, July 11 **Litho.** *Perf. 12x12½*
C661 AP169 3.50p multicolored .25 .20

Apotheosis of Spanish Language, by Luis Alberto Acuña — AP170

1978, Aug. 9 *Perf. 14*
C662 AP170 Strip of 3 4.75 4.75
a.-c. 11p, any single 1.10 1.10
Millennium of Spanish language.

Presidential Guard AP171

Figure, Muisca Culture AP172

1978, Aug. 16 *Perf. 13½x14*
C663 AP171 9p multicolored .45 .45
Presidential Guard Battalion, 50th anniv.

1978, Sept. 12 **Litho.** *Perf. 12½*
C664 AP172 3.50p multicolored .30 .20

Apse of Carmelite Church — AP173

1978, Oct. 12 *Perf. 13*
C665 AP173 30p multicolored 2.50 .40
Souvenir Sheet
Perf. 13½x14
C666 AP173 50p multicolored 3.50 3.50
ESPAMER '78 Philatelic Exhibition, Bogota, Oct. 12-21.

Owl, Gold Ornament, Calima AP174

Virgin and Child, by Gregorio Vasquez AP175

No. C669, Gold frog, Quimbaya culture. No. C670, Gold nose pendant, Tairona, horiz.

1978-80 **Litho.** *Perf. 12½*
C667 AP174 3.50p multi .40 .20
C668 AP174 4p multi ('79) .25 .20
C669 AP174 4p multi ('79) .40 .20
C670 AP174 5p multi ('80) .60 .20
Nos. C667-C670 (4) 1.65 .80

1978, Nov. 28 *Perf. 13½x14*
C671 AP175 2.50p multicolored .25 .20
Christmas 1978.

Bull Ring, Cathedral, Manizales AP176

1979, Jan. 6 **Litho.** *Perf. 14*
C672 AP176 7p multicolored .60 .20
Manizales Fair.

Children Playing Hopscotch, and IYC Emblem — AP177

No. C674, Child at blackboard and UNESCO emblem. No. C675, The Paper Collector, by Omar Gordillo, and UN emblem.

1979, July 19 *Perf. 13½x14, 14x13½*
C673 AP177 8p multi .40 .30
C674 AP177 12p multi, horiz. .55 .45
C675 AP177 12p multi .55 .45
Nos. C673-C675 (3) 1.50 1.20
International Year of the Child.

Rio Prado Hydroelectric Station — AP178

1979, Aug. 24 *Perf. 13½x14*
C676 AP178 5p multicolored .50 .20

Tomb, 6th Century — AP179

1979, Sept. 25 **Litho.** *Perf. 14*
C677 AP179 8p multicolored .55 .35
San Augustin Archaeological Park.

Gonzalo Jimenez de Quesada, by C. Leudo AP180

1979, Oct. 11 *Perf. 12*
C678 AP180 20p multicolored 1.50 .50
Gonzalo Jimenez de Quesada (1500-1579), Spanish conquistador.

Hill, Penny Black, Colombia No. 1 — AP181

1979, Oct. 23 *Perf. 13½x14*
C679 AP181 15p multicolored .60 .20
Sir Rowland Hill (1795-1879), originator of penny postage.

Amazon Region — AP182

Tourism: 14p, San Fernando Fortress.

1979 **Litho.** *Perf. 13½x14*
C680 AP182 7p multicolored .40 .20
C681 AP182 14p multicolored 1.10 .60
Issue dates: 7p, Nov. 16; 14p, Nov. 9.
See Nos. C717-C719.

Nativity — AP183

Creche Sculptures: No. C682, Three Kings and soldiers. No. C684, Shepherds.

1979, Nov. 30   *Perf. 12*
C682 AP183 3p multicolored   .35 .35
C683 AP183 3p multicolored   .35 .35
C684 AP183 3p multicolored   .35 .35
  a.   Strip of 3, #C682-C684   1.40 1.40

Christmas 1979.

AP184

Magdalena Bridge, Avianca emblem.

1979, Dec. 5   *Perf. 14*
C685 AP184 15p multicolored   .60 .20

Barranquilla, 350th anniversary; Avianca National Airline, 60th anniversary.

1980, Feb. 15   *Perf. 13½x14*

Boy Playing Flute, by Judith Leyster.

C686 AP185 6p multicolored   .45 .20

2nd Intl. Music Competition, Ibague, Dec. 1979.

Gen. Antonio José de Sucre, 150th Death Anniversary AP186

1980, Feb. 15   Litho.   *Perf. 12½x12*
C687 AP186 12p multicolored   .45 .20

The Watchman, by Edgar Negret AP187

1980, Feb. 26   *Perf. 12x12½*
C688 AP187 25p multicolored   1.75 .80

Virgin Mary, by Real del Sarte, 1929 AP188

1980, May 23   Litho.   *Perf. 14x13½*
C689 AP188 12p multicolored   .30 .20

Apparition of the Virgin Mary to Sister Catalina Labouri Gontard, 150th anniv.

San Gil Produce Market, by Luis Roncancio — AP189

1980, May 27   *Perf. 13½x14*
C690 AP189 12p multicolored   .50 .25

Pres. Enrique Olaya Herrera, by Miguel Diaz Vargas — AP190

1980, Oct. 28   Litho.   *Perf. 12*
C691 AP190 20p multicolored   1.00 .40

Enrique Olaya Herrera (1880-1936), president, 1930-1934.

The Boy Fishing in a Bucket AP191

Christmas (Christmas Stories by Rafael Pombo): No. C693, The Frog and the Mouse. No. C694, The Seven Lives of the Cat.

1980, Nov. 21   Litho.   *Perf. 14½*
C692 AP191 4p multicolored   .20 .20
C693 AP191 4p multicolored   .20 .20
C694 AP191 4p multicolored   .20 .20
  Nos. C692-C694 (3)   .60 .60

28th World Golf Cup, Cajica — AP192

1980, Dec. 9   Litho.   *Perf. 13½x14*
C695 AP192 30p multicolored   3.75 .50

Bolivar Type

Simon Bolivar Death Sesquicentennial: 6p, Portrait, last words to Colombia, vert.

1980, Dec. 17   *Perf. 12*
C696 A400   6p multicolored   .60 .45

St. Peter Claver Holding Cross AP193

1981, Jan. 13   *Perf. 14½*
C697 AP193 15p multicolored   .50 .20

St. Peter Claver (1580-1654), helped American Indians.

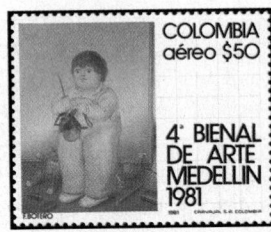

Sculptured Bird, San Augustin AP194

Archaeological Finds: No. C699, Funeral chamber, Tierradentro. No. C700, Chamber hallway, Tierradentro. No. C701, Statue of man, San Augustin.

1981, May 12   Litho.   *Perf. 14*
C698 AP194 7p multicolored   1.00 .20
C699 AP194 7p multicolored   1.00 .20
C700 AP194 7p multicolored   1.00 .20
C701 AP194 7p multicolored   1.00 .20
  a.   Block of 4, #C698-C701   5.00 5.00

See Nos. C707-C710D.

Child with Hobby Horse, by Fernando Botero — AP195

4th Biennial Arts show, Medellin: 20p, Square Abstract, by Omar Rayo. 25p, Flowers, by Alejandro Obregon.

1981, May 15   *Perf. 12*
C702 AP195 20p multicolored   .85 .20
C703 AP195 25p multicolored   1.00 .30
C704 AP195 50p multicolored   1.75 .75
  Nos. C702-C704 (3)   3.60 1.25

8th South American Swimming Championships, Medellin — AP196

1981, June 5
C705 AP196 15p multicolored   .50 .25

Santamaria Bull Ring, 50th Anniv. — AP197

1981, June 9   Litho.   *Perf. 12*
C706 AP197 30p multicolored   2.00 1.25

Quimbaya Culture — AP197a

1981, Sept. 23   Litho.   *Perf. 14*
    Yellow Background
C707   9p Man   1.00 .20
C708   9p Seated man   1.00 .20
C709   9p Seal, print   1.00 .20
C710   9p Jug   1.00 .20
  e.   AP197a Block of 4, #C707-C710   5.00 3.50

Calima Culture — AP197b

1981, Dec. 17
    White Background
C710A   9p Anthropomorphic container   1.25 .20
C710B   9p Jar   1.25 .20
C710C   9p Anthropomorphic jar   1.25 .20
C710D   9p Urn   1.25 .20
  f.   AP197b Block of 4, #C710A-C710D   6.00 4.50

Fruit AP198

1981, Nov. 3   Litho.   *Perf. 14*
C711   Block of 6   22.50 20.00
  a.-f.   AP198 25p, any single   3.00 .80

Revolt of the Comuneros, 200th Anniv. — AP199

1981, Nov. 21   Litho.   *Perf. 12*
C712 AP199 20p multicolored   .55 .30

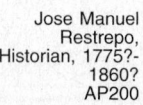

Jose Manuel Restrepo, Historian, 1775?-1860? historiador
AP200

Andres Bello, 1780?-1865
AP201

1981, Dec. 1   Litho.   Perf. 12
C713 AP200 35p multicolored   1.00   .35

1981, Dec. 11   Litho.   Perf. 12
C714 AP201 18p multicolored   .50   .20

Colombia's Admission to UPU, 100th Anniv.
AP202

30p, No. 103. 50p, Hemispheres, Nos. 104-108.

1981   Litho.   Perf. 12
C715 AP202 30p multicolored   1.00   .35

Size: 100x70mm

Imperf

C716 AP202 50p multicolored   3.00   3.00

Issued: No. C715, Dec. 18. No. C716, Dec. 28.

Tourism Type of 1979

1982   Litho.   Perf. 12
C717 AP182 20p Solano Bay   .50   .20
C718 AP182 20p Tota Lake, Boyaca   .50   .20
C719 AP182 20p Corrales, Boya-ca   .50   .20
Nos. C717-C719 (3)   1.50   .60

Issued: No. C717, 6/2; others, 6/16.

1982 World Cup — AP202a

Players and team emblems: a, "America." b, "A. B." c, "Cali." d, "C." e, "C/D." f, "Junior F.B.C." g, "D/M." h, Stadium. i, "M." j, "Club Atletico Nacional." k, "D/P." l, "Quindio." m, "Santa Fe." n, "T." o, "Santa Marta."

1982, June 21   Perf. 14
C720   Sheet of 15   10.00   6.75
a.-o. AP202a 9p, any single   .70   .30

Bogota Gun Club Centenary
AP202b

1982, July 16   Perf. 12
C721 AP202b 20p multicolored   .50   .20

Gold Crocodile Figure, Tairona Culture
AP202c

Tairona Culture Exhibit, Gold Museum: Various figures. Nos. C723-C727 vert.

1982, July 28

Gold, Black and:

C722 AP202c 25p light brown   1.60   .45
C723 AP202c 25p bright pink   1.60   .45
C724 AP202c 25p green   1.60   .45
C725 AP202c 25p dark blue   1.60   .45
C726 AP202c 25p violet   1.60   .45
C727 AP202c 25p red   1.60   .45
Nos. C722-C727 (6)   9.60   2.70

Government Buildings, Pereira — AP203

1982, Aug. 4   Litho.   Perf. 12
C728 AP203 35p multicolored   1.00   .40

Biplane in Flight, by Edgar Antonio Bustos
AP204

1982, Aug. 5   Perf. 14
C729 AP204 18p multicolored   .50   .20

American Air Forces Cooperation System.

Magdalena River
AP205

1982, Oct. 21   Litho.   Perf. 12
C730 AP205 30p multicolored   1.25   .35

Marquez Type

1982, Dec. 10   Perf. 13½x14
C731 A412 25p gray & blue   .60   .20
C732 A412 30p gray & brown   .85   .20

San Andres Archipelago — AP206

1983, Apr. 9   Litho.   Perf. 12
C733 AP206 25p Liberty Fort   .50   .20

Opening of Las Gaviotas (The Seagulls) Ecological Center, Bogota — AP207

1983, June 1   Litho.
C734 AP207 12p multicolored   .30   .20

50th Anniv. of Radio Amateurs League
AP208

1983, June 11   Perf. 14x13½
C735 AP208 12p multicolored   .30   .20

Bolivar Type

1983, July 24   Perf. 12
C736 A417 30p multicolored   .60   .20
C737 A417 100p multicolored   2.00   1.50

Botanical Exhibition Type

1983, Aug. 18   Perf. 14
C738 A418 12p Begonia guaduensis   .55   .20
C739 A418 12p Chinchona ovaliflora   .55   .20
C740 A418 40p Begonia urticae   2.90   .40
Nos. C738-C740 (3)   4.00   .80

Cartagena, 450th Anniv. — AP208a

1983, Sept. 9   Litho.   Perf. 12
C740A AP208a 12p Customs Square   .35   .20
C740B AP208a 35p Historic sites, Cartagena   .90   .30

Painting Type

1983, Oct. 5   Litho.   Perf. 12
C741 A420   30p multicolored   .50   .20

Scouting Year
AP209

Coffee Beans
AP210

1983, Oct. 24
C742 AP209 12p multicolored   .25   .20

1984, Mar. 28   Litho.   Perf. 14½x14
C743 AP210 14p multicolored   .25   .20

Marandua City Type

1984, Sept. 28   Perf. 12
C744 A427 30p multicolored   .50   .20

AP211

AP212

1984, Nov. 2
C745 AP211 45p multicolored   .70   .25

45th Cong. of Americanists, Bogota, 1985.

Christmas Type

1984, Dec. 14
C746 A428 14p multicolored   .30   .20

1985, Feb. 15

Design: Dove, map and flags of Colombia, Mexico, Costa Rica and Venezuela.

C747 AP212 40p multicolored   .70   .30

Contadora Group of Latin American countries.

Gomez Type

1985, Feb. 25
C748 A432 40p multicolored   .70   .30

Birds — AP213

AP214

1985
C749 AP213 14p Dryocopus lineatus nuperus   .70   .25

C750 AP213 20p Xiphorhynchus
　　　　　picus　　　　　1.40　.25
C751 AP213 50p Eriocnemis
　　　　　cupreoventris　3.00　.30
C752 AP213 55p Momotus
　　　　　momota　　　3.75　.30
　Nos. C749-C752 (4)　8.85　1.10
Issued: 14p, 4/12; 20p, 50p, 8/6; 55p, 8/29.

1985, July 15
C753 AP214 20p multicolored　.30　.20
Admiral Padilla Naval School, 50th anniv.

1985
Census
AP215

1985, Oct. 15　　　　　**Perf. 12**
C754 AP215 20p multicolored　.40　.20

Christmas Type

1985, Dec. 4　**Litho.**　**Perf. 13**
C755 A436 20p Girl, Christmas
　　　　　tree　　　　.30　.20

Alfonso Lopez
Pumarejo (1886-
1959), President,
1934-38, 1942-
45 — AP216

1986, Jan. 31
C756 AP216 24p multicolored　.30　.20

Coffee
Berries,
Natl.
Cycling
Team
AP217

1986, Feb. 4
C757 AP217 60p multicolored　1.00　.60
Natl. Coffee Producers Assoc. sponsorship
of natl. cycling team, 25th anniv.

Fauna Type of 1985

1986, Feb. 18
C758 A433 50p Pudu mephis-
　　　　　tophiles　　　1.50　.25

World
Communications
Day — AP218

Intl. Peace
Year — AP219

1986, May 17　**Litho.**　**Perf. 13**
C759 AP218 50p multicolored　.65　.25

1986, June 13　**Litho.**　**Perf. 13**
C760 AP219 55p multicolored　.65　.25

AP220

AP221

1986, July 1　**Litho.**　**Perf. 13**
C761 AP220 24p Portrait, papal
　　　　　arms　　　1.50　.20
C762 AP220 55p Portrait, Me-
　　　　　dellin cathe-
　　　　　dral, horiz.　1.50　.25
C763 AP220 60p Blessing
　　　　　crowd, horiz.　1.50　.25
　Nos. C761-C763 (3)　4.50　.70
Souvenir Sheet
C764 AP220 200p Praying, Ma-
　　　　　donna of Bo-
　　　　　gota　　　3.00　3.00
　Visit of Pope John Paul II.
Nos. C762-C763 each printed in sheets of
20 with se-tenant labels picturing religious
symbols.

1986, July 15　　　　**Perf. 12**
C765 AP221 25p multicolored　.30　.20
Enrique Santos Montejo (1886-1971),
journalist.

Bach,
Handel and
Schutz,
Composers
AP222

1986, July 17　　　　**Perf. 13**
C766 AP222 70p Bach　1.50　.40
C767 AP222 100p Text, music　2.00　.55

Salesian
Order
Education
in
Colombia,
Cent.
AP223

1986, July 23　　　　**Perf. 12**
C768 AP223 25p De La Salle,
　　　　　founder　.30　.20

Completion
of Coal
Mining
Complex,
El Cerrejon
AP224

1986, July 29　**Litho.**　**Perf. 12**
C769 AP224 55p multi　.80　.20

AP225

Natl. Constitution, Cent. — AP226

25p, The Five Signators, by R. Vasquez,
detail, & Bogota Cathedral. 200p, Pres. Nunez
& Miguel Antonio Caro, Natl. Council of Delegates chairman, & Presidential Palace,
constitution.

1986, Aug. 5　**Litho.**　**Perf. 14**
C770 AP225 25p multi　.30　.20
Souvenir Sheet
Perf. 12
C771 AP226 200p multi　2.25　2.25

Poet Type
Federico Garcia Lorca (1898-1936), poet,
and birthplace, Fuentevaqueros, Granada,
Spain.

1986, Sept. 26　**Litho.**　**Perf. 12**
C772 A445 60p multi　.70　.25

Gratitude
for Intl. Aid
after the
Armero
Mudslide
Disaster
AP227

1986, Nov. 13
C773 AP227 50p multi　.55　.20

Christmas
AP228

Wood sculpture: Virgin Mestiza, Nerina.

1986, Dec. 19　**Litho.**　**Perf. 12**
C774 AP228 25p multi　.30　.20

The Apotheosis of Popayan, by
Ephrain Martinez Zambrano (1898-
1956) — AP229

1987, Jan. 13
C775 100p Popayan riding horse 1.50　.75
C776 100p Onlookers　1.50　.75
　a. AP229 Pair, #C775-C776　3.50　3.50

AP230

AP231

1987, Mar. 16　**Litho.**　**Perf. 12**
C777 AP230 30p multi　.40　.20
The Conversion of St. Augustine of Hippo,
1600th anniv.

Type of 1987
30p, Phoenicopterus ruber. 35p,
Pseudemys scripta, horiz. No. C780, Crax
alberti. No. C781, Symphysodon aequifas-
ciatum, horiz.

Perf. 14½x14, 14x14½
1987-89　　　　　**Wmk. 334**
C778 A446a 30p lake　　　.35　.20
C779 A446a 35p dark red brn　.40　.20
C780 A446a 45p dark blue gray　.30　.20
C781 A446a 45p blue　　　.30　.20
　Nos. C778-C781 (4)　1.35　.80
　Issue dates: 30p, June 8. 35p, Dec. 24. No.
C780, Dec. 6, 1988. No. C781, June 23, 1989.

Perf. 13½x13
1987, Apr. 10　　　　**Unwmk.**
C783 AP231 25p multi　.30　.20
Natl. University School of Mining, Medellin,
cent.

Purebred
Horses
AP232

1987, June 17　　　　**Perf. 12**
C784 AP232 60p White horse　1.00　.25
C785 AP232 70p Black horse　1.00　.30

El Espectador
Newspaper,
Cent.
AP233

Design: Frontispieces from 1887, 1915,
1948, 1974 and portraits of founder Don Fidel
Cano, editors Don Luis Cano, Luis Gabriel
Cano Isaza and Alfonso Cano Isaza.

1987, July 24　　　　**Perf. 12½x12**
C786 AP233 60p multi　.75　.25

Intl. Year of
Shelter for the
Homeless
AP234

1987, Sept. 21 *Perf. 14*
C787 AP234 60p multi 1.10 .25

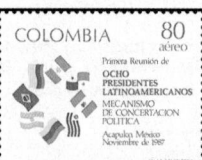

Flags
AP235

1987, Nov. 27 Litho. *Perf. 13x13½*
C788 AP235 80p multi .80 .30
Ist Meeting of the eight Latin-American
Presidents, Acapulco, Nov.

Christmas
AP236

1987, Dec. 8 Litho. *Perf. 14*
C789 AP236 30p multi .45 .20

Rural
Telephone
System
AP237

1988, Feb. 4 Litho. *Perf. 14*
C790 AP237 70p multi .80 .30

Founding of
Bogota, 450th
Anniv. — AP238

1988, Apr. 11 Litho. *Perf. 12*
C791 AP238 70p multi .75 .25

Bogota,
450th
Anniv.
AP238a

Unwmk.
1988, July 1 Litho. *Perf. 12*
C792 AP238a 80p Modern district,
vert. .75 .25
C793 AP238a 90p Colonial district .85 .30

Gold
Artifacts
AP239

Artifacts in the Gold Museum: 70p, Mask.
80p, Two-headed human figure inside a circle,
Muisca tribe. 90p, Ritual figure of the
Quimbaya.

1988 *Perf. 12*
C794 AP239 70p multi .65 .30
C795 AP239 80p multi .75 .25
C796 AP239 90p multi 1.00 .35
Nos. C794-C796 (3) 2.40 .90
Issue dates: 70p, May 13; 80p, 90p, Oct. 7.

Human Rights Type
Perf. 14x14½
1988, July 1 Engr. Wmk. 334
C797 A452 40p Communication,
horiz. .40 .20

AP240

AP241

1988, Sept. 28 Litho. *Perf. 12*
C798 AP240 80p multi .70 .20
Zipa Tisquesusa (d. 1538), Chibcha Indian
leader during revolt against Spanish
Conquistadors.

1988, Nov. 23 Litho. *Perf. 12*
C799 AP241 40p multi .50 .20
Christmas.

Agustin Nieto Caballero (1889-1975),
Educator — AP242

Unwmk.
1989, Mar. 18 Litho. *Perf. 12*
C800 AP242 100p multi .75 .25

Pres. Laureano
Gomez (1889-
1965)
AP243

1989, Mar. 29
C801 AP243 45p multi .30 .20

Intl. Coffee Organization — AP244

1989, Apr. 3
C802 AP244 110p multi .90 .30

12th Session of
the UN
Commission on
Human
Rights — AP245

1989, Apr. 28
C803 AP245 100p multi .90 .25

French
Revolution,
Bicent.
AP246

1989, June 29 Litho. *Perf. 12*
C804 AP246 100p multi .75 .25

PHILEXFRANCE '89 — AP247

a, Bananas, tropical fruits. b, Fruits, flowers.
c, Birds, animals. d, Precious gems, metals
and mineral resources. e, View of fields,
Colombian carrying produce basket. f, Waterfall. g, Fish, coast. Illustration reduced.

1989 Litho. *Perf. 14*
C805 AP247 Pane of 7 17.50 17.50
a.-g. 110p any single 1.75 .40
No. C805 printed in sheets containing
panes of 7, rouletted between.

Souvenir Sheet

Los Lanceros, by R. Arenas
Betancur — AP248

1989 Litho. *Perf. 12*
C806 AP248 250p multicolored 1.75 1.25

Human Rights Type
Perf. 14½x14
1989, Aug. 18 Engr. Wmk. 334
C807 A452 55p Family .40 .20

Natl. Anti-Drugs
Campaign
AP249

Unwmk.
1989, Aug. 23 Litho. *Perf. 12*
C808 AP249 115p multicolored .90 .25

America
Issue
AP250

UPAE emblem and artifacts or customs of
pre-Columbian peoples: 115p, Quimbaya,
Calima or Tolima gold smiths. 130p, Potter and
Sinu ceramic figurine.

1989 *Perf. 12*
C809 AP250 115p multicolored 1.00 .25
C810 AP250 130p multicolored 1.10 .30
Issue dates: 115p, Oct. 12; 130p, Aug. 23.

Joaquin Quijano Mantilla (1878-1944),
Journalist — AP251

1989, Sept. 29 *Perf. 12*
C811 AP251 170p multicolored 1.20 .40

Arts and Crafts in
Barro-Raquira
AP252

1989 Litho. *Perf. 12*
C812 AP252 55p multicolored .40 .20
Christmas.

Boeing 767
AP253

1989, Dec. 5 Litho. *Perf. 12*
C813 AP253 130p multicolored .90 .30

Bolivar Installed at the Congress of Angostura, by Tito Salas — AP254

1989, Dec. 12
C814 AP254 130p multicolored   .90 .30
   Creation of the Republic, 1819.

Fathers of the Nation Leaving the Constitutional Convention AP255

1989, Dec. 12
C815 AP255 130p shown   .90 .30
C816 AP255 130p Arms   .90 .30
C817 AP255 130p Temple of the
                  Rosary   .90 .30
   Nos. C815-C817 (3)   2.70 .90
   Constitution of the Republic, 1821.

Arms Type of Regular Issue, 1982
1990, Mar. 1   Litho.   Perf. 12
C818 A372 60p Velez   .30 .20

Presidential Summit, Cartagena AP256

1990, Feb. 15   Litho.   Perf. 12
C819 AP256 130p Plaza de la
                 Aduana   .55 .20

Colombian National Radio, 50th Anniv. — AP257

1990, Feb. 16   Litho.   Perf. 12
C820 AP257 150p multicolored   1.00 .20

Teresa Cuervo Borda (1889-1976), Art Historian — AP258

1990, Mar. 28   Litho.   Perf. 12
C821 AP258 60p multicolored   .35 .20

Second Latin American Theater Festival, Bogota — AP259

1990, Apr. 10
C822 AP259 150p buff, tan &
                gold   .80 .25

Santander Type
   No. C823, Santander holding the Constitution. No. C824, Central Cemetery, Bogota and National Pantheon. No. C825, Santander, as organizer of public education. No. C826, "Postman of New Granada" (Man and burro) by Joseph Brown and Jose Maria del Castillo, horiz. 500p, Santander on death bed.

1990, May 6   Perf. 14x13½
C823 A470 60p multicolored   .30 .20
C824 A470 60p multicolored   .30 .20
C825 A470 70p multicolored   .40 .20
C826 A470 70p multicolored   .40 .20
   Nos. C823-C826 (4)   1.40 .80

Souvenir Sheet
Perf. 12
C827 A470 500p multi   2.00 1.50
   No. C827 contains one 54x40mm stamp.

First Postage Stamp, 150th Anniv. AP260

1990, May 6   Perf. 14
C828 AP260 150p multicolored   .80 .25

Trans-Caribbean Fiber Optic Cable — AP261

1990, May 19   Perf. 12
C829 AP261 150p multicolored   .80 .25

Institute of Industrial Development, 25th Anniv. — AP262

1990, May 22
C830 AP262 60p multicolored   .40 .20

Souvenir Sheet

World Cup Soccer Championships, Italy — AP263

1990, June 8
C831 AP263 500p multicolored   3.00 2.25

AP264

AP265

1990, June 27
C832 AP264 130p multicolored   .60 .20
   Organization of American States, cent.

1990, July 26
C833 AP265 170p multicolored   .80 .25
   Museum of Gold, 50th Anniv.

Dolphins, Marine Birds AP266

1990, Oct. 12   Litho.   Perf. 12
C834 AP266 150p shown   1.50 .20
C835 AP266 170p Jungle fauna,
              vert.   1.50 .25

AP267

AP268

1990, Nov. 16   Litho.   Perf. 12
C836 AP267 70p multicolored   .40 .20
   Monastery of Our Lady of Las Lajas.

1991, Feb. 8   Litho.   Perf. 12
C837 AP268 170p multicolored   .80 .30
   Newspaper Publishing, 200th Anniv.

AP269

AP270

1990, Nov. 1   Litho.   Perf. 12
C838 AP269 70p multicolored   .40 .20
   Christmas.

1991, May 31   Litho.   Perf. 14
   Whales and Dolphins: 80p, Megaptera novaeangliae, breaching. 170p, Megaptera novaeangliae, diving. 190p, Inia geoffrensis, Sotalia fluviatilis, horiz.
C839 AP270 80p multicolored   .90 .20
C840 AP270 170p multicolored   1.90 .30
C841 AP270 190p multicoloed   2.10 .30
   Nos. C839-C841 (3)   4.90 .80

America Issue AP271

1991, Oct. 11   Litho.   Perf. 14
C842 AP271 90p shown   .45 .20
C843 AP271 190p Ship arriving
              in New World   .85 .25

Adoration of the Magi — AP272

1991, Dec. 20   Litho.   Perf. 14
C844 AP272 90p multicolored   .45 .20
   Christmas.

AP273

AP274

1991, Dec. 2
C845 AP273 190p Country flags .85 .25
Fifth summit of Latin American presidents.

1992, Feb. 8 Litho. *Perf. 12*
C846 AP274 210p multicolored 1.00 .30
8th UNCTAD Conference, Cartagena.

Proclamation of New Constitution, July 4, 1991 — AP275

1991, Nov. 27 Litho. *Perf. 14*
C847 AP275 90p multicolored .40 .20

Export Products
AP276

Copyright Protection
AP277

1992, Mar. 11 *Perf. 12*
C848 AP276 90p Flowers .40 .20
C849 AP276 210p Fruits, vegetables, horiz. 1.10 .30

1992, Apr. 13 Litho. *Perf. 12*
C850 AP277 190p multicolored .85 .25

1992 Summer Olympics
AP278

1992, June 4 Litho. *Perf. 14*
C851 AP278 110p multicolored .75 .30

Earth Summit '92
AP279

a, Tree, mountain landscape. b, Birds in tree.

1992, June 2 Litho. *Perf. 14*
C852 A279 230p Pair, #a.-b. 2.10 1.40

America Issue
AP280

Paintings: 230p, Discovery of America by Christopher Columbus, by Salvador Dali. 260p, Magical America, Myth and Legend, by Alfredo Vivero.

1992, July 22 *Perf. 14x13½*
C853 AP280 230p multicolored 1.00 .70
C854 AP280 260p multicolored 1.10 .75

McDonnell Douglas MD83
AP281

1992, Sept. 22 Litho. *Perf. 12*
C855 AP281 110p multicolored .50 .30

Curtain of Colon Theatre
AP282

1992, Oct. 12 Litho. *Perf. 12*
C856 AP282 230p multicolored 1.00 .65

AP283

AP284

1992, Nov. 27 Litho. *Perf. 12*
C857 AP283 230p Gloria Lara, 1938-82 1.00 .65

1993, June 7 Litho. *Perf. 12*
C858 AP284 220p multicolored .95 .60
1993 American Soccer Cup, Ecuador.

Intl. Year of Indigenous People — AP285

1993, July 1 *Perf. 14*
C859 AP285 460p multicolored 2.00 1.25

South American Eliminations for 1994 World Cup Soccer Championships, US — AP286

1993, July 31 Litho. *Perf. 12*
C860 AP286 220p multicolored .95 .50

AP287

AP288

America Issue (Endangered species): a, 220p, Saguinus oedipus. b, 220p, Porphyrula martinica. c, 460p, Rupicola peruviana. d, 520p, Trichecus manatus.

1993, Oct. 19 Litho. *Perf. 12*
C861 AP287 Block of 4, #a.-d. 7.50 7.50

1994, Mar. 21 Litho. *Perf. 12*
C862 AP288 630p multicolored 2.25 1.40
Intl. Decade for Natural Disaster Reduction.

Beatification of Josemaria Escriva de Balaguer — AP289

1994, May 17 Litho. *Perf. 13½x14*
C863 AP289 560p multicolored 1.90 1.25

First Airmail Delivery, 75th Anniv. AP290

Design: 270p, William Knox Martin, airplane over Port Colombia, 1919.

1994, July 29 Litho. *Perf. 14*
C864 AP290 270p multicolored 1.00 .55

Natl. Institute of Medical Law & Forensic Sciences, 80th Anniv. AP291

1994, Oct. 27 Litho. *Perf. 12*
C865 AP291 560p multicolored 1.90 1.25

Sociedad Colombo-Alemana de Transportes Aereos (SCADTA), 75th Anniv. — AP292

1995, Jan. 2 Litho. *Perf. 12*
C866 AP292 330p No. C15 1.10 .50

Flora and Fauna — AP293

Iguana iguana: No. C867a, Facing right. b, Facing left.
Rain forest: No. C868a, Nuts on branch, flowers. b, Waterfall, hanging red flower.

1995, Jan. 17
C867 AP293 650p Pair, #a.-b. 4.50 3.00
C868 AP293 750p Pair, #a.-b. 5.50 4.00
Nos. C867-C868 are continuous designs.

SCADTA, 75th Anniv. AP294

1995, Mar. 30 Litho. *Perf. 14*
C869 AP294 330p No. C9 1.50 .75

FAO, 50th Anniv. AP295

1995, Apr. 25 Litho. *Perf. 13x13½*
C870 AP295 750p multicolored   2.25 1.25

Andres Bello Organization, 25th Anniv. — AP296

Colombian Firefighters, Cent. — AP297

1995, Apr. 27   *Perf. 13½x13*
C871 AP296 650p multicolored   2.00 .85

1995, May 5   *Perf. 12*
C872 AP297 330p multicolored   1.10 .45

Fenalco, 50th Anniv. — AP298

UN, 50th Anniv. — AP299

1995, May 25   *Perf. 13½*
C873 AP298 330p multicolored   1.10 .45

1995, June 21   *Perf. 12*
C874 AP299 750p multicolored   1.50 1.00

First Pacific Ocean Games — AP300

1995, June 23
C875 AP300 750p multicolored   2.25 1.25

11th Summit of Non-Aligned Countries, Cartagena — AP302

1995, Oct. 13   Litho.   *Perf. 12*
C877 AP302 650p multicolored   1.50 .90

Motion Pictures, Cent. AP303

Design: 330p, Charlie Chaplin and Jackie Coogan in "The Kid," Estela López Pomareda in "Maria," first Colombian feature length film.

1995, Oct. 19   *Perf. 14*
C878 AP303 330p black & sepia   .90 .45

AP304

AP305

1995, Nov. 23   *Perf. 12*
C879 AP304 650p multicolored   1.90 .90

Andes Development Corporation (CAF), 25th Anniv.

1995, Nov. 21   *Perf. 14*
Fight against illegal drug trafficking: No. C880, Locating illegally grown plants. No. C881, Hands in handcuffs, horiz.

C880 AP305 330p multicolored   .70 .45
C881 AP305 330p multicolored   .70 .45

Miniature Sheet of 16

Myths and Legends — AP306

Madre-Monte: a.-d.
La Llorona: e.-h.
El Mohán: i.-l.
Hombre Caimán: m.-p.
Background color changes from top to bottom rows. Top row is blue. Row 2 is blue

green. Row 3 is green. Row 4 is lilac. Each design comes in all four colors.

1995, Dec. 6
C882 AP306 750p #a.-p.   27.50 27.50
    See No. C886.

José Asunción Silva (1865-96), Poet AP307

1996, Apr. 23   Litho.   *Perf. 12*
C883 AP307 400p multicolored   .90 .40

Isla de Providencia AP308

Policarpa Salavarrieta (1796-1817), Patriot — AP309

1996, Apr. 25   *Perf. 14*
C884 AP308 800p multicolored   2.25 .80

1996, Apr. 26
C885 AP309 900p multicolored   2.50 .85

Myths and Legends Type

Designs: a, Kogui Creation. b, Yonna Wayu. c, Jaguar Man. d, Master of the Animals.

1996, Aug. 12   Litho.   *Perf. 13½x14*
C886 AP306 900p Block of 4,
    #a.-d.   13.00 13.00

Metropolitan Basilica, Medellin AP310

1996, July 12
C887 AP310 400p multicolored   1.10 .55

National Archives Building AP311

1996, July 30   Litho.   *Perf. 14*
C888 AP311 400p multicolored   1.10 .40

CERLALC, 25th Anniv. AP312

1996, Aug. 16   Litho.   *Perf. 12*
C889 AP312 800p multicolored   2.10 1.00
    UNESCO.

Pioneers in Petroleum Industry — AP313

a, Jorge Isaacs, pumping oil. b, Francisco Burgos Rubio, refinery at night. c, Diego Martínez Camargo, derrick. d, Prisciliano Cabrales Lora, off-shore drilling. e, Manuel María Palacio, oil tanker loading offshore. f, Roberto De Mares, refinery, lake. g, General Virgilio Barco Maldonado, men positioning equipment. h, Roustabout, "ECOPETROL" emblem.

1996, Sept. 5   Litho.   *Perf. 13½x14*
C890 AP313 800p Block of 8,
    #a.-h.   20.00 20.00

Colombian Golf Federation, 50th Anniv. AP314

1996, Sept. 19   Litho.   *Perf. 12*
C891 AP314 400p multicolored   1.25 .50

Covenant for the Children AP315

1997, Feb. 28   Litho.   *Perf. 14*
C892 AP315 400p multicolored   1.40 .55

AP316

AP317

1997, Apr. 25   *Perf. 12*
C893 AP316 800p multicolored   1.75 1.40
Motion pictures in Colombia, cent.

1997, May 13   **Litho.**   *Perf. 12*
C894 AP317 400p multicolored   1.50 .50
Social Security Institute, 50th anniv.

Ericsson in Colombia, Cent. — AP318

1997, May 22   *Perf. 13½x14*
C895 AP318 900p multicolored   2.50 1.40

Bogotá Colonial Bldg., Home of Natl.
Mint and Numismatic
Museum — AP319

1997, July 10   *Perf. 12*
C896 AP319 800p multicolored   2.50 1.40

Phytelephas Seemannii — AP320

1997, July 23   *Perf. 13½x14*
C897 AP320 900p multicolored   3.00 .90

Cordoba
Cattle Fair
AP321

1997, June 21   *Perf. 14*
C898 AP321 400p multicolored   1.25 .45

Personalities — AP322

No. C899: a, Cacique Gaitana, 16th cent., Indian resistance leader. b, Josefa Acevedo de Gómez (1803-61), writer. c, Domingo Bioho (d. 1621), black leader. d, Soledad Acosta de Samper (1831-1913), historian. e, Maria Cano Márquez (1897-1967), popular leader. f, Manuel Quintín Lame (1880-1967), native leader. g, Ezequiel Uricoechea (1834-80), linguist, naturalist. h, Juan Rodríguez Freyle (1566-1642), colonial reporter. i, Gerardo Reichel-Dolmatoff (1912-94), archaeologist. j, Ramón de Zubiría (1922-95), writer, educator. k, Esteban Jaramillo (1874-1947), economist. l, Pedro Fermín de Vargas (1762-c. 1810), economist.

No. C900: a, Luis Carlos "el tuerto" López (1879-1950), poet. b, Aurelio Arturo (1906-74), poet. c, Enrique Pérez Arbeláez (1896-1972), botanist. d, José Maria González Benito (1843-1903), mathematician, astronomer. e, José Manuel Rivas Sacconi (1917-91), diplomat. f, Eduardo Lemaitre Román (1914-94), historian. g, Diójenes Arrieta (1848-93), politician. h, Gabriel Turbay Abunader (1901-47), politician, diplomat. i, Guillermo Echavarría Misas (1888-1985), aviation pioneer. j, Juan Friede Alter (1901-90), historian. k, Fabio Lozano Torrijos (1865-1947), diplomat. l, Lino de Pombo (1797-1862), engineer, diplomat.

1997, Dec. 19   **Litho.**   *Perf. 13½x14*
Sheets of 12
C899 AP322 500p #a.-l.   22.50 22.50
C900 AP322 500p #a.-l.   22.50 22.50

Colombian Society of Orthopedic
Surgery and Traumatology, 50th
Anniv. — AP323

1997   *Perf. 12*
C901 AP323 1000p multicolored   3.00 1.00

AP324

AP325

1998, Apr. 30   **Litho.**   *Perf. 14*
C902 AP324 1000p multicolored   3.00 .80
Organization of American States, 50th anniv.

1998, May 22
C903 AP325 1000p bl & org   3.00 .80
4th Bolivar Philatelic Exhibition, Santa Fe de Bogota.

World Health
Organization,
50th
Anniv. — AP326

1998, Apr. 7   *Perf. 12*
C904 AP326 1100p multicolored   3.00 1.00

1998 World Cup Soccer
Championships, France — AP327

Stylized designs: a, Foot. b, Soccer ball. c, Hand.

1998, June 9   **Litho.**   *Perf. 14*
C905 AP327 1100p Strip of 3,
    #a.-c.   9.00 9.00

Intl. Year of the Ocean — AP328

1998, May 22   *Perf. 12*
C906 AP328 1100p ARC Gloria   3.50 .95

Myths and Legends — AP329

Designs: a, Bochica. b, Chimingagua. c, Bachue and Huitica.

Perf. 13¼x12¾
1998, Nov. 27   **Litho.**
C907 AP329 1000p Strip of 3,
    #a.-c.   15.00 15.00

AIR POST SPECIAL DELIVERY STAMPS

> **Catalogue values for unused stamps in this section are for Never Hinged items.**

Post Horn
and Wings
APSD1

Unwmk.
1958, May 19   **Litho.**   *Perf. 12*
CE1   APSD1 25c dk bl & red   .55 .20

1959
CE2   APSD1 25c dk bl & red   .50 .20

Jet Plane and Envelope — APSD2

1963, Oct. 4   *Perf. 14*
CE3   APSD2 50c red & blk   .25 .20

Aviation Type
80c, Boeing 727 jet, 1966.

Perf. 14x13½
1966, Dec. 14   **Photo.**   **Unwmk.**
CE4   AP96 80c crim & multi   .55 .25

AIR POST REGISTRATION STAMPS

**Issued by Sociedad Colombo-
Alemana de Transportes Aereos
(SCADTA)**

No. C41 Overprinted
in Red

1923   **Wmk. 116**   *Perf. 14x14½*
CF1   AP6   20c gray   4.75 1.10

No. C58 Overprinted in
Black

1929   **Wmk. 127**   *Perf. 14*
CF2   AP8   20c carmine   8.00 7.00

Same Overprint on No. C71
CF3   AP10 20c carmine   6.50 6.00

Colombian Government Issues
Same Overprint on No. C86

1932
CF4   AP8   20c carmine   6.50 6.00

No. C100 Overprinted

CF5   AP12 20c car & ol blk   6.00 1.25
For surcharge see No. C118.

SPECIAL DELIVERY STAMPS

Special Delivery
Messenger — SD1

1917   Unwmk.   Engr.   _Perf. 14_
E1   SD1   5c gray green   60.00 150.00

Catalogue values for unused
stamps in this section, from this
point to the end of the section, are
for Never Hinged items.

SD2

1987, July 31   Litho.   _Perf. 14_
E2   SD2   25p emerald & ver   .30   .30
E3   SD2   30p emerald & ver   .35   .35

REGISTRATION STAMPS

R1   R2

1865   Unwmk.   Litho.   _Imperf._
F1   R1   5c black   87.50 47.50
F2   R2   5c black   110.00 50.00

R3   R4

1870
White Paper
Vertical Lines in Background
F3   R3   5c black   3.00   2.50
F4   R4   5c black   3.00   2.50
Horizontal Lines in Background
F5   R3   5c black   10.00   8.50
F6   R4   5c black   3.00   2.50
    Nos. F3-F6 (4)   19.00 16.00
Reprints of Nos. F3 to F6 show either
crossed lines or traces of lines in background.

R5

R6

1881   _Imperf._
F7   R5   10c violet   60.00 52.50
  a.   Sewing machine perf.   67.50 60.00
  b.   Perf. 11   75.00 62.50

1883   _Perf. 12, 13½_
F8   R6   10c red, _orange_   2.00   2.50

R7

1889-95   _Perf. 12, 13½_
F9   R7   10c red, _grysh_   9.50   4.50
F10   R7   10c red, _yelsh_   9.50   4.50
F11   R7   10c dp brn, _rose_
             buff ('95)   2.00   1.60
F12   R7   10c yel brn, _lt buff_
             ('92)   2.00   1.60
    Nos. F9-F12 (4)   23.00 12.20
    Nos. F9-F12 exist imperf. Values same as
    for perf.

R9

1902   _Imperf._
F13   R9   20c red brown, _blue_   1.60   1.60
  a.   Sewing machine perf.   4.75   4.75
  b.   Perf. 12   4.75   4.75

Medellín Issue

R10

1902   _Perf. 12_
Laid Paper
F16   R10   10c blk vio   15.00 15.00
  a.   Wove paper   21.00 21.00

Regular Issue
1903   _Imperf._
F17   R9   20c blue, _blue_   1.60   1.60
  a.   Sewing machine perf.   4.75   4.75
  b.   Perf. 12   4.75   4.75

R11

1904   Pelure Paper   _Imperf._
F19   R11   10c purple   3.75   3.75
  a.   Sewing machine perf.   5.00   3.75
  b.   Perf. 12   6.25   5.00

R12

    Imprint: "J. L. Arango"
1904   _Perf. 12_
Wove Paper
F20   R12   10c purple   2.50   .60
  a.   Imperf., pair   7.75   7.75

    Imprint: "Lit. Nacional"
1909   _Perf. 10, 14, 10x14, 14x10_
F21   R12   10c purple   2.75   .85
  a.   Imperf., pair   6.25   6.25
    For overprints see Nos. LF1-LF4.

Execution at Cartagena in
1816 — R13

1910, July 20   Engr.   _Perf. 12_
F22   R13   10c red & black   21.00 90.00
    Centenary of National Independence.

Pier at Puerto Colombia — R14

Tequendama Falls — R15

Perf. 11, 11½, 14, 11½x14
1917, Aug. 25
F23   R14   4c green & ultra   .55   3.50
  a.   Center inverted   575.00 575.00
F24   R15   10c deep blue   8.00   .60

R16

1925   Litho.   _Perf. 10x13½_
F25   R16   (10c) blue   4.25   1.90
  a.   Imperf., pair   15.00 12.50
  b.   Perf. 13½x10   7.50   5.00

ACKNOWLEDGMENT OF RECEIPT STAMPS

AR1   AR2

1893   Unwmk.   Litho.   _Perf. 13½_
H1   AR1   5c ver, _blue_   4.75   4.75

1894   _Perf. 12_
H2   AR1   5c vermilion   4.50   5.00

1902-03   _Imperf._
H3   AR2   10c blue, _blue_   3.50   5.00
  a.   10c, blue, _greenish blue_   3.50   5.00
  b.   Sewing machine perf.   3.50   5.00
  c.   Perf. 12   3.50   5.00

    The handstamp "AR" in circle is
believed to be a postmark.

AR2a

Purple Handstamp
1903   _Imperf._
H4   AR2a   10c black, _pink_   25.00 25.00

AR3

1904   Pelure Paper   _Imperf._
H12   AR3   5c pale blue   10.50 10.50
  a.   Perf. 12   10.50 10.50

No. 307 Overprinted
in Black, Green or
Violet

H13   A86   5c carmine   17.50 17.50

AR4

1904   _Perf. 12_
H16   AR4   5c blue   3.25   2.75
  a.   Imperf., pair   8.75   8.75
    For overprints see Nos. LH1-LH2.

General José
Acevedo y
Gómez — AR5

1910, July 20   Engr.
H17   AR5   5c orange & green   7.00 _17.50_
    Centenary of National Independence.

Sabana Station   Map of
AR6   Colombia
               AR7

1917   _Perf. 14_
H18   AR6   4c bister brown   5.50   6.00
H19   AR7   5c orange brown   5.50   4.50
  a.   Imperf., pair   14.00

LATE FEE STAMPS

LF1   LF2

1886   Unwmk.   Litho.   _Perf. 10½_
I1   LF1   2½c blk, _lilac_   4.00   3.25
  a.   Imperf., pair   15.00 15.00

1892   _Perf. 12, 13½_
I2   LF2   2½c dk bl, _rose_   3.50   2.50
  a.   Imperf., pair   15.00
I3   LF2   2½c ultra, _pink_   3.50   2.50

LF3

LF4

1902   Imperf.
I4	LF3	5c purple, *rose*	1.00	1.00
a.		Perf. 12	2.10	2.10

1914   Perf. 10, 13½
I6	LF4	2c vio brown	5.00	5.00
I7	LF4	5c blue green	5.00	4.25

Retardo   *Retardo*
           1921

Overprints illustrated above are unauthorized and of private origin.

POSTAGE DUE STAMPS

These are not, strictly speaking, postage due stamps but were issued to cover an additional fee, "Sobreporte," charged on mail to foreign countries with which Colombia had no postal conventions.

D1

D2

D3

1866   Unwmk.   Litho.   Imperf.
J1	D1	25c black, *blue*	80.00	55.00
J2	D2	50c black, *yellow*	55.00	*80.00*
J3	D3	1p black, *rose*	160.00	*125.00*
		Nos. J1-J3 (3)	295.00	260.00

DEPARTMENT STAMPS

These stamps are said to be for interior postage, to supersede the separate issues for the various departments.

Regular Issues Handstamped in Black, Violet, Blue or Green — a

Correos Departamentales

On Stamps of 1904
1909   Unwmk.   Perf. 12
L1	A94	½c yellow	2.50	2.50
a.		Imperf., pair	7.50	7.50
L2	A94	1c yel grn	3.75	2.50
L3	A94	2c red	5.50	3.75
a.		Imperf., pair	15.00	15.00
L4	A94	5c blue	6.25	4.00
L5	A94	10c violet	8.75	8.75
L6	A94	20c black	14.00	12.50
L7	A95	1p brown	22.50	21.00

On Stamp of 1902
L8	A83	10p dk brn, *rose*	25.00	25.00
		Nos. L1-L8 (8)	88.25	80.00

On Stamps of 1908
Perf. 10, 13, 13½ and Compound
L9	A94	½c orange	2.50	2.50
a.		Imperf., pair	7.50	7.50
L10	A94	1c green	5.00	4.00
a.		Without imprint	6.25	6.25

L11	A94	2c red	5.50	4.00
a.		Imperf., pair		
L12	A94	5c blue	5.50	4.00
a.		Imperf., pair	15.00	15.00
L13	A94	10c violet	7.50	7.50

On Tolima Stamp of 1888
Perf. 10½
L14	A23	1p red brn	15.00	15.00
		Nos. L9-L14 (6)	41.00	37.00

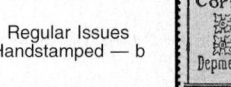
Correos Depmentales

Regular Issues Handstamped — b

On Stamps of 1904
Perf. 12
L15	A94	½c yellow	2.50	2.50
L16	A94	1c yellow grn	4.25	3.75
L17	A94	2c red	7.50	6.25
L18	A94	5c blue	7.50	6.25
L19	A94	10c violet	10.00	7.50
L20	A94	20c black	14.00	14.00
L21	A94	1p brown	25.00	25.00
		Nos. L15-L21 (7)	70.75	65.25

On Stamps of 1908
Perf. 10, 13, 13½
L22	A94	½c orange	2.75	2.75
L23	A94	1c yellow grn	7.75	7.75
L24	A94	2c red	6.25	6.25
a.		Imperf., pair	15.00	15.00
L25	A94	5c light blue	7.50	6.25
		Nos. L22-L25 (4)	24.25	23.00

The handstamps on Nos. L1-L25 are, as usual, found inverted and double.

DEPARTMENT REGISTRATION STAMPS

Registration Stamps Handstamped like Nos. L1-L25
On Registration Stamp of 1904
1909   Unwmk.   Perf. 12
LF1	R12 (a)	10c purple	30.00	30.00
LF2	R12 (b)	10c purple	30.00	30.00

On Registration Stamp of 1909
Perf. 10, 13
LF3	R12 (a)	10c purple	30.00	30.00
LF4	R12 (b)	10c purple	30.00	30.00
		Nos. LF1-LF4 (4)	120.00	120.00

Nos. LF1-LF4 exist imperf. Value per pair, $125.

DEPARTMENT ACKNOWLEDGMENT OF RECEIPT STAMPS

Acknowledgment of Receipt Stamp of 1904 Handstamped like Nos. L1-L25
1909   Unwmk.   Perf. 12
LH1	AR4 (a)	5c blue	30.00	30.00
a.		Imperf., pair	125.00	
LH2	AR4 (b)	5c blue	30.00	30.00
a.		Imperf., pair	125.00	

LOCAL STAMPS FOR THE CITY OF BOGOTA

A1

Pelure Paper
1889   Unwmk.   Litho.   Perf. 12
LX1	A1	½c black	1.10	1.10
a.		Imperf., pair	7.25	7.25

Impressions on bright blue and blue-gray paper were not regularly issued.

A2

A3

White Wove Paper
1896   Perf. 12, 13½
LX2	A2	½c black	1.10	1.10

1903   Imperf.
LX3	A3	10c black, *pink*	7.25	1.40
a.		Perf. 12	7.25	1.40

OFFICIAL STAMPS

Stamps of 1917-1937 Overprinted in Black or Red:

a

b

1937   Unwmk.   Perf. 11, 12, 13½
O1	A131 (a)	1c green	.20	.20
O2	A157 (a)	10c dp org	.20	.20
O3	A107 (b)	30c olive bis	2.10	1.00
O4	A129 (b)	40c brn & yel		
		brn	1.60	.80
O5	A114 (b)	50c car	1.60	.80
O6	A107 (b)	1p lt bl	13.00	5.50
O7	A107 (b)	2p org	15.00	6.50
O8	A107 (b)	5p gray	47.50	*52.50*
O9	A118 (b)	10p dk brn	110.00	*125.00*

Wmk. 229
Perf. 12½
O10	A132 (a)	2c red	.20	.20
O11	A133 (a)	5c brn	.20	.20
O12	A160 (a)	12c dp bl (R)	1.00	.50
O13	A136 (b)	20c dk bl (R)	1.60	.80
		Nos. O1-O13 (13)	194.20	194.20

Tall, wrong font "I's" in OFICIAL exist on all stamps with "a" overprint.

POSTAL TAX STAMPS

"Greatest Mother" PT1

Perf. 11½
1935, May 27   Unwmk.   Litho.
RA1	PT1	5c olive blk & scar	4.00	1.25

Required on all mail during Red Cross Week in 1935 (May 27-June 3) and in 1936.

Mother and Child — PT2

Perf. 10½, 10½x11
1937, May 24   Unwmk.
RA2	PT2	5c red	2.75	.90

Required on all mail during Red Cross Week. The tax was for the Red Cross.

Ministry of Posts and Telegraphs Building

PT3   PT4

1939-45   Litho.   Perf. 10½, 12½
RA3	PT3	¼c dp bl	.20	.20
RA3A	PT3	¼c dk vio brn ('45)	.20	.20
RA4	PT3	½c pink	.20	.20
RA5	PT3	1c violet	.30	.20
RA5A	PT3	1c yel org ('45)	1.50	.60
RA6	PT3	2c pck grn	.55	.25
RA7	PT3	20c lt brn	4.50	1.50
		Nos. RA3-RA7 (7)	7.45	3.15

Obligatory on all mail. The tax was for the construction of the new Communications Building.

The 25c of type PT3 and PT4 were not usable on postal matter.

For overprint see No. 561.

Perf. 12½x13
1940, Jan. 20   Engr.   Wmk. 229
RA8	PT4	¼c ultra	.25	.20
RA9	PT4	½c carmine	.25	.20
RA10	PT4	1c violet	.25	.20
RA11	PT4	2c bl grn	.30	.25
RA12	PT4	20c brown	1.25	.25
		Nos. RA8-RA12 (5)	2.30	1.10

See note after No. RA7. See No. RA18.

"Protection" — PT5

1940, Apr. 25   Wmk. 255   Perf. 12
RA13	PT5	5c rose carmine	.30	.25

See No. RA17.

Postal Tax Stamps of 1939 Surcharged in Black

1943   Unwmk.   Perf. 10½
RA14	PT3	½c on 1c violet	.25	.20
a.		Inverted surcharge	2.00	
RA15	PT3	½c on 2c pck grn	.25	.20
RA16	PT3	½c on 20c lt brn	.25	.20
		Nos. RA14-RA16 (3)	.75	.60

Types of 1940
Imprint: "Litografia Colombia Bogota S.A."

1944   Litho.   Perf. 11
RA17	PT5	5c dark rose	.40	.20

Imprint: "Lito-Colombia Bogota-Colombia"
RA18	PT4	¼c ultra	.20	.20

Ministry of Posts and Telegraphs Building — PT6

1945-48   Wmk. 255   Engr.   Perf. 12
RA19	PT6	¼c ultra	.20	.20
RA20	PT6	¼c sepia ('46)	.20	.20
RA21	PT6	½c car rose	.20	.20
RA22	PT6	½c dp mag ('46)	.20	.20
RA23	PT6	1c vio ('46)	.20	.20
RA23A	PT6	1c red org ('46)	.20	.20
RA24	PT6	2c grn ('46)	.20	.20
RA25	PT6	20c brn ('46)	.90	.36
a.		20c red brown ('48)	.60	.25
		Nos. RA19-RA25 (8)	2.30	1.70

These stamps were obligatory on all mail. The surtax was for the construction of the new

Communications Building. See Nos. 603, RA33. For overprints see Nos. 562-564.

No. 469
Overprinted in Carmine

1946, May 25
RA26 A176 5c dull brown .35 .20

The surtax was for the Red Cross.

Ministry of Posts and Telegraphs Building — PT7

1946 Unwmk. Litho. Perf. 11
RA27 PT7 3c blue .20 .20

No. 490 Overprinted in Carmine

1947 Wmk. 255 Perf. 12
RA28 A196 20c gray black 3.75 2.25

Arms of Colombia and Red Cross — PT8   PT9

Perf. 12½
1947, Sept. Unwmk. Engr.
RA29 PT8 5c car lake .25 .20

The surtax of Nos. RA29 and RA40 was for the Red Cross. See No. RA40.

No. 466 Overprinted Like No. RA28 in Carmine
RA30 A136 20c dark blue 16.00 12.50

> Catalogue values for unused stamps in this section, from this point to the end of the section, are for Never Hinged items.

Type of 1945
1947 Wmk. 255 Engr. Perf. 12
RA33 PT6 1c olive bister .30 .20

Black Surcharge
1948 Unwmk. Litho. Perf. 11
RA36 PT9 1c on 5c lt brn .30 .20
RA37 PT9 1c on 10c lt vio .30 .20
RA38 PT9 1c on 25c red .30 .20
RA39 PT9 1c on 50c ultra .30 .20
    Nos. RA36-RA39 (4) 1.20 .80

Type of 1947
1948 Perf. 10½
RA40 PT8 5c vermilion .25 .20

Ministry of Posts and Telegraphs Building — PT10   Mother and Child — PT11

1948-50 Wmk. 255 Engr. Perf. 12
RA41 PT10 1c rose car ('49) .30 .20
RA42 PT10 2c green ('50) .30 .20
RA43 PT10 3c blue .30 .20
RA44 PT10 5c gray .30 .20
RA45 PT10 10c purple .30 .20
    Nos. RA41-RA45 (5) 1.50 1.00

A 25c stamp of type PT10 was for use on telegrams, later for regular postage. See Nos. 602, 604. For overprints and surcharge see Nos. C227-C230, C238, C283, RA51.

Unwmk.
1950, May 25 Litho. Perf. 11
Dark Blue Surcharge
RA46 PT11 5c on 2c gray, red, blk & yel 1.25 .40
  a. "195" instead of "1950" 2.50 2.50
  b. Top bar and "19" of "1950" omitted 2.50 2.50

Marginal perforations omitted, creating 26 straight-edged stamps in each sheet of 44. Surtax for Red Cross.

No. 574 Overprinted in Black

1950, May 26 Wmk. 255 Perf. 12
RA47 A176 5c blue .25 .20
  a. Inverted overprint 2.50

Telegraph Stamp Surcharged in Black
RA48 A253a 8c on 50c org yel .25 .20

Fiscal stamps of type A253a were available for postal use after May 9, 1952. See Nos. 605-608.

Arms and Cross — PT12   Bartolome de Las Casas Aiding Youth — PT13

Perf. 12½
1951, May Unwmk. Engr.
RA49 PT12 5c red .25 .25
RA50 PT13 5c carmine .25 .25

The surtax was for the Red Cross.

No. RA43 Surcharged with New Value in Black
1951 Wmk. 255 Perf. 12
RA51 PT10 1c on 3c blue .25 .20

Type of 1951
Engraved; Cross Lithographed
1953 Unwmk. Perf. 12½
RA52 PT13 5c grn & car .35 .25

Surtax of Nos. RA52-RA60 for the Red Cross.

No. C254 Overprinted with Cross and Bar in Carmine
1954
RA53 AP42 5c lilac rose 2.00 .90

St. Peter Claver Offering Gifts to Slaves — PT14

Engraved; Cross Typographed
1955, May 2 Unwmk. Perf. 13
RA54 PT14 5c dp plum & red .30 .25

Death of St. Peter Claver, 300th anniv.

Jean Henri Dunant and Santiago Samper Brush PT15

Photo.; Red Cross & "Cruz Roja" Engr.
1956, June 1 Unwmk. Perf. 13
RA55 PT15 5c brown & red .30 .25

Nurses and Ambulances PT16

1958, June 2 Photo. Perf. 12
RA56 PT16 5c gray & red .30 .25

St. Louisa de Marillac and Church PT17

No. RA58, Henri Dunant and battle scene.

1960, Sept. 1 Litho. Perf. 11
RA57 PT17 5c brown & rose .30 .20
RA58 PT17 5c vio blue & rose .30 .20

No. RA57 for 3rd cent. of the Sisters of Charity. No. RA58 for cent. (in 1959) of the Red Cross idea.

Manuelita de la Cruz — PT18   Red Cross Worker, Patient — PT19

1961, Nov. 2 Engr. Perf. 13
RA59 PT18 5c dull pur & red .25 .20
RA60 PT18 5c brown & red .25 .20

Issued in memory of Red Cross Nurse Manuelita de la Cruz, who died in the line of

duty during the floods of 1955. Obligatory on domestic mail for a month.

1965, Apr. 30 Photo. Perf. 12
RA61 PT19 5c blue gray & red .25 .20

Obligatory on domestic mail during May.

Nurse's Cap — PT20

Red Cross — PT21

1967, June 1 Litho. Perf. 12
RA62 PT20 5c brt bl & red .25 .20

1969, July 1 Litho. Perf. 12x12½
RA63 PT21 5c vio bl & red .25 .20

Child Care — PT22

1970, July 1 Litho. Perf. 12½x12
RA64 PT22 5c light bl & red .25 .20

ANTIOQUIA

ant-ē-ʹō-kē-ə

Originally a State, now a Department of the Republic of Colombia. Until the revolution of 1885, the separate states making up the United States of Colombia were sovereign governments in their own right. On August 4, 1886, the National Council of Bogotá, composed of two delegates from each state, adopted a new constitution which abolished the sovereign rights of states, which then became departments with governors appointed by the President of the Republic. The nine original states represented at the Bogotá Convention retained some of their previous rights, as management of their own finances, and all issued postage stamps until as late as 1904. For Panama's issues, see Panama Nos. 1-30.

Coat of Arms
A1   A2

A3   A4

Wove Paper

1868		Unwmk.	Litho.	Imperf.	
1	A1	2½c blue		1,000.	750.
2	A2	5c green		750.	575.
3	A3	10c lilac		3,000.	1,000.
4	A4	1p red		675.	750.

Reprints of Nos. 1, 3 and 4 are on a bluish white paper and all but No. 3 have scratches across the design.

A5

A6

A7

A8

A9

A10

1869

5	A5	2½c blue	3.75	3.25
6	A6	5c green	5.50	5.00
7	A7	5c green	5.50	5.00
8	A8	10c lilac	6.25	3.50
9	A9	20c brown	6.25	3.50
10	A10	1p rose red	14.50	13.00
a.		1p vermilion	27.50	25.00
		Nos. 5-10 (6)	41.75	33.25

Reprints of Nos. 7, 8 and 10 are on a bluish white paper; reprints of Nos. 5 and 10a on white paper. The 10c blue is believed to be a reprint.

A11

A12

A13

A14

A15

A16

A17

A18

1873

12	A11	1c yellow grn	5.25	4.00
a.		1c green	5.25	4.00
13	A12	5c green	8.75	6.50
14	A13	10c lilac	25.00	21.00
15	A14	20c yellow brn	8.75	7.50
a.		20c dark brown	8.75	7.50

16	A15	50c blue	2.00	1.75
17	A16	1p vermilion	3.75	3.00
18	A17	2p black, yellow	8.75	8.00
19	A18	5p black, rose	65.00	55.00

A19

A20

Liberty Head
A21   A22

Pedro Justo
Berrio — A23

1875-85

20	A19	1c blk, grn, unglazed ('76)	1.60	1.40
a.		Glazed paper	2.25	1.90
b.		1c blk, lt grn, laid paper ('85)	3.75	3.50
21	A19	1c black ('76)	1.10	1.00
a.		Laid paper	160.00	110.00
22	A19	1c bl grn ('85)	2.25	1.90
23	A19	1c red lil, laid paper ('85)	2.25	1.90
24	A20	2½c blue	2.25	1.90
a.		Pelure paper ('78)	1,500.	1,100.
25	A21	5c green	16.00	14.50
a.		Laid paper	160.00	87.50
26	A22	5c green	16.00	14.50
a.		Laid paper	160.00	87.50
27	A23	10c lilac	25.00	21.00
a.		Laid paper	160.00	125.00
28	A20	10c vio, pelure paper ('78)	900.00	675.00

Arms — A24   Liberty — A25

A26   A27

1878-85

29	A24	2½c blue, pelure paper	2.75	2.50
30	A24	2½c green ('83)	2.50	2.10
a.		Laid paper ('83)	80.00	55.00
31	A24	2½c blk, buff ('85)	7.25	6.50
32	A25	5c green ('83)	4.50	4.00
a.		Pelure paper	32.50	27.50
b.		Laid paper ('82)	40.00	13.00
33	A25	5c violet ('83)	9.50	7.50
a.		5c blue violet ('83)	9.50	7.50
34	A26	10c vio, laid paper ('82)	190.00	65.00
35	A26	10c scar ('83)	2.50	2.10
a.		Tete beche pair	110.00	110.00
36	A27	20c brown ('83)	4.50	4.00
a.		Laid paper ('82)	6.00	5.50

A28   A29

Liberty — A30   Coat of Arms — A31

1883-85

37	A28	5c brown	4.50	3.50
a.		Laid paper	225.00	87.50
38	A28	5c green ('85)	140.00	45.00
a.		Laid paper ('85)	160.00	75.00
39	A28	5c yel, laid paper ('85)	5.50	4.50
40	A29	10c bl grn, laid paper	5.50	4.75
41	A29	10c bl, bl ('85)	5.50	4.50
42	A29	10c lil, laid paper ('85)	12.00	7.50
a.		Wove paper ('85)	125.00	80.00
43	A30	20c bl, laid paper ('85)	4.50	4.00

1886

Wove Paper

55	A31	1c grn, pink	.65	.55
56	A31	2½c blk, orange	.65	.55
57	A31	5c ultra, buff	2.00	1.75
a.		5c blue, buff	3.75	3.25
58	A31	10c rose, buff	1.75	1.60
a.		Transfer of 50c in stone of 10c	140.00	140.00
59	A31	20c dk vio, buff	1.75	1.60
61	A31	50c yel brn, buff	3.25	2.75
62	A31	1p yel, grn	5.25	4.50
63	A31	2p green, vio	5.25	4.50
		Nos. 55-63 (8)	20.55	17.80

1887-88

64	A31	1c red, vio	.50	.45
65	A31	2½c lil, pale lil	.50	.60
66	A31	5c car, buff	.65	.65
67	A31	5c red, grn	3.75	1.75
68	A31	10c brn, grn	.65	.80
		Nos. 64-68 (5)	6.05	4.25

Medellin Issue

A32   A33

A34   A35

1888

				Typeset	
69	A32	2½c blk, yellow	16.00	14.50
70	A33	5c blk, yellow	8.75	7.50
71	A34	5c red, yellow	5.25	4.50
		Nos. 69-71 (3)	30.00	26.50

Two varieties of No. 69, six of No. 70 and ten of No. 71.

1889

72	A35	2½c red	8.00	6.75

Ten varieties including "eentavos."

Regular Issue

Coat of Arms
A36   A37

A38   A39

A40   A41

1889

		Litho.	Perf. 13½	
73	A36	1c blk, rose	.25	.25
74	A36	2½c blk, blue	.25	.25
75	A36	5c blk, yellow	.30	.30
76	A36	10c blk, green	.30	.30
		Nos. 73-76 (4)	1.10	1.10

1890

78	A37	20c blue	1.40	1.40
79	A38	50c vio brn	2.50	2.50
a.		Transfer of 20c in stone of 50c	95.00	95.00
80	A38	50c green	2.25	2.25
81	A39	1p red	2.00	2.00
82	A40	2p blk, mag	14.50	14.50
83	A41	5p blk, org red	22.50	22.50
		Nos. 78-83 (6)	45.15	45.15

Nos. 73-76, 82-83 exist imperf.
The so-called "errors" of Nos. 73 to 76, printed on paper of wrong colors, are essays or, possibly, reprints. They exist perforated and imperforate.
See No. 96.

A42   A43

A44   A45

1890

		Typeset	Perf. 14	
84	A42	2½c blk, buff	2.25	2.25
85	A43	5c blk, orange	2.25	2.25
86	A44	10c blk, buff	7.00	7.00
87	A44	10c blk, rose	9.00	9.00
88	A45	20c blk, orange	9.00	9.00
		Nos. 84-88 (5)	29.50	29.50

20 varieties of the 5c, 10 each of the other values.

A46   A47

1892

		Litho.	Perf. 13½	
89	A46	1c brn, brnsh	.40	.40
90	A46	2½c pur, lil	.40	.40
92	A46	5c blk, gray	1.10	.55
a.		Transfer of 2½c in stone of 5c	200.00	
		Nos. 89-92 (3)	1.90	1.35

1893

93	A46	1c blue	.25	.25
94	A46	2½c green	.40	.40
95	A46	5c vermilion	.25	.25
96	A36	10c pale brown	.25	.25
		Nos. 93-96 (4)	1.15	1.15

1896

			Perf. 14	
97	A47	2c gray	.25	.25
98	A47	2c lilac rose	.25	.25
99	A47	2½c brown	.25	.25
100	A47	2½c steel blue	.25	.25
101	A47	3c orange	.25	.25
102	A47	3c olive grn	.25	.25
103	A47	5c green	.25	.25
104	A47	5c yellow buff	.30	.30
105	A47	10c brown vio	.55	.55
106	A47	10c violet	.55	.55
107	A47	20c brown org	1.40	1.40
108	A47	20c brown	1.40	1.40
109	A47	50c gray brn	1.40	1.40
110	A47	50c rose	1.40	1.40
111	A47	1p blue & blk	17.50	17.50

112	A47	1p rose red & blk	17.50	17.50
113	A47	2p orange & blk	55.00	55.00
114	A47	2p dk grn & blk	55.00	55.00
115	A47	5p red vio & blk	95.00	95.00
116	A47	5p purple & blk	95.00	95.00
		Nos. 97-116 (20)	343.75	343.75

#115-116 with centers omitted are proofs.

General José María
Córdoba — A48

1899   **Perf. 11**

117	A48	½c grnsh bl	.20	.20
118	A48	1c slate blue	.20	.20
119	A48	2c slate brown	.20	.20
120	A48	3c red	.20	.20
121	A48	4c bister brown	.20	.20
122	A48	5c green	.20	.20
123	A48	10c scarlet	.20	.20
124	A48	20c gray violet	.20	.20
125	A48	50c olive bister	.20	.20
126	A48	1p greenish blk	.20	.20
127	A48	2p olive gray	.20	.20
		Nos. 117-127 (11)	2.20	2.20

Numerous part-perf. and imperf. varieties of Nos. 117-127 exist.

A49   A50

A50a

1901   **Typeset**   **Perf. 12**

128	A49	1c red	.25	.25
129	A50	1c ultra	.65	.65
130	A50	1c bister	.65	.65
130A	A50a	1c dull red	.65	.65
130B	A50a	1c ultra	4.50	4.50
		Nos. 128-130B (5)	6.70	6.70

Eight varieties of No. 128, four varieties of Nos. 129-130B.

A51   A52

Atanasio Girardot   Dr. José Félix Restrepo
A53   A54

1902   **Litho.**   **Wove Paper**

131	A51	1c brt rose	.25	.25
a.		Laid paper	.65	.65
b.		Imperf., pair	2.75	
132	A51	2c blue	.25	.25
a.		Transfer of 3c in stone of 2c	6.00	6.00
133	A51	3c green	.25	.25
a.		Imperf., pair	5.00	
134	A51	4c dull violet	.25	.25
135	A52	5c rose red	.25	.25
136	A53	10c rose lilac	.25	.25
a.		Small head	5.75	5.75
b.		10c rose	.25	.25
137	A53	20c gray green	.25	.25
138	A53	30c brt rose	.25	.25
139	A53	40c blue	.25	.25
140	A53	50c brn, yel	.25	.25

Laid Paper

141	A54	1p purple & blk	.80	.80
142	A54	2p rose & blk	.80	.80
143	A54	5p sl bl & blk	1.50	1.50
		Nos. 131-143 (13)	5.60	5.60

1903

Wove Paper

143A	A51	1c blue	.25	.25
144	A51	2c violet	.25	.25
a.		Imperf.	3.00	

A55   A56

A57

Designs: 1p, Francisco Antonio Zea. 2p, Custodio Garcia Rovira. 3p, La Pola (Policarpa Salavarrieta). 4p, J. M. Restrepo. 5p, José Fernández Madrid. 10p, Juan del Corral.

1903-04

145	A55	4c yellow brn	.25	.25
146	A55	5c blue	.25	.25
147	A56	10c yellow	.25	.25
148	A56	20c purple	.25	.25
149	A56	30c brown	.65	.65
150	A56	40c green	.65	.65
151	A56	50c rose	.25	.25
152	A57	1p olive gray	.65	.65
153	A57	2p purple	.65	.65
154	A57	3p dark blue	.65	.65
155	A57	4p dull red	1.10	1.10
156	A57	5p red brown	3.25	1.60
157	A57	10p scarlet	7.00	4.00
		Nos. 145-157 (13)	15.85	11.20

Nos. 145-146, 151, 153-157 exist imperf. Value of pairs, $4 to $5.

Manizales Issue

Stamps of these designs are local private post issues.

OFFICIAL STAMPS Stamps of 1903-04 with overprint "OFICIAL" were never issued.

REGISTRATION STAMPS

R1

1896   **Unwmk.**   **Litho.**   **Perf. 14**

F1	R1	2½c rose	1.25	1.25
F2	R1	2½c dull blue	1.25	1.25

Córdoba
R2

R3

R4

1899   **Perf. 11**

F3	R2	2½c dull blue	.25	.25
F4	R3	10c red lilac	.25	.25

1902   **Perf. 12**

F5	R4	10c purple, blue	.30	.30
a.		Imperf.	—	

ACKNOWLEDGMENT OF RECEIPT STAMPS

AR1

1902-03   **Unwmk.**   **Litho.**   **Perf. 12**

H1	AR1	5c black, rose	1.10	1.10
H2	AR1	5c slate ('03)	.35	.35

LATE FEE STAMPS

Córdoba — LF1

1899   **Unwmk.**   **Litho.**   **Perf. 11**

I1	LF1	2½c dark green	.30	.30
a.		Imperf., pair	3.00	

LF2   LF3

1901   **Typeset**   **Perf. 12**

I2	LF2	2½c red violet	.80	.80
a.		2½c purple	.80	.80

1902   **Litho.**

I3	LF3	2½c violet	.25	.25

City of Medellin

Stamps of the designs shown were not issued by any governmental agency but by the Sociedad de Mejoras Publicas.

BOLIVAR

bə-'lē-ˌvär

Originally a State, now a Department of the Republic of Colombia. (See Antioquia.)

A1

1863-66   **Unwmk.**   **Litho.**   **Imperf.**

1	A1	10c green	1,200.	600.00
a.		Five stars below shield	2,500.	2,400.
2	A1	10c red ('66)	27.50	30.00
a.		Diagonal half used as 5c on cover		120.00
b.		Five stars below shield	80.00	72.50
3	A1	1p red	6.75	7.75

Fourteen varieties of each. Counterfeits of Nos. 1 and 1a exist.

Coat of Arms
A2   A3

A4   A5

1873

4	A2	5c blue	7.25	7.25
5	A3	10c violet	7.25	7.25
6	A4	20c yellow green	32.50	32.50
7	A5	80c vermilion	65.00	65.00
		Nos. 4-7 (4)	112.00	112.00

A6   A7

A8   Bolívar — A9

1874-78

8	A6	5c blue	27.50	14.00
9	A7	5c blue ('78)	8.00	7.25
10	A8	10c violet ('77)	4.00	3.75
		Nos. 8-10 (3)	39.50	25.00

Dated "1879"

1879 White Wove Paper Perf. 12½
11	A9	5c blue	.30	.30
a.		Imperf., pair	.90	
12	A9	10c violet	.25	.25
13	A9	20c red	.30	.30
a.		20c green (error)	11.00	11.00

Bluish Laid Paper
15	A9	5c blue	.30	.30
a.		Imperf., pair	2.25	
16	A9	10c violet	1.60	1.60
a.		Imperf., pair	4.50	
17	A9	20c red	.40	.40
a.		Imperf., pair	2.00	
		Nos. 11-17 (6)	3.15	3.15

Stamps of 80c and 1p on white wove paper and 1p on bluish laid paper were prepared but not placed in use.

Dated "1880"

1880 White Wove Paper Perf. 12½
19	A9	5c blue	.30	.30
a.		Imperf., pair	1.60	
20	A9	10c violet	.40	.40
a.		Imperf., pair	1.60	
21	A9	20c red	.40	.40
a.		20c green (error)	14.00	14.00
23	A9	80c green	2.50	2.50
24	A9	1p orange	2.75	2.75
a.		Imperf., pair	5.50	
		Nos. 19-24 (5)	6.35	6.35

Bluish Laid Paper
25	A9	5c blue	.30	.30
a.		Imperf., pair	1.40	
26	A9	10c violet	2.50	2.50
27	A9	20c red	.40	.40
a.		Imperf., pair	3.00	
28	A9	1p orange	450.00	
a.		Imperf.	475.00	

A11   A12

A13   A15

A16

Dated "1882"
White Wove Paper

1882 Perf. 12, 16x12
29	A11	5c blue	.35	.35
30	A12	10c lilac	.25	.25
31	A13	20c red	.35	.35
33	A15	80c green	.65	.65
34	A16	1p orange	.65	.65
		Nos. 29-34 (5)	2.25	2.25

Nos. 29, 30 and 34 are known imperforate. They are printer's waste and were not issued through post offices.

A17   A18

1882 Engr. Perf. 12
35	A17	5p blue & rose red	.65	.65
a.		Imperf., pair	5.25	
b.		Perf. 16	8.00	6.75
c.		Perf. 14	6.75	6.75

36	A17	10p brown & blue	1.75	1.75
a.		Imperf., pair	8.75	
b.		Perf. 16	7.25	6.00
c.		Rouletted	8.75	8.75

Dated "1883"

1883 Litho. Perf. 12, 16x12
37	A11	5c blue	.25	.25
a.		Imperf., pair	1.00	
b.		Perf. 12	12.00	2.40
38	A12	10c lilac	.30	.30
39	A13	20c red	.30	.30
41	A15	80c green	.30	.30
42	A16	1p orange	1.60	1.60
a.		Perf. 16x12	2.25	2.25
		Nos. 37-42 (5)	2.75	2.75

1884

Dated "1884"
43	A11	5c blue	.30	.30
a.		Perf. 12	16.00	16.00
44	A12	10c lilac	.25	.25
45	A13	20c red	.25	.25
a.		Perf. 12	8.00	8.00
47	A15	80c green	.30	.35
a.		Perf. 12	4.00	4.00
48	A16	1p orange	.30	.30
		Nos. 43-48 (5)	1.40	1.45

1885

Dated "1885"
49	A11	5c blue	.20	.20
50	A12	10c lilac	.20	.20
51	A13	20c red	.20	.20
53	A15	80c green	.25	.25
54	A16	1p orange	.30	.30
		Nos. 49-54 (5)	1.15	1.15

The note after No. 34 will also apply to imperforate stamps of the 1884-85 issues.

1891 Perf. 14
55	A18	1c black	.30	.30
56	A18	5c orange	.30	.30
a.		Imperf., pair	.90	
57	A18	10c carmine	.30	.30
58	A18	20c blue	.65	.65
59	A18	50c green	.95	.95
60	A18	1p purple	.95	.95
		Nos. 55-60 (6)	3.45	3.45

For overprint see Colombia No. 169.

Bolívar
A19

José
Fernández
Madrid
A20

Manuel
Rodriguez
Torices
A21

José María
García de
Toledo
A22

1903 Laid Paper Imperf.
62	A19	50c dk bl, *pink*	.65	.65
a.		Bluish paper	.65	.65
63	A19	50c sl grn, *pink*	.65	.65
a.		Rose paper	2.25	2.25
b.		Greenish blue paper	3.25	3.25
c.		Yellow paper	4.50	4.50
d.		Brown paper	4.50	4.50
e.		Salmon paper	8.00	8.00
64	A19	50c pur, *pink*	2.25	2.25
a.		White paper	4.50	4.50
b.		Brown paper	4.50	4.50
c.		Greenish blue paper	4.50	4.50
d.		Lilac paper	4.50	4.50
e.		Rose paper	4.00	4.00
f.		Yellow paper	4.50	4.50
g.		Salmon paper	6.50	6.50
h.		As "a," wove paper	9.75	9.75
65	A20	1p org, *sal*	.65	.65
a.		Yellow paper	5.00	5.00
b.		Greenish blue paper	16.00	16.00
66	A20	1p gray grn, *lil*	1.60	1.60
a.		Yellow paper	7.00	7.00
b.		Salmon paper	8.00	8.00
c.		Green paper	8.00	8.00
d.		White wove paper	12.00	
67	A21	5p car rose, *lil*	.65	.65
a.		Brown paper	1.25	1.25
b.		Yellow paper	1.25	1.25
c.		Greenish blue paper	5.00	5.00
d.		Bluish paper	6.50	6.50
e.		Salmon paper	8.00	8.00
f.		Rose paper	9.75	9.75

68	A22	10p dk bl, *bluish*	1.40	1.40
a.		Greenish blue paper	1.40	1.40
b.		Rose paper	8.00	8.00
c.		Salmon paper	8.00	8.00
d.		Yellow paper	8.00	8.00
e.		Brown paper	9.00	9.00
f.		Lilac paper	12.00	12.00
g.		White paper	9.75	9.75
69	A22	10p pur, *grnsh bl*	3.75	3.75
a.		Bluish paper	8.00	8.00
b.		Rose paper	7.25	7.25
c.		Yellow paper	8.00	8.00
d.		Brown paper	8.00	8.00
		Nos. 62-69 (8)	11.60	11.60

Sewing Machine Perf.
Laid Paper
70	A19	50c dk bl, *pink*	1.10	1.10
a.		Bluish paper	1.10	1.10
71	A19	50c sl grn, *pink*	2.25	2.25
72	A19	50c pur, *grnsh bl*	4.50	4.50
a.		White paper	4.50	4.50
b.		White wove paper	8.00	
73	A20	1p org, *sal*	2.25	2.25
74	A20	1p gray grn, *lil*	9.75	9.75
a.		Yellow paper	9.75	9.75
75	A21	5p car rose, *yel*	1.75	1.75
a.		Lilac paper	4.50	4.50
b.		Brown paper	4.50	4.50
c.		Bluish paper	6.00	6.00
d.		White wove paper	9.75	
76	A22	10p dk bl, *grnsh bl*	5.00	5.00
a.		Bluish paper	7.50	7.50
b.		Yellow paper	9.75	9.75
c.		As "b," wove paper	12.00	
77	A22	10p pur, *grnsh bl*	7.50	7.50
a.		Bluish paper	13.00	13.00
b.		Rose paper	8.50	8.50
c.		Yellow paper	13.00	13.00
		Nos. 70-77 (8)	34.10	34.10

José María del
Castillo y
Rada — A23

Manuel
Anguiano — A24

Pantaleón C.
Ribón — A25

1904 Sewing Machine Perf.
89	A23	5c black	.25	.25
90	A24	10c brown	.25	.25
91	A25	20c red	.30	.30
92	A25	20c red brown	.65	.65
		Nos. 89-92 (4)	1.45	1.45

Imperf., pairs
89a	A23	5c black	4.00	4.00
90a	A24	10c brown	3.00	3.00
91a	A25	20c red	7.25	7.25
92a	A25	20c red brown	7.25	7.25

A26

A27

A28

1904 Imperf.
93	A26	½c black	.65	.65
a.		Tête bêche pair	3.75	3.75

94	A27	1c blue	1.25	1.25
95	A28	2c purple	1.40	1.40
		Nos. 93-95 (3)	3.30	3.30

REGISTRATION STAMPS

Simón Bolívar

R1   R2
White Wove Paper
Perf. 12½, 16x12

1879 Unwmk. Litho.
F1	R1	40c brown	.75	.75

Bluish Laid Paper
F2	R1	40c brown	.75	.75
a.		Imperf., pair	3.50	

Dated "1880"

1880

White Wove Paper
F3	R1	40c brown	.35	.35

Bluish Laid Paper
F4	R1	40c brown	.75	.75
a.		Imperf., pair	3.50	

Dated "1882" to "1885"
White Wove Paper

1882-85 Perf. 16x12
F5	R2	40c brown (1882)	.35	.35
F6	R2	40c brown (1883)	.30	.30
F7	R2	40c brown (1884)	.30	.30
F8	R2	40c brown (1885)	.30	.30
		Nos. F5-F8 (4)	1.25	1.25

Perf. 12
F5a	R2	40c	19.00	
F6a	R2	40c	16.00	
F7a	R2	40c	16.00	
F8a	R2	40c	16.00	
		Nos. F5a-F8a (4)	67.00	

R3

Laid Paper

1903 Imperf.
F9	R3	20c orange, *rose*	.65	.65
a.		Salmon paper	1.25	1.25
b.		Greenish blue paper	6.50	6.50

Sewing Machine Perf.
F10	R3	20c orange, *rose*	2.75	2.75
a.		Salmon paper	2.75	2.75
b.		Greenish blue paper	6.50	6.50

R4

1904

Wove Paper
F11	R4	5c black	3.25	3.25

ACKNOWLEDGMENT OF RECEIPT STAMPS

AR1   AR2

1903   Unwmk.   Litho.   *Imperf.*
Laid Paper

H1	AR1 20c org, *rose*	2.75	2.75
a.	Yellow paper	1.40	1.40
b.	Greenish blue paper	5.50	5.50
H2	AR1 20c dk bl, *yel*	2.25	2.25
a.	Brown paper	3.75	3.75
b.	Rose paper	2.75	2.75
c.	Salmon paper	7.50	7.50
d.	Greenish blue paper	7.50	7.50

Sewing Machine Perf.

H3	AR1 20c org, *grnsh bl*	6.75	6.75
a.	Yellow paper	7.75	7.75
H4	AR1 20c dk bl, *yel*	7.75	7.75
a.	Lilac paper	7.75	7.75
	Nos. H1-H4 (4)	19.50	19.50

1904
Wove Paper

H5	AR2 2c red	1.25	1.25

LATE FEE STAMPS

LF1

1903   Unwmk.   Litho.   *Imperf.*
Laid Paper

I1	LF1 20c car rose, *bluish*	.65	.65
I2	LF1 20c pur, *bluish*	.65	.65
a.	Rose paper	2.25	2.25
b.	Brown paper	2.25	2.25
c.	Lilac paper	2.25	2.25
d.	Yellow paper	7.00	7.00

Sewing Machine Perf.

I3	LF1 20c car rose, *bluish*	3.75	3.75
I4	LF1 20c pur, *bluish*	3.75	3.75
a.	Rose paper	6.50	6.50
b.	Lilac paper	6.50	6.50
c.	Yellow paper	12.00	12.00
	Nos. I1-I4 (4)	8.80	8.80

BOYACA
bō-yä-cä

Originally a State, now a Department of the Republic of Colombia. (See Antioquia.)

Diego Mendoza
Pérez — A1

1902   Unwmk.   Litho.   *Perf. 13½*
Wove Paper

1	A1 5c blue green	.80	.80
a.	Bluish paper	95.00	95.00
b.	Imperf., pair	16.00	16.00

Laid Paper
Perf. 12

2	A1 5c green	110.00	110.00

Coat of Arms
A2   A3

Gen. Próspero
Pinzón — A4

A5

Monument of
Battle of
Boyacá — A6

President José
Manuel
Marroquin — A7

1903   Litho.   *Imperf.*

4	A2 10c dark gray	.30	.30
5	A3 20c red brown	.35	.35
6	A5 1p red	3.25	3.25
a.	1p claret	3.75	3.75
8	A6 5p black, *rose*	1.25	1.25
a.	5p black, *buff*	12.00	12.00
9	A7 10p black, *buff*	1.25	1.25
a.	10p black, *rose*	12.00	12.00
b.	As "a,"tête bêche pair	24.00	
	Nos. 4-9 (5)	6.40	6.40

Perf. 12

10	A2 10c dark gray	.35	.35
11	A3 20c red brown	.40	.40
12	A4 50c green	.35	.35
13	A4 50c dull blue	2.50	2.50
14	A5 1p red	.35	.35
a.	1p claret	3.00	3.00
16	A6 5p black, *rose*	11.00	11.00
a.	5p black, *buff*	9.50	9.50
17	A7 10p black, *buff*	1.10	1.10
a.	10p black, *rose*	11.00	11.00
b.	Tête bêche pair	12.00	12.00
	Nos. 10-17 (7)	16.05	16.05

Statue of Bolívar — A8

1904

18	A8 10c orange	.25	.25
a.	Imperf., pair	3.75	3.75

CAUCA

Stamps of these designs were issued by a provincial post between 1879(?) and 1890.

Stamps of this design are believed to be of private origin and without official sanction.

Items inscribed "No hay estampillas" (No stamps available) and others inscribed "Manuel E. Jiménez" are considered by specialists to be receipt labels, not postage stamps.

CUNDINAMARCA
kün-di-nə-'mär-kə

Originally a State, now a Department of the Republic of Colombia. (See Antioquia.)

Coat of Arms
A1   A2

1870   Unwmk.   Litho.   *Imperf.*

1	A1 5c blue	5.25	5.25
2	A2 10c red	16.00	16.00

The counterfeits, or reprints, show traces of the cuts made to deface the dies.

A3   A4

A5   A6

1877-82

3	A3 10c red ('82)	3.50	3.50
a.	Laid paper ('77)	4.50	4.50
4	A4 20c green ('82)	7.50	7.50
a.	Laid paper ('77)	12.00	12.00
7	A5 50c purple ('82)	8.25	8.25
8	A6 1p brown ('82)	12.00	12.00
	Nos. 3-8 (4)	31.25	31.25

A7   Redrawn

1884

10	A7 5c blue	.80	.80
11	A7 5c blue (redrawn)	.80	.80
a.	Tête bêche pair	80.00	80.00

The redrawn stamp has no period after "COLOMBIA."

A8

A9

A10

A11

1883   Typeset

13	A8 10c black, *yellow*	14.00	14.00
14	A9 50c black, *rose*	14.00	14.00
15	A10 1p black, *brown*	37.50	37.50
16	A11 2r black, *green*	*2,200.*	

Typeset varieties exist: 4 of the 10c, 2 each of 50c and 1p.
Some experts doubt that No. 16 was issued. The variety without signature and watermarked "flowers" is believed to be a proof. Forgeries exist.

A12

1886   Litho.

17	A12 5c blue	.80	.80
18	A12 10c red	5.00	5.00
19	A12 10c red, *lilac*	2.75	2.75
20	A12 20c green	4.25	4.25
a.	20c yellow green	5.00	
21	A12 50c purple	5.50	5.50
22	A12 1p orange brown	5.75	5.75
	Nos. 17-22 (6)	24.05	24.05

Nos. 17 to 22 have been reprinted. The colors are aniline and differ from those of the original stamps. The impression is coarse and blurred.

A13   A14

A15   A16

A17   A18

A19   A20

A21

1904   **Perf. 10½, 12**

23	A13	1c orange	.25	.25
24	A14	2c gray blue	.25	.25
25	A15	3c rose	.35	.35
26	A15	5c olive grn	.35	.35
27	A16	10c pale brn	.35	.35
28	A17	15c pink	.35	.35
29	A18	20c blue, *grn*	.35	.35
30	A18	20c blue	.60	.60
31	A19	40c blue	.60	.60
32	A19	40c blue, *buff*	21.00	21.00
33	A20	50c red vio	.60	.60
34	A21	1p gray grn	.60	.60
		Nos. 23-34 (12)	25.65	25.65

     Imperf

23a	A13	1c orange	.75	.75
24a	A14	2c blue	.75	.75
b.		2c slate	6.50	6.50
25a	A15	3c rose	.90	.90
26a	A15	5c olive green	1.60	1.60
27a	A16	10c pale brown	2.00	2.00
28a	A17	15c pink	.50	.50
29a	A18	20c blue, *green*	2.00	2.00
30a	A18	20c blue	2.00	2.00
31a	A19	40c blue	.70	.70
32a	A19	40c blue, *buff*	21.00	21.00
33a	A20	50c red violet	.70	.70
34a	A21	1p gray green	.70	.70
		Nos. 23a-34a (12)	33.60	33.60

REGISTRATION STAMPS

R1

1883   **Unwmk.**   **Imperf.**

F1	R1	black, *orange*	17.00	17.00

R2

1904   **Perf. 12**

F2	R2	10c bister	.85	.85
a.		Imperf.	3.75	3.75

Magdalena

Items inscribed "No hay estampillas" (No stamps available) are considered by specialists to be not postage stamps but receipt labels.

Panama

Issues of Panama as a state and later Department of Colombia are listed with the Republic of Panama issues (Nos. 1-30).

SANTANDER

săn-,tän-'de͟͟ə͟r

Originally a State, now a Department of the Republic of Colombia.
(See Antioquia.)

Coat of Arms
A1   A2

1884   **Unwmk.**   **Litho.**   **Imperf.**

1	A1	1c blue	.30	.30
a.		1c gray blue	.50	.50

2	A2	5c red	.50	.50
3	A2	10c bluish purple	1.90	1.90
a.		Tête bêche pair	—	—
			2.70	2.70
		Nos. 1-3 (3)	2.70	2.70

No. 2 exists unofficially perforated 14.

A3   A4

1886   **Imperf.**

4	A3	1c blue	.90	.90
5	A3	5c red	.30	.30
6	A3	10c red violet	.50	.50
a.		10c deep violet	.50	.50
b.		Inscribed "CINCO CENTAVOS"	26.00	26.00
		Nos. 4-6 (3)	1.70	1.70

The numerals in the upper corners are omitted on No. 5, while on No. 6 there are no numerals in the side panels. No. 6 exists unofficially perforated 12.

1887

7	A4	1c blue	.25	.25
a.		1c ultramarine	1.75	1.75
8	A4	5c red	1.75	1.75
9	A4	10c violet	5.50	5.50
		Nos. 7-9 (3)	7.50	7.50

A5   A6

A7

1889   **Perf. 11½ and 13½**

10	A5	1c blue	.35	.35
11	A6	5c red	1.25	1.25
12	A7	10c purple	.45	.45
a.		Imperf., pair	16.00	20.00
		Nos. 10-12 (3)	2.05	2.05

A8   A9

1892   **Perf. 13½**

13	A8	5c red, *rose buff*	1.00	1.00

1895-96

14	A9	5c brown	.70	.70
15	A9	5c yel grn ('96)	.70	.70

A10   A11

A12

1899   **Perf. 10**

16	A10	1c black, *green*	.35	.35
17	A11	5c black, *pink*	.35	.35

     Perf. 13½

18	A12	10c blue	.70	.70
a.		Perf. 12	1.00	1.00
		Nos. 16-18 (3)	1.40	1.40

A13

1903   **Imperf.**

19	A13	50c red	.60	.60
a.		50c rose	.60	.60
b.		"SANTENDER"	2.50	2.50
c.		"Corrcos"	2.50	2.50
d.		"Correos"	2.50	2.50
e.		Tête bêche pair	4.75	4.75
f.		Pair, one without overprint	2.75	2.75

The overprint "Correos de Departamento Bucaramanga" on the 50c red revenue stamp has been proved to be a cancellation.

A14   A15

Arms   Locomotive
A16   A17

A18   A19

A20

1904   **Imperf.**

22	A14	5c dark green	.25	.25
a.		5c yellow green	.40	.40
24	A15	10c rose	.20	.20
25	A16	20c brown violet	.20	.20
26	A17	50c yellow	.20	.20
27	A18	1p black	.20	.20
28	A19	5p dark blue	.35	.35
29	A20	10p carmine	.40	.40
		Nos. 22-29 (7)	1.80	1.80

1905

30	A14	5c pale blue	.45	.45
31	A15	10c red brown	.45	.45
32	A16	20c yellow green	.45	.45
33	A17	50c red violet	.60	.60
34	A18	1p dark blue	.60	.60
35	A19	5p pink	.60	.60
36	A20	10p red	1.60	1.60
		Nos. 30-36 (7)	4.75	4.75

A21

1907   **Imperf.**

37	A21	½c on 50c rose	.80	*1.60*

City of Cucuta

Stamps of these and similar designs on white and yellow paper, with and without surcharges of ½c, 1c or 2c, are believed to have been produced without government authorization.

TOLIMA

tə-lē-mə

Originally a State, now a Department of the Republic of Colombia.
(See Antioquia.)

A1

1870   **Unwmk.**   **Typeset**   **Imperf.**
     White Wove Paper

1	A1	5c black	62.50	62.50
2	A1	10c black	75.00	75.00
a.		Vert. se-tenant pair	1,500.	1,500.

Printed from two settings. Setting I, ten types of 5c. Setting II, six types of 5c and four types of 10c.

     Blue Laid Batonné Paper

3	A1	5c black	*950.00*	

     Buff Laid Batonné Paper

4	A1	5c black	150.00	100.00

     Blue Wove Paper

5	A1	5c black	70.00	45.00

     Blue Vertically Laid Paper

6	A1	5c black	110.00	70.00
a.		Paper with ruled blue vertical lines		

     Blue Horizontally Laid Paper

7	A1	5c black	100.00	75.00

     Blue Quadrille Paper

8	A1	5c black	150.00	80.00

Ten varieties each of Nos. 3-5 and 7; 20 varieties each of Nos. 6 and 8.

Official imitations were made in 1886 from new settings of the type. There are only 2 varieties of each value. They are printed on blue and white paper, wove, batonné, laid, etc.

A2   A3

A4   A5

     Yellowish White Wove Paper

1871   **Litho.**   **Imperf.**

9	A2	5c deep brown	2.25	2.25
a.		5c red brown	2.25	2.25
b.		Value reads "CINGO"	40.00	40.00
10	A3	10c blue	6.25	6.25
11	A4	50c green	8.00	8.00
12	A5	1p carmine	13.00	13.00
		Nos. 9-12 (4)	29.50	29.50

The 5p stamps, type A2, are bogus varieties made from an altered die of the 5c.

The 10c, 50c and 1 peso stamps have been reprinted on bluish white wove paper. They are from new plates and most copies show traces of fine lines with which the dies had been defaced. Reprints of the 5c have a large cross at the top. The 10c on laid batonné paper is known only as a reprint.

A6   A7

A8

A9

1879

Grayish or White Wove Paper

14	A6	5c yellow brown	.45	.45
a.		5c purple brown	.45	.45
15	A7	10c blue	.50	.50
16	A8	50c green, *bluish*	.50	.50
a.		White paper	1.60	1.60
17	A9	1p vermilion	2.25	2.25
a.		1p carmine rose	9.00	9.00
		Nos. 14-17 (4)	3.70	3.70

A10

Coat of Arms — A12

1883   *Imperf.*

18	A6	5c orange	.45	.45
19	A7	10c vermilion	.95	.95
20	A10	20c violet	1.50	1.50
		Nos. 18-20 (3)	2.90	2.90

1884   *Imperf.*

23	A12	1c gray	.20	.20
24	A12	2c rose lilac	.20	.20
a.		2c slate	.20	.20
25	A12	2½c dull orange	.20	.20
26	A12	5c brown	.20	.20
27	A12	10c blue	.35	.35
a.		10c slate	.25	.25
28	A12	20c lemon	.35	.35
a.		Laid paper	5.00	5.00
29	A12	25c black	.30	.30
30	A12	50c green	.30	.30
31	A12	1p vermilion	.40	.40
32	A12	2p violet	.60	.60
a.		Value omitted	30.00	30.00
33	A12	5p yellow	.40	.40
34	A12	10p lilac rose	1.10	1.10
a.		Laid paper	30.00	30.00
b.		10p gray	175.00	
		Nos. 23-34 (12)	4.60	4.60

A13

A14

Condor with Long Wings Touching Flagstaffs
A15   A16

1886   *Litho.*   *Perf. 10½, 11*
White Paper

36	A13	5c brown	1.40	1.40
a.		5c yellow brown	1.40	1.40
b.		Imperf., pair	17.50	
37	A14	10c blue	3.75	3.75
a.		Imperf., pair	17.50	
38	A15	50c green	3.25	3.25
a.		Imperf., pair	17.50	
39	A16	1p vermilion	2.75	2.75
a.		Imperf., pair	26.00	
		Nos. 36-39 (4)	11.15	11.15

No. 38 has been reprinted in pale gray green, perforated 10½, and No. 39 in bright vermilion, perforated 11½. The impressions show many signs of wear.

Lilac Tinted Paper

36c	A13	5c orange brown	12.50	12.50
37b	A14	10c blue	12.50	12.50
38b	A15	50c green	9.25	9.25
39b	A16	1p vermilion	8.25	8.25
		Nos. 36c-39b (4)	42.50	42.50

Items similar to A15 and A16 but with condor with long wings and upper flag-staffs omitted are forgeries.

A17

A18

A19

A20

Condor with Short Wings
A19   A20

1886   **White Paper**   *Perf. 12*

44	A19	1c gray	6.25	6.25
45	A17	2c rose lilac	6.50	6.50
46	A18	2½c dull org	19.00	19.00
47	A19	5c brown	8.50	8.00
48	A20	10c blue	8.00	8.00
49	A20	20c lemon	6.50	6.50
a.		Tête bêche pair	275.00	275.00
50	A20	25c black	6.25	6.25
51	A20	50c green	3.75	3.75
52	A20	1p vermilion	5.00	4.25
53	A20	2p violet	7.25	7.25
b.		Tête bêche pair	190.00	190.00
54	A20	5p orange	13.00	13.00
55	A20	10p lilac rose	7.50	7.50
		Nos. 44-55 (12)	97.50	96.25

Imperf., Pairs

44a	A19	1c	17.00
47a	A19	5c	29.00
48a	A20	10c	29.00
52a	A20	1p	21.00
53a	A20	2p	26.00
54a	A20	5p	40.00
55a	A20	10p	17.00

A23

1888   *Perf. 10½*

62	A23	5c red	.20	.20
63	A23	10c green	.30	.30
64	A23	50c blue	.75	.75
65	A23	1p red brown	1.90	1.90
		Nos. 62-65 (4)	3.15	3.15

For overprint see Colombia No. L14.

1895   *Perf. 12, 13½*

66	A23	1c blue, *rose*	.25	.25
67	A23	2c grn, *lt grn*	.25	.25
68	A23	5c red	.20	.20
69	A23	10c green	.50	.50
70	A23	20c blue, *yellow*	.30	.30
71	A23	1p brown	2.10	2.10
		Nos. 66-71 (6)	3.60	3.60

Imperf., Pairs

62a	A23	5c	8.75
63a	A23	10c	12.00
64a	A23	50c	14.50 14.50
65a	A23	1p	21.00
66a	A23	1c	21.00
67a	A23	2c	21.00
70a	A23	20c	24.00

"No Hay Estampillas"
Items inscribed "No hay estampillas" (No stamps available) are considered by specialists to be not postage stamps but receipt labels.

"Honda Issue"
This item seems to be of private origin.

A24

A25

A26

A27

A28

A29

A30

A31

Sewing Machine or Regular Perf. 12
1903-04   *Litho.*

79	A24	4c black, *green*	.25	.25
80	A25	10c dull blue	.25	.25
81	A26	20c orange	.50	.50
82	A27	50c black, *rose*	.25	.25
a.		50c black, *buff*	.20	.20
84	A28	1p brown	.20	.20
85	A29	2p gray	.20	.20
86	A30	5p red	.20	.20
a.		Tête bêche pair	8.00	12.00
87	A31	10p black, *blue*	.25	.25
a.		10p black, *light green*	.25	.25
b.		10p black, *grn, glazed*	3.75	3.75
		Nos. 79-87 (8)	2.10	2.10

Imperf

79a	A24	4c black, *green*	.25	.25
80a	A25	10c dull blue	.20	.20
81a	A26	20c orange	1.25	1.25
82b	A27	50c black, *rose*	1.75	1.75
c.		50c black, *buff*	1.75	1.75
84a	A28	1p brown	.20	.20
85a	A29	2p gray	.25	.25
86b	A30	5p red	.25	.25
c.		Tête bêche pair	12.00	16.00
87c	A31	10p black, *blue*	2.50	2.50
d.		Tête bêche pair		
e.		10p black, *light green*	3.75	3.75
f.		10p black, *green, glazed*	19.00	19.00
		Nos. 79a-87c (8)	6.65	6.65

COMORO ISLANDS

ˈkä-mə-ˌrō ˈī-lənds

LOCATION — In Mozambique Channel between Madagascar and Mozambique
GOVT. — Republic
AREA — 838 sq. mi.
POP. — 562,723 (1999 est.)
CAPITAL — Moroni

The Comoro Archipelago consists of the islands of Mayotte, Anjouan, Grand Comoro (Grande Comore) and Moheli, which issued their own stamps as French protectorates or colonies from 1887-1914. The archipelago was attached to Madagascar from 1914 to 1946, when it became a separate French territory. In July 1975, Anjouan, Grand Comoro and Moheli united to declare independence as the State of Comoro. Mayotte remained French.

100 Centimes = 1 Franc

> **Catalogue values for all unused stamps in this country are for Never Hinged items.**

Anjouan Bay — A2

Comoro Woman Grinding Grain — A3

Moroni Mosque on Grand Comoro A4

1950   Unwmk.   Engr.   *Perf. 13*

30	A2	10c blue	.50	.30
31	A2	50c green	.50	.30
32	A2	1fr dk ol brn	.50	.30
33	A3	2fr brt grn	.80	.65
34	A3	5fr purple	1.40	1.00
35	A3	6fr vio brn	1.60	1.20
36	A4	7fr red	1.60	1.25
37	A4	10fr dk grn	1.60	1.25
38	A4	11fr dp ultra	2.00	1.50
		Nos. 30-38 (9)	10.50	7.75

Imperforates
Most Comoro Islands stamps exist imperforate in issued and trial colors, and also in small presentation sheets in issued colors.

Common Design Types pictured following the introduction.

Military Medal Issue
Common Design Type
1952   **Engraved and Typographed**
39	CD101	15fr multi	60.00 45.00

Mosque of Ouani, Anjouan — A5

Coelacanth A6

1952-54   **Engr.**
40 A5 15fr dark brown   4.00   3.00
41 A5 20fr red brown   5.50   4.25
42 A6 40fr aqua & indigo
      ('54)   36.00 18.00
    Nos. 40-42 (3)   45.50 25.25

FIDES Issue
Common Design Type
Design: 9fr, Women at water pump.

1956   **Unwmk.**   **Perf. 13x12½**
43 CD103 9fr dp vio   2.75 1.60

Human Rights Issue
Common Design Type
1958   **Engr.**   **Perf. 13**
44 CD105 20fr ol grn & dk bl   15.00 11.00

Flower Issue
Common Design Type
1959   **Photo.**   **Perf. 12½x12**
45 CD104 10fr Colvillea   6.50 4.50

View of
Dzaoudzi
and Radio
Symbol
A8

Comoro radio station: 25fr, Radio tower and
radio waves over Islands.

1960, Dec. 23   **Engr.**   **Perf. 13**
46 A8 20fr maroon, vio bl & grn   1.75 1.25
47 A8 25fr ultra, brn & grn   2.00 1.00

Harpa
Conoidalis — A9

Sea Shells: 50c, Cypraecassis rufa. 2fr,
Murex ramosus. 5fr, Turbo marmoratus. 20fr,
Pterocera scorpio. 25fr, Charonia tritonis.

1962, Jan. 13   **Photo.**
Shells in Natural Colors
48 A9 50c lilac & brn   1.40 1.40
49 A9 1fr yel & red   1.50 1.50
50 A9 2fr pale grn & pink   2.75 2.75
51 A9 5fr yel & grn   4.25 4.25
52 A9 20fr salmon & brn   11.50 11.50
53 A9 25fr bister & pink   15.00 15.00
    Nos. 48-53,C5-C6 (8)   84.90 76.40

Wheat
Emblem
and Globe
A10

1963, Mar. 21   **Engr.**   **Perf. 13**
54 A10 20fr choc & dk grn   5.50 4.50

FAO "Freedom from Hunger" campaign.

Red Cross Centenary Issue
Common Design Type
1963, Sept. 2   **Unwmk.**   **Perf. 13**
55 CD113 50fr emer, gray & car 9.50 8.00

Human Rights Issue
Common Design Type
1963, Dec. 10   **Engr.**
56 CD117 15fr dk red & yel grn 9.50 8.00

Tobacco   Grand Comoro
Pouch — A13   Canoe — A14

Designs: 4fr, Censer. 10fr, Carved lamp.

1963, Dec. 27   **Perf. 13**
Size: 22x36mm
57 A13 3fr multi   .95 .95
58 A13 4fr org, dp cl & sl
      grn   1.00 1.00
59 A13 10fr org brn, dk red
      brn & grn   1.90 1.90
    Nos. 57-59,C8-C9 (5)   18.85 12.60

Philatec Issue
Common Design Type
1964, Mar. 31
60 CD118 50fr dk bl, red & grn 4.75 4.75

1964, Aug. 7   **Photo.**   **Perf. 13x12½**
Design: 30fr, Boutre felucca.

Size: 22x37mm
61 A14 15fr multi   3.50 3.50
62 A14 30fr lt grn & multi   5.50 5.50
    Nos. 61-62,C10-C11 (4)   20.50 13.25

Spiny Lobster — A15

Designs: 12fr, Hammerhead shark, horiz.
20fr, Turtle, horiz. 25fr, Merou fish.

1965, Dec. 20   **Engr.**   **Perf. 13**
63 A15 1fr grn, lil & ocher   1.00 .95
64 A15 12fr org red, slate &
      gray   2.10 1.60
65 A15 20fr org, red & bl grn   4.50 3.00
66 A15 25fr bl grn, dk brn &
      red   6.75 3.25
    Nos. 63-66 (4)   14.35 8.80

Hotel
Itsandra,
Moroni
A16

Design: 15fr, Lake Salé, Grand Comoro.

1966, Dec. 19   **Photo.**   **Perf. 12½x13**
67 A16 15fr multi   1.25 .95
68 A16 25fr multi   1.50 1.00
    Nos. 67-68,C18-C19 (4)   16.75 10.20

Comoro
Sunbird
A17

Birds: 10fr, Malachite kingfisher. 15fr,
Rothschild's fody. 30fr, Cuckoo-roller.

1967, June 20   **Photo.**   **Perf. 12½x13**
Size: 36x23mm
69 A17 2fr ocher & multi   2.75 2.75
70 A17 10fr lil & multi   6.00 5.25
71 A17 15fr yel grn & multi   7.25 6.50
72 A17 30fr pink & multi   13.50 13.50
    Nos. 69-72,C20-C21 (6)   53.00 42.50

For surcharge see No. 133.

WHO Anniversary Issue
Common Design Type
1968, May 4   **Engr.**   **Perf. 13**
73 CD126 40fr grn, vio & dp car 3.25 3.25

Surgeonfish
A19

Design: 25fr, Imperial angelfish.

1968, Aug. 1   **Engr.**   **Perf. 13**
Size: 36x22mm
74 A19 20fr vio bl, yel & red
      brn   3.50 3.50
75 A19 25fr Prus bl, dk bl &
      org   4.25 4.25
    Nos. 74-75,C23-C24 (4)   25.75 17.00

For surcharge & overprint see #C52, C74.

Human Rights Year Issue
Common Design Type
1968, Aug. 10   **Engr.**   **Perf. 13**
76 CD127 60fr brn, grn & org   4.00 4.00

Msoila
Prayer Rug
and Praying
Man — A20

Each stamp shows a different prayer
position.

1969, Feb. 27   **Engr.**   **Perf. 13**
77 A20 20fr bl grn, rose red &
      pur   1.40 .95
78 A20 30fr pur, rose red & bl
      grn   1.60 1.40
79 A20 45fr rose red, pur & bl
      grn   3.00 1.75
    Nos. 77-79 (3)   6.00 4.10

Vanilla
Flower
A21

Design: 15fr, Flower of ylang-ylang tree.
25fr, Poinsettia (country name at upper left).

1969-70   **Photo.**   **Perf. 12½x13**
Size: 36x23mm
80 A21 10fr multi   1.90 .85
81 A21 15fr multi   2.10 .95
82 A21 25fr multi ('70)   4.25 2.10
    Nos. 80-82,C26-C28 (6)   29.50 17.90

Issue dates: #80-81, Mar. 20. #82, Mar. 5.

ILO Issue
Common Design Type
1969, Nov. 24   **Engr.**   **Perf. 13**
83 CD131 5fr org, emerald &
      gray   1.60 1.20

UPU Headquarters Issue
Common Design Type
1970, May 20   **Engr.**   **Perf. 13**
84 CD133 65fr pur, bl grn & red
      brn   5.50 2.75

Chiromani
Costume,
Anjouan — A22

Friday
Mosque — A23

25fr, Bouiboui costume, Grand Comoro.

1970, Oct. 30   **Photo.**   **Perf. 12½x13**
85 A22 20fr grn, yel & red   1.40 1.10
86 A22 25fr brn, yel & dk bl   2.10 1.25

1970, Dec. 18   **Engr.**   **Perf. 13**
87 A23 5fr rose car, grn &
      grnsh bl   .75 .75
88 A23 10fr dp lil, grn & vio   1.10 1.00
89 A23 40fr cop red, grn & dp
      brn   1.75 1.75
    Nos. 87-89 (3)   3.60 3.50

Great White   Pyrostegia
Egret — A24   Venusta — A25

Birds: 10fr, Comoro pigeon. 15fr, Green-
backed heron. 25fr, Comoro blue pigeon.
35fr, Humbolt's flycatcher. 40fr, Allen's
gallinule.

1971, Mar. 12   **Photo.**   **Perf. 12½x13**
90 A24 5fr multi   1.50 .80
91 A24 10fr yel & multi   2.00 .80
92 A24 15fr bl & multi   3.25 1.75
93 A24 25fr org & multi   4.75 2.00
94 A24 35fr yel grn & multi   6.50 2.50
95 A24 40fr gray & multi   8.00 3.25
    Nos. 90-95 (6)   26.00 11.10

For overprint see No. 145.

1971, July 19   **Photo.**   **Perf. 13**
Flowers: 3fr, Dogbane, horiz. 20fr,
Frangipani.

Size: 22x36mm, 36x22mm
96 A25 1fr ver & grn   .95 .85
97 A25 3fr yel, grn & red   1.40 1.00
98 A25 20fr ver & multi   3.50 2.50
    Nos. 96-98,C37-C38 (5)   17.35 11.50

For surcharges see Nos. 131-132, C75, C83.

Lithograph
Cone
A26

Sea Shells: 10fr, Pacific lettered cone. 20fr,
Aulicus cone. 35fr, Polita nerita. 60fr, Snakehead cowrie.

1971, Oct. 4
99 A26 5fr lt ultra & multi   1.25 1.00
100 A26 10fr multi   1.75 1.40
101 A26 20fr vio & multi   3.75 2.25
102 A26 35fr lt bl & multi   7.25 4.75
103 A26 60fr lt vio & multi   9.50 3.50
    Nos. 99-103 (5)   23.50 10.90

For surcharge see No. 150.

De Gaulle Issue
Common Design Type
Designs: 20fr, Gen. de Gaulle, 1940. 35fr,
Pres. de Gaulle, 1970.

1971, Nov. 9   **Engr.**   **Perf. 13**
104 CD134 20fr dk car & blk   4.75 4.00
105 CD134 35fr dk car & blk   5.50 4.75

Louis Pasteur, Slides, Microscope A27

1972, Aug. 2
106 A27 65fr indigo, org, & ol brn 5.50 4.75
Sesquicentennial of the birth of Louis Pasteur (1822-1895), chemist.

Type of Air Post Issue 1971
Designs: 10fr, View of Goulaivoini. 20fr, Bay, Mitsamiouli. 35fr, Gate and fountain, Foumbouni. 50fr, View of Moroni.

1973, June 28		**Photo.**	**Perf. 13**	
107	AP10	10fr bl & multi	.85	.65
108	AP10	20fr grn & multi	1.50	1.10
109	AP10	35fr bl & multi	2.10	1.60
110	AP10	50fr bl & multi	2.60	2.25
		Nos. 107-110,C53 (5)	16.55	12.10

For overprint see No. 143.

Bank of Madagascar and Comoros — A28

Buildings in Moroni: 15fr, Post and Telecommunications Administration. 20fr, Prefecture.

1973, July 10		**Photo.**	**Perf. 13x12½**	
111	A28	5fr multi	.65	.55
112	A28	15fr multi	.90	.80
113	A28	20fr multi	1.25	1.00
		Nos. 111-113 (3)	2.80	2.35

For surcharge see No. 134.

Salimata Hamissi Mosque A29

20fr, Zaouiyat Chaduli Mosque, vert.

Perf. 12½x13, 13x12½

1973, Oct. 20			**Photo.**	
114	A29	20fr multi	1.25	.95
115	A29	35fr multi	2.10	1.25

For surcharges see Nos. 135, 138.

Cheikh Mausoleum A30

Design: 50fr, Mausoleum of President Said Mohamed Cheikh (different view).

1974, Mar. 16		**Engr.**	**Perf. 13**	
116	A30	35fr grn, ol brn & blk	1.75	1.25
117	A30	50fr grn, ol brn & blk	2.50	1.75

For surcharge see No. 140.

Koran Stand, Anjouan A31

Designs: 15fr, Carved combs, vert. 20fr, 3-legged table, vert. 75fr, Sugar press.

1974, May 10		**Photo.**	**Perf. 12½x13**	
118	A31	15fr emer & multi	1.40	1.00
119	A31	20fr grn & multi	1.90	1.10
120	A31	35fr multi	2.90	1.90
121	A31	75fr multi	5.00	3.00
		Nos. 118-121 (4)	11.20	7.00

For overprints and surcharge see #137, 141, 149.

UPU Emblem, Symbolic Postmark A32

1974, Oct. 9		**Engr.**	**Perf. 13x12½**	
122	A32	30fr multi	2.00	1.75

Centenary of Universal Postal Union. For surcharge see No. 155.

Bracelet A33

1975, Feb. 28		**Engr.**	**Perf. 13**	
123	A33	20fr shown	1.10	.95
124	A33	35fr Diadem	1.90	1.25
125	A33	120fr Saber	5.00	3.25
126	A33	135fr Dagger	7.00	4.00
		Nos. 123-126 (4)	15.00	9.45

For surcharges see Nos. 136, 142, 151, 154.

Mohani Village, Moheli — A34

50fr, Djoezi Village, Moheli. 55fr, Chirazi tombs.

1975, May 26		**Photo.**	**Perf. 13**	
127	A34	30fr vio bl & multi	2.00	1.40
128	A34	50fr Prus bl & multi	3.25	2.10
129	A34	55fr grn & multi	4.75	3.25
		Nos. 127-129 (3)	10.00	6.75

For overprints and surcharge see #139, 146, 148.

Scuba Diver Photographing Coelacanth — A35

1975, June 27		**Engr.**	**Perf. 13**	
130	A35	50fr multi	8.25	5.75

1975 coelacanth expedition. For overprint see No. 147.

STATE OF COMORO

In 1978 the islands' name became the Federal and Islamic Republic of the Comoros.

Issues of 1971-75 Surcharged and Overprinted with Bars and: "ETAT COMORIEN" in Black, Silver or Red.

Tambourine Player — A36

#153, Women dancers & tambourine players.

Printing & Perforations as Before, Photogravure (A36)

1975			**Perf. 13 (A36)**	
131	A25	5fr on 1fr	.40	.20
132	A25	5fr on 3fr	.40	.20
133	A17	10fr on 2fr	.60	.20
134	A28	15fr on 20fr (R)	.80	.20
135	A29	15fr on 20fr (S)	.80	.20
136	A33	15fr on 20fr	.80	.20
137	A31	20fr	1.00	.20
138	A29	25fr on 35fr	1.00	.20
139	A34	30fr	1.00	.60
140	A30	30fr on 35fr	1.00	.30
141	A31	30fr on 35fr	1.00	.30
142	A33	30fr on 35fr	1.00	.60
143	AP10	35fr	1.25	.75
144	SP2	35fr on 35fr + 10fr	1.25	.75
145	A24	40fr	1.50	.80
146	A34	50fr	1.90	1.90
147	A35	50fr	1.90	.95
148	A34	50fr on 55fr (S)	1.90	.95
149	A31	75fr	2.00	.55
150	A26	75fr on 60fr (S)	2.00	.55
151	A33	100fr on 120fr	2.50	.90
152	A36	100fr bl & multi	2.50	.90
153	A36	100fr on 150fr (S)	2.50	.90
154	A33	200fr on 135fr	6.00	2.40
155	A32	500fr on 30fr	12.00	6.75
		Nos. 131-155 (25)	49.00	22.45

Nos. 152-153 exist without overprint or surcharge. Value, each $90.
No. 155 exists with red surcharge. Value $12.

Litho. & Embossed "Gold Foil" Stamps
These stamps generally are of a different design format than the rest of the issue. Since there is a commemorative inscription tieing them to the issue a separate illustration is not being shown.

Apollo-Soyuz — A37

Spacecraft and astronauts: 10fr, Soyuz lift-off, Alexei A. Leonov and Valeri N. Kubasov, vert. 30fr, Apollo lift-off, Thomas P. Stafford, Vance D. Brand, Donald K. Slayton, vert. 50fr, Meeting in space. 100fr, Chairman Brezhnev, President Ford talking with astronauts and cosmonauts. 200fr, Spacecraft preparing to dock. 400f, Return to Earth. 500fr, Spacecraft, mission emblems. 1500fr, Apollo-Soyuz crew. No. 164, Preparing to dock, diff.

1975, Dec. 15		**Litho.**	**Perf. 13½**	
156	A37	10fr multicolored	.20	.20
157	A37	30fr multicolored	.50	.25
158	A37	50fr multicolored	.80	.55
159	A37	100fr multicolored	1.40	.60
160	A37	200fr multicolored	2.75	1.25
161	A37	400fr multicolored	5.00	2.50
		Nos. 156-161 (6)	10.65	5.35

Litho. & Embossed
Size: 45x45mm
162 A37 1500fr gold & multi 17.50 —

Souvenir Sheets
Litho.
163 A37 500fr multicolored 5.50 1.75

Litho. & Embossed
164 A37 1500fr gold & multi 17.50 —

Nos. 159-164 are airmail. No. 163 contains one 64x44mm stamp. No. 164 contains one 45x45mm stamp.
No. 162 exists in a souvenir sheet of 1. Value $50.
For overprints see Nos. 477-478.

A38

American Revolution, Bicent. — A39

Designs: 15fr, Lewis and Clark, Blackfoot Indian. 25fr, John C. Fremont, Kit Carson, Indian dancer. 35fr, Daniel Boone, Buffalo Bill Cody, wagon train. 40fr, Richard E. Egan, Johnny Frey, Pony Express. 75fr, Henry Wells, William G. Fargo, stagecoach. 400fr, Frontiersman, Indian. 500fr, Leland Stanford, Thomas C. Dunant, transcontinental railroad. 1000fr, George Washington, winter at Valley Forge. 1500fr, John Paul Jones, ship.

1976, Jan. 15			**Litho.**	
165	A38	15fr multicolored	.20	.20
166	A38	25fr multicolored	.45	.25
167	A38	35fr multicolored	.75	.35
168	A38	40fr multicolored	.85	.45
169	A38	75fr multicolored	1.50	.60
170	A38	500fr multicolored	6.25	2.50
		Nos. 165-170 (6)	10.00	4.35

Litho. & Embossed
171 A39 1000fr gold & multi 13.50 —

Souvenir Sheets
Litho.
172 A38 400fr multicolored 5.50 1.75

Litho. & Embossed
173 A39 1500fr gold & multi 16.50 —

Nos. 170-173 are airmail. See Nos. 230, 232 and note after No. 479.
No. 171 exists in a souvenir sheet of 1. Value $55.

1976 Winter Olympics, Innsbruck — A40

1976, Mar. 30				**Litho.**
174	A40	5fr Women's figure skating	.20	.20
175	A40	30fr Slalom skiing	.25	.20
176	A40	35fr Speed skating	.35	.20
177	A40	50fr Downhill skiing	.60	.35
178	A40	200fr Ski jumping	2.10	1.00
179	A40	400fr Cross country skiing	4.50	1.25
		Nos. 174-179 (6)	8.00	3.20

Litho. & Embossed
Size: 56x35mm
180 A40 1000fr Downhill skier, hockey 13.00 —

Souvenir Sheets
Litho.
181 A40 500fr Hockey 5.50 1.75

Litho. & Embossed
182 A40 1000fr Olympic Rings 11.00 —

Nos. 178-182 are airmail. Nos. 181-182 contain one 58x35mm stamp. For overprint see No. 471.
No. 162 exists in a souvenir sheet of 1. Value $45.

1976 Summer Olympics,
Montreal — A41

1976, Mar. 30 Litho.
183 A41 20fr Runner, Athens,
1896 .20 .20
184 A41 25fr Sprints .25 .20
185 A41 40fr High jump, Paris,
1900 .45 .20
186 A41 75fr High jump 1.00 .45
187 A41 100fr Women stretching,
St. Louis, 1904 1.10 .50
188 A41 500fr Uneven parallel
bars 6.00 1.75
Nos. 183-188 (6) 9.00 3.30

Souvenir Sheet

189 A41 400fr Olympic Stadium,
Montreal 4.50 1.25

Nos. 187-189 are airmail.
For overprint see No. 476.

Fairy Tales — A42

1976, June 28
190 A42 15fr Hansel & Gretel .20 .20
191 A42 30fr Alice in Wonder-
land .50 .20
192 A42 35fr Pinocchio .65 .20
193 A42 40fr Good Little Henry .65 .25
194 A42 50fr Peter and the
Wolf 1.00 .25
195 A42 400fr Thousand and
One Nights 6.50 2.00
Nos. 190-195 (6) 9.50 3.10

#195 is airmail. #190-191, 193, 195 are vert.

Invention of Telephone, Cent. — A43

Designs: 10fr, A. G. Bell, 1st telephone.
25fr, Charles Bourseul, Paris-London phone
service, 1891. 75fr, Philipp Reis, telephone
operators. 100fr, Earth to Moon to Earth communications. 200fr, Satellite. 400fr, Ship-to-
Satellite communications. No. 201, Satellite in
orbit, antenna. No. 203, Global
communications.

1976, July 1
196 A43 10fr multicolored .20 .20
197 A43 25fr multicolored .25 .20
198 A43 75fr multicolored .75 .30
199 A43 100fr multicolored 1.00 .50
200 A43 200fr multicolored 2.25 .90
201 A43 500fr multicolored 5.50 1.75
Nos. 196-201 (6) 9.95 3.85

Souvenir Sheets

202 A43 400fr multicolored 4.50 1.25
203 A43 500fr multicolored 5.50 1.75

Nos. 199-203 are airmail. Nos. 202-203
contain a 73x44mm stamp. For overprint see
No. 472.

Comoro Flag, Map and Government
Buildings — A44

1976, Nov. 18 Litho. Perf. 13½
204 A44 30fr multi .75 .30
205 A44 50fr multi 1.25 .30

1st anniversary of independence.
For overprints and surcharges see Nos.
353-372.

Viking Probe to
Mars — A45

Designs: 5fr, Nicolaus Copernicus, rocket
launch. 10fr, Albert Einstein, Carl Sagan,
Thomas Young, Viking probe orbit-
ing Mars. 35fr, Discovery of America by Vikings, horiz. 100fr, Flag, Viking landing on
Mars. 500fr, Viking emblem, surface of Mars,
horiz. 400fr, Viking probe. No. 212, Wagon
train, frontiersman, rocket launch. No. 214,
Viking on Martian surface, robotic shovel.

1976, Nov. 23
206 A45 5fr multicolored .20 .20
207 A45 10fr multicolored .20 .20
208 A45 25fr multicolored .25 .30
209 A45 35fr multicolored 1.10 .30
210 A45 100fr multicolored 1.75 .40
211 A45 500fr multicolored 10.50 1.50
Nos. 206-211 (6) 14.00 2.90

Litho. & Embossed
Size: 57x39mm

212 A45 1500fr gold & multi 14.00 —

Souvenir Sheets
Litho.

213 A45 400fr multicolored 5.00 1.50

Litho. & Embossed

214 A45 1500fr gold & multi 15.00 —

American Revolution, bicentennial. Nos.
211-214 are airmail. No. 213 contains one
60x42mm stamp.
No. 212 exists in a souvenir sheet of 1.
Value $50.

UN Postal Administration, 25th
Anniv. — A46

Designs: 15fr, UN #24, irrigating field. 30fr,
UN #43, doctor, nurse. 50fr, UN #162, mother
holding child. 75fr, UN #42, communications
satellite in orbit. 200fr, UN #32, Concorde,
Zeppelin. 400fr, UN #18, cargo plane. 500fr,
People passing letters around globe.

1976, Nov. 25 Litho.
215 A46 15fr multicolored .20 .20
216 A46 30fr multicolored .30 .20
217 A46 50fr multicolored .60 .30
218 A46 75fr multicolored .80 .30
219 A46 200fr multicolored 2.50 .90
220 A46 400fr multicolored 5.00 1.50
Nos. 215-220 (6) 9.40 3.00

Souvenir Sheet

221 A46 500fr multicolored 5.00 2.00

Nos. 219-221 are airmail. No. 221 contains
one 57x40mm stamp. For overprints see Nos.
282-284, 473.

Comoro Flag, UN Headquarters and
Emblem — A47

1976, Nov. 25
222 A47 40fr multi 1.40 .30
223 A47 50fr multi 1.90 .40

1st anniv. of UN membership.

Type of 1976 and

US Bicentennial — A48

Civil War Battles: 10fr, Fort Sumter, Lincoln.
30fr, Bull Run, Gen. P.G.T. Beauregard, vert.
50fr, Antietam, Gen. Joseph E. Johnston.
100fr, Gettysburg, Gen. Meade. 200fr, Chatta-
nooga, Gen. Sherman, vert. 400fr, Appomat-
tox, Gen. Pickett. 500fr, Surrender at Appo-
mattox, Generals Lee and Grant. 1000fr,
Lincoln, battlefield. No. 230, Pres. Kennedy,
lunar lander.

1976, Dec. 30 Litho.
224 A48 10fr multicolored .20 .20
225 A48 30fr multicolored .30 .20
226 A48 50fr multicolored .65 .25
227 A48 100fr multicolored 1.10 .45
228 A48 200fr multicolored 2.50 .80
229 A48 400fr multicolored 5.00 1.50
Nos. 224-229 (6) 9.75 3.40

Litho. & Embossed
Size: 61x51mm

230 A39 1500fr gold & multi 17.00 —

Souvenir Sheets
Litho.

231 A48 500fr multicolored 6.50 1.75

Litho. & Embossed

232 A39 1000fr gold & multi 9.50 —

American Revolution bicentennial. Nos.
227-232 are airmail. No. 231 contains one
60x42mm stamp.
No. 230 exists in a souvenir sheet of 1.
Value $50.

Endangered Species — A49

1976, Dec. 30 Litho.
233 A49 15fr Andean condor,
vert. .30 .20
234 A49 20fr Australian tiger
cat .45 .20
235 A49 35fr Leopard, vert. 1.00 .20
236 A49 40fr White rhinoceros 1.25 .45
237 A49 75fr Nyala, vert. 3.00 .55
238 A49 400fr Orangutan 8.00 1.50
Nos. 233-239 (1) .30 .20

Souvenir Sheet

239 A49 500fr Lemur, vert. 7.00 1.75

Nos. 238-239 airmail. No. 239 contains one
40x58mm stamp.
See note after No. 479.

Endangered Species — A50

1977, Apr. 14
240 A50 10fr Wolf .20 .20
241 A50 30fr Aye-aye .45 .20
242 A50 40fr Cephalopus zebra .85 .25
243 A50 50fr Giant tortoise 1.00 .25
244 A50 200fr Ocelot 3.25 .75
245 A50 400fr Penguin 6.25 1.50
Nos. 240-245 (6) 12.00 3.15

Souvenir Sheet

246 A50 500fr Sumatran tiger 8.50 1.50

Nos. 244-246 airmail. No. 246 contains one
58x40mm stamp.

Giffard
Airship, 1851
and Paris-St.
Germain
Train, 1837,
France — A51

Airships & Locomotives: 25fr, Santos-
Dumont's airship, 1906, Brazilian Tander
120FIN, Brazil. 50fr, Astra, 1914, Trans-Sibe-
rian Express, 1905, Russia. 75fr, R.34, 1919,
Southern Belle, 1910, Great Britain. 200fr,
Navy airship, Pacific Class locomotive, 1930,
US. No. 252, Hindenburg, Rheingold Express,
1933, Germany. No. 253, Graf-Zeppelin,
1928, Nord-Express Type 231, 1925,
Germany.

1977, Apr. 14
247 A51 20fr multicolored .30 .20
248 A51 25fr multicolored .30 .20
249 A51 50fr multicolored .75 .25
250 A51 75fr multicolored 1.10 .25
251 A51 200fr multicolored 2.75 .60
252 A51 500fr multicolored 6.25 1.60
Nos. 247-252 (6) 11.45 3.10

Souvenir Sheet

253 A51 500fr multi, horiz. 6.00 2.00

Nos. 251-253 are airmail. No. 253 contains
one 58x39mm stamp.

Nobel Prize, 75th Anniv. — A52

Nobel Prize winners: 30fr, Medicine. 40fr,
Physics. 50fr, Literature. 100fr, Physics. 200fr,
Chemistry. 400fr, Peace.

1977, July 7
254 A52 30fr multicolored .75 .20
255 A52 40fr multicolored .75 .20
256 A52 50fr multicolored 1.25 .25
257 A52 100fr multicolored 3.25 .25
258 A52 200fr multicolored 5.50 .75
259 A52 400fr multicolored 12.50 1.25
Nos. 254-259 (6) 24.00 2.90

Souvenir Sheet

260 A52 500fr Nobel medal 5.50 1.75

Nos. 258-260 are airmail.
See note after No. 479.

Peter Paul Rubens, 400th Birth Anniv. — A53

Portraits: 20fr, Portrait of the Artist's Daughter, Clara. 25fr, Suzanne Fourment. 50fr, Toilet of Venus, (detail). 75fr, Ceres (detail). 200fr, Young Woman with Blonde Braided Hair. No. 266, Helene Fourment in her Wedding Dress. No. 267, Self-portrait.

1977, July 7
261	A53	20fr multicolored	.20	.20
262	A53	25fr multicolored	.30	.20
263	A53	50fr multicolored	.65	.25
264	A53	75fr multicolored	1.10	.30
265	A53	200fr multicolored	2.50	.60
266	A53	500fr multicolored	6.25	1.50
		Nos. 261-266 (6)	11.00	3.05

Souvenir Sheet
267	A53	500fr multicolored	5.50	1.75

Nos. 265-267 are airmail.
See note after No. 479.

Fish A54

1977, Nov. 21
268	A54	30fr Swordfish	.50	.20
269	A54	40fr Gaterin	1.00	.20
270	A54	50fr Sea scorpion	1.75	.20
271	A54	100fr Chaetodon lunula	3.25	.45
272	A54	200fr Amphiprion	4.00	.75
273	A54	400fr Tetrodon	7.50	1.50
		Nos. 268-273 (6)	18.00	3.30

Souvenir Sheet
274	A54	500fr Coelacanth	8.00	2.00

Nos. 272-274 airmail. No. 274 contains one 52x47mm stamp.

Space Exploration — A55

1977, Nov. 21
275	A55	30fr Jupiter lander	.30	.20
276	A55	50fr Voyager probe, Uranus, vert.	.60	.20
277	A55	75fr Pioneer probe, Venus	1.00	.25
278	A55	100fr Space shuttle, vert.	1.10	.40
279	A55	200fr Viking III, Mars	2.50	.60
280	A55	400fr Apollo-Soyuz, vert.	5.00	1.25
		Nos. 275-280 (6)	10.50	2.90

Souvenir Sheet
281	A55	500fr Allegory of the Sun	5.00	1.75

Nos. 279-281 airmail. No. 281 contains one 52x42mm stamp.

No. 219 Overprinted in One Line in Gold, Silver or Red
"Paris-New-York - 22 Nov. 1977"

1977, Nov. 22
282	A46	200fr multicolored	5.00	2.75
283	A46	200fr multicolored (S)	30.00	—
284	A46	200fr multicolored (R)	10.00	—
		Nos. 282-284 (3)	45.00	2.75

Birds — A56

1978, Feb. 6
285	A56	15fr Porphyrula alleni	.35	.20
286	A56	20fr M. superciliosus	.60	.20
287	A56	35fr Alcedo vintsioides johannae	.95	.20
288	A56	40fr Terpsiphone	1.25	.25
289	A56	75fr Nectarinia comorensis	2.10	.30
290	A56	400fr Egretta alba	10.75	1.50
		Nos. 285-290 (6)	16.00	2.65

Souvenir Sheet
291	A56	500fr Foudia eminentissima, horiz.	7.50	1.75

Nos. 290-291 are airmail. For overprint and surcharges see Nos. 444-448.

World Cup Soccer Championships, Argentina — A57

Designs: 30fr, Greece, 5th. cent. B.C. 50fr, Brittany, 19th cent. 75fr, London, 14th cent. 100fr, Italy, 18th cent. 200fr, England, 19th cent. 400fr, English Cup match, 1891. 500fr, English Cup final, 1962. No. 298, Player, satellite. No. 300, Players.

1978, Feb. 6
292	A57	30fr multicolored	.30	.20
293	A57	50fr multicolored	.60	.20
294	A57	75fr multicolored	.75	.20
295	A57	100fr multicolored	1.10	.40
296	A57	200fr multicolored	2.50	.60
297	A57	400fr multicolored	5.00	1.25
		Nos. 292-297 (6)	10.25	2.95

Litho. & Embossed
Size: 60x42mm
298	A57	1000fr gold & multi	11.00	—

Souvenir Sheets
Litho.
299	A57	500fr multicolored	6.00	1.75

Litho. & Embossed
300	A57	1000fr gold & multi	10.00	4.00

Nos. 296-300 are airmail. No. 300 contains one 60x42mm stamp.
No. 298 exists in a souvenir sheet of 1. Value $50.
For overprints and surcharges see Nos. 402-408, 449-453.

Composers — A58

1978, Apr. 5 Litho.
301	A58	30fr J.S. Bach	.90	.20
302	A58	40fr W.A. Mozart	1.10	.20
303	A58	50fr Berlioz	1.50	.30
304	A58	100fr Verdi	3.00	.30
305	A58	200fr Tchaikovsky	4.50	.60

306	A58	400fr George Gershwin	9.00	1.25
		Nos. 301-306 (6)	20.00	2.85

Souvenir Sheet
307	A58	500fr Beethoven	9.00	1.75

Nos. 305-307 are airmail. For overprints and surcharges see Nos. 454-458.

Albrecht Durer, 450th Death Anniv. — A59

Portraits: 20fr, Oswolt Krel. 25fr, Elspeth Tucher. 50fr, Hieronymus Holzschuher. 75fr, Young Woman. 200fr, Emperor Maximilian I. No. 313, Young Woman, (detail). No. 314, Self-portrait.

1978, Apr. 5
308	A59	20fr multicolored	.20	.20
309	A59	25fr multicolored	.30	.20
310	A59	50fr multicolored	.65	.20
311	A59	75fr multicolored	1.00	.30
312	A59	200fr multicolored	2.50	.60
313	A59	500fr multicolored	6.00	1.60
		Nos. 308-313 (6)	10.65	3.20

Souvenir Sheet
314	A59	500fr multicolored	5.50	1.75

Nos. 312-314 airmail. No. 314 contains one 42x52mm stamp. See note after No. 479.

Issues Not Valid for Postage
The government changed in May 1978. A number of sets that had not been issued seem to have been invalid for postage until they were overprinted with the new country name. These are a set of 9 for the 25th anniv. of Elizabeth's coronation, a set of 7 for butterflies, a set of 6 for the 10th Intl. Communications Year, a set of 7 for the history of aviation, a set of 9 for Rubens, and a set of 9 for Durer.
These sets, unoverprinted, exist both mint and cancelled to order. They are no scarcer than the previous listed issues.
See note after No. 479.

Islamic Republic
Nos. 204-205 Surcharged and Overprinted with 3 Lines and: "République / Fédérale / et Islamique / des Comores"

1978, July 24 Litho. Perf. 13½
353	A44	30fr multi	.30	—
354	A44	40fr on 30fr multi	.30	—
355	A44	50fr multi	.50	—
356	A44	100fr on 50fr multi	.90	—
		Nos. 353-356 (3)	1.50	

Nos. 353 and 355 were also overprinted to commemorate World Cup Soccer winner; Albrecht Dürer; Railroad anniversary; Voyager I and II; 1980 Olympic Games; World Cup Soccer, Espana '82.

Nos. 353, 355 Overprinted

1978, July 25 Litho. Perf. 13½
357	A44	30fr multi	7.00	—
358	A44	50fr multi	12.00	—

Coronation of Queen Elizabeth II, 25th anniv.

Nos. 353, 355 Overprinted

1978, July 26 Litho. Perf. 13½
359	A44	30fr multi	6.00	—
360	A44	50fr multi	9.00	—

Birth of Capt. James Cook, 250th anniv.

Nos. 353, 355 Overprinted

1978, July 31 Litho. Perf. 13½
365	A44	30fr multi	6.00	—
366	A44	50fr multi	10.00	—

Intl. Civil Aviation Organization.

Nos. 353, 355 Overprinted

1978, Aug. 3 Litho. Perf. 13½
371	A44	30fr multi	11.00	—
372	A44	50fr multi	11.00	—

Intl. Year of the Child (in 1979).

Europe-Africa A66

Various satellites or spacecraft.

1978, Dec. 16
386	A66	10fr multicolored	.20	.20
387	A66	25fr multicolored	.20	.20
388	A66	35fr multicolored	.40	.20
389	A66	50fr multicolored	.65	.20
390	A66	100fr multicolored	1.10	.60
391	A66	500fr multicolored	5.50	1.25
		Nos. 386-391 (6)	8.05	2.65

Souvenir Sheet
392	A66	500fr multicolored	5.50	1.75

Nos. 390-392 airmail. No. 392 contains one 61x40mm stamp.

Sir Rowland Hill — A67

1978, Dec. 16
393	A67	20fr Saxony #1	.20	
394	A67	30fr Netherlands #1	.30	.20
395	A67	40fr Great Britain #2	.60	.20
396	A67	75fr US #2	.75	.30
397	A67	200fr France #33	2.10	.60
398	A67	400fr Basel #3L1	4.50	1.25
		Nos. 393-398 (6)	8.45	2.75

Litho. & Embossed
Size: 39x58mm

| 399 | A67 | 1500fr British Guiana #13 | 13.00 | — |

Souvenir Sheets
Litho.

| 400 | A67 | 500fr Moheli, Mayotte, Anjouan, Grand Comoro #1 | 5.50 | 1.75 |

Litho. & Embossed

| 401 | A67 | 1500fr Hill, Mauritius #3 | 13.00 | — |

Nos. 397-401 are airmail. No. 400 contains one 57x49mm stamp. No. 401 contains one 58x39mm stamp.
No. 399 exists in a souvenir sheet of 1. Value $40.

Nos. 292-297 Ovptd. in Black & Silver

1978, Dec. 16
402	A57	30fr multicolored	.30	.20
403	A57	50fr multicolored	.60	.20
404	A57	75fr multicolored	.90	.20
405	A57	100fr multicolored	1.10	.45
406	A57	200fr multicolored	2.25	.60
407	A57	400fr multicolored	4.75	1.25
		Nos. 402-407 (6)	9.90	2.90

Souvenir Sheet

| 408 | A57 | 500fr multicolored | 5.50 | 1.25 |

Nos. 406-407 are airmail.
Exists with Country name in red on silver. Value approx. triple those of overprints in black.

Galileo and Voyager I — A68

Exploration of Solar System: 30fr, Kepler and Voyager II. 40fr, Copernicus and Voyager I, 100fr, Huygens and Voyager II. 200fr, William Herschel and Voyager II. 400fr, Urbain Leverrier and Voyager II. 500fr, Voyagers I and II, symbolic solar system.

1979, Feb. 19 **Litho.** **Perf. 13**
409	A68	20fr multi	.20	.20
410	A68	30fr multi	.30	.20
411	A68	40fr multi	.50	.20
412	A68	100fr multi	1.10	.25
413	A68	200fr multi	1.90	.50
414	A68	400fr multi	4.00	1.00
		Nos. 409-414 (6)	8.00	2.35

Souvenir Sheet

| 415 | A68 | 500fr multi | 5.00 | 1.50 |

Nos. 413-415 airmail.

Philidor, Anderssen, Steinitz and King — A69

100fr, Chess pieces and board, Venetian chess player. 500fr, Chess Grand Masters Alekhine, Spassky, Fischer, and bishop.

1979, Feb. 19
416	A69	40fr multi	.65	.20
417	A69	100fr multi	1.25	.20
418	A69	500fr multi	5.50	1.50
		Nos. 416-418 (3)	7.40	1.90

Chess Grand Masters. No. 418 airmail.

Nos. 419-425 are reserved for Summer Olympics set of 6 with one souvenir sheet, released Mar. 28, 1979.

Charaxes Defulvata — A71

Birds: 50fr, Leptosomus discolor. 75fr, Bee eater.

1979, Apr. 10 **Litho.** **Perf. 12½**
426	A71	30fr multi	1.50	.30
427	A71	50fr multi	3.75	.60
428	A71	75fr multi	6.25	1.00
		Nos. 426-428 (3)	11.50	1.90

Otto Lilienthal and Glider — A72

History of Aviation: No. 430, Wright brothers and Flyer A. No. 431, Louis Bleriot and Bleriot XI. 100fr, Claude Dornier and Dornier-Wal hydrofoil. 200fr, Charles Lindbergh and Spirit of St. Louis.

1979, May 2 **Perf. 13**
Black Overprint and Surcharge
429	A72	30fr multi	.50	.50
430	A72	50fr multi	.80	.80
431	A72	50fr on 75fr multi	.80	.80
432	A72	100fr multi	1.60	1.60
433	A72	200fr multi	2.50	2.50
		Nos. 429-433 (5)	6.20	6.20

No. 433 airmail.
For unoverprinted stamps see note after No. 314.

Papilio Dardanus Cenea — A73

Butterflies: 15fr, Papilio dardanus. 30fr, Chrysiridia croesus. 50fr, Precis octavia. 75fr, Bunaea alcinoe.

1979, May 2
Black Overprint and Surcharge
434	A73	5fr on 20fr multi	.20	.20
435	A73	15fr multi	.35	.20
436	A73	30fr multi	.70	.45
437	A73	50fr multi	1.40	.95
438	A73	75fr multi	2.25	1.50
		Nos. 434-438 (5)	4.90	3.30

For unoverprinted stamps see note after No. 314.

Man Reading Proclamation — A74

1979, May 2 **Litho.** **Perf. 13½**
Black Surcharge and Overprint
439	A74	5fr on 25fr coronation coach	.20	.20
440	A74	10fr Drummer	.30	.30
441	A74	50fr on 40fr with crown, orb, scepter	.70	.70
442	A74	50fr on 200fr shown	1.10	1.10
443	A74	100fr St. Edward's Crown	1.40	1.40
		Nos. 439-443 (5)	3.70	3.70

No. 442 is airmail.
For unoverprinted stamps see note after No. 314.

Nos. 285-289 (Birds) Overprinted or Surcharged like A72-A74
1979, May 2 **Litho.** **Perf. 13**
444	A56	15fr multi	.30	.30
445	A56	30fr on 35fr multi	.70	.70
446	A56	50fr on 20fr multi	1.25	1.25
447	A56	50fr on 40fr multi	1.25	1.25
448	A56	200fr on 75fr multi	4.00	4.00
		Nos. 444-448 (5)	7.50	7.50

Nos. 292-296 (Soccer) Overprinted or Surcharged like A72-A74
1979, May 2 **Litho.** **Perf. 13**
449	A57	1fr on 100fr multi	.20	.20
450	A57	2fr on 75fr multi	.20	.20
451	A57	3fr on 50fr multi	.20	.20
452	A57	50fr multi	.90	.55
453	A57	200fr multi	2.25	2.25
		Nos. 449-453 (5)	3.75	3.40

No. 453 airmail.

Nos. 301-305 (Composers) Overprinted or Surcharged like A72-A74
1979, May 2 **Perf. 13½**
454	A58	5fr on 100fr multi	.20	.20
455	A58	30fr multi	1.25	1.25
456	A58	40fr multi	1.75	1.75
457	A58	50fr multi	2.25	2.25
458	A58	50fr on 200fr multi	3.50	3.50
		Nos. 454-458 (5)	8.95	8.95

No. 458 airmail.

Intl. Year of the Child — A75

Intl. Year of the Child emblem and: 20fr, Astronaut on moon, child in astronaut costume. 30fr, Luger, child with snowboard. 40fr, Woman from Dürer painting, child practicing Chinese calligraphy. 100fr, Steam locomotive, child with toy train. 200fr, Adults and children playing soccer. 400fr, Olympic rower, child in rowboat.

500fr, Karl Benz, boy in toy car, horiz. No. 465A, Louis Blériot, child with remote-control airplane, horiz. No. 465B, Capt. James Cook, child with teddy bear and toy gun, horiz.

1979, May 30 **Litho.** **Perf. 13½**
459	A75	20fr multi	.20	.20
460	A75	30fr multi	.30	.30
461	A75	40fr multi	.40	.40
462	A75	100fr multi	1.00	1.00
463	A75	200fr multi	2.00	2.00
464	A75	400fr multi	4.00	4.00
		Nos. 459-464 (6)	7.90	7.90

Souvenir Sheet

| 465 | A75 | 500fr multi | 5.75 | 5.75 |

Litho. & Embossed
Size: 51x42mm

| 465A | A75 | 1500fr gold & multi | 13.50 | 13.50 |

Souvenir Sheet
Perf. 13¼

| 465B | A75 | 1500fr gold & multi | — | |

Nos. 463-465A are airmail. Nos. 465 and 465B each contain one 51x42mm stamp.

Litchi Nuts — A76

1979, June 15 **Litho.** **Perf. 12½**
466	A76	60fr shown	1.00	.30
467	A76	70fr Papayas	1.25	.45
468	A76	100fr Avocados	1.40	.55
469	A76	125fr Bananas	1.90	.90
		Nos. 466-469 (4)	5.55	2.20

For surcharges see Nos. 515, 533.

Basketball Players — A77

1979, Aug. 28 **Litho.** **Perf. 13**
| 470 | A77 | 200fr multi | 2.50 | 1.40 |

Indian Ocean Olympics.

Nos. 176, 198, 218, 187, 159-160 and Type A78 Overprinted in Black

Nimbus Weather Satellite — A78

No. 475, Apollo-Soyuz. No. 479, Molniya.

Printing & Perfs. as Before, Litho. (A78)
1979, Sept. 15 **Perf. 13 (A78)**
471	A40	35fr multi	.70	.70
472	A43	75fr multi	1.50	1.50
473	A46	75fr multi	1.50	1.50
474	A78	75fr multi	1.50	1.50
475	A78	100fr multi	2.10	2.10
476	A41	100fr multi	2.10	2.10
477	A37	100fr multi	2.10	2.10
478	A37	200fr multi	4.25	4.25
479	A78	200fr multi	4.25	4.25
		Nos. 471-479 (9)	20.00	20.00

Nos. 476-479 airmail.
For type A78 see note after No. 314.

Nos. 166-167, 169, 235-236, 257, 262, 309, 311, the unissued Rubens set (4 values) and Durer set (5 values) exist with this overprint, supposedly also issued Sept. 15.

Dugout on Beach A80

Anjouan Puppet — A81

1980, Jan. 4 **Litho.** **Perf. 13**
498 A80 60fr multi 1.00 .25
499 A81 100fr multi 1.50 .45

For surcharge see No. 534.

Sultan Said Ali — A82

1980, Feb. 20 **Perf. 12½x13**
500 A82 40fr shown .60 .20
501 A82 60fr Sultan Ahmed .75 .25

Sherlock Holmes, Doyle — A83

1980, Feb. 25 **Perf. 12½**
502 A83 200fr multi 4.75 1.75

Sir Arthur Conan Doyle (1859-1930), writer.
For surcharge see No. 513.

Grand Mosque, Holy Ka'aba, Mecca — A84

1980, Mar. 12 **Perf. 13x12½**
503 A84 75fr multi 1.00 .40

Hegira, 1500th anniv.
For surcharge see No. 514.

Year of the Holy City of Jerusalem A85

1980, Mar. 12 **Perf. 13x13½**
504 A85 60fr multi .75 .40

Kepler, Copernicus and Pluto — A86

1980, Apr. 30 **Litho.** **Perf. 12½**
505 A86 400fr multi 4.50 2.25

Discovery of Pluto, 50th anniversary.
For surcharge see No. 531.

Muscle System, Avicenna — A87

1980, Apr. 30 **Engr.** **Perf. 13**
506 A87 60fr multi .75 .40

Avicenna, Arab physician, birth millennium.

Soccer Players — A88

World Cup Soccer 1982; Various soccer scenes. 60fr, 150fr, 500fr, vert.

1981, Feb. 20 **Litho.** **Perf. 12½**
507 A88 60fr multi .65 .20
508 A88 75fr multi .75 .20
509 A88 90fr multi 1.25 .25
510 A88 100fr multi 1.10 .45
511 A88 150fr multi 1.90 .60
Nos. 507-511 (5) 5.65 1.70

Souvenir Sheet
512 A88 500fr multi 5.00 1.50

For overprints & surcharge see #532, 555-560.

Nos. 502-503, 469 Surcharged and

Merops Superciliosus A89

Perf. 12½, 13x12½ (No. 514)
1981, Feb. **Litho.**
Red, Black or Blue Surcharge
513 A83 15fr on 200fr multi .50 .50
514 A84 20fr on 75fr multi .50 .50
515 A76 40fr on 125fr multi (Bk) 1.50 1.50
516 A89 60fr on 75fr multi (Bl) 3.00 3.00
Nos. 513-516 (4) 5.50 5.50

A90

Space Exploration: 50fr, Apollo program, vert. 75fr, 100fr, 500fr, Columbia space shuttle.

1981, July 13 **Litho.** **Perf. 14**
517 A90 50fr multi .60 .20
518 A90 75fr multi .75 .20
519 A90 100fr multi 1.25 .30
520 A90 450fr multi 6.00 1.50
Nos. 517-520 (4) 8.60 2.20

Souvenir Sheet
521 A90 500fr multi 5.00 1.50

For overprints and surcharges see Nos. 599, 804F.

Prince Charles and Lady Diana, Buckingham Palace — A91

1981, Sept. 1 **Litho.** **Perf. 14½**
522 A91 125fr shown 1.10 .30
523 A91 200fr Highwood House 1.75 .60
524 A91 450fr Carnarvon Castle 3.75 1.25
a. Souvenir sheet of 3 6.75 2.00
Nos. 522-524 (3) 6.60 2.15

Royal wedding. No. 524a contains Nos. 522-524 in changed colors.
For overprints see Nos. 551-553.

Official Stamp Flag Type

1981, Oct. **Litho.** **Perf. 13**
526 O1 5fr multi .20 .20
527 O1 15fr multi .20 .20
528 O1 25fr multi .30 .20
529 O1 35fr multi .40 .20
530 O1 75fr multi .75 .35
Nos. 526-530 (5) 1.85 1.15

Nos. 505, 509, 468, 499 Surcharged

1981, Nov. **Litho.** **Perf. 12½**
531 A86 5fr on 400fr multi .40 .40
532 A88 20fr on 90fr multi .80 .20
533 A76 45fr on 100fr multi 2.00 1.00
534 A81 45fr on 100fr multi 2.00 .20
Nos. 531-534 (4) 5.20 1.60

75th Anniv. of Grand Prix — A92

Designs: Winners and their Cars.

1981, Dec. 28 **Litho.** **Perf. 12½**
535 A92 20fr Mercedes, 1914 .30 .20
536 A92 20fr Delage, 1925 .65 .20
537 A92 75fr Rudi Caracciola, 1926 .90 .25
538 A92 90fr Stirling Moss, 1955 1.10 .35
539 A92 150fr Maserati, 1957 1.60 .45
Nos. 535-539 (5) 4.55 1.45

Souvenir Sheet
Perf. 13
540 A92 500fr Changing wheels, vert. 6.00 1.75

For overprint see No. 600.

Scouting Year — A93

1982, Jan. 5 **Perf. 12½**
541 A93 50fr Climbing rocks .60 .20
542 A93 75fr Boating .85 .25
543 A93 250fr Sailing 3.00 .90
544 A93 350fr Sailing, diff. 3.75 1.10
Nos. 541-544 (4) 8.20 2.45

Souvenir Sheet
Perf. 13
545 A93 500fr Baden-Powell 6.50 1.75

For overprint see No. 601.

21st Birthday of Princess of Wales — A94

Various portraits of Princess Diana.

1982, July 1 **Litho.** **Perf. 14**
546 A94 200fr multi 2.50 .60
547 A94 300fr multi 3.25 .90

Souvenir Sheet
548 A94 500fr multi 5.50 1.50

Johannes von Goethe (1749-1832) A95

1982, July
549 A95 75fr multi .75 .25
550 A95 350fr multi 3.75 .90

Nos. 522-524a Overprinted in Blue: "NAISSANCE ROYALE 1982"

1982, July 31 **Perf. 14½**
551 A91 125fr multi 1.50 .60
552 A91 200fr multi 2.50 .90
553 A91 450fr multi 4.50 2.00
a. Souvenir sheet of 3 8.75 8.75
Nos. 551-553 (3) 8.50 3.50

Birth of Prince William of Wales, June 21.

Nos. 507-512 Overprinted with Finalists and Score in Red

1982, Sept. 20 **Litho.** **Perf. 12½**
555 A88 60fr multi .65 .25
556 A88 75fr multi .75 .35
557 A88 90fr multi 1.00 .45
558 A88 100fr multi 1.10 .45
559 A88 150fr multi 1.40 .60
Nos. 555-559 (5) 4.90 2.10

Souvenir Sheet
560 A88 500fr multi 5.00 1.50

Italy's victory in 1982 World Cup.

Paintings by Norman Rockwell A96

1982, Oct. 11   Litho.   Perf. 14
561	A96	60fr	1931	.65	.25
562	A96	75fr	1925	.70	.25
563	A96	100fr	1922	1.25	.25
564	A96	150fr	1919	1.40	.55
565	A96	200fr	1924	2.00	.60
566	A96	300fr	1918	3.50	1.00
		Nos. 561-566 (6)		9.50	2.90

Sultans of Anjouan — A97

1982, Dec.   Perf. 12½x13, 13x12½
567	A97	30fr	Said Mohamed Sidi, vert.	.40	.20
568	A97	60fr	Ahmed Abdallah, vert.	.75	.25
569	A97	75fr	Salim	1.00	.25
570	A97	300fr	Sidi, Abdallah	3.50	1.40
		Nos. 567-570 (4)		5.65	2.10

Landscapes — A98

1983, Sept. 30   Litho.   Perf. 13
571	A98	60fr	D'Ziani Lake	.75	.30
572	A98	100fr	Sunset	1.25	.45
573	A98	175fr	Anjouan, vert.	2.00	.75
574	A98	360fr	Itsandra	4.00	1.25
575	A98	400fr	Anjouan, diff.	5.00	1.60
		Nos. 571-575 (5)		13.00	4.35

For surcharge see No. 815S.

Woman from Moheli A99

1983, Oct. 17   Litho.   Perf. 12½x13
576	A99	30fr	shown	.40	.20
577	A99	45fr	Woman, diff.	.55	.20
578	A99	50fr	Man from Mayotte	.55	.20
		Nos. 576-578 (3)		1.50	.60

Horses — A100

1983, Nov. 30   Litho.   Perf. 13
579	A100	75fr	Arabian	.70	.25
580	A100	100fr	Anglo-Arabian	1.25	.30
581	A100	125fr	Lippizaner	1.50	.40
582	A100	150fr	Tennessee	1.75	.50
583	A100	200fr	Appaloosa	2.00	.70
584	A100	300fr	Pure English	3.50	1.00
585	A100	400fr	Clydesdale	4.75	1.25
586	A100	500fr	Andalusian	6.50	1.50
		Nos. 579-586 (8)		21.95	5.90

Double Portrait, by Raphael A101

1983, Dec. 30   Litho.   Perf. 13
587	A101	100fr	shown	1.25	.45
588	A101	200fr	Girl, fresco detail	2.50	.80
589	A101	300fr	St. George Killing Dragon	3.25	.90
590	A101	400fr	Balthazar Castiglione	5.50	1.25
		Nos. 587-590 (4)		12.50	3.40

For surcharges see Nos. 703, 800E, 815M.

Ships and Automobiles — A102

1984, Oct. 9   Litho.   Perf. 12½
591	A102	100fr	William Fawcett	1.25	.30
592	A102	100fr	De Dion, 1885	1.50	.30
593	A102	150fr	Lightning	1.90	.45
594	A102	150fr	Benz Victoria, 1893	2.25	.60
595	A102	200fr	Rapido	2.50	.75
596	A102	200fr	Columbia Electric, 1901	3.00	.75
597	A102	350fr	Sindia	4.50	1.00
598	A102	350fr	Fiat, 1902	5.00	1.10
		Nos. 591-598 (8)		21.90	5.25

For surcharge see No. 812Q.

Souvenir Sheets
Nos. 521, 540, 545, C126, C131 Ovptd. with Exhibition in Black, Blue, Red or Gold

1985, Mar. 11   Perf. 14, 13
599	A90	500fr	'85 / HAMBOURG (Bk)	5.00	5.00
600	A92	500fr	TSUKUBA EXPO '85 (Bl)	5.00	5.00
601	A93	500fr	ARGENTINA '85/BUENOS AIRES (R)	5.00	5.00
602	AP31	500fr	Rome, ITALIA '85 emblem (R)	5.00	5.00
603	AP32	500fr	OLYM-PHILEX/ '85 / LAUSANNE (G)	5.00	5.00
		Nos. 599-603 (5)		25.00	25.00

Nos. 602-603 airmail.

Victor Hugo (1802-1885), Author, Pantheon, Paris — A103

Anniversaries and events: 200fr, IYY, Jules Verne (1828-1905), author. 300fr, IYY, Mark Twain (1835-1910), author. 450fr, Queen Mother, 85th birthday, vert. 500fr, Statue of Liberty, cent., vert.

1985, May 27   Litho.   Perf. 13
604	A103	100fr	multi	1.25	.30
605	A103	200fr	multi	2.25	.60
606	A103	300fr	multi	3.50	.90
607	A103	450fr	multi	5.00	1.25
608	A103	500fr	multi	6.00	1.50
		Nos. 604-608 (5)		18.00	4.55

For surcharges see Nos. 704, 800A.

Sea Shells — A104

1985, Oct. 23   Perf. 14
609	A104	75fr	Lambis chiragra	1.00	.20
610	A104	125fr	Strombe lentifinosum	1.50	.35
611	A104	200fr	Tonna gala	2.50	.60
612	A104	300fr	Cymbium glans	4.00	.90
613	A104	450fr	Lambis crocata	6.00	1.40
		Nos. 609-613 (5)		15.00	3.45

Comoros Admission to UN, 10th Anniv. — A105

1985, Nov. 12   Litho.   Perf. 13x12½
614	A105	5fr	multi	.20	.20
615	A105	30fr	multi	.30	.20
616	A105	75fr	multi	.90	.25
617	A105	125fr	multi	1.40	.50
618	A105	400fr	multi	4.50	1.50
		Nos. 614-618 (5)		7.30	2.65

For surcharge see No. 800F.

Moroni Rotary Club, 20th Anniv. — A106

1985, Nov. 30   Perf. 13
619	A106	25fr	multi	.30	.20
620	A106	75fr	multi	.90	.40
621	A106	125fr	multi	1.40	.45
622	A106	500fr	multi	5.00	2.00
		Nos. 619-622 (4)		7.60	3.05

Mushrooms — A107

1985, Dec. 24   Perf. 13½
623	A107	75fr	Boletus edulis	1.00	.30
624	A107	125fr	Sarcoscypha coccinea	1.50	.45
625	A107	200fr	Hypholoma fasciculare	2.50	.60
626	A107	350fr	Astraeus hygrometricus	4.00	.90
627	A107	500fr	Armillariella mellea	7.00	1.50
		Nos. 623-627 (5)		16.00	3.75

For surcharge see No. 815R.

Health Year A108

1986, Oct. 2   Litho.   Perf. 15x14½
628	A108	25fr	Pediatric examination	.35	.20
629	A108	100fr	Weighing child	1.50	.60
630	A108	200fr	Immunization	2.75	1.25
		Nos. 628-630 (3)		4.60	2.05

For surcharge see No. 705.

Musical Instruments A109

1986, Dec. 24   Litho.   Perf. 13
631	A109	75fr	Ndzoumara	.90	.40
632	A109	125fr	Ndzedze	1.25	.60
633	A109	210fr	Gaboussi	2.10	.90
634	A109	500fr	Ngoma	6.00	1.75
		Nos. 631-634 (4)		10.25	3.65

For surcharges see Nos. 796P, 796T, 800L, 815A.

Role of Women in National Development — A110

1987, Mar. 7   Litho.   Perf. 13
635	A110	75fr	Working fields	.80	.30
636	A110	125fr	Harvesting crops, vert.	1.40	.45
637	A110	1000fr	Basketweaving	11.00	3.00
		Nos. 635-637 (3)		13.20	3.75

Service Organizations — A111

Emblems and activities: 75fr, Nos. 642, Kiwanis or 643c, Rotary Intl. for child survival. 125fr, No. 641, Kiwanis or 643b, Lions Intl. for aid to the handicapped. 210fr, No. 643a, Kiwanis helping poor and homeless children.

1988   Litho.   Perf. 13½
638	A111	75fr	dk bl, lt bl & multi	.75	.30
639	A111	125fr	dk brn, lt brn & multi	1.40	.45
640	A111	210fr	org, yel & multi	2.25	.75

641 A111 425fr red, pink &
 multi 4.50 1.75
642 A111 500fr bl, yel & multi 6.00 2.00
643 Strip of 3 13.00 6.00
 a. A111 210fr grn, lt grn & multi 2.10 .75
 b. A111 425fr pur, pink & multi 4.50 1.75
 c. A111 500fr red, orange & multi 6.00 2.00
 Nos. 638-643 (6) 27.90 11.25

For surcharges see Nos. 654-656, 815B, 815W.

1988 Olympics, Calgary and
Seoul — A113

1988 **Litho.** **Perf. 13½**
644 A112 75fr Women's figure skating .65 .20
645 A112 100fr Running 1.00 .30
646 A112 125fr Women's
 speed skating 1.00 .40
647 A112 150fr Equestrian 1.50 .50
648 A112 350fr Two-man luge 3.25 .90
649 A112 400fr Biathlon 4.00 1.40
650 A112 500fr Pole vault 4.00 1.25
651 A112 600fr Soccer 6.00 1.50
 Nos. 644-651 (8) 21.40 6.45

Souvenir Sheets
652 A113 750fr Women's
 downhill ski-
 ing, satellite 7.75 1.50
653 A113 750fr Track, satellite 7.75 1.50

Nos. 649 and 651-653 are airmail.
For surcharges see Nos. 800C, 800M, 815V.

**No. 643 and Service Organization
Types Surcharged**

No. 655, like #643b. No. 656, like #643c.

1988, July 18 **Litho.** **Perf. 13½**
654 Strip of 3 5.50 5.00
 a. A111 75fr on 210fr #643a .65 .45
 b. A111 200fr on 425fr #643b 1.75 .90
 c. A111 300fr on 500fr #643c 2.75 1.25
655 A111 125fr on 425fr pur, lt
 pur & multi, blk
 letters 1.10 .60
656 A111 400fr on 500fr car,
 pink & multi 3.75 2.00
 Nos. 654-656 (3) 10.35 7.60

Nos. 655-656 not issued without surcharge.

Discovery of
America, 500th
Anniv. (in
1992) — A114

Designs: 75fr, Christopher Columbus, *Santa Maria*. 125fr, Martin Alonzo Pinzon (c. 1441-1493), *Pinta*. 150fr, Vicente Yanez Pinzon (c. 1460-1523), *Nina*. 250fr, Search for Cipango, legendary rich islands off the coast of Asia. 375fr, *Santa Maria* shipwrecked. 450fr, Preparing for 4th voyage. 750fr, Samana Cay landing.

1988, Apr. 18 **Litho.** **Perf. 13½**
657 A114 75fr multi .65 .20
658 A114 125fr multi 1.10 .30
659 A114 150fr multi 1.50 .45

660 A114 250fr multi 2.10 .75
661 A114 375fr multi 3.75 1.00
662 A114 450fr multi 4.50 1.25
 Nos. 657-662 (6) 13.60 3.95

Souvenir Sheet
663 A114 750fr multi, horiz. 7.75 1.50

Nos. 661-663 airmail. No. 663 contains one 42x30mm stamp.
For surcharges see Nos. 702, 815D.

1992
Summer
Olympics,
Barcelona
A115

1988, Apr. 18
664 A115 75fr Discus, vert. .60 .20
665 A115 100fr shown .90 .30
666 A115 125fr Cycling 1.75 .45
667 A115 150fr Wrestling 2.25 .50
668 A115 375fr Basketball, vert. 5.25 1.00
669 A115 600fr Tennis, vert. 8.25 1.25
 Nos. 664-669 (6) 19.00 3.70

Souvenir Sheet
670 A115 750fr Marathon, vert. 7.75 1.50

Nos. 668-670 are airmail.

Famous
Men — A116

Rotary Intl. — A117

150fr, Yuri Gagarin (1934-68), USSR, cosmonaut. 300fr, Jean-Henri Dunant, Red Cross founder. 400fr, Roger Clemens, baseball player. 500fr, Gary Kasparov, USSR, 1985 world chess champion. 600fr, Paul Harris, US, Rotary founder. 750fr, Neil Armstrong walking on the Moon, John F. Kennedy. #678, The Thinker by Rodin, Rotary Intl. emblem.

1988, Dec. 6 **Litho.** **Perf. 13½**
671 A116 150fr multi 1.75 .50
672 A116 300fr multi 1.75 .50
673 A116 400fr multi 1.75 .50
674 A116 500fr multi 1.75 .50
675 A116 600fr multi 1.75 .50
 a. Souv. sheet of 5, #671-675 +
 label 10.00
 Nos. 665-669 (5) 18.40 3.50

Litho. & Embossed
676 A117 1500fr gold & multi 15.00 —

Souvenir Sheets
Litho.
677 A116 750fr multi 7.75 1.50

Litho. & Embossed
678 A117 1500fr gold & multi 15.00 —

Intl. Red Cross, 125th anniv. (300fr), Rotary Intl. (600fr, Nos. 676, 678). Nos. 674-678 are airmail.

#672-673 exist in souv. sheets of 1.
No. 676 exists in a souvenir sheet of 1. Value $42.50.

Inventors and
Sportsmen
A118

Portraits and modes of transportation: Designs: 75fr, Alain Prost, F-1 MacLaren-Honda. 125fr, George Stephenson and locomotive *Borsig* of 1935. 500fr, Ettore Bugatti (1881-1947), 1939 Bugatti Aravis Type 57. 600fr, Rudolf Diesel (1858-1913) and V200 BB diesel-electric locomotive. 750fr, Dennis Conner, captain of the *Stars and Stripes*, winner of the 1987 America's Cup. No. 684, Michael Fay, patron of the *New Zealand*, an entry in the America's Cup. No. 685, Enzo Ferrari and 1989 Ferrari Formula 1, horiz.

1988, Dec. 27 **Litho.** **Perf. 13½**
679 A118 75fr multi .75 .45
680 A118 125fr multi 1.25 .25
681 A118 500fr multi 5.00 1.25
682 A118 600fr multi 6.00 1.25
683 A118 750fr multi 7.00 1.25
684 A118 1000fr multi 10.00 1.25
 Nos. 679-684 (6) 30.00 5.70

Souvenir Sheet
685 A118 1000fr multi 10.00 1.50

Nos. 683-685 are airmail.
#679-684 exist in souv. sheets of 1.

Scouts,
Butterflies and
Birds — A119

Scouts involved in various activities and species: 50fr, Gathering specimens, *Papilio nireus aristophontes oberthur* female. 75fr, Studying specimen and male. 150fr, Cooking out, *Charaxes fulvescens separanus poulton*. 375fr, Picking mushrooms, *Lonchura cucullatus*. 450fr, Examining specimen, *Charaxes castor comoranus rothschild*. 500fr, Identifying specimen, *Zosterops maderaspatana*. 750fr, Studying specimens, *Foudia omissa* and *Charaxes paradoxa lathy* female. No. 692, Photographing specimen, *Junonia rhadama*. No. 694, Examining specimen, *Agapornis cana cana*.

1989 **Litho.**
686 A119 50fr multi .50 .20
687 A119 75fr multi .60 .20
688 A119 150fr multi 1.40 .30
689 A119 375fr multi 4.00 .75
690 A119 450fr multi 4.75 1.00
691 A119 500fr multi 5.75 1.25
 Nos. 686-691 (6) 17.00 3.70

Litho. & Embossed
692 A119 1500fr gold & multi 13.00 —

Souvenir Sheets
Litho.
693 A119 750fr multi 12.00 1.50

Litho. & Embossed
694 A119 1500fr gold & multi 13.00 —

Nos. 690-694 are airmail. Issue dates: Nos. 692, 694, May 15; others, Mar. 15.
No. 692 exists in a souvenir sheet of 1. Value $42.50.
For surcharges see Nos. 800D, 815T.

Gold
Medalists
of the
1988
Summer
Olympics
A120

Communication satellites, various equestrians and their mounts: 75fr, Nicole Uphoff, West Germany, individual dressage, and Aussat K3. 150fr, Pierre Durand, France, individual jumping, and Brazilsat. 375fr, Janos Martinek, Hungary, individual modern pentathlon, and ECS 4. 600fr, Mark Todd, New Zealand, individual three-day event, and Olympus. 750fr, Team jumping, West Germany, and satellite. No. 699, Pierre Durand, France, individual show jumping. No. 701, Nicole Uphoff, West Germany, individual dressage.

1989, Apr. 10 **Litho.** **Perf. 13½**
695 A120 75fr multi .65 .20
696 A120 150fr multi 1.25 .35
697 A120 375fr multi 3.00 .75
698 A120 600fr multi 5.00 1.25
 Nos. 695-698 (4) 9.90 2.55

Litho. & Embossed
699 A120 1500fr gold & multi 13.00 —

Souvenir Sheets
Litho.
700 A120 750fr multi 6.75 1.50

Litho. & Embossed
701 A120 1500fr gold & multi 13.00 —

No. 701 contains one 39x38mm stamp. Nos. 698-701 are airmail.
No. 699 exists in a souvenir sheet of 1. Value $45.
For surcharges see Nos. 796Q, 804I.

**Nos. 660, 588, 605 and 630
Surcharged**

1989 **Litho.** **Perfs. as Before**
702 A114 25fr on 250fr #660 .20 .20
703 A101 150fr on 200fr #588 1.25 .50
704 A103 150fr on 200fr #605 1.25 .50
705 A108 150fr on 200fr #630 1.25 .50
 Nos. 702-705 (4) 3.95 1.70

1992 Summer
Olympics,
Barcelona
A121

1989, Apr. 26 **Litho.** **Perf. 13½**
706 A121 75fr Running .65 .20
707 A121 150fr Soccer 1.25 .40
708 A121 300fr Tennis 2.50 .60
709 A121 375fr Baseball 3.25 .80
710 A121 500fr Pommel horse 4.00 1.00
711 A121 600fr Table tennis 5.00 1.25
 Nos. 706-711 (6) 16.65 4.25

Souvenir Sheet
712 A121 750fr Equestrian 6.75 1.50

Nos. 710-712 are airmail.
For surcharges see Nos. 796J, 796K, 800J, 812R.

Dr. Joseph-Ignace Guillotin (1738-
1814) — A122

French Revolution, Bicent.: 150fr, French artillery, Gen. Francois-Christophe Kellermann (1735-1820). 375fr, Royalist insurgents & leader, Jean Cottereau (1757-94). 600fr, King Louis XVI (1774-92), troops. 1000fr, Storming of the Bastille & Jacques Necker, statesman (1732-1804). #717, Lafayette, Mounier, Sieyes & Declaration of the Rights of Man and Citizen. #719, Robespierre & St. Just before the Convention on 9 Thermidor.

1989, Oct. 25 **Litho.** **Perf. 13½**
713 A122 75fr multicolored .70 .20
714 A122 150fr multicolored 1.25 .35
715 A122 375fr multicolored 3.00 .60
716 A122 600fr multicolored 5.00 1.25
 Nos. 713-716 (4) 9.95 2.40

Litho. & Embossed
717 A122 1500fr gold & multi 13.00 —

Souvenir Sheets
Litho.

718 A122 1000fr multicolored   8.50 1.75

Litho. & Embossed

719 A122 1500fr gold & multi   13.00

Philexfrance 1989. No. 716-719 are airmail. No. 714 incorrectly inscribed "Francois-Etienne."

Nos. 713-716 exist in souvenir sheets of 1. No. 717 exists in a souvenir sheet of 1. Value $22.

For surcharges see Nos. 796B, 800W, 804J.

Airport Pavilion A124

Designs: 10fr, 25fr, Airport pavilion. 50fr, 75fr, 150fr, Federal Assembly.

1990, Apr. 1   Litho.   Perf. 13

722	A124	5fr brn, org & brt red	.20	.20
723	A124	10fr brn, org & brt bl	.20	.20
724	A124	25fr brn, org & brt grn	.20	.20
725	A124	50fr blk & brt red	.45	.20
726	A124	75fr blk & brt bl	.75	.30
727	A124	150fr blk & grn	1.40	.60
		Nos. 722-727 (6)	3.20	1.70

World Cup Soccer Championships, Italy — A125

Players from: 50fr, Brazil. 75fr, England. 100fr, Federal Republic of Germany. 150fr, Belgium. 375fr, Italy. 600fr, Argentina. 750fr, Argentina and Italy.

1990   Litho.   Perf. 13½

728	A125	50fr multicolored	.45	.20
729	A125	75fr multicolored	.65	.30
730	A125	100fr multicolored	.80	.35
731	A125	150fr multicolored	1.10	.45
732	A125	375fr multicolored	3.00	1.00
733	A125	600fr multicolored	5.00	1.25
		Nos. 728-733 (6)	11.00	3.55

Litho. & Embossed

734 A125 1500fr gold & multi   13.00 5.00

Souvenir Sheets
Litho.

735 A125 750fr multicolored   6.75 1.50

Litho. & Embossed

736 A125 1500fr gold & multi   13.00 —

Nos. 732-736 are airmail. No. 734 exists in a souvenir sheet of 1. Value $22.50.

For surcharges see Nos. 796L, 796O, 804K.

Telecom '91 A125a

1990, Oct. 29   Litho.   Perf. 13½

736A	A125a	75fr Emblem, vert.	.75	.60
736B	A125a	150fr shown	1.60	1.25
		Nos. 736A-736B exist imperf.		

A126

Designs: 75fr, Hubble Space Telescope placed in orbit. 150fr, Pope John Paul II, Pres. Gorbachev meet Dec. 3, 1989. 200fr, Kevin Mitchell, San Francisco Giants, Natl. League Most Valuable Player, 1989. 250fr, De Gaulle, France, and Adenauer, West Germany, meet in Sept. 1962. 300fr, Cassini probe to Titan, 2002. 375fr, Bullet train and Concorde, France. 450fr, Gary Kasparov, World Chess Champion. 500fr, Paul Harris (1868-1947), founder of Rotary Intl.

1990, Nov. 26   Litho.   Perf. 13½

737	A126	75fr sil & multi	.75	.25
738	A126	150fr sil & multi	1.50	.40
739	A126	200fr sil & multi	2.00	.40
740	A126	250fr sil & multi	2.50	.40
741	A126	300fr sil & multi	3.00	.50
742	A126	375fr sil & multi	3.75	.65
743	A126	450fr sil & multi	4.50	1.00
744	A126	500fr sil & multi	5.25	.75
		Nos. 737-744 (8)	23.25	4.35

Nos. 743-744 are airmail. #738, 744 exist in souv. sheets of 1. For surcharges see Nos. 796A, 796R, 800I, 804A, 804L, 815E, 815U.

A127

A128

Winter Olympics participants: 75fr, Edi Reinalter, Switzerland, slalom, 1948. 100fr, Canadian hockey team, 1924. 375fr, Gratia Van der Oye, women's slalom, Holland, 1936. 600fr, Heikki Hasu, Finland, combined cross country and ski jumping, 1948. 750fr, Helene Engelman & Alfred Berger, Austria, pairs figure skating, 1924. No. 751, Speed skater, horiz. No. 751A, Luge, horiz.

1990, Dec. 10

746	A127	75fr multicolored	.60	.20
747	A127	100fr multicolored	.75	.30
748	A127	375fr multicolored	3.50	1.00
749	A127	600fr multicolored	6.00	1.25
		Nos. 746-749 (4)	10.85	2.75

Souvenir Sheet

750 A127 750fr multicolored   8.25 1.50

Litho. & Embossed
Souvenir Sheet

751 A127 1500fr gold & multi   16.00 —

Souvenir Sheet

751A A127 1500fr gold & multi   15.00 —

1992 Winter Olympics, Albertville. Nos. 748-751A are airmail. No. 750 contains one 36x41mm stamp.

No. 751 exists in a souvenir sheet of 1. Value $22.

For surcharges see Nos. 796M, 800K, 804M, 812S.

1991, May 17   Litho.   Perf. 13½

Ground station, Moroni Volo-Volo.

752	A128	75fr multicolored	1.00	.20
753	A128	150fr multicolored	1.60	.45
754	A128	225fr multicolored	2.40	.75
755	A128	300fr multicolored	3.50	1.00
756	A128	500fr multicolored	5.50	1.25
		Nos. 752-756 (5)	14.00	3.65

For surcharge see 815N.

Indian Ocean Conference — A129

1991, June 17

757	A129	75fr multicolored	.30	.20
758	A129	150fr multicolored	.90	.75
759	A129	225fr multicolored	1.40	1.00
		Nos. 757-759 (3)	2.60	1.95

World War II, 50th Anniv. A130

Actors, Films: 150fr, Errol Flynn, Objective Burma. 300fr, Henry Fonda, The Longest Day. 450fr, Humphrey Bogart, Sahara.

1991, Aug. 5

760	A130	150fr sil & multi	1.75	.45
761	A130	300fr sil & multi	3.25	.75
762	A130	450fr sil & multi	5.00	.90
		Nos. 760-762 (3)	10.00	2.10

No. 762 is airmail. Nos. 760-762 exist in souvenir sheets of 1.

For surcharges see Nos. 796D, 800H, 804B, 804G.

A131

Charles de Gaulle A132

De Gaulle and: 125fr, Battle of Koufra. 375fr, Battle of Britain. 500fr, Battle of Monte Cassino. 1000fr, Airplanes. 1500fr, De Gaulle at podium.

1991, Aug. 5   Litho.   Perf. 13½

763	A131	125fr multi	1.25	.30
764	A131	375fr multi	2.75	.75
765	A131	500fr multi	4.50	.90
		Nos. 763-765 (3)	8.50	1.95

Souvenir Sheet

766 A131 1000fr multi   12.00 2.00

Litho. & Embossed

767 A132 1500fr gold & multi   16.00 —

Nos. 765-767 are airmail. No. 767 exists in souvenir sheet of 1. Value $20.

For surcharges see Nos. 796G, 804N, 816I.

Anniversaries and Events — A133

Designs: 100fr, Satellite Columbus in polar orbit. 150fr, Gandhi. 250fr, Jean-Henri Dunant. 300fr, Wolfgang Amadeus Mozart. 375fr, Brandenburg Gate. 400fr, Konrad Adenauer. 450fr, Elvis Presley. 500fr, Ferdinand von Zeppelin.

1991, Nov. 18   Litho.   Perf. 13½

768	A133	100fr multicolored	1.25	.30
769	A133	150fr multicolored	1.60	.35
770	A133	250fr multicolored	2.50	.60
771	A133	300fr multicolored	3.25	.60
772	A133	375fr multicolored	4.50	.90
773	A133	400fr multicolored	4.50	.90
774	A133	450fr multicolored	5.50	1.00
a.		Souv. sheet, #771, 774		
775	A133	500fr multicolored	5.50	1.00
a.		Souv. sheet, #772-773, 775		
		Nos. 768-775 (8)	28.60	5.65

Nobel Peace Prize, 90th anniv. (#770). Mozart, bicent. of death (#771). Brandenburg Gate, bicent. (#772). Konrad Adenauer, 25th anniv. of death (#773). Elvis Presley, 15th anniv. of death (in 1992) (#774). Count Zeppelin, 75th anniv. of death (in 1992) (#775).

Nos. 774-775 are airmail. Nos. 768-775 exist in souvenir sheets of 1. Value, set $50.

For surcharges see Nos. 796F, 796H, 800G, 804C, 804O, 815F, 815O, 816J.

Mushrooms — A134

1992, Mar. 23   Litho.   Perf. 13½

776	A134	75fr Cepe comestible	.80	.40
777	A134	150fr Geastre en etoile	1.90	.60
778	A134	600fr Pezize ecarlate	8.25	1.50
		Nos. 776-778 (3)	10.95	2.50

No. 778 is airmail. Nos. 776-778 exist imperf. and in souvenir sheets of one.

Shells A135

1992, Mar. 23

779	A135	125fr Conus textile	1.60	.50
780	A135	150fr Cypraecassis rufa	2.10	.65
781	A135	500fr Leporicypraea mappa	6.50	1.90
		Nos. 779-781 (3)	10.20	3.05

Souvenir Sheet

782 A135 750fr Nautilus pompilius   10.50 2.00

Nos. 781-782 are airmail. Nos. 779-781 exist imperf. and in souvenir sheets of one. No. 782 exists imperf.

For surcharges see Nos. 800N, 816K.

Space
Programs
A136

Designs: 75fr, Mercury rocket, chimpanzee
Ham, US. 125fr, Mars Observer, US. No. 785,
Veronica rocket, cat Felix, France. No. 786,
Mars rover, US, Mars car, USSR. 500fr,
Phobos project, USSR. 600fr, Sputnik II, dog
Laika, USSR. 1000fr, Viking, US, vert.

1992, Mar. 30		**Litho.**	**Perf. 13½**	
783	A136	75fr multicolored	1.25	.25
784	A136	125fr multicolored	1.75	.30
785	A136	150fr multicolored	2.25	.70
786	A136	150fr multicolored	2.10	.70
787	A136	500fr multicolored	6.50	1.25
a.		Souv. sheet, #784, 786-787	15.00	7.00
788	A136	600fr multicolored	7.75	1.40
a.		Souv. sheet, #783, 785, 788		
		Nos. 783-788 (6)	21.60	4.60

Souvenir Sheet

789	A136	1000fr multicolored	13.00	2.25

Nos. 787-789 are airmail. Nos. 783-788
exist imperf. and in souvenir sheets of one.
No. 789 contains one 30x42mm stamp.
For surcharges see Nos. 800O, 804Q.

Voyages
of
Discovery
A137

Designs: 75fr, Space shuttle Endeavour,
sailing ship Endeavour, Capt. Cook. 100fr,
Satellite, sailing ship Golden Hinde, Sir Francis Drake. 150fr, ISO observation satellite,
sailing ship Susan Constant, John Smith.
225fr, Probe B, sailing ship Discovery, Robert
F. Scott. 375fr, Magellan probe over Venus,
sailing ship, Ferdinand Magellan. 500fr,
Newton probe, sailing ship Sao Gabriel, Vasco
da Gama.
1000fr, Hermes-Columbus space shuttle,
Columbus and his fleet.

1992, May 28		**Litho.**	**Perf. 13½**	
790	A137	75fr multicolored	1.25	.25
791	A137	100fr multicolored	1.40	.30
792	A137	150fr multicolored	2.25	.45
793	A137	225fr multicolored	2.75	.75
794	A137	375fr multicolored	5.25	1.00
795	A137	500fr multicolored	6.00	1.25
a.		Souvenir sheet of 6, #790-795	18.90	4.00
		Nos. 790-795 (6)	18.90	4.00

Souvenir Sheet

796	A137	1000fr multicolored	13.00	2.25

Nos. 794-796 are airmail. Nos. 790-795
exist imperf. in souvenir sheets of one.
For surcharges see Nos. 796E, 800P, 804P.

Various Stamps Surcharged

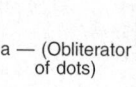

a — (Obliterator
of dots)

Methods and Perfs as Before
1992-95

796A	A126	10fr on 300fr #741	—
796B	A122	15fr on 375fr #715	—
796C	AP41	25fr on 210fr	
		#C164	
796D	A130	25fr on 300fr #761	—
796E	A137	25fr on 375fr #794	—

796F	A133	35fr on 400fr #773		
796G	A131	50fr on 375fr #764		
796H	A133	50fr on 375fr #772		
796I	AP34	50fr on 475fr		
		#C138		
796J	A121	75fr on 300fr #708	—	
796K	A121	75fr on 375fr #709	—	
796L	A125	75fr on 375fr #732	—	
796M	A127	75fr on 375fr #748	—	
796N	AP42	75fr on 600fr		
		#C170		
796O	A125	100fr on 375fr #732	—	
796P	A109	100fr on 210fr #633	—	
796Q	A120	150fr on 375fr #697	—	
796R	A127	150fr on 375fr #742	—	
796S	AP40	150fr on 450fr		
		#C162		
796T	A109	150fr on 500fr #634	—	
796U	AP42	150fr on 500fr		
		#C169		

No. 796J exists with quadruple surcharge.
No. 796Q exists with inverted surcharge and
with double surcharge, one inverted.

Organization of
African Unity,
30th
Anniv. — A138

1993, Feb. 15		**Litho.**	**Perf. 13½x13**	
797	A138	25fr blue & multi	.20	.20
798	A138	50fr pink & multi	.50	.20
		Perf. 12		
799	A138	75fr green & multi	1.40	.45
800	A138	150fr vermilion & multi	2.25	1.00
		Nos. 797-800 (4)	4.35	1.85

Various Stamps Surcharged

b — (Bar
obliterator)

Methods and Perfs as Before
1992-95

800A	A103	50fr on 450fr #607	
x.		Zero in surcharge thin at top and bottom	
800B	AP47	75fr on 800fr	
		#C192	
800C	A112	100fr on 350fr #648	—
800D	A119	100fr on 375fr #689	—
g.		Zero in surcharge thin at top and bottom	
y.		150fr on 375fr #689 (error)	
800E	A101	100fr on 400fr #590	—
800F	A105	100fr on 400fr #618	—
h.		Zero in surcharge thin at top and bottom	
800G	A133	100fr on 400fr #773	—
i.		Zero in surcharge thin at top and bottom	
800H	A130	125fr on 450fr #762	—
800I	A126	150fr on 250fr #740	—
z.		Zero in surcharge thin at top and bottom	
800J	A121	150fr on 375fr #709	—
800K	A127	150fr on 375fr #748	—
a.		Zero in surcharge thin at top and bottom	
800L	A109	150fr on 500fr #634	—
k.		Zero in surcharge thin at top and bottom	
800M	A112	150fr on 500fr #650	—
b.		Zero in surcharge thin at top and bottom	
800N	A135	150fr on 500fr #781	—
800O	A136	150fr on 500fr #787	—
800P	A137	150fr on 500fr #795	—
c.		Zero in surcharge thin at top and bottom	
800Q	AP41	150fr on 500fr	—
		#C165	
d.		Zero in surcharge thin at top and bottom	
800R	AP44	150fr on 500fr	—
		#C177	
l.		Zero in surcharge thin at top and bottom	
m.		Denomination above oblitera-tor	
n.		As "l," denomination above obliterator	

800S	AP45	150fr on 500fr	
		#C181	
e.		Zero in surcharge thin at top and bottom	
800T	AP42	150fr on 500fr	
		#C185	
o.		Zero in surcharge thin at top and bottom	
800U	AP47	150fr on 500fr	
		#C191	
800V	AP50	150fr on 500fr	
		#C212	
p.		Zero in surcharge thin at top and bottom	
800W	A122	150fr on 600fr #716	

Surcharge on No. 800W is sideways reading
top to bottom. Nos. 800B and 800F exist with
inverted surcharge, Nos. 800F, 800R, 800W,
and perhaps other values exist with misplaced
surcharge.
No. 800F exists with zeros in surcharge in
different sizes.

1994 World Cup
Soccer
Championships,
U.S. — A139

Intl. Telecommunications Day — A140

1993, May 12		**Litho.**	**Perf. 13x12½**	
801	A139	25fr red & multi	.20	.20
802	A139	75fr brown & multi	.65	.30
803	A139	100fr blue & multi	1.40	.40
804	A139	150fr green & multi	1.60	.60
		Nos. 801-804 (4)	3.85	1.50

Various Stamps Surcharged Type
"b" in Black or Red
Methods and Perfs as Before
1992-95

804A	A126	200fr on 300fr #741	—
s.		Zero in surcharge thin at top and bottom	
804B	A130	200fr on 300fr #761	—
804C	A133	200fr on 300fr #771	—
w.		Zero in surcharge thin at top and bottom	
804D	AP45	200fr on 300fr	—
		#C180	
x.		Zero in surcharge thin at top and bottom	
804E	AP47	200fr on 300fr	—
		#C190	
t.		Zero in surcharge thin at top and bottom	
804F	A90	200fr on 450fr #520	—
u.		Overprint right side up	
y.		Overprint right side up, zero in surcharge thin at top and bottom	
804G	A130	200fr on 450fr #762	—
a.		Zero in surcharge thin at top and bottom	
b.		As "a," two obliterators	
804H	AP40	200fr on 450fr	—
		#C162	
c.		Zero in surcharge thin at top and bottom	
804I	A120	225fr on 375fr #697	—
804J	A122	225fr on 375fr #715	—
804K	A125	225fr on 375fr #732	—
804L	A126	225fr on 375fr #742	—
804M	A127	225fr on 375fr #748	—
v.		"f" in surcharge omitted	
804N	A127	225fr on 375fr #764	—
804O	A133	225fr on 375fr #772	—
804P	A137	225fr on 375fr #794	—
804Q	A136	225fr on 500fr #787	—

Red Surcharge

804R	AP40	200fr on 300fr	
		#C161	

Surcharge on No. 804F is inverted.
No. 804D exists with "020fr" surcharge and
with zeroes in surcharge in different sizes.
Nos. 804D and 804F exists with zeroes in
surcharge in different sizes.

1993, May 17				
805	A140	50fr red & multi	.40	.20
806	A140	75fr blue & multi	.65	.30
807	A140	100fr green & multi	1.10	.40
808	A140	150fr black & multi	1.60	.60
		Nos. 805-808 (4)	3.75	1.50

Miniature Sheet

Prehistoric
Animals
A141

Designs: a, 75fr, Edaphosaurus. b, 75fr,
Moschops. c, 75fr, Sauroctonus. d, 75fr,
Ornitholestes. e, 75fr, Kentrosaurus. f, 75fr,
Compsognathus. g, 75fr, Styracosaurus. h,
75fr, Acanthopolis. i, 150fr, Edmontonia. j,
150fr, Struthiomimus. k, 450fr,
Dromiceiomimus. l, 450fr, Iguanodon. m,
150fr, Diatryma. n, 150fr, Uintatherium. o,
525fr, Synthetoceras. p, 525fr, Euryapteryx.
1200fr, Tyrannosaurus rex.

1994, Apr. 5		**Litho.**	**Perf. 13½**	
809	A141	Sheet of 16, #a.-p.	22.50	9.00

Souvenir Sheet

810	A141	1200fr multicolored	13.00	3.00

No. 810 is airmail and contains one
42x60mm stamp.

Miniature Sheets

Flora — A142

Flowers: No. 811a, 75fr, Hibiscus syriacus.
150fr, Pyrostegia venusta. 525fr, Allamanda
cathartica.
Vegetables: No. 811b, 75fr, Anacardier.
150fr, Manioc. 525fr, Cacao.
Mushrooms: No. 811c, 75fr, Suillus lutens.
150fr, Lycogala epidendron. 525fr, Clathrus
ruber.
Butterflies, insects: No. 812a, 75fr, Colotis
zoe. b, 150fr, Acherontia atropos. c, 525fr,
Danaus chrysippus. d, 75fr, Charaxes
comoranus. e, 150fr, Euchloron megaera. f,
450fr, Papilio phorbanta. g, 75fr, Hypurgus
ova. h, 150fr, Onthophagus catta. i, 450fr,
Echinosoma bolivari.

1994, May 24		**Litho.**	**Perf. 13½**	
811	A142	Sheet of 9	16.00	5.50
a.		Strip of 3	4.25	1.50
b.		Strip of 3	4.25	1.50
c.		Strip of 3	4.25	1.50
d.		Souvenir sheet of 3, #811a	16.00	5.00
e.		Souvenir sheet of 3, #811b	16.00	5.00
f.		Souvenir sheet of 3, #811c	16.00	5.00
812	A142	Sheet of 9, #a.-i.	15.00	5.00
j.		Souv. sheet of 3, #812a-812c	16.00	5.00
k.		Souv. sheet of 3, #812d-812f	16.00	5.00
l.		Souv. sheet of 3, #812g-812i	16.00	5.00

For surcharges see No. 826F.

Independence, 20th Anniv. — A142a

Designs: 100fr, 200fr, 300fr, Maps of Grand Comoro, Moheli, Mayotte and Anjouan.

1995 (?)   **Litho.**   *Perf. 13x12¾*
812M	A142a	100fr multi	—
812N	A142a	200fr multi	—
812O	A142a	300fr multi	—

For surcharge see No. 826M.

Various Stamps Surcharged in Gold

c — (Wide numerals, obliterator of small sqares in grid)

Methods and Perfs as Before

1996, Dec.
812P	AP40	200fr on 300fr #C161	—
812Q	A102	200fr on 350fr #598	—
812R	A121	200fr on 375fr #709	—
v.		"2" same size as "0"	—
812S	A127	200fr on 375fr #748	—
812T	AP31	200fr on 400fr #C125	—
812U	AP44	200fr on 500fr #C177	—

Size of numerals and obliteration grids varies.

A143	A144

Diana, Princess of Wales (1961-97): Various portraits.

1997, Dec. 15   **Litho.**   *Perf. 14*
813	A143	150fr Sheet of 12, #a.-l.	10.00 4.00
814	A143	375fr Sheet of 6, #a.-f.	12.00 5.00

Souvenir Sheet
815	A143	1000fr multicolored	5.50 2.25

Various Stamps Surcharged Type "c" in Black

Methods and Perfs as Before

1996, Dec.
815A	A109	200fr on 210fr #633	—
815B	A111	200fr on 210fr #640	—
815C	AP41	200fr on 210fr #C164	—
815D	A114	200fr on 250fr #660	—
815E	A126	200fr on 250fr #740	—
815F	A133	200fr on 250fr #770	—
815G	AP30	200fr on 250fr #C116	—
815H	AP38	200fr on 250fr #C151	—
815I	AP38	200fr on 250fr #C152	—
x.		Pair, #815H-815I + label	—
815J	AP42	200fr on 250fr #C168	—
815K	AP42	200fr on 250fr #C184	—
815L	AP28	200fr on 260fr #C110	—
815M	A101	200fr on 300fr #589	—
y.		With gold obliterator over old value	—

815N	A128	200fr on 300fr #755	—
815O	A133	200fr on 300fr #771	—
815P	AP31	200fr on 300fr #C124	—
815Q	AP37	200fr on 300fr #C150	—
815R	A107	200fr on 350fr #626	—
815S	A98	200fr on 360fr #574	—
815T	A119	200fr on 375fr #689	—
815U	A126	200fr on 375fr #742	—
815V	A112	200fr on 400fr #649	—
815W	A111	200fr on 425fr #641	—

Size of surcharge numerals and obliteration grid varies. Black surcharge on No. 815My is misplaced. No. 815Q exists with misplaced surcharge that is faintly tripled, a surcharge with thinner zeroes, and a pair containing No. C150 next to No. 815Q with misplaced surcharge that is faintly tripled and has thinner zeroes. No. 815W exists with an inverted surcharge and with a double surcharge, one inverted.

1997, Dec. 15   **Litho.**   *Perf. 14*
816	A144	200fr Mother Teresa (1910-97)	1.50 .45

No. 816 was issued in sheets of 9.

Aromatic Plants
A144a

Designs: 25fr, 50fr, 1000fr, Piper nigrum. 100fr, 125fr, 200fr, Cinnamomum ceylanicum. 300fr, Syzigium aromaticum. 500fr, Myristica fragrans.

1997, Dec. 15   **Litho.**   *Perf. 14*
816A	A144a	25fr multi	—
816B	A144a	50fr multi	—
816C	A144a	100fr multi	—
816D	A144a	125fr multi	—
816E	A144a	200fr multi	—
816F	A144a	300fr multi	—
816G	A144a	500fr multi	—
816H	A144a	1000fr multi	—

Various Stamps Surcharged Type "c" in Black

Methods and Perfs as Before

1996, Dec.
816I	A131	200fr on 500fr #765	—
816J	A133	200fr on 500fr #775	—
816K	A135	200fr on 500fr #781	—
816L	AP42	200fr on 500fr #C169	—
816M	AP42	200fr on 500fr #C185	—
816N	AP42	200fr on 600fr #C170	—
816O	AP42	200fr on 600fr #C186	—

Size of surcharge and obliteration grid varies.

Vertical Pairs from No. B4 Surcharged with Silver Bar to Obliterate Surtax

Methods and Perfs as before.

1996, Dec.
816P		Surcharged pair of #B4a, B4e	—
t.		SP3 200fr on 200fr+10fr Galileo	—
u.		SP3 200fr on 200fr+10fr Planet A & 3 stars	—
816Q		Surcharged pair of #B4b, B4f	—
v.		SP3 200fr on 200fr+10fr Copernicus	—
w.		SP3 200fr on 200fr+10fr ICE	—
816R		Surcharged pair of #B4c, B4g	—
x.		SP3 200fr on 200fr+10fr Kepler	—
y.		SP3 200fr on 200fr+10fr Planet A & 5 stars	—
816S		Surcharged pair of #B4d, B4h	—
z.		SP3 200fr on 200fr+10fr Halley	—
aa.		SP3 200fr on 200fr+10fr Vega	—

A full sheet of Nos. 816P-816S is not known to exist.

Cats
A145

Designs, vert: 75fr, Silver banded. 150fr, Lac de Van. No. 819, 200fr, European short hair. No. 820, 200fr, Somali. No. 821, 375fr,

Japanese bobtail. No. 822, 375fr, Egyptian mau.

No. 823, each 375fr: a, Poupée de chiffon. b, Maine coon. c, Norwegian forest cat. d, Persian. e, Droop-eared. f, Marbled American short hair.

No. 824, each 375fr: a, Manx. b, Cashmere. c, British shorthair. d, Cornish rex. e, American curl. f, Ocicat.

No. 825, 1500fr, Silver-chocolate Somali. No. 826, 1500fr, Chocolate Persian, vert.

1998, June 3   **Litho.**   *Perf. 14*
817-822	A145	Set of 6	7.50 7.50

Sheets of 6
823-824	A145	Set of 2	24.00 24.00

Souvenir Sheets
825-826	A145	Set of 2	17.50 6.00

No. C215D Surcharged Type "c" in Red or Black

Methods and Perfs as Before

1997 (?)
826A	AP52a	100fr on 225fr	—
826B	AP52a	200fr on 225fr	—
826C	AP52a	200fr on 225fr (Bk)	—
826D	AP52a	500fr on 225fr	—
826E	AP52a	600fr on 225fr	—

Size of surcharge numerals varies. No. 826B exists with inverted surcharge, No. 826C exists with double surcharge.

No. 811 Surcharged on Six Stamps

d — (Obliterator of Triangles and Wavy Lines)

Methods and Perfs as Before

1998 (?)
826F		Sheet of 9	—
g.		A142 200fr on 150fr Pyrostegia venusta	
h.		A142 200fr on 150fr Manioc	
i.		A142 200fr on 150fr Lycogala epidendron	
j.		A142 200fr on 525fr Allamanda cathartica	
k.		A142 200fr on 525fr Cacao	
l.		A142 200fr on 525fr Clathrus ruber	

The three 75fr stamps on the sheet received no surcharge.

No. 812O Surcharged

e — (Obliterator of Bars, Dots, and Semicircles)

Methods and Perfs as Before

1998 (?)
826M	A142a	100fr on 300fr	—

Size of surcharge numerals varies.

Marine Life
A146

No. 827, each 150fr: a, Pomacanthus imperator. b, Cephalopholis miniatus. c, Diver. d, Nautilus pompilius. e, Sphyraena barracuda. f, Manta birostris. g, Lutjanus sebae. h,

Chaetodonplus duboulayi. i, Amphiprion bicinctus.

No. 828, vert , each 150fr: a, Istiophorus platypterus. b, Sterna fuscata. c, Larus pipixcan. d, Hippocampus kuda. e, Amphiprion ocellaris (2 fish). f, Octopus vulgaris. g, Chaetodon striatus. h, Actini aquina. i, Acanthurus leucosternon.

No. 829: a, Diomedea exulans. b, Delphinus delphis. c, Sailboat. d, Sphyrna zygaena. e, Loligo forbesi. f, Galeocerdo cuvieri. g, Pomacanthus imperator, diff. h, Amphiprion ocellaris (1 fish). i, Forcipiger flavissimus. j, Electrophorus electricus. k, Dermochelys coriaoea. l, Asterias rubens.

No. 830, 1500fr, Mastigias papua, vert. No. 831, 1500fr, Sepia officinalis. No. 832, 1500fr, Zancius canescens.

1998, Aug. 10   **Litho.**   *Perf. 14*

Sheets of 9 or 12
827-828	A146	Set of 2	13.00 13.00
829	A146	200fr #a.-l.	12.00 12.00

Souvenir Sheets
830-832	A146	Set of 3	22.50 22.50

Nos. 830-832 each contain one 51x38mm or 38x51mm stamp.

Betty Boop — A146a

No. 832A: b, Wearing hula skirt, dancing. c, With dog, wearing blue dress, in pink heart. d, Wearing polka dot dress. e, In bathtub. f, Face in red heart. g, Holding top hat. h, With flamingos. i, With dog, Wearing red dress, blue ribbon. j, Wearing hula skirt, on surf board. 1125fr, With fishing pole.

1998   **Litho.**   *Perf. 13¼*
832A	A146a	300fr Sheet of 9, #b-j	16.00 16.00

Souvenir Sheet
832K	A146a	1125fr multi	7.00 7.00

No. 832A contains nine 35x41mm stamps.

Popeye — A146b

No. 832L: m, Wimpy. n, Popeye, Olive Oyl, ship's wheel. o, Swee'Pea. p, Head of Popeye. q, Popeye. r, Head of Olive Oyl. s, Jeep. t, Olive Oyl. u, Brutus.

No. 832V, 1125fr, Popeye with spinach can. No. 832W, 1125fr, Like #832Ln, horiz.

1998
832L	A146b	450fr Sheet of 9, #m-u	24.00 24.00

Souvenir Sheets
832V-832W	A146b	Set of 2	14.00 14.00

No. 832L contains nine 35x51mm stamps, No. 832W contains one 60x50mm stamp.

Coelacanth — A147

World Wildlife Fund: a, Swimming right, colored background. b, Swimming right, white background. c, In net. d, Swimming left.
No. 833E: f, Like #833a. g, Like #833d. h, Like #833c. i, Like #833b.

1998
833   A147   200fr Strip of 4, #a-
      d   6.00   6.00
833E   A147   375fr Sheet of 4, #f-i   37.50

No. 833 was issued in sheets of 3 vertical strips.
No. 833E exists imperf. Value $45.

I Love Lucy — A147a

No. 833F, vert. — Lucy: g, With black ribbon in hair. h, Wearing burlap sack. i, With trapeze in mouth. j, With one arm raised. k, On telephone. l, Wearing red and white apron. m, Wearing bright green dress. n, Wearing blue dress. o, With fishing gear.
1125fr, With Ricky, with fishing gear.

1998   **Litho.**   **Perf. 13¼**
833F   A147a   250fr Sheet of
      9, #g-o   13.00   13.00
Souvenir Sheet
833P   A147a   1125fr multi   7.00   7.00

No. 833F contains nine 35x51mm stamps.

Diana, Princess of Wales (1961-97) A148

Nos. 834-835, 835J, Various portraits.
No. 836, 1125fr, Wearing scarf, green dress. No. 837, 1125fr, Wearing black and white hat and outfit.

1998   **Litho.**   **Perf. 13½**
Sheets of 9
834   A148   250fr #a.-i.   13.00   13.00
835   A148   350fr #a.-i.   18.00   18.00
835J   A148   450fr #k.-s.   24.00   24.00
Souvenir Sheets
836-837   A148   Set of 2   13.00   13.00

Nos. 835, 835J contain 42x51mm stamps.
Nos. 836-837 each contain one 42x60mm stamp.

Entertainers A149

#838: Various portraits of Grace Kelly (Princess Grace of Monaco) (1929-92).
#839: Various portraits of Frank Sinatra (1915-98).

1998
Sheets of 9
838   A149   300fr #a.-i.   16.00   16.00
839   A149   500fr #a.-i.   26.50   26.50

Classic Automobiles — A150

No. 840, each 150fr: a, 1936 Jaguar SS. b, 1939 Lincoln Continental. c, 1903 Mercedes. d, 1936 MG-TA. e, 1946 Oldsmobile Custom Cruiser 98. f, 1933 Pontiac. g, 1940 Rolls-Royce Silver Ghost 40/50. h, 1950 Studebaker Starlight Coupe. i, 1932 Ford V8.
No. 841, each 150fr: a, 1927 Alfa Romeo RLSS. b, 1933 DuPont Model G. c, Bentley Speed Six. d, 1932 Cadillac 355. e, 1955 Corvette. f, 1934 Chrysler Airflow. g, Buick Coupe deVille. h, Model T Ford. i, 1920 Duesenberg Model A.
No. 842, 1500fr, Rolls-Royce Phantom II Continental. No. 843, 1500fr, 1927 Daimler Double Six.

1998, Oct. 29   **Litho.**   **Perf. 14**
Sheets of 9
840-841   A150   Set of 2   13.00   13.00
Souvenir Sheets
842-843   A150   Set of 2   17.00   17.00

Birds — A151

No. 844, 75fr, Macareux moine. No. 845, 75fr, Calliste à tête verte. No. 846, 150fr, Soutmanga de la reine Christine. No. 847, 150fr, Rale d'eau. No. 848, 200fr, Lophophore replendissant. No. 849, 200fr, Francolin noir. No. 850, 375fr, Mesia à oreillonis argentes. No. 851, 375fr, Mérion splendide.
No. 852: a, Canard plongeur austral. b, Garrot a ceil d'or. c, Harle huppé. d, Canard colvert. e, Canard branchu. f, Sarcelle elegante.
No. 853: a, Emérillon. b, Nyctale de tengmalm. c, Aigle royal d, Kétoupa malais. e, Caracara. f, Chouette à lunettes
No. 854, Jacana du mexique. No. 855, Toucan de cuvier.

1999, Jan. 23   **Litho.**   **Perf. 14**
844-851   A151   Set of 8   8.50   8.50
Sheets of 6, #a-f
852-853   A151   375fr Set of 2   22.50   22.50
Souvenir Sheets
854-855   A151   1500fr Set of 2   16.00   16.00

Fauna A152

No. 856, vert, each 150fr: a, Giraffa camaloprdalis. b, Macaca fusata. c, Loxodonta africana. d, Ovis dalli. e, Phoenicopterus ruber. f, Orcinus orca. g, Ursus horribilis. h, Lemur catta.
No. 857, vert, each 150fr: a, Pongo pygmaeus. b, Ceratotherium simum. c, Ailuropoda melanoleuca. d, Tursiops truncartus. e, Felis caracel. g, Eudyptes chrysocome. h, Panthera uncia.
No. 858, vert, each 150fr: a, Phascolarctos cinereus. b, Ammotragus levia. c, Hippopatamus amphibius. d, Saimiri boliviensis. e, Acinonyx jubatus. f, Gorilla gorilla. g, Branta sandvicensis. h, Thalarctos maritimus.
No. 859, each 150fr: a, Panthera tigris. b, Phoca groenlandica. c, Acipenser sturio. d, Lepidochelys kempii. e, Ailuropoda melanoleuca. f, Isurus oxyrinchus. g, Chelydra serpentina. h, Eretmochelys imbricata.
Each 1500fr: No. 860: Pan troglodytes, vert. No. 861, Panthera tigris altaica, vert. No. 862, Oryx gazella, vert. No. 863, Hippotigris zebra. No. 864, Diceros bicornis. No. 865, Panthera leo. No. 866, Amazona viridgenalis. No. 867, Pygoscelis papua, vert.

1999, Jan. 25
Sheets of 8
856-859   A152   Set of 4   25.00   25.00
Souvenir Sheets
860-867   A152   Set of 8   65.00   65.00

Fish A153

No. 868, 75fr, Pomacantus imperator. No. 869, 75fr, Heniochus intermedium. No. 870, 150fr, Mirolaprichthys. No. 871, 150fr, Pomacanthus paru. No. 872, 375fr, Ostzacion tuberculatus. No. 873, 375fr, Colisa calia.
No. 874, each 150fr: a, Coris aygula. b, Chromis caeruleys. c, Euxiphipops navarchus. d, Pseudobalistes fuscus. e, Zebrasoma flavescens. f, Mycteroperca urba. g, Epinephelus flavocaeruleus. h, Equetus lanceolatus. i, Acanthurus leucostemon.
No. 875, each 150fr: a, Chaetodon tinkeri. b, Ostzaciidae. c, Seatophagus argus. d, Adioryx coruscus. e, Pygoplites diacanthus. f, Paracanthurus hepatus. g, Chaetodon plebius. h, Lythrypnus dalli. i, Myrichthys oculatus.
Each 1500fr: No. 876, Amphipzion percula. No. 877, Cymnothorne undulatus.

1998, Oct.-Nov.   **Litho.**   **Perf. 14**
868-873   A153   Set of 6   7.00   7.00
Sheets of 9
874-875   A153   Set of 2   14.00   14.00
Souvenir Sheets
876-877   A153   Set of 2   16.00   16.00

Marine Life — A154

No. 878, 75fr, Tubastrea aurea. No. 879, 75fr, Condylachtis gigantea. No. 880, 150fr, Paracanthurus hepatus. No. 881, 150fr, Balistoides conspicillum. No. 882, 200fr, Diodon holocanthus. No. 883, 200fr, Sebastes rubrivintus. No. 884, 375fr, Trygonorhina fasciata. No. 885, 375fr, Phocoenoides dalli.
No. 886, each 150fr: a, Epinephelus guttatus. b, Diademichthys lineatus. c, Plotosus lineatus. d, Rhinomuraena quaesita. e, Zanclus cornutus. f, Persephona punctata. g, Murex pecten. h, Tetrosomus gibbosus.
No. 887, each 150fr: a, Lythrypnus dalli. b, Premnas biaculeatus. c, Pseudanthias tuka. d, Capros aper. e, Balistoides conspicillum. f, Oreaster reticulatus. g, Octopus joubini. h, Fasciolaris tulipa.

Each 1500fr: No. 888, S. picturatus. No. 889, Megaptera novaeangliae.

1999
878-885   A154   Set of 8   8.50   8.50
Sheets of 8
886-887   A154   Set of 2   17.00   17.00
Souvenir Sheets
888-889   A154   Set of 2   19.00   19.00

Prehistoric Animals — A155

No. 890, each 150fr: a, Meganeura. b, Archaeopteryx. c, Peteinosaurus. d, Eudimorphodon. e, Brachiosaurus. f, Gallimimus. g, Tarbosaurus. h, Parasaurolophus. i, Sauropelta. j, Herrarasaurus. k, Stegosaurus. l, Lambeosaurus.
No. 891, each 150fr: a, Ramphorhinchus. b, Quetzalcoatlus. c, Pterodactylus. d, Pteranodon. e, Dimorphodon. f, Camarasaurus. g, Tenontosaurus. h, Protoceratops. i, Coelurosaurus. j, Mixosaurus. k, Ceresiosaurus. l, Sharovipteryx.
Each 1500fr: No. 892, Ceratosaurus. No. 893, Mesosaurus. No. 894, Megazostrodon. No. 895, Diatryma.

1999
Sheets of 12
890-891   A155   Set of 2   19.00   19.00
Souvenir Sheets
892-895   A155   Set of 4   32.50   32.50

Prehistoric Animals, Lemurs and Butterflies — A156

Prehistoric animals — No. 895A — Prehistoric sea creatures: b, Eurhinodelphis. c, Stenopterygius. d, Ichthyosaurus. e, Pakicetus. f, Xenacanthus. g, Zygorhiza. h, Basilosaurus. i, Mesosaurus. j, Cetotherium. No. 896: a, Elasmosaurus (b). b, Quetzalcoatl (c). c, Mesadactylus (b). d, Dimorphodon (e). e, Rhamphorhynchus (c, d, f, i). f, Pteranodon (c, i). g, Pterodactylus (h). h, Eudimorphodon (i). i, Ornithodesmus (g, h).
Lemurs — No. 897: a, Haplorhinien primitif. b, Aye aye (c, e, f). c, Lemur vari. d, Indri. e, Makis varis (f, i). f, Potto. g, Lemur catta. h, Lemur macaos. i, Microcebe souris.
Butterflies — No. 898: a, Charaxes nobilis. b, Charaxes eupale. c, Charaxes brutus. d, Lobobunea turlini. e, Papilio nobilis. f, Athletes gigas. g, Papilio antimachus. h, Epiphora albida. i, Papilio zalmoxis.

1998   **Perf. 13¼x13½**
Sheets of 9
895A   A156   150fr #b-j   6.50   6.50
896   A156   200fr #a.-i.   9.75   9.75
897   A156   250fr #a.-i.   12.00   12.00
898   A156   300fr #a.-i.   14.50   14.50

See Nos. 928-933.

A157

Endangered Species — A157a

Designs: 75fr, Galago crassicaudatus. 150fr, Vulpes vulpes. 200fr, Anomalurus pusillus. 375fr, Loxodonta africana, vert.

Primates, vert: Nos. 903a-903c, Various views of Pan troglodytes. Nos. 903d-903f, Various views of gorilla gorilla. Nos. 903g-903i, Various views of pongo pygmaeus.

No. 904, each 375fr: a, Tragelaphus strepsiceros. b, Capra hircus. c, Egretta alba. d, Tockus flavirostris.

No. 905, each 375fr: a, Ursus maritimus. b, Megaptera novaeangliae. c, Phoca vitulina. d, Aptenodytes forsteri.

No. 906, each 375fr: a, Pelecanus occidentalis. b, Orcinus orca. c, Delphinus delphis. d, Iguana iguana.

No. 907: a, Panthera tigris altaica. b, Camelus bactrianus. c, Canus lupus. d, Cuon alpinus. e, Rangifer tarandus dawsoni. f, Gulo gulo.

Each 1500fr: No. 908, Loxodonta africana, vert. No. 909, Ursus thibetanus.

Perf. 14, 14½x14 (#904-906)

1999, Jan. 25		**Litho.**		
899-902	A157	Set of 4	4.50	4.50
903	A157	150fr Sheet of 9, #a.-i.	8.00	8.00
		Sheets of 4		
904-906	A157a	Set of 3	24.00	24.00
		Sheet of 6		
907	A157	375fr #a.-f.	12.00	12.00
		Souvenir Sheets		
908-909	A157	Set of 2	16.00	16.00

Mushrooms
A158   A159

No. 910, 75fr, Russula xerampelina. No. 911, 75fr, Catathelasma imperiale. No. 912, 150fr, Cortinarius violaceus. No. 913, 150fr, Cortinarius camphoratus. No. 914, 200fr, Rozites caperata. No. 915, 200fr, Coprinus picaceus. No. 916, 375fr, Coprinus cromatus. No. 917, 375fr, Russula cavipes.

No. 918, each 150fr: a, Boletus edulis. b, Suillus grevillei. c, Boletinus cavipes. d, Morchella esculenta. e, Morchella conica. f, Clitocybe dealbata. g, Hygrocybe nigrescens. h, Clitocybe geotropa. i, Lepiota cristata.

No. 919, each 150fr: a, Amanita citrina. b, Amanita phalloides. c, Cortinarius praestans. d, Phallus impudicus. e, Cortinarius bicolor. f, Cortinarius renidens. g, Lactarius torminosus. h, Boletus satanas. i, Cystolepiota bucknalii.

No. 920, each 375fr: a, Amanita muscaria. b, Coprinus comatus. c, Clitocybe odora. d, Cantharellus cibarius. e, Mycena epipterygia. f, Marasmius oreades.

No. 921, each 375fr: a, Boletus edulis. b, Laccaria laccata. c, Agaricus campestris. d, Hypholoma fasciculare. e, Lepiota procera. f, Russula aurata.

Each 1500fr: No. 922, Ramaria aurea, horiz. No. 923, Panellus serotinus. No. 924, Macrolepiota procera. No. 925, Amanita muscaria. No. 926, Hebeloma crustuliniforme. No. 927, Lepiota molybdites.

1999		**Litho.**		**Perf. 14**
910-917	A158	Set of 8	8.50	8.50
		Sheets of 9		
918-919	A158	Set of 2	14.00	14.00
		Sheets of 6		
920-921	A159	Set of 2	24.00	24.00

Souvenir Sheets

922-925	A158	Set of 4	32.50	32.50
926-927	A159	Set of 2	16.00	16.00

Raptors — A160

No. 927A — Birds: b, Souimanga royal. c, Martin-pecheur huppe. d, Pie-grieche. e, Barbican a tete roughe. f, Beau-marquet. g, Rollier a poitrine lilas. h, Pintade vulturine. i, Grenadier. j, Outarde korhaon.

No. 928: a, Sparrow hawk. b, Red-tailed buzzard. c, Dark kite. d, African fish eagle. e, Bald eagle. f, Fawn-colored vulture. g, Peregrine falcon. h, Osprey. i, Harpie eagle.

Dinosaurs — No. 929: a, Dilophosaurus. b, Megalosaurus. c, Ceratosaurus. d, Coelophysis. e, Tyrannosaurus. f, Deinonychus. g, Allosaurus. h, Stegosaurus. i, Albertosaurus.

Gems — No. 930: a, Ruby. b, Liroconite. c, Emerald. d, Euclase. e, Diamond. f, Chrysoberyl. g, Plancheite. h, Kasolite. i, Indigolite.

Meteorites — No. 931: a, Martian. b, Antarctic. c, C2 Chondrite. d, Archondrite. e, Octaedrite moyenne. f, Iron. g, Tektite. h, Chondrite olivine. i, Iron, diff.

Mushrooms — No. 932: a, Paxillus atrotomentosus. b, Craterellus cornucopioides. c, Boletus satanas. d, Clavaria truncata. e, Phallus impudicus. f, Scleroderma aurantiacum. g, Amanita citrina. h, Catathe lasma. i, Inocybe fastigiata.

1125fr, Wulfenite.

1998				**Perf. 13¼x13½**
		Sheets of 9		
927A	A160	175fr #b-j	8.00	8.00
928	A160	200fr #a.-i.	9.75	9.75
929	A160	250fr #a.-i.	11.50	11.50
930	A160	375fr #a.-i.	17.50	17.50
931	A160	400fr #a.-i.	19.00	19.00
932	A160	400fr #a.-i.	19.00	19.00

Souvenir Sheet

933	A160	1125fr multicolored	5.75	5.75

No. 933 contains one 36x51mm stamp. Captions on Nos. 928e and 928h are transposed.
See Nos. 896-898.

Submarines — A161

No. 934: a, USS Salt Lake City, US. b, Le Terrible, France. c, Amethyste, France.

1999		**Litho.**		**Perf. 13¼**
934	A161	150fr Sheet of 3, #a-c	3.00	3.00

Automobiles — A161a

No. 935: a, Cadillac Eldorado, Cadillac Series 62, US. b, Aston Martin DB2 IV Mark III, Austin Healey. c, Alfa Romeo Superlegera, Alfa Romeo Giuletta.
1125fr, Aston Martin DB5.

1999				
935	A161a	200fr Sheet of 3, #a-c	3.50	3.50
		Souvenir Sheet		
935D	A161a	1125fr multi	7.00	7.00

No. 935D contains one 51x30mm stamp.

Motorcycles — A162

No. 935E: f, Honda NR. g, Christian Leliard and motorcycle. h, Joe S. Wright and motorcycle.

1999				
935E	A162	250fr Sheet of 3, #f-h	4.50	4.50

Helicopters — A162a

No. 936: a, Westland Wessex. b, MIL MI-8. c, Sikorsky 5-76 Spirit.

1999				
936	A162a	300fr Sheet of 3, #a-c	5.50	5.50

Dogs and Sleds A163

No. 937: a, Alaskan malamute, US. b, Greenlandic. c, Siberian husky.

1999				
937	A163	400fr Sheet of 3, #a-c	7.00	7.00

Airplanes A164

No. 938: a, Tupolev Tu-160. b, Lockheed F-117A. c, Rafale C.01.
No. 939: a, Ilyshin Il-76. b, Boeing E-3. c, Concorde.
1125fr, Concorde, diff.

1999		**Litho.**		**Perf. 13¼**
		Sheets of 3		
938	A164	375fr #a.-c.	6.50	6.50
939	A164	450fr #a.-c.	8.00	8.00
		Souvenir Sheet		
940	A164	1125fr mulicolored	7.00	7.00

No. 940 contains one 50x30mm stamp.

Trains A165

No. 941: a, Series E. b, Series 9100. c, Kitson-Still I-C-I.
No. 942: a, HST 125. b, TGV. c, RTG.
1125fr, Sereis DD40AX.

1999		**Litho.**		**Perf. 13¼**
		Sheets of 3		
941	A165	400fr #a.-c.	7.25	7.25
942	A165	500fr #a.-c.	9.00	9.00
		Souvenir Sheet		
943	A165	1125fr mulicolored	7.00	7.00

No. 943 contains one 50x30mm stamp.

Space Achievements — A166

#944: a, Shuttles Discovery, Buran. b, Ariane V. c, John Glenn, Saturn V.
#945: a, Valentina Tereshkova, Soyuz 4. b, Dogs Laika, Bielka. c, Yuri Gagarin, Vostok 1.
1125fr, Space Shuttle Discovery, John Glenn.

1999		**Litho.**		**Perf. 13¼**
		Sheets of 3		
944	A166	500fr #a.-c.	9.00	9.00
945	A166	600fr #a.-c.	11.00	11.00
		Souvenir Sheet		
946	A166	1125fr multi	7.00	7.00

No. 946 contains one 51x30mm stamp.

Teams in 1998 World Cup Soccer Tournament — A167

Players in 1998 World Cup Soccer Tournament — A168

No. 947, 150fr: a, Italy. b, Chile. c, Cameroun. d, Austria. e, Netherlands. f, Belgium. g, South Korea. h, Mexico.

No. 948, 250fr: a, Brazil. b, Scotland. c, Morocco. d, Norway. e, Spain. f, Nigeria. g, Paraguay. h, Bulgaria.

No. 949, 300fr: a, France. b, South Africa. c, Saudi Arabia. d, Denmark. e, Germany. f, United States. g, Yugoslavia. h, Iran.

No. 950, 500fr: a, England. b, Colombia. c, Romania. d, Tunisia. e, Argentina. f, Croatia. g, Jamaica. h, Japan.

No. 951, 350fr: a, Desailly, French flag. b, Ronaldo, Brazilian flag. c, Suker, Croatian flag. d, Kluivert, Netherlands flag. e, French players, World Cup trophy. f, Brazilian player (yellow and green shirt). g, Croatian player (checked shirt). h, Netherlands player (orange shirt).

1998	Litho.		**Perf. 13x13½**	
	Sheets of 8, #a-h			
947-950	A167	Set of 4	50.00	50.00
951	A168	multi	14.50	14.50

Trucks — A169

No. 952: a, Truck with ornamentation over cab. b, Blue truck. c, Green truck. d, Yellow truck.

1999	Litho.		**Perf. 13¼**
952	A169	350fr Sheet of 4, #a-d	— —

Automobile Racing, Chess, Tennis and Table Tennis, Fishing and Diving — A170

No. 953, 250fr — Automobile racing: a, Giuseppe Farina and Alfa 1500. b, Juan Fangio and Mercedes 2.5L. c, Jack Brabham and Cooper Climax 2.5L. d, Jim Clark and Lotus Climax 1.5L.

No. 954, 300fr — Chess players: a, Garry Kasparov. b, Akiba Rubinstein. c, Max Euwe. d, Mikhail Botvinnik.

No. 955, 375fr — Fishing and diving: a, Shark fishing. b, Sport fishing. c, Diver, back half of shark. d, Diver, front half of shark.

No. 956, 500fr — Chess players: a, Bent Larsen. b, José Raúl Capablanca. c, Boris Spassky. d, Bobby Fischer.

No. 957, 600fr — Tennis and table tennis: a, Female tennis player. b, Male table tennis player. c, Female table tennis player. d, Male tennis player.

No. 958, 1125fr — Chess players: a, Samuel Reshevsky. b, Vassili Smyslov.

No. 959, 1125fr — Fishing and diving: a, Sport fishing, diff. b, Divers and marine life.

No. 960, 1125fr — Tennis and table tennis: a, Male table tennis player, diff. b, Women tennis players.

1999			**Perf. 13¼**	
	Sheets of 4, #a-d			
953-957	A170	Set of 5	47.50	47.50
	Souvenir Sheets of 2, #a-b			
958-960	A170	Set of 3	21.00	21.00

Nos. 816E, 816G Surcharged

Methods and Perfs. As Before
2001, June 16			
963	A144a	100fr on 500fr multi	— —
964	A144a	125fr on 200fr multi	— —

Traditional Costumes A171

Designs: 125fr, Woman. No. 966, 150fr, No. 969, 300fr, Woman, diff. No. 967, 150fr, No. 968, 300fr, Man.

2002, Apr. 8	Litho.		**Perf. 13¼x13**
965-969	A171	Set of 5	8.50 8.50

Flowers — A172

Designs: 50fr, Cananga odorata. 600fr, Vanilla planifolia.

2003, Oct. 9			
970-971	A172	Set of 2	5.25 5.25

Marine Mammals A173

Designs: 75fr, Peponocephala electra. 1000fr, Megaptera novaeangliae.

2003, Oct. 9			**Perf. 13x13¼**
972-973	A173	Set of 2	9.00 9.00

Wood Handicrafts A174

Designs: 100fr, Carved door. 300fr, Candleholder.

2003, Oct. 9			**Perf. 13¼x13**
974-975	A174	Set of 2	3.25 3.25

Orchids — A175

Orchid color: 50fr, White. 75fr, Yellow. 100fr, Mauve. 600fr, Red.

2003, Oct. 9			
976-979	A175	Set of 4	6.50 6.50

Diplomatic Relations Between Comoro Islands and People's Republic of China, 30th Anniv. — A176

No. 980: a, 125fr, Chinese President Hu Jintao and Comoro Islands President Azali Assoumani, country flags. b, 125fr, Coelacanth, Worldwide Fund for Nature emblem, country arms. c, 300fr, Comoros Islands Broadcasting Center, country arms. d, 600fr, Comoros Islands People's Palace, country flags.

2006, Jan. 1	Litho.		**Perf. 12**
980	A176	Block of 4, #a-d	5.75 5.75

Comoro Islands postal officials have declared as "illegal" the following items:

Impressionist Paintings, sheet of five 500fr stamps.

Paintings in the Louvre, six different sheets of two 500fr stamps.

American Actors and Actresses, four different sheets of four 350fr stamps.

European Astronauts, three souvenir sheets of one 500fr stamp.

Disneyland, 50th anniv., souvenir sheet of one 500fr stamp.

Léopold Sédar Senghor (1906-2001), First President of Senegal — A177

Colors: No. 981, 125fr, Green and multicolored. No. 982, 125fr, Yellow and multicolored, vert. No. 983, 300fr, Green and black. No. 983A, 300fr, Blue and multicolored. No. 984, 300fr, Red violet and black, vert. 350fr, Purple and multicolored, vert. 500fr, Brown and black, vert.

Perf. 13x13¼, 13¼x13
2007, June 1			Litho.
981-986	A177	Set of 7	9.50 9.50

Medicinal Plants — A178

Designs: 75fr, Cymbopogon citratus. 125fr, Ocimum suave. 150fr, Aloe molucaca. 250fr, Like 75fr. 300fr, Like 150fr. 500fr, Like 125fr.

2007, June 1			**Perf. 13¼x13**
987-992	A178	Set of 6	7.75 7.75

SEMI-POSTAL STAMPS

Anti-Malaria Issue
Common Design Type

Perf. 12½x12
1962, Apr. 7	Engr.		Unwmk.
B1	CD108	25fr + 5fr brt pink	4.00 4.00

WHO drive to eradicate malaria.

Nurse Feeding Infant — SP1

Mother and Child — SP2

1967, July 3	Engr.		**Perf. 13**
B2	SP1	25fr + 5fr multi	3.25 3.25

For the Red Cross.

1974, Aug. 10	Engr.		**Perf. 13**
B3	SP2	35fr + 10fr red & dk brn	2.75 2.75

For the Red Cross.
For surcharge see No. 144.

Miniature Sheet

Space Achievements SP3

World Philatelic Programs emblems (stamp collecting or Halley's Comet) and astronomer or satellite: a, Galileo. b, Copernicus. c, Kepler. d, Halley. e, Planet A, Japan, and 3 stars. f, ICE, US. g, Planet A, 5 stars. h, Vega, USSR.

1988	Litho.		**Perf. 13½**
B4		Sheet of 8	15.00 15.00
a.-h.	SP3	200fr +10fr multi	1.50 1.50

See No. C193.
For surcharges see Nos. 816P-816S.

AIR POST STAMPS

Comoro Village — AP1

Comoro Men and Moroni Mosque — AP2

Design: 200fr, Mosque of Ouani, Anjouan.

1950-54	Unwmk.	Engr.		**Perf. 13**	
C1	AP1	50fr grn & red brn		4.50	1.40
C2	AP2	100fr dk brn & red		6.75	1.75
C3	AP1	200fr dk grn, rose brn & pur ('54)		26.00	9.50
	Nos. C1-C3 (3)			37.25	12.65

Liberation Issue
Common Design Type

1954, June 6			
C4	CD102	15fr sepia & red	47.50 24.00

Madrepora Fructicosa — AP3

100fr, Coral, shells and sea anemones.

1962, Jan. 13 Photo. Perf. 12½x13
C5   AP3 100fr multi   16.00 16.00
C6   AP3 500fr multi   32.50 24.00

Telstar Issue
Common Design Type

1962, Dec. 5 Engr. Perf. 13
C7   CD111 25fr dp vio, dl pur &
                         red lil   6.50 4.75

Type of Regular Issue
Unwmk.

1963, Dec. 27 Photo. Perf. 13
Size: 26½x48mm
C8   A13 65fr Baskets   5.00 3.50
C9   A13 200fr Pendant   10.00 5.25

Boat Type of Regular Issue

1964, Aug. 7 Photo. Perf. 13
Size: 27x48mm
C10 A14 50fr Mayotte pirogue   4.50 1.75
C11 A14 85fr Schooner   7.00 2.50

Olympic Torch and Boxers — AP4

Order of Star of Grand Comoro — AP5

1964, Oct. 10 Engr. Perf. 13
C12 AP4 100fr red brn, dk brn &
                    gray grn   7.50 7.50
18th Olympic Games, Tokyo, Oct. 10-25.

1964, Dec. 10 Photo. Perf. 13
C13 AP5 500fr multi   20.00 20.00

ITU Issue
Common Design Type

1965, May 17 Engr. Perf. 13
C14 CD120 50fr gray, grnsh bl
                    & ol   24.00 17.50

French Satellite A-1 Issue
Common Design Type

Designs: 25fr, Diamant rocket and launching installations. 30fr, A-1 satellite.

1966, Jan. 17 Engr. Perf. 13
C15 CD121 25fr dk pur & ultra 4.50 4.50
C16 CD121 30fr dk pur & ultra 6.00 6.00
a.   Strip of 2, #C15-C16 + label 11.00 11.00

French Satellite D-1 Issue
Common Design Type

1966, May 16 Engr. Perf. 13
C17 CD122 30fr dk grn, org &
                    brn   4.00 4.00

Old Gun Battery, Dzaoudzi — AP6

200fr, Ksar Castle, Mutsamudu, vert.

1966, Dec. 19 Photo. Perf. 13
C18 AP6 50fr multi   5.00 2.50
C19 AP6 200fr multi   9.00 5.75

Bird Type of Regular Issue

Birds: 75fr, Madagascar paradise flycatchers. 100fr, Blue-cheeked bee eaters.

1967, June 20 Photo. Perf. 13
Size: 27x48mm
C20 A17 75fr yel grn & multi 10.50 6.50
C21 A17 100fr lt bl & multi   13.00 8.00

Woman Skier — AP7

1968, Apr. 29 Engr. Perf. 13
C22 AP7 70fr brt grn, lt bl & choc 6.50 4.75
10th Winter Olympic Games, Grenoble,
France, Feb. 6-18, 1968.

Fish Type of Regular Issue

50fr, Moorish idol. 90fr, Diagramma
lineatus.

1968, Aug. 1 Engr. Perf. 13
Size: 47½x27mm
C23 A19 50fr plum blk & yel   8.00 4.00
C24 A19 90fr brt grn, yel & gray
                    grn   10.00 5.25
For surcharge & overprint see #C52, C74.

Swimmer, Butterfly Stroke — AP8

1969, Jan. 27 Photo. Perf. 12½
C25 AP8 65fr ver, grnsh bl & blk 5.25 3.50
19th Olympic Games, Mexico City, 10/12-27.

Flower Type of Regular Issue

50fr, Heliconia sp. 85fr, Tuberose. 200fr,
Orchid (angraecum eburneum).

1969, Mar. 20 Photo. Perf. 13
Size: 27x48mm
C26 A21 50fr multi, vert.   4.75 3.50
C27 A21 85fr multi, vert.   5.50 4.50
C28 A21 200fr multi, vert.   11.00 6.00
     Nos. C26-C28 (3)   21.25 14.00

Concorde Issue
Common Design Type

1969, Apr. 17 Engr.
C29 CD129 100fr pur & brn
                    org   24.00 16.00

View of EXPO, Globe and Moon — AP9

90fr, Geisha, map of Japan & EXPO
emblem.

1970, Sept. 13 Photo. Perf. 13
C30 AP9 60fr slate & multi   4.50 2.40
C31 AP9 90fr multi   5.50 3.25
EXPO '70 International Exposition, Osaka,
Japan, Mar. 15-Sept. 13.

Sunset over Mutsamudu — AP10

Map of Archipelago — AP11

Designs: 20fr, Sada Village, Mayotte. 65fr,
Old Iconi Palace, Grand Comoro. 85fr,
Nioumatchoua Island, Moheli.

1971, May 3 Photo. Perf. 13
C32 AP10 15fr dk bl & multi   1.20 .65
C33 AP10 20fr multi   1.75 .80
C34 AP10 65fr grn & multi   3.75 1.60
C35 AP10 85fr bl & multi   5.50 2.50
Engr.
C36 AP11 100fr brn red, grn &
                    vio bl   7.50 5.50
     Nos. C32-C36 (5)   19.70 11.05
See #107-110, C45-C49, C53, C62-C64.
For overprints & surcharges see #143, C69,
C71, C73, C76-C77, C79-C80, C82, C84.

Flower Type of Regular Issue

Flowers: 60fr, Hibiscus schizopetalus. 85fr,
Acalypha sanderii.

1971, July 19 Photo. Perf. 13
Size: 27x48mm
C37 A25 60fr grn, ver & yel   5.00 2.40
C38 A25 85fr grn, red & yel   6.50 4.75
For surcharge see No. C75.

Mural, Moroni Airport — AP12

Designs: 85fr, Mural in Arrival Hall, Moroni
Airport. 100fr, View of Moroni Airport.

1972, Mar. 30 Photo. Perf. 13
C39 AP12 65fr gray & multi   2.00 .85
C40 AP12 85fr gray & multi   2.25 1.20
Engr.
C41 AP12 100fr brn, bl & slate
                    grn   4.00 2.10
     Nos. C39-C41 (3)   8.25 4.15
New airport in Moroni.

Eiffel Tower and Moroni Telephone
Exchange — AP13

75fr, Frenchman and Comoro Islander talking on telephone, radio tower and beacons.

1972, Apr. 24
C42 AP13 35fr dl red & gray   1.25 .85
C43 AP13 75fr dk car, vio & bl 2.25 .95
First radio-telephone connection between
France and Comoro Islands.

Underwater Spear-fishing — AP14

1972, July 5 Engr. Perf. 13
C44 AP14 70fr vio bl, brt grn &
                    mar   8.75 5.50
For surcharge see No. C78.

Types of 1971
1972, Nov. 15 Photo.
Designs: 20fr, Cape Sima. 35fr, Bambao
Palace. 40fr, Domoni Palace. 60fr, Gomajou
Peninsula. 100fr, Map of Anjouan Island.
C45 AP10 20fr brn & multi   .90 .65
C46 AP10 35fr dk grn & multi   1.20 .80
C47 AP10 40fr bl & multi   1.75 .95
C48 AP10 60fr grnsh blk &
                    multi   2.50 1.60
Engr.
C49 AP11 100fr mar, bl & sl
                    grn   13.50 7.25
     Nos. C45-C49 (5)   19.85 11.25

Pres. Said Mohamed Cheikh
(1904-70) AP15

1973, Mar. 16 Photo. Perf. 13
C50 AP15 20fr multi   1.25 .80
C51 AP15 35fr multi   1.60 1.00
For overprints see Nos. C70, C72.

No. C24 Surcharged

1973, Apr. 30 Engr. Perf. 13
C52 A19 120fr on 90fr multi   13.00 7.25
Intl. Commission for Coelacanth Studies.

Map of Grand Comoro AP16

1973, June 28   **Engr.**   *Perf. 13*
C53 AP16 135fr vio, bl & dk brn   9.50 6.50

See Nos. C65, C68. For surcharges see Nos. C90-C92.

Karthala Volcano AP17

1973, July 16   **Photo.**   *Perf. 13x12½*
C54 AP17 120fr multi   7.50 5.50

Eruption of Karthala, Sept. 1972.
For surcharge see No. C89.

Armauer G. Hansen — AP18

Design: 150fr, Nicolaus Copernicus (1473-1543), Polish astronomer.

1973, Sept. 5   **Engr.**   *Perf. 13*
C55 AP18 100fr brn, dk bl & sl
       grn   7.00 3.50
C56 AP18 150fr grnsh bl, vio bl &
       choc   8.00 5.25

Cent. of the discovery of the Hansen bacillus, the cause of leprosy.
For overprint & surcharge see #C81, C93.

Pablo Picasso (1881-1973) — AP19

1973, Sept. 30   **Photo.**
C57 AP19 200fr blk & multi   12.00 9.75
Souvenir Sheet
C58 AP19 100fr blk & multi   16.00 14.50

For overprint see No. C87.

Order of the Star of Anjouan — AP20

Said Omar ben Soumeth — AP21

1974, Jan. 7   **Photo.**   *Perf. 13*
C59 AP20 500fr brn, bl & gold   13.00 9.50

For overprint see No. C95.

1974, Jan. 31   *Perf. 13x13½, 13½x13*

135fr, Grand Mufti Said Omar, horiz.

C60 AP21 135fr blk & multi   4.50 2.75
C61 AP21 200fr blk & multi   5.50 3.50

For overprint & surcharge see #C85, C88.

Types of 1971-73

Designs (Views on Mayotte): 20fr, Moya Beach. 35fr, Chiconi. 90fr, Port Mamutzu. 120fr, Map of Mayotte.

1974, Aug. 31   **Photo.**   *Perf. 13*
C62 AP10 20fr bl & multi   1.20 .95
C63 AP10 35fr grn & multi   2.50 2.00
C64 AP10 90fr multi   6.25 3.50
       Engr.
C65 AP16 120fr ultra & grn   9.00 5.50
   Nos. C62-C65 (4)   18.95 11.95

Jet Take-off — AP22

1975, Jan. 10   **Engr.**   *Perf. 13*
C66 AP22 135fr multi   7.25 4.75

First direct route Moroni-Hahaya-Paris.
For surcharge see No. C86.

Rotary Emblem, Meeting House, Map — AP23

1975, Feb. 23   **Photo.**   *Perf. 13*
C67 AP23 250fr multi   10.50 7.25

Rotary Intl., 70th anniv., Moroni Rotary Club, 10th anniv.
For surcharge see No. C94.

Map Type of 1973

Design: 230fr, Map of Moheli, horiz.

1975, May 26   **Engr.**   *Perf. 13*
C68 AP16 230fr ocher, ol grn &
       bl   11.00 8.00

STATE OF COMORO
Issues of 1968-75 Surcharged and Overprinted with Bars and: "ETAT COMORIEN" in Black, Silver, Red or Orange

1975		Printing & Perfs. as Before		
C69	AP10	10fr on 20fr #C62	.60	.20
C70	AP15	20fr (S)	1.00	.20
C71	AP10	30fr on 35fr (R)		
		#C63	1.00	.20
C72	AP15	35fr (S)	1.25	.75
C73	AP10	40fr (O)	1.50	.75
C74	A19	50fr	1.90	1.00
C75	A25	75fr on 60fr	2.00	1.10
C76	AP10	75fr on 60fr	2.00	1.10
C77	AP10	75fr on 65fr (O)	2.00	1.10
C78	AP14	75fr on 70fr	2.00	1.10
C79	AP11	100fr #C36	2.50	1.50
C80	AP11	100fr #C49	2.50	1.50
C81	AP18	100fr	2.50	1.50
C82	AP10	100fr on 85fr (O)	2.50	1.50
C83	A25	100fr on 85fr	2.50	1.50
C84	AP10	100fr on 90fr	2.50	1.50
C85	AP21	100fr on 135fr (S)	2.50	1.50
C86	AP22	100fr on 135fr	2.50	1.50
C87	AP19	200fr (S)	6.00	3.50
C88	AP21	200fr (S)	6.00	3.50
C89	AP17	200fr on 120fr	6.00	3.50
C90	AP16	200fr on 120fr	6.00	3.50
C91	AP16	200fr on 135fr	6.00	3.50
C92	AP16	200fr on 230fr	6.00	3.50
C93	AP18	400fr on 150fr	10.00	5.25
C94	AP23	400fr on 250fr	10.00	5.25
C95	AP20	500fr	12.00	7.25
		Nos. C69-C95 (27)	103.25	58.25

See postage section for airmail stamps that are part of joint postage/airmail sets.

Rotary Emblem, Landscape AP26

1979, July 31   **Litho.**   *Perf. 13x12½*
C107 AP26 400fr multi   7.00 3.00

Rotary International.

IYC Emblem, Mother and Child — AP27

1979, July 31   *Perf. 13x13½*
C108 AP27 250fr multi   3.50 3.50

Intl. Year of the Child. See No. CB1. For surcharges see Nos. C121, C202.

Dimadjou Dispensary, Map of Southern Africa, Emblem AP28

1980, Feb. 23   **Litho.**   *Perf. 12½*
C109 AP28 100fr shown   1.25 .40
C110 AP28 260fr Globe, Concorde, emblem   3.00 1.00

Rotary International, 75th anniv. and Moroni Rotary Club, 15th anniv. (100fr).
For surcharges see Nos. 815L, C119-C120.

First Transatlantic Flight, 50th Anniversary — AP29

1980, May 30   **Litho.**   *Perf. 13*
C111 AP29 200fr multi   2.50 1.25

No. C111 Surcharged in Blue

1981, Feb.   **Litho.**   *Perf. 13*
C112 AP29 30fr on 200fr multi   1.00 .35

The Dove and the Rainbow, by Picasso — AP30

Picasso Birth Centenary: 70fr, Still Life on a Sideboard. 150fr, Studio with Plaster Head. 250fr, Bowl and Pot, vert. 500fr, The Red Tablecloth.

1981, June 30   **Litho.**   *Perf. 12½*
C113 AP30 40fr multi   .55 .20
C114 AP30 70fr multi   .95 .20
C115 AP30 150fr multi   1.90 .50
C116 AP30 250fr multi   3.25 .70
C117 AP30 500fr multi   6.25 1.50
   Nos. C113-C117 (5)   12.90 3.10

For surcharges see Nos. 815G, C118.

#C114, C109-C110, CB1 Surchd.

1981, Nov.   **Litho.**   *Perf. 12½, 13*
C118 AP30 10fr on 70fr multi   .40 .40
C119 AP28 10fr on 100fr multi   .80 .80
C120 AP28 50fr on 260fr multi   2.00 .20
C121 AP27 50fr on 200fr+30fr
       multi   2.00 .20
   Nos. C118-C121 (4)   5.20 1.60

Manned Flight Bicentenary — AP31

Balloons. 100fr, 200fr, 300fr, 500fr vert.

1983, Apr. 20   **Litho.**   *Perf. 13*
C122 AP31 100fr Montgolfiere,
       1783   1.00 .30
C123 AP31 200fr Lunardi, 1784   1.90 .50
C124 AP31 300fr Blanchard and
       Jeffries, 1785   3.25 .90
C125 AP31 400fr Giffard, 1852   4.50 1.25
   Nos. C122-C125 (4)   10.65 2.95
Souvenir Sheet
C126 AP31 500fr Paris Siege.
       1870   5.50 1.50

For overprints and surcharges see Nos. 602, 812T, 815P.

Pre-Olympic Year Sailing — AP32

1983, June 30 Litho. Perf. 13
C127	AP32	150fr	Type 470	1.50	.40
C128	AP32	200fr	Flying Dutch-man	2.25	.50
C129	AP32	300fr	Type 470, diff.	3.25	.90
C130	AP32	400fr	Finn	4.75	1.00
			Nos. C127-C130 (4)	11.75	2.80

Souvenir Sheet
C131	AP32	500fr	Soling	5.50	1.50

For overprint and surcharge see Nos. 603, C206.

1984 Summer Olympics — AP33

1984, July 10 Litho. Perf. 13
C132	AP33	60fr	Basketball	.50	.20
C133	AP33	100fr	Basketball, diff.	.90	.40
C134	AP33	165fr	Basketball, diff.	1.50	.65
C135	AP33	175fr	Baseball, horiz.	1.60	.65
C136	AP33	200fr	Baseball, horiz.	1.90	.80
			Nos. C132-C136 (5)	6.40	2.70

Souvenir Sheet
C137	AP33	500fr	Basketball, diff.	8.00	1.50

Nos. C132-C134 vert.

Development Conference AP34

1984, July 2 Litho. Perf. 13
C138	AP34	475fr	Tools for development	5.50	2.00

For surcharge see No. 796I.

Audubon Bicentenary — AP35

1985, Jan. 15 Litho. Perf. 13
C139	AP35	100fr	Hirundo rustica, vert.	1.25	.40
C140	AP35	125fr	Icterus galbula, vert.	1.50	.50
C141	AP35	150fr	Buteo lineatus	2.00	.60
C142	AP35	500fr	Sphyropieus varius	5.25	2.00
			Nos. C139-C142 (4)	10.00	3.50

Moroni Port Missile Defense — AP36

No. C146, Ngome Ntsoudjini Scout troop.

1985, May 20 Litho. Perf. 13x12½
C145	AP36	200fr	multi	3.25	1.25
C146	AP36	200fr	multi	3.25	1.25
a.			Pair, #C145-C146 + label	6.75	6.75

PHILEXAFRICA '85, Lome.
For surcharges see Nos. C207-C208.

Natl. Flag, Sun, Outline Map of Islands — AP37

1985, July 6
C147	AP37	10fr	multi	.30	.20
C148	AP37	15fr	multi	.30	.20
C149	AP37	125fr	multi	2.25	.60
C150	AP37	300fr	multi	5.50	1.50
			Nos. C147-C150 (4)	8.35	2.50

Natl. independence, 10th anniv.
For surcharge see No. 815Q.

Runners — AP38

1985, Nov. 12
C151	AP38	250fr	shown	2.75	1.75
C152	AP38	250fr	Mining	2.75	1.75
a.			Pair, #C151-C152 + label	6.00	6.00

PHILEXAFRICA '85, Lome, Togo, 11/16-24.
For surcharges see Nos. 815H-815I, C204-C205.

Air Transport Union, UTA, 50th Anniv. — AP39

1985, Dec. 30 Litho. Perf. 13
C153	AP39	25fr	F-AOUL seaplane	.20	.20
C154	AP39	75fr	Camel driver, DC-8	.75	.30
C155	AP39	100fr	Noratlas and Heron DC-4s	1.10	.40
a.			Souv. sheet of 3, #C153-C155, perf. 12½	3.50	2.25
C156	AP39	125fr	UTA cargo plane	1.40	.60

Size: 40x52mm
Perf. 12½x13
C157	AP39	1000fr	Aircraft, 1935-1985	12.00	6.00
a.			Souv. sheet of 2, #C156-C157, perf. 12½	13.00	8.00
			Nos. C153-C157 (5)	15.45	7.50

Halley's Comet — AP40

Comets, astronomers and probes.

1986, Mar. 7 Perf. 13
C158	AP40	125fr	Edmond Halley, Giotto probe	1.25	.45
C159	AP40	150fr	Giacobini-Zinner, 1959	1.50	.50
C160	AP40	225fr	Encke, 1961	2.50	.90
C161	AP40	300fr	Bradfield, 1980	3.00	1.25
C162	AP40	450fr	Planet A probe	5.00	1.75
			Nos. C158-C162 (5)	13.25	4.85

For surcharges see Nos. 796S, 804H, 804R, 812P.

1986 World Cup Soccer Championships, Mexico — AP41

Various soccer plays.

1986, June 11 Litho. Perf. 13
C163	AP41	125fr	multi	1.25	.45
C164	AP41	210fr	multi	2.25	.80
C165	AP41	500fr	multi	5.50	2.00
C166	AP41	600fr	multi	6.00	2.25
			Nos. C163-C166 (4)	15.00	5.50

For surcharges see Nos. 796C, 800Q, 815C.

Tennis at the 1988 Summer Olympics — AP42

Various players.

1987, Jan. 28 Litho. Perf. 13½
C167	AP42	150fr	multi	1.75	.45
C168	AP42	250fr	multi	3.00	.75
C169	AP42	500fr	multi	5.50	1.50
C170	AP42	600fr	multi	6.75	1.75
			Nos. C167-C170 (4)	17.00	4.45

For overprints and surcharges see Nos. 796N, 796U, 815J, 816L, 816N, C183-C186, C203.

World Wildlife Fund — AP43

Various pictures of the mongoose lemur.

1987, Feb. 18 Perf. 13
C171	AP43	75fr	multi, vert.	2.50	.50
C172	AP43	100fr	multi	3.50	.75
C173	AP43	125fr	multi	5.50	1.00
C174	AP43	500fr	multi	6.50	1.25
			Nos. C171-C174 (4)	18.00	3.50

1988 Winter Olympics, Calgary AP44

AP45

Aviation History AP46

1987, Apr. 10 Litho. Perf. 13½
C175	AP44	150fr	Slalom	1.25	.45
C176	AP44	225fr	Ski jumping	2.25	.75
C177	AP44	500fr	Women's giant slalom	5.50	1.60
C178	AP44	600fr	Luge	6.00	2.25
			Nos. C175-C178 (4)	15.00	5.05

For surcharges see Nos. 800R, 812U.

Designs: 200fr, Inventors Didier Daurat and Raymond Vanier with 1935 Air Blue F-ANR1. 300fr, Farman biplane, 1st scheduled airmail delivery, Paris-LeMans-St. Nazaire, Aug. 17, 1918. 500fr, Bleriot aircraft, 1st scheduled airmail delivery, Villacoublay-Vendome-Poitiers-Pauillac, Oct. 15, 1913. 1000fr, Henri Pequet and his aircraft, Feb. 18, 1911.

1987, Dec. 29 Litho. Perf. 13
C179	AP45	200fr	multi	2.25	.65
C180	AP45	300fr	multi	3.25	1.00
C181	AP45	500fr	multi	5.50	1.60

Perf. 12½x13
C182	AP46	1000fr	multi	11.00	2.25
			Nos. C179-C182 (4)	22.00	5.50

Airmail history exposition, Allahabad.
For surcharges see Nos. 800S, 804D.

Nos. C167-C170 Ovptd. in Red for 1988 Olympic Tennis Champions

Overprint includes name of athlete and "Medaille d'or / Seoul" or "Medaille / d'argent / Seoul."

1988, Nov. Litho. Perf. 13½
C183	AP42	150fr	"Miloslav Mecir / (Tchec.)"	1.25	.75
C184	AP42	250fr	"Tim Mayotte / (U.S.A.)"	1.90	1.40
C185	AP42	500fr	"Steffi Graf / (R.F.A.)"	5.00	2.75
C186	AP42	600fr	"Gabriela Sabatini / (Argentine)"	6.00	3.75
			Nos. C183-C186 (4)	14.15	8.65

For surcharges see Nos. 800T, 815K, 816M, 816O.

Early Aviators and Aircraft — AP47

100fr, Alberto Santos-Dumont (1873-1932), & Bagatelle, 1st documented power flight in Europe, Oct. 23, 1906. 150fr, Wright Brothers & Flyer A. 200fr, Louis Bleriot (1872-1936) & Bleriot XI, 1st crossing of the English Channel in a heavier-than-air craft, July 25, 1909. 300fr, Henri Farman (1874-1958) & Voisin biplane, 1st fixed-route 1-kilometer circular flight, Jan. 13, 1908. 500fr, Gabriel (1880-1973) & Charles (1882-1912) Voisin, established 1st biplane factory (1908), & Voisin biplane. 800fr, Roland Garros (1888-1918), 1st trans-Mediterranean flight, Sept. 23, 1913.

1988, Dec. 7 Litho. Perf. 13
C187	AP47	100fr	pur	.90	.45
C188	AP47	150fr	brt lil rose	1.60	.60
C189	AP47	200fr	blk	2.00	.90
C190	AP47	300fr	dark yel org	3.00	.90

C191 AP47 500fr dark blue   5.00   1.50
C192 AP47 800fr lt olive grn   7.50   3.00
Nos. C187-C192 (6)   20.00   7.35

For surcharges see Nos. 800B, 800U, 804E, C209.

Souvenir Sheet

Space Achievements — AP48

Design: World Philatelic Programs stamp collecting emblem, Soviet satellite and Edmond Halley.

1988   **Litho.**   **Perf. 13½**
C193 AP48 750fr multi   8.00   1.50

Nos. C108, C168, C151-C152, C128, C145-C146 and C189 Surcharged

		1989	**Litho.**	**Perfs. as Before**		
C202	AP27	5fr on 250fr #C108			.20	.20
C203	AP42	25fr on 250fr #C168			.20	.20
C204	AP38	50fr on 250fr #C151			.50	.20
C205	AP38	50fr on 250fr #C152			.50	.20
a.		Pair, #C204-C205 + label			1.25	1.25
C206	AP32	150fr on 200fr #C128			1.40	.60
C207	AP36	150fr on 200fr #C145			1.40	.60
C208	AP36	150fr on 200fr #C146			1.40	.60
a.		Pair, #C207-C208 + label			6.00	6.00
C209	AP47	150fr on 200fr #C189			1.40	.60
		Nos. C202-C209 (8)			7.00	3.20

World Cup Soccer, Championships, Italy — AP50

Various soccer plays and map of Italy.

1990, June   **Litho.**   **Perf. 13**
C210 AP50 75fr multicolored   .60   .30
C211 AP50 150fr multicolored   1.40   .60
C212 AP50 500fr multicolored   4.25   1.90
C213 AP50 1000fr multicolored   8.75   4.00
Nos. C210-C213 (4)   15.00   6.80

For surcharge see No. 800V.

Souvenir Sheet

Garry Kasparov, Anatoly Karpov, Russian Chess Champions — AP51

Litho. & Embossed
1991, Aug. 5   **Perf. 13½**
C214 AP51 1500fr gold & multi   12.00   —
World Chess Championships.

1992 Summer Olympics, Barcelona AP52

Litho. & Embossed
1992, July 28   **Perf. 13½**
C215 AP52 1500fr gold & multi   26.50   12.00

Sculpted Table — AP52a

1994 (?)   **Litho.**   **Perf. 13¼x13½**
Background Color
C215A AP52a 15fr blue   —   —
C215B AP52a 75fr green   —   —
C215C AP52a 100fr pink   —   —
C215D AP52a 225fr orange   —   —

For surcharges see Nos. 826A-826E.

Sea Turtles AP53

1995   **Litho.**   **Perf. 13½x13¼**
Frame Color
C216 AP53 10fr blue   25.00   25.00
C217 AP53 25fr pink
C218 AP53 30fr green   25.00   25.00
C219 AP53 50fr lilac   50.00   50.00

No. C215A Surcharged in Blue Violet

Perf. 13¼x13½
2001, June 16   **Litho.**
C220 AP52a 300fr on 15fr   —   —

AIR POST SEMI-POSTAL STAMP

Type of Air Post 1979
Design: IYC emblem, mother and son.

1979, July 31   **Photo.**   **Perf. 13½x13**
CB1 AP27 200fr + 30fr multi   3.50   3.50
International Year of the Child.
For surcharge see No. C121.

POSTAGE DUE STAMPS

Anjouan Mosque
D1

Coelacanth
D2

1950 Unwmk. Engr.   Perf. 14x13
J1 D1 50c deep green   1.20   .95
J2 D1 1fr black brown   1.20   1.00

1954
J3 D2 5fr dk brown & green   1.10   1.00
J4 D2 10fr gray & red brown   1.50   1.50
J5 D2 20fr indigo & blue   2.75   2.50
Nos. J3-J5 (3)   5.35   5.00

Hibiscus
D3

2fr, 15fr, 40fr, 50fr, vertical.

1977, Nov. 19   **Litho.**   **Perf. 13½**
J6 D3 1fr shown   .35   .20
J7 D3 2fr Pineapple   .35   .20
J8 D3 5fr White butterfly   .35   .20
J9 D3 10fr Chameleon   .35   .20
J10 D3 15fr Blooming banana   .35   .20
J11 D3 20fr Orchids   .35   .20
J12 D3 30fr Allamanda cathartica   .50   .20
J13 D3 40fr Cashews   .95   .20
J14 D3 50fr Custard apple   1.10   .20
J15 D3 100fr Breadfruit   2.10   .75
J16 D3 200fr Vanilla   4.50   .95
J17 D3 500fr Ylang ylang   10.75   1.50
Nos. J6-J17 (12)   22.00   5.00

OFFICIAL STAMPS

Comoro Flag — O1

Perf. 13x12½
1979-85   **Litho.**   **Unwmk.**
O1 O1 5fr multi   .20   .20
O2 O1 10fr multi   .20   .20
O3 O1 20fr multi   .20   .20
O4 O1 30fr multi   .50   .20
O5 O1 40fr multi   .65   .25
O6 O1 60fr multi ('80)   .60   .25
O7 O1 75fr multi ('85)   .40   .25
O8 O1 100fr multi   1.25   .60
Nos. O1-O8 (8)   4.00   2.15

See Nos. 526-530.

Pres. Said Mohamed Cheikh (1904-1970) — O2

1980-85
O9 O2 100fr multi   1.00   .40
O10 O2 125fr multi ('85)   2.00   1.50
O11 O2 400fr multi   3.00   1.25
Nos. O9-O11 (3)   6.00   3.15

CONGO, DEMOCRATIC REPUBLIC

ˌde-mə-ˈkra-tik ri-ˈpə-blik of ˈkäŋˌgō

LOCATION — Central Africa
GOVT. — Republic
AREA — 895,348 sq. mi. (estimated)
POP. — 22,480,000 (est. 1971)
CAPITAL — Kinshasa (Leopoldville)

Congo was an independent state, founded by Leopold II of Belgium, until 1908 when it was annexed to Belgium as a colony. Congo became an independent republic in 1960. The name was changed to Republic of Zaire, Oct. 28, 1971. In 1998 some issues again used the name Congo Democratic Republic. See Zaire in Vol. 6 for later issues.

100 Centimes = 1 Franc
100 Sengi = 1 Li-Kuta,
100 Ma-Kuta = 1 Zaire (1967)

> **Catalogue values for all unused stamps in this country are for Never Hinged items.**

Belgian Congo Flower Issue of 1952-53 Overprinted or Surcharged

Perf. 11½
1960, June 30   **Photo.**   **Unwmk.**
Flowers in Natural Colors
Size: 21x25½mm
Granite Paper
323 A86 10c dp plum & ocher
324 A86 10c on 15c red & yel grn   .20   .20
325 A86 20c grn & gray   .20   .20
326 A86 40c grn & sal   .20   .20
327 A86 50c on 60c bl grn & pink   .20   .20
328 A86 50c on 75c dp plum & gray   .20   .20
329 A86 1fr car & yel   .30   .20
330 A86 1.50fr vio & ap grn   .30   .20
331 A86 2fr ol grn & buff   .30   .20
332 A86 3fr ol grn & pink   .45   .20
333 A86 4fr choc & lil   1.50   1.00
334 A86 5fr dp plum & lt bl grn   .55   .20
335 A86 6.50fr dk car & lil   .70   .20
336 A86 8fr grn & lt yel   .80   .30
337 A86 10fr dp plum & pale ol   1.50   .90
338 A86 20fr vio bl & dl sal   3.50   .80

Nos. 324, 327-328 exist without "CONGO" overprint but with surcharge, also without surcharge but with "CONGO." Inverted and double overprints exist. Values from $10 to $50 each.

Overprinted

Size: 22x32mm
339 A86 50fr dp plum & gray bl   19.00   6.00
340 A86 100fr grn & buff   45.00   10.00
Nos. 323-340 (18)   75.10   20.80

Belgian Congo Animal Issue, Nos. 306-317, Overprinted or Surcharged in Red, Blue, Black or Brown

341	A92	10c bl & brn (R)	.20	.20
342	A93	20c red org & sl (Bl)	.20	.20
343	A92	40c brn & bl (Bk)	.20	.20
344	A93	50c brt ultra, red & sep (R)	.20	.20
345	A92	1fr brn, grn & blk (Br)	.20	.20
346	A92	1.50fr blk & org yel (R)	.20	.20
347	A92	2fr crim, blk & brn (Bl)	.45	.20
348	A93	3.50fr on 3fr blk, gray & lil rose (Bk)	.65	.20
349	A92	5fr brn, dk brn & brt grn (Br)	.85	.20
350	A93	6.50fr bl, brn & org yel (R)	1.00	.20
a.		Black overprint	1.75	.60
351	A92	8fr org brn, ol bis & lil (Br)	1.25	.40
352	A93	10fr multi (R)	1.60	.60
		Nos. 341-352 (12)	7.00	3.00

Inverted and double overprints exist. Values from $15 to $20 each.

Same Overprint on Belgian Congo No. 318

1960

353	A94	50c gldn brn, ocher & red brn	1.00	1.00

Same Overprint and Surcharge of New Value on Belgian Congo Nos. 321-322

Inscription in French

354	A95	3.50fr on 3fr gray & red	1.00	.70

Inscription in Flemish

355	A95	3.50fr on 3fr gray & red	1.00	.70
		Nos. 353-355 (3)	3.00	2.40

Nos. 353-355 are known with inverted overprints. Value, each $10.

Map of Congo A93a

1960   **Photo.**   **Perf. 11½**

356	A93a	20c brown	.20	.20
357	A93a	50c rose red	.20	.20
358	A93a	1fr green	.20	.20
359	A93a	1.50fr red brn	.20	.20
360	A93a	2fr rose car	.20	.20
361	A93a	3.50fr lilac	.20	.20
362	A93a	5fr brt bl	.20	.20
363	A93a	6.50fr gray	.25	.20
364	A93a	10fr orange	.50	.20
365	A93a	20fr ultra	.90	.25
		Nos. 356-365 (10)	3.05	2.05

Congo's Independence.
Exists imperf.
For overprints see Nos. 371-380.

Flag, People and Broken Chain — A94

1961, Jan. 4   Unwmk.   Perf. 11½

Flag in Blue and Yellow

366	A94	2fr rose vio	.25	.20
367	A94	3.50fr vermilion	.25	.20
368	A94	6.50fr yel brn	.25	.20
369	A94	10fr brt grn	.35	.20
370	A94	20fr car rose	.50	.30
		Nos. 366-370 (5)	1.60	1.10

Signing of the Independence Agreement by Belgium, Jan. 4, 1959.

Nos. 356-365 Overprinted in Blue, Black or Red: "Conference Coquilhatville Avril Mai 1961"

1961

371	A93a	20c brn (Bl)	1.75	1.75
372	A93a	50c rose red (Bk)	1.75	1.75
373	A93a	1fr grn (R)	1.75	1.75
374	A93a	1.50fr red brn (Bl)	1.75	1.75
375	A93a	2fr rose car (Bk)	1.75	1.75
376	A93a	3.50fr lil (Bl)	1.75	1.75
377	A93a	5fr brt bl (R)	1.75	1.75
378	A93a	6.50fr gray (R)	1.75	1.75
379	A93a	10fr org (Bk)	1.75	1.75
380	A93a	20fr ultra (R)	1.75	1.75
		Nos. 371-380 (10)	17.50	17.50

Coquilhatville Conf., Apr.-May, 1961.
Nos. 371-380 exist with inverted overprints. Value $15 each.

Pres. Joseph Kasavubu — A95

Kasavubu and Map of Congo — A96

10fr-100fr, Kasavubu in uniform and map.

Perf. 11½

1961, June 30   Unwmk.   Photo.

Portrait and Inscription in Dark Brown

381	A95	10c yellow	.20	.20
382	A95	20c dp rose	.20	.20
383	A95	40c bl grn	.20	.20
384	A95	50c salmon	.20	.20
385	A95	1fr lilac	.20	.20
386	A95	1.50fr lt brn	.20	.20
387	A95	2fr brt grn	.20	.20
388	A96	3.50fr rose pink	.20	.20
389	A96	5fr gray	6.50	.20
390	A96	6.50fr ultra	1.00	.20
391	A96	8fr olive	1.00	.20
392	A96	10fr lt vio	2.25	.80
393	A93	20fr orange	2.25	.20
394	A95	50fr lt bl	3.75	.35
395	A95	100fr apple green	6.25	.55
		Nos. 381-395 (15)	24.60	4.10

First anniversary of independence.
Exists imperf. Value, set $70.

Nos. 381-387, 389 and 392 Overprinted: "REOUVERTURE du PARLEMENT JUILLET 1961"

1961

Portrait and Inscription in Dark Brown

396	A95	10c yellow	.20	.20
397	A95	20c dp rose	.20	.20
398	A95	40c bl grn	.20	.20
399	A95	50c salmon	.55	.35
400	A95	1fr lilac	.55	.35
401	A95	1.50fr lt brn	1.50	1.00
402	A95	2fr brt grn	1.50	1.00
403	A96	5fr gray	1.50	1.00
404	A95	10fr lt vio	1.50	1.00
		Nos. 396-404 (9)	7.70	5.30

Congolese parliament re-opening, 7/1961.
Nos. 396-404 exist with inverted overprints. Value $9 each.

Dag Hammarskjold and Map of Africa with Congo — A97

Malaria Eradication Emblem and Mosquito — A98

1962, Jan. 20   Photo.   Perf. 11½

Gray Background

405	A97	10c dk brn	.20	.20
406	A97	20c Prus bl	.20	.20
407	A97	30c brown	.20	.20
408	A97	40c dk bl	.20	.20
409	A97	50c brn red	.20	.20
410	A97	3fr ol grn	5.00	2.00
411	A97	6.50fr dk vio	1.50	.50
412	A97	8fr red brn	1.75	.50
		Nos. 405-412 (8)	9.25	3.85

Souvenir Sheet

Imperf

413	A97	25fr blk brn	10.00	10.00
a.		Overprint in green	4.50	4.50

Dag Hammarskjold, Sec. Gen. of the UN, 1953-61.
No 413a is overprinted "30 Juin 1962" on stamp and "2eme Anniversaire de l'Independance" on sheet margin. Issued June 30, 1962.
For overprints see Nos. 417-424.

1962, June 15

Granite Paper

414	A98	1.50fr yel, blk & dk red	.20	.20
415	A98	2fr yel grn, brn & bl grn	.30	.20
416	A98	6.50fr ultra, blk & mar	.40	.20
		Nos. 414-416 (3)	.90	.60

WHO drive to eradicate malaria.

Nos. 405-412 Overprinted in Blue, Purple, Black or Carmine

1962, Oct. 15

Gray Background

417	A97	10c dk brn (Bl)	.20	.20
418	A97	20c Prus bl (P)	.20	.20
419	A97	30c brn (Bk)	.20	.20
420	A97	40c dk bl (C)	.20	.20
421	A97	50c brn red (Bl)	2.50	1.00
422	A97	3fr ol grn (P)	.20	.20
423	A97	6.50fr dk vio (Bk)	.25	.20
424	A97	8fr red brn (C)	.40	.20
		Nos. 417-424 (8)	4.15	2.40

Reorganization of Adoula administration.
Inverted overprints exist. Value, $8.00 each.

Canceled to Order

Starting in 1963, values in the used column are for "canceled to order" stamps. Postally used copies sell for much more.

A99

1963, Jan. 28   Engr.   Perf. 10½x13

425	A99	2fr dull purple	1.50	1.00
426	A99	4fr red	.20	.20
427	A99	7fr dark blue	.25	.20
428	A99	20fr slate green	.50	.20
		Nos. 425-428 (4)	2.45	1.60

Congo's 1st participation at the UPU Cong., New Delhi, Mar. 1963.
An imperf sheet containing No. 428 in brown exists. Value $30.
For overprints see Nos. 468-471.

Shoebill — A100

Birds: 10c, Pelicans. 20c, Crested guinea fowl, horiz. 30c, Openbill. 40c, White-bellied storks, horiz. 2fr, Marabou. 3fr, Greater flamingos, horiz. 4fr, Congolese peacock. 5fr, Hartlaub ducks, horiz. 6fr, Secretary bird. 7fr, Black-casqued hornbill, horiz. 8fr, Sacred ibis and nest. 10fr, Crowned crane, horiz. 20fr, Saddle-bill stork, horiz.

1963   Unwmk.   Photo.   Perf. 11½

429	A100	10c pink, ultra & ocher	.20	.20
430	A100	20c rose red, bl & blk	.20	.20
431	A100	30c grn, ocher & blk	.20	.20
432	A100	40c gray, org & blk	.20	.20
433	A100	1fr brn, emer & gray	.20	.20
434	A100	2fr gray, red & ind	3.25	.60
435	A100	3fr ol grn, blk & rose	.20	.20
436	A100	4fr car rose, vio bl & grn	.20	.20
437	A100	5fr lake, lt bl & blk	.45	.20
438	A100	6fr pur, yel & blk	3.50	.60
439	A100	7fr bl grn, blk & ind	.55	.20
440	A100	8fr yel, org & blk	.65	.20
441	A100	10fr bl, blk & rose	.65	.20
442	A100	20fr cit, red & blk	1.20	.20
		Nos. 429-442 (14)	11.65	3.60

Nos. 436 and 438 exist in imperf sheets of one. Value, each $40.

Cinchona Ledgeriana — A101

Red Cross Nurse — A102

10c, 30c, 5fr, Strophanthus sarmentosus.

Perf. 12½x13½, 13½x12½

1963, May 25   Engr.   Unwmk.

Cross in Red

443	A101	10c vio & dl grn	.20	.20
444	A101	20c magenta & bl	.20	.20
445	A101	30c grn & org	.20	.20
446	A101	40c bl & vio	.20	.20
447	A101	5fr ol & rose claret	.20	.20
448	A101	7fr org & blk	.20	.20
449	A102	9fr gray olive & red	.20	.20
450	A102	20fr purple & red	2.50	1.00
		Nos. 443-450 (8)	3.90	2.40

International Red Cross centenary.
A souvenir sheet of three contains imperf. 5fr, 7fr, and 20fr stamps similar to Nos. 447, 448 and 450, but in changed colors. Size: 109x75mm. Value $30.

Men Joining Hands and Map of Congo A103

1963, June 29   Photo.   Perf. 11½

451	A103	4fr multi	1.25	.50
452	A103	5fr multi	.20	.20
453	A103	9fr multi	.20	.20
454	A103	12fr multi	.35	.20
		Nos. 451-454 (4)	2.00	1.10

Issued to celebrate national reconciliation.

Bulldozer and Kabambare Sewer, Leopoldville — A104

Designs: 30c, 5fr, 12fr, Excavator and blueprint. 50c, 9fr, Building Ituri road.

1963, July 1　　Engr.　　Unwmk.

455	A104	20c multi	.20	.20
456	A104	30c multi	.20	.20
457	A104	50c multi	.20	.20
458	A104	3fr multi	1.50	.60
459	A104	5fr multi	.20	.20
460	A104	9fr multi	.20	.20
461	A104	12fr multi	.20	.20
		Nos. 455-461 (7)	2.70	1.80

Issued to publicize aid to Congo by the European Economic Community.

Leopoldville Airport N'Djili — A105

5fr, 7fr, 50fr, Tail assembly and airport.

1963, Nov. 30　　Photo.　　Perf. 11½

462	A105	2fr gray, yel & red brn	.20	.20
463	A105	5fr mag, vio & yel	.20	.20
464	A105	6fr bl, yel & dk brn	1.75	.60
465	A105	7fr multi	.20	.20
466	A105	30fr lil, yel & ol	.40	.25
467	A105	50fr multi	.65	.30
		Nos. 462-467 (6)	3.40	1.75

Issued to publicize Air Congo.
For surcharge see No. 606.

Nos. 425-428 Overprinted with Silver Frame on Three Sides and Black Inscription: "15e anniversaire / 10 DECEMBRE 1948 / DROITS DE L'HOMME / 10 DECEMBRE 1963"

Engraved and Typographed

1963, Dec. 10　　Perf. 10½x13

468	A99	2fr dull purple	.20	.20
469	A99	4fr red	.20	.20
470	A99	7fr dark blue	.25	.20
471	A99	20fr slate green	.35	.20
		Nos. 468-471 (4)	1.00	.80

Universal Declaration of Human Rights, 15th anniv.
Nos. 468-471 exist with side date panels transposed ("1963" at left, "1948" at right). Value, each $15.

Laboratory Technician and Atomic Emblem A106

1.50fr, 60fr, University.　8fr, 75fr, First African nuclear reactor.　25fr, 100fr, University and crest.

1964, Feb. 1　　Photo.　　Perf. 14x12½

472	A106	50c multi	.20	.20
473	A106	1.50fr multi	.20	.20
474	A106	8fr multi	3.00	2.75
475	A106	25fr multi	.20	.20
476	A106	30fr multi	.35	.20
477	A106	60fr multi	.60	.35
478	A106	75fr multi	.70	.60
479	A106	100fr multi	1.25	1.00
a.		Souv. sheet of 3	7.00	7.00
		Nos. 472-479 (8)	6.50	5.50

Lovanium University, Leopoldville, 10th anniv.
No. 479a contains 3 imperf. multicolored stamps: 20fr, design as 50c; 30fr, as 8fr; 100fr.

Belgian Congo Issues of 1952-59 Overprinted "REPUBLIQUE DU CONGO" and Surcharged in Black on Overprinted Metallic Panels

1964　　　　　　Perf. 11½

480	A93	1fr on 20c red org & sl (#307)	.20	.20
481	A86	2fr on 1.50fr (#273)	11.00	3.75
482	A93	5fr on 6.50fr (#315)	.80	.25
483	A86	8fr on 6.50fr (#278)	1.10	.35

Republic Issues of 1960-61 Surcharged in Black on Overprinted Metallic Rectangles or Ovals

484	A86	1fr on 6.50fr (#335)	.20	.20
485	A93	1fr on 20c (#342)	.20	.20
486	A86	2fr on 1.50fr (#330)	.20	.20
487	A95	3fr on 20c (#382)	.55	.25
488	A93	4fr on 40c (#383)	.55	.25
489	A93	5fr on 6.50fr ("Congo" red) (#350)	.80	.25
a.		"Congo" black		.20

490	A93a	6fr on 6.50fr (#363)	.80	.25
491	A93a	7fr on 20c (#356)	.80	.25
		Nos. 480-491 (12)	17.20	6.40

Pole Vault A107

7fr, 20fr, Javelin, vert. 8fr, 100fr, Hurdling.

Perf. 11½

1964, July 13　　Unwmk.　　Photo.

Granite Paper

492	A107	5fr gray, dk brn & car	.20	.20
493	A107	7fr rose, vio & emer	.95	.35
494	A107	8fr org, yel, red brn & vio bl	.20	.20
495	A107	10fr bl, vio brn & mag	.20	.20
496	A107	20fr gray grn, red brn & ver	.25	.20
497	A107	100fr lil, dk brn & grn	.95	.25
a.		Souv. sheet of 3	10.00	10.00
		Nos. 492-497 (6)	2.75	1.40

18th Olympic Games, Tokyo, Oct. 10-25. No. 497a contains 3 imperf. stamps (20fr orange & dark brown, pole vault; 30fr citron and dark brown, hurdling; 100fr dull green and dark brown, javelin). Sheet issued Sept. 10.

National Palace, Leopoldville — A108

1964, Sept. 15

Granite Paper

498	A108	50c lil rose & bl	.20	.20
499	A108	1fr bl & lil rose	.20	.20
500	A108	2fr brn red & vio	.20	.20
501	A108	3fr emer & red	.20	.20
502	A108	4fr org & vio bl	.20	.20
503	A108	5fr gray vio & emer	.20	.20
504	A108	6fr sep & org	.20	.20
505	A108	7fr gray ol & red brn	.20	.20
506	A108	8fr rose red & vio bl	2.00	.30
507	A108	9fr vio bl & rose red	.20	.20
508	A108	10fr brn ol & grn	.20	.20
509	A108	20fr bl & brn vio	.20	.20
510	A108	30fr dk car rose & grn	.25	.20
511	A108	40fr ultra & dk car rose	.35	.20
512	A108	50fr brn org & grn	.40	.20
513	A108	100fr slate & ver	.85	.20
		Nos. 498-513 (16)	6.05	3.30

For overprints and surcharges see Nos. 574-577, 593-598, 609-615, 670-671, 673-674, 676-677, 680, 684-687.

Pres. John F. Kennedy (1917-63) A109

1964, Dec. 8　　Photo.　　Perf. 13½

514	A109	5fr dk bl & blk	.20	.20
515	A109	6fr rose claret & blk	.20	.20
516	A109	9fr brn & blk	.20	.20
517	A109	30fr pur & blk	.55	.20
518	A109	40fr dl grn & blk	3.50	1.00
519	A109	60fr red brn & blk	1.20	.35
		Nos. 514-519 (6)	5.85	2.15

Souvenir Sheet

520	A109	150fr blk & mar	6.50	6.50

Rocket and Unisphere A110

Basketball A111

Engraved and Typographed

1965, Mar. 1　　Unwmk.　　Perf. 12

521	A110	50c lil & blk	.20	.20
522	A110	1.50fr bl & lil	.20	.20
523	A110	2fr red brn & brt grn	.20	.20
524	A110	10fr brt grn & dk red	1.00	.55
525	A110	18fr vio bl & blk	.20	.20
526	A110	27fr rose red & grn	.35	.20
527	A110	40fr gray & org	.45	.20
		Nos. 521-527 (7)	2.60	1.75

New York World's Fair, 1964-65.

1965, Apr.　　Photo.　　Perf. 13½

6fr, 40fr, Soccer, horiz. 15fr, 60fr, Volleyball.

528	A111	5fr blk, grnsh bl & ocher	.20	.20
529	A111	6fr blk, bl gray & crim	.20	.20
530	A111	15fr blk, org & yel grn	.20	.20
531	A111	24fr blk, rose lil & brt grn	.40	.20
532	A111	40fr blk, brt grn & ultra	2.00	.70
533	A111	60fr blk, bl & red lil	.70	.20
		Nos. 528-533 (6)	3.70	1.70

First African Games, Leopoldville, Mar. 31-Apr. 7, 1965.
For surcharges see Nos. 604-605.

Earth and Satellites A112

Designs: 9fr, 15fr, 20fr, 40fr, Satellites at left, globe at right.

Perf. 14x14½

1965, June 28　　Photo.　　Unwmk.

534	A112	6fr blk, sal & vio	.20	.20
535	A112	9fr blk, lt grn & gray	.20	.20
536	A112	12fr org, gray & blk	.20	.20
537	A112	15fr grn, ultra & blk	.20	.20
538	A112	18fr blk, lt grn & gray	1.50	.40
539	A112	20fr blk, sal & vio	.20	.20
540	A112	30fr grn, ultra & blk	.25	.20
541	A112	40fr org, gray & blk	.35	.20
		Nos. 534-541 (8)	3.10	1.80

Cent. of the ITU.

Congolese Paratrooper and Parachutes A113

1965, July 5　　　　　Perf. 13x14

542	A113	5fr brt bl & brn	.20	.20
543	A113	6fr org & brn	.20	.20
544	A113	7fr br grn & brn	.40	.25
545	A113	9fr brt pink & brn	.20	.20
546	A113	18fr lem & brn	.20	.20
		Nos. 542-546 (5)	1.20	1.05

Fifth anniversary of independence.

Matadi Harbor and ICY Emblem — A114

ICY Emblem and: 8fr, 25fr, Katanga mines. 9fr, 60fr, Tshopo Dam, Stanleyville.

1965, Oct. 25　　Photo.　　Perf. 13x14

547	A114	6fr ultra, blk & yel	.20	.20
548	A114	8fr org red, blk & bl	.20	.20
549	A114	9fr bl grn, blk & brn org	.20	.20
550	A114	12fr car rose, blk & gray	1.00	.35
551	A114	25fr ol, blk & rose red	.20	.20
552	A114	60fr gray, blk & org	.65	.20
		Nos. 547-552 (6)	2.45	1.35

International Cooperation Year, 1965.
For overprints and surcharges see Nos. 559-560, 607-608.

Soldiers Giving First Aid — A115

The Army Serving the Country: 7fr, Bridge building. 9fr, Feeding child. 19fr, Maintenance of telegraph lines. 20fr, House building. 30fr, Soldier and flag. (19fr, 20fr, 30fr, vert.)

Perf. 12½x13, 13x12½

1965, Nov. 17

553	A115	5fr sal, brn & red	.20	.20
554	A115	7fr yel & grn	.20	.20
555	A115	9fr ol & brn	.20	.20
556	A115	19fr brt grn & brn	1.10	.60
557	A115	20fr lt bl & brn	.30	.20
558	A115	30fr multi	.50	.20
		Nos. 553-558 (6)	2.50	1.60

See Nos. 582-586. For surcharges see Nos. 602, 678-679, 683.

Nos. 551-552 Overprinted with UN Emblem and "6e Journée Météorologique Mondiale / 23.3.66." on Metallic Strip

1966, Mar. 23　　Photo.　　Perf. 13x14

559	A114	25fr ol & blk	1.40	.55
560	A114	60fr gray & blk	1.40	.65

6th World Meteorological Day.

Woman's Head and Goat — A116

10fr, Sculptured heads.　12fr, Sitting figure and two heads, vert. 53fr, Figure with earrings and kneeling woman with bowl, vert.

Perf. 11½x13, 13x11½

1966, Apr. 23　　Litho.　　Unwmk.

561	A116	10fr red, blk & gray	.20	.20
562	A116	12fr grn, blk & bl	.25	.20
563	A116	15fr dp bl, blk & lil	.30	.20
564	A116	53fr dp rose, blk & vio bl	1.50	1.10
		Nos. 561-564 (4)	2.25	1.70

Intl. Negro Arts Festival, Dakar, Senegal, Apr. 1-24.

Pres. Joseph Desiré Mobutu and Fishing Industry A117

Pres. Mobutu and: 4fr, Pyrethrum harvest. 6fr, Building industry.　8fr, Winnowing rice. 10fr, Cotton harvest.　12fr, Banana harvest. 15fr, Coffee harvest. 24fr, Pineapple harvest. No. 573a, Pres. Mobutu without cap, and men rolling up sleeves.

1966, May 1　　Photo.　　Perf. 11½

565	A117	2fr dk brn & dk bl	.20	.20
566	A117	4fr brn & org	.20	.20
567	A117	6fr dk brn & ol	.75	.60
568	A117	8fr dk brn & brt grnsh bl	.20	.20
569	A117	10fr dk brn & brn red	.20	.20
570	A117	12fr dk brn & vio	.20	.20

571	A117	15fr dk brn & lt ol grn	.20 .20
572	A117	24fr dk brn & lil rose	.25 .20
		Nos. 565-572 (8)	2.20 2.00

Souvenir Sheet
Perf. 11x11½

573		Sheet of 4	2.25 2.25
a.	A117	15fr red, black & ultra	.50 .50

Lt. Gen. Joseph Desiré Mobutu, Pres. of Congo, and publicizing the "Back to Work" campaign.
For surcharges see Nos. 601, 603, 616, 619-624, 672, 675, 681-682.

Nos. 510-513 Overprinted

1966, June 13   *Perf. 11½*

574	A108	30fr dk car rose & grn	1.10 1.10
575	A108	40fr ultra & dk car rose	1.20 1.20
576	A108	50fr brn org & grn	1.40 1.40
577	A108	100fr slate & ver	1.40 1.40
		Nos. 574-577 (4)	5.10 5.10

Inauguration of WHO Headquarters, Geneva.

Soccer Player — A118

30fr, 2 soccer players. 50fr, 3 soccer players. 60fr, Jules Rimet Cup, soccer ball & globe.

1966, July 25   Photo.   *Perf. 14*

578	A118	10fr ocher, vio & brt grn	.20 .20
579	A118	30fr brt rose lil, vio & ap grn	.45 .20
580	A118	50fr ap grn, Prus bl & tan	1.50 1.00
581	A118	60fr brt grn, dk brn & gold	1.50 .50
		Nos. 578-581 (4)	3.65 1.90

World Cup Soccer Championship, Wembley, England, July 11-30.
For overprints see Nos. 587-590.

Army Type of 1965

The Army Serving the Country: 2fr, Soldiers giving first aid. 6fr, Feeding child. 10fr, House building, vert. 18fr, Bridge building. 24fr, Soldier and flag, vert.

1966, Aug. 8   *Perf. 12½x13, 13x12½*

582	A115	2fr ver, ind & red	.20 .20
583	A115	6fr ultra red brn	.20 .20
584	A115	10fr yel grn & red brn	.75 .50
585	A115	18fr car rose & vio	.20 .20
586	A115	24fr multi	.25 .20
		Nos. 582-586 (5)	1.60 1.30

#578-581 Overprinted in Black ("a"), Carmine or Green ("b"):
"FINALE / ANGLETERRE-ALLEMAGNE / 4-2"

1966, Nov. 14   Photo.   *Perf. 14*

587	A118	10fr pair, B and C	.60 .60
588	A118	30fr pair, B and G	2.25 2.00
589	A118	50fr pair, B and C	3.50 3.50
590	A118	60fr pair, B and G	4.50 3.75
		Nos. 587-590 (4)	10.85 8.85

England's victory in the World Soccer Cup Championship. The two colors of the overprint alternate in the sheets.

Souvenir Sheets

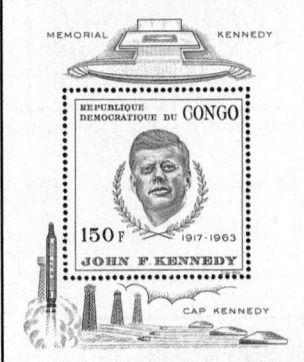

Pres. John F. Kennedy — A119

1966, Dec. 28   Engr.   *Perf. 13*

591	A119	150fr brown	22.50 17.50
592	A119	150fr slate	22.50 17.50

Issued in memory of Pres. John F. Kennedy. No. 591 has slate green, No. 592 deep orange marginal design. Two imperf. sheets exist: 150fr brown with violet blue margin and 150fr slate with lilac margin. Size: 65x76mm. Values, $20 each.

Nos. 498-503 Surcharged in Black, Red or Maroon

1967, Sept. 11   Photo.   *Perf. 11½*

593	A108	1k on 2fr	.20 .20
a.		Inverted overprint	5.00
594	A108	3k on 5fr	.20 .20
595	A108	5k on 4fr	.35 .20
596	A108	6.60k on 1fr (R)	.50 .20
a.		Inverted overprint	5.00
597	A108	9.60k on 50c	.70 .30
a.		Inverted overprint	5.00
598	A108	9.80k on 3fr (M)	.75 .50
		Nos. 593-598 (6)	2.70 1.60

Souvenir Sheet

Map of Africa, Torch — A120

599	A120	50k grnsh bl, blk & red	2.50 2.50

4th meeting of the Org. for African Unity, Kinshasa (Leopoldville), Sept. 9-11.
No. 599 in other colors was not a postal issue.

Souvenir Sheet

Horn Blower and EXPO Emblem — A121

1967, Sept. 28   Engr.   *Perf. 11½*

600	A121	50k dk brn	3.50 3.50

EXPO '67, International Exhibition, Montreal, Apr. 28-Oct. 27, 1967.

Nos. 565-566 and 582 Overprinted: "NOUVELLE CONSTITUTION 1967" and Surcharged with New Value on Metallic Panel in Magenta or Brown
Perf. 11½, 12½x13

1967, Oct. 9   Photo.

601	A117	4k on 2fr (M)	.25 .20
602	A115	5k on 2fr (B)	.45 .20
603	A117	21k on 4fr (M)	1.50 .90
		Nos. 601-603 (3)	2.20 1.30

Promulgation of the Constitution, June 4, 1967.

Nos. 528 and 530 Surcharged with New Value and Overprinted: "1ers Jeux Congolais / 25/6 au 2/7/1967 / Kinshasa"

1967, Oct. 16   Photo.   *Perf. 13½*

604	A111	1k on 5fr multi	.35 .20
605	A111	9.60k on 15fr multi	.75 .65

First Congolese Games, Kinshasa, June 25-July 2, 1967.

No. 465 Surcharged with New Value and Overprinted: "1er VOL BAC / ONE ELEVEN / 14/5/67"

1967, Oct. 16   Photo.   *Perf. 11½*

606	A105	9.60k on 7fr multi	1.20 .25

1st flight of the BAC 111 in the service of Air Congo, May 14, 1967.

Nos. 547 and 549 Surcharged in Red or Black: "JOURNEE MONDIALE / DE L'ENFANCE / 8-10-67"

1968, Feb. 10   Photo.   *Perf. 13x14*

607	A114	1k on 6fr (R)	.35 .20
608	A114	9k on 9fr (B)	1.00 .70

Intl. Children's Day. The surcharge is on a rectangle printed in metallic ink.

Nos. 498, 504 and 501 Surcharged in Blue or Red: "Année Internationale / du Tourisme 24-10-1967"

1968, Feb. 10   *Perf. 11½*

609	A108	5k on 50c lil rose & bl (Bl)	.45 .25
610	A108	10k on 6fr sepia & org (R)	.65 .55
611	A108	15k on 3fr emer & red (R)	1.00 1.00
		Nos. 609-611 (3)	2.10 1.80

International Tourist Year. The surcharge is on a rectangle printed in metallic ink.

Nos. 500, 498 and 502 Surcharged in Black, Violet Blue or Gold

1968, July   Photo.   *Perf. 11½*

612	A108	1k on 2fr	.30 .20
613	A108	2k on 50c (VBl)	.45 .25
614	A108	2k on 50c (G)	.45 .25
615	A108	9.60k on 4fr	2.00 1.10
		Nos. 612-615 (4)	3.20 1.80

The surcharge on No. 612 consists of a black rectangle and new denomination in upper right corner; the surcharge on No. 613 has a violet blue rectangle with denomination printed in white on it; on No. 614 the rectangle is gold and the denomination black; on No. 615 the rectangle is black and the denomination white.

No. 565 Surcharged in White on Black Rectangle

1968, Oct.   Photo.   *Perf. 11½*

616	A117	10k on 2fr dk brn & dk bl	.70 .20

Leopard
A122

1968, Nov. 5   Litho.   *Perf. 10½*

617	A122	2k brt grnsh bl & blk	.30 .20
618	A122	9.60k red & blk	1.50 .20

Mobutu Type of 1966 Surcharged

1968, Dec. 20   Photo.   *Perf. 11½*

619	A117	15s on 2fr sep & brt bl	.20 .20
620	A117	1k on 6fr sep & brn	.20 .20
621	A117	3k on 10fr sep & emer	.20 .20
622	A117	5k on 12fr sep & org	.35 .20
623	A117	20k on 15fr sep & brt grn	1.25 .50
624	A117	50k on 24fr sep & brt lil	3.25 1.50
		Nos. 619-624 (6)	5.45 2.80

Human Rights Flame — A123

1968, Dec. 30   *Perf. 12½x13*

625	A123	2k lt ultra & brt grn	.20 .20
626	A123	9.60k grn & dp car	.75 .30
627	A123	10k brt lil & brn	.75 .35
628	A123	40k org brn & pur	2.50 1.25
		Nos. 625-628 (4)	4.20 2.10

International Human Rights Year.

Type of 1968 Overprinted in Gold

1969, Jan. 27   Photo.   *Perf. 12½x13*

629	A123	2k ap grn & red brn	.20 .20
630	A123	9.60k rose & emer	.75 .30
631	A123	10k gray & ultra	.75 .35
632	A123	40k grnsh bl & pur	2.50 1.25
		Nos. 629-632 (4)	4.20 2.10

4th summit meeting of OCAM (Organisation Communitee Afrique et Malgache), Kinshasa, Jan. 27.

Kinshasa Fair Emblem and Cotton Boll — A124

Fair Emblem and: 6k, Copper. 9.60k, Coffee. 9.80k, Diamond. 11.60k, Oil palm fruits.

1969, May 2   Photo.   *Perf. 12½x13*

633	A124	2k brt pur, gold & red lil	.25 .20
634	A124	6k grn, gold & bl grn	.95 .50

635 A124 9.60k brn, gold & lt
brn 1.25 .40
636 A124 9.80k ultra & gold 1.40 .60
637 A124 11.60k hn brn, gold &
brn 1.60 .90
Nos. 633-637 (5) 5.45 2.60

Kinshasa Fair, Limete, June 30-July 21.

Fair Entrance, Emblem — A125

Fair Emblem and: 3k, Gecomin Mining Co.
Pavilion. 10k, Administration Building. 25k,
Pavilion of the Organization for African Unity.

1969, June 30 **Photo.** **Perf. 11½**
Granite Paper
638 A125 2k brt rose lil & gold .20 .20
639 A125 3k blue & gold .20 .20
640 A125 10k lt ol grn & gold .80 .40
641 A125 25k copper red & gold 1.80 1.00
Nos. 638-641 (4) 3.00 1.80

Kinshasa Fair, Limete, June 30-July 21.

Congo
Arms — A126

Pres.
Mobutu — A127

1969, July-Sept. **Litho.** **Perf. 14**
642 A126 10s org & blk .20 .20
643 A126 15s ultra & blk .20 .20
644 A126 30s brt grn & blk .20 .20
645 A126 60s brt rose lil &
blk .20 .20
646 A126 90s dp bister & blk .20 .20
Perf. 13
647 A127 1k sky bl & multi .20 .20
648 A127 2k org & multi .20 .20
649 A127 3k multi .30 .20
650 A127 5k brt rose &
multi .40 .20
651 A127 6k ultra & multi .40 .25
652 A127 9.60k multi .75 .40
653 A127 10k lt lil & multi 1.00 .50
654 A127 20k yel & multi 1.75 1.00
655 A127 50k multi 5.00 2.50
656 A127 100k fawn & multi 10.00 6.00
Nos. 642-656 (15) 21.00 12.45

Well Driller, by Oscar
Bonnevalle — A128

Paintings: 4k, Preparation of cocoa, by
Jean Van Noten. 8k, Dock workers, by Con-
stantin Meunier. 10k, Poultry shop, by Henri
Evenepoel. 15k, Steel industry, by Constantin
Meunier.

Perf. 13x14, 14x13 (8k)
1969, Dec. 15 **Litho.**
Size: 41x41mm
657 A128 3k multi .20 .20
658 A128 4k multi .20 .20
Size: 28x41mm
659 A128 8k multi .50 .30
Size: 41x41mm
660 A128 10k multi .75 .40
661 A128 15k multi 1.50 .70
Nos. 657-661 (5) 3.15 1.80

50th anniv. of the ILO.

Souvenir Sheet

Adoration of the Kings, by
Rubens — A129

1969, Dec. **Engr.** **Perf. 13**
662 A129 50k red lilac 5.50 5.50

Issued for Christmas 1969.

Pres.
Mobutu,
Map
and
Flag of
Congo
A130

1970, June 30 **Litho.** **Perf. 13½x13**
663 A130 10s multi .20 .20
664 A130 90s pur & multi .20 .20
665 A130 1k brn & multi .20 .20
666 A130 2k multi .20 .20
667 A130 7k multi .35 .20
668 A130 10k multi .55 .25
669 A130 20k multi 1.25 .60
Nos. 663-669 (7) 2.95 1.85

10th anniversary of independence.

Issues of 1964-1966 Surcharged

Perf. 11½, 12½x13, 13x12½
1970, Sept. 24 **Photo.**
670 A108 10s on 1fr (#499) .25 .20
671 A108 20s on 2fr (#500) .25 .20
672 A117 20s on 2fr (#565) 1.00 .50
673 A108 30s on 3fr (#501) .25 .20
674 A108 40s on 4fr (#502) .25 .20
675 A117 40s on 4fr (#566) 1.00 .50
676 A108 60s on 7fr (#505) 3.00 1.75
677 A108 90s on 9fr (#507) 3.00 1.75
678 A115 90s on 9fr (#555) .60 .40
679 A115 1k on 7fr (#554) .60 .40
680 A108 1k on 6fr (#504) .50 .20
681 A117 1k on 12fr (#570) 2.75 1.75
682 A117 2k on 24fr (#572) 1.25 .50
683 A115 2k on 24fr (#586) 1.25 .50
684 A108 3k on 30fr (#510) 2.25 1.25
685 A108 4k on 40fr (#511) .50 .20
686 A108 5k on 50fr (#512) 9.00 5.00
687 A108 10k on 100fr (#513) 2.25 1.25
Nos. 670-687 (18) 29.95 16.75

Telecommunications Building,
Geneva — A131

Designs: 2k, 6.60k, UPU Headquarters,
Bern. 9.80k, 10k, 11k, UN Headquarters, NY.

1970, Oct. 24 **Photo.** **Perf. 11½**
688 A131 1k pink & grn .20 .20
689 A131 2k org & grn .20 .20
690 A131 6.60k grnsh bl & rose
car .40 .25
691 A131 9.60k yel & vio bl .50 .35
692 A131 9.80k lt ultra & brn .50 .35
693 A131 10k lt pur & brn .50 .35
694 A131 11k rose & brn .70 .45
Nos. 688-694 (7) 3.00 2.15

ITU; new UPU Headquarters, Bern; 25th
anniv. of the UN.

Pres. Mobutu, Congolese Flag and
Arch — A132

1970, Nov. 24 **Litho.** **Perf. 13**
695 A132 2k yel & multi .20 .20
696 A132 10k bl & multi 1.00 .50
697 A132 20k red & multi 2.50 1.50
Nos. 695-697 (3) 3.70 2.20

Fifth anniversary of new government.

Apollo 11
in Flight
A133

Designs: 2k, Astronaut and spacecraft on
moon. 7k, Pres. Mobutu decorating astronauts' wives. 10k, Pres. Mobutu with Neil A.
Armstrong, Col. Edwin E. Aldrin, Jr. and Lt.
Col. Michael Collins. 30k, Armstrong, Aldrin
and Collins in space suits.

1970, Dec. 24 **Perf. 13x13½**
698 A133 1k bl & blk .30 .20
699 A133 2k brt pur & blk .50 .25
700 A133 7k dl org & blk 1.50 .85
701 A133 10k rose red & blk 2.00 1.25
702 A133 30k grn & blk 5.50 3.50
Nos. 698-702 (5) 9.80 6.05

Visit of US Apollo 11 astronauts and their
wives to Kinshasa.

Metopodontus Savagei — A134

Designs: Various insects of Congo.

1971, Jan. 25 **Photo.** **Perf. 11½**
703 A134 10s dl rose & multi .75 .30
704 A134 50s gray & multi .75 .30
705 A134 90s multi .75 .30
706 A134 1k citron & multi .75 .30
707 A134 2k gray grn & multi .75 .30
708 A134 3k lt vio & multi 1.75 .60
709 A134 5k bl & multi 5.00 2.00
710 A134 10k multi 7.00 2.50
711 A134 30k grn & multi 16.00 6.75
712 A134 40k ocher & multi 25.00 10.00
Nos. 703-712 (10) 58.50 23.35

Colotis Protomedia — A135

Various butterflies and moths of Congo.

1971, Feb. 24
713 A135 10s lt ultra & multi .75 .35
714 A135 20s choc & multi .75 .35
715 A135 70s dp org & multi .75 .35
716 A135 1k vio bl & multi .75 .35
717 A135 3k multi 1.75 .60
718 A135 5k dk grn & multi 4.75 1.50
719 A135 10k multi 6.25 2.00
720 A135 15k emer & multi 11.00 3.50
721 A135 25k yel & multi 17.50 4.50
722 A135 40k multi 24.00 11.00
Nos. 713-722 (10) 68.25 24.50

UN Emblem,
Racial
Unity — A136

1971, Mar. 21 **Photo.** **Perf. 11½**
723 A136 1k lt grn & multi .20 .20
724 A136 4k gray & multi .20 .20
725 A136 5k lt lil & multi .40 .25
726 A136 10k lt bl & multi .90 .35
Nos. 723-726 (4) 1.70 1.00

Intl. year against racial discrimination.

Hypericum
Bequaertii
A137

Flowers: 4k, Dissotis brazzae. 20k, Begonia wollastonii. 25k, Cassia alata.

1971, May 24 **Litho.** **Perf. 14**
727 A137 1k multi 1.00 1.00
728 A137 4k multi 1.75 .45
729 A137 20k multi 9.25 2.50
730 A137 25k multi 12.00 3.25
Nos. 727-730 (4) 24.00 6.45

Obelisk at
N'sele, Pres.
Mobutu
A138

1971, May 20 **Photo.** **Perf. 11½**
731 A138 4k gold & multi .55 .20

4th anniversary of the People's Revolutionary Movement.

Radar
Station
A139

Designs: 1k, Waves. 6k, Map of Africa with
telecommunications network.

1971, June 25 **Photo.** **Perf. 11½**
732 A139 1k rose & multi .20 .20
733 A139 3k yel & multi .55 .35
734 A139 6k lt bl & multi 1.40 1.00
Nos. 732-734 (3) 2.15 1.55

3rd World Telecommunications Day, May 17
(1k); opening of satellite telecommunications
ground station, Kinshasa, June 30 (3k); Pan-
African telecommunication system (6k).

Grass
Monkeys
A140

Designs: 20s, Moustached monkeys, vert.
70s, De Brazza's monkeys. 1k, Yellow
baboons. 3k, Pygmy chimpanzee, vert. 5k,
Mangabeys, vert. 10k, Owlfaced monkeys.
15k, Diana monkeys. 25k, Black-and-white
colobus, vert. 40k, L'Hoest's monkeys, vert.

1971, Aug.

735	A140	10s vio & multi	.75	.35
736	A140	20s lt bl & multi	.75	.35
737	A140	70s ocher & multi	1.25	.45
738	A140	1k gray & multi	1.25	.45
739	A140	3k rose & multi	2.00	1.00
740	A140	5k brn & multi	4.50	2.50
741	A140	10k multi	8.75	4.75
742	A140	15k multi	14.00	6.50
743	A140	25k brt bl & multi	23.50	11.00
744	A140	40k red & multi	32.50	16.00
	Nos. 735-744 (10)		89.25	43.35

Hotel Inter-Continental,
Kinshasa — A141

1971, Oct. 2   Photo.   Perf. 13

745	A141	2k silver & multi	.25	.25
746	A141	12k gold & multi	.55	.25

Man Reading
A142

Designs: 2.50k, Open book and abacus. 7k, Five letters surrounding symbolic head.

1971, Oct. 24

747	A142	50s multi	.20	.20
748	A142	2.50k multi	.20	.20
749	A142	7k multi	1.40	1.00
	Nos. 747-749 (3)		1.80	1.40

Fight against illiteracy.

Succeeding issues are listed in Vol. 6 under Zaire. Beginning in 1998, Zaire reverted to using the Congo name, at least temporarily. Until the situation is resolved, the current stamps inscribed "Congo" will be listed under Zaire.

SEMI-POSTAL STAMPS

Women
Carrying
Food,
Wheat
Emblem,
and
Tractor
SP22

1963, Mar. 21   Photo.   Perf. 14x13

B48	SP22	5fr + 2fr multi	.25	.20
B49	SP22	9fr + 4fr multi	.45	.20
B50	SP22	12fr+ 6fr multi	.50	.25
B51	SP22	20fr+ 10fr multi	2.25	1.75
	Nos. B48-B51 (4)		3.45	2.40

FAO "Freedom from Hunger" campaign. No. B51 exists in an imperf sheet of one, in light and dark violet. Value $30.

CONGO, PEOPLE'S REPUBLIC

'pē-pəls ri-'pə-blik of

'käŋ₋gō

(ex-French)

LOCATION — West Africa at equator
GOVT. — Republic
AREA — 132,046 sq. mi.
POP. — 2,716,814 (1999 est.)
CAPITAL — Brazzaville

The former French colony of Middle Congo became a member state of the French Community on November 28, 1958, and achieved independence on August 15, 1960. For some years before 1958, the colony was joined with three other French territories to form French Equatorial Africa. Issues of Middle Congo (1907-1933) are listed under that heading.

100 Centimes = 1 Franc

Catalogue values for all unused stamps in this country are for Never Hinged items.

Allegory of New Republic A7

1959　Unwmk.　Engr.　Perf. 13
89　A7　25fr brn, dp claret, org & ol　　.60　.25

1st anniv. of the proclamation of the Republic.

Imperforates

Most stamps of the Republic of the Congo exist imperforate in issued and trial colors, and also in small presentation sheets in issued colors.

Common Design Types pictured following the introduction.

C.C.T.A. Issue
Common Design Type

1960　Unwmk.　Perf. 13
90　CD106　50fr dl grn & plum　　.80　.80

President Fulbert Youlou — A8　　Flag, Map and UN Emblem — A9

1960
91　A8　15fr grn, blk & car　　.35　.35
92　A8　85fr indigo & car　　2.00　.45

1961, Mar. 11　　Perf. 13
Flag in Green, Yellow & Red
93　A9　5fr vio brn & dk bl　　.25　.20
94　A9　20fr org & dk bl　　.45　.25
95　A9　100fr grn & dk bl　　2.00　.80
　　　Nos. 93-95 (3)　　2.70　1.25

Congo's admission to United Nations.

Rainbow Runner A10

Fish: 50c, 3fr, Rainbow runner. 1fr, 2fr, Sloan's viperfish. 5fr, Hatchet fish. 10fr, A deep-sea fish.

1961, Nov. 28　　　Engr.
96　A10　50c brn, ol grn & sal　　.35　.20
97　A10　1fr bl grn & sepia　　.35　.20
98　A10　2fr ultra, sep & dk grn　　.35　.20
99　A10　3fr dk bl, grn & salmon　　.50　.30
100　A10　5fr red brn, grn & blk　　.80　.40
101　A10　10fr blue & red brn　　1.75　.50
　　　Nos. 96-101 (6)　　4.10　1.80

Brazzaville Market — A11

1962, Mar. 23　Unwmk.　Perf. 13
102　A11　20fr blk, red & grn　　.60　.20

Abidjan Games Issue
Common Design Type

20fr, Boxing. 50fr, Running, finish line.

1962, July 21　Photo.　Perf. 12½x12
103　CD109　20fr car, brt pink, brn & blk　　.45　.25
104　CD109　50fr car, brt pink, brn & blk　　.90　.30
　　　Nos. 103-104,C7 (3)　　3.85　1.80

African-Malgache Union Issue
Common Design Type

1962, Sept. 8
105　CD110　30fr multicolored　　1.00　.40

Waves Around Globe A11a

Design: 100fr, Orbit patterns around globe.

1963, Sept. 19　　　Perf. 12½
106　A11a　25fr org, grn & ultra　　.50　.30
107　A11a　100fr lt red brn, bl & plum　　1.60　.90

Issued to publicize space communications.

King Makoko's Collar — A12

Unwmk.
1963, Oct. 21　Engr.　Perf. 13
108　A12　10fr showm　　.45　.25
109　A12　15fr Kebekebe mask　　.60　.25

UNESCO Emblem, Scales and Tree A12a

1963, Dec. 10　Unwmk.　Perf. 13
110　A12a　25fr grn, dk bl & brn　　.70　.30

15th anniv. of the Universal Declaration of Human Rights.

Barograph and WMO Emblem A12b

1964, Mar. 23　　　Engr.
111　A12b　50fr grn, red brn & ultra　1.00　.60

Fourth World Meteorological Day.

Mechanic with Machine — A13

1964, Apr. 8
112　A13　20fr grnsh bl, mag & dk brn　　.60　.30

Training of technicians.

Corn and Tools A14

1964, Apr. 24　Unwmk.　Perf. 13
113　A14　80fr brn, grn & brn car　1.10　.60

Importance of manual labor.

Diaboua Ballet A15

Kébékébé Dance — A16　　Carved Figure — A17

1964, May 8　　　Engr.
114　A15　30fr multicolored　　1.25　.30
115　A16　60fr multicolored　　2.25　.65

1964, May 22
116　A17　50fr brn red & sepia　　1.50　.55

Classroom A18

1964, May 26
117　A18　25fr dk brn, red & blue　　.60　.30

Issued to publicize education.

Type of Air Post Issue, 1963, Inscribed: "1er ANNIVERSAIRE DE LA REVOLUTION/FETE NATIONALE/15 AOUT 1964"

1964, Aug. 15　Photo.　Perf. 13x12
118　AP5　20fr lt bl, red, ocher, dk brn & grn　　.50　.20

1st anniv. of the revolution and Natl. Feast Day, Aug. 15.

Fire Squid A19

15fr, Johnson's deep-sea angler (fish).

1964, Oct. 20　Engr.　Perf. 13
119　A19　2fr ver, lt grn & brn　　.80　.50
120　A19　15fr vio, lt ol grn & dp cl 2.75　1.50

Cooperation Issue
Common Design Type

1964, Nov. 7　Unwmk.　Perf. 13
121　CD119　25fr car, brt grn & dk brn　　.60　.35

Communications Emblems — A20

1965, Jan. 1　Litho.　Perf. 12½x13
122　A20　25fr ol, red brn & blk　　.50　.25

Issued to commemorate the establishment of the national postal administration.

Sitatunga — A21　　Dancer on Stilts — A22

Design: 20fr, Elephant, horiz.

1965, Mar. 15　Engr.　Perf. 13
123　A21　15fr redsh brn, dl grn & bl　　.90　.40
124　A21　20fr blk, dp bl & sl grn　　.90　.40
125　A22　85fr lil & multi　　3.50　1.50
　　　Nos. 123-125 (3)　　5.30　2.30

Pres. Alphonse Massamba-Debat A23

1965-66　Photo.　Perf. 12x12½
126　A23　20fr dk brn, grn & yel　　.25　.20
127　A23　25fr brn, bl grn, emer & blk ('66)　　.30　.20

128 A23 30fr brn, bl grn, org & blk
('66) .45 .20
Nos. 126-128 (3) 1.00 .60

Soccer
Player
A24

Designs: 25fr, Games' emblem (map of
Africa and runners). 50fr, Field ball player.
85fr, Runner. 100fr, Bicyclist.

1965, July 17 Photo. Perf. 12½
Size: 28x28mm
129 A24 25fr blk, red, yel & grn .50 .30
Size: 34x34mm
130 A24 40fr yel grn & multi .70 .45
131 A24 50fr red & multi .70 .45
132 A24 85fr blk & multi 1.25 .65
133 A24 100fr yel & multi 1.75 .75
a. Min. sheet of 5, #129-133 7.50 7.50
Nos. 129-133 (5) 4.90 2.60

1st African Games, Brazzaville, July 18-25.

Arms of
Congo — A25

1965, Nov. 15 Litho. Perf. 12½x13
134 A25 20fr multicolored .50 .20

Cooperative
Village
A26

30fr, Gymnastic drill team with streamers.

1966, Feb. 18 Perf. 12½x13
135 A26 25fr multicolored .50 .25
136 A26 30fr multicolored .50 .30

Sculptured
Mask — A27

Designs: 30fr, Weaver, painting. 85fr,
String instrument, painting, horiz.

Perf. 13x12½, 12½x13
1966, Apr. 9 Photo.
137 A27 30fr multicolored .70 .30
138 A27 85fr multicolored 1.90 .70
139 A27 90fr multicolored 2.25 1.00
Nos. 137-139 (3) 4.85 2.00

Intl. Negro Arts Festival, Dakar, Senegal,
4/1-24.

Men and
Clocks
A28

1966, Apr. 15 Perf. 12½x12
140 A28 70fr pale brn, ocher & dk
brn 1.00 .30

Introduction of the shorter work day (less
lunch time, earlier quitting time).

WHO Headquarters, Geneva — A29

1966, May 3 Photo. Perf. 12½x13
141 A29 50fr org yel, vio & bl .80 .40

Inauguration of the WHO Headquarters,
Geneva.

Church of St.
Peter Claver
A30

Women's
Basketball
A31

1966, June 15 Photo. Perf. 13x12½
142 A30 70fr multicolored 1.00 .40

1966, July 15 Engr. Perf. 13

Sport: 1fr, Women's volleyball, horiz. 3fr,
Women's field ball, horiz. 5fr, Athletes of various races. 10fr, Torch bearer. 15fr, Soccer
and gold medal of First African Games.

143 A31 1fr ultra, choc & ol .20 .20
144 A31 2fr choc, grn & bl .25 .20
145 A31 3fr dk grn, dk car &
choc .25 .20
146 A31 5fr slate, emer & choc .30 .20
147 A31 10fr dl bl, dk grn & vio .55 .20
148 A31 15fr vio, car & choc .75 .30
Nos. 143-148 (6) 2.30 1.30

Jules Rimet
Cup and
Globe
A32

1966, July 15 Photo. Perf. 12½x12
149 A32 30fr brt red, gold, blk & bl .90 .45

8th World Soccer Cup Championship, Wembley, England, July 11-30.

Savorgnan
de Brazza
School
A33

1966, Sept. 15 Photo. Perf. 12½x12
150 A33 30fr dk pur, grn, yel & blk .60 .25

Pointe-Noire Railroad Station — A34

1966, Oct. 15 Engr. Perf. 13
151 A34 60fr grn, red & brn 1.25 .60

Student with
Microscope
A35

Balumbu Mask
A36

1966, Nov. 28 Engr. Perf. 13
152 A35 90fr brn, grn & ind 1.25 .70

20th anniv. of UNESCO.

1966, Dec. 12 Engr. Perf. 13

Masks: 10fr, Kuyu. 15fr, Bakwélé. 20fr,
Batéké.

153 A36 5fr car rose & dk brn .45 .20
154 A36 10fr Prus bl & brn .50 .20
155 A36 15fr sep, dl org & dk bl .60 .20
156 A36 20fr dp bl & multi .80 .20
Nos. 153-156 (4) 2.35 .80

Order of the
Revolution and
Map — A37

Learning
the
Alphabet
A38

Design: 45fr, Harvesting and loading sugar
cane, and sugar mill.

Perf. 12x12½, 12½x12
1967, Mar. 15 Photo.
157 A37 20fr org & multi .50 .30
158 A38 25fr blk, ocher & dk car .60 .35
159 A38 45fr blk, yel grn & lt bl 1.00 .30
Nos. 157-159 (3) 2.10 .95

Issued to honor the members of the Order
of the Revolution (20fr); to publicize the literacy campaign (25fr); to publicize, sugar production (45fr).

Mahatma
Gandhi — A39

Fruit
Vendor — A40

1967, Apr. 21 Engr. Perf. 13
160 A39 90fr bl & blk 2.25 .75

Issued in memory of Mohandas K. Gandhi
(1869-1948), Hindu nationalist leader.

1967, June Photo. Perf. 13x12½

Dolls: 5fr, "Elegant Lady." 25fr, Woman
pounding saka-saka. 30fr, Mother and child.

161 A40 5fr gold & multi .25 .20
162 A40 10fr yel grn & multi .45 .20
163 A40 15fr lt ultra & multi .50 .20
164 A40 30fr multicolored .60 .20
Nos. 161-164 (4) 1.80 .80

ITY
Emblem,
Village and
Waterfall
A41

1967, July 5 Engr. Perf. 13
165 A41 60fr rose cl, org & ol grn .70 .40

Issued for International Tourist Year, 1967.

Symbols of
Cooperation
A42

Arms of
Brazzaville
A43

Europafrica Issue, 1967
1967, July 20 Photo. Perf. 12x12½
166 A42 50fr multicolored .90 .30

1967, Aug. 15 Litho. Perf. 12½x13
167 A43 30fr yel & multi .60 .35

Fourth anniversary of the revolution.

UN Emblem,
Dove and
People — A44

Boy and
UNICEF
Emblem — A45

1967, Oct. 24 Photo. Perf. 13x12½
168 A44 90fr bl, dk brn, red brn &
yel 1.60 .60

Issued for United Nations Day, Oct. 24.

1967, Dec. 11 Engr. Perf. 13
169 A45 90fr mar, blk & ultra 1.60 .60

21st anniv. of UNICEF.

Albert
Luthuli,
Dove and
Globe
A46

1968, Jan. 29 Engr. Perf. 13
170 A46 30fr brt grn & ol bis .60 .35

Albert Luthuli (1899-1967) of South Africa,
winner of 1960 Nobel Peace Prize.

Arms of Pointe
Noire — A47

1968, Feb. 20 Litho. Perf. 12½x13
171 A47 10fr brt pink & multi .50 .30

Motherhood
A48

Mayombe
Viaduct
A49

1968, May 25   Engr.   Perf. 13
172 A48 15fr dk car rose, sky bl &
          blk   .50   .30
Issued for Mother's Day.

1968, June 24
173 A49 45fr maroon, slate grn &
          bl   1.75 .45

A50

1968, July 29 Photo.   Perf. 13x12½
174 A50 5fr Daimler, 1889   .45   .20
175 A50 20fr Berliet, 1897   .90   .30
176 A50 60fr Peugeot, 1898   1.75   .40
177 A50 80fr Renault, 1900   2.75   .70
178 A50 85fr Fiat, 1902   3.25   .90
     Nos. 174-178,C67-C68 (7)   17.85 6.00

Tanker, Refinery and Map of Area
Served — A50a

1968, July 30   Perf. 12½
179 A50a 30fr multicolored   .80   .30
Issued to commemorate the opening of the
Port Gentil (Gabon) Refinery, June 12, 1968.

WHO Emblem and
Tree of Life — A51

1968, Nov. 28   Engr.   Perf. 13
180 A51 25fr dk grn, red & dp lil   .50   .30
20th anniv. of WHO.

Development Bank Issue
Common Design Type
1969, Sept. 10   Engr.   Perf. 13
181 CD130 25fr car rose, grn &
           ocher   .35   .20
182 CD130 30fr bl, grn & ocher   .35   .20

Bicycle
A52

Bicycles & Motorcycles: 75fr, Hirondelle.
80fr, Folding bicycle. 85fr, Peugeot. 100fr,
Excelsior Manxman. 150fr, Norton. 200fr,

Brough Superior "Old Bill." 300fr, Matchless
and N.L.G.-J.A.P.S.

1969, Oct. 6   Engr.   Perf. 13
183 A52 50fr multicolored   1.25   .30
184 A52 75fr multicolored   1.50   .30
185 A52 80fr multicolored   1.75   .40
186 A52 85fr multicolored   2.00   .50
187 A52 100fr multicolored   3.00   .85
188 A52 150fr multicolored   4.00 1.00
189 A52 200fr multicolored   5.25 1.75
190 A52 300fr multicolored   9.50 2.75
     Nos. 183-190 (8)   28.25 7.85

Mayombe
Train and
Tourist Year
Emblem
A53

40fr, Train and Mbamba Tunnel, vert.

Perf. 13x12½, 12½x13
1969, Oct. 20   Photo.
191 A53 40fr multicolored   1.50   .40
192 A53 60fr multicolored   2.50   .65
Issued for African Tourist Year.

Loutete
Cement
Works
A54

Loutete Cement Works: 15fr, Mixing tower,
vert. 25fr, Cable transport, vert. 30fr, General
view of plant.

1969, Dec. 10   Engr.   Perf. 13
193 A54 10fr dk gray, rose cl &
          dk ol   .25   .20
194 A54 15fr Prus bl, red brn &
          pur   .50   .20
195 A54 25fr mar, brn & Prus bl   .60   .20
196 A54 30fr vio brn, ultra & blk   .70   .20
a.   Min. sheet of 4, #193-196   2.75 2.75
      Nos. 193-196 (4)   2.05   .80

ASECNA Issue
Common Design Type
1969, Dec. 12
197 CD132 100fr dull brown   1.60   .40

Pineapple
Harvest
and ILO
Emblem
A55

30fr, Worker at lathe and ILO emblem.

1969, Dec. 20   Engr.   Perf. 13
198 A55 25fr bl, olive & brn   .35   .25
199 A55 30fr rose red, choc & slate .50   .25
50th anniv. of the ILO.

SOTEXCO
Textile
Plant,
Kinsoundi
A56

20fr, Women in spinnery. 25fr, Hand-print-
ing textiles. 30fr, Checking woven cloth.

1970, Jan. 20
200 A56 15fr grn, blk & lil   .45   .20
201 A56 20fr plum, car & sl grn   .45   .20
202 A56 25fr bl, slate & brn   .60   .20
203 A56 30fr gray, car rose & brn   .60   .25
     Nos. 200-203 (4)   2.10   .85

Hotel
Cosmos,
Brazzaville
A57

1970, Jan. 30
204 A57 90fr slate grn, bl & red
          brn   1.25   .30

**The status of the three sets for
Kennedy, etc., Summer Olympics,
and Baroque paintings is not certain.**

Linzolo
Church — A58

Diosso
Gorge
A59

Design: 90fr, Foulakari waterfall.

1970   Engr.   Perf. 13
205 A58 25fr multicolored   .60   .20
206 A59 70fr multicolored   1.50   .30
207 A59 90fr multicolored   2.25   .40
     Nos. 205-207 (3)   4.35   .90
Issue dates: 25fr, Feb. 10; others, Feb. 25.

Volvaria
Esculenta — A60

Mushrooms: 10fr, Termitomyces entolo-
moides. 15fr, Termitomyces microcarpus. 25fr,
Termitomyces aurantiacus. 30fr, Termitomyces mammiformis. 50fr, Tremella
fuciformis.

1970, Mar. 31   Photo.   Perf. 13
208 A60 5fr multicolored   6.75 1.00
209 A60 10fr multicolored   9.00 1.40
210 A60 15fr multicolored   13.50 2.00
211 A60 25fr multicolored   22.50 4.00
212 A60 30fr multicolored   32.50 5.75
213 A60 50fr multicolored   70.00 10.00
     Nos. 208-213 (6)   154.25 24.15

Laying
Coaxial
Cable
A61

Design: 30fr, Full view of rail car; 3 cable
layers on railway roadbed.

1970, Apr. 30   Engr.   Perf. 13
214 A61 25fr dk brn & multi   1.00   .30
215 A61 30fr brn & multi   1.10   .60
Issued to publicize the laying of the coaxial
cable linking Brazzaville and Pointe Noire.
For surcharges see Nos. 263-264.

UPU Headquarters Issue
Common Design Type
1970, May 20
216 CD133 30fr dk pur, gray & mag .70 .25

Mother Feeding
Child — A62

Dag
Hammarskjold,
UN
Emblem — A63

Design: 90fr, Mother nursing infant.

1970, May 30   Photo.
217 A62 85fr vio bl & multi   1.00   .30
218 A62 90fr lil & multi   1.10   .40
Issued for Mother's Day.

1970, June 20   Engr.   Perf. 13
UN Emblem and: No. 220, Trygve Lie,
horiz. No. 221, U Thant, horiz.
219 A63 100fr scar, dk red & dk
          pur   1.40   .80
220 A63 100fr dk red, ultra & ind   1.40   .80
221 A63 100fr grn, emer & dk
          red   1.40   .80
a.   Souv. sheet of 3, #219-221   5.50 5.50
      Nos. 219-221 (3)   4.20 2.40
25th anniv. of the UN and to honor its Sec-
retaries General.

Brillantaisia
Vogeliana
A64

Sternotomis
Variabilis — A65

Plants and Beetles: 2fr, Plectranthus decur-
rens. 3fr, Myrianthemum mirabile. 5fr, Con-
narus griffonianus. 15fr, Chelorrhina polyphe-
mus. 20fr, Metopodontus savagei.

Perf. 12½x12, 12x12½
1970, June 30   Photo.
222 A64 1fr dk grn & multi   .45   .25
223 A64 2fr multicolored   .45   .25
224 A64 3fr indigo & multi   .50   .25
225 A64 5fr lemon & multi   1.00   .25
226 A65 10fr lilac & multi   2.25   .40
227 A65 15fr orange & multi   3.00   .40
228 A65 20fr multicolored   3.25   .60
     Nos. 222-228 (7)   10.90 2.40
For surcharge see No. 288.

Stegosaurus — A66

Prehistoric Fauna: 20fr, Dinotherium, vert.
60fr, Brachiosaurus, vert. 80fr,
Arsinoitherium.

1970, July 20
229 A66 15fr dl grn, ocher & red
          brn   .80   .30
230 A66 20fr lt bl & multi   2.75   .65
231 A66 60fr lt bl & multi   5.75   .95
232 A66 80fr lt bl & multi   7.50 1.75
     Nos. 229-232 (4)   16.80 3.65

Mikado 141, 1932
A67

Locomotives: 60fr, Steam locomotive 130+032, 1947. 75fr, Alsthom BB 1100, 1962. 85fr, Diesel BB BB 302, 1969.

1970, Aug. 20   Engr.   Perf. 13
233	A67	40fr mag, bl grn & blk	2.75 .80
234	A67	60fr blk, bl & grn	3.00 .90
235	A67	75fr red, bl & blk	4.50 1.25
236	A67	85fr car, sl grn & ocher	7.00 1.75
		Nos. 233-236 (4)	17.25 4.70

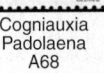

Cogniauxia Padolaena
A68

Green Night Adder
A69

Tropical Flowers: 2fr, Celosia cristata. 5fr, Plumeria acutifolia. 10fr, Bauhinia variegata. 15fr, Poinsettia. 20fr, Thunbergia grandiflora.

1971, Feb. 10   Photo.   Perf. 12x12½
237	A68	1fr lil & multi	.25 .20
238	A68	2fr yel & multi	.25 .20
239	A68	5fr ultra & multi	.25 .20
240	A68	10fr yel & multi	1.10 .20
241	A68	15fr multicolored	1.60 .30
242	A68	20fr dk red & multi	2.75 .40
		Nos. 237-242 (6)	6.20 1.50

Perf. 12x12½, 12½x12
1971, June 26   Photo.

Reptiles: 10fr, African Egg-eating snake, horiz. 15fr, Flap-necked chameleon. 20fr, Nile crocodile, horiz. 25fr, Rock python, horiz. 30fr, Gaboon viper. 40fr, Brown house snake, horiz. 45fr, Jameson's mamba.

243	A69	5fr multicolored	.40 .20
244	A69	10fr multicolored	.40 .20
245	A69	15fr multicolored	1.40 .20
246	A69	20fr red & multi	2.25 .25
247	A69	25fr grn & multi	3.00 .35
248	A69	30fr multicolored	3.75 .75
249	A69	40fr bis & multi	4.25 .95
250	A69	45fr multicolored	5.75 1.00
		Nos. 243-250 (8)	21.20 3.90

Pseudimbrasia Deyrollei — A70

Caterpillars: 15fr, Bunaea alcinoe, vert. 20fr, Epiphora vacuna ploetzi. 25fr, Imbrasia eblis. 30fr, Imbrasia dione, vert. 40fr, Holocera angulata.

1971, July 3   Perf. 13
251	A70	10fr ver, blk & grn	1.00 .20
252	A70	15fr multicolored	1.50 .30
253	A70	20fr yel grn, blk & ocher	2.25 .40
254	A70	25fr multicolored	3.50 .60
255	A70	30fr red, blk & yel	5.00 .90
256	A70	40fr bl, blk & org	6.75 1.25
		Nos. 251-256 (6)	20.00 3.65

Boy Scout — A70a

Scouts, Lord Baden-Powell — A70b

Designs: c, Scout facing left. d, Scout facing forward. e, Lord Baden-Powell.

Embossed on Metallic Foil
1971, July 14   Die Cut Perf. 10½
256A	A70a	90fr Block of 4, #b.-e, silver	10.00 10.00
256F	A70b	1000fr gold	30.00 30.00

No. 256F is airmail.

Cymothoe Sangaris
A71

Butterflies and Moths: 40fr, Papilio dardanus, vert. 75fr, Iolaus timon. 90fr, Papilio phorcas, vert. 100fr, Euchloron megaera.

1971, Oct. 15   Perf. 12½x12, 12x12½
257	A71	30fr yel & multi	1.75 .40
258	A71	40fr grn & multi	3.25 .65
259	A71	75fr multicolored	5.25 1.25
260	A71	90fr multicolored	7.00 1.90
261	A71	100fr ultra & multi	9.50 2.50
		Nos. 257-261 (5)	26.75 6.70

Black and White Men Working Together — A72

1971, Oct. 30   Perf. 13x12½
262	A72	50fr org & multi	.65 .35

Intl. Year Against Racial Discrimination.

Nos. 214-215 Surcharged

1971, Nov. 18   Engr.   Perf. 13
263	A61	30fr on 25fr multicolored	.50 .30
264	A61	40fr on 30fr multicolored	.75 .35

Inauguration of cable service between Brazzaville and Pointe Noire. Words of surcharge arranged differently on No. 264.

Map of Congo — A73

1971, Dec. 31   Photo.   Perf. 12½x13
265	A73	30fr bl & multi	.35 .20
266	A73	40fr yel grn & multi	.45 .20
267	A73	100fr gray & multi	1.10 .40
		Nos. 265-267 (3)	1.90 .80

"Labor, Democracy, Peace."

Lion — A74

2fr, African elephants. 3fr, Leopard. 4fr, Hippopotamus. 5fr, Gorilla, vert. 20fr, Potto. 30fr, De Brazza's monkey. 40fr, Pygmy chimpanzee, vert.

1972, Jan. 31   Engr.   Perf. 13
268	A74	1fr grn & multi	.35 .20
269	A74	2fr dk red & multi	.50 .20
270	A74	3fr red brn & multi	.80 .20
271	A74	4fr vio & multi	1.00 .20
272	A74	5fr brn & multi	1.10 .25
273	A74	20fr org & multi	2.75 .35
274	A74	30fr ocher & multi	3.50 .45
275	A74	40fr Prus bl & multi	5.25 .75
		Nos. 268-275 (8)	15.25 2.60

WHO, 25th Anniv. — A75

Perf. 12½x13, 13x12½
1973, June 30   Typo.
276	A75	40fr WHO Emblem	.60 .20
277	A75	50fr WHO emblem, horiz.	.70 .20

Kronenbourg Brewery — A76

Brewery Trademark and: 40fr, Laboratory. 75fr, Vats and controls. 85fr, Automatic control room. 100fr, Pressure room. 250fr, Bottling plant.

1973, July 15   Engr.   Perf. 13
278	A76	30fr red & multi	.50 .20
279	A76	40fr red & multi	.60 .20
280	A76	75fr red & multi	1.00 .30
281	A76	85fr red & multi	1.50 .40
282	A76	100fr red & multi	1.60 .55
283	A76	250fr red & multi	3.25 1.00
		Nos. 278-283 (6)	8.45 2.65

Kronenbourg Brewery, Brazzaville.

Golwe Locomotive, 1935 — A77

Locomotives: 40fr, Diesel, 1935. 75fr, Diesel Whithcomb, 1946. 85fr, Diesel CC200.

1973, Aug. 1   Engr.   Perf. 13
284	A77	30fr indigo & multi	2.00 .50
285	A77	40fr vio bl & multi	3.00 .85
286	A77	75fr multicolored	4.25 1.50
287	A77	85fr multicolored	5.50 2.75
		Nos. 284-287 (4)	14.75 5.60

No. 225 Surcharged and Overprinted in Ultramarine

1973, Aug. 16   Photo.   Perf. 12½x12
288	A64	100fr on 5fr multicolored	1.75 .60

African solidarity in drought emergency.

African Postal Union Issue
Common Design Type
1973, Sept. 12   Engr.   Perf. 13
289	CD137	100fr bl grn, vio & brn	1.50 .45

Bees, Beehive, Honeycomb
A78

1973, Dec. 10   Engr.   Perf. 13
290	A78	30fr sl grn, dk red & bl	1.10 .20
291	A78	40fr sl bl, sl grn & lt grn	1.50 .20

"Work and economy."

Family, UN and FAO Emblems
A79

40fr, Grain, emblems. 100fr, Grain, emblems, vert.

1973, Dec. 10
292	A79	30fr dk car & dk brn	.50 .20
293	A79	40fr dk grn, yel & ind	.60 .20
294	A79	100fr grn, brn & org	1.40 .40
		Nos. 292-294 (3)	2.50 .80

World Food Program, 10th anniversary.

Amilcar Cabral, Cattle and Child — A80

1974, July 15   Engr.   Perf. 13
295	A80	100fr multicolored	1.00 .60

First death anniversary of Amilcar Cabral (1924-1973), leader of anti-Portuguese guerrilla activity in Portuguese Guinea.

Félix Eboué, Cross of Lorraine
A81

1974, Aug. 31 **Litho.** **Perf. 13**
296 A81 30fr bl & multi .60 .30
297 A81 40fr brt pink & multi 1.00 .60

Félix A. Eboué (1884-1944), Governor of Chad, first colonial governor to join Free French in WWII, 30th death anniversary.

Pineapples
A82

1974, Nov. 12
298 A82 30fr shown .60 .30
299 A82 30fr Bananas .70 .30
300 A82 30fr Safous .70 .30
301 A82 40fr Avocados 1.25 .30
302 A82 40fr Mangos 1.25 .30
303 A82 40fr Papaya 1.25 .30
304 A82 40fr Orange 1.25 .30
Nos. 298-304 (7) 7.00 2.10

Charles de Gaulle and Conference Building — A83

1974, Nov. 25 **Engr.** **Perf. 13**
305 A83 100fr multicolored 3.25 1.90

Brazzaville Conference, 25th anniversary.

George Stephenson and Various Locomotives — A84

1974, Dec. 15
306 A84 75fr slate green & olive 4.00 1.00

George Stephenson (1781-1848), English inventor and railroad founder.

UDEAC Issue

Presidents and Flags of Cameroun, CAR, Congo, Gabon and Meeting Center — A84a

1974, Dec. 8 **Photo.** **Perf. 13**
307 A84a 40fr gold & multi .60 .20

See note after Cameroun No. 595.
See No. C195.

Irish Setter
A85

1974, Dec. 15 **Photo.** **Perf. 13x13½**
308 A85 30fr shown 1.25 .30
309 A85 40fr Borzoi 1.50 .30
310 A85 75fr Pointer 3.25 .75
311 A85 100fr Great Dane 4.50 .80
Nos. 308-311 (4) 10.50 2.15

1974, Dec. 15

Designs: Cats.

312 A85 30fr Havana chestnut 1.25 .30
313 A85 40fr Red Persian 1.50 .30
314 A85 75fr Blue British 3.25 .75
315 A85 100fr African serval 4.50 .80
Nos. 312-315 (4) 10.50 2.15

Labor Party Flags and People
A86

40fr, Hands holding flowers and tools.

1974, Dec. 31 **Engr.** **Perf. 13x12½**
316 A86 30fr red & multi .50 .20
317 A86 40fr red & multi .60 .25

5th anniversary of Congolese Labor Party and of introduction of red flag.

Symbols of Development — A87

U Thant and UN Headquarters — A88

Paul G. Hoffman and UN Emblem
A89

Perf. 13x12½, 12½x13
1975, Feb. 28 **Litho.**
318 A87 40fr multicolored .60 .25
319 A88 50fr light blue & multi .60 .25
320 A89 50fr yellow & multi .60 .25
Nos. 318-320 (3) 1.80 .75

National economic development.

Woman Breaking Bonds, Women's Activities, Map of Congo
A91

1975, June 20 **Litho.** **Perf. 12½**
322 A91 40fr gold & multi .60 .25

Revolutionary Union of Congolese Women, URFC, 10th anniversary.

CARA Soccer Team — A92

Design: 40fr, Team captain and manager receiving trophy, vert.

1975, July 15 **Litho.** **Perf. 12½**
323 A92 30fr multicolored .50 .25
324 A92 40fr multicolored .60 .25

CARA team, winners of African Soccer Cup 1974.

Citroen, 1935 — A93

Designs: Early autombiles.

1975, July 17 **Perf. 12**
325 A93 30fr shown .90 .40
326 A93 40fr Alfa Romeo, 1911 1.10 .40
327 A93 50fr Rolls Royce, 1926 1.40 .55
328 A93 75fr Duryea, 1893 2.75 .70
Nos. 325-328 (4) 6.15 2.05

Tipoye Transport — A94

1975, Aug. 5
329 A94 30fr shown .90 .40
330 A94 40fr Dugout canoe 1.00 .65

Traditional means of transportation.

Raising Red Flag — A95

1975, Aug. 15
331 A95 30fr shown .50 .20
332 A95 40fr National Conference .60 .25

2nd anniv. of installation of popular power (30fr) and 3rd anniv. of Natl. Conf. (40fr).

Line Fishing — A96

Woman Pounding "Foufou" — A97

Traditional Fishing: 30fr, Trap fishing, horiz. 60fr, Spear fishing. 90fr, Net fishing, horiz.

1975, Aug. 31 **Litho.** **Perf. 12**
333 A96 30fr multicolored .80 .25
334 A96 40fr multicolored .80 .30
335 A96 60fr multicolored 1.25 .50
336 A96 90fr multicolored 2.50 1.00
Nos. 333-336 (4) 5.35 2.05

1975, Sept. 5

Household Tasks: No. 338, Woman chopping wood. 40fr, Woman preparing manioc, horiz.

337 A97 30fr multicolored .60 .20
338 A97 30fr multicolored .60 .20
339 A97 40fr multicolored .90 .25
Nos. 337-339 (3) 2.10 .65

Musical Instruments
A98

1975, Sept. 20 **Perf. 12½**
340 A98 30fr Esanga .75 .20
341 A98 40fr Kalakwa 1.25 .25
342 A98 60fr Likembe 1.50 .30
343 A98 75fr Ngongui 2.00 .40
Nos. 340-343 (4) 5.50 1.15

Dzeke (Congolese) Shell Money — A99

Ancient Money: No. 346, like No. 344. Nos. 345, 347, Okengo, Congolese, iron bar. 40fr, Gallic coin, c. 60 B.C. 50fr, Roman denarius, 37 B.C. 60fr, Danubian coin, 2nd cent. B.C. 85fr, Greek stater, 4th cent. B.C.

1975-76 **Engr.** **Perf. 13**
344 A99 30fr red & multi .60 .20
345 A99 30fr vio & multi .60 .20
346 A99 35fr ol & multi .90 .25
347 A99 35fr dk car rose & multi .90 .25
348 A99 40fr Prus bl & brn .90 .20
349 A99 50fr Prus bl & ol 1.00 .20
350 A99 60fr dk grn & brn 1.25 .35
351 A99 85fr mag & sl grn 2.10 .45
Nos. 344-351 (8) 8.25 2.20

Nos. 346-347 inscribed "1976" and issued Mar. 1976; others issued Oct. 5, 1975.

1974, Dec. 15

Perf. 13
Map of China and Mao Tse-tung — A90

1975, Mar. 9 **Engr.** **Perf. 13**
321 A90 75fr multicolored 4.50 1.50
25th anniv. of the PRC.

Moschops — A100

Pre-historic Animals: 70fr, Tyrannosaurus.
95fr, Cryptocleidus. 100fr, Stegosaurus.

1975, Oct. 15   Litho.   Perf. 13
352 A100 55fr multicolored   2.25   .30
353 A100 75fr multicolored   3.25   .35
354 A100 95fr multicolored   5.75   .75
355 A100 100fr multicolored   8.00   1.25
    Nos. 352-355 (4)   19.25   2.65

Albert Schweitzer
(1875-1965),
Medical
Missionary — A101

1975, Oct. 15   Engr.
356 A101 75fr ol, brn & red   1.50   .40

Alexander
Fleming
A102

Designs: No. 358, André Marie Ampère.
No. 359, Clement Ader.

1975, Nov. 15   Engr.   Perf. 13
357 A102 60fr brn, grn & blk   1.00   .30
358 A102 95fr blk, red & grn   1.40   .40
359 A102 95fr red, blue & indigo   1.60   .40
    Nos. 357-359 (3)   4.00   1.10

Fleming (1881-1955), developer of penicillin; Ampère (1775-1836), physicist; Ader
(1841-1925), aviation pioneer.

UN Emblem "ONU" and "30" — A103

1975, Dec. 20   Engr.   Perf. 13
360 A103 95fr car, ultra & grn   1.25   .45
    United Nations, 30th anniversary.

Women's Broken Chain — A104

Design: 60fr, Equality between man and
woman, globe, IWY emblem.

1975, Dec. 20   Litho.   Perf. 12½
361 A104 35fr mag, ocher & gray   .60   .20
362 A104 60fr ultra, brn & blk   .70   .30
    International Women's Year, 1975.

Pres. Marien Ngouabi, Flag and
Workers — A105

Echo of the
P.C.T.
A106

1975, Dec. 31   Perf. 12½x12, 13x12½
363 A105 30fr multicolored   .50   .20
364 A106 35fr multicolored   .50   .20

6th anniversary of the Congolese Labor
Party (P.C.T.). See No. C215.

A.G. Bell
and 1876
Telephone
A107

1976, Apr. 25   Litho.   Perf. 12½x13
365 A107 35fr yel, brn & org brn   .50   .20

Cent. of 1st telephone call by Alexander
Graham Bell, Mar. 10, 1876. See No. C229.

Women
Selling Fruit
and
Vegetables
A108

1976, Sept. 19   Litho.   Perf. 12½x13
366 A108 35fr shown   .50   .20
367 A108 60fr Market scene   1.00   .30

Congolese
Coiffure — A109

Designs: Various women's hair styles.

1976, Oct. 10   Litho.   Perf. 13
368 A109 35fr multicolored   .60   .20
369 A109 60fr multicolored   1.00   .25
370 A109 95fr multicolored   1.50   .35
371 A109 100fr multicolored   2.00   .40
    Nos. 368-371 (4)   5.10   1.20

Pole Vault,
Map of
Central
Africa
A110

95fr, Long jump and map of Central Africa.

1976, Oct. 25   Perf. 12½
372 A110 60fr yel & multi   .70   .25
373 A110 95fr yel & multi   1.25   .40
    Nos. 372-373,C230-C231 (4)   6.45   2.50

Gold medalists, 1st Central African Games,
Yaoundé, July 27-30, 1975.

Antelope
A111

1976, Oct. 27   Litho.   Perf. 12½
Size: 36x36mm
374 A111 5fr shown   .55   .20
375 A111 10fr Buffalos   .65   .20
376 A111 15fr Hippopotamus   1.00   .30
377 A111 20fr Wart hog   2.00   .35
378 A111 25fr Elephants   2.25   .40
    Nos. 374-378 (5)   6.45   1.45

1976, Dec. 8
Designs: Birds.
Size: 26x36mm
379 A111 5fr Saddle-bill storks   1.00   .25
Size: 36x36mm
380 A111 10fr Malachite kingfish-
            er   1.25   .25
381 A111 20fr Crowned cranes   3.00   .60
    Nos. 379-381 (3)   5.25   1.10

Bicycling, Map of
Participants
A112

Heliotrope
A113

1976, Dec. 21   Photo.   Perf. 12½x13
382 A112 35fr shown   .35   .20
383 A112 60fr Fieldball   .60   .25
384 A112 80fr Running   1.00   .35
385 A112 95fr Soccer   1.25   .40
    Nos. 382-385 (4)   3.20   1.20

First Central African Games, Libreville,
Gabon, June-July 1976.

1976, Dec. 23   Photo.   Perf. 12½x13
Flowers: 5fr, Water lilies. 15fr, Bird-of-paradise flower.
386 A113 5fr multicolored   .25   .20
387 A113 10fr multicolored   .35   .20
388 A113 15fr multicolored   .60   .20
    Nos. 386-388 (3)   1.20   .60

Torch and
Olive
Branches
A114

1976, Dec. 25   Litho.   Perf. 12½x13
389 A114 35fr multicolored   .45   .20
    National Pioneer Movement.

The Spirit of '76 — A115

125fr, Pulling down George III statue. 150fr,
Battle of Princeton. 175fr, Generals of Revolu-
tionary War. 200fr, Burgoyne's surrender at
Saratoga. 500fr, Battle of Lexington.

1976, Dec. 29   Litho.   Perf. 14
390 A115 100fr multicolored   1.00   .25
391 A115 125fr multicolored   1.10   .35
392 A115 150fr multicolored   1.60   .40
393 A115 175fr multicolored   2.00   .50
394 A115 200fr multicolored   2.25   .60
    Nos. 390-394 (5)   7.95   2.10

Souvenir Sheet
395 A115 500fr multicolored   5.75   1.50
    American Bicentennial.

Dugout
Canoe
Race
A116

Design: 60fr, 2-man dugout canoes.

1977, Mar. 27   Litho.   Perf. 13x13½
396 A116 35fr multicolored   .60   .20
397 A116 60fr multicolored   1.00   .35
    Dugout canoe races on Congo River.

Lilan Goua
A117

Fresh-water Fish: 15fr, Liko ko. 25fr, Liyan
ga. 35fr, Mbessi. 60fr, Mongandza.

1977, June 15   Perf. 12½
398 A117 10fr multicolored   .75   .20
399 A117 15fr multicolored   .90   .20
400 A117 25fr multicolored   1.00   .30
401 A117 35fr multicolored   2.00   .30
402 A117 60fr multicolored   3.00   .45
    Nos. 398-402 (5)   7.65   1.35

Traditional Headdress — A118

1977, June 30   Litho.   Perf. 12½
403 A118 35fr shown   .45 .30
404 A118 60fr Leopard cap   .90 .35
    See Nos. C234-C235.

Bondjo Wrestling
A119

40fr, 50fr, Bondjo wrestling, diff. 40fr, horiz.

1977, July 15
405 A119 25fr multicolored   .50 .20
406 A119 40fr multicolored   .55 .20
407 A119 50fr multicolored   .65 .30
    Nos. 405-407 (3)   1.70 .70

"Schwaben" LZ 10, 1911 — A120

Zeppelins: 60fr, "Viktoria Luise." LZ 11, 1913. 100fr, LZ 120. 200fr, LZ 127. 300fr, "Graf Zeppelin II" LZ 130.

1977, Aug. 5   Litho.   Perf. 11
408 A120 40fr multicolored   .50 .20
409 A120 60fr multicolored   .75 .25
410 A120 100fr multicolored   1.25 .30
411 A120 200fr multicolored   2.50 .60
412 A120 300fr multicolored   4.00 .95
    Nos. 408-412 (5)   9.00 2.30

History of the Zeppelin. Exist imperf. See No. C236.

Coat of Arms and Rising Sun
A121

1977, Aug. 15
413 A121 40fr multicolored   .50 .20
    14th anniversary of the revolution.

Victor Hugo and The Hunchback of Notre Dame — A122

Designs (Hugo and): 60fr, Les Miserables. 100fr, Les Travailleurs de la Mer (octopus).

1977, Aug. 20   Engr.   Perf. 13
414 A122 35fr multicolored   .75 .30
415 A122 60fr multicolored   1.00 .30
416 A122 100fr multicolored   1.50 .45
    Nos. 414-416 (3)   3.25 1.05

Victor Hugo (1802-1885), French novelist.

Mao Tse-tung
A123

Lithographed; Gold Embossed
1977, Sept. 9   Perf. 12x12½
417 A123 400fr red & gold   12.00 7.00
    Chairman Mao Tse-tung (1893-1976), Chinese Communist leader, 1st death anniv.

Peter Paul Rubens
A124

1977, Sept. 20   Gold Embossed
418 A124 600fr gold & lt bl   15.00 7.50
    Peter Paul Rubens (1577-1640), painter.

Child Leading Blind Woman Across Street
A125

1977, Oct. 22   Litho.   Perf. 12½x13
419 A125 35fr multicolored   .60 .25
    World Health Day: To see is life.

Paul Kamba and Records
A126

1977, Oct. 29
420 A126 100fr multicolored   1.00 .45
    Paul Kamba (1912-1950), musician.

Trajan Vuia and Flying Machine — A127

Designs: 75fr, Louis Bleriot and plane. 100fr, Roland Garros and plane. 200fr, Charles Lindbergh and Spirit of St. Louis. 300fr, Tupolev Tu-144. 500fr, Lindbergh and Spirit of St. Louis over ship in Atlantic.

1977, Nov. 18   Litho.   Perf. 14
421 A127 60fr multicolored   .60 .20
422 A127 75fr multicolored   .90 .25
423 A127 100fr multicolored   1.10 .30
424 A127 200fr multicolored   2.25 .50
425 A127 300fr multicolored   3.25 .70
    Nos. 421-425 (5)   8.10 1.95

Souvenir Sheet
426 A127 500fr multicolored   5.75 1.25
    History of aviation.

Elizabeth II and Prince Philip
A128

Design: 300fr, Elizabeth II wearing Crown.

1977, Dec. 21
427 A128 250fr multicolored   2.25 .65
428 A128 300fr multicolored   2.75 .70
    Reign of Queen Elizabeth II, 25th anniv. See #C239. For overprints see #468-469, C244.

King Baudouin
A129

Design: No. 430, Charles de Gaulle.

1977, Dec. 21
429 A129 200fr multicolored   2.25 .65
430 A129 200fr multicolored   2.25 .65
    King Baudouin of Belgium and Charles de Gaulle, president of France.

Ambete Sculpture
A130

Congolese art: 85fr, Babembe sculpture.

1978, Feb. 18   Engr.   Perf. 13
431 A130 35fr lt brn & multi   .65 .25
432 A130 85fr lt grn & multi   1.50 .45

St. Simon, by Rubens
A131

Rubens Paintings: 140fr, Duke of Lerma. 200fr, Madonna and Saints. 300fr, Rubens and his Wife Helena Fourment. 500fr, Farm at Laeken.

1978, Mar. 7   Litho.   Perf. 13½x14
433 A131 60fr gold & multi   .60 .20
434 A131 140fr gold & multi   1.50 .30
435 A131 200fr gold & multi   2.25 .45
436 A131 300fr gold & multi   3.50 .65
    Nos. 433-436 (4)   7.85 1.60

Souvenir Sheet
437 A131 500fr gold & multi   5.75 1.40
    Peter Paul Rubens, 400th birth anniv.

Pres. Ngouabi and Microphones — A132

60fr, Ngouabi at his desk, horiz. 100fr, Portrait.

Perf. 12½x13, 13x12½
1978, Mar. 18   Litho.
438 A132 35fr multicolored   .45 .20
439 A132 60fr multicolored   .50 .25
440 A132 100fr multicolored   .90 .40
    Nos. 438-440 (3)   1.85 .85

Pres. Marien Ngouabi, 1st death anniv.

Ferenc Puskas and Argentina '78 Emblem — A133

Players and Emblem: 75fr, Giacinto Facchetti. 100fr, Bobby Moore. 200fr, Raymond Kopa. 300fr, Pele. 500fr, Franz Beckenbauer.

1978, Apr. 4   Perf. 14x13½
441 A133 60fr multicolored   .60 .20
442 A133 75fr multicolored   .70 .25
443 A133 100fr multicolored   1.10 .25
444 A133 200fr multicolored   2.25 .55
445 A133 300fr multicolored   3.25 .75
    Nos. 441-445 (5)   7.90 2.00

Souvenir Sheet
446 A133 500fr multicolored   6.25 1.25
    11th World Cup Soccer Championship, Argentina, June 1-25.
    For overprints see Nos. 481-486.

Pearl S. Buck and Chinese Women — A134

Nobel Prize winners: 75fr, Fridtjof Nansen, refugees and Nansen passport. 100fr, Henri Bergson, book and flame. 200fr, Alexander Fleming and Petri dish. 300fr, Gerhart Hauptmann and book. 500fr, Henri Dunant and Red Cross Station.

1978, Apr. 29
447	A134	60fr multicolored	.60	.25
448	A134	75fr multicolored	.70	.25
449	A134	100fr multicolored	1.10	.30
450	A134	200fr multicolored	2.00	.50
451	A134	300fr multicolored	2.75	.60
	Nos. 447-451 (5)		7.15	1.90

Souvenir Sheet
452	A134	500fr multicolored	5.75	1.40

African Buffalos A135

Endangered animals and Wildlife Fund Emblem: 35fr, Okapi, vert. 85fr, Rhinoceros. 150fr, Chimpanzee, vert. 200fr, Hippopotamus. 300fr, Buffon's kob, vert.

1978 Perf. 14½
453	A135	35fr multicolored	1.25	.45
454	A135	60fr multicolored	1.75	.55
455	A135	85fr multicolored	4.25	.85
456	A135	150fr multicolored	6.00	1.25
457	A135	200fr multicolored	8.00	1.75
458	A135	300fr multicolored	15.00	2.50
	Nos. 453-458 (6)		36.25	7.35

Issue dates: 35fr, Aug. 11; others, July 11.

Emblem, Young People, Gun and Fist — A136

1978, July 28 Perf. 12½
459	A136	35fr multicolored	.50	.30

11th World Youth Festival, Havana, 7/28-8/5.

Pyramids and Camels — A137

Seven Wonders of the Ancient World: 50fr, Hanging Gardens of Babylon. 60fr, Statue of Zeus, Olympia. 95fr, Colossus of Rhodes. 125fr, Mausoleum of Halicarnassus. 150fr, Temple of Artemis, Ephesus. 200fr, Lighthouse, Alexandria. 300fr, Map of Eastern Mediterranean showing locations. 50fr, 60fr, 95fr, 125fr, 200fr, vertical.

1978, Aug. 12 Litho. Perf. 14
460	A137	35fr multicolored	.50	.20
461	A137	50fr multicolored	.60	.20
462	A137	60fr multicolored	.75	.20
463	A137	95fr multicolored	1.00	.30

464	A137	125fr multicolored	1.25	.45
465	A137	150fr multicolored	1.75	.55
466	A137	200fr multicolored	2.25	.75
467	A137	300fr multicolored	3.25	1.00
	Nos. 460-467 (8)		11.35	3.65

Nos. 427-428 Overprinted in Silver: "ANNIVERSAIRE DU COURONNEMENT 1953-1978"

1978, Sept. Litho. Perf. 14
468	A128	250fr multicolored	2.25	.90
469	A128	300fr multicolored	2.75	1.25

25th anniversary of coronation of Queen Elizabeth II. See No. C244.

Kwame Nkrumah and Map of Africa — A138

1978, Sept. 23 Litho. Perf. 13x12½
470	A138	60fr multicolored	.60	.40

Nkrumah (1909-72), Pres. of Ghana.

Wild Boar Hunt — A139

Local hunting and fishing: 50fr, Fish smoking. 60fr, Hunter with spears and dog, vert.

1978 Litho. Perf. 12
471	A139	35fr multicolored	2.00	.25
472	A139	50fr multicolored	.60	.25
473	A139	60fr multicolored	3.00	.25
	Nos. 471-473 (3)		5.60	.75

Issue dates: 35fr, 60fr, Oct. 5; 50fr, Oct. 10.

View of Kalchreut, by Dürer — A140

Paintings by Dürer: 150fr, Elspeth Tucher, vert. 250fr, "The Great Piece of Turf," vert. 350fr, Self-portrait, vert.

1978, Nov. 23 Litho. Perf. 14
474	A140	65fr multicolored	.60	.20
475	A140	150fr multicolored	1.40	.35
476	A140	250fr multicolored	2.25	.65
477	A140	350fr multicolored	3.50	.90
	Nos. 474-477 (4)		7.75	2.10

Albrecht Dürer (1471-1528), German painter.

Basketmaker A141

Productive Labor: 90fr, Woodcarver. 140fr, Women hoeing field.

1978, Nov. 18 Litho. Perf. 12½
Size: 25x36mm
478	A141	85fr multicolored	.70	.40
479	A141	90fr multicolored	1.00	.40

Size: 27x48mm
Perf. 12
480	A141	140fr multicolored	1.50	.65
	Nos. 478-480 (3)		3.20	1.45

Nos. 441-446 Overprinted in Silver:
a. "1962 VAINQUEUR: BRESIL"
b. "1966 VAINQUEUR: / GRANDE BRETAGNE"
c. "1970 VAINQUEUR: / BRESIL"
d. "1974 VAINQUEUR: / ALLEMAGNE (RFA)"
e. "1978 VAINQUEUR: / ARGENTINE"
f. "ARGENTINE-PAYS BAS 3-1/25 juin 1978"

1978, Nov. Perf. 14x13½
481	A133 (a)	60fr multicolored	.60	.25
482	A133 (b)	75fr multicolored	.70	.35
483	A133 (c)	100fr multicolored	1.00	.45
484	A133 (d)	200fr multicolored	2.00	.65
485	A133 (e)	300fr multicolored	2.75	1.00
	Nos. 481-485 (5)		7.05	2.70

Souvenir Sheet
486	A133 (f)	500fr multicolored	5.75	2.40

Winners, World Soccer Cup Championships 1962-1978.

Heart and Charts A142

1978, Dec. 16 Engr. Perf. 13
487	A142	100fr multicolored	1.00	.45

Fight against hypertension.

Party Emblem and Road — A143

1978, Dec. 31 Litho. Perf. 12½x12
488	A143	60fr multicolored	.60	.25

Congolese Labor Party, 9th anniversary.

Capt. Cook, Polynesians and House — A144

Capt. James Cook (1728-1779): 150fr, Island scene. 250fr, Polynesian longboats. 350fr, Capt. Cook's ships off Hawaii.

1979, Jan. 16 Perf. 14½
489	A144	65fr multicolored	.60	.20
490	A144	150fr multicolored	1.40	.35
491	A144	250fr multicolored	2.25	.60
492	A144	350fr multicolored	3.50	1.00
	Nos. 489-492 (4)		7.75	2.15

Pres. Marien Ngouabi — A145

1979, Mar. 18 Litho. Perf. 12
493	A145	35fr multicolored	.35	.20
494	A145	60fr multicolored	.50	.25

Assassination of President Ngouabi, 2nd anniv.

"1979," IYC Emblem, Child A146

A146a

1979, Apr. 30 Litho. Perf. 12½x13
495	A146	45fr multicolored	.45	.20
496	A146	75fr multicolored	.90	.35

Souvenir Sheet
Perf. 14½
496A	A146a	250fr multicolored	2.75	1.00

International Year of the Child.
Issued: 45fr, 75fr, Apr. 30; 250fr, Sept. 5.

Pottery Vases and Solanum — A147

Design: 150fr, Mail runner, Concorde, train, UPU emblem, envelope.

1979, June 8 Litho. Perf. 13
497	A147	60fr multicolored	1.25	.60

Engr.
498	A147	150fr multicolored	2.75	1.25

Philexafrique II, Libreville, Gabon, June 8-17. Nos. 497, 498 each printed in sheets of 10 with 5 labels showing exhibition emblem.

Rowland Hill, Diesel Locomotive, Germany No. 78 — A148

Designs (Rowland Hill and): 100fr, Old steam locomotive and France No. B10. 200fr, Diesel locomotive and US No. 245. 300fr, Steam locomotive and England-Australia First Aerialpost vignette, 1919. 500fr, Electric train, Concorde and Middle Congo No. 75.

1979, June 30 Perf. 14
499	A148	65fr multicolored	.60	.20
500	A148	100fr multicolored	1.00	.25
501	A148	200fr multicolored	2.25	.50
502	A148	300fr multicolored	2.75	.75
	Nos. 499-502 (4)		6.60	1.70

Souvenir Sheet
503	A148	500fr multicolored	5.75	1.25

Sir Rowland Hill (1795-1879), originator of penny postage.

Salvador Allende, Flags,
Demonstrators — A149

1979, July 21   Litho.   Perf. 12½
504 A149 100fr multicolored   1.00 .45
Salvador Allende, president of Chile.

Old Man Telling Stories — A150

1979, July 28
505 A150 45fr multicolored   .60 .25
Story telling as education.

Handball
Players
A151

75fr, Players and ball. 250fr, Pres. Ngouabi,
cup on map of Africa, player.

1979, July 31   Litho.   Perf. 12½
Size: 40x30mm, 30x40mm
506 A151 45fr multi   .60 .20
507 A151 75fr multi, vert.   1.00 .25
Size: 22x40mm
Perf. 12x12½
508 A151 250fr multicolored   2.75 1.00
Marien Ngouabi Handball Cup.

Map and Flag of
Congo — A152

1979, Aug. 15
509 A152 50fr multicolored   .45 .25
16th anniversary of revolution.

Souvenir Sheet

Virgin and Child, by Dürer — A153

1979, Aug. 13   Perf. 13½
510 A153 500fr red brn & lt grn   6.50 2.50
Albrecht Dürer (1471-1528), German
engraver and painter.

Bach and Contemporary
Instruments — A155

#512, Albert Einstein, astronauts on moon.

1979, Sept. 10   Perf. 13½
511 A155 200fr multicolored   2.25 .75
512 A155 200fr multicolored   2.25 .75

Yoro
Fishing
Port
A156

1979, Sept. 26   Litho.   Perf. 12½
513 A156 45fr shown   .60 .20
514 A156 75fr Port at night   .90 .35

Mukukulu Dam — A157

1979, Oct. 5   Perf. 12½x12
515 A157 20fr multicolored   .25 .20
516 A157 45fr multicolored   .70 .25

Emblem,
Control
Tower, Jets
A158

1979, Dec. 12   Litho.   Perf. 12½
517 A158 100fr multicolored   1.10 .50
ASECNA (Air Safety Board), 20th anniv.

Congolese
Labor
Party, 10th
Anniversary
A159

1979, Dec. 31
518 A159 45fr multicolored   .45 .20

A160

A161

1980, Mar. 30   Litho.   Perf. 12½
519 A160 45fr multicolored   .45 .20
520 A160 95fr multicolored   .90 .30
Post Office, 15th Anniversary.

1980, May 5
521 A161 100fr multicolored   3.50 1.00
Visit of Pope John Paul II.

Rotary International, 75th
Anniversary — A162

1980, May 10   Litho.   Perf. 12½
522 A162 150fr multicolored   1.50 .50

Pointe
Noire
Foundry
A163

1980, June 18   Litho.   Perf. 12½
523 A163 30fr shown   .20 .20
524 A163 35fr Different view   .50 .20

Claude Chappe, Tower — A164

1980, June 21   Litho.   Perf. 12½
525 A164 200fr multicolored   2.25 1.00
Claude Chappe (1763-1805), French
engineer.

Mossaka Harbor — A165

1980, June 23
532 A165 45fr shown   .50 .20
533 A165 90fr Different view   1.00 .25

Papilio Dardanus
(Front and
Back) — A167

Human Rights
Emblem,
People — A169

July 31st Hospital — A168

1980, July 12   Litho.   Perf. 12½
534 A167 5fr shown   .80 .30
535 A167 15fr Kalima aethi-
                 ops   1.50 .30
536 A167 20fr Papilio
                 demodocus   1.50 .40
537 A167 60fr Euphaedra   4.00 .75
538 A167 90fr Hypolimnas
                 misippus   7.25 1.00
     Nos. 534-538 (5)   15.05 2.75
Souvenir Sheet
539 A167 300fr Charaxes
                 smaragdalis   20.00 17.00
Nos. 534-536 also exist perf 12½x13. Values the same.

1980, July 31
540 A168 45fr multicolored   .60 .25

1980, Aug. 2
541 A169 350fr shown   2.75 1.00
542 A169 500fr Man breaking
                 chain   4.50 1.50
Human Rights Convention, 32nd anniv.

Citizens
and
Congolese
Arms
A170

1980, Aug. 15   Perf. 12½
543 A170 75fr shown   .70 .30
544 A170 95fr Dove on flag,
                 fists, vert.   .90 .30
545 A170 150fr Dove holding
                 Congolese arms   1.40 .60
     Nos. 543-545 (3)   3.00 1.20
August 13-15th Revolution, 17th anniv.

Coffee and Cocoa Trees on Map of Congo — A171

Coffee and Cocoa Day: 95fr, Branches, map of Congo.

1980, Aug. 18   *Perf. 13½x13*
546 A171 45fr multicolored   .50 .20
547 A171 95fr multicolored   1.00 .40

Logging A172

1980, Aug. 28
548 A172 70fr shown   .80 .30
549 A172 75fr Wood transport   .80 .30

Pres. Neto of Angola, 1st Death Anniv. — A173   Lark — A174

1980, Sept. 11
550 A173 100fr multicolored   .90 .30

1980, Sept. 17

Designs: Birds.

551 A174 45fr multi, horiz.   1.00 .30
552 A174 75fr multi, horiz.   1.25 .30
553 A174 90fr multi, horiz.   1.50 .35
554 A174 150fr multicolored   2.25 .50
555 A174 200fr multicolored   3.25 1.00
556 A174 250fr multicolored   3.75 1.25
   a   Souv. sheet of 6, #551-556   5.00 5.00
    Nos. 551-556 (6)   13.00 3.70

World Tourism Conference, Manila, Sept. 27 — A175

1980, Sept. 27   Litho.   *Perf. 13½x13*
557 A175 100fr multicolored   .90 .35

First Day of School Term — A176

1980, Oct. 2   Photo.   *Perf. 13*
558 A176 50fr multicolored   .50 .20

First House in Brazzaville — A177

Brazzaville Centenary: 65fr, First native village. 75fr, Old Town Hall, 1912. 150fr, View from bank of Bacongo, 1912. 200fr, Meeting of explorer Savorgnan de Brazza and chief Makoko, 1880.

1980, Oct. 3   Litho.   *Perf. 12½*
559 A177 45fr multicolored   .50 .20
560 A177 65fr multicolored   .70 .30
561 A177 75fr multicolored   1.00 .40
562 A177 150fr multicolored   1.75 .65
563 A177 200fr multicolored   2.25 1.00
    Nos. 559-563 (5)   6.20 2.55

Boys on Bank of Congo River — A178

1980, Oct. 30
564 A178 80fr shown   .70 .25
565 A178 150fr Djoue Bridge   1.60 .40

Revolutionary Stadium and Athletes — A179

1980, Nov. 20   *Perf. 13x12½*
566 A179 60fr multicolored   .70 .25

Rebuilt Railroad Bridge over Congo River A180

1980, Nov. 29   *Perf. 13x13½*
567 A180 75fr multicolored   .90 .30

Mangoes, Loudima Fruit Packing Station A181

1980, Dec. 2   *Perf. 13*
568 A181 10fr shown   .25 .20
569 A181 25fr Oranges   .50 .20
570 A181 40fr Citrons   .60 .20
571 A181 85fr Mandarins   1.10 .30
    Nos. 568-571 (4)   2.45 .90

African Postal Union, 5th Anniversary A182

1980, Dec. 24   *Perf. 13½*
572 A182 100fr multicolored   .90 .30

Moungouni Earth Satellite Station A183

1980, Dec. 30   *Perf. 12½*
573 A183 75fr multicolored   .60 .20

Hertzian Wave Communication, Brazzaville — A184

1980, Dec. 30   *Perf. 12½x12*
574 A184 150fr multicolored   1.25 .40

1980 African Handball Champion Team — A185

Perf. 12½x13, 13x12½
1981, Jan. 26   Litho.
575 A185 100fr Receiving cup, vert.   1.10 .35
576 A185 150fr shown   1.30 .60

Pres. Denis Sassou-Nguesso — A186

1981, Feb. 5   Litho.   *Perf. 12½*
577 A186 45fr multicolored   .45 .20
578 A186 75fr multicolored   .60 .20
579 A186 100fr multicolored   .90 .25
    Nos. 577-579 (3)   1.95 .65

Columbia Space Shuttle Orbiting Earth — A187

Space Conquest: 100fr, Luna 17, 1970. 200fr, 300fr, 500fr, Columbia space shuttle, 1981.

1981, May 4   Litho.   *Perf. 14x13½*
580 A187 100fr multicolored   1.00 .25
581 A187 150fr multicolored   1.40 .40
582 A187 200fr multicolored   2.00 .55
583 A187 300fr multicolored   2.75 .80
    Nos. 580-583 (4)   7.15 2.00
    Souvenir Sheet
584 A187 500fr multicolored   5.00 1.40
    For overprint see No. 725.

Fight Against Apartheid — A188

Twin Palm Tree of Louingui — A189

1981, May 5   Litho.   *Perf. 12½*
585 A188 100fr deep blue   .90 .25

1981, May 22   *Perf. 12x12½*
586 A189 75fr multicolored   1.00 .25

13th World Telecommunications Day — A190

1981, June 6   *Perf. 12½*
587 A190 120fr multicolored   1.25 .30

Rubber Extraction — A191

1981, June 27   *Perf. 13*
588 A191 50fr shown   .60 .20
589 A191 70fr Sap draining   .90 .30

Intl. Year of the Disabled
A192

1981, June 29   **Engr.**
590 A192 45fr multicolored   .45 .20
See No. B7.

Bird Trap — A194

Designs: Animal traps. 10fr vert.

1981, July
596 A194 5fr multicolored   1.10 .20
597 A194 10fr multicolored   1.10 .20
598 A194 15fr multicolored   1.10 .20
599 A194 20fr multicolored   1.10 .20
600 A194 30fr multicolored   1.60 .25
601 A194 35fr multicolored   2.25 .30
   Nos. 596-601 (6)   8.25 1.35

Mausoleum of King Maloango — A195

1981, July 4   **Litho.**   **Perf. 12½**
602 A195 75fr shown   .70 .20
603 A195 150fr Mausoleum, por-
       trait   1.25 .40

Prince Charles and Lady Diana, Coach
A196

Royal wedding: Couple and coaches.

1981, Sept. 1   **Litho.**   **Perf. 14½**
604 A196 100fr multicolored   1.00 .25
605 A196 200fr multicolored   2.00 .55
606 A196 300fr multicolored   3.25 .80
   Nos. 604-606 (3)   6.25 1.60

Souvenir Sheet
607 A196 400fr multicolored   4.00 1.10

World Food Day — A197

1981, Oct. 16   **Litho.**   **Perf. 13½x13**
608 A197 150fr multicolored   1.40 .55

12th World UPU Day
A198

1981, Oct. 24   **Engr.**   **Perf. 13x12½**
609 A198 90fr multicolored   .90 .25

Royal Guard
A199

1981, Oct. 31   **Litho.**   **Perf. 12½x13**
610 A199 45fr multicolored   .60 .20

Eradication of Manioc Beetle — A200

Natl. Red Cross — A201

1981, Nov. 18   **Litho.**   **Perf. 12½**
611 A200 75fr multicolored   1.00 .25

1981, Nov. 18   **Perf. 13**
612 A201 10fr Bandaging patient   .20 .20
613 A201 35fr Treating child   .45 .20
614 A201 60fr Drawing well water   .70 .25
   Nos. 612-614 (3)   1.35 .65

Giant Baobab ("Tree of Savorgnan de Brazza")
A202

1981, Dec. 19   **Litho.**   **Perf. 13**
615 A202 45fr multicolored   .90 .20
616 A202 75fr multicolored   1.25 .30

Fetish Figure — A203

Designs: Various carved figures.

1981, Dec. 19   **Perf. 13x12½**
617 A203 15fr multicolored   .20 .20
618 A203 25fr multicolored   .25 .20
619 A203 45fr multicolored   .45 .20

620 A203 50fr multicolored   .60 .20
621 A203 60fr multicolored   .70 .20
   Nos. 617-621 (5)   2.20 1.00

Nos. 617, 618 and 620 also exist perf 12½x13. Values the same.

Caves of Bangou
A204

1981, Dec. 29   **Perf. 13x13½**
622 A204 20fr multicolored   .45 .20
623 A204 25fr multicolored   .45 .20

King Makoko and His Queen, Ivory Sculptures by R. Engongodzo — A205

Perf. 13½x13, 13x13½
1982, Feb. 27   **Litho.**
624 A205 25fr Woman, vert.   .35 .20
625 A205 35fr Woman, diff.,
       vert.   .45 .20
626 A205 100fr shown   1.00 .30
   Nos. 624-626 (3)   1.80 .70

George Stephenson (1781-1848) and Inter City 125, Gt. Britain — A206

Locomotives: 150fr, Sinkansen Bullet Train, Japan. 200fr, Advanced Passenger Train, Gt. Britain. 300fr, TGV-001, France.

1982, Mar. 2   **Litho.**   **Perf. 12½**
627 A206 100fr multicolored   1.00 .25
628 A206 150fr multicolored   1.60 .40
629 A206 200fr multicolored   2.25 .55
630 A206 300fr multicolored   3.25 .80
   Nos. 627-630 (4)   8.10 2.00

Scouting Year
A207

1982, Apr. 13   **Litho.**   **Perf. 13**
631 A207 100fr Looking through
       binoculars   1.25 .25
632 A207 150fr Reading map   1.50 .40
633 A207 200fr Helping woman   2.25 .55
634 A207 300fr Crossing rope
       bridge   3.25 .80
   Nos. 631-634 (4)   8.25 2.00

Souvenir Sheet
635 A207 500fr Hiking, horiz.   5.00 1.75
   For overprint see No. 726.

Franklin Roosevelt
A208

1982, June 12   **Litho.**   **Perf. 13**
636 A208 150fr shown   1.75 .60
637 A208 250fr Washington   2.75 .85
638 A208 350fr Goethe   3.75 1.10
   Nos. 636-638 (3)   8.25 2.55

21st Birthday of Princess Diana, July 1 — A209

1982, June 12   **Perf. 14**
639 A209 200fr Candles   2.00 .55
640 A209 300fr "21"   2.75 .80

Souvenir Sheet
641 A209 500fr Diana   5.00 1.40

5-Year Plan, 1982-1986
A210

Perf. 13x12½, 12½x13
1982, June 19
642 A210 60fr Road construc-
       tion   .70 .20
643 A210 100fr Communications,
       vert.   1.10 .30
644 A210 125fr Operating room
       equipment, vert.   1.40 .35
645 A210 150fr Hydroelectric
       power, vert.   1.60 .40
   Nos. 642-645 (4)   4.80 1.25

ITU Plenipotentiary Conference, Nairobi — A211

1982, June 26   **Perf. 13**
646 A211 300fr multicolored   2.75 .90

Nos. 604-607 Overprinted in Blue: "NAISSANCE ROYALE 1982"
1982, July 30   **Perf. 14½**
647 A196 100fr multicolored   .90 .30
648 A196 200fr multicolored   1.75 .60
649 A196 300fr multicolored   2.75 1.00
   Nos. 647-649 (3)   5.40 1.90

Souvenir Sheet
650 A196 400fr multicolored   3.50 2.50
   Birth of Prince William of Wales, June 21.

Nutrition Campaign A212

1982, July 24   Litho.   Perf. 12½
651 A212 100fr multicolored   1.00   .25

WHO African Headquarters, Brazzaville — A213

1982, July 24   Litho.   Perf. 12½
652 A213 125fr multicolored   1.00   .45

TB Bacillus Centenary — A214

1982, Aug. 7   Perf. 12½x12
653 A214 250fr Koch, bacillus   3.00   1.10

Pres. Sassou-Nguesso and 1980 Simba Prize — A215

1982, Oct. 20   Litho.   Perf. 13
654 A215 100fr multicolored   .90   .30

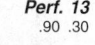
Turtles — A216

Various turtles and tortoises.

1982, Dec. 1
655 A216 30fr multicolored   .75   .20
656 A216 45fr multicolored   1.00   .25
657 A216 55fr multicolored   1.50   .30
    Nos. 655-657 (3)   3.25   .75

Boy Gathering Coconuts — A217

Nest in Tree Trunk — A218

1982, Dec. 11
658 A217 100fr multicolored   .90   .30

1982, Dec. 29   Perf. 12½
659 A218 40fr shown   1.25   .20
660 A218 75fr Nests in palm tree   1.50   .20
661 A218 100fr Woven nest on thorn branch   1.60   .25
    Nos. 659-661 (3)   4.35   .65

Hertzian Wave Communication Network — A219

1982, Dec. 30   Perf. 13x12½
662 A219 45fr multicolored   .45   .20
663 A219 60fr multicolored   .50   .20
664 A219 95fr multicolored   .90   .30
    Nos. 662-664 (3)   1.85   .70

30th Anniv. of Customs Cooperation Council — A220

1983, Jan. 26   Litho.   Perf. 12½x13
665 A220 100fr Headquarters   .90   .30

Mausoleum of Pres. Marien Ngouabi — A221

1983, Feb. 8   Perf. 13
666 A221 60fr multicolored   .50   .20
667 A221 80fr multicolored   .80   .20

Ironsmiths — A222

1983   Perf. 12½
668 A222 45fr shown   .50   .20
669 A222 150fr Weaver, vert.   1.25   .50
Issue dates: 45fr, Mar. 5; 150fr, Feb. 24.

Carved Chess Pieces, by R. Engongonzo — A223

Various pieces.

1983, Feb. 26   Perf. 13
670 A223 40fr multicolored   .40   .20
671 A223 60fr multicolored   1.00   .20
672 A223 95fr multicolored   2.00   .50
    Nos. 670-672 (3)   3.40   .90

Easter 1983 A224

Raphael drawings. 200fr, 400fr vert.

1983, Apr. 20   Litho.   Perf. 13
673 A224 200fr Transfiguration study   2.00   .50
674 A224 300fr Deposition from Cross   3.25   .65
675 A224 400fr Christ in Glory   4.50   .85
    Nos. 673-675 (3)   9.75   2.00

Seashells A225

1983   Litho.   Perf. 15x14
675A A225 25fr multicolored   150.00   65.00
676 A225 35fr multicolored   1.25   .30
677 A225 65fr multicolored   1.60   .35
Dated 1982.

A226   A227

Various traditional combs.

1983, May   Perf. 14
678 A226 30fr multicolored   .35   .20
679 A226 70fr multicolored   .90   .20
680 A226 85fr multicolored   1.00   .20
    Nos. 678-680 (3)   2.25   .60

Litho. & Engr.
1983, Aug. 10   Perf. 12½x13
681 A227 60fr multicolored   .45   .20
682 A227 100fr multicolored   .90   .30
    20th anniv. of revolution.

Centenary of the Arrival of Christian Missionaries — A228

Churches and Clergymen: 150fr, A. Carrie, Church of the Sacred Heart, Loango, vert. 250fr, Msgr. Augouard; St. Louis, Liranga; St. Joseph, Linzolo.

1983, Aug. 23   Perf. 12½
683 A228 150fr multicolored   1.60   .40
684 A228 250fr multicolored   2.75   .70

Local Flowers — A229

1984, Jan. 20   Litho.   Perf. 12½
685 A229 5fr Liana thunderaie, vert.   .20   .20
686 A229 15fr Bougainvillea   .35   .20
687 A229 20fr Anthurium, vert.   .50   .20
688 A229 45fr Allamanda   1.00   .20
689 A229 75fr Hibiscus, vert.   1.40   .30
    Nos. 685-689 (5)   3.45   1.10

35th Anniv. of World Peace Council A230

1984, Mar. 31   Litho.   Perf. 13x12½
690 A230 50fr multicolored   .45   .20
691 A230 100fr multicolored   .90   .30

Anti-Nuclear Arms Campaign A231

1984, May 31   Litho.   Perf. 12x12½
692 A231 200fr Explosion, victims   1.75   .50

Agriculture Day A232

Perf. 13x13½, 13½x13
1984, June 30 Litho.
693	A232	10fr Rice	.20	.20
694	A232	15fr Pineapples	.20	.20
695	A232	60fr Manioc, vert.	.60	.25
696	A232	100fr Palm tree, map, vert.	1.10	.35
		Nos. 693-696 (4)	2.10	1.00

Congress Palace — A233

1984, July 27 *Perf. 13*
697	A233	60fr multicolored	.50	.20
698	A233	100fr multicolored	.90	.30

Chinese-Congolese cooperation.

CFCO-Congo Railways, 50th Anniv. — A234

1984, July 30 *Perf. 13½*
699	A234	10fr Loulombo Station	.25	.20
700	A234	25fr Les Bandas Chinese Labor Camp	.45	.20
701	A234	125fr "50"	2.00	.70
702	A234	200fr Admin. bldg.	4.50	1.00
		Nos. 699-702 (4)	7.20	2.10

Locomotives — A235

Ships on the Congo River — A236

1984, Aug. 24 *Perf. 12½*
703	A235	100fr CC 203	1.10	.35
704	A236	100fr Tugboat	1.10	.35
705	A235	150fr BB 103	1.60	.50
706	A236	150fr Pusher tugboat	1.60	.50
707	A235	300fr BB-BB 301	3.25	1.10
708	A236	300fr Dredger	3.25	1.10
709	A235	500fr BB 420 L'Eclair	5.25	1.75
710	A236	500fr Cargo ship	5.25	1.75
		Nos. 703-710 (8)	22.40	7.40

World Fisheries Year A237

1984, Oct. 16 *Perf. 13½*
711	A237	5fr Basket of fish	.25	.20
712	A237	20fr Net fishermen in boat	.45	.20
713	A237	25fr School of fish	.60	.20
714	A237	40fr Net fisherman	1.00	.25
715	A237	55fr Trawler	1.60	.30
		Nos. 711-715 (5)	3.90	1.15

Anti-polio Campaign A238

M'Bamou Palace Hotel, Brazzaville A239

1984, Oct. 30
716	A238	250fr Disabled men, hand	2.75	.90
717	A238	300fr Target, disabled women, horiz.	3.25	1.00

1984, Dec. 15 *Perf. 14½*
718	A239	60fr multicolored	.45	.20
719	A239	100fr multicolored	.90	.30

Fauna A240

1984, Dec. *Perf. 15x14½*
720	A240	30fr Pangolin	3.75	.75
721	A240	70fr Bat	8.00	1.50
722	A240	85fr Civet cat	9.75	2.00
		Nos. 720-722 (3)	21.50	4.25

Congo River Logging A241

1984, Dec. *Perf. 13½x13*
723	A241	60fr Log raft, crew hut	.60	.25
724	A241	100fr Tugboat pushing logs	1.25	.35

Souvenir Sheets
Nos. 584, 635 Ovptd. with Exhibition in Black or Green

1985, Mar. 8 *Perf. 14x13½, 13*
725	A187	500fr TSUKUBA EXPO '85	5.75	4.50
726	A207	500fr ITALIA '85 emblem, ROME (G)	5.75	4.50

See Nos. C336-C337.

Zonocerus Variegatus — A242

1985, Mar. 15 *Perf. 13*
727	A242	125fr multicolored	1.75	.35

Burial of a Teke Chief — A243

1985, Apr. 30 *Perf. 12½*
728	A243	225fr multicolored	2.25	.75

Edible Fruit A244

Perf. 13½, 13 (#732A), 13½x13¼ (#732B)
1985, June 15
729	A244	5fr Trichoscypha acuminata, vert.	.20	.20
730	A244	10fr Aframomum africanum	.20	.20
730A	A244	90fr like #730		
731	A244	125fr Gambeya lacuurtiana	1.40	.40
732	A244	150fr Landolphia jumelei	1.75	.55
732A	A244	205fr like #731		
732B	A244	300fr Like #732	—	—

Sizes: #729, 22x36mm, #731, 732A, 36x22mm.
Nos. 730A, 732A, 732B inscribed "Congo" only.
For overprints, see Nos. 1170, 1183-1185.
Compare type A244 with type A352.

Lions Club Intl., 30th Anniv. — A245

1985, June 25 *Perf. 12½*
733	A245	250fr Flag, District 403B	2.25	.70

Russian Soldier, Kremlin, Fall of Berlin A246

1985, July 27 *Perf. 12*
734	A246	60fr multicolored	.50	.20

Defeat of Nazi Germany, end of World War II, 40th anniv.

Lady Olave Baden-Powell, Girl Guides Founder — A247

Anniversaries and events: 150fr, Girl Guides, 75th anniv. 250fr, Jacob Grimm, fabulist; Sleeping Beauty. 350fr, Johann Sebastian Bach, composer; European Music Year, St. Thomas Church organ, Leipzig. 450fr, Queen Mother, 85th birthday, vert. 500fr, Statue of Liberty, cent., vert.

1985, Aug. 26 *Perf. 13*
735	A247	150fr multicolored	1.60	.50
736	A247	250fr multicolored	2.25	.90
737	A247	350fr multicolored	2.75	1.25
738	A247	450fr multicolored	3.50	1.60
739	A247	500fr multicolored	5.00	2.00
		Nos. 735-739 (5)	15.10	6.25

PHILEXAFRICA '85, Lome, Togo, Nov. 16-24 — A248

1985, Oct. 10 *Perf. 13x12½*
740	A248	250fr shown	2.25	1.00
741	A248	250fr Airport, postal van	2.25	1.00
a.		Pair, #740-741 + label	5.25	5.25

Mushrooms — A249

1985, Dec. 14 Litho. *Perf. 13*
742	A249	100fr Coprinus, vert.	1.50	.35
743	A249	150fr Cortinarius	2.25	.50
744	A249	200fr Armillariella mellea	3.00	.85
745	A249	300fr Dictyophora	4.00	1.25
746	A249	400fr Crucibulum vulgare	6.00	1.50
		Nos. 742-746 (5)	16.75	4.45

Arbor Day — A250

Children's Hoop Races — A251

1986, Mar. 6 *Perf. 13½*
747	A250	60fr Planting sapling	.45	.20
748	A250	200fr Map, lifecycle diagram	1.90	.90

1986, Apr. 30 *Perf. 12½*
749	A251	5fr Two boys	.20	.20
750	A251	10fr One boy	.20	.20
751	A251	60fr Three boys, horiz.	.50	.20
a.		Souvenir sheet of 3, #749-751	1.25	1.00
		Nos. 749-751 (3)	.90	.60

A252

A253

1986, June 5   Litho.   Perf. 13½
752 A252 60fr Garbage disposal   .50   .20
753 A252 125fr Dumping garbage   1.00   .40

Intl. Environment Day.

1986, July 15   Litho.   Perf. 13x12½
Traditional Modes of Transporting Goods:
5fr, Basket on head, child in sling carrier. 10fr, Child in carrier on hip, large basket strapped to forehead. 60fr, Man carrying load on shoulder.
754 A253 5fr multicolored   .20   .20
755 A253 10fr multicolored   .60   .20
756 A253 60fr multicolored   .30   .20
      Nos. 754-756 (3)   1.10   .65

Mission of the Sisters of St. Joseph of Cluny, Cent. A254

1986, Aug. 19   Litho.   Perf. 12½x13
757 A254 230fr multicolored   2.40   1.25

A255

A256

1986, Aug. 30   Litho.   Perf. 13½
758 A255 40fr multicolored   .45   .20
759 A255 60fr multicolored   .55   .20
760 A255 100fr multicolored   1.00   .35
      Nos. 758-760 (3)   2.00   .75

UNESCO intl. communications development program.

1986, Sept. 15   Litho.   Perf. 13½
761 A256 100fr multicolored   .90   .30

Intl. Peace Year.

World Food Day
A257

1986, Oct. 16
762 A257 75fr Food staples   .80   .25
763 A257 120fr Mother feeding child   1.25   .40

UN Child Survival Campaign A258

Mothers, children and pinwheels in various designs.

1986, Oct. 27
764 A258 15fr multi, vert.   .20   .20
765 A258 30fr multi   .25   .20
766 A258 70fr multi, vert.   .70   .30
      Nos. 764-766 (3)   1.15   .70

A258a

A259

1986, Dec. 5   Litho.   Perf. 12x12½
766A A258a 100fr multicolored   1.50   .35

27th Soviet Communist Party congress.

1987, Feb. 10   Litho.   Perf. 13½
767 A259 30fr multicolored   .25   .20
768 A259 45fr multicolored   .45   .20
769 A259 75fr multicolored   .70   .25
770 A259 120fr multicolored   1.10   .35
      Nos. 767-770 (4)   2.50   1.00

Election of President Sassou-Nguesso, head of the Organization of African States.

Traditional Wedding A260

1987, Feb. 18   Litho.   Perf. 12½x13
771 A260 5fr multicolored   .20   .20
772 A260 15fr multicolored   .25   .20
773 A260 20fr multicolored   .25   .20
      Nos. 771-773 (3)   .70   .60

The Blue Lake — A261

1987, July 16   **Perf. 12½**
774 A261 5fr multicolored   .20   .20
775 A261 15fr multicolored   .20   .20
776 A261 75fr multicolored   1.00   .30
777 A261 120fr multicolored   1.25   .40
      Nos. 774-777 (4)   2.65   1.10

Pres. Marien Ngouabi A262

Congress of African Scientists A263

1987, July 16   **Perf. 13**
778 A262 75fr multicolored   .75   .30
779 A262 120fr multicolored   1.25   .40

Tenth death anniv.

1987, Sept. 10   Perf. 13x12½
780 A263 15fr multicolored   .20   .20
781 A263 90fr multicolored   .70   .30
782 A263 230fr multicolored   2.00   .80
      Nos. 780-782 (3)   2.90   1.30

4th African Games, Nairobi — A264

1987, Oct. 30   **Perf. 12½**
783 A264 75fr multicolored   .75   .40
784 A264 120fr multicolored   1.25   .60

Raoul Follereau (1903-1977), Philanthropist — A265

1987, Oct. 20   **Perf. 13½**
785 A265 120fr multicolored   1.50   .60

Cure leprosy.

FAO, 40th Anniv. — A266

1987, Nov. 17   **Perf. 12½**
786 A266 300fr multicolored   2.75   1.10

Anti-Apartheid Campaign A267

Nelson Mandela A268

Perf. 13½x15, 14½x15
1987, Sept. 21   **Litho.**
787 A267 60fr multicolored   .60   .20
788 A268 240fr multicolored   2.25   .75

Natl. UNICEF Vaccination Campaign — A269

Africa Fund — A270

Perf. 13½x14½, 14½x13½
1987, Sept. 28
789 A269 30fr Inoculating adults, horiz.   .25   .20
790 A269 45fr shown   .50   .20
791 A269 500fr Inoculating children, horiz.   5.25   2.00
      Nos. 789-791 (3)   6.00   2.40

No. 791 is airmail.

1987, Sept. 28   Perf. 13½x15
792 A270 25fr multicolored   .25   .20
793 A270 50fr multicolored   .40   .20
794 A270 70fr multicolored   .75   .25
      Nos. 792-794 (3)   1.40   .65

Self-sufficiency in Food Production by the Year 2000 — A271

1987, Nov. 20   Litho.   Perf. 13½
795 A271 20fr multicolored   .25   .20
796 A271 55fr multicolored   .60   .20
797 A271 100fr multicolored   1.00   .35
      Nos. 795-797 (3)   1.85   .75

Simon Kimbangu (b. 1887), Founder of the Church of Christ on Earth — A272

1987, Nov. 28   **Perf. 12½**
798 A272 75fr Kimbangu, vert.   .70   .30
799 A272 120fr Kimbangu, parrot, vert.   1.10   .40
800 A272 240fr Kimbanguist Church, Nkamba   2.75   1.00
a.   Souvenir sheet of 3, #798-800   5.75   5.00
      Nos. 798-800 (3)   4.55   1.70

October Revolution, Russia, 70th Anniv. — A273

Lenin inspecting revolutionary troops, Red Square, from an unspecified painting.

1988, Feb. 19   Litho.   Perf. 12½x12
801 A273 75fr multicolored   1.60   .60
802 A273 120fr multicolored   2.25   1.00

African Writers
Opposing
Apartheid — A274

Intl. Fund for
Agricultural
Development
(IFAD), 10th
Anniv. — A275

1988, Apr. 6 **Litho.** *Perf. 13½*
803 A274 15fr multicolored .20 .20
804 A274 60fr multicolored .50 .25
805 A274 75fr multicolored .80 .30
Nos. 803-805 (3) 1.50 .75

For overprint see #1157.

1988, Apr. 30
806 A275 240fr multicolored 2.00 .85

Invention of the Telegraph by Samuel
Morse, 150th Anniv. (in 1987) — A276

1988, Apr. 28
807 A276 90fr Morse, vert. .90 .30
808 A276 120fr shown 1.10 .40

A277

A278

1988, Sept. 20 **Litho.** *Perf. 13½*
809 A277 5fr Eucalyptus trees,
Brazzaville .30 .20
810 A277 10fr Stop cutting down
trees .30 .20

Fight against desertification.

1988, Aug. 12 **Litho.** *Perf. 13½*

Campaigns: No. 812, Return to the Land
Campaign (farming). 120fr, Self-sufficiency in
food production.

811 A278 75fr shown .75 .30
812 A278 75fr multicolored .75 .30
813 A278 120fr multicolored .90 .40
Nos. 811-813 (3) 2.40 1.00

Congo Revolution, 25th anniv.

Yoro
Fishing
Village
A279

1988, Sept. 1
814 A279 35fr shown .45 .20
815 A279 40fr Liberty Place .45 .20

Intl. Day for
the Fight
Against
AIDS
A280

1988, Dec. 1 **Litho.** *Perf. 13½*
816 A280 60fr shown .45 .20
817 A280 75fr Emblem .70 .20
818 A280 180fr Modified UN emblem, campaign
emblem 1.75 .60
Nos. 816-818 (3) 2.90 1.00

Natl. Committee for the Fight Against AIDS
and Evangelical Anglican Church of Congo
anti-AIDS campaign.

February 5
Movement,
10th Anniv.
A281

1989, Apr. 21 **Litho.** *Perf. 13½*
819 A281 75fr Rally .75 .30
820 A281 120fr Pres. Sassou-
Nguesso, natl.
achievements .90 .40

UN
Declaration
of Human
Rights,
40th Anniv.
(in 1988)
A282

1989, May 19 *Perf. 13*
821 A282 120fr multicolored .90 .40
822 A282 350fr multicolored 2.50 1.20

Marien
Nguabi,
Founder of
Congo
Labor Party
A282a

1989, July 31 **Litho.** *Perf. 12½x13*
822A A282a 240fr red & yellow 2.00 .75

Red Cross
and Red
Crescent
Societies,
125th
Anniv.
A283

120fr, Dunant, emblem, Congo Red Cross.

1989, Sept. 19 **Litho.** *Perf. 13*
823 A283 75fr shown .90 .40
824 A283 120fr multicolored 1.00 .65

No. 824 is airmail.

Organization of
African Unity,
25th
Anniv. — A284

1989, Oct. 19 **Litho.** *Perf. 12½*
825 A284 120fr multicolored 1.10 .40

African Development Bank, 25th
Anniv. — A285

1989, Dec. 22 **Litho.** *Perf. 12½x13*
826 A285 75fr multicolored .75 .35
827 A285 120fr multicolored 1.00 .40

WHO, 40th
Anniv. (in
1988)
A286

1989, Dec. 28 **Litho.** *Perf. 12½*
828 A286 60fr shown .75 .35
829 A286 75fr Blood donation,
vert. .90 .50

See Nos. 846-847 for overprints.

Congo Labor
Party (PCT), 20th
Anniv. — A287

1989, Dec. 22 **Litho.** *Perf. 13x12½*
830 A287 75fr multicolored .75 .35
831 A287 120fr multicolored 1.10 .40

Cacti
A288

Perf. 12½x13, 13x12½
1989, Nov. 22
832 A288 35fr Opuntia phaea-
cantha discata .35 .20
833 A288 40fr Opuntia ficus indica .50 .20
834 A288 60fr Opuntia erinacea .90 .25
835 A288 75fr Opuntia rufida 1.25 .30
836 A288 120fr Opuntia leptocau-
lis 1.75 .45
Nos. 832-836 (5) 4.75 1.40

Souvenir Sheet
Perf. 12½
837 A288 220fr Opuntia com-
presa 5.00 2.10

Nos. 832-833, 835 and 837 vert. No. 837
contains one 32x40mm stamp.

1992 Winter
Olympics,
Albertville
A289

1989, Dec. 22 *Perf. 12½*
838 A289 75fr Ice dancing .60 .25
839 A289 80fr Nordic skiing .60 .30
840 A289 100fr Speed skating .90 .35
841 A289 120fr Luge 1.10 .45
842 A289 200fr Alpine skiing 1.75 .70
843 A289 240fr Ice hockey 2.25 .85
844 A289 400fr Ski jumping 3.25 1.40
Nos. 838-844 (7) 10.45 4.30

Souvenir Sheet
Perf. 13
845 A289 500fr Bobsled 4.50 2.40

No. 845 contains one 32x40mm stamp.

Nos. 828-829 Ovptd. "NOTRE
PLANETE, NOTRE SANTE PENSER
GLOBALEMENT AGIR
LOCALEMENT" in 3 or 5 Lines
1989, Dec. 28 *Perf. 12½*
846 A286 60fr multicolored .75 .45
847 A286 75fr multicolored .90 .60

Health care for everyone.

Intl. Literacy
Year — A290

1990, June 26 **Litho.** *Perf. 13½*
848 A290 75fr bl, blk & yel .75 .35

Birds
A291

Designs: 25fr, Tourterelle des bois. 50fr,
Fauvette pitchou, vert. 70fr, Faucon crecerelle,
vert. 150fr, Perroquet gris, vert.

1990, July 10

849	A291	25fr multicolored	.35	.25
850	A291	50fr multicolored	.70	.30
851	A291	70fr multicolored	1.10	.55
852	A291	150fr multicolored	2.10	1.25
		Nos. 849-852 (4)	4.25	2.35

Dance Masks — A292

Flowering Plants — A293

1990, July 24   **Perf. 13**

853	A292	120fr Mondo	1.10	.40
854	A292	360fr Bapunu	3.50	1.25
855	A292	400fr Kwele	4.00	1.50
		Nos. 853-855 (3)	8.60	3.15

For overprints see #1172, 1173.

1990, Sept. 15   **Litho.**   **Perf. 12½**

856	A293	30fr Tournesol (sunflower)	.25	.20
857	A293	45fr Cassia alata, horiz.	.45	.20
858	A293	75fr Oeillette (opium poppy)	.70	.25
859	A293	90fr Acalypha sanderil	1.00	.35
		Nos. 856-859 (4)	2.40	1.00

1992 Summer Olympics, Barcelona — A294

1990, June 28   **Litho.**   **Perf. 13½**

860	A294	100fr Street scene, vert.	1.00	.30
861	A294	150fr shown	1.40	.35
862	A294	200fr Sailing, diff.	1.75	.40
863	A294	240fr Marketplace	2.25	.55
864	A294	350fr Harbor	3.50	.75
865	A294	500fr Monument, vert.	4.75	.90
		Nos. 860-865 (6)	14.65	3.25

Souvenir Sheet

866	A294	750fr Cathedral, vert.	5.50	3.50

Nos. 864-865 airmail. Nos. 860-865 exist in miniature sheets of 1.

Royal Necklaces A295

1990, Aug. 18   **Litho.**   **Perf. 13½**

867	A295	75fr shown	.75	.35
868	A295	100fr Necklace, diff.	1.00	.60

Boy Scouts Observing Nature A296

Scout: 35fr, Photographing butterfly, Euphaedra eusimoides. 40fr, Picking mushrooms, Armillaria mellea. 75fr, Drawing butterfly, Palla decius. 80fr, Using magnifying glass, Kallima ansorgei. 500fr, Using microscope, Cortinarius speciocissimus. 600fr, Feeding butterfly, Graphium illyris. 1500fr, Photographing butterfly, Berberia plistonax, horiz. 750fr, Photographing mushrooms, Volvariella bombycina.

1991, June 8   **Litho.**   **Perf. 13½**

869	A296	35fr multicolored	.20	.20
870	A296	40fr multicolored	.45	.20
871	A296	75fr multicolored	.60	.20
872	A296	80fr multicolored	.70	.20
873	A296	500fr multicolored	4.00	1.25
874	A296	600fr multicolored	4.00	1.25
a.		Min. sheet of 4, #869, 871-872, 874	7.50	3.75
		Nos. 869-874 (6)	9.95	3.30

Litho. & Embossed

874B	A296	1500fr gold & multi	32.50	—

Souvenir Sheet

875	A296	750fr multicolored	5.25	2.25

Nos. 869-874 exist in souvenir sheets of 1. Nos. 873-875 are airmail.

Medicinal Plants — A297

Designs: 15fr, Ocimum viride. 20fr, Kalanchoe pinnata, vert. 30fr, Euphorbia hirta. 60fr, Catharanthus roseus, vert. 75fr, Bidens pilosa, vert. 100fr, Brillantaisia patula, vert. 120fr, Cassia occidentalis, vert.

1991, Jan. 30   **Litho.**   **Perf. 11½**

876	A297	15fr multicolored	.20	.20
877	A297	20fr multicolored	.25	.20
878	A297	30fr multicolored	.25	.20
879	A297	60fr multicolored	.50	.25
880	A297	75fr multicolored	.70	.35
881	A297	100fr multicolored	1.00	.55
882	A297	120fr multicolored	1.10	.75
		Nos. 876-882 (7)	4.00	2.50

Mushrooms A298

1991, Mar. 25   **Litho.**   **Perf. 13**

883	A298	30fr Amanita rubescens	.30	.20
883A	A298	45fr Catathelasma imperiale	.40	.20
883B	A298	75fr Amanita caesarea	.75	.25
883C	A298	90fr Boletus regius	.90	.25
883D	A298	120fr Pluteus cervinus	1.10	.40
883E	A298	150fr Boletus chrysenteron	1.50	.60
883F	A298	200fr Agaricus arvensis	2.10	.75
		Nos. 883-883F (7)	7.05	2.65

Souvenir Sheet
Perf. 12½

883G	A298	350fr Boletus versipellis, horiz.	5.00	2.00

No. 883G contains one 40x32mm stamp.

Trains — A298a

Designs: 60fr, Dr-16, Finland. 75fr, TGV, France. 120fr, S350, Italy. 200fr, DE24000, Turkey. 250fr, DE1024, Germany.

1991, Apr. 10 Litho.   **Perf. 12½x12¼**

883H	A298a	60fr multi		
883I	A298a	75fr multi	.65	.30
883J	A298a	120fr multi	1.10	.45
883K	A298a	200fr multi	2.00	.75
883L	A298a	250fr multi	2.75	1.00

Dated 1990.

African Tourism Year — A299

1991, Apr. 15   **Litho.**   **Perf. 13½**

884	A299	75fr shown	.75	.35
885	A299	120fr Zebra, map	1.10	.60

Allegory of New Republic — A300

1991, May 13   **Litho.**   **Perf. 13**

888	A300	15fr blue	.20	.20
889	A300	30fr brt grn	.25	.20
890	A300	60fr org yel	.30	.20
891	A300	75fr brt pink	.50	.30
892	A300	120fr dk brown	.90	.45
		Nos. 888-892 (5)	2.15	1.35

Trans-Siberian Railroad, Cent. — A301

1991, June 6   **Litho.**   **Perf. 13**

899	A301	120fr Map	1.50	.50
900	A301	240fr Map, train	2.75	1.20

Telecom 91 — A302

1991, June 29   **Litho.**   **Perf. 13**

901	A302	75fr multicolored	.75	.30
902	A302	120fr multi, vert.	1.10	.60

6th World Forum and Exposition on Telecommunications, Geneva, Switzerland.

Insects — A303

A304

1991, July 2   **Perf. 12½**

903	A303	75fr Peanut beetle	.90	.25
904	A303	120fr Centaur, horiz.	1.25	.45
905	A303	200fr Coffee beetle	2.00	.75
906	A303	300fr Goliath beetle	3.00	1.50
		Nos. 903-906 (4)	7.15	2.95

1991, July 16   **Litho.**   **Perf. 12½**

907	A304	75fr Water conservation	.75	.35

Amnesty Intl., 30th Anniv. A305

Designs: 40fr, Candle, sun, vert. 75fr, "30," broken chains, vert.

1991, Aug. 13   **Perf. 13½**

908	A305	40fr multicolored	.35	.20
909	A305	75fr multicolored	.60	.25
910	A305	80fr multicolored	.70	.35
		Nos. 908-910 (3)	1.65	.80

Congo Postage Stamps, Cent. — A306

75fr, Similar to French Congo #1. 120fr, Similar to French Congo #35. 240fr, Similar to Congo Republic #89. 500fr, Similar to French Congo #1, 35 and Congo Republic #89.

Litho. & Engr.

1991, Aug.   **Perf. 13x13½**

911	A306	75fr beige & dk grn	.80	.30
912	A306	120fr beige, dk grn & brn	1.10	.45
913	A306	240fr multicolored	2.25	1.10
914	A306	500fr multicolored	4.50	2.00
a.		Strip of 4, #911-914	10.00	9.00

Ducks A307

1991, Aug. 8   **Litho.**   **Perf. 12½**

915	A307	75fr Anas acuta	1.25	.30
916	A307	120fr Somateria mollissima, vert.	1.50	.45
917	A307	200fr Anas clypeata, vert.	2.00	.75
918	A307	240fr Anas platyrhynchos	3.50	1.00
		Nos. 915-918 (4)	8.25	2.50

Automobiles and Space — A308

Designs: 35fr, Ferrari 512S by Pininfarina. 40fr, Vincenzo Lancia, Lancia Stratos by Bertone. 75fr, Maybach Zeppelin type 12, Wilhelm Maybach. 80fr, Mars Observer, 1992. 500fr, Magellan probe surveying Venus. 600fr, Magnification of Sun, Ulysses probe. 750fr, Crew of Apollo 11.

		1991, Aug. 23	**Litho.**	**Perf. 13½**
919	A308	35fr multicolored	.30	.20
920	A308	40fr multicolored	.30	.20
921	A308	75fr multicolored	.60	.30
922	A308	80fr multicolored	.65	.30
923	A308	500fr multicolored	4.25	2.25
924	A308	600fr multicolored	5.00	2.50
		Nos. 919-924 (6)	11.10	5.75

Souvenir Sheet

925	A308	750fr multicolored	6.50	3.50

Nos. 923-925 are airmail. No. 925 contains one 60x42mm stamp.

Butterflies A309

		1991, Aug. 31		**Perf. 11½**
926	A309	75fr Petit bleu	1.00	.30
927	A309	120fr Charaxe	1.25	.50
928	A309	240fr Papillon feuille, vert.	1.75	.80
929	A309	300fr Papillon de l'oranger, vert.	3.00	1.00
		Nos. 926-929 (4)	7.00	2.60

For overprints see Nos. 1156, 1165.

Celebrities and Organizations — A310

Designs: 100fr, Bo Jackson, baseball and football player. 150fr, Nick Faldo, golfer. 200fr, Rickey Henderson, Barry Bonds, baseball players. 240fr, Garry Kasparov, World Chess Champion. 300fr, Starving child, Lions and Rotary Clubs emblems. 350fr, Wolfgang Amadeus Mozart. 400fr, De Gaulle, Churchill. 500fr, Jean-Henri Dunant, founder of Red Cross. 750fr, De Gaulle, vert.

		1991, Sept. 2		**Perf. 13½**
930	A310	100fr multicolored	.85	.40
931	A310	150fr multicolored	1.25	.60
932	A310	200fr multicolored	1.60	.80
933	A310	240fr multicolored	1.90	.95
934	A310	300fr multicolored	2.40	1.25
935	A310	350fr multicolored	2.75	1.40
936	A310	400fr multicolored	3.75	1.60
937	A310	500fr multicolored	4.50	2.00
		Nos. 930-937 (8)	19.00	9.00

Souvenir Sheet

938	A310	750fr multicolored	6.50	3.50

Nos. 936-938 are airmail. No. 938 contains one 35x50mm stamp.
For overprint, see No. 1199.

Gen. Charles de Gaulle in Africa — A311

120fr, De Gaulle, Free French flag, vert. 240fr, De Gaulle, Appeal of Brazzaville, 1940.

		1991, Sept. 2	**Perf. 13½x13, 13x13½**
939	A311	75fr multicolored	.90	.40
940	A311	120fr multicolored	1.10	.60
941	A311	240fr multicolored	2.25	1.20
		Nos. 939-941 (3)	4.25	2.20

A312

Paintings — A313

		1991, Oct. 12		**Perf. 11½**
942	A312	75fr multicolored	.75	.35
943	A313	120fr multicolored	1.10	.45

Discovery of America, 500th Anniv. (in 1992) — A314

20fr, Portrait of Christopher Columbus by Sebastian Del Pombo. 35fr, Portrait of Columbus. 40fr, Portrait of Columbus facing right. 55fr, Santa Maria. 75fr, Nina. 150fr, Pinta. 200fr, Arms & signature of Columbus.

		1991, May 30		**Perf. 13**
944	A314	20fr multicolored	.35	.20
945	A314	35fr multicolored	.35	.20
946	A314	40fr multicolored	.45	.35
947	A314	55fr multicolored	.60	.35
948	A314	75fr multicolored	.85	.35
949	A314	150fr multicolored	1.60	.85
950	A314	200fr multicolored	2.10	1.00
		Nos. 944-950 (7)	6.30	3.30

Primates A315

		1991, Dec. 13	**Litho.**	**Perf. 13**
951	A315	30fr Cercopithecus diana	.40	.20
952	A315	45fr Pan troglodytes	.50	.20
953	A315	60fr Theropithecus gelada	.85	.20
954	A315	75fr Papio hamadry- as	1.25	.35
955	A315	90fr Macaca nemes- trina	1.50	.50
956	A315	120fr Gorilla gorilla	1.75	.50
957	A315	240fr Mandrillus sphinx	3.75	.75
		Nos. 951-957 (7)	10.00	2.70

Souvenir Sheet

958	A315	250fr Gorilla gorilla	4.25	1.50

Nos. 953-958 are vert.

Anniversaries and Events A316

Designs: 50fr, Launching of Sputnik II with dog, Laika, 1957. 75fr, Mahatma Gandhi and Martin Luther King, Jr. 1964. 120fr, Launching of Meteosat and ERS-1 over Europe and Africa. 240fr, Maybach Zeppelin automobile and Ferdinand von Zeppelin, 75th death anniversary. 300fr, Konrad Adenauer, 25th death anniversary and opening of the Brandenburg Gate, 1989. 500fr, Pope John Paul II's visit to Africa. 600fr, Elvis Presley, American entertainer.

		1992, Feb. 4	**Litho.**	**Perf. 13½**
959	A316	50fr multicolored	.75	.25
960	A316	75fr multicolored	.75	.25
961	A316	120fr multicolored	1.25	.45
962	A316	240fr multicolored	2.75	.85
963	A316	300fr multicolored	2.50	.80
964	A316	500fr multicolored	5.25	1.40
a.		Souvenir sheet of 3, #960, 963-964	11.50	5.75
		Nos. 959-964 (6)	13.25	4.00

Souvenir Sheet

965	A316	600fr multicolored	6.00	2.40

Nos. 959-964 exist in souvenir sheets of 1. Nos. 962, 964-965 are airmail.

Explorers A317

Birds — A318

Genoa '92: 75fr, Juan de la Cosa, nautical chart. 95fr, Martin Alonso Pinzon, astrolabe. 120fr, Alonso de Ojeda, hour glass. 200fr, Vicente Yanez Pinzon, sun dial. 250fr, Bartholomew Columbus, quadrant.
400fr, Columbus, flag, horiz.

		1992, Oct. 21	**Litho.**	**Perf. 13**
966	A317	75fr multicolored	1.00	.30
967	A317	95fr multicolored	1.10	.30
968	A317	120fr multicolored	1.75	.30
969	A317	200fr multicolored	2.25	.40
970	A317	250fr multicolored	2.75	.50
		Nos. 966-970 (5)	8.85	1.80

Souvenir Sheet

971	A317	400fr multi	14.00	14.00

1992, Oct. 21

Designs: 60fr, Sagittarius serpentarius. 75fr, Ephippiorhynchus senegalensis. 120fr, Bugeranus carunculatus. 200fr, Ardea melanocephala. 250fr, Phoenicopterus ruber roseus.
400fr, Balearica regulorum.

972	A318	60fr multicolored	.70	.20
973	A318	75fr multicolored	.80	.20
974	A318	120fr multicolored	1.10	.30
975	A318	200fr multicolored	2.00	.40
976	A318	250fr multicolored	2.75	.50
		Nos. 972-976 (5)	7.35	1.60

Souvenir Sheet

977	A318	400fr multi	4.00	1.00

For overprint, see No. 1191.

Wild Cats — A319

		1992, Nov. 21	**Litho.**	**Perf. 13**
978	A319	45fr Panthera leo	.50	.50
979	A319	60fr Panthera tigris	.60	.60
980	A319	75fr Lynx lynx	.70	.70
981	A319	95fr Caracal caracal	.80	.80
982	A319	250fr Leopardus pardalis	2.25	2.25
		Nos. 978-982 (5)	4.85	4.85

Souvenir Sheet

983	A319	400fr Acinonyx jubatus	4.50	1.75

No. 983 contains one 32x40mm stamp.

1992 Winter Olympics, Albertville — A320

1992 Summer Olympics, Barcelona A321

Gold medalists: 150fr, N. Mishkutyonok, A. Dmitriev, pairs figure skating, Unified team. 200fr, I. Appelt, H. Winkler, G. Haldacher, T. Schroll, 4-man bobsled, Austria. 500fr, Gunda Niemann, speed skating, Germany. 600fr, Bjorn Daehlie, cross-country skiing, Norway. 750fr, Alberto Tomba, giant slalom, Italy.

		1992, Dec. 21	**Litho.**	**Perf. 13½**
984	A320	150fr multicolored	1.25	1.25
985	A320	200fr multicolored	1.60	1.60
986	A320	500fr multicolored	4.00	4.00
987	A320	600fr multicolored	4.75	4.75
		Nos. 984-987 (4)	11.60	11.60

Souvenir Sheet

988	A320	750fr multicolored	6.00	6.00

Nos. 986-988 are airmail. No. 988 contains one 35x50mm stamp. Name on No. 987 spelled incorrectly.

1992, Dec. 21

Barcelona landmarks, Olympic event: 75fr, Steeple of La Sagrada Familia, baseball. 100fr, The Muse, Palace of Music, running. 150fr, Cupola interior, long jump. 200fr, St. Paul Hospital, pole vault. 400fr, Sculpture, by Miro, shot put. 500fr, Galley, Maritime Museum, table tennis. 750fr, La Sagrada Familia, tennis.

989	A321	75fr multicolored	.60	.30
990	A321	100fr multicolored	.80	.40
991	A321	150fr multicolored	1.25	.60
992	A321	200fr multicolored	1.60	.80
993	A321	400fr multicolored	3.25	3.25
994	A321	500fr multicolored	4.00	4.00
		Nos. 989-994 (6)	11.50	9.35

Souvenir Sheet

995	A321	750fr multicolored	6.00	6.00

Nos. 993-995 are airmail.

Christmas A321a

Paintings: 95fr, The Madonna of the Grand Duke, by Raphael. 120fr, Virgin and Child, by Francesco Mazzo. 200fr, The Madonna with a Book, by Botticelli. 250fr, The Madonna Carondelet, by Fra Bartolommeo. 400fr, Madonna and Child, by Raphael.

1992, Dec. 20 Litho. Perf. 12½

995A	A321a	95fr multicolored	1.25	.30
995B	A321a	120fr multi	2.00	.65
995C	A321a	200fr multicolored	2.75	.75
995D	A321a	250fr multicolored	3.25	1.25
		Nos. 995A-995D (4)	9.25	2.95

Souvenir Sheet

995E	A321a	400fr multicolored	4.50	1.90

Nos. 995A-995E were not available until late 1993.
For overprint, see No. 1192.

Birds of Prey — A322

A323

1993, Jan. 15 Litho. Perf. 12½x13

996	A322	45fr Charognard	.50	.20
997	A322	75fr Vulture	1.50	.30
998	A322	120fr Eagle	2.00	.65
		Nos. 996-998 (3)	4.00	1.15

1993, Dec. 21 Litho. Perf. 13½

Traditional ceramics.

999	A323	45fr Liloko	.60	.30
1000	A323	75fr Mbeya	.95	.50
1001	A323	120fr Jug with ladles, Mbeya	1.40	.85
		Nos. 999-1001 (3)	2.95	1.65

1994 World Cup Soccer
Championships, United States — A324

Design: 75fr, Player stretching to kick ball. 95fr, Goalie diving to stop ball. 120fr, Player stretching to kick ball. 200fr, Player kicking. 250fr, Goalie catching ball. 400fr, Players competing for ball.

1993, Jan. 15 Litho. Perf. 12¾

1002	A324	75fr multi	1.20	.80
1003	A324	95fr multi	1.25	1.10
1004	A324	120fr multi	2.10	1.40
1005	A324	200fr multi	3.00	2.10
1006	A324	250fr multi	3.50	2.75

Souvenir Sheet
Perf. 12½

1007	A324	400fr multi	—	—

No. 1007 contains one 40x32mm stamp.

Wild Animals
A325

Designs: 60fr, Damaliscus lunatus. 75fr, Gazella granti. 95fr, Equus quagga. 120fr, Panthera pardus. 200fr, Syncerus caffer. 250fr, Hippopotamus ampibius. 350fr, Panthera leo.

1993, Feb. 20 Litho. Perf. 13

1008	A325	60fr Damaliscus lunatus	.75	.20
1009	A325	75fr Gazella granti	1.25	.20
1010	A325	95fr Equus quagga	1.40	.30
1011	A325	120fr Panthera pardus	1.90	.30
1012	A325	200fr Syncerus caffer	2.75	.40
1013	A325	250fr Hippopotamus amphibius	3.50	.40
1014	A325	300fr Necrosyrtes monachu	4.25	.40
1015	A325	350fr Panthera leo	4.75	.75
a.		Sheet of 8, #1008-1015	20.00	20.00
		Nos. 1008-1015 (8)	20.55	2.95

No. 1015a is a continuous design.

Wild Flowers — A326

Designs: 75fr, Hibiscus schizopetalus. 95fr, Pentas lanceolata. 120fr, Ricinus communis. 200fr, Delonix regia. 250fr, Stapelia gigantea.

1993, May 20 Litho. Perf. 12½

1016	A326	75fr multicolored	1.25	.30
1017	A326	95fr multicolored	1.75	.40
1018	A326	120fr multicolored	3.00	.50
1019	A326	200fr multicolored	5.25	1.00
1020	A326	250fr multicolored	6.50	1.60
		Nos. 1016-1020 (5)	17.75	3.80

Deep Sea Submersibles A327

1993, June 25

1021	A327	75fr Transport PC-1202	1.60	.75
1022	A327	95fr J. Sea Link 1	2.00	1.00
1023	A327	120fr Nemo	2.50	1.25
1024	A327	200fr Robot	4.25	2.25
1025	A327	250fr Alvin	5.50	2.75
		Nos. 1021-1025 (5)	15.85	8.00

Souvenir Sheet

1026	A327	400fr Star III	9.00	6.75

No. 1026 contains one 32x40mm stamp.

1996 Summer Olympic Games, Atlanta A329

Designs: 50fr, Equestrian. 75fr, Cycling. 120fr, Sailing. 240fr, shown. 300fr, Hurdles. 500fr, Women's basketball. 750fr, Running.

1993, Apr. 26 Litho. Perf. 13½

1030-1035	A329	Set of 6	10.00	4.00
1035a		Sheet of 6, #1030-1035	10.00	5.00

Souvenir Sheet

1036	A329	750fr multicolored	6.50	1.50

Nos. 1030-1036 exist imperf. Nos. 1030-1035 exist in souvenir sheets of 1.

Brasiliana '93 — A330

Birds: 75fr, Vidua whydah. 95fr, Vidua regia. 120fr, Steganura paradisea. 200fr, Vidua macroura. 250fr, Anthreptes platura. 400fr, Coliuspasser macrourus, horiz.

1993, July 15 Litho. Perf. 12x12½

1037-1041	A330	Set of 5	13.00	13.00

Souvenir Sheet

1042	A330	400fr multicolored	12.00	12.00

Prehistoric Animals — A331

1993, Aug. 20 Litho. Perf. 13

1043	A331	75fr Ichthyostega	1.75	1.25
1044	A331	95fr Archaeopteryx	2.25	1.60
1045	A331	120fr Brachiosaurus	3.00	2.10
1046	A331	200fr Tyrannosaurus	4.75	3.50
1047	A331	250fr Pteranodon, vert.	6.50	4.25
		Nos. 1043-1047 (5)	18.25	12.70

Souvenir Sheet

1048	A331	400fr Brontosaurus	13.00	6.50

No. 1048 contains one 32x40mm stamp.

Powered Flight, 90th Anniv. — A332

Designs: 75fr, Wilbur Wright, Model B airplane, vert. 95fr, Orville Wright and Model B biplane, vert. 120fr, First flight by Orville Wright. 200fr, Flight at Kitty Hawk. 250fr, Wright Brothers and airplane.

Perf. 12⅛x12½, 12½x12¼
1993, Dec. 17 Litho.

1049	A332	75fr multi	.60	.60
1050	A332	95fr multi	.75	.75
1051	A332	120fr multi	.90	.90
1052	A332	200fr multi	1.60	1.60
1053	A332	250fr multi	2.10	2.10
		Nos. 1049-1053 (5)	5.95	5.95

Evolution of the Elephant A333

1994, June 20 Litho. Perf. 12½

1054	A333	25fr Palaeomastodon	1.00	.50
1055	A333	45fr Mammut	1.75	.90
1056	A333	50fr Amebelodon	2.00	1.00
1057	A333	75fr Platybelodon	3.00	1.50
1058	A333	120fr Mammuthus	4.75	2.40
		Nos. 1054-1058 (5)	12.50	6.30

Protection of Nature — A335

Designs: 50fr, Choeropsis liberiensis. 90fr, Hyemoschus aquaticus. 205fr, Taurotragus euryceros, vert. 300fr, Redunca redunca, vert.

1994, Aug. 27 Litho. Perf. 12½

1063	A335	50fr multicolored	.65	.30
1064	A335	90fr multicolored	1.10	.30
1065	A335	205fr multicolored	2.50	1.10
1066	A335	300fr multicolored	3.25	1.60
		Nos. 1063-1066 (4)	7.50	3.30

For overprint see #1167.

Seaplanes — A336

Designs: 30fr, Cant Z-505, Italy. 45fr, Martin Mariner PBM-3, US. No. 1069, E-59, Russia. No. 1070, Short Sunderland, Great Britain. No. 1071, Martin Mars XPB2M-1, US. 400fr, Boeing 314, US.

1994, Sept. 2 Litho. Perf. 12½

1067	A336	30fr multicolored	.40	.40
1068	A336	45fr multicolored	.65	.65
1069	A336	90fr multicolored	1.50	1.50
1070	A336	90fr multicolored	1.50	1.50
1071	A336	90fr multicolored	1.50	1.50
		Nos. 1067-1071 (5)	5.55	5.55

Souvenir Sheet

1071A	A336	400fr multicolored	5.00	2.50

No. 1071A contains one 40x32mm stamp.

Intl. Year of the Family — A337

1995, Jan. 28 Litho. Perf. 12½

1072	A337	90fr shown	1.10	.40
1073	A337	205fr African map, child	2.25	1.00
1074	A337	300fr Family, native huts	3.50	1.50
		Nos. 1072-1074 (3)	6.85	2.90

For overprint see No. 1168.

Insects — A338

1994, July 24 Litho. Perf. 12½

1075	A338	90fr Tarantula	1.90	.40
1076	A338	205fr Spider	4.50	1.10
1077	A338	240fr Ladybug	5.00	1.25
		Nos. 1075-1077 (3)	11.40	2.75

Souvenir Sheet

1078	A338	400fr Bee	4.75	2.00

Costumes — A338a

1995 **Litho.** **Perf. 12¾x12½**
1078A	A338a	90fr M'Bochi	2.00	1.00
1078B	A338a	205fr Téké	2.50	1.25
1078C	A338a	500fr Loango	6.00	2.00
	Nos. 1078A-1078C (3)		10.50	4.25

Rotary Intl., 90th Anniv. A339

Designs: 90fr, Polio victim. No. 1080, Playing ball with children. 205fr, Children with food. 300fr, Delivering polio vaccine. 1500fr, Paul Harris, Rotary emblem.

1996, Feb. 6 **Litho.** **Perf. 14**
1079	A339	90fr multicolored	.60	.25
1080	A339	205fr multicolored	1.25	.50
1081	A339	205fr multicolored	1.25	.50
1082	A339	300fr multicolored	1.60	.60
	Nos. 1079-1082 (4)		4.70	1.85

Souvenir Sheet
1083	A339	1500fr multicolored	7.50	3.25

For overprint, see Mo. 1201.

18th World Scout Jamboree, The Netherlands — A340

Designs: No. 1084, Handshake. No. 1085, Scout helping another with arm sling. 205fr, Saving life in water. 300fr, Lord Baden-Powell. 1000fr, Scout salute.

1996, Feb. 6 **Litho.** **Perf. 14**
1084	A340	90fr multicolored	.45	.20
1085	A340	90fr multicolored	.45	.20
1086	A340	205fr multicolored	1.10	.50
1087	A340	300fr multicolored	1.75	.50
	Nos. 1084-1087 (4)		3.75	1.30

Souvenir Sheet
1088	A340	1000fr multicolored	4.25	2.10

1998 World Cup Soccer Tournament A340a

Various players. Denominations: 90fr, 150fr, 205fr, 300fr, 400fr, 500fr.

1996 **Litho.** **Perf. 12¾**
1088A-1088F	A340a	Set of 6	7.25	7.25

Souvenir Sheet
Perf. 13¼x13
1088G	A340a	1000fr Player's legs	4.50	4.50

No. 1088G contains one 40x31mm stamp.

Antique Automobiles — A341

90fr, 1936 Armstrong Siddeley Twelve. 150fr, 1935 Aston Martin Mark II. 205fr, 1938 Morris 8. 300fr, 1955-62 MG Series MGA. 400fr, 1932 SS1. 500fr, 1938 Alvis 25 SB.

1996, Apr. 30 **Litho.** **Perf. 12½x12**
1089	A341	90fr multicolored	.45	.20
1090	A341	150fr multicolored	.75	.40
1091	A341	205fr multicolored	1.00	.50
1092	A341	300fr multicolored	1.50	.75
1093	A341	400fr multicolored	2.00	1.00
1094	A341	500fr multicolored	2.50	1.25
	Nos. 1089-1094 (6)		8.20	4.10

Domestic Cats — A342

90fr, Persian. 150fr, Siamese. 205fr, Norwegian forest. 300fr, Exotic shorthair. 400fr, Maine coon. 500fr, Red abyssinian. 1000fr, Turkish Angora.

1996, Mar. 10 **Perf. 13x12½**
1095	A342	90fr multicolored	.45	.20
1096	A342	150fr multicolored	.75	.40
1097	A342	205fr multicolored	1.00	.50
1098	A342	300fr multicolored	1.50	.75
1099	A342	400fr multicolored	2.00	1.00
1100	A342	500fr multicolored	2.50	1.25
	Nos. 1095-1100 (6)		8.20	4.10

Souvenir Sheet
1101	A342	1000fr multicolored	5.00	2.50

No. 1101 contains one 32x40mm stamp.

1996 Summer Olympic Games, Atlanta A343

1996 **Perf. 13x12½, 12½x13**
1102	A343	90fr Fencing, vert.	.50	.25
1103	A343	150fr Archery, vert.	.80	.40
1104	A343	205fr Basketball, vert.	1.10	.55
1105	A343	300fr Baseball, vert.	1.60	.80
1106	A343	400fr Volleyball	2.25	1.10
1107	A343	500fr 2-man kayak	2.50	1.25
	Nos. 1102-1107 (6)		8.75	4.35

Souvenir Sheet
1108	A343	1000fr Judo, vert.	5.25	2.50

No. 1108 contains one 32x40mm stamp.

Flowers — A344

Designs: 90fr, Nerium oleander. 150fr, Eucaliptus globulus. 205fr, Centaurea cyanus. 300fr, Coffea arabica. 400fr, Hibiscus sabdariffa. 500fr, Cassia angustifolia.

1996, May 10 **Perf. 12½**
1109	A344	90fr multicolored	.50	.25
1110	A344	150fr multicolored	.80	.40
1111	A344	205fr multicolored	1.10	.55

1112	A344	300fr multicolored	1.60	.80
1113	A344	400fr multicolored	2.25	1.10
1114	A344	500fr multicolored	2.50	1.25
	Nos. 1109-1114 (6)		8.75	4.35

Mother Carrying Baby — A345

1996 **Litho.** **Perf. 13**
1115	A345	40fr blue	4.00	2.00
1116	A345	50fr violet brown	5.00	2.50
1117	A345	90fr orange	9.00	4.50
1118	A345	100fr green blue	10.00	5.00
1119	A345	115fr gray	11.00	5.50
1120	A345	205fr brown	20.00	10.00
	Nos. 1115-1120 (6)		59.00	29.50

It has been stated that this set was not issued.
See #1145-1150.
For overprint, see No. 1185A.

A346

1996, Aug. 31 **Litho.** **Perf. 13½**
1121	A346	90fr orange & multi	.45	.30
1122	A346	205fr green & multi	1.00	.60

Investiture of Pres. Pascal Lissouba, 4th anniv.

Owls — A347

1996, Mar. 29 **Perf. 14½**
1123	A347	90fr Tyto alba	.70	.25
1124	A347	205fr Bubo poensis	1.40	.50
1125	A347	300fr Scotopelia peli	2.00	.90
1126	A347	500fr Asio capensis	3.25	1.50
	Nos. 1123-1126 (4)		7.35	3.15

Military Aircraft — A348

Designs: 90fr, Vought-Sikorsky Vindicator SB2U-1. 150fr, Grumman Wildcat F4F-3. 205fr, North American SNJ-2. 300fr, Brewster Bermuda. 400fr, Blackburn Skua 1. 500fr, Mitsubishi Type 98-1.
1000fr, P-40 Warhawk (Flying Tigers).

1996, June 24 **Litho.** **Perf. 12½x12**
1127	A348	90fr multicolored	.45	.20
1128	A348	150fr multicolored	.75	.30
1129	A348	205fr multicolored	1.00	.50
1130	A348	300fr multicolored	1.50	.75
1131	A348	400fr multicolored	2.00	1.00
1132	A348	500fr multicolored	2.50	1.25
	Nos. 1127-1132 (6)		8.20	4.00

Souvenir Sheet
Perf. 13
1133	A348	1000fr multicolored	5.00	2.50

No. 1133 contains one 32x40mm stamp.

Aquatic Flowers — A348a

Design: 90fr, Cyrtosperma senegalense.

1996, July 3 **Litho.** **Perf. 14x14¼**
1133A	A348a	90fr multi	.50	.50

An additional stamp was issued in this set. The editors would like to examine it.

Crocodilians A348b

1996, July 16 **Litho.** **Perf. 14**
1133C	A348b	205fr Nile crocodile	—	—
1133D	A348b	255fr Gavial	—	—
1133E	A348b	300fr Caiman	—	—

United Nations, 50th Anniv. — A348c

1996 **Litho.** **Perf. 12½**
1133F	A348c	300fr multi	—	—

Arctocebus Calabarensis A349

a, 90fr, With young. b, 205fr, Touching leaf. c, 300fr, Climbing to left. d, 255fr, Walking on branch.

1998, June 3 **Litho.** **Perf. 14**
1134	A349	Strip of 4, #a.-d.	4.50	4.50

No. 1134 issued in sheets of 12 stamps. World Wildlife Fund.

Endangered Species — A350

#1135, Kabus defassa, vert. #1136, Caphalophus sylvicutor. 205fr, Potamochoerus porcus. 300fr, Tragelaplus spekei.

1996 **Litho.** **Perf. 14**
1135	A350	90fr multi	.55	.25
1136	A350	90fr multi, vert.	.55	.25
1137	A350	205fr multi, vert.	1.10	.45
1138	A350	300fr multi	1.60	.65
	Nos. 1135-1138 (4)		3.80	1.60

Diana, Princess of Wales (1961-97) A351

#1139-1141: Various portraits with white rose.
Diana, rose, famous people in sheet margin: 750fr, Henry Kissinger, vert. No. 1143, Mother Teresa, vert. No. 1144, Hillary Clinton, vert.

1998, Aug. 31   Litho.   Perf. 14
Sheets of 6

1139	A351	205fr #a.-f.	4.25	2.00
1140	A351	255fr #a.-f., vert.	5.25	2.75
1141	A351	300fr #a.-f., vert.	6.25	3.00

Souvenir Sheets

1142	A351	750fr multicolored	2.50	1.25
1143-1144	A351	1000fr each	3.50	1.75

Stamps of Type A345 inscribed only "Congo" ovptd.

1998   Litho.   Perf. 13

1145	A345	40fr	
1146	A345	50fr violet brown	
1147	A345	90fr orange	
1148	A345	100fr green blue	— —
1149	A345	115fr gray	
1150	A345	205fr brown	

A352

Designs: 90fr, Aframomum africanum. 205fr, Gambeya lacuurtiana (37x24mm). 300fr, Landolphia jumeli.

Perf. 13½x13¼, 13 (#1152)

1998   Litho.

1151	A352	90fr multi	
1152	A352	205fr multi	
1153	A352	300fr multi	

No. 1153 has denomination in yellow.

No. 732A Overprinted

No. 929 Overprinted

1998   Litho.   Perf. 13

1155	A244	205fr multi	— —
1156	A309	300fr multi	— —

An additional stamp was issued in this set. The editors would like to examine them.

Nos. 732B, 804, 854, 855, 929, 1066, 1074, 1118, 1133D Ovptd. Like

and

A355

Perfs. as before, Perf. 14 (#1164), Perf. 13½x13¼ (#1170)
Methods as before, Litho. (#1164, 1170)

1998

1157	A274	60fr multi (#804)	
1159	A345	100fr green blue (#1118)	
1164	A348b	255fr multi (#1133D)	
1165	A309	300fr multi (#929)	
1167	A335	300fr multi (#1066)	
a.		Overprint reading horizontally	
1168	A337	300fr multi (#1074)	
1169	A355	300fr multi	— —
1170	A244	300fr multi (#732B)	— —
a.		Overprint reading horizontally	
1172	A292	360fr multi (#854)	— —
a.		Inverted overprint	
1173	A292	400fr multi (#855)	— —

Numbers have been reserved for additional overprinted stamps. Overprint reads horizontally on Nos. 1157, 1159, 1169, 1172 and 1173, vertically reading down on Nos. 1164, 1167, 1168 and 1170, and vertically reading up on No. 1165. No. 1170 has white denomination.
The editors would like to see examples of No. 1169 without the overprint.

1998 World Cup Soccer Championships, France — A358

Designs: 90fr, Netherlands, 4th place. 205fr, Croatia, bronze medal. 300fr, Brazil, silver medal. 500fr, France, gold medal.

1998, Nov. 16   Litho.   Perf. 13x13¼
1175-1178   A358   Set of 4   — —

Masks — A359

Perf. 13¼x13½

1998, Nov. 20   Litho.

1179	A359	90fr Kwele wood mask	
1180	A359	150fr Kwele wood mask	
1181	A359	205fr Teke/Tsangui wood mask	
1182	A359	205fr Kuyu wood mask	

No. 732B Overprinted

Type I — Unserifed Upper and Lower Case Letters, 7x3mm

Type II — Serifed Upper and Lower Case Letters, 12x3mm

Type III — Upper Case Letters, 9x2mm

Methods and Perfs as Before

1999 ?

1183	A244	300fr multi (I)	— —
1184	A244	300fr multi (II)	— —
1185	A244	300fr multi (III)	— —

No. 1119 Overprinted Like No. 1149 But With Wider "G" In Overprint
Method and Perf. As Before

1999 ?
1185A   A345   115fr gray   — —

Nos. 934, 975, 995B, 1082, C342-C343 Overprinted Like No. 1157 and

A359a

Methods as Before, Litho. (#1204)
1999 ?   Perf. as Before, 12½ (#1204)

1187	AP120	200fr multi (#C342)	— —
1188	AP120	200fr multi (#C343)	— —
a.		Horiz. pair, #1187-1188, + central label	— —
1191	A318	200fr multi (#975)	— —
1192	A321a	200fr multi (#995B)	— —
1199	A310	300fr multi (#934)	— —
1201	A339	300fr multi (#1082)	— —
1204	A359a	300fr multi	— —

The editors would like to see examples of No. 1204 without the overprint. Overprint reads horizontally on No. 1204, horizontally and inverted on Nos. 1187-1188, vertically reading down on Nos. 1191 and 1199, and vertically reading up on Nos. 1192 and 1201.

PhilexFrance 99 — A360

Design: 205fr, Raffia cloth with tassels. 300fr, Woven raffia cloth.

1999, July 2   Litho.   Perf. 13x13¼

1211	A360	205fr multi	— —
1212	A360	300fr multi	— —

First French Postage Stamp, 150th Anniv. A361

Litho. With Hologram
1999   Perf. 13x13¼
1213   A361   300fr multi   — —

Central African Economic and Monetary Community Week — A363

Designs: 90fr, Map and flags. 205fr, Map and circle of flags.

1999   Litho.   Perf. 14½

1227	A363	90fr multi	— —
1228	A363	205fr multi	— —

Additional stamps may exist in this set. The editors would like to examine any examples.

Third Pan-African Music Festival — A364

Designs: 120fr, Emblem. 270fr, Map of Africa with drummers.

2001, Aug. 4   Litho.   Perf. 13½x13
1229-1230   A364   Set of 2   1.60   1.60

Independence, 40th Anniv. — A365

Designs: 90fr, Dove, vine, map, hands, people. 205fr, Tools, clasped and opened hands, map.

2001, Nov. 15   Litho.   Perf. 13¼x13
1231-1232   A365   Set of 2   — —

Birds — A366

Designs: 90fr, Egretta garzetta. 120fr, Ardea cenerea. 205fr, Ardea perpurea. 270fr, Ciconia nigra.

2001   Perf. 13¼

1233	A366	90fr multi	— —
1234	A366	120fr multi	— —
1234B	A366	205fr multi	— —
1235	A366	270fr multi	— —

Two additional stamps were issued in this set. The editors would like to examine any examples.

Type of A345 Inscribed "REPUBLIQUE DU CONGO" Overprinted "LEGAL" Like No. 1145
2001 ?   Litho.   Perf. 13
1236   A345   90fr blue   — —

Fruit — A367

Designs: 40fr, Mbila esobe. 50fr, Ikami. 70fr, Tsia, vert. 80fr, Bamou. 120fr, Malombo. 270fr, Ntondolo, vert.

2002, June 25 Litho. *Perf. 13½*
1237-1242 A367 Set of 6 — —

Birds — A368

Designs: 40fr, Calao (hornbill). 80fr, Cigogne blanche (white stork). 120fr, Grue cendrée (gray crane). 270fr, Marabout.

2002, July 23 *Perf. 13½x13*
1243-1246 A368 Set of 4 — —

Elephants A369

Designs; 120fr, Mammoth. 270fr, Elephant on savannah, horiz. 350fr, Elephant, horiz. 500fr, Forest elephant near lake.

Perf. 13¼x13, 13x13¼
2003, June 20
1247-1250 A369 Set of 4 5.75 5.75

Flowers — A370

Designs: 120fr, Muflier (antirrhinum). 270fr, Pivoine (peony). 400fr, Petunia. 600fr, Mauve (mallow), horiz.

2003, July 6
1251-1254 A370 Set of 4 6.50 6.50

Moringa Olifera — A371

Highlighted portion: 30fr, Bark. 70fr, Root. 90fr, Leaves. 115fr, Seeds and open pod. 120fr, Flowers. 360fr, Pod.

2005, Feb. 3 Litho. *Perf. 13¼x13*
1255-1260 A371 Set of 6 3.25 3.25
Dated 2004.

Fruits — A372

Designs: 120fr, Custard apple. 200fr, Tangerine. 270fr, Guava. 360fr, Grapefruit.

2005, July 13 Litho. *Perf. 13½*
1261-1264 A372 Set of 4 7.25 7.25

Albert Einstein (1879-1955), Physicist — A373

2005, Aug. 17 Litho. *Perf. 13¼x13*
1265 A373 400fr multi 4.25 4.25

A374

Brazzaville, 125th Anniv. — A375

2005, Oct. 3 *Perf. 13¼x13*
1266 A374 120fr multi 1.10 1.10
Perf. 13½x13¼
1267 A375 360fr multi 3.25 3.25

Pope Benoît XVI A376

Pope Benedict XVI: 360fr, Waving. 500fr, Holding crucifix.

2005, Nov. 28 *Perf. 13¼x13½*
1268-1269 A376 Set of 2 3.75 3.75

Coat of Arms — A377

Colors: 30fr, Dark brown. 40fr, Red. 50fr, Bister brown. 60fr, Dark green.

2006, Jan. 4 Litho. *Perf. 13½*
1270-1273 A377 Set of 4 2.25 2.25

Denis Sassou-Nguesso, President of African Union — A378

2006, Mar. 14 Litho. *Perf. 13x13¼*
1274 A378 500fr multi 2.40 2.40

Léopold Sédar Senghor (1906-2001), First President of Senegal — A379

2006, May 15
1275 A379 360fr multi 1.75 1.75

Animals — A380

Designs: 40fr, Crocodile. 50fr, Pangolin, horiz. 60fr, Lizard, horiz. 120fr, Cat, horiz.

2006 Litho. *Perf. 13¼x13, 13x13¼*
1276-1279 A380 Set of 4 1.10 1.10

World Religion Day A381

2007 *Perf. 13½x13*
1280 A381 120fr multi .55 .55

Opening of Pierre Savorgnan de Brazza Memorial, Brazzaville A382

Memorial and: 120fr, Statue. 500fr, Photo of Savorgnan de Brazza. 1000fr, Statue, diff.

2008 *Perf. 13¼*
1281-1283 A382 Set of 3 7.00 7.00

Pan-African Postal Union, 30th Anniv. — A383

2010 Litho. *Perf. 13½x13¼*
1284 A383 360fr multi 2.50 2.50

SEMI-POSTAL STAMPS

Anti-Malaria Issue
Common Design Type

1962, Apr. 7 Engr. *Perf. 12½x12*
B3 CD108 25fr + 5fr bister 1.25 1.00

Freedom from Hunger Issue
Common Design Type

1963, Mar. 21 Unwmk. *Perf. 13*
B4 CD112 25fr + 5fr vio bl, bl
grn & brn 1.25 1.00

Boy Suffering from Sleeping Sickness SP1

Fight Against Communicable Diseases; 40fr+5fr, Examination, treatment, vert.

1981, June 6 Litho. *Perf. 13*
B5 SP1 40fr + 5fr multi .60 .25
B6 SP1 65fr + 10fr multi 1.00 .30

IYD Type of 1981

1981, June 29 *Perf. 12½*
B7 A192 75fr + 5fr multi .90 .35

AIR POST STAMPS

Olympic Games Issue
French Equatorial Africa No. C37
Surcharged in Red Like Chad No. C1

1960 Unwmk. Engr. *Perf. 13*
C1 AP8 250fr on 500fr grnsh
blk, blk & sl 7.50 7.50
17th Olympic Games, Rome, 8/25-9/11.

Helicrysum Mechowiam — AP1

Flowers: 200fr, Cogniauxia podolaena. 500fr, Thesium tencio.

1961, Sept. 28 Engr. *Perf. 13*
C2 AP1 100fr grn, lil & yel 3.25 1.25
C3 AP1 200fr bl grn, yel & brn 5.25 1.75
C4 AP1 500fr brn red, yel & sl
grn 16.00 5.00
Nos. C2-C4 (3) 24.50 8.00

Air Afrique Issue
Common Design Type

1961, Nov. 25 Unwmk. *Perf. 13*
C5 CD107 50fr lil rose, sl grn &
grn 1.75 .90

Loading Timber, Pointe-Noire Harbor — AP2

1962, June 8 Photo. *Perf. 12½x12*
C6 AP2 50fr multicolored 1.50 .90
Opening of the Intl. Fair and Exhib., Pointe-Noire, June 8-11.

Abidjan Games — AP3

Costus Spectabilis AP4

1962, July 21   **Perf. 12x12½**
C7   AP3 100fr Basketball   2.50 1.25

1963   **Unwmk.**   **Perf. 13**

Design: 250fr, Mountain acanthus.

C8   AP4 100fr multicolored   4.00 1.75
C9   AP4 250fr multicolored   8.00 3.25

Brazzaville City Hall and Pres. Fulbert Youlou — AP4a

1963, Aug.   **Photo.**   **Perf. 13x12**
C10   AP4a 100fr multicolored   150.00 125.00

African Postal Union Issue
Common Design Type
1963, Sept. 8   **Perf. 12½**
C13   CD114 85fr pur, ocher & red   1.25 .75

Air Afrique Issue, 1963
Common Design Type
    Perf. 13x12
1963, Nov. 19   **Unwmk.**   **Photo.**
C14   CD115 50fr multicolored   .85 .50

Liberty Place, Brazzaville — AP5

1963, Nov. 28
C15   AP5 25fr multicolored   1.00 .40
    See No. 118.

Europafrica Issue
Common Design Type
1963, Nov. 30   **Perf. 12x13**
C16   CD116 50fr gray, yel & dk
      brn   1.75 1.00

Timber Industry — AP6

1964, May 12   **Engr.**   **Perf. 13**
C17   AP6 100fr grn, brn red & blk   2.25 1.10

Chiefs of State Issue

Map and Presidents of Chad, Congo, Gabon and CAR AP6a

1964, June 23   **Photo.**   **Perf. 12½**
C18   AP6a 100fr multicolored   1.75 1.00
    See note after Central African Republic No. C19.

Europafrica Issue, 1964

Sunburst, Wheat, Cogwheel and Globe — AP7

1964, July 20   **Perf. 12x13**
C19   AP7 50fr yel, Prus bl & mar   1.25 .75
    See note after Cameroun No. 402.

Hammer Thrower, Olympic Flame and Stadium — AP8

50fr, 100fr, vert.

1964, July 30   **Engr.**   **Perf. 13**
C20   AP8   25fr shown   .55 .30
C21   AP8   50fr Weight lifter   .95 .60
C22   AP8   100fr Volleyball   2.25 1.10
C23   AP8   200fr High jump   3.75 2.25
   a.   Min. sheet of 4, #C20-C23   9.00 9.00
      Nos. C20-C23 (4)   7.50 4.25

18th Olympic Games, Tokyo, 10/10-25/64.

Communications Symbols — AP8a

1964, Nov. 2   **Litho.**   **Perf. 12½x13**
C24   AP8a 25fr dl rose & dk brn   .60 .45
    See note after Chad No. C19.

Town Hall, Brazzaville — AP9

1965, Jan. 30   **Photo.**   **Perf. 12½**
C25   AP9 100fr multicolored   1.75 .75

Coupling Hooks — AP10

1965, Feb. 27   **Photo.**   **Perf. 13x12**
C26   AP10 50fr multicolored   1.00 .75
    Economic Europe-Africa Association.

Breguet Dial Telegraph, ITU Emblem and Telstar — AP11

1965, May 17   **Engr.**   **Perf. 13**
C27   AP11 100fr dk bl, ocher &
      brn   2.25 .75
    Cent. of the ITU.

Pope John XXIII (1881-1963), St. Peter's Cathedral — AP12

    Perf. 12½x13
1965, June 26   **Photo.**   **Unwmk.**
C28   AP12 100fr gldn brn & multi   1.60 .75

Pres. John F. Kennedy — AP13

Log Rolling — AP14

Portraits: 25fr on 50fr, Patrice Lumumba, premier of Congo Republic (ex-Belgian). 50fr, Sir Winston Churchill. 80fr, Barthélémy Boganda, premier of Central African Republic.

1965, June   **Perf. 12½**
C29   AP13 25fr on 50fr dk
      brn & red   .50 .40
   a.   Surcharge omitted   35.00 35.00
C30   AP13 50fr dk brn &
      yel grn   1.10 1.00
C31   AP13 80fr dk brn & bl   2.00 1.50
C32   AP13 100fr dk brn &
      org yel   2.75 2.25
   a.   Min. sheet of 4, #C29-C32   6.25 6.25
      Nos. C29-C32 (4)   6.35 5.15

A second miniature sheet contains one each of Nos. C29a, C30-C32. Value, $50. Issued: 25fr, 80fr, 6/25; 50fr, 100fr, #C32a, 6/26.

1965, Aug. 14   **Engr.**   **Perf. 13**
C33   AP14 50fr grn, brn & red brn   .80 .50
    Issued to publicize national unity.

World Map and Symbols of Agriculture and Industry — AP15

1965, Oct. 18   **Engr.**   **Perf. 13**
C34   AP15 50fr dk bl, blk, brn &
      org   1.50 .90
    International Cooperation Year, 1965.

Abraham Lincoln — AP16

1965, Dec. 15   **Photo.**   **Perf. 13**
C35   AP16 90fr pink & multi   1.25 .60
    Centenary of death of Abraham Lincoln.

Charles de Gaulle, Torch and Map of Africa — AP17

1966, Feb. 28   Engr.   Perf. 13
C36 AP17 500fr dk red, dk grn
& dk red brn   35.00 26.00
22nd anniv. of the Brazzaville Conf.

D-1 Satellite over Brazzaville Space Tracking Station — AP18

Grain, Atom Symbol and Map of Africa and Europe — AP19

1966, May 15   Engr.   Perf. 13
C37 AP18 150fr blk, dl red & bl
grn   2.25 1.25

1966, July 20   Photo.   Perf. 12x13
C38 AP19 50fr multicolored   1.25 .75
See note after Gabon No. C46.

Pres. Massamba-Debat and President's Palace — AP20

3rd anniv. of the Revolution: 30fr, Robespierre and storming of the Bastille. 50fr, Lenin and storming of the Winter Palace.

1966, Aug. 15   Photo.   Perf. 12x12½
C39 AP20 25fr multicolored   .45 .30
C40 AP20 30fr multicolored   .65 .30
C41 AP20 50fr multicolored   1.60 .50
a.   Souv. sheet of 3, #C39-C41   2.25 2.25
Nos. C39-C41 (3)   2.70 1.10

Air Afrique Issue, 1966
Common Design Type

1966, Aug. 31   Photo.   Perf. 13
C42 CD123 30fr lilac, lemon & blk   .60 .25

Dr. Albert Schweitzer — AP21

1966, Sept. 4   Photo.   Perf. 12½
C43 AP21 100fr red, blk, bl & li-
lac   2.00 1.25
Issued to honor Dr. Albert Schweitzer (1875-1965), medical missionary.

AP22

AP23

1966, Dec. 26   Photo.   Perf. 13
C44 AP22 100fr Crab, micro-
scope and pa-
goda   1.50 1.00
9th Intl. Anticancer Cong., Tokyo. 10/23-29.

1967   Photo.   Perf. 13
Birds: 50fr, Social Weaver. 75fr, European Bee-eater. 100fr, Lilac-breasted roller. 150fr, Regal sunbird. 200fr, Crowned cranes. 250fr, Secretary bird. 300fr, Knysna touraco.

C45 AP23 50fr multicolored   1.60 .75
C46 AP23 75fr multicolored   3.25 1.00
C47 AP23 100fr multicolored   3.25 1.00
C48 AP23 150fr multicolored   4.25 2.25
C49 AP23 200fr multicolored   7.50 2.50
C50 AP23 250fr multicolored   9.50 5.00
C51 AP23 300fr multicolored   13.50 5.00
Nos. C45-C51 (7)   42.85 15.50
Issued: #C45-C47, 2/13; others, 6/20.

Shackled Hands AP24

1967, May 24   Photo.   Perf. 12½x13
C52 AP24 500fr multicolored   8.50 3.00
Issued for African Liberation Day.

Sputnik 1, Explorer 6 and Earth — AP25

Space Craft: 75fr, Ranger 6, Lunik 2 and moon. 100fr, Mars 1, Mariner 4 and Mars. 200fr, Gemini, Vostok and earth.

1967, Aug. 1   Engr.   Perf. 13
C53 AP25 50fr multicolored   .65 .30
C54 AP25 75fr multicolored   1.10 .35
C55 AP25 100fr multicolored   1.60 .60
C56 AP25 200fr multicolored   2.75 1.50
Nos. C53-C56 (4)   6.10 2.75
Space explorations.

African Postal Union Issue, 1967
Common Design Type

1967, Sept. 9   Engr.   Perf. 13
C57 CD124 100fr ver, ol & emer   1.25 .60

Boy Scouts, Tents and Jamboree Emblem — AP26

Design: 70c, Borah Peak, Idaho; tents, Scout sign and Jamboree emblem.

1967, Sept. 29
C58 AP26 50fr multicolored   1.00 .30
C59 AP26 70fr multicolored   1.40 .50
12th Boy Scout World Jamboree, Farragut State Park, ID, Aug. 1-9.

Sikorsky S-43 and Map of Africa — AP27

1967, Oct. 2   Photo.   Perf. 13
C60 AP27 30fr multicolored   .65 .30
30th anniv. of the 1st airmail connection by Aeromaritime Lines from Casablanca to Pointe-Noire.

Men of Four Races Dancing on Globe — AP28

1968, Feb 8   Engr.   Perf. 13
C61 AP28 70fr dk brn, ultra & em-
er   1.25 .60
Friendship among peoples.

The Oath of the Horatii, by Jacques Louis David — AP29

Paintings: 25fr, On the Barricades, by Delacroix. No. C63, Grandfather and Grandson, by Ghirlandajo, vert. No. C64, The Demolition of the Bastille, by Hubert Robert. 200fr, Negro Woman Arranging Peonies, by Jean F. Bazille.

1968   Photo.   Perf. 12x12½, 12½x12
C62 AP29 25fr multicolored   1.75 .35
C63 AP29 30fr multicolored   .90 .30
C64 AP29 30fr multicolored   1.75 .50

C65 AP29 100fr multicolored   2.25 .90
C66 AP29 200fr multicolored   5.00 1.75
Nos. C62-C66 (5)   11.65 3.80
Issue dates: Nos. C62, C64, Aug. 15. Nos. C63, C65-C66, Mar. 20.
See Nos. C78-C81, C111-C115.

Early Automobile Type
1968, July 29   Photo.   Perf. 13x12½
C67 A50 150fr Ford, 1915   3.50 1.75
C68 A50 200fr Citroen, 1922   5.25 1.75

Europafrica Issue

Square Knot — AP30

1968, July 20   Photo.   Perf. 13
C69 AP30 50fr multicolored   1.00 .50
5th anniv. of the economic agreement between the European Economic Community and the African and Malgache Union.

Martin Luther King, Jr. — AP31

Robert F. Kennedy — AP32

1968, Aug. 5   Perf. 12½
C70 AP31 50fr lt grn, Prus grn &
blk   1.10 .40

1968, Sept. 30 Photo. Perf. 13x12½
C71 AP32 50fr dp car, ap grn & blk .85 .40

Running — AP33

Olympic Rings and: 20fr, Soccer, vert. 60fr, Boxing, vert. 85fr, High jump.

1968, Dec. 27   Engr.   Perf. 13
C72 AP33 5fr emer, brt bl &
choc   .25 .20
C73 AP33 20fr dk bl, brn & dk
grn   .45 .25
C74 AP33 60fr mar, brt grn &
choc   .90 .60
C75 AP33 85fr blk, car rose &
choc   1.75 .85
Nos. C72-C75 (4)   3.35 1.90
19th Olympic Games, Mexico City, 10/12-27.

PHILEXAFRIQUE Issue

G. De Gueidan, by Nicolas de Largillière AP34

1968, Dec. 30   Photo.   Perf. 12½
C76 AP34 100fr pink & multi   3.00 1.75

Issued to publicize PHILEXAFRIQUE, Philatelic Exhibition, in Abidjan, Feb. 14-23. Printed with alternating pink label.
See Nos. C89-C93.

2nd PHILEXAFRIQUE Issue
Common Design Type

Design: 50fr, Middle Congo No. 72 and Pointe-Noire harbor.

1969, Feb. 14   Engr.   Perf. 13
C77 CD128 50fr car rose, sl grn
        & bis brn   1.75 1.75

Painting Type of 1968.

Paintings: 25fr, Battle of Rivoli, by Carle Vernet. 50fr, Battle of Marengo, by Jacques Augustin Pajou. 75fr, Battle of Friedland, by Horace Vernet. 100fr, Battle of Jena, by Charles Thevenin.

1969, May 20   Photo.   Perf. 12x12½
C78 AP29 25fr vio bl & multi   1.25 .45
C79 AP29 50fr cop red & multi   1.75 .80
C80 AP29 75fr grn & multi   3.00 1.10
C81 AP29 100fr brn & multi   5.00 1.40
    Nos. C78-C81 (4)   11.00 3.75

Bicentenary of birth of Napoleon I.

Ernesto Ché Guevara — AP35

1969, June 10   Photo.   Perf. 12½
C82 AP35 90fr brn, org & blk   1.00 .50

Issued in memory of Ernesto Ché Guevara (1928-1967), Cuban revolutionist.

Doll, Train and Space Toy — AP36

1969, June 20   Engr.   Perf. 13
C83 AP36 100fr mag, org & gray   1.50 .75

International Toy Fair, Nuremberg, Germany.

Europafrica Issue, 1969

Ribbon Tied Around Bar — AP37

1969, Aug. 5   Photo.   Perf. 13x12
C84 AP37 50fr bl grn, lil & blk   .90 .35

See note after Chad No. C11.

Armstrong, Aldrin and Collins — AP38

Souvenir Sheet

Design: No. C85b, Blast-off from Moon.

Embossed on Gold Foil
1969, Sept. 15   Imperf.
C85 AP38 1000fr #a-b   40.00 37.50

See note after Algeria No. 427. No. C85 contains one each of Nos. C85a and C85b with simulated perforations.

Painter, Poto-Poto School — AP39

150fr, Sculpture lesson (man, infant and sculpture). 200fr, Potter working on vase.

1970, Feb. 20   Engr.   Perf. 13
C86 AP39 100fr multicolored   2.25 .60
C87 AP39 150fr multicolored   3.00 .95
C88 AP39 200fr multicolored   4.50 1.75
    Nos. C86-C88 (3)   9.75 3.30

Painting Type (Philexafrique)

Paintings: 150fr, Child with Cherries, by John Russell. 200fr, Erasmus, by Hans Holbein the Younger. 250fr, "Silence" (head), by Bernardino Luini. 300fr, Scene from the Massacre of Scio, by Delacroix. 500fr, The Capture of Constantinople by the Crusaders, by Delacroix.

1970   Photo.   Perf. 12½
C89 AP34 150fr lil & multi   4.50 1.50
C90 AP34 200fr multicolored   5.75 1.75
C91 AP34 250fr brn & multi   6.25 2.25
C92 AP34 300fr multicolored   8.00 3.25
C93 AP34 500fr brn & multi   13.50 4.50
    Nos. C89-C93 (5)   38.00 13.25

Aurichalcite — AP40

1970, Mar. 20
C94 AP40 100fr shown   5.25 1.75
C95 AP40 150fr Dioptase   8.00 2.50

Lenin — AP41

Karl Marx — AP42

1970, June 25   Photo.   Perf. 12½
C96 AP41 45fr shown   1.00 .35
C97 AP41 75fr Lenin, seated   1.75 .50

Centenary of the birth of Lenin (1870-1924), Russian communist leader.

1970, July 10   Engr.   Perf. 13
Design: No. C99, Friedrich Engels.
C98 AP42 50fr emer, dk brn & dk
        red   1.50 .35
C99 AP42 50fr ultra, dk brn & dk
        red   1.50 .35

Karl Marx (1818-1883) and Friedrich Engels (1820-1895), German socialist writers.

Otto Lilienthal's Glider, 1891 — AP43

Designs: 50fr, "Spirit of St. Louis," Lindbergh's first transatlantic solo flight, 1927. 70fr, Sputnik 1, first satellite in space. 90fr, First man on the moon, Apollo 11, 1969.

1970, Sept. 5   Engr.   Perf. 13
C100 AP43 45fr dp car, bl & ol
        bis   1.00 .30
C101 AP43 50fr emer, sl grn &
        brn   1.00 .35
C102 AP43 70fr brt bl, ol bis &
        dp car   1.25 .50
C103 AP43 90fr brn, bl & ol gray   1.90 .75
    Nos. C100-C103 (4)   5.15 1.90

Forerunners of space exploration.

Saint on Horseback AP44

Marilyn Monroe and NYC — AP45

Designs from Stained Glass Windows, Brazzaville Cathedral: 150fr, Saint with staff. 250fr, The Elevation of the Host, from rose window.

1970, Dec. 10   Photo.   Perf. 12½
C104 AP44 100fr multicolored   1.40 .50
C105 AP44 150fr multicolored   1.90 .85
C106 AP44 250fr multicolored   3.25 1.75
    a.   Souv. sheet of 3, #C104-C106   6.75 6.75
    Nos. C104-C106 (3)   6.55 3.10

Christmas 1970.

1971, Mar. 16   Engr.   Perf. 13

Portraits: 150fr, Martine Carol and Paris. 200fr, Erich von Stroheim and Vienna. 250fr, Sergei Eisenstein and Moscow.

C107 AP45 100fr brt grn, red
        brn & ultra   7.00 .50
C108 AP45 150fr brn, brt lil &
        ultra   7.00 .75
C109 AP45 200fr choc & ultra   7.00 1.10
C110 AP45 250fr brt grn, brn
        vio & ultra   7.00 1.25
    Nos. C107-C110 (4)   28.00 3.60

History of motion pictures.

Painting Type of 1968

Paintings: 100fr, Christ Carrying Cross, by Paolo Veronese. 150fr, Christ on the Cross, Burgundian School, 1500, vert. 200fr, Descent from the Cross, by Rogier van der Weyden. 250fr, Christ Laid in the Tomb, Flemish School, 1500, vert. 500fr, Resurrection, by Hans Memling, vert.

1971, Apr. 26   Photo.   Perf. 13
C111 AP29 100fr green & multi   1.75 .75
C112 AP29 150fr green & multi   2.75 .90
C113 AP29 200fr green & multi   4.00 1.10
C114 AP29 250fr green & multi   4.50 1.60
C115 AP29 500fr green & multi   10.00 3.00
    Nos. C111-C115 (5)   23.00 7.35

Easter 1971.

Map of Africa and Telecommunications System — AP46

1971, June 18   Photo.   Perf. 12½
C116 AP46 70fr bl, gray & dk brn   .80 .30
C117 AP46 85fr bl, lil rose & dk
        brn   1.25 .35
C118 AP46 90fr grn, yel & dk brn   1.60 .70
    Nos. C116-C118 (3)   3.65 1.35

Pan-African telecommunications system.

Globe and Waves — AP47

1971, June 19
C119 AP47 65fr lt bl & multi   .70 .30

3rd World Telecommunications Day.

Japanese Mask
and Play — AP48

Olympic Torch
and
Rings — AP49

Design: 150fr, Japanese and African women, symbolic leaves.

1971, June 28　Engr.　Perf. 13
C120　AP48　75fr lil, blk & mag　1.00　.70
C121　AP48　150fr dk brn, brn red
　　　　& red lil　1.60　1.10

PHILATOKYO '71 International Stamp Exhibition, Tokyo, Apr. 20-30.

13th World Boy Scout Jamboree, Japan, gold foil 1000fr airmail and silver foil souv. sheet of four 90fr, issued July 14. Nos. 71C01-71C02.

1971, July 20　Engr.　Perf. 13
350fr, Olympic rings and various sports.
C122　AP49　150fr multi　1.90　.95
C123　AP49　350fr multi, horiz.　4.50　2.50

Pre-Olympic Year, 1971.

Scout Emblem, Japanese Dragon and
African Carved Canoe — AP50

Designs (Boy Scout Emblem and): 90fr, Japanese mask and African boy, vert. 100fr, Japanese woman and African drummer, vert. 250fr, Congolese mask.

1971, Aug. 25
C124　AP50　85fr multicolored　1.10　.30
C125　AP50　90fr multicolored　1.25　.35
C126　AP50　100fr multicolored　1.60　.45
C127　AP50　250fr multicolored　3.25　.90
　　　Nos. C124-C127 (4)　7.20　2.00

13th Boy Scout World Jamboree, Asagiri Plain, Japan, Aug. 2-10.

Olympic Rings and Running — AP51

Designs (Olympic Rings and): 85fr, Hurdles. 90fr, Weight lifting, boxing, discus, running, javelin. 100fr, Wrestling. 150fr, Boxing.

1971, Sept. 30
C128　AP51　75fr plum, bl & dk
　　　　brn　.75　.35
C129　AP51　85fr scar, sl & dk
　　　　brn　.85　.35
C130　AP51　90fr vio bl & dk brn　1.10　.60

C131　AP51　100fr brn & slate　1.40　.60
C132　AP51　150fr grn, red & dk
　　　　brn　2.40　1.00
　　　Nos. C128-C132 (5)　6.50　2.90

75th anniv. of the 1st modern Olympic Games.

Congo No. C36 and de
Gaulle — AP52

Pres. Marien
Ngouabi's Tribute
to de
Gaulle — AP53

Design: No. C135, Charles de Gaulle.

1971, Nov. 9
C133　AP52　500fr slate grn &
　　　　multi　18.00　15.00

**Lithographed; Gold Embossed
Perf. 12½**
C134　AP53　1000fr gold, grn
　　　　& red　27.50　20.00
C135　AP53　1000fr gold, grn
　　　　& red　27.50　20.00
　a.　Pair, #C134-C135　55.00　55.00

Charles de Gaulle (1890-1970), president of France.

**African Postal Union Issue, 1971
Common Design Type**

Design: 100fr, Allegory of Congo Republic (woman) and UAMPT Building, Brazzaville.

1971, Nov. 13　Photo.　Perf. 13x13½
C136　CD135　100fr bl & multi　1.40　.75

Flag of Congo Republic and
"Revolution" — AP54

1971, Nov. 30
C137　AP54　100fr red & multi　1.75　.60

8th anniversary of revolution.

Workers and Flag — AP55

40fr, Flag of Congo Republic and sun.

1971, Dec. 31　Photo.　Perf. 13x12½
C138　AP55　30fr multicolored　.50　.25
C139　AP55　40fr red & multi　1.10　.40

2nd anniv. of founding of Congolese Labor Party (#C138), and adoption of red flag (#C139).

Book Year
Emblem — AP56

1972, June 3　Litho.　Perf. 12½
C140　AP56　50fr red, grn & yel　.85　.40

International Book Year 1972.

Congolese Soccer Team — AP57

#C142, Captain of winning team and cup, vert.

1973, Feb. 22　Photo.　Perf. 13
C141　AP57　100fr ultra, red & blk　1.50　.75
C142　AP57　100fr red, yel & blk　1.50　.75

Girl Holding Bird,
Environment
Emblem — AP58

1973, Mar. 5　　　Engr.
C143　AP58　85fr org, slate grn &
　　　　bl　1.75　.90

UN Conference on Human Environment, Stockholm, Sweden, June 5-16, 1972.

Miles Davis
AP59

Designs: 140fr, Ella Fitzgerald. 160fr, Count Basie. 175fr, John Coltrane.

1973, Mar. 5　Photo.　Perf. 13x13½
C144　AP59　125fr multicolored　4.00　.95
C145　AP59　140fr multicolored　4.00　1.00
C146　AP59　160fr multicolored　5.00　1.50
C147　AP59　175fr multicolored　5.00　1.50
　　　Nos. C144-C147 (4)　18.00　4.95

Black American jazz musicians.

Olympic Rings, Hurdling — AP60

1973, Mar. 15　Engr.　Perf. 13
C148　AP60　100fr shown　1.10　.60
C149　AP60　150fr Pole vault, vert.　1.75　.90
C150　AP60　250fr Wrestling　2.75　1.50
　　　Nos. C148-C150 (3)　5.60　3.00

20th Olympic Games, Munich, 8/26-9/11/72.

Refinery and Storage Tanks,
Djéno — AP61

Designs: 230fr, Off-shore drilling platform, vert. 240fr, Workers assembling drill, vert. 260fr, Off-shore drilling installation.

1973, Mar. 20
C151　AP61　180fr red, bl & indi-
　　　　go　3.25　1.50
C152　AP61　230fr red, bl & blk　4.00　1.50
C153　AP61　240fr red, ind & brn　4.50　1.60
C154　AP61　260fr red, bl & blk　7.25　2.25
　　　Nos. C151-C154 (4)　19.00　6.85

Oil installations, Pointe-Noire.

Astronauts, Landing Module and Lunar
Rover on Moon — AP62

1973, Mar. 31
C155　AP62　250fr multicolored　4.50　1.75

Apollo 17 US moon mission, 12/7-19/72.

ITU Emblem,
Symbols of
Communications
AP63

1973, May 24　Engr.　Perf. 13
C156　AP63　120fr multicolored　2.25　.90

5th International Telecommunications Day.

White Horse, by Delacroix — AP64

Designs: Paintings by Eugene Delacroix.

1973, June 30　Photo.　Perf. 13
C157　AP64　150fr shown　2.25　1.50
C158　AP64　250fr Lion sleeping　5.00　2.40
C159　AP64　300fr Lion and tiger　5.25　2.40
　　　Nos. C157-C159 (3)　12.50　6.40

See Nos. C169-C171.

Copernicus and Heliocentric
System — AP65

1973, June 30　　　Engr.
C160　AP65　50fr multicolored　1.00　.45

500th anniversary of the birth of Nicolaus Copernicus (1473-1543), Polish astronomer.

Plane, Ship, Rocket, Village, Sun and Clouds — AP66

1973, July
C161 AP66 50fr red & multi 1.40 .60
Cent. of intl. meteorological cooperation.

Pres. Marien Ngouabi — AP67

1973, Aug. 12 Photo. Perf. 13
C162 AP67 30fr multicolored .35 .20
C163 AP67 40fr aqua & multi .45 .20
C164 AP67 75fr red & multi 1.00 .35
 Nos. C162-C164 (3) 1.80 .75

10th anniversary of independence.

Stamps, Album, African Woman AP68

40fr, #C167, Stamps in shape of map of Congo, album, globe. #C168, Like 30fr.

1973, Aug. 12
C165 AP68 30fr pur & multi 1.90 .30
C166 AP68 40fr multicolored .25 .20
C167 AP68 100fr dk brn & multi 3.75 .80
C168 AP68 100fr ocher & multi .90 .40
 Nos. C165-C168 (4) 6.80 1.70

Nos. C165, C168 for the 10th anniv. of the revolution, Nos. C166-C167 the Intl. Philatelic Exhib., Brazzaville.

Painting Type of 1973 Inscribed "EUROPAFRIQUE"

Designs: Details from "Earth and Paradise," by Jan Brueghel, the Elder.

1973, Oct. 10 Photo. Perf. 13
C169 AP64 100fr Spotted hyena 3.00 1.50
C170 AP64 100fr Leopard and lion 3.00 1.50
C171 AP64 100fr Elephant and creatures 3.00 1.50
 Nos. C169-C171 (3) 9.00 4.50

US and Russian Spacecraft Docking — AP69

Design: 80fr, US and USSR spacecraft docked in space and emblems of 1975 joint space mission.

1973, Oct. 15 Engr. Perf. 13
C172 AP69 40fr bl, red & brn .50 .35
C173 AP69 80fr red, grn & bl 1.10 .50
Planned joint US and Soviet space missions.

For overprint see No. C251.

UPU Monument, Satellites, Big Dipper — AP70

1973, Nov. 20 Engr. Perf. 13
C174 AP70 80fr vio bl & lt bl 1.00 .35
Universal Postal Union Day.

Astronauts Working in Space — AP71

40fr, Spacecraft & Skylab docking in space.

1973, Nov. 30
C175 AP71 30fr ultra, sl grn & choc .60 .20
C176 AP71 40fr mag, org & sl grn .60 .25
Skylab, first space laboratory.

Goalkeeper, Soccer — AP72

Design: 100fr, Soccer player kicking ball.

1973, Dec. 20
C177 AP72 40fr sl grn, sepia & brn .75 .25
C178 AP72 100fr pur, red & slate grn 1.90 .75

World Soccer Cup, Munich, 1974.

John F. Kennedy (1917-1963) AP73

1973, Dec. 20 Photo. Perf. 12½
C179 AP73 150fr ultra, gold & blk 1.75 .90

Runners — AP74

Flag over Map of Congo — AP75

1973, Dec. 20 Engr. Perf. 13
C180 AP74 40fr sl grn, red & brn .60 .25
C181 AP74 100fr red, sl grn, & brn 1.75 .75
2nd African Games, Lagos, Nigeria.

1973, Dec. 31 Photo.
C182 AP75 40fr dp grn & multi .50 .25
4th anniversary of Congolese Labor Party and of the Congo Red Flag.

Soccer and Games Emblem — AP76

1974, June 20 Photo. Perf. 13
C183 AP76 250fr multicolored 3.75 1.90
World Cup Soccer Championship, Munich, June 13-July 7.

Astronauts Yuri A. Gagarin and Alan B. Shepard — AP77

Designs: 30fr, Space, globe, Russian and American flags with names of astronauts who perished in space. 100fr, Alexei Leonov and Neil A. Armstrong in space and on moon.

1974, June 30 Engr. Perf. 13
C184 AP77 30fr red, ultra & brn .45 .20
C185 AP77 40fr red, bl & brn .60 .25
C186 AP77 100fr car, grn & brn 1.40 .90
 Nos. C184-C186 (3) 2.45 1.35
For overprint see No. C254.

Soccer Game Superimposed on Ball — AP78

Link-up Emblem, Stages of Link-up — AP79

1974, July 31 Photo. Perf. 13
C187 AP78 250fr multicolored 3.50 1.75
Germany's victory in World Cup Soccer Championship.

1974, Aug. 8 Engr. Perf. 13
300fr, Spacecraft docking over globe.
C188 AP79 200fr pur, bl & red 2.25 1.10
C189 AP79 300fr multi, horiz. 3.50 1.50
Russo-American space cooperation.
For overprint see No. C255.

Symbols of Communications, UPU Emblem — AP80

1974, Aug. 10
C190 AP80 500fr blk & red 6.75 3.00
Centenary of Universal Postal Union.
For surcharge see No. C194.

Lenin and Pendulum Trace Pattern — AP81

1974, Sept. 16 Engr. Perf. 13
C191 AP81 150fr multicolored 2.10 1.10
Lenin (1870-1924).

Churchill and Order of the Garter AP82

Marconi and Wireless Telegraph AP83

1974, Oct. 1 Litho. Perf. 13
C192 AP82 200fr lt grn & multi 3.00 1.25
C193 AP83 200fr lt ultra & multi 3.00 1.25

No. C190 Surcharged in Violet Blue with New Value, 2 Bars and: "9 OCTOBER 1974"

1974, Oct. 9
C194 AP80 300fr on 500fr multi 4.25 2.75
Universal Postal Union Day.

UDEAC Issue

Presidents and Flags of Cameroun, CAR, Gabon and Congo — AP83a

1974, Dec. 8 Photo. Perf. 13
C195 AP83a 100fr gold & multi 1.00 .50
See note after Cameroun No. 595.

Regatta at Argenteuil, by
Monet — AP84

Impressionist Paintings: 40fr, Seated
Dancer, by Degas. 50fr, Girl on Swing, by
Renoir. 75fr, Girl with Straw Hat, by Renoir.
All vertical.

1974, Dec. 15
C196	AP84	30fr gold & multi	1.50	.35
C197	AP84	40fr gold & multi	2.00	.35
C198	AP84	50fr gold & multi	2.75	.50
C199	AP84	75fr gold & multi	3.25	.80
		Nos. C196-C199 (4)	9.50	2.00

National
Fair
AP85

1974, Dec. 20
C200	AP85	30fr multicolored	.90	.35

National Fair, Aug. 24-Sept. 8.

Flags of Participating Nations, Map of
Africa — AP86

1974, Dec. 20   **Perf. 13**
C201	AP86	40fr ultra & multi	.65	.35

Conference of Chiefs of State of Central and
East Africa, Brazzaville, Aug. 31-Sept. 2.

"Five
Weeks in a
Balloon," by
Jules Verne
AP87

Design: 50fr, "Around the World in 80
Days," by Jules Verne.

1975, June 30   **Litho.**   **Perf. 12½**
C202	AP87	40fr multicolored	1.40	.50
C203	AP87	50fr multicolored	1.75	1.00

Jules Verne (1828-1905), French science
fiction writer, 70th death anniversary.

Paris-Brussels Train, 1890 — AP88

Design: 75fr, Santa Fe, 1880.

1975, June 30
C204	AP88	50fr ocher & multi	2.00	.75
C205	AP88	75fr lt bl & multi	4.25	.90

Soyuz and Apollo-Soyuz
Emblem — AP89

Design: 100fr, Apollo and emblem.

1975, July 20   **Litho.**   **Perf. 12½**
C206	AP89	95fr org, blk & mag	1.25	.50
C207	AP89	100fr vio, bl & blk	1.40	.60

Apollo Soyuz space test project (Russo-
American space cooperation), launching July
15; link-up, July 17.
For overprints see Nos. C252-C253.

Bicycling and Montreal Olympic
Emblem — AP90

Designs (Montreal Olympic Emblem and):
40fr, Boxing, vert. 50fr, Basketball, vert. 95fr,
High jump. 100fr, Javelin. 150fr, Running.

Perf. 12½x13, 13x12½

1975, Oct. 30   **Photo.**
C208	AP90	40fr multicolored	.50	.25
C209	AP90	50fr red & multi	.60	.25
C210	AP90	85fr bl & multi	1.00	.35
C211	AP90	95fr org & multi	1.10	.45
C212	AP90	100fr multicolored	1.40	.50
C213	AP90	150fr gold & multi	1.75	.80
		Nos. C208-C213 (6)	6.35	2.60

Pre-Olympic Year 1975.

Map of Africa,
Sports and
Flags — AP91

Workers and
Flag — AP92

1975, Dec. 20   **Litho.**   **Perf. 12½**
C214	AP91	30fr multicolored	.60	.35

1st African Games, Brazzaville, 10th anniv.

1975, Dec. 31   **Litho.**   **Perf. 12½**
C215	AP92	60fr multicolored	.60	.25

Congolese Labor Party (P.C.T.), 6th anniv.

Alphonse Fondere — AP93

Historic Ships: 5fr, like 30fr. 10fr, 40fr,
Hamburg, 1839. 15fr, 50fr, Gomer, 1831. 20fr,
60fr, Great Eastern, 1858. 95fr, J.M. White II,
1878.

1976   **Engr.**   **Perf. 13**
C216	AP93	5fr multicolored	.25	.20
C217	AP93	10fr multicolored	.25	.20
C218	AP93	15fr multicolored	.30	.20
C219	AP93	20fr multicolored	.50	.20
C220	AP93	30fr multicolored	.75	.25
C221	AP93	40fr multicolored	1.00	.35
C222	AP93	50fr multicolored	1.25	.50
C223	AP93	60fr multicolored	1.75	.60
C224	AP93	95fr multicolored	2.50	1.00
		Nos. C216-C224 (9)	8.55	3.50

Issued: #C216-C219, May; #C220-C224,
Mar. 7.

Europafrica Issue 1976

Peasant Family, by Louis Le
Nain — AP94

Paintings: 80fr, Boy with Top, by Jean B.
Chardin. 95fr, Venus and Aeneas, by Nicolas
Poussin. 100fr, The Rape of the Sabine
Women, by Jacques Louis David.

1976, Mar. 20   **Litho.**   **Perf. 12½**
C225	AP94	60fr gold & multi	1.25	.45
C226	AP94	80fr gold & multi	1.40	.70
C227	AP94	95fr gold & multi	1.90	.70
C228	AP94	100fr gold & multi	2.10	.85
		Nos. C225-C228 (4)	6.65	2.70

Nos. C225-C228 printed in sheets of 8
stamps and horizontal gutter with commemorative inscription.

Telephone Type of 1976

1976, Apr. 25   **Litho.**   **Perf. 12½x13**
C229	A107	60fr pink, mar & crim	.90	.30

Sports Type of 1976

Designs: 150fr, Runner and map of Central
Africa. 200fr, Discus and map.

1976, Oct. 25   **Perf. 12½**
C230	A110	150fr multicolored	1.75	.75
C231	A110	200fr multicolored	2.75	1.10

Map of Africa, Flag
and OAU
Headquarters
AP95

1976, Dec. 16   **Typo.**   **Perf. 13x14**
C232	AP95	60fr multicolored	.70	.35

13th anniv. of the Organization for African
Unity.

Europafrica Issue

Map of Europe and Africa — AP96

1977, June 28   **Litho.**   **Perf. 13**
C233	AP96	75fr multicolored	.90	.45

Headdress Type of 1977

1977, June 30   **Perf. 12½**

250fr, Two straw caps. 300fr, Beaded cap.
C234	A118	250fr multicolored	2.75	1.50
C235	A118	300fr multicolored	3.00	1.75

Zeppelin Type of 1977
Souvenir Sheet

Design: 500fr, LZ 127 over US Capitol.

1977, Aug. 5   **Litho.**   **Perf. 11**
C236	A120	500fr multicolored	6.75	2.00

No. C236 exists imperf.

Checkerboard
AP97

1977, Aug. 20   **Engr.**   **Perf. 13**
C237	AP97	60fr red & blk	.90	.35

Lomé Convention on General Agreement on
Tariffs and Trade (GATT).

Newton, Intelsat Satellite and Classical
"Planets" — AP98

1977, Aug. 25
C238	AP98	140fr multicolored	2.00	.90

Isaac Newton (1642-1727), natural philosopher and mathematician.

Elizabeth II Type of 1977
Souvenir Sheet

Design: 500fr, Royal family on balcony.

1977, Dec. 21   **Litho.**   **Perf. 14**
C239	A128	500fr multicolored	5.75	1.75

For overprint see No. C244.

Mallard
AP99

Birds: 75fr, Purple heron, vert. 150fr, Reed
warbler, vert. 240fr, Hoopoe, vert.

1978, May 22   **Perf. 13x12½, 12½x13**
C240	AP99	65fr multicolored	1.10	.50
C241	AP99	75fr multicolored	1.40	.50
C242	AP99	150fr multicolored	3.25	1.00
C243	AP99	240fr multicolored	4.75	1.75
		Nos. C240-C243 (4)	10.50	3.75

Souvenir Sheet

No. C239 Overprinted in Silver:
"ANNIVERSAIRE DU /
COURONNEMENT / 1953-1978"

1978, Sept.   **Litho.**   **Perf. 14**
C244   A128   500fr multicolored   4.50   3.00

25th anniv. of coronation of Elizabeth II.

Philexafrique II-Essen Issue
Common Design Types

No. C245, Leopard and Congo No. C243.
No. C246, Eagle and Wurttemberg No. 1.

1978, Nov. 1   **Litho.**   **Perf. 12½**
C245   CD138   100fr multicolored   2.00   1.10
C246   CD139   100fr multicolored   2.00   1.10
 a.   Pair, #C245-C246   5.25   5.25

Map of Africa,
Satellites
AP100

Map of Africa and
People — AP101

1978, Nov. 25   **Engr.**   **Perf. 13**
C247   AP100   100fr multicolored   1.25   .50

Pan-African Telecommunications Network,
PANAFEL.

1979, Aug. 2   **Litho.**   **Perf. 12½**
C248   AP101   45fr multicolored   .50   .25
C249   AP101   75fr multicolored   .85   .40

5th Conference of Panafrican Youth Movement, Brazzaville, Aug. 2-7.

Abala
Peasant
Woman
AP102

1979, Aug. 20
C250   AP102   150fr multicolored   1.75   .90

Nos. C173, C206-C207, C186, C189
Overprinted "ALUNISSAGE APOLLO
XI / JUILLET 1969" and Emblem
Perf. 13, 12½

1979, Nov. 5   **Engr., Litho.**
C251   AP69   80fr multicolored   1.00   .90
C252   AP89   95fr multicolored   1.50   1.00
C253   AP89   100fr multicolored   2.00   1.00
C254   AP77   100fr multicolored   2.00   1.00
C255   AP79   300fr multicolored   3.50   2.75
 Nos. C251-C255 (5)   10.00   6.65

Apollo 11 moon landing, 10th anniversary.

Runner, Olympic Rings — AP103

Pre-Olympic Year: 100fr, Boxing. 200fr,
Fencing. 300fr, Soccer. 500fr, Moscow '80
emblem.

1979   **Litho.**   **Perf. 13½**
C256   AP103   65fr multi   .50   .20
C257   AP103   100fr multi   1.00   .25
C258   AP103   200fr multi, vert.   2.00   .50
C259   AP103   300fr multi, vert.   2.50   .75
C260   AP103   500fr multi, vert.   5.00   1.25
 Nos. C256-C260 (5)   11.00   2.95

Cross-Country
Skiing — AP104

Lake Placid '80 Emblem and: 60fr, Slalom.
200fr, Ski jump, 350fr, Downhill skiing, horiz.
500fr, Woman skier.

1979, Dec   **Perf. 14½**
Size: 24x42mm, 42x24mm
C261   AP104   40fr multicolored   .45   .20
C262   AP104   60fr multicolored   .60   .20
C263   AP104   200fr multicolored   2.00   .45
C264   AP104   300fr multicolored   3.50   .90
Size: 31½x46½mm
Perf. 14
C265   AP104   500fr multicolored   5.00   1.40
 Nos. C261-C265 (5)   11.55   3.15

13th Winter Olympic Games, Lake Placid,
NY, Feb. 12-24, 1980.

Overprinted with Names of Winners

1980, Apr. 28
C266   AP104   40fr Zimiatov   .40   .20
C267   AP104   60fr Moser-Proell   .50   .25
C268   AP104   200fr Tomanen   1.90   .75
C269   AP104   350fr Stock   3.50   1.25
C270   AP104   500fr Stenmark-
               Wenzel   4.75   1.90
 Nos. C266-C270 (5)   11.05   4.35

Long Jump, Olympic Rings — AP105

1980, May 2   **Litho.**   **Perf. 14½**
C271   AP105   75fr multi, vert.   .90   .20
C272   AP105   150fr multi   1.40   .30
C273   AP105   250fr multi, vert.   2.25   .50
C274   AP105   350fr multi, vert.   3.25   .70
 Nos. C271-C274 (4)   7.80   1.70

Souvenir Sheet

C275   AP105   500fr multi   5.00   1.60

22nd Summer Olympic Games, Moscow,
July 19-Aug. 3.
For overprints see Nos. C292-C296.

Stadium, Mascot, Madrid Club
Emblem — AP106

Stadium, Mascot and Club Emblem: 75fr,
Zaragoza. 100fr, Madrid Athletic Club. 150fr,
Valencia. 175fr, Spain. 250fr, Barcelona.

1980, June 23   **Litho.**   **Perf. 14x13½**
C276   AP106   60fr multicolored   .60   .20
C277   AP106   75fr multicolored   .60   .20
C278   AP106   100fr multicolored   1.00   .25

C279   AP106   150fr multicolored   1.40   .35
C280   AP106   175fr multicolored   1.60   .50
 Nos. C276-C280 (5)   5.20   1.50

Souvenir Sheet

C281   AP106   250fr multicolored   2.75   1.25

World Soccer Cup 1982.
For overprints see Nos. C298-C303.

Adoration of the Shepherds — AP107

Rembrandt Paintings: 100fr, The Burial.
200fr, Christ at Emmaus. 300fr, Annunciation,
vert. 500fr, Crucifixion, vert.

1980, July 4   **Perf. 12½**
C282   AP107   65fr multicolored   .70   .30
C283   AP107   100fr multicolored   1.10   .50
C284   AP107   200fr multicolored   2.25   .60
C285   AP107   300fr multicolored   3.25   .85
C286   AP107   500fr multicolored   5.75   1.50
 Nos. C282-C286 (5)   13.05   3.75

Albert Camus (1913-1960),
Writer — AP108

Design: 150fr, Jacques Offenbach (1819-
1880), composer, vert.

1980, July 5   **Engr.**   **Perf. 13**
C287   AP108   100fr multicolored   1.25   .50
C288   AP108   200fr multicolored   2.25   1.25

Raffia Dancing Skirts — AP109

Traditional Dancing Costumes: 300fr, Tam-
tam dancers, vert. 350fr, Masks.

1980, Aug. 6   **Litho.**   **Perf. 13½**
C289   AP109   250fr multicolored   2.75   .95
C290   AP109   300fr multicolored   3.25   1.50
C291   AP109   350fr multicolored   4.00   1.90
 Nos. C289-C291 (3)   10.00   4.35

Nos. C271-C275 Overprinted with
Winner and Country

75fr, Dombrowki (RDA), 150fr, Saneiev
(URSS), 250fr, Simeoni (IT), 350fr, Thompson
(GB)

1980, Nov. 14   **Litho.**   **Perf. 14½**
C292   AP105   75fr multicolored   .70   .30
C293   AP105   150fr multicolored   1.40   .60
C294   AP105   250fr multicolored   2.25   .90
C295   AP105   350fr multicolored   3.25   1.50
 Nos. C292-C295 (4)   7.60   3.30

Souvenir Sheet

C296   AP105   500fr multicolored   5.00   4.00

The Studio by Picasso — AP109a

1981, July 4   **Perf. 12½**
C296A   AP109a   100fr shown   1.40   .50
C296B   AP109a   150fr Land-
                scape   2.00   .75
C296C   AP109a   200fr Cannes
                Studio   2.50   1.00
C296D   AP109a   300fr Still Life   4.50   1.50
C296E   AP109a   500fr Still Life,
                diff.   6.75   2.50
 Nos. C296A-C296E (5)   17.15   6.25

1st Seminar
on
Petroleum,
Gas and
Energy
Alternatives,
Brazzaville
AP109b

45fr, Emblem, oil platform, other energy
sources. 100fr, Emblem, map, oil platforms.
150fr, Map, other energy sources. 200fr, Maps
of Africa, Congo, oil worker.

1981   **Litho.**   **Perf. 12½**
C296F   AP109b   45fr multi   20.00   13.00
C296G   AP109b   75fr multi   32.50   19.00
C296H   AP109b   100fr multi   45.00   27.50
C296I   AP109b   150fr multi   65.00   40.00
C296J   AP109b   200fr multi   90.00   50.00
 Nos. C296F-C296J (5)   252.50   149.50

1350th Anniv. of
Mohamed's
Death at
Medina — AP110

1982, July 17   **Litho.**   **Perf. 13**
C297   AP110   400fr Medina
              Mosque min-
              aret   3.75   1.75

Nos. C276-C281 Overprinted with
Finalists and/or Scores in Black on
Silver

1982, Oct. 7   **Litho.**   **Perf. 14x13½**
C298   AP106   60fr multicolored   .50   .25
C299   AP106   75fr multicolored   .60   .30
C300   AP106   100fr multicolored   .90   .45
C301   AP106   150fr multicolored   1.40   .60
C302   AP106   175fr multicolored   1.50   .60
 Nos. C298-C302 (5)   4.90   2.20

Souvenir Sheet

C303   AP106   250fr multicolored   2.25   1.90

30th Anniv. of Amelia Earhart's
Transatlantic Flight — AP111

1982, Dec. 4   **Engr.**   **Perf. 13**
C304   AP111   150fr multicolored   1.25   .75

Wind
Surfing
AP112

Various wind surfing scenes, 1984 Olympic Games, 100fr, 300fr, 400fr vert.

1983, June 4   *Litho.*   *Perf. 13*
C305 AP112 100fr multicolored   .90   .25
C306 AP112 200fr multicolored   1.75   .50
C307 AP112 300fr multicolored   2.75   .70
C308 AP112 400fr multicolored   3.50 1.00
    Nos. C305-C308 (4)   8.90 2.45
       Souvenir Sheet
C309 AP112 500fr multicolored   5.00 2.50

For overprint see No. C336.

Manned Flight Bicentenary AP113

Various balloons.

1983, June 7
C310 AP113 100fr Montgolfiere, 1783   1.10   .20
C311 AP113 200fr Flesselles, 1784   2.10   .40
C312 AP113 300fr Auguste Piccard, 1931   3.00   .60
C313 AP113 400fr Don Piccard   4.50   .90
    Nos. C310-C313 (4)   10.70 2.10
       Souvenir Sheet
C314 AP113 500fr Mail transport balloon, 1870   5.75 1.60

For overprint see No. C337.

Christmas 1983 AP114

Various Virgin and Child Paintings by Botticelli.

1984, Jan. 21   *Litho.*   *Perf. 13*
C315 AP114 150fr multicolored   1.25   .50
C316 AP114 350fr multicolored   3.00 1.10
C317 AP114 500fr multicolored   4.50 1.50
    Nos. C315-C317 (3)   8.75 3.10

Vase of Flowers, by Manet (1832-83) AP115

Paintings: 200fr, Small Holy Family, by Raphael. 300fr, La Belle Jardiniere, by Raphael. 400fr, Virgin of Loretto, by Raphael. 500fr, Portrait of Richard Wagner (1813-83), by Giuseppe Tivoli.

1984, Feb. 24   *Litho.*   *Perf. 13*
C318 AP115 100fr multicolored   .90   .30
C319 AP115 200fr multicolored   1.90   .70
C320 AP115 300fr multicolored   2.75 1.00
C321 AP115 400fr multicolored   3.75 1.40
C322 AP115 500fr multicolored   5.00 1.50
    Nos. C318-C322 (5)   14.30 4.90

1984 Summer Olympics — AP116

1984, Mar. 31   *Perf. 13*
C323 AP116 45fr Judo, vert.   .45   .20
C324 AP116 75fr Judo, diff.   .70   .25
C325 AP116 150fr Wrestling   1.40   .50
C326 AP116 175fr Fencing   1.60   .60
C327 AP116 350fr Fencing, diff.   3.25 1.10
    Nos. C323-C327 (5)   7.40 2.65
       Souvenir Sheet
C328 AP116 500fr Boxing   5.00 2.50

1984 Summer Olympic Gold Medalists — AP117

Sailing/yachting: 100fr, Stephan Van Den Berg, Netherlands, Windglider Class. 150fr, US, Soling Class. 200fr, Spain, 470 Class. 500fr, US, Flying Dutchman Class.

1984, Dec. 18   *Litho.*   *Perf. 13*
C329 AP117 100fr multi, vert.   1.00   .45
C330 AP117 150fr multi   1.40   .65
C331 AP117 200fr multi   2.00   .90
C332 AP117 500fr multi, vert.   4.50 2.25
    Nos. C329-C332 (4)   8.90 4.25

Virgin and Child, by Giovanni Bellini (c. 1430-1516) — AP118

Religious paintings: 100fr, Holy Family, by Andrea del Sarto (1486-1530). 400fr, Virgin with Angels, by Cimabue (c. 1240-1302).

1985, Feb. 12   *Litho.*   *Perf. 13*
C333 AP118 100fr multi, vert.   1.00   .45
C334 AP118 200fr multi   2.00   .90
C335 AP118 400fr multi, vert.   3.75 1.75
    Nos. C333-C335 (3)   6.75 3.10

Christmas 1984.

      Souvenir Sheets
Nos. C309, C314 Ovptd. with Exhibition in Blue or Green

1985, Mar. 8   *Perf. 13*
C336 AP112 500fr OLYMPHILEX '85 / LAUSANNE (B)   5.00 4.00
C337 AP113 500fr MOPHILA '85 / HAMBURG (G)   5.00 4.00

Audubon Birth Bicentenary — AP119

Illustrations of North American bird species by Audubon. Nos. C338-C339 vert.

1985, Apr. 11   *Perf. 13½*
C338 AP119 100fr Passiformes fringillidae   1.00   .45
C339 AP119 150fr Eudocimus ruber   1.50   .65
C340 AP119 200fr Buteo jamaicensis   1.90   .90
C341 AP119 350fr Camptorhynchus labradorius   3.75 1.50
    Nos. C338-C341 (4)   8.15 3.50

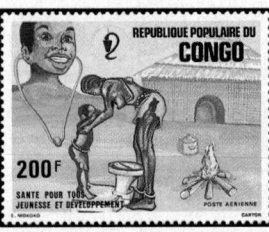

PHILEXAFRICA '85, Lome — AP120

Youths in public service activities.

1985, May 20   *Perf. 13*
C342 AP120 200fr Community health care   2.25 1.50
C343 AP120 200fr Agriculture   2.25 1.50
   a.   Pair, #C342-C343 + label   5.75 5.75

Admission to UN, 25th Anniv. — AP121

1985, Aug. 13
C344 AP121 190fr multicolored   1.75   .75

UN, 40th Anniv. — AP122

1985, Oct. 25   *Perf. 12½*
C345 AP122 180fr Rainbow, emblem   1.60   .65

Christmas — AP123

Paintings: 100fr, The Virgin and the Infant Jesus, by David. 200fr, Adoration of the Magi, by Hieronymus Bosch (1450-1516). 400fr, Virgin and Child, by Van Dyck.

1985, Dec. 20   *Litho.*   *Perf. 13*
C346 AP123 100fr multicolored   .90   .35
C347 AP123 200fr multicolored   1.90   .75
C348 AP123 400fr multicolored   3.50 1.75
    Nos. C346-C348 (3)   6.30 2.85

Nos. C346-C347 vert.

Halley's Comet — AP124

1986, Feb. 17
C349 AP124 125fr Halley, comet   1.00   .50
C350 AP124 150fr West's Comet, 1976   1.25   .60
C351 AP124 225fr Ikeya Seki's Comet, 1965   1.75   .90
C352 AP124 300fr Trajectory diagram   2.25 1.25
C353 AP124 350fr Comet, Vega probe   2.75 1.50
    Nos. C349-C353 (5)   9.00 4.75

Nos. C350-C351 vert.

Cosmos-Frantel Hotel — AP125

1986, May 1   *Perf. 13½*
C354 AP125 250fr multicolored   2.50   .90

1986 World Cup Soccer Championships, Mexico — AP126

Various soccer plays.

1986, July 22   *Litho.*   *Perf. 13*
C355 AP126 150fr multicolored   1.25   .60
C356 AP126 250fr multicolored   2.00 1.00
C357 AP126 440fr multicolored   3.75 1.75
C358 AP126 600fr multicolored   6.50 2.50
    Nos. C355-C358 (4)   13.50 5.85

Air Africa, 25th Anniv. — AP127

1986, Nov. 29   *Litho.*   *Perf. 13½*
C359 AP127 200fr multicolored   1.75   .75

1988 Winter Pre-Olympics, Calgary — AP128

1986, Dec. 15   *Perf. 13*
C360 AP128 150fr Downhill skiing   1.25   .60
C361 AP128 250fr Bobsled   2.25 1.00

C362 AP128 440fr Women's cross-country skiing 4.00 1.50
C363 AP128 600fr Ski jumping 5.75 2.40
Nos. C360-C363 (4) 13.25 5.45

Nos. C361-C362 vert.

Christmas
AP129

Paintings by Rogier van der Weyden (c.1399-1464): 250fr, Virgin and Child. 440fr, The Nativity. 500fr, Virgin with Carnation.

1986, Dec. 23 **Perf. 13½**
C364 AP129 250fr multicolored 2.25 1.00
C365 AP129 440fr multicolored 4.50 1.75
C366 AP129 500fr multicolored 5.00 2.10
Nos. C364-C366 (3) 11.75 4.85

Crocodiles, World Wildlife
Fund — AP130

1987, Jan. 22 **Perf. 13**
C367 AP130 75fr Osteolaemus tetraspis 2.75 1.10
C368 AP130 100fr Crocodylus cataphractus 3.25 1.25
C369 AP130 125fr Osteolaemus tetraspis, diff. 4.50 1.75
C370 AP130 150fr Crocodylus cataphractus, diff. 5.00 3.00
Nos. C367-C370 (4) 15.50 7.10

1988 Summer Olympics,
Seoul — AP131

1987, July 11 **Litho.** **Perf. 13**
C371 AP131 100fr Backstroke .90 .35
C372 AP131 200fr Freestyle 1.75 .75
C373 AP131 300fr Breaststroke 2.75 1.10
C374 AP131 400fr Butterfly 3.50 1.40
Nos. C371-C374 (4) 8.90 3.60
Souvenir Sheet
C375 AP131 750fr Start of event 6.75 3.50

Launch of Sputnik, First Artificial
Satellite, 30th Anniv. — AP132

1987, June 5 **Perf. 12½x12**
C376 AP132 60fr multicolored .50 .25
C377 AP132 240fr multicolored 2.25 1.10

Butterflies — AP133

1987, Sept. 4 **Perf. 12½**
C378 AP133 75fr Precis epicleli 1.00 .30
C379 AP133 120fr Deilephila nerii 1.75 .45
C380 AP133 450fr Euryphene senegalensis 5.25 1.75
C381 AP133 550fr Precis almanta 7.00 2.40
Nos. C378-C381 (4) 15.00 4.90

Coubertin, Eternal Flame and Greece
No. 125 — AP134

Cameo portrait, athletes and stamps: 120fr, Runners, France No. 198. 350fr, Congo Republic No. C22, hurdler. 600fr, High jump, Congo Republic No. C75.

1987, Nov. 4
C382 AP134 75fr shown .80 .30
C383 AP134 120fr multicolored 1.10 .45
C384 AP134 350fr multicolored 3.50 1.25
C385 AP134 600fr multicolored 5.25 2.10
Nos. C382-C385 (4) 10.65 4.10

Pierre de Coubertin (1863-1937), promulgator of the modern Olympics.

Arrival of Schweitzer in Lambarene,
75th Anniv. — AP135

1988, Apr. 17 **Litho.** **Perf. 12½**
C386 AP135 240fr multicolored 2.75 1.25

Dr. Albert Schweitzer (1875-1965), Nobel Peace Prize winner of 1952, founded Lambarene Hospital, Gabon, in 1913.

1988 Summer Olympics,
Seoul — AP136

Pentathlon: 75fr, Swimming. 170fr, Cross-country running, vert. 200fr, Shooting. 600fr, Equestrian. 700fr, Fencing.

1988, June 10 **Litho.** **Perf. 13**
C387 AP136 75fr multicolored .70 .25
C388 AP136 170fr multicolored 1.60 .60
C389 AP136 200fr multicolored 1.75 .70
C390 AP136 600fr multicolored 5.00 2.00
Nos. C387-C390 (4) 9.05 3.55
Souvenir Sheet
C391 AP136 750fr multicolored 6.75 3.75

Elimination Matches, 1990 World Cup
Soccer Championships — AP137

Various athletes and cities in Italy.

1989, June 15 **Litho.** **Perf. 13**
C392 AP137 75fr Bari .60 .30
C393 AP137 120fr Rome 1.00 .45
C394 AP137 500fr Florence 4.75 1.90
C395 AP137 550fr Naples 5.25 2.00
Nos. C392-C395 (4) 11.60 4.65

PHILEXFRANCE '89 — AP138

Paintings: 300fr, Storming of the Bastille, July 14, 1789, from a gouache by J.P. Houel. 400fr, Eiffel Tower, by G. Seurat.

1989, June 22
C396 AP138 300fr multicolored 2.75 1.10
C397 AP138 400fr multicolored 3.75 1.50

French revolution, bicent. (300fr); Eiffel Tower, cent. (400fr).

First Moon
Landing,
20th Anniv.
AP139

Man's first step on the Moon: No. C398, Astronaut on ladder. No. C399, Conducting experiments on the Moon's surface.

1989, June 22
C398 AP139 400fr multicolored 3.75 1.50
C399 AP139 400fr multicolored 3.75 1.50

World Cup Soccer Championships,
Italy — AP140

Various soccer plays and architecture.

1990, June 8 **Litho.** **Perf. 13**
C400 AP140 120fr multicolored 1.00 .50
C401 AP140 240fr multicolored 2.10 .95
C402 AP140 500fr multicolored 4.25 2.00
C403 AP140 600fr multicolored 5.25 2.40
Nos. C400-C403 (4) 12.60 5.85

Pan African
Postal Union,
10th Anniv.
AP141

1991, Jan. 10 **Litho.** **Perf. 13½**
C404 AP141 60fr shown .50 .25
C405 AP141 120fr Emblem .95 .50

1992 Winter
Olympics,
Albertville
AP142

1991, June 8 **Litho.** **Perf. 13½**
C406 AP142 120fr Ice hockey 1.40 .60
C407 AP142 300fr Speed skating 3.00 1.50
Litho. & Embossed
C408 AP142 1500fr Slalom skiing 15.00 15.00

Numbers have been reserved for souvenir sheets in this set.

1992
Summer
Olympics,
Barcelona
AP143

#C411, Equestrian. #C412, Long jump.

1992 Litho. & Embossed **Perf. 13½**
C411 AP143 1500fr gold & multi 16.00 16.00
Souvenir Sheet
C412 AP143 1500fr gold & multi 21.00 21.00

Anniversaries
AP144

Designs: 90fr, Victor Schoelcher, missionary, death cent. 205fr, Martin Luther King, civil rights reformer, 25th death anniv. 300fr, Claude Chappe (1763-1805), bicent. of visual telegraph.

1993 **Litho.** **Perf. 14**
C413 AP144 90fr multicolored 1.00 .50
C414 AP144 205fr multicolored 2.50 1.25
C415 AP144 300fr multicolored 3.50 1.75
Nos. C413-C415 (3) 7.00 3.50

1994 Winter Olympics, Lillehammer
AP145

1993, Apr. 26   **Litho.**   *Perf. 13*
C416 AP145 400fr Ice dancing   3.50 1.40
C417 AP145 600fr Ice hockey   6.00 1.75

Souvenir Sheet
C418 AP145 750fr Downhill skiing   7.00 4.00

Nos. C416-C417 exist in imperf. souvenir sheets of 1. Nos. C416-C418 exist imperf.

AIR POST SEMI-POSTAL STAMPS

Hathor Pillar — SPAP1

Unwmk.
1964, Mar. 9   **Engr.**   *Perf. 13*
CB1 SPAP1 10fr + 5fr vio & chnt   .90 .50
CB2 SPAP1 25fr + 5fr org brn & slate grn   1.10 .70
CB3 SPAP1 50fr + 5fr slate grn & brn red   2.25 1.60
Nos. CB1-CB3 (3)   4.25 2.80

UNESCO world campaign to save historic monuments in Nubia.

POSTAGE DUE STAMPS

Messenger — D6

MH. 1521 Broussard Plane — D7

Early Transportation: 1fr, Litter. 2fr, Canoe. 5fr, Bicyclist. 10fr, Steam locomotive. 25fr, Seaplane.

Unwmk.
1961, Dec. 4   **Engr.**   *Perf. 11*
J34 D6 50c ultra, ol bis & red   .20 .20
  a. Pair, #J34, J40   .25
J35 D6 1fr red brn, red & grn   .20 .20
  a. Pair, #J35, J41   .30
J36 D6 2fr grn, ultra & brn   .20 .20
  a. Pair, #J36, J42   .40
J37 D6 5fr pur & gray brn   .25 .25
  a. Pair, #J37, J43   .50
J38 D6 10fr bl, grn & chocolate   .70 .70
  a. Pair, #J38, J44   1.40 1.40
J39 D6 25fr bl, dk grn & dk brn   1.60 1.60
  a. Pair, #J39, J45   3.25

Modern transportation: 1fr, Land Rover. 2fr, River boat transporting barge. 5fr, Trailer-truck. 10fr, Diesel locomotive. 25fr, Boeing 707 jet plane.

J40 D7 50c ultra, olive bis & red   .20 .20
J41 D7 1fr red & grn   .20 .20
J42 D7 2fr ultra, grn & brn   .20 .20
J43 D7 5fr pur & gray brn   .25 .25
J44 D7 10fr dk grn & chocolate   .70 .70
J45 D7 25fr bl, dk grn & sepia   1.60 1.60
Nos. J34-J45 (12)   6.30 6.30

Pairs printed tête bêche, se-tenant at the base.

Flowers — D8

Flowers: 2fr, Phaeomeria magnifica. 5fr, Millettia laurentii. 10fr, Tuberose. 15fr, Pyrostegia venusta. 20fr, Hibiscus.

1971, Mar. 25   **Photo.**   *Perf. 12x12½*
J46 D8 1fr multi   .35 .35
J47 D8 2fr multi   .45 .45
J48 D8 5fr pink & multi   .55 .55
J49 D8 10fr dk grn & multi   .70 .70
J50 D8 15fr multi   1.10 1.10
J51 D8 20fr multi   1.40 1.40
Nos. J46-J51 (6)   4.55 4.55

Flowers and Fruit — D9

1986, June 5   **Litho.**   *Perf. 13*
J52 D9 5fr Passiflora quadrangulares   .25 .25
J53 D9 10fr Cannaceae, vert.   .45 .45
J54 D9 15fr Ananas comosus, vert.   .55 .55
Nos. J52-J54 (3)   1.25 1.25

OFFICIAL STAMPS

Coat of Arms — O1

Perf. 14x13
1968-70   **Unwmk.**   **Typo.**
O1 O1 1fr multi ('70)   .20 .20
O2 O1 2fr multi ('70)   .20 .20
O3 O1 5fr multi ('70)   .20 .20
O4 O1 10fr multi ('70)   .25 .20
O5 O1 25fr emer & multi   .45 .20
O6 O1 30fr red & multi   .60 .20
O7 O1 50fr multi ('70)   1.10 .50
O8 O1 85fr multi ('70)   2.25 .90
O9 O1 100fr multi ('70)   2.75 1.10
O10 O1 200fr multi ('70)   3.75 2.00
Nos. O1-O10 (10)   11.75 5.70

COOK ISLANDS

ˈkuk ˈī-lənds

(Rarotonga)

LOCATION — South Pacific Ocean, northeast of New Zealand
GOVT. — Internal self-government, linked to New Zealand
AREA — 91 sq. mi.
POP. — 19,103 (1996)
CAPITAL — Avarua

Fifteen islands in Northern and Southern groups extend over 850,000 square miles of ocean.

Separate stamp issues used by Aitutaki (1903-32 and 1972 onward) and Penrhyn Islands (1902-32 and 1973 onward). Niue is included geographically, but administered separately. It continues to issue separate stamps.

12 Pence = 1 Shilling
20 Shillings = 1 Pound
100 Cents = 1 Dollar (1967)

> **Catalogue values for unused stamps in this country are for Never Hinged items, beginning with Scott 127 in the regular postage section, Scott B1 in the semi-postal section, Scott C1 in the air post section, Scott CB1 in the air post semi-postal section and Scott O16 in the official section.**

Watermarks

Wmk. 61 — Single-lined N Z and Star Close Together

Wmk. 62 — Single-lined N Z and Star Wide Apart

Wmk. 253 — Multiple N Z and Star

A1

1892   **Unwmk.**   **Typo.**   *Perf. 12½*
Toned Paper
1 A1 1p black   32.50 30.00
2 A1 1½p violet   47.50 45.00
  a. Imperf, pair   19,000.
3 A1 2½p blue   47.50 45.00
4 A1 10p carmine   160.00 150.00
Nos. 1-4 (4)   287.50 270.00

White Paper
5 A1 1p black   32.50 30.00
  a. Vert. pair, imperf. between   11,000.
6 A1 1½p violet   47.50 45.00
7 A1 2½p blue   47.50 45.00
8 A1 10p carmine   160.00 150.00
Nos. 5-8 (4)   287.50 270.00

Nos. 1-8 were printed in sheets of 60 (6x10), from a setting of six slightly different cliches.

Queen Makea Takau — A2

Wrybill (Torea) — A3

1893-94   **Wmk. 62**   *Perf. 12x11½*
9 A2 1p brown   47.50 52.50
10 A2 1p blue ('94)   13.00 2.50
11 A2 1½p brt violet   12.00 8.50
12 A2 2½p rose   47.50 27.50
13 A2 5p olive gray   22.50 16.00
14 A2 10p green   82.50 57.50
Nos. 9-14 (6)   225.00 164.50

Perf. 12½ examples of Nos. 10, 12 are from a part of the normal perf. 12x11½ sheets. They were caused by a partial deviation of the original perforating.

1898-1900   *Perf. 11*
15 A3 ½p blue ('00)   6.50 9.00
  a. "d" omitted at upper right   1,750.
16 A2 1p brown   22.50 21.00
17 A2 1p blue   6.00 5.50
18 A3 1½p violet   12.00 7.50
19 A3 2p chocolate   11.00 8.50
20 A2 2½p car rose   22.50 10.50
21 A2 5p olive gray   27.50 21.00
22 A3 6p red violet   22.50 29.00
23 A2 10p green   26.00 57.50
24 A3 1sh car rose   57.50 57.50
Nos. 15-24 (10)   214.00 227.00

No. 17 Surcharged in Black

1899
25 A2 ½p on 1p blue   40.00 50.00
  a. Double surcharge   1,000. 1,200.
  b. Inverted surcharge   1,200. 1,100.

No. 16 Overprinted in Black

1901
26 A2 1p brown   210.00 160.00
  a. Inverted overprint   2,400. 1,900.
  c. Double overprint   1,900. 1,900.

Some single stamps were overprinted by favor. Other varieties could exist. Forgeries exist.

Types of 1893-98

1902   **Unwmk.**
27 A3 ½p green   7.00 7.00
  a. Vert. pair, imperf. horiz.   1,400.
28 A2 1p rose   14.00 12.50
29 A2 2½p dull blue   15.00 25.00
Nos. 27-29 (3)   36.00 44.50

1902   **Wmk. 61**   *Perf. 11*
30 A3 ½p green   3.25 3.75
31 A2 1p rose   4.75 3.50
32 A2 1½p brt violet   4.75 10.00
33 A3 2p chocolate   6.50 12.00
  a. Figures of value omitted   2,750. 3,600.
  b. Perf. 11x14   2,250.
34 A2 2½p dull blue   4.50 8.25
35 A2 5p olive gray   42.50 57.50
36 A3 6p purple   37.50 32.50
37 A2 10p blue green   55.00 120.00
38 A3 1sh car rose   55.00 82.50
  a. Perf. 11x14   2,750.
Nos. 30-38 (9)   213.75 330.00

1909-19   *Perf. 14, 14x14½, 14½x14*
39 A3 ½p green, perf 14½x14 ('11)   8.00 9.50
  a. ½p dp grn, perf 14 ('15)   7.00 17.50
  b. As "a," wmk upright   9.50 17.50
40 A2 1p red, wmk. sideways ('09)   15.00 5.00
41 A2 1½p purple, perf 14x15 ('16)   14.00 4.75
42 A3 2p dp brown ('19)   6.00 57.50
43 A2 10p dp green ('18)   25.00 110.00
44 A3 1sh car rose ('19)   32.50 110.00
Nos. 39-44 (6)   96.00 296.75

Nos. 39-40 are on both ordinary and chalky paper; Nos. 41-44 on chalky paper.

New Zealand Stamps of 1909-19 Surcharged in Dark Blue or Red

1919   **Typo.**   *Perf. 14x15*
48 A43 ½p yel green (R)   .45 1.25
  a. Pair, one without surcharge
49 A42 1p carmine   1.25 3.50
50 A47 1½p brown org (R)   .60 .90
51 A43 2p yellow (R)   1.75 2.00
52 A43 3p chocolate   3.25 15.00

Engr.   **Perf. 14x14½**

53	A44	2½p dull blue (R)	2.75	2.50
54	A45	3p violet brown	2.75	2.00
55	A45	4p purple	2.25	4.25
56	A44	4½p dark green	2.25	9.50
57	A46	6p car rose	2.00	5.50
58	A44	7½p red brown,		
		perf 14x13½	2.10	6.50
59	A45	9p ol green (R)	3.75	17.50
60	A44	1sh vermilion	2.75	18.00
		Nos. 48-60 (13)	27.90	88.40

The Polynesian surcharge restates the denomination of the basic stamp.

Landing of Capt. Cook A4

Avarua Waterfront A5

Capt. James Cook — A6

Palm — A7

Houses at Arorangi — A8

Avarua Harbor — A9

1920   **Unwmk.**   **Engr.**   **Perf. 14**

61	A4	½p green & black	4.75	25.00
62	A5	1p car & black	5.50	25.00
a.		Center inverted	700.00	
63	A6	1½p blue & black	10.00	10.00
64	A7	3p red brn & blk	2.50	6.50
65	A8	6p org & red brn	3.75	10.00
66	A9	1sh vio & black	6.00	20.00
		Nos. 61-66 (6)	32.50	96.50

The stamps overprinted or inscribed "Rarotonga" were used throughout the Cook Islands.
For surcharges see Nos. 78, 79.

New Zealand Postal-Fiscal Stamps of 1906-13 Overprinted in Red or Dark Blue

a

Perf. 14, 14½, 14x14½

1921   **Typo.**   **Wmk. 61**

67	PF1	2sh blue (R)	32.50	65.00
68	PF1	2sh6p brown	22.50	60.00
69	PF1	5sh green (R)	32.50	77.50
70	PF1	10sh claret	90.00	140.00
71	PF2	£1 rose	140.00	250.00
		Nos. 67-71 (5)	317.50	592.50

Types of 1920 Issue

1924-26   **Engr.**   **Perf. 14**

72	A4	½p yel grn & black	5.25	10.00
73	A5	1p carmine & black	7.00	2.50

Issued: ½p, May 13, 1926; 1p, Nov. 10, 1924.

New Zealand Stamps of 1926 Overprinted Type "a" in Red

1926-28   **Typo.**   **Perf. 14, 14½x14**

74	A56	2sh blue ('27)	17.50	47.50
a.		2sh dark blue	12.00	47.50
75	A56	3sh violet ('28)	19.00	50.00

Rarotongan Chief (Te Po) — A10

Avarua Harbor — A11

1927, Oct. 15   **Engr.**   **Perf. 14**

76	A10	2½p dk bl & red brn	7.50	29.00
77	A11	4p dull vio & bl grn	12.00	20.00

No. 63 Surcharged in Red

1931   **Unwmk.**

78	A6	2p on 1½p blue & blk	11.00	3.25

Same Surcharge on Type of 1920
Wmk. 61

79	A6	2p on 1½p blue & blk	5.50	13.00

No. 79 was not issued without surcharge.

New Zealand Postal-Fiscal Stamps of 1931-32 Overprinted Type "a" in Blue or Red

1931, Nov. 12   **Typo.**

80	PF5	2sh6p dp brown (Bl)	12.00	26.00
81	PF5	5sh green (R)	21.00	65.00
82	PF5	10sh dk car (Bl)	45.00	110.00
83	PF5	£1 pink (Bl) ('32)	105.00	190.00
		Nos. 80-83 (4)	183.00	391.00

See Nos. 103-108, 124A-126C.

Landing of Capt. Cook — A12

Capt. James Cook — A13

Double Canoe — A14

Islanders Unloading Ship — A15

View of Avarua Harbor — A16

R.M.S. Monowai — A17

King George V — A18

Unwmk.
1932, Mar. 16   **Engr.**   **Perf. 13**
Center in Black

84	A12	½p deep green	4.00	19.00
a.		Perf. 14	32.50	105.00
85	A13	1p brown lake	7.75	5.25
a.		Center inverted	8,500.	8,500.
b.		Perf. 14	17.50	28.00
86	A14	2p brown	3.50	6.50
b.		Perf. 14	10.00	24.00
87	A15	2½p dark ultra	18.00	65.00
b.		Perf. 14	18.00	65.00

Perf. 14

88	A16	4p ultra	12.00	65.00
a.		Perf. 13	25.00	75.00
b.		Perf. 14x13	35.00	130.00
89	A17	6p orange	5.00	17.50
a.		Perf. 13	30.00	57.50
90	A18	1sh deep violet	13.00	26.00
		Nos. 84-90 (7)	63.25	204.25

Nos. 84 to 90 were available for postage in Aitutaki, Penrhyn and Rarotonga and replaced the special issues for those islands.
Inverted centers of the 1p and 2p are from printers waste.

1933-36   **Wmk. 61**   **Perf. 14**

91	A12	½p dp grn & blk	1.20	5.25
92	A13	1p dk car & black ('35)	1.50	2.40
93	A14	2p brn & blk ('36)	1.75	.60
94	A15	2½p dk ultra & blk	1.75	2.50
95	A16	4p blue & black	1.75	.60
96	A17	6p org & blk ('36)	2.00	2.50
97	A18	1sh dp vio & blk ('36)	29.00	42.50
		Nos. 91-97 (7)	38.95	56.35

See Nos. 116-121.

Silver Jubilee Issue

Types of 1932 Overprinted in Black or Red

1935, May 7

98	A13	1p dk car & brn red	.65	2.00
99	A15	2½p dk ultra & bl (R)	1.10	3.50
100	A17	6p dull org & green	5.00	8.50
		Nos. 98-100 (3)	6.75	14.00
		Set, never hinged	10.00	

The vertical spacing of the overprint is wider on No. 100.

New Zealand Stamps of 1926 Overprinted in Black

b

1936, July 15   **Typo.**   **Perf. 14**

101	A56	2sh blue	15.00	50.00
102	A56	3sh violet	15.00	80.00

New Zealand Postal-Fiscal Stamps of 1931-35 Overprinted Type "b" in Black or Red

1932-36

103	PF5	2sh6p brown ('36)	32.50	90.00
104	PF5	5sh grn (R) ('36)	35.00	120.00
105	PF5	10sh dk car ('36)	75.00	225.00
106	PF5	£1 pink ('36)	110.00	275.00
107	PF5	£3 lt grn (R)	400.00	650.00
108	PF5	£5 dk blue (R)	225.00	375.00
		Nos. 103-108 (6)	877.50	1,735.

Issue dates: Mar. 1932, July 15, 1936.

New Zealand Stamps of 1937 Overprinted in Black

Perf. 14x13½

1937, June 1   **Engr.**   **Wmk. 253**

109	A78	1p rose carmine	.20	.20
110	A78	2½p dark blue	.25	.20
111	A78	6p vermilion	.35	.30
		Nos. 109-111 (3)	.80	.70
		Set, never hinged	2.50	

King George VI A19

Village and Palms A20

Coastal Scene with Canoe — A21

1938, May 2   **Wmk. 61**   **Perf. 14**

112	A19	1sh dp violet & blk	7.50	15.00
113	A20	2sh dk red brn & blk	15.00	19.00
114	A21	3sh yel green & blue	37.50	42.50
		Nos. 112-114 (3)	60.00	76.50
		Set, never hinged	100.00	

See Nos. 122-124.

Mt. Ikurangi behind Avarua — A22

Perf. 13½x14

1940, Sept. 2   **Engr.**   **Wmk. 253**
115 A22 3p on 1½p violet & blk   .80   .80

Issued only with surcharge. Stamps without surcharge are from the printer's archives.

Types of 1932-38

1944-46		**Engr.**		**Perf. 14**
116	A12	½p dk ol grn & blk ('45)	1.00	4.50
117	A13	1p dk car & blk ('45)	1.50	1.25
118	A14	2p brn & blk ('46)	.90	7.00
119	A15	2½p dk bl & blk ('45)	.60	2.00
120	A17	4p blue & black	2.50	15.00
121	A17	6p org & black	1.00	2.50
122	A19	1sh dp vio & blk	1.00	3.50
123	A20	2sh dk red brn & blk	27.50	50.00
124	A21	3sh yel green & blue ('45)	25.00	40.00
		Nos. 116-124 (9)	61.00	125.75
		Set, never hinged	100.00	

New Zealand Nos. AR76, AR78, AR85 and Type of 1931 Postal-Fiscal Stamps Overprinted Type "b" in Black or Red

1943-50		**Wmk. 253**	**Typo.**	**Perf. 14**
124A	PF5	2sh6p brn ('46)	11.50	22.50
125	PF5	5sh green (R)	7.75	22.50
126	PF5	10sh dp pink ('48)	35.00	90.00
126A	PF5	£1 pink ('47)	40.00	97.50
126B	PF5	£3 lt grn (R) ('46)	47.50	190.00
126C	PF5	£5 dk bl (R) ('50)	175.00	425.00
		Nos. 124A-126C (6)	316.75	847.50
		Set, never hinged	550.00	

For surcharges see Nos. 192-194.

> **Catalogue values for unused stamps in this section, from this point to the end of the section, are for Never Hinged items.**

Peace Issue

New Zealand Nos. 248, 250, 254 and 255 Overprinted in Black or Blue:

    c   d

Perf. 13x13½, 13½x13

1946, June 1				**Engr.**
127	A94 (c)	1p emerald	.50	.20
128	A96 (d)	2p rose vio (Bl)	.50	.50
129	A100(c)	6p org red & red brn	1.00	.70
130	A101(c)	8p brn lake & blk (Bl)	.80	.70
		Nos. 127-130 (4)	2.80	2.10

Ngatangiia Channel, Rarotonga A23

Capt. James Cook Statue and Map of Cook Islands — A24

Designs: 1p, Cook and map of Hervey Isls. 2p, Rev. John Williams, his ship Messenger of Peace, and map of Rarotonga. 3p, Aitutaki map and palms. 5p, Mail plane landing at Rarotonga airport. 6p, Tongareva (Penrhyn) scene. 8p, Islander's house, Rarotonga. 2sh, Thatched house, mat weaver. 3sh, Steamer Matua offshore.

Perf. 13½x13, 13x13½

1949, Aug.1		**Engr.**		**Wmk. 253**
131	A23	½p brown & violet	.25	1.25
132	A23	1p green & orange	4.00	2.50
133	A23	2p carmine & brn	2.50	2.50
134	A23	3p ultra & green	2.25	2.50
135	A23	5p purple & grn	7.00	4.00
136	A23	6p car rose & blk	7.00	3.25
137	A23	8p orange & olive	.75	4.75
138	A24	1sh chocolate & bl	6.50	4.75
139	A24	2sh rose car & brn	4.75	16.00
140	A24	3sh bl grn & lt ultra	12.50	29.00
		Nos. 131-140 (10)	47.50	68.50

For surcharge see No. 147.

Coronation Issue
Type of New Zealand

1953, May 25		**Photo.**		**Perf. 14x14½**
145	A113	3p brown	1.10	1.10
146	A114	6p slate black	2.10	2.10

No. 135 Surcharged with New Value and Two Dots

1960, Apr. 1		**Engr.**		**Perf. 13½x13**
147	A23	1sh6p on 5p purple & grn	.75	.75

Tiare Maori — A25   Fishing God — A26

Queen Elizabeth II — A27

Island Scene A28

3sh, Administration building, Mangaia. 5sh, Ship in Rarotonga harbor. 3p, 5p, 6p, 1sh, horiz.

Perf. 13½x13, 13x13½
Litho.; Engr.; (1sh6p)

1963, June 4				
148	A25	1p shown	.75	.70
149	A26	2p shown	.30	.50
150	A25	3p Frangipani	.70	.70
151	A26	5p Fairy tern	8.25	2.00
152	A26	6p Hibiscus	1.10	.75
153	A26	8p Bonito	4.50	1.50
154	A25	1sh Oranges	1.00	.75
155	A27	1sh6p shown	2.75	2.00
156	A28	2sh gray & brown	2.00	1.10
157	A28	3sh emer & brown	2.00	1.75
158	A28	5sh ultra & brown	16.00	5.00
		Nos. 148-158 (11)	39.35	16.75

For overprints and surcharges see #167-169, 179-181, 183-184, 186-190.

Solar Eclipse and Palm Tree — A29

1965, May 31		**Litho.**		**Perf. 13x13½**
159	A29	6p black, lt blue & yel	.40	.40

Observation of the solar eclipse on Manuae Island, May 30, 1965. Exists imperf.
For surcharge see No. 185.

Flag of New Zealand and Map of Cook Islands A30

Designs: 10p, London Missionary Society Church and graveyard. 1sh, Reading of Proclamation of Cession, Oct. 8, 1900, and Queen Elizabeth II. 1sh9p, Nikao School and flag of New Zealand.

Perf. 13½x13

1965, Sept. 16				**Wmk. 253**
160	A30	4p blue & red	.20	.20
161	A30	10p multicolored	.20	.20
162	A30	1sh multicolored	.20	.20
163	A30	1sh9p multicolored	.60	.60
		Nos. 160-163 (4)	1.20	1.20

Establishment of internal self-government.
For surcharges see Nos. 182, 191.

Nos. 160-162 and 156-158 Overprinted in Red: "In Memoriam / Sir Winston Churchill / 1874-1965"

1966, Jan. 24		**Litho.**		**Wmk. 253**
164	A30	4p blue & red	.75	.30
165	A30	10p multicolored	2.25	.60
a.		Inverted overprint	275.00	
166	A30	1sh multicolored	2.25	.90
167	A28	2sh gray & brown	2.25	1.60
168	A28	3sh emer & black	2.25	1.60
169	A28	5sh ultra & brown	2.75	2.25
		Nos. 164-169 (6)	12.50	7.25

Statesman and WWII leader.

Adoration of the Wise Men, by Fra Angelico — A31

Paintings: 2p, Nativity, by Hans Memling, vert. 4p, Adoration of the Wise Men, by Velazquez. 10p, Adoration of the Wise Men, by Hieronymus Bosch. 1sh6p, Adoration of the Shepherds, by Jose Ribera, vert.

Perf. 13x14½, 14½x13

1966, Nov. 28		**Photo.**		**Unwmk.**
170	A31	1p multicolored	.20	.20
171	A31	2p multicolored	.20	.20
172	A31	4p multicolored	.20	.20
173	A31	10p multicolored	.55	.55
174	A31	1sh6p multicolored	.65	.65
		Nos. 170-174 (5)	1.80	1.80

Christmas. Issued in sheets of 6 with ornamental gold border.

Perf. 13x12, 12x13

170a	A31	1p	.45	.55
171a	A31	2p	14.00	11.50
172a	A31	4p	1.10	1.00
173a	A31	10p	2.40	4.50
174a	A31	1sh6p	30.00	6.75
		Nos. 170a-174a (5)	47.95	24.30

Tennis and Queen Elizabeth A32

Sport: 1p, Women's basketball and Games' emblem. 4p, Boxing and team emblem. 7p, Soccer and Queen Elizabeth II.

1967, Jan. 12				**Perf. 13½**
175	A32	½p brt olive & multi	.20	.20
176	A32	1p brt blue & multi	.20	.20
177	A32	4p purple & multi	.20	.20
178	A32	7p red & multi	.20	.20
		Nos. 175-178,C10-C11 (6)	1.25	1.25

Second South Pacific Games, Noumea, New Caledonia, Dec. 8-18, 1966.

Nos. 148-155, 157-161 Surcharged with New Value or Black or Red

Pair (#181b), with Type I on left (#181) and Type II on right (#181a)

1967				
179	A25	1c on 1p	.45	1.75
180	A26	2c on 2p	.20	.20
181	A25	2½c on 3p (I)	.20	.20
a.		Type II	.20	.20
b.		Pair, #181 and #181a	.45	.45
182	A30	3c on 4p	.20	.20
183	A26	4c on 5p	9.00	.40
184	A25	5c on 6p	.20	.20
185	A29	5c on 6p	5.00	1.25
186	A26	7c on 8p	.25	.20
187	A25	10c on 1sh	.20	.20
188	A27	15c on 1sh6p (R)	2.00	1.10
189	A28	30c on 3sh (R)	22.50	5.50
190	A28	50c on 5sh (R)	4.00	2.00
191	A30	$1 on 10p (R)	17.00	8.00
		Nos. 179-191 (13)	61.20	21.20

Issued: 2c, 2½c, 3c, 5c, 7c, 10c, 4/3; others 5/4.
No. 191 is surcharged "10/ $1.00" and 3 bars over old value.
Numerous varieties of surcharge include wrong-font "c," thin numerals, etc.

Nos. 126A, 126B and 126C Surcharged in Red
Wmk. 253

1967, June 6		**Typo.**		**Perf. 14**
192	PF5	$2 on £1 pink	80.00	200.00
193	PF5	$6 on £3 lt green	140.00	225.00
194	PF5	$10 on £5 dk blue	250.00	375.00
		Nos. 192-194 (3)	470.00	800.00

Frequently found with stained gum.

Stamp of 1892, Village and Queen Victoria A33

Designs: 3c (4p), PO, Rarotonga, and Elizabeth II. 8c (10p), View of Avarua, Rarotonga, and 10p stamp of 1892. 18c (1sh9p), Map of Cook Islands, DC-3, S.S. Moana Roa and Capt. Cook.

				Perf. 13½
1967, July 3		**Photo.**		**Unwmk.**
195	A33	1c (1p) multi	.20	.20
196	A33	3c (4p) multi	.20	.20
197	A33	8c (10p) multi	.35	.35
198	A33	18c (1sh9p) multi	1.50	.80
a.		Souvenir sheet of 4, #195-198	3.50	3.50
		Nos. 195-198 (4)	2.25	1.55

75th anniv. of the 1st Cook Islands stamps. Issued in sheets of 8 stamps and 1 label with inscription in yellow margin.

Hibiscus — A34

Elizabeth II A35

Elizabeth II and Flowers — A36

Flowers: 1c, Rose of Sharon. 2c. 15c, Frangipani. 2½c, Butterfly pea. 3c, Suva queen and Queen Elizabeth II. 4c, Water lily. 5c, Bauhania. 6c, Yellow hibiscus. 8c, Alamanda and Queen Elizabeth II. 9c, Stephanotis. 10c, Flaymboyant poinciana. 20c, Thunbergia. 25c, Canna lily and Queen Elizabeth II. 30c, Poinsettia. 50c, Gardenia.

The $4 exists with "FOUR DOLLARS" in two widths: type 1, 32½mm; type 2, 33½mm.

1967-69   Photo.   Perf. 14x13½

199	A34	½c gold & multi	.30	.20
200	A34	1c gold & multi	.30	.20
201	A34	2c gold & multi	.30	.20
202	A34	2½c gold & multi	.45	.20
203	A34	3c gold & multi	1.00	.20
204	A34	4c *Walter Lily*	1.40	*1.75*
205	A34	4c *Water Lily*	3.75	1.50
206	A34	5c gold & multi	.70	.20
207	A34	6c gold & multi	.75	.20
208	A34	8c gold & multi	.75	.20
209	A34	9c gold & multi	.75	.20
210	A34	10c gold & multi	.75	.20
211	A34	15c gold & multi	.75	.20
212	A34	20c gold & multi	8.50	.50
213	A34	25c gold & multi	1.50	.60
214	A34	30c gold & multi	1.25	.70
215	A34	50c gold & multi	1.90	1.00
216	A35	$1 gold & multi	4.00	2.25
217	A35	$2 gold & multi	9.00	3.50
218	A36	$4 multi, type 2		
		('68)	6.00	9.00
a.		Type 1	35.00	50.00
219	A36	$6 multi ('68)	3.75	7.50
219A	A36	$8 multi ('69)	11.00	11.00
220	A36	$10 multi ('68)	7.00	12.00
		Nos. 199-220 (23)	65.85	53.50

Nos. 199-220 (except No. 204) were reprinted in 1970/71 with the fluorescent printing described below. Value, set: unused $60; used $35.

For surcharges see Nos. 290-291, 305-309, B1-B13, B17-B18, B20. For overprints see Nos. 277-283, 302-304, 315, 351-356, O1-O15.

Fluorescence

Since 1968 a number of stamps have been issued with a "fluorescent security underprinting" in a multiple coat of arms pattern. Some issues have this underprint, some do not.

Stamps issued both with and without the underprint are Nos. 199-203, 205-220, 283, 290-291.

From Nos. 292-296 onward, all stamps have this underprint unless otherwise noted.

Ia Orana Maria, by Gauguin A37

Gauguin Paintings: 3c, Riders on the Beach. 5c, Still Life with Flowers. 8c, Whispered Words. 15c, Maternity. 22c, Why Are You Angry?

1967, Oct. 23   Photo.   Perf. 13½

221	A37	1c gold & multi	.25	.25
222	A37	3c gold & multi	.25	.25
223	A37	5c gold & multi	.25	.25
224	A37	8c gold & multi	.25	.25
225	A37	15c gold & multi	.40	.40
226	A37	22c gold & multi	.60	.60
a.		Souvenir sheet of 6, #221-226	4.50	4.50
		Nos. 221-226 (6)	2.00	2.00

#221-226 are printed in sheets of 6 (3x2).

Holy Family by Rubens — A38

Paintings: 3c, Adoration of the Magi, by Albrecht Durer. 4c, The Lucca Madonna, by Jan Van Eyck. 8c, Adoration of the Shepherds, by Jacopo da Bassano. 15c, Nativity, by El Greco. 25c, Madonna and Child, by Antonio Allegri da Correggio.

1967, Dec. 4   Perf. 12x13

227	A38	1c gold & multi	.20	.20
228	A38	3c gold & multi	.20	.20
229	A38	4c gold & multi	.20	.20
230	A38	8c gold & multi	.20	.20
231	A38	15c gold & multi	.30	.30
232	A38	25c gold & multi	.35	.35
		Nos. 227-232 (6)	1.45	1.45

Christmas.

Capt. Cook and Matavai Bay, Tahiti, by Sydney Parkinson A39

1c, Ships off Huahine Island, Tahiti, by John & James Clevely. 2c, town & harbor of Kamchatka, by John Webber, & Queen Elizabeth II. 4c, "The Ice Islands" (Antarctica), by William Hodges.

1968, Sept. 12   Photo.   Perf. 13

233	A39	½c gold & multi	.20	.20
234	A39	1c gold & multi	.20	.20
235	A39	2c gold & multi	.20	.20
236	A39	4c gold & multi	.20	.20
		Nos. 233-236,C12-C15 (8)	6.45	6.45

Bicent. of Capt. Cook's 1st voyage of discovery. Printed in sheets of 10 stamps and 2 labels (3x4). Labels show portraits of Elizabeth II and Cook.

Gymnast A40

1968, Oct. 21

237	A40	1c Sailing	.20	.20
238	A40	5c shown	.20	.20
239	A40	15c High jump	.20	.20
240	A40	20c Woman diver	.35	.20
241	A40	30c Bicyclist	.70	.20
242	A40	50c Woman hurdler	.55	.30
		Nos. 237-242 (6)	2.20	1.30

19th Olympic Games, Mexico City, Oct. 12-27. Printed in sheets of 10 stamps and 2 labels (3x4).

Virgin and Child, by Titian — A41

Paintings: 4c, Holy Family, by Raphael. 10c, Madonna of the Rosary, by Murillo. 20c, Adoration of the Magi, by Memling. 30c, Adoration of the Magi, by Ghirlandajo.

1968, Dec. 2   Photo.   Perf. 13

243	A41	1c gold & multi	.20	.20
244	A41	4c gold & multi	.20	.20
245	A41	10c gold & multi	.20	.20
246	A41	20c gold & multi	.30	.30
247	A41	30c gold & multi	.45	.45
a.		Souv. sheet, #243-247 + label	2.50	2.50
		Nos. 243-247 (5)	1.35	1.35

Issued in sheets of 6 (2x3).

Training on Ropeway A42

Designs: ½c, Boy Scouts cooking over campfire. 5c, Training with signal flags, and Queen Elizabeth II. 10c, Planting a tree. 20c, Erecting a hut. 30c, Lord Baden-Powell, lake and mountains (visit to Rarotonga in 1935).

1969, Feb. 6   Photo.   Perf. 13½

248	A42	½c multicolored	.25	.25
249	A42	1c multicolored	.25	.25
250	A42	5c multicolored	.25	.25
251	A42	10c multicolored	.25	.25
252	A42	20c multicolored	.30	.30
253	A42	30c multicolored	.55	.55
		Nos. 248-253 (6)	1.85	1.85

5th Natl. Boy Scout Jamboree, Christchurch, New Zealand, Jan. 2-12.
Issued in sheets of 10 stamps and 2 labels (4x3).

Soccer — A43

#254b, Pole vault. #255a, Weight lifting. #255b, Basketball, Elizabeth II. #256a, Long jump. #256b, Tennis. #257a, Running. #257b, Javelin, Elizabeth II. #258b, Boxing. #258b, Golf.

Perf. 13½x13

1969, July 7   Photo.   Unwmk.

254	A43	½c Pair, #a.-b.	.70	.70
255	A43	1c Pair, #a.-b.	.70	.70
256	A43	4c Pair, #a.-b.	1.50	1.50
257	A43	10c Pair, #a.-b.	2.10	2.10
258	A43	15c Pair, #a.-b.	3.50	3.50
c.		Souv. sheet #254-258 + 2 labels	9.50	9.50
		Nos. 254-258 (5)	8.50	8.50

3rd South Pacifc Games, Port Moresby, Papua and New Guinea, Aug. 13-23.
Issued in sheets of 10.

Map of Cook Islands and Capt. Cook — A44

Map of Cook Islands and: 5c, Premier Albert Henry of Cook Islands. 25c, Coat of arms of New Zealand. 30c, Queen Elizabeth II.

1969, Oct. 8   Photo.   Perf. 13

264	A44	5c red & multi	.50	.50
265	A44	10c lemon & multi	1.50	1.50
266	A44	25c green & multi	.75	.75
267	A44	30c blue & multi	.75	.75
		Nos. 264-267 (4)	3.50	3.50

South Pacific Conf., Noumea, Oct. 1969.

Madonna and Child, by Filippo Lippi A45

Paintings: 4c, Holy Family, by Baccio della Porta. 10c, Madonna and Child, by Anton Raphael Mengs. 20c, Madonna and Child, by Le Maitre de Flemalle. 30c, Madonna and Child by Correggio.

1969, Nov. 21   Photo.   Perf. 13½

268	A45	1c buff & multi	.20	.20
269	A45	4c buff & multi	.20	.20
270	A45	10c buff & multi	.20	.20
271	A45	20c buff & multi	.25	.25
272	A45	30c buff & multi	.25	.25
a.		Souv. sheet, #268-272 + label	2.00	2.00
		Nos. 268-272 (5)	1.10	1.10

Issued in sheets of 8 stamps, one label with portrait of Queen Elizabeth II.

Resurrection of Christ, by Raphael — A46

The Resurrection of Christ by: 8c, Dirk Bouts. 20c, Albert Altdorfer. 25c, Murillo.

1970, Mar. 12   Photo.   Perf. 13½
Size: 25½x56mm

273	A46	4c gold & multi	.25	.25
274	A46	8c gold & multi	.25	.25
275	A46	20c gold & multi	.25	.25
276	A46	25c gold & multi	.25	.25
a.		Souv. sheet, #273-276 + 2 labels	1.75	1.75
		Nos. 273-276 (4)	1.00	1.00

Easter 1970.
Printed in sheets of 8 stamps and a label (3x3) showing portrait of Queen Elizabeth II and name of painting and painter.
See Nos. 316-318.

Nos. 205, 208, 211-212, 214, 217 Overprinted: "KIA ORANA / APOLLO 13 /ASTRONAUTS / Te Atua to / Tatou Irinakianga"

1970, Apr.   Perf. 14x13½

277	A34	4c gold & multi	.30	.30
278	A34	8c gold & multi	.30	.30
279	A34	15c gold & multi	.30	.30
280	A34	20c gold & multi	.40	.40
281	A34	30c gold & multi	.55	.55
282	A35	$2 gold & multi	1.75	1.75

No. 218 Overprinted: "KIA ORANA / APOLLO 13 /ASTRONAUTS"

283	A36	$4 gold & multi	3.25	3.25
		Nos. 277-283 (7)	6.85	6.85

Splashdown of Apollo 13 west of Rarotonga, Apr. 17, 1970.
Issued: #277-282, 4/17; $4, 4/30.
Values for Nos. 283, 290-291 are for stamps with fluorescence. Stamps without fluorescence sell for more.

Queen Elizabeth II, Prince Philip, Princess Anne and Prince Charles — A47

Design: 30c, Wedgwood bust of Capt. Cook and "Endeavour." $1, Royal visit commemorative coin, obverse and reverse.

1970, June 12   Photo.   Perf. 13½

284	A47	5c gold & multi	.50 .30
285	A47	30c gold & multi	1.75 1.50
286	A47	$1 gold & multi	5.00 4.50
a.		Souv. sheet, #284-286 + label	12.00 12.00
		Nos. 284-286 (3)	7.25 6.30

Visit of the British royal family.

Nos. 284-286 Overprinted in Silver or Black: "Fifth Anniversary Self-Government August 1970"

1970, Aug. 27   Photo.   Perf. 13½

287	A47	5c gold & multi (S)	.50 .20
288	A47	30c gold & multi	1.50 1.00
289	A47	$1 gold & multi	2.50 1.40
		Nos. 287-289 (3)	4.50 2.60

5th anniv. of self-government. The overprint on No. 287 is arranged in one line around 3 sides of the design; the overprint on Nos. 288-289 is in 3 horizontal lines.

Nos. 219A-220 Surcharged

1970, Nov. 11   Photo.   Perf. 14x13½

290	A36	$4 on $8 multi	4.25 4.25
291	A36	$4 on $10 multi	3.00 3.00

In each sheet of 15, 3 stamps have 2 surcharged bars instead of one. See second note after No. 283.

Nativity
A48

Illuminations from 14th Century Robert de Lisle Psalter: 4c, Angel and shepherds. 10c, The Circumcision. 20c, The Adoration of the Kings. 30c, The Presentation at the Temple.

1970, Nov. 30   Photo.   Perf. 13½

292	A48	1c gold & multi	.20 .20
293	A48	4c gold & multi	.20 .20
294	A48	10c gold & multi	.30 .30
295	A48	20c gold & multi	.35 .35
296	A48	30c gold & multi	.45 .45
a.		Souv. sheet, #292-296 + label	2.75 2.75
		Nos. 292-296 (5)	1.50 1.50

Christmas.
Issued in sheets of 5 stamps and a label (3x2) showing portrait of Queen Elizabeth II and source of design.

Nos. 214-215 Overprinted "PLUS 20c // UNITED // KINGDOM // SPECIAL // MAIL SERVICE"

1971

296B	A34	30c +20c multi	.40 .60
296C	A34	50c +20c multi	1.25 2.25

Issued: 30c, 2/25; 50c, 3/8.
Nos. 214-215 were issued to prepay regular postage plus the fee of a private carrier who had contracted to deliver mail within the United Kingdom during a postal strike. The strike ended on March 8, and these stamps were withdrawn March 12.

Queen Elizabeth II and Prince
Philip — A49

Designs: 4c, Royal family at Balmoral. 10c, Prince Philip sailing. 15c, Prince Philip as polo player. 25c, Prince Philip and royal yacht.

1971, Mar. 11   Litho.   Perf. 13½

297	A49	1c brt blue & multi	.20 .20
298	A49	4c brt blue & multi	.30 .30
299	A49	10c brt blue & multi	.75 .75
300	A49	15c brt blue & multi	1.10 1.10
301	A49	25c brt blue & multi	1.90 1.90
a.		Souv. sheet, #297-301 + 2 labels	6.00 6.00
		Nos. 297-301 (5)	4.25 4.25

Visit of Prince Philip, Duke of Edinburgh to Rarotonga, Feb. 27, 1971. Printed in sheets of 10 stamps and 2 labels showing Queen Elizabeth II commemorative coin and a portrait of Prince Philip.

Nos. 210, 213-
214 Overprinted

1971, Sept. 8   Photo.   Perf. 14x13½

302	A34	10c gold & multi	.65 .65
303	A34	25c gold & multi	.65 .65
304	A34	30c gold & multi	.65 .65
		Nos. 302-304 (3)	1.95 1.95

4th South Pacific Games, Papeete, French Polynesia, Sept. 8-19.

Nos. 202, 205, 208-209 and 211 Surcharged with New Value and Three Bars

1971, Oct. 20

305	A34	10c on 2½c multi	.20 .20
306	A34	10c on 4c multi	.20 .20
307	A34	10c on 8c multi	.20 .20
308	A34	10c on 9c multi	.20 .20
309	A34	10c on 15c multi	.20 .20
		Nos. 305-309 (5)	1.00 1.00

Rocket over
Moon — A51

Madonna and
Child, by
Bellini — A50

Christmas: Paintings of the Madonna and Child, by Giovanni Bellini.

1971, Nov. 30   Perf. 13½

310	A50	1c gold & multi	.20 .20
311	A50	4c gold & multi	.20 .20
312	A50	10c gold & multi	.30 .30
313	A50	20c gold & multi	.60 .60
314	A50	30c gold & multi	.90 .90
a.		Souv. sheet, #310-314 + label	3.00 3.00
		Nos. 310-314 (5)	2.20 2.20

See No. B14.

No. 216 Overprinted: "SOUTH PACIFIC / COMMISSION / FEB. 1947-1972"

1972, Feb. 17   Photo.   Perf. 14x13½

315	A35	$1 gold & multi	1.00 1.00

South Pacific Commission, 25th anniv.

Easter Type of 1970

Illuminations from 14th century Robert de Lisle Psalter: 5c, St. John. 10c, Christ crucified. 30c, Virgin Mary.

1972, Mar. 6   Photo.   Perf. 13½
Size: 21x68mm

316	A46	5c gold & multi	.20 .20
317	A46	10c gold & multi	.20 .20
318	A46	30c gold & multi	.50 .50
a.		Souvenir sheet of 3, #316-318	1.50 1.50
		Nos. 316-318 (3)	.90 .90

Printed in sheets of 12.
For surcharges see Nos. B15-B16, B19.

#319a, Shown. #319b, Earth over moon. #320a, Landing module and astronaut. #320b, Astronaut collecting moon rocks. #321a, Earth and rocket over moon. #321b, Lunar rover and astronaut. #322a, Helicopter over raft in Pacific. #322b, Capsule and parachutes.

1972, Apr. 17

319	A51	5c Pair, #a.-b.	.20 .20
320	A51	10c Pair, #a.-b.	.60 .60
321	A51	25c Pair, #a.-b.	1.75 1.75
322	A51	25c Pair, #a.-b.	2.25 2.25
c.		Souvenir sheet of 8	7.50 7.50
		Nos. 319-322 (4)	4.80 4.80

Apollo moon explorations.
No. 322c contains Nos. 319-322 arranged in 2 blocks of 4 divided by a map showing splashdown area of Apollo X, XII and XIII.
For surcharges see Nos. B21-B24.

High Jump,
Olympic
Rings — A52

Rest on Flight to
Egypt, by
Caravaggio — A53

1972, June 26

327	A52	10c shown	.30 .30
328	A52	25c Running	.65 .65
329	A52	30c Boxing	.65 .65
a.		Souv. sheet, #327-329 + label	2.50 2.50
		Nos. 327-329 (3)	1.60 1.60

20th Olympic Games, Munich, Aug. 26-Sept. 10. Sheets of 8 stamps and label.
See No. B29.

1972, Oct. 11   Photo.   Perf. 13½

Paintings: 5c, Virgin of the Swallows, by Guercino. 10c, Virgin with Green Cushion, by Andrea Solario. 20c, Virgin and Child, by Lorenzo di Credi. 30c, Virgin and Child, by Giovanni Bellini.

330	A53	1c gold & multi	.30 .30
331	A53	5c gold & multi	.30 .30
332	A53	10c gold & multi	.40 .40
333	A53	20c gold & multi	.75 .75
334	A53	30c gold & multi	1.25 1.25
a.		Souv. sheet, #330-334 + label	4.50 4.50
		Nos. 330-334 (5)	3.00 3.00

Christmas. See No. B30.

Princess
Elizabeth and
Prince
Philip — A54

Designs: 5c, Wedding ceremony, Westminster Abbey. 15c, Bridal portrait. 30c, Official wedding picture of royal family.

1972, Nov. 20
Size: 29x40mm

335	A54	5c silver & multi	.40 .40
336	A54	10c silver & multi	.55 .55

Size: 40x40mm

337	A54	15c silver & multi	.70 .70

Size: 66x40mm

338	A54	30c silver & multi	.85 .85
		Nos. 335-338 (4)	2.50 2.50

25th anniversary of the marriage of Queen Elizabeth II and Prince Philip.
Nos. 335-337 printed in sheets of 8 stamps and one label; No. 338 in sheets of 6.

1c Coin
with
Queen
Elizabeth II
and Taro
Leaf
A55

Queen Elizabeth II Coins: 2c, Pineapples. 5c, Hibiscus. 10c, Oranges. 20c, Fairy terns. 50c, Bonito. $1, Tangaroa, Polynesian god of creation, vert.

1973, Mar. 15   Photo.   Perf. 13x13½
Size: 37x24mm

339	A55	1c dp car, blk & gold	.20 .20
340	A55	2c blue, blk & gold	.20 .20
341	A55	5c green, blk & gold	.20 .20

Size: 46x30mm

342	A55	10c vio, blue, blk & sil	.25 .25
343	A55	20c dk green, blk & sil	.40 .40
344	A55	50c dp car, black & sil	.60 .60

Size: 32x54½mm

345	A55	$1 blue, blk & silver	.90 .90
		Nos. 339-345 (7)	2.75 2.75

Coinage commemorating silver wedding anniversary of Queen Elizabeth II.
Printed in sheets of 20 stamps and label showing Westminster Abbey.

"Noli me
Tangere," by
Titian — A56

Paintings: 10c, Descent from the Cross, by Rubens. 30c, The Lamentation of Christ, by Dürer.

1973, Apr. 9

346	A56	5c gold & multi	.20 .20
347	A56	10c gold & multi	.40 .40
348	A56	30c gold & multi	.50 .50
a.		Souvenir sheet of 3, #346-348	1.40 1.40
		Nos. 346-348 (3)	1.10 1.10

Easter. Printed in sheets of 15 stamps and one label.
See Nos. 378-380, B31-B33, B39-B41.

Queen Elizabeth
II in Coronation
Regalia — A57

1973, June 1   Photo.   Perf. 14x13½

349	A57	10c gold & multi	1.25 1.25

Souvenir Sheet
Perf. 13½x14½

350	A57	50c gold & multi	3.75 3.75

20th anniv. of the coronation of Queen Elizabeth II. No. 349 printed in sheets of 5 stamps and one label.

Nos. 206, 208, 210, 212-214
Overprinted: "TENTH ANNIVERSARY / CESSATION OF / NUCLEAR TESTING / TREATY"

1973, July 25   Photo.   Perf. 14x13½

351	A34	5c gold & multi	.20	.20
352	A34	8c gold & multi	.20	.20
353	A34	10c gold & multi	.20	.20
354	A34	20c gold & multi	.20	.20
355	A34	25c gold & multi	.50	.50
356	A34	30c gold & multi	.50	.50
		Nos. 351-356 (6)	1.80	1.80

Nuclear Test Ban Treaty, 10th anniv. and as protest against French nuclear testing on Mururoa atoll.

Tipairua — A58

Historic South Pacific sailing vessels.

1973, Sept. 17   Photo.   Perf. 13½x13

357	A58	½c shown	.30	.30
358	A58	1c Wa'a Kaulua	.30	.30
359	A58	1½c Tainui	.30	.30
360	A58	5c War canoe	.85	.85
361	A58	10c Pahi	1.00	1.00
362	A58	15c Amatasi	1.25	1.25
363	A58	25c Vaka	1.75	1.75
		Nos. 357-363 (7)	5.75	5.75

Annunciation
A59

Designs from 15th Century Prayer Book: 5c, The Visitation. 10c, Adoration of the Shepherds. 20c, Adoration of the Kings. 30c, Slaughter of the Innocents.

1973, Oct. 30   Photo.   Perf. 13x13½

364	A59	1c multicolored	.20	.20
365	A59	5c multicolored	.20	.20
366	A59	10c multicolored	.20	.20
367	A59	20c multicolored	.25	.25
368	A59	30c multicolored	.45	.45
a.		Souv. sheet, #364-368 + label	1.25	1.25
		Nos. 364-368 (5)	1.30	1.30

Christmas. See Nos. B34-B38.

1973, Nov. 14   Photo.   Perf. 14

369	A60	25c shown	.30	.30
370	A60	30c Mark Phillips	.50	.50
371	A60	50c Princess and Mark Phillips	.70	.70
a.		Souv. sheet, #369-371 + label	1.75	1.75
		Nos. 369-371 (3)	1.50	1.50

Princess
Anne — A60

Wedding of Princess Anne and Capt. Mark Phillips.

Running and Games Emblem A61

1c, Diving. 3c, Boxing. 10c, Weight lifting. 30c, Bicycling. 50c, Discobolus.

1974, Jan. 24   Photo.   Perf. 14

372	A61	1c multi, vert.	.20	.20
373	A61	3c multi, vert.	.20	.20
374	A61	5c multi	.20	.20
375	A61	10c multi	.25	.25
376	A61	30c multi	.75	.75
		Nos. 372-376 (5)	1.60	1.60

Souvenir Sheet

377	A61	50c multi, vert.	2.00	2.00

10th British Commonwealth Games, Christchurch, New Zealand, Jan. 24-Feb. 2. No. 377 contains one stamp 35x45mm.

Easter Type of 1973
Dated "1974"

Paintings: 5c, Jesus Carrying Cross, by Raphael. 10c, Jesus in the Arms of God, by El Greco. 30c, Descent from the Cross, by Caravaggio.

1974, Mar. 25   Perf. 13½x13

378	A56	5c gold & multi	.20	.20
379	A56	10c gold & multi	.25	.25
380	A56	30c gold & multi	.65	.65
a.		Souvenir sheet of 3, #378-380	2.00	2.00
		Nos. 378-380 (3)	1.10	1.10

Easter. See Nos. B39-B41.

Phallicium Glaucum A62

Queen Elizabeth II — A63

Queen and Shells — A64

Cook Islands sea shells. The designs of the 2c, 5c, 10c, 30c include portrait of Queen Elizabeth II.

1974-75   Photo.   Perf. 13½

381	A62	½c shown	.20	.20
382	A62	1c Vasum turbinellus	.20	.20
383	A62	1½c Corculum cardissa	.20	.20
384	A62	2c Terebellum terebellum	.20	.20
385	A62	3c Aulica vespertilio	.20	.20
386	A62	4c Strombus gibberulus	.20	.20
387	A62	5c Cymatium pileare	.20	.20
388	A62	6c Cyprae caput-serpentis	.20	.20
389	A62	8c Bursa granularis	.20	.20
390	A62	10c Tenebra muscaria	.20	.20
391	A62	15c Mitra mitra	.35	.35
392	A62	20c Natica alapillonis roding	.55	.55
393	A62	25c Gloripallium pallium	.65	.65
394	A62	30c Conus miles	.80	.80
395	A62	50c Conus textile	1.25	1.10
396	A62	60c Oliva sericea roding	2.00	1.10

397	A63	$1 multicolored	3.00	2.00
398	A63	$2 multi ('75)	6.25	4.00

Perf. 14x13½

399	A64	$4 multi ('75)	9.50	6.00
400	A64	$6 multi ('75)	15.00	9.50
401	A64	$8 multi ('75)	19.00	11.50
402	A64	$10 multi ('75)	24.00	16.00
		Nos. 381-402 (22)	84.35	55.55

Issued: 50c, 60c, $1, 8/26; $2, 1/27; $4, 3/17; $6, 4/29; $8, 5/30; $10, 6/30; others, 5/17.
For surcharges & overprints see #488-498, 526-528, 991, O16-O26, O30-O31.

Soccer Player and Map of Oceania A65

50c, Munich stadium & map of Oceania. $1, Soccer player, Munich stadium & World Cup.

**1974, July 5   Photo.   Perf. 13½
Size: 31x29mm**

403	A65	25c multicolored	.35	.35
404	A65	50c multicolored	.75	.75

Size: 68x28½mm

405	A65	$1 multicolored	1.25	1.25
a.		Souvenir sheet of 3, #403-405	2.75	2.75
		Nos. 403-405 (3)	2.35	2.35

World Cup Soccer Championship, Munich, June 13-July 7. Nos. 403-405 printed in sheets of 8 and commemorative label.

$2.50 Capt. Cook Silver Coin — A66

Commemorative Silver Coins: $7.50, $7.50 coin with Queen Elizabeth II on obverse; Capt. Cook, map of Islands and "Resolution" on reverse. $2.50 coin shows "Resolution," "Adventure" and globe on reverse.

1974, July 22   Photo.   Perf. 14

406	A66	$2.50 sil, vio & blk	11.00	7.25
407	A66	$7.50 grn, sil & blk	29.00	22.50
a.		Souvenir sheet of 2, #406-407	45.00	30.00

Bicentenary of Capt. Cook's 2nd voyage of discovery. Nos. 406-407 printed in sheets of 5 and commemorative label.

Cook Islands Nos. 1, 49, 62, 66, 77 — A67

Stamps of Cook Islands: 25c, DC-3 over old Rarotonga landing strip, and No. 19. 30c, Rarotonga Post Office, UPU emblem and No. 65. 50c, UPU emblem and Nos. 1, 19, 49, 62, 65-66 and 77.

1974, Sept. 16   Photo.   Perf. 13½x14

408	A67	10c gold & multi	.20	.20
409	A67	25c gold & multi	.55	.55
410	A67	30c gold & multi	.65	.65
411	A67	50c gold & multi	1.25	1.25
a.		Souv. sheet of 4, #408-411, perf. 13½	2.75	2.75
		Nos. 408-411 (4)	2.65	2.65

Cent. of UPU. Nos. 408-411 printed in sheets of 8 and commemorative label.

Virgin and Child, with St. John, by Raphael — A68

Paintings: 5c, Holy Family, by Andrea del Sarto. 10c, Nativity, by Correggio. 20c, Holy Family, by Rembrandt. 30c, Nativity, by Van der Weyden.

1974, Oct. 15   Photo.   Perf. 13½

412	A68	1c multicolored	.20	.20
413	A68	5c multicolored	.20	.20
414	A68	10c multicolored	.20	.20
415	A68	20c multicolored	.65	.65
416	A68	30c multicolored	.95	.95
a.		Souv. sheet, #412-416 + label	2.50	2.50
		Nos. 412-416 (5)	2.20	2.20

Christmas 1974. Nos. 412-416 printed in sheets of 15 and one label showing Queen Elizabeth II.
See Nos. B42-B46.

Churchill and Blenheim Palace A69

Sir Winston Churchill (1874-1965) and: 10c, Parliament. 25c, Chartwell. 30c, Buckingham Palace. 50c, St. Paul's Cathedral.

1974, Nov. 20   Photo.   Perf. 14

417	A69	5c violet & multi	.20	.20
418	A69	10c maroon & multi	.25	.25
419	A69	25c dk blue & multi	.50	.50
420	A69	30c brown & multi	.65	.65
421	A69	50c multicolored	1.25	1.25
a.		Souv. sheet, #417-421 + label	3.50	3.50
		Nos. 417-421 (5)	2.85	2.85

Nos. 417-421 printed in sheets of 5 stamps and one label showing $100 commemorative gold coin.

Vasco Nunez de Balboa — A70

5c, Ferdinand Magellan & route around South America. 10c, Juan Sebastian de Elcano & ship. 25c, Andres de Urdaneta & ship. 25c, Miguel Lopez de Legaspi & ship.

1975, Feb. 3   Perf. 13½

422	A70	1c multicolored	.35	.20
423	A70	5c multicolored	.35	.20
424	A70	10c multicolored	1.25	.35
425	A70	25c multicolored	3.00	1.10
426	A70	30c multicolored	3.50	1.25
		Nos. 422-426 (5)	8.45	3.10

16th century explorers of the Pacific Ocean.

Apollo and Apollo-Soyuz Emblem — A71

Apollo-Soyuz Emblem &: #427b, Soyuz. #428a, Aleksei A. Leonov & Valery N. Kubasov. #428b, Donald K. Slayton, Vance D. Brand & Thomas P. Stafford. #429a, Cosmonaut inside Soyuz capsule. #429b, American astronauts inside Apollo capsule.

1975, July 15 Photo.   *Perf. 13½*

427	A71	25c Pair, #a.-b.	1.00	1.00
428	A71	30c Pair, #a.-b.	1.25	1.25
429	A71	50c Pair, #a.-b.	2.00	2.00
c.		Souvenir sheet of 6, #427-429	4.25	4.25
		Nos. 427-429 (3)	4.25	4.25

Apollo Soyuz space test project (Russo-American space cooperation), launching July 15; link-up, July 17. Printed sheets of 18 stamps and 2 labels showing flags.

$100 Gold Commemorative Coin — A72

1975, Aug. 8 Photo.   *Perf. 13½x13*

| 433 | A72 | $2 gold & dp violet | 6.00 | 5.75 |

Bicentenary of the completion of Capt. Cook's second voyage of discovery.

Cook Islands' Flag, Map of Islands and New Zealand A73

Prime Minister Sir Albert Henry — A74

Design: 25c, View of Rarotonga and flag.

1975, Aug. 8 *Perf. 13½x13, 13x13½*

434	A73	5c gold & multi	.60	.20
435	A74	10c gold & multi	.75	.20
436	A73	25c gold & multi	1.90	.55
		Nos. 434-436 (3)	3.25	.95

Tenth anniversary of self-government.

Virgin and Child, 15th Century, Flemish — A75

Paintings: 10c, Madonna in the Field, by Raphael. 15c, Holy Family, by Raphael. 20c, Adoration of the Shepherds, by J. B. Mayno. 35c, Annunciation, by Murillo.

1975, Dec. 1 Photo.   *Perf. 13½*

437	A75	6c gold & multi	.20	.20
438	A75	10c gold & multi	.20	.20
439	A75	15c gold & multi	.30	.30
440	A75	20c gold & multi	.40	.40
441	A75	35c gold & multi	.65	.65
a.		Souv. sheet, #437-441 + label	1.90	1.90
		Nos. 437-441 (5)	1.75	1.75

Christmas. See Nos. B47-B51.

Descent from the Cross, by Raphael A76

Paintings: 15c, Pieta, by Veronese. 35c, Pieta, by El Greco.

1976, Mar. 29 Photo.   *Perf. 13½*

442	A76	7c gold & multi	.20	.20
443	A76	15c gold & multi	.60	.60
444	A76	35c gold & multi	1.40	1.40
a.		Souvenir sheet of 3, #442-444	2.25	2.25
		Nos. 442-444 (3)	2.20	2.20

Easter. Nos. 442-444 printed in sheets of 20 with label showing Queen Elizabeth II. See Nos. B52-B54.

Benjamin Franklin and "Resolution" — A77

Designs: $2, Capt. James Cook and "Resolution." $3, Cook, "Resolution" and Franklin.

1976, May 29 Photo.   *Perf. 13½*

| 445 | A77 | $1 gold & multi | 5.50 | 3.00 |
| 446 | A77 | $2 gold & multi | 11.50 | 6.25 |

Souvenir Sheet

Perf. 13

| 447 | A77 | $3 gold & multi | 15.00 | 8.50 |

American Bicentennial. No. 447 contains one stamp 73x31mm. Nos. 445-446 printed in sheets of 5 and corner label with Franklin's request to assist Capt. Cook.
For overprint see No. O29.

Nos. 445-447 Overprinted "Royal Visit July 1976"

1976, July 6   *Perf. 13½*

| 448 | A77 | $1 gold & multi | 2.50 | 2.00 |
| 449 | A77 | $2 gold & multi | 6.25 | 5.75 |

Souvenir Sheet

Perf. 13

| 450 | A77 | $3 gold & multi | 11.00 | 7.75 |

Visit of Queen Elizabeth II and Prince Philip to the United States.

High Hurdles — A78

15c, Field hockey. 30c, Fencing. 35c, Soccer.

1976, July 22   *Perf. 13½*

451	A78	7c Pair, #a.-b.	.25	.25
452	A78	15c Pair, #a.-b.	.50	.50
453	A78	30c Pair, #a.-b.	1.25	1.25
454	A78	35c Pair, #a.-b.	1.50	1.50
c.		Souvenir sheet of 8, #451-454	4.50	4.50
		Nos. 451-454 (4)	3.50	3.50

21st Olympic Games, Montreal, Canada, 7/17-8/1. Printed in sheets of 10 stamps + 2 labels.

The Visitation — A80

Designs: 10c, Virgin and Child. 15c, Adoration of the Shepherds. 20c, Adoration of the Kings. 35c, Holy Family. After painted Renaissance altar sculptures.

1976, Oct. 12 Photo.   *Perf. 14x13½*

459	A80	6c gold & multi	.20	.20
460	A80	10c gold & multi	.20	.20
461	A80	15c gold & multi	.25	.25
462	A80	20c gold & multi	.35	.35
463	A80	35c gold & multi	.60	.60
a.		Souv. sheet, #459-463 + label	1.75	1.75
		Nos. 459-463 (5)	1.60	1.60

Christmas. Nos. 459-463 printed in sheets of 20 with label showing Queen Elizabeth II. See Nos. B55-B59.

$5 Silver Coin, 1976 — A81

1976, Nov. 15 Photo.   *Perf. 13½*

| 464 | A81 | $1 multicolored | 3.00 | 2.25 |

National Wildlife and Conservation Day. Issued in sheets of 5 stamps and commemorative label.
See Nos. 502, 536.

A82

#465a, Crown. #465b, Elizabeth II in Coronation Vestments. #466a, Westminster Abbey. #466b, Coach in procession. #467a, Queen and Prince Philip after coronation. 467b, Investiture of Sir Albert Henry, Premier of Cook Islands, 1974.

1977, Feb. 7 Photo.   *Perf. 13½x13*

465	A82	25c Pair, #a.-b.	.50	.40
466	A82	50c Pair, #a.-b.	1.25	1.00
467	A82	$1 Pair, #a.-b.	2.50	2.00
c.		Souv. sheet, #465-467, perf. 13	4.00	3.50
		Nos. 465-467 (3)	4.25	3.40

Reign of Queen Elizabeth II, 25th anniv. Printed in sheets of 8.
For overprints see No. O27.

Crucifixion, by Rubens — A83

Virgin and Child, by Memling — A84

Paintings by Rubens: 15c, Christ Between the Thieves. 35c, Descent from the Cross.

1977, Mar. 28 Photo.   *Perf. 14x13½*

471	A83	7c gold & multi	.50	.50
472	A83	15c gold & multi	.50	.50
473	A83	35c gold & multi	1.40	1.40
a.		Souv. sheet, #471-473, perf 13	2.50	2.50
		Nos. 471-473 (3)	2.40	2.40

Easter 1977, and 400th birth anniv. of Peter Paul Rubens (1577-1640), Flemish painter. Nos. 471-473 printed in sheets of 24 stamps and corner label with portrait of Queen Elizabeth II and description.
See Nos. B60-B62.

1977, Oct. 3 Photo.   *Perf. 13½*

Virgin and Child by: 10c, Hans Memling. 15c, Geertgen Tot Sin Jans. 20c, Carlo Crivelli. 35c, School of Henry Blex.

474	A84	6c gold & multi	.25	.25
475	A84	10c gold & multi	.25	.25
476	A84	15c gold & multi	.25	.25
477	A84	20c gold & multi	.45	.45
478	A84	35c gold & multi	.80	.80
a.		Souv. sheet, #474-478 + label	2.25	2.25
		Nos. 474-478 (5)	2.00	2.00

Christmas. Nos. 474-478 printed in sheets of 24 and label. See Nos. B63-B67.

$5-silver Coin, 1977 — A85

1977, Nov. 15 Photo.   *Perf. 13½*

| 479 | A85 | $1 silver & multi | 3.00 | 1.40 |

National Wildlife Conservation Day. No. 479 issued in sheets of 5 and one label.

Capt. Cook, by Nathaniel Dance and "Resolution" — A86

$1, "Capt. Cook Landing at Owyhee" and Capt. Cook. $2, Cook Islands $200 commemorative coin, 1978, and Cook Monument, Hawaii, 1825.

1978, Jan. 20 Litho.   *Perf. 13½*

480	A86	50c gold & multi	.90	.90
481	A86	$1 gold & multi	1.60	1.60
482	A86	$2 gold & multi	3.25	3.25
a.		Souvenir sheet of 3, #480-482	6.00	6.00
		Nos. 480-482 (3)	5.75	5.75

Bicentennial of Capt. Cook's arrival in Hawaii.
Nos. 480-482 issued in sheets of 5 with corner label showing ship off Hawaiian coast.
For overprints see Nos. 499-501a.

Pieta, by Rogier van der Weyden A87

Paintings, National Gallery, London: 35c, Burial of Jesus, by Michelangelo. 75c, Jesus at Emmaus, by Caravaggio.

1978, Mar. 20 Photo. Perf. 13½x13

483	A87	15c gold & multi	.20	.20
484	A87	35c gold & multi	.50	.50
485	A87	75c gold & multi	1.10	1.10
a.		Souv. sheet, #483-485 + label	1.75	1.75
		Nos. 483-485 (3)	1.80	1.80

Easter. Nos. 483-485 printed in sheets of 5 and corner label showing National Gallery. See Nos. B68-B70.

A88

A89

Souvenir Sheets

1978, June 6 Photo. Perf. 13

486	Sheet of 4 + 2 labels	1.50	1.50
a.	A88 50c shown	.40	.40
b.	A88 50c Lion of England	.40	.40
c.	A88 50c Imperial State Crown	.40	.40
d.	A88 50c Tangaroa figure	.40	.40
487	Sheet of 4 + label	1.50	1.50
a.	A88 70c like 486a	.40	.40
b.	A88 70c Scepter with Cross	.40	.40
c.	A88 70c St. Edward's Crown	.40	.40
d.	A88 70c Rarotongan staff god	.40	.40
e.	Souv. sheet of 8, #486a-487b + label	3.00	3.00

Coronation of Queen Elizabeth II, 25th anniv.

Nos. 381, 383, 388-389, 393-396 Surcharged with New Value and Three Bars in Silver, Black or Gold

1978, Nov. 10 Photo. Perf. 13½

488	A62	5c on 1½c multi (S)	.25	.25
489	A62	7c on ½c multi	.35	.35
490	A62	10c on 6c multi (G)	.50	.50
491	A62	10c on 8c multi (G)	.50	.50
492	A62	15c on ½c multi	.80	.80
493	A62	15c on 25c multi (S)	.80	.80
494	A62	15c on 30c multi	.80	.80
495	A62	15c on 50c multi (S)	.80	.80
496	A62	15c on 60c multi (G)	.80	.80
497	A62	17c on ½c multi	.95	.95
498	A62	17c on 50c multi (S)	.95	.95
		Nos. 488-498 (11)	7.50	7.50

See Nos. 526-528.

Nos. 480-482a Overprinted in Black on Silver Panel

1978, Nov. 13 Litho. Perf. 13½

499	A86	50c gold & multi	1.00	1.00
500	A86	$1 gold & multi	2.00	2.00
501	A86	$2 gold & multi	4.00	4.00
a.		Souvenir sheet of 3, #499-501	18.00	18.00
		Nos. 499-501 (3)	7.00	7.00

250th anniv. of Capt. Cook's birth. Similar overprint in 4 lines was applied to labels. Label of No. 501a overprinted only with dates 1728, 1978.

Coin Type of 1976

$1, $5 Silver coin, 1978 (Polynesian warbler).

1978, Nov. 15 Photo. Perf. 13½

502	A81	$1 multicolored	2.25	2.00

National Wildlife and Conservation Day. Sheets of 24 containing 4 panes of 6.

1978, Dec. 8 Photo. Perf. 13

Virgin and Child by: 15c, Rogiervan der Weyden. 17c, Carlo Crivelli. 35c, Murillo.

503	A89	15c multicolored	.45	.45
504	A89	17c multicolored	.60	.60
505	A89	35c multicolored	.95	.95
a.		Souvenir sheet of 3, #503-505	2.25	2.25
		Nos. 503-505 (3)	2.00	2.00

Christmas. See Nos. B71-B73.

A90

A91

Descent from the Cross, by Gaspar de Crayer (Details): 10c, Pieta. 12c, St. John. 15c, Mary Magdalene. 20c, Cherubs.

1979, Apr. 5 Photo. Perf. 13

506	A90	10c multicolored	.30	.30
507	A90	12c multicolored	.30	.30
508	A90	15c multicolored	.35	.35
509	A90	20c multicolored	.75	.75
		Nos. 506-509 (4)	1.70	1.70

Easter. See No. B74.

1979, July 23 Photo. Perf. 14x13½

20c, Capt. Cook, by John Weber. 30c, Resolution, by Henry Roberts. 35c, Endeavour. 50c, Death of Capt. Cook, by George Carter.

510	A91	20c multicolored	.55	.55
511	A91	30c multicolored	.75	.75
512	A91	35c multicolored	.85	.85
513	A91	50c multicolored	1.10	1.10
a.		Souvenir sheet of 4	3.50	3.50
		Nos. 510-513 (4)	3.25	3.25

Capt. Cook (1728-1779), explorer. No. 513a contains 4 stamps similar to Nos. 510-513 with black frames.

Sir Rowland Hill, Originator of Penny Postage — A92

#514a, Postrider. #514b, Stagecoach. #514c, Automobile. #514d, Streamlined train. #515a, Cap-Horniers, sailing ship. #515b, River steamer. #515c, Liner Deutschland. #515d, Liner United States. #516a, Balloon Neptune. #516b, Junkers F13. #516c, Graf Zeppelin. #516d, Concorde.

1979, Sept. 10 Perf. 14½

514	A92	30c Block of 4, #a.-d.	1.40	1.40
515	A92	35c Block of 4, #a.-d.	1.60	1.60
516	A92	50c Block of 4, #a.-d.	2.50	2.50
e.		Souv. sheet of 12, #514-516	6.00	6.00
		Nos. 514-516 (3)	5.50	5.50

Nos. 381, 383, 396 Surcharged in Gold or Silver

1979, Sept. 12 Photo. Perf. 13½

526	A62	6c on ½c multi	.20	.20
527	A62	10c on 1½c multi (S)	.30	.30
528	A62	15c on 60c multi	.40	.40
		Nos. 526-528 (3)	.90	.90

Nos. 526-528 have 3 thick bars of equal length over old value.

Girl and Baby, IYC Emblem — A93

IYC Emblem and: 50c, Boy playing tree drum. 65c, Children dancing.

1979, Oct. 10 Perf. 13

529	A93	30c multicolored	.35	.35
530	A93	50c multicolored	.60	.60
531	A93	65c multicolored	.80	.80
		Nos. 529-531 (3)	1.75	1.75

See No. B75.

Apollo 11 Emblem — A94

50c, Apollo 11 crew, lunar map. 60c, Astronaut walking on moon. 65c, Splashdown.

1979, Nov. 7 Perf. 14

532	A94	30c multicolored	.40	.40
533	A94	50c multicolored	.60	.60
534	A94	60c multicolored	.75	.75
535	A94	65c multicolored	.85	.85
a.		Souv. sheet, #532-535, perf. 13	3.50	3.50
		Nos. 532-535 (4)	2.60	2.60

Apollo 11 moon landing, 10th anniv.

Coin Type of 1976

$1, $5 Silver coin, 1979 (Rarotonga fruit dove).

Perf. 13½x14½

1979, Nov. 15 Photo.

536	A81	$1 multicolored	2.00	2.00

National Wildlife and Conservation Day.

Christmas Tree Ornaments — A95

1979, Dec. 14 Perf. 14

Christmas (Flowers and): 10c, Star. 12c, Bells and candle. 15c, Ancestral statue.

537	A95	6c multicolored	.20	.20
538	A95	10c multicolored	.20	.20
539	A95	12c multicolored	.20	.20
540	A95	15c multicolored	.20	.20
		Nos. 537-540,B76-B79 (8)	1.80	1.80

See also Nos. C16-C19, CB1-CB4.

A96

Bible illustrations by Gustave Dore, 1833-1883: #541a, Flagellation. #541b, Jesus Wearing Crown of Thorns. #542a, Jesus Mocked. #542b, Jesus Falls. #543a, The Crucifixion. #543b, Descent from the Cross.

1980, Mar. 31 Photo. Perf. 13

541	A96	20c Pair, #a.-b.	.60	.60
542	A96	30c Pair, #a.-b.	.90	.90
543	A96	35c Pair, #a.-b.	1.00	1.00
		Nos. 541-543 (3)	2.50	2.50

Easter. See Nos. 553, B80-B83.

Doves with Olive Branch, Rotary Emblem A97

1980, May 27 Photo. Perf. 14

547	A97	30c shown	.45	.45
548	A97	35c Flowers	.50	.50
549	A97	50c Flags, globe	.70	.70
		Nos. 547-549 (3)	1.65	1.65

Rotary Intl., 75th anniv. See No. B87.

Easter Type of 1980 and:

New Zealand No. 1 — A98

#550a, Postrider. #550b, Coach. #550c, Automobile. #550d, Train.
New Zealand #2 and: #551a, Sailing ship. #551b, River steamer. #551c, Transatlantic liner (facing left). #551d, Transatlantic liner (facing right).
New Zealand #3 and: #552a, 1870-71 mail balloon. #552b, 1919 plane. #552c, Graf Zeppelin. #552d, Concorde.

1980, Aug. 22 Photo. Perf. 14

550	A98	30c Block of 4, #a.-d.	1.50	1.25
551	A98	35c Block of 4, #a.-d.	2.00	1.75
552	A98	50c Block of 4, #a.-d.	3.00	2.50
e.		Souvenir sheet of 12	7.50	6.50
		Nos. 550-552 (3)	6.50	5.50

Souvenir Sheet

Perf. 13

553	A96	Sheet of 6, #541-543	5.00	3.50

ZEAPEX '80, New Zealand Intl. Stamp Exhib., Auckland, Aug. 23-31. #552e contains of #550-552 arranged horizontally (4x3). #553 has black on gold overprint: "ZEAPEX / '80 / Auckland / +10c" in margin.

Queen Mother Elizabeth, 80th Birthday — A99

1980, Sept. 22   **Photo.**   *Perf. 13*
554 A99 50c multicolored   1.00 1.00

Souvenir Sheet
555 A99 $2 multicolored   2.00 2.00

No. 554 issued in sheets of 9 (3x3).

Johannes Kepler, Spacecraft — A100

Designs: Nos. 556a, 559a, Kepler, spacecraft (diff.). No. 559b, Kepler, lunar rover, astronaut on moon. Nos. 557a-558b, Jules Verne, various scenes from From Earth to Moon, vert.

1980, Nov. 7   **Photo.**   *Perf. 13*
556 A100 12c Pair, #a-b   .50 .50
557 A100 20c Pair, #a-b   .50 .50
558 A100 30c Pair, #a-b   1.25 1.25
   a.   Souvenir sheet, #557-558   2.50 2.50
559 A100 50c Pair, #a-b   2.75 2.75
   a.   Souv. sheet, #556, 559   3.50 3.50
    Nos. 556-559 (4)   5.00 5.00

Death anniversaries of Johannes Kepler, German astronomer and Jules Verne, French science fiction writer.

Burning Bush Coral — A101

Daisy Coral — A102

#564a, 570a, 576a, Siphonogorgia. #564b, 570b, 576b, Pavona practorta. #564c, 570c, 576c, Stylaster echinatus. #564d, 570d, 576d, Stylaster echinatus. #565a, 571a, 577a, Millepora alcicornis. #565b, 571b, 577b, Junceella gemmaea. #565c, 571c, 577c, Fungia fungites. #565d, 571d, 577d, Heliofungia actiniformis. #566a, 572a, 578a, Distichopora violacea. #566b, 572b, 578b, Stylaster. #566c, 572c, 578c, Gonipora. #566d, 572d, 578d, Caulastraea echinulata. #567a, 573a, 579a, Ptilosarcus gurneyi. #567b, 573b, 579b, Stylophora pistillata. #567c, 573c, 579c, Melithaea squamata. #567d, 573d, 579d, Porites andrewsi. #568a, 574a, 580a, Lobophyllia bemprichii. #568b, 574b, 580b, Palauastrea ramosa. #568c, 574c, 580c, Bellonella indica. #568d, 574d, 580d, Pectinia alcicornis. #569a, 575a, 581a, Sarcophyton digitatum. #569b, 575b, 581b, Melithaea albitincta. #569c, 575c, 581c, Plerogyra sinuosa. #569d, 575d, 581d, Dendrophyllia gracilis.

1980-82   *Perf. 13½x13*
Strips of 4 (#564-575) or Blocks of 4 (#576-581)

564	A101	1c #a.-d.	.25	.25
565	A101	3c #a.-d.	.30	.30
566	A101	4c #a.-d.	.35	.35
567	A101	5c #a.-d.	.45	.45
568	A101	6c #a.-d.	.60	.60
569	A101	8c #a.-d.	.70	.70
570	A101	10c #a.-d.	.90	.90
571	A101	12c #a.-d.	1.10	1.10
572	A101	15c #a.-d.	1.40	1.40
573	A101	20c #a.-d.	1.60	1.60
574	A101	25c #a.-d.	2.25	2.25
575	A101	30c #a.-d.	2.50	2.50
576	A101	35c #a.-d.	3.00	3.00
577	A101	40c #a.-d.	4.00	4.00
578	A101	60c #a.-d.	5.25	5.25
579	A101	70c #a.-d.	5.75	5.75
580	A101	80c #a.-d.	6.25	6.25
581	A101	$1 #a.-d.	7.00	7.00

    Perf. 14x13½

582	A102	$2 like #566c	5.50	5.50
583	A102	$3 like #565d	7.75	7.75
584	A102	$4 like #567b	10.00	10.00
585	A102	$6 like #564c	15.00	15.00
586	A102	$10 like #569b	22.50	22.50
		Nos. 564-586 (23)	104.40	104.40

Issued: 1-8c, 11/21/80; 10-30c, 12/19/80; 35-60c, 3/16/81; 70c, 80c, 4/13/81; $1, 5/20/81; $2, $3, 11/27/81; $4, $6, 1/11/82; $10, 3/5/82.

For surcharges see Nos. 710-714, 716, 738, 740, 811-815, 953-954, 956-957, 959, 961-962, 964, 978-979, 984-986, B109-B111, O50-O53. For overprints see Nos. 992, 1049.

Annunciation, 13th Century Prayerbook Illustration — A102a

1980, Dec. 1   **Photo.**   *Perf. 14*
652 A102a 15c shown   .20 .20
653 A102a 30c Visitation   .40 .40
654 A102a 40c Nativity   .50 .50
655 A102a 50c Epiphany   .70 .70
   a.   Souvenir sheet of 4, #652-655   2.00 2.00
    Nos. 652-655 (4)   1.80 1.80

Christmas. See Nos. B88-B91.

Crucifixion, 12th Cent. Prayerbook Illustration — A103

1981, Apr. 10   *Perf. 14*
656 A103 15c shown   .20 .20
657 A103 25c Placing in Tomb   .40 .40
658 A103 40c Marys at the Tomb   .60 .60
    Nos. 656-658 (3)   1.20 1.20

Easter. See Nos. B92-B95.

Prince Charles and Lady Diana — A104

1981, July 29   **Photo.**   *Perf. 14*
659 A104 $1 Charles   1.00 1.00
660 A104 $2 shown   2.50 2.50
   a.   Souv. sheet of 2, #659-660   4.00 4.00

Royal Wedding. Issued in sheets of 4. For overprints and surcharges see Nos. 679-680, 715, 835, 980-981, B97-B98.

Soccer Players — A105

Designs: Various soccer players.

1981, Oct 20   **Photo.**   *Perf. 14*
661 A105 20c Pair, #a.-b.   1.00 1.00
662 A105 30c Pair, #a.-b.   1.75 1.75
663 A105 35c Pair, #a.-b.   2.25 2.25
664 A105 50c Pair, #a.-b.   3.00 3.00
    Nos. 661-664 (4)   8.00 8.00

ESPANA '82 World Cup Soccer Championships. See No. B96.

Virgin and Child, by Rubens — A107

Christmas: Rubens Paintings.

1981, Dec. 14   **Photo.**   *Perf. 14x13½*
669 A107 8c shown   .50 .50
670 A107 15c Coronation of St. Catherine   .50 .50
671 A107 40c Adoration of the Shepherds   1.50 1.50
672 A107 50c Adoration of the Kings   1.75 1.75
    Nos. 669-672 (4)   4.25 4.25

Souvenir Sheets

1982, Jan. 18
673 A107 75c +5c like #669   1.10 1.10
674 A107 75c +5c like #670   1.10 1.10
675 A107 75c +5c like #671   1.10 1.10
676 A107 75c +5c like #672   1.10 1.10

Surtax was for school children. See No. B99.

21st Birthday of Princess Diana A108

#677a, 21st Birthday. #677b, 1 July 1982. #678a, Wedding portrait. #678b, 1 July 1982. #678d, $1.25, #678e, $2.50, both inscribed "21st Birthday / 1 July 1982."

1982, June 21   **Photo.**   *Perf. 14*
677 A108 $1.25 Pair, #a.-b.   4.50 4.50
678 A108 $2.50 Pair, #a.-b.   9.50 9.50
   c.   Souv. sheet of 2, #d.-e.   8.50 8.50

Issued in sheets of 4. See Nos. 681-682. For surcharges and overprints see Nos. 739-740, 833-834, 982.

Nos. 659-660a Overprinted

#680d, $1; #680e, $2, both inscribed "21 JUNE 1982 ROYAL BIRTH."

1982, July 12
679 A104 $1 Pair, #a.-b.   2.25 2.25
680 A104 $2 Pair, #a.-b.   4.75 4.75
   c.   Souv. sheet of 2, #d.-e.   5.00 5.00

Issued in sheets of 4. For surcharges see Nos. 987-988.

Design A108 Inscribed

#682d, $1.25; #682e, $2.50, both inscribed "Royal Birth / June 1982."

1982, Aug. 3
681 A108 $1.25 Pair, #a.-b.   3.75 3.75
682 A108 $2.50 Pair, #a.-b.   7.25 7.25
   c.   Souv. sheet of 2, #d.-e.   7.50 7.50

Issued in sheets of 4.

Serenade, by Norman Rockwell (1894-1978) A109

1982, Sept. 10   **Photo.**   *Perf. 14*
683 A109 5c shown   .20 .20
684 A109 10c The Hikers   .20 .20
685 A109 20c The Doctor and the Doll   .30 .30
686 A109 30c Home From Camp   .45 .45
    Nos. 683-686 (4)   1.15 1.15

Christmas A110

Princess Diana Holding Prince William. Various Details from Virgin with Garlands, by Rubens.

1982, Nov. 30   **Photo.**   *Perf. 14*
687 A110 35c multicolored   1.50 1.10
688 A110 48c multicolored   2.00 1.50
689 A110 60c multicolored   2.25 1.75
690 A110 $1.70 multicolored   6.75 6.75
    Nos. 687-690 (4)   12.50 11.10

Souvenir Sheets
Perf. 13½

691		Sheet of 4	8.50	8.50
a.	A110	60c like 35c	2.00	2.00
b.	A110	60c like 48c	2.00	2.00
c.	A110	60c like #689	2.00	2.00
d.	A110	60c like $1.70	2.00	2.00
692	A110	75c + 5c like 35c	3.00	3.00
693	A110	75c + 5c like 48c	3.00	3.00
694	A110	75c + 5c like 60c	3.00	3.00
695	A110	75c + 5c like $1.70	3.00	3.00

No. 691 contains 4 stamps (27x32mm., showing only painting details) plus 2 labels showing Diana and William. Nos. 692-695 show Diana and William (27x39mm), multicolored margins show painting details. Surtax was for child welfare.

Commonwealth Day — A111

#696a, Tangaroa statue. #696b, Rarotonga oranges. #696c, Rarotonga Airport. #696d, Prime Minister Thomas Davis.

1983, Mar. 14   **Photo.**   *Perf. 14*
696 A111 60c Block of 4, #a.-d.   3.00 3.00

For overprints see No. O46.

Scouting Year — A112

1983, Apr. 5   Photo.   *Perf. 13x13½*
700	A112	12c Pair, #a.-b., shown	.75 .75
701	A112	36c Pair, #a.-b., Camping	2.25 2.25
702	A112	48c Pair, #a.-b., Rope swing	2.75 2.75
703	A112	60c Pair, #a.-b., Tree planting	3.50 3.50
		Nos. 700-703 (4)	9.25 9.25

Souvenir Sheet of 8
704	#a.-d.	8.00 8.00

#704 contains 2 each of #700-703 with 2c surtax.

Nos. 700-704 Overprinted: "XV
WORLD JAMBOREE ALBERTA
CANADA 1983"

1983, July 4   Photo.   *Perf. 13x13½*
705	A112	12c Pair, #a.-b.	.50 .50
706	A112	36c Pair, #a.-b.	2.25 2.25
707	A112	48c Pair, #a.-b.	2.75 2.75
708	A112	60c Pair, #a.-b.	3.50 3.50
		Nos. 705-708 (4)	9.00 9.00

Souvenir Sheet of 8
709	A112	#a.-d.	8.00 8.00

Nos. 569, 572, 574-575, 579, 587, 660
Surcharged in Black or Gold

Perf. 13½x13, 14x13½, 14

1983, Aug. 12   Photo.

Strips of 4, #a.-d. (#710-713) or
Block of 4, #a.-d. (#714)
710	A101	18c on 8c #569	3.50 3.50
711	A101	36c on 15c #572	5.75 5.75
712	A101	36c on 30c #575	5.75 5.75
713	A101	48c on 25c #574	9.25 9.25
714	A101	72c on 70c #579	14.00 14.00
715	A104	96c on $2 #660 (G)	4.50 4.50
716	A102	$5.60 on $6 #585 (G)	29.00 29.00
		Nos. 710-716 (7)	71.75 71.75

A114

A115

1983, Sept. 9   *Perf. 14*
732		Pair	.85 .85
a.	A114	6c Gt. Britain	.40 .40
b.	A115	6c Cook Islds. Group Federal flag	.40 .40
733		Pair	1.10 1.10
a.	A114	12c Raratonga ensign	.55 .55
b.	A115	12c New Zealand	.55 .55
734		Pair	1.25 1.25
a.	A114	15c Cook Islds, 1973-79	.65 .65
b.	A115	15c Cook Islds, 1983	.65 .65
c.		Souvenir sheet of 6, #732-734	2.25 2.25
735		Pair	2.00 2.00
a.	A114	20c like #732a	.95 .95
b.	A115	20c like #732b	.95 .95
736		Pair	2.50 2.50
a.	A114	30c like #733a	1.25 1.25
b.	A115	30c like #733b	1.25 1.25
737		Pair	3.00 3.00
a.	A114	35c like #734a	1.50 1.50
b.	A115	35c like #734b	1.50 1.50
c.		Souvenir sheet of 6, #735-737	4.75 4.75
		Nos. 732-737 (6)	10.70 10.70

Nos. 732-737 have different background landscapes; Nos. 735-737 airmail with silver background. Nos. 734c, 737c perf. 13½.

**Nos. 576, 586, 678 Surcharged in
Black or Gold**

Perf. 13½x13, 14x13½, 14
1983, Aug. 30   Photo.

Block of 4, #a.-d.
738	A101	36c on 35c #576	5.75 5.75

Pair, #a.-b. (#739)
739	A108	96c on $2.50	9.25 9.25
740	A102	#678 (G)	
		$5.60 on $10 #586 (G)	22.50 22.50
		Nos. 738-740 (3)	37.50 37.50

Satellite Earth
Station — A116

Designs: Various satellites in orbit.

1983, Oct. 10   Litho.   *Perf. 13½*
744	A116	36c multicolored	.80 .80
745	A116	48c multicolored	1.25 1.25
746	A116	60c multicolored	1.40 1.40
747	A116	96c multicolored	2.25 2.25
		Nos. 744-747 (4)	5.70 5.70

Souvenir Sheet
748	A116	$2 multicolored	4.00 4.00

World Communications Year.

Christmas
A117

Manned Flight
Bicent. — A118

Raphael Paintings: 12c, La Belle Jardiniere. 18c, Madonna and Child with Five Saints. 36c, Madonna and Child with Saint John. 48c, Madonna of the Fish. 60c, Madonna of the Baldacchino.

1983   Photo.   *Perf. 14*
749	A117	12c multicolored	.90 .90
750	A117	18c multicolored	.90 .90
751	A117	36c multicolored	1.60 1.60
752	A117	48c multicolored	2.00 2.00
753	A117	60c multicolored	3.00 3.00
		Nos. 749-753 (5)	8.40 8.40

Souvenir Sheets
Perf. 13½
754		Sheet of 5	4.00 4.00
a.	A117	12c + 3c like #749	.30 .30
b.	A117	18c + 3c like #750	.35 .35
c.	A117	36c + 3c like #751	.70 .70
d.	A117	48c + 3c like #752	.90 .90
e.	A117	60c + 3c like #753	1.10 1.10
755	A117	85c + 5c like #749	1.60 1.60
756	A117	85c + 5c like #750	1.60 1.60

757	A117	85c + 5c like #751	1.60 1.60
758	A117	85c + 5c like #752	1.60 1.60
759	A117	85c + 5c like #753	1.60 1.60

Nos. 749-753 issued in sheets of 5 + label. Surtax was for children's charities.
Issued: #749-754, Nov. 14; others, Dec. 9.

1984, Jan. 16   Photo.   *Perf. 13*

Various balloons.
760	A118	36c 1st manned flight, 1783	.65 .65
761	A118	48c Ascent of Adorne, Strasbourg, 1784	.80 .80
762	A118	60c 1785	.90 .90
763	A118	72c Man on horse, 1785	1.25 1.25
764	A118	96c Godard's aerial acrobatics, 1850	1.40 1.40
		Nos. 760-764 (5)	5.00 5.00

Souvenir Sheets
765	A118	$2.50 Blanchard & Jefferies, 1785	4.25 4.25
766		Sheet of 5	7.75 7.75
a.	A118	36c + 5c like 36c	.90 .90
b.	A118	48c + 5c like 48c	1.10 1.10
c.	A118	60c + 5c like 60c	1.50 1.50
d.	A118	72c + 5c like 72c	1.75 1.75
e.	A118	96c + 5c like 96c	2.25 2.25

#765 contains 1 stamp 30x48mm, perf. 13½.

Save the
Whales
Campaign
A119

1984, Feb. 10   Photo.   *Perf. 13*
767	A119	10c Cuvier's beaked whale	.40 .40
768	A119	18c Risso's dolphin	.60 .60
769	A119	20c True's beaked whale	.70 .70
770	A119	24c Long-finned pilot whale	.90 .90
771	A119	30c Narwhal	1.10 1.10
772	A119	36c Beluga whale	1.25 1.25
773	A119	42c Common dolphin	1.60 1.60
774	A119	48c Commerson's dolphin	1.75 1.75
775	A119	60c Bottle-nosed dolphin	2.25 2.25
776	A119	72c Sowerby's whale	2.75 2.75
777	A119	96c Common porpoise	3.25 3.25
778	A119	$2 Boutu	7.75 7.75
		Nos. 767-778 (12)	24.30 24.30

1984 Summer
Olympics
A120

Posters of Various Summer Olympics. 72c, 96c, $1.20 airmail.

1984, Mar. 8   Photo.   *Perf. 13½*
779	A120	18c Athens, 1896	.35 .35
780	A120	24c Paris, 1900	.40 .40
781	A120	36c St. Louis, 1904	.65 .65
782	A120	48c London, 1948	.85 .85
783	A120	60c Tokyo, 1964	1.00 1.00
784	A120	72c Berlin, 1936	1.25 1.25
785	A120	96c Rome, 1960	1.75 1.75
786	A120	$1.20 Los Angeles, 1932	2.25 2.25
		Nos. 779-786 (8)	8.50 8.50

For overprints see Nos. 826-828.

Nos. 582-586 Surcharged and:

Coral — A121

1c, Siphonogorgia. 2c, Millepora alcicornis. 3c, Distichopora violacea. 5c, Ptilosarcus gurneyi. 10c, Lobophyllia bemprichii. 12c, Sarcophyton digitatum. 14c, Pavona praetorta. 18c, Junceela gemmacea. 20c, Stylaster. 24c, Stylophora pistillata. 30c, Palauastrea ramosa. 36c, Melithaea albitincta. 40c, Stylaster echinatus. 42c, Fungia fungites. 48c, Goniopora. 50c, Melithaea squamata. 52c, Bellonella indica. 55c, Plerogyra sinuosa. 60c, Tubastraea. 70c, Heliofungia actinformis. 85c, Caulastraea echinulata. 96c, Porites andrewsi. $1.10, Pectinia alcicornis. $1.20, Dendrophyllia gracilis.

1984   *Perf. 13½x13*
787	A121	1c multi	.20 .20
788	A121	2c multi	.20 .20
789	A121	3c multi	.20 .20
790	A121	5c multi	.20 .20
791	A121	10c multi	.20 .20
792	A121	12c multi	.20 .20
793	A121	14c multi	.30 .30
794	A121	18c multi	.40 .40
795	A121	20c multi	.40 .40
796	A121	24c multi	.50 .50
797	A121	30c multi	.60 .60
798	A121	36c multi	.75 .75
799	A121	40c multi	.80 .80
800	A121	42c multi	.90 .90
801	A121	48c multi	.95 .95
802	A121	50c multi	1.00 1.00
803	A121	52c multi	1.00 1.00
804	A121	55c multi	1.40 1.40
805	A121	60c multi	1.60 1.60
806	A121	70c multi	1.75 1.75
807	A121	85c multi	2.00 2.00
808	A121	96c multi	2.25 2.25
809	A121	$1.10 multi	3.00 3.00
810	A121	$1.20 multi	3.25 3.25

Perf. 14x13½
Size: 59½x38½mm
811	A102	$3.60 on $2 #582	8.00 8.00
812	A102	$4.20 on $3 #583	8.75 8.75
813	A102	$5 on $4 #584	10.50 10.50
814	A102	$7.20 on $6 #585	15.00 15.00
815	A102	$9.60 on $10 #586	17.50 17.50
		Nos. 787-815 (29)	83.80 83.80

Issued: #787-801, 3/23; #802-810, 5/15; #811-813, 6/28; #814, 7/20; #815, 8/10.
For surcharges & overprints see #948-952, 955, 958, 960, 963, 965-967, B105-B108, O32-O45.

Nos. 784-786 Overprinted With
Winners

1984, Aug. 24   Photo.   *Perf. 13½*
826	A120	72c Team Dressage, Germany	1.00 1.00
827	A120	96c Daley Thompson, U.K.	1.50 1.50
828	A120	$1.20 Carl Lewis, USA	1.90 1.90
		Nos. 826-828 (3)	4.40 4.40

1984 Summer Olympics. Nos. 826-828 airmail.

AUSIPEX '84 — A123

1984, Sept. 20
829	A123	36c Captain Cook's cottage	1.60 1.60
830	A123	48c The Endeavour	2.10 2.10
831	A123	60c Cook's landing	2.50 2.50
832	A123	$2 Portrait, by John Webber	8.50 8.50
a.		Souv. sheet, #829-832, 90c ea	11.00 11.00
b.		Sheet of 4, STAMPEX '86 emblem	10.50 10.50
		Nos. 829-832 (4)	14.70 14.70

No. 832b issued Aug. 4, 1986, for STAMPEX '86, Adelaide, Aug. 4-10; margin ovptd. with exhibition emblem, stamp picturing James Cook ovptd. with gold circle and black "Stampex 86 / Adelaide."

Nos. 677-678 Ovptd. & Surcharged in Gold

No. 659 Ovptd. & Surcharged in Silver

1984, Oct. 15		**Photo.**	**Perf. 14**	
833	A108	$1.25 Pair, #a.-b.	2.50	2.50
834	A108	$2.50 Pair, #a.-b.	6.75	6.75
835	A104	$3 on $1 No. 659	4.75	4.75
		Nos. 833-835 (3)	14.00	14.00

Nos. 833-835 printed in sheets of 4 stamps.

A124

A125

Christmas (Paintings): 36c, Virgin on Throne with Child, by Giovanni Bellini (c. 1430-1516). 48c, Virgin and Child, 15th century, artist unknown. 60c, Virgin and Child with Saints, by Alvise Vivarini (c. 1446-1505). 96c, Virgin and Child with Angels, by Hans Memling (c. 1435-1494). $1.20, Adoration of the Magi, by Giovanni Tiepolo (1696-1770).

1984				
838	A124	36c multicolored	.70	.70
839	A124	48c multicolored	1.00	1.00
840	A124	60c multicolored	1.25	1.25
841	A124	96c multicolored	2.00	2.00
842	A124	$1.20 multicolored	2.50	2.50
		Nos. 838-842 (5)	7.45	7.45

Souvenir Sheets
Perf. 13½

843		Sheet of 5	5.75	5.75
a.	A124	36c +5c like #838	.70	.70
b.	A124	48c +5c like #839	.85	.85
c.	A124	60c +5c like #840	1.00	1.00
d.	A124	96c +5c like #841	1.50	1.50
e.	A124	$1.20 +5c like #842	1.75	1.75
844	A124	95c + 5c like #838	1.75	1.75
845	A124	95c + 5c like #839	1.75	1.75
846	A124	95c + 5c like #840	1.75	1.75
847	A124	95c + 5c like #841	1.75	1.75
848	A124	95c + 5c like #842	1.75	1.75

Surtax of No. 843 for children's organizations, of Nos. 844-848 for youth education. Issued: #838-843, 11/21; #844-848, 12/10.

1985, Apr. 23			**Perf. 13x13½**	

Illustrations of North American bird species by artist, naturalist John J. Audubon.

849	A125	30c Downy woodpecker	1.50	1.50
850	A125	55c Black-throated blue warbler	2.75	2.75

851	A125	65c Yellow-throated warbler	3.00	3.00
852	A125	75c Chestnut-sided warbler	3.75	3.75
853	A125	95c Dickcissel	4.75	4.75
854	A125	$1.15 White-crowned sparrow	4.75	4.75
		Nos. 849-854 (6)	20.50	20.50

Souvenir Sheets

855	A125	$1.30 Red-cockaded woodpecker	3.00	3.00
856	A125	$2.80 Seaside sparrow	5.25	5.25
857	A125	$5.30 Zenaida dove	10.75	10.75

Audubon birth bicentenary.

Locomotives — A126

1985, May 14		**Litho.**	**Perf. 14x13½**	
858	A126	20c Kingston Flyer, New Zealand	.20	.20
859	A126	55c Class 640, Italy	.40	.40
860	A126	65c Gotthard, Switzerland	.50	.50
861	A126	75c Union Pacific 6900, US	.60	.60
862	A126	95c Super Continental, Canada	.80	.80
863	A126	$1.15 TGV, France	.90	.90
864	A126	$2.20 Flying Scotsman, U.K.	1.75	1.75
865	A126	$3.40 Orient Express, Europe	2.50	2.50
		Nos. 858-865 (8)	7.65	7.65

Intl. Youth Year — A127

Paintings: 55c, Helena Fourment, by Rubens. 65c, Vigee-Lebrun and Daughter, by Elizabeth Vigee-Lebrun (1755-1842). 75c, On the Terrace, by Renoir. $1.30, Young Mother Sewing, by Mary Cassatt (1845-1926).

1985, June 6		**Photo.**	**Perf. 13x13½**	
866	A127	55c multicolored	3.50	3.50
867	A127	65c multicolored	4.00	4.00
868	A127	75c multicolored	4.50	4.50
869	A127	$1.30 multicolored	7.50	7.50
		Nos. 866-869 (4)	19.50	19.50

Souvenir Sheet

870		Sheet of 4	11.00	11.00
a.	A127	55c + 10c like #866	1.75	1.75
b.	A127	65c + 10c like #867	2.10	2.10
c.	A127	75c + 10c like #868	2.40	2.40
d.	A127	$1.30 + 10c like #869	3.75	3.75

Surtax for youth organizations.

Queen Mother, 85th Birthday A128

Portraits: 65c, Lady Elizabeth, 1908, by Mable Hankey. 75c, Duchess of York, 1923, by Savely Sorine. $1.15, Duchess of York, 1925, by Philip De Laszlo. $2.80, $5.30, Queen Elizabeth, 1938, by Sir Gerald Kelly.

1985, June 28				
871	A128	65c multi	.80	.80
872	A128	75c multi	.95	.95
873	A128	$1.15 multi	1.50	1.50
874	A128	$2.80 multi	3.25	3.25

874A		Sheet of 4 ('86)	5.50	5.50
b.-e.		A128 55c, like #871-874	1.50	1.50
		Nos. 871-874A (5)	12.00	12.00

Souvenir Sheet

875	A128	$5.30 multi	7.50	7.50

Nos. 871-874 printed in sheets of four. #874A issued 8/4/86, for 86th birthday. For surcharges see Nos. B114, B116, B122, B134, B140.

A129

A130

Portraits of prime ministers.

1985, July 29				
876	A129	30c Albert Henry, 1965-78	1.25	1.25
877	A129	50c Sir Thomas Davis, 1978-83	2.50	2.50
878	A129	65c Geoffrey Henry, 1983	3.00	3.00
		Nos. 876-878 (3)	6.75	6.75

Souvenir Sheet

879		Sheet of 3	5.75	5.75
a.	A129	55c like #876	1.75	1.75
b.	A129	55c like #877	1.75	1.75
c.	A129	55c like #878	1.75	1.75

Self-government, 20th anniv.

1985, July 29			**Perf. 14**	
880	A130	55c Golf	4.50	4.50
881	A130	65c Rugby	5.00	5.00
882	A130	75c Tennis	5.75	5.75
		Nos. 880-882 (3)	15.25	15.25

Souvenir Sheet

883		Sheet of 3	15.00	15.00
a.	A130	55c + 10c like #880	4.50	4.50
b.	A130	65c + 10c like #881	4.50	4.50
c.	A130	75c + 10c like #882	4.50	4.50

South Pacific Mini Games, Rarotonga, July 31-Aug. 10. Surtax for the benefit of the Mini Games.

A131

A132

Seahorse & conf. emblems: 55c, South Pacific Bureau for Economic Cooperation. 65c, No. 887b, South Pacific Forum. 75c, No. 887c, Pacific Islands Conf.

1985, July 29			**Perf. 14**	
884	A131	55c blk, scar & gold	1.40	1.40
885	A131	65c blk, vio & gold	1.60	1.60
886	A131	75c blk, brt grn & gold	1.75	1.75
		Nos. 884-886 (3)	4.75	4.75

Souvenir Sheet

887		50c Sheet of 3, #a.-c.	3.50	3.50

Pacific islands conf., Rarotonga, 7/30-8/10.

1985

Virgin and Child paintings by Botticelli.

888	A132	55c Madonna of the Magnificent	1.75	1.75
889	A132	65c Madonna with Pomegranate	2.25	2.25
890	A132	75c Madonna with Child & Six Angels	2.75	2.75
891	A132	95c Madonna & Child with St. John	3.50	3.50
		Nos. 888-891 (4)	10.25	10.25

Souvenir Sheets
Perf. 13½

892	A132	$2.75 Sheet of 4	6.50	6.50
a.	A132	50c like #888	1.40	1.40
b.	A132	50c like #889	1.40	1.40
c.	A132	50c like #890	1.40	1.40
d.	A132	50c like #891	1.40	1.40

Imperf

893	A132	$1.20 like #888	2.50	2.50
894	A132	$1.45 like #889	2.75	2.75
895	A132	$2.20 like #890	4.50	4.50
896	A132	$2.75 like #891	5.25	5.25

Christmas. Issue dates: Nos. 888-892, Nov. 18; Nos. 893-896, Dec. 9.

Halley's Comet — A133

Elizabeth II, 60th Birthday — A134

Paintings: 55c, No. 902a, The Eve of the Deluge, by John Martin (1789-1854). 65c, No. 902b, Lot and His Daughters, by Lucas van Leyden (1494-1533). 75c, No. 902c, Auspicious Comet, 1587, anonymous. $1.25, No. 902d, Events Following Charles I, by Herman Saftleven (1609-1658). $2, No. 902e, Ossian Receiving Napoleonic Officers, by Anne Louis Girodet-Trioson (1764-1824). $4, Halley's Comet over the Thames, 1759, by Samuel Scott (1702-1772).

1986, Mar. 13		**Photo.**	**Perf. 14**	
897	A133	55c multicolored	1.40	1.40
898	A133	65c multicolored	1.75	1.75
899	A133	75c multicolored	2.10	2.10
900	A133	$1.25 multicolored	4.00	4.00
901	A133	$2 multicolored	5.75	5.75
		Nos. 897-901 (5)	15.00	15.00

Souvenir Sheets
Perf. 13½

902		Sheet of 5 + label	6.50	6.50
a.-e.		A133 70c, each single	1.25	1.25
903	A133	$4 multicolored	7.50	7.50

For surcharges see Nos. B113, B115, B117, B123, B129.

1986, Apr. 21			**Perf. 13x13½**	

Various portraits.

904	A134	95c multi	1.75	1.75
905	A134	$1.25 multi	2.10	2.10
906	A134	$1.50 multi	2.40	2.40
		Nos. 904-906 (3)	6.25	6.25

Souvenir Sheets

907	A134	$1.10 like #904	2.75	2.75
908	A134	$1.95 like #905	5.00	5.00
909	A134	$2.45 like #906	7.25	7.25

For surcharges see Nos. 972-974, B118, B124, B127, B136-B137, B139.

AMERIPEX '86 — A135

Designs: $1, US No. 1, The Resolution, Rarotonga. $1.50, Downtown Chicago. $2, No. 398, Benjamin Franklin, The Resolution.

1986, May 21   Photo.   Perf. 14

910	A135	$1 multi	3.50	3.50
911	A135	$1.50 multi	5.25	5.25
912	A135	$2 multi	6.75	6.75
		Nos. 910-912 (3)	15.50	15.50

For surcharges see Nos. B119, B128, B130.

Statue of Liberty, Cent. — A136

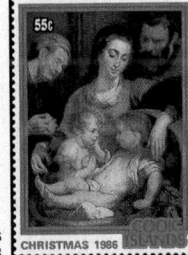

Wedding of Prince Andrew and Sarah Ferguson — A137

1986, July 4

913	A136	$1 Head	1.25	1.25
914	A136	$1.25 Torch	1.50	1.50
915	A136	$2.75 Liberty Is.	3.50	3.50
		Nos. 913-915 (3)	6.25	6.25

For surcharges see Nos. B120, B125, B132.

1986, July 23

916	A137	$1 Sarah Ferguson	1.00	1.00
917	A137	$2 Prince Andrew	2.00	2.00

Size: 60x33½mm
Perf. 13½x13

918	A137	$3 Couple	3.00	3.00
		Nos. 916-918 (3)	6.00	6.00

Nos. 916-918 each printed in sheets of 4.
For surch. see #975-977, B121, B131, B135.

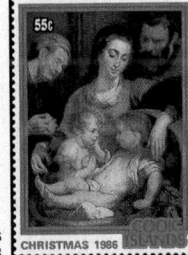

Christmas A138

Paintings by Rubens: 55c, No. 922a, The Holy Family. $1.30, $6.40, No. 922b, Virgin with Garland. $2.75, No. 922c, Adoration of Magi.

1986, Nov. 17   Litho.   Perf. 13½

919	A138	55c multi	1.75	1.75
920	A138	$1.30 multi	4.00	4.00
921	A138	$2.75 multi	8.25	8.25
		Nos. 919-921 (3)	14.00	14.00

Souvenir Sheets

922		Sheet of 3	18.00	18.00
a.-c.		A138 $2.40, any single	5.75	5.75
923	A138	$6.40 multi	19.00	19.00

No. 922 contains 3 stamps 38½x49mm.
For surcharges see Nos. B100-B104, B112, B126, B133, B138, B141.

Stamps of 1980-84 Surcharged in Black

1987, Feb.   Litho.   Perfs. as before
Strips of 4, #a.-d. (#953, 954, 956, 957) or
Blocks of 4, #a.-d. (#959, 961, 962, 964)

948	A121	5c on 1c #787	.20	.20
949	A121	5c on 2c #788	.20	.20
950	A121	5c on 3c #789	.20	.20
951	A121	5c on 12c #792	.20	.20
952	A121	5c on 14c #793	.20	.20
953	A101	10c on 15c #572	.55	.55
954	A101	10c on 25c #574	.55	.55
955	A101	18c on 24c #796	.20	.20
956	A101	18c on 12c #571	1.10	1.10
957	A101	18c on 12c #573	1.10	1.10
958	A101	55c on 52c #803	.90	.90
959	A101	55c on 35c #576	3.25	3.25
960	A101	65c on 42c #800	1.00	1.00
961	A101	65c on 50c #577	4.50	4.50
962	A101	65c on 60c #578	4.50	4.50
963	A101	75c on 48c #801	1.25	1.25
964	A101	75c on 70c #579	4.50	4.50
965	A121	95c on 96c #808	1.50	1.50
966	A121	95c on $1.10 #809	1.50	1.50
967	A121	95c on $1.20 #810	1.50	1.50

Stamps of 1981-86 Surcharged in Black (A102), Black and Gold (#968-970, A137) or Gold (#971, A134, A104, A108)

968	A123	$1.30 on 36c #829	1.90	1.90
969	A123	$1.30 on 48c #830	1.90	1.90
970	A123	$1.30 on 60c #831	1.90	1.90
971	A123	$1.30 on $2 #832	1.90	1.90
972	A134	$2.80 on 95c #904	4.25	4.25
973	A134	$2.80 on $1.25 #905	4.25	4.25
974	A134	$2.80 on $1.50 #906	4.25	4.25
975	A137	$2.80 on $1 #916	4.25	4.25
976	A137	$2.80 on $2 #917	4.25	4.25
977	A137	$2.80 on $3 #918	4.25	4.25
978	A102	$6.40 on $4 #584	9.25	9.25
979	A102	$7.20 on $6 #585	10.50	10.50
980	A104	$9.40 on $1 #659	14.50	14.50
981	A104	$9.40 on $2 #660	14.50	14.50

Pair, #a.-b.

982	A108	$9.40 on $2.50 #678	29.00	29.00
		Nos. 948-982 (35)	139.75	139.75

Issued: 5c, #955, 958, 960, 963, 95c, $6.40, $7.20, 2/10; 10c, #956-957, 959, 961-962, 964, 2/11; $12.30; $2.80, $9.40, 2/12.
For surcharge see No. B111.

Stamps of 1980-82 Surcharged in Black (A102) or Gold (A104)

Perfs. as before

1987, June 17   Photo.

984	A102	$2.80 on $2 #582	3.25	3.25
985	A102	$5 on $3 #583	5.50	5.50
986	A102	$9.40 on $10 #586	10.00	10.00

Pairs, #a.-b.

987	A104	$9.40 on $1 #679	20.00	20.00
988	A104	$9.40 on $2 #680	20.00	20.00
		Nos. 984-988 (5)	58.75	58.75

Souvenir Sheet

989	A104	$9.20 on #680c	19.00	19.00

Nos. 399 and 584 Ovptd. "ROYAL / WEDDING / FORTIETH / ANNIVERSARY" in Black on Gold Bar

1987, Nov. 20   Photo.   Perf. 14x13½

991	A64	$4 on #399	5.00	5.00
992	A102	$4 on #584	5.00	5.00

Christmas — A139

The Holy Family, religious paintings by Rembrandt in European museums: $1.25, No. 996a, The Louvre, Paris. $1.50, No. 996b, $6, The Holy Family with Angels, The Hermitage, Leningrad. $1.95, No. 996c, The Alte Pinakothek, Munich.

1987, Dec. 7   Photo.   Perf. 13½

993	A139	$1.25 multi	3.25	3.25
994	A139	$1.50 multi	4.50	4.50
995	A139	$1.95 multi	5.75	5.75
		Nos. 993-995 (3)	13.50	13.50

Souvenir Sheets

996		Sheet of 3	10.00	10.00
a.-c.		A139 $1.15 any single	3.00	3.00

Perf. 13x13½

997	A139	$6 multi	12.00	12.00

Size of Nos. 996a-996c: 49 ½x38 ½mm. No. 997 contains 1 stamp 39 ½x31 ½mm.

1988 Summer Olympics, Seoul A140

Designs: a, Cook Islands commemorative silver coin (obverse and reverse) issued on Aug. 20, 1987, for the '88 Summer Games. b, Seoul Olympic Park, torch and emblem. c, Steffi Graf, women's tennis champion, and '88 gold medal.

1988, Apr. 26   Photo.   Perf. 13½x14

998		Strip of 3	17.00	17.00
a.-c.		A140 $1.50 multicolored	5.75	5.75

Souvenir Sheet
Perf. 13½

999	A140	$10 multi	19.00	19.00

Participation of national athletes in the Olympics for the first time, introduction of tennis as an Olympic gold-medal event.
No. 999 contains one stamp 114x47mm combining the designs of Nos. 998a-998c.

Nos. 998-999 Ovptd. for Olympic Winners
a. "MILOSLAV MECIR CZECHO-SLOVAKIA GOLD MEDAL WINNER MEN'S TENNIS"
b. "TIM MAYOTTE UNITED STATES GABRIELA SABATINI ARGENTINA SILVER MEDAL WINNERS"
c. "GOLD MEDAL WINNER STEFFI GRAF WEST GERMANY"
d. "GOLD MEDAL WINNER SEOUL OLYMPIC GAMES STEFFI GRAF dash> WEST GERMANY"

1988, Oct. 12   Photo.   Perf. 13½x14

1000		Strip of 3	15.00	15.00
a.-c.		A140 $1.50 multicolored	5.00	5.00

Souvenir Sheet
Perf. 13½

1001	A140(d)	$10 on No. 999	17.50	17.50

Margin of No. 1001 ovptd.: "STEFFI GRAF, WINNER OF AUSTRALIAN OPEN 24 JULY 1988, FRENCH OPEN / 4 JUNE 1988, WIMBLEDON 2 JULY 1988, U.S. OPEN 10 SEPTEMBER 1988. / FIRST GRAND SLAM WINNER IN 18 YEARS. GOLD MEDAL WINNER SEOUL / OLYMPICS 1 OCTOBER 1988."

Christmas A141

Paintings by Albrecht Durer: 70c, Virgin and Child. 85c, Virgin and Child, diff. 95c, Virgin and Child, diff. $1.25, Virgin and Child, diff. $6.40, The Nativity.

1988, Nov. 11   Perf. 13½

1002	A141	70c multi	3.25	3.25
1003	A141	85c multi	3.75	3.75
1004	A141	95c multi	4.25	4.25
1005	A141	$1.25 multi	5.75	5.75
		Nos. 1002-1005 (4)	17.00	17.00

Souvenir Sheet

1006	A141	$6.40 multi	11.00	11.00

No. 1006 contains one stamp 45x60mm.

Scene and Left Half of Mission Emblem A142

1st Moon Landing, 20th Anniv. — A144

#1007a, Launch vehicle in space. #1007b, *Eagle* landing on Moon. #1008a, Astronaut descending ladder. #1008, Astronaut on Moon. #1009a, Seismic experiment. #1009b, Solar wind experiment. #1010a, Liftoff from Moon. #1010b, Splashdown and recovery.
The "b" stamps have the right half of the emblem.

1989, July 14   Photo.   Perf. 13

1007	A142	40c Pair, #a.-b.	3.25	3.25
1008	A142	55c Pair, #a.-b.	5.00	5.00
1009	A142	65c Pair, #a.-b.	6.00	6.00
1010	A142	75c Pair, #a.-b.	6.75	6.75
		Nos. 1007-1010 (4)	21.00	21.00

Souvenir Sheet

1011	A144	$4.20 Armstrong and Aldrin	11.00	11.00

Printed with continuous designs.

World Wildlife Fund A145

Endangered bird species.

1989, Oct. 4   Photo.   Perf. 13½x13

1016	A145	15c *Pomarea dimidiata*	1.50	1.50
1017	A145	20c *Pomarea dimidiata* (two)	2.25	2.25
1018	A145	65c *Ptilinopus rarotongensis* (two)	6.00	6.00
1019	A145	70c *Ptilinopus rarotongensis*	6.75	6.75
		Nos. 1016-1019 (4)	16.50	16.50

Souvenir Sheets
Without WWF Emblem
Perf. 13½

1020	A145	$1 like 15c	3.25	3.25
1021	A145	$1.25 like 20c	3.75	3.75
1022	A145	$1.50 like 65c	4.25	4.25
1023	A145	$1.75 like 70c	4.75	4.75

World Wildlife Fund. #1020-1023 are airmail and contain one 52x34mm stamp; decorative margins continue the designs.
For overprints see Nos. C24-C27.

Christmas — A146

Details of *Adoration of the Magi,* by Rubens: 70c, Witnesses. 85c, Madonna. 95c, Christ child. $1.50, Attendant. $6.40, Entire painting.

1989, Nov. 24 Photo. Perf. 13½x13

1024	A146	70c multicolored	2.25	2.25
1025	A146	85c multicolored	2.50	2.50
1026	A146	95c multicolored	3.00	3.00
1027	A146	$1.50 multicolored	4.75	4.75
		Nos. 1024-1027 (4)	12.50	12.50

Souvenir Sheet
Perf. 13½

1028	A146	$6.40 multicolored	17.50	17.50

No. 1028 contains one 45x60mm stamp.

Religious History A147

70c, John Williams, LMS Mission Church. 85c, Bernardine Castanie, Roman Catholic Church. 95c, Osborne J.P. Widstoe, Church of Jesus Christ of Latter Day Saints. $1.60, J.E. Caldwell, Seventh Day Adventist Church.

1990, Feb. 19 Photo. Perf. 13½x13

1029	A147	70c multicolored	1.25	1.25
1030	A147	85c multicolored	1.50	1.50
1031	A147	95c multicolored	1.75	1.75
1032	A147	$1.60 multicolored	3.00	3.00
		Nos. 1029-1032 (4)	7.50	7.50

Souvenir Sheet
Perf. 13½

1033		Sheet of 4	8.50	8.50
a.	A147	90c like 70c	1.90	1.90
b.	A147	90c like 85c	1.90	1.90
c.	A147	90c like 95c	1.90	1.90
d.	A147	90c like $1.60	1.90	1.90

No. 1033 contains 4 36x36mm stamps.

Penny Black, 150th Anniv. — A148

Paintings: 85c, No. 1038a, *Woman Writing a Letter,* by Gerard Terborch (1617-1681). $1.15, No. 1038b, *Portrait of George Gisze,* by Hans Holbein the Younger. $1.55, No. 1038c, *Portrait of Mrs. John Douglas,* by Thomas Gainsborough. $1.85, No. 1038d, *Portrait of a Gentleman,* by Albrecht Durer.

1990, May 2 Photo. Perf. 13½

1034	A148	85c multicolored	1.75	1.75
1035	A148	$1.15 multicolored	2.50	2.50
1036	A148	$1.55 multicolored	3.25	3.25
1037	A148	$1.85 multicolored	4.00	4.00
		Nos. 1034-1037 (4)	11.50	11.50

Souvenir Sheet

1038		Sheet of 4	15.00	15.00
a.-d.	A148	$1.05 any single	3.50	3.50

The margin of No. 1038 pictures the Stamp World '90 emblem and Great Britain #1-2.

1992 Olympics A149

Designs: a. Summer Games, Barcelona (runners). b. Eternal flame, commemorative coin obverse (Queen Elizabeth II) and reverse (athletes). c. Winter Games, Albertville (skier).

1990, June 15 Photo. Perf. 14

1039		Strip of 3	19.00	19.00
a.-c.	A149	$1.85 any single	6.00	6.00

Queen Mother, 90th Birthday A150

1990, July 20 Photo. Perf. 13½

1040	A150	$1.85 multicolored	6.50	6.50

Souvenir Sheet

1041	A150	$6.40 multicolored	12.00	12.00

Christmas A151

Paintings: 70c, Adoration of the Magi by Memling. 85c, The Holy Family by Lotto. 95c, Madonna and Child with Saints John and Catherine by Titian. $1.50, The Holy Family by Titian. $6.40, Madonna and Child Enthroned, Surrounded by Saints by Vivarini.

1990, Nov. 29 Litho. Perf. 14

1042	A151	70c multicolored	2.00	2.00
1043	A151	85c multicolored	2.75	2.75
1044	A151	95c multicolored	3.00	3.00
1045	A151	$1.50 multicolored	4.75	4.75
		Nos. 1042-1045 (4)	12.50	12.50

Souvenir Sheet

1046	A151	$6.40 multicolored	18.00	18.00

For overprints and surcharges see Nos. 1251, 1254, 1257-1258.

Souvenir Sheet

1992 Olympic Games — A152

1991, Feb. 12 Perf. 13½

1047	A152	$6.40 multicolored	19.00	19.00

Discovery of America 500th Anniv. (in 1992) — A153

1991, Feb. 14 Photo. Perf. 13½x13

1048	A153	$1 multicolored	4.25	4.25

No. 586 Ovptd. "65th BIRTHDAY" in Gold

1991, Apr. 22 Litho. Perf. 14x13½

1049	A102	$10 multicolored	18.00	18.00

Christmas A154

Paintings: 70c, Adoration of the Child, by Delle Notti (Gerrit van Honthorst). 85c, Birth of the Virgin, by Murillo. $1.15, Adoration of the Shepherds, by Rembrandt. $1.50, Adoration of the Shepherds, by Le Nain. $6.40, Madonna and Child, by Fra Filippo Lippi, vert.

1991, Nov. 12 Litho. Perf. 14

1050	A154	70c multicolored	1.00	1.00
1051	A154	85c multicolored	3.00	3.00
1052	A154	$1.15 multicolored	4.25	4.25
1053	A154	$1.50 multicolored	5.75	5.75
		Nos. 1050-1053 (4)	14.00	14.00

Souvenir Sheet

1054	A154	$6.40 multicolored	15.00	15.00

For overprints and surcharges see Nos. 1252-1253, 1255-1256.

Marine Life — A155

A155a

5c, Red-breasted maori wrasse. 10c, Blue sea star. 15c, Black & gold angelfish. 20c, Spotted pebble crab. 25c, Black-tipped cod. 30c, Spanish dancer. 50c, Royal angelfish. 80c, Squirrel fish. 85c, Red pencil sea urchin. 90c, Red-spot rainbow fish. $1, Black-lined maori wrasse. $2, Longnose butterflyfish. $3, Red-spot rainbow fish. $5, Blue sea star. $7, Royal angelfish. $10, Spotted pebble crab. $15, Red pencil sea urchin.

1992-94 Litho. Perf. 14½x13½

1058	A155	5c multi	.40	.40
1059	A155	10c multi	.40	.40
1062	A155	15c multi	.40	.40
1064	A155	20c multi	.50	.50
1065	A155	25c multi	.55	.55
1066	A155	30c multi	.65	.65
1071	A155	50c multi	1.10	1.10
1076	A155	80c multi	1.75	1.75
1077	A155	85c multi	1.75	1.75
1078	A155	90c multi	1.75	1.75
1080	A155	$1 multi	2.00	2.00
1081	A155	$2 multi	3.75	3.75
1082	A155a	$3 multi	4.50	4.50
1083	A155a	$5 multi	8.00	8.00
1085	A155a	$7 multi	12.00	12.00
1087	A155a	$10 multi	17.00	17.00
1089	A155a	$15 multi	25.00	25.00
		Nos. 1058-1089 (17)	81.50	81.50

Issued: 85c, 90c, $1, $2, 3/23/92; $3, $5, 10/25/93; $7, 12/6/93; $10, 1/31/94; $15, 9/9/94; others, 1/22/92.

See Nos. 1154-1176 for stamps with buff border. For overprints see Nos. O54-O68.

Endangered Wildlife — A156

#1095, Tiger. #1096, Asiatic elephant. #1097, Grizzly bear. #1098, Black rhinoceros. #1099, Chimpanzee. #1100, Asian bighorn. #1101, Heavisides dolphin. #1102, Eagle owl. #1103, Bee hummingbird. #1104, Feliscon-color cougar. #1105, European otter. #1106, Red kangaroo.

1992 Litho. Perf. 14

1095-1106		$1.15 Set of 12	30.00	30.00

Issued: #1095, 4/6; #1096, 4/7; #1097, 4/8; #1098, 4/9; #1099, 4/10; #1100, 4/11; #1101, 7/13; #1102, 7/14; #1103, 7/15; #1104, 7/16; #1105, 7/17; #1106, 7/18.
See Nos. 1119-1124, 1134-1138.
For surcharges see Nos. 1239-1250.

Discovery of America, 500th Anniv. — A157

1992, May 22 Litho. Perf. 14x14½

1107	A157	$6 multicolored	11.00	11.00

Souvenir Sheet
Perf. 15x14

1107A	A157	$10 Coming ashore	13.00	13.00

Issued: #1107, May 22. #1107A, Sept. 21.
No. 1107A contains one 40x30mm stamp.

1992 Summer Olympics, Barcelona — A158

Designs: No. 1108a, $50 coin, soccer players. b, Flags of Spain, Cook Islands, Barcelona medal. c, $10 coin, basketball players. No. 1109a, Runners. b, $10, $50 coins. c, Cyclists. $6.40, Javelin.

1992, July 24 Litho. Perf. 13

1108	A158	$1.75 Strip of 3, #a.-c.	12.00	12.00
1109	A158	$2.25 Strip of 3, #a.-c.	15.00	15.00

Souvenir Sheet

1110	A158	$6.40 multicolored	19.00	19.00

6th Festival of Pacific Arts, Rarotonga A159

80c, UNESCO poster. 85c, $1, $1.75, Different carvings of Rarotongan fertility god, Tangaroa.

1992, Oct. 16   Litho.   Perf. 15x14

1111	A159	80c multicolored	1.75	1.75
1112	A159	85c multicolored	2.00	2.00
1113	A159	$1 multicolored	2.40	2.40
1114	A159	$1.75 multicolored	3.75	3.75
		Nos. 1111-1114 (4)	9.90	9.90

For overprints see #1231-1234.

Ovptd. "ROYAL VISIT"

1992, Oct. 16

1115	A159	80c on #1111	2.10	2.10
1116	A159	85c on #1112	2.50	2.50
1117	A159	$1 on #1113	2.50	2.50
1118	A159	$1.75 on #1114	4.75	4.75
		Nos. 1115-1118 (4)	11.85	11.85

Endangered Wildlife Type of 1992

1992   Litho.   Perf. 14

1119	A156	$1.15 Jackass penguin	2.50	2.50
1120	A156	$1.15 Asian lion	2.50	2.50
1121	A156	$1.15 Peregrine falcon	2.50	2.50
1122	A156	$1.15 Persian fallow deer	2.50	2.50
1123	A156	$1.15 Key deer	2.50	2.50
1124	A156	$1.15 Alpine ibex	2.50	2.50
		Nos. 1119-1124 (6)	15.00	15.00

Issued: #1119, 11/2; #1120, 11/3; #1121, 11/4; #1122, 11/5; #1123, 11/6; #1124, 11/7.

Christmas
A160

Paintings by El Parmigianino: 70c, Worship of Shepherds. 85c, $6.40, Virgin with Long Neck. $1.15, Virgin with Rose. $1.90, St. Margaret's Virgin.

1992, Nov. 20   Litho.   Perf. 13½

1125	A160	70c multicolored	1.10	1.10
1126	A160	85c multicolored	1.75	1.75
1127	A160	$1.15 multicolored	2.25	2.25
1128	A160	$1.90 multicolored	4.00	4.00
		Nos. 1125-1128 (4)	9.10	9.10

Souvenir Sheet

1129	A160	$6.40 multicolored	12.50	12.50

No. 1129 contains one 36x47mm stamp.

Queen Elizabeth II's Accession to the Throne, 40th Anniv. — A161

Various portraits of Queen Elizabeth II.

1992, Dec. 10   Litho.   Perf. 14

1130	A161	80c multicolored	1.25	1.25
1131	A161	$1.15 multicolored	2.00	2.00
1132	A161	$1.50 multicolored	3.25	3.25
1133	A161	$1.95 multicolored	4.50	4.50
		Nos. 1130-1133 (4)	11.00	11.00

Endangered Wildlife Type of 1992

1993   Litho.   Perf. 14

1134	A156	$1.15 English mandrill	3.00	3.00
1135	A156	$1.15 Gorilla	3.00	3.00
1136	A156	$1.15 Vanessa atlanta	3.00	3.00
1137	A156	$1.15 Sichuan takin	3.00	3.00
1138	A156	$1.15 Ring tailed lemur	3.00	3.00
		Nos. 1134-1138 (5)	15.00	15.00

Issued: #1134, Feb. 1; #1135, Feb. 2; #1136, Feb. 3; #1137, Feb. 4; #1138, Feb. 5.

Coronation of Queen Elizabeth II, 40th Anniv. — A162

Designs: $1, Coronation ceremony. $2, Coronation portrait. $3, Queen, family on balcony, Buckingham Palace.

1993, June 2   Litho.   Perf. 14

1139	A162	$1 multicolored	2.25	2.25
1140	A162	$2 multicolored	4.75	4.70
1141	A162	$3 multicolored	7.00	7.00
		Nos. 1139-1141 (3)	14.00	13.95

Christmas
A163

Paintings: 70c, Virgin with Child, by Filippo Lippi. 85c, Bargellini Madonna, by Lodovico Carracci. $1.15, Virgin of the Curtain, by Raphael. $2.50, Holy Family, by Il Bronzino. $4, Saint Zachary Virgin, by Il Parmigianino.

1993, Nov. 8   Litho.   Perf. 14

1142	A163	70c multicolored	1.25	1.25
1143	A163	85c multicolored	1.75	1.75
1144	A163	$1.15 multicolored	2.25	2.25
1145	A163	$2.50 multicolored	4.50	4.50

Size: 32x47mm

Perf. 13½

1146	A163	$4.00 multicolored	7.75	7.75
		Nos. 1142-1146 (5)	17.50	17.50

1994 Winter Olympics, Lillehammer — A164

1994, Feb. 11   Litho.   Perf. 13½x14

1147	A164	$5 multicolored	10.00	10.00

1994 World Cup Soccer Championships, US — A165

1994, June 17   Litho.   Perf. 14

1148	A165	$4.50 multicolored	10.00	10.00

First Manned Moon Landing, 25th Anniv. — A166

Apollo 11 emblem and: No. 1149a, First step onto Moon, US flag. No. 1149b, Astronaut carrying experiment packs on Moon. No. 1150a, Astronaut, US flag. No. 1150b, Flag, reflection shown in astronaut's visor.

1994, July 20

1149	A166	$2.25 Pair, #a.-b. + label	9.00	9.00
1150	A166	$2.25 Pair, #a.-b. + label	9.00	9.00

Living Reef Type of 1992

1994, Oct. 24   Litho.   Perf. 14½x13½

Size: 41x31mm

Buff & Multicolored

1154	A155	5c like #1058	.50	.50
1158	A155	15c like #1062	.50	.50
1160	A155	20c like #1064	.60	.60
1161	A155	25c like #1065	.65	.65
1162	A155	30c like #1066	.75	.75
1167	A155	50c like #1071	1.40	1.40
1172	A155	80c like #1076	2.25	2.25
1173	A155	85c like #1077	2.40	2.40
1174	A155	90c like #1078	2.50	2.50
1176	A155	$1 like #1080	2.75	2.75
		Nos. 1154-1176 (10)	14.30	14.30

Miniature Sheet

The Return of Tommy Tricker — A167

Scenes from film: a, Three people in canoe. b, Traditional dancers. c, Couple walking on beach. d, Aerial view of island. e, Girls performing hand gestures. f, Girls walking along sand bar.

1994, Nov. 23   Litho.   Perf. 14

1191	A167	85c Sheet of 6, #a.-f.	16.00	16.00

See No. 1213.

Christmas — A168

Paintings: No. 1192a, The Virgin and Child, by Morales. b, Adoration of Kings, by Gerard David. c, Adoration of Kings, by Vinc Foppa. d, The Madonna & Child with St. Joseph & Infant Baptist, by Baroccio.
No. 1193a, Madonna with Iris, in style of Durer. b, Adoration of Shepherds, by Le Nain. c, The Virgin and Child, by follower of Leonardo. d, The Mystic Nativity, by Botticelli.

1994, Nov. 30   Litho.   Perf. 14

1192	A168	85c Block of 4, #a.-d.	7.75	7.75
1193	A168	$1 Block of 4, #a.-d.	8.75	8.75

Robert Louis Stevenson (1850-94), Writer — A169

Adventure scenes from books: a, "Treasure Island." b, "David Balfour." c, "Dr. Jekyll and Mr. Hyde." d, "Kidnapped."

1994, Dec. 12   Perf. 14x15

1194	A169	$1.50 Block of 4, #a.-d.	14.00	14.00

UN, 50th Anniv. — A170

$4.50, FAO, 50th anniv.

1995   Litho.   Perf. 13x13½

1195	A170	$4.75 multicolored	8.50	8.50

Perf. 13½

1196	A170	$4.50 multicolored	8.00	8.00

Each issued in sheets of 4.
Issued: $4.75, 7/17; $4.50, 10/12.

Queen Mother, 95th Birthday — A172

1995, Aug. 31

1197	A172	$5 multicolored	15.00	15.00

End of World War II, 50th Anniv. — A173

Designs: a, German surrender, Rheims. b, Japanese surrender, Tokyo Bay.

1995, Sept. 4   Perf. 13

1198	A173	$3.50 Pair, #a.-b.	25.00	25.00

No. 1198 was issued in sheets of 4 stamps.

Year of the Sea Turtle A174

Designs: 85c, Green turtle in water. $1, Hawksbill turtle in water. $1.75, Green turtle nesting. $2.25, Hawksbill turtle hatchlings leaving nest.

1995, Nov. 20   Litho.   Perf. 14

1199	A174	85c multicolored	2.50	2.50
1200	A174	$1 multicolored	3.50	3.50
1201	A174	$1.75 multicolored	5.25	5.25
1202	A174	$2.25 multicolored	7.25	7.25
		Nos. 1199-1202 (4)	18.50	18.50

1996 Summer Olympics, Atlanta A175

1996, Jan. 12   Litho.   Perf. 14

1203	A175	85c Discus	1.75	1.75
1204	A175	$1 Torch bearer	2.25	2.25
1205	A175	$1.50 Sprinting	3.25	3.25
1206	A175	$1.85 Gymnastics	4.25	4.25
1207	A175	$2.10 Archery	5.00	5.00
1208	A175	$2.50 Javelin	5.50	5.50
		Nos. 1203-1208 (6)	22.00	22.00

Queen Elizabeth
II, 70th
Birthday — A176

Designs: $1.90, No. 1212a, In blue hat,
coat. $2.25, No. 1212b, Wearing tiara. $2.75,
No. 1212c, In robes of Order of the Garter.

1996, June 21   Perf. 14
1209 A176 $1.90 multicolored   4.00   4.00
1210 A176 $2.25 multicolored   5.00   5.00
1211 A176 $2.75 multicolored   5.50   5.50
      Nos. 1209-1211 (3)   14.50 14.50

Sheet of 3
1212 A176 $2.50 #a.-c. + label   17.50 17.50
Nos. 1209-1211 were issued in sheets of 4.

**"The Return of Tommy Tricker" Type of
1994**
No. 1213a-1213f, like #1191a-1191f.

1997, Aug. 28   Litho.   Perf. 14
1213 A167 90c Sheet of 6,
      #a.-f.   12.00 12.00

Nos. 1213a-1213f Overprinted in Silver

a

b

1997, Sept. 12   Litho.   Perf. 14
1214 A167 90c Sheet 6, #a.-f.   9.00   9.00

#1214a, 1214d-1214e are overprinted type
"a"; #1214b-1214c, 1214f type "b."

Butterflies
A177

5c, Lampides boeticus (female). 10c,
Vanessa atalanta. 15c, Lampides boeticus
(male). 20c, Papilio godeffroyi. 25c, Danaus
hamata. 30c, Xois sesara. 50c, Vagrans
egista. 70c, Parthenos sylvia. 80c, Hyblaea
sanguinea. 85c, Melanitis leda. 90c,
Ascalapha odorata. $1, Precis villida. $1.50,
Parthenos sylvia. $2, Lampides boeticus. $3,
Precis villida. $4, Melanitis leda. $5, Vagrans
egista. $7, Hyblaea sanguinea. $10, Vanessa
atalanta. $15, Papilio godeffroyi.

1997-98   Litho.   Perf. 13
1215 A177   5c multi   .20   .20
1216 A177   10c multi   .20   .20
1217 A177   15c multi   .20   .20
1218 A177   20c multi   .30   .30
1219 A177   25c multi   .35   .35
1220 A177   30c multi   .40   .40
1221 A177   50c multi   .65   .65
1222 A177   70c multi   .95   .95
1223 A177   80c multi   1.10   1.10
1224 A177   85c multi   1.10   1.10
1225 A177   90c multi   1.25   1.25
1226 A177 $1 multi   1.40   1.40

Perf. 13½
Size: 41x25mm

1226A A177 $1.50 multi   1.90   1.90
1226B A177 $2 multi   2.75   2.75
1226C A177 $3 multi   3.75   3.75
1226D A177 $4 multi   5.50   5.50

1226E A177 $5 multi   6.50   6.50
1226F A177 $7 multi   10.00 10.00
1226G A177 $10 multi   13.50 13.50
1226H A177 $15 multi   18.00 18.00
      Nos. 1215-1226H (20)   70.00 70.00

Issued: 5c, 10c, 15c, 20c, 25c, 30c, 50c,
70c, 10/22/97; 80c, 85c, 90c, $1, 11/12/97;
$1.50, $2, $3, 3/11/98; $4, $5, 6/19/98; $7,
$10, 9/18/98; $15, 11/13/98.
For surcharges, see Nos. 1259-1264.

Queen Elizabeth II and Prince Philip,
50th Wedding Anniv.
A178

1997, Nov. 20   Perf. 14
1227 A178 $2 multicolored   3.25   3.25

Souvenir Sheet
1228 A178 $5 like #1227,
      close-up   10.00 10.00
No. 1228 is a continuous design.

Diana, Princess of
Wales (1961-
97) — A179

1998, Mar. 18   Litho.   Perf. 14
1229 A179 $1.15 shown   1.75   1.75

Souvenir Sheet
1230 A179 $3.50 like #1229   5.25   5.25
No. 1229 was issued in sheets of 5 + label.
See No. B142.

Nos. 1111-1114 Ovptd.

No. 1231

**Printing Methods and Perfs as
before**
1999, Dec. 31
1231 A159 80c on #1111   1.25   1.25
1232 A159 85c on #1112   1.25   1.25
1233 A159 $1 on #1113   1.50   1.50
1234 A159 $1.75 on #1114 2.50   2.50
      Nos. 1231-1234 (4)   6.50   6.50

Queen Mother, 100th Birthday — A180

No. 1235: a, As child. b, As young woman.
c, Wearing green hat. d, Wearing tiara.

2000, Oct. 20   Litho.   Perf. 14
1235 A180 $4.50 Sheet of 4,
      #a-d   20.00 20.00

Souvenir Sheet
1236 A180 $6 Wearing blue
      hat   7.00   7.00

2000 Summer Olympics,
Sydney — A181

No. 1237: a, Ancient runner. b, Track and
field. c, Ancient archery. d, Archery.

2000, Nov. 14
1237 A181 $1.75 Sheet of 4,
      #a-d   11.00 11.00

Souvenir Sheet
1238 A181 $3.90 Torch bearer   4.50   4.50

Nos. 1095-1106 Surcharged in Gold

2001, Apr. 30   Litho.   Perf. 14
1239 A156 80c on $1.15
      #1101   1.00   1.00
1240 A156 80c on $1.15
      #1102   1.00   1.00
1241 A156 80c on $1.15
      #1103   1.00   1.00
1242 A156 80c on $1.15
      #1104   1.00   1.00
1243 A156 80c on $1.15
      #1105   1.00   1.00
1244 A156 80c on $1.15
      #1106   1.00   1.00
1245 A156 90c on $1.15
      #1095   1.25   1.25
1246 A156 90c on $1.15
      #1096   1.25   1.25
1247 A156 90c on $1.15
      #1097   1.25   1.25
1248 A156 90c on $1.15
      #1098   1.25   1.25
1249 A156 90c on $1.15
      #1099   1.25   1.25

1250 A156 90c on $1.15
      #1100   1.25   1.25
      Nos. 1239-1250 (12)   13.50 13.50

Nos. 1042-1045, 1050-1053
Surcharged or Overprinted in Black or
Gold

2002, Nov. 11   Litho.   Perf. 14
1251 A151 20c on 70c #1042   .20   .20
1252 A154 20c on 70c #1050   .20   .20
1253 A154 80c on $1.15
      #1052 (G)   1.50   1.50
1254 A151 85c on #1043   1.60   1.60
1255 A154 85c on #1051   1.60   1.60
1256 A154 90c on $1.50
      #1053   1.75   1.75
1257 A151 95c on #1044   1.90   1.90
1258 A151 $1 on $1.50
      #1045   2.25   2.25
      Nos. 1251-1258 (8)   11.00 11.00

Nos. 1226A-1226F Surcharged

Methods and Perfs As Before
2003, June 30
1259 A177 20c on $1.50
      #1226A   .30   .30
1260 A177 80c on $2 #1226B 1.00   1.00
1261 A177 85c on $3 #1226C 1.25   1.25
1262 A177 85c on $4 #1226D 1.25   1.25
1263 A177 90c on $5 #1226E 1.50   1.50
1264 A177 90c on $7 #1226F 1.50   1.50
      Nos. 1259-1264 (6)   6.80   6.80

Obliterator on Nos. 1260-1264 is a Moai
head.

United We
Stand — A182

2003, Sept. 30   Litho.   Perf. 14
1265 A182 90c multi   3.00   3.00

Printed in sheets of 4.

2004
Summer
Olympics,
Athens
A183

Designs: 40c, Poster for 1992 Barcelona
Olympics. 60c, Pancration, horiz. $1, Cycling,
horiz. $2, Gold medal, 1936 Berlin Olympics.

2004, Sept. 29   Litho.   Perf. 14¼
1266-1269 A183   Set of 4   6.50   6.50

Worldwide Fund for Nature
(WWF) — A184

Birds of Suwarrow National Park: 80c, Cook Islands reed warblers. 90c, Mangaia kingfishers. $1.15, Rarotonga starlings. $1.95, Atiu swiftlets.

2005, June 13   Litho.   Perf. 14
1270-1273 A184 Set of 4   8.00 8.00

Each stamp printed in sheets of 4.

Pope John Paul II
(1920-2005)
A185

2005, Nov. 11
1274 A185 $1.35 multi   2.40 2.40

Printed in sheets of 5 + label.

A186

A187

A188

Designs: 5c, Black-lined Maori wrasse. 10c, Blue lorikeets. 20c, Daisy coral. 30c, Ocean sunfish. 40c, Female Lampides boeticus butterfly. 50c, Rarotonga starlings.

No. 1285: a, Mangaia kingfishers. b, Cook Islands reef warblers. c, Rarotonga starlings, diff. d, Matiu swiftlets.

No. 1286: a, Male Lampides boeticus. b, Vagrans egista. c, Melantis leda. d, Female Lampides boeticus, diff.

No. 1287: a, Daisy coral, diff. b, Hydroid coral. c, Sea star. d, Smooth sea star.

No. 1288: a, Black-tipped cod. b, Red spot rainbow fish. c, Black-lined Maori wrasse, diff. d, Fish (incorrectly identified as Smooth sea star).

No. 1289: a, Three Ocean sunfish, Latin name at LL. b, Three Ocean sunfish, large clump of seaweed, Latin name at LR. c, Two Ocean sunfish, diver. d, Three Ocean sunfish, small clump of seaweed at top, Latin name at LR.

No. 1290: a, Blue lorikeets on palm branch. b, Blue lorikeets in tree hollow. c, Blue lorikeets and white flowers. d, Blue lorikeets and pink flowers.

No. 1291 — Queen Elizabeth II and: a, Hawksbill turtle. b, Leatherback turtle. c, Green turtle. d, Olive ridley turtle.

No. 1292 — Queen Elizabeth II and: a, Sowerby's whales. b, Cuvier's beaked whales. c, Bottle-nosed dolphin. d, Commerson's dolphins.

$7.50, Queen Elizabeth II, fish and marine life. $10, Queen Elizabeth II, butterflies and flowers. $15, Queen Elizabeth II and birds. Illustrations A187 and A188 reduced.

2007   Litho.   Perf. 13¼
1279 A186 5c multi   .20   .20
1280 A186 10c multi   .20   .20
1281 A186 20c multi   .30   .30
1282 A186 30c multi   .45   .45
1283 A186 40c multi   .60   .60
1284 A186 50c multi   .75   .75

Size: 48x27mm
Perf. 14x14¾
1285   Block of 4   4.75   4.75
a.-d. A186 80c Any single   1.10   1.10
1286   Block of 4   5.25   5.25
a.-d. A186 90c Any single   1.25   1.25
1287   Block of 4   5.75   5.75
a.-d. A186 $1 Any single   1.40   1.40
1288   Block of 4   6.50   6.50
a.-d. A186 $1.10 Any single   1.60   1.60
1289   Block of 4   7.00   7.00
a.-d. A186 $1.20 Any single   1.75   1.75
1290   Block of 4   11.50   11.50
a.-d. A186 $2 Any single   2.75   2.75

Perf. 13¾
1291   Block of 4   19.00   19.00
a.-d. A187 $3 Any single   4.75   4.75
1292   Block of 4   31.00   31.00
a.-d. A187 $5 Any single   7.75   7.75

Perf. 13¼
1293 A188 $7.50 multi   12.00   12.00
1294 A188 $10 multi   15.50   15.50
1295 A188 $15 multi   24.00   24.00
Nos. 1279-1295 (17)   144.75 144.75

Issued: Nos. 1279-1290, 3/20; No. 1291, 10/10; No. 1292, 11/13; Nos. 1293-1295, 12/10.

Miniature Sheet

2008 Summer Olympics,
Beijing — A189

No. 1296: a, 40c, Weight lifting. b, 60c, High jump. c, $1, Swimming. d, $1.50, Running.

2008, July 28   Litho.   Perf. 14¾x14
1296 A189 Sheet of 4, #a-d   5.25 5.25

Pacific Mini-
Games,
Rarotonga
A190

Designs: 20c, Shot put and discus. 80c, High jump. 90c, Weight lifting. $3, Running.

2009, Sept. 21   Litho.   Perf. 13¾
1297-1300 A190 Set of 4   7.25 7.25
1300a   Souvenir sheet,
           #1297-1300   7.25 7.25

Nos. 1297-1300 Overprinted in Gold
with Names of Winners

Overprint text: 20c, Daniel Kilama / New Caledonia / Men's Discus Throw / 27th Sept. 2009. 80c, Johanna Sui / Tahiti / Women's High Jump / 24th Sept. 2009. 90c, Yukio Peter / Nauru / 84kg Clean & Jerk / 1st Oct. 2009. $3, Niko Verekauta / Fiji / Men's 100 metres / 24th Sept. 2009.

2009, Oct. 21   Litho.   Perf. 13¾
1301-1304 A190 Set of 4   7.25 7.25
1304a   Souvenir sheet,
           #1301-1304   7.25 7.25

Flowers — A191

Designs: 10c, Catharanthus roseus. 20c, Ixora casei. 30c, Hibiscus rosa-sinensis cultivar. 40c, Heliconia psittacorum. 50c, Hibiscus schizopetalus, vert. 70c, Alpinia purpurata, vert. 80c, Bougainvillea spectabilis. 90c, Hibiscus rosa-sinensis. $1, Nymphaea capensis. $1.10, Euphorbia pulcherrima. $1.20, Impatiens walleriana. $2, Anthurium andraeanum. $3, Chrysanthemum cultivar. $4, Acalypha pendula, vert. $5, Heliconia rostrata, vert. $7.50, Tagetes patular cultivar. $10, Phalaenopsis cultivar. $20, Catharanthus roseus, diff.

2010, Sept. 10   Litho.   Perf. 13¾
Sizes: 60x37mm, 37x60mm
1305 A191 10c multi   .20   .20
1306 A191 20c multi   .30   .30
1307 A191 30c multi   .45   .45
1308 A191 40c multi   .60   .60
1309 A191 50c multi   .75   .75
1310 A191 70c multi   1.00   1.00
1311 A191 80c multi   1.25   1.25
1312 A191 90c multi   1.40   1.40
1313 A191 $1 multi   1.50   1.50
1314 A191 $1.10 multi   1.60   1.60
1315 A191 $1.20 multi   1.75   1.75
1316 A191 $2 multi   3.00   3.00
1317 A191 $3 multi   4.50   4.50
1318 A191 $4 multi   5.75   5.75
1319 A191 $5 multi   7.25   7.25
1320 A191 $7.50 multi   11.00   11.00
1321 A191 $10 multi   14.50   14.50
1322 A191 $20 multi   29.00   29.00
Nos. 1305-1322 (18)   85.80   85.80

See Nos. 1328-1337.
For overprints see Nos. O70-O84.

ANZAC
Day
A192

Designs: 80c, Girl Guides in parade. 90c, Boy Scouts in parade. $1.10, Monument, vert. $1.20, Cook Islands flag, vert.
No. 1327: a, Church interior. b, Church exterior.

Perf. 14¾x14¼, 14¼x14¾
2010, Sept. 14
1323-1326 A192 Set of 4   6.00 6.00

Souvenir Sheet
1327 A192 $3 Sheet of 2, #a-b   9.00 9.00

**Flower Type of 2010 in Smaller
Sizes**

Designs as before.

2010, Oct. 27   Litho.   Perf. 14
Sizes: 42x28mm, 28x42mm
1328 A191 10c multi   .20   .20
1329 A191 20c multi   .30   .30
1330 A191 30c multi   .50   .50
1331 A191 50c multi   .80   .80
1332 A191 80c multi   1.25   1.25
1333 A191 90c multi   1.50   1.50
1334 A191 $1 multi   1.60   1.60
1335 A191 $1.10 multi   1.75   1.75
1336 A191 $1.20 multi   1.90   1.90
1337 A191 $2 multi   3.25   3.25
Nos. 1328-1337 (10)   13.05   13.05

Expo
2010,
Shanghai
A193

Designs: 80c, Anthurium flower. 90c, Angelfish. $1.10, Fish near ocean floor. $1.20, Coconuts.
$6, Palm tree and ocean, vert.

2010, Oct. 27   Perf. 14¾x14¼
1338-1341 A193 Set of 4   6.50 6.50

Souvenir Sheet
Perf. 14¼
1342 A193 $6 multi   9.75 9.75
No. 1342 contains one 38x50mm stamp.

Miniature Sheet

Aerial Views of Islands — A194

No. 1343: a, 10c, Aitutaki. b, 10c, Penrhyn. c, 20c, Palmerston. d, 20c, Mitiaro. e, 30c, Rarotonga. f, 30c, Takutea. g, 50c, Atiu. h, 70c, Suwarrow. i, 80c, Pukapuka. j, 80c, Nassau. k, 90c, Mangaia. l, 90c, Manihiki. m, 90c, Manuae. n, $1.10, Rakahanga. o, $1.20, Mauke.

2010, Nov. 8   Perf. 14
1343 A194 Sheet of 15, #a-o   14.00 14.00

SEMI-POSTAL STAMPS

Catalogue values for unused stamps in this section are for Never Hinged items.

Nos. 203-204,
223, 210, 213,
215-216
Surcharged

Perf. 14x13½, 13½
1968, Feb. 12   Photo.
B1 A34 3c + 1c multi   .20   .20
B2 A34 4c + 1c multi   .20   .20
B3 A37 5c + 2c multi   .20   .20
B4 A34 10c + 2c multi   .25   .25
B5 A34 25c + 5c multi   .40   .40
B6 A34 50c + 10c multi   .90   .90
B7 A35 $1 + 10c multi   1.75   1.75
Nos. B1-B7 (7)   3.90   3.90

Surtax for the victims of hurricane of Dec. 15-18, 1967. The surcharge on No. B3 is printed on a silver rectangle. The surcharge on No. B7 is in smaller type with serifs, measuring 7½mm in depth.

Nos. 210, 213-214 Surcharged in
Ultramarine

1971, Sept. 8   Photo.   Perf. 14x13½
B8   A34 10c + 1c multi   .25   .25
B9   A34 10c + 3c multi   .25   .25
B10 A34 25c + 1c multi   .65   .65
B11 A34 25c + 3c multi   .65   .65
B12 A34 30c + 1c multi   .75   .75
B13 A34 30c + 3c multi   .75   .75
Nos. B8-B13 (6)   3.30   3.30

4th South Pacific Games, Papeete, French Polynesia, Sept. 8-19.

Christmas Type of Regular Issue
Souvenir Sheet

50c+5c, Holy Family in a Garland of Flowers, by Jan Brueghel and Pieter van Avont.

1971, Nov. 30   **Photo.**   *Perf. 13½*
B14	A50	50c + 5c gold & multi	1.75 1.75

No. B14 contains one stamp 45x40mm.

Nos. 316-318, 211, 213 and 215
Surcharged in Red or Black

a   b

1972, Mar. 30   **Photo.**   *Perf. 13½*
B15	A46(a)	5c + 2c multi (R)	.20 .20
B16	A46(a)	10c + 2c multi (R)	.20 .20
B17	A34(b)	15c + 5c multi	.35 .35
B18	A34(b)	25c + 5c multi	.65 .65
B19	A46(b)	30c + 5c multi (R)	.75 .75
B20	A34(b)	50c + 10c multi	1.40 1.40
		Nos. B15-B20 (6)	3.55 3.55

Surtax for victims of hurricane of Mar. 22-26.

Nos. 319-322c with Surcharge Similar
to Type "a"

1972, May 24   **Photo.**   *Perf. 13½*
B21	A51	5c + 2c, pair, #a.-b.	.25 .25
B22	A51	10c + 2c, pair, #a.-b.	.45 .45
B23	A51	25c + 2c, pair, #a.-b.	1.00 1.00
B24	A51	30c + 2c, pair, #a.-b.	1.50 1.50
c.		Souvenir sheet of 8	4.25 4.25
		Nos. B21-B24 (4)	3.20 3.20

Surtax for victims of hurricane of Mar. 22-26. Stamps of No. B24c each surcharged 3c.

Olympic Type of Regular Issue
Souvenir Sheet

50c+5c, Pierre de Coubertin, Olympic rings.

1972, June 26
B29	A52	50c + 5c multi	2.50 2.50

Christmas Type of Regular Issue
Souvenir Sheet

Design: 50c+5c, Nativity, by Correggio.

1972, Oct. 11   **Photo.**   *Perf. 13½*
B30	A53	50c + 5c multi	1.50 1.25

No. B30 contains one stamp 30x40mm.

Easter Type of Regular Issue
Souvenir Sheets

1973, Apr. 30   **Photo.**   *Perf. 13½x14*
B31	A56	50c + 5c like #346	.80 .80
B32	A56	50c + 5c like #347	.80 .80
B33	A56	50c + 5c like #348	.80 .80
		Nos. B31-B33 (3)	2.40 2.40

Surtax was for school children.

Christmas Type of Regular Issue
Souvenir Sheets

1973, Dec. 3   **Photo.**   *Perf. 13x13½*
B34	A59	50c + 5c like #364	.50 .50
B35	A59	50c + 5c like #365	.50 .50
B36	A59	50c + 5c like #366	.50 .50
B37	A59	50c + 5c like #367	.50 .50
B38	A59	50c + 5c like #368	.50 .50
		Nos. B34-B38 (5)	2.50 2.50

Surtax was for school children.

Easter Type of 1973
Dated "1974"
Souvenir Sheets

1974, Apr. 22   *Perf. 13½x14*
B39	A56	50c + 5c like #378	.65 .65
B40	A56	50c + 5c like #379	.65 .65
B41	A56	50c + 5c like #380	.65 .65
		Nos. B39-B41 (3)	1.95 1.95

Christmas Type of 1974
Souvenir Sheets

1974   **Photo.**   *Perf. 13½x13*
B42	A68	50c + 5c like #412	.50 .50
B43	A68	50c + 5c like #413	.50 .50
B44	A68	50c + 5c like #414	.50 .50
B45	A68	50c + 5c like #415	.50 .50
B46	A68	50c + 5c like #416	.50 .50
		Nos. B42-B46 (5)	2.50 2.50

Christmas Type of 1975
Souvenir Sheets

1975, Dec. 1   *Perf. 13½*
B47	A75	75c + 5c like #437	.75 .75
B48	A75	75c + 5c like #438	.75 .75
B49	A75	75c + 5c like #439	.75 .75
B50	A75	75c + 5c like #440	.75 .75
B51	A75	75c + 5c like #441	.75 .75
		Nos. B47-B51 (5)	3.75 3.75

Size of stamps: 23x40mm.

Easter Type of 1976
Souvenir Sheets

1976, May 3   **Photo.**   *Perf. 13½*
B52	A76	60c + 5c like #442	.75 .75
B53	A76	60c + 5c like #443	.75 .75
B54	A76	60c + 5c like #444	.75 .75
		Nos. B52-B54 (3)	2.25 2.25

Size of stamps: 36x36mm.

Christmas Type of 1976
Souvenir Sheets

1976, Nov. 2   **Photo.**   *Perf. 14x13½*
B55	A80	75c + 5c like #459	.80 .80
B56	A80	75c + 5c like #460	.80 .80
B57	A80	75c + 5c like #461	.80 .80
B58	A80	75c + 5c like #462	.80 .80
B59	A80	75c + 5c like #463	.80 .80
		Nos. B55-B59 (5)	4.00 4.00

Easter Type of 1977
Souvenir Sheets

1977, Apr. 18   **Photo.**   *Perf. 13½x14*
B60	A83	60c + 5c like #471	.75 .75
B61	A83	60c + 5c like #472	.75 .75
B62	A83	60c + 5c like #473	.75 .75
		Nos. B60-B62 (3)	2.25 2.25

Size of stamps: 30x42mm.

Christmas Type of 1977
Souvenir Sheets

1977, Oct. 31   **Photo.**   *Perf. 14x13½*
B63	A84	75c + 5c like #474	.75 .75
B64	A84	75c + 5c like #475	.75 .75
B65	A84	75c + 5c like #476	.75 .75
B66	A84	75c + 5c like #477	.75 .75
B67	A84	75c + 5c like #478	.75 .75
		Nos. B63-B67 (5)	3.75 3.75

Easter Type of 1978
Souvenir Sheets

1978, Apr. 10   **Photo.**   *Perf. 14x13½*
B68	A87	60c + 5c like #483	.70 .60
B69	A87	60c + 5c like #484	.70 .60
B70	A87	60c + 5c like #485	.70 .60
		Nos. B68-B70 (3)	2.10 1.80

Christmas Type of 1978
Souvenir Sheets

1979, Jan. 12   **Photo.**   *Perf. 13*
B71	A89	75c + 5c like #503	.70 .70
B72	A89	75c + 5c like #504	.70 .70
B73	A89	75c + 5c like #505	.70 .70
		Nos. B71-B73 (3)	2.10 2.10

Easter Type of 1979
Souvenir Sheet

1979, Apr. 5   **Photo.**   *Perf. 13*
B74		Sheet of 4	1.00 1.00
a.		A90 10c + 2c like #506	.20 .20
b.		A90 12c + 2c like #507	.20 .20
c.		A90 15c + 2c like #508	.25 .25
d.		A90 20c + 2c like #509	.35 .35

IYC Type of 1979
Souvenir Sheet

1979, Oct. 10
B75		Sheet of 3	2.25 2.25
a.		A93 30c + 5c like #529	.45 .45
b.		A93 50c + 5c like #530	.75 .75
c.		A93 65c + 5c like #531	.90 .90

Christmas Type of 1979

1980, Jan. 15   **Photo.**   *Perf. 14*
B76	A95	6c + 2c like #537	.20 .20
B77	A95	10c + 2c like #538	.20 .20
B78	A95	12c + 2c like #539	.25 .25
B79	A95	15c + 2c like #540	.35 .35
		Nos. B76-B79 (4)	1.00 1.00

Easter Type of 1980
Souvenir Sheets

1980, Mar. 31   **Photo.**   *Perf. 13*
B80	A96	Sheet of 6, #a.-f.	2.25 2.25

#B80 contains #541-543, each stamp with 2c surcharge.

1980, Apr. 23
Souvenir Sheets
B81	A96	75c + 5c like #541a	.75 .75
B82	A96	75c + 5c like #541b	.75 .75
B83	A96	75c + 5c like #542a	.75 .75
B84	A96	75c + 5c like #542b	.75 .75
B85	A96	75c + 5c like #543a	.75 .75
B86	A96	75c + 5c like #543b	.75 .75
		Nos. B81-B86 (6)	4.50 4.50

Surtax was for school children.

Rotary Type of 1980
Souvenir Sheet

1980, May 27   **Photo.**   *Perf. 14*
B87		Sheet of 3	1.75 1.75
a.		A97 30c + 3c like #547	.45 .45
b.		A97 35c + 3c like #548	.55 .55
c.		A97 50c + 3c like #549	.75 .75

Christmas Type of 1980
Souvenir Sheets

1981, Jan. 9   **Photo.**   *Imperf.*
B88	A102a	75c + 5c like #652	.75 .75
B89	A102a	75c + 5c like #653	.75 .75
B90	A102a	75c + 5c like #654	.75 .75
B91	A102a	75c + 5c like #655	.75 .75
		Nos. B88-B91 (4)	3.00 3.00

Easter Type of 1981
Souvenir Sheet

1981, Apr. 10   **Photo.**   *Perf. 13½*
B92		Sheet of 3	1.50 1.50
a.		A103 15c + 2c like #656	.25 .25
b.		A103 25c + 2c like #657	.50 .50
c.		A103 40c + 2c like #658	.75 .75

1981, Apr. 28   *Imperf.*
B93	A103	75c + 5c like #656	1.25 1.25
B94	A103	75c + 5c like #657	1.25 1.25
B95	A103	75c + 5c like #658	1.25 1.25
		Nos. B93-B95 (3)	3.75 3.75

Surtax was for school children.

Espana '82 Soccer Type
Souvenir Sheet

1981   **Photo.**   *Perf. 13½*
B96	A105	Sheet of 8, #a.-h.	7.00 7.00

#B96 contains #661-664, each stamp with 3c surcharge.

Royal Wedding Type of 1981
Nos. 659-660a Surcharged in Black

1981, Nov. 10   **Photo.**   *Perf. 14*
B97	A104	$1 + 5c multi	2.00 2.00
B98	A104	$2 + 5c multi	4.00 4.00
a.		Souvenir sheet of 2	6.00 6.00

Intl. Year of the Disabled. No. B98a contains Nos. B97-B98 each with 10c surtax, which was for benefit of the disabled; black overprint in margin.

Christmas Type of 1981
Souvenir Sheet

1981, Dec. 14   **Photo.**   *Perf. 13½*
B99		Sheet of 4	3.50 3.50
a.		A107 8c + 3c like #669	.25 .25
b.		A107 15c + 3c like #670	.40 .40
c.		A107 40c + 3c like #671	1.10 1.10
d.		A107 50c + 3c like #672	1.40 1.40

Surtax was for school children.

Nos. 919-923 Surcharged "FIRST PAPAL VISIT TO SOUTH PACIFIC / POPE JOHN PAUL II / *NOV 21-24 1986* " and Value in Silver

1986, Nov. 21   **Litho.**   *Perf. 13½*
B100	A138	55c + 10c multi	3.25 3.25
B101	A138	$1.30 + 10c multi	6.75 6.75
B102	A138	$2.75 + 10c multi	13.00 13.00
		Nos. B100-B102 (3)	23.00 23.00

Souvenir Sheets
B103		Sheet of 3	17.50 17.50
a.-c.		A138 $2.40 + 10c on Nos. 922a-922c, any single	5.75 5.75
B104	A138	$6.40 + 50c multi	17.50 17.50

No. B103 ovptd. in margin "VISIT TO SOUTH PACIFIC / OF POPE JOHN PAUL II" and "FIRST PAPAL VISIT / NOVEMBER 21-24 1986." No. B104 ovptd. around margin only, "*FIRST PAPAL VISIT TO SOUTH PACIFIC NOVEMBER 21-24 1986" and "PRE-CHRISTMAS VISIT OF HIS HOLINESS POPE JOHN PAUL II."

For surcharge see No. B112.

Stamps of 1982 and 1987 Surcharged "HURRICANE RELIEF" in Sans-serif Capitals Plus New Value

Perfs. as before

1987, June 30   **Photo.**
Surcharged +25c
B105	A121	55c on #958	1.10 1.10
B106	A121	65c on #960	1.25 1.25
B107	A121	75c on #963	1.40 1.40
B108	A121	95c on #965	1.60 1.60

Surcharged +50c
B109	A101	$2.80 on #582	4.50 4.50
B110	A101	$5 on #583	7.75 7.75
B111	A102	$6.40 on #978	9.50 9.50
		Nos. B105-B111 (7)	27.10 27.10

Stamps of 1985-86 Surcharged "HURRICANE RELIEF / +50c" in Silver or Black

1987   *Perfs. as before*
Surcharged +50c
B112	A138	55c on #B100	1.40 1.40
B113	A133	55c on #897 (B)	1.40 1.40
B114	A128	65c on #871	1.50 1.50
B115	A133	65c on #898	1.50 1.50
B116	A128	75c on #872	1.60 1.60
B117	A133	75c on #899	1.60 1.60
B118	A134	95c on #908 (B)	1.90 1.90
B119	A135	$1 on #910	2.10 2.10
B120	A136	$1 on #913	2.10 2.10
B121	A137	$1 on #916	2.10 2.10
B122	A128	$1.15 on #873	2.25 2.25
B123	A133	$1.25 on #900	2.25 2.25
B124	A134	$1.25 on #905	2.25 2.25
B125	A136	$1.25 on #914 (B)	2.25 2.25
B126	A134	$1.30 on #920	2.50 2.50
B127	A134	$1.50 on #906 (B)	2.50 2.50
B128	A135	$1.50 on #911 (B)	2.50 2.50
B129	A133	$2 on #901 (B)	3.25 3.25
B130	A135	$2 on #912 (B)	3.25 3.25
B131	A137	$2 on #917	3.25 3.25
B132	A136	$2.75 on #915	4.50 4.50
B133	A138	$2.75 on #921	4.50 4.50
B134	A128	$2.80 on #874	4.50 4.50
B135	A137	$3 on #918	4.75 4.75
		Nos. B112-B135 (24)	61.70 61.70

Souvenir Sheets
B136	A134	$1.10 on #907 (B)	2.00 2.00
B137	A134	$1.95 on #908	3.25 3.25
B138		on #922	
a.-c.			11.00 11.00
B139	A134	$2.45 on #909 (B)	3.75 3.75
B140	A128	$5.30 on #875	7.25 7.25
B141	A138	$6.40 on #B104	8.50 8.50
		Nos. B136-B141 (6)	35.50 35.50

Issued: #B118, B121, B124, B127, B131, B135-B137, B139-B140, 7/31; others 6/30.

No. 1230 Surcharged "CHILDREN'S / CHARITIES" in Silver
Souvenir Sheet

1998, Nov. 20   **Litho.**   *Perf. 14*
B142	A179	$3.50 +$1 multi	5.75 5.75

AIR POST STAMPS

Stamps of 1936-63 Overprinted and Surcharged

Airmail

Perf. 13x13½, 13½x13

Litho., Engr.

			1966, Apr. 22		**Wmk. 253**
C1	A25	6p on #152		.90	.25
C2	A26	7p on 8p #153		1.25	.25
C3	A25	10p on 3p #150		.85	.35
C4	A25	1sh on #154		.90	.45
C5	A27	1sh6p on #155		1.50	1.25
C6	A26	2sh3p on 3sh #157		1.25	1.00
C7	A28	5sh on #158		2.00	1.75
C8	A28	10sh on 2sh #156		2.50	8.00

Perf. 14

Typo.

C9	PF5	£1 on #106		15.00	16.00
a.	Airplane missing			35.00	50.00
	Nos. C1-C9 (9)			26.15	29.25

#C9a occurs on all stamps from the right vertical column of the sheet due to a lack of airplane symbols. The size and position of the airplane symbol varies in relation to "Airmail" on the other stamps. The surcharges are printed on silver ovals.

2nd So. Pacific Games' Type

Sport: 10p, Women runners and Games' emblem. 2sh3p, Runner and team emblem.

Perf. 13½

			1967, Jan. 12	**Unwmk.**	**Photo.**
C10	A32	10p org & multi		.20	.20
C11	A32	2sh3p multi		.25	.25

Capt. Cook Type of Regular Issue

6c, The "Resolution" and "Discovery" Beating Through the Ice, by Webber. 10c, The Island of Otaheite, by Hodges, and Queen Elizabeth II. 15c, View of Karakakooa (Kealakekua), Hawaii, by Webber. 25c, The Landing at Middleburg, Tonga, by Hodges, & Captain Cook. (All horiz.)

			1968, Sept. 12	**Photo.**	**Perf. 13**
C12	A39	6c gold & multi		.65	.65
C13	A39	10c gold & multi		1.00	1.00
C14	A39	15c gold & multi		1.25	1.25
C15	A39	25c gold & multi		2.75	2.75
	Nos. C12-C15 (4)			5.65	5.65

See note after No. 236.

Christmas Type of 1979

			1979, Dec. 14	**Photo.**	**Perf. 14**
C16	A95	20c like #537		.25	.25
C17	A95	25c like #538		.35	.35
C18	A95	30c like #539		.40	.40
C19	A95	35c like #540		.50	.50
	Nos. C16-C19 (4)			1.50	1.50

Franklin D. Roosevelt — AP1

80c, Benjamin Franklin. $1.40, George Washington, by Gilbert Stuart.

			1982, Sept. 30	**Photo.**	**Perf. 14**
C20	AP1	60c multicolored		.90	.90
C21	AP1	80c multicolored		1.10	1.10
C22	AP1	$1.40 multicolored		2.00	2.00
a.	Souvenir sheet of 3			5.25	5.25
	Nos. C20-C22 (3)			4.00	4.00

No. C22a contains Nos. C20-C22, perf. 13½ with portraits in square frames.

No. C22 Overprinted in Gold and Black

			1983, Aug. 12	**Photo.**	**Perf. 14**
C23	AP1	96c on $1.40 multi		2.00	2.00

Endangered Bird Species Type
Souvenir Sheets

Nos. 1020-1023 Overprinted

			1990, Dec. 5	**Litho.**	**Perf. 13½**
C24	A145	$1 Flycatcher		4.25	4.25
C25	A145	$1.25 Flycatchers		5.00	5.00
C26	A145	$1.50 Fruit dove		6.50	6.50
C27	A145	$1.75 Fruit doves		7.25	7.25
	Nos. C24-C27 (4)			23.00	23.00

Birdpex '90, 20th Intl. Ornithological Cong., New Zealand.

AIR POST SEMI-POSTAL STAMPS

> **Catalogue values for unused stamps in this section are for Never Hinged items.**

Christmas Type of 1979

			1980, Jan. 15	**Photo.**	**Perf. 14**
CB1	A95	20c + 4c like #C16		.40	.40
CB2	A95	25c + 4c like #C17		.45	.45
CB3	A95	30c + 4c like #C18		.50	.50
CB4	A95	35c + 4c like #C19		.65	.65
	Nos. CB1-CB4 (4)			2.00	2.00

OFFICIAL STAMPS

Flower Issue of 1967-69 Overprinted or Surcharged in Black on Silver

1975 Photo. Unwmk. Perf. 14x13½

O1	A34	1c multi (#200)		.25
O2	A34	2c multi (#201)		.25
O3	A34	3c multi (#203)		.25
O4	A34	4c multi (#205)		.25
O5	A34	5c on 2½c multi (#202)		.25
O6	A34	8c multi (#208)		.30
O7	A34	10c on 6c multi (#207)		.35
O8	A34	18c on 20c multi (#212)		.45
O9	A34	25c on 9c multi (#209)		.70
O10	A34	30c on 15c multi (#211)		.80
O11	A34	50c multi (#215)		.90
O12	A35	$1 multi (#216)		1.60
O13	A35	$2 multi (#217)		2.50
O14	A36	$4 multi (#218)		4.50
O15	A36	$6 multi (#219)		5.50
	Nos. O1-O15 (15)			18.85

No. O1-O15 were not sold to the public unused. Arrangement of surcharge varies on different denominations.

Silver panel on Nos. O14-O15 measures 26½x6mm and is rounded at both ends.

Issue dates: 1c-$2, Mar. 17; $4-$6, May 19.

> **Catalogue values for unused stamps in this section, from this point to the end of the section, are for Never Hinged items.**

Nos. 381-382, 389, 393-396, 467, 446 Overprinted or Surcharged in Silver or Black

O.H.M.S.

Photo., Litho.

			1978, Oct. 19		**Perf. 13½**
O16	A62	1c multi (S)		.85	.20
O17	A62	2c on ½c multi		.85	.20
O18	A62	5c on ½c multi		.95	.20
O19	A62	10c on 8c multi (S)		1.10	.20
O20	A62	15c on 50c multi (S)		1.25	.20
O21	A62	18c on 60c multi (S)		1.25	.20
O22	A62	25c multicolored		1.60	.25
O23	A62	30c multi (S)		1.60	.30
O24	A62	35c on 60c multi (S)		1.60	.35
O25	A62	50c multi (S)		2.10	.50
O26	A62	60c multi (S)		2.40	.60
O27	A82	$1 Pair, #a.-b. (S)		10.00	2.00
O29	A77	$2 multicolored		7.25	2.00
O30	A64	$4 multi ('79)		13.50	4.00
O31	A64	$6 multi ('79)		13.50	6.50
	Nos. O16-O31 (15)			59.80	17.70

Diagonal overprints on No. O27. Overprint on No. O29: 19x4mm.

Nos. 790-791, 795, 797, 799, 805, 807, 809-810 Ovptd. or Surcharged "O.H.M.S." in Silver

			1985, July 10	**Photo.**	**Perf. 13½x13**
O32	A121	5c multi		.55	.55
O33	A121	10c multi		.55	.55
O34	A121	20c multi		.65	.65
O35	A121	30c multi		.65	.65
O36	A121	40c multi		.65	.65
O37	A121	55c on 85c multi		.80	.80
O38	A121	60c multi		.80	.80
O39	A121	$1.10 multi		1.25	1.25
O40	A121	$2 on $1.20 multi		2.50	2.50
	Nos. O32-O40 (9)			8.40	8.40

Nos. 792-794, 802, 806, 696 and 583-586 Ovptd. or Surcharged "O.H.M.S." in Silver, Gold (75c) or Black and Silver ($5, $18)

			1986-90	**Photo.**	**Perfs. as Before**
O41	A121	12c multi		5.00	5.00
O42	A121	14c multi		5.00	5.00
O43	A121	18c multi		5.00	5.00
O44	A121	50c multi		6.25	6.25
O45	A121	70c multi		6.75	6.75
O46	A111	75c on 60c, #a.-d.		13.50	13.50
O50	A102	$5 on $3 multi		17.00	17.00
O51	A102	$9 on $4 multi		9.00	9.00
O52	A102	$14 on $6 multi		14.00	14.00
O53	A102	$18 on $10 multi		20.00	20.00
	Nos. O41-O53 (10)			101.50	101.50

Issued: $9, 5/30/89; $14, 7/12/89; $18, 6/4/90; others 5/5/86.

Nos. 1058-1059, 1062, 1064-1066, 1071, 1076-1078, 1080-1083, 1085 Ovptd. "O.H.M.S." in Silver

			1995-98	**Litho.**	**Perf. 14½x13½**
O54	A155	5c multicolored		.50	.50
O55	A155	10c multicolored		.50	.50
O56	A155	15c multicolored		.65	.65
O57	A155	20c multicolored		.70	.70
O58	A155	25c multicolored		.75	.75
O59	A155	30c multicolored		.80	.80
O60	A155	50c multicolored		1.00	1.00
O61	A155	80c multicolored		1.60	1.60
O62	A155	85c multicolored		1.60	1.60
O63	A155	90c multicolored		1.60	1.60
O64	A155	$1 multicolored		1.90	1.90
O65	A155	$2 multicolored		3.00	3.00
O66	A155a	$3 multicolored		4.75	4.75
O67	A155a	$5 multicolored		5.75	5.75
O68	A155a	$7 multicolored		8.50	8.50
O69	A155a	$10 multi		10.50	10.50
	Nos. O54-O69 (16)			44.10	44.10

Overprint on Nos. O66-O69 has larger, sans serif letters.

Nos. O66-O69 were not sold unused to local customers.

Issued: 5c-90c, 2/24/95; $1-$2, 5/15/95; $3-$7, 7/17/98; $10, 11/12/98.

Nos. 1305-1319 Overprinted in Gold

			2010, Oct. 12	**Litho.**	**Perf. 13¾**
			Sizes: 60x37mm, 37x60mm		
O70	A191	10c multi		.20	.20
O71	A191	20c multi		.30	.30
O72	A191	30c multi		.50	.50
O73	A191	40c multi		.65	.65
O74	A191	50c multi		.80	.80
O75	A191	70c multi		1.10	1.10
O76	A191	80c multi		1.25	1.25
O77	A191	90c multi		1.50	1.50
O78	A191	$1 multi		1.60	1.60
O79	A191	$1.10 multi		1.75	1.75
O80	A191	$1.20 multi		1.90	1.90
O81	A191	$2 multi		3.25	3.25
O82	A191	$3 multi		4.75	4.75
O83	A191	$4 multi		6.50	6.50
O84	A191	$5 multi		8.00	8.00
	Nos. O70-O84 (15)			34.05	34.05

Overprint reads up on vertical stamps.

CORFU

kor-'fü

LOCATION — An island in the Ionian Sea opposite the Greek-Albanian border
GOVT. — A department of Greece
AREA — 245 sq. mi.
POP. — 114,620 (1938)
CAPITAL — Corfu

In 1922 Italy occupied Corfu (Kerkyra) during a controversy with Greece over the assassination of an Italian official in Epirus. Italy again occupied Corfu in 1941-43.

100 Centesimi = 1 Lira
100 Lepta = 1 Drachma

Watermark

Wmk. 140 —
Crown

Wmk. 252 —
Crowns

ISSUED UNDER ITALIAN OCCUPATION

Italian Stamps of 1901-23 Overprinted

1923, Sept. 20		**Wmk. 140**	**Perf. 14**	
N1	A48	5c green	8.00	12.00
N2	A48	10c claret	8.00	12.00
N3	A48	15c slate	8.00	12.00
N4	A50	20c brown orange	8.00	12.00
N5	A49	30c orange brown	8.00	12.00
N6	A49	50c violet	8.00	12.00
N7	A49	60c blue	8.00	12.00
a.		Vert. pair, one without overprint	1,500.	
N8	A46	1 l brown & green	8.00	12.00
		Nos. N1-N8 (8)	64.00	96.00
		Set, never hinged	145.00	

Italian Stamps of 1901-23 Surcharged

1923, Sept. 24				
N9	A48	25 l on 10c claret	72.50	40.00
N10	A49	60 l on 25c blue	11.00	
N11	A49	70 l on 30c org brn	11.00	
N12	A49	1.20d on 50c violet	32.00	40.00
N13	A46	2.40d on 1 l brn & grn	32.00	40.00
N14	A46	4.75d on 2 l grn & org	16.00	
		Nos. N9-N14 (6)	174.50	
		Set, never hinged	420.00	

Nos. N10, N11, N14 were not placed in use.

Issue for Corfu and Paxos

Nos. N15-N34, NC1-NC12, NJ1-NJ11 and NRA1-NRA3 have been extensively counterfeited, some with forged cancellations.

Stamps of Greece, 1937-38, Overprinted in Black

Perf. 12x13½, 12½x12, 13½x12				
1941, June 5			**Wmk. 252**	
N15	A69	5 l brn red & blue	6.75	3.50
a.		Inverted overprint	67.50	40.00
b.		Double overprint	100.00	100.00
N16	A70	10 l bl & brn red (On 397)	2.50	2.50
N17	A70	10 l bl & brn red (On 413)	1,500.	1,200.
N18	A71	20 l black & grn	2.50	2.50
a.		Inverted overprint	100.00	40.00
N19	A72	40 l green & blk	3.50	3.50
a.		Inverted overprint	100.00	40.00
b.		Double overprint	100.00	100.00
N20	A73	50 l brown & blk	2.50	2.50
a.		Inverted overprint	67.50	40.00
N21	A74	80 l ind & yel brn	3.50	3.50
N22	A67	1d green	17.00	15.00
N23	A84	1.50d green	13.00	13.00
N24	A75	2d ultra	9.50	5.00
N25	A67	3d red brown	17.00	15.00
N26	A76	5d red	8.50	6.75
N27	A77	6d olive brown	8.50	6.75
N28	A78	7d dark brown	11.00	8.50
N29	A67	8d deep blue	30.00	30.00
N30	A79	10d red brown	675.00	350.00
N31	A80	15d green	26.50	25.00
N32	A81	25d dark blue	25.00	25.00
N33	A84	30d org brn	120.00	120.00
N34	A67	100d carmine lake	400.00	325.00
		Nos. N15-N34 (20)	2,882.	2,163.
		Set, never hinged	5,000.	

AIR POST STAMPS

Greece Nos. C37 and C26-C35, Overprinted Like Nos. N15-N34

Perf. 12½x12, 13x12½, 13½x12½				
1941, June 5			**Unwmk.**	
NC1	D3	50 l dk brown	21.00	10.00
NC2	AP16	1d red	1,000.	425.00
NC3	AP17	2d gray blue	25.00	20.00
NC4	AP18	5d violet	30.00	17.00
NC5	AP19	7d deep ultra	30.00	17.00
NC6	AP20	10d bister brn (On C26)	1,350.	775.00
NC7	AP20	10d brown org (On C35)	100.00	60.00
NC8	AP21	25d rose	150.00	65.00
NC9	AP22	30d dk grn	190.00	100.00
NC10	AP23	50d violet	150.00	75.00
a.		Double overprint		550.00
NC11	AP24	100d brown	1,700.	1,000.

On No. C36

Serrate Roulette 13½

NC12	D3	50 l vio brn	120.00	39.00
a.		On No. C36a		
		Nos. NC1-NC12 (12)	4,866.	2,603.
		Set, never hinged	7,500.	

POSTAGE DUE STAMPS

Postage Due Stamps of Greece, 1913-35 Overprinted Like #N15-N34

1941, June 5			**Unwmk.**	
Serrate Roulette 13½				
NJ1	D3	10 l carmine	8.50	8.50
NJ2	D3	25 l ultra	13.00	8.50
NJ3	D3	80 l lilac brown	1,500.	425.00

Perf. 12½x13, 13½x12½				
NJ4	D3	1d lt bl (On J80)	2,500.	1,150.
NJ5	D3	2d light red	17.00	17.00
NJ6	D3	5d gray	34.00	34.00
NJ7	D3	10d gray green	30.00	30.00
NJ8	D3	15d red brown	34.00	30.00
NJ9	D3	25d light red	34.00	30.00
NJ10	D3	50d orange	34.00	30.00
NJ11	D3	100d slate green	850.00	600.00
		Nos. NJ1-NJ11 (11)	5,054.	2,363.

POSTAL TAX STAMPS

Greece Nos. RA61-RA63, Overprinted Like Nos. N15-N34
Wmk., Unwmk.

1941, June 5			**Perf. 13½**	
NRA1	PT7	10 l brt rose, *pale rose*	3.50	6.50
NRA2	PT7	50 l gray grn, *pale green*	4.25	6.50
NRA3	PT7	1d dull blue, *lt blue*	39.00	34.00
		Nos. NRA1-NRA3 (3)	46.75	47.00
		Set, never hinged	105.00	

Stamps overprinted "CORFU" were replaced by Italian stamps overprinted "Isole Jonie." See Ionian Islands.

COSTA RICA

ˌkäs-tə-'rē-kə

LOCATION — Central America between Nicaragua and Panama
GOVT. — Republic
AREA — 19,730 sq. mi.
POP. — 3,674,490 (1999 est.)
CAPITAL — San Jose

8 Reales = 100 Centavos = 1 Peso
100 Centimos = 1 Colon (1900)

Catalogue values for unused stamps in this country are for Never Hinged items, beginning with Scott 238 in the regular postage section, Scott C117 in the air post section, Scott CE1 in the air post special delivery section, Scott E1 in the special delivery section, and Scott RA1 in the postal tax section.

Watermarks

Wmk. 215 — Small Star in Shield, Multiple

Wmk. 229 — Wavy Lines

Wmk. 334 — Rectangles

Values for unused stamps are for examples with original gum as defined in the catalogue introduction. Very fine examples of Nos. 1-22 will have perforations just clear of the design on one or more sides due to the placement of the stamps on the plates and to imperfect perforating methods.

Coat of Arms — A1

1863		**Unwmk.**	**Engr.**	**Perf. 12**
1	A1	½r blue	.40	1.10
a.		½r light blue	.40	1.10
b.		Pair, imperf. horiz.	3,500.	
2	A1	2r scarlet	1.75	2.25
3	A1	4r green	16.00	16.00
4	A1	1p orange	42.50	42.50
		Nos. 1-4 (4)	60.65	61.85

The ½r was printed from two plates. The second is in light blue with little or no sky over the mountains.
Imperforate stamps of Nos. 1-2 are corner stamps from poorly perforated sheets.

Nos. 1-3 Surcharged in Red or Black:

a

b

c

d

e

1881-82				
	Red or Black Surcharge			
7	A1(a)	1c on ½r ('82)	3.00	6.00
a.		On No. 1a	15.00	
8	A1(b)	1c on ½r ('82)	18.00	30.00
9	A1(c)	2c on ½r, #1a	3.00	2.75
a.		On No. 1	8.00	
12	A1	5c on ½r	15.00	
13	A1(d)	5c on ½r ('82)	65.00	
14	A1(d)	10c on 2r (Bk) ('82)	72.50	—
15	A1(e)	20c on 4r ('82)	300.00	—

Overprints with different fonts and "OFICIAL" were never placed in use, and are said to have been surcharged to a dealer's order. The ½r surcharged "DOS CTS" is not a postage stamp. It probably is an essay.
Postally used examples of Nos. 7-15 are rare. Nos. 13-15 exist with a favor cancel having a hyphen between "San" and "Jose." Values same as unused. Fake cancellations exist.
Counterfeits exist of surcharges on Nos. 7-15.

Gen. Prospero Fernández A6

President Bernardo Soto Alfaro A7

1883, Jan. 1
16	A6	1c green	3.00	1.50
17	A6	2c carmine	3.25	1.50
18	A6	5c blue violet	32.50	2.00
19	A6	10c orange	150.00	12.00
20	A6	40c blue	3.00	3.00
		Nos. 16-20 (5)	191.75	20.00

Unused examples of 40c usually lack gum.
For overprints see Nos. O1-O20, O24, Guanacaste 1-38, 44.

1887
21	A7	5c blue violet	7.00	.50
22	A7	10c orange	4.00	3.00

Unused examples of 5c usually lack gum.
For overprints see Nos. O22-O23, Guanacaste 42-43, 45.

A8

A9

1889

Black Overprint
23	A8	1c rose	5.00	3.00
24	A9	5c brown	7.00	3.00

Vertical and inverted overprints are fakes.
For overprints see Guanacaste 47-54.

President Soto Alfaro
A10   A11

A12   A13

A14   A15

A16   A17

A18   A19

1889   *Perf. 14-16 & Compound*
25	A10	1c brown	.35	.45
a.		Horiz. pair, imperf. vert	150.00	
b.		Imperf. pair	100.00	
c.		Horiz. or vert. pair, imperf. btwn.	150.00	
26	A11	2c dark green	.35	.45
a.		Imperf., pair	50.00	
b.		Vert. pair, imperf. horiz.	125.00	
c.		Horiz. pair, imperf. btwn.	125.00	
27	A12	5c orange	.45	.35
a.		Imperf., pair		250.00
b.		Horiz. pair, imperf. btwn.	150.00	

28	A13	10c red brown	.40	.35
a.		Vert. or horiz. pair, imperf. btwn.	150.00	
29	A14	20c yellow green	.30	.35
a.		Vert. pair, imperf. horiz.	200.00	
b.		Horizontal pair, imperf. btwn.	150.00	
30	A15	50c rose red	1.00	
		Telegram cancel		.75
31	A16	1p blue	1.25	
		Telegram cancel		.75
32	A17	2p dull violet	6.00	
a.		2p slate	6.00	
		Telegram cancel		4.00
33	A18	5p olive green	25.00	
		Telegram cancel		10.00
34	A19	10p black	100.00	
		Telegram cancel		45.00
		Nos. 25-34 (10)	135.10	1.95

Nos. 30-34 normally were used on telegrams and most examples were removed from the forms and sold by the government.
Most unused examples of No. 34 have no gum or only part gum. These sell for somewhat less.
For overprints see Nos. O25-O30, Guanacaste 55-67.

Arms of Costa Rica
A20   A21

A22   A23

A24   A25

A26   A27

A28   A29

1892   *Perf. 12-15 & Compound*
35	A20	1c grnsh blue	.30	.40
36	A21	2c yellow	.30	.40
37	A22	5c red lilac	.30	.25
a.		5c violet	60.00	.30
38	A23	10c lt green	.80	.35
a.		Horiz. pair, imperf. btwn.	—	100.00
39	A24	20c scarlet	12.00	.20
a.		Horiz. pair, imperf. btwn.	—	100.00
40	A25	50c gray blue	4.00	4.25
41	A26	1p green, *yel*	1.25	1.00
42	A27	2p brown red, *lilac*	3.00	1.00
a.		2p rose red, *pale lil*	12.00	1.00
43	A28	5p dk blue, *blue*	2.00	1.00
44	A29	10p brown, *pale buff*	35.00	5.00
a.		10p brown, *yellow*	—	
		Nos. 35-44 (10)	58.95	13.85

Imperfs. of Nos. 35-44 are proofs.
For overprints see Nos. O31-O36.

Statue of Juan Santamaría
A30

Juan Mora Fernández
A31

Braulio Carrillo ("Branlio" on stamp) — A33

View of Port Limón — A32

National Theater — A34

José M. Castro — A35

Birris Bridge — A36

Juan Rafael Mora — A37

Jesús Jiménez — A38

Coat of Arms — A39

1901, Jan.   *Perf. 12-15½*
45	A30	1c green & blk	3.25	.30
a.		Horiz. pair, imperf. btwn.	150.00	
46	A31	2c ver & blk	1.25	.30
47	A32	5c gray blue & blk	3.25	.30
a.		Vert. pair, imperf. btwn.	—	150.00
48	A33	10c ocher & blk	3.25	.35
49	A34	20c lake & blk	22.50	.25
a.		Vert. pair, imperf. btwn.	150.00	
50	A35	50c dull lil & dk bl	5.50	1.00
51	A36	1col ol bis & blk	110.00	3.50
52	A37	2col car rose & dk grn	16.00	3.00
53	A38	5col brown & blk	75.00	3.50
54	A39	10col yel grn & brn red	29.00	3.00
		Nos. 45-54 (10)	269.00	15.50

The 2c exists with center inverted. Value $77,500.
Nos. 45-57 in other colors are private reprints made in 1948. They have little value.
For surcharge and overprints see Nos. 58, 78, O37-O44.

Remainders

In 1914 the government sold a large quantity of stamps at very much less than face value. The lot included most regular issues from 1901 to 1911 inclusive, postage due stamps of 1903 and Official stamps of 1901-03. These stamps were canceled with groups of thin parallel bars. The higher valued used stamps, such as Nos. 64, 65-68a, sell for much less than the values quoted, which are for stamps with regular postal cancellations. A few sell for much higher prices.

José M. Cañas — A40

Julián Volio — A41

Eusebio Figueroa Oreamuno — A42

1903   *Perf. 13½, 14, 15*
55	A40	4c red vio & blk	2.00	.70
56	A41	6c olive grn & blk	7.25	4.00
57	A42	25c gray lil & brn	16.00	.30
		Nos. 55-57 (3)	25.25	5.00

See note on private reprints following #54.
For overprints see Nos. 81, O45-O47.

No. 49 Surcharged in Black:

1905
58	A34	1c on 20c lake & blk	.60	.60
a.		Inverted surcharge	10.00	10.00
b.		Diagonal surcharge	.60	.60

Examples surcharged in other colors are proofs.

Statue of Juan Santamaria
A43

Juan Mora Fernández
A44

José M. Cañas
A45

Mauro Fernández
A46

Braulio Carrillo — A47

Julián Volio — A48

Eusebio Figueroa Oreamuno
A49

José M. Castro
A50

Jesús
Jiménez — A51

Juan Rafael
Mora — A52

Eusebio
Figueroa
Oreamuno
A59

Jesús Jiménez
A60

A61

A62

A63

Liberty with Torch
of
Freedom — A65

Perf. 11x14, 14 (1c, 5c, 10c, 25c)

1907				**Unwmk.**	
59	A43	1c red brn & ind	8.00	.40
a.		Perf. 11x14	60.00	3.00
b.		Imperf pair	15.00	
60	A44	2c yel grn & blk	3.00	.30
a.		Perf. 14	3.00	.30
b.		Imperf pair	15.00	
61	A45	4c car & indigo	12.00	2.50
a.		Perf. 14	500.00	45.00
b.		Imperf pair	15.00	
62	A46	5c yel & dull bl	3.00	.30
a.		Perf. 11x14	60.00	1.00
b.		Imperf pair	15.00	
63	A47	10c blue & blk	10.00	.50
a.		Perf. 11x14	20.00	1.00
b.		Imperf pair	30.00	
64	A48	20c olive grn & blk	25.00	6.00
a.		Perf. 14	25.00	6.00
		Remainder cancel	—	2.00
b.		Imperf pair	—	
65	A49	25c gray lil & blk	3.00	3.00
		Remainder cancel	—	1.00
a.		Perf. 11x14	150.00	50.00
b.		Imperf pair	—	
66	A50	50c red lil & blue	75.00	25.00
		Remainder cancel	—	2.00
a.		Perf. 14	175.00	50.00
b.		Imperf pair	100.00	
67	A51	1col brown & blk	25.00	20.00
a.		Perf. 14	25.00	20.00
		Remainder cancel	—	2.00
b.		Imperf pair	—	
68	A52	2col claret & grn	160.00	100.00
		Remainder cancel	—	3.00
a.		Perf. 14	300.00	150.00
b.		Imperf pair	200.00	
		Nos. 59-68 (10)	324.00	158.00

The remainder cancel value applies to both perforations.

The imperforate varieties of the above set are valued without gum. Ungummed stamps were probably placed on the market in London, while gummed stamps appear to have been sent to Costa Rica and accepted for postal use. There is a small premium for gummed stamps.

The 1c, 2c, 5c, 20c, 50c, 1 col and 2 col exist with center inverted. Value, set $62,500.

Nos. 59-68 exist with papermaker's watermark.

No. 65b with brown vignette is a proof. Value, pair $40. The actual No. 65b (black vignette) is worth much more.

For overprints see Nos. 77, 79-80, 82-84, O48-O55, O60-O64.

Statue of Juan
Santamaria
A53

Juan Mora
Fernández
A54

José M.
Cañas
A55

Mauro
Fernández
A56

Braulio
Carrillo — A57

Julián
Volio — A58

1910 — Perf. 12

69	A53	1c brown	.25	.20
70	A54	2c dp green	.30	.20
71	A55	4c scarlet	.35	.35
72	A56	5c orange	1.00	.20
73	A57	10c deep blue	.40	.20
74	A58	20c olive grn	.50	.35
75	A59	25c dp violet	17.00	1.50
76	A60	1col dk brown	.50	.50
		Nos. 69-76 (8)	20.30	3.50

For overprints and surcharge see Nos. 111C-111J, B1, C2, O56-O59.

No. 60a Overprinted
in Red

1911 — Perf. 14

77	A44	2c yel grn & blk	3.00	1.10
a.		Inverted overprint	6.00	5.00
b.		Double overprint, both inverted	45.00	

Stamps of 1901-07
Overprinted in Red or
Black

78	A30	1c grn & blk (R)	3.00	1.00
a.		Black overprint	32.50	18.00
b.		Inverted overprint		
79	A43	1c red brn & ind (Bk)	1.25	.40
a.		Inverted overprint	4.50	3.50
b.		Double overprint	5.50	5.00
80	A44	2c yel grn & blk (Bk)	1.00	.40
a.		Inverted overprint	3.75	3.50
b.		Dbl. ovpt., one as on No. 77	40.00	27.50
c.		Double overprint, one inverted	15.00	15.00
d.		Pair, one stamp No. 77	25.00	18.00
e.		Perf. 11x14	30.00	1.00

No. 55 Overprinted in
Black

81	A40	4c red vio & blk	1.50	.65

Stamps of 1907
Overprinted in Blue,
Black or Rose

Perf. 14, 11x14 (#83, 84)

82	A46	5c yel & bl (Bl)	2.00	.25
a.		"Habilitada"	3.25	2.50
b.		"2911"	5.50	3.25
c.		Roman "I" in "1911"	4.00	2.50
d.		Double overprint	5.50	5.00
e.		Inverted overprint	6.00	3.75
f.		Black overprint	—	2.00
g.		Triple overprint	6.00	
h.		Vert. pair, imperf. horiz.	100.00	
83	A47	10c blue & blk (Bk)	5.00	1.40
a.		As #83, Roman "I" in "1911"	7.00	5.00
c.		As #83, double overprint	20.00	11.50
d.		Perf. 14	45.00	5.25
84	A47	10c blue & blk (R)	15.00	13.50
a.		Roman "I" in "1911"	100.00	100.00
c.		Perf. 14	100.00	100.00
		Nos. 77-84 (8)	31.75	18.70

Many counterfeits of overprint exist.

Telegraph Stamps Surcharged in Rose, Blue or Black

1911			**Perf. 12**	
86	A61	1c on 10c bl (R)	.50	.25
a.		"Coereos"	7.75	6.00
b.		Inverted surcharge		
87	A61	1c on 10c bl (Bk)	210.00	87.50
a.		"Coereos"	8.75	6.00
88	A61	1c on 25c vio (Bk)	.50	.25
b.		Pair, one without surcharge	20.00	
c.		Double surcharge	9.00	
e.		Double surch., one inverted	12.50	
89	A61	1c on 50c red brn (Bl)	.55	.40
a.		Inverted surcharge	5.50	5.00
b.		Double surcharge	4.50	
90	A61	1c on 1col brn (R)	.55	.40
91	A61	1c on 5col red (Bl)	1.00	.55
92	A61	1c on 10col dk brn (R)	1.50	.70

		Perf. 14		
93	A62	2c on 5c brn org (Bk)	3.50	1.90
a.		Inverted surcharge	9.00	3.75
b.		"Coereos" inverted	17.50	
c.		Double surcharge	9.00	

		Perf. 14x11		
94	A62	2c on 10c bl (R)	100.00	100.00
a.		Perf. 14	350.00	350.00
b.		"Coereos" inverted	2,000.	
c.		As "b," perf. 14	2,000.	—
95	A62	2c on 50c cl (Bk)	1.00	.55
a.		Inverted surcharge	4.50	3.25
b.		Double surcharge	12.50	
c.		Perf. 14	45.00	20.00
96	A62	2c on 1col brn (Bk)	1.25	.70
a.		Inverted surcharge	12.50	
b.		Double surcharge	16.00	
c.		Perf. 14	2.00	.80
97	A62	2c on 2col car (Bk)	1.25	.60
a.		Inverted surcharge	8.00	5.00
b.		"Coereos" inverted	10.00	5.50
c.		Double surcharge		
d.		Perf. 14	27.50	16.00
98	A62	2c on 5col grn (Bk)	1.00	.70
a.		Inverted surcharge	10.00	7.00
b.		"Coereos" inverted	16.00	4.25
c.		Perf. 14	6.00	3.00
99	A62	2c on 10col mar (Bk)	1.50	.70
a.		"Coereos" inverted	400.00	
b.		Perf. 14	6.00	3.00

		Perf. 12		
100	A63	5c on 5c org (Bl)	.40	.25
a.		Double surcharge	27.50	16.00
b.		Inverted surcharge	27.50	9.50
c.		Pair, one without surcharge	16.00	

Counterfeits exist of Nos. 87, 94 and all minor varieties. Genuine used examples of No. 94 are rare and have a cancel only used on registered mail. Genuine "Coereos" errors do not exist on No. 87. Used examples of No. 94 with target cancels are counterfeits. No. 94c is unique. All examples of Nos. 94b and 94c have stains and are valued thus.

Nos. 93-99 exist with papermaker's watermark.

Coffee Plantation — A64

1921, June 17 — Litho. — Perf. 11½

103	A64	5c bl & blk	3.00	3.00
a.		Tête bêche pair	15.00	6.50
b.		Imperf., pair	40.00	
c.		As "a," imperf.	150.00	

Centenary of coffee raising in Costa Rica.

1921 — Typo. — Perf. 11

104	A65	5c violet	1.00	.40
a.		Imperf, pair	100.00	

Cent. of Central American independence. Beware of trimmed singles that look like No. 104a.

For overprint see No. 111.

Juan Mora and Julio Acosta — A66

1921, Sept. 15 — Perf. 11½

105	A66	2c orange & blk	1.75	1.75
106	A66	3c green & blk	1.75	1.75
107	A66	6c scarlet & blk	3.00	3.00
108	A66	15c dk blue & blk	5.00	5.00
109	A66	30c orange brn & blk	6.50	6.50
		Nos. 105-109 (5)	18.00	18.00

Centenary of Central American independence. Issue requested by Costa Rican Philatelic Society. Authorized by decree calling for 2,000 of 30c and 5,000 each of other values. Nos. 105-109 imperf were not regularly issued. Inverted centers exist of both perf and imperf. They are rare. Used values are for Independence commemorative cancel.

Each sheet of 20 (4x5) contains 5 tête-bêche pairs. Value, set of 5 pairs $40.

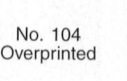

Simón Bolívar — A67

1921 — Engr. — Perf. 12

110	A67	15c deep violet	.75	.25

For overprint No. 110a see set following No. 111. For surcharge see No. 148

No. 104
Overprinted

1922 — Perf. 11

111	A65	5c violet	.75	.40
a.		Inverted overprint	10.00	
b.		Double overprint	15.00	

Stamps of 1910-1921
Overprinted in Blue,
Red, Black or Gold

1922 — Perf. 12

111C	A53	1c brown (Bl)	.30	.20
111D	A54	2c deep green (R)	.40	.20
111E	A55	4c scarlet	.30	.20
111F	A56	5c orange	2.00	.20

111G	A57	10c deep blue (R)	.75	.40
111H	A67	15c deep violet (G)	4.00	2.00
		Nos. 111C-111H (6)	7.75	3.40

Inverted overprints occur on all values. Value, set $20. Counterfeits predominate.

No. 72 Overprinted

1923
| 111J | A56 5c orange | 3.00 | .75 |
| k. | "VD." for "UD." | 75.00 | 75.00 |

Jesús Jiménez — A68

1923, June 18   Litho.   Perf. 11½
112	A68	2c brown	.40	.40
113	A68	4c green	.40	.40
114	A68	5c blue	.60	.40
115	A68	20c carmine	.85	.50
116	A68	1col violet	1.10	1.25
		Nos. 112-116 (5)	3.35	2.95

Pres. Jesús Jiménez (1823-98). Nos. 112-116, imperf, were not regularly issued. Value, set $5.
For overprints see Nos. O65-O69.

National Monument A70

Harvesting Coffee — A71   Banana Growing — A73

General Post Office A74

Columbus Soliciting Aid of Isabella A75

Christopher Columbus A76

Columbus at Cariari A77

Map of Costa Rica — A78

Manuel M. Gutiérrez — A79

1923-26   Engr.   Perf. 12
117	A70	1c violet	.25	.20
118	A71	2c yellow	.50	.20
119	A73	4c deep green	.75	.30
120	A74	5c light blue	1.50	.20
121	A74	5c yellow grn ('26)	.50	.20
122	A75	10c red brown	3.00	.20
123	A75	10c car rose ('26)	.50	.20
124	A76	12c carmine rose	10.00	3.00
125	A77	20c deep blue	10.00	.65
126	A78	40c orange	11.00	3.00
127	A79	1col olive green	2.40	.80
		Nos. 117-127 (11)	40.40	8.95

See #151-156. For surcharges & overprints see #136-140, 147, 189, 218, C2.

Rodrigo Arias Maldonado — A80

1924   Perf. 12½
| 128 | A80 2c dark green | .25 | .20 |
| a. | Perf. 14 | .50 | .25 |

See No. 162.

Map of Guanacaste A81

Mission at Nicoya A82

1924   Litho.   Perf. 12
129	A81	1c carmine rose	.30	.20
130	A81	2c violet	.40	.20
131	A81	5c green	.40	.20
132	A81	10c orange	2.25	.50
133	A82	15c light blue	1.00	.50
134	A82	20c gray black	2.00	1.00
135	A82	25c light brown	3.00	1.50
		Nos. 129-135 (7)	9.35	4.10

Centenary of annexation of Province of Guanacaste to Costa Rica. Exist imperf. Value, set, $50.

Stamps of 1923 Surcharged:

a

b

1925
136	A74(a)	3c on 5c lt blue	.30	.20
137	A75(a)	6c on 10c red brn	.40	.25
138	A78(a)	30c on 40c orange	1.50	.40

139	A79(b)	45c on 1col ol grn	1.75	.50
a.		Double surcharge	250.00	
		Nos. 136-139 (4)	3.95	1.35

No. 124 Surcharged

1926
| 140 | A76 10c on 12c car rose | 1.50 | .30 |

College of San Luis, Cartago A83

Chapui Asylum, San José — A84

Normal School, Heredia A85

Ruins of Ujarrás A86

1926   Unwmk.   Engr.   Perf. 12½
143	A83	3c ultra	.55	.20
144	A84	6c dark brown	.55	.25
145	A85	30c deep orange	2.00	.40
146	A86	45c black violet	4.00	1.60
		Nos. 143-146 (4)	7.10	2.45

For surcharges see Nos. 190-190D, 217.

No. 124 Surcharged in Black:

1928, Jan. 7   Perf. 12
| 147 | A76 10c on 12c car rose | 4.75 | 4.75 |

Issued in honor of Col. Charles A. Lindbergh during his Good Will Tour of Central America. The surcharge was privately reprinted using an original die. Reprints can be distinguished by distinct dots under the "10s." All errors and inverted surcharges are reprints.

No. 110 Surcharged

1928
| 148 | A67 5(c) on 15c dp violet | .25 | .25 |
| a. | Inverted surcharge | 35.00 | |

Type I — A88

Type II

Type III

Type IV

Type V

Surcharge Typo. (I-V) & Litho. (V)
1929   Perf. 12½
149	A88 5c on 2col car (I)	.50	.20
a.-d.	Types II-V	.60	.20
e.	Type V (litho.)	3.00	3.00

Telegraph Stamp Surcharged for Postage as in 1929, Surcharge Lithographed

1929
| 150 | A88 13c on 40c deep grn | .35 | .25 |
| a. | Inverted surcharge | 1.00 | 1.00 |

Excellent counterfeits exist of No. 150a.

Types of 1923-26 Issues Dated "1929" Imprint of Waterlow & Sons

1930   Size: 26x21½mm   Perf. 12½
151	A70	1c dark violet	.70	.20
155	A74	5c green	.70	.20
156	A75	10c carmine rose	.70	.20
		Nos. 151-156 (3)	2.10	.60

Juan Rafael Mora — A89

1931, Jan. 29
| 157 | A89 13c carmine rose | .60 | .20 |

For surcharge see No. 209.

Seal of Costa Rica Philatelic Society ("Octubre 12 de 1932") — A90

1932, Oct. 12   Perf. 12
158	A90	3c orange	.25	.20
159	A90	5c dark green	.40	.25
160	A90	10c carmine rose	.50	.25
161	A90	20c dark blue	.85	.40
		Nos. 158-161 (4)	2.00	1.10

Phil. Exhib., Oct. 12, 1932. See #179-183.

Maldonado Type of 1924

1934, Aug. 11   Perf. 12½
| 162 | A80 3c dark green | .20 | .20 |

Red Cross Nurse — A91

1935, May 31   *Perf. 12*
163 A91 10c rose carmine   7.50 .25

50th anniv. of the founding of the Costa Rican Red Cross Society.

Air View of Cartago A92

Miraculous Statuette and View of Cathedral A93

Vision of 1635 — A94

1935, Aug. 1   *Perf. 12½*
164 A92 5c green   .20 .20
165 A93 10c carmine   .20 .20
166 A92 30c orange   .20 .20
167 A94 45c dark violet   1.00 1.00
168 A93 50c blue black   1.00 1.00
    Nos. 164-168 (5)   2.60 2.15

Tercentenary of the Patron Saint, Our Lady of the Angels, of Costa Rica.

Map of Cocos Island A95

1936, Jan. 29   *Perf. 14, 11½ (25c)*
169 A95 4c ocher   .50 .20
170 A95 8c dark violet   .65 .25
171 A95 25c orange   .80 .25
172 A95 35c brown vio   .95 .25
173 A95 40c brown   1.25 .40
174 A95 50c yellow   1.50 .60
175 A95 2col yellow grn   11.00 10.00
176 A95 5col green   30.00 25.00
    Nos. 169-176 (8)   46.65 36.95

Exist imperf. Value, set, $50.
For surcharges see #196-200, C55-C56.

Map of Cocos Island and Ships of Columbus A96

1936, Dec. 5   *Perf. 12*
177 A96 5c green   .40 .25
178 A96 10c carmine rose   .55 .25

For overprints see Nos. 247, O80-O81.

Seal of Costa Rica Philatelic Society ("Diciembre 1937") — A97

1937, Dec. 15
179 A97 2c dark brown   .45 .20
180 A97 3c black   .45 .20
181 A97 5c green   .45 .20
182 A97 10c orange red   .45 .20
    Nos. 179-182 (4)   1.80 .80

Souvenir Sheet
Imperf
183   Sheet of 4   6.50 4.00
a.   A97 2c dark brown   .20 .20
b.   A97 3c black   .20 .20
c.   A97 5c green   .20 .20
d.   A97 10c orange red   .20 .20

Phil. Exhib., Dec. 1937.

Purple Guaria Orchid, National Flower — A98

Tuna — A99

Native with Donkey Carrying Bananas A101

3c, Cacao pod. 10c, Coffee harvesting.

1937-38   **Wmk. 229**   *Perf. 12½*
184 A98 1c green & vio ('38)   .55 .20
185 A98 3c chocolate ('38)   .55 .20

Unwmk.   *Perf. 12*
186 A99 2c olive gray   .40 .20
187 A101 5c dark green   .55 .20
188 A101 10c carmine rose   .90 .25
    Nos. 184-188 (5)   2.95 1.05

National Exposition.

No. 125 Overprinted in Black

1938, Sept. 23   **Unwmk.**   *Perf. 12*
189 A77 20c deep blue   1.50 .30

No. 146 Surcharged in Red:

a

b

---

c

d

e

1940   *Perf. 12½*
190 A86(a) 15c on 45c blk vio   .60 .30
190A A86(b) 15c on 45c blk vio   .60 .30
190B A86(c) 15c on 45c blk vio   .60 .30
190C A86(d) 15c on 45c blk vio   .60 .30
190D A86(e) 15c on 45c blk vio   .60 .30
    Nos. 190-190D (5)   3.00 1.50

#190D exists with inverted surcharge. Value, $5.

Allegory A103

Overprinted "Dia Panamericano de la Salud / 2 Diciembre 1940" and Arc

1940, Dec. 2   **Engr.**   *Perf. 12½*
191 A103 5c green   .25 .25
192 A103 10c rose carmine   .40 .25
193 A103 20c deep blue   .90 .55
194 A103 40c brown   1.60 1.60
195 A103 55c orange yellow   3.25 2.50
    Nos. 191-195 (5)   6.40 5.15

Pan-American Health Day. See #C46-C54. Exist without overprint.

Stamps of 1936 Surcharged in Black:

1941   *Perf. 14, 11½*
196 A95 15c on 25c orange   .50 .50
197 A95 15c on 35c brn vio   .50 .50
198 A95 15c on 40c brown   .50 .50
199 A95 15c on 2col yel grn   .50 .50
200 A95 15c on 5col green   1.00 1.00
    Nos. 196-200 (5)   3.00 3.00

Nos. 196-200 exist with surcharge inverted. Value, set of 5, $20.

National Stadium A104

Engr.; Flags Typo. in Natl. Colors
1941, May 8   *Perf. 12½*
201 A104 5c green   .70 .25
a.   Flags omitted   200.00
202 A104 10c orange   .55 .30
203 A104 15c car rose   .80 .40
204 A104 25c dk blue   .85 .55
205 A104 40c chestnut   3.25 1.40
206 A104 50c purple   4.25 2.00
207 A104 75c red orange   6.75 5.75
208 A104 1col dk carmine   13.00 10.50
    Nos. 201-208 (8)   30.15 21.15

Caribbean and Central American Soccer Championship. See #C57-C66, C121-C123.

No. 157 Surcharged in Black

1941, July 26   *Perf. 12*
209 A89 5c on 13c car rose   .20 .20

Cleto González Víquez — A105

Design: 5c, José Rodriguez.

1941-45   **Engr.**   *Perf. 12½*
210 A105 3c dp orange   .25 .20
210A A105 3c dp plum ('43)   .25 .20
210B A105 3c carmine ('45)   .25 .20
211 A105 5c dp violet   .25 .20
211A A105 5c brown blk ('43)   .25 .20
    Nos. 210-211A (5)   1.25 1.00

See No. 256.

Old University of Costa Rica A106

New National University A107

1941, Aug. 26   *Perf. 12*
212 A106 5c green   .40 .25
213 A107 10c yellow org   .40 .25
214 A106 15c lilac rose   .75 .25
215 A107 25c dull blue   1.00 .35
216 A106 50c fawn   7.50 2.25
    Nos. 212-216 (5)   10.05 3.35

National University, founded in 1940. See Nos. C74-C80.

Nos. 144, 189 Surcharged in Black or Red

1942, April   *Perf. 12½, 12*
217 A84 5c on 6c dk brn   .35 .20
218 A77 15c on 20c dp bl (R)   .65 .25

Nos. 217-218 exist with inverted surcharge. Value, each $10.

Torch of Freedom, "Victory" and Flags of American Nations A108

Juan Mora Fernández A109

1942, Sept. 25   *Perf. 12*
219 A108 5c rose   .30 .20
220 A108 5c yellow grn   .30 .20
221 A108 5c purple   .30 .20
222 A108 5c dp blue   .30 .20
223 A108 5c red orange   .30 .20
    Nos. 219-223 (5)   1.50 1.00

For overprints see Nos. 238-241.

1943-47   Engr.

Designs: 2c, Bruno Carranza. 3c, Tomas Guardia. 5c, Manuel Aguilar. 15c, Francisco Morazan. 25c, Jose M. Alfaro. 50c, Francisco M. Oreamuno. 1col, Jose M. Castro. 2col, Juan Rafael Mora.

224	A109	1c red lilac	.20	.20
225	A109	2c black	.20	.20
226	A109	3c deep blue	.20	.20
227	A109	5c brt blue grn	.20	.20
a.		5c bright green ('47)	.20	.20
228	A109	15c scarlet	.20	.20
229	A109	25c brt ultra	1.00	.20
230	A109	50c dp violet	3.00	.45
231	A109	1col black brown	4.00	2.00
232	A109	2col deep orange	5.00	3.00
		Nos. 224-232 (9)	14.00	6.65

See Nos. 344-368, C81-C91A, C124-C127, C154-C158, C179-C181, C768-C772, C790-C794, C854-C858. For surcharges see Nos. C154-C158, C182, C184-C185.

View of San Ramón A118

1944, Jan. 19

233	A118	5c dark green	.20	.20
234	A118	10c orange	.20	.20
235	A118	15c rose pink	.30	.20
236	A118	40c gray black	1.25	.80
237	A118	50c deep blue	2.40	1.60
		Nos. 233-237 (5)	4.35	3.00

100th anniv. of the founding of the City of San Ramón. See Nos. C94-C102.

Catalogue values for unused stamps in this section, from this point to the end of the section, are for Never Hinged items.

Nos. 220-223 Overprinted in Red or Black

1944, Sept. 18

238	A108	5c yel green	.30	.20
239	A108	5c purple (R)	.30	.20
240	A108	5c dp blue (R)	.30	.20
241	A108	5c red orange	.30	.20
		Nos. 238-241 (4)	1.20	.80

Amicable settlement of a boundary dispute with Panama. This overprint also exists on No. 219.

Mauro Fernández (1844-1905), Statesman — A119

Unwmk.
1945, July 21   Engr.   *Perf. 14*

242	A119	20c deep green	.30	.20

For surcharge see No. 246.

Coffee Harvesting — A120

1945, Oct. 9   *Perf. 12*

243	A120	5c dk green & blk	.30	.20
244	A120	10c orange & blk	.30	.20
245	A120	20c car rose & blk	.50	.20
		Nos. 243-245 (3)	1.10	.60

No. 242 Surcharged in Red Brown
1946   Unwmk.   *Perf. 14*

246	A119	15c on 20c dp green	.30	.20

Exists with inverted surcharge. Value, $6.

No. O80 Overprinted in Red

1947, Mar. 19   *Perf. 12*

247	A96	5c green	.30	.20

Exist with inverted overprint. Value, $6.

Cervantes — A121   A122

Wmk. 215
1947, Nov. 10   Engr.   *Perf. 14*

249	A121	30c deep blue	.45	.20
250	A121	55c deep carmine	.80	.20

Miguel de Cervantes Saavedra, novelist, playwright & poet, 400th birth anniv.

1947, Aug. 26   Unwmk.   *Perf. 12*

251	A122	5c brt green	.20	.20
252	A122	10c car rose	.20	.20
253	A122	15c ultra	.25	.20
254	A122	25c orange red	.35	.25
255	A122	50c lilac	.55	.30
		Nos. 251-255,C160-C167 (13)	7.10	5.90

Franklin D. Roosevelt. For surcharges see Nos. C224-C226.

Small Portrait Type of 1941

Design: 3c, Bishop Bernardo A. Thiel.

1948   *Perf. 12½*

256	A105	3c deep ultra	.25	.20

Old University of Costa Rica A123

1953, June 25   Litho.   *Perf. 12*
Black Surcharge

257	A123	5c on 10c green	.35	.25

Revenue Stamp Surcharged in Red or Blue — A124

1955-56   Unwmk.   Engr.   *Perf. 12*

258	A124	5c on 2c emerald	.25	.20
259	A124	15c on 2c emer (Bl)	.25	.20
260	A124	55c on 2c emer ('56)	.25	.20
		Nos. 258-260,C341-C344 (7)	2.25	1.85

For surcharges see #C341-C344, C431-C433.

Justo A. Facio A125   Anglo-Costa Rican Bank A126

1960, Apr. 20   Photo.   *Perf. 13½*

261	A125	10c brown red	.40	.25

Centenary of the birth (in 1859) of Prof. Justo A. Facio. Exists imperf. Value, $35.

Nos. RA12-RA15 Surcharged in Red

1963, Mar.

262	PT3	10c on 5c dk car	.40	.25
263	PT3	10c on 5c sepia	.40	.25
264	PT3	10c on 5c dull grn	.40	.25
265	PT3	10c on 5c blue	.40	.25
		Nos. 262-265 (4)	1.60	1.00

1963   Unwmk.   *Perf. 13½*

266	A126	10c gray	.35	.25

Centenary of the Anglo-Costa Rican Bank.

Arms of San José — A127

Alberto M. Brenes Mora — A128

Coats of Arms: 35c, Cartago. 50c, Heredia. 55c, Alajuela. 65c, Guanacaste. 1col, Puntarenas. 2col, Limon.

1969, Sept. 14   Litho.   *Perf. 14x13½*

267	A127	15c multicolored	.30	.20
268	A127	35c multicolored	.30	.20
269	A127	50c gray & multi	.30	.20
270	A127	55c buff & multi	.30	.20
271	A127	65c multicolored	.75	.25
272	A127	1col pink & multi	2.75	.40
273	A127	2col multicolored	3.75	.60
		Nos. 267-273 (7)	8.45	2.05

1976, Mar. 1   Litho.   *Perf. 10½*

274	A128	1col violet blue	.65	.25
		Nos. 274,C653-C657 (6)	9.15	4.40

Prof. Alberto Manuel Brenes Mora, botanist, birth centenary.

Map of Costa Rica, Reader with Book — A129

1978, July 17   Litho.   *Perf. 13½*

275	A129	50c multicolored	.40	.25

National five-year literacy plan.

A130   A131

1983, May 17   Litho.   *Perf. 13x13½*

276	A130	10c multicolored	.40	.25
277	A130	50c multicolored	.35	.20
278	A130	10col multicolored	1.40	.30
		Nos. 276-278 (3)	2.15	.75

World Communications Year.

1983, May 30   Litho.   *Perf. 10½*

279	A131	20col black	2.40	.55

1st World Cong. of Human Rights, 1982.

UPU Membership Centenary — A132

1983, June 30   Litho.   *Perf. 16*

280	A132	3col #17, monument	1.25	.20
281	A132	10col #20, San Jose post office	2.40	.50

French Alliance Centenary — A133

1983, July 21   Litho.   *Perf. 11*

282	A133	12col Scene in San Jose, by Christina Fournier	2.00	.55

Christmas 1983 — A134

Nativity tableau in continuous design.

1983, Dec. 5   Litho.   *Perf. 13½*

283		1.50col multi	.25	.20
284		1.50col multi	.25	.20
285		1.50col multi	.25	.20
a.		A134 Strip of 3, #283-285	1.60	1.60

Costa Rican Gardens Association.

Fishery Development Administration A135

1983, Dec. 19   Litho.   *Perf. 13½*

286	A135	8.50col multi	.80	.30

Local Birds — A136

1984, Jan. 9　　Litho.　　Perf. 13½

287	A136	10c Quetzal	.55	.25
288	A136	50c Cyanerpes cyaneus	.65	.25
289	A136	1col Turdus grayi	.65	.25
290	A136	1.50col Momotus momota	.65	.25
291	A136	3col Colibri thalassinus	1.50	.25
292	A136	10col Notiochelindon cyanoleuca	4.75	.30
		Nos. 287-292 (6)	8.75	1.55

Dated 1983. 10c, 1.50col, 3col vert.

José Joaquin Mora, Hero of 1856 Independence Campaign — A137

Paintings, Juan Santamaria Museum, San José: 1.50col, Pancha Carrasco. 3 col, Death of Juan Santamaria, horiz. 8.50col, Juan Rafael Mora Porras.

1984, Apr. 10　　Litho.　　Perf. 10½

293	A137	50c multi	.20	.20
294	A137	1.50col multi	.20	.20
295	A137	3col multi	.25	.20
296	A137	8.50col multi	.80	.55
		Nos. 293-296 (4)	1.45	1.15

For surcharge see No. 440.

Jesus Bonilla Chavarria, Composer A138

Musicians and Composers: 5col, Benjamin Gutierrez (b. 1937). 12col, Pilar Jimenez (1835-1922). 13col, Jose Daniel Zuniga Zeledon (1889-1981).

1984, May 30　　Litho.　　Perf. 13½

297	A138	3.50col black & lil	.30	.20
298	A138	5col black & pink	.40	.25
299	A138	12col black & grn	1.00	.80
300	A138	13col black & yel	1.25	.90
		Nos. 297-300 (4)	2.95	2.15

Figurines, Jade Museum — A139

1984 Summer Olympics A140

1984, June 27　　Litho.　　Perf. 13½

301	A139	4col Man (pendant)	.80	.25
302	A139	7col Seated man	1.60	.40
303	A139	10col Dish, horiz.	2.10	.90
		Nos. 301-303 (3)	4.50	1.15

1984, July 27

304	A140	1col Basketball	.20	.20
305	A140	8col Swimming	.65	.20
306	A140	10col Bicycling	.90	.40
307	A140	14col Running	1.25	.65
308	A140	20col Boxing	1.60	1.25
309	A140	30col Soccer	2.50	1.40
		Nos. 304-309 (6)	7.10	4.10

Public Street Lighting Centenary A141

1984, Aug. 9　　Litho.　　Perf. 10½
310　A141　6col Street scene by Luis Chacon　　.55　.40

10th Natl. Stamp Exhibition, Sept. 10-16 — A142

1984, Sept. 10　　Litho.　　Perf. 10½

311	A142	10col Natl. monument	.90	.55
312	A142	10col Juan Mora Fernandez monument	.90	.55
a.		Min. sheet, 2 each #311-312	15.00	10.00

Natl. Arms — A143

1984, Oct. 29　　Engr.　　Perf. 14x13½

313	A143	100col dk green	8.00	3.75
314	A143	100col yel org	8.00	3.75

Detail from Sistine Virgin by Raphael — A144

1984, Dec. 7　　Litho.　　Perf. 10½

315	3col multicolored	.25	.20
316	3col multicolored	.25	.20
a.	A144 Pair, #315-316	2.00	2.00

20th Intl. Bicycle Race, Costa Rica — A146

1984, Dec. 19　　Litho.　　Perf. 13½
317　A146　6col multi　　.65　.30

Intl. Youth Year A147

1985, Jan. 31　　　　　　Perf. 10½
322　A147　11col IYY emblem, #C476　　1.60　.55

Scouting Movement, 75th anniv.

Labor Monument, San Jose — A148

Natl. values: 11col, Freedom of speech-wooden hand printing press. 13col, Neutrality-dove, natl. flag, outline map.

1985, Feb. 28

323	A148	6col shown	.80	.30
324	A148	11col bl, blk & yel	1.25	.50
325	A148	13col multi	1.40	.55
		Size: 68x38mm		
326	A148	30col Nos. 323-325	4.00	1.10
		Nos. 323-326 (4)	7.45	2.45

Natl. Red Cross Cent., UN 40th Anniv. A149

1985, May 3　　　　　　Perf. 10½

327	A149	3col No. 163, horiz.	2.00	.25
328	A149	5col No. C120	3.00	.25

Club Emblem A150

1st Club Pres., Ricardo Saprissa Ayma A151

Design: No. 330, Hands holding soccer ball.

1985, July 16　　　　　　Perf. 10½

329	A150	3col multi	.50	.20
330	A150	3col multi	.50	.20
a.		Pair, #329-330	1.50	1.00
331	A151	6col multi	1.00	.30
		Nos. 329-331 (3)	2.00	.70

Saprissa Soccer Club, 50th Anniv.

Orchids — A152

11th Natl. Philatelic Exposition A153

1985, Dec. 3

332	A152	6col Brassia arcuigera	3.50	.80
333	A152	6col Encyclia peraltensis	3.50	.80
334	A152	6col Maxillaria especie	3.50	.80
a.		Strip of 3, #332-334	14.50	5.00
335	A152	13col Oncidium turialbae	4.00	1.40
336	A152	13col Trichopilia marginata	4.00	1.40
337	A152	13col Stanhopea ecornuta	4.00	1.40
a.		Strip of 3, #335-337	16.50	5.50
		Nos. 332-337 (6)	22.50	6.60

1985, Dec. 3　　Litho.　　Perf. 13½
338　A153　20col No. C41　　1.25　.55

Christmas 1985 — A153a

1985, Dec. 12　　Litho.　　Perf. 10½
338A　A153a　3col multi　　.40　.25

Compulsory Education, Cent. A154

Designs: 3col, Primary school, horiz. 30col, Mauro Fernandez Acuna, founder.

1986, Feb. 28　　　　　　Perf. 13½

339	A154	3col pale yel & brn	.20	.20
340	A154	30col pale pink & brn	1.60	.80

Agriculture Students — A155

1986, Mar. 21　　　　　　Perf. 10½

341		10col Students on farm	.50	.25
342		10col IDB emblem	.50	.25
343		10col Capo Bianco fisherman	.50	.25
a.		A155 Strip of 3, #341-343	3.00	3.00
		Nos. 341-343 (3)	1.50	.75

Inter-American Development Bank Annual Governors' Assembly, San Jose.

Presidents Type of 1943

Designs: Nos. 344, 349, 354, 359, 364, Francisco J. Orlich Bolmarcich, 1962-66.
Nos. 345, 350, 355, 360, 365, Jose Joaquin Trejos Fernandez, 1966-70.
Nos. 346, 351, 356, 361, 366, Daniel Oduber Quiros, 1974-78.
Nos. 347, 352, 357, 362, 367, Rodrigo Carazo Odio, 1978-82.
Nos. 348, 353, 358, 363, 368, Luis Alberto Monge Alvarez, 1982-86.

1986, May 12　　Litho.　　Perf. 10½

344	A109	3col turq blue	.40	.20
345	A109	3col turq blue	.40	.20
346	A109	3col turq blue	.40	.20
347	A109	3col turq blue	.40	.20
348	A109	3col turq blue	.40	.20
a.		Strip of 5, #344-348	2.25	1.90
349	A109	6col yel brn	.65	.25
350	A109	6col yel brn	.65	.25
351	A109	6col yel brn	.65	.25
352	A109	6col yel brn	.65	.25
353	A109	6col yel brn	.65	.25
a.		Strip of 5, #349-353	5.00	4.50
354	A109	10col brn org	.95	.30
355	A109	10col brn org	.95	.30

356	A109	10col brn org	.95	.30
357	A109	10col brn org	.95	.30
358	A109	10col brn org	.95	.30
a.		Strip of 5, #354-358	8.25	8.00
359	A109	11col slate gray	1.25	.40
360	A109	11col slate gray	1.25	.40
361	A109	11col slate gray	1.25	.40
362	A109	11col slate gray	1.25	.40
363	A109	11col slate gray	1.25	.40
a.		Strip of 5, #359-363	10.00	9.00
364	A109	13col olive	1.60	.45
365	A109	13col olive	1.60	.45
366	A109	13col olive	1.60	.45
367	A109	13col olive	1.60	.45
368	A109	13col olive	1.60	.45
a.		Strip of 5, #364-368	13.50	10.50
		Nos. 344-368 (25)	24.25	8.00
		Nos. 348a-368a (5)	39.00	

1986 World Cup Soccer
Championships, Mexico — A156

1986, May 30   Litho.   Perf. 13½

369	A156	1col Players	.30	.20
370	A156	1col Character trade- mark, vert.	.30	.20
371	A156	4col as No. 370	1.40	.20
372	A156	6col as No. 369	2.00	.25
373	A156	11col Players, diff.	1.40	.45
		Nos. 369-373 (5)	8.00	1.25

A second printing of No. 370 differs in paper
and shade from the first printing, but the most
obvious difference is in the absence of the
initials "LIL" by the left foot of the soccer
player. Unused stamps are rare. Value for
used, $3.

Intl. Peace
Year — A157

Gold Museum,
Central Bank of
Costa
Rica — A158

Peace in many languages: a, "Hoa binh,"
etc. b, "Vrede," etc. c, "Pace," etc.

1986, July 31   Litho.   Perf. 10½

374		Strip of 3	4.50	1.25
a.-c.	A157 5col, any single		.55	.25

1986, Sept. 19   Perf. 10½

Designs: Various undescribed works of Pre-
Columbian art.

375		Strip of 5	6.00	1.00
a.-e.	A158 6col any single		.40	.25
376		Strip of 5	10.50	2.00
a.-e.	A158 13col any single		.80	.40

Exist perf 13½, value $11.50 for the two
strips of 5 unused

A159

Fauna and Flora — A160

1986, Dec. 16   Litho.   Perf. 13x13½

377	A159	2col Centurio senex	.20	.20
378	A159	3col Glossophaga soricina	.45	.20
379	A159	4col Ectophylla al- ba	.60	.20
380	A159	5col Ectophylla al- ba, diff.	.85	.20
381	A159	6col Agalychnis callidryas	1.00	.25
382	A159	10col Dendrobates pumilio	1.40	.25
383	A159	11col Hyla ebraccata	1.60	.40
384	A159	20col Phyllobates lugubris	2.40	.65
		Nos. 377-384 (8)	8.50	2.35

Souvenir Sheet
Perf. 12½x12

385	A160	50col Agalychnis callidryas, diff.	60.00	40.00

Natl. Science and
Technology
Day — A161

Mural (detail), by Francisco Amighetti,
Clorito Picado Social Security Clinic.

1987, July 31   Litho.   Perf. 10½

386	A161	8col multi	4.00	.25

Natl.
Museum,
Cent.
A162

Artifacts: No. 387a, Dowel-shaped figure of
a man. No. 387b, Ape-like carved stone figurine. No. 387c, Polished stone ritual figure. No.
387d, Carved granite capital. No. 387e, Two-
legged pot. No. 388a, Bowl. No. 388b, Sculpture. No. 388c, Water jar.

1987, Aug. 7

387		Strip of 5	5.00	2.40
a.-e.	A162 8col any single, vert.		.40	.25
388		Strip of 3	5.00	2.75
a.-c.	A162 15col any single		.65	.25
		Nos. 387-388 (2)	10.00	5.15

Horse-drawn
Wagon — A163

1987, Oct. 26

389	A163	20col shown	.95	.50
390	A163	20col Street in old San Jose	.95	.50
a.		Pair, #389-390	2.00	2.00

391	A163	20col Provincial coat of arms	.95	.50
		Nos. 389-391 (3)	2.85	1.50

City of San Jose, 250th anniv. Rotary Club,
60th anniv.

Columbus
Day
A164

1987, Oct. 26   Perf. 10½

392	A164	30col Map, 16th cent.	2.25	.65

Day of the Race; 495th anniv. of Columbus's departure from Palos, Spain, on first
journey to the New World.

Discovery of
America, 500th
Anniv. (in
1992) — A165

Pres. Oscar Arias,
1987 Nobel Peace
Prize
Winner — A166

Maps of Honduras, Nicaragua, Costa Rica
and Panama, believed to be Asia by Columbus: No. 393, Costa Rica, 16th cent. No. 394,
Map of "Asia" by Bartholomeu Columbus
(1461-1514).

1987, Nov. 20   Litho.   Perf. 13½

393	A165	4col yel & dk red brn	.25	.25
394	A165	4col yel & dk red brn	.25	.25
a.		Pair, #393-394	2.00	2.00

1987, Dec. 2   Perf. 10½

395	A166	10col multi	2.50	.30

Two Houses,
a Watercolor
by Fausto
Pacheco
(1899-1966)
A167

1987, Dec. 22   Litho.   Perf. 10½

396	A167	1col multi	.55	.30

Intl. Year of Shelter for the Homeless.

17th General
Conference for
the
Preservation of
Natural
Resources
A168

1988, Feb. 1   Litho.   Perf. 13½

397	A168	5col Green turtle	.80	.25
398	A168	5col Emblem, golden toad	.80	.25
399	A168	5col Blue butterfly	.80	.25
a.		A168 Strip of 3, #397-399	2.50	2.50

Intl. Red Cross
and Red Crescent
Organizations,
125th
Annivs. — A169

1988, Apr. 18   Litho.   Perf. 10½

400	A169	30col lt blue & dark red	1.40	.65

North and
South
Campaign
A170

1988, June 6   Photo.   Perf. 11½
Granite Paper

401	A170	18col Adult education	2.40	.25
402	A170	20col Cultural radio programs	2.40	.25

Cultural cooperation with Liechtenstein. See
Liechtenstein #886-887. For overprint see
#C921.

A171   A172

1988, June 27   Litho.   Perf. 10½

403	A171	3col dk blue, dark red & yel	.40	.20

Anglo-Costa Rican Bank, 125th anniv.

1988, Sept. 16   Litho.   Perf. 13½

404	A172	25col Character trade- mark	.95	.50
405	A172	25col Games emblem	.95	.50
a.		Pair, #404-405	2.40	2.40

1988 Summer Olympics, Seoul.

Girls' High
School,
Cent.
A173

1988, Oct. 17   Litho.   Perf. 10½

406	A173	10col Student, court- yard	.50	.25

A174   A175

1988, Nov. 18

407	A174	10col gray, greenish bl & red brn	.40	.25

Educator Omar Dengo (1888-1928) and the
Teachers' College, Heredia.

1988, Nov. 28   Perf. 13½

Indian glass-bead and lion-tooth necklace.

408	A175	4col multi	.25	.25

Discovery of America, 500th anniv. (in 1992).

A176   A177

1988, Dec. 26   Litho.   Perf. 10½

409	A176	2col Observation tower	.65	.30

Natl. Meteorological Institute, cent. For
surcharge see No. 439.

1989, Feb. 28

Designs: Indigenous flora.

410	A177	5col	*Eschweilera costarricensis*	.50	.25
411	A177	10col	*Heliconia wagneriana*	.95	.25
412	A177	15col	*Heliconia lophocarpa*	1.25	.25
413	A177	20col	*Aechmea magdalenae*	1.50	.25
414	A177	25col	*Psammisia ramiflora*	1.75	.25
415	A177	30col	*Passiflora vitifolia*	2.25	.25
			Nos. 410-415 (6)	8.20	1.50

A178

A179

1989, July 1   Litho.   Perf. 10½

416	A178	30col	Nation at Arms	1.40	.50

French Revolution, bicent.

1989, Aug. 28   Litho.   Perf. 13½

417	A179	10col	Sugar mill	.65	.25

Grecia County, 151st anniv.
For overprints see Nos. RA106-RA109.

America
Issue — A180

UPAE emblem and pre-Columbian stone carvings: 50col, Three-footed bench for grinding corn. 100col, Sphere.

Litho. & Engr.
Perf. 12½x12

1989, Oct. 12   Wmk. 334

418	A180	50col	multi	2.50	1.10
419	A180	100col	multi	5.50	1.75

For overprint see No. C916.

A181   A182

Perf. 10½

1989, Oct. 23   Litho.   Unwmk.

420	A181	10col	Orchid	2.00	.25

"100 Years of Democracy" summit of Presidents.

Perf. 13½

1989, Nov. 27   Litho.   Unwmk.

421	A182	18col	Map, H.F. Pittier, emblem	.80	.25

Natl. Geographic Institute, cent.
For surcharge see No. 452.

America
Issue — A183

Pre-Columbian gold frog figurine and facing portraits of Ferdinand V and Isabella I on gold coin struck by Spain from 1476 to 1516.

1989, Dec. 4   Perf. 10½

422	A183	4col	multicolored	.25	.20

Discovery of America, 500th anniv. (in 1992).

Natl.
Theater,
Cent.
A184

Perf. 10½

1990, Feb. 27   Litho.   Unwmk.

423	A184	5col	Coffee Allegory	.65	.30

World Cup Soccer
Championships,
Italy — A185

1990, June 1   Litho.   Perf. 10½

424	A185	5col	multicolored	.25	.20

Univ. of
Costa
Rica, 50th
Anniv.
A187

1990, Aug. 24   Litho.   Perf. 10½

426	A187	18col	multicolored	.75	.25

Education,
Democracy,
Peace — A188

Litho. & Engr.

1990, Oct. 31   Perf. 12½

427	A188	100col	shown	2.25	1.10
428	A188	200col	Flag as map	4.50	1.75
429	A188	500col	National arms	12.00	4.50
			Nos. 427-429 (3)	18.75	7.35

"Invisible" security printing is sometimes visible.
For overprints see Nos. 448, C920.

Hospitals   America Issue
A190   A191

#431, St. Vincent de Paul Hospital, Heredia.
#432, Natl. Psychiatric hospital.

1990, Dec. 18   Engr.   Perf. 13x12½

431	A190	50col	multicolored	1.25	.30
432	A190	100col	multicolored	2.75	.65

1990, Dec. 21   Litho.   Perf. 10½

433	A191	18col	Ara macao	1.00	.40
434	A191	18col	Ara ambigua	1.00	.40
a.			Pair, #433-434	6.00	6.00
435	A191	24col	Cassia grandis	1.90	1.90
436	A191	24col	Tabebuia ochracea	1.90	1.90
a.			Pair, #435-436	6.00	6.00
			Nos. 433-436 (4)	5.80	4.60

Costa Rica-Panama Border Treaty,
50th Anniv. — A192

Designs: a, Flags, national arms. b, Presidents. c, Map.

1991, May 24   Litho.   Perf. 10½

437	A192	10col	Strip of 3, #a.-c.	1.60	.55

Discovery of
America, 500th
Anniv. (in
1992) — A193

1991, Oct. 11   Litho.   Perf. 13½

438	A193	4col	multicolored	.70	.20

Nos. 409, 296 Surcharged

1991, Oct. 21   Litho.   Perf. 10½

439	A176	1col on 2col #409		.30	.20
440	A137	3col on 8.50col #296		.30	.20

Former Presidents,
Supreme Court of
Justice — A194

Designs: a, Benito Serrano Jimenez. b, Luis Davila Solera. c, Fernando Baudrit Solera. d, Alejandro Alvarado Garcia.

Perf. 14½x13½

1992, Feb. 28   Litho.

441	A194	5col	Strip of 4, #a.-d.	1.75	.80

A sheet exists containing an unissued 5th stamp. Value, sheet $500.

DINADECO,
Natl.
Directorate of
Community
Development,
25th Anniv.
A195

1992, Apr. 28   Litho.   Perf. 10½

442	A195	15col	multicolored	1.50	.35

Compare with No. C505.

A196   A197

1992, May 26   Litho.   Perf. 13½

443	A196	15col	lake & black	1.25	.35

Dr. Solon Nunez Frutos, public health pioneer.

1992, July 17   Litho.   Perf. 13

Solar Eclipse: a, Total eclipse. b, Post Office Bldg. during eclipse. c, Partial eclipse.

444	A197	45col	Strip of 3, #a.-c.	8.25	3.25

A198   A199

1992, Aug. 14   Litho.   Perf. 13½

445	A198	35col	multicolored	1.40	.40

Interamerican Institute for Agricultural Cooperation, 50th anniv.

1992, Nov. 5   Litho.   Perf. 10½

446	A199	2col	Waterfall	.25	.20
447	A199	15col	Coastline	.40	.20

Cocos Island, 450th anniv. of discovery.

No. 427 Ovptd. "CENTENARIO / DE LIMON"

Litho. & Engr.

1992, Nov. 27   Perf. 12½

448	A188	100col	black & blue	2.10	1.00

America
Issue
A200

1992, Dec. 15   Litho.   Perf. 10½

449	A200	15col	Anolis townsendi	*2.50*	.25
450	A200	35col	Pinaroloxias inornata	*4.50*	.40

Natl. Theater
A201

Detail from painting "Allegory of Fine Arts," by Roberto Fontana.

1993, Jan. 29   Litho.   Perf. 10½

451	A201	20col	multicolored	.80	.25

No. 421 Surcharged

1993, Mar. 26   Litho.   Perf. 13½
452 A182 5col on 18col multi   .50   .20

   50,000 stamps originally were overprinted with a tiny block and four thin bars over the value, but this was considered unacceptable. So these stamps plus 1,550,000 unoverprinted stamps were overprinted with the large black square and surcharge, as shown.

Protection of the Dolphin A202

1993, May 17   Litho.   Perf. 10½
453 A202 10col Delphinus
             delphis   1.60   .40
454 A202 20col Stenella
             coeruleoalbus   3.25   .40

Costa Rican Civil Service, 40th Anniv. — A203

1993, May 28   Litho.   Perf. 13½
455 A203 5col multicolored   .45   .25

Costa Rican Chamber of Industries, 50th Anniv. A204

1993, July 15   Perf. 10½
456 A204 45col multicolored   1.40   .90

School of Communication Sciences, University of Costa Rica, 25th Anniv. — A205

1993, Aug. 19   Litho.   Perf. 13½
457 A205 20col black, blue & red   .50   .30

Protection of the Tropical Rain Forest — A206

1993, Aug. 27   Perf. 10½
458 A206 2col Passiflora vitifolia   .60   .20
459 A206 35col Gurania megis-
             tantha   1.40   .55

Social Guarantees and Labor Code, 50th Anniv. A207

1993, Sept. 14   Litho.   Perf. 10½
460 A207 20col multicolored   .50   .30

A208   A209

1993, Oct. 25   Litho.   Perf. 13½
461 A208 45col multicolored   1.00   .70

   Intl. Assoc. of Professional Custom-House Agents, 15th Congress.

1993, Nov. 26   Perf. 10½
462 A209 20col multicolored   .65   .30

   Miguel Angel Castro Carazo (1893-1960), educator and humanitarian.
   For surcharge see No. 481.

A211   A212

1993, Dec. 23   Litho.   Perf. 10½
464 A211 20col multicolored   .55   .30

   Law School of Costa Rica, 150th anniv.

1994, Mar. 18   Litho.   Perf. 13
465 A212 20col Natl. Theater   .55   .30

Marine Life — A213

   5col, Cyphoma gibbosum. 10col, Ophioderma rubicundum. 15col, Myripristis jacobus. 20col, Holocanthus passer. 35col, Paranthias furcifer. 45col, Tubastraea coccinea. 50col, Acanthaster planci. 55col, Ocypode. 70col, Arothron meleagris. 100col, Thalassoma lucasanum.

Litho. & Embossed
1994, Apr. 29   Perf. 12½x12
466 A213 5col multicolored   .40   .20
467 A213 10col multicolored   .80   .20
468 A213 15col multicolored   1.25   .30
469 A213 20col multicolored   1.60   .35
470 A213 35col multicolored   2.75   .55
471 A213 45col multicolored   3.50   .75
472 A213 50col multicolored   4.00   .85
473 A213 55col multicolored   4.50   .95
474 A213 70col multicolored   5.50   1.25
     Nos. 466-474 (9)   24.30   5.40

Souvenir Sheet
Perf. 13
475 A213 100col multicolored   11.00   8.00

America Issue A214

   Illustrations from 19th century Book of Figueroa: a, Man on horseback. b, Back of ox carrying bundles.

1994, Dec. 19   Litho.   Perf. 10½
476 A214 20col Pair, #a.-b. + la-
             bel   1.75   1.40

   No. 476 is a continuous design.

Rotary Intl., 90th Anniv. — A215

1995, Mar.   Litho.   Perf. 13½
477 A215 20col multicolored   .90   .40

Antonio Jose de Sucre (1795-1830) A216

Guanacaste Institute, 50th Anniv. A217

   Design: 30col, Jose Marti (1853-95).

1995, June   Litho.   Perf. 10½
478 A216 10col multicolored   .25   .25
479 A216 30col multicolored   .65   .65

1995, July 24   Perf. 13½
480 A217 50col grn, blk & bis   1.00   1.00

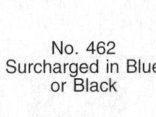

No. 462 Surcharged in Blue or Black

1995, Sept. 11   Litho.   Perf. 10½
481 A209 5col on 20col multi   .30   .25

UN, 50th Anniv. — A218

13th Natl. Philatelic Expo — A219

1995, Oct. 24   Litho.   Perf. 10½
482 A218 5col multicolored   .40   .25

1995, Dec. 1

   Paintings by Lola Fernández: No. 483, Noviembre. No. 484, Enero.

483 A219 50col multicolored   1.00   1.00
484 A219 50col multicolored   1.00   1.00
a.   Pair, Nos. 483-484   3.00   3.00

America Issue A220

   30col, Jabiru mycteria. #486, View of coast. #487, River, trees. 50col, Atta cephalotes.

1995, Dec. 25   Litho.   Rouletted 13½
485 A220 30col multicolored   1.50   .80
486 A220 40col multicolored   1.50   1.25
487 A220 40col multicolored   1.50   1.25
a.   Pair, #486-487   3.50   3.00
488 A220 50col multicolored   2.00   1.50
a.   Souvenir sheet, #485-488   12.00   8.00
     Nos. 485-488 (4)   6.50   4.80

Seaport City of Limón A221

   Designs: a, Early picture of steam train. b, Photo of ship in port, 1922. c, Aerial view of seaport, 1995. d, Painting of fruit seller, by Diego Villalobos. e, Drawing of Calipso singers, by Jorge Esquivel.

1996, Jan. 31   Litho.   Perf. 10½
489 A221 30col Strip of 5, #a.-e.   3.25   3.25

Jerusalem, 3000th Anniv. — A222

1996, May 17   Litho.   Perf. 13½
490 A222 30col multicolored   .80   .65

1996 Summer Olympic Games, Atlanta A223

   Olympic swimmers, coaches from Costa Rica: a, F. Rivas, M.M. Paris. b, S. Poll, R. Yglesias. c, C. Poll, A. Cruz.

1996, July 18   Litho.   Perf. 10½
491 A223 5col Strip of 3, #a.-c.   1.60   1.60

   No. 491 is a continuous design.

A224   A225

First lady, presidents: a, Juana del Castillo. b, Juan Mora Fernández. c, J.M. Castro Madriz. d, Pacífica Fernández.

1996, Sept. 13   **Litho.**   **Perf. 10½**
492 A224 30col Block of 4, #a.-d.   3.00   3.00
  Independence, 175th anniv. No. 492 was issued in sheets of 16 stamps.

1996, Oct. 4   **Litho.**   **Perf. 13½**
493 A225 15col multicolored   .40   .25
  Aqueducts and sewage systems, 35th anniv. Exists imperf.

A226

America issue (Paintings): No. 494, Black from Lemon, by Manuel da la Cruz González. No. 495, Peasant Women, by Gonzalo Morales Alvarado, vert.

1996, Dec. 16   **Perf. 10½**
494 A226 45col multicolored   1.10   .85
495 A226 45col multicolored   1.10   .85

A227

Entrance of the Saints at San Ramón, parade of people: a, Building with palm trees on top. b, Church on hill. c, Tree, holy family.

1997, Aug. 14   **Litho.**   **Perf. 13½**
496 A227 30col Strip of 3, #a.-c.   3.00   1.60
  Costa Rican traditions.

School of Fine Arts, Cent. A228

1997, Sept. 24   **Perf. 10½**
497 A228 50col multicolored   1.40   .70

Radio Netherlands, 50th Anniv. — A229

1997, Sept. 26   **Perf. 13½**
498 A229 45col multicolored   1.10   .65
  Exists imperf.

14th Natl. Philatelic Exhibition A230

1997, Oct. 9   **Perf. 10½**
499 A230 30col Postmen   .65   .40
  America Issue.

Church of the Immaculate Conception, Heredia, Bicent. — A231

1997, Nov. 10   **Litho.**   **Perf. 10½**
502 A231 50col multicolored   1.25   1.00

Second Republic, 50th Anniv. — A232

Former Pres. José Figueres demolishing wall of Fort Bellavista: 10col, 45col, Complete photo. 30col, Detail of Figueres' head. 50col, Hammer head hitting wall.

Litho. & Engr.
1998, Mar. 30   **Perf. 12½**
503 A232 10col multicolored   .60   .30
504 A232 30col multicolored   .90   .30
505 A232 45col multicolored   1.40   .30
506 A232 50col multicolored   1.50   .40
  a.   Souvenir sheet of 2, #504, 506   4.50   3.25

Natl. University, 25th Anniv. — A233

1998, July 27   **Litho.**   **Perf. 10½**
507 A233 50col multicolored   1.50   1.10

Butterflies A234

10col, Caligo memnon. 15col, Morpho peleides. 20col, Papilio thoas. 30col, Siproeta stelenes. 35col, Ascia monuste. 40col, Parides iphidamas. 45col, Smyrna blonfildia. 50col, Callicore pitheas. 55col, Historis odius. 60col, Danaus plexippus.

1998, July 16
508 A234 10col multicolored   .80   .30
509 A234 15col multicolored   1.25   .40
510 A234 20col multicolored   1.75   .60
511 A234 30col multicolored   2.50   .90
512 A234 35col multicolored   3.00   1.10
513 A234 40col multicolored   3.25   1.25
514 A234 45col multicolored   3.50   1.40
515 A234 50col multicolored   4.00   1.50
516 A234 55col multicolored   4.50   1.75
517 A234 60col multicolored   5.50   1.90
  Nos. 508-517 (10)   30.05   11.10

1998 World Cup Soccer Championships, France — A235

1998, Feb. 27   **Litho.**   **Perf. 10½**
518 A235 50col multicolored   1.25   1.00

A236   A237

1998, Nov. 30   **Litho.**   **Perf. 13½**
519 A236 50col brn, yel brn & lt yel   2.00   .80
  Carmen Lyra (1888-1949), author.

1998, Dec. 11   **Litho.**   **Perf. 13½**
520 A237 50col multicolored   1.60   1.00
  Gandhi (1869-1948).

Intl. Union for the Conservation of Nature, 50th Anniv. A238

Turtles: a, 70col, Rhinociemmys pulcherrima. b, 60col, Trachemys scripta. c, 70col, Chelydra serpentina.

1998, Dec. 1
521 A238 Strip of 3, #a.-c.   7.50   7.50

Mushrooms A239

a, Morchella esculenta. b, Boletus edulis.

1999, July 2   **Litho.**   **Perf. 10½**
522 A239 50col Pair, #a.-b.   4.50   4.50

SOS Children's Villages, 50th Anniv. — A240

1999, June   **Litho.**   **Perf. 10½**
523 A240 50col multicolored   1.50   .80

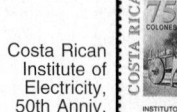

Costa Rican Institute of Electricity, 50th Anniv. A241

1999, Sept. 21   **Litho.**   **Perf. 13¼**
524 A241 75col multi   .80   .60

A242   A243

1999, Oct. 7   **Engr.**   **Perf. 13¾x14**
525 A242 300col violet   3.00   3.00
  Archbishop Víctor M. Sanabria (1899-1952). See No. 538.

1999, Oct. 29   **Litho.**   **Perf. 13¼**
526 A243 50col multi   .80   .50
  Intl. Year of Older Persons.

Supreme Election Tribunal, 50th Anniv. A244

1999, Nov. 5   **Perf. 10½**
527 A244 70col multi   1.00   .75

UPU, 125th Anniv. A245   Carmen Granados (1915-99), Humorist A246

1999, Dec. 1   **Perf. 13¼**
528 A245 75col multi   .90   .70

1999, Dec. 1
529 A246 50col multi   .90   .60

America Issue, A New Millennium Without Arms — A247

1999, Dec. 1
530 A247 50col shown   .75   .50
531 A247 70col Face, hands, diff.   1.00   .70

PhilexFrance '99 — A248

1999, Dec. 1
532 A248 300col shown   5.00   3.50
533 A248 300col Flower, Eiffel Tower   5.00   3.50

Natl. Bank, 50th Anniv. — A249

No. 534 — Pre-Columbian artifacts: a, Jaguar. b, Scorpion. c, Bat. d, Crab. e, Beast with horns.
No. 535 — Obverse and reverse of coins: a, Gold, from 1825. b, Gold, from 1850. c, Silver one-eighth peso. d, Gold 20-peso. e, 1935 1-colon.

2000, Jan. 28   Litho.   Perf. 13¼
534   A249 Vert. strip of 5   9.50 7.00
a.-e. A249 60col Any single   1.25 1.00
535   A249 Vert. strip of 5   22.50 12.50
a.-e. A249 90col Any single   3.00 1.50

2000 Summer Olympics, Sydney — A250

No. 536, 60col: a, Taekwando. b, Cycling. c, Swimming. d, Soccer.
No. 537, 70col: a, Running. b, Boxing. c, Men's rings. d, Tennis.

2000, Aug. 31
Blocks of 4, #a-d
536-537 A250   Set of 2   10.00 10.00
There were two printings of Nos. 536-537. In the first printing, colors are paler, and the green Olympic ring is misregistered on Nos. 536a-536d. In the second, colors are more intense, and the green ring is properly registered. Values the same.

Famous Person Type of 1999
Pres. Rafael A. Calderón Guardia (1900-70).

2000, Sept. 14   Engr.   Perf. 12½
538   A242 100col deep blue   1.10 .50
a.   Perf 13¾x14   3.25 1.50

Paintings by Max Jiménez — A251

No. 539: a, Fishermen in Cojimar. b, Adamant.

2000, Nov.   Litho.   Perf. 10½
539   A251 Horiz. pair   4.00 2.50
a.-b. A251 50col Either single   1.00 .50

America Issue, Fight Against AIDS — A252

Designs: 60col, Stylized people. 90col, Stylized person.

2000, Dec.   Perf. 13¼
540-541 A252 Set of 2   2.50 2.00

Christmas — A253

2000, Dec.
542 A253 100col multi   1.60 1.25

America Issue — UNESCO World Heritage A254

Birds form Cocos Island Natl. Park: 95col, Coccyzus ferrugineus. 115col, Pinaroloxias inornata.

2001, Apr. 5   Litho.   Perf. 10½
543-544 A254   Set of 2   4.50 3.50

Costa Rica — Netherlands Diplomatic Relations, 150th Anniv. — A255

2001, July 20
545 A255 65col multi   1.00 .75

No. 429 Surcharged

2001   Method and Perf. As Before
546 A188 65col on 500col multi   1.00 .75
547 A188 80col on 500col multi   1.25 1.00
548 A188 95col on 500col multi   1.50 1.10
     Nos. 546-548 (3)   3.75 2.85
Issued: No. 846, 8/24. Nos. 547-548, 9/7.

Third Hispanic-Costa Rican Exposition — A256

Orchids: a, Guaria turrialba. b, Tricopilia.

2001, Oct. 5   Litho.   Perf. 13¼
549 A256 65col Horiz. pair, #a-b   2.50 2.50

Campaign Against Child Labor — A257

2001, Nov. 15   Perf. 13¼
550 A257 100col multi   1.60 1.25

Pres. Tomás Guardia (1832-82) and Locomotive — A258

2001, Nov. 21
551 A258 65col multi   2.00 .80
A second printing of No. 551 was issued in 2002. It features a lighter beige and has yellow gum. This printing of 500 sheets of 15 stamps was made to complete the contract. Value, unused $25.

Costa Rican Team for 2002 World Cup Soccer Championships, Japan and Korea — A259

2002, Mar. 15   Perf. 10½
552 A259 65col multi   .80   .60

No. 428 Surcharged in Red

Litho. & Engr.
2002, Jan. 24   Perf. 12½
553 A188 65col on 200col multi   1.00 .75

America Issue — Youth, Education and Literacy — A260

Designs: 65col, Children and globe. 100col, Blind person reading Braille.

Litho. & Embossed
2002, Mar.   Perf. 10½
554-555 A260   Set of 2   2.50 2.00

Taiwan Friendship Bridge A261

2002, Apr. 3   Litho.
556 A261 95col multi   1.25 1.00

16th Rio Group Congress A262

2002, Apr. 10
557 A262 65col blue & green   1.00 .75

Pan-American Health Organization, Cent. — A263

No. 558: a, People (red denomination at UR). b, Emblem. c, Mother and child (black denomination at LR). d, Child and man (red denomination at LR).
50col, Emblem.

2002, July 5
558 A263 10col Block of 4, #a-d   .65   .65
559 A263 50col multi   .70   .70

In Remembrance of Sept. 11, 2001 Terrorist Attacks — A264

Litho. & Embossed
2002, Sept. 11
560 A264 110col multi   1.50 1.50

Marine Life of Uvita Island A265

Designs: No. 561, 75col, Gorgona flabellum. No. 562, 75col, Ulva lactuca. No. 563, 75col, Cittarium pica. No. 564, 75col, Liriope tetraphyla.

Litho & Embossed
2002, Sept. 25
561-564 A265   Set of 4   6.00 6.00

Space Exploration — A266

No. 565: a, Dr. Franklin Chang-Diaz, astronaut, and space shuttle. b, Phanaeus changdiazi and satellite.

Litho. & Embossed
2003, June 15   Perf. 10½
565 A266 115col Horiz. pair,
          #a-b   4.00 4.00

Coco Island National Park — A267

No. 566: a, Denomination at UR. b, Denomination at UL.

2003, Aug. 1
566 A267 75col Horiz. pair, #a-b   3.00 3.00

America Issue - Fish — A268

No. 567: a, Archocentrus sajica. b, Astatheros diquis.

2003
567 A268 110col Horiz. pair,
          #a-b   5.00 5.00

Scenes from Cocorí, by Joaquín
Gutiérrez — A269

No. 568: a, Boy, turtle, monkey and bird. b,
Boy looking at reflection in water. c, Toucan in
tree, boy and monkey on ground. d, Sailor, girl
and boy. e, Boy, bird on branch. f, Jaguar,
turtle armadillo, monkey, boy and father. g,
Boy and monkey pushing turtle. h, Monkey
with open arms, turtle, boy. i, Mother and boy.
j, Mother, boy, rose bush. k, Boy, father playing musical instrument (80x150mm).

Litho. & Embossed

2003, Sept. 3   **Perf. 10½**
568   A269   Sheet of 11   9.50 9.50
a.-j.   25col Any single   .50 .50
k.   225col multi   4.25 4.25

National Anthem, Cent. — A270

No. 569: a, Lyricist José María Zeledón
(24x35mm). b, Flag, text of anthem
(49x35mm).

2003, Sept. 10   **Litho.**
569   A270 75col Horiz. pair, #a-b 2.75 2.75

Election of Pope John
Paul II, 25th
Anniv. — A271

2003, Oct. 16   Litho.   Perf. 13¼x13½
570   A271 130col multi   2.50 2.50

Charles Lindbergh's Flight to Costa
Rica, 75th Anniv. — A272

Litho. & Embossed
2003, Dec. 16   Perf. 13½x13¼
571   A272 110col multi   2.00 2.00

Guayabo de Turrialba Archaeological
Monument — A273

2003, Dec. 18
572   A273 110col multi   2.00 2.00

America
Issue
A274

Flora: No. 573, 75col, Ceiba pentandra. No.
574, 75col, Tetranema floribundum. 90col,
Ceiba pentandra, diff. 110col, Tetranema
gamboanum.

2004, Mar. 23   Litho.   Perf. 10½
573-576 A274   Set of 4   6.00 6.00

Volcanoes
A275

Designs: 85col, Arenal. 120col, Irazú.
140col, Poás.

2004-05   **Perf. 10½**
577-579 A275   Set of 3   6.00 6.00
577a   Perf. 13¼ ('05)   1.50 1.50
578a   Perf. 13¼ ('05)   2.00 2.00
579a   Perf. 13¼ ('05)   2.50 2.50

Issued: Nos. 577-579, 6/24/04; 577a, 578a,
579a, 2005.
Nos. 577a, 578a and 579a have printer's
inscription "LIL S.A."

2004
Summer
Olympics,
Athens
A276

No. 580 — Various athletes in: a, Blue. b,
Yellow orange. c, Green. d, Red.

2004, July 15
580   Horiz. strip of 4   8.00 8.00
a.-d.   A276 120col Any single   2.00 2.00

Dr. Miguel Angel Rodríguez,
Organization of American States
President
A277

2004, Sept. 15
581   A277 120col multi   2.00 2.00

FIFA (Fédération Internationale de
Football Association), Cent. — A278

No. 582: a, Emblem (34x34mm). b, Soccer
player and field (39x34mm).

2004, Feb. 15   Litho.   Perf. 10½
582   A278 140col Horiz. pair, #a-b 5.00 5.00

Rotary
International,
Cent. — A279

No. 583: a, Emblem and frog. b, Centenary
emblem. c, Emblem and butterfly.

2005, Feb. 23
583   Horiz. strip of 3   7.50 7.50
a.-c.   A279 140col Any single   2.50 2.50

Souvenir Sheet

Popes — A280

No. 584: a, Pope John Paul II (1920-2005).
b, Pope Benedict XVI.

2005, Aug. 22
584   A280 140col Sheet of 4, 2
          each #a-b   10.00 10.00

An imperf. sheet lacking postal validity
exists. Value, $150.

Intl. Year of Physics — A281

No. 585: a, Albert Einstein (1879-1955). b,
Max Planck (1858-1947).

2005, June 7
585   Horiz. pair   3.50 3.50
a.-b.   A281 95col Either single 1.75 1.75

Flora and
Fauna in
National
Parks — A282

No. 586: a, Passiflora vitifolia. b, Dryas iulia
moderata. c, Potos flavus.

2005, Oct. 11   Litho.   Perf. 10½
586   Strip of 3   4.50 4.50
a.-c.   A282 85col Any single   1.40 1.40

America Issue,
Fight Against
Poverty — A283

No. 587: a, Child at computer. b, Man saw-
ing wood. c, Medical worker.

2005, Oct. 19
587   Strip of 3   6.50 6.50
a.-c.   A283 120col Any single 2.10 2.10

Intl. Year
of Sports
and
Physical
Education
A284

2005, Dec. 6
588   A284 85col multi   1.50 1.50

Cartago Sport Club, Cent. — A285

2006, Mar. 20
589   A285 85col multi   1.75 1.75

Miniature Sheet

National Campaign Against
Nicaraguan Pres. William Walker,
150th Anniv. — A286

No. 590: a, Juan Rafael Mora, National
Monument. b, Juan Santamaría Monument,
barracks. c, Map (50x40mm). d, Gen. José
María Cañas, Santa Rosa House. e, Luis
Molina, Joaquín Bernardo Calvo.

2006, Apr. 7
590   A286 85col Sheet of 5, #a-e 8.50 8.50

2006 World Cup Soccer
Championships, Germany — A287

2006, May 15
591   A287 120col multi   2.40 2.40

America Issue, Energy
Conservation — A288

2006, July 31   Litho.   Perf. 10½
592   A288 155col multi + label 3.00 3.00

Miniature Sheet

Birds and Marine Life of Cocos Island — A289

No. 593: a, Sula sula. b, Mycteroperca olfax. c, Zanclus cornutis. d, Eretmochely imbricaas. e, Tursiops truncatus. f, Myripristis berndti. g, Dendroica petechia aureola. h, Carcharhinus limbatus. i, Anous stolidus. j, Acarus rubroviolaceus.

2006, Aug. 25   Litho.   Perf. 10½
593 A289 180col Sheet of 10, #a-j   35.00 35.00

Pres. José Figueres Ferrer (1906-90) — A290

2006, Sept. 25   Perf. 10½
594 A290 115col gray & multi + label   2.25 2.25
Souvenir Sheet
Imperf
595 A290 1000col tan & multi   20.00 20.00

Fruits A291

No. 596: a, Hymenaea courbaril. b, Bixa orellana. c, Garcinia intermedia.

2006, Oct. 12   Perf. 10½
596   Strip of 3   9.00 9.00
a.-c. A291 155col Any single   3.00 3.00

National Symbols — A292

No. 597: a, Flag. b, Coat of arms.

2006, Nov. 27
597 A292 155col Pair, #a-b   6.00 6.00
Printed in sheets containing two pairs.

Pres. Francisco J. Orlich (1907-69) — A293

2007, Mar. 7
598 A293 115col multi   2.25 2.25

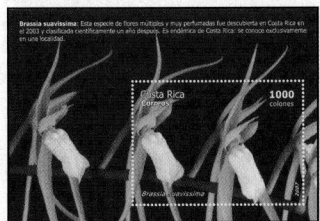

Orchids — A294

No. 599: a, Guarianthe skinneri (pink flowers). b, Galeandra arundinis. c, Encyclia ossenbachiana. d, Dracula inexperata. e, Guarianthe skinneri (white flowers). f, Kefersteinia retanae. g, Coryanthes kaiseriana. h, Psychopsis krameriana. i, Chondroscaphe yamilethae. j, Cattleya dowiana.
1000col, Brassia suavissima.

2007, Mar. 19   Litho.   Perf. 10½
599 A294 180col Sheet of 10, #a-j   35.00 35.00
Souvenir Sheet
Imperf
600 A294 1000col multi   20.00 20.00
No. 599 contains ten 45x37mm stamps. No. 600 has simulated perforations.

Salesian Order in Costa Rica, Cent. — A295

2007, Apr. 30   Perf. 10½
601 A295 110col multi   2.25 2.25

Miniature Sheet

Pre-Columbian Art — A296

No. 602: a, Frog-shaped gold pendant (25x45mm). b, Bird-shaped jadeite pendant (25x45mm). c, Stone metate, horiz. (50x30mm). d, Ceramic censer with alligator (25x45mm). e, Stone figure of warrior (25x45mm).

2007, May 4
602 A296 155col Sheet of 5, #a-e   15.00 15.00

America Issue, Education For All — A297

No. 603: a, 115col, Teacher and students. b, 155col, Family around fire.

2007, June 8
603 A297 Horiz. pair, #a-b   5.50 5.50

Plasma Technology — A298

No. 604: a, Astronaut and spacecraft's robot arm. b, Plasma containment vessel.

2007, July 6
604 A298 240col Horiz. pair, #a-b 9.50 9.50

Guanacaste Musical Instruments — A299

Designs: No. 605, 115col, Marimba. No. 606, 115col, Quijongo, vert. (30x50mm).

2007, July 25
605-606 A299   Set of 2   4.50 4.50
Nos. 605-606 were printed in sheets containing two of each stamp + label.

Virgin of the Angels Icon, 225th Anniv. as Patron of Cartago — A300

No. 607 — Icon with denomination at: a, LR. b, LL.
1000col, Interior of Cartago Basilica, vert.

2007, July 27
607 A300 115col Horiz. pair, #a-b 4.50 4.50
Souvenir Sheet
608 A300 1000col multi   20.00 20.00
No. 608 contains one 75x115mm stamp.

Fauna of National Parks — A301

No. 609: a, Oxybelis fulgidus. b, Stagmomantis sp. c, Heliodoxa jacula. d, Pulsatrix perspicillata.

2007, Aug. 17   Litho.   Perf. 10½
609   Horiz. strip of 4   18.00 18.00
a.-d. A301 235col Any single   4.50 4.50

2007 Special Olympics, Shanghai — A302

No. 610: a, Cycling. b, Swimming. c, Running.

2007, Sept. 10
610   Horiz. strip of 3   14.00 14.00
a.-c. A302 240col Any single   3.50 3.50

Accounts of My Aunt Panchita, Children's Book by Carmen Lyra — A303

No. 611, vert. — Text: a, Por qué Tío Conejo tiene las orejas tan largas. b, La Mica. c, Uvieta. d, Tío Conejo y los caites de su abuela.
1000col, De como Tío Conejo salió de un apuro.

2007, Oct. 18
611 A303 100col Sheet of 4, #a-d   8.00 8.00
Souvenir Sheet
612 A303 1000col multi   20.00 20.00
No. 611 contains four 37x50mm stamps.

Ox Cart Heritage — A304

No. 613: a, Man with oxen. b, Decorated wheel.

2007, Nov. 23
613 A304 180col Vert. pair, #a-b, + central label   7.00 7.00

Esquipulas II Central American Peace Accords, 20th Anniv. — A305

No. 614 — Nobel Peace medal of Pres. Oscar Arias Sánchez: a, Reverse (three men). b, Obverse (Alfred Nobel).

2007, Dec. 10
614 A305 135col Horiz. pair, #a-b 5.25 5.25

Dr. Fernando Centeno Güell (1907-93), Poet and Educator — A306

2008, Feb. 14
615 A306 115col multi   2.25 2.25

Churches — A307

No. 616: a, Our Lord of Agony Chapel, Guanacaste. b, San Francisco Church, San José. c, Our Lady of Sorrow Church, San José. d, Santa Ana Church, San José. e, Our Lady of Carmel Cathedral, Puntarenas. f, San Bartolomé Apóstol Church, Heredia.

1000col, Our Lady of Mercy Parish Church, San José.

2008, Mar. 17
616 A307   230col Sheet of 6,
    #a-f   27.50 27.50
    Souvenir Sheet
617 A307 1000col multi   20.00 20.00

No. 616 contains six 40x40mm stamps.

Souvenir Sheet

Women's Superior College, 120th Anniv. — A308

2008, Mar. 31
618 A308 1000col multi   20.00 20.00

Miniature Sheet

Marine Mammals — A309

No. 619: a, Megaptera novaengliae, side view. b, Sotalia guianensis. c, Stenella attenuata. d, Megaptera novaengliae flukes.

2008, June 16   Litho.   **Perf. 10½**
619 A309 240col Sheet of 4,
    #a-d   19.00 19.00

Intl. Year of Planet Earth — A310

No. 620: a, San Vicente Cataracts. b, Santa Elena Peninsula.

2008, July 1
620   Pair   7.00 7.00
   a.-b. A310 175col Either single   3.50 3.50

Miniature Sheet

Art — A311

No. 621: a, La Ultima Escena, by Rudy Espinoza. b, Mujer que Avanza, sculpture by Crisanto Badilla. c, Transitoriedad del Hombre, by Miguel Hernández. d, Arquetipo, by Lola Fernández.

2008, July 3
621 A311 240col Sheet of 4,
    #a-d   19.00 19.00

Miniature Sheet

Ministry of Labor and Social Security, 80th Anniv. — A312

No. 622 — Details from mural "The Second Republic," by Luccio Ranucci: a, Man with hat, striped pole. b, Woman with basket of fruit. c, Man and woman embracing. d, Man carrying sack on head.

2008, Aug. 28   Litho.   **Perf. 10½**
622 A312 240col Sheet of 4,
    #a-d   19.00 19.00

Masks — A313

No. 623 — Masks with background colors of: a, 115col, Brown orange. b, 155col, Green.

2008, Oct. 31
623 A313   Horiz. pair, #a-b   5.50 5.50

Hogar Crea Drug Rehabilitation Centers in Costa Rica, 25th Anniv. — A314

2009, Feb. 25   Litho.   **Perf. 10½**
624 A314 160col multi   3.20 3.20

Carlos Luis Fallas (1906-66), Author — A315

2009, Apr. 30   Litho.   **Perf. 10½**
625 A315 150col multi   2.00 2.00

Miniature Sheet

Children's Literature — A316

No. 626: a, Tolo, the Giant North Wind (kite), by Adela Ferreto de Saénz. b, The Ship of the Stars (ship and boy), by Alfredo Cardona Peña. c, Old Stories (rabbit and gourds), by María Leal de Noguera. d, Paul's Music (boy holding box), by Lara Ríos.

2009, May 27
626 A316 65col Sheet of 4, #a-d   5.00 5.00

Alberto Martén, Economist, Solidarity Movement Founder — A317

2009, June 19
627 A317 135col multi   2.50 2.50

Miniature Sheet

Costa Rican Electrical Institute (ICE), 60th Anniv. — A318

No. 628: a, People and ICE building. b, Construction workers in tunnel. c, Lineman on ladder. d, Computers and satellite dishes. e, Houses and windmills. f, Hand planting seedling, girl.

2009, June 30
628 A318   340col Sheet of 6,
    #a-f   32.50 32.50

Diplomatic Relations Between Costa Rica and Switzerland — A319

2009, July 8
629 A319 225col multi   3.75 3.75

Miniature Sheet

National Parks — A320

No. 630: a, Arenal Volcano. b, Celeste River. c, Cerro Chirripó. d, Cocos Island. e, Monteverde. f, Poás Volcano. g, Tortuguero.

2009, Aug. 24
630 A320 240col Sheet of 7, #a-g 8.25 8.25

America Issue, Traditional Games — A321

No. 631: a, Marbles. b, Kite flying.

2009, Sept. 9   Litho.   Perf. 10½
631   Horiz. pair   1.40 1.40
a.-b. A321 135col Either single   .70   .70

Intl. Holocaust Remembrance Day — A322

2010, Jan. 27   Perf. 13¼
632 A322 500col gray & black   3.00 3.00

Miniature Sheet

Locomotives — A323

No. 633: a, Steam locomotive, 1889. b, Electric Series AEG locomotive, 1926. c, Yellow and white Apolo Series Diesel-electric locomotive, 1990. d, Blue, white and red Diesel-electric locomotive, 1979-80.

2010, May 4   Litho.   Perf. 10½
633 A323 200col Sheet of 4, #a-d 3.25 3.25

America Issue, National Symbols — A324

2010, June 24
634   Horiz. pair   2.40 2.40
a. A324 280col Turdus grayi   1.10 1.10
b. A324 340col Odocoileus virginianus 1.25 1.25

Miniature Sheet

Endangered Birds — A325

No. 635: a, 400col, Platalea ajaja. b, 400col, Icterus mesomelas. c, 1000col, Morphnus guianensis. d, 1000col, Harpia harpyja.

2010, June 24   Litho.   Perf. 10½
635 A325 Sheet of 4, #a-d 10.50 10.50

University Anniversaries — A326

No. 636: a, Mural by Eduardo Torijano at University of Costa Rica. b, Monument to Disarmament, Work and Peace by Thelvia Marin at Univeristy for Peace.

2010, Aug. 26
636 A326 500col Pair, #a-b   4.00 4.00

University of Costa Rica, 70th anniv., University for Peace, 30th anniv.

POSTAL-FISCAL STAMPS

From April 1884 through September 1889 revenue stamps were permitted for postal use, when post offices exhausted supplies of regular postage stamps.

Used values are for stamps with postal cancels.

PF1   PF2

1884   Engr.   Perf. 12
AR1 PF1 1c rose   .50 5.00
AR2 PF1 2c light blue   20.00 5.00
1888
AR3 PF2 5c brown   .50 3.00
AR4 PF2 10c blue   .25 3.00

SEMI-POSTAL STAMPS

No. 72 Surcharged in Red

1922   Unwmk.   Perf. 12
B1 A56 5c + 5c orange   1.00 .40

Issued for the benefit of the Costa Rican Red Cross Society. In 1928, owing to a temporary shortage of the ordinary 5c stamp, No. B1 was placed on sale as a regular 5c stamp, the surtax being disregarded.

Discus Thrower SP1   Trophy SP2

Parthenon SP3

1924   Litho.   Imperf.
B2 SP1 5c dark green   1.60 2.00
B3 SP2 10c carmine   1.60 2.00
B4 SP3 20c dark blue   20.00 20.00
a.   Tête bêche pair   60.00 60.00
                 Perf. 12
B5 SP1 5c dark green   1.60 2.25
B6 SP2 10c carmine   1.60 2.25
B7 SP3 20c dark blue   3.50 4.00
a.   Tête bêche pair   16.00 20.00
   Nos. B2-B7 (6)   29.90 32.50

These stamps were sold at a premium of 10c each, to help defray the expenses of athletic games held at San José in Dec. 1924.

AIR POST STAMPS

Airplane AP1

Perf. 12½
1926, June 4   Unwmk.   Engr.
C1 AP1 20c ultramarine   3.00 .65

No. 123 Overprinted

1930, Mar. 14   Perf. 12
C2 A75 10c carmine rose 2.00 .25

Inverted or double overprints are fakes.

AP3

1930-32   Perf. 12½
C3 AP3 5c on 10c dk brn ('32) .40 .25
C4 AP3 20c on 50c ultra   .50 .25
C5 AP3 40c on 50c ultra   .60 .25
   Nos. C3-C5 (3)   1.50 .75

The existence of genuine inverted or double surcharges of Nos. C3-C5 is in doubt.

Telegraph Stamp Overprinted

1930, Mar. 19
C6 AP3 1col orange   2.00 .50

No. O79 Surcharged in Red

1930, Mar. 11
C7 O7 8c on 1col lilac & blk   .80 .65
C8 O7 20c on 1col lilac & blk 1.25 .70
C9 O7 40c on 1col lilac & blk 2.40 1.50
C10 O7 1col on 1col lilac & blk 3.50 2.00
   Nos. C7-C10 (4)   7.95 4.85

AP6   AP7

Red Surcharge on Revenue Stamps
1931-32   Perf. 12
C11 AP6 2col on 2col gray
             grn   35.00 35.00
C12 AP6 3col on 5col lil brn 35.00 35.00
C13 AP6 5col on 10col gray
             blk   35.00 35.00
   Nos. C11-C13 (3)   105.00 105.00

There were two printings of this issue which were practically identical in the colors of the stamps and the surcharges.

Nos. C11 and C13 have the date "1929" on the stamp, No. C12 has "1930."

Black Overprint on Telegraph Stamp
1932, Mar. 8   *Perf. 12½*

C14	AP7	40c green	3.00	.30
a.		Inverted overprint	32.50	27.50

Unofficial "proofs," inverts and double overprints were made from a defaced plate.

Mail Plane about to Land
AP8

Allegory of Flight
AP9

1934, Mar. 14   *Perf. 12*

C15	AP8	5c green	.25	.25
C16	AP8	10c carmine rose	.25	.25
C17	AP8	15c chocolate	.40	.25
C18	AP8	20c deep blue	.40	.25
C19	AP8	25c deep orange	.55	.25
C20	AP8	40c olive blk	1.75	.25
C21	AP8	50c gray blk	.85	.25
C22	AP8	60c orange yel	1.50	.25
C23	AP8	75c dull violet	2.75	.50
C24	AP9	1col deep rose	1.50	.25
C25	AP9	2col lt blue	7.50	.95
C26	AP9	5col black	7.50	4.75
C27	AP9	10col red brown	10.00	8.00
		Nos. C15-C27 (13)	35.20	16.45

Nos. C15-C27 with holes punched through were for use of government officials.
See Nos. C216-C219. For overprints see Nos. C67-C73, C92-C93, C103-C116, CO1-CO13.

Airplane over Poás Volcano — AP10

1937, Feb. 10

C28	AP10	1c black	.45	.35
C29	AP10	2c brown	.45	.35
C30	AP10	3c dk violet	.45	.35
		Nos. C28-C30 (3)	1.35	1.05

First Fair of Costa Rica.

Puntarenas — AP11

National Bank
AP12

Perf. 12, 12½
1937, Dec. 15   *Unwmk.*

C31	AP11	2c black gray	.25	.20
C32	AP11	5c green	.30	.20
C33	AP11	20c deep blue	.30	.20
C34	AP11	1.40col olive brn	2.50	2.50
		Nos. C31-C34 (4)	3.35	3.10

1938, Jan. 11   *Wmk. 229*   *Perf. 12½*

C35	AP12	1c purple	.25	.20
C36	AP12	3c red orange	.25	.20
C37	AP12	10c carmine rose	.30	.20
C38	AP12	75c brown	2.50	2.00
		Nos. C35-C38 (4)	3.30	2.60

Nos. C31-C38 for the Natl. Products Exposition held at San José, Dec. 1937.

Airport Administration Building, La Sabana — AP13

1940, May 2   *Engr.*   *Unwmk.*

C39	AP13	5c green	.30	.25
C40	AP13	10c rose pink	.30	.25
C41	AP13	25c lt blue	.40	.25
C42	AP13	35c red brown	.40	.25
C43	AP13	60c red org	.55	.40
C44	AP13	75c violet	1.40	1.00
C45	AP13	2.35col turq grn	6.50	5.50
		Nos. C39-C45 (7)	9.85	7.90

Opening of the Intl. Airport at La Sabana.

Duran Sanatorium
AP14

Overprinted "Dia Panamericano de la Salud / 2 Diciembre 1940" and Bar in Black

1940, Dec. 2   *Perf. 12*

C46	AP14	10c scarlet	.25	.25
C47	AP14	15c purple	.25	.25
C48	AP14	25c lt blue	.50	.40
C49	AP14	35c bister brn	.70	.65
C50	AP14	60c pck green	1.00	.95
C51	AP14	75c olive	2.75	2.50
C52	AP14	1.35col red org	8.75	8.00
C53	AP14	5col sepia	45.00	40.00
C54	AP14	10col red lilac	140.00	100.00
		Nos. C46-C54 (9)	199.20	153.00

Pan-American Health Day. Nos. C46-C54 exist without overprint. Value, set $5,000.

No. 174 Surcharged in Black or Blue

1940, Dec. 17   *Perf. 14*

C55	A95	15c on 50c yel (Bk)	1.00	1.00
C56	A95	30c on 50c yel (Bl)	1.00	1.00

Pan-American Aviation Day, proclaimed by President F. D. Roosevelt.
The 15c surcharge exists normal and inverted on No. 171, Value, normal $30. Inverted surcharge is worth more.

International Soccer Game at National Stadium — AP15

1941, May 8   *Perf. 12*

C57	AP15	15c red	.80	.25
C58	AP15	30c dp ultra	.90	.25
C59	AP15	40c red brn	.95	.35
C60	AP15	50c purple	1.40	.80
C61	AP15	60c brt green	1.60	.90
C62	AP15	75c yel org	2.75	1.40
C63	AP15	1col dull vio	4.75	4.50
C64	AP15	1.40col rose	9.50	8.75

C65	AP15	2col blue grn	20.00	17.50
C66	AP15	5col black	52.50	37.50
		Nos. C57-C66 (10)	95.15	72.20

Caribbean and Central American Soccer Championship. See Nos. C121-C123. For surcharges see Nos. C145-C147.

Air Post Stamps of 1934
Overprinted or Surcharged in Black

1941, June 2

C67	AP8	5c on 20c dp bl	.20	.20
C68	AP8	15c on 20c dp bl	.20	.20
C69	AP8	40c on 75c dl vio	.35	.20
C70	AP9	65c on 1col dp rose	.65	.50
C71	AP9	1.40col on 2col lt bl	3.25	3.25
C72	AP9	5col black	12.00	12.00
C73	AP9	10col red brn	14.50	12.50
		Nos. C67-C73 (7)	31.15	28.85

Issued in commemoration of the settlement of the Costa Rica-Panama border dispute.
Nos. C67-C73 are found with hyphen omitted in overprint.
Nos. C67-C69 exist with inverted overprint. Value, each, $35.

University Types of 1941

1941, Aug. 26   *Perf. 12*

C74	A107	15c salmon	.25	.25
C75	A106	30c lt blue	.30	.25
C76	A107	40c orange	.40	.30
C77	A106	60c turq green	.50	.40
C78	A107	1col violet	1.90	1.90
C79	A106	2col black	4.75	4.75
C80	A107	5col sepia	16.00	16.00
		Nos. C74-C80 (7)	24.10	23.85

Portrait Type of 1943-47

Designs: 40c, Manuel Aguilar. No. C83, Francisco Morazan. No. C83A, Jose R. De Gallegos. 50c, Jose M. Alfaro. 60c, Francisco M. Oreamuno. 65c, Jose M. Castro. 85c, Juan Rafael Mora. 1col, Jose M. Montealegre. 1.05col, Braulio Carrillo. 1.15col, Jesus Jimenez. 1.40col, Bruno Carranza. 2col, Tomas Guardia.

1943-45   *Engr.*

C81	A109	10c rose pink	.20	.20
C82	A109	40c blue	.30	.20
C82A	A109	40c car rose	.30	.20
C83	A109	45c magenta	.50	.30
C83A	A109	45c black	.25	.20
C84	A109	50c turq grn	1.75	.25
C84A	A109	50c red org	.40	.25
C85	A109	60c brt ultra	.65	.25
C85A	A109	60c brt green	.25	.25
C86	A109	65c scarlet	.95	.30
C86A	A109	65c brt ultra	.30	.25
C87	A109	85c dp org	1.25	.50
C87A	A109	85c dull pur	1.60	.65
C88	A109	1col black	1.60	.50
C88A	A109	1col scarlet	.65	.40
C88B	A109	1.05col bis brn	.90	.55
C89	A109	1.15col red brn	2.10	1.75
C89A	A109	1.15col green	3.00	1.25
C90	A109	1.40col dp vio	3.25	2.40
C90A	A109	1.40col org yel	1.75	1.60
C91	A109	2col black	5.25	1.25
C91A	A109	2col olive grn	1.60	.50
		Nos. C81-C91A (22)	28.80	13.95

Issued: Nos. C82A, C83A, C84A, C85A, C86A, C87A, C88A, C88B, C89A, C90A, C91A, 1945.
See Nos. C124-C127, C179-C181. For surcharges see Nos. C154-C158, C182, C184-C185.

Nos. C26-C27 Overprinted in Red or Blue

1943, Sept. 16

C92	AP9	5col black (R)	4.50	3.00
C93	AP9	10col red brown (Bl)	5.25	3.25

Mercury and Plane
AP31

1944, Jan. 19

C94	AP31	10c red orange	.20	.20
C95	AP31	15c dk carmine	.20	.20
C96	AP31	40c brt ultra	.40	.20
C97	AP31	45c dp red lil	.40	.30
C98	AP31	60c turq green	.55	.40
C99	AP31	1col dk red brn	1.60	.80
C100	AP31	1.40col gray blk	8.75	5.85
C101	AP31	5col violet	24.00	16.00
C102	AP31	10col black	70.00	62.50
		Nos. C94-C102 (9)	106.10	85.85

City of San Ramón founding, 100th anniv.

No. CO10 With Additional Overprint in Black

1944, Nov. 22

C103	AP9	1col deep rose	2.00	.95
a.		Blue overprint	100.00	100.00

Nos. CO1-CO13 Overprinted in Carmine or Black

1945, Jan. 12   *Unwmk.*   *Perf. 12*

C104	AP8	5c green	.60	.50
C105	AP8	10c car rose (Bk)	.60	.55
C106	AP8	15c chocolate	.60	.55
C107	AP8	20c deep blue	.50	.40
C108	AP8	25c dp org (Bk)	.60	.60
C109	AP8	40c olive blk	.35	.35
C110	AP8	50c gray blk	.60	.60
C111	AP8	60c org yel (Bk)	.90	.35
C112	AP8	75c dull violet	.75	.50
C113	AP9	1col dp rose (Bk)	.75	.35
C114	AP9	2col light blue	8.00	4.50
C115	AP9	5col black	8.00	5.50
C116	AP9	10col red brn (Bk)	11.00	8.25
		Nos. C104-C116 (13)	33.25	23.00

No. C104 exists inverted & overprinted in black. This is probably a trial color. Value, $50.

> **Catalogue values for unused stamps in this section, from this point to the end of the section, are for Never Hinged items.**

AP32

Telegraph Stamps Overprinted in Black or Carmine

1945, Feb. 28   *Unwmk.*   *Perf. 12½*

C117	AP32	40c green (C)	.30	.20
C118	AP32	50c ultra (C)	.30	.20
C119	AP32	1col orange (Bk)	1.00	.40
		Nos. C117-C119 (3)	1.60	.80

No. C117 exists with inverted overprint. Value, $10.

Florence
Nightingale
and Edith
Cavell
AP33

1945   **Engr.**
C120 AP33 1col black & car   1.00 .50

Costa Rican Red Cross Soc., 60th anniv.
For surcharge see No. C183.

Soccer Type of 1941
Inscribed: "Febrero 1946"

1946, May 13   **Perf. 12**
C121 AP15 25c green   1.60 .65
C122 AP15 30c dull yellow   2.00 .65
C123 AP15 55c deep blue   2.40 .65
   Nos. C121-C123 (3)   6.00 1.95

Portrait Type of 1943-47

Designs: 25c, Aniceto Esquivel. 30c,
Vicente Herrera. 55c, Prospero Fernandez.
75c, Bernardo Soto.

1946, May 12
C124 A109 25c blue   .20 .20
C125 A109 30c red brown   .25 .20
C126 A109 55c plum   .40 .30
C127 A109 75c blue green   .60 .40
   Nos. C124-C127 (4)   1.45 1.10

Hospital of
St. John of
God
AP38

1946, June 24   **Unwmk.**   **Perf. 12½**
Center in Black
C128 AP38 5c yellow grn   .40 .20
C129 AP38 10c dk brown   .50 .20
C130 AP38 15c carmine   .50 .20
C131 AP38 25c dk blue   .50 .20
C132 AP38 30c dp orange   .95 .25
C133 AP38 40c olive grn   .50 .20
C134 AP38 50c violet   .95 .25
C135 AP38 60c dk sl grn   1.90 .55
C136 AP38 75c brown   1.40 .40
   a. Horiz. pair, imperf. btwn.   100.00
C137 AP38 1col blue   1.90 .35
C138 AP38 2col brn org   2.40 .80
C139 AP38 3col dk vio brn   4.75 2.00
C140 AP38 5col yellow   6.50 2.40
   Nos. C128-C140 (13)   23.15 8.00

Nos. C128, C129, C132 and C135 exist
imperf.

Rafael
Iglesias — AP39

3col, Ascensión Esquivel. 5col, Cleto González Viquez. 10col, Ricardo Jiménez
Oreamuno.

1947, Jan. 15   **Wmk. 215**   **Perf. 14**
Center in Black
C141 AP39 2col blue   2.00 1.25
C142 AP39 3col dp car   2.75 1.60
C143 AP39 5col dk green   4.75 2.00
C144 AP39 10col orange   7.25 5.25
   Nos. C141-C144 (4)   16.75 10.10

Nos. C141-C144 also exist in a souvenir
sheet of 4. Value, $600. The sheet in sepia is a
proof and worth less.

Nos. C121-C123 Surcharged in Black

1947, May 5   **Unwmk.**   **Perf. 12**
C145 AP15 15c on 25c green   .95 .80
C146 AP15 15c on 30c dull yel   .95 .80
C147 AP15 15c on 55c dp blue   .95 .80
   Nos. C145-C147 (3)   2.85 2.40

Nos. C145-C147 exist with inverted
surcharge.

Columbus
in Cariari
AP43

1947, May 18   **Engr.**   **Perf. 12½**
Center in Black
C148 AP43 25c green   .30 .20
C149 AP43 30c dp ultra   .40 .20
C150 AP43 40c red orange   .50 .20
C151 AP43 45c violet   .65 .30
C152 AP43 50c brt carmine   .70 .20
C153 AP43 65c brown org   2.00 .95
   Nos. C148-C153 (6)   4.55 2.05

For surcharges see Nos. C178, C220-C223.

Nos. C84A, C85A, C127, C88A, and
C88B Surcharged with New Value in
Black or Red

1947, June 3   **Perf. 12**
C154 A109 15c on 50c red org   .40 .30
C155 A109 15c on 60c brt grn
     (R)   .40 .30
C156 A109 15c on 75c bl grn (R)   .40 .30
C157 A109 15c on 1col scar   .55 .50
C158 A109 15c on 1.05col bis
     brn   .40 .30
   Nos. C154-C158 (5)   2.15 1.70

No. C155 is known with black surcharge.
Value, $10. No. C156 with inverted surcharge.
Value, $10.

Early Steam Locomotive — AP44

1947, Nov. 10   **Perf. 12½**
C159 AP44 35c bl grn & blk   2.40 .55

Electric railroad to the Pacific coast, 50th
anniv.

Roosevelt Type of Regular Issue

1947, Aug. 26   **Perf. 12**
C160 A122 15c green   .20 .20
C161 A122 30c car rose   .20 .20
C162 A122 45c red brown   .20 .20
C163 A122 65c orange yel   .25 .20
C164 A122 75c blue   .30 .20
C165 A122 1col olive grn   .50 .35
C166 A122 2col black   1.40 1.00
C167 A122 5col scarlet   2.50 2.40
   Nos. C160-C167 (8)   5.55 4.60

For surcharges see Nos. C224-C226.

National Theater   Rafael Iglesias
AP46   AP47

1948, Jan. 26   **Perf. 12½**
Center in Black
C168 AP46 15c brt ultra   .25 .20
C169 AP46 20c red   .25 .20
C170 AP47 35c dk green   .40 .20
C171 AP46 45c purple   .50 .25
C172 AP46 50c carmine   .50 .25
C173 AP46 75c red violet   1.10 .80
C174 AP46 1col olive   2.00 1.10
C175 AP46 2col red brn   3.25 1.60
C176 AP47 5col org yel   5.25 4.00
C177 AP47 10col brt blue   12.00 8.00
   Nos. C168-C177 (10)   25.50 16.60

50th anniversary of National Theater.

No. C150
Surcharged
in Carmine

1948, Apr. 21
C178 AP43 35c on 40c   1.10 .50

Exists with surcharge inverted.

Portrait Type of 1943-47

5c, Salvador Lara. 15c, Carlos Duran.

1948   **Engr.**   **Perf. 12**
C179 A109 5c sepia   .20 .20
C180 A109 10c olive brown   .20 .20
C181 A109 15c violet   .20 .20
   Nos. C179-C181 (3)   .60 .60

Nos. C88B, C120,
C89A and C90A
Surcharged in Carmine
or Black

Perf. 12½, 12
1949, Aug. 28   **Unwmk.**
C182 A109 35c on 1.05col bis   .35 .20
C183 AP33 50c on 1col blk & car   .60 .45
   a. 2nd & 3rd lines both read "125
     Aniversario"   5.00 3.00
C184 A109 55c on 1.15col grn   .85 .70
C185 A109 55c on 1.40col org
     yel (Bk)   .90 .60
   Nos. C182-C185 (4)   2.70 1.95

125th anniv. of the annexation of the prov-
ince of Guanacaste.
Overprint differs on No. C183, with "Guana-
caste" in capitals, and lower case "a" in
"Anexion."
The variety "I" for "i" in "Anexion" is found on
Nos. C182, C184 and C185.

Symbols of
UPU
AP48

1950, Jan. 11   **Photo.**   **Perf. 11½**
C186 AP48 15c lilac rose   .20 .20
C187 AP48 25c chalky blue   .40 .40
C188 AP48 1col gray green   .55 .55
   Nos. C186-C188 (3)   1.15 1.15

75th anniv. of the UPU.

Battle of
El Tejar,
Cartago
AP49

Occupation of   Bull (Cattle
Limón — AP50   Raising) — AP51

25c, Lucha ranch. 35c, Trenches of San
Isidro Battalion. 55c, 75c, Observation post.
80c, 1col, Dr. Carlos Luis Valverde.

Inscribed: "Guerra de Liberacion
Nacional 1948"
Engraved; Center Photogravure
1950, July 20   **Perf. 12½**
Center in Black
C189 AP49 15c brt car   .20 .20
C190 AP50 20c dull green   .20 .20
C191 AP49 25c dull blue   .30 .20
C192 AP49 35c chestnut   .40 .20
C193 AP49 55c lilac   .70 .20
C194 AP50 75c red org   1.10 .30
C195 AP50 80c gray   1.10 .50
C196 AP50 1col org yel   1.50 .55
   Nos. C189-C196 (8)   5.50 2.35

2nd anniv. of the War for Natl. Liberation.

Inscribed: "Feria Nacional
Agricola Ganadera e Industrial
Cartago 1950"

1950, July 27

1c, 10c, 2col, Bull. 2c, 30c, 3col, Tuna fishing. 3c, 65c, Pineapple. 5c, 50c, 5col,
Bananas. 45c, 80c, 10col, Coffee picker.

Center in Black
C197 AP51 1c brt green   .55 .25
C198 AP51 2c brt blue   .55 .25
C199 AP51 3c chocolate   .65 .25
C200 AP51 5c dp ultra   .65 .25
C201 AP51 10c green   .65 .25
C202 AP51 30c purple   .65 .25
C203 AP51 45c vermilion   .70 .25
C204 AP51 50c blue gray   .80 .25
C205 AP51 65c dk blue   .80 .25
C206 AP51 80c dp rose   2.00 .65
C207 AP51 2col org yel   4.00 1.60
C208 AP51 3col blue   7.25 4.00
C209 AP51 5col carmine   10.50 6.50
C210 AP51 10col dp claret   10.50 6.50
   Nos. C197-C210 (14)   40.25 21.50

National Agricultural, Livestock and Industrial Fair, Cartago, 1950.
For surcharge see No. RA1.

Queen
Isabella I
and
Caravels of
Columbus
AP52

Unwmk.
1952, Mar. 4   **Engr.**   **Perf. 13**
C211 AP52 15c carmine   .30 .20
C212 AP52 20c orange   .55 .20
C213 AP52 25c ultra   .80 .20
C214 AP52 55c dp green   2.75 .25
C215 AP52 2col violet   5.25 .50
   Nos. C211-C215 (5)   9.65 1.35

Birth of Queen Isabella I of Spain, 500th
anniv.

Mail Plane Type of 1934

1952-53   **Perf. 12**
C216 AP8 5c blue   .40 .25
C217 AP8 10c green   .40 .25
C218 AP8 15c car rose ('53)   .55 .25
C219 AP8 35c purple   1.40 .25
   Nos. C216-C219 (4)   2.75 1.00

Nos. C216-C217 were reprinted in 1953 in
different shades. Values the same.

Nos. C149-C151, C153 Surcharged
in Red: "HABILITADO PARA
CINCO CENTIMOS 1953"

1953, Apr. 24   **Perf. 12½**
Center in Black
C220 AP43 5c on 30c dp ultra   2.00 1.50
C221 AP43 5c on 40c red org   .40 .30
C222 AP43 5c on 45c vio   .40 .30
C223 AP43 5c on 65c brn org   .40 .30
   Nos. C220-C223 (4)   3.20 2.40

Nos. C161-C163
Surcharged in Black

1953, Apr. 11   **Perf. 12**
C224 A122 15c on 30c car rose   .30 .20
C225 A122 15c on 45c red brn   .30 .20
C226 A122 15c on 65c org yel   .30 .20
   Nos. C224-C226 (3)   .90 .60

Refinery of Vegetable Oils and Fats — AP53

Industries: 10c, Pottery. 15c, Sugar. 20c, Soap. 25c, Lumber. 30c, Matches. 35c, Textiles. 40c, Leather. 45c, Tobacco. 50c, Preserving. 55c, Canning. 60c, General. 65c, Metals. 75c, Pharmaceuticals. 80c, Pharmaceuticals. 1col, Paper. 2col, Rubber. 3col, Airplane maintenance. 5col, Marble. 10col, Beer.

Engraved; Center Photogravure

1954-59		Unwmk.	*Perf. 13x12½*	
		Center in Black		
C227	AP53	5c red	.25	.20
C228	AP53	10c dk blue	.25	.20
C229	AP53	15c green	.25	.20
C230	AP53	20c violet	.25	.20
C231	AP53	25c magenta	.30	.20
C232	AP53	30c purple	.65	.40
C233	AP53	35c red vio	.40	.20
C234	AP53	40c black	.65	.30
C235	AP53	45c dk green	1.25	.40
C236	AP53	50c vio brown	.80	.20
C237	AP53	55c yellow	.65	.20
C238	AP53	60c brown	1.50	.65
C239	AP53	65c carmine	1.75	.95
C240	AP53	75c violet	2.40	.80
C240A	AP53	80c pur & gray	1.25	.80
C241	AP53	1col blue	.80	.40
a.		Imperf., pair	100.00	
C242	AP53	2col rose pink	2.40	1.25
C243	AP53	3col ol grn	3.25	2.00
C244	AP53	5col black	5.25	1.60
C245	AP53	10col yellow	14.50	9.50
		Nos. C227-C245 (20)	38.80	20.65

Issued: 30c, 35c, 60c, 65c, 75c, 2col, 3col, Oct. 20; 80c, Oct. 2, 1959; others, Sept. 1.
See Nos. C252-C255. For surcharges and overprint, see Nos. C314-C315, C334-C336, RA2, RA11.

Globe, Rotary Emblem AP54 — Map of Costa Rica AP55

25c, Hand protecting boy. 40c, 2col, Hospital. 45c, Globe & palm leaves. 60c, Lighthouse.

1956, Feb. 7		Engr.	*Perf. 12*	
C246	AP54	10c green	.20	.20
C247	AP54	25c dk blue	.20	.20
C248	AP54	40c dk brown	.50	.40
C249	AP54	45c brt red	.30	.25
C250	AP54	60c dk red vio	.50	.20
C251	AP54	2col yel org	1.25	.65
		Nos. C246-C251 (6)	2.95	2.00

50th anniv. of Rotary Intl. (in 1955).

Industries Type of 1954

Designs as in 1954.

Engraved; Center Photogravure

1956, Feb. 17			*Perf. 12*	
		Center in Black		
C252	AP53	5c ultra	.30	.20
C253	AP53	10c violet blue	.40	.20
C254	AP53	15c orange yel	.50	.20
C255	AP53	75c red orange	.80	.30
		Nos. C252-C255 (4)	2.00	.90

1957, June 21   Engr.   *Perf. 13½x13*

10c, Map of Guanacaste. 15c, Inn. 20c, House of Santa Rosa. 25c, Gen. Jose Manuel Quiros. 30c, Old Presidential Palace. 35c, Joaquin Bernardo Calvo. 40c, Luis Molina. 45c, Gen. Jose Joaquin Mora. 50c, Gen. Jose Maria Canas. 55c, Juan Santamaria monument. 60c, National monument. 65c, Antonio Vallerriestra. 70c, Ramon Castilla y Marquesado. 75c, San Carlos fortress. 80c, Francisco Maria Oreamuno. 1col, Pres. Juan Rafael Mora.

C256	AP55	5c lt blue	.25	.25
C257	AP55	10c green	.30	.25
C258	AP55	15c dp orange	.30	.25
C259	AP55	20c lt brown	.30	.25

C260	AP55	25c vio blue	.40	.25
C261	AP55	30c violet	.50	.25
C262	AP55	35c car rose	.55	.25
C263	AP55	40c slate	.55	.25
C264	AP55	45c rose red	.65	.25
C265	AP55	50c ultra	.70	.25
C266	AP55	55c ocher	1.10	.25
C267	AP55	60c brt car	.95	.30
C268	AP55	65c carmine	1.10	.30
C269	AP55	70c orange yel	1.25	.30
C270	AP55	75c emerald	1.25	.30
C271	AP55	80c dk brown	1.60	.40
C272	AP55	1col black	1.75	.40
		Nos. C256-C272 (17)	13.50	4.75

Centenary of War of 1856-57.

Cleto Gonzalez Viquez — AP56

Highway and Gonzalez Viquez AP57

Designs: 10c, Ricardo Jimenez Oreamuno. 20c, Puntarenas wharf and Jimenez. 35c, Post and Telegraph Bldg. and Jimenez. 55c, Pipeline and Gonzalez Viquez. 80c, National Library and Gonzalez Viquez. 1col, Electric train and Jimenez. 2col, Gonzales and Jimenez.

1959, Nov. 23		Engr.	*Perf. 13½*	
C274	AP56	5c car & ultra	.20	.20
C275	AP56	10c red & gray	.20	.20
		Perf. 13½x13		
C276	AP57	15c dk bl grn & blk	.20	.20
C277	AP57	20c car & brn	.50	.20
C278	AP57	35c rose lil & bl	.20	.20
C279	AP57	55c olive & vio	.50	.20
C280	AP57	80c ultra	.60	.35
C281	AP57	1col orange & mar	.85	.50
C282	AP57	2col gray & mar	2.00	1.60
		Nos. C274-C282 (9)	5.25	3.65

For surcharge and overprint see Nos. C337, C339.

Soccer AP58

Designs: Various soccer scenes.

1960, Mar. 7		Unwmk.	*Perf. 13½*	
			Photo.	
C283	AP58	10c black	.30	.30
C284	AP58	25c ultra	.30	.30
C285	AP58	35c red orange	.30	.30
C286	AP58	50c red brown	.40	.30
C287	AP58	85c Prus green	1.10	.90
C288	AP58	5col dp claret	2.50	2.50
		Nos. C283-C288 (6)	4.90	4.60

Souvenir Sheet

Imperf

C289	AP58	2col blue	6.50	6.50

3rd Pan-American Soccer Games, San José, Mar. 1960.
Nos. C283-C288 exist imperf. Value, pair $150.

WRY Uprooted Oak Emblem — AP59

1960, Apr. 7		Unwmk.	*Perf. 11½*	
		Granite Paper		
C290	AP59	35c vio bl, blk & yel	.30	.25
C291	AP59	85c black & brt pink	.65	.55

Refugee Year, July 1, 1959-June 30, 1960.

Banner and "OEA" — AP60

35c, "OEA" in oval. 55c, Clasped hands. 2col, "OEA" & map of Americas. 5col, Flags forming bird. 10col, Map of Costa Rica, flags & "OEA."

1960, Aug. 15		Litho.	*Perf. 10*	
C292	AP60	25c black & multi	.20	.20
a.		Multi, impression sideways	60.00	
C293	AP60	35c multicolored	.30	.30
a.		Pair, imperf. between	60.00	
C294	AP60	55c multicolored	.50	.40
C295	AP60	5col multicolored	3.00	2.75
C296	AP60	10col black & multi	5.00	4.50
		Nos. C292-C296 (5)	9.00	8.15

Souvenir Sheet

Imperf

C297	AP60	2col multicolored	2.75	2.75

Pan-American Conf., San Jose, Aug. 15.

St. Louisa de Marillac and Orphanage — AP61

St. Vincent de Paul — AP62

25c, St. Vincent & old seminary. 50c, St. Louisa & sickroom. 1col, St. Vincent & new seminary.

1960, Oct. 26		Engr.	*Perf. 14x13½*	
C298	AP61	10c green	.25	.25
C299	AP61	25c carmine	.25	.25
C300	AP61	50c dk blue	.25	.25
C301	AP61	1col brown org	.40	.30
C302	AP62	5col brown	2.10	1.75
		Nos. C298-C302 (5)	3.25	2.80

St. Vincent (1581?-1660) and St. Louisa (1591-1660). Nos. C298-C302 exist imperf.

Runner AP63

Sports: 2c, Woman swimmer. 3c, Bicyclist. 4c, Weight lifter. 5c, Woman tennis player. 10c, Boxers. 25c, Soccer player. 85c, Basketball player. 1col, Baseball batter. 5col, Romulus and Remus statue. 10col, Pistol marksman.

1960, Dec. 14		Photo.	Unwmk.	
		Designs in Black		
C303	AP63	1c brt yellow	.20	.20
C304	AP63	2c lt blue	.20	.20
C305	AP63	3c dp rose	.20	.20
C306	AP63	4c yellow	.25	.20
C307	AP63	5c brt yel grn	.25	.20

C308	AP63	10c pink	.25	.20
C309	AP63	25c lt bl grn	.25	.20
C310	AP63	85c lilac	1.25	.80
C311	AP63	1col gray	1.40	1.00
C312	AP63	10col lt violet	10.50	8.00
		Nos. C303-C312 (10)	14.75	11.20

Souvenir Sheets

Perf. 14x13½

C313	AP63	5col multi	6.00	6.00

17th Olympic Games, Rome, 8/25-9/11. Nos. C303-C313 exist imperf.

No. C255 Surcharged and Overprinted in Blue or Ultramarine: "XV Campeonato Mundial de Beisbol de Aficionados"

Engraved and Photogravure

1961, Apr. 21			*Perf. 12*	
		Center in Black		
C314	AP53	25c on 75c red org (Bl)	.25	.20
C315	AP53	75c red orange (U)	.55	.20

15th Amateur Baseball Championships.

Alberto Brenes C. AP64 — Miguel Obregon AP65

No. C317, Manuel Aguilar. No. C318, Agustin Gutierrez L. No. C319, Vicente Herrera.

1961, June 12		Photo.	*Perf. 12*	
C316	AP64	10c deep claret	.25	.25
C317	AP64	10c blue	.25	.25
C318	AP64	25c bright violet	.25	.25
C319	AP64	25c gray	.25	.25
		Nos. C316-C319 (4)	1.00	1.00

First Continental Congress of Lawyers, San José, June 11-15. Exist imperf.
See Nos. C330-C333.

1961, July 19		Litho.	*Perf. 13½*	
C320	AP65	10c Prussian green	.40	.25

Birth centenary of Prof. Miguel Obregon L. Exists imperf. Value $50.

UN Food and Agriculture Organization AP66

UN day (UN Organizations): 20c, WHO. 25c, ILO. 30, ITU. 35c, World Meteorological Organization. 45c, UNESCO. 85c, ICAO. 5col, "United Nations" holding the world. 10col, Int. Bank for Reconstruction and Development.

			Perf. 11½	
1961, Oct. 24		Unwmk.	Engr.	
C321	AP66	10c lt green	.20	.20
C322	AP66	20c orange	.20	.20
C323	AP66	25c Prus grn	.20	.20
C324	AP66	30c dk blue	.20	.20
C325	AP66	35c carmine rose	.90	.25
C326	AP66	45c violet	.30	.20
C327	AP66	85c blue	.65	.55
C328	AP66	10col dk sl grn	5.25	4.50
		Nos. C321-C328 (8)	7.90	6.30

Souvenir Sheet

Imperf

C329	AP66	5col ultra	4.50	4.50

For overprint see No. C338.

Portrait Type of 1961

No. C330, Dr. José Maria Soto Alfaro. No. C331, Dr. Elias Rojas Roman. No. C332, Dr. Andres Saenz Llorente. No. C333, Dr. Juan José Ulloa Giralt.

1961   **Photo.**   *Perf. 13½*

C330	AP64 10c blue green	.25	.20
C331	AP64 10c violet	.25	.20
C332	AP64 25c dark gray	.30	.20
C333	AP64 25c deep claret	.30	.20
	Nos. C330-C333 (4)	1.10	.80

9th Congress of Physicians of Central America and Panama.

Nos. C229, C236 and C280 Surcharged in Black, Orange or Red

Engraved; Center Photogravure

1962   *Perf. 13x12½, 13½x13*

C334	AP53 10c ("10") on 15c	.20	.20
C334A	AP53 10c ("c0.10") on 15c (R)	.20	.20
C335	AP53 25c on 15c	.20	.20
C336	AP53 35c on 50c (O)	.30	.20

Engr.

C337	AP57 85c on 80c (R)	.95	.80
	Nos. C334-C337 (5)	1.85	1.60

No. C336 exists with double surcharge. Value, $35.

Nos. C324 and C282 Overprinted in Red: "II CONVENCION FILATELICA CENTROAMERICANA SETIEMBRE 1962"

1962, Sept. 12   *Perf. 11½, 13½x13*

C338	AP66 30c dark blue	.55	.40
C339	AP57 2col gray & mar	1.60	1.25

2nd Central American Phil. Convention.

Revenue Stamp Surcharged with New Values and "CORREO AEREO" in Red

1962   **Engr.**   *Perf. 12*

C341	A124 25c on 2c emer	.20	.20
C342	A124 35c on 2c emer	.20	.20
C343	A124 45c on 2c emer	.40	.30
C344	A124 85c on 2c emer	.70	.55
	Nos. C341-C344 (4)	1.40	1.20

Arms and Malaria Eradication Emblem AP67

1963, Feb. 14   **Photo.**   *Perf. 11½*

C345	AP67 25c brt rose	.20	.20
C346	AP67 35c brown org	.25	.20
C347	AP67 45c ultra	.30	.25
C348	AP67 85c blue grn	.65	.50
C349	AP67 1col dk blue	1.10	.65
	Nos. C345-C349 (5)	2.50	1.80

WHO drive to eradicate malaria.

Central American Tapir — AP68

Designs: 5c, Paca. 25c, Jaguar. 30c, Ocelot. 35c, Whitetail deer. 40c, Manatee. 85c, White-throated capuchin monkey. 5col, White-lipped peccary.

Perf. 13½

1963, May   **Unwmk.**   **Photo.**

C354	AP68 5c yel ol & brn	.25	.20
C355	AP68 10c orange & sl	.30	.20
C356	AP68 25c blue & yel	.50	.35
C357	AP68 30c lt yel grn & brn	.70	.40
C358	AP68 35c bis & red brn	1.00	.40
C359	AP68 40c emer & sl bl	1.25	.55
C360	AP68 85c green & blk	4.00	.55
C361	AP68 5col gray grn & choc	12.00	4.00
	Nos. C354-C361 (8)	20.00	6.65

Stamp of 1863 and Packet "Monarch" — AP69

Issue of 1863 and: 2col, Recaredo Bonilla Carrillo, Postmaster, 1862-63. 3col, Burros, overland mail transport, 1839. 10col, Burro railway car.

1963, June 26   **Litho.**

C362	AP69 25c dl rose & chlky bl	.25	.20
C363	AP69 2col gray bl & org	1.75	1.25
C364	AP69 3col bister & emer	3.00	2.00
C365	AP69 10col dl grn & ocher	10.50	6.00
	Nos. C362-C365 (4)	15.50	9.45

Centenary of Costa Rica's stamps. No. C362 is inscribed "William Le Lacheur," the builder and captain of the "Monarch."

Souvenir Sheets

REPUBLICA DE COSTA RICA

+ COSTA RICA CORREO AEREO

SAN JOSE

₡5 1 CENTENARIO DEL SELLO POSTAL

PRIMER CENTENARIO DEL SELLO POSTAL

Stamps of 1863 and San José Postmark — AP70

Perf. 13½, Imperf.

1963, June 26   **Unwmk.**

C366	AP70 5col bl, red, grn & org	5.50	5.50

Cent. of Costa Rica's stamps. In 1968 examples of No. C366 were overprinted "2-4 Agosto 1968" and "III Exposicion Filatelica Nacional / 'Costa Rica 68'". Value, $10.50.

Animal Type of 1963 Surcharged in Red

No. C367, Little anteater. No. C368, Gray fox. No. C369, Armadillo. No. C370, Great anteater.

1963, Sept. 14   **Photo.**   *Perf. 13½*

C367	AP68 10c on 1c brt grn & org brn	1.10	.30
C368	AP68 25c on 2c org yel & ol grn	1.10	.30
C369	AP68 35c on 3c bluish grn & brn	1.50	.30
C370	AP68 85c on 4c dp rose & dk brn	2.75	.65
	Nos. C367-C370 (4)	6.45	1.55

Examples of #C370 exist without surcharge.

Pres. Kennedy AP71

Ancestral Figure AP72

Portraits — Presidents: 25c, Francisco J. Orlich, Costa Rica. 30c, Julio A. Rivera, El Salvador. 35c, Miguel Ydigoras F., Guatemala. 85c, Dr. Ramon Villeda M., Honduras. 1col, Luis A. Somoza, Nicaragua. 3col, Roberto F. Chiari, Panama.

1963, Dec. 7   **Unwmk.**   *Perf. 14*

Portraits in Black Brown

C371	AP71 25c violet brn	.30	.25
C372	AP71 30c brt lil rose	.30	.25
C373	AP71 35c ocher	.30	.25
C374	AP71 85c gray blue	.50	.25
C375	AP71 1col orange brn	.55	.30
C376	AP71 3col lt ol grn	2.50	1.60
C377	AP71 5col gray	3.25	2.25
	Nos. C371-C377 (7)	7.70	5.15

Meeting of Central American Presidents with Pres. John F. Kennedy, San José, Mar. 18-20, 1963.

1963-64   **Photo.**   *Perf. 12*

Ancient Art: 5c, Dog, horiz. 10c, Ornamental stool, horiz. 25c, Male figure. 30c, Ceremonial dancer. 35c, Ceramic vase. 50c, Frog. 55c, Bell. 75c, Six-limbed figure. 85c, Seated man. 90c, Bird-shaped jug. 1col, Twin human beaker, horiz. 2col, Alligator, horiz. 3col, Twin-tailed lizard. 5col, Figure under arch. 10col, Polished stone figure.

C378	AP72 5c lt yel grn & Prus grn	.25	.25
C379	AP72 10c buff & dk grn	.25	.25
C380	AP72 25c rose & dk brn	.25	.25
C381	AP72 30c ocher & Prus grn ('64)	.25	.25
C382	AP72 35c sal & sl grn	.25	.25
C383	AP72 45c lt bl & dk brn	.25	.25
C384	AP72 50c dl bl & dk brn	.40	.25
C385	AP72 55c yel grn & dk brn	.55	.25
C386	AP72 75c ocher & dk red brn	.55	.25
C387	AP72 85c yel & red brn	1.40	1.40
C388	AP72 90c cit & red brn ('64)	1.75	1.75
C389	AP72 1col lt bl & dk brn ('64)	1.00	.30
C390	AP72 2col buff & dk grn ('64)	1.60	.65
C391	AP72 3col yel grn & dk brn ('64)	5.25	.95
C392	AP72 5col cit & sep ('64)	5.25	5.25
C393	AP72 10col rose lil & sl	8.75	8.75
	Nos. C378-C393 (16)	28.00	21.30

For surcharges and overprint see Nos. C395, C397-C398, C400, C426-C428.

Flags of Central American States — AP73

1964, Mar. 11   *Perf. 14*

C394	AP73 30c bl, gray, red & blk	1.00	.35

Central American Independence issue. For surcharge see No. C396.

Nos. C381, C394 and C387 Surcharged

1964, Oct.   *Perf. 12, 14*

C395	AP72 5c on 30c	.55	.25
C396	AP73 15c on 30c	.55	.25
C397	AP72 15c on 85c	.55	.25
	Nos. C395-C397 (3)	1.65	.75

No. C388 Surcharged: "C 0.15 / CONFERENCIA POSTAL / DE PARIS — 1864"

1964, Nov. 22   *Perf. 12*

C398	AP72 15c on 90c cit & red brn	.50	.25

Paris Postal Conference.

Alfredo Gonzalez F. — AP74

1965, June   **Photo.**   *Perf. 12*

C399	AP74 35c dk blue green	3.25	.25

50th anniv. of the National Bank and honoring Alfredo Gonzalez Flores (1877-1962), 1st governor of the bank.

No. C390 Overprinted: "75 ANIVERSARIO / ASILO CHAPUI / 1890-1965"

1965, Aug. 14   **Unwmk.**   *Perf. 12*

C400	AP72 2col buff & dk grn	1.40	.80

75th anniv. of Chapui Asylum, San José.

Girl, FAO Emblem and Hands Holding Grain — AP75

Church of Nicoya — AP76

FAO Emblem and: 15c, Map of Costa Rica and silos, horiz. 50c, World population chart and children. 1col, Plane over map of Costa Rica, horiz.

1965, Oct. 25   **Litho.**   *Perf. 14*

C401	AP75 15c lt brn & blk	.25	.25
C402	AP75 35c black & yel	.25	.25
C403	AP75 50c ultra & dk grn	.25	.25
C404	AP75 1col grn, blk & sil	.40	.25
	Nos. C401-C404 (4)	1.15	1.00

FAO "Freedom from Hunger" campaign.

1965, Dec. 20   *Perf. 13½x14*

5c, Leonidas Briceno B. 15c, Scroll dated "25 de Julio de 1964." 35c, Map of Guanacaste and Nicoya peninsula. 50c, Dancing couple. 1col, Map showing local products.

C405	AP76 5c red brn & blk	.40	.25
C406	AP76 10c blue & gray	.40	.25
C407	AP76 15c bis & slate	.40	.25
C408	AP76 35c blue & slate	.40	.25
C409	AP76 50c gray & vio bl	.55	.25
C410	AP76 1col buff & slate	1.10	.40
	Nos. C405-C410 (6)	3.25	1.65

Acquisition of the Nicoya territory.

Runner and Olympic Rings AP77

Pres. Kennedy Speaking in San José Cathedral AP78

Olympic Rings and Emblem: 10c, Bicyclists. 40c, Judo. 65c, Basketball. 80c, Soccer. 1col, Hands holding torches, and Mt. Fuji.

1965, Dec. 23 — Perf. 13x13½

C411	AP77	5c bister & multi	.20	.20
C412	AP77	10c lt lil & multi	.20	.20
C413	AP77	40c multicolored	.20	.20
C414	AP77	65c lemon & multi	.25	.20
C415	AP77	80c tan & multi	.40	.20
C416	AP77	1col multicolored	.50	.30
a.		Souvenir sheet of 2	6.00	3.00
		Nos. C411-C416 (6)	1.75	1.30

18th Olympic Games, Tokyo, Oct. 10-25, 1964. No. C416a contains two 1col stamps, one like No. C416, the other with gray background replacing yellow orange.

No. C416a was issued both perf and imperf. Same values.

Nos. C411-C416 exist imperf.

Perf. 13½x13, 13x13½
1965, Dec. 23 — Litho. — Unwmk.

Designs: 45c, Friendship 7 capsule circling globe, and Kennedy, horiz. 85c, Kennedy and John, Jr. 1col, Curtis-Lee Mansion and flame from Kennedy grave, Arlington, Va.

C417	AP78	45c brt bl & lil	.25	.20
C418	AP78	55c org & brt bl	.30	.25
C419	AP78	85c gray, dk brn & red brn	.55	.40
C420	AP78	1col multicolored	.65	.50
a.		Souvenir sheet of 2	1.25	1.25
		Nos. C417-C420 (4)	1.75	1.35

President John F. Kennedy (1917-63). No. C420a contains two 1col stamps, one like No. C420, the other with green background replacing dark blue. Exists with light blue background instead of green; value $150.

No. C420a was issued both perf and imperf. Same values.

Nos. C417-C420 exist imperf.

For surcharges see Nos. C429-C430.

Firemen with Hoses — AP79

Designs: 5c, Fire engine "Knox," horiz. 10c, 1866 fire pump. 35c, Fireman's badge. 50c, Emblem and flags of Confederation of Central American Fire Brigades.

1966, Mar. 12 — Litho. — Perf. 11

C421	AP79	5c black & red	.30	.20
C422	AP79	10c bister & red	.40	.20
C423	AP79	15c blk, red brn & red	.55	.20
C424	AP79	35c black & yel	.95	.25
C425	AP79	50c dk blue & red	2.00	.50
		Nos. C421-C425 (5)	4.20	1.35

Centenary of San José Fire Brigade.

Nos. C381, C383, C386 and C418-C419 Surcharged

a

b

1966, Dec. — Photo. — Perf. 12

C426	AP72(a)	15c on 30c	.20	.20
C427	AP72(a)	15c on 45c	.20	.20
C428	AP72(a)	35c on 75c	.25	.20

Litho. — Perf. 13x13½

C429	AP78(a)	35c on 55c	.25	.20
C430	AP78(b)	50c on 85c	.45	.20
		Nos. C426-C430 (5)	1.35	1.00

Revenue Stamps (Basic Type of A124) Surcharged

1967, Jan. — Engr. — Perf. 12

C431	A124	15c on 5c blue	.25	.20
C432	A124	35c on 10c claret	.30	.20
C433	A124	50c on 20c rose red	.50	.25
		Nos. C431-C433 (3)	1.05	.65

Central Bank of Costa Rica — AP80

1967, Mar. 1 — Litho. — Perf. 11

C434	AP80	5c brt green	.35	.25
C435	AP80	15c brown	.35	.25
C436	AP80	35c scarlet	.35	.25
		Nos. C434-C436 (3)	1.05	.75

Power Lines — AP81

Telecommunications Building, San Pedro — AP82

Electrification Program: 15c, Telephone Central. 25c, La Garita Dam. 35c, Rio Mache Reservoir. 50c, Cachi Dam.

1967, Apr. 24 — Litho. — Perf. 11

C437	AP81	5c dark gray	.25	.25
C438	AP81	10c brt rose	.25	.25
C439	AP81	15c brown org	.25	.25
C440	AP82	25c brt ultra	.25	.25
C441	AP82	35c brt green	.30	.25
C442	AP82	50c red brown	.40	.30
		Nos. C437-C442 (6)	1.70	1.55

Chondrorhyncha Aromatica AP83

Institute Emblem AP84

Orchids: 10c, Miltonia endresii. 15c, Stanhopea cirrhata. 25c, Trichopilia suavis. 35c, Odontoglossum schlieperianum. 50c, Cattleya skinneri. 1col, Cattleya dowiana. 2col, Odontoglossum chiriquense.

1967, June 15 — Engr. — Perf. 13x13½
Orchids in Natural Colors

C443	AP83	5c multicolored	.20	.20
C444	AP83	10c olive & multi	.40	.30
C445	AP83	15c multicolored	.55	.30
C446	AP83	25c multicolored	.95	.30
C447	AP83	35c dull vio & multi	1.25	.30
C448	AP83	50c brown & multi	1.60	.30
C449	AP83	1col vio & multi	3.50	.80

C450	AP83	2col dk ol bis & multi	6.00	1.50
		Nos. C443-C450 (8)	14.45	4.00

Issued for the University Library.

1967, Oct. 6 — Litho. — Perf. 13x13½

C451	AP84	50c vio bl, lt bl & bl	.40	.20

Inter-American Agriculture Institute, 25th anniv.

Church of Solitude — AP85

LACSA Emblem — AP86

Costa Rican Churches: 10c, Basilica of Santo Domingo, Heredia. 15c, Cathedral of Tilaran. 25c, Cathedral of Alajuela. 30c, Mercy Church. 35c, Basilica of Our Lady of Angels. 40c, Church of St. Raphael, Heredia. 45c, Ujarras ruins. 50c, Ruins of parish church, Cartago. 55c, Cathedral of San José. 65c, Parish church, Puntarenas. 75c, Church of Orosi. 80c, Cathedral of St. Isidro, the General. 85c, St. Ramon Church. 90c, Church of the Abandoned. 1col, Coronado Church. 2col, Church of St. Teresita. 3col, Parish Church, Heredia. 5col, Carmelite Church. 10col, Limon Cathedral.

1967, Dec. 15 — Engr. — Perf. 12½

C452	AP85	5c green	.20	.20
C453	AP85	10c blue	.25	.20
C454	AP85	15c lilac	.25	.20
C455	AP85	25c dull yel	.25	.20
C456	AP85	30c orange brn	.25	.20
C457	AP85	35c lt blue	.25	.20
C458	AP85	40c dp orange	.30	.20
C459	AP85	45c dl bl grn	.30	.20
C460	AP85	50c olive	.40	.20
C461	AP85	55c brown	.40	.20
C462	AP85	65c car rose	.65	.25
C463	AP85	75c sepia	.70	.30
C464	AP85	80c yellow	1.40	.45
C465	AP85	85c violet blk	1.60	.45
C466	AP85	90c emerald	1.60	.65
C467	AP85	1col slate	1.25	.35
C468	AP85	2col brt green	5.50	1.75
C469	AP85	3col orange	7.25	3.00
C470	AP85	5col vio blue	8.00	3.00
C471	AP85	10col carmine	9.75	4.50
		Nos. C452-C471 (20)	40.55	16.70

Nos. C452 and C454 exist imperf; Nos. C455 and C470 exist imperf horiz.

See Nos. C561-C576.

Perf. 13x13½, 13½x13
1967, Dec. 12 — Litho. & Engr.

45c, LACSA emblem, jet, horiz. 50c, Decorated wheel, anniversary emblem.

C472	AP86	40c ultra, grnsh bl & gold	.25	.20
C473	AP86	45c blk, pale grn, ultra & gold	.30	.20
C474	AP86	50c blue & multi	.40	.25
		Nos. C472-C474 (3)	.95	.65

20th anniv. (in 1966) of Lineas Aereas Costaricenses, LACSA, Costa Rican Airlines.

Scout Directing Traffic AP87

Runner AP88

Designs: 25c, Campfire under tree. 35c, Flag of Costa Rica, Scout flag and emblem. 50c, Encampment, horiz. 65c, Photograph of first Scout troop, horiz.

1968, Mar. 15 — Perf. 13

C475	AP87	15c lt bl, blk & lt brn	.20	.20
C476	AP87	25c lt ultra, vio bl & org	.25	.20
C477	AP87	35c blue & multi	.40	.25

C478	AP87	50c multicolored	.65	.30
C479	AP87	65c sal, dk bl & brn	.80	.40
		Nos. C475-C479 (5)	2.30	1.35

Costa Rican Boy Scouts, 50th anniversary.

1969, Jan. 17 — Litho. — Perf. 10x11

Sports: 40c, Women's running. 55c, Boxing. 65c, Bicycling. 75c, Weight lifting. 1col, High diving. 3col, Rifle shooting.

C481	AP88	30c multi	.20	.20
C482	AP88	40c multi	.20	.20
C483	AP88	55c multi	.25	.20
C484	AP88	65c lil & multi	.30	.20
C485	AP88	75c multi	.30	.20
C486	AP88	1col multi	.40	.25
C487	AP88	3col multi	1.60	.95
		Nos. C481-C487 (7)	3.25	2.20

19th Olympic Games, Mexico City, 10/12-27.

Philatelic Exhibition Emblem — AP89

1969, June 5 — Litho. — Perf. 11x10

C488	AP89	35c multicolored	.20	.20
C489	AP89	40c pink & multi	.20	.20
C490	AP89	50c lt blue & multi	.25	.20
C491	AP89	2col multicolored	.95	.55
		Nos. C488-C491 (4)	1.60	1.15

4th Natl. Philatelic Exhib., San José, 6/5-8.

ILO Emblem AP90

1969, Oct. 29 — Litho. — Perf. 10

C492	AP90	35c bl grn & blk	.25	.20
C493	AP90	50c scarlet & blk	.25	.20

50th anniv. of the ILO.

Soccer — AP91

Stylized Crab — AP92

Designs: 65c, Soccer ball, map of North and Central America. 85c, Soccer player. 1col, Two players in action.

1969, Nov. 23 — Litho. — Perf. 11x10

C494	AP91	65c gray & multi	.30	.20
C495	AP91	75c multicolored	.30	.25
C496	AP91	85c multicolored	.40	.30
C497	AP91	1col pink & multi	.55	.40
		Nos. C494-C497 (4)	1.55	1.15

Issued to publicize the 4th Soccer Championships (CONCACAF), Nov. 23-Dec. 7.

1970, May 14 — Litho. — Perf. 12½

C498	AP92	10c blk & lil rose	.25	.25
C499	AP92	15c blk & yel	.25	.25
C500	AP92	50c blk & brn org	.25	.25
C501	AP92	1.10col blk & emer	.55	.25
		Nos. C498-C501 (4)	1.30	1.00

10th Inter-American Cancer Cong., 5/22-29.

Costa Rica No. 124, Magnifying Glass and Stamps — AP93

2col, Father, son with stamps, album.

1970, Sept. 14   **Litho.**   *Perf. 11*
C502 AP93 1col ultra, brn & car
      rose   1.00   .25
C503 AP93 2col blk, pink & ultra   1.25   .55

The 5th National Philatelic Exhibition.

EXPO Emblem and Costa Rican
Cart — AP94

EXPO Emblem and: 10c, Japanese floral arrangement, vert. 35c, Pavilion and Tower of the Sun. 40c, Japanese tea ceremony. 45c, Woman picking coffee, vert. 55c, Earth seen from moon, vert.

1970, Oct. 22   **Litho.**   *Perf. 13x13½*
C504 AP94 10c multicolored   .25   .20
C505 AP94 15c green & multi   .25   .20
C506 AP94 35c blue & multi   .55   .20
C507 AP94 40c gray & multi   .65   .20
C508 AP94 45c multicolored   .70   .20
C509 AP94 55c black & multi   1.90   .90
     Nos. C504-C509 (6)   4.30 1.30

EXPO '70 International Exhibition, Osaka, Japan, Mar. 15-Sept. 13.

Escazu Valley, by Margarita
Bertheau — AP95

Paintings: 25c, "Irazu," by Rafael A. Garcia, vert. 80c, Shore landscape, by Teodorico Quiros. 1col, "The Other Face," by Cesar Valverde. 2.50col, Mother and Child, by Luis Daell, vert.

1970, Nov. 4   **Litho.**   *Perf. 12½*
C510 AP95 25c multi   .80   .30
C511 AP95 45c multi   .80   .30
C512 AP95 80c multi   1.25   .55
C513 AP95 1col multi   1.25   .65
C514 AP95 2.50col multi   2.50 2.00
     Nos. C510-C514 (5)   6.60 3.80

Arms of Costa
Rica,
1964 — AP96

National
Theater
AP97

Various Coats of Arms, dated: 10c, Nov. 27, 1906. 15c, Sept. 29, 1848. 25c, Apr. 21, 1840. 35c, Nov. 22, 1824. 50c, Nov. 2, 1824. 1col, Mar. 6, 1824. 2col, May 10, 1823.

1971, Feb. 10   **Litho.**   *Perf. 14x13½*
C515 AP96 5c buff & multi   .40   .25
C516 AP96 10c multi   .40   .25
C517 AP96 15c yel & multi   .50   .25
C518 AP96 25c pink & multi   .50   .25
C519 AP96 35c multi   .65   .25
C520 AP96 50c rose & multi   .70   .25

C521 AP96 1col beige & multi   .80   .40
C522 AP96 2col multi   1.60   .80
     Nos. C515-C522 (8)   5.55 2.70

1971, Apr. 14   **Litho.**   *Perf. 11*
C523 AP97 2col plum   .40   .30

Organization of American States meeting.

José
Matias
Delgado,
Manuel
José
Arce
AP98

Flag of Costa
Rica — AP99

Independence Leaders: 10c, Miguel Larreinaga and Manuel Antonio de la Cerda, Nicaragua. 15c, José Cecilio del Valle, Dionisio de Herrera, Honduras. 35c, Pablo Alvarado and Florencio del Castillo, Costa Rica. 50c, Antonio Larrazabal and Pedro Molina, Guatemala. 2col, Costa Rica coat of arms.

1971, Sept. 14   *Perf. 13*
C524 AP98 5c multi   .25   .25
C525 AP98 10c multi   .25   .25
C526 AP98 15c gray, brn & blk   .25   .25
C527 AP98 35c multi   .25   .25
C528 AP98 50c multi   .25   .25
C529 AP99 1col multi   .25   .25
C530 AP99 2col multi   .40   .40
     Nos. C524-C530 (7)   1.90 1.90

Central American independence, sesqui.

Soccer Federation
Emblem — AP100

Children of the
World — AP101

1971, Dec. 6
C531 AP100 50c multi   .30   .25
C532 AP100 60c multi   .30   .25

50th anniv. of Soccer Federation of Costa Rica.

1972, Jan. 11   *Perf. 12½*
C533 AP101 50c multi   .25   .20
C534 AP101 1.10col red & multi   .40   .25

25th anniv. (in 1971) of UNICEF.

Tree of
Guanacaste
AP102

Designs: 40c, Hermitage, Liberia. 55c, Petroglyphs, Rincón Brujo. 60c, Painted head, sculpture from Curubandé, vert.

1972, Feb. 28   *Perf. 11*
C535 AP102 20c brn, ol & brt grn   .40   .25
C536 AP102 40c brn & ol   .40   .25
C537 AP102 55c blk & brn   .40   .25
C538 AP102 60c blk, buff & ver   .40   .25
     Nos. C535-C538 (4)   1.60 1.00

Bicentenary of the founding of the city of Liberia, Guanacaste.

Farm and
Family — AP103

Inter-American
Exhibitions
AP104

Designs: 45c, Cattle, dairy products and meat, horiz. 50c, Kneeling figure with plant. 10col, Farmer and map of Americas.

1972, June 30   **Litho.**   *Perf. 12½*
C539 AP103 20c multi   .30   .25
C540 AP103 45c multi   .30   .25
C541 AP103 50c dp yel, grn &
       blk   .30   .25
C542 AP103 10col brn, org & blk   2.50 1.75
     Nos. C539-C542 (4)   3.40 2.50

30th anniversary of the Inter-American Institute of Agricultural Sciences.

1972, Aug. 26   **Litho.**   *Perf. 13*
C543 AP104 50c orange & brn   .20   .20
C544 AP104 2col blue & vio   .40   .30

4th Interamerican Philatelic Exhibition, EXFILBRA, Rio de Janeiro, Aug. 26-Sept. 2.

First Book Printed
in Costa
Rica — AP105

Intl. Book Year: 50c, 5col, Natl. Library, horiz.

1972, Dec. 7   **Litho.**   *Perf. 12½*
C545 AP105 20c brt blue   .40   .25
C546 AP105 50c gold & multi   .40   .25
C547 AP105 75c multicolored   .40   .25
C548 AP105 5col multicolored   1.90   .95
     Nos. C545-C548 (4)   3.10 1.70

Road to
Irazú
Volcano
AP106

1972-73   *Perf. 11x11½, 11½x11*
C549 AP106 5c like 20c   .30   .25
C550 AP106 15c Coco-Culebra
       Bay   .30   .25
C551 AP106 20c shown   .30   .25
C552 AP106 25c like 15c   .30   .25
C553 AP106 40c Manuel Antonio
       Beach   .30   .25
C554 AP106 45c Tourist Office
       emblem   .30   .25
C555 AP106 50c Lindora Lake   .30   .25
C556 AP106 60c San Jose P.O.,
       vert.   .30   .25
C557 AP106 80c like 40c   .40   .25
C558 AP106 90c like 45c   .40   .25
C559 AP106 1col like 50c   .40   .25
C560 AP106 2col like 60c   .70   .50
     Nos. C549-C560 (12)   4.30 3.25

Tourism year of the Americas.
Issued: 20c, 25c, 80c, 90c, 1col, 2col, 12/26; others, 3/21/73.
No. C555 exists with inverted center, used only. Value $10,000.

Church Type of 1967

Designs as before.

1973, July 16   **Engr.**   *Perf. 12½*
C561 AP85 5c slate grn   .25   .25
C562 AP85 10c olive   .25   .25
C563 AP85 15c orange   .25   .25
C564 AP85 25c brown   .25   .25
C565 AP85 30c rose claret   .25   .25
C566 AP85 35c violet   .25   .25
C567 AP85 40c brt green   .25   .25
C568 AP85 45c dull yellow   .25   .25
C569 AP85 50c rose magenta   .25   .25
C570 AP85 55c blue   .25   .25
C571 AP85 65c black   .30   .25
C572 AP85 75c rose red   .40   .25
C573 AP85 80c yellow grn   .45   .25
C574 AP85 85c lilac   .50   .25
C575 AP85 90c brt pink   .55   .25
C576 AP85 1col dark blue   .65   .25
     Nos. C561-C576 (16)   5.35 4.00

Human Rights
Flame — AP107

OAS
Emblem — AP108

1973, Dec. 10   **Photo.**   *Perf. 10½*
C577 AP107 50c black & red   .40   .25

25th anniversary of the Universal Declaration of Human Rights.

1973, Dec. 17   **Litho.**   *Perf. 10½*
C578 AP108 20c dk bl & dp car   .40   .25

25th anniv. of the OAS.

Joaquin Vargas
Calvo — AP109

AP110

1974, Jan. 14
C579 AP109 20c shown   .40   .25
C580 AP109 20c Alejandro
       Monestel   .40   .25
C581 AP109 20c Julio Mata   .40   .25
C582 AP109 20c Julio Fonseca   .40   .25
C583 AP109 2col Rafael A.
       Chaves   .90   .30
C584 AP109 5col Manuel M. Gutierrez   2.10 1.25
     Nos. C579-C584 (6)   4.60 2.55

Costa Rican composers honored by the National Symphony Orchestra.

Revenue Stamps Overprinted in Black
"Habilitado para Correo Aereo"

1974, Apr. 5   **Engr.**   *Perf. 12*
C585 AP110 50c brown   .20   .20
C586 AP110 1col violet   .30   .20
C587 AP110 2col orange   .70   .40
C588 AP110 5col olive   1.75 1.75
     Nos. C585-C588 (4)   2.95 2.55

Telephone
Building, San
Pedro — AP111

EXFILMEX 74
Emblem
AP112

Designs: 65c, Rio Macho Control, horiz. 85c, Turbines, Rio Macho Center. 1.25col, Cachi Dam and reservoir, horiz. 2col, I.C.E. Headquarters.

1974, July 30　Litho.　Perf. 10½
C589	AP111	50c gold & multi	.20	.20
C590	AP111	65c gold & multi	.25	.20
C591	AP111	85c gold & multi	.30	.20
C592	AP111	1.25col gold & multi	.40	.25
C593	AP111	2col gold & multi	.80	.40
	Nos. C589-C593 (5)		1.95	1.25

25th anniversary of Costa Rican Electrical Institute (I.C.E.).

1974, Aug. 22　　　　　Perf. 13
C594	AP112	65c green	.20	.20
C595	AP112	3col lilac rose	.65	.40

5th Inter-American Philatelic Exhibition, EXFILMEX-74 UPU, Mexico City, Oct. 26-Nov. 3.

Map of Costa Rica, 4-S Emblem AP113

50c, Young harvesters and 4-S emblem.

1974, Oct. 7　Litho.　Perf. 12x11
C596	AP113	20c brt green	.40	.25
C597	AP113	50c multicolored	.40	.25

25th anniversary of 4-S Clubs of Costa Rica (similar to US 4-H Clubs).

Roberto Brenes
Mesen — AP114

"Life Insurance"
AP115

Designs: 85c, "Love and Death," manuscript. 5col, Hands of writer, horiz.

1974, Oct. 14　Litho.　Perf. 10½
C598	AP114	20c black & brn	.20	.20
C599	AP114	85c black & red	.25	.20
C600	AP114	5col black & red brn	1.60	.90
	Nos. C598-C600 (3)		2.05	1.30

Mesen, educator & writer, birth centenary.

1974, Oct. 30　　　　　Perf. 14

Designs: 20c, Ricardo Jiménez Oreamuno and Tomás Soley Güell, horiz. 50c, Harvest Insurance (hand holding shovel), horiz. 85c, Maritime insurance (hand holding paper boat). 1.25col, INS emblem. 2col, Workers rehabilitation (arm with crutch). 2.50col, Workers' Compensation (hand holding wrench). 20col, Fire insurance (hands protecting house).

C601	AP115	20c multi	.20	.20
C602	AP115	50c multi	.20	.20
C603	AP115	65c multi	.20	.20
C604	AP115	85c multi	.20	.20
C605	AP115	1.25col multi	.30	.20
C606	AP115	2col multi	.55	.25

C607	AP115	2.50col multi	.65	.40
C608	AP115	20col multi	4.50	4.50
	Nos. C601-C608 (8)		6.80	6.15

Costa Rican Insurance Institute (Instituto Nacional de Seguros, INS), 50th anniversary. For surcharges see Nos. C721-C722.

WPY
Emblem — AP116

Oscar J. Pinto
F. — AP117

1974, Nov. 13　Litho.　Perf. 11x11½
C609	AP116	2col vio bl & red	.50	.25

World Population Year.

1974, Dec. 2　　　　　Perf. 13

Designs: 50c, Alberto Montes de Oca D., champion sharpshooter. 1col, Eduardo Garnier, sports promoter. O. J. Pinto, introducer of soccer.

C610	AP117	20c gray & dk bl	.20	.20
C611	AP117	50c gray & dk bl	.20	.20
C612	AP117	1col gray & dk bl	.50	.25
	Nos. C610-C612 (3)		.90	.65

First Central American Olympic Games, held in Guatemala, 1973.

Mormodes
Buccinator
AP118

Masdevallia
Ephippium
AP119

Designs: Orchids.

1975, Mar. 7　Litho.　Perf. 10½, 13½
C613	AP118	25c *shown*	.65	.25
C614	AP118	25c *Gongora clavi-odora*	.65	.25
C615	AP119	25c *shown*	.65	.25
C616	AP119	25c *Encyclia spondiadum*	.65	.25
a.	Block of 4, #C613-C616		2.60	1.25
b.	As "a," perf. 10½		1.60	1.25
C617	AP118	65c *Lycaste skinneri alba*	1.60	.25
C618	AP118	65c *Peristeria elata*	1.60	.25
C619	AP119	65c *Miltonia roezelii*	1.60	.25
C620	AP119	65c *Brassavola digbyana*	1.60	.25
a.	Block of 4, #C617-C620, perf. 13½		6.50	2.25
b.	As "a," perf. 10½		16.00	2.25
C621	AP118	80c *Epidendrum mirabile*	2.25	.30
C622	AP118	80c *Barkeria lindleyana*	2.25	.30
C623	AP119	80c *Cattleya skinneri*	2.25	.30
C624	AP119	80c *Sobralia macrantha*	2.25	.30
a.	Block of 4, #C621-C624		9.00	2.50
b.	As "a," perf. 10½		16.00	2.50
C625	AP118	1.40col *Lycaste cruenta*	2.75	.40
C626	AP118	1.40col *Oncidium obryzatum*	2.75	.40
C627	AP119	1.40col *Gongora armeniaca*	2.75	.40
C628	AP119	1.40col *Sievekingia suavis*	2.75	.40
a.	Block of 4, #C625-C628		11.00	4.50

b.	As "a," perf. 10½		9.75	4.50

Perf. 13½
C629	AP118	1.75col *Hexisea imbricata*	1.60	.40
C630	AP118	2.15col *Warcewiczella discolor*	1.60	.55
C631	AP119	2.50col *Oncidium krameri-anum*	2.75	1.10
C632	AP119	3.25col *Cattleya dowiana*	3.25	1.40
	Nos. C613-C632 (20)		38.20	8.25

5th National Orchid Exhibition.
Nos. C613-C628 were printed in both perforations on two different papers: dull finish and shiny. Nos. C629-C632 were printed on shiny paper.
Most examples of Nos. C617-C620, perf 10½, were surcharged.
For overprints and surcharges see Nos. C715-C720, C723-C728.

Radio Club
Emblem
AP120

Members' Flags and
Emblem — AP121

Design: 2col, Federation emblem.

1975, Apr. 16　Litho.　Perf. 13½
C633	AP120	1col blk & red lil	.50	.20
C634	AP121	1.10col multi	.55	.25
C635	AP120	2col black & bl	.95	.25
	Nos. C633-C635 (3)		2.00	.70

16th Central American Radio Amateurs' Convention, San José, May 2-4.

Nicoya Beach
AP122

Designs: 75c, Driving cattle. 1col, Colonial Church, Nicoya. 3col, Savannah riders, vert.

1975, Aug. 1　Litho.　Perf. 13½
C636	AP122	25c gray & multi	.20	.20
C637	AP122	75c gray & multi	.25	.25
C638	AP122	1col gray & multi	.30	.25
C639	AP122	3col gray & multi	1.00	.85
	Nos. C636-C639 (4)		1.75	1.55

Sesqui. of annexation of Nicoya District.

Costa
Rica #158
AP123

Designs (Type A90 of 1932): No. C641, #159. No. C642, #160. No. C643, #161.

1975, Aug. 14　Litho.　Perf. 12
C640	AP123	2.20col blk & org	.40	.35
C641	AP123	2.20col blk & dk grn	.40	.35
C642	AP123	2.20col blk & car rose	.40	.35
C643	AP123	2.20col blk & dk bl	.40	.35
a.	Block of 4, #C640-C643		4.00	4.00

6th Natl. Phil. Exhib., San José, Aug. 14-17. For surcharges see Nos. C885-C892.

IWY Emblem
AP124

1975, Oct. 9　Litho.　Perf. 10½
C644	AP124	40c vio bl & red	.20	.20
C645	AP124	1.25col blk & ultra	.40	.20

International Women's Year 1975.

UN Emblem
AP125

UN, 30th Anniv.: 60c, UN General Assembly, horiz. 1.20col, UN Headquarters, NY.

1975, Oct. 24　　　　　Perf. 12
C646	AP125	10c bl & blk	.25	.25
C647	AP125	60c multi	.25	.25
C648	AP125	1.20col multi	.40	.25
	Nos. C646-C648 (3)		.90	.75

The Visitation,
by Jorge
Gallardo
AP126

"20-30" Club
Emblem — AP127

Paintings by Jorge Gallardo: 1col, Nativity and Star. 5col, St. Joseph in his Workshop, Virgin and Child.

1975, Nov. 3　　　　　Perf. 10½
C649	AP126	50c multi	.30	.25
C650	AP126	1col multi	.50	.25
C651	AP126	5col multi	1.75	.70
	Nos. C649-C651 (3)		2.55	1.20

Christmas 1975.

1976, Jan. 16　Litho.　Perf. 12
C652	AP127	1col multi	.40	.20

"20-30" Club of Costa Rica, 20th anniv.

Quercus Brenessi
Trel — AP128

"Literary
Development"
AP129

Plants: 30c, Maxillaria albertii schecht. 55c, Calathea brenesii standl. 2col, Brenesia costaricensis schlecht. 10col, Philodendron brenesii standl.

1976, Mar. 1   **Perf. 10½**
C653	AP128	5c multi	.50	.25
C654	AP128	30c multi	.50	.25
C655	AP128	55c multi	.75	.25
C656	AP128	2col tan & multi	1.25	.40
C657	AP128	10col multi	5.50	3.00
		Nos. C653-C657 (5)	7.90	3.45

Prof. Alberto Manuel Brenes Mora, botanist, birth centenary.

1976, Apr. 9   **Litho.**   **Perf. 16**

Designs: 1.10col, Man holding book, stylized. 5col, Costa Rican flag emanating from book, horiz.

C658	AP129	15c multi	.25	.25
C659	AP129	1.10col multi	.25	.25
C660	AP129	5col multi	.95	.80
		Nos. C658-C660 (3)	1.45	1.30

Publishing in Costa Rica.
Nos. C658-C660 exist imperf.

Postrider, 1839 — AP130

Costa Rica No. 13, Post Office AP131

Designs: 65c, Costa Rica No. 14 and Post Office. 85c, Costa Rica No. 15 and Post Office. 2col, UPU Monument, Bern, vert.

1976, May 24   **Perf. 10½**
C661	AP130	20c apple grn & blk	.30	.25
C662	AP131	50c bister & multi	.30	.25
C663	AP131	65c multi	.30	.25
C664	AP131	85c multi	.30	.25
C665	AP130	2col blk & lt bl	.80	.50
		Nos. C661-C665 (5)	2.00	1.50

Cent. of UPU (in 1974).
Nos. C662-C664 exist without the surcharges on reproductions of Nos. 13-15.

Telephones, 1876 and 1976 — AP132

Designs: 2col, Wall telephone. 5col, Alexander Graham Bell.

1976, June 28
C666	AP132	1.60col lt bl & blk	.40	.25
C667	AP132	2col multicolored	.50	.25
C668	AP132	5col yellow & blk	1.25	.95
		Nos. C666-C668 (3)	2.15	1.45

Centenary of first telephone call by Alexander Graham Bell, Mar. 10, 1876.

Inverted Center Stamp of 1901 and Association Emblems — AP133

Design: 5col, 1901 stamp between Costa Rican Philatelic Society and Interamerican Philatelic Federation emblems.

1976, Nov. 11   **Litho.**   **Perf. 10½**
C669	AP133	50c multi	.20	.20
C670	AP133	1col multi	.20	.20
C671	AP133	2col multi	.40	.20
		Nos. C669-C671 (3)	.80	.60

Souvenir Sheet
Perf. 12
C672	AP133	5col multi	5.25	2.50

7th Natl. Phil. Exhib. and 9th Plenary Assembly of the Interamerican Phil. Fed. (FIAF), San José, Nov. 1976.
No. C670 exists in colors of No. C671.
No. C671 exists on thin dull paper, with bright gum. Value, mint, $25.
No. C672 was issued both perf and imperf. Same values.

"Seeing Eye" and Map of Costa Rica AP134

Amadeo Quiros Blanco — AP135

1976, Nov. 22   **Perf. 16**
C673	AP134	35c black & blue	.20	.20
C674	AP135	2col multicolored	.55	.40

General Audit Office, 25th anniversary.

Nurse Attending Child — AP136

LACSA Circling Globe — AP137

1.10col, National Children's Hospital, horiz.

1976, Nov. 29
C675	AP136	90c multi	.25	.20
C676	AP136	1.10col multi	.40	.25

5th Panamerican Congress of Pediatric Surgery and 12th Congress of Pediatrics.

1976, Dec. 1   **Perf. 10½**

Designs: 1.20col, Route map. 3col, LACSA emblem and Costa Rican flag.

C677	AP137	1col multi	.25	.20
C678	AP137	1.20col multi	.40	.25
C679	AP137	3col multi	1.10	.70
		Nos. C677-C679 (3)	1.75	1.15

Costa Rican Air Lines (LACSA), 30th anniversary.

Boston Tea Party AP138

US Bicent.: 5col, Declaration of Independence. 10col, Ringing Liberty Bell to announce Independence, vert.

1976, Dec. 24
C680	AP138	2.20col multi	.40	.30
C681	AP138	5col multi	1.00	.70
C682	AP138	10col multi	1.75	1.40
		Nos. C680-C682 (3)	3.15	2.40

Tree of Guanacaste AP139

Felipe J. Alvarado AP140

Designs (Rotary Emblem and): 60c, Dr. Paul Blanco Cervantes Hospital, horiz. 3col, Map of Costa Rica, horiz. 10col, Paul Harris.

1977, Mar. 31   **Litho.**   **Perf. 16**
C683	AP139	40c multi	.20	.20
C684	AP140	50c multi	.20	.20
C685	AP139	60c multi	.20	.20
C686	AP139	3col multi	.95	.65
C687	AP140	10col multi	3.25	2.50
		Nos. C683-C687 (5)	4.80	3.75

Rotary Club of San José, 50th anniversary.

Boruca Cloth AP141

Design: 1.50col, Painted wood ornament.

1977, Feb. 22
C688	AP141	75c multi	.20	.20
C689	AP141	1.50col multi	.30	.20

Natl. Artisan & Small Industry Program.

Juana Pereira AP142

Alonso de Anguciana de Gamboa AP143

Designs: 1col, First Church of Our Lady of the Angels, horiz. 1.10col, Our Lady of the Angels (gold sculpture). 1.25col, Crown of Our Lady of the Angels.

1977, June 6   **Litho.**   **Perf. 10½**
C690	AP142	50c multi	.25	.25
C691	AP142	1col multi	.25	.25
C692	AP142	1.10col multi	.25	.25
C693	AP142	1.25col multi	.40	.25
		Nos. C690-C693 (4)	1.15	1.00

50th anniv. of the coronation of Our Lady of the Angels, patron saint of Costa Rica.

1977, July 4   **Litho.**   **Perf. 10½**

Designs: 75c, Church of Esparza. 1col, Statue of Our Lady of Candlemas. 2col, Statue of Diego de Artieda y Chirino.

C694	AP143	35c multi	.20	.20
C695	AP143	75c multi	.20	.20
C696	AP143	1col multi	.30	.20
C697	AP143	2col multi	.65	.40
		Nos. C694-C697 (4)	1.35	1.00

400th anniv. of the founding of Esparza. For surcharge see No. C883.

CARE Emblem and Child — AP144

1col, CARE emblem and soybeans, horiz.

1977, Sept. 14   **Litho.**   **Perf. 16**
C698	AP144	80c multi	.25	.20
C699	AP144	1col multi	.40	.20

20th anniversary of CARE (relief organization) in Costa Rica.

Institute's Emblem — AP145

First Map of Americas, 1540 — AP146

1977, Oct. 21   **Litho.**   **Perf. 16**
C700	AP145	50c blk & multi	.50	.20
C701	AP146	1.40col blk & multi	.95	.40

Hispanic Cultural Institute of Costa Rica, 25th anniversary.

Mercy Church, by Ricardo Ulloa B. AP147

Health Ministry Emblem AP148

Paintings: 1col, Christ, by Floria Pinto de Herrero. 5col, St. Francis and the Birds, by Louisa Gonzalez Y Saenz.

1977, Nov. 9   **Litho.**   **Perf. 10½**
C702	AP147	50c multi	.40	.25
C703	AP147	1col multi	.40	.20
C704	AP147	5col multi	1.75	.70
		Nos. C702-C704 (3)	2.55	1.15

1977, Nov. 16   **Perf. 16**
C705	AP148	1.40col multi	.40	.20

Creation of Ministry of Health.

Picnic — AP149

San Martin — AP150

Designs: 50c, Weaver. 2col, Beach scene. 5col, Fruit and vegetable market. 10col, Swans on lake.

1978, Mar. 21   **Litho.**   **Perf. 10½**
C706	AP149	50c blk & multi	.20	.20
C707	AP149	1col blk & multi	.40	.20
C708	AP149	2col blk & multi	1.00	.25
C709	AP149	5col blk & multi	1.90	.85
C710	AP149	10col blk & multi	2.50	1.90
		Nos. C706-C710 (5)	6.00	3.40

Conf. of Latin American Tourist Organizations.

1978, Aug. 7   **Litho.**   **Perf. 10½**
C711	AP150	5col multi	1.25	.80

Gen. José de San Martin (1778-1850), soldier and statesman, fought for South American independence.

Geographical Institute Emblem — AP151

University Federation Emblem — AP152

1978, Aug. 28   Litho.   Perf. 12½
C712 AP151 5col multi   1.25 .65

Pan-American Geography and History Institute, 50th anniversary. Exists imperf.

1978, Sept. 18   Perf. 11
C713 AP152 80c ultra   .40 .20

Central American University Federation, 30th anniversary.

Emblems — AP153

1978, Oct. 24   Perf. 16
C714 AP153 2col aqua, blk &
             gold   .55 .40

6th Interamerican Philatelic Exhibition, Argentina 78, Buenos Aires, Oct. 1978.

Nos. C629-C631 Overprinted: "50 Aniversario del / primer vuelo de PAN AM / en Costa Rica / 1928-1978"

1978, Nov. 1   Litho.   Perf. 13½
C715 AP118 1.75col multi   .55 .30
C716 AP118 2.15col multi   .70 .40
C717 AP119 2.50col multi   .95 .55
      Nos. C715-C717 (3)   2.20 1.25

1st Pan Am flight in Costa Rica, 50th anniv.

Nos. C629-C631 Overprinted: "50 Aniversario de la / visita de Lindbergh a / Costa Rica 1928-1978"

1978, Nov. 1
C718 AP118 1.75col multi   1.40 .30
C719 AP118 2.15col multi   1.60 .40
C720 AP119 2.50col multi   2.10 .50
      Nos. C718-C720 (3)   5.10 1.20

50th anniversary of Lindbergh's visit.

Nos. C603 and C607 Surcharged with New Value, 4 Bars and: "Centenario del / Asilo Carlos / Maria Ulloa / 1878-1978"

1978, Nov. 8   Perf. 14
C721 AP115 50c on 65c multi   .25 .20
C722 AP115 2col on 2.50col multi   .55 .25

Asilo Carlos Maria Ulloa, birth centenary.

No. C617-C620, C630-C631 Surcharged with New Value and 4 Bars
Perf. 10½, 13½

1978, Nov. 13   Litho.
C723 AP118 50c on 65c   .65 .60
C724 AP118 50c on 65c   .65 .60
C725 AP119 50c on 65c   .65 .60
C726 AP119 50c on 65c   .65 .60
  a.   Block of 4, #C723-C726   2.75 2.75
C727 AP118 1.20col on 2.15col   1.25 .55
C728 AP119 2col on 2.50col   1.25 .55
      Nos. C723-C728 (6)   5.10 3.50

Nos. C723-C726, perf. 13½, value $20, unused, $10, used, each. No. C726a, unused, $400.

Star over Map of Costa Rica — AP154

"Flying Men," Chorotega AP155

1978, Nov. 13   Perf. 10½
C729 AP154 50c blue & blk   .20 .20
C730 AP154 1col rose lil & blk   .25 .20
C731 AP154 5col orange & blk   1.40 .65
  a.   Strip of 3, #C729-C731   2.00 2.00

Christmas 1978. Nos. C729-C731 printed in sheets of 100 and se-tenant in sheet of 15 (3x5). Value, se-tenant sheet, $20.

1978, Nov. 20   Perf. 11½

Designs: 1.20col, Oviedo giving his History of Indies to Duke of Calabria, horiz. 10col, Lord of Oviedo's coat of arms.

C732 AP155 85c multi   .25 .25
C733 AP155 1.20col blk & lt bl   .25 .25
C734 AP155 10col multi   2.00 2.00
      Nos. C732-C734 (3)   2.50 2.50

500th birth anniv. of Gonzalo Fernandez de Oviedo, 1st chronicler of Spanish Indies.

Msgr. Domingo Rivas AP156

San José Cathedral AP157

1978, Dec. 6   Perf. 16, 13½ (20col)
C735 AP156 1col black & indigo   .20 .20
C736 AP157 20col multicolored   3.75 3.50

Centenary of the Cathedral of San José.

View of Coco Island AP158

Designs: 2.10, 3, 5 col, various views of Coco Island. 10col, Installation of memorial plaque, people and flag. 5, 10col vert.

1979, Apr. 30   Litho.   Perf. 10½
C737 AP158 90c multi   .40 .20
C738 AP158 2.10col multi   .80 .40
C739 AP158 3col multi   1.25 .55
C740 AP158 5col multi   1.90 1.00
C741 AP158 10col multi   3.75 2.25
  a.   Souv. sheet, #C737-C741   12.00 12.00
      Nos. C737-C741 (5)   8.10 4.40

Visit of Pres. Rodrigo Carazo Odio to Coco Island, June 24, 1978, in the interest of national defense.
No. C741a exists imperf. Value $750.

Shrimp AP159

Designs: 85c, Mahogany snapper. 1.80col, Corvina. 3col, Crayfish. 10col, Tuna.

1979, May 14   Litho.   Perf. 13½
C742 AP159 60c multi   .50 .25
C743 AP159 85c multi   .50 .25
C744 AP159 1.80col multi   .95 .25
C745 AP159 3col multi   1.40 .55
C746 AP159 10col multi   5.00 3.50
      Nos. C742-C746 (5)   8.35 4.80

Marine life protection.

Hungry Nestlings, IYC Emblem AP160

Microwave Transmitters, Mt. Irazu AP161

1979, May 24   Perf. 11
C747 AP160 1col multi   .80 .20
C748 AP160 2col multi   1.60 .50
C749 AP160 20col multi   10.50 5.50
      Nos. C747-C749 (3)   12.90 6.20

International Year of the Child.

1979, June 28   Litho.   Perf. 14

Design: 1col, Arenal Dam, horiz.

C750 AP161 1col multi   .25 .25
C751 AP161 5col multi   1.10 .70

Costa Rican Electricity Institute, 30th anniversary.

Costa Rica No. 1 and Rowland Hill AP162

Design: 10col, Penny Black and Hill.

1979, July 16   Perf. 13
C752 AP162 5col lil rose & bl
             gray   1.25 .55
C753 AP162 10col dl bl & blk   2.40 1.25

Sir Rowland Hill (1795-1879), originator of penny postage.

Poverty, by Juan Ramon Bonilla AP163

National Sculpture Contest: 60c, Hope, by Hernan Gonzalez. 2.10col, Cattle, by Victor M. Bermudez, horiz. 5col, Bust of Clorito Picado, by Juan Rafael Chacon. 20col, Mother and Child, by Francisco Zuniga.

1979, July 16   Litho.   Perf. 12
C754 AP163 60c multi   .25 .20
C755 AP163 1col multi   .30 .20
C756 AP163 2.10col multi   .65 .25
C757 AP163 5col multi   1.60 1.10
C758 AP163 20col multi   5.25 2.50
      Nos. C754-C758 (5)   8.05 4.25

Danaus Plexippus — AP164

Butterflies: 1col, Phoebis philea. 1.80col, Rothschildia. 2.10col, Prepona omphale. 2.60col, Marpesia marcella. 4.05col, Morpho cypris.

1979, Aug. 31   Litho.   Perf. 13½
C759 AP164 60c multi   3.00 .40
C760 AP164 1col multi   5.00 .40
C761 AP164 1.80col multi   7.00 .65
C762 AP164 2.10col multi   10.00 1.25
C763 AP164 2.60col multi   10.00 2.50
C764 AP164 4.05col multi   18.00 3.50
      Nos. C759-C764 (6)   53.00 8.70

SOS Emblem, Houses AP165

Children's Drawings: 5col, 5.50col, Landscapes, diff.

1979, Sept. 18
C765 AP165 2.50col multi   .95 .40
C766 AP165 5col multi   2.00 .60
C767 AP165 5.50col multi   2.40 .90
      Nos. C765-C767 (3)   5.35 1.90

SOS Children's Villages, 30th anniversary.

President Type of 1943

Presidents of Costa Rica: 60c, Rafael Yglesias C. 85c, Ascension Esquivel Ibarra. 1col, Cleto Gonzalez Viquez. 2col, Ricardo Jimenez Oreamuno.

1979, Oct. 8   Litho.   Perf. 13½
C768 A109 10c dk blue   .20 .20
C769 A109 60c dull purple   .20 .20
C770 A109 85c red orange   .25 .20
C771 A109 1col red orange   .30 .20
C772 A109 2col brown   .65 .40
  a.   Strip of 5, #C768-C772   1.75 1.40
      Nos. C768-C772 (5)   1.60 1.20

Printed in sheets of 100 and se-tenant in sheets of 25 (5x5).
See Nos. C790-C794.

Holy Family, Creche AP167

Reforestation AP168

1979, Nov. 16   Litho.   Perf. 12½
C773 AP167 1col multi   .25 .20
C774 AP167 1.60col multi   .65 .25

Christmas 1979.

1980, Jan. 14   Litho.   Perf. 11
C775 AP168 1col multi   .20 .20
C776 AP168 3.40col multi   .65 .50

Anatomy Lesson, by Rembrandt AP169

1980, Feb. 7   Litho.   Perf. 10½
C777 AP169 10col multi   4.00 1.75

Legal medicine teaching in Costa Rica, 50th anniversary.

Rotary Intl., 75th Anniv. — AP170

Gulf of Nicoya, Satellite Photo — AP171

1980, Feb. 26 **Perf. 16**
C778 AP170 2.10col multi .35 .25
C779 AP170 5col multi 1.00 .65

1980, Mar. 10 **Litho.** **Perf. 12½**
C780 AP171 2.10col Puerto Li- mon .35 .25
C781 AP171 5col multi 1.00 .65

14th Intl. Symposium on Remote Sensing of the Environment, San José, Apr. 23-30. Exist imperf.

Soccer, Moscow '80 Emblem — AP172

Poas Volcano AP173

1980, Apr. 16 **Litho.** **Perf. 10½**
C782 AP172 1col shown .50 .20
C783 AP172 3col Bicycling 8.00 .75
C784 AP172 4.05col Baseball 8.00 1.00
C785 AP172 20col Swim- ming 8.00 5.00
Nos. C782-C785 (4) 24.50 6.95

22nd Summer Olympic Games, Moscow, July 19-Aug. 3.

1980, May 14 **Litho.** **Perf. 10½**
C786 AP173 1col shown .25 .20
C787 AP173 2.50col Cahuita Beach .55 .40

National Parks Service, 10th anniversary.

José Maria Zeledon Brenes, Score — AP174

Design: 10col, Manuel Maria Gutierrez.

1980, June 25 **Litho.** **Perf. 12½**
C788 AP174 1col multi .25 .20
C789 AP174 10col multi 1.60 1.40

National anthem composed by Brenes (words) and Gutierrez (music). Nos. C788-C789 exist imperf.

President Type of 1943

1col, Alfredo Gonzalez F. 1.60col, Federico Tinoco G. 1.80col, Francisco Aguilar B. 2.10col, Julio Acosta G. 3col, Leon Cortes C.

1980, Aug. 14 **Litho.** **Perf. 11**
C790 A109 1col dk red .25 .20
C791 A109 1.60col slate bl .40 .20
C792 A109 1.80col brown .40 .20
C793 A109 2.10col dull green .50 .25
C794 A109 3col dark purple .80 .50
Nos. C790-C794 (5) 2.35 1.35

8th Natl. Phil. Exhib. — AP175

Fruits — AP176

1980, Sept. 11 **Perf. 13½**
C795 AP175 5col multi .80 .60
C796 AP175 20col multi 3.25 2.75

1980, Sept. 24 **Perf. 10½**
C797 AP176 10c shown .20 .20
C798 AP176 60c Cacao .50 .20
C799 AP176 1col Coffee .80 .20
C800 AP176 2.10col Bananas 1.60 .25
C801 AP176 3.40col Flowers 2.00 .50
C802 AP176 5col Sugar cane 2.40 .95
Nos. C797-C802 (6) 7.50 2.30

Giant Tree, by Jorge Carvajal AP177

Virgin and Child, by Raphael AP178

Paintings: 2.10col, Secret Look, by Rolando Cubero. 2.45col, Consuelo, by Fernando Carballo. 3col, Volcano, by Lola Fernandez. 4.05col, attending Mass, by Francisco Amighetti.

1980, Oct. 22 **Litho.** **Perf. 10½**
C803 AP177 1col multi .40 .20
C804 AP177 2.10col multi .55 .25

Size: 28x30mm

C805 AP177 2.45col multi .70 .30

Size: 22x36mm

C806 AP177 3col multi .80 .40
C807 AP177 4.05col multi 1.25 .50
Nos. C803-C807 (5) 3.70 1.65

1980, Nov. 11 **Perf. 13½**

Christmas 1980: 10col, Virgin and Child and St. John, by Raphael.

C808 AP178 1col multi .40 .30
C809 AP178 10col multi 2.40 1.75

Juan Santamaria International Airport AP179

1980, Dec. 11 **Litho.** **Perf. 10½**
Sizes: 30x30mm, 31x25mm (1.30col), 25x32mm (2.60col)
C810 AP179 1col Caldera Harbor .25 .20
C811 AP179 1.30col shown .40 .20
C812 AP179 2.10col Rio Frio Railroad Bridge .80 .40
C813 AP179 2.60col Highway to Colon .80 .40
C814 AP179 5col Huetar post office 1.25 .80
Nos. C810-C814 (5) 3.50 2.00

Paying your taxes means progress. For surcharge see No. C884.

Repertorio Americano Cover, J. Garcia Monge and Signature — AP180

1981, Jan. 2 **Litho.** **Perf. 10½**
C815 AP180 1.60col multi .30 .20
C816 AP180 3col multi .60 .40

Birth centenary of J. Garcia Monge, founder of Repertorio Americano journal.

Arms of Aserri (Site of Cornea Bank) AP181

Harpia Harpyja AP182

1981, Jan. 28 **Litho.** **Perf. 13½**
C817 AP181 1col shown .25 .20
C818 AP181 1.80col Eye .55 .25
C819 AP181 5col Rojas 1.60 .80
Nos. C817-C819 (3) 2.40 1.25

Establishment of human cornea bank, founded by Abelardo Rojas.

1980, Dec. 23 **Perf. 11**
C820 AP182 2.10col shown 1.60 .40
C821 AP182 2.50col Ara macao 2.10 .55
C822 AP182 3col Felis con- color 2.75 .65
C823 AP182 5.50col Ateles ge- offrovi 5.50 1.10
Nos. C820-C823 (4) 11.95 2.70

Medical and Surgical Clinic AP183

1981, Apr. 8 **Litho.** **Perf. 10½**
C824 AP183 5c multi .20 .20
C825 AP183 10c multi .20 .20
C826 AP183 50c multi .20 .20
C827 AP183 1.30col multi .40 .20
C828 AP183 3.40col multi .55 .50
C829 AP183 4.05col multi, vert. .80 .55
Nos. C824-C829 (6) 2.35 1.85

University of Costa Rica, 40th anniversary.

Mail Transport by Horse — AP184

1981, May 6 **Litho.** **Perf. 10½**
C830 AP184 1col shown .25 .20
C831 AP184 2.10col Train, 1857 .55 .25
C832 AP184 10col Mail carri- ers, 1858 2.40 1.60
Nos. C830-C832 (3) 3.20 2.05

Heinrich von Stephan (1831-97), UPU founder.

13th World Telecommunications Day — AP185

1981, May 18 **Perf. 11**
C833 AP185 5col multi 3.00 .60
C834 AP185 25col multi 7.50 4.00

Bishop Bernardo Thiel AP186

Juan Santamaria AP187

1981, June 8 **Litho.** **Perf. 10½**
C835 Strip of 5, stained glass windows 2.75 2.75
a. AP186 1col Sts. Peter & Paul .20 .20
b. AP186 1col St. Vincent de Paul .20 .20
c. AP186 1col Death of St. Joseph .20 .20
d. AP186 1col Archangel Michael .20 .20
e. AP186 1col Holy Family .20 .20
C836 AP186 2col shown .65 .40

Consecration of Bernardo Augusto Thiel as Bishop of San Jose.

1981, June 26 **Perf. 13½**
C837 AP187 1col shown .25 .20
C838 AP187 2.45col Alajuela Ca- thedral, horiz. .50 .40

Alajuela province.

Potters — AP188

1981, July 10 **Litho.** **Perf. 10½**
C839 AP188 15c shown .20 .20
C840 AP188 1.60col Bricklayers .25 .20
C841 AP188 1.80col Farmers .25 .20
C842 AP188 2.50col Fishermen .25 .20
C843 AP188 3col Nurse, pa- tient .40 .20
C844 AP188 5col Children, traffic po- liceman .70 .25
Nos. C839-C844 (6) 2.05 1.25

Model of New Natl. Archives AP189

Natl. Archives Centenary: 1.40col, Leon Fernandez Bonilla, founder, vert. 2col, Arms, vert. 3col, St. Thomas University, former headquarters.

1981, Aug. 24 **Litho.** **Perf. 13½**
C845 AP189 1.40col multi .30 .25
C846 AP189 2col multi .50 .25
C847 AP189 3col multi .65 .50
C848 AP189 3.50col multi .70 .60
Nos. C845-C848 (4) 2.15 1.60

Men Reaching for Sun, Map AP190

1981, Sept. 9   Litho.   Perf. 11
C849 AP190 1col Man in wheelchair, stairs, vert. .30 .20
C850 AP190 2.60col Man reaching for scale, vert. .80 .20
C851 AP190 10col shown 3.50 .80
Nos. C849-C851 (3) 4.60 1.20
Intl. Year of the Disabled.

World Food Day — AP191

1981, Oct. 16   Litho.   Perf. 10½
C852 AP191 5col multi .40 .25
C853 AP191 10col multi .80 .55

President Type of 1943

1col, Rafael A. Calderon Guardia, 1940. 2col, Teodoro Picado Michalski, 1944. 3col, José Figueres Ferrer, 1953. 5col, Otilio Ulate Blanco, 1949. 10col, Mario Echandi Jimenez, 1958.

1981, Dec. 7   Litho.   Perf. 13½
C854 A109 1col pink .55 .55
C855 A109 2col orange .55 .55
C856 A109 3col green .70 .55
C857 A109 5col dk bl 1.25 .90
C858 A109 10col blue 2.50 2.00
Nos. C854-C858 (5) 5.55 4.55

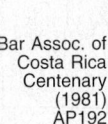

Bar Assoc. of Costa Rica Centenary (1981) AP192

1982, Mar. 22   Litho.   Perf. 13½
C859 AP192 1col Emblem, horiz. .20 .20
C860 AP192 2col E. Figueroa, 1st pres. .20 .20
C861 AP192 20col Bar building, horiz. 2.50 1.40
Nos. C859-C861 (3) 2.90 1.80

National Progress AP193

1982   Perf. 10½
C862 AP193 95c Housing .20 .20
C863 AP193 1.15col Agricultural fair .20 .20
C864 AP193 1.45col Education .20 .20
C865 AP193 1.65col Drinkable water .20 .20
C866 AP193 1.80col Rural medical care .20 .20
C867 AP193 2.10col Recreational areas .25 .20
C868 AP193 2.35col Natl. Theater Square .40 .20
C869 AP193 2.60col Communications .40 .20
C870 AP193 3col Electric railroad .55 .20
C871 AP193 4.05col Irrigation .55 .45
Nos. C862-C871 (10) 3.15 2.25

Issue dates: 1.80col, 2.10col, 2.60col, 3col, 4.05col, May 5; others, June 16.

City of Alajuela Bicentenary AP194

Perez Zeledon County, 50th Anniv. (1981) AP195

Designs: 5col, Central Park Fountain. 10col, Juan Santamaria Historical and Cultural Museum, horiz. 15col, Church of Christ of Esquipulas. 20col, Monsignor Esteban Lorenzo de Tristan, 25col, Father Juan Manuel Lopez del Corral.

1982, Aug. 9
C872 AP194 5col multi .55 .30
C873 AP194 10col multi 1.25 .55
C874 AP194 15col multi 1.75 1.25
C875 AP194 20col multi 2.40 1.25
C876 AP194 25col multi 3.00 1.60
Nos. C872-C876 (5) 8.95 4.95

1982, Aug. 30

Designs: 10c, Saint's Stone. 50c, Monument to Mothers. 1col, Pedro Perez Zeledon. 1.25col, St. Isidore Labrador Church. 3.50col, Municipal Building, horiz. 4.25col, Arms.

C877 AP195 10c multi .20 .20
C878 AP195 50c multi .20 .20
C879 AP195 1col multi .20 .20
C880 AP195 1.25col multi .20 .20
C881 AP195 3.50col multi .40 .25
C882 AP195 4.25col multi .55 .25
Nos. C877-C882 (6) 1.75 1.30

Nos. C695 and C813 Surcharged

1982, Oct. 28   Litho.   Perf. 10½
C883 AP143 3col on 75c multi .40 .25
C884 AP179 5col on 2.60col multi .55 .25

Nos. C640-C643 Surcharged and Overprinted: "IX EXPOSICION FILATELICA - 1982"

1982, Oct. 28   Perf. 12
C885 AP123 8.40col on #C640 .55 .40
C886 AP123 8.40col on #C641 .55 .40
C887 AP123 8.40col on #C642 .55 .40
C888 AP123 8.40col on #C643 .55 .40
C889 AP123 9.70col on #C640 .65 .55
C890 AP123 9.70col on #C641 .65 .55
C891 AP123 9.70col on #C642 .65 .55
C892 AP123 9.70col on #C643 .65 .55
Nos. C885-C892 (8) 4.80 3.80

9th Natl. Stamp Exhibition.

TB Bacillus Centenary AP196

Pan-American Blood Donors' Society, 7th Cong. — AP197

1982, Nov. 19   Perf. 13½
C893 AP196 1.50col Koch .20 .20
C894 AP196 3col Koch, slide .40 .20
C895 AP196 3.30col Health Ministry .40 .20
Nos. C893-C895 (3) 1.00 .60

1982, Nov. 25   Perf. 11
C896 AP197 30col Natl. Blood Assoc. emblem 2.00 1.40
C897 AP197 50col Cong. emblem 3.25 2.00

AP198

AP199

1982, Dec. 13   Litho.   Perf. 10½
C898 AP198 8.40col Emblem, horiz. .55 .25
C899 AP198 9.70col Emblem, diff. .80 .40
C900 AP198 11.70col Handshake, horiz. .80 .40
C901 AP198 13.05col Emblem, diff., horiz. .95 .50
Nos. C898-C901 (4) 3.10 1.55

Inter-Governmental Migration Committee, 30th anniv.

1983, Jan. 3   Perf. 16
4.80col, St. Francis of Assisi, by El Greco. 7.40col, Portrait, diff.
C902 AP199 4.80col multi .55 .25
C903 AP199 7.40col multi .80 .25
For surcharges see Nos. C908-C911.

Visit of Pope John Paul II AP200

Bolivar, by Francisco Zuniga Chavarria AP201

1983, Mar. 1   Litho.   Perf. 10½
C904 AP200 5col multi 2.75 .25
C905 AP200 10col multi 2.75 .50
C906 AP200 15col multi 6.00 .75
Nos. C904-C906 (3) 11.50 1.50

1983, July 22   Litho.   Perf. 16
C907 AP201 10col multi 1.10 .25

Nos. C902-C903 Surcharged

1983, Sept. 23   Litho.   Perf. 16
C908 AP199 10c on 4.80col .25 .25
C909 AP199 50c on 4.80col .25 .25
C910 AP199 1.50col on 7.40col .25 .25
C911 AP199 3col on 7.40col .25 .25
Nos. C908-C911 (4) 1.00 1.00

LACSA Costa Rica Airlines, 40th Anniv. — AP202

Various childrens' drawings.

1986, Dec. 12   Litho.   Perf. 13½
C912 AP202 1col Adriana E. Hidalgo .55 .20
C913 AP202 7col Osvaldo A.G. Vega 3.50 .30
C914 AP202 16col David V. Rodriguez 8.00 .75
Nos. C912-C914 (3) 12.05 1.25

Nos. C912-C913 exist perf 11. Unused examples are rare. Value used, $5 each.

Roman Macaya Lahmann, Aviation Pioneer AP203

1988, Sept. 26   Litho.   Perf. 10½
C915 AP203 10col multi .50 .20

No. 418 Ovptd.

1990, Nov. 5
C916 A180 50col multicolored 1.60 .55

Bagging Coffee Beans — AP204

Perf. 10½
1990, Nov. 16   Litho.   Unwmk.
C917 AP204 50col multicolored 2.10 .50

AP205

AP206

1990, Dec. 6
C918 AP205 50col blue & black 1.75 .50
First postage stamps, 150th anniv.

1991, Mar. 25   Litho.   Perf. 10½
Banana Picker, 1897, by Alleardo Villa.
C919 AP206 30col multicolored 2.00 .40
National Theater.

No. 428 Overprinted

Litho. & Engr.
1991, Sept. 13   Perf. 12½
C920 A188 200col 6.75 1.75
12th Natl. Philatelic Exposition.

No. 402 Overprinted

1991, Oct. 11   Litho.   Perf. 11½
Granite Paper
C921 A170 20col multicolored   2.25   .75
Basketball, cent.

Social Security Administration, 50th Anniv. AP207

1991, Nov. 1   Litho.   Perf. 13½
C922 AP207 15col multicolored   2.50   .30

La Poesia by Vespasiano Bignami — AP208

1992, Jan. 24   Litho.   Perf. 10½
C923 AP208 35col multicolored   3.50   .70
National Theater.

Discovery of America, 500th Anniv. AP209

Columbus' ships: a, Nina. b, Santa Maria. c, Pinta.

1992, Oct. 8   Litho.   Perf. 13½
C924 AP209 45col Strip of 3,
#a.-c.   4.00   1.50

Intl. Arts Festival — AP210

1993, Mar. 15   Litho.   Perf. 13½
C925 AP210 45col multicolored   1.40   .50

Telecommunications Institute, 30th Anniv. — AP211

1993, Nov. 25   Litho.   Perf. 13½
C926 AP211 45col multicolored   1.00   .70

Ministry of the Interior, 150th Anniv. AP212

1994, Mar. 8   Litho.   Perf. 10½
C927 AP212 45col multicolored   1.00   .70

Intl. Year of the Family — AP213

1994, May 5   Litho.   Perf. 10½
C928 AP213 45col multicolored   1.00   1.00

LACSA, 50th Anniv. AP214

1996, Mar. 29   Litho.   Perf. 10½
C929 AP214 5col   Douglas DC-3   .25   .25
C930 AP214 10col Curtiss C-46   .25   .25
C931 AP214 20col Beechcraft   .40   .40
C932 AP214 30col DC-6B   .65   .65
C933 AP214 35col BAC 1-11   .70   .70
C934 AP214 40col Convair CV
                     440   .90   .90
C935 AP214 45col Electra L-188   .95   .95
C936 AP214 50col Boeing 727-
                     200   1.00   1.00
C937 AP214 55col Douglas DC-8   1.25   1.25
C938 AP214 60col Airbus A320   1.40   1.40
        Nos. C929-C938 (10)   7.75   7.75

No. C932 Surcharged

2001, Oct. 5   Litho.   Perf. 10½
C939 AP214 5col on 30col multi   .40   .25

10th Intl. Art Festival — AP215

2006, Mar. 17   Litho.   Perf. 10½
C940 AP215 120col multi   1.90   1.90

AIR POST SPECIAL DELIVERY STAMPS

Catalogue values for unused stamps in this section are for Never Hinged items.

UPU Headquarters and Monument, Bern — APSD1

Perf. 10x11
1970, May 20   Litho.   Unwmk.
CE1 APSD1 35c multi   .75   .25
CE2 APSD1 60c multi   .75   .25

Opening of the UPU Headquarters in Bern. The red and black label attached to the 60c is inscribed "EXPRES." Values are for stamps with label attached.
Stamps with labels removed were used for regular airmail.

AIR POST OFFICIAL STAMPS

Air Post Stamps of 1934 Overprinted in Red

1934		**Unwmk.**	**Perf. 12**	
CO1	AP8	5c green	.25	.25
CO2	AP8	10c car rose	.25	.25
CO3	AP8	15c chocolate	.50	.50
CO4	AP8	20c deep blue	.80	.80
CO5	AP8	25c deep org	.80	.80
CO6	AP8	40c olive blk	.80	.80
CO7	AP8	50c gray blk	.80	.80
CO8	AP8	60c org yel	.95	.95
CO9	AP8	75c dull vio	.95	.95
CO10	AP9	1col deep rose	1.60	1.60
CO11	AP9	2col light blue	4.75	4.75
CO12	AP9	5col black	8.00	8.00
CO13	AP9	10col red brown	12.00	12.00
		Nos. CO1-CO13 (13)	32.45	32.45

For overprints see Nos. C103-C116.

SPECIAL DELIVERY STAMPS

Catalogue values for unused stamps in this section are for Never Hinged items.

Winged Letter SD1

Unwmk.
1972, Mar. 20   Litho.   Perf. 11
E1 SD1 75c brown & red   .30   .30
E2 SD1 1.50col blue & red   .50   .40

1973   Perf. 11x12
E3 SD1 75c green & red   .30   .30

1973, Nov. 5   Litho.   Perf. 12
E4 SD1 75c lilac & orange   1.50   .75
Exists perf 11x11½.

Concorde SD2

1976, May 17   Litho.   Perf. 16
E5 SD2 1col vermilion & multi   .75   .75

SD3

SD4

1979, June 15   Litho.   Perf. 12½
E6 SD3 2col multi   .90   .50

1980, Dec. 18   Litho.   Perf. 12½
E7 SD4 2col multi   .80   .50

1982, Dec. 20   Litho.   Perf. 11
E8 SD4 4col multi   .65   .40

POSTAGE DUE STAMPS

D1

D2

1903   Unwmk.   Engr.   Perf. 14
Numerals in Black
J1	D1	5c slate blue	6.75	1.25
J2	D1	10c brown orange	6.75	1.25
J3	D1	15c yellow green	3.50	1.75
J4	D1	20c carmine	4.75	1.75
J5	D1	25c slate gray	4.75	2.40
J6	D1	30c brown	6.00	2.50
J7	D1	40c olive bister	6.75	2.50
J8	D1	50c red violet	6.75	2.50
		Nos. J1-J8 (8)	46.00	15.90

1915   Litho.   Perf. 12
J9	D2	2c orange	1.25	.55
J10	D2	4c dark blue	1.25	.55
J11	D2	8c gray green	1.25	.55
J12	D2	10c violet	1.25	.55
J13	D2	20c brown	1.25	.55
		Nos. J9-J13 (5)	6.25	2.75

OFFICIAL STAMPS

Values for unused stamps are for examples with original gum as defined in the catalogue introduction. Examples without gum have probably been used and are so regarded.
Very fine examples of Nos. O1-O24 will have perforations just clear of the design on one or more sides.
Nos. O1-O55, to about 1915, normally were not canceled when affixed to official mail. Occasionally they were canceled in a foreign country of destination. Used values are for favor-canceled stamps or for stamps without gum.

Regular Issues Overprinted

Overprinted in Red, Black, Blue or Green

1883-85		Unwmk.	Perf. 12	
O1	A6	1c green (R)	2.00	1.10
O2	A6	1c green (Bk)	4.00	1.10
O3	A6	2c carmine (Bk)	4.00	1.40
O4	A6	2c carmine (Bl)	2.40	1.60
O5	A6	5c blue vio (R)	7.00	3.00
O6	A6	10c orange (G)	10.00	4.00
O7	A6	40c blue (R)	10.00	4.00
		Nos. O1-O7 (7)	39.40	16.20

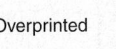

Overprinted

1886				
O8	A6	1c green (Bk)	3.50	1.10
O9	A6	2c carmine (Bk)	3.50	1.60
O10	A6	5c blue vio (R)	24.00	11.00
O11	A6	10c orange (Bk)	24.00	11.00
		Nos. O8-O11 (4)	55.00	24.70

Overprinted

O12	A6	1c green (Bk)	3.50	1.00
O13	A6	2c carmine (Bk)	3.50	1.40
O14	A6	5c blue vio (R)	24.00	11.00
O15	A6	10c orange (Bk)	24.00	11.00
		Nos. O12-O15 (4)	55.00	24.40

Nos. O8-O11 and O12-O15 exist se-tenant in vertical pairs.

Overprinted in Black

O16	A6	5c blue vio	60.00	35.00
O17	A6	10c orange	—	275.00

Overprinted

1887				
O18	A6	1c green	1.25	.55
O19	A6	2c carmine	1.25	.50
O21	A6	10c orange	37.50	24.00
c.		Double overprint	42.50	
O22	A7	5c blue vio	12.00	3.50
O23	A7	10c orange	.90	.50
c.		Double overprint	27.50	
O24	A6	40c blue	1.25	.50
		Nos. O18-O24 (6)	54.15	29.55

Overprinted "OFICAL"

O18a	A6	1c green	14.50	14.50
O19a	A6	2c carmine	14.50	14.50
O22a	A7	5c blue violet	14.50	
O23a	A7	10c orange	14.50	3.50
O24a	A6	40c blue	17.00	17.00
		Nos. O18a-O24a (5)	60.50	

Dangerous counterfeits exist of Nos. O18a-O24a.

Without Period

O18b	A6	1c green	14.50	10.00
O19b	A6	2c carmine	14.50	10.00
O22b	A7	5c blue violet	14.50	10.00
O23b	A7	10c orange	14.50	10.00
		Nos. O18b-O23b (4)	58.00	40.00

Nos. O18b-O23b are from a separate plate without periods. No. O23 exists without period (position 32). These must be collected in pairs.

Issues of 1889-1901 Overprinted

1889			Perf. 14, 15	
O25	A10	1c brown	.25	.20
O26	A11	2c dk green	.25	.20
O27	A12	5c orange	.25	.20
O28	A13	10c red brown	.25	.20
O29	A14	20c yellow grn	.40	.20
O30	A15	50c rose red	1.40	1.40
		Nos. O25-O30 (6)	2.80	2.40

1892				
O31	A20	1c grnsh blue	.25	.25
O32	A21	2c yellow	.25	.25
O33	A22	5c violet	.25	.25
O34	A23	10c lt green	3.50	1.60
O35	A24	20c scarlet	.25	.20
O36	A25	50c gray blue	.65	.55
		Nos. O31-O36 (6)	5.15	3.10

1901-02				
O37	A30	1c green & blk	.40	.40
O38	A31	2c ver & blk	.40	.40
O39	A32	5c gray bl & blk	.40	.40
O40	A33	10c ocher & blk	.80	.80
O41	A34	20c lake & blk	1.25	1.25
O42	A35	50c lilac & dk bl	10.00	4.00
O43	A36	1col ol bis & blk	17.50	10.00
		Nos. O37-O43 (7)	30.75	17.25

No. 46 Overprinted in Green

1903				
O44	A31	2c ver & blk	3.00	3.00
b.		"PROVISIORO"	10.00	10.00
d.		Inverted overprint	10.00	10.00
f.		As "b," inverted	13.00	10.00

Counterfeit overprints exist.

Regular Issue of 1903 Overprinted Like Nos. O25-O43

1903			Perf. 14, 12½x14	
O45	A40	4c red vio & blk	1.40	1.40
O46	A41	6c ol grn & blk	1.75	1.75
O47	A42	25c gray lil & brn	9.50	6.00
		Nos. O45-O47 (3)	12.65	9.15

Counterfeit overprints exist.

Regular Issue of 1907 Overprinted

1908			Perf. 14	
O48	A43	1c red brn & ind	.20	.20
O49	A44	2c yel grn & blk	.20	.20
O50	A45	4c car & ind	.20	.20
O51	A46	5c yel & dull bl	.20	.20
O52	A47	10c blue & blk	.80	.80
O53	A49	25c gray lil & blk	.30	.20
O54	A50	50c red lil & bl	.55	.55
O55	A51	1col brown & blk	1.25	1.25
		Nos. O48-O55 (8)	3.70	3.60

Various varieties of the overprint and basic stamps exist.
Imperf examples of Nos. O48, O49, O53 were found in 1970.

Regular Issue of 1910 Overprinted in Black

1917				
O56	A56	5c orange	.40	.40
a.		Inverted overprint	6.00	3.50
O57	A57	10c deep blue	.25	.25
a.		Inverted overprint	3.50	3.50

No. 74 Surcharged

1920		Red Surcharge	Perf. 12	
O58	A58	15c on 20c olive grn	.55	.55

Nos. 72, 61, 59, 65-67 Surcharged or Overprinted

1921		Black Surcharge	Perf. 12	
O59	A56	10c on 5c orange	.50	.50
a.		"10 CTS." inverted	17.50	
			Perf. 14	
O60	A45	4c car & indigo	.40	.40
a.		"1291" for "1921"	12.00	
O61	A43	6c on 1c red brn & ind	.55	.55
O62	A49	20c on 25c gray lil & blk	.55	.55

Overprinted like No. O60

O63	A50	50c red lil & bl	2.50	1.75
O64	A51	1col brown & blk	5.00	3.00
		Nos. O59-O64 (6)	9.50	6.75

Nos. O60 to O64 exist with date and new values inverted. These may be printer's waste but probably were deliberately made.

Regular Issue of 1923 Overprinted

1923			Perf. 11½	
O65	A68	2c brown	.20	.20
O66	A68	4c orange	.20	.20
O67	A68	5c blue	.40	.40
O68	A68	20c carmine	.25	.25
O69	A68	1col violet	.55	.55
		Nos. O65-O69 (5)	1.55	1.55

Nos. O65 to O69 exist imperforate but were not regularly issued in that condition.

O7

1926		Unwmk.	Engr.	Perf. 12½	
O70	O7	2c ultra & blk		.25	.25
O71	O7	3c mag & blk		.25	.25
O72	O7	4c lt bl & blk		.25	.25
O73	O7	5c grn & blk		.25	.25
O74	O7	6c ocher & blk		.25	.25
O75	O7	10c rose red & blk		.25	.25
O76	O7	20c ol grn & blk		.25	.25
O77	O7	30c red org & blk		.25	.25
O78	O7	45c brown & blk		.25	.25
O79	O7	1col lilac & blk		.50	.50
		Nos. O70-O79 (10)		2.75	2.75

See Nos. O82-O94. For surcharges see Nos. C7-C10.

Regular Issue of 1936 Overprinted in Black

1936		Unwmk.	Perf. 12	
O80	A96	5c green	.25	.25
O81	A96	10c carmine rose	.25	.25

Type of 1926

1937			Perf. 12½	
O82	O7	2c vio & blk	.20	.20
O83	O7	3c bis brn & blk	.20	.20
O84	O7	4c rose car & blk	.20	.20
O85	O7	5c ol grn & blk	.20	
O86	O7	8c blk brn & blk	.20	
O87	O7	10c rose lake & blk	.20	
O88	O7	20c ind & blk	.20	.20
O89	O7	40c red org & blk	.25	.25
O90	O7	55c dk vio & blk	.25	
O91	O7	1col brn vio & blk	.30	.30
O92	O7	2col gray bl & blk	.70	.70
O93	O7	5col dl yel & blk	3.00	3.00
O94	O7	10col blue & blk	20.00	20.00
		Nos. O82-O94 (13)	25.90	

Nine stamps of this series exist with perforated star (2c, 3c, 4c, 20c, 40c, 1col, 2col, 5col, 10col). These were issued to officials for postal purposes. Unpunched stamps were sold to collectors but had no franking power. Values for unused are for unpunched.

POSTAL TAX STAMPS

Catalogue values for unused stamps in this section are for Never Hinged items.

Most postal tax issues were to benefit the Children's Village and were obligatory on all mail during Dec.

No. C198 Surcharged in Red: "Sello de Navidad Pro-Ciudad de Los Niños 5 5"

Engraved; Center Photogravure

1958		Unwmk.	Perf. 12½	
RA1	AP51	5c on 2c brt bl & blk	.30	.25

Similar Surcharge in Green on Type of 1954

Design: Like No. C228, pottery.

RA2	AP53	5c on 10c dk bl & blk	.50	.25
a.		Inverted surcharge	8.50	

Father Edward J. Flanagan PT1 — Father Peralta PT2

Paintings: No. RA4, Boy by El Greco. No. RA5, Boy by Jose Ribera. No. RA6, Girl by Amadeo Modigliani.

			Perf. 13½	
1959, Nov. 25		Unwmk.	Photo.	
RA3	PT1	5c green	.65	.25
RA4	PT1	5c dl gray vio	.65	.25
RA5	PT1	5c olive	.65	.25
RA6	PT1	5c lilac rose	.65	.25
		Nos. RA3-RA6 (4)	2.60	1.00

Nos. RA3-RA6 exist imperf.

1960		Litho.	Perf. 14	

Designs: No. RA8, Girl by Renoir. No. RA9, Boys with cups by Velazquez. No. RA10, Singing children, sculpture by F. Zuñiga.

RA7	PT2	5c chocolate	.65	.25
RA8	PT2	5c dp org	.65	.25
RA9	PT2	5c plum	.65	.25
RA10	PT2	5c grysh bl	.65	.25
		Nos. RA7-RA10 (4)	2.60	1.00

Nos. RA7-RA10 exist imperf.

No. C229 Surcharged Like Nos. RA1-RA2

Engraved; Center Photogravure

1961   *Perf. 13x12½*
RA11 AP53 5c on 15c grn & blk   .40   .25

Nicolas, Son of Rubens — PT3

Boys in Workshop — PT4

Designs: No. RA13, Madonna by Bellini. RA14, Angel playing stringed instrument by Melozzo. RA15, Msgr. Rubén Odio H.

1962   **Photo.**   *Perf. 13½*
RA12 PT3 5c dark carmine   .70   .25
RA13 PT3 5c sepia   .70   .25
RA14 PT3 5c dull green   .70   .25
RA15 PT3 5c blue   .70   .25
   Nos. RA12-RA15 (4)   2.80 1.00

For surcharges see Nos. 262-265.

Type of 1962, Inscribed "1963"
Designs as before

1963   **Photo.**   *Perf. 13½*
RA16 PT3 5c sepia (RA12)   .45   .25
RA17 PT3 5c ultra (RA13)   .45   .25
RA18 PT3 5c dk car (RA14)   .45   .25
RA19 PT3 5c black (RA15)   .45   .25
   Nos. RA16-RA19 (4)   1.80 1.00

1964   **Litho.**   *Perf. 12½*
Designs: No. RA21, Two playing boys. No. RA22, Teacher and children. No. RA23, Priest with boys.

RA20 PT4 5c bright green   .40   .25
RA21 PT4 5c rose lilac   .40   .25
RA22 PT4 5c blue   .40   .25
RA23 PT4 5c brown   .40   .25
   Nos. RA20-RA23 (4)   1.60 1.00

Brother Casiano de Madrid PT5

Christmas Ornaments PT6

Designs: No. RA25, National Children's Hospital. No. RA26, Poinsettia. No. RA27, Santa Claus with children (diamond).

1965, Dec. 10   **Litho.**   *Perf. 10*
RA24 PT5 5c red brown   .25   .25
RA25 PT5 5c green   .25   .25
RA26 PT5 5c red   .25   .25
RA27 PT5 5c ultra   .25   .25
   Nos. RA24-RA27 (4)   1.00 1.00

1966   **Litho.**   *Perf. 11*
RA28 PT6 5c shown   .25   .25
RA29 PT6 5c Angel   .25   .25
RA30 PT6 5c Church   .25   .25
RA31 PT6 5c Reindeer   .25   .25
   Nos. RA28-RA31 (4)   1.00 1.00

General Post Office, San José — PT7

1967, Mar.   **Litho.**   *Perf. 11*
RA32 PT7 10c blue   .40   .25

No. RA32 was issued as a postal tax stamp to be used by organizations normally allowed free postage. On Dec. 15, 1972, it was authorized for use as an ordinary postage stamp.

Madonna and Child — PT8

Star of Bethlehem, Mother and Child — PT9

1967   **Litho.**   *Perf. 11*
RA33 PT8 5c olive green   .25   .25
RA34 PT8 5c dp lil rose   .25   .25
RA35 PT8 5c brt blue   .25   .25
RA36 PT8 5c grnsh blue   .25   .25
   Nos. RA33-RA36 (4)   1.00 1.00

1968, Dec.   **Litho.**   *Perf. 12½*
RA37 PT9 5c gray   .25   .25
RA38 PT9 5c rose red   .25   .25
RA39 PT9 5c dk rose brn   .25   .25
RA40 PT9 5c bister brn   .25   .25
   Nos. RA37-RA40 (4)   1.00 1.00

Madonna and Child — PT10

Christ Child, Star — PT11

1969, Dec.   **Litho.**   *Perf. 12½*
RA41 PT10 5c dk blue   .25   .25
RA42 PT10 5c orange   .25   .25
RA43 PT10 5c brown red   .25   .25
RA44 PT10 5c blue green   .25   .25
   Nos. RA41-RA44 (4)   1.00 1.00

1970, Dec.   **Litho.**   *Perf. 12½*
RA45 PT11 5c brt purple   .35   .25
RA46 PT11 5c lilac rose   .35   .25
RA47 PT11 5c olive   .35   .25
RA48 PT11 5c ocher   .35   .25
   Nos. RA45-RA48 (4)   1.40 1.00

Christ Child and "PAX" — PT12

Madonna and Child — PT13

1971, Nov. 29
RA49 PT12 5c dk blue   .25   .25
RA50 PT12 10c orange   .25   .25
RA51 PT12 10c brown   .25   .25
RA52 PT12 10c green   .25   .25
   Nos. RA49-RA52 (4)   1.00 1.00

1972, Nov. 30   *Perf. 11x11½*
RA53 PT13 10c dk blue   .25   .25
RA54 PT13 10c brt red   .25   .25
RA55 PT13 10c lilac   .25   .25
RA56 PT13 10c green   .25   .25
   Nos. RA53-RA56 (4)   1.00 1.00

Madonna and Child — PT14

Boys Eating Cake, by Murillo — PT15

1973, Nov. 30   **Litho.**   *Perf. 12½*
RA57 PT14 10c purple   .25   .25
RA58 PT14 10c car rose   .25   .25
RA59 PT14 10c gray   .25   .25
RA60 PT14 10c orange brn   .25   .25
   Nos. RA57-RA60 (4)   1.00 1.00

1974, Nov. 25   *Perf. 13*
Paintings: No. RA62, Virgin and Child, with St. John, by Raphael. No. RA63, Maternity, by Juan R. Bonilla. No. RA64, Praying Child, by Reynolds.

RA61 PT15 10c brt pink   .30   .25
RA62 PT15 10c rose lilac   .30   .25
RA63 PT15 10c dk gray   .30   .25
RA64 PT15 10c violet bl   .30   .25
   Nos. RA61-RA64 (4)   1.20 1.00

See No. RA110.

"Happy Dreams," by Sonia Romero PT16

Virgin and Child, by Hans Memling PT17

Paintings: No. RA66, Virgin with Carnation, by Leonardo da Vinci. No. RA67, Children with Tortoise, by Francisco Amighetti. No. RA68, Boy with Pigeon, by Picasso.

1975, Nov. 25   **Litho.**   *Perf. 10½*
RA65 PT16 10c gray   .30   .25
RA66 PT16 10c red lilac   .30   .25
RA67 PT16 10c orange brown   .30   .25
RA68 PT16 10c brt blue   .30   .25
   Nos. RA65-RA68 (4)   1.20 1.00

1976, Nov. 24   **Litho.**   *Perf. 10½*
Paintings: No. RA70, Girl with Sombrero, by Auguste Renoir. No. RA71, Meditation (boy), by Floria Pinto de Herrero. No. RA72, Gaston de Mezerville (boy), by Lolita Zeller de Peralta.

RA69 PT17 10c rose lilac   .30   .25
RA70 PT17 10c rose carmine   .30   .25
RA71 PT17 10c gray   .30   .25
RA72 PT17 10c violet blue   .30   .25
   Nos. RA69-RA72 (4)   1.20 1.00

Boy's Head, by Amparo Cruz — PT18

Boy with Kite — PT19

Paintings: No. RA74, Girl's head, by Rubens. No. RA75, Girl and infant, by Cristina Fournier. No. RA76, Mariano Goya, by Goya.

1977, Nov.   *Perf. 10½*
RA73 PT18 10c gray olive   .30   .25
RA74 PT18 10c rose red   .30   .25
RA75 PT18 10c brt ultra   .30   .25
RA76 PT18 10c brt rose lil   .30   .25
   Nos. RA73-RA76 (4)   1.20 1.00

1978, Nov. 20   **Litho.**   *Perf. 12½*
Designs: Nos. RA78-RA79, Girl flying kite.

RA77 PT19 10c magenta   .30   .25
RA78 PT19 10c slate   .30   .25
RA79 PT19 10c lilac   .30   .25
RA80 PT19 10c violet blue   .30   .25
   Nos. RA77-RA80 (4)   1.20 1.00

Boy Leaning on Tree — PT20

Boy on Swing — PT21

1979, Nov. 19   **Litho.**   *Perf. 12½*
RA81 PT20 10c blue   .25   .25
RA82 PT20 10c orange   .25   .25
RA83 PT20 10c magenta   .25   .25
RA84 PT20 10c green   .25   .25
   Nos. RA81-RA84 (4)   1.00 1.00

1980, Nov. 18   **Litho.**   *Perf. 12½*
RA85 PT21 10c brt blue   .25   .25
RA86 PT21 10c brt yellow   .25   .25
RA87 PT21 10c crimson rose   .25   .25
RA88 PT21 10c brt green   .25   .25
   Nos. RA85-RA88 (4)   1.00 1.00

Boy Riding Toy Car PT22

Youth Running Machine PT23

1981, Nov. 19   **Litho.**   *Perf. 11*
RA89 PT22 10c blue   .25   .25
RA90 PT22 10c green   .25   .25
RA91 PT22 10c brt ultra   .25   .25
RA92 PT22 10c orange   .25   .25
   Nos. RA89-RA92 (4)   1.00 1.00

1982, Nov. 19   **Litho.**   *Perf. 10½*
RA93 PT23 10c red   .25   .25
RA94 PT23 10c gray   .25   .25
RA95 PT23 10c purple   .25   .25
RA96 PT23 10c grnsh blue   .25   .25
   Nos. RA93-RA96 (4)   1.00 1.00

Youths Working on Wheelchair PT24

Girl on Bicycle PT25

1983, Nov. 24   **Litho.**   *Perf. 16*
RA97 PT24 10c red   .25   .25
RA98 PT24 10c orange   .25   .25
RA99 PT24 10c ultra   .25   .25
RA100 PT24 10c green   .25   .25
   Nos. RA97-RA100 (4)   1.00 1.00

   Christmas 1983.

1984, Nov. 20   **Litho.**   *Perf. 10½*
RA101 PT25 10c violet   .60   .25

   Christmas 1984.

Taking a Child in Out of the Cold PT26

Depressed Child PT27

1985, Dec. 1   **Litho.**   *Perf. 13*
RA102 PT26 10c dull brown   .60   .25

   Christmas 1985.

1986, Dec. 1   **Litho.**   *Perf. 10½*
RA103 PT27 10c lemon   .60   .25

   Christmas stamps, 25th anniv.; Christmas 1986.

Christmas
PT28

Teaching
Children
PT29

1987, Dec. 1　　Litho.　　Perf. 10½
RA104　PT28　10c dk ol bis & brt
　　　　bl　　　　　　　　.40　.25

No postal tax stamp was issued for 1988.

1989, Dec. 1　　Litho.　　Perf. 13½
RA105　PT29　1col blue, blk & brt
　　　　apple grn　　　　　.40　.25

Christmas 1989.

No. 417 Ovptd. in
Red, Blue, Green,
or Orange

1990, Nov. 16　　Litho.　　Perf. 13½
RA106　A179　10col multi (R)　　.90　.25
RA107　A179　10col multi (Bl)　　.90　.25
RA108　A179　10col multi (G)　　.90　.25
RA109　A179　10col multi (O)　　.90　.25
　　Nos. RA106-RA109 (4)　3.60　1.00

No. RA109 exists with a silver overprint.

Art Type of 1974
Design: 10col, Praying Child, by Reynolds.

1991, Nov. 18　　Litho.　　Perf. 10½
RA110　PT15　10col dark ultra　.90　.25

PT30　　　　　　PT31

Boy in workshop.

1992, Dec. 1　　Litho.　　Perf. 10½
RA111　PT30　10col red　　　.30　.20

Christmas.

1993, Nov. 17
RA112　PT31　10col multicolored　.25　.20

Christmas.

PT32　　　　　　PT33

1994, Nov. 23　　Litho.　　Perf. 10½
RA113　PT32　11col lilac & slate　.40　.20

Christmas.
No. RA113 exists imperf.

1995, Dec. 1　　　　　　Perf. 13½
Painting of mother and child, by Claudio
Carazo.

RA114　PT33　12col multicolored　.55　.25
　a.　Miniature sheet, #RA114 + 5
　　　labels　　　　　　　3.25　3.25

No. RA114a contains 4 progressive proofs
of No. RA114 + one label of text and sold for
112col.
Christmas.

PT34　　　　　　　PT35

1996, Dec. 1　　Litho.　　Perf. 10½
RA115　PT34　14col　Sculpture　.55　.25

1997, Dec. 1
Bust of Antonio Obando Chan, by Olger Villegas Cruz.

RA116　PT35　15col multicolored　.40　.30
Christmas.

PT36

Designs: a, Flower. b, Flower up close, one
in background. c, Berries on branch.

1998　　　　　　　　Perf. 13½
RA117　PT36　16col　Strip of 3,
　　　　#a.-c.　　　　1.40　1.25
Christmas.

Children's
Village
PT37

1999, Dec. 1　　Litho.　　Perf. 13¼
RA118　PT37　17col multi　　.45　.25

Child — PT38

Color: a, Green. b, Red. c, Blue. d, Brown.

2000, Dec. 1　　Litho.　　Perf. 10½
RA119　　Horiz. strip of 4　4.00　2.00
　a.-d.　PT38 20col Any single　.50　.30

Child
Examining
Stamp — PT39

Panel color: a, Purple. b, Green. c, Red. d,
Orange.

2001, Dec. 1　　Litho.　　Perf. 10½
RA120　　Horiz. strip of 4　1.60　1.25
　a.-d.　PT39 21col Any single　.35　.30

Child — PT40

Panel color: a, Purple. b, Blue. c, Orange. d,
Green.

2002　　　　Litho.　　Perf. 10½
RA121　　Horiz strip of 4　1.40　1.40
　a.-d.　PT40 22col Any single　.30　.30

Child Pointing at
Star — PT41

No. RA122 — Background color: a, Purple.
b, Green. c, Red. d, Yellow orange.

2003, Dec. 1　　Litho.　　Perf. 13½x13¼
RA122　　Horiz. strip of 4　1.40　1.40
　a.-d.　PT41 23col Any single　.30　.30

Three
Magi — PT42

No. RA123 — Magi in: a, Lemon. b, Green.
c, Purple. d, Red violet.

2004　　　　Litho.　　Perf. 13¼
RA123　　Horiz. strip of 4　1.75　1.75
　a.-d.　PT42 25col Any single　.40　.40

Children — PT43

No. RA124 — Denomination color: a, White.
b, Buff. c, Dull orange. d, Red.

2005, Dec. 1　　Litho.　　Perf. 10½
RA124　　Horiz. strip of 4　1.75　1.75
　a.-d.　PT43 28col Any single　.40　.40

Surtax for Children's Village.

Child
Reading
PT44

No. RA125 — Frame color: a, Yellow bister.
b, Dull brown. c, Olive green. d, Orange
brown.

2006, Dec. 1　　Litho.　　Perf. 10½
RA125　　Horiz. strip of 4　2.25　2.25
　a.-d.　PT44 32col Any single　.55　.55

Children's
Art — PT45

No. RA126: a, Family and hearts. b, Children at school. c, Children on playground
equipment. d, Boy on skateboard.

2007, Dec. 1　　Litho.　　Perf. 10½
RA126　　Horiz. strip of 4　2.25　2.25
　a.-d.　PT45 35col Any single　.55　.55

Surtax for Children's Village.

Children's
Art — PT46

No. RA127: a, Child flying kite, by Luis Paul-
ino Murillo Méndez. b, Boy and jaguar, by
David Malavassi Zúñiga. c, Bird and sailboat,
by Valeria Vargas Arias. d, Child in water, by
Dannia María Berrocal Fonseca.

2008, Dec. 1　　Litho.　　Perf. 13½
RA127　　Horiz. strip of 4　2.50　2.50
　a.-d.　PT46 40col Any single　.60　.60

Surtax for Children's Village.

Miniature Sheet

Masquerade Costumes — PT47

No. RA128: a, Devil and man in purple hat.
b, Bull and clown. c, Grim reaper. d, Stilt
walker and tall woman.

2009, Dec. 1　　Litho.　　Perf. 10½
RA128　PT47　45col　Sheet of 4,
　　　　#a-d　　　　.90　.90

Surtax for Children's Village.

GUANACASTE

ˌgwä-nə-ˈkästä

(A province of Costa Rica)

LOCATION — Northwestern coast of
Central America
AREA — 4,000 sq. mi. (approx.)
POP. — 69,531 (estimated)
CAPITAL — Liberia

Residents of Guanacaste were
allowed to buy Costa Rican stamps,
overprinted "Guanacaste," at a discount
from face value because of the province's isolation and climate, which
makes it difficult to keep mint stamps.
Use was restricted to the province.
Counterfeits of most Guanacaste
overprints are plentiful.

For 5c stamps between Nos. 5-43,
unused examples without gum sell for
slightly more than the used value.

Very fine examples of Nos. 1-54 will
have perforations just clear of the
design on one or more sides.

Dangerous counterfeits exist of Nos.
1-63.

On Issue of 1883
Overprinted Horizontally in Black

16mm

1885 Unwmk. Perf. 12

1	A6	1c green	4.00	3.25
2	A6	2c carmine	4.00	3.25
a.		"Gnanacaste"	250.00	
3	A6	10c orange	35.00	21.00
a.		"Gnanacaste"	500.00	

Same Overprint in Red

4	A6	1c green	4.00	3.25
a.		"Gnanacaste"	200.00	
b.		Overprinted in black & red	300.00	
5	A6	5c blue violet	30.00	4.00
a.		"Gnanacaste"	350.00	
6	A6	40c blue	25.00	21.00

Overprinted Horizontally in Black

17½mm

7	A6	1c green	10.00	7.00
8	A6	2c carmine	10.00	7.00
9	A6	5c blue violet	45.00	15.00
10	A6	10c orange	60.00	35.00
11	A6	40c blue	60.00	60.00

Same Overprint in Red

12	A6	5c blue violet	500.00	175.00
13	A6	40c blue	2,000.	

Overprinted Horizontally in Black

18½mm — c

14	A6	2c carmine	10.00	7.00
15	A6	10c orange	100.00	75.00

Same Overprint in Red

16	A6	1c green	7.00	7.00
a.		Double ovpt., one in blk	250.00	
17	A6	5c blue violet	45.00	15.00
18	A6	40c blue	75.00	75.00

Same Overprint, Vertically in Black

19	A6	1c green	5,000.	
20	A6	2c carmine	4,250.	
21	A6	5c blue violet	700.00	175.00
22	A6	10c orange	120.00	120.00

(overprint type specimens)

e f g h i

Overprinted Type e, Vertically

23	A6	1c green	3,000.	2,000.
24	A6	2c carmine	700.00	300.00
25	A6	5c blue violet	400.00	75.00
26	A6	10c orange	75.00	75.00

Overprinted Type f, Vertically

27	A6	1c green	2,000.	2,000.
28	A6	2c carmine	700.00	400.00
29	A6	5c blue violet	400.00	125.00
30	A6	10c orange	100.00	100.00

Overprinted Type g, Vertically

31	A6	1c green	2,500.	2,500.
32	A6	2c carmine	1,000.	1,000.
33	A6	5c blue violet	600.00	200.00
34	A6	10c orange	150.00	150.00

Overprinted Type h, Vertically

35	A6	1c green	2,000.	1,500.
36	A6	2c carmine	500.00	300.00
37	A6	5c blue violet	350.00	75.00
38	A6	10c orange	60.00	60.00

Overprinted Type i, Vertically

39	A6	1c green	—	
39A	A6	2c carmine	275.00	
40	A6	5c blue violet	20.00	
41	A6	10c orange	200.00	

On Issues of 1883-87

Overprinted Horizontally in Black

1888-89

42	A7	5c blue violet	15.00	3.00

Overprinted Horizontally in Black

43	A7	5c blue violet	15.00	3.00

Overprinted Horizontally in Black

44	A6	2c carmine	3.00	
45	A7	10c orange	3.00	

Inverted overprints are fakes.

On Issue of 1889
Overprinted Like Nos. 7-13, Horizontally

1889

47	A8	2c blue	20.00	

Vertically

48	A8	2c blue (c)	250.00	
49	A8	2c blue (e)	75.00	
51	A8	2c blue (f)	75.00	
52	A8	2c blue (g)	250.00	
54	A8	2c blue (h)	75.00	

Nos. 47-54 are overprinted "Correos." Stamps without "Correos" are known postally used. Unused examples are valued the same as Nos. 47-54, unused. The 1c without "Correos" is known postally used. The 1c with "Correos" is counterfeit.

On Nos. 25-33

Overprinted Horizontally in Black

1889 Perf. 14 and 15

55	A10	1c brown	10.00	3.50
56	A11	2c dark green	4.50	1.50
57	A12	5c orange	6.75	2.10
58	A13	10c red brown	6.75	2.10
59	A14	20c yellow green	1.00	.70
60	A15	50c rose red	1.75	1.50
61	A16	1p blue	4.50	4.50
62	A17	2p violet	6.75	6.75
63	A18	5p olive green	37.50	37.50
		Nos. 55-63 (9)	79.50	60.15

Nos. 61-63 with remainder cancels sell for about half the used values shown.

Overprinted "GUAGACASTE"

60a	A15	50c rose red	325.00	325.00
61a	A16	1p blue	325.00	325.00
62a	A17	2p violet	400.00	400.00
63a	A18	5p olive green	600.00	600.00

Values for Nos. 60a-63a used are for examples with remainder cancels.

Overprinted Horizontally in Black

64	A10	1c brown	2.25	1.50
a.		Vert. pair, imperf. between		

65	A11	2c dark green	2.25	1.50
66	A12	5c orange	2.25	1.50
67	A13	10c red brown	2.25	1.50
		Nos. 64-67 (4)	9.00	6.00

CRETE

'krēt

LOCATION — An island in the Mediterranean Sea south of Greece
GOVT. — A department of Greece
AREA — 3,235 sq. mi.
POP. — 336,150 (1913)
CAPITAL — Canea

Formerly Crete was a province of Turkey. After an extended period of civil wars, France, Great Britain, Italy and Russia intervened and declaring Crete an autonomy, placed it under the administration of Prince George of Greece as High Commissioner. In October, 1908, the Cretan Assembly voted for union with Greece and in 1913 the union was formally effected.

40 Paras = 1 Piaster
4 Metallik = 1 Grosion (1899)
100 Lepta = 1 Drachma (1900)

Issued Under Joint Administration of France, Great Britain, Italy and Russia
British Sphere of Administration
District of Heraklion (Candia)

A1 A2

Handstamped

1898		**Unwmk.**	**Imperf.**
1	A1	20pa red	450.00 250.00

1898		**Litho.**	**Perf. 11½**
2	A2	10pa blue	9.00 3.00
a.		Horiz. pair, imperf. btwn.	275.00
b.		Imperf., pair	275.00
3	A2	20pa green	15.50 3.00
a.		Imperf., pair	275.00

1899			
4	A2	10pa brown	9.50 3.00
a.		Horiz. pair, imperf. btwn.	
b.		Imperf., pair	275.00
5	A2	20pa rose	21.00 3.00

Used values for Nos. 2-5 are for stamps canceled by the straight-line "Heraklion" town postmark. Stamps canceled with any other postmark used for postal duty are scarce and worth much more.
Counterfeits exist of Nos. 1-5.

Russian Sphere of Administration
District of Rethymnon

Coat of Arms
A3 A4

1899		**Handstamped**	**Imperf.**
10	A3	1m green	12.50 5.50
11	A3	2m black	10.00 5.50
12	A3	2m rose	300.00 300.00
13	A4	1m blue	80.00 50.00

Nos. 10-13 exist on both wove and laid papers. Counterfeits exist.

Poseidon's Trident — A5a
A5

1899 Litho. Perf. 11½
With Control Mark Overprinted in Violet
Without Stars at Sides

14	A5	1m orange	80.	60.
15	A5	2m orange	80.	60.
16	A5	1gr orange	80.	70.
17	A5	1m green	80.	80.
18	A5	2m green	80.	60.
19	A5	1gr green	80.	70.
20	A5	1m yellow	80.	60.
21	A5	2m yellow	80.	60.
22	A5	1gr yellow	80.	60.
23	A5	1m rose	80.	75.
24	A5	2m rose	80.	60.
25	A5	1gr rose	80.	70.
26	A5	1m violet	80.	60.
27	A5	2m violet	80.	60.
28	A5	1gr violet	80.	75.
29	A5	1m blue	80.	60.
30	A5	2m blue	80.	60.
31	A5	1gr blue	80.	60.
32	A5	1m black	1,000.	975.
33	A5	2m black	1,000.	975.
34	A5	1gr black	1,000.	975.

With Stars at Sides

35	A5a	1m blue	25.00	15.00
36	A5a	2m blue	10.00	8.00
37	A5a	1gr blue	15.00	10.00
38	A5a	1m rose	50.00	40.00
39	A5a	2m rose	15.00	10.00
40	A5a	1gr rose	10.00	10.00
41	A5a	1m green	30.00	20.00
42	A5a	2m green	10.00	10.00
43	A5a	1gr green	10.00	10.00
44	A5a	1m violet	30.00	15.00
45	A5a	2m violet	15.00	5.25
46	A5a	1gr violet	15.00	10.00
		Nos. 35-46 (12)	240.00	168.25

Nearly all of Nos. 14 to 46 may be found without control mark, with double control marks and in various colors.
Counterfeits exist of Nos. 14-46.

Issued by the Cretan Government

Hermes — A6

Hera — A7

Prince George of Greece — A8

Talos — A9

Minos — A10

St. George and the Dragon — A11

1900, Mar. 1   **Engr.**   **Perf. 14**

50	A6	1 l violet brown	.30	.30
51	A7	5 l green	1.50	.30
52	A8	10 l red	1.75	.35
53	A7	20 l carmine rose	6.50	1.25
		Nos. 50-53 (4)	10.05	2.20

See #64-71. For overprints and surcharges see #54-63, 72-73, 85, 88, 93, 97-99, 108, 111.

Overprinted

Red Overprint

54	A8	25 l blue	3.00	.85
55	A6	50 l lilac	3.00	1.25
56	A9	1d gray violet	13.00	11.00
57	A10	2d brown	27.50	25.00
58	A11	5d green & blk	125.00	125.00
		Nos. 54-58 (5)	171.50	163.10

Black Overprint

59	A8	25 l blue	3.00	.85
60	A6	50 l lilac	3.00	1.75
61	A9	1d gray violet	12.50	4.50
a.		Inverted overprint	450.00	450.00
62	A10	2d brown	25.00	22.50
63	A11	5d green & blk	65.00	65.00
		Nos. 59-63 (5)	108.50	94.60

1901

Without Overprint

64	A6	1 l bister	.90	.90
65	A7	20 l orange	4.75	.90
66	A8	25 l blue	11.00	.60
67	A6	50 l lilac	30.00	22.50
68	A6	50 l ultra	13.50	13.00
69	A9	1d gray violet	33.00	25.00
70	A10	2d brown	12.50	10.00
71	A11	5d green & blk	15.00	12.00
		Nos. 64-71 (8)	120.65	84.90

No. 64 is a revenue stamp that was used for postage for short periods in 1901 and 1904.

Types A6 to A8 in olive yellow, and types A9 to A11 in olive yellow and black are revenue stamps.

See note following No. 53.

Surcharges with the year "1922" on designs A6, A8, A9, A11, A13, A15-A23 and D1 are listed under Greece.

No. 66 Overprinted in Black

1901

72	A8	25 l blue	32.50	1.00
a.		First letter of ovpt. invtd.	325.00	275.00

No. 65 Surcharged in Black

1904, Dec.

73	A7	5 l on 20 l orange	4.50	1.00
a.		Without "5" at right	100.00	75.00

Mycenaean Seal — A12   Britomartis (Cortyna Coin) — A13

Prince George — A14

Kydon and Dog (Cydonia Coin) — A15

Triton (Itanos Coin) — A16   Ariadne (Knossos Coin) — A17

Zeus as Bull Abducting Europa (Cortyna Coin) A18

Palace of Minos Ruins, Knossos A19

Arkadi Monastery and Mt. Ida — A20

1905, Feb. 15

74	A12	2 l dull violet	1.90	.45
75	A13	5 l yellow grn	5.00	1.00
76	A14	10 l red	5.00	.65
77	A15	20 l blue grn	5.50	1.00
78	A16	25 l ultra	6.50	1.10
79	A17	50 l yellow brn	7.50	4.75
80	A18	1d rose car & dp brn	62.50	60.00
81	A19	3d orange & blk	50.00	40.00
82	A20	5d ol grn & blk	25.00	20.00
		Nos. 74-82 (9)	168.90	128.40

For overprints see Nos. 86-87, 89, 91-92, 94-95, 104, 106, 109-110, 112-113, 115-120.

The so-called revolutionary stamps of 1905 were issued for sale to collectors and, so far as can be ascertained, were of no postal value whatever.

A. T. A. Zaimis A21

Prince George Landing at Suda A22

1907, Aug. 28

83	A21	25 l blue & blk	37.50	1.25
84	A22	1d green & blk	13.00	11.00

Administration under a High Commissioner. For overprints see Nos. 90, 105, 107.

Stamps of 1900-1907 Overprinted in Black

1908, Sept. 21

85	A6	1 l violet brn	.60	.50
86	A12	2 l dull violet	.65	.50
87	A13	5 l yellow grn	.90	.50
88	A8	10 l red	1.75	.65
89	A15	20 l blue grn	4.50	.70
90	A21	25 l blue & blk	11.00	2.50
91	A17	50 l yellow brn	11.00	4.00
92	A18	1d rose car & dp brn	67.50	70.00
93	A10	2d brown	10.50	10.50
94	A19	3d orange & blk	40.00	37.50
95	A20	5d ol grn & blk	32.50	32.50
		Nos. 85-95 (11)	180.90	159.85

This overprint exists inverted and double, as well as with incorrect, reversed, misplaced and omitted letters. Similar errors are found on the Postage Due and Official stamps with this overprint.

Hermes by Praxiteles — A23

1908

96	A23	10 l brown red	3.25	.90
a.		Pair, one without overprint	25.00	
b.		Inverted overprint	25.00	
c.		Double overprint	35.00	

Nos. 96 and 114 were not regularly issued without overprint.
For overprints see Nos. 103, 114.

No. 53 Surcharged

1909

97	A7	5 l on 20 l car rose	125.00	130.00

Forgeries exist of No. 97.

On No. 65

98	A7	5 l on 20 l orange	1.75	1.25
a.		Inverted surcharge		

Overprinted on Nos. 64, J1

99	A6	1 l bister	1.75	1.75
100	D1	1 l red	1.75	1.75

No. J4 Surcharged

101	D1	2 l on 20 l red	1.75	1.75
b.		Inverted surcharge	75.00	
c.		Second letter of surcharge "D" instead of "P"	50.00	50.00

No. J4 Surcharged

102	D1	2 l on 20 l red	1.60	1.40

Overprinted in Black:

a

b

c **ЄΛΛΑΣ**

103	A23(a)	10 l brown red	4.75	1.25
a.		Inverted overprint	85.00	
104	A15(a)	20 l blue grn	6.25	1.25
105	A21(c)	25 l blue & blk	12.50	4.00
106	A17(c)	50 l yellow brn	10.00	5.25
107	A22(b)	1d green & blk	13.50	11.00
108	A10(a)	2d brown	13.50	13.50
109	A19(b)	3d org & blk	97.50	77.50
110	A20(b)	5d ol grn & blk	37.50	37.50
		Nos. 103-110 (8)	195.50	151.25

Stamps of 1900-08 Overprinted in Red or Black

1909-10

111	A6	1 l violet brown	.45	.25
112	A12	2 l dull violet	.45	.25
113	A13	5 l yellow green	.45	.25
114	A23	10 l brown red (Bk)	.85	.25
115	A15	20 l blue green	3.00	.70
116	A16	25 l ultra	3.50	.75
117	A17	50 l yellow brn	9.00	6.75
118	A18	1d rose car & dp brn (Bk)	70.00	70.00
119	A19	3d orange & blk	55.00	55.00
120	A20	5d ol grn & blk	45.00	40.00
		Nos. 111-120 (10)	187.70	174.20

POSTAGE DUE STAMPS

D1

1901   **Unwmk.**   **Litho.**   **Perf. 14**

J1	D1	1 l red	.30	.30
J2	D1	5 l red	.95	.60
J3	D1	10 l red	1.50	.60
J4	D1	20 l red	1.90	1.50
J5	D1	40 l red	14.00	14.00
J6	D1	50 l red	14.00	14.00
J7	D1	1d red	22.50	21.00
J8	D1	2d red	14.00	14.00
		Nos. J1-J8 (8)	69.15	66.00

For overprints and surcharges see Nos. 100-102, J9-J26.

Surcharged in Black   Overprinted

1901

J9	D1	1d on 1d red	12.00	12.00

1908

J10	D1	1 l red	.60	.50
J11	D1	5 l red	1.10	.85
J12	D1	10 l red	1.25	.90
J13	D1	20 l red	3.00	2.25

J14	D1	40 l red	10.00	10.00
J15	D1	50 l red	10.00	10.00
J16	D1	1d red	150.00	150.00
J17	D1	1d on 1d red	10.00	10.00
J18	D1	2d red	18.50	17.50
		Nos. J10-J18 (9)	204.45	202.00

Nos. J10-J18 exist with inverted overprint. See note after No. 95. Counterfeits of No. J16 exist.

Overprinted

1910

J19	D1	1 l red	.60	.30
J20	D1	5 l red	1.40	.25
J21	D1	10 l red	1.00	.50
J22	D1	20 l red	4.25	1.75
J23	D1	40 l red	10.00	9.00
J24	D1	50 l red	12.50	11.00
J25	D1	1d red	27.50	27.50
J26	D1	2d red	27.50	27.50
		Nos. J19-J26 (8)	84.75	77.80

OFFICIAL STAMPS

O1   O2

Unwmk.

			Perf. 14	
1908, Jan. 14		**Litho.**		
O1	O1	10 l dull claret	20.00	2.50
O2	O2	30 l blue	42.50	2.50

Nos. O1-O2 exist imperf.

Overprinted   Overprinted

O3	O1	10 l dull claret	20.00	2.50
O4	O2	30 l blue	42.50	2.50

See note after No. 95.

1910

O5	O1	10 l dull claret	2.50	2.00
O6	O2	30 l blue	2.50	2.00

Nos. O5-O6 remained in use until 1922, nine years after union with Greece.

CROATIA

krō-'ā-sh e͏̦,-ə

LOCATION — Southeastern Europe
GOVT. — Independent state
AREA — 44,453 sq. mi.
POP. — 7,000,000 (approx.)
CAPITAL — Zagreb

The Independent Croatian State of 1941-45 became part of the Yugoslav Federation in 1945.

Croatia declared its independence in 1991.

100 Paras = 1 Dinar
100 Banica = 1 Kuna

> Catalogue values for unused stamps in this country are for Never Hinged items, beginning with Scott 1 in the regular postage section, Scott B1 in the semi-postal section, Scott C1 in the airmail section and Scott RA1 in the postal tax section.

Watermark

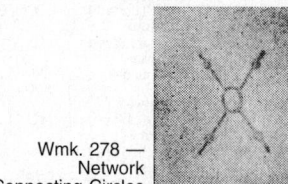

Wmk. 278 —
Network Connecting Circles

Yugoslavia Nos. 143 to 148B Overprinted in Black

Perf. 12½

			Unwmk.	Typo.
1941, Apr. 12				
1	A16	50p orange	3.50	4.75
a.		Inverted overprint	225.00	
2	A16	1d yellow grn	3.50	4.25
a.		Double overprint	110.00	
3	A16	1.50d red	4.00	2.10
a.		Double overprint	110.00	
4	A16	2d deep magenta	4.75	3.00
5	A16	3d dull red brn	7.75	8.00
a.		Double overprint	110.00	
6	A16	4d ultra	9.00	9.00
7	A16	5d dark blue	9.00	9.00
8	A16	5.50d dk violet brn	10.25	10.75
a.		Double overprint	110.00	
		Nos. 1-8 (8)	51.75	50.85

Counterfeit overprints exist of Nos. 1-8, especially the inverted and double overprint varieties.

Yugoslavia Nos. 142 to 154 Overprinted in Black

1941, Apr. 21				
9	A16	25p black	.40	.50
a.		Inverted overprint	75.00	
b.		Double overprint	75.00	
10	A16	50p orange	.40	.50
a.		Inverted overprint	75.00	
11	A16	1d yellow grn	.40	.50
a.		Double overprint	—	
12	A16	1.50d red	.65	.50
a.		Double overprint	150.00	
13	A16	2d deep magenta	.65	.50
14	A16	3d dull red brn	.80	.95
15	A16	4d ultra	.95	1.40
16	A16	5d dark blue	1.50	1.40
a.		Inverted overprint	200.00	
17	A16	5.50d dk violet brn	1.60	1.40
a.		Inverted overprint	375.00	
b.		Double overprint	200.00	
18	A16	6d slate blue	2.00	2.50
19	A16	8d sepia	3.00	2.40
20	A16	12d brt violet	3.75	3.25
a.		Inverted overprint	375.00	
21	A16	16d dull violet	4.00	4.75
a.		Double overprint		200.00
22	A16	20d blue	5.25	5.75
23	A16	30d bright pink	7.75	10.00
		Nos. 9-23 (15)	33.10	36.30

The overprint exists double, both inverted, on Nos. 16, 18 and 19.

Yugoslavia Nos. 147, 148 Surcharged in Black

1941, May 16				
24	A16	1d on 3d dull red brn	.45	.45
a.		Inverted overprint	75.00	
b.		Double overprint	75.00	
25	A16	2d on 4d ultra	.45	.45
a.		Inverted overprint	75.00	
b.		Double overprint	75.00	

Postage Due Stamps of Yugoslavia, Nos. J28, J30 to J32, Overprinted in Black

1941, May 17				
26	D4	50p violet	.45	.45
27	D4	2d deep blue	1.25	1.25
28	D4	5d orange	1.60	1.40
29	D4	10d chocolate	2.00	1.60
		Nos. 26-29 (4)	5.30	4.70

Counterfeit cancellations exist for Nos. 1-29 on cover.

Imperforates

Nearly all Croatian stamps, from No. 30 through 80, B3 through B76, J6 through J25, O1 through O24 and RA1 through RA7 exist imperforate, imperforate vertically, and imperforate horizontally. These are primarily from the special Ministerial Albums issued by the State Printing Office.

Ozalj Castle — A1

Designs: 50b, City of Jajce. 75b, Old Warasdin. 1k, Velebit Mountains. 1.50k, Zelanjak. 2k, Zagreb Cathedral. 3k, Osjek Cathedral. 4k, Drina River. No. 38, Korjic. No. 39, Zemun. 6k, Dubrovnik. 7k, Save River. 8k, Sarajevo. 10k, Plitvice. 12k, Klis Fortress, Split. 20k, Hvar. 30k, Syrmia. 50k, Senj. 100k, Banjaluka (without "F.I.").

			Perf. 11¼	
1941-43		**Unwmk.**		**Photo.**
Ordinary Paper				
30	A1	25b henna	.20	.20
31	A1	50b slate blue	.20	.20
32	A1	75b dk olive grn	.20	.20
33	A1	1k Prussian green	.20	.20
34	A1	1.50k deep green	.20	.20
35	A1	2k carmine lake	.20	.20
36	A1	3k brown red	.20	.20
37	A1	4k deep ultra	.20	.20
38	A1	5k black	2.25	1.25
39	A1	5k blue	.25	.20
40	A1	6k lt olive brn	.25	.20
41	A1	7k orange red	.30	.20
42	A1	8k chestnut	.50	.30
43	A1	10k dark plum	1.00	.45
44	A1	12k olive brown	1.40	.50
45	A1	20k golden brown	1.00	.40
46	A1	30k black brown	1.40	.50
47	A1	50k dk slate green	2.50	1.40
48	A1	100k violet	4.25	3.25
		Nos. 30-48 (19)	16.70	10.25

Nos. 30-48 exist with a variety of perforations, including 11¼x10¾ and 12.
Nos. 31, 35 and 43 exist on thin to pelure paper, as does No. 32, though the latter was not issued to the public. Shades of all values exist.
For overprints and surcharge see #49-51, 53.

Tête bêche Pairs

30a	A1	25b	1.75	2.75
31a	A1	50b	2.00	3.50
33a	A1	1k	2.50	4.00
34a	A1	1.50k	2.75	5.00
35a	A1	2k	3.00	6.00
37a	A1	4k	3.95	6.50
38a	A1	5k	7.00	7.50
40a	A1	6k	4.00	7.00
41a	A1	7k	4.50	7.25

42a	A1	8k	5.00	8.00
43a	A1	10k	5.50	9.50
45a	A1	20k	6.50	10.00
46a	A1	30k	7.25	11.00
47a	A1	50k	13.00	13.00
		Nos. 30a-47a (14)	68.70	101.00

Types of 1941 Overprinted in Brown or Green

1942, Apr. 9				
49	A1	2k dark brown	.50	.40
50	A1	5k dark carmine	.85	.85
51	A1	10k dark blue green (G)	1.50	1.25
		Nos. 49-51 (3)	2.85	2.50

First anniversary of Croatian independence. The overprint exists double on No. 50.
Tête bêche pairs of Nos. 49-51 are from Ministerial Albums.

Banjaluka ("F.I." at upper right) — A20

1942, June 13				
52	A20	100k violet	4.50	4.50

Banjaluka Philatelic Exhibition.
Exists in se-tenant pair with No. 48. Value unused, $225.

No. 35 Surcharged in Red Brown with New Value and Bar

1942, June 23				
53	A1	25b on 2k carmine lake	.60	.60
a.		Tête bêche pair	3.50	3.50

No. 53 exists with double surcharge. It is not scarce.

Trakoscan Castle — A21

Catherine Zrinski — A23

Design: 12.50k, Citadel of Veliki Tabor.

1943, Mar. 28				
Pelure Paper				
54	A21	3.50k brown carmine	.75	.65
55	A21	12.50k violet black	1.00	.95

Nos. 54 was reissued in 1944 on ordinary paper, perf 12. Value the same for both varieties. No. 55 also exists on ordinary paper. It is scarce.

1943, June 7   Engr.   Perf. 12¼x12½

2k, Fran Krsto Frankopan. 3.50k, Peter Zrinski.

Various Frames

56	A23	1k dark blue	.40	.40
57	A23	2k dark olive green	.40	.40
58	A23	3.50k dark red	.50	.55
		Nos. 56-58 (3)	1.30	1.35

Many perforation varieties of this issue exist, including 12x12½, 12½x13, 12½, 13, 12½x14, 13x12½, and 14x12½.

Rugjer
Boscovich — A26

Ante
Pavelich — A27

1943, Dec. 13   **Perf. 11**
59	A26	3.50k copper red	.50	.40
60	A26	12.50k dk violet brn	.65	.50

Rugjer Boscovich (1711-1787). Mathematician and physicist.

1943-44   **Litho.**   **Perf. 12½, 14**
61	A27	25b orange ver	.30	.20
62	A27	50b Prus blue	.30	.20
63	A27	75b olive green	.30	.20
64	A27	1k lt green	.30	.20
65	A27	1.50k dull gray vio	.30	.20
66	A27	2k rose lake	.30	.20
67	A27	3k rose brown	.30	.20
68	A27	3.50k bright blue	.30	.20
a.		3.50k dark blue, perf. 11½	4.00	4.75
69	A27	4k brt red violet	.30	.20
70	A27	5k ultra	.30	.20
71	A27	8k orange brn	.35	.20
72	A27	9k rose pink	.35	.20
73	A27	10k violet brn	.40	.20
74	A27	12k dk olive bis	.45	.25
75	A27	12.50k gray black	.55	.25
76	A27	18k dull brown	.70	.30
77	A27	32k dark brown	.75	.30
78	A27	50k grnsh blue	1.40	.50
79	A27	70k orange	1.75	.90
80	A27	100k violet	3.00	1.50
		Nos. 61-80 (20)	12.70	6.60

Nos. 61 and 63 measure 20½x26mm. Nos. 62 and 64-80 measure 22x27½mm.

Nos. 61, 63, 67, 70, 71 and 72 are perf 12½. Nos. 62, 64-66, 68, 69, 73 and 75-80 are perf 14. No. 74 exists either perf 12½ or 14.

Issue dates: 2k, 1943; No. 68a, June 13, 1943, Pavelich's Saint's Day; others, 1944.

"Labor Day
1945" — A28

1945   **Photo.**   **Perf. 11½**
81	A28	3.50k red brown	.85	1.60

From 1951 to 1972 44 labels were circulated by a Croatian Government in Exile. These had no postal value.

GOVT. — Independent state
AREA — 21,823 sq. mi.
POP. — 4,676,865 (1999 est.)
CAPITAL — Zagreb

Croatia declared its independence from Yugoslavia in 1991.

100 Paras = 1 Dinar (1991)
100 Lipa = 1 Kuna (1994)

Nos. RA20, RA20a Surcharged in Black and Gold

1991, Nov. 21   **Litho.**   **Perf. 14**
100	PT10	4d on 1.20d #RA20	.90	.90
a.		Perf. 11x10½	.80	.80
b.		Perf. 11	8.50	8.50

A35

A36

1991, Dec. 10   **Perf. 12**
101	A35	30d multicolored	2.00 2.00

Declaration of independence, 10/8/91.

1991, Dec. 11   **Perf. 12**

Christmas: Creche figures of the Holy Family from Kosljun Monastery.
102	A36	4d multicolored	1.10 1.10

No. RA21 Surcharged in Black and Gold

1992, Jan. 3   **Perf. 10½x11**
103	PT11	20d on 1.70d #RA21	6.25 6.00

Croatian
Arms — A37

1992, Jan. 15   **Perf. 11x10½**
104	A37	10d multicolored	.65	.65
a.		Perf. 14	.35	.35

See No. RA22.

1992 Winter
Olympics,
Albertville
A38

1992, Feb. 4   **Perf. 11x10½**
105	A38	30d multicolored	1.40 1.40

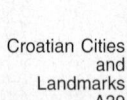

Croatian Cities
and
Landmarks
A39

A39a

Designs: 6d, Knin. 7d, Eltz Castle, Vukovar. 20d, Church, Ilok. 30d, Starcevic Street, Gospic. 45d, Rector's Palace, Dubrovnik. 50d, St. Jakov's Cathedral, Sibenik. 100d, Vinkovci. 200d, Pazin, vert. No. 115, Beli Manastir. 500d, Slavonski Brod. 1000d, Varazdin. 2000d, Karlovac. 5000d, Zadar, vert. 10,000d, Vis.

1992-94   **Perf. 14**
107	A39	6d multicolored	.20	.20
108	A39	7d multicolored	.20	.20
109	A39	20d multicolored	.35	.35
a.		Perf. 11x10½	1.00	
110	A39	30d multicolored	.40	.40
111	A39	45d multicolored	1.10	1.10
112	A39	50d multicolored	1.10	1.10
113	A39a	100d multicolored	.65	.65
114	A39a	200d multicolored	.35	.35
115	A39	300d multicolored	1.00	1.00
117	A39a	500d multicolored	1.40	1.20
118	A39a	1000d multicolored	1.00	.70
119	A39a	2000d multicolored	2.00	1.50
120	A39a	5000d multicolored	3.00	2.50
121	A39a	10,000d multicolored	5.50	5.00
		Nos. 107-121 (14)	18.25	16.25

Issued: 6d, 4/18; 7d, 4/8; #109, 2/28; #109a, 9/9; 30d, 5/21; 45d, 4/14; 50d, 4/28; 115, 6/26; 100d, 12/14; 500d, 2/9/93; 1000d, 3/16/93; 200d, 4/22/93; 2000d, 5/20/93; 5000d, 9/24/93; 10,000d, 2/22/94.
See Nos. 355-356, 437A, 456.

Statue of King
Tomislav — A40

1992, May 5   **Engr.**   **Perf. 12½ Horiz.**
Coil Stamp
124	A40	10d dark green	.35 .25

Railroad
Station,
Zagreb,
Cent. — A41

1992, June 30   **Litho.**   **Perf. 14**
125	A41	30d multicolored	.50 .25

Matica, Society of
Knowledge and
Literacy, 150th
Anniv. — A42

1992, July 8
126	A42	20d red, gold & black	.35 .25

Bishop Josip Juraj Strossmayer,
Founder — A43

1992, July 9
127	A43	30d multicolored	.45 .45

Croatian Academy of Arts and Sciences, 125th anniv., in 1991.

1992 Summer
Olympics,
Barcelona
A44

Design: 105d, Abstract design.

1992, July 25
128	A44	40d shown	.50	.20
129	A44	105d multicolored	1.25	1.25

Flowers
A45

Designs: 30d, Edraianthus pumilio. 85d, Degenia velebitica, vert.

1992, July 28
130	A45	30d multicolored	.40	.40
131	A45	85d multicolored	1.00	1.00

Wildlife — A46

40d, Monticola solitarius. 75d, Elaphe situla.

1992, July 31
132	A46	40d multicolored	.50	.50
133	A46	75d multicolored	.90	.90

Discovery of
America,
500th
Anniv. — A47

Europa: 30d, 60d, Sailing ship. 75d, 130d, Indian in Chicago, by Ivan Mestrovic (1883-1962).

1992, Sep. 4   **Litho.**   **Perf. 14**
134	A47	30d multicolored	.20	.20
135	A47	60d multicolored	.60	.60
136	A47	75d red & black	.75	.75
137	A47	130d red, blk & gold	1.10	1.10
		Nos. 134-137 (4)	2.65	2.65

Issued: 30d, 75d, July 31; others, Sept. 4.

A48

A49

1992, Oct. 2
138 A48 40d multicolored .35 .35
139 A48 130d multi, diff. 1.00 1.00

Declaration of Croatian Literary Language, 25th Anniv. (#133). Spelling reform by Dr. Ivan Broz, cent. (#134).

1992, Oct. 16
140 A49 90d multicolored .65 .40

City of Samobor, 750th Anniv.

Gift of the St. Juraj Church by Archbishop Mucimir, 1100th Anniv. — A50

1992, Oct. 30
141 A50 60d multicolored .50 .40

Reign of King Bela IV, 750th Anniv. — A51

1992, Nov. 16   Litho.   Perf. 14
142 A51 180d multicolored 1.00 1.00

Christmas A52

1992, Dec. 7
143 A52 80d multicolored .40 .35

Blaz Lorkovic (1839-1892), Scientist — A53

Kolo Literature Review, 150th Anniv. — A54

1992, Dec. 21
144 A53 250d multicolored 1.00 1.00

1992, Dec. 22
145 A54 300d multicolored 1.25 1.25

Ivan Bunic-Vucic (1592-1658) A55

1992, Dec. 29
146 A55a 350d multicolored 1.25 1.25

— A55a

800th Anniversary of Krapina
1993, Jan. 15
146A A55a 300d multicolored .80 .80

Nikola Tesla (1856-1943), Physicist A56

1993, Jan. 30
147 A56 250d multicolored .80 .80

Self-Portrait, by Ferdo Quiquerez (1845-1893) A57

1993, Feb. 10
148 A57 100d multicolored .50 .50

Wildlife — A58

1993, Feb. 23   Litho.   Perf. 14
149 A58 500d Cervus elaphus .90 .80
150 A58 550d Haliaeetus albicilla .95 .80

Self-Portrait, by Zlatko Sulentic (1893-1971) A59

1993, Mar. 17
151 A59 350d multicolored .65 .55

Lipik Health and Convalescent Home, Cent. — A60

1993, Apr. 22   Litho.   Perf. 14
152 A60 400d multicolored .75 .75

Ivan Goran Kovacic (1913-1943), Author — A61

1993, Apr. 24
153 A61 200d multicolored .35 .35

59th PEN Congress, Dubrovnik A62

1993, Apr. 24
154 A62 800d multicolored 1.40 1.40

Ivan Kukuljevic (1816-89), Politician, Historian, Writer — A63

1993, May 2   Litho.   Perf. 14
155 A63 500d multicolored .75 .75

Croatian Natl. Theatre, Split, Cent. — A64

Pag, 500th Anniv. — A65

1993, May 6   Litho.   Perf. 14
156 A64 600d multicolored .75 .75

1993, May 18
157 A65 800d multicolored .90 .90

Croatian Membership in United Nations, 1st Anniv. — A66

1993, May 22
158 A66 500d multicolored .60 .60

Europa A67

Contemporary paintings by: 700d, Ivo Dulcic (1916-75). 1000d, Miljenko Stancic (1926-77). 1100d, Ljubo Ivancic (b. 1925).

1993, June 5
159 A67 700d multicolored .65 .65
160 A67 1000d multicolored .90 .90
161 A67 1100d multicolored 1.10 1.10
a.   Min. sheet, 2 each #159-161 8.00 8.00
     Nos. 159-161 (3) 2.65 2.65

Intl. Art Biennial, Venice — A68

Works of art by: 250d, Milivoj Bijelic. 600d, Ivo Dekovic. 1000d, Zeljko Kipke.

1993, June 10   Litho.   Perf. 14
162 A68 250d multicolored .35 .35
a.   Souvenir sheet of 4 1.00 1.00
163 A68 600d multicolored 1.00 1.00
a.   Souvenir sheet of 4 3.00 3.00
164 A68 1000d multicolored 1.40 1.40
a.   Souvenir sheet of 4 4.00 4.00
     Nos. 162-164 (3) 2.75 2.75

1993 Mediterranean Games — A69

1993, June 15   Litho.   Perf. 14
165 A69 700d multicolored .75 .75

Adolf Waldinger (1843-1904), Painter — A70

1993, June 16
166 A70 300d multicolored .40 .40

Famous Croatian Battles A71

1993, July 6   **Litho.**   **Perf. 14**
167 A71 800d Krbavskom, 1493   .75   .75
168 A71 1300d Sisak, 1593   1.25   1.25

Miroslav Krleza (1893-1981),
Writer — A72

1993, July 7
169 A72 400d multicolored   .40   .40

Croatian
Membership in
UPU, 1st
Anniv. — A73

1993, July 20   **Litho.**   **Perf. 14**
170 A73 1800d multicolored   1.40   .80

Vlaho Paljetak
(1893-1944),
Composer
A74

1993, Aug. 7
171 A74 500d multicolored   .45   .45

Stamp
Day — A75

1993, Sept. 9   **Litho.**   **Perf. 14**
172 A75 600d multicolored   .75   .75

Map of Istria,
1620 — A76

1993, Sept. 20
173 A76 2200d multicolored   1.40   1.40

Incorporation of Istria, Rijeka and Zadar into
Croatia, 50th anniv.

Tadija Smiciklas
(1843-1914),
Historian — A77

1993, Oct. 1
174 A77 800d black, gold & red   .60   .60

Archaelogical
Museum,
Split,
Cent. — A78

1993, Oct. 27
175 A78 1000d multicolored   .60   .60

A79

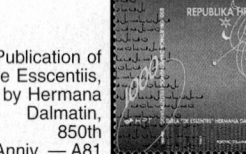

A80

1993, Nov. 17   **Litho.**   **Perf. 14**
176 A79 3000d multicolored   1.60   1.60

Uprising of 13th Pioneer Battalion, Vil-
lefranche-de-Rouergue, France, 50th anniv.

1993, Nov. 18
900d, Josip Eugen Tomic (1843-1906),
writer.
177 A80 900d multicolored   .50   .50

Publication of
De Esscentiis,
by Hermana
Dalmatin,
850th
Anniv. — A81

1993, Nov. 30
178 A81 1000d multicolored   .80   .60

Christmas
A82

Paintings: 1000d, Christmas at the Front, by
Miroslav Sutej. 4000d, Birth of Christ, 15th
cent. fresco, Marienkirch of Dvigrad.

1993, Dec. 3
179 A82 1000d multicolored   .75   .50
180 A82 4000d multicolored   2.75   1.75

Organized Skiing
in Croatia,
Cent. — A83

1993, Dec. 15
181 A83 1000d multicolored   1.00   .75

Croatian
Natl. Guard,
125th Anniv.
A84

1993, Dec. 22
182 A84 1100d multicolored   1.00   .75

Printers of
Senj, 500th
Anniv. — A85

1994, Jan. 29
183 A85 2200d multicolored   1.25   .80

1994 Winter
Olympics,
Lillehammer
A86

1994, Feb. 12
184 A86 4000d multicolored   2.10   1.75

Dinosaurs from
Western
Istria — A87

a, 2400d, Iguanodons. b, 4000d, Map,
skeleton.

1994, Mar. 7
185 A87 Pair, #a.-b.   3.75   3.75

Nos. 185a-185b are a continuous design.

Zora
Dalmatinska
Magazine,
150th
Anniv. — A88

1994, Mar. 15
186 A88 800d multicolored   .50   .35

Croatian
University,
Zagreb, 325th
Anniv. — A89

Design: 2200d, University building, Emperor
Leopold I's seal, vice-chancellor's chain.

1994, Apr. 19   **Litho.**   **Perf. 14**
187 A89 2200d multicolored   1.20   .75

Protect the
Environment
A90

ILO, 75th
Anniv. — A91

1994, Apr. 22   **Litho.**   **Perf. 14**
188 A90 3800d Canis lupus   2.00   1.75

1994, May 2
189 A91 1000d multicolored   .60   .40

A92

Europa — A93

European inventions, discoveries: 3800d,
Faust Vrancic (1551-1617), parachute. 4000d,
Slavoljub Penkala (1871-1922), fountain pen.

1994, May 16
190 A92 3800d multicolored   *2.25*   *2.00*
191 A93 4000d multicolored   *2.75*   *2.00*

A94

A95

1994, June 3
192 A94 2.40k Iris croatica   1.25   .60
193 A94 4k Colchicum visianii   2.00   1.25

1994, June 7
Drazen Petrovic (1964-93), basketball
player.
194 A95 1k multicolored   .75   .55

Tourism in Croatia, 150th Anniv. — A96

Designs: 80 l, Plitvice Lakes Natl. Park. 1k, Waterfalls, Krka River. 1.10k, Kornati Islands Natl. Park. 2.20k, Kopacki Trscak nature reserve. 2.40k Sailboats, Opatijska Riviera resort. 3.80k, Brijuni islands. 4k, Trakoscan castle, Zagorje.

1994, June 15   Litho.   Perf. 14

196	A96	80 l multicolored	.55	.25
197	A96	1k multicolored	.60	.30
198	A96	1.10k multicolored	.70	.35
199	A96	2.20k multicolored	1.50	.40
200	A96	2.40k multicolored	1.75	.60
201	A96	3.80k multicolored	2.75	.75
202	A96	4k multicolored	3.00	1.00
a.		Min. sheet of 7, #196-202 + 2 labels	10.00	7.00
		Nos. 196-202 (7)	10.85	3.65

Croatian Musicians A97

Designs: 1k, Kresimir Baranovic (1894-1975), composer, vert. 2.20k, Vatroslav Lisinski (1819-54), composer, vert. 2.40k, Pauline song-book (1644), harpist.

1994, June 20

211	A97	1k multicolored	.50	.35
212	A97	2.20k multicolored	1.10	.75
213	A97	2.40k multicolored	1.25	.85
		Nos. 211-213 (3)	2.85	1.95

Croatian Fraternal Union, Cent. — A98

1994, Aug. 15   Litho.   Perf. 14

214	A98	2.20k multicolored	1.40	1.40

A99

A100

1994, Aug. 31

215	A99	80 l multicolored	.50	.50

Intl. Year of the Family.

1994, Sept. 10

216	A100	1k multicolored	.60	.60

Intl. Olympic Committee, cent.

Visit of Pope John Paul II — A101

1994, Sept. 10

217	A101	1k multicolored	.75	.60

No. 217 printed with se-tenant label.

Antoine de Saint-Exupery (1900-44), Aviator, Author A102

1994, Sept. 20

218	A102	3.80k multicolored	1.90	1.25

13th Intl. Congress on Early Christian Archeology A103

1994, Sept. 23

219	A103	4k multicolored	2.00	1.25

No. 219 printed with se-tenant label.

Modern Croatian Paintings A104

Designs: 2.40k, Still Life with Fruits and Basket, by Marino Tartaglia, 1926. 3.80k, In the Park, by Milan Steiner, c. 1918. 4k, Self-portrait, by Vilko Gecan, 1929.

1994, Oct. 12

220	A104	2.40k multicolored	1.25	.75
221	A104	3.80k multicolored	1.90	1.25
222	A104	4k multicolored	2.00	1.25
		Nos. 220-222 (3)	5.15	3.25

Ivan Belostenec (1594-1675), Writer & Lexicographer A105

1994, Nov. 9

223	A105	2.20k multicolored	1.10	.90

City of Zagreb, Zagreb Bishopric, 900th Anniv. — A106

Designs: No. 224a, 1k, Zagreb exchange building, designed by V. Kovacic, S. Penkala's airplane, Cibona office tower, designed by Hrzic, Pitesa and Serbetic. b, 1k, Maxi Cat, by Zlatko Grgic, Zagreb School of Animated Film. c, 1k, St. Mark's Church, Gradec; photo of gas lantern, by Toso Dabac. d, 4k, Late Gothic bishop's staff, Valvasor's view of Zagreb. 13.50k, Zagreb street scene, Penkala's airplane, vert.

1994, Nov. 16

224	A106	Strip of 4, #a.-d.	4.25	4.25

Souvenir Sheet

225	A106	13.50k multicolored	7.75	7.75

No. 224 is a continuous design. No. 225 contains one 24x48mm stamp.

Christmas A107

Design: 1k, Epiphany, by unknown sculptor.

1994, Dec. 1   Litho.   Perf. 14

226	A107	1k multicolored	.60	.50

Virgin Mary's Sanctuary, Loreto, 700th Anniv. — A108

Design: 4k, The Moving of the Holy House, by Giovanni Battista Tiepolo.

1994, Dec. 10

227	A108	4k multicolored	2.00	1.50

Necktie in Croatia — A109

Tie designs: 1.10k, Businessman's, 1995. 3.80k, English Dandy, 1810. 4k, Croatian soldier, 1630.

1995, Jan. 19   Litho.   Perf. 14

228	A109	1.10k multicolored	.65	.40
229	A109	3.80k multicolored	2.00	1.40
230	A109	4k multicolored	2.10	1.75
a.		Souvenir sheet of 3, #228-230	5.00	5.00
		Nos. 228-230 (3)	4.75	3.55

Croatian Monasteries — A110

1k, Jesuit Monastery, Zagreb, 350th anniv. 2.40k, Franciscan Monastery, Visovac, 550th anniv.

1995, Feb. 16

231	A110	1k multicolored	.50	.30
232	A110	2.40k multicolored	1.25	.95

Hunting Dogs — A111

Designs: 2.20k, Istrian short-haired. 2.40k, Posavinian. 3.80k, Istrian wire-haired.

1995, Mar. 9   Litho.   Perf. 14

233	A111	2.20k multicolored	1.00	.75
234	A111	2.40k multicolored	1.25	.80
235	A111	3.80k multicolored	1.75	1.40
		Nos. 233-235 (3)	4.00	2.95

Town of Split, 1700th Anniv. — A112

#236: a, 1k, Drawing of reconstruction of Diocletian's Palace. b, 2.20k, "Split Harbour," by Emanuel Vidovic, 1937. c, 4k, Modern view of town, bust of Marko Marulic by Ivan Mestrovic.
13.40k, Buildings, vert.

1995, Apr. 20   Litho.   Perf. 14

236	A112	Strip of 3, #a.-c.	4.25	4.25

Souvenir Sheet

237	A112	13.40k multicolored	6.50	6.50

No. 237 contains one 24x48mm stamp.

World Team Handball Championships, Iceland — A113

1995, May 4

238	A113	4k multicolored	2.00	1.25

Peace & Freedom A114

Europa: 2.40k, Clearing storm clouds. 4k, Hands of angel, by Francisco Robba.

1995, May 9

239	A114	2.40k multicolored	*1.75*	*1.25*
240	A114	4k multicolored	*2.25*	*1.60*

Anti-Austria Demonstrations, 150th Anniv. — A115

1995, May 15

241	A115	1.10k multicolored	.75	.45
242	A115	3.80k multicolored	1.50	1.10

Croatian surrender to British forces at Bleiburg, 50th anniv. (#242).

Independence Day — A116

1995, May 30   Litho.   Perf. 14

243	A116	1.10k multicolored	.75	.40

Croatian Sculptures at Venice Biennial, 1995 — A117

2.20k, Installation (a part), by Martina Kramer. 2.40k, Paracelsus Paraduchamps, by Mirko Zrinscak, vert. 4k, Shadows, by Goran Petercol.

1995, June 8		**Litho.**	**Perf. 14**	
244	A117	2.20k multicolored	1.00	.65
245	A117	2.40k multicolored	1.10	.75
246	A117	4k multicolored	1.90	1.75
		Nos. 244-246 (3)	4.00	3.15

St. Anthony of Padua (1195-1231) — A118

1995, June 13				
247	A118	1k multicolored	.50	.30

Marine Life — A119

1995, June 29		**Litho.**	**Perf. 14**	
248	A119	2.40k Caretta caretta	1.25	.95
249	A119	4k Tursiops truncatus	2.25	1.50

Liberation of the City of Knin — A120

1995, Aug. 5		**Litho.**	**Perf. 14**	
250	A120	1.30k multicolored	.70	.55

Krka River Hydroelectric Power Plant, Cent. — A121

1995, Aug. 28				
251	A121	3.60k multicolored	1.60	.90

Stamp Day — A122

1995, Sept. 9		**Litho.**	**Perf. 14**	
252	A122	1.30k multicolored	.70	.70

Franz von Suppe (1819-95), Composer A123

1995, Sept. 15			
253	A123	6.50k multicolored	3.25 2.00

See Austria Nos. 1686-1687.

Liberation of Petrinja from Turkish Rule, 400th Anniv. — A124

1995, Sept. 21			
254	A124	2.20k multicolored	1.10 .90

Croatian Music — A125

Composers, conductors: 1.20k, Ivo Tijardovic (1895-1976). 1.40k, Lovro Von Matacic (1899-1985). 6.50k, Jakov Gotovac (1895-1982).

1995, Sept. 23				
255	A125	1.20k multicolored	.60	.55
256	A125	1.40k multicolored	.75	.60
257	A125	6.50k multicolored	3.50	2.50
		Nos. 255-257 (3)	4.85	3.65

Herman Bollé (1845-1926), Architect — A126

2.40k, Izidor Krsnjavi (1845-1927), painter. 3.60k, Croatian National Theatre, cent.

1995, Oct. 14		**Litho.**	**Perf. 14**	
258	A126	1.80k multicolored	.80	.50
259	A126	2.40k multicolored	1.00	.70
260	A126	3.60k multicolored	1.75	1.25
		Nos. 258-260 (3)	3.55	2.45

Croatian Towns — A127

1995, Oct. 20				
261	A127	1k Bjelovar	.55	.55
262	A127	1.30k Osijek, vert.	.65	.65
263	A127	1.40k Cakovec, vert.	.70	.70
264	A127	2.20k Rovinj	1.25	1.25
265	A127	2.40k Korcula	1.40	1.40
266	A127	3.60k Zupanja	1.75	1.75
		Nos. 261-266 (6)	6.30	6.30

See No. 448.

UN, FAO, 50th Anniv. — A128

No. 268, "5, 0" in form of cracker, FAO.

1995, Oct. 24				
267	A128	3.60k multicolored	1.60	1.00
268	A128	3.60k multicolored	1.60	1.00
a.		Pair, #267-268	3.75	3.75

Croatian Scientists — A129

1k, Spiro Brusina (1845-1908). 2.20k, Bogoslav Sulek (1816-95). 6.50k, Front of European language dictionary, published by Faust Vrancic (1551-1617).

1995, Oct. 30				
269	A129	1k multicolored	.65	.30
270	A129	2.20k multicolored	1.10	.75
271	A129	6.50k multicolored	3.25	2.50
		Nos. 269-271 (3)	5.00	3.55

Institute for Blind Children, Cent. — A130

1995, Nov. 23		**Litho.**	**Perf. 14**	
272	A130	1.20k multicolored	.65	.45

Christmas A131

1995, Dec. 1				
273	A131	1.30k multicolored	.65	.45

Maroc Polo's Return from China, 700th Anniv. A132

1995, Dec. 7			
274	A132	3.60k multicolored	1.75 1.50

Liberated Towns A133

1995, Dec. 16				
275	A133	20 l Hrvatska Kostajnica	.25	.25
276	A133	30 l Slunj	.25	.25
277	A133	50 l Gracac	.35	.35
278	A133	1.20k Drnis, vert.	.70	.70
279	A133	6.50k Glina	3.00	3.00
280	A133	10k Obrovac, vert.	4.50	4.50
		Nos. 275-280 (6)	9.05	9.05

Incunabula A134

Designs: 1.40k, Lectionary of Bernardin of Split. 3.60k, Spovid Opcena (General Confession).

Spirituality of the Croats A135   Political Anniversaries A136

Designs: No. 283, Mosaic of St. Marko Krizevcanin (1589-1619), Catholic martyr. No. 284, Veneration of Miraculous Crucifix, St. Guido's Church, Rijeka, 700th anniv. No. 285, Ivan Merz (1896-1928), Catholic educator.

1996, Jan. 18		**Litho.**	**Perf. 14**	
283	A135	1.30k multicolored	.60	.50
284	A135	1.30k multicolored	.60	.50
285	A135	1.30k multicolored	.60	.50
a.		Strip of 3, Nos. 283-285	2.00	2.00

1.20k, Rakovica Uprising by Eugen Kvaternik, 125th anniv., horiz. 1.40k, Ante Starcevic (1823-96). 2.20k, Constitution of Neutral Peasant Republic of Croatia, 75th anniv., Stjepan Radic (1871-1928). 3.60k, Labin Republic, 75th anniv.

1996, Feb. 28				
286	A136	1.20k multicolored	.60	.50
287	A136	1.40k multicolored	.70	.60
288	A136	2.20k multicolored	.95	.80
289	A136	3.60k multicolored	1.75	1.40
		Nos. 286-289 (4)	4.00	3.30

Institute for Pharmacognosy, University of Zagreb, Cent. — A137

1996, Mar. 23		**Litho.**	**Perf. 14**	
290	A137	6.50k multicolored	3.00	2.00

Croatian Music — A138

a, Vinko Jelić (1596-1636), composer. b, First performance of opera "Love and Music." c, Josip Stolcer Slavenski (1896-1955), composer. d, "Lijepa Nasa," Croatian national anthem, 150th anniv.

1996, Mar. 28			
291	A138	2.20k Strip of 4, #a.-d.	4.00 4.00

A139   A140

Famous Women Writers (Europa): 2.20k, Cvijeta Zuzoric (b. 1551 or 1552). 3.60k, Ivana Brlic Mazuranic (1874-1938).

1996, Apr. 11		**Litho.**	**Perf. 14**	
292	A139	2.20k multicolored	1.75	1.25
293	A139	3.60k multicolored	2.25	1.50

The Zrinskis and The Frankopans: 1.30k, Nikola Subic Zrinski of Sziget (1508-56). 1.40k, Nikola Zrinski (1620-64). 2.20k, Petar Zrinski (1621-71). 2.40k, Katarina Zrinska

(1625-73). 3.60k, Fran Krsto Frankopan (1643-71).

1996, Apr. 30
294	A140	1.30k multicolored	.60	.50
295	A140	1.40k multicolored	.70	.55
296	A140	2.20k multicolored	1.10	.90
297	A140	2.40k multicolored	1.25	1.00
298	A140	3.60k multicolored	1.75	1.25
a.		Sheet of 5, #294-298	5.50	5.00
		Nos. 294-298 (5)	5.40	4.20

Natl. Guard, 5th Anniv. A141

Flowers A142

1996, May 28 — Litho. — Perf. 14
299	A141	1.30k multicolored	.65	.45

Designs: 2.40k, Campanula istriaca. 3.60k, Centaurea ragusina.

1996, June 5
300	A142	2.40k multicolored	1.25	1.25
301	A142	3.60k multicolored	1.75	1.75

England '96, European Soccer Championship A143

1996, June 8
302	A143	2.20k red & black	1.10	.90

Father Ferdinand Konscak's Expedition to Lower California, 250th Anniv. — A144

1996, June 10
303	A144	2.40k multicolored	1.25	1.00

1996 Summer Olympics, Atlanta A145

1996, July 4
304	A145	3.60k multicolored	1.75	1.25

A146 — A147

1996, July 4
305	A146	1.40k multicolored	.75	.60

Josip Fon, founder of Croatian Sokol Gymnastics Society, 150th birth anniv.

1996, Sept. 9 — Litho. — Perf. 14
306	A147	1.30k multicolored	.65	.35

Croatian postage stamps, 5th anniv.

1st Written Reference, Zumberak Region, 700th Anniv. — A148

1996, Sept. 14
307	A148	2.20k multicolored	1.10	1.10

A149 — A150

1996, Sept. 19
308	A149	1.30k multicolored	.65	.45

First written record of fishing in Croatia, 1000th anniv.

Events of the early Middle Ages: 1.20k, Vekenega's Book of Gospels, 900th anniv. 1.40k, Visit by Saxon Benedictine abbot Gottschalk (805-870), to Duke Trpimir's court, 1150th anniv.

1996, Sept. 19
309	A150	1.20k multicolored	.65	.50
310	A150	1.40k multicolored	.75	.55

Scientists A151

Designs: a, Gjuro Pilar (1846-93), geologist. b, Frane Bulic (1846-1934), archeologist. c, Ante Sercer (1896-1968), otolaryngologist.

1996, Oct. 4 — Litho. — Perf. 14
311	A151	2.40k Strip of 3, #a.-c.	3.50	3.50

Beginning of Higher Education in Croatia, 600th Anniv. — A152

Oldest preserved Croatian text written in Latin script, "Order and Law" of Dominican nuns, Zadar.

1996, Oct. 16 — Perf. 13½
312	A152	1.40k multicolored	.75	.50

Paintings — A153

Designs: 1.30k, Rain, by Menci Clement Crncic (1865-1930). 1.40k, The Peljesac-Korcula Channel, by Mato Celestin Medovic (1857-1919). 3.60k, Pink Dream, by Vlaho Bukovac (1855-1922).

1996, Nov. 7 — Litho. — Perf. 14
313	A153	1.30k multicolored	.60	.60
314	A153	1.40k multicolored	.70	.70
315	A153	3.60k multicolored	1.75	1.75
		Nos. 313-315 (3)	3.05	3.05

UNICEF, 50th Anniv. — A154

1996, Nov. 15
316	A154	3.60k multicolored	1.75	1.40

City of Osijek, 800th Anniv. A155

Christmas A156

Views of city: No. 317, River bank, church, coat of arms. No. 318, Boats in water, view looking down covered walkway through building.

1996, Dec. 2 — Litho. — Perf. 14
317	A155	2.20k multicolored	1.00	.75
318	A155	2.20k multicolored	1.00	.75
a.		Pair, #317-318	2.25	2.25

1996, Dec. 3
319	A156	1.30k multicolored	.70	.50

First Croatian Savings Bank, Zagreb, 150th Anniv. — A157

Design: 3.60k, Publishing of "The Bases of Corn Trade," by Josip Sipus, bicent.

1996, Dec. 14
320	A157	2.40k multicolored	1.10	.80
321	A157	3.60k multicolored	1.90	1.25

Motion Pictures, Cent. — A158

Designs: a, Shooting of film, "Vatroslav Lisinski," Oktavijan Miletic, cameraman, director. b, Characters from animated series, "Professor Baltazar." c, Mirjana Bohanec, Relja Basic in "Who Sings Means No Harm."

1997, Jan. 16 — Litho. — Perf. 14
322	A158	1.40k Strip of 3, #a.-c.	2.25	2.25

Great Europeans A159

Designs: 2.20k, Miguel de Cervantes (1547-1676), author. 3.60k, Johannes Gutenberg (1397-1468), printer, horiz.

1997, Feb. 7
323	A159	2.20k multicolored	.75	.65
324	A159	3.60k multicolored	1.25	1.10

Legends A160

Europa: 1.30k, Home Genies, from story, "Stribor's Forest." 3.60k, "Vili Joze," by Vladimir Nazor, vert.

1997, Mar. 6 — Litho. — Perf. 14
325	A160	1.30k multicolored	1.00	1.00
326	A160	3.60k multicolored	2.50	2.50

Fauna of Croatia — A161

1997, Apr. 22 — Litho. — Perf. 14
327	A161	1.40k Pinna nobilis	.65	.65
328	A161	2.40k Radziella styx	1.10	1.10
329	A161	3.60k Tonna galea	1.75	1.75
		Nos. 327-329 (3)	3.50	3.50

Admission of Croatia to UN, 5th Anniv. A162

1997, May 22 — Litho. — Perf. 14
330	A162	6.50k Pres. Franjo Tudjman	3.75	3.75

First Croatian Esperantist Conference, 90th Anniv. A163

Ludwig Lazarus Zamenhof, conf. logo.

1997, May 31
331	A163	1.20k multicolored	.60	.45

Congress of Intl. Amateur Rugby Federation, Dubrovnik A164

1997, June 6
332	A164	2.20k multicolored	1.00	.80

Siege of Vukovar, Serbo-Croatian War, 1991 — A165

Painting by Zlatko Kauzlaric Atac.

1997, June 8 — Litho. — Perf. 14
333	A165	6.50k multicolored	3.25	3.25

Croatian Kings — A166

1.30k, King Peter Svacic, 900th death anniv. 2.40k, King Stephen Drzislav, 1000th death anniv.

1997, July 3
334 A166 1.30k multicolored .60 .60
335 A166 2.40k multicolored 1.25 1.25

16th Century Courier from Dubrovnik A167

1997, Sept. 9   Litho.   Perf. 14
336 A167 2.30k multicolored 1.10 .90
Stamp Day.

Croatian Olympic Medals — A168

Designs: 1k, Tennis, bronze, Barcelona, 1992. 1.20k, Basketball, silver, Barcelona 1992. 1.40k, Water polo, silver, Atlanta, 1996. 2.20k, Handball, gold, Atlanta, 1996.

1997, Sept. 10
337 A168 1k multicolored .40 .40
338 A168 1.20k multicolored .50 .50
Size: 27x31mm
339 A168 1.40k multicolored .60 .60
340 A168 2.20k multicolored .90 .90
Nos. 337-340 (4) 2.40 2.40

Defense of Sibenik — A169

Designs: No. 341, Fort, airplanes. No. 342, Turkish cavalry, fort.

1997, Sept. 18
341 A169 1.30k multicolored .50 .50
342 A169 1.30k multicolored .50 .50
a. Pair, #341-342 1.25 1.25
Serbo-Croatian War, 1991 (#341). War with the Turks, 350th anniv. (#342).

Anniversaries A170

No. 343: a, Frane Petric (1529-97), philosopher. b, Vicko Lovrin, 16th century painter. c, Frano Krsinic (1897-1982), sculptor. d, Dubravko Dujsin (1894-1947), actor.

1997, Oct. 17   Litho.   Perf. 14
343 A170 1.40k Strip of 4, #a.-d. 3.00 3.00

A171

A172

1997, Oct. 23
344 A171 2.20k multicolored 1.00 .70
345 A172 3.60k multicolored 1.75 1.00
Use of Croatian language in parliament, 150th anniv. (#344).
Croatian Grammar School, Zadar, cent. (#345).

Palaeontological Finds in Croatia — A173

Designs: 1.40k, Gomphotherium angustidens. 2.40k, Viviparus novskaensis.

1997, Nov. 6
346 A173 1.40k multicolored .60 .60
347 A173 2.40k multicolored 1.10 1.10

Modern Art A174

Paintings: 1.30k, Painter in the Pond, by Nikola Masic (1852-1902). 2.20k, Angelus, by Emanuel Vidovic (1870-1953). 3.60k, Tree in the Snow, by Slava Raskaj (1877-1906).

1997, Nov. 14
348 A174 1.30k multicolored .60 .45
349 A174 2.20k multicolored .90 .55
350 A174 3.60k multicolored 1.75 1.25
Nos. 348-350 (3) 3.25 2.25

Contemporary Christmas Painting, by Ivan Antolcic — A175

"Birth of Jesus," by Isidor Krsnjavi A176

1997, Nov. 28   Litho.   Perf. 13½
351 A175 1.30k multicolored .60 .40
Perf. 14
352 A176 3.60k multicolored 1.75 1.10

Croatian Literature — A177

1997, Dec. 18   Perf. 14
353 A177 1k shown .55 .40
354 A177 1.20k Book, words .60 .40
Printing of the translation of "Electra," by Dominko Zlataric, 400th anniv. (No. 353). Publication of "The Best of Folk Speech and the Illyric or Croatian Language," by Filip Grabovac, 250th anniv. (No. 354).

Cities and Landmarks Type of 1992
1997   Litho.   Perf. 14
355 A39 5 l Ilok .25 .25
356 A39 10 l Dubrovnik .25 .25

Events and Festivals — A178

Europa: 1.45k, Varazdin Baroque Evenings, musical notes. 4k, Dubrovnik Summer Festival.

1998, Jan. 23   Perf. 13½
357 A178 1.45k multicolored 1.00 1.00
358 A178 4k multicolored 2.50 2.50

1998 Winter Olympic Games, Nagano — A179

1998, Feb. 7   Perf. 14
359 A179 2.45k multicolored .80 .55

Croatian Events of 1848 — A180

a, 1.60k, Flag, battle near Moor. b, 4k, Portrait of Ban Josip Jelacic. c, 1.60k, Croatian Assembly.

1998, Mar. 25   Litho.   Perf. 14
360 A180 Strip of 3, #a.-c. 3.25 3.25
No. 360b is 21x32mm.

Ante Topic Mimara (1898-1987), Art Collector, Painter A181

1998, Apr. 7   Litho.   Perf. 14
361 A181 2.65k multicolored 1.25 .90

A182   A183

Mushrooms: a, 1.30k, Amanita caesarea. b, 7.20k, Morchella conica. c, 1.30k, Lactarius deliciosus.

1998, Apr. 22
362 A182 Strip of 3, #a.-c. 4.75 4.75

1998, May 8
363 A183 1.50k multicolored .75 .65
Archbishop Alojzije Stepinac (1898-1960).

27th European Regional Conference of Interpol, Dubrovnik A184

1998, May 13
364 A184 2.45k multicolored 1.25 .90

Souvenir Sheet

Expo '98, Lisbon — A185

1998, June 3   Litho.   Perf. 14
365 A185 14.85k Fishing boat, Falkusa 6.75 6.75

1998 World Cup Soccer Championships, France — A186

1998, June 10
366 A186 4k multicolored 2.00 1.50

Writers
A187

1.20k, Juraj Barakovic (1548-1628). 1.50k, Milan Begovic (1876-1948). 1.60k, Mate Balota (Mijo Mirkovic, 1898-1963). 2.45k, Antun Gustav Matos (1873-1914). 2.65k, Matija Antun Relkovic (1732-98). 4.00k, Antun Branko Simic (1898-1925).

1998, June 13   **Litho.**   **Perf. 14**
367	A187	1.20k multicolored	.60	.50
368	A187	1.50k multicolored	.70	.60
369	A187	1.60k multicolored	.75	.70
370	A187	2.45k multicolored	1.00	.90
371	A187	2.65k multicolored	1.10	1.00
372	A187	4k multicolored	1.75	1.60
		Nos. 367-372 (6)	5.90	5.30

19th Conference of the Countries of the Danube Region, Osijek — A188

1998, June 15
373 A188 1.80k multicolored   .90 .65

Stjepan Betlheim (1898-1970), Psychiatrist A189

1998, July 22
374 A189 1.50k multicolored   .70 .50

Souvenir Sheet

Croatian Soccer Team, Bronze Medalists at 1998 World Cup Soccer Championships, France — A190

Portions of team picture, denomination: a, red, LL. b, yellow, CR (player in yellow & blue shirt). c, yellow, CL. d, yellow, LR.

1998, July 24
375 A190 4k Sheet of 4, #a.-d.   7.75 7.75

Croatian Ships — A191

1.20k, Serilia Liburnica. 1.50k, Condura Croatica. 1.60k, Dubrovnik carrack. 1.80k, Bracera. 2.45k, Ship from the Neretva. 2.65k, Bark. 4k, Training ship, "Villa Velebita." 7.20k, Passenger ship, "Amorella." 20k, Missile gun boat, "Kralj Petar Kresimir IV."

1998, Aug. 27   **Litho.**   **Perf. 14**
376	A191	1.20k multi	.70	.70
376A	A191	1.50k multi	.80	.80
376B	A191	1.60k multi	.85	.85
376C	A191	1.80k multi	.90	.90
376D	A191	2.45k multi	1.30	1.30
376E	A191	2.65k multi	1.50	1.50
376F	A191	4k multi	2.00	2.00
376G	A191	7.20k multi	3.50	3.50
376H	A191	20k multi	9.25	9.25
i.		Sheet of 9, #376-376H +		
		3 labels	20.00	20.00
		Nos. 376-376H (9)	20.80	20.80

Stamp Day — A192

1998, Sept. 9
377 A192 1.50k multicolored   .75 .50

Bishopric of Sibenik, 700th Anniv. — A193

1998, Sept. 29   **Litho.**   **Perf. 14**
378 A193 4k multicolored   1.90 1.90

Pope John Paul II, Second Visit to Croatia A194

1998, Oct. 2
379 A194 1.50k multicolored   1.10 1.10

History of Public Transportation A195

Designs: a, 1.50k, Horse tram. b, 1.50k, First automobile in Zagreb, 1901. c, 7.20k, Zagreb funicular. d, 1.50k, Karlovac-Rijeka Railway Line, 1873. e, 1.50k, New Highway, Zagreb-Rijeka.

1998, Oct. 23   **Litho.**   **Perf. 14**
380 A195 Strip of 5, #a.-e.   6.75 6.75
No. 380c is 20x24mm.

Christmas — A196

Adoration of the Shepherds, by Juraj Julije Klovic (1498-1578).

1998, Nov. 21   **Perf. 14x13**
381 A196 1.50k multicolored   .80 .75
See Vatican City No. 1088.

Father Luka Ibrisimovic (1620-98) A197

1998, Nov. 30   **Litho.**   **Perf. 14**
382 A197 1.90k multicolored   .90 .75

Universal Declaration of Human Rights, 50th Anniv. — A198

1998, Dec. 10
383 A198 5k multicolored   2.25 2.25

Modern Art A199

Paintings: 1.90k, Paromlin Road, by Josip Vanista. 2.20k, Cypresses, by Frano Simunovic, vert. 5k, Koma, by Dalibor Martinis, vert.

1998, Dec. 15
384	A199	1.90k multicolored	.90	.90
385	A199	2.20k multicolored	1.00	1.00
386	A199	5k multicolored	2.50	2.50
		Nos. 384-386 (3)	4.40	4.40

Zagreb Intl. Trade Fair — A200

1999, Jan. 21   **Litho.**   **Perf. 14**
387 A200 1.80k multicolored   .90 .80

Cardinal Juraj Haulik (1788-1869), Archbishop of Zagreb — A201

Photo. & Engr.
1999, Jan. 28   **Perf. 11½**
388 A201 5k multicolored   2.25 2.25
See Slovakia 321.

National Parks — A202

Europa: 1.80k, Mljet Island. 5k, Lonja Field.

1999, Mar. 12   **Litho.**   **Perf. 14**
389	A202	1.80k multicolored	1.60	1.60
390	A202	5k multicolored	2.75	2.75

Vipera Ursinii — A203

World Wildlife Fund: a, One coiled in grass and rock. b, Two. c, Head. d, One coiled on rock.

1999, Apr. 27   **Litho.**   **Perf. 14**
391 A203 2.20k Strip of 4, #a.-d. 4.25 4.25

Council of Europe, 50th Anniv. — A204

1999, May 5
392 A204 2.80k multicolored   1.25 1.25

19th Convention of the Foundation of European Carnival Cities, Dubrovnik — A205

1999, May 8
393 A205 2.30k multicolored   1.10 1.00

Croatian Coins — A206

Designs: a, 2.30k, Obv., rev. of 1849 kreutzer. b, 5k, One kuna.

1999, May 30   **Litho.**   **Perf. 14**
394 A206 Pair, #a.-b.   3.25 3.25
Minting of Jelacic kreutzer, 150th anniv. (#394a). Croatian kuna, 5th anniv. (#394b).

Famous Croats — A207

1.80k, Vladimir Nazor (1876-1949), poet. 2.30k, Ferdo Livadic (1799-1879), composer. 2.50k, Ivan Rendic (1849-1932), sculptor. 2.80k, Milan Lenuci (1849-1924), architect. 3.50k, Vjekoslav Klaic (1849-1929), historian, muscician. 4k, Emilij Laszowski (1868-1949), historian. 5k, Antun Kanizlic (1699-1777), poet, missionary.

1999, June 18
395	A207	1.80k multicolored	.70	.70
396	A207	2.30k multicolored	1.00	.90
397	A207	2.50k multicolored	1.25	1.10
398	A207	2.80k multicolored	1.40	1.40
399	A207	3.50k multicolored	1.50	1.50
400	A207	4k multicolored	1.75	1.75
401	A207	5k multicolored	2.25	2.25
		Nos. 395-401 (7)	9.85	9.60

Euphrasian Basilica, Porec — A208

1999, June 25
402 A208 4k multicolored   1.60 1.60

2nd World Military Games, Zagreb A209

1999, Aug. 7   **Litho.**   **Perf. 14**
403 A209 2.30k multicolored   1.10 .90

Discovery of Early Krapina Man, Cent. — A210

Designs: a, 1.80k, Bones, rendition of Krapina man. b, 4k, Ancient bones, paleontologist Dragutin Gorjanovic-Kramberger.

1999, Aug. 23
404 A210 Pair, #a.-b.   3.25 3.25

Stamp Day and UPU, 125th Anniv. — A211

1999, Sept. 9   Litho.   *Perf. 14*
405 A211 2.30k multicolored   1.10 1.00

Paulist Order in Lepoglava, 600th Anniv. — A212

a, Lace, Jesus Expelling the Money Changers from Temple, by Ivan Ranger, altar angel from St. Mary's Church, Lepoglava. b, St. Mary's Church facade, altar angel. c, St. Elizabeth, lace.

1999, Sept. 11   Litho.
406 A212 5k Strip of 3, #a.-c.   6.75 6.75

150th Anniv. of "Jelacic March" by Johann Strauss the Elder — A213

1999, Sept. 16   Litho.
407 A213 3.50k multicolored   1.75 1.75

World Ozone Layer Protection Day A214

1999, Sept. 16   Litho.
408 A214 5k multicolored   2.25 2.10

Grammar School Anniversaries A215

1999, Oct. 15   Litho.   *Perf. 14*
409 A215 2.30k Pazin, cent.   1.00 .90
410 A215 3.50k Pozega, 300th anniv.   1.50 1.25

Andrija Hebrang (1899-1949), Politician — A216

1999, Oct. 21
411 A216 1.80k multicolored   .85 .75

Our Lady of the Rose Garden, by Blaz Jurjev Trogiranin A217

1999, Oct. 28
412 A217 5k multicolored   2.00 1.90
Christmas, opening of exhibition of Croatian religious art and artifacts, Vatican City.

Christmas — A218

1999, Nov. 24   Litho.   *Perf. 14*
413 A218 2.30k multicolored   1.10 1.00

Modern Art A219

Designs: 2.30k, Winter Landscape, by Gabrijel Jurkic (1886-1974). 3.50k, Klek, by Oton Postruznik (1900-78). 5k, Stone Table, by Ignjat Job (1895-1936), vert.

1999, Dec. 15
414 A219 2.30k multicolored   1.15 1.15
415 A219 3.50k multicolored   1.50 1.50
416 A219 5k multicolored   2.10 2.10
   Nos. 414-416 (3)   4.75 4.75

Pres. Franjo Tudjman (1922-99) — A220

1999, Dec. 16   *Vignette Color*
417 A220 2.30k black   1.00 .95
418 A220 5k blue   2.25 1.90

Millennium A221

2000, Jan. 1   Litho.   *Perf. 14*
419 A221 2.30k multi   1.40 1.25

Valentine's Day — A222

2000, Feb. 1
420 A222 2.30k multi   1.75 1.50

Split Grammar School, 300th Anniv. — A223

2000, Mar. 25   Litho.   *Perf. 14*
421 A223 2.80k multi   1.25 1.10

Croatian Writers' Assoc., 100th Anniv. — A224

2000, Apr. 22   Litho.   *Perf. 14*
422 A224 2.30k black & red   2.50 2.40

A225

A227

A226

A228

A229

(1.80k) Lo Schiavone (Andrija Medulic, c. 1500-63), painter; (2.30k) Matija Petar Katancic (1750-1825), writer; (2.80k) Marija Ruzicka-Strozzi (1850-1937), actress; (3.50k) Marko Marulic (1450-1524), writer; (5k) Blaz Jurjev Trogiranin (c. 1390-1450), painter.

2000, Apr. 22
423 A225 1.80k multi   .70 .65
424 A226 2.30k multi   1.00 .95
425 A227 2.80k multi   1.25 1.10
426 A228 3.50k multi   1.60 1.40
427 A229 5k multi   2.25 1.90
   Nos. 423-427 (5)   6.80 6.00

Europa, 2000
Common Design Type and

A230

2000, May 9
428 A230 2.30k multi   1.40 1.25
429 CD17 5k multi   3.00 2.25

Independence Day — A231

2000, May 30   Litho.   *Perf. 14*
430 A231 2.30k multi   1.10 1.00

Souvenir Sheet

Expo 2000, Hanover — A232

2000, June 1
431 A232 14.40k multi   6.50 6.50

Flora — A233

No. 432: a, 3.50k, Micromeria croatica. b, 5k, Geranium dalmaticum.

2000, June 5
432 A233 Pair, #a-b   4.00 4.00
   c.   Booklet pane of 10 #432a   15.00
     Booklet, #432c   16.00
   d.   Booklet pane of 10 #432b   20.00
     Booklet, #432d   21.00

Kastav Statute, 600th Anniv. — A234

2000, June 6
433 A234 1.80k multi   .85 .80

World Mathematics Year — A235

2000, June 15
434 A235 3.50k multi   1.75 1.60

Ivan Ranger
(1700-53),
Artist — A236

2000, June 19
435 A236 1.80k multi .85 .75

Souvenir Sheet

Baska Stone Tablet, 900th
Anniv. — A237

2000, June 24
436 A237 16.70k multi 7.50 7.50

Archdeacon
Toma of Split
(1200-68)
A238

2000, July 10
437 A238 3.50k multi 1.75 1.50

Type of 1992-94 Redrawn
2000, Aug. 1 Litho. Perf. 14
437A A39a 3.50k Vis 1.75 1.25
No. 437A has "HP" and post horn in LR
corner.

Stamp Day — A239

No. 438: a, 2.30k, Austria #5. b, 2.30k, Automatic mail sorting equipment.
2000, Sept. 9 Litho. Perf. 14
438 A239 Pair, #a-b 2.40 2.40
First stamps used in Croatia, 150th anniv.
(#438a).

2000 Summer
Olympics,
Sydney
A240

2000, Sept. 15
439 A240 5k multicolored 3.00 3.00

Altarpiece,
Church of the
Blessed Virgin
Mary, Ostarije
A241

2000, Nov. 23
440 A241 2.30k multi 1.10 .95
a. Booklet pane of 10 11.00
Booklet, #440a 11.50

Modern
Art
A242

Designs: 1.80k, Korcula, by Vladimir Varlaj.
2.30k, Brusnik, by Duro Tiljak. 5k, Boats, by
Ante Kastelacic.

2000, Dec. 1
441-443 A242 Set of 3 4.50 4.00
See Nos. 471-473.

Start of New
Millennium
A243

2001, Jan. 1 Litho. Perf. 14
444 A243 2.30k multi 1.85 1.60

Souvenir Sheet

Equestrian Statue of
Charlemagne — A244

2001, Jan. 19
445 A244 14.40k multi 7.00 7.00
Crowning of Charlemagne as Emperor of
the Romans, 1200th anniv. (in 2000).

Dzore Drzic (1461-1501),
Writer — A245

2001, Mar. 15 Litho. Perf. 14
446 A245 2.80k multi 1.40 1.25

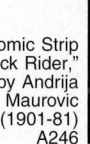

Comic Strip
"Black Rider,"
by Andrija
Maurovic
(1901-81)
A246

2001, Mar. 29
447 A246 5k multi 2.25 2.00

Makarska
A247

2001, Mar. 30
448 A247 2.30k multi 1.00 .80
a. Perf. 14 syncopated .85 .85
Issued: No. 448a, 6/2/06.

Janica
Kostelic,
Skier — A248

2001, Apr. 19 Litho. Perf. 14
449 A248 2.80k multi 2.40 2.00

Kastel Stafilic
Olive Trees,
1500th
Anniv. — A249

2001, Apr. 20
450 A249 1.80k multi .85 .75

Europa — A250

No. 451: a, 3.50k, Denomination at R. b, 5k,
Denomination at L.
2001, May 9
451 A250 Horiz. pair, #a-b 3.25 3.25

World No
Smoking
Day — A251

2001, May 31
452 A251 2.50k multi 1.25 1.10

Butterflies
A252

Designs: 2.50k, Parnassius apollo. 2.80k,
Maculinea teleius. 5k, Coenonympha
oedippus.
2001, June 5
453-455 A252 Set of 3 5.00 5.00

Type of 1992 Redrawn
2001, June 21 Litho. Perf. 14
456 A39 2.80k Eltz Castle,
Vukovar 1.25 1.25
a. Perf. 14 syncopated 1.10 1.10
No. 456 has "1991-2001" inscription, and
"HP" and post horn at LL.
Issued: No. 456a, 6/19/06.

Souvenir Sheet

Trsteno Arboretum — A253

2001, July 12 Litho. Perf. 14
457 A253 14.40k multi 6.50 6.50

World
Esperanto
Congress,
Zagreb — A254

2001, July 21
458 A254 5k multi 2.40 2.40

Refugee
Organizations,
50th Anniv.
A255

Designs: 1.80k, UN High Commissioner for
Refugees. 5k, Intl. Organization for Migration.

2001, July 28
459-460 A255 Set of 2 3.00 3.00

Victory of
Goran
Ivanisevic at
Wimbledon
A256

2001, Aug. 31
461 A256 2.50k multi 2.40 2.10
Printed in sheets of 9 + label.

Stamp
Day — A257

2001, Sept. 9
462 A257 2.50k multi .90 .80
Printed in sheets of 16 + 4 labels.

Native Dog
Breeds
A258

Designs: 1.80k, Croatian sheepdog. 5k,
Dalmatian.

2001, Oct. 4
463-464 A258 Set of 2 3.50 3.50

Independence, 10th Anniv. — A259

2001, Oct. 8
465 A259 2.30k multi 1.25 1.10

Printed in sheets of 25 + 5 labels.

Year of Dialogue Among Civilizations — A260

2001, Oct. 9
466 A260 5k multi 3.00 3.00

Fortresses — A261

Designs: 1.80k, Klis, 16th cent. 2.50k, Ston, 14th-15th cents. 3.50k, Sisak, 16th cent.

2001, Oct. 26 Litho. Perf. 14
467-469 A261 Set of 3 3.50 3.50

See Nos. 499-501, 525-527, 565-567, 594-596.

Adoration of the Magi Altarpeice, Church of the Visitation of Mary, Cucerje — A262

2001, Nov. 22 Litho. Perf. 14
470 A262 2.30k multi 1.10 1.00
a. Booklet pane of 10 11.00 11.00
Complete booklet, #470a 11.00

Modern Art Type of 2000

Designs: No. 471, 2.50k, Maternité du Port-Royal, by Leo Junek. No. 472, 2.50k, Amphitheater Ruins, by Vjekoslav Parac. 5k, Nude with a Baroque Figure, by Slavko Sohaj, vert.

2001, Dec. 1
471-473 A242 Set of 3 5.00 5.00

Croatian Nobel Laureates — A263

Laureates: 2.80k, Lavoslav (Leopold) Ruzicka, Chemistry, 1939. 3.50k, Vladimir Prelog, Chemistry, 1975. 5k, Ivo Andric, Literature, 1961.

2001, Dec. 5
474-476 A263 Set of 3 5.50 5.50

Famous Croats and Events — A264

Designs: 1.80k, Ivan Gucetic (1451-1502), writer. 2.30k, Dobrisa Cesaric (1902-80), writer. 2.50k, Publishing of Juraj Rattkay's History of Croatian Rulers, 350th anniv. 2.80k, Franjo Vranjanin Laurana (c. 1420-1502), sculptor. 3.50k, Beatification of Bishop Augustin Kazotic (c. 1260-1323), 300th anniv. 5k, Matko Laginja (1852-1930), politician and writer.

2002, Jan. 24 Litho. Perf. 14
477-482 A264 Set of 6 8.25 8.25

2002 Winter Olympics, Salt Lake City — A265

2002, Feb. 8
483 A265 5k multi 2.25 2.25

Croatian Chamber of Economy, 150th Anniv. — A266

2002, Feb. 16
484 A266 2.50k multi 1.25 1.25

Souvenir Sheet

Trpimir's Deed of Gift, 1150th Anniv. — A267

2002, Mar. 4
485 A267 14.40k multi 6.50 6.50

Franjo Cardinal Kuharic (1919-2002) A268

2002, Mar. 25
486 A268 2.30k multi 1.00 1.00

Divan, by Vlaho Bukovac — A269

Litho. & Engr.
2002, Apr. 23 Perf. 11¾
487 A269 5k multi 2.25 2.25

See Czech Republic No. 3169.

Royal Borough of Krizevci, 750th Anniv. — A270

2002, Apr. 24 Litho. Perf. 14
488 A270 1.80k multi .85 .85

Varazdin Post Office, Cent. — A271

2002, Apr. 26
489 A271 2.30k multi 1.10 1.10

Europa — A272

Clown color: a, 3.50k, Orange. b, 5k, Blue.

2002, May 9 Litho. Perf. 14
490 A272 Horiz. pair, #a-b 4.50 4.50

2002 World Cup Soccer Championships, Japan and Korea — A273

Stylized players facing: a, 3.50k, Left. b, 5k, Right.

2002, May 15
491 A273 Horiz. pair, #a-b 4.25 4.25

World Bowling Championships, Osijek — A274

2002, May 18
492 A274 3.50k multi 1.50 1.50

Oak Trees — A275

Designs: 1.80k, Quercus rober. 2.50k, Quercus petraea. 2.80k, Quercus ilex.

2002, June 5
493-495 A275 Set of 3 3.25 3.25
493a Booklet pane of 10 6.00 —
Complete booklet, #493a 6.25
494a Booklet pane of 10 12.00 —
Complete booklet, #494a 12.50
495a Booklet pane of 10 14.75 —
Complete booklet, #495a 15.25

15th World Animated Films Festival, Zagreb — A276

2002, June 18
496 A276 5k multi 2.25 2.25

Lace — A277

Lace from: 3.50k, Pag Island, Croatia. 5k, Liedekerke, Belgium.

2002, July 13 Photo. Perf. 11½
497-498 A277 Set of 2 4.25 4.25

See Belgium Nos. 1927-1928.

Fortresses Type of 2001

Designs: No. 499, 2.50k, Nehaj, 16th cent. No. 500, 2.50k, Skocibuha, 16th cent. 5k, Veliki Tabor, 16th cent.

2002, Sept. 20 Litho. Perf. 14
499-501 A261 Set of 3 4.50 4.50

Old Slavonic Academy, Krk, Cent. — A278

2002, Oct. 3 Litho. & Embossed
502 A278 4k red & black 1.75 1.75

Children's Help Line 48 26 051, 5th Anniv. — A279

2002, Oct. 15 Litho.
503 A279 2.30k multi 1.00 1.00

Christmas A280

2002, Nov. 21
504 A280 2.30k multi 1.25 1.25
a. Booklet pane of 10 12.50
Complete booklet, #504a 13.00

Modern Art Type of 2002

Designs: No. 505, 2.50k, Flowers on the Window, by Antun Motika (1902-92), vert. No. 506, 2.50k, The Girl in the Boat, by Milivoj Uzelac (1897-1977), vert. 5k, On the Drava River, by Krsto Hegedusic (1901-75).

2002, Dec. 2 Litho. Perf. 14
505-507 A242 Set of 3 5.00 5.00

Zagreb Bishopric, 150th Anniv. — A281

2002, Dec. 11
508 A281 2.80k multi   1.40 1.40

Printed in sheets of 19 + label.

Pavao Ritter Vitezovic (1652-1713), Writer — A282

2002, Dec. 13
509 A282 2.30k multi   1.00 1.00

Pacta Conventa, 900th Anniv. — A283

2002, Dec. 14
510 A283 3.50k multi   1.50 1.50

Fairies From Stories by Ivana Brlic Mazuranic — A284

No. 511: a, 2.30k, Kosjenka, fairy character from *Regoc*. b, 2.80k, Tintilinic, fairy character from *Suma Striborova*.

2003, Jan. 15
511 A284   Horiz. pair, #a-b   2.25 2.25

St. Valentine's Day — A285

Litho. With Foil Application
2003, Feb. 1
512 A285 2.30k multi   1.00 1.00

Astronomy and Meteorology A286

No. 513: a, 1.80k, Zagreb Astronomical Observatory, cent. b, 3.50k, Meteorological

---

measurements in Zagreb, 150th anniv.; Meteorological station on Zavizan, 50th anniv.

2003, Feb. 17   **Litho.**
513 A286   Pair, #a-b   2.40 2.40

Souvenir Sheet

Croatia, 2003 World Handball Champions — A287

No. 514: a, Five team members, one wearing red shirt. b, Eight team members, one with arm extended. c, Six team members. d, Four team members, one wearing blue shirt.

2003, Feb. 20
514 A287   4k Sheet of 4, #a-d   7.00 7.00

Paulist High School, Lepoglava, 500th Anniv. — A288

2003, Mar. 1
515 A288 5k multi   2.25 2.25

Missal of Hrvoje Vukcic Hrvatinic, 600th Anniv. — A289

2003, Mar. 25
516 A289 5k multi   2.25 2.25

Land Mine Danger A290

2003, Apr. 8
517 A290 2.30k multi   1.00 1.00

Alpine Skiing World Cup Victories of Janica and Ivica Kostelic A291

No. 518: a, Janica. b, Ivica.

2003, Apr. 16
518 A291   3.50k Pair, #a-b   5.25 5.25

Printed in sheets containing 4 vertical pairs and 2 labels.

Christian Institutions in Rome Founded by Croatian Roman Brotherhood of St. Jerome, 550th Anniv. — A292

2003, Apr. 22
519 A292 2.80k multi   1.25 1.25

Famous Croatians A293

Designs: 1.80k, Antun Soljan (1932-93), writer. 2.30k, Hanibal Lucic (1485-1553), writer. 5k, Federiko Benkovic (1667-1753), painter.

2003, Apr. 22
520-522 A293   Set of 3   4.00 4.00

Poster for Performance of Marya Delvard, by Tomislav Krizman, 1907 — A294

Poster for Performance of "The Firebird," by Boris Bucan, 1983 — A295

2003, May 9   **Litho.**   *Perf. 14*
523 A294 3.50k multi   *1.50 1.50*
524 A295   5k multi   *2.25 2.25*

Europa.

Fortresses Type of 2001

Designs; 1.80k, Kostajnica, 15th-18th cent. 2.80k, Slavonski Brod, 18th cent. 5k, Minceta Tower, 15th cent., vert.

2003, May 13
525-527 A261   Set of 3   4.25 4.25

Visit of Pope John Paul II — A296

2003, June 2
528 A296 2.30k multi   1.60 1.60

Rodents A297

Designs: 2.30k, Sciuris vulgaris. 2.80k, Glis glis. 3.50k, Castor fiber.

2003, June 5
529-531 A297   Set of 3   3.75 3.75
   531a   Booklet pane, 6 #529, 2
     each #530-531   12.00   —
     Complete booklet, #531a   12.00

Souvenir Sheet

Robe of King Ladislaus, 11th Cent. — A298

2003, June 13
532 A298 10k multi   4.50 4.50

Stamp Day — A299

2003, Sept. 9   **Litho.**   *Perf. 14*
533 A299 2.30k multi   1.10 1.10

Souvenir Sheet

Primosten Vineyards — A300

Litho. with Foil Application
2003, Sept. 19
534 A300 10k multi   4.50 4.50

Ursuline Sisters in Croatia, 300th Anniv. — A301

2003, Oct. 20   **Litho.**
535 A301 2.50k multi   1.10 1.10

Christmas A302

2003, Nov. 20   **Litho.**   *Perf. 14*
536 A302 2.30k multi   1.00 1.00

Self-Adhesive
Serpentine Die Cut 5¼
537 A302 2.30k multi   1.40 1.40

Modern Art A304

Designs: 1.80k, Flower Girl II, by Slavko Kopac, vert. No. 539, 3.50k, Dry Stone Wall 5-71, by Oton Gliha. No. 540, 3.50k, Pont des Arts, by Josip Racic.

2003, Nov. 21   *Perf. 14*
538-540 A304 Set of 3   4.50 4.50

See Nos. 568-570, 604-606, 636-638, 668-670, 712-714.

18th World Women's Handball Championships — A305

2003, Dec. 1
541 A305 5k multi   2.25 2.25

Musicians — A306

No. 542: a, Josip Hatze (1879-1959), composer. b, Zagreb Soloists, 50th anniv.

2004, Jan. 5   **Litho.**   *Perf. 14*
542 A306 5k Horiz. pair, #a-b   5.25 5.25

Hval's Manuscript, 600th Anniv. — A307

2004, Jan. 22
543 A307 2.30k multi   1.60 1.60

European Boxing Championships, Pula — A308

2004, Feb. 19   **Litho.**   *Perf. 14*
544 A308 2.80k multi   1.40 1.40

Worldwide Fund for Nature (WWF) — A309

Ardea purpurea: a, In grass. b, Standing with head extended. c, With young. d, In flight.

2004, Mar. 22
545   Strip or block of 4   9.50 9.50
   a.-d. A309 5k Any single   2.25 2.25

Famous Croats — A310

Designs: 2.30k, Ivan Lucic (1604-79), historian. No. 547, 3.50k, Antun Vrancic (1504-75), archbishop, writer. No. 548, 3.50k, St. Jerome, sculpture by Andrija Alesi (c. 1425-1504). 10k, Printing of Croatian grammar book, by Bartol Kasic (1575-1650), 400th anniv.

2004, Apr. 22
546-549 A310 Set of 4   8.75 8.75

Souvenir Sheet

Risnjak National Park — A311

2004, Apr. 22
550 A311 10k multi   5.25 5.25

Martyrdom of St. Domnio, 1700th Anniv. — A312

2004, May 7
551 A312 3.50k multi   1.75 1.75

Europa A313

Designs: No. 552, 3.50k, Summer vacation items. No. 553, 3.50k, Winter vacation items.

2004, May 9
552-553 A313 Set of 2   4.00 4.00

FIFA (Fédération Internationale de Football Association), Cent. A314

2004, May 21   **Litho.**   *Perf. 14*
554 A314 2.50k multi   1.25 1.25

Medicinal Herbs — A315

Designs: 2.30k, Rosa canina. 2.80k, Viola odorata. 3.50k, Mentha piperita.

2004, June 5
555-557 A315   Set of 3   4.75 4.75
555a   Booklet pane of 10   12.00   —
   Complete booklet, #555a   12.50
556a   Booklet pane of 10   15.00   —
   Complete booklet, #556a   15.50
557a   Booklet pane of 10   20.00   —
   Complete booklet, #557a   21.00

Nos. 555-557 are impregnated with a floral scent.

Intl. Marionette Union Congress, Intl. Puppetry Art Festival, Rijeka A316

2004, June 6
558 A316 3.50k multi   1.75 1.75

European Soccer Championships, Portugal — A317

2004, June 12
559 A317 3.50k multi   1.75 1.75
Values are for stamps with surrounding selvage.

Restoration of Old Bridge, Mostar, Bosnia & Herzegovina A318

2004, July 23   **Litho.**   *Perf. 14*
560 A318 3.50k multi   1.75 1.75

2004 Summer Olympics, Athens — A319

2004, Aug. 13
561 A319 3.50k multi   1.75 1.75

Virovitica A320

2004, Aug. 16
562 A320 5k multi   2.50 2.50

Zagreb Post Office, Cent. A321

2004, Sept. 9
563 A321 2.30k multi   1.25 1.25
Printed in sheets of 16 + 4 labels.

Father Andrija Kacic Miosic (1704-60), Poet — A322

2004, Sept. 15
564 A322 2.80k multi   1.40 1.40

Fortresses Type of 2001

Designs: No. 565, 3.50k, Dubovac, 15th-19th cent. No. 566, 3.50k, Gripe, 17th cent. No. 567, 3.50k, Valpovo, 15th-18th cent.

2004, Sept. 29
565-567 A261 Set of 3   5.50 5.50

Modern Art Type of 2003

Designs: No. 568, 2.30k, Self-portrait, by Miroslav Kraljevic, vert. No. 569, 2.30k, Noon in Supetar, by Jerolim Mise, vert. No. 570, 2.30k, Stari Grad, by Juraj Plancic, vert.

2004, Nov. 15   **Litho.**   *Perf. 14*
568-570 A304 Set of 3   3.75 3.75

Christmas A323

2004, Nov. 25
571 A323 2.30k multi   1.25 1.25

Antun and Stjepan Radic and Plowman — A324

2004, Dec. 22   **Litho.**   *Perf. 14*
572 A324 7.20k multi   3.75 3.75
Croatian People's Peasant Party, Cent.

Fairy Tale Characters — A325

No. 573: a, Mermaid Halugica. b, Dwarf Pedalj Muza Lakat Brade.

2005, Jan. 14
573 A325 5k Horiz. pair, #a-b   5.25 5.25

World Conference on the Information Society, Tunis — A326

2005, Feb. 10
574 A326 2.80k multi   1.40 1.40

Values are for stamps with surrounding selvage.

Souvenir Sheet

Bust of Livia Drusilla — A327

2005, Feb. 24
575 A327 10k multi   6.00 6.00

Souvenir Sheet

Expo 2005, Aichi, Japan — A328

2005, Mar. 25   *Perf.*
576 A328 10k multi   6.00 6.00

Pope John Paul II (1920-2005) A329

2005, Apr. 8   *Perf. 14*
577 A329 2.30k multi   1.40 1.40

World Music Days, Zagreb A330

Stjepan Sulek (1914-86), Composer A331

2005, Apr. 15
578 A330 2.30k multi   1.25 1.25
579 A331 2.30k multi   1.25 1.25

Insects — A332

Designs: 1.80k, Coccinella septempunctata. 2.30k, Rosalia alpina. 3.50k, Lucanus cervus.

2005, Apr. 22
580-582 A332   Set of 3   4.00 4.00

Liberation of Western Slavonia, 10th Anniv. A333

2005, May 1
583 A333 1.80k multi   .95 .95

Dr. Josip Buturac (1905-93), Historian — A334

2005, May 6
584 A334 2.80k multi   1.40 1.40

Europa — A335

No. 585: a, Loaf of bread. b, Glass of wine.

2005, May 9
585 A335 3.50k Horiz. pair, #a-b   *3.50 3.50*

Coast of Hvar Island — A336

No. 586: a, Rock at L, tree tops at bottom. b, Tree tops at LL. c, Rock at R. d, Canoe, rock at R. e, Small rock in center. f, Rocks at UL, trees. g, Rocks at R, trees. h, Tree tops at LL corner, rock at UR corner. i, Rocks at UL and LL corners. j, Rocks at LL.

2005, May 24   *Litho.*   *Perf. 14*
586 A336   Booklet pane of
           10   16.00   —
a.-e.   1.80k Any single   1.10 1.10
f.-j.   3.50k Any single   1.75 1.75
      Complete booklet, #586   17.00

Kresimir Cosic (1948-95), Basketball Player — A337

2005, May 25
587 A337 3.50k multi   1.75 1.75

Printed in sheets of 9 + 1 label.

Krapanj Island Sponge and Coral Diving — A338

2005, June 2   *Litho.*
588 A338 3.50k multi   1.90 1.90

Portions of the design were applied by a thermographic process producing a shiny, raised effect.

Emperor Constantine's Bath, Varazdinske Toplice A339

2005, June 20   *Perf. 14*
589 A339 1.80k multi   1.00 1.00

Intl. Fire Brigade Olympics, Varazdin A340

2005, July 15
590 A340 2.30k multi   1.25 1.25

Printed in sheets of 8 + 2 labels.

European Philatelic Cooperation, 50th Anniv. (in 2006) A341

Designs: 7.20k, Vignette of #134. 8k, Stylized gull.

2005, Sept. 8
591-592 A341   Set of 2   *8.00 8.00*
592a   Souvenir sheet, #591-592   70.00 70.00

Europa stamps, 50th anniv. (in 2006).

Telegraph A342

2005, Sept. 9
593 A342 2.30k multi   1.25 1.25

First overhead telegraph lines in Croatia, 155th anniv., Stamp Day.

Fortresses Type of 2001

Designs: 1k, Ilok, 14th-15th cents. 2.30k, Motovun, 13th-15th cents., vert. 3.50k, St. Nicholas, 16th cent.

2005, Sept. 15
594-596 A261   Set of 3   3.50 3.50

Famous People — A343

Designs: 1k, Adam Baltazar Krcelic (1715-78), historian. No. 598, 2.30k, Dragutin Tadijanovic (b. 1905), poet. No. 599, 2.30k, Tin Ujevic (1891-1955), poet. 2.80k, Madonna and Child, by Juraj Culinovic (c.1433-1504).

2005, Nov. 4
597-600 A343   Set of 4   4.50 4.50

Clock Tower, Rijeka — A344

2005, Nov. 10   *Litho.*   *Perf. 14*
601 A344 3.50k multi   1.90 1.90
a.   Perf. 14 syncopated   1.90 1.90

Issued: No. 601a, 6/12/06.

Christmas A345

2005, Nov. 22   *Perf. 14*
602 A345 2.30k multi   1.25 1.25

Booklet Stamp
Self-Adhesive
Serpentine Die Cut 5¼

603 A345 2.30k multi   1.25 1.25
a.   Booklet pane of 10   12.50 12.50
     Complete booklet, #603a   12.50 12.50

Modern Art Type of 2003

Designs: 1.80k, Zadar, by Edo Murtic. 5k, Meander, by Julije Knifer. 10k, Drawing, by Miroslav Sutej, vert.

2005, Dec. 1   *Perf. 14*
604-606 A304   Set of 3   9.00 9.00

Davis Cup and Members of Croatian Tennis Team — A346

2005, Dec. 22   *Litho.*   *Perf. 14*
607 A346 5k multi   2.50 2.50

Croatia, winners of 2005 Davis Cup. Printed in sheets of 9 + label.

Composers A347

Designs: 1.80k, Boris Papandopulo (1906-91). 2.30k, Milo Cipra (1906-85). 2.80k, Ivan Brkanovic (1906-87).

2006, Jan. 17
608-610 A347   Set of 3   3.50 3.50

2006 Winter Olympics, Turin — A348

2006, Feb. 10
611 A348 3.50k multi   1.75 1.75

Rembrandt (1606-69), Painter A349

2006, Mar. 7
612 A349 5k multi 2.50 2.50

Famous Men — A350

Designs: No. 613, 1k, Andrija Ljudevit Adamic (1766-1828), merchant. No. 614, 1k, Josip Kozarac (1858-1906), writer. 5k, Vanja Radaus (1906-75), sculptor. 7.20k, Ljubo Karaman (1886-1971), art historian.

2006, Mar. 21   Perf. 14 Syncopated
613-616 A350 Set of 4 7.00 7.00

European Track and Field Championships, Göteborg, Sweden — A351

2006, Apr. 4
617 A351 2.30k multi 1.10 1.10

2006 World Cup Soccer Championships, Germany A352

2006, Apr. 4
618 A352 2.80k multi 1.40 1.40

Flag and Crowd — A353

No. 619 — Location and placement of denomination: a, At left, with denomination above crowd. b, At right, with top of numerals over red in flag. c, At left, with top of "8" and "0" above white in flag. d, At left, with serif of "1" above red in flag. e, At left, with entire denomination above red in flag. f, At right, with parts of "5" and "0" above red in flag. g, At right, with entire denomination above red in flag. h, At right, with entire denomination above white in flag. i, At left, with entire denomination above red in flag. j, At right, with denomination above crowd.

2006, Apr. 25
619 A353 Booklet pane of
10 15.00 —
a.-e. 1.80k Any single 1.00 1.00
f.-j. 3.50k Any single 2.00 2.00
Complete booklet, #619 16.00

Europa — A354

No. 620: a, Denomination at left. b, Denomination at right.

2006, May 9
620 A354 3.50k Horiz. pair, #a-b 3.25 3.25

Worldwide Fund for Nature (WWF) A355

No. 621 — Various views of Sterna albifrons with denomination in: a, Gray. b, Dull green. c, Yellow orange. d, Red.

2006, May 23
621 Strip of 4 10.00 10.00
a.-d. A355 5k Any single 2.40 2.40

Croatian Automobile Club, Cent. — A356

Perf. 13¾x14 Syncopated
2006, June 4
622 A356 5k multi 2.50 2.50

Aquatic Flowers A357

Designs: 2.30k, Nymphaea alba. 2.80k, Nuphar lutea. 3.50k, Menyanthes trifoliata.

2006, June 5   Perf. 14 Syncopated
623-625 A357 Set of 3 4.25 4.25
623a Booklet pane of 10 11.50
Complete booklet, #623a 11.50
624 Booklet pane of 10 13.50 13.50
Complete booklet, #624a 13.50
625a Booklet pane of 10 17.00 17.00
Complete booklet, #625a 17.00

Nikola Tesla (1856-1943), Inventor — A358

Perf. 14x13½ Syncopated
2006, July 10   Litho.
626 A358 3.50k multi 2.00 2.00

Bjelovar, 250th Anniv. A359

Perf. 14 Syncopated
2006, Aug. 22   Litho.
627 A359 2.80k multi 1.40 1.40

Stamp Day — A360

2006, Sept. 9   Litho. & Embossed
628 A360 2.30k multi 1.10 1.10

Jewish Community of Zagreb, 200th Anniv. — A361

Perf. 14¼x13¾ Syncopated
2006, Sept. 15   Litho.
629 A361 5k multi 2.50 2.50

Fortresses Type of 2001

Designs: No. 630, 1k, St. Mary of Mercy Church, Vrboska, 16th cent. No. 631, 1k, Church of the Holy Spirit, Sudurad, 16th cent. 7.20k, Frankapan Citadel, Ogulin, 16th cent.

Perf. 13¾x14¼ Syncopated
2006, Sept. 21
630-632 A261 Set of 3 4.75 4.75

White Cane Safety Day — A362

Perf. 14 Syncopated
2006, Oct. 15   Litho. & Embossed
633 A362 1.80k black & red 1.25 1.25

Christmas A363

Perf. 14¼ Syncopated
2006, Nov. 27   Litho.
634 A363 2.30k multi 1.10 1.10

Booklet Stamp
Self-Adhesive
Serpentine Die Cut 5¼

635 A363 2.30k multi 1.10 1.10
a. Booklet pane of 10 11.00
Complete booklet, #635a 11.00

Modern Art Type of 2003

Designs: 1k, Still Life, by Vladimir Becic. 1.80k, Composition Tyma 3, by Ivan Picelj.

10k, Self-portrait as Hunter, by Nasta Rojc, vert.

2006, Dec. 1   Perf. 14 Syncopated
636-638 A304 Set of 3 6.25 6.25

Classical Gymnasium, Zagreb, 400th Anniv. — A364

Perf. 14 Syncopated
2007, Jan. 9   Litho.
639 A364 5k multi 2.50 2.50

Fairy Tale Characters — A365

No. 640: a, Monster Orko. b, Devil Macic.

2007, Jan. 18
640 A365 2.30k Horiz. pair, #a-b 2.25 2.25

National and University Library, Zagreb, 400th Anniv. A366

2007, Feb. 22
641 A366 5k multi 2.50 2.50

Crustaceans A367

Designs: 1.80k, Palinurus elephas. 2.30k, Nephrops norvegicus. 2.80k, Astacus astacus.

2007, Mar. 15
642 A367 1.80k multi .90 .90
a. Booklet pane of 10 9.00
Complete booklet, #642a 9.00
643 A367 2.30k multi 1.10 1.10
a. Booklet pane of 10 11.00
Complete booklet, #643a 11.00
644 A367 2.80k multi 1.50 1.50
a. Booklet pane of 10 15.00
Complete booklet, #644a 15.00
Nos. 642-644 (3) 3.50 3.50

Native Breeds of Farm Animals A368

Designs: 2.80k, Istrian ox. 3.50k, Posavina horse. 5k, Dalmatian donkey.

2007, Mar. 20
645-647 A368 Set of 3 5.50 5.50

Europa — A369

No. 648: a, Scouting emblem and dove. b, Scout neckerchief.

2007, Apr. 16
648 A369 3.50k Horiz. pair, #a-b   3.25 3.25
Scouting, cent.

Scientists — A370

Designs: 5k, Andrija Mohorovicic (1857-1936), seismologist. 7.20k, Duro Baglivi (1668-1707), physician.

Perf. 14x13½ Syncopated
2007, Apr. 23
649-650 A370   Set of 2   5.75 5.75

Souvenir Sheet

World Championship Victory of Croatian Water Polo Team — A371

No. 651: a, Man with red shirt at right, denomination at UL. b, Man with red shirt at LR, denomination at UR. c, Man with red shirt at left, denomination at UR.

Litho. With Foil Application
2007, May 3   *Perf. 14¼ Syncopated*
651 A371 5k Sheet of 3, #a-c   7.50 7.50

World Table Tennis Championships, Zagreb — A372

Perf. 14 Syncopated
2007, May 21   Litho. & Embossed
652 A372 3.50k multi   1.75 1.75

Starting with No. 652 some stamps have an imprinted wing-shaped tagging design that looks like a watermark.

Diplomatic Relations Between Croatia and People's Republic of China, 15th Anniv. — A373

No. 653: a, "China" in Glagolithic letters. b, "Croatia" in Chinese characters.

2007, May 30   Litho.   *Perf. 12*
653 A373 5k Horiz. pair, #a-b   5.00 5.00

Zagreb City Museum, Cent. — A374

2007, May 31   *Perf. 14 Syncopated*
654 A374 2.30k multi   1.25 1.25

Souvenir Sheet

Red Lake — A375

2007, June 8
655 A375 10k multi   5.00 5.00

First Croatian Philatelic Exhibition, Cent. — A376

Perf. 14 Syncopated
2007, Sept. 9   Litho. & Embossed
656 A376 2.80k multi   1.50 1.50

Stamp Day.

Lighthouses — A377

Designs: No. 657, 5k, St. John on the Sea Lighthouse. No. 658, 5k, Porer Lighthouse. No. 659, 5k, Savudrija Lighthouse.

Perf. 13¾x14¼ Syncopated
2007, Sept. 14   Litho.
657-659 A377   Set of 3   7.75 7.75

Veprinac Statute, 500th Anniv. — A378

Perf. 14¼x13¾ Syncopated
2007, Oct. 2
660 A378 2.70k multi   1.40 1.40

City Views — A379

Designs: 1.80k, Omis. 2.30k, Koprivnica, horiz. 2.80k, Krk.

2007, Oct. 30   *Perf. 14 Syncopated*
661 A379 1.80k multi   1.00 1.00
662 A379 2.30k multi   1.25 1.25
663 A379 2.80k multi   1.50 1.50
    Nos. 661-663 (3)   3.75 3.75

Blanka Vlasic, 2007 World Women's High Jump Champion A380

2007, Nov. 8
664 A380 2.30k multi   1.25 1.25

Christmas A381

Perf. 14¼ Syncopated
2007, Nov. 15   Litho.
665 A381 2.30k multi   1.25 1.25

Booklet Stamp
Self-Adhesive
Serpentine Die Cut 5¼
666 A381 2.30k multi   1.25 1.25
a.   Booklet pane of 10   12.50
    Complete booklet, #666a   12.50

Marija Juric Zagorka (1873-1957), Writer — A382

Perf. 14¼x13¾ Syncopated
2007, Nov. 16
667 A382 7.20k multi   3.50 3.50

Modern Art Type of 2003

Designs: 2.80k, Area by the Sava River, by Branko Senoa. No. 669, 5k, Pegasus's Garden, by Ferdinand Kulmer. No. 670, 5k, Bridgeport, by Ivan Benkovic.

Perf. 14 Syncopated
2007, Dec. 1   Litho.
668-670 A304   Set of 3   6.25 6.25

New Year 2008 — A383

2007, Dec. 5
671 A383 1.80k multi   .90 .90

Composers A384

Designs: No. 672, 2.30k, Igor Kuljeric (1938-2006). No. 673, 2.30k, Krsto Odak (1888-1965).

2008, Jan. 22
672-673 A384   Set of 2   2.40 2.40

Publication of *Arithmetika Horvatszka*, by Mijo Silobod Bolsic, 250th Anniv. — A385

Perf. 13¾x14 Syncopated
2008, Jan. 25
674 A385 3.50k multi   1.75 1.75

Steam Locomotives — A386

Designs: No. 675, 5k, MAV 601/JZ 32. No. 676, 5k, MAV 651/JZ 31.

2008, Feb. 15
675-676 A386   Set of 2   5.25 5.25
Nos. 675-676 were printed in sheets of 6 containing three of each stamp.

St. Nicholas Church, Cavtat A387

Perf. 14 Syncopated
2008, Mar. 8   Litho.
677 A387 7.20k multi   3.50 3.50

2008 Summer Olympics, Beijing A388

2008, Mar. 11
678 A388 5k multi   2.50 2.50
Printed in sheets of 9 + label.

Flowers — A389

Designs: 1.80k, Helleborus niger. 2.80k, Onosma stellulata. 3.50k, Lonicera glutinosa.

2008, Mar. 20
679 A389 1.80k multi   1.00 1.00
a.   Booklet pane of 10   10.00   —
    Complete booklet, #679a   10.00
680 A389 2.80k multi   1.50 1.50
a.   Booklet pane of 10   15.00   —
    Complete booklet, #680a   15.00
681 A389 3.50k multi   1.75 1.75
a.   Booklet pane of 10   17.50   —
    Complete booklet, #681a   17.50
    Nos. 679-681 (3)   4.25 4.25

Famous Writers — A390

Designs: 2.30k, Petar Zoranic (1508-c. 1569), novelist. 2.80k, Silvije Strahimir Kranjcevic (1865-1908), poet. 7.20k, Marin Drzic (1508-67), dramatist.

Perf. 14 Syncopated

2008, Apr. 22   Litho.
682-684 A390   Set of 3   6.25 6.25

Waterfall, Plitvice Lakes National Park — A391

No. 685 — Part of waterfall with: a, Country name in white, denomination at UL, "HP" symbol in white at LL. b, Country name in white, denomination at UR, "HP" symbol in white at LL, green foliage at UL. c, Country name in black, denomination at UR. d, Country name in white, denomination at UR, "HP" symbol in black at LL. e, Country name in white, denomination at UR, "HP" symbol in white at LL, green foliage at UR. f, Country name in white, denomination in black at LR, "HP" symbol in black at LL, rock with foliage in center. g, Country name in white, denomination in black at LR, "HP" symbol in black at LL, all rocks covered by spray. h, Country name in black, denomination at LR. i, Country name in white, denomination in white at LR. j, Country name in white, denomination in black at LR, "HP" symbol in white at LL.

Perf. 14 Syncopated

2008, Apr. 25   Litho.
685   Booklet pane of 10   17.50 —
   a.-j.   A391 3.50k Any single   1.75 1.75
   Complete booklet, #685   17.50

2008 Volkswagen Beetle — A392

2008, May 8
686 A392 2.30k multi + label   1.25 1.25

Europa A393

Designs: 3.50k, Insured envelope with wax seal. 5k, Airmail envelope.

2008, May 9   Litho.
687 A393 3.50k multi   1.60 1.60
   Litho. & Embossed
688 A393   5k multi   2.40 2.40

Portions of the design of No. 687 were applied using a thermographic process producing a shiny raised effect.

UEFA Euro 2008 Soccer Championships, Austria and Switzerland — A394

2008, May 14   Litho.   **Perf. 14x13½**
689 A394 3.50k multi   1.75 1.75

Values are for stamps with surrounding selvage. Printed in sheets of 9 + label.

Adris Group — A395

2008, May 16   **Perf. 14 Syncopated**
690 A395 2.30k multi + label   1.25 1.25

Souvenir Sheet

Ivan Vucetic (1858-1925), Fingerprint Classifier — A396

2008, Apr. 20
691 A396 10k multi   5.25 5.25

Souvenir Sheet

Expo Zaragoza 2008 — A397

Litho. With Foil Application
2008, June 16
692 A397 10k multi   5.25 5.25

Souvenir Sheet

Lujzinske Road, 200th Anniv. — A398

No. 693 — Parts of map of Lujzinske Road with denomination in: a, Red. b, Green. c, White.

Perf. 14x13½ Syncopated
2008, June 17   Litho.
693 A398 5k Sheet of 3, #a-c   7.50 7.50

Western Union — A399

2008, July 11   **Perf. 14 Syncopated**
694 A399 3.50k multi + label   1.50 1.50

Postal Workers' Games — A400

Litho. With Foil Application
2008, Sept. 9   **Perf. 14 Syncopated**
695 A400 2.80k multi   1.40 1.40

Stamp Day.

Lighthouses A401

Designs: No. 696, 5k, Pinida Lighthouse. No. 697, 5k, Vnetak Lighthouse. No. 698, 5k, Zaglav Lighthouse.

Perf. 14¼x13¾ Syncopated
2008, Sept. 12   Litho.
696-698 A401   Set of 3   7.50 7.50

Order of St. Clare, Split, 700th Anniv. — A402

2008, Sept. 16
699 A402 2.80k multi   1.50 1.50

Details From Native Costumes A403

Costume from: 10 l, Sunja. 20 l, Bistra. 50 l, Bizovac. 1k, Ravni Kotari. 10k, Pag.

2008, Sept. 30   **Perf. 14 Syncopated**
700-704 A403   Set of 5   6.00 6.00
   703a   Perf. 14 ('10)   .35 .35
   704a   Sheet of 5, #700-704 + label   6.00 6.00

European Healthy Cities Movement, 20th Anniv. — A404

2008, Oct. 17   **Perf. 14¼ Syncopated**
705 A404 2.80k multi + label   1.50 1.50

Collegium Ragusinum, Dubrovnik, 350th Anniv. — A405

Perf. 14¼x13¾ Syncopated
2008, Nov. 7   **Litho. & Embossed**
706 A405 7.20k multi   3.75 3.75

Intl. Amateur Radio Union Region 1 Conference, Cavtat — A406

Perf. 13¾x14¼ Syncopated
2008, Nov. 14   Litho.
707 A406 3.50k multi   1.75 1.75

The Book on the Art of Trading, by Benedikt Kotruljevic, 550th Anniv. of Publication A407

Perf. 14¼x13¾ Syncopated
2008, Oct. 22   Litho.
708 A407 2.80k multi   1.50 1.50

New Year's Day — A408

Perf. 14 Syncopated
2008, Nov. 21   Litho.
709 A408 1.80k multi   .95 .95

Christmas A409

2008, Nov. 27   **Perf. 14 Syncopated**
710 A409 2.80k multi   1.50 1.50

Booklet Stamp
Self-Adhesive

711	A409	2.80k multi	1.00 1.00
a.		Booklet pane of 10	10.00
		Complete booklet, #711a	10.00

Modern Art Type of 2003

Designs: 1.65k, Two Trees at the Foot of a Hill, by Oskar Herman. 1.80k, Carousel, by Nevenka Djordjevic. 6.50k, Still Life, by Ivo Rezek.

Perf. 14 Syncopated
2008, Dec. 1   **Litho.**

712-714 A304 Set of 3   5.00 5.00

Zora Choral Society, 150th Anniv. — A410

Perf. 14x13¾ Syncopated
2008, Dec. 5

715 A410 1.65k multi   .90 .90

Ivan Mestrovic (1883-1962), Sculptor — A411

Perf. 14 Syncopated
2008, Dec. 15   **Litho.**

716 A411 5k multi   1.90 1.90

21st Men's World Handball Championships — A412

Perf. 13¾x14¼ Syncopated
2009, Jan. 16   **Litho. & Embossed**

717 A412 3.50k multi   1.25 1.25

Printed in sheets of 9 + label

Bruno Bjelinski (1909-92), Composer A413

Josip Andreis (1909-82), Musicologist A414

Perf. 14¼x13¾ Syncopated
2009, Jan. 21   **Litho.**

718	A413	1.80k multi	.80 .80
719	A414	3.50k multi	1.50 1.50

Street and Bridge, Sisak — A415

2009, Jan. 22   **Perf. 14 Syncopated**

720 A415 8k multi   3.50 3.50

Remains of St. Tryphon in Kotor, 1200th Anniv. — A416

No. 721 — St. Tryphon: a, Drawing. b, Sculpture from altarpiece, Kotor Cathedral.

2009, Feb. 3   **Perf. 14¼ Syncopated**

721 A416 3.50k Horiz. pair, #a-b   3.00 3.00

Fairy Tale Characters — A417

No. 722: a, Svarozic. b, Bjesomar.

2009, Feb. 27

722 A417 1.65k Horiz. pair, #a-b   1.50 1.50

Souvenir Sheet

Protection of Polar Regions and Glaciers — A418

No. 723: a, Sun over glacier. b, Intl. Polar Year emblem and glacier.

2009, Mar. 27   **Litho. & Embossed**

723 A418 5k Sheet of 2, #a-b   4.50 4.50

Easter A419

Perf. 14 Syncopated
2009, Mar. 30   **Litho.**

724 A419 3.50k multi   1.60 1.60

Entry Into NATO A420

2009, Apr. 4

725 A420 8k multi   3.50 3.50

Juraj Sizgoric (1445-c. 1509), Poet — A421

Juraj Habdelic (1609-78), Writer — A422

Ljudevit Gaj (1809-72), Writer, Illyrian Movement Leader — A423

Petar Segedin (1909-98), Writer — A424

Perf. 14¼x13¾ Syncopated
2009, Apr. 22

726	A421	3.50k multi	1.50	1.50
727	A422	3.50k multi	1.50	1.50
728	A423	5k multi	2.25	2.25
729	A424	5k multi	2.25	2.25
		Nos. 726-729 (4)	7.50	7.50

Europa — A425

No. 730 — Image of space from Hubble Space Telescope with red diamond at: a, Left. b, Right.

Perf. 14x13½ Syncopated
2009, May 9   **Litho.**

730 A425 8k Horiz. pair, #a-b   7.00 7.00

Intl. Year of Astronomy. Values are for stamps with surrounding selvage.

Franciscans in Cakovec, 350th Anniv. — A426

2009, May 20   **Perf. 14 Syncopated**

731 A426 3.50k multi   1.60 1.60

Souvenir Sheet

King Andrew's Charter Proclaiming Varazdin as Free Royal Borough, 800th Anniv. — A427

Perf. 14 Syncopated
2009, June 9   **Litho.**

732 A427 15k multi   6.50 6.50

Souvenir Sheet

St. John, Sculpture by Ivan Duknovic (c. 1440-1509) — A428

2009, June 23   **Perf. 14**

733 A428 10k multi   4.50 4.50

Zagreb Jazz Quartet, 50th Anniv. A429

2009, June 29

734 A429 10.70k multi   4.75 4.75

Fish — A430

Designs: 3.50k, Acipenser naccarii. No. 736, 5k, Knipowitschia mrakovcici. No. 737, 5k, Ballerus sapa.

2009, Sept. 1   Litho.   Perf. 14
735	A430	3.50k multi	1.60	1.60
a.		Booklet pane of 10	16.50	—
		Complete booklet, #735a	16.50	
736	A430	5k multi	2.25	2.25
a.		Booklet pane of 10	22.50	—
		Complete booklet, #736a	22.50	
737	A430	5k multi	2.25	2.25
a.		Booklet pane of 10	22.50	—
		Complete booklet, #737a	22.50	
		Nos. 735-737 (3)	6.10	6.10

Stamp Day — A431

2009, Sept. 9
738	A431	3.50k multi	1.60	1.60

Croatian Post Inc., 10th Anniv.

Lighthouses A432

Designs: No. 739, 3.50k, Gruica Lighthouse. No. 740, 3.50k, Strazica Lighthouse. 8k, Voscica Lighthouse.

2009, Sept. 11
739-741	A432	Set of 3	4.25	4.25

Franciscan Order, 800th Anniv. — A433

2009, Sept. 17   Litho.   Perf. 14
742	A433	3.50k multi	1.50	1.50

Souvenir Sheet

Stone Buildings — A434

No. 743 — Stone building in: a, Pazin, Croatia. b, Kopriva na Krasu, Slovenia.

2009, Sept. 25
743	A434	8k Sheet of 2, #a-b	7.00	7.00

See Slovenia No. 812.

St. Martin's Hermit Chapel, Podsused, 800th Anniv. A435

2009, Oct. 29
744	A435	3.50k multi	1.50	1.50

National Folk Dance Ensemble, 60th Anniv. A436

2009, Nov. 11
745	A436	3.50k multi	1.50	1.50

Rights of the Child A437

2009, Nov. 20
746	A437	3.50k multi	1.50	1.50

Declaration of the Rights of the Child, 50th anniv.; UN Convention on the Rights of the Child, 20th anniv.

New Year's Day — A438

2009, Nov. 24   Litho.   Perf. 14
747	A438	3.50k multi	1.50	1.50

Serpentine Die Cut 5¼
Booklet Stamp
Self-Adhesive
748	A438	3.50k multi	1.50	1.50
a.		Booklet pane of 10	15.00	
		Complete booklet, #748a	15.00	

Modern Art Type of 2003

Designs: No. 749, 1.80k, Gray Sail, by Zlatko Prica. No. 750, 1.80k, A Bosom Full of Wind, by Nives Kavuric Kurtovic, vert. No. 751, 1.80k, Flora, by Ordan Petlevski.

2009, Dec. 1   Litho.   Perf. 14
749-751	A304	Set of 3	2.50	2.50

A439

Christmas A440

2009, Dec. 4   Litho.   Perf. 14
752	A439	3.50k multi	1.60	1.60
753	A440	8k multi	3.50	3.50

Christmas Type of 2009
Serpentine Die Cut 5¼
2009, Dec. 4   Litho.
Booklet Stamp
Self-Adhesive
754	A439	3.50k multi	1.50	1.50
a.		Booklet pane of 10	15.00	
		Complete booklet, #754a	15.00	

Statute of Lastovo, 700th Anniv. — A441

2010, Jan. 8   Litho.   Perf. 14
755	A441	3.50k multi	1.40	1.40

2010 Winter Olympics, Vancouver A442

2010, Feb. 12   Perf. 14¼x14
756	A442	3.50k multi	1.40	1.40

Souvenir Sheet

Peonies — A443

No. 757: a, Paeonia mascula. b, Paeonia officinalis.

2010, Mar. 8   Litho.   Perf. 14
757	A443	3k Sheet of 2, #a-b	2.25	2.25

Embroidery A444

Embroidery from: 1.60k, Primorje. 3.10k, Medimurje. 4.60k, Posavina. 7.10k, Draganic.

2010, Mar. 15
758-761	A444	Set of 4	6.25	6.25
761a		Sheet of 4, #758-761	6.25	6.25

Fruit A445

Designs: 1k, Fragaria vesca. No. 763, Vitis vinifera. No. 764, Ribes uva-crispa.

2010, Mar. 16   Litho. & Embossed
762	A445	1k multi	.40	.40
a.		Booklet pane of 10	4.00	—
		Complete booklet, #762a	4.00	
763	A445	4k multi	1.50	1.50
a.		Booklet pane of 10	15.00	—
		Complete booklet, #763a	15.00	
764	A445	4k multi	1.50	1.50
a.		Booklet pane of 10	15.00	—
		Complete booklet, #764a	15.00	
		Nos. 762-764 (3)	3.40	3.40

Easter A446

2010, Mar. 19   Litho.   Perf. 14
765	A446	3.10k multi	1.25	1.25

Establishment of Bjelovar-Krizevci Diocese — A447

2010, Mar. 19
766	A447	6.50k multi	2.40	2.40

Printed in sheets of 8 + 2 labels.

Steam Locomotives — A448

No. 767: a, Series MAV 326/JZ 125. b, Series SüdB 18.

2010, Mar. 29
767		Vert. pair + central label	5.25	5.25
a.-b.	A448	7.10k Either single	2.60	2.60

Capuchin Order in Croatia, 400th Anniv. — A449

2010, Apr. 15
768	A449	6.10k multi	2.25	2.25

Famous Men — A450

Designs: 1.60k, Grgo Gamulin (1910-97), art historian. 3.10k, Janko Polic Kamov (1886-1910), writer. 4.50k, Ivan Matetic Ronjgov (1880-1960), composer. 6.10k, Marko Antun de Dominis (1560-1624), archbishop and physicist.

2010, Apr. 22
769-772 A450 Set of 4   5.75 5.75

Souvenir Sheet

Expo 2010, Shanghai — A451

2010, Apr. 29
773 A451 10k multi   3.75 3.75

Europa — A452

No. 774 — Children's book and: a, Fairy on branch, fairy with horn. b, Fairy looking at butterfly, fairy on flower.

Litho. With Foil Application
2010, May 7   **Perf. 14**
774 A452 7.10k Horiz. pair, #a-b   5.00 5.00

Souvenir Sheet

Lubenice — A453

2010, May 21   **Litho.**
775 A453 10k multi   3.50 3.50

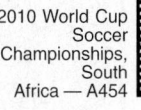

2010 World Cup Soccer Championships, South Africa — A454

2010, June 11
776 A454 4.50k multi   1.50 1.50
Printed in sheets of 9 + label.

Lighthouses A455

Designs: No. 781, 3.10k, Vir Lighthouse. No. 782, 3.10k, Veli Rat Lighthouse. No. 783, 3.10k, Tajer Lighthouse.

2010, Sept. 7   **Litho.**   **Perf. 14**
781-783 A455 Set of 3   3.25 3.25

Souvenir Sheet

Minerals — A456

No. 784: a, Calcite from Brac. b, Agate from Lepoglava.

Litho. & Embossed (#784a), Litho.
2010, Oct. 15
784 A456 3.10k Sheet of 2, #a-b   2.40 2.40

Souvenir Sheet

Dubrovnik Tramway, Cent. — A457

2010, Nov. 22   **Litho.**   **Perf. 14**
785 A457 15k multi   5.50 5.50

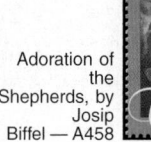

Adoration of the Shepherds, by Josip Biffel — A458

2010, Nov. 25
786 A458 3.10k multi   1.25 1.25
Christmas.

A459

A460

2010, Dec. 1   **Litho.**   **Perf. 14**
788 A459 3.10k multi   1.25 1.25
Croatian Journalist Society, cent.

2010, Dec. 6
789 A460 1.60k multi   .60 .60
New Year 2011.

___

SEMI-POSTAL STAMPS

> **Catalogue values for unused stamps in this section are for Never Hinged items.**

Types of Yugoslavia, 1941, Overprinted in Gold "NEZAVISNA / DRZAVA / HRVATSKA"
          Perf. 11½
1941, May 10   **Unwmk.**   **Engr.**
B1 SP80 1.50d + 1.50d bl blk   17.50 17.50
B2 SP81 4d + 3d choc   17.50 17.50
Panes of 16 stamps and 9 labels.
This overprint exists on Yugoslavia No. B124. Value $2,500.

In 1941, 5,000 sets of Yugoslavia Nos. 142-154 were overprinted "NEZAVISNA DRZAVA HRVATSKA 10. IV. 1941" and with a small shield in red or blue. Sold for double face value. Value: set, $550.

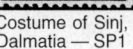

Costume of Sinj, Dalmatia — SP1

Soldiers with Arms of the Axis States — SP4

Designs (Costumes): 2k+2k, Travnik, Bosnia. 4k+4k, Turopolje, Croatia.

1941, Oct. 12   **Photo.**   **Perf. 10½x10**
B3 SP1 1.50k + 1.50k Prus
       bl & red   1.00 1.00
B4 SP1 2k + 2k ol brn &
       red   1.25 1.25
B5 SP1 4k + 4k brn lake
       & red   2.25 2.25
    Nos. B3-B5 (3)   4.50 4.50
The surtax aided the Croatian Red Cross. Panes of 20 stamps and 5 labels.

1941, Dec. 3   **Perf. 11**
B6 SP4 4k + 2k blue   3.25 4.00
The surtax was used for Croatian Volunteers in the East.
Issued in panes of 100 stamps.

Model Plane — SP5

Model Plane — SP6

Designs: 3k+3k, Boy with model plane. 4k+4k, Model seaplane in flight.

1942, Mar. 25
B7 SP5 2k + 2k sepia   1.90 1.90
B8 SP6 2.50k + 2.50k dl grn   1.90 1.90
B9 SP5 3k + 3k brn car   1.90 1.90
B10 SP6 4k + 4k dp bl   1.90 1.90
    Nos. B7-B10 (4)   7.60 7.60
Nos. B7-B10 were issued both in panes of 25 and in panes of 24 plus label.

> Values for used souvenir sheets are for those with special philatelic cancels. Faked postal cancellations on souvenir sheets are common, especially using cancellers stolen after WWII. Genuine postal cancellations are the exception and sell for much more. Expertization is recommended.

Souvenir Sheets
      Perf. 11
B11   Sheet of 2   55.00 52.50
  a.   SP5 2k+8k brown carmine   14.00 14.00
  b.   SP5 3k+12k deep blue   14.00 14.00
       Imperf
B12   Sheet of 2   55.00 52.50
  a.   SP5 2k+8k deep blue   14.00 14.00
  b.   SP5 3k+12k brown carmine   14.00 14.00
The sheets measure 125x110mm.
Aviation Exposition of Zagreb. The surtax aided society of Croatian Wings (Hrvatska Krila).
Nos. B11-B12 exist with colors of stamps and inscriptions transposed, with missing colors and with one stamp missing.

Boy Trumpeters SP10

Triumphal Arch — SP11

Mother and Child — SP12

1942, July 5   **Perf. 11½**
B13 SP10 3k + 1k lake   1.50 1.50
B14 SP11 4k + 2k dk brn   1.60 1.60
B15 SP12 5k + 5k dp bl grn   2.40 2.40
    Nos. B13-B15 (3)   5.50 5.50
The surtax was for national welfare.
Issued in panes of 25.

Matthew Gubec SP13

Ante Starcevich SP14

SP15

1942, Nov. 22   *Perf. 14½*
B16 SP13 3k + 6k dark red   .80 .80
B17 SP14 4k + 7k sepia   .80 .80

Souvenir Sheets
Perf. 12, Imperf.

B18 SP15 5k + 20k dull blue   27.50 27.50

Heroes of Senj, May 9, 1937. Nos. B16-B17 were printed in panes of 16 + 9 labels, each bearing a hero's name. The surtax aided the Natl. Youth Soc.

Sestine Peasant SP16

Croatian Labor Corpsman SP20

Designs: 3k+1k, Slavonian peasant. 4k+2k, Bosnian peasant. 10k+5k, Dalmatian peasant. 13k+6k, Sestine peasant.

1942, Oct. 4   *Perf. 11½*
B20 SP16 1.50k + 50b org brn
        & red   1.50 1.50
B21 SP16 3k + 1k dl pur &
        red   1.50 1.50
B22 SP16 4k + 2k dp bl &
        red   2.25 2.25
B23 SP16 10k + 5k dk ol bis
        & red   3.25 3.25
B24 SP16 13k + 6k rose lake
        & red   6.00 6.00
    Nos. B20-B24 (5)   14.50 14.50

The surtax aided the Croatian Red Cross. Issued in panes of 24 stamps plus label.

1943, Jan. 17 Wmk. 278 Perf. 11

Designs: 3k+3k, Corpsman with wheelbarrow. 7k+4k, Corpsman plowing.

B25 SP20 2k + 1k ol gray &
        sepia   4.75 *5.00*
B26 SP20 3k + 3k brn & sepia   4.75 *5.00*
B27 SP20 7k + 4k gray bl &
        sepia   4.75 *5.00*
    Nos. B25-B27 (3)   14.25 *15.00*

The surtax aided the State Labor Service (Drzavna Radna Sluzba). Issued in panes of 9.

Arms of Zagreb and "Golden Bull" — SP23

1943, Mar. 21   **Unwmk.**
B28 SP23 3.50k (+ 6.50k) ultra   4.50 *4.75*

700th anniversary of Zagreb's "Golden Bull," a Magna Carta of civic rights and privileges granted to the city in 1242 by King Bela because the Croats annihilated Tartar hordes at Grobnik.
Issued in panes of 8 with marginal inscriptions.

Ante Pavelich — SP24

Sailor at Sea of Azov — SP26

1943, Apr. 10   *Perf. 13¾14*
B29 SP24 5k + 3k copper red   .60 .60
   a. Sheetlet of 16 #B29 + 9 labels   12.00 12.00
B30 SP24 7k + 5k dark green   .60 .60
   a. Sheetlet of 16 #B30 + 9 labels   12.00 12.00

Surtax aided the National Youth Society. Nos. B29-B30 were issued in panes of 100 stamps. Nos. B29a and B30a were issued Apr. 12 and are perf 14½.

Souvenir Sheets
1943, May 17   *Perf. 12, Imperf.*
B31 SP24 12k + 8k dp ultra   32.50 32.50

1943, July 1   *Perf. 11*

Designs: 2k+1k, Flier at Sevastopol and Rzhev. 3.50k+1.50k, Infantrymen at Stalingrad. 9k+4.50k, Panzer Division at Don River.

B33 SP26   1k + 50b grn   .40 .25
B34 SP26   2k + 1k dk red   .40 .25
B35 SP26 3.50k + 1.50k dk bl   .40 .25
B36 SP26   9k + 4.50k chestnut   .40 .25
    Nos. B33-B36 (4)   1.60 1.00

Souvenir Sheets
Perf. 11, Imperf.

B37 Sheet of 4   7.50 7.50
   a. SP26 1k+50b dark blue   1.40 *1.40*
   b. SP26 2k+1k green   1.40 *1.40*
   c. SP26 3.50k+1.50k dk red brown 1.40 *1.40*
   d. SP26 9k+4.50k bluish black 1.40 *1.40*

Surtax aided the National Youth Society. Issued to honor the Croatian Legion which fought with the Germans in Russia. The surtax aided the Legion.
Issued in panes of 100.

St. Mary's Church and Cistercian Cloister, Zagreb, in 1650
SP31

1943, Sept. 12 Engr. Perf. 14½
B39 SP31 18k + 9k dl gray vio   5.50 *6.00*

Souvenir Sheet
Perf. 12½
B40 SP31 18k + 9k blk brn   16.00 16.00
Croatian Phil. Soc. Exhibition at Zagreb. No. B39 issued in pane of 40.

No. B39   **HRVATSKO MORE**
Overprinted in   **8. IX.**
Red   **1943.**

1943, Sept. 12
B41 SP31 18k + 9k dl gray vio   12.00 *14.00*

Return to Croatia of the Dalmatian and Croatian coasts.
The overprint exists inverted, double, and double, one inverted.

Mother and Children — SP33

Nurse and Patient — SP34

1943, Oct. 3 Litho. Perf. 11
Cross in Red
B42 SP33 1k + 50b bl grn   .75 .75
B43 SP33 2k + 1k bril car   .75 .75
B44 SP33 3.50k + 1.50k brt
        bl   .75 .75
B45 SP34 8k + 3k red brn   .90 .90
B46 SP34 9k + 4k yel grn   1.00 1.00
B47 SP33 10k + 5k dp vio   1.00 1.00
B48 SP34 12k + 6k brt ultra   1.25 1.25
B49 SP33 12.50k + 6k dk brn   1.75 1.75
B50 SP34 18k + 8k brn org   2.00 2.00
B51 SP34 32k + 12k dk
        gray   3.25 3.25
    Nos. B42-B51 (10)   13.40 13.40

The surtax aided the Croatian Red Cross. Issued in panes of 100.

Post Horn and Arms — SP35

Carrier Pigeon and Plane — SP36

Mercury — SP37

Winged Wheel — SP38

1944, Feb. 3
B52 SP35 7k + 3.50k ol bis &
        red   .90 .90
B53 SP36 16k + 8k bl & dk bl   .90 .90
B54 SP37 24k + 12k red & rose
        red   .90 .90
B55 SP38 32k + 16k gray & red   .90 .90
    Nos. B52-B55 (4)   3.60 3.60

The surtax benefited communications and railway employees. Panes of 9.

St. Sebastian — SP39

War Invalids SP40

Statue of Ancient Croatian King — SP41

Death of King Peter Svacic, 1097 — SP42

1944, Feb. 15
B56 SP39 7k + 3.50k org red &
        rose car   1.00 1.00
B57 SP40 16k + 8k yel grn & dk
        grn   1.00 1.00
B58 SP41 24k + 12k yel brn &
        red   1.00 1.00
B59 SP42 32k + 16k bl & dk bl   1.00 1.00
    Nos. B56-B59 (4)   4.00 4.00

The surtax aided wounded war victims. Issued in panes of eight stamps, with marginal inscriptions and a central label picturing St. Sebastian.

Black Legion in Combat — SP43

Guarding the Drina — SP44

Jure Francetic — SP45

1944, May 22 Photo. Imperf.
B60 SP43 3.50k + 1.50k brn
        red   .20 .20
B61 SP44 12.50k + 6.50k slate
        bl   .20 .20
B62 SP45 18k + 9k olive
        brn   .20 .20
    Nos. B60-B62 (3)   .60 .60

Third anniversary of Croatian independence. The surtax aided the National Youth Society. Panes of 20.

Perf. 14½
B63 SP45 12.50k + 287.50k int
        blk   12.00 *14.50*

Issued to commemorate Jure Francetic. Issued in pane of 30.

Labor Corpsmen Marching SP46

Corpsman Digging SP47

Designs: 18k+9k, Officer instructing corpsman. 32k+16k, Pavelich reviewing Labor Corps. Panes of 8 plus label.

1944, Aug. 20   Perf. 11½, 12½, 14½   Engr.

B65	SP46	3.50k + 1k dk red	.50	.50
B66	SP47	12.50k + 6k sepia	.50	.50
B67	SP47	18k + 9k dk bl	.50	.50
B68	SP47	32k + 16k gray grn	.50	.50
		Nos. B65-B68 (4)	2.00	2.00

Nos. B68 exists only perf 12½, while B65-B67 exist perf 11½, 12½ or 14½. Values are for copies perf 11½ or 12½. Values Nos. B65-B67 perf 14½, $5 each unused or used.

Souvenir Sheet
Perf. 12½

B69	SP47	32k + 16k dk brn, cr	4.50	5.00

The surtax aided the State Labor Service (Drzavna Radna Sluzba).

Palm Leaf — SP51

1944, Nov. 12   Litho.   Perf. 11

B70	SP51	2k + 1k dl grn & red	.45	.45
B71	SP51	3.50k + 1.50k car lake & red	.45	.45
B72	SP51	12.50k + 6k ind & red	.45	.45
		Nos. B70-B72 (3)	1.35	1.35

The surtax aided the Croatian Red Cross. Panes of 16.

Men of Storm Division — SP52

70k+70k, Soldiers of Storm Division in action. 100k+100k, Storm Division emblem.

1944   Unwmk.   Litho.   Perf. 11

B73	SP52	50k + 50k brick red	145.00	160.00
B74	SP52	70k + 70k sepia	145.00	160.00
B75	SP52	100k + 100k chlky, pale & dp bl	145.00	160.00
		Nos. B73-B75 (3)	435.00	480.00

Nos. B73-B75 issued in panes of 20.

Souvenir Sheet

B76		Sheet of 3	1,600.	1,600.
a.		SP52 50k + 50k brick red	450.00	450.00
b.		SP52 70k + 70k sepia	450.00	450.00
c.		SP52 100k + 100k chalky, pale & deep blue	450.00	450.00

Nos. B76a to B76c are inscribed "O. A." in brick red at right below design. The sheet measures 216x132mm. The surtax aided the First Croatian Storm Division. Counterfeits are plentiful.

Postman SP55   Telephone Line Repairman SP56

24k+12k, Switchboard operator. 50k+25k, 100k+50k, Postman delivering parcel.

1945   Photo.

B77	SP55	3.50k + 1.50k sl gray	.40	.40
B78	SP56	12.50k + 6k brn car	.40	.40
B79	SP56	24k + 12k dk grn	.40	.40
B80	SP56	50k + 25k brn vio	.40	.40
		Nos. B77-B80 (4)	1.60	1.60

Souvenir Sheet

B81	SP56	100k + 50k dp brn	11.00	11.00

The surtax on #B77-B81 aided employees of the P.T.T. Panes of 8.

Famous Croatians SP60

#B100, Ban Josip Jelacic (1801-59). #B101, Dr. Ante Starcevic (1823-96). 7d + 3d, Stjepan Radic (1871-1928).

1992   Litho.   Perf. 11x10½

B100	SP60	4d +2d multi	.65	.65
B101	SP60	4d +2d multi	.35	.35

Perf. 14

B102	SP60	7d +3d multi	.35	.35
		Nos. B100-B102 (3)	1.35	1.35

Issued: #B100, 2/1; #B101, 3/4; #B102, 4/2.

The surcharge on Nos. B100-B102 was initially an obligatory tax on all internal and overseas mail. From May 15, 1992, these stamps were valid for postage at their 6d or 10d face values.

AIR POST STAMPS

> Catalogue values for unused stamps in this section are for Never Hinged items.

Airplane, Zagreb Cathedral and Port of Dubrovnik AP1

Airplane Over Ruins of Diocletian's Palace, Split — AP2

Coat of Arms, Aiplane, Zagreb Cathedral and Pula Amphitheatre AP3

Paper Airplane Made From Picture of Osijek Cathedral AP4

1991-92   Litho.   Perf. 11x10½

C1	AP1	1d multicolored	.30	.20
a.		Perf. 14	.20	.20
C2	AP2	2d multicolored	.90	.25
a.		Perf. 14	.20	.20
C3	AP3	3d multicolored	.45	.20
C4	AP4	4d multicolored	.40	.20
		Nos. C1-C4 (4)	2.05	.85

Issued: #C1, 9/9/91; #C1a, 6/24/92; #C2, 10/9/91; #C2a, 1992; #C3, 11/20/91; #C4, 2/14/92.

POSTAGE DUE STAMPS

Yugoslavia Nos. J28-J32 Overprinted in Black

1941, Apr. 26   Unwmk.   Perf. 12½

J1	D4	50p violet	.40	.65
a.		Double overprint	150.00	
b.		50p rose violet	9.00	18.00
c.		As "b," double overprint		200.00
J2	D4	1d deep magenta	.40	.65
a.		Inverted overprint	200.00	
b.		Double overprint		300.00
J3	D4	2d deep blue	10.00	20.00
a.		Double overprint	300.00	
J4	D4	5d orange	1.25	2.00
a.		Double overprint	300.00	
J5	D4	10d chocolate	6.00	12.00
		Nos. J1-J5 (5)	18.05	35.30
		Set, never hinged	40.00	

Counterfeit overprints exist, particularly of Nos. J3 and J5.

D1

D2

1941, Sept. 12   Litho.   Perf. 11

J6	D1	50b carmine lake	.20	.50
J7	D1	1k carmine lake	.20	.50
J8	D1	2k carmine lake	.30	.70
J9	D1	5k carmine lake	.50	1.00
J10	D1	10k carmine lake	.75	1.40
		Nos. J6-J10 (5)	1.95	4.10
		Set, never hinged	4.00	

1943   Perf. 11½, 12x12½, 12½
Size: 24x24mm

J11	D2	50b lt blue & gray	.20	.25
J12	D2	1k lt blue & gray	.20	.25
J13	D2	2k lt blue & gray	.20	.25
J14	D2	4k lt blue & gray	.20	.35
J15	D2	5k lt blue & gray	.20	.40
J16	D2	6k lt blue & gray	.20	.45
J17	D2	10k blue & indigo	.20	.40
J18	D2	15k blue & indigo	.20	1.10
J19	D2	20k blue & indigo	.65	1.60
		Nos. J11-J19 (9)	2.25	5.05
		Set, never hinged	4.50	

1942, July 30   Perf. 10½, 11½
Size: 25x24¼mm

J20	D2	50b lt blue & gray	.20	.40
J21	D2	1k lt blue & gray	.25	.50
J22	D2	2k lt blue & gray	.25	.50
J23	D2	5k lt blue & gray	.25	.50
J24	D2	10k lt blue & blue	.65	1.10
J25	D2	20k lt blue & blue	.90	1.60
		Nos. J20-J25 (6)	2.50	4.60
		Set, never hinged	6.00	

Nos. J21-J25 exist both perf 10½ and 11½. No. J20 exists only perf 11½.

OFFICIAL STAMPS

Croatian Coat of Arms
O1   O2

1942-43   Unwmk.   Litho.
Ordinary Paper
Perf. 11½

O1	O1	25b rose lake	.20	.20
O2	O1	50b slate blk	.20	.20
O3	O1	75b gray grn	.20	.20
O4	O1	1k orange brn	.20	.20
O5	O1	2k turq blue	1.10	1.10
O6	O1	3k vermilion	.20	.20
O7	O1	4k brown vio	.20	.20
O8	O1	5k ultra, thin paper	.25	.40
O9	O1	6k brt violet	.20	.20
O10	O1	10k lt green	.20	.30
O11	O1	12k brown rose	.20	.35
O12	O1	20k dark blue	.25	.40
O13	O2	30k brn vio & gray	.25	.40
O14	O2	40k vio blk & gray	.30	.50
O15	O2	50k brn lake & gray	.65	1.00
O16	O2	100k black & pink	.65	1.00
		Nos. O1-O16 (16)	5.25	6.85
		Set, never hinged	8.00	

Perf. 10½

O1a	O1	25b rose lake	.20	.20
O2a	O1	50b slate blk	.20	.20
O3a	O1	75b gray grn	.20	.20
O4a	O1	1k orange brn	.20	.20
O5a	O1	2k turq blue	1.10	2.00
O6a	O1	3k vermilion	.20	.20
O7a	O1	4k brown vio	.20	.20
O8a	O1	5k ultra	.95	1.75
O9a	O1	6k brt violet	1.40	2.50
O10a	O1	10k lt green	.20	.20
O11a	O1	12k brown rose	1.25	2.25
O12a	O1	20k dark blue	1.25	2.25
O13a	O2	30k brn vio & gray	.25	.40
O14a	O2	40k vio blk & gray	.30	.50
O15a	O2	50k brn lake & gray	.65	1.00
O16a	O2	100k black & pink	.65	1.00
		Nos. O1a-O16a (16)	9.20	15.05
		Set, never hinged	15.00	

1943-44   Thin Paper   Perf. 11½

O17	O1	25b claret	.20	.20
O18	O1	50b gray	.20	.20
O19	O1	75b dull green	.20	.20
O20	O1	1k orange brn	.20	.20
O21	O1	2k slate blue	.20	.20
O22	O1	3.50k car rose	.20	.20
a.		Ordinary paper	3.00	3.00
O23	O1	6k brt red vio	.20	.20
O24	O1	12.50k deep orange	.20	.20
a.		Ordinary paper	2.00	2.00
		Set, never hinged	1.50	

POSTAL TAX STAMPS

> Catalogue values for unused stamps in this section are for Never Hinged items.

Nurse and Soldier — PT1   Wounded Soldier — PT2

1942, Oct. 4   Unwmk.   Litho.   Perf. 11

RA1	PT1	1k olive grn & red	.85	.80

The tax aided the Croatian Red Cross. Issued in sheets of 24 plus label.

No. RA1 can be found with a red cross printed on the nurse's hat. The original design included this element, but it was removed from the final approved design. Early printings of No. RA1, probably trial printings, included the red cross.

1943, Oct. 3

RA2	PT2	2k blue & red	.70	.70

The tax aided the Croatian Red Cross.

Ruins — PT3

Wounded Soldier — PT4

1944, Jan. 1   Photo.   Perf. 12
RA3 PT3 1k dk slate green   .25   .25
RA4 PT4 2k carmine lake   .30   .30
RA5 PT4 5k black   .35   .35
RA6 PT4 10k deep blue   .55   .40
RA7 PT4 20k brown   1.10   .90
Nos. RA3-RA7 (5)   2.55   2.20

Interior of Zagreb Cathedral PT10

1991, Apr. 1   Litho.   Perf. 14
RA20 PT10 1.20d black & gold   .65   .55
a.   Perf. 11x10½   .85   .80
b.   Perf. 11   15.00   12.00
c.   Imperf   .90   .90
Worker's Fund. Required on mail during April 1991.
For surcharges see Nos. 100, 100a.

Shrine of the Virgin, 700th Anniv. PT11

1991, May 16   Perf. 10½x11
RA21 PT11 1.70d multicolored   .65 .55
a.   Imperf   .80 .70
Workers' Fund. Required on mail May 16-31.

Croatian Arms Type of 1992

1991, July 1   Perf. 11x10½
RA22 A37 2.20d multicolored   .70 .60
a.   Imperf   .95 .75
Required on mail during July.

Members of Parliament PT12

1991, Aug. 1   Perf. 11x10½
RA23 PT12 2.20d multicolored   .70 .60
a.   Imperf   .95 .80
Worker's Fund. Required on mail during Aug.

Red Cross and Tuberculosis PT13

1991, Sept 14   Perf. 11
RA24 PT13 2.20d blue & red   .50 .45
Required on mail Sept. 14-21.

Re-erection of Ban Josip Jelacic Equestrian Statue, Zagreb PT14

1991, Nov. 1   Perf. 11x10½
RA25 PT14 2.20d multicolored   .50 .45
a.   Imperf.   .65 .50
Worker's Fund. Required on mail during Nov.

New Constitution PT15

1991, Dec. 2   Litho.   Perf. 10¾x10½
Language of Inscription
RA26 PT15 2.20d English   2.25   2.00
RA27 PT15 2.20d Croatian   .80   .70
RA28 PT15 2.20d French   2.25   2.00
RA29 PT15 2.20d German   2.25   2.00
RA30 PT15 2.20d Russian   2.25   2.00
RA31 PT15 2.20d Spanish   2.25   2.00
a.   Vert. strip, #RA26-RA31   14.00   14.00
Nos. RA26-RA31 (6)   12.05   10.70
Nos RA26-RA31 were printed in sheet containing 15 of No. RA27, 2 each of the other stamps and five labels. Obligatory on mail Dec. 2-31.
Sheet exists imperf. Value $225.

"VUKOVAR" with Barbed Wire — PT16

1992, Jan. 1   Litho.   Perf. 11x10½
RA32 PT16 2.20d black & brown   .70 .55
a.   Imperf.   1.00 .90
Vukovar Refugee's Fund. Required on mail during Jan.

Red Cross PT17

Red Cross and Solidarity PT18

1992   Perf. 11
RA33 PT17 3d red & black   .25 .20
RA34 PT18 3d red & black   .25 .20
Issued: No. RA33, May 8. No. RA34, June 1. No. RA33 was required on mail May 8-15; No. RA34, June 1-7.

Madonna of Bistrica — PT19

Red Cross — PT20

1992, Aug. 1   Litho.   Perf. 14
RA35 PT19 5d blue & gold   .45 .40
Required on mail, Aug. 1-8.

1992, Sept. 21   Litho.   Perf. 11
RA36 PT20 5d black & red   .40 .25
Required on mail Sept. 14-21.

St. George Slaying Dragon PT21

1992, Nov. 4   Perf. 14
RA37 PT21 15d multicolored   .30 .25
Cancer Research League. Required on mail Nov. 4-11.
See No. RA43.

Red Cross — PT22

1993, May 8   Litho.   Rough Perf. 11
RA38 PT22 80d black & red   .40 .25
Required on mail May 8-15.

Red Cross and Solidarity PT23

1993, June 1
RA39 PT23 100d black & red   .40 .25
Required on mail June 1-7.

Cardinal Stepinac (1898-1960) PT24

1993, July 15   Litho.   Perf. 14
RA40 PT24 150d multicolored   .40 .25
Required on mail July 15-22.

Zrinski-Frankopan Foundation — PT25

Design: 200d, Gen. Peter Zrinski (1621-1671), Politician and Fran Krsto Frankopan, Count of Tersat (1643-1671), Poet.

1993, Aug. 12   Litho.   Perf. 14
RA41 PT25 200d gray & blue   .40 .25
Required on mail Aug. 12-19.

Red Cross Campaign Against Tuberculosis PT26

1993, Sept. 14   Litho.   Perf. 11
RA42 PT26 300d gray, red & black   .45 .40
Required on mail Sept. 14-21.

St. George Slaying Dragon Type of 1992

1993, Oct. 11   Litho.   Perf. 14
RA43 PT21 400d multicolored   .45 .40
Cancer Research League. Required on mail Oct. 11-31.

Save the Children of Croatia PT27

1993, Nov. 1   Perf. 13½x14
RA44 PT27 400d multicolored   .45 .40
Required on mail Nov. 1-30.

Croatian Red Cross — PT28

1994, May 5   Litho.   Perf. 11
RA45 PT28 500d multicolored   .40 .25
Required on mail May 5-15.

Red Cross Solidarity PT29

Ludberg Church PT30

1994, May 5   Litho.   Perf. 11
RA46 PT29 50 l multicolored   .45 .40
Required on mail June 1-7.

1994, July 15   Perf. 14
RA47 PT30 50 l multicolored   .40 .25
Required on mail July 15-22.

Save the Children of Croatia — PT31

St. George
Slaying
Dragon — PT32

1994, Aug. 16   Litho.   Perf. 14
RA48   PT31 50 l multicolored   .40   .25
   Required on mail Aug. 16-29.

1994, Sept. 1
RA49   PT32 50 l multicolored   .40   .25
   Cancer Research League. Required on mail
Sept. 1-8.

PT33   PT34

1994, Sept. 14   Perf. 11
RA50   PT33 50 l blk, grn & red   .65   .40
   Red Cross Campaign against Tuberculosis.
Required on mail Sept. 14-21.

1994, Oct. 15   Litho.   Perf. 14
RA51   PT34 l multicolored   .35   .25
   Town of Slavonski Brod, 750th anniv.

Homage to
Olympia, by
Ivan Lackovic
PT35

Intl. Olympic
Committee,
Cent. — PT36

   Designs: a, Tennis. b, Soccer. c, Basketball.
d, Team handball. e, Canoeing, kayaking. f,
Water polo. g, Track and field. h, Gymnastics.

1994, Nov. 2   Litho.   Perf. 14
RA52   PT35 50 l Pair, #a.-b.   1.40   1.25
   Miniature Sheets of 8
RA53   PT36 50 l #a.-h.   6.25   6.25
RA54   PT36 50 l #a.-h.   6.25   6.25
   Nos. RA52b, RA53a, RA53d-RA53e,
RA53h, RA54b-RA54c, RA54f-RA54g have
IOC centennial emblem. Others have emblem
of Croatian Olympic Committee.
   Required on mail Nov. 2-15.

Natl. Olympic
Committee
PT37

   Designs: a, Rowing. b, Pétanque. c, Monument to Drazen Petrovic, Olympic Park, Lausanne. d, Tennis. e, Basketball.

1995, Apr. 17   Litho.   Perf. 14
RA55   PT37 50 l Strip of 5, #a.-
         e.   2.25   2.25
   Required on mail Apr. 17-30.

Red Cross Stamps
PT38   PT39

1995, May 8   Perf. 11
RA56   PT38 50 l multicolored   .45   .25
   Required on mail May 8-15.

1995, June 1
RA57   PT39 50 l multicolored   .45   .25
   Required on mail June 1-7.

Sts. Peter and
Paul Cathedral,
Osijek — PT40

1995, July 17   Perf. 14
RA58   PT40 65 l multicolored   .45   .40
   Required on mail July 17-30.

Holy Mother of
Freedom
PT41

   Design: No. RA59, Like No. RA60, but with
black surcharge on white panel. #RA60, Croatian Pieta, by Ivan Lackovic. #RA61, Gedenk-
statte Church Project.

1995, Aug. 14   Litho.   Perf. 14
RA59   PT41 65 l on 50 l multi   1.75   1.75
RA60   PT41 65 l multicolored   .40   .35
RA61   PT41 65 l multicolored   .40   .35
   Nos. RA59-RA61 (3)   2.55   2.45
   No. RA59 not issued without surcharge.
Examples without surcharge are printer's
waste. Required on mail Aug. 14-27.

Red Cross and   Save the Croatian
Tuberculosis   Children
PT42   PT43

1995, Sept. 14   Litho.   Perf. 11
RA62   PT62 65 l multicolored   .45   .40
   Required on mail Sept. 14-21.

1995, Oct. 16   Perf. 14
RA63   PT43 65 l multicolored   .45   .40
   Required on mail Oct. 16-29.

PT44

PT45

   Performance scene: a, Woman seated at
top of steps. b, Gathering of people. c, People,
large statue in background.

1995, Oct. 16
RA64   PT44 65 l Strip of 3, #a.-
         c.   1.40   1.40
   Croatian Natl. Theater, Zagreb, cent. No.
RA64 has continuous design. Required on
mail 10/16-29.

1995, Nov. 6   Litho.   Perf. 14
RA65   PT45 65 l multicolored   .45   .35
   Fight against drugs. Required on mail Nov.
20-30.

PT46

1995, Nov. 20   Litho.   Perf. 14x13¾
RA66   PT46 65 l multicolored   .45   .35
   Croatian Anti-Cancer League. Required on
mail Nov. 20-30.

PT47   PT48

1996, Feb. 15   Litho.   Perf. 14x13½
RA67   PT47 65 l multicolored   .45   .35
   Croatian Anti-Cancer League. Required on
mail Feb. 15-28.

1996, Mar. 18   Litho.   Perf. 14
RA68   PT48 65 l multicolored   .50   .35
   Sanctuary of the Virgin Mary of Bistrica.
Required on mail Mar. 18-31.

Croatian
Olympic
Committee
PT49

1996, Apr. 17   Litho.   Perf. 14
RA69   PT49 65 l multi   .60   .35
   No. RA69 exists imperf. and in booklets,
which were not placed on sale. Required on
mail Apr. 17-30.

PT50   PT51

1996, May 8   Litho.   Perf. 11
RA70   PT50 65 l multicolored   .45   .35
   Red Cross. Required on mail May 8-15.

1996, June 6   Litho.   Perf. 11
RA71   PT51 65 l multicolored   .45   .35
   Red Cross Solidarity Week. Required on
mail June 1-7.

PT52

1996, June 14   Litho.   Perf. 14x13½
RA72   PT52 65 l multicolored   .45   .35
   For Croatian children. Required on mail
6/14-27.

PT53

1996, July 3   Litho.   Perf. 14
RA73   PT53 65 l multicolored   .45   .35
   Osijek, 800th anniv. Required on mail July
3-16.

PT54

PT55

1996, July 17   Litho.   Perf. 14
RA74   PT54 65 l multicolored   .45   .35
   Renovation of Dakovo Cathedral. Required
on mail July 17-30.

1996, Aug. 1   Litho.   Perf. 14
RA75   PT55 65 l multicolored   .45   .35
   Split, 1700th anniv. Required on mail Aug.
1-14.

PT56   PT57

1996, Aug. 16   Litho.   *Perf. 14x13½*
RA76 PT56 65 l multicolored   .45   .35
Aid to Vukovar. Required on mail 8/16-29.

1996, Sept. 1   Litho.   *Perf. 14*
RA77 PT57 65 l multicolored   .55   .35
Fight against drugs. Required on mail Sept. 1-12.

PT58

1996, Sept. 14   Litho.   *Perf. 11*
RA78 PT58 65 l multicolored   .45   .35
Red Cross Tuberculosis Week. Required on mail Sept. 14-21.

PT59

1996, Oct. 10   Litho.   *Perf. 14*
RA79 PT59 65 l multicolored   .55   .35
Isolation of insulin, 75th anniv. Required on mail Oct. 10-17.

PT60   PT61

1996, Nov. 11   Litho.   *Perf. 14*
RA80 PT60 65 l multicolored   .50   .35
Remete pilgrimage. Required on mail Nov. 11-24.

1997, Jan. 6   Litho.   *Perf. 14*
RA81 PT61 65 l multicolored   .45   .35
Antun Mihanovic (1796-1861), natl. anthem lyricist. Required on mail Jan. 6-26.

House of Dr. Ante Starcevic
PT62

1997, Jan. 27   Litho.   *Perf. 14*
RA82 PT62 65 l multicolored   .45   .35
Required on mail Jan. 27-Feb. 14.

PT63   PT64

1997, Feb. 15   Litho.   *Perf. 14*
RA83 PT63 65 l multicolored   .45   .35
Croatian Anti-Cancer League. Required on mail Feb. 15-28.

1997, May 8   Litho.   *Perf. 10½x11*
RA84 PT64 65 l multicolored   .80   .50
   a.   Perf 10 ½   .80   .50
   b.   Perf 11   35.00
Red Cross. Required on mail May 8-15.

Numerous charity stamps were issued between 1997 and 2001, but their use on mail was not obligatory.

Red Cross Solidarity Week — PT65

2001, Dec. 8   Litho.   *Perf. 14*
RA85 PT65 1.15k red & black   .60   .50
Obligatory on mail Dec. 8-15.

Red Cross Week — PT66

2002, May 8
RA86 PT66 1.15k multi   .70   .60
Obligatory on mail May 8-15.

Red Cross Anti-Tuberculosis Week — PT67

2002, Sept. 14
RA87 PT67 1.15k multi   .60   .50
Obligatory on mail Sept. 14-21.

Red Cross Solidarity Week — PT68

2002, Dec. 8
RA88 PT68 1.15k multi   .60   .50
Obligatory on mail Dec. 8-15.

Red Cross Week — PT69

2003, May 8
RA89 PT69 1.15k multi   .75   .60
Obligatory on mail May 8-15.

Red Cross Anti-Tuberculosis Week — PT70

2003, Sept. 14
RA90 PT70 1.15k multi   .75   .60
Obligatory on mail Sept. 14-21.

Red Cross Solidarity Week — PT71

2003, Dec. 8
RA91 PT71 1.15k multi   .75   .60
Obligatory on mail Dec. 8-15.

Red Cross Week — PT72

2004, May 8
RA92 PT72 1.15k multi   1.00   .75
Obligatory on mail May 8-15.

Red Cross Anti-Tuberculosis Week — PT73

2004, Sept. 14
RA93 PT73 1.15k multi   1.00   .75
Obligatory on mail Sept. 14-21.

Red Cross Solidarity Week — PT74

2004, Dec. 8
RA94 PT74 1.15k multi   1.00   .75
Obligatory on mail Dec. 8-15.

Red Cross Week — PT75

2005, May 8   Litho.   *Perf. 14*
RA95 PT75 1.15k multi   .75   .75
Obligatory on mail May 8-15.

Red Cross Anti-Tuberculosis Week — PT76

2005, Sept. 14
RA96 PT76 1.15k multi   .75   .75
Obligatory on mail Sept. 14-21.

Red Cross Solidarity Week — PT77

2005, Dec. 8
RA97 PT77 1.15k multi   .75   .75
Obligatory on mail Dec. 8-15.

Red Cross Week — PT78

2006, May 8   Litho.   *Perf. 14*
RA98 PT78 1.15k multi   .75   .75
Obligatory on mail May 8-15.

Red Cross Anti-Tuberculosis Week — PT79

2006, Sept. 14
RA99 PT79 1.15k multi   .75   .75
Obligatory on mail Sept. 14-21.

Red Cross Solidarity Week — PT80

2006, Dec. 8
RA100 PT80 1.15k multi   .75   .75
Obligatory on mail Dec. 8-15.

Red Cross Anti-
Tuberculosis
Week — PT85

2008, Sept. 14   Litho.   Perf. 14¼
RA105 PT85 1.15k multi   .45   .45
Obligatory on mail Sept. 14-21.

Scott Album Accessories

SPECIALTY/NATIONAL SERIES BINDERS
National series pages are punched for 3-ring and 2-post binders. The 3-ring binder is available in two sizes. The 2-post binder comes in one size. All Scott binders are covered with a tough green leatherette material that is washable and reinforced at stress points for long wear.

3-RING BINDERS & SLIPCASES
With the three ring binder, pages lay flat and the rings make turning the pages easy. The locking mechanism insure that the rings won't pop open even when the binder is full.

Item			Retail	AA*
ACBR01	Small 3-Ring Binder	Holds up to 100 pages	$39.99	**$32.99**
ACBR03	Large 3-Ring Binder	Holds up to 250 pages	$39.99	**$32.99**
ACSR01	Small 3-Ring Slipcase		$32.50	**$26.99**
ACSR03	Large 3-Ring Slipcase		$37.50	**$26.99**
ACC102	3-Ring Black Protector Sheets		$4.99	**$3.99**
ACC107	Glassine Interleaving		$11.99	**$10.25**

LARGE 2-POST BINDER & SLIPCASE
For the traditional Scott collector, we offer the standard hinge post binder. Scott album pages are punched with rectangular holes that fit on rectangular posts. The posts and pages are held by a rod that slides down from the top. With the post binder pages do not lie flat. However, filler strips are available for a minimal cost.

Item			Retail	AA*
ACBS03	Large 2-Post Binder	Holds up to 250 pages	$54.99	**$46.99**
ACSS03	Large 2-Post Slipcase		$37.50	**$26.99**
ACC101	2-Post Green Protector Sheets		$4.99	**$3.99**
ACC107	Glassine Interleaving		$11.99	**$10.25**

SCOTT UNIVERSAL BINDER
The Scott Universal Binder is designed to hold any Scott album page. Two round posts can be mounted to accomodate pages punched to fit 3-ring or 2-post binders. Pages will not lie flat when housed in the Universal Binder. Matches Scott 2-post and 3-ring binders in looks. The Universal Binder will hold approximately 150 pages.

Item			Retail	AA*
ACBU	Universal Binder	Holds up to 150 pages	$39.99	**$32.99**
ACSS03	Universal Slipcase		$37.50	**$26.99**

BLANK PAGES
High quality paper developed exclusively for each specific album series. Ideal for developing your own album pages to be integrated with your album.

SPECIALTY/NATIONAL SERIES PAGES (20 PGS PER PACK)

Item		Retail	AA
ACC110	Specialty Blank Pages	$8.99	**$6.99**
ACC111	Specialty Quadrille*	$13.99	**$11.99**
ACC120	National Blank Pages	$8.99	**$6.99**
ACC121	National Quadrille*	$13.99	**$11.99**

ORDER ONLINE
Get the AMOS ADVANTAGE Discount

ORDERING INFORMATION
*AA prices apply to paid subscribers of Amos Hobby titles, or for orders placed online.
Prices, terms and product availability subject to change.
Shipping & Handling:
United States: 10% of order total.
Minimum charge $6.99 Maximum charge $45.00.
Canada: 15% of order total.
Minimum charge $19.99 Maximum charge $50.00.
Foreign orders are shipped via FedEx Economy Intl. and billed actual freight.

Order from **SCOTT**

Call **1-800-572-6885**

Visit **www.amosadvantage.com**

CUBA

'kyü-bə

LOCATION — The largest island of the West Indies; south of Florida
GOVT. — Former Spanish possession
AREA — 44,206 sq. mi.
POP. — 11,096,395 (1999 est.)
CAPITAL — Havana

Formerly a Spanish possession, Cuba made several unsuccessful attempts to gain her freedom, which finally led to the intervention of the US in 1898. In that year under the Treaty of Paris, Spain relinquished the island to the US in trust for its inhabitants.

In 1902 a republic was established and the Cuban Congress took over the government from the military authorities.

8 Reales Plata = 1 Peso
100 Centesimos = 1 Escudo or Peseta (1867)
1000 Milesimas =
100 Centavos = 1 Peso

Catalogue values for unused stamps in this country are for Never Hinged items, beginning with Scott 402 in the regular postage section, Scott B3 in the semipostal section, Scott C38 in the airpost section, Scott CB1 in the airpost semi-postal section, Scott E13 in the special delivery section, and Scott RA1 in the postal tax section.

Pen cancellations are common on the earlier stamps of Cuba. Stamps so canceled sell for very much less than those with postmark cancellations.

Watermarks

Wmk. 104 — Loops

Loops from different rows may or may not be directly opposite each other.

Wmk. 105 — Crossed Lines

Wmk. 106 — Star

Wmk. 229 — Wavy Lines

Wmk. 320

Wmk. 321 — "R de C"

Wmk. 376 — "R de C"

Issued under Spanish Dominion

Used also in Puerto Rico: Nos. 1-3, 9-14, 17-21, 32-34, 35A-37, 39-41, 43-45, 47-49, 51-53, 55-57.
Used also in the Philippines: Nos. 2-3.
Identifiable cancellations of those countries will increase the value of the stamps.

Queen Isabella II — A1

Blue Paper

1855	**Typo.**	**Wmk. 104**	**Imperf.**
1	A1	½r p blue green	75.00	6.00
a.		½r p blackish green	87.50	11.00
2	A1	1r p gray green	65.00	4.00
3	A1	2r p carmine	500.00	12.00
4	A1	2r p orange red	1,000.	19.00
a.		2r p vermilion	1,100.	20.00
		Nos. 1-4 (4)	1,640.	41.00

See Nos. 9-14. For surcharges see Nos. 5-8, 15.

Counterfeit surcharges are plentiful.

Nos. 3-4 Surcharged

1855-56			
5	A1	¼r p on 2r p car	775.00	210.00
a.		Without fraction bar	1,700.	625.00
6	A1	¼r p on 2r p org red	600.00	160.00
a.		Without fraction bar	—	—

Surcharged

 Y ¼

7	A1	¼r p on 2r p car	675.00	200.00
a.		Without fraction bar	2,000.	1,000
8	A1	¼r p on 2r p org red	1,050.	425.00
a.		Without fraction bar		1,200.

The "Y ¼" surcharge met the "Ynterior" rate for delivery within the city of Havana.

Rough Yellowish Paper

1856			**Wmk. 105**
9	A1	½r p yellow grn	6.75	.85
10	A1	1r p green	800.00	18.00
a.		1r p emerald	1,150.	21.00
11	A1	2r p orange red	400.00	16.00

White Smooth Paper

1857			**Unwmk.**
12	A1	½r p blue	3.50	.80
13	A1	1r p gray green	3.25	.80
a.		1r p pale yellow green	3.00	3.25
14	A1	2r p dull rose	18.50	3.25
		Nos. 12-14 (3)	25.25	4.85

Surcharged

 Y ¼

1860			
15	A1	¼r p on 2r p dl rose	240.00	85.00
a.		1 of ¼ inverted	350.00	150.00
b.		"1⅕" instead of "1 ¼"		—

Queen Isabella II
A2	A3

1862-64			**Imperf.**
16	A2	¼r p black	16.00	19.00
17	A3	¼r p blk, buff ('64)	18.00	17.00
18	A3	½r p green ('64)	4.75	.80
19	A3	½r p grn, pale rose ('64)	11.00	2.00
20	A3	1r p bl, sal ('64)	4.75	1.00
a.		Diagonal half used as ½r p on cover		125.00
21	A3	2r p ver, buff ('64)	25.00	6.00
a.		2r p red, buff	30.00	6.75
		Nos. 16-21 (6)	79.50	45.80

No. 17 Overprinted in Black

 66

1866			
22	A3	¼r p black, buff	80.00	85.00

Exists with handstamped "1866."

A5	A6

1866			
23	A5	5c dull violet	47.50	29.00
24	A5	10c blue	4.50	1.00
25	A5	20c green	2.25	1.00
a.		Diag. half used as 10c on cover		150.00
26	A5	40c rose	13.00	8.00
		Nos. 23-26 (4)	67.25	39.00

For the Type A5 20c in dull lilac, see Spain No. 87.

Stamps Dated "1867"

1867			**Perf. 14**
27	A5	5c dull violet	55.00	21.00
28	A5	10c blue	29.00	1.40
a.		Imperf., pair	110.00	6.50
b.		Diagonal half used as 5c on cover		140.00
29	A5	20c green	18.00	1.90
a.		Imperf., pair	110.00	4.00
b.		Diag. half used as 10c on cover		150.00
30	A5	40c rose	18.00	10.00
		Nos. 27-30 (4)	120.00	34.30

Stamps Dated "1868"

1868			
31	A6	5c dull violet	18.50	9.50
32	A6	10c blue	4.25	1.75
a.		Diagonal half used as 5c on cover		200.00
33	A6	20c green	6.00	3.00
a.		Diag. half used as 10c on cover		200.00
34	A6	40c rose	15.50	8.00
a.		Diag. half used as 20c on cover		200.00
		Nos. 31-34 (4)	44.25	22.25

Nos. 31-34 Overprinted in Black

1868			
35	A6	5c dull violet	75.00	32.50
35A	A6	10c blue	75.00	32.50
b.		Diag. half used as 5c on cover		275.00
36	A6	20c green	75.00	32.50
37	A6	40c rose	75.00	32.50
		Nos. 35-37 (4)	300.00	130.00

1869			**Stamps Dated "1869"**
38	A6	5c rose	40.00	14.50
39	A6	10c red brown	4.25	1.75
a.		Diagonal half used as 5c on cover		140.00
40	A6	20c orange	7.25	2.25
41	A6	40c dull violet	32.50	9.50
		Nos. 38-41 (4)	84.00	28.00

Nos. 38-41 Ovptd. Like Nos. 35-37

42	A6	5c rose	165.00	42.50
43	A6	10c red brown	52.50	32.50
a.		Diagonal half used as 5c on cover		—
44	A6	20c orange	45.00	32.50
a.		Diag. half used as 10c on cover		—
45	A6	40c dull violet	72.50	32.50
		Nos. 42-45 (4)	335.00	140.00

"Espana"
A8	A9

1870			**Perf. 14**
46	A8	5c blue	210.00	60.00
47	A8	10c green	2.75	.85
a.		Diagonal half used as 5c on cover		200.00
48	A8	20c red brown	2.75	.85
a.		Diag. half used as 10c on cover		240.00
49	A8	40c rose	250.00	35.00

1871			
50	A9	12c red lilac	23.00	10.00
a.		Imperf., pair	85.00	85.00
51	A9	25c ultra	2.75	.85
a.		Imperf., pair	40.00	40.00
b.		Diagonal half used as 12c on cover		200.00
52	A9	50c gray green	2.75	.85
a.		Imperf., pair	47.50	32.50
b.		Diagonal half used as 25c on cover		200.00
53	A9	1p yel brown	32.50	9.00
a.		Imperf., pair	100.00	100.00
		Nos. 50-53 (4)	61.00	20.70

King Amadeo — A10

1873			**Perf. 14**
54	A10	12½c dark green	25.00	14.00
55	A10	25c gray	2.25	.85
a.		Diagonal half used as 12½c on cover		95.00
b.		25c lilac	6.00	1.10

c.	As "b," half used as 12½c on cover			110.00
56	A10	50c brown	1.60	.80
a.	Imperf., pair		55.00	—
b.	Half used as 25c on cover			90.00
57	A10	1p red brown	325.00	52.50
a.	Diagonal half used as 50c on cover			275.00

"España"
A11

Coat of Arms
A12

1874

58	A11	12½c brown	18.00	8.25
a.	Half used as 5c on cover			140.00
59	A11	25c ultra	.90	.55
a.	Diagonal half used as 12½c on cover			100.00
60	A11	50c dp violet	1.60	.80
a.	Diagonal half used as 25c on cover			110.00
61	A11	50c gray	1.60	.80
a.	Diagonal half used as 25c on cover			110.00
62	A11	1p carmine	225.00	60.00
a.	Imperf., pair		600.00	210.00
	Nos. 58-62 (5)		247.10	70.40

Examples of Nos. 61, 63-65, 67-87 with fine impressions in slightly different colors are proofs.

1875

63	A12	12½c lt violet	.90	.90
a.	Imperf., pair		75.00	
64	A12	25c ultra	.40	.30
a.	Imperf., pair		75.00	
b.	Diagonal half used as 12½c on cover			70.00
65	A12	50c blue green	.45	.35
a.	Imperf., pair		75.00	
b.	Diag. half used as 25c on cover			80.00
66	A12	1p brown	7.50	4.75
b.	Diag. half used as 50c on cover			125.00
	Nos. 63-66 (4)		9.25	6.30

King Alfonso XII
A13   A14

1876

67	A13	12½c green	2.25	1.50
a.	12½c emerald green		2.50	2.00
68	A13	25c gray	1.00	.35
a.	Diagonal half used as 12½c on cover			90.00
c.	25c pale violet		1.75	.30
d.	25c bluish gray		2.25	.35
69	A13	50c ultra	1.00	.40
a.	Imperf., pair		16.00	16.00
b.	Diag. half used as 25c on cover			75.00
70	A13	1p black	10.00	3.50
a.	Imperf., pair		40.00	40.00
b.	Diag. half used as 50c on cover			125.00
	Nos. 67-70 (4)		14.25	5.75

1877

71	A14	10c lt green	24.00	
72	A14	12½c gray	5.75	2.50
a.	Imperf., pair		32.50	
b.	Diagonal half used on cover			62.50
73	A14	25c dk green	.55	.50
a.	Imperf., pair		32.50	
b.	Diagonal half used as 12½c on cover			62.50
74	A14	50c black	.55	.50
a.	Imperf., pair		32.50	
b.	Half used as 25c on cover			72.50
75	A14	1p brown	24.00	12.00
	Nos. 71-75 (5)		54.85	

No. 71 was not placed in use.

Stamps Dated "1878"

1878

76	A14	5c blue	.60	.45
77	A14	10c black	70.00	
78	A14	12½c brown bis	3.50	1.75
a.	12½c olive brown		3.75	1.50
c.	Diagonal half used on cover			65.00
79	A14	25c yel green	.25	.20
b.	No. 79 or 79c, diagonal half used as 12½c on cover			60.00
c.	25c deep green		.25	.20

80	A14	50c dk blue grn	.40	.20
b.	Diagonal half used as 25c on cover			60.00
81	A14	1p carmine	11.00	4.50
b.	1p rose		8.00	3.50
	Nos. 76-81 (6)		85.75	7.10

No. 77 was not placed in use.

Imperf., Pairs

76a	A14	5c blue	22.50	22.50
77a	A14	10c black	140.00	
78b	A14	12½c brown bister	22.50	22.50
79a	A14	25c deep green	22.50	22.50
80a	A14	50c dk blue green	110.00	
81a	A14	1p carmine	75.00	

Stamps Dated "1879"

1879

82	A14	5c slate black	.60	.25
83	A14	10c orange	150.00	75.00
84	A14	12½c rose	.60	.25
85	A14	25c ultra	.50	.25
a.	Diagonal half used as 12½c on cover			80.00
b.	Imperf., pair		45.00	32.50
86	A14	50c gray	.50	.25
a.	Diag. half used as 25c on cover			80.00
87	A14	1p olive bister	17.00	9.50
	Nos. 82-87 (6)		169.20	85.50

A15

A16

A17

1880

88	A15	5c green	.40	.20
89	A15	10c lake	90.00	
a.	Double impression of frame and lettering		110.00	
90	A15	12½c gray	.40	.20
91	A15	25c gray blue	.40	.20
a.	Diagonal half used as 12½c on cover			75.00
92	A15	50c brown	.50	.20
a.	Diagonal half used as 25c on cover			65.00
93	A15	1p yellow brn	5.50	2.50
a.	Diagonal half used as 50c on cover			90.00
	Nos. 88-93 (6)		97.20	3.30

No. 89 was not placed in use.

1881

94	A16	1c green	.30	.20
95	A16	2c lake	45.00	
96	A16	2½c olive bister	.50	.30
97	A16	5c gray blue	.30	.20
a.	Diag. half used as 2½c on cover			55.00
98	A16	10c yellow brown	.40	.20
a.	Diagonal half used as 5c on cover			55.00
99	A16	20c dark brown	5.00	4.00
	Nos. 94-99 (6)		51.50	4.90

No. 95 was not placed in use.

1882

100	A17	1c green	.50	.35
a.	Diag. half used as ½c on cover			50.00
101	A17	2c lake	2.40	.35
a.	Diag. half used as 1c on cover			50.00
102	A17	2½c dk brown	5.25	1.75
a.	Diag. half used as 2½c on cover			55.00
103	A17	5c gray blue	2.40	.50
a.	Diag. half used as 2½c on cover			55.00
104	A17	10c olive bister	.65	.20
a.	Diag. half used as 5c on cover			50.00
105	A17	20c red brown	90.00	27.50
a.	Diag. half used as 10c on cover			110.00
	Nos. 100-105 (6)		101.20	30.65

See Nos. 121-131. For surcharges see Nos. 106-120.

Issue of 1882 Surcharged or Overprinted in Black, Blue or Red:

a

b

c

d

e

1883

Type "a"

106	A17	5 on 5c (R)	2.50	1.50
a.	Triple surcharge		22.50	22.50
b.	Double surcharge		29.00	29.00
c.	Inverted surcharge		16.50	16.50
d.	Without "5" in surcharge			
e.	Dbl. surch., types "a" & "d"			
107	A17	10 on 10c (Bl)	2.50	1.50
a.	Inverted surcharge		26.00	26.00
b.	Double surcharge			
108	A17	20 on 20c	32.50	26.00
a.	"10" instead of "20"		75.00	75.00
b.	Double surcharge			

Type "b"

109	A17	5 on 5c (R)	2.50	1.50
a.	Inverted surcharge		26.00	26.00
b.	Double surcharge		22.50	22.50
110	A17	10 on 10c (Bl)	8.25	4.00
a.	Inverted surcharge		32.00	32.00
111	A17	20 on 20c	82.50	40.00
a.	Double surcharge			
b.	Dbl. surch., types "b" & "c"			

Type "c"

112	A17	5 on 5c (R)	2.10	1.40
a.	Inverted surcharge		32.00	32.00
b.	Dbl. surch., types "c" & "d"		—	
113	A17	10 on 10c (Bl)	8.25	4.00
a.	Inverted surcharge		37.50	37.50
b.	Double surcharge		37.50	37.50
114	A17	20 on 20c	52.50	30.00
a.	"10" instead of "20"		95.00	75.00
b.	Double surcharge		95.00	95.00
c.	Dbl. surch., types "a" & "c"			

Type "d"

115	A17	5 on 5c (R)	2.10	1.50
a.	Inverted surcharge		32.00	32.00
b.	Double surcharge		26.00	26.00
116	A17	10 on 10c (Bl)	3.25	2.25
a.	Inverted surcharge		32.00	32.00
b.	Double surcharge		29.00	29.00
117	A17	20 on 20c	77.50	30.00
a.	Dbl. surch., types "a" & "d"			

Type "e"

118	A17	5c gray blue (R)	2.50	2.00
a.	Double overprint		35.00	35.00
119	A17	10c olive bis (Bl)	6.00	5.50
a.	Double overprint		37.50	37.50
120	A17	20c red brown	190.00	50.00
a.	Double overprint		250.00	250.00
	Nos. 106-120 (15)		474.95	201.15

Handstamped overprints and surcharges are counterfeits.
Numerous other varieties exist.

Type of 1882

Original

1st retouch

2d retouch

The differences between the stamps of 1882 and the various retouches are as follows:

Original state: The medallion is surrounded by a heavy line of color of nearly even thickness, touching the horizontal line below the word "Cuba" (or "Filipinas," "Puerto Rico," as the case may be); the opening in the hair above the temple is narrow and pointed.

1st retouch: The line around the medallion is thin, except at the upper right, and does not touch the horizontal line above it; the opening in the hair is slightly wider and a trifle rounded; the lock of hair above the forehead is shaped like a broad "V" and ends in a point; there is a faint white line below it, which is not found on the stamps in the original state. Owing to wear of the plate the shape of the lock of hair and the width of the white line below it vary.

2nd retouch: The opening in the hair forms a semi-circle; the lock above the forehead is

1883-86

121	A17	1c grn, 2nd retouch	110.00	45.00
122	A17	2½c olive bister	.40	.20
124	A17	2½c violet	.40	.25
a.	2½c red lilac ('85)		.85	.50
b.	2½c ultramarine		95.00	
125	A17	5c gray bl, 1st retouch	2.25	.30
a.	Diag. half used as 2½c on cover			45.00
126	A17	5c gray bl, 2nd retouch	22.50	2.50
a.	Diag. half used as 2½c on cover			50.00
127	A17	10c brn, 1st retouch	2.75	.50
a.	Diagonal half used as 5c on cover			40.00
c.	Imperf, pair		300.00	—
128	A17	20c olive bister	13.00	2.75
	Nos. 121-128 (7)		151.30	51.50

1888

129	A17	2½c red brown	1.60	.90
130	A17	10c blue	1.25	.80
a.	Diagonal half used as 5c on cover			175.00
131	A17	20c brnsh gray	12.00	4.00
	Nos. 129-131 (3)		14.85	5.70

King Alfonso XIII
A18   A19

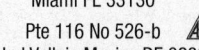

1890-97

132	A18	1c gray brown	15.50	6.50
133	A18	1c ol gray ('91)	9.00	3.50
134	A18	1c ultra ('94)	4.00	.40
135	A18	1c dk vio ('96)	1.10	.30
136	A18	2c slate blue	8.25	2.50
137	A18	2c lilac brn ('91)	1.75	.55
138	A18	2c rose ('94)	36.00	6.00
139	A18	2c claret ('96)	9.00	.85
140	A18	2½c emerald	11.50	4.50
141	A18	2½c salmon ('91)	55.00	10.00
142	A18	2½c lilac ('94)	3.75	.20
143	A18	2½c rose ('96)	.80	.20
144	A18	5c olive gray	.95	.70
b.		Diagonal half used as 2½c on cover		55.00
145	A18	5c emerald ('91)	1.00	.50
b.		Diagonal half used as 2½c on cover		55.00
146	A18	5c sl blue ('96)	.60	.20
b.		Diagonal half used as 2½c on cover		55.00
147	A18	10c brown violet	3.50	.85
b.		Diagonal half used as 5c on cover		55.00
148	A18	10c claret ('91)	2.25	.50
b.		Diagonal half used as 5c on cover		55.00
149	A18	10c emerald ('96)	2.75	.20
150	A18	20c dk violet	.95	.65
151	A18	20c ultra ('91)	11.00	8.00
152	A18	20c red brn ('94)	30.00	11.00
153	A18	20c violet ('96)	16.50	5.50
b.		Diagonal half used as 10c on cover		55.00
154	A18	40c orange brn ('97)	36.00	12.50
155	A18	80c lilac brn ('97)	52.50	19.00
		Nos. 132-155 (24)	313.65	95.20

Imperf., Pairs

134a	A18	1c ultramarine	85.00
135a	A18	1c dark violet	90.00
138a	A18	2c rose	85.00
139a	A18	2c claret	90.00
142a	A18	2½c lilac	85.00
143a	A18	2½c rose	95.00
145a	A18	5c emerald	85.00
146a	A18	5c slate blue	85.00
148a	A18	10c claret	80.00
149a	A18	10c emerald	95.00
152a	A18	20c red brown	125.00
153a	A18	20c violet	125.00
154a	A18	40c orange brown	115.00
155a	A18	80c red brown	175.00

1898

156	A19	1m orange brn	.25	.20
157	A19	2m orange brn	.25	.20
158	A19	3m orange brn	.25	.20
159	A19	4m orange brn	5.25	1.60
160	A19	5m orange brn	.30	.25
161	A19	1c black vio	.30	.25
162	A19	2c dk blue grn	.30	.25
163	A19	3c dk brown	.30	.25
164	A19	4c orange	15.50	4.00
165	A19	5c car rose	1.10	.25
166	A19	6c dk blue	.35	.25
167	A19	8c gray brown	1.10	.40
168	A19	10c vermilion	1.10	.40
169	A19	15c slate green	5.25	.40
170	A19	20c maroon	.70	.25
171	A19	40c dark lilac	2.50	.40
172	A19	60c black	2.75	.40
173	A19	80c red brown	16.50	8.00
174	A19	1p yel green	16.50	8.00
175	A19	2p slate blue	32.50	8.00
		Nos. 156-175 (20)	103.05	33.95

Nos. 156-160 were issued for use on newspapers.

Nos. 156-175 exist imperf. Value, unused pairs, $1,500.

For surcharges see Nos. 176-189C, 196-200.

King Alfonso XIII
A19　　　N2

Issued under Administration of the United States
Puerto Principe Issue

Issues of Cuba of 1898 and 1896
Surcharged:

a　　　　　　b

Numeral in ( ) after color indicates printing.

1898-99
Black Surcharge on Nos. 156-158, 160

Types a, c, d, e, f, g and h are 17½mm high, the others are 19½mm high.

176	A19 (a)	1c on 1m org	50.00	30.00
		brn		
177	A19 (b)	1c on 1m org	45.00	35.00
		brn		
a.		Broken figure "1"	75.00	65.00
b.		Inverted surcharge		200.00
d.		As "a," inverted		250.00

c　　　　　　d

178	A19 (c)	2c on 2m org	24.00	20.00
a.		Inverted surcharge	250.00	50.00
179	A19 (d)	2c on 2m org	40.00	35.00
		brn		
a.		Inverted surcharge	350.00	100.00

k　　　　　　l

179B	A19 (k)	3c on 1m org	300.	175.
		brn		
c.		Double surcharge	1,500.	750.

An unused example is known with "cents" omitted.

179D	A19 (l)	3c on 1m org	1,500.	750.
		brn		
e.		Double surcharge	—	—

e　　　　　　f

179F	A19 (e)	3c on 2m org		1,500.
		brn		

Value is for examples with minor faults.

179G	A19 (f)	3c on 2m org	—	2,000.
		brn		

Value is for examples with minor faults.

180	A19 (e)	3c on 3m org	30.	30.
		brn		
a.		Inverted surcharge		110.
181	A19 (f)	3c on 3m org	75.	75.
		brn		
a.		Inverted surcharge		200.

g　　　　　　h

i　　　　　　j

182	A19 (g)	5c on 1m org	700.	200.
		brn		
a.		Inverted surcharge		500.
183	A19 (h)	5c on 1m org	1,300.	500.
		brn		
a.		Inverted surcharge		700.
184	A19 (g)	5c on 2m org	750.	275.
		brn		
185	A19 (h)	5c on 2m org	1,500.	500.
		brn		
186	A19 (g)	5c on 3m org	650.	175.
		brn		
a.		Inverted surcharge	1,200.	700.

187	A19 (h)	5c on 3m org	400.	
		brn		1,000.
a.		Inverted surcharge		
188	A19 (g)	5c on 5m org	80.	60.
		brn	400.	200.
a.		Inverted surcharge		
b.		Double surcharge	—	
189	A19 (h)	5c on 5m org	350.	250.
		brn		425.
a.		Inverted surcharge		
b.		Double surcharge		

The 2nd printing of Nos. 188-189 has shiny ink. Values are for the 1st printing.

189C	A19 (i)	5c on 5m org		7,500.
		brn		

Black Surcharge on No. P25

190	N2 (g)	5c on ½m bl	250.	75.
a.		Inverted surcharge	500.	150.
b.		Pair, one without surcharge		500.

Value for 190b is for pair with unsurcharged stamp at right. Also exists with unsurcharged stamp at left.

191	N2 (h)	5c on ½m bl	300.	90.
		grn		
a.		Inverted surcharge		200.
192	N2 (i)	5c on ½m bl	550.	200.
		grn		
a.		Dbl. surch., one diagonal		11,500.
193	N2 (j)	5c on ½m bl	800.	300.
		grn		

Red Surcharge on No. 161

196	A19 (k)	3c on 1c blk	65.	35.
		vio		
a.		Inverted surcharge		325.
197	A19 (l)	3c on 1c blk	125.	55.
		vio		
a.		Inverted surcharge		400.
198	A19 (i)	5c on 1c blk	25.	30.
		vio		
a.		Inverted surcharge		125.
b.		Surcharge vert. reading up		3,500.
c.		Double surcharge	400.	600.
d.		Double invtd. surch.		—

Value for No. 198b is for surcharge reading up. One example is known with surcharge reading down.

199	A19 (j)	5c on 1c blk	55.	55.
		vio		
a.		Inverted surcharge		250.
b.		Vertical surcharge		2,000.
c.		Double surcharge	1,000.	700.

m

200	A19 (m)	10c on 1c blk	20.	50.
a.		Broken figure "1"	40.	100.

Black Surcharge on Nos. P26-P30

201	N2 (k)	3c on 1m bl	350.	350.
		grn		
a.		Inverted surcharge		450.
b.		"EENTS"	550.	450.
c.		As "b," inverted		850.
202	N2 (l)	3c on 1m bl	550.	400.
		grn		
a.		Inverted surcharge		850.
203	N2 (k)	3c on 2m bl	850.	400.
		grn	1,250.	500.
a.		"EENTS"		1,150.
b.		Inverted surcharge		
c.		As "a," inverted		950.
204	N2 (l)	3c on 2m bl	1,250.	600.
		grn		
a.		Inverted surcharge		750.
205	N2 (k)	3c on 3m bl	900.	400.
		grn		750.
a.		Inverted surcharge		
b.		"EENTS"	1,250.	450.
c.		As "b," inverted		700.
206	N2 (l)	3c on 3m bl	1,200.	550.
		grn		
a.		Inverted surcharge		700.
211	N2 (i)	5c on 1m bl		1,800.
		grn		
212	N2 (j)	5c on 1m bl		2,500.
		grn		
213	N2 (i)	5c on 2m bl		2,250.
		grn		
214	N2 (j)	5c on 2m bl		1,800.
		grn		1,900.
a.		"EENTS"		
215	N2 (i)	5c on 3m bl		1,750.
		grn		
216	N2 (j)	5c on 3m bl	550.	
		grn		1,000.
a.		"EENTS"		
217	N2 (i)	5c on 4m bl		1,000.
		grn		
218	N2 (j)	5c on 4m bl	2,500.	900.
		grn	3,000.	1,500.
a.		"EENTS"		2,000.
b.		Inverted surcharge		2,000.
c.		As "a," inverted		

217	N2 (i)	5c on 4m bl	2,500.	900.
		grn		
218	N2 (j)	5c on 4m bl		1,500.
		grn		2,000.
a.		Inverted surcharge		

219	N2 (i)	5c on 8m bl	2,500.	1,250.
		grn		
a.		Inverted surcharge		1,500.
b.		"EENTS"	—	1,800.
c.		As "b," inverted		2,500.
220	N2 (j)	5c on 8m bl		2,000.
		grn		
a.		Inverted surcharge		2,500.

Beware of forgeries of the Puerto Principe issue. Obtaining expert opinions is recommended.

United States Stamps Nos. 279, 267, 267b, 279Bf, 279Bh, 268, 281, 282C and 283 Surcharged in Black

1899　　Wmk. 191　　Perf. 12

221	A87	1c on 1c yel		
		grn	5.00	.40
222	A88	2c on 2c reddish car, III	10.00	.75
b.		2c on 2c vermilion, type III	10.00	.75
222A	A88	2c on 2c reddish car, IV	6.00	.40
c.		2c on 2c vermilion, IV	6.00	.40
d.		As No. 222A, inverted surcharge	5,500.	5,000.
223	A88	2½c on 2c reddish car, III	5.00	.80
b.		2½c on 2c vermilion, III	5.00	.80
223A	A88	2½c on 2c reddish car, IV	3.50	.50
c.		2½c on 2c vermilion, IV	3.50	.50
224	A89	3c on 3c purple	14.00	1.75
a.		Period between "B" and "A"	40.00	35.00
225	A91	5c on 5c blue	14.00	2.00
226	A94	10c on 10c brn, I	25.00	6.50
b.		"CUBA" omitted	6,500.	4,000.
226A	A94	10c on 10c brn, II	6,000.	
		Nos. 221-226 (8)	82.50	13.10

The 2½c was sold and used as a 2c stamp.

Excellent counterfeits of this and the preceding issue exist, especially inverted and double surcharges.

Issues of the Republic under US Military Rule

Statue of Columbus　　　Royal Palms
A20　　　　　　　　A21

"Cuba" — A22　　　Ocean Liner — A23

Cane Field — A24

1899　　Wmk. US-C (191C)　　Perf. 12

227	A20	1c yellow green	3.50	.20
228	A21	2c carmine	3.50	.20
a.		scarlet	3.50	
b.		Booklet pane of 6	5,000.	
229	A22	3c purple	3.50	.25
230	A23	5c blue	4.50	.30
231	A24	10c brown	11.00	.80
		Nos. 227-231 (5)	26.00	1.75

No. 228b was issued by the Republic.
See Nos. 233-237. For surcharge see No. 232.

Issues of the Republic

No. 229 Surcharged in Carmine

1902, Sept. 30

232	A22 1c on 3c purple	1.50	.50
a.	Inverted surcharge	150.00	150.00
b.	Surcharge sideways (numeral horizontal)	200.00	200.00
c.	Double surcharge	200.00	200.00

Counterfeits of the errors are plentiful.

Re-engraved

The re-engraved stamps of 1905-07 may be distinguished from the issue of 1899 as follows:

ORIGINAL   RE-ENGRAVED

1c — The ends of the label inscribed "Centavo" are rounded instead of square.

2c — The foliate ornaments, inside the oval disks bearing the numerals of value, have been removed.

5c — Two lines forming a right angle have been added in the upper corners of the label bearing the word "Cuba."

10c — A small ball has been added to each of the square ends of the label bearing the word "Cuba."

1905   **Unwmk.**   **Perf. 12**

233	A20 1c green	1.60	.20
234	A21 2c rose	1.10	.20
a.	Booklet pane of 6	150.00	
236	A23 5c blue	37.50	1.00
237	A24 10c brown	3.25	.50
	Nos. 233-237 (4)	43.45	1.90

Maj. Gen. Antonio Maceo — A26

1907

238	A26 50c gray bl & blk	1.10	.80

Bartolomé Masó A27   Máximo Gómez A28

Julio Sanguily A29

Ignacio Agramonte A30

Calixto García A31

José M. Rodriquez y Rodriquez (Mayia) A32

Carlos Roloff — A33

1910, Feb. 1

239	A27 1c grn & vio	.85	.25
a.	Center inverted	260.00	260.00
240	A28 2c car & grn	1.60	.25
a.	Center inverted	575.00	575.00
241	A29 3c vio & bl	1.10	.25
242	A30 5c bl & grn	16.00	.80
243	A31 8c ol & vio	1.10	.30
244	A32 10c brn & bl	6.75	.65
a.	Center inverted	850.00	
245	A26 50c vio & blk	1.60	.50
246	A33 1p slate & blk	7.75	4.00
	Nos. 239-246 (8)	36.75	7.00
	Set, never hinged	50.00	

1911-13

247	A27 1c green	.55	.25
248	A28 2c car rose	.70	.25
a.	Booklet pane of 6 ('13)	82.50	
250	A30 5c ultra	1.75	.25
251	A31 8c ol grn & blk	1.10	.60
252	A33 1p black	5.00	2.00
	Nos. 247-252 (5)	9.10	3.35
	Set, never hinged	16.00	

Map of Cuba — A34

1914-15

253	A34 1c green	.90	.25
a.	Booklet pane of 6	100.00	
254	A34 2c car rose	1.10	.25
a.	Booklet pane of 6	100.00	
255	A34 2c red ('15)	1.75	.25
a.	Booklet pane of 6	100.00	
256	A34 3c violet	5.50	.35
257	A34 5c blue	7.50	.25
258	A34 8c ol grn	6.00	.70
259	A34 10c brown	11.00	.35
260	A34 10c ol grn ('15)	13.00	.55
261	A34 50c orange	85.00	10.00
262	A34 1p gray	125.00	24.00
	Nos. 253-262 (10)	256.75	36.95
	Set, never hinged	450.00	

Complete set of eight 1914 stamps, imperf. pairs, value $1,500.

Nos. 253, 254, 256 and E5 exist with "1917 GOB./CONSTITUCIONAL/CAMAGUEY" overprint. These were not authorized.

Gertrudis Gómez de Avellaneda, Cuban Poetess (1814-73) A34a

1914

263	A34a 5c blue	14.00	5.00
	Never hinged	22.50	

José Martí A35

José de la Luz Caballero A37

Ignacio Agramonte A39

José A. Saco — A41

Carlos Manuel de Céspedes — A43

Máximo Gómez A36

Calixto García A38

Tomás Estrada Palma A40

Antonio Maceo — A42

1917-18   **Unwmk.**   **Perf. 12**

264	A35 1c bl grn	.75	.25
a.	Booklet pane of 6	40.00	
b.	Booklet pane of 30	250.00	
265	A36 2c rose	.80	.25
a.	Booklet pane of 6	50.00	
b.	Booklet pane of 30	210.00	
266	A36 2c lt red ('18)	.65	.25
a.	Booklet pane of 6	50.00	
267	A37 3c violet	.85	.25
a.	Imperf. pair	275.00	
b.	Booklet pane of 6	50.00	
268	A38 5c dp bl	.80	.25
269	A39 8c red brn	4.25	.25
270	A40 10c yel brn	2.40	.25
271	A41 20c gray grn	14.00	1.60
272	A42 50c dl rose	14.00	.70
273	A43 1p black	14.50	.70
	Nos. 264-273 (10)	53.00	4.75
	Set, never hinged	77.50	

1925-28   **Wmk. 106**   **Perf. 12**

274	A35 1c bl grn	1.10	.25
a.	Booklet pane of 6	350.00	
275	A36 2c brt rose	1.20	.25
a.	Booklet pane of 6	75.00	
b.	Booklet pane of 30	350.00	
276	A38 5c dp bl	2.50	.25
277	A39 8c red brn ('28)	5.75	.65
278	A40 10c yel brn ('27)	7.00	.70
279	A41 20c olive grn	11.00	1.10
	Nos. 274-279 (6)	28.55	3.20
	Set, never hinged	40.00	

1926   **Imperf.**

280	A35 1c blue green	1.40	1.00
281	A36 2c brt rose	1.40	1.00
282	A38 5c deep blue	1.75	1.40
	Nos. 280-282 (3)	4.55	3.40
	Set, never hinged	5.00	

See Nos. 304-310. For overprint and surcharge see Nos. 317-318, 644.

Arms of Republic A44

1927, May 20   **Unwmk.**   **Perf. 12**

283	A44 25c violet	16.00	3.50
	Never hinged	24.00	

25th anniversary of the Republic. For surcharges see Nos. 355, C3.

Tomás Estrada Palma A45

Designs: 2c, Gen. Gerardo Machado. 5c, Morro Castle. 8c, Havana Railway Station. 10c, Presidential Palace. 13c, Tobacco Plantation. 20c, Treasury Building. 30c, Sugar Mill. 50c, Havana Cathedral. 1p, Galician Clubhouse, Havana.

1928, Jan. 2   **Wmk. 106**

284	A45 1c deep green	.50	.30
285	A45 2c brt rose	.50	.30
286	A45 5c deep blue	1.40	.50
287	A45 8c lt red brn	3.00	1.10
288	A45 10c bister brn	1.25	.80
289	A45 13c orange	1.75	.80
290	A45 20c olive grn	2.10	.95
291	A45 30c dk violet	4.25	.75
292	A45 50c carmine rose	6.50	2.75
293	A45 1p gray black	13.00	6.25
	Nos. 284-293 (10)	34.25	14.50
	Set, never hinged	52.50	

Sixth Pan-American Conference.

Capitol, Havana A55

1929, May 18

294	A55 1c green	.40	.35
295	A55 2c carmine rose	.40	.30
296	A55 5c blue	.55	.40

297	A55	10c bister brn	1.10 .50
298	A55	20c violet	3.75 2.75
		Nos. 294-298 (5)	6.20 4.30
		Set, never hinged	11.50

Opening of the Capitol, Havana.

Hurdler — A56

1930, Mar. 15   **Engr.**

299	A56	1c green	.75 .45
300	A56	2c carmine	.75 .50
301	A56	5c deep blue	1.00 .50
302	A56	10c bister brn	2.00 .95
303	A56	20c violet	12.00 3.25
		Nos. 299-303 (5)	16.50 5.65
		Set, never hinged	24.00

2nd Central American Athletic Games.

Types of 1917 Portrait Issue
Flat Plate Printing

1930-45 Wmk. 106 Engr. *Perf. 10*

304	A35	1c blue green	.80 .25
a.		Booklet pane of 6	50.00
b.		Booklet pane of 30	—
305	A36	2c brt rose	75.00 —
a.		Booklet pane of 6	1,200.
305B	A37	3c dk rose vio ('42)	4.00 .75
c.		Booklet pane of 6	42.50
306	A38	5c dk blue	2.75 .20
306A	A39	8c red brn ('45)	2.75 .25
307	A40	10c brown	2.75 .25
a.		10c yellow brown ('35)	3.50 .75
307B	A41	20c olive grn ('41)	4.75 .75
		Nos. 304-307B (7)	92.80 2.45

Nos. 305 and 305B were printed for booklet panes and all examples have straight edges.
For surcharge see No. 644.

Rotary Press Printing

308	A35	1c blue grn	1.10 .25
309	A36	2c brt rose	1.10 .25
a.		Booklet pane of 50	—
310	A37	3c violet	1.50 .25
a.		3c dull violet ('38)	1.10 .25
b.		3c rose violet ('41)	1.10 .25
c.		Booklet pane of 50	—
		Nos. 308-310 (3)	3.70 .75

Flat plate stamps measure 18½x21½mm; rotary press, 19x22mm.

The Mangos of Baragua — A57

War Memorial — A61

Battle of Mal Tiempo A58

Battle of Coliseo A59

Maceo, Gómez and Zayas A60

Wmk. 229

1933, Apr. 23   Photo.   *Perf. 12½*

312	A57	3c dk brown	1.40 .30
313	A58	5c dk blue	1.25 .40
314	A59	10c emerald	2.40 .40
315	A60	13c red	2.75 1.10
316	A61	20c black	5.50 3.00
		Nos. 312-316 (5)	13.30 5.20
		Set, never hinged	22.50

War of Independence and dedication of the "Soldado Invasor" (the American Army that came to the aid of the revolution against Spain) monument.

Types of 1917 Issues with Carmine or Black Overprint Reading Up or Down

Rotary Press Printing
Wmk. 106

1933, Dec. 23   Engr.   *Perf. 10*

317	A35	1c blue green (C)	1.75 .25

With Additional Surcharge of New Value and Bars

318	A37	2c on 3c vio (Bk)	1.75 .25

Establishment of a revolutionary junta.
Catalogue values for Nos. 317-318 unused are for examples with overprint reading up. Values for overprint reading down, $4.

Dr. Carlos J. Finlay — A62

1934, Dec. 3   Engr.   *Perf. 10*

319	A62	2c dark carmine	1.00 .50
320	A62	5c dark blue	2.75 1.50
		Set, never hinged	6.00

Cent. of the birth of Dr. Carlos J. Finlay (1833-1915), physician-biologist who found that a mosquito transmitted yellow fever.

Pres. José Miguel Gómez — A63

Gómez Monument A64

1936, May   *Perf. 10*

322	A63	1c green	1.50 .40
323	A64	2c carmine	2.25 .50
		Set, never hinged	7.00

Unveiling of a monument to Gen. José Miguel Gómez, ex-president.

Matanzas Issue

Map of Cuba A65

2c, Map of Free Zone. 4c, S. S. "Rex" in Matanzas Bay. 5c, Ships in Matanzas Bay. 8c, Caves of Bellamar. 10c, Valley of Yumuri. 20c, Yumuri River. 50c, Ships Leaving Port.

Wmk. 229

1936, May 5   Photo.   *Perf. 12½*

324	A65	1c blue green	.40 .25
325	A65	2c red	.60 .25
326	A65	4c claret	1.00 .25
327	A65	5c ultra	1.50 .25
328	A65	8c orange brn	2.50 .70
329	A65	10c emerald	2.75 .70
330	A65	20c brown	5.25 2.50
331	A65	50c slate	9.75 3.50
		Nos. 324-331,C18-C21,CE1,E8 (14)	45.65 21.85
		Set, never hinged	60.00

Exist imperf. Value 20% more.

"Peace and Work" A73

Máximo Gómez Monument — A74

Torch — A75

"Independence" — A76

"Messenger of Peace" — A77

1936, Nov. 18   *Perf. 12½*

332	A73	1c emerald	.50 .25
333	A74	2c crimson	.60 .30
334	A75	4c maroon	.70 .30
335	A76	5c ultra	2.75 .55
336	A77	8c dk green	4.00 1.20
		Nos. 332-336,C22-C23,E9 (8)	19.30 7.20
		Set, never hinged	35.00

Maj. Gen. Máximo Gómez, birth centenary. Issued both perf and imperf. Values for imperfs are approx. 400% higher.

Sugar Cane — A78

Primitive Sugar Mill — A79

Modern Sugar Mill — A80

Wmk. 106

1937, Oct. 2   Engr.   *Perf. 10*

337	A78	1c yellow green	1.40 .40
338	A79	2c red	.80 .25
339	A80	5c bright blue	1.75 .40
		Nos. 337-339 (3)	3.95 1.05
		Set, never hinged	6.25

Cuban sugar cane industry, 400th anniv.

Argentine Emblem — A81

Mountain Scene (Bolivia) — A82

Arms of Brazil — A83

Canadian Scene — A84

Camilo Henriquez (Chile) A85

Gen, Francisco de Paula Santander (Colombia) A86

Natl. Monument (Costa Rica) — A87

Autograph of José Marti (Cuba) — A88

Columbus Lighthouse (Dominican Rep.) — A89

Juan Montalvo (Ecuador) — A90

Abraham Lincoln
(US)
A91

Quetzal and
Scroll
(Guatemala)
A92

Arms of Haiti
A93

Francisco
Morazán
(Honduras)
A94

Fleet of
Columbus — A95

Wmk. 106

1937, Oct. 13   Engr.   Perf. 10

340	A81	1c deep green	.70	.70
341	A82	1c green	.70	.70
342	A83	2c carmine	.70	.70
343	A84	2c carmine	.70	.70
344	A85	3c violet	1.60	1.60
345	A86	3c violet	1.60	1.60
346	A87	4c bister brown	1.90	1.90
347	A88	4c bister brown	3.50	3.50
348	A89	5c blue	1.75	1.75
349	A90	5c blue	1.75	1.75
350	A91	8c citron	6.25	6.25
351	A92	8c citron	3.00	3.00
352	A93	10c maroon	3.00	3.00
353	A94	10c maroon	3.00	3.00
354	A95	25c rose lilac	32.50	32.50
		Nos. 340-354,C24-C29,E10-E11 (23)	122.15	122.15
		Set, never hinged	160.00	

Nos. 340-354 were sold by the Cuban PO for 3 days, Oct. 13-15, during which no other stamps were sold. They were postally valid for the full face value. Proceeds from their three-day sale above 30,000 pesos were paid by the Cuban POD to the Assoc. of American Writers and Artists. Remainders were overprinted "SVP" (Without Postal Value).

No. 283
Surcharged
in Green

1937, Nov. 19   Unwmk.   Perf. 12

355	A44	10c on 25c violet	12.50	4.00
		Never hinged	19.00	

Centenary of Cuban railroads.

Ciboney Indian
and
Cigar — A96

Cigar and
Globe — A97

Tobacco Plant and
Cigars — A98

1939, Aug. 28   Wmk. 106   Perf. 10

356	A96	1c yellow green	.40	.25
357	A97	2c red	.55	.25
358	A98	5c brt ultra	.95	.30
		Nos. 356-358 (3)	1.90	.80
		Set, never hinged	3.00	

General Calixto García
A99   A100

1939, Nov. 6   Perf. 10, Imperf.

359	A99	2c dark red	.75	.25
360	A100	5c deep blue	1.00	.40
		Set, never hinged	3.00	

Birth centenary of General Garcia.
Values are for perf examples. Value of imperfs approx. 20% higher.

Gonzalo de
Quesada — A101

1940, Apr. 30   Engr.   Perf. 10

361	A101	2c rose red	1.25	.50
		Never hinged	2.00	

Pan American Union, 50th anniversary.

Rotary Club
Emblem, Cuban
Flag and
Tobacco
Plant — A102

Lions Emblem,
Cuban Flag and
Royal
Palms — A103

1940, May 18   Wmk. 106   Perf. 10

362	A102	2c rose red	1.75	.75
		Never hinged	3.00	

Rotary Intl. Convention held at Havana.

1940, July 23

363	A103	2c orange vermilion	1.75	.75
		Never hinged	3.00	

Lions International Convention, Havana.

Dr.
Nicolás J.
Gutiérrez
A104

1940, Oct. 28

364	A104	2c orange ver	1.00	.30
365	A104	5c blue	1.25	.30
a.		Sheet of four, imperf., unwmkd.	4.50	3.00
		Never hinged	6.50	
b.		As "a," black overprint ('51)	6.00	4.75
		Never hinged	9.00	
		Set, never hinged	3.00	

100th anniv. of the publication of the 1st Cuban Medical Review, "El Repertorio Medico Habanero."

No. 365a contains 2 each of Nos. 364-365 imperf. and sold for 25c.

For overprint see No. C43A.

In 1951 No. 365a was overprinted in black: "50 Aniversario Descubrimiento Agente Transmisor de la Flebre Amarilla por el Dr. Carlos J. Finlay Honor a los Martires de la Ciencia 1901 1951." The overprint is illustrated over No. C43A, but does not include the plane and "Correo Aereo."

Major General
Guillermo
Moncada — A105

Moncada
Riding into
Battle
A106

1941, June 25

366	A105	3c dk brown, *buff*	1.50	.50
367	A106	5c bright blue	1.50	.50
		Set, never hinged	4.50	

Maj. Gen. Guillermo Moncada (1841-96).

Globe Showing
Western
Hemisphere
A107

"Labor: Wealth of
America" — A109

Maceo,
Bolívar,
Juárez,
Lincoln
and Arms
of Cuba
A108

Tree of
Fraternity,
Havana
A110

Statue of
Liberty — A111

Perf. 10, Imperf.

1942, Feb. 23   Wmk. 106

368	A107	1c emerald	.25	.20
369	A108	3c orange brown	.40	.20
370	A109	5c blue	.70	.20
371	A110	10c red violet	1.75	1.00
372	A111	13c red	1.25	.65
		Nos. 368-372 (5)	4.35	2.25
		Set, never hinged	7.00	

Spirit of Democracy in the Americas.

The imperforate varieties are without gum. Value, set mint $10, used $5.

Ignacio Agramonte
Loynaz — A112

Rescue of
Sanguily
by
Agramonte
A113

1942, Apr. 10   Perf. 10

373	A112	3c bister brn	1.00	.50
374	A113	5c brt blue, *bluish*	2.00	1.00
		Set, never hinged	4.00	

100th anniv. of the birth of Ignacio Agramonte Loynaz, patriot.

"Unmask the Fifth Columnists" — A114

"Be Careful,
The Fifth
Column is
Spying on
You" — A115

"Destroy it. The Fifth Column is like a
Serpent" — A116

"Fulfill your Patriotic Duty by
Destroying the Fifth Column" — A117

"Don't be Afraid of the Fifth Column.
Attack it" — A118

1943, July 5

375	A114	1c dk blue grn	.40	.25
376	A115	3c red	.70	.25
377	A116	5c brt blue	.70	.25
378	A117	10c dull brown	2.50	.70
379	A118	13c dull rose vio	3.50	1.50
		Nos. 375-379 (5)	7.80	2.95
		Set, never hinged	12.00	

General Eloy Alfaro and Flags of Cuba and Ecuador A119

1943, Sept. 20
380 A119 3c green   1.20 .30
   Never hinged   2.00

General Eloy Alfaro of Ecuador, 100th birth anniv.

Retirement Security A120

1943, Nov. 8   Wmk. 106   Perf. 10
381 A120 1c yellow green   .50 .30
382 A120 3c vermilion   .50 .30
383 A120 5c bright blue   .80 .40

1944, Mar. 18
384 A120 1c bright yel grn   1.10 .40
385 A120 3c salmon   1.10 .40
386 A120 5c light blue   2.25 1.10
   Nos. 381-386 (6)   6.25 2.90
   Set, never hinged   11.00

Half the proceeds from the sale of Nos. 381-386 were used for the Communications Ministry Employees' Retirement Fund.

Portrait of Columbus — A121

Bartolomé de Las Casas — A122

First Statue of Columbus at Cárdenas — A123

Discovery of Tobacco A124

Columbus Sights Land A125

1944, May 19
387 A121 1c dk yellow grn   .30 .20
   a. Pair, imperf horiz.   75.00
388 A122 3c brown   .45 .20
389 A123 5c brt blue   .80 .20
390 A124 10c dark violet   2.50 .75
391 A125 13c dark red   4.00 1.75
   Nos. 387-391,C36-C37 (7)   11.05 4.25
   Set, never hinged   17.00

450th anniv. of the discovery of America.

Major General Carlos Roloff — A126

Americas Map and 1st Brazilian Postage Stamps — A127

1944, Aug. 21
392 A126 3c violet   1.25 .30
   Never hinged   2.00

Maj. Gen. Carlos Roloff, 100th birth anniv.

1944, Dec. 20   Engr.
393 A127 3c brown orange   2.00 .75
   Never hinged   3.00

Cent. of the 1st postage stamps of the Americas, issued by Brazil in 1843.

Seal of the Society — A128

Luis de las Casas and Luis Maria Penalyer A129

1945, Oct. 5   Wmk. 106   Perf. 10
394 A128 1c yellow green   .50 .20
395 A129 2c scarlet   1.25 .25
   Set, never hinged   2.75

Sesquicentenary of the founding of the Economic Society of Friends of the Country.

Aged Couple A130

1945, Dec. 27
396 A130 1c dk yellow grn   .20 .20
397 A130 2c scarlet   .40 .20
398 A130 5c cobalt blue   .90 .20

1946, Mar. 26
399 A130 1c brt yellow grn   .75 .20
400 A130 2c salmon pink   .45 .20
401 A130 5c light blue   .75 .25
   Nos. 396-401 (6)   3.45 1.25
   Set, never hinged   5.00

See note after No. 386.

Catalogue values for unused stamps in this section, from this point to the end of the section, are for Never Hinged items.

Gabriel de la Concepcion Valdés Plácido A131

1946, Feb. 5
402 A131 2c scarlet   1.00 .30

Cent. of the death of the poet Gabriel de la Concepcion Valdés.

Manuel Marquez Sterling — A132

Globe and Cross — A133

1946, Apr. 30
403 A132 2c scarlet   2.25 .30

Founding of the Manuel Marquez Sterling Professional School of Journalism, 3th anniv.

1946, July 4   Engr.
404 A133 2c scarlet, pink   1.25 .20

80th anniv. of the Intl. Red Cross.

Cow and Milkmaid — A134

Franklin D. Roosevelt — A135

1947, Feb. 20   Wmk. 106   Perf. 10
405 A134 2c scarlet   2.00 .40

1947 National Livestock Exposition.

1947, Apr. 12
406 A135 2c vermilion   1.50 .40

2nd anniv. of the death of Franklin D. Roosevelt.

Antonio Oms Sarret and Aged Couple A136

1947, Oct. 20
407 A136 1c dp yellow grn   .50 .30
408 A136 2c scarlet   .50 .30
409 A136 5c lt blue   1.00 .55
   Nos. 407-409 (3)   2.00 1.15

See note after No. 386.

Marta Abreu Arenabio de Estevez — A137

"Charity" — A138

Marta Abreu Monument, Santa Clara A139

"Patriotism" A140

1947, Nov. 29
410 A137 1c dp yellow grn   .55 .30
411 A138 2c scarlet   1.00 .30
412 A139 5c brt blue   2.00 .40
413 A140 10c dk violet   3.50 1.00
   Nos. 410-413 (4)   7.05 2.00

Birth cent. of Marta Abreu Arenabio de Estevez, philanthropist and humanitarian.

Armauer Hansen A141

1948, Apr. 9
414 A141 2c rose carmine   1.75 .40

International Leprosy Congress, Havana.

Mother and Child A142

1948, Oct. 15   **Engr.**
415 A142 1c yellow grn   .40   .25
416 A142 2c scarlet   .50   .25
417 A142 5c brt blue   1.20   .40
    Nos. 415-417 (3)   2.10   .90
    See note after No. 386.

Death of José Martí — A143

Martí Rowing to Shore — A144

1948, Nov. 10   **Wmk. 106**   **Perf. 10**
418 A143 2c scarlet   .75   .25
419 A144 5c brt blue   2.25   .45
    50th anniversary of the death of José Martí, patriot (in 1945).

Tobacco Picking — A145   Liberty Carrying Flag and Cigars — A146

Cigar and Arms of Cuba — A147

1948, Dec. 6
Size: 22½x26mm
420 A145 1c green   .35   .25
421 A146 2c rose car   .65   .30
422 A147 5c brt blue   1.25   .30
    Nos. 420-422 (3)   2.25   .85

    Cuba's tobacco industry. See Nos. 445-447. For overprints and surcharge see Nos. 448-451, 512.

Equestrian Statue of Gen. Antonio Maceo — A148

Sword Salute to Maceo A149

    Designs: 2c, Portrait of Maceo. 5c, Mausoleum, El Cacahual. 10c, East to West invasion. 20c, Battle of Peralejo. 50c, Declaration of Baragua. 1p, Death of Maceo at San Pedro.

1948, Dec. 15   **Wmk. 229**   **Perf. 12½**
423 A148   1c blue green   .40   .20
424 A148   2c red   .45   .20
425 A148   5c blue   .60   .20
426 A149   8c black & brown   .90   .40
427 A149 10c brown & bl grn   .90   .25
428 A149 20c blue & car   3.50   1.10
429 A149 50c car & ultra   5.75   2.75
430 A149   1p black & violet   12.50   4.25
    Nos. 423-430 (8)   25.00   9.35
    Birth cent. (in 1945) of Maceo.

Symbol of Pharmacy A150   Morro Lighthouse A151

1948, Dec. 28   **Perf. 10**
431 A150 2c rose carmine   1.40   .40
    1st Pan-American Congress of Pharmacy, Havana, Dec. 1948.

1949, Jan. 17   **Wmk. 229**   **Perf. 12½**
432 A151 2c carmine   1.75   .40
    Centenary (in 1944) of the erection of the Morro Lighthouse.

Jagua Castle, Cienfuegos A152

1949, Jan. 27   **Wmk. 106**   **Perf. 10**
433 A152 1c yellow green   .75   .30
434 A152 2c rose red   1.50   .30
    200th anniv. of the construction of Jagua Castle and the cent. of the publication of the 1st newspaper in Cienfuegos.

Manuel Sanguily y Garritt — A153

Map of Isle of Pines — A154

1949, Mar. 31
435 A153 2c rose red   .75   .30
436 A153 5c blue   2.00   .30
    Manuel Sanguily y Garritt (1848-1925), cabinet member, editor, author.

1949, Apr. 26
437 A154 5c rose red   2.00   .75
    20th anniv. of the recognition of Cuban ownership of the Isle of Pines.

Ismael Cespedes — A155

1949, Sept. 28
438 A155 1c yellow green   .60   .30
439 A155 2c scarlet   .60   .30
440 A155 5c brt blue   1.25   .30
    Nos. 438-440 (3)   2.45   .90
    See note after No. 386.

Gen. Enrique Collazo — A156

Enrique José Varona — A157

1950, Feb. 28   **Engr.**   **Perf. 10**
441 A156 2c scarlet   .75   .20
442 A156 5c brt blue   2.00   .45
    Centenary (in 1948) of the birth of General Enrique Collazo.

1950, Feb. 28
443 A157 2c scarlet   .75   .20
444 A157 5c brt blue   2.00   .20
    Centenary of the birth of Enrique José Varona, writer and patriot.

Tobacco Types of 1948
1950, June 20   **Re-engraved**
        Size: 21x25mm
445 A145 1c green   1.10   .30
446 A146 2c rose red   1.10   .30
447 A147 5c blue   1.75   .30
    Nos. 445-447 (3)   3.95   .90
    The re-engraved stamps show slight differences in many minor details.
    For overprints and surcharge see #448-451, 512.

No. 446 Overprinted in Black

1950, Apr. 27
448 A146 2c rose red   1.75   .30
    Natl. Bank of Cuba opening, Apr. 27, 1950.

Re-engraved Tobacco Types of 1950 Overprinted in Carmine

1950, May 18
449 A145 1c yellow green   .50   .30
450 A146 2c lilac rose   .75   .30
451 A147 5c light blue   1.50   .30
    Nos. 449-451 (3)   2.75   .90
    75th anniv. (in 1949) of the UPU.
    No. 451 exists with surcharge inverted.

Manuel Balanzategui, Antonio L. Pausa and Train Wreck A158

Fernando Figueredo — A159

1950, Sept. 21   **Engr.**
452 A158 1c yellow grn   1.50   .75
453 A158 2c scarlet   1.50   .75
454 A158 5c brt blue   4.25   1.25
    Nos. 452-454 (3)   7.25   2.75

1951, Mar. 17   **Wmk. 106**   **Perf. 10**
455 A159 1c green   1.50   .20
456 A159 2c scarlet   1.50   .20
457 A159 5c brt blue   2.75   .20
    Nos. 455-457 (3)   5.75   .60

    Three-fourths of the proceeds from the sale of these stamps were used for the Communication Ministry Employees' Retirement Fund. See Nos. 474, C51-C56, E15. For surcharges see Nos. 474, C51-C56, E15.

Miguel Teurbe Tolón and Flag — A160   Narciso Lopez — A161

Emilia Teurbe Tolón Sewing Flag — A162   Cuban Flag — A163

Engraved and Lithographed
1951, July 3   **Wmk. 229**   **Perf. 13**
458 A160   1c Prus grn, ultra & red   .75   .30
459 A161   2c red & gray blk   1.00   .30
460 A162   5c ultra & red   2.10   .45
461 A163 10c rose vio, bl & red   3.25   .60
    Nos. 458-461,C41-C43,E13 (8)   24.85   5.40

    Centenary of adoption of Cuba's flag.

Clara Louise Maass and Hospitals A164

Hospitals: Lutheran Memorial, Newark, N.J. and Las Animas, Havana.

Wmk. 106

1951, Aug. 24   **Engr.**   *Perf. 10*
462 A164 2c scarlet   2.00 .50

75th anniv. of the birth of Clara Louise Maass, (1876-1901), American nurse and martyr in yellow fever fight.

Airmail Type and

José Raul Capablanca — A165

Capablanca Club, Havana A166

Wmk. 229

1951, Nov. 1   **Photo.**   *Perf. 13*
463 A165 1c blue grn & org   3.50 .65
464 AP27 2c rose car & dk brn   4.50 1.25
465 A166 5c black & dp ultra   9.00 1.90
Nos. 463-465,C44-C46,E14 (7) 67.00 13.60

Jose Raul Capablanca, World Chess titlist (1921). Value imperf., set of 7 pairs, $1,500.

Antonio Guiteras Holmes — A167

Guiteras Preparing Social Legislation A168

Fort of the Morrillo A169

Wmk. 106

1951, Oct. 22   **Engr.**   *Perf. 10*
466 A167 1c yellow green   .45 .20
467 A168 2c rose carmine   .75 .25
468 A169 5c deep blue   1.50 .40
Nos. 466-468,C47-C49 (6) 14.85 4.55

16th anniv. of the Action of the Morrillo and to honor Antonio Guiteras Holmes, who was killed there.
Souvenir sheets containing stamps similar to Nos. 466-468, but in different colors, are listed as Nos. C49a-C49b.

Poinsettia A170

Maj. Gen. José Maceo A171

1951, Dec. 1   **Engr. and Typo.**
469 A170 1c green & car   3.50 .25
470 A170 2c rose car & grn   4.00 .50

See Nos. 498-499.

1952, Feb. 6   **Engr.**
471 A171 2c yellow brown   .75 .20
472 A171 5c indigo   1.50 .20

Birth centenary of Maceo.

Isabella I — A172

Receipt of Autonomy A173

1952, Feb. 22
473 A172 2c bright red   2.00 .50

500th anniv. of the birth of Queen Isabella I of Spain.
Souvenir sheets containing 2c stamps of type A172 are listed as Nos. C50a-C50b.

Type of 1951 Surcharged in Green
1952, Mar. 18
474 A159 10c on 2c yel brn   2.00 .40

Wmk. 106

1952, May 27   **Engr.**   *Perf. 12½*

Designs: 2c, Tomas Estrada Palma and Luis Estevez Romero. 5c, Barnet, Finlay, Guiteras and Nuñez. 8c, Capitol. 20c, Map, Central Highway. 50c, Sugar Mill.

Centers in Black

475 A173 1c dk green   .25 .20
476 A173 2c dk carmine   .30 .20
477 A173 5c dk blue   .45 .20
478 A173 8c dk brown car   .70 .20
479 A173 20c dk olive grn   1.75 .40
480 A173 50c dp orange   3.50 .80
Nos. 475-480,C57-C60,E16 (11) 14.90 4.40

50th anniv. of the Republic of Cuba.

Hands Holding Coffee Beans A174

Designs: 2c, Map and man picking coffee beans. 5c, Farmer with pan of beans.

1952, Aug. 22   **Wmk. 229**   *Perf. 13½*
481 A174 1c green   .50 .25
482 A174 2c rose red   1.25 .30
483 A174 5c dk vio bl & aqua   1.75 .40
Nos. 481-483 (3) 3.50 .95

Bicentenary of coffee cultivation.

Col. Charles Hernandez y Sandrino A175

Alonso Alvarez de la Campa A176

1952, Oct. 7   **Wmk. 106**   *Perf. 10*
484 A175 1c yellow grn   .30 .30
485 A175 2c scarlet   .55 .30
486 A175 5c blue   .65 .30
487 A175 8c black   1.75 .45
488 A175 10c brown red   1.75 .45
489 A175 20c brown   6.50 3.75
Nos. 484-489,C63-C72,E17 (17) 49.15 25.15

See note after No. 457.

Frame Engraved; Center in Black
1952, Nov. 27

Portraits: 2c, Carlos A. Latorre. 3c, Anacleto Bermudez. 5c, Eladio G. Toledo. 8c, Angel Laborde. 10c, Jose M. Medina. 13c, Pascual Rodriguez. 20c, Carlos Verdugo.

490 A176 1c green   .40 .20
491 A176 2c carmine   .75 .25
492 A176 3c purple   .90 .25
493 A176 5c blue   .90 .60
494 A176 8c bister brn   2.00 .50
495 A176 10c orange brn   1.50 .50
496 A176 13c lilac rose   3.00 .75
497 A176 20c olive grn   4.50 1.25
Nos. 490-497,C73-C74 (10) 20.70 6.10

Execution of 8 medical students, 81st anniv.

Christmas Type of 1951
Dated "1952-1953"
Frame Engr.; Center Typo.
1952, Dec. 1

Centers: Tree.

498 A170 1c yel grn & car   5.00 1.75
499 A170 3c vio & dk grn   5.00 1.75

Birthplace of José Martí — A177

Marti at St. Lazarus Quarry — A178

No. 501, Court martial. No. 502, Martiano house, Havana. No. 504, El Abra ranch, Isle of Pines. No. 505, Symbols, "Marti the Poet." No. 506, Marti and Bolivar statue, Caracas. No. 507, At desk in New York. No. 508, House where revolutionary party was formed. No. 509, 1st issue of "Patria."

1953   **Engr.**   *Perf. 10*
500 A177 1c dk grn & red brn   .50 .20
501 A177 1c dk grn & red brn   .50 .20
502 A177 3c purple & brn   .55 .20
503 A177 3c purple & brn   .55 .20
504 A177 5c dp bl & dk brn   1.00 .20
505 A177 5c ultra & brn   1.00 .20
506 A178 10c red brn & blk   2.00 .40
507 A178 10c dk brn & blk   2.00 .40
508 A178 13c dk ol grn & dk brn   3.25 .80
509 A177 13c dk ol grn & brn   3.25 1.00
Nos. 500-509,C79-C89 (21) 34.70 12.90

Centenary of birth of José Marti.

Rafael Montoro Valdez — A179

Francisco Carrera Justiz — A180

1953, Mar. 5
510 A179 3c dark violet   2.00 .30

Rafael Montoro Valdez, statesman, birth cent.

1953, Mar. 9
511 A180 3c rose red   2.50 .30

Francisco Carrera Justiz, educator, statesman.

No. 446 Surcharged with New Value
1953, June 16
512 A146 3c on 2c rose red   2.00 .25

Board of Accounts Bldg., Havana — A181

1953, Nov. 3   **Engr.**
513 A181 3c blue   .90 .45
Nos. 513,C90-C91 (3) 6.50 2.25

1st Intl. Cong. of Boards of Accounts, Havana, Nov. 2-9.

Miguel Coyula Llaguno — A182

Communications Assoc. Flag — A183

Designs: 3c, 8c, Enrique Calleja Hensell. 10c, Antonio Ginard Rojas.

1954   **Dated 1953**
514 A182 1c green   .30 .20
515 A182 3c rose red   .30 .20
516 A182 5c blue   1.40 .20
517 A182 8c brn car   2.25 .40
518 A182 10c brown   3.50 .65
Nos. 514-518,C92-C95,E19 (10) 25.35 8.10

Nos. 515 and 517 show the same portrait, but inscriptions are arranged differently. See note after No. 457.

Carlos J. Finlay A184

Serafin Sanchez A184a

Portraits: 1c, José Marti. 2c, Maximo Gomez. 3c, José de la Luz Caballero. 4c, Miguel Aldama. 5c, Calixto Garcia. 8c, Ignacio Agramonte. 10c, Tomas Estrada Palma. 20c, José Antonio Saco. 50c, Antonio Maceo. 1p, Carlos Manuel de Cespedes.

1954-56   **Wmk. 106**   *Perf. 10*
519 A184 1c green   .45 .20
520 A184 2c rose car   .45 .20
521 A184 3c violet   .45 .20
521A A184 4c red lil ('56)   .50 .20
522 A184a 5c slate bl   .60 .20
523 A184a 8c car lake   .90 .20
524 A184 10c sepia   .90 .20
525 A184a 13c org red   .75 .20

525A	A184a	14c gray ('56)	1.25	.20
526	A184	20c olive	2.50	.20
527	A184a	50c org yel	3.50	.45
528	A184a	1p orange	7.00	.45
		Nos. 519-528 (12)	19.25	2.90

See Nos. 674-680. For surcharges see Nos. 636, 641-643.

Maj. Gen. José M. Rodriguez — A185

Design: 5c, Gen. Rodriguez on horseback.

1954, June 8   **Engr.**   ***Perf. 12½***
Center in Dark Brown

529	A185	2c dark carmine	.75	.25
530	A185	5c deep blue	2.00	.40

Cent. of the birth of Maj. Gen. José Maria Rodriguez (in 1851).

Gen. Batísta Sanatorium — A186

1954, Sept. 21   **Wmk. 106**   ***Perf. 10***

531	A186	3c deep blue	1.25	.25

See No. C107.

Santa Claus — A187   Maria Luisa Dolz — A188

1954, Dec. 15

532	A187	2c dk grn & car	5.00	1.25
533	A187	4c car & dk grn	5.00	1.25

Christmas 1954.

1954, Dec. 23

534	A188	4c deep blue	1.75	.30

Cent. of the birth of Maria Luisa Dolz, educator and defender of women's rights. See No. C108.

Cuban Flag and Scouts Saluting A189

1954, Dec. 27   ***Perf. 12½***

535	A189	4c dark green	2.25	.30

Issued to publicize the national patrol encampment of the Boy Scouts of Cuba.

Rotary Emblem and Paul P. Harris — A190

1955, Feb. 23   **Engr.**   **Wmk. 106**

536	A190	4c blue	1.50	.25

Rotary International, 50th anniversary. See No. C109.

Maj. Gen. Francisco Carrillo — A191

Portrait: 5c, Gen. Carrillo standing.

1955, Mar. 8   ***Perf. 10***

537	A191	2c brt red & dk bl	.75	.25
538	A191	5c dk bl & dk brn	1.50	.30

Cent. of the birth of Maj. Gen. Francisco Carrillo (1851-1926).

Stamp of 1885 and Convent of San Francisco — A192

Designs (including 1855 stamp): 4c, Volanta carriage. 10c, Havana, 19th century. 14c, Captain general's residence.

1955, Apr.   ***Perf. 12½***

539	A192	2c lil rose & dk grnsh bl	.95	.20
540	A192	4c ocher & dk grn	1.25	.30
541	A192	10c ultra & dk red	3.00	.85
542	A192	14c grn & dp org	7.00	2.00
		Nos. 539-542,C110-C113 (8)	20.55	6.60

Cent. of Cuba's 1st postage stamps.

Maj. Gen. Mario G. Menocal A193   Gen. Emilio Nuñez A194

Portraits: 10c, J. G. Gomez. 14c, A. Sanchez de Bustamante.

1955, June 22

543	A193	2c dark green	.65	.20
544	A194	4c lilac rose	.80	.20
545	A193	10c deep blue	1.50	.40
546	A194	14c gray violet	3.00	.90
		Nos. 543-546,C114-C116,E20 (8)	18.95	5.95

See note after No. 457.

Turkey — A195   Gen. Emilio Nuñez — A196

1955, Dec. 15   **Engr.**

547	A195	2c slate grn & dk car	5.00	1.50
548	A195	4c rose lake & brt grn	5.00	1.50

Christmas 1955.

1955, Dec. 27

549	A196	4c claret	1.10	.45
		Nos. 549,C127-C128 (3)	6.35	1.90

Cent. of the birth of Gen. Emilio Nunez, Cuban revolutionary hero.

Francisco Cajigal de la Vega (1695-1777) A197   Julian del Casal A198

1956, Mar. 27   ***Perf. 12½***

552	A197	4c rose brn & slate bl	1.10	.55

Cuban post bicent. See No. C129.

1956, May 2

Portraits: 4c, Luisa Perez de Zambrana. 10c, Juan Clemente Zenea. 14c, José Joaquin Palma.

Portraits in Black

553	A198	2c green	.50	.20
554	A198	4c rose lilac	.50	.20
555	A198	10c blue	1.25	.20
556	A198	14c violet	2.50	.20
		Nos. 553-556,C131-C133,E21 (8)	14.75	3.50

See note after No. 457.

Victor Muñoz — A199   Masonic Temple, Havana — A200

1956, May 13

557	A199	4c brown & green	1.25	.55

Victor Munoz (1873-1922), founder of Mother's Day in Cuba. See No. C134.

1956, June 5

558	A200	4c blue	1.50	.55

See No. C135.

Virgin of Charity, El Cobre — A201   "The Cry of Yara" — A202

1956, Sept. 8   ***Perf. 12½***

559	A201	4c brt blue & yel	1.25	.30

Issued in honor of Our Lady of Charity of Cobre, patroness of Cuba. See No. C149.

1956, Oct. 10

560	A202	4c dk grn & brn	1.40	.30

Cuba's independence from Spain.

Raimundo G. Menocal A203

The Three Wise Men — A204

1956, Dec. 3   **Wmk. 106**   ***Perf. 12½***

561	A203	4c dark brown	1.25	.30

Cent. of the birth of Prof. Raimundo G. Menocal, physician.

1956, Dec. 1

562	A204	2c red & slate grn	4.50	1.25
563	A204	4c slate grn & red	4.50	1.25

Christmas 1956.

Martin Morua Delgado — A205   Boy Scouts at Campfire — A206

1957, Jan. 30

564	A205	4c dark green	1.00	.30

Delgado, patriot, birth cent.

1957, Feb. 22   **Wmk. 106**   ***Perf. 12½***

565	A206	4c slate grn & red	1.50	.40

Cent. of the birth of Lord Baden-Powell, founder of the Boy Scouts. See No. C152.

"The Blind," by M. Vega A207

Paintings: 4c, "The Art Critics" by M. Melero. 10c, "Volanta in Storm" by A. Menocal. 14c, "The Convalescent" by L. Romañach.

1957, Mar.   **Engr.**   ***Perf. 12½***
Side and Lower Inscriptions in Dark Brown

566	A207	2c olive green	.50	.25
567	A207	4c orange red	.90	.30
568	A207	10c olive green	1.25	.50
569	A207	14c ultra	1.50	.55
		Nos. 566-569,C153-C155,E22 (8)	13.80	4.25

See note after No. 457.

Emblem of Philatelic Club of Cuba A208   Juan F. Steegers A209

1957, Apr. 24

570	A208	4c ocher, blue & red	1.50	.30

Issued for Stamp Day, Apr. 24, and the National Philatelic Exhibition. See No. C156.

1957, Apr. 30

571	A209	4c blue	1.00	.30

Juan Francisco Steegers y Perera (1856-1921), dactyloscopy pioneer. See No. C157.

Victoria Bru Sanchez A210

Joaquin de Aguero in Battle of Jucaral A211

1957, June 3   Wmk. 106   Perf. 12½
572 A210 4c indigo   1.25 .30

1957, July 4
573 A211 4c dark green   1.00 .30

Issued to honor Joaquin de Aguero, Cuban freedom fighter and patriot. See No. C162.

Boy, Dogs and Cat — A212

Col. Rafael Manduley del Rio — A213

1957, July 17
574 A212 4c Prus green   2.00 .55

Mrs. Jeanette Ryder, founder of the Humane Society of Cuba. See Nos. C163-C163a.

1957, July 31
575 A213 4c Prus green   2.75 1.50

Issued to honor Col. Manduley del Rio, patriot, on the cent. of his birth (in 1856).

Palace of Justice A214

1957, Sept. 2   Engr.   Perf. 12½
576 A214 4c blue gray   1.25 .40

Opening of the new Palace of Justice in Havana. See No. C165.

Generals of the Liberation — A215

1957, Sept. 26
577 A215 4c dl grn & red brn   1.00 .30
578 A215 4c dl bl & red brn   1.00 .30
579 A215 4c rose & brown   1.00 .30
580 A215 4c org yel & brn   1.00 .30
581 A215 4c lt violet & brn   1.00 .30
    Nos. 577-581 (5)   5.00 1.50

Generals of the army of liberation.

1st Publication Printed in Cuba — A216

Patio — A217

1957, Oct. 18   Wmk. 106   Perf. 12½
582 A216 4c slate blue   1.00 .40
    Nos. 582,C167-C168 (3)   3.75 1.15

José Marti National Library.

1957, Nov. 19
583 A217 4c red brn & grn   1.00 .40
    Nos. 583,C173-C174 (3)   4.90 1.40

Cent. of the 1st Cuban Normal School.

Trinidad, Founded 1514 — A218

Fortifications, Havana, 1611 — A219

Views: 10c, Padre Pico street, Santiago de Cuba. 14c, Church of Our Lady, Camaguey.

1957, Dec. 17   Engr.   Perf. 12½
584 A218 2c brown & indigo   .30 .20
585 A219 4c slate grn & brn   .70 .20
586 A219 10c sepia & red   1.25 .30
587 A219 14c green & dk red   1.75 .25
    Nos. 584-587,C175-C177,E23
    (8)   12.05 3.40

See note after No. 457.

Nativity — A220

1957, Dec. 20
588 A220 2c multicolored   3.50 .90
589 A220 4c multicolored   3.50 .90

Christmas 1957.

Dayton Hedges and Ariguanabo Textile Factory A221

1958, Jan. 30   Wmk. 106   Perf. 12½
590 A221 4c blue   1.50 .75

Issued to honor Dayton Hedges, founder of Cuba's textile industry. See No. C178.

Dr. Francisco Dominguez Roldan — A222

José Ignacio Rivero y Alonso — A223

1958, Feb. 21
591 A222 4c green   1.25 .30

Roldan (1864-1942), who introduced radiotherapy and physiotherapy to Cuba.

1958, Apr. 1
592 A223 4c lt olive green   1.25 .70

José Ignacio Rivero y Alonso, editor of Diario de la Marina, 1919-44. See No. C179.

Map of Cuba and Mail Route, 1756 A224

1958, Apr. 24   Perf. 12½
593 A224 4c dk grn, aqua & buff 1.00 .30

Issued for Stamp Day, Apr. 24 and the National Philatelic Exhibition. See No. C180.

Maj. Gen. José Miguel Gomez A225

Nicolas Ruiz Espadero A226

1958, June 6   Wmk. 106   Perf. 12½
594 A225 4c slate   1.00 .40

Maj. Gen. José Miguel Gomez, President of Cuba, 1909-13. See No. C181.

1958, June 27   Perf. 12½

Indigo Emblem

Musicians: 4c, Ignacio Cervantes. 10c, José White. 14c, Brindis de Salas.

595 A226 2c brown   .60 .20
596 A226 4c dark gray   .60 .20
597 A226 10c olive green   .80 .20
598 A226 14c red   1.10 .25

Green Emblem

Physicians: 2c, Tomas Romay Chacon. 4c, Angel Arturo Aballi. 10c, Fernando Gonzalez del Valle. 14c, Vicente Antonio de Castro.

599 A226 2c brown   .70 .20
600 A226 4c gray   1.10 .20
601 A226 10c dark carmine   .80 .20
602 A226 14c dark blue   1.10 .20

Red Emblem

Lawyers: 2c, Jose Maria Garcia Montes. 4c, Jose A. Gonzalez Lanuza. 10c, Juan B. Hernandez Barreiro. 14c, Pedro Gonzalez Llorente.

603 A226 2c sepia   .50 .20
604 A226 4c gray   .80 .20
605 A226 10c olive grn   1.00 .20
606 A226 14c slate blue   1.10 .20
    Nos. 595-606 (12)   10.20 2.45

For surcharges see Nos. 629-631.

Carlos de la Torre — A227

1958, Aug. 29   Engr.   Wmk. 321
607 A227 4c violet blue   1.50 .40
    Nos. 607,C182-C184 (4)   32.00 5.50

Dr. Carlos de la Torre y Huerta (1858-1950), naturalist. For surcharge see No. 632.

Poey's "Memorias" Title Page — A228

Felipe Poey — A229

1958, Sept. 26   Wmk. 106
608 A228 2c black & lt violet   .80 .25
609 A229 4c brown black   .95 .25
    Nos. 608-609,C185-C191,E26-
    E27 (11)   79.75 22.60

Felipe Poey (1799-1891), naturalist.

Theodore Roosevelt — A230

Cattleyopsis Lindenii Orchid — A231

1958, Oct. 27   Perf. 12½
610 A230 4c gray green   1.25 .40

Theodore Roosevelt, birth cent. See No. C192.

Engraved and Photogravure
1958, Dec. 16   Wmk. 321   Perf. 12½

4c, Oncidium Guibertianum Orchid.

611 A231 2c multicolored   4.50 1.25
612 A231 4c multicolored   4.50 1.25

Christmas. For surcharge see No. 633.

Flag and Revolutionary A232

Gen. Adolfo Flor Crombet (1848-95) A233

Engr. & Typo.
1959, Jan. 28   Wmk. 321
613 A232 2c car rose & gray   .75 .30

Day of Liberation, Jan. 1, 1959.

1959, Mar. 18   Engr.   Wmk. 106
614 A233 4c slate green   1.10 .40

For surcharge see No. 634.

Maria Teresa
Garcia Montes
A234

Carlos Manuel
de Cespedes
A235

1959, Nov. 11   **Perf. 12½**
615 A234 4c brown   1.10   .40

Maria Teresa Garcia Montes (1880-1930), founder of the Musical Arts Society. See No. C198. For surcharge see No. 635.

1959, Oct. 10   Wmk. 106   Perf. 12½

Presidents: No. 617, Salvador Cisneros Betancourt. No. 618, Manuel de Jesus Calvar. No. 619, Bartolomé Maso. No. 620, Juan B. Spotorno. No. 621, Tomas Estrada Palma. No. 622, Francisco Javier de Céspedes. No. 623, Vicente Garcia.

616	A235	2c slate blue	.55	.20
617	A235	2c green	.55	.20
618	A235	2c deep violet	.55	.20
619	A235	2c orange brown	.55	.20
620	A235	4c dark carmine	.70	.25
621	A235	4c deep brown	.70	.25
622	A235	4c dark gray	.70	.25
623	A235	4c dark violet	.70	.25
		Nos. 616-623 (8)	5.00	1.80

Issued to honor former Cuban presidents.

No. B3 Surcharged in Red:
"HABILITADO PARA / 2¢"

1960
624 SP2 2c on 2c + 1c car & ultra   1.00   .20

See No. C199.

Rebel Attack on Moncada Barracks
A236

Designs: 2c, Rebels disembarking from "Granma." 10c, Battle of the Uvero. 12c, Map of Cuba and rebel ("The Invasion").

1960, Jan. 28   **Wmk. 320**
625	A236	1c gray ol, bl & ver	.25	.20
626	A236	2c bl, gray ol & brn	.70	.20
627	A236	10c bl, gray ol & red	1.75	.65
628	A236	12c brt bl, brn & grn	2.40	.30
		Nos. 625-628,C200-C202 (7)	17.10	3.75

First anniversary of revolution.

Stamps of 1956-59 Surcharged with New Value in Carmine or Silver

1960, Feb. 3
629	A226	1c on 4c dk gray & ind	.50	.20
630	A226	1c on 4c gray & grn	.50	.25
631	A226	1c on 4c gray & red	.50	.20
632	A227	1c on 4c violet bl	.50	.20
633	A231	1c on 4c multi (S)	.60	.50
634	A233	1c on 4c slate grn	.50	.20
635	A234	1c on 4c brown	.50	.20
636	A184a	2c on 14c gray	.90	.20
		Nos. 629-636,C203-C204 (10)	8.00	3.25

17th Olympic Games, Rome, Aug. 25-Sept. 11 — A238

Statues: 2c, Mambi Victorioso (Battle of San Juan Hill), Santiago de Cuba. 10c, Marta Abreo de Estevez. 12c, Ignacio Agramonte, Camaguey.

Wmk. 321
1960, Mar. 28   Engr.   Perf. 12½
637	A237	1c brn & dk bl	.25	.20
638	A237	2c green & red	.30	.20
639	A237	10c choc & red	.90	.20
640	A237	12c gray ol & vio	1.25	.45
		Nos. 637-640,C206-C208 (7)	7.40	2.85

See note after No. 386.

Nos. 521A, 522 and 525 Surcharged "HABILITADO / PARA / 2¢" in Violet Blue, Red or Black

1960   **Wmk. 106**   **Perf. 10**
641	A184	2c on 4c red lil (VB)	.80	.40
642	A184a	2c on 5c sl bl (R)	1.25	.40
643	A184	2c on 13c org red	1.25	.40

No. 307B Surcharged "HABILITADO / 10¢"

644	A41	10c on 20c ol grn	1.25	.50
		Nos. 641-644 (4)	4.55	1.70

Wmk. 321
1960, Sept. 22   Engr.   Perf. 12½
645	A238	1c Sailboats	.45	.25
646	A238	2c Marksman	.55	.25
		Nos. 645-646,C212-C213 (4)	3.30	1.25

For souvenir sheet see No. C213a.

Camilo Cienfuegos and View of Escolar
A239

1960, Oct. 27   Litho.   Unwmk.
647 A239 2c brn, bl, grn & red   1.25   .20

1st anniv. of the death of Camilo Cienfuegos, revolutionary hero.

Morning Glory
A240

Tobacco and Christmas Hymn
A241

1960   **Litho.**   **Perf. 12½**
648	A240	1c red	.75	.75
649	A241	1c Tobacco	1.50	1.50
650	A241	1c Mariposa	1.50	1.50
651	A241	1c Guaiacum	1.50	1.50
652	A241	1c Coffee	1.50	1.50
	a.	Block of 4, #649-652	7.00	
653	A240	2c ultra	1.00	1.00
654	A241	2c Tobacco	3.00	3.00
655	A241	2c Mariposa	3.00	3.00
656	A241	2c Guaiacum	3.00	3.00
657	A241	2c Coffee	3.00	3.00
	a.	Block of 4, #654-657	14.00	
658	A240	10c ocher	3.00	2.50
659	A241	10c Tobacco	10.00	6.00
660	A241	10c Mariposa	10.00	6.00
661	A241	10c Guaiacum	10.00	6.00
662	A241	10c Coffee	10.00	6.00
	a.	Block of 4, #659-662	47.50	
		Nos. 648-662 (15)	62.75	46.25

Issued for Christmas 1960.
Nos. 648-662 were printed in three sheets of 25. Nine stamps of type A240 form a center cross, stamps of type A241 form a block of

four in each corner with the musical bars joined in an oval around the floral designs.

"Public Capital for Economic Benefit" — A242

Designs: 2c, Chart and symbols of agriculture and industry. 6c, Cogwheels.

Perf. 11½
1961, Jan. 10   Unwmk.   Photo.
663	A242	1c yel, blk & org	.40	.20
664	A242	2c bl, blk & red	.40	.20
665	A242	6c yel, red org & blk	1.00	.25
		Nos. 663-665,C215-C218 (7)	9.90	2.70

Issued to publicize the conference of underdeveloped countries, Havana.

Jesus Menéndez and Sugar Cane — A243

1961, Jan. 22   Litho.   Perf. 12½
666 A243 2c dk grn & brn   .60   .25

Jesus Menéndez, leader in sugar industry.

Same Overprinted in Red: "PRIMERO DE MAYO 1961 ESTAMOS VENCIENDO"

1961, May 2
667 A243 2c dk grn & brn   1.50   .25

Issued for May Day, 1961.

Dove and UN Emblem — A244

1961, Apr. 12   Litho.   Perf. 12½
668	A244	2c red brn & yel grd	.60	.20
669	A244	10c emer & rose lil	1.25	.45
	a.	Souv. sheet, #668-669, imperf.	5.00	
		Nos. 668-669,C222-C223 (4)	3.95	1.40

15th anniv. (in 1960) of the UN.

Stamp Day
A245

Stamp Day: 1c, Revolutionary 10c stamp of 1874, 1868 "cancel." 2c, #238, 1902 "cancel." 10c, #613, 1959 "cancel."

1961, Apr. 24   **Unwmk.**
670	A245	1c dull rose & dk grn	.35	.20
671	A245	2c salmon & dk grn	.40	.20
672	A245	10c pale grn, car rose & blk	2.00	.40
		Nos. 670-672 (3)	2.75	.80

For overprint see No. 681.

Hand Releasing Dove — A246

1961, July 26   **Perf. 12½**
673 A246 2c blk, red, yel & gray   1.50   .25

26th of July (1953) movement, Castro's revolt against Fulgencio Batista.
Burelage on back consisting of wavy lines and diagonal rows of "CUBA CORREOS" in pale salmon.

Portrait Type of 1954

Designs: Same as before. On the 2c, "1833" is replaced by "?."

Wmk. 321 (Nos. 674, 676); Unwmkd.
Perf. 12½ (Nos. 674, 676); Rouletted
1961-69   **Engr.**
674	A184	1c brown red	.50	.20
675	A184	1c lt blue ('69)	.30	.20
676	A184a	2c slate green	.50	.20
677	A184a	2c yel grn ('69)	.30	.20
678	A184	3c org ('64)	1.50	.20
679	A184	13c brn ('64)	1.50	.30
680	A184	20c lilac ('69)	1.75	.25
		Nos. 674-680 (7)	6.35	1.55

Issued: #674, 676, 8/1; #678-679, 12/764; others, 9/69.
For Nos. 675, 677-680, see embargo note following No. 702.

No. 672 Ovptd. in Red

Perf. 12½
1961, Oct. 7   Litho.   Unwmk.
681 A245 10c pale grn, car rose & blk   2.00   .45

1st Official Phil. Exhib., Havana, Oct. 7-17.

Education Year — A247

Designs: One letter (per stamp) of "CUBA," book and various quotations by Jose Marti about the virtues of literacy.

1961, Nov. 22
682	A247	1c pale grn, red & blk	.20	.20
683	A247	2c blue, red & blk	.20	.20
684	A247	10c vio, red & blk	.90	.25
685	A247	12c org, red & blk	1.75	.60
		Nos. 682-685 (4)	3.05	1.25

A248

Christmas
A249

1c, Snails. 2c, Birds, vert. 10c, Butterflies.

1961, Dec. 1
686	A248	1c Polymita flammulata	.50	.20
687	A249	1c Polymita fulminata	.50	.20
688	A249	1c Polymita nigrofasciata	.50	.20

689	A249	1c Polymita fus-colimbata	.50	.20
690	A249	1c Polymita rose-olimbata	.50	.20
a.		Block of 5 + label, Nos. 686-690	2.50	1.50
691	A248	2c Cuban grassquit	2.00	.50
692	A249	2c Cuban macaw	2.00	.50
693	A249	2c Cuban trogon	2.00	.50
694	A249	2c Bee hummingbird	2.00	.50
695	A249	2c Ivory-billed woodpecker	2.00	.50
a.		Block of 5 + label, Nos. 691-695	12.50	4.00
696	A248	10c Othreis toddi	3.00	1.00
697	A249	10c Uranidia boisduvalii	3.00	1.00
698	A249	10c Phoebis avellaneda	3.00	1.00
699	A249	10c Phaloe cubana	3.00	1.00
700	A249	10c Papilio gundlachianus	3.00	1.00
a.		Block of 5 + label, Nos. 696-700	15.00	7.50
		Nos. 686-700 (15)	27.50	8.50

Stamps of the same denomination printed se-tenant in sheets of 20 stamps plus 5 labels picturing bells and star. Stamps of Type A249 are arranged in blocks of 4; Type A248 stamps and labels form a cross in sheet.

See Nos. 760-774, 912-926, 1025-1039, 1179-1193, 1303-1317, 1464-1478, 1572-1586.

3rd Anniv. of the Revolution A250

1962, Jan. 3

701	A250	1c multi	.85	.35
702	A250	2c multi	1.75	.45

See Nos. C226-C228.

Cuban goods have been embargoed by the United States since a Feb. 7, 1962 proclamation by President Kennedy, but according to the Office of Foreign Assets Control of the Treasury Department, used Cuban stamps can be imported and sold without limitation, and unused stamps may be imported for personal use, but not resold.

Natl. Militia A251

Silhouettes of militiamen and women and their peace-time occupations: 1c, Farmer. 2c, Welder. 3c, Seamstress.

1962, Feb. 26

703	A251	1c blue grn & blk	.30	.20
704	A251	2c deep blue & blk	.60	.25
705	A251	10c brt org & blk	2.10	.55
		Nos. 703-705 (3)	3.00	1.00

Bay of Pigs Invasion, 1st Anniv. — A252

1962, Apr. 17

706	A252	2c multi	.45	.20
707	A252	3c multi	.45	.20
708	A252	10c multi	3.00	.65
		Nos. 706-708 (3)	3.90	1.05

1st West Indies Packet A253

1962, Apr. 24

709	A253	10c red & gray	3.25	.90

Stamp Day. See No. E32.

Intl. Labor Day — A254

1962, May 1

710	A254	2c ocher & blk	.35	.20
711	A254	3c ver & blk	.75	.25
712	A254	10c greenish blue & blk	2.50	.70
		Nos. 710-712 (3)	3.60	1.15

Natl. Sports Institute (INDER) Emblem and Athletes — A255

1962, July 25 Wmk. 321

713	A255	1c Judo	.35	.20
714	A255	1c Discus	.35	.20
715	A255	1c Gymnastics	.35	.20
716	A255	1c Wrestling	.35	.20
717	A255	1c Weight lifting	.35	.20
718	A255	2c Roller skating	.35	.20
719	A255	2c Equestrian	.35	.20
720	A255	2c Archery	.35	.20
721	A255	2c Bicycling	.35	.20
722	A255	2c Bowling	.35	.20
723	A255	3c Power boating	1.00	.20
724	A255	3c One-man kayak	1.00	.20
725	A255	3c Swimming	1.00	.20
726	A255	3c Sculling	1.00	.20
727	A255	3c Yachting	1.00	.20
728	A255	9c Soccer	.90	.35
729	A255	9c Volleyball	.90	.35
730	A255	9c Baseball	.90	.35
731	A255	9c Basketball	.90	.35
732	A255	9c Tennis	.90	.35
733	A255	9c Boxing	.90	.35
734	A255	10c Underwater fishing	.90	.35
735	A255	10c Model-plane flying	.90	.35
736	A255	10c Pistol shooting	.90	.35
737	A255	10c Water polo	.90	.35
738	A255	13c Paddleball	1.00	.50
739	A255	13c Fencing	1.00	.50
740	A255	13c Sports Palace	1.00	.50
741	A255	13c Chess	1.00	.50
742	A255	13c Jai alai	1.00	.50
		Nos. 713-742 (30)	22.50	9.00

Stamps of the same denomination printed se-tenant in sheets of 25. Various combinations possible.

CORREOS DE CUBA

9th Anniv. of the Revolution A256

Attack on Moncada Barracks: Abel Santamaria and: 2c, Barracks under siege. 3c, Children at Moncada School.

1962, July 26

743	A256	2c brn car & dark ultra	.65	.35
744	A256	3c dark ultra & brn car	1.10	.55

8th World Youth Festival for Peace and Friendship, Helsinki, July 28-Aug. 6 — A257

1962, July 28

745	A257	2c Dove, emblem	1.00	.25
746	A257	3c Hand grip, emblem	1.75	.55
a.		Min. sheet of 2, Nos. 745-746, imperf.	6.50	6.50

9th Central American and Caribbean Games, Kingston, Jamaica, Aug. 11-25 A258

1962, Aug. 27

747	A258	1c Boxing	.20	.20
748	A258	2c Tennis	.20	.20
749	A258	3c Baseball	.20	.20
750	A258	13c Fencing	2.40	.80
		Nos. 747-750 (4)	3.00	1.40

A259

First Natl. Congress of the Federation of Cuban Women — A260

1962, Oct. 1

751	A259	9c rose, blk & grn	1.10	.25
752	A260	13c blk, grn & lt blue	2.40	.65

Latin American University Games — A261

1962, Oct. 13 Wmk. 106

753	A261	1c Running	.40	.20
754	A261	2c Baseball	.85	.20
755	A261	3c Basketball	1.25	.20
756	A261	13c World map	2.50	.50
		Nos. 753-756 (4)	5.00	1.15

World Health Organization Campaign to Eradicate Malaria — A262

Designs: 1c, Magnified specimen of the parasitic protozoa, microscope. 2c, Swamp and mosquito. 3c, Chemist's structural formulas for quinine, cinchona plant.

1962, Dec. 14

757	A262	1c multi	.50	.25
758	A262	2c multi	.50	.25
759	A262	3c multi	1.75	.45
		Nos. 757-759 (3)	2.75	.95

Christmas Type of 1961

2c, Reptiles. 3c, Insects, vert. 10c, Rodents.

1962, Dec. 21 Unwmk.

760	A248	2c Epicrates angulifer	.65	.20
761	A249	2c Cricosaurus typica	.65	.20
762	A249	2c Anolis equestris	.65	.20
763	A249	2c Tropidophis wrighti	.65	.20
764	A249	2c Cyclura macleayi	.65	.20
a.		Block of 5 + label, Nos. 760-764	3.50	1.50
765	A248	3c Cubispa turquino	1.00	.60
766	A249	3c Chrysis superba	1.00	.60
767	A249	3c Essostruta roberto	1.00	.60
768	A249	3c Hortensia conciliata	1.00	.60
769	A249	3c Lachnopus argus	1.00	.60
a.		Block of 5 + label, Nos. 765-769	5.50	4.50
770	A248	10c Monophyllus cubanus	4.00	1.25
771	A249	10c Capromys pilorides	4.00	1.25
772	A249	10c Capromys prehensilis	4.00	1.25
773	A249	10c Solenodon cubensis	4.00	1.25
774	A249	10c Capromys pilorides (Blanca)	4.00	1.25
a.		Block of 5 + label, Nos. 770-774	21.00	9.00
		Nos. 760-774 (15)	28.25	10.25

Christmas 1962. See note after No. 700.

Around 1962 a 1ctv. label picturing Fidel Castro was used as a voluntary contribution stamp. It is not inscribed "Correos" and was not valid for postage.

Soviet Space Flights — A263

Spacecraft and cosmonauts: 1c, Vostok 1, Yuri A. Gagarin, Apr. 12, 1961. 2c, Vostok 2, Gherman S. Titov, Aug. 6-7, 1961. 3c, Vostok 3, Andrian G. Nikolaev, Aug. 11-15, 1962, and Vostok 4, Pavel R. Popovich, Aug. 12-15, 1962. 9c, Vostok 5, Valery F. Bykovsky, June 14-19, 1963. 13c, Vostok 6, Valentina V. Tereshkova, June 16-19, 1963.

1963-64 Wmk. 321

775	A263	1c ultra, red & yel	.35	.20
776	A263	2c grn, red & rose lake	.65	.25
777	A263	3c yel, vio & ver	.65	.25
778	A263	9c red, dark vio & yel	1.25	.45
779	A263	13c dark blue green, dull red brown & yel	3.25	.70
		Nos. 775-779 (5)	6.15	1.85

Issued: 1c, 2c, 3c, 2/26/63; others, 8/15/64.

Attack of the Presidential Palace, 6th Anniv. — A264

9c, Guerillas attacking palace. 13c, Four student leaders. 30c, Jose A. Echeverria, Menelao Mora.

1963, Mar. 13

780	A264	9c dark red & blk	1.10	.20
781	A264	13c chalky blue & sep	1.40	.45
782	A264	30c org & grn	3.50	1.00
		Nos. 780-782 (3)	6.00	1.65

4th Pan American Games, Sao Paulo, Brazil, Apr. 20-May 5 — A265

1963, Apr. 20
783	A265	1c Baseball	1.25	.35
784	A265	13c Boxing	3.25	.65

Stamp Day A266

3c, Mask mailbox, 19th cent. 10c, Mask mailbox at the Plaza de la Catedral, Havana.

1963, Apr. 25
785	A266	3c black & dark org	1.00	.25
786	A266	10c black & pur	2.50	.50

See Nos. 828-829, 956-957 and 1102-1103.

Labor Day — A267

1963, May 1
787	A267	3c shown	.50	.20
788	A267	13c Four workers	1.75	.60

Intl. Children's Week, June 1-7 — A268

1963, June 1
789	A268	3c blue blk & bister brn	.50	.20
790	A268	30c blue blk & red	2.75	.80

Ritual Effigy — A269

Broken Chains at Moncada A270

Taino Civilization artifacts: 3c, Wood-carved throne, horiz. 9c, Stone-carved figurine.

1963, June 29
791	A269	2c org & red brn	.75	.20
792	A269	3c ultra & red brn	.90	.25
793	A269	9c rose & gray	1.60	.45
		Nos. 791-793 (3)	3.25	.90

Montane Anthropology Museum, 60th anniv.

1963, July 26

2c, Attack on the Presidential Palace. 3c, The insurrection. 7c, Strike of April 9. 9c, Triumph of the revolution. 10c, Agricultural

reform and nationalization of industry. 13c, Bay of Pigs victory.
794	A270	1c pink & blk	.20	.20
795	A270	2c lt blue & vio brn	.20	.20
796	A270	3c lt vio & brn	.20	.20
797	A270	7c apple green & rose	.25	.20
798	A270	9c olive bister & rose vio	.50	.30
799	A270	10c beige & sage grn	1.50	.50
800	A270	13c pale org & slate blue	2.25	.90
		Nos. 794-800 (7)	5.10	2.50

Indigenous Fruit — A271

1963, Aug. 19
801	A271	1c Star apple	.20	.20
802	A271	2c Cherimoya	.20	.20
803	A271	3c Cashew nut	.35	.20
804	A271	10c Custard apple	2.00	.45
805	A271	13c Mangoes	2.50	1.40
		Nos. 801-805 (5)	5.25	2.45

Geometric Shapes A272

View of a Town — A273

Designs: No. 806, Circle, triangle, square, vert. No. 807, Roof, window, vert. No. 808, View of a town. No. 809, View of a town in blue. No. 810, View of a town in olive bister and red. No. 811, Circle, triangle, vert. No. 812, House, roof and doorway, vert. No. 813, House, girders.

1963, Sept. 29   **Unwmk.**
806	A272	3c multi	.50	.20
807	A272	3c multi	.50	.20
808	A273	3c multi	.50	.20
809	A273	3c multi	.50	.20
810	A273	13c multi	1.50	.55
811	A272	13c multi	1.50	.55
812	A272	13c multi	1.50	.55
813	A272	13c multi	1.50	.55
		Nos. 806-813 (8)	8.00	3.00

7th Intl. Congress of the Intl. Union of Architects.

Ernest Hemingway (1899-1961), American Author — A274

Hemingway and: 3c, The Old Man and the Sea. 9c, For Whom the Bell Tolls. 13c, Hemingway Museum (former residence), San Francisco de Paula, near Havana.

1963, Dec. 5   **Wmk. 321**
814	A274	3c brn & lt blue	.75	.20
815	A274	9c sage grn & pink	1.75	.20
816	A274	13c blk & yel grn	3.00	.60
		Nos. 814-816 (3)	5.50	1.00

Natl. Museum, 50th Anniv. — A275

Works of art: 2c, El Zapateo (Dance), by Victor P. Landaluze. 3c, Abduction of the Mulatto Women, by Carlos Enriquez, vert. 9c, Greek Panathean amphora, vert. 13c, My Beloved (bust of a young woman), by Jean Antoine Houdon, vert.

1964, Mar. 19   **Unwmk.**
817	A275	2c multi	.20	.20
818	A275	3c multi	.80	.20
819	A275	9c multi	1.10	.40
820	A275	13c multi	2.40	.65
		Nos. 817-820 (4)	4.50	1.45

General Strike on Apr. 9, 6th Anniv. — A276

Rebel leaders: 2c, Bernardo Juan Borrell. 3c, Marcelo Salado. 10c, Oscar Lucero. 13c, Sergio Gonzalez.

1964, Apr. 9
821	A276	2c blk, yel grn & dull org	.40	.20
822	A276	3c blk, red & dull org	.70	.20
823	A276	10c blk, pur & beige	1.25	.30
824	A276	13c blk, brt blue & beige	2.50	.60
		Nos. 821-824 (4)	4.85	1.30

Bay of Pigs Invasion, 3rd Anniv. A277

Designs: 3c, Fish in net. 10c, Victory Monument. 13c, Fallen eagle, vert.

1964, Apr. 17
825	A277	3c multi	.30	.20
826	A277	10c multi	.70	.35
827	A277	13c multi	2.00	.70
		Nos. 825-827 (3)	3.00	1.25

Stamp Day Type of 1963

3c, Vicente Mora Pera, 1st postal director. 13c, Unissued provisional stamp, 1871.

1964, Apr. 24
828	A266	3c ocher & dull lil	.50	.20
829	A266	13c dull vio & lt olive grn	2.50	.50

Labor Day — A278

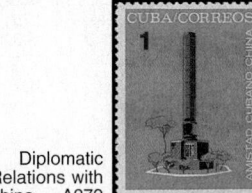

Diplomatic Relations with China — A279

1964, May 1
830	A278	3c Industry	.40	.20
831	A278	13c Agriculture	1.60	.55

1964, May 15

Designs: 1c, China Monument, Havana. 2c, Cuban and Chinese farmers. 3c, Natl. flags.
832	A279	1c multi	.35	.20
833	A279	2c org brn, blk & apple grn	.70	.20
834	A279	3c multi	1.40	.20
		Nos. 832-834 (3)	2.45	.60

15th UPU Congress, Vienna, May-June A280

1964, May 29
835	A280	13c Hemispheres on world map	.85	.30
836	A280	30c Heinrich von Stephan	1.90	.80
837	A280	50c UPU Monument, Bern	4.00	1.40
		Nos. 835-837 (3)	6.75	2.50

Development of Natl. Industry A281

1964, June 16
838	A281	1c Fish	.40	.20
839	A281	2c Cow	.60	.20
840	A281	13c Chickens	2.50	.60
		Nos. 838-840 (3)	3.50	1.00

Merchant Fleet — A282

1964, June 30
841	A282	1c Rio Jibacoa	.25	.20
842	A282	2c Camilo Cienfuegos	.40	.20
843	A282	3c Sierra Maestra	.60	.20
844	A282	9c Bahia de Siguanea	1.25	.50
845	A282	10c Oriente	3.50	.90
		Nos. 841-845 (5)	6.00	2.00

Unification of Viet Nam — A283

Designs: 2c, Vietnamese guerrilla, American soldier. 3c, Northerner and southerner shaking hands over map of united Viet Nam. 10c, Ox-drawn plow, machinised harvester. 13c, Natl. flags and profiles of Cuban and Vietnamese farmers.

1964, July 20
846	A283	2c multi	.30	.20
847	A283	3c multi	.45	.20
848	A283	10c multi	1.00	.25
849	A283	13c multi	2.75	.60
		Nos. 846-849 (4)	4.50	1.25

11th Anniv. of the Revolution A284

1964 Summer Olympics, Tokyo, Oct. 10-25 A285

Designs: 3c, Raul Gomez Garcia and poem. 13c, Cover of La Historia Me Absolvera, by Fidel Castro.

1964, July 25
850	A284	3c red, tan & blk	.50	.20
851	A284	13c multi	3.00	.40

1964, Oct. 10   Wmk. 376   Perf. 10
852	A285	1c Gymnastics	.30	.20
853	A285	2c Rowing	.30	.20
854	A285	3c Boxing	.30	.20
855	A285	7c Running, horiz.	.70	.20
856	A285	10c Fencing, horiz.	1.50	.55
857	A285	13c Foil, cleats, oar, boxing glove, sun, horiz.	2.50	.85
		Nos. 852-857 (6)	5.60	2.20

Satellite and Globe A286

Satellite and Partial Globe A287

No. C31 and Partial Globe A288

Various satellites and rockets.

1964, Oct. 15
858	A286	1c shown	.20	.20
859	A286	1c shown	.20	.20
860	A287	1c Globe LL	.20	.20
861	A287	1c Globe UR	.20	.20
862	A287	1c Globe UL	.20	.20
a.		Block of 5 + label, Nos. 858-862	1.00	1.00
863	A286	2c Spacecraft and globe	.55	.20
864	A287	2c Globe LR	.55	.20
865	A287	2c Globe LL	.55	.20
866	A287	2c Globe UR	.55	.20
867	A287	2c Globe UL	.55	.20
a.		Block of 5 + label, Nos. 863-867	3.00	1.50
868	A286	3c Satellite and globe	.75	.35
869	A287	3c Globe LR	.75	.35
870	A287	3c Globe LL	.75	.35
871	A287	3c Globe UR	.75	.35
872	A287	3c Globe UL	.75	.35
a.		Block of 5 + label, Nos. 868-872	4.00	2.50
873	A286	9c Satellite and globe, diff	1.75	.70
874	A287	9c Globe LR	1.75	.70
875	A287	9c Globe LL	1.75	.70
876	A287	9c Globe UR	1.75	.70
877	A287	9c Globe UL	1.75	.70
a.		Block of 5 + label, Nos. 873-877	11.00	5.00
878	A286	13c Satellite and globe, diff.	2.40	1.75
879	A287	13c Globe LR	2.40	1.75
880	A287	13c Globe LL	2.40	1.75
881	A287	13c Globe UR	2.40	1.75

882	A287	13c Globe UL	2.40	1.75
a.		Block of 5 + label, Nos. 878-882	16.00	10.00
883	A288	50c blk & lt grn	4.00	2.50
a.		Souvenir sheet of one, Wmk. 321	15.00	12.50
		Nos. 858-883 (26)	32.25	18.50

Experimental Cuban postal rocket flight, 25th anniv. Stamps of the same denomination printed se-tenant in sheets of 20 stamps and 5 inscribed labels. Stamps of Type A287 arranged in blocks of 4 with a complete globe in center of block; Type A286 stamps and labels form a cross in center of sheet. Inscribed "1939-Cohete Postal Cubano-1964." No. 883a contains one 46x28mm stamp.

Type of A288 Ovptd. in Silver

1964, Oct. 17   Unwmk.
884	A288	50c dark red brown & lt grn	5.00	1.50

No. 884 not issued without overprint.

40th Death Anniv. of Lenin — A289

Havana Zoo — A290

Designs: 13c, Lenin Mausoleum, horiz. 30c, Lenin, star, hammer and sickle.

1964, Nov. 7   Wmk. 376
885	A289	3c org & blk	.40	.20
886	A289	13c pur, pink & blk	1.10	.35
887	A289	30c blue & blk	2.25	.80
		Nos. 885-887 (3)	3.75	1.35

1964, Nov. 25
888	A290	1c Leopard, horiz.	.30	.20
889	A290	2c Elephant	.30	.20
890	A290	3c Fallow deer	.30	.20
891	A290	4c Kangaroo, horiz.	.30	.20
892	A290	5c Lions, horiz.	.40	.20
893	A290	6c Eland, horiz.	.50	.20
894	A290	7c Zebra, horiz.	.50	.20
895	A290	8c Hyena, horiz.	.75	.20
896	A290	9c Tiger, horiz.	.75	.20
897	A290	10c Guanaco, horiz.	.80	.20
898	A290	13c Chimpanzees, horiz.	.90	.20
899	A290	20c Peccary, horiz.	1.10	.25
900	A290	30c Raccoon	1.60	.60
901	A290	40c Hippopotamus, horiz.	2.75	1.00
902	A290	50c Tapir, horiz.	3.00	1.40
903	A290	60c Dromedary	4.50	1.90
904	A290	70c Bison, horiz.	4.75	1.90
905	A290	80c Black bear	5.00	2.40
906	A290	90c Water buffalo, horiz.	5.50	2.40

Size: 47x32mm
907	A290	1p Deer in nature park, horiz.	9.25	3.00
		Nos. 888-907 (20)	43.25	17.65

Heroes of the 1895 War of Independence — A291

1964, Dec. 7
908	A291	1c Jose Marti	.20	.20
909	A291	2c Antonio Maceo	.40	.20
910	A291	3c Maximo Gomez	.75	.35
911	A291	13c Calixto Garcia	1.90	.70
		Nos. 908-911 (4)	3.25	1.45

Christmas Type of 1961

2c, Coral. 3c, Jellyfish. 10c, Starfish, sea-urchins.

1964, Dec. 18
912	A248	2c Dwarf cup coral	.80	.30
913	A249	2c Eusmilia fastigiata	.80	.30
914	A249	2c Acropora palmata	.80	.30
915	A249	2c Acropora profilera	.80	.30
916	A249	2c Diploria labyrinthiformis	.80	.30
a.		Block of 5 + label, Nos. 912-916	4.50	2.00
917	A248	3c Condylactis gigantea	1.25	.50
918	A249	3c Physalia physalis	1.25	.50
919	A249	3c Aurelia aurita	1.25	.50
920	A249	3c Linuche unguiculata	1.25	.50
921	A249	3c Cassiopea frondosa	1.25	.50
a.		Block of 5 + label, Nos. 917-921	7.50	3.00
922	A248	10c Neocrinus blakei	2.25	1.00
923	A249	10c Eucidaris tribuloidas	2.25	1.00
924	A249	10c Tripneutes	2.25	1.00
925	A249	10c Ophiocoma echinata	2.25	1.00
926	A249	10c Oreaster celiculatus	2.25	1.00
a.		Block of 5 + label, Nos. 922-926	12.50	7.00
		Nos. 912-926 (15)	21.50	9.00

Christmas 1964. See note after No. 700.

Dr. Tomas Romay (1764-1849), Physician and Scientist — A292

Romay Monument — A293

Designs: 2c, First vaccination against small-pox. 3c, Portrait and treatise on vaccination.

1964, Dec. 21
927	A292	1c blk & olive brn	.50	.20
928	A292	2c blk & tan	.50	.20
929	A293	3c olive & dark red brown	.60	.20
930	A293	10c bister & blk	2.40	.40
		Nos. 927-930 (4)	4.00	1.00

Second Declaration of Havana A294

Map of Latin America and ripples or map of Cuba and peasant breaking shackles under text from the Declaration of Havana: No. 931a, 932a "Visperas de su muerte..." No. 931b, 932b, "Un continente, que juntos suponen represento..." No. 931c, 932c, "Y no se ocultaran ni el gobierna..." No. 931d, 932d, "Millones de mulatos latinamericanos que saben..." No. 931e, "A labran la tierra en condiciones..."

1964, Dec. 23
931		Strip of 5	5.00	3.50
a.-e.	A294	3c any single	.75	.40
932		Strip of 5	15.00	12.50
a.-e.	A294	13c any single	1.75	1.50

Nos. 931-932 printed in sheets of 25 (5x5).

Dioramas in New Cuban Postal Museum — A295

1965, Jan. 4
Yellow & Black Border
933	A295	13c Maritime Post	3.25	.85
934	A295	30c Insurrection Post	2.50	1.25

Souvenir Sheet
Imperf
935		Sheet of 2	8.50	7.50
a.		A295 13c like #933, blue & blk border	1.00	1.00
b.		A295 30c like #934, blue & blk border	3.00	3.00
		Nos. 933-935 (3)	14.25	9.60

Stamps in No. 935 have simulated perforations; buff margin is inscribed "PRECIO 50c" LR.

Fishing Fleet — A296

1965, May 1
936	A296	1c Schooner	.20	.20
937	A296	2c Omicron	.30	.20
938	A296	3c Victoria	.45	.20
939	A296	9c Cardenas	.70	.30
940	A296	10c Sigma	2.75	.60
941	A296	13c Lambda	4.25	1.00
		Nos. 936-941 (6)	8.65	2.50

Intl. Women's Day — A297

1965, Mar. 8
942	A297	3c Lidia Doce	1.10	.30
943	A297	13c Clara Zetkin	1.60	.60

Technical Revolution — A298

Designs: 3c, Jose Antonio Echeverria University School. 13c, Stylized symbols of science and research, molecular structure and satellite dish.

1965, Mar. 31

944	A298	3c tan, blk & dark red brn	.50	.20
945	A298	13c multi	2.50	.70

Cosmonauts, Rocket — A299

30c, Cosmonauts Pavel I. Balyayev, Aleksei A. Leonov taking first space walk.

1965, Apr. 2

946	A299	30c dark blue, blk & brn	2.50	.70
947	A299	50c brt pink & blue blk	4.50	1.40

Flight of Voskhod 2, the first man to walk in space, Mar. 17.

Abstract Wood Carving by Eugenio Rodriguez — A300

Abraham Lincoln — A301

Paintings in the Natl. Museum, Havana: 3c, Garden with Sunflowers, by Victor Manuel. 10c, Abstract, by Wilfredo Lam, horiz. 13c, Children, by Enrique Ponce, horiz.

1965, Apr. 12

948	A300	2c multi	.35	.20
		Size: 35x46mm		
949	A300	3c multi	.55	.20
		Size: 46x35mm		
950	A300	10c multi	1.50	.45
		Size: 43x37mm		
951	A300	13c multi	2.50	.80
		Nos. 948-951 (4)	4.90	1.65

1965, Apr. 15

Designs: 1c, Log cabin, birth site, horiz. 2c, Memorial, Washington, DC, horiz. 3c, Monument, Washington, DC. 13c, Portrait, quote.

952	A301	1c yel bister, red brn & gray	.20	.20
953	A301	2c lt blue & dark blue	.45	.20
954	A301	3c red org, blk & blue blk	1.25	.35
955	A301	13c org, blk & blue blk	2.50	.60
		Nos. 952-955 (4)	4.40	1.35

Stamp Day Type of 1963

Stamp Day 1965: 3c, 18th Cent. postmarks and packet. 13c, No. C16 and airplanes over capital.

1965, Apr. 24

956	A266	3c sep & dark org	3.00	.25
957	A266	13c brt blue, sal rose & blk	2.75	.60

Intl. Quiet Sun Year — A302

Intl. Telecommunications Union, Cent. — A303

1965, May 10

958	A302	1c Sun, Earth's magnetic pole, horiz.	.25	.20
959	A302	2c Sun Year emblem	.25	.20
960	A302	3c Earth's magnetic field, horiz.	.55	.20
961	A302	4c Atmospheric currents, horiz.	.60	.20
962	A302	30c Solar rays on planet surface	2.10	.55
963	A302	50c Effect on satellite orbits, horiz.	2.75	1.40
a.		Souv. sheet of one, imperf.	8.00	8.00
b.		As "a," changed colors	14.00	14.00
		Nos. 958-963 (6)	6.50	2.75

Stamps in Nos. 963a-963b have simulated perforations.

Stamp in No. 963b is blue blk, Prus blue, org yel & red. Issued Oct. 10 for the Philatelic Space Exhibition, Havana, Oct. 10-17.

1965, May 17

964	A303	1c Station, horiz.	.20	.20
965	A303	2c Satellite	.20	.20
966	A303	3c Telstar, horiz.	.30	.20
967	A303	10c Telstar, receiving station	1.10	.25
968	A303	30c ITU emblem, horiz.	3.00	.90
		Nos. 964-968 (5)	4.80	1.75

9th Communist World Youth and Students Congress — A304

1965, June 10

969	A304	13c Flags of Cuba and Algeria, emblem	1.50	.30
970	A304	30c Flags, guerrillas	2.50	.80

Matias Perez, Cuban Aeronautics Pioneer — A305

1965, June 23

971	A305	3c pink & blk	1.75	.95
972	A305	13c dull vio & blk, diff.	2.75	.95

Flowers and Maps of Their Locations A306

1965, July 20

973	A306	1c Rosa canina, Europe	.20	.20
974	A306	2c Chrysanthemum hortorum, Asia	.30	.20
975	A306	3c Strelitzia reginae, Africa	.30	.30
976	A306	4c Dahlia pinnata, No. America	.30	.20
977	A306	5c Cattleya labiata, So. America	1.60	.20
978	A306	13c Grevillea banksii, Oceania	3.25	.95
979	A306	30c Brunfelsia nitida, Cuba	4.75	1.60
		Nos. 973-979 (7)	10.70	3.65

1st Natl. Games — A307

1965, July 25

980	A307	1c Swimming	.20	.20
981	A307	2c Basketball	.35	.20
982	A307	3c Gymnastics	.70	.25
983	A307	30c Hurdling	2.75	.70
		Nos. 980-983 (4)	4.00	1.35

Revolution Museum Opening A308

1965, July 26

984	A308	1c Anti-tank guns	.20	.20
985	A308	2c Tanks	.20	.20
986	A308	3c Bazookas	.20	.20
987	A308	10c Uniform, guerillas	.75	.25
988	A308	13c Compass, yacht Granma	2.10	.45
		Nos. 984-988 (5)	3.45	1.30

A309

1965, Aug. 20

989	A309	1c Finlay's signature	.20	.20
990	A309	2c Anopheles mosquito	.20	.20
991	A309	3c Portrait	.35	.20
992	A309	7c Microscope	.45	.20
993	A309	9c Dr. Claudio Delgado	.75	.25
994	A309	10c Monument	1.90	.30
995	A309	13c Discussing theory with doctors	3.00	.65
		Nos. 989-995 (7)	6.85	2.00

Carlos J. Finlay (1833-1915), discovered transmission of yellow fever via aedes aegypti (not anopheles) mosquito. Nos. 990-995 vert.

Butterflies A310

1965, Sept. 22 — Unwmk.

996	A310	2c Dismorphia cubana	.50	.20
997	A310	2c Anetia numidia briarea	.50	.20
998	A310	2c Carathis gortynoides	.50	.20
999	A310	2c Hymenitis cubana	.50	.20
1000	A310	2c Eubaphe heros	.50	.20
a.		Strip of 5, Nos. 996-1000	3.75	2.50
1001	A310	3c Lycorea ceres demeter	.75	.20
1002	A310	3c Eubaphe disparitis	.75	.20
1003	A310	3c Siderone nemesis	.75	.20
1004	A310	3c Syntomidopsis variegata	.75	.20
1005	A310	3c Ctenuchidia virgo	.75	.20
a.		Strip of 5, Nos. 1001-1005	5.00	3.25
1006	A310	13c Prepona antimache crossina	3.00	.80
1007	A310	13c Sylepta reginalis	3.00	.80
1008	A310	13c Chlosyne perezi perezi	3.00	.80
1009	A310	13c Anaea clytemnestra iphigenia	3.00	.80
1010	A310	13c Anetia cubana	3.00	.80
a.		Strip of 5, Nos. 1006-1010	17.00	8.25
		Nos. 996-1010 (15)	21.25	6.00

Cuban Mint, 50th Anniv. A311

Coins (obverse and reverse).

1965, Oct. 13

1011	A311	1c 20 centavos, 1962	.30	.20
1012	A311	2c 1 peso, 1934	.30	.20
1013	A311	3c 40 centavos, 1962	.30	.20
1014	A311	8c 1 peso, 1915	.80	.20
1015	A311	10c Marti peso, 1953	1.90	.40
1016	A311	13c 20 pesos, 1915	2.75	.50
		Nos. 1011-1016 (6)	6.35	1.70

Tropical Fruit — A312

1965, Nov. 15 — Perf. 12½

1017	A312	1c Oranges	.20	.20
1018	A312	2c Custard apples	.20	.20
1019	A312	3c Papayas	.20	.20
1020	A312	4c Bananas	.35	.20
1021	A312	10c Avocado	.60	.20
1022	A312	13c Pineapple	.95	.70
1023	A312	20c Guavas	2.50	.70
1024	A312	50c Marmalade plums	5.50	1.25
		Nos. 1017-1024 (8)	10.50	3.65

Christmas Type of 1961

Birds.

1965, Dec. 1

1025	A248	3c Icterus galbula	1.60	1.25
1026	A249	3c Passerina ciris	1.60	1.25
1027	A249	3c Setophaga ruticillar	1.60	1.25
1028	A249	3c Dendroica tusca	1.60	1.25
1029	A249	3c Pheucticus ludovicianus	1.60	1.25
a.		Block of 5 + label, Nos. 1025-1029	9.00	7.25
1030	A248	5c Pyranga olivacea	1.75	1.75
1031	A249	5c Dendroica dominica	1.75	1.75
1032	A249	5c Vermivora pinus	1.75	1.75
1033	A249	5c Protonotaria citrea	1.75	1.75
1034	A249	5c Wilsonia citrina	1.75	1.75
a.		Block of 5 + label, Nos. 1030-1034	10.00	10.00
1035	A248	13c Passerina cyanea	4.00	3.00

1036	A249	13c	Anas discors	4.00	3.00
1037	A249	13c	Aix sponsa	4.00	3.00
1038	A249	13c	Spatula clypeata	4.00	3.00
1039	A249	13c	Nycticorax hoactli	4.00	3.00
a.			Block of 5 + label, Nos. 1035-1039	21.00	20.00
			Nos. 1025-1039 (15)	36.75	30.00

Christmas 1965. See note after No. 700.

Intl. Athletic Competition, Havana, 7th Anniv. — A313

1965, Dec. 11   Wmk. 376   Perf. 10

1040	A313	1c	Hurdling	.20	.20
1041	A313	2c	Discus	.20	.20
1042	A313	3c	Shot put	.55	.20
1043	A313	7c	Javelin	.55	.25
1044	A313	9c	High jump	.70	.35
1045	A313	10c	Hammer throw	1.40	.60
1046	A313	13c	Running	2.00	.90
			Nos. 1040-1046 (7)	5.60	2.70

Fish in the Natl. Aquarium — A314

1965, Dec. 5   Unwmk.   Perf. 12½

1047	A314	1c	Echeneis naucrates	.25	.20
1048	A314	2c	Katsuwonus pelamis	.25	.20
1049	A314	3c	Abudefduf saxatilis	.55	.20
1050	A314	4c	Istiophorus	.65	.20
1051	A314	5c	Epinephelus striatus	.65	.20
1052	A314	10c	Lutianus analis	.80	.30
1053	A314	13c	Ocyurus chrysurus	2.75	.80
1054	A314	30c	Holocentrus ascensionis	4.50	1.25
			Nos. 1047-1054 (8)	10.40	3.35

Andre Voisin (d. 1964), French Naturalist — A315

1965, Dec. 21   Wmk. 376

1055	A315	3c	shown	1.00	.25
1056	A315	13c	Portrait, flags, microscope, plant	2.50	.55

Transportation — A316

1965, Dec. 30

1057	A316	1c	Skoda bus, Czechoslovakia	.20	.20
1058	A316	2c	Ikarus bus, Hungary	.20	.20
1059	A316	3c	Leyland bus, G.B.	.25	.20

1060	A316	4c	TEM-4 locomotive, USSR	3.00	.70
1061	A316	7c	BB-69.000 locomotive, France	3.00	.70
1062	A316	10c	Remolcador tugboat, DDR	1.25	.35
1063	A316	13c	15 de Marzo freighter, Spain	2.00	.60
1064	A316	20c	Ilyushin 18 jet, USSR	2.50	1.00
			Nos. 1057-1064 (8)	12.40	3.95

7th Anniv. of the Revolution A317

A318

1966, Jan. 2

1065	A317	1c	Guerrillas	.25	.20
1066	A317	2c	Commander and tank	.25	.20
1067	A317	3c	Sailor, patrol boat	.90	.20
1068	A318	10c	Jet aircraft	1.90	.45
1069	A318	13c	Rocket	2.25	.70
			Nos. 1065-1069 (5)	5.55	1.75

Conference of Asian, African and South American Countries, Havana — A319

1966, Jan. 3

1070	A319	2c	Emblem at R	.20	.20
1071	A319	3c	Emblem at L	.40	.20
1072	A319	13c	Emblem at center	2.10	.55
			Nos. 1070-1072 (3)	2.70	.95

Guardalabarca Beach — A320

1966, Feb. 10

1073	A320	1c	shown	.30	.20
1074	A320	2c	Gran Piedra mountain	.30	.20
1075	A320	3c	Guama Village	.90	.20
1076	A320	13c	Soroa waterfall, vert.	2.50	.60
			Nos. 1073-1076 (4)	4.00	1.20

11th Medical and 7th Natl. Dental Congresses — A321

1966, Feb. 28   Wmk. 376

1077	A321	3c	multi	.30	.20
1078	A321	13c	multi, diff.	1.50	.55

Folk Art A322

1966, Feb. 28   Unwmk.

1079	A322	1c	Afro-cuban ritual puppet	.20	.20
1080	A322	2c	Sombreros	.20	.20
1081	A322	3c	Ceramic vase	.25	.20
1082	A322	7c	Lanterns, lamp	.25	.20
1083	A322	9c	Table lamp	.80	.20
1084	A322	10c	Shark, wood sculpture	1.25	.30
1085	A322	13c	Snail-shell necklace, earrings	2.50	.60
			Nos. 1079-1085 (7)	5.45	1.90

Nos. 1079-1083 vert.

Chelsea College, by Canaletto — A323

Ceramics and paintings in the National Museum: 1c, Ming vase. 3c, Portrait of a Lady, by Goya. 13c, Portrait of Fayum, encaustic painting. Nos. 1086, 1088-1089 vert.

1966, Mar. 31   Wmk. 376

1086	A323	1c	multi	.20	.20
1087	A323	2c	multi	.85	.20
1088	A323	3c	multi	.75	.25
1089	A323	13c	multi	3.00	.70
			Nos. 1086-1089 (4)	4.80	1.35

First Man in Space, 5th Anniv. A324

Designs: 1c, Konstantin Eduardovich Tsiolkovsky (1857-1935), Soviet rocket and space sciences pioneer. 2c, Cosmonauts in training, vert. 3c, Yuri Gagarin, rocket, Earth. 7c, Cosmonauts Nikolaev and Popovich, vert. 9c, Tereshkova and Bykovsky. 10c, Komarov, Feoktistov and Yegorov. 13c, Leonov taking first space walk.

1966, Apr. 12

1090	A324	1c	multi	.20	.20
1091	A324	2c	multi	.20	.20
1092	A324	3c	multi	.35	.20
1093	A324	7c	multi	.60	.20
1094	A324	9c	multi	.85	.25
1095	A324	10c	multi	1.10	.30
1096	A324	13c	multi	2.25	.55
			Nos. 1090-1096 (7)	5.55	1.90

Bay of Pigs Invasion, 5th Anniv. A325

1966, Apr. 17

1097	A325	2c	Tank	.20	.20
1098	A325	3c	Burning ship, plane crash	.95	.20
1099	A325	9c	Tank in ditch	.40	.20
1100	A325	10c	Soldier, gunners	1.75	.20
1101	A325	13c	Operations map	3.00	.70
			Nos. 1097-1101 (5)	6.30	1.50

Stamp Day Type of 1963

Designs: 3c, Cuban Postal Museum interior. 13c, No. 613 and stamp collector.

1966, Apr. 24

1102	A266	3c	sage grn & sal rose	1.25	.20
1103	A266	13c	brn, sal rose & blk	3.50	.80

Stamp Day 1966. 1st Anniv. of the Cuban Postal Museum (No. 1102); 1st anniv. of the Cuban Philatelic Federation (No. 1103).

Flowers and Symbols of Industry — A326

1966, May 1

1104	A326	2c	Anvil	.20	.20
1105	A326	3c	Machete	.30	.20
1106	A326	10c	Hammer	.70	.25
1107	A326	13c	Hemisphere, gearwheel	1.75	.90
			Nos. 1104-1107 (4)	2.95	1.55

Labor Day.

Opening of the World Health Organization Headquarters, Geneva — A327

Views of WHO headquarters and emblem or emblem on flag.

1966, May 3

1108	A327	2c	blk & yel org	.20	.20
1109	A327	3c	blk, lt blue & yel org	.70	.20
1110	A327	13c	blk, lt blue & yel org	2.10	.55
			Nos. 1108-1110 (3)	3.00	.95

10th Central American and Caribbean Games, Puerto Rico, June 11-25 A328

1966, June 11

1111	A328	1c	Running, vert.	.20	.20
1112	A328	2c	Rifle shooting	.30	.20
1113	A328	3c	Baseball, vert.	.45	.20
1114	A328	7c	Volleyball, vert.	.45	.20
1115	A328	9c	Soccer, vert.	.80	.20
1116	A328	10c	Boxing, vert.	1.40	.20
1117	A328	13c	Basketball, vert.	3.50	.55
			Nos. 1111-1117 (7)	7.10	1.75

Progress in Education A329

Designs: 1c, Makarenko School, Playa de Tarara. 2c, Natl. Literacy Campaign Museum. 3c, Lantern, literacy campaign emblem for 1961. 10c, Frank Pais education team in the mountains. 13c, Farmer, factory worker.

1966, June 15

1118	A329	1c	grn & blk	.20	.20
1119	A329	2c	yel, olive bister & blk	.20	.20
1120	A329	3c	brt blue, lt blue & blk	.30	.20

1121 A329 10c golden brn, brn &
    blk .90 .25
1122 A329 13c multi 2.40 .45
    Nos. 1118-1122 (5) 4.00 1.30

1st Graduating class of Makarenko School (1c), 5th anniv. of the Natl. Literacy Campaign (3c), 4th anniv. of agricultural and industrial trade education (13c).

12th Congress of the Cuban Labor Organization — A330

1966, Aug. 12
1123 A330 3c multi .75 .25

Sea Shells — A331

1966, Aug. 25   **Unwmk.**
1124 A331 1c Liguus flammellus .35 .20
1125 A331 2c Cypraea zebra .45 .20
1126 A331 3c Strombus pugilis .70 .20
1127 A331 7c Aequipecten muscosu .80 .25
1128 A331 9c Liguus fasciatus crenatus .90 .25
1129 A331 10c Charonia variegata 1.75 .40
1130 A331 13c Liguus fasciatus archeri 3.50 .80
    Nos. 1124-1130 (7) 8.45 2.30

Breeding Messenger Pigeons — A332

1966, Sept. 18   **Wmk. 376**
1131 A332 1c shown .40 .20
1132 A332 2c Timer .40 .20
1133 A332 3c Coops .40 .20
1134 A332 7c Breeder tending coops .80 .25
1135 A332 9c Pigeons in yard .80 .35
1136 A332 10c Two men, message 2.50 .50

Size: 47x32mm
1137 A332 13c Baracoa to Havana championship flight, July 26, 1959 3.75 .90
    Nos. 1131-1137 (7) 9.05 2.60

Provincial and Natl. Coats of Arms, Map of Cuba — A333

17th World Chess Olympiad, Havana — A334

1966, Oct. 10
1138 A333 1c Pinar del Rio .20 .20
1139 A333 2c Havana .30 .20
1140 A333 3c Matanzas .30 .20
1141 A333 4c Las Villas .40 .20
1142 A333 5c Camaguey .60 .20

1143 A333 9c Oriente 1.00 .45
Size: 30x48mm
1144 A333 13c National arms 2.25 .55
    Nos. 1138-1144 (7) 5.05 2.00

1966, Oct. 18
1145 A334 1c Pawn .30 .20
1146 A334 2c Rook .30 .20
1147 A334 3c Knight .50 .20
1148 A334 9c Bishop 1.00 .25
1149 A334 10c Queen, games, horiz. 2.40 .25
1150 A334 13c King and emblem, horiz. 3.25 .60
    Nos. 1145-1150 (6) 7.75 1.70

Souvenir Sheet
Imperf
1151 A334 30c Capablanca Vs. Lasker, 1914, horiz. 12.00 12.00

No. 1151 contains one 49½x31mm stamp.

Cuban-Soviet Diplomatic Relations — A335

1966, Nov. 7
1152 A335 2c Lenin Hospital .20 .20
1153 A335 3c Oil tanker, world map .35 .20
1154 A335 10c Workers, gearwheels 1.10 .25
1155 A335 13c Agriculture 2.25 .70
    Nos. 1152-1155 (4) 3.90 1.35

2nd Song Festival A336

Cuban composers and their compositions.

1966, Nov. 18
1156 A336 1c Amadeo Roldan .20 .20
1157 A336 2c Eduardo Sanchez de Fuentes .30 .20
1158 A336 3c Moises Simons .30 .20
1159 A336 7c Jorge Anckermann .80 .20
1160 A336 9c Alejandro G. Caturla .80 .25
1161 A336 10c Eliseo Grenet .30 .45
1162 A336 13c Ernesto Lecuona 4.00 .90
    Nos. 1156-1162 (7) 9.40 2.40

Viet Nam War — A337

Flag of Viet Nam and: 2c, US aircraft discharging bombs, dead cattle. 3c, Gas mask and victims. 13c, US bombs, women and children.

1966, Nov. 23
1163 A337 2c multi .40 .20
1164 A337 3c multi .60 .20
1165 A337 13c multi 2.00 .60
    Nos. 1163-1165 (3) 3.00 1.00

10th Anniv. of Successful Revolution Campaigns — A338

Revolution leaders, scenes of the insurrection.

1966, Nov. 30
1166 A338 1c Antonio Fernandez .20 .20
1167 A338 2c Candido Gonzalez .20 .20
1168 A338 3c Jose Tey .20 .20
1169 A338 7c Tony Aloma .30 .20
1170 A338 9c Otto Parellada .60 .20
1171 A338 10c Juan Manuel Marquez 2.00 .50
1172 A338 13c Frank Pais 1.90 .80
    Nos. 1166-1172 (7) 5.40 2.30

Intl. Leisure Time and Recreation Seminar — A339

1966, Dec. 2
1173 A339 3c shown .20 .20
1174 A339 9c World map, stopwatch, eye 1.40 .25
1175 A339 13c Earth, clock, emblem 1.75 .60
    Nos. 1173-1175 (3) 3.35 1.05

1st Natl. Telecommunications Forum — A340

1966, Dec. 12
1176 A340 3c shown .75 .20
1177 A340 10c Satellite in orbit 3.75 .25
1178 A340 13c Shell, satellite 5.50 .70
    a. Souv. sheet of 3, #1176-1178, imperf 15.00 15.00
    Nos. 1176-1178 (3) 10.00 1.15

No. 1178a sold for 30c.

Christmas Type of 1961
1966, Dec. 20   **Unwmk.**
1179 A248 1c Cypripedium eurylochus .90 .20
1180 A249 1c Cattleya speciosissima .90 .20
1181 A249 1c Cattleya mendelii majestica .90 .20
1182 A249 1c Cattleya trianae amesiana .90 .20
1183 A249 1c Cattleya labiata macfarlanei .90 .20
    a. Block of 5 + label, #1179-1183 5.00 1.00
1184 A248 3c Cypripedium morganiae burfordense 1.40 .20
1185 A249 3c Cattleya Countess of Derby 1.40 .20
1186 A249 3c Cypripedium hookerae volunteanum 1.40 .20
1187 A249 3c Cattleya warscewiczii reginae burfordense 1.40 .20
1188 A249 3c Cypripedium stonei cannartae 1.40 .20
    a. Block of 5 + label, #1184-1188 8.00 1.00

1189 A248 13c Cattleya mendelii Duchess of Montrose 5.00 .50
1190 A249 13c Oncidium macranthum 5.00 .50
1191 A249 13c Cypripedium stonei platytoenium 5.00 .50
1192 A249 13c Cattleya dowiana aurea 5.00 .50
1193 A249 13c Laelia anceps 5.00 .50
    a. Block of 5 + label, #1189-1193 27.50 2.75
    Nos. 1179-1193 (15) 36.50 4.50

Christmas 1966. See note after No. 700.

8th Anniv. of the Revolution — A341

1967, Jan. 2
1194 A341 3c Liberation, 1959 .30 .20
1195 A341 3c Agrarian Reform, 1960 .30 .20
1196 A341 3c Education, 1961 .30 .20
1197 A341 3c Agriculture, 1965 .30 .20
    a. Strip of 4, Nos. 1194-1197 1.25 .90
1198 A341 13c Rodin's Thinker, Planning, 1962 1.90 .45
1199 A341 13c Organization, 1963 1.90 .45
1200 A341 13c Economy, 1964 1.90 .45
1201 A341 13c Solidarity, 1966 1.90 .45
    a. Strip of 4, Nos. 1198-1201 7.75 4.25
    Nos. 1194-1201 (8) 8.80 2.60

Nos. 1198-1201 vert.

Spring, by Jorge Arche — A342

Paintings in the Natl. Museum: 1c, Coffee Machine, by Angel Acosta Leon, vert. 2c, Country People, by Eduardo Abela, vert. 13c, Still-life, by Amelia Pelaez, vert. 30c, Landscape, by Gonzalo Escalante.

1967, Feb. 27
1202 A342 1c multi .30 .20
1203 A342 2c multi .50 .20
1204 A342 3c multi .70 .20
1205 A342 13c multi 2.00 .80
1206 A342 30c multi 5.50 1.50
    Nos. 1202-1206 (5) 9.00 2.90

Natl. Events, Mar. 13, 1957 A343

1967, Mar. 13   **Wmk. 376**
1207 A343 3c Attack on Presidential Palace .20 .20
Size: 41x28mm
1208 A343 13c Landing of Corynthia 2.50 .70
1209 A343 30c Cienfuegos revolt 2.40 .80
    Nos. 1207-1209 (3) 5.10 1.70

Evolution of Man — A344

Prehistoric men: 2c, Australopithecus. 3c, Pithecanthropus erectus. 4c, Sinanthropus pekinensis. 5c, Neanderthal man. 13c, Cromagnon man carving tusk. 20c, Cro-magnon man painting petroglyph.

1967, Mar. 31   **Unwmk.**

1210	A344	1c multi	.30	.20
1211	A344	2c multi	.50	.20
1212	A344	3c multi	.50	.20
1213	A344	4c multi	.75	.20
1214	A344	5c multi	1.10	.25
1215	A344	9c multi	3.75	.50
1216	A344	20c multi	7.50	.90
	Nos. 1210-1216 (7)		14.40	2.45

Stamp Day A345

Carriages.

1967, Apr. 24

1217	A345	3c Victoria	.35	.20
1218	A345	9c Volante	2.00	.45
1219	A345	13c Quitrin	3.00	.80
	Nos. 1217-1219 (3)		5.35	1.45

EXPO '67, Montreal, Apr. 28-Oct. 27 — A346

1967, Apr. 28

1220	A346	1c Cuban pavilion	.40	.20
1221	A346	2c Space exploration	.40	.20
1222	A346	3c Petroglyph, hieroglyph	.55	.20
1223	A346	13c Agriculture, computer technology	3.00	.70
1224	A346	20c Athletes	3.50	.80
	Nos. 1220-1224 (5)		7.85	2.10

Botanical Gardens, Sequicentennial A347

Flowering plants.

1967, May 30

1225	A347	1c Eugenia malaccencis	.20	.20
1226	A347	2c Jacaranda filicifolia	.20	.20
1227	A347	3c Coroupita guianensis	.45	.20
1228	A347	4c Spathodea campanulata	.45	.20
1229	A347	5c Cassia fistula	.90	.20
1230	A347	13c Plumieria alba	2.75	.55
1231	A347	20c Erythrina poeppigiana	4.75	.65
	Nos. 1225-1231 (7)		9.70	2.20

Natl. Ballet — A348

1967, June 15

1232	A348	1c Giselle	.35	.20
1233	A348	2c Swan Lake	.35	.20
1234	A348	3c Don Quixote	.50	.20
1235	A348	4c Calaucan	1.00	.20
1236	A348	13c Swan Lake	2.75	.70
1237	A348	20c Nutcracker	4.00	1.25
	Nos. 1232-1237 (6)		8.95	2.75

Intl. Ballet Festival, Havana.

5th Pan American Games, Winnipeg, Canada, July 22-Aug. 7 — A349

1st Conference of Latin American Solidarity Organization (OLAS) — A350

1967, July 22

1238	A349	1c Baseball, horiz.	.20	.20
1239	A349	2c Swimming, horiz.	.35	.20
1240	A349	3c Basketball	.50	.20
1241	A349	4c Gymnastic rings	.85	.20
1242	A349	5c Water polo	1.00	.20
1243	A349	13c Weight lifting, horiz.	3.00	.45
1244	A349	20c Javelin	4.75	.80
	Nos. 1238-1244 (7)		10.65	2.25

1967, July 28   **Wmk. 376**

Portrait of representative, map of South American homeland: No. 1245, Camilo Torres, Colombia. No. 1246, Luis de la Puente Uceda, Peru. No. 1247, Luis A. Turcios Lima, Guatemala. No. 1248, Fabricio Ojeda, Venezuela.

1245	A350	13c pale grn, blk & red	2.00	.50
1246	A350	13c lil, blk & red	2.00	.50
1247	A350	13c dark chalky blue, blk & red	2.00	.50
1248	A350	13c golden brn, blk & red	2.00	.50
	Nos. 1245-1248 (4)		8.00	2.00

Portrait of Sonny Rollins, by Alan Davie — A351

Bathers, by Gustave Singier A352

Modern Art: No. 1250, Twelve Selenites, by Felix Labisse. No. 1251, Night of the Drinker, by Friedensreich Hundertwasser. No. 1252, Figure, by Mariano. No. 1253, All-Souls, by Wilfredo Lam. No. 1254, Darkness and Cracks, by Antonio Tapies. No. 1256, Torso of a Muse, by Jean Arp. No. 1257, Figure, by M.W. Svanberg. No. 1258, Oppenheimer's Information, by Erro. No. 1259, Where Cardinals Are Born, by Max Ernst. No. 1260, Havana Landscape, by Portocarrero. No. 1261, EG 12, by Victor Vasarely. No. 1262, Frisco, by Alexander Calder. No. 1263, The Man with the Pipe, by Picasso. No. 1264, Abstract Composition, by Sergei Poliakoff. No. 1265, Painting, by Bram van Velde. No. 1266, Sower of Fires, by R. Matta. No. 1267, The Art of Living, by Rene Magritte. No. 1268, Poem, by Joan Miro. No. 1269, Young Tigers, by Jean Messanger. No. 1270, Painting, by M. Vieira da Silva. No. 1271, Live Cobra, by Pierre Alechinsky. No. 1272, Stalingrad, by Asger Jorn. 30c, Warriors, by Edouard Pignon. 50c, Cloister, a mural at the exhibition representing the Salon de Mayo pictures.

1967, July 29   **Unwmk.**

1249	A351	1c shown	.80	.20
1250	A351	1c multi	.80	.20
1251	A351	1c multi	30.00	15.00
1252	A351	1c multi	.80	.20
1253	A351	1c multi	.80	.20
a.		Strip of 5, Nos. 1249-1253	4.50	1.50

Sizes: 36½x54mm, 36½x53mm, 36½x45mm, 36½x41mm

1254	A352	2c multi	.80	.20
1255	A352	2c shown	.80	.20
1256	A352	2c multi	.80	.20
1257	A352	2c multi	.80	.20
1258	A352	2c multi	.80	.20
a.		Strip of 5, Nos. 1254-1258	4.50	2.50

Sizes: 36½x54mm, 36½x40mm, 36½x42mm, 36½x49mm

1259	A352	3c multi	1.50	.20
1260	A352	3c multi	1.50	.20
1261	A352	3c multi	1.50	.20
1262	A352	3c multi	1.50	.20
1263	A352	3c multi	1.50	.20
a.		Strip of 5, Nos. 1259-1263	7.50	3.50

Sizes: 35x15mm, 35x67mm, 35x46½mm, 35x55mm

1264	A352	4c multi	1.75	.80
1265	A352	4c multi	1.75	.80
1266	A352	4c multi	1.75	.80
1267	A352	4c multi	1.75	.80
1268	A352	4c multi	1.75	.80
a.		Strip of 5, Nos. 1264-1268	9.00	4.00

Sizes: 49x32mm, 49x35mm, 49x46mm

1269	A351	13c multi	4.50	2.75
1270	A351	13c multi	4.50	2.75
1271	A351	13c multi	4.50	2.75
1272	A351	13c multi	4.50	2.75
a.		Strip of 4, Nos. 1269-1272	19.00	11.00

Size: 54x32mm

1273	A351	30c multi	17.50	11.00
	Nos. 1249-1273 (25)		88.95	43.80

Souvenir Sheet

Imperf

1274	A351	50c multi		25.00	12.50

Salon de Mayo Art Exhibition, Havana. No. 1274 contains one 88x45mm stamp with simulated perforations. Issued Oct. 7.

World Underwater Fishing Championships — A353

1967, Sept. 5

1275	A353	1c Green moray	.20	.20
1276	A353	2c Octopus	.20	.20
1277	A353	3c Great barracuda	.20	.20
1278	A353	4c Blue shark	.75	.20
1279	A353	5c Spotted jewfish	1.60	.25
1280	A353	13c Sting ray	3.25	.70
1281	A353	20c Green turtle	6.50	.85
	Nos. 1275-1281 (7)		12.70	2.60

Soviet Space Program A354

1967, Oct. 4   **Wmk. 376**

1282	A354	1c Sputnik 1	.20	.20
1283	A354	2c Lunik 3	.20	.20
1284	A354	3c Venusik	.20	.20
1285	A354	4c Cosmos	.40	.20
1286	A354	5c Mars 1	.65	.20
1287	A354	9c Electron 1 & 2	.75	.25
1288	A354	10c Luna 9	1.10	.45
1289	A354	13c Luna 10	2.50	.60
a.		Souv. sheet of 8, #1282-1289, imperf.	15.00	15.00
	Nos. 1282-1289 (8)		6.00	2.30

Stamps in #1289a have simulated perfs.

50th Anniv. of the October Revolution, Russia A355

Paintings: 1c, Storming the Winter Palace, by Sokolov-Skalia and Miasnikov. 2c, Lenin Addressing Congress, by W.A. Serov. 3c, Lenin, by H.D. Nalbandian. 4c, Lenin Explaining Electrification Map, by L.A. Schmatko. 5c, Dawn of the Five-Year Plan, by J.D. Romas. 13c, Kusnetzkroi Steel Furnace No. 1, by P. Kotov. 30c, Victory, by A. Krivonogov.

1967, Nov. 7   **Unwmk.**

1290	A355	1c 64x36mm	.20	.20
1291	A355	2c 48x36mm	.20	.20
1292	A355	3c	.45	.20
1293	A355	4c 48x36mm	.45	.20
1294	A355	5c 50x36mm	3.75	.50
1295	A355	13c 36x50mm	3.00	.50
1296	A355	30c 50x36mm	4.00	.85
	Nos. 1290-1296 (7)		12.05	2.65

Castle of the Royal Forces, Havana — A356

Historic architecture: 2c, Iznaga Tower, Trinidad, vert. 3c, Castle of Our Lady of the Angels, Cienfuegos. 4c, St. Francis de Paula Church, Havana. 13c, St. Francis Convent, Havana. 30c, Castle del Morro, Santiago de Cuba.

1967, Nov. 7   **Wmk. 376**
Sizes: 26x47mm (1c), 41x29mm (3c, 4c), 38½x31mm (13c)

1297	A356	1c multi	.20	.20
1298	A356	2c multi	.20	.20
1299	A356	3c multi	.65	.20
1300	A356	4c multi	.65	.20
1301	A356	13c multi	3.25	.50
1302	A356	30c multi	5.00	1.00
	Nos. 1297-1302 (6)		9.95	2.20

Christmas Type of 1961

Birds.

1967, Dec. 20

1303	A248	1c Struthia came-lus australis		1.75	.60
1304	A249	1c Chysolophus pictus		1.75	.60
1305	A249	1c Ciconia ciconia ciconia		1.75	.60
1306	A249	1c Balearica pavonina		1.75	.60
1307	A249	1c Dromiceius novaehollandiae		1.75	.60
a.		Block of 5 + label, Nos. 1303-1307		10.00	3.25
1308	A248	3c Anodorhynchus hyacinthus		2.40	1.00
1309	A249	3c Psittacus erithacus		2.40	1.00
1310	A249	3c Domicella garrula		2.40	1.00
1311	A249	3c Ramphastos sulfuratus		2.40	1.00
1312	A249	3c Kakatoe galerita galerita		2.40	1.00
a.		Block of 5 + label, Nos. 1308-1312		14.00	5.50
1313	A248	13c Phoenicopterus ruber		4.50	1.75
1314	A249	13c Pelecanus erythrorhynchos		4.50	1.75
1315	A249	13c Alopochen aegyptiacus		4.50	1.75
1316	A249	13c Dendronessa galericulata		4.50	1.75
1317	A249	13c Chenopsis atrata		4.50	1.75
a.		Block of 5 + label, Nos. 1313-1317		25.00	9.00
		Nos. 1303-1317 (15)		43.25	16.75

Christmas 1967. See note after No. 700.

Ernesto "Che" Guevara (1928-1967), Revolution Leader — A356a

1968, Jan. 3

1318	A356a	13c blk, dark red & buff	2.50	.55

Cultural Congress, Havana — A357

Abstract designs: No. 1319, Independence fostering culture. No. 1320, Integral formation of man. No. 1321, Responsibility of intellectuals. No. 1322, Relationship between culture and the mass media. No. 1323, The arts versus science and technology.

1968, Jan. 4

1319	A357	3c multi, vert.	.20	.20
1320	A357	3c multi, vert.	.20	.20
1321	A357	13c multi, vert.	1.50	.40
1322	A357	13c multi, vert.	1.75	.50
1323	A357	30c multi	2.40	.85
		Nos. 1319-1323 (5)	6.05	2.15

Canaries and Breeding Cycles A358

1968, Apr. 13

1324	A358	1c F.C.C. 4016	.20	.20
1325	A358	2c A.C.C. 774	.20	.20
1326	A358	3c A.C.C. 122	.40	.20

1327	A358	4c F.C.C. 4477	.40	.25
1328	A358	5c A.C.C. 117	.75	.20
1329	A358	13c A.N.R. 1175	4.00	.55
1330	A358	20c A.C.C. 777	5.50	.70
		Nos. 1324-1330 (7)	11.45	2.30

Stamp Day A359

Paintings: 13c, The Village Postman, by J. Harris. 30c, The Philatelist, by G. Sciltian.

1968, Apr. 24 — Unwmk.

1331	A359	13c multi	2.00	.50
1332	A359	30c multi	3.00	.70

World Health Organization, 20th Anniv. — A360

1968, May 10 — Wmk. 376

1333	A360	13c Nurse, mother, child	1.60	.55
1334	A360	30c Surgeons	2.10	.80

Intl. Children's Day — A361

1968, June 1

1335	A361	3c multi	1.25	.25

Seville Camaguey Flight, 35th Anniv. — A362

1968, June 20

1336	A362	13c Plane Four Winds	2.25	.45
1337	A362	30c Capt. Barberan, Lt. Collar, pilots	2.75	.60

Natl. Food Production — A363

1968, June 29

1338	A363	1c Yellow tuna, can	.25	.20
1339	A363	2c Cow, dairy products	.25	.20
1340	A363	3c Rooster, eggs	.50	.25
1341	A363	13c Rum, sugar cane	3.00	.50
1342	A363	20c Crayfish, box	3.50	.70
		Nos. 1338-1342 (5)	7.50	1.85

Attack of Moncada Barracks, 15th Anniv. A364

1968, July 26 — Size: 43x29mm (13c)

1343	A364	3c Siboney farmhouse	.20	.20
1344	A364	13c Assault route, Santiago de Cuba	1.75	.55
1345	A364	30c Students, school	3.00	.80
		Nos. 1343-1345 (3)	4.95	1.55

Committee for the Defense of the Revolution, 8th Anniv. — A365

1968, Sept. 28

1346	A365	3c multi	2.00	.20

Guerilla Day A366

Che Guevara and: 1c, Rifleman and "En Cualquier Lugar..." 3c, Machine gunners and "Crear tres muchos Viet Nam." 9c, Silhouette of battalion and "Este Tipo De Lucha..." 10c, Guerillas cheering and "Hoy aquilatamos..." 13c, Map of Caribbean, So. America and "Hasta La Victoria Siempre."

1968, Oct. 8

1347	A366	1c gold, brt blue grn & blk	.20	.20
1348	A366	3c gold, org brn blk	.20	.20
1349	A366	9c multi	.60	.20
1350	A366	10c gold, lt olive grn & blk	1.40	.20
1351	A366	13c gold, red org & blk	2.50	.70
		Nos. 1347-1351 (5)	4.90	1.50

Cuban War of Independence, Cent. — A367

Independence fighters and scenes.

1968, Oct. 10 — Unwmk.

1352	A367	1c C.M. de Cespedes, broken wheel	.20	.20
1353	A367	1c E. Betances, horsemen, flag	.20	.20
1354	A367	1c I. Agramonte, Clavellinas Monument	.20	.20
1355	A367	1c A. Maceo, Baragua Protest	.20	.20

1356	A367	1c J. Marti, horsemen	.20	.20
a.		Strip of 5, Nos. 1352-1356	1.00	1.00
1357	A367	3c M. Gomez, The Invasion	.25	.20
1358	A367	3c J.A. Mella, declaration	.25	.20
1359	A367	3c A. Guiteras, El Morrillo monument	.25	.20
1360	A367	3c A. Santamaria, attack on Moncada Barracks	.25	.20
1361	A367	3c F. Pais memorial	.25	.20
a.		Strip of 5, Nos. 1357-1361	1.75	1.00
1362	A367	9c J. Echeverria, student protest	1.25	.20
1363	A367	13c C. Cienfuegos, insurrection	3.00	.70
1364	A367	30c Che Guevara, 1st Declaration of Havana	3.50	1.10
		Nos. 1352-1364 (13)	10.00	4.00

Souvenir Sheet

The Burning of Bayamo, by J.E. Hernandez Giro — A368

1968, Oct. 18 — Imperf.

1365	A368	50c multi		9.00	9.00

Natl. Philatelic Exhibition, independence cent. Stamp in No. 1365 has simulated perforations.

19th Summer Olympics, Mexico City, Oct. 12-27 — A369

1968, Oct. 21 — Perf. 12½

1366	A369	1c Parade of athletes	.20	.20
1367	A369	2c Women's basketball, vert.	.20	.20
1368	A369	3c Hammer throw, vert.	.20	.20
1369	A369	4c Boxing	.20	.20
1370	A369	5c Water polo	.45	.20
1371	A369	13c Pistol shooting	3.00	.55

Size: 32x50mm

1372	A369	30c Mexican flag, calendar stone	4.50	.80
		Nos. 1366-1372 (7)	8.75	2.35

Souvenir Sheet
Imperf

1373	A369	50c Running	15.00	4.00

Stamp in #173 has simulated perforations.

Civilian Activities of the Armed Forces A370

1968, Dec. 2 — Wmk. 376 — Perf. 12½

1374	A370	3c Crop dusting	.20	.20
1375	A370	9c Che Guevara's Brigade	.60	.20
1376	A370	10c Road building	1.00	.25
1377	A370	13c Plowing, harvesting	2.10	.70
		Nos. 1374-1377 (4)	3.90	1.35

San Alejandro School of Painting, Sesquicentennial — A371

Paintings: 1c, Manrique de Lara's Family, by Jean Baptiste Vermay, vert. 2c, Seascape, by Leopoldo Romanach. 3c, Wild Cane, by Antonio Rodriguez, vert. 4c, Self-portrait, by Miguel Melero, vert. 5c, The Lottery List, by Jose Joaquin Tejada. 13c, Portrait of Nina, by Armando B. Menocal, vert. 30c, Landscape, by Esteban B. Chartrand. 50c, Siesta, by Guillermo Collazo.

1968, Dec. 30 **Unwmk.**
Sizes: 38x48mm (1c, 3c), 39x50mm (4c, 13c), 53x36mm (30c)
1378	A371	1c multi	.20	.20
1379	A371	2c multi	.20	.20
1380	A371	3c multi	.30	.20
1381	A371	4c multi	.30	.20
1382	A371	5c multi	1.40	.40
1383	A371	13c multi	4.00	.70
1384	A371	30c multi	6.25	1.10
	Nos. 1378-1384 (7)		12.65	3.00

Souvenir Sheet
Imperf
1385	A371	50c multi	9.00	3.50

No. 1385 contains one 52x41½mm stamp that has simulated perforations.

10th Anniv. of the Revolution A372

1969, Jan. 3 **Wmk. 376** **Perf. 12½**
1386	A372	13c multi	2.00	.60

Villaclarenos Rebellion, Cent. — A373

1969, Feb. 6
1387	A373	3c Gutierrez and Sanchez	1.00	.25

Women's Day — A374

Design: Mariana Grajales, rose and statue.

1969, Mar. 8
1388	A374	3c multi	1.25	.25

Cuban Pioneers and Young Communists Unions — A375

1969, Apr. 4
1389	A375	3c Pioneers	.40	.20
1390	A375	13c Young Communists	2.25	.80

Guaimaro Assembly, Cent. — A376

1969, Apr. 10
1391	A376	3c dark brn	1.00	.25

The Postman, by Jean C. Cazin A377

Paintings: 30c, Portrait of a Young Man, by George Romney.

1969, Apr. 24 **Unwmk.**
1392	A377	13c multi	2.50	.60

Size: 35½x43½mm
1393	A377	30c multi	4.00	.90

Stamp Day.

Agrarian Reform, 10th Anniv. A378

1969, May 17 **Wmk. 376**
1394	A378	13c multi	2.25	.70

Marine Life A379

1969, May 20 **Unwmk.**
1395	A379	1c Petrochirus bahamensis	.20	.20
1396	A379	2c Stenopus hispidus	.40	.20
1397	A379	3c Panulirus argus	.40	.20
1398	A379	4c Callinectes sapidus	.50	.20
1399	A379	5c Gecarcinus ruricola	.50	.20
1400	A379	13c Macrobrachium carcinus	3.50	.45
1401	A379	30c Carpilius coralinus	5.25	.80
	Nos. 1395-1401 (7)		10.75	2.25

Intl. Labor Organization, 50th Anniv. — A380

1969, June 6 **Wmk. 376**
1402	A380	3c shown	.45	.20
1403	A380	13c Blacksmith breaking chains	2.25	.70

Paintings in the Natl. Museum — A381

Designs: 1c, Flowers, by Raul Milian, vert. 2c, Annunciation, by Antonia Eiriz. 3c, Factory, by Marcelo Pogolotti, vert. 4c, Territorial Waters, by Luis Martinez Pedro, vert. 5c, Miss Sarah Gale, by John Hoppner, vert. 13c, Two Women Wearing Mantilla, by Ignacio Zuloaga. 30c, Virgin and Child, by Francisco de Zurbaran.

1969, June 15 **Unwmk.**
1404	A381	1c 39x59mm	.20	.20
1405	A381	2c	.20	.20
1406	A381	3c 39½x49mm	1.10	.20
1407	A381	4c 39½x43mm	.30	.20
1408	A381	5c 39½x45½mm	.30	.20
1409	A381	13c 38x41½mm	2.10	.70
1410	A381	30c 39x45mm	3.25	.90
	Nos. 1404-1410 (7)		7.45	2.60

Broadcasting Institute — A382

1969, July 5 **Wmk. 376**
1411	A382	3c shown	.40	.25
1412	A382	13c Hemispheres, tower	2.10	.80
1413	A382	1p Waves on graph	5.00	1.75
	Nos. 1411-1413 (3)		7.50	2.80

Fish A383

1969, July 20 **Unwmk.**
1414	A383	1c Apogon maculatus	.20	.20
1415	A383	2c Bodianus rufus	.20	.20
1416	A383	3c Microspathodon chrysurus	.40	.20
1417	A383	4c Gramma loreto	.40	.20
1418	A383	5c Chromis marginatus	.60	.20
1419	A383	13c Myripristis jacobus	3.75	.55
1420	A383	30c Nomeus gronovii, vert.	5.25	.90
	Nos. 1414-1420 (7)		10.80	2.45

Natl. Film Industry, 10th Anniv. — A384

1969, Aug. 5 **Wmk. 376**
1421	A384	1c Poster	.20	.20
1422	A384	3c Documentaries	.20	.20
1423	A384	13c Cartoons	3.00	.60
1424	A384	30c Entertainers	3.50	.70
	Nos. 1421-1424 (4)		6.90	1.70

Napoleon in Milan, by Andrea Appiani — A385

Paintings in the Napoleon Museum, Havana: 2c, Hortensia de Beauharnais, by Francois Gerard. 3c, Napoleon as First Consul, by J.B. Regnault. 4c, Elisa Bonaparte, by Robert Lefevre. 5c, Napoleon Planning Coronation Ceremony, by J.G. Vibert, horiz. 13c, Napoleon as Cuirassier Corporal, by Jean Meissonier. 30c, Napoleon Bonaparte, by LeFevre.

1969, Aug. 20 **Unwmk.**
1425	A385	1c	.20	.20
1426	A385	2c 41½x55mm	.25	.20
1427	A385	3c 45½x56mm	.25	.20
1428	A385	4c 43x62½mm	.45	.20
1429	A385	5c 63x47½mm	.70	.30
1430	A385	13c 43x62½mm	3.25	.70
1431	A385	30c 45x59½mm	4.25	.90
	Nos. 1425-1431 (7)		9.35	2.70

See Nos. 2448-2453.

Cuba's Victory at the 17th World Amateur Baseball Championships, Santo Domingo — A386

1969, Sept. 11
1432	A386	13c multi	2.75	.60

No. 1432 printed se-tenant with inscribed label listing finalists.

Alexander von Humboldt (1769-1859), German Naturalist — A387

1969, Sept. 14
1433	A387	3c Surinam eel	.20	.20
1434	A387	13c Night ape	2.50	1.00
1435	A387	30c Condors	4.00	.85
	Nos. 1433-1435 (3)		6.70	2.05

World Fencing Championships,
Havana — A388

Designs: 1c, Ancient Egyptians in combat. 2c, Roman gladiators. 2c, Viking and Norman. 4c, Medieval tournament. 5c, French musketeers. 13c, Japanese samurai. 30c, Mounted Cubans, War of Independence. 50c, Modern fencers.

1969, Oct. 2

1436	A388	1c multi	.20	.20
1437	A388	2c multi	.20	.20
1438	A388	3c multi	.20	.20
1439	A388	4c multi	.40	.20
1440	A388	5c multi	.65	.20
1441	A388	13c multi	3.00	.45
1442	A388	30c multi	4.75	.80
		Nos. 1436-1442 (7)	9.40	2.25

Souvenir Sheet

Imperf

1443	A388	50c multi	12.00	5.00

Stamp in No. 1443 has simulated perforations.

Natl. Revolutionary Militia, 10th Anniv. — A389

1969, Oct. 26   Wmk. 376
1444	A389	3c multi	1.25	.25

Disappearance of Maj. Camilo Cienfuegos, 10th Anniv. — A390

1969, Oct. 28
1445	A390	13c multi	2.50	.60

Agriculture — A391

1969, Nov. 2   Unwmk.
1446	A391	1c Strawberries, grapes	.25	.20
1447	A391	1c Onions, asparagus	.25	.20
1448	A391	1c Rice	.25	.20
1449	A391	1c Banana	.25	.20
a.		Strip of 4, #1446-1449	1.00	.80
1450	A391	3c Pineapple, vert.	.50	.50
1451	A391	3c Tobacco, vert.	.50	.50
1452	A391	3c Citrus fruits, vert.	.50	.50
1453	A391	3c Coffee, vert.	.50	.50
1454	A391	3c Rabbits, vert.	.50	.50
a.		Strip of 5, #1450-1454	2.75	2.50
1455	A391	10c Pigs, vert.	.50	.50
1456	A391	13c Sugar cane	2.75	.60
1457	A391	30c Bull	4.00	.85
		Nos. 1446-1457 (12)	10.75	4.95

Sporting Events — A392

1969, Nov. 15
1458	A392	1c 2nd Natl. Games	.25	.20
1459	A392	2c 11th Anniv. Games	.25	.20
1460	A392	3c Barrientos Commemorative, vert.	.25	.20
1461	A392	10c 2nd Olympic Trials, vert.	.40	.20
1462	A392	13c 6th Socialist Bicycle Race, vert.	2.75	.80
1463	A392	30c 6th Capablanca Memorial Chess Championships, vert.	4.00	1.25
		Nos. 1458-1463 (6)	7.90	2.85

Christmas Type of 1961

Flowering plants.

1969, Dec. 1
1464	A248	1c Plumbago capensis	.40	.20
1465	A249	1c Petrea volubilis	.40	.20
1466	A249	1c Clitoria ternatea	.40	.20
1467	A249	1c Duranta repens	.40	.20
1468	A249	1c Ruellia tuberosa	.40	.20
a.		Block of 5 + label, Nos. 1464-1468	3.00	1.00
1469	A248	3c Turnera ulmifolia	1.00	.25
1470	A249	3c Thevetia peruviana	1.00	.25
1471	A249	3c Hibiscus elatus	1.00	.25
1472	A249	3c Allamanda cathartica	1.00	.25
1473	A249	3c Cosmos sulphureus	1.00	.25
a.		Block of 5 + label, Nos. 1469-1473	6.00	1.25
1474	A248	13c Delonix regia	2.25	1.00
1475	A249	13c Neriun oleander	2.25	1.00
1476	A249	13c Cordia sebestena	2.25	1.00
1477	A249	13c Lochnera rosea	2.25	1.00
1478	A249	13c Jatropha integerrima	2.25	1.00
a.		Block of 5 + label, Nos. 1474-1478	11.00	5.00
		Nos. 1464-1478 (15)	18.25	7.25

Christmas 1969. See note after No. 700.

Zapata Swamp Fauna — A393

1969, Dec. 15
1479	A393	1c Trelanorhynus variabilis	.20	.20
1480	A393	2c Hyla insulsa	.20	.20
1481	A393	3c Atractosteus tristoechus	.20	.20
1482	A393	4c Capromys nana	.20	.20
1483	A393	5c Crocodylus rhombifer	.20	.20
1484	A393	13c Amazona leucocephala	4.50	.55
1485	A393	30c Agelaius phoeniceus assimilis	5.00	1.00
		Nos. 1479-1485 (7)	10.50	2.55

Nos. 1482, 1484-1485 vert.

Tourism
A394

1970, Jan. 25   Wmk. 376
1486	A394	1c Jibacoa Beach	.20	.20
1487	A394	3c Trinidad City	.20	.20
1488	A394	13c Santiago de Cuba	1.90	.80
1489	A394	30c Vinales Valley	2.75	1.00
		Nos. 1486-1489 (4)	5.05	2.20

Medicinal Plants — A395

1970, Feb. 10   Unwmk.
1490	A395	1c Guarea guara	.20	.20
1491	A395	3c Ocimum sanctum	.20	.20
1492	A395	10c Canella winterana	.45	.20
1493	A395	13c Bidens pilosa	2.25	.70
1494	A395	30c Turnera ulmifolia	2.75	.85
1495	A395	50c Picramnia pentandra	4.00	1.00
		Nos. 1490-1495 (6)	9.85	3.15

11th Central American and Caribbean Games, Panama, Feb. 28-Mar. 14 — A396

1970, Feb. 28   Wmk. 376
1496	A396	1c Weight lifting	.20	.20
1497	A396	3c Boxing	.20	.20
1498	A396	10c Gymnastics	.20	.20
1499	A396	13c Running	2.40	.65
1500	A396	30c Fencing	3.50	.90
		Nos. 1496-1500 (5)	6.50	2.15

Souvenir Sheet

Imperf

1501	A396	50c Baseball	12.00	6.00

No. 1501 contains one 50x37mm stamp that has simulated perforations.

EXPO '70, Osaka, Japan, Mar. 15-Sept. 13 — A397

1970, Mar. 15
1502	A397	1c Enjoying life	.20	.20
1503	A397	2c Improving on nature, vert.	.40	.20
1504	A397	3c Better living standard	.40	.20
1505	A397	13c Intl. cooperation, vert.	2.75	.55
1506	A397	30c Cuban pavilion	4.00	.80
		Nos. 1502-1506 (5)	7.75	1.95

Speleological Soc., 30th Anniv. — A398

Petroglyphs in Cuban caves: 1c, Ambrosio Cave, Varadero Matanzas. 2c, Cave No. 1, Punta del Este, Isle of Pines. 3c, Pichardo Cave, Cubitas Camaguey Mountains. 4c, Ambrosio Cave, diff. 5c, Cave No. 1, diff. 13c, Garcia Ribiou Cave, Havana. 30c, Cave No. 2, Punta del Este.

1970, Mar. 28   Unwmk.

Sizes: 29x45mm (1c, 3c, 4c, 13c)
1507	A398	1c multi	.20	.20
1508	A398	2c shown	.20	.20
1509	A398	3c multi	.20	.20
1510	A398	4c multi	.20	.20
1511	A398	5c multi	.20	.20
1512	A398	13c multi	2.25	.70
1513	A398	30c multi	4.75	.80
		Nos. 1507-1513 (7)	8.00	2.50

Aviation Pioneers — A399

1970, Apr. 10
1514	A399	3c Jose D. Blino	1.00	.20
1515	A399	13c Adolfo Teodore	3.50	.70

Lenin Birth Centenary — A400

Paintings and quotes: 1c, Lenin in Kazan, by O. Vishniakov. 2c, Young Lenin, by V. Prager. 3c, Second Socialist Party Congress, by Y. Vinogradov. 4c, First Manifesto, by F. Golubkov. 5c, First Day of Soviet Power, by N. Babasiuk. 13c, Lenin in Smolny, by M. Sokolov. 30c, Autumn in Gorky, by A. Varlamov. 50c, Lenin at Gorky, by N. Baskakov.

1970, Apr. 22

Sizes: 67½x46mm (1c, 4c, 5c)
1516	A400	1c multi	.20	.20
1517	A400	2c shown	.20	.20
1518	A400	3c multi	.20	.20
1519	A400	4c multi	.20	.20
1520	A400	5c multi	.20	.20
1521	A400	13c multi	2.75	.55
1522	A400	30c multi	3.25	.70
		Nos. 1516-1522 (7)	7.00	2.25

Souvenir Sheet

Imperf

1523	A400	50c multi	13.00	6.50

No. 1523 contains one 48x46mm stamp that has simulated perforations.

Stamp Day — A401

1970, Apr. 24
1524	A401	13c The Letter, by J. Arche	3.00	.60

Size: 30x44mm
1525 A401 30c Portrait of A Cadet, Anonymous 3.75 .80

Da Vinci's Anatomical Drawing, Earth, Moon — A402

1970, May 17 **Wmk. 376**
1526 A402 30c multi 3.50 .60
World Telecommunications Day.

Ho Chi Minh (1890-1969), President of North Viet Nam — A403

1970, May 19 **Unwmk.**
1527 A403 1c Vietnamese fisherman .20 .20
Size: 32x44mm
1528 A403 3c Two women .50 .20
1529 A403 3c Plowing field .50 .20
Size: 33x45mm
1530 A403 3c Teacher, students in air-raid shelter .50 .20
1531 A403 3c Nine women in paddy .70 .20
Size: 34x41½mm
1532 A403 3c Camouflaged machine shop .70 .20
Size: 34x39mm
1533 A403 13c shown 3.25 .70
Nos. 1527-1533 (7) 6.35 1.90

Cuban Cigar Industry A404

1970, July 5
1534 A404 3c Plantation, Eden cigar band .20 .20
1535 A404 13c Factory, El Mambi band 2.25 .70
1536 A404 30c Packing cigars, Lopez Hermanos band 3.25 1.00
Nos. 1534-1536 (3) 5.70 1.90

Projected Sugar Production: Over 10 Million Tons — A405

1970, July 26
1537 A405 1c Cane-crushing .20 .20
1538 A405 2c Sowing and crop dusting .20 .20

1539 A405 3c Cutting sugar cane .25 .20
1540 A405 10c Transporting cane 5.00 .45
1541 A405 13c Modern cutting machine 1.50 .25
1542 A405 30c Intl. Brigade, cane cutters, vert. 2.25 .70
1543 A405 1p Sugar warehouse 4.00 2.00
Nos. 1537-1543 (7) 13.40 4.00

Pedro Figueredo (d. 1870), Composer — A406

Versions of the Natl. Anthem.

1970, Aug. 17
1544 A406 3c 1868 Version .30 .20
1545 A406 20c 1898 Version 2.75 .60

Women's Federation, 10th Anniv. — A407

1970, Aug. 23
1546 A407 3c multi 1.00 .50

Militia, by Servando C. Moreno — A408

Paintings in the Natl. Museum: 2c, Washerwomen, by Aristides Fernandez. 3c, Puerta del Sol, Madrid, by L. Paret Y Alcazar. 4c, Fishermen's Wives, by Joaquin Sorolla. 5c, Portrait of a Woman, by Thomas de Keyser. 13c, Mrs. Edward Foster, by Sir Thomas Lawrence. 30c, Tropical Gypsy, by Victor M. Garcia.

1970, Aug. 31
1547 A408 1c shown .20 .20
Size: 45x41mm
1548 A408 2c multi .20 .20
1549 A408 3c multi .20 .20
Size: 40x41mm
1550 A408 4c multi .20 .20
Size: 38x45½mm
1551 A408 5c multi .20 .20
1552 A408 13c multi 2.50 .50
1553 A408 30c multi 4.00 .80
Nos. 1547-1553 (7) 7.50 2.30
See #1640-1646, 1669-1675, 1773-1779.

Havana Declaration, 10th Anniv. — A409

1970, Sept. 2
1554 A409 3c Jose Marti Square .75 .20

Committee for the Defense of the Revolution, 10th Anniv. A410

1970, Sept. 28
1555 A410 3c multi .55 .20

39th Sugar Technician's Assoc. (ATAC) Conference — A411

1970, Oct. 11
1556 A411 30c multi 3.25 .70

Wildlife — A412

1970, Oct. 20
1557 A412 1c Numida meleagris galeata .70 .20
1558 A412 2c Dendrocygna arborea .80 .20
1559 A412 3c Phasianus colchicus torquatus .95 .20
1560 A412 4c Zenaida macroura macroura 1.10 .20
1561 A412 5c Colinus virginianus cubanensis 1.25 .25
1562 A412 13c Sus scrofa 2.00 1.00
1563 A412 30c Odocoileus virginianus 3.25 1.50
Nos. 1557-1563 (7) 10.05 3.55

Black-magic Feast, by M. Puente — A413

Afro-Cuban folk paintings: 3c, Hat Dance, by V.P. Landaluze. 10c, Los Hoyos Conga Dance, by Domingo Ravenet. 13c, Climax of the Rumba, by Eduardo Abela.

1970, Nov. 5
Sizes: 36x48½mm (3c, 13c), 44½x44mm (10c)
1564 A413 1c shown .20 .20
1565 A413 3c multi .35 .20
1566 A413 10c multi .90 .45
1567 A413 13c multi 2.50 .70
Nos. 1564-1567 (4) 3.95 1.55

Road Safety Week A414

1970, Nov. 15
1568 A414 3c Zebra, road signs 1.10 .20
1569 A414 9c Prudence the Bear 1.60 .25

Intl. Education Year — A415

1970, Nov. 20
1570 A415 13c Abacus, "a" 2.50 .25
1571 A415 30c Cow, microscope 3.25 .70

Christmas Type of 1961
Birds.

1970, Dec. 1
1572 A248 1c Dives atroviolaceus .80 .20
1573 A249 1c Glaucidium siju siju .80 .20
1574 A249 1c Todus multicolor .80 .20
1575 A249 1c Xiphidiopicus percussus percussus .80 .20
1576 A249 1c Ferminia cerverai .80 .20
a. Block of 5 + label, Nos. 1572-1576 5.00 1.00
1577 A248 3c Teretistris fornsi 1.75 .35
1578 A249 3c Myadestes elisabeth elisabeth 1.75 .35
1579 A249 3c Polioptila lembeyei 1.75 .35
1580 A249 3c Vireo gundlachii gundlachii 1.75 .35
1581 A249 3c Teretistris fernandinae 1.75 .35
a. Block of 5 + label, Nos. 1577-1581 10.00 2.00
1582 A248 13c Torreornis inexpectata inexpectata 2.50 .90
1583 A249 13c Chondrohierax wilsonii 2.50 .90
1584 A249 13c Accipiter gundlachi 2.50 .90
1585 A249 13c Starnoenas cyanocephala 2.50 .90
1586 A249 13c Aratinga euops 2.50 .90
a. Block of 5 + label, Nos. 1582-1586 15.00 5.00
Nos. 1572-1586 (15) 25.25 7.25
Christmas 1970. See note after No. 700.

Camilo Cienfuegos Military Academy — A416

1970, Dec. 2
1587 A416 3c multi 1.25 .25

7th Congress of the Intl. Organization of Journalists — A417

1971, Jan. 4
1588 A417 13c multi 2.25 .50

World Meteorology Day — A418

1971, Feb. 16
Size: 39½x35½mm (3c)
1589	A418	1c Class, weather chart, computer, vert.	.20	.20
1590	A418	3c Weather map	.20	.20
1591	A418	8c Equipment, vert.	1.00	.25
1592	A418	30c shown	4.75	1.25
		Nos. 1589-1592 (4)	6.15	1.90

6th Pan American Games, Cali, Colombia — A419

1971, Feb. 20
1593	A419	1c Emblem, vert.	.20	.20
1594	A419	2c Women's running, vert.	.20	.20
1595	A419	3c Rifle shooting	.20	.20
1596	A419	4c Gymnastics, vert.	.20	.20
1597	A419	5c Boxing, vert.	.20	.20
1598	A419	13c Water polo	2.40	.30
1599	A419	30c Baseball	3.00	.55
		Nos. 1593-1599 (7)	6.40	1.85

Porcelain and Mosaics in the Metropolitan Museum, Havana — A420

Designs: 1c, Parisian vase, 19th cent. 3c, Mexican bowl, 17th cent. 10c, Parisian vase, diff. 13c, Colosseum, Italian mosaic, 19th cent. 20c, Mexican bowl, 17th cent. 30c, St. Peter's Square, Italian mosaic, 19th cent.

1971, Mar. 11
Sizes: 34½x53mm (1c, 10c), 46x53mm (3c), 42x48mm (20c)
1600	A420	1c multi	.20	.20
1601	A420	3c multi	.20	.20
1602	A420	10c multi	.40	.20
1603	A420	13c shown	2.25	.25
1604	A420	20c multi	2.25	.55
1605	A420	30c multi	2.75	.65
		Nos. 1600-1605 (6)	8.05	2.05

See Nos. 1699-1705.

Natl. Child Centers, 10th Anniv. — A421

1971, Apr. 10
| 1606 | A421 | 3c multi | .75 | .20 |

Manned Space Flight 10th Anniv. — A422

Cosmonauts in training.

1971, Apr. 12
1607	A422	1c multi	.20	.20
1608	A422	2c multi, diff.	.20	.20
1609	A422	3c multi, diff.	.20	.20
1610	A422	4c multi, diff.	.20	.20
1611	A422	5c multi, diff.	.20	.20
1612	A422	13c multi, diff.	2.25	.30
1613	A422	30c multi, diff.	3.25	.65
		Nos. 1607-1613 (7)	6.50	1.95

Souvenir Sheet
Imperf
| 1614 | A422 | 50c multi | 10.00 | 10.00 |

Stamp in #1614 has simulated perf.

Bay of Pigs Invasion, 10th Anniv. A423

1971, Apr. 17
| 1615 | A423 | 13c multi | 2.00 | .60 |

Stamp Day — A424

Packets: 13c, Jeune Richard attacking Windsor Castle, 1807. 30c, Orinoco.

1971, Apr. 24
| 1616 | A424 | 13c multi | 2.40 | .80 |
| 1617 | A424 | 30c multi | 3.50 | 1.00 |

Cuban Intl. Broadcast Service, 10th Anniv. — A425

1971, May 1   **Wmk. 376**
| 1618 | A425 | 3c multi | .40 | .20 |
| 1619 | A425 | 50c multi | 4.50 | .90 |

Orchids A426

1971, May 15
1620	A426	1c Cattleya skinnerii	.20	.20
1621	A426	2c Vanda hibrida	.20	.20
1622	A426	3c Cypripedium collossum		.20
1623	A426	4c Cypripedium gloucophyllum		.20
1624	A426	5c Vanda tricolor	.25	.20
1625	A426	13c Cypripedium mowgh	2.40	.45
1626	A426	30c Cypripedium solum	4.75	.85
		Nos. 1620-1626 (7)	8.20	2.30

See Nos. 1677-1683 and 1780-1786.

Enrique Loynaz del Castillo (b. 1861), Composer — A427

1971, June 5   **Wmk. 376**
| 1627 | A427 | 3c Portrait, Invasion Hymn | .90 | .25 |

Bee Keeping — A428

1971, June 20   **Unwmk.**
1628	A428	1c Egg, larvae, pupa	.20	.20
1629	A428	3c Worker	.20	.20
1630	A428	9c Drone	.45	.20
1631	A428	13c Defense of hive	2.25	.30
1632	A428	30c Queen	3.50	.80
		Nos. 1628-1632 (5)	6.60	1.70

Children's Drawings — A429

1971, Aug. 30
Size: 45x39mm
| 1633 | A429 | 1c Sailboat | .20 | .20 |
| 1634 | A429 | 3c The Little Train | .85 | .20 |

Sizes: 45½x35½mm (9c, 13c), 47x37½mm (10c)
1635	A429	9c Sugar Cane Cutter	.20	.20
1636	A429	10c Return of the Fishermen	.40	.20
1637	A429	13c The Zoo	1.60	.30

Size: 47x42mm
| 1638 | A429 | 20c House and Garden | 2.50 | .55 |

Size: 31½x50mm
| 1639 | A429 | 30c Landscape | 2.75 | .85 |
| | | Nos. 1633-1639 (7) | 8.50 | 2.50 |

Art Type of 1970

Paintings in the Natl. Museum: 1c, St. Catherine of Alexandria, by F. Zurburan. 2c, The Cart, by Federico Americo. 3c, St. Christopher and Child, by J. Bassano. 4c, Little Devil, by Rene Portocarrero. 5c, Portrait of a Woman, by Nicolas Maes. 13c, Phoenix, by Raul Martinez. 30c, Sir William Pitt, by Thomas Gainsborough.

1971, Sept. 20
1640	A408	1c 31x55mm	.20	.20
1641	A408	2c 48x37mm	.20	.20
1642	A408	3c 31x55mm	.20	.20
1643	A408	4c 37x48mm	.25	.20
1644	A408	5c 37x48mm	.40	.20
1645	A408	13c 39x48½mm	2.25	.45
1646	A408	30c 39x48½mm	3.25	.75
		Nos. 1640-1646 (7)	6.75	2.20

Sport Fishing — A431

1971, Oct. 30
1647	A431	1c Albula vulpes	.20	.20
1648	A431	2c Seriola species	.20	.20
1649	A431	3c Micropterus salmoides		.20
1650	A431	4c Coryphaena hippurus	.25	.20
1651	A431	5c Megalops atlantica	.30	.20
1652	A431	13c Acanthocybium solandri	2.00	.55
1653	A431	30c Makaira ampla	3.25	.95
		Nos. 1647-1653 (7)	6.40	2.50

19th World Amateur Baseball Championships — A432

1971, Nov. 22   **Wmk. 376**
| 1654 | A432 | 3c shown | .25 | .25 |
| 1655 | A432 | 1p Globe as baseball | 6.25 | 1.40 |

Execution of Medical Students, Cent. A433

Paintings: 3c, Dr. Fermin Valdez Dominguez, anonymous. 13c, Execution of the Medical Students, by M. Mesa. 30c, Capt. Federico Capdevila, anonymous.

1971, Nov. 27   **Unwmk.**
Size: 61½x46mm (13c)
1656	A433	3c multi	.35	.20
1657	A433	13c multi	1.90	.40
1658	A433	30c multi	3.00	.55
		Nos. 1656-1658 (3)	5.25	1.15

Spindalis Zena Pretrei — A434

Birds: 1c, Falco sparverius sparverioides vigors. 2c, Glaucidium siju siju. 3c, Priotelus temnurus temnurus. 4c, Saurothera merlini merlini. 5c, Nesoceleus fernandinae. 30c, Mimocichla plumbea rubripes. 50c, Chlorostilbon ricordii ricordii and Archilochus colubris. Nos. 1659-1663 vert.

1971, Dec. 10

1659	A434	1c multi	.40	.20
1660	A434	2c multi	.40	.20
1661	A434	3c multi	.65	.20
1662	A434	4c multi	.70	.25
1663	A434	5c multi	.90	.25
1664	A434	13c shown	1.60	.55
1665	A434	30c multi	3.25	1.75

Nos. 1659-1665 (7) 7.90 3.40

Size: 55½x29mm

1666	A434	50c multi	6.00	1.75

Death centenary of Ramon de la Sagra, naturalist.

Cuba's Victory at the World Amateur Baseball Championships — A435

1971, Dec. 8   **Wmk. 376**

1667	A435	13c multi	2.00	.60

UNICEF, 25th Anniv. — A436

1971, Dec. 11

1668	A436	13c multi	2.50	.70

Art Type of 1970

Paintings in the Natl. Museum: 1c, Arrival of an Ambassador, by Vittore Carpaccio. 2c, Senora Malpica, by G. Collazo. 3c, La Chorrera Tower, by Esteban Chartrand. 4c, Creole Landscape, by Carlos Enriquez. 5c, Sir William Lemon, by George Romney. 13c, Landscape, by Henry Cleenewerk. 30c, Valencia Beach, by Joaquin Sorolla y Bastida.

1972, Jan. 25   **Unwmk.**

1669	A408	1c 50x33mm	.20	.20
1670	A408	2c 27½x52mm	.20	.20
1671	A408	3c 50x33mm	.20	.20
1672	A408	4c 35x43mm	.20	.20
1673	A408	5c 35x43mm	.20	.20
1674	A408	13c 43x33mm	2.00	.40
1675	A408	30c 43x33mm	3.50	.95

Nos. 1669-1675 (7) 6.50 2.35

Academy of Sciences, 10th Anniv. — A437

1972, Feb. 20   **Wmk. 376**

1676	A437	13c Capitol Type of 1929	2.00	.50

Orchid Type of 1971

1972, Feb. 25   **Unwmk.**

1677	A426	1c Brasso cattleya sindorossiana	.20	.20
1678	A426	2c Cypripedium doraeus	.20	.20
1679	A426	3c Cypripedium exul	.20	.20
1680	A426	4c Cypripedium rosy dawn	.20	.20
1681	A426	5c Cypripedium champolliom	.20	.20
1682	A426	13c Cypripedium bucolique	2.75	.65
1683	A426	30c Cypripedium sullanum	3.50	.80

Nos. 1677-1683 (7) 7.25 2.45

Eduardo Agramonte (1849-1872), Revolutionary, Physician — A438

1972, Mar. 8

1684	A438	3c Portrait by F. Martinez	.60	.20

World Health Day — A439

1972, Apr. 7   **Wmk. 376**

1685	A439	13c multi	2.00	.50

Soviet Space Program — A440

1972, Apr. 12   **Unwmk.**

1686	A440	1c Sputnik 1	.20	.20
1687	A440	2c Vostok 1	.20	.20
1688	A440	3c Valentina Tereshkova	.20	.20
1689	A440	4c Alexei Leonov	.20	.20
1690	A440	5c Lunokhod 1, moon vehicle	.20	.20
1691	A440	13c Linking Soyuz capsules	2.10	.40
1692	A440	30c Victims of Soyuz 11 accident	2.50	.70

Nos. 1686-1692 (7) 5.60 2.10

Stamp Day — A441

Designs: 13c, Postmaster-Gen. Vicente Mora Pera, by Ramon Loy. 30c, Soldier's Letter, Cuba to Venezuela, 1897.

1972, Apr. 24

1693	A441	13c shown	1.75	.50

Size: 48x39mm

1694	A441	30c multi	2.75	.55

Labor Day — A442

Jose Marti, Ho Chi Minh — A443

3rd Conference Against War in Indo-China, May 19 — A444

1972, May 1   **Wmk. 376**

1695	A442	3c multi	.90	.25

1972, May 19

1696	A443	3c shown	.40	.20
1697	A444	13c shown	1.60	.40
1698	A443	30c Roses, conference emblem	2.00	.55

Nos. 1696-1698 (3) 4.00 1.15

Metropolitan Museum Type of 1971

Portraits: 1c, Salvador del Muro, by J. Del Rio. 2c, Luis de las Casas, by Del Rio. 3c, Cristopher Columbus, anonymous. 4c, Tomas Gamba, by V. Escobar. 5c, Maria Galarraga, by Escobar. 13c, Isabel II, by Federico Madrazo. 30c, Carlos III, by Miguel Melero.

1972, May 25   **Unwmk.**

Size: 34x43½mm

1699	A420	1c multi	.20	.20
1700	A420	2c multi	.20	.20
1701	A420	3c multi	.20	.20
1702	A420	4c multi	.40	.20
1703	A420	5c multi	.40	.20

Size: 34x51½mm

1704	A420	13c multi	2.00	.40
1705	A420	30c multi	2.50	.70

Nos. 1699-1705 (7) 5.90 2.10

Children's Songs Competition, Natl. Library A445

1972, June 5   **Wmk. 376**

1706	A445	3c multi	.80	.25

Thoroughbred Horses — A446

1972, June 30   **Unwmk.**

1707	A446	1c Tarpan	.20	.20
1708	A446	2c Kertag	.20	.20
1709	A446	3c Creole	.20	.20
1710	A446	4c Andalusian	.20	.20
1711	A446	5c Arabian	.20	.20
1712	A446	13c Quarter horse	3.00	.55
1713	A446	30c Pursang	3.50	.80

Nos. 1707-1713 (7) 7.50 2.35

Frank Pais (d. 1957), Educator, Revolutionary — A447

1972, July 26   **Wmk. 376**

1714	A447	13c blk & red	1.75	.50

1972 Summer Olympics, Munich, Aug. 26-Sept. 10 — A448

1972, Aug. 26   **Unwmk.**

1715	A448	1c Athlete, emblems, vert.	.20	.20
1716	A448	2c "M," boxing	.20	.20
1717	A448	3c "U," weight lifting	.20	.20
1718	A448	4c "N," fencing	.20	.20
1719	A448	5c "I," rifle shooting	.20	.20
1720	A448	13c "C," running	2.00	.35
1721	A448	30c "H," basketball	2.50	.65

Nos. 1715-1721 (7) 5.50 2.00

Souvenir Sheet

Imperf

1722	A448	50c Gymnastics	6.00	1.90

Stamp in No. 1722 has simulated perforations.

Intl. Hydrological Decade — A449

Landscapes: 1c, Tree Trunks, by Domingo Ramos. 3c, Cyclone, by Tiburcio Lorenzo. 8c, Vinales, by Ramos. 30c, Forest and Brook, by Antonio R. Morey, vert.

1972, Sept. 20

1723	A449	1c multi	.20	.20
1724	A449	3c multi	.20	.20
1725	A449	8c multi	.80	.20
1726	A449	30c multi	2.50	.55

Nos. 1723-1726 (4) 3.70 1.15

Butterflies from the Gundlach Collection — A450

1972, Sept. 25

1727	A450	1c Papilio thoas oviedo	.20	.20
1728	A450	2c Papilio devilliers	.20	.20
1729	A450	3c Papilio polixenes polixenes	.20	.20
1730	A450	4c Papilio androgeus epidaurus	.20	.20
1731	A450	5c Papilio cayguanabus	.30	.20

1732 A450 13c Papilio an-
draemon her-
nandezi 3.50 .85
1733 A450 30c Papilio celadon 4.75 1.10
Nos. 1727-1733 (7) 9.35 2.95

A451

Miguel de Cervantes Saavedra (1547-
1616), Spanish Author — A452

Paintings by A. Fernandez: 3c, In La
Mancha, vert. 13c, Battle with Wine Skins.
30c, Don Quixote de La Mancha, vert. 50c,
Scene from Don Quixote, by Jose Moreno
Carbonero.

1972, Sept. 29
Size: 34½x46mm (3c, 30c)
1734 A451 3c multi .20 .20
1735 A451 13c shown 2.10 .50
1736 A451 30c multi 2.25 .55
Nos. 1734-1736 (3) 4.55 1.25
Souvenir Sheet
Perf. 12½ on 3 Sides
1737 A452 50c shown 5.00 2.25

Guerrilla Day, 5th Anniv. — A453

1972, Oct. 8
1738 A453 3c Ernesto "Che"
Guevara .20 .20
1739 A453 13c Tamara "Tania"
Bunke 2.25 .50
1740 A453 30c Guido "Inti"
Peredo 2.50 .60
Nos. 1738-1740 (3) 4.95 1.30

Traditional
Musical
Instruments
A454

1972, Oct. 25
1741 A454 3c Abwe (rattles) .20 .20
1742 A454 13c Bonko enchemiya
(drum) 2.25 .45
1743 A454 30c Iya (drum) 2.50 .55
Nos. 1741-1743 (3) 4.95 1.20

MATEX '72, 3rd Natl. Philatelic
Exhibition, Matanzas — A455

1972, Nov. 18 **Wmk. 376**
1744 A455 13c No. 467 2.50 .45
1745 A455 30c No. C49 3.00 .55
Nos. 1744-1745 printed se-tenant with
insribed labels picturing Type A232, emblem
of the Cuban Philatelic Federation.

Historic
Ships
A456

1972, Nov. 30 **Unwmk.**
1746 A456 1c Viking long boat,
6th-9th cent. .20 .20
1747 A456 2c Caravel, 15th
cent., vert. .20 .20
1748 A456 3c Galleass, 16th
cent. .20 .20
1749 A456 4c Galleon, 17th
cent., vert. .30 .20
1750 A456 5c Clipper, 19th
cent. .35 .20
1751 A456 13c Steam packet,
19th cent. 2.10 .75
Size: 52½x29mm.
1752 A456 30c Atomic icebreaker
Lenin 6.00 1.25
Nos. 1746-1752 (7) 9.35 3.00

UNESCO Save Venice
Campaign — A457

1972, Dec. 8
1753 A457 3c Lion of St. Mark .20 .20
1754 A457 13c Bridge of Sighs,
vert. 1.75 .45
1755 A457 30c St. Mark's Cathedral 2.25 .85
Nos. 1753-1755 (3) 4.20 1.50

Cuba, World
Amateur
Baseball
Champion in
1972 — A458

Sport Events,
1972 — A459

1972, Dec. 15
1756 A458 3c Umpire 1.25 .30

1972, Dec. 22
1757 A459 1c shown .20 .20
1758 A459 2c Pole vault .20 .20
1759 A458 3c like No. 1756 .20 .20
1760 A458 4c Wrestling .20 .20
1761 A458 5c Fencing .20 .20
1762 A458 13c Boxing 1.75 .55
1763 A458 30c Marlin 2.50 .80
Nos. 1757-1763 (7) 5.25 2.35
Barrientos Memorial Athletics Championships, 11th Amateur Baseball Championships,
Cerro Pelado Intl. Tournament, Central American and Caribbean Fencing Tournament,

Giraldo Cordova Tournament, Ernest Hemingway Natl. Fishing Contest.
No. 1759 inscribed "XI serie nacional de
beisbol aficionado."

Medals
Won by
Cubans at
the 1972
Summer
Olympics,
Munich
A460

1c, Bronze, Women's 100-meter. 2c,
Bronze, women's relay. 3c, Gold, 54kg boxing.
4c, Silver, 81kg boxing. 5c, Bronze, 51kg boxing. 13c, Gold, 87kg boxing. 30c, Gold, silver
cup, heavyweight boxing. 50c, Bronze,
basketball.

1973, Jan. 28
1764 A460 1c multi .20 .20
1765 A460 2c multi .20 .20
1766 A460 3c multi .20 .20
1767 A460 4c multi .20 .20
1768 A460 5c multi .20 .20
1769 A460 13c multi 1.75 .60
1770 A460 30c multi 2.25 .90
Nos. 1764-1770 (7) 5.00 2.50
Souvenir Sheet
Imperf
1771 A460 50c multi 6.00 2.25
Stamp in No. 1771 has simulated
perforations.

A461

A462

Portrait by A.M. Esquivel.

1973, Feb. 10
1772 A461 13c multi 2.25 .45
Gertrudis Gomez de Avellaneda (1814-
1873), poet.

Art Type of 1970
Paintings in the Natl. Museum: 1c, Bathers
in the Lagoon, by C. Enriquez. 2c, Still-life, by
W.C. Heda. 3c, Gallantry, by P. Landaluze. 4c,
Return in the Late Afternoon, by C. Troyon. 5c,
Elizabetta Mascagni, by F.X. Fabre. 13c, The
Picador, by De Lucas Padilla, horiz. 30c, In the
Garden, by Arburu Morell.

1973, Feb. 28
Sizes: 36x46mm, 46x36mm
1773 A408 1c multi .20 .20
1774 A408 2c multi .20 .20
1775 A408 3c multi .20 .20
1776 A408 4c multi .20 .20
1777 A408 5c multi .20 .20
1778 A408 13c multi 1.60 .55
1779 A408 30c multi 2.25 .80
Nos. 1773-1779 (7) 4.85 2.35

Orchid Type of 1971
1973, Mar. 26
1780 A426 1c Dendrobium hybrid .20 .20
1781 A426 2c Cypripedium exul .20 .20
1782 A426 3c Vanda miss. joaquin rose marie .20 .20
1783 A426 4c Phalaenopsis
schilleriana .20 .20
1784 A426 5c Vanda gilbert
tribulet .40 .20
1785 A426 13c Dendrobium hybrid, diff. 3.00 .55

1786 A426 30c Arachnis catherine 3.50 .80
Nos. 1780-1786 (7) 7.70 2.35

1973, Apr. 7 **Wmk. 376**
1787 A462 10c multi, *buff* 1.25 .30
World Health Day. World Health Organization, 25th anniv.

Anti-Polio Campaign — A463

1973, Apr. 9 **Unwmk.**
1788 A463 3c multi .70 .25

Soviet Space Program — A464

1973, Apr. 12
1789 A464 1c Soyuz rocket
launch, vert. .20 .20
1790 A464 2c Luna 1, Moon .20 .20
1791 A464 3c Luna 16 taking-
off from Moon,
vert. .20 .20
1792 A464 4c Venus 7 .20 .20
1793 A464 5c Molnia 1, vert. .20 .20
1794 A464 13c Mars 3 1.25 .70
1795 A464 30c Radar observation ship, Yuri
Gagarin 3.50 .85
Nos. 1789-1795 (7) 5.75 2.55

Stamp
Day
A465

Postmarks: 13c, Santiago de Cuba, 1760.
30c, Havana, 1760.

1973, Apr. 24
1796 A465 13c multi 1.90 .50
1797 A465 30c multi 2.10 .60
See Nos. 1888-1891.

Portrait by A.
Espinosa
A466

1973, May 11
1798 A466 13c multi 1.50 .45
Maj.-Gen. Ignacio Agramonte (1841-1873).

Birthplace, Torun, and
Inventions — A467

Copernicus Monument,
Warsaw — A468

1973, May 25
1799 A467 3c shown .20 .20
1800 A467 13c Copernicus,
spacecraft 1.60 .45
1801 A467 30c Manuscript,
Frombork Tower 3.00 .60
Nos. 1799-1801 (3) 4.80 1.25

Souvenir Sheet
Perf. 12½ on 3 Sides
1802 A468 50c shown 6.50 2.25

500th anniversary of the birth of Nicolaus
Copernicus (1473-1543), Polish astronomer.

Improvement of School
Education — A469

1973, June 12 **Wmk. 376**
1803 A469 13c multi 1.50 .25

Cattle — A470

1973, June 28 **Unwmk.**
1804 A470 1c Jersey .20 .20
1805 A470 2c Charolaise .20 .20
1806 A470 3c Creole .20 .20
1807 A470 4c Swiss .25 .20
1808 A470 5c Holstein .25 .20
1809 A470 13c Santa Gertrudis 1.60 .40
1810 A470 30c Brahman 3.25 .75
Nos. 1804-1810 (7) 5.95 2.15

A471

A472

1973, July 10 **Wmk. 376**
1811 A471 13c multi 1.50 .30

10th Communist Festival of Youths and Students, East Berlin.

1973, July 26 **Unwmk.**
1812 A472 3c Siboney Farm,
Santiago de Cu-
ba .35 .25
1813 A472 13c Moncada Barracks 1.50 .30
1814 A472 30c Revolution Plaza,
Havana 2.25 .45
Nos. 1812-1814 (3) 4.10 1.00

20th anniv. of the Revolution.

10th Anniv. of the Revolutionary
Navy — A473

1973, Aug. 3 **Wmk. 376**
1815 A473 3c Midshipman, missile frigate .85 .30

Interior,
by
Manuel
Vicens
A474

Paintings in the Natl. Museum: 1c, Amalia of
Saxony, by J.K. Rossler. 3c, Margarita of Aus-
tria, by J. Pantoja de la Cruz. 4c, City Hall
Official, anonymous. 5c, View of Santiago de
Cuba, by Hernandez Giro. 13c, The Catalan,
by J.J. Tejada. 30c, Alley in Guayo, by Tejada.

1973, Aug. 30 **Unwmk.**
Sizes: 26½x41mm (1c, 3c),
28½x39mm (4c, 13c, 30c)
1816 A474 1c multi .20 .20
1817 A474 2c multi .20 .20
1818 A474 3c multi .25 .20
1819 A474 4c multi .25 .20
1820 A474 5c multi .25 .20
1821 A474 13c multi 1.90 .60
1822 A474 30c multi 2.50 .70
Nos. 1816-1822 (7) 5.55 2.30

WMO
Emblem,
Paintings
by J.
Madrazo
A475

1973, Sept. 4
1823 A475 8c Spring .75 .20
1824 A475 8c Summer .75 .20
1825 A475 8c Fall .75 .20
1826 A475 8c Winter .75 .20
Nos. 1823-1826 (4) 3.00 .80

World Meterological Organization, cent.
Nos. 1823-1826 printed se-tenant in strips of
4; frame reversed on 2nd and 4th stamp in
strip.

A476

A477

27th World and 1st Pan American Weight
Lifting Championships: Various weightlifting
positions.

1973, Sept. 12
1827 A476 1c multi, diff. .20 .20
1828 A476 2c shown .20 .20
1829 A476 3c multi, diff. .20 .20
1830 A476 4c multi, diff. .20 .20
1831 A476 5c multi, diff. .20 .20
1832 A476 13c multi, diff. 1.60 .45
1833 A476 30c multi, diff. 2.75 .90
Nos. 1827-1833 (7) 5.35 2.35

1973, Sept. 28
Flowering plants.
1834 A477 1c Erythrina stan-
dleyana .20 .20
1835 A477 2c Lantana camara .20 .20
1836 A477 3c Canavalia maritima .20 .20
1837 A477 4c Dichromena
colorata .20 .20
1838 A477 5c Borrichia
arborescens .20 .20
1839 A477 13c Anguria pedata 2.10 .65
1840 A477 30c Cordia sebestena 3.25 .90
Nos. 1835-1840 (6) 6.15 2.35

8th World Trade Union Congress,
Varna, Bulgaria — A478

1973, Oct. 5 **Wmk. 376**
1841 A478 13c multi 1.50 .35

Cuban Natl. Ballet,
25th Anniv. — A479

Sea
Shells — A480

1973, Oct. 28 **Unwmk.**
1842 A479 13c gold & brt ultra 2.00 .40

1973, Oct. 29
1843 A480 1c Liguus fasciatus
fasciatus .20 .20
1844 A480 2c Liguus fasciatus
guitarti .20 .20
1845 A480 3c Liguus fasciatus
whartoni .20 .20
1846 A480 4c Liguus fasciatus
angelae .20 .20
1847 A480 5c Liguus fasciatus
trinidadense .20 .20
1848 A480 13c Liguus blainianus 2.75 .70
1849 A480 30c Liguus vittatus 3.75 .85
Nos. 1843-1849 (7) 7.50 2.55

Maps of
Cuba
A481

1973, Oct. 29
1850 A481 1c Juan de la Cosa,
1502 .20 .20
1851 A481 3c Ortelius, 1572 .25 .20
1852 A481 13c Bellini, 1762 1.75 .20
1853 A481 40c 1973 2.10 .80
Nos. 1850-1853 (4) 4.30 1.45

15th Anniversary of the
Revolution — A482

1974, Jan. 2
1854 A482 1c No. 625 .20 .20
1855 A482 3c No. 626 .25 .20
1856 A482 13c No. C200 4.00 .55
1857 A482 40c No. C201 1.60 .80
Nos. 1854-1857 (4) 6.05 1.75

Woman, by F.
Ponce de
Leon — A483

Amilcar
Cabral — A484

Portraits in the Camaguey Museum: 3c,
Mexican Girls, by J. Arche. 8c, Young Woman,
by A. Menocal. 10c, Mulatto Woman Drinking
from Coconut, by L. Romanach. 13c, Head of
an Old Man, by J. Arburu.

1974, Jan. 10
1858 A483 1c multi .20 .20
1859 A483 3c multi. .20 .20
1860 A483 10c multi .35 .20
1861 A483 13c multi 1.10 .25
1862 A483 13c multi 1.60 .40
Nos. 1858-1862 (5) 3.45 1.25

1974, Jan. 20
1863 A484 13c multi 1.40 .25

Amilcar Cabral, Guinea-Bissau freedom
fighter, 1st death anniv.

Lenin, by I.V. Kosmin — A485

12th Central American and Caribbean Games, Santo Domingo — A486

1974, Jan. 21
1864 A485 30c multi 3.00 .55
50th death anniv. of Lenin.

1974, Feb. 8
1865 A486 1c Emblem .25 .20
1866 A486 2c Javelin .25 .20
1867 A486 3c Boxing .25 .20
1868 A486 4c Baseball, horiz. .25 .20
1869 A486 13c Basketball, horiz. 1.60 .20
1870 A486 30c Volleyball, horiz. 2.40 .70
Nos. 1865-1870 (6) 5.00 1.70

Portrait by F. Martinez — A487

Portrait of a Man, by J.B. Vermay — A488

1974, Feb. 27
1871 A487 13c multi 1.40 .20
Carlos M. de Cespedes (d. 1874), patriot.

1974, Mar. 7
Paintings in the Natl. Museum: 2c, The Wet Nurse, by C.A. Van Loo. 3c, Cattle in River, by R. Morey. 4c, Village, by Morey. 13c, Faun and Bacchus, by Rubens. 30c, Young Woman Playing Cards, by R. Madrazo.

1872 A488 1c shown .20 .20
1873 A488 2c multi .20 .20
1874 A488 3c multi .20 .20
1875 A488 4c multi .20 .20
1876 A488 13c multi 1.40 .20
1877 A488 30c multi 2.50 .55
Nos. 1872-1877 (6) 4.70 1.60

Council for Mutual Economic Assistance (COMECON), 25th Anniv. — A489

1974, Mar. 15
1878 A489 30c Comecon building, Moscow 2.00 .70

Visit of Leonid I. Brezhnev to Cuba, Jan. 28-Feb. 3 — A490

1974, Mar. 28
1879 A490 13c Jose Marti, Lenin, flags 2.00 .30
1880 A490 30c Brezhnev, Fidel Castro 2.10 .55
Nos. 1879-1880 (2) 4.10 .85

Science Fiction A491

Paintings by A. Sokolov.

1974, Apr. 12
1881 A491 1c Martian Crater .25 .20
1882 A491 2c Fiery Labyrinth .25 .20
1883 A491 3c Amber Wave .25 .20
1884 A491 4c Flight Through Space .25 .20
1885 A491 13c Planet in Nebula 2.00 .25
1886 A491 30c World of Two Suns 3.25 .60
Nos. 1881-1886 (6) 6.25 1.65
Cosmonauts Day.

UPU, Cent. A492

1974, Apr. 15
1887 A492 30c Letter, 1874 2.50 .60

Stamp Day Type of 1973
Postmarks.

1974, Apr. 24
1888 A465 1c Havana .25 .20
1889 A465 3c Matanzas .40 .20
1890 A465 13c Trinidad 1.50 .20
1891 A465 20c Guana Vacoa 2.25 .35
Nos. 1888-1891 (4) 4.40 .95

18th Sports Congress of Friendly Armies — A493

1974, May 5 Wmk. 376
1892 A493 3c multi .80 .20

Felipe Poey (1799-1891), Naturalist — A494

Designs: 1c, 4c, Butterflies. 2c, 13c, Sea shells. 3c, 30c, 50c, Fish.

1974, May 26 Perf. 12½x12
1893 A494 1c Eumaeus atala atala .20 .20
1894 A494 2c Pineria terebra .20 .20
1895 A494 3c Chaetodon sedentarius .20 .20
1896 A494 4c Eurema dina dina .80 .20
1897 A494 13c Hemitrochus fuscolabiata 2.75 .45
1898 A494 30c Eupomacentrus partitus 3.50 .55
Nos. 1893-1898 (6) 7.65 1.80

Souvenir Sheet
Imperf
1899 A494 50c Apogon binotatus 7.00 2.50
Stamp in #1899 has simulated perforations.

Havana Philharmonic Orchestra, 50th Anniv. — A495

1c, Antonio Mompo, cello. 3c, Cesar Perez Sentenat, piano. 5c, Pedro Mercado, trumpet. 10c, Pedro Sanjuan, Havana Philharmonic emblem. 13c, Roberto Ondina, flute.

1974, June 8 Perf. 12½
1900 A495 1c multi .25 .20
1901 A495 3c multi .25 .20
1902 A495 5c multi .25 .20
1903 A495 10c multi 1.40 .25
1904 A495 13c multi 1.75 .25
Nos. 1900-1904 (5) 3.90 1.10

Garden Flowers — A496

1974, June 12
1905 A496 1c Heliconia humilis .20 .20
1906 A496 2c Anthurium andraeanum .20 .20
1907 A496 3c Canna generalis .20 .20
1908 A496 4c Alpinia purpurata .25 .20
1909 A496 13c Gladiolus grandiflorus 1.75 .20
1910 A496 30c Amomum capitatum 4.50 .60
Nos. 1905-1910 (6) 7.10 1.60

A497

A498

World Amateur Boxing Championships: Emblem and various boxers.

Perf. 12x12½
1974, Aug. 24 Litho. Unwmk.
1911 A497 1c multi .20 .20
1912 A497 3c multi .35 .20
1913 A497 13c multi 1.60 .20
Nos. 1911-1913 (3) 2.15 .65

1974, Aug. 28 Perf. 13
Extinct birds.
1914 A498 1c Dodo .40 .20
1915 A498 3c Ara de Cuba (parrot) .40 .20
1916 A498 8c Passenger pigeon .85 .20
1917 A498 10c Moa 2.75 .55
1918 A498 13c Great auk 3.50 .80
Nos. 1914-1918 (5) 7.90 1.95

Pres. Salvador Allende of Chile (d. 1973) A499

1974, Sept. 11
1919 A499 13c multi 1.25 .45

Wildflowers A500

Model Aircraft — A501

1974, Sept. 14 Perf. 13x12½
1920 A500 1c Suriana maritima .20 .20
1921 A500 3c Cassia ligustrina .20 .20
1922 A500 8c Flaveria linearis .30 .20
1923 A500 10c Stachytarpheta jamaicensis 2.10 .25
1924 A500 13c Bacopa monnieri 3.50 .85
Nos. 1920-1924 (5) 6.30 1.70

1974, Sept. 22 Perf. 12½
1925 A501 1c shown .20 .20
1926 A501 3c Sky diving .20 .20
1927 A501 8c Glider .45 .20
1928 A501 10c Crop dusting 1.25 .20
1929 A501 13c Commercial aviation 2.00 .25
Nos. 1925-1929 (5) 4.10 1.10
Civil Aeronautic Institute, 10th anniv. Nos. 1927-1929 horiz.

History of Cuban Baseball — A502

1974, Oct. 3 Perf. 13
1930 A502 1c Indians playing ball .20 .20
1931 A502 3c 1st Official game, 1874 .20 .20
1932 A502 8c Emilio Sabourin .40 .20
1933 A502 10c Umpire, players, 1974 1.25 .20

1934 A502 13c Latin-American Stadium, Havana   2.10   .25
Nos. 1930-1934 (5)   4.15 1.05
Nos. 1930-1932 vert.

Mambi 10c Stamp (Revolutionary Junta Issue), Cent. — A503

1974, Oct. 10
1935 A503 13c multi   1.50   .25

16th Conference of Customs Organizations of Socialist Countries — A504

1974, Oct. 15
1936 A504 30c Comecon Building, Moscow   2.00   .55

Disappearance of Major Camilo Cienfuegos, 15th Anniv. — A505

Wmk. 376
1974, Oct. 28   **Litho.**   *Perf. 13*
1937 A505 3c multi   .75   .20

8th World Mining Conference — A506

1974, Nov. 3
1938 A506 13c multi   1.50   .25

Petroleum Institute, 15th Anniv. — A507

1974, Nov. 20
1939 A507 3c multi   .70   .20

Intersputnik Earth Station Opening — A508

1974, Nov. 30   **Unwmk.**
1940 A508 3c shown   .25   .20
1941 A508 13c Satellite, satellite dish   1.25   .20
1942 A508 1p Satellite, flags   3.25 1.10
Nos. 1940-1942 (3)   4.75 1.50

Philatelic Federation, 10th Anniv. — A509

1974, Nov. 30   *Perf. 12½x13*
1943 A509 30c multi   2.40   .45

Souvenir Sheet

Mercury — A510

1974, Dec. 6   *Imperf.*
1944 A510 50c multi   6.00 1.25
4th Natl. Phil. Exhib., Havana.

1st World Peace Congress, 25th Anniv. — A511

1974, Dec. 16   **Wmk. 376**   *Perf. 13*
1945 A511 30c *F. Joliot-Curie*, by Picasso   3.00   .45

Ruben Martinez Villena (b. 1899), Revolutionary — A512

1974, Dec. 20   **Unwmk.**
1946 A512 3c red org & yel   .75   .20

Souvenir Sheet

Cuban Victories, 1st Amateur Boxing Championships — A513

1975, Jan. 6   **Litho.**   *Imperf.*
1947 A513 50c Trophy   6.00 1.25

The Word, by Marcelo Pogolotti A514

Paintings in the Natl. Museum: 2c, *The Silk-Cotton Tree,* by Henry Cleenewerk. 3c, *Landscape,* by Guillermo Collazo. 5c, *Still-life,* by Francisco Peralta. 13c, *Maria Wilson,* by Federico Martinez, vert. 30c, *The Couple,* by Mariano Fortuny.

1975, Jan. 20   *Perf. 13*
1948 A514 1c multi   .20   .20
1949 A514 2c multi   .20   .20
1950 A514 3c multi   .20   .20
1951 A514 5c multi   .25   .20
1952 A514 13c multi   1.50   .25
1953 A514 30c multi   2.75   .45
Nos. 1948-1953 (6)   5.10 1.50

Intl. Women's Year A515

1975, Feb. 6
1954 A515 13c multi   1.25   .25

Fishing Industry A516

Various fish and fishing vessels.

1975, Feb. 22
1955 A516 1c Long-finned tuna   .20   .20
1956 A516 2c Tuna   .20   .20
1957 A516 3c Mediterranean grouper   .20   .20
1958 A516 8c Hake   .20   .20
1959 A516 13c Prawn   1.10   .70
1960 A516 30c Lobster   3.25   .70
Nos. 1955-1960 (6)   5.15 2.20

Minerals — A517

1975, Mar. 15   **Litho.**   *Perf. 13x12½*
1961 A517 3c Nickel   .40   .20
1962 A517 13c Copper   1.60   .20
1963 A517 30c Chromium   2.75   .45
Nos. 1961-1963 (3)   4.75   .85

Cosmonaut's Day — A518

1975, Apr. 12   *Perf. 13x12½, 12½x13*
1964 A518 1c Cosmodrome   .20   .20
1965 A518 2c Probe, vert.   .20   .20
1966 A518 3c Eclipse   .20   .20
1967 A518 5c Threshold to Space   .40   .20
1968 A518 13c Midday on Mars   1.50   .25
1969 A518 30c Cosmonaut's view of Earth   2.50   .45
Nos. 1964-1969 (6)   5.00 1.50

The future of space.

Stamp Day A519

Various covers.

1975, Apr. 24   *Perf. 13*
1970 A519 3c multi   .20   .20
1971 A519 13c multi   1.40   .25
1972 A519 30c multi   2.10   .40
Nos. 1970-1972 (3)   3.70   .85

Victory Over Fascism, 30th Anniv. — A520

Design: Raising red flag over Reichstag, Berlin.

1975, May 9   *Perf. 13x12½*
1973 A520 30c multi   2.00   .40

A521

Works in the Decorative Art Museum — A522

1c, Sevres porcelain vase, vert. 2c, Meissen porcelain statue *Shepherdess and Dancers,* vert. 3c, Chinese porcelain dish *Lady with Parasol.* 5c, Chinese screen detail *The Phoenix,* vert. 13c, *Allegory of Music,* by Francois Boucher (1703-70), vert. 30c, *Portrait of a Lady,* by L. Tocque, vert. 50c, *The Swing,* by Hubert Robert (1733-1808).

1975, May 10   Perf. 12½x13, 13x12½
1974	A521	1c multi	.20 .20
1975	A521	2c multi	.20 .20
1976	A521	3c shown	.25 .20
1977	A521	5c multi	.40 .20
1978	A521	13c multi	1.50 .20
1979	A521	30c multi	2.00 .40
		Nos. 1974-1979 (6)	4.55 1.40

Souvenir Sheet
Perf. 13x12½ on 3 Sides
1980	A522	50c shown	5.50 1.25

No. 1980 contains one 25x39mm stamp.

Intl. Children's Day — A523

Wmk. 376
1975, May 31   Litho.   Perf. 13
1981	A523	3c multi	.50 .20

Indigenous Birds — A524

1975, June 18   Unwmk.
1982	A524	1c *Vireo gundlachi*	.25 .20
1983	A524	2c *Gymnoglaux lawrenci*	.25 .20
1984	A524	3c *Aratingo eoups*	.25 .20
1985	A524	5c *Staroenas cyanocephala*	.40 .20
1986	A524	13c *Chondrohierax wilsoni*	1.75 .40
1987	A524	30c *Cyanolimnas cerverai*	2.50 .70
		Nos. 1982-1987 (6)	5.40 1.90

See Nos. 2121-2125, 2180-2182, C276-C276.

Scientific Investigation Center, 10th Anniv. — A525

1975, July 1   Perf. 12½
1988	A525	13c multi	1.40 .20

Irrigation and Drainage Commission, 25th Anniv. — A526

1975, Aug. 2   Perf. 13
1989	A526	13c multi	1.40 .20

Afforestation A527

1975, Aug. 20
1990	A527	1c *Cedrela mexicana*	.20 .20
1991	A527	3c *Swietenia mahogani*	.40 .20
1992	A527	5c *Calophyllum brasiliense*	.40 .20
1993	A527	13c *Hibiscus tiliaceus*	1.10 .25
1994	A527	30c *Pinus caribaea*	1.75 .40
		Nos. 1990-1994 (5)	3.85 1.25

Cuban Women's Federation, 15th Anniv. — A528

1975, Aug. 23
1995	A528	3c multi	.50 .20

Intl. Conference on the Independence of Puerto Rico — A529

1975, Sept. 5   Litho.
1996	A529	13c multi	1.00 .20

A530

A531

7th Pan American Games, Mexico: Aztec calendar stone and various athletes.

1975, Sept. 20   Perf. 12½x13
1997	A530	1c Baseball	.25 .20
1998	A530	3c Boxing	.25 .20
1999	A530	5c Basketball	.25 .20
2000	A530	13c High jump	1.50 .30
2001	A530	30c Weight lifting	2.10 .30
		Nos. 1997-2001 (5)	4.35 1.20

Souvenir Sheet
Imperf
2002	A530	50c Stone, emblem	4.00 1.25

1975, Sept. 28   Perf. 12½x13
2003	A531	3c multi	.50 .20

Revolutionary Defense Committees (CDR), 15th anniv.

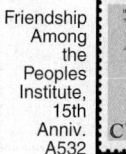

Friendship Among the Peoples Institute, 15th Anniv. A532

1975, Oct. 8   Perf. 12½x13
2004	A532	3c multi	.30 .20

Natl. Bank, 25th Anniv. A533

Designs: 1-peso coins and banknotes identified by serial numbers.

1975, Oct. 13   Perf. 13x12½
2005	A533	13c Coin, 1915	1.10 .25
2006	A533	13c C882736A, 1934	1.10 .25
2007	A533	13c A000387A, 1946	1.10 .25
2008	A533	13c 933906, 1964	1.10 .25
2009	A533	13c K000000, 1976	1.10 .25
a.		Strip of 5, Nos. 2005-2009	6.00 1.50
		Nos. 2005-2009 (5)	5.50 1.25

Locomotives — A534

1975, Oct. 28   Unwmk.   Perf. 12½
2010	A534	1c *La Junta,* 1837	.20 .20
2011	A534	3c Steam engine 2-8-0 *No. 12*	.30 .20
2012	A534	5c Diesel TEM 4 *No. 51010*	.30 .20
2013	A534	13c Diesel DVM 9 *I-7 55*	2.50 .25

2014	A534	30c Diesel M 62K *No. 61601*	3.00 .45
		Nos. 2010-2014 (5)	6.30 1.30

Railway history.

Development of the Textile Industry — A535

1975, Nov. 10   Perf. 13x12½
2015	A535	13c Bobbins, flag, loom operator	1.25 .20

Veterinary Medicine — A536

Parasites and host species.

1975, Nov. 25   Litho.   Perf. 13
2016	A536	1c *Haemonchus,* lamb	.25 .20
2017	A536	2c *Ancylostoma caninum,* dog	.25 .20
2018	A536	3c *Dispharynx nasuta,* rooster	.25 .20
2019	A536	5c *Gasterophilus intestinalis,* horse	.25 .20
2020	A536	13c *Ascaris lumbricoides,* pig	1.40 .20
2021	A536	30c *Boophilus microplus,* bull	2.50 .40
		Nos. 2016-2021 (6)	4.90 1.40

Manuel Ascunce Domenech Educational Detachment A537

1975, Nov. 27   Litho.
2022	A537	3c multi	.40 .20

Development of Agriculture and Irrigation — A538

1975, Dec. 15   Litho.   Perf. 13x12½
2023	A538	13c Irrigation	1.25 .20

1st Communist Party Congress — A539

1975, Dec. 17   Perf. 12½x13, 13x12½
2024	A539	3c "1," revolutionaries, vert.	.20 .20
2025	A539	13c shown	1.10 .30
2026	A539	30c Party leaders	1.50 .30
		Nos. 2024-2026 (3)	2.80 .70

8th Latin-American Obstetrics and Gynecology Congress — A540

1976, Jan. 24   **Perf. 13**
2027 A540 3c multi   .60   .20

Paintings in Natl. Museums — A541

Designs: 1c, *Seated Woman*, by Victor Manuel, vert. 2c, *Garden*, by Santiago Rusinol. 3c, *Guadalquivir River*, by Manuel Barron y Carrillo. 5c, *Self-portrait*, by Jan Havicksz Steen, vert. 13c, *Portrait of a Woman*, by Louis Michel Van Loo, vert. 30c, *La Chula*, by Jose Arburu Morell, vert.

Perf. 13, 12½ (3c, 30c)
1976, Jan. 30
Sizes: 29x40mm (1c, 5c, 13c), 40x29mm (2c), 44x27mm (3c), 27x44mm (30c)

2028 A541 1c multi   .20   .20
2029 A541 2c multi   .20   .20
2030 A541 3c multi   .25   .20
2031 A541 5c multi   .25   .20
2032 A541 13c multi   1.40   .25
2033 A541 30c multi   2.25   .50
   Nos. 2028-2033 (6)   4.55 1.55

10th Cong. of Ministers from Socialist Communications Organizations, Feb. 12, Havana — A542

1976, Feb. 12   **Litho.**   **Perf. 13**
2034 A542 13c multi   1.40   .20

Hunting Dogs A543

1976, Feb. 20
2035 A543 1c American fox-
     hound   .25   .20
2036 A543 2c Labrador retriev-
     er   .25   .20
2037 A543 3c Borzoi   .25   .20
2038 A543 5c Irish setter   .25   .20
2039 A543 13c Pointer   2.40   .30
2040 A543 30c Cocker spaniel   3.25   .40
   Nos. 2035-2040 (6)   6.65 1.50

Socialist Constitution — A544

1976, Feb. 24   **Perf. 12½**
2041 A544 13c Natl. flag, arms,
     anthem   1.40   .25

Chess Champions — A545

Designs: 1c, Ruy Lopez Segura and chessboard. 2c, Francois Philidor and frontispiece of his book, *Analysis of the Game of Chess*. 3c, Wilhelm Steinitz and knight. 13c, Emanuel Lasker and king. 30c, Jose Raul Capablanca learning to play chess as a small boy.

1976, Mar. 15   **Perf. 13x12½**
2042 A545 1c multi   .20   .20
2043 A545 2c multi   .20   .20
2044 A545 3c multi   .25   .20
2045 A545 13c multi   1.75   .25
2046 A545 30c multi   1.90   .55
   Nos. 2042-2046 (5)   4.30 1.40

Havana Radio Intl. Broadcasts, 15th Anniv. — A546

1976, Mar. 26
2047 A546 50c multi   2.00   .70

World Health Day — A547

1976, Apr. 7
2048 A547 30c multi   1.50   .45

1976, Apr. 10   **Perf. 12½x13**
2049 A548 3c multi   .60   .20

Child Care Centers, 15th Anniv. — A548

1st Manned Space Flight, 15th Anniv. A549

1976, Apr. 12   **Perf. 13**
2050 A549 1c Gagarin, lift-off   .20   .20
2051 A549 2c V. Tesreshkova,
     rockets   .20   .20
2052 A549 3c A. Leonov's
     space walk, vert.   .25   .20
2053 A549 5c Spacecraft, vert.   .40   .20
2054 A549 13c Spacecraft, diff.,
     vert.   1.10   .20
2055 A549 30c Space link-up   1.75   .35
   Nos. 2050-2055 (6)   3.90 1.35

Bay of Pigs Invasion, 15th Anniv. — A550

1976, Apr. 17   **Perf. 13x12½, 12½x13**
2056 A550 3c shown   .25   .20
2057 A550 13c Bomber, pilot   .95   .20
2058 A550 30c Soldiers exulting,
     vert.   1.75   .45
   Nos. 2056-2058 (3)   2.95   .85

Natl. Militia, 17th anniv. (3c); Air Force, 15th anniv. (13c); proclamation of the socialist revolution, 15th anniv. (30c).

Nat. Assoc. of Small Farmers (ANAP), 15th Anniv. — A551

1976, May 17   **Perf. 13x12½**
2059 A551 3c multi   .60   .20

1976 Summer Olympics, Montreal — A552

1976, May 25   **Perf. 12½x13**
2060 A552 1c Volleyball   .20   .20
2061 A552 2c Basketball   .20   .20
2062 A552 3c Long jump   .20   .20
2063 A552 4c Boxing   .25   .20
2064 A552 5c Weight lifting   .25   .20
2065 A552 13c Judo   1.10   .20
2066 A552 30c Swimming   1.75   .45
   Nos. 2060-2066 (7)   3.95 1.65

Souvenir Sheet
Imperf
2067 A552 50c Character trade-
     mark (beaver)   4.00 1.25
   See Nos. 2106, 2112.

Modern Secondary Schools — A553

1976, June 12   **Litho.**   **Perf. 13**
2068 A553 3c red, pale grn & blk   .60   .20

Indigenous Birds — A554

1976, June 15   **Perf. 13x12½**
2069 A554 1c *Teretistris fornsi*   .30   .20
2070 A554 2c *Glaucidium siju*   .30   .20
2071 A554 3c *Nesoceleus fer-
     nandinae*   .40   .25
2072 A554 5c *Todus mutlicolor*   .70   .25

2073 A554 13c *Accipiter gun-
     dlachi*   1.40   .25
2074 A554 30c *Priotelus
     temnurus*   3.25   .80
   Nos. 2069-2074 (6)   6.35 1.95

EXPO '76, USSR A555

1976, July 5   **Perf. 12½x13, 13x12½**
2075 A555 1c Anatomical scan-
     ning device   .20   .20
2076 A555 3c Child, doe   .20   .20
2077 A555 10c Cosmonauts   .50   .20
2078 A555 30c Tupolev super-
     sonic jet   2.50   .55
   Nos. 2075-2078 (4)   3.40 1.15

Public health and industrial safety (1c), environmental protection (3c), space exploration (10c) and modern transportation (30c). Nos. 2075-2077 vert.

Death Cent. of "El Inglesito" A556

1976, Aug. 4   **Perf. 13**
2079 A556 13c Henry M. Reeve   .70   .20

Portrait of G. Collazo, by Jean Dabour — A557

Paintings by Collazo: 2c, *The Art Lovers*, horiz. 3c, *The Patio*. 5c, *Coconut Tree*. 13c, *New York Studio*, horiz. 30c, *R. Emelina Collazo*.

Perf. 13, 12½x13 (5c, 30c), 13x12½ (13c)
1976, Sept. 2
Sizes: 33x44mm, 44x33mm (2c), 31x46mm (5c, 30c), 46x31mm (13c)

2080 A557 1c multi   .20   .20
2081 A557 2c multi   .20   .20
2082 A557 3c multi   .20   .20
2083 A557 5c multi   .20   .20
2084 A557 13c multi   .65   .25
2085 A557 30c multi   2.10   .50
   Nos. 2080-2085 (6)   3.55 1.55

Camilo Cienfuegos Military Schools, 10th Anniv. — A558

1976, Sept. 23   **Perf. 13**
2086 A558 3c multi   .40   .20

Development of the Merchant Marine — A559

Various cargo and passenger ships.

1976, Oct. 2			Perf. 12½	
2087	A559	1c multi	.30	.20
2088	A559	2c multi	.30	.20
2089	A559	3c multi	.30	.20
2090	A559	5c multi	.45	.20
2091	A559	13c multi	1.40	.45
2092	A559	30c multi	2.75	.80
	Nos. 2087-2092 (6)		5.50	2.05

8th Intl. Health Film Festival of Socialist Countries, Havana — A560

1976, Oct. 4			Perf. 13x12½	
2093	A560	3c multi	.40	.20

5th Intl. Ballet Festival, Havana A561

Scenes from ballets. 2c, 5c, 13c, 30c vert.

1976, Nov. 6			Perf. 13	
2094	A561	1c Apollo	.20	.20
2095	A561	2c The River and the Forest	.20	.20
2096	A561	3c Giselle	.20	.20
2097	A561	5c Oedipus Rex	.25	.20
2098	A561	13c Carmen	1.10	.20
2099	A561	30c Vital Song	2.10	.35
	Nos. 2094-2099 (6)		4.05	1.35

3rd Military Games A562

1976, Nov. 25			Perf. 13	
2100	A562	3c multi	.50	.20

Granma Landings, 20th Anniv. — A563

1976, Dec. 2			Perf. 13x12½	
2101	A563	1c Landing craft	.20	.20
2102	A563	3c Landing force	.20	.20
2103	A563	13c Castro, soldiers	1.00	.20
2104	A563	30c Globe, rifles	1.60	.55
	Nos. 2101-2104 (4)		3.00	1.15

Souvenir Sheet

Cuban Landscape, by F. Cadava — A564

1976, Dec. 8			Perf. 13x13½	
2105	A564	50c multi	5.25	2.00

CIENFUEGOS '76, 5th natl. phil. exhib.

Summer Olympics Type of 1976 and

Victory of Cuban Athletes at the Montreal Games — A565

1976, Dec. 10			Perf. 12½x13	
2106	A565	1c Volleyball	.20	.20
2107	A565	2c Hurdles	.20	.20
2108	A565	3c Running (starting blocks)	.25	.20
2109	A565	8c Boxing	.25	.20
2110	A565	13c Running (finish line)	.85	.20
2111	A565	30c Judo	1.75	.45
	Nos. 2106-2111 (6)		3.50	1.45

Souvenir Sheet
Imperf

2112	A552	50c like No. 2063	5.00	1.25

Paintings in the Natl. Museum A566

1c, Golden Cross Inn, by S. Scott. 3c, Portrait of a Man, by J.C. Verspronck, vert. 5c, Venetian Landscape, by Francesco Guardi. 10c, Valley Corner, by H. Cleenewerck, vert. 13c, F. Xaviera Paula, anonymous, vert. 30c, F. de Medici, by C. Allori, vert.

Perf. 13, 12½x13 (3c, 10c, 30c), 12½ (13c)

1977, Jan. 18
Sizes: 40x29mm, 27x42mm (3c, 10c, 30c), 27x43½mm (13c)

2113	A566	1c multi	.20	.20
2114	A566	3c multi	.20	.20
2115	A566	5c multi	.20	.20
2116	A566	10c multi	.55	.20
2117	A566	13c multi	.85	.20
2118	A566	30c multi	2.10	.40
	Nos. 2113-2118 (6)		4.10	1.40

Rural Transport A567

1977, Feb. 15			Perf. 13	
2119	A567	3c multi	.80	.20

Constitution of Popular Government — A568

1976, Dec. 1			Perf. 13x12½	
2120	A568	13c multi	.70	.20

Bird Type of 1975

1977, Feb. 25			Perf. 13	
2121	A524	1c Xiphidiopicus percussus	.40	.25
2122	A524	4c Tiaris canora	.45	.25
2123	A524	10c Dives atroviolaceus	.95	.25
2124	A524	13c Ferminia cerverai	1.40	.25
2125	A524	30c Mellisuga helenae	2.75	.65
	Nos. 2121-2125 (5)		5.95	1.65

Lenin Park Aquarium, Havana — A569

1977, Mar. 15				
2126	A569	1c Chichlasoma meeki	.20	.20
2127	A569	3c Barbus tetrazona tetrazona	.20	.20
2128	A569	5c Cyprinus carpio	.20	.20
2129	A569	10c Betta splendens	.30	.20
2130	A569	13c Pterophyllum scalare, vert.	1.25	.25
2131	A569	30c Hemigrammus caudovittatus	2.50	.50
	Nos. 2126-2131 (6)		4.65	1.55

Sputnik (1st Artificial Satellite), 20th Anniv. — A570

1c, DDR No. 370, Sputnik. 3c, Hungary No. 1216, Luna 16. 5c, North Korean Intl. Geophysical Year 10-won stamp of 1958, Cosmos. 10c, Poland No. 822, Sputnik 3. 13c, Yugoslavia No. 870, Earth, Moon. 30c, Cuba No. 866, Earth, Moon. 50c, Russia No. 2021, Sputnik.

1977, Apr. 12			Perf. 13x12½	
2132	A570	1c multi	.25	.20
2133	A570	3c multi	.25	.20
2134	A570	5c multi	.25	.20
2135	A570	10c multi	.35	.20
2136	A570	13c multi	1.10	.20
2137	A570	30c multi	1.90	.40
	Nos. 2132-2137 (6)		4.10	1.40

Souvenir Sheet
Imperf

2138	A570	50c multi	4.25	1.25

No. 2138 has simulated perfs.

Antonio Maria Romeu (1876-1955), Composer — A571

1977, May 10		Litho.	Perf. 13	
2139	A571	3c multi	.35	.20

See No. C251.

Flowering Plants — A572

1977, May 31

2140	A572	1c Hibiscus rosa sinensis	.20	.20
2141	A572	2c Nerium oleander	.20	.20
2142	A572	5c Allamanda cathartica	.20	.20
2143	A572	10c Pelargonium zonale	.40	.20
	Nos. 2140-2143 (4)		1.00	.80

Dr. Juan Tomas Roig (b. 1877), botanist. See Nos. C252-C254.

Fire Prevention Week — A573

1977, June 20

2144	A573	1c shown	.20	.20
2145	A573	2c Horse-drawn fire pump, diff.	.20	.20
2146	A573	6c Early motorized vehicle	.25	.20
2147	A573	10c Modern truck	.50	.20
2148	A573	13c Turntable-ladder truck	.90	.20
2149	A573	30c Crane vehicle	1.90	.40
	Nos. 2144-2149 (6)		3.95	1.40

Natl. Decorations (Ribbons and Medals of Honor) — A574

1977, July 26			Perf. 12x12½	
2150	A574	1c shown	.25	.20
2151	A574	3c multi, diff.	.25	.20

See Nos. C255-C256.

Paintings by Jorge Arche — A575

Perf. 13x12½, 12½x13 (10c), 13 (5c)
1977, Aug. 25
  Sizes: 26x38mm, 29x40mm (5c),
    38x26mm (10c)

2152	A575	1c	Portrait of Mary	.20 .20
2153	A575	3c	Jose Marti	.20 .20
2154	A575	5c	Portrait of Aristides	.20 .20
2155	A575	10c	Bathers	.50 .20
		Nos. 2152-2155 (4)		1.10 .80

Nos. 2152-2154 vert. See Nos. C257-C259.

4th Military Spartakiad (Summer Sports) — A576

1977, Sept. 10   **Perf. 13**

2156	A576	1c	Boxing	.20 .20
2157	A576	3c	Volleyball	.20 .20
2158	A576	5c	Parachuting	.20 .20
2159	A576	10c	Running	.35 .20
		Nos. 2156-2159 (4)		.95 .80

See Nos. C260-C261.

Intl. Airmail Service, 50th Anniv. A577

Designs: 1c, Biplane and No. C62. 2c, Three-engine plane and Cuba-Key West 1st flight cachet, Oct. 28, 1927. 5c, Flying boat and intl. airmail service 1st flight cachet. 10c, Jet aircraft and Havana-Madrid cachet, Apr. 26, 1948.

1977, Oct. 27 **Litho.** **Perf. 12x12½**

2160	A577	1c	multi	.20 .20
2161	A577	2c	multi	.20 .20
2162	A577	5c	multi	.20 .20
2163	A577	10c	multi	.50 .20
		Nos. 2160-2163 (4)		1.10 .80

See Nos. C263-C264.

October Revolution, Russia, 60th Anniv. — A578

1977, Nov. 7   **Perf. 13x12½**

2164	A578	3c	Cruiser Aurora	.20 .20
2165	A578	13c	Lenin, Flags	.40 .20
2166	A578	30c	Hammer, sickle, symbols of agriculture, technology	1.40 .40
		Nos. 2164-2166 (3)		2.00 .80

Felines, Havana Zoo — A579

1977, Nov. 24 **Litho.** **Perf. 13**

2167	A579	1c	Cat	.20 .20
2168	A579	2c	Black panther	.20 .20
2169	A579	8c	Puma	.25 .20
2170	A579	10c	Leopard	1.10 .20
		Nos. 2167-2170 (4)		1.75 .80

See Nos. C266-C267.

Martyrs of the Revolution, 20th Death Annivs. — A580

1977, Dec. 2   **Perf. 12½x12**

2171	A580	3c	Cienfuegos Uprising	.20 .20
2172	A580	20c	Siege on the Presidential Palace	1.00 .20

See No. C268.

Intl. Measurement System — A581

1977, Dec. 9

2173	A581	3c	multi	.40 .20

Havana University, 250th Anniv. — A582

1978, Jan. 5   **Perf. 13x12½**

2174	A582	3c	multi	.25 .20

See Nos. C270-C271.

Landscape with Figures, by J. Pilliment — A583

Paintings in the Natl. Museum of Art: 1c, *Seated Woman,* by R. Madrazo, vert. 4c, *Girl,* by J. Sorolla, vert. 10c, *The Cow,* by E. Abela.

Perf. 12x12½, 13 (4c, 6c, 10c)
1978, Feb. 20
  Sizes: 27x42mm, 29x40mm (4c),
    40x29mm (6c, 10c)

2175	A583	1c	multi	.20 .20
2176	A583	4c	multi	.20 .20
2177	A583	6c	shown	.20 .20
2178	A583	10c	multi	.60 .20
		Nos. 2175-2178 (4)		1.20 .80

See Nos. C273-C274.

Frontier Troops, 15th Anniv. — A584

1978, Mar. 5   **Perf. 13**

2179	A584	13c		1.50 .25

Bird Type of 1975
Perf. 13, 12½x12 (4c)
1978, Mar. 10 **Size: 42x27mm**

2180	A524	1c	Myadestes elisabeth	.45 .20
2181	A524	4c	Palioptila lembeyei	.55 .20
2182	A524	10c	Teretistris fernandinae	1.40 .25
		Nos. 2180-2182 (3)		2.40 .65

Name of bird inscribed below vignette. See Nos. C275-C276.

Cosmonaut's Day — A585

1978, Apr. 12   **Perf. 13**

2183	A585	1c	Intercosmos, vert.	.20 .20
2184	A585	2c	Luna 24	.20 .20
2185	A585	5c	Venus 9, vert.	.35 .20
2186	A585	10c	Cosmos	.35 .20
		Nos. 2183-2186 (4)		1.10 .80

See Nos. C278-C279.

9th World Trade Unions Congress, Prague — A586

1978, Apr. 16

2187	A586	30c	ver, deep brn & blk	1.00 .45

Cactus Flowers — A587

1978, May 15 **Perf. 12½x13 (1c), 13**

2188	A587	1c	Melocactus guitarti	.25 .20
2189	A587	4c	Leptocereus wrightii	.25 .20
2190	A587	6c	Opuntia militaris	.25 .20
2191	A587	10c	Cylindropuntia hystrix	.65 .25
		Nos. 2188-2191 (4)		1.40 .85

Natl. Botanical Gardens. See #C281-C282.

Lenin Park Aquarium, Havana — A588

1978, June 15   **Perf. 13**

2192	A588	1c	Barbus arulios	.25 .20
2193	A588	4c	Hiphessobrycon flammeus	.25 .20
2194	A588	6c	Poecilia reticulata	.30 .20
2195	A588	10c	Colis lalia	.65 .20
		Nos. 2192-2195 (4)		1.45 .80

See Nos. C286-C287.

MEDELLIN '78, 13th Central American and Caribbean Games — A589

1978, July 1

2196	A589	1c	Basketball, vert.	.25 .20
2197	A589	3c	Boxing, vert.	.25 .20
2198	A589	5c	Weight lifting, vert.	.25 .20
2199	A589	10c	Fencing	.45 .20
		Nos. 2196-2199 (4)		1.20 .80

See Nos. C288-C289.

Attack on Moncada Barracks, 25th Anniv. — A590

1978, July 26

2200	A590	3c	multi	.25 .20

See Nos. C290-C291.

World Youth and Students Festival, Havana A591

Natl. flags and views of host cities.

1978, July 28

2201	A591	3c	Prague, 1947	.25 .20
2202	A591	3c	Budapest, 1949	.25 .20
2203	A591	3c	Berlin, 1951	.25 .20
2204	A591	3c	Bucharest, 1953	.25 .20
2205	A591	3c	Warsaw, 1955	.25 .20
a.		Strip of 5, Nos. 2201-2205		1.40 1.40
		Nos. 2201-2205 (5)		1.25 1.00

See Nos. C292-C297.

Young Workers' Army, 5th Anniv. — A592

1978, Aug. 3

2206	A592	3c	multi	.30 .20

Tuna Industry A593

1978, Aug. 30   **Perf. 12½x12**

2207	A593	1c	Tuna boat	.20 .20
2208	A593	2c	Processing ship	.20 .20
2209	A593	5c	Shrimp boat	.20 .20
2210	A593	10c	Inshore stern trawler	.40 .20
		Nos. 2207-2210 (4)		1.00 .80

See Nos. C298-C299.

Paintings by Amelia Pelaez del Casal
(1896-1968) — A594

Perf. 13x12½, 13 (3c, 6c), 12½x13
1978, Sept. 15
2211 A594 1c *The White Mantle* .20 .20
2212 A594 3c *Still-life with Flowers,* vert. .20 .20
2213 A594 6c *Women,* vert. .20 .20
2214 A594 10c *Fish,* vert. .45 .20
Nos. 2211-2214 (4) 1.05 .80
See Nos. C301-C303.

African
Fauna,
Havana
Zoo
A595

1978, Oct. 20 **Perf. 13**
2215 A595 1c Rhinoceros .25 .20
2216 A595 4c Okapi, vert. .25 .20
2217 A595 6c Mandrill .25 .20
2218 A595 10c Giraffe, vert. .65 .20
Nos. 2215-2218 (4) 1.40 .80
See Nos. C307-C308.

Natl. Ballet, 30th Anniv. — A596

1978, Oct. 28 **Perf. 13x12½**
2219 A596 3c *Grande Pas de
Quatre* .25 .20
See Nos. C309-C310.

A597

A598

Flowers of the Pacific: Various species.

1978, Nov. 30 **Litho.** **Perf. 13**
2220 A597 1c multi .20 .20
2221 A597 4c multi .20 .20
2222 A597 6c multi .25 .20
2223 A597 10c multi .50 .20
Nos. 2220-2223 (4) 1.15 .80
See Nos. C311-C312.

1979, Jan. 1 **Perf. 12½x13 (3c), 13**
2224 A598 3c Castro, soldier .20 .20
2225 A598 13c Industry .50 .20
2226 A598 1p Flag, globe, flame 3.25 1.25
Nos. 2224-2226 (3) 3.95 1.65
Triumph of the Revolution, 20th anniv.

Doves and
Pigeons
A599

1979, Jan. 30 **Perf. 13**
2227 A599 1c *Starnoenas cyanocephala* .35 .20
2228 A599 3c *Geotrygon chysia* .40 .20
2229 A599 7c *Geotrygon
caniceps* .40 .20
2230 A599 8c *Geotrygon montana* .50 .20
2231 A599 13c *Columba
leucocephala* .90 .25
2232 A599 30c *Columba inornata* 1.90 .80
Nos. 2227-2232 (6) 4.45 1.85

Paintings
in the
Natl.
Museum
of Art
A600

Designs: 1c, *Genre Scene,* by David
Teniers. 3c, *Arrival of Spanish Troops,* by J.
Louis Meissonier. 6c, *A Joyful Gathering,* by
Sir David Wilkie. 10c, *A Robbery,* by E. De
Lucas Padilla. 13c, *Tea Time,* by R. Madrazo,
vert. 30c, *Peasants in Front of a Tavern,* by
Adriaen van Ostade.

1979, Feb. 20
2233 A600 1c multi .20 .20
2234 A600 3c multi .20 .20
2235 A600 6c multi .30 .20
2236 A600 10c multi .45 .20
2237 A600 13c multi .80 .20
2238 A600 30c multi 1.75 .30
Nos. 2233-2238 (6) 3.70 1.30
See Nos. 2262-2267, C317.

Marine
Flora — A601

1979, Mar. 20
2239 A601 3c *Nymphaea
capensis* .20 .20
2240 A601 10c *Nymphaea ampla* .40 .20
2241 A601 13c *Nymphaea
coerulea* .65 .25
2242 A601 30c *Nymphaea rubra* 1.50 .40
Nos. 2239-2242 (4) 2.75 1.05
All are incorrectly inscribed "Nymphaca."

A602

A603

1979, Mar. 24
2243 A602 3c multi .25 .25
Cuban film industry, 20th anniv.

1979, Apr. 12
2244 A603 1c Rocket launch .20 .20
2245 A603 4c Soyuz .20 .20
2246 A603 6c Salyut .35 .20
2247 A603 10c Link-up .50 .20
2248 A603 13c Soyuz, Salyut .85 .20
2249 A603 30c Parachute landing 1.90 .25
Nos. 2244-2249 (6) 4.00 1.25
Cosmonaut's Day. See No. C315.

6th Summit Meeting of Non-Aligned
Countries — A604

1979, Apr. 17
2250 A604 3c Understanding,
cooperation .25 .20
2251 A604 13c Fight colonialism .50 .20
2252 A604 30c New world economic order 1.40 .40
Nos. 2250-2252 (3) 2.15 .80

House of the Americas Museum, 20th
Anniv. — A605

1979, Apr. 28 **Perf. 13x12½**
2253 A605 13c Cuna Indian tapestry .40 .20

Agrarian Reform,
20th
Anniv. — A606

1979, May 17 **Perf. 12½x12**
2254 A606 3c multi .40 .20

Souvenir Sheet

The Party, by Jules Pascin — A607

1979, May 18 **Perf. 13**
2255 A607 50c multi 3.50 1.25
PHILASERDICA '79 phil. exhib., Sofia.

Nocturnal Butterflies — A608

1979, May 25
2256 A608 1c *Eulepidotis rec-
timargo* .20 .20
2257 A608 4c *Othreis materna* .20 .20
2258 A608 6c *Noropsis hierog-
lyphica* .40 .20
2259 A608 10c *Heterochroma* .40 .20
2260 A608 13c *Melanchroia
regnatrix* .80 .20
2261 A608 30c *Attera gemmata* 2.00 .45
Nos. 2256-2261 (6) 4.00 1.45

Art Type of 1979

Paintings by Victor Emmanuel Garcia (d.
1969): 1c, *Main Avenue, Paris.* 3c, *Portrait of
Enmita.* 6c, *San Juan River, Matanzas.* 10c,
Woman Carrying Hay. 13c, *Still-life with Vase.*
30c, *Street at Night.* Nos. 2262-2267 vert.

1979, June 15
2262 A600 1c multi .20 .20
2263 A600 3c multi .20 .20
2264 A600 6c multi .20 .20
2265 A600 10c multi .30 .20
2266 A600 13c multi .45 .20
2267 A600 30c multi 1.60 .45
Nos. 2262-2267 (6) 2.95 1.45
See No. C317.

World
Peace
Council,
30th Anniv.
A609

1979, June 29 **Perf. 12½x13**
2268 A609 30c multi 1.00 .35

1980 Summer Olympics,
Moscow — A610

1979, July 30 **Perf. 13x12½**
2269 A610 1c Wrestling .30 .20
2270 A610 4c Boxing .30 .20
2271 A610 6c Women's volleyball .30 .20
2272 A610 10c Shooting .40 .20
2273 A610 13c Weight lifting .65 .20
2274 A610 30c High jump 2.10 .30
Nos. 2269-2274 (6) 4.05 1.30

Roses — A611

A612

1979, Aug. 20   **Perf. 13**
2275	A611	1c *Rosa eglanteria*	.25	.20
2276	A611	2c *Rosa centifolia anemonoides*	.25	.20
2277	A611	3c *Rosa indica vulgaris*	.25	.20
2278	A611	5c *Rosa eglanteria punicea*	.25	.20
2279	A611	10c *Rosa sulfurea*	.30	.20
2280	A611	13c *Rosa muscosa alba*	.50	.20
2281	A611	20c *Rosa gallica purpurea velutina*	1.00	.25
		Nos. 2275-2281 (7)	2.80	1.45

1979, Aug. 30
2282	A612	13c multi	.50	.20

Council for Mutual Economic Assistance, 30th anniv.

Cubana Airlines, 50th Anniv. A613

Various aircraft.

1979, Oct. 8
2283	A613	1c Ford trimotor	.20	.20
2284	A613	2c Sikorsky S-38	.20	.20
2285	A613	3c Douglas DC-3	.35	.20
2286	A613	4c Brittania	.35	.20
2287	A613	13c Ilyushin IL-14	.90	.20
2288	A613	40c Tupolev TU-104	2.50	.40
		Nos. 2283-2288 (6)	4.50	1.40

Disappearance of Camilo Cienfuegos, 20th Anniv. — A614

1979, Oct. 28
2289	A614	3c multi	.30	.20

Reinoso, Sugar Cane and Blossom A615

1979, Nov. 12
2290	A615	13c multi	.75	.20

Sugar Cane Research Institute, 15th anniv., and sesquicentennial of the birth of Alvaro Reinoso.

Zoo Animals A616

1979, Nov. 15
2291	A616	1c Chimpanzees	.20	.20
2292	A616	2c Leopards	.20	.20
2293	A616	3c Deer	.20	.20
2294	A616	4c Lion cubs	.20	.20
2295	A616	5c Bear cubs	.20	.20
2296	A616	13c Squirrels	.30	.20
2297	A616	30c Pandas	.70	.30
2298	A616	50c Tiger cubs	1.40	.60
		Nos. 2291-2298 (8)	3.40	2.10

Insects A617

1980, Jan. 25
2299	A617	1c *Rhina oblita*	.20	.20
2300	A617	5c *Odontocera josemartii*, vert.	.20	.20
2301	A617	6c *Pinthocoelium columbinum*	.20	.20
2302	A617	10c *Calasoma splendida*, vert.	.50	.20
2303	A617	13c *Homophileurus cubanus*, vert.	.95	.20
2304	A617	30c *Heterops dimidiata*, vert.	2.10	.70
		Nos. 2299-2304 (6)	4.15	1.70

1980 Summer Olympics, Moscow — A618

1980, Feb. 20   **Perf. 12½**
2305	A618	1c Weight lifting	.25	.20
2306	A618	2c Shooting	.25	.20
2307	A618	5c Javelin	.30	.20
2308	A618	6c Wrestling	.30	.20
2309	A618	8c Judo	.30	.20
2310	A618	10c Running	.30	.20
2311	A618	13c Boxing	.65	.20
2312	A618	30c Women's volleyball	1.60	.60
		Nos. 2305-2312 (8)	3.95	2.00

Souvenir Sheet
Imperf
2313	A618	50c Mischa character	3.00	1.60

No. 2313 contains one 32x40mm stamp.

Paintings in the Natl. Museum A619

Designs: 1c, *The Oak Trees*, by Henry Joseph Harpignies, vert. 4c, *Family Reunion*, by Willem van Mieris, vert. 6c, *Domestic Fowl*, by Melchior De Hondecoeter, vert. 9c, *Innocence*, by William A. Bougereau, vert. 13c, *Venetial Scene II*, by Michele Marieschi. 30c, *Spanish Peasant Woman*, by Joaquin Dominguez Bequer, vert.

Perf. 12½, 13 (9c, 30c), 12½x13 (13c)

1980, Mar. 11
    Sizes: 29x40mm, 40x29mm (4c),
    28x42mm (9c, 30c), 38x26mm (13c)
2314	A619	1c multi	.20	.20
2315	A619	4c multi	.20	.20
2316	A619	6c multi	.20	.20
2317	A619	9c multi	.65	.20
2318	A619	13c multi	.85	.20
2319	A619	30c multi	1.90	.65
		Nos. 2314-2319 (6)	4.00	1.65

Souvenir Sheet

LONDON '80 — A620

1980, Apr. 1   **Perf. 13**
2320	A620	50c *Malvern Hall*, by John Constable	3.50	1.60

Intercosmos Program — A621

1980, Apr. 12
2321	A621	1c Emblem, flags	.20	.20
2322	A621	4c Astrophysics	.20	.20
2323	A621	6c Satellite communications	.20	.20
2324	A621	10c Meteorology	.45	.20
2325	A621	13c Biology and medicine	.60	.20
2326	A621	30c Surveying satellite	1.90	.65
		Nos. 2321-2326 (6)	3.55	1.65

Cuban Postage Stamps, 125th Anniv. — A622

1980, Apr. 24   **Perf. 12½**
2327	A622	30c Nos. 1, 7 and 613	1.25	.45

Orchids — A623

1980, May 20   **Perf. 13**
2328	A623	1c *Bletia purpurea*	.25	.20
2329	A623	4c *Oncidium leiboldii*	.25	.20
2330	A623	6c *Epidendrum cochieatum*	.25	.20
2331	A623	10c *Cattleyopsis lindenii*	.50	.20
2332	A623	13c *Encyclia fucata*	.90	.20
2333	A623	30c *Encyclia phoenicea*	1.90	.60
		Nos. 2328-2333 (6)	4.05	1.60

Marine Mammals — A624

1980, June 20
2334	A624	1c *Tursiops truncatus*	.50	.20
2335	A624	3c *Megaptera novaeangliae*, vert.	.50	.20
2336	A624	13c *Ziphius cavirostris*	1.50	.20
2337	A624	30c *Monachus tropicalis*	3.50	.50
		Nos. 2334-2337 (4)	6.00	1.10

Urban Reform Campaign, 20th Anniv. — A625

Nationalization of Foreign Industry, 20th Anniv. — A626

1980, July 26   **Perf. 13x12½, 12½x13**
2338	A625	3c multi	.20	.20
2339	A626	13c multi	.35	.20

Moncada Program.

Colonial Copperware A627

Perf. 12½, 12½x13 (13c)
1980, July 29
    Sizes: 27x43½mm, 38x26mm (13c)
2340	A627	3c Wine pitcher, 19th cent.	.20	.20
2341	A627	13c Oil jar, 18th cent.	.70	.20
2342	A627	30c Lidded pitcher, 19th cent.	1.40	.30
		Nos. 2340-2342 (3)	2.30	.70

Cuban Women's Federation, 20th Anniv. — A628

1980, Aug. 23   **Perf. 13**
2343	A628	3c multi	.40	.20

Souvenir Sheet

ESPAMER '80, Madrid — A629

Design: *Clotilde Passing Through the Country Garden*, by Joaquin Sorolla y Bastida.

1980, Aug. 29
2344 A629 50c multi 3.50 1.60
Postage stamps of Spain, 130th anniv.

1st Havana Declaration, 20th Anniv. — A630

1980, Sept. 2
2345 A630 13c multi .50 .20

Construction of Naval Vessels in Cuba, 360th Anniv. — A631

Ships under construction: 1c, *Our Lady of Atocha*, galleon, 1620. 3c, *El Rayo*, warship, 1749. 7c, *Santisima Trinidad*, 1769. 10c, *Santisima Trinidad*, diff., 1805, vert. 13c, Steamships *Congreso* and *Colon*, 1851. 30c, Cardenas and Chullima shipyards.

1980, Sept. 15
2346 A631 1c multi .20 .20
2347 A631 3c multi .20 .20
2348 A631 7c multi .20 .20
2349 A631 10c multi .50 .20
2350 A631 13c multi .95 .20
2351 A631 30c multi 1.60 .60
Nos. 2346-2351 (6) 3.65 1.60

A633

A634

1980, Sept. 26 Perf. 13
2354 A633 13c multi .60 .20
Fidel Castro's 1st speech before the UN General Assembly, 20th anniv.

1980, Sept. 28 Perf. 13x12½
2355 A634 3c multi .30 .20
Revolutionary defense committees, 20th anniv.

Souvenir Sheet

ESSEN '80, 49th Intl. Philatelic Federation Congress — A635

Painting: *Portrait of a Lady*, by Ludger Tom Ring The Younger.

1980, Oct. 2 Litho. Perf. 13
2356 A635 50c multi 3.75 1.25

Early Locomotives — A636

1980, Oct. 15
2357 A636 1c Josefa .25 .20
2358 A636 2c Chaparra Sugar Co. No. 22 .25 .20
2359 A636 7c Steam storage locomotive .25 .20
2360 A636 10c 2-4-2 locomotive .40 .20
2361 A636 13c 2-4-0 locomotive .65 .20
2362 A636 30c Oil combustion engine, 1909 1.60 .60
Nos. 2357-2362 (6) 3.40 1.60

Lighthouses A637

1980, Oct. 30
2363 A637 3c Roncali, San Antonio .20 .20
2364 A637 13c Jagua, Cienfuegos .70 .20
2365 A637 30c Maisi Point, Guantanamo 1.60 .25
Nos. 2363-2365 (3) 2.50 .65
See Nos. 2440-2442, 2553-2555, 2614-2616.

Victory of Cuban Athletes at the 1980 Summer Olympics, Moscow — A638

1980, Nov. 10 Litho. Perf. 12½x12
2366 A638 13c Bronze medals .50 .20
2367 A638 30c Silver medals 1.10 .25
2368 A638 50c Gold medals 2.25 .55
Nos. 2366-2368 (3) 3.85 1.00
Nos. 2366-2368 each printed se-tenant with label containing statistical data.

Wildflowers A639

1980, Nov. 20 Perf. 13
2369 A639 1c Pancratium arenicolum .20 .20
2370 A639 4c Urechites lutea .25 .20
2371 A639 6c Solanum elaegnifolium .30 .20
2372 A639 10c Hamelia patens .50 .20
2373 A639 13c Morinda royoc .95 .20
2374 A639 30c Centrosema virginianum 2.25 .40
Nos. 2369-2374 (6) 4.45 1.40

Souvenir Sheet

7th Natl. Stamp Exhibition — A640

1980, Nov. 22
2375 A640 50c Mail train 3.00 1.25

2nd Communist Party Congress A641

1980, Dec. 17
2376 A641 3c shown .20 .20
2377 A641 13c Industry, communication .40 .20
2378 A641 30c Athletics, elderly, education 1.10 .25
Nos. 2376-2378 (3) 1.70 .65

Paintings in the Natl. Museum of Art A642

Designs: 1c, *Lady Mayo*, by Anton Van Dyck, vert. 6c, *The Spinner*, by Giovanni Battista Piazzeta, vert. 10c, *Daniel Collyer*, by Francis Cotes, vert. 13c, *Gardens, Palma de Mallorca*, by Santiago Rusinol Prats. 20c, *Landscape with Roadway and Houses*, by Frederick Waters Watts. 50c, *Landscape with Sheep*, by Jean-Francois Millet.

1981, Jan. 20
2379 A642 1c multi .20 .20
2380 A642 6c multi .20 .20
2381 A642 10c multi .50 .20
2382 A642 13c multi .60 .20
2383 A642 20c multi 1.00 .30
2384 A642 50c multi 2.10 .60
Nos. 2379-2384 (6) 4.60 1.70
See Nos. 2510-2515.

Pelagic Fish A643

1981, Feb. 25
2385 A643 1c *Isurus oxyrhynchus* .25 .20
2386 A643 3c *Lampris regius* .25 .20
2387 A643 10c *Istiophorus platypterus* .45 .20
2388 A643 13c *Mola mola*, vert. 1.75 .25
2389 A643 30c *Coruphaena hippurus* 1.10 .40
2390 A643 50c *Tetrapturus albidus* 2.00 .95
Nos. 2385-2390 (6) 5.80 2.20

1982 World Cup Soccer Championships, Spain — A644

Globe and various soccer players.

1981, Mar. 20 Perf. 12½
2391 A644 1c multi .20 .20
2392 A644 2c multi .20 .20
2393 A644 3c multi .20 .20
2394 A644 10c multi, vert. .45 .20
2395 A644 13c multi, vert. .45 .20
2396 A644 50c multi 1.75 .65
Nos. 2391-2396 (6) 3.25 1.65

Souvenir Sheet
Perf. 13
2397 A644 1p Soccer ball, flag 4.75 2.00
No. 2397 contains one 40x32mm stamp.

Opening of the 1st Kindergarten, 20th Anniv. — A645

1981, Apr. 10 Perf. 13
2398 A645 3c multi .65 .20

1st Man in Space, 20th Anniv. A646

Designs: 1c, Jules Verne, Russian scientist Konstantin E. Tsiolkovski, and Sergei P. Korolev, designer of the 1st Soviet spacecraft, vert. 2c, Yuri Gagarin, 1st man in space. 3c, Valentina Tereshkova, 1st woman in space, and *Vostok 6*. 5c, Aleksei A. Leonov, 1st man to walk in space. 13c, Konstantin Feoktistov, Boris Yegorov and Vladimir Komarov, *Voskhod 1* crew, 1st 3-man orbital flight. 30c, Valeri Ryumen and Leonid Popov, set a space endurance record. 50c, Arnaldo Tamayo, 1st Cuban cosmonaut, and Soviet cosmonaut Yuri Romanenko on joint space flight, vert.

1981, Apr. 12 — *Perf. 12½*
2399	A646	1c multi	.20	.20
2400	A646	2c multi	.20	.20
2401	A646	3c multi	.20	.20
2402	A646	5c multi	.20	.20
2403	A646	13c multi	.45	.20
2404	A646	30c multi	1.00	.35
2405	A646	50c multi	2.25	.60
		Nos. 2399-2405 (7)	4.50	1.95

A647

Designs: 3c, Rocket, aircraft. 13c, Hand raising gun.

1981, Apr. 19 — *Litho. Perf. 13*
2406	A647	3c multi, vert.	.20	.20
2407	A647	13c multi, vert.	.40	.20
2408	A647	30c multi	.95	.60
		Nos. 2406-2408 (3)	1.55	1.00

Creation of armed forces (DAAFAR) (3c), Bay of Pigs Invasion, 20th Anniv. (13c), Proclamation of the socialist revolution (30c).

Attack on Goicuria Barracks, 25th Anniv. — A648

1981, Apr. 29
2409	A648	3c multi	.30	.20

Natl. Assoc. of Small Farmers (ANAP), 20th Anniv. A649

1981, May 17
2410	A649	3c multi	.50	.20

Souvenir Sheet

WIPA '81 — A650

1981, May 22 — *Litho.*
2411	A650	50c Austria No. 643	4.00	1.50

Fighting Cocks A651

1981, May 25 — *Perf. 12½x13, 13x12½*
2412	A651	1c Canelo, vert.	.20	.20
2413	A651	3c Cenizo	.20	.20
2414	A651	7c Blanco, vert.	.25	.20
2415	A651	13c Pinto, vert.	.50	.20
2416	A651	30c Giro	1.60	.35
2417	A651	50c Jabao, vert.	2.40	.60
		Nos. 2412-2417 (6)	5.15	1.75

Ministry of the Interior, 20th Anniv. — A652

1981, June 6 — *Perf. 13*
2418	A652	13c multi	.40	.20

Souvenir Sheet

Mother and Child, by Zlatka Dabova — A653

1981, June 14
2419	A653	50c gold, sil & blk	2.25	1.10

Bulgaria, 1300th anniv. BULGARIA '81 phil. exhib.

Horse-drawn Carriages — A654

1981, June 25
2420	A654	1c Streetcar	.20	.20
2421	A654	4c Bus	.20	.20
2422	A654	9c Breake	.25	.20
2423	A654	13c Landau	.40	.20
2424	A654	30c Phaeton	1.40	.45
2425	A654	50c Funeral coach	2.50	.75
		Nos. 2420-2425 (6)	4.95	2.00

House in the Country, by Mario Caridad — A655

1981, July 15 — *Perf. 12½*
2426	A655	30c multi	1.25	.30

Intl. Year of the Disabled.

Sandinistas, 25th Anniv. — A656

1981, July 23 — *Perf. 13*
2427	A656	13c multi	.50	.20

State Institutions, 20th Annivs. — A657

1981, July 26 — *Perf. 12½*
2428	A657	3c multi	.20	.20
2429	A657	13c multi, diff.	.45	.20
2430	A657	30c multi, diff.	1.25	.25
		Nos. 2428-2430 (3)	1.90	.65

Institute for Sports, Physical Education and Recreation (3c); Radio Havana (13c); and Ministry of Foreign Trade (MINCEX) (30c).

Carlos J. Finlay and Cent. of His Theory of Biological Vectors — A658

1981, Aug. 14 — *Perf. 13*
2431	A658	13c multi	1.00	.20

Nonaligned Countries Movement, 20th Anniv. — A659

1981, Sept. 1
2432	A659	50c multi	1.50	.80

Horses — A660

Nos. 2433-2437 vert.

1981, Sept. 15 — *Perf. 13*
Size: 29x40mm
2433	A660	1c multi	.20	.20
2434	A660	3c multi, diff.	.20	.20
2435	A660	8c multi, diff.	.20	.20
2436	A660	13c multi, diff.	.35	.20
2437	A660	30c multi, diff.	1.10	.45

Size: 68x27mm
Perf. 12½
2438	A660	50c Herd	1.75	.75
		Nos. 2433-2438 (6)	3.80	2.00

Souvenir Sheet

Idyll in a Tea House, by Kitagawa Utamaro — A661

1981, Oct. 9 — *Perf. 13*
2439	A661	50c multi	2.75	1.25

PHILATOKYO '81.

Lighthouse Type of 1980

1981, Oct. 15 — *Litho.*
2440	A637	3c North Rock	.20	.20
2441	A637	13c Lucrecia Point	.50	.20
2442	A637	40c East Guano	2.10	.50
		Nos. 2440-2442 (3)	2.80	.90

Jose Marti Natl. Library, 80th Anniv. — A662

Sugar mills, lithographs from *Los Ingenios*, by Eduardo Laplante (b. 1818): 3c, Flor de Cuba, 1838. 13c, El Progreso, 1845. 30c, Santa Teresa, 1847.

1981, Oct. 18 — *Perf. 12½x12*
2443	A662	3c multi	.20	.20
2444	A662	13c multi	.35	.20
2445	A662	30c multi	1.25	.55
		Nos. 2443-2445 (3)	1.80	.95

Pablo Picasso (b. 1881) and No. 1263 A663

1981, Oct. 25 — *Perf. 12½x13*
2446	A663	30c multi	1.25	.40

Souvenir Sheet

ESPAMER '81, Buenos Aires — A664

1981, Nov. 13 — *Perf. 13*
2447	A664	1p Packet	4.00	2.00

Art Type of 1969

Paintings in the Napoleon Museum: 1c, *Napoleon in Coronation Costume*, anonymous. 3c, *Napoleon with Landscape in the Background*, by Jean Horace Vernet. 10c, *Bonaparte in Egypt*, by Edouard Detaille. 13c, *Napoleon on Horseback*, by Hippolyte Belange. 30c, *Napoleon in Normandy*, by Belange. 50c, *Death of Napoleon*, anonymous.

1981, Dec. 1 — *Perf. 12½*
Sizes: 42x58mm, 58x42mm (3c, 13c, 30c, 50c)
2448	A385	1c multi	.20	.20
2449	A385	3c multi, horiz.	.20	.20
2450	A385	10c multi	.40	.20
2451	A385	13c multi, horiz.	.40	.20

2452	A385	30c multi, horiz.	1.25	.40
2453	A385	50c multi, horiz.	2.10	.70
		Nos. 2448-2453 (6)	4.55	1.90

Napoleon Museum, 20th anniv.

25th Anniv. A665

1981, Dec. 2   *Perf. 13*

2454	A665	3c Revolutionaries, vert.	.20	.20
2455	A665	20c Marksman	.45	.20
2456	A665	1p Yacht *Granma*	5.25	1.40
		Nos. 2454-2456 (3)	5.90	1.80

November 30th insurrection (3c); creation of the revolutionary armed forces (20c); and disembarking of revolutionary forces (1p).

Fauna — A666

1981, Dec. 14   Litho.   *Perf. 12½x12*

2457	A666	1c Hummingbird	.60	.20
2458	A666	2c Parakeet	.95	.20
2459	A666	5c Hutia	.20	.20
2460	A666	20c Almiqui	.65	.20
2461	A666	35c Manatee	1.25	.25
2462	A666	40c Crocodile	1.00	.55
		Nos. 2457-2462 (6)	4.65	1.60

Fernando Ortiz, Folklorist, Birth Cent. A667

1981, Dec. 20   *Perf. 12½x13*

2463	A667	3c Portrait by Jorge Arche y Silva	.20	.20
2464	A667	10c Hanging idol	.40	.20
2465	A667	30c Arara drum	1.50	.45
2466	A667	50c Chango statue	2.25	.70
		Nos. 2463-2466 (4)	4.35	1.55

Literacy Campaign, 20th Anniv. — A668

1981, Dec. 25   *Perf. 12½x12*

2467		5c Conrado Benitez	.30	.20
2468		5c Manuel Asunce	.30	.20
a.		A668 Pair, #2467-2468	.75	.25
		Nos. 2467-2468 (2)	.60	.40

A669

1982 World Cup Soccer Championships, Spain — A670

Various athletes.

1982, Jan. 15   *Perf. 13*

2469	A669	1c multi, vert.	.20	.20
2470	A669	2c multi, vert.	.20	.20
2471	A669	5c multi, vert.	.20	.20
2472	A669	10c multi, vert.	.30	.20
2473	A669	20c shown	.70	.20
2474	A669	40c multi	1.25	.50
2475	A669	50c multi, vert.	1.60	.70
		Nos. 2469-2475 (7)	4.45	2.20

Souvenir Sheet

| 2476 | A670 | 1p shown | 5.00 | 2.50 |

No. 2476 contains one 32x40mm stamp.

10th World Trade Unions Congress, Havana — A671

1982, Feb. 10   Litho.

| 2477 | A671 | 30c Lazaro Pena, delegate | 1.00 | .40 |

Exports — A673

3c, Sugar (processing plant). 4c, Lobster (fishing boat). 6c, Canned fruits. 7c, Agricultural machinery. 8c, Nickel (passenger jet, industrial complex, car). 9c, Rum. 10c, Coffee. 30c, Fresh fruit. 50c, Tobacco. 1p, Cement. Nos. 2489-2493 vert.

1982, Feb. 26   *Perf. 12x12½, 12½x12*

2484	A673	3c lt grn	.20	.20
2485	A673	4c car rose	.20	.20
2486	A673	6c dull blue	.25	.20
2487	A673	7c brt org	.40	.20
2488	A673	8c brt vio	.40	.20
2489	A673	9c slate	.40	.20
2490	A673	10c dull red brn	.50	.20
2491	A673	30c bister	.75	.25
2492	A673	50c orange	2.10	.40
2493	A673	1p olive bister	4.00	1.25
		Nos. 2484-2493 (10)	9.20	3.30

Tulips A674

1982, Mar. 30   *Perf. 12½x13*

2494	A674	1c Greenland	.20	.20
2495	A674	3c Mariette	.25	.20
2496	A674	8c Ringo	.25	.20
2497	A674	20c La Tulipe Noire	.80	.20
2498	A674	30c Jewel of Spring	1.40	.25
2499	A674	50c Orange Parrot	1.90	.60
		Nos. 2494-2499 (6)	4.80	1.65

Communist Youth Organization, 20th Anniv. — A675

1982, Apr. 4   *Perf. 13*

| 2500 | A675 | 5c multi | .30 | .20 |

2nd UN Congress on the Peaceful Use of Outer Space — A676

1982, Apr. 12

2501	A676	1c *Mars*	.20	.20
2502	A676	3c *Venera*	.20	.20
2503	A676	6c *Salyut-Soyuz* link-up	.25	.20
2504	A676	20c *Lunokhod* moon vehicle	.50	.20
2505	A676	30c *Venera* with heat shield	1.40	.30
2506	A676	50c *Intelsat-4a*	2.00	.60
		Nos. 2501-2506 (6)	4.55	1.70

Cover A677

1982, Apr. 24   *Perf. 12½x12*

| 2507 | A677 | 20c Havana-Veracruz | .75 | .25 |
| 2508 | A677 | 30c Havana-Tampico | 1.25 | .25 |

Stamp Day. English post office, 1842-1877 (20c); and French post office, 1862-1877 (30c).

Broadcasting and Television Institute (ICRT), 20th Anniv. — A678

1982, May 24   *Perf. 12x12½*

| 2509 | A678 | 30c multi | 1.00 | .25 |

Art Type of 1981 With Larger Type

Paintings in the Natl. Museum of Art: 1c, *Portrait of a Youth* (girl), by Jean B. Greuze, vert. 3c, *Procession in Brittany,* by Jules Breton. 9c, *Landscape,* by Jean Piliment. 20c, *Late Afternoon,* by William A. Bourgueran, vert. 30c, *Tiger,* by Ferdinand V.E. Delacroix. 40c, *The Chair,* by Wilfredo Lam, vert.

Perf. 13, 13x12½ (3c), 12x12½ (20c, 40c), 12½x12 (30c)

1982, May 31   Litho.

2510	A642	1c 29x40mm	.20	.20
2511	A642	3c 46x36mm	.20	.20
2512	A642	9c 40x29mm	.25	.20
2513	A642	20c 27x42mm	.65	.25
2514	A642	30c 42x27mm	1.25	.40
2515	A642	40c 27x42mm	2.00	.40
		Nos. 2510-2515 (6)	4.55	1.65

Souvenir Sheet

PHILEXFRANCE '82 — A679

1982, June 7   *Perf. 13*

| 2516 | A679 | 1p Steamship *Louisiana* at St. Nazaire | 5.00 | 2.50 |

DEPORFILEX '82 — A680

1982, June 10   *Perf. 13x12½*

| 2517 | A680 | 20c Hurdler, No. 300 | 1.50 | .25 |

Reptiles A681

1982, June 15   *Perf. 13*

2518	A681	1c *Pseudemys decussata*	.20	.20
2519	A681	2c *Tropidophis pardalis*	.20	.20
2520	A681	3c *Crocodylus rhombifer*	.25	.20
2521	A681	20c *Cyclura nubila*	.85	.20
2522	A681	30c *Anolis allisonis*	1.25	.30
2523	A681	50c *Alsophis cantherigerus*	2.40	.50
		Nos. 2518-2523 (6)	5.15	1.60

Butterflies — A672

1982, Feb. 25   *Perf. 12½*

2478	A672	1c *Euptoieta hegesia*	.20	.20
2479	A672	4c *Metamorpha stelenes insularis*	.20	.20
2480	A672	5c *Heliconius charithonius ramsdeni*	.20	.20
2481	A672	20c *Phoebis avellaneda*	1.40	.30
2482	A672	30c *Hamadryas ferox diasia*	2.25	.55
2483	A672	50c *Marpesia eleuchea*	4.00	.95
		Nos. 2478-2483 (6)	8.25	2.40

George Dimitrov (1882-1949), Bulgarian Prime Minister — A682

1982, June 18
2524 A682 30c multi 1.00 .25

Koch, Bacillus A683

1982, July 18
2525 A683 20c multi 1.25 .25

Discovery of the tubercle bacillus by Dr. Robert Koch, cent.

14th Central American and Caribbean Games — A684

1982, Aug. 1
2526 A684 1c Baseball .20 .20
2527 A684 2c Boxing .20 .20
2528 A684 10c Water polo .35 .20
2529 A684 20c Javelin .80 .30
2530 A684 35c Weight lifting 1.25 .50
2531 A684 50c Volleyball 2.00 .55
Nos. 2526-2531 (6) 4.80 1.95

Hydraulic Development Plan, 20th Anniv. — A685

5c, Fruit, *Eichornia crassipes*, ship. 20c, Arid soil, *Nymphaea alba*, irrigation & reservoir systems.

1982, Aug. 9
2532 A685 5c multi .40 .20
2533 A685 20c multi 1.25 .25

Souvenir Sheet

DEPORFILEX '82, Intl. Stamp and Coin Exhibition — A686

1982, Aug. 10 Litho.
2534 A686 1p Cuco, character trademark 4.75 2.25

14th Central American and Caribbean Games.

Namibia Day — A687

1982, Aug. 26
2535 A687 50c multi 1.75 .75

1982 World Cup Soccer Championships, Spain — A688

Various athletes.

1982, Aug. 30
2536 A688 5c multi .20 .20
2537 A688 20c multi .75 .30
2538 A688 30c multi 1.10 .40
2539 A688 50c multi 1.90 .80
Nos. 2536-2539 (4) 3.95 1.70

Also exist in miniature sheets of 16 + 9 labels containing 4 each Nos. 2536-2539 in blocks of 4.

Natl. Folklore Ensemble, 20th Anniv. — A689

Paintings by V.P. Landaluze.

1982, Sept. 10
2540 A689 20c *Little Devil*, vert. .80 .25
2541 A689 30c *Day of Kings* 1.10 .45

Prehistoric Fauna — A690

1982, Sept. 15 Litho.
2542 A690 1c *Ornimegalonyx oteroi*, vert. .65 .25
2543 A690 5c *Crocodylus rhombifer* .20 .20
2544 A690 7c *Aquila borrasi*, vert. 2.75 .40
2545 A690 20c *Geocapromys colombianus* .65 .20
2546 A690 35c *Megalocnus rodens*, vert. 1.00 .50
2547 A690 50c *Nesophontes micrus* 1.40 .65
Nos. 2542-2547 (6) 6.65 2.20

15th Death Anniv. of Che Guevara — A691

1982, Oct. 8 *Perf. 13x12½*
2548 A691 20c multi .70 .25

Discovery of America, 490th Anniv. — A692

1982, Oct. 12 *Perf. 13*
2549 A692 5c shown 1.10 .25
2550 A692 20c *Santa Maria*, vert. 1.25 .40
2551 A692 35c *Pinta*, vert. 1.90 .90
2552 A692 50c *Nina*, vert. 2.40 1.10
Nos. 2549-2552 (4) 6.65 2.65

Lighthouse Type of 1980

1982, Oct. 25
2553 A637 5c Jutias Caye 1.00 .20
2554 A637 20c Paredon Grande Caye 2.75 .20
2555 A637 30c Morro Santiago de Cuba 3.75 .45
Nos. 2553-2555 (3) 7.50 .85

George Washington, 250th Birth Anniv. — A693

Designs: Quotations and anonymous oil paintings, 18th-19th cent.

1982, Oct. 29 *Perf. 12x12½*
2556 A693 5c multi .25 .20
2557 A693 20c multi, diff. .75 .20

Souvenir Sheet

8th Natl. Philatelic Exposition, Ciego de Avila — A694

1982, Nov. 13
2558 A694 1p Paddle steamer *Almendares* 5.00 2.50

8th Congress of the Cuban Philatelic Federation, Nov. 13-22.

Lenin Natl. Park, 10th Anniv. A695

1982, Dec. 28
2559 A695 5c multi .65 .20

Chess Champion Jose Raul Capablanca and King — A696

1982, Dec. 29
2560 A696 5c shown .25 .20
2561 A696 20c Rook 1.10 .25
2562 A696 30c Knight 1.40 .50
2563 A696 50c Queen 2.25 .80
a. Bklt. pane of 4, Nos. 2560-2563 20.00 10.00
Nos. 2560-2563 (4) 5.00 1.75

Exist in sheets of 4+2 labels picturing chessmen.

USSR, 60th Anniv. — A697

1982, Dec. 30 *Perf. 13x12½*
2564 A697 30c multi 1.25 .25

World Communications Year — A698

1983, Jan. 24 Litho. *Perf. 13*
2565 A698 20c multi .75 .25

No. 507 and Birthplace — A699

1983, Jan. 28 *Perf. 13x12½*
2566 A699 5c multi .30 .20

Jose Marti (b. 1853), writer, revolution leader.

1984 Summer Olympics, Los Angeles A700

1983, Jan. 31 *Perf. 13*
2567 A700 1c Javelin .20 .20
2568 A700 5c Volleyball .25 .20
2569 A700 6c Basketball .25 .20
2570 A700 20c Weight lifting .80 .20
2571 A700 30c Wrestling 1.10 .40
2572 A700 50c Boxing 1.75 .60
   a.   Block of 6, #2567-2572 4.50 1.80
    Nos. 2567-2572 (6) 4.35 1.80

Souvenir Sheet
Perf. 13½x13
2573 A700 1p Judo 5.00 2.50

No. 2573 contains one 32x40mm stamp.

Radio Rebelde, 25th Anniv. — A701

1983, Feb. 24 *Perf. 13*
2574 A701 20c multi .70 .20

Karl Marx, Death Cent. A702

1983, Mar. 14
2575 A702 30c multi 1.00 .40

1st Manned Balloon Flight, Bicent. — A703

Various balloons.

1983, Mar. 30
2576 A703 1c multi .20 .20
2577 A703 3c multi .20 .20
2578 A703 5c multi .20 .20
2579 A703 7c multi .35 .20
2580 A703 30c multi 2.10 .70
2581 A703 50c multi 2.10 .70
    Nos. 2576-2581 (6) 5.15 2.20

Souvenir Sheet
2582 A703 1p Jose D. Blino 4.00 2.00

No. 2582 contains one 32x40mm stamp.

Cosmonauts' Day — A704

1983, Apr. 12 *Litho.*
2583 A704 1c *Vostok 1* .20 .20
2584 A704 4c Satellite *Frances D1* .20 .20
2585 A704 5c *Mars 2* .20 .20
2586 A704 20c *Soyuz* .75 .20
2587 A704 30c Meteorological satellite 1.10 .50
2588 A704 50c Intercosmos satellite 1.75 .70
    Nos. 2583-2588 (6) 4.20 2.00

Stamp Day A705

1983, Apr. 24
2589 A705 20c Havana-Key West cover .75 .30
2590 A705 30c Spain-Havana cover 1.25 .30

1st Intl. airmail services.

Souvenir Sheet

TEMBAL '83, Basel — A706

1983, May 21 *Perf. 13½x13*
2591 A706 1p Weasel 5.00 2.50

Simon Bolivar, Liberator of South America A707

1983, July 24 *Perf. 12½x13*
2592 A707 5c Jose Rafael de las Heras .20 .20
2593 A707 20c Bolivar .60 .20

Attack of Moncada Barracks, 30th Anniv. — A708

Designs: 5c, Jose Marti, Moncada barracks. 20c, Abel Santamaria, Jose Luis Tasende and Boris Luis Santa Coloma, martyrs, vert. 30c, *History Will Absolve Me*, declaration of Fidel Castro, vert.

1983, July 26 *Perf. 13*
2594 A708 5c multi .20 .20
2595 A708 20c multi .70 .20
2596 A708 30c multi .90 .50
    Nos. 2594-2596 (3) 1.80 .90

Souvenir Sheet

Alberto Santos-Dumont (1873-1932) — A709

1983, July 29 *Perf. 13x13½*
2597 A709 1p Dumont's aircraft 5.00 2.50

BRASILIANA '83, Rio; 140th anniv. of 1st stamp issued in the Americas.

9th Pan American Games, Caracas — A710

1983, Aug. 14 *Perf. 13x12½*
2598 A710 1c Weight lifting .20 .20
2599 A710 2c Volleyball .20 .20
2600 A710 3c Baseball .20 .20
2601 A710 20c High jump .75 .20
2602 A710 30c Basketball 1.10 .50
2603 A710 50c Boxing 1.75 .70
    Nos. 2598-2603 (6) 4.20 2.00

Port, by Claude Joseph Vernet — A711

1983, Sept. 5
2604 A711 30c multi 1.75 .55

French alliance, cent.

Pres. Salvador Allende of Chile (d. 1973) — A712

1983, Sept. 12
2605 A712 20c multi .70 .20

1st Congress of Farmers at Arms, 25th Anniv. — A713

1983, Sept. 21 *Perf. 12½x12*
2606 A713 5c multi .25 .20

Raphael, 500th Birth Anniv. — A714

1983, Sept. 30 *Litho.* *Perf. 13*
2607 A714 1c *Girl with Veil* .20 .20
2608 A714 2c *The Cardinal* .20 .20
2609 A714 5c *Francesco M. Della Rovere* .20 .20
2610 A714 20c *Portrait of a Youth* .75 .20
2611 A714 30c *Magdalena Doni* 1.10 .40
2612 A714 50c *La Fornarina* 1.75 .65
    Nos. 2607-2612 (6) 4.20 1.85

State Quality Seal A715

1983, Oct. 14
2613 A715 5c multi .40 .20

Lighthouse Type of 1980

1983, Oct. 20
2614 A637 5c Carapachibey .20 .20
2615 A637 20c Cadiz Bay .80 .30
2616 A637 30c Gobernadora Point 2.00 .80
    Nos. 2614-2616 (3) 3.00 1.30

Turtles A716

1983, Nov. 15
2617 A716 1c *Eretmochelys imbricata* .20 .20
2618 A716 2c *Lepidochelys kempi* .20 .20
2619 A716 5c *Chrysemys decussata* .25 .20
2620 A716 20c *Caretta caretta* .80 .20
2621 A716 30c *Chelonia mydas* 1.40 .25
2622 A716 50c *Dermochelys coriacea* 2.75 .75
    Nos. 2617-2622 (6) 5.60 1.80

World Communications Year — A717

1983, Nov. 23
2623	A717	1c	Bell's Gallow Frame, telephone	.20	.20
2624	A717	5c	Telegram, airmail	.20	.20
2625	A717	10c	Satellite, satellite dish	.45	.20
2626	A717	20c	Television, radio	.75	.20
2627	A717	30c	24th Communications conf.	1.10	.40
			Nos. 2623-2627 (5)	2.70	1.20

Nos. 319 and 990 A718

150 ANIV. NACIMIENTO DE CARLOS J. FINLAY

1983, Dec. 3   Perf. 13x12½
2628	A718	20c	multi	.70	.25

See note after No. 320.

Flowers, Birds A719   Flowers A720

1983, Dec. 20   Perf. 13
2629	A719	5c	Opuntia dillenii	.55	.20
2630	A719	5c	Euphorbia podocarpifolia	.55	.20
2631	A719	5c	Dinema cubincola	.55	.20
2632	A719	5c	Guaiacum officinale	.55	.20
2633	A719	5c	Magnolia cubensis	.55	.20
a.			Strip of 5, Nos. 2629-2633	4.00	2.00
2634	A719	5c	Jatropha angustifolia	.55	.20
2635	A719	5c	Cochlospermum vitifolium	.55	.20
2636	A719	5c	Tabebuia lepidota	.55	.20
2637	A719	5c	Kalmiella ericoides	.55	.20
2638	A719	5c	Jatropha integerrima	.55	.20
2639	A719	5c	Melocactus actinacanthus	.55	.20
2640	A719	5c	Cordia sebestana	.55	.20
2641	A719	5c	Tabernae-montana apoda	.55	.20
2642	A719	5c	Lantana camara	.55	.20
2643	A719	5c	Cordia gerascanthus	.55	.20
a.			Block of 10, Nos. 2634-2643	6.50	4.00
2644	A719	5c	Tiaris canora	.55	.20
2645	A719	5c	Phaethon lepturus	.55	.20
2646	A719	5c	Myadestes elisabeth	.55	.20
2647	A719	5c	Saurothera merlini	.55	.20
2648	A719	5c	Polioptila lembeyei	.55	.20
a.			Strip of 5, Nos. 2644-2648	4.00	2.00
2649	A719	5c	Mellisuga helenae	.55	.20
2650	A719	5c	Mimus polyglottos	.55	.20
2651	A719	5c	Todus multicolor	.55	.20
2652	A719	5c	Amazona leucocephala	.55	.20
2653	A719	5c	Ferminia cerverai	.55	.20
2654	A719	5c	Pelecanus occidentalis	.55	.20
2655	A719	5c	Melanerpes superciliaris	.55	.20
2656	A719	5c	Mimocichla plumbea	.55	.20
2657	A719	5c	Aratinga euops	.55	.20

2658	A719	5c	Sturnella magna	.55	.20
a.			Block of 10, Nos. 2649-2658	6.50	4.00
			Nos. 2629-2658 (30)	16.50	6.00

Souvenir Sheets
2658B	A719	100c	Hedychium coronarium	5.00	4.50
2658C	A719	100c	Priotelus temnurus	5.00	4.50

1983, Dec. 30   Perf. 12½
2659	A720	60c	Tobacco	1.75	.55
2660	A720	70c	Lily	2.25	.60
2661	A720	80c	Mariposa	2.50	.70
2662	A720	90c	Orchid	3.50	1.00
			Nos. 2659-2662 (4)	10.00	2.85

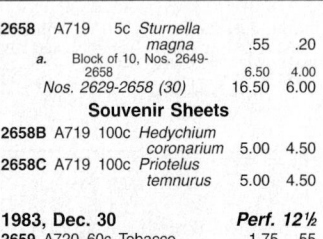

25th Anniv. of the Revolution — A721

1983, Dec. 31   Litho.   Perf. 13
2663	A721	5c	shown	.20	.20
2664	A721	20c	Flags, Santa Clara Rlwy. tracks	3.50	1.00

25th Anniv. of the Revolution — A722

1984, Jan. 8
2665		20c	Guevara, Castro	.70	.25
2666		20c	Star	.70	.25
2667		20c	PCC emblem, workers	1.75	.80
a.			A722 Strip of 3, #2665-2667	3.25	1.50
			Nos. 2665-2667 (3)	3.15	1.30

Lenin, 60th Death Anniv. A723

60 ANIVERSARIO DE LA MUERTE DE V.I. LENIN

1984, Jan. 21   Perf. 12½x12
2668	A723	30p	Spasski Tower, Russia Nos. 295, 265	1.25	.25

Cuban Labor Union, 45th Anniv. A724

1984, Jan. 28   Perf. 13
2669	A724	5c	multi	.25	.20

Butterflies — A725

1984, Jan. 31   Perf. 13x12½
2670	A725	1c	Ixias balice	.20	.20
2671	A725	2c	Phoebis avellaneda	.20	.20
2672	A725	3c	Anthocaris sara	.20	.20
2673	A725	5c	Victorina	.25	.20

2674	A725	20c	Heliconius cydno cydnides	.80	.20
2675	A725	30c	Parides gundlachianus calzadillae	1.40	.65
2676	A725	50c	Catagramma sorana	2.40	.95
			Nos. 2670-2676 (7)	5.45	2.60

Marine Mammals — A726

1984, Feb. 15   Perf. 12x12½, 12½x12
2677	A726	1c	Grampus griseus, vert.	.25	.20
2678	A726	2c	Delphinus delphis, vert.	.25	.20
2679	A726	5c	Physeter catodon	.25	.20
2680	A726	6c	Stenella plagiodon, vert.	.25	.20
2681	A726	10c	Pseudorca crassidens	.70	.20
2682	A726	30c	Tursiops truncatus, vert.	1.60	.40
2683	A726	50c	Megaptera novaeangliae	2.75	.70
			Nos. 2677-2683 (7)	6.05	2.10

Augusto C. Sandino (1893-1934), Nicaraguan Revolutionary — A727

1984, Feb. 21   Perf. 13
2684	A727	20c	multi	.70	.25

Red Cross in Cuba, 75th Anniv. — A728

1984, Mar. 10
2685	A728	30c	Flag, No. 404	1.25	.35

Cuban Film Industry, 25th Anniv. A729

1984, Mar. 24
2686	A729	20c	multi	.80	.30

Caribbean Flowers — A730

1984, Mar. 29
2687	A730	1c	Brownea grandiceps	.20	.20
2688	A730	2c	Couroupita guianensis	.20	.20

2689	A730	5c	Triplaris surinamensis	.20	.20
2690	A730	20c	Amherstia nobilis	.80	.30
2691	A730	30c	Plumieria alba	1.10	.50
2692	A730	50c	Delonix regia	2.00	.90
			Nos. 2687-2692 (6)	4.50	2.30

Cosmonauts' Day — A731

1984, Apr. 12
2693	A731	2c	Electron 1, 1964	.20	.20
2694	A731	3c	Electron 2, 1964	.20	.20
2695	A731	5c	Intercosmos 1, 1969	.20	.20
2696	A731	10c	Mars 5, 1974	.40	.20
2697	A731	30c	Soyuz, 1969	1.10	.50
2698	A731	50c	USSR-Bulgaria space flight, 1979	2.00	.90
			Nos. 2693-2698 (6)	4.10	2.20

Souvenir Sheet
Perf. 12½
2699	A731	1p	Luna 1, 1959	4.00	2.00

No. 2699 contains one 32x40mm stamp.

Mothers' Day — A732

1984, Apr. 19   Perf. 13
2700	A732	20c	Red roses	.80	.30
2701	A732	20c	Pink roses	.80	.30

Stamp Day — A733

Designs: Mural, by R. Rodriguez Radillo (details).

1984, Apr. 24   Perf. 13x12½
2702	A733	20c	Mexican runner	.80	.30
2703	A733	30c	Egyptian boatman	1.10	.50

See Nos. 2787-2788, 2860-2861, 3025-3026, 3122-3123, 3213-3214.

Souvenir Sheet

ESPANA '84, Madrid — A734

1984, Apr. 27   Perf. 13x13½
2704	A734	1p	Clipper ship	4.75	2.25

Women's Basketball, 1984 Summer Olympics A735

1984, May 5 *Perf. 13*
2705 A735 20c multi 1.25 .35

Agrarian Reform Act, 25th Anniv. — A736

1984, May 17 *Perf. 13½x13*
2706 A736 5c multi .40 .20

Banco Popular de Ahorro, 1st Anniv. — A737

1984, May 18 *Perf. 13*
2707 A737 5c multi .40 .20

Early Locomotives — A738

1984, June 11 *Perf. 12½x12*
2708 A738 1c multi .25 .20
2709 A738 4c multi, diff. .25 .20
2710 A738 5c multi, diff. .25 .20
2711 A738 10c multi, diff. .40 .20
2712 A738 30c multi, diff. 1.25 .40
2713 A738 50c multi, diff. 2.10 .80
Nos. 2708-2713 (6) 4.50 2.00

Souvenir Sheet

19th UPU Congress, HAMBURG '84 — A739

1984, June 19 *Perf. 13x13½*
2714 A739 1p Nos. 73, 232 4.50 2.25

Intl. Olympic Committee, 90th Anniv. — A740

1984, June 23 *Perf. 13*
2715 A740 30c Coubertin, torch-
bearer 1.40 .50

Children's Day A741

1984, July 15 *Perf. 12½x13*
2716 A741 5c multi .25 .20

1984 Summer Olympics, Los Angeles A742

1984, July 28 *Perf. 13*
2717 A742 1c Wrestling .20 .20
2718 A742 3c Discus .20 .20
2719 A742 5c Volleyball .20 .20
2720 A742 20c Boxing .80 .30
2721 A742 30c Basketball 1.10 .50
2722 A742 50c Weight lifting 2.00 .90
Nos. 2717-2722 (6) 4.50 2.30
Souvenir Sheet
Perf. 12½
2723 A742 1p Baseball 4.50 2.25
No. 2723 contains one 32x40mm stamp.

Emilio Roig de Leuchsenring (1889-1964), Historian A743

1984, Aug. 8 *Perf. 13*
2724 A743 5c multi .25 .20

Friendship Games, Aug. 18-26, Havana — A744

1984, Aug. 18
2725 A744 3c Volleyball .20 .20
2726 A744 5c Women's volleyball .35 .20
2727 A744 8c Water polo .35 .20
2728 A744 30c Boxing 1.25 .35
Nos. 2725-2728 (4) 2.15 .95

Cattle Breeding A745

1984, Sept. 20
2729 A745 2c Artificial pastures .20 .20
2730 A745 3c Cuban carib .20 .20
2731 A745 5c Charolaise, vert. .25 .20
2732 A745 30c Cuban cebu, vert. 1.25 .40
2733 A745 50c White-udder 2.25 .75
Nos. 2729-2733 (5) 4.15 1.75

Souvenir Sheet

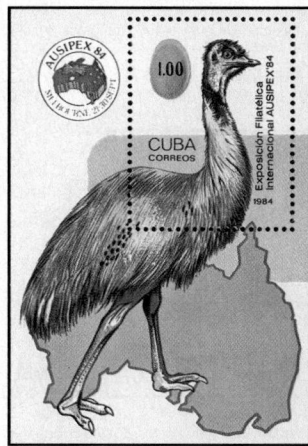

AUSIPEX '84, Sept. 21-30, Melbourne — A746

1984, Sept. 21 *Perf. 12½*
2734 A746 1p Emu 5.00 2.75

Fauna — A747

1984, Oct. 10 *Perf. 13*
2735 A747 1c Polymita .20 .20
2736 A747 2c Solenodon
cubanus .20 .20
2737 A747 3c Alsophis
cantherigerus .20 .20
2738 A747 4c Osteopilus
septentrionalis .20 .20
2739 A747 5c Mellisuga
helenae .55 .20
2740 A747 10c Capromys me-
lanurus .30 .20
2741 A747 30c Todus multicolor 2.40 .95
2742 A747 50c Parrots (cotorra) 3.75 1.25
Nos. 2735-2742 (8) 7.80 3.40

Souvenir Sheet

ESPAMER '85, Havana — A748

1984, Oct. 12
2743 Sheet of 4+2 la-
bels 5.00 2.50
a. A748 5c Ferdinand, Isabella .20 .20
b. A748 20c Departure from Palos 1.50 .70
c. A748 30c Nina, Pinta, Santa
Maria 2.25 1.10
d. A748 50c Landing in America 1.00 .50
Columbus Day.

Souvenir Sheet

9th Natl. Phil. Exhibition, Oct. 20-28, Santiago de Cuba — A749

1984, Oct. 20 *Perf. 12½*
2744 A749 1p multicolored 4.50 2.25

Natl. Revolutionary Militia, 25th Anniv. — A750

1984, Oct. 26 *Perf. 12½x13*
2745 A750 5c multi .30 .20

Disappearance of Camilo Cienfuegos, 25th Anniv. — A751

1984, Oct. 28 *Perf. 13x12½*
2746 A751 5c multi .40 .20

UN Child Survival Campaign A752

1984, Nov. 11 *Perf. 13*
2747 A752 5c Breast-feeding .40 .20

Classic Automobiles — A753

1984, Nov. 25
2748 A753 1c 1909 Morgan .20 .20
2749 A753 2c 1922 Austin .20 .20
2750 A753 5c 1903 De Dion-
Bouton .20 .20
2751 A753 20c 1908 Ford Model
T .95 .20
2752 A753 30c 1885 Benz 1.50 .35
2753 A753 50c 1910 Benz 2.75 .70
Nos. 2748-2753 (6) 5.80 1.85

Postal Museum, 20th Anniv. — A754

1985, Jan. 2   *Perf. 13x12½*
2754 A754 20c multi   .75   .25

Portrait of Celia Sanchez, by E. Escobedo
A755

1985, Jan. 11   *Perf. 13*
2755 A755 5c multi   .40   .20

Celia Sanchez (1920-1980), party leader.

PORTO '85, Intl. Pigeon Exhibition — A756

1985, Jan. 23
2756 A756 20c multi   1.25   .25

1986 World Cup Soccer Championships, Mexico — A757

Athletes and Flags of previous host nations.

1985, Jan. 25
2757	A757	1c Chile, 1962	.20	.20
2758	A757	2c Great Britain, 1966	.20	.20
2759	A757	3c Mexico, 1970	.20	.20
2760	A757	4c Federal Republic of Germany, 1974	.25	.20
2761	A757	5c Argentina, 1978	.25	.20
2762	A757	30c Spain, 1982	1.40	.50
2763	A757	50c Sweden, 1958	2.25	.65
		Nos. 2757-2763 (7)	4.75	2.15

Souvenir Sheet
Perf. 12½
2764 A757 1p Mexico, 1986   4.00   2.00

No. 2764 contains one 40x32mm stamp.

Bacanao Natl. Park — A758

Dinosaurs.

1985, Feb. 14   *Perf. 13x12½*
2765	A758	1c Pteranodon	.30	.20
2766	A758	2c Brontosaurus	.30	.20
2767	A758	4c Iguanodontus	.30	.20
2768	A758	5c Estegosaurus	.30	.20
2769	A758	8c Monoclonius	.50	.20
2770	A758	30c Corythosaurus	1.50	.50
2771	A758	50c Tyrannosaurus	2.75	.70
		Nos. 2765-2771 (7)	5.95	2.20

13th Congress of the Postal Unions of the Americas, Havana — A759

Design: Uruguay #196, congress emblem and Brazil #287.

1985, Mar. 11   *Perf. 12½x12*
2772 A759 20c multi   2.50   .70

ESPAMER '85 — A760

Indian activities: 1c, Playing ball. 2c, Medicine man preparing calumet and other ritual items. 5c, Net and spear fishing. 20c, Potter. 30c, Hunting. 50c, Hollowing-out canoe, decorating paddle. 1p, Cooking.

1985, Mar. 19   *Perf. 12½x13*
2773	A760	1c multi	.20	.20
2774	A760	2c multi	.20	.20
2775	A760	5c multi	.40	.20
2776	A760	20c multi	.40	.25
2777	A760	30c multi	.65	.40
2778	A760	50c multi	2.75	.80
		Nos. 2773-2778 (6)	4.60	2.05

Souvenir Sheet
Perf. 12½
2779 A760 1p multi   5.00   2.50

No. 2779 contains one 32x40mm stamp. An imperf. souvenir sheet exists containing Nos. 2773-2779.

Cosmonauts' Day — A761

Designs: 2c, Spacecraft orbiting Moon. 3c, Two spacecraft. 10c, Space walkers linked. 13c, Space walkers welding. 20c, *Vostok 2.* 50c, *Lunokhod 1* moon vehicle.

1985, Apr. 12   *Perf. 13x12½*
2780	A761	2c multi	.20	.20
2781	A761	3c multi	.20	.20
2782	A761	10c multi	.45	.20
2783	A761	13c multi	.65	.20
2784	A761	20c multi	.75	.25
2785	A761	50c multi	2.50	.70
		Nos. 2780-2785 (6)	4.75	1.75

12th Youth and Students Festival, Moscow A762

1985, Apr. 19   *Perf. 13*
2786 A762 30c Lenin Mausoleum   .65   .50

Stamp Day Type of 1984

Mural, by R. Rodriguez Radillo (1967), details: 20c, Roman charioteer (courier of *Cursus Publicus*). 35c, Medieval nobleman, monks (monastic messenger mail).

1985, Apr. 24   *Perf. 13x12½*
2787	A733	20c multi	.80	.25
2788	A733	35c multi	1.10	.40

Mothers' Day — A763

1985, May 2   *Perf. 13*
2789	A763	1c Peonies	.20	.20
2790	A763	4c Carnations	.20	.20
2791	A763	5c Dahlias	.20	.20
2792	A763	13c Roses	.45	.20
2793	A763	30c Roses, diff.	.75	.20
2794	A763	50c Tulips	2.00	.55
		Nos. 2789-2794 (6)	3.80	1.55

50th Death Anniv. of Antonio Guiteras and Carlos Aponte, Revolutionaries — A764

1985, May 9   *Perf. 12½x12*
2795 A764 5c multi   .25   .25

End of WWII, 40th Anniv. A765

1985, May 10
2796	A765	5c shown	.20	.20
2797	A765	20c Soviet memorial, Berlin-Treptow	.65	.30
2798	A765	30c Dove	1.10	.55
		Nos. 2796-2798 (3)	1.95	1.05

Souvenir Sheet

ARGENTINA '85, Buenos Aires — A766

1985, June 5   *Perf. 13½x13*
2799 A766 1p *Vulture gryphus*   4.50   2.25

Motorcycle, Cent. — A767

1985, June 28   *Perf. 13*
2800	A767	2c 1885 Daimler	.20	.20
2801	A767	5c 1910 Kaiser Tricycle	.25	.20
2802	A767	10c 1925 Fanomobile	.55	.20
2803	A767	30c 1926 Mars A20	1.50	.30
2804	A767	50c 1936 Simson BSW	2.75	.70
		Nos. 2800-2804 (5)	5.25	1.60

Development of Health Care Since the Revolution — A768

1985, July 18   *Perf. 12½x12*
2805 A768 5c Hospitals   .25   .20

Federation of Cuban Women (FMC), 25th Anniv. — A769

1985, Aug. 23
2806 A769 5c multi   .25   .20

No. 2806 printed se-tenant with label picturing federation emblem.

Universiade Games, Japan — A770

1985, Aug. 27   *Perf. 13*
2807 A770 50c multi   1.75   .55

1st Havana Declaration, 25th Anniv. — A771

1985, Sept. 2
2808 A771 5c Jose Marti statue, revolutionaries .40 .20

Souvenir Sheet

ITALIA '85 — A772

1985, Sept. 25 Perf. 12½
2809 A772 1p Roman galley 5.00 2.50

Revolutionary Defense Committees (CDR), 25th Anniv. — A773

1985, Sept. 28 Perf. 13
2810 A773 5c multi .25 .20

Aquarium Fish — A774

1985, Sept. 30 Litho.
2811 A774 1c Centropyge argi .25 .20
2812 A774 3c Holacanthus tricolor .25 .20
2813 A774 5c Chaetodon capistratus .25 .20
2814 A774 10c Chaetodon sedentarius .40 .25
2815 A774 20c Chaetodon ocellatus .95 .50
2816 A774 50c Holacanthus ciliaris 2.40 1.60
Nos. 2811-2816 (6) 4.50 2.95

Communist Party Central Committee, 20th Anniv. — A775

1985, Oct. 1
2817 A775 5c multi .40 .20

Souvenir Sheet

EXFILNA '85 — A776

1985, Oct. 18
2818 A776 1p Spain No. C45, Cuba No. 387 5.00 2.50

UN, 40th Anniv. — A777

1985, Oct. 24
2819 A777 20c multi .90 .25

Sites on the UNESCO World Heritage List — A778

Designs: 2c, Plaza Vieja, 16th cent. 5c, Royal Army Castle, c. 1558. 20c, Havana Cathedral, c. 1748. 30c, Captains-General Palace (Havana City Museum), 1776. 50c, The Temple, 1827.

1985, Nov. 25
2820 A778 2c multi .25 .20
2821 A778 5c multi .25 .20
2822 A778 20c multi .95 .25
2823 A778 30c multi 1.50 .45
2824 A778 50c multi 2.40 .60
Nos. 2820-2824 (5) 5.35 1.70

1986 World Cup Soccer Championships, Mexico — A779

Various athletes.

1986, Jan. 20
2825 A779 1c multi .20 .20
2826 A779 4c multi .20 .20
2827 A779 5c multi .20 .20
2828 A779 10c multi .30 .20
2829 A779 30c multi 1.10 .30
2830 A779 50c multi 1.60 .55
Nos. 2825-2830 (6) 3.60 1.65

Souvenir Sheet
Perf. 13½x13
2831 A779 1p multi 4.50 2.25
No. 2831 contains one 32x40mm stamp.

3rd Communist Party Congress, Havana — A780

1986, Feb. 4 Perf. 13
2832 A780 5c shown .20 .20
2833 A780 20c Party and natl. flags, emblem 1.25 .25

Natl. Sports Institute (INDER), 25th Anniv. A781

1986, Feb. 23
2834 A781 5c multi .30 .20

A782 A783

1986, Feb. 23
2835 A782 5c multi .30 .20
Ministry of Domestic Trade, 25th anniv.

1986, Feb. 25 Perf. 12½x12
Exotic flowers in the Botanical Gardens.
2836 A783 1c Tecomaria capensis .20 .20
2837 A783 3c Michelia champaca .20 .20
2838 A783 5c Thunbergia grandiflora .25 .20
2839 A783 8c Dendrobium phalaenopsis .30 .20
2840 A783 30c Allamanda violacea 1.25 .25
2841 A783 50c Rhodactus bleo 1.90 .40
Nos. 2836-2841 (6) 4.10 1.45

Gundlach and Birds — A784

1986, Mar. 14 Litho. Perf. 13½x13
2842 A784 1c Agelaius assimilis .30 .20
2843 A784 3c Dendroica pityophila .30 .20
2844 A784 7c Myiarchus sagrae .55 .40
2845 A784 9c Dendroica petechia gundlachi .70 .50
2846 A784 30c Geotrygon caniceps 3.00 2.00
2847 A784 50c Colaptes auratus chrysocaulosus 4.75 3.25
Nos. 2842-2847 (6) 9.60 6.55
Juan Cristobal Gundlach (d. 1896), ornithologist.

Pioneers Youth Organization, 25th Anniv. — A785

1986, Apr. 3 Perf. 13
2848 A785 5c Induction .30 .20

150th Birth Anniv. of Maximo Gomez — A786

1986, Apr. 4
2849 A786 20c multi .90 .25

A787

1986, Apr. 10 Perf. 12½
2850 A787 5c multi .40 .20
Kindergartens, 25th anniv.

A788

1986, Apr. 12 Perf. 13x13½
1st Man in Space, 25th Anniv.: 1c, Vostok and rocket designer Sergei Korolev. 2c, Yuri Gagarin, Vostok 1. 5c, Valentina Tereshkova, Vostok 6. 20c, Salyut-Soyuz space link. 30c, Capsule landing. 50c, Soyuz rocket launch. 1p, Konstantin Tsiolkovski (1857-1935), rocket scientist.

2851 A788 1c multi .20 .20
2852 A788 2c multi .20 .20
2853 A788 5c multi .20 .20
2854 A788 20c multi .60 .20
2855 A788 30c multi .80 .25
2856 A788 50c multi 1.75 .55
Nos. 2851-2856 (6) 3.75 1.60

Souvenir Sheet
Perf. 12½
2857 A788 1p multi 4.50 2.25
No. 2857 contains one 32x40mm stamp.

Natl. Flag and No. 2407 A789

1986, Apr. 19 — Perf. 13
2858 A789 5c shown .20 .20
2859 A789 20c Banners, natl. crest 1.10 .20

Bay of Pigs invasion, 25th anniv. (5c); Proclamation of Socialist Revolution, 25th anniv. (20c).

Stamp Day Type of 1984
Mural, by R. Rodriguez Radillo (1967), details.

1986, Apr. 24 — Perf. 13x12½
2860 A733 20c Mail coach, 18th-19th cent. .75 .20
2861 A733 30c Pony Express 1.00 .25

Radio Havana, 25th Anniv. — A790

1986, May 1
2862 A790 5c multi .40 .20

EXPO '86, Vancouver — A791

Locomotives: 1c, *Stourbridge Lion*, 1829, US. 4c, Stephenson's *Rocket*, 1829, GB. 5c, 1st Russian locomotive, 1845. 8c, Seguin's locomotive, 1830, France. 30c, 1st Canadian locomotive, 1836. 50c, Urban locomotive, Belgian Grand Central Rlwy., 1872. 1p, US locomotive pulling Cuban sugar train, 1837.

1986, May 2 — Litho. — Perf. 12½x12
2863 A791 1c multi .20 .20
2864 A791 4c multi .20 .20
2865 A791 5c multi .20 .20
2866 A791 8c multi .25 .20
2867 A791 30c multi .80 .30
2868 A791 50c multi 2.10 .55
Nos. 2863-2868 (6) 3.75 1.65

Souvenir Sheet
Perf. 13x13½
2869 A791 1p multi 5.00 2.50

No. 2869 contains one 40x32mm stamp.

Assoc. of Small Farmers, (ANAP), 25th Anniv. — A792

1986, May 17 — Perf. 13
2870 A792 5c multi .40 .20

Intl. Peace Year A793

1986, June 2
2871 A793 30c multi 1.00 .25

Ministry of the Interior (MININT), 25th Anniv. — A794

1986, June 6
2872 A794 5c multi .40 .20

Martin Luther King, Jr. A795

1986, June 27 — Perf. 13½x13
2873 A795 20c multi 1.00 .25

Bonifacio Byrne (d. 1936), Poet A796

1986, July 5 — Perf. 13
2874 A796 5c multi .30 .20

Cuban Union of Writers and Artists (UNEAC), 25th Anniv. — A797

Sandinista Movement in Nicaragua (FSLN), 25th Anniv. — A798

1986, July 10 — Perf. 13x12½
2875 A797 5c multi .30 .20

1986, July 23 — Perf. 13x12
Augusto Cesar Sandino and Carlos Fonseca.
2876 A798 20c multi .75 .25

Ministry of Transportation, 25th Anniv. — A799

1986, Aug. 1 — Perf. 13
2877 A799 5c multi .50 .25

7th University Games of Central America and the Caribbean A800

1986, Aug. 9
2878 A800 20c multi 1.00 .25

Souvenir Sheet

STOCKHOLMIA '86 — A801

Designs: a, 2c Mambi Revolutionary stamp of 1897. b, Sweden Type A7, cancellation.

1986, Aug. 28 — Perf. 12½
2879 A801 Sheet of 2 4.50 2.25
a.-b. 50c multi

Nonaligned Countries Movement, 25th Anniv. — A802

1986, Sept. 1 — Perf. 13½x13
2880 A802 50c multi 2.00 .45

Orchids — A803

1986, Sept. 15 — Perf. 12½
2881 A803 1c *Cattleya hardyana* .20 .20
2882 A803 4c *Brassolaelio cattleya* .20 .20
2883 A803 5c *Phalaenopsis marget moses* .25 .20
2884 A803 10c *Laelio cattleya prism palette* .30 .20
2885 A803 30c *Phalaenopsis violacea* 1.25 .30
2886 A803 50c *Disa uniflora* 1.90 .50
Nos. 2881-2886 (6) 4.10 1.60

Latin American History — A804

Pre-Columbian artifacts: No. 2887, Mayan dwelling and votive jade sculpture. No. 2888, Inca vase and Tiahuanacu sun gate (Bolivia). No. 2889, Spain No. C47, discovery of America 500th anniv. emblem, scroll. No. 2890, Diaguitan duck-shaped pitcher and Pucara de Quitor ruins (Chile). No. 2891, San Agustin Archaeological Park megaliths and Quimbayan sculpture (Colombia). No. 2892, Moler grinding stone and Chorotega ceramic figurine. No. 2893, Tabaco idol and Indian

dwelling (Cuba). No. 2894, Spain No. C38. No. 2895, Taino dwelling and chair (Dominica). No. 2896, Tolita statue and Ingapirca Castle ruins. No. 2897, Maya vase and Tikal Temple (Guatemala). No. 2898, Copan ruins and Maya idol. No. 2899, Spain No. C37. No. 2900, Chichen Itza Temple and Zapotecan urn (Mexico). No. 2901, Punta de Zapote megaliths and Ometepe ceramic figurine. No. 2902, Tonosi lidded ceramic bowl and Barriles monoliths. No. 2903, Ruins at Machu-Picchu and Inca statue (Peru). No. 2904, Spain No. C49. No. 2905, Teepees and triangular sculpture (Puerto Rico). No. 2906, Fertility statue from Santa Ana and Santo Domingo Cave.

1986, Oct. 12 — Perf. 13
2887 A804 1c multi .20 .20
2888 A804 1c multi .20 .20
2889 A804 1c multi .20 .20
2890 A804 1c multi .20 .20
2891 A804 1c multi .20 .20
a. Strip of 5, Nos. 2887-2891 1.00 1.00
2892 A804 5c multi .20 .20
2893 A804 5c multi .20 .20
2894 A804 5c multi .20 .20
2895 A804 5c multi .20 .20
2896 A804 5c multi .20 .20
a. Strip of 5, Nos. 2892-2896 1.00 1.00
2897 A804 10c multi .30 .20
2898 A804 10c multi .30 .20
2899 A804 10c multi .30 .20
2900 A804 10c multi .30 .20
2901 A804 10c multi .30 .20
a. Strip of 5, Nos. 2897-2901 1.50 1.00
2902 A804 20c multi .70 .30
2903 A804 20c multi .70 .30
2904 A804 20c multi .70 .30
2905 A804 20c multi .70 .30
2906 A804 20c multi .70 .30
a. Strip of 5, Nos. 2902-2906 3.50 1.50
Nos. 2887-2906 (20) 7.00 4.50

Discovery of America, 500th anniv. (in 1992). See Nos. 2966-2985, 3065-3084, 3253-3272, 3463-3466.

Intl. Brigades, Spain, 50th Anniv. — A805

1986, Oct. 14 — Perf. 12½x12
2907 A805 30c multi .75 .35

Paintings in the Natl. Museum A806

Designs: 2c, *Two Children*, by Gutierrez de la Vega, vert. 4c, *Sed*, by Jean-Georges Vibert. 6c, *Virgin and Child*, by Niccolo Abbate, vert. 10c, *Bullfight*, by Eugenio de Lucas Velazquez. 30c, *The Five Senses*, anonymous. 50c, *Arrival at Thomops Castle*, by Jean Louis Ernest.

1986, Nov. 5 — Perf. 13
2908 A806 2c multi .25 .20
2909 A806 4c multi .25 .20
2910 A806 6c multi .25 .20
2911 A806 10c multi .40 .20
2912 A806 30c multi 1.10 .30
2913 A806 50c multi 1.90 .55
Nos. 2908-2913 (6) 4.15 1.65

Anniversaries — A807

1986, Dec. 2 — Litho. — Perf. 12½
2914 A807 5c *Granma* .45 .20

Size: 26x38mm
2915 A807 20c Soldier, rifle, flag 1.50 .20

Granma Landings, 30th anniv. (5c); Revolutionary Armed Forces, 30th anniv. (20c).

Scholarship Program, 25th
Anniv. — A808

1986, Dec. 22   *Perf. 13*
2916 A808 5c Guevara, students   .30   .20

Natl. Literacy
Campaign, 25th
Anniv. — A809

1986, Dec. 25   *Perf. 13x12½*
2917 A809 5c Marti, man learning to write   .30   .20

Siege
of La
Plata,
30th
Anniv.
A810

1987, Jan. 17   *Perf. 12½x12*
2918 A810 5c Map, revolutionaries   .30   .20

Paintings
in the
Natl.
Museum
A811

3c, *Gypsy*, by Joaquin Sorolla. 5c, *Sir Wal-
ter Scott*, by Sir John W. Gordon. 10c, *Farm
Meadows*, by Alfred de Breanski. 20c, *Still-life*,
by Isaac van Duynen. 30c, *Landscape with
Figures*, by Francesco Zuccarelli. 40c, *The
Failure* (defeated bullfighter), by Ignacio
Zuloaga.

1987, Feb. 5   *Perf. 13*
2919 A811 3c multi, vert.   .25   .20
2920 A811 5c multi, vert.   .25   .20
2921 A811 10c multi   .40   .20
2922 A811 20c multi   1.00   .25
2923 A811 30c multi   1.10   .30
2924 A811 40c multi, vert.   1.60   .50
    Nos. 2919-2924 (6)   4.60   1.65

Siege of the Presidential Palace, 30th
Anniv. — A812

1987, Mar. 13   *Perf. 12½x12*
2925 A812 5c Palace, van,
Echeverra   .30   .20

Lazarus Ludwig Zamenhof and Russia
Type A77 — A813

1987, Mar. 16   *Perf. 13½x13*
2926 A813 30c multi   1.00   .30

      Esperanto, cent.

Souvenir Sheet

EXFILNA '87, 10th Natl. Stamp
Exposition, Holguin — A814

1987, Mar. 28   *Perf. 13x13½*
2927 A814 1p Nos. 552, C129   4.50   2.25

25th Anniv. and 5th Cong. of the
Youth Communist League
(U.J.C.) — A815

1987, Apr. 4   *Perf. 13*
2928 A815 5c multi   .30   .20

Intercosmos, 20th
Anniv. — A816

1987, Apr. 12   Litho.   *Perf. 12½x12*
2929 A816 3c *Intercosmos 1*   .20   .20
2930 A816 5c *Intercosmos 2*   .20   .20
2931 A816 10c *TD*   .30   .20
2932 A816 20c *Cosmos 93*   .75   .25
2933 A816 30c *Prognoz*   1.00   .30
2934 A816 50c *Vostok 3*   1.60   .55
    Nos. 2929-2934 (6)   4.05   1.70

Souvenir Sheet
Perf. 13½x13

2935 A816 1p Rocket, *Vostok 3*   4.50   2.25
   No. 2935 contains one 32x40mm stamp.

Stamp
Day
A817

Stamped covers and canceled stamps.

1987, Apr. 24   *Perf. 13*
2936 A817 30c Havana, 1890   1.25   .30
2937 A817 50c Santiago de Cu-
ba, 1869   2.10   .60

Mothers'
Day — A818

   Various dahlias and roses.

1987, May 2
2938 A818 3c multi   .20   .20
2939 A818 5c multi   .20   .20
2940 A818 10c multi   .25   .20
2941 A818 13c multi   .30   .20
2942 A818 30c multi   .70   .25
2943 A818 50c multi   1.25   .50
    Nos. 2938-2943 (6)   2.90   1.55

Bone-lengthening Procedure (Femur in
Frame) — A819

1987, May 4
2944 A819 5c multi   .30   .20

   ORTOPEDIA '87, medical congress for
orthopedists from Spanish and Portuguese-
speaking countries, Havana.

Cuban
Broadcasting
and Television
Institute, 25th
Anniv. — A820

1987, May 24   *Perf. 13*
2945 A820 5c multi   .30   .20

Battle
of
Uvero,
30th
Anniv.
A821

1987, May 28   *Perf. 13½x13*
2946 A821 5c Views of monument, Sierra
Maestra Mts.   .30   .20

CAPEX
'87 — A822

   Natl. flags, stamps and 19th cent. mail carriers pictured on cigarette cards: 3c, Messenger, llamas and Bolivia Type A9. 5c, Early p.o.,
automobile and France Type A17. 10c, Messengers riding elephants and Thailand Type
A2. 20c, Messenger riding camel and stamp of
Egypt, 1879. 30c, Mail troika and stamp of
Russia. 50c, Post rider and stamp of Indo-
China. 1p, Post rider and Mambi Revolutionary
stamp.

1987, June 15   *Perf. 12½x13*
2947 A822 3c multi   .20   .20
2948 A822 5c multi   .20   .20
2949 A822 10c multi   .25   .20
2950 A822 20c multi   .50   .25
2951 A822 30c multi   .70   .25
2952 A822 50c multi   1.25   .50
    Nos. 2947-2952 (6)   3.10   1.60

Souvenir Sheet
Perf. 13½x13

2953 A822 1p multi   4.50   2.25
   No. 2953 contains one 32x40mm stamp.

Dinosaur
Exhibits,
Bacanao
Natl.
Park
A823

1987, June 25   *Perf. 13*
2954 A823 3c multi   .25   .20
2955 A823 5c multi   .25   .20
2956 A823 10c multi   .40   .20
2957 A823 20c multi   .90   .25
2958 A823 35c multi   1.40   .30
2959 A823 40c multi   1.60   .40
    Nos. 2954-2959 (6)   4.80   1.55

Frank Pais (d. 1957), Teacher and
Student Leader — A824

1987, July 30   *Perf. 12½x12*
2960 A824 5c Pais, Rafael Maria
Mendive Universi-
ty   .30   .20

10th Pan American Games,
Indianapolis — A825

1987, Aug. 8
2961 A825 50c multi   1.75   .45

   Printed se-tenant with inscribed label picturing the 1991 Havana Games character
trademark.

Siege
of
Cienfuegos,
30th
Anniv. — A826

1987, Sept. 5   *Perf. 13*
2962 A826 5c Memorial   .30   .20

Souvenir Sheet

HAFNIA '87, Denmark — A827

1987, Sept. 16 **Perf. 13½x13**
2963 A827 1p Danish mailman, 1887, Type A6   4.50 2.25

Souvenir Sheet

ESPAMER '87, La Coruna, Oct. 2-12 — A828

1987, Oct. 2
2964 A828 1p La Coruna Port, 1525   4.50 2.25

20th Heroic Guerrillas Day — A829

1987, Oct. 8 **Perf. 12½x12**
2965 A829 50c Coins, #1364   1.25 .55

Latin American History Type of 1986

Indians and birds: #2966, Tehuelche Indian of Argentina, *Habia rubica.* #2967, *Ramphastos cuvieri,* Tibirica Indian of Brazil. #2968, Spain #C31 & discovery of America 500th anniv. emblem. #2969, *Vulture gryphus,* Lautaro Indian of Chile. #2970, Calarca Indian of Colombia, *Opisthocomus hoazin.* #2971, *Priotelus temnurus,* Hatuey Indian of Cuba. #2972, *Columbigallina passerina,* Enriquillo Indian of the Dominican Republic. #2973, Spain #427. #2974, *Semnornis ramphastinus,* Indian of Ecuador. #2975, *Pharomachrus mocinno,* Tecum Uman Indian of Guatemala. #2976, Anacaona Indian of Haiti, *Aramus guarauna.* #2977, Lempira Indian of Honduras, *Diglossa baritula.* #2978, Spain #C42. #2979, *Onychorhinchus mexicanus,* Cuauhtemoc Indian of Mexico. #2980, *Setofaga picta,* Nicarao Indian of Nicaragua. #2981, *Rupicola peruviana,* Atahualpa Indian of Peru. #2982, Atlacatl Indian of El Salvador, *Bluteo jamaicensis.* #2983, Spain #432. #2984, Abayuba Indian of Uruguay, *Phytotoma rutila.* #2985, Guaycaypuro Indian of Venezuela, *Ara arauna.*

1987, Oct. 12 **Perf. 13**
2966 A804 1c multi   .20 .20
2967 A804 1c multi   .20 .20
2968 A804 1c multi   .20 .20
2969 A804 1c multi   .20 .20
2970 A804 1c multi   .20 .20
   a. Strip of 5, Nos. 2966-2970   1.00 1.00
2971 A804 5c multi   .40 .20
2972 A804 5c multi   .40 .20
2973 A804 5c multi   .40 .20
2974 A804 5c multi   .40 .20
2975 A804 5c multi   .40 .20
   a. Strip of 5, Nos. 2971-2975   2.00 1.00
2976 A804 10c multi   .65 .20
2977 A804 10c multi   .65 .20
2978 A804 10c multi   .65 .20
2979 A804 10c multi   .65 .20
2980 A804 10c multi   .65 .20
   a. Strip of 5, Nos. 2976-2980   3.25 1.00
2981 A804 20c multi   1.00 .40
2982 A804 20c multi   1.00 .40
2983 A804 20c multi   1.00 .40
2984 A804 20c multi   1.00 .40
2985 A804 20c multi   1.00 .40
   a. Strip of 5, Nos. 2981-2985   5.00 2.00
   Nos. 2966-2985 (20)   11.25 5.00

Discovery of America, 500th anniv. (in 1992). *Vultur* is spelled incorrectly on No. 2969.

October Revolution, Russia, 70th Anniv. — A830

1987, Nov. 7 **Perf. 12½x12**
2986 A830 30c Soviet spacecraft, Russia No. 379   1.00 .25

Cuban Railway, 150th Anniv. — A831

Stamps on stamps.

1987, Nov. 19 **Perf. 13x12½**
2987 A831 3c No. 453   .20 .20
2988 A831 5c No. 1061   .20 .20
2989 A831 10c No. 2010   .25 .20
2990 A831 20c No. 2011   .55 .20
2991 A831 35c No. 2360   1.00 .30
2992 A831 40c No. 2361   1.25 .40
   Nos. 2987-2992 (6)   3.45 1.50

Souvenir Sheet
Perf. 13x13½
2993 A831 1p No. 355   4.75 2.25

No. 2993 contains 40x32mm one stamp. An imperf. sheet containing Nos. 2987-2992 exists, inscribed to promote the 17th Pan American Railway Congress. Value, $7.

San Alejandro Art School, 170th Anniv. — A832

Paintings: 1c, *Landscape,* by Domingo Ramos. 2c, *Portrait of Rodriguez Morey,* by Eugenio Gonzalez Olivera. 3c, *Landscape with Malangas and Palm Trees,* by Valentin Sanz Carta. 5c, *Wagons,* by Eduardo Morales. 10c, *Portrait of Elena Herrera,* by Armando Menocal, vert. 30c, *Rape of Dejanira,* by Miguel Melero, vert. 50c, *The Card Player,* by Leopoldo Romanach.

1988, Jan. 12 **Perf. 13x12½, 12½x13**
2994 A832 1c multi   .20 .20
2995 A832 2c multi   .20 .20
2995A A832 3c multi   .20 .20
2996 A832 5c multi   .20 .20
2997 A832 10c multi   .30 .20
2998 A832 30c multi   .85 .25
2999 A832 50c multi   1.50 .50
   Nos. 2994-2999 (7)   3.45 1.75

Poisonous Mushrooms A833

1988, Feb. 15 **Perf. 13**
3000 A833 1c *Boletus satanas*   .20 .20
3001 A833 2c *Amanita citrina*   .20 .20
3002 A833 3c *Tyloplus felleus*   .25 .20
3003 A833 5c *Paxillus involutus*   .25 .20

3004 A833 10c *Inocybe patouillardii*   .55 .25
3005 A833 30c *Amanita muscaria*   1.50 .55
3006 A833 50c *Hypholoma fasciculare*   2.40 1.00
   Nos. 3000-3006 (7)   5.35 2.60

Radio Rebelde, 30th Anniv. — A834

1988, Feb. 24 **Perf. 12½x12**
3007 A834 5c multi   .30 .20

Monuments A835

1988 **Litho.** **Perf. 13**
3008 A835 5c Mario Munoz, Santiago de Cuba   .45 .20
3009 A835 5c Frank Pais Memorial, eternal flame   .45 .20

Battle fronts, 30th annivs. Issue dates: No. 3008, Mar. 5. No. 3009, Mar. 11.

Mothers' Day — A836

1988, Mar. 30
3010 A836 1c Red roses   .20 .20
3011 A836 2c Pale pink roses   .20 .20
3012 A836 3c Daisies   .20 .20
3013 A836 5c Dahlias   .20 .20
3014 A836 13c White roses   .30 .20
3015 A836 35c Carnations   .90 .25
3016 A836 40c Pink roses   1.10 .30
   Nos. 3010-3016 (7)   3.10 1.55

Cosmonauts' Day — A837

1988, Apr. 12
3017 A837 2c *Gorizont*   .20 .20
3018 A837 3c *Mir-Kvant* space link   .20 .20
3019 A837 4c *Signo 3*   .20 .20
3020 A837 5c Mars, space probe   .20 .20
3021 A837 10c *Phobos*   .30 .20
3022 A837 30c *Vega*   .85 .25
3023 A837 50c Spacecraft   1.50 .50
   Nos. 3017-3023 (7)   3.45 1.75

Souvenir Sheet
Perf. 13½x13
3024 A837 1p Spacecraft, diff.   4.25 2.00

No. 3024 contains one 32x40mm stamp.

Stamp Day Type of 1984

Mural, by R. Rodriguez Radillo (1967) details: 30c, Mail coach, telegraph operator. 50c, Passenger pigeon.

1988, Apr. 24 **Perf. 13x12½**
3025 A733 30c multi   1.10 .40
3026 A733 50c multi   1.90 .50

Institute for Research on Sugar Cane and Byproducts (ICIDCA), 25th Anniv. — A838

1988, May 23 **Perf. 12½x12**
3027 A838 5c multi   .40 .20

Cubana Airlines Transatlantic Flights — A839

1988, May 25
3028 A839 2c Madrid, 1948   .20 .20
3029 A839 4c Prague, 1961   .20 .20
3030 A839 5c Berlin, 1972   .20 .20
3031 A839 10c Luanda, 1975   .30 .20
3032 A839 30c Paris, 1983   1.00 .25
3033 A839 50c Moscow, 1987   1.60 .50
   Nos. 3028-3033 (6)   3.50 1.55

Souvenir Sheet

FINLANDIA '88 — A840

1988, June 1 **Perf. 12½**
3034 A840 1p Steam packet
   Furst Menschikoff 4.00 2.00

Postal Union of the Americas and Spain (UPAE) Conference on Stamps of the Americas, Havana — A841

1988, June 20 **Perf. 12½x12**
3035 A841 20c multi   1.25 .35

Beetles A842

1988, June 30 **Perf. 13**
3036 A842 1c *Megasoma elephas fabricus*   .20 .20
3037 A842 3c *Platycoelia flavoscutellata ohaus,* vert.   .20 .20
3038 A842 4c *Plusiotis argenteola bates*   .25 .20
3039 A842 5c *Heterosternus oberthuri ohaus*   .25 .20
3040 A842 10c *Odontotaenius zodiacus truqui*   .40 .20
3041 A842 35c *Chrysophora chrysochlora latreille,* vert.   1.25 .30
3042 A842 40c *Phanaeus leander waterhouse*   1.60 .50
   Nos. 3036-3042 (7)   4.15 1.80

Jose Raul Capablanca (1888-1942), Chess Champion — A843

1988, July 15   Perf. 12½x13, 13x12½
3043 A843 30c Chessmen, vert.   .65   .30
3044 A843 40c J. Corza,
               Capablanca   .90   .30
3045 A843 50c Lasker,
               Capablanca   .95   .40
3046 A843 1p Winning config-
               uration, 1921,
               vert.   2.40   .90
3047 A843 3p Portrait by E.
               Valderrama,
               vert.   7.25 2.40
3048 A843 5p Chessmen,
               Capablanca   13.00 4.50
      Nos. 3043-3048 (6)   25.15 8.80

Souvenir Sheets
3049   Sheet of 2   1.60   .80
  a.   A843 30c No. 464, vert.   .60   .40
  b.   like No. 3043, size: 32x40mm .60   .40
3050   Sheet of 2   2.10 1.05
  a.   A843 40c No. 465   .70   .40
  b.   like No. 3044, size: 40x32mm .70   .40
3051   Sheet of 2   3.00 1.50
  a.   A843 50c No. C44   .75   .50
  b.   like No. 3045, size: 40x32mm .75   .50
3052   Sheet of 2   5.50 2.75
  a.   A843 1p No. 464, vert.   2.10 1.00
  b.   like No. 3046, size: 32x40mm 2.10 1.00
3053   Sheet of 2   16.00 8.00
  a.   A843 3p No. C46, vert.   6.25 3.00
  b.   like No. 3047, size: 32x40mm 6.25 3.00
3054   Sheet of 2   27.50 13.50
  a.   A843 5p No. C45, vert.   10.50 5.00
  b.   like No. 3048, size: 32x40mm 10.50 5.00
      Nos. 3049-3054 (6)   55.70 27.60

Attack on Moncada Barracks, 35th Anniv. A844

1988, July 26   Perf. 13
3055 A844 5c blk, yel ocher &
            red   .30   .20

Souvenir Sheet

PRAGA '88 — A845

1988, Aug. 26   Perf. 12½
3056 A845 1p Czechoslovakia
            #45   4.00 2.00

Czechoslovakian postage stamps, 70th anniv.

Revolutionary Invasion Force, 30th Anniv. — A846

1988, Aug. 31   Perf. 12½x12
3057 A846 5c multi   .30   .20

World Marxist Review, 30th Anniv. A847

1988, Sept. 1   Perf. 13
3058 A847 30c multi   1.25   .35

Locomotives — A848

1988, Sept. 19   Perf. 12½x13
3059 A848 20c Stephenson's
               Rocket, 1837   .50   .25
3060 A848 30c Miller, US,
               1839   .95   .45
3061 A848 50c La Junta   2.00   .90
3062 A848 1p J.G. Brill trol-
               ley, US, 1922   3.50 1.25
3063 A848 2p TEM 4K,
               USSR, c.
               1960   6.75 3.00
3064 A848 5p CAP 9 electric,
               c. 1988   15.00 8.00
      Nos. 3059-3064 (6)   28.70 13.85

Latin American History Type of 1986

Natl. arms & patriots: #3065, San Martin, Argentina. #3066, M.A. Padilla, Bolivia. #3067, #390 & discovery of America 500th anniv. emblem. #3068, Tiradentes, Brazil. #3069, O'Higgins, Chile. #3070, A. Narino, Colombia. #3071, Marti, Cuba. #3072, #391 & emblem. #3073, Duarte, Dominican Republic. #3074, Sucre, Ecuador. #3075, M.J. Arce, El Salvador. #3076, Dessalines, Haiti. #3077, #C36 & emblem. #3078, Hidalgo, Mexico. #3079, J.D. Estrada, Nicaragua. #3080, Diaz, Paraguay. #3081, F. Bolognesi, Peru. #3082, #C37 & emblem. #3083, Artigas, Uruguay. #3084, Bolivar, Venezuela.

1988, Oct. 12   Perf. 13
3065 A804 1c multi   .20   .20
3066 A804 1c multi   .20   .20
3067 A804 1c multi   .20   .20
3068 A804 1c multi   .20   .20
3069 A804 1c multi   .20   .20
  a.   Strip of 5, Nos. 3065-3069 1.00   .50
3070 A804 5c multi   .20   .20
3071 A804 5c multi   .20   .20
3072 A804 5c multi   .20   .20
3073 A804 5c multi   .20   .20
3074 A804 5c multi   .20   .20
  a.   Strip of 5, Nos. 3070-3074 1.00   .50
3075 A804 10c multi   .25   .20
3076 A804 10c multi   .25   .20
3077 A804 10c multi   .25   .20
3078 A804 10c multi   .25   .20
3079 A804 10c multi   .25   .20
  a.   Strip of 5, Nos. 3075-3079 1.50   .75
3080 A804 20c multi   .45   .20
3081 A804 20c multi   .45   .20
3082 A804 20c multi   .45   .20
3083 A804 20c multi   .45   .20
3084 A804 20c multi   .45   .20
  a.   Strip of 5, Nos. 3080-3084 2.25 1.25
  b.   Sheet of 20, Nos. 3065-
         3084   7.50 7.50
      Nos. 3065-3084 (20)   5.50 4.00

Discovery of America, 500th anniv. (in 1992).

Havana Museum, 20th Anniv. — A849

Design: Captain-General's Palace and Maces of Municipal Havana.

1988, Oct. 16   Litho.   Perf. 12½x12
3085 A849 5c multi + label   .40   .20

Anniversaries — A850

1988, Oct. 28   Perf. 13
3086 A850 5c Swan Lake   .60   .20
3087 A850 5c Theater in 1838
               and 1988   .60   .20
  a.   Pair, Nos. 3086-3087   1.25   .40

Natl. Ballet, 40th anniv. (No. 3086); Grand Theater of Havana, 150th anniv. (No. 3087).

Intl. Literacy Year A851

1988, Dec. 5
3088 A851 5c multi   .30   .20

UN Declaration of Human Rights, 40th Anniv. — A851a

1988, Dec. 10
3088A A851a 30c multi   1.25   .35

Battle of Santa Clara, 30th Anniv. — A852

1988, Dec. 28   Perf. 13x12½
3089 A852 30c Monument, Che
               Guevara Plaza   1.25   .35

30th Anniv. of the Revolution — A853

1989, Jan. 1   Perf. 13
3090 A853 5c multi   .20   .20
3091 A853 20c multi   .65   .20
3092 A853 30c multi   .85   .25
3093 A853 50c multi   1.75   .50
      Nos. 3090-3093 (4)   3.45 1.15

Edible Mushrooms — A854

1989, Jan. 10
3094 A854 2c Pleurotus levis   .20   .20
3095 A854 3c Pleurotus
               floridanus   .20   .20
3096 A854 5c Amanita caesa-
               rea   .20   .20
3097 A854 10c Lentinus cubensis .45   .20
3098 A854 40c Pleurotus os-
               treatus (brown)   1.60   .40
3099 A854 50c Pleurotus os-
               treatus (yellow) 1.75   .50
      Nos. 3094-3099 (6)   4.40 1.70
      2c, 3c, 5c, 40c, 50c, vert.

Souvenir Sheet

INDIA '89 — A855

1989, Jan. 20
3100 A855 1p Indian River Post,
               1858   4.00 2.00

Central Organization of Cuban Trade Unions (CTC), 50th Anniv. — A856

1989, Jan. 28   Perf. 12½
3101 A856 5c No. 2477, CTC
               emblem   .30   .20

Butterflies A857

1989, Feb. 15
3102 A857 1c Metamorpho dido   .20   .20
3103 A857 3c Callithea saphhira .20   .20
3104 A857 5c Papilio zagreus   .20   .20
3105 A857 10c Mynes sestia   .30   .20
3106 A857 30c Papilio dardanus 1.40   .30
3107 A857 50c Catagranma
               sorana   2.50   .65
      Nos. 3102-3107 (6)   4.80 1.75

1990 World Cup Soccer Championships, Italy — A858

Various athletes.

1989, Mar. 15   Perf. 13
3108 A858 1c multi   .20   .20
3109 A858 3c multi, diff.   .20   .20
3110 A858 5c multi, diff.   .20   .20
3111 A858 10c multi, diff.   .25   .20
3112 A858 30c multi, diff.   1.25   .25
3113 A858 50c multi, diff.   2.10   .40
      Nos. 3108-3113 (6)   4.20 1.45

Souvenir Sheet
Perf. 12½
3114 A858 1p multi, diff., horiz. 4.00 2.00

No. 3114 contains one 40x32mm stamp.

Natl. Revolutionary Police (PNR), 30th Anniv. — A859

1989, Mar. 23   *Perf. 13*
3115 A859 5c multi   .30 .20

Cosmonauts' Day — A860

Spacecraft and rocket mail covers: 1c, *Zodiac* and cover, Australia 1934. 3c, Lighthouse and cover, India, 1934. 5c, Cover, England, 1934. 10c, *Icarus* and cover, The Netherlands, 1935. 40c, *La Douce France* and cover, France, 1935. 50c, Rocket mail cover, Cuba, 1939.

1989, Apr. 12
3116 A860 1c multi   .20 .20
3117 A860 3c multi   .20 .20
3118 A860 5c multi   .20 .20
3119 A860 10c multi   .20 .20
3120 A860 40c multi   1.10 .40
3121 A860 50c multi   1.40 .55
    Nos. 3116-3121 (6)   3.30 1.75

Stamp Day Type of 1984

Details of mural by R. Rodriguez Radillo (1967): 30c, Mail coach, Satellite dish. 50c, Galleon, longboats, train, passenger pigeon, horses.

1989, Apr. 24   **Litho.**   *Perf. 13x12½*
3122 A733 30c multi   .65 .30
3123 A733 50c multi   4.75 2.00

Casa de Las Americas, 30th Anniv. A861

1989, Apr. 28   *Perf. 12½x13*
3124 A861 5c multi   .30 .20

Souvenir Sheet

BULGARIA '89 — A862

1989, May 1   *Perf. 12½*
3125 A862 1p Bulgaria No. 346   4.50 2.25
    58th FIP Congress and 101st anniv. of Bulgarian Railways.

Cuban Postal Code A863

1989, May 5   *Perf. 13*
3126 A863 5c multi   .30 .20

Mothers' Day — A864

Perfume bottles and flowers.

1989, May 10
3127 A864 1c Habano, tobacco   .20 .20
3128 A864 3c Violeta, violets   .20 .20
3129 A864 5c Mariposa, mariposa   .25 .20
3130 A864 13c Coral Negro, roses   .35 .20
3131 A864 30c Ala Alonso, jasmine   1.00 .30
3132 A864 50c D'Man, lemon blossoms   1.75 .70
    Nos. 3127-3132 (6)   3.75 1.80

Agrarian Reform Law, 30th Anniv. — A865

1989, May 17   *Perf. 12x12½*
3133 A865 5c multi   .30 .20

Council for Mutual Economic Assistance (CAME), 40th Anniv. A866

1989, June 1   **Litho.**   *Perf. 12½x13*
3134 A866 30c multi   1.25 .25

13th World Communist Youth and Student Festival, Pyongyang — A867

1989, July 1   **Litho.**   *Perf. 12½*
3135 A867 30c multi   1.25 .25

Souvenir Sheet

Rouget de Lisle Singing *La Marseillaise*, by Pils — A868

1989, July 7   *Perf. 13*
3136 A868 1p multi   4.00 2.00
    PHILEXFRANCE '89, French revolution bicent. and Cuban revolution 30th anniv.

BRASILIANA '89 — A869

Exotic birds.

1989, July 28   **Litho.**   *Perf. 12½*
3137 A869 1c *Ramphastos toco*   .20 .20
3138 A869 3c *Agamia agami*   .20 .20
3139 A869 5c *Eudocimus ruber*   .25 .20
3140 A869 10c *Psophia leucoptera*   .40 .20
3141 A869 35c *Harpia harpyja*   1.50 .50
3142 A869 50c *Cephatopterus ornatus*   2.00 .70
    Nos. 3137-3142 (6)   4.55 2.00

Warships A870

1989, Sept. 29   **Litho.**   *Perf. 12½*
3143 A870 1c *El Fenix*   .20 .20
3144 A870 3c *Triunfo*   .20 .20
3145 A870 5c *El Rayo*   .20 .20
3146 A870 10c *San Carlos*   .30 .20
3147 A870 30c *San Jose*   1.25 .40
3148 A870 50c *San Genaro*   1.90 .70
    Nos. 3143-3148 (6)   4.05 1.90

America Issue — A871

UPAE emblem and pre-Columbian art: 5p, Stone carving, Indians in dugout canoe. 20p, Petroglyph, Indian drawing on stone wall.

1989, Oct. 12   *Perf. 12½x12*
3149 A871 5c multi   .20 .20
3150 A871 20c multi   .80 .40

Latin American History — A872

Writers and orchids: No. 3151, Domingo Sarmiento (1811-1888), Argentine educator, and *Govenia utriculata*. No. 3152, Joaquim Maria Machado de Assis (1839-1908), Brazilian novelist, and *Laelia grandis*. No. 3153, Salvador No. 69 and discovery of America anniv. emblem. No. 3154, Jorge Isaacs (1837-1895), Colombian novelist, and *Cattleya trianae*. No. 3155, Alejo Carpentier, Cuban writer, and *Cochleanthes discolor*. No. 3156, Pablo Neruda (1904-1973), Chilean poet, and *Oxalis adenophylla*. No. 3157, Pedro Urena, Dominican writer, and *Epidendrum fragrans*. No. 3158, Salvador No. 86 and anniv. emblem. No. 3159, Juan Montalvo (1832-1889), Ecuadorian satirist, and *Miltonia vexillaria*. No. 3160, Miguel Asturias (1899-1974), Guatemalan writer awarded the 1966 Lenin Peace Prize and 1967 Nobel Prize for literature, and *Odontoglossum rossii*. No. 3161, Jose C. del Valle, Honduran writer, and *Laelia anceps*. No. 3162, Alfonso Reyes (1889-1959), Mexican poet, and *Laelia anceps alba*. No. 3163, Salvador No. 87 and anniv. emblem. No. 3164, Ruben Dario (1867-1917), Nicaraguan poet, and *Brassavola acaulis*. No. 3165, Belisario Porras (1856-1942), president of Panama, and *Pescatorea celina*. No. 3166, Ricardo Palma (1833-1919), Peruvian writer, and *Coryanthes leucocorys*. No. 3167, Eugenio Maria de Hostos (1839-1903), Puerto Rican writer, and *Guzmania berteroniana*. No. 3168, Salvador No. 88 and anniv. emblem. No. 3169, Jose E. Rodo (1872-1917), Uruguayan philosopher, essayist, and *Cypella hebertii*. No. 3170, Romulo Gallegos, Venezuelan writer, and *Cattleya mossiae*.

1989, Oct. 27   **Litho.**   *Perf. 13*
3151 A872 1c multicolored   .20 .20
3152 A872 1c multicolored   .20 .20
3153 A872 1c multicolored   .20 .20
3154 A872 1c multicolored   .20 .20
3155 A872 1c multicolored   .20 .20
   a.   Strip of 5, Nos. 3151-3155   1.00 .50
3156 A872 5c multicolored   .20 .20
3157 A872 5c multicolored   .20 .20
3158 A872 5c multicolored   .20 .20
3159 A872 5c multicolored   .20 .20
3160 A872 5c multicolored   .20 .20
   a.   Strip of 5, Nos. 3156-3160   1.00 .50
3161 A872 10c multicolored   .35 .20
3162 A872 10c multicolored   .35 .20
3163 A872 10c multicolored   .35 .20
3164 A872 10c multicolored   .35 .20
3165 A872 10c multicolored   .35 .20
   a.   Strip of 5, Nos. 3161-3165   2.00 1.00
3166 A872 20c multicolored   .55 .25
3167 A872 20c multicolored   .55 .25
3168 A872 20c multicolored   .55 .25
3169 A872 20c multicolored   .55 .25
3170 A872 20c multicolored   .55 .25
   a.   Strip of 5, Nos. 3166-3170   3.00 1.50
   b.   Sheet of 20, #3151-3170   8.00 8.00
    Nos. 3151-3170 (20)   6.50 4.25

Discovery of America 500th anniv. (in 1992).

Disappearance of Camilo Cienfuegos, 30th Anniv. — A873

1989, Oct. 28
3171 A873 5c multicolored   .30 .20

Founding of the City of Trinidad, 475th Anniv. A874

1989, Nov. 6   *Perf. 12½x13*
3172 A874 5c multicolored   .30 .20

Paintings in the Natl. Museum — A875

Designs: 1p, *Familiar Scene*, by Antoine Faivre. 2p, *Flowers*, by Emile Jean Horace Vernet (1789-1863). 5p, *The Judgement of Paris*, by Charles Le Brun (1619-1690). 20p, *Outskirts of Nice*, by Eugene Louis Boudin (1824-1898). 30p, *Portrait of Sarah Bernhardt*, by G.J.V. Clairin. 50p, *Fishermen in Port*, by C.J. Vernet.

Perf. 12½, 12½x13 (30p)
1989, Nov. 20 Litho.
Size of 30p: 36x46mm

3173	A875	1c multicolored	.20	.20
3174	A875	2c multicolored	.20	.20
3175	A875	5c multicolored	.20	.20
3176	A875	20c multicolored	.85	.20
3177	A875	30c multicolored	1.10	.20
3178	A875	50c multicolored	2.25	.55
		Nos. 3173-3178 (6)	4.80	1.55

11th Pan-American Games, Havana, 1991 — A876

1989, Dec. 15 Litho. **Perf. 12½**

3179	A876	5c Cycling	.25	.20
3180	A876	5c Fencing	.25	.20
3181	A876	5c Water polo	.25	.20
3182	A876	5c Shooting	.25	.20
3183	A876	5c Archery	.25	.20
3184	A876	20c Tennis, vert.	.65	.25
3185	A876	30c Swimming, vert.	1.10	.25
3186	A876	35c Diving, vert.	1.40	.30
3187	A876	40c Field hockey	1.50	.30
3188	A876	50c Basketball, vert.	2.25	.65
		Nos. 3179-3188 (10)	8.15	2.75

Jose Marti's *Golden Age*, Cent. — A877

1989, Dec. 20 **Perf. 13**
3189 A877 5c scar, light blue & blk .40 .20

Cuban Postal Museum, 25th Anniv. — A878

1990, Jan. 2 **Perf. 13x12½**
3190	A878	5c *Almendares*	.20	.20
3191	A878	30c Mail train	2.50	.80

Speleological Soc., 50th Anniv. — A879

1990, Jan. 15 **Perf. 12½**
3192 A879 30c multicolored 2.00 .35

1990 World Cup Soccer Championships, Italy — A880

Various Italian architecture and athletes: No. 3193a, Dribbling (in red and blue). No. 3193b, Heading (in red and green). No. 3193c, Kicking (in green). 10c, Goalie catching ball. 30c, Dribbling, diff. 50c, Kicking, diff. 1p, Goalie catching ball, diff.

1990, Jan. 30 Litho. **Perf. 12½**
3193		Strip of 3	.50	.25
a.-c.		A880 5c any single	.20	.20
3194	A880	10c multicolored	.25	.20
3195	A880	30c multicolored	1.25	.30
3196	A880	50c multicolored	2.10	.55
a.		Sheet of 6, #3193a-3193c, 3194-3196 + 3 labels	4.25	2.10
		Nos. 3193-3196 (4)	4.10	1.30

Souvenir Sheet
3197 A880 1p multicolored 3.50 1.75

No. 3193 has a continuous design picturing The Colosseum.

1992 Summer Olympics, Barcelona — A881

1990, Feb. 20 Litho. **Perf. 12½**
3198	A881	1c Baseball	.20	.20
3199	A881	4c Running	.20	.20
3200	A881	5c Basketball	.20	.20
3201	A881	10c Women's volley- ball	.45	.20
3202	A881	30c Wrestling	1.10	.30
3203	A881	50c Boxing	2.00	.65
		Nos. 3198-3203 (6)	4.15	1.75

Souvenir Sheet
3204 A881 1p High jump 4.00 2.00

Nos. 3198-3201 and 3203 are vert. No. 3204 contains one 40x32mm stamp.

75th Universal Esperanto Congress — A882

1990, Mar. 7
3205 A882 30c Tower of Babel 1.25 .35

No. 3205 printed se-tenant with inscribed label publicizing the congress.

1992 Winter Olympics, Albertville — A883

1990, Mar. 30 Litho. **Perf. 13**
3206 A883 1p multicolored 4.50 2.25

Cosmonauts' Day — A884

Spacecraft and rocket mail covers: 1c, Austria, 1932. 2c, Germany, 1933. 3c, Netherlands, 1934. 10c, Belgium, 1935. 30c, Yugoslavia, 1935. 50c, United States, 1936.

1990, Apr. 12 **Perf. 12½**
3207	A884	1c multicolored	.20	.20
3208	A884	2c multicolored	.20	.20
3209	A884	3c multicolored	.20	.20
3210	A884	10c multicolored	.25	.20
3211	A884	30c multicolored	1.10	.20
3212	A884	50c multicolored	2.00	.55
		Nos. 3207-3212 (6)	3.95	1.55

Stamp Day Type of 1984

Details of mural by R. Rodriguez Radillo (1967): 30c, Train station. 50c, Jet aircraft in flight.

1990, Apr. 24 **Perf. 13x12½**
3213	A733	30c multicolored	2.40	.75
3214	A733	50c multicolored	1.40	.45

Labor Day, Cent. A885

1990, Apr. 30 **Perf. 13**
3215 A885 5c multicolored .40 .20

Souvenir Sheet

Great Britain No. 1 on Cover — A886

1990, May 3
3216 A886 1p multicolored 4.00 2.00

Stamp World London '90, Penny Black 150th anniv.

Penny Black, 150th Anniv. A887

Portraits of Sir Rowland Hill and stamps of Great Britain.

1990, May 6 Litho. **Perf. 12½x12**
3217	A887	2c No. 1	.20	.20
3218	A887	3c No. 2	.20	.20
3219	A887	5c Type A5	.20	.20
3220	A887	10c No. 5	.25	.20
3221	A887	30c First day post- mark	1.25	.20
3222	A887	50c 5 #1 on Mulready envelope	2.25	.60
		Nos. 3217-3222 (6)	4.35	1.60

Celia Sanchez Manduley (1920-1980) — A888

1990, May 9 **Perf. 12½x13**
3223 A888 5c multicolored .50 .20

Ho Chi Minh (1890-1969), Vietnamese Communist Party Leader — A889

1990, May 19 **Perf. 12½**
3224 A889 50c multicolored 1.40 .45

Oceanography Institute, 25th Anniv. — A890

Designs: 5c, Specimen analysis and *Lachnolaimus maximus*. 30c, Research ship, fish, coral reef. 50c, Specimen collection and *Panulirus argus*.

1990, June 18 Litho. **Perf. 12½**
3225	A890	5c multicolored	.20	.20
3226	A890	30c multicolored	1.00	.20
3227	A890	50c multicolored	1.60	.40
		Nos. 3225-3227 (3)	2.80	.85

5th Latin American Botanical Conference A891

1990, June 25 Litho. **Perf. 12½**
3228	A891	3c Banara minu- tiflora	.20	.20
3229	A891	5c Oplonia nan- nophylla	.20	.20
3230	A891	10c Jacquinia brun- nescens	.50	.20
3231	A891	30c Rondeletia brachycarpa	1.60	.20
3232	A891	50c Rondeletia odorata	2.40	.60
		Nos. 3228-3232 (5)	4.90	1.40

Tourism
A892

1990, June 30

3233	A892	5c Wind surfing	.20	.20
3234	A892	10c Spear fishing	.35	.20
3235	A892	30c Deep sea fishing	1.00	.20
3236	A892	40c Hunting	1.60	.55
		Nos. 3233-3236 (4)	3.15	1.15

Nos. 3233, 3236 vert.

Art
Treasures
A893

5c, "La Flauta Del Dios Pan." 20c, "Un Pastor." 50c, "Ganimedes." 1p, "Venus Anadiomenes."

1990, July 20

3237	A893	5c multicolored	.20	.20
3238	A893	20c multicolored	.60	.25
3239	A893	50c multicolored	1.60	.40
3240	A893	1p multicolored	2.50	.85
a.		Sheet of 4, #3237-3240	5.00	5.00
		Nos. 3237-3240 (4)	4.90	1.70

Birds
A894

1990, Aug. 24   Litho.   Perf. 13

3241	A894	2c Podiceps cristatus	.20	.20
3242	A894	3c Gallirallus australis	.20	.20
3243	A894	5c Nestor notabilis	.25	.20
3244	A894	10c Xenicus longipes	.50	.20
3245	A894	30c Cracticus torquatus	1.50	.35
3246	A894	50c "Prosthemadera" novaeseelandiae	2.40	.65
		Nos. 3241-3246 (6)	5.05	1.80

Souvenir Sheet

3247	A894	1p Kiwi	4.50	2.25

New Zealand '90. No. 3247 contains one 39x31mm stamp.

8th UN
Congress on
Crime
Prevention
A895

1990, Aug. 27   Litho.   Perf. 12½

3248	A895	50c blue, silver & red	1.75	.45

Discovery of America, 500th Anniv. (in 1992) — A896

1990, Oct. 12   Litho.   Perf. 12½

3249	A896	5c Ship, shore	.25	.20
3250	A896	20c Columbus, village	1.00	.35

Cuban Television, 40th Anniv. — A897

1990, Oct. 12   Litho.   Perf. 13

3251	A897	5c multicolored	.35	.20

Nationalization of Railroads, 30th Anniv. — A898

1990, Oct. 13   Perf. 13x12½

3252	A898	50c multicolored	2.40	.75

Latin American History Type of 1986

Latin American stamps or flags and costumes: No. 3253, Argentina. No. 3254, Bolivia. No. 3255, Argentina No. 91. No. 3256, Colombia. No. 3257, Costa Rica. No. 3258, Cuba. No. 3259, Chile. No. 3260, Dominican Republic No. 110. No. 3261, Ecuador. No. 3262, El Salvador. No. 3263, Guatemala. No. 3264, Mexico. No. 3265, Puerto Rico No. 133. No. 3266, Nicaragua. No. 3267, Panama. No. 3268, Paraguay. No. 3269, Peru. No. 3270, El Salvador No. 103. No. 3271, Puerto Rico. No. 3272, Venezuela.

1990, Oct. 27   Perf. 12½

3253	A804	1c multicolored	.20	.20
3254	A804	1c multicolored	.20	.20
3255	A804	1c multicolored	.20	.20
3256	A804	1c multicolored	.20	.20
3257	A804	1c multicolored	.20	.20
a.		Strip of 5, Nos. 3253-3257	1.00	.50
3258	A804	5c multicolored	.20	.20
3259	A804	5c multicolored	.20	.20
3260	A804	5c multicolored	.20	.20
3261	A804	5c multicolored	.20	.20
3262	A804	5c multicolored	.20	.20
a.		Strip of 5, Nos. 3258-3262	1.00	.50
3263	A804	10c multicolored	.30	.20
3264	A804	10c multicolored	.30	.20
3265	A804	10c multicolored	.30	.20
3266	A804	10c multicolored	.30	.20
3267	A804	10c multicolored	.30	.20
a.		Strip of 5, Nos. 3263-3267	1.50	.75
3268	A804	20c multicolored	.85	.20
3269	A804	20c multicolored	.85	.20
3270	A804	20c multicolored	.85	.20
3271	A804	20c multicolored	.85	.20
3272	A804	20c multicolored	.85	.20
a.		Strip of 5, Nos. 3268-3272	4.50	2.25
b.		Sheet of 20, #3253-3272	5.00	5.00
		Nos. 3253-3272 (20)	7.75	4.00

Discovery of America, 500th anniv. (in 1992).

11th Jai Alai
World
Championships
A899

1990, Nov. 14   Litho.   Perf. 12½

3273	A899	30c multicolored	1.25	.40

No. 3273 printed with se-tenant label.

11th Pan American Games,
Havana — A900

1990, Nov. 15   Litho.   Perf. 12½

3274	A900	5c Judo	.20	.20
3275	A900	5c Sailing	.20	.20
3276	A900	5c Kayak	.20	.20
3277	A900	5c Rowing	.20	.20
3278	A900	5c Equestrian	.20	.20
3279	A900	10c Table tennis	.30	.20
3280	A900	20c Men's gymnastics, vert.	.60	.25
3281	A900	30c Baseball, vert.	.90	.25
3282	A900	35c Team handball, vert.	1.10	.35
3283	A900	50c Soccer, vert.	1.60	.70
		Nos. 3274-3283 (10)	5.50	2.75

See Nos. 3311-3320.

A901

1990, Nov. 20   Litho.   Perf. 13

3284	A901	5c Boxing	.20	.20
3285	A901	30c Baseball	1.10	.25
3286	A901	50c Volleyball	1.90	.50
		Nos. 3284-3286 (3)	3.20	.95

16th Central American and Caribbean Games, Mexico.

Butterflies
A902

1991, Jan. 25   Litho.   Perf. 12½

3287	A902	2c Chioides marmorosa	.25	.20
3288	A902	3c Composia fidelissima	.25	.20
3289	A902	5c Danaus plexippus	.35	.20
3290	A902	10c Hypolimnas misippus	.50	.20
3291	A902	30c Hypna iphigenia	1.40	.25
3292	A902	50c Hemiargus ammon	2.25	.50
		Nos. 3287-3292 (6)	5.00	1.55

Jose Luis Guerra Aguiar (1914-1990),
Director of Postal Museum — A903

1991, Feb. 17   Litho.   Perf. 12½

3293	A903	5c multicolored	.45	.20

A904

A905

1991, Feb. 20

3294	A904	1c Long jump	.20	.20
3295	A904	2c Javelin	.20	.20
3296	A904	3c Field hockey	.20	.20
3297	A904	5c Weight lifting	.20	.20
3298	A904	40c Cycling	1.25	.35
3299	A904	50c Gymnastics	1.75	.50
		Nos. 3294-3299 (6)	3.80	1.65

Souvenir Sheet

3300	A904	1p Torchbearer	3.50	1.75

1992 Summer Olympics, Barcelona.

1991, Apr. 12   Litho.   Perf. 13

1st Man in Space, 30th anniv.: 5c, Yuri Gagarin. No. 3302, Cosmonaut Y. Romanenko. No. 3303, Cosmonaut A. Tamayo. No. 3304, Mir space station. No. 3305, Mir space station, docked Soyuz, earth. 50c, Soviet space shuttle Buran.

3301	A905	5c multicolored	.20	.20
3302	A905	10c multicolored	.20	.20
3303	A905	10c multicolored	.20	.20
a.		Pair, #3302-3303	.40	.20
3304	A905	30c multicolored	1.00	.20
3305	A905	30c multicolored	1.00	.20
a.		Pair, #3304-3305	2.00	1.00
3306	A905	50c multicolored	1.60	.50
a.		Sheet of 6, #3301-3306	4.50	—
		Nos. 3301-3306 (6)	4.20	1.50

Proclamation of
the Socialist
Revolution, 30th
Anniv. — A906

Design: 50c, Ship, jet on fire.

1991, Apr. 19   Perf. 12½

3307	A906	5c multicolored	.20	.20
3308	A906	50c multicolored	1.60	.80

Bay of Pigs invasion, 30th anniv., No. 3308.

Stamp Day
A907

Details from mural by R. Rodriguez Radillo: 30c, Rocket lift-off. 50c, Dish antenna, horiz.

1991, Apr. 24   Perf. 12½x13, 13x12½

3309	A907	30c multicolored	1.00	.30
3310	A907	50c multicolored	1.75	.40

11th Pan American Games Type of 1990

1991, May 15		**Litho.**	**Perf. 12½**	
3311	A900	5c Volleyball	.20	.20
3312	A900	5c Rhythmic gymnastics	.20	.20
3313	A900	5c Synchronized swimming	.20	.20
3314	A900	5c Weight lifting	.20	.20
3315	A900	5c Baseball	.20	.20
3316	A900	10c Bowling	.25	.20
3317	A900	20c Boxing	.55	.25
3318	A900	30c Running	.85	.25
3319	A900	35c Wrestling	1.10	.30
3320	A900	50c Karate	1.50	.50
		Nos. 3311-3320 (10)	5.25	2.50

Nos. 3311-3315 & 3317 are vert.

Airships
A908

Designs: 5c, First ellipsoidal, 1784, J.B.M. Meusnier. 10c, First with steam engine, 1852, H. Giffard. 20c, First with gas engine, 1872, P. Haenlein. 30c, First with gasoline engine, 1896, H. Wolfert. 50c, First rigid aluminum, 1897, D. Schwarz. 1p, LZ-129 Hindenburg, 1936, F. von Zeppelin.

1991, July 1		**Litho.**	**Perf. 13**	
3321	A908	5c multicolored	.20	.20
3322	A908	10c multicolored	.35	.20
3323	A908	20c multicolored	.70	.30
3324	A908	30c multicolored	.90	.50
3325	A908	50c multicolored	1.60	.95
3326	A908	1p multicolored	3.25	1.60
		Nos. 3321-3326 (6)	7.00	3.75

Espamer '91, Buenos Aires, Argentina.

Simon Bolivar
A909

1991, June 22		**Litho.**	**Perf. 12½x13**	
3327	A909	50c multicolored	2.00	.60

Amphictyonic Cong. of Panama, 165th anniv.

Birds
A910

Designs: 45c, Melanerpes superciliaris. 50c, Myadestes elisabeth. 2p, Priotelus temnurus. 4p, Tiaris canora. 5p, Campephilus principalis. 10p, Amazona leucocephala, horiz. 16.45p, Mellisuga helenae, horiz.

1991, July 15		**Perf. 12½x13, 13x12½**		
3328	A910	45c multicolored	1.25	.40
3329	A910	50c multicolored	1.50	.50
3330	A910	2p multicolored	5.25	2.00
3331	A910	4p multicolored	10.00	3.50
3332	A910	5p multicolored	12.50	4.25
3333	A910	10p multicolored	25.00	6.50
3334	A910	16.45p multicolored	40.00	13.00
		Nos. 3328-3334 (7)	95.50	30.15

Tourism — A911

Designs: No. 3335, Varadero Beach, vert. No. 3336, Cayo Largo, vert. No. 3337, Artillerymen at fortress San Carlos de la Cabana. No. 3338, Tres Reyes del Morro Castle.

1991, July 30				
3335	A911	20c multicolored	.60	.20
3336	A911	20c multicolored	.60	.20
3337	A911	30c multicolored	1.00	.30
3338	A911	30c multicolored	1.00	.30
		Nos. 3335-3338 (4)	3.20	1.00

Panamfilex '91 — A912

11th Pan American Games venues: 5c, Pan American Stadium. 20c, Swimming venue. 30c, Multisports center. 50c, Velodrome. 1p, Havana City Coliseum and Sports Center.

1991, Aug. 4		**Litho.**	**Perf. 12½**	
3339	A912	5c multicolored	.20	.20
3340	A912	20c multicolored	.60	.30
3341	A912	30c multicolored	.80	.50
3342	A912	50c multicolored	1.50	.90
		Nos. 3339-3342 (4)	3.10	1.90
		Souvenir Sheet		
3343	A912	1p multicolored	3.50	1.75

No. 3343 contains one 40x32mm stamp.

Paintings
A913

5c, Kataoka Dengoemon Takafusa, by Utagawa Kuniyoshi. 10c, Evening Walk, by Hosoda Eishi. 20c, Courtesans, by Torii Kiyonaga. 30c, Conversation, by Utamaro. 50c, Bridge at Inari-bashi, by Hiroshige. 1p, On the Terrace, by Kiyonaga.

1991, Sept. 9		**Litho.**	**Perf. 12½x13**	
3344	A913	5c multicolored	.20	.20
3345	A913	10c multicolored	.35	.20
3346	A913	20c multicolored	.70	.30
3347	A913	30c multicolored	.90	.40
3348	A913	50c multicolored	1.60	.75
3349	A913	1p multicolored	3.25	1.75
		Nos. 3344-3349 (6)	7.00	3.60

Phila Nippon '91, Tokyo.

Souvenir Sheet

1992 Winter Olympics, Albertville — A914

1991, Sept. 25		**Litho.**	**Perf. 12½**	
3350	A914	1p multicolored	3.50	1.75

Cuban Communist Party, 4th Congress
A915

1991, Oct. 10				
3351	A915	5c shown	.20	.20
3352	A915	50c Congress symbol	1.75	.50

Discovery of America, 500th Anniv. (in 1992) — A916

Designs: 5c, Columbus, Vicente and Martin Pinzon. 20c, Santa Maria, Nina and Pinta.

1991, Oct. 12				
3353	A916	5c multicolored	.25	.20
3354	A916	20c multicolored	1.25	.25

Jose Marti
A917

1991, Oct. 15		**Perf. 13x12½**		
3355	A917	50c multicolored	2.00	.40

Publication of "Simple Verses," cent.

Latin American History
A918

Stamps or musicians and instruments: No. 3356, Julian Aguirre, Argentina, charango. No. 3357, Eduardo Caba, Bolivia, antara. No. 3358, Chile #2. No. 3359, Heitor Villalobos, Brazil, resonator trumpet. No. 3360, Guillermo Uribe-Holguin, Colombia, drum. No. 3361,

Miguel Failde, Cuba, claves. No. 3362, Enrique Soro, Chile, drum. No. 3363, Chile #57. No. 3364, Segundo L. Moreno, Ecuador, xylophone. No. 3365, Ricardo Castillo, Guatemala, marimba. No. 3366, Carlos Chavez, Mexico, guitar. No. 3367, Luis A. Delgadillo, Nicaragua, maracas. No. 3368, Chile #69. No. 3369, Alfredo De Saint-Malo, Panama, mejorana. No. 3370, Jose Asuncion Flores, Paraguay, harp. No. 3371, Daniel Alomia, Peru, flute. No. 3372, Juan Morell y Campos, Puerto Rico, cuatro. No. 3373, Chile #72. No. 3374, Eduardo Farini, Uruguay, drums. No. 3375, Juan V. Lecuna, Venezuela, cuatro, diff.

1991, Oct. 27			**Perf. 13**	
3356	A918	1c multicolored	.20	.20
3357	A918	1c multicolored	.20	.20
3358	A918	1c multicolored	.20	.20
3359	A918	1c multicolored	.20	.20
3360	A918	1c multicolored	.20	.20
a.		Strip of 5, #3356-3360	1.00	.50
3361	A918	5c multicolored	.20	.20
3362	A918	5c multicolored	.20	.20
3363	A918	5c multicolored	.20	.20
3364	A918	5c multicolored	.20	.20
3365	A918	5c multicolored	.20	.20
a.		Strip of 5, #3361-3365	1.00	.50
3366	A918	10c multicolored	.40	.20
3367	A918	10c multicolored	.40	.20
3368	A918	10c multicolored	.40	.20
3369	A918	10c multicolored	.40	.20
3370	A918	10c multicolored	.40	.20
a.		Strip of 5, #3366-3370	2.00	1.00
3371	A918	20c multicolored	.80	.20
3372	A918	20c multicolored	.80	.20
3373	A918	20c multicolored	.80	.20
3374	A918	20c multicolored	.80	.20
3375	A918	20c multicolored	.80	.20
a.		Strip of 5, #3371-3375	4.00	2.00
b.		Sheet of 20, #3356-3375	8.00	—
		Nos. 3356-3375 (20)	8.00	4.00

Discovery of America, 500th anniv. in 1992 (Nos. 3358, 3363, 3368, 3373).

Jose Marti Pioneers Organization, 1st Congress
A919

1991, Oct. 29				
3376	A919	5c multicolored	.35	.20

Toussaint L'Ouverture (1743-1803) — A920

1991, Nov. 20		**Perf. 12½x13**		
3377	A920	50c multicolored	2.00	.40

Haitian Revolution, Bicent.

Cuban Revolutionary Armed Forces, 35th Anniv. — A921

Design: 50c, Landing of the Granma expedition, 35th anniv., vert.

		Perf. 12½x12, 12x12½		
1991, Dec. 2			**Litho.**	
3378	A921	5c multicolored	.25	.20
3379	A921	50c multicolored	1.75	.40

Gen. Ignacio Agramonte (1841-1873),
Revolutionary Hero — A922

1991, Dec. 23   Litho.   Perf. 12½x13
3380 A922   5c multicolored   .30   .20

Souvenir Sheet

1992 Winter Olympics,
Albertville — A923

1992, Jan. 15   Perf. 13
3381 A923 1p multicolored   3.50 1.75

1992 Summer Olympics,
Barcelona — A924

1992, Jan. 20   Litho.   Perf. 13x12½
3382 A924   3c Table tennis   .20   .20
3383 A924   5c Handball   .20   .20
3384 A924 10c Shooting   .30   .20
3385 A924 20c Long jump, vert. .60   .20
3386 A924 35c Judo   1.25   .40
3387 A924 50c Fencing   1.60   .40
       Nos. 3382-3387 (6)   4.15 1.60
Souvenir Sheet
Perf. 12½
3388 A924 100c Rhythmic gym-
            nastics, vert.   3.50 1.75

No. 3388 contains one 32x40mm stamp.

Environmental
Protection
A925

1992, Feb. 10   Perf. 13
3389 A925   5c Terraced hillsides .25 .20
3390 A925 20c Save the whales   .60 .25
3391 A925 35c Ozone hole over
            Antarctica   1.25   .40
3392 A925 40c Nuclear disarma-
            ment   1.40   .40
       Nos. 3389-3392 (4)   3.50 1.25

Dogs
A926

1992, Mar. 10   Litho.   Perf. 13x12½
3393 A926   5c Boxer   .20   .20
3394 A926 10c Great dane   .20   .20
3395 A926 20c German shep-
            herd   .65   .20
3396 A926 30c Various breeds   1.10   .25
3397 A926 35c Doberman pin-
            scher   1.10   .30
3398 A926 40c Fox terrier   1.40   .40
3399 A926 50c Poodle   1.75   .50
       Nos. 3393-3399 (7)   6.40 2.05
Souvenir Sheet
Perf. 12½
3400 A926   1p Bichon frise, vert. 4.00 2.00

No. 3400 contains one 32x40mm stamp.
Nos. 3401-3404 will not be assigned.

Union of Young
Communists,
30th
Anniv. — A928

1992, Apr. 4   Litho.   Perf. 13
3405 A928   5c multicolored   .35   .20

Cuban Revolutionary Party,
Cent. — A929

1992, Apr. 10   Perf. 13x12½
3406 A929   5c multicolored   .25   .20
3407 A929 50c multicolored   1.75   .50

Discovery of America, 500th
Anniv. — A930

1992, Apr. 14   Perf. 12½
3408 A930   5c Landing at Bariay .25 .20
3409 A930 20c Landing at San
            Salvador   .70   .25

Granada '92 Philatelic
Exhibition — A931

Views of the Alhambra, Granada: 5c, With
Sierra Nevada mountains beyond. 10c, Arches
at sunset. 20c, Interior architecture. 30c, Patio,
fountain of lions. 35c, Bedroom. 50c, View of
Albaicin.

1992, Apr. 17   Perf. 13
3410 A931   5c multicolored   .20   .20
3411 A931 10c multicolored   .25   .20
3412 A931 20c multicolored   .75   .20
3413 A931 30c multicolored   1.25   .25
3414 A931 35c multicolored   1.50   .40
3415 A931 50c multicolored   2.10   .50
       Nos. 3410-3415 (6)   6.05 1.75

La Bodeguita Del Medio Restaurant,
50th Anniv. — A932

1992, Apr. 26
3416 A932 50c multicolored   1.75   .50

Fish
A933

1992, May 15   Litho.   Perf. 12½
3417 A933   5c Holacanthus
            isabelita   .20   .20
3418 A933 10c Equetus lanceo-
            latus   .25   .20
3419 A933 20c Acanthurus
            coeruleus   .65   .20
3420 A933 30c Abudefduf saxa-
            tilis   1.10   .25
3421 A933 50c Microspathodon
            chrysurus   1.90   .50
       Nos. 3417-3421 (5)   4.10 1.35

Orchids — A934

1992, June 20   Litho.   Perf. 12½
3422 A934   3c Cattleya hibrida   .20   .20
3423 A934   5c Phalaenopsis   .20   .20
3424 A934 10c Cattleyopsis
            lindenii   .20   .20
3425 A934 30c Bletia purpurea   1.00   .25
3426 A934 35c Oncidium luridum 1.10   .30
3427 A934 40c Vanda hibrida   1.40   .40
       Nos. 3422-3427 (6)   4.10 1.55

Soroa Orchid Garden, 40th anniv.

Mellisuga Helenae — A935

1992, July 7   Perf. 13
3428 A935   5c Sitting on nest   .40   .25
3429 A935 10c Wings extended   .60   .30
3430 A935 20c Sitting on branch 1.25   .40
3431 A935 30c In flight   2.00 1.00
       Nos. 3428-3431 (4)   4.25 1.95

World Wildlife Fund.

Tourism
A936

1992, July 15   Litho.   Perf. 12½
3432 A936 10c Guardalavaca
            Beach   .35   .20
3433 A936 20c Bucanero Hotel   .60   .20
3434 A936 30c Sailing ship, Ha-
            vana   1.10   .40
3435 A936 50c Varadero Beach   1.50   .50
       Nos. 3432-3435 (4)   3.55 1.30

Souvenir Sheet

Expo '92, Seville — A937

1992, July 27   Litho.   Perf. 13
3436 A937 1.50p multicolored   4.50 2.25

1992
Summer
Olympics,
Barcelona
A938

Athlete, sport: 5c, Eligio (Kid Chocolate)
Sardinas, boxing. 35c, Ramon Fonst, fencing.
40c, Sergio Martinez, cycling. 50c, Martin
Dihigo, baseball.

1992, July 20   Litho.   Perf. 12½x13
3437 A938   5c multicolored   .20   .20
3438 A938 35c multicolored   1.10   .30
3439 A938 40c multicolored   1.25   .40
3440 A938 50c multicolored   1.75   .60
       Nos. 3437-3440 (4)   4.30 1.50

Olymphilex '92.

Discovery of America, 500th
Anniv. — A939

5c, Alvarez Cabral. 10c, Alonso Pinzon. 20c,
Alonso de Ojeda. 30c, Amerigo Vespucci. 35c,
Prince Henry the Navigator. 40c, Bartolomeu
Dias. 1p, Columbus' fleet.

1992, Sept. 18   Litho.   Perf. 12½
3441 A939   5c multicolored   .20   .20
3442 A939 10c multicolored   .30   .20
3443 A939 20c multicolored   .70   .20
3444 A939 30c multicolored   1.10   .30
3445 A939 35c multicolored   1.25   .30
3446 A939 40c multicolored   1.50   .40
       Nos. 3441-3446 (6)   5.05 1.60
Souvenir Sheet
Perf. 13
3447 A939   1p multi, vert.   3.25 1.60

Genoa '92. No. 3447 contains one
32x40mm stamp.

1992 Summer Olympics Medal
Winners, Barcelona — A940

Medals and participants in events: No. 3448, Bronze, 4x100-meter relay, women's high jump, and women's 800-meter. No. 3449, Gold, high jump, women's discus. No. 3450, Silver, 4x400-meter relay, bronze, discus. No. 3451, Gold and silver, boxing. No. 3452, Gold, baseball. No. 3453, Gold, women's volleyball. No. 3454, Gold, silver, and bronze, judo. No. 3455, Gold and bronze, Greco-Roman and freestyle wrestling. No. 3456, Silver and bronze, fencing, silver, weight lifting.

1992, Sept. 24   Litho.   Perf. 13

3448	A940	5c multicolored	.20	.20
3449	A940	5c multicolored	.20	.20
3450	A940	5c multicolored	.20	.20
3451	A940	20c multicolored	.65	.20
3452	A940	20c multicolored	.65	.20
3453	A940	20c multicolored	.65	.20
3454	A940	50c multicolored	1.75	.50
3455	A940	50c multicolored	1.75	.50
3456	A940	50c multicolored	1.75	.50
	Nos. 3448-3456 (9)		7.80	2.70

6th World Track and Field Cup, Havana A941

1992, Sept. 24   Litho.   Perf. 13

3457	A941	5c High jump	.20	.20
3458	A941	20c Javelin	.65	.20
3459	A941	30c Hammer throw	1.00	.25
3460	A941	40c Long jump, vert.	1.40	.40
3461	A941	50c Hurdles, vert.	1.75	.50
	Nos. 3457-3461 (5)		5.00	1.55

Souvenir Sheet

3462	A941	1p Women's relay	3.50	1.75

No. 3462 contains one 40x32mm stamp.

Latin American History Type of 1986

Discovery of America: No. 3463a, Columbus, Queen Isabella. b, Columbus at Rabida Monastery. c, Columbus, pointing up, outlining his plan. d, Columbus, with scroll, before Salamanca Council. e, Departure of Columbus' fleet from Palos.

No. 3464a, Three ships stopping at Canary Islands. b, Columbus speaking to crew. c, Land sighted, Oct. 12, 1492. d, Columbus landing in New World. e, Meeting natives.

No. 3465a, Grounding of Santa Maria at Hispanola. b, Arrival of Nina at Palos. c, Columbus welcomed in Barcelona. d, Columbus describes his voyage to Ferdinand and Isabella. e, Departure of fleet from Cadiz on second voyage.

No. 3466a, King and Queen welcome Columbus. b, Fleet on Columbus' third voyage. c, Columbus deported from Hispanola to Spain as prisoner. d, Columbus on ship, fourth voyage. e, Death of Columbus, May 20, 1506 in Valladolid.

1992, Oct. 3   Perf. 13

3463	A804	1c Strip of 5, #a.-e.	.65	.30
3464	A804	5c Strip of 5, #a.-e.	.65	.30
3465	A804	10c Strip of 5, #a.-e.	1.25	.75
3466	A804	20c Strip of 5, #a.-e.	4.00	1.50
	Nos. 3463-3466 (4)		6.55	2.85

Jose Maria
Chacon y Calvo
(1892-1969),
Historian
A942

1992, Oct. 29   Perf. 13

3467	A942	30c multicolored	1.00	.40

Churches
A943

Designs: 5c, Basilica of Nuestra Senora de la Caridad del Cobre. 20c, Santa Maria del Rosario Church. 30c, Espiritu Santo Church. 50c, Santo Angel Custodio Church.

1992, Nov. 10   Litho.   Perf. 12½

3468	A943	5c multicolored	.20	.20
3469	A943	20c multicolored	.75	.20
3470	A943	30c multicolored	1.00	.25
3471	A943	50c multicolored	2.00	.30
	Nos. 3468-3471 (4)		3.95	.95

Development of the Diesel
Engine — A944

1993, Jan. 20   Litho.   Perf. 12½

3472	A944	5c Truck	.20	.20
3473	A944	10c Automobile	.20	.20
3474	A944	30c Tugboat	.55	.40
3475	A944	40c Locomotive	2.50	1.25
3476	A944	50c Tractor	1.00	.65
	Nos. 3472-3476 (5)		4.45	2.70

Souvenir Sheet

3477	A944	1p Rudolf Diesel	3.50	1.75

No. 3477 contains one 40x32mm stamp. Rudolf Diesel, 80th anniv. of death (#3477).

Davis Cup Tennis Competition — A945

Various tennis players in action.

Perf. 12x12½, 12½x12

1993, Feb. 10   Litho.

3478	A945	5c multi, vert.	.20	.20
3479	A945	20c multi, vert.	.60	.25
3480	A945	30c multi, vert.	.90	.40
3481	A945	35c multicolored	1.00	.50
3482	A945	40c multicolored	1.25	.60
	Nos. 3478-3482 (5)		3.95	1.95

Souvenir Sheet

Perf. 12½

3483	A945	1p multicolored	2.50	1.25

No. 3483 contains one 40x32mm stamp.

Scientists
A946

Designs: 3c, Pierre-Paul-Emile Roux (1853-1933), bacteriologist. 5c, Carlos J. Finlay (1833-1915), suggested mosquito as carrier of yellow fever. 10c, Ivan Petrovich Pavlov (1849-1936), physiologist, investigated conditioned reflexes. 20c, Louis Pasteur, chemist, developer of pasteurization. 30c, Santiago Ramon y Cajal (1852-1934), histologist, isolated the neuron. 35c, Sigmund Freud, psychoanalyst. 40c, Wilhelm Conrad Roentgen, physicist, discoverer of x-ray. 50c, Joseph Lister, surgeon, introduced principle of antisepsis. 1p, Robert Koch, bacteriologist, developer of tuberculin, vert.

1993, Mar. 3   Litho.   Perf. 12½

3484	A946	3c multicolored	.20	.20
3485	A946	5c multicolored	.20	.20
3486	A946	10c multicolored	.25	.20
3487	A946	20c multicolored	.55	.25
3488	A946	30c multicolored	.80	.40
3489	A946	35c multicolored	.90	.50
3490	A946	40c multicolored	1.10	.60
3491	A946	50c multicolored	1.25	.65
	Nos. 3484-3491 (8)		5.25	3.00

Souvenir Sheet

3492	A946	1p multicolored	2.75	1.40

Bicycles — A947

Bicycles designed by: 3c, Leonardo da Vinci, 15th cent. 5c, Karl Von Drais de Sauerbrun, 1813. 10c, Ernest Michaux, 1856. 20c, James Starley, 1869. 30c, Harry Lawson, 1879. 35c, Guaso (Cuba), 1992.

1993, Apr. 14   Perf. 13

3493	A947	3c multicolored	.20	.20
3494	A947	5c multicolored	.20	.20
3495	A947	10c multicolored	.45	.20
3496	A947	20c multicolored	.90	.25
3497	A947	30c multicolored	1.40	.40
3498	A947	35c multicolored	1.50	.50
	Nos. 3493-3498 (6)		4.65	1.75

Cuban Natl. Museum, 80th Anniv. A948

Paintings by Joaquin Sorolla y Bastida (1863-1923): 3c, Child Eating Watermelon, 1920, vert. 5c, Valencian Fisherwomen, 1909. 10c, Regattas. 20c, Contadina, 1889. 40c, Summer, 1904. 50c, Boats on the Ocean, 1908.

1993, May 29   Litho.   Perf. 13x12½

3499	A948	3c multicolored	.20	.20

Perf. 12½x13

3500	A948	5c multicolored	.30	.20
3501	A948	10c multicolored	.35	.20
3502	A948	20c multicolored	.65	.25
3503	A948	40c multicolored	1.25	.60
3504	A948	50c multicolored	1.75	.65
	Nos. 3499-3504 (6)		4.50	2.10

Water Birds A949

Perf. 12½, 13x12½ (5, 30c)

1993, June 15

3505	A949	3c Jacana spinosa	.20	.20
3506	A949	5c Ardea herodias, vert.	.20	.20
3507	A949	10c Himantopus mexicanus	.40	.20
3508	A949	20c Nycticorax nycticorax	.80	.25
3509	A949	30c Grus canadensis, vert.	1.10	.40
3510	A949	50c Aramus guarauna	2.25	.65
	Nos. 3505-3510 (6)		4.95	1.90

Brasiliana '93. Nos. 3506, 3510 are 27x44mm.

Anniversaries — A950

#3511, Jose Marti, Moncada Barracks. #3512, "History Will Absolve Me," declaration of Fidel Castro, Marti. #3513, Jose Marti, Rafael M. Mendive, vert. #3514, Carlos Manuel de Cespedes, gear wheels.

1993, July 26   Litho.   Perf. 13

3511	A950	5c multicolored	.20	.20
3512	A950	5c multicolored	.20	.20
3513	A950	5c multicolored	.20	.20
3514	A950	5c multicolored	.20	.20
	Nos. 3511-3514 (4)		.80	.80

Attack on Moncada Barracks, 40th anniv. (#3511). Declaration of Fidel Castro, 40th anniv. (#3512). Birth of Jose Marti, 140th anniv. (#3513). Declaration of the Ten Years' War, 125th anniv. (#3514).

Flowers from Cienfuegos Botanical Gardens A951

1993, Aug. 20

3515	A951	3c Sedum allantoides	.20	.20
3516	A951	5c Heliconia caribaea	.20	.20
3517	A951	10c Anthurium andraeanum	.35	.20
3518	A951	20c Pseudobombax ellipticum	.70	.25
3519	A951	35c Ixora coccinea	1.10	.50
3520	A951	50c Callistemon specious	1.90	.65
	Nos. 3515-3520 (6)		4.45	2.00

Bangkok '93, Intl. Philatelic Exhibition A952

Butterflies: 3c, Battus devillievs. 5c, Anteos maerula. 20c, Ascia monuste evonima. 30c, Junonia coenia. 35c, Anartia jatrophae guantanamo. 50c, Hypolimnas misippus.

1993, Sept. 10   Litho.   Perf. 13

3521	A952	3c multicolored	.20	.20
3522	A952	5c multicolored	.25	.20
3523	A952	20c multicolored	.70	.25
3524	A952	30c multicolored	1.00	.40
3525	A952	35c multicolored	1.10	.40
3526	A952	50c multicolored	1.60	.65
	Nos. 3521-3526 (6)		4.85	2.10

Endangered Species A953

1993, Oct. 12   Litho.   Perf. 13

3527	A953	5c Phoenicopterus ruber	.25	.20
3528	A953	50c Ajaia ajaja	1.75	.65

Latin American Revolutionaries A954

Flags, map and: No. 3529, Simon Bolivar. No. 3530, Jose Marti. No. 3531, Benito Juarez, Mexican President. No. 3532, Ernesto "Che" Guevara.

1993, Oct. 27 **Litho.** **Perf. 13**
3529	A954	50c multicolored	1.40	.65
3530	A954	50c multicolored	1.40	.65
3531	A954	50c multicolored	1.40	.65
3532	A954	50c multicolored	1.40	.65
a.		Block of 4, #3529-3532	7.25	3.50
		Nos. 3529-3532 (4)	5.60	2.60

17th Central American and Caribbean Games, Ponce, Puerto Rico — A955

1993, Nov. 10 **Litho.** **Perf. 12½**
3533	A955	5c Swimming	.20	.20
3534	A955	10c Pole vault	.20	.20
3535	A955	20c Boxing	.70	.25
3536	A955	35c Gymnastics, vert.	1.10	.40
3537	A955	50c Baseball, vert.	1.60	.65
		Nos. 3533-3537 (5)	3.80	1.70

Souvenir Sheet
| 3538 | A955 | 1p Basketball | 3.75 | 1.75 |

No. 3538 contains one 40x32mm stamp.

Mariana Grajales (1808-93), Patriot — A956

Peter I. Tchaikovsky (1840-93), Composer A957

1993, Nov. 27 **Perf. 13**
| 3539 | A956 | 5p multicolored | .30 | .20 |

1993, Nov. 30
3540	A957	5c Portrait	.20	.20
3541	A957	20c Swan Lake Ballet	.65	.25
3542	A957	30c Statue	.90	.40
3543	A957	50c Museum, horiz.	1.25	.65
		Nos. 3540-3543 (4)	3.00	1.50

A958

A959

1994, Jan. 1 **Litho.** **Perf. 13**
| 3544 | A958 | 5c multicolored | .30 | .20 |

35th anniv. of the Revolution.

1994, Jan. 1

Various soccer players.

3545	A959	5c multicolored	.20	.20
3546	A959	20c multicolored	.60	.25
3547	A959	30c multicolored	.85	.40
3548	A959	35c multicolored	.95	.40
3549	A959	40c multicolored	1.25	.50
3550	A959	50c multicolored	1.40	.65
		Nos. 3545-3550 (6)	5.25	2.40

Souvenir Sheet
| 3551 | A959 | 1p multicolored | 3.00 | 1.50 |

1994 World Cup Soccer Championships, US. No. 3551 contains one 40x31mm stamp.

Cats A960

1994, Feb. 15 **Litho.** **Perf. 12½**
3552	A960	5c Blue Persian	.20	.20
3553	A960	10c Havana	.25	.20
3554	A960	20c Maine coon	.70	.25
3555	A960	30c Blue British shorthair	1.00	.40
3556	A960	35c Bicolor Persian	1.10	.40
3557	A960	50c Gold chinchilla	1.60	.65
		Nos. 3552-3557 (6)	4.85	2.10

Souvenir Sheet
Perf. 13
| 3558 | A960 | 1p Abyssinian, vert. | 4.00 | 2.00 |

No. 3558 contains one 30x38mm stamp.

Medicinal Plants — A961

Designs: 5c, Salvia officinalis. 10c, Aloe barbadensis. 20c, Helianthus annuus. 30c, Matricaria chamomilla. 40c, Calendula officinalis. 50c, Tilia platyphyllos.

1994, Mar. 30 **Litho.** **Perf. 12½**
3559	A961	5c multicolored	.25	.20
3560	A961	10c multicolored	.25	.20
3561	A961	20c multicolored	.65	.25
3562	A961	30c multicolored	.90	.40
3563	A961	40c multicolored	1.25	.50
3564	A961	50c multicolored	1.50	.65
		Nos. 3559-3564 (6)	4.80	2.20

Carriages — A962

Designs: 5c, Public coach, 1860. 10c, Coach of Ferdinand VII, Maria Louisa. 30c, Louis XV-style coach. 35c, Elizabeth II gala

day's coach. 40c, Catalina II's summer coach. 50c, Volanta habanera.

1994, Apr. 20 **Perf. 12½x12**
3565	A962	5c multicolored	.20	.20
3566	A962	10c multicolored	.25	.20
3567	A962	30c multicolored	1.00	.40
3568	A962	35c multicolored	1.10	.40
3569	A962	40c multicolored	1.40	.50
3570	A962	50c multicolored	1.60	.65
		Nos. 3565-3570 (6)	5.55	2.35

No. 3570 is 68x37mm.

Aquaculture — A963

Designs: 5c, Crassostrea rhizophorae. 20c, Cardisoma guanhumi. 30c, Tilapia melanopleura. 35c, Hippospongia lachne. 40c, Panulirus argus. 50c, Cyprinus carpio.

1994, May 10 **Litho.** **Perf. 12½**
3571	A963	5c multicolored	.35	.20
3572	A963	20c multicolored	.60	.25
3573	A963	30c multicolored	.85	.40
3574	A963	35c multicolored	1.00	.40
3575	A963	40c multicolored	1.25	.50
3576	A963	50c multicolored	1.50	.65
		Nos. 3571-3576 (6)	5.55	2.40

Intl. Olympic Committee, Cent. — A964

1994, June 23 **Litho.** **Perf. 12½**
3577	A964	5c Flag, runners	.20	.20
3578	A964	30c Flag, world map	.85	.40
3579	A964	50c Flag, Olympic flame	1.50	.65
		Nos. 3577-3579 (3)	2.55	1.25

Scientists A965

Designs: 5c, Michael Faraday (1791-1867), physicist. 10c, Marie Curie (1867-1934), physical chemist. 20c, Pierre Curie (1859-1906), chemist. 30c, Albert Einstein (1879-1955), physicist, mathematician. 40c, Max Planck (1858-1947), theoretical physicist. 50c, Otto Hahn (1879-1968), physical chemist.

1994, July 20 **Litho.** **Perf. 12½**
3580	A965	5c multicolored	.20	.20
3581	A965	10c multicolored	.25	.20
3582	A965	20c multicolored	.70	.25
3583	A965	30c multicolored	1.00	.40
3584	A965	40c multicolored	1.40	.50
3585	A965	50c multicolored	1.75	.65
		Nos. 3580-3585 (6)	5.30	2.20

Cactus Flowers A966

Designs: 5c, Opuntia dillenii. 10c, Opuntia millspaughii, vert. 30c, Leptocereus santamarinae. 35c, Pereskia marcanoi. 40c, Dendrocereus nudiflorus, vert. 50c, Pilocereus robinii.

1994, Aug. 15 **Litho.** **Perf. 12½**
3586	A966	5c multicolored	.20	.20
3587	A966	10c multicolored	.30	.20
3588	A966	30c multicolored	1.00	.40
3589	A966	35c multicolored	1.10	.40
3590	A966	40c multicolored	1.50	.50
3591	A966	50c multicolored	1.75	.65
		Nos. 3586-3591 (6)	5.85	2.35

Souvenir Sheet

2nd Spanish-Cuban Philatelic Exhibition, Havana — A967

Design: 1p, Cuban postal rocket, #C31.

1994, Sept. 18
| 3592 | A967 | 1p multicolored | 3.00 | 1.50 |

Experimental postal rocket flight, 55th anniv.

Dogs A968

1994, Sept. 20
3593	A968	5c Rough collie	.25	.20
3594	A968	20c American cocker spaniel	.70	.25
3595	A968	30c Dalmatian	.95	.40
3596	A968	40c Afghan hound	1.40	.50
3597	A968	50c English cocker spaniel	1.60	.65
		Nos. 3593-3597 (5)	4.90	2.00

Cayo Largo Island A969

Fauna: 15c, Carpilius corallinus. 65c, Cyclura nubila, vert. 75c, Pelecanus occidentalis. 4p, Chelonia mydas.

1994, Sept. 30 **Litho.** **Perf. 12½**
3598	A969	15c multicolored	.30	.20
3599	A969	65c multicolored	1.50	.90
3600	A969	75c multicolored	1.75	1.00
3601	A969	1p multicolored	2.50	1.25
		Nos. 3598-3601 (4)	6.05	3.35

A970

A971

1994, Oct. 28
3602 A970 15c multicolored .50 .20

Camilo Cienfuegos Gorriaran, revolutionary, 35th anniv. of disappearance.

1994, Oct. 30

Fauna of the Caribbean: 10c, Epinephelus flavolimbatus, horiz. No. 3604, Phoenicopterus ruber. No. 3605, Aetobatus narinari. No. 3606, Istiophorus platypterus, horiz. No. 3607, Tursiops truncatus, horiz. No. 3608, Pelecanus occidentalis.

3603	A971	10c multicolored	.30	.20
3604	A971	15c multicolored	.30	.20
3605	A971	15c multicolored	.30	.20
3606	A971	15c multicolored	.30	.20
3607	A971	65c multicolored	1.75	.90
3608	A971	65c multicolored	1.75	.90
	Nos. 3603-3608 (6)		4.70	2.60

ICAO, 50th Anniv. A972

1994, Nov. 9
3609 A972 65c multicolored 1.75 .90

Zoological Garden, Havana, 55th Anniv. — A973

1994, Nov. 14 Litho. Perf. 13
3610 A973 15c Bronze monument .25 .20
3611 A973 65c Ara chloroptera 1.40 .90
3612 A973 75c Carduelis carduelis 1.60 1.00
Nos. 3610-3612 (3) 3.25 2.10

Cuban Philatelic Federation, 30th Anniv. — A974

1994, Nov. 20
3613 A974 15c multicolored .50 .20

America Issue — A975

Postal transportation: 15c, 18th Cent. Spanish galleon, maritime postal service, vert. 65c,

19th Cent. postal rider, insurgent postal service.

1994, Dec. 12
3614 A975 15c multicolored .25 .20
3615 A975 65c multicolored 1.75 .90

Postal Museum, 30th Anniv. — A976

1995, Jan. 2
3616 A976 15c multicolored .50 .20

Lizards — A977

Designs: 15c, Anolis baracoae. 65c, Sphaerodactylus ramsdeni. 75c, Leiocephalus raviceps. 85c, Sphaerodactylus ruibali. 90c, Anolis ophiolepis. 1p, Sphaerodactylus armasi.

1994, Nov. 30 Litho. Perf. 12½
3617 A977 15c multicolored .30 .20
3618 A977 65c multicolored 1.60 .90
3619 A977 75c multicolored 1.75 1.00
3620 A977 85c multicolored 2.00 1.25
3621 A977 90c multicolored 2.25 1.25
3622 A977 1p multicolored 2.50 1.40
Nos. 3617-3622 (6) 10.40 6.00

Cuban War of Independence, Cent. — A978

1995, Feb. 24 Litho. Perf. 12½
3623 A978 15c Jose Marti, flag .50 .20

Pan American Games, Mar del Plata, Argentina — A979

1995, Mar. 11 Litho. Perf. 13
3624 A979 10c Boxing, vert. .20 .20
3625 A979 15c Weight lifting, vert. .25 .20
3626 A979 65c Volleyball, vert. 1.10 .80
3627 A979 75c Wrestling 1.25 1.00
3628 A979 85c Baseball 1.50 1.00
3629 A979 90c High jump 1.60 1.10
Nos. 3624-3629 (6) 5.90 4.30

National Aquarium, 35th Anniv. — A980

Fish: 10c, Holacanthus cillaris. 15c, Hypoplectrus guttavarius. 65c, Anisotremus virginicus. 75c, Amblycirrhitus pinos. 85c, Pomaacanthus paru. 90c, Acanthurus coeruleus.

1995, Apr. 28 Litho. Perf. 13
3630 A980 10c multicolored .25 .20
3631 A980 15c multicolored .30 .20
3632 A980 65c multicolored 1.40 .70
3633 A980 75c multicolored 1.50 .80
3634 A980 85c multicolored 2.00 1.10
3635 A980 90c multicolored 2.00 1.10
Nos. 3630-3635 (6) 7.45 4.10

FAO, 50th Anniv. A981

1995, Apr. 7 Litho. Perf. 13
3636 A981 75c multicolored 1.40 1.00

First Cuban Postage Stamp, 140th Anniv. — A982

65c, Ornamental letter drop, envelope.

1995, Apr. 24 Litho. Perf. 12½
3637 A982 15c black & blue green .30 .20
3638 A982 65c multicolored 1.40 .75

Jose Marti, Death Cent. A983

Designs: 15c, Marti killed in combat, signature, portrait. 65c, Landing of Marti, Cuban patriots on Playitas beach. 75c, Montecristi Manifesto signed in Dominican Republic. Marti. 85c, Meeting of Marti, Maceo, Gomez at La Mejorana Farm. 90c, Marti's mausoleum, Santiago, Cuba, vert.

1995, May 19 Perf. 12½x13, 13x12½
3639 A983 15c multicolored .25 .20
3640 A983 65c multicolored 1.25 .80
3641 A983 75c multicolored 1.40 1.00
3642 A983 85c multicolored 1.75 1.00
3643 A983 90c multicolored 1.75 1.10
Nos. 3639-3643 (5) 6.40 4.10

Antonio Maceo (1845-96), Revolutionary — A984

1995, June 14 Litho. Perf. 12½
3644 A984 15c multicolored .60 .20

Butterflies — A985

Designs: 10c, Dione vanillae. 15c, Eunica tatila. 65c, Melete salacia. 75c, Greta cubana. 85c, Eurema daira. 90c, Phoebis sennae.

1995, June 20 Perf. 12½x13
3645 A985 10c multicolored .25 .20
3646 A985 15c multicolored .25 .20
3647 A985 65c multicolored 1.25 .80
3648 A985 75c multicolored 1.40 1.00
3649 A985 85c multicolored 1.75 1.00
3650 A985 90c multicolored 1.75 1.10
Nos. 3645-3650 (6) 6.65 4.30

World War II Combat Planes — A986

Designs: 10c, Supermarine "Spitfire," Great Britain. 15c, IL-2, Russia. 65c, Curtiss P-40, US. 75c, Messerschmitt Bf-109, Germany. 85c, Morane-Saunier 406, France.

1995, July 30 Litho. Perf. 12½
3651 A986 10c multicolored .30 .20
3652 A986 15c multicolored .30 .20
3653 A986 65c multicolored 1.40 .80
3654 A986 75c multicolored 1.60 1.00
3655 A986 85c multicolored 1.90 1.00
Nos. 3651-3655 (5) 5.50 3.20

A987

A988

1995, Aug. 6 Litho. Perf. 12½
3656 A987 15c multicolored .50 .20

Ernesto Lecuona, composer, pianist, birth cent.

1995, Aug. 10
Color of Horse or Horses
3657 A988 10c golden brown, white .40 .20
3658 A988 15c white, horiz. .40 .20
3659 A988 65c dark brown, white 1.75 .80
3660 A988 75c red brown 2.10 1.00
3661 A988 85c tan 2.50 1.00
3662 A988 90c white 2.50 1.10
Nos. 3657-3662 (6) 9.65 4.30

Singapore '95.

Souvenir Sheet

Beijing Intl. Stamp & Coin Expo '95 — A989

1995, Aug. 28 Perf. 13
3663 A989 50c multicolored 1.25 .75

1996 Summer Olympics, Atlanta — A990

1995, Sept. 25   Litho.   Perf. 13
3664	A990	10c Wrestling	.20	.20
3665	A990	15c Weight lifting	.25	.20
3666	A990	65c Women's volley-ball	1.10	.80
3667	A990	75c Women's athletics	1.25	1.00
3668	A990	85c Baseball	1.50	1.00
3669	A990	90c Women's judo	1.60	1.10
		Nos. 3664-3669 (6)	5.90	4.30

Souvenir Sheet
3670	A990	1p Boxing	3.00	1.50

No. 3670 contains one 30x36mm stamp.

Cuban Sugar Industry, 400th Anniv. A991

Paintings from "Los Ingenios," by Edouard Laplante, 1852: 15c, Steam train, sugar factory. 65c, Sugar factory, tower, bridge.

1995, Oct. 3
3671	A991	15c multicolored	1.75	.35
3672	A991	65c multicolored	1.00	.70

UN, 50th Anniv. A992

1995, Oct. 24   Litho.   Perf. 13
3673	A992	65c multicolored	1.10	.80

Zoological Gardens, Havana — A993

Designs: 10c, Panthera leo, vert. 15c, Equus grevyi. 65c, Pongo pygmaeus, vert. 75c, Elephas maximus. 85c, Sciurus vulgaris. 90c, Procyon lotor.

1995, Oct. 30   Litho.   Perf. 13
3674	A993	10c multicolored	.25	.20
3675	A993	15c multicolored	.30	.20
3676	A993	65c multicolored	1.25	.80
3677	A993	75c multicolored	1.50	1.00
3678	A993	85c multicolored	1.90	1.00
3679	A993	90c multicolored	2.10	1.10
		Nos. 3674-3679 (6)	7.30	4.30

UNESCO, 50th Anniv. — A994

UNESCO World Culture and National Heritage sites: 65c, Santa Clara de Asis Convent. 75c, San Francisco de Asis Minor Basilica.

1995, Nov. 4
3680	A994	65c multicolored	1.10	.80
3681	A994	75c multicolored	1.25	1.00

Orchids — A995

Designs: 5c, Epidendrum porpax. 10c, Cyrtopodium punctatum. 15c, Polyrrhiza lindeni. 40c, Bletia patula. 45c, Galeandra beyrichii. 50c, Vanilla dilloniana. 65c, Macradenia lutescens. 75c, Oncidium luridum. 85c, Ionopsis utricularioides.

1995, Nov. 10   Perf. 12½
3681A	A995	5c multicolored	.30	.20
3681B	A995	10c multicolored	.50	.20
3681C	A995	15c multicolored	.65	.20
3682	A995	40c multicolored	.80	.55
3683	A995	45c multicolored	.90	.55
3684	A995	50c multicolored	1.00	.65
3685	A995	65c multicolored	1.25	.80
3686	A995	75c multicolored	1.40	1.00
3687	A995	85c multicolored	1.75	1.00
		Nos. 3681A-3687 (9)	8.55	5.15

Issued: 40c-85c, 11/10/95; 5c-15c, 6/28/96.

Motion Pictures, Cent. — A996

1995, Dec. 7   Perf. 13
3688	A996	15c Lumiere Brothers	.30	.20
3689	A996	15c Marilyn Monroe	.30	.20
3690	A996	15c Marlene Dietrich	.30	.20
3691	A996	15c Vittorio DeSica	.30	.20
3692	A996	15c Charlie Chaplin	.30	.20
3693	A996	15c Greta Garbo	.30	.20
3694	A996	65c Humphrey Bogart	1.40	.80
3695	A996	75c Montaner	1.60	1.00
3696	A996	85c Cantinflas	1.90	1.00
		Nos. 3688-3696 (9)	6.70	4.00

Souvenir Sheet

4th Cuban-Spanish Philatelic Exhibition, Havana — A997

1995, Dec. 11   Litho.   Perf. 13
3697	A997	1p multicolored	3.00	1.50

America Issue — A998

1995, Dec. 12
3698	A998	15c Centurus superciliaris	.35	.20
3699	A998	65c Todus multicolor	1.60	.80

Generals Who Died in 1895 War — A999

Designs: No. 3700, Alfonso Goulet Goulet, Francisco Adolfo Crombet Ballon. No. 3701, Jesus Calvar O, Jose Guillermo Moncada, Tomas Jordan. No. 3702, Francisco Borrero Lavadi, Francisco Inchaustegui Cabrera.

1995, Dec. 20   Perf. 12½
3700	A999	15c multicolored	.35	.20
3701	A999	15c multicolored	.35	.20
3702	A999	15c multicolored	.35	.20
a.		Strip of 3, #3700-3702	1.10	.90
		Nos. 3700-3702 (3)	1.05	.60

See Nos. 3758-3760.

Island of Coco Cay, Jardines del Rey A1000

Bird, scenic view: 10c, Sterna antillarum, aerial view of island. 15c, Eudocimus albus, people on beach. 45c, Spindalis zena, couple on steps of resort complex. 50c, Turdus plumbeus, resort. 65c, Mimus polyglottos, resort. 75c, Phoenicopterus ruber, couple in pool at resort.

1995, Dec. 23
3703	A1000	10c multicolored	.20	.20
3704	A1000	15c multicolored	.30	.20
3705	A1000	45c multicolored	1.00	.55
3706	A1000	50c multicolored	1.10	.60
3707	A1000	65c multicolored	1.40	.80
3708	A1000	75c multicolored	1.60	1.00
		Nos. 3703-3708 (6)	5.60	3.35

Patriots — A1001

Designs: 15c, Carlos M. de Céspedes (1819-74). 65c, José Marti (1853-95). 75c, Antonio Maceo (1845-96). 1.05p, Ignacio Agramonte (1841-73). 2.05p, Máximo Gómez (1836-1905). 3p, Calixto Garcia (1839-98).

1996, Jan. 10
3709	A1001	15c green	.25	.20
3710	A1001	65c blue	1.10	.80
3711	A1001	75c carmine	1.25	1.00
3712	A1001	1.05p lilac	1.90	1.40
3713	A1001	2.05p brown	3.75	2.50
3714	A1001	3p light brown	5.25	3.75
		Nos. 3709-3714 (6)	13.50	9.65

See Nos. 3755-3757.

Organization of Solidarity of the Peoples of Africa, Asia and Latin America (OSPAAAL), 30th Anniv. — A1002

1996, Jan. 14
3715	A1002	65c multicolored	1.50	.75

Scientists — A1003

10c, Leonardo da Vinci (1452-1519). 15c, Mikhail V. Lomonosov (1711-65), atmospheric scientist. 65c, James Watt (1736-1819), engineer, inventor. 75c, Guglielmo Marconi (1874-1937), physicist. 85c, Charles R. Darwin (1809-82), naturalist.

1996, Jan. 30   Litho.   Perf. 12½
3716	A1003	10c multicolored	.35	.20
3717	A1003	15c multicolored	.35	.20
3718	A1003	65c multicolored	1.75	.80
3719	A1003	75c multicolored	2.00	1.00
3720	A1003	85c multicolored	2.25	1.00
		Nos. 3716-3720 (5)	6.70	3.20

1996 Summer Olympics, Atlanta — A1004

1996, Feb. 15   Litho.   Perf. 12½
3721	A1004	10c Athletics, vert.	.30	.20
3722	A1004	15c Weight lifting, vert.	.30	.20
3723	A1004	65c Judo, vert.	1.40	.80
3724	A1004	75c Wrestling	1.60	1.00
3725	A1004	85c Boxing	1.90	1.00
		Nos. 3721-3725 (5)	5.50	3.20

Souvenir Sheet
3726	A1004	1p Baseball, vert.	3.00	1.50

No. 3726 contains one 40x32mm stamp.

Espamer '96, Aviation and Space, Philatelic Exhibition, Seville — A1005

1996, Mar. 4
3727	A1005	15c C-4 Autogiro	.25	.20
3728	A1005	65c CASA C-352	1.25	.80
3729	A1005	75c Alcotan C-201	1.60	1.00
3730	A1005	85c CASA C-212	1.75	1.00
		Nos. 3727-3730 (4)	4.85	3.00

Juan C. Gundlach (1810-1896), Ornithologist — A1006

Birds: 10c, Ceryle alcyon. 15c, Setophaga ruticilla. 65c, Geothlypis trichas. 75c, Passerina ciris. 85c, Bombycilla cedrorum. 1p, Vireo gundlachi.

1996, Mar. 15   Perf. 12½
3731	A1006	10c multicolored	.30	.20
3732	A1006	15c multicolored	.30	.20
3733	A1006	65c multicolored	1.40	.80
3734	A1006	75c multicolored	1.60	1.00
3735	A1006	85c multicolored	1.90	1.00
		Nos. 3731-3735 (5)	5.50	3.20

Souvenir Sheet
3736	A1006	1p multicolored	3.75	1.90

No. 3736 contains one 40x32mm stamp.

Souvenir Sheet

ESPAMER '96, Stamp Exhibition of America and Europe, Seville — A1007

1996, Mar. 14   Litho.   Perf. 12½
3737 A1007 1p multicolored   3.00 1.50

First Man in Space, 35th Anniv. — A1008

Designs: 15c, Yuri A. Gagarin (1934-68). 65c, Spaceship, map showing orbital route.

1996, Apr. 12   Litho.   Perf. 12½
3738 A1008 15c multi   .25   .20
3739 A1008 65c multi, horiz.   1.10   .80

Bay of Pigs Invasion, 35th Anniv. — A1009

1996, Apr. 19
3740 A1009 15c shown   .35   .20
3741 A1009 65c Natl. flags   1.60   .80

Cuban Sailing Ships A1010

Designs: 10c, Bahama. 15c, Santísima Trinidad. 65c, Príncipe de Asturias. 75c, San Pedro de Alcántara. 85c, Santa Ana. 1p, San Genaro.

1996, May 8   Litho.   Perf. 12½
3742 A1010 10c multicolored   .20   .20
3743 A1010 15c multicolored   .30   .20
3744 A1010 65c multicolored   1.40   .80
3745 A1010 75c multicolored   1.60 1.00
3746 A1010 85c multicolored   1.75 1.00
      Nos. 3742-3746 (5)   5.25 3.20

Souvenir Sheet

3747 A1010 1p multicolored   2.00 1.00
    CAPEX '96. No. 3747 contains one 40x32mm stamp.

Fauna of the Caribbean A1011

Designs: 10c, Todus multicolor. No. 3749, Eulampis jugularis. No. 3750, Aix sponsa. No. 3751, Chaetodon ocellatus. No. 3752, Papilio cresphontes. No. 3753, Hypoplectrus indigo.

1996, June 18   Litho.   Perf. 12½
3748 A1011 10c multicolored   .30   .20
3749 A1011 15c multicolored   .30   .20
3750 A1011 15c multicolored   .30   .20
3751 A1011 15c multicolored   .30   .20
3752 A1011 65c multicolored   1.40   .80
3753 A1011 65c multicolored   1.40   .80
      Nos. 3748-3753 (6)   4.00 2.40

Jose M. Maceo Grajales (1849-96), Revolutionary War Leader — A1012

1996, July 5
3754 A1012 15c multicolored   .50   .20

Patriot Type of 1996

Designs: 10c. Serafin Sánchez. 85c, Juan Gualberto Gomez. 90c, Quintin Bandera.

1996, July 10
3755 A1001 10c orange   .20   .20
3756 A1001 85c olive   1.75 1.00
3757 A1001 90c olive brown   2.00 1.10
      Nos. 3755-3757 (3)   3.95 2.30

Generals Who Died in 1895 War Type of 1995

#3758, Esteban Tamayo (1843-96), Angel Guerra (1842-96). #3759, Juan Fernández Ruz (1821-96), José Maria Aguirre (1843-96), Serafin Sánchez (1846-96). #3760, Juan Bruno Zayas (1867-96), Pedro Vargas Sotomayor (1868-96).

1996, July 30
3758 A999 15c multicolored   .35   .20
3759 A999 15c multicolored   .35   .20
3760 A999 15c multicolored   .35   .20
  a.   Strip of 3, #3758-3760   1.70   .90
      Nos. 3758-3760 (3)   1.05   .60

Santiago de Cuba — A1013

Flower, scenic view: 15c, Jacaranda arborea, beach. 65c, Begonia bissei, Fort San Pedro de la Roca. 75c, Byrsonima crassifolia, palm trees, mountains, vert. 85c, Pereskia zinniiflora, church, vert.

Perf. 13x12½, 12½x13
1996, Sept. 27   Litho.
3761 A1013 15c multicolored   .30   .20
3762 A1013 65c multicolored   1.40   .80
3763 A1013 75c multicolored   1.60 1.00
3764 A1013 85c multicolored   1.75 1.00
      Nos. 3761-3764 (4)   5.05 3.00

Steam Locomotives — A1014

Designs: 10c, Baldwin 0-4-2, 1878. 15c, American 2-6-0, 1904. 65c, Baldwin 4-6-0, 1906. 75c, Rogers 2-4-4, 1914. 90c, Baldwin 2-8-0, 1920.

1996, Sept. 30   Perf. 12½
3765 A1014 10c multicolored   .30   .20
3766 A1014 15c multicolored   .30   .20
3767 A1014 65c multicolored   1.40   .80
3768 A1014 75c multicolored   1.60   .90
3769 A1014 90c multicolored   1.75 1.00
      Nos. 3765-3769 (5)   5.35 3.10

Traditional Costumes A1015

America Issue: 15c, Free black couple, 19th cent. 65c, Guayabera couple, 20th cent.

1996, Oct. 12   Litho.   Perf. 12½
3770 A1015 15c multicolored   .35   .20
3771 A1015 65c multicolored   1.60   .80

UNICEF, 50th Anniv. — A1016

1996, Nov. 8   Litho.   Perf. 12½
3772 A1016 15c multicolored   .50   .20

World Chess Championship Won by José Raúl Capablanca, 75th Anniv. — A1017

Designs: 15c, Portrait, chess board. 65c, Portrait, seated at chess board. 75c, Rook with top shaped as world, portrait. 85c, Playing chess as a child. 90c, In championship match, 1921.

1996, Nov. 30   Litho.   Perf. 12½
3773 A1017 15c multicolored   .25   .20
3774 A1017 65c multicolored   1.25   .80
3775 A1017 75c multicolored   1.40 1.00
3776 A1017 85c multicolored   1.60 1.00
3777 A1017 90c multicolored   1.75 1.10
      Nos. 3773-3777 (5)   6.25 4.10

Revolutionary Armed Forces and Return of Castro from Mexico, 40th Anniv. — A1018

1996, Dec. 2
3778 A1018 15c Yacht Granma   .25   .20
3779 A1018 65c Armed forces   1.60 1.00

Maj. Gen. Antonio Maceo (1845-96) — A1019

Designs: 10c, Monument, Santiago, vert. No. 3781, Portrait, vert. No. 3782, Monument, Duaba. 65c, Detail of painting showing Maceo dying from combat wounds. 75c, Maceo, young man and monument, San Pedro.

1996, Dec. 7
3780 A1019 10c multicolored   .20   .20
3781 A1019 15c multicolored   .30   .20
3782 A1019 15c multicolored   .30   .20
3783 A1019 65c multicolored   1.60 1.10
3784 A1019 75c multicolored   1.90 1.40
      Nos. 3780-3784 (5)   4.30 3.10

Medals Won at 1996 Summer Olympic Games, Atlanta — A1020

Medal, sport: No. 3785a, Gold, judo. b, Bronze, wrestling.
No. 3786: a, Gold, weight lifting. b, Gold, wrestling. c, Silver, fencing. d, Silver, swimming.
No. 3787: a, Gold, women's volleyball. b, Gold, boxing. c, Silver, women's running. d, Gold, baseball.

1996, Dec. 10
3785 A1020 10c Pair, #a-b + 4
             labels   .50   .25
3786 A1020 15c Block, #a-d + 2
             labels   1.25   .65
3787 A1020 65c Block, #a-d + 2
             labels   5.00 2.50
      Nos. 3785-3787 (3)   6.75 3.40

New Year 1996 (Year of the Rat) — A1021

1996, Dec. 28   Litho.   Perf. 12½
3788 A1021 15c multicolored   .50   .25

Espamer '98 — A1022

Locomotives: 15c, Minho Douro 0-6-0, Portugal. No. 3790, Vulcan Iron Works 0-4-0, Brazil. No. 3791, Baldwin 2-6-0, Dominican Republic. No. 3792, American Locomotive Co. 2-6-4, Panama. No. 3793, Baldwin 0-4-0, Puerto Rico. No. 3794, Slaughter, Gruning Co. 0-4-0, Spain. No. 3795, Yorkshire Engine Co. 4-4-0, Argentina. No. 3796, 2-6-0 Paraguay. No. 3797, H.K. Porter Co. 2-8-2, Chile. No. 3798, 2-6-0, Mexico.
1p, Baldwin 0-4-2 (1884), Cuba.

1996, Dec. 30
3789 A1022 15c multicolored   .30   .20
3790 A1022 65c multicolored   1.50   .85
3791 A1022 65c multicolored   1.50   .85
3792 A1022 65c multicolored   1.50   .85
3793 A1022 65c multicolored   1.50   .85
3794 A1022 65c multicolored   1.50   .85
3795 A1022 75c multicolored   1.75 1.00
3796 A1022 75c multicolored   1.75 1.00
3797 A1022 75c multicolored   1.75 1.00
3798 A1022 75c multicolored   1.75 1.00
      Nos. 3789-3798 (10)   14.80 8.45

Souvenir Sheet

3799 A1022 1p multicolored   3.50 1.75
    No. 3799 contains one 36x28mm.

Hong Kong '97, Intl. Philatelic Exhibition — A1023

Cats: 10c, Brown-point Siamese, vert. No. 3801, Japanese bobtail. No. 3802, Burmese, vert. No. 3803, Singapore. No. 3804, Korat. 1p, Blue-point Siamese.

1997, Jan. 15   **Litho.**   **Perf. 12½**
3800 A1023 10c multicolored   .25 .20
3801 A1023 15c multicolored   .30 .20
3802 A1023 15c multicolored   .30 .20
3803 A1023 65c multicolored   1.75 1.00
3804 A1023 75c multicolored   2.10 1.10
   Nos. 3800-3804 (5)   4.70 2.70

Souvenir Sheet
3805 A1023 1p multicolored   4.00 2.00

No. 3805 contains one 40x31mm stamp.

Motion Pictures, Cent. A1024

Film scenes from: 15c, "El Romance del Palmar," directed by Ramón Peón. 65c, "Memorias del Subdesarrollo," directed by Tomás Gutiérrez Alea, vert.

1997, Jan. 24   **Litho.**   **Perf. 13**
3806 A1024 15c multicolored   .30 .20
3807 A1024 65c multicolored   1.60 1.00

Zoo Animals A1025

Designs: 10c, Camelus dromedarius. No. 3809, Ailuropada melanoleuca. No. 3810, Cerothoterium simun. 75c, Pongo pygmaeus. 90c, Bison bonasus.

1997, Feb. 20   **Litho.**   **Perf. 12½**
3808 A1025 10c multicolored   .25 .20
3809 A1025 15c multicolored   .30 .20
3810 A1025 15c multicolored   .30 .20
3811 A1025 75c multicolored   1.75 1.00
3812 A1025 90c multicolored   2.00 1.10
   Nos. 3808-3812 (5)   4.60 2.70

New Year 1997 (Year of the Ox) — A1026

1997, Feb. 22
3813 A1026 15c multicolored   .50 .25

Attack on the Presidential Palace, 40th Anniv. — A1027

1997, Mar. 13   **Litho.**   **Perf. 12½**
3814 A1027 15c Menelao Mora Morales   .60 .20

1998 World Cup Soccer Championships, France — A1028

Action scenes: 10c, Three players. No. 3816, Player in green, player in blue & yellow. No. 3817, Player in yellow & black, player in green. 65c, Player in yellow & blue, player in blue and red. 75c, Player in red & blue, player in yellow & black. 1p, Player down.

1997, Mar. 25
3815 A1028 10c multicolored   .25 .20
3816 A1028 15c multicolored   .30 .20
3817 A1028 15c multicolored   .30 .20
3818 A1028 65c multicolored   1.75 1.00
3819 A1028 75c multicolored   2.00 1.25
   Nos. 3815-3819 (5)   4.60 2.85

Souvenir Sheet
3820 A1028 1p multicolored   2.40 1.25

No. 3820 contains one 40x31mm stamp.

Young Communist League (UJC), 35th Anniv. — A1029

1997, Apr. 4
3821 A1029 15c multicolored   .75 .20

Paddle Steamer Caledonia — A1030

Stamp Day: 15c, Maritime Postal Service, 170th anniv. 65c, Air Postal Service, 70th anniv.

1997, Apr. 24   **Litho.**   **Perf. 12½**
3822 A1030 15c multicolored   .40 .25
3823 A1030 65c multicolored   1.60 .95

Death of Generals in War of 1895, 102nd Anniv. — A1031

#3824, Adolfo de Castillo, Enrique del Junco Cruz-Muñoz. #3825, Alberto Rodríguez Acosta, Mariano Sánchez Vaillant.

1997, May 18   **Litho.**   **Perf. 12½**
3824 A1031 15c multicolored   .30 .20
3825 A1031 15c multicolored   .30 .20
   a.   Pair, #3824-3825   .65 .30

Gen. Gregorio Luperon, Death Cent. — A1032

1997, May 20
3826 A1032 65c multicolored   1.60 1.00

Butterflies — A1033

Designs: 10c, Eurema nicippe. No. 3828, Eurema dina. No. 3829, Colobura dirce clementi. 65c, Vanesa atalanta. 85c, Kricogonia castalia.

1997, May 20
3827 A1033 10c multicolored   .25 .20
3828 A1033 15c multicolored   .30 .20
3829 A1033 15c multicolored   .30 .20
3830 A1033 65c multicolored   1.60 .90
3831 A1033 85c multicolored   1.90 1.00
   Nos. 3827-3831 (5)   4.35 2.50

Cuban Assoc. of the UN, 50th Anniv. A1034

1997, May 31
3832 A1034 65c multicolored   1.60 .95

Chinese In Cuba, 150th Anniv. — A1035

1997, May 29   **Perf. 13**
3833 A1035 15c multicolored   .90 .50

14th World Festival of Youth and Students A1036

Designs: 10c, Dove holding olive twig, rainbow. No. 3835, Children playing on playground equipment, vert. No. 3836, Monument with arms extended. 65c, Maj. Ernesto "Che" Guevara, revolutionary hero. 75c, Monument, diff.

1997, July 28   **Litho.**   **Perf. 12½**
3834 A1036 10c multicolored   .25 .20
3835 A1036 15c multicolored   .30 .20
3836 A1036 15c multicolored   .30 .20
3837 A1036 65c multicolored   1.60 .95
3838 A1036 75c multicolored   1.90 1.00
   Nos. 3834-3838 (5)   4.35 2.55

Frank País (1934-57), Revolutionary Hero — A1037

1997, July 30
3839 A1037 15c multicolored   .50 .20

Seven Wonders of the Ancient World A1038

Designs: 10c, Lighthouse of Alexandria. No. 3841, Pyramids of Egypt. No. 3842, Gardens of Semiramis at Babylon. No. 3843, Colossus at Rhodes. No. 3844, Mausoleum of Halicarnassus. No. 3845, Statue of Zeus at Olympia. 75c, Temple of Artemis at Ephesus.

1997, July 30
3840 A1038 10c multicolored   .20 .20
3841 A1038 15c multicolored   .30 .20
3842 A1038 15c multicolored   .30 .20
3843 A1038 15c multicolored   .30 .20
3844 A1038 65c multicolored   1.60 .95
3845 A1038 65c multicolored   1.60 .95
3846 A1038 75c multicolored   1.75 1.00
   Nos. 3840-3846 (7)   6.05 3.70

Independence of India, 50th Anniv. — A1039

1997, Aug. 15
3847 A1039 15c Mahatma Gandhi   .50 .20

Caribbean Birds — A1040

#3848, Sicalis flaveola. #3849, Eubucco bourcierii. #3850, Trogon curucui. #3851, Amazona leucocephala. #3852, Amazona ochrocephala. #3853, Hylocharis eliciae. #3854, Carduelis carduelis.

1997, Aug. 15
3848 A1040 15c multicolored   .30 .20
3849 A1040 15c multicolored   .30 .20
3850 A1040 15c multicolored   .30 .20
3851 A1040 15c multicolored   .30 .20
3852 A1040 65c multicolored   1.60 1.00
3853 A1040 65c multicolored   1.60 1.00
3854 A1040 75c multicolored   1.90 1.10
   Nos. 3848-3854 (7)   6.30 3.90

Famous Composers — A1041

10c, Liszt. #3856, Chopin. #3857, Bach. #3858, Beethoven. 65c, Ignacio Cervantes (1847-1905). 75c, Mozart.

1997, Sept. 15   Litho.   Perf. 12½
3855	A1041	10c multicolored	.50	.20
3856	A1041	15c multicolored	.50	.25
3857	A1041	15c multicolored	.50	.25
3858	A1041	15c multicolored	.50	.25
3859	A1041	65c multicolored	1.75	.95
3860	A1041	75c multicolored	1.90	1.00
	Nos. 3855-3860 (6)		5.65	2.90

Tourism in Pinar del Rio — A1042

Bird, scene: 10c, Myadestes elisabeth, Viñales Valley. 15c, Corvus nasicus, Jutia Key. 65c, Dendroica pityophila, Soroa Falls. 75c, Tyrannus cubensis, San Juan River.

1997, Sept. 27   Litho.
3861	A1042	10c multi	.40	.20
3862	A1042	15c multi	.40	.25
3863	A1042	65c multi, vert.	1.60	.95
3864	A1042	75c multi, vert.	1.75	1.00
	Nos. 3861-3864 (4)		4.15	2.40

Caribbean Flowers — A1043

Designs: No. 3865, Hibiscus elatus (majagua). No. 3866, Cordia sebestena (vomitel). No. 3867, Bidens pilosa (romerillo). No. 3868, Catharanthus roseus (vicaria). 65c, Reullia tuberosa (salta perico). 75c, Turnera ulmifolia (marilope).

1997, Sept. 30
3865	A1043	15c multicolored	.40	.25
3866	A1043	15c multicolored	.40	.25
3867	A1043	15c multicolored	.40	.25
3868	A1043	15c multicolored	.40	.25
3869	A1043	65c multicolored	1.60	.95
3870	A1043	75c multicolored	1.75	.95
	Nos. 3865-3870 (6)		4.95	2.90

Eastern University, 50th Anniv. — A1044

1997, Oct. 1   Perf. 13
3871	A1044	15c multicolored	.50	.25

Che Guevara (1928-67), 5th Cuban Communist Party Congress A1045

1997, Oct. 8
3872	A1045	15c Flags	.40	.25
3873	A1045	15c Text, Guevara	1.60	.95
3874	A1045	75c Portrait of Guevara	1.75	.95
	Nos. 3872-3874 (3)		3.75	2.15

America Issue — A1046

1997, Oct. 12   Litho.   Perf. 13
3875	A1046	15c 19th cent. postman	.50	.25
3876	A1046	65c 20th cent. postman	1.60	.85

Hominids — A1047

Designs: 10c, Australopithecus. No. 3878, Pithecanthropus (Java man). No. 3879, Sinanthropus (Peking man). No. 3880, Neanderthal. 65c, Cro-magnon man. 75c, Oberkassel man.

1997, Oct. 30   Perf. 12½
3877	A1047	10c multicolored	.30	.20
3878	A1047	15c multicolored	.50	.25
3879	A1047	15c multicolored	.50	.25
3880	A1047	15c multicolored	.50	.25
3881	A1047	65c multicolored	1.75	.95
3882	A1047	75c multicolored	1.90	.95
	Nos. 3877-3882 (6)		5.45	2.85

October Revolution, 80th Anniv. — A1048

1997, Nov. 7   Perf. 12½
3884	A1048	75c multicolored	1.75	1.00

Cuban Railroad, 160th Anniv. — A1049

10c, John Bull, 1830, UK. No. 3886, Old Ironsides, Baldwin, 1832, US. No. 3887, Baldwin Pacific Type 4-6-2, 1910-13, US. 65c, TE.M4:1 diesel electric, 1970, USSR. 75c, TE.114-K, diesel electric, 1975, USSR.

1997, Nov. 19   Litho.   Perf. 12½
3885	A1049	10c multicolored	.25	.20
3886	A1049	15c multicolored	.30	.20
3887	A1049	15c multicolored	.30	.20
3888	A1049	65c multicolored	1.60	.95
3889	A1049	75c multicolored	1.75	.95
	Nos. 3885-3889 (5)		4.20	2.50

UN Conference on Commerce and Employment, Havana, 50th Anniv. — A1050

1997, Nov. 21
3890	A1050	65c multicolored	1.50	.95

Victor Manuel Garcia, Painter, Birth Cent. A1051

1997, Dec. 29   Litho.   Perf. 12½
3891	A1051	15c #1553, Garcia	.50	.25

Visit of Pope John Paul II A1052

Pope John Paul II, different coats of arms, and: 65c, Havana Cathedral. 75c, Basilica of Our Lady of Charity, Cobre, vert.
No. 3894, vert: a, Pope John Paul II greeting Fidel Castro. b, Pope waving.

1998, Jan. 18   Litho.   Perf. 12½
3892	A1052	65c multicolored	1.50	.95
3893	A1052	75c multicolored	1.75	.95

Souvenir Sheet of 2
3894	A1052	50c #a.-b.	3.00	1.50
	Nos. 3894a-3894b are 32x40mm.			

Assassination of Jesus Menendez, 50th Anniv. — A1053

1998, Jan. 22
3895	A1053	15c multicolored	.55	.25

1998 World Cup Soccer Championships, France — A1054

Various soccer plays: 10c, 2 players. #3897, Player in black & yellow. #3898, Player on ground, 1 in striped shirt. #3899, 3 players, 2 in striped shirts. #3900, 3 players, 2 in blue shirts.
1p, Player with #11 on sleeve.

1998, Feb. 10   Litho.   Perf. 12½
3896	A1054	10c multi, vert.	.50	.20
3897	A1054	15c multi, vert.	.60	.25
3898	A1054	15c multi, vert.	.60	.25
3899	A1054	65c multi	2.10	1.00
3900	A1054	65c multi	2.10	1.00
	Nos. 3896-3900 (5)		5.90	2.70

Souvenir Sheet
Perf. 13
3901	A1054	1p multicolored	3.00	1.50
	No. 3901 contains one 40x32mm stamp.			

Capt. Isabel Rubio Diaz, Medical Aide During Revolution, Death Cent. — A1055

1998, Feb. 15   Perf. 13
3902	A1055	15c multicolored	.65	.25

Brig. Gen. Vidal Ducasse Reeve (1852-98) A1056

1998, Feb. 19   Perf. 12½
3903	A1056	15c multicolored	.65	.25
	No. 3903 inscribed "Revee."			

"Radio Rebelde," 40th Anniv. — A1057

1998, Feb. 23
3904	A1057	15c multicolored	.65	.25

Fire Engines A1058

Designs: 10c, 1901 Shand Mason & Co., London. No. 3905, 1905 Horse-drawn municipal fire wagon, Havana, 1905. No. 3906, 1921 American-La France Fire Engine Co. 65c, 1952 Chevrolet 6400, US. 75c, 1956 American-La France Foamite Co., US.

1998, Mar. 10
3905	A1058	10c multicolored	.40	.20
3906	A1058	15c multicolored	.45	.25
3907	A1058	15c multicolored	.45	.25
3908	A1058	65c multicolored	1.50	.90
3909	A1058	75c multicolored	1.75	.90
	Nos. 3905-3909 (5)		4.55	2.50

Protest of Baragua, 120th Anniv. — A1059

1998, Mar. 15
3910	A1059	15c multicolored	.65	.25

Victory at Cuito Cuanavale, Angola, 10th Anniv. — A1060

1998, Mar. 23   Litho.   Perf. 12½
3911 A1060 15c multicolored   .65 .25

New Year 1998 (Year of the Tiger) — A1061

1998, Mar. 30
3912 A1061 15c multicolored   .65 .25

Dogs — A1062

1998, Apr. 15   Litho.   Perf. 12½
3913 A1062 10c Chihuahua   .40 .20
3914 A1062 15c Beagle   .45 .25
3915 A1062 15c Xoloitzcuintle   .45 .25
3916 A1062 65c German pointer   1.60 1.00
3917 A1062 75c Chow chow   1.90 1.25
   Nos. 3913-3917 (5)   4.80 2.95

Evolution of the Chimpanzee A1063

Pan troglodytes and: 10c, Proconsul. No. 3919, Cranium. No. 3920, Right hand and foot. 65c, New-born chimpanzee. 75c, Map of Africa showing chimpanzee's range.

1998, May 15   Litho.   Perf. 12½
3918 A1063 10c multicolored   .40 .20
3919 A1063 15c multicolored   .40 .25
3920 A1063 15c multicolored   .40 .25
3921 A1063 65c multicolored   1.60 1.25
3922 A1063 75c multicolored   1.75 1.25
   Nos. 3918-3922 (5)   4.55 3.20

Lisbon '98, World Stamp Exhibition — A1064

Deep sea fish: No. 3923, Raja batis. No. 3924, Eurypharynx pelecanoides. 65c, Cauliophryne. 75c, Chauliodus sloani.

1998, May 22   Litho.   Perf. 12½
3923 A1064 15c multicolored   .40 .25
3924 A1064 15c multicolored   .40 .25
3925 A1064 65c multicolored   1.60 1.10
3926 A1064 75c multicolored   1.80 1.25
   Nos. 3923-3926 (4)   4.20 2.85

Souvenir Sheet

Juvalux '98, World Stamp Exhibition for Youth Philately and Postal History, Luxembourg — A1065

1998, May 20   Litho.   Perf. 12½
3927 A1065 1p Postman on bicycle   3.00 1.50

Federico Garcia Lorca (1898-1936), Poet — A1066

1998, June 2
3928 A1066 75c multicolored   2.25 1.25

Intl. Year of the Oceans A1067

#3929, Canarreos flower coral, coral crab, small fish. #3030, French angel fish, brain coral, gorgonia.

1998, June 5
3929 A1067 65c multicolored   1.50 1.00
3930 A1067 65c multicolored   1.50 1.00
   a.   Pair, #3929-3930   3.50 1.75

Diana, Princess of Wales (1961-97) A1068

Various portraits, color of clothes: No. 3931, Pale yellow and pink. No. 3932, Black and white. No. 3933, Multicolored print. No. 3934, Red. No. 3935, Pink and black plaid. 65c, White. 75c, Blue.

1998, June 30   Litho.   Perf. 13
3931 A1068 10c multicolored   .30 .20
3932 A1068 10c multicolored   .30 .20
3933 A1068 10c multicolored   .30 .20
3934 A1068 15c multicolored   .40 .25
3935 A1068 15c multicolored   .40 .25
3936 A1068 65c multicolored   1.90 1.10
3937 A1068 75c multicolored   2.10 1.25
   Nos. 3931-3937 (7)   5.70 3.45

Expo 2000, Hanover A1069

#3938, Mascot, "Twipsy." #3939, Mascot in London, 1851. #3940, Mascot in Brussels, 1958. #3941, German flag, map of Germany. 65c, Mascot in Paris, 1889. 75c, Mascot on top of world, fireworks.

1998, July 31   Perf. 12½
3938 A1069 15c multi, vert.   .40 .25
3939 A1069 15c multi   .40 .25
3940 A1069 15c multi   .40 .25
3941 A1069 15c multi   .40 .25
3942 A1069 65c multi, vert.   1.90 1.00
3943 A1069 75c multi   2.10 1.25
   Nos. 3938-3943 (6)   5.60 3.25

Maracaibo '98, 18th Central America and Caribbean Games — A1070

1998, Aug. 8
3944 A1070 15c multicolored   .50 .20

Attack on Moncada Barracks, 45th Anniv. — A1071

Designs: 15c, Siboney farmhouse, Abel Santamaría. 65c, Barracks, José Marti.

1998, July 26   Litho.   Perf. 13
3945 A1071 15c multicolored   .40 .25
3946 A1071 65c multicolored   1.90 .95

Democratic Republic of Korea, 50th Anniv. — A1072

1998, Sept. 8   Litho.   Perf. 13
3947 A1072 75c Kim Il Sung (1912-94)   2.25 1.10

Japanese Immigration to Cuba, Cent. — A1073

1998, Sept. 9   Litho.   Perf. 13
3948 A1073 75c multicolored   2.25 1.10

Orchids A1074

10c, Coelogyne flaccida. #3950, Dendrobium fimbriatum. #3951, Arunding graminifolia. #3952, Bletia patula. #3953, Phaius tankervilliaea.

1998, Sept. 10
3949 A1074 10c multicolored   .30 .20
3950 A1074 15c multicolored   .50 .25
3951 A1074 15c multicolored   .50 .25
3952 A1074 65c multicolored   1.90 1.00
3953 A1074 65c multicolored   1.90 1.00
   Nos. 3949-3953 (5)   5.10 2.70

5th Congress of the Revolution Defense Committees A1075

1998, Sept. 25   Litho.   Perf. 13
3954 A1075 15c multicolored   .45 .20

World Tourism Day — A1076

Holguin Province, reptiles: 10c, Looking through gateway, city of Gibara, anolis equestris, vert. 15c, Mayabe Valley, anolis vermiculatus, vert. 65c, Guardalavaca Beach, anolis allisoni. 75c, Mayari pine forest, anolis mestrei.

1998, Sept. 27
3955 A1076 10c multicolored   .30 .20
3956 A1076 15c multicolored   .50 .25
3957 A1076 65c multicolored   1.90 .95
3958 A1076 75c multicolored   2.10 1.25
   Nos. 3955-3958 (4)   4.80 2.65

Women Who Aided Cuban Revolutionary Movements A1077

America Issue: 65c, Bernarda Toro Pelegrin (1852-1911). 75c, Maria Magdalena Cabrales Issac (1842-1905).

1998, Oct. 12
3959 A1077 65c multicolored   1.90 .95
3960 A1077 75c multicolored   2.10 1.25

World Wildlife Fund Protected Fauna — A1078

Cuban Natl. Ballet, 50th Anniv. — A1079

Arantinga Euops: 10c, Two on tree branch. 15c, One looking out of nest. 65c, One on tree branch. 75c, One up close.

1998, Oct. 21
3961 A1078 10c multicolored .45 .30
3962 A1078 15c multicolored .65 .50
3963 A1078 65c multicolored 2.75 .95
3964 A1078 75c multicolored 3.25 1.25
    Nos. 3961-3964 (4) 7.10 3.00

1998, Oct. 28
3965 A1079 15c Swan Lake .50 .25
3966 A1079 65c Giselle 1.90 .95

Massacre of O'Farrill and Goicuria, 40th Anniv. — A1080

Rogelio Perea, Angel Ameijeiras, Pedro Gutiérrez.

1998, Nov. 8
3967 A1080 15c multicolored .45 .20

Battle of Guisa, 40th Anniv. A1081

Design: Capt. Braulio Coroneaux, tank.

1998, Nov. 30   Litho.   Perf. 12½
3968 A1081 15c multicolored .45 .20

A1082

A1083

1998, Dec. 10   Litho.   Perf. 12½
3969 A1082 65c multicolored 1.90 .95
    Universal Declaration of Human Rights, 50th anniv.

1998, Dec. 11   Perf. 13
    Calixto Garcia Iñiguez (1839-98), revolutionary Major General.
3970 A1083 65c multicolored 1.90 .95

Padre Félix Varela (1788-1853) — A1084

1998, Dec. 16
3971 A1084 75c multicolored 2.25 1.10

War for Independence, Cent. — A1085

War heroes, historical scene: No. 3972, Carlos Manuel de Céspedes. No. 3973, Ignacio Agramonte. No. 3974, Máximo Gómez. No. 3975, José Maceo. No. 3976, Salvador Cisneros. No. 3978, Calixto Garcia. No. 3979, Adolfo Flor. No. 3980, Serafin Sánchez. 65c, José Marti. 75c, Antonio Maceo.

1998, Dec. 25   Litho.   Perf. 12½
3972 A1085 15c multicolored .45 .25
3973 A1085 15c multicolored .45 .25
3974 A1085 15c multicolored .45 .25
3975 A1085 15c multicolored .45 .25
3976 A1085 15c multicolored .45 .25
3977 A1085 15c multicolored .45 .25
3978 A1085 15c multicolored .45 .25
3979 A1085 15c multicolored .45 .25
3980 A1085 65c multicolored 1.90 .95
3981 A1085 75c multicolored 2.10 1.10
    a.   Sheet of 10, #3972-3981 + 3
        labels 8.00 8.00
    Nos. 3972-3981 (10) 7.60 4.05

Battle for Palma Soriano, 40th Anniv. A1086

1998, Dec. 27   Litho.   Perf. 13
3982 A1086 15c multicolored .45 .20

Cuban Revolution, 40th Anniv. — A1087

a, Boat, soldiers in water. b, Fidel Castro with soldier. c, Castro giving speech, pigeons.

1999, Jan. 1
3983 A1087 65c Strip of 3, #a.-c. 4.75 2.40

Natl. Revolutionary Police, 40th Anniv. — A1088

1999, Jan. 5
3984 A1088 15c multicolored .50 .20

Cuban Workers' Trade Union Organization, 60th Anniv. — A1089

1999, Jan. 28   Litho.   Perf. 12½
3985 A1089 15c multicolored .45 .20

New Year 1999 (Year of the Rabbit) — A1090

1999, Feb. 5   Perf. 13
3986 A1090 75c multicolored 1.60 1.10

Lenin (1870-1924) — A1091

1999, Feb. 21   Litho.   Perf. 12½
3987 A1091 75c multicolored 1.60 1.10

Dinosaurs — A1092

1999, Mar. 10
3988 A1092 10c Ornithosuchus .30 .25
3989 A1092 15c Saltopus .50 .25
3990 A1092 15c Bactrosaurus .50 .25
3991 A1092 65c Protosuchus 1.90 .95
3992 A1092 75c Mussaurus 2.10 1.10
    Nos. 3988-3992 (5) 5.30 2.80

Cuban Musicians — A1093

1999, Mar. 22   Perf. 13
3993 A1093 5c Dámaso Pérez
        Prado .20 .20
3994 A1093 15c Benny Moré .50 .25
3995 A1093 15c Chano Pozo .50 .25
3996 A1093 35c Miguelito
        Valdés 1.25 .50
3997 A1093 65c Bola de Nieve 1.90 .95
3998 A1093 75c Rita Montaner 2.10 1.10
    Nos. 3993-3998 (6) 6.45 3.25

Simón Bolivar's Visit to Cuba, Bicent. A1094

1999, Mar. 25
3999 A1094 65c Portrait 1.90 .95
4000 A1094 65c Monument 1.90 .95
    a.   Pair, #3999-4000 4.25 2.00

State Security Organization, 40th Anniv. — A1095

1999, Mar. 26   Litho.   Perf. 12½
4001 A1095 65c multicolored 1.90 .95

Souvenir Sheet

China '99 World Philatelic Exhibition — A1096

1999, Apr. 10   Litho.   Perf. 12½
4002 A1096 1p Giant panda 3.00 1.50

Stamp Day A1097

1999, Apr. 24
4003 A1097 15c Postal rocket .50 .20
4004 A1097 65c Post rider 1.90 .80
    Test of Cuban Postal Rocket, 60th anniv. Insurgent Postal Service, 130th anniv.

Casa de las Américas, 40th
Anniv. — A1098

1999, Apr. 24
4005 A1098 65c multicolored   1.90 .80

Souvenir Sheet

IBRA '99, World Philatelic Exhibition,
Nuremberg — A1099

1999, Apr. 27
4006 A1099 1p Train   3.00 1.50

Agrarian
Reform
Law,
40th
Anniv.
A1100

1999, May 17
4007 A1100 65c multicolored   1.60 .80

Felipe
Poey,
Scientist,
Birth
Bicent.
A1101

Fish: 5c, Gramma loreto Poey. 15c, Liopro-
poma rubre Poey. 40c, Hypoplectrus gummigutta. #74011, Stegastes dorsopunicans.
1p, Portrait of Poey, hypoplectrus
guttavarius.

1999, May 26   Litho.   Perf. 12½
4008 A1101 5c multicolored   .20 .20
4009 A1101 15c multicolored   .40 .20
4010 A1101 65c multicolored   1.90 .80
4011 A1101 65c multicolored   1.90 .80
    Nos. 4008-4011 (4)   4.40 2.00
Souvenir Sheet
Perf. 13¼x13
4012 A1101 1p multicolored   3.00 1.00
No. 4012 contains one 32x40mm stamp.

Souvenir Sheet

Philexfrance '99, World Philatelic
Exhibition — A1102

Sculpture in sheet margin: "1814," by Jean
Louis Meissonier (1815-1891).

1999, June 2   Perf. 13
4013 A1102 1p multicolored   3.00 1.50

1999 Pan-American Games,
Winnipeg — A1103

1999, June 25   Litho.   Perf. 13
4014 A1103 15c Baseball   .40 .20
4015 A1103 65c Volleyball, vert 1.90 .80
4016 A1103 75c Boxing   2.10 .90
    Nos. 4014-4016 (3)   4.40 1.90

People's
Republic
of China,
50th
Anniv.
A1104

5c, Victory at Wioming, by Gao Hong. 15c,
Nanchang Insurrection, by Cai Lang. 40c, Red
Army Crossing a Swamp, by Gao Quan. 65c,
Occupation of the Presidential Palace, by
Cheng Yifei and Wei Jingshan. 75c, Proclama-
tion of the People's Republic of China, by
Dong Xiwen.

1999, Aug. 21   Litho.   Perf. 12¾
4017 A1104 5c multicolored   .20 .20
4018 A1104 15c multicolored   .40 .25
4019 A1104 40c multicolored   1.10 .70
4020 A1104 65c multicolored   1.75 1.10
4021 A1104 75c multicolored   2.00 1.40
    Nos. 4017-4021 (5)   5.45 3.65

China 1999 World Philatelic Exhibition,
Beijing — A1105

No. 4022, Morning Glories, by Qi Baishi.
No. 4023, Three Galloping Horses, by Xu
Beihong. No. 4024, Hunan Woman, by Fu
Baoshi. No. 4025, Birthplace of Luxun, by Wu
Guanzhong. No. 4026, Horse Riders, by
Huangzhou. 40c, Pine Tree, by He Xiangning.
65c, Sleep, by Jin Shangyi. 75c, Poetic Scene
in Xun Yang, by Chen Yifei.

1999, Aug. 22   Litho.   Perf. 13
4022 A1105 5c multicolored   .20 .20
4023 A1105 5c multicolored   .20 .20
4024 A1105 15c multicolored   .40 .25
4025 A1105 15c multicolored   .40 .25
4026 A1105 15c multicolored   .40 .25
4027 A1105 40c multicolored   1.10 .70
4028 A1105 65c multicolored   1.75 1.10
4029 A1105 75c multicolored   2.00 1.25
    a.   Sheet of 8, #4022-4029 + la-
         bel   8.00 8.00
    Nos. 4022-4029 (8)   6.45 4.20

UPU,
125th
Anniv.
A1106

1999, Sept. 16   Litho.   Perf. 12¾
4030 A1106 75c multicolored   1.50 1.00

World
Tourism
Day
A1107

Butterflies and Havana tourist sites: 10c,
Antia numidia, Morro Castle. 15c, Papilio
polyxenes, Havana Cathedral. 65c, Dryas
julia, Convent of San Francisco. 75c, Eueides
cleobaea, Capitol.

1999, Sept. 27   Perf. 12½x12¾
4031 A1107 10c multicolored   .25 .20
4032 A1107 15c multicolored   .40 .25
4033 A1107 65c multicolored   1.75 1.00
4034 A1107 75c multicolored   2.00 1.10
    Nos. 4031-4034 (4)   4.40 2.55

Expo
2000,
Hanover,
Germany
A1108

5c, World map, Expo 2000 emblem. #4036,
"Twipsy" mascot, vert. #4037, "Twipsy" and
1876 Philadelphia Exposition. #4038,
"Twipsy" and 1970 Osaka Exposition. 65c,
"Twipsy" and 2000 Exposition. 75c, "Twipsy"
and 1967 Montreal Exposition.

1999, Oct. 1   Perf. 12¾
4035 A1108 5c multicolored   .20 .20
4036 A1108 15c multicolored   .35 .25
4037 A1108 15c multicolored   .35 .25
4038 A1108 15c multicolored   .35 .25
4039 A1108 65c multicolored   1.60 1.00
4040 A1108 75c multicolored   2.00 1.10
    Nos. 4035-4040 (6)   4.85 3.05

Cubana Airlines, 70th Anniv. — A1109

1999, Oct. 8   Perf. 12½x12¼
4041 A1109 15c Fokker   .35 .25
4042 A1109 15c DC-10   .35 .25
4043 A1109 65c A-320   1.60 1.00
4044 A1109 75c DC-3   2.00 1.10
    Nos. 4041-4044 (4)   4.30 2.60

America Issue,
A New
Millennium
Without
Arms — A1110

1999, Oct. 12   Perf. 12¾
4045 A1110 15c Pigeon, mush-
           room cloud   .40 .25
4046 A1110 65c Dove, globe   1.60 1.10

National Instiutions, 40th
Anniv. — A1111

1999, Oct. 16   Perf. 12¾
4047 A1111 15c MINFAR   .35 .25
4048 A1111 65c Natl. Revolution-
           ary Militia   1.50 1.00

Disappearance
of Camilo
Cienfuegos,
40th
Anniv. — A1112

1999, Oct. 28   Litho.   Perf. 12¾
4049 A1112 15c multicolored   1.40 .25

Souvenir Sheet

12th Congress of Cuban Philatelic
Federation — A1113

1999, Dec. 11   Perf. 13
4050 A1113 1p multicolored   2.50 1.25

Ernest Hemingway (1899-1961),
Writer — A1114

1999, Dec. 15   Perf. 12½x12¼
4051 A1114 65c multicolored   1.50 1.00

9th Summit of Ibero-American Heads
of State and Government,
Havana — A1115

Designs: 65c, Plaza Vieja. 75c, Plaza of St.
Francis of Assisi.
1p, Plaza de Armas.

1999, Nov. 5   Litho.   Perf. 12¾x12½
4052 A1115 65c multi   1.50 1.00
4053 A1115 75c multi   1.60 1.10
Souvenir Sheet
Perf. 13
4054 A1115 1p multi   2.50 1.25

No. 4054 contains one 40x31mm stamp.

Rubén Martínez Villena (1899-1934),
Revolutionary — A1116

1999, Dec. 20   Perf. 12½x12¾
4055 A1116 15c multi   .40 .25

Dr. Tomás
Romay Chacón
(1764-1849)
A1117

1999, Dec. 21   Perf. 13
4056 A1117 65c multi   1.40 .90

New Year 2000 (Year of the
Dragon) — A1118

2000, Jan. 10   Perf. 12½
4057 A1118 15c multi   .40 .25

Folklore
A1119

Paintings depicting Cuban folklore by Con-
cepción Ferrant (1882-1968): 10c, Rumba
Caliente. 15c, Cachumba. 65c, En Casa de un
Babalao. 75c, Tata Cuñengue.

2000, Jan. 26   Perf. 12½x12¾
4058 A1119 10c multi   .25 .25
4059 A1119 15c multi   .35 .30
4060 A1119 65c multi   1.40 1.00
4061 A1119 75c multi   1.60 1.10
    Nos. 4058-4061 (4)   3.60 2.65

Butterflies — A1120

10c, Helcyra superba. No. 4063, Pantaporia
punctata. No. 4064, Neptis themis. 65c,
Curetis acuta. 75c, Chrysozephyrus ataxus.

2000, Feb. 25   Perf. 12¾
4062 A1120 10c multi   .30 .30
4063 A1120 15c multi   .40 .30
4064 A1120 15c multi   .40 .30
4065 A1120 65c multi   1.60 1.25
4066 A1120 75c multi   1.90 1.40
    Nos. 4062-4066 (5)   4.60 3.50

Bangkok 2000 Stamp Exhibition.

Group of 77 South Summit,
Havana — A1121

2000, Apr. 7   Litho.   Perf. 13x12½
4067 A1121 75c multi   2.00 1.25

Lenin, 130th
Anniv. of
Birth — A1122

2000, Apr. 22   Perf. 12¾
4068 A1122 75c multi   2.00 1.25

Che
Guevara
in
Congo,
35th
Anniv.
A1123

2000, Apr. 24
4069 A1123 65c multi   1.75 1.10

Stamp
Day — A1124

Designs: 65c, Cuba #2, building. 90c, Airplane, cover, Jaime Gonzáles, pilot of first
experimental airmail flight in Cuba.

2000, Apr. 24
4070 A1124 65c multi   1.75 1.10
4071 A1124 90c multi   2.25 1.50

Capt. San Luis
(Eliseo Reyes),
Military Hero
(1940-67)
A1125

2000, Apr. 27
4072 A1125 65c multi   1.75 1.10

The
Stamp
Show
2000,
London
A1126

Locomotives: 5c, 1882 Baldwin 0-6-0. 10c,
1895 Baldwin 2-8-0. 15c, 1912 Baldwin 2-8-0.
65c, 1919 Alco 2-8-0. 75c, 1925 Alco 2-8-2.
1p, 1920 Henschel 2-6-0.

2000, May 5   Perf. 12¾
4073 A1126 5c multi   .20 .20
4074 A1126 10c multi   .30 .25
4075 A1126 15c multi   .40 .30
4076 A1126 65c multi   1.60 1.10
4077 A1126 75c multi   1.90 1.25
    Nos. 4073-4077 (5)   4.40 3.10
Souvenir Sheet
Perf. 13
4078 A1126 1p multi   3.00 1.50

No. 4078 contains one 40x32mm stamp.

WIPA 2000 Philatelic Exhibition,
Vienna — A1127

Airships of: 10c, Henri Giffart, 1852. 15c,
Albert and Gaston Tissandier, 1883, vert. 50c,
Charles Renard and Arthur Krebs, 1884. 65c,
Pierre and Paul Lebaudy, 1903. 75c, August
von Perseval, 1906.
1p, Ferdinand von Zeppelin.

Perf. 12½x12¼, 12¼x12½
2000, May 18
4079 A1127 10c multi   .35 .25
4080 A1127 15c multi   .50 .30
4081 A1127 50c multi   1.40 .90
4082 A1127 65c multi   1.90 1.10
4083 A1127 75c multi   2.10 1.25
    Nos. 4079-4083 (5)   6.25 3.80
Souvenir Sheet
Perf. 12½
4084 A1127 1p multi   3.00 1.50

No. 4084 contains one 40x32mm stamp.

Second World
Meeting of
Friendship and
Solidarity With
Cuba — A1128

2000, June 23   Litho.   Perf. 12¾
4085 A1128 65c multi   1.50 1.10

José de la Luz y Caballero (1800-62),
Educator — A1129

2000, July 11   Perf. 12½x12¼
4086 A1129 65c multi   1.50 1.10

Amadeo Roldan (1900-39),
Violinist — A1130

2000, July 12   Perf. 12¾
4087 A1130 65c multi   1.50 1.10

La Edad de
Oro, by José
Marti — A1131

5c, Bebé y El Señor Don Pomposo. 10c, La
Muñeca Negra. 15c, Nene Traviesa. 50c, Los
Dos Ruiseñores. 65c, Frontispiece of La Edad
de Oro. 75c, El Camarón Encantado.

2000, July 20
4088-4093 A1131 Set of 6   6.00 4.25
4093a   Sheet of 6, #4088-4093 6.00 6.00

Latin American Association for
Integration — A1132

2000, Aug. 12
4094 A1132 65c multi   1.75 1.25

Souvenir Sheet

Olymphilex 2000, Sydney — A1133

2000, Aug. 17 *Perf. 13*
4095 A1133 1p multi 2.25 1.10

2000 Summer Olympics, Sydney A1134

Designs: 5c, Runners. 15c, Soccer. 65c, Baseball. 75c, Cycling.

2000, Aug. 20 *Perf. 12¾*
4096-4099 A1134 Set of 4 4.50 4.00

Dr. Pedro Kouri Esmeja (1900-64) A1135

2000, Aug. 21 *Litho.*
4100 A1135 65c multi 1.75 1.25

Federation of Cuban Women, 40th Anniv. — A1136

2000, Aug. 23
4101 A1136 15c multi .40 .30

España 2000 Intl. Philatelic Exhibition — A1137

Designs: 10c, 1851 Havana-Bilbao stampless cover, ship. No. 4103, 15c, Spain #1, Cibeles Fountain, Madrid. No. 4104, 15c, 1850 Zaragoza-Cadiz cover, Palacio de Cristal, Madrid. 65c, Spain #1-5, Palacio de Comunicaciones, Madrid. 75c, Cuba #1, Centro Gallego, Havana.

2000, Sept. 7 *Perf. 12¾x12½*
4102-4106 A1137 Set of 5 4.75 3.00
4106a Sheet of 5, #4102-4106 + label 4.75 4.75

Souvenir Sheet
Perf. 12½
4107 A1137 100c Queen Isabella II, vert. 3.00 2.25

No. 4107 contains one 32x40mm stamp.

Beaches — A1138

#4108, Coconuts Bay, PRC. #4109, Varadero Beach, Cuba.

2000, Sept. 26 *Perf. 12½x12¼*
4108-4109 A1138 15c Set of 2 .80 .80
4109a Pair, #4108-4109 .80 .80

See People's Republic of China No. 3052.

World Tourism Day — A1139

Marine life: 10c, Eretmochelys imbricata, vert. 15c, Epinephelus striatus, vert. 65c, Pomacanthus paru. 75c, Anisotremus surinamensis.

Perf. 12½x12¾, 12¾x12½
2000, Sept. 27
4110-4113 A1139 Set of 4 4.00 2.00

Committees of Defense of the Revolution, 40th Anniv. — A1140

2000, Sept. 28 *Perf. 12¾*
4114 A1140 15c multi .40 .30

America Issue — AIDS Prevention A1141

Ribbon, heart-shaped map and: 15c, Family. 65c, Couple.

2000, Oct. 12
4115-4116 A1141 Set of 2 2.75 1.25

Cuban Military in Angola, 25th Anniv. — A1142

2000, Nov. 7
4117 A1142 75c multi 2.00 1.40

Visit by Alexander von Humboldt, Bicent. — A1143

Humboldt and: 15c, House in Trinidad. 65c, House in Havana, Political Essay on the Island of Cuba.

2000, Dec. 19 *Litho.* *Perf. 12¾*
4118-4119 A1143 Set of 2 2.50 1.25

20th Pan-American Railway Congress A1144

2000, Sept. 18 *Litho.* *Perf. 12¾*
4120 A1144 65c multi 1.75 1.25

Millennium — A1145

Snails: a, Polymita versicolor. b, Polymita picta iolimbata. c, Polymita picta roseolimbata. d, Polymita picta picta. e, Polymita picta nigrolimbata.

2000, Dec. 20
4121 A1145 65c Block of 5, #a-e, + label 8.00 4.00

New Year 2001 (Year of the Snake) — A1146

2001, Jan. 10
4122 A1146 15c multi .50 .25

Hong Kong 2001 Stamp Exhibition — A1147

Birds: 5c, Aix galericulata. 10c, Chrysolophus pictus. 15c, Ardea cinerea. 65c, Gallus gallus. 75c, Streptotelia decaocto.

2001, Jan. 25 *Perf. 12¾*
4123-4127 A1147 Set of 5 4.50 3.25

Souvenir Sheet
Perf. 12½
4128 A1147 1p Grus grus 3.00 1.25

No. 4128 contains one 32x40mm stamp.

National Institute for Sport Physical Education and Recreation, 40th Anniv. — A1148

2001, Feb. 23 *Perf. 12½x12¼*
4129 A1148 65c multi 1.60 .80

UN High Commissioner for Refugees, 50th Anniv. — A1149

2001, Mar. 15 *Perf. 12¾x12½*
4130 A1149 65c multi 1.50 .75

Antique Locomotives — A1150

Locomotives from, 10c, 1863. 15c, 1876. 40c, 1885. 65c, 1914. 75c, 1932.

2001, Mar. 20   **Perf. 12½x12¼**
4131-4135 A1150   Set of 5   4.75 2.40

105th Interparliamentary Union Congress, Havana — A1151

2001, Mar. 30   **Perf. 12¾**
4136 A1151 65c multi   1.75 .80

Bay of Pigs Invasion, 40th Anniv. — A1152

2001, Apr. 19   **Perf. 12¾x12½**
4137 A1152 65c multi   1.50 .75

Cats and Dogs A1153

Designs: 10c, Cats, emblem of Cat Aficionados Association. No. 4139, 15c, Dogs, Cats, emblem of Aniplant. No. 4140, 15c, Dogs, emblem of Cynological Federation of Cuba. 65c, Dogs, emblem of Sporting Dog Federation of Cuba. 75c, Dogs, cats.

2001, Apr. 25   **Perf. 12½x12¾**
4138-4142 A1153   Set of 5   4.00 2.00

Radio Havana, 40th Anniv. — A1154

2001, May 1   **Perf. 12½x12¼**
4143 A1154 65c multi   1.50 .75

Tourism Convention — A1155

2001, May 7   **Perf. 12¾x12½**
4144 A1155 65c multi   1.50 .75

Belgica 2001 Intl. Stamp Exhibition, Brussels A1156

Designs: 5c, St. Michel Cathedral. 10c, Sablon Church, horiz. 15c, Royal Residence, horiz. 65c, Sacred Heart Basilica, horiz. 75c, Atomium.
1p, Royal Palace.

2001, May 10   **Perf. 12¾**
4145-4149 A1156   Set of 5   4.00 2.00
         Souvenir Sheet
         Perf. 12½
4150 A1156 100c multi   2.40 1.25

No. 4150 contains one 32x40mm stamp.

Interior Ministry, 40th Anniv. A1157

2001, June 6   **Perf. 12¾**
4151 A1157 65c multi   1.75 .80

Phila Nippon '01, Japan A1158

Japanese trains: 5c., JR 500. 10c, JR 700. 15c, MAX 1. 65c, MAX 2. 75c, 300.

2001, June 20   Litho.   **Perf. 12¾**
4152-4156 A1158   Set of 5   3.75 1.50
         Souvenir Sheet
         Perf. 12½
4157 A1158 100c Zero   2.40 1.25

No. 4157 contains one 40x32mm stamp.

Republic of San Marino, 1700th Anniv. — A1159

2001, July 20   Litho.   **Perf. 12½x12¼**
4158 A1159 75c multi   1.75 .75

Aquaculture — A1160

Designs: 5c, Tinca tinca. 10c, Rana temporaria. 15c, Cardisoma guanhumi. 65c, Mytius edulis. 75c, Tilapia mariae.
1p, Potamobius pallipes.

2001, Sept. 17   **Perf. 12¾**
4159-4163 A1160   Set of 5   3.75 1.50
         Souvenir Sheet
         Perf. 12½
4164 A1160 1p multi   2.40 1.25

No. 4164 contains one 40x32mm stamp.

Recovery of Raw Materials, 40th Anniv. — A1161

2001, Sept. 21   **Perf. 12¾x12½**
4165 A1161 65c multi   1.60 .75

Tourism — A1162

Designs: 10c, Valle de Viñales. 15c, Trinidad. 65c, Sirena Beach, Cayo Largo del Sur. 75c, Morro Castle, Havana.

2001, Sept. 27
4166-4169 A1162   Set of 4   3.75 1.75

Year of Dialogue Among Civilizations A1163

2001, Oct. 9   **Perf. 12¾**
4170 A1163 65c multi   1.50 .75

America Issue — UNESCO World Heritage A1164

Flora and fauna from Desembarco del Granma Natl. Park: 15c, Tetramicra malpighiarum. 65c, Liggus vittatus.

2001, Oct. 12   **Perf. 12½x12¾**
4171-4172 A1164   Set of 2   1.75 .85

José Marti National Library, Cent. A1165

2001, Oct. 18   **Perf. 12¾**
4173 A1165 15c multi   .35 .25

Cuban Airliner Explosion Near Barbados, 25th Anniv. — A1166

Various details of painting.

2001, Oct. 22
4174   Horiz. strip of 5   3.25 1.60
   a.   A1166 5c shown   .20 .20
   b.   A1166 10c multi   .20 .20
   c.   A1166 15c multi   .35 .20
   d.   A1166 50c multi   1.10 .55
   e.   A1166 65c multi   1.40 .90

Eduardo R. Chibas, Communist Leader, Cent. of Birth — A1167

2001, Nov. 27   Litho.   **Perf. 13**
4175 A1167 65c multi   1.60 .80

Napoleonic Museum, 40th Anniv. — A1168

Equestrian statues of Napoleon and map of battle of: No. 4176, 10c, Eylau. No. 4177, 10c, Marengo. 65c, Waterloo. 75c, Aboukir.

2001, Dec. 1   **Perf. 12¾x12½**
4176-4179 A1168   Set of 4   3.75 1.75

Pablo de la Torriente Brau (1901-36), Poet — A1169

2001, Dec. 12   **Perf. 12¾**
4180 A1169 75c multi   1.75 .80

Cuban Federation of Pigeon Fanciers, 4th Congress A1170

Pigeons: No. 4181, 65c, Empedrado oscura 2021-61-ME. No. 4182, 65c, Empedrado claro 2241-55-ME. No. 4183, 65c, Mosaico 1561-66-HM. No. 4184, 65c, Mosaico, 3013-67-HM. No. 4185, 65c Bronceado, 338-59-HE.

2001, Dec. 14   **Perf. 12½**
4181-4185 A1170   Set of 5   7.00 3.50

Film Stars Who Never Won Academy Awards A1171

Designs: 5c, Tyrone Power. No. 4187, 10c, Ava Gardner. No. 4188, 10c, Steve McQueen. No. 4189, 15c, Rita Hayworth. No. 4190, 15c, Marilyn Monroe. No. 4191, 15c, James Dean. No. 4192, 65c, Rock Hudson. No. 4193, 65c, Natalie Wood. 75c, Richard Burton.

2001, Dec. 20
4186-4194 A1171   Set of 9   8.00 3.50
  a. Sheet of 9, #4186-4194   8.00 3.50

New Year 2002 (Year of the Horse) — A1172

2002, Jan. 21 Litho. Perf. 12½x12¾
4195 A1172 15c multi   .45 .30

Cigar Production — A1173

Cigars and: 5c, Hat, Cuba No. 358, tobacco leaf. 10c, Clock, cigar cylinder. 15c, Map of Cuba, Simon Bolivar. 65c, Cuba Nos. 356, 357, map, cigar smoker. 75c, Flag, tobacco field, man.
  1p, Fidel Castro, map, star.

2002, Feb. 15   Perf. 12¾
4196-4200 A1173   Set of 5   4.00 2.00
Souvenir Sheet
Perf. 1313¼
4201 A1173 1p multi   2.50 1.25

Fourth Havana Festival, Cohiba brand, 36th anniv. No. 4201 contains one 40x32mm stamp.

Second UPAEP Information Workshop — A1174

2002, Feb. 21   Perf. 12½x12¼
4202 A1174 65c multi   1.50 .75

Explorers A1175

Explorers: 5c, Reading map. 15c, Tying knots. 50c, Starting campfire for cooking. 65c, Starting fire. 75c, Using orientation techniques.

2002, Mar. 20   Perf. 12½
4203-4207 A1175   Set of 5   5.00 2.50
  a. Sheet of 5, #4203-4207, + label   7.00 3.50

Union of Young Communists, 40th Anniv. — A1176

2002, Apr. 4   Perf. 12½x12¼
4208 A1176 15c multi   .30 .25

ExpoVid 2002 Wine Event — A1177

Designs: 15c, Cigar smokers, wine bottles and glasses, map of wine producing areas. 65c, Wine glass and barrels. 75c, Wine glass and vineyard.

2002, June 5   Perf. 12¾x12½
4209-4211 A1177   Set of 3   3.50 1.75

2002 World Cup Soccer Championships, Japan and Korea — A1178

Player and flag from: No. 4212, 15c, South Korea. No. 4213, 15c, France. No. 4214, 15c, Germany. No. 4215, 15c, Brazil. No. 4216, 15c, Spain. 65c, Argentina. 75c, Italy. 85c, Japan.

2002, Apr. 21   Litho.   Perf. 12½
4212-4219 A1178   Set of 8   6.50 3.25
  4219a   Sheet #4212-4219   8.50 4.25
Souvenir Sheet

Hispano-Cubano Philatelic Exposition — A1179

2002, Apr. 27   Perf. 13
4220 A1179 1p multi   2.25 1.10

Juan Tomas Roig, Botanist, 125th Anniv. of Birth A1180

Designs: 5c, Bust of Roig, experimental agronomic station, Santiago de las Vegas. 10c, Bust and house of Roig. 15c, Roig, laboratory glassware and Nicotiana tabacum. 50c, Building, Allophyllum roiggi, and sculpture of Roig. 65c, Roig, laboratory glassware and botanical dictionary.

2002, May 10   Perf. 12½x12¾
4221-4225 A1180   Set of 5   3.25 1.50
  4225a   Sheet, #4221-4225, + label   5.00 2.40

Medi Cuba Suiza — A1181

2002, June 18   Perf. 12¾x12½
4226 A1181 75c multi   1.60 .80

Mushrooms A1182

Designs: 5c, Amanita junquillea. 15c, Lepiota puellaris. 45c, Cortinarius cumatilis. 65c, Pholliota adiposa. 75c, Coprinus comatus.

2002, June 20   Perf. 12¾
4227-4231 A1182   Set of 5   4.50 2.25
  4231a   Sheet, #4227-4231, + label   8.00 4.00

Nicolás Guillén (1902-89), Poet — A1183

2002, July 10   Perf. 12¾x12½
4232 A1183 65c multi   1.75 .90

Dockers, By Marcelo Pogolotti (1902-88) A1184

2002, July 12   Perf. 12¾
4233 A1184 15c multi   .50 .30

Agostinho Neto (1922-79), Pres. of Angola — A1185

2002, Sept. 17   Perf. 12¾x12½
4234 A1185 65c multi   1.75 .90

España 2002 Youth Philatelic Exposition, Salamanca — A1186

Birds: 5c, Calidris minutilla. 10c, Tringa melanoleucas. 15c, Charadius semipalmatus. 65c, Pluvialis squatarola. 75c, Arenaria interpres.
  1p, Porzana carolina.

2002, Sept. 20   Perf. 12½x12¼
4235-4239 A1186   Set of 5   4.75 2.25
  4239a   Sheet, #4235-4239, + label   8.00 4.00
Souvenir Sheet
Perf. 13
4240 A1186 1p multi   2.50 1.25

No. 4240 contains one 40x31mm stamp.

Third Intl. Meeting of War Correspondents — A1187

2002, Oct. 7   Perf. 12¾
4241 A1187 65c multi   1.75 .90

Ernesto "Che" Guevara (1928-67), Revolutionary Leader — A1188

Various depictions of Guevara: 5c, 10c, 15c, 50c, 65c, 75c.

2002, Oct. 8   Litho.
4242-4247 A1188   Set of 6   5.25 2.75
  4247a   Sheet, #4242-4247   30.00 6.00

America Issue — Youth, Education and Literacy — A1189

Designs: 15c, Emblem of Literacy Army, man with book, teacher with student. 65c, Building, flag, children at computer.

2002, Oct. 12   Perf. 12½x12¼
4248-4249 A1189   Set of 2   2.00 1.00

Old Automobiles — A1190

Designs: No. 4250, 5c, 1956 Pontiac Catalina. No. 4251, 5c, 1957 Mercury Monterrey. 15c, 1959 Cadillac Fleetwood. 65c, Hudson Hornet. 75c, 1957 Chevrolet Bel Air. 85c, 1957 Mercedes-Benz 190SL.

2002, Oct. 19				Perf. 12¾	
4250-4255	A1190	Set of 6		6.00	3.50
a.	Sheet, #4250-4255, + 6 labels			16.00	4.00

15th Intercontinental Baseball Cup — A1191

Baseball players: 5c, G. Mesa. 15c, A. Pacheco. 50c, O. Linares. 65c, O. Kindelan. 75c, L. Ulacia.

2002, Nov. 1					
4256-4260	A1191	Set of 5		5.00	3.00
4260a	Sheet of 5, #4256-4260 + 4 labels			15.00	4.75

20th Havana Intl. Fair — A1192

2002, Nov. 3					
4261	A1192	65c multi		1.75	.90

Railroads, 165th Anniv. — A1193

Designs: 5c, Rocket. 15c, Miller. 50c, Vulcan. 65c, Consolidation. 75c, Mikado.

2002, Nov. 12				Perf. 12½x12¼	
4262-4266	A1193	Set of 5		5.00	3.00
a.	Sheet, #4262-4266, + label			15.00	3.75

Camagüey Ballet, 35th Anniv. — A1194

Designs: 65c, Twelve dancers. 75c, Two dancers.

2002, Dec. 1				Perf. 12¾	
4267-4268	A1194	Set of 2		3.50	2.00

Pan-American Health Organization, Cent. — A1195

2002, Dec. 2					
4269	A1195	65c multi		1.50	.90

Paintings of Wilfredo Lam (1902-82) A1196

Designs: 15c, Emi Cosinca, 1950. 45c, Yo Soy, 1949. 65c, Retrado de H.H., 1941-42. 75c, Mujer Sentada, 1951.

2002, Dec. 8				Perf. 12¾	
4270-4273	A1196	Set of 4		5.00	3.00
a.	Sheet, #4270-4273, + 4 labels			14.00	3.00

Dulce M. Loynaz (1902-97), Writer A1197

2002, Dec. 19				Perf. 12½x12¾	
4274	A1197	65c multi		1.50	.90

Souvenir Sheet

Tursiops Truncatus — A1198

2002, Dec. 20				Perf. 12½	
4275	A1198	1p multi		3.00	1.50

Fifth National Philatelic Competition.

Prehistoric and Modern-Day Animals — A1199

Designs: 5c, Megaloceros, Cervus elaphus. 10c, Theropithecus, Papio anubis. 15c, Coelodonta, Diceros bicornis. 45c, Canis dirus, Canis lupus. 65c, Ursus spelaeus, Ursus arctos. 75c, Smilodon, Panthera leo. 1p, Mammuthus primigenius.

2002, Dec. 27				Perf. 12½x12¼	
4276-4281	A1199	Set of 6		5.00	2.00

Souvenir Sheet
Perf. 13

4282	A1199	1p multi		2.75	1.10

No. 4282 contains one 40x32mm stamp.

New Year 2003 (Year of the Ram) A1200

Ram with background in: No. 4283, 15c, Green. No. 4284, 15c, Red.

2003, Jan. 6				Perf. 12½	
4283-4284	A1200	Set of 2		.80	.40

San Alejandro Academy for Arts, 185th Anniv. — A1201

Paintings by: 5c, Amelia Pelaez. 15c, René Portocarrero. 65c, Mario Carreña, horiz. 75c, Servando Cabrera.

2003, Jan. 12				Perf. 12¾	
4285-4288	A1201	Set of 4		4.00	2.00

José Martí (1853-95), Patriot — A1202

Designs: 15c, Birthplace. No. 4290, 65c, Martí and text. No. 4291, 65c, Martí, sky and text, horiz. 75c, Portrait. 1p, Martí, horiz.

2003, Jan. 28				Perf. 12¾	
4289-4292	A1202	Set of 4		5.00	2.50

Souvenir Sheet
Perf. 12½

4293	A1202	1p multi		2.75	1.40

No. 4293 contains one 40x32mm stamp.

Arrival of Europeans at Havana, 510th Anniv. — A1203

Various Cuban stamps and: No. 4294, 15c, Woman with Cigar boxes, map of Cuba (diamond-shaped). No. 4295, 15c, Men at table holding cigars and drinks (diamond-shaped). 50c, Tobacco farmer, field, hands rolling cigar. 65c, Building, Trinidad. 75c, Cigar, building, palm tree, people in room. 1p, Indian lighting cigar, vert.

2003, Feb. 6				Perf. 12½	
4294-4298	A1203	Set of 5		5.00	2.50

Souvenir Sheet

4299	A1203	1p multi		2.75	1.40

No. 4299 contains one 32x40mm stamp.

Radio Rebelde, 45th Anniv. A1204

2003, Feb. 13				Perf. 12¾	
4300	A1204	65c multi		1.50	.85

Félix Varela (1788-1853), Priest — A1205

2003, Feb. 25				Perf. 12½	
4301	A1205	65c multi		1.50	.85

Military Units, 45th Anniv. — A1206

Designs: No. 4302, 15c, 2nd Frank Pais Front. No. 4303, 15c, 3rd Mario Muñoz Front.

2003				Perf. 12¾	
4302-4303	A1206	Set of 2		1.10	.55

Issued: No. 4302, 3/5; No. 4303, 3/11.

16th World Sexology Congress A1207

2003, Mar. 11					
4304	A1207	65c multi		1.50	.85

Transportation and Shipping — A1208

Designs: 5c, Container ship. 10c, Truck. 15c, Train. 65c, Airplane and delivery van. 75c, Airplane and delivery van, diff.

2003, Apr. 10				Perf. 12½	
4305-4309	A1208	Set of 5		4.00	2.00

Flora & Fauna — A1209

Designs: 5c, Nymphaea ampla, Lepisosteus tristoechus. 10c, Magnolia grandiflora, Spindalis zena pretrei. 15c, Lillium candidum, Polymita picta. 65c, Strelitzia regiae, Solenodon cubanus. 75c, Hibiscus rosasinensis, Mellysuga helenae.

2003, May 15
4310-4314 A1209 Set of 5 4.00 2.00

Pan American Games, Santo Domingo, Dominican Republic A1210

Designs: 5c, Kayaking. 15c, Judo. 50c, Track. 65c, Volleyball.

2003, June 27 **Perf. 12½x12¾**
4315-4318 A1210 Set of 4 3.00 1.50

Attack on Moncada Barracks, 50th Anniv. — A1211

Designs: 15c, Men and barracks. 65c, Fidel Castro, text.

2003, July 26 **Perf. 12¾**
4319-4320 A1211 Set of 2 1.75 .75

Railroads A1212

Designs: 5c, Three-wheeled handcar, 1930-35. 10c, Crane, 1920. 15c, B-B 120/120 E locomotive, 1925. 65c, DVM-9 Ganz Mavag locomotive, 1969. 75c, 2-6-0 locomotive, 1905.

2003, Aug. 7
4321-4325 A1212 Set of 5 4.00 2.00

UN Conference to Combat Desertification — A1213

2003, Aug. 25 **Perf. 12½x12¼**
4326 A1213 65c multi 1.50 .85

Expo Bangkok A1214

Wildlife: 5c, Nyctea scandiaca. 10c, Fratercula arctica. 15c, Sula bassana. 65c, Ursus maritimus. 75c, Alopex lagopus. 1p, Pagolphilus groenlandicus.

2003, Aug. 28 **Perf. 12¾**
4327-4331 A1214 Set of 5 4.00 2.00

Souvenir Sheet
Perf. 12½
4332 A1214 1p multi 2.75 1.40
No. 4332 contains one 32x40mm stamp.

Butterflies and Flowers — A1215

Designs: 5c, Dione juno, Gardenia jasminoides. 15c, Apatura ilia, Chrysanthemus sinence. 65c, Inachis io, Hibiscus rosasinensis. 75c, Marpesia iole, Althaea rosea. 1p, Danaus plexippus, Zantedeschia aethiopica, vert.

2003, Sept. 11 **Litho.** **Perf. 12½**
4333-4336 A1215 Set of 4 4.00 2.00
Souvenir Sheet
4337 A1215 1p multi 2.75 1.40
No. 4337 contains one 32x40mm stamp.

Ecotourism — A1216

Bird and location: 10c, Aratinga eops, Baracoa. 15c, Xiphiopicus percussus, Valle de los Ingenios. 65c, Tiaris canora, Sierra Maestra. 75c, Priotelus temnurus, Granma.

2003, Sept. 27 **Perf. 12¾x12½**
4338-4341 A1216 Set of 4 4.00 2.00

Worldwide Fund for Nature (WWF) — A1217

Crocodylus rhombifer: No. 4342, 15c, Eggs and hatchling. No. 4343, 15c, Adult at water's edge. 65c, Capturing prey. 75c, With open mouth.

2003, Sept. 30 **Litho.** **Perf. 12¾**
4342-4345 A1217 Set of 4 5.00 2.50
4345a Sheet, 4 each #4342-4345 20.00 12.50

America Issue — Flora and Fauna — A1218

Designs: 15c, Xiphidiopicus percussus. 65c, Encyclia phoenicea.

2003, Oct. 12
4346-4347 A1218 Set of 2 1.75 .85

35th Baseball World Cup — A1219

Cuban players: 5c, Antonio Muñoz. 10c, Lourdes Gourriel. No. 4350, 15c, Jorge L. Valdes. No. 4351, 15c, Lazaro Vargas. 65c, Lazaro Valle. 75c, Javier Mendez. 1p, Players celebrating, vert.

2003, Oct. 17 **Perf. 12½x12¼**
4348-4353 A1219 Set of 6 4.50 2.25
Souvenir Sheet
Perf. 12½
4354 A1219 1p multi 2.75 1.40
No. 4354 contains one 32x40mm stamp.

Ballet — A1220

Designs: No. 4355, 65c, National Ballet of Cuba, 55th anniv. No. 4356, 65c, Alicia Alonso as Giselle, 60th anniv., vert.

Perf. 12¾x12½, 12½x12¾
2003, Oct. 28
4355-4356 A1220 Set of 2 3.00 1.50

Powered Flight, Cent. — A1221

Emblem and: 5c, Wright Brothers. 15c, Pitcairn PA-5. 65c, Stearman C-3MB. 75c, Douglas M-2.

2003, Dec. 17 **Perf. 12½x12¼**
4357-4360 A1221 Set of 4 4.00 2.00

Cuban Revolution, 45th Anniv. — A1222

2004, Jan. 1 **Perf. 12¾**
4361 A1222 65c multi 1.50 .85

Expocuba, 15th Anniv. — A1223

2004, Jan. 4 **Perf. 12½x12¼**
4362 A1223 65c multi 1.50 .85

2004 Summer Olympics, Athens — A1224

Sports: 10c, Baseball. 15c (#4363A), Track. 65c, Boxing. 75c, Equestrian.

2004, Jan. 6 **Litho.**
4363-4365 A1224 Set of 4 3.75 1.90

New Year 2004 (Year of the Monkey) A1225

Monkey with denomination in: No. 4366, 15c, Blue. No. 4367, 15c, Orange.

2004, Jan. 9 **Perf. 12¾**
4366-4367 A1225 Set of 2 1.00 .50

Julio A. Mella (1903-29), Communist Leader A1226

2004, Jan. 10
4368 A1226 65c multi 1.50 1.10

José Martí (1853-95) — A1227

Designs: No. 4369, 5c, Martí in 1862, Colegio San Pablo, Prado No. 88. No. 4370, 5c, Martí's father, Mariano, Tapineria No. 16, Valencia. No. 4371, 5c, Martí's mother, Leonor Pérez, birthplace, Paula No. 41. No. 4372, 10c, Martí's high school, 1862, Martí, Fermín Valdés Domínguez, 1869. No. 4373, 10c, Martí in 1869, Havana Royal Jail. No. 4374, 15c, Martí in 1870, El Abra farm, Isle of Pines. No. 4375, 15c, Martí in 1870, Martí Forge. No. 4376, 15c, Martí and son, José Francisco, 1879, Guanabacoa Lyceum. 65c, Martí and son, 1879, Mercaderes Law Offices. 75c, Martí in 1895, La Jatía farm, Oriente.

2004, Jan. 28 **Perf. 12½x12¼**
4369-4378 A1227 Set of 10 4.75 2.75
See Nos. 4525-4535, 4570-4578, 4691-4700, 4800-4807.

Town of Santa María de Puerto del
Principe, 490th Anniv. — A1228

2004, Feb. 2   **Perf. 12¾x12½**
4379 A1228 15c multi   .50 .25

Trolleys
A1229

Designs: 5c, Santiago. 10c, Havana. 15c,
Camagüey. 65c, Matanzas. 75c, Camagüey,
diff.
  1p, Havana, diff.

2004, Feb. 20   **Perf. 12¾**
4380-4384 A1229   Set of 5   3.75 1.90
Souvenir Sheet
Perf. 12½
4385 A1229 1p multi   2.50 1.25
No. 4385 contains one 40x32mm stamp.

Souvenir Sheet

Cuba — Mexico Binational Philatelic
Exhibition — A1230

2004, Feb. 25   **Perf. 12½**
4386 A1230 1p multi   2.50 1.25

EGREM Recording Co., 40th
Anniv. — A1231

Recording artists: 10c, Cascarita, Julio Cue-
vas. 15c, Carlos Puebla. 65c, Benny Maré.
75c, Compay Segundo.

2004, Mar. 24   **Perf. 12¾**
4387-4390 A1231   Set of 4   3.50 1.75

España 2004 Intl. Philatelic
Exhibition — A1232

Dogs: 5c, Spanish pointer. 10c, Spanish
hound. 15c, Mallorquin bulldog. 65c, Catalan
sheepdog. 75c, Pyrenean mastiff.
  1p, Spanish mastiff.

2004, Mar. 24   **Perf. 12½x12¼**
4391-4395 A1232   Set of 5   3.75 1.90
Souvenir Sheet
Perf. 12½
4396 A1232 1p multi   2.50 1.25
No. 4396 contains one 40x32mm stamp.

National Police, 45th Anniv. — A1233

2004, Mar. 26   **Perf. 12½x12¼**
4397 A1233 15c multi + label   .35 .20

Souvenir Sheet

Second Cuban Sports
Olympiad — A1234

2004, Apr. 18   **Perf. 12½**
4398 A1234 1p multi   2.50 1.25

Nature and Man
Foundation, 10th
Anniv. — A1235

2004, May 16 Litho.   **Perf. 12¼x12½**
4399 A1235 65c multi   1.50 .75

FIFA (Fédération Internationale de
Football Association), Cent. — A1236

FIFA emblem and various players: 10c, 15c,
65c, 75c.

2004, May 21   **Perf. 12¾**
4400-4403 A1236   Set of 4   3.50 1.75

Pets
A1237

Designs: 5c, Parakeets. 10c, Fish. 15c,
Dogs. 65c, Cats. 75c, Finches.
  1p, Horse, horiz.

2004, June 25   **Perf. 12½x12¾**
4404-4408 A1237   Set of 5   3.75 1.90
Souvenir Sheet
Perf. 12½
4409 A1237 1p multi   2.50 1.25
No. 4409 contains one 40x32mm stamp.

Intl. Chess
Federation, 80th
Anniv. — A1238

Chess players: 15c, Maria Teresa Mora.
65c, José Raúl Capablanca, horiz. 75c,
Ernesto "Che" Guevara.

2004, July 20   **Perf. 12¾**
4410-4412 A1238   Set of 3   3.50 1.75

Minerals — A1239

Designs: 5c, Corundum. 10c, Thenardite.
15c, Uraninite. 65c, Realgar. 75c, Fluorite.
  1p, Copper.

2004, July 30   **Perf. 13**
4413-4417 A1239   Set of 5   3.50 1.75
Souvenir Sheet
Perf. 12½
4418 A1239 1p multi   2.50 1.25
No. 4418 contains one 40x32mm stamp.

Convention Hall, 25th Anniv. — A1240

2004, Sept. 3   **Perf. 12¾**
4419 A1240 65c multi   1.50 1.25

Cuban Aviation, 75th Anniv. — A1241

Designs: 15c, Lockheed Constellation. 65c,
IL-62M. 75c, Airbus 330.

2004, Oct. 8   **Perf. 12½x12¼**
4420-4422 A1241   Set of 3   3.50 1.75

America Issue — A1242

Map of Cuba and: 15c, Bird over islands.
65c, Fish and marine life.

2004, Oct. 12   Set of 2   1.75 .90
4423-4424 A1242

Marine Mammals — A1243

Designs: 5c, Delphinus delphis. 10c, Lagenorhynchus obliquidens. 15c, Stenella attenuata. 65c, Grampus griseus. 75c, Tursiops
truncatus.
  1p, Orcinus orca.

2004, Oct. 20   **Perf. 12½x12¼**
4425-4429 A1243   Set of 5   3.50 1.75
Souvenir Sheet
Perf. 13
4430 A1243 1p multi   2.50 1.25
No. 4430 contains one 40x32mm stamp.

Disappearance
of Camilo
Cienfuegos,
45th Anniv.
A1244

2004, Oct. 28   **Perf. 12¾**
4431 A1244 65c multi   1.50 .75

Railroad Stations, Cent. — A1245

Designs: 15c, Agramonte Station, 1906
ALCO No. 48 4-6-0. 65c, Aguacate Station,
1907 BLW No. 57 4-6-0. 75c, Guira de Melina
Station, 1903 ALCO No. 7 4-4-0.

2004, Nov. 10   **Perf. 13**
4432-4434 A1245   Set of 3   3.50 1.75

Souvenir Sheet

13th Philatelic Congress, Havana — A1245a

2004, Nov. 20   Litho.   Perf. 12½
4434A A1245a 1p multi   2.25 2.25

Founding of San Cristóbal de la Habana, 485th Anniv. A1246

Designs: 15c, Temple. 65c, Painting showing priest in red vestments at base of tree. 75c, Paintig showing group of men at base of tree.

Perf. 12½x12¾
2004, Nov. 30   Litho.
4435-4437 A1246   Set of 3   3.00 1.50

Latin American Parliament Foundation, 40th Anniv. — A1246a

2004, Nov. 30   Litho.   Perf. 12¾
4437A A1246a 65c multi   1.40 .70

Ministry of Foreign Affairs, 45th Anniv. — A1247

2004, Dec. 23   Perf. 12½x12¼
4438 A1247 65c multi   1.40 .70

Alejo Carpentier (1904-80), Writer — A1248

2004, Dec. 26   Perf. 12¾
4439 A1248 65c multi   1.40 .70

First Baseball Game in Cuba, 130th Anniv. — A1249

Baseball players: 5c, Rey Vicente Anglada. 10c, Braudilio Vinent. 15c, Rogelio Garcia. 65c, Luis G. Casanova. 75c, Victor Mesa. 1p, Martin Dihigo, vert.

2004, Dec. 27   Perf. 12½x12¼
4440-4444 A1249   Set of 5   5.25 2.50
Souvenir Sheet
Perf. 12½
4445 A1249 1p multi   2.25 1.10
No. 4445 contains one 32x40mm stamp.

Jose L. Guerra Aguiar Cuban Postal Museum, 40th Anniv. — A1250

Designs: 15c, Plaza Mayor, Trinidad and 1855 Trinidad to Barcelona cover. 65c, Charity Sanctuary, El Cobre and 1861 El Cobre to Santiago de Cuba cover. 85c, Matanzas Cathedral, Matanzas and 1848 Mantanzas to Havana cover.

2005, Jan. 2   Perf. 12¾x12½
4446-4448 A1250   Set of 3   3.50 1.75

New Year 2005 (Year of the Rooster) A1251

Designs: No. 4449, 15c, Rooster in air. No. 4450, 15c, Rooster on ground.

2005, Jan. 4   Perf. 12¼x12½
4449-4450 A1251   Set of 2   .60 .30

Ministry of Information Technology and Communications, 5th Anniv. — A1252

2005, Jan. 12   Perf. 12½x12¼
4451 A1252 65c multi   1.40 .70

Dinosaurs — A1253

Designs: 5c, Carnotaurus. 10c, Oviraptor. 30c, Parasaurolophus. 65c, Sauropelta. 90c, Iguanodon. 1p, Velociraptor.

2005, Jan. 20 Litho. Perf. 12½x12¼
4452-4456 A1253   4.25 2.10
Souvenir Sheet
Perf. 13
4457 A1253 1p multi   2.25 1.10
No. 4457 contains one 40x32mm stamp.

Miguel de Cervantes and Title Page of *Don Quixote* — A1254

2005, Jan. 24   Perf. 12¾x12½
4458 A1254 65c multi   1.40 .70
Publication of *Don Quixote*, 400th anniv.

Bridges A1255

Designs: 10c, Bacunayagua Bridge. 15c, La Concordia Bridge. 50c, El Triunfo Bridge. 65c, Yayabo Bridge. 75c, Canimar Bridge. 1p, Plaza Bridge.

2005, Feb. 5   Perf. 13x12¾
4459-4463 A1255   Set of 5   4.75 2.40
Souvenir Sheet
Perf. 13
4464 A1255 1p multi   2.25 1.10
No. 4464 contains one 40x32mm stamp.

Cuban Telecommunications Enterprise, 10th Anniv. — A1256

2005, Feb. 24   Perf. 12½x12¾
4465 A1256 90c multi   1.90 .95

Parrots — A1257

Designs: 5c, Amazona ochrocephala, Amazona leucocephala. 10c, Agapornis personata, Agapornis fischeri. 15c, Cacatua galerita, Cacatua leadbeateri. 65c, Psittacula krameri, Psittacula himalayana, vert. 1.05p, Aratinga guarouba, Aratinga euops. 1p, Ara macao, Ara araruana, Anodorhynchus hyacythus.

Perf. 12½x12¼, 12¼x12½
2005, Feb. 23   Litho.
4466-4470 A1257   Set of 5   4.25 2.10
Souvenir Sheet
Perf. 13
4471 A1257 1p multi   2.25 1.10
No. 4471 contain one 32x40mm stamp.

Cats A1258

Various cats: 5c, 10c, 40c, 65c, 75c. 10c is vert.

2005, Mar. 15   Perf. 12¾
4472-4476 A1258   Set of 5   4.25 2.10
Perf. 12¾
4477 A1258 1p Two cats, vert.   2.25 1.10
No. 4477 contains one 32x40mm stamp.

Cuba — Canada Diplomatic Relations, 60th Anniv. — A1259

2005, Mar. 20   Perf. 12¾x12½
4478 A1259 65c multi   1.40 .70

Wildlife — A1260

2005, Mar. 21   **Perf. 12½x12¼**
4479 A1260 15c Manatee   .30 .20
4480 A1260 65c Parrot   1.40 .70
4481 A1260 75c Crocodile   1.50 .75
4482 A1260 90c Hummingbird   1.90 .95
    Nos. 4479-4482 (4)   5.10 2.60

World Water
Day — A1261

2005, Mar. 22   **Perf. 13**
4483 A1261 90c multi   1.90 .95

Boats — A1262

Designs: 10c, Fishing boat, fish. 20c, Schooner, fish. 30c, Bonito boat, bonito. 45c, Shrimp boat, shrimp. 90c, Lobster boat, lobster.
   1p, Cargo ship, horiz.

2005, Apr. 15   **Perf. 12½**
4484-4488 A1262   Set of 5   4.25 2.10
    Souvenir Sheet
4489 A1262 1p multi   2.25 1.10

First Cuban Postage Stamps, 150th
Anniv. — A1263

Designs: 15c, St. Francis of Assisi Convent, Cuba #1. 65c, Morro Lighthouse, Cuba #2. 75c, Colonial Post Office, Cuba #3.

2005, Apr. 24   **Perf. 12¾x12½**
4490-4492 A1263   Set of 3   3.50 1.75

Social Security For All — A1264

2005, May 5   **Litho.**
4493 A1264 65c multi   1.40 .70

Major General Máximo Gómez (1836-1905) — A1265

2005, June 17   **Perf. 12½**
4494 A1265 1.05p multi   2.25 1.10

    Souvenir Sheet

Santiago de Cuba, 490th
Anniv. — A1266

2005, July 4   **Perf. 13**
4495 A1266 1p multi   2.25 1.10

16th World Youth and Student Festival,
Venezuela — A1267

2005, July 29   **Perf. 12¾x12½**
4496 A1267 65c multi   1.40 .70

Dances
A1268

Parrot and: No. 4497, 65c, Samba dancers and Brazilian flag. No. 4498, 65c, Son dancers, Cuban flag.

2005, Aug. 15   **Perf. 12¾**
4497-4498 A1268   Set of 2   2.75 1.50
    See Brazil Nos. 2967-2968.

Cuban — Soviet Space Flight, 25th
Anniv. — A1269

No. 4499: a, Cosmonaut Arnaldo Tamayo Mendez. b, Cosmonaut Yuri Romanenko.

2005, Sept. 18   **Perf. 12½**
4499 A1269 90c Horiz. pair, #a-b   4.00 2.00

Albert Einstein's
Visit to Cuba,
75th
Anniv. — A1270

Designs: 65c, Caricature of Einstein. 75c, Equation for energy, Einstein writing.

2005, Sept. 21
4500-4501 A1270   Set of 2   4.00 2.00

Locomotives — A1271

Designs: 5c, DSB B40, 1869. 10c, Great Northern, 1902. No. 4504, 15c, Minaret, 1929. No. 4505, 15c, C. F. White, 1885. 2.05p, Western Pacific FP7A 805D.
   1p, 14th No. 4 Krauss & Co., 1884.

2005, May 10   **Litho.**   **Perf. 12¾**
4502-4506 A1271   Set of 5   5.50 2.75
    Souvenir Sheet
    Perf. 13
4507 A1271 1p multi   2.25 1.10
   No. 4507 contains one 40x32mm stamp.

Zoo Animals
A1272

Designs: 10c, Loxodonta africana. 15c, Acunonyx jubatus, horiz. 50c, Synceros caffer, horiz. 65c, Giraffa camelopardalis. 75c, Panthera leo.
   1p, Equus burchelli, horiz.

2005, July 21   **Perf. 12¾**
4508-4512 A1272   Set of 5   4.75 2.40
    Souvenir Sheet
    Perf. 13
4513 A1272 1p multi   2.25 1.10
   No. 4513 contains one 40x32mm stamp.

Santiago de Cuba, 490th
Anniv. — A1273

2005, Sept. 22   **Perf. 12¾x12½**
4514 A1273 75c multi   1.60 .80

Revolutionary Defense Committees,
45th Anniv. — A1274

2005, Sept. 28   **Perf. 12½x12¼**
4515 A1274 50c multi   1.10 .55

Diplomatic Relations Between Cuba
and People's Republic of China, 45th
Anniv. — A1275

No. 4516: a, Chinese General Secretary Hu Jintao and Cuban Pres. Fidel Castro. b, Great Wall of China and Morro Castle, Havana.

2005, Sept. 28   **Perf. 13x13¼**
4516 A1275 15c Horiz. pair, #a-b   1.00 .50

America Issue,
Fight Against
Poverty
A1276

Designs: 50c, Starving children, map of Africa. 75c, Woman and child, map of South America.

2005, Oct. 12   **Perf. 12¾**
4517-4518 A1276   Set of 2   2.75 1.40

Horses
A1277

Breeds: 10c, Gelderlander. 20c, Arabian. 30c, Quarterhorse. 65c, Wild horses. 75c, Lipizzaner.
   100c, Holsteiner, vert.

2005, Oct. 21   **Perf. 12¾**
4519-4523 A1277   Set of 5   4.25 2.10
    Souvenir Sheet
    Perf. 12¾x12½
4524 A1277 100c multi   2.25 1.10
   No. 4524 contains one 32x40mm stamp.

    José Martí Type of 2004

Martí and: No. 4525, 5c, Central University, Madrid, 1871. No. 4526, 5c, Zaragoza University, 1871. No. 4527, 5c, F. Valdés Dominguez, Teatro Principal, Zaragoza, 1872. No. 4528, 10c, Victor Hugo House, Paris, 1872. No. 4529, 10c, Moneda No. 12, Mexico City, 1875. No. 4530, 15c, Normal School, Guatemala City, 1876. No. 4531, 15c, San Ildefonso No. 40, Mexico City, 1894. No. 4532, 15c, Plaza de Guardiola, Mexico City, 1894. 65c, Plaza Bolívar, Caracas, 1885. 75c, Santa María College, Caracas, 1893.
   1p, Martínez Ibor Tobacco Factory, Tampa, 1892.

2005, Oct. 20   **Perf. 12½x12¼**
4525-4534 A1227   Set of 10   4.75 2.40
    Souvenir Sheet
    Perf. 13
4535 A1227 1p multi   2.25 1.10
   No. 4535 contains one 40x32mm stamp.

World Summit on the Information Society, Tunis — A1278

2005, Nov. 16　　**Perf. 12½x12¼**
4536　A1278　75c multi　　1.60　.80

Establishment of Local Delivery of Mail in Havana, 150th Anniv. — A1279

Designs 15c, Cuba #7, cover to Havana. 65c, Cuba #16, Colonial Havana mailbox.

2005, Nov. 19　　**Perf. 12¾x12½**
4537-4538　A1279　Set of 2　　1.60　.80

Cuban Men Convicted of Terrorism Imprisoned In the United States A1280

2005, Nov. 25　　**Perf. 12½x12¾**
4539　A1280　65c multi　　2.00　1.00

Europa Stamps, 50th Anniv. (in 2006) A1281

Designs: 1.30p, Spain #1126, Castilla de la Fuerza, Havana. 2.05p, Spain #1010, Santisima Church, Trinidad, Cuba. 2.55p, Spain #1526, Morro Castle, Santiago de Cuba. 3.90p, Spain #1263, San Cristóbal Cathedral, Havana.

2005, Nov. 30　　**Perf. 12½**
4540-4543　A1281　Set of 4　　20.00　10.00
4543a　　Souvenir sheet, #4540-4543　　20.00　10.00

Nos. 4540-4543, 4543a exist imperf. Values, same.

Jewelry A1282

Jewelry by: 5c, Antonio Barcala. 10c, Raúl Valladares. 45c, Carlos de la Torre. 65c, J. Carlo Rafart. 75c, Osvaldo Castilla. 1p, 19th cent. jewelry in Gold Museum.

2005, Dec. 1　　**Perf. 12¾**
4544-4548　A1282　Set of 5　　4.25　2.10

Souvenir Sheet
Perf. 12½
4549　A1282　1p multi　　2.25　1.10
No. 4549 contains one 32x40mm stamp.

Friendship Among the Peoples Institute, 45th Anniv. — A1283

2005, Dec. 14　　**Perf. 12¾x12½**
4550　A1283　1.05p multi　　2.25　1.10

Snails and Mushrooms A1284

Designs: 10c, Clathrus cancellatus. 20c, Polymita genus picta. 30c, Lepiota puellaris. 65c, Polymita genus muscarum. 75c, Clitocybe infundibuliformis. 1p, Polymita genus versicolor, horiz.

2005, Dec. 15　　**Perf. 12¾**
4551-4555　A1284　Set of 5　　4.25　2.10

Souvenir Sheet
Perf. 13
4556　A1284　1p multi　　2.25　1.10
No. 4556 contains one 40x32mm stamp.

Hotel Inglaterra, 130th Anniv. — A1285

2005, Dec. 23　　**Perf. 12¾x12½**
4557　A1285　65c multi　　1.40　.70

New Year 2006 (Year of the Dog) — A1286

Designs: No. 4558, 15c, Shih tzu. No. 4559, 15c, Pug.

2006, Jan. 4　　**Perf. 12¼x12½**
4558-4559　A1286　Set of 2　　.60　.30

Organization of Solidarity of the People of Asia, Africa and Latin America, 40th Anniv. A1287

2006, Jan. 16　　**Perf. 12¾**
4560　A1287　65c multi　　1.40　.70

Establishment of Cuban Postal Service, 250th Anniv. — A1288

Stampless cover and: 75c, Horse and rider. 2.05p, Ship.

2006, Mar. 1　　**Perf. 12½x12¼**
4561-4562　A1288　Set of 2　　6.00　3.00

OPEC Intl. Development Fund, 30th Anniv. — A1289

2006, Mar. 23　　**Litho.**
4563　A1289　75c multi　　1.60　.80

Souvenir Sheet

Havana '06 Intl. Philatelic Exhibition — A1290

2006, Mar. 25　　**Perf. 12½**
4564　A1290　1p multi　　2.25　1.10

Pope John Paul II (1920-2005) — A1291

Designs: 65c, Pope, Mass in Santa Clara. 75c, Mass in Camagüey (44x27mm). 90c, Mass in Santiago de Cuba (44x27mm). 1.05p, Pope, Mass in Havana.

2006, Apr. 2　　**Perf. 12½x12¼**
4565-4568　A1291　Set of 4　　7.25　3.75

Bay of Pigs Invasion, 45th Anniv. — A1292

2006, Apr. 17　　**Perf. 12¼x12½**
4569　A1292　65c multi　　1.40　.70

José Martí Type of 2004

Martí and: No. 4570, Madame Griffou's Hotel, New York, 1890. No. 4571, Gonzalo de Quesada, 116 West 64th Street, New York, 1893. No. 4572, Son, José Francisco, 324 Classon Ave., New York, 1885. No. 4573, Masonic Temple, New York, 1888.
No. 4574: a, Cajobabo beach, Gomez monument. b, Martí monument, monument at Dos Ríos.
Martí and: 75c, Hardman Hall, New York, 1891. 85c, Office, 120 Front Street, New York, 1891. 90c, María Mantilla, Bath Beach, Long Island.
1p, Home of Teodoro Pérez, Cayo Hueso, 1893.

2006, May 19　Litho.　Perf. 12½x12¼
4570　A1227　5c multi　　.20　.20
4571　A1227　5c multi　　.20　.20
4572　A1227　10c multi　　.20　.20
4573　A1227　10c multi　　.20　.20
4574　A1227　15c Horiz. pair, #a-b　.65　.65
4575　A1227　75c multi　　1.60　1.60
4576　A1227　85c multi　　1.90　1.90
4577　A1227　90c multi　　1.90　1.90
　　Nos. 4570-4577 (8)　　6.85　6.85

Souvenir Sheet
Perf. 13
4578　A1227　1p multi　　2.25　2.25
No. 4578 contains one 40x32mm stamp.

Prehistoric Animals — A1293

Designs: 5c, Dsungaripetrus, Yangchuanosaurus. 10c, Pterodactylus, Sprinosaurus. 30c, Pteranodon, Pachycephalosaurus. 35c, Scaphognathus, Muttaburrasaurus. 65c, Quetzalcoatlus, Stegosaurus. 1.05p, Sordes, Saichania. 1p, Stenonychosaurus, vert.

2006, May 24　　**Perf. 12½x12¼**
4579-4584　A1293　Set of 6　　5.50　5.50

Souvenir Sheet
Perf. 12½
4585　A1293　1p multi　　2.25　2.25
No. 4585 contains one 32x40mm stamp.

Ministry of the Interior, 45th Anniv. — A1294

2006, June 6　　**Perf. 12½x12¼**
4586　A1294　75c multi　　1.60　1.60

Fowl — A1295

Designs: 5c, Chickens. No. 4588, 15c, Turkeys. No. 4589, 15c, Guinea fowl. 45c, Geese. 50c, Pheasants. 75c, Peafowl.
1p, Ducks.

2006, June 15   **Perf. 12½x12¼**
4587-4592 A1295   Set of 6   4.50 4.50
Souvenir Sheet
Perf. 13
4593 A1295 1p multi   2.25 2.25
No. 4593 contains one 40x32mm stamp.

Cerro Pelado Declaration, 40th Anniv. — A1296

Designs: 65c, Ship, man and crowd. 75c, People in cargo hoist. 85c, Men assisting woman down ship's stairs, flags of Cuba and Puerto Rico.

2006, June 25   **Perf. 12½x12¾**
4594-4596 A1296   Set of 3   4.75 4.75

2006 World Cup Soccer Championships, Germany — A1296a

Various Cuban soccer players: 15c, 45c, 65c, 75c.

2006, June   **Litho.**   **Perf. 12¾**
4596A-4596D A1296a   Set of 4   4.00 4.00

Genetic Engineering and Biotechnology Center, 20th Anniv. — A1297

2006, July 1   **Perf. 12½x12¼**
4597 A1297 65c multi   1.40 1.40

Comic Strips by Virgilio Martinez — A1298

Designs: 15c, Pucho y Sus Perrerias. 65c, Cucho.

2006, July 16   **Perf. 12¾x12¼**
4598-4599 A1298   Set of 2   1.75 1.75

Airplanes — A1299

Designs: 10c, Granville GeeBee R2. No. 4601, 15c, Bücker Jungmann. No. 4602, 15c, Comte AC-4 Gentleman. 50c, Mustang TF-51. 75c, Supermarine Spitfire. 85c, Lavochkin La-9.
1p, Bücker Jungmeister.

2006, July 20   **Perf. 12¾**
4600-4605 A1299   Set of 6   5.50 5.50
Souvenir Sheet
Imperf
4606 A1299 1p multi   2.25 2.25
No. 4606 contains one 36x28mm stamp.

Dogs — A1300

Designs: 5c, Bulldog. 10c, American cocker spaniel. 15c, Shar-pei. 20c, Airedale terrier. 35c, Pomeranian. 2.05p, Dalmatian.
1p, Whippet, vert.

2006, Aug. 18   **Perf. 12½x12¼**
4607-4612 A1300   Set of 6   6.25 6.25
Souvenir Sheet
Perf. 13
4613 A1300 1p multi   2.25 2.25

Recovery of Raw Materials, 45th Anniv. — A1301

Designs: 15c, Ernesto "Che" Guevara. 65c, Cuban and recovery program flags.

2006, Aug. 24   **Perf. 12¾**
4614-4615 A1301   Set of 2   1.75 1.75

14th Congress of Non-Aligned Countries, Havana A1302

2006, Sept. 10
4616 A1302 65c multi   1.40 1.40

Pedro Santacilia, Benito Juárez and Mexico House, Havana — A1303

2006, Sept. 15   **Perf. 12½x12¼**
4617 A1303 65c multi   1.40 1.40
Benito Juárez (1806-72), President of Mexico.

Souvenir Sheet

7th Hispano-Cuban Philatelic Exposition — A1304

No. 4618: a, Statue, arms of Cuba, denomination at LR. b, Statue, arms of Spain, denomination at LL.

2006, Sept. 20   **Imperf.**
4618 A1304 50c Sheet of 2, #a-b 2.25 2.25

España 06 World Philatelic Exposition, Malaga, Spain — A1305

Designs: 5c, Rio Hanabanilla. 10c, Laguna Bacanao. 15c, Sierra de la Gran Piedra. 20c, Valle de los Ingenios. 50c, Laguna del Tesoro. 75c, Sierra Maestra.
1p, Valle de Viñales.

2006, Sept. 20   **Perf. 12¾**
4619-4624 A1305   Set of 6   3.75 3.75
Souvenir Sheet
Perf. 13
4625 A1305 1p multi   2.25 2.25
No. 4625 contains one 40x32mm stamp.

America Issue, Energy Conservation — A1306

Equipment for harnessing energy source: No. 4626, 65c, Petroleum. No. 4627, 65c, Water. No. 4628, 65c, Solar. No. 4629, 65c, Wind.

2006, Oct. 12   **Perf. 12¾**
4626-4629 A1306   Set of 4   5.50 5.50

Saiz Brothers Association, 20th Anniv. A1307

2006, Oct. 18
4630 A1307 75c multi   1.60 1.60

20th Intl. Ballet Festival, Havana A1308

Dancers: 75c, Alicia Alonso and Igor Youskévitch. 85c, Alonso.

2006, Oct. 28   **Perf. 12¼x12½**
4631-4632 A1308   Set of 2   3.50 3.50

A1309

Belgica '06 Intl. Youth Philately Exposition, Belgium — A1310

Trains: 5c, Rocket and Intercity Diesel-electric. 10c, Turbine locomotive, Diesel-electric locomotive. 15c, Shinkasen and City of Los Angeles. 65c, Steam locomotive, Diesel locomotive. 75c, TEE Diesel-electric, TGV electric. 85c, Brisbane electric monorail, Wuppertal monorail.
No. 4639: a, Steam locomotive. b, Diesel locomotive.

2006, Nov. 2   **Perf. 12¾**
4633-4638 A1309   Set of 6   5.50 5.50
Souvenir Sheet
Perf. 12½
4639 A1310 50c Sheet of 2, #a-b 2.25 2.25

TeleFood Emblem — A1311

2006, Nov. 11   **Perf. 12¾**
4640 A1311 75c multi   1.60 1.60

Animals Serving Man — A1312

Designs: 5c, Equus caballus, Greek horse-drawn chariot. 15c, Camelus dromedarius, Ibn Battuta on camel. 30c, Capra aegagrus, Roman musician. 40c, Lama lama, Peruvian pre-Columbian ceramic llama. 50c, Felis catus, painting by Kuniyoshi Utagawa. 1.05p, Elephas maximus, elephant with Indian caparison.
1p, Canis familiaris, Grecian with dog.

2006, Oct. 1 Litho. Perf. 12½x12¼
4641-4646 A1312 Set of 6 5.50 5.50
Souvenir Sheet
Perf. 12½
4647 A1312 1p multi 2.25 2.25
No. 4647 contains one 40x32mm stamp.

Fire Fighting and Rescue Equipment — A1313

Designs: 5c, 1899 Horse-drawn ambulance, Brazil, and megaphone. 10c, Fireman's hat, and 1898 Merryweather fire truck, England. 20c, 1910 Laurin & Klement fire truck, Bohemia, and fire hydrant. 30c, 1939 American La France ladder truck, US, and badge. 45c, 1925 Leyland Motors pumper motorcycle, United Kingdom, and portable hose and tank. 90c, Brussels fire badge and 1930 Magirus ladder truck, Germany.
1p, Fireman spraying water, vert.

2006, Nov. 13 Perf. 12¾
4648-4653 A1313 Set of 6 4.50 4.50
Souvenir Sheet
Perf. 12½
4654 A1313 1p multi 2.25 2.25
No. 4654 contains one 32x40mm stamp.

Santiago Rebellion, 50th Anniv. — A1314

2006, Nov. 30 Perf. 12½x12¼
4655 A1314 65c multi 1.40 1.40

Governmental Reorganization, 30th Anniv. — A1315

2006, Dec. 2
4656 A1315 75c multi 1.60 1.60

Granma Landings, 50th Anniv. — A1316

Revolutionary Armed Forces, 50th Anniv. — A1317

2006, Dec. 2 Perf. 13
4657 A1316 65c multi 1.40 1.40
4658 A1317 65c multi 1.40 1.40

General Antonio Maceo Grajales (1845-96) — A1317a

2006, Dec. 7 Litho. Perf. 12½x12¼
4658A A1317a 1.05p multi 2.10 2.10

Intl. Film and Television School, 20th Anniv. — A1318

2006, Dec. 15 Perf. 12¾
4659 A1318 75c multi 1.60 1.60

Martí Forge Museum, 55th Anniv. — A1319

2006, Dec. 15 Perf. 12½x12¼
4660 A1319 90c multi 1.90 1.90

Literacy Campaign, 45th Anniv. A1320

2006, Dec. 19 Perf. 12¾
4661 A1320 65c multi 1.40 1.40

Major General Ignacio Agramonte y Loinaz (1841-73) — A1321

2006, Dec. 23 Perf. 12½x12¼
4662 A1321 65c multi 1.40 1.40

Special Education, 45th Anniv. — A1322

2007, Jan. 4 Perf. 12¾
4663 A1322 85c multi 1.75 1.75

Francesa Pharmacy, 125th Anniv. A1323

2007, Jan. 18 Litho.
4664 A1323 65c multi 1.40 1.40

Electric Trains A1324

Designs: 5c, First American electric locomotive, 1895. 10c, Locomotive, Netherlands. 15c, Interurban train, Australia. 65c, High-speed train, Italy. 85c, Helensburgh-Bridgeton train, Great Britain. 1.05p, Lyon-St. Etienne interurban train, France.
1p, High-speed train, Germany.

2007, Jan. 18 Perf. 12¾
4665-4670 A1324 Set of 6 6.00 6.00
Souvenir Sheet
Imperf
4671 A1324 1p multi 2.25 2.25
No. 4671 contains one 40x32mm stamp with simulated perforations.

12th Intl. Information Fair and Convention — A1325

2007, Feb. 12 Perf. 12½x12¼
4672 A1325 75c multi 1.60 1.60

Cats A1326

Designs: 10c, Two cats. No. 4674, 15c, Kitten with paw raised. No. 4675, 15c, Cat. 50c, Cat and telephone. 75c, Cat with ball. 90c, Cat, diff.
1p, Cat, diff.

2007, Feb. 14 Perf. 12¾
4673-4678 A1326 Set of 6 5.50 5.50
Souvenir Sheet
Imperf
4679 A1326 1p multi 2.25 2.25
No. 4679 contains one 40x32mm stamp with simulated perforations.

Fifth Congress of Cuban Pigeon Fanciers Federation — A1327

2007, Feb. 24 Perf. 12¾
4680 A1327 75c multi 1.60 1.60

Souvenir Sheet

Patria Newspaper, 115th Anniv. — A1328

Imperf. With Simulated Perforations
2007, Mar. 14
4681 A1328 1p multi 2.25 2.25

Animals in National Zoo — A1329

Designs: 5c, Ara ararauana. 10c, Tsetudo elephantopus. 15c, Balearica regulorum. 20c, Procyon lotor. 45c, Panthera pardus. 2.05p, Pongo pygmaeus.
1p, Giraffa camelopardalis, vert.

2007, Mar. 31 Perf. 12½x12¼
4682-4687 A1329 Set of 6 6.50 6.50
Souvenir Sheet
Imperf
4688 A1329 1p multi 2.25 2.25
No. 4688 contains one 32x40mm stamp with simulated perforations.

Raúl Roa García (1907-82), Foreign Minister A1330

2007, Apr. 18 Perf. 12¾
4689 A1330 65c multi 1.40 1.40

Union of Young Communists, 45th Anniv. — A1331

2007, Apr. 4 Perf. 12½x12¼
4690 A1331 75c multi 1.60 1.60

José Martí Type of 2004
Martí and: No. 4691, 5c, Cuban High School, Tampa, 1892. No. 4692, 5c, Casa de los Pedrosa, Tampa, 1892. No. 4693, 10c, Hotel Duval, Cayo Hueso, 1891. No. 4694, 10c, Hotel Cherokee, Tampa, 1891. No. 4695, 15c, Cayo Hueso Committee, 1891 (68x28mm). No. 4696, 15c, F. Valdés Domínguez, Gato Brothers Cigar Factory, Cayo Hueso, 1894. 35c, Club San Carlos, Cayo Hueso, 1892. 40c, Hotel Myrtle Bank, Kingston, 1892. 50c, Gen. Francisco Gómez Toro, Friends of the Country Society Building, Santo Domingo, 1894. 65c, Máximo Gómez, Gómez's house, Montecristi.

2007, Apr. 10 Perf. 12½x12¼
4691-4700 A1227 Set of 10 5.50 5.50

World Food Program Children's Art
Exhibition, 10th Anniv. — A1332

2007, May 3   Litho.   Perf. 12¾
4701 A1332 65c multi   1.40 1.40

Folklore
Union — A1333

2007, May 7   Perf. 12¼x12½
4702 A1333 75c multi   1.60 1.60

Islands and Wildlife — A1334

Designs: 5c, Cayo Guillermo, pelican. No.
4704, 15c, Cayo Las Brujas, sea gull. No.
4705, 15c, Cayo Levisa, conches. 20c, Cayo
Santa Maria, iguana. 50c, Cayo Ensenachos,
plover. 85c, Cayo Largo, Carey turtle.
1p, Cayo Coco, flamingos.

2007, May 8   Perf. 12½x12¼
4703-4708 A1334   Set of 6   4.25 4.25
Souvenir Sheet
Imperf
4709 A1334 1p multi   2.25 2.25
No. 4709 contains one 40x32mm stamp.

Singers and
Songwriters
A1335

Designs: 5c, Benny Moré. 10c, Ignacio
Piñeiro. 30c, Arsenio Rodríguez. 35c, Miguelito Cuní. 65c, Pio Leyva. 75c, Ibrahim Ferrer.
1p, Miguel Matamoros.

2007, May 10   Perf. 12¾
4710-4715 A1335   Set of 6   4.75 4.75
Souvenir Sheet
Imperf
4716 A1335 1p multi   2.25 2.25
No. 4716 contains one 32x40mm stamp
with simulated perforations.

Souvenir Sheet

Martí Studies Youth Seminary, 35th
Anniv. — A1336

2007, May 19   Imperf.
4717 A1336 1p multi   2.25 2.25

Cuban Radio and Television Institute,
45th Anniv. — A1337

2007, May 24   Perf. 12½x12¼
4718 A1337 3p multi   6.50 6.50

Integral Development Group of the
Capital, 20th Anniv. — A1338

2007, May 25   Litho.
4719 A1338 65c multi   1.40 1.40

Cuban
Admission to
the United
Nations, 60th
Anniv.
A1339

2007, May 29   Perf. 12¾
4720 A1339 65c multi   1.40 1.40

2007 Pan American Games, Rio de
Janeiro — A1340

Designs: No. 4721, 15c, Fencing. No. 4722,
15c, Boxing. 20c, Wrestling. 45c, Running.
65c, Gymnastics. 75c, Cycling.
1p, Games emblem, vert.

2007, June 20   Perf. 12¾
4721-4726 A1340   Set of 6   5.00 5.00
Souvenir Sheet
Imperf
4727 A1340 1p multi   2.25 2.25
No. 4727 contains one 32x40mm stamp.

Third Technological Transfer and Intl.
Trade Workshop — A1341

2007, July 3   Perf. 12½x12¼
4728 A1341 65c multi   1.40 1.40

Frank País (1934-57), Revolutionary
Hero — A1342

2007, July 30   Perf. 12¾
4729 A1342 65c multi   1.40 1.40

Radio Cubana,
85th Anniv.
A1343

2007, Aug. 22   Perf. 12¾
4730 A1343 65c multi   1.40 1.40

Seven
Wonders
of the
Modern
World
A1344

Designs: 10c, Great Wall of China. 15c,
Petra, Jordan. 20c, Christ the Redeemer
Statue, Brazil. 40c, Machu Picchu, Peru. 65c,
Chichén Itzá Pyramids, Mexico. 75c, Roman
Colosseum. 85c, Taj Mahal, India.

2007, Aug. 16   Litho.   Perf. 12¾
4731-4737 A1344   Set of 7   6.25 6.25

Transportation — A1345

Designs: 10c, Cocotaxis (40x29mm). 15c,
Lada 2105 taxi (40x29mm). 30c, Girón VI bus
(40x29mm). 40c, Bus trailer on truck
(44x27mm). 75c, DAF articulated bus
(44x27mm). 85c, Yutong bus (44x27mm).
1p, La Gaviota train.

Perf. 12¾, 12½x12¼ (#4741-4743)
2007, Sept. 3
4738-4743 A1345   Set of 6   5.25 5.25
Souvenir Sheet
Imperf
4744 A1345 1p multi   2.00 2.00
No. 4744 contains one 40x32mm stamp
with simulated perforations.

Central Youth
Club, 20th
Anniv. — A1346

2007, Sept. 8   Perf. 12¼x12½
4745 A1346 65c multi   1.40 1.40

Cubans
Convicted of
Espionage by
United States
A1347

Designs: No. 4746, 65c, Raised hand with
"Cuban Five" emblem. No. 4747, 65c, Fer-
nando González Liort. No. 4748, 65c, Gerardo
Hernández Nordelo. No. 4749, 65c, Antonio
Guerrero Rodriguez. No. 4750, 65c, Ramón
Labañino Salazar. No. 4751, 65c, René Gon-
zález Schwerert.

2007, Sept. 12   Perf. 12¾
4746-4751 A1347   Set of 6   8.00 8.00

Tree Planting Campaign — A1348

2007, Oct. 24   Perf. 12½x12¼
4752 A1348 65c multi   1.40 1.40

Rose
Varieties
A1349

Designs: 5c, Pink Parfait. No. 4754, 15c,
Alison Wheatcroft. No. 4755, 15c, Prima Ballerina. 45c, Fragrant Cloud. 50c, Blue Moon.
75c, Grandmère Jenny.
1p, Rosa highdownensis.

2007, Oct. 25   Perf. 12¾
4753-4758 A1349   Set of 6   4.25 4.25
Souvenir Sheet
Imperf
4759 A1349 1p multi   2.00 2.00
No. 4759 contains one 40x32mm stamp
with simulated perforations.

International Design
Conference — A1350

Designs: 75c, Electronic machine. 85c,
Caricatures.

2007, Oct. 26   Perf. 12½x12¼
4760-4761 A1350   Set of 2   3.25 3.25

Souvenir Sheet

International Air Mail Service From Cuba, 80th Anniv. — A1351

2007, Oct. 27 *Imperf.*
4762 A1351 1p multi 2.00 2.00
Seventh Natl. Philatelic Championship. No. 4762 has simulated perforations.

Protected Animals — A1352

Designs: 5c, Eretmochelys imbricata. 10c, Trichechus manatus. 20c, Mesocapromys sanfelipensis. 30c, Mesocapromys nanus. 45c, Epinephelus itajara. 85c, Balistes vetula. 1p, Chelonia mydas.

2007, Nov. 15 *Perf. 12½x12¼*
4763-4768 A1352 Set of 6 4.00 4.00
Souvenir Sheet
Imperf
4769 A1352 1p multi 2.00 2.00
No. 4769 contains one 40x32mm stamp with simulated perforations.

Cuban UNESCO Commission, 60th Anniv. — A1353

2007, Nov. 17 *Perf. 12½x12¼*
4770 A1353 65c multi 1.40 1.40

Cuban Railroads, 170th Anniv. — A1354

2007, Nov. 19 *Perf. 12¾*
4771 A1354 3p multi 6.00 6.00

Camagüey Ballet, 40th Anniv. — A1355

2007, Dec. 1 *Litho.*
4772 A1355 75c multi 1.50 1.50

Infomed Health Network, 15th Anniv. — A1356

2007, Dec. 15
4773 A1356 65c green & black 1.40 1.40

Federation of University Students, 85th Anniv. — A1357

2007, Dec. 20
4774 A1357 65c multi 1.40 1.40

Seven Marvels of Cuban Civil Engineering — A1358

Designs: 5c, White Aqueduct, Havana. 10c, Sewer system, Havana. 20c, Central Highway, Santiago. 30c La Bahia Tunnel, Havana. 85c, Bacunayagua Bridge, Matanzas. 90c, La Farola Viaduct, Guantánamo. 1p, FOSCA Building, Havana.

2007, Dec. 31 *Perf. 12¾*
4775-4780 A1358 Set of 6 5.00 5.00
Souvenir Sheet
Imperf
4781 A1358 1p multi 2.00 2.00
No. 4781 contains one 40x32mm stamp with simulated perforations.

World Ozone Layer Protection Day, 20th Anniv. — A1359

2007 *Perf. 12¾*
4782 A1359 65c multi 1.40 1.40

Tourism — A1360

No. 4783, 75c — El Yunque, Baracoa and: a, Atlantea perezi. b, Polymita picta.
No. 4784, 75c — Alexander von Humboldt National Park and: a, Eleutherodactylus iberia. b, Solenodon cubanus.

2007 *Litho.*
Horiz. Pairs, #a-b
4783-4784 A1360 Set of 2 6.00 6.00

Miniature Sheet

America Issue, Education For All — A1361

No. 4785: a, Teacher and children, children in uniforms, girl at computer. b, Students at table. c, Students, flag, marchers. d, Artist, people sitting in front of building, man at computer.

2007
4785 A1361 75c Sheet of 4, #a-d 6.00 6.00

Ernesto "Che" Guevara (1928-67) — A1362

Designs: 65c, Guevara sitting with other men. 75c, Monument to Guevara, La Higuera, Bolivia. 85c, Guevara and text. 90c, Guevara and marchers.

2007 *Perf. 12½x12¼*
4786-4789 A1362 Set of 4 6.50 6.50
4789a Miniature sheet, #4786-4789 6.50 6.50

Historic Central City of Cienfuegos — A1363

Buildings: 15c, City Hall. 65c, San Lorenzo and Santo Tomás College. 75c, Tomás Terry Theater. 85c, Ferrer Palace. 1p, Gazebo, José Martí Park.

2007 *Litho.* *Perf. 12¾*
4790-4793 A1363 Set of 4 5.00 5.00
Souvenir Sheet
Imperf
4794 A1363 1p multi 2.00 2.00
No. 4794 contains one 40x32mm stamp with simulated perforations.

University of Havana, 280th Anniv. — A1364

2008, Jan. 5 *Litho.* *Perf. 12½x12¼*
4795 A1364 65c multi 1.40 1.40

2008 Summer Olympics, Beijing — A1365

Designs: 15c, Baseball. 45c, Swimming. 65c, Discus. 75c, Volleyball.

2008, Jan. 18 *Perf. 12¾*
4796-4799 A1365 Set of 4 4.00 4.00

José Martí Type of 2004

Designs: No. 4800, 15c, Martí at Twilight Park, New York, 1892, vert. No. 4801, 15c, Martí with members of Cuban Revolutionary Party, 1892, vert. 30c, Martí, and family of Carme Miyares, Sandy Hill, New York, 1893, vert. 40c, Mausoleum, Santa Ifigenia, vert. 45c, Martí, tomb of Félix Varela, San Agustín. 50c, Martí, Dellundé House, Cabo Haitiano. 65c, Hanábana Memorial, Matanzas. 85c, Cover from 1889 in Postal Museum.

2008, Jan. 28
4800-4807 A1227 Set of 8 7.00 7.00

Subway Trains and Stations — A1366

Trains and stations in: No. 4808, 15c, New York. No. 4809, 15c, Paris. 30c, Caracas. 65c, Madrid. 75c, Mexico City. 1.05p, Tokyo.
No. 4814: a, 1866 London Underground train. b, Modern London Underground train, Westminster station emblem.

2008, Feb. 15 *Perf. 12½x12¼*
4808-4813 A1366 Set of 6 6.25 6.25
Souvenir Sheet
Imperf
4814 A1366 50c Sheet of 2, #a-b 2.00 2.00
No. 4814 contains two 39x24mm stamps with simulated perforations.

Radio Rebelde, 50th Anniv. A1367

2008, Feb. 24 *Perf. 12¾*
4815 A1367 75c multi 1.50 1.50

Frontier Guards, 45th Anniv. A1368

2008, Mar. 3
4816 A1368 65c multi 1.40 1.40

Dr. Mario Muñoz Monroy Third Guerrilla Front, 50th Anniv. — A1369

2008, Mar. 6 Litho. *Perf. 12¾*
4817 A1369 75c multi 1.50 1.50

Aquaculture — A1370

Designs: 65c, Penaeus vannamei. 75c, Ctenopharyngodon idella. 85c, Clarias gariepinus.
1p, Oreochromis aurea.

2008, Apr. 8 *Perf. 12½x12¼*
4818-4820 A1370 Set of 3 4.50 4.50
Souvenir Sheet
Imperf
4821 A1370 1p multi 2.00 2.00
No. 4821 contains one 31x28mm stamp.

Souvenir Sheet

Cuban Postal Stationery, 130th Anniv. — A1371

2008, Apr. 24 *Imperf.*
4822 A1371 1p multi 2.00 2.00

Bohemia Magazine, Cent. — A1372

2008, May 10 *Perf. 12¾*
4823 A1372 65c multi 1.40 1.40

Second Frank Pais Front, 50th Anniv. — A1373

2008, Mar. 11 Litho. *Perf. 12¾*
4824 A1373 65c multi 1.40 1.40

Birds — A1374

Designs: 5c, Cartacuba (Cuban tody). 10c, Ruiseñor (nightingale). 15c, Carpintero verde (green woodpecker). 50c, Tocororo (Cuban trogon). 65c, Catey (parakeet), horiz. 75c, Cabrerito de la Ciénaga (Zapata sparrow), horiz. 90c, Zunzuncito (hummingbird), horiz. 1.05p, Juan Chiví (Cuban vireo), horiz.

2008, May 22
4825-4832 A1374 Set of 8 8.50 8.50
"Wings of Liberty" Symposium, Cuban National Museum of Natural History.

Visit of Indonesian Pres. Sukarno, 48th Anniv. — A1375

Sukarno and: No. 4833, 65c, Fidel Castro (shown). No. 4834, 65c, Ernesto "Che" Guevara.

2008 Litho. *Perf. 12½x12¼*
4833-4834 A1375 Set of 2 2.60 2.60

Flora and Fauna at Ramsar Sites in Cuba and Iran — A1376

No. 4835: a, Cyanolimnas cerverai and Nymphaea ampla, Ciénaga de Zapata, Cuba. b, Nelumbo nucifera and Porphyrio porphyrio, Anzali, Iran.

2008, Oct. 16 Litho. *Perf. 12½x12¼*
4835 Horiz. pair with central label 3.00 3.00
a.-b. A1376 75c Either single 1.50 1.50
See Iran No. 3003.

Cuban Literature, 400th Anniv. — A1377

Designs: 15c, Emblem written backward on torn page. 75c, Snails. 2.05p, White star in red triangle.

2008, Oct. 20 *Perf. 12¼x12½*
4836-4838 A1377 Set of 3 6.00 6.00

National Ballet, 60th Anniv. A1378

Designs: 10c, Dancers in Swan Lake (El Lago de los Cisnes). 15c, Dancers in Giselle. 50c, Dancers in Coppélia, horiz. 65c, Dancer in Romeo and Juliet, horiz. 75c, Dancers in The Nutcracker (Cascanueces), horiz. 85c, Scenery for Sleeping Beauty (La Bella Durmiente del Bosque), horiz.
1p, Ballerina at Intl. Ballet Festival, Havana.

2008, Oct. 28 *Perf. 12¾*
4839-4844 A1378 Set of 6 6.00 6.00
Souvenir Sheet
Imperf
4845 A1378 1p multi 2.00 2.00
No. 4845 has simulated perforations.

Vilma Espín Guillois (1930-2007), Wife of Pres. Raúl Castro — A1379

2008 *Perf. 12¾*
4846 A1379 65c multi 1.40 1.40

Joséito Fernández (1908-79), Singer A1380

2008
4847 A1380 65c multi 1.40 1.40

Dr. Carlos J. Finlay (1833-1915), Yellow Fever Researcher A1381

2008
4848 A1381 65c multi 1.40 1.40

José Raúl Capablanca (1888-1942), World Chess Champion — A1382

Designs: 1.05p, Capablanca playing chess. 2.05p, Capablanca seated, vert.

2008 *Perf. 12½x12¼, 12¼x12½*
4849-4850 A1382 Set of 2 6.25 6.25

Dogs — A1383

Designs: 10c, Neapolitan mastiff. 15c, Golden retriever. 40c, Rottweiler. 65c, Shetland sheepdog. 85c, Chow chow. 90c, Boxer.
1p, Chihuahua.

2008 *Perf. 12¾*
4851-4856 A1383 Set of 6 6.25 6.25
Souvenir Sheet
Imperf
4857 A1383 1p multi 2.00 2.00

Owls and Butterflies A1384

Designs: No. 4858, 15c, Tyto alba, Lycaena dispar. No. 4859, 15c, Bubo bubo, Lolana iolas. 45c, Strix nebulosa, Vanessa cardui. 65c, Strix aluco, Colias erate. 75c, Asio otus, Aporia crataegi. 85c, Strix uralensis, Colias hecla.
1p, Anthocharis damone butterfly, horiz.

2008 *Perf. 12¾*
4858-4863 A1384 Set of 6 6.00 6.00
Souvenir Sheet
Imperf
4864 A1384 1p multi 2.00 2.00
No. 4864 contains one 40x32mm stamp. EFIRO 2008 Intl. Philatelic Exhibition, Romania (No. 4864).

Animals in National Zoo — A1385

Designs: 5c, Panthera leo. 10c, Ailurus fulgens. 15c, Cacatua galerita. 30c, Crocodylus rhombifer. 40c, Phoenicopterus ruber. 2.05p, Equus burchelli.
1p, Loxodonta africana.

2008 *Perf. 12½x12¼*
4865-4870 A1385 Set of 6 6.25 6.25
Souvenir Sheet
Imperf
4871 A1385 1p multi 2.00 2.00
No. 4871 contains one 40x32mm stamp with simulated perforations.

Ernesto "Che" Guevara (1928-67), Revolutionary Leader — A1386

Designs: 65c, Guevara as infant with mother, birthplace in Rosario, Argentina. 75c, Guevara as boy, childhood home, Villa Nydia. 85c, Guevara as young man, Guevara on bicycle. 1.05p, Guevara on raft, Guevara with cigar.

2008　　　　　　　　**Perf. 12¾**
4872-4875　A1386　Set of 4　6.75　6.75
4875a　Souvenir sheet, #4872-
　　　4875　　　　　　　　　6.75　6.75

America Issue, National
Holidays — A1387

Designs: 15c, Starting Day of the War of Independence. 65c, Liberation Day. 75c, Labor Day. 2.05p, National Rebellion Day.

2008　Litho.　　**Perf. 12½x12¼**
4876-4879　A1387　　　　7.25　7.25
4879a　Souvenir sheet of 4,
　　　#4876-4879　　　　　7.25　7.25

Tourism
A1388

Buildings in: No. 4880, 15c, Havana. No. 4881, 15c, Trinidad. 30c, Sancti Spiritus. 65c, Camagüey. 75c, Bayamo. 85c, Santiago de Cuba.
1p, Baracoa.

2008　　　　　　　**Perf. 12¼x12½**
4880-4885　A1388　Set of 6　5.75　5.75
Souvenir Sheet
Imperf
4886　A1388　1p multi　　　2.00　2.00
　No. 4886 contains one 32x40mm stamp with simulated perforations.

Gran Caribe Hotels, 50th Anniv. A1389

Designs: 5c, Hotel Habana Riviera. 10c, Hotel Habana Libre, vert. 15c, Hotel Deauville, vert. 50c, Hotel Victoria, vert. 65c, Hotel Presidente.
1p, Hotel Sevilla, vert.

2008　　　　　　　　**Perf. 12¾**
4887-4891　A1389　Set of 5　3.00　3.00
Souvenir Sheet
Imperf
4892　A1389　1p multi　　　2.00　2.00
　No. 4892 contains one 32x40mm stamp with simulated perforations.

Carlos de la Torre y la Huerta (1858-1950), Naturalist — A1390

De la Torre y la Huerta and: 5c, Hand holding shells. 15c, Polymita picta nigrolimbata, light blue background. 50c, Polymita picta nigrolimbata, pink background. 65c, Polymita picta iolimbata. 75c, Polymita picta nigrolimbata, light green background. 90c, Polymita picta fuscolimbata.
1p, Liguus fasciatus.

2008　　　　　　　**Perf. 12½x12¼**
4893-4898　A1390　Set of 6　6.00　6.00
Souvenir Sheet
Imperf
4899　A1390　1p multi　　　2.00　2.00
　No. 4899 contains one 40x32mm stamp with simulated perforations.

Paleolithic Man and Animals — A1391

Designs: 10c, Australopithecus afarensis and Megatherium. 15c, Australopithecus africanus and Toxodon. 50c, Australopithecus robustus and Bison. 65c, Homo habilis and Hippidion. 75c, Homo erectus and Megantereon. 90c, Neanderthal man and Mammoths.
1p, Coelodonts.

2008　　　　　　　　**Perf. 12¾**
4900-4905　A1391　Set of 6　6.25　6.25
Souvenir Sheet
Imperf
4906　A1391　1p multi　　　2.00　2.00
　No. 4906 contains one 45x34mm stamp with simulated perforations.

A1392

Transportation

Designs: 15c, 1802 steam carriage of Richard Trevithick. 30c, 1829 steam carriage of Sir Goldsworthy Gurney. 40c, 1832 steam carriage of William Church. 65c, 1858 steam carriage of Thomas Rickett. 75c, 1890 Motorwagen of Karl Benz. 85c, 1836 steam omnibus of Walter Hancock.
1p, 1958 Panhard-Levassor automobile.

2008　　　　　　　**Perf. 12½x12¼**
4907-4912　A1392　Set of 6　6.25　6.25
Souvenir Sheet
Imperf
4913　A1392a　1p multi　　　2.00　2.00
　No. 4913 has simulated perforations.

Matanzas, 315th Anniv. — A1393

Designs: 15c, Building arches, Plaza de la Vigía. 40c, Palacio Junco Provincial Museum.

50c, Fire house. 75c, Palace of Justice. 85c, Sauto Theater. 90c, Palace of Government.
1p, Unknown Soldier's Monument, vert.

2008　　　　　　　　**Perf. 12½x12¼**
4914-4919　A1393　Set of 6　7.25　7.25
Souvenir Sheet
Imperf
4920　A1393　1p multi　　　2.00　2.00
　No. 4920 has simulated perforations.

Triumph of the Cuban Revolution, 50th Anniv. — A1394

No. 4921, 15c: a, Liberation Day (man with wide-brimmed hat at left). b, Liberation Day (tank at left). c, Arrival of Fidel Castro in Havana. d, First march. e, Fidel Castro, Revolutionary Government Prime Minister, addressing crowd. f, Camilo Cienfuegos dissolves Bureau for the Repression of Communist Activities. g, Granting of Cuban citizenship to Ernesto "Che" Guevara. h, Fidel Castro's first visit to Venezuela. i, Creation of the P.N.R. (National Revolutionary Police). j, Creation of State Security organizations. k, Creation of T.G.F. (Border Guard). l, Agrarian Reform Law. m, Takeover of Cuban telephone system. n, Creation of the F.M.C. (Federation of Cuban Women). o, Creation of the C.D.R. (Committees for the Defense of the Revolution). p, Start of literacy campaign. q, Creation of I.N.D.E.R. (Institute of Sports, Physical Education and Recreation). r, Radio across Cuba. s, Designation of Guevara as Industry Minister. t, Creation of Union of Young Communists. u, Creation of the Civil Defense. v, Creation of the National Civil Defense Committee. w, First sugar harvest. x, Guevara speaks at the United Nations.
　No. 4922, 15c: a, Constitution of the Central Committee of the Cuban Communist Party. b, Day of the Heroic Guerrilla. c, Free distribution of Guevara's diary. d, First National Education and Cultural Congress. e, First Congress of the P.C.C. (Cuban Communist Party). f, First Rural Education Congress. g, Establishment in Cuba of Intl. Children's Day. h, Vaccinations in Cuba, 205th anniv. i, Creation of M.I.N.A.Z. (Cuban Ministry of Sugar). j, Creation of I.N.P. (National Fishing Institute). k, Development of fishing industry. l, 11th World Youth and Student Festival. m, Cuban cosmonaut. n, Day of Cuban Science (building at right). o, Day of Cuban Science (building at left). p, Family doctors and nurses. q, Elimination of apartheid, 15th anniv. r, Beginning of Battle of Ideas. s, Social security. t, Creation of the E.I.E.D. u, National culture (ballet dancer at left). v, National culture (guitarists at right). w, Battle of Ideas program (classroom at right). x, Battle of Ideas program (people waving flags at right).
　No. 4923, 1p, Cuban flags. No. 4924, 1p, Revolution Plaza, Havana.

2009, Jan. 1　Litho.　**Perf. 12¾**
Sheets of 24, #a-x
4921-4922　A1394　Set of 2　14.50　14.50
Souvenir Sheets
Imperf
4923-4924　A1394　Set of 2　4.00　4.00
　Nos. 4923-4924 have simulated perforations.

Second World Baseball Classic A1395

Designs: 5c, Batter swinging at ball. 10c, Play at home plate. 15c, Fielder stretching to catch ball. 45c, Pitcher in wind-up. 65c, Runner sliding into base. 75c, Runner and fielder watching ball.
1p, Cuban team.

2009, Jan. 27　　　　　**Perf. 12¾**
4925-4930　A1395　Set of 6　4.50　4.50

Souvenir Sheet
Imperf
4931　A1395　1p multi　　　2.00　2.00
　No. 4931 has simulated perforations.

Souvenir Sheet

Cuban Workers' Union, 70th
Anniv. — A1396

2009, Jan. 29　　　　　*Imperf.*
4932　A1396　1p multi　　　2.00　2.00
　No. 4932 has simulated perforations.

Santa María del Puerto de Príncipe, 495th Anniv. A1397

2009, Feb. 2　　　　　**Perf. 12¾**
4933　A1397　90c multi　　　1.90　1.90

Souvenir Sheet

13th Intl. Information Fair and Convention, Havana — A1398

2009, Feb. 9　　　　　*Imperf.*
4934　A1398　1p multi　　　2.00　2.00
　No. 4934 has simulated perforations.

Art — A1399

Designs: 15c, Coloritmo, by Alejandro Otero. 30c, Atmósfera Cromoplástica IV, by Luis Tomasello. 40c, Autopista del Sur, by León Ferrari. 65c, Tridim-L, by Victor Vasarely. 75c, Untitled work, by Jesús Soto. 85c, Untitled work, by Julio Le Parc.
1p, Physicromie 105, by Carlos Cruz Diez, horiz.

2009, Feb. 25　　　　　**Perf. 12¾**
4935-4940　A1399　Set of 6　6.25　6.25
Souvenir Sheet
Imperf
4941　A1399　1p multi　　　2.00　2.00
　No. 4941 has simulated perforations.

High Speed Trains
A1400

Designs: No. 4942, 15c, Acela Express, US. No. 4943, 15c, AVE, Spain. 30c, ATP Eurostar, Great Britain. 65c, ICE, Germany. 75c, ICN, Switzerland. 1.05p, TGV, France.
No. 4948: a, Shinkansen Model 500, Japan. b, Shinkansen Model 700, Japan.

2009, Feb. 27   *Perf. 12½x12¼*
4942-4947 A1400   Set of 6   6.25 6.25
Souvenir Sheet
Imperf
4948 A1400 50c Sheet of 2, #a-b 2.00 2.00
No. 4948 has simulated perforations.

Cuban Arts and Cinematographic Industry Institute, 50th Anniv. — A1401

Designs: No. 4949, 10c, Actress from *La Bella del Alhambra*. No. 4950, 10c, Actress from *Reina y Rey*. No. 4951, 15c, Character from animated film *Elpidio Valdés*. No. 4952, 15c, Actresses from *Lucía*. 45c, Actor from *Primera Carga al Machete*. 65c, Actor from *El Hombre de Maisinicú*. 75c, Actor and actress from *Clandestinos*. 90c, Actress from *Retrato de Teresa*. 1.05p, Santiago Alvarez, ICAIC reporter.
1p, Scene from *Fresa y Chocolate*.

2009, Mar. 24   *Perf. 12½x12¼*
4949-4957 A1401   Set of 9   8.75 8.75
Souvenir Sheet
Imperf
4958 A1401 1p multi   2.00 2.00
No. 4958 has simulated perforations.

State Security Organizations, 50th Anniv. — A1402

2009, Mar. 26   *Perf. 12¼x12½*
4959 A1402 65c multi   1.40 1.40

Motorcycles — A1403

Designs: 10c, Cagiva Mito N1. 15c, Honda CBR 900. 30c, Hyosung-GT 8. 65c, Kawasaki ZX-7R 750cc. 75c, Gussi MGS. 90c, Ducati Monster 900.
1p, Hyosung-GT 125-R-LD, vert.

2009, Apr. 8   *Perf. 12¾*
4960-4965 A1403   Set of 6   6.25 6.25
Souvenir Sheet
Imperf
4966 A1403 1p multi   2.00 2.00
China 2009 World Philatelic Exhibition, Luoyang. No. 4966 has simulated perforations.

Cats
A1404

Designs: 10c, Cat and kittens. 15c, Kittens and baseball. 40c, Two cats clawing fabric. 65c, Two cats on tile floor. 75c, Cat. 1.05p, Cat eating food.
1p, Two cats on roof, vert.

2009, Apr. 12   *Perf. 12¾*
4967-4972 A1404   Set of 6   6.25 6.25
Souvenir Sheet
Imperf
4973 A1404 1p multi   2.00 2.00
No. 4973 has simulated perforations.

Tourism
A1405

Art from hotels and restaurants: No. 4974, 10c, Stained-glass window, by René Portocarrero, Bodeguita del Medio Restaurant. No. 4975, Detail from mural, by Amelia Peláez, Hotel Habana Libre Tryp. 45c, Painting by Domingo Ramos, Hotel Nacional de Cuba, horiz. 65c, Detail from mural, by Mariano Rodríguez, Hotel Bello Caribe, horiz. 75c, Detail from mural, by Raúl Martínez, Hotel Bella Caribe, horiz. 85c, Mural, by Manuel A. Sosabravo, Hotel Habana Libre Tryp, horiz.
1p, Mural by various artists, Hotel Inglaterra, horiz.

2009, Apr. 21   *Perf. 12¾*
4974-4979 A1405   Set of 6   6.00 6.00
Souvenir Sheet
Imperf
4980 A1405 1p multi   2.00 2.00
No. 4980 has simulated perforations.

Haydee Santamaría Cuadrado (1922-80), Founder of Casa de las Americas — A1406

2009, Apr. 28   *Perf. 12¾*
4981 A1406 3p multi   6.00 6.00

World Heritage Sites
A1407

Designs: 15c, Havana. 45c, Cienfuegos. 50c, Trinidad. 1.05p, Camagüey.

2009, May 8   *Litho.*
4982-4985 A1407   Set of 4   4.50 4.50
4985a   Souvenir sheet, #4982-4985   4.50 4.50

Parrots
A1408

Designs: 5c, Guacamayo sereno. 10c, Guacamayo azul-dorado. 15c, Guacamayo de hombro rojo. No. 4989, 20c, Guacamayo cuellodorado. No. 4990, Guacamayo de Jacinto. 65c, Guacamayo escarlata. 75c, Guacamayo frente rojo. 90c, Guacamayo militar.

2009, May 16
4986-4993 A1408   Set of 8   6.00 6.00

Institute of Design, 25th Anniv. — A1409

2009, May 28   *Perf. 12½x12¼*
4994 A1409 65c multi   1.40 1.40

Souvenir Sheet

Ernesto Guevara Central Palace of Pioneers, 30th Anniv. — A1410

2009, June 1   *Imperf.*
4995 A1410 1p multi   2.00 2.00
No. 4995 has simulated perforations.

National Revolutionary Police, 50th Anniv. — A1411

2009, June 6   *Perf. 12½x12¼*
4996 A1411 1.05p multi   2.10 2.10

FORDES Gallery, 5th Anniv. — A1412

2009, June 14
4997 A1412 75c multi   1.50 1.50

Zoo Animals
A1413

Designs: 5c, Ceratotherium simum. 10c, Syncerus caffer caffer. 15c, Acinonyx jubatus,

vert. 30c, Papio hamadryas, vert. 40c, Struthio camelus, vert. 2.05p, Lycaon pictus, vert.
1p, Hippopotamus amphibius.

2009, June 20   *Perf. 12¾*
4998-5003 A1413   Set of 6   6.25 6.25
Souvenir Sheet
Imperf
5004 A1413 1p multi   2.00 2.00
No. 5004 contains one 47x30mm stamp with simulated perforations.

Cuban Cuisine — A1414

Designs: 40c, Arroz con pollo a la chorrera (chicken with rice). 45c, Plátano maduro frito (fried plantains). 50c, Frijoles negros dormidos (black beans with onion).

2009, June 29   *Perf. 12½x12¼*
5005-5007 A1414   Set of 3   2.75 2.75

Diplomatic Relations Between Cuba and Sri Lanka, 50th Anniv. — A1415

2009, July 29   *Perf. 12¼x12½*
5008 A1415 1.05p multi   2.10 2.10

Peace and National Sovereignty Movement, 60th Anniv. — A1416

2009, Aug. 4   *Perf. 12¾*
5009 A1416 65c multi   1.40 1.40

Los Malagones Peasant Militia, 50th Anniv. — A1417

2009, Aug. 31   *Perf. 12¼x12½*
5010 A1417 90c multi   1.90 1.90

Havana Convention Center, 30th
Anniv. — A1418

2009, Sept. 3   **Perf. 12¾**
5011 A1418 50c multi   1.00 1.00

Tourism
A1419

Birds: 15c, Coloptes fernandinae. 40c, Torreonis inexpectata. 50c, Ferminia cerverai. 65c, Agelaius assimilis. 75c, Mellisuga helenae. 90c, todus multicolor.
1p, Aratinga euops.

2009, Sept. 14   **Perf. 12¾**
5012-5017 A1419   Set of 6   6.75 6.75
Souvenir Sheet
Imperf
5018 A1419 1p multi   2.00 2.00
No. 5018 has simulated perforations.

People's
Republic
of China,
60th
Anniv.
A1420

2009, Sept. 28   **Litho.**   **Perf. 12¾**
5019 A1420 85c multi   1.75 1.75

Cubana Airlines, 80th Anniv. — A1421

Designs: 5c, Ford Trimotor. 15c, Sikorsky S-38B. 45c, DC-3. 50c, DC-4. 65c, IL-62M. 75c, IL-96 300.
1p, Tu-204.

2009, Oct. 8   **Perf. 12½x12¼**
5020-5025 A1421   Set of 6   5.25 5.25
Souvenir Sheet
Imperf
5026 A1421 1p multi   2.00 2.00
No. 5026 has simulated perforations.

America Issue,
Traditional
Games
A1422

Designs: 15c, Kite. 65c, Top. 75c, Dominos. 2.05p, Jacks.

2009, Oct. 12   **Perf. 12¾**
5027-5030 A1422   Set of 4   7.25 7.25
5030a   Souvenir sheet, #5027-
      5030   7.25 7.25

Souvenir Sheet

First Rocket Mail Flight in Cuba, 70th
Anniv. — A1423

2009, Oct. 15   **Imperf.**
5031 A1423 1p multi   2.00 2.00

Ministry of the Revolutionary Armed
Forces, 50th Anniv. — A1424

2009, Oct. 16   **Perf. 12¾**
5032 A1424 75c multi   1.50 1.50

Disappearance of Camilo Cienfuegos,
50th Anniv. — A1425

2009, Oct. 28   **Perf. 12½x12¼**
5033 A1425 65c multi   1.40 1.40

Rights of the
Child
Convention,
20th Anniv.
A1426

2009, Nov. 20   **Perf. 12¾**
5034 A1426 1.05p multi   2.10 2.10

Cuban
Federation of
Sport Fishing,
30th
Anniv. — A1427

Designs: 15c, Fisherman pulling fish into boat. 30c, Fisherman in water holding rod and fish. 45c, Sailfish and boat. No. 5038, 65c, Fisherman in water holding rod and fish, horiz. 75c, Fish on line, two fishermen in boat, horiz. 85c, Fishermen on sea wall, horiz.
No,. 5041, 65c, Tilapia, horiz

Perf. 12¼x12½, 12½x12¼
2009, Nov. 21
5035-5040 A1427   Set of 6   6.50 6.50
Souvenir Sheet
Imperf
5041 A1427 65c multi   1.40 1.40
No. 5041 has simulated perforations.

Ministry of Foreign Relations, 50th
Anniv. — A1428

2009, Dec. 23   **Perf. 12½x12¼**
5042 A1428 1.05p multi   2.10 2.10

José L. Guerra Aguiar Cuban Postal
Museum, 45th Anniv. — A1430

2010, Jan. 2   **Litho.**   **Perf. 12½x12¼**
5044 A1430 65c multi   1.40 1.40

A1431

A1432

A1433

New
Year
2010
(Year of
the
Tiger)
A1434

2010, Jan. 5   **Perf. 12¾**
5045 A1431 15c multi   .30 .30
5046 A1432 15c multi   .30 .30
5047 A1433 15c multi   .30 .30
5048 A1434 15c multi   .30 .30
   a.   Souvenir sheet, #5045-5048   1.25 1.25
   Nos. 5045-5048 (4)   1.20 1.20

January 1960 Speech of Fidel Castro,
50th Anniv. — A1435

2010, Jan. 15   **Perf. 12½x12¼**
5049 A1435 65c multi   1.40 1.40

Diplomatic Relations Between Cuba
and Indonesia, 50th Anniv. — A1436

2010, Jan. 22
5050 A1436 85c multi   1.75 1.75

Association of Rebel Youth, 50th
Anniv. — A1437

2010, Jan. 28
5051 A1437 3p multi   6.00 6.00

Trains
A1438

Designs: 5c, Fidel Castro leaving train. 10c, DF7G-C locomotive. 15c, Tank car. 65c, Flat car carrying shipping containers. 75c, Box cars. 1.05p, DF7K-C locomotive.
1p, Locomotive at end of track, vert.

2010, Jan. 29   **Perf. 12¾**
5052-5057 A1438   Set of 6   5.50 5.50
Souvenir Sheet
Imperf
5058 A1438 1p multi   2.00 2.00

Diplomatic Relations Between Cuba
and India, 50th Anniv. — A1439

2010, Feb. 10   **Perf. 12¾**
5059 A1439 85c multi   1.75 1.75

National Aquarium, 50th
Anniv. — A1440

Designs: 10c, Bispira brunnea. No. 5061, 15c, Hypoplectrus gummigutta. No. 5062, 15c, Holocanthus ciliaris. 50c, Seal. 75c, Epinephelus guttatus. 85c, Tursiops truncatus. 1p, Acanthurus coeruleus.

2010, Feb. 12   *Perf. 12¾*
5060-5065 A1440 Set of 6   5.00 5.00
Souvenir Sheet
Imperf
5066 A1440 1p multi   2.00 2.00
No. 5066 has simulated perforations.

A1441

La Colmenita Youth Theater Company, 20th Anniv. — A1442

2010, Feb. 14   *Perf. 12¾*
5067 A1441 50c multi   1.00 1.00
5068 A1442 50c multi   1.00 1.00

Underwater Photography — A1443

Designs: 10c, Fish and coral. 15c, Coral and starfish. 45c, Crab and sea anemone. 50c, Sponges and feather duster worms. 75c, Sea cucumber and coral. 85c, Sea horse and diver photographing tube worm. 1p, Fish and diver.

2010, Feb. 20   *Perf. 12½x12¼*
5069-5074 A1443 Set of 6   5.75 5.75
Souvenir Sheet
Imperf
5075 A1443 1p multi   2.00 2.00

Central Planning, 50th Anniv. — A1444

2010, Mar. 11   *Perf. 12½x12¼*
5076 A1444 75c multi   1.50 1.50

Dogs and Art — A1445

Designs: 10c, Peruvian hairless dog, Mochica figurine of dog, Peru. 15c, Bichon Frise, pitcher depicting hunter and dogs. 40c, Neapolitan mastiff, Roman mosaic of hunter and dog. 65c, Chihuahua, figurine of dog, map of Colima, Mexico. 75c, Pug, Chinese painting

of hunters and dog. 90c, King Charles spaniel, The Birth of Louis XIII, by Peter Paul Rubens. 1p, Pharaoh hound, Egyptian painting from tomb of Ipy.

2010, Mar. 12   *Perf. 12¾*
5077-5082 A1445 Set of 6   6.00 6.00
Souvenir Sheet
Imperf
5083 A1445 1p multi   2.00 2.00
No. 5083 has simulated perforations.

Diplomatic Relations Between Cuba and Canada, 65th Anniv. — A1446

2010, Mar. 16   *Perf. 12¾*
5084 A1446 65c multi   1.40 1.40

Bilateral Relations Between Cuba and Namibia, 20th Anniv. A1447

2010, Mar. 24   *Litho.*
5085 A1447 85c multi   1.75 1.75

2010 World Cup Soccer Championships, South Africa — A1448

Flags of competing nations, various soccer players and list of teams in: 15c, Groups A and B. 45c, Groups C and D. 65c, Groups E and F. 75c, Groups G and H.

2010, Mar. 24
5086-5089 A1448 Set of 4   4.00 4.00

Congress of the Young Communist's League — A1449

2010, Apr. 2
5090 A1449 65c multi   1.40 1.40

National Symphonic Orchestra, 50th Anniv. — A1450

Designs: 15c, Amadeo Roldán (1900-39), composer. 30c, Gonzalo Roig (1890-1970), composer. 40c, Enrique González Mántici (1912-74), composer. 75c, Manuel Duchesne

Cuzán, General director of National Symphonic Orchestra.

2010, Apr. 11   *Perf. 12½x12¼*
5091-5094 A1450 Set of 4   3.25 3.25

Diplomatic Relations Between Cuba and Cambodia, 50th Anniv. — A1451

2010, Apr. 15
5095 A1451 85c multi   1.75 1.75

Cuban National Chorus, 50th Anniv. — A1452

2010, Apr. 17   *Litho.*
5096 A1452 90c multi   1.90 1.90

First Cuban Computer, 40th Anniv. — A1453

2010, Apr. 18   *Perf. 12¾*
5097 A1453 75c multi   1.50 1.50

First Cuban Stamps, 155th Anniv. — A1454

Designs: 75c, Matanzas mail box, 1859, bicyclist in front of building. 85c, Cuba #147, account book of first postal administrator, 1765.

2010, Apr. 24   *Perf. 12½x12¼*
5098-5099 A1454 Set of 2   3.25 3.25

Tourism A1455

Designs: 15c, Santiago de Cuba. 20c, Guantánamo. 35c, Holguín. 65c, Camagüey. 75c, Granma. 90c, Las Tunas. 1p, Santiago de Cuba, diff.

2010, May 4   *Perf. 12¼x12½*
5100-5105 A1455 Set of 6   6.00 6.00
Souvenir Sheet
Imperf
5106 A1455 1p multi   2.00 2.00

ICAIC Latin American Newsreels, 50th Anniv. — A1456

2010, June 1   *Perf. 12¾*
5107 A1456 75c multi   1.50 1.50

Flora and Fauna A1457

Designs: 15c, Dellia sp. 35c, Bietia purpurea. 40c, Anolis equestris. 65c, Broughtonia orgiesiana. 75c, Priotrochatella stellata. 85c, Todus multicolor. 1p, Pinus caribaea.

Perf. 12½x12¼, 12¼x12½
2010, June 11
5108-5113 A1457 Set of 6   6.50 6.50
Souvenir Sheet
Imperf
5114 A1457 1p multi   2.00 2.00

Expo 2010, Shanghai — A1458

Map of China, aviation posters and aircraft: 5c, Savoia-Marchetti 55X. 10c, Farman 60 Goliath. 15c, Fokker VII. 45c, Koolhoven F.K. 50. 65c, Junkers 52/3M. 85c, Latécoère 28. 1p, Handley Page 42E.

2010, Apr. 26 Litho.   *Perf. 12½x12¼*
5115-5120 A1458 Set of 6   4.50 4.50
Souvenir Sheet
Imperf
5121 A1458 1p multi   2.00 2.00
No. 5121 has simulated perforations.

Writings of José Martí — A1459

Designs: No. 5122, 15c, *La Patria Libre*, white warbler, flag similar to Chile's. No. 5123, 15c, *La Nacion*, great antshrike, flag of Argentina. No. 5124, 15c, *Revista Universal*, king vulture, flag of Mexico. No. 5125, 15c, Proclamation of President of Paraguay, plantcutter, flag of Paraguay. No. 5126, 15c, *Patria*, hummingbird, flag of Cuba. No. 5127, 15c, Montecristi Manifesto, woodpecker, flag similar to Dominican Republic's. No. 5128, 15c, *La República Española y la Revolucion Cubana*, house sparrow and flag similar to Spain's, vert. No. 5129, 15c, *Mis Hijos* (translation of Victor Hugo's *Mes Fils*), long-tailed tit, flag of France, vert. No. 5130, 15c, *Guatemala*, quetzal, flag of Guatemala, vert. 65c, Pamphlet for International Monetary Conference, crested gallito, flag of Uruguay, vert. 75c, *Revista Venezolana*, troupial, flag of Venezuela, vert. 90c, Books of poetry, quill pen and inkwell, vert.

Perf. 12½x12¼, 12¼x12½
2010, May 19
5122-5133 A1459 Set of 12   7.50 7.50

Birds Endemic to Various Countries — A1460

Designs: 5c, Eumomota superciliosa, Nicaragua. 10c, Priotelus temnurus, Cuba. 15c, Amazona imperialis, Dominica. No. 5137, 20c, Amazona guildingii, St. Vincent and the Grenadines. No. 5138, 20c, Fregata magnificent, Antigua and Barbuda. 65c, Vultur gryphus, Bolivia. 75c, Icterus icterus, Venezuela, vert. 90c, Turdus rufiventris, Brazil, vert.

			Perf. 12¾
2010, May 26			
5134-5141	A1460	Set of 8	6.00 6.00

Ernest Hemingway Intl. Fishing Tournament, 60th Anniv. — A1461

Emblem and: No. 5142, 65c, Fishing boat, rod and reel. No. 5143, 65c, Ernest Hemingway. No. 5144, 65c, Swordfish. No. 5145, 65c Trophy.

			Perf. 12¼x12½
2010, May 29			
5142-5145	A1461	Set of 4	5.25 5.25

Dr. Enrique Hart Ramírez (1900-89), Judge — A1462

			Perf. 12¾
2010, June 1			
5146	A1462	65c multi	1.40 1.40

Diplomatic Relations Between Cuba and North Korea, 50th Anniv. — A1463

			Litho.
2010, Aug. 29			
5147	A1463	85c multi	1.75 1.75

La Caridad Theater, Santa Clara, 125th Anniv. A1464

Designs: 15c, Theater in 1885. 30c, Theater in 2010. 75c, Theater interior. 90c, Marta Abreu de Estévez (1845-1909), philanthropist, vert.

2010, Sept. 8			
5148-5151	A1464	Set of 4	4.25 4.25

Architectural Arches of Havana — A1465

Designs: 15c, Elliptical arch. 65c, Mixtilinear arch. 75c, Polylobular arch.

			Perf. 12½x12¼
2010, Sept. 9			
5152-5154	A1465	Set of 3	3.25 3.25

Lighthouses A1466

Maps and: No. 5155, 15c, Cayo Jutía Lighthouse, Pinar del Rio. No. 5156, 15c, Cayo Cruz del Padre Lighthouse, Matanzas. No. 5157, 15c, Cayo Lucrecia Lighthouse, Holguin. 2.05p, Morro Lighthouse, Santiago de Cuba.

			Perf. 12¼x12½
2010, Sept. 15			
5155-5158	A1466	Set of 4	5.00 5.00
5158a		Souvenir sheet, #5155-5158	5.00 5.00

Electric Automobiles — A1467

Designs: 5c, 1893 Jeantaud and Raffard. 10c, 1903 American Pope-Tribune. 15c, 1903 STAE. 20c, Matra Zoom. 45c, Zilent. 75c, Jeep Treo. 1p, Aptera, vert.

			Perf. 12¾
2010, Sept. 20			
5159-5164	A1467	Set of 6	3.50 3.50

Souvenir Sheet

Imperf

5165	A1467	1p multi	2.00 2.00

Portugal 2010 Intl. Philatelic Exhibition. No. 5165 has simulated perforations.

Tourism — A1468

Designs: 20c, Papilio androgeus epidaurus, Viñales National Park. 50c, Mesocapromys enanus, Ciénaga de Zapata National Park. 75c, Trichechus manatus manatus, Alejandro de Humboldt National Park. 90c, Amazona leucocephala, Desembarco del Granma National Park.

			Perf. 12½x12¼
2010, Sept. 27			
5166-5169	A1468	Set of 4	4.75 4.75

Diplomatic Relations Between Cuba and People's Republic of China, 50th Anniv. — A1469

Designs: No. 5170, 15c, Chinese Army, flag of People's Republic of China. No. 5171, 15c, Chinese landscape, arms of People's Republic of China. No. 5172, 85c, Cuban soldiers, horses and boat, flag of Cuba. No. 5173, 85c, Cuban landscape, arms of Cuba.

2010, Sept. 28			
5170-5173	A1469	Set of 4	4.00 4.00

SEMI-POSTAL STAMPS

Common Design Types pictured following the introduction.

Curie Issue
Common Design Type
Wmk. 106

1938, Nov. 23		**Engr.**	**Perf. 10**
B1	CD80	2c + 1c salmon	4.00 1.00
B2	CD80	5c + 1c deep ultra	4.00 1.40
	Set, never hinged		12.00

40th anniv. of the discovery of radium by Pierre and Marie Curie. Surtax for the benefit of the Intl. Union for the Control of Cancer.

> Catalogue values for unused stamps in this section, from this point to the end of the section, are for Never Hinged items.

"Agriculture" Supporting "Industry" SP2

Engr., Center Typo.

1959, May 7	**Wmk. 321**	**Perf. 12½**	
B3	SP2	2c + 1c car & ultra	.70 .20

Agricultural reforms. See No. CB1. For surcharges see Nos. 624, C199.

Nurse — SP3

Wmk. 229

1959, Sept. 22	**Photo.**	**Perf. 12½**	
B4	SP3	2c + 1c crimson rose	.40 .25

Exists imperf, value about double.

AIR POST STAMPS

Seaplane over Havana Harbor AP1

Wmk. 106

1927, Nov. 1	**Engr.**	**Perf. 12**	
C1	AP1	5c dark blue	5.00 1.00
	Never hinged		8.00

For overprint see No. C30.

Type of 1927 Issue Overprinted

1928, Feb. 8			
C2	AP1	5c carmine rose	4.00 1.60
	Never hinged		6.00

No. 283 Surcharged in Red

1930, Oct. 27			**Unwmk.**
C3	A44	10c on 25c violet	3.50 1.60
	Never hinged		4.75

Airplane and Coast of Cuba — AP3

For Foreign Postage

1931, Feb. 26	**Wmk. 106**	**Perf. 10**	
C4	AP3	5c green	.45 .20
C5	AP3	10c dk blue	.45 .20
C6	AP3	15c rose	.90 .30
C7	AP3	20c brown	.90 .20
C8	AP3	30c dk violet	1.25 .20
C9	AP3	40c dp orange	2.75 .35
C10	AP3	50c olive grn	3.25 .35
C11	AP3	1p black	5.25 .90
	Nos. C4-C11 (8)		15.20 2.70
	Set, never hinged		25.00

See No. C40. For surcharges see Nos. C16-C17, C203, C225.

Airplane AP4

For Domestic Postage

1931-46

C12	AP4	5c rose vio ('32)	.40 .20
a.	5c brown violet ('36)		.40 .20
C13	AP4	10c gray blk	.40 .20
C14	AP4	20c car rose	3.25 .90
C14A	AP4	20c rose pink ('46)	1.40 .25
C15	AP4	50c dark blue	5.25 .90
	Nos. C12-C15 (5)		10.70 2.45
	Set, never hinged		17.00

See #C130. For overprints see #C31, E29-E30.

Type of 1931 Surcharged in Black

1935, Apr. 24			**Perf. 10**
C16	AP3	10c + 10c red	11.00 9.50
	Never hinged		18.00
a.	Double surcharge		110.00

Imperf

C17	AP3	10c + 10c red	25.00 25.00
	Never hinged		35.00

Matanzas Issue

Air View of Matanzas AP5

10c, Airship "Macon." 20c, Airplane "The Four Winds." 50c, Air View of Fort San Severino.

Wmk. 229
1936, May 5   Photo.   Perf. 12½
C18 AP5 5c violet .75 .30
C19 AP5 10c yellow orange .90 .50
C20 AP5 20c green 3.25 1.90
C21 AP5 50c greenish slate 8.00 3.75
Nos. C18-C21 (4) 12.90 6.45
Set, never hinged 20.00

Exist imperf. Value 20% more.

"Lightning" AP9

Allegory of Flight AP10

1936, Nov. 18
C22 AP9 5c violet 2.00 1.10
C23 AP10 10c orange brown 2.75 1.50
Set, never hinged 6.00

Major Gen. Maximo Gomez, birth cent.

Flat Arch (Panama) — AP11

Carlos Antonio López (Paraguay) — AP12

Inca Gate, Cuzco (Peru) — AP13

Atlacatl (Salvador) AP14

José Enrique Rodó (Uruguay) AP15

Simón Bolívar (Venezuela) AP16

Wmk. 106
1937, Oct. 13   Engr.   Perf. 10
C24 AP11 5c red 7.00 7.00
C25 AP12 5c red 7.00 7.00
C26 AP13 10c blue 7.00 7.00
C27 AP14 10c blue 7.00 7.00
C28 AP15 20c green 9.50 9.50
C29 AP16 20c green 9.50 9.50
Nos. C24-C29 (6) 47.00 47.00
Set, never hinged 60.00

See note after No. 354.

Type of 1927 Overprinted in Black

1938, May   Wmk. 106
C30 AP1 5c dark orange 5.00 1.60
Never hinged 7.00

1st airplane flight from Key West to Havana, made by Domingo Rosillo, 1913.

Type of 1931-32 Overprinted

1939, Oct. 15
C31 AP4 10c emerald 40.00 6.50
Never hinged 60.00

Issued in connection with an experimental postal rocket flight held at Havana.

Sir Rowland Hill, Map of Cuba and First Stamps of Britain, Spanish Cuba and Republic of Cuba — AP17

1940, Nov. 28   Engr.   Wmk. 106
C32 AP17 10c brown 4.50 2.00
Never hinged 7.50

Souvenir Sheet
Unwmk.   Imperf.
C33 Sheet of 4 15.00 11.00
Never hinged 25.00
a. AP17 10c light brown 2.75 1.25
Never hinged 3.50

Cent. of the 1st postage stamp.
Sheet sold for 60c.

No. C33 exists with each of the four stamps overprinted in black: "Exposicion de la ACNU/24 de Octubre de 1951/Dia de las Naciones" and "Historia de la Aviacion" in lower margin. Value, $80.
For overprints see Nos. C39, C211.

Poet José Heredia and Palms AP18

Heredia and Niagara Falls — AP19

1940, Dec. 30   Wmk. 106
C34 AP18 5c emerald 2.00 1.00
C35 AP19 10c greenish slate 3.00 1.60
Set, never hinged 7.50

Death cent. of José Maria Heredia y Campuzano (1803-39), poet and patriot.

First Cuban Land Sighted by Columbus AP20

Columbus Lighthouse AP21

1944, May 19
C36 AP20 5c olive green .90 .40
C37 AP21 10c slate black 2.10 .75

450th anniv. of the discovery of America.

Catalogue values for unused stamps in this section, from this point to the end of the section, are for Never Hinged items.

Conference of La Mejorana (Meceo, Gomez and Marti) AP22

1948, May 21   Wmk. 229   Perf. 12½
C38 AP22 8c org yel & blk 3.00 .80

50th anniv. of the start of the War of 1895.

Souvenir Sheet
No. C33 Overprinted in Ultramarine

1948, May 21   Unwmk.   Imperf.
C39 AP17 Sheet of 4 15.00 9.50

The overprint is applied in the center of the sheet, so that a part of the overprint falls on each stamp.
American Air Mail Soc. Convention, Havana, May 21 to 23, 1948. The sheets sold for 60c each.

Type of 1931
1948, June 15   Wmk. 106   Perf. 10
C40 AP3 8c orange brown 2.40 .80

Narciso Lopez Landing at Cárdenas AP23

Flag on Cuban Fort — AP24

Flag on Morro Castle, Havana — AP25

Engraved and Lithographed
1951, July 3   Wmk. 229   Perf. 13
C41 AP23 5c ol grn, ultra & red 2.25 .30
C42 AP24 8c red brn, bl & red 3.50 .30
C43 AP25 25c gray blk, bl & red 5.00 1.90
Nos. C41-C43 (3) 10.75 2.50

Centenary of adoption of Cuba's flag.

Souvenir Sheet
No. 365a Overprinted in Green

Illustration reduced.

1951, Aug. 24   Unwmk.   Imperf.
C43A Sheet of 4 12.00 9.00

50th anniv. of the discovery of the cause of yellow fever by Dr. Carlos J. Finlay, and to honor the martyrs of science.

Postage Type and

Resignation Play of Dr. Lasker AP26

Capablanca Making "The Exact Play" — AP27

Wmk. 229
1951, Nov. 1   Photo.   Perf. 13
C44 AP26 5c shown 5.00 .80
C45 AP27 8c shown 9.00 1.25
C46 A165 25c Capablanca 15.00 3.25
Nos. C44-C46 (3) 29.00 5.30

30th anniv. of the winning of the World Chess title by José Raul Capablanca.

Morrillo Types of Regular Issue
Wmk. 106
1951, Nov. 22   Engr.   Perf. 10
C47 A167 5c violet 2.40 .70
C48 A168 8c deep green 3.25 1.00
C49 A169 25c dark brown 6.50 2.00
a. Souv. sheet of 6, black brown, perf. 13 50.00 35.00
b. Souv. sheet of 6, green, imperf. 200.00 125.00
Nos. C47-C49 (3) 12.15 2.75

Nos. C49a and C49b contain one each of the 1c, 2c and 5c of types A167-A169 and of the 5c, 8c and 25c airmail stamps of types A167-A169. Sheets are unwatermarked and measure 124x133mm.

Isabella Type of Regular Issue, 1952
1952, Feb. 22
C50 A172 25c purple 4.00 1.25
a. Souv. sheet of 2, perf. 11 19.00 19.00
b. Souv. sheet of 2, imperf. 24.00 24.00

Nos. C50a and C50b contain one each of a 2c of type A172 and a 25c air-mail stamp of type A172. In No. C50a, the 2c and marginal inscriptions are brown carmine; the 25c, dark blue. In No. C50b, the 2c and marginal inscriptions are dark blue; the 25c, brown carmine. Sheets measure 108x18mm.

Type of Regular Issue of 1951 Surcharged in Various Colors

1952, Mar. 18
Color: Yellow Brown

C51	A159	5c on 2c	.90	.30
C52	A159	8c on 2c (C)	1.75	.30
C53	A159	10c on 2c (Bl)	1.75	.30
C54	A159	25c on 2c (V)	2.75	1.50
C55	A159	50c on 2c (C)	8.75	3.00
C56	A159	1p on 2c (Bl)	20.00	12.00
	Nos. C51-C56 (6)		35.90	17.40

Country School AP32

Entrance, University of Havana — AP33

10c, Presidential Mansion. 25c, Banknote.

Wmk. 106
1952, May 27   Engr.   Perf. 12½
Centers Various Shades of Green

C57	AP32	5c dark purple	.45	.20
C58	AP33	8c dark red	.70	.20
C59	AP32	10c deep blue	1.40	.20
C60	AP32	25c dark violet brn	2.40	1.00
	Nos. C57-C60 (4)		4.95	1.60

Foundation of the Republic of Cuba, 50th anniv.

Plane and Map — AP34

Agustín Parlá — AP35

1952, July 22   Engr.   Perf. 10

C61	AP34	8c black	1.50	.55
a.	Souv. sheet, 8c deep blue		15.00	10.00
b.	Souv. sheet, 8c deep green		15.00	10.00
C62	AP35	30c ultra	4.00	1.60
a.	Souv. sheet, 25c deep blue		15.00	10.00
b.	Souv. sheet, 25c deep green		15.00	10.00

30th anniv. of the Key West-Mariel flight of Agustin Parla.
The four souvenir sheets are perf. 11.

Col. Charles Hernandes y Sandrino — AP36

1952, Oct. 7

C63	AP36	5c orange	.80	.30
C64	AP36	8c brt yel grn	.80	.30
C65	AP36	10c dk brown	1.00	.30
C66	AP36	15c dk Prus grn	1.90	.80
C67	AP36	20c aqua	2.50	1.00
C68	AP36	25c crimson	1.90	1.00
C69	AP36	30c dk vio bl	5.25	2.50
C70	AP36	45c rose lilac	5.25	3.50
C71	AP36	50c indigo	3.00	2.50
C72	AP36	1p bister	10.50	5.00
	Nos. C63-C72 (10)		32.90	17.20

Three-fourths of the proceeds from the sale were used for the Communications Ministry Employees' Retirement Fund.

Entrance, University of Havana — AP37

F. V. Dominguez, M. Estebanez and F. Capdevila — AP38

Engr.; Center Typo.
1952, Nov. 27

C73	AP37	5c indigo & dk blue	1.75	.40
C74	AP38	25c org & dk grn	5.00	1.40

Execution of 8 medical students, 81st anniv.

AP39

Lockheed Constellation Airliners — AP40

1953, May 22   Engr.

C75	AP39	8c orange brn	1.25	.20
C76	AP39	15c scarlet	2.25	.70

Typographed and Engraved

C77	AP40	2p dp green & dk brn	27.50	10.00
C78	AP40	5p blue & dk brn	55.00	17.50
	Nos. C75-C78 (4)		86.00	28.40

See Nos. C120-C121. For surcharge, see No. C224.

Page of Manifesto of Montecristi — AP42

House of Maximo Gomez AP43

#C79, Marti in Kingston, Jamaica, #C80, With Workers in Tampa, Florida. #C83, Marti addressing liberating army. #C84, Portrait. #C85, Dos Rios obelisk. #C86, Marti's first tomb. #C87, Present tomb. #C88, Monument in Havana. #C89, Martian forge.

1953   Engr.   Perf. 10

C79	AP42	5c dk car & blk	.30	.20
C80	AP42	5c dk car & blk	.30	.20
C81	AP43	8c dk green & blk	.65	.20
C82	AP42	8c dk green & blk	.65	.20
C83	AP43	10c dk blue & dk car	1.75	.75
C84	AP42	10c dk blue & dk car	1.75	.75
C85	AP42	15c violet & gray	1.10	.90
C86	AP42	15c violet & gray	1.10	.90
C87	AP42	25c brown & car	3.75	1.25
C88	AP42	25c brown & car	3.75	1.25
C89	AP43	50c yellow & bl	5.00	2.50
	Nos. C79-C89 (11)		19.80	9.10

Cent. of the birth of José Marti.

Board of Accounts Building — AP44

25c, Plane above Board of Accounts Bldg.

Miguel Coyula Llaguno AP45

Antonio Ginard Rojas AP46

1953, Nov. 3

C90	AP44	8c rose carmine	2.10	.70
C91	AP44	25c dk gray grn	3.50	1.10

1st Intl. Cong. of Boards of Account, Havana, Nov. 2-9, 1953.

Designs: 10c, Gregorio Hernandez Saez. 1p, Communications Association Flag.

1954

C92	AP45	5c dark blue	.65	.25
C93	AP46	8c red violet	.80	.25
C94	AP46	10c orange	1.40	.35
C95	AP45	1p black	9.50	4.50
	Nos. C92-C95 (4)		12.25	5.35

See note after No. C72.

Alvaro Reinoso — AP47

Plane and Harvesters Cutting Cane AP48

Designs in Lower Triangle: 5c, Four-engine Plane and Cane Field. 10c, Tractor pulling loaded wagons. 15c, Train of sugar cane. 20c, Modern mill. 25c, Evaporators. 30, Sacks of sugar. 40c, Loading sugar on ship. 45c, Ox cart. 50c, Primitive sugar mill.

1954, Apr. 27   Engr.

C96	AP47	5c yellow green	.45	.20
C97	AP48	8c brown	1.25	.50
C98	AP48	10c dark green	1.25	.50
C99	AP48	15c henna brn	3.00	.50
C100	AP48	20c blue	1.25	.20
C101	AP48	25c scarlet	.95	.20
C102	AP48	30c lilac rose	2.50	.95
C103	AP48	40c deep blue	5.00	1.25
C104	AP48	45c violet	4.00	2.50
C105	AP48	50c brt blue	4.00	1.60
C106	AP47	1p dk gray blue	11.00	3.25
	Nos. C96-C106 (11)		34.65	11.65

For surcharges see Nos. C204.

Sanatorium Type of Regular Issue
1954, Sept. 21   Wmk. 106   Perf. 10

C107	A186	9c deep green	2.50	.65

Dolz Type of Regular Issue, 1954
1954, Dec. 23

C108	A188	12c carmine	2.00	.70

Rotary Type of Regular Issue, 1955
1955, Feb. 23

C109	A190	12c carmine	2.50	.65

Stamps of 1855 and 1905, Palace of Fine Arts AP52

Designs (including 2 stamps): 12c, Plaza de la Fraternidad. 24c, View of Havana. 30c, Plaza de la Republica.

1955, Apr. 24   Perf. 12½

C110	AP52	8c dk grnsh bl & grn	1.00	.35
C111	AP52	12c dk ol grn & red	1.10	.35

C112	AP52	24c dk red & ultra	2.00	.95
C113	AP52	30c dp org & brn	4.25	1.60
	Nos. C110-C113 (4)		8.35	3.10

Cent. of Cuba's 1st postage stamps.

Mariel Bay — AP53

Views: 12c, Varadero beach. 1p, Vinales valley.

1955, June 22   Wmk. 106

C114	AP53	8c dk car & dk grn	.75	.25
C115	AP53	12c dk ocher & brt bl	1.75	.55
C116	AP53	1p dk grn & ocher	7.50	2.50
	Nos. C114-C116 (3)		10.00	3.30

See note after No. C72.

Map of Crocier's 1914 Flight — AP54

Design: 30c, Crocier in plane.

1955, July 4   Perf. 10

C117	AP54	12c red & dk grn	1.00	.25
C118	AP54	30c dk grn & mag	3.00	.80

35th anniv. of the death of Jaime Gonzalez Crocier, aviation pioneer.

Cuban Museum, Tampa, Fla. — AP55

1955, July 1   Engr.   Perf. 12½

C119	AP55	12c red & dk brn	2.10	.65

Cent. of Tampa's incorporation as a town.

Lockheed Type of 1953
Typographed and Engraved
1955, Sept. 21   Wmk. 106

C120	AP40	2p bl & ol grn	20.00	6.50
C121	AP40	5p dp rose & ol grn	42.50	15.00

Wright Brothers' Plane and Stamps AP56

Designs: 12c, Spirit of St. Louis. 24c, Graf Zeppelin. 30c, Constellation passenger plane. 50c, Convair jet fighter.

Engraved and Photogravure
1955, Nov. 12   Wmk. 106   Perf. 12½
Inscription and Plane in Black

C122	AP56	8c car & bl	1.00	.35
C123	AP56	12c yel grn & car	2.25	.70
C124	AP56	24c vio & car	6.75	2.50
C125	AP56	30c bl & red org	5.75	3.25
C126	AP56	50c ol grn & red org	7.75	4.00
a.	Souvenir sheet of 5		47.50	26.00
	Nos. C122-C126 (5)		23.50	10.80

International Centenary Philatelic Exhibition in Havana, Nov. 12-19, 1955.
No. C126a is printed on thick paper and measures 140x178mm. It contains one each of Nos. C122-C126 with the background of each stamp printed in a different color from the perforated stamps.

"Three Friends" and Gen. Emilio Nuñez AP57

Design: 12c, Landing on the Cuban Coast.

1955, Dec. 27   Engr.   Unwmk.
C127 AP57 8c ultra & dk car   2.00 .55
C128 AP57 12c grn & dk red brn 3.25 .90
Gen. Emilio Nuñez, Cuban revolutionary hero, birth cent.

Post Type of Regular Issue, 1956
Bishop P. A. Morell de Santa Cruz (1694-1768).

1956, Mar. 27   Wmk. 106
C129 A197 12c dk brn & grn   2.10 .55

Plane Type of 1931-46
1956   Engr.   Perf. 10
C130 AP4 50c greenish blue   3.00 1.00

Portrait Type of Regular Issue, 1956
1956, May 2   Perf. 12½
Portraits: 8c, Gen. Julio Sanguily. 12c, Gen. José Maria Aguirre. 30c, Col. Ernesto Fonts Sterling.

Portraits in Black
C131 A198 8c brown   1.25 .20
C132 A198 12c dull yellow   2.00 .25
C133 A198 30c indigo   3.00 1.50
Nos. C131-C133 (3)   5.85 1.95
See note after No. C72.

Mother and Child — AP60   Masonic Temple Havana — AP61

1956, May 13 Wmk. 106 Perf. 12½
C134 AP60 12c ultra & red   2.50 .40
Issued in honor of Mother's Day 1956.

1956, June 5
C135 AP61 12c olive green   2.75 .55

Pigeon AP62

Gundlach Hawk — AP63

Birds: 8c, Wood duck. 19c, Herring gulls. 24c, White pelicans. 29c, Common merganser. 30c, Quail. 50c, Herons (great white, great blue and Wurdemann's). 1p, Northern caracara. 2p, Middle American jacana. 5p, Ivory-billed woodpecker.

1956
C136 AP62 8c blue   .50 .20
C137 AP62 12c gray blue   7.50 .20
C138 AP63 14c green   1.75 .25
C139 AP63 19c redsh brn   1.10 .55
C140 AP63 24c lilac rose   1.25 .55
C141 AP62 29c green   1.90 .55
C142 AP62 30c dk olive bis   2.25 .80
C143 AP63 50c slate blk   4.25 1.10
C144 AP63 1p dk car rose   6.50 2.25
C145 AP62 2p rose violet   13.00 4.25
C146 AP63 5p brt red   35.00 8.75
Nos. C136-C146 (11)   75.00 19.45

See Nos. C205, C235-C237. For surcharges and overprints, see Nos. C147, C151, C197, C209-C210

Type of 1956 Surcharged

Design: 24c, White pelicans.

1956, July 13
C147 AP63 8c on 24c deep org 2.50 .75
Opening of the new building of the Cuba Philatelic Club, Havana, July 14, 1956.

Hubert de Blanck — AP64   Church of Our Lady of Charity — AP65

1956, July 6
C148 AP64 12c ultra   2.00 .40
Hubert de Blanck (1856-1932), composer.

1956, Sept. 8
C149 AP65 12c green & carmine   2.75 .55
a. Souvenir sheet of 2, imperf. 14.00 9.50
Issued in honor of Our Lady of Charity of Cobre, patroness of Cuba.
No. C149a contains one each of Nos. 559 and C149. No. C149a exists with yellow of No. 559 omitted.

Benjamin Franklin AP66

1956, Oct. 5   Engr.   Perf. 12½
C150 AP66 12c red brown   2.00 .55

Type of 1956 Surcharged in Blue

Design: 2p, Middle American jacana.

1956, Oct. 26   Wmk. 106
C151 AP62 12c on 2p dark gray 2.40 .95
Issued in honor of the 12th Inter-American Press Association Conference, Havana.

Lord Baden-Powell AP67

1957, Feb. 22
C152 AP67 12c slate   2.40 .70
Centenary of the birth of Lord Baden-Powell, founder of the Boy Scouts.

Hanabanilla Waterfall AP68

12c, Sierra de Cubitas. 30c, Puerto Boniato.

1957, Mar. 29
C153 AP68 8c blue & red   .75 .20
C154 AP68 12c green & red   2.40 .50
C155 AP68 30c ol grn & dk pur 3.00 .70
Nos. C153-C155 (3)   6.00 1.00
See note after No. 457.

Philatelic Club, Havana AP69   Fingerprint AP70

1957, Apr. 24 Wmk. 106 Perf. 12½
C156 AP69 12c yel, grn & brn 1.75 .40
Stamp Day, and the Natl. Phil. Exhib.

1957, Apr. 30
C157 AP70 12c claret brown   1.75 .40
Birth cent. (in 1856) of Juan Francisco Steegers y Perera, dactyloscopy pioneer.

Baseball Player — AP71

1957, May 17 Wmk. 106 Perf. 12½
C158 AP71 8c shown   1.25 .40
C159 AP71 12c Ballerina   2.00 .50
C160 AP71 24c Girl diver   2.75 1.25
C161 AP71 30c Boxers   4.00 1.60
Nos. C158-C161 (4)   10.00 3.75
Issued to honor young Cuban athletes.

Joaquin de Aguero AP72   Jeanette Ryder AP73

1957, July 4
C162 AP72 12c indigo   1.50 .40
Issued to honor Joaquin de Aguero, Cuban freedom fighter and patriot.

1957, July 17
C163 AP73 12c dk red brn   2.50 .55
a. Pair, #574, C163   7.00 3.50
Mrs. Jeanette Ryder, founder of the Humane Society of Cuba.

José M. de Heredia y Girard — AP74   John Robert Gregg — AP75

1957, Aug. 16   Engr.   Wmk. 106
C164 AP74 8c dk blue vio   1.50 .30
José Maria de Heredia y Girard (1842-1905), Cuban born French poet.

Justice Type of Regular Issue, 1957
1957, Sept. 2   Perf. 12½
C165 A214 12c green   2.00 .50

1957, Oct. 1
C166 AP75 12c dark green   2.00 .70
90th anniv. of the birth of John Robert Gregg, inventor of the Gregg shorthand system.

D. Figarola Caneda — AP76

José Marti National Library AP77

1957, Oct. 18 Wmk. 106 Perf. 12½
C167 AP76 8c ultra   .75 .25
C168 AP77 12c chocolate   2.00 .50
José Marti National Library.

Map of Cuba and UN Emblem AP78

1957, Oct. 24
C169 AP78 8c dk green & brn 1.00 .25
C170 AP78 12c car rose & grn 1.50 .55
C171 AP78 30c ind & brt pink 3.50 1.25
Nos. C169-C171 (3)   6.00 2.05
Issued for United Nations Day, 1957.

Map of Cuba and Florida AP79

1957, Oct. 28
C172 AP79 12c dk red brn & bl 1.90 .80
30th anniv. of airmail service from Key West to Havana.

Type of Regular Issue, 1957 and

Stairway and Bell Tower AP80

Design: 12c, Facade of Normal School.

1957, Nov. 19   Engr.   Perf. 12½
C173 A217 12c indigo & ocher   1.40   .40
C174 AP80 30c dk car & gray   2.50   .60

View Types of Regular Issue, 1957

Views: 8c, El Viso Fort, El Caney. 12c, Sancti Spiritus Church. 30c, Concordia Bridge, Matanzas.

1957, Dec. 17   Perf. 12½
C175 A218 8c dk gray & red   .80   .30
C176 A219 12c brown & gray   1.50   .40
C177 A218 30c red brn & bl gray   2.75   .75
      Nos. C175-C177 (3)   5.00   1.35

See note after No. C72.

Hedges Types of Regular Issue, 1958

8c, Dayton Hedges & Matanzas rayon factory.

1958, Jan. 30   Wmk. 106   Perf. 12½
C178 A221 8c green   2.00   .80

Diario de la Marina Building — AP81

1958, Apr. 1
C179 AP81 29c black   3.50   1.10

Jose Ignacio Rivero y Alonso, editor of the newspaper, Diario de la Marina.

Map Showing Sea Mail Route, 1765 AP82

1958, Apr. 24   Wmk. 106   Perf. 12½
C180 AP82 29c dk bl aqua & buff 4.75 1.25

Issued for Stamp Day, Apr. 24, and the National Philatelic Exhibition.

Gen. Gomez in Battle — AP83   Snail (Polymita Picta) — AP84

1958, June 6   Engr.
C181 AP83 12c slate green   2.00   .55

Issued in honor of Maj. Gen. José Miguel Gomez, President of Cuba, 1909-13.

1958, Aug. 29   Wmk. 321   Perf. 12½

12c, Megalocnus Rodens. 30c, Ammonite.

C182 AP84 8c gray, red & yel   6.50   1.25
C183 AP84 12c brn, yel grn   9.50   1.75
C184 AP84 30c grn, pink   14.50   2.10
      Nos. C182-C184 (3)   30.50   5.10

Centenary of the birth of Dr. Carlos de la Torre, naturalist.

Papilio Caiguanabus AP85

Cuban Sea Bass — AP86

12c, Teria gundlachia. 14c, Teria ebriola. 19c, Nathalis felicia. 29c, Butter Hamlet. 30c, Tattler.

1958, Sept. 26 Wmk. 106 Perf. 12½
C185 AP85 8c multicolored   3.00   .65
C186 AP85 12c emer, blk & org   3.50   .65
C187 AP85 14c multicolored   5.25   .95
C188 AP85 19c bl, blk & yel   6.75   1.25
C189 AP86 24c multicolored   7.50   1.25
C190 AP86 29c blk, brn & ultra   11.00   1.60
C191 AP86 30c blk, yel grn &
                   sep   16.00   2.25
      Nos. C185-C191 (7)   53.00   8.60

Felipe Poey (1799-1891), naturalist.

Battle of San Juan Hill, 1898 — AP87

Wmk. 106
1958, Oct. 27   Engr.   Perf. 12½
C192 AP87 12c black brown   2.75   .50

Birth centenary of Theodore Roosevelt.

UNESCO Building, Paris — AP88

Design: 30c, "UNESCO" and map of Cuba.

1958, Nov. 7
C193 AP88 12c dk slate grn   1.50   .50
C194 AP88 30c dp ultra   3.00   1.60

UNESCO Headquarters in Paris opening, Nov. 3.

Postal Notice of 1765 — AP89   Musical Arts Building — AP90

Design: 30c, Administrative postal book of St. Cristobal, Havana, 1765.

1959, Apr. 24   Wmk. 321   Perf. 12½
C195 AP89 12c Prus blue & sep 1.50   .40
C196 AP89 30c sepia & Prus bl 2.50   1.40

Issued for Stamp Day, Apr. 24, and the National Philatelic Exhibition.

Type of 1956 Surcharged with New Value, Bar and "ASTA" Emblem in Dark Blue

1959, Oct. 17   Wmk. 321   Perf. 12½
C197 AP63 12c on 1p emerald   2.40   1.25

Issued to publicize the meeting of the American Soc. of Travel Agents, Oct. 17-23.

Wmk. 106
1959, Nov. 11   Engr.   Perf. 12½
C198 AP90 12c yellow green   3.00   .70

40th anniversary of the Musical Arts Society.

No. CB1 Surcharged in Red: "HABILITADO PARA / 12c"

Engr. & Typo.
1960   Wmk. 321   Perf. 12½
C199 SPAP1 12c on 12 + 3c car
                   & grn   2.25   .75

Type of Regular Issue, 1960

8c, Battle of Santa Clara. 12c, Rebel forces entering Havana. 29c, Bank-note changing hands ("Clandestine activities in the cities").

Wmk. 320
1960, Jan. 28   Engr.   Perf. 12½
C200 A236 8c bl, gray ol & sal   2.25   .50
C201 A236 12c gray ol & ocher   3.25   .40
C202 A236 29c gray & car   6.50   1.50
      Nos. C200-C202 (3)   12.00   2.00

Nos. C9 and C104 Surcharged "12c" in Red

1960, Feb. 3   Wmk. 106
C203 AP3   12c on 40c dp org   1.75   .65
C204 AP48 12c on 45c vio   1.75   .65

Pigeon Type of 1956

1960, Feb. 12   Wmk. 321
C205 AP62 12c brt blue grn   2.00   .55

Statue Type of Regular Issue, 1960.

Statues: 8c, José Marti, Matanzas. 12c, Heroes of the Cacarajicara, Pinar del Rio. 30c, Cosme de la Torriente, Isle of Pines, horiz.

1960, Mar. 28   Perf. 12½
C206 A237 8c gray & car   .70   .25
C207 A237 12c blue & car   1.25   .25
C208 A237 30c violet & brn   2.75   1.25
      Nos. C206-C208 (3)   4.70   1.75

See note after No. 386.

Type of 1956 and No. C33 Overprinted in Dark Blue

1960, Apr. 24   Wmk. 321   Perf. 12½
C209 AP62 8c orange yel   .65   .40
C210 AP62 12c cerise   1.75   .65

Souvenir Sheet
C211 AP17   Sheet of 4   35.00 35.00

Stamp Day, 4/24/60, and Natl. Phil. Exhib. No. C211 has added marginal inscription in dark blue for cent. of the ¼r on 2r (No. 15).

Type of Olympic Games Issue, 1960

Wmk. 321
1960, Sept. 22   Engr.   Perf. 12½
C212 A238 8c Boxer   .80   .25
C213 A238 12c Runner   1.50   .50
   a.   Souvenir sheet of 4   5.50   5.50

17th Olympic Games, Rome, Aug. 25-Sept. 11. No. C213a contains one each imperf. of types of Nos. 645-646 and Nos. C212-C213 in dark blue.

No. C3 and Flight Symbols of 1930, 1960 — AP91

1960, Oct. 30   Litho.   Unwmk.
C214 AP91 8c multicolored   3.50   2.00

30th anniv. of national air mail service.

Sword of Sheaf of Wheat — AP92

12c, Two workers, horiz. 30c, Three maps, horiz. 50c, Hand inscribed "Peace" in 5 languages.

1961, Jan. 10   Photo.   Perf. 11½
Granite Paper
C215 AP92 8c multicolored   .60   .20
C216 AP92 12c multicolored   2.00   .20
C217 AP92 30c black & red   .65   .65
C218 AP92 50c blk, bl & red   3.00   1.00
      Nos. C215-C218 (4)   7.00   1.90

Conf. of Underdeveloped Countries, Havana.

José Marti and "Declaration of Havana" — AP93

Background in Spanish, English or French.

1961, Jan. 28   Litho.   Perf. 12½
C219 AP93 8c pale grn, blk &
                   red   1.25   .85
C220 AP93 12c org yel, blk &
                   blk   1.75   1.00
C221 AP93 30c pale bl, blk &
                   pale brn   4.00   3.50
   a.   Souvenir sheet of 3   15.00 15.00
      Nos. C219-C221 (3)   7.00   5.35

Declaration of Havana, Sept. 1, 1960. Sheets of 25 are imprinted in margin "E" for Spanish, "I" for English or "F" for French. No. C221a contains one each of Nos. C219-C221, imperf. The 8c has background in Spanish, the 12c in English and the 30e in French.

UN Type of 1961

1961, Apr. 12   Unwmk.   Perf. 12½
C222 A244 8c dp car & yel   .60   .25
C223 A244 12c brt ultra & org   1.50   .50
   a.   Souv. sheet of 2, #C222-
          C223, imperf.   10.00 10.00

Nos. C76 and C7 Surcharged

Wmk. 106
1961, Oct. 1   Engr.   Perf. 10
C224 AP39 8c on 15c No. C76   1.00   .40
C225 AP3   8c on 20c No. C7   1.00   .40

Revolution Anniv. Type of 1962

Perf. 12½
1962, Jan. 3   Litho.   Unwmk.
C226 A250 8c multi   .85   .30
C227 A250 12c multi   1.90   .55
C228 A250 30c multi   2.50   .90
      Nos. C226-C228 (3)   5.25   1.75

1st Sugarcane Harvest in Socialist Cuba, 1st Anniv. — AP94

1962, Jan. 16
C229 AP94 8c salmon pink &
                   dark brn   1.00   .20
C230 AP94 12c bluish lil & blk 2.50   .45

Cuban goods have been embargoed by the United States since a Feb. 7, 1962 proclamation by President Kennedy, but according to the Office of Foreign Assets Control of the Treasury Department, used Cuban stamps can be imported and sold without limitation, and unused stamps may be imported for personal use, but not resold.

Intl.
Radio
Service
AP95

1962, Mar. 26   **Wmk. 321**
C231 AP95 8c multi   1.10   .25
C232 AP95 12c multi   2.25   .55
C233 AP95 30c multi   3.25   1.25
C234 AP95 1p multi   7.00   3.25
   Nos. C231-C234 (4)   13.60   5.30

Bird Type of 1956

1962, July 20   **Engr.**   **Wmk. 321**
C235 AP63 1p like #C144, royal blue   5.75   5.75
C236 AP62 2p like #C145, dark red   17.00   15.00
C237 AP63 5p like #C146, rose lake   37.50   32.50
   Nos. C235-C237 (3)   60.25   53.25

PRAGA '62 — AP96

1962, Aug. 18   **Litho.**
C238 AP96 31c Czechoslovakia No. 1080   3.50   1.50

Souvenir Sheet
Imperf
C239 AP96 31c like No. C238   17.50   12.00
   No. C239 contains one 60x35½mm stamp.

Achievements of the
Revolution — AP97

1966, July 26   **Wmk. 376**   **Perf. 12½**
C240 AP97 1c Agrarian reform   .20   .20
C241 AP97 2c Industrialization   .20   .20
C242 AP97 3c Urban reform   .50   .20
C243 AP97 7c Eradication of unemployment   .50   .20
C244 AP97 9c Education   .95   .20
C245 AP97 10c Public health   2.10   .20
C246 AP97 13c Excerpt from *La Historia Me Absolvera*, by Castro   2.75   .45
   Nos. C240-C246 (7)   7.20   1.65

Camaguey-Seville Flight, 35th
Anniv. — AP98

1971, Jan. 12   **Unwmk.**
C247 AP98 13c Aircraft   2.75   .25
C248 AP98 30c Map, Lieut. Menendez Palaez   3.25   .70

Havana-Santiago de Chile Direct Air
Service, 1st Anniv. — AP99

1972, June 26   **Wmk. 376**
C249 AP99 25c multi   3.00   .75

6th Congress of Latin American and
Caribbean Exporters of Sugar,
Havana — AP100

Perf. 12½x12
1977, Feb. 28   **Unwmk.**
C250 AP100 13c multi   .75   .20

Composer Type of 1977

1977, May 10   **Perf. 13**
C251 A571 13c Jorge Ankerman and score   1.00   .20

Flower Type of 1977

1977, May 31
C252 A572 13c *Caesalpinia pulcherrima*   .85   .20
C253 A572 30c *Catharanthus roseus*   1.75   .50

Souvenir Sheet
Perf. 13½x13
C254 A572 50c Juan Tomas Roig   4.00   .90
   No. C254 contains one 32x40mm stamp.

Natl. Decorations Type of 1977

1977, July 26   **Perf. 12x12½**
C255 A574 13c multi, diff.   .80   .20
C256 A574 30c multi, diff.   1.50   .45

Art Type of 1977
Paintings by Jorge Arche: 13c, *My Wife and I*, vert. 30c, *Domino Players*. 50c, *Self-portrait*, vert.

1977, Aug. 25   **Perf. 13x12½**
Size: 26x38mm
C257 A575 13c multi   .65   .20
Size: 40x29mm
Perf. 13
C258 A575 30c multi   1.60   .40
Souvenir Sheet
Perf. 13½x13
C259 A575 50c multi   4.00   4.00
   No. C259 contains one 32x40mm stamp.

Spartakiad Type of 1977
1977, Sept. 10   **Perf. 13**
C260 A576 13c Grenade-throwing   .60   .20
C261 A576 30c Rifle-shooting, horiz.   1.50   .40

10th Heroic
Guerrilla's
Day
AP101

1977, Oct. 8   **Perf. 12½x13**
C262 AP101 13c Guerrilla fighters   1.00   .20

Airmail Service Type of 1977
1977, Oct. 27   **Perf. 12x12½**
C263 A577 13c Havana-Mexico cachet   .85   .20
C264 A577 30c Havana-Prague cachet   1.75   .55

Souvenir Sheet

Adoration of the Magi, by
Rubens — AP102

1977, Nov. 18   **Perf. 13**
C265 AP102 50c multi   4.00   4.00
   Ruben's 400th birth anniv.

Havana Zoo Type of 1977
1977, Nov. 24
C266 A579 13c Tiger   1.25   .20
C267 A579 30c Lion   1.90   .55

Revolution Martyrs Type of 1977
1977, Dec. 2   **Perf. 12½x12**
C268 A580 13c *Corynthia* landing   .75   .20

Pan American Health Organization
(OPS), 75th Anniv. — AP103

1977, Dec. 2
C269 AP103 13c multi   .75   .20

Havana University Type of 1978
1978, Jan. 5   **Perf. 13x12½**
C270 A582 13c Crossed sabres, university   .75   .20
C271 A582 30c University, statue, crowd   1.10   .50

Portrait of Jose
Marti (b. 1853),
by A. Menocal
AP104

1978, Jan. 28
C272 AP104 13c multi   .80   .20

Art Type of 1978
Paintings in the Nat. Museum of Art: 13c, *El Guadalquivir*, by M. Barron. 30c, *Portrait of H.E. Ridley*, by J.J. Masqueries, vert.

1978, Feb. 20   **Perf. 12½x12, 13**
Sizes: 42x27mm, 29x40mm
C273 A583 13c multi   1.00   .20
C274 A583 30c multi   1.10   .40

Bird Type of 1975
1978, Mar. 10   **Perf. 12½x12, 13**
Size: 42x27mm, 27x42mm
C275 A524 13c *Torreornis inexpectata*, horiz.   1.60   .50
C276 A524 30c *Ara tricolor*   2.40   1.10

Baragua Protest,
Cent. — AP105

1978, Mar. 15   **Perf. 13x13½**
C277 AP105 13c *Antonio Maceo*, by A. Melero   .70   .25

Cosmonaut's Day Type of 1978
1978, Apr. 12   **Perf. 13**
C278 A585 13c *Venus 10*   .70   .20
Size: 36x46mm
Perf. 12½x13
C279 A585 30c *Lunokhod 2*, vert.   1.25   .50

SOCFILEX '78, Budapest — AP106

1978, May 7   **Perf. 13x12½**
C280 AP106 30c Parliament, Hungary No. 217   1.75   .55

Cactus Type of 1978
1978, May 15   **Perf. 13**
C281 A587 13c *Rhodocactus cubensis*   .90   .25
C282 A587 30c *Harrisia taetra*   1.90   .35

World Telecommunications
Day — AP107

1978, May 17
C283 AP107 30c multi   1.25   .45

Organization of
African Unity,
15th
Anniv. — AP108

1978, May 25   **Perf. 13x12½**
C284 AP108 30c multi   1.00   .45

Souvenir Sheet

CAPEX '78, Toronto — AP109

1978, June 9   **Perf. 13x13½**
C285 AP109 50c *Niven, Wales,*
       by G.H. Rus-
       sell   3.50 2.25

Aquarium Type of 1978

1978, June 15   **Perf. 13**
C286 A588 13c *Carassias*
       auratus, vert.   1.90 .25
C287 A588 30c *Symphysodon*
       aequifasciata
       axelrodi   3.00 .50

MEDELLIN Games Type of 1978

1978, July 1
C288 A589 13c Volleyball   .60 .20
C289 A589 30c Running   1.25 .45

Attack on Moncada Type of 1978

1978, July 26
C290 A590 13c Soldiers bearing
       rifles   .45 .20
C291 A590 30c Stylized dove,
       banners   1.10 .35

Youth Festival Type of 1978

Natl. flags and views of host cities.

1978, July 28
C292 A591 13c Moscow, 1957   .70 .20
C293 A591 13c Vienna, 1959   .70 .20
C294 A591 13c Helsinki, 1962   .70 .20
C295 A591 13c Sofia, 1968   .70 .20
C296 A591 13c Berlin, 1973   .70 .20
   a.   Strip of 5, Nos. C292-C296   3.75 1.75
     Nos. C292-C296 (5)   3.50 1.00
     Size: 46x36mm
     Perf. 13x12½
C297 A591 30c Havana, 1978   1.50 .35

Tuna Industry Type of 1978

1978, Aug. 30   **Perf. 12½x12**
C298 A593 13c Stern trawler   .90 .25
C299 A593 30c Refrigerator ship   1.60 .60

Souvenir Sheet

PRAGA '78 — AP110

1978, Sept. 8   **Perf. 13**
C300 AP110 50c *Marina,* by A.
       Brandeis   3.75 2.00

Art Type of 1978

Paintings by Amelia Pelaez del Casal (1896-1968).

1978, Sept. 15   **Perf. 12x12½, 13**
C301 A594 13c *Yellow Flowers,*
       vert.   .55 .20
C302 A594 30c *Still-life in Blue,*
       vert.   1.25 .45

Souvenir Sheet
Perf. 13½x13

C303 A594 50c *Portrait of Ame-*
       lia, by L.
       Romanach, vert. 4.00 .90

No. C303 contains one 32x40mm stamp.

Socialist Communication Organizations
Congress (OSS), 20th
Anniv. — AP111

1978, Sept. 25   **Perf. 13**
C304 AP111 30c multi   1.25 .25

Souvenir Sheet

EXFILNA '78, 6th Natl. Philatelic
Exposition — AP112

1978, Oct. 10   **Imperf.**
C305 AP112 50c 1st Postal Card,
       issued in 1878 3.25 2.00

No. C305 has simulated perfs.

Intl. Anti-
Apartheid
Year — AP113

1978, Oct. 16   **Perf. 12½**
C306 AP113 13c multi   1.60 1.00

Zoo Type of 1978

1978, Oct. 20   **Perf. 13**
C307 A595 13c *Acinonyx jubatos* 1.00 .25
C308 A595 30c *Loxodonta afri-*
       cana, vert.   2.40 .65

Natl. Ballet Type of 1978

1978, Oct. 28   **Perf. 12½x13**
C309 A596 13c *Giselle,* vert.   .85 .25
C310 A596 30c *Genesis,* vert.   1.60 .30

Pacific Flora Type of 1978

1978, Nov. 30   **Perf. 13**
C311 A597 13c multi, diff.   .80 .25
C312 A597 30c multi, diff.   1.60 .30

25th Death Anniv. of Julius and Ethel
Rosenberg, American Communists
Executed for Espionage — AP114

1978, Dec. 20
C313 AP114 13c multi   .60 .20

Julio A.
Mella
(d. 1929)
AP115

1979, Jan. 10
C314 AP115 13c multi   .60 .20

Cosmonaut's Day Type of 1979
Souvenir Sheet

1979, Apr. 12   **Perf. 13½x13**
C315 A603 50c Orbital complex   3.75 2.00

No. C315 contains one 32x40mm stamp.

Intl. Year of the Child — AP116

1979, June 1   **Perf. 13x12½**
C316 AP116 13c multi   1.00 .20

Art Type of 1979

1979, June 15   **Perf. 13½x13**
C317 A600 50c *Portrait of Victor*
       Emmanuel Gar-
       cia, by J. Arche,
       vert.   3.50 1.75

No. C317 contains one 32x40mm stamp.

CARIFESTA
'79, Festival
of
Caribbean
Peoples,
Havana
AP117

1979, July 16   **Perf. 12½x13**
C318 AP117 13c multi   .75 .20

10th World Universiade Games,
Mexico City — AP118

1979, Sept. 1   **Perf. 13x12½**
C319 AP118 13c grn, pale grn &
       gold   .75 .20

6th Conference of Nonaligned
Countries — AP119

1979, Sept. 3
C320 AP119 50c Convention Pal-
       ace   1.75 .90

Sir Rowland Hill (d. 1879), Originator
of Penny Postage — AP120

1979, Sept. 4   **Perf. 13½x13**
C321 AP120 30c Hill, casket   1.50 .25

SOCFILEX '79, Bucharest — AP121

Illustration reduced.

1979, Oct. 25   **Perf. 12½**
C322 AP121 30c Romania No.
       683, flags   1.40 .40

Intl. Radio Consultative Committee
(CCIR), 50th Anniv. — AP122

1979, Nov. 30   **Perf. 12½x12**
C323 AP122 30c Ground receiv-
       ing station   1.40 .40

1st Soviet-Cuban Joint Space
Flight — AP123

1980, Sept. 23   **Perf. 12½**
C324 AP123 13c multi   .50 .20
C325 AP123 30c multi   1.50 .35

Capt. Mariano Barberan, Lt. Joaquin Collar, and Their Airplane Cuatro Vientos. — AP124

1993, June 11   Litho.   Perf. 13
C326 AP124 30c multicolored   1.00   .45
1st Flight Seville-Camaguey, 60th anniv.

AIR POST SEMI-POSTAL STAMP

Catalogue values for unused stamps in this section are for Never Hinged items.

Farm Couple and Factory SPAP1

Engr. & Typo.
1959, May 7   Wmk. 321   Perf. 12½
CB1 SPAP1 12c + 3c car & grn   2.00   .80
Agricultural reforms. See No. C199.

AIR POST SPECIAL DELIVERY STAMPS

Matanzas Issue

Matanzas Harbor APSD1

Wmk. 229
1936, May 5   Photo.   Perf. 12½
CE1 ASPD1 15c light blue   4.50 3.50
  Never hinged   7.00
Exists imperf. Value $6.50 unused, $4.50 used.

SPECIAL DELIVERY STAMPS

Issued under Administration of United States

US No. E5 Surcharged in Red

1899   Wmk. 191   Perf. 12
E1 SD3 10c blue   130.   100.
a.   No period after "CUBA"   575.   400.

Issue of the Republic under US Military Rule

Special Delivery Messenger SD2

Printed by the US Bureau of Engraving and Printing

1899   Wmk. US-C (191C)
Inscribed: "Immediata"
E2 SD2 10c orange   52.50 15.00

Issues of the Republic

Inscribed: "Inmediata"

1902   Perf. 12
E3 SD2 10c orange   3.00 1.00

J. B. Zayas SD3

1910   Unwmk.
E4 SD3 10c orange & blue 20.00 3.25
  Never hinged   30.00
a.   Center inverted   1,250.

Airplane and Morro Castle SD4

1914, Feb. 24   Perf. 12
E5 SD4 10c dark blue   15.00 1.25
Exists imperf. Value, pair $500.

1927   Wmk. Star (106)
E6 SD4 10c deep blue   12.00   .50
  Never hinged   18.00

1935   Perf. 10
E7 SD4 10c blue   12.00   .40
  Never hinged   15.00

Matanzas Issue

Mercury SD5

Wmk. Wavy Lines (229)
1936, May 5   Photo.   Perf. 12½
E8 SD5 10c deep claret   4.50 3.50
  Never hinged   7.00
Exists imperf. Value $7.50 unused, $5 used.

"Triumph of the Revolution" — SD6

1936, Nov. 18
E9 SD6 10c red orange   6.00 2.00
  Never hinged   8.00
Maj. Gen. Máximo Gómez (1836-1905).

Temple of Quetzalcoatl (Mexico) SD7

Ruben Dario (Nicaragua) SD8

Wmk. 106
1937, Oct. 13   Engr.   Perf. 10
E10 SD7 10c deep orange   6.25 6.25
E11 SD8 10c deep orange   6.25 6.25
  Set, never hinged   15.00

Issued for the benefit of the Association of American Writers and Artists. See note after No. 354.

Letter and Symbols of Transportation — SD9

1945, Oct. 30
E12 SD9 10c olive brown   1.40   .40
  Never hinged   3.00

Catalogue values for unused stamps in this section, from this point to the end of the section, are for Never Hinged items.

Governor's Building, Cárdenas SD10

Engraved and Lithographed
1951, July 3   Wmk. 229   Perf. 13
E13 SD10 10c henna brn, ultra & red   7.00 1.25
Cent. of the adoption of Cuba's flag.

Chess Type of Regular Issue, 1951
1951, Nov. 1   Photo.
E14 A166 10c dk grn & rose brn   21.00 4.50

Type of Regular Issue of 1951 Surcharged in Red Violet

Wmk. 106
1952, Mar. 18   Engr.   Perf. 10
E15 A159 10c on 2c yel brn   6.00 1.40

Arms and Bars from National Hymn — SD12

Roseate Tern — SD13

1952, May 27   Perf. 12½
E16 SD12 10c dp org & bl   3.00   .80
Republic of Cuba founding, 50th anniv.

Type of Air Post Stamps of 1952 Inscribed: "Entrega Especial"
1952, Oct. 7   Perf. 10
E17 AP36 10c pale olive grn   4.75 2.40
Three-fourths of the proceeds from the sale of No. E17 were used for the Communications Ministry Employees' Retirement Fund.

1953, July 28
E18 SD13 10c blue   5.75 1.60

Gregorio Hernandez Saez SD14

Felix Varela SD15

1954, Feb. 23
E19 SD14 10c olive green   5.25 1.10

1955, June 22   Perf. 12½
E20 SD15 10c brown car   3.00   .95
See note after No. E17.

Portrait Type of Regular Issue, 1956
Inscribed: "Entrega Especial"
Portrait: 10c, Jose Jacinto Milanes.

1956, May 2   Wmk. 106
E21 A198 10c dk car rose & blk   3.75   .75
See note after No. E17.

Painting Type of Regular Issue, 1957, Inscribed: "Entrega Especial"
10c, "Yesterday" by E. Garcia Cabrera.

1957, Mar. 15   Engr.   Perf. 12½
E22 A207 10c dk brn & turq bl   3.50 1.25
See note after No. E17.

View Type of Regular Issue, 1957, Inscribed: "Entrega Especial."
10c, Independence square, Pino del Rio.

1957, Dec. 17
E23 A218 10c dk pur & brn   3.00 1.00
See note after No. E17.

View in Havana and Messenger SD16

1958, Jan. 10   Engr.
E24 SD16 10c blue   2.00   .80
E25 SD16 20c green   2.50   .80
See Nos. E28, E31.

Fish Type of Air Post Issue, 1958, Inscribed "Entrega Especial."
Fish: 10c, Blackfish snapper. 20c, Mosquitofish.

1958, Sept. 26 Wmk. 106 Perf. 12½
E26 AP86 10c blk, bl, pink & yel   6.00 2.50
E27 AP86 20c blk, ultra & pink   19.00 11.00
See note after No. C191.

Messenger Type of 1958
1960   Wmk. 321   Perf. 12½
E28 SD16 10c brt vio   3.50   .80

Plane Type of Air Post Issue, of 1931-46, Surcharged in Black or Red: "HABILITADO ENTREGA ESPECIAL 10¢"
1960   Wmk. 106   Perf. 10
E29 AP4 10c on 20c car rose   3.00   .50
E30 AP4 10c on 50c grnsh bl (R)   3.00   .50

Messenger Type of 1958
1961, June 28 Wmk. 321 Perf. 12½
E31 SD16 10c orange   3.50   .80

West Indies Packet Type of 1962
Perf. 12½
1962, Apr. 24   Litho.   Unwmk.
E32 A253 10c buff, dull ultra & brn   7.50 1.75

POSTAGE DUE STAMPS

Issued under Administration of the United States

Postage Due Stamps of the United States Nos. J38, J39, J41 and J42 Surcharged in Black Like Nos. 221-226A

D2

1899		Wmk. 191		Perf. 12
J1	D2	1c dp claret	45.00	5.25
J2	D2	2c dp claret	45.00	5.25
a.		Inverted surcharge		4,000.
J3	D2	5c dp claret	45.00	5.25
J4	D2	10c dp claret	27.50	2.50
		Nos. J1-J4 (4)	162.50	18.25

Issues of the Republic

D1

1914		Unwmk. Engr.		Perf. 12
J5	D1	1c carmine rose	8.00	1.25
J6	D1	2c carmine rose	10.00	1.25
J7	D1	5c carmine rose	15.00	2.50
		Nos. J5-J7 (3)	33.00	5.00

1927-28				
J8	D1	1c rose red	4.50	.90
J9	D1	2c rose red	6.75	.90
J10	D1	5c rose red	8.00	1.25
		Nos. J8-J10 (3)	19.25	3.05

NEWSPAPER STAMPS

Issued under Spanish Dominion

N1   N2

1888		Unwmk. Typo.		Perf. 14
P1	N1	½m black	.25	.25
P2	N1	1m black	.25	.30
P3	N1	2m black	.25	.30
P4	N1	3m black	1.60	1.00
P5	N1	4m black	2.10	2.00
P6	N1	8m black	8.00	8.50
		Nos. P1-P6 (6)	12.45	12.35

1890				
P7	N2	½m red brown	.55	.65
P8	N2	1m red brown	.55	.65
P9	N2	2m red brown	.90	.95
P10	N2	3m red brown	1.10	1.10
P11	N2	4m red brown	8.25	5.50
P12	N2	8m red brown	8.25	5.50
		Nos. P7-P12 (6)	19.60	14.35

1892				
P13	N2	½m violet	.25	.30
P14	N2	1m violet	.25	.30
P15	N2	2m violet	.25	.30
P16	N2	3m violet	1.10	.35
P17	N2	4m violet	4.25	1.90
P18	N2	8m violet	8.75	3.00
		Nos. P13-P18 (6)	14.85	6.15

1894				
P19	N2	½m rose	.25	.30
a.		Imperf. pair	40.00	40.00
P20	N2	1m rose	.50	.35
P21	N2	2m rose	.55	.35
P22	N2	3m rose	2.10	1.40
P23	N2	4m rose	3.50	1.60
P24	N2	8m rose	6.00	4.00
		Nos. P19-P24 (6)	12.90	8.00

1896				
P25	N2	½m blue green	.25	.30
P26	N2	1m blue green	.25	.30
P27	N2	2m blue green	.25	.30
P28	N2	3m blue green	2.75	1.50

P29	N2	4m blue green	5.75	7.00
P30	N2	8m blue green	10.50	10.00
		Nos. P25-P30 (6)	19.75	19.40

For surcharges see Nos. 190-193, 201-220.

POSTAL TAX STAMPS

Catalogue values for unused stamps in this section are for Never Hinged items.

Mother and Child — PT1   Nurse with Child — PT2

1938, Dec. 1		Wmk. Star. (106) Engr.		Perf. 10
RA1	PT1	1c bright green	1.60	.25

The tax benefited the National Council of Tuberculosis fund for children's hospitals. Obligatory on all mail during December and January. This note applies also to Nos. RA2-RA4, RA7-RA10, RA12-RA15, RA17-RA21.

1939, Dec. 1				
RA2	PT2	1c orange vermilion	.90	.25

"Health" Protecting Children — PT3

1940, Dec. 1				
RA3	PT3	1c deep blue	.90	.25

Mother and Child — PT4   Victory — PT5

1941, Dec. 1				
RA4	PT4	1c olive bister	.95	.25

1942-44				
RA5	PT5	½c orange	.40	.25
RA6	PT5	½c gray ('44)	.95	.25

Issued: No. RA5, 7/1/42; No. RA6, 10/3/44.

Type of 1941 Overprinted "1942" in Black

1942, Dec. 1				
RA7	PT4	1c salmon	1.10	.30
a.		Inverted overprint	75.00	65.00

As PT3 — PT6   As PT4 — PT7

1943, Dec. 1				
RA8	PT6	1c brown	.95	.25

1949, Dec. 9				
RA9	PT7	1c blue	.65	.25

Type of 1949 Inscribed: "1950"

1950, Dec. 1				Engr.
RA10	PT7	1c rose red	.65	.25

Proposed Communications Building
PT8   PT10

Woman Holding Child Aloft — PT9   Child — PT11

1951, June 5		Wmk. 106		Perf. 10
RA11	PT8	1c violet	.95	.25

The tax was to help build a new Communications Building. This note applies also to Nos. RA16, RA34, RA43.

1951, Dec. 1				
RA12	PT9	1c violet blue	.55	.25
RA13	PT9	1c brown carmine	.55	.25
RA14	PT9	1c olive bister	.55	.25
RA15	PT9	1c deep green	.55	.25
		Nos. RA12-RA15 (4)	2.20	1.00

1952, Feb. 8				
RA16	PT10	1c slate blue	.40	.25

See Nos. RA34, RA43.

1952, Dec. 1				
RA17	PT11	1c rose carmine	.95	.25
RA18	PT11	1c yellow green	.95	.25
RA19	PT11	1c blue	.95	.25
RA20	PT11	1c orange	.95	.25
		Nos. RA17-RA20 (4)	3.80	1.00

Hands Reaching for Lorraine Cross PT12   Child's Head, Lorraine Cross PT13

1953, Dec. 1				Perf. 9½
RA21	PT12	1c rose carmine	.65	.30

1954, Nov. 1				Perf. 9½x10
RA22	PT13	1c rose red	.95	.30
RA23	PT13	1c violet	.95	.30
RA24	PT13	1c bright blue	.95	.30
RA25	PT13	1c emerald	.95	.30
		Nos. RA22-RA25 (4)	3.80	1.20

The tax benefited the Natl. Council of Tuberculosis fund for children's hospitals. Obligatory on all mail during Nov., Dec., Jan. & Feb. This note also applies to Nos. RA26-RA33, RA35-RA42.

Rose and Watering Can PT14   Child and Protective Hands PT15

1955, Nov. 1				
RA26	PT14	1c red orange	.95	.30
RA27	PT14	1c red lilac	.95	.30
RA28	PT14	1c bright blue	.95	.30
RA29	PT14	1c orange yellow	.95	.30
		Nos. RA26-RA29 (4)	3.80	1.20

1956, Nov. 1				
RA30	PT15	1c rose red	.95	.30
RA31	PT15	1c yellow brown	.95	.30
RA32	PT15	1c bright blue	.95	.30
RA33	PT15	1c emerald	.95	.30
		Nos. RA30-RA33 (4)	3.80	1.20

Building Type of 1952

1957, Jan. 18				Perf. 10
RA34	PT10	1c rose red	.95	.30

Mother and Child by Silvia Arrojo Fernandez PT16   National Council of Tuberculosis PT17

1957, Nov. 1		Wmk. 321 Engr.		Perf. 10
RA35	PT16	1c dull rose	.90	.30
RA36	PT16	1c bright blue	.90	.30
RA37	PT16	1c gray	.90	.30
RA38	PT16	1c emerald	.90	.30
		Nos. RA35-RA38 (4)	3.60	1.20

1958				
RA39	PT17	1c rose red	.50	.30
RA40	PT17	1c red brown	.50	.30
RA41	PT17	1c gray	.50	.30
RA42	PT17	1c emerald	.50	.30
		Nos. RA39-RA42 (4)	2.00	1.20

Building Type of 1952

1958				Wmk. 321
RA43	PT10	1c rose red	.95	.30

CURACAO

ˈcər-ə-sau

LOCATION — North of Venezuela, east of Aruba in Caribbean Sea
AREA — 171 sq. mi.
POP. — 135,822 (2005)
CAPITAL — Willemstad

On Oct. 10, 2010, Curaçao, formerly part of Netherlands Antilles, became a constituent state within the Kingdom of the Netherlands. Stamps issued from 1873 to 1949 inscribed "Curaçao" were valid in all islands that comprised the Netherlands Antilles. These stamps are listed under "Netherlands Antilles."

100 Cents = 1 Gulden

> **Catalogue values for all unused stamps in this country are for Never Hinged items.**

Map of Curaçao and West Indies, Arms and Flag
A1

Perf. 13¾

2010, Oct. 10   Litho.   Unwmk.
1   A1   111c multi   1.25   1.25

CYPRUS

ˈsī-prəs

LOCATION — An island in the Mediterranean Sea off the coast of Turkey
GOVT. — Republic
AREA — 3,572 sq. mi.
POP. — 754,064 (1999 est.)
CAPITAL — Nicosia

The British Crown Colony of Cyprus became a republic in 1960.
Turkey invaded Cyprus in 1974 resulting in the the northern 40% of the island becoming the Turkish Republic of Northern Cyprus. No other country recognizes this division of the island.
See Turkey in Volume 6.

12 Pence = 1 Shilling
40 Paras = 1 Piaster
9 Piasters = 1 Shilling
20 Shillings = 1 Pound
1000 Milliemes = 1 Pound (1955)
100 Cents = 1 Cyprus Pound (1983)
100 Cents = 1 Euro (2008)

> **Catalogue values for unused stamps in this country are for Never Hinged items, beginning with Scott 156 in the regular postage section and Scott RA1 in the postal tax section.**

Values for unused stamps are for examples with original gum as defined in the catalogue introduction. Very fine examples of Nos. 1, 2 and 7-10 will have perforations touching the design on at least one or more sides due to the narrow spacing of the stamps on the plates and to imperfect perforation methods. Stamps with perfs clear on all four sides are scarce and will command higher prices.

Watermark

Wmk. 344 — Map of Cyprus and KC/K Delta

Queen Victoria — A1

CYPRUS
A2

CYPRUS
A4

CYPRUS
A6

CYPRUS
A3

CYPRUS
A5

CYPRUS
30 PARAS
A7

Various Watermarks as in Great Britain (#20, 23, 25, 27 & 29)

1880   Typo.   Perf. 14
1	A1	½p rose (P 15)	125.00	115.00
		Plate 12	225.00	300.00
		Plate 19	5,750.	950.00
b.		Double overprint (P 15)		40,000.
2	A2	1p red (P 216)	19.00	55.00
		Plate 217	16.00	57.50
		Plate 174	1,500.	1,500.
		Plate 181	500.00	210.00
		Plate 184	20,000.	2,750.
		Plate 193	825.00	
		Plate 196	700.00	
		Plate 201	19.00	57.50
		Plate 205	80.00	57.50
		Plate 208	130.00	65.00
		Plate 215	16.00	57.50
		Plate 218	24.00	65.00
		Plate 220	500.00	450.00
b.		Double overprint (P 218)	6,000.	
		Double overprint (P 208)	25,000.	
c.		Pair, one without ovpt. (P 208)	25,000.	
3	A3	2½p claret (P 14)	3.75	12.00
		Plate 15	5.00	32.50
4	A4	4p lt ol grn (P 16)	140.00	240.00
5	A5	6p ol gray (P 16)	575.00	750.00
6	A6	1sh green (P 13)	800.00	525.00

Black Surcharge

7	A7	30 paras on 1p red (P 216)	130.00	95.00
		Plate 201	160.00	110.00
		Plate 217	210.00	210.00
		Plate 220	175.00	190.00
b.		Dbl. surch., one invtd. (P 220)	1,800.	1,450.
		Dbl. surch., one invtd. (P 216)	6,500.	

No. 2 Surcharged

HALF-PENNY

18mm Long

1881
8	A2	½p on 1p (205, 216)	82.50	100.00
		Plate 174	225.00	375.00
		Plate 181	190.00	225.00
		Plate 201	110.00	140.00
		Plate 205	80.00	100.00
		Plate 208	225.00	350.00
		Plate 215	825.00	925.00
		Plate 217	1,000.	875.00
		Plate 218	550.00	675.00
		Plate 220	325.00	400.00

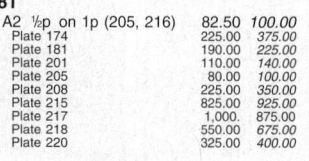

POSTAGE
HALF-PENNY

16mm Long

9	A2	½p on 1p (P 201)	140.00	190.00
		Plate 216	400.00	450.00
		Plate 218		17,500.
a.		Double surcharge (P 201, 216)	3,500.	2,900.

POSTAGE
HALF-PENNY

13mm Long

10	A2	½p on 1p red (P 215)	52.50	75.00
		Plate 205	375.00	
		Plate 217	175.00	100.00
		Plate 218	90.00	125.00
c.		Double surcharge (P 215)	550.00	700.00
		Double surcharge (P 205)	875.00	
e.		Triple surcharge (P 215)	875.00	
		Triple surcharge (P 205)	4,750.	
		Triple surcharge (P 217)		
		Triple surcharge (P 218)	4,750.	
h.		Quadruple surch. (P 205, 215)	6,500.	
j.		"CYPRUS" double (P 218)	6,000.	

A8

1881, July   Typo.   Wmk. 1
11	A8	½pi emerald green	210.00	52.50
12	A8	1pi rose	425.00	37.50
13	A8	2pi ultramarine	525.00	37.50
14	A8	4pi olive green	1,050.	325.00
15	A8	6pi olive gray	1,900.	525.00

Postage and revenue stamps of Cyprus with "J.A.B." (the initials of Postmaster J.A. Bulmer) in manuscript, or with "POSTAL SURCHARGE" (with or without "J. A. B."), were not Postage Due stamps but were employed for accounting purposes between the chief PO at Larnaca and the sub-offices.
See Nos. 19-25, 28-37. For surcharges see Nos. 16-18, 26-27.

½   ½
HALF PIASTRE
A9

30 PARAS
A10

Black Surcharge

1882   Wmk. 1
16	A9	½pi on ½pi grn	750.00	92.50
17	A10	30pa on 1pi rose	1,750.	140.00
a.		Double surcharge, one inverted	1,400.	850.00

1884   Wmk. 2
18	A9	½pi on ½pi green	190.00	10.00
a.		Double surcharge		3,200.

See Nos. 26, 27.

1882-94   Die B

For description of Dies A and B see "Dies of British Colonial Stamps" in Table of Contents.

19	A8	½pi green	9.00	1.75
20	A8	30pa violet	7.50	10.00
21	A8	1pi rose	15.50	4.50
22	A8	2pi blue	17.50	2.10
23	A8	4pi pale ol grn	55.00	37.50
24a	A8	6pi	225.00	725.00
25a	A8	12pi	175.00	425.00
		Nos. 19-25a (7)	504.50	1,205.

Die A
19a	A8	½pi	22.50	2.75
b.		½pi emerald	6,000.	500.00
20a	A8	30pa lilac	80.00	25.00
21a	A8	1pi	110.00	3.50
22a	A8	2pi	160.00	3.50
23a	A8	4pi	600.00	45.00
24	A8	6pi olive gray	67.50	21.00
25	A8	12pi brown org	225.00	45.00
		Nos. 19a-25 (7)	1,265.	145.75

CYPRUS
½   ½
HALF PIASTRE
A11

Type I — Figures "½" 8mm apart.
Type II — Figures "½" 6mm apart.
The space between the fraction bars varies from 5½ to 8½mm but is usually 6 or 8mm.

Black Surcharge Type I

1886   Wmk. 2
26	A11	½pi on ½pi grn	475.00	15.00
a.		Type II	300.00	100.00
b.		Double surcharge, type II		

Wmk. 1
27	A11	½pi on ½pi grn	8,750.	500.00
a.		Type II	23,000.	

No. 27a probably is a proof.

1894-96   Wmk. 2
28	A8	½pi grn & car rose	5.25	1.75
29	A8	30pa violet & green	3.00	2.00
30	A8	1pi rose & ultra	8.00	1.75
31	A8	2pi ultra & mar	10.00	1.75
32	A8	4pi ol green & vio	21.00	9.50
33	A8	6pi ol gray & grn	18.00	29.00
34	A8	9pi brown & rose	22.50	25.00
35	A8	12pi brn org & blk	22.50	70.00
36	A8	18pi slate & brown	60.00	60.00
37	A8	45pi dk vio & ultra	125.00	175.00
		Nos. 28-37 (10)	295.25	375.75

CYPRUS
HALF PIASTRE
King Edward VII
A12

CYPRUS
TEN PARAS
King George V
A13

1903   Typo.
38	A12	½pi grn & car rose	8.00	1.40
39	A12	30pa violet & green	17.00	4.00
40	A12	1pi carmine rose & ultra	26.00	4.50
41	A12	2pi ultra & mar	82.50	17.00
42	A12	4pi ol green & vio	40.00	22.50
43	A12	6pi ol brown & grn	50.00	140.00
44	A12	9pi brn & car rose	125.00	225.00
45	A12	12pi org brn & blk	19.00	72.50
46	A12	18pi black & brown	100.00	175.00
47	A12	45pi dk vio & ultra	250.00	600.00
		Nos. 38-47 (10)	717.50	1,261.

1904-07   Wmk. 3
48	A12	5pa bis & blk ('07)	1.25	1.75
49	A12	10pa org & grn ('07)	5.00	1.50
50	A12	½pi grn & car rose	7.75	1.25
51	A12	30pa reddish violet & green	20.00	2.25
52	A12	1pi car rose & ultra	10.00	1.10
53	A12	2pi ultra & maroon	12.00	2.00
54	A12	4pi ol grn & red vio	20.00	11.00
55	A12	6pi ol brn & green	24.00	17.00
56	A12	9pi brn & car rose	50.00	9.75
57	A12	12pi org brn & blk	32.50	50.00
58	A12	18pi black & brown	45.00	14.00
59	A12	45pi dk vio & ultra	110.00	175.00
		Nos. 48-59 (12)	337.50	286.60

1912
61a	A13	10pa org yel & br grn	2.75	1.60
62	A13	½pi grn & car rose	2.25	.35
63	A13	30pa violet & green	3.25	2.00

64	A13	1pi car & ultra	5.25	2.25
65	A13	2pi ultra & maroon	8.50	2.50
66	A13	4pi ol grn & red vio	5.50	6.25
67	A13	6pi ol brn & green	4.75	11.00
68	A13	9pi brn & car rose	32.50	30.00
69	A13	12pi org brn & blk	22.50	52.50
70	A13	18pi black & brown	37.50	45.00
71	A13	45pi dl vio & ultra	110.00	160.00
		Nos. 61-71 (11)	236.25	314.75

1921-23　　　　　　　　Wmk. 4

72	A13	10pa orange & grn	14.00	12.00
73	A13	10pa gray & yellow	16.00	9.50
74	A13	30pa violet & grn	3.25	1.75
75	A13	30pa green	9.00	1.75
76	A13	1pi rose & ultra	25.00	40.00
77	A13	1pi violet & car	4.00	5.00
78	A13	1½pi orange & blk	12.00	6.50
79	A13	2pi ultra & red vio	30.00	22.50
80	A13	2pi rose & ultra	14.50	27.50
81	A13	2¾pi ultra & red vio	9.00	12.00
82	A13	4pi ol grn & red vio	17.50	22.50
83	A13	6pi ol brn & green	27.50	87.50
84	A13	9pi brn & carmine	40.00	92.50
85	A13	18pi black & brn	80.00	175.00
86	A13	45pi dl vio & ultra	250.00	325.00
		Nos. 72-86 (15)	551.75	841.00

Wmk. 3

87	A13	10sh grn & red, yel	425.00	875.00
88	A13	£1 vio & black, red	1,300.	2,500.

Years of issue: Nos. 73, 75, 77-78, 80-81, 87-88, 1923; others, 1921.

A14

1924-28　　Chalky Paper　　Wmk. 4

89	A14	¼pi gray & brn org	1.75	.55
90	A14	½pi gray blk & blk	5.00	14.00
91	A14	½pi grn & dp grn ('25)	2.50	1.10
92	A14	¾pi grn & dp grn	3.50	1.10
93	A14	¾pi gray blk & blk ('25)	3.75	1.00
94	A14	1pi brn vio & org brown	2.25	1.75
95	A14	1½pi org & black	2.75	13.00
96	A14	1½pi carmine ('25)	4.50	1.50
97	A14	2pi car & green	3.50	19.00
98	A14	2pi org & black ('25)	13.00	4.25
99	A14	2½pi ultra ('25)	4.50	1.50
100	A14	2¾pi ultra & dull vio	3.75	4.50
101	A14	4pi ap grn & vio	4.50	4.50
102	A14	4½pi black & yel, emer	4.00	4.75
103	A14	6pi grn ol & grn	4.50	8.00
104	A14	9pi brn & dk vio	8.00	5.00
105	A14	12pi org brn & blk	12.00	65.00
106	A14	18pi blk & org	22.50	5.75
		Revenue cancel		1.00
107	A14	45pi gray vio & ultra	52.50	42.50
		Revenue cancel		1.50
108	A14	90pi grn & red, yel	110.00	225.00
		Revenue cancel		3.00
109	A14	£5 blk, yel ('28)	3,200.	7,750.
		Revenue cancel		250.00

Wmk. 3

110	A14	£1 vio & black, red	350.00	800.00
		Revenue cancel		10.00
		Nos. 89-108 (20)	268.75	423.75

Nos. 96 and 99 are on ordinary paper.

Silver Coin of Amathus — A15

Philosopher Zeno — A16

Map of Cyprus — A17

Discovery of Body of St. Barnabas — A18

Cloisters of Bella Paise Monastery — A19

Badge of the Colony — A20

Hospice of Umm Haram at Larnaca — A21

Statue of Richard Coeur de Lion, London — A22

St. Nicholas Cathedral, Famagusta — A23

King George V — A24

Perf. 12

1928, Feb. 1　　Engr.　　Wmk. 4

114	A15	¾pi dark violet	3.50	1.60
115	A16	1pi Prus bl & blk	4.00	2.00
116	A17	1½pi red	6.00	2.50
117	A18	2½pi ultramarine	4.75	2.75
118	A19	4pi dp red brown	8.50	9.00
119	A20	6pi dark blue	12.00	27.50
120	A21	9pi violet brown	10.00	14.00
121	A22	18pi dk brn & blk	27.50	30.00
122	A23	45pi dp blue & vio	52.50	62.50
123	A24	£1 ol brn & deep blue	275.00	400.00
		Nos. 114-123 (10)	403.75	551.85

50th year of Cyprus as a British colony.

Ruins of Vouni Palace — A25

Columns at Salamis — A26

Peristerona Church — A27

Soli Theater — A28

Kyrenia Castle and Harbor — A29

Kolossi Castle — A30

St. Sophia Cathedral — A31

Bairakdar Mosque — A32

Queen's Window, St. Hilarion Castle — A33

Buyuk Khan, Nicosia — A34

Forest Scene — A35

1934, Dec. 1　　Engr.　　Perf. 12½

125	A25	¼pi yel brn & ultra	1.40	1.10
		Never hinged	2.00	
a.		Vert. pair, imperf. between	47,500.	30,000.
126	A26	½pi green	1.90	1.25
		Never hinged	2.00	
a.		Vert. pair, imperf. between	17,500.	19,000.
127	A27	¾pi violet & blk	3.25	.45
		Never hinged	4.25	
a.		Vert. pair, imperf. between	47,500.	
128	A28	1pi brown & blk	2.75	2.00
		Never hinged	4.25	
a.		Vert. pair, imperf. between	25,000.	25,000.
b.		Horiz. pair, imperf. btwn.	17,500.	
129	A29	1½pi rose red	3.75	1.75
		Never hinged	5.25	
130	A30	2½pi dark ultra	4.50	2.40
		Never hinged	7.00	
131	A31	4½pi dk car & blk	4.50	5.00
		Never hinged	12.50	
132	A32	6pi blue & black	12.00	18.00
		Never hinged	25.00	
133	A33	9pi dl vio & blk brown	14.00	7.50
		Never hinged	27.50	
134	A34	18pi ol grn & black	52.50	42.50
		Never hinged	110.00	
135	A35	45pi blk & emer	92.50	77.50
		Never hinged	190.00	
		Nos. 125-135 (11)	193.05	159.45
		Set, never hinged	389.75	

Common Design Types pictured following the introduction.

Silver Jubilee Issue
Common Design Type

1935, May 6　　　　Perf. 11x12

136	CD301	¾pi gray blk & ultra	2.25	1.50
137	CD301	1½pi car & dk bl	5.25	3.50
138	CD301	2½pi ultra & brn	4.75	2.00
139	CD301	9pi brn vio & ind	19.00	25.00
		Nos. 136-139 (4)	31.25	32.00
		Set, never hinged	50.00	

Coronation Issue
Common Design Type

1937, May 12　　　　Perf. 11x11½

140	CD302	¾pi dark gray	.35	.20
141	CD302	1½pi dark carmine	.60	.85
142	CD302	2½pi deep ultra	1.25	1.40
		Nos. 140-142 (3)	2.20	2.45
		Set, never hinged	7.00	

Ruins of Vouni Palace — A36

Columns at Salamis — A37

Peristerona Church — A38

Soli Theater — A39

Kyrenia Castle and Harbor — A40

Kolossi Castle — A41

Map of Cyprus — A42

Bairakdar Mosque — A43

Citadel, Famagusta — A44

Buyuk Khan — A45

Forest Scene A46   King George VI A47

1938-44   Wmk. 4   Perf. 12½

143	A36	¼pi yel brn & ultra	.20	.20
144	A37	½pi green	.40	.20
145	A38	¾pi violet & blk	9.00	.65
146	A39	1pi orange	.50	.20
a.		Perf. 13½x12½ ('44)	375.00	30.00
		Never hinged	600.00	
147	A40	1½pi rose car	3.25	1.90
147A	A40	1½pi lt vio ('43)	.35	.35
147B	A38	2pi carmine & blk ('42)	.45	.20
c.		Perf. 12½x13½ ('44)	2.00	7.50
		Never hinged	2.50	
148	A41	2½pi ultramarine	13.00	4.25
148A	A41	3pi dp ultra ('42)	1.00	.20
149	A42	4½pi gray	.45	.20
150	A43	6pi blue & black	.80	1.25
151	A44	9pi dk vio & blk	1.25	.20
152	A45	18pi ol grn & blk	2.50	1.10
153	A46	45pi blk & emer	11.50	3.25
154	A47	90pi blk & brt vio	21.00	6.50
155	A47	£1 ind & dl red	45.00	30.00
		Nos. 143-155 (16)	110.65	50.65
		Set, never hinged	290.00	

See Nos. 164-166.

Catalogue values for unused stamps in this section, from this point to the end of the section, are for Never Hinged items.

Peace Issue
Common Design Type

1946, Oct. 21   Engr.   Perf. 13½x14

156	CD303	1½pi purple	.40	.20
157	CD303	3pi deep blue	.40	.30

Silver Wedding Issue
Common Design Types

1948, Dec. 20   Photo.   Perf. 14x14½

158	CD304	1½pi purple	1.00	.40

Engr.; Name Typo.
Perf. 11½x11

159	CD305	£1 dark blue	57.50	77.50

UPU Issue
Common Design Types
Perf. 13½, 11x11½

1949, Oct. 10   Engr.   Wmk. 4

160	CD306	1½pi violet	.45	1.40
161	CD307	2pi deep carmine	1.75	1.75
162	CD308	3pi indigo	.80	1.10
163	CD309	9pi rose violet	2.00	3.00
		Nos. 160-163 (4)	5.00	7.25

Types of 1938-43

1951, July 2   Engr.   Perf. 12½

164	A37	½pi purple	3.00	.50
165	A40	1½pi deep green	4.00	1.00
166	A41	4pi deep ultra	4.25	.90
		Nos. 164-166 (3)	11.25	2.40

Coronation Issue
Common Design Type

1953, June 2   Perf. 13½x13

167	CD312	1½pi brt grn & black	1.75	1.00

Carobs A48   Copper Pyrites Mine A49

St. Hilarion Castle A50

Queen Elizabeth II and Cyprian Coin Devices — A51

Designs: 3m, Grapes. 5m, Oranges. 15m, Troodos forest. 20m, Aphrodite beach. 25m, Coin of Paphos. 30m, Kyrenia. 35m, Harvest in Mesaoria. 40m, Famagusta harbor. 100m, Hala Sultan Tekke. 250m, Kanakaria church. £1, Queen Elizabeth II and devices of Byzantium, Lusignan, Ottoman Empire and Venice.

Perf. 11½

1955, Aug. 1   Engr.   Wmk. 4

168	A48	2m chocolate	.20	.50
169	A48	3m violet blue	.20	.20
170	A48	5m orange	1.00	.20
171	A49	10m gray grn & chocolate	1.25	.20
172	A49	15m indigo & olive	3.50	.50
173	A49	20m ultra & brown	1.25	.25
174	A49	25m aquamarine	3.25	.70
175	A49	30m carmine & blk	3.00	.20
176	A49	35m aqua & orange	1.25	.50
177	A49	40m choc & dk grn	2.00	.75

Perf. 13½

178	A50	50m red brn & aqua	2.10	.30
179	A50	100m bl green & mag	13.00	.60
180	A50	250m vio brn & dk blue gray	14.00	12.00

Perf. 11x11½

181	A51	500m lilac rose & grnsh gray	32.50	14.00
182	A51	£1 grnsh gray & brn red	29.00	47.50
		Revenue cancel		1.00
		Nos. 168-182 (15)	107.50	78.40

Republic

Nos. 168-182 Overprinted in Dark Blue

1960, Aug. 16   Ovpt. 10x6½mm

183	A48	2m chocolate	.20	.50
184	A48	3m violet blue	.20	.20
185	A48	5m orange	.20	.20

Overprint 12½x11mm

186	A49	10m gray grn & choc	.25	.20
187	A49	15m indigo & ol	.45	.30
188	A49	20m ultra & brn	.50	.50
a.		Double overprint		11,000.
189	A49	25m aquamarine	.60	.60
190	A49	30m car & black	.75	.20
a.		Double overprint		40,000.
191	A49	35m aqua & org	1.00	.70
192	A49	40m choc & dk grn	1.10	1.25

2-line overprint 2½mm apart

193	A50	50m red brown & aqua	1.25	.75
194	A50	100m bl grn & mag	3.00	2.00
195	A50	250m vio brn & dk blue gray	10.50	6.00

2-line overprint 22mm apart

196	A51	500m lil rose & grnsh gray	47.50	25.00
197	A51	£1 grnsh gray & brn red	87.50	52.50
		Nos. 183-197 (15)	155.00	91.00

The overprint, in Greek and Turkish, reads "Republic of Cyprus."

Map of Cyprus — A52

Wmk. 314

1960, Aug. 16   Engr.   Perf. 11½

198	A52	10m brown & green	.25	.20
199	A52	30m blue & brown	1.00	.70
200	A52	100m purple & black	2.75	2.25
		Nos. 198-200 (3)	4.00	3.15

Independence of Republic of Cyprus.

Europa Issue, 1961

Nineteen Doves Flying as One CD4

Perf. 14x13½

1962, Mar. 19   Litho.   Unwmk.

201	CD4	10m lilac	.30	.20
202	CD4	40m deep ultra	.90	.35
203	CD4	100m emerald	.90	.60
		Nos. 201-203 (3)	2.10	1.15

Admission of Cyprus to Council of Europe.

Malaria Eradication Emblem A54

1962, May 14   Perf. 14x13½

204	A54	10m gray green & blue	.25	.20
205	A54	30m red brown & black	.50	.50

WHO drive to eradicate malaria.

Iron Age Jug — A55

St. Barnabas Church, Salamis A56

Designs: 5m, Grapes. 10m, Head of Apollo. 15m, St. Sophia Church, Nicosia. 30m, Temple of Apollo. 35m, Head of Aphrodite. 40m, Skiing on Mt. Troodos. 50m, Ruins of Gymnasium, Salamis. 100m, Hala Sultan Tekke (sheep, Salt Lake Larnaca and tomb). 250m, Bella Paise Monastery. 500m, Cyprus mouflon. £1, St. Hilarion Castle.

Perf. 13½x14, 14x13½

1962, Sept. 17   Wmk. 344

206	A55	3m dk brn & sal	.20	.30
207	A55	5m dull green & red lilac	.20	.20
208	A55	10m dk slate grn & yel green	.20	.20
209	A55	15m dk brn & rose vio	.40	.20
210	A56	25m salmon & brn	.45	.20
211	A56	30m lt bl & dk bl	.25	.20
212	A55	35m dk bl & pale grn	.45	.20
213	A56	40m vio bl & dk bl	1.50	1.75
214	A56	50m olive bis & dk grn	.60	.20
215	A55	100m brn & yel brn	4.25	.30
216	A55	250m tan & black	11.00	2.40
217	A55	500m brown & olive	21.00	9.00
218	A56	£1 gray & green	22.50	30.00
		Nos. 206-218 (13)	63.00	45.15

Wmk. 344 is found in two positions: normal or inverted on vertical stamps, and reading up or down on horizontal stamps.
For overprints see Nos. 232-236, 265-268. For surcharge see No. 273.

Europa Issue, 1962
Common Design Type
Perf. 14x13½

1963, Jan. 28   Wmk. 344
Size: 36x20mm

219	CD5	10m ultra & black	3.75	.20
220	CD5	40m red & black	15.00	1.40
221	CD5	150m green & black	57.50	2.75
		Nos. 219-221 (3)	76.25	4.35

Cypriot Farm Girl — A57   Cub Scout and Tents — A58

75m, Statue of Demeter, goddess of agriculture.

1963, Mar. 21   Perf. 13½x14

222	A57	25m blk, ultra & ocher	.60	.45
223	A57	75m dk car, gray & blk	3.50	1.75

FAO "Freedom from Hunger" campaign.

1963, Aug. 21   Wmk. 344

20m, Sea Scout. 150m, Boy Scout & mouflon.

224	A58	3m multicolored	.20	.20
225	A58	20m multicolored	.40	.25
226	A58	150m multicolored	2.00	2.50
a.		Souvenir sheet of 3	150.00	150.00
		Nos. 224-226 (3)	2.60	2.95

Boy Scout movement in Cyprus, 50th anniv. #226a contains 3 imperf. stamps similar to #224-226 with simulated perforations. Sold for 250m.

Red Cross Nurse — A59

Children's Home, Kyrenia A60

Perf. 13½x14, 14x13½
1963, Sept. 9   Litho.   Wmk. 344

227	A59	10m multicolored	1.00	.20
228	A60	100m multicolored	4.00	4.00

Intl. Red Cross, cent.

Europa Issue, 1963

Stylized Links, Symbolizing Unity — CD6

1963, Nov. 4   Perf. 14x13½

229	CD6	20m multicolored	5.75	.70
230	CD6	30m multicolored	6.50	.70
231	CD6	150m multicolored	42.50	3.75
		Nos. 229-231 (3)	54.75	5.15

Nos. 208, 211, 213-215 Overprinted in Ultramarine

1964, May 5   Perf. 13½x14, 14x13½

232	A55	10m dk sl grn & yel grn	.25	.20
233	A55	30m lt blue & dk blue	.30	.20
234	A55	40m vio bl & dull bl	.80	.30
235	A55	50m ol bis & dk grn	.50	.35
236	A55	100m brn & yel brown	.85	.75
		Nos. 232-236 (5)	2.70	1.80

Decision by the UN and its Security Council to help restore the country to normality and to seek a solution of its problems.

Clay Mask and Soli Theater A62

Designs: 35m, Curium theater. 50m, Salamis theater. 100m, Performance of "Othello" in front of Othello Tower.

1964, June 15   Perf. 13½x14

237	A62	15m multicolored	.50	.20
238	A62	35m multicolored	.50	.25
239	A62	50m multicolored	.50	.25
240	A62	100m multicolored	1.90	2.25
		Nos. 237-240 (4)	3.40	2.95

400th anniversary of Shakespeare's birth.

Boxers A63

14th century B.C. art: 10m, Runners, vert. 75m, Chariot.

1964, July 6   Perf. 13½x14, 14x13½

241	A63	10m brn, bis & blk	.20	.20
242	A63	25m gray bl, bl & brn	.30	.25
243	A63	75m brick red, blk & brn	.75	.80
a.		Souvenir sheet of 3	10.00	13.50
		Nos. 241-243 (3)	1.25	1.25

18th Olympic Games, Tokyo, Oct. 10-25, 1964. No. 243a contains three imperf. stamps similar to Nos. 241-243 with gray marginal inscription. Sheet sold for 250m; the difference between face value and selling price went for the promotion of classical athletics in Cyprus.

Symbolic Daisy CD7

Satyr Drinking Wine, 5th Century B.C. Statuette A65

Modern Winery A66

Europa Issue, 1964
Perf. 13½x14
1964, Sept. 14   Litho.   Wmk. 344

244	CD7	20m bis brn & red brn	2.50	.35
245	CD7	30m lt blue & dk blue	3.25	.35
246	CD7	150m grn & ol grn	30.00	2.75
		Nos. 244-246 (3)	35.75	3.45

CEPT, 5th anniv. The 22 petals of the flower symbolize the 22 members of the organization.

Perf. 14x13½, 13½x14
1964, Oct. 26   Wmk. 344

Cypriot Wine Industry: 10m, Dionysus and Acme drinking wine, 3rd century mosaic. 50m, Commandaria wine, Knight Templar and Kolossi Castle.

247	A66	10m multicolored	.50	.20
248	A65	40m multicolored	.95	1.25
249	A65	50m multicolored	.95	.30
250	A66	100m multicolored	2.50	2.00
		Nos. 247-250 (4)	4.90	3.75

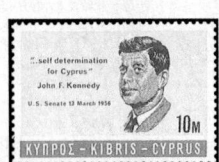

Pres. John F. Kennedy (1917-1963) — A67

Perf. 14x13½
1965, Feb. 15   Litho.   Wmk. 344

251	A67	10m violet blue	.20	.20
252	A67	40m green	.50	.45
253	A67	100m rose claret	.65	.45
a.		Souvenir sheet of 3	5.00	7.00
		Nos. 251-253 (3)	1.35	1.10

No. 253a contains 3 imperf. stamps similar to Nos. 251-253 with simulated perforations. Sold for 250m, 100m going to charitable organizations in Cyprus.

Old Couple — A68

Mother and Children by A. Diamantis — A69

45m, Man with broken leg (accident insurance).

1965, Apr. 12   Perf. 13½x14

254	A68	30m dull green & tan	.30	.20
255	A68	45m dk vio bl, bl & gray	.50	.30

Perf. 13½x12½

256	A69	75m buff & red brown	1.50	2.00
		Nos. 254-256 (3)	2.30	2.50

Introduction of Social Insurance Law.

ITU Emblem, Old and New Communication Equipment — A70

1965, May 17   Litho.   Perf. 14x13½

257	A70	15m brn, yel & black	.75	.25
258	A70	60m grn, lt grn & black	8.50	3.25
259	A70	75m dk & lt bl & black	9.75	4.50
		Nos. 257-259 (3)	19.00	8.00

ITU, cent.

ICY Emblem A71

1965, May 17   Wmk. 344

260	A71	50m multicolored	1.25	.20
261	A71	100m multicolored	2.00	.90

International Cooperation Year.

Europa Issue, 1965

Leaves and Fruit CD8

Perf. 14x13½
1965, Sept. 27   Litho.   Wmk. 344

262	CD8	5m org, org brn & black	1.10	.25
263	CD8	45m lt grn, org brn & black	5.25	.80
264	CD8	150m gray, org brn & black	19.00	2.75
		Nos. 262-264 (3)	25.35	3.80

Nos. 206, 208, 211 and 216 Overprinted in Dark Blue

1966, Jan. 31   Perf. 13½x14, 14x13½

265	A55	3m dk brn & salmon	.35	.40
266	A55	10m dk sl grn & yel green	.35	.20
267	A56	30m lt bl & dk blue	.35	.20
268	A56	250m tan & black	1.25	2.40
		Nos. 265-268 (4)	2.30	3.20

UN General Assembly's resolution to mediate the dispute between Greeks and Turks on Cyprus, Dec. 18, 1965.

St. Barnabas, Ancient Icon — A73

Chapel over Tomb of St. Barnabas A74

Bishop Anthemios of Constantine Dreaming of St. Barnabas, Discovering Tomb, etc. — A75

Design: 15m, Discovery of body of St. Barnabas (scene as in type A18).

Perf. 13x14, 14x13
1966, Apr. 25   Litho.   Wmk. 344

269	A73	15m multicolored	.20	.20
270	A74	25m multicolored	.20	.20
271	A73	100m multicolored	.90	1.75

Size: 110x91mm
Imperf

272	A75	250m multicolored	6.50	12.00
		Nos. 269-272 (4)	7.80	14.15

1900th anniv. of the death of St. Barnabas.

No. 206 Surcharged with New Value and Three Bars
Perf. 13½x14
1966, May 30   Litho.   Wmk. 344

273	A55	5m on 3m dk brn & sal	.50	.25

Gen. K. S. Thimayya A76

1966, June 6   Perf. 14x13½

274	A76	50m tan & black	.40	.25

In memory of Gen. Kodendera Subayya Thimayya (1906-1965), commander of the UN Peace-keeping Force on Cyprus.

Europa Issue, 1966

Symbolic Sailboat — CD9

Perf. 13½x14

1966, Sept. 26   Litho.   Wmk. 344

275	CD9	20m multicolored	.50	.20
276	CD9	30m multicolored	.50	.25
277	CD9	150m multicolored	3.75	1.40
		Nos. 275-277 (3)	4.75	1.85

Stavrovouni Monastery A78

St. Nicholas Cathedral, Famagusta A79

Ingot Bearer, Bronze Age — A80

Designs: 5m, St. James' Church, Tricomo, vert. 10m, Zeno of Citium, marble bust, vert. 15m, Ship from 7th cent. BC vase, horiz. 20m, Silver coin, 4th cent. BC (head of Hercules with lion skin). 25m, Sleeping Eros (1st cent. marble statue; horiz.). 35m, Hawks on 11th cent. gold and enamel scepter from Curium. 40m, Marriage of David (7th cent. silver disc). 50m, Silver coin of Alexander the Great showing Hercules and Zeus, horiz. 100m, Bird catching fish on 7th cent. BC jug. 500m, The Rape of Ganymede (3rd cent. mosaic). £1, Aphrodite (1st cent. marble statue).

Perf. 12x12½, 12½x12

1966, Nov. 21   Litho.   Wmk. 344

278	A78	3m bl, dl yel, grn & black	.60	.20
279	A78	5m dk bl, ol & blk	.20	.20
280	A78	10m olive & black	.25	.20

Perf. 14x13½, 13½x14

281	A79	15m grn, blk & red brn	.25	.20
282	A79	20m red brn & blk	1.75	1.40
283	A79	25m red brn, gray & black	.55	.20
284	A79	30m aqua, tan & blk	.75	.30
285	A79	35m dk car, yel & blk	.75	.45
286	A79	40m brt bl, gray & blk	1.00	.45
287	A79	50m org brn, gray & blk	1.50	.20
288	A79	100m gray, buff, blk & red	5.00	.20

Perf. 13x14

289	A80	250m dull yel, grn & blk	1.50	.50
290	A80	500m multicolored	3.50	1.00
291	A80	£1 gray, lt gray & black	3.00	7.00
		Nos. 278-291 (14)	20.60	12.50

Electric Power Station, Limassol — A81

Arghaka-Maghounda Dam — A82

Designs: 35m, Troodos Highway. 50m, Cyprus Hilton Hotel. 100m, Ships in Famagusta Harbor.

Perf. 14x13½, 13½x14

1967, Apr. 10   Litho.   Wmk. 344

292	A81	10m lt brn, dark brn & yellow	.20	.20
293	A82	15m lt bl, bl & grn	.25	.25
294	A82	35m dark gray, indigo & dark grn	.35	.35
295	A82	50m gray, olive & blue	.35	.35
296	A82	100m gray, ind & bl	.35	.35
		Nos. 292-296 (5)	1.50	1.50

1st development program, 1962-66, completion.

Europa Issue, 1967
Common Design Type

1967, May 2   Perf. 13x14
Size: 21x37mm

297	CD10	20m yel grn & olive	.50	.20
298	CD10	30m rose vio & pur	.50	.25
299	CD10	150m pale brn & brn	3.25	1.25
		Nos. 297-299 (3)	4.25	1.70

Javelin Thrower, Map of Eastern Mediterranean and "Victory" — A83

Map of Eastern Mediterranean, Victory Statue and: 35m, Runner. 100m, High jumper. 250m, Amphora, map of Eastern Mediterranean and Victory statue.

Perf. 13½x13

1967, Sept. 4   Litho.   Wmk. 344

300	A83	15m multicolored	.20	.20
301	A83	35m multicolored	.35	.30
302	A83	100m multicolored	.75	.75

Size: 97x77mm
Imperf

303	A83	250m multicolored	3.50	6.50
		Nos. 300-303 (4)	4.80	7.75

Cyprus-Crete-Salonika Athletic Games.

Marble Forum at Salamis, Church of St. Barnabas and Bellapais Abbey A84

ITY Emblem and: 40m, Famagusta Beach. 50m, Plane and Nicosia International Airport. 100m, Youth Hostel and skiing on Mt. Troodos.

Perf. 13½x13

1967, Oct. 16   Litho.   Wmk. 344

304	A84	10m multicolored	.20	.20
305	A84	40m multicolored	.20	1.00
306	A84	50m multicolored	.30	.20
307	A84	100m multicolored	.50	1.00
		Nos. 304-307 (4)	1.20	2.40

Intl. Tourist Year, 1967.

St. Andrew, 6th Century Mosaic — A85

Crucifixion, 15th Century — A86

The Three Kings, 15th Century Fresco — A87

1967, Nov. 8   Perf. 13x13½

308	A85	25m multicolored	.30	.20
309	A86	50m multicolored	.30	.20
310	A87	75m multicolored	.30	.20
		Nos. 308-310 (3)	.90	.60

St. Andrew's Monastery, cent. (25m); Exhibition of Art of Cyprus, Paris, Nov. 7, 1967-Jan. 3, 1968 (50m); 20th anniv. of UNESCO (75m).

Human Rights Flame and Stars — A88

Designs: 90m, Human Rights flame and UN emblem. 250m, Scroll showing Article One of the Declaration of Human Rights.

Perf. 13½x14

1968, Mar. 18   Litho.   Wmk. 344

311	A88	50m multicolored	.20	.20
312	A88	90m multicolored	.40	.60

Size: 110x90mm
Imperf

313	A88	250m multicolored	2.00	4.50
		Nos. 311-313 (3)	2.60	5.30

Intl. Human Rights Year.

Europa Issue, 1968
Common Design Type

1968, Apr. 29   Perf. 14x13½

314	CD11	20m multicolored	.40	.25
315	CD11	30m dk car rose, gray brn & blk	.50	.25
316	CD11	150m multicolored	2.00	1.25
		Nos. 314-316 (3)	2.90	1.75

Boy Holding Milk, UNICEF Emblem A89

Aesculapius and WHO Emblem — A90

Perf. 14x13½, 13½x14

1968, Sept. 2   Wmk. 344

317	A89	35m dk red, lt brn & blk	.30	.20
318	A90	50m gray ol, blk & grn	.30	.20

21st anniv. of UNICEF (No. 317), 20th anniv. of the WHO (No. 318).

Discus Thrower — A91

ILO Emblem — A92

25m, Runners. 100m, Stadium, Mexico City.

Perf. 13½x14, 14x13½

1968, Oct. 24   Litho.

319	A91	10m multicolored	.20	.20
320	A91	25m vio blue & multi	.20	.20
321	A91	100m blue & multi, horiz.	.30	1.25
		Nos. 319-321 (3)	.70	1.65

19th Olympic Games, Mexico City, 10/12-27.

Perf. 12x13½

1969, Mar. 3   Wmk. 344

322	A92	50m bl, vio bl & org brn	.25	.25
323	A92	90m gray, blk & org brn	.25	.25

ILO, 50th anniv.

Ancient Map of Cyprus A93

Design: 50m, Medieval map of Cyprus.

Perf. 13½x13

1969, Apr. 7   Wmk. 344

324	A93	35m multicolored	.30	.30
325	A93	50m olive & multi	.30	.30

1st Intl. Congress of Cypriot Studies.

Europa Issue, 1969

"EUROPA" and "CEPT" CD12

1969, Apr. 28   Litho.   Perf. 14x13½

326	CD12	20m bl, blk & gray	.55	.20
327	CD12	30m cop red, blk & ocher	.55	.20
328	CD12	150m grn, blk & yel	1.90	.85
		Nos. 326-328 (3)	3.00	1.25

CEPT, 10th anniv.

European Roller — A95

Birds: 15m, Audouin's gull. 20m, Cyprus warbler. 30m, Eurasian jay, vert. 40m, Hoopoe, vert. 90m, Eleonora's falcon, vert.

Perf. 13½x12, 12x13½

		1969, July 7	**Wmk. 344**	
329	A95	5m multicolored	.55	.20
330	A95	15m multicolored	.75	.20
331	A95	20m multicolored	.75	.20
332	A95	30m multicolored	.80	.25
333	A95	40m multicolored	.95	.30
334	A95	90m multicolored	2.25	4.50
		Nos. 329-334 (6)	6.05	5.65

Nativity, Mural, 1192 A96

Christmas: 45m, Nativity, mural in Church of Ayios Nicolaos tis Steghis, 14th century. 250m, Virgin and Child between Archangels Michael and Gabriel, mosaic in Church of Panayia Angeloktistos, 6th-7th centuries. Design of 20m is a mural in Church of Panayia tou Arakos, Lagoudhera.

		1969, Nov. 24 Litho.	**Perf. 13½x13**	
335	A96	20m multicolored	.20	.20
336	A96	45m multicolored	.30	.25

Size: 109x89mm

Imperf

337	A96	250m dk blue & multi	7.00	*11.00*
		Nos. 335-337 (3)	7.50	11.45

Mahatma Gandhi A97

		1970, Jan. 26	**Perf. 14x13½**	
338	A97	25m multicolored	.35	.35
339	A97	75m multicolored	1.40	1.50

Birth cent. of Mohandas K. Gandhi (1869-1948), leader in India's struggle for independence.

Europa Issue, 1970

Interwoven Threads CD13

		1970, May 4 Litho.	**Wmk. 344**	
340	CD13	20m brn, yel & org	.40	.25
341	CD13	30m brt bl, yel & org	.40	.25
342	CD13	150m brt rose lil, yel & orange	1.90	1.40
		Nos. 340-342 (3)	2.70	1.90

Landscape with Flowers — A99

Designs: Various landscapes with flowers.

Perf. 13x14

		1970, Aug. 3 Litho.	**Wmk. 344**	
343	A99	10m multicolored	.25	.20
344	A99	50m multicolored	.25	.20
345	A99	90m multicolored	.85	*1.10*
		Nos. 343-345 (3)	1.35	1.50

European Nature Conservation Year.

Education Year Emblem — A100

Grapes and Partridge (Mosaic) A101

UN Emblem, Dove, Globe and Wheat A102

Perf. 13x14, 14x13

		1970, Sept. 7 Litho.	**Wmk. 344**	
346	A100	5m tan, blk & brn	.25	.20
347	A101	15m multicolored	.25	.20
348	A102	75m multicolored	.25	.20
		Nos. 346-348 (3)	.75	.60

Intl. Education Year (No. 346); 50th General Assembly of the Intl. Vine and Wine Office (No. 347); 25th anniv. of the UN (No. 348).

Virgin and Child, Mural from Podhithou Church, 16th Century — A103

Perf. 14x14½

		1970, Nov. 23 Photo.	**Unwmk.**	
349	A103	Strip of three	.45	.45
a.		25m Left angel	.20	.20
b.		25m Virgin and Child	.20	.20
c.		25m Right angel	.20	.20
350	A103	75m multicolored	.35	.35

Christmas.

Design of No. 349 is same as No. 350, but divided by perforation into 3 stamps with 25m denomination each. Size of No. 349: 71x46mm; size of No. 350: 42x31mm.

Cotton Napkin — A104

Festive Costume — A105

Drinking Cup, 7th Cent. B.C. A106

Mouflon from Mosaic Pavement, 3rd Century — A107

Cypriot Art: 5m, St. George, bas-relief on pine board, 19th cent. 20m, kneeling donors, painting, Church of St. Mamas, 1465. 25m, Mosaic head, 5th cent. A.D. 30m, Athena mounting horse-drawn chariot, terracotta figurine, 5th cent. B.C. 40m, Shepherd playing pipe, 14th cent. fresco. 50m, Woman's head, limestone, 3rd cent. B.C. 75m, Angel, mosaic, 6th cent. 90m, Mycenaean silver bowl, 14th cent. B.C. 500m, Woman and tree, decoration from amphora, 7th-6th cent. B.C. £1, God statue (horned helmet), from Enkomi, 12th cent. B.C., vert.

Perf. 12½x13½ (A104), 13x14 (A105), 14x13 (A106), 13½x13, 13x13½ (A107)

		1971, Feb. 22 Litho.	**Wmk. 344**	
351	A104	3m blk, red & brn	.40	.50
352	A104	5m citron, red brn & black	.20	.20
353	A105	10m multicolored	.20	.30
354	A106	15m bister brn, blk & slate	.25	.20
355	A105	20m slate, red brn & black	.45	.50
356	A105	25m multicolored	.35	.20
357	A106	30m multicolored	.35	.20
358	A105	40m gray & multi	1.25	1.10
359	A105	50m bl, bis & blk	1.00	.20
360	A105	75m cit & multi	2.25	1.25
361	A106	90m multicolored	2.50	2.50
362	A107	250m lt red brn, brn & black	1.90	.40
363	A107	500m tan & multi	1.00	.50
364	A107	£1 multicolored	1.90	.75
		Nos. 351-364 (14)	14.00	8.80

For surcharges & overprints see #403, 424-427, 444, RA1.

Europa Issue, 1971

"Fraternity, Co-operation, Common Effort" — CD14

		1971, May 3 Litho.	**Perf. 14x13½**	
		Size: 36½x23½mm		
365	CD14	20m lt bl, vio bl & blk	.30	.20
366	CD14	30m brt yel grn, grn & blk	.30	.20
367	CD14	150m yel, grn & blk	2.00	1.25
		Nos. 365-367 (3)	2.60	1.65

Archbishop Kyprianos, 1821 — A109

Paintings: 30m, Young Greek Taking Oath, horiz. 100m, Bishop Germanòs of Patras Declaring Greek Independence.

Perf. 13x13½, 13½x13

		1971, July 9	**Wmk. 344**	
368	A109	15m multicolored	.20	.20
369	A109	30m multicolored	.20	.20
370	A109	100m multicolored	.30	.30
		Nos. 368-370 (3)	.70	.70

150th anniversary of Greek independence.

Arch and Castle A110

Tourist Publicity: 25m, Decorated gourd and sun over shore, vert. 60m, Mountain road, vert. 100m, Village church.

Perf. 13½x13, 13x13½

		1971, Sept. 20		
371	A110	15m vio bl & multi	.20	.20
372	A110	25m ocher & multi	.20	.20
373	A110	60m green & multi	.25	.25
374	A110	100m blue & multi	.25	.25
		Nos. 371-374 (4)	.90	.90

Virgin and Child — A111

Heart and Electrocardiogram — A112

		1971, Nov. 22	**Perf. 13½x14**	
375	A111	10m shown	.20	.20
376	A111	50m The Three Kings	.20	.20
377	A111	100m Shepherds	.30	.30
a.		Strip of 3, Nos. 375-377	.75	.75

Christmas.

		1972, Apr. 11	**Perf. 13½x12½**	
378	A112	15m bister & multi	.20	.20
379	A112	50m brown & multi	.30	.30

"Your heart is your health," World Health Day.

Europa Issue 1972

Sparkles, Symbolic of Communications CD15

		1972, May 22	**Perf. 12½x13½**	
380	CD15	20m brn, org & fawn	.60	.30
381	CD15	30m pur, org & lilac	.60	.55
382	CD15	150m dk ol, org & brt green	4.75	1.60
		Nos. 380-382 (3)	5.95	2.45

Archery, Olympic and Motion Emblems A114

		1972, July 24	**Perf. 14x13½**	
383	A114	10m shown	.25	.20
384	A114	40m Wrestling	.35	.25
385	A114	100m Soccer	.65	1.25
		Nos. 383-385 (3)	1.25	1.70

20th Olympic Games, Munich, 8/26-9/11.

Apollo, Silver Stater, Marion, 5th Century B.C. A115

Silver Staters of Cyprus: 30m, Eagle's head, Paphos, c. 460 B.C. 40m, Pallas Athena, Lapithos, 388-387 B.C. 100m, Sphinx (obverse) and lotus flower (reverse), Idalion, c. 460 B.C.

1972, Sept. 25   Litho.   Wmk. 344
Coins in Silver

386	A115	20m lt grnsh bl & blk	.20	.20
387	A115	30m pale bl & silver	.20	.20
388	A115	40m ol bister & black	.35	.30
389	A115	100m pale brn & blk	1.25	1.10
		Nos. 386-389 (4)	2.00	1.80

Bathing the Christ Child — A116

Christmas: 20m, The Three Kings. 100m, Nativity. 250m, The Nativity, 1466, mural in Church of the Holy Cross, Platanistasa. The designs of the 10m, 20m, 100m, show details from mural shown entirely on 250m.

1972, Nov. 20   Litho.   Perf. 13½x14

390	A116	10m multicolored	.30	.30
391	A116	20m multicolored	.30	.30
392	A116	100m multicolored	.40	.40

Size: 110x90mm
Imperf

393	A116	250m multicolored	2.75	2.75
		Nos. 390-393 (4)	3.75	3.75

Landscape, Troodos Mountains A117

100m, FIS Congress emblem and map of Cyprus.

Perf. 14x13½
1973, Mar. 13   Wmk. 344

394	A117	20m blue & multi	.20	.20
395	A117	100m blue & multi	.40	.40

29th Meeting of the Intl. Ski Fed. (FIS), Nicosia, June 1973.

Europa Issue 1973

Post Horn of Arrows CD16

1973, May 7   Size: 37x21mm

396	CD16	20m dl bl & multi	.50	.25
397	CD16	30m multicolored	.50	.35
398	CD16	150m multicolored	3.25	1.50
		Nos. 396-398 (3)	4.25	2.10

Archbishop's Palace, Nicosia — A119

Traditional Architecture: 30m, Konak, Nicosia, 18th century, vert. 50m, House, Gourri, 1850, vert. 100m, House, Rizokarpaso, 1772.

1973, July 23   Perf. 14x13, 13x14

399	A119	20m multicolored	.20	.20
400	A119	30m multicolored	.20	.20
401	A119	50m multicolored	.20	.20
402	A119	100m multicolored	.50	.50
		Nos. 399-402 (4)	1.10	1.10

No. 354 Surcharged

1973, Sept. 24   Perf. 14x13

403	A106	20m on 15m multi	.45	.45

Cyprus Scout Emblem — A120

EEC Emblem A122

CYPRUS KIBRIS

Cyprus Airways Emblem — A121

35m, FAO emblem. 100m, INTERPOL emblem.

1973, Sept. 24   Perf. 13x14, 14x13

404	A120	10m brn ol, ol & buff	.40	.35
405	A121	25m pur, bl & plum	.30	.30
406	A121	35m grn, gray grn & citron	.30	.30
407	A122	50m black & blue	.30	.30
408	A120	100m brown & fawn	.60	.60
		Nos. 404-408 (5)	1.90	1.85

60th anniv. of Cyprus Boy Scout Organ.; association of Cyprus with EEC; 10th anniv. of FAO; 25th anniv. of Cyprus Airways; 50th anniv. of Intl. Criminal Police Organization.

Archangel Gabriel — A123

Virgin and Child — A124

Christmas: 100m, Panaya tou Araka Church, horiz. Designs of 10m, 20m are from wall paintings in Arakas Church.

1973, Nov. 26   Wmk. 344

409	A123	10m multicolored	.20	.20
410	A124	20m multicolored	.20	.20
411	A124	100m multicolored	.60	.60
		Nos. 409-411 (3)	1.00	1.00

Grapes — A125

Rape of Europa — A126

1974, Mar. 18   Litho.   Perf. 13x14

412	A125	25m shown	.25	.20
413	A125	50m Grapefruit	.30	.20
414	A125	50m Oranges	.30	.20
415	A125	50m Lemons	.30	.30
a.		Strip of 3, #413-415	1.25	1.25
		Nos. 412-415 (4)	1.15	.90

Europa Issue 1974
1974, Apr. 29

Design shows a silver stater of Marion, second half of 5th century B.C.

416	A126	10m org brn & multi	.60	.30
417	A126	40m multicolored	.60	.60
418	A126	150m dk car & multi	2.75	1.40
		Nos. 416-418 (3)	3.95	2.30

Solon, 3rd Century Mosaic A127

Designs: 10m, Front page of "History of Cyprus," by Archimandrite Kyprianos, 1788, vert. 100m, St. Neophytos, mural, vert. 250m, Maps of Cyprus and Greek Islands, by Abraham Ortelius, 1584.

Perf. 13x14, 14x13
1974, July 22   Litho.   Wmk. 344

419	A127	10m multicolored	.20	.20
420	A127	25m multicolored	.20	.20
421	A127	100m multicolored	.85	.85

Size: 110x90mm
Imperf

422	A127	250m multicolored	3.25	3.50
		Nos. 419-422 (4)	4.50	4.75

2nd Intl. Congress of Cypriot Studies, Nicosia, Sept. 15-21. No. 422 has simulated perforations.

Nos. 353, 358-359, 362 Overprinted

Perf. 13x14, 13½x13
1974, Oct. 14   Litho.

424	A105	10m multicolored	.25	.25
425	A105	40m multicolored	.35	.35
426	A105	50m multicolored	.35	.35
427	A107	250m multicolored	.80	.80
		Nos. 424-427 (4)	1.75	1.75

UN Security Council Resolution No. 353 to end hostilities on Cyprus. Overprint is in 3 lines on No. 427.

Virgin and Child, 1466 A129

Adoration of the Kings, c. 1500 — A130

Christmas: 100m, Flight into Egypt, mural, Monastery Church of Ayios Meophytos, c. 1500. (50m is from same church). Mural on 10m is in Church of Stavros tou Ahiasmati.

Perf. 14x13, 13x14
1974, Dec. 2   Wmk. 344

429	A129	10m multicolored	.20	.20
430	A130	50m multicolored	.20	.20
431	A129	100m multicolored	.40	.40
		Nos. 429-431 (3)	.80	.80

Disabled Persons, Emblem — A131

Council of Europe Flag — A132

1975, Feb. 17   Unwmk.   Perf. 14½

432	A131	30m ocher & ultra	.20	.20
433	A132	100m multicolored	.70	.60

8th European Meeting of the Intl. Society for the Rehabilitation of Disabled Persons (30m; design shows society's emblem); 25th anniv. of Council of Europe (100m).

First Mail Coach in Cyprus A133

1975, Feb. 17

434	A133	20m multicolored	.20	.20
435	A133	50m ultra & multi	1.10	.40

Centenary (in 1974) of UPU.

The Distaff, by Michael Kashalos — A134

Europa (Paintings): 30m, Still Life, by Christoforos Savva. 150m, Virgin and Child of Liopetri, by Georghios P. Georghiou.

Perf. 13½x14½
1975, Apr. 28   Photo.

436	A134	20m multicolored	.30	.20
437	A134	30m multicolored	.35	.20
438	A134	150m multicolored	1.00	.60
a.		Strip of 3, #436-438	1.75	1.75

Red Cross Flag over Cyprus — A135

Nurse and Nurses Emblem A136

Steatite Female Figure, c. 3000 B.C. — A137

Perf. 12½x13½, 13½x12½
1975, Aug. 4   Litho.   Wmk. 344
439 A135 25m blue green & red   .25   .20
440 A136 30m dp blue & lt grn   .30   .25
441 A137 75m multicolored   .45   .40
    Nos. 439-441 (3)   1.00   .85

Cyprus Red Cross, 25th anniv.; Intl. Nurses' Day 1975; IWY.

Submarine Cable — A138

International Telephone A139

Perf. 12½x13½, 13½x12½
1975, Oct. 13   Litho.
442 A138 50m multicolored   .40   .20
443 A139 100m purple & org   .65   .45

Telecommunications achievements.

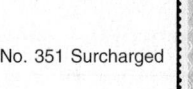

No. 351 Surcharged

1976, Jan. 5   Perf. 12½x13½
444 A104 10m on 3m multi   .45   .45

Vessel in Shape of Woman, 19th Century — A140

Composite Vessel, 2100-2000 B.C. — A141

Europa: 100m, Byzantine goblet, 15th cent.

Perf. 13x14
1976, May 3   Litho.   Wmk. 344
445 A140 20m violet & multi   .35   .20
446 A141 60m gray & multi   .80   .70
447 A140 100m brown & multi   1.60   .95
    Nos. 445-447 (3)   2.75   1.85

Self-help Housing A142

Cyprus Airways Jet — A143

Designs: 25m, Women sewing in front of tents. 30m, Aforestation.

1976, May 3   Perf. 14x13
448 A142 10m multicolored   .20   .20
449 A142 25m multicolored   .20   .20
450 A142 30m multicolored   .20   .20
451 A143 60m multicolored   .40   .40
    Nos. 448-451 (4)   1.00   1.00

Re-activation of the economy.

Terracotta Statue, 7th-6th Centuries B.C. — A144

Bronze Plate with Inscription, Idalion, 5th Century B.C. A145

Designs: 10m, Limestone head of bearded man, 5th cent. B.C. 20m, Gold necklace, Lamboussa, 6th cent. A.D. 25m, Terracotta warrior on horseback, 7th cent. B.C. 30m, Limestone figure, priest of Aphrodite, 5th cent. B.C. 50m, Mycenaean crater, 13th cent. B.C. 60m, Limestone sarcophagus, Amathus, 550-500 B.C. 100m, Gold bracelet, Lamboussa, 6th cent. A.D. 250m, Silver dish, Lamboussa, 6th cent. A.D. 500m, Bronze stand, 12th cent. B.C. £1, Marble statue of Artemis, Larnaca, 4th cent. B.C.

Perf. 12x13½
1976, June 7   Wmk. 344
Size: 22x33mm
452 A144 5m brn & multi   .20   .75
453 A144 10m gray & multi   .20   .65
Size: 24x37mm, 37x24mm
Perf. 13x14, 14x13
454 A144 20m red & multi   .20   .60
455 A144 25m lt brn & blk   .20   .20
456 A144 30m green & multi   .20   .20
457 A145 40m bis gray & blk   .20   .60
458 A145 50m brn & multi   .20   .20
459 A145 60m dk brn & multi   .25   .20
460 A145 100m crim & multi   .40   .60
Size: 28x40mm
Perf. 13x12½
461 A144 250m dk bl & multi   .90   1.50
462 A144 500m yel & multi   1.75   1.75
463 A144 £1 slate & multi   3.75   3.50
    Nos. 452-463 (12)   8.45   10.75

George Washington A146

1976, July 5   Perf. 13x13½
464 A146 100m multicolored   .70   .60

American Bicentennial.

Montreal Olympic Games Emblem — A147

Various Sports A148

100m, like 60m, with different sports.

1976, July 5   Unwmk.   Perf. 14
465 A147 20m yel, blk & dk car   .20   .20
466 A148 60m ultra & multi   .30   .30
467 A148 100m lilac & multi   .50   .50
    Nos. 465-467 (3)   1.00   1.00

21st Olympic Games, Montreal, Canada, July 17-Aug. 1.

Children in Library — A149

Low-cost Housing Development A150

Hands Shielding Eye — A151

Perf. 13½x14, 13x13½
1976, Sept. 27   Litho.   Wmk. 344
468 A149 40m black & multi   .30   .30
469 A150 50m multicolored   .25   .20
470 A151 80m ultra & multi   .45   .35
    Nos. 468-470 (3)   1.00   .85

Books for Children (40m); Habitat, UN Conference on Human Settlements, Vancouver, Canada, May 31-June 11 (50m); World Health Day: Foresight prevents blindness (80m).

Archangel Michael — A152

Christmas: 15m, Archangel Gabriel. 150m, Nativity. Icons in Ayios Neophytis Monastery, 16th century.

1976, Nov. 15   Unwmk.   Perf. 12½
471 A152 10m multicolored   .20   .20
472 A152 15m multicolored   .20   .20
473 A152 150m multicolored   .85   .75
    Nos. 471-473 (3)   1.25   1.15

Landscape, by A. Diamantis — A154

Europa (Paintings): 60m, Trees and Meadow, by T. Kanthos. 120m, Harbor, by V. Ioannides.

Perf. 13½x13
1977, May 2   Litho.   Unwmk.
475 A154 20m multicolored   .30   .20
476 A154 60m multicolored   .70   .40
477 A154 120m multicolored   1.25   .90
    Nos. 475-477 (3)   2.25   1.50

Cyprus No. 196 — A155

Perf. 13x13½
1977, June 13   Litho.   Wmk. 344
478 A155 120m multicolored   .55   .40

25th anniv. of reign of Queen Elizabeth II.

Silver Tetradrachm of Demetrios Poliorcetes — A156

Ancient Coins of Cyprus: 10m, Bronze coin of Emperor Trajan. 60m, Silver Tetradrachm of Ptolemy VIII. 100m, Gold octadrachm of Arsinoe II.

1977, June 13   Unwmk.   Perf. 14
479 A156 10m multicolored   .25   .20
480 A156 40m multicolored   .30   .20
481 A156 60m multicolored   .40   .30
482 A156 100m multicolored   .55   .50
    Nos. 479-482 (4)   1.50   1.20

Archbishop Makarios (1913-1977), Pres. of Cyprus — A157

20m, Archbishop in full vestments. 250m, Head.

Perf. 13x14
1977, Sept. 10   Litho.   Unwmk.
483 A157 20m multicolored   .20   .20
484 A157 60m multicolored   .25   .20
485 A157 250m multicolored   .95   .85
    Nos. 483-485 (3)   1.40   1.25

Handicrafts A158

Sputnik over Earth — A159

Designs: 40m, Map of Cyprus. 60m, Gold medals and sports emblems.

Perf. 13½x12

1977, Oct. 17		**Wmk. 344**	
486	A158	20m multicolored	.20 .20
487	A158	40m multicolored	.20 .20
488	A158	60m multicolored	.25 .25
489	A159	80m multicolored	.35 .30
	Nos. 486-489 (4)		1.00 .95

Revitalization of handicrafts (20m); Man and the biosphere (40m); Gold medals won by secondary school students in France for long jump and 200 meter race (60m); 60th anniv. of Bolshevik Revolution (80m).

Nativity A160

Christmas (Children's Drawings): 10m, Three Kings following the star. 150m, Flight into Egypt.

Perf. 14x13½

1977, Nov. 21		**Litho.**	**Unwmk.**
490	A160	10m multicolored	.20 .20
491	A160	40m multicolored	.20 .20
492	A160	150m multicolored	.60 .55
	Nos. 490-492 (3)		1.00 .95

Demetrios Libertis (1866-1937) — A161

150m, Vasilis Michaelides (1849-1917).

1978, Mar. 6	**Wmk. 344**	**Perf. 14x13**	
493	A161	40m bister & olive	.20 .20
494	A161	150m gray, ver & blk	.60 .55

Cypriot poets.

Chrysorrhogiatissa Monastery — A162

Europa: 75m, Kolossi Castle. 125m, Municipal Library, Paphos.

Perf. 14½x13

1978, Apr. 24		**Litho.**	**Unwmk.**
495	A162	25m multicolored	.30 .20
496	A162	75m multicolored	.80 .40
497	A162	125m multicolored	1.40 .70
	Nos. 495-497 (3)		2.50 1.30

Makarios as Archbishop 1950-1977 A163

"The Great Leader" — A164

Archbishop Makarios: 25m, Exiled, Seychelles, 1956-1957. 50m, President of Cyprus, 1960-1977. 75m, Soldier of Christ. 100m, Freedom fighter.

Perf. 14x14½

1978, Aug. 3		**Litho.**	**Unwmk.**
498	A163	15m multicolored	.20 .20
499	A163	25m multicolored	.20 .20
500	A163	50m multicolored	.25 .25
501	A163	75m multicolored	.35 .35
502	A163	100m multicolored	.50 .50
a.	Strip of 5, #498-502		1.50 1.50

Size: 110x80mm

Imperf

503	A164	300m multicolored	3.50 2.50
	Nos. 498-503 (6)		5.00 4.00

Archbishop Makarios, President of Cyprus.

Blood Cells with Low Hemoglobin A165

Bust of Aristotle A166

Heads and Human Rights Emblem A167

Wilbur and Orville Wright, Flyer I A168

Perf. 13x14, 14x13

1978, Oct. 23		**Unwmk.**	**Litho.**
504	A165	15m multicolored	.20 .20
505	A166	35m multicolored	.20 .20
506	A167	75m black	.35 .35
507	A168	125m multicolored	.50 .50
	Nos. 504-507 (4)		1.25 1.25

Anemia prevention (15m); 2300th birth anniv. of Aristotle (35m); 30th anniv. of Universal Declaration of Human Rights (75m); 75th anniv. of first powered flight (125m).

Kiti Icon Stand — A169

Christmas: 35m, Athienou icon stand. 150m, Omodhos icon stand.

1978, Dec. 4		**Perf. 14x14½**	
508	A169	15m multicolored	.20 .20
509	A169	35m multicolored	.20 .20
510	A169	150m multicolored	.75 .75
	Nos. 508-510 (3)		1.15 1.15

Venus Statue from Soli A170

125m, Birth of Venus, by Botticelli (detail).

1979, Mar. 12	**Litho.**	**Perf. 14x13½**	
511	A170	75m multicolored	.40 .40
512	A170	125m multicolored	.60 .60

Mail Coach, Envelope and Truck A171

Europa: 75m, Old telephone, dish antenna and satellite. 125m, Steamship, jet and envelopes.

1979, Apr. 30	**Litho.**	**Perf. 14x13½**	
513	A171	25m multicolored	.55 .25
514	A171	75m multicolored	.95 .40
515	A171	125m multicolored	2.75 1.00
	Nos. 513-515 (3)		4.25 1.65

Peacock Wrasse A172

Designs: 50m, Black partridge, vert. 75m, Cyprus cedar, vert. 125m, Mule.

Perf. 13½x12½, 12½x13½

1979, June 25		**Litho.**	
516	A172	25m multicolored	.25 .20
517	A172	50m multicolored	.50 .40
518	A172	75m multicolored	.50 .35
519	A172	125m multicolored	.75 .55
	Nos. 516-519 (4)		2.00 1.50

Children Holding Globe, UNESCO Emblem — A173

Dove, Magnifying Glass, Album A174

Lord Kitchener, Map of Cyprus A175

Soccer A177

Rotary Emblem — A178

1979, Oct. 1	**Litho.**	**Perf. 12½**	
520	A173	15m multicolored	.20 .20
521	A174	25m multicolored	.20 .20
522	A175	50m multicolored	.25 .25
523	A176	75m multicolored	.30 .20
524	A177	100m multicolored	.50 .45
525	A178	125m multicolored	.55 .50
	Nos. 520-525 (6)		2.00 1.85

Intl. Bureau of Education, Geneva, 50th anniv.; Cyprus Philatelic Society, 20th anniv.; Horatio Herbert Kitchener's survey of Cyprus, cent.; IYC; European Soccer Assoc., 25th anniv.; Rotary Club of Cyprus, 75th anniv.

Jesus, Icon, 12th Century — A179

Christmas (Icons): 35m, Nativity, 16th cent. 150m, Virgin and Child, 12th cent.

Perf. 13½x14, 13x14

1979, Nov. 5		**Litho.**	
Sizes: 24x37mm; 27x40mm (35m)			
526	A179	15m multicolored	.20 .20
527	A179	35m multicolored	.20 .20
528	A179	150m multicolored	.50 .40
	Nos. 526-528 (3)		.90 .80

Cyprus No. 1, Nicosia Cancel A180

Cyprus Stamp Centenary: 125m, #3, Kyrenia cancel. 175m, #6, Larnaca cancel. 500m, #1-6.

1980, Mar. 17	**Litho.**	**Perf. 14x13**	
529	A180	40m multicolored	.20 .20
530	A180	75m multicolored	.50 .50
531	A180	175m multicolored	.75 .75

Size: 105x85mm

Imperf

532	A180	500m multicolored	2.00 2.00
	Nos. 529-532 (4)		3.45 3.45

Holy Cross, St. Barnabas Church, Ayiasmati — A181

Europa: 125m, Zenon of Citium, Ny Carlsberg Glyptothek, Copenhagen.

1980, Apr. 28		**Perf. 12½**	
533	A181	40m multicolored	.25 .20
534	A181	125m multicolored	.45 .30

Smiling Child, IYC Emblem A176

Sailing, Moscow '80 Emblem A182

1980, June 23   Litho.   Perf. 14x13
535 A182 40m shown .20 .20
536 A182 125m Swimming .40 .40
537 A182 200m Gymnast .70 .70
    Nos. 535-537 (3) 1.30 1.30

22nd Summer Olympic Games, Moscow, July 19-Aug. 3.

Gold Necklace — A183

Clay Amphora — A184

Archaeological finds on Cyprus, 12th cent. B.C. to 3rd cent. A.D. 15m, 40m, 150m, 500m, horiz.

Perf. 13½x14, 14x13½
1980, Sept. 15   Litho.   Wmk. 344
538 A183 10m shown .30 .30
539 A184 15m Bronze cow .30 .30
540 A184 25m shown .30 .30
541 A184 40m Lion, gold ring .40 .40
542 A184 50m Bronze caul-
            dron .40 .40
543 A184 75m Stele 1.50 1.50
544 A184 100m Clay jug 1.10 1.10
545 A184 125m Warrior, terra-
            cotta bust 1.10 1.10
546 A184 150m Lions attack-
            ing bull 1.75 1.75
547 A184 175m Faience and
            enamel vase 1.25 1.25
548 A184 200m Warrior god,
            bronze 1.25 1.25
549 A184 500m Stone bowl 1.25 1.25
550 A183 £1 Ivory plaque 1.50 1.50
551 A183 £2 Leda and the
            swan, mosaic 2.75 2.75
    Nos. 538-551 (14) 15.15 15.15

For surcharges see Nos. 584, 600-611.

Cyprus Flag — A185

Archbishop Makarios — A187

Treaty Signing Establishing Republic, 20th Anniversary — A186

1980, Oct. 1   Perf. 13½x14, 14x13
552 A185 40m multicolored .20 .20
553 A186 125m multicolored .45 .45
554 A187 175m multicolored .65 .65
    Nos. 552-554 (3) 1.30 1.30

Dove and Woman A188

Perf. 14x13
1980, Nov. 29   Litho.   Wmk. 344
555 A188 40m shown .20 .20
556 A188 125m Dove and man .60 .60
  a.   Pair, #555-556 .80 .80

Intl. Palestinian Solidarity Day.

Pulpit, Tripiotis Church, Nicosia — A189

Christmas: 100m, Iconostatis (Holy Door), Panayia Church, Paralimni. 125m, Pulpit, Ayios Lazaros Church, Larnaca.

1980, Nov. 29   Perf. 13½x14
557 A189 25m multicolored .20 .20
    Size: 24x37mm
558 A189 100m multicolored .35 .35
    Size: 21x37mm
559 A189 125m multicolored .45 .45
    Nos. 557-559 (3) 1.00 1.00

Europa Issue 1981

Folk Dance — A190

1981, May 4   Photo.   Perf. 14
560 A190 40m shown .35 .20
561 A190 175m Dance, diff. .75 .50

Self-portrait, by Leonardo Da Vinci — A191

The Last Supper, by Da Vinci — A192

Perf. 13½x14, 12½x13½
1981, June 15   Wmk. 344   Litho.
562 A191 50m shown .40 .30
563 A192 125m shown .85 .70
564 A191 175m Lace pattern, Mi-
            lan Cathedral 1.25 1.00
    Nos. 562-564 (3) 2.50 2.00

Da Vinci's visit to Cyprus, 500th anniv.

Ophrys Kotschyi — A193

Designs: Orchids.

1981, July 6   Perf. 13½x14
565 A193 25m shown .40 .40
566 A193 50m Orchis puntulata .75 .75
567 A193 75m Ophrys argolica
            elegantis 1.10 1.10
568 A193 150m Epipactis vera-
            trifolia 2.00 2.00
  a.   Block of 4, #565-568 4.25 4.25
    Nos. 565-568 (4) 4.25 4.25

Prince Charles and Lady Diana, St. Paul's Cathedral A194

Perf. 14x13
1981, Sept. 28   Wmk. 344
569 A194 200m multicolored 1.00 1.00

Royal wedding.

Heinrich von Stephan (1831-1897), UPU Founder — A195

World Food Day (Oct. 16) A196

Intl. Year of the Disabled A197

European Campaign for Urban Renaissance — A198

1981, Sept. 28
570 A195 25m multicolored .20 .20
571 A196 40m multicolored .20 .20
572 A197 125m multicolored .55 .55
573 A198 150m multicolored .60 .60
    Nos. 570-573 (4) 1.55 1.55

Our Lady of the Angels, Transfiguration Church, Palekhori A199

Christmas (Frescoes): 100m, Christ, Madonna of Arakas Church, Lagoudera, vert.

125m, Baptism of Christ, Our Lady of Assinou Church, Nikitari.

1981, Nov. 16   Perf. 12½
574 A199 25m multicolored .25 .20
575 A199 100m multicolored .65 .35
576 A199 125m multicolored .80 .45
    Nos. 574-576 (3) 1.70 1.00

Bathing Aphrodite, Sculpture, Soloi, 250 B.C. — A200

Design: 175m, Aphrodite Emerging from the Water, by Titian, 16th cent.

Perf. 13½x14
1982, Apr. 12   Litho.   Wmk. 344
577 A200 125m multicolored .90 .70
578 A200 175m multicolored 1.25 1.10

Europa Issue 1982

Liberation by Emperor Nicephorus II Phocas, 965 A.D. A201

Perf. 12½
1982, May 3   Photo.   Unwmk.
579 A201 40m shown .50 .20
580 A201 175m Conversion of
            Sergius Paulus,
            45 A.D. .85 .75

Mosaic Chrismon A202

Cultural Heritage: 125m, King of Palaepaphos (High Priest of Aphrodite), sculpture, vert. 225m, Theseus Struggling with the Minotaur, mosaic.

1982, July 5   Litho.   Wmk. 344
581 A202 50m multicolored .25 .25
582 A202 125m multicolored .70 .70
583 A202 225m multicolored 1.25 1.25
    Nos. 581-583 (3) 2.20 2.20

No. 543 Surcharged
1982, Sept. 6   Litho.   Perf. 13½x14
584 A184 100m on 75m multi .60 .60

Scouting Year A203

Christmas A204

Perf. 13½x12½, 12½x13½
1982, Nov. 8   Wmk. 344
585 A203 100m Emblem, horiz. .50 .50
586 A203 125m Baden-Powell .60 .60
587 A203 175m Camp site, horiz. .80 .80
    Nos. 585-587 (3) 1.90 1.90

Perf. 12½, 13½x14 (100m)
1982, Dec. 6

Designs: 25m, 250m, Christ Giving Holy Communion (bread, 25m: wine, 250m) to the Apostles, St. Neophytos Monastery Church,

Paphos, horiz. 100m, Chalice, Church of St. Savvas, Nicosia.

588	A204	25m multicolored	.20	.20
589	A204	100m multicolored	.40	.40
590	A204	250m multicolored	1.00	1.00
		Nos. 588-590 (3)	1.60	1.60

A204a

1983, Mar. 14   *Perf. 14x13½*

591	A204a	50m Cyprus Forest Industries, Ltd.	.20	.20
592	A204a	125m Mosaic, 3rd cent.	.35	.35
593	A204a	150m Dancers	.45	.45
594	A204a	175m Royal Exhibition Building, Melbourne	.50	.50
		Nos. 591-594 (4)	1.50	1.50

Commonwealth Day.

Europa A205

50m, Cyprosyllabic script funerary stele, 6th cent. B.C. 200m, Copper ore, Enkomi ingot, 1400-1250 BC, bronze jug, 2nd cent.

1983, May 3   **Photo.**   *Perf. 14½x14*

595	A205	50m multicolored	.25	.20
596	A205	200m multicolored	.75	.50

Local Butterflies A206

Wmk. 344

1983, June 28   **Litho.**   *Perf. 12½*

597	A206	60m Pararge aegeria	.50	.50
598	A206	130m Aricia medon	1.00	1.00
599	A206	250m Glaucopsyche paphos	1.90	1.90
		Nos. 597-599 (3)	3.40	3.40

Nos. 538-549 Surcharged

Perf. 13½x14, 14x13½

1983, Oct. 3   **Litho.**   **Wmk. 344**

600	A183	1c on 10m multi	.25	.25
601	A184	2c on 15m multi	.25	.25
602	A184	3c on 25m multi	.25	.25
603	A184	4c on 40m multi	.25	.25
604	A184	5c on 50m multi	.30	.30
605	A184	6c on 75m multi	.30	.30
606	A184	10c on 100m multi	.55	.55
607	A184	13c on 125m multi	.75	.75
608	A184	15c on 150m multi	.90	.90
609	A184	20c on 200m multi	1.25	1.25
610	A184	25c on 175m multi	1.60	1.60
611	A184	50c on 500m multi	2.75	2.75
		Nos. 600-611 (12)	9.40	9.40

Electricity Authority of Cyprus, 30th Anniv. — A207

World Communications Year — A208

Intl. Maritime Org., 25th Anniv. — A209

Universal Declaration of Human Rights, 35th Anniv. — A210

Nicos Kazantzakis, 100th Birth Anniv. — A211

Archbishop Makarios III, 70th Birth Anniv. — A212

1983, Oct. 31   **Litho.**   *Perf. 13½x14*

612	A207	3c multicolored	.20	.20
613	A208	6c multicolored	.20	.20
614	A209	13c multicolored	.40	.40
615	A210	15c multicolored	.45	.45
616	A211	20c multicolored	.65	.65
617	A212	25c multicolored	.80	.80
		Nos. 612-617 (6)	2.70	2.70

Christmas — A213

Designs: 4c, Belfry, St. Lazaros Church, Larnaca. 13c, Belfry, St. Varvara Church, Kaimakli, Nicosia. 20c, Belfry, St. Ioannis Church, Larnaca.

1983, Dec. 12   *Perf. 12½x14*

618	A213	4c multicolored	.25	.25
619	A213	13c multicolored	.75	.75
620	A213	20c multicolored	1.10	1.10
		Nos. 618-620 (3)	2.10	2.10

Waterside Cafe at the Marina, Larnaca — A214

19th Century engravings. Size of 6c: 41x27mm; 75c, 110x85mm.

Perf. 14½x14 (6c), 14, Imperf. (75c)

1984, Mar. 6

621	A214	6c shown	.20	.20
622	A214	20c Bazaar, Larnaca	.65	.65
623	A214	30c East Gate, Nicosia	.95	.95
624	A214	75c St. Lazarus Church Interior, Larnaca	2.50	2.50
		Nos. 621-624 (4)	4.30	4.30

Europa (1959-1984) — A215

1984, Apr. 30   **Wmk. 344**   *Perf. 12½*

625	A215	6c multicolored	.40	.20
626	A215	15c multicolored	.90	.75

1984 Summer Olympics A216

1984, June 18   **Litho.**   *Perf. 14*

627	A216	3c Running	.20	.20
628	A216	4c Olympic column	.20	.20
629	A216	13c Swimming	.60	.60
630	A216	20c Gymnastics	.90	.90
		Nos. 627-630 (4)	1.90	1.90

Turkish Invasion, 10th Anniv. A217

1984, July 20   **Litho.**   *Perf. 14x13½*

631	A217	15c Prisoners, barbed wire	.45	.45
632	A217	20c Map	.60	.60

Cyprus Philatelic Society, 25th Anniv. — A218

Cyprus Soccer Assoc., 50th Anniv. A219

George Papanicolaou (1883-1962), Cancer Researcher — A220

Medieval Map A221

1984, Oct. 15   **Wmk. 344**   *Perf. 12½*

633	A218	6c multicolored	.30	.30
634	A219	10c multicolored	.50	.50
635	A220	15c multicolored	.85	.85
636	A221	25c multicolored	1.60	1.60
		Nos. 633-636 (4)	3.25	3.25

Intl. Symposium of Cyprus Cartography and First Intl. Symposium on Medieval Paleography (25c).

1984, Nov. 26   **Litho.**   *Perf. 12½*

637	A222	4c St. Mark	.30	.30
638	A222	13c Gospel page (St. Mark)	1.00	1.00
639	A222	20c St. Luke	1.50	1.50
		Nos. 637-639 (3)	2.80	2.80

Landscapes — A223

Perf. 15x14, 14x15

1985, Mar. 18   **Litho.**

640	A223	1c Autumn at Platania	.20	.65
641	A223	2c Ayia Napa Monastery	.20	.65
642	A223	3c Phine Village	.20	.65
643	A223	4c Kykko Monastery	.20	.35
644	A223	5c Beach at Makronissos	.20	.20
645	A223	6c Village Street, Omodhos, vert.	.20	.20
646	A223	10c Sea view	.35	.35
647	A223	13c Water sports	.45	.45
648	A223	15c Beach at Protaras	.55	.55
649	A223	20c Forestry, vert.	.65	.65
650	A223	25c Sunrise at Protaras, vert.	1.00	.85
651	A223	30c Village houses, Pera Orinis	1.40	1.00
652	A223	50c Apollo Hylates Sanctuary	2.75	1.25
653	A223	£1 Troodos Mountain, vert.	6.00	2.50
654	A223	£5 Personification of Autumn, Dionyssos House, vert.	21.00	19.00
		Nos. 640-654 (15)	35.35	29.30

For surcharges see Nos. 684-685, 712.

Europa A224

6c, Ceramic figures playing the double flute, lyre and tambourine, 7th-6th cent. B.C. 15c, Cypriot violin, lute, flute, the Fourth Women's Dance from the Cyprus Suite.

1985, May 6   **Litho.**   *Perf. 12½*

655	A224	6c multicolored	.60	.40
656	A224	15c multicolored	1.40	1.10

Republic of Cyprus, 25th Anniv. — A225

UN 40th Anniv. — A229

Natl. Liberation Movement, 30th Anniv. — A226

Christmas — A222

Intl. Youth Year A227

Solon Michaelides (1905-1979), Conductor, European Music Year — A228

Perf. 14½ (#657), 14½x14, 15 (#661)
1985, Sept. 23   Litho.

657 A225 4c multicolored .40 .40
658 A226 6c multicolored .55 .55
659 A227 13c multicolored 1.10 1.10
660 A228 15c multicolored 1.25 1.25
661 A229 20c multicolored 1.60 1.60
    Nos. 657-661 (5) 4.90 4.90

Christmas — A230

Murals of the St. Ioannis Lampadistis Monastery, Kalopanyiotis: 4c, Virgin Mary's Visit to Elizabeth. 13c, The Nativity. 20c, The Candlemas, Church of Our Lady of Assinous, Nikitari.

1985, Nov. 18   Litho.   Perf. 12½

662 A230 4c multicolored .35 .35
663 A230 13c multicolored 1.00 1.00
664 A230 20c multicolored 1.65 1.65
    Nos. 662-664 (3) 3.00 3.00

Hellenistic Platinum Spoon A231

Designs: 20c, Ionian helmet, foot of a sculpture. 25c, Union of Eros and Intellect personified, abstract. 30c, Statue profile.

1986, Feb. 17   Perf. 15x14

665 A231 15c multicolored .90 .90
666 A231 20c multicolored 1.25 1.25
667 A231 25c multicolored 1.60 1.60
668 A231 30c multicolored 2.00 2.00
   a.   Souv. sheet of 4, #665-668 19.00 19.00
    Nos. 665-668 (4) 5.75 5.75

Construction of the New Archaeological Museum, Nicosia. Department of Antiquities, 50th anniv. No. 668a sold for £1.

Europa Issue

Mouflon, Cedar Trees A232

1986, Apr. 28   Litho.   Perf. 14x13

669 A232 7c shown .40 .35
670 A232 17c Flamingos, Larnaca Salt Lake 1.50 1.25

Seashells A233

1986, July 1   Perf. 14x13½

671 A233 5c Chlamys pesfelis .50 .50
672 A233 7c Charonia variegata .60 .60
673 A233 18c Murex brandaris 1.60 1.60
674 A233 25c Cypraea spurca 2.10 2.10
    Nos. 671-674 (4) 4.80 4.80

Overseas Cypriots Year A234

Halley's Comet A235

Anniversaries and events.

Perf. 13½x13
1986, Oct. 13   Litho.   Wmk. 344

675 A234 15c multicolored 1.25 1.25
676 A235 18c shown 1.75 1.75
677 A235 18c Comet tail, Edmond Halley 1.75 1.75
   a.   Pair, #676-677 3.50 3.50
    Nos. 675-677 (3) 4.75 4.75

No. 677a has continuous design.

Road Safety A236

1986, Nov. 10   Perf. 14x13

678 A236 5c Pedestrian crossing .75 .75
679 A236 7c Helmet, motorcycle controls 1.25 1.25
680 A236 18c Seatbelt, rearview mirror 3.00 3.00
    Nos. 678-680 (3) 5.00 5.00

Intl. Peace Year, Christmas A237

Nativity frescoes (details): 5c, Church of Panayia tou Araka. 15c, Church of Panayia tou Moutoulla. 17c, Church of St. Nicholaos tis Steyis.

1986, Nov. 24   Perf. 13½x14

681 A237 5c multicolored .50 .50
682 A237 15c multicolored 1.50 1.50
683 A237 17c multicolored 1.90 1.90
    Nos. 681-683 (3) 3.90 3.90

Nos. 645 and 647 Surcharged

Perf. 14x15, 15x14
1986, Oct. 13   Litho.   Wmk. 344

684 A223 7c on 6c multi 1.10 1.10
685 A223 18c on 13c multi 2.25 2.25

Miniature Sheet

Troodos Churches on UNESCO World Heritage List — A238

Churches and frescoes: a, Assinou, Nikitari. b, Moutoulla, Moutoullas. c, Podithou, Galata. d, Ayios Ioannis Lampadistis, Kalopanayiotis. e, Timios Stavros, Pelentri. f, Stavros Áyiasmati, Platanistasa. g, Archangelos Pedoula, Pedoulas. h, Ayios Nicolaos tis Steyis, Kakopetria. i, Araka, Lagoudera.

Perf. 12½
1987, Apr. 22   Photo.   Unwmk.

686   Sheet of 9 12.00 12.00
   a.-i.   A238 15c any single 1.25 1.25

Europa Issue

Modern Architecture A239

Perf. 14x13½
1987, May 11   Litho.   Wmk. 344

687 A239 7c Central Bank of Cyprus .50 .40
688 A239 18c Cyprus Communications Authority 1.00 .90

Ships Named Kyrenia A240

1987, Oct. 3

689 A240 2c The Kyrenia, Kyrenia Castle .50 .30
690 A240 3c Kyrenia II, Perama Shipyard .70 .75
691 A240 5c Kyrenia II, Paphos .90 .50
692 A240 17c Kyrenia II, NY Harbor 1.90 1.50
    Nos. 689-692 (4) 4.00 3.05

Blood Donation Coordinating Committee, 10th Anniv. — A241

European Campaign for Countryside — A242

TROODOS '87 — A243

Perf. 14x13½
1987, Nov. 2   Litho.   Wmk. 344

693 A241 7c multicolored .60 .55
694 A242 15c multicolored 1.40 1.25
695 A243 20c multicolored 2.00 1.75
    Nos. 693-695 (3) 4.00 3.55

Christmas A244

1987, Nov. 30   Perf. 14

696 A244 5c Babe in a manger .40 .40
697 A244 15c Ornament 1.40 1.40
698 A244 17c Fruit bowl 1.75 1.75
    Nos. 696-698 (3) 3.55 3.55

Cyprus Customs Union in Cooperation with the EEC — A245

Perf. 13x13½
1988, Jan. 11   Wmk. 344

699 A245 15c Natl. and EEC flags 1.25 1.25
700 A245 18c Maps 1.60 1.60

A246

Europa (Communication and transportation): No. 701, Electronic mail (Intelpost). No. 702, Cellular telephone system. No. 703, Cyprus Airways, technology vs. ecology (jet, 3 flamingos). No. 704, Cyprus Airways (jet, 4 flamingos).

1988, May 9   Perf. 14x14½

701 A246 7c multicolored .55 .45
702 A246 7c multicolored .55 .45
   a.   Pair, #701-702 1.25 1.25
703 A246 18c multicolored 2.00 1.50
704 A246 18c multicolored 2.00 1.50
   a.   Pair, #703-704 5.00 5.00
    Nos. 701-704 (4) 5.10 3.90

1988 Summer Olympics, Seoul — A247

Unwmk.
1988, June 27   Photo.   Perf. 12
Granite Paper

705 A247 5c Sailing .45 .30
706 A247 7c Track .50 .50
707 A247 10c Marksmanship .55 .55
708 A247 20c Judo 1.25 1.25
    Nos. 705-708 (4) 2.75 2.60

Non-Aligned Foreign Minister's Conference — A248

Designs: 10c, Natl. coat of arms. 50c, Jawaharlal Nehru, Tito, Gamal Abdel Nasser and Makarios III (1913-77).

Perf. 14x13½
1988, Sept. 5   Litho.   Wmk. 344
709 A248 1c shown   .25 .25
710 A248 10c multicolored   .65 .65
711 A248 50c multicolored   3.00 3.00
 Nos. 709-711 (3)   3.90 3.90

No. 643 Surcharged

1988, Oct. 3   Litho.   Perf. 15x14
712 A223 15c on 4c multi   1.90 1.40

A249

A250

Christmas.

Perf. 13½x14
1988, Nov. 28   Litho.   Wmk. 344
713 A249 5c Candlemas   .45 .25
714 A249 15c Madonna and child   .95 .30
715 A249 17c Adoration of the
           Magi   1.40 1.40
 Nos. 713-715 (3)   2.80 1.95

1988, Dec. 10
716 A250 25c lt ultra & int blue 1.40 1.40
UN Declaration of Human Rights, 40th anniv.

3rd Games of Small European States, Nicosia A251

Perf. 13½
1989, Apr. 10   Litho.   Unwmk.
717 A251 1c Discus   .40 .30
718 A251 5c Javelin   .40 .30
719 A251 15c Wrestling .90 .70
720 A251 18c Running   1.10 1.10
 Size: 110x80mm
 Imperf
721 A251 £1 Mythological wo-
           man, laurel,
           bird   9.00 9.00
 Nos. 717-721 (5)   11.80 11.40

Various Children's Games A252

Perf. 13x13½
1989, May 8   Litho.   Unwmk.
722 A252 7c multi (5 boys)   .85 .75
723 A252 7c multi (6 boys)   .85 .75
 a.   Pair, #722-723   1.90 1.90

724 A252 18c multi (6 boys) 1.25 1.10
725 A252 18c multi (5 boys) 1.25 1.10
 a.   Pair, #724-725   2.75 2.75
 Nos. 722-725 (4)   4.20 3.70
 Europa.

French Revolution, Bicent. — A253

Perf. 11½
1989, July 7   Litho.   Unwmk.
Granite Paper
726 A253 18c multicolored   1.60 1.60

A254

A255

1989, Sept. 4   Perf. 13½
727 A254 15c multicolored   .70 .65
728 A255 30c multicolored   1.50 1.40

15c for Interparliamentary Union, cent. 30c for 9th Non-Aligned Summit Conf., Belgrade.

Apiculture A256

Annivs. & Events — A257

1989, Oct. 15   Perf. 13½x14
729 A256 3c Honeycomb   .55 .30
730 A256 10c Gathering nectar 1.00 .60
731 A256 15c Gathering nectar,
           diff.   1.25 .60
732 A256 18c Queen, worker
           bees   1.50 1.50
 Nos. 729-732 (4)   4.30 3.00

1989, Nov. 13

Designs: 3c, Armenian earthquake. 5c, Cyprus Philatelic Society. 7c, European Cancer Year. 17c, World Food Day.

733 A257 3c multicolored   .40 .40
734 A257 5c multicolored   .55 .30
735 A257 7c multicolored   .95 .95
736 A257 17c multicolored   1.40 1.40
 Nos. 733-736 (4)   3.30 3.05

A258

A259

Mosaics, 3rd-5th Cent. A260

Details: 1c, Winter, from *The Four Seasons*, House of Dionysos. 2c, Personification of Crete, from *Theseus Slaying the Minotaur*, Villa of Theseus. 3c, Centaur and Maenad, from *The Dionysiac Procession*, House of Aion, vert. 4c, *Poseidon and Amymone*, House of Dionysos. 5c, Leda, from *Leda and the Swan*, House of Aion. 7c, Apollon, from *Apollo and Marsyas*, House of Aion. 10c, Hermes and Dionysos, from *Hermes Presenting Dionysos to Tropheus*, House of Aion, vert. 15c, Cassiopeia, from *Cassiopeia and the Nereids*, House of Aion. 18c, Orpheus Playing the Lyre, House of Orpheus. 20c, Nymphs preparing bath, from *Hermes Presenting Dionysos to Tropheus*, vert. 25c, Amazon holding double ax and reins, House of Orpheus, vert. 40c, Doris, one of 3 Nereids in *Cassiopeia and the Nereids*, House of Aion. 50c, Hercules and the lion, from *The First Labor of Hercules*, House of Orpheus. £1, *Apollon and Daphne*, House of Dionysos. £3, Cupid hunting, Villa of Theseus.

Perf. 13, 13x13½ (2c, 4c, 18c, 40c),
13½x13 (3c, 10c, 20c, 25c)
1989, Dec. 29
737 A258 1c multicolored   .60 1.25
738 A259 2c multicolored   .60 1.25
739 A259 3c multicolored   .75 1.50
740 A259 4c multicolored   1.00 1.50
741 A258 5c multicolored   1.00   .30
742 A258 7c multicolored   1.25   .35
743 A259 10c multicolored 1.50   .40
744 A258 15c multicolored 2.50   .65
745 A258 18c multicolored 2.50   .70
746 A259 20c multicolored 3.00 1.10
747 A259 25c multicolored 3.00 1.10
748 A259 40c multicolored 4.25 2.25

Perf. 13½x14
749 A260 50c multicolored   3.25 2.25
750 A260 £1 multicolored   7.00 4.50
751 A260 £3 multicolored   15.00 12.00
 Nos. 737-751 (15)   47.20 31.10

UNESCO World Literacy Year — A261

83rd Interparliamentary Conference, Nicosia — A262

Lions Europa Forum A263

Anniversaries & events.

1990, Apr. 3   Perf. 14x13½
752 A261 15c multicolored   .80 .80
753 A262 17c multicolored   .95 .95
754 A263 18c multicolored 1.25 1.25
 Nos. 752-754 (3)   3.00 3.00

Europa A264

Post Offices.

1990, May 10   Litho.   Perf. 13x13½
755 A264 7c Paphos   1.00 .45
756 A264 18c Limassol City
           Center   1.75 1.25

European Year of Tourism — A265

Designs: 5c, Hotel and Catering Institute, 25th anniv. 7c, Holy Church of St. Lazarus, 1100th anniv. 15c, Female silhouette, butterflies. 18c, Male silhouette, birds.

1990, July 9   Perf. 14
757 A265 5c multicolored   .65 .60
758 A265 7c multicolored   .85 .80
759 A265 15c multicolored 2.25 1.75
760 A265 18c multicolored 2.60 2.60
 Nos. 757-760 (4)   6.35 5.75

Republic of Cyprus, 30th Anniv. A266

1990, Sept. 29   Photo.   Perf. 11½
761 A266 15c Sun   .85 .60
762 A266 17c shown   1.10 .70
763 A266 18c Fish   1.40 .80
764 A266 40c Birds, flowers 3.00 3.00
 Size: 90x90mm
 Imperf
765 A266 £1 Stylized bird 7.00 7.00
 Nos. 761-765 (5)   13.35 12.10

Flowers — A267   Christmas — A268

1990, Nov. 5   Litho.   Perf. 13½x13
766 A267 2c Chionodoxa
           lochiae   .45 .75
767 A267 3c Pancrayium mari-
           timum   .65 .75
768 A267 5c Paeonia mascula .95 .65
769 A267 7c Cyclamen cyprium 1.25 1.00
770 A267 15c Tulipa cypria 2.50 2.25
771 A267 18c Crocus cyprius 2.75 2.75
 Nos. 766-771 (6)   8.55 8.15

1990, Dec. 3   Perf. 13½x14
772 A268 5c Nativity   .90 .30
773 A268 15c Virgin and Child 1.90 .45
774 A268 17c Nativity, diff. 2.25 1.90
 Nos. 772-774 (3)   5.05 2.65

Mosaics From Kanakaria Church — A269

1991, Mar. 28   Photo.   Perf. 12
Granite Paper
775	A269	5c Archangel	.80	.20
776	A269	15c Christ Child	.85	.75
777	A269	17c St. James	1.75	1.75
778	A269	18c St. Matthew	2.00	2.00
		Nos. 775-778 (4)	5.40	4.70

Europa A270

1991, May 6   Litho.   Perf. 13x13½
779	A270	7c Spacecraft Ulysses	.75	.40
780	A270	18c Spacecraft Giotto	1.60	1.10

Oenanthe Cypriaca (Cyprus Wheatear) A271

1991, July 4   Litho.   Perf. 13½
781	A271	5c Juvenile bird	1.25	.50
782	A271	7c Autumn plumage	1.50	.50
783	A271	15c Male bird	1.75	.75
784	A271	30c Female bird	2.75	2.75
		Nos. 781-784 (4)	7.25	4.50

UN High Commissioner for Refugees, 40th Anniv. — A272

1991, Oct. 7   Litho.   Perf. 14x13½
785	A272	5c shown	.40	.25
786	A272	15c Legs	1.50	.75
787	A272	18c Faces	1.90	1.90
		Nos. 785-787 (3)	3.80	2.90

Christmas A273

A274

1991, Nov. 25   Litho.   Perf. 13½
788	A273	5c Nativity scene	.40	.25
789	A273	15c St. Basil	.95	.85
790	A273	17c Baptism of Jesus	1.25	1.25
a.		Strip of 3, #788-790	3.00	3.00
		Strips of 3 are from sheets of 9.		

1992, Apr. 3   Litho.   Perf. 12
Granite Paper
791	A274	10c Swimming	1.10	.60
792	A274	20c Long jump	1.75	1.25
793	A274	30c Running	2.50	2.50
794	A274	35c Discus	2.75	2.75
		Nos. 791-794 (4)	8.10	7.10
		1992 Summer Olympics, Barcelona.		

Expo '92, Seville A275

10th Youth Under 16 European Soccer Tournament — A276

Opening of University of Cyprus A277

1992, Apr. 20   Litho.   Perf. 14
795	A275	20c multicolored	2.00	.95
796	A276	25c multicolored	2.10	1.25
797	A277	30c multicolored	2.10	2.10
		Nos. 795-797 (3)	6.20	4.30

Discovery of America, 500th Anniv. A278

1992, May 29   Litho.   Perf. 13x13½
798	A278	10c Map	1.00	.90
799	A278	10c Embarkation at Palos	1.00	.90
a.		Pair, #798-799	2.25	2.25
800	A278	30c Three ships	1.50	1.25
801	A278	30c Columbus	1.50	1.25
a.		Pair, #800-801	3.25	3.25
		Nos. 798-801 (4)	5.00	4.30
		Europa.		

Reptiles A279

Designs: 7c, Chamaeleo chamaeleon. 10c, Lacerta laevis troodica. 15c, Mauremys caspica. 20c, Coluber cypriensis.

1992, Sept. 14   Litho.   Perf. 14x13½
802	A279	7c multicolored	1.10	.40
803	A279	10c multicolored	1.25	.65
804	A279	15c multicolored	1.75	1.10
805	A279	20c multicolored	2.25	2.25
		Nos. 802-805 (4)	6.35	4.40

Intl. Maritime and Shipping Conference — A280

Unwmk.
1992, Nov. 9   Litho.   Perf. 14
806	A280	50c multicolored	4.50	4.50

Christmas A281

Church wall paintings: 7c, , "Virgin Mary Greeting Elizabeth," Church of Timios Stavros, Pelendri. 15c, "The Virgin and Child," Church of Panayia tou Araka. 20c, "Holy Mother Odigitria," Church of Ayios Nicolaos tis Steyis.

1992, Nov. 9   Perf. 13½x14
807	A281	7c multicolored	.65	.35
808	A281	15c multicolored	1.10	.75
809	A281	20c multicolored	1.75	1.75
		Nos. 807-809 (3)	3.50	2.85

A282

A283

1993, Feb. 15   Litho.   Perf. 14
810	A282	10c multicolored	1.00	.80
		Pancyprian Gymnasium, cent.		

1993, Apr. 3   Perf. 13½x14, 14x13½
Europa: 10c, Bronze sculpture, Motherhood, by N. Dymiotis (1930-1990). 30c, Applique, Motherhood, by Savva (1924-1968), horiz.
811	A283	10c multicolored	.90	.65
812	A283	30c multicolored	1.60	1.25

13th European Cup for Women Athletes A284

Scouting in Cyprus, 80th Anniv. — A285

Water Skiing Moufflon Encouragement Cup — A286

Archbishop Makarios III, 80th Anniv. of Birth — A287

Perf. 13½x14, 14x13½
1993, May 24   Litho.
813	A284	7c multicolored	.60	.40
814	A285	10c multicolored	.80	.55
815	A286	20c multicolored	1.40	1.40
a.		Inscribed "MUFFLON"	25.00	
816	A287	25c multicolored	2.00	2.00
		Nos. 813-816 (4)	4.80	4.35

Fish — A288

1993, Sept. 6   Litho.   Perf. 14x13½
817	A288	7c Holocentrus ruber	.70	.35
818	A288	15c Scorpaena scrofa	1.10	.70
819	A288	20c Serranus scriba	1.25	1.25
820	A288	30c Balistes capriscus	2.40	2.40
		Nos. 817-820 (4)	5.45	4.70

Maritime Cyprus A289

1993, Oct. 4   Perf. 14
821	A289	25c multicolored	2.50	2.50

12th Commonwealth Summit Conference — A290

1993, Oct. 4   Perf. 14x13½
822	A290	35c red brown & tan	2.40	2.40
823	A290	40c olive brown & tan	3.00	3.00

Christmas A291

7c, Carved wooden cross, Stavrovouni Monastery. 20c, Crucifixion, cross from Lefkara Church. 25c, Nativity, cross from Pedoulas Church.

1993, Nov. 22   Litho.   Perf. 13½x14
824	A291	7c multicolored	.40	.30
825	A291	20c multicolored	.95	.95
		Perf. 14x13½		
826	A291	25c multi, horiz.	1.40	1.40
		Nos. 824-826 (3)	2.75	2.65

Copper Industry A292

Europa: 10c, Early smelting of copper. 30c, Map, boat, copper ingot.

1994, Mar. 1   Litho.   Perf. 13x13½
827 A292 10c multicolored   .70 1.90
828 A292 30c multicolored   1.25 1.10

Persons with Special Needs — A293

Intl. Olympic Committee, Cent. — A294

World Gymnasiade, Nicosia — A295

Intl. Year of the Family — A296

1994, May 9   Litho.   Perf. 13
829 A293 7c multicolored   .65   .35
830 A294 15c multicolored   1.10   .65
831 A295 20c multicolored   1.40 1.40
832 A296 25c multicolored   1.75 1.75
    Nos. 829-832 (4)   4.90 4.15

Turkish Invasion and Occupation of Cyprus, 20th Anniv. — A297

1994, June 27   Litho.   Perf. 14
833 A297 10c Human rights   .90   .40
834 A297 50c Cultural heritage 3.50 3.50

Trees — A298

7c, Pinus nigra. 15c, Cedrus libani. 20c, Quercus alnifolia. 30c, Arbutus andrachne.

1994, Oct. 10   Litho.   Perf. 13½
835 A298 7c multicolored   .75   .40
836 A298 15c multicolored   1.25   .80
837 A298 20c multicolored   1.40 1.40
838 A298 30c multicolored   2.10 2.10
    Nos. 835-838 (4)   5.50 4.70

ICAO, 50th Anniv. A299

1994, Nov. 21   Litho.   Perf. 14
839 A299 30c multicolored   3.25 3.25

Christmas A300

Designs: 7c, Virgin Mary (Vlahernitissa). 20c, Nativity. 25c, Archangel Michael.

1994, Nov. 21   Perf. 13½
840 A300 7c multicolored   .90   .50
841 A300 20c multicolored   2.10 1.25
842 A300 25c multicolored   3.00 3.00
    Nos. 840-842 (3)   6.00 4.75

Traditional Costumes — A301

Costumes: 1c, Female, Phapos. 2c, Bridal, Karpess. 3c, Female, Phapos, diff. 5c, Female, Messaoria. 7c, Bridegroom's. 10c, Shepherd's, Messaoria. 15c, Festive female, Nicosia. 20c, Festive female, Karpass. 25c, Female, Mountain-Pitsillia. 30c, Festive female, Karpass, diff. 35c, Rural male. 40c, Plain festive male, Messaoria. 50c, Urban male. £1, Urban festive female, Sarka.

1994, Dec. 27   Litho.   Perf. 13½x13
843 A301 1c multicolored   .40   .40
844 A301 2c multicolored   .60   .60
845 A301 3c multicolored   .65   .65
846 A301 5c multicolored   .80   .80
847 A301 7c multicolored   .85   .85
848 A301 10c multicolored   1.25 1.25
849 A301 15c multicolored   2.10 2.10
850 A301 20c multicolored   2.10 2.10
851 A301 25c multicolored   2.40 2.40
852 A301 30c multicolored   2.40 2.40
853 A301 35c multicolored   2.40 2.40
854 A301 40c multicolored   2.75 2.75
855 A301 50c multicolored   4.25 4.25
856 A301 £1 multicolored   7.75 7.75
    a.   Inscribed "1998"   7.75 7.75
    Nos. 843-856 (14)   30.70 30.70

Third Intl. Congress of Cypriot Studies — A302

Excavations: 20c, Hearth room, Ashlar building, Paliotaverna. 30c, Hall, Agios Demetrios area, Kalavasos. £1, Old Nicosia Archbishorpic building, 18th cent.

1995, Feb. 27   Litho.   Perf. 14
859 A302 20c multicolored   1.40 1.40
860 A302 30c multicolored   2.00 2.00

Size: 107x71mm
Imperf
861 A302 £1 multicolored   6.25 6.25
    Nos. 859-861 (3)   9.65 9.65

A303   A304

Liberation Monument, Nicosia: a, People walking left. b, Statue of Liberty, prisoners leaving prison. c, People walking right.

1995, Mar. 31   Litho.   Perf. 13x14
862   Strip of 3   4.75 4.75
    a.-c. A303 20c any single 1.50 1.50

No. 862 is a continuous design.
Formation of EOKA (Natl. Organization of Cypriot Struggle), 40th anniv.

1995, May 8   Litho.   Perf. 13½
Europa: 10c, Concentration camp prisoners, dove, rainbow, map of Europe. 30c, Prisoner, dove.

863 A304 10c multicolored   1.00   .75
864 A304 30c multicolored   2.00 1.60

Liberation of the concentration camps, 50th anniv.

Health A305

7c, Proper nutrition, exercise. 10c, Fight against AIDS. 15c, Fight against illegal drugs. 20c, Stop smoking campaign.

1995, June 26   Litho.   Perf. 13½
865 A305 7c multi, vert.   .35   .30
866 A305 10c multi   .80   .80
867 A305 15c multi   .85   .85
868 A305 20c multi, vert.   1.25 1.25
    Nos. 865-868 (4)   3.25 3.20

European Cultural Month A306

1995, Sept. 18   Litho.   Perf. 13x13½
869 A306 20c shown   .95   .95
870 A306 25c Map of Europe,
                building   1.25 1.25

Souvenir Sheet

Eurofilex '95 A307

Designs: a, Dove carrying letter, stars. b, Stars, exhibition emblem.

1995, Sept. 18   Litho.   Perf. 14
871   Sheet of 2   9.50 9.50
    a.-b. A307 50c any single 4.25 4.25

A limited number were surcharged £5 on each stamp and sold at "Europhilex '95" on Oct. 27 and 28, 1995.

UN, 50th Anniv. A308

Volleyball, Cent. — A309

European Conservation Year — A310

World Clay Target Shooting Championships — A311

Perf. 13x13½, 13½x13
1995, Oct. 24   Litho.
872 A308 10c multicolored   .70   .70
873 A309 15c multicolored   1.10   .85
874 A310 20c multicolored   1.60 1.25
875 A311 25c multicolored   1.90 1.90
    Nos. 872-875 (4)   5.30 4.70

Christmas A312

Various reliquaries, Kykko Monastery.

1995, Nov. 27   Litho.   Perf. 13½x13
876 A312 7c multicolored   .60   .45
877 A312 20c multicolored   1.40 1.10
878 A312 25c multicolored   1.75 1.75
    Nos. 876-878 (3)   3.75 3.30

A313

A314

A315

Anniversaries and
Events — A316

1996, Jan. 4 Litho. Perf. 13½x13
879	A313	10c multicolored	1.00	.75
880	A314	20c multicolored	1.75	1.25
881	A315	35c multicolored	2.75	2.75
882	A316	40c multicolored	2.75	2.75
	Nos. 879-882 (4)		8.25	7.50

Pancyprian Organization of Large Families, 25th anniv. (#879). Motion pictures, cent. (#880). UNICEF, 50th anniv. (#881). 13th Conf. of Commonwealth Speakers and Presiding Officers (#882).

Portraits of Women
A317   A318

1996, Apr. 8 Litho. Perf. 14
883	A317	10c multicolored	1.10	.50
884	A318	30c multicolored	2.40	1.40

Europa.

1996 Summer Olympics, Atlanta
A319

1996, June 10 Litho. Perf. 13
885	A319	10c High jump	.90	.35
886	A319	20c Javelin	1.25	.70
887	A319	25c Wrestling	1.75	1.00
888	A319	30c Swimming	2.10	2.10
	Nos. 885-888 (4)		6.00	4.15

Mills of
Cyprus — A320

1996, Sept. 23 Litho. Perf. 13
889	A320	10c Watermill	.95	.70
890	A320	15c Olivemill	1.40	1.00
891	A320	20c Windmill	1.50	1.40
892	A320	25c Handmill	2.25	2.25
	Nos. 889-892 (4)		6.10	5.35

Icons, Religious Landmarks
A321

Designs: No. 893, Icon of Our Lady of Iberia, Moscow. No. 894, Holy Monastery of Stavrovouni, Cyprus. No. 895, Icon of St. Nicholas, Cyprus. No. 896, Iveron Mother of God Resurrection Gate, Moscow.

1996, Nov. 13 Litho. Perf. 11½
893	A321	30c multicolored	2.40	2.40
894	A321	30c multicolored	2.40	2.40
895	A321	30c multicolored	2.40	2.40
896	A321	30c multicolored	2.40	2.40
a.	Block of 4, #893-896		10.00	10.00

See Russia No. 6356.

Christmas
A322

Paintings from Church of the Virgin of Asinou: 7c, Detail from Nativity. 20c, Virgin Mary between Archangels Gabriel and Michael. 25c, Christ bestowing blessings, vert.

1996, Dec. 2 Perf. 13x13½, 13½x13
897	A322	7c multicolored	1.00	.50
898	A322	20c multicolored	2.25	1.25
899	A322	25c multicolored	2.75	2.75
	Nos. 897-899 (3)		6.00	4.50

Easter
A323

1997, Mar. 24 Litho. Perf. 13x13½
900	A323	15c The Last Supper	1.50	.75
901	A323	25c The Crucifixion	2.00	2.00

A324

A325

1997, Mar. 24 Perf. 13½x13
902	A324	30c multicolored	4.50	3.75

European Men's Clubs Basketball Cup finals.

1997, May 5 Litho. Perf. 13½x13

Europa (Stories and Legends): 30c, Man in red cape fighting Death, eagle above.
903	A325	15c shown	1.00	.50
904	A325	30c multicolored	2.00	1.10

Insects
A326

10c, Oedipoda miniata. 15c, Acherontia atropos. 25c, Daphnis nerii. 35c, Ascalaphus macaronius.

1997, June 30 Litho. Perf. 13x13½
905	A326	10c multicolored	1.10	.60
906	A326	15c multicolored	1.60	.80
907	A326	25c multicolored	2.25	1.60
908	A326	35c multicolored	2.75	2.75
	Nos. 905-908 (4)		7.70	5.75

Archbishop Makarios III (1913-77), 1st Pres. of Cyprus Republic
A327

1997, Aug. 1 Litho. Perf. 13x13½
909	A327	15c multicolored	1.50	1.50

Christmas
A328

Frescoes from Church of Ayios Ioannis Lambadestis: 10c, Nativity. 25c, Magi on way to Bethlehem. 30c, Flight into Egypt.

1997, Nov. 17 Litho. Perf. 13½x13
910	A328	10c multicolored	.95	.65
911	A328	25c multicolored	2.40	1.40
912	A328	30c multicolored	2.75	2.75
	Nos. 910-912 (3)		6.10	4.80

Minerals
A329

1998, Mar. 9 Litho. Perf. 13x13½
913	A329	10c Green jasper	.60	.40
914	A329	15c Iron pyrite	.90	.65
915	A329	25c Gypsum	1.40	1.40
916	A329	30c Chalcedony	1.75	1.75
	Nos. 913-916 (4)		4.65	4.20

1998 World Cup Soccer
Championships, France — A330

1998, May 4 Litho. Perf. 14
917	A330	35c multicolored	3.25	1.75

Europa
A331

Festivals, holidays: 15c, "Katakklysmos" Larnaca. 30c, People watching proclamation of independence, 1960.

1998, May 4
918	A331	15c multicolored	1.10	.55
919	A331	30c multicolored	2.40	1.60

Ovis Gmelini Ophion
A332

World Wildlife Fund: No. 920, Male, female, calf. No. 921, Group running. No. 922, Male up close. No. 923, Male with front legs up on rock, one grazing.

1998, June 22 Litho. Perf. 13x13½
920	A332	25c multicolored	1.50	1.50
921	A332	25c multicolored	1.50	1.50
922	A332	25c multicolored	1.50	1.50
923	A332	25c multicolored	1.50	1.50
a.	Block of 4, #920-923		6.25	6.25

Issued in sheets of 16.

World Stamp Day
A333

1998, Oct. 9 Litho. Perf. 14
924	A333	30c multicolored	3.00	3.00
a.	Booklet pane of 8		26.00	
	Complete booklet, #924a		29.00	

A334   A335

1998, Oct. 9
925	A334	50c multicolored	2.25	2.25

Universal Declaration of Human Rights, 50th anniv.

1998, Nov. 16 Litho. Perf. 14

Christmas (Scenes from paintings in the Church of the Virgin of Théosképasti, Kalopanayiotis): 10c, The Annunciation. 25c, The Nativity. 30c, Baptism of Christ.
926	A335	10c multicolored	.40	.40
927	A335	25c multicolored	1.10	1.10
928	A335	30c multicolored	3.25	3.25
a.	Souvenir sheet, #926-928		4.75	4.75
	Nos. 926-928 (3)		4.75	4.75

Mushrooms — A336

10c, Pleurotus eryngii. 15c, Lactarius deliciosus. 25c, Sparassis crispa. 30c, Morchella elata.

1999, Mar. 4 Litho. Perf. 13½x13½
929	A336	10c multicolored	.55	.55
930	A336	15c multicolored	1.10	.70
931	A336	25c multicolored	1.60	1.60
932	A336	30c multicolored	1.75	1.75
	Nos. 929-932 (4)		5.00	4.60

Natl. Parks and Nature Preserves
A337

1999, May 6   Litho.   Perf. 14
933 A337 15c Tripylos Reserve   .90   .50
934 A337 30c Lara Reserve   1.60 1.00
a.   Booklet pane, 4 each #933-934   11.00
      Complete booklet, #934a   12.00

Europa.

Council of Europe, 50th Anniv. A338

1999, May 6
935 A338 30c multicolored   2.10 2.10

4000 Years of Hellenism — A339

a, Sanctuary of Apollo Hylates, Kourion. b, Mycenaean "Krater of the Warriors," Athens. c, Mycenaean amphoral krater, Cyprus Museum. d, Sanctuary of Apollo Epikourios, Delphi.

1999, June 28   Litho.   Perf. 13½x13
936 A339 25c Block of 4, #a.-d.   6.25 6.25

See Greece No. 1938.

UPU, 125th Anniv. A340

1999, Sept. 30   Litho.   Perf. 14
937 A340 15c shown   1.25   .90
938 A340 35c "125"   2.75 2.00

Souvenir Sheet

Maritime Cyprus Shipping Conference A341

Cyprus flag and: a, Container ship. b, Binoculars, chart, cap. c, Ship with yellow stripe on tower. d, Tanker.

1999, Sept. 30
939 A341 25c Sheet of 4, #a.-d.   5.50 5.50

Souvenir Sheet

Turkish Invasion of Cyprus, 25th Anniv. — A342

1999, Nov. 11   Litho.   Imperf.
940 A342 30c multicolored   2.75 2.75

A343   A344

1999, Nov. 11   Perf. 14
941 A343 10c Angel   .70   .55
942 A343 25c Magi   1.40 1.25
943 A343 30c Madonna and child 1.60 1.60
      Nos. 941-943 (3)   3.70 3.40

Christmas.

Souvenir Sheet
2000, Mar. 30   Litho.   Perf. 13¼x13
Miss Universe 2000: a, 15c, Woman, stars. b, 35c, Armless nude statue of woman.
944 A344   Sheet of 2, #a.-b.   3.00 3.00

Jewelry — A345

Various pieces of jewelry. #945-952 vert.

2000, Mar. 30   Litho.   Perf. 14
945 A345 10c multi   .45   .45
946 A345 15c multi   .60   .60
947 A345 20c multi   .80   .80
948 A345 25c multi   1.00 1.00
949 A345 30c multi   1.25 1.25
950 A345 35c multi   1.40 1.40
951 A345 40c multi   1.60 1.60
952 A345 50c multi   2.25 2.25
953 A345 75c multi   3.00 3.00
954 A345 £1 multi   4.00 4.00
955 A345 £2 multi   8.00 8.00
956 A345 £3 multi   12.00 12.00
      Nos. 945-956 (12)   36.35 36.35

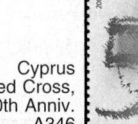

Cyprus Red Cross, 50th Anniv. A346

2000, May 9   Litho.   Perf. 13x13¼
957 A346 15c multi   2.25 2.25

Memorial to Heroes of 1955-59 Independence Struggle — A347

2000, May 9   Perf. 13¼x13
958 A347 15c multi   2.40 2.40

Europa, 2000
Common Design Type
2000, May 9   Perf. 14
959 CD17 30c multi   2.10 1.40

World Meteorological Org., 50th Anniv. — A348

2000, May 9
960 A348 30c multi   2.25 2.25

European Convention of Human Rights, 50th Anniv. A349

2000, June 29   Litho.   Perf. 13x13¼
961 A349 30c multi   3.00 3.00

Churches Damaged Under Turkish Occupation A350

Designs: 10c, Monastery of Antifonitis, Kalograia, vert. 15c, Church of St. Themonianos, Lysi, vert. 25c, Church of Panagia Kanakaria, Lytrhagkomi. 30c, Avgasida Monastery Church, Milia.

Perf. 13¼x13, 13x13¼
2000, June 29
962 A350 10c multi   1.10   .60
963 A350 15c multi   1.50   .80
964 A350 25c multi   2.00 1.60
965 A350 30c multi   2.40 2.40
      Nos. 962-965 (4)   7.00 5.40

2000 Summer Olympics, Sydney A351

Designs: 10c, Archery. 15c, Pommel horse. 25c, Diving. 35c, Trampoline.

2000, Sept. 14   Litho.   Perf. 13x13½
966-969 A351   Set of 4   6.00 6.00

Christmas — A352

Gospel covers: 10c, Annunciation. 25c, Nativity. 30c, Baptism of Jesus.

2000, Nov. 2   Perf. 13½x13
970-972 A352   Set of 3   5.00 5.00

Pavlos Liasides (1901-85), Poet — A353

2001, Mar. 12   Litho.   Perf. 13¼x13
973 A353 13c multi   1.25   .65

Commonwealth Day, 25th Anniv. — A354

2001, Mar. 12   Perf. 13x13¼
974 A354 30c multi   2.75 2.75

UN High Commissioner for Refugees, 50th Anniv. — A355

2001, Mar. 12
975 A355 30c multi   2.50 2.50

Europa A356

Designs: 20c, Bridge over Diarizos River. 30c, Akaki River.

2001, May 3
976-977 A356   Set of 2   4.00 2.00
977a   Booklet pane, 4 each
      #976-977   17.00
      Booklet, #977a   19.00

Crabs A357

Designs: 13c, Parthenope massena. 20c, Calappa granulata. 25c, Ocypode cursor. 30c, Pagurus bernhardus.

2001, June 7
978-981 A357   Set of 4   8.00 8.00

Loukis Akritas (1909-65), Writer A358

Christmas A359

2001, Oct. 25   Litho.   Perf. 13½x13
982 A358 20c multi   2.00   .90

2001, Oct. 25
Holy Monastery of Macheras, 800th anniv.: 13c, Icon of Madonna. 25c, Monastery building. 30c, Crucifix.
983-985 A359   Set of 3   4.50 4.50

Cats — A360

No. 986, 20c: a, Red brown panel. b, Green panel.
No. 987, 25c: a, Dark brown panel. b, Orange brown panel.

2002, Mar. 21 Litho. Perf. 13x13½
Horiz. Pairs, #a-b
986-987 A360 Set of 2 7.25 7.25

Europa — A361

Designs: 20c, Equestrian act. 30c, Tight-rope walker.

2002, May 9 Perf. 13½x13
988-989 A361 Set of 2 4.00 2.00
  a. Booklet pane, 4 each #988-989 17.00 —
      Booklet, #989a 19.00

Medicinal
Plants
A362

Designs: 13c, Myrtus communis. 20c, Lavandula stoechas. 25c, Capparis spinosa. 30c, Ocimum basilicum.

2002, June 13 Perf. 13x13½
990-993 A362 Set of 4 7.25 7.25

Mother Teresa
(1910-97) — A363

2002, Sept. 12 Litho. Perf. 13½x13
994 A363 40c multi 4.00 4.00

Intl. Teachers' Day — A364

No. 995: a, 13c, Blackboard and teachers. b, 30c, Computer and teachers.

2002, Sept. 12 Perf. 13x13½
995 A364 Horiz. pair, #a-b 3.75 3.75

Cyprus-Europhilex 02 Philatelic
Exhibition — A365

No. 996: a, Seal, 490-470 B.C. (red brown background). b, Silver coin of Timoharis, 5th-4th cent B.C. (blue background) c, Silver coin of Stasioikos, 449 B.C. (yellow background).
No. 997: a, Clay oil lamp, 2nd cent. A.D. (olive green background). b, Clay statue of Europa on a bull, 7th-6th cent. B.C. (yellow background). c, Clay oil lamp, 1st cent. B.C. (lilac background)
No. 998: a, 15th cent. map of eastern Crete and western Cyprus, and statue of Aphrodite, 1st cent. B.C. b, Map of eastern Cyprus, and Abduction of Europe, by Francesco di Giorgio.

2002, Sept. 22
996 Horiz. strip of 3 5.25 5.25
  a.-c. A365 20c Any single 1.75 1.75
997 Horiz. strip of 3 7.25 7.25
  a.-c. A365 30c Any single 2.40 2.40
Souvenir Sheet
998 Sheet of 2, #a-b 10.50 10.50
  a.-b. A365 50c Any single 4.00 4.00

Christmas
A366

Wall painting in Church of Metamorphosis Sotiros, Palechori: 13c, Nativity, detail. 25c, Angels, detail. 30c, Entire painting (37x37mm).

Perf. 13x13½, 13¾ (30c)
2002, Nov. 21
999-1001 A366 Set of 3 5.25 5.25

Antique
Automobiles
A367

No. 1002: a, 20c, 1946 Triumph Roadster 1800. b, 25c, 1917 Ford Model T. c, 30c, 1932 Baby Ford.

2003, Mar. 20 Litho. Perf. 13x13½
1002 A367 Vert. strip of 3, #a-c 6.50 6.50

Europa — A368

2003, May 8 Perf. 13½x13
Color of Triangles
1003 A368 20c yellow 1.00 .65
  a. Perf. 13½x13¾ on 3 sides 1.75 1.10
1004 A368 30c red 1.60 1.00
  a. Perf. 13½x13¾ on 3 sides 3.00 1.60
  b. Booklet pane, 4 each
      #1003a-1004a 20.00 —
      Complete booklet, #1004b 24.00

European Ministers
of Education, 7th
Conference — A369

2003, June 12 Litho. Perf. 13½x13
1005 A369 30c multi 2.25 2.25

Worldwide Fund for Nature
(WWF) — A370

Mediterranean horseshoe bat: a, In flight. b, Close-up. c, Hanging from rock. d, With open mouth.

2003, June 12 Perf. 13x13½
1006 A370 25c Block of 4, #a-b 7.50 7.50

Birds of Prey — A371

No. 1007, 20c: a, Eleonora's falcon. b, Eleonora's falcons in flight.
No. 1008, 25c: a, Head of Imperial eagle. b, Imperial eagles in flight.
No. 1009, 30c: a, Owl on branch. b, Owl in flight, eggs.

2003, Sept. 25 Litho. Perf. 14
Horiz. pairs, #a-b
1007-1009 A371 Set of 3 9.50 9.50

Famous
Men
A372

Designs: No. 1010, 5c, Constantinos Spyridakis (1903-76), Education minister. No. 1011, 5c, Tefkros Anthias (1903-68), poet (23x31mm).

Perf. 13x13¼, 13¼x13
2003, Nov. 13
1010-1011 A372 Set of 2 1.60 1.60

Christmas
A373

Details of Nativity icon from church in Kourdali: 13c, Angels. 30c, Three Magi on horses. 40c, Entire icon (37x60mm).

Perf. 13¾x13¼, 13¾x14 (40c)
2003, Nov. 13
1012-1014 A373 Set of 3 5.25 5.25

FIFA (Fédération
Internationale de
Football
Association),
Cent. — A374

Perf. 13¼x13¾
2004, Mar. 11 Litho.
1015 A374 30c multi 2.10 2.10

UEFA (European
Soccer Union),
50th
Anniv. — A375

2004, Mar. 11 Perf. 13¼x13
1016 A375 30c multi 2.10 2.10

Yiannos
Kranidiotis
(1947-99),
Politician
A376

2004, May 1 Perf. 13¼x13½
1017 A376 20c multi 1.25 1.25

Admission to European Union — A377

2004, May 1 Perf. 14¼x14
1018 A377 30c multi 2.10 2.10

Europa
A378

Cliff and: 20c, Amphitheater, ship. 30c, Family at seashore, sculpture

2004, May 1 Perf. 13¾x13¼
1019 A378 20c multi 1.25 .60
  a. Perf. 13⅜ on 3 sides 1.50 .70
1020 A378 30c multi 1.75 .90
  a. Perf. 13⅜ on 3 sides 2.00 1.10
  b. Booklet pane, 4 each #1019a,
      1020a 16.00 —
      Complete booklet, #1020b 18.00

2004 Summer Olympics,
Athens — A379

Designs: 13c, Equestrian. 20c, Runners. 30c, Swimmers. 40c, Athletes, man in robe.

2004, June 10 Litho. Perf. 13¼x13
1021-1024 A379 Set of 4 5.75 5.75

Mammals — A380

No. 1025, 20c — Tursiops truncatus: a, Blue background. b, White background.
No. 1026, 30c — Vulpes vulpes indutus: a, Green background. b, White background.
No. 1027, 40c, Lepus europaeus cyprium: a, Orange brown background. b, White background.

2004, Sept. 9 Litho. Perf. 13¾x13½
Horiz. Pairs, #a-b
1025-1027 A380 Set of 3 13.00 13.00

Georgios
Philippou
Pierides (1904-
99),
Writer — A381

Emilios
Chourmouzios
(1904-73),
Writer — A382

2004, Nov. 11   *Perf. 13¼x13*
1028 A381 5c multi .55 .55
1029 A382 5c multi .55 .55

Christmas
A383

Details from icon depicting the birth of Christ, Monastery of Chrysoroyiatissa: 13c, Angels. 30c, Magi on horseback. 40c, Annunciation, vert. (37x60mm).
£1, Adoration of the Shepherds.

Perf. 13¾x13¼, 13¾x14 (40c)
2004, Nov. 11
1030-1032 A383 Set of 3 6.00 6.00
Souvenir Sheet
Perf. 13¾ on 3 Sides
1033 A383 £1 multi 7.00 7.00
No. 1033 contains one 37x38mm stamp.

Carolina Pelendritou, Swimming Gold Medalist at 2004 Paralympics A384

2005, Mar. 3   Litho.   *Perf. 13¼x13¾*
1034 A384 20c multi 1.40 1.40

Rotary International, Cent. — A385

2005, Mar. 3
1035 A385 40c multi 2.75 2.75

Natl. Organization of Cypriot Struggle (EOKA), 50th Anniv. — A386

2005, Mar. 3
1036 A386 50c multi 2.75 2.75

Europa — A387

Table with food and: 20c, Purple grapes, sailboat. 30c, Green grapes, steamship.

2005, May 5   *Perf. 13½x13*
White Frame All Around
1037 A387 20c multi .90 .90
1038 A387 30c multi 1.40 1.40

Booklet Stamps
White Frame on 3 Sides
Perf. 13½ on 3 Sides
1039 A387 20c multi 1.25 .75
1040 A387 30c multi 1.75 1.25
   a. Horiz. pair, #1039-1040 3.25 2.25
   b. Booklet pane, 4 #1040a 13.50 —
     Complete booklet, #1040b 15.00
   Nos. 1037-1040 (4) 5.30 4.30

Dogs — A388

Designs: 13c, German shepherd. 20c, Hungarian vizsla. 30c, Labrador retriever. 40c, Dalmatian.

2005, June 16   Litho.   *Perf. 13¼*
1041-1044 A388 Set of 4 8.00 8.00
1044a   Booklet pane, #1041-1044 8.50
    Complete booklet, #1044a 8.50

Christmas
A389

Icons: 13c, Annunciation to the Shepherds. 30c, Adoration of the Magi. 40c, Madonna and Child, vert. (38x60mm).

Perf. 13¼, 13¾x14 (40c)
2005, Nov. 10   Litho.
1045-1047 A389 Set of 3 4.25 4.25

Souvenir Sheet

Europa Stamps, 50th Anniv. — A390

No. 1048: a, Cyprus #246. b, Cyprus #202. c, Cyprus #220. d, Cyprus #231.

2006, Feb. 23   Litho.   *Perf. 13¾*
1048 A390 30c Sheet of 4, #a-d 6.00 6.00

Postal Museum, 25th Anniv. A391

2006, Mar. 30   *Perf. 13¾x13¼*
1049 A391 25c multi 1.25 1.25

Rembrandt (1606-69), Painter A392

2006, Mar. 30
1050 A392 40c multi 2.00 2.00

2006 World Cup Soccer Championships, Germany A393

2006, Mar. 30   *Perf. 13¼x13¾*
1051 A393 50c multi 2.50 2.50

Souvenir Sheet

Folk Dances — A394

No. 1052 — Folk dancers from: a, Cyprus. b, India.

2006, Apr. 12   *Perf. 13x13½*
1052 A394 40c Sheet of 2, #a-b 4.00 4.00
   See India No. 2151.

Europa — A395

2006, May 4   *Perf. 13½x13*
1053 A395 30c grn & multi 1.40 1.40
   a. Perf. 13½x13¾ on 3 sides 1.40 1.40
1054 A395 40c red & multi 1.75 1.75
   a. Perf. 13½x13¾ on 3 sides 1.75 1.75
   b. Booklet pane, 4 each #1053a-1054a 13.00 —
     Complete booklet, #1054b 13.00

Organ Transplantation — A396

2006, June 15   Litho.   *Perf. 13¼*
1055 A396 13c multi .65 .65

Fruit — A397

Designs: 20c, Elaeagnus angustifolia. 25c, Mespilus germanica, horiz. 60c, Opuntia ficus barbarica.

Perf. 13¼x13½, 13½x13¼
2006, June 15
1056-1058 A397 Set of 3 5.25 5.25

Fire Trucks A398

Designs: 13c, Bedford water carrier. 20c, Hino pump water tender. 50c, Bedford ladder truck.

2006, Sept. 14   *Perf. 13¾x13¼*
1059-1061 A398 Set of 3 4.25 4.25

Nicos Nicolaides (1884-1956), Writer — A399

2006, Nov. 16   Litho.   *Perf. 13½x13*
1062 A399 5c multi .25 .25

Christmas — A400

Items from Agiou Eleftheriou Church: 13c, Carved wood iconostasis. 30c, Cross. 40c, Bas-relief of cross, spear and sponge.

2006, Nov. 16   *Perf. 13¼x13¾*
1063-1065 A400 Set of 3 4.25 4.25

St. Xenon, the Postman — A401

Litho. & Embossed
2007, Feb. 8   *Imperf.*
1066 A401 £1 multi 4.75 4.75

Echinoderms — A402

No. 1067: a, Antedon mediterranea. b, Centrostephanus longispinus. c, Astropecten jonstoni. d, Ophioderma longicadum.

2007, Feb. 8   Litho.   *Perf. 13¾x13¼*
1067   Horiz. strip of 4 4.75 4.75
   a.-d. A402 25c Any single 1.10 1.10

Motorcycles A403

Designs: 13c, 1972 Triumph Daytona. 20c, 1941 Matchless. 40c, 1940 BSA. 60c, 1939 Ariel Red Hunter.

2007, Mar. 15
1068-1071 A403 Set of 4 6.25 6.25

Treaty of Rome, 50th Anniv. — A404

2007, May 3 Perf. 13¼x13¾
1072 A404 30c multi 1.40 1.40

Europa — A405

Scouting emblem in gold, knot in: 30c, Light blue. 40c, Buff.

Litho. & Embossed With Foil Application
2007, May 3
1073-1074 A405 Set of 2 3.25 3.25
1074a Booklet pane, 4 each #1073-1074, perf. on 3 sides 13.00 —
Complete booklet, #1074a 13.00
Scouting, cent.

Social Insurance, 50th Anniv. — A406

No. 1075: a, Text in Greek. b, Text in English.

2007, June 14 Litho. Perf. 13x13¼
1075 A406 40c Horiz. pair, #a-b 3.75 3.75

Miniature Sheet

Cyprus Throughout the Ages — A407

No. 1076: a, Skeleton of pygmy hippopotamus, 10,000 B.C. b, Stone vessel, 7000 B.C. c, Choirokoitia Settlement, 7000 B.C. d, Female terracotta figurine, 3000 B.C. e, Terracotta vessel, 2000 B.C. f, Greek inscriptions on bronze skewer, 1000 B.C. g, Bird-shaped vessel, 800 B.C. h, Map of ancient kingdoms of Cyprus.

2007, Oct. 2 Perf. 13¾
1076 A407 25c Sheet of 8, #a-h 9.75 9.75
See Nos. 1101, 1116, 1138.

Neoclassical Buildings A408

Designs: 13c, Limassol District Administration Building. 15c, National Bank of Greece Building, Nicosia. 20c, Archaeological Research Unit Building, Nicosia. 30c, National Art Gallery, Nicosia. 40c, Paphos Municipal Library. 50c, A. G. Leventis Foundation Office Building, Nicosia. £1, Limassol Municipal Library. £3, Phaneromeni Gymnasium, Nicosia.

2007, Oct. 2 Perf. 13¾x13½
1077 A408 13c multi .65 .65
1078 A408 15c multi .75 .75
1079 A408 20c multi 1.00 1.00
1080 A408 30c multi 1.50 1.50
1081 A408 40c multi 2.00 2.00
1082 A408 50c multi 2.40 2.40
1083 A408 £1 multi 5.00 5.00
1084 A408 £3 multi 14.50 14.50
Nos. 1077-1084 (8) 27.80 27.80

Christmas — A409

Murals from Chapel of St. Themonianus, Lysi: 13c, Virgin Mary. 30c, Archangel Gabriel. 40c, Christ Pantocrator (35x45mm).

Perf. 14x13¾, 13¾ (40c)
2007, Nov. 15
1085-1087 A409 Set of 3 4.25 4.25

100 Cents = 1 Euro
Souvenir Sheet

Introduction of Euro Currency — A410

No. 1088: a, Statue of Aphrodite, map of Cyprus. b, Sleeping Lady statue.

2008, Jan. 1 Litho. Perf. 13¾
1088 A410 €1 Sheet of 2, #a-b 6.00 6.00
See Malta No. 1329.

Anemone Flowers — A411

Variously colored Anemone coronaria flowers with background colors of: 26c, Blue. 34c, Red. 51c, Green. 68c, Yellow orange.

2008, Mar. 6 Perf. 13¼x13¾
1089-1092 A411 Set of 4 5.50 5.50

Europa — A412

Designs: 51c, Closed and open envelopes. 68c, Envelopes and mail boxes.

2008, May 2 Litho. Perf. 13¼x13¾
1093-1094 A412 Set of 2 3.75 3.75
1094a Booklet pane, 4 each #1093-1094, perf. 13¼x13¾ on 3 sides 15.00 —
Complete booklet, #1094a 15.00

Souvenir Sheet

Fourth Intl. Congress of Cypriot Studies, Nicosia — A413

2008, May 2 Perf. 13¾ on 3 Sides
1095 A413 85c multi 2.75 2.75

12th Francophone Summit, Quebec — A414

2008, June 5 Litho. Perf. 13¾
1096 A414 85c multi 2.75 2.75

2008 Summer Olympics, Beijing A415

Designs: 22c, Sailboarding. 34c, High jump. 43c, Tennis. 51c, Shooting.

2008, June 5 Perf. 13x13¼
1097-1100 A415 Set of 4 4.75 4.75

Cyprus Throughout the Years Type of 2007
Miniature Sheet

No. 1101: a, Coin from Archaic period, 750 B.C.-480 B.C. b, Ship from Archaic period. c, Bust of Kimon the Athenian and ship, Classical period, 480 B.C.-310 B.C. d, Tomb of the Kings, Hellenistic period, 310 B.C.-30 B.C. e, Coin from Hellenistic period. f, Painting of St. Paul from Roman period, 30 B.C.-A.D. 324. g, Bust of Septimus Severus from Roman period. h, Granting of church privileges from Early Byzantine period, 324-841.

2008, Oct. 2 Litho. Perf. 13¾
1101 A407 43c Sheet of 8, #a-h 9.50 9.50

Christmas — A416

Icons from church, Pelendri: 22c, Archangel Gabriel. 51c, Archangel Michael. 68c, Madonna and Child.

2008, Nov. 13 Perf. 13¼x13
1102-1104 A416 Set of 3 3.75 3.75

Cooperative Movement, Cent. A417

2009, Mar. 12 Litho. Perf. 13¾
1105 A417 26c multi .70 .70

Louis Braille (1809-52), Educator of the Blind A418

2009, Mar. 12 Litho. & Embossed
1106 A418 68c multi 1.90 1.90

Introduction of the Euro, 10th Anniv. A419

Reverse of Cyprus: 51c, Cent coin. 68c, 2-euro coin.

2009, Mar. 12 Litho.
1107-1108 A419 Set of 2 3.25 3.25

Intl. Year of Planet Earth — A420

No. 1109: a, Western Hemisphere. b, Eastern Hemisphere.

2009, May 4 Litho. Perf. 13x13¼
1109 A420 51c Horiz. pair, #a-b 3.00 3.00

Europa — A421

Constellations: 51c, Cassiopeia. 68c, Andromeda.

2009, May 4 — Perf. 13¼x13¾

1110-1111	A421	Set of 2	3.50 3.50
1111a	Booklet pane of 8, 4 each #1110-1111, perf. 13¼x13¾ on 3 sides		14.00 —
	Complete booklet, #1111a		14.00 —

Intl. Year of Astronomy.

18th Games of the Small States of Europe, Cyprus — A422

Designs: 22c, Tennis. 34c, Sailing. 43c, Cycling.

2009, June 1 — Litho. — Perf. 13¼x13¾

1112-1114	A422	Set of 3	2.75 2.75

Souvenir Sheet

Cyprus Philatelic Society, 50th Anniv. — A423

Litho. & Embossed With Foil Application

2009, June 1 — Perf. 13¾

1115	A423	85c multi	2.40 2.40

Cyprus Throughout the Years Type of 2007
Miniature Sheet

No. 1116: a, St. Paraskevi Church, 9th cent. b, Monastery of St. John Chrysostom, 1090-1100. c, Lusignan coat of arms, 1192-1489. d, Chronicle of Leontios Machairas, 15th cent. e, Queen Caterina Cornaro cedes Cyprus to Venice, 1489. f, Venetian Walls, Nicosia, 1567-70. g, Ottoman siege of Nicosia, 1570. h, Larnaca Aqueduct, 18th cent.

2009, Sept. 10 — Litho. — Perf. 13¾

1116	A407	43c Sheet of 8, #a-h	10.00 10.00

Domesticated Birds — A424

Designs: 22c, Pigeon. 34c, Turkey. 43c, Rooster. 51c, Duck.

2009, Sept. 10 — Perf. 13¾x13¼

1117-1120	A424	Set of 4	4.50 4.50

European Court of Human Rights, 50th Anniv. A425

2009, Nov. 12 — Litho. — Perf. 13x13¼

1121	A425	51c multi	1.60 1.60

A426

Christmas A427

Design: 68c, Solid silver star.

Perf. 13¼x13¾

2009, Nov. 12 — Litho.

1122	A426	22c shown	.65 .65

Litho. & Embossed With Foil Application

1123	A427	51c shown	1.60 1.60
1124	A427	68c multi	2.10 2.10
		Nos. 1122-1124 (3)	4.35 4.35

Republic of Cyprus, 50th Anniv. A428

Denomination color: 68c, Bister. 85c, Blue.

Litho. & Embossed With Foil Application

2010, Jan. 27 — Perf. 13¾x13¼

1125-1126	A428	Set of 2	4.25 4.25

Expo 2010, Shanghai A429

2010, Mar. 17 — Litho. — Perf. 13x13¼

1127	A429	51c multi	1.40 1.40

2010 World Cup Soccer Championships, South Africa — A430

2010, Mar. 17 — Perf. 13¾

1128	A430	€1.71 multi	4.75 4.75

Barnyard Animals A431

Designs: 22c, Pig. 26c, Sheep. 34c, Goat. 43c, Cow. €1.71, Rabbit.

2010, Mar. 17 — Perf. 13¾x13¼

1129-1133	A431	Set of 5	8.00 8.00

Europa — A432

No. 1134 — Stack of books and: a, Sun, flowers, tree, snails, bees. b, Tree, bees.

2010, May 5 — Perf. 13¼x13¾

1134	A432	51c Horiz. pair, #a-b	2.75 2.75
c.		Booklet pane of 8, 4 each #1134a-1134b, perf. 13¼x13¾ on 3 sides	11.00 —
		Complete booklet, #1134c	11.00 —

Visit of Pope Benedict XVI — A433

2010, June 4 — Perf. 13¾x14¼

1135	A433	51c multi	1.25 1.25

Cyprus Railway — A434

No. 1136 — Locomotive with denomination in: a, Black. b, White. 85c, Train, map of stations.

2010, June 4 — Perf. 13¾x13¼

1136	A434	43c Pair, #a-b	2.10 2.10

Souvenir Sheet

1137	A434	85c multi	2.10 2.10

Cyprus Through the Ages Type of 2007
Miniature Sheet

No. 1138: a, Treaties of Sevres, 1920, and Lausanne, 1923. b, Burnt Government House, 1931. c, Imprisoned graves, 1955-59. d, Statue of Gregoris Afxentiou (1928-57), anticolonialist leader. e, Presidential Palace, 1960. f, Black Summer 1974, painting by Telemachos Kanthou. g, Pres. Tassou Papadopoulos signing Treaty of Accession to the European Union, 2004. h, Flag of Cyprus.

2010, Oct. 1 — Litho. — Perf. 13¾

1138	A407	43c Sheet of 8, #a-h	9.50 9.50

Souvenir Sheet

Viticulture — A435

No. 1139: a, Wine barrels, wine glass. b, Grapes, pitcher.

Perf. 14 on 3 Sides

2010, Nov. 10 — Litho.

1139	A435	51c Sheet of 2, #a-b	2.75 2.75

See Romania No.

Nativity — A436

Christmas Ornament A437

Perf. 13½x13¾

2010, Nov. 10 — Litho.

1140	A436	22c shown	.60 .60

Litho. With Foil Application
Perf. 13¾

1141	A437	51c shown	1.40 1.40
1142	A437	68c Ornament, diff.	1.90 1.90
		Nos. 1140-1142 (3)	3.90 3.90

POSTAL TAX STAMPS

Catalogue values for unused stamps in this section are for Never Hinged items.

Unless otherwise stated, Cyprus postal tax stamps are for the Refugee Fund.

No. 352 Surcharged

Perf. 12x12½

1974, Dec. 2 — Wmk. 344

RA1	A104	10m on 5m multi	.60 .60

Old Woman and Child — PT1

Child and Barbed Wire — PT2

1974, Oct. 1 — Perf. 12½x13½

RA2	PT1	10m gray & black	.50 .50

Perf. 13x12½

1977, Jan. 10 — Litho. — Wmk. 344

RA3	PT2	10m black	.50 .50

Inscribed 1984

1984, June 18 — Perf. 13x12½

RA4	PT2	1c black	.50 .50

There are two types of No. RA4.

Inscribed 1988 — PT3

1988-2007   Perf. 13x12½
Design Size 22x28mm
RA5 PT3 1c black & pale gray   .50   .50
Perf. 11½x12
RA6 PT3 1c Inscribed 1989   .50   .50
RA7 PT3 1c Inscribed 1990   .50   .50
Unwmk.
Perf. 13
RA8 PT3 1c Inscribed 1991   .50   .50
RA9 PT3 1c Inscribed 1992   .50   .50
RA10 PT3 1c Inscribed 1993   .50   .50
RA11 PT3 1c Inscribed 1994   .50   .50
Perf. 14½x13¾
Design Size 21x24.5mm
RA12 PT3 1c Inscribed 1995   .50   .50
RA13 PT3 1c Inscribed 1996   .50   .50
RA14 PT3 1c Inscribed 1997   .50   .50
RA15 PT3 1c Inscribed 1998   .50   .50
RA16 PT3 1c Inscribed 1999   .50   .50
RA17 PT3 1c Inscribed 2000   .50   .50
RA18 PT3 1c Inscribed 2001   .50   .50
Size: 22x27mm
Perf. 12¾
RA19 PT3 1c Inscribed 2002   .50   .50
RA20 PT3 1c Inscribed 2003   .50   .50
Perf. 12¾x13
RA21 PT3 1c Inscribed 2004   .50   .50
RA22 PT3 1c Inscribed 2005   .50   .50
RA23 PT3 1c Inscribed 2006   .50   .50
Perf. 13½x14
RA24 PT3 1c Inscribed 2007   .40   .40
Nos. RA5-RA24 (20)   9.90 9.90

Issued: #RA5, 9/12/88; #RA6, 9/4/89; #RA7, 9/29/90; #RA8, 10/7/91; #RA9, 11/9/92; #RA10, 1993; #RA11, 11/21/94; #RA12, 10/24/95; #RA13, 6/10/96; #RA14, 6/30/97; #RA15, 1998; #RA16, 1999; #RA17, 2000; #RA18, 2001. #RA19, 2002. #RA20, 2003. #RA21, 11/11/04. #RA22, 6/16/05. #RA23, 5/4/06. #RA24, 3/15/07.

Child and Barbed Wire With Denomination in Euro Currency — PT4

2008, Jan. 1   Litho.   Perf. 13½x14
RA25 PT4 2c dk gray & gray   .40   .40

Type of 2008
2009-10   Litho.   Perf. 13½x14
Inscribed "2009"
RA26 PT4 2c blk & lilac gray   .40   .40
Inscribed "2010"
RA27 PT4 2c blk & tan   .40   .40

CYRENAICA
ˌsir-ə-ˈnā-ə-kə

LOCATION — In northern Africa bordering on the Mediterranean Sea
GOVT. — Italian colony
AREA — 75,340 sq. mi.
POP. — 225,000 (approx. 1934)
CAPITAL — Bengasi (Benghazi)

Cyrenaica was an Italian Colony. In 1949 Great Britain granted the Amir of Cyrenaica autonomy in internal affairs. Cyrenaica was incorporated into the kingdom of Libya in 1951.

100 Centesimi = 1 Lira
1000 Milliemes = 1 Pound (1950)

Catalogue values for unused stamps in this country are for Never Hinged items, beginning with Scott 65 in the regular postage section, Scott J1 in the postage due section.

Used values in italics are for postally used stamps. CTO's sell for about the same as unused, hinged stamps.

Watermark

Wmk. 140 — Crown

Propaganda of the Faith Issue

Italy Nos. 143-146 Overprinted

1923, Oct. 24   Wmk. 140   Perf. 14
1 A68 20c ol grn & brn org   11.00   47.50
2 A68 30c claret & brn org   11.00   47.50
3 A68 50c violet & brn org   6.00   55.00
4 A68 1 l blue & brown orange   6.00   75.00
Nos. 1-4 (4)   34.00 225.00
Set, never hinged   80.00

Fascisti Issue

Italy Nos. 159-164 Overprinted in Red or Black

1923, Oct. 29   Unwmk.   Perf. 14
5 A69 10c dk grn (R)   10.00   17.00
6 A69 30c dk vio (R)   10.00   17.00
7 A69 50c brn car   10.00   21.00
Wmk. 140
8 A70 1 l blue   10.00   47.50
9 A70 2 l brown   10.00   55.00
10 A71 5 l blk & bl (R)   10.00   80.00
Nos. 5-10 (6)   60.00 237.50
Set, never hinged   140.00

Manzoni Issue

Italy Nos. 165-170 Overprinted in Red

1924, Apr. 1   Perf. 14
11 A72 10c brn red & blk   12.00   67.50
12 A72 15c bl grn & blk   12.00   67.50
13 A72 30c blk & slate   12.00   67.50
14 A72 50c org brn & blk   12.00   67.50
15 A72 1 l bl & blk   72.50 375.00
   a. Double overprint   1,200.
      Never hinged   1,800.
16 A72 5 l vio & blk   475.00 2,800.
Nos. 11-16 (6)   595.50 3,445.
Set, never hinged   1,500.

Vertical overprints on Nos. 11-14 are essays. On Nos. 15-16 the overprint is vertical at the left.
All examples of No. 15a are poorly centered.

Victor Emmanuel Issue

Italy Nos. 175-177 Overprinted

1925-26   Unwmk.   Perf. 11
17 A78 60c brn car   .85   8.50
18 A78 1 l dark blue   .85   8.50
19 A78 1.25 l dk bl ('26)   3.50   21.00
   a. Perf. 13½   250.00 725.00
      Never hinged   575.00
      Nos. 17-19 (3)   5.20   38.00
Set, never hinged   13.00
Issue dates: Nov. 1925, July 1926.

Saint Francis of Assisi Issue

Italian Stamps of 1926 Overprinted

1926, Apr. 12   Wmk. 140   Perf. 14
20 A79 20c gray green   2.50   13.50
21 A80 40c dark violet   2.50   13.50
22 A81 60c red brown   2.50   24.00

Overprinted in Red

Unwmk.
23 A82 1.25 l dk bl, perf. 11   2.50   34.00
24 A83 5 l + 2.50 l ol grn   6.75   67.50
Nos. 20-24 (5)   16.75 152.50
Set, never hinged   40.00

Volta Issue

Type of Italy 1927, Overprinted

1927, Oct. 10   Wmk. 140   Perf. 14
25 A84 20c purple   6.75   38.00
26 A84 50c dp org   8.50   24.00
27 A84 1.25 l brt bl   13.50   60.00
Nos. 25-27 (3)   28.75 122.00
Set, never hinged   67.50

Monte Cassino Issue

Types of 1929 Issue of Italy, Overprinted in Red or Blue

1929, Oct. 14
28 A96 20c dk grn (R)   6.00   21.00
29 A96 25c red org (Bl)   6.00   21.00
30 A98 50c + 10c crim (Bl)   6.00   24.00
31 A98 75c + 15c ol brn (R)   6.00   24.00
32 A96 1.25 l + 25c dk vio (R)   13.50   42.50
33 A98 5 l + 1 l saph (R)   13.50   47.50

Overprinted in Red

Unwmk.
34 A100 10 l + 2 l gray brn   13.50   67.50
Nos. 28-34 (7)   64.50 247.50
Set, never hinged   157.50

Royal Wedding Issue

Type of Italian Stamps of 1930 Overprinted

1930, Mar. 17   Wmk. 140
35 A101 20c yel grn   1.75   5.00
36 A101 50c + 10c dp org   1.25   8.50
37 A101 1.25 l + 25c rose red   1.25   17.00
Nos. 35-37 (3)   4.25   30.50
Set, never hinged   10.25

Ferrucci Issue

Types of Italian Stamps of 1930, Overprinted in Red or Blue

1930, July 26
38 A102 20c violet (R)   6.00   6.00
39 A103 25c dk grn (R)   6.00   6.00
40 A103 50c black (R)   6.00   12.00
41 A103 1.25 l dp bl (R)   6.00   21.00
42 A104 5 l + 2 l dp car   12.00   39.00
Nos. 38-42 (5)   36.00   84.00
Set, never hinged   90.00

Virgil Issue
Types of Italian Stamps of 1930 Overprinted in Red or Blue

1930, Dec. 4
43 A106 15c vio blk   1.25   10.00
44 A106 20c org brn (Bl)   1.25   4.25
45 A106 25c dk grn   1.25   4.25
46 A106 30c lt brn (Bl)   1.25   4.25
47 A106 50c dl vio   1.25   4.25
48 A106 75c rose red (Bl)   1.25   8.50
49 A106 1.25 l gray bl   1.25   10.00
Unwmk.
50 A106 5 l + 1.50 l dk vio   3.75   47.50
51 A106 10 l + 2.50 l ol brn (Bl)   3.75   72.50
Nos. 43-51 (9)   16.25 165.50
Set, never hinged   39.00

Saint Anthony of Padua Issue
Types of Italian Stamps of 1931 Overprinted in Blue or Red

1931, May 7   Wmk. 140
52 A116 20c brown (Bl)   1.75   21.00
53 A116 25c green (R)   1.75   6.75
54 A118 30c gray brn (Bl)   1.75   6.75
55 A118 50c dl vio (R)   1.75   6.75
56 A120 1.25 l slate bl (R)   1.75   21.00
Overprinted like Nos. 23-24 in Red or Black
Unwmk.
57 A121 75c black (R)   1.75   38.00
58 A122 5 l + 2.50 l dk brn   8.50   77.50
Nos. 52-58 (7)   19.00 177.75
Set, never hinged   46.50

Carabineer
A1

1934, Oct. 16   Photo.   Wmk. 140

59	A1	5c dk ol grn & brn	4.25	21.00
60	A1	10c brn & blk	4.25	21.00
61	A1	20c scar & indigo	4.25	17.00
62	A1	50c pur & brn	4.25	17.00
63	A1	60c org brn & ind	4.25	25.00
64	A1	1.25 l dk bl & grn	4.25	42.50
		Nos. 59-64 (6)	25.50	143.50
		Set, never hinged	60.00	

2nd Colonial Art Exhibition held at Naples.
See Nos. C24-C29.

> Catalogue values for unused stamps in this section, from this point to the end of the section, are for Never Hinged items.

Autonomous State

Senussi Warrior
A2   A3

Perf. 12½

1950, Jan. 16   Unwmk.   Engr.

65	A2	1m dark brown	.65	2.25
66	A2	2m rose car	.85	2.00
67	A2	3m orange	.85	2.00
68	A2	4m dark green	4.25	3.25
69	A2	5m gray	1.10	1.25
70	A2	8m red orange	1.25	1.50
71	A2	10m purple	1.25	1.50
72	A2	12m red	1.25	1.50
73	A2	20m deep blue	1.25	1.50
74	A3	50m choc & ultra	6.75	8.50
75	A3	100m bl blk & car rose	21.00	42.50
76	A3	200m vio & pur	25.00	67.50
77	A3	500m dk grn & org	110.00	135.00
		Nos. 65-77 (13)	175.45	270.25

SEMI-POSTAL STAMPS

Many issues of Italy and Italian Colonies include one or more semipostal denominations. To avoid splitting sets, these issues are generally listed as regular postage unless all values carry a surtax.

Holy Year Issue
Italian Semi-Postal Stamps of 1924 Overprinted in Black or Red

1925, June 1   Wmk. 140   Perf. 12

B1	SP4	20c + 10c dk grn & brn	3.50	24.00
B2	SP4	30c + 15c dk brn & brn	3.50	25.00
B3	SP4	50c + 25c vio & brn	3.50	24.00
B4	SP4	60c + 30c dp rose & brn	3.50	30.00
B5	SP8	1 l + 50c dp bl & vio (R)	3.50	38.00
B6	SP8	5 l + 2.50 l org brn & vio (R)	3.50	55.00
		Nos. B1-B6 (6)	21.00	196.00
		Set, never hinged	48.00	

Colonial Institute Issue

"Peace" Substituting
Spade for
Sword — SP1

1926, June 1   Typo.   Perf. 14

B7	SP1	5c + 5c brown	1.00	10.00
B8	SP1	10c + 5c olive grn	1.00	10.00
B9	SP1	20c + 5c blue grn	1.00	10.00
B10	SP1	40c + 5c brown red	1.00	10.00
B11	SP1	60c + 5c orange	1.00	10.00
B12	SP1	1 l + 5c blue	1.00	21.00
		Nos. B7-B12 (6)	6.00	71.00
		Set, never hinged	15.00	

Surtax for Italian Colonial Institute.

Types of Italian Semi-Postal Stamps of 1926 Overprinted like Nos. 17-19

1927, Apr. 21   Unwmk.   Perf. 11

B13	SP10	40c + 20c dk brn & blk	2.50	38.00
B14	SP10	60c + 30c brn red & ol brn	2.50	38.00
B15	SP10	1.25 l + 60c dp bl & blk	2.50	60.00
a.		Double overprint	1,100.	
		Never hinged	1,600.	
B16	SP10	5 l + 2.50 l dk grn & blk	4.25	85.00
		Nos. B13-B16 (4)	11.75	221.00
		Set, never hinged	30.00	

The surtax on these stamps was for the charitable work of the Voluntary Militia for Italian National Defense.

Allegory of Fascism
and Victory — SP2

1928, Oct. 15   Wmk. 140   Perf. 14

B17	SP2	20c + 5c bl grn	3.50	13.50
B18	SP2	30c + 5c red	3.50	13.50
B19	SP2	50c + 10c purple	3.50	24.00
B20	SP2	1.25 l + 20c dk bl	4.25	30.00
		Nos. B17-B20 (4)	14.75	81.00
		Set, never hinged	36.75	

46th anniv. of the Societa Africana d'Italia. The surtax aided that society.

Types of Italian Semi-Postal Stamps of 1926 Overprinted in Red or Black like Nos. 52-56

1929, Mar. 4   Unwmk.   Perf. 11

B21	SP10	30c + 10c red & blk	4.25	24.00
B22	SP10	50c + 20c vio & blk	4.25	27.50
B23	SP10	1.25 l + 50c brn & bl	5.00	47.50
B24	SP10	5 l + 2 l ol grn & blk (Bk)	5.00	85.00
		Nos. B21-B24 (4)	18.50	184.00
		Set, never hinged	47.50	

Surtax for the charitable work of the Voluntary Militia for Italian Natl. Defense.

Types of Italian Semi-Postal Stamps of 1926 Overprinted in Black or Red like Nos. 52-56

1930, Oct. 20   Perf. 14

B25	SP10	30c + 10c dk grn & bl grn (Bk)	28.00	47.50
B26	SP10	50c + 20c dk grn & vio	28.00	65.00
B27	SP10	1.25 l + 30c ol brn & red	28.00	80.00
B28	SP10	5 l + 1.50 l ind & grn	87.50	225.00
		Nos. B25-B28 (4)	171.50	417.50
		Set, never hinged	400.00	

Surtax for the charitable work of the Voluntary Militia for Italian Natl. Defense.

Sower — SP3

1930, Nov. 27   Photo.   Wmk. 140

B29	SP3	50c + 20c ol brn	4.25	24.00
B30	SP3	1.25 l + 20c dp bl	4.25	24.00
B31	SP3	1.75 l + 20c green	4.25	27.50
B32	SP3	2.55 l + 50c purple	8.00	42.50
B33	SP3	5 l + 1 l dp car	8.00	65.00
		Nos. B29-B33 (5)	28.75	183.00
		Set, never hinged	68.00	

25th anniv. of the Italian Colonial Agricultural Institute. The surtax was for the aid of that institution.

AIR POST STAMPS

Air Post Stamps of Tripolitania, 1931, Overprinted in Blue like Nos. 38-42

1932, Jan. 7   Wmk. 140   Perf. 14

C1	AP1	50c rose car	1.75	.45
C2	AP1	60c dp org	5.00	13.00
C3	AP1	80c dl vio	5.00	21.00
		Nos. C1-C3 (3)	11.75	34.45
		Set, never hinged	29.25	

Air Post Stamps of
Tripolitania, 1931,
Overprinted in Blue

1932, May 12

C4	AP1	50c rose car	1.75	2.10
C5	AP1	80c dull violet	5.00	24.00
		Set, never hinged	16.50	

This overprint was also applied to the 60c, Tripolitania No. C9. The overprinted stamp was never used in Cyrenaica, but was sold at Rome in 1943 by the Postmaster General for the Italian Colonies. Value $10.

Arab on
Camel — AP2

Airplane in
Flight
AP3

1932, Aug. 8   Photo.

C6	AP2	50c purple	13.00	.20
C7	AP2	75c brn rose	13.00	15.00
C8	AP2	80c deep blue	13.00	30.00
C9	AP3	1 l black	5.00	.20
C10	AP3	2 l green	5.00	15.00
C11	AP3	5 l deep car	10.00	30.00
		Nos. C6-C11 (6)	59.00	90.40
		Set, never hinged	140.00	

For surcharges and overprint see #C20-C23.

Graf Zeppelin Issue

Zeppelin
and Clouds
forming
Pegasus
AP4

Zeppelin
and Ancient
Galley
AP5

Zeppelin
and Giant
Bowman
AP6

1933, Apr. 15

C12	AP4	3 l dk brn	11.00	135.00
C13	AP5	5 l purple	11.00	135.00
C14	AP6	10 l dp grn	11.00	250.00
C15	AP5	12 l deep blue	11.00	275.00
C16	AP4	15 l carmine	11.00	275.00
C17	AP6	20 l black	11.00	375.00
		Nos. C12-C17 (6)	66.00	1,445.
		Set, never hinged	160.00	

North Atlantic Crossing Issue

Airplane Squadron and
Constellations — AP7

1933, June 1

C18	AP7	19.75 l grn & dp bl	21.00	700.00
C19	AP7	44.75 l red & indigo	21.00	700.00
		Set, never hinged	100.00	

Type of 1932 Overprinted and Surcharged

1934, Jan. 20

C20	AP3	2 l on 5 l org brn	4.25	87.50
C21	AP3	3 l on 5 l yel grn	4.25	87.50
C22	AP3	5 l ocher	4.25	100.00
C23	AP3	10 l on 5 l rose	6.00	100.00
		Nos. C20-C23 (4)	18.75	375.00
		Set, never hinged	39.00	

For use on mail to be carried on a special flight from Rome to Buenos Aires.

Transport
Plane
AP8

Venus of
Cyrene
AP9

1934, Oct. 9

C24	AP8	25c sl bl & org red	4.25	21.00
C25	AP8	50c dk grn & ind	4.25	17.00
C26	AP8	75c dk brn & org red	4.25	17.00
a.		Imperf.	2,600.	
		Never hinged	3,600.	

C27 AP9 80c org brn & ol
grn | 4.25 | 21.00
C28 AP9 1 l scar & ol grn | 4.25 | 25.00
C29 AP9 2 l dk bl & brn | 4.25 | 42.50
Nos. C24-C29 (6) | 25.50 | 143.50
Set, never hinged | 60.00

2nd Colonial Arts Exhib. held at Naples.

AIR POST SEMI-POSTAL STAMPS

King Victor
Emmanuel
III
SPAP1

Wmk. 104

1934, Nov. 5	Photo.		Perf. 14
CB1 SPAP1 25c + 10c			
gray grn	6.75	25.00
CB2 SPAP1 50c + 10c			
brn	6.75	25.00
CB3 SPAP1 75c + 15c			
rose			
red	6.75	25.00
CB4 SPAP1 80c + 15c			
brn blk	6.75	25.00
CB5 SPAP1 1 l + 20c			
red brn	6.75	25.00
CB6 SPAP1 2 l + 20c brt			
bl	6.75	25.00
CB7 SPAP1 3 l + 25c			
pur	24.00	130.00
CB8 SPAP1 5 l + 25c			
org	24.00	130.00
CB9 SPAP1 10 l + 30c dp			
vio	24.00	130.00
CB10 SPAP1 25 l + 2 l dp			
grn	24.00	130.00
Nos. CB1-CB10 (10)	136.50	670.00
Set, never hinged	336.00

65th birthday of King Victor Emmanuel III
and the non-stop flight, Rome-Mogadiscio.

AIR POST SEMI-POSTAL OFFICIAL STAMP

Type of Air Post Semi-Postal Stamps,
1934, Overprinted Crown and
"SERVIZIO DI STATO" in Black

1934, Nov. 5	Wmk. 140	Perf. 14
CBO1 SPAP1 25 l + 2 l cop		
red		2,750.

POSTAGE DUE STAMPS

Catalogue values for unused
stamps in this section are for
Never Hinged items.

D1

Perf. 12½

1950, July 1	Unwmk.	Engr.
J1 D1 2m dark brown	77.50	110.00
J2 D1 4m deep green	77.50	110.00
J3 D1 8m scarlet	77.50	110.00
J4 D1 10m vermilion	77.50	120.00
J5 D1 20m orange yel	77.50	120.00
J6 D1 40m deep blue	77.50	160.00
J7 D1 100m dark gray	77.50	250.00
Nos. J1-J7 (7)	542.50	980.00

CZECHOSLOVAKIA

‚che-kə-slō-'vä-kē-ə

LOCATION — Central Europe
GOVT. — Republic
AREA — 49,355 sq. mi.
POP. — 15,395,970 (1983 est.)
CAPITAL — Prague

The Czechoslovakian Republic consists of Bohemia, Moravia and Silesia, Slovakia and Ruthenia (Carpatho-Ukraine). In March 1939, a German protectorate was established over Bohemia and Moravia, as well as over Slovakia which had meanwhile declared its independence. Ruthenia was incorporated in the territory of Hungary. These territories were returned to the Czechoslovak Republic in 1945, except for Ruthenia, which was ceded to Russia. Czechoslovakia became a federal state on Jan. 2, 1969. On Jan. 1, 1993 Czechoslovakia separated into Slovakia and the Czech Republic. See Volume 5 for the stamps of Slovakia.

100 Haleru = 1 Koruna

> Catalogue values for unused stamps in this country are for Never Hinged items, beginning with Scott 142 in the regular postage section, B144 in the semi-postal section, Scott C19 in the air post section, Scott EX1 in the personal delivery section, and Scott J58 in the postage due section, Scott O1 int the officials section, and Scott P14 in the newspaper section.

Watermarks

Wmk. 107 —
Linden Leaves
(Vertical)

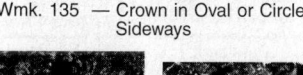
Wmk. 135 — Crown in Oval or Circle, Sideways

Wmk. 136

Wmk. 136a

Wmk. 341 —
Striped Ovals

Stamps of Austria overprinted "Ceskoslovenska Republika," lion and "Cesko Slovensky Stat," "Provisorni Ceskoslovenska Vlada" and Arms, and "Ceskoslovenska Statni Posta" and Arms were made privately. A few of them were passed through the post but all have been pronounced unofficial and unauthorized by the Postmaster General.

During the occupation of part of Northern Hungary by the Czechoslovak forces, stamps of Hungary were overprinted "Cesko Slovenska Posta," "Ceskoslovenska Statni Posta" and Arms, and "Slovenska Posta" and Arms. These stamps were never officially issued though examples have passed the post.

Hradcany at
Prague — A1

1918-19   Unwmk.   Typo.   Imperf.

1	A1	3h red violet	.20	.20
2	A1	5h yellow green	.20	.20
3	A1	10h rose	.20	.20
4	A1	20h bluish green	.20	.20
5	A1	25h deep blue	.25	.20
6	A1	30h bister	.45	.20
7	A1	40h red orange	.45	.20
8	A1	100h brown	1.25	.20
9	A1	200h ultra	2.25	.20
10	A1	400h purple	3.50	.20

On the 3h-40h "Posta Ceskoslovenska" is in white on a colored background; on the higher values the words are in color on a white background.
The 25h in ultramarine was not valid for postage.
Nos. 1-6 exist as tete-beche gutter pairs.
See #368, 1554, 1600. For surcharges see #B130, C1, C4, J15, J19-J20, J22-J23, J30.

Perf. 11½, 13½

13	A1	5h yellow green	.80	.20
a.		Perf. 11 ½x10¾	2.50	.55
14	A1	10h rose	.40	.20
15	A1	20h bluish green	.40	.20
a.		Perf. 11 ½	.40	.20
16	A1	25h deep blue	.40	.20
a.		Perf. 11 ½	1.50	.65
20	A1	200h ultra	4.25	.20
		Nos. 1-10,13-16,20 (15)	15.40	3.00

All values of this issue exist with various private perforations and examples have been used on letters.
The 3h, 30h, 40h, 100h and 400h formerly listed are now known to have been privately perforated.
For overprints see Eastern Silesia Nos. 2, 5, 7-8, 14, 16, 18, 30.

A2

Type II — Sun behind cathedral. Colorless foliage in foreground.
Type III — Without sun. Shaded foliage in foreground.
Type IV — No foliage in foreground. Positions of buildings changed. Letters redrawn.

1919   Imperf.

23	A2	1h dark brown (II)	.20	.20
25	A2	5h blue green (IV)	.40	.20
27	A2	15h red (IV)	.85	.20
29	A2	25h dull violet (IV)	.65	.20
30	A2	50h dull violet (II)	.40	.20
31	A2	50h dark blue (IV)	.40	.20
32	A2	60h orange (III)	1.60	.20
33	A2	75h slate (IV)	1.20	.20
34	A2	80h olive grn (III)	.95	.20

36	A2	120h gray black (IV)	2.50	.35
38	A2	300h dark green (III)	8.00	.65
39	A2	500h red brown (IV)	8.50	.50
40	A2	1000h violet (III)	19.00	.20
a.		1000h bluish violet	42.50	2.40
		Nos. 23-40 (13)	44.65	4.50

For overprints see Eastern Silesia Nos. 1, 3-4, 6, 9-13, 15, 17, 20-21.

1919-20   Perf. 11½, 13¾, 13¾x11½

41	A2	1h dk brown (II)	.20	.20
42	A2	5h blue grn (IV), perf. 13 ½	.75	.20
a.		Perf. 11 ½	25.00	4.00
43	A2	10h yellow grn (IV)	.40	.20
a.		Imperf.	25.00	19.00
b.		Perf. 11¾	13.00	1.25
44	A2	15h red (IV)	.40	.20
a.		Perf. 11 ½x10 ¾	30.00	4.50
b.		Perf. 11 ½x13 ¾	85.00	22.50
c.		Perf. 13¾x10 ¾	125.00	26.00
45	A2	20h rose (IV)	.40	.20
a.		Imperf.	100.00	95.00
46	A2	25h dull vio (IV), perf. 11 ½	.65	.25
a.		Perf. 11 ½x10 ¾	5.00	1.10
b.		Perf. 13¾x10 ¾	175.00	40.00
47	A2	30h red violet (IV)	.35	.20
a.		Imperf.	190.00	190.00
b.		Perf. 13¾x13 ½	550.00	175.00
c.		30h deep violet	.70	.20
d.		As "c," perf. 13¾x13 ½	625.00	190.00
e.		As "c," imperf.	190.00	140.00
50	A2	60h orange (III)	.30	.20
a.		Perf. 13¾x13 ½	25.00	6.25
53	A2	120h gray black (IV)	3.75	.95
		Nos. 41-53 (9)	7.20	2.60

Nos. 43a, 45a, 47a and 47e were imperforate by accident and not issued in quantities as were Nos. 23 to 40.
Rouletted stamps of the preceding issues are said to have been made by a postmaster in a branch post office at Prague, or by private firms, but without authority from the Post Office Department.
The 50, 75, 80, 300, 500 and 1000h have been privately perforated.
Unlisted color varieties of types A1 and A2 were not officially released, and some are printer's waste.
For surcharges and overprints see Nos. B131, C2-C3, C5-C6, J16-J18, J21, J24-J29, J31, J42-J43, Eastern Silesia 22-29.

Pres. Thomas
Garrigue
Masaryk — A4

1920   Perf. 13½

61	A4	125h gray blue	1.50	.20
a.		125h ultramarine	40.00	19.00
62	A4	500h slate, grysh	4.75	2.50
63	A4	1000h blk brn, brnsh	8.00	5.00
		Nos. 61-63 (3)	14.25	7.70

Nos. 61, 61a, 63 imperf. were not regularly issued. Values: unused singles, No. 61 $30; No. 61a $150; No. 62 $30; No. 63 $40.
For surcharge and overprints, see Nos. B131, Eastern Silesia 31-32.

Carrier Pigeon with
Letter — A5

Czechoslovakia
Breaking Chains to
Freedom — A6

Hussite
Priest — A7

Agriculture and
Science — A8

Two types of 40h:
Type I: 9 leaves by woman's hip.
Type II: 10 leaves by woman's hip.

1920   Perf. 14

65	A5	5h dark blue	.20	.20
a.		Perf. 13¾	325.00	150.00
66	A5	10h blue green	.20	.20
a.		Perf. 13¾	225.00	110.00
67	A5	15h red brown	.20	.20
68	A6	20h rose	.20	.20
69	A6	25h lilac brown	.20	.20
70	A6	30h red violet	.20	.20
71	A6	40h red brown (I)	.60	.20
a.		As "b," tête bêche pair	6.75	2.00
b.		Perf. 13 ½	1.50	.20
c.		Type II	.25	.20
72	A6	50h carmine	.50	.20
73	A6	60h dark blue	.50	.20
a.		As "b," tête bêche pair	6.00	4.00
b.		Perf. 13 ½	2.00	.25

Photo.

74	A7	80h purple	.20	.20
75	A7	90h black brown	.30	.20

Typo.

76	A8	100h dark green	1.00	.20
77	A8	200h violet	1.50	.20
78	A8	300h vermilion	3.50	.20
a.		Perf. 13¾x13 ½	7.00	.35
79	A8	400h brown	6.00	.45
80	A8	500h deep green	7.00	.45
a.		Perf. 13¾x13 ½	100.00	5.50
81	A8	600h deep violet	9.00	.45
a.		Perf. 13¾x13 ½	275.00	7.00
		Nos. 65-81 (17)	31.30	4.15

No. 69 has background of horizontal lines.
Imperfs. were not regularly issued.
Nos. 71 and 73 exist as tete-beche gutter pairs.
For surcharges and overprint see Nos. C7-C9, J44-J56.

1920-25   Perf. 14

Two types of 20h:
Type I: Base of 2 is long, interior of 0 is angular.
Type II: Base of 2 is short, interior of 0 is an oval.
Two types of 25h:
Type I: Top of 2 curves up.
Type II: Top of 2 curves down.

82	A5	5h violet	.20	.20
a.		As "b," tête bêche pair	2.00	1.00
b.		Perf. 13 ½	1.00	.35
83	A5	10h olive bister	.20	.20
a.		As "b," tête bêche pair	2.25	1.50
b.		Perf. 13 ½	.80	.20
84	A5	20h deep orange (I)	1.00	.20
a.		As "b," tête bêche pair	30.00	14.00
b.		Perf. 13 ½	6.00	.60
c.		Type II	.20	.20
85	A5	25h blue green (I)	.20	.20
a.		Type II	.20	.20
86	A6	30h deep violet ('25)	3.00	.20
87	A6	50h yellow green	1.00	.20
a.		As "b," tête bêche pair	60.00	27.50
b.		Perf. 13 ½	12.00	.20
88	A6	100h dark brown	1.00	.20
a.		Perf. 13 ½	15.00	.20
89	A6	150h rose	4.50	.50
a.		Perf. 13 ½	80.00	1.10
90	A6	185h orange	3.00	.20
91	A6	250h dark green	5.00	.25
		Nos. 82-91 (10)	19.10	2.35

Imperfs. were not regularly issued.
Nos. 82-84, 87 exist as tete-beche gutter pairs.

Type of 1920 Issue Redrawn

Type I — Rib of leaf below "O" of POSTA is straight and extends to tip. White triangle above book is entirely at left of twig. "P" has a stubby, abnormal appendage.
Type II — Rib is extremely bent; does not reach tip. Triangle extends at right of twig. "P" like Type I.
Type III — Rib of top left leaf is broken in two. Triangle like Type II. "P" has no appendage.

1923   Perf. 13¾, 13¾x13½

92	A8	100h red, yellow, III, perf. 14x13 ½	1.00	.20
a.		Type I, perf. 13¾	1.25	.20
b.		Type I, perf. 13¾x13 ½	1.25	.20
c.		Type II, perf. 13¾	1.50	.20
d.		Type II, perf. 13¾x13 ½	1.50	.20
e.		Type III, perf. 13¾	7.00	.20
93	A8	200h blue, yellow, II, perf. 14	5.00	.20
a.		Type II, perf. 13¾x13 ½	8.50	.25
b.		Type III, perf. 13¾	8.50	.25
c.		Type III, perf. 13¾x13 ½	52.50	.50
94	A8	300h violet, yellow, I, perf. 13¾	3.75	.20
a.		Type II, perf. 13¾	35.00	.50
b.		Type II, perf. 13¾x13 ½	50.00	.50
c.		Type III, perf. 13¾x13 ½	7.00	.20
d.		Type III, perf. 13¾	24.00	.35
		Nos. 92-94 (3)	9.75	.60

President Masaryk
A9   A10

Perf. 13¾x13½, 13¾

1925		Photo.	Wmk. 107
		Size: 19½x23mm	
95	A9	40h brown orange	.75 .20
96	A9	50h olive green	1.50 .20
97	A9	60h red violet	1.75 .20
		Nos. 95-97 (3)	4.00 .60

Distinctive Marks of the Engravings.

I, II, III — Background of horizontal lines in top and bottom tablets. Inscriptions in Roman letters with serifs.

IV — Crossed horizontal and vertical lines in the tablets. Inscriptions in Antique letters without serifs.

I, II, IV — Shading of crossed diagonal lines on the shoulder at the right.

III — Shading of single lines only.

I — "T" of "Posta" over middle of "V" of "Ceskoslovenska." Three short horizontal lines in lower part of "A" of "Ceskoslovenska."

II — "T" over right arm of "V." One short line in "A."

III — "T" as in II. Blank space in lower part of "A."

IV — "T" over left arm of "V."

Wmk. Horizontally (107)
Engr.
I. First Engraving
Size: 19¾x22½mm

98	A10	1k carmine	.85	.20
99	A10	2k deep blue	2.00	.25
100	A10	3k brown	4.00	.65
101	A10	5k blue green	1.40	.45
		Nos. 98-101 (4)	8.25	1.55

Wmk. Vertically (107)
Size: 19¼x23mm

101A	A10	1k carmine	100.00	4.00
101B	A10	2k deep blue	100.00	12.50
101C	A10	3k brown	250.00	12.50
101D	A10	5k blue green	5.00	2.00
		Nos. 101A-101D (4)	455.00	31.00

II. Second Engraving
Wmk. Horizontally (107)
Size: 19x21½mm

102	A10	1k carmine	50.00	.50
103	A10	2k deep blue	3.50	.25
104	A10	3k brown	3.50	.50
		Nos. 102-104 (3)	57.00	1.25

III. Third Engraving
Size: 19-19½x21½-22mm
Perf. 10

105	A10	1k carmine rose	1.00	.20
a.		Perf. 14	15.00	.20

IV. Fourth Engraving
Size: 19x22mm

1926			**Perf. 10**	
106	A10	1k carmine rose	1.00	.20

Perf. 14

| 108 | A10 | 3k brown | 4.50 | .20 |

There is a 2nd type of No. 106: with long mustache. Same values. See No. 130, design SP3.

Karlstein Castle — A11

1926, June 1		Engr.	**Perf. 10**	
109	A11	1.20k red violet	.50	.30
110	A11	1.50k car rose	.30	.20
111	A11	2.50k dark blue	3.00	.30
		Nos. 109-111 (3)	3.80	.80

See Nos. 133, 135.

 Karlstein Castle — A12
Pernstein Castle — A13

 Orava Castle A14
Masaryk A15

 Strahov Monastery — A16

 Hradcany at Prague A17

 Great Tatra — A18

1926-27		Engr.	Wmk. 107	
114	A13	30h gray green	1.25	.20
115	A14	40h red brown	.50	.20
116	A15	50h deep green	.50	.20
117	A15	60h red vio, lil	.85	.20
118	A16	1.20k red violet	4.00	1.50

Perf. 13½

119	A17	2k blue	.75	.20
a.		2k ultramarine	6.00	.75
120	A17	3k deep red	1.50	.20
121	A18	4k brn vio ('27)	4.75	.40
122	A18	5k dk grn ('27)	14.00	2.25
		Nos. 114-122 (9)	28.10	5.35

No. 116 exists in two types. The one with short, straight mustache at left sells for several times as much as that with longer wavy mustache.
See Nos. 137-140.

Coil Stamps
Perf. 10 Vertically

123	A12	20h brick red	.50	.40
a.		Vert. pair, imperf. horiz.	100.00	
124	A13	30h gray green	.35	.20
a.		Vert. pair, imperf. horiz.	100.00	
125	A15	50h deep green	.25	.20
		Nos. 123-125 (3)	1.10	.80

See No. 141.

1927-31		Unwmk.	**Perf. 10**	
126	A13	30h gray green	.25	.20
127	A14	40h deep brown	.70	.20
128	A15	50h deep green	.20	.20
129	A15	60h red violet	.70	.20
130	A10	1k carmine rose	1.10	.20
131	A15	1k deep red	.75	.20
132	A16	1.20k red violet	.40	.20
133	A11	1.50k carmine ('29)	.55	.20
134	A13	2k dp grn ('29)	.60	.20
135	A11	2.50k dark blue	5.50	.30
136	A14	3k red brown ('31)	.60	.20
		Nos. 126-136 (11)	11.25	2.30

No. 130 exists in two types. The one with longer mustache at left sells for several times as much as that with the short mustache.

1927-28			**Perf. 13½**	
137	A17	2k ultra	.85	.20
138	A17	3k deep red ('28)	1.90	.65
139	A18	4k brown violet ('28)	6.00	1.00
140	A18	5k dark green ('28)	6.25	.50
		Nos. 137-140 (4)	15.00	2.35

Coil Stamp

1927			**Perf. 10 Vertically**	
141	A12	20h brick red	.50	.20

> **Catalogue values for unused stamps in this section, from this point to the end of the section, are for Never Hinged items.**

 Hradec Castle A19

 Brno Cathedral A25

 Masaryk — A27

10th anniv. of Czech. independence: 40h, Town Hall, Levoca. 50h, Telephone exchange, Prague. 60h, Town of Jasina. 1k, Hluboka Castle. 1.20k, Pilgrims' House, Velehrad. 2.50k, Great Tatra. 5k, Old City Square, Prague.

1928, Oct. 22			**Perf. 13½**	
142	A19	30h black	.20	.20
143	A19	40h red brown	.25	.25
144	A19	50h dark green	.30	.30
145	A19	60h orange red	.35	.25
146	A19	1k carmine	.50	.50
147	A19	1.20k brown vio	.90	.90
148	A25	2k ultra	1.25	1.25
149	A19	2.50k dark blue	2.75	2.75
150	A27	3k dark brown	2.00	2.00
151	A25	5k deep violet	4.00	4.00
		Nos. 142-151 (10)	12.50	12.50

From one to three sheets each of Nos. 142-148, perf 12½, appeared on the market in the early 1950's.

 Coat of Arms — A29

1929-37			**Perf. 10**	
152	A29	5h dark ultra ('31)	.20	.20
153	A29	10h bister brn ('31)	.20	.20
154	A29	20h red	.20	.20
155	A29	25h green	.20	.20
156	A29	30h red violet	.20	.20
157	A29	40h dk brown ('37)	1.50	.20
a.		40h red brown ('29)	4.00	.20
		Nos. 152-157 (6)	2.50	1.20

Coil Stamp
Perf. 10 Vertically

158	A29	20h red	.20	.20

For overprints, see Bohemia and Moravia Nos. 1-5, Slovakia Nos. 2-6.

 St. Wenceslas A30

 Founding St. Vitus' Cathedral A31

Design: 3k, 5k, St. Wenceslas martyred.

1929, May 14			**Perf. 13½**	
159	A30	50h gray green	.50	.20
160	A30	60h slate violet	.80	.20
161	A31	2k dull blue	1.50	.50
162	A30	3k brown	2.00	.50
163	A30	5k brown violet	7.50	4.00
		Nos. 159-163 (5)	12.30	5.40

Millenary of the death of St. Wenceslas.

 Statue of St. Wenceslas and National Museum, Prague — A33

1929			**Perf. 10**	
164	A33	2.50k deep blue	1.00	.20

 Brno Cathedral A34

 Tatra Mountain Scene A35

Design: 5k, Old City Square, Prague.

1929, Oct. 15			**Perf. 13½**	
165	A34	3k red brown	3.00	.20
166	A35	4k indigo	9.50	.55
167	A35	5k gray green	11.00	.50
		Nos. 165-167 (3)	23.50	1.25

See No. 183.

 A37

Type I

Type II

Two types of 50h:

I — A white space exists across the bottom of the vignette between the coat, shirt and tie and the "HALERU" frame panel.

II — An extra frame line has been added just above the "HALERU" panel which finishes off the coat and tie shading evenly.

1930, Jan. 2			**Perf. 10**	
168	A37	50h myrtle green (II)	.20	.20
a.		Type I	1.25	.20
169	A37	60h brown violet	1.00	.20
170	A37	1k brown red	.40	.20
		Nos. 168-170 (3)	1.60	.60

See No. 234.

Coil Stamp

1931			**Perf. 10 Vertically**	
171	A37	1k brown red	1.25	.65

 President Masaryk — A38

 St. Nicholas' Church, Prague — A39

1930, Mar. 1			**Perf. 13½**	
175	A38	2k gray green	2.00	.50
176	A38	3k red brown	3.25	.50
177	A38	5k slate blue	7.50	2.00
178	A38	10k gray black	20.00	5.00
		Nos. 175-178 (4)	32.75	8.00

Eightieth birthday of President Masaryk. Nos. 175-178 were each issued in sheets with ornamental tabs at the bottom. Value, set with tabs $65.50.

1931, May 15				
183	A39	10k black violet	18.00	3.25

Krivoklat Castle — A40 Krumlov Castle — A42

Design: 4k, Orlik Castle.

1932, Jan. 2 **Perf. 10**
184 A40 3.50k violet 4.50 1.50
185 A40 4k deep blue 4.50 .75
186 A42 5k gray green 5.50 .75
  Nos. 184-186 (3) 14.50 3.00

A43 A44

Miroslav Tyrs — A45

1932, Mar. 16
187 A43 50h yellow green .75 .25
188 A43 1k brown carmine 2.00 .25
189 A44 2k dark blue 12.00 .60
190 A44 3k red brown 17.50 .60
  Nos. 187-190 (4) 32.25 1.70

1933, Feb. 1
191 A45 60h dull violet .30 .20

Miroslav Tyrs (1832-84), founder of the Sokol movement; and the 9th Sokol Congress (#187-190).

First Christian Church at Nitra
A46 A47

1933, June 20
192 A46 50h yellow green .60 .30
193 A47 1k carmine rose 9.00 .60

Prince Pribina who introduced Christianity into Slovakia and founded there the 1st Christian church in A.D. 833.

All gutter pairs are vertical. Values unused: No. 192 $350; No. 193 $10,000.

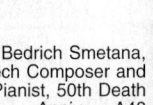

Bedrich Smetana, Czech Composer and Pianist, 50th Death Anniv. — A48

1934, Mar. 26 **Engr.** **Perf. 10**
194 A48 50h yellow green .40 .20

Consecration of Legion Colors at Kiev, Sept. 21, 1914 — A49

Ensign Heyduk with Colors A51 Legionnaires A52

1k, Legion receiving battle flag at Bayonne.

1934, Aug. 15 **Perf. 10**
195 A49 50h green .70 .20
196 A49 1k rose lake .85 .20
197 A51 2k deep blue 3.50 .40
198 A52 3k red brown 6.00 .50
  Nos. 195-198 (4) 11.05 1.30

20th anniv. of the Czechoslovakian Legion which fought in WWI.

Antonin Dvorák, (1841-1904), Composer — A53

1934, Nov. 22
199 A53 50h green .40 .20

Pastoral Scene — A54

1934, Dec. 17 **Perf. 10**
200 A54 1k claret .65 .20
  a. Souv. sheet of 15, perf. 13½ 200.00 300.00
  b. As "a," single stamp 10.00 12.50
201 A54 2k blue 1.75 .65
  a. Souv. sheet of 15, perf. 13½ 1,000. 1,000.
  b. As "a," single stamp 42.50 29.00

Centenary of the National Anthem.
Nos. 200-201 were each issued in sheets of 100 stamps and 12 blank labels.
Nos. 200a & 201a have thick paper, darker shades, no gum. Forgeries exist.

President Masaryk
A55 A56

1935, Mar. 1
202 A55 50h green, buff .35 .20
203 A55 1k claret, buff .40 .20
204 A56 2k gray blue, buff 2.00 .60
205 A56 3k brown, buff 3.25 .60
  Nos. 202-205 (4) 6.00 1.60

85th birthday of President Masaryk.
Nos. 204-205 were each issued in sheets of 100 stamps and 12 blank labels. Value with attached labels: mint $30; used $10.
See No. 235.

Monument to Czech Heroes at Arras, France — A57

1935, May 4
206 A57 1k rose .85 .20
207 A57 2k dull blue 3.00 .75

20th anniversary of the Battle of Arras.
Nos. 206-207 were each issued in sheets of 100 stamps and 12 blank labels. Value, set with attached labels: mint $22.50; used $10.

Gen. Milan Stefánik A58 Sts. Cyril and Methodius A59

1935, May 18
208 A58 50h green .20 .20

1935, June 22
209 A59 50h green .40 .20
210 A59 1k claret .55 .20
211 A59 2k deep blue 2.00 .90
  Nos. 209-211 (3) 2.95 .90

Millenary of the arrival in Moravia of the Apostles Cyril and Methodius.

Masaryk — A60

Statue of Macha, Prague — A61

1935, Oct. 20 **Perf. 12½**
212 A60 1k rose lake .20 .20

No. 212 exists imperforate. See No. 256. For overprints see Bohemia and Moravia Nos. 9-10, Slovakia 12.

1936, Apr. 30
213 A61 50h deep green .20 .20
214 A61 1k rose lake .50 .20

Karel Hynek Macha (1810-1836), Bohemian poet.
Nos. 213-214 were each issued in sheets of 100 stamps and 12 blank labels. Value, set with attached labels: mint $2; used 80c.

Jan Amos Komensky (Comenius) — A61a

Pres. Eduard Benes A62 Gen. Milan Stefánik A63

1936
215 A61a 40h dark blue .20 .20
216 A62 50h dull green .20 .20
217 A63 60h dull violet .20 .20
  Nos. 215-217 (3) .60 .60

See #252, 255. For overprints see Bohemia and Moravia #6, 8, Slovakia 7, 9-11.

Castle Palanok near Mukacevo A64 Town of Banska Bystrica A65

Castle at Zvikov — A66 Ruins of Castle at Strecno — A67

Castle at Cesky Raj A68 Palace at Slavkov (Austerlitz) A69

Statue of King George of Podebrad A70

Town Square at Olomouc — A71

Castle Ruins at Bratislava A72

1936, Aug. 1
218 A64 1.20k rose lilac .20 .20
219 A65 1.50k carmine .20 .20
220 A66 2k dark blue green .20 .20
221 A67 2.50k dark blue .40 .20
222 A68 3k brown .40 .20
223 A69 3.50k dark violet 1.60 .55
224 A70 4k dark violet .65 .20
225 A71 5k green .65 .20
226 A72 10k blue 1.10 .55
  Nos. 218-226 (9) 5.40 2.50

Nos. 224-226 were each issued in sheets of 100 stamps and 12 blank labels. Value, with attached labels: mint $7; used $2.75.
For overprints and surcharge see Nos. 237-238, 254A, Bohemia and Moravia 11-12, 14-19, Slovakia 13-14, 16-23.

President Benes — A73 Soldiers of the Czech Legion — A74

1937, Apr. 26 **Unwmk.** **Perf. 12½**
227 A73 50h deep green .20 .20

For overprints see Nos. 236, Slovakia 8.

1937, June 15
228 A74 50h deep green .20 .20
229 A74 1k rose lake .40 .20

20th anniv. of the Battle of Zborov.
Nos. 228-229 were each issued in sheets of 100 stamps and 12 blank labels. Value, set with attached labels: mint $4; used $2.

Cathedral at Prague — A75　　Jan Evangelista Purkyne — A76

1937, July 1
230 A75　2k green　　　1.00 .20
231 A75　2.50k blue　　1.50 .80
Founding of the "Little Entente," 16th anniv.
Nos. 230-231 were each issued in sheets with blank labels. Value, set with attached labels: mint $22.50; used $11.

1937, Sept. 2
232 A76　50h slate green　　.25 .20
233 A76　1k dull rose　　　.30 .20
150th anniv. of the birth of Purkyne, Czech physiologist.
Nos. 232-233 were printed in sheets of 100 with 12 decorated labels. Value, set with labels, $1.

Masaryk Types of 1930-35
1937, Sept.　　　　**Perf. 12½**
234 A37　50h black　　　.20 .20
With date "14.IX. 1937" in design
235 A56　2k black　　　.30 .20
Death of former President Thomas G. Masaryk on Sept. 14, 1937.
No. 235 was issued in sheets of 100 stamps and 12 inscribed labels. Value, with attached label: mint $1.20; used 60c.

International Labor Bureau Issue

Stamps of 1936-37 Overprinted in Violet or Black

1937, Oct. 6　　　　**Perf. 12½**
236 A73　50h dp green (Bk)　.40 .25
237 A65　1.50k carmine (V)　.40 .25
238 A66　2k dp green (V)　.70 .50
　　Nos. 236-238 (3)　　1.50 1.00

Bratislava Philatelic Exhibition Issue
Souvenir Sheet

A77

1937, Oct. 24　　　　**Perf. 12½**
239 A77　Sheet of 2　　2.50 3.25
　a.　50h dark blue　　.80 1.20
　b.　1k brown carmine　.80 1.20
The stamps show a view of Poprad Lake (50h) and the tomb of General Milan Stefanik (1k).
No. 239 overprinted with the Czechoslovak arms and "Czecho-Slovak Participation New York World's Fair 1939, Czecho-Slovak Pavilion" were privately produced to finance Czechoslovak participation in the exhibition. The overprint exists in black, green, red, blue, gold and silver.
No. 239 overprinted "Liberation de la Tchechoslovaquie, 28-X-1945" etc., was sold at a philatelic exhibition in Brussels, Belgium.

St. Barbara's Church, Kutna Hora — A79　　Peregrine Falcon, Sokol Emblem — A80

1937, Dec. 4
240 A79　1.60k olive green　　.20 .20
For overprints see Bohemia and Moravia Nos. 13, Slovakia 15.

1938, Jan. 21
241 A80　50h deep green　　.20 .20
242 A80　1k rose lake　　.25 .20
10th Intl. Sokol Games.
Nos. 241-242 were each issued in sheets of 100 stamps and 12 inscribed labels. Value, set with attached labels: mint $2; used $1.50.
Imperf. copies of No. 242 are essays.

Legionnaires
A81　　　　A82

Legionnaire — A83

1938
243 A81　50h deep green　　.20 .20
244 A82　50h deep green　　.20 .20
245 A83　50h deep green　　.20 .20
　　Nos. 243-245 (3)　　.60 .60
20th anniv. of the Battle of Bachmac, Vouziers and Doss Alto.
Nos. 243-245 were each issued in sheets of 100 stamps and 12 inscribed labels. Value, set with attached labels $1.25, mint or used.

Jindrich Fügner, Co-Founder of Sokol Movement — A84

1938, June 18　　　　**Perf. 12½**
246 A84　50h deep green　　.20 .20
247 A84　1k rose lake　　.20 .20
248 A84　2k slate blue　　.40 .20
　　Nos. 246-248 (3)　　.80 .60
10th Sokol Summer Games.
Nos. 246-248 were each issued in sheets of 100 stamps and 12 inscribed labels. Value, set with attached labels: mint $2.50; used $2.

View of Pilsen — A85　　Cathedral of Kosice — A86

1938, June 24
249 A85　50h deep green　　.20 .20
Provincial Economic Council meeting, Pilsen.

No. 249 was issued in sheets of 150 stamps and 10 labels depicting a flower within a cogwheel. Value, with attached label 40c, mint or used.
For overprint see Bohemia & Moravia #7.

1938, July 15　　　　**Perf. 12½**
250 A86　50h deep green　　.20 .20
Kosice Cultural Exhibition.

Prague Philatelic Exhibition Issue
Souvenir Sheet

Vysehrad Castle — Hradcany — A87

1938, June 26　　　　**Perf. 12½**
251 A87　Sheet of 2　　5.00 5.00
　a.　50h dark blue　　1.50 1.50
　b.　1k deep carmine　1.50 1.50
　　　See No. 3036.

Stefánik Type of 1936
1938, Nov. 21
252 A63　50h deep green　　.20 .20

Allegory of the Republic — A89

1938, Dec. 19　　　　**Unwmk.**
253 A89　2k lt ultra　　.30 .20
254 A89　3k pale brown　　.50 .40
20th anniv. of Independence.
Nos. 253-254 were each issued in sheets of 100 stamps and 12 blank labels. Value, set with attached labels $2.50, mint or used.
See No. B153.

"Wir sind frei!"
Stamps of Czechoslovakia, 1918-37, overprinted with a swastika in black or red and "Wir sind frei!" were issued locally and unofficially in 1938 as Czech authorities were evacuating and German authorities arriving. They appeared in the towns of Asch, Karlsbad, Reichenberg-Maffersdorf, Rumburg, etc.
The overprint, sometimes including a surcharge or the town name (as in Karlsbad), exists on many values of postage, air post, semi-postal, postage due and newspaper stamps.

No. 226 Surcharged in Orange Red

1939, Jan. 18　Unwmk.　Perf. 12½
254A A72　300h on 10k blue　1.25 1.60
Opening of the Slovakian Parliament.
No. 254A was issued in sheets of 100 stamps with 12 blank labels. Value, set with attached labels, mint $4.

View of Jasina — A89a

Perf. 12½
1939, Mar. 15　Engr.　Unwmk.
254B A89a　3k ultra　25.00 90.00
Inauguration of the Carpatho-Ukraine Diet, Mar. 2, 1939.
Printed for use in the province of Carpatho-Ukraine but issued in Prague at the same time.
Used value is for red commemorative cancel.

The stamps formerly listed as Czechoslovakia Nos. 255, 256 and C18 are now listed with Bohemia and Moravia and Slovakia. No. 255 is now Slovakia 23A. No. 256 and C18 are now listed as Bohemia and Moravia 1A and C1, respectively.

Masaryk Type of 1935 with hyphen in Cesko-Slovensko
1939, Apr. 23
256 A60　1k rose lake　　.20 .20

Linden Leaves and Buds — A90

1945　　**Photo.**　　**Perf. 14**
256A A90　10h black　　.20 .20
257 A90　30h yellow brown　.20 .20
258 A90　50h dark green　.20 .20
258A A90　60h dark blue　.20 .20
Engr.
(Buds Open)
Perf. 12½
259 A90　60h blue　　.20 .20
259A A90　80h orange ver　.20 .20
260 A90　1.20k rose　　.20 .20
261 A90　3k violet brown　.20 .20
262 A90　5k green　　.20 .20
　　Nos. 256A-262 (9)　1.80 1.80
Compare with Bohemia-Moravia type A1.

Thomas G. Masaryk — A91　　Coat of Arms — A92

1945-46　　**Photo.**　　**Perf. 12**
262A A91　5h dull violet ('46)　.20 .20
262B A91　10h orange yel ('46)　.20 .20
262C A91　20h dk brown ('46)　.20 .20
263 A91　50h brt green　.20 .20
264 A91　1k orange red　.20 .20
265 A91　2k chalky blue　.25 .25
　　Nos. 262A-265 (6)　1.25 1.25

1945　　　　**Imperf.**
266 A92　50h olive gray　.20 .20
267 A92　1k brt red vio　.20 .20
268 A92　1.50k dk carmine　.20 .20
269 A92　2k deep blue　.20 .20
269A A92　2.40k henna brn　.30 .20
270 A92　3k brown　　.20 .20
270A A92　4k dk slate grn　.20 .20
271 A92　6k violet blue　.25 .20
271A A92　10k sepia　　.40 .20
　　Nos. 266-271A (9)　2.15 1.80
Nos. 266, 268, 269, 270 and 271 exist in 2 printings. Stamps of the 1st printing have a coarse impression and are on thin, hard paper in sheets of 100; all values exist in the 2nd printing, with fine impressions on thick, soft wove paper in sheets of 200. Values are the same.

Staff Capt. Ridky (British Army) — A93

Dr. Miroslav Novak (French Army) — A94

Capt. Otakar Jaros (Russian Army) — A95

Staff Capt. Stanislav Zimprich (Foreign Legion) — A96

2nd Lt. Jiri Kral (French Air Force) A97

Josef Gabcik (Parachutist) A98

Staff Capt. Alois Vasatko (Royal Air Force) A99

Private Frantisek Adamek (British Colonial Service) A100

1945, Aug. 18   Engr.   Perf. 11½x12½

272	A93	5h intense blue	.20	.20
273	A94	10h dark brown	.20	.20
274	A95	20h brick red	.20	.20
275	A96	25h rose red	.20	.20
276	A97	30h purple	.20	.20
277	A98	40h sepia	.20	.20
278	A99	50h dark olive	.20	.20
279	A100	60h violet	.20	.20
280	A93	1k carmine	.20	.20
281	A94	1.50k lake	.20	.20
282	A95	2k ultra	.20	.20
283	A96	2.50k deep violet	.20	.20
284	A97	3k sepia	.20	.20
285	A98	4k rose lilac	.20	.20
286	A99	5k myrtle green	.20	.20
287	A100	10k brt ultra	.65	.20
		Nos. 272-287 (16)	3.65	3.20

Flags of Russia, Great Britain, US and Czechoslovakia — A101

View of Banská Bystrica A102

Patriot Welcoming Russian Soldier, Turciansky A103

Ruins of Castle at Sklabina A104

Czech Patriot, Strecno A105

1945, Aug. 29   Photo.   Perf. 10

288	A101	1.50k brt carmine	.20	.20
289	A102	2k brt blue	.20	.20
290	A103	4k dark brown	.20	.20
291	A104	4.50k purple	.25	.25
292	A105	5k deep green	.50	.50
		Nos. 288-292 (5)	1.35	1.35

National uprising against the Germans. A card contains one each of Nos. 288-292 on thin cardboard, ungummed. Size: 148x210mm. Sold for 50k. Value, $20 unused, $100 used.

A106   A107

A108

Stefánik — Benes — Masaryk — A108

1945-47   Engr.   Perf. 12, 12½

293	A106	30h rose violet	.20	.20
294	A107	60h blue	.20	.20
294A	A106	1k red org ('47)	.20	.20
295	A108	1.20k car rose	.20	.20
295A	A108	1.20(k) rose lil ('46)	.20	.20
296	A106	2.40(k) rose	.20	.20
297	A107	3k red violet	.20	.20
297A	A108	4k dark blue ('46)	.20	.20
298	A108	5k Prus green	.20	.20
299	A107	7k gray	.20	.20
300	A106	10k gray blue	.35	.20
300A	A106	20k sepia ('46)	.75	.20
		Nos. 293-300A (12)	3.10	2.40

1945   Photo.   Perf. 14

301	A108	50h brown	.20	.20
302	A106	80h dark green	.20	.20
303	A107	1.60(k) olive green	.20	.20
304	A108	15k red violet	.55	.20
		Nos. 301-304 (4)	1.15	.80

Statue of Kozina and Chod Castle, Domazlice A109

Red Army Soldier A110

1945, Nov. 28   Engr.   Perf. 12½

305	A109	2.40k rose carmine	.20	.20
306	A109	4k blue	.25	.25

250th anniv. of the death of Jan Sladky Kozina, peasant leader. Nos. 305-306 were issued in sheets of 100 stamps with 12 blank labels. Value, set with attached labels, mint $6.

1945, Mar. 26   Litho.   Imperf.

307	A110	2k crimson rose	.40	.40
308	A110	5k slate black	1.25	1.25
309	A110	6k ultramarine	1.25	1.25
		Nos. 307-309 (3)	2.90	2.90

Souvenir Sheet

1945, July 16

Gray Burelage

310		Sheet of 3	4.00	4.00
	a.	A110 2k crimson rose	.75	.75
	b.	A110 5k slate black	.75	.75
	c.	A110 6k ultramarine	.75	.75

Return of Pres. Benes, Apr., 1945.

Clasped Hands — A112

Karel Havlícek Borovsky — A113

1945   Rouletted 12½

311	A112	1.50k brown red	2.25	2.25
312	A112	9k red orange	.50	.50
313	A112	13k orange brown	.65	.65
314	A112	20k blue	1.75	1.75
		Nos. 311-314 (4)	5.15	5.15

1946, July 5   Engr.   Perf. 12½

315	A113	1.20k gray black	.20	.20

Borovsky (1821-56), editor and writer. Issued in sheets of 100 stamps and 12 inscribed labels. Value with attached label: $1.25.

Old Town Hall, Brno — A114

Hodonin Square — A115

Perf. 12½x12, 12x12½

1946, Aug. 3   Engr.   Unwmk.

316	A114	2.40k deep rose	.20	.20
317	A115	7.40k dull violet	.30	.20

See No. B159.

President Eduard Benes — A116

1946, Oct. 28

318	A116	60h indigo	.20	.20
319	A116	1.60k dull green	.20	.20
320	A116	3k red lilac	.20	.20
321	A116	8k sepia	.25	.20
		Nos. 318-321 (4)	.85	.80

Flag, Symbols — A117

Saint Adalbert — A118

1947, Jan. 1   Perf. 12½

322	A117	1.20k Prus green	.20	.20
323	A117	2.40k deep green	.20	.20
324	A117	4k deep blue	.80	.25
		Nos. 322-324 (3)	1.20	.65

Czechoslovakia's two-year reconstruction and rehabilitation program. Nos. 322-324 each issued in sheets of 100 stamps and 12 inscribed labels. Value, set with attached labels, $3.

1947, Apr. 23

326	A118	1.60k gray	.50	.30
327	A118	2.40k rose carmine	.80	.65
328	A118	5k blue green	1.00	.40
		Nos. 326-328 (3)	2.30	1.35

950th anniv. of the death of Saint Adalbert, Bishop of Prague. Nos. 326-328 each issued in sheets of 100 stamps and 12 monogrammed labels. Value, set with attached labels, $40.

Grief — A119

Allegorical Figure — A120

1947, June 10   Engr.

329	A119	1.20k black	.30	.25
330	A119	1.60k slate black	.40	.40
331	A120	2.40k brown violet	.50	.50
		Nos. 329-331 (3)	1.20	1.15

Destruction of Lidice, 5th anniversary. Nos. 329-331 each issued in sheets of 100 stamps and 12 inscribed labels. Value, set with attached labels, $10.

World Federation of Youth Symbol — A121

Thomas G. Masaryk — A122

1947, July 20

332	A121	1.20k violet brown	.50	.40
333	A121	4k slate	.50	.40

World Youth Festival held in Prague, July 20-Aug. 17.

1947, Sept. 14

334	A122	1.20k gray blk, buff	.20	.20
335	A122	4k blue blk, cream	.40	.20

Death of Masaryk, 10th anniv. Nos. 334-335 each issued in sheets of 100 stamps and 12 inscribed labels. Value, with attached labels, $7.50.

Msgr. Stefan Moyses A123

1947, Oct. 19

336	A123	1.20k rose violet	.20	.20
337	A123	4k deep blue	.35	.20

150th anniversary of the birth of Stefan Moyses, first Slovakian chairman of the Slavic movement. Each issued in sheets of 100 stamps and 12 labels with "MOYSES" and floral decoration. Value, set with attached labels, $9.50.

"Freedom from Social Oppression" A124

1947, Oct. 26   Photo.   Perf. 14
338 A124 2.40k brt carmine   .40   .30
339 A124 4k brt ultra   .50   .25

Russian revolution of Oct., 1917, 30th anniv.

Benes
A125

"Czechoslovakia"
Greeting Sokol
Marchers
A126

1948, Feb. 15   Photo.
Size: 17½x21½mm
340 A125 1.50k brown   .20   .20
Size: 19x23mm
341 A125   2k deep plum   .20   .20
342 A125   5k brt ultra   .20   .20
     Nos. 340-342 (3)   .60   .60

1948, Mar. 7   Engr.   Perf. 12½
343 A126 1.50k brown   .20   .20
344 A126   3k rose carmine   .20   .20
345 A126   5k blue   .60   .20
     Nos. 343-345 (3)   1.00   .60

The 11th Sokol Congress.
Nos. 343-345 each issued in sheets of 100 stamps and 12 labels depicting dates and bouquet. Values, set with attached labels: mint $2.50; used $1.50.

King Charles
IV — A127

St. Wenceslas,
King Charles
IV — A128

1948, Apr. 7
346 A127 1.50k black brown   .20   .20
347 A128   2k dark brown   .20   .20
348 A128   3k brown red   .20   .20
349 A127   5k dark blue   .40   .20
     Nos. 346-349 (4)   1.00   .80

600th anniv. of the foundation of Charles University, Prague.
Nos. 346-349 each issued in sheets of 100 stamps and 12 inscribed labels. Value, set with attached labels, $6.

Czech
Peasants in
Revolt
A129

Jindrich Vanicek
A130

Unwmk.
1948, May 14   Photo.   Perf. 14
350 A129 1.50k dk olive brown   .20   .20

Centenary of abolition of serfdom.

1948, June 10   Engr.   Perf. 12½
Designs: 1.50k, 2k, Josef Scheiner.
351 A130   1k dark green   .20   .20
352 A130 1.50k sepia   .20   .20
353 A130   2k gray blue   .20   .20
354 A130   3k claret   .25   .20
     Nos. 351-354 (4)   .85   .80

11th Sokol Congress, Prague, 1948.
Nos. 351-354 each issued in sheets of 100 stamps and 12 labels depicting a sunflower. Values, set with attached labels: $3.75 mint; $3 used.

Frantisek Palacky
& F. L.
Rieger — A131

Miloslav Josef
Hurban — A132

1948, June 20   Unwmk.
355 A131 1.50k gray   .20   .20
356 A131   3k brown carmine   .20   .20

Constituent Assembly at Kromeriz, cent.
Nos. 355-356 each issued in sheets of 100 stamps and 12 labels depicting a wreath. Value, set with attached labels, $1.50.

1948, Aug. 27   Perf. 12½
3k, Ludovit Stur. 5k, Michael M. Hodza.
357 A132 1.50k dark brown   .20   .20
358 A132   3k carmine lake   .20   .20
359 A132   5k indigo   .25   .20
     Nos. 357-359 (3)   .65   .60

Cent. of 1848 insurrection against Hungary.
Nos. 357-359 each issued in sheets of 100 stamps and 12 labels depicting signatures. Values, set with attached labels: mint $3.50; used 1.50.

Eduard Benes
A133

Czechoslovak Family
A134

1948, Sept. 28
360 A133 8k black   .20   .20

President Eduard Benes, 1884-1948.

1948, Oct. 28   Perf. 12½x12
361 A134 1.50k deep blue   .20   .20
362 A134   3k rose carmine   .20   .20

Czechoslovakia's Independence, 30th anniv.
Nos. 361-362 each issued in sheets of 100 stamps and 12 labels depicting dates, leaves. Value, set with attached labels, $1.50.

Pres. Klement
Gottwald — A135

1948-49   Perf. 12½
Size: 18½x23½mm
363 A135 1.50k dk brown   .20   .20
364 A135   3k car rose   .40   .20
   a.   3k rose brown   1.20   .20
365 A135   5k gray blue   .25   .20
Size: 23½x29mm
366 A135 20k purple   1.10   .20
     Nos. 363-366 (4)   1.95   .80

No. 366 was issued in sheets of 100 stamps and 12 monogrammed labels. Value, with attached label, $3.
See Nos. 373, 564, 600-604.

Souvenir Sheet
1948, Nov. 23   Unwmk.   Imperf.
367 A135 30k rose brown   4.50   3.50

52nd birthday of Pres. Klement Gottwald (1896-1953).

Hradcany Castle Type of 1918
Souvenir Sheet
1948, Dec. 18
368 A1 10k dk blue violet   3.00   2.40

1st Czech postage stamp, 30th anniv.

Czechoslovak
and Russian
Workmen
Shaking
Hands — A138

Lenin — A139

1948, Dec. 12   Perf. 12½
369 A138 3k rose carmine   .20   .20

5th anniv. of the treaty of alliance between Czechoslovakia and Russia.
No. 369 issued in sheets of 100 stamps and 12 labels depicting Czech and Soviet flags. Value with attached label 60c.

1949, Jan. 21   Engr.   Perf. 12½
370 A139 1.50k violet brown   .30   .20
371 A139   5k deep blue   .30   .30

25th anniversary of the death of Lenin.
Nos. 370-371 each issued in sheets of 100 stamps and 12 labels depicting torch. Value, set with attached labels: mint $1.75; used $1.50.

Gottwald Type of 1948 Inscribed:
"UNOR 1948" and

Gottwald
Addressing
Meeting
A140

1949, Feb. 25   Photo.   Perf. 14
372 A140 3k red brown   .20   .20
Perf. 12½
Engr.
Size: 23½x29mm
373 A135 10k deep green   .60   .25

1st anniv. of Gottwald's speech announcing the appointment of a new government. No. 372 exists in a souvenir sheet of 1. It was not sold to the public.
No. 373 issued in sheets of 100 stamps and 12 inscribed labels. Values with attached label: mint $3; used $2.

A141

A142

Writers: 50h, P. O. Hviezdoslav. 80h, V. Vancura. 1k, J. Sverma. 2k, Julius Fucik. 4k, Jiri Wolker. 8k, Alois Jirasek.

1949   Photo.   Perf. 14
374 A141 50h violet brown   .20   .20
375 A141 80h scarlet   .20   .20
376 A141   1k dk olive green   .20   .20
377 A141   2k brt blue   .40   .20
Perf. 12½
Engr.
378 A141   4k olive green   .40   .20
379 A141   8k brown black   .50   .20
     Nos. 374-379 (6)   1.90   1.20

1949, May 20
3k, Stagecoach and Train. 5k, Postrider and post bus. 13k, Sailing ship and plane.
380 A142   3k brown carmine   1.25   1.25
381 A142   5k deep blue   .80   .40
382 A142 13k deep green   1.25   .80
     Nos. 380-382 (3)   3.30   2.45

75th anniv. of the UPU.

Reaping
A143

Communist
Emblem and
Workers
A144

Workman, Symbol
of Industry — A145

Perf. 12½x12, 12x12½
1949, May 24   Unwmk.
383 A143 1.50k deep green   .50   .45
384 A144   3k brown carmine   .50   .45
385 A145   5k deep blue   .50   .45
     Nos. 383-385 (3)   1.50   1.35

No. 384 for the 9th meeting of the Communist Party of Czechoslovakia, 5/25/49.
Nos. 383-385 each issued in sheets of 100 stamps and 12 inscribed labels. Value, set with attached labels, $15.

Bedrich
Smetana and
Natl. Theater,
Prague — A146

Aleksander
Pushkin — A147

1949, June 4   Perf. 12½x12
386 A146 1.50k dull green   .20   .20
387 A146   5k deep blue   .55   .20

Birth of Bedrich Smetana, composer, 125th anniv.

1949, June 6   Perf. 12x12½
388 A147 2k olive gray   .30   .25

Birth of Aleksander S. Pushkin, 150th anniv.

Frederic Chopin
and
Conservatory,
Warsaw
A148

1949, June 24   Perf. 12½x12
389 A148 3k dark red   .40   .20
390 A148 8k violet brown   .75   .20

Cent. of the death of Frederic F. Chopin.

Globe and Ribbon — A149

Zvolen Castle — A150

1949, Aug. 20 **Perf. 12½x12**
391 A149 1.50k violet brown .40 .40
392 A149 5k ultra .95 .95

50th Prague Sample Fair, Sept. 11-18, 1949.

Starting in October, 1949, some commemorative sets included one "blocked" value, which could be obtained only by purchasing the complete set. These restricted values were printed in smaller quantities than other stamps in the set and were typically sold for more than face value.

1949, Aug. 28 **Perf. 12½**
393 A150 10k rose lake .75 .20

Early Miners — A151

Miner of Today — A152

Design: 5k, Mining Machine.

1949, Sept. 11 **Perf. 12½**
394 A151 1.50k sepia .80 .60
395 A152 3k carmine rose 6.50 2.50
396 A151 5k deep blue 5.00 1.75
  Nos. 394-396 (3) 12.30 4.85

700th anniv. of the Czechoslovak mining industry; 150th anniv. of the miner's laws.

Construction Workers — A153

Joseph V. Stalin — A154

1949, Dec. 11 **Perf. 12½**
397 A153 1k shown 3.50 1.60
398 A153 2k Machinist 2.50 .80

2nd Trade Union Congress, Prague, 1949.

1949, Dec. 21 **Unwmk.**

Design: 3k, Stalin facing left.

Cream Paper
399 A154 1.50k greenish gray 1.25 .60
400 A154 3k claret 4.75 2.00

70th birthday of Joseph V. Stalin.

Skier — A155

Efficiency Badge — A156

Engr., Photo. (3k)
1950, Feb. 15 **Perf. 12½, 13½**
401 A155 1.50k gray blue 3.25 1.50
402 A156 3k vio brn, cr 3.25 1.50
403 A155 5k ultramarine 2.40 1.25
  Nos. 401-403 (3) 8.90 4.25

51st Ski Championship for the Tatra cup, Feb. 15-26, 1950.

Vladimir V. Mayakovsky, Poet, 20th Death Anniv. — A157

1950, Apr. 14 **Engr.** **Perf. 12½**
404 A157 1.50k dark brown 2.50 1.25
405 A157 3k brown red 2.50 1.25

See Nos. 414-417, 422-423, 432-433, 464-465, 477-478.

Soviet Tank Soldier and Hradcany A158

2k, Hero of Labor medal. 3k, Two workers (militiamen) and Town Hall, Prague. 5k, Text of government program and heraldic lion.

1950, May 5
406 A158 1.50k gray green .40 .25
407 A158 2k dark brown 1.25 1.25
408 A158 3k brown red .25 .20
409 A158 5k dark blue .55 .25
  Nos. 406-409 (4) 2.45 1.95

5th anniv. of the Czechoslovak People's Democratic Republic.

Factory and Young Couple with Tools A159

Designs: 2k, Steam shovel. 3k, Farmer and farm scene. 5k, Three workers leaving factory.

1950, May 9 **Engr.**
410 A159 1.50k dark green 2.00 .95
411 A159 2k dark brown 2.00 .95
412 A159 3k rose red 1.25 .40
413 A159 5k deep blue 1.25 .40
  Nos. 410-413 (4) 6.50 2.70

Canceled to Order
The government philatelic department started about 1950 to sell canceled sets of new issues. Values in the second ("used") column are for these canceled-to-order stamps. Postally used stamps are worth more.

Portrait Type of 1950
Design: S. K. Neumann.

1950, June 5 **Unwmk.** **Perf. 12½**
414 A157 1.50k deep blue .40 .20
415 A157 3k violet brown 1.25 .75

Stanislav Kostka Neumann (1875-1947), journalist and poet.

1950, June 21
Design: Bozena Nemcova.
416 A157 1.50k deep blue 1.25 .75
417 A157 7k dark brown .30 .20

Bozena Nemcova (1820-1862), writer.

Liberation of Colonies A160

Designs: 2k, Allegory, Fight for Peace. 3k, Group of Students. 5k, Marching Students with flags.

1950, Aug. 14
418 A160 1.50k dark green .20 .20
419 A160 2k sepia .85 .55
420 A160 3k rose carmine .20 .20
421 A160 5k ultra .40 .35
  Nos. 418-421 (4) 1.65 1.30

2nd International Students World Congress, Prague, Aug. 12-24, 1950.

Portrait Type of 1950
Design: Zdenek Fibich.

1950, Oct. 15
422 A157 3k rose brown .90 .55
423 A157 8k gray green .35 .20

Zdenek Fibich, musician, birth centenary.

Miner, Soldier and Farmer A161

Czech and Soviet Soldiers A162

1950, Oct. 6
424 A161 1.50k slate 1.25 1.25
425 A162 3k carmine rose .40 .40

Issued to publicize Czech Army Day.

Prague Castle, 16th Century A163

Prague, 1493 A164

3k, Prague, 1606. 5k, Prague, 1794.

1950, Oct. 21 **Perf. 14**
426 A163 1.50k black 4.50 3.00
427 A164 2k chocolate 4.50 3.00
428 A164 3k brown car 4.50 3.00
429 A164 5k gray 4.50 3.00
  a. Block of 4, #426-429 25.00 16.00

See Nos. 434-435.

Communications Symbols — A165

1950, Oct. 25 **Perf. 12½**
430 A165 1.50k chocolate .40 .20
431 A165 3k brown carmine .85 .30

1st anniv. of the foundation of the Intl. League of P.T.T. Employees.

Portrait Type of 1950
Design: J. Gregor Tajovsky.

1950, Oct. 26
432 A157 1.50k brown 1.00 .60
433 A157 5k deep blue .65 .30

10th anniversary of the death of J. Gregor Tajovsky (1874-1940), Slovakian writer.

Scenic Type of 1950
Design: Prague, 1950.

1950, Oct. 28
434 A164 1.50k indigo .40 .20
  a. Souvenir sheet of 4, imperf. 40.00 20.00
435 A164 3k brown car .80 .50

Czech and Soviet Steel Workers A166

1950, Nov. 4 **Unwmk.**
436 A166 1.50k chocolate .50 .35
437 A166 5k deep blue .95 .60

Issued to publicize the 2nd meeting of the Union of Czechoslovak-Soviet Friendship.

Dove by Picasso A167

1951, Jan. 20 **Photo.** **Perf. 14**
438 A167 2k deep blue 4.75 3.00
439 A167 3k rose brown 3.25 1.50

1st Czechoslovak Congress of Fighters for Peace, held in Prague.

Julius Fucik — A168

1951, Feb. 17 **Engr.** **Perf. 12½**
440 A168 1.50k gray .80 .80
441 A168 5k gray blue 1.60 1.60

Drop Hammer — A169

Installing Gear — A170

1951, Feb. 24
442 A169 1.50k gray blk .20 .20
443 A170 3k violet brn .20 .20
444 A169 4k gray blue .60 .50
  Nos. 442-444 (3) 1.00 .90

Women Machinists A171

Apprentice Miners A172

Designs: 3k, Woman tractor operator. 5k, Women of different races.

1951, Mar. 8   Photo.   Perf. 14
445 A171 1.50k olive brown .40 .30
446 A171 3k brown car 1.60 1.25
447 A171 5k blue .80 .50
Nos. 445-447 (3) 2.80 2.05

International Women's Day, Mar. 8.

1951, Apr. 12   Engr.   Perf. 12½
448 A172 1.50k gray .55 .50
449 A172 3k red brown .20 .20

Plowing A173

Collective Cattle Breeding A174

1951, Apr. 28   Photo.   Perf. 14
450 A173 1.50k brown .80 .80
451 A174 2k dk green 1.60 1.60

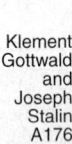

Tatra Mountain Recreation Center — A175

Mountain Recreation Centers: 2k, Beskydy (Beskids). 3k, Krkonose (Carpathians).

1951, May 5   Engr.   Perf. 12½
452 A175 1.50k deep green .20 .20
453 A175 2k dark brown 1.10 .95
454 A175 3k rose brown .30 .20
Nos. 452-454 (3) 1.60 1.35

Issued to publicize the summer opening of trade union recreation centers.

Klement Gottwald and Joseph Stalin A176

Factory Militiaman A177

Red Army Soldier and Partisan A178

Marx, Engels, Lenin and Stalin A179

1951   Unwmk.   Perf. 12½
455 A176 1.50k olive gray .80 .25
456 A177 2k red brown .40 .20
457 A178 3k rose brown .40 .20
458 A176 5k deep blue 2.00 1.40
459 A179 8k gray .80 .25
Nos. 455-459 (5) 4.40 2.30

30th anniv. of the founding of the Czechoslovak Communist Party.

A180   A181

Design: 1k, 2k, Antonin Dvorák. 1.50k, 3k, Bedrich Smetana.

1951, May 30
460 A180 1k redsh brown .40 .20
461 A180 1.50k olive gray 1.60 .80
462 A180 2k dk redsh brn 1.60 .80
463 A180 3k rose brown .40 .20
Nos. 460-463 (4) 4.00 2.00

International Music Festival, Prague. Nos. 461 and 462 were each issued in sheets of 10 stamps. Value, $350 each.

Portrait Type of 1950

1951, June 21
Portrait: Bohumir Smeral (facing right).
464 A157 1.50k dark gray .80 .65
465 A157 3k rose brown .40 .20

10th anniv. of the death of Bohumir Smeral, political leader.

1951, June 21
466 A181 1k shown .75 .35
467 A181 1.50k Discus .75 .35
468 A181 3k Soccer 1.50 .35
469 A181 5k Skier 3.50 1.50
Nos. 466-469 (4) 6.50 2.55

Issued to honor the 9th Congress of the Czechoslovak Sokol Federation.

Scene from "Fall of Berlin" A182

Scene from "The Great Citizen" A183

1951, July 14
470 A182 80h rose brown .40 .40
471 A183 1.50k dark gray .40 .40
472 A183 4k gray blue 1.60 1.25
Nos. 470-472 (3) 2.40 2.05

Intl. Film Festival, Karlovy Vary, July 14-29.

Alois Jirásek — A184

"Fables and Fate" A185

Design: 4k, Scene from "Reign of Tabor."

1951, Aug. 23   Engr.   Perf. 12½
473 A184 1.50k gray .55 .20
474 A184 5k dark blue 2.40 1.25

Photo.
Perf. 14
475 A185 3k dark red .55 .20
476 A185 4k dark brown .55 .20
Nos. 473-476 (4) 4.05 1.85

Cent. of the birth of Alois Jirásek, author. No. 474 was issued in a sheet of 10 stamps. Value: mint $550.

Portrait Type of 1950

Design: Josef Hybes (1850-1921), co-founder of Czech Communist Party.

1951, July 21   Engr.
477 A157 1.50k chocolate .20 .20
478 A157 2k rose brown .80 .65

"Ostrava Region" — A186

Mining Iron Ore — A187

1951, Sept. 9
479 A186 1.50k dk brown .20 .20
480 A187 3k rose brown .20 .20
481 A186 5k deep blue 1.25 1.00
Nos. 479-481 (3) 1.65 1.40

Miner's Day, Sept. 9, 1951.

Soldiers on Parade — A188

1k, Gunner and field gun. 1.50k, Klement Gottwald. 3k, Tankman and tank. 5k, Aviators.

Photo. (80h, 5k), Engr.
1951, Oct. 6   Perf. 14 (80h, 5k), 12½
Inscribed: "Den CS Armady 1951"
482 A188 80h olive brown .35 .30
483 A188 1k dk olive grn .35 .30
484 A188 1.50k sepia .35 .30
485 A188 3k claret .80 .40
486 A188 5k blue 2.00 .80
Nos. 482-486 (5) 3.85 2.10

Issued to publicize Army Day, Oct. 6, 1951.

Stalin and Gottwald — A189

Lenin, Stalin and Soldiers — A190

1951, Nov. 3   Engr.   Perf. 12½
487 A189 1.50k sepia .20 .20
488 A190 3k red brown .20 .20
489 A189 4k deep blue 1.25 .80
Nos. 487-489 (3) 1.65 1.20

Issued to publicize the month of Czechoslovak-Soviet friendship, 1951.

Peter Jilemnicky A191

Ladislav Zapotocky A192

1951, Dec. 5   Unwmk.
491 A191 1.50k redsh brown .25 .20
492 A191 2k dull blue .95 .40

Peter Jilemnicky (1901-1949), writer.

1952, Jan. 12   Perf. 11½
493 A192 1.50k brown red .20 .20
494 A192 4k gray 1.25 .55

Centenary of the birth of Ladislav Zapotocky, Bohemian socialist pioneer.

Jan Kollar — A193

Lenin and Lenin Hall — A194

1952, Jan. 30   Unwmk.   Perf. 11½
495 A193 3k dark carmine .20 .20
496 A193 5k violet blue 1.25 .80

Jan Kollar (1793-1852), poet.

1952, Jan. 30   Perf. 12½
497 A194 1.50k rose carmine .30 .20
498 A194 5k deep blue 1.25 .80

6th All-Russian Party Conf., 40th anniv.

Emil Holub and African — A195

Gottwald Metallurgical Plant — A196

1952, Feb. 21   Perf. 11½
499 A195 3k red brown .50 .30
500 A195 5k gray 2.00 1.10

Death of Emil Holub, explorer, 50th anniv.

1952, Feb. 25   Photo.   Perf. 14
Designs: 2k, Foundry. 3k, Chemical plant.
501 A196 1.50k sepia .25 .20
502 A196 2k red brown 1.50 .75
503 A196 3k scarlet .25 .20
Nos. 501-503 (3) 2.00 1.15

CZECHOSLOVAKIA

Student, Soldier and Worker — A197

Youths of Three Races — A198

Youths Carrying Flags — A204

1952, Mar. 21   Unwmk.   Perf. 14
504 A197 1.50k blue .20 .20
505 A198 2k olive black .25 .20
506 A197 3k lake 1.25 .80
Nos. 504-506 (3) 1.70 1.20

International Youth Day, Mar. 25, 1952.

1952, May 1
519 A204 3k brown red .45 .25
520 A204 4k dk red brown 2.00 1.75

Issued to publicize Labor Day, May 1, 1952.

Lidice, Symbol of a New Life — A210

1952, June 10   Perf. 12½
532 A210 1.50k dk violet brn .20 .20
533 A210 5k dark blue 1.25 .75

Destruction of Lidice, 10th anniversary.

17th Century Mining Towers — A217

Jan Zizka — A218

Designs: 1.50k, Coal Excavator. 2k, Peter Bezruc mine. 3k, Automatic coaling crane.

1952, Sept. 14   Perf. 12½
548 A217 1k sepia 1.40 .90
549 A217 1.50k dark blue .20 .20
550 A217 2k olive gray .20 .20
551 A217 3k violet brown .20 .20
Nos. 548-551 (4) 2.00 1.50

Miners' Day, Sept. 14, 1952. No. 550 also for the 85th anniv. of the birth of Peter Bezruc (Vladimir Vasek), poet.

1952, Oct. 5   Engr.   Perf. 11½
Inscribed: ". . . . Armady 1952,"

Designs: 2k, Fraternization with Russians. 3k, Marching with flag.

552 A218 1.50k rose lake .20 .20
553 A218 2k olive bister .20 .20
554 A218 3k dk car rose .20 .20
555 A218 4k gray 1.90 .95
Nos. 552-555 (4) 2.50 1.55

Issued to publicize Army Day, Oct. 5, 1952.

Souvenir Sheet

Statues to Bulgarian Partisans and to Soviet Army — A219

1952, Oct. 18   Unwmk.   Perf. 12½
556 A219 Sheet of 2 110.00 25.00
a. 2k deep carmine 35.00 7.50
b. 3k ultramarine 35.00 7.50

National Philatelic Exhibition, Bratislava, Oct. 18-Nov. 2, 1952.

1952, Nov. 7
558 A221 2k brown black　　1.60 1.25
559 A221 3k carmine　　　　.20 .20

35th anniv. of the Russian Revolution and to publicize Czechoslovak-Soviet friendship.

1952, Nov. 15　Photo.　Perf. 14
560 A222 2k brown　　　　1.40 .80
561 A222 3k red　　　　　.20 .20

Issued to publicize the first State Congress of the Czechoslovak Red Cross.

Matej Louda, Hussite Leader, Painted by Mikulas Ales
A223

3k, Dragon-killer Trutnov, painted by Ales.

1952, Nov. 18　Engr.　Perf. 11½
562 A223 2k red brown　　　.40 .20
563 A223 3k grnsh gray　　　.80 .25

Mikulas Ales, painter, birth cent.

Gottwald Type of 1948-49

1952, June 2　Unwmk.　Perf. 12½
Size: 19x24mm
564 A135 1k dark green　　　.60 .20

"Peace"　　　　　Dove by
Flags — A224　　Picasso — A225

1952, Dec. 12　Photo.　Perf. 14
565 A224 3k red brown　　　.40 .20
566 A224 4k deep blue　　　1.50 1.00

Issued to publicize the Congress of Nations for Peace, Vienna, Dec. 12-19, 1952.

1953, Jan. 17

Design: 4k, Czech Family.

567 A225 1.50k dark brown　　.20 .20
568 A225 4k slate blue　　　.80 .50

2nd Czechoslovak Peace Congress.

Smetana
Museum — A226

Design: 4k, Jirásek Museum.

1953, Feb. 10　Engr.　Perf. 11½
569 A226 1.50k dk violet brn　.20 .20
570 A226 4k dark gray　　　1.50 .90

Prof. Zdenek Nejedly, 75th birth anniv.

Martin　　　　　　Jaroslav
Kukucin — A227　　Vrchlicky — A228

Designs: 2k, Karel Jaromir Erben. 3k, Vaclav Matej Kramerius. 5k, Josef Dobrovsky.

1953, Feb. 28
571 A227 1k gray　　　.20 .20
572 A228 1.50k olive　　.20 .20
573 A228 2k rose lake　　.20 .20
574 A228 3k lt brown　　.75 .50
575 A228 5k slate blue　1.50 1.10
　Nos. 571-575 (5)　2.85 2.20

Issued to honor Czech writers and poets: 1k, 25th anniv. of death of Kukucin. 1.50k, birth cent. of Vrchlicky. 2k, cent. of completion of "Kytice" by Erben. 3k, birth bicent. of Kramerius. 5k, birth bicent. of Dobrovsky.

Militia — A229

Gottwald — A230

Design: 8k, Portraits of Stalin and Gottwald and Peoples Assembly.

Perf. 13½x14
1953, Feb. 25　Photo.　Unwmk.
576 A229 1.50k deep blue　.20 .20
577 A230 3k red　　　　.20 .20
578 A229 8k dark brown　2.40 1.00
　Nos. 576-578 (3)　2.80 1.40

5th anniv. of the defeat of the attempt to reinstate capitalism.

Book and
Torch — A231

Design: 3k, Bedrich Vaclavek.

1953, Mar. 5　Engr.　Perf. 11½
579 A231 1k sepia　　　1.60 .80
580 A231 3k orange brown　.20 .20

Bedrich Vaclavek (1897-1943), socialist writer.

Stalin Type of 1949
Inscribed "21 XII 1879-5 III 1953"
1953, Mar. 12
581 A154 1.50k black　　.35 .25

Death of Joseph Stalin, Mar. 5, 1953.

Mother and
Child — A232

Girl
Revolutionist
A233

1953, Mar. 8
582 A232 1.50k ultra　　.20 .20
583 A233 2k brown red　1.25 .75

International Women's Day.

Klement
Gottwald — A234

1953, Mar. 19
584 A234 1.50k black　　.20 .20
585 A234 3k black　　　.20 .20

Souvenir Sheet
Imperf
586 A234 5k black　　　6.00 4.00

Death of Pres. Klement Gottwald, 3/14/53.

Josef Pecka, Ladislav Zapotocky and
Josef Hybes — A236

1953, Apr. 7　Unwmk.　Perf. 11½
587 A236 2k lt violet brn　　.20 .20

75th anniversary of the first congress of the Czech Social Democratic Party.

Cyclists — A237

1953, Apr. 29
588 A237 3k deep blue　　.75 .35

6th International Peace Bicycle Race, Prague-Berlin-Warsaw.

Medal of
"May 1,
1890"
A238

Designs: 1.50k, Lenin and Stalin. 3k, May Day Parade. 8k, Marx and Engels.

Engraved and Photogravure
1953, Apr. 30　Perf. 11½x11, 14
589 A238 1k chocolate　　1.50 .75
590 A238 1.50k dark gray　.20 .20
591 A238 3k carmine lake　.20 .20
592 A238 8k dk gray green　.35 .20
　Nos. 589-592 (4)　2.25 1.35

Issued to publicize Labor Day, May 1, 1953.

Sowing
Grain — A239

Dam — A240

1953, May 8　Photo.　Perf. 14
593 A239 1.50k shown　　.35 .20
594 A239 7k Reaper　　1.60 1.40

Socialization of the village.

Welder — A241

Design: 3k, Iron works.

1953, May 8　Perf. 11½
595 A240 1.50k gray　　1.25 .60
596 A241 2k blue gray　.20 .20
597 A240 3k red brown　.20 .20
　Nos. 595-597 (3)　1.65 1.00

Josef　　　　　Leos
Slavik — A242　Janacek — A243

1953, June 19　Photo.
598 A242 75h dp gray blue　.75 .20
599 A243 1.60k dark brown　1.00 .20

Issued on the occasion of the International Music Festival, Prague, 1953.

Gottwald Type of 1948-49
Perf. 12½ (15h, 1k), 11½ (20h, 3k)
1953
600 A135 15h yellow green　.35 .20
601 A135 20h dk violet brn　.50 .20
602 A135 1k purple　　　1.25 .20
603 A135 3k brown car　　.20 .20
604 A135 3k gray　　　　.80 .20
　Nos. 600-604 (5)　3.10 1.00

Nos. 600-604 vary slightly in size.

Pres. Antonin
Zapotocky — A244

1953, June 19　Perf. 14
605 A244 30h violet blue　.75 .20
606 A244 60h cerise　　1.00 .20

Julius Fucik　　　Book and
A245　　　　　　Carnation
　　　　　　　　A246

1953, Sept. 8　Engr.　Perf. 12½
607 A245 40h dk violet brn　.30 .20
608 A246 60h pink　　　.50 .30

10th anniv. of the death of Julius Fucik, Communist leader executed by the Nazis.

Miner and
Flag — A247

Design: 60h, Oil field and workers.

1953, Sept. 10　Perf. 11½
609 A247 30h gray　　　.25 .20
610 A247 60h brown vio　1.25 .50

Miner's Day, Sept. 10, 1953.

Volleyball
Game — A248

Motorcyclist
A249

Design: 60h, Woman throwing javelin.

1953, Sept. 15
611 A248 30h brown red 5.25 1.50
612 A249 40h dk violet brn 3.25 1.00
613 A248 60h rose violet 2.75 1.00
Nos. 611-613 (3) 11.25 3.50

Hussite Warrior
A250

Pres. Antonin
Zapotocky
A251

Designs: 60h, Soldier presenting arms. 1k,
Red army soldiers.

1953, Oct. 8
614 A250 30h brown .30 .20
615 A250 60h rose lake .65 .20
616 A250 1k brown red 1.50 1.25
Nos. 614-616 (3) 2.45 1.65

Issued to publicize Army Day, Oct. 3, 1953.

1953 Unwmk. Perf. 11½, 12½
617 A251 30h violet blue .45 .20
618 A251 60h carmine rose .80 .20

#617 is perf. 11½ & measures 19x23mm,
#618 perf. 12½ & 18½x23½mm.
See No. 780.

Charles Bridge
and Prague
Castle — A252

Korean and Czech
Girls — A253

1953, Aug. 15 Engr. Perf. 11½
619 A252 5k gray 4.00 .20

1953, Oct. 11 Perf. 11x11½
620 A253 30h dark brown 2.40 1.60

Czechoslovakia's friendship with Korea.

Flags, Hradcany Castle and
Kremlin — A254

Designs: 60h, Lomonosov University, Moscow. 1.20k, Lenin Ship Canal.

1953, Nov. 7
621 A254 30h dark gray .80 .55
622 A254 60h dark brown 1.25 1.00
623 A254 1.20k ultra 4.00 2.00
Nos. 621-623 (3) 6.05 3.55

Czechoslovak-Soviet friendship month.

Emmy Destinn,
Ópera
Singer — A255

National Theater,
Prague — A256

Portrait: 2k, Eduard Vojan, actor.

1953, Nov. 18 Perf. 14
624 A255 30h blue black 1.25 .75
625 A256 60h brown .40 .40
626 A255 2k sepia 3.25 1.25
Nos. 624-626 (3) 4.90 2.40

Natl. Theater founding, 70th anniv.

Josef
Manes — A257

Vaclav
Hollar — A258

1953, Nov. 28 Perf. 11x11½
627 A257 60h brown carmine .35 .20
628 A257 1.20k deep blue 1.50 .90

Issued to honor Josef Manes, painter.

1953, Dec. 5

Portrait: 1.20k, Head framed, facing right.

629 A258 30h brown black .35 .20
630 A258 1.20k dark brown 1.50 .65

Vaclav Hollar, artist and etcher.

Leo N.
Tolstoi — A259

1953, Dec. 29 Unwmk.
631 A259 60h dark green .35 .20
632 A259 1k chocolate 1.50 .65

Leo N. Tolstoi, 125th birth anniv.

Locomotive — A260

Design: 1k, Plane loading mail.

Engraved, Center Photogravure
1953, Dec. 29 Perf. 11½x11
633 A260 60h brn org & gray vio 1.50 .50
634 A260 1k org brn & brt bl 4.00 1.25

Lenin — A261

Lenin Museum, Prague — A262

1954, Jan. 21 Engr. Perf. 11½
635 A261 30h dark brown .45 .20
636 A262 1.40k chocolate 1.50 .90

30th anniversary of the death of Lenin.

Klement
Gottwald — A263

Design: 2.40k, Revolutionist with flag.

1954, Feb. 18 Perf. 11x11½, 14x13½
637 A263 60h dark brown .30 .20
638 A263 2.40k rose lake 4.25 1.50

25th anniversary of the fifth congress of the
Communist Party in Czechoslovakia.
No. 638 was issued in a sheet of 10 stamps.
Value, $80.

Gottwald
Mausoleum,
Prague — A264

Gottwald
and
Stalin
A265

1.20k, Lenin & Stalin mausoleum, Moscow.

1954, Mar. 5 Perf. 11½, 14x13½
639 A264 30h olive brown .35 .20
640 A265 60h deep ultra .35 .20
641 A264 1.20k rose brown 2.25 1.00
Nos. 639-641 (3) 2.95 1.40

1st anniv. of the deaths of Stalin and
Gottwald.
No. 641 was issued in a sheet of 10 stamps.
Value, $100.

Two
Runners — A266

Group of
Hikers — A267

Design: 1k, Woman swimmer.

1954, Apr. 24 Perf. 11½
642 A266 30h dark brown 2.40 1.25
643 A267 80h dark green 8.00 4.00
644 A266 1k dk violet blue 2.00 .80
Nos. 642-644 (3) 12.40 6.05

No. 643 was issued in a sheet of 10 stamps.
Value, $240.

Nurse — A268

Designs: 15h, Construction worker. 40h,
Postwoman. 45h, Ironworker. 50h, Soldier.
75h, Lathe operator. 80h, Textile worker. 1k,
Farm woman. 1.20k, Scientist and microscope. 1.60k, Miner. 2k, Physician and baby.
2.40k, Engineer. 3k, Chemist.

1954 Perf. 12½x12, 11½x11
645 A268 15h dark green .30 .20
646 A268 20h lt violet .35 .20
647 A268 40h dark brown .45 .20
648 A268 45h dk gray blue .35 .20
649 A268 50h dk gray green .45 .20
650 A268 75h deep blue .45 .20
651 A268 80h violet brown .45 .20
652 A268 1k green .75 .20
653 A268 1.20k dk violet blue .45 .20
654 A268 1.60k brown blk 1.10 .20
655 A268 2k orange brown 1.60 .20
656 A268 2.40k violet blue 1.50 .20
657 A268 3k carmine 1.50 .20
Nos. 645-657 (13) 9.70 2.60

Antonin
Dvořák — A269

Prokop
Divis — A270

40h, Leos Janacek. 60h, Bedrich Smetana.

1954, May 22 Perf. 11x11½
658 A269 30h violet brown 2.50 .30
659 A269 40h brick red 3.00 .40
660 A269 60h dark blue .80 .25
Nos. 658-660 (3) 6.30 .95

"Year of Czech Music," 1954.

1954, June 15
661 A270 30h gray .40 .20
662 A270 75h violet brown 1.60 .65

200th anniv. of the invention of a lightning
conductor by Prokop Divis.

Slovak
Insurrectionist
A271

Anton P.
Chekhov
A272

Design: 1.20k, Partisan woman.

1954, Aug. 28 Perf. 11½
663 A271 30h brown orange .20 .20
664 A271 1.20k dark blue .95 .75

Slovak national uprising, 10th anniv.

1954, Sept. 24
665 A272 30h dull gray grn .30 .20
666 A272 45h dull gray brn 1.25 .65

50th anniv. of the death of Chekhov, writer.

Soviet Representative Giving
Agricultural Instruction — A273

Designs: 60h, Soviet industrial instruction.
2k, Dancers (cultural collaboration).

1954, Nov. 6   *Perf. 11½x11*
667 A273 30h yellow brown   .20   .20
668 A273 60h dark blue   .20   .20
669 A273 2k vermilion   1.40   1.25
     Nos. 667-669 (3)   1.80   1.65
Czechoslovak-Soviet friendship month.

Jan Neruda — A274

60h, Janko Jesensky. 1.60k, Jiri Wolker.

1954, Nov. 25   *Perf. 11x11½*
670 A274 30h dark blue   .85   .20
671 A274 60h dull red   1.40   .50
672 A274 1.60k sepia   .35   .20
     Nos. 670-672 (3)   2.60   .90
Issued to honor Czechoslovak poets.

View of Telc A275

Views: 60h, Levoca. 3k, Ceske Budejovice.

1954, Dec. 10   **Engr. & Photo.**
673 A275 30h black & bis   .65   .20
674 A275 60h brown & bis   .65   .20
675 A275 3k black & bis   2.40   1.60
     Nos. 673-675 (3)   3.70   2.00

Pres. Antonin Zapotocky A276   Attacking Soldiers A278

1954, Dec. 18   **Engr.**   *Perf. 11½*
676 A276 30h black brown   .55   .20
677 A276 60h dark blue   .55   .20

Souvenir Sheet
Imperf
678 A276 2k deep claret   20.00   8.00
70th birthday of Pres. Antonin Zapotocky. See Nos. 829-831.

1954, Oct. 3   *Perf. 11½*
Design: 2k, Soldier holding child.
679 A278 60h dark green   .30   .20
680 A278 2k dark brown   1.60   1.25
    Army Day, Oct. 6, 1954.

Woman Holding Torch — A279

Comenius University Building A280

Design: 45h, Ski jumper.

1955, Jan. 20   **Engr.**
681 A279 30h red   2.40   .50

Engraved and Photogravure
682 A279 45h black & blue   4.00   .50
First National Spartacist Games, 1955.

1955, Jan. 28   **Engr.**   *Perf. 11½*
Design: 75h, Jan A. Komensky medal.
683 A280 60h deep green   .30   .20
684 A280 75h chocolate   1.60   .80
35th anniversary of the founding of Comenius University, Bratislava.

Czechoslovak Automobile A281

60h, Textile worker. 75h, Lathe operator.

1955, Mar. 15   **Unwmk.**
685 A281 45h dull green   1.50   .45
686 A281 60h dk violet blue   .60   .20
687 A281 75h sepia   .90   .20
     Nos. 685-687 (3)   3.00   .85

Woman Decorating Soviet Soldier — A282

Stalin Memorial, Prague — A283

Designs: 35h, Tankman with flowers. 60h, Children greeting soldier.

1955, May 5   **Engr.**   *Perf. 11½*
688 A282 30h blue   .35   .20
689 A282 35h dark brown   1.50   .75
690 A282 60h cerise   .35   .20
Photo.
691 A283 60h sepia   .35   .20
     Nos. 688-691 (4)   2.55   1.35
10th anniv. of Czechoslovakia's liberation.

Music and Spring — A284   Foundry Worker — A285

Design: 1k, Woman with lyre.

1955, May 12   **Engr. & Photo.**
692 A284 30h black & pale blue   .35   .25
693 A284 1k black & pale rose   1.50   1.50
International Music Festival, Prague, 1955.

1955, May 12   **Engr.**
Design: 45h, Farm workers.
694 A285 30h violet   .20   .20
695 A285 45h green   1.40   .75
Issued to publicize the third congress of the Trade Union Revolutionary Movement.

Woman Athlete — A286   Jakub Arbes — A287

60h, Dancing couple. 1.60k, Athlete.

1955, June 21
696 A286 20h violet blue   1.00   .50
697 A286 60h green   .35   .20
698 A286 1.60k red   .75   .30
     Nos. 696-698 (3)   2.10   1.00
Issued to publicize the first National Spartacist Games, Prague, June-July, 1955.

1955
Portraits: 30h, Jan Stursa. 40h, Elena Marothy-Soltesova. 60h, Josef Vaclav Sladek. 75h, Alexander Stepanovic Popov. 1.40k, Jan Holly. 1.60k, Pavel Josef Safarik.
699 A287 20h brown   .25   .20
700 A287 30h black   .25   .20
701 A287 40h gray green   .75   .20
702 A287 60h black   .50   .20
703 A287 75h claret   1.75   .70
704 A287 1.40k black, *cr*   .50   .20
705 A287 1.60k dark blue   .50   .20
     Nos. 699-705 (7)   4.50   1.90
Various anniversaries of prominent Slavs.

Girl and Boy of Two Races — A288   Costume of Ocova, Slovakia — A289

1955, July 20
706 A288 60h violet blue   .75   .20
5th World Festival of Youth in Warsaw, July 31-Aug. 14.

1955, July 25
Regional Costumes: 75h, Detva man, Slovakia. 1.60k, Chodsko man, Bohemia. 2k, Hana woman, Moravia.

Frame and Outlines in Brown
707 A289 60h orange & rose   9.00   6.00
708 A289 75h orange & lilac   3.75   3.75
709 A289 1.60k blue & orange   11.00   6.75
710 A289 2k yellow & rose   11.00   6.75
     Nos. 707-710 (4)   34.75   23.25
Nos. 707-710 were each issued in sheets of 10 stamps. Value, $360.

Carp A290

Designs: 30h, Beetle. 35h, Gray Partridge. 1.40k, Butterfly. 1.50k, Hare.

1955, Aug. 8   **Engr. & Photo.**
711 A290 20h sepia & lt bl   2.40   .35
712 A290 30h sepia & pink   1.60   .30
713 A290 35h sepia & buff   1.60   .75
714 A290 1.40k sepia & cream   7.75   4.50
715 A290 1.50k sepia & lt grn   2.60   1.00
     Nos. 711-715 (5)   15.95   6.90

Tabor A291

45h, Prachatice. 60h, Jindrichuv Hradec.

1955, Aug. 26   **Engr.**
716 A291 30h violet brown   .35   .20
717 A291 45h rose carmine   1.50   .75
718 A291 60h sage green   .75   .20
     Nos. 716-718 (3)   2.60   1.15
Issued to publicize the architectural beauty of the towns of Southern Bohemia.

Souvenir Sheet

Various Views of Prague — A292

1955, Sept. 10   **Engr.**   *Perf. 14x13½*
719 A292   Sheet of 5   24.00   27.50
   a.   30h gray black   4.50   5.25
   b.   45h gray black   4.50   5.25
   c.   60h rose lake   4.50   5.25
   d.   75h rose lake   4.50   5.25
   e.   1.60k gray black   4.50   5.25
International Philatelic Exhibition, Prague, Sept. 10-25, 1955. Size: 145x110mm. Exists imperf., value $40.

Motorcyclists A293   Workers, Soldier and Pioneer A294

1955, Aug. 28
720 A293 60h violet brown   3.00   .75
30th International Motorcycle Races at Gottwaldov, Sept. 13-18, 1955.

1955, Oct. 6   **Unwmk.**   *Perf. 11½*
Army Day: 60h, Tanks and planes.
721 A294 30h violet brown   .35   .20
722 A294 60h slate   1.75   1.25

Hans Christian Andersen — A295

Portraits: 40h, Friedrich von Schiller. 60h, Adam Mickiewicz. 75h, Walt Whitman.

1955, Oct. 27
723 A295 30h brown red   .35   .20
724 A295 40h dark blue   2.25   1.00
725 A295 60h deep claret   .35   .20
726 A295 75h greenish black   .75   .35
     Nos. 723-726 (4)   3.70   1.75
Issued in honor of these four poets and to mark the 100th anniversary of the publication of Walt Whitman's "Leaves of Grass."

Railroad Bridge A296

30h, Train crossing bridge. 60h, Train approaching tunnel. 1.60k, Miners' housing project.

Inscribed: "Stavba Socialismu"

1955, Dec. 15

727	A296	20h dull green	.40	.20
728	A296	30h violet brown	.80	.20
729	A296	60h slate	.80	.20
730	A296	1.60k carmine rose	.55	.20
		Nos. 727-730 (4)	2.55	.80

Issued to publicize socialist public works.

Hydroelectric Plant — A297

Jewelry — A298

2nd Five Year Plan: 10h, Miner with drill. 25h, Building construction. 30h, Harvester. 60h, Metallurgical plant.

Inscribed: "Druhy Petilety Plan 1956-1960."

1956, Feb. 20   **Perf. 11½x11**

731	A297	5h violet brown	.30	.20
732	A297	10h gray black	.30	.20
733	A297	25h dk car rose	.55	.20
734	A297	30h green	.35	.20
735	A297	60h violet blue	.55	.20
		Nos. 731-735 (5)	2.05	1.00

1956, Mar. 17   **Perf. 11x11½**

736	A298	30h shown	.55	.20
737	A298	45h Glassware	4.00	2.00
738	A298	60h Ceramics	.80	.20
739	A298	75h Textiles	.65	.30
		Nos. 736-739 (4)	6.00	2.70

Products of Czechoslovakian industries.

Karlovy Vary (Karlsbad) A299

"We Serve our People" A300

Various Spas: 45h, Marianske Lazne (Marienbad). 75h, Piestany. 1.20k, Tatry Vysne Ruzbachy (Tatra Mountains).

1956, Mar. 17

740	A299	30h olive green	1.50	.30
741	A299	45h brown	1.20	.30
742	A299	75h claret	6.00	4.00
743	A299	1.20k ultra	.80	.30
		Nos. 740-743 (4)	9.50	4.90

Issued to publicize Czechoslovakian spas.

1956, Apr. 9   **Photo.**   **Perf. 11x11½**

Designs: 60h, Russian War Memorial, Berlin. 1k, Tank crewman with standard.

744	A300	30h olive brown	.75	.20
745	A300	60h carmine rose	.75	.20
746	A300	1k ultra	4.75	3.00
		Nos. 744-746 (3)	6.25	3.40

Exhibition: "The Construction and Defense of our Country," Prague, Apr., 1956.

Cyclists — A301

Girl Basketball Players — A302

Athletes and Olympic Rings — A303

Engraved and Photogravure

1956, Apr. 25   **Unwmk.**   **Perf. 11½**

747	A301	30h green & lt blue	4.00	.40
748	A302	45h dk blue & car	1.60	.40
749	A303	75h brown & lemon	1.25	.80
		Nos. 747-749 (3)	6.85	1.60

9th Intl. Peace Cycling Race, Warsaw-Berlin-Prague, May 1-15, 1956 (No. 747). 5th European Womens' Basketball Championship (No. 748). Summer Olympics, Melbourne, Nov. 22-Dec. 8, 1956 (No. 749).

Mozart — A304

Home Guard — A305

45h, Josef Myslivecek. 60h, Jiri Benda. 1k, Bertramka House, Prague. 1.40k, Xaver Dusek (1731-99) and wife Josepha. 1.60k, Nostic Theater, Prague.

1956, May 12   **Engr.**

Design in Gray Black

750	A304	30h bister	1.50	.35
751	A304	45h gray green	13.50	9.00
752	A304	60h pale rose lilac	1.50	.35
753	A304	1k salmon	1.90	.35
754	A304	1.40k lt blue	4.50	.75
755	A304	1.60k lemon	3.00	.35
		Nos. 750-755 (6)	25.90	11.15

200th anniv. of the birth of Wolfgang Amadeus Mozart and to publicize the International Music Festival in Prague.

1956, May 25

756	A305	60h violet blue	.75	.20

Issued to commemorate the first meeting of the Home Guard, Prague, May 25-27, 1956.

Josef Kajetan Tyl — A306

River Patrol — A307

Portraits: 20h, Ludovit Stur. 30h, Frana Sramek. 1.40k, Karel Havlicek Borovsky.

1956, June 23

757	A306	20h dull purple	.75	.20
758	A306	30h blue	.45	.20
759	A306	60h black	.45	.20
760	A306	1.40k claret	3.00	1.75
		Nos. 757-760 (4)	4.65	2.35

Issued to honor various Czechoslovakian writers. See Nos. 781-784, 873-876.

1956, July 8   **Perf. 11x11½**

Design: 60h, Guard and dog.

761	A307	30h ultra	.85	.25
762	A307	60h green	.60	.20

Issued to honor men of Frontier Guard.

Type of 1956 and

Steeplechase — A308

1956, Sept. 8   **Unwmk.**   **Perf. 11½**

763	A308	60h indigo & bister	3.00	.80
764	A308	80h brown vio & vio	1.75	.40
765	A303	1.20k slate & orange	3.00	1.75
		Nos. 763-765 (3)	7.75	2.95

Steeplechase, Pardubice, 1956 (No. 763). Marathon race, Kosice, 1956 (No. 764). Olympic Games, Melbourne, Nov. 22-Dec. 8 (No. 765).

Woman Gathering Grapes — A309

Fishermen — A310

35h, Women gathering hops. 95h, Logging.

1956, Sept. 20   **Engr.**

766	A309	30h brown lake	.35	.20
767	A309	35h gray green	.35	.20
768	A310	80h dark blue	.75	.20
769	A310	95h chocolate	2.25	1.00
		Nos. 766-769 (4)	3.70	1.60

Issued to publicize natural resources.

European Timetable Conf., Prague, Nov. 9-13 — A311

A312

Locomotives: 10h, 1846. 30h, 1855. 40h, 1945. 45h, 1952. 60h, 1955. 1k, 1954.

1956, Nov. 9   **Unwmk.**   **Perf. 11½**

770	A311	10h brown	1.50	.30
771	A312	30h gray	3.00	.30
772	A312	40h green	4.50	.45

773	A312	45h brown car	13.50	6.75
774	A312	60h indigo	3.00	.30
775	A312	1k ultra	5.25	.45
		Nos. 770-775 (6)	30.75	8.55

Costume of Moravia — A313

Regional Costumes (women): 1.20k, Blata, Bohemia. 1.40k, Cicmany, Slovakia. 1.60k, Novohradsko, Slovakia.

1956, Dec. 15   **Perf. 13½**

776	A313	30h brn, ultra & car	1.60	1.60
777	A313	1.20k brn, car & ultra	2.75	.40
778	A313	1.40k brn, ocher & ver	8.25	2.75
779	A313	1.60k brn, car & grn	3.25	.80
		Nos. 776-779 (4)	15.85	5.55

See Nos. 832-835.
Nos. 776-779 each were issued in sheets of 10 stamps. Value, $160.

Zapotocky Type of 1953

1956, Oct. 7   **Unwmk.**   **Perf. 12½**

780	A251	30h blue	.75	.20

Portrait Type of 1956

15h, Ivan Olbracht. 20h, Karel Toman. 30h, F. X. Salda. 1.60k, Terezia Vansova.

1957, Jan. 18   **Engr.**   **Perf. 11½**

781	A306	15h dk red brn, cr	.30	.20
782	A306	20h dk green, cr	.30	.20
783	A306	30h dk brown, cr	.30	.20
784	A306	1.60k dk blue, cr	.60	.20
		Nos. 781-784 (4)	1.50	.80

Issued in honor of Czechoslovakian writers.

Kolin Cathedral — A315

Views: No. 786, Banska Stiavnica. No. 787, Uherske Hradiste. No. 788, Karlstein. No. 789, Charles Bridge, Prague. 1.25k, Moravska Trebova.

1957, Feb. 23

785	A315	30h dk blue gray	.30	.20
786	A315	30h rose violet	.45	.20
787	A315	60h deep rose	.45	.20
788	A315	60h gray green	.45	.20
789	A315	60h brown	.60	.20
790	A315	1.25k gray	2.50	1.50
		Nos. 785-790 (6)	4.75	2.50

Anniversaries of various towns and landmarks.

Komensky Mausoleum, Naarden A316

Jan A. Komensky A317

Farm Woman — A318

Old Prints: 40h, Komensky teaching. 1k, Sun, moon, stars and earth.

Perf. 11½x11, 14 (A317)

			Unwmk.	
1957, Mar. 28		**Engr.**		
791	A316	30h pale brown	.45	.20
792	A316	40h dark green	.45	.20
793	A317	60h chocolate	3.00	.75
794	A316	1k carmine rose	.60	.20
		Nos. 791-794 (4)	4.50	1.35

300th anniv. of the publication of "Didactica Opera Omnia" by J. A. Komensky (Comenius). No. 793 issued in sheets of four.

			Perf. 11½	
1957, Mar. 22				
795	A318	30h lt blue green	.75	.20

3rd Cong. of Agricultural Cooperatives.

Cyclists A319

Woman Archer A320

Boxers — A321

Rescue Team A322

1957, Apr. 30		**Perf. 11½x11, 11x11½**		
796	A319	30h sepia & ultra	.60	.20
797	A319	60h dull grn & bis	2.25	1.25
798	A320	60h gray & emer	.45	.20
799	A321	60h sepia & org	.45	.20
800	A322	60h violet & choc	.75	.20
		Nos. 796-800 (5)	4.50	2.05

10th Intl. Peace Cycling Race, Prague-Berlin-Warsaw (#796-797). Intl. Archery Championships (#798). European Boxing Championships, Prague (#799). Mountain Climbing Rescue Service (#800).

Jan V. Stamic — A323

Musicians: No. 802, Ferdinand Laub. No. 803, Frantisek Ondricek. No. 804, Josef B.

Foerster. No. 805, Vitezslav Novak. No. 806, Josef Suk.

			Perf. 11½	
1957, May 12				
801	A323	60h purple	.35	.20
802	A323	60h black	.35	.20
803	A323	60h slate blue	.35	.20
804	A323	60h brown	.35	.20
805	A323	60h dull red brn	.90	.20
806	A323	60h blue green	.35	.20
		Nos. 801-806 (6)	2.65	1.20

Spring Music Festival, Prague.

Josef Bozek — A324

School of Engineering A325

60h, F. J. Gerstner. 1k, R. Skuhersky.

1957, May 25				
807	A324	30h bluish black	.20	.20
808	A324	60h gray brown	.35	.20
809	A324	1k rose lake	.35	.20
810	A325	1.40k blue violet	.75	.20
		Nos. 807-810 (4)	1.65	.80

School of Engineering in Prague, 250th anniv.

Pioneer and Philatelic Symbols A326

Design: 60h, Girl and carrier pigeon.

Engraved and Photogravure

			Perf. 11½	
1957, June 8				
811	A326	30h olive grn & org	.50	.20

		Engr.	Perf. 13½	
812	A326	60h brn & vio bl	1.50	1.00

Youth Philatelic Exhibition, Pardubice. No. 812 was printed in miniature sheets of 4. Value $12.

"Grief" A327

Motorcyclists A328

Design: 60h, Rose, symbol of new life.

1957, June 10				
813	A327	30h black	.40	.20
814	A327	60h blk & rose red	1.40	.45

Destruction of Lidice, 15th anniversary. No. 814 was issued in a sheet of 10 stamps. Value, $28.

			Perf. 11½	
1957, July 5				
815	A328	60h dk gray & blue	1.50	.30

32nd International Motorcycle Race.

Karel Klic — A329

Josef Ressel — A330

1957, July 5				
816	A329	30h gray black	.60	.20
817	A330	60h violet blue	.60	.20

Klic, inventor of photogravure, and Ressel, inventor of the ship screw.

Chamois — A331

Gentian A332

Designs: 30h, Brown bear. 60h, Edelweiss. 1.25k, Tatra Mountains.

		Engr.	Perf. 11½	
1957, Aug. 28				
818	A331	20h emer & brnsh gray	1.10	.35
819	A331	30h lt blue & brn	1.10	.20
820	A332	40h gldn brn & vio bl	2.00	.35
821	A332	60h yellow & grn	1.10	.20
		Size: 48x28½mm		
822	A332	1.25k ol grn & bis	2.00	1.00
		Nos. 818-822 (5)	7.30	2.10

Tatra Mountains National Park.

"Marycka Magdonova" A333

Man Holding Banner of Trade Union Cong. A334

Engraved and Photogravure

			Unwmk.	Perf. 11½	
1957, Sept. 15					
823	A333	60h black & dull red		.45	.20

90th birthday of Petr Bezruc, poet and author of "Marycka Magdonova."

				Engr.	
1957, Sept. 28					
824	A334	75h rose red		.45	.20

4th Intl. Trade Union Cong., Leipzig, 10/4-15.

Television Transmitter and Antennas — A335

Design: 60h, Family watching television.

			Perf. 11½	
1957, Oct. 19		**Engr.**		
825	A335	40h dk blue & car	.30	.20
826	A335	60h redsh brown & emer	.45	.20

Issued to publicize the television industry.

Worker, Globe and Lenin A336

60h, Worker, factory, hammer and sickle.

			Perf. 12x11½	
1957, Nov. 7				
827	A336	30h claret	.20	.20
828	A336	60h gray blue	.25	.20

Russian Revolution, 40th anniversary.

Zapotocky Type of 1954 dated: 19 XII 1884-13 XI 1957

			Unwmk.	Perf. 11½	
1957, Nov. 18					
829	A276	30h black		.25	.20
830	A276	60h black		.25	.20

Souvenir Sheet

Imperf

831	A276	2k black	4.00	2.00

Death of Pres. Antonin Zapotocky.

Costume Type of 1956

Regional Costumes: 45h, Pilsen woman, Bohemia. 75h, Slovacko man, Moravia. 1.25k, Hana woman, Moravia. 1.95k, Teshinsko woman, Silesia.

			Perf. 13½	
1957, Dec. 18		**Engr.**		
832	A313	45h brn, bl & dk red	4.25	1.50
833	A313	75h dk brn, red & grn	3.00	.80
834	A313	1.25k dk brn, scar & ocher	5.25	1.50
835	A313	1.95k sepia, bl & ver	6.00	3.75
		Nos. 832-835 (4)	18.50	7.55

Nos. 832-835 each was issued in sheets of 10 stamps. Value, set $200.

A337

A338

Designs: 30h, Radio telescope and observatory. 45h, Meteorological station in High Tatra. 75h, Sputnik 2 over Earth.

			Perf. 11½	
1957, Dec. 20				
836	A337	30h violet brn & yel	2.00	.65
837	A338	45h sepia & lt bl	.50	.35
838	A337	75h claret & blue	2.75	1.00
		Nos. 836-838 (3)	5.25	2.00

IGY, 1957-58. No. 838 also for the launching of Sputnik 2, Nov. 3, 1957.

Girl Skater — A339

Litomysl Castle — A340

Designs: 40h, Canoeing. 60h, Volleyball. 80h, Parachutist. 1.60k, Soccer.

1958, Jan. 25   Engr.   Perf. 11½x12

839	A339	30h rose violet	3.50	.25
840	A339	40h blue	.70	.20
841	A339	60h redsh brown	.70	.20
842	A339	80h violet blue	2.00	.50
843	A339	1.60k brt green	.65	.20
		Nos. 839-843 (5)	7.55	1.35

Issued to publicize various sports championship events in 1958.

1958, Feb. 10   Perf. 11½

Design: 60h, Bethlehem Chapel.

844	A340	30h green	.30	.20
845	A340	60h redsh brown	.30	.20

80th anniversary of the birth of Zdenek Nejedly, restorer of Bethlehem Chapel.

Giant Excavator A341

Jewelry — A342

Peace Dove and: 60h, Soldiers, flame and banner, horiz. 1.60k, Harvester and rainbow, horiz.

1958, Feb. 25

846	A341	30h gray violet & yel	.20	.20
847	A341	60h gray brown & car	.30	.20
848	A341	1.60k green & dull yel	.50	.20
		Nos. 846-848 (3)	1.00	.60

10th anniv. of the "Victorious February."

Engraved and Photogravure
1958   Unwmk.   Perf. 11½

Designs: 45h, Dolls. 60h, Textiles. 75h, Kaplan turbine. 1.20k, Glass.

849	A342	30h rose car & blue	.40	.20
850	A342	45h rose red & pale lil	.40	.20
851	A342	60h violet & aqua	.60	.20
852	A342	75h ultra & salmon	1.50	.75
853	A342	1.20k blue grn & pink	.60	.20
		Nos. 849-853 (5)	3.50	1.55

Issued for the Universal and International Exposition at Brussels.

King George of Podebrad — A343

Design: 60h, View of Prague, 1628.

1958, May 19   Engr.

854	A343	30h carmine rose	.50	.20
855	A343	60h violet blue	.30	.20

Issued to publicize the National Archives Exhibition, Prague, May 15-Aug. 15.

"Towards the Stars" — A344

Women of Three Races — A345

Boy, Girl and Globes A346

1958, May 26

856	A344	30h carmine rose	.95	.35
857	A345	45h rose violet	.25	.20
858	A346	60h blue	.25	.20
		Nos. 856-858 (3)	1.45	.75

The Soc. for Dissemination of Political and Cultural Knowledge (#856). 4th Cong. of the Intl. Democratic Women's Fed. (#857). 1st World Trade Union Conf. of Working Youths, Prague, July 14-20 (#858).

Grain, Hammer and Sickle A347

Atomic Reactor A348

45h, Map of Czechoslovakia, hammer & sickle.

1958, May 26

859	A347	30h dull red	.25	.20
860	A347	45h green	.25	.20
861	A348	60h dark blue	.25	.20
		Nos. 859-861 (3)	.75	.60

11th Congress of the Czech Communist Party and the 15th anniv. of the Russo-Czechoslovakian Treaty.

Karlovy Vary A349

Various Spas: 40h, Podebrady. 60h, Marianske Lazne. 80h, Luhacovice. 1.20k, Strbske Pleso. 1.60k, Trencianske Teplice.

1958, June 25

862	A349	30h rose claret	.45	.20
863	A349	40h redsh brown	.45	.20
864	A349	60h gray green	.30	.20
865	A349	80h sepia	.45	.20
866	A349	1.20k violet blue	.60	.20
867	A349	1.60k lt violet	1.20	.75
		Nos. 862-867 (6)	3.45	1.75

Telephone Operator A350

Pres. Novotny A351

Design: 45h, Radio transmitter.

1958, June 20

868	A350	30h black & brn org	.40	.20
869	A350	45h black & lt grn	.50	.20

Conference of Postal Ministers of Communist Countries, Prague, June 30-July 9.

1958-59   Perf. 12½

870	A351	30h brt violet blue	.80	.20
b.		Perf. 11½	.80	.20
870A	A351	30h violet ('59)	4.50	1.75
871	A351	60h carmine rose	.50	.20

Perf. 11½
Redrawn

871A	A351	60h rose red	.50	.20
		Nos. 870-871A (4)	6.30	2.35

On No. 871 the top of the "6" turns down; on No. 871A it is open.

Czechoslovak Pavilion, Brussels — A352

1958, July 15   Engr. & Photo.

872	A352	1.95k lt blue & bis brn	.90	.20

Czechoslovakia Week at the Universal and International Exhibition at Brussels.

Portrait Type of 1956

30h, Julius Fucik. 45h, G. K. Zechenter 60h, Karel Capek. 1.40k, Svatopluk Cech.

1958, Aug. 20   Engr.   Perf. 11½

873	A306	30h rose red	.40	.20
874	A306	45h violet	2.10	.50
875	A306	60h dk blue gray	.75	.20
876	A306	1.40k gray	.75	.20
		Nos. 873-876 (4)	4.00	1.10

Death anniversaries of four famous Czechs.

The Artist and the Muse — A353

1958, Aug. 20   Perf. 14

877	A353	1.60k black	4.50	1.25

85th birthday of Max Svabinsky, artist and engraver.

No. 877 was printed in miniature sheets of 4. Value $24.

Children's Hospital, Brno — A354

Designs: 60h, New Town Hall, Brno. 1k, St. Thomas Church. 1.60k, View of Brno.

1958, Sept. 6   Unwmk.   Perf. 11½
Size: 40x23mm

878	A354	30h violet	.20	.20
879	A354	60h rose red	.20	.20
880	A354	1k brown	.45	.20

Perf. 14
Size: 50x28mm

881	A354	1.60k dk slate grn	1.90	1.75
		Nos. 878-881 (4)	2.75	2.35

Natl. Phil. Exhib., Brno, Sept. 9. No. 881 sold for 3.10k, including entrance ticket to exhibition. Issued in sheets of four. Value, $10.

Lepiota Procera — A355

Children on Beach — A356

Mushrooms: 40h, Boletus edulis. 60h, Krombholzia rufescens. 1.40k, Amanita muscaria L. 1.60k, Armillariella mellea.

1958, Oct. 6   Perf. 14

882	A355	30h dk brn, grn & buff	1.60	.80
883	A355	40h vio brn & brn org	2.40	.80
884	A355	60h black, red & buff	3.25	.80
885	A355	1.40k brown, scar & grn	4.00	2.25
886	A355	1.60k blk, red brn & ol	13.00	5.75
		Nos. 882-886 (5)	24.25	10.40

Nos. 882-886 were each issued in a miniature sheet of 10 stamps. Value, set $240.

1958, Oct. 24   Unwmk.   Perf. 14

45h, Mother, child and bird. 60h, Skier.

887	A356	30h blue, yel & red	.40	.25
888	A356	45h ultra & carmine	1.60	.85
889	A356	60h brown, blue & yel	.40	.25
		Nos. 887-889 (3)	2.40	1.35

UNESCO Headquarters in Paris opening, Nov. 3.

Bozek's Steam Car of 1815 A357

Designs: 45h, "Präsident" car of 1897. 60h, "Skoda" sports car. 80h, "Tatra" sedan. 1k, "Autocar Skoda" bus. 1.25k, Trucks.

Engraved and Photogravure
1958, Dec. 1   Perf. 11½x11

890	A357	30h vio blk & buff	.75	.20
891	A357	45h ol & lt ol grn	.75	.30
892	A357	60h ol gray & sal	1.75	.30
893	A357	80h claret & bl grn	1.10	.30
894	A357	1k brn & lt yel grn	1.50	.30
895	A357	1.25k green & buff	2.25	.45
		Nos. 890-895 (6)	8.10	1.75

Issued to honor the automobile industry.

Stamp of 1918 and Allegory — A358

1958, Dec. 18   Engr.   Perf. 11x11½
896 A358 60h dark blue gray   1.25 .30

1st Czechoslovakian postage stamp, 40th anniv.

Ice Hockey A359

30h, Girl throwing javelin. 60h, Ice hockey. 1k, Hurdling. 1.60k, Rowing. 2k, High jump.

1959, Feb. 14   Perf. 11½x11
897 A359 20h dk brown & gray   .65 .20
898 A359 30h red brn & org brn   .45 .20
899 A359 60h dk bl & pale grn   .80 .20
900 A359 1k maroon & citron   .65 .20
901 A359 1.60k dull vio & lt bl   .95 .20
902 A359 2k red brn & lt bl   2.00 1.00
       Nos. 897-902 (6)   5.50 2.00

Congress Emblem — A360   "Equality of All Races" — A361

60h, Industrial & agricultural workers, emblem.

1959, Feb. 27   Perf. 11½
903 A360 30h maroon & lt blue   .45 .20
904 A360 60h dk blue & yellow   .45 .20

4th Agricultural Cooperative Cong. in Prague.

1959, Mar. 23
Designs: 1k, "Peace." 2k, Mother and Child: "Freedom for Colonial People."

905 A361 60h gray green   .30 .20
906 A361 1k gray   .45 .20
907 A361 2k dk gray blue   1.50 .50
       Nos. 905-907 (3)   2.25 .90

10th anniversary of the signing of the Universal Declaration of Human Rights.

Girl Holding Doll — A362   Frederic Joliot Curie — A363

40h, Pioneer studying map. 60h, Pioneer with radio. 80h, Girl pioneer planting tree.

1959, Mar. 28   Engr. & Photo.
908 A362 30h violet bl & yel   .45 .25
909 A362 40h indigo & ultra   .45 .25
910 A362 60h black & lilac   .45 .25
911 A362 80h brown & lt green   1.00 .25
       Nos. 908-911 (4)   2.35 1.00

10th anniv. of the Pioneer organization.

1959, Apr. 17   Engr.
912 A363 60h sepia   1.60 .30

Frederic Joliot Curie and the 10th anniversary of the World Peace Movement.

"Reaching for the Moon" — A364   Town Hall Pilsen — A365

1959, Apr. 17
913 A364 30h violet blue   1.25 .30

2nd Cong. of the Czechoslovak Assoc. for the Propagation of Political and Cultural knowledge.

1959, May 2
Designs: 60h, Part of steam condenser turbine. 1k, St. Bartholomew's Church, Pilsen. 1.60k, Part of lathe.

914 A365 30h lt brown   .25 .25
915 A365 60h violet & lt grn   .30 .25
916 A365 1k violet blue   .40 .25
917 A365 1.60k black & yellow   1.60 1.10
       Nos. 914-917 (4)   2.55 1.85

2nd Pilsen Stamp Exhib. in connection with the centenary of the Skoda (Lenin) armament works.

Factory and Emblem A366

Inscribed: "IV Vseodborovy sjezd, 1959"

1959, May 13
918 A366 30h shown   .50 .20
919 A366 60h Dam   .30 .20

4th Trade Union Congress.

Zvolen Castle A367

1959, June 13
920 A367 60h gray olive & yel   .75 .20

Regional Stamp Exhibition, Zvolen, 1959.

Frantisek Benda — A368   Aurel Stodola — A369

30h, Vaclav Kliment Klicpera. 60h, Karel V. Rais. 80h, Antonin Slavicek. 1k, Peter Bezruc.

1959, June 22   Perf. 11½x11
921 A368 15h violet blue   .25 .20
922 A368 30h orange brown   .25 .20
923 A369 40h dull green   .25 .20
924 A369 60h dull red brn   .35 .20
925 A369 80h dull violet   .65 .20
926 A368 1k dark brown   .65 .25
       Nos. 921-926 (6)   2.40 1.25

View of the Fair Grounds A370

Designs: 60h, Fair emblem and world map. 1.60k, Pavilion "Z."

Inscribed: "Mezinarodni Veletrh Brne 6.-20.IX. 1959"

Engraved and Photogravure
1959, July 20   Unwmk.   Perf. 11½
927 A370 30h lilac & yellow   .25 .20
928 A370 60h dull blue   .25 .20
929 A370 1.60k dk blue & bister   .75 .20
       Nos. 927-929 (3)   1.25 .60

International Fair at Brno, Sept. 6-20.

Revolutionist and Flag — A371

Slovakian Fighter — A372

1.60k, Linden leaves, sun and factory.

Perf. 11½
1959, Aug. 29   Unwmk.   Engr.
930 A371 30h black & rose   .20 .20
931 A372 60h carmine rose   .25 .20
932 A371 1.60k dk blue & yel   .45 .20
       Nos. 930-932 (3)   .90 .60

Natl. Slovakian revolution, 15th anniv. and Slovakian Soviet Republic, 40th anniv.

Alpine Marmots A373

1959, Sept. 25   Engr. & Photo.
933 A373 30h shown   1.60 .25
934 A373 40h Bison   1.10 .40
935 A373 60h Lynx, vert.   3.25 .25
936 A373 1k Wolf   3.25 .25
937 A373 1.60k Red deer   2.75 .55
       Nos. 933-937 (5)   11.95 1.70

Tatra National Park, 10th anniv.

Lunik 2 Hitting Moon and Russian Flag A374

1959, Sept. 23   Perf. 11½
938 A374 60h dk red & lt ultra   1.90 .30

Issued to commemorate the landing of the Soviet rocket on the moon, Sept. 13, 1959.

Stamp Printing Works, Peking A375

1959, Oct. 1
939 A375 30h pale green & red   .40 .20

10 years of Czechoslovakian-Chinese friendship.

Haydn — A376

Great Spotted Woodpecker A377

Design: 3k, Charles Darwin.

1959, Oct. 16   Engr.   Perf. 11½
940 A376 60h violet black   .50 .20
941 A376 3k dark red brown   1.50 .70

150th death anniv. of Franz Joseph Haydn, Austrian composer, and 150th birth anniv. of Charles Darwin, English naturalist.

1959, Nov. 16   Perf. 14
Birds: 30h, Blue tits. 40h, Nuthatch. 60h, Golden oriole. 80h, Goldfinch. 1k, Bullfinch. 1.20k, European kingfisher.

942 A377 20h multicolored   1.50 .60
943 A377 30h multicolored   1.50 .60
944 A377 40h multicolored   6.50 1.50
945 A377 60h multicolored   1.50 .60
946 A377 80h multicolored   2.50 .90
947 A377 1k multicolored   2.75 .90
948 A377 1.20k multicolored   5.00 1.25
       Nos. 942-948 (7)   21.25 6.35

Nos. 942-948 were each issued in miniature sheets of 10. Value, set $250.

Nikola Tesla A378

Designs: 30h, Alexander S. Popov. 35h, Edouard Branly. 60h, Guglielmo Marconi. 1k, Heinrich Hertz. 2k, Edwin Howard Armstrong and research tower, Alpine, N. J.

Engraved and Photogravure
1959, Dec. 7   Perf. 11½
949 A378 25h black & pink   .65 .20
950 A378 30h black & orange   .25 .20
951 A378 35h black & lt vio   .25 .20
952 A378 60h black & blue   .25 .20
953 A378 1k black & lt grn   .30 .20
954 A378 2k black & bister   1.90 .40
       Nos. 949-954 (6)   3.60 1.40

Issued to honor inventors in the fields of telegraphy and radio.

Gymnast — A379

2nd Winter Spartacist Games: 60h, Skier. 1.60k, Basketball players.

1960, Jan. 20   **Perf. 11½**
955 A379   30h salmon pink & brn   1.10   .20
956 A379   60h lt blue & blk   1.10   .20
957 A379   1.60k bister & brn   1.00   .25
    Nos. 955-957 (3)   3.20   .65

1960, June 15   **Unwmk.**
Designs: 30h, Two girls in "Red Ball" drill. 60h, Gymnast with stick. 1k, Three girls with hoops.
958 A379   30h lt grn & rose claret   .65   .20
959 A379   60h pink & black   .50   .20
960 A379   1k ocher & vio bl   .85   .20
    Nos. 958-960 (3)   2.00   .60
2nd Summer Spartacist Games, Prague, June 23-July 3.

River Dredge Boat A380

Ships: 60h, River tug. 1k, Tourist steamer. 1.20k, Cargo ship "Lidice."

1960, Feb. 22   **Perf. 11½**
961 A380   30h slate grn & sal   3.00   .30
962 A380   60h maroon & pale bl   1.60   .30
963 A380   1k dk violet & yel   2.75   .30
964 A380   1.20k lilac & pale grn   4.00   .90
    Nos. 961-964 (4)   11.35   1.80

Ice Hockey Players — A381

Design: 1.80k, Figure skaters.

1960, Feb. 27
965 A381   60h sepia & lt blue   2.40   .50
966 A381   1.80k black & lt green   7.25   2.00
8th Olympic Winter Games, Squaw Valley, Calif., Feb. 18-29, 1960.

1960, June 15   **Unwmk.**
Designs: 1k, Running. 1.80k, Women's gymnastics. 2k, Rowing.
967 A381   1k black & orange   1.00   .30
968 A381   1.80k black & sal pink   1.60   .40
969 A381   2k black & blue   2.50   .95
    Nos. 967-969 (3)   5.10   1.65
17th Olympic Games, Rome, 8/25-9/11.

Trencin Castle — A382

Castles: 10h, Bezdez. 20h, Kost. 30h, Pernstein. 40h, Kremnica. 50h, Krivoklát castle. 60h, Karlstein. 1k, Smolenice. 1.60k, Kokorin.

1960-63   **Engr.**   **Perf. 11½**
970 A382   5h gray violet   .30   .20
971 A382   10h black   .30   .20
972 A382   20h brown org   .40   .20
973 A382   30h green   .30   .20
974 A382   40h brown   .40   .20
974A A382   50h black ('63)   4.00   .20
975 A382   60h rose red   .45   .20
976 A382   1k lilac   .45   .20
977 A382   1.60k dark blue   .90   .20
    Nos. 970-977 (9)   7.50   1.80

1961, Oct.   **Wmk. 341**
977A A382   30h green   3.25   .40

Lenin — A383   Soldier Holding Child — A384

1960, Apr. 22   **Unwmk.**
978 A383   60h gray olive   1.60   .20
90th anniversary of the birth of Lenin.

1960, May 5   **Engr. & Photo.**
Designs: No. 980, Child eating pie. No. 981, Soldier helping concentration camp victim. No. 982, Welder and factory, horiz. No. 983, Tractor driver and farm, horiz.
979 A384   30h maroon & lt blue   .35   .20
980 A384   30h dull red   .35   .20
981 A384   30h green & dull blue   .40   .20
982 A384   60h dk blue & buff   .35   .20
983 A384   60h redsh brn & yel grn   .40   .20
    Nos. 979-983 (5)   1.85   1.00
15th anniversary of liberation.

Steelworker — A385

Design: 60h, Farm woman and child.

1960, May 24
984 A385   30h maroon & gray   .20   .20
985 A385   60h green & pale blue   .30   .20
1960 parliamentary elections.

Red Cross Nurse Holding Dove A386

Fire Fighters A387

1960, May 26   **Unwmk.**
986 A386   30h brown car & bl   .40   .20
987 A387   60h dk blue & pink   .60   .20
3rd Congress of the Czechoslovakian Red Cross (No. 986), and the 2nd Fire Fighters' Congress (No. 987).

Hand of Philatelist with Tongs and Two Stamps — A388

Design: 1k, Globe and 1937 Bratislava stamp (shown in miniature on 60h).

1960, July 11   **Perf. 11½**
988 A388   60h black & dull yel   .80   .20
989 A388   1k black & blue   1.00   .20
Issued to publicize the National Stamp Exhibition, Bratislava, Sept. 24-Oct. 9.
See Nos. C49-C50.

Stalin Mine, Ostrava-Hermanovice — A390

Viktorin Cornelius, Lawyer — A391

Designs: 20h, Power station, Hodonin. 30h, Gottwald iron works, Kuncice. 40h, Harvester. 60h, Oil refinery.

1960, July 25
992 A390   10h black & pale grn   .30   .20
993 A390   20h maroon & lt bl   .30   .20
994 A390   30h indigo & pink   .30   .20
995 A390   40h green & pale lilac   .30   .20
996 A390   60h dk blue & yel   .30   .20
    Nos. 992-996 (5)   1.50   1.00
Issued to publicize the new five-year plan.

1960, Aug. 23   **Engr.**
Portraits: 20h, Karel Matej Capek-Chod, writer. 30h, Hana Kvapilova, actress. 40h, Oskar Nedbal, composer. 60h, Otakar Ostrcil, composer.
997 A391   10h black   .40   .20
998 A391   20h red brown   .45   .20
999 A391   30h rose red   .65   .20
1000 A391   40h dull green   1.60   .80
1001 A391   60h gray violet   .45   .20
    Nos. 997-1001 (5)   3.55   1.60
See Nos. 1037-1041.

Skoda Sports Plane Flying Upside Down A392

1960, Aug. 28   **Engr. & Photo.**
1002 A392   60h violet blue & blue   1.50   .30
1st aerobatic world championships, Bratislava.

Constitution and "Czechoslovakia" — A393

1960, Sept. 18
1003 A393   30h violet bl & pink   .40   .20
Proclamation of the new socialist constitution.

Workers Reading Newspaper — A394

Man Holding Newspaper — A395

1960, Sept. 18
1004 A395   30h slate & ver   .25   .20
1005 A395   60h black & rose   .25   .20
Day of the Czechoslovak Press, Sept. 21, 1960, and 40th anniv. of the Rudé Právo paper.

Globes and Laurel A396

1960, Sept. 18   **Engr.**
1006 A396   30h dk blue & bister   .40   .20
World Federation of Trade Unions, 15th anniv.

Black-crowned Night Heron — A397   Doronicum Clusii (Thistle) — A398

Birds: 30h, Great crested grebe. 40h, Lapwing. 60h, Gray heron. 1k, Graylag goose, horiz. 1.60k, Mallard, horiz.

Engraved and Photogravure
1960, Oct. 24   **Unwmk.**   **Perf. 11½**
Designs in Black
1007 A397   25h pale vio blue   .90   .20
1008 A397   30h pale citron   .80   .20
1009 A397   40h pale blue   .90   .20
1010 A397   60h pink   .60   .20
1011 A397   1k pale yellow   1.75   .20
1012 A397   1.60k lt violet   4.50   1.25
    Nos. 1007-1012 (6)   9.45   2.35

1960, Nov. 21   **Engr.**   **Perf. 14**
Flowers: 30h, Cyclamen. 40h, Primrose. 60h, Hen-and-chickens. 1k, Gentian. 2k, Pasqueflower.
1013 A398   20h black, yel & grn   .85   .85
1014 A398   30h black, car rose & grn   .85   .85
1015 A398   40h black, yel & grn   .85   .85
1016 A398   60h black, pink & grn   .85   .85
1017 A398   1k black, bl, vio & grn   2.50   .85
1018 A398   2k black, lil, yel & grn   3.25   1.60
    Nos. 1013-1018 (6)   9.15   5.85

Alfons Mucha — A399

1960, Dec. 18   **Engr.**   **Perf. 11½x12**
1019 A399   60h dk blue gray   3.25   .20
Day of the Czechoslovak Postage Stamp and birth cent. of Alfons Mucha, designer of the 1st Czechoslovakian stamp (Type A1).

Rolling-mill Control Bridge — A400

Athletes with Flags — A401

Designs: 30h, Turbo generator. 60h, Ditch-digging machine.

1961, Jan. 20 Unwmk. Perf. 11½
1020	A400	20h blue	.30	.20
1021	A400	30h rose	.30	.20
1022	A400	60h brt green	.30	.20
		Nos. 1020-1022 (3)	.90	.60

Third Five-Year Plan.

Perf. 11x11½, 11½x11
1961, Feb. 20 Engr. & Photo.

Designs: No. 1024, Motorcycle race, horiz. 40h, Sculling, horiz. 60h, Ice skater. 1k, Rugby. 1.20k, Soccer. 1.60k, Long-distance runners.

1023	A401	30h rose red & bl	.30	.20
1024	A401	30h dk blue & car	.30	.20
1025	A401	40h dk gray & car	.50	.20
1026	A401	60h lilac & blue	.50	.20
1027	A401	1k ultra & yel	.50	.20
1028	A401	1.20k green & buff	.75	.20
1029	A401	1.60k sepia & salmon	2.00	1.00
		Nos. 1023-1029 (7)	4.85	2.20

Various sports events.

Exhibition Emblem A402

Rocket Launching A403

1961, Mar. 6 Engr. Perf. 11½
1030	A402	2k dk blue & red	2.40	.20

"Praga 1962" International Stamp Exhibition, Prague, Sept. 1962.

1961, Mar. 6 Engr. & Photo.

30h, Sputnik III, horiz. 40h, As 20h, but inscribed "Start Kosmicke Rakety k Venusi — 12.II.1961". 60h, Sputnik I, horiz. 1.60h, Interplanetary station, horiz. 2k, Similar to type A404, without commemorative inscription.

1031	A403	20h violet & pink	.40	.20
1032	A403	30h dk green & buff	.80	.20
1033	A403	40h dk red & yel grn	.80	.20
1034	A403	60h violet & buff	.95	.20
1035	A403	1.60k dk bl & pale grn	.65	.20
1036	A403	2k mar & pale bl	2.40	1.10
		Nos. 1031-1036 (6)	6.00	2.25

Issued to publicize Soviet space research.

Portrait Type of 1960

No. 1037, Jindrich Mosna. No. 1038, Pavol Orszagh Hviezdoslav. No. 1039, Alois Mrstik. No. 1040, Joza Uprka. No. 1041, Josef Hora.

1961, Mar. 27 Perf. 11½
1037	A391	60h green	.30	.20
1038	A391	60h dark blue	.65	.20
a.		"ORSZACH" instead of "ORSZAGH"	400.00	100.00
1039	A391	60h dull claret	.80	.20
1040	A391	60h gray	.65	.20
1041	A391	60h sepia	.30	.20
		Nos. 1037-1041 (5)	2.70	1.00

Man Flying into Space A404

1961, Apr. 13
1042	A404	60h car & pale bl	.80	.20
1043	A404	3k ultra & yel	2.40	.80

1st man in space, Yuri A. Gagarin, Apr. 12, 1961. See No. 1036.

Flute Player — A405

Blast Furnace and Mine, Kladno — A406

1961, Apr. 24 Engr.
1044	A405	30h shown	.55	.20
1045	A405	30h Dancer	.55	.20
1046	A405	60h Lyre player	.80	.20
		Nos. 1044-1046 (3)	1.90	.60

Prague Conservatory of Music, 150th anniv.

1961, Apr. 24
1047	A406	3k dull red	.75	.20

Marching Workers — A407

Woman with Hammer and Sickle — A408

Klement Gottwald Museum A409

Designs: No. 1050, Lenin Museum. No. 1051, Crowd with flags. No. 1053, Man saluting Red Star.

1961, May 10
1048	A407	30h dull violet	.30	.20
1049	A409	30h dark blue	.30	.20
1050	A409	30h redsh brown	.30	.20
1051	A407	60h vermilion	.30	.20
1052	A408	60h dark green	.30	.20
1053	A408	60h carmine	.30	.20
		Nos. 1048-1053 (6)	1.80	1.20

Czech Communist Party, 40th anniversary.

Puppet — A410

Designs: Various Puppets.

Engraved and Photogravure
1961, June 20 Unwmk. Perf. 11½
1054	A410	30h ver & yel	.30	.20
1055	A410	40h sepia & bluish grn	.30	.20
1056	A410	60h vio bl & sal	.30	.20
1057	A410	1k green & lt blue	.30	.20
1058	A410	1.60k mar & pale vio	1.10	.35
		Nos. 1054-1058 (5)	2.30	1.15

Woman, Map of Africa and Flag of Czechoslovakia — A411

1961, June 26
1059	A411	60h red & blue	.40	.20

Issued to publicize the friendship between the people of Africa and Czechoslovakia.

Map of Europe and Fair Emblem A412

Fair emblem and: 60h Horizontal boring machine, vert. 1k, Scientists' meeting and nuclear physics emblem.

1961, Aug. 14 Perf. 11½
1060	A412	30h dk bl & pale grn	.30	.20
1061	A412	60h green & pink	.30	.20
1062	A412	1k vio brn & lt bl	.60	.25
		Nos. 1060-1062 (3)	1.20	.65

International Trade Fair, Brno, Sept. 10-24.

Sugar Beet, Cup of Coffee and Bags of Sugar A413

Charles Bridge, St. Nicholas Church and Hradcany A414

1961, Sept. 18 Unwmk. Perf. 11½
1063	A413	20h shown	.20	.20
1064	A413	30h Clover	.20	.20
1065	A413	40h Wheat	.20	.20
1066	A413	60h Hops	.20	.20
1067	A413	1.40k Corn	.50	.30
1068	A413	2k Potatoes	2.00	.80
		Nos. 1063-1068 (6)	3.30	1.90

1961, Sept. 25
1069	A414	60h violet bl & car	1.20	.20

26th session of the Governor's Council of the Red Cross Societies League, Prague.

Orlik Dam and Kaplan Turbine A415

Designs: 30h, View of Prague, flags and stamps. 40h, Hluboká Castle, river and fish. 60h, Karlovy Vary and cup. 1k, Pilsen and beer bottle. 1.20k, North Bohemia landscape and vase. 1.60k, Tatra mountains, boots, ice pick and rope. 2k, Ironworks, Ostrava Kuncice and pulley. 3k, Brno and ball bearing. 4k, Bratislava and grapes. 5k, Prague and flags.

1961 Unwmk. Perf. 11½
Size: 41x23mm
1070	A415	20h gray & blue	1.60	.55
1071	A415	30h vio blue & red	.30	.20
1072	A415	40h dk blue & lt grn	1.60	.85
1073	A415	60h dk blue & yel	1.75	.85
1074	A415	1k mar & grn	1.25	.85
1075	A415	1.20k green & pink	1.75	.85
1076	A415	1.60k brn & vio bl	1.75	1.25
1077	A415	2k blk & ocher	2.00	1.25
1078	A415	3k ultra & yel	2.00	.55
1079	A415	4k purple & sal	2.40	1.10

Perf. 13½
Engr.
Size: 50x29mm
1080	A415	5k multicolored	27.00	17.50
		Nos. 1070-1080 (11)	43.40	25.80

"PRAGA 1962 World Exhib. of Postage Stamps," Aug. 18-Sept. 2, 1962. No. 1080 was printed in sheet of 4. Value $150.

Globe A416

Engraved and Photogravure
1961, Nov. 27 Perf. 11½
1081	A416	60h red & ultra	.50	.20

Issued to publicize the Fifth World Congress of Trade Unions, Moscow, Dec. 4-16.

Orange Tip Butterfly A417

Bicyclists A418

Designs (butterflies): 20h, Zerynthia hypsipyle Sch. 30h, Apollo. 40h, Swallowtail. 60h, Peacock. 80h, Mourning cloak (Camberwell beauty). 1k, Underwing (moth). 1.60k, Red admiral. 2k, Brimstone (sulphur).

1961, Nov. 27 Engr.
1082	A417	15h multicolored	.90	.30
1083	A417	20h multicolored	.90	.30
1084	A417	30h multicolored	.90	.30
1085	A417	40h multicolored	.90	.30
1086	A417	60h multicolored	.90	.30
1087	A417	80h multicolored	2.75	.90
1088	A417	1k multicolored	3.00	.90
1089	A417	1.60k multicolored	3.00	.90
1090	A417	2k multicolored	7.50	3.00
		Nos. 1082-1090 (9)	20.75	7.20

Printed in sheets of ten. Value, set $275.

Engraved and Photogravure
1962, Feb. 5 Unwmk. Perf. 11½

Sports: 40h, Woman gymnast. 60h, Figure skaters. 1k, Woman bowler. 1.20k, Goalkeeper, soccer. 1.60k, Discus thrower.

1091	A418	30h black & vio bl	.20	.20
1092	A418	40h black & yel	.20	.20
1093	A418	60h slate & grnsh bl	.40	.20
1094	A418	1k black & pink	.40	.20
1095	A418	1.20k black & green	.40	.20
1096	A418	1.60k blk & dull grn	2.00	.95
		Nos. 1091-1096 (6)	3.60	1.95

Various 1962 sports events.
No. 1095 does not have the commemorative inscription.

Karel Kovarovic — A419

Frantisek Zaviska and Karel Petr A420

20h, Frantisek Skroup. 30h, Bozena Nemcova. 60h, View of Prague & staff of Aesculapius. 1.60k, Ladislav Celakovsky. 1.80k, Miloslav Valouch & Juraj Hronec.

1962, Feb. 26 Engr.
1097	A419	10h red brown	.20	.20
1098	A419	20h violet blue	.20	.20
1099	A419	30h brown	.20	.20
1100	A420	40h claret	.20	.20
1101	A419	60h black	.20	.20
1102	A419	1.60k slate green	.50	.20
1103	A420	1.80k dark blue	.60	.20
		Nos. 1097-1103 (7)	2.10	1.40

Various cultural personalities and events.

Miner and Flag A421

1962, Mar. 19 Engr. & Photo.
1104 A421 60h indigo & rose .25 .20

30th anniv. of the miners' strike at Most.

"Man Conquering Space" — A422

Soviet Spaceship Vostok 2 — A423

40h, Launching of Soviet space rocket. 80h, Multi-stage automatic rocket. 1k, Automatic station on moon. 1.60k, Television satellite.

1962, Mar. 26
1105	A422	30h dk red & lt blue	.40	.20
1106	A422	40h dk blue & sal	.40	.20
1107	A423	60h dk blue & pink	.40	.20
1108	A422	80h rose vio & lt grn	.60	.20
1109	A422	1k indigo & citron	.40	.20
1110	A423	1.60k green & buff	2.40	.75
		Nos. 1105-1110 (6)	4.60	1.75

Issued to publicize space research.

Polar Bear — A424

Zoo Animals: 30h, Chimpanzee. 60h, Camel. 1k, African and Indian elephants, horiz. 1.40k, Leopard, horiz. 1.60k, Przewalski horse, horiz.

1962, Apr. 24 Unwmk. Perf. 11½
Design and Inscriptions in Black
1111	A424	20h grnsh blue	.75	.20
1112	A424	30h violet	.75	.20
1113	A424	60h orange	.75	.20
1114	A424	1k green	.90	.20

1115	A424	1.40k carmine rose	.90	.20
1116	A424	1.60k lt brown	2.00	1.25
		Nos. 1111-1116 (6)	6.05	2.25

Child and Grieving Mother — A425

60h, Flowers growing from ruins of Lezáky.

1962, June 9 Engr. & Photo.
1118 A425 30h black & red .45 .20
1119 A425 60h black & dull bl .85 .20

20th anniversary of the destruction of Lidice and Lezáky by the Nazis.

1962, June 9
1120 A426 60h dull grn & yel .40 .20

1,200th anniversary of the discovery of the medicinal springs of Teplice.

Malaria Eradication Emblem, Cross and Dove A427

Soccer Goalkeeper A428

3k, Dove and malaria eradication emblem.

1962, June 18
1121 A427 60h black & crimson .20 .20
1122 A427 3k dk blue & yel 1.40 .60

WHO drive to eradicate malaria.

1962, June 20 Unwmk. Perf. 11½
1123 A428 1.60k green & yellow 1.50 .20

Czechoslovakia's participation in the World Cup Soccer Championship, Chile, May 30-June 17. See No. 1095.

Soldier in Swimming Relay Race A429

"Agriculture" A430

Designs: 40h, Soldier hurdling. 60h, Soccer player. 1k, Soldier with rifle in relay race.

1962, July 20
1124	A429	30h green & lt ultra	.20	.20
1125	A429	40h dk purple & yel	.20	.20
1126	A429	60h brown & green	.20	.20
1127	A429	1k dk blue & sal pink	.35	.20
		Nos. 1124-1127 (4)	.95	.80

2nd Summer Spartacist Games of Friendly Armies, Prague, Sept., 1962.

1962 Engr. Perf. 13½

Designs: 60h, Astronaut in capsule. 80h, Boy with flute, horiz. 1k, Workers of three races, horiz. 1.40k, Children dancing around

tree. 1.60k, Flying bird, horiz. 5k, View of Prague, horiz.

1128	A430	30h multicolored	1.50	.90
1129	A430	60h multicolored	.70	.55
a.		Miniature sheet of 8	20.00	20.00
1130	A430	80h multicolored	2.40	1.60
1131	A430	1k multicolored	2.40	1.60
1132	A430	1.40k multicolored	2.40	1.60
1133	A430	1.60k multicolored	4.00	4.00
		Nos. 1128-1133 (6)	13.40	10.25

Souvenir Sheet
1134 A430 5k multicolored 13.00 10.00
a. Imperf. 60.00 48.00

"PRAGA 1962 World Exhib. of Postage Stamps," 8/18-9/2/62. No. 1133 also for FIP Day, Sept. 1. Printed in sheets of 10. Value: Nos. 1128-1133 $150; No. 1134 $80.

No. 1129a contains 4 each of Nos. 1128-1129 and 2 labels arranged in 2 rows of 2 se-tenant pairs of Nos. 1128-1129 with label between. Sold for 5k, only with ticket.

No. 1134 contains one 51x30mm stamp. Sold only with ticket.

Children in Day Nursery and Factory A431

Sailboat and Trade Union Rest Home, Zinkovy — A432

Engraved and Photogravure
1962, Oct. 29 Unwmk. Perf. 11½
1135 A431 30h black & lt blue .20 .20
1136 A432 60h brown & yellow .20 .20

Cruiser "Aurora" A433

1962, Nov. 7
1137 A433 30h black & gray bl .20 .20
1138 A433 60h black & pink .20 .20

Russian October revolution, 45th anniv.

Cosmonaut and Worker — A434

Lenin — A435

1962, Nov. 7
1139 A434 30h dark red & blue .20 .20
1140 A435 60h black & dp rose .20 .20

40th anniversary of the USSR.

Symbolic Crane — A436

40h, Agricultural products, vert. 60h, Factories.

1962, Dec. 4
1141 A436 30h dk red & yel .20 .20
1142 A436 40h gray blue & yel .20 .20
1143 A436 60h black & dp rose .30 .20
Nos. 1141-1143 (3) .70 .60

Communist Party of Czechoslovakia, 12th cong.

Ground Beetle — A437

Table Tennis — A438

Beetles: 30h, Cardinal beetle. 60h, Stag beetle, vert. 1k, Great water beetle. 1.60k, Alpine longicorn, vert. 2k, Ground beetle, vert.

1962, Dec. 15 Engr. Perf. 14
1144	A437	20h multicolored	1.00	.40
1145	A437	30h multicolored	1.00	.40
1146	A437	60h multicolored	1.00	.40
1147	A437	1k multicolored	2.00	.60
1148	A437	1.60k multicolored	4.00	.60
1149	A437	2k multicolored	6.00	2.00
		Nos. 1144-1149 (6)	15.00	4.40

Nos. 1144-1149 were each printed in sheets of 10. Value, set $200.

Engraved and Photogravure
1963, Jan. Perf. 11½

Sports: 60h, Bicyclist. 80h, Skier. 1k, Motorcyclist. 1.20k, Weight lifter. 1.60k, Hurdler.

1150	A438	30h black & dp grn	.20	.20
1151	A438	60h black & orange	.20	.20
1152	A438	80h black & ultra	.20	.20
1153	A438	1k black & violet	.40	.20
1154	A438	1.20k blk & pale brn	.40	.20
1155	A438	1.60k blk & car	.85	.20
		Nos. 1150-1155 (6)	2.25	1.20

Various 1963 sports events.

Industrial Plant, Laurel and Star — A439

Symbol of Child Welfare Home — A440

Industrial Plant and Symbol of Growth — A441

1963, Feb. 25 Unwmk. Perf. 11½
1156 A439 30h carmine & lt bl .20 .20
1157 A440 60h black & car .20 .20
1158 A441 60h black & red .20 .20
Nos. 1156-1158 (3) .60 .60

15th anniv. of the "Victorious February" and 5th Trade Union Cong.

Artists' Guild Emblem — A442

Juraj Jánosik — A443

Eduard Urx — A444

National Theater, Prague — A445

#1163, Woman reading to children. #1164, Juraj Pálkovic. 1.60k, Max Svabinsky.

Engr. & Photo.; Engr. (A444)
1963, Mar. 25   Unwmk.   Perf. 11½
1159 A442	20h black & Prus bl	.20	.20
1160 A443	30h car & lt bl	.20	.20
1161 A444	30h carmine	.20	.20
1162 A445	60h dl red brn & lt bl	.20	.20
1163 A444	60h green	.20	.20
1164 A444	60h black	.25	.20
1165 A444	1.60k brown	.50	.20
Nos. 1159-1165 (7)		1.75	1.40

Various cultural personalities and events.

Boy and Girl with Flag A446

Television Transmitter A447

Engraved and Photogravure
1963, Apr. 18   Perf. 11½
| 1166 A446 | 30h slate & rose red | .35 | .20 |

The 4th Congress of Czechoslovak Youth.

1963, Apr. 25
40h, Television camera, mast and set, horiz.
| 1167 A447 | 40h buff & slate | .40 | .20 |
| 1168 A447 | 60h dk red & lt blue | .40 | .20 |

Czechoslovak television, 10th anniversary.

Rocket to the Sun A448

50h, Rockets & Sputniks leaving Earth. 60h, Spacecraft to & from Moon. 1k, 3k, Interplanetary station & Mars 1. 1.60k, Atomic rocket & Jupiter. 2k, Rocket returning from Saturn.

1963, Apr. 25
1169 A448	30h red brn & buff	.65	.20
1170 A448	50h slate & bluish grn	.65	.20
1171 A448	60h dk green & yel	.65	.20
1172 A448	1k dk gray & sal	.80	.20
1173 A448	1.60k gray brn & lt grn	.80	.20
1174 A448	2k dk purple & yel	2.50	.75
Nos. 1169-1174 (6)		6.05	1.75

Souvenir Sheet
Imperf
| 1175 A448 | 3k Prus grn & org red | 14.50 | 7.25 |

No. 1175 issued for 1st Space Research Exhib., Prague, Apr. 1963.

Studio and Radio A449

1k, Globe inscribed "Peace" & aerial mast, vert.

1963, May 18   Unwmk.   Perf. 11½
| 1176 A449 | 30h choc & pale grn | .40 | .20 |
| 1177 A449 | 1k bluish grn & lilac | .40 | .20 |

40th anniversary of Czechoslovak radio.

Tupolev Tu-104B Turbojet A450

Design: 1.80k, Ilyushin Il-18 Moskva.

1963, May 25
| 1178 A450 | 80h violet & lt bl | 1.25 | .40 |
| 1179 A450 | 1.80k dk blue & lt grn | 2.00 | .40 |

40th anniversary of Czechoslovak airlines.

9th Cent. Ring, Map of Moravian Settlements A451

Woman Singing A452

1.60k, Falconer, 9th cent. silver disk.

1963, May 25
| 1180 A451 | 30h lt green & blk | .25 | .20 |
| 1181 A451 | 1.60k dull yel & blk | .75 | .20 |

1100th anniversary of Moravian empire.

1963, May 25   Engr.
| 1182 A452 | 30h bright red | .60 | .20 |

60th anniversary of the founding of the Moravian Teachers' Singing Club.

Kromeriz Castle and Barley — A453

Centenary Emblem, Nurse and Playing Child — A454

Engraved and Photogravure
1963, June 20   Unwmk.   Perf. 11½
| 1183 A453 | 30h slate grn & yel | .60 | .20 |

Natl. Agricultural Exhib. and 700th anniv. of Kromeriz.

1963, June 20
| 1184 A454 | 30h dk gray & car | .50 | .20 |

Centenary of the International Red Cross.

Bee, Honeycomb and Emblem A455

Liberec Fair Emblem — A456

1963, June 20
| 1185 A455 | 1k brown & yellow | .75 | .20 |

19th Intl. Beekeepers Cong., Apimondia, 1963.

1963, July 13
| 1186 A456 | 30h black & dp rose | .40 | .20 |

Liberec Consumer Goods Fair.

Town Hall, Brno — A457

Cave, Moravian Karst — A458

Design: 60h, Town Hall tower, Brno.

1963, July 29
| 1187 A457 | 30h lt blue & maroon | .35 | .20 |
| 1188 A457 | 60h pink & dk blue | .35 | .20 |

International Trade Fair, Brno.

1963, July 29
#1190, Trout, Hornad Valley. 60h, Great Hawk Gorge. 80h, Macocha mountains.
1189 A458	30h brown & lt bl	.80	.20
1190 A458	30h dk bl & dull grn	.95	.20
1191 A458	60h green & blue	.80	.20
1192 A458	80h sepia & pink	.80	.20
Nos. 1189-1192 (4)		3.35	.80

Blast Furnace A459

1963, Aug. 15   Unwmk.   Perf. 11½
| 1193 A459 | 60h blk & bluish grn | .40 | .20 |

30th Intl. Cong. of Iron Founders, Prague.

White Mouse A460

1963, Aug. 15
| 1194 A460 | 1k black & carmine | .65 | .20 |

2nd Intl. Pharmacological Cong., Prague.

Farm Machinery for Underfed Nations — A461

1963, Aug. 15   Engr.
| 1195 A461 | 1.60k black | .50 | .20 |

FAO "Freedom from Hunger" campaign.

Wooden Toys — A462

1963, Sept. 2   Engr.   Perf. 13½
Folk Art (Inscribed "UNESCO"): 80h, Cock and flowers. 1k, Flowers in vase. 1.20k, Janosik, Slovak hero. 1.60k, Stag. 2k, Postilion.
1196 A462	60h red & vio bl	.75	.30
1197 A462	80h multi	.75	.30
1198 A462	1k multi	.75	.30
1199 A462	1.20k multi	.75	.30
1200 A462	1.60k multi	.75	.30
1201 A462	2k multi	3.25	1.75
Nos. 1196-1201 (6)		7.00	3.25

Nos. 1196-1201 were printed in sheets of 10. Value, set $150.

Canoeing A463

Tree and Star — A464

Sports: 40h, Volleyball. 60h, Wrestling. 80h, Basketball. 1k, Boxing. 1.60k, Gymnastics.

Engraved and Photogravure
1963, Oct. 26   Perf. 11½
1202 A463	30h indigo & grn	.35	.20
1203 A463	40h red brn & lt bl	.35	.25
1204 A463	60h brn red & yel	.40	.20
1205 A463	80h dk pur & dp org	.50	.25
1206 A463	1k ultra & dp rose	.70	.35
1207 A463	1.60k vio bl & ultra	2.75	1.40
Nos. 1202-1207 (6)		5.05	2.65

1964 Olympic Games, Tokyo.

1963, Dec. 11   Unwmk.   Perf. 11½
Design: 60h, Star, hammer and sickle.
| 1208 A464 | 30h bis brn & lt bl | .30 | .20 |
| 1209 A464 | 60h carmine & gray | .30 | .20 |

Russo-Czechoslovakian Treaty, 20th anniv.

Atom Diagrams Surrounding Head — A465

Chamois — A466

1963, Dec. 12   Engr.
| 1210 A465 | 60h dark purple | .40 | .20 |

3rd Congress of the Association for the Propagation of Scientific Knowledge.

1963, Dec. 14   Perf. 14

40h, Alpine ibex. 60h, Mouflon. 1.20k, Roe deer. 1.60k, Fallow deer. 2k, Red deer.

1211	A466	30h multi	1.50	.35
1212	A466	40h multi	1.50	.35
1213	A466	60h brn, yel & grn	1.50	.35
1214	A466	1.20k multi	2.50	1.00
1215	A466	1.60k multi	3.00	1.25
1216	A466	2k multi	6.00	2.50
		Nos. 1211-1216 (6)	16.00	5.80

Nos. 1211-1216 were each issued in sheets of 10 stamps. Value, set $140.

Figure Skating — A467

Ice Hockey — A468

80h, Skiing, horiz. 1k, Field ball player.

Engraved and Photogravure

1964, Jan. 20   Unwmk.   Perf. 11½

1217	A467	30h violet bl & yel	.30	.20
1218	A467	80h dk blue & org	.45	.20
1219	A467	1k brown & lilac	.75	.20
		Nos. 1217-1219 (3)	1.50	.60

Intl. University Games (30h, 80h) and the World Field Ball Championships (1k).

1964, Jan. 20

1220	A468	1k shown	.85	.35
1221	A468	1.80k Toboggan	1.00	.60
1222	A468	2k Ski jump	2.50	2.25
		Nos. 1220-1222 (3)	4.35	3.20

9th Winter Olympic Games, Innsbruck, Jan. 29-Feb. 9, 1964.

Magura Rest Home, High Tatra — A469

Design: 80h, Slovak National Insurrection Rest Home, Low Tatra.

1964, Feb. 19   Unwmk.   Perf. 11½

1223	A469	60h green & yellow	.30	.20
1224	A469	80h violet bl & pink	.30	.20

Skiers and Ski Lift A470

60h, Automobile camp, Telc. 1k, Fishing, Spis Castle. 1.80k, Lake & boats, Cesky Krumlov.

1964, Feb. 19   Engr. & Photo.

1225	A470	30h dk vio brn & bl	.40	.20
1226	A470	60h slate & car	.45	.20
1227	A470	1k brown & olive	.80	.20
1228	A470	1.80k slate grn & org	1.25	.35
		Nos. 1225-1228 (4)	2.90	.95

Moses, Day and Night by Michelangelo — A471

Designs: 60h, "A Midsummer Night's Dream," by Shakespeare. 1k, Man, telescope and heaven, vert. 1.60k, King George of Podebrad (1420-71).

1964, Mar. 20

1229	A471	40h black & yel grn	.45	.20
1230	A471	60h slate & car	.30	.20
1231	A471	1k black & lt blue	1.10	.20
1232	A471	1.60k black & yellow	1.25	.20
a.		Souvenir sheet of 4 ('88)	9.50	6.50
		Nos. 1229-1232 (4)	3.10	.80

400th anniv. of the death of Michelangelo (40h); 400th anniv. of the birth of Shakespeare (60h); 400th anniv. of the birth of Galileo (1k); 500th anniv. of the pacifist efforts of King George of Podebrad (1.60k).

No. 1232a for PRAGA '88.

Yuri A. Gagarin — A472

Astronauts: 60h, Gherman Titov. 80h, John H. Glenn, Jr. 1k, Scott M. Carpenter, vert. 1.20k, Pavel R. Popovich and Andrian G. Nikolayev. 1.40k, Walter M. Schirra, vert. 1.60k, Gordon L. Cooper, vert. 2k, Valentina Tereshkova and Valeri Bykovski, vert.

1964, Apr. 27   Unwmk.   Perf. 11½
Yellow Paper

1233	A472	30h black & vio bl	.55	.25
1234	A472	60h dk grn & dk car	.25	.20
1235	A472	80h dk car & vio	.55	.20
1236	A472	1k ultra & rose vio	.25	.25
1237	A472	1.20k ver & ol gray	.55	.35
1238	A472	1.40k black & dl grn	1.40	.50
1239	A472	1.60k pale pur & Prus grn	3.25	1.50
1240	A472	2k dk blue & red	1.10	.40
		Nos. 1233-1240 (8)	7.90	3.65

World's first 10 astronauts.

Creeping Bellflower A473   Film "Flower" and Karlovy Vary Colonnade A474

Flowers: 80h, Musk thistle. 1k, Chicory. 1.20k, Yellow iris. 1.60k, Gentian. 2k, Corn poppy.

1964, June 15   Engr.   Perf. 14

1241	A473	60h dk grn, lil & org	1.25	.25
1242	A473	80h blk, grn & red lil	1.25	.25
1243	A473	1k vio bl, grn & pink	1.25	.45
1244	A473	1.20k black, yel & grn	1.25	.30
1245	A473	1.60k violet & grn	3.00	.40
1246	A473	2k vio, red & grn	7.00	2.00
		Nos. 1241-1246 (6)	15.00	3.65

Nos. 1241-1246 were each issued in sheets of 10. Value, set $225.

Engraved and Photogravure
1964, June 20   Unwmk.   Perf. 13½

1247	A474	60h black, blue & car	2.00	.50

14th Intl. Film Festival at Karlovy Vary, July 4-19.

Silesian Coat of Arms — A475

Young Miner of 1764 — A476

1964, June 20   Perf. 11½

1248	A475	30h black & yel	.30	.20

150th anniv. of the Silesian Museum, Opava.

1964, June 20

1249	A476	60h sepia & lt grn	.30	.20

Mining School at Banska Stiavnica, bicent.

Skoda Fire Engine A477

1964, June 20

1250	A477	60h car rose & lt bl	1.25	.20

Voluntary fire brigades in Bohemia, cent.

Gulls, Hradcany Castle, Red Cross — A478   Human Heart — A479

1964, July 10

1251	A478	60h car & bluish gray	.55	.20

4th Czechoslovak Red Cross Congress at Prague.

1964, July 10

1252	A479	1.60k ultra & car	1.25	.20

4th European Cardiological Cong. at Prague.

Partisans, Girl and Factories A480

Battle Scene, 1944 — A481

Design: 60h, Partisans and flame.

Engraved and Photogravure
1964, Aug. 17   Unwmk.   Perf. 11½

1253	A480	30h brown & red	.20	.20
1254	A480	60h dk blue & red	.20	.20
1255	A481	60h black & red	.20	.20
		Nos. 1253-1255 (3)	.60	.60

20th anniv. of the Slovak Natl. Uprising; No. 1255, 20th anniv. of the Battles of Dukla Pass.

Hradcany at Prague — A482   Discus Thrower and Pole Vaulter — A483

Design: 5k, Charles Bridge and Hradcany.

1964, Aug. 30   Perf. 11½x12

1256	A482	60h black & red	.65	.20

Souvenir Sheet
      Engr.   Imperf.

1257	A482	5k deep claret	4.00	3.25

Millenium of the Hradcany, Prague. No. 1257 stamp size: 30x50mm.

Engraved and Photogravure
1964, Sept. 2   Perf. 13½

Designs: 60h, Bicycling, horiz. 1k, Soccer. 1.20k, Rowing. 1.60k, Swimming, horiz. 2.80k, Weight lifting, horiz.

1258	A483	60h multi	1.00	.30
1259	A483	80h multi	1.00	.30
1260	A483	1k multi	1.00	.30
1261	A483	1.20k multi	1.00	.30
1262	A483	1.60k multi	1.00	.30
1263	A483	2.80k multi	5.00	2.00
		Nos. 1258-1263 (6)	10.00	3.50

Issued to commemorate the 18th Olympic Games, Tokyo, Oct. 10-25.

Nos. 1258-1263 were issued in sheets of 10. Value, set $200.

Miniature Sheet

Space Ship Voskhod I, Astronauts and Globe — A484

1964, Nov. 12   Unwmk.   Perf. 11½

1264	A484	3k dk bl & dl lil, buff	6.00	4.00

Russian 3-man space flight of Vladimir M. Komarov, Boris B. Yegorov and Konstantin Feoktistov, Oct. 12-13.

Steam Engine and Atomic Power Plant — A485

Diesel Engine "CKD Praha" — A486

1964, Nov. 16   Engr.

1265	A485	30h dull red brown	.25	.20

Engraved and Photogravure

1266	A486	60h green & salmon	.75	.20

Traditions and development of engineering; No. 1265 for 150th anniv. of the First Brno Engineering Works, No. 1266 for the engineering concern CKD Praha.

European Redstart — A487

Birds: 60h, Green woodpecker. 80h, Hawfinch. 1k, Black woodpecker. 1.20k, European robin. 1.60k, European roller.

1964, Nov. 16   **Litho.**   **Perf. 10½**
1267	A487	30h multicolored	1.25	.30
1268	A487	60h black & multi	1.25	.30
1269	A487	80h multicolored	1.50	.35
1270	A487	1k multicolored	2.00	.40
1271	A487	1.20k lt vio bl & blk	2.00	.40
1272	A487	1.60k yellow & blk	4.00	1.00
		Nos. 1267-1272 (6)	12.00	2.75

Dancer A488

"In the Sun" Pre-school Children A489

Designs: 60h, "Over the Obstacles," teenagers. 1k, "Movement and Beauty," woman flag twirler. 1.60k, Runners at start.

Engraved and Photogravure
1965   **Unwmk.**   **Perf. 11½**
1273	A488	30h red & lt blue	.20	.20

Perf. 11½x12
1274	A489	30h vio bl & car	.20	.20
1275	A489	60h brown & ultra	.20	.20
1276	A489	1k black & yellow	.25	.20
1277	A489	1.60k maroon & gray	.60	.20
		Nos. 1273-1277 (5)	1.45	1.00

3rd Natl. Spartacist Games. Issue dates: No. 1273, Jan. 3; Nos. 1274-1277, May 24.

Mountain Rescue Service — A490

Designs: No. 1279, Woman gymnast. No. 1280, Bicyclists. No. 1281, Women hurdlers.

1965, Jan. 15   **Unwmk.**   **Perf. 11½**
1278	A490	60h violet & blue	.30	.20
1279	A490	60h maroon & ocher	.30	.20
1280	A490	60h black & carmine	.30	.20
1281	A490	60h green & yellow	.30	.20
		Nos. 1278-1281 (4)	1.20	.80

Mountain Rescue Service (#1278); 1st World Championship in Artistic Gymnastics, Prague, Dec. 1965 (#1279); World Championship in Indoor Bicycling, Prague, Oct. 1965 (#1280); "Universiada 1965," Brno (#1281).

Arms and View, Beroun — A491

Designs: No. 1283, Town Square, Domazlice. No. 1284, Old and new buildings, Frydek-Mystek. No. 1285, Arms and view, Lipnik. No. 1286, Fortified wall, City Hall and Arms, Policka. No. 1287, View and hops, Zatek. No. 1288, Small fortress and rose, Terezin.

1965, Feb. 15
1282	A491	30h vio bl & lt bl	.30	.20
1283	A491	30h dull pur & yel	.30	.20
1284	A491	30h slate & gray	.30	.20
1285	A491	30h green & bis	.30	.20
1286	A491	30h brown & tan	.30	.20
1287	A491	30h dk blue & cit	.30	.20
1288	A491	30h black & rose	.30	.20
		Nos. 1282-1288 (7)	2.10	1.40

Nos. 1282-1287 for 700th anniv. of the founding of various Bohemian towns; No. 1288 the 20th anniv. of the liberation of the Theresienstadt (Terezin) concentration camp.

Sun's Corona A492

Space Research: 30h, Sun. 60h, Exploration of the Moon. 1k, Twin space craft, vert. 1.40k, Space station. 1.60k, Exploration of Mars, vert. 2k, USSR and US Meteorological collaboration.

1965, Mar. 15   **Perf. 12x11½, 11½x12**
1289	A492	20h rose & red lilac	.25	.20
1290	A492	30h rose red & yel	.25	.20
1291	A492	60h bluish blk & yel	.25	.20
1292	A492	1k pur & pale bl	.50	.20
1293	A492	1.40k black & salmon	.50	.20
1294	A492	1.60k black & pink	.50	.20
1295	A492	2k bluish blk & lt bl	*1.50*	*1.00*
		Nos. 1289-1295 (7)	3.75	2.20

Space research; Nos. 1289-1290 also for the Intl. Quiet Sun Year, 1964-65.

Frantisek Ventura, Equestrian; Amsterdam, 1928 — A493

Czechoslovakian Olympic Victories: 30h, Discus, Paris, 1900. 60h, Running, Helsinki, 1952. 1k, Weight lifting, Los Angeles, 1932. 1.40k, Gymnastics, Berlin, 1936. 1.60k, Double sculling, Rome, 1960. 2k, Women's gymnastics, Tokyo, 1964.

1965, Apr. 16   **Perf. 11½x12**
1296	A493	20h choc & gold	.25	.20
1297	A493	30h indigo & emer	.25	.20
1298	A493	60h ultra & gold	.25	.20
1299	A493	1k red brn & gold	.35	.25
1300	A493	1.40k dk sl grn & gold	.80	.65
1301	A493	1.60k black & gold	.85	.65
1302	A493	2k maroon & gold	1.25	.50
		Nos. 1296-1302 (7)	4.00	2.65

Astronauts Virgil Grissom and John Young — A494

Designs: No. 1304, Alexei Leonov floating in space. No. 1305, Launching pad at Cape Kennedy. No. 1306, Leonov leaving space ship.

1965, Apr. 17   **Perf. 11x11½**
1303	A494	60h slate bl & lil rose	.45	.20
1304	A494	60h vio blk & blue	.45	.20
1305	A494	3k slate bl & lil rose	1.75	1.00
a.		Pair, #1303, 1305	3.75	2.00
1306	A494	3k vio blk & blue	1.75	1.00
a.		Pair, #1304, 1306	3.75	2.00
		Nos. 1303-1306 (4)	4.40	2.40

Issued to honor American and Soviet astronauts. Printed in sheets of 25; one sheet contains 20 No. 1303 and 5 No. 1305, the other sheet contains 20 No. 1304 and 5 No. 1306.

Russian Soldier, View of Prague and Guerrilla Fighters A495

Designs: No. 1308, Blast furnace, workers and tank. 60h, Worker and factory. 1k, Worker and new constructions. 1.60k, Woman farmer, new farm buildings and machinery.

1965, May 5   **Engr.**   **Perf. 13½**
1307	A495	30h dk red, blk & ol	.40	.20
1308	A495	30h multicolored	.40	.20
1309	A495	60h vio bl, red & blk	.40	.20
1310	A495	1k dp org, blk & brn	.65	.20
1311	A495	1.60k yel, red & blk	.70	.20
		Nos. 1307-1311 (5)	2.55	1.00

20th anniv. of liberation from the Nazis. Nos. 1307-1311 were each printed in sheets of 10. Value, set $85.

Slovakian Kopov Dog A496

Dogs: 40h, German shepherd. 60h, Czech hunting dog with pheasant. 1k, Poodle. 1.60k, Czech terrier. 2k, Afghan hound.

1965, June 10   **Perf. 12x11½**
1312	A496	30h black & red org	.50	.20
1313	A496	40h black & yellow	.50	.20
1314	A496	60h black & ver	.80	.20
1315	A496	1k black & dk car rose	1.10	.30
1316	A496	1.60k black & orange	1.50	.35
1317	A496	2k black & orange	3.00	1.25
		Nos. 1312-1317 (6)	7.40	2.50

World Dog Show at Brno and the International Dog Breeders Congress, Prague.

UN Headquarters Building, NY — A497

Emblems: 60h, UN & inscription. 1.60k, ICY.

1965, June 24   **Perf. 12x11½**
1318	A497	60h dk red brn & yel	.30	.20
1319	A497	1k ultra & lt blue	.75	.25
1320	A497	1.60k gold & dk red	.70	.35
		Nos. 1318-1320 (3)	1.75	.80

20th anniv. of the UN and the ICY, 1965.

Trade Union Emblem A498

1965, June 24   **Engr.**
1321	A498	60h dk red & ultra	.65	.20

Intl. Trade Union Federation, 20th anniv.

Women and Globe — A499

1965, June 24   **Perf. 11½x12**
1322	A499	60h violet blue	.40	.20

20th anniv. of the Intl. Women's Federation.

Children's House (Burgraves' Palace), Hradcany A500

Matthias Tower — A501

1965, June 25   **Perf. 11½**
1323	A500	30h slate green	.30	.20
1324	A501	60h dark brown	.30	.20

Issued to publicize the Hradcany, Prague.

Marx and Lenin — A502

1965, July 1   **Engr. & Photo.**
1325	A502	60h car rose & gold	.40	.20

6th conf. of Postal Ministers of Communist Countries, Peking, June 21-July 15.

Joseph Navratil — A503

Jan Hus — A504

Gregor Johann Mendel A505

Costume Jewelry A506

Bohuslav Martinu A507

Seated Woman and University of Bratislava A508

ITU Emblem and Communication Symbols A509

Macromolecular Symposium Emblem A510

Design: No. 1327, Ludovit Stur (diff. frame).

	1965		Unwmk.	Perf. 11½	
1326	A503	30h	black & fawn	.20	.20
1327	A503	30h	black & dull grn	.20	.20
1328	A504	60h	black & crimson	.20	.20
1329	A505	60h	vio bl & red	.20	.20
1330	A506	60h	purple & gold	.20	.20
1331	A507	60h	black & orange	.20	.20
1332	A508	60h	brn, yel	.20	.20
1333	A509	1k	orange & blue	.35	.20
1334	A510	1k	black & dp org	.35	.20
	Nos. 1326-1334 (9)			2.10	1.80

No. 1326, Navratil (1798-1865), painter; No. 1327, Stur (1815-56), Slovak author and historian; No. 1328, the 550th anniv. of the death of Hus, religious reformer;

No. 1329, cent. of publication of Mendel's laws of inheritance; No. 1330 publicizes the "Jablonec 1965" costume jewelry exhib.; No. 1331, Martinu (1890-1959), composer; No. 1332, 500th anniv. of the founding of the University of Bratislava as Academia Istropolitana; No. 1333, cent. of the ITU; No. 1334, Intl. Symposium on Macromolecular Chemistry, Prague, Sept. 1-8.

Issued: No. 1333, 7/10.

"Young Woman at her Toilette," by Titian — A512

Miniature Sheet

1965, Aug. 12
1336	A512	5k multicolored	6.00	4.00

Hradcany Art Gallery. #1336 contains one stamp.

Help for Flood Victims — A513

Rescue of Flood Victims A514

1965, Sept. 6   **Engr.**
1337	A513	30h violet blue	.20	.20

Engraved and Photogravure
1338	A514	2k dk ol grn & ol	.65	.45

Help for Danube flood victims in Slovakia.

Dotterel A515

Mountain Birds: 60h, Wall creeper, vert. 1.20k, Lesser redpoll. 1.40k, Golden eagle, vert. 1.60k, Ring ouzel. 2k, Eurasian nutcracker, vert.

1965, Sept. 20   **Litho.**   **Perf. 11**
1339	A515	30h	multi	1.40	.20
1340	A515	60h	multi	1.25	.20
1341	A515	1.20k	multi	1.40	.20
1342	A515	1.40k	multi	2.40	.40
1343	A515	1.60k	multi	1.60	.50
1344	A515	2k	multi	6.25	2.40
	Nos. 1339-1344 (6)			14.30	3.90

Levoca — A516

Medicinal Plants — A517

Views of Towns: 10h, Jindrichuv Hradec. 20h, Nitra. 30h, Kosice. 40h, Hradec Králové. 50h, Telc. 60h, Ostrava. 1k, Olomouc. 1.20k, Ceske Budejovice. 1.60k, Cheb. 2k, Brno. 3k, Bratislava. 5k, Prague.

Engraved and Photogravure
1965-66   **Perf. 11½x12**
Size: 23x19mm
1345	A516	5h	black & yel	.20	.20
1346	A516	10h	ultra & ol bis	.65	.20
1347	A516	20h	black & lt bl	.20	.20
1348	A516	30h	vio bl & lt grn	.20	.20
1348A	A516	40h	dk brn & lt bl ('66)	.20	.20
1348B	A516	50h	black & ocher ('66)	.50	.20
1348C	A516	60h	red & gray ('66)	1.00	.20
1348D	A516	1k	pur & pale grn ('66)	.65	.20

Perf. 11½x11
Size: 30x23mm
1349	A516	1.20k	slate & lt bl	.55	.20
1350	A516	1.60k	indigo & yel	.80	.20
1351	A516	2k	sl grn & pale yel	.75	.20
1352	A516	3k	brn & yel	1.00	.20
1353	A516	5k	black & pink	1.40	.20
	Nos. 1345-1353 (13)			8.10	2.60

1965, Dec. 3   **Engr.**   **Perf. 14**
1354	A517	30h	Coltsfoot	.40	.20
1355	A517	60h	Meadow saffron	.40	.20
1356	A517	80h	Corn poppy	1.25	.20
1357	A517	1k	Foxglove	1.25	.40
1358	A517	1.20k	Arnica	1.75	.75
1359	A517	1.60k	Cornflower	1.75	.75
1360	A517	2k	Dog rose	4.25	2.00
	Nos. 1354-1360 (7)			11.05	4.50

Nos. 1354-1360 were each printed in sheets of 10. Value, set $200.

Strip of "Stamps" — A518

Engraved and Photogravure
1965, Dec. 18   **Perf. 11½**
1361	A518	1k dark red & gold	4.00	2.25

Issued for Stamp Day, 1965.

Romain Rolland (1866-1944), French Writer A519

Symbolic Musical Instruments & Names of Composers A520

Portraits: No. 1362, Stanislav Sucharda (1866-1916), sculptor. No. 1363, Ignac Josef Pesina (1766-1808), veterinarian. No. 1365, Donatello (1386-1466), Italian sculptor.

1966, Feb. 14   **Engr.**   **Perf. 11½**
1362	A519	30h	deep green	.25	.20
1363	A519	30h	violet blue	.25	.20
1364	A519	60h	rose lake	.25	.20
1365	A519	60h	brown	.25	.20
	Nos. 1362-1365 (4)			1.00	.80

1966, Jan. 15   **Engr. & Photo.**
1366	A520	30h black & gold	.65	.20

Czech Philharmonic Orchestra, 70th anniv.

Figure Skating Pair A521

#1368, Man skater. #1369, Volleyball player, spiking, vert. 1k, Volleyball player, saving, vert. 1.60k, Woman skater. 2k, Figure skating pair.

1966, Feb. 17
1367	A521	30h	dk car rose	.30	.20
1368	A521	60h	green	.30	.20
1369	A521	60h	carmine & buff	.30	.20
1370	A521	1k	vio & lt bl	.40	.20
1371	A521	1.60k	brown & yellow	.50	.20
1372	A521	2k	blue & grnsh bl	2.40	.40
	Nos. 1367-1372 (6)			4.20	1.40

#1367-1368, 1371-1372 for the European Figure Skating Championships, Bratislava; #1369-1370 for the World Volleyball Championships.

Souvenir Sheet

Girl Dancing — A522

1966, Mar. 21   **Engr.**   **Imperf.**
1373	A522	3k slate bl, red & bl	4.00	2.75

Cent. of the opera "The Bartered Bride" by Bedrich Smetana.

"Ajax" 1841 A523

Locomotives: 30h, "Karlstejn" 1865. 60h, Steam engine, 1946. 1k, Steam engine with tender, 1946. 1.60k, Electric locomotive, 1964. 2k, Diesel locomotive, 1964.

1966, Mar. 21   **Perf. 11½x11**
Buff Paper
1374	A523	20h	sepia	1.40	.25
1375	A523	30h	dull violet	1.75	.25
1376	A523	60h	dull purple	1.25	.25
1377	A523	1k	dark brown	1.40	.50
1378	A523	1.60k	dk blue grn	2.40	.40
1379	A523	2k	dark red	4.75	2.10
	Nos. 1374-1379 (6)			12.95	3.75

European Perch A524

30h, Brown trout, vert. 1k, Carp. 1.20k, Northern pike. 1.40k, Grayling. 1.60k, Eel.

Perf. 13x13½, 13½x13
1966, Apr. 22   **Litho.**   **Unwmk.**
1380	A524	30h	multi	.75	.20
1381	A524	60h	multi	.75	.20
1382	A524	1k	multi	1.75	.20
1383	A524	1.20k	multi	.75	.20
1384	A524	1.40k	multi	1.25	.25
1385	A524	1.60k	multi	3.50	1.10
	Nos. 1380-1385 (6)			8.75	2.15

Intl. Fishing Championships, Svit, Sept. 3-5.

WHO Headquarters, Geneva — A525

Engraved and Photogravure
1966, Apr. 25   **Perf. 12x11½**
1386	A525	1k dk blue & lt blue	.50	.20

Opening of the WHO Headquarters, Geneva.

Symbolic Handshake and UNESCO Emblem A526

1966, Apr. 25   **Perf. 11½**
1387	A526	60h bister & olive gray	.30	.20

20th anniv. of UNESCO.

Prague Castle Issue

Belvedere Palace and St. Vitus' Cathedral A527

Crown of St. Wenceslas, 1346 — A528

Design: 60h, Madonna, altarpiece from St. George's Church.

1966, May 9   **Engr.**   **Perf. 11½**
1388 A527 30h dark blue   .50   .20

Engraved and Photogravure
1389 A527 60h blk & yel bis   .75   .20

Souvenir Sheet
Engr.
1390 A528 5k multi   6.50 3.25
See Nos. 1537-1539.

Tiger Swallowtail A529

Butterflies and Moths: 60h, Clouded sulphur. 80h, European purple emperor. 1k, Apollo. 1.20k, Burnet moth. 2k, Tiger moth.

1966, May 23   **Engr.**   **Perf. 14**
1391 A529 30h multi   .90   .25
1392 A529 60h multi   .90   .25
1393 A529 80h multi   1.25   .40
1394 A529 1k multi   1.90   .60
1395 A529 1.20k multi   1.90   .50
1396 A529 2k multi   5.50 2.00
   Nos. 1391-1396 (6)   12.35 4.00

Nos. 1391-1396 were issued in sheets of 10. Value, set $250.

Flags of Russia and Czechoslovakia — A530

Designs: 60h, Rays surrounding hammer and sickle "sun." 1.60k, Girl's head and stars.

Engraved and Photogravure
1966, May 31   **Perf. 11½**
1397 A530 30h dk bl & crim   .20   .20
1398 A530 60h bl & red   .20   .20
1399 A530 1.60k red & dk bl   .30   .20
   Nos. 1397-1399 (3)   .70   .60

13th Congress of the Communist Party of Czechoslovakia.

Dakota Chief — A531

Model of Molecule — A532

Designs: 20h, Indians, canoe and tepee, horiz. 30h, Tomahawk. 40h, Haida totem poles. 60h, Kachina, good spirit of the Hopis. 1k, Indian on horseback hunting buffalo, horiz. 1.20k, Calumet, Dakota peace pipe.

1966, June 20
Size: 23x40mm
1400 A531 20h vio bl & dp org   .25   .20
1401 A531 30h blk & dl org   .25   .20
1402 A531 40h blk & lt bl   .25   .20
1403 A531 60h grn & yel   .25   .20
1404 A531 1k pur & emer   .40   .20
1405 A531 1.20k vio bl & rose lil   .65   .30
Perf. 14
Engr.
Size: 23x37mm
1406 A531 1.40k multi   1.60   .90
   Nos. 1400-1406 (7)   3.65 2.20

Cent. of the Náprstek Ethnographic Museum, Prague, and "The Indians of North America" exhibition.

No. 1406 was issued in sheets of 10. Value $60.

Engraved and Photogravure
1966, July 4   **Unwmk.**   **Perf. 11½**
1407 A532 60h blk & lt bl   .50   .20

Czechoslovak Chemical Society, cent.

"Guernica" by Pablo Picasso — A533

1966, July 5
Size: 75x30mm
1408 A533 60h blk & pale bl   3.20 1.60

30th anniversary of International Brigade in Spanish Civil War.

Sheets of 15 stamps and 5 labels inscribed "Picasso-Guernica 1937." Values: with tab attached, $3.75; sheet $75.

Pantheon, Bratislava A534

Atom Symbol and Sun A535

Designs: No. 1410, Devin Castle and Ludovit Stur. No. 1411, View of Nachod. No. 1412, State Science Library, Olomouc.

1966, July 25   **Engr.**
1409 A534 30h dl pur   .30   .20
1410 A534 60h dk bl   .35   .20
1411 A534 60h green   .35   .20
1412 A534 60h sepia   .30   .20
   Nos. 1409-1412 (4)   1.30   .80

No. 1409, Russian War Memorial, Bratislava; No. 1410, the 9th cent. Devin Castle as symbol of Slovak nationalism; No. 1411, 700th anniv. of the founding of Nachod; No. 1412, the 400th anniv. of the State Science Library, Olomouc.

Engraved and Photogravure
1966, Aug. 29   **Perf. 11½**
1413 A535 60h blk & red   .40   .20

Issued to publicize Jachymov (Joachimsthal), where pitchblende was first discovered, "cradle of the atomic age."

Brno Fair Emblem — A536

Olympia Coin and Olympic Rings — A537

1966, Aug. 29
1414 A536 60h blk & red   .40   .20

8th International Trade Fair, Brno.

1966, Aug. 29

Design: 1k, Olympic flame, Czechoslovak flag and Olympic rings.

1415 A537 60h blk & gold   .30   .20
1416 A537 1k dk bl & red   1.10   .30

70th anniv. of the Olympic Committee.

Missile Carrier, Tank and Jet Plane A538

1966, Aug. 31
1417 A538 60h blk & apple grn   .40   .20

Issued to commemorate the maneuvers of the armies of the Warsaw Pact countries.

Mercury A539

30h, Moravian silver thaler, 1620, reverse & obverse, vert. 1.60k, Old & new buildings of Brno State Theater. 5k, Intl. Trade Fair Administration Tower & postmark, vert.

1966, Sept. 10
1418 A539 30h dk red & blk   .45   .20
1419 A539 60h org & blk   .45   .20
1420 A539 1.60k blk & brt grn   .85   .25
   Nos. 1418-1420 (3)   1.75   .65

Souvenir Sheet
1421 A539 5k multi   3.50 3.50

Brno Philatelic Exhibition, Sept. 11-25. No. 1421 contains one 30x40mm stamp.

First Meeting in Orbit — A540

30h, Photograph of far side of Moon & Russian satellite. 60h, Photograph of Mars & Mariner 4. 80h, Soft landing on Moon. 1k, Satellite, laser beam & binary code. 1.20k, Telstar over Earth & receiving station.

1966, Sept. 26   **Perf. 11½**
1422 A540 20h vio & lt grn   .25   .20
1423 A540 30h blk & sal pink   .25   .20
1424 A540 60h slate & lilac   .35   .20
1425 A540 80h dk pur & lt bl   .35   .20
1426 A540 1k blk & vio   .40   .20
1427 A540 1.20k red & bl   2.25   .60
   Nos. 1422-1427 (6)   3.85 1.60

Issued to publicize American and Russian achievements in space research.

Badger A541

Game Animals: 40h, Red deer, vert. 60h, Lynx. 80h, Hare. 1k, Red fox. 1.20k, Brown bear, vert. 2k, Wild boar.

1966, Nov. 28   **Litho.**   **Perf. 13½**
1428 A541 30h multi   .60   .20
1429 A541 40h multi   .60   .20
1430 A541 60h multi   .50   .20
1431 A541 80h multi   .20
     (europaens)   1.25   .25
a.   80h multi *(europaeus)*   6.00 3.50
1432 A541 1k multi   .90   .30
1433 A541 1.20k multi   1.25   .50
1434 A541 2k multi   3.00 1.25
   Nos. 1428-1434 (7)   8.10 2.90

The sheet of 50 of the 80h contains 40 with misspelling "europaens" and 10 with "europaeus."

"Spring" by Vaclav Hollar, 1607-77 A542

Paintings: No. 1436, Portrait of Mrs. F. Wussin, by Jan Kupecky (1667-1740). No. 1437, Snow Owl by Karel Purkyne (1834-1868). No. 1438, Tulips by Vaclav Spála (1885-1964). No. 1439, Recruit by Ludovít Fulla (1902-1980).

1966, Dec. 8   **Engr.**   **Perf. 14**
1435 A542 1k black   3.75 3.50
1436 A542 1k multicolored   5.25 1.90
1437 A542 1k multicolored   2.40 1.90
1438 A542 1k multicolored   2.40 1.90
1439 A542 1k multicolored   19.00 16.00
   Nos. 1435-1439 (5)   32.80 25.20

Printed in sheets of 4 stamps and 2 labels. The labels in sheet of No. 1435 are inscribed "Vaclav Hollar 1607-1677" in fancy frame. Other labels are blank. Value, set $150.
See No. 1484.

Symbolic Bird — A543

Engraved and Photogravure
1966, Dec. 17   **Perf. 11½**
1440 A543 1k dp blue & yel   1.25   .80

Issued for Stamp Day.

Youth — A544

1967, Jan. 16   **Perf. 11½**
1441 A544 30h ver & lt bl   .30   .20

5th Cong. of the Czechoslovak Youth Org.

Symbolic Flower and Machinery A545

1967, Jan. 16
1442 A545 30h carmine & yel .30 .20
6th Trade Union Congress, Prague.

Parents with Dead Child — A545a

1967, Jan. 16 **Perf. 11½**
1442A A545a 60h black & salmon on .30 .20
"Peace and Freedom in Viet Nam."

View of Jihlava and Tourist Year Emblem A546

Views and Tourist Year Emblem: 40h, Spielberg Castle and churches, Brno. 1.20k, Danube, castle and churches, Bratislava. 1.60k, Vlatava River bridges, Hradcany and churches, Prague.

1967, Feb. 13 **Engr.** **Perf. 11½**
Size: 40x23mm
1443 A546 30h brown violet .25 .20
1444 A546 40h maroon .25 .20
Size: 75x30mm
1445 A546 1.20k violet blue .60 .20
1446 A546 1.60k black 2.00 .80
    Nos. 1443-1446 (4) 3.10 1.40

International Tourist Year, 1967.

Black-tailed Godwit — A547

Birds: 40h, Shoveler, horiz. 60h, Purple heron. 80h, Penduline tit. 1k, Avocet. 1.40k, Black stork. 1.60k, Tufted duck, horiz.

1967, Feb. 20 **Litho.** **Perf. 13½**
1447 A547 30h multi .60 .30
1448 A547 40h multi .60 .30
1449 A547 60h multi .60 .30
1450 A547 80h multi .60 .30
1451 A547 1k multi .85 .30
1452 A547 1.40k multi 1.10 .60
1453 A547 1.60k multi 4.50 1.20
    Nos. 1447-1453 (7) 8.85 3.30

Solar Research and Satellite — A548

Space Research: 40h, Space craft, rocket and construction of station. 60h, Man on moon and orientation system. 1k, Exploration of solar system and rocket. 1.20k, Lunar satellites and moon photograph. 1.60k, Planned lunar architecture and moon landing.

Engraved and Photogravure
1967, Mar. 24 **Perf. 11½**
1454 A548 30h yel & dk red .30 .20
1455 A548 40h vio bl & blk .45 .20
1456 A548 60h lilac & grn .45 .20
1457 A548 1k brt pink & sl .45 .20
1458 A548 1.20k lt violet & blk .70 .20
1459 A548 1.60k brn lake & blk 2.40 .60
    Nos. 1454-1459 (6) 4.75 1.60

Gothic Painting, by Master Theodoric A549

Designs: 40h, "Burning of Master Hus," from Litomerice Hymnal. 60h, Modern glass sculpture. 80h, "The Shepherdess and the Chimney Sweep," Andersen fairy tale, painting by J. Trnka. 1k, Section of pressure vessel from atomic power station. 1.20k, Three ceramic figurines, by P. Rada. 3k, Montreal skyline and EXPO '67 emblem.

1967, Apr. 10 **Engr.** **Perf. 14**
Size: 37x23mm
1460 A549 30h multi .20 .20
1461 A549 40h multi .20 .20
1462 A549 60h multi .20 .20
1463 A549 80h multi .25 .20
1464 A549 1k multi 1.00 .20
1465 A549 1.20k multi 1.25 .60
    Nos. 1460-1465 (6) 3.10 1.65
Souvenir Sheet
Perf. 11½
Size: 40x30mm
1466 A549 3k multi 3.00 2.50

EXPO '67, International Exhibition, Montreal, Apr. 28-Oct. 27, 1967.
Nos. 1460-1465 were each issued in a miniature sheet of 10 stamps. Value, set $75.
No. 1466 exists imperf.

Canoe Race A550

Women Playing Basketball — A551

#1468, Wheels, dove & emblems of Warsaw, Berlin, Prague. 1.60k, Canoe slalom.

Perf. 12x11½, 11½x12
1967, Apr. 17 **Engr. & Photo.**
1467 A550 60h black & brt bl .20 .20
1468 A550 60h black & salmon .20 .20
1469 A551 60h blk & grnsh bl .20 .20
1470 A551 1.60k black & brt vio 1.40 .55
    Nos. 1467-1470 (4) 2.00 1.15

No. 1467, 5th Intl. Wild-Water Canoeing Championships; No. 1468, 20th Warsaw-Berlin-Prague Bicycle Race: No. 1469, Women's Basketball Championships; No. 1470, 10th Intl. Water Slalom Championships.

"Golden Street" — A552

Designs: 60h, Interior of Hall of King Wenceslas. 5k, St. Matthew, from illuminated manuscript, 11th century.

1967, May 9 **Perf. 11½x11**
1471 A552 30h rose claret .25 .20
1472 A552 60h bluish black .50 .20
Souvenir Sheet
Perf. 11½
1473 A552 5k multicolored 2.75 2.50
Issued to publicize the Castle of Prague.

Stylized Lyre with Flowers — A553

Old-New Synagogue, Prague — A554

1967, May 10 **Perf. 11½**
1474 A553 60h dull pur & brt grn .30 .20
Prague Music Festival.

1967, May 22 **Perf. 11½**
30h, Detail from Torah curtain, 1593. 60h, Prague Printer's emblem, 1530. 1k, Mikulov jug, 1804. 1.40k, Memorial for Concentration Camp Victims 1939-45, Pincas Synagogue (menorah & tablet). 1.60k, Tombstone of David Gans, 1613.

1475 A554 30h dull red & lt bl .30 .20
1476 A554 60h blk & lt grn .20 .20
1477 A554 1k dk bl & rose lil .35 .20
1478 A554 1.20k dk brn & mar .65 .20
1479 A554 1.40k black & yellow .55 .20
1480 A554 1.60k green & yel 4.50 2.75
    Nos. 1475-1480 (6) 6.55 3.75

Issued to show Jewish relics. The items shown on the 30h, 60h and 1k are from the State Jewish Museum, Prague.

"Lidice" A555

Prague Architecture A556

1967, June 9 **Unwmk.** **Perf. 11½**
1481 A555 30h black & brt rose .30 .20
Destruction of Lidice by the Nazis, 25th anniv.

1967, June 10 **Engr. & Photo.**
1482 A556 1k black & gold .45 .20
Issued to publicize the 9th Congress of the International Union of Architects, Prague.

Peter Bezruc A557

1967, June 21
1483 A557 60h dull rose & blk .30 .20
Peter Bezruc, poet & writer, birth cent.

Painting Type of 1966
2k, Henri Rousseau (1844-1910), self-portrait.

Issued in sheets of 4. Value $12.50.

1967, June 22 **Engr.** **Perf. 11½**
1484 A542 2k multicolored 2.00 1.60

Praga 68, World Stamp Exhibition, Prague, June 22-July 7, 1968. Printed in sheets of 4 stamps (2x2), separated by horizontal gutter with inscription and picture of Natl. Gallery, site of Praga 68.

View of Skalitz — A558

#1486, Mining tower & church steeple, Pribram. #1487, Hands holding book & view of Presov.

1967, Aug. 21 **Engr.** **Perf. 11½**
1485 A558 30h violet blue .20 .20
1486 A558 30h slate green .20 .20
1487 A558 30h claret .20 .20
    Nos. 1485-1487 (3) .60 .60

Towns of Skalitz, Pribram, Presov, annivs.

Colonnade and Spring, Karlovy Vary and Communications Emblem — A559

1967, Aug. 21 **Engr. & Photo.**
1488 A559 30h violet bl & gold .30 .20
5th Sports & Cultural Festival of the Employees of the Ministry of Communications, Karlovy Vary.

Ondrejov Observatory and Galaxy — A560

1967, Aug. 22 **Engr.**
1489 A560 60h vio bl, rose lil & sil 1.50 .25
13th Cong. of the Intl. Astronomical Union. No. 1489 was issued in a sheet of 10 stamps. Value, set $32.

Orchid — A561

Flowers from the Botanical Gardens: 30h, Cobaea scandens. 40h, Lycaste deppei. 60h, Glottiphyllum davisii. 1k, Anthurium. 1.20k, Rhodocactus. 1.40k, Moth orchid.

1967, Aug. 30 **Litho.** **Perf. 12½**
1490 A561 20h multicolored .40 .20
1491 A561 30h pink & multi .40 .20
1492 A561 40h multicolored .55 .20
1493 A561 60h lt blue & multi .55 .20
1494 A561 1k multicolored .75 .20
1495 A561 1.20k lt yellow & multi .90 .30
1496 A561 1.40k multicolored 2.40 .70
    Nos. 1490-1496 (7) 5.95 2.00

Red Squirrel A562

Animals from the Tatra National Park: 60h, Wild cat. 1k, Ermine. 1.20k, Dormouse. 1.40k, Hedgehog. 1.60k, Pine marten.

Engraved and Photogravure

1967, Sept. 25   **Perf. 11½**

1497	A562	30h black, yel & org	.35	.25
1498	A562	60h black & buff	.35	.25
1499	A562	1k black & lt blue	.40	.25
1500	A562	1.20k brn, pale grn & yel	.70	.25
1501	A562	1.40k blk, pink & yel	.80	.25
1502	A562	1.60k black, org & yel	3.50	1.25
		Nos. 1497-1502 (6)	6.10	2.50

Rockets and Weapons — A563

1967, Oct. 6   **Engr.**   **Perf. 11½**

1503	A563	30h slate green	.30	.20

Day of the Czechoslovak People's Army.

Cruiser "Aurora" Firing at Winter Palace A564

Designs: 60h, Hammer and sickle emblems and Red Star, vert. 1k, Hands reaching for hammer and sickle, vert.

1967, Nov. 7   **Engr. & Photo.**

1504	A564	30h black & dk car	.20	.20
1505	A564	60h black & dk car	.20	.20
1506	A564	1k black & dk car	.20	.20
		Nos. 1504-1506 (3)	.60	.60

Russian October Revolution, 50th anniv.

The Conjurer, by Frantisek Tichy A565

Paintings: 80h, Don Quixote, by Cyprian Majernik. 1k, Promenade in the Park, by Norbert Grund. 1.20k, Self-portrait, by Peter J. Brandl. 1.60k, Saints from Jan of Jeren Epitaph, by Czech Master of 1395.

1967, Nov. 13   **Engr.**   **Perf. 11½**

1507	A565	60h multi	.35	.25
1508	A565	80h multi	.50	.30
1509	A565	1k multi	.75	.50
1510	A565	1.20k multi	.75	.50
1511	A565	1.60k multi	3.25	2.75
		Nos. 1507-1511 (5)	5.60	4.30

Nos. 1507-1511 were issued in sheets of 4. Value, set $27.50.

See Nos. 1589-1593, 1658-1662, 1711-1715, 1779-1783, 1847-1851, 1908-1913, 2043-2047, 2090-2093, 2147-2151, 2265-2269, 2335-2339, 2386-2390, 2437-2441, 2534-2538, 2586-2590, 2634-2638, 2810-2813, 2843-2847, 2872-2874, 2908-2910, 2936-2938, 2973-2975, 2995, 3001-3002, 3028-3030, 3054-3055, 3075-3076, 3105-3107, 3133-3135, 3160-3162, 3188-3190, 3224-3226, 3233, 3255-3257, 3287-3289, 3323-3325, 3359-3361, 3401-3402.

Pres. Antonin Novotny — A566

1967, Dec. 9   **Engr.**   **Perf. 11½**

1512	A566	2k blue gray	1.60	.20
1513	A566	3k brown	1.60	.20

Czechoslovakia Nos. 65, 71 and 81 of 1920 — A567

1967, Dec. 18

1514	A567	1k maroon & silver	1.60	1.10

Issued for Stamp Day.

Symbolic Flag and Dates — A568

1968, Jan. 15   **Engr.**   **Perf. 11½**

1515	A568	30h red, dk bl & ultra	.80	.20

50th anniversary of Czechoslovakia. No. 1515 was issued in a sheet of 10. Value, $25.

Figure Skating and Olympic Rings — A569

Olympic Rings and: 1k, Ski course. 1.60k, Toboggan chute. 2k, Ice hockey.

1968, Jan. 29   **Engr. & Photo.**

1516	A569	60h blk, yel & ocher	.30	.20
1517	A569	1k ol grn, lt bl & lem	.60	.20
1518	A569	1.60k blk, lil & bl grn	.80	.20
1519	A569	2k blk, ap grn & lt bl	1.25	.65
		Nos. 1516-1519 (4)	2.95	1.25

10th Winter Olympic Games, Grenoble, France, Feb. 6-18.

Factories and Rising Sun — A570

Design: 60h, Workers and banner.

1968, Feb. 25   **Perf. 11½x12**

1520	A570	30h car & dk bl	.20	.20
1521	A570	60h car & dk bl	.20	.20

20th anniversary of February Revolution.

Map of Battle of Sokolow A571

Human Rights Flame — A572

1968, Mar. 8   **Perf. 11½**

1522	A571	30h blk, brt bl & car	.40	.20

Engr.

1523	A572	1k rose carmine	1.25	.50

25th anniv. of the Battle of Sokolow, Mar. 8, 1943, against the German Army, No. 1522; Intl. Human Rights Year, No. 1523.

Janko Kral and Liptovsky Mikulas — A573

Karl Marx — A574

Girl's Head — A575

Arms and Allegory — A576

Head — A577

1968, Mar. 25   **Engr.**

1524	A573	30h green	.30	.20
1525	A574	30h claret	.25	.20

Engraved and Photogravure

1526	A575	30h dk red & gold	.25	.20
1527	A576	30h dk blue & dp org	.25	.20
1528	A577	1k multicolored	.50	.20
		Nos. 1524-1528 (5)	1.55	1.00

The writer Janko Kral and the Slovak town Liptovsky Mikulas (No. 1524); 150th anniv. of the birth of Karl Marx (No. 1525); cent. of the cornerstone laying of the Prague Natl. Theater (No. 1526); 150th anniv. of the Prague Natl. Museum (No. 1527); 20th anniv. of WHO (1k).

Symbolic Radio Waves A578

No. 1530, Symbolic television screens.

1968, Apr. 29   **Perf. 11½**

1529	A578	30h blk, car & vio bl	.20	.20
1530	A578	30h blk, car & vio bl	.20	.20

45th anniv. of Czechoslovak broadcasting (#1529), 15th anniv. of television (#1530).

Olympic Rings, Mexican Sculpture and Diver — A579

Olympic Rings and: 40h, Runner and "The Sanctification of Quetzalcoatl." 60h, Volleyball and Mexican ornaments. 1k, Czechoslovak and Mexican Olympic emblems and carved altar. 1.60k, Soccer and ornaments. 2k, View of Hradcany, weather vane and key.

1968, Apr. 30

1531	A579	30h black, bl & car	.20	.20
1532	A579	40h multi	.20	.20
1533	A579	60h multi	.20	.20
1534	A579	1k multi	.35	.20
1535	A579	1.60k multi	.35	.20
1536	A579	2k black & multi	1.75	.40
		Nos. 1531-1536 (6)	3.05	1.40

19th Olympic Games, Mexico City, 10/12-27.

Prague Castle Types of 1966

Designs: 30h, Tombstone of Bretislav I. 60h, Romanesque door knocker, St. Wenceslas Chapel. 5k, Head of St. Peter, mosaic from Golden Gate of St. Vitus Cathedral.

1968, May 9   **Perf. 11½**

1537	A527	30h multicolored	.40	.20
1538	A527	60h black, red & cit	.40	.20

Souvenir Sheet
Engr.

1539	A528	5k multicolored	2.50	2.50

Pres. Ludvik Svoboda — A580

1968-70   **Engr.**   **Perf. 11½**

1540	A580	30h ultramarine	.20	.20
1540A	A580	50h green ('70)	.20	.20
1541	A580	60h maroon	.20	.20
1541A	A580	1k rose car ('70)	.30	.20
		Nos. 1540-1541A (4)	.90	.80

Shades exist of No. 1541A.

"Business," Sculpture by Otto Gutfreund A581

Cabaret Performer, by Frantisek Kupka — A582

Designs (The New Prague): 40h, Broadcasting Corporation Building. 60h, New Parliament. 1.40k, Tapestry by Jan Bauch "Prague 1787." 3k, Presidential standard.

Engr. & Photo.; Engr. (2k)
1968, June 5

1542	A581	30h black & multi	.20	.20
1543	A581	40h black & multi	.20	.20
1544	A581	60h dk brn & multi	.20	.20
1545	A581	1.40k dk brn & multi	.40	.20
1546	A582	2k indigo & multi	.85	.70
1547	A581	3k black & multi	.85	.30
		Nos. 1542-1547 (6)	2.70	1.80

Designs (The Old Prague): 30h, St. George's Basilica. 60h, Renaissance fountain. 1k, Villa America-Dvorak Museum, 18th cent. building. 1.60k, Emblem from the House of Three Violins, 18th cent. 2k, Josefina, by Josef Manes. 3k, Emblem of Prague, 1475.

1968, June 21 *Perf. 11½*

1548	A581	30h green, gray & yel	.20	.20
1549	A581	60h dk vio, ap grn & gold	.20	.20
1550	A581	1k black, lt bl & pink	.30	.20
1551	A581	1.60k slate grn & multi	.55	.20
1552	A582	2k brown & multi	1.25	.60
1553	A581	3k blk, yel, bl & pink	1.25	.60
		Nos. 1548-1553 (6)	3.75	2.00

Nos. 1542-1553 publicized the Praga 68 Philatelic Exhibition. Nos. 1542-1545, 1547-1551, 1553 issued in sheets of 15 + 15 labels with Praga 68 emblem and inscription.

Nos. 1546, 1552 issued in sheets of 4 (2x2) with one horizontal label between top and bottom rows showing Praga 68 emblem. Values for sheets of 4, each $8.

Souvenir Sheet

View of Prague and Emblems — A583

Engraved and Photogravure
1968, June 22 *Imperf.*

1554	A583	10k multicolored	3.00	2.50

Praga 68 and 50th anniv. of Czechoslovak postage stamps. Sold only together with a 5k admission ticket to the Praga 68 philatelic Exhibition. Value $20.

Madonna with the Rose Garlands, by Dürer — A584

1968, July 6 *Perf. 11½*

1555	A584	5k multicolored	3.00	1.75

FIP Day, July 6. Issued in sheets of 4 (2x2) with one horizontal label between, showing Praga 68 emblem. Value, $25.

Stagecoach on Rails — A585

Design: 1k, Steam and electric locomotives.

1968, Aug. 6

1556	A585	60h multicolored	.45	.20
1557	A585	1k multicolored	1.60	.60

No. 1556: 140th anniv. of the horse-drawn railroad Ceské Budejovice to Linz; No. 1557: cent. of the Ceské Budejovice to Plzen railroad.

6th Intl. Slavonic Cong. in Prague — A586

1968, Aug. 7 *Perf. 11½*

1558	A586	30h vio blue & car	.40	.20

Ardspach Rocks and Ammonite — A587

60h, Basalt formation & frog skeleton fossil. 80h, Rocks, basalt veins & polished agate. 1k, Pelecypoda (fossil shell) & Belanske Tatra mountains. 1.60k, Trilobite & Barrande rock formation.

1968, Aug. 8

1559	A587	30h black & citron	.20	.20
1560	A587	60h black & rose cl	.20	.20
1561	A587	80h black, lt vio & pink	.30	.20
1562	A587	1k black & lt blue	.40	.20
1563	A587	1.60k black & bister	1.40	.65
		Nos. 1559-1563 (5)	2.50	1.45

Issued to publicize the 23rd International Geological Congress, Prague, Aug. 8-Sept. 3.

Raising Slovak Flag A588

60h, Slovak partisans, and mountain.

1968, Sept. 9 *Engr.* *Perf. 11½*

1564	A588	30h ultra	.20	.20
1565	A588	60h red	.20	.20

No. 1564 for the Slovak Natl. Council, No. 1565 the 120th anniv. of the Slovak national uprising.

Flowerpot, by Jiri Schlessinger (age 10) — A589

Drawings by Children in Terezin Concentration Camp: 30h, Jew and Guard, by Jiri Beutler (age 10). 60h, Butterflies, by Kitty Brunnerova (age 11).

Engraved and Photogravure
1968, Sept. 30 *Perf. 11½*

Size: 30x23mm

1566	A589	30h blk, buff & rose lil	.30	.20
1567	A589	60h black & multi	.30	.20

Perf. 12x11½

Size: 41x23mm

1568	A589	1k black & multi	.95	.20
		Nos. 1566-1568 (3)	1.55	.60

30th anniversary of Munich Pact.

Arms of Regional Capitals A590

Arms of Prague — A591

1968, Oct. 21 *Perf. 11½*

1569	A590	60h Banská Bystrica	.20	.20
1570	A590	60h Bratislava	.20	.20
1571	A590	60h Brno	.20	.20
1572	A590	60h Ceské Budejovice	.20	.20
1573	A590	60h Hradec Králové	.20	.20
1574	A590	60h Kosice	.20	.20
1575	A590	60h Ostrava (horse)	.20	.20
1576	A590	60h Plzen	.20	.20
1577	A590	60h Ustí nad Labem	.20	.20

Perf. 11½x16

1578	A591	1k shown	.75	.20
		Nos. 1569-1578 (10)	2.55	2.00

#1578 issued in sheets of 10. Value, $15. See #1652-1657, 1742-1747, 1886-1888, 2000-2001.

Flag and Linden Leaves A592

Bohemian Lion Breaking Chains (Type SP1 of 1919) — A593

Design: 60h, Map of Czechoslovakia, linden leaves, Hradcany in Prague and Castle in Bratislava.

1968, Oct. 28 *Perf. 12x11½*

1579	A592	30h dp blue & mag	.30	.20
1580	A592	60h blk, gold, red & ultra	.30	.20

Souvenir Sheet
Engr.

Perf. 11½x12

1581	A593	5k red	3.50	2.75

Founding of Czechoslovakia, 50th anniv.

Ernest Hemingway A594 / Cinderlad A595

Caricatures: 30h, Karel Capek (1890-1938), writer. 40h, George Bernard Shaw. 60h, Maxim Gorki. 1k, Pablo Picasso. 1.20k, Taikan Yokoyama (1868-1958), painter. 1.40k, Charlie Chaplin.

Engraved and Photogravure
1968, Nov. 18 *Perf. 11½x12*

1582	A594	20h black, org & red	.20	.20
1583	A594	30h black & multi	.30	.20
1584	A594	40h blk, lic & car	.30	.20
1585	A594	60h black, sky bl & grn	.20	.20
1586	A594	1k black, brn & yel	.45	.20
1587	A594	1.20k black, dp car & vio	.45	.20
1588	A594	1.40k black, brn & dp org	1.75	.40
		Nos. 1582-1588 (7)	3.65	1.60

Cultural personalities of the 20th cent. and UNESCO. See Nos. 1628-1633.

Painting Type of 1967

Czechoslovakian Art: 60h, Cleopatra II, by Jan Zrzavy (1890-1977). 80h, Black Lake (man and horse), by Jan Preisler (1872-1918). 1.20k, Giovanni Francisci as a Volunteer, by Peter Michal Bohun (1822-1879). 1.60k, Princess Hyacinth, by Alfons Mucha (1860-1939). 3k, Madonna and Child, woodcarving, 1518, by Master Paul of Levoca.

1968, Nov. 29 *Engr.* *Perf. 11½*

1589	A565	60h multi	.75	.35
1590	A565	80h multi	.75	.35
1591	A565	1.20k multi	.75	.35
1592	A565	1.60k multi	.75	.35
1593	A565	3k multi	2.50	2.50
		Nos. 1589-1593 (5)	5.50	3.90

Nos. 1589-1593 were issued in sheets of 4. Value, set $30.

1968, Dec. 18 *Engr. & Photo.*

Slovak Fairy Tales: 60h, The Proud Lady. 80h, The Ruling Knight. 1k, Good Day, Little Bench. 1.20k, The Spellbound Castle. 1.80k,

The Miraculous Hunter. The designs are from illustrations by Ludovit Fulla for "Slovak Stories."

1594	A595	30h multi	.25 .20
1595	A595	60h multi	.25 .20
1596	A595	80h multi	.40 .20
1597	A595	1k multi	.55 .20
1598	A595	1.20k multi	.55 .20
1599	A595	1.80k multi	1.50 .65
		Nos. 1594-1599 (6)	3.50 1.65

Czechoslovakia Nos. 2 and 3 — A596

1968, Dec. 18

1600 A596 1k violet bl & gold .95 .65

50th anniv. of Czechoslovakian postage stamps.

Crescent, Cross and Lion and Sun Emblems A597

ILO Emblem A598

60h, 12 crosses in circles forming large cross.

1969, Jan. 31 **Perf. 11½**

1601 A597 60h black, red & gold .20 .20
1602 A597 1k black, ultra & red .35 .20

No. 1601: 50th anniv. of the Czechoslovak Red Cross. No. 1602: 50th anniv. of the League of Red Cross Societies.

1969, Jan. 31

1603 A598 1k black & gray .30 .20

50th anniv. of the ILO.

Cheb Pistol A599

Historical Firearms: 40h, Italian pistol with Dutch decorations, c. 1600. 60h, Wheellock rifle from Matej Kubik workshop c. 1720. 1k, Flintlock pistol, Devieuxe workshop, Liege, c. 1760. 1.40k, Duelling pistols, from Lebeda workshop, Prague, c. 1835. 1.60k, Derringer pistols, US, c. 1865.

1969, Feb. 18

1604	A599	30h black & multi	.20 .20
1605	A599	40h black & multi	.20 .20
1606	A599	60h black & multi	.20 .20
1607	A599	1k black & multi	.25 .20
1608	A599	1.40k black & multi	.35 .20
1609	A599	1.60k black & multi	1.00 .50
		Nos. 1604-1609 (6)	2.20 1.50

Bratislava Castle, Muse and Book — A600

#1611, Science symbols & emblem (Brno University). #1612, Harp, laurel & musicians' names. #1613, Theatrical scene. #1614, Arms of Slovakia, banner & blossoms. #1615, School, outstretched hands & woman with linden leaves.

1969, Mar. 24 **Engr.** **Perf. 11½**

1610 A600 60h violet blue .20 .20

Engraved and Photogravure

1611	A600	60h blk, gold & slate	.20 .20
1612	A600	60h gold, blue, blk & red	.20 .20
1613	A600	60h black & rose red	.20 .20
1614	A600	60h rose red, sil & bl	.20 .20
1615	A600	60h black & gold	.20 .20
		Nos. 1610-1615 (6)	1.20 1.20

50th anniv. of: Komensky University in Bratislava (#1610); Brno University (#1611); Brno Conservatory of Music (#1612); Slovak Natl. Theater (#1613); Slovak Soviet Republic (#1614); cent. of the Zniev Gymnasium (academic high school) (#1615).

Baldachin-top Car and Four-seat Coupé of 1900-1905 — A601

Designs: 1.60k, Laurin & Klement Voiturette, 1907, and L & K touring car with American top, 1907. 1.80k, First Prague bus, 1907, and sectionalized Skoda bus, 1967.

1969, Mar. 25 **Engr. & Photo.**

1616	A601	30h blk, lil & lt grn	.65 .20
1617	A601	1.60k blk, org brn & lt bl	.80 .20
1618	A601	1.80k multi	1.40 .60
		Nos. 1616-1618 (3)	2.85 1.00

Peace, by Ladislav Guderna — A602

1969, Apr. 21 **Perf. 11**

1619 A602 1.60k multi .50 .35

20th anniv. of the Peace Movement. Issued in sheets of 15 stamps and 5 tabs.

Horse and Rider, by Vaclav Hollar — A603

Old Engravings of Horses: 30h, Prancing Stallion, by Hendrik Goltzius, horiz. 80h, Groom Leading Horse, by Matthäus Merian, horiz. 1.80k, Horse and Soldier, by Albrecht Dürer. 2.40k, Groom and Horse, by Johann E. Ridinger.

1969, Apr. 24 **Perf. 11x11½, 11½x11**
Yellowish Paper

1620	A603	30h dark brown	.20 .20
1621	A603	80h violet brown	.20 .20
1622	A603	1.60k slate	.45 .20
1623	A603	1.80k sepia	.50 .20
1624	A603	2.40k multi	2.40 .60
		Nos. 1620-1624 (5)	3.75 1.40

M. R. Stefánik as Astronomy Professor and French General — A604

1969, May 4 **Engr.** **Perf. 11½**

1625 A604 60h rose claret .40 .20

Gen. Milan R. Stefánik, 50th death anniv.

St. Wenceslas Pressing Wine, Mural by the Master of Litomerice — A605

Design: No. 1627, Coronation banner of the Estates, 1723, with St. Wenceslas and coats of arms of Bohemia and Czech Crown lands.

1969, May 9 **Engr.** **Perf. 11½**

1626 A605 3k multicolored 2.00 1.40
1627 A605 3k multicolored 2.00 1.40

Issued to publicize the art treasures of the Castle of Prague.
Issued in sheets of 4. Value, set $20.
See Nos. 1689-1690.

Caricature Type of 1968

Caricatures: 30h, Pavol Orszagh Hviezdoslav (1849-1921), Slovak writer. 40h, Gilbert K. Chesterton (1874-1936), English writer. 60h, Vladimir Mayakovski (1893-1930), Russian poet. 1k, Henri Matisse (1869-1954), French painter. 1.80k, Ales Hrdlicka (1869-1943), Czech-born American anthropologist. 2k, Franz Kafka (1883-1924), Austrian writer.

Engraved and Photogravure
1969, June 17 **Perf. 11½x12**

1628	A594	30h blk, red & bl	.20 .20
1629	A594	40h blk, bl & lt vio	.20 .20
1630	A594	60h blk, rose & yel	.20 .20
1631	A594	1k black & multi	.20 .20
1632	A594	1.80k blk, ultra & ocher	.20 .20
1633	A594	2k blk, yel & brt grn	1.50 .50
		Nos. 1628-1633 (6)	2.50 1.50

Issued to honor cultural personalities of the 20th century and UNESCO.

"Music," by Alfons Mucha — A606

Paintings by Mucha: 60h, "Painting." 1k, "Dance." 2.40k, "Ruby" and "Amethyst."

1969, July 14 **Perf. 11½x11**
Size: 30x49mm

1634	A606	30h black & multi	1.00 .20
1635	A606	1k black & multi	1.00 .20
1636	A606	1k black & multi	1.25 .20

Size: 39x51mm

1637	A606	2.40k black & multi	2.75 1.25
		Nos. 1634-1637 (4)	6.00 1.85

Alfons Mucha (1860-1930), painter and stamp designer (Type A1).
No. 1637 was issued in sheets of 4. Value $18.

Pres. Svoboda and Partisans A607

No. 1639, Slovak fighters and mourners.

1969, Aug. 29 **Perf. 11**

1638 A607 30h ol grn & red, *yel* .20 .20
1639 A607 30h vio bl & red, *yel* .20 .20

25th anniversary of the Slovak uprising and of the Battle of Dukla.

Tatra Mountain Stream and Gentians — A608

Designs: 60h, Various views in Tatra Mountains. No. 1644, Mountain pass and gentians. No. 1645, Houses, Krivan Mountain and autumn crocuses.

1969, Sept. 8 **Engr.** **Perf. 11**
Size: 71x33mm

1640	A608	60h gray	.25 .20
1641	A608	60h dark blue	.25 .20
1642	A608	60h dull gray vio	.25 .20

Perf. 11½
Size: 40x23mm

1643	A608	1.60k multi	.80 .20
1644	A608	1.60k multi	1.60 .50
1645	A608	1.60k multi	.80 .20
		Nos. 1640-1645 (6)	3.95 1.50

20th anniv. of the creation of the Tatra Mountains Natl. Park.
Nos. 1640-1642 are printed in sheets of 15 (3x5) with 5 labels showing mountain plants. Value, set with tabs $2.50.
Nos. 1643-1645 were issued in sheets of 10. Value, $55.

Bronze Belt Ornaments A609

Archaeological Treasures from Bohemia and Moravia: 30h, Gilt ornament with 6 masks. 1k, Jeweled earrings. 1.80k, Front and back of lead cross with Greek inscription. 2k, Gilt strap ornament with human figure.

Engraved and Photogravure
1969, Sept. 30 **Perf. 11½x11**

1646	A609	20h gold & multi	.20 .20
1647	A609	30h gold & multi	.20 .20
1648	A609	1k red & multi	.25 .20
1649	A609	1.80k dull org & multi	.65 .20
1650	A609	2k gold & multi	2.00 .40
		Nos. 1646-1650 (5)	3.30 1.20

"Mail Circling the World" A610

1969, Oct. 1 **Engr.** **Perf. 12**

1651 A610 3.20k multi .95 .60

16th UPU Cong., Tokyo, Oct. 1-Nov. 14. Issued in sheets of 4. Value $9.

Coat of Arms Type of 1968
Engraved and Photogravure
1969, Oct. 25 **Perf. 11½**

1652	A590	50h Bardejov	.25 .20
1653	A590	50h Hranice	.25 .20
1654	A590	50h Kezmarok	.25 .20
1655	A590	50h Krnov	.25 .20
1656	A590	50h Litomerice	.25 .20
1657	A590	50h Manetin	.25 .20
		Nos. 1652-1657 (6)	1.50 1.20

Painting Type of 1968

Designs: 60h, Requiem, 1944, by Frantisek Muzika. 1k, Resurrection, 1380, by the Master of the Trebon Altar. 1.60k, Crucifixion, 1950, by Vincent Hloznik. 1.80k, Girl with Doll, 1863, by Julius Bencur. 2.20k, St. Jerome, 1357-67, by Master Theodorik.

1969, Nov. 25 *Perf. 11½*
1658	A565	60h multi	1.00	.25
1659	A565	1k multi	1.00	.25
1660	A565	1.60k multi	1.10	.40
1661	A565	1.80k multi	1.40	.50
1662	A565	2.20k multi	3.00	2.00
		Nos. 1658-1662 (5)	7.50	3.40

Nos. 1658-1662 were each issued in sheets of 4. Value, set $40.

Symbolic Sheet of Stamps — A611

1969, Dec. 18 *Perf. 11½x12*
| 1663 | A611 | 1k dk brn, ultra & gold | .30 | .30 |

Issued for Stamp Day 1969.

Ski Jump — A612

Designs: 60h, Long distance skier. 1k, Ski jump and slope. 1.60k, Woman skier.

1970, Jan. 6 *Perf. 11½*
1664	A612	50h multi	.20	.20
1665	A612	60h multi	.20	.20
1666	A612	1k multi	.20	.20
1667	A612	1.60k multi	.60	.30
		Nos. 1664-1667 (4)	1.20	.90

Intl. Ski Championships "Tatra 1970."

Ludwig van Beethoven — A613

Portraits: No. 1669, Friedrich Engels (1820-95), German socialist. No. 1670, Maximilian Hell (1720-92), Slovakian Jesuit and astronomer. No. 1671, Lenin, Russian Communist leader. No. 1672, Josef Manes (1820-71), Czech painter. No. 1673, Comenius (1592-1670), theologian and educator.

1970, Feb. 17 **Engr.** *Perf. 11x11½*
1668	A613	40h black	.20	.20
1669	A613	40h dull red	.20	.20
1670	A613	40h yellow brn	.20	.20
1671	A613	40h dull red	.20	.20
1672	A613	40h brown	.20	.20
1673	A613	40h black	.20	.20
		Nos. 1668-1673 (6)	1.20	1.20

Anniversaries of birth of Beethoven, Engels, Hell, Lenin and Manes, 300th anniv. of the death of Comenius, and to honor UNESCO.

Bells A614

80h, Machine tools & lathe. 1k, Folklore masks. 1.60k, Angel & Three Wise Men, 17th cent. icon from Koniec. 2k, View of Orlik Castle, 1787, by F. K. Wolf. 3k, "Passing through Koshu down to Mishima" from Hokusai's 36 Views of Fuji.

**Engraved and Photogravure
1970, Mar. 13** *Perf. 11½x11*
Size: 40x23mm
1674	A614	50h multi	.20	.20
1675	A614	80h multi	.20	.20
1676	A614	1k multi	.25	.20

Size: 50x40mm
Perf. 11½
1677	A614	1.60k multi	.55	.30
1678	A614	2k multi	.75	.35
1679	A614	3k multi	1.90	1.00
		Nos. 1674-1679 (6)	3.85	2.25

EXPO '70 Intl. Exhib., Osaka, Japan, Mar. 15-Sept. 13, 1970. Nos. 1674-1676 issued in sheets of 50, Nos. 1677-1679 in sheets of 4. Value, set of 3 sheets, $28.

Kosice Townhall, Laurel and Czechoslovak Arms — A615

1970, Apr. 5 *Perf. 11*
| 1680 | A615 | 60h slate, ver & gold | .40 | .20 |

Government's Kosice Program, 25th anniv.

"The Remarkable Horse" by Josef Lada — A616

Lenin — A617

Paintings by Josef Lada: 60h, Autumn, 1955, horiz. 1.80k, "The Water Sprite." 2.40k, Children in Winter, 1943, horiz.

1970, Apr. 21 *Perf. 11½*
1681	A616	60h black & multi	.30	.20
1682	A616	1k black & multi	.45	.20
1683	A616	1.80k black & multi	.80	.20
1684	A616	2.40k black & multi	1.60	.40
		Nos. 1681-1684 (4)	3.15	1.00

1970, Apr. 22

Design: 60h, Lenin without cap, facing left.
| 1685 | A617 | 30h dk red & gold | .20 | .20 |
| 1686 | A617 | 60h black & gold | .20 | .20 |

Lenin (1870-1924), Russian communist leader.

Fighters on the Barricades — A618

No. 1688, Lilac, Russian tank and castle.

1970, May 5 *Perf. 11x11½*
| 1687 | A618 | 30h dull pur, gold & bl | .20 | .20 |
| 1688 | A618 | 30h dull grn, gold & red | .20 | .20 |

No. 1687: 25th anniv. of the Prague uprising. No. 1688: 25th anniv. of the liberation of Czechoslovakia from the Germans.

Prague Castle Art Type of 1969
#1689, Bust of St. Vitus, 1486. #1690, Hermes and Athena, by Bartholomy Springer (1546-1611), mural from White Tower.

1970, May 7 **Engr.** *Perf. 11½*
| 1689 | A605 | 3k maroon & multi | 2.40 | 1.50 |
| 1690 | A605 | 3k lt blue & multi | 2.40 | 1.50 |

Nos. 1689-1690 were issued in sheets of 4. Value, set of 2 sheets, $20.

Compass Rose, UN Headquarters and Famous Buildings of the World — A619

**Engraved and Photogravure
1970, June 26** *Perf. 11*
| 1691 | A619 | 1k black & multi | .40 | .20 |

25th anniv. of the UN. Issued in sheets of 15 (3x5) and 5 labels showing UN emblem. Value of single with tab attached: unused 75c; used 40c.

Cannon from 30 Years' War and Baron Munchhausen — A620

Historical Cannons: 60h, Cannon from Hussite war and St. Barbara. 1.20k, Cannon from Prussian-Austrian war, and legendary cannoneer Javurek. 1.80k, Early 20th century cannon and spaceship "La Colombiad" (Jules Verne). 2.40k, World War I cannon and "Good Soldier Schweik."

1970, Aug. 31 *Perf. 11½*
1692	A620	30h black & multi	.20	.20
1693	A620	60h black & multi	.20	.20
1694	A620	1.20k black & multi	.20	.20
1695	A620	1.80k black & multi	.30	.20
1696	A620	2.40k black & multi	1.60	.65
		Nos. 1692-1696 (5)	2.50	1.45

"Rude Pravo" (Red Truth) A621

1970, Sept. 21 *Perf. 11½x11*
| 1697 | A621 | 60h car, gold & blk | .20 | .20 |

50th anniv. of the Rude Pravo newspaper.

"Great Sun" House Sign and Old Town Tower Bridge, Prague — A622

60h, "Blue Lion" & Town Hall Tower, Brno. 1k, Gothic corner stone & Town Hall Tower, Bratislava. 1.40k, Coat of Arms & Gothic Tower, Bratislava, & medallion. 1.60k, Moravian Eagle & Gothic Town Hall Tower, Brno.

1.80k, "Black Sun" & "Green Frog" house signs & New Town Hall, Prague.

1970, Sept. 23 *Perf. 11x11½*
1698	A622	40h black & multi	.25	.20
1699	A622	60h black & multi	.25	.20
1700	A622	1k black & multi	.25	.20
1701	A622	1.40k black & multi	1.40	.50
1702	A622	1.60k black & multi	.30	.20
1703	A622	1.80k black & multi	.95	.20
		Nos. 1698-1703 (6)	3.40	1.50

Germany-Uruguay Semifinal Soccer Match — A623

Designs: 20h, Sundisk Games' emblem and flags of participating nations. 60h, England-Czechoslovakia match and coats of arms. 1k, Romania-Czechoslovakia match and coats of arms. 1.20k, Brazil-Italy, final match and emblems. 1.80k, Brazil-Czechoslovakia match and emblems.

1970, Oct. 29 *Perf. 11½*
1704	A623	20h blk & multi	.25	.20
1705	A623	40h blk & multi	.25	.20
1706	A623	60h blk & multi	.25	.20
1707	A623	1k blk & multi	.35	.20
1708	A623	1.20k blk & multi	.40	.20
1709	A623	1.80k blk & multi	1.90	.30
		Nos. 1704-1709 (6)	3.40	1.30

9th World Soccer Championships for the Jules Rimet Cup, Mexico City, 5/30-6/21.

Congress Emblem — A624

1970, Nov. 9 **Engr. & Photo.**
| 1710 | A624 | 30h blk, gold, ultra & red | .20 | .20 |

Congress of the Czechoslovak Socialist Youth Federation.

Painting Type of 1967
Paintings: 1k, Seated Mother, by Mikulas Galanda. 1.20k, Bridesmaid, by Karel Svolinsky. 1.40k, Walk by Night, 1944, by Frantisek Hudecek. 1.80k, Banska Bystrica Market, by Dominik Skutecky. 2.40k, Adoration of the Kings, from the Vysehrad Codex, 1085.

1970, Nov. 27 **Engr.** *Perf. 11½*
1711	A565	1k multi	.65	.25
1712	A565	1.20k multi	.80	.45
1713	A565	1.40k multi	.65	.30
1714	A565	1.80k multi	1.00	.45
1715	A565	2.40k multi	3.25	2.10
		Nos. 1711-1715 (5)	6.35	3.55

Nos. 1711-1715 were each issued in sheets of 4. Value, set $30.

Radar A625

Designs: 40h, Interkosmos 3, geophysical satellite. 60h, Kosmos meteorological satellite. 1k, Astronaut and Vostok satellite. No. 1720, Interkosmos 4, solar research satellite. No. 1720A, Space satellite (Sputnik) over city. 1.60k, Two-stage rocket on launching pad.

1970-71 **Engr. & Photo.** *Perf. 11*
1716	A625	20h black & multi	.20	.20
1717	A625	40h black & multi	.20	.20
1718	A625	60h black & multi	.20	.20
1719	A625	1k black & multi	.20	.20
1720	A625	1.20k black & multi	.20	.20

1720A A625 1.20k black & multi
('71) .30 .20
1721 A625 1.60k black & multi 1.40 .35
Nos. 1716-1721 (7) 2.70 1.55

"Interkosmos," the collaboration of communist countries in various phases of space research.
Issued: #1720A, 11/15/71; others, 11/30/70.

Face of Christ on Veronica's Veil — A626

Slovak Ikons, 16th-18th Centuries: 60h, Adam and Eve in the Garden, vert. 2k, St. George and the Dragon. 2.80k, St. Michael, vert.

1970, Dec. 17   Engr.   Perf. 11½
Cream Paper
1722 A626 60h multi .90 .40
1723 A626 1k multi 1.25 .55
1724 A626 2k multi 1.60 .70
1725 A626 2.80k multi 2.25 1.40
Nos. 1722-1725 (4) 6.00 3.05

Nos. 1722-1725 were each issued in sheets of 4. Value, set $32.50.

Carrier Pigeon Type of 1920 — A627

Engraved and Photogravure
1970, Dec. 18   Perf. 11x11½
1726 A627 1k red, blk & yel grn .40 .30
Stamp Day.

Song of the Barricades, 1938, by Karel Stika — A628

Czech and Slovak Graphic Art: 50h, Fruit Grower's Barge, 1941, by Cyril Bouda. 60h, Moon (woman) Searching for Lilies of the Valley, 1913, by Jan Zrzavy. 1k, At the Edge of Town (working man and woman), 1931, by Koloman Sokol. 1.60k, Summer, 1641, by Vaclav Hollar. 2k, Gamekeeper and Shepherd of Orava Castle, 1847, by Peter M. Bohun.

Engr. & Photo.; Engr. (40h, 60h, 1k)
1971, Jan. 28   Perf. 11½
1727 A628 40h brown .25 .20
1728 A628 50h black & multi .25 .20
1729 A628 60h slate .25 .20
1730 A628 1k black .30 .20
1731 A628 1.60k black & buff .30 .20
1732 A628 2k black & multi 1.40 .30
Nos. 1727-1732 (6) 2.75 1.30

Saris Church   Bell Tower,
A629   Hronsek
A630

Designs: 1k, Roofs and folk art, Horácko. 2.40k, House, Jicin. 3k, House and folk art, Melnik. 3.60k, Church of St. Bartholomew, Chrudim. 5k, Watch Tower, Nachod. 5.40k, Baroque house, Posumavi. 6k, Cottage, Orava. 9k, Cottage, Turnov. 10k, Old houses, Liptov. 14k, House and wayside bell stand. 20k, Houses, Cicmany.

Engraved and Photogravure
1971-72   Perf. 11½x11, 11x11½
1733 A630 1k multi .25 .20
1734 A629 1.60k multi 1.60 .20
1735 A630 2k multi 2.40 .20
1736 A629 2.40k multi 1.40 .30
1736A A630 3k multi ('72) 2.40 .20
1737 A629 3.60k multi 1.90 .20
1737A A630 5k multi ('72) 2.40 .20
1738 A629 5.40k multi 1.25 .20
1739 A630 6k multi 3.75 .20
1740 A630 9k multi 1.50 .20
1740A A629 10k multi ('72) 3.50 .20
1741 A629 14k multi 3.75 .25
1741A A629 20k multi ('72) 4.00 .30
Nos. 1733-1741A (13) 30.10 2.85

Nos. 1736A, 1738, 1740 are horizontal. See No. 2870.

Coat of Arms Type of 1968

1971, Mar. 26   Perf. 11½
1742 A590 60h Zilina .20 .20
1743 A590 60h Levoca .20 .20
1744 A590 60h Ceska Trebova .20 .20
1745 A590 60h Uhersky Brod .20 .20
1746 A590 60h Trutnov .20 .20
1747 A590 60h Karlovy Vary .20 .20
Nos. 1742-1747 (6) 1.20 1.20

"Fight of the Communards and Rise of the International" — A631

Design: No. 1749, World fight against racial discrimination, and "UNESCO."

1971, Mar. 18   Perf. 11
1748 A631 1k multicolored .30 .20
1749 A631 1k multicolored .30 .20

No. 1748 for cent. of the Paris Commune. No. 1749 for the Year against Racial Discrimination. Issued in sheets of 15 stamps and 5 labels. Value for single with attached tab, each 40c.

A632   A633

Edelweiss, mountaineering map & equipment.

1971, Apr. 27   Perf. 11½x11
1750 A632 30h multicolored .25 .20
50th anniversary of Slovak Alpine Club.

1971, Apr. 27   Perf. 11½
1751 A633 30h Singer .25 .20
50th anniversary of Slovak Teachers' Choir.

Abbess' Crosier, 16th Century A634

No. 1753, Allegory of Music, 16th cent. mural.

1971, May 9
1752 A634 3k gold & multi 1.90 1.40
1753 A634 3k blk, dk brn & buff 2.50 1.40

Nos. 1752-1753 were each issued in sheets of 4. Value, set $22.50.
See Nos. 1817-1818, 1884-1885, 1937-1938, 2040-2041, 2081-2082, 2114-2115, 2176-2177, 2238-2239, 2329-2330, 2384-2385, 2420-2421.

Lenin A635

40h, Hammer & sickle allegory. 60h, Raised fists. 1k, Star, hammer & sickle.

1971, May 14   Perf. 11
1754 A635 30h blk, red & gold .20 .20
1755 A635 40h blk, ultra, red & gold .20 .20
1756 A635 60h blk, ultra, red & gold .20 .20
1757 A635 1k blk, ultra, red & gold .30 .20
Nos. 1754-1757 (4) .90 .80

Czechoslovak Communist Party, 50th anniv.

Star, Hammer-Sickle Emblems — A636

60h, Hammer-sickle emblem, fist & people, vert.

Perf. 11½x11, 11x11½
1971, May 24   Engr. & Photo.
1758 A636 30h blk, red, gold & yel .20 .20
1759 A636 60h blk, red, gold & bl .20 .20

14th Congress of Communist Party of Czechoslovakia.

Ring-necked Pheasant — A637

Designs: 60h, Rainbow trout. 80h, Mouflon. 1k, Chamois. 2k, Stag. 2.60k, Wild boar.

1971, Aug. 17   Perf. 11½x11
1760 A637 20h orange & multi .20 .20
1761 A637 60h lt blue & multi .20 .20
1762 A637 80h yellow & multi .20 .20
1763 A637 1k lt green & multi .35 .20
1764 A637 2k lilac & multi .50 .20
1765 A637 2.60k bister & multi 2.25 .65
Nos. 1760-1765 (6) 3.70 1.65

World Hunting Exhib., Budapest, Aug. 27-30.

Diesel   Gymnasts and
Locomotive   Banners
A638   A639

1971, Sept. 2   Perf. 11x11½
1766 A638 30h lt bl, blk & red .40 .20
Cent. of CKD, Prague Machine Foundry.

1971, Sept. 2   Perf. 11½x11½
1767 A639 30h red brn, gold & ultra .20 .20
50th anniversary of Workers' Physical Exercise Federation.

Road Intersections and Bridge — A640

1971, Sept. 2   Engr. & Photo.
1768 A640 1k blk, gold, red & bl .30 .20

14th World Highways and Bridges Congress. Sheets of 25 stamps and 25 labels printed se-tenant with continuous design. Value, single with attached tab, 40c.

Chinese Fairytale, by Eva Bednarova A641

Designs: 1k, Tiger and other animals, by Mirko Hanak. 1.60k, The Miraculous Bamboo Shoot, by Yasuo Segawa, horiz.

Perf. 11½x11, 11x11½
1971, Sept. 10
1769 A641 60h multi .20 .20
1770 A641 1k multi .30 .20
1771 A641 1.60k multi .45 .20
Nos. 1769-1771 (3) .95 .60

Bratislava BIB 71 biennial exhibition of illustrations for children's books.

Apothecary Jars and Coltsfoot — A642

Intl. Pharmaceutical Cong.: 60h, Jars and dog rose. 1k, Scales and adonis vernalis. 1.20k, Mortars and valerian. 1.80k, Retorts and chicory. 2.40k, Mill, mortar and henbane.

1971, Sept. 20   Perf. 11½x11
Yellow Paper
1772 A642 30h multi .20 .20
1773 A642 60h multi .20 .20
1774 A642 1k multi .20 .20
1775 A642 1.20k multi .20 .20
1776 A642 1.80k multi .35 .20
1777 A642 2.40k multi 1.40 .45
Nos. 1772-1777 (6) 2.55 1.45

Painting Type of 1967

Paintings: 1k, "Waiting" (woman's head), 1967, by Imro Weiner-Král. 1.20k, Resurrection, by Master of Vyssi Brod, 14th century. 1.40k, Woman with Pitcher, by Milos Bazovsky. 1.80k, Veruna Cudova (in folk costume), by Josef Mánes. 2.40k, Detail from "Feast of the Rose Garlands," by Albrecht Dürer.

1971, Nov. 27   *Perf. 11½*
1779	A565	1k multi	.40	.30
1780	A565	1.20k multi	.95	.45
1781	A565	1.40k multi	.75	.30
1782	A565	1.80k multi	1.40	.60
1783	A565	2.40k multi	2.40	.95
		Nos. 1779-1783 (5)	5.90	2.60

Nos. 1779-1783 were each issued in sheets of 4. Value, set $28.

Workers Revolt in Krompachy, by Julius Nemcik — A643

1971, Nov. 28   *Perf. 11x11½*
1784	A643	60h multi	.30	.20

History of the Czechoslovak Communist Party.

Wooden Dolls and Birds — A644

Folk Art and UNICEF Emblem: 80h, Jug handles, carved. 1k, Horseback rider. 1.60k, Shepherd carrying lamb. 2k, Easter eggs and rattle. 3k, "Zbojnik," folk hero.

1971, Dec. 11   *Perf. 11½*
1785	A644	60h multi	.30	.20
1786	A644	80h multi	.65	.20
1787	A644	1k multi	.30	.20
1788	A644	1.60k multi	.30	.20
1789	A644	2k multi	.30	.45
1790	A644	3k multi	2.00	.60
		Nos. 1785-1790 (6)	3.85	1.85

25th anniv. of UNICEF.
Nos. 1785-1790 were each issued in sheets of 10. Value, set $50.

Runners, Parthenon, Czechoslovak Olympic Emblem — A645

Designs: 40h, Women's high jump, Olympic emblem and plan for Prague Stadium. 1.60k, Cross-country skiers, Sapporo '72 emblem and ski jump in High Tatras. 2.60k, Discus thrower, Discobolus and St. Vitus Cathedral.

1971, Dec. 16   **Engr. & Photo.**
1791	A645	30h multi	.20	.20
1792	A645	40h multi	.20	.20
1793	A645	1.60k multi	.25	.20
1794	A645	2.60k multi	1.50	.75
		Nos. 1791-1794 (4)	2.15	1.35

75th anniversary of Czechoslovak Olympic Committee (30h, 2.60k); 20th Summer Olympic Games, Munich, Aug. 26-Sept. 10, 1972 (40h); 11th Winter Olympic Games, Sapporo, Japan, Feb. 3-13, 1972 (1.60k).

Post Horns and Lion — A646

1971, Dec. 17   *Perf. 11x11½*
1795	A646	1k blk, gold, car & bl	.30	.20

Stamp Day.

Figure Skating — A647

Olympic Emblems and: 50h, Ski jump. 1k, Ice hockey. 1.60k, Sledding, women's.

1972, Jan. 13   *Perf. 11½*
1796	A647	40h pur, org & red	.20	.20
1797	A647	50h dk bl, org & red	.20	.20
1798	A647	1k mag, org & red	.35	.20
1799	A647	1.60k bl grn, org & red	1.60	.30
		Nos. 1796-1799 (4)	2.35	.90

11th Winter Olympic Games, Sapporo, Japan, Feb. 3-13.

"Lezáky" — A648

No. 1801, Boy's head behind barbed wire, horiz. No. 1802, Hand rising from ruins. No. 1803, Soldier and banner, horiz.

1972, Feb. 16
1800	A648	30h blk, dl org & red	.20	.20
1801	A648	30h blk & brn org	.20	.20
1802	A648	60h blk, yel & red	.20	.20
1803	A648	60h sl grn & multi	.20	.20
		Nos. 1800-1803 (4)	.80	.80

30th anniv. of: destruction of Lezáky (No. 1800) and Lidice (No. 1802); Terezin concentration camp (No. 1801); Czechoslovak Army unit in Russia (No. 1803).

Book Year Emblem A649

Steam and Diesel Locomotives A650

1972, Mar. 17   *Perf. 11½x11*
1804	A649	1k blk & org brn	.30	.20

International Book Year 1972.

1972, Mar. 17   *Perf. 11½x11*
1805	A650	30h multi	.75	.20

Centenary of the Kosice-Bohumin railroad.

"Pasture," by Vojtech Sedlacek A651

Designs: 50h, Dressage, by Frantisek Tichy. 60th, Otakara Kubina, by Vaclav Fiala. 1k, The Three Kings, by Ernest Zmetak. 1.60k, Woman Dressing, by Ludovit Fulla.

1972, Mar. 27   *Perf. 11½x11*
1806	A651	40h multi	.20	.20
1807	A651	50h multi	.20	.20
1808	A651	60h multi	.20	.20
1809	A651	1k multi	.30	.20
1810	A651	1.60k multi	1.60	1.60
		Nos. 1806-1810 (5)	2.50	2.40

Czech and Slovak graphic art.
1.60k issued in sheets of 4. Value $12.
See #1859-1862, 1921-1924.

Ice Hockey A652

Design: 1k, Two players.

1972, Apr. 7   *Perf. 11*
1811	A652	60h blk & multi	.20	.20
1812	A652	1k blk & multi	.40	.20

World and European Ice Hockey Championships, Prague.
For overprint see Nos. 1845-1846.

Bicycling, Olympic Rings and Emblem A653

1972, Apr. 7
1813	A653	50h shown	.20	.20
1814	A653	1.60k Diving	.40	.20
1815	A653	1.80k Canoeing	.55	.20
1816	A653	2k Gymnast	1.10	.40
		Nos. 1813-1816 (4)	2.25	1.00

20th Olympic Games, Munich, 8/26-9/11.

Prague Castle Art Type of 1971

Designs: No. 1817, Adam and Eve, column capital, St. Vitus Cathedral. No. 1818, Czech coat of arms (lion), c. 1500.

1972, May 9   *Perf. 11½*
1817	A634	3k blk & multi	3.20	1.90
1818	A634	3k blk, red, sil & gold	1.60	.95

Nos. 1817-1818 were each issued in sheets of 4. Value, set $20.

Andrej Sladkovic (1820-1872), Poet — A654

#1820, Janko Kral (1822-1876), poet. #1821, Ludmilla Podjavorinska (1872-1951), writer. #1822, Antonin Hudecek (1872-1941), painter. #1823, Frantisek Bilek (1872-1941), sculptor. #1824, Jan Preisler (1872-1918), painter.

1972, June 14   *Perf. 11*
1819	A654	40h pur, ol & bl	.20	.20
1820	A654	40h dk grn, bl & yel	.20	.20
1821	A654	40h blk & multi	.20	.20
1822	A654	40h brn, grn & bl	.20	.20
1823	A654	40h choc, grn & org	.20	.20
1824	A654	40h grn, sl & dp org	.20	.20
		Nos. 1819-1824 (6)	1.20	1.20

Men with Banners — A655

1972, June 14   *Perf. 11x11½*
1825	A655	30h dk vio bl, red & yel	.20	.20

8th Trade Union Congress, Prague.

Art Forms of Wire A656

Ornamental Wirework: 60h, Plane and rosette. 80h, Four-headed dragon and ornament. 1k, Locomotive and loops. 2.60k, Tray and owl.

1972, Aug. 28   *Perf. 11½x11*
1826	A656	20h sal & multi	.20	.20
1827	A656	60h multi	.20	.20
1828	A656	80h pink & multi	.30	.20
1829	A656	1k multi	.40	.20
1830	A656	2.60k rose & multi	1.40	.45
		Nos. 1826-1830 (5)	2.50	1.25

"Jiskra" A657

Engr. & Photo.
1972, Sept. 27   *Perf. 11½x11*
Size: 40x22mm

Multicolored Design on Blue Paper
1831	A657	50h shown	.20	.20
1832	A657	60h "Mir"	.20	.20
1833	A657	80h "Republika"	.20	.20

Size: 48x29mm
Perf. 11x11½
1834	A657	1k "Kosice"	.30	.20
1835	A657	1.60k "Dukla"	.45	.20
1836	A657	2k "Kladno"	1.40	.55
		Nos. 1831-1836 (6)	2.75	1.55

Czechoslovak sea-going vessels.

Hussar, 18th Century Tile — A658

1972, Oct. 24   *Perf. 11½x11*
1837	A658	30h shown	.20	.20
1838	A658	60h Janissary	.20	.20
1839	A658	80h St. Martin	.25	.20
1840	A658	1.60k St. George	.45	.20
1841	A658	1.80k Nobleman's guard	.70	.20
1842	A658	2.20k Slovakian horseman	1.40	.60
		Nos. 1837-1842 (6)	3.20	1.60

Horsemen from 18th-19th century tiles or enamel paintings on glass.

Worker, Flag Hoisted on Bayonet A659

Star, Hammer and Sickle A660

1972, Nov. 7   **Perf. 11x11½**
1843 A659 30h gold & multi   .20   .20
1844 A660 60h rose car & gold   .20   .20

55th anniv. of the Russian October Revolution (30h); 50th anniv. of the Soviet Union (60h).

Nos. 1811-1812 Overprinted in Violet Blue or Black

1972   **Perf. 11**
1845 A652 60h multi (VBl)   8.00   6.50
1846 A652 1k multi (Bk)   8.00   6.50

Czechoslovakia's victorious ice hockey team. The overprint on the 60h (shown) is in Czech and reads CSSR/MISTREM/SVETA; the overprint on the 1k is in Slovak.

Painting Type of 1967

Designs: 1k, "Nosegay" (nudes and flowers), by Max Svabinsky. 1.20k, Struggle of St. Ladislas with Kuman nomad, anonymous, 14th century. 1.40k, Lady with Fur Hat, by Vaclav Hollar. 1.80k, Midsummer Night's Dream, 1962, by Josef Liesler. 2.40k, Pablo Picasso, self-portrait.

1972, Nov. 27   **Engr. & Photo.**
1847 A565 1k multi   .60   .40
1848 A565 1.20k multi   .80   .55
1849 A565 1.40k blk & cream   .95   .70
1850 A565 1.80k multi   1.25   1.10
1851 A565 2.40k multi   2.75   2.75
   Nos. 1847-1851 (5)   6.35   5.50

Nos. 1847-1851 were each issued in sheets of 4. Value, set $30.

Goldfinch A661

Songbirds: 60h, Warbler feeding young cuckoo. 80h, Cuckoo. 1k, Black-billed magpie. 1.60k, Bullfinch. 3k, Song thrush.

1972, Dec. 15
     Size: 30x48½mm
1852 A661 60h yel & multi   .20   .20
1853 A661 80h multi   .20   .20
1854 A661 1k lt bl & multi   .20   .20
     Engr.
     Size: 30x23mm
1855 A661 1.60k multi   1.50   .80
1856 A661 2k multi   1.50   .80
1857 A661 3k multi   1.50   .80
   Nos. 1852-1857 (6)   5.10   3.00

Nos. 1855-1857 were each issued in a sheet of 10. Value, set $45.

Post Horn and Allegory — A662

1972, Dec. 18   **Engr. & Photo.**
1858 A662 1k blk, red lil & gold   .30   .30
Stamp Day.

Art Type of 1972

Designs: 30h, Flowers in Window, by Jaroslav Grus. 60h, Quest for Happiness, by Josef Balaz. 1.60k, Balloon, by Kamil Lhotak. 1.80k, Woman with Viola, by Richard Wiesner.

1973, Jan. 25   **Perf. 11½x11**
1859 A651 30h multi   .20   .20
1860 A651 60h multi   .20   .20
1861 A651 1.60k multi   .35   .20
1862 A651 1.80k multi   1.40   .35
   Nos. 1859-1862 (4)   2.15   .95

Czech and Slovak graphic art.

Tennis Player — A663   Figure Skater — A664

Torch and Star — A665

1973, Feb. 22   **Perf. 11**
1863 A663 30h vio & multi   .20   .20
1864 A664 60h blk & multi   .20   .20
1865 A665 1k multi   .30   .20
   Nos. 1863-1865 (3)   .70   .60

80th anniversary of the tennis organization in Czechoslovakia (30h); World figure skating championships, Bratislava (60h); 3rd summer army Spartakiad of socialist countries (1k).

Star and Factories A666

Workers' Militia, Emblem and Flag — A667

1973, Feb. 23
1866 A666 30h multi   .20   .20
1867 A667 60h multi   .20   .20

25th anniversary of the Communist revolution in Czechoslovakia and of the Militia.

Capt. Jan Nalepka, Major Antonin Sochor and Laurel A668

Torch &: 40h, Evzen Rosicky, Mirko Nespor & ivy leaves. 60h, Vlado Clementis, Karol Smidke & linden leaves. 80h, Jan Osoha,

Josef Molak & oak leaves. 1k, Marie Kuderikova, Jozka Jaburkova & rose. 1.60k, Vaclav Sinkule, Eduard Urx & palm leaf.

1973, Mar. 20
     Yellow Paper
1868 A668 30h blk, ver & gold   .30   .20
1869 A668 40h blk, ver & grn   .30   .20
1870 A668 60h blk, ver & gold   .30   .20
1871 A668 80h blk, ver & gold   .30   .20
1872 A668 1k blk, ver & gold   .40   .20
1873 A668 1.60k blk, ver & sil   .85   .20
   Nos. 1868-1873 (6)   2.45   1.20

Fighters against and victims of Fascism and Nazism during German Occupation.

Virgil I. Grissom, Edward H. White, Roger B. Chaffee — A669

Designs: 20h, Soviet planetary station "Venera." 30h, "Intercosmos" station. 40h, Lunokhod on moon. 3.60k, Vladimir M. Komarov, Georgi T. Dobrovolsky, Vladislav N. Volkov, Victor I. Patsayev. 5k, Yuri A. Gagarin. Two types of 3.60k: type I, Cosmonaut on background of cross-hatched lines; type 2, Cosmonaut on background of parallel diagonal lines.

1973, Apr. 12   **Perf. 11½x11**
     Size: 40x22mm
1874 A669 20h multi   .20   .20
1875 A669 30h multi   .20   .20
1876 A669 40h multi   .20   .20
     Engr.
     Perf. 11½
     Size: 49x30mm
1877 A669 3k multi   .80   .50
1878 A669 3.60k multi, type 1   1.25   1.10
  a.   Type 2   25.00   15.00
1879 A669 5k multi   3.00   2.00
   Nos. 1874-1879 (6)   5.65   4.20

In memory of American and Russian astronauts.
Nos. 1877-1879 were each issued in sheets of 4. Values: set (with No. 1878) $30; mset (with No. 1878a) $120.

Radio — A670

Telephone and Map of Czechoslovakia A671

Television A672

1973, May 1   **Perf. 11½x11**
1880 A670 30h blk & multi   .20   .20
1881 A671 30h lt bl, pink & blk   .20   .20
1882 A672 30h dp bl & multi   .20   .20
   Nos. 1880-1882 (3)   .60   .60

Czechoslovak anniversaries: 50 years of broadcasting (No. 1880); 20 years of telephone service to all communities (No. 1881); 20 years of television (No. 1882).

Coat of Arms and Linden Branch — A673

1973, May 9   **Perf. 11x11½**
1883 A673 60h red & multi   .20   .20

25th anniv. of the Constitution of May 9.

Prague Castle Art Type of 1971

No. 1884, Royal Legate, 14th century. No. 1885, Seal of King Charles IV, 1351.

1973, May 9   **Perf. 11½**
1884 A634 3k blue & multi   1.50   1.10
1885 A634 3k gold, grn & dk brn   3.00   2.25

Nos. 1884-1885 were each issued in sheets of 4. Value, set $16.

Coat of Arms Type of 1968

1973, June 20
1886 A590 60h Mikulov   .20   .20
1887 A590 60h Zlutice   .35   .20
1888 A590 60h Smolenice   .35   .20
   Nos. 1886-1888 (3)   .90   .60

Coats of arms of Czechoslovakian cities.

Heraldic Colors of Olomouc and Moravia — A674

1973, Aug. 23   **Engr. & Photo.**
1889 A674 30h multi   .25   .20

University of Olomouc, 400th anniv.

Anthurium — A675

1973, Aug. 23   **Perf. 11½**

Sizes: 60h, 1k, 2k, 30x50mm; 1.60k, 1.80k, 3.60k, 23x39mm.

1890 A675 60h Tulips   .75   .35
1891 A675 1k Rose   .75   .35
1892 A675 1.60k shown   .40   .35
1893 A675 1.80k Iris   .40   .35
1894 A675 2k Chrysanthemum   1.90   1.00
1895 A675 3.60k Cymbidium   .75   .35
   Nos. 1890-1895 (6)   4.95   2.75

Flower Show, Olomouc, Aug. 18-Sept. 2. 60h, 1k, 2k issued in sheets of 4, others in sheets of 10. Value, set $100.

Hunting Dogs A676

1973, Sept. 5
1896 A676 20h Irish setter   .45   .20
1897 A676 30h Czech terrier   .45   .20
1898 A676 40h Bavarian hunting dog   .65   .20
1899 A676 60h German pointer   .65   .20
1900 A676 1k Cocker spaniel   1.00   .20
1901 A676 1.60k Dachshund   2.40   .50
   Nos. 1896-1901 (6)   5.60   1.50

Czechoslovak United Hunting Org., 50th anniv.

St. John, the
Baptist, by
Svabinsky
A677

Works by Max Svabinsky: 60h, "August Noon" (woman). 80h, "Marriage of True Minds" (artist and muse). 1k, "Paradise Sonata I" (Adam dreaming of Eve). 2.60k, Last Judgment, stained glass window, St. Vitus Cathedral.

1973, Sept. 17   Litho. & Engr.
1902 A677 20h blk & pale grn .25 .20
1903 A677 60h black & buff   .25 .20

Engr.
1904 A677 80h black   .75 .20
1905 A677 1k slate green   .75 .25
1906 A677 2.60k multi   1.90 1.25
    Nos. 1902-1906 (5)   3.90 2.10

Centenary of the birth of Max Svabinsky (1873-1962), artist and stamp designer. 20h and 60h issued in sheets of 25; 80h and 1k se-tenant in sheets of 4 checkerwise (value $5); 2.60k in sheets of 4 (value $12).

Trade Union
Emblem
A678

1973, Oct. 15   Engr. & Photo.
1907 A678 1k red, bl & yel   .25 .20

8t (valueh Congress of the World Federation of Trade Unions, Varna, Bulgaria.

Painting Type of 1967

1k, Boy from Martinique, by Antonin Pelc. 1.20k, "Fortitude" (mountaineer), by Martin Benka. 1.80k, Rembrandt, self-portrait. 2k, Pierrot, by Bohumil Kubista. 2.40k, Ilona Kubinyiova, by Peter M. Bohun. 3.60k, Virgin and Child (Veveri Madonna), c. 1350.

1973, Nov. 27   Perf. 11½
1908 A565 1k multi, vio bl
       inscriptions   2.50 1.25
  a. 1k multi, black inscriptions 10.00 10.00
1909 A565 1.20k multi   2.50 1.25
1910 A565 1.80k multi   .80 .80
1911 A565 2k multi   .80 .80
1912 A565 2.40k multi   .80 .80
1913 A565 3.60k multi   .80 .80
    Nos. 1908-1913 (6)   8.20 5.70

Sheets of 4. Nos. 1910-1913 printed se-tenant with gold and black inscription on gutter. Value, set $35. No. 1908a in sheet of 4, value $45.

Central background light bluish green on No. 1908, grayish blue on No. 1908a.

Postilion — A679

1973, Dec. 18
1914 A679 1k gold & multi   .30 .20

Stamp Day 1974 and 55th anniversary of Czechoslovak postage stamps. Printed with 2 labels showing telephone and telegraph. Value of single with two labels, 60c.

Bedrich   Pablo Neruda,
Smetana — A681   Chilean
            Flag — A682

"CSSR" — A680   Comecon
            Building,
            Moscow — A683

1974, Jan. 1
1915 A680 30h red, gold & ultra .20 .20

5th anniversary of Federal Government in the Czechoslovak Socialist Republic.

1974, Jan. 4   Perf. 11x11½
1916 A681 60h shown   .20 .20
1917 A681 60h Josef Suk .20 .20
1918 A682 60h shown   .20 .20
    Nos. 1916-1918 (3)   .60 .60

Smetana (1824-84), composer; Suk (1874-1935), composer, and Pablo Neruda (Neftali Ricardo Reyes, 1904-73), Chilean poet.

1974, Jan. 23
1919 A683 1k gold, red & vio bl .25 .20

25th anniversary of the Council of Mutual Economic Assistance (COMECON).

Symbols of Postal Service — A684

1974, Feb. 20   Perf. 11½
1920 A684 3.60k multi   .95 .45

BRNO '74 National Stamp Exhibition, Brno, June 8-23.
No. 1920 was issue both in normal sheets of 25 stamps and in sheets containing 16 stamps se-tenant with 9 labels depicting Brno. Values: single stamp with attached tab $2.25; full sheet of 16 stamps and 9 labels $85.

Art Type of 1972

Designs: 60h, Tulips 1973, by Josef Broz. 1k, Structures 1961 (poppy and building), by Orest Dubay. 1.60k, Bird and flowers (Golden Sun-Glowing Day), by Adolf Zabransky. 1.80k, Artificial flowers, by Frantisek Gross.

1974, Feb. 21   Perf. 11½x11
1921 A651 60h multi   .25 .20
1922 A651 1k multi   .30 .20
1923 A651 1.60k multi   .40 .20
1924 A651 1.80k multi 1.10 .30
    Nos. 1921-1924 (4)   2.05 .90

Czech and Slovak graphic art.

Oskar Benes and Vaclav
Prochazka — A685

40h, Milos Uher, Anton Sedlacek. 60h, Jan Hajecek, Marie Sedlackova. 80h, Jan Sverma, Albin Grznar. 1k, Jaroslav Neliba, Alois

Hovorka. 1.60k, Ladislav Exnar, Ludovit Kukorelli.

1974, Mar. 21   Perf. 11½x11
1925 A685 30h indigo & multi   .25 .20
1926 A685 40h indigo & multi   .25 .20
1927 A685 60h indigo & multi   .25 .20
1928 A685 80h indigo & multi   .25 .20
1929 A685 1k indigo & multi   .30 .20
1930 A685 1.60k indigo & multi .85 .25
    Nos. 1925-1930 (6)   2.15 1.25

Partisan commanders and fighters.

"Water,
the
Source
of
Energy"
A686

Symbolic Designs: 1k, Importance of water for agriculture. 1.20k, Study of the oceans. 1.60k, "Hydrological Decade." 2k, Struggle for unpolluted water.

1974, Apr. 25   Engr.   Perf. 11½
1931 A686 60h multi   .65 .25
1932 A686 1k multi   .65 .25
1933 A686 1.20k multi   1.25 .45
1934 A686 1.60k multi   1.25 .45
1935 A686 2k multi   2.40 1.75
    Nos. 1931-1935 (5)   6.20 3.15

Hydrological Decade (UNESCO), 1965-1974.
Nos. 1931-1935 were each issued in sheets of 4. Value $30.

Allegory
Holding
"Molniya," and
Ground
Station — A687

Sousaphone
A688

1974, Apr. 30   Engr. & Photo.
1936 A687 30h vio bl & multi   .25 .20

"Intersputnik," first satellite communications ground station in Czechoslovakia.

Prague Castle Art Type of 1971

No. 1937, Golden Cock, 17th century locket. No. 1938, Glass monstrance, 1840.

1974, May 9   Engr.   Perf. 11½
1937 A634 3k gold & multi   1.60 1.25
1938 A634 3k blk & multi   2.40 1.60

Nos. 1937-1938 werre each issued in sheets of 4. Value, set $20.

Engraved and Photogravure
1974, May 12   Perf. 11x11½
1939 A688 20h shown   .20 .20
1940 A688 30h Bagpipe   .20 .20
1941 A688 40h Violin, by Martin
            Benka   .20 .20
1942 A688 1k Pyramid piano .20 .20

1943 A688 1.60k Tenor quinton,
            1754   .80 .20
    Nos. 1939-1943 (5)   1.60 1.00

Prague and Bratislava Music Festivals. The 1.60k also commemorates 25th anniversary of Slovak Philharmonic Orchestra.

Child — A689

1974, June 1   Perf. 11½
1944 A689 60h multi   .20 .20

Children's Day. Design is from illustration for children's book by Adolf Zabransky.

Globe, People and Exhibition
Emblems — A690

Design: 6k, Rays and emblems symbolizing "Oneness and Mutuality."

1974, June 1
1945 A690 30h multi   .25 .20
1946 A690 6k multi   1.50 .75

BRNO 74 Natl. Stamp Exhib., Brno, June 8-23.
Nos. 2171-2172 were each issued both in sheet of 50 stamps and in sheets of 16 stamps and 14 labels. Values: stamps with attached labels, $1.75; sheet of 16 stamps and 14 labels $75.

Resistance   Actress Holding
Fighter — A691   Tragedy and
            Comedy
            Masks — A692

1974, Aug. 29   Perf. 11½
1947 A691 30h multi   .20 .20

Slovak National Uprising, 30th anniversary.

1974, Aug. 29
1948 A692 30h red, sil & blk   .20 .20

Bratislava Academy of Music and Drama, 25th anniversary.

Slovak Girl with
Flower — A693

1974, Aug. 29
1949 A693 30h multi   .20 .20

SLUK, Slovak folksong and dance ensemble, 25th anniversary.

Hero and Leander A694

Design: 2.40k, Hero watching Leander swim the Hellespont. No. 1952, Leander reaching shore. No. 1953, Hero mourning over Leander's body. No. 1954, Hermione, Leander's sister. No. 1955, Mourning Cupid. Designs are from 17th century English tapestries in Bratislava Council Palace.

1974-76
1950	A694	2k multi	1.25	1.10
1951	A694	2.40k multi	1.50	1.25
1952	A694	3k multi	1.00	.45
1953	A694	3.60k multi	1.75	1.75
1954	A694	3.60k multi	2.50	1.10
1955	A694	3.60k multi	.85	.60
		Nos. 1950-1955 (6)	8.85	6.25

Issued: Nos. 1950-1951, 9/25/74; Nos. 1952, 1954, 8/29/75; Nos. 1953, 1955, 5/9/76. Nos. 1950-1951 were each issued in sheets of 6, with 2 blank labels; Nos. 1952-1955 were issued in sheets of 4. Value, set $50.

Soldier Standing Guard, Target, 1840 — A695

Painted Folk-art Targets: 60h, Landscape with Pierrot and flags, 1828. 1k, Diana crowning champion marksman, 1832. 1.60k, Still life with guitar, 1839. 2.40k, Salvo and stag in flight, 1834. 3k, Turk and giraffe, 1831.

1974, Sept. 26   *Perf. 11½*
Size: 30x50mm
1956	A695	30h black & multi	.25	.20
1957	A695	60h black & multi	.25	.20
1958	A695	1k black & multi	.30	.20

Engr.
Perf. 12
Size: 40x50mm
1959	A695	1.60k green & multi	.50	.45
1960	A695	2.40k sepia & multi	.90	.75
1961	A695	3k multi	3.00	3.00
		Nos. 1956-1961 (6)	5.20	4.80

Nos. 1959-1961 were each issued in sheets of 4. Value, set $28.

UPU Emblem and Postilion — A696

UPU Cent. (UPU Emblem and): 40h, Mail coach. 60h, Railroad mail coach, 1851. 80h, Early mail truck. 1k, Czechoslovak Airlines mail plane. 1.60k, Radar.

Engraved and Photogravure
1974, Oct. 9   *Perf. 11½*
1962	A696	30h multi	.20	.20
1963	A696	40h multi	.20	.20
1964	A696	60h multi	.20	.20
1965	A696	80h multi	.20	.20
1966	A696	1k multi	.40	.20
1967	A696	1.60k multi	1.25	.25
		Nos. 1962-1967 (6)	2.45	1.25

Sealed Letter — A697

Stylized Bird — A698

Postal Code Symbol — A698a

20h, Post Horn, Old Town Bridge Tower. #1971, Carrier pigeon. #1979, Map of Czechoslovakia with postal code numbers.

1974, Oct. 31   *Perf. 11½x11*
1968	A699	20h multi	.20	.20
1969	A697	30h brn, bl & red	.20	.20
1970	A699	40h multi	.20	.20
1971	A697	60h bl, yel & red	.20	.20
		Nos. 1968-1971 (4)	.80	.80

Nos. 1968-1971 were reissued in 1979, printed on fluorescent paper. Value, set $15. See No. 2675.

Coil Stamps
1975   **Photo.**   *Perf. 14*
1976	A698	30h brt bl	.20	.20
1977	A698	60h carmine	.20	.20

1976   *Perf. 11½*
1978	A698a	30h emer	.20	.20
1979	A698a	60h scar	.20	.20

Nos. 1976-1979 have black control number on back of every fifth stamp.

Ludvik Kuba, Self-portrait, 1941 — A700

Paintings: 1.20k, Violinist Frantisek Ondricek, by Vaclav Brozik. 1.60k, Vase with Flowers, by Otakar Kubin. 1.80k, Woman with Pitcher, by Janko Alexy. 2.40k, Bacchanalia, c. 1635, by Karel Skreta.

1974, Nov. 27   **Engr.**   *Perf. 11½*
1980	A700	1k multi	.50	.24
1981	A700	1.20k multi	.80	.40
1982	A700	1.60k multi	.80	.60
1983	A700	1.80k multi	1.00	.40
1984	A700	2.40k multi	2.50	1.75
		Nos. 1980-1984 (5)	5.60	3.45

Czech and Slovak art. Nos. 1980-1984 were each issued in sheets of 4. Value, set $28. See Nos. 2209-2211, 2678-2682, 2721-2723, 2743, 2766-2768.

Post Horn — A701

Engraved and Photogravure
1974, Dec. 18   *Perf. 11x11½*
1985	A701 1k multicolored		.30	.20

Stamp Day.

Still-life with Hare, by Hollar — A702

Designs: 1k, The Lion and the Mouse, by Vaclav Hollar. 1.60k, Deer Hunt, by Philip Galle. 1.80k, Grand Hunt, by Jacques Callot.

1975, Feb. 26   *Perf. 11½x11*
1988	A702	60h blk & buff	.25	.25
1989	A702	1k blk & buff	.25	.25
1990	A702	1.60k blk & yel	.25	.25
1991	A702	1.80k blk & buff	1.25	.65
		Nos. 1988-1991 (4)	2.00	1.40

Hunting scenes from old engravings.

Guns Pointing at Family A703

Young Woman and Globe — A704

Designs: 1k, Women and building on fire. 1.20k, People and roses. All designs include names of destroyed villages.

1975, Feb. 26   *Perf. 11*
1992	A703	60h multi	.20	.20
1993	A703	1k multi	.20	.20
1994	A703	1.20k multi	.30	.20
		Nos. 1992-1994 (3)	.70	.60

Destruction of 14 villages by the Nazis, 30th anniversary.

1975, Mar. 7   *Perf. 11½x11*
1995	A704 30h red & multi		.20	.20

International Women's Year 1975.

Little Queens, Moravian Folk Custom A705

Folk Customs: 1k, Straw masks (animal heads and blackened faces), Slovak. 1.40k, The Tale of Maid Dorothea (executioner, girl, king and devil). 2k, Drowning of Morena, symbol of death and winter.

1975, Mar. 26   **Engr.**   *Perf. 11½*
1996	A705	60h blk & multi	.45	.25
1997	A705	1k blk & multi	.80	.45
1998	A705	1.40k blk & multi	.90	.65
1999	A705	2k blk & multi	1.10	.85
		Nos. 1996-1999 (4)	3.25	2.20

Nos. 1996-1999 were each issued in sheets of four. Value $15.

Coat of Arms Type of 1968
Engraved and Photogravure
1975, Apr. 17   *Perf. 11½*
2000	A590	60h Nymburk	.25	.20
2001	A590	60h Znojmo	.25	.20

Coats of arms of Czechoslovakian cities.

Czech May Uprising — A706

Liberation by Soviet Army — A707

Czechoslovak-Russian Friendship — A708

Engr. & Photo.; Engr. (A707)
1975, May 9
2002	A706 1k multi		.25	.20
2003	A707 1k multi		.25	.20
2004	A708 1k multi		.75	.60
		Nos. 2002-2004 (3)		

30th anniv. of the May uprising of the Czech people and of liberation by the Soviet Army; 5th anniv. of the Czechoslovak-Soviet Treaty of Friendship, Cooperation and Mutual Aid.

Adolescents' Exercises — A709

Designs: 60th, Children's exercises. 1k, Men's and women's exercises.

Engraved and Photogravure
1975, June 15   *Perf. 12x11½*
2005	A709	30h lil & multi	.20	.20
2006	A709	60h multi	.20	.20
2007	A709	1k vio & multi	.25	.20
		Nos. 2005-2007 (3)	.65	.60

Spartakiad 1975, Prague, June 26-29. Nos. 2005-2007 each issued in sheets of 30 stamps and 40 labels, showing different Spartakiad emblems. Value, set with tabs, $1.

Datrioides Microlepis and Sea Horse — A710

Tropical Fish (Aquarium): 1k, Beta splendens regan and pterophyllum scalare. 1.20k, Carassius auratus. 1.60k, Amphiprion percula and chaetodon sp. 2k, Pomacanthodes semicirculatus, pomocanthus maculosus and paracanthorus hepatus.

1975, June 27   *Perf. 11½*
2008	A710	60h multi	.20	.20
2009	A710	1k multi	.35	.20
2010	A710	1.20k multi	.40	.20

2011	A710	1.60k multi	.55	.20
2012	A710	2k multi	1.75	.50
		Nos. 2008-2012 (5)	3.25	1.30

Pelicans, by Nikita Charushin — A711

Book Illustrations: 30h, The Dreamer, by Lieselotte Schwarz. 40h, Hero on horseback, by Val Muntenau. 60h, Peacock, by Klaus Ensikat. 80h, Man on horseback, by Robert Dubravec.

1975, Sept. 5

2013	A711	20h multi	.25	.20
2014	A711	30h multi	.25	.20
2015	A711	40h multi	.30	.20
2016	A711	60h multi	.30	.20
2017	A711	80h multi	.60	.20
		Nos. 2013-2017 (5)	1.70	1.00

Bratislava BIB 75 biennial exhibition of illustrations for children's books.

Nos. 2013-2017 issued in sheets of 25 stamps and 15 labels with designs and inscriptions in various languages. Value, set with attached labels, $2.50.

Strakonice, 1951 — A712

Designs: Motorcycles.

1975, Sept. 29   *Perf. 11½*

2018	A712	20h shown	.20	.20
2019	A712	40h Jawa 250, 1945	.20	.20
2020	A712	60h Jawa 175, 1935	.20	.20
2021	A712	1k ITAR, 1921	.20	.20
2022	A712	1.20k ORION, 1903	.25	.20
2023	A712	1.80k Laurin & Klement, 1898	1.40	.40
		Nos. 2018-2023 (6)	2.45	1.40

Study of Shortwave Solar Radiation — A713

Soyuz-Apollo Link-up in Space — A714

60h, Study of aurora borealis & Oréol satellite. 1k, Study ofionosphere & cosmic radiation. 2k, Copernicus, radio map of the sun & satellite.

1975, Sept. 30

2024	A713	30h multi	.20	.20
2025	A713	60h yel, rose red & vio	.20	.20
2026	A713	1k bl, yel & vio	.20	.20
2027	A713	2k red, vio & yel	.35	.20
		Engr.		
2028	A714	5k vio & multi	2.00	1.50
		Nos. 2024-2028 (5)	2.95	2.30

International cooperation in space research. No. 2028 issued in sheets of 4. Value $15. The design of No. 2026 appears to be inverted.

Slovnaft, Petrochemical Plant — A715

Designs: 60h, Atomic power station. 1k, Construction of Prague subway. 1.20k, Construction of Friendship pipeline. 1.40k, Combine harvesters. 1.60k, Apartment house construction.

Engraved and Photogravure
1975, Oct. 28

2029	A715	30h multi	.20	.20
2030	A715	60h multi	.20	.20
2031	A715	1k multi	.25	.20
2032	A715	1.20k multi	.25	.20
2033	A715	1.40k multi	.25	.20
2034	A715	1.60k multi	.75	.30
		Nos. 2029-2034 (6)	1.90	1.30

Socialist construction, 30th anniversary. Nos. 2029-2034 printed se-tenant with labels. Value, set with attached labels, $2.50.

Pres. Gustav Husak — A716

1975, Oct. 28   **Engr.**

2035	A716 30h ultra	.20	.20
2036	A716 60h rose red	.20	.20

Prague Castle Art Type of 1971

3k, Gold earring, 9th cent. 3.60k, Arms of Premysl Dynasty & Bohemia from lid of leather case containing Bohemian crown, 14th cent.

1975, Oct. 29

2040	A634	3k blk, grn, pur & gold	.95	.50
2041	A634	3.60k red & multi	2.00	1.60

Nos. 2040-2041 each issued in sheets of 4. Value, set $15.

Miniature Sheet

Ludvik Svoboda, Road Map, Buzuluk to Prague, Carnations — A717

1975, Nov. 25

2042	A717 10k multi	9.00	7.00

Pres. Ludvik Svoboda, 80th birthday. Exists imperf. Value, $40 unused, $25 used.

Art Type of 1967

Paintings: 1k, "May 1975" (Woman and doves for 30th anniv. of peace), by Zdenek Sklenar. 1.40k, Woman in national costume, by Eugen Nevan. 1.80k, "Liberation of Prague," by Alena Cermakova, horiz. 2.40k, "Fire 1938" (woman raising fist), by Josef Capek. 3.40k, Old Prague, 1828, by Vincenc Morstadt.

1975, Nov. 27   **Engr.**   *Perf. 11½*

2043	A565	1k blk, buff & brn	.30	.20
2044	A565	1.40k multi	.65	.30
2045	A565	1.80k multi	.65	.30
2046	A565	2.40k multi	1.60	.75
2047	A565	3.40k multi	1.60	1.25
		Nos. 2043-2047 (5)	4.80	2.80

Nos. 2043-2047 were each issued in sheets of 4. Value, set $22.50.

Carrier Pigeon — A718

Engraved and Photogravure
1975, Dec. 18   *Perf. 11½*

2048	A718 1k red & multi	.30	.20

Stamp Day 1975.

Frantisek Halas — A719

Wilhelm Pieck — A720

Frantisek Lexa — A721

Jindrich Jindrich — A722

Ivan Krasko — A723

1976, Feb. 25   *Perf. 11½*

2049	A719	60h multi	.20	.20
2050	A720	60h multi	.20	.20
2051	A721	60h multi	.20	.20
2052	A722	60h multi	.20	.20
2053	A723	60h multi	.20	.20
		Nos. 2049-2053 (5)	1.00	1.00

Halas (1901-49), poet; Pieck (1876-1960), pres. of German Democratic Republic; Lexa (1876-1960), professor of Egyptology; Jindrich (1876-1967), composer and writer; Krasko (1876-1958), Slovak poet. No. 2051 printed in sheets of 10, others in sheets of 50. Value, No. 2051 sheet, $5.00.

Ski Jump, Olympic Emblem A724

Winter Olympic Games Emblem and: 1.40k, Figure skating, women's. 1.60k, Ice hockey.

1976, Mar. 22   *Perf. 12x11½*

2054	A724	1k gold & multi	.20	.20
2055	A724	1.40k gold & multi	.20	.20
2056	A724	1.60k gold & multi	1.00	.30
		Nos. 2054-2056 (3)	1.40	.70

12th Winter Olympic Games, Innsbruck, Austria, Feb. 4-15.

Javelin and Olympic Rings — A725

1976, Mar. 22   *Perf. 11½*

2057	A725	2k shown	.25	.20
2058	A725	3k Relay race	.40	.20
2059	A725	3.60k Shot put	1.40	.90
		Nos. 2057-2059 (3)	2.05	1.30

21st Olympic Games, Montreal, Canada, July 17-Aug. 1.

Table Tennis — A726

1976, Mar. 22   *Perf. 11x12*

2060	A726 1k multi	.30	.20

European Table Tennis Championship, Prague, Mar. 26-Apr. 4.

Symbolic of Communist Party — A727   Worker, Derrick, Emblem — A728

1976, Apr. 12   *Perf. 11x12*

2061	A727	30h gold & multi	.20	.20
2062	A728	60h gold & multi	.20	.20

15th Congress of the Communist Party of Czechoslovakia.

Radio Prague Orchestra A729

Dancer, Violin, Tragic Mask — A730

Actors — A731

Folk Dancers A732

Film
Festival — A733

1976, Apr. 26　　　　**Perf. 11½**
2063 A729 20h gold & multi　　　.20 .20
2064 A730 20h pink & multi　　　.20 .20
2065 A731 20h lt bl & multi　　　.20 .20
2066 A732 30h blk & multi　　　.20 .20
2067 A733 30h vio bl, rose & grn　.20 .20
　　Nos. 2063-2067 (5)　　　1.00 1.00

Czechoslovak Radio Symphony Orchestra, Prague, 50th anniv. (No. 2063); Academy of Music and Dramatic Art, Prague, 50th anniv. (No. 2064); Nova Scena Theater Co., Bratislava, 30th anniv. (No. 2065); Intl. Folk Song and Dance Festival, Straznice, 30th anniv. (No. 2066); 20th Intl. Film Festival, Karlovy Vary (No. 2067).

Hammer and Sickle
A734　　　　　　A735

Design: 6k, Hammer and sickle, horiz.

1976, May 14
2068 A734 30h gold, red & dk bl　.20 .20
2069 A735 60h gold, red & dp
　　　　　car　　　　　　.20 .20

Souvenir Sheet

2070 A735 6k red & multi　　1.75 1.75
Czechoslovak Communist Party, 55th anniv. #2070 contains a 50x30mm stamp.

Ships in Storm,
by Frans Huys
(1522-1562)
A736

Old Engravings of Ships: 60h, by Václav Hollar (1607-77). 1k, by Regnier Nooms Zeeman (1623-68). 2k, by Francois Chereau (1680-1729).

Engraved and Photogravure
1976, July 21　　　**Perf. 11x11½**
2071 A736 40h buff & blk　　.25 .20
2072 A736 60h gray, buff & blk　.25 .20
2073 A736 1k lt grn, buff & blk　.25 .20
2074 A736 2k lt bl, buff & blk　1.25 .40
　　Nos. 2071-2074 (4)　　　2.00 1.00

"UNESCO"
A737

1976, July 30　　　　**Perf. 11½**
2075 A737 2k gray & multi　　.40 .45
30th anniversary of UNESCO. Issued in sheets of 10. Value $8.

Souvenir Sheet

Hands
Holding
Infant,
Globe
and
Dove
A738

1976, July 30
2076　　Sheet of 2　　　4.00 3.50
　a. A738 6k multi　　　2.50 2.00
European Security and Cooperation Conference, Helsinki, Finland, 2nd anniv.

Merino
Ram — A739

Couple
Smoking, WHO
Emblem and
Skull — A740

Designs: 40h, Bern-Hana milk cow. 1.60k, Kladruby stallion Generalissimus XXVII.

1976, Aug. 28　　　**Perf. 11½x12**
2077 A739 30h multi　　　.20 .20
2078 A739 40h multi　　　.20 .20
2079 A739 1.60k multi　　.35 .20
　　Nos. 2077-2079 (3)　　　.75 .60

Bountiful Earth Exhibition, Ceske Budejovice, Aug. 28-Sept. 12.

1976, Sept. 7　　　**Perf. 12x11½**
2080 A740 2k multi　　　.50 .30
Fight against smoking, WHO drive against drug addiction.
Printed in sheets of 10 (2x5) with WHO emblems and inscription in margin. Value $10.

Prague Castle Art Type of 1971
Designs: 3k, View of Prague Castle, by F. Hoogenberghe, 1572. 3.60k, Faun and Satyr, sculptured panel, 16th century.

1976, Oct. 22　　**Engr.**　　**Perf. 11½**
2081 A634 3k multi　　　2.50 2.10
2082 A634 3.60k multi　　.90 .60
Nos. 2081-2082 were each issued in sheets of 4. Value $15.

Guernica 1937,
by Imro Weiner-
Kral
A741

1976, Oct. 22
2083 A741 5k multi　　　.80 .40
40th anniv. of the Intl. Brigade in Spain.

Zebras
A742

20h, Elephants. 30h, Cheetah. 40h, Giraffes. 60h, Rhinoceros. 3k, Bongos.

Engraved and Photogravure
1976, Nov. 3　　**Perf. 11½x11, 11x11½**
2084 A742 10h multi　　　.25 .20
2085 A742 20h multi, vert.　.25 .20
2086 A742 30h multi　　　.30 .20
2087 A742 40h multi, vert.　.45 .20
2088 A742 60h multi　　　.45 .20
2089 A742 3k multi, vert.　2.25 .65
　　Nos. 2084-2089 (6)　　　3.95 1.65

African animals in Dvur Kralove Zoo.

Art Type of 1967
Paintings of Flowers: 1k, by Peter Matejka. 1.40k, by Cyril Bouda. 2k, by Jan Breughel. 3.60k, J. Rudolf Bys.

1976, Nov. 27　　**Engr.**　　**Perf. 11½**
2090 A565 1k multi　　　.75 .50
2091 A565 1.40k multi　　1.50 .90
2092 A565 2k multi　　　1.50 .90
2093 A565 3.60k multi　　.90 .50
　　Nos. 2090-2093 (4)　　　4.65 2.80

Nos. 2090-2093 were each issued in sheets of 4, with emblem and name of Praga 1978 on horizontal gutter. Value, set $25.

Postrider, 17th Century, and
Satellites — A743

1976, Dec. 18　　**Engr. & Photo.**
2094 A743 1k multi　　　.25 .20
Stamp Day 1976.

Ice　　　　　　Arms of
Hockey — A744　　Vranov — A745

1977, Feb. 11　　　　**Perf. 11½**
2095 A744 60h shown　　.20 .20
2096 A744 1k Biathlon　　.20 .20
2097 A744 1.60k Ski jump　.95 .25
2098 A744 2k Downhill skiing　.25 .20
　　Nos. 2095-2098 (4)　　　1.60 .85

6th Winter Spartakiad of Socialist Countries' Armies.

1977, Feb. 20

Coats of Arms of Czechoslovak towns.
2099 A745 60h shown　　　.20 .20
2100 A745 60h Kralupy & Vltavou　.20 .20
2101 A745 60h Jicin　　　.20 .20
2102 A745 60h Valasske Mezirici　.20 .20
　　Nos. 2099-2102 (4)　　　.80 .80

See Nos. 2297-2300.

Window, Michna
Palace — A746

Prague Renaissance Windows: 30h, Michna Palace. 40h, Thun Palace. 60h, Archbishop's Palace, Hradcany. 5k, St. Nicholas Church.

1977, Mar. 10
2103 A746 20h multi　　　.20 .20
2104 A746 30h multi　　　.20 .20
2105 A746 40h multi　　　.20 .20

2106 A746 60h multi　　　.20 .20
2107 A746 5k multi　　　1.50 .60
　　Nos. 2103-2107 (5)　　　2.30 1.40

PRAGA 1978 International Philatelic Exhibition, Prague, Sept. 8-17, 1978.

Children,
Auxiliary
Police
A747

1977, Apr. 21　　　　**Perf. 11½**
2108 A747 60h multi　　　.25 .20
Auxiliary Police, 25th anniversary.

Warsaw,
Polish Flag,
Bicyclists
A748

Congress
Emblem — A749

Designs: 60h, Berlin, DDR flag, bicyclists. 1k, Prague, Czechoslovakian flag, victorious bicyclist. 1.40k, Bicyclists on highways, modern views of Berlin, Prague and Warsaw.

1977, May 7
2109 A748 30h multi　　　.25 .20
2110 A748 60h multi　　　.25 .20
2111 A748 1k multi　　　.60 .20
2112 A748 1.40k multi　　.40 .20
　　Nos. 2109-2112 (4)　　　1.50 .80

30th International Bicycle Peace Race Warsaw-Prague-Berlin.

1977, May 25　　　　**Perf. 11½**
2113 A749 30h car, red & gold　.20 .20
9th Trade Union Congress, Prague 1977.

Prague Castle Art Type of 1971
Designs: 3k, Onyx footed bowl, 1350. 3.60k, Bronze horse, 1619.

1977, June 7　　　　**Engr.**
2114 A634 3k multi　　　1.25 1.10
2115 A634 3.60k multi　　1.10 1.10
Nos. 2114-2115 were each issued in sheets of 4. Value, set $13.

French Postrider, 19th Century,
PRAGA '78 Emblem — A750

Postal Uniforms: 1k, Austrian, 1838. 2k, Austrian, late 18th century. 3.60k, Germany, early 18th century.

1977, June 8　　**Engr. & Photo.**
2116 A750 60h multi　　　.25 .20
2117 A750 1k multi　　　.25 .20
2118 A750 2k multi　　　.40 .20
2119 A750 3.60k multi　　1.50 .60
　　Nos. 2116-2119 (4)　　　2.40 1.20

PRAGA 1978 International Philatelic Exhibition, Prague, Sept. 8-17, 1978.
Nos. 2116-2119 were each issued both in sheets of 50 and in sheets of 4 stamps with 4 inscribed labels and 2 blank labels. Value, set of sheets of 4, $16.

Coffeepots, Porcelain Mark — A751

Mlada Boleslav Costume — A752

Czechoslovak Porcelain and Porcelain Marks: 30h, Urn. 40h, Vase. 60h, Cup and saucer, jugs. 1k, Candlestick and plate. 3k, Cup and saucer, coffeepot.

1977, June 15

2120	A751	20h multi	.20 .20
2121	A751	30h multi	.20 .20
2122	A751	40h multi	.20 .20
2123	A751	60h multi	.20 .20
2124	A751	1k multi	.20 .20
2125	A751	3k multi	1.10 .95
	Nos. 2120-2125 (6)		2.10 1.35

1977, Aug. 31   Engr.   Perf. 11½

PRAGA Emblem and Folk Costumes from: 1.60k, Vazek. 3.60k, Zavadka. 5k, Belkovice.

2126	A752	1k multi	1.25 .95
2127	A752	1.60k multi	1.25 .95
2128	A752	3.60k multi	1.25 .95
2129	A752	5k multi	1.25 .95
	Nos. 2126-2129 (4)		5.00 3.80

Issued in sheets of 10 and in sheets of 8 plus 2 labels showing PRAGA '78 emblem. Value, set: sheets of 10 $50; sheets of 8 $40.

Old Woman, Devil and Spinner, by Viera Bombova A753

Book Illustrations: 60h, Bear and tiger, by Genadij Pavlisin. 1k, Coach drawn by 4 horses (Hans Christian Andersen), by Ulf Lovgren. 2k, Bear and flamingos (Lewis Carroll), by Nicole Claveloux. 3k, King with keys, and toys, by Jiri Trnka.

1977, Sept. 9   Engr. & Photo.

2130	A753	40h multi	.20 .20
2131	A753	60h multi	.20 .20
2132	A753	1k multi	.20 .20
2133	A753	2k multi	.25 .20
2134	A753	3k multi	1.00 .35
	Nos. 2130-2134 (5)		1.85 1.15

Prize-winning designs, 6th biennial exhibition of illustrations for children's books, Bratislava.

Globe, Violin, Doves, View of Prague — A754

1977, Sept. 28   Perf. 11½

2135	A754	60h multi	.25 .20

Congress of International Music Council of UNESCO, Prague and Bratislava.

Souvenir Sheets

"For a Europe of Peace" A755

1.60k, "For a Europe of Cooperation." 2.40k, "For a Europe of Social Progress."

1977, Oct. 3

2136		Sheet of 2	.50 .50
a.	A755	60h multi	.20 .20
2137		Sheet of 2	1.00 1.00
a.	A755	1.60k multi	.25 .25
2138		Sheet of 2	2.00 1.75
a.	A755	2.40k multi	.50 .50

2nd European Security and Cooperation Conference, Belgrade. Nos. 2136-2138 each contain 2 stamps and 2 blue on buff inscriptions and ornaments.

S. P. Korolev, Sputnik I Emblem — A756

Sailors, Cruiser Aurora — A757

30h, Yuri A. Gagarin & Vostok I. 40h, Alexei Leonov. 1k, Neil A. Armstrong & footprint on moon. 1.60k, Construction of orbital space station.

1977, Oct. 4

2139	A756	20h multi	.20 .20
2140	A756	30h multi	.20 .20
2141	A756	40h multi	.20 .20
2142	A756	1k multi	.20 .20
2143	A756	1.60k multi	.60 .20
	Nos. 2139-2143 (5)		1.40 1.00

Space research, 20th anniv. of 1st earth satellite.

1977, Nov. 7

2144	A757	30h multi	.20 .20

60th anniv. of Russian October Revolution.

"Russia," Arms of USSR, Kremlin A758

"Science" A759

1977, Nov. 7

2145	A758	30h multi	.20 .20

55th anniversary of the USSR.

1977, Nov. 17

2146	A759	3k multi	.50 .20

Czechoslovak Academy of Science, 25th anniversary.

Art Type of 1967

Paintings: 2k, "Fear" (woman), by Jan Murdoch. 2.40k, Jan Francisci, portrait by Peter M. Bohun. 2.60k, Vaclav Hollar, self-portrait, 1647. 3k, Young Woman, 1528, by Lucas Cranach. 5k, Cleopatra, by Rubens.

1977, Nov. 27   Engr.   Perf. 11½

2147	A565	2k multi	.80 .45
2148	A565	2.40k multi	1.25 1.10
2149	A565	2.60k multi	1.25 1.10

2150	A565	3k multi	.80 .70
2151	A565	5k multi	1.60 1.60
	Nos. 2147-2151 (5)		5.70 4.95

Nos. 2147-2151 were each issued in sheets of 4. Value, set $28.

View of Bratislava, by Georg Hoefnagel — A760

Design: 3.60k, Arms of Bratislava, 1436.

1977, Dec. 6

2152	A760	3k multi	1.90 1.60
2153	A760	3.60k multi	.80 .50

Nos. 2152-21531 were each issued in sheets of 4. Value, set $12.50.

See Nos. 2174-2175, 2270-2271, 2331-2332, 2364-2365, 2422-2423, 2478-2479, 2514-2515, 2570-2571, 2618-2619.

Stamp Pattern and Post Horn — A761

1977, Dec. 18   Engr. & Photo.

2154	A761	1k multi	.25 .20

Stamp Day.

Zdenek Nejedly — A762

Karl Marx — A763

1978, Feb. 10   Perf. 11½

2155	A762	30h multi	.20 .20
2156	A763	40h multi	.20 .20

Zdenek Nejedly (1878-1962), musicologist and historian; Karl Marx (1818-1883), political philosopher.

Civilians Greeting Guardsmen — A764

Intellectual, Farm Woman and Steel Worker, Flag — A765

1978, Feb. 25

2157	A764	1k gold & multi	.20 .20
2158	A765	1k gold & multi	.20 .20

30th anniv. of "Victorious February" (No. 2157), and Natl. Front (No. 2158). See note after 2190.

Yuri A. Gagarin, Vostok I — A766

10k Coin, 1964, and 25k Coin, 1965 — A767

Design: 30h, 3.60k, like No. 2140.

Engraved; Overprint Photogravure (Blue and carmine on 30h, green and lilac rose on 3.60k)

1978, Mar. 2   Perf. 11½x12

2159	A766	30h dk red	.20 .20
2160	A766	3.60k vio bl	2.40 2.40

Capt. V. Remek, 1st Czechoslovakian cosmonaut on Russian spaceship Soyuz 28, Mar. 2-9.

1978, Mar. 14   Engr. & Photo.

40h, Medal for Culture, 1972. 1.40k, Charles University medal, 1948. 3k, Ferdinand I medal, 1568. 5k, Gold florin, 1335.

2161	A767	20h sil & multi	.20 .20
2162	A767	40h sil & multi	.20 .20
2163	A767	1.40k gold & multi	1.00 .20
2164	A767	3k gold & multi	.35 .20
2165	A767	5k gold & multi	.35 .20
	Nos. 2161-2165 (5)		2.10 1.00

650th anniversary of Kremnica Mint.

Tire Tracks and Ball — A768

Congress Emblem — A769

1978, Mar. 15

2166	A768	60h multi	.25 .20

Road safety.

1978, Apr. 16   Perf. 11½

2167	A769	1k multi	.25 .20

9th World Trade Union Cong., Prague 1978.

Shot Put and Praha '78 Emblem A770

1k, Pole vault. 3.60k, Women runners.

1978, Apr. 26

2168	A770	40h multi	.30 .30
2169	A770	1k multi	.40 .30
2170	A770	3.60k multi	.90 .50
	Nos. 2168-2170 (3)		1.60 1.10

5th European Athletic Championships, Prague 1978.

Ice Hockey — A771

Designs: 30h, Hockey. 2k, Ice hockey play.

1978, Apr. 26
2171	A771	30h multi	.30	.25
2172	A771	60h multi	.20	.20
2173	A771	2k multi	.40	.20
		Nos. 2171-2173 (3)	.90	.65

5th European Ice Hockey Championships and 70th anniversary of Bandy hockey.

Bratislava Type of 1977

Designs: 3k, Bratislava, 1955, by Orest Dubay. 3.60k, Fishpound Square, Bratislava, 1955, by Imro Weiner-Kral.

1978, May 9   **Engr.**   **Perf. 11½**
2174	A760	3k multi	.95	.80
2175	A760	3.60k multi	1.25	.80

Nos. 2174-2175 were each issued in sheets of 4. Value, set $12.

Prague Castle Art Type of 1971

3k, King Ottokar II, detail from tomb. 3.60k, Charles IV, detail from votive panel by Jan Ocka.

1978, May 9
2176	A634	3k multi	1.25	.60
2177	A634	3.60k multi	4.00	2.40

Nos. 2176-2177 were each issued in sheets of 4. Value, set $20.

Ministry of Post, Prague A772

Engraved and Photogravure
1978, May 29   **Perf. 12x11½**
2178	A772	60h multi	.25	.20

14th session of permanent COMECOM Commission (Ministers of Post and Telecommunications of Socialist Countries).

Palacky Bridge A773

Prague Bridges and PRAGA '78 Emblem: 40h, Railroad bridge. 1k, Bridge of May 1. 2k, Manes Bridge. 3k, Svatopluk Cech Bridge. 5.40k, Charles Bridge.

1978, May 30
2179	A773	20h blk & multi	.20	.20
2180	A773	40h blk & multi	.20	.20
2181	A773	1k blk & multi	.20	.20
2182	A773	2k blk & multi	.20	.20
2183	A773	3k blk & multi	.45	.20
2184	A773	5.40k blk & multi	1.50	.75
		Nos. 2179-2184 (6)	2.75	1.75

PRAGA 1978 International Philatelic Exhibition, Prague, Sept. 8-17.

St. Peter and Apostles, Clock Tower, and Emblem A774

Town Hall Clock, Prague, by Josef Manes, and PRAGA '78 Emblem: 1k, Astronomical clock. 2k, Prague's coat of arms. 3k, Grape harvest (September). 3.60k, Libra. 10k, Arms surrounded by zodiac signs and scenes symbolic of 12 months, horiz. 2k, 3k, 3.60k show details from design of 10k.

1978, June 20   **Perf. 11½x11**
2185	A774	40h multi	.20	.20
2186	A774	1k multi	.20	.20
2187	A774	2k multi	.25	.20
2188	A774	3k multi	1.50	.20
2189	A774	3.60k multi	.75	.25
		Nos. 2185-2189 (5)	2.90	1.20

Souvenir Sheet
Perf. 12x12
2190	A774	10k multi	10.00 7.50

PRAGA'78 Intl. Philatelic Exhibition, Prague, Sept. 8-17. No. 2190 contains one 50x40mm stamp. Sheet exists imperf. Value $30.

A non-valid souvenir sheet contains 4 imperf. examples of No. 2157. Sold only with PRAGA ticket.

Folk Dancers — A775

1978, July 7   **Perf. 11½x12**
2191	A775	30h multi	.20	.20

25th Folklore Festival, Vychodna.

Overpass and PRAGA Emblem — A776

1k, 2k, Modern office buildings, diff. 6k, Old & new Prague. 20k, Charles Bridge & Old Town, by Vincent Morstadt, 1828.

1978   **Perf. 12x11½**
2192	A776	60h blk & multi	.20	.20
2193	A776	1k blk & multi	.20	.20
2194	A776	2k blk & multi	.20	.20
2195	A776	6k blk & multi	1.50	.75
		Nos. 2192-2195 (4)	2.10	1.35

Souvenir Sheet
Engr.
2196	A776	20k multi	9.50 7.50

PRAGA 1978 Intl. Phil. Exhib., Prague, Sept. 8-17. No. 2196 also for 60th anniv. of Czechoslovak postage stamps. No. 2196 contains one 61x45mm stamp.
Issued: #2192-2195, 9/8; #2196, 9/10.

Souvenir Sheet

Apollo's Companion, by Titian — A777

#2197b, King Midas. Stamps show details from "Apollo Flaying Marsya" by Titian.

1978, Sept. 12   **Perf. 11½**
2197		Sheet of 2	11.00 8.75
a.	A777	10k multi	5.00 4.25
b.	A777	10k multi	5.00 4.25

Titian (1488-1576), Venetian painter. No. 2197 with dark blue marginal inscription "FIP" was sold only with entrance ticket to PRAGA Philatelic Exhibition. Value $25.

Exhibition Hall — A778

Engraved and Photogravure
1978, Sept. 13   **Perf. 11½x11**
2198	A778	30h multi	.20	.20

22nd International Engineering Fair, Brno.

Postal Newspaper Service — A779

TV Screen, Headquarters and Logo — A780

Newspaper, Microphone A781

1978, Sept. 21   **Perf. 11½**
2199	A779	30h multi	.20	.20
2200	A780	30h multi	.20	.20
2201	A781	30h multi	.20	.20
		Nos. 2199-2201 (3)	.60	.60

Postal News Service, 25th anniv.; Czechoslovakian television, 25th anniv.; Press, Broadcasting and Television Day.

Sulky Race A782

Pardubice Steeplechase: 10h, Falling horses and jockeys at fence. 30h, Race. 40h, Horses passing post. 1.60k, Hurdling. 4.40k, Winner.

1978, Oct. 6   **Perf. 12x11½**
2202	A782	10h multi	.20	.20
2203	A782	20h multi	.20	.20
2204	A782	30h multi	.20	.20
2205	A782	40h multi	.20	.20
2206	A782	1.60k multi	.25	.20
2207	A782	4.40k multi	1.50	.65
		Nos. 2202-2207 (6)	2.55	1.65

Woman Holding Arms of Czechoslovakia A783

1978, Oct. 28   **Perf. 11½**
2208	A783	60h multi	.20	.20

60th anniversary of independence.

Art Type of 1974

2.40k, Flowers, by Jakub Bohdan (1660-1724). 3k, The Dream of Salas, by Ludovit Fulla, horiz. 3.60k, Apostle with Censer, Master of the Spissko Capitals (c. 1480-90).

1978, Nov. 27   **Engr.**
2209	A700	2.40k multi	.70	.55
2210	A700	3k multi	.90	.80
2211	A700	3.60k multi	3.25	2.50
		Nos. 2209-2211 (3)	4.85	3.85

Slovak National Gallery, 30th anniversary. Nos. 2209-2211 were each issued in sheets of 4. Value, set $25.

Musicians, by Jan Könyves — A784

Slovak Ceramics: 30h, Janosik on Horseback, by Jozef Franko. 40h, Woman in Folk Costume by Michal Polasko. 1k, Three Girls Singing, by Ignac Bizmayer. 1.60k, Janosik Dancing, by Ferdis Kostka.

Engraved and Photogravure
1978, Dec. 5   **Perf. 11½x12**
2212	A784	20h multi	.20	.20
2213	A784	30h multi	.20	.20
2214	A784	40h multi	.20	.20
2215	A784	1k multi	.20	.20
2216	A784	1.60k multi	1.00	.30
		Nos. 2212-2216 (5)	1.80	1.10

Alfons Mucha and his Design for 1918 Issue — A785

1978, Dec. 18   **Perf. 11½**
2217	A785	1k multi	.25	.20

60th Stamp Day.

COMECON Building, Moscow — A786

1979, Jan. 1   **Perf. 11½**
2218	A786	1k multi	.25	.20

Council for Mutual Economic Aid (COMECON), 30th anniversary.

Woman's Head and Grain — A787

Woman, Workers, Child, Doves — A788

1979, Jan. 1
2219	A787	30h multi	.20	.20
2220	A788	60h multi	.20	.20

United Agricultural Production Assoc., 30th anniv. (30h); Czechoslovakian Federation, 10th anniv. (60h).

Soyuz 28, Rockets and Capsule — A789

60h, Astronauts Aleksei Gubarev and Vladimir Remek on launching pad, vert. 1.60k, Soviet astronauts J. Romanenko and G. Grecko, Salyut 6 and recovery ship. 2k, Salyut-Soyuz orbital complex, post office in space and Czechoslovakia No. 2153. 4k, Soyuz 28, crew after landing and trajectory map, vert. 10k, Gubarev and Remek, Intercosmos emblem, arms of Czechoslovakia and USSR.

1979, Mar. 2

2221	A789	30h multi	.20	.20
2222	A789	60h multi	.20	.20
2223	A789	1.60k multi	.20	.20
2224	A789	2k multi	1.60	.30
2225	A789	4k multi	.80	.25
	Nos. 2221-2225 (5)		3.00	1.15

Souvenir Sheet

2226	A789	10k multi	5.00	3.50

1st anniv. of joint Czechoslovak-Soviet space flight. Size of No. 2226: 76x93mm (stamp 39x55mm). No. 2226 has Cyrillic inscription, No. 2455a does not. No. 2226 exists imperf. Value, $22.50.

Alpine Bellflowers A790 — Stylized Satellite, Dial, Tape A791

Mountain Flowers: 20h, Crocus. 30h, Pinks. 40h, Alpine hawkweed. 3k, Larkspur.

1979, Mar. 23   **Perf. 11½**

2227	A790	10h multi	.20	.20
2228	A790	20h multi	.20	.20
2229	A790	30h multi	.20	.20
2230	A790	40h multi	.20	.20

Perf. 14

2231	A790	3k multi	1.50	.75
	Nos. 2227-2231 (5)		2.30	1.55

Mountain Rescue Service, 25th anniversary. The 3k exists perf. 11½. Value, $40 unused, $20 used.
The 3k was issued in sheets of 10. Values: perf 14 (No. 2231), $25; perf 11½, $400.

1979, Apr. 2

2232	A791	10h multi	.20	.20

Telecommunications research, 30th anniv.

Artist and Model, Dove, Bratislava Castle — A792

Cog Wheels, Transformer and Student — A793

Musical Instruments, Bratislava Castle — A794

Pioneer Scarf, IYC Emblem — A795

Red Star, Man, Child and Doves — A796

1979, Apr. 2

2233	A792	20h multi	.20	.20
2234	A793	20h multi	.20	.20
2235	A794	30h multi	.20	.20
2236	A795	30h multi	.20	.20
2237	A796	60h multi	.20	.20
	Nos. 2233-2237 (5)		1.00	1.00

Fine Arts Academy, Bratislava, 30th anniv.; Slovak Technical University, 40th anniv.; Radio Symphony Orchestra, Bratislava, 30th anniv.; Young Pioneers, 30th anniv. and IYC; Peace Movement, 30th anniversary.

Prague Castle Art Type of 1971

3k, Burial crown of King Ottokar II. 3.60k, Portrait of Mrs. Reitmayer, by Karel Purkyne.

1979, May 9   **Perf. 11½**

2238	A634	3k multi	2.10	1.75
2239	A634	3.60k multi	1.00	.60

Nos. 2238-2239 were each issued in sheets of 4. Value, set $15.

Arms of Vlachovo Brezi, 1538 — A797

Animals in Heraldry: 60h, Jesenik, 1509 (bear and eagle). 1.20k, Vysoke Myto, 1471 (St. George slaying dragon). 1.80k, Martin, 1854 (St. Martin giving coat to beggar). 2k, Zebrak, 1674 (mythological beast).

1979, May 25   **Perf. 11½x12**

2240	A797	30h multi	.20	.20
2241	A797	60h multi	.20	.20
2242	A797	1.20k multi	.20	.20
2243	A797	1.80k multi	1.25	.40
2244	A797	2k multi	.80	.20
	Nos. 2240-2244 (5)		2.65	1.20

Forest, Thriving and Destroyed — A798

Designs: 1.80k, Water. 3.60k, City. 4k, Cattle. All designs show good and bad environment, separated by exclamation point; Man and Biosphere emblem.

1979, June 22   Engr.   Perf. 11½

2245	A798	60h multi	.20	.20
2246	A798	1.80k multi	.30	.25
2247	A798	3.60k multi	1.75	.75
2248	A798	4k multi	1.25	.40
	Nos. 2245-2248 (4)		3.50	1.60

Man and Biosphere Program of UNESCO. Nos. 2245-2248 were each issued in sheets of 10. Value, set $40.

Blast Furnace — A799

Engraved and Photogravure
1979, Aug. 29   Perf. 11x11½

2249	A799	30h multi		.20	.20

Slovak National Uprising, 35th anniversary.

Frog and Goat A800

Book Illustrations (IYC Emblem and): 40h, Knight on horseback. 60h, Maidens. 1k, Boy with sled following rooster. 3k, King riding flying beast.

1979, Apr. 2   Perf. 11½x11

2250	A800	20h multi	.20	.20
2251	A800	40h multi	.20	.20
2252	A800	60h multi	.20	.20
2253	A800	1k multi	.20	.20
2254	A800	3k multi	1.50	.90
	Nos. 2250-2254 (5)		2.30	1.30

Prize-winning designs, 7th biennial exhibition of illustrations for children's books, Bratislava; International Year of the Child. Printed with labels showing story characters. Value, set with attached labels, $4.75.

"Bone Shaker" Bicycles, 1870 A801

Bicycles from: 20h, 1978. 40h, 1910. 60h, 1886. 3.60k, 1820.

1979, Sept. 14   Perf. 12x11½

2255	A801	20h multi	.20	.20
2256	A801	40h multi	.20	.20
2257	A801	60h multi	.20	.20
2258	A801	2k multi	.40	.20
2259	A801	3.60k multi	1.50	.50
	Nos. 2255-2259 (5)		2.50	1.30

Bracket Clock, 18th Century A802

Designs: 18th century clocks.

1979, Oct. 1   Perf. 11½

2260	A802	40h multi	.20	.20
2261	A802	60h multi	.20	.20
2262	A802	80h multi	.85	.20
2263	A802	1k multi	.25	.20
2264	A802	2k multi	.50	.20
	Nos. 2260-2264 (5)		2.00	1.00

Art Type of 1967

Paintings: 1.60k, Sunday by the River, by Alois Moravec. 2k, Self-portrait, by Gustav Mally. 3k, Self-portrait, by Ilia Yefimovic Repin. 3.60k, Horseback Rider, by Jan Bauch. 5k, Dancing Peasants, by Albrecht Dürer.

1979, Nov. 27   Engr.   Perf. 12

2265	A565	1.60k multi	.40	.35
2266	A565	2k multi	.60	.50
2267	A565	3k multi	.60	.50
2268	A565	3.60k multi	2.00	1.75
2269	A565	5k multi	1.60	1.25
	Nos. 2265-2269 (5)		5.20	4.35

Nos. 2265-2269 were each issued in sheets of 4. Value, set $25.

Bratislava Type of 1977

Designs: 3k, Bratislava Castle on the Danube, by L. Janscha, 1787. 3.60k, Bratislava Castle, stone engraving by Wolf, 1815.

1979, Dec. 5

2270	A760	3k multi	1.25	.80
2271	A760	3.60k multi	1.80	1.50

Nos. 2270-2272 were each issued in sheets of 4. Value, set $15.

Stamp Day — A803

Engraved and Photogravure
1979, Dec. 18   Perf. 11½x12

2272	A803	1k multi		.25	.20

Electronic Circuits — A804

Designs: 50h, Satellite dish. 2k, Airplane. 3k, Computer punch tape.

1979-80   Photo.   Perf. 11½x12
Coil Stamps

2273	A804	50h red	.20	.20
2274	A804	1k brown	.25	.20
2275	A804	2k green ('80)	.30	.20
2276	A804	3k lake ('80)	.45	.25
	Nos. 2273-2276 (4)		1.20	.85

The 1k comes in two shades.

Runners and Dove A805

Engraved and Photogravure
1980, Jan. 29   Perf. 12x11½

2289	A805	50h multi		.20	.20

50th Intl. Peace Marathon, Kosice, Oct. 4.

Downhill Skiing — A806

1980, Jan. 29   Perf. 11½x12

2290	A806	1k shown	.30	.25
2291	A806	2k Speed skating	.95	.35
2292	A806	3k Four-man bobsled	.80	.35
	Nos. 2290-2292 (3)		2.05	.95

13th Winter Olympic Games, Lake Placid, NY, Feb. 12-24.

Basketball — A807

1980, Jan. 29   **Perf. 11½**
2293	A807	40h shown	.25	.25
2294	A807	1k Swimming	.35	.25
2295	A807	2k Hurdles	1.50	.35
2296	A807	3.60k Fencing	1.10	.30
		Nos. 2293-2296 (4)	*3.20*	*1.15*

22nd Olympic Games, Moscow, 7/19-8/3.

Arms Type of 1977

1980, Feb. 20   **Perf. 11½**
2297	A745	50h Bystrice Nad Pern-stejnem	.20	.20
2298	A745	50h Kunstat	.20	.20
2299	A745	50h Rozmital Pod Trem-sinem	.20	.20
2300	A745	50h Zlata Idka	.20	.20
		Nos. 2297-2300 (4)	*.80*	*.80*

Theatrical Mask — A808

Slovak National Theater, Actors — A809

1980, Mar. 1
2301	A808	50h multi	.20	.20
2302	A809	1k multi	.25	.20

50th Jiraskuv Hronov Theatrical Ensemble Review; Slovak National Theater, Bratislava, 60th anniversary.

Mouse in Space, Satellite — A810   Police Corps Banner, Emblem — A811

Intercosmos: 1k, Weather map, satellite. 1.60k, Intersputnik television transmission. 4k, Camera, satellite. 5k, Czech satellite station, 1978, horiz. 10k, Intercosmos emblem, horiz.

1980, Apr. 12   **Perf. 11½x12, 12x11½**
2303	A810	50h multi	.25	.25
2304	A810	1k multi	.35	.25
2305	A810	1.60k multi	2.10	.25
2306	A810	4k multi	.90	.50
2307	A810	5k multi	1.25	.60
		Nos. 2303-2307 (5)	*4.85*	*1.85*

Souvenir Sheet
2308	A810	10k multi	3.25	2.50

Intercosmos cooperative space program.
No. 2305 was issued in a sheet of 10. Value, $25.
No. 2308 exists imperf. Value, $40.

1980, Apr. 17   **Perf. 11½**
2309	A811	50h multi	.20	.20

National Police Corps, 35th anniversary.

Lenin's 110th Birth Anniversary — A812

Design: #2311, Engels's 160th birth anniv.

1980, Apr. 22
2310	A812	1k tan & brn	.25	.20
2311	A812	1k lt grn & brn	.25	.20

Old and Modern Prague, Czech Flag, Bouquet A813

Boy Writing "Peace" A814

Pact Members' Flags, Dove — A815

Czech and Soviet Arms, Prague and Moscow Views A816

1980, May 6   **Perf. 12x11½**
2312	A813	50h multi	.20	.20
2313	A814	1k multi	.20	.20
2314	A815	1k multi	.20	.20
2315	A816	1k multi	.20	.20
		Nos. 2312-2315 (4)	*.80*	*.80*

Liberation by Soviet army, 35th anniv.; Soviet victory in WWII, 35th anniv.; Signing of Warsaw Pact (Bulgaria, Czechoslovakia, German Democratic Rep., Hungary, Poland, Romania, USSR), 25th anniv.; Czechoslovak-Soviet Treaty of Friendship, Cooperation and Mutual Aid, 10th anniv.

Souvenir Sheet

UN, 35th Anniv. A817

1980, June 3   **Engr.**   **Perf. 12**
2316		Sheet of 2	3.50	2.75
a.		A817 4k multicolored	1.50	1.25

Athletes Parading Banners in Strahov Stadium, Prague, Spartakiad Emblem — A818

Engraved and Photogravure

1980, June 3   **Perf. 12x11½**
2317	A818	50h shown	.20	.20
2318	A818	1k Gymnast, vert.	.20	.20

Spartakiad 1980, Prague, June 26-29.

Aechmea Fasciata — A819   A820

1980, Aug. 13   **Perf. 12**
2319	A819	50h *Gerbera Jamesonii*	.50	.25
2320	A819	1k *Aechmea fasciata*	2.40	.80
2321	A819	2k *Strelitzia reginae*	.65	.25
2322	A819	4k *Paphiopedilum*	2.50	.40
		Nos. 2319-2322 (4)	*6.05*	*1.70*

Olomouc and Bratislava Flower Shows.
Nos. 2319-2322 were each issued in sheets of 10. Value, set $70.

1980, Sept. 24   **Perf. 11½x12**

Designs: Folktale character embroideries.
2323	A820	50h Chad girl	.20	.20
2324	A820	1k Punch and dog	.20	.20
2325	A820	2k Dandy and Posy	.75	.20
2326	A820	4k Lion and moon	1.30	.75
2327	A820	5k Wallachian dance	.65	.20
		Nos. 2323-2327 (5)	*3.10*	*1.55*

National Census A821

1980, Sept. 24   **Perf. 12x11½**
2328	A821	1k multi	.25	.20

Prague Castle Type of 1971

Designs: 3k, Old Palace gateway. 4k, Armorial lion, 16th century.

1980, Oct. 28   **Perf. 12**
2329	A634	3k multi	1.25	1.10
2330	A634	4k multi	1.00	.65

Nos. 2329-2330 were each issued in sheets of 4. Value, set $18.

Bratislava Type of 1977

3k, View across the Danube, by J. Eder, 1810. 4k, The Old Royal Bridge, by J.A. Lantz, 1820.

1980, Oct. 28
2331	A760	3k multi	1.60	1.40
2332	A760	4k multi	1.25	.80

Nos. 2331-2332 were each issued in sheets of 4. Value, set $16.

10th Anniversary of Socialist Youth Federation — A822

1980, Nov. 9   **Perf. 12x11½**
2333	A822	50h multi	.20	.20

No. 2137 Overprinted in Red: 3. / MEZINARODNI VELETRH ZNAMEK / ESSEN '80

1980, Nov. 18
2334	A755	1.60k multi	20.00	15.00

Czechoslovak Day/ ESSEN '80, 3rd International Stamp Exhibition. No. 2334 has overprinted red marginal inscription.

Art Type of 1967

Designs: 1k, Pavel Jozef Safarik, by Jozef B. Klemens. 2k, Peasant Revolt mosaic, Anna Podzemna. 3k, St. Lucia, 14th century statue. 4k, Waste Heaps, by Jan Zrzavy, horiz. 5k, Labor, sculpture by Jan Stursa.

1980, Nov. 27   **Engr.**   **Perf. 12**
2335	A565	1k multi	.95	1.10
2336	A565	2k multi	1.10	.95
2337	A565	3k multi	.55	.50
2338	A565	4k multi	.65	.55
2339	A565	5k multi	.65	.55
		Nos. 2335-2339 (5)	*3.90*	*3.65*

Nos. 2335-2339 were each issued in sheets of 4. Value, set $27.

Stamp Day — A823

Engraved and Photogravure

1980, Dec. 18   **Perf. 11½x12**
2340	A823	1k multi	.25	.20

7th Five-year Plan, 1981-1985 A824

1981, Jan. 1   **Perf. 11½**
2341	A824	50h multi	.20	.20

International Year of the Disabled A825

1981, Feb. 24
2342	A825	1k multi	.25	.20

Landau, 1800 A826

1981, Feb. 25   **Perf. 12x11½**
2343	A826	50h shown	.20	.20
2344	A826	1k Mail coach, 1830	.25	.20
2345	A826	3.60k Mail sled, 1840	1.25	.60
2346	A826	5k 4-horse mail coach, 1860	.85	.45
2347	A826	7k Open carriage, 1840	1.25	.85
a.		Sheet of 4	13.00	10.00
		Nos. 2343-2347 (5)	*3.80*	*2.30*

WIPA '81 Intl. Philatelic Exhibition, Vienna, Austria, May 22-31. #2347a issued May 10.

Wolfgang Amadeus Mozart — A827

Famous Men: #2348, Joesph Hlavka (1831-1908). #2349, Juraj Hronec (1881-1959). #2350, Jan Sverma (1901-44). #2351, Mikulas Schneider-Trnavsky (1881-1958). #2352, B. Bolzano (1781-1848). #2353, Dimitri Shostakovich, composer. #2354, George Bernard Shaw, playwright.

1981, Mar. 10   **Perf. 11½**
2348	A827	50h multi	.20	.20
2349	A827	50h multi	.20	.20
2350	A827	50h multi	.20	.20
2351	A827	50h multi	.20	.20
2352	A827	1k multi	.75	.35
2353	A827	1k multi	.25	.20
2354	A827	1k multi	.25	.20
2355	A827	1k multi	.25	.20
		Nos. 2348-2355 (8)	*2.30*	*1.75*

Souvenir Sheet

Yuri Gagarin A828

1981, Apr. 5   **Perf. 12**
2356   Sheet of 2   4.50 4.00
   a.   A828 6k multicolored   2.00 1.60
20th anniv. of 1st manned space flight.

Workers and Banner A829

1981, Apr. 6   **Perf. 12x11½**
2357 A829   50h shown   .20 .20
2358 A829   1k Hands holding
            banner   .25 .20
2359 A829   4k Worker holding
            banner, vert.   .35 .25
     Nos. 2357-2359 (3)   .80 .65
Czechoslovakian Communist Party, 60th anniv.

Congress Emblem, View of Prague — A830

1981, Apr. 6
2360 A830   50h shown   .20 .20
2361 A830   1k Bratislava   .25 .20
16th Communist Party Congress.

Agriculture Museum, 90th Anniv. A831

Natl. Assembly Elections A832

1981, May 14   **Perf. 11½x12**
2362 A831   1k multi   .25 .20

1981, June 1
2363 A832   50h multi   .20 .20

Bratislava Type of 1977

Designs: 3k, Bratislava Castle, by G.B. Probst, 1760. 4k, Grassalkovic Palace, by C. Bschor, 1815.

1981, June 10   **Perf. 12**
2364 A760   3k multi   1.50 1.40
2365 A760   4k multi   1.25 .90
Nos. 2364-2365 were each issued in sheets of 4. Value, set $18.

Uran and Red October Hotels A833

Successes of Socialist Achievements Exhibition: 1k, Brno-Bratislava Highway, Jihlava. 2k, Nuclear power station, Jaslovske Bohunice.

1981, June 10   **Perf. 12x11½**
2366 A833   80h multi   .20 .20
2367 A833   1k multi   .20 .20
2368 A833   2k multi   .20 .20
     Nos. 2366-2368 (3)   .60 .60

Border Defense Units, 30th Anniv. A834

Civil Defense, 30th Anniv. A835

Army Cooperation, 30th Anniv. — A836

Rysy Youth Mountain Climbing Contest A837

Engraved and Photogravure
1981, July 11   **Perf. 11½**
2369 A834   40h multi   .20 .20
2370 A835   50h multi   .20 .20
2371 A836   1k multi   .25 .20
2372 A837   3.60k multi   .75 .30
     Nos. 2369-2372 (4)   1.40 .90

30th Natl. Festival of Amateur Puppet Ensembles — A838

1981, July 2   **Perf. 11½**
2373 A838   2k Punch and Devil   .50 .20

Souvenir Sheet

Guernica, by Pablo Picasso — A839

1981, July 2   **Engr.**   **Perf. 11½x12**
2374 A839   10k multi   3.50 2.50
Picasso's birth centenary; 45th anniv. of Intl. Brigades in Spain.

Cat Holding Flower, by Etienne Delessert A840

8th Biennial Exhibition of Children's Book Illustrations (Designs by): 50h, Albin Brunovsky, vert. 1k, Adolf Born. 2k, Vive Tolli. 10k, Suekichi Akaba.

Engraved and Photogravure
1981, Sept. 5   **Perf. 11½**
2375 A840   50h multi   .20 .20
2376 A840   1k multi   .25 .20
2377 A840   2k multi   .40 .20
2378 A840   4k multi   .95 .40
2379 A840   10k multi   2.00 .75
     Nos. 2375-2379 (5)   3.80 1.75

Prague Zoo, 50th Anniv. — A841

1981, Sept. 28   **Perf. 11½x12**
2380 A841   50h Gorillas   .45 .20
2381 A841   1k Lions   .80 .20
2382 A841   7k Przewalski's hor-
            ses   2.25 .80
     Nos. 2380-2382 (3)   3.50 1.20

Anti-smoking Campaign A842

1981, Oct. 27   **Perf. 12**
2383 A842   4k multi   1.00 .60
No. 2383 was issued in sheets of 10, containing 8 stamps and 2 labels. Values: single with label attached, $1.50; sheet, $14.

Prague Castle Art Type of 1971

Designs: 3k, Carved dragon, Palais Lobkovitz, 16th cent. 4k, St. Vitus Cathedral, by J. Sember and G. Dobler, 19th cent.

1981, Oct. 28
2384 A634   3k multi   .75 .45
2385 A634   4k multi   1.75 1.40
Nos. 2384-2385 were each issued in sheets of 4. Value, set $13.

Art Type of 1967

Designs: 1k, View of Prague, by Vaclav Hollar (1607-1677). 2k, Czechoslovak Academy medallion, engraved by Otakar Spaniel (1881-1955). 3k, Jihoceska Vysivka, by Zdenek Sklenar (b. 1910). 4k, Still Life, by A.M. Gerasimov (1881-1963). 5k, Standing Woman, by Pablo Picasso (1881-1973).

1981, Nov. 27   **Engr.**   **Perf. 12**
2386 A565   1k multi   2.40 1.60
2387 A565   2k multi   .65 .30
2388 A565   3k multi   .80 .50
2389 A565   4k multi   .95 .65
2390 A565   5k multi   2.40 1.25
     Nos. 2386-2390 (5)   7.20 4.30
Nos. 2386-2390 were each issued in sheets of 4. Value, set $35.
Sheets of No. 2390 exist with center gutter inscribed with Philexfrance 82 and FIP emblems. Value, $22.

Stamp Day — A843

Engraved and Photogravure
1981, Dec. 18   **Perf. 11½x12**
2391 A843   1k Engraver Edward
            Karel   .25 .20

Russian Workers' Party, Prague Congress, 70th Anniv. — A844

1982, Jan. 18   **Perf. 12**
2392 A844   2k Lenin   .50 .20
   a.   Sheet of 4   5.00 4.00
No. 2392 issued in sheet of 8. Value $5.

1982 World Cup Soccer A845

Designs: Various soccer players.

1982, Jan. 29   **Perf. 12x11½**
2393 A845   1k multi   .25 .20
2394 A845   3.60k multi   .70 .30
2395 A845   4k multi   1.40 .50
     Nos. 2393-2395 (3)   2.35 1.00

10th World Trade Union Congress, Havana — A846

Arms of Hrob — A847

1982, Feb. 10   **Perf. 11½**
2396 A846   1k multi   .25 .20

1982, Feb. 10   **Perf. 12x11½**

Arms of various cities.

2397 A847   50h shown   .20 .20
2398 A847   50h Nove Mesto Nad
            Metuji   .20 .20
2399 A847   50h Trencin   .20 .20
2400 A847   50h Mlada Boleslav   .20 .20
     Nos. 2397-2400 (4)   .80 .80
See Nos. 2499-2502, 2542-2544, 2595-2597, 2783-2786.

50th Anniv. of the Great Strike at Most — A848

1982, Mar. 23   **Perf. 11½**
2401 A848   1k multi   .25 .20

60th Intl. Railway Union Congress — A849

1982, Mar. 23   **Perf. 12x11½**
2402 A849   6k Steam locomotive,
            1922, electric,
            1982   3.25 .95

10th Workers'
Congress, Prague
A850

George
Dimitrov
A851

1982, Apr. 15
2403 A850 1k multi .25 .20

1982, May 1
2404 A851 50h multi .20 .20

A852

10th Lidice Intl.
Children's
Drawing
Contest — A853

Engravings: 40h, The Muse Euterpe Playing a Flute, by Crispin de Passe (1565-1637). 50h, The Lute Player, by Jacob de Gheyn (1565-1629). 1k, Woman Flautist, by Adriaen Collaert (1560-1618). 2k, Musicians in a Hostel, by Rembrandt (1606-1669). 3k, Hurdygurdy Player, by Jacques Callot (1594-1635).

1982, May 18   Perf. 11½x12
2405 A852 40h multi .20 .20
2406 A852 50h multi .20 .20
2407 A852 1k multi .20 .20
2408 A852 2k multi .30 .20
2409 A852 3k multi 1.10 .60
   Nos. 2405-2409 (5) 2.00 1.40

1982, May 18
2410 A853 2k multi 1.60 1.25
   Issued in sheets of 6. Value $10.

40th Anniv. of
Destruction of
Lidice and
Lezaky — A854

1982, June 4   Perf. 11½
2411 A854 1k Girl, rose .45 .20
2412 A854 1k Hands, barbed wire .45 .20

Souvenir Sheet

UN Disarmament Conference — A855

1982, June 4   Perf. 12
2413   Sheet of 2 12.00 8.00
   a. A855 6k Woman holding doves 5.50 3.50

Souvenir Sheet

2nd UN Conference on Peaceful Uses
of Outer Space, Vienna, Aug. 9-
21 — A856

1982, Aug. 9   Engr. & Photo.
2414   Sheet of 2 16.00 12.00
   a. A856 5k multi 6.00 4.00

Krivoklat
Castle
A857

1982, Aug. 31   Perf. 12x11½
2415 A857 50h shown .25 .20
2416 A857 1k Statues
           (Krivoklat) .25 .20
2417 A857 2k Nitra Castle .30 .20
2418 A857 3k Pottery, lock (Nitra) .40 .35
   a. Souv. sheet of 4, #2415-2418 2.00 1.60
   Nos. 2415-2418 (4) 1.20 .95

50th Anniv. of Zizkov
Hill Natl.
Monument — A858

1982, Sept. 16
2419 A858 1k multi .25 .20

Prague Castle Art Type of 1971

Designs: 3k, St. George and the Dragon, 1373. 4k, Tomb of King Vratislav I, 10th cent.

1982, Sept. 28   Perf. 12
2420 A634 3k multi 2.00 1.40
2421 A634 4k multi 1.10 1.10

Nos. 2420-2421 were each issued in sheets of 4. Value, set $13.

Bratislava Type of 1977

Designs: 3k, Paddle steamer, Parnik, 1818. 4k, View from Bridge, 19th cent.

1982, Sept. 29
2422 A760 3k multi 1.40 1.00
2423 A760 4k multi 1.10 1.00

Nos. 2422-2423 were each issued in sheets of 4. Value, set $18.

European Danube
Commission — A859

1982, Sept. 29   Perf. 11½x12
2424 A859 3k Steamer, Bratislava Bridge .80 .35
   a. Souvenir sheet of 4 5.00 4.00
2425 A859 3.60k Ferry, Budapest 1.25 .50
   a. Souvenir sheet of 4 7.00 6.00

16th Communist Party
Congress — A860

1982, Oct. 28   Perf. 12x11½
2426 A860 20h Agriculture .20 .20
2427 A860 1k Industry .20 .20
2428 A860 3k Engineering .35 .35
   Nos. 2426-2428 (3) .75 .75

30th Anniv. of
Academy of
Sciences — A861

1982, Oct. 29   Perf. 11½
2429 A861 6k Emblem .90 .35

65th Anniv. of October
Revolution — A862

Design: 1k, 60th anniv. of USSR.

1982, Nov. 7   Perf. 12x11½
2430 A862 50h multi .20 .20
2431 A862 1k multi .25 .20

Jaroslav Hasek,
Writer, Sculpture by
Josef
Malejovsky — A863

Sculptures: 2k, Jan Zrzavy, freedom fighter, by Jan Simota. 4.40k, Leos Janacek, composer, by Milos Axman. 6k, Martin Kukucin, freedom fighter, by Jan Kulich. 7k, Peaceful Work, by Rudolf Pribis.

Engraved and Photogravure
1982, Nov. 26   Perf. 11½x12
2432 A863   1k multi .20 .20
2433 A863   2k multi .25 .20
2434 A863   4.40k multi .85 .20
2435 A863   6k multi 1.20 .30
2436 A863   7k multi 1.50 .75
   Nos. 2432-2436 (5) 4.00 1.65

Nos. 2432-2436 were each issued in sheets of 4. Value, set $30.

Art Type of 1967

1k, Revolution in Spain, by Josef Sima (1891-1971). 2k, Woman Dressing, by Rudolf Kremlicka (1886-1932). 3k, The Girl Bride, by Dezider Milly (1906-1971). 4k, Performers, by Jan Zelibsky (b. 1907). 5k, The Complaint of the Birds, by Emil Filla (1882-1953).

1982, Nov. 27   Perf. 12
2437 A565 1k multi .65 .45
2438 A565 2k multi 1.25 1.00
2439 A565 3k multi .85 .85
2440 A565 4k multi .85 .85
2441 A565 5k multi 2.00 1.00
   Nos. 2437-2441 (5) 5.60 4.15

Nos. 2437-2441 were each issued in sheets of 4. Value, set $28.

Stamp Day — A864

1982, Dec. 8   Perf. 11½
2442 A864 1k Engraver Jaroslav Goldschmied
           (1890-1977) .25 .20

A865

A866

1983, Jan. 10   Engr.   Perf. 12x11½
2443 A865 50h dark blue .20 .20

Pres. Gustav Husak, 70th birthday. See No. 2686.

1983, Feb. 24   Engr. & Photo.
Designs: 50h, Jaroslav Hasek (1882-1923), writer. 1k, Julius Fucik (1903-1943), antifascist martyr. 2k, Martin Luther (1483-1546). 5k, Johannes Brahms (1833-1897), composer.

2444 A866 50h multi .20 .20
2445 A866 1k multi .20 .20
2446 A866 2k multi .25 .20
   a.   Souvenir sheet of 4 24.00 12.50
2447 A866 5k multi .85 .80
   Nos. 2444-2447 (4) 1.50 .80

Nordposta '83 Intl. Stamp Exhibition, Hamburg.
No. 2446a issued Nov. 1.

Workers
Marching
A867

Family — A868

1983, Feb. 25   Perf. 11½
2448 A867 50h multi .20 .20
2449 A868 1k multi .25 .20

35th anniv. of "Victorious February" (50h), and Natl. Front (1k).

World
Communications
Year — A869

Perf. 11½, 12x11½ (2k)
1983, Mar. 16
2450 A869 40h multi .20 .20
2451 A869 1k multi .20 .20
2452 A869 2k multi .30 .20
2453 A869 3.60k multi .60 .20
   Nos. 2450-2453 (4) 1.30 .80

Various wave patterns. 2k, 40x23mm; 3.60k, 49x19mm.

7th World Ski-
jumping
Championships
A870

1983, Mar. 16   Perf. 11½
2454 A870 1k multi .25 .20

Souvenir Sheet

5th Anniv. of Czechoslovak-USSR Intercosmos Cooperative Space Program — A871

1983, Apr. 12   **Perf. 12**
2455   Sheet of 2   13.00 9.50
   a.   A871 10k multi   4.75 4.00

See No. 2226.

Protected Species — A872

1983, Apr. 28   **Perf. 12x11½**
2456 A872   50h Butterfly, violets   .30 .20
2457 A872   1k Water lilies, frog   .65 .20
2458 A872   2k Pine cones, crossbill   .65 .30
2459 A872 3.60k Herons   .80 .35
2460 A872   5k Gentians, lynx   1.10 .45
2461 A872   7k Stag   2.50 1.00
   Nos. 2456-2461 (6)   6.00 2.50

A873   A874

Soviet Marshals.

1983, May 5   **Perf. 11½**
2462 A873 50h Ivan S. Konev   .20 .20
2463 A873   1k Andrei I. Sheremenko   .20 .20
2464 A873   2k Rodion J. Malinovsky   .25 .20
   Nos. 2462-2464 (3)   .65 .60

30th anniv. of Czechoslovak-Soviet defense treaty.

1983, July 13   **Perf. 12**
2465 A874   2k multi   .40 .25
   a.   Souvenir sheet of 4   6.50 5.50

World Peace and Life Congress, Prague. No. 2465 issued in sheets of 8. Value $10.

Emperor Rudolf II by Adrian De Vries (1560-1626) A875

Art treasures of the Prague Castle: 5k, Kinetic relief, Timepiece, Rudolf Svoboda.

1983, Aug. 25   **Perf. 11½**
2466 A875 4k multi   .90 .60
2467 A875 5k multi   .90 .60

Nos. 2466-2467 were each issued in sheets of 6. Value, set $15.

See Nos. 2518-2519, 2610-2611, 2654-2655, 2717-2718, 2744-2745, 2792-2793.

9th Biennial of Illustrations for Children and Youth — A876

Illustrators: 50h, Oleg K. Zotov, USSR. 1k, Zbigniew Rychlicki, Poland. 4k, Lisbeth Zwerger, Austria. 7k, Antonio Dominques, Angola.

1983, Sept. 9   **Engr. & Photo.**
2468 A876 50h multi   .20 .20
2469 A876   1k multi   .20 .20
2470 A876   4k multi   .35 .20
2471 A876   7k multi   .75 .30
   a.   Souv. sheet of 4, #2468-2471   5.00 3.00
   Nos. 2468-2471 (4)   1.50 .90

World Communications Year — A877

Emblems and aircraft.

1983, Sept. 30   **Perf. 11½**
2472 A877 50h red & black   .20 .20
2473 A877   1k red & black, vert.   .20 .20
2474 A877   4k red & black   .75 .25
   Nos. 2472-2474 (3)   1.15 .65

60th anniv. of the Czechoslovak Airlines.

16th Party Congress Achievements — A878

1983, Oct. 20   **Perf. 12x11½**
2475 A878 50h Civil engineering construction   .20 .20
2476 A878   1k Chemical industry   .20 .20
2477 A878   3k Health services   .40 .20
   Nos. 2475-2477 (3)   .80 .60

Bratislava Type of 1977

Designs: 3k, Two sculptures, Viktor Tilgner (1844-96). 4k, Mirbachov Palace, 1939, by Julius Schubert (1888-1947).

1983, Oct. 28   **Perf. 12**
2478 A760 3k multi   1.50 1.25
2479 A760 4k multi   1.25 1.00

Nos. 2478-2479 were each issued in sheets of 4 stamps. Value, set $16.

Natl. Theater, Prague, Centenary — A879

1983, Nov. 8   **Engr.**   **Perf. 11½**
2480 A879 50h Natl. Theater building   .20 .20
2481 A879   2k State Theater, Natl. Theater   .30 .20

Messenger of Mourning, by Mikolas Ales — A880

Designs: 2k, Genius, theater curtain by Vojtech Hynais (1854-1925). 3k, Music, Lyric drawings by Frantisek Zenisek (1849-1916). 4k, Symbolic figure of Prague, by Vaclav Brozik (1851-1901). 5k, Hradcany Castle, by Julius Marak (1832-1899).

1983, Nov. 18   **Engr.**
2482 A880 1k multi   1.20 .75
2483 A880 2k multi   1.50 1.10
2484 A880 3k multi   .90 .45
2485 A880 4k multi   1.40 .45
2486 A880 5k multi   1.10 .60
   Nos. 2482-2486 (5)   6.10 3.35

Nos. 2482-2486 were each issued in sheets of 4 stamps. Value, set $35.

Warrior with Sword and Shield, Engraving, 17th Cent. — A881

Engravings of Costumes: 50h, Bodyguard of Rudolf II, by Jacob de Gheyn (1565-1629). 1k, Lady with Lace Collar, by Jacques Callot (1592-1635). 4k, Lady, by Vaclav Hollar (1607-77). 5k, Man, by Antoine Watteau (1684-1721).

Engraved and Photogravure

1983, Dec. 2   **Perf. 11½x12**
2487 A881 40h multi   .20 .20
2488 A881 50h multi   .20 .20
2489 A881   1k multi   .20 .20
2490 A881   4k multi   .75 .20
2491 A881   5k multi   1.25 .75
   Nos. 2487-2491 (5)   2.60 1.55

Stamp Day — A882

1983, Dec. 18
2492 A882 1k Karl Seizinger (1889-1978), #114   .25 .20

Czechoslovak Federation, 15th Anniv. — A883

1984, Jan. 1   **Perf. 11½**
2493 A883 50h Bratislava, Prague Castles   .20 .20

35th Anniv. of COMECON A884

1984, Jan. 23
2494 A884 1k Headquarters, Moscow   .25 .20

1984 Winter Olympics A885

1984, Feb. 7   **Perf. 12x11½**
2495 A885 2k Cross-country skiing   .40 .20
2496 A885 3k Hockey   .50 .20
   a.   Souvenir sheet of 4   5.00 4.00
2497 A885 5k Biathlon   1.25 .35
   Nos. 2495-2497 (3)   2.15 .75

Intl. Olympic Committee, 90th Anniv. — A886

1984, Feb. 7   **Perf. 11½x12**
2498 A886 7k Rings, runners, torch   1.25 .35

City Arms Type of 1982

1984, Mar. 1   **Perf. 12x11½**
2499 A847 50h Kutna Hora   .20 .20
2500 A847 50h Turnov   .20 .20
2501 A847   1k Martin   .25 .20
2502 A847   1k Milevsko   .25 .20
   Nos. 2499-2502 (4)   .90 .80

Intercosmos Space Program — A887

Various satellites. Nos. 2503-2507 se-tenant with labels showing flags.

1984, Apr. 12   **Perf. 11½x12**
2503 A887 50h multi   .20 .20
2504 A887   1k multi   .20 .20
2505 A887   2k multi   .35 .20
2506 A887   4k multi   .75 .40
2507 A887   5k multi   1.40 .50
   Nos. 2503-2507 (5)   2.90 1.50

Resistance Heroes — A888

Designs: 50h, Vendelin Opatrny (1908-44). 1k, Ladislav Novomesky (1904-44). 2k, Rudolf Jasiok (1919-44). 4k, Jan Nalepka (1912-43).

1984, May 9   **Perf. 11x11½**
2508 A888 50h multi   .20 .20
2509 A888   1k multi   .20 .20
2510 A888   2k multi   .30 .20
2511 A888   4k multi   .50 .20
   Nos. 2508-2511 (4)   1.20 .80

Music Year — A889

1984, May 11   **Perf. 11½**
2512 A889 50h Instruments   .20 .20
2513 A889   1k Organ pipes, vert.   .30 .20

Bratislava Type of 1977

Designs: 3k, Vintners' Guild arms, 19th cent. 4k, View of Bratislava (painting commemorating shooting competition, 1827).

1984, June 1   *Perf. 12*
2514 A760 3k multi   1.10 .85
2515 A760 4k multi   1.60 1.10

Nos. 2514-2515 were each issued in sheets of 4 stamps. Value, set $15.

Central Telecommunications Building, Bratislava — A890

1984, June 1   *Perf. 11½*
2516 A890 2k multi   .35 .20

A891   A893

1984, June 12   *Perf. 12*
2517 A891 5k UPU emblem, dove, globe   3.25 2.75

1984 UPU Congress. Issued in sheet of 4 with and without Philatelic Salon text. Values, $40 with text, $12 without text.

Prague Castle Type of 1983

Designs: 3k, Crowing rooster, St. Vitus Cathedral, 19th cent. 4k, King David from the Roundnice, Book of Psalms illuminated manuscript, Bohemia, 15th cent.

1984, Aug. 9   *Engr. & Photo.*
2518 A875 3k multi   1.25 .80
2519 A875 4k multi   1.60 .50

Nos. 2518-2519 were each issued in sheets of 6 stamps. Value, set $18.

1984, Aug. 28   *Perf. 11½x12*

Playing cards.
2520 A893 50h Jack of Spades, 16th cent.   .20 .20
2521 A893 1k Queen of spades, 17th cent.   .20 .20
2522 A893 2k 9 of hearts, 18th cent.   .25 .20
2523 A893 3k Jack of clubs, 18th cent.   .35 .20
2524 A893 5k King of hearts, 19th cent.   1.00 .20
    Nos. 2520-2524 (5)   2.00 1.00

Slovak Natl. Uprising, 40th Anniv. A894

1984, Aug. 29   *Perf. 12x11½*
2525 A894 50h Family, factories, flowers   .20 .20

Battle of Dukla Pass (Carpathians), 40th Anniv. — A895

1984, Sept. 8   *Perf. 11½x12*
2526 A895 2k Soldiers, flag   .40 .20

1984 Summer Olympics A896

1984, Sept. 9   *Perf. 12x11½*
2527 A896 1k Pole vault   .20 .20
2528 A896 2k Bicycling   .40 .20
2529 A896 3k Rowing   .60 .35
2530 A896 5k Weight lifting   1.00 .45
   a.   Souv. sheet of 4, #2527-2530   4.00 3.25
    Nos. 2527-2530 (4)   2.20 1.20

16th Party Congress Goals and Projects — A897

1984, Oct. 28   *Perf. 12x11½*
2531 A897 1k Communications   .20 .20
2532 A897 2k Transportation   .25 .20
2533 A897 3k Transgas pipeline   .35 .25
   a.   Souvenir sheet of 3   2.00 1.60
    Nos. 2531-2533 (3)   .80 .65

Art Type of 1967

1k, The Milevsky River, by Karel Stehlik (b. 1912). 2k, Under the Trees, by Viktor Barvitius (1834-1902). 3k, Landscape with Flowers, by Zolo Palugyay (1898-1935). 4k, King in Palace, Visehrad Codex miniature, 1085. 5k, View of Kokorin Castles, by Antonin Manes. #2534-2537 horiz.; issued in sheets of 4.

1984, Nov. 16   *Perf. 11½*
2534 A565 1k multi   3.00 .90
2535 A565 2k multi   3.00 .90
2536 A565 3k multi   2.00 .50
2537 A565 4k multi   3.00 .70
2538 A565 5k multi   3.00 .70
    Nos. 2534-2538 (5)   14.00 3.70

Nos. 2534-2538 were each issued in sheets of 4 stamps. Value, set $60.

Students' Intl., 45th Anniv. A898   Birth Cent., Antonin Zapotocky A899

1984, Nov. 17
2539 A898 1k Head, dove   .25 .20

Engr. & Photo.
1984, Dec. 18   *Perf. 11½*
2540 A899 50h multi   .25 .20

Stamp Day — A900

1984, Dec. 18   *Perf. 11½x12*
2541 A900 1k Engraver Bohumil Heinz (1894-1940)   .25 .20

City Arms Type of 1982

1985, Feb. 5   *Perf. 12x11½*
2542 A847 50h Kamyk nad Vltavou   .20 .20
2543 A847 50h Havirov   .20 .20
2544 A847 50h Trnava   .20 .20
    Nos. 2542-2544 (3)   .60 .60

University of Applied Arts, Prague, Centenary — A901

1985, Feb. 6   *Perf. 11½x12*
2545 A901 3k Art and Pleasure, sculpture   .40 .20

Trnava University, 350th Anniv. — A902

1985, Feb. 6   *Perf. 11½x12*
2546 A902 2k Town of Trnava   .40 .20

Military Museum Exposition — A903

1985, Feb. 7   *Perf. 11½x12, 12x11½*
2547 A903 50h Armor, crossbow, vert.   .20 .20
2548 A903 1k Medals, vert.   .20 .20
2549 A903 2k Biplane, spacecraft   .40 .20
    Nos. 2547-2549 (3)   .80 .60

Vladimir I. Lenin (1870-1924), 1st Chairman of Russia — A904

1985, Mar. 15   *Engr.*   *Perf. 12*
2550 A904 2k multi   .80 .40

No. 2550 printed in sheets of 6 stamps. Value $5.

UN 40th Anniv., Peace Year 1986 A905

1985, Mar. 15
2551 A905 6k UN, Peace Year emblems   2.75 2.40

Issued in sheets of 4 stamps. Value $12.

A906   A907

Engraved and Photogravure
1985, Apr. 5   *Perf. 11½*
2552 A906 4k Natl. arms, twig, crowd   .60 .20

Kosice govt. plan, Apr. 5, 1945.

1985, Apr. 5
2553 A907 50h Natl. arms, flag, soldiers   .20 .20

Natl. Security Forces, 40th anniv.

Halley's Comet, INTERCOSMOS Project Vega — A908

Design: Emblem, space platform, interstellar map, intercept data.

1985, Apr. 12   *Perf. 12x11½*
2554   Sheet of 2   12.00 9.50
   a.   A908 5k multicolored   5.00 3.25

Project Vega, a joint effort of the USSR, France, German Democratic Republic, Austria, Poland, Bulgaria and CSSR, was for the geophysical study of Halley's Comet, Dec. 1984-Mar. 1986.

European Ice Hockey Championships, Prague, Apr. 17-May 3 — A909

1985, Apr. 13
2555 A909 1k Hockey players, emblem   .25 .20

No. 2555 Ovptd. "CSSR MISTREM SVETA" in Violet Blue
1985, May 31   *Perf. 12x11½*
2556 A909 1k multi   2.50 2.50

Natl. Chess Org., 80th Anniv. — A910

1985, Apr. 13   *Perf. 11½*
2557 A910 6k Emblem, game board, chessmen   1.25 .50

Anniversaries — A911

1985, May 5   *Perf. 11½x12*
2558 A911 1k May Uprising, 1945   .20 .20
2559 A911 1k Soviet Army in CSSR, 1945   .20 .20
2560 A911 1k Warsaw Treaty, 1950   .20 .20
2561 A911 1k Czech-Soviet Treaty, 1970   .20 .20
    Nos. 2558-2561 (4)   .80 .80

Spartakiad '85, Strahov Stadium, Prague, June 27 — A912

Designs: 50h, Gymnasts warming up with rackets and balls. 1k, Rhythmic gymnastics floor exercise, Prague Castle.

1985, June 3   *Perf. 11½, 11½x12*
2562 A912 50h multi   .20 .20

Size: 53x22mm
2563 A912 1k multi   .20 .20

WWII Anti-Fascist Political Art — A913

Drawings and caricatures: 50h, Fire, and From the Concentration Camp, by Joseph Capek (1887-1945). 2k, The Conference on Disarmament in Geneva, 1927 and The Prophecy of Three Parrots, 1933, by Frantisek Bidlo (1895-1945). 4k, The Unknown Warrior to Order, 1936, and The Almost Peaceful Dove, 1937, by Antonin Pelc (1895-1967).

1985, June 4   **Perf. 12x11½**
2564 A913 50h multi .20 .20
2565 A913 2k multi .30 .20
2566 A913 4k multi .60 .40
    Nos. 2564-2566 (3) 1.10 .80

Helsinki Conference on European Security and Cooperation, 10th Anniv. — A914

1985, July 1   **Engr. & Photo.**
2567 A914 7k multi 2.25 1.50
   a.   Souvenir sheet of 4   12.00 8.00

An imperf. souv. sheet similar to No. 2567a was issued June 1, 1988 for FINLANDIA '88 and PRAGA '88. Value $40.

12th World Youth Festival, Moscow A915

1985, July 2
2568 A915 1k Kremlin, youths .20 .20

A916

A918

1985, Sept. 3   **Perf. 11½**
2569 A916 50h multi .20 .20
Federation of World Trade Unions, 40th anniv.

Bratislava Type of 1977

Designs: 3k, Castle and river, lace embroidery by Elena Holeczyova (1906-1983). 4k, Pottery cups and mugs, 1600-1500 B.C.

1985, Sept. 4   **Engr.**   **Perf. 12**
2570 A760 3k multi 1.60 .45
2571 A760 4k multi 2.10 .60
Nos. 2570-2571 were each issued in sheets of 4 stamps. Value, set $18.

Engraved and Photogravure
1985, Sept. 5   **Perf. 11½**
Children's book illustrations: 1k, Rocking Horse, by Kveta Pacovska, USSR. 2k, Fairies, by Gennadij Spirin, USSR. 3k, Butterfly and

Girl, by Kaarina Kaila, Finland. 4k, Boy and Animals, by Erick Ingraham, US.
2572 A918 1k multi .20 .20
2573 A918 2k multi .30 .20
2574 A918 3k multi .45 .25
2575 A918 4k multi .60 .25
   a.   Souv. sheet of 4, #2572-2575   4.00 3.00
   Nos. 2572-2575 (4) 1.55 1.00
10th biennial of illustrations.

5-Year Development Plan — A919

1985, Oct. 28   **Perf. 12x11½**
2576 A919 50h Construction machinery .20 .20
2577 A919 1k Prague subway, map .20 .20
2578 A919 2k Modern textile spinning .20 .20
   Nos. 2576-2578 (3) .60 .60
16th Communist Party Congress goals.

Prague   A921
Castle — A920

Engr., Engr. & Photo. (3k)
1985, Oct. 28   **Perf. 12**
2579 A920 2k Presidential Palace Gate, 1768 .40 .40
2580 A920 3k St. Vitus' Cathedral .50 .50
Nos. 2579-2580 were each issued in sheets of 6 stamps. Value, set $9.

Engraved and Photogravure
1985, Nov. 23   **Perf. 11½x12**
Glassware: 50h, Pitcher, Near East, 4th cent. 1k, Venetian pitcher, 16th cent. 2k, Bohemian goblet, c. 1720. 4k, Harrachov Bohemian vase, 18th cent. 6k, Jablonec Bohemian vase, c. 1900.
2581 A921 50h multi .20 .20
2582 A921 1k multi .20 .20
2583 A921 2k multi .30 .20
2584 A921 4k multi .50 .20
2585 A921 6k multi 1.00 .35
   Nos. 2581-2585 (5) 2.20 1.15
Arts and Crafts Museum, Prague, cent.

Art Type of 1967

Designs: 1k, Young Woman in a Blue Gown, by Jozef Ginovsky (1800-1857). 2k, Lenin on the Charles Bridge, Prague, 1952, by Martin Sladky (b. 1920). 3k, Avenue of Poplars, 1935, by Vaclav Rabas (1885-1954). 4k, The Martyrom of St. Dorothea, 1516, by Hans Baldung Grien (c. 1484-1545). 5k, Portrait of Jasper Schade van Westrum, 1645, by Frans Hals (c. 1581-1666).

1985, Nov. 27   **Engr.**   **Perf. 12**
2586 A565 1k multi 1.60 .80
2587 A565 2k multi 1.10 .35
2588 A565 3k multi 1.50 .35
2589 A565 4k multi .90 .50
2590 A565 5k multi .90 .50
   Nos. 2586-2590 (5) 6.00 2.50
Nos. 2586-2590 were each issued in sheets of 4 stamps. Value, set $30.

Bohdan Roule (1921-1960), Engraver — A922

Engraved and Photogravure
1985, Dec. 18   **Perf. 11½x12**
2591 A922 1k multicolored .25 .20
Stamp Day 1985.

Intl. Peace Year — A923

1986, Jan. 2
2592 A923 1k multi .25 .20

Philharmonic Orchestra, 90th Anniv. — A924

EXPO '86, Vancouver A925

1986, Jan. 2   **Perf. 11½**
2593 A924 1k Victory Statue, Prague .25 .20

1986, Jan. 23   **Perf. 11½**
Design: Z 50 LS monoplane, Cenyerth Prague-Kladno locomotive, Sahara Desert rock drawing, 5th-6th cent. B.C.
2594 A925 4k multicolored .75 .20

City Arms Type of 1982

1986, Feb. 10   **Perf. 12x11½**
     Size: 42x54mm
2595 A847 50h Myjava .20 .20
2596 A847 50h Vodnany .20 .20
2597 A847 50h Zamberk .20 .20
   Nos. 2595-2597 (3) .60 .60

17th Natl. Communist Party Congress, Prague, Mar. 24 — A926

1986, Mar. 20   **Perf. 11½**
2598 A926 50h shown .20 .20
2599 A926 1k Industry .20 .20

Natl. Communist Party, 65th Anniv. — A927

1986, Mar. 20   **Perf. 12x11½**
2600 A927 50h Star, man, woman .20 .20
2601 A927 1k Hammer, sickle, laborers .20 .20

Natl. Front Election Program A928

1986, Mar. 28
2602 A928 50h multi .20 .20

Karlovy Vary Intl. Film Festival, 25th Anniv. — A929

1986, Apr. 3   **Perf. 11½**
2603 A929 1k multi .25 .20

A930

A931

1986, Apr. 8   **Engr. & Photo.**
2604 A930 1k multi .25 .20
Spring of Prague Music Festival.

1986, Apr. 25
2605 A931 50h multi .40 .20
Prague-Moscow air service, 50th anniv.

Intl. Olympic Committee, 90th Anniv. — A932

1986, May 12   **Perf. 11½x12**
2606 A932 2k multi .30 .20

1986 World Cup Soccer Championships, Mexico — A933

1986, May 15   **Perf. 12x11½**
2607 A933 4k multi .80 .40

Women's World Volleyball Championships, Prague — A934

1986, May 19
2608 A934 1k multi .25 .20

Souvenir Sheet

Intl. Philatelic Federation, FIP, 60th Anniv. — A935

1986, June 3   **Engr.**   **Perf. 12**
2609 A935 20k multi   6.50 5.00

Exists imperf and with perforations between stamps omitted. Values, $12 and $25, respectively.

Prague Castle Type of 1983

Designs: 2k, Jewelled funerary pendant, 9th cent. 3k, Allegory of Blossoms, sculpture by Jaroslav Horejc (1886-1983), St. Vitus' Cathedral.

1986, June 6   **Engr.**   **Perf. 12**
2610 A875 2k multi   .30 .30
2611 A875 3k multi   .70 .45

Nos. 2610-2611 were each issued in sheets of 6 stamps. Value, set $10.

UN Child Survival Campaign — A937

Toys.

Engraved and Photogravure
1986, Sept. 1   **Perf. 11½**
2612 A937 10h Rooster   .20 .20
2613 A937 20h Horse and rider   .20 .20
2614 A937 1k Doll   .25 .20
2615 A937 2k Doll, diff.   .50 .20
2616 A937 3k Tin omnibus, c. 1910   .65 .30
Nos. 2612-2616 (5)   1.80 1.10

UNICEF, 40th anniv.

Registration, Cent. — A938

1986, Sept. 2   **Perf. 11½x12**
2617 A938 4k Label, mail coach   .45 .20

Bratislava Type of 1977
1986, Sept. 11   **Engr.**   **Perf. 12**
2618 A760 3k Sigismund Gate   1.25 .80
2619 A760 4k St. Margaret, bas-relief   1.25 .65

Nos. 2618-2619 were each issued in sheets of 4 stamps. Value, set $12.

Owls — A939

Engraved and Photogravure
1986, Sept. 18   **Perf. 11½**
2620 A939 50h Bubo bubo   .80 .20
2621 A939 2k Asio otus   .95 .35
2622 A939 3k Strix aluco   1.60 .35
2623 A939 4k Tyto alba   1.60 .45
2624 A939 5k Asio flammeus   2.25 6.75
Nos. 2620-2624 (5)   7.20 8.10

Souvenir Sheet

Intl. Brigades in Spain — A940

Theater curtain: Woman Savaged by Horses, 1936, by Vladimir Sychra (1903-1963), Natl Gallery, Prague.

1986, Oct. 1   **Engr.**   **Perf. 12**
2625   Sheet of 2   4.50 3.50
   a. A940 5k multi   2.00 1.25

Locomotives and Streetcars — A941

Engraved and Photogravure
1986, Oct. 6   **Perf. 12x11½**
2626 A941 50h KT-8   .20 .20
2627 A941 1k E458.1   .20 .20
2628 A941 3k T466.2   .75 .30
2629 A941 5k M152.0   .80 .20
Nos. 2626-2629 (4)   1.95 .90

Paintings in the Prague and Bratislava Natl. Galleries — A942

Designs: 1k, The Circus Rider, 1980, by Jan Bauch (b. 1898). 2k, The Ventriloquist, 1954, by Frantisek Tichy (1896-1961). 3k, In the Circus, 1946, by Vincent Hloznik (b. 1919). 6k, Clown, 1985, by Karel Svolinsky (1896-1986).

1986, Oct. 13   **Engr.**   **Perf. 12**
2630 A942 1k multi   1.25 .65
2631 A942 2k multi   1.60 .85
2632 A942 3k multi   1.60 .85
2633 A942 6k multi   1.10 .95
Nos. 2630-2633 (4)   5.55 3.30

Nos. 2630-2633 were each issued in sheets of 4 stamps. Value, set $30.

Art Type of 1967

1k, The Czech Lion, May 1918, by Vratislav H. Brunner (1886-1928). 2k, Boy with Mandolin, 1945, by Jozef Sturdik (b. 1920). 3k, Metra Building, 1984, by Frantisek Gross (1909-1985). 4k, Portrait of Maria Maximiliana at Sternberk, 1665, by Karel Skreta (1610-1674). 5k, Adam & Eve, 1538, by Lucas Cranach (1472-1553).

1986, Nov. 3   **Engr.**   **Perf. 12**
2634 A565 1k multi   3.00 2.25
2635 A565 2k multi   3.00 2.25
2636 A565 3k multi   3.00 2.25
2637 A565 4k multi   3.00 2.25
2638 A565 5k multi   3.00 2.25
Nos. 2634-2638 (5)   15.00 11.25

Nos. 2634-2638 were each issued in sheets of 4 stamps. Value, set $100.

Stamp Day — A943

Design: V.H. Brunner (1886-1928), stamp designer, and No. 88.

Photo. & Engr.
1986, Dec. 18   **Perf. 11½x12**
2639 A943 1k multicolored   .25 .20

World Cyclocross Championships, Jan. 24-25, Central Bohemia — A944

1987, Jan. 22   **Perf. 11½**
2640 A944 6k multi   .80 .20

Czechoslovakian Bowling Union, 50th Anniv. — A945

1987, Jan. 22   **Perf. 11½**
2641 A945 2k multi   .35 .20

State Decorations — A946

Designs: 50h, Gold Stars of Socialist Labor and Czechoslovakia. 2k, Order of Klement Gottwald. 3k, Order of the Republic. 4k, Order of Victorious February. 5k, Order of Labor.

1987, Feb. 4   **Perf. 12x11½**
2642 A946 50h multi   .20 .20
2643 A946 2k multi   .25 .20
2644 A946 3k multi   .30 .20
2645 A946 4k multi   .45 .20
2646 A946 5k multi   .60 .40
Nos. 2642-2646 (5)   1.80 1.20

Butterflies — A947

1987, Mar. 4
2647 A947 1k Limenitis populi   .80 .20
2648 A947 2k Smerinthus ocellatus   1.25 .30
2649 A947 3k Pericallia matronula   1.60 .45
2650 A947 4k Saturnia pyri   1.60 .45
Nos. 2647-2650 (4)   5.25 1.40

Natl. Nuclear Power Industry A948

1987, Apr. 6
2651 A948 5k multi   .60 .20

11th Revolutionary Trade Union Movement Congress, Apr. 14-17, Prague — A949

1987, Apr. 7   **Perf. 11½**
2652 A949 1k multi   .20 .20

Souvenir Sheet

INTERCOSMOS, 20th Anniv. — A950

Cosmonauts Alexei Gubarev of the USSR & Vladimir Remek of Czechoslovakia, rocket & emblem.

1987, Apr. 12   **Engr.**   **Perf. 12**
2653   Sheet of 2   8.00 6.50
   a. A950 10k multi   3.25 2.00
   b. Souv. sheet of 4, litho. & engr., imperf.   10.00 8.00

No. 2653b issued Nov. 15, 1987.

Prague Castle Art Treasures Type of 1983

Designs: 2k, Three Saints, stained-glass window detail, c. 1870, St. Vitus Cathedral, by Frantisek Sequens (1830-1896). 3k, Coat of Arms, New Land Rolls Hall, 1605.

1987, May 9   **Perf. 11½**
2654 A875 2k multi   .40 .30
2655 A875 3k dk red, slate gray & yel org   .60 .45

Nos. 2634-2638 were each issued in sheets of 6 stamps. Value, set $9.

PRAGA '88 A951

Photo. & Engr.
1987, May 12   **Perf. 12x11½**
2656 A951 3k Telephone, 1894   .80 .20
2657 A951 3k Postal van, 1924   .80 .30
2658 A951 4k Locomotive tender, 1907   .80 .30
2659 A951 4k Tram, 1900   .80 .30
2660 A951 5k Steam roller, 1936   .80 .30
Nos. 2656-2660 (5)   4.00 1.40

Printed in sheets of 8 + 2 labels picturing telephone or vehicles. Value $40.
Nos. 2657-2658 were also printed in sheets of 4 + label picturing vehicles. Value, $30 for both sheets.

Destruction of Lidice and Lezaky, 45th Anniv. — A952

Drawings: No. 2661, When the Fighting Ended, 1945, by Pavel Simon. No. 2662, The End of the game, 1945, by Ludmila Jirincova.

1987, June   **Perf. 11½**
2661 A952 1k blk, cerise & vio   .20 .20
2662 A952 1k blk, gold, pale lil & cerise   .20 .20

Union of Czechoslovakian Mathematicians and Physicists, 125th Anniv. — A953

Designs: No. 2663, Prague Town Hall mathematical clock, Theory of Functions diagram. No. 2664, J.M. Petzval (1807-1891), J. Strouhal (1850-1922) and V. Jarnik (1897-1970). No. 2665, Geographical measurement from A.M. Malletta's book, 1672, earth fold and Brownian motion diagrams.

1987, July 6   *Perf. 11½x12*

2663	A953	50h multi	.20	.20
2664	A953	50h multi	.20	.20
2665	A953	50h multi	.20	.20
		Nos. 2663-2665 (3)	.60	.60

A954

A955

Award-winning illustrations.

1987, Sept. 3   *Perf. 11½*

2666	A954	50h Asun Balzola, Spain	.20	.20
2667	A954	1k Frederic Clement, France	.20	.20
2668	A954	2k Elzbieta Gaudasinska, Poland	.40	.25
a.		Souv. sheet of 2 + label	2.50	1.75
2669	A954	4k Marija Lucija Stupica, Yugoslavia	.80	.50
		Nos. 2666-2669 (4)	1.60	1.15

11th Biennial of Children's Book Illustration, Sept. 11-Oct. 30, Bratislava.

1987, Sept. 23

2670	A955	50h Eternal flame, flower	.20	.20

Theresienstadt Memorial for the victims from 23 European countries who died in the Small Fortress, Terezin, a Nazi concentration camp.

Socialist Communications Organization, 30th Anniv. — A956

1987, Sept. 23

2671	A956	4k Emblem, satellite, dish receiver	.40	.20

Jan Evangelista Purkyne (1787-1869), Physiologist A957

1987, Sept. 30

2672	A957	7k multicolored	.80	.20

Views of Bratislava — A958

Designs: 3k, Male and female figures supporting an oriel, Arkier Palace, c. 1552. 4k, View of Bratislava from Ware Conterfactur de Stadt Presburg, from an engraving by Hans Mayer, 1563.

1987, Oct. 1   Engr.   *Perf. 12*

2673	A958	3k multicolored	.50	.35
2674	A958	4k multicolored	.70	.45

Each printed in sheets of 4 with Bratislava Castle (from Mayer's engraving) between. Value, set $6.50.
See #2719-2720, 2763-2764, 2800-2801.

Type of 1974
Photo. & Engr.

1987, Nov. 1   *Perf. 12x11½*

2675	A699	1k Post rider	.20	.20

PRAGA '88, Aug. 26-Sept. 4, 1988. No. 2675 printed se-tenant with label picturing exhibition emblem. Value for single with attached label 40c.

October Revolution, Russia, 70th Anniv. — A959

Establishment of the Union of Soviet Socialist Republics, 65th Anniv. — A960

1987, Nov. 6   *Perf. 12x11½*

2676	A959	50h multicolored	.20	.20
2677	A960	50h multicolored	.20	.20

Art Type of 1974

Paintings in national galleries: 1k, Enclosure of Dreams, by Kamil Lhotak (b. 1912). 2k, Tulips, by Ester Simerova-Martincekova (b. 1909). 3k, Triptych with Bohemian Landscape, by Josef Lada (1887-1957). 4k, Accordion Player, by Josef Capek (1887-1945). 5k, Self-portrait, by Jiri Trnka (1912-1969).

1987, Nov. 18   Engr.   *Perf. 12*

2678	A700	1k multi	3.25	.75
2679	A700	2k multi	4.50	1.60
2680	A700	3k multi	4.00	1.10
2681	A700	4k multi	2.75	.80
2682	A700	5k multi	4.25	1.25
		Nos. 2678-2682 (5)	18.75	5.50

Czech and Slovak art.
Nos. 2678-2682 were each issued in sheets of 4. Value, set $80.

69th Stamp Day — A961

Portrait of Jacob Obrovsky (1882-1949), stamp designer, Bohemian Lion (Type SP1), sketch of a lion and PRAGA '88 emblem.

Photo. & Engr.

1987, Dec. 18   *Perf. 11½x12*

2683	A961	1k multicolored	.25	.20

No. 2683 printed in sheet of four with eight labels se-tenant with stamps, inscribed "100 Years of the National Philatelic Movement in Czechoslovakia" in Czech. The four labels between the "blocks of six" are blank. Value, sheet $3.

Czechoslovak Republic, 70th Anniv. — A962

1988, Jan. 1   *Perf. 12x11½*

2684	A962	1k Woman, natl. arms, linden branch	.25	.20

Natl. Front, 40th Anniv. — A963

1988, Feb. 25   *Perf. 11½*

2685	A963	50h multicolored	.25	.20

Husak Type of 1983
Photo. & Engr.

1988, Jan. 10   *Perf. 12x11½*

2686	A865	1k brt rose & dk carmine	.25	.20

Olympics — A965

1988, Feb. 1   *Perf. 11½x12*

2687	A965	50h Ski jumping, ice hockey	.20	.20
2688	A965	1k Basketball, soccer	.20	.20
2689	A965	6k Discus, weight lifting	.80	.40
		Nos. 2687-2689 (3)	1.20	.80

Exist in souv. sheets of 2, imperf. between and in souv. sheets of 2, imperf. Value, each set, $16.

Victorious February, 40th Anniv. — A966

Statue of Klement Gottwald by Rudolf Svoboda.

1988, Feb. 25   *Perf. 11½*

2690	A966	50h multicolored	.20	.20

No. 2690 exists in a souvenir sheet of two No. 2690 and two postally invalid imperf impressions of No. 637. Value $9. Sheet exists imperf. Value $12.

Classic Automobiles — A967

1988, Mar. 1   *Perf. 12x11½*

2691	A967	50h 1914 Laurin & Klement	.20	.20
2692	A967	1k 1902 Tatra NW Type B	.20	.20
2693	A967	2k 1905 Tatra NW Type E	.30	.20
2694	A967	3k 1929 Tatra 12 Normandie	.60	.25
2695	A967	4k 1899 Meteor	.80	.40
a.		Bklt. pane, 2 3k, 3 4k + label	6.00	6.00
		Complete booklet, #2695a	7.00	
		Nos. 2691-2695 (5)	2.10	1.25

Postal Museum, 70th Anniv. A968

Praga '88 emblem and: 50h, Postman, Malostranske Namesti Square p.o., Prague, c. 1742, and Velka Javorina television transmitter, 1979. 1k, Telecommunications Center, Mlada Boleslav, 1986, and Carmelite Street p.o., Prague, c. 1792. 2k, Prague 1 (1873) and Bratislava 56 (1984) post offices. 4k, Communications Center, Prachatice (1982), postman and Maltetske Nameski Square p.o., Prague, c. 1622.

1988, Mar. 10

2696	A968	50h multi	.20	.20
2697	A968	1k multi	.20	.20
2698	A968	2k multi	.25	.20
2699	A968	4k multi	.45	.25
a.		Souv. sheet, 2 ea #2698-2699	2.25	1.25
		Nos. 2696-2699 (4)	1.10	.85

In No. 2699a the top pair of Nos. 2698-2699 is imperf. at top and sides.

A969

1988, Mar. 29   *Perf. 11½*

2700	A969	50h multicolored	.20	.20

Matice Slovenska Cultural Assoc., 125th anniv.

A970

1988, May 12   **Photo. & Engr.**

PRAGA '88. (Exhibition emblem and aspects of the Museum of Natl. Literature, Prague): 1k, Gate and distant view of museum. 2k, Celestial globe, illuminated manuscript, bookshelves and ornately decorated ceiling. 5k, Illuminated "B" and decorated binder of a medieval Bible. 7k, Celestial globe, illuminated manuscript, Zodiacal signs (Aries and Leo), view of museum.

2701	A970	1k multicolored	.30	.25
a.		Souvenir sheet of 4	1.50	1.25
2702	A970	2k multicolored	.65	.40
a.		Souvenir sheet of 4	3.25	2.00
2703	A970	5k multicolored	.95	.60
a.		Souvenir sheet of 4	5.75	4.75
2704	A970	7k multicolored	2.00	.95
a.		Souvenir sheet of 4	11.00	9.00
b.		Souv. sheet of 4, imperf., #2701-2704	4.00	3.50
		Nos. 2701-2704 (4)	3.90	2.20

PRAGA '88 — A971

Exhibition emblem and fountains, Prague.

1988, June 1   *Perf. 11½x12*

2705	A971	1k Waldstein Palace	.35	.20
2706	A971	2k Old town square	.45	.20
2707	A971	3k Charles University	.90	.25
2708	A971	4k Prague Castle	1.25	.30
a.		Souv. sheet of 4, #2705-2708	4.00	2.00
		Nos. 2705-2708 (4)	2.95	.95

Souvenir Sheet

Soviet-US Summit Conference on Arms Reduction, Moscow — A972

Design: The capital, Washington, and the Kremlin, Moscow.

1988, June 1   *Perf. 12x11½*
2709 A972 4k blue blk, dark red & gold   2.50 1.50

Exists imperf. Value $8.

PRAGA '88 A973

Exhibition emblem and modern architecture, Prague: 50h, Trade Unions Central Recreation Center. 1k, Koospol foreign trade company. 2k, Motol Teaching Hospital. 4k, Culture Palace.

1988, July 1   *Perf. 12x11½*
2710 A973 50h multicolored   .20 .20
2711 A973 1k blk, lt blue & bister   .20 .20
2712 A973 2k multicolored   .20 .20
   a. Souv. sheet, 2 1k, 2 2k + 4 labels, imperf.   2.00 1.50
2713 A973 4k multicolored   .50 .35
   a. Souv. sheet, 2 50h, 2 4k + 4 labels, imperf.   2.00 1.50
   Nos. 2710-2713 (4)   1.10 .95

Souvenir Sheet

PRAGA '88 — A974

Design: Exhibition emblem and Alfons Mucha (1860-1939), designer of first Czech postage stamp.

1988, Aug. 18   Engr.   *Perf. 12*
2714 A974 Sheet of 2   5.50 3.25
   a. 5k multicolored   2.40 1.25

Czech postage stamps, 70th anniv.

Souvenir Sheets

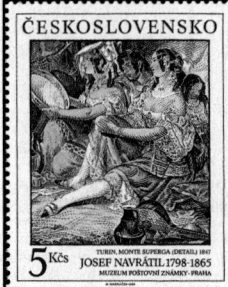

PRAGA '88 A975

5k, *Turin, Monte Superga,* by Josef Navratil (1798-1865), Postal Museum, Prague. Details of *Bacchus and Ariadne,* by Sebastiano Ricci (1659-1734), Natl. Gallery, Prague: No. 2716a, Ariadne. No. 2716b, Bacchus and creatures.

1988
2715 Sheet of 2   6.50 4.00
   a. A975 5k multi   2.75 1.60
2716 Sheet of 2   10.50 6.00
   a.-b. A975 10k any single   4.80 2.40

#2716 exists with emblem and inscription "DEN F.I.P. JOURNEE DE LA FEDERATION INTERNATIONALE DE PHILATELIE." Value $12.
Issue dates: 5k, Aug. 19; 10k, Aug. 26.

Prague Castle Type of 1983

2k, Pottery jug, 17th cent. 3k, *St. Catherine with Angel,* 1580, by Paolo Veronese.

1988, Sept. 28   Engr.   *Perf. 12*
2717 A875 2k shown   .50 .50
2718 A875 3k multi   1.25 .70

Nos. 2717-2718 were each issued in sheets of 6. Value, set $12.

Bratislava Views Type of 1987

3k, *Hlavne Square, circa 1840* an etching by R. Alt-Sandman, 1840. 4k, *Ferdinand House, circa 1850,* a pen-and-ink drawing by V. Reim.

1988, Oct. 19
2719 A958 3k multicolored   .50 .50
2720 A958 4k multicolored   1.25 1.25

Nos. 2719-2720 were each issued in sheets of 4. Value, set $9.

Art Type of 1974

Paintings in natl. galleries: 2k, *With Bundles,* 1931, by Martin Benka (1888-1971). 6k, *Blue Bird,* 1903, by Vojtech Preissig (1873-1944). 7k, *A Jaguar Attacking a Rider,* c. 1850, by Eugene Delacroix (1798-1863).

1988, Nov. 17   Engr.   *Perf. 12*
2721 A700 2k multicolored   2.75 1.40
2722 A700 6k multicolored   4.25 2.00
2723 A700 7k multicolored   4.25 2.00
   Nos. 2721-2723 (3)   11.25 5.40

Czech and Slovak art.

Nos. 2721-2723 were each issued in sheets of 4. Value, set $55.

Stamp Day — A978

Design: 1k, Jaroslav Benda (1882-1970), illustrator and stamp designer.

Photo. & Engr.

1988, Dec. 18   *Perf. 11½x12*
2724 A978 1k multicolored   .25 .20

Paris-Dakar Rally — A979

Trucks: 50h, Earth, Motokov Liaz. 1k, Liaz, globe. 2k, Earth, Motokov Tatra. No. 607. 4k, Map of racecourse, turban, Tatra.

1989, Jan. 2   *Perf. 12x11½*
2725 A979 50h multicolored   .20 .20
2726 A979 1k multicolored   .30 .20
2727 A979 2k multicolored   .45 .20
2728 A979 4k multicolored   .80 .30
   Nos. 2725-2728 (4)   1.75 .90

Czechoslovakian Federation, 20th Anniv. — A980

1989, Jan. 1
2729 A980 50h multicolored   .20 .20

Jan Botto (1829-1881) A981

Taras Grigorievich Shevchenko (1814-1861) A982

Jean Cocteau (1889-1963) A983

Charlie Chaplin (1889-1977) A984

Jawaharlal Nehru (1889-1964) and "UNESCO" — A985

Famous men: No. 2732, Modest Petrovich Musorgsky (1839-1881).

Photo. & Engr.

1989, Mar. 9   *Perf. 12x11½*
2730 A981 50h brn blk & lt blue green   .20 .20
2731 A982 50h shown   .20 .20
2732 A982 50h multicolored   .20 .20
2733 A983 50h red brn, grnh blk & org brn   .20 .20
2734 A984 50h blk, int blue & dark red   .20 .20
2735 A985 50h brn blk & lt yel green   .20 .20
   Nos. 2730-2735 (6)   1.20 1.20

Shipping Industry A986

1989, Mar. 27
2736 A986 50h *Republika*   .20 .20
2737 A986 1k *Pionyr,* flags   .20 .20
2738 A986 2k *Brno,* flags   .35 .20
2739 A986 3k *Trinec*   .60 .20
2740 A986 4k Flags, mast, *Orlik*   .80 .30
2741 A986 5k *Vltava,* communication hardware   1.00 .30
   Nos. 2736-2741 (6)   3.15 1.40

Pioneer Organization, 40th Anniv. — A987

Photo. & Engr.

1989, Apr. 20   *Perf. 11½*
2742 A987 50h multi   .20 .20

Art Type of 1974

Details of *Feast of Rose Garlands,* 1506, by Albrecht Durer, Natl. Gallery, Prague: a, Virgin and Child. b, Angel playing mandolin.

1989, Apr. 21   Engr.   *Perf. 12*
Miniature Sheet
2743 Sheet of 2   10.00 5.00
   a.-b. A700 10k any single   4.50 2.00

Prague Castle Art Type of 1983

2k, Bas-relief picturing Kaiser Karl IV, from Kralovske tomb by Alexander Colin (c. 1527-1612). 3k, Self-portrait, by V.V. Reiner (1689-1743).

1989, May 9   Photo. & Engr.
2744 A875 2k dark red, sepia & buff   .40 .30
2745 A875 3k multi   .60 .40

Nos. 2744-2745 were each issued in sheets of 6. Value, set $7.

Souvenir Sheet

PHILEXFRANCE '89, French Revolution Bicent. — A988

1989, July 14   Engr.   *Perf. 12*
2746 A988 5k brt blue, blk & dk red   2.00 1.50

Haliaeetus albicilla — A989

Photo. & Engr.

1989, July 17   *Perf. 12x11½*
2747 A989 1k multicolored   .50 .20

World Wildlife Fund — A990

Toads and newts.

1989, July 18   *Perf. 11½x12*
2748 A990 2k *Bombina bombina*   1.40 .35
2749 A990 3k *Bombina variegata*   1.70 .45
2750 A990 4k *Triturus alpestris*   1.90 .65
2751 A990 5k *Triturus montandoni*   2.25 .85
   Nos. 2748-2751 (4)   7.25 2.30

Slovak Folk Art Collective, 40th Anniv. — A991

1989, Aug. 29 **Perf. 12x11½**
2752 A991 50h multicolored .20 .20

Slovak Uprising, 45th Anniv. — A992

Photo. & Engr.
1989, Aug. 29 **Perf. 11½x12**
2753 A992 1k multicolored .20 .20

A993 A994

Award-winning illustrations.

1989, Sept. 4 **Perf. 11½**
2754 A993 50h Hannu Taina, Finland .20 .20
2755 A993 1k Aleksander Aleksov, Bulgaria .20 .20
2756 A993 2k Jurgen Spohn, West Berlin .25 .20
2757 A993 4k Robert Brun, Czechoslovakia .75 .20
a. Souvenir sheet of 2 2.00 .80
Nos. 2754-2757 (4) 1.40 .80

12th Biennial of Children's Book Illustration, Bratislava.

1989, Sept. 5 **Engr.** **Perf. 11½x12**

Poisonous mushrooms.

2758 A994 50h *Nolanea verna* .30 .25
2759 A994 1k *Amanita phalloides* .40 .40
2760 A994 2k *Amanita virosa* .55 .50
2761 A994 3k *Cortinarius orellanus* .90 .70
2762 A994 5k *Galerina marginata* 1.00 .70
Nos. 2758-2762 (5) 3.15 2.55

Nos. 2758-2762 were each issued in sheets of 10. Value, set $40.

Bratislava Views Type of 1987

Views of Devin, a Slavic castle above the Danube, Bratislava.

1989, Oct. 16 **Engr.** **Perf. 12**
2763 A958 3k Castle, flower .65 .65
2764 A958 4k Castle, urn .85 .85
Nos. 2763-2764 were each issued in sheets of 4. Value, set $7.

Jan Opletal (1915-39) — A996

Photo. & Engr.
1989, Nov. 17 **Perf. 12x11½**
2765 A996 1k multicolored .20 .20

Intl. Student's Day. Funeral of Opletal, a Nazi victim, on Nov. 15, 1939, sparked student demonstrations that resulted in the closing of all universities in occupied Bohemia and Moravia.

Art Type of 1974

Paintings in Natl. Galleries: 2k, *Nirvana*, c. 1920, by Anton Jasusch (1882-1965). 4k, *Winter Evening in Town*, c. 1907, by Jakub

Schikaneder (1855-1924), horiz. 5k, *The Bakers*, 1926, by Pravoslav Kotik (1889-1970), horiz.

1989, Nov. 27 **Engr.** **Perf. 12**
2766 A700 2k multicolored .90 .55
2767 A700 4k multicolored 1.60 1.10
2768 A700 5k multicolored 1.50 1.10
Nos. 2766-2768 (3) 4.00 2.75

Nos. 2766-2768 were each issued in sheets of 4. Value, set $17.

Stamp Day — A997

Design: Portrait of Cyril Bouda, stamp designer, art tools and falcon.

Photo. & Engr.
1989, Dec. 18 **Perf. 11½x12**
2769 A997 1k multicolored .25 .20

A998

A999

Photo. & Engr.
1990, Jan. 8 **Perf. 11½x12**
2770 A998 1k multicolored .60 .20

UNESCO World Literacy Year. Printed setenant with inscribed label picturing UN and UNESCO emblems. Value, single with label attached 75c.

1990, Jan. 9 **Perf. 11½**

Famous men: No. 2771, Karel Capek, writer. No. 2772, Thomas G. Masaryk. 1k, Lenin. 2k, Emile Zola, French writer. 3k, Jaroslav Heyrovsky (1890-1987), chemical physicist. 10k, Bohuslav Martinu (1890-1959), composer.

2771 A999 50h multicolored .20 .20
2772 A999 50h multicolored .20 .20
2773 A999 1k multicolored .20 .20
2774 A999 2k multicolored .30 .20
2775 A999 3k multicolored .50 .30
2776 A999 10k multicolored 1.60 .90
Nos. 2771-2776 (6) 3.00 2.00

#2771, 2775-2776 inscribed "UNESCO."

Pres. Vaclav Havel A1000

Handball Players A1001

1990, Jan. 9 **Perf. 12x11½**
2777 A1000 50h red, brt vio & bl .30 .20
See Nos. 2879, 2948.

1990, Feb. 1 **Perf. 11½**
2778 A1001 50h multicolored .20 .20

1990 Men's World Handball Championships, Czechoslovakia.

Flora — A1002

A1003

Photo. & Engr.
1990, Mar. 1 **Perf. 11½**
2779 A1002 50h *Antirrhinum majus* .65 .25
2780 A1002 1k *Zinnia elegans* .90 .25
2781 A1002 3k *Tigridia pavonia* 1.25 .30
Perf. 12x12½
2782 A1002 5k *Lilium candidum* 1.60 .90
Nos. 2779-2782 (4) 4.40 1.70

No. 2782 was issued in a sheet of 10. Value, $20.

City Arms Type of 1982

Photo. & Engr.
1990, Mar. 28 **Perf. 12x11½**
2783 A847 50h Prostejov .20 .20
2784 A847 50h Bytca .20 .20
2785 A847 50h Sobeslav .20 .20
2786 A847 50h Podebrady .20 .20
Nos. 2783-2786 (4) .80 .80

1990, Apr. 16 **Perf. 11½x12**
2787 A1003 1k brn vio, rose & buff .60 .20
Visit of Pope John Paul II.

World War II Liberation A1004

Photo. & Engr.
1990, May 5 **Perf. 11½**
2788 A1004 1k multicolored .25 .20

Souvenir Sheet

150th Anniv. of the Postage Stamp — A1005

1990, May 6 **Engr.** **Perf. 12**
2789 A1005 7k multicolored 4.00 1.50
Stamp World London 90.

A1006

A1007

Photo. & Engr.
1990, May 8 **Perf. 11½**
2790 A1006 1k multicolored .60 .20
World Cup Soccer Championships, Italy.

1990, June 1
2791 A1007 1k multicolored .60 .20
Free elections.

Prague Castle Type of 1983
1990, June 6, 1990 **Engr.**
2792 A875 2k Gold and jeweled hand .60 .30
2793 A875 3k Medallion .90 .45

Art treasures of Prague Castle.

Nos. 2792-2793 were each issued in sheets of 6. Value, set $12.

Helsinki Conference, 15th Anniv. — A1008

Photo & Engr.
1990, June 21 **Perf. 12x11½**
2794 A1008 7k multicolored 1.10 .60

Dr. Milada Horakova A1009

1990, June 25 **Perf. 12x11½**
2795 A1009 1k multicolored .30 .20

Intercanis Dog Show, Brno — A1010

Designs: 50h, Poodles, 1k, Afghan hound, Irish wolfhound, greyhound. 4k, Czech terrier, bloodhound, Hannoverian hound. 7k, Cavalier King Charles Spaniel, cocker spaniel, American cocker spaniel.

1990, July 2
2796 A1010 50h multicolored .65 .25
2797 A1010 1k multicolored 1.00 .25
2798 A1010 4k multicolored 1.60 .45
2799 A1010 7k multicolored 2.25 .75
Nos. 2796-2799 (4) 5.50 1.70

Bratislava Art Type of 1987

1990 **Engr.** **Perf. 12**
2800 A958 3k Ancient Celtic coin .80 .40
2801 A958 4k Gen. Milan Stefanik .80 .50

Issue dates: 3k, Sept. 29. 4k, July 21. Nos. 2800-2801 were each issued in sheets of 4. Value, set $8.

Grand Pardubice Steeplechase, Cent. — A1011

Photo. & Engr.
1990, Sept. 7 **Perf. 12x11½**
2802 A1011 50h multicolored .20 .20
2803 A1011 4k multi, diff. .70 .35

Protected Animals — A1012

Litho. & Engr.

1990, Oct. 1   **Perf. 12x11**
2804	A1012	50h Marmota marmota	1.00	.25
2805	A1012	1k Felis silvestris	1.60	.25
2806	A1012	4k Castor fiber	1.75	.45
2807	A1012	5k Plecotus auritus	2.25	.75
		Nos. 2804-2807 (4)	6.60	1.70

Conf. of Civic Associations, Helsinki — A1013

Litho. & Engr.

1990, Oct. 15   **Perf. 12x11½**
2808	A1013	3k blue, gold & yel	.50	.30

Christmas — A1014

Photo. & Engr.

1990, Nov. 15   **Perf. 11½x12**
2809	A1014	50h multicolored	.20	.20

Art Type of 1967

Works of art: 2k, Krucemburk by Jan Zrzavy (1890-1977), horiz. 3k, St. Agnes of Bohemia from the St. Wenceslas Monument, Prague by Josef V. Myslbek (1848-1922). 4k, The Slavs in their Homeland by Alfons Mucha (1860-1939). 5k, St. John the Baptist by Auguste Rodin (1840-1917).

1990, Nov. 27   **Engr.**   **Perf. 11½**
2810	A565	2k multicolored	1.50	.50
2811	A565	3k multicolored	1.75	1.75
2812	A565	4k multicolored	2.10	.60
2813	A565	5k multicolored	2.50	.60
		Nos. 2810-2813 (4)	7.85	3.45

Nos. 2810-2813 were each issued in sheets of 4. Value, set $35.

Karel Svolinsky (1896-1986), Vignette from No. 1182 — A1016

1990, Dec. 18   **Photo. & Engr.**
2814	A1016	1k multicolored	.25	.20

Stamp Day.

A1017   A1018

1991, Jan. 10   **Perf. 11½**
2815	A1017	1k multicolored	.30	.20

European Judo Championships, Prague.

1991, Jan. 10

Design: A. B. Svojsik (1876-1938), Czech Scouting Founder.
2816	A1018	3k multicolored	1.00	.20

Scouting in Czechoslovakia, 80th Anniv.

Bethlehem Chapel, Prague, 600th Anniv. — A1019

1991, Feb. 4   **Perf. 12x11½**
2817	A1019	50h multicolored	.25	.20

Wolfgang Amadeus Mozart (1756-1791), Old Theatre — A1020

1991, Feb. 4
2818	A1020	1k multicolored	.20	.20

Steamship Bohemia, 150th Anniv. — A1021

1991, Feb. 4   **Perf. 11½x12**
2819	A1021	5k multicolored	1.00	.30

Famous Men A1022

Designs: No. 2820, Antonin Dvorak (1841-1904), composer. No. 2821, Andrej Kmet (1841-1908), botanist. No. 2822, Jaroslav Seifert (1901-1986), poet, Nobel laureate for Literature. No. 2823, Jan Masaryk (1886-1948), diplomat. No. 2824, Alois Šenefelder (1771-1834), lithographer.

1991, Feb. 18   **Perf. 12x11½**
2820	A1022	1k multicolored	.20	.20
2821	A1022	1k multicolored	.30	.20
2822	A1022	1k multicolored	.40	.20
2823	A1022	1k multicolored	.50	.20
2824	A1022	1k multicolored	.60	.20
		Nos. 2820-2824 (5)	2.00	1.00

#2820-2824 printed with se-tenant labels. See No. 2831.

Europa — A1023   A1024

Photo. & Engr.

1991, May 6   **Perf. 11½x12**
2825	A1023	6k blk, bl & red	2.50	.75

Photo. & Engr.

1991, May 10   **Perf. 11½x12**
2826	A1024	1k multicolored	.25	.20

General Exhibition in Prague, cent.

Antarctic Treaty, 30th Anniv. A1025

1991, May 20   **Perf. 12x11½**
2827	A1025	8k multicolored	1.75	.60

Castles — A1026   Scenic Views — A1027

1991, June 3   **Perf. 11½**
2828	A1026	50h Blatna	.40	.20
2829	A1026	1k Bouzov	.50	.20
2830	A1026	3k Kezmarok	.60	.20
		Nos. 2828-2830 (3)	1.50	.60

Famous Men Type

Design: Jan Palach (1948-1969), Student.

Photo. & Engr.

1991, Aug. 9   **Perf. 12x11½**
2831	A1022	4k black	2.00	.30

Printed se-tenant with label.

Photo. & Engr.

1991, Aug. 28   **Perf. 11½**
2832	A1027	4k Krivan mountains	1.00	.60
2833	A1027	4k Rip mountain	1.00	.60

A1028   A1029

Illustrations by: 1k, Binette Schroeder, Germany. 2k, Stasys Eidrigevicius, Poland.

Photo. & Engr.

1991, Sept. 2   **Perf. 11½**
2834	A1028	1k multicolored	.40	.20
2835	A1028	2k multicolored	.40	.20

13th Biennial Exhibition of Children's Book Illustrators, Bratislava.

1991, Sept. 27   **Engr.**   **Perf. 11½**

Design: Father Andrej Hlinka (1864-1938), Slovak nationalist.
2836	A1029	10k blue black	1.60	.30

Art of Prague and Bratislava A1030

Designs: No. 2837, Holy Infant of Prague. No. 2838, Blue Church of Bratislava.

1991, Sept. 30
2837	A1030	3k multicolored	1.25	.75
2838	A1030	3k multicolored	1.25	.75

Nos. 2837-2838 were each issued in sheets of 8. Value, set $20.

Flowers A1031   Christmas A1033

Photo. & Engr.

1991, Nov. 3   **Perf. 12x11½**
2839	A1031	1k Gagea bohemica	.40	.20
2840	A1031	2k Aster alpinus	.75	.25
2841	A1031	5k Fritillaria meleagris	2.00	.30
2842	A1031	11k Daphne cneorum	3.25	.45
		Nos. 2839-2842 (4)	6.40	1.20

Art Type of 1967

Paintings: 2k, Everyday Homelife by Max Ernst. 3k, Lovers by Auguste Renoir. 4k, Head of Christ by El Greco. 5k, Coincidence by Ladislav Guderna. 7k, Two Maidens by Utamaro.

1991, Nov. 3   **Engr.**   **Perf. 11½**
2843	A565	2k multicolored	1.25	.45
2844	A565	3k multicolored	1.60	.65
2845	A565	4k multicolored	2.40	.75
2846	A565	4k multicolored	2.40	.95
2847	A565	7k multicolored	3.25	1.60
		Nos. 2843-2847 (5)	10.90	4.40

Nos. 2843-2847 were each issued in sheets of 4. Value, set $47.50.

1991, Nov. 19
2848	A1033	50h multicolored	.30	.20

Stamp Day — A1034

Martin Benka (1888-1971), stamp engraver.

Photo. & Engr.

1991, Dec. 18   **Perf. 11½x12**
2849	A1034	2k multicolored	.45	.20

1992 Winter Olympics, Albertville — A1035

1992, Jan. 6   **Perf. 11½**
2850	A1035	1k Biathlon	.25	.20

Photo. & Engr.

1992, May 21   **Perf. 11½**
2851	A1035	2k Tennis	.30	.20

1992 Summer Olympics, Barcelona.

Souvenir Sheet

Jan Amos Komensky (Comenius),
Educator — A1036

1992, Mar. 5   **Engr.**
2852 A1036 10k multicolored   5.00 4.75

World Ice Hockey
Championships,
Prague and
Bratislava — A1037

1992, Mar. 31   **Photo. & Engr.**
2853 A1037 3k multicolored   .75 .20

Traffic
Safety
A1038

1992, Apr. 2
2854 A1038 2k multicolored   .50 .20

Expo '92,
Seville — A1039

1992, Apr. 2
2855 A1039 4k multicolored   .75 .20

Discovery of America, 500th
Anniv. — A1040

1992, May 5   **Engr.**
2856 A1040 22k multicolored   2.75 2.75
Europa. Printed in sheets of 8. Value $25.

Czechoslovak Military Actions in
WWII — A1041

Designs: 1k, J. Kubis and J. Gabcik, assassins of Reinhard Heydrich, 1942. 2k, Pilots flying for France and Great Britain. 3k, Defense of Tobruk. 6k, Capture of Dunkirk, 1944-45.

1992, May 21   **Engr.**   **Perf. 12x11½**
2857 A1041 1k multicolored   .50 .20
2858 A1041 2k multicolored   .60 .20
2859 A1041 3k multicolored   .75 .25
2860 A1041 6k multicolored   1.60 .35
   Nos. 2857-2860 (4)   3.45 1.00

A1042   A1043

Photo. & Engr.
1992, June 10   **Perf. 11½**
2861 A1042 2k multicolored   .30 .20
Czechoslovakian Red Cross.

1992, June 30
2862 A1043 1k multicolored   .30 .20
Junior European Table Tennis Championships, Topolcany.

Beetles
A1044

1992, July 15
2863 A1044 1k Polyphylla fullo   .80 .25
2864 A1044 2k Ergates faber   1.10 .40
2865 A1044 3k Meloe violaceus   2.25 .55
2866 A1044 4k Dytiscus latissimus   2.25 .75
   Nos. 2863-2866 (4)   6.40 1.95
The 1k exists with denomination omitted.

Troja
Castle
A1045

1992, Aug. 28   **Engr.**   **Perf. 11½**
2867 A1045 6k shown   2.75 1.00
2868 A1045 7k Statue of St. Martin, vert.   4.00 1.10
2869 A1045 8k Lednice Castle   4.00 1.25
   Nos. 2867-2869 (3)   10.75 3.35
Nos. 2867-2869 were each issued in sheets of 8. Value, set $85.

Chrudim Church Type of 1971
Photo. & Engr.
1992, Aug. 28   **Perf. 11½x11**
2870 A629 50h multicolored   .75 .20

Postal
Bank — A1045a

Photo. & Engr.
1992, Aug. 28   **Perf. 11½x12**
2870A A1045a 20k multicolored   5.00 1.10

Antonius Bernolak, Georgius
Fandly — A1046

Photo. & Engr.
1992, Oct. 6   **Perf. 12x11½**
2871 A1046 5k multicolored   1.50 .50
Slovakian Educational Society, bicent.

Cesky
Krumlov — A1046a

Photo. & Engr.
1992, Oct. 19   **Perf. 11½x12**
2871A A1046a 3k brick red & brn   .90 .20
   See No. 2890.

Painting Type of 1967
6k Old Man on a Raft, by Koloman Sokol. 7k, Still Life of Grapes and Raisins, by Georges Braque, horiz. 8k, Abandoned Corset, by Toyen.

Perf. 11½x12, 12x11½
1992, Nov. 2   **Engr.**
2872 A565 6k multicolored   2.50 .95
2873 A565 7k multicolored   4.00 1.10
2874 A565 8k multicolored   4.00 1.25
   Nos. 2872-2874 (3)   10.50 3.30
Nos. 2872-2874 were each issued in sheets of 4. Value, set $45.

Christmas — A1047

Photo. & Engr.
1992, Nov. 9   **Perf. 12x11½**
2875 A1047 2k multicolored   .80 .20

Jindra Schmidt (1897-1984), Graphic
Artist and Engraver — A1048

Photo. & Engr.
1992, Dec. 18   **Perf. 11½x12**
2876 A1048 2k multicolored   .80 .20
Stamp Day.

On January 1, 1993, Czechoslovakia split into Czech Republic and Slovakia. Czech Republic listings continue here. Slovakia can be found in Volume 5.

CZECH REPUBLIC
AREA — 30,449 sq. mi.
POP. — 10,280,513 (1999 est.)

Natl. Arms
A1049

Photo. & Engr.
1993, Jan. 20   **Perf. 11**
2877 A1049 3k multicolored   .45 .20

1993 World
Figure Skating
Championships,
Prague
A1050

1993, Feb. 25   **Perf. 11½x11**
2878 A1050 2k multicolored   .50 .20

Havel Type of 1990 Inscribed "Ceska
Republika"
Photo. & Engr.
1993, Mar. 2   **Perf. 12x11½**
2879 A1000 2k vio, vio brn & blue   .40 .20

St. John Nepomuk, Patron Saint of
Czechs, 600th Death Anniv. — A1051

1993, Mar. 11
2880 A1051 8k multicolored   1.00 .35
See Germany No. 1776; Slovakia No. 158.

Holy Hunger, by
Mikulas
Medek — A1052

1993, Mar. 11   **Perf. 11½**
2881 A1052 14k multicolored   6.00 2.00
Europa.

Sacred
Heart
Church,
Prague
A1053

1993, Mar. 30   **Engr.**   **Perf. 11½**
2882 A1053 5k multicolored   3.00 .35

Brevnov Monastery, 1000th
Anniv. — A1054

Litho. & Engr.
1993, Apr. 12   **Perf. 12x11½**
2883 A1054 4k multicolored   .65 .25

1993 Intl. Junior
Weight Lifting
Championships,
Cheb — A1055

Photo. & Engr.
1993, May 12   **Perf. 11½**
2884 A1055 6k multicolored   1.00 .35

Clock Tower and Church, Brno — A1056

1993, June 16   Engr.   Perf. 12x11½
2885 A1056 8k multicolored   1.20 1.20
Brno, 750th anniv.

Arrival of St. Cyril and St. Methodius, 1130th Anniv. — A1057

1993, June 22   Photo. & Engr.
2886 A1057 8k multicolored   1.00 .50
See Slovakia No. 167.

Souvenir Sheet

State Arms — A1058

1993, June 22   Perf. 11½
2887 A1058 8k Sheet of 2   3.00 3.00

Architecture Type of 1992 Inscribed "Ceska Republika" and

A1059

Cities: 1k, Ceske Budejovice. 2k, Usti Nad Labem. #2890, like #2871A. #2890A, Brno. 5k, Plzen. 6k, Slany. 7k, Ostrava. 8k, Olomouc. 10k, Hradec Kralove. 20k, Prague. 50k, Opava.

Perf. 12x11½, 11½x12
1993-94   Photo. & Engr.
2888 A1059 1k dp cl & org   .20 .20
2889 A1059 2k red vio & bl   1.00 .20
2890 A1046a 3k gray bl & red   1.00 .20
  Complete booklet, 5 #2890   6.00
2891 A1059 3k dk bl & red   .35 .20
  Complete booklet, 5 #2891   5.00
2892 A1059 5k bluish green & brn   .60 .25
2893 A1059 6k grn & org yel   .75 .30
2894 A1059 7k blk brn & grn   .85 .30
2895 A1059 8k dp vio & yel   .95 .30
2896 A1059 10k olive gray & red   1.20 .40
2897 A1059 20k red & blue   2.50 .75
2898 A1059 50k brn & grn   6.00 1.75
  Nos. 2888-2898 (11)   15.40 4.85

Issued: No. 2891, 3/30/94; 6k, 10/1/94; 7k, 11/23/94; others, 7/1/93.

World Rowing Championships, Racice A1060

Photo. & Engr.
1993, Aug. 18   Perf. 11½
2901 A1060 3k multicolored   .50 .20

A1061   Trees — A1062

Famous men: 2k, August Sedlacek (1843-1926), historian. 3k, Eduard Cech (1893-1960), mathematician.

1993, Aug. 26   Perf. 12x11½
2902 A1061 2k multicolored   .40 .20
2903 A1061 3k multicolored   .55 .20

1993, Oct. 26   Perf. 11½
2904 A1062 5k Quercus robur   .75 .30
2905 A1062 7k Carpinus betulus   1.00 .40
2906 A1062 9k Pinus silvestris   1.50 .50
  Nos. 2904-2906 (3)   3.25 1.20

Christmas — A1063

A1064

Photo. & Engr.
1993, Nov. 8   Perf. 11½
2907 A1063 2k multicolored   .30 .20

Art Type of 1967 Inscribed "CESKA REPUBLIKA"

Paintings: 9k, Strahovska Madonna, by "Bohemian Master" in the year 1350. 11k, Composition, by Miro, horiz. 14k, Field of Green, by Van Gogh, horiz.

1993   Engr.   Perf. 11½x12
2908 A565 9k multicolored   2.25 2.25
  Perf. 12x11½
2909 A565 11k multicolored   2.25 2.25
2910 A565 14k multicolored   3.50 3.50
  Nos. 2908-2910 (3)   8.00 8.00

Issued: 11k, 14k, Nov. 8; 9k, Dec. 15.
Nos. 2908-2910 were each issued in sheets of 4. Value $35.

Photo. & Engr.
1994, Jan. 19   Perf. 11½
2911 A1064 2k multicolored   .30 .20
Intl. Year of the Family.

Jan Kubelik (1880-1940), Composer A1065

Photo. & Engr.
1994, Jan. 19   Perf. 11½
2912 A1065 3k multicolored   .40 .25

UNESCO — A1065a

Designs: 2k, Voltaire (1694-1778), philosopher. 6k, Georgius Agricola (1494-1555), mineralogist, humanist.

1994, Feb. 2   Perf. 12x11½
2913 A1065a 2k multicolored   .25 .20
2914 A1065a 6k multicolored   .80 .35

A1066   A1067

Photo. & Engr.
1994, Feb. 2   Perf. 11½
2915 A1066 5k multicolored   .65 .35
1994 Winter Olympics, Lillehammer.

Photo. & Engr.
1994, May 4   Perf. 11½
Europa (Marco Polo &): #2916, Stylized animals, Chinese woman. #2917, Stylized animals.
2916 A1067 14k multicolored   1.75 1.75
2917 A1067 14k multicolored   1.75 1.75
  a. Pair, #2916-2917   3.50 3.50

A1068   A1070

Architectural Sights — A1069

1994, May 18
2918 A1068 5k Eduard Benes   .60 .20

1994, May 18
UNESCO: 8k, Houses at the square, Telc. 9k, Cubist house designed by Chochol, Prague.
2919 A1069 8k multicolored   1.00 .75
2920 A1069 9k multicolored   1.10 .75

Photo. & Engr.
1994, June 1   Perf. 11½
2921 A1070 2k Children's Day   .40 .20

Dinosaurs — A1071

Perf. 11½x11, 11x11½
1994, June 1   Litho.
2922 A1071 2k Stegosaurus   .75 .20
2923 A1071 3k Apatosaurus   1.00 .25
2924 A1071 5k Tarbosaurus, vert.   1.25 .35
  Nos. 2922-2924 (3)   3.00 .80

A1072

A1073

Photo. & Engr.
1994, June 1   Perf. 11½x11
2925 A1072 8k multicolored   1.10 .50
1994 World Cup Soccer Championships, US.

1994, June 15   Perf. 11x11½
2926 A1073 2k multicolored   .35 .20
12th Pan-Sokol Rally, Prague.

Intl. Olympic Committee, Cent. — A1074

1994, June 15
2927 A1074 7k multicolored   .90 .50

UPU, 120th Anniv. A1075

1994, Aug. 3   Engr.   Perf. 11½
2928 A1075 11k multicolored   1.50 1.00

Songbirds — A1076

Designs: 3k, Saxicola torquata. 5k, Carpodacus erythrinus. 14k, Luscinia svecica.

Photo. & Engr.
1994, Aug. 24   Perf. 11x11½
2929 A1076 3k multicolored   .45 .25
2930 A1076 5k multicolored   .75 .30
2931 A1076 14k multicolored   1.80 .80
  Nos. 2929-2931 (3)   3.00 1.35

Historic Race Cars — A1077

Photo. & Engr.
1994, Oct. 5   Perf. 11½
2932 A1077 2k 1900 NW   .25 .20
  Complete booklet, 10 #2932   3.00
2933 A1077 3k 1908 L&K   .55 .20
  Complete booklet, 5 #2933   3.50
2934 A1077 9k 1912 Praga   1.40 .50
  Nos. 2932-2934 (3)   2.20 .90

Christmas — A1078

Photo. & Engr.
1994, Nov. 9   **Perf. 11½**
2935 A1078 2k multicolored   .45 .20

Art Type of 1967 Inscribed "CESKA REPUBLIKA"

Engraving or paintings: 7k, Stary Posetilec A Zena, by Lucas Van Leyden. 10k, Moulin Rouge, by Henri de Toulouse-Lautrec. 14k, St. Vitus Madonna, St. Vitus Cathedral, Prague.

1994, Nov. 9   **Engr.**   **Perf. 12**
2936 A565 7k multicolored   .95 .95
2937 A565 10k multicolored   1.40 1.40
2938 A565 14k multicolored   2.00 2.00
    Nos. 2936-2938 (3)   4.35 4.35

Nos. 2936-2938 were each printed in sheets of 4. Value, set $14.

World Tourism Organization, 20th Anniv. A1079

Czech Stamp Production A1080

Photo. & Engr.
1995, Jan. 2   **Perf. 11x12**
2939 A1079 8k green blue & red   .95 .50

1995, Jan. 20
2940 A1080 3k Design N1   .60 .25

Czech Republic & European Union Association Agreement A1081

1995, Jan. 20 Litho.   **Perf. 13½x12½**
2941 A1081 8k multicolored   .95 .65

Famous Men A1082

Designs: 2k, Johannes Marcus Marci (1595-1667). 5k, Ferdinand Peroutka (1895-1978). 7k, Premysl Pitter (1895-1976).

Photo. & Engr.
1995, Feb. 1   **Perf. 12x11**
2942 A1082 2k multicolored   .25 .20
2943 A1082 5k multicolored   .60 .25
2944 A1082 7k multicolored   .85 .35
    Nos. 2942-2944 (3)   1.70 .80

Theater Personalities — A1083

Designs: No. 2945, Jiri Voskovec (1905-81). No. 2946, Jan Werich (1905-80). No. 2947, Jaroslav Jezek (1906-42). 22k, Caricatures of Voskovec, Werich, and Jezek with piano.

1995   **Photo. & Engr.**   **Perf. 12x11**
2945 A1083 3k multicolored   .50 .25
    Complete booklet, 3 #2945   2.00
2946 A1083 3k multicolored   .50 .25
    Complete booklet, 3 #2946   2.00
2947 A1083 3k multicolored   .50 .25
    Complete booklet, 3 #2947   2.00
   a.   Strip of 3, #2945-2947   1.75 1.50
    Complete booklet, 2 #2947a   4.00
    Nos. 2945-2947 (3)   1.50 .75

Souvenir Sheet
Photo.
Perf. 12
2947B A1083 22k yellow & black   2.50 2.50

Issued: 3k, 3/15; 22k, 9/20.

Havel Type of 1990 Inscribed "Ceska Republika"
Photo. & Engr.
1995, Mar. 22   **Perf. 12x11½**
2948 A1000 3.60k bl, vio & mag   .45 .20
    Complete booklet, 5 #2948   4.00

Rural Architecture A1084

1995, Mar. 22   **Perf. 11½**
2949 A1084 40h shown   .20 .20
2950 A1084 60h Homes, diff.   .20 .20

European Nature Conservation Year — A1085

1995, Apr. 12
2951 A1085 3k Bombus terrestris   .35 .30
    Complete booklet, 5 #2951   4.00
2952 A1085 5k Mantis religiosa   .60 .30
    Complete booklet, 5 #2952   4.50
2953 A1085 6k Calopteryx splendens   .75 .30
    Complete booklet, 5 #2953   5.00
    Nos. 2951-2953 (3)   1.70 .90

Peace & Freedom A1086

Photo. & Engr.
1995, May 3   **Perf. 11½**
2954 A1086 9k Rose, profiles   1.20 .35
2955 A1086 14k Butterfly, profiles   1.75 .75

Europa.

Natural Beauties in Czech Republic A1087

Designs: 8k, "Stone Organ" scenic mountain. 9k, Largest sandstone bridge in Europe.

Photo. & Engr.
1995, May 3   **Perf. 11½**
2956 A1087 8k multicolored   .95 .95
2957 A1087 9k multicolored   1.00 1.00

Nos. 2956-2957 were each issued in sheets of 8. Value, set $17.50.

Children's Day — A1088

First Train from Vienna to Prague, 150th Anniv. A1089

Photo. & Engr.
1995, June 1   **Perf. 11½**
2958 A1088 3.60k multicolored   .60 .25

3k, Chocen Tunnel. 9.60k, Entering Prague.

1995, June 21
2959 A1089 3k multicolored   .35 .25
    Complete booklet, 5 #2959   2.00
2960 A1089 9.60k multicolored   1.15 .50

World Wrestling Championships, Prague A1090

Photo. & Engr.
1995, Sept. 6   **Perf. 11½**
2961 A1090 3k multicolored   .55 .25

Cartoon Characters A1091

Designs: 3k, Man playing violin, woman washing, by Vladimir Rencin. 3.60k, Angel, naked man, by Vladimir Jiranek. 5k, Circus trainer holding ring for champagne cork to pop through, by Jiri Sliva.

1995, Sept. 6
2962 A1091 3k multicolored   .45 .25
    Complete booklet, 5 #2962   2.00
2963 A1091 3.60k multicolored   .55 .25
    Complete booklet, 5 #2963   2.50
2964 A1091 5k multicolored   .75 .30
    Complete booklet, 5 #2964   3.50
    Nos. 2962-2964 (3)   1.75 .80

A1092   A1093

1995, Sept. 20 Litho.   **Perf. 13½x13**
2965 A1092 3k multicolored   .35 .20

SOS Children's Villages, 25th anniv.

Photo. & Engr.
1995-97   **Perf. 12x11½**

Designs: 2.40k, Gothic. 3k, Secession. 3.60k, Romance. 4k, Classic portal; 4.60k, Rococo. 9.60k, Renaissance Portal. 12.60k, Cubist. 14k, Baroque.

2966 A1093 2.40k red & green   .30 .20
2967 A1093 3k grn & bl   .35 .20
2967A A1093 3.60k pur & grn   .45 .20
2968 A1093 4k blue & red   .50 .20
    Complete booklet, 5 #2967A   3.00
2968A A1093 4.60k multicolored   .55 .20
2969 A1093 9.60k blue & red   1.10 .45
2969A A1093 12.60k red brn & bl   1.50 .45
2970 A1093 14k grn & pur   1.60 .60
    Nos. 2966-2970 (8)   6.35 2.50

Issued: 9.60k, 9/27; 2.40k, 14k, 10/11; 3k, 3.60k, 10/25; 4k, 6/12/96; 4.60k, 3/26/97; 12.60k, 6/25/97.

UN, 50th Anniv. A1094

1995, Oct. 11 Litho.   **Perf. 12x11½**
2971 A1094 14k multicolored   1.90 .80

Wilhelm Röntgen (1845-1923), Discovery of the X-Ray, Cent. — A1095

1995, Oct. 11   **Photo. & Engr.**
2972 A1095 6k blk, buff & bl vio   .85 .35

Art Type of 1967 Inscribed "CESKA REPUBLIKA"

Designs: 6k, Parisiene, by Ludek Marold. 9k, Vase of Flowers, by J.K. Hirschely. 14k, Portrait of J. Malinsky, by Antonín Machek.

1995, Nov. 8   **Perf. 12**
2973 A565 6k multicolored   .95 .95
2974 A565 9k multicolored   1.25 .65
2975 A565 14k multicolored   2.00 1.00
    Nos. 2973-2975 (3)   4.20 2.10

Nos. 2973-2975 were each printed in sheets of 4. Value, set $13.50.

Christmas — A1096

1995, Nov. 8   **Perf. 11½**
2976 A1096 3k multicolored   .60 .20
    Complete booklet, 3 #2976   2.00

Czech Philharmonic Orchestra, Cent. — A1097

Photo. & Engr.
1996, Jan. 2   **Perf. 12x11½**
2977 A1097 3.60k multicolored   .45 .25

Tradition of Czech Stamp Production — A1098

Photo. & Engr.
1996, Jan. 20   **Perf. 11½x12**
2978 A1098 3.60k Design A5 of 1920   .45 .25

Vera Mencikova (1906-44), Chess Player — A1099

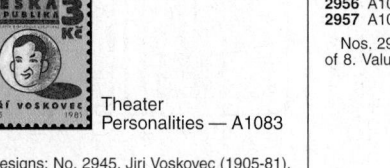

Photo. & Engr.
1996, Feb. 14　　　　　　**Perf. 12x11½**
2979　A1099　6k multicolored　　　　.75　.35

Easter — A1100

1996, Mar. 13　　　　　**Perf. 11½x12**
2980　A1100　3k multicolored　　　　.45　.20
　　　Complete booklet, 5 #2980　　2.00

Josef Sudek
(1896-1976),
Photographer
A1101

Photo. & Engr.
1996, Mar. 13　　　　　　　**Perf. 11**
2981　A1101　9.60k multicolored　　1.25　.60

Rulers from House of
Luxembourg — A1102

Designs: a, John of Luxembourg (1296-1346). b, Charles IV (1316-78). c, Wenceslas IV. (1361-1419). d, Sigismund (1368-1437).

1996, Mar. 27　　**Engr.**　　**Perf. 11½**
2982　A1102　14k Sheet of 4, #a.-
　　　　d. + label　　　　　6.75　6.75

Jiri Guth-
Jurkovsky,
Participant in
First Modern
Olympic
Games, Athens
A1103

Photo. & Engr.
1996, Mar. 27　　　　　　　**Perf. 11½**
2983　A1103　9.60k multicolored　　1.90　.60
　　　Modern Olympic Games, cent.

World Wildlife
Fund — A1104

Ema Destinnova
(1878-1930),
Singer — A1105

Designs: a, 3.60k, Eliomys quercinus. b, 5k, Dryomys nitedula. c, 6k, Spermophilus citellus. d, 8k, Sicista betulina.

Photo. & Engr.
1996, Apr. 24　　　　　**Perf. 11½x12**
2984　A1104　Block of 4, #a.-d.　3.00　3.00
　　　Issued in sheets of 8 stamps. Value $9.

Photo. & Engr.
1996, May 2　　　　　　　**Perf. 11½**
2985　A1105　8k multicolored　　　.90　.40
　　　　　　　　Europa.
　　　No. 2985 was issued in sheets of 10. Value $11.

A1106　　　　　　　　A1107

Photo. & Engr.
1996, May 15　　　　　　**Perf. 11x11½**
2986　A1106　12k multicolored　　1.40　.65
　　　Jean Gaspart Deburau (1796-1846), mime.

1996, May 29
2987　A1107　3k multicolored　　　.35　.20
　　　1996 Summmer Olympic Games, Atlanta.

Intl. Children's
Day — A1108

Photo. & Engr.
1996, May 29　　　　　　　**Perf. 11½**
2988　A1108　3k multicolored　　　.35　.20

Architectural
Sites — A1109

UNESCO: 8k, St. Nepomuk Church, Zelena Hora. 9k, Loretta Tower, Prague.

1996, June 26　　　**Engr.**　　**Perf. 11½**
2989　A1109　8k multicolored　　1.00　1.00
2990　A1109　9k multicolored　　1.10　1.10
　　　Nos. 2989-2990 were each issued in sheets of 8. Value, set $16.
　　　See Nos. 3056-3057.

UNICEF,
50th
Anniv.
A1110

Photo. & Engr.
1996, Sept. 11　　　　　　**Perf. 12x11**
2991　A1110　3k multicolored　　　.35　.20

Horses
A1111　　　　　　　A1112

Photo. & Engr.
1996, Sept. 25　　　　　　**Perf. 11x11½**
2992　A1111　3k multicolored　　　.50　.20
2993　A1112　3k multicolored　　　.50　.20
　a.　Pair, #2992-2993　　　　1.00　.75
　　　Complete booklet, 3 #2992, 2
　　　　#2993　　　　　　　3.00
　　　Complete booklet, 2 #2992, 3
　　　　#2993　　　　　　　3.00

Souvenir Sheet

Vaclav Havel, 60th Birthday — A1113

1996, Oct. 5
2994　A1113　Sheet of 2　　　1.50　1.50
　a.　6k red & blue　　　　　.80　.50

Art Type of 1967 Inscribed "CESKA
REPUBLICA"
　The Baroque Chair, by Endre Nemes (1909-85).

1996, Oct. 5　　　**Engr.**　　**Perf. 11½**
2995　A565　20k multicolored　　2.50　2.50
　　　No. 2995 was issued in sheets of 4. Value $10.
　　　See Slovakia No. 255; Sweden No. 2199.

Tycho Brahe (1546-1601),
Astronomer — A1114

Photo. & Engr.
1996, Oct. 9　　　　　　**Perf. 11½x11**
2996　A1114　5k multicolored　　　.75　.30

Biplanes
A1115

1996, Oct. 9
2997　A1115　7k Letov S1 (1920)　.85　.40
2998　A1115　8k Aero A11 (1925)　.95　.45
2999　A1115　10k Avia BH21
　　　　　　(1925)　　　　1.20　.55
　　　Nos. 2997-2999 (3)　　　3.00　1.40

Christmas
A1116

Photo. & Engr.
1996, Nov. 13　　　　　　　**Perf. 11½**
3000　A1116　3k multicolored　　　.45　.20
　　　Complete booklet, 5 #3000　3.50

Art Type of 1967 Inscribed "CESKA
REPUBLICA"
　Designs: 9k, Garden of Eden, by Josef Váchal (1884-1969), horiz. 11k, Breakfast, by Georg Flegel (1566-1638).

1996, Nov. 13　　**Engr.**　　**Perf. 11½**
3001　A565　9k multicolored　　1.25　1.25
3002　A565　11k multicolored　　1.60　1.60
　　　Nos. 3001-3002 were each issued in sheets of 4. Value, set $10.

Czech Stamp
Production — A1117

Photo. & Engr.
1997, Jan. 20　　　　　**Perf. 11½x12**
3003　A1117　3.60k #68, bl & red　.40　.25

Easter — A1118　　　Flowers — A1119

Photo. & Engr.
1997, Mar. 12　　　　　　　**Perf. 11½**
3004　A1118　3k multicolored　　　.65　.20
　　　Complete booklet, 5 #3004　4.00

1997, Mar. 12　　　　　　**Perf. 11x11½**
　3.60k, Erythronium dens-canis. 4k, Calla palustris. 5k, Cypripedium calceolus. 8k, Iris pumila.

3005　A1119　3.60k multicolored　.45　.20
　　　Complete booklet, 5 #3005　2.50
3006　A1119　4k multicolored　　.45　.25
　　　Complete booklet, 5 #3006　2.50
3007　A1119　5k multicolored　　.60　.30
　　　Complete booklet, 5 #3007　3.50
3008　A1119　8k multicolored　　.95　.45
　　　Complete booklet, 5 #3008　5.00
　　　Nos. 3005-3008 (4)　　　2.45　1.20

A1120　　　　　　　　A1121

Jewish Monuments in Prague: 8k, Altneuschul Synagogue. 10k, Tombstone of Rabbi Judah Loew MaHaRal.

1997, Apr. 30   *Perf. 11½*
3009 A1120 8k multicolored .90 .45
3010 A1120 10k multicolored 1.10 .55
  a.   Sheet, 4 each #3009-3010   8.00 4.00

See Israel Nos. 1302-1303.

1997, Mar. 26   **Litho.**   *Perf. 13x13½*

Greetings stamp.

3011 A1121 4k Girl with cats .50 .25

A1122   A1123

1997, Apr. 23   **Engr.**   *Perf. 11½*
3012 A1122 7k deep violet .85 .40
St. Adalbert (956-97). See Germany No. 1964, Hungary No. 3569, Poland No. 3337, Vatican City No. 1040.

Photo. & Engr.
1997, Apr. 30   *Perf. 11½x12*

Europa (Stories and Legends): No. 3013, Queen, knight with sword, lion, snakes. No. 3014, Man riding in chariot drawn by chickens, King looking through window.

3013 A1123 8k multicolored 1.25 1.25
3014 A1123 8k multicolored 1.25 1.25

Nos. 3013-3014 were each issued in sheets of 8. Value, set $16.

Souvenir Sheet

Collections of Rudolf II (1522-1612), Prague Exhibition A1124

Designs: a, 6k, Musical instruments, flowers, face of bearded man. b, 8k, Rudolf II wearing laurel wreath, holding rose, Muses. c, 10k, Rudolf II, skull, moth's wings, tree, flowers, leaves, fruit.

1997, May 14   **Engr.**   *Perf. 12*
3015 A1124 Sheet of 3, #a.-c. 2.75 2.75

Intl. Children's Day — A1125

Photo. & Engr.
1997, May 28   *Perf. 11½*
3016 A1125 4.60k multicolored .55 .25

Frantisek Krizik (1847-1941), Electrical Engineer, Inventor of Arc Lamp — A1126

Photo. & Engr.
1997, June 25   *Perf. 12x11½*
3017 A1126 6k multicolored .70 .25

European Swimming & Diving Championships, Prague — A1127

Photo. & Engr.
1997, Aug. 27   *Perf. 11½*
3018 A1127 11k multicolored 1.50 .40

"The Good Soldier Schweik," by Jaroslav Hasek, 110th Anniv. — A1128

4k, Mrs. Müller, Schweik in wheelchair. 4.60k, Lt. Lukás, Col. Kraus von Zillergut, dog. 6k, Schweik smoking pipe, winter scene.

Photo. & Engr.
1997, Sept. 10   *Perf. 12x11½*
3019 A1128 4k multicolored .50 .20
  a.   Booklet pane of 8 + 4 labels   4.50
      Complete booklet, #3019a   4.50
3020 A1128 4.60k multicolored .55 .20
  a.   Booklet pane of 8 + 4 labels   5.00
      Complete booklet, #3020a   5.00
3021 A1128 6k multicolored .70 .30
  a.   Booklet pane of 8 + 4 labels   6.00
      Complete booklet, #3021a   6.00
Nos. 3019-3021 (3) 1.75 .70

Praga 1998, Intl. Stamp Exhibition — A1129

#3022, Lesser Town, Prague Castle. #3023, Old Town, bridges over Vltava River.

Photo. & Engr.
1997, Sept. 24   *Perf. 11½*
3022 A1129 15k multicolored 1.80 .70
3023 A1129 15k multicolored 1.80 .70
  a.   Souvenir sheet, #3022-3023 + 2 labels   3.50 3.00

Historic Service Vehicles A1130

Designs: 4k, Postal bus, Prague. 4.60k, Sentinel truck, Skoda. 8k, Fire truck, Tatra.

1997, Oct. 8   *Perf. 12x11½*
3024 A1130 4k multicolored .45 .20
      Complete booklet, 5 #3024   2.50
3025 A1130 4.60k multicolored .55 .25
      Complete booklet, 5 #3025   3.50
3026 A1130 8k multicolored .95 .40
      Complete booklet, 5 #3026   5.00
Nos. 3024-3026 (3) 1.95 .85

A1131   A1132

Photo. & Engr.
1997, Nov. 12   *Perf. 11½*
3027 A1131 4k multicolored .50 .20
      Complete booklet, 5 #3027   2.75

Christmas.

Art Type of 1967 Inscribed "CESKA REPUBLIKA"

7k, Landscape with Chateau in Chantilly, by Antonín Chittussi (1847-91). 12k, The Prophets Came Out of the Desert, by Frantisek Bílek (1872-1941). 1 6k, Parisian Antiquarians, by T. F. Simon (1877-1942).

1997, Nov. 12   **Engr.**   *Perf. 12*
3028 A565 7k multi, horiz. .85 .85
3029 A565 12k multi 1.40 1.40
3030 A565 16k multi 1.90 1.90
Nos. 3028-3030 (3) 4.15 4.15

Nos. 3028-3030 were each issued in sheets of 4. Value, set $17.

1998, Jan. 20   **Litho.**   *Perf. 11½x12*
3031 A1132 7k multicolored .85 .30

1998 Winter Olympic Games, Nagano.

Tradition of Czech Stamp Production — A1133

Photo. & Engr.
1998, Jan. 20   *Perf. 12x11½*
3032 A1133 12.60k Type A8 1.50 .55
  a.   Booklet pane of 8 + 4 labels   12.50
      Complete booklet, #3032a   12.50

Pres. Václav Havel A1134   Love A1135

1998, Jan. 22
3033 A1134 4.60k dark grn & red .55 .20

See No. 3114.

1998, Feb. 4   *Perf. 11½*
3034 A1135 4k multicolored .50 .20
      Complete booklet, 5 #3034   2.50

Skibob World Championship, Spindleruv Mlyn — A1136

1998, Feb. 25
3035 A1136 8k multicolored 1.00 .35

Prague Philatelic Exhibition Type of 1938
Souvenir Sheet

1998, Feb. 25   **Engr.**   *Perf. 12x11½*
3036 A87 Sheet of 2 7.50 4.50
  a.   30k like #251a   4.00 2.00

Prague '98, Intl. Philatelic Exhibition.

Easter — A1137

Photo. & Engr.
1998, Mar. 25   *Perf. 11x11½*
3037 A1137 4k multicolored .55 .20
      Complete booklet, 5 #3037   2.75

Ondrejov Observatory, Cent. — A1138

1998, Mar. 25   *Perf. 12x11½*
3038 A1138 4.60k multicolored .55 .20

Czech Ice Hockey Team, Gold Medalists at Nagano Winter Olympic Games — A1139

1998, Apr. 1   **Litho.**   *Perf. 11½x12*
3039 A1139 23k Dominik Hasek 3.00 2.25
No. 3039 was issued in a sheet with two labels.

Charles University and New Town, Prague, 650th Anniv. — A1140

Designs: a, 15k, Hands forming arch, University seal. b, 22k, Charles IV (1316-78), Holy Roman Emperor, King of Bohemia. c, 23k, Groin vault, St. Vitus Cathedral, Prague.

1998, Apr. 1   **Engr.**   *Perf. 12*
3040 A1140 Sheet of 3, #a.-c. 7.50 5.00

World Book and Copyright Day — A1141

1998, Apr. 23   **Litho.**   *Perf. 12x11½*
3041 A1141 10k multicolored 1.20 .45

Nature Conservation A1142

1998, Apr. 23   *Perf. 13x13½*
3042 A1142 4.60k Perdix perdix .55 .20
3043 A1142 4.60k Lyrurus tetrix .55 .20
  a.   Pair, #3042-3043   1.10 .60
3044 A1142 8k Cervus elaphus .95 .35
3045 A1142 8k Alces alces .95 .35
  a.   Pair, #3044-3045   1.90 1.10
Nos. 3042-3045 (4) 3.00 1.10

Natl. Festivals and Holidays A1143

Europa: 11k, King's Ride. 15k, Wearing masks for Carnival.

Litho. & Engr.

1998, May 5		**Perf. 11½**	
3046	A1143 11k multicolored	1.25	.55
3047	A1143 15k multicolored	1.75	.75

Intl. Children's Day — A1144

Designs: 4k, Two satyr musicians. 4.60k, Character riding on fish.

Photo. & Engr.

1998, May 27		**Perf. 11½**	
3048	A1144 4k multicolored	.45	.20
a.	Booklet of 6 +4 labels	3.00	
	Complete booklet, #3048a	3.00	
3049	A1144 4.60k multicolored	.55	.20
a.	Booklet of 6 + 4 labels	3.50	
	Complete booklet, #3049a	3.50	

Famous Men — A1145

Designs: 4k, Frantisek Kmoch (1848-1912), bandleader, composer. 4.60k, Frantisek Palacky (1798-1876), historian, politician. 6k, Rafael Kubelík (1914-96), composer, conductor.

Photo. & Engr.

1998, May 27		**Perf. 11½x12**	
3050	A1145 4k multicolored	.45	.20
3051	A1145 4.60k multicolored	.55	.20
3052	A1145 6k multicolored	.70	.25
	Nos. 3050-3052 (3)	1.70	.65

Revolt of 1848, 150th Anniv. A1146

1998, May 27		**Perf. 12x11½**	
3053	A1146 15k multicolored	1.90	.75

Art Type of 1967 Inscribed "CESKA REPUBLIKA"

Praga 1998 Intl. Stamp Exhibition, works of art: 22k, Amorfa Dvoubarevna Fuga, by Frantisek Kupka (1871-1957), horiz. 23k, Escape, by Paul Gauguin (1848-1903), horiz.

1998, June 17   Engr.   Perf. 12

3054	A565 22k multicolored	2.50	1.75
3055	A565 23k multicolored	2.75	1.75

Nos. 3054-3055 were each issued in sheets of 4. Value, set $22.

UNESCO World Heritage Sites Type of 1996

8k, St. Barbara Cathedral, Kutná Hora, horiz. 11k, The Chateau of Valtice, horiz.

1998, Oct. 7   Engr.   Perf. 11½x12

3056	A1109 8k multicolored	.95	.40
3057	A1109 11k multicolored	1.25	.60

Nos. 3056-3057 were each issued in sheets of 8. Value, set $17.50.

Czechoslovak Republic, 80th Anniv. — A1147

Designs based on World War I recruitment posters by Vojtech Preissig (1873-1944): 4.60k, Soldiers holding flags, guns. 5k, Three soldiers marching. 12.60k, Flags waving from city buildings.

Perf. 11½x11¾

1998, Oct. 28   Litho. & Engr.

3058	A1147 4.60k multicolored	.85	.40
3059	A1147 5k multicolored	.90	.40
3060	A1147 12.60k multicolored	2.25	.90
	Nos. 3058-3060 (3)	4.00	1.70

No. 3060 was issued in sheets of 6+2 labels. Value $30.

Christmas A1148

Designs: 4k, People following star. 6k, Angel blowing trumpet over town, vert.

Photo. & Engr.

1998, Nov. 18		**Perf. 11½**	
3061	A1148 4k multicolored	.45	.20
	Complete booklet, 5 #3061	2.50	
3062	A1148 6k multicolored	.70	.25
	Complete booklet, 5 #3062	4.00	

Signs of the Zodiac — A1149

1998-2000		**Perf. 12x11½**	
3063	A1149 1k Capricorn	.20	.20
3064	A1149 10k Aquarius	1.20	.25
3065	A1149 9k Libra	1.00	.25
3066	A1149 8k Cancer	.95	.25
3067	A1149 20k Sagittarius	2.25	.45

Photo. & Engr.

Perf. 11¾x11¼

3068	A1149 5k Taurus	.55	.25
	Booklet, 5 #3068	2.75	
3069	A1149 5.40k Scorpio	.60	.25
	Booklet, 5 #3069	3.00	
3070	A1149 2k Virgo	.25	.20
3071	A1149 40h Pisces	.20	.20
3072	A1149 12k Leo	1.40	.30
3073	A1149 17k Gemini	2.00	.65
3074	A1149 26k Aries	3.00	.95
	Nos. 3063-3074 (12)	13.60	4.20

Issued: 1k, 10k, 11/18; 9k, 5/5/99; 8k, 20k, 9/8/99; 5k, 5.40k, 12/8/99; 2k, 5/9/00. 40h, 1/20/01. 12k, 2/21/01. 17k, 9/1/02. 26k, 2/12/03.

Art Type of 1967 Inscribed "CESKA REPUBLIKA"

15k, Painting from the Greater Cycle, 1902, by Jan Preisler (1872-1918), horiz. 16k, Spinner, by Josef Navrátil (1798-1865).

1998, Dec. 9   Perf. 12

3075	A565 15k multicolored	1.75	1.00
3076	A565 16k multicolored	1.80	1.00

Nos. 3075-3076 were each issued in sheets of 4. Value, set $14.50.

A1150   A1151

Photo. & Engr.

1999, Jan. 20		**Perf. 11½x11¾**	
3077	A1150 4.60k #164	.50	.20
a.	Booklet pane of 8 + 4 labels	4.00	
	Complete booklet, #3077a	4.00	

Tradition of Czech stamp production.

Photo. & Engr.

1999, Feb. 17   Perf. 11½

Domestic cats.

3078	A1151 4.60k shown	.55	.20
	Complete booklet, 5 #3078	2.75	
3079	A1151 5k Adult, kitten	.55	.25
	Complete booklet, 5 #3079	2.75	
3080	A1151 7k Two cats	.80	.30
	Complete booklet, 5 #3080	4.00	
	Nos. 3078-3080 (3)	1.90	.75

Easter — A1152   A1153

Photo. & Engr.

1999, Mar. 10		**Perf. 11¼x11½**	
3081	A1152 3k multicolored	.35	.20

Perf. 12¾x13¼

1999, Mar. 10   Litho.

Protected birds: No. 3082, Merops apiaster. No. 3083, Upupa epops.
Protected butterflies: No. 3084, Catocala electa. No. 3085, Euphydryas maturna.

3082	A1153 4.60k multicolored	.55	.20
3083	A1153 4.60k multicolored	.55	.20
a.	Pair, #3082-3083	1.10	.60
	Complete booklet, 3 #3082, 2 #3083	2.75	
3084	A1153 5k multicolored	.55	.20
3085	A1153 5k multicolored	.55	.20
a.	Pair, #3084-3085	1.10	.60
	Complete booklet, 3 #3084, 2 #3085	2.75	

Nature conservation.

Czech Republic's Entry Into NATO — A1154

Photo. & Engr.

1999, Mar. 12		**Perf. 12x11½**	
3086	A1154 4.60k multicolored	.55	.20

Council of Europe, 50th Anniv. A1155

Photo. & Engr.

1999, Apr. 14		**Perf. 11¾x11¼**	
3087	A1155 7k multicolored	.90	.40

Natl. Olympic Committee, Cent. — A1156

Design: Josef Rössler-Orovsky (1869-1933), founder of Czech Olympic Committee.

1999, Apr. 14		**Perf. 11¼x11¾**	
3088	A1156 9k multicolored	1.00	.35

Europa A1157

Natl. Parks: 11k, Sumava. 17k, Podyji.

1999, May 5		**Perf. 11¾x11¼**	
3089	A1157 11k multicolored	1.25	.40
3090	A1157 17k multicolored	2.00	.65

Nos. 3089-3090 were each issued in sheets of 8. Value, set $27.

Ferda the Ant, Pytlik the Beetle and Ladybird A1158

Photo. & Engr.

1999, May 26		**Perf. 11½x11¼**	
3091	A1158 4.60k multicolored	.55	.20
	Complete booklet, 8 #3091	4.50	

Bridges A1159

1999, May 26 Engr.		**Perf. 11¾**	
3092	A1159 8k Stádlec, vert.	.90	.40
3093	A1159 11k Cernvír	1.25	.60

Nos. 3092-3094 were each issued in sheets of 8. Value, set $17.50.

Souvenir Sheet

Paleontologist Joachim Barrande (1799-1883) and Trilobite Fossils — A1160

a, 13k, Barrande, fossils. b, 31k, Delphon forbesi, Ophioceras simplex, Carolicrinus barrandei.

1999, June 23 Engr.		**Perf. 11¾**	
3094	A1160 Sheet of 2, #a.-b. + 2 labels	5.00	4.00

Jihlava Mining Rights, 750th Anniv. A1161

Photo. & Engr.

1999, June 23 *Perf. 11¾x11¼*
3095 A1161 8k multicolored .90 .35
a. Bklt. pane of 8 + 4 labels 7.25
   Complete booklet, #3095a 7.50

UPU, 125th Anniv. — A1162

Litho. & Engr.

1999, June 23 *Perf. 11¾*
3096 A1162 9k multicolored 1.00 .40

Issued se-tenant with two labels.

Vincenc Preissnitz (1799-1851), Hydrotherapy Advocate A1163

Photo. & Engr.

1999, Sept. 8 *Perf. 11¼*
3097 A1163 4.60k multicolored .50 .25

UNESCO.

Carved Beehives A1164 | Cartoons by Miroslav Bartak A1165

Designs: 4.60k, Woman. 5k, St. Joseph and Infant Jesus. 7k, Chimney sweep.

Photo. & Engr.

1999, Sept. 29 *Perf. 11¼x11½*
3098 A1164 4.60k multi .55 .25
   Complete booklet, 5 #3098 2.75
3099 A1164 5k multi .60 .25
   Complete booklet, 5 #3099 3.00
3100 A1164 7k multi .80 .30
   Complete booklet, 5 #3100 4.00
   Nos. 3098-3100 (3) 1.95 .80

1999, Oct. 20

Designs: 4.60k, Doctor in clown mask, infant. 5k, Dog with pipe. 7k, Night seeping through window sill.

3101 A1165 4.60k multi .55 .25
3102 A1165 5k multi .60 .25
3103 A1165 7k multi .80 .30
   Nos. 3101-3103 (3) 1.95 .80

Souvenir Sheet

Beuron Art School — A1166

Designs: a, 11k, Mater Dei, 1898. b, 13k, Pantocrator, 1911.

Litho. & Engr.

1999, Oct. 20 *Perf. 11¾*
3104 A1166 Sheet of 2, #a.-b. 3.00 2.25

Art Type of 1967 Inscribed "CESKA REPUBLIKA"

Designs: 13k, Red Orchid, by Jindrich Styrsky (1899-1942). 17k, Landscape with Marsh, by Julius Marák (1832-99). 26k, Monument, by Frantisek Hudecek (1909-90).

1999, Nov. 10 **Engr.** *Perf. 11¾*
3105 A565 13k multi 1.50 1.00
3106 A565 17k multi 2.00 1.50
3107 A565 26k multi 3.00 2.00
   Nos. 3105-3107 (3) 6.50 4.50

Nos. 3105-3107 were each issued in sheets of 4. Value, set $26.

A1167 | A1168

Photo. & Engr.

1999, Nov. 10 *Perf. 11¼x11½*
3108 A1167 3k multi .35 .20

Christmas.

Photo. & Engr.

2000, Jan. 20 *Perf. 11¼x11¾*
3109 A1168 5.40k #B151 .60 .25
a. Bklt. pane of 8 + 4 labels 5.00
   Booklet, #3109a 5.00

Tradition of Czech stamp production.

Brno 2000 Philatelic Exhibition — A1169

Designs: 5k, 1593 view of Brno. 50k, St. James's Church, vert.

2000, Jan. 20 *Perf. 11¾x11¼*
3110 A1169 5k multi .60 .20

Souvenir Sheet
Perf. 11¼x11¾
3111 A1169 50k multi 6.00 4.25

No. 3110 printed in sheets of 35 stamps and 30 labels.

Kutna Hora Royal Mining Law, 700th Anniv. — A1170

2000, Mar. 1 *Perf. 11¼x11¾*
3112 A1170 5k multi .60 .25
a. Booklet pane of 8 + 4 labels 5.00
   Booklet, #3112a 5.00

Souvenir Sheet

Pres. Thomas Garrigue Masaryk (1850-1937) — A1171

2000, Mar. 1 **Engr.** *Perf. 11¾*
3113 A1171 17k multi 2.00 1.50

Pres. Havel Type of 1998
Photo. & Engr.

2000, Mar. 1 *Perf. 11¾x11¼*
3114 A1134 5.40k Prus bl & org brn .60 .25

Easter — A1172

Photo. & Engr.

2000, Apr. 5 *Perf. 11¼x11½*
3115 A1172 5k multi .60 .25

Souvenir Sheet

Prague, 2000 European City of Culture — A1173

No. 3116: a, 9k, Statue of man. b, 11k, Statue of harpist. c, 17k, Statue of King Charles IV.

Litho. & Engr.

2000, Apr. 5 *Perf. 11¾*
3116 A1173 #a-c + 3 labels 4.25 4.25

Souvenir Sheet

Trains — A1174

No. 3117: a, 8k, Train from 1900. b, 15k, Train from 2000.

Litho. & Engr.

2000, May 5 *Perf. 11¾*
3117 A1174 Sheet of 2, #a-b, +3 labels 3.00 3.00

Czech Personalities A1175

5k, Vítezslav Nezval (1900-58), writer. 8k, Gustav Mahler (1860-1911), composer.

Photo. & Engr.

2000, May 5 *Perf. 11¼x11¾*
3118-3119 A1175 Set of 2 1.60 .50

Europa, 2000
Common Design Type

2000, May 5 **Litho.** *Perf. 12¾x13¼*
3120 CD17 9k multi 1.00 .40

Intl. Children's Year — A1176

Photo. & Engr.

2000, May 31 *Perf. 11½x11¼*
3121 A1176 5.40k multi .60 .20
a. Booklet pane of 8 + 2 labels 5.00
   Booklet, #3121a 5.00

1995 Proof of Fermat's Last Theorem by Andrew Wiles A1177

2000, May 31 *Perf. 11¾x11¼*
3122 A1177 7k multi .80 .25

Intl. Mathematics Year.

Prague Landmarks — A1178

Designs: 9k, Charles Bridge tower. 11k, St. Nicholas's Church. 13k, Town Hall.

2000, June 28		**Engr.**	**Perf. 11¾**	
3123-3125	A1178	Set of 3	4.00	1.10

Mushrooms — A1179

No. 3126, 5k: a, Geastrum pouzarii. b, Boletus satanoides.
No. 3127, 5.40k: a, Morchella pragensis. b, Verpa bohemica.

Photo. & Engr.

2000, June 28		**Perf. 11¼x11½**	
		Pairs, #a-b	
3126-3127	A1179	Set of 2	2.40	.70
	Booklet, 3 #3126a, 2 #3126b	3.50	
	Booklet, 3 #3127b, 2 #3127a	3.50	

Meeting of Intl. Monetary Fund and World Bank Group, Prague — A1180

2000, Aug. 30		**Perf. 11¾x11¼**	
3128	A1180	7k multi	.80	.25

Ancient Olympics A1181

2000, Aug. 30			
3129	A1181	9k multi	1.00	.35

2000 Summer Olympics, Sydney — A1182

2000, Aug. 30			
3130	A1182	13k multi	1.50	.45

Hunting — A1183

No. 3131: a, 5k, Falconry. b, 5k, Deer at feed trough.
No. 3132: a, 5.40k, Ducks and blind. b, 5.40k, Deer and blind.

Photo. & Engr.

2000, Oct. 4		**Perf. 11¼x11¾**	
		Horiz. Pairs, #a-b	
3131-3132	A1183	Set of 2	2.40	.55
	Booklet, 3 #3131a, 2 #3131b	3.50	
	Booklet, 3 #3132a, 2 #3132b	3.50	

Art Type of 1967 Inscribed "CESKA REPUBLIKA"

Designs: 13k, St. Luke the Evangelist, by Master Theodoricus. 17k, Simeon With Infant

Jesus, by Petr Jan Brandl. 26k, Brunette, by Alfons Mucha.

2000, Nov. 15		**Engr.**	**Perf. 11¾**	
3133-3135	A565	Set of 3	7.00	4.50

Nos. 3133-3135 were each issued in sheets of 4. Value, set $27.

Christmas — A1184

Photo. & Engr.

2000, Nov. 15		**Perf. 11¼x11½**	
3136	A1184	5k multi	.60	.20

End of Millennium A1185   Advent of New Millennium A1186

2000, Nov. 22			
3137	A1185	9k multi	1.00	.35
2001, Jan. 2			
3138	A1186	9k multi	1.00	.35

Tradition of Czech Stamp Production A1187

2001, Jan. 20		**Perf. 11¼x11¾**	
3139	A1187	5.40k #474	.60	.25
a.	Booklet pane of 8 + 4 labels	5.00	
	Booklet, #3139a	5.00	

Jan Amos Komensky (Comenius, 1592-1670), Theologian — A1188

Photo. & Engr.

2001, Mar. 14		**Perf. 11¼x11½**	
3140	A1188	9k red & black	1.00	.35

Souvenir Sheet

Architecture — A1189

No. 3141: a, 13k, Church and decorations, Jakub. b, 17k, Arcade decorations, Bucovice Castle. c, 31k, Dance Hall, Prague.

2001, Mar. 28		**Engr.**	**Perf. 11¾x11½**	
3141	A1189	Sheet of 3, #a-c	7.50	4.50

Easter — A1190

Photo. & Engr.

2001, Mar. 28		**Perf. 11¼x11½**	
3142	A1190	5.40k multi	.60	.25

Souvenir Sheet

Allegory of Art, by Vaclav Vavrinec Reiner — A1191

Litho. & Engr.

2001, Apr. 18		**Perf. 11¾**	
3143	A1191	50k multi	6.00	4.25

Europa A1192

Photo. & Engr.

2001, May 9		**Perf. 11¾x11¼**	
3144	A1192	9k pur & lilac	1.00	.35

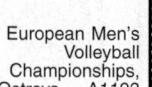

European Men's Volleyball Championships, Ostrova — A1193

Photo. & Engr.

2001, May 9		**Perf. 11¼x11½**	
3145	A1193	12k multi	1.50	.50

Intl. Children's Day — A1194   Famous Men — A1195

Photo. & Engr.

2001, May 30		**Perf. 11¼x11½**	
3146	A1194	5.40k multi	.60	.25
a.	Booklet pane of 8 + 2 labels	5.00	
	Booklet, #3146a	5.00	

2001, May 30

Designs: 5.40k, Frantisek Skroup (1801-62), composer. 16k, Frantisek Halas (1901-49), writer.

3147-3148	A1195	Set of 2	2.50	.80

Congratulations A1196

2001, June 20

3149	A1196	5.40k multi	.60	.25
	Booklet, 5 #3149	3.00	

Dogs — A1197

No. 3150: a, West Highland terrier. b, Beagle.
No. 3151: a, German shepherd. b, Golden retriever.

Photo. & Engr.

2001, June 20		**Perf. 11½x11¼**	
3150		Pair	1.40	1.00
a.-b.	A1197 5.40k Any single	.65	.25
	Booklet, 3 #3150a, 2 #3150b	3.25	
	Booklet, 3 #3150b, 2 #3150a	3.25	
3151		Pair	1.40	1.00
a.-b.	A1197 5.40k Any single	.65	.25
	Booklet, 3 #3151a, 2 #3151b	3.25	

Zoo Animals A1198

No. 3152: a, Pongo pygmaeus. b, Panthera tigris altaica.
No. 3153: a, Ailurus fulgens. b, Fennecus zerda.

Photo. & Engr.

2001, Sept. 5		**Perf. 11¾x11¼**	
3152		Pair	1.40	1.00
a.-b.	A1198 5.40k Any single	.65	.25
	Booklet, 3 #3152b, 2 #3152a	3.25	
3153		Pair	1.40	1.00
a.-b.	A1198 5.40k Any single	.65	.25
	Booklet, 3 #3153b, 2 #3153a	3.25	

UNESCO World Heritage Sites A1199

Designs: 12k, Kormeríz Castle and Gardens. 14k, Holasovice Historical Village Restoration.

2001, Oct. 9		**Engr.**	**Perf. 11½x11¾**	
3154-3155	A1199	Set of 2	3.00	1.25

See Nos. 3177-3178, 3267-3268.

Year of Dialogue Among Civilizations A1200

Photo. & Engr.

2001, Oct. 9		**Perf. 11¼x11½**	
3156	A1200	9k multi	1.00	.35

Mills A1201   Christmas A1202

Designs: 9k, Windmill. 14.40k, Water mill.

2001, Oct. 9			
3157-3158	A1201	Set of 2	3.00	1.00

Photo. & Engr.

2001, Nov. 14		**Perf. 11¼x11½**	
3159	A1202	5.40k multi		

Art Type of 1967 Inscribed "CESKA REPUBLIKA"

Designs: 12k, The Annunciation of the Virgin Mary, by Michael J. Rentz. 17k, The Sans Souci Bar in Nimes, by Cyril Bouda. 26k, The Goose Keeper, by Vaclav Brozík.

2001, Nov. 14 **Engr.** **Perf. 11¾**
3160-3162 A565 Set of 3 6.75 4.25

Nos. 3160-3162 were each issued in sheets of 4. Value, set $25.

Tradition of Czech Stamp Production — A1203

Photo. & Engr.
2002, Jan. 20 **Perf. 11¼x11¾**
3163 A1203 5.40k Type A89 .60 .25
a. Booklet pane of 8 + 4 labels 5.00
Booklet, #3163a 5.00

2002 Winter Olympics, Salt Lake City — A1204

2002, Jan. 30 **Perf. 11¼**
3164 A1204 12k multi 1.40 .45

For overprint, see No. 3168.

2002 Winter Paralympics, Salt Lake City — A1205

2002, Jan. 30 **Perf. 11¼x11½**
3165 A1205 5.40k multi .60 .25

Composers Jaromír Vejvoda (1902-88), Josef Poncar (1902-86) and Karel Vacek (1902-82) — A1206

2002, Mar. 6 **Perf. 11¾x11¼**
3166 A1206 9k multi 1.00 .35

Easter — A1207

2002, Mar. 6 **Perf. 11¼x11½**
3167 A1207 5.40k multi .60 .25

No. 3164 Overprinted in Blue

Photo. & Engr.
2002, Mar. 8 **Perf. 11¼**
3168 A1204 12k multi 1.40 .65

Divan, by Vlaho Bukovac (1855-1922) — A1208

Litho. & Engr.
2002, Apr. 23 **Perf. 11¾**
3169 A1208 17k multi 2.25 1.40

Printed in sheets of 4 + 2 labels. Value $9. See Croatia No. 487.

Europa A1209

Photo. & Engr.
2002, May 7 **Perf. 11¾x11¼**
3170 A1209 9k multi 1.00 .35

Souvenir Sheet

Czech Culture and France — A1210

No. 3171: a, 23k, Klávesy Piana-Jezero, by Frantisek Kupka. b, 31k, Man with Broken Nose, sculpture by Auguste Rodin.

Perf. 11¾x11½
2002, May 7 **Litho. & Engr.**
3171 A1210 Sheet of 2, #a-b 6.25 4.00

Intl. Children's Day — A1211

Photo. & Engr.
2002, May 29 **Perf. 11¼x11½**
3172 A1211 5.40k multi .60 .25
a. Booklet pane of 8 + 2 labels 5.00
Complete booklet, #3172a 5.00

Margaritifera Margaritifera A1212

2002, June 6
3173 A1212 9k multi 1.00 .35

Jan Hus (1372-1415), Religious Leader — A1213

2002, June 19
3174 A1213 9k multi + label 1.00 .35

Souvenir Sheet

Worldwide Fund for Nature (WWF) — A1214

Butterflies: a, 5.40k, Maculinea nausithous. b, 5.40k, Maculinea alcon. c, 9k, Maculinea teleius. d, 9k, Maculinea arion.

Litho. & Engr.
2002, June 19 **Perf. 11¾**
3175 A1214 Sheet of 4, #a-d + 4 labels 3.50 2.75

Pansy — A1215

Photo. & Engr.
2002, Sept. 1 **Perf. 11¾x11¼**
3176 A1215 6.40k multi .75 .25

See Nos. 3220-3221, 3262-3263, 3293-3294, 3340, 3345-3347, 3363-3366.

World Heritage Sites Type of 2001

Designs: 12k, Litomysl Castle. 14k, Holy Trinity Column, Olomouc, vert.

Perf. 11½x11¾, 11¾x11½
2002, Sept. 11 **Engr.**
3177-3178 A1199 Set of 2 2.75 2.00

Nos. 3177-3178 were each issued in sheets of 8. Value, set $25.

Emil Zátopek (1922-2000), Olympic Long Distance Runner — A1216

Photo. & Engr.
2002, Sept. 11 **Perf. 11¼x11¾**
3179 A1216 9k multi 1.00 .35

Pres. Havel Type of 1998
Photo. & Engr.
2002, Nov. 6 **Perf. 11¾x11¼**
3180 A1134 6.40k pur & blue .75 .25

St. Nicholas' Day A1217

Christmas A1218

2002, Nov. 6 **Perf. 11¼x11½**
3181 A1217 6.40k multi .75 .25
a. Booklet pane of 8 + 2 labels 6.00
Complete booklet, #3181a 6.00

2002, Nov. 13
3182 A1218 6.40k multi .75 .25

NATO Summit, Prague — A1219

2002, Nov. 14 **Perf. 11¼x11¾**
3183 A1219 9k multi 1.00 .30

Furniture — A1220

Designs: 6.40k, Armchair, 17th cent. 9k, Sewing table with hemispheric cover, 1820. 12k, Dressing table with mirror, 1860. 17k, Art deco amchair, 1923.

2003, Dec. 11
3184-3187 A1220 Set of 4 5.50 2.25

Art Type of 1967 Inscribed "CESKA REPUBLIKA"

Designs: 12k, The Abandoned, by Jaroslav Panuska, horiz. 20k, St. Wenceslas, by Mikolás Ales. 26k, Portrait of a Young Man with a Lute, by Jan Petr Molitor.

2002, Dec. 11 **Engr.** **Perf. 11¾**
3188-3190 A565 Set of 3 7.25 3.75

Nos. 3188-3190 were each issued in sheets of 4. Value, set $27.

Souvenir Sheet

10. VÝROČÍ
ČESKÉ REPUBLIKY

Czech Republic, 10th Anniv. — A1221

Litho. & Engr.
2003, Jan. 1 *Perf. 11¾*
3191 A1221 25k multi 3.00 1.60

Tradition of Czech Stamp Production — A1222

Photo. & Engr.
2003, Jan. 20 *Perf. 11¼x11¾*
3192 A1222 6.40k Type A75 .75 .25
  a.   Booklet pane of 8 + 2 labels 6.00 —
    Complete booklet, #3192a 6.00

Famous Men — A1223

Designs: 6.40k, Jaroslav Vrchlicky (1853-1912), poet. 8k, Josef Thomayer (1853-1927), physician and writer.

2003, Feb. 12 *Perf. 11½x11¼*
3193-3194 A1223 Set of 2 1.60 .50

Easter — A1224

2003, Mar. 26 *Perf. 11¼x11½*
3195 A1224 6.40k multi .75 .25

Roses Above Prague — A1225

Perf. 12¾x13¼
             Litho.
3196 A1225 6.40k multi + label .75 .35
  Labels could be personalized.
  Issued in sheets of 9 stamps and 12 labels. Value $9.

Lace A1226

Designs: 6.40k, Netted lace. 9k, Bobbin lace.

Photo. & Engr.
2003, Mar. 26 *Perf. 11¼*
3197 A1226 6.40k bl, dk bl & red .75 .25
  a.   Booklet pane of 6 + 4 labels 4.50 —
    Complete booklet, #3197a 4.50
3198 A1226 9k dk bl, bl & red 1.00 .35
  a.   Booklet pane of 6 + 4 labels 6.00 —
    Complete booklet, #3197a 6.00

Europa — A1227

Litho. & Engr.
2003, May 7 *Perf. 11¾*
3199 A1227 9k multi 1.00 .65

Geologic Attractions — A1228

Designs: 12k, Sandstone towers, Hrubá Skála Region. 14k, Punkva Caves, Moravian karst area.

2003, May 7 Engr. *Perf. 11½x11¾*
3200-3201 A1228 Set of 2 3.25 2.00
  Nos. 3200-3201 were each issued in sheets of 8. Value, set $25.

Mach and Sebestova, Children's Television Show Characters — A1229

Photo. & Engr.
2003, May 28 *Perf. 11¼x11½*
3202 A1229 6.40k multi .75 .35

First Electric Railway, Tábor — Bechyne, Cent. A1230

2003, May 28 *Perf. 11¾x11¼*
3203 A1230 10k multi 1.25 .50

A1231   A1233

A1232

Observation towers: No. 3204, 6.40k, Klet. No. 3205, 6.40k, Slovanka.

2003, May 28 *Perf. 11¼x11½*
3204-3205 A1231 Set of 2 1.60 .50

2003, June 25 *Perf. 11¾x11¼*
3206 A1232 9k multi 1.00 .35
  European Shooting Championships, Plzen and Brno.

2003, June 25 *Perf. 11¼x11½*
3207 A1233 9k multi 1.00 .35
  Josef Dobrovsky (1753-1829), linguist.

Pres. Vaclav Klaus — A1234

Photo. & Engr.
2003 *Perf. 11¾x11¼*
3208 A1234 6.40k buff, red & vio bl .75 .35
3209 A1234 6.50k Prus bl & pur .75 .35
  Issued: 6.40k, 7/30; 6.50k, 11/5. See No. 3264.

Souvenir Sheet

Tropical Fish — A1235

No. 3210: a, 12k, Betta splendens (27x44mm). b, 14k, Pterophyllum scalare (27x44mm). c, 16k, Carassius auratus (54x44mm). d, 20k, Symphysodon aequifasciatus (54x44mm).

Litho. & Engr.
2003, Sept. 10 *Perf. 11¾*
3210 A1235 Sheet of 4, #a-d 7.50 5.00

Oriental Carpets A1236

Designs: 9k, Turkish prayer carpet, 19th cent. 12k, Turkish carpet, 18th cent.

2003, Oct. 1 Engr. *Perf. 11¾*
3211-3212 A1236 Set of 2 2.50 1.75
  Nos. 3211-3212 were each issued in sheets of 4. Value, set $10.

Tympanum, Porta Coeli Monastery, Predklásterí — A1237

Photo. & Engr.
2003, Oct. 15 *Perf. 11¾x11¼*
3213 A1237 6.50k multi .75 .45
  a.   Booklet pane of 8 + 4 labels 6.00 —
    Complete booklet, #3213a 6.00

Birds of Prey — A1238

Designs: 6.50k, Milvus milvus. 8k, Falco peregrinus. 9k, Hieraaetus pennatus.

2003, Oct. 15 *Perf. 11¼x11½*
3214 A1238 6.50k multi .75 .25
    Booklet, 5 #3214 3.75
3215 A1238 8k multi .90 .30
    Booklet, 5 #3215 4.50
3216 A1238 9k multi 1.00 .30
    Booklet, 5 #3216 5.00
    Nos. 3214-3216 (3) 2.65 .85

Czech Fire Fighters, 140th Anniv. A1239

Fire engines: 6.50k, Wooden fire engine, 1822. 9k, Motorized fire engine, 1933. 12k, CAS 8/Avia Daewoo fire truck, 2002.

2003, Oct. 15 *Perf. 11¾x11¼*
3217-3219 A1239 Set of 3 3.50 1.50

Flower Type of 2002
Designs: 50h, Cornflower (chrpa). 6.50k, Dahlia (jirina).

2003, Oct. 22
3220 A1215 50h multi .20 .20
3221 A1215 6.50k multi .75 .25

Roses Over Prague Type of 2003 and

Prague Castle Lantern — A1240

2003, Oct. 22 Litho. *Perf. 12¾x13¼*
3222 A1225 6.50k multi + label .75 .25
3223 A1240 9k multi + label 1.00 .30
  Labels could be personalized.
  Nos. 3222-3223 were each issued in sheets of 9 stamps and 12 labels. Value, set $17.50.

Art Type of 1967 Inscribed "CESKA REPUBLIKA"
Designs: 17k, Poor Countryside, by Max Svabinsky, horiz. 20k, Autumn in Veltrusy, by Antonín Slavícek. 26k, Eleanora de Toledo, by Agnolo Bronzino.

2003, Nov. 5 Engr. *Perf. 11¾*
3224-3226 A565 Set of 3 7.75 4.00
  Nos. 3224-3226 were each issued in sheets of 4. Value, set $30.

Christmas
A1241

Photo. & Engr.
2003, Nov. 5   *Perf. 11¼x11½*
3227 A1241 6.50k multi   .75 .35

Tradition of Czech
Stamp Production
A1242

Photo. & Engr.
2004, Jan. 20   *Perf. 11¼x11¾*
3228 A1242 6.50k Vignette of
              #1703   .75 .35
  a.   Booklet pane of 8 + 4 labels   6.00
      Complete booklet, #3228a   6.00

Church of the Assumption of the Virgin
Mary, Brno — A1243

2004, Feb. 18   **Engr.**   *Perf. 11¾*
3229 A1243 17k multi   2.00 1.00

Brno 2005 Philatelic Exhibition.
No. 3229 was issued in sheets of 4. Value
$8.

Industrial
Building
Historical
Preservation
A1244

Designs: 6.50k, Busek's Water Forging
Hammer, Lniste. 17k, Iron Furnace, Stará Hut
u Adamova.

Photo. & Engr.
2004, Feb. 18   *Perf. 11½x11¼*
3230-3231 A1244   Set of 2   2.75 .90

Easter
A1245

2004, Mar. 17
3232 A1245 6.50k multi   .75 .25

**Art Type of 1967 Inscribed "CESKA
REPUBLIKA"**

Design: Prometheus, by Antonín
Procházka.

2004, Mar. 17   *Perf. 11¾*
3233 A565 26k multi   3.25 1.60

Brno 2005 Philatelic Exhibition. No. 3233
was issued in sheets of 4. Value $12.

World Ice Hockey
Championships,
Prague and
Ostrava — A1246

Photo. & Engr.
2004, Apr. 14   *Perf. 11¼x11¾*
3234 A1246 12k multi   1.50 .50

Admission to
European
Union
A1247

Photo. & Engr.
2004, May 1   *Perf. 11¼*
3235 A1247 9k multi   1.00 .35

Admission to the European
Union — A1248

2004, May 1   **Litho.**   *Perf. 11¾x11¼*
3236 A1248 9k multi   1.00 .35

No. 3236 was issued in sheets of 10. Value
$8.

Europa
A1249

2004, May 5   *Perf. 11¼*
3237 A1249 9k multi   1.00 .35

Composers of
Czech
Operas — A1250

Designs: 6.50k, Dalibor, by Bedrich
Smetana (1824-84). 8k, Jakobín, by Antonín
Dvorák (1841-1904). 10k, Její Pastorkyna, by
Leos Janácek (1854-1928).

Photo. & Engr.
2004, May 5   *Perf. 11¼x11¾*
3238-3240 A1250   Set of 3   3.00 1.10

For Children
A1251

Photo. & Engr.
2004, May 26   *Perf. 11½x11¼*
3241 A1251 6.50k multi   .75 .25
  a.   Booklet pane of 8 + 2 labels   6.00
      Complete booklet, #3241a   6.00

Statue of Radegast,
by Albín
Polásek — A1252

2004, May 26   *Perf. 11¼x11½*
3242 A1252 6.50k multi   .75 .25

Brno 2005 Philatelic Exhibition.

Tourist Attractions — A1253

Designs: 12k, Holy Mountain, Príbram. 14k,
Holy Shrine, Bystrice pod Hostynem.

2004, May 26   **Engr.**   *Perf. 11½x11¾*
3243-3244 A1253   Set of 2   3.25 1.50

Nos. 3243-3244 were each issued in sheets
of 8. Value, set $24.

A1254   A1255

Photo. & Engr.
2004, June 23   *Perf. 11¼x11¾*
3245 A1254 6.50k multi   .75 .25

2004 Paralympics, Athens.

2004, June 23
3246 A1255 9k multi   1.00 .35

2004 Summer Olympics, Athens.

Petrarch (1304-74), Poet — A1256

2004, June 23   *Perf. 11¾x11¼*
3247 A1256 14k multi   1.75 .60

Famous
Trees — A1257

Designs: 6.50k, Singing lime tree, Telecí. 8k,
Jan Zizka oak tree, Podhradí.

Photo. & Engr.
2004, Sept. 8   *Perf. 11¼x11½*
3248 A1257 6.50k multi   .75 .25
      Complete booklet, 5 #3248   3.75
3249 A1257   8k multi   .90 .30
      Complete booklet, 5 #3249   4.50

Miniature Sheet

Parrots — A1258

No. 3250: a, 12k, Melopsittacus undulatus.
b, 14k, Agapornis personata. c, 16k, Psittacula
krameri. d, 20k, Ara chloroptera.

Litho. & Engr.
2004, Sept. 8   *Perf. 11¾*
3250 A1258   Sheet of 4, #a-d, +
           4 labels   7.50 4.50

Compulsory School
Attendance, 230th
Anniv. — A1259

Photo. & Engr.
2004, Sept. 29   *Perf. 11¼x11½*
3251 A1259 6.50k multi   .75 .25

Baby
Carriages — A1260

Carriages made about: 12k, 1880. 14k,
1890. 16k, 1900.

2004, Oct. 20
3252-3254 A1260   Set of 3   5.25 2.00

**Art Type of 1967 Inscribed "CESKA
REPUBLIKA"**

Designs: 20k, On the Outskirts of the Cesky
Ráj Region, by Alois Bubák, horiz. 22k, The
Long, the Broad and the Sharpsight, by Hanus
Schwaiger. 26k, The Spring, by Vojtéch
Hynais.

2004, Nov. 10   **Engr.**   *Perf. 11¾*
3255-3257 A565   Set of 3   8.50 4.25

Nos. 3255-3257 were each issued in sheets
of 4. Value, set $32.

Christmas — A1261

Photo. & Engr.
2004, Nov. 10   *Perf. 11¼x11½*
3258 A1261 6.50k multi   .75 .25

Tradition of Czech Stamp Production
A1262

2005, Jan. 18 *Perf. 11¼x11¾*
3259 A1262 6.50k Design of
#975 .75 .30
a. Booklet pane of 8 + 4 labels 6.00
Complete booklet, #3259a 6.00

Peacock and Bugler Portal
Decoration — A1263

2005, Jan. 18 Litho. *Perf. 12¾x13¼*
3260 A1263 7.50k multi + label .85 .30
Labels could be personalized for an additional fee.
Issued in sheets of 9 stamps and 12 labels. Value $8.
See No. 3372.

Souvenir Sheet

Moonscape, by Petr Ginz — A1264

Perf. 11¾x11½
2005, Jan. 18 Litho. & Engr.
3261 A1264 31k multi 3.75 2.00

Flower Type of 2002
Designs: 7.50k, Lily (lilie). 19k, Fuchsia (fuchsie).

Photo. & Engr.
2005 *Perf. 11¾x11¼*
3262 A1215 7.50k multi .85 .30
3263 A1215 19k multi 2.25 .85
Issued: 7.50k, 1/20; 19k, 3/2.

Pres. Vaclav Klaus Type of 2003
2005, Feb. 9
3264 A1234 7.50k claret & red .85 .30

Granny, by Bozena Nemcová, 150th Anniv. of Publication
A1265

2005, Feb. 9 *Perf. 11¼x11¾*
3265 A1265 7.50k multi .85 .30

Easter — A1266

Photo. & Engr.
2005, Mar. 2 *Perf. 11¼x11½*
3266 A1266 7.50k multi .85 .30

UNESCO World Heritage Sites Type of 2001
Designs: 14k, St. Prokop's Basilica, Trebíc, vert. 16k, Villa Tugendhat, Brno.

Perf. 11¾x11½, 11½x11¾
2005, Mar. 23 **Engr.**
3267-3268 A1199 Set of 2 3.50 1.90
Nos. 3267-32682 were each issued in sheets of 8. Value, set $28.

Famous Men — A1267

Designs: 7.50k, Bohuslav Brauner (1855-1935), chemist. 12k, Adalbert Stifter (1805-68), writer, painter. 19k, Mikulás Dacicky of Heslov (1555-1626), poet.

Photo. & Engr.
2005, Apr. 13 *Perf. 11¼x11¾*
3269-3271 A1267 Set of 3 4.50 1.60

Europa
A1268

2005, May 4 Litho. *Perf. 11¼*
3272 A1268 9k multi 1.00 .35

Battle of Austerlitz, Bicent. — A1269

Napoleon Before the Battle of Austerlitz, by Louis-François Lejeune — A1270

Photo. & Engr.
2005, May 4 *Perf. 11¾x11¼*
3273 A1269 19k multi 2.25 .90
Souvenir Sheet
Litho. & Engr.
Perf. 11¾
3274 A1270 30k multi 3.50 2.25
Brno 2005 Stamp Exhibition (#3274). See France No. 3115.

Kremílek and Vochomurka, by Václav Ctvrtek — A1271

Photo. & Engr.
2005, May 25 *Perf. 11¼x11½*
3275 A1271 7.50k multi .85 .30
a. Booklet pane of 8 + 2 labels 7.00
Complete booklet, #3275a 7.00

A1272 A1273

2005, May 25 *Perf. 11¼x11¾*
3276 A1272 12k multi 1.40 .75
Intl. Year of Physics.

2005, June 22
3277 A1273 9k multi 1.00 .50
2005 European Baseball Championships.

Souvenir Sheet

Protected Flora and Fauna of the Krkonose Mountains — A1274

No. 3278: a, 12k, Viola lutea sudetica, Hedysarum hedysaroides (44x28mm). b, 14k, Cinclus cinclus, Leucojum vernum (44x28mm). c, 15k, Sorex alpinus, Salamandra salamandra, Primula minima (44x54mm). d, 22k, Mt. Snezka, Luscinia svecica svecica, Aeschna coerulea, Pneumonanthe asclepiadea (44x54mm).

Litho. & Engr.
2005, June 22 *Perf. 11¾*
3278 A1274 Sheet of 4, #a-d, +
4 labels 7.50 4.25

Church Bells — A1275

Bells from: 7.50k, Benesov, 1322, Havlíckuv Brod, 1335. 9k, Dobrs, 1561, 1596. 12k, Olomouc, 1827.

Photo. & Engr.
2005, Sept. 7 *Perf. 11½x11¾*
3279 A1275 7.50k multi .85 .30
Complete booklet, 5 #3279 4.25
3280 A1275 9k multi 1.00 .40
Complete booklet, 5 #3280 5.00
3281 A1275 12k multi 1.40 .50
Complete booklet, 5 #3281 7.00
Nos. 3279-3281 (3) 3.25 1.20

Tractors
A1276

Designs: 7.50k, 1923 John Deere 15/27. 9k, 1921 Lanz Bulldog HL-12, 1596. 18k, 1937 Skoda HT 40.

2005, Sept. 21 *Perf. 11½x11¼*
3282 A1276 7.50k multi .85 .30
Complete booklet, 5 #3282 4.25
3283 A1276 9k multi 1.00 .35
Complete booklet, 5 #3283 5.00
3284 A1276 18k multi 2.00 .75
Complete booklet, 5 #3284 10.00
Nos. 3282-3284 (3) 3.85 1.40

World Summit on the Information Society, Tunis
A1277

2005, Sept. 21 *Perf. 11¼*
3285 A1277 9k org & violet 1.00 .35

Curling
A1278

Photo. & Engr.
2005, Oct. 12 *Perf. 11¾x11¼*
3286 A1278 17k multi 2.00 .70

Art Type of 1967 Inscribed "CESKA REPUBLIKA"
Designs: 22k, Summer Landscape, by Adolf Kosárek. 25k, Deinotherium, by Zdenék Burian. 26k, Osiky Near Velké Nemcice, by Alois Kalvoda.

2005, Nov. 9 **Engr.** *Perf. 11¾*
3287-3289 A565 Set of 3 8.50 5.25
Nos. 3287-3289 were each issued in sheets of 4. Value, set $32.50.

A1279

Christmas
A1280

Photo. & Engr.

2005, Nov. 9		**Perf. 11¼x11½**	
3290	A1279 7.50k multi	.85	.30

Perf. 11½x11¼

| 3291 | A1280 9k multi | 1.00 | .35 |

Tradition of Czech
Stamp Production
A1281

Photo. & Engr.

2006, Jan. 20		**Perf. 11¼x11¾**	
3292	A1281 7.50k Portion of #C59	.85	.30
a.	Booklet pane of 8 + 2 labels	7.00	—
	Complete booklet, #3292a	7.00	

Flower Type of 2002

Designs: 11k, Marshmallow (ibisek). 24k,
Daffodil (narcis).

2006		**Perf. 11¾x11¼**	
3293	A1215 11k multi	1.25	.45
3294	A1215 24k multi	2.75	1.00

Issued: 11k, 2/1; 24k, 2/22.

Flowers — A1282

Flowers, Grapes, Glass of
Wine — A1283

2006		**Litho.**	**Perf. 12¾x13¼**	
3295	A1282 10k multi + label	1.10	.60
3296	A1283 12k multi + label	1.40	.75

Issued: 10k, 2/1; 12k, 2/22. Labels could be
personalized for an additional fee.
Nos. 3295-3296 were issued in sheets of 9
stamps and 12 labels. Value, set $22.50.
See No. 3373.

Madonna of Zbraslav — A1284

2006, Feb. 8		**Engr.**	**Perf. 11¾**	
3297	A1284 25k multi		3.00	1.75

Printed in sheets of 4. Value $11.

2006 Winter Paralympics,
Turin — A1285

Photo. & Engr.

2006, Feb. 8		**Perf. 11¾x11¼**	
3298	A1285 7.50k multi	.85	.30

2006 Winter
Olympics,
Turin — A1286

2006		**Perf. 11¼x11¾**	
3299	A1286 9k multi	1.00	.40

**With "K. NEUMANNOVA / ZLATA
MEDAILE" Overprinted in Red
Reading Up**

3300	A1286 9k multi	1.00	.40

Issued: No. 3299, 2/8; No. 3300, 3/15.

Famous
Men — A1287

Designs: 11k, Frantisek Josef Gerstner
(1756-1832), mathematician and educator.
12k, Jaroslav Jezek (1906-42), composer.
19k, Sigmund Freud (1856-1939),
psychoanalyst.

2006, Feb. 22		**Perf. 11½x11¼**	
3301-3303	A1287	Set of 3	4.75 1.75

Easter — A1288

2006, Mar. 22		**Perf. 11¼x11½**	
3304	A1288 7.50k multi	.85	.30

Osek Monastery — A1289

Kokorinsko Capstones — A1290

2006, Mar. 22		**Engr.**	**Perf. 11½x11¾**	
3305	A1289 12k multi	1.40	.65
3306	A1290 15k multi	1.75	.85

Nos. 3305-3306 were each issued in sheets
of 8. Value, set $25.

Love — A1291

Photo. & Engr.

2006, Apr. 26		**Perf. 11¼x11½**	
3307	A1291 7.50k multi	.85	.35
	Complete booklet, 5 #3307	4.25	

Europa
A1292

Silhouette of person and: 10k, Horse. 20k,
Dog.

2006, May 3		**Perf. 11¾x11¼**	
3308-3309	A1292	Set of 2	3.50 1.40

Rumcajs, Manka
and Cipísek, by V.
Ctvrtek — A1293

Photo. & Engr.

2006, May 31		**Perf. 11¼x11½**	
3310	A1293 7.50k multi	.85	.35
a.	Booklet pane of 8 + 2 labels	7.00	—
	Complete booklet, #3310a	7.00	

A1294   A1295

2006, June 14		**Perf. 11¼x11¾**	
3311	A1294 19k multi	2.25	.90

Kamenice Pass, Czech Switzerland
National Park.

2006, June 14

Jewelry with garnets: 15k, Silver brooch
with pearl, 1904. 18k, Gold pendant, 1930.

3312-3313	A1295	Set of 2	4.00 1.75

Miniature Sheet

Bohemian Kings of Premyslid
Dynasty — A1296

No. 3314: a, 12k, Otakar I Premysl (c. 1155-
1230). b, 14k, Václav (Wenceslas) I (1205-53).
c, 15k, Otakar II Premysl (1230-78). d, 22k,
Václav (Wenceslas) II (1271-1305). e, 28k,
Václav (Wenceslas) III (1289-1306).

2006, June 14		**Engr.**	**Perf. 11¾**	
3314	A1296 Sheet of 5, #a-e, + label		10.50 6.00

Souvenir Sheet

Mosaic of Prague Castle, by Giovanni
Castrucci — A1297

2006, Sept. 13		**Litho. & Engr.**	**Perf. 11¾**	
3315	A1297 35k multi		4.00 2.00

Cacti — A1298

No. 3316: a, Gymnocalycium denudatum. b,
Obregonia denegrii.
No. 3317: a, Astrophytum asterias. b, Cintia
knizei.

Perf. 11¼x11¾

2006, Sept. 13　　**Litho.**
3316　A1298　7.50k Pair, #a-b　1.75　.90
　　Complete booklet, 2 #3316a, 3
　　#3316b　　4.25
3317　A1298　10k Pair, #a-b　2.40　1.25
　　Complete booklet, 2 #3317a, 3
　　#3317b　　6.00

Ecology
A1299

2006, Sept. 27　　**Perf. 11¾x11¼**
3318　A1299　7.50k multi　　.70　.35

Christmas — A1300

2006, Oct. 11　　**Perf. 12¾x13¼**
3319　A1300　7.50k multi + label　.70　.35

Printed in sheets of 9 stamps + 12 labels. Labels could be personalized.

Vrtbovská Garden, Prague — A1301

Photo. & Engr.
2006, Oct. 11　　**Perf. 11½x11¾**
3320　A1301　7.50k multi　　.70　.35
　a.　Booklet pane of 8 + 4 labels　5.75　—
　　Complete booklet, #3320a　5.75

Praga 2008 Intl. Philatelic Exhibition, Prague.

Wooden Churches — A1302

Designs: 7.50k, Church of the Virgin Mary, Broumov. 19k, Church of St. Andrew, Hodslavice.

Photo. & Engr.
2006, Oct. 11　　**Perf. 11¾x11¼**
3321-3322　A1302　Set of 2　3.25　1.60

Art Type of 1967 Inscribed "CESKA REPUBLIKA"

Designs: 22k, Still Life with Fruit, by Jan Davidsz de Heem. 25k, Montenegrin Madonna, by Jaroslav Cermák. 28k, Pod Suchym Skalim, by Frantisek Kaván, horiz.

2006, Nov. 8　**Engr.**　**Perf. 11¾**
3323-3325　A565　Set of 3　9.00　4.50

Christmas — A1303

Photo. & Engr.
2006, Nov. 8　　**Perf. 11¾x11½**
3326　A1303　7.50k multi　　.75　.35

Emblem of Praga 2008 Intl. Philatelic Exhibition — A1304

2006, Dec. 1　　**Litho.**
3327　A1304　7.50k multi　　.75　.35

See Nos. 3341, 3368.

Czech Technical University, Prague, 300th Anniv. — A1305

Photo. & Engr.
2007, Jan. 10　　**Perf. 11¾x11½**
3328　A1305　9k multi　　1.00　.50

Famous Men — A1306

Designs: 7.50k, Frána Srámek (1877-1952), writer. 19k, Karel Slavoj Amerling (1807-84), educator.

2007, Jan. 10　　**Perf. 11½x11¼**
3329-3330　A1306　Set of 2　3.00　1.40

Tradition of Czech Stamp Production A1307

2007, Jan. 20　　**Perf. 11½x11¾**
3331　A1307　7.50k Type A242　.70　.35
　a.　Booklet pane of 8 + 4 labels　5.75　—
　　Complete booklet, #3331a　5.75

Cancer Prevention A1308

Photo. & Engr.
2007, Feb. 21　　**Perf. 11¼x11½**
3332　A1308　7.50k multi　　.70　.35

Snake — A1309

Perf. 11¼x11¾
2007, Feb. 21　　**Litho.**
3333　A1309　12k multi　　1.40　.70

Oriental Art A1310

Designs: 12k, Girl with a Puppet, by Kunisawa Utagawa. 24k, Siva, Parvati and Ganesa, 19th cent. Indian glass painting.

Litho. & Engr.
2007, Feb. 21　　**Perf. 11¾**
3334-3335　A1310　Set of 2　4.25　2.10

Easter — A1311

Photo. & Engr.
2007, Mar. 14　　**Perf. 11¼x11½**
3336　A1311　7.50k multi　　.75　.35

Model of Mala Strana Area of Prague, by Antonín Langweil — A1312

2007, Mar. 14　　**Perf. 11¾x11¼**
3337　A1312　7.50k multi　　.75　.35

Praga 2008 Intl. Philatelic Exhibition, Prague.

Stoclet House, Brussels, Designed by Josef Hoffmann — A1313

Designs: 20k, Building interior. 35k, Building exterior.

2007, Mar. 26　　**Perf. 11¼x11¾**
3338-3339　A1313　Set of 2　6.50　3.25

See Belgium Nos. 2228-2229.

Flowers Type of 2006
Perf. 12¾x13¼
2007, Mar. 26　　**Litho.**
3340　A1282　11k multi + label　1.25　.60

Label could be personalized for an additional fee.

Praga 2008 Emblem Type of 2006
2007, Apr. 4　　**Perf. 11¾x11½**
3341　A1304　11k blue & multi　1.25　.60

Spas A1314

Designs: 12k, Jurkovic House, Luhacovice. 15k, Gocár Pavillion, Lázne Bohdanec.

2007, Apr. 4　**Engr.**　**Perf. 11½x11¾**
3342-3343　A1314　Set of 2　3.25　1.75

Europa A1315

Photo. & Engr.
2007, May 9　　**Perf. 11¼**
3344　A1315　11k multi　　1.25　.60

Scouting, cent.

Flowers Type of 2002

Designs: 1k, Cyclamen (bramborik). 15k, Tropaeolum (lichorerisnice). 23k, Geranium (pelargonie).

Photo. & Engr.
2007　　**Perf. 11¾x11¼**
3345　A1215　1k multi　　.25　.25
3346　A1215　15k multi　　1.75　.90
3347　A1215　23k multi　　2.50　1.25
　Nos. 3345-3347 (3)　4.50　2.40

Issued: 1k, 23k, 5/9. 15k, 9/5.

Fast Arrows, Comic Strip by Jaroslav Foglar A1316

Photo. & Engr.
2007, May 30　　**Perf. 11¾x11¼**
3348　A1316　7.50k multi　　.75　.35
　a.　Booklet pane of 8 + 4 labels　6.00　—
　　Complete booklet, #3348a　6.00

Historic Stoves — A1317

Designs: 7.50k, Gothic era stove, Olomouc, and tile. 12k, Renaissance era stove, Rícany u Prahy and tile.

Photo. & Engr.
2007, June 20　　**Perf. 11½x11¾**
3349　A1317　7.50k multi　　.70　.35
　　Complete booklet, 5 #3349　3.50
3350　A1317　12k multi　　1.25　.60
　　Complete booklet, 5 #3350　6.25

Souvenir Sheet

Vaclav Hollar (1607-77), Engraver — A1318

Litho. & Engr.

2007, June 20   **Perf. 11¾**
3351 A1318 35k multi + 2 labels   4.25 2.10

Souvenir Sheet

Charles Bridge, Prague, 650th Anniv. — A1319

2007, June 20
3352 A1319 45k multi   5.25 3.00

Praga 2008 World Philatelic Exhibition.

First Movie Theater in Prague, Cent. A1320

Photo. & Engr.

2007, Sept. 5   **Perf. 11¾x11¼**
3353 A1320 7.50k multi   .75 .35

Didactica Opera Omnia, by Comenius, 350th Anniv. — A1321

2007, Sept. 5
3354 A1321 12k multi   1.40 .75

Miniature Sheet

Flora and Fauna of the White Carpathians — A1322

No. 3355: a, 9k, Ophrys holosericea (27x44mm). b, 10k, Colias myrmidone, Anacamptis pyramidalis (27x44mm). c, 11k, Ophrys apifera (27x44mm). d, 12k, Coracias garrulus, Gymnadenia densiflora (54x44mm).

Litho. & Engr.

2007, Sept. 5   **Perf. 11¾**
3355 A1322   Sheet of 4, #a-d, +   5.00 2.75
           4 labels

Emil Holub (1847-1902), Naturalist — A1323

Photo. & Engr.

2007, Oct. 3   **Perf. 11¾x11¼**
3356 A1323 11k multi   1.25 .65

Water Towers — A1324

Towers in: 7.50k, Karviná. 18k, Plzen.

2007, Oct. 3   **Perf. 11¼x11¾**
3357-3358 A1324   Set of 2   3.00 1.50

Art Type of 1967 Inscribed "CESKA REPUBLIKA"

Designs: 22k, Vrbicany Castle, by Amálie Mánesova, horiz. 25k, Way to Bechnye Castle, by Otakar Lebeda. 28k, Montmartre, by Sobeslav Hippolyt Pinkas, horiz.

2007, Nov. 7   **Engr.**   **Perf. 11¾**
3359-3361 A565   Set of 3   9.00 4.50

Christmas — A1325

Photo. & Engr.

2007, Nov. 7   **Perf. 11¼x11½**
3362 A1325 7.50k multi   .85 .40

Flower Type of 2002

Design: 2.50k, Gaillardia (kokarda); 3k, Azalea (azalka); 10k, Rose (ruze); 21k, Gerbera daisy (gerbera).

Photo. & Engr.

2007-08   **Perf. 11¾x11¼**
3363 A1215 2.50k multi   .30 .20
3364 A1215   3k multi   .40 .20
3365 A1215   10k multi   1.25 .60
3366 A1215   21k multi   2.60 1.40
      Nos. 3363-3366 (4)   4.55 2.40

Issued: 2.50k, 12/12/07; 3k, 3/19/08; 10k, 1/30/08; 21k, 3/5/08.

Czech Republic's Entry Into Schengen Border-Free Zone A1326

2007, Dec. 19   **Litho.**   **Perf. 11¼**
3367 A1326 10k multi   1.10 .55

Praga 2008 Emblem Type of 2006

2007, Dec. 19   **Perf. 11¾x11¼**
3368 A1304 18k bl grn & blue   2.00 1.00

Tradition of Czech Stamp Production A1327

Photo. & Engr.

2008, Jan. 20   **Perf. 11¼x11¾**
3369 A1327 10k Type A311   1.25 .60
   a.   Booklet pane of 8 + 4 labels   10.00
      Complete booklet, #3369a   10.00

Famous Men — A1328

Designs: 11k, Karel Klostermann (1848-1923), writer. 14k, Josef Kajetán Tyl (1808-56), playwright.

2008, Jan. 20   **Perf. 11¼x11½**
3370-3371 A1328   Set of 2   3.00 1.50

Peacock and Bugler Type of 2005 and Flowers, Grapes and Glass of Wine Type of 2006 Redrawn

2008, Jan. 30 Litho.   **Perf. 12¾x13¼**
3372 A1263 10k multi + label   1.25 .60
3373 A1283 17k multi + label   2.00 1.00

Nos. 3372-3373 were issued in sheets of 9 stamps and 12 labels. Labels could be personalized for an additional fee.

George of Podebrady (1420-71), King of Bohemia — A1329

Photo. & Engr.

2008, Feb. 20   **Perf. 11¼x11¾**
3374 A1329 12k multi   1.50 .75

Intl. Year of Planet Earth A1330

2008, Feb. 20   **Litho.**   **Perf. 11¼**
3375 A1330 18k multi   2.25 1.10

Easter A1331

Photo. & Engr.

2008, Mar. 5   **Perf. 11½x11¼**
3376 A1331 10k multi   1.25 .60

Bath Servant Zuzana Carrying King Wenceslas IV Over the Vltava River, by J. Navrátil — A1332

2008, Mar. 5   **Perf. 11¾x11¼**
3377 A1332 10k multi   1.25 .60
   a.   Booklet pane of 8 + 4 labels   10.00
      Complete booklet, #3377a   10.00

Praga 2008 Intl. Philatelic Exhibition, Prague.

Publication of Orbis Pictus, Children's Picture Book, by Comenius, 350th Anniv. — A1333

2008, Mar. 19   **Perf. 11¼x11¾**
3378 A1333 10k multi   1.25 .60

Mountaintop Hotel With Broadcast Tower, Jested — A1334

Hradec Kralové Buildings and Monuments A1335

2008, Mar. 19   **Engr.**   **Perf. 11½**
3379 A1334 12k multi   1.50 .75
3380 A1335 15k multi   1.90 .95

Pres. Klaus Type of 2003

Photo. & Engr.

2008, Apr. 2   **Perf. 11¾x11¼**
3381 A1234 12k multi   1.25 .60

A1336   A1337

Items in National Technical Museum: 10k, Reichenbach-Ertel astronomical theodolite, c. 1830. 14k, 1935 Jawa 750 sports car, horiz. 18k, Märky, Bromovsky-Schulz gasoline combustion engine, c. 1889.

Perf. 11¼x11¾, 11¾x11¼
2008, Apr. 16   **Photo. & Engr.**
3382-3384 A1336   Set of 3   5.25 2.60

National Technical Museum, Prague, cent.

2008, Apr. 16   **Perf. 11¼x11¾**
3385 A1337 17k multi   2.10 1.10

Czech Hockey Association, cent.

Europa A1338

2008, May 7   **Litho.**   **Perf. 11¾x11¼**
3386 A1338 17k multi   2.10 1.10

The Doggy's and Pussy's Tales, Children's Book by Josef Capek A1339

Photo. & Engr.

2008, May 28 Perf. 11½x11¼
3387 A1339 10k multi 1.40 .70
  a. Booklet pane of 8 + 2 labels 11.50 —
    Complete booklet, #3387a 11.50

Souvenir Sheet

Ledeburk Gardens, Prague — A1340

Litho. & Engr.

2008, May 28 Perf. 11¾
3388 A1340 51k multi 6.75 3.25
Praga 2008 World Philatelic Exhibition.

Miniature Sheet

Flora and Fauna of Trebon Basin UNESCO Biosphere Reservation — A1341

No. 3389: a, 10k, Alcedo atthis (28x44mm). b, 12k, Lutra lutra and Spiraea salicifolia (54x44mm). c, 14k, Haliaeetus albicilla (54x44mm). d, 18k, Netta rufina and Nymphaea alba (54x44mm).

2008, May 28
3389 A1341 Sheet of 4, #a-d, + 7.00 3.50
    3 labels

2008 Paralympics, Beijing — A1342

Perf. 11¾x11¼
2008, June 18 Litho.
3390 A1342 10k multi 1.40 .70

2008 Summer Olympics, Beijing — A1343

2008, June 18
3391 A1343 18k multi 2.40 1.25

Explorers — A1344

Designs: 12k, Ferdinand Stolicka (1838-74), explorer of Himalayas. 21k, Alois Musil (1868-1944), explorer of Jordanian desert.

2008, June 18 Photo. & Engr.
3392-3393 A1344 Set of 2 4.50 2.25

Children's Book Illustration by Josef Palacek — A1345

2008, Sept. 3 Litho. Perf. 12¾x13¼
3394 A1345 10k multi + label 1.25 .60
Printed in sheets of 9 stamps + 12 labels. Labels could be personalized.

Emmaus Monastery, Prague — A1346

Photo. & Engr.
2008, Sept. 3 Perf. 11¼x11¾
3395 A1346 10k multi 1.25 .60
Praga 2008 World Philatelic Exhibition.

Applied Art Designers' Association, Cent. — A1347

2008, Sept. 3 Perf. 11¾x11¼
3396 A1347 26k multi 3.25 1.60

Karel Plicka (1894-1987), Photographer — A1348

Litho. & Engr.
2008, Sept. 12 Perf. 11¾
3397 A1348 35k multi + 2 labels 4.25 2.10
See Slovakia No. 548.

Souvenir Sheet

Mail Coach — A1349

2008, Sept. 12
3398 A1349 35k multi 4.25 2.10
Praga 2008 Intl. Stamp Exhibition, Prague, and 2008 Vienna Intl. Stamp Exhibition. See Austria No. 2172.

Stoves — A1350

Stove from: 10k, Sternberk Castle. 17k, Archbishop's Palace, Prague.

Photo. & Engr.
2008, Oct. 15 Perf. 11¼x11¾
3399 A1350 10k multi 1.10 .55
  Complete booklet, 5 #3399 5.50
3400 A1350 17k multi 1.90 .95
  Complete booklet, 5 #3400 9.50

Art Type of 1967 Inscribed "CESKA REPUBLIKA"

Designs: 23k, Vltava River at Klecany, by Zdenka Braunerová, horiz. 26k, Autumn Road, by Otakar Nejedly.

2008, Nov. 5 Engr. Perf. 11¾
3401-3402 A565 Set of 2 6.00 3.00

Souvenir Sheet

Allegory of Water, by Jan Jakub Hartman — A1351

2008, Nov. 5 Litho. & Engr.
3403 A1351 30k multi 3.50 1.75

Basket With Apples — A1352

Winter Scene — A1353

Mechanical Christmas Display — A1354

Photo. & Engr.
2008, Nov. 5 Perf. 11¼x11½
3404 A1352 10k multi 1.10 .55
Litho.
Perf. 12¾x13¼
3405 A1353 10k multi + label 1.10 .55
Souvenir Sheet
Litho. & Engr.
Perf. 11¾
3406 A1354 30k multi 3.50 1.75
Christmas. No. 3405 was printed in sheets of 9 stamps + 12 labels. Labels could be personalized.

Czech Republic Presidency of European Union, January to June 2009 — A1355

Perf. 11¾x11¼
2008, Nov. 25 Litho.
3407 A1355 17k multi + label 2.00 .90

Louis Braille (1809-52), Educator of the Blind — A1356

Charles Darwin (1809-82), Naturalist — A1357

2009, Jan. 2 Photo. & Engr.
3408 A1356 10k multi 1.10 .55
3409 A1357 12k multi 1.25 .60

Tradition of Czech Stamp Production A1358

2009, Jan. 20 Perf. 11¼x11¾
3410 A1358 10k Design of #980 1.00 .50
  a. Booklet pane of 8 + 4 labels 8.25
    Complete booklet, #3410a 8.25

Nordic World Skiing Championships, Liberec — A1359

Perf. 11¾x11¼
2009, Feb. 11 Litho.
3411 A1359 18k multi 1.90 1.90

Souvenir Sheet

Preservation of Polar Regions and Glaciers — A1360

Litho. & Engr.
2009, Feb. 11 **Perf. 11¾**
3412 A1360 35k multi 3.75 1.90

Easter A1361

Photo. & Engr.
2009, Mar. 18 **Perf. 11½x11¼**
3413 A1361 10k multi 1.10 .55

Lu Tung-pin, by Unknown Chinese Artist — A1362

Mythical Beings, by Unknown Balinese Artist — A1363

Litho. & Engr.
2009, Mar. 18 **Perf. 11¾**
3414 A1362 18k multi 2.00 1.00
3415 A1363 24k multi 2.75 1.40

Souvenir Sheet

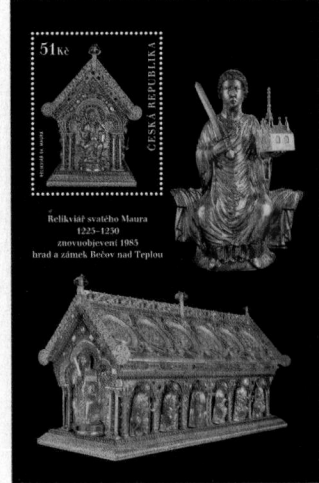

Reliquary of St. Maurus, Becov nad Teplou Castle — A1364

2009, Apr. 8
3416 A1364 51k multi 5.75 3.00

Pardubice to Liberec Rail Line, 150th Anniv. — A1365

Photo. & Engr.
2009, Apr. 22 **Perf. 11¾x11¼**
3417 A1365 10k multi 1.25 .60

Industry and Trade Ministry Building, 75th Anniv. A1366

Photo. & Engr.
2009, Apr. 22 **Perf. 11¾x11½**
3418 A1366 10k multi 1.25 .60

Europa A1367

2009, May 6 Litho. **Perf. 11¼**
3419 A1367 17k multi 2.00 1.00
Intl. Year of Astronomy.

Buildings A1368

Designs: 12k, Cistercian Monastery, Vyssí Brod. 14k, Horsovsky Castle, Tyn.

2009, May 6 Engr. **Perf. 11¾x11½**
3420-3421 A1368 Set of 2 3.00 1.50

Marionettes Spejbl and Hurvínek — A1369

Photo. & Engr.
2009, May 27 **Perf. 11¼x11½**
3422 A1369 10k multi 1.25 .60
   a. Booklet pane of 8 + 2 labels 9.00 —
     Complete booklet, #3422a 9.00

Rabbi Jehuda Löw (c. 1525-1609) A1370

2009, May 27 Litho. **Perf. 11¼x11¾**
3423 A1370 21k multi 2.50 1.25
Printed in sheets of 5 + 4 labels.

Granting of Religious Freedom by Rudolf II, 400th Anniv. A1371

Photo. & Engr.
2009, June 17 **Perf. 11¼**
3424 A1371 26k multi 3.00 1.50

Intl. Firefighters' Games, Ostrava — A1372

Perf. 11¾x11¼
2009, June 17 Litho.
3425 A1372 17k multi 2.00 1.00

Miniature Sheet

Krivoklát UNESCO Biosphere Reservation — A1373

No. 3426: a, 10k, Eudia pavonia (44x27mm). b, 12k, Aglia tau, Cervus elaphus (44x54mm). c, 14k, Bubo bubo, Lunaria

rediviva, Ciconia nigra (44x54mm). d, 17k, Tyto alba, Krivoklát Castle (44x54mm).

Litho. & Engr.
2009, Sept. 2 **Perf. 11¾**
3426 A1373 Sheet of 4, #a-d, + 4 labels 6.25 3.25

Souvenir Sheet

Bohemian-Moravian Highlands — A1374

2009, Sept. 2
3427 A1374 43k multi 5.00 2.50

Windmill, Ruprechtov A1375

Water Mill, Hoslovice A1376

Photo. & Engr.
2009, Sept. 23 **Perf. 11¼x11½**
3428 A1375 10k multi 1.25 .60
   Complete booklet, 5 #3428 6.25
Perf. 11½x11¼
3429 A1376 12k multi 1.40 .70
   Complete booklet, 5 #3429 7.00

Czech National Anthem, 175th Anniv. — A1377

2009, Oct. 14 **Perf. 11¼x11¾**
3430 A1377 10k multi 1.25 .60

Barbora Markéta Eliásová (1874-1957), Travel Writer — A1378

2009, Oct. 14 **Perf. 11¾x11¼**
3431 A1378 18k multi 2.10 1.10

Stoves — A1379

Designs: 10k, Empire stove, Litomysl Castle. 14k, Biedermeier stove, Vyskov Castle.

2009, Oct. 14		**Perf. 11¼x11¾**		
3432	A1379	10k multi	1.25	.60
	Complete booklet, 5 #3432		6.25	
3433	A1379	14k multi	1.60	.80
	Complete booklet, 5 #3433		8.00	

Protest Rallies of Nov. 17, 1939, and Nov. 17, 1989 — A1380

2009, Nov. 4		**Litho.**		
3434	A1380	14k multi	1.60	.80

Art Type of 1967 Inscribed "CESKA REPUBLIKA"

Designs: 24k, Canal Lock in Moret, by Alfred Sisley, horiz. 26k, Alley, by Alfred Justitz, horiz.

2009, Nov. 4		**Engr.**	**Perf. 11¾**	
3435-3436	A565	Set of 2	5.75	3.00

Souvenir Sheet

Oldrich and Bozena, by Frantisek Zenísek — A1381

Litho. & Engr.				
2009, Nov. 4		**Perf. 11¾**		
3437	A1381	34k multi	4.00	2.00

Christmas — A1382

Photo. & Engr.				
2009, Nov. 4		**Perf. 11¼x11½**		
3438	A1382	10k multi	1.25	.60

Tradition of Czech Stamp Production A1383

2010, Jan. 20		**Perf. 11¼x11¾**		
3439	A1383	10k Vignette of #2121	1.10	.55
a.	Booklet pane of 8 + 4 labels		9.00	—
	Complete booklet, #3439a		9.00	

Magdalena Dobromila Rettigová (1785-1845), Writer — A1384

2010, Jan. 20		**Perf. 11¾x11¼**		
3440	A1384	12k multi	1.25	.65

2010 Winter Olympics, Vancouver — A1385

2010, Feb. 10		**Perf. 11¼x11¾**		
3441	A1385	18k multi	1.90	.95

2010 Winter Paralympics, Vancouver — A1386

2010, Feb. 10				
3442	A1386	18k multi	1.90	.95

Souvenir Sheet

Expo 2010, Shanghai — A1387

2010, Feb. 10		**Litho.**		
3443	A1387	35k multi + 3 labels	3.75	1.90

Easter A1388

Photo. & Engr.				
2010, Mar. 10		**Perf. 11½x11¼**		
3444	A1388	10k multi	1.10	.55

Martina Sáblíková, Gold Medalist at 2010 Winter Olympic Games — A1389

Perf. 11¼x11¾				
2010, Mar. 24		**Litho.**		
3445	A1389	10k multi	1.10	.55

Souvenir Sheet

Karel Hynek Macha (1810-36), Writer — A1390

Perf. 11½x11¾				
2010, Mar. 10		**Litho. & Engr.**		
3446	A1390	43k multi	4.75	2.40

Enrique Stanko Vráz (1860-1932), Travel Writer — A1391

Photo. & Engr.				
2010, Apr. 14		**Perf. 11¾x11¼**		
3447	A1391	24k multi	2.50	1.25

19th Century Transcaucasian Carpets — A1392

Designs: 21k, Kasim Usak carpet. 24k, Celaberd carpet.

Litho. & Engr.				
2010, Apr. 14		**Perf. 11¾**		
3448-3449	A1392	Set of 2	4.75	2.40

Prague Castle — A1394

2010, May 5		**Engr.**	**Perf. 11¾**	
3451	A1394	17k brown	1.75	.85

Prague Castle in the Art of the Postage Stamp Exhibition, Prague. Printed in sheets of 4 + label.

Dásenka, Children's Book by Karel Capek A1395

2010, May 5		**Litho.**	**Perf. 11¼**	
3452	A1395	17k multi	1.75	.85

Europa.

Children's Book Illustration by Helena Zmatlíková (1923-2005) A1396

Photo. & Engr.				
2010, May 26		**Perf. 11¼x11½**		
3453	A1396	10k multi	.95	.45
a.	Booklet pane of 8 + 2 labels		7.75	
	Complete booklet, #3453a		7.75	

Alphonse Mucha (1860-1939), Illustrator — A1397

Designs: E, Gismonda. Z, Zodiac.

Serpentine Die Cut 14¼x14½				
2010, May 26			**Litho.**	
Booklet Stamps				
Self-Adhesive				
3454	A1397	E multi	1.60	.80
a.	Booklet pane of 6		9.75	
Size: 43x54mm				
Serpentine Die Cut 14½				
3455	A1397	Z multi	1.75	.85
a.	Booklet pane of 6		10.50	

No. 3454 sold for 17k and No. 3455 sold for 18k on day of issue.

Zd'árské Hills Protected Landscape — A1398

Photo. & Engr.				
2010, June 16		**Perf. 11¾x11½**		
3456	A1398	10k multi	1.00	.50

Marriage of John of Luxembourg and Elizabeth of Bohemia, 700th Anniv. — A1399

Photo. & Engr.				
2010, June 16		**Perf. 11¾x11¼**		
3457	A1399	17k multi	1.75	.85

Accession to the throne of Bohemia by the House of Luxembourg. See Luxembourg No. 1292.

Astronomical Clock, Prague, 600th Anniv. — A1400

2010, June 16		**Litho.**		
3458	A1400	21k multi	2.10	1.10

Towns — A1401

Designs: 12k, Klatovy. 14k, Stramberk.

2010, June 16			Engr.	
3459-3460	A1401	Set of 2	2.60	1.25

Czech Republic, Winners of 2010 World Ice Hockey Championships A1402

Perf. 11¼x11¾

2010, June 23			Litho.	
3461	A1402	10k multi	1.00	.50

SEMI-POSTAL STAMPS

Nos. B1-B123 were sold at 1½ times face value at the Philatelists' Window of the Prague P.O. for charity benefit. They were available for ordinary postage.

Almost all stamps between Nos. B1-B123 are known with misplaced or inverted overprints and/or in pairs with one stamp missing the overprint.

The overprints of Nos. B1-B123 have been well forged.

Austrian Stamps of 1916-18 Overprinted in Black or Blue

a

Two sizes of type A40:
Type I: 25x30mm.
Type II: 26x29mm.

1919			Perf. 12½	
B1	A37	3h brt violet	.20	.25
B2	A37	5h lt green	.20	.25
B3	A37	6h dp orange (Bl)	.60	.80
B4	A37	6h dp orange (Bk)	2,000.	2,000.
B5	A37	10h magenta	.80	1.00
B6	A37	12h lt blue	.80	.80
B7	A42	15h dull red	.20	.25
B8	A42	20h dark green	.20	.25
a.		20h green	55.00	40.00
B9	A42	25h blue	.35	.20
B10	A42	30h dull violet	.35	.35
B11	A39	40h olive grn	.40	.40
B12	A39	50h dk green	.40	.40
B13	A39	60h dp blue	.40	.40
B14	A39	80h orange brn	.40	.40
B15	A39	90h red violet	.80	.80
B16	A39	1k car, yel (Bl)	.60	.60
B17	A39	1k car, yel (Bk)	62.50	62.50
B18	A40	2k light blue (I)	3.25	3.25
a.		2k dark blue (II)	3,000.	2,000.
B19	A40	3k car rose (I)	37.50	32.50
a.		3k claret (I)	2,500.	900.00
B20	A40	4k yellow grn (I)	20.00	15.00
a.		4k deep green (I)	55.00	45.00
B21	A40	10k violet	300.00	160.00
a.		10k deep violet	375.00	275.00
b.		10k black violet	450.00	300.00

The used value of No. B18a is for a stamp that has only a Czechoslovakian cancellation. Some examples of Austria No. 160, which

were officially overprinted with type "a" and sold by the post office, had previously been used and lightly canceled with Austrian cancellations. These canceled-before-overprinting stamps, which were postally valid, sell for about one-fourth as much.

Granite Paper

B22	A40	2k light blue	4.00	2.90
B23	A40	3k carmine rose	10.00	8.25

The 4k and 10k on granite paper with this overprint were not regularly issued.
Excellent counterfeits of Nos. B1-B23 exist.

Austrian Newspaper Stamps Overprinted

b

Imperf
On Stamp of 1908

B26	N8	10h carmine	3,500.	2,000.

On Stamps of 1916

B27	N9	2h brown	.20	.20
B28	N9	4h green	.40	.40
B29	N9	6h deep blue	.40	.40
B30	N9	10h orange	5.00	5.00
B31	N9	30h claret	1.60	1.60
		Nos. B27-B31 (5)	7.60	7.60

Austrian Special Handling Stamps Overprinted in Blue or Black Stamps of 1916 Overprinted

c

Perf. 12½

B32	SH1	2h claret, yel (Bl)	25.00	25.00
B33	SH1	5h dp grn, yel (Bk)	1,900.	825.00

Stamps of 1917 Overprinted

d

B34	SH2	2h cl, yel (Bl)	.25	.35
a.		Vert. pair, imperf. btwn.	250.00	
B35	SH2	2h cl, yel (Bk)	60.00	35.00
B36	SH2	5h grn, yel (Bk)	.25	.25

Austrian Air Post Stamps, #C1-C3, Overprinted Type "c" Diagonally

B37	A40	1.50k on 2k lil	175.00	175.00
B38	A40	2.50k on 3k ocher	175.00	175.00
B39	A40	4k gray	1,250.	800.00

1919
Austrian Postage Due Stamps of 1908-13 Overprinted Type "b"

B40	D3	2h carmine	6,500.	2,750.
B41	D3	4h carmine	25.00	15.00
B42	D3	6h carmine	12.50	8.00
B43	D3	14h carmine	90.00	35.00
B44	D3	25h carmine	45.00	20.00
B45	D3	30h carmine	600.00	300.00
B46	D3	50h carmine	1,200.	825.00

Austria Nos. J49-J56 Overprinted Type "b"

B47	D4	5h rose red	.20	.30
B48	D4	10h rose red	.20	.30
B49	D4	15h rose red	.20	.30
B50	D4	20h rose red	2.00	2.00
B51	D4	25h rose red	2.00	2.00
B52	D4	30h rose red	.65	.65
B53	D4	40h rose red	2.00	2.00
B54	D4	50h rose red	600.00	250.00

Austria Nos. J57-J59 Overprinted Type "a"

B55	D5	1k ultra	12.50	10.00
B56	D5	5k ultra	55.00	35.00
B57	D5	10k ultra	475.00	200.00

Austria Nos. J47-J48, J60-J63 Overprinted Type "c" Diagonally

B58	A22	1h gray	32.50	30.00
B59	A23	15h on 2h vio	150.00	110.00
B60	A38	10h on 24h blue	120.00	85.00
B61	A38	15h on 36h vio	1.00	1.00
B62	A38	20h on 54h org	90.00	85.00
B63	A38	50h on 42h choc	1.00	1.00

Hungarian Stamps Ovptd. Type "b"

1919		Wmk. 137	Perf. 15	

On Stamps of 1913-16

B64	A4	1f slate	4,000.	1,600.
B65	A4	2f yellow	3.50	2.50
B66	A4	3f orange	45.00	25.00
B67	A4	6f olive green	4.50	4.50
B68	A4	50f lake, bl	1.25	1.00
B69	A4	60f grn, sal	50.00	20.00
B70	A4	70f red brn, grn	4,000.	1,600.

On Stamps of 1916

B71	A8	10f rose	475.00	175.00
B72	A8	15f violet	250.00	100.00

On Stamps of 1916-18

B73	A9	2f brown orange	.20	.20
B74	A9	3f red lilac	.20	.20
B75	A9	5f green	.20	.20
B76	A9	6f grnsh blue	.60	.60
B77	A9	10f rose red	1.40	2.25
B78	A9	15f violet	.25	.25
B79	A9	20f gray brown	14.00	14.00
B80	A9	25f dull blue	1.00	.80
B81	A9	35f brown	10.00	10.00
B82	A9	40f olive green	3.25	2.50

Overprinted Type "d"

B83	A10	50f red vio & lil	1.25	1.60
B84	A10	75f brt bl & pale bl	1.25	1.60
B85	A10	80f yel grn & pale grn	1.25	1.60
B86	A10	1k red brn & cl	2.50	2.00
B87	A10	2k ol brn & bis	10.00	10.00
B88	A10	3k dk vio & ind	37.50	37.50
B89	A10	5k dk brn & lt brn	140.00	90.00
B90	A10	10k vio brn & vio	1,800.	800.00

Overprinted Type "b"
On Stamps of 1918

B91	A11	10f scarlet	.25	.25
B92	A11	20f dark brown	.30	.30
B93	A11	25f deep blue	1.40	1.25
B94	A12	40f olive grn	4.00	3.25
B95	A12	50f lilac	67.50	25.00

On Stamps of 1919

B96	A13	10f red	10.00	8.00
B97	A13	20f dk brn	10,000.	

Same Overprint On Hungarian Newspaper Stamp of 1914
Imperf

B98	N5	(2f) orange	.20	.30

Same Overprint On Hungarian Special Delivery Stamp
Perf. 15

B99	SD1	2f gray grn & red	.25	.35

Same Ovpt. On Hungarian Semi-Postal Stamps

B100	SP3	10f + 2f rose red	.80	.80
B101	SP4	15f + 2f violet	1.25	1.25
B102	SP5	40f + 2f brn car	7.00	3.50
		Nos. B98-B102 (5)	9.50	6.20

Hungarian Postage Due Stamps of 1903-18 Overprinted Type "b"

1919		Wmk. 135	Perf. 11½, 12	
B103	D1	50f green & black	525.00	525.00

Wmk. Crown (136, 136a)
Perf. 11½x12, 15

B104	D1	1f green & black	1,200.	1,000.
B105	D1	2f green & black	1,000.	750.
B106	D1	12f green & black	4,250.	3,000.
B107	D1	50f green & black	275.	150.

Wmk. Double Cross (137)
Perf. 15
On Stamps of 1914

B110	D1	1f green & black	1,250.	600.
B111	D1	2f green & black	700.	550.
B112	D1	5f green & black	1,325.	900.
B113	D1	12f green & black	5,250.	4,000.
B114	D1	50f green & black	275.	150.

On Stamps of 1915-18

B115	D1	1f green & red	175.00	140.00
B116	D1	2f green & red	1.00	.80
B117	D1	5f green & red	12.50	10.00
B118	D1	6f green & red	1.50	1.50
B119	D1	10f green & red	.60	.60
a.		Pair, one without overprint		
B120	D1	12f green & red	2.00	2.00
B121	D1	15f green & red	7.50	5.00

B122	D1	20f green & red	1.00	1.00
B123	D1	30f green & red	80.00	70.00
		Nos. B115-B123 (9)	281.10	230.90

Excellent counterfeits of Nos. B1-B123 exist.

Bohemian Lion Breaking its Chains — SP1

Mother and Child — SP2

Perf. 11½, 13¾ and Compound

1919		Typo.	Unwmk.	

Pinkish Paper

B124	SP1	15h gray green	.20	.20
a.		15h light green	32.50	25.00
B125	SP1	25h dark brown	.20	.20
a.		25h light brown	5.00	4.00
B126	SP1	50h dark blue	.20	.20

Photo.
Yellowish Paper

B127	SP2	75h slate	.20	.20
B128	SP2	100h brn vio	.20	.20
B129	SP2	120h vio, yel	.20	.20
		Nos. B124-B129 (6)	1.20	1.25

Values are for perf 13¾. Other perfs are valued higher.

Nos. B124-B126 commemorate the 1st anniv. of Czechoslovak independence. Nos. B127-B129 were sold for the benefit of Legionnaires' orphans. Imperforates exist.
See No. 1581.

Regular Issues of Czechoslovakia Surcharged in Red:

a

b

1920			Perf. 13¾	
B130	A1(a)	40h + 20h bister	.50	.80
B131	A2(a)	60h + 20h green	.50	.80
B132	A4(b)	125h + 25h gray bl	2.00	2.25
		Nos. B130-B132 (3)	3.00	3.85

President Masaryk — SP3

Wmk. Linden Leaves (107)

1923		Engr.	Perf. 13¾x14¾	
B133	SP3	50h gray green	.75	.50
B134	SP3	100h carmine	1.00	.80
B135	SP3	200h blue	3.00	2.75
B136	SP3	300h dark brown	3.25	4.00
		Nos. B133-B136 (4)	8.00	8.05

5th anniv. of the Republic.
The gum was applied through a screen and shows the monogram "CSP" (Ceskoslovenska Posta). These stamps were sold at double their face values, the excess being given to the Red Cross and other charitable organizations.

International Olympic Congress Issue

Semi-Postal Stamps of 1923 Overprinted in Blue or Red

1925

B137	SP3	50h gray green	10.00	8.50
B138	SP3	100h carmine	14.50	12.00
B139	SP3	200h blue (R)	72.50	55.00
	Nos. B137-B139 (3)		97.00	75.50
	Set, never hinged		175.00	

These stamps were sold at double their face values, the excess being divided between a fund for post office clerks and the Olympic Games Committee.

Sokol Issue

Semi-Postal Stamps of 1923 Overprinted in Blue or Red

1926

B140	SP3	50h gray green	1.60	*4.00*
B141	SP3	100h carmine	3.25	*4.00*
B142	SP3	200h blue (R)	15.00	12.50
a.	Double overprint			
B143	SP3	300h dk brn (R)	20.00	20.00
	Nos. B140-B143 (4)		39.85	40.50
	Set, never hinged		140.00	

These stamps were sold at double their face values, the excess being given to the Congress of Sokols, June, 1926.

Catalogue values for unused stamps in this section, from this point to the end of the section, are for Never Hinged items.

Midwife Presenting Newborn Child to its Father; after a Painting by Josef Manes

SP4   SP5

1936 Unwmk. Engr. Perf. 12½

B144	SP4	50h + 50h green	.65	.65
B145	SP5	1k + 50h claret	1.00	1.00
B146	SP4	2k + 50h blue	2.75	2.75
	Nos. B144-B146 (3)		4.40	4.40

"Lullaby" by Stanislav Sucharda
SP6

SP7

1937 Perf. 12½

B147	SP6	50h + 50h dull green	.50	.20
B148	SP6	1k + 50h rose lake	.80	.60
B149	SP7	2k + 1k dull blue	2.25	1.25
	Nos. B147-B149 (3)		3.55	2.05

President Masaryk and Little Girl in Native Costume — SP8

1938 Perf. 12½

B150	SP8	50h + 50h deep green	.65	.50
B151	SP8	1k + 50h rose lake	.85	.65

Souvenir Sheet
Imperf

B152	SP8	2k + 3k black	5.00	5.00

88th anniv. of the birth of Masaryk (1850-1937).
Nos. B150-B151 were each issued in sheets of 100 stamps and 12 blank labels. Value, set of singles with attached labels: mint $3.75; used $2.50.

Allegory of the Republic Type
Souvenir Sheet

1938 Perf. 12½

B153	A89	2k (+ 8k) dark blue	4.00	4.00

The surtax was devoted to national relief for refugees.

"Republic" and Congress Emblem SP10

St. George Slaying the Dragon SP11

1945 Engr.

B154	SP10	1.50k + 1.50k car rose	.20	.20
B155	SP10	2.50k + 2.50k blue	.25	.20

Students' World Cong., Prague, 11/17/45.

1946

B156	SP11	2.40k + 2.60k car rose	.20	.20
B157	SP11	4k + 6k blue	.45	.20

Souvenir Sheet
Imperf

B158	SP11	4k + 6k blue	1.50	1.50

1st anniv. of Czechoslovakia's liberation. The surtax aided WW II orphans.
Nos. B156-B157 were each issued in sheets of 100 stamps and 12 inscribed labels. Value for set of singles with attached labels, mint or used $4.

Old Town Hall Type of 1946
Souvenir Sheet

1946, Aug. 3 Imperf.

B159	A114	2.40k rose brown	1.25	.80

Brno Natl. Stamp Exhib., Aug., 1946. The sheet was sold for 10k.

"You Went Away" — SP14

"You Remained Ours" — SP15

"You Came Back" — SP16

1946, Oct. 28 Photo. Perf. 14

B160	SP14	1.60k + 1.40k red brn	.40	.40
B161	SP15	2.40k + 2.60k scarlet	.40	.40
B162	SP16	4k + 4k deep blue	.75	.75
	Nos. B160-B162 (3)		1.55	1.55

The surtax was for repatriated Slovaks.

Barefoot Boy — SP17

Woman and Child — SP18

2k+1k, Mother and child. 3k+1k, Little girl.

Perf. 12½

1948, Dec. 18 Unwmk. Engr.

B163	SP17	1.50k + 1k rose lilac	.35	.20
B164	SP17	2k + 1k dp blue	.20	.20
B165	SP17	3k + 1k rose car	.35	.20
	Nos. B163-B165 (3)		.90	.60

The surtax was for child welfare. Nos. B163-B165 were each issued in sheets of 100 stamps and 12 inscribed labels. Value for set of singles with attached labels: mint $3.50; used $1.75.

1949, Dec. 18 Perf. 12½

Design: 3k+1k, Man lifting child.

B166	SP18	1.50k + 50h gray	4.00	1.60
B167	SP18	3k + 1k claret	6.00	2.50

The surtax was for child welfare.

SP19

Dove Carrying Olive Branch — SP20

1949, Dec. 18

B168	SP19	1.50k + 50h claret	4.50	1.50
B169	SP20	3k + 1k rose red	4.50	1.50

The surtax was for the Red Cross.

AIR POST STAMPS

Nos. 9, 39-40, 20, and Types of 1919 Surcharged in Red, Blue or Green:

1920 Unwmk. Imperf.

C1	A1	14k on 200h (R)	21.00	18.00
a.	Inverted surcharge		125.00	
C2	A2	24k on 500h (Bl)	50.00	30.00
a.	Inverted surcharge		225.00	

C3	A2	28k on 1000h (G)	32.50	30.00
a.	Inverted surcharge		150.00	
b.	Double surcharge		200.00	
	Nos. C1-C3 (3)		103.50	78.00

Perf. 13¾

C4	A1	14k on 200h (R)	22.50	*30.00*
a.	Perf. 13¾x13½		95.00	95.00
C5	A2	24k on 500h (Bl)	45.00	*70.00*
a.	Perf. 13¾x13½		100.00	100.00

Perf. 13¾x13½

C6	A2	28k on 1000h (G)	20.00	27.50
a.	Inverted surcharge		400.00	—
b.	Perf. 13¾		475.00	700.00
c.	As "b," invtd. surcharge		350.00	—
	Nos. C4-C6 (3)		87.50	127.50
	Nos. C1-C6 (6)		191.00	205.50

Excellent counterfeits of the overprint are known.

Stamps of 1920 Surcharged in Black or Violet:

1922, June 15 Perf. 13¾

C7	A8	50h on 100h dl grn	1.50	1.50
a.	Inverted surcharge		150.00	
b.	Double surcharge		160.00	
C8	A8	100h on 200h vio	4.00	3.25
a.	Inverted surcharge		150.00	
C9	A8	250h on 400h brn (V)	6.00	7.50
a.	Inverted surcharge		275.00	
	Nos. C7-C9 (3)		11.50	12.25
	Set, never hinged		20.00	

Fokker Monoplane AP3

Smolik S 19 AP4

Smolik S 19 — AP5

Fokker over Prague AP6

1930, Dec. 16 Engr. Perf. 13½

C10	AP3	50h deep green	.20	.20
C11	AP3	1k deep red	.25	.25
C12	AP4	2k dark green	.60	.55
C13	AP4	3k red violet	1.25	1.00
C14	AP5	4k indigo	1.00	.80
C15	AP5	5k red brown	1.50	1.50
C16	AP6	10k vio blue	3.50	3.50
a.	10k ultra		10.00	10.00
C17	AP6	20k gray violet	3.00	3.00
	Nos. C10-C17 (8)		12.80	10.80

Two types exist of the 50h, 1k and 2k, and three types of the 3k, differing chiefly in the size of the printed area. A "no hill at left" variety of the 3k exists.
Imperf. examples of Nos. C10-C17 are proofs.

Perf. 12

C10a	AP3	50h deep green	2.75	*4.75*
C11a	AP3	1k deep red	18.00	*22.50*
C12a	AP4	2k dark green	15.00	*22.50*
C14a	AP5	4k indigo	2.25	*3.75*
C17a	AP6	20k gray violet	3.00	*7.50*

Perf. 12x13½, 13½x12

C11b	AP3	1k deep red	4.00	*7.50*
C12b	AP4	2k dark green	11.00	*19.00*

Perf. 13¾x12¼

C17b	AP6	20k gray violet	1,750.

Perf. 12½

C15a	AP5	5k red brown	2,000.

Catalogue values for unused stamps in this section, from this point to the end of the section, are for Never Hinged items.

Capt. Frantisek Novak — AP7

Plane over Bratislava Castle — AP8

Plane over Charles Bridge, Prague — AP9

1946-47   Perf. 12½

C19	AP7	1.50k rose red	.25	.20
C20	AP7	5.50k dk gray bl	.50	.20
C21	AP7	9k sepia ('47)	.85	.20
C22	AP8	10k dl grn	.85	.35
C23	AP8	16k violet	1.50	.60
C24	AP8	20k light blue	1.60	1.10
C25	AP9	24k dk bl, cr	1.00	.65
C26	AP9	24k rose lake	1.75	1.00
C27	AP9	50k dk gray bl	3.25	2.60
	Nos. C19-C27 (9)		11.55	6.90

No. C25 was issued June 12, 1946, for use on the first Prague-New York flight.

Nos. C22, C24-C27 were each issued in sheets of 100 stamps and 12 labels depicting airplane over globe. Values for singles with attached labels (mint/used): C22, $2/$1.50; C24, $4/$3; C25, $7.50/$4; C26, $5.50/$4.50; C27, $9/$7.50.

Nos. C19-C24, C26-C27 Surcharged with New Value and Bars in Various Colors

1949, Sept. 1   Perf. 12½

C28	AP7	1k on 1.50k (Bl)	.20	.20
C29	AP7	3k on 5.50k (C)	.35	.20
C30	AP7	6k on 9k (Br)	.55	.20
C31	AP7	7.50k on 16k (C)	.75	.25
C32	AP8	8k on 10k (G)	.75	.75
C33	AP8	12.50k on 20k (Bl)	1.10	.55
C34	AP9	15k on 24k rose lake (Bl)	2.75	1.00
C35	AP9	30k on 50k (Bl)	2.00	.90
	Nos. C28-C35 (8)		8.45	4.05

Karlovy Vary (Karlsbad) — AP10

1951, Apr. 2   Engr.   Perf. 13½

C36	AP10	6k shown	3.00	1.50
C37	AP10	10k Piestany	3.00	1.50
C38	AP10	15k Marienbad	5.50	1.50
C39	AP10	20k Silac	8.50	4.90
	Nos. C36-C39 (4)		20.00	8.50

Nos. C36-C39 were each issued in a sheet of 10 stamps. Value, set $950.

View of Cesky Krumlov — AP11

Views: 1.55k, Olomouc. 2.35k, Banska Bystrica. 2.75k, Bratislava. 10k, Prague.

1955   Perf. 11½
Cream Paper

C40	AP11	80h olive green	.80	.20
C41	AP11	1.55k violet brn	1.10	.35
C42	AP11	2.35k violet blue	1.50	.20
C43	AP11	2.75k rose brown	2.25	.35
C44	AP11	10k indigo	4.50	2.00
	Nos. C40-C44 (5)		10.15	3.10

Issue dates: 10k, Feb. 20. Others, Mar. 28.

Airline: Moscow-Prague-Paris — AP12

2.35k, Airline: Prague-Cairo-Beirut-Damascus.

Engraved and Photogravure
1957, Oct. 15   Unwmk.   Perf. 11½

C45	AP12	75h ultra & rose	.75	.20
C46	AP12	2.35k ultra & org yel	.75	.20

Planes at First Czech Aviation School, Pardubice — AP13

Design: 1.80k, Jan Kaspar and flight of first Czech plane, 1909.

1959, Oct. 15

C47	AP13	1k gray & yel	.20	.20
C48	AP13	1.80k blk & pale bl	.75	.20

50th anniv. of Jan Kaspar's 1st flight Aug. 25, 1909, at Pardubice.

Mail Coach, Plane and Arms of Bratislava — AP14

Design: 2.80k, Helicopter over Bratislava.

1960, Sept. 24   Unwmk.   Perf. 11½

C49	AP14	1.60k dk bl & gray	1.50	.90
C50	AP14	2.80k grn & buff	2.00	1.10

Issued to publicize the National Stamp Exhibition, Bratislava, Sept. 24-Oct. 9.

AP15   AP16

Designs: 60h, Prague hails Gagarin. 1.80k, Gagarin, rocket and dove.

1961, June 22

C51	AP15	60h gray & car	.30	.20
C52	AP15	1.80k gray & blue	.50	.20

No. C51 commemorates Maj. Gagarin's visit to Prague, Apr. 28-29; No. C52 commemorates the first man in space, Yuri A. Gagarin, Apr. 12, 1961.

1962, May 14   Engr.   Perf. 14

"PRAGA" emblem and: 80h, Dove & Nest of Eggs. 1.40k, Dove. 2.80k, Symbolic flower with five petals. 4.20k, Five leaves.

C53	AP16	80h multicolored	.75	.35
C54	AP16	1.40k blk, dk red & bl	1.90	1.50
C55	AP16	2.80k multicolored	1.90	1.50
C56	AP16	4.20k multicolored	2.25	1.50
	Nos. C53-C56 (4)		6.80	4.85

PRAGA 1962 World Exhibition of Postage Stamps, Aug. 18-Sept. 2, 1962.
Nos. C53-C56 were each issued in sheets of 10. Value, set $110.

Vostok 5 and Lt. Col. Valeri Bykovski AP17

2.80k, Vostok VI & Lt. Valentina Tereshkova.

1963, June 26

C57	AP17	80h slate bl & pink	.50	.20
C58	AP17	2.80k dl red brn & lt bl	2.00	.30

Space flights of Valeri Bykovski, June 14-19, and Valentina Tereshkova, first woman astronaut, June 16-19, 1963.

PRAGA 1962 Emblem, View of Prague and Plane — AP18

Designs: 60h, Istanbul '63 (Hagia Sophia). 1k, Philatec Paris 1964 (Ile de la Cité). 1.40k, WIPA 1965 (Belvedere Palace, Vienna). 1.60k, SIPEX 1966 (Capitol, Washington). 2k, Amphilex '67 (harbor and old town, Amsterdam). 5k, PRAGA 1968 (View of Prague).

Engraved and Photogravure
1967, Oct. 30   Perf. 11½
Size: 30x50mm

C59	AP18	30h choc, yel & rose	.20	.20
C60	AP18	60h dk grn, yel & lil	.20	.20
C61	AP18	1k blk, brick red & lt bl	.35	.20
C62	AP18	1.40k vio, yel & dp org	.40	.20
C63	AP18	1.60k ind, tan & lil	.35	.20
C64	AP18	2k dk grn, org & red	.40	.25

Size: 40x50mm

C65	AP18	5k multi	2.25	1.25
	Nos. C59-C65 (7)		4.15	2.50

PRAGA 1968 World Stamp Exhibition, Prague, June 22-July 7, 1968. No. C59-C64 issued in sheets of 15 stamps and 15 bilingual labels. Values, set of singles with attached labels: mint $6.50; used $4.50. No. C65 issued in sheets of 4 stamps and one center label. Value $15.

Glider L-13 — AP19

Airplanes: 60h, Sports plane L-40. 80h, Aero taxi L-200. 1k, Crop-spraying plane Z-37. 1.60k, Aerobatics trainer Z-526. 2k, Jet trainer L-29.

1967, Dec. 11

C66	AP19	30h multi	.25	.25
C67	AP19	60h multi	.25	.25
C68	AP19	80h multi	.25	.25
C69	AP19	1k multi	.30	.25
C70	AP19	1.60k multi	.50	.25
C71	AP19	2k multi	1.60	.90
	Nos. C66-C71 (6)		3.15	2.15

Charles Bridge, Prague, and Balloon — AP20

Designs: 1k, Belvedere, fountain and early plane. 2k, Hradcany, Prague, and airship.

1968, Feb. 5   Unwmk.   Perf. 11½

C72	AP20	60h multicolored	.30	.20
C73	AP20	1k multicolored	.45	.30
C74	AP20	2k multicolored	.75	.30
	Nos. C72-C74 (3)		1.50	.80

PRAGA 1968 World Stamp Exhibition, Prague, June 22-July 7, 1968.
Nos. C72-C74 were each issued in a sheet of 10 stamps. Value, set $30.

Astronaut, Moon and Manhattan AP21

Design: 3k, Lunar landing module and J. F. Kennedy Airport, New York.

1969, July 21

C75	AP21	60h blk, vio, yel & sil	.20	.20
C76	AP21	3k blk, bl, ocher & sil	1.00	.50

Man's 1st landing on the moon, July 20, 1969, US astronauts Neil A. Armstrong and Col. Edwin E. Aldrin, Jr., with Lieut. Col. Michael Collins piloting Apollo 11.
Nos. C75-C76 printed with label inscribed with names of astronauts and European date of moon landing. Values for pair of singles with attached labels: mint $2; used $1.

TU-104A over Bitov Castle AP22

Designs: 60h, IL-62 over Bezdez Castle. 1.40k, TU-13A over Orava Castle. 1.90k, IL-18 over Veveri Castle. 2.40k, IL-14 over Pernstejn Castle. 3.60k, TU-154 over Trencin Castle.

1973, Oct. 24   Engr.   Perf. 11½

C77	AP22	30h multi	.20	.20
C78	AP22	60h multi	.20	.20
C79	AP22	1.40k multi	.25	.20
C80	AP22	1.90k multi	.40	.20
C81	AP22	2.40k multi	1.50	.75
C82	AP22	3.60k multi	.70	.20
	Nos. C77-C82 (6)		3.25	1.75

50 years of Czechoslovakian aviation. Nos. C77-C82 were each printed in sheets of 10. Values, set: mint $60; used $30.

Old Water Tower and Manes Hall — AP23

Designs (Praga 1978 Emblem, Plane Silhouette and): 1.60k, Congress Hall. 2k, Powder Tower, vert. 2.40k, Charles Bridge and Old Bridge Tower. 4k, Old Town Hall on Old Town Square, vert. 6k, Prague Castle and St. Vitus' Cathedral, vert.

Engraved and Photogravure

1976, June 23			Perf. 11½	
C83	AP23	60h ind & multi	.20	.20
C84	AP23	1.60k ind & multi	.25	.20
C85	AP23	2k ind & multi	.35	.20
C86	AP23	2.40k ind & multi	.40	.20
C87	AP23	4k ind & multi	.80	.20
C88	AP23	6k ind & multi	2.00	.80
	Nos. C83-C88 (6)		4.00	1.90

PRAGA 1978 International Philatelic Exhibition, Prague, Sept. 8-17, 1978.

Zeppelin, 1909 and 1928 — AP24

PRAGA '78 Emblem and: 1k, Ader, 1890, L'Eole & Dunn, 1914. 1.60k, Jeffries-Blanchard balloon, 1785. 2k, Otto Lilienthal's glider, 1896. 4.40k, Jan Kaspar's plane, Pardubice, 1911.

1977, Sept. 15			Perf. 11½	
C89	AP24	60h multi	.20	.20
C90	AP24	1k multi	.30	.20
C91	AP24	1.60k multi	.35	.20
C92	AP24	2k multi	.45	.20
C93	AP24	4.40k multi	2.25	.50
	Nos. C89-C93 (5)		3.55	1.30

History of aviation.
Nos. C89-C93 were each issued in sheets of 30 stamps, 15 labels depicting the exhibition emblem, and 5 blank labels. Values for set of singles with attached inscribed labels: mint $5; used $2.50.

SPECIAL DELIVERY STAMPS

Doves — SD1

1919-20		Unwmk. Typo.	Imperf.	
E1	SD1	2h red vio, yel	.20	.20
E2	SD1	5h yel grn, yel	.20	.20
E3	SD1	10h red brn, yel ('20)	.80	.80
	Nos. E1-E3 (3)		1.20	1.20

For overprints and surcharge see Nos. P11-P13, Eastern Silesia E1-E2.

1921			White Paper
E1a	SD1	2h red violet	9.50
E2a	SD1	5h yellow green	6.50
E3a	SD1	10h red brown	140.00
	Nos. E1a-E3a (3)		156.00

It is doubted that Nos. E1a-E3a were regularly issued.

PERSONAL DELIVERY STAMPS

Catalogue values for unused stamps in this section are for Never Hinged items.

PD1

Design: No. EX2, "D" in each corner.

1937	Unwmk. Photo.		Perf. 13½	
EX1	PD1	50h blue	.20	.25
EX2	PD1	50h carmine	.20	.25

PD3

1946			Perf. 13½	
EX3	PD3	2k deep blue	.50	.75

POSTAGE DUE STAMPS

D1

1918-20		Unwmk. Typo.	Imperf.	
J1	D1	5h deep bister	.20	.20
J2	D1	10h deep bister	.20	.20
J3	D1	15h deep bister	.20	.20
J4	D1	20h deep bister	.30	.20
J5	D1	25h deep bister	.45	.20
J6	D1	30h deep bister	.45	.20
J7	D1	40h deep bister	.60	.20
J8	D1	50h deep bister	.75	.20
J9	D1	100h blk brn	1.50	.20
J10	D1	250h orange	11.00	1.40
J11	D1	400h scarlet	15.00	1.40
J12	D1	500h gray grn	7.50	.20
J13	D1	1000h purple	7.50	.25
J14	D1	2000h dark blue	22.50	.60
	Nos. J1-J14 (14)		68.15	5.65

For surcharges and overprints see Nos. J32-J41, J57, Eastern Silesia J1-J11.

Nos. 1, 33-34, 10 Surcharged in Blue

1922				
J15	A1	20h on 3h red vio	.30	.20
J16	A2	50h on 75h slate	1.50	.20
J17	A2	60h on 80h olive grn	.80	.20
J18	A2	100h on 80h olive grn	3.00	.20
J19	A1	200h on 400h purple	4.00	.20
	Nos. J15-J19 (5)		9.60	1.00

Same Surcharge on Nos. 1, 10, 30-31, 33-34, 36, 40 in Violet

1923-26				
J20	A1	10h on 3h red vio	.20	.20
J21	A1	20h on 3h red vio	.30	.20
J22	A1	30h on 3h red vio	.20	.20
J23	A1	40h on 3h red vio	.20	.20
J24	A2	50h on 75h slate	1.25	.20
J25	A2	60h on 50h dk vio ('26)	4.00	1.25
J26	A2	60h on 50h dk bl ('26)	4.00	1.50
J27	A2	60h on 75h slate	.50	.20
J28	A2	100h on 80h ol grn	27.50	.20
J29	A2	100h on 120h gray blk	1.00	.20
J30	A1	100h on 400h pur ('26)	1.00	.20
J31	A2	100h on 1000h dp vio ('26)	1.60	.20
	Nos. J20-J31 (12)		41.75	4.75

Postage Due Stamp of 1918-20 Surcharged in Violet

1924				
J32	D1	50h on 400h scar	.90	.25
J33	D1	60h on 400h scar	3.25	.60
J34	D1	100h on 400h scar	2.00	.25
	Nos. J32-J34 (3)		6.15	1.10

Postage Due Stamps of 1918-20 Surcharged with New Values in Violet as in 1924

1925				
J35	D1	10h on 5h bister	.25	.25
J36	D1	20h on 5h bister	.25	.25
J37	D1	30h on 15h bister	.25	.25
J38	D1	40h on 15h bister	.25	.25
J39	D1	50h on 250h org	1.10	.25
J40	D1	60h on 250h org	1.50	.60
J41	D1	100h on 250h org	2.25	.25
	Nos. J35-J41 (7)		5.85	2.10

Stamps of 1918-19 Surcharged with New Values in Violet as in 1922

1926			Perf. 14, 11½	
J42	A2	30h on 15h red	.50	.30
J43	A2	40h on 15h red	.50	.30

On #J44-J49   On #J50-J56

1926		Violet Surcharge	Perf. 14	
J44	A8	30h on 100h dk grn	.20	.20
J45	A8	40h on 200h violet	.25	.20
J46	A8	40h on 300h ver	.95	.20
a.		Perf. 14x13½		60.00
J47	A8	50h on 500h dp grn	.50	.20
a.		Perf. 14x13½	2.75	
J48	A8	60h on 400h brown	1.00	.20
J49	A8	100h on 600h dp vio	2.50	.35
a.		Perf. 14x13½	30.00	1.25
	Nos. J44-J49 (6)		5.40	1.40

1927			Violet Overprint	
J50	A6	100h dark brown	.55	.20
a.		Perf. 13½	200.00	10.00

Surcharged with New Value in Violet

J51	A6	40h on 185h org	.20	.20
J52	A6	50h on 20h car	.20	.20
a.		50h on 50h carmine (error)	55,000.	
J53	A6	50h on 150h rose	.20	.20
a.		Perf. 13½	12.50	2.00
J54	A6	60h on 25h brown	.25	.20
J55	A6	60h on 185h orange	.55	.20
J56	A6	100h on 25h brown	.55	.20
	Nos. J50-J56 (7)		2.50	1.40

No. J52a is known only used.

No. J12 Surcharged in Violet   200

1927			Imperf.	
J57	D1	200h on 500h gray grn	8.00	2.50

Catalogue values for unused stamps in this section, from this point to the end of the section, are for Never Hinged items.

D5

1928			Perf. 14x13½	
J58	D5	5h dark red	.20	.20
J59	D5	10h dark red	.20	.20
J60	D5	20h dark red	.20	.20
J61	D5	30h dark red	.20	.20
J62	D5	40h dark red	.20	.20
J63	D5	50h dark red	.20	.20
J64	D5	60h dark red	.20	.20
J65	D5	1k ultra	.20	.20
J66	D5	2k ultra	.50	.20
J67	D5	5k ultra	.75	.20
J68	D5	10k ultra	1.90	.20
J69	D5	20k ultra	3.75	.30
	Nos. J58-J69 (12)		8.50	2.50

D6

1946-48		Photo.	Perf. 14	
J70	D6	10h dark blue	.20	.20
J71	D6	20h dark blue	.20	.20
J72	D6	50h dark blue	.35	.20
J73	D6	1k carmine rose	.35	.20
J74	D6	1.20k carmine rose	.35	.20
J75	D6	1.50k carmine rose ('48)	.35	.20
J76	D6	1.60k carmine rose	.35	.20
J77	D6	2k carmine rose ('48)	.35	.20
J78	D6	2.40k carmine rose	.35	.20
J79	D6	3k carmine rose	.70	.20
J80	D6	4k carmine rose	.70	.20
J81	D6	6k carmine rose ('48)	1.00	.20
	Nos. J70-J81 (12)		5.25	2.40

D7   D8

1954-55		Engr.	Perf. 12½, 11½	
J82	D7	5h gray green ('55)	.20	.20
J83	D7	10h gray green ('55)	.20	.20
J84	D7	30h gray green	.20	.20
J85	D7	50h gray green ('55)	.20	.20
J86	D7	60h gray green ('55)	.20	.20
J87	D7	95h gray green	.35	.20
J88	D8	1k violet	.35	.20
J89	D8	1.20k violet ('55)	.35	.20
J90	D8	1.50k violet	.70	.20
J91	D8	1.60k violet ('55)	.45	.20
J92	D8	2k violet	.85	.20
J93	D8	3k violet	1.10	.20
J94	D8	5k violet ('55)	1.40	.25
	Nos. J82-J94 (13)		6.55	2.65

Perf. 11½ stamps are from a 1963 printing which lacks the 95h, 1.60k, and 2k.

Stylized Flower — D9

Designs: Various stylized flowers.

Engraved and Photogravure

1971-72			Perf. 11½	
J95	D9	10h vio bl & pink	.20	.20
J96	D9	20h vio & lt bl	.20	.20
J97	D9	30h emer & lil rose	.20	.20
J98	D9	60h pur & emer	.20	.20
J99	D9	80h org & vio bl	.20	.20
J100	D9	1k dk red & emer	.25	.20
J101	D9	1.20k grn & org	.20	.20
J102	D9	2k blue & red	.40	.20
J103	D9	3k blk & yel	.50	.20
J104	D9	4k brn & ultra	.85	.20
J105	D9	5.40k red & lilac	1.40	.20
J106	D9	6k brick red & org	1.40	.20
	Nos. J95-J106 (12)		5.60	2.40

All except 5.40k issued in 1972.

OFFICIAL STAMPS

Catalogue values for unused stamps in this section are for Never Hinged items.

Coat of Arms — O1

1945		Unwmk. Litho.	Perf. 10½x10	
O1	O1	50h dp slate grn	.20	.20
O2	O1	1k dp bl vio	.20	.20
O3	O1	1.20k plum	.20	.20
O4	O1	1.50k crimson rose	.20	.20
O5	O1	2.50k bright ultra	.20	.20
O6	O1	5k dk vio brn	.30	.20
O7	O1	8k rose pink	.30	.30
	Nos. O1-O7 (7)		1.60	1.50

Redrawn

1947   Photo.   Perf. 14

O8	O1	60h red	.20	.20
O9	O1	80h dk olive grn	.20	.20
O10	O1	1k dk lilac gray	.20	.20
O11	O1	1.20k dp plum	.20	.20
O12	O1	2.40k dk car rose	.20	.20
O13	O1	4k brt ultra	.20	.20
O14	O1	5k dk vio brn	.20	.20
O15	O1	7.40k purple	.20	.20
		Nos. O8-O15 (8)	1.60	1.60

There are many minor changes in design, size of numerals, etc., of the redrawn stamps.

NEWSPAPER STAMPS

Windhover — N1

1918-20   Unwmk.   Typo.   Imperf.

P1	N1	2h gray green	.20	.20
P2	N1	5h green ('20)	.20	.20
a.		5h dark green	.40	.40
P3	N1	6h red	.30	.25
P4	N1	10h dull violet	.20	.20
P5	N1	20h blue	.20	.20
P6	N1	30h gray brown	.20	.20
P7	N1	50h orange ('20)	.30	.20
P8	N1	100h red brown ('20)	.40	.20
		Nos. P1-P8 (8)	2.00	1.65

Nos. P1-P8 exist privately perforated.
For surcharges and overprints see Nos. P9-P10, P14-P16, Eastern Silesia P1-P5.

Stamps of 1918-20 Surcharged in Violet

1925-26

P9	N1	5h on 2h gray green	.50	.40
P10	N1	5h on 6h red ('26)	.25	.40

Special Delivery Stamps of 1918-20 Overprinted in Violet

1926

P11	SD1	5h apple grn, yel	.20	.20
a.		5h dull green, yellow	.50	.40
P12	SD1	10h red brn, yel	.20	.20

With Additional Surcharge of New Value

P13	SD1	5h on 2h red vio, yel	.35	.35
		Nos. P11-P13 (3)	.75	.75

Catalogue values for unused stamps in this section, from this point to the end of the section, are for Never Hinged items.

Newspaper Stamps of 1918-20 Overprinted in Violet

1934

P14	N1	10h dull violet	.20	.20
P15	N1	20h blue	.20	.20
P16	N1	30h gray brown	.20	.20
		Nos. P14-P16 (3)	.60	.60

Overprinted for use by commercial firms only.

Carrier Pigeon — N2

1937   Imperf.

P17	N2	2h bister brown	.20	.20
P18	N2	5h dull blue	.20	.20
P19	N2	7h red orange	.20	.20
P20	N2	9h emerald	.20	.20
P21	N2	10h henna brown	.20	.20
P22	N2	12h ultra	.20	.20
P23	N2	20h dark green	.20	.20
P24	N2	50h dark brown	.20	.20
P25	N2	1k olive grn	.20	.20
		Nos. P17-P25 (9)	1.80	1.80

For overprint see Slovakia Nos. P1-P9.

Bratislava Philatelic Exhibition Issue
Souvenir Sheet

1937   Imperf.

P26	N2	10h henna brn, sheet of 25	4.00	4.00

Newspaper Delivery Boy — N4

1945   Unwmk.   Typo.   Imperf.

P27	N4	5h dull blue	.20	.20
P28	N4	10h red	.20	.20
P29	N4	15h emerald	.20	.20
P30	N4	20h dark slate green	.20	.20
P31	N4	25h bright red vio	.20	.20
P32	N4	30h ocher	.20	.20
P33	N4	40h red orange	.20	.20
P34	N4	50h brown red	.20	.20
P35	N4	1k slate gray	.20	.20
P36	N4	5k deep vio blue	.20	.20
		Nos. P27-P36 (10)	2.00	2.00

CZECHOSLOVAK LEGION POST

The Czechoslovak Legion in Siberia issued these stamps for use on its mail and that of local residents. Forgeries exist.

For more detailed listings of Czechoslovak Legion Post issues, see the *Classic Specialized Catalogue of Stamps and Covers.*

Russia No. 79 Overprinted

1918   Typo.   Perf. 14x14½

A1	A15	10k dark blue	2,500.

No. A1 was sold for a few days in Chelyabinsk. It was withdrawn because of a spelling error ("CZESZKJA," instead of "CZESZKAJA).

This overprint was also applied to Russia Nos. 73-78, 80-81, 83-85, 119-121, 123 and 130-131. These were trial printings, never sold to the public, although favor-cancelled covers exist.

Urn and Cathedral at Irkutsk — A1

Armored Railroad Car — A2

Sentinel — A3

1919-20   Litho.   Imperf.

1	A1	25k carmine	10.50	—
a.		Perf 11½ ('20)	15.00	—
2	A2	50k yellow green	10.50	—
a.		Perf 11½ ('20)	15.00	—
3	A3	1r red brown	19.00	—
a.		Perf 11½ ('20)	22.50	—

Originals of Nos. 1-3 and 1a-3a have a crackled yellow gum. Ungummed remainders, which were given a white gum, exist imperforate and perforated 11½ and 13¼. Value per set, $3.

Lion of Bohemia — A4

Two types: 1 — 6 points on star-like mace head at right of goblet; large saber handle; measures 20x25¼mm. 2 — 5 points on mace head; small saber handle; measures 19½x25mm.

Perce en Arc in Blue

1920   Embossed

4	A4	(25k) blue & rose	3.00	—

No. 4 Overprinted

1920

5	A4	(25k) bl & rose	10.00	—

Both types of No. 4 received overprint.

No. 5 Surcharged with New Values in Green

6	A4	2k bl & rose	35.00	
7	A4	3k bl & rose	35.00	
8	A4	5k bl & rose	35.00	
9	A4	10k bl & rose	35.00	
10	A4	15k bl & rose	35.00	
11	A4	25k bl & rose	35.00	
12	A4	35k bl & rose	35.00	
13	A4	50k bl & rose	35.00	
14	A4	1r bl & rose	35.00	
		Nos. 6-14 (9)	315.00	

BOHEMIA AND MORAVIA

Catalogue values for unused stamps in this country are for never hinged items, beginning with Scott 20 in the regular postage section, Scott B1 in the semipostal section, Scott J1 in the postage due section, and Scott P1 in the newspaper section.

Masaryk Type of Czechoslovakia with hyphen in "Cesko-Slovensko"

Masaryk — A60

1939, Apr. 23

1A	A60	1k rose lake	.20	.20

Prepared by Czechoslovakia prior to the German occupation March 15, 1939. Subsequently issued for use in Bohemia and Moravia.
See No. C1.

German Protectorate

Stamps of Czechoslovakia, 1928-39, Overprinted in Black

Perf. 10, 12½, 12x12½

1939, July 15   Unwmk.

1	A29	5h dk ultra	.20	1.25
2	A29	10h brown	.20	1.25
3	A29	20h red	.20	1.25
4	A29	25h green	.20	1.25
5	A29	30h red vio	.20	1.25
6	A61a	40h dk bl	2.50	5.00
7	A85	50h dp grn	.20	1.25
8	A63	60h dl vio	2.50	5.00
9	A60	1k rose lake (212)	.75	1.75
10	A60	1k rose lake (256)	.30	1.25
11	A64	1.20k rose lilac	3.00	5.00
12	A65	1.50k carmine	2.50	5.75
13	A79	1.60k olive grn	5.00	5.75
a.		"Mähnen"	32.50	75.00
14	A66	2k dk bl grn	1.10	4.00
15	A67	2.50k dk bl	3.00	5.00
16	A68	3k brown	3.00	5.75
17	A70	4k dk vio	9.50	6.50
18	A71	5k green	3.50	10.00
19	A72	10k blue	4.75	15.00
		Nos. 1-19 (19)	42.60	83.25
		Set, never hinged	60.00	

The size of the overprint varies, Nos. 1-10 measure 17½x15½mm, Nos. 11-16 19x18mm, Nos. 17 and 19 28x17½mm and No. 18 23½x23mm.

Catalogue values for unused stamps in this section, from this point to the end of the section, are for never hinged items.

Linden Leaves and Closed Buds — A1

1939-41   Photo.   Perf. 14

20	A1	5h dark blue	.20	.20
21	A1	10h blk brn	.20	.40
22	A1	20h crimson	.20	.30
23	A1	25h dk bl grn	.20	.30
24	A1	30h dp plum	.20	.30
24A	A1	30h golden brn ('41)	.20	.30
25	A1	40h orange ('40)	.20	.20
26	A1	50h slate grn ('40)	.20	.20
		Nos. 20-26 (8)	1.60	2.30

See Nos. 49-51.

Castle at Zvikov — A2

Karlstein Castle — A3

St. Barbara's
Church, Kutna
Hora — A4

Cathedral at
Prague — A5

Brno
Cathedral — A6

Town Square,
Olomouc — A7

1939　　　Engr.　　　Perf. 12½

27	A2	40h dark blue	.20	.30
28	A3	50h dk bl grn	.20	.30
29	A4	60h dl vio	.20	.30
30	A5	1k dp rose	.20	.30
31	A6	1.20k rose lilac	.40	.60
32	A6	1.50k rose car	.20	.30
33	A7	2k dk bl grn	.20	.50
34	A7	2.50k dark blue	.20	.30
		Nos. 27-34 (8)	1.80	2.90

No. 31 measures 23½x29½mm, No. 42
measures 18½x23mm.
See #52-53, 53B. For overprints see #60-
61.

Zlin — A8

Iron Works at
Moravská
Ostrava — A9

Prague — A10

1939-40

35	A8	3k dl rose vio	.20	.30
36	A9	4k slate ('40)	.20	.40
37	A10	5k green	.50	.80
38	A10	10k lt blue	.40	1.00
39	A10	20k yel brn	1.25	2.00
		Nos. 35-39 (5)	2.55	4.50

Types of 1939 and

Neuhaus
A11

Lainsitz Bridge near
Bechyne
A14

Pernstein
Castle — A12

Samson Fountain,
Budweis — A15

Pardubice
Castle — A13

Kromeriz
A16

Wallenstein
Palace,
Prague — A17

1940　　　Engr.　　　Perf. 12½

40	A11	50h dk bl grn	.20	.20
41	A12	80h dp bl	.25	.40
42	A6	1.20k vio brn	.40	.25
43	A13	2k gray grn	.20	.20
44	A14	5k dk bl grn	.20	.20
45	A15	6k brn vio	.20	.50
46	A16	8k slate grn	.20	.30
47	A17	10k blue	.45	.30
48	A10	20k sepia	1.10	1.60
		Nos. 40-48 (9)	3.20	3.95

No. 42 measures 18½x23mm; No. 31,
23½x29½mm.

Types of 1939-40

1941

49	A1	60h violet	.20	.20
50	A1	80h red org	.20	.20
51	A1	1k brown	.20	.20
52	A5	1.20k rose red	.20	.20
53	A4	1.50k lil rose	.20	.25
53A	A13	2k light blue	.20	.20
53B	A6	2.50k ultra	.20	.20
53C	A12	3k olive	.20	.20
		Nos. 49-53C (8)	1.60	1.65

Nos. 49-51 show buds open. Nos. 52 and
53B measure 18¾x23½mm and have no
inscriptions below design.
For overprints see Nos. 60-61.

Antonin
Dvorák — A18

1941, Aug. 25　Engr.　Perf. 12½

54	A18	60h dull lilac	.50	.60
55	A18	1.20k sepia	.50	.60

Antonin Dvorák (1841-1904), composer.
Nos. 54-55 were issued in sheets of 50
stamps and 50 alternating inscribed labels.
Value for set of singles with attached labels,
unused or used, $1.50.

Farming
Scene — A19

Factories — A20

1941, Sept. 7　Photo.　Perf. 13½

56	A19	30h dk red brn	.20	.30
57	A19	60h dark green	.20	.30
58	A20	1.20k dk plum	.20	.30
59	A20	2.50k sapphire	.25	.65
		Nos. 56-59 (4)	.85	1.55

Issued to publicize the Prague Fair.

Nos. 52 and 53B
Overprinted in Blue
or Red

1942, Mar. 15　　　Perf. 12½

60	A5	1.20k rose red (Bl)	.70	.80
61	A6	2.50k ultra (R)	.80	1.25

3rd anniv. of the Protectorate of Bohemia
and Moravia.

Adolf Hitler
A21

17th Century
Messenger
A22

1942　　　Photo.　　　Perf. 14

Size: 17½x21½mm

62	A21	10(h) gray blk	.20	.25
63	A21	30(h) bister brn	.20	.25
64	A21	40(h) slate blue	.20	.25
65	A21	50(h) slate grn	.20	.25
66	A21	60(h) purple	.20	.25
67	A21	80(h) org ver	.20	.25

Perf. 12½
Engr.
Size: 18x21mm

68	A21	1k dl brn	.20	.25
69	A21	1.20(k) carmine	.20	.30
70	A21	1.50(k) claret	.20	.30
71	A21	1.60(k) Prus grn	.20	.30
72	A21	2k light blue	.20	.30
73	A21	2.40(k) fawn	.20	.30

Size: 18½x24mm

74	A21	2.50(k) ultra	.20	.30
75	A21	3k olive grn	.20	.30
76	A21	4k brt red vio	.20	.30
77	A21	5k myrtle grn	.20	.30
78	A21	6k claret brn	.20	.40
79	A21	8k indigo	.20	.40

Size: 23½x29¾mm

80	A21	10k dk gray grn	.25	1.00
81	A21	20k gray vio	.40	1.00
82	A21	30k red	.75	2.00
83	A21	50k deep blue	1.50	3.00
		Nos. 62-83 (22)	6.50	12.25

1943, Jan. 10　Photo.　Perf. 13½

84	A22	60h dark rose violet	.40	.40

Stamp Day.

Scene from "Die
Meistersinger"
A23

Richard Wagner
A24

Scene from
"Siegfried" — A25

1943, May 22

85	A23	60h violet	.20	.20
86	A24	1.20k carmine rose	.20	.20
87	A25	2.50k deep ultra	.20	.20
		Nos. 85-87 (3)	.60	.60

Richard Wagner (1813-83).

St. Vitus'
Cathedral,
Prague — A26

Adolf
Hitler — A27

1944, Nov. 21　Engr.　Perf. 12½

88	A26	1.50k dull rose brn	.25	.25
89	A26	2.50k dull lilac blue	.25	.35

1944

90	A27	4.20k green	.50	.50

SEMI-POSTAL STAMPS

Catalogue values for unused
stamps in this section are for
never hinged items.

Nurse and
Wounded
Soldier — SP1

Perf. 13½

1940, June 29　Photo.　Unwmk.

B1	SP1	60h + 40h indigo	.90	1.10
B2	SP1	1.20k + 80h deep plum	.90	1.25

Surtax for German Red Cross.
Nos. B1-B2 were issued in sheets of 50
stamps and 50 alternating inscribed labels.
Value for set of singles with attached labels:
unused $3; used $4.

Red Cross Nurse
and Patient — SP2

1941, Apr. 20

B3	SP2	60h + 40h indigo	.40	.60
B4	SP2	1.20k + 80h dp plum	.40	.65

Surtax for German Red Cross.
Nos. B3-B4 were issued in sheets of 50
stamps and 50 alternating inscribed labels.
Value for set of singles with attached labels:
unused $1.80; used $2.75.

Old Theater,
Prague — SP3

Mozart — SP4

1941, Oct. 26

B5	SP3	30h + 30h brown	.20	.20
B6	SP3	60h + 60h Prus grn	.20	.20
B7	SP4	1.20k + 1.20k scar	.25	.25
B8	SP4	2.50k + 2.50k dk bl	.45	.55
		Nos. B5-B8 (4)	1.10	1.20

150th anniversary of Mozart's death.
Labels alternate with stamps in sheets of
Nos. B5-B8. The labels with Nos. B5-B6 show
two bars of Mozart's opera "Don Giovanni."
Those with Nos. B7-B8 show Mozart's piano.
Value for set of singles with attached labels:
unused $2; used $3.25.

Adolf
Hitler — SP5

Nurse and
Soldier — SP6

1942, Apr. 20   Engr.   Perf. 12½

B9	SP5	30h + 20h dl brn vio	.25	.25
B10	SP5	60h + 40h dl grn	.25	.25
B11	SP5	1.20k + 80h dp claret	.25	.35
B12	SP5	2.50k + 1.50k dl bl	.35	.55

Nos. B9-B12 (4)   1.10   1.40

Hitler's 53rd birthday.
Nos. B9-B12 were issued in sheets of 100 stamps and 12 blank labels. Value for set of singles with attached labels: unused $3; used $2.25.

1942, Sept. 4   Perf. 13½

B13	SP6	60h + 40h deep blue	.25	.25
B14	SP6	1.20k + 80h dp plum	.25	.25

The surtax aided the German Red Cross.

Emperor
Charles IV
SP7

Peter Parler
SP8

John the Blind,
King of
Bohemia — SP9

Adolf
Hitler — SP10

1943, Jan. 29

B15	SP7	60h + 40h violet	.20	.20
B16	SP8	1.20k + 80h carmine	.20	.20
B17	SP9	2.50k + 1.50k vio bl	.20	.20

Nos. B15-B17 (3)   .60   .60

The surtax was for the benefit of the German wartime winter relief.

1943, Apr. 20   Engr.   Perf. 12½

B18	SP10	60h + 1.40k dl vio	.25	.25
B19	SP10	1.20k + 3.80k carmine	.25	.30

Hitler's 54th birthday.
Nos. B18-B19 were issued in sheets of 100 stamps and 12 blank labels. Value for set of singles with attached labels: unused $1.10; used 60c.

Deathmask of
Reinhard
Heydrich — SP11

Eagle and Red
Cross — SP12

1943, May 28   Photo.   Perf. 13½

B20	SP11	60h + 4.40k black	.75	1.60

No. B20 exists in a souvenir sheet containing a single stamp. It was given to high Nazi officials attending a ceremony one year after Heydrich's assassination. Value $15,000.

1943, Sept. 16   Perf. 13

B21	SP12	1.20k + 8.80k blk & car	.50	.50

The surtax aided the German Red Cross.

Native Costumes
SP13

Nazi Emblem,
Arms of
Bohemia,
Moravia
SP14

1944, Mar. 15   Perf. 13½

B22	SP13	1.20(k) + 3.80(k) rose lake	.25	.25
B23	SP14	4.20(k) + 10.80(k) golden brn	.25	.25
B24	SP13	10k + 20k saph	.25	.40

Nos. B22-B24 (3)   .75   .90

Fifth anniversary of protectorate.

Adolf
Hitler — SP15

Bedrich
Smetana — SP16

1944, Apr. 20

B25	SP15	60h + 1.40k olive blk	.30	.30
B26	SP15	1.20k + 3.80k slate grn	.30	.30

1944, May 12   Engr.   Perf. 12½

B27	SP16	60h + 1.40k dk gray grn	.25	.25
B28	SP16	1.20k + 3.80k brn car	.25	.25

Bedrich Smetana (1824-84), Czech composer and pianist.

AIR POST STAMP

Catalogue values for unused stamps in this section are for never hinged items.

Type of Czechoslovakia 1930 with hyphen in "Cesko-Slovensko"

Fokker Monoplane — AP3

1939, Apr. 22   Perf. 13½

C1	AP3	30h rose lilac	.20	.20

Prepared by Czechoslovakia prior to the German occupation March 15, 1939. Subsequently issued for use in Bohemia and Moravia. See No. 1A.

PERSONAL DELIVERY STAMPS

PD1

1939-40   Unwmk.   Photo.   Perf. 13½

EX1	PD1	50h indigo & blue ('40)	1.25	2.00
EX2	PD1	50h carmine & rose	1.60	2.50

POSTAGE DUE STAMPS

Catalogue values for unused stamps in this section are for never hinged items.

D1

1939-40   Unwmk.   Typo.   Perf. 14

J1	D1	5h dark carmine	.25	.30
J2	D1	10h dark carmine	.25	.30
J3	D1	20h dark carmine	.25	.30
J4	D1	30h dark carmine	.25	.30
J5	D1	40h dark carmine	.25	.30
J6	D1	50h dark carmine	.25	.30
J7	D1	60h dark carmine	.25	.30
J8	D1	80h dark carmine	.25	.30
J9	D1	1k bright ultra	.25	.40
J10	D1	1.20k brt ultra ('40)	.30	.40
J11	D1	2k bright ultra	1.00	1.25
J12	D1	5k bright ultra	1.10	1.60
J13	D1	10k bright ultra	1.60	2.00
J14	D1	20k bright ultra	3.25	3.25

Nos. J1-J14 (14)   9.50   11.30

OFFICIAL STAMPS

Catalogue values for unused stamps in this section are for never hinged items.

Numeral
O1

Eagle
O2

Unwmk.
1941, Jan. 1   Typo.   Perf. 14

O1	O1	30h ocher	.25	.20
O2	O1	40h indigo	.25	.20
O3	O1	50h emerald	.25	.20
O4	O1	60h slate grn	.25	.20
O5	O1	80h org red	.80	.20
O6	O1	1k red brn	.40	.20
O7	O1	1.20k carmine	.40	.20
O8	O1	1.50k dp plum	.65	.20
O9	O1	2k brt bl	.65	.20
O10	O1	3k olive	.65	.20
O11	O1	4k red vio	.80	.50
O12	O1	5k org yel	2.00	1.00

Nos. O1-O12 (12)   7.35   3.50

1943, Feb. 15

O13	O2	30(h) bister	.20	.30
O14	O2	40(h) indigo	.20	.30
O15	O2	50(h) yel grn	.20	.30
O16	O2	60(h) dp vio	.20	.30
O17	O2	80(h) org red	.20	.30
O18	O2	1k chocolate	.20	.30
O19	O2	1.20(k) carmine	.20	.30
O20	O2	1.50(k) brn red	.20	.30
O21	O2	2k lt bl	.20	.30
O22	O2	3k olive	.20	.30
O23	O2	4k red vio	.20	.30
O24	O2	5k dk grn	.20	.50

Nos. O13-O24 (12)   2.40   3.80

NEWSPAPER STAMPS

Catalogue values for unused stamps in this section are for never hinged items.

Carrier Pigeon — N1

1939   Unwmk.   Typo.   Imperf.

P1	N1	2h ocher	.20	.30
P2	N1	5h ultra	.20	.30
P3	N1	7h red orange	.20	.30

P4	N1	9h emerald	.20	.30
P5	N1	10h henna brown	.20	.30
P6	N1	12h dark ultra	.20	.30
P7	N1	20h dark green	.20	.30
P8	N1	50h red brown	.20	.40
P9	N1	1k greenish gray	.25	.80

Nos. P1-P9 (9)   1.85   3.30

No. P5 Overprinted in
Black

1940

P10	N1	10h henna brown	.40	.65

Overprinted for use by commercial firms.

N2

1943, Feb. 15

P11	N2	2(h) ocher	.20	.20
P12	N2	5(h) light blue	.20	.20
P13	N2	7(h) red orange	.20	.20
P14	N2	9(h) emerald	.20	.20
P15	N2	10(h) henna brown	.20	.20
P16	N2	12(h) dark ultra	.20	.20
P17	N2	20(h) dark green	.20	.20
P18	N2	50(h) red brown	.20	.20
P19	N2	1k slate green	.20	.20

Nos. P11-P19 (9)   1.80   1.80

DAHOMEY

də-'hō-mē

LOCATION — West coast of Africa
AREA — 43,483 sq. mi.
POP. — 3,030,000 (est. 1974)
CAPITAL — Porto-Novo

Formerly a native kingdom including Benin, Dahomey was annexed by France in 1894. It became part of the colonial administrative unit of French West Africa in 1895. Stamps of French West Africa superseded those of Dahomey in 1945. The Republic of Dahomey was proclaimed Dec. 4, 1958.

The republic changed its name to the People's Republic of Benin on Nov. 30, 1975. See Benin for stamps issued after that date.

100 Centimes = 1 Franc

Catalog values for unused stamps in this country are for Never Hinged items, beginning with Scott 137 in the regular postage section, Scott B15 in the semipostal section, Scott C14 in the airpost section, Scott CQ1 in the airpost parcel post section, Scott J29 in the postage due section, and Scott Q1 in the parcel post section.

See French West Africa No. 71 for stamp inscribed "Dahomey" and "Afrique Occidentale Francaise."

Navigation and Commerce — A1

Perf. 14x13½

1899-1905   Typo.   Unwmk.
Name of Colony in Blue or Carmine

1	A1	1c black, *lil bl* ('01)	1.60	1.60
2	A1	2c brown, *buff* ('04)	2.40	1.60
3	A1	4c claret, *lav* ('04)	2.40	2.40
4	A1	5c yellow grn ('04)	6.50	4.00
5	A1	10c red ('01)	5.50	3.25
6	A1	15c gray ('01)	5.50	5.50
7	A1	20c red, *grn* ('04)	19.00	15.00
8	A1	25c black, *rose* ('99)	20.00	20.00
9	A1	25c blue ('01)	21.00	17.00
10	A1	30c brown, *bis* ('04)	24.00	12.00
11	A1	40c red, *straw* ('04)	24.00	15.00
12	A1	50c brn, *az* (name in red) ('01)	24.00	22.50
12A	A1	50c brn, *az* (name in bl) ('05)	32.50	24.00
13	A1	75c dp vio, *grn* ('04)	85.00	55.00
14	A1	1fr brnz grn, *straw* ('04)	40.00	32.50
15	A1	2fr violet, *rose* ('04)	110.00	72.50
16	A1	5fr red lilac, *lav* ('04)	135.00	105.00
		Nos. 1-16 (17)	558.40	404.95

Perf. 13½x14 stamps are counterfeits.
For surcharges see Nos. 32-41.

Gen. Louis Faidherbe A2

Oil Palm — A3

Dr. Noel Eugène Ballay A4

1906-07   Perf. 13½x14
Name of Colony in Red or Blue

17	A2	1c slate	1.60	1.60
18	A2	2c chocolate	2.40	1.60
19	A2	4c choc, *gray bl*	4.00	3.25
20	A2	5c green	9.50	3.25
21	A2	10c carmine (B)	22.50	4.00
22	A3	20c black, *azure*	14.50	13.00
23	A3	25c blue, *pnksh*	16.00	13.00
24	A3	30c choc, *pnksh*	16.00	14.50
25	A3	35c black, *yellow*	87.50	19.00
26	A3	45c choc, *grnsh* ('07)	21.00	14.50
27	A3	50c deep violet	21.00	17.50
28	A3	75c blue, *orange*	24.00	22.00
29	A4	1fr black, *azure*	32.00	24.00
30	A4	2fr blue, *pink*	110.00	110.00
31	A4	5fr car, *straw* (B)	100.00	105.00
		Nos. 17-31 (15)	482.00	360.20

#2-3, 6-7, 9-13 Surcharged in Black or Carmine

1912   Perf. 14x13½
Spacing between figures of surcharge 1.5mm (5c), 2mm (10c)

32		5c on 2c brn, *buff*	2.00	*2.40*
33		5c on 4c claret, *lav* (C)	1.60	*2.00*
a.		Double surcharge	275.00	
34		5c on 15c gray (C)	2.00	*2.40*
35		5c on 20c red, *grn*	2.00	*2.40*
36		5c on 25c blue (C)	2.00	*2.40*
a.		Inverted surcharge	220.00	
37		5c on 30c brown, *bis* (C)	2.00	*2.40*
38		10c on 40c red, *straw*	2.00	*2.40*
a.		Inverted surcharge	325.00	
39		10c on 50c brn, *az*, name in bl (C)	2.40	*2.75*
40		10c on 50c brn, *az*, name in red (C)	1,125.	*1,300.*
41		10c on 75c violet, *org*	7.25	8.00
a.		Double surcharge	*5,500.*	
		Nos. 32-39,41 (9)	23.25	27.15

Two spacings between the surcharged numerals are found on Nos. 32 to 41. For detailed listings, see the *Scott Classic Specialized Catalogue of Stamps and Covers.*

Man Climbing Oil Palm — A5

1913-39   Perf. 13½x14

42	A5	1c violet & blk	.25	.30
43	A5	2c choc & rose	.30	.40
44	A5	4c black & brn	.30	.40
45	A5	5c yel grn & blk grn	1.20	.55
46	A5	5c vio brn & vio ('22)	.50	.55
47	A5	10c org red & rose	1.60	.80
a.		Half used as 5c on wrapper or printed matter		—
48	A5	10c yel grn & bl grn ('22)	.75	.90
49	A5	10c red & ol ('25)	.40	.40
50	A5	15c brn org & dk vio ('17)	.80	.80
51	A5	20c gray & red brown	.75	.75
52	A5	20c bluish grn & grn ('26)	.40	.40
53	A5	20c mag & blk ('27)	.40	.40
54	A5	25c ultra & dp blue	2.00	1.60
55	A5	25c vio brn & org ('22)	1.20	.95
56	A5	30c choc & vio	2.75	2.40
57	A5	30c red org & rose ('22)	3.25	3.25

58	A5	30c yellow & vio ('25)	.40	.40
59	A5	30c dl grn & grn ('27)	.40	.40
60	A5	35c brown & blk	.80	.80
61	A5	35c bl grn & grn ('38)	.40	.30
62	A5	40c black & red org	.80	.80
63	A5	45c gray & ultra	.80	.80
64	A5	50c chocolate & brn	6.50	6.00
a.		Half used as 25c on cover		500.00
65	A5	50c ultra & bl ('22)	1.60	1.60
66	A5	50c brn red & bl ('26)	1.20	1.20
67	A5	55c gray grn & choc ('38)	.70	.55
68	A5	60c vio, *pnksh* ('25)	.40	.40
69	A5	65c yel brn & ol grn ('26)	1.20	1.20
70	A5	75c blue & violet	1.20	1.20
71	A5	80c henna brn & ultra ('38)	.40	.40
72	A5	85c dk bl & ver ('26)	1.60	1.60
73	A5	90c rose & brn red ('30)	.80	.75
74	A5	90c yel bis & red org ('39)	1.20	.80
75	A5	1fr blue grn & blk	1.20	1.20
76	A5	1fr dk bl & ultra ('26)	1.60	1.60
77	A5	1fr yel brn & lt red ('28)	1.60	1.20
78	A5	1fr dk red & red org ('38)	1.05	.95
79	A5	1.10fr vio & bis ('28)	5.50	*6.00*
80	A5	1.25fr dp bl & dk brn ('33)	17.50	8.75
81	A5	1.50fr dk bl & lt bl ('30)	1.30	.80
82	A5	1.75fr dk brn & dp buff ('33)	4.00	2.00
83	A5	1.75fr ind & ultra ('38)	1.45	.95
84	A5	2fr yel org & choc	1.20	*1.60*
85	A5	3fr red violet ('30)	2.75	1.75
86	A5	5fr violet & dp bl	2.40	2.75
		Nos. 42-86 (45)	78.80	63.60

The 1c gray and yellow green and 5c dull red and black are Togo Nos. 193a, 196a.

Nos. 47a and 64a were authorized for use in Paouignan during the last part of November 1921. Other values exist as bisects but were not authorized.

For surcharges see #87-96, B1, B8-B11.

Type of 1913 Surcharged

1922-25

87	A5	60c on 75c vio, *pnksh*	1.20	1.20
a.		Double surcharge	200.00	
88	A5	65c on 15c brn org & dk vio ('25)	2.00	2.00
89	A5	85c on 15c brn org & dk vio ('25)	2.00	2.00
		Nos. 87-89 (3)	5.20	5.20

Stamps and Type of 1913-39 Surcharged with New Value and Bars

1924-27

90	A5	25c on 2fr org & choc	1.20	1.20
91	A5	90c on 75c cer & brn red ('27)	2.00	2.00
92	A5	1.25fr on 1fr dk bl & ultra (R) ('26)	1.60	1.60
93	A5	1.50fr on 1fr dk bl & grnsh bl ('27)	2.75	2.75
94	A5	3fr on 5fr olvn & dp org ('27)	10.50	10.50
95	A5	10fr on 5fr bl vio & red brn ('27)	8.00	8.00
96	A5	20fr on 5fr ver & dl grn ('27)	8.75	8.75
		Nos. 90-96 (7)	34.80	34.80

Common Design Types pictured following the introduction.

Colonial Exposition Issue
Common Design Types

1931		Engr.		Perf. 12½
		Name of Country in Black		
97	CD70	40c deep green	6.25	6.25
98	CD71	50c violet	6.25	6.25
99	CD72	90c red orange	6.25	6.25
100	CD73	1.50fr dull blue	6.25	6.25
		Nos. 97-100 (4)	25.00	25.00

Paris International Exposition Issue
Common Design Types

1937		Engr.		Perf. 13
101	CD74	20c deep violet	2.00	2.00
102	CD75	30c dark green	2.00	2.00
103	CD76	40c carmine rose	2.00	2.00
104	CD77	50c dark brown	1.60	1.60
105	CD78	90c red	1.60	1.60
106	CD79	1.50fr ultra	2.00	2.00
		Nos. 101-106 (6)	11.20	11.20

Souvenir Sheet
Imperf

107	CD77	3fr dp blue & blk	8.75	*10.00*

Caillié Issue
Common Design Type

1939, Apr. 5		Engr.		Perf. 12½x12
108	CD81	90c org brn & org	1.00	1.00
109	CD81	1.40fr org & org	1.40	1.40
110	CD81	2.25fr ultra & dk blue	1.50	1.50
		Nos. 108-110 (3)	3.90	3.90

New York World's Fair Issue
Common Design Type

1939				Engr.
111	CD82	1.25fr carmine lake	1.20	1.20
112	CD82	2.25fr ultra	1.20	1.20

Man Poling a Canoe — A7

Pile House A8

Sailboat on Lake Nokoué — A9

Dahomey Warrior — A10

1941				Perf. 13
113	A7	2c scarlet	.25	.25
114	A7	3c deep blue	.25	.25
115	A7	5c brown violet	.70	.70
116	A7	10c green	.30	.30
117	A7	15c black	.25	.25
118	A8	20c violet brown	.30	.30
119	A8	30c dk violet	.30	.30
120	A8	40c scarlet	.70	.70
121	A8	50c slate green	.95	.95
122	A8	60c black	.30	.30
123	A8	70c brt red violet	1.20	1.20
124	A8	80c brown black	1.20	1.20
125	A9	1fr violet	1.20	1.20
126	A9	1.30fr brown violet	1.20	1.20
127	A9	1.40fr green	1.20	1.20
128	A9	1.50fr brt rose	1.20	1.20
129	A9	2fr brown orange	1.20	1.20
130	A10	2.50fr dark blue	1.20	1.20
131	A10	3fr scarlet	1.20	1.20
132	A10	5fr slate green	1.20	1.20

133	A10	10fr violet brown	2.00	2.00
134	A10	20fr black	2.40	2.40
		Nos. 113-134 (22)	20.70	20.70

Nos. 121, 122 without "RF," see Nos. 136A-136B.

Pile House and Marshal Pétain A11

1941   *Perf. 12½x12*
135 A11 1fr green .80 —
136 A11 2.50fr blue .80 —

For surcharges see Nos. B14A-B14B.

Type of 1941 without "RF"

1944   *Perf. 13*
136A A8 50c slate green 1.20
136B A8 60c black 1.20

Nos. 136A-136B were issued by the Vichy government in France, but were not placed on sale in Dahomey.

> **Catalogue values for unused stamps in this section, from this point to the end of the section, are for Never Hinged items.**

Republic

Village Ganvié — A12

Unwmk.

1960, Mar. 1   **Engr.**   *Perf. 12*
137 A12 25fr dk blue, brn & red .55 .20

For overprint see No. 152.

Imperforates
Most Dahomey stamps from 1960 onward exist imperforate in issued and trial colors, and also in small presentation sheets in issued colors.

C.C.T.A. Issue
Common Design Type

1960, May 16
138 CD106 5fr rose lilac & ultra .45 .20

Emblem of the Entente — A13   Prime Minister Hubert Maga — A14

Council of the Entente Issue

1960, May 29 Photo.   *Perf. 13x13½*
139 A13 25fr multicolored .55 .30

1st anniv. of the Council of the Entente (Dahomey, Ivory Coast, Niger and Upper Volta).

1960, Aug.   **Engr.**   *Perf. 13*
140 A14 85fr deep claret & blk 1.60 .90

Issued on the occasion of Dahomey's proclamation of independence, Aug. 1, 1960.
For surcharge see No. 149.

Weaver — A15   Doves, UN Building and Emblem — A16

2fr, 10fr, Wood sculptor. 3fr, 15fr, Fisherman and net, horiz. 4fr, 20fr, Potter, horiz.

1961, Feb. 17   **Engr.**   *Perf. 13*
141 A15 1fr rose, org & red lilac .20 .20
142 A15 2fr bister brn & choc .20 .20
143 A15 3fr green & orange .20 .20
144 A15 4fr olive bis & claret .20 .20
145 A15 6fr rose, lt vio & ver .40 .20
146 A15 10fr blue & green .55 .40
147 A15 15fr red lilac & violet .75 .40
148 A15 20fr bluish vio & Prus bl .90 .55
    Nos. 141-148 (8) 3.40 2.35

For surcharges see Nos. 1374, Q1-Q7.

No. 140 Surcharged with New Value, Bars and: "Président de la République"

1961, Aug. 1
149 A14 100fr on 85fr dp cl & blk 3.25 3.25

First anniversary of Independence.

1961, Sept. 20   **Unwmk.**   *Perf. 13*
150 A16 5fr multicolored .35 .25
151 A16 60fr multicolored 1.10 .80

1st anniv. of Dahomey's admission to the UN. See #C16 and souvenir sheet #C16a.

No. 137 Overprinted: "JEUX SPORTIFS D'ABIDJAN 24 AU 31 DECEMBRE 1961"

1961, Dec. 24
152 A12 25fr dk blue, brn & red .55 .30

Abidjan Games, Dec 24-31.

Interior of Burned-out Fort Ouidah and Wrecked Car — A17

1962, July 31 Photo.   *Perf. 12½*
153 A17 30fr multicolored .60 .45
154 A17 60fr multicolored 1.40 .60

Evacuation of Fort Ouidah by the Portuguese, and its occupation by Dahomey. 1st anniv.

African and Malgache Union Issue
Common Design Type

1962, Sept. 8   *Perf. 12½x12*
155 CD110 30fr red lil, bluish grn, red & gold .90 .90

Red Cross Nurses and Map — A18

1962, Oct. 5   **Engr.**   *Perf. 13*
156 A18 5fr blue, choc & red .30 .20
157 A18 20fr blue, dk grn & red .60 .45
158 A18 25fr blue, brown & red .65 .45
159 A18 30fr blue, black & red .85 .70
    Nos. 156-159 (4) 2.40 1.80

Ganvié Woman in Canoe — A19

Peuhl Herdsman and Cattle — A20

Designs: 3fr, 65fr, Bariba chief of Nikki. 15fr, 50fr, Ouidah witch doctor, rock python. 20fr, 30fr, Nessoukoué women carrying vases on heads, Abomey. 25fr, 40fr, Dahomey girl. 60fr, Peuhl herdsman and cattle. 85fr, Ganvié woman in canoe.

1963, Feb. 18   **Unwmk.**   *Perf. 13*
160 A19 2fr grnsh blue & vio .20 .20
161 A19 3fr blue & black .20 .20
162 A20 5fr brown, blk & grn .45 .20
163 A19 15fr brn, bl grn & red brn .45 .20
164 A19 20fr green, blk & car .40 .20
165 A20 25fr dk brn, bl & bl grn .50 .20
166 A19 30fr brn org, choc & mag .75 .40
167 A20 40fr choc, grn & brt bl 1.25 .40
168 A19 50fr blk, grn, brn & red brn 2.00 .55
169 A20 60fr choc, org red & ol 5.50 1.00
170 A19 65fr orange brn & choc 2.25 .65
171 A19 85fr brt blue & choc 3.25 1.00
    Nos. 160-171 (12) 17.20 5.20

For surcharges see Nos. 211, 232, Benin 655A, 690F, 700, 722, 1375, 1417.

Boxers — A21

Designs: 1fr, 20fr, Soccer goalkeeper, horiz. 2fr, 5fr, Runners.

1963, Apr. 11   **Engr.**
172 A21 50c green & blue .20 .20
173 A21 1fr olive, blk & brn .20 .20
174 A21 2fr olive, blue & brn .20 .20
175 A21 5fr brown, crim & blk .20 .20
176 A21 15fr dk violet & brn .45 .20
177 A21 20fr multicolored .70 .55
    Nos. 172-177 (6) 1.95 1.55

Friendship Games, Dakar, Apr. 11-21.
For surcharges & overprint see Benin #697, 704, 1372, 1382, 1384.

President's Palace, Cotonou — A22

1963, Aug. 1 Photo.   *Perf. 12½x12*
178 A22 25fr multicolored .45 .20

Third anniversary of independence.

Gen. Toussaint L'Ouverture — A23   UN Emblem, Flame, "15" — A24

1963, Nov. 18 Unwmk.   *Perf. 12x13*
179 A23 25fr multicolored .40 .20
180 A23 30fr multicolored .70 .20
181 A23 100fr ultra, brn & red 1.40 .80
    Nos. 179-181 (3) 2.50 1.20

Pierre Dominique Toussaint L'Ouverture (1743-1803), Haitian gen., statesman and descendant of the kings of Allada (Dahomey). For overprint, see Benin No. 1367. For surcharge, see Benin No. 1466.

1963, Dec. 10   *Perf. 12*
182 A24 4fr multicolored .20 .20
183 A24 6fr multicolored .20 .20
184 A24 25fr multicolored .45 .20
    Nos. 182-184 (3) .85 .60

15th anniversary of the Universal Declaration of Human Rights. For surcharge, see Benin No. 1377.

Somba Dance — A25

Regional Dances: 3fr, Nago dance, Pobe-Ketou, horiz. 10fr, Dance of the baton. 15fr, Nago dance, Ouidah, horiz. 25fr, Dance of the Sakpatassi. 30fr, Dance of the Nessouhouessi, horiz.

1964, Aug. 8   **Engr.**   *Perf. 13*
185 A25 2fr red, emerald & blk .20 .20
186 A25 3fr dull red, blue & grn .20 .20
187 A25 10fr purple, blk & red .40 .20
188 A25 15fr magenta, blk & grn .40 .20
189 A25 25fr Prus blue, brn & org .80 .30
190 A25 30fr dk red, choc & org 1.00 .40
    Nos. 185-190 (6) 3.00 1.50

Runner — A26

1964, Oct. 20 Photo.   *Perf. 11*
191 A26 60fr shown 1.90 1.00
192 A26 85fr Bicyclist 3.00 1.40

18th Olympic Games, Tokyo, Oct. 10-25.

Cooperation Issue
Common Design Type

1964, Nov. 7   **Engr.**   *Perf. 13*
193 CD119 25fr org, vio & dk brn .80 .35

UNICEF Emblem, Mother and Child — A27

IQSY Emblem and Apollo — A28

25fr, Mother holding child in her arms.

1964, Dec. 11   Unwmk.   Perf. 13
194 A27 20fr yel grn, dk red & blk   .40   .20
195 A27 25fr blue, dk red & blk   .60   .45

18th anniv. of UNICEF. For overprint, see Benin No. 1368.

1964, Dec. 22   Photo.   Perf. 13x12½

100fr, IQSY emblem, Nimbus weather satellite.

196 A28   25fr green & lt yellow   .55   .20
197 A28 100fr deep plum & yellow   1.60   .95

International Quiet Sun Year, 1964-65.

Abomey Tapestry — A29

Designs (Abomey tapestries): 25fr, Warrior and fight scenes. 50fr, Birds and warriors, horiz. 85fr, Animals, ship and plants, horiz.

1965, Apr. 12   Photo.   Perf. 12½
198 A29 20fr multicolored   .80   .20
199 A29 25fr multicolored   .95   .40
200 A29 50fr multicolored   1.50   .80
201 A29 85fr multicolored   3.00   1.10
    a.   Min. sheet of 4, #198-201   8.00   8.00
    Nos. 198-201 (4)   6.25   2.50

Issued to publicize the local rug weaving industry.

Baudot Telegraph Distributor and Ader Telephone A30

1965, May 17   Engr.   Perf. 13
202 A30 100fr lilac, org & blk   2.10   1.60

Cent. of the ITU.

Cotonou Harbor — A31

100fr, Cotonou Harbor, denomination at left.

1965, Aug. 1   Photo.   Perf. 12½
203 A31   25fr multicolored   .90   .20
204 A31 100fr multicolored   2.10   1.10
    a.   Pair, #203-204   3.75   2.10

The opening of Cotonou Harbor. No. 204a has a continuous design.
For surcharges see Nos. 219-220.

Cybium Tritor A32

Fish: 25fr, Dentex filosus. 30fr, Atlantic sail-fish. 50fr, Blackish tripletail.

1965, Sept. 20   Engr.   Perf. 13
205 A32 10fr black & brt blue   .75   .20
206 A32 25fr brt blue, org & blk   1.00   .55
207 A32 30fr violet bl & grnsh bl   1.50   .80
208 A32 50fr black, gray bl & org   2.50   1.00
    Nos. 205-208 (4)   5.75   2.55

For surcharge see Benin No. 911.

Independence Monument — A33

1965, Oct. 28   Photo.   Perf. 12x12½
209 A33 25fr gray, black & red   .40   .20
210 A33 30fr lt ultra, black & red   .65   .20

October 28 Revolution, 2nd anniv. For surcharge, see Benin No. 1385.

No. 165 Surcharged

1965, Nov.   Engr.   Perf. 13
211 A20 1fr on 25fr   .30   .20

Porto Novo Cathedral A34

Designs: 50fr, Ouidah Pro-Cathedral, vert. 70fr, Cotonou Cathedral.

1966, Mar. 21   Engr.   Perf. 13
212 A34 30fr Prus bl, vio brn & grn   .55   .20
213 A34 50fr vio brn, Prus bl & brn   .70   .50
214 A34 70fr grn, Prus bl & vio brn   1.25   .75
    Nos. 212-214 (3)   2.50   1.45

Jewelry — A35

Designs: 30fr, Architecture. 50fr, Musician. 70fr, Crucifixion, sculpture.

1966, Apr. 4   Engr.   Perf. 13
215 A35 15fr dull red brn & blk   .45   .20
216 A35 30fr dk brn, ultra & brn red   .70   .45
217 A35 50fr brt blue & dk brn   1.10   .55
218 A35 70fr red brown & blk   2.25   .85
    Nos. 215-218 (4)   4.50   2.05

International Negro Arts Festival, Dakar, Senegal, Apr. 1-24.

Nos. 203-204 Surcharged

1966, Apr. 24   Photo.   Perf. 12½
219 A31 15fr on 25fr multi   .55   .35
220 A31 15fr on 100fr multi   .55   .35
    a.   Pair, #219-220   1.50   1.10

Fifth anniversary of the Cooperation Agreement between France and Dahomey.

WHO Headquarters from the East — A36

1966, May 3   Perf. 12½x13
    Size: 35x22½mm
221 A36 30fr multicolored   .55   .20

Inauguration of the WHO Headquarters, Geneva. See No. C32.

Boy Scout Signaling A37

Designs: 10fr, Patrol standard with pennant, vert. 30fr, Campfire and map of Dahomey, vert. 50fr, Scouts building foot bridge.

1966, Oct. 17   Engr.   Perf. 13
222 A37   5fr dk brn, ocher & red   .20   .20
223 A37 10fr black, grn & rose cl   .20   .20
224 A37 30fr org, red brn & pur   .55   .35
225 A37 50fr vio bl, grn & dk brn   .95   .45
    a.   Min. sheet of 4, #222-225   2.75   2.75
    Nos. 222-225 (4)   1.90   1.20

Clappertonia Ficifolia — A38

Lions Emblem, Dancing Children, Bird — A39

Flowers: 3fr, Hewittia sublobata. 5fr, Butterfly pea. 10fr, Water lily. 15fr, Commelina forskalaei. 30fr, Eremomastax speciosa.

1967, Feb. 20   Photo.   Perf. 12x12½
226 A38   1fr multicolored   .20   .20
227 A38   3fr multicolored   .35   .20
228 A38   5fr multicolored   .55   .20
229 A38 10fr multicolored   .90   .35
230 A38 15fr multicolored   1.10   .55
231 A38 30fr multicolored   2.10   .90
    Nos. 226-231 (6)   5.20   2.40

For surcharges see Benin Nos. 707, 715, 1376, 1390, 1402.

Nos. 170-171 Surcharged with New Value and Heavy Bar

1967, Mar. 1   Engr.   Perf. 13
232 A19 30fr on 65fr   .85   .60
    a.   Double surcharge   36.00
233 A19 30fr on 85fr   .85   .60
    a.   Double surcharge   60.00
    b.   Inverted surcharge   60.00

1967, Mar. 20
234 A39 100fr dl vio, dp bl & grn   1.50   1.10

50th anniversary of Lions International.

EXPO '67 "Man in the City" Pavilion A40

Design: 70fr, "The New Africa" exhibit.

1967, June 12   Engr.   Perf. 13
235 A40 30fr green & choc   .70   .20
236 A40 70fr green & brn red   1.50   .65

EXPO '67, International Exhibition, Montreal, Apr. 28-Oct. 27, 1967. See No. C57 and miniature sheet No. C57a.
For surcharges see Benin No. 897.

Europafrica Issue, 1967

Trade (Blood) Circulation, Map of Europe and Africa — A41

1967, July 20   Photo.   Perf. 12x12½
237 A41 30fr multicolored   .55   .20
238 A41 45fr multicolored   .80   .45

For surcharge, see Benin No. 1386.

Scouts Climbing Mountain, Jamboree Emblem A42

70fr, Jamboree emblem, Scouts launching canoe.

1967, Aug. 7   Engr.   Perf. 13
239 A42 30fr brt bl, red brn & sl   .50   .20
240 A42 70fr brt bl, sl grn & dk brn   1.25   .65

12th Boy Scout World Jamboree, Farragut State Park, Idaho, Aug. 1-9. For souvenir sheet see No. C59a.
For surcharges see Benin Nos. 902, 912, 1391.

Rhone River and Olympic Emblems A43

Designs (Olympic Emblems and): 45fr, View of Grenoble, vert. 100fr, Rhone Bridge, Grenoble, and Pierre de Coubertin.

1967, Sept. 2   Engr.   Perf. 13
241 A43   30fr bis, dp bl & grn   .70   .40
242 A43   45fr ultra, grn & brn   .90   .55
243 A43 100fr choc, grn & brt bl   1.90   1.00
    a.   Min. sheet of 3, #241-243   4.00   4.00
    Nos. 241-243 (3)   3.50   1.95

10th Winter Olympic Games, Grenoble, Feb. 6-18, 1968.
For surcharges, see Benin No. 903, 1392.

Monetary Union Issue
Common Design Type

1967, Nov. 4   Engr.   Perf. 13
244 CD125 30fr grn, dk car & dk brn   .65   .65

Animals from the Pendjari Reservation A45

Designs: 15fr, Cape Buffalo. 30fr, Lion. 45fr, Buffon's kob. 70fr, African slender-snouted crocodile. 100fr, Hippopotamus.

1968, Mar. 18   Photo.   Perf. 12½x13
245 A45 15fr multicolored   .75   .20
246 A45 30fr purple & multi   .90   .50
247 A45 45fr blue & multi   1.75   .60
248 A45 70fr multicolored   3.00   .75
249 A45 100fr multicolored   5.50 2.25
    Nos. 245-249 (5)   11.90 4.30

See Nos. 252-256.
For surcharges see No. 310, Benin Nos. 655E, 725, 1415, 1420, 1421.

WHO Emblem A46

1968, Apr. 22   Engr.   Perf. 13
250 A46 30fr multicolored   .60   .20
251 A46 70fr multicolored   1.40   .70

20th anniv. of WHO. For surcharges, see Benin Nos. 1387, 1465.

Animals from the Pendjari Reservation A47

Animals: 5fr, Warthog. 30fr, Leopard. 60fr, Spotted hyena. 75fr, Anubius baboon. 90fr, Hartebeest.

1969, Feb. 10   Photo.   Perf. 12½x12
252 A47 5fr dark brown & multi   .25   .20
253 A47 30fr deep ultra & multi   1.00   .50
254 A47 60fr dark green & multi   1.75   .70
255 A47 75fr dark blue & multi   4.00 1.00
256 A47 90fr dark green & multi   5.50 2.25
    Nos. 252-256 (5)   12.50 4.65

For surcharges, see Benin Nos. 708, 1438.

Heads, Symbols of Agriculture and Science, and Globe A48

1969, Mar. 10   Engr.   Perf. 13
257 A48 30fr orange & multi   .50   .20
258 A48 70fr maroon & multi   1.50   .70

50th anniv. of the ILO.
For surcharges see Benin Nos. 904, 913.

Arms of Dahomey — A49

1969, June 30   Litho.   Perf. 13½x13
259 A49 5fr yellow & multi   .35   .30
260 A49 30fr orange red & multi   1.25   .45

See No. C101.

Development Bank Issue

Cornucopia and Bank Emblem — A50

1969, Sept. 10   Photo.   Perf. 13
261 A50 30fr black, grn & ocher   .75   .55

African Development Bank, 5th anniv.
For surcharge see Benin No. 905.

Europafrica Issue

Ambary (Kenaf) Industry, Cotonou A51

Design: 45fr, Cotton industry, Parakou.

1969, Sept. 22   Litho.   Perf. 14
262 A51 30fr multicolored   1.00   .50
263 A51 45fr multicolored   1.25   .75

See Nos. C105-C105a.

Sakpata Dance and Tourist Year Emblem — A52

Dances and Tourist Year Emblem: 30fr, Guelede dance. 45fr, Sato dance.

1969, Dec. 15   Litho.   Perf. 14
264 A52 10fr multicolored   .45   .30
265 A52 30fr multicolored   .90   .45
266 A52 45fr multicolored   1.25   .55
    Nos. 264-266 (3)   2.60 1.30

See No. C108. For surcharges see Benin Nos. 690J, 1054B, 1388, 1433.

UN Emblem, Garden and Wall — A53

1970, Apr. 6   Engr.   Perf. 13
267 A53 30fr ultra, red org & slate .70   .20
268 A53 40fr ultra, brn & sl grn   .90   .50

25th anniversary of the United Nations.
For surcharge see No. 294. For overprint see Benin 647B.

ASECNA Issue
Common Design Type

1970, June 1   Engr.   Perf. 13
269 CD132 40fr red & purple   .90   .55

For surcharges, see Benin Nos. 906, 1396.

Mt. Fuji, EXPO '70 Emblem, Monorail Train — A54

1970, June 15   Litho.   Perf. 13½x14
270 A54 5fr green, red & vio bl   .40   .20

EXPO '70 International Exhibition, Osaka, Japan, 3/15-9/13/70. See Nos. C124-C125.

Alkemy, King of Ardres — A55

40fr, Sailing ships "La Justice" & "La Concorde," Ardres, 1670. 50fr, Matheo Lopes, ambassador of the King of Ardres & his coat of arms. 200fr, Louis XIV & fleur-de-lis.

1970, July 6   Engr.   Perf. 13
271 A55 40fr brt grn, ultra & brn   .65   .20
272 A55 50fr dk car, choc & emer   .90   .40
273 A55 70fr gray, lemon & choc   1.40   .65
274 A55 200fr Prus bl, dk car & choc 3.50 1.25
    Nos. 271-274 (4)   6.45 2.50

300th anniv. of the mission from the King of Ardres to the King of France, and of the audience with Louis XIV on Dec. 19, 1670.
For surcharges see Benin Nos. 724, 914.

Star of the Order of Independence A56

Bariba Warrior A57

1970, Aug. 1   Photo.   Perf. 12
275 A56 30fr multicolored   .40   .20
276 A56 40fr multicolored   .60   .20

10th anniversary of independence.
For surcharge see Benin Nos. 720, 1464.

1970, Aug. 24   Perf. 12½x13

Designs: 2fr, 50fr, Two horsemen. 10fr, 70fr, Horseman facing left.

277 A57 1fr yellow & multi   .20   .20
278 A57 2fr gray grn & multi   .30   .20
279 A57 10fr blue & multi   .35   .20
280 A57 40fr yellow grn & multi   1.40   .35
281 A57 50fr gold & multi   1.75   .50
282 A57 70fr lilac rose & multi   2.10   .80
    Nos. 277-282 (6)   6.10 2.25

For surcharges see Benin Nos. 350-351, 613, 703, 1373, 1401.

Globe and Heart A58

Design: 40fr, Hands holding heart, vert.

1971, June 7   Engr.   Perf. 13
283 A58 40fr red, green & dk brn   .90   .35
284 A58 100fr green, red & blue   1.75   .90

For surcharges see Benin Nos. 617, 647A, 712, 907, 1429.

Intl. year against racial discrimination.

Ancestral Figures and Lottery Ticket — A59

King Behanzin's Emblem (1889-1894) A60

1971, June 24   Litho.   Perf. 14
285 A59 35fr multicolored   .65   .20
286 A59 40fr multicolored   .80   .35

4th anniv. of the National Lottery.
For overprint and surcharge, see Benin Nos. 710, 1430.

Photo.; Litho. (25fr, 135fr)
1971-72   Perf. 12½

Emblems of the Kings of Abomey: 25fr, Agoliagbo (1894-1900). 35fr, Ganyehoussou (1620-45), bird and cup, horiz. 100fr, Guezo (1818-58), bull, tree and birds. 135fr, Ouegbadja (1645-85), horiz. 140fr, Glèle (1858-89), lion and sword, horiz.

287 A60 25fr multicolored   .55   .20
288 A60 35fr green & multi   .90   .20
289 A60 40fr green & multi   1.25   .55
290 A60 100fr red & multi   2.25   .90
291 A60 135fr multicolored   3.25 1.40
292 A60 140fr brown & multi   3.75 1.90
    Nos. 287-292 (6)   11.95 5.15

Issued: 25fr, 135fr, 7/17/72; others, 8/3/71.
For surcharges and overprint, see Benin #614, 634B, 791, 1369, 1422, 1431, 1467, 1470.

Kabuki Actor, Long-distance Skiing — A61

Brahms and "Soir d'été" — A62

1972, Feb.   Engr.   Perf. 13
293 A61 35fr dk car, brn & bl grn 1.60   .75

11th Winter Olympic Games, Sapporo, Japan, Feb. 3-13. See No. C153.

No. 268 Surcharged

1972
294 A53 35fr on 40fr multi   .65   .35

1972, June 29   Engr.   Perf. 13

Design: 65fr, Brahms, woman at piano & music, horiz.

295 A62 30fr red brn, blk & lilac 2.00   .80
296 A62 65fr red brn, blk & lilac 3.25 1.50

75th anniversary of the death of Johannes Brahms (1833-1897), German composer.
For surcharge see Benin Nos. 654B, 718, 1389.

The Hare and The Tortoise, by La Fontaine — A63

Fables: 35fr, The Fox and The Stork, vert. 40fr, The Cat, The Weasel and Rabbit.

1972, Aug. 28　　Engr.　　Perf. 13
297 A63 10fr multicolored　　　　1.75 .75
298 A63 35fr dark red & multi　　3.25 1.25
299 A63 40fr ultra & multi　　　　4.25 1.75
　　　Nos. 297-299 (3)　　　　　9.25 3.75

Jean de La Fontaine (1621-1695), French fabulist. For surcharges, see Benin Nos. 1380, 1393, 1397.

West African Monetary Union Issue
Common Design Type
1972, Nov. 2　　Engr.　　Perf. 13
300 CD136 40fr choc, ocher & gray .65 .20

Dr. Hansen, Microscope, Bacilli — A65

Design: 85fr, Portrait of Dr. Hansen.

1973, May 14　　Engr.　　Perf. 13
301 A65 35fr ultra, vio brn & brn　.50 .30
302 A65 85fr yel grn, bis & ver　1.10 .75

Centenary of the discovery by Dr. Armauer G. Hansen of the Hansen bacillus, the cause of leprosy.
For surcharges see Benin Nos. 655G, 1084, 1437.

Arms of Dahomey — A66

1973, June 25　　Photo.　　Perf. 13
303 A66 5fr ultra & multi　　　　.20 .20
304 A66 35fr ocher & multi　　　.40 .20
305 A66 40fr red orange & multi　.60 .20
　　　Nos. 303-305 (3)　　　　1.20 .60

For overprint and surcharge see Benin Nos. 690A, 1403.

INTERPOL Emblem and Spiderweb A67

Design: 50fr, INTERPOL emblem and communications symbols, vert.

1973, July　　　　　　　　Engr.
306 A67 35fr ver, grn & brn　　.60 .30
307 A67 50fr green, brn & red　1.00 .45

50th anniversary of International Criminal Police Organization (INTERPOL).
For overprints and surcharges, see Benin Nos. 634A, 810, 1434, 1471.

Education in Hygiene and Nutrition A68

WHO, 25th Anniv.: 100fr, Prenatal examination and care, WHO emblem.

1973, Aug. 2　　Photo.　　Perf. 12½x13
308 A68 35fr multicolored　　　.50 .30
309 A68 100fr multicolored　　1.50 .65

For surcharges, see Benin Nos. 655B, 1439.

No. 248 Surcharged with New Value, 2 Bars, and Overprinted in Red: "SECHERESSE SOLIDARITE AFRICAINE"

1973, Aug. 16
310 A45 100fr on 70fr multi　　2.10 1.00

African solidarity in drought emergency.

African Postal Union Issue
Common Design Type
1973, Sept. 12　　Engr.　　Perf. 13
311 CD137 100fr red, purple & blk 1.25 .55

For surcharges, see Benin Nos. 690I, 1440.

Epinephelus Aeneus — A69

Fish: 15fr, Drepane africana. 35fr, Pragus ehrenbergi.

1973, Sept. 18
312 A69 5fr slate blue & indigo　1.00 .30
313 A69 15fr black & brt blue　　1.50 .35
314 A69 35fr emerald, ocher & sep　　　　　　　　　3.50 .60
　　　Nos. 312-314 (3)　　　　6.00 1.25

For surcharges, see Benin No. 1378, 1383, 1394.

Chameleon A70

40fr, Emblem over map of Dahomey, vert.

1973, Nov. 30　　Photo.　　Perf. 13
315 A70 35fr olive & multi　　　.55 .30
316 A70 40fr multicolored　　　1.25 .35

1st anniv. of the Oct. 26 revolution.

The Chameleon in the Tree — A71

Designs: 5fr, The elephant, the hen and the dog, vert. 10fr, The sparrowhawk and the dog, vert. 25fr, The chameleon in the tree. 40fr, The eagle, the viper and the hen.

1974, Feb. 14　　Photo.　　Perf. 13
317 A71 5fr emerald & multi　　.40 .20
318 A71 10fr slate blue & multi　.50 .20
319 A71 25fr slate blue & multi　.90 .30
320 A71 40fr light blue & multi　1.40 .45
　　　Nos. 317-320 (4)　　　3.20 1.15

For surcharges and overprint see Benin Nos. 709, 908, 1363, 1370, 1379, 1381, 1432.

German Shepherd — A72

1974, Apr. 25　　Photo.　　Perf. 13
321 A72 40fr shown　　　　　1.50 .35
322 A72 50fr Boxer　　　　　1.75 .35
323 A72 100fr Saluki　　　　3.50 .80
　　　Nos. 321-323 (3)　　　6.75 1.50

For surcharges, see Benin No. 1398, 1435, 1441.

Council Issue

Map and Flags of Members A73

1974, May 29　　Photo.　　Perf. 13x12½
324 A73 40fr blue & multi　　　.80 .20

15th anniversary of the Council of Accord.

Locomotive 232, 1911 — A74

Designs: Locomotives.

1974, Sept. 2　　Photo.　　Perf. 13x12½
325 A74 35fr shown　　　　　.75 .30
326 A74 40fr Freight, 1877　　1.50 .30
327 A74 100fr Crampton, 1849　2.25 1.00
328 A74 200fr Stephenson, 1846 4.50 1.60
　　　Nos. 325-328 (4)　　　9.00 3.20

For surcharges see Benin Nos. 654E, 690K, 727, 909, 1395, 1399, 1442, 1444.

Globe, Money, People in Bank A75

1974, Oct. 31　　Engr.　　Perf. 13
329 A75 35fr multicolored　　　.50 .35

World Savings Day. For surcharge, see Benin No. 1468.

Dompago Dance, Hissi Tribe — A76

Flags of Dahomey and Nigeria over Africa — A77

Folk Dances: 25fr, Fetish Dance, Vaudou-Tchinan. 40fr, Bamboo Dance, Agbehoun. 100fr, Somba Dance, Sandoua, horiz.

1975, Aug. 4　　Litho.　　Perf. 12
330 A76 10fr yellow & multi　　.50 .20
331 A76 25fr dk green & multi　1.00 .20
332 A76 40fr red & multi　　　1.25 .50
333 A76 100fr multicolored　　2.25 .60
　　　Nos. 330-333 (4)　　　5.00 1.50

For surcharges and overprints see Benin Nos. 655D, 713, 1371, 1414, 1443.

1975, Aug. 11　　Photo.　　Perf. 12½x13
Design: 100fr, Arrows connecting maps of Dahomey and Nigeria, horiz.
334 A77 65fr multicolored　　　.75 .25
335 A77 100fr green & multi　　1.00 .45

Year of intensified cooperation between Dahomey and Nigeria.
For surcharges & overprint see Benin Nos. 690H, 701, 899, 901, 1419, 1423.

Map, Pylons, Emblem — A78

Benin Electric Community Emblem and Pylon — A79

1975, Aug. 18
336 A78 40fr multicolored　　　.75 .35
337 A79 150fr multicolored　　2.00 1.00

Benin Electric Community and Ghana-Togo-Dahomey cooperation.
For surcharges see Benin #601, 900, 910, 1400.

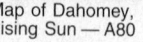

Map of Dahomey, Rising Sun — A80

Albert Schweitzer, Nurse, Patient — A81

1975, Aug. 25　　Photo.　　Perf. 12½x13
338 A80 35fr multicolored　　　.50 .20

Cooperation Year for the creation of a new Dahoman society.
For overprint see Benin No. 690E. For surcharge, see Benin No. 1362.

1975, Sept. 22　　Engr.　　Perf. 13
339 A81 200fr olive, grn & red brn　　　　　　　　　5.00 1.50

Birth centenary of Albert Schweitzer (1875-1965), medical missionary and musician.
For surcharges, see Benin Nos. 655F, 1445.

Woman Speaking on Telephone, IWY Emblem — A82

150fr, IWY emblem and linked rings.

1975, Oct. 20   Engr.   Perf. 12½x13
340 A82 50fr Prus blue & lilac   .75 .35
341 A82 150fr emerald, brn & org   2.00 .80

International Women's Year 1975.
For surcharges, see Benin Nos. 655C, 1436, 1469.

SEMI-POSTAL STAMPS

Regular Issue of 1913 Surcharged in Red

1915   Unwmk.   Perf. 14x13½
B1 A5 10c + 5c orange
            red & rose   1.60 1.60

Curie Issue
Common Design Type
1938   Perf. 13
B2 CD80 1.75fr + 50c brt
            ultra   9.50 9.50

French Revolution Issue
Common Design Type
1939   Photo.
Name and Value Typo. in Black
B3 CD83 45c + 25c green   9.50 9.50
B4 CD83 70c + 30c brown   9.50 9.50
B5 CD83 90c + 35c red org   9.50 9.50
B6 CD83 1.25fr + 1fr rose pink 9.50 9.50
B7 CD83 2.25fr + 2fr blue   9.50 9.50
    Nos. B3-B7 (5)   47.50 47.50

Postage Stamps of 1913-38 Surcharged in Black

1941   Perf. 13½x14
B8 A5 50c + 1fr brn red &
            bl   3.25 3.25
B9 A5 80c + 2fr hn brn &
            ultra   7.25 7.25
B10 A5 1.50fr + 2fr dk bl & lt bl 7.25 7.25
B11 A5 2fr + 3fr yel org &
            choc   7.25 7.25
    Nos. B8-B11 (4)   25.00 25.00

Common Design Type and

Radio Operator — SP1

Senegalese Artillerymen SP2

1941   Photo.   Perf. 13½
B12 SP1 1fr + 1fr red   1.20
B13 CD86 1.50fr + 3fr claret 1.20
B14 SP2 2.50fr + 1fr blue   1.20
    Nos. B12-B14 (3)   3.60

Surtax for the defense of the colonies.
Nos. B12-B14 were issued by the Vichy government in France, but were not placed on sale in Dahomey.

Nos. 135-136
Surcharged in Black or Red

1944   Engr.   Perf. 12½x12
B14A 50c + 1.50fr on 2.50fr deep
            blue (R)   .80
B14B + 2.50fr on 1fr green   .80

Colonial Development Fund.
Nos. B14A-B14B were issued by the Vichy government in France, but were not placed on sale in Dahomey.

> **Catalogue values for unused stamps in this section, from this point to the end of the section, are for Never Hinged items.**

Republic
Anti-Malaria Issue
Common Design Type
1962, Apr. 7   Engr.   Perf. 12½x12
B15 CD108 25fr + 5fr orange brn .55 .55

Freedom from Hunger Issue
Common Design Type
1963, Mar. 21   Unwmk.   Perf. 13
B16 CD112 25fr + 5fr ol, brn red &
            brn   .65 .65

AIR POST STAMPS

Common Design Type
1940   Unwmk.   Engr.   Perf. 12½
C1 CD85 1.90fr ultra   .40 .40
C2 CD85 2.90fr dk red   .55 .55
C3 CD85 4.50fr dk gray grn   .80 .80
C4 CD85 4.90fr yel bister   .95 .95
C5 CD85 6.90fr deep org   1.30 1.30
    Nos. C1-C5 (5)   4.00 4.00

Common Design Types
1942
C6 CD88 50c car & bl   .30
C7 CD88 1fr brn & blk   .30
C8 CD88 2fr dk grn & red brn .50
C9 CD88 3fr dk bl & scar   .95
C10 CD88 5fr vio & brn red 1.05

Frame Engr., Center Typo.
C11 CD89 10fr ultra, ind & org 1.05
C12 CD89 20fr rose car, mag &
            gray blk   1.10
C13 CD89 50fr yel grn, dl grn &
            dp bl   1.90 3.25
    a. 50fr yellow green, dull green &
            pale blue   2.75 3.75
    Nos. C6-C13 (8)   7.15

Nos. C6-C12 were issued by the Vichy government in France, but were not placed on sale in Dahomey.

> **Catalogue values for unused stamps in this section, from this point to the end of the section, are for Never Hinged items.**

Republic

Somba House — AP4

Design: 500fr, Royal Court of Abomey.

1960, Apr. 1   Unwmk.   Engr.   Perf. 13
C14 AP4 100fr multi   3.25 .80
C15 AP4 500fr multi   13.50 4.00

For overprint see Benin No. C419. For surcharges, see Benin Nos. C541, C609.

Type of Regular Issue, 1961
1961, Sept. 20
C16 A16 200fr multi   3.00 2.25
    a. Souv. sheet of 3, #150-151, C16 6.00 6.00

Air Afrique Issue
Common Design Type
1962, Feb. 17   Perf. 13
C17 CD107 25fr ultra, blk & org brn .70 .30

Palace of the African and Malgache Union, Cotonou — AP5

1963, July 27   Photo.   Perf. 13x12
C18 AP5 250fr multi   4.00 2.00

Assembly of chiefs of state of the African and Malgache Union held at Cotonou in July.

African Postal Union Issue
Common Design Type
1963, Sept. 8   Unwmk.   Perf. 12½
C19 CD114 25fr brt bl, ocher & red .60 .25

See note after Cameroun No. C47.

Boeing 707 — AP6

Boeing 707: 200fr, On the ground. 300fr, Over Cotonou airport. 500fr, In the air.

1963, Oct. 25   Perf. 13
C20 AP6 100fr multi   2.00 .60
C21 AP6 200fr multi   3.00 2.00
C22 AP6 300fr multi   5.00 2.00
C23 AP6 500fr multi   10.00 2.50
    Nos. C20-C23 (4)   20.00 7.10

For surcharges see Nos. CQ1-CQ5, Benin No. C610.

Priests Carrying Funerary Boat, Isis Temple, Philae — AP7

1964, Mar. 9   Unwmk.   Perf. 13
C24 AP7 25fr vio bl & brn   1.50 .75

UNESCO world campaign to save historic monuments in Nubia.

Weather Map and Symbols — AP8

1965, Mar. 23   Photo.   Perf. 12½
C25 AP8 50fr multi   .80 .55

Fifth World Meteorological Day.

ICY Emblem and Men of Various Races — AP9

1965, June 26   Engr.   Perf. 13
C26 AP9 25fr dl pur, mar & grn .40 .20
C27 AP9 85fr dp bl, mar & sl grn .90 .65

International Cooperation Year, 1965

Winston Churchill — AP10

1965, June 15   Photo.   Perf. 12½
C28 AP10 100fr multi   2.10 1.75

For surcharge, see Benin No. C611.

Abraham Lincoln — AP11

1965, July 15   Perf. 13
C29 AP11 100fr multi   1.65 1.00

Centenary of death of Lincoln
For surcharge see No. C55.

John F. Kennedy and Arms of Dahomey — AP12

1965, Nov. 22   Photo.   Perf. 12½
C30 AP12 100fr dp grn & blk 2.25 1.10

President John F. Kennedy (1917-63).
For surcharge see No. C56.

Dr. Albert Schweitzer and
Patients — AP13

1966, Jan. 17   Photo.   Perf. 12½
C31   AP13 100fr multi   2.50 1.25
Dr. Albert Schweitzer (1875-1965), medical
missionary, theologian and musician.
For surcharge see Benin No. C435.

WHO Type of Regular Issue

Design: WHO Headquarters from the West.

1966, May 3   Unwmk.   Perf. 13
Size: 47x28mm
C32   A36 100fr ultra, yel & blk   1.75 1.50

Pygmy
Goose — AP14

Broad-billed
Rollers — AP15

Birds: 100fr, Fiery-breasted bush-shrike.
250fr, Emerald cuckoos. 500fr, Emerald
starling.

1966-67   Perf. 12½
C33   AP14 50fr multi   2.00   .55
C34   AP14 100fr multi   3.00   .85
C35   AP15 200fr multi   10.00 2.25
C36   AP15 250fr multi   10.00 3.00
C37   AP14 500fr multi   15.00 6.00
    Nos. C33-C37 (5)   40.00 12.65

Issued: 50fr, 100fr, 500fr, 6/13/66; others,
1/20/67.
For surcharges see Nos. C107, Benin Nos.
1472, C353-C355, C357, C368, C426, C436,
C550, C590.

Industrial
Symbols — AP16

1966, July 21   Photo.   Perf. 12x13
C38   AP16 100fr multi   1.60   .80
Agreement between European Economic
Community & the African & Malagache Union,
3rd anniv.

Pope Paul VI and St. Peter's,
Rome — AP17

Pope Paul
VI and UN
General
Assembly
AP18

70fr, Pope Paul VI and view of NYC.

1966, Aug. 22   Engr.   Perf. 13
C39   AP17 50fr multi   .75   .45
C40   AP17 70fr multi   .95   .55
C41   AP18 100fr multi   1.75 1.00
    a. Min. sheet of 3, #C39-C41 4.50 4.50
    Nos. C39-C41 (3)   3.45 2.00
Pope Paul's appeal for peace before the UN
General Assembly, Oct. 4, 1965.

Air Afrique Issue, 1966
Common Design Type
1966, Aug. 31   Photo.   Perf. 12½
C42   CD123 30fr dk vio, blk & gray   .75   .20

"Science" — AP20

Designs: 45fr, "Art" (carved female statue),
vert. 100fr, "Education" (book and letters).

1966, Nov. 4   Engr.   Perf. 13
C43   AP20 30fr mag, ultra & vio
                         brn   .45   .20
C44   AP20 45fr mar & grn   .80   .55
C45   AP20 100fr blk, mar & brt bl 1.90 1.00
    a. Min. sheet of 3, #C43-C45 3.25 3.25
    Nos. C43-C45 (3)   3.15 1.75
20th anniversary of UNESCO.

Madonna
by Alessio
Baldovinetti
AP21

Christmas: 50fr, Nativity after 15th century
Beaune tapestry. 100fr, Adoration of the
Shepherds, by José Ribera.

1966, Dec. 25   Photo.   Perf. 12½x12
C46   AP21 50fr multi   3.25 2.25
C47   AP21 100fr multi   4.50 3.25
C48   AP21 200fr multi   9.00 5.00
    Nos. C46-C48 (3)   16.75 10.50
See Nos. C95-C96, C109-C115. For
surcharge see No. C60. For overprint, see
Benin No. C544.

1967, Apr. 10   Perf. 12½x12
Paintings by Ingres: No. C49, Self-portrait,
1804. No. C50, Oedipus and the Sphinx.
C49   AP21 100fr multi   3.00 1.50
C50   AP21 100fr multi   3.00 1.50
Jean Auguste Dominique Ingres (1780-
1867), French painter.

Three-master Suzanne — AP22

Windjammers: 45fr, Three-master Esmeralda, vert. 80fr, Schooner Marie Alice, vert.
100fr, Four-master Antonin.

1967, May 8   Perf. 13
C51   AP22 30fr multi   1.00   .50
C52   AP22 45fr multi   1.25   .75
C53   AP22 80fr multi   2.25 1.25
C54   AP22 100fr multi   3.00 1.50
    Nos. C51-C54 (4)   7.50 4.00
For overprint and surcharges see Benin
Nos. C369, C420, C606, C612.

Nos. C29-C30 Surcharged

1967, May 29   Photo.   Perf. 13, 12½
C55   AP11 125fr on 100fr   2.00 1.25
C56   AP12 125fr on 100fr   2.00 1.25
50th anniv. of the birth of Pres. John F.
Kennedy.

EXPO '67 "Man
In Space"
Pavilion — AP23

1967, June 12   Engr.   Perf. 13
C57   AP23 100fr dl red & Prus bl 2.25   .75
    a. Min. sheet of 3, #235-236, C57 4.00 4.00
EXPO '67, International Exhibition, Mon-
treal, Apr. 28-Oct. 27, 1967.

Europafrica Issue, 1967

Konrad
Adenauer,
by Oscar
Kokoschká
AP24

1967, July 19   Photo.   Perf. 12½x12
C58   AP24 70fr multi   1.50   .75
    a. Souv. sheet of 4   7.00 7.00
Konrad Adenauer (1876-1967), chancellor
of West Germany (1949-1963). For
surcharges, see Benin Nos. C572, C602.

Jamboree
Emblem, Ropes
and World
Map — AP25

1967, Aug. 7   Engr.   Perf. 13
C59   AP25 100fr lil, sl grn & dp bl 1.90   .75
    a. Souv. sheet of 3, #239-240,
        C59   4.00 4.00
12th Boy Scout World Jamboree, Farragut
State Park, Idaho, Aug. 1-9.

No. C48 Surcharged in Red

1967, Aug. 12   Photo.   Perf. 12½x12
C60   AP21 150fr on 200fr   3.00 2.25
    a. "150F" omitted   300.00 300.00
Riccione, Italy Stamp Exhibition.

African Postal Union Issue, 1967
Common Design Type
1967, Sept. 9   Engr.   Perf. 13
C61   CD124 100fr red, brt lil &
                        emer   1.25   .75
For surcharge see Benin No. C471.

Charles de
Gaulle
AP26

1967, Nov. 21   Photo.   Perf. 12½x13
C62   AP26 100fr multi   3.25 2.00
    a. Souv. sheet of 4   15.00 15.00
Pres. Charles de Gaulle of France on the
occasion of Pres. Christophe Soglo's state
visit to Paris, Nov. 1967.

Madonna,
by Matthias
Grunewald
AP27

Paintings: 50fr, Holy Family by the Master
of St. Sebastian, horiz. 100fr, Adoration of the
Magi by Ulrich Apt the Elder. 200fr, Annunciation, by Matthias Grunewald.

1967, Dec. 11 **Photo.** *Perf. 12½*
C63 AP27 30fr multi .55 .45
C64 AP27 50fr multi 1.10 .60
C65 AP27 100fr multi 2.00 1.25
C66 AP27 200fr multi 5.00 2.00
Nos. C63-C66 (4) 8.65 4.30
Christmas 1967.

Venus de Milo and Mariner 5 — AP28

Gutenberg Monument, Strasbourg Cathedral AP29

#C68, Venus de Milo and Venus 4 Rocket.

1968, Feb. 17 **Photo.** *Perf. 13*
C67 AP28 70fr grnsh bl & multi 1.50 .75
C68 AP28 70fr dp bl & multi 1.50 .75
a. Souv. sheet of 2, #C67-C68 3.50 3.50
Explorations of the planet Venus, Oct. 18-19, 1967.
For surcharges see Nos. C103-C104, Benin No. C587.

1968, May 20 **Litho.** *Perf. 14x13½*
Design: 100fr, Gutenberg Monument, Mainz, and Gutenberg press.
C69 AP29 45fr grn & org 1.00 .40
C70 AP29 100fr dk & lt bl 2.00 1.00
a. Souv. sheet of 2, #C69-C70 3.75 3.75
500th anniv. of the death of Johann Gutenberg, inventor of printing from movable type.
For surcharge see Benin No. C516.

Martin Luther King, Jr. — AP30

Designs: 30fr, "We must meet hate with creative love" in French, English and German. 100fr, Full-face portrait.

Perf. 12½, 13½x13
1968, June 17 **Photo.**
Size: 26x46mm
C71 AP30 30fr red brn, yel & blk .60 .35
Size: 26x37mm
C72 AP30 55fr multi 1.00 .45
C73 AP30 100fr multi 1.50 .90
a. Min. sheet of 3, #C71-C73 4.00 4.00
Nos. C71-C73 (3) 3.10 1.70
Martin Luther King, Jr. (1929-68), American civil rights leader.
For surcharges, see Benin Nos. C517, C561, C613.

Robert Schuman — AP31

45fr, Alcide de Gasperi. 70fr, Konrad Adenauer.

1968, July 20 **Photo.** *Perf. 13*
C74 AP31 30fr dp yel, blk & grn .40 .40
C75 AP31 45fr org, dk brn & ol .85 .50
C76 AP31 70fr multi 1.40 .50
Nos. C74-C76 (3) 2.65 1.40
5th anniversary of the economic agreement between the European Economic Community and the African and Malgache Union.
For surcharges, see Benin Nos. C462, C562, C603.

Battle of Montebello, by Henri Philippoteaux — AP32

Paintings: 45fr, 2nd Zouave Regiment at Magenta, by Riballier. 70fr, Battle of Magenta, by Louis Eugène Charpentier. 100fr, Battle of Solferino, by Charpentier.

1968, Aug. 12 *Perf. 12½x12*
C77 AP32 30fr multi .90 .50
C78 AP32 45fr multi 1.25 .65
C79 AP32 70fr multi 2.50 1.25
C80 AP32 100fr multi 3.25 1.00
Nos. C77-C80 (4) 7.90 3.40
Issued for the Red Cross. For surcharges, see Benin Nos. C574, C594, C614.

Mail Truck in Village — AP33

Designs: 45fr, Mail truck stopping at rural post office. 55fr, Mail truck at river bank. 70fr, Mail truck and train.

1968, Oct. 7 **Photo.** *Perf. 13x12½*
C81 AP33 30fr multi .80 .50
C82 AP33 45fr multi 1.00 .55
C83 AP33 55fr multi 1.50 .55
C84 AP33 70fr multi 3.75 1.00
Nos. C81-C84 (4) 7.05 2.60
For surcharges see Benin Nos. C352, C357A, C584.

Aztec Stadium, Mexico City — AP34

45fr, Ball player, Mayan sculpture, vert. 70fr, Wrestler, sculpture from Uxpanapan, vert. 150fr, Olympic Stadium, Mexico City.

1968, Nov. 20 **Engr.** *Perf. 13*
C85 AP34 30fr dp cl & sl grn .60 .30
C86 AP34 45fr ultra & dk rose brn 1.10 .60
C87 AP34 70fr sl grn & dk brn 1.60 .65
C88 AP34 150fr dk car & dk brn 2.25 1.25
a. Min. sheet of 4, #C85-C88 5.50 5.50
Nos. C85-C88 (4) 5.55 2.80
19th Olympic Games, Mexico City, Oct. 12-27. No. C88a is folded down the vertical gutter separating Nos. C85-C86 se-tenant at left and Nos. C87-C88 se-tenant at right.
For overprint and surcharges see Benin Nos. C457, C461, C513.

The Annunciation, by Foujita — AP35

Paintings by Foujita: 30fr, Nativity, horiz. 100fr, The Virgin and Child. 200fr, The Baptism of Christ.

Perf. 12x12½, 12½x12
1968, Nov. 25 **Photo.**
C89 AP35 30fr multi .80 .55
C90 AP35 70fr multi 1.60 .80
C91 AP35 100fr multi 1.75 1.25
C92 AP35 200fr multi 4.00 2.75
Nos. C89-C92 (4) 8.15 5.35
Christmas 1968. For surcharges, see Benin Nos. C563, C615, C648.

PHILEXAFRIQUE Issue
Painting: Diderot, by Louis Michel Vanloo.

1968, Dec. 16 *Perf. 12½x12*
C93 AP35 100fr multi 3.50 3.50
PHILEXAFRIQUE, Philatelic Exhibition in Abidjan, Feb. 14-23. Printed with alternating label.
For surcharges, see Benin Nos. C522, C629.

2nd PHILEXAFRIQUE Issue
Common Design Type
50fr, Dahomey #119 and aerial view of Cotonou.

1969, Feb. 14 **Engr.** *Perf. 13*
C94 CD128 50fr bl, brn & pur 2.10 2.10
For surcharge see Benin No. C467.

Christmas Painting Type
Paintings: No. C95, Virgin of the Rocks, by Leonardo da Vinci. No. C96, Virgin with the Scales, by Cesare da Sesto.

1969, Mar. 17 **Photo.** *Perf. 12½x12*
C95 AP21 100fr vio & multi 1.75 1.00
C96 AP21 100fr grn & multi 1.75 1.00
Leonardo da Vinci (1452-1519).

General Bonaparte, by Jacques Louis David AP36

Paintings: 60fr, Napoleon I in 1809, by Robert J. Lefevre. 75fr, Napoleon on the Battlefield of Eylau, by Antoine Jean Gros, horiz. 200fr, Gen. Bonaparte at Arcole, by Gros.

1969, Apr. 14 **Photo.** *Perf. 12½x12*
C97 AP36 30fr multi 1.50 1.25
C98 AP36 60fr multi 2.75 1.75
C99 AP36 75fr multi 3.00 2.50
C100 AP36 200fr multi 7.25 5.50
Nos. C97-C100 (4) 14.50 11.00
Bicentenary of the birth of Napoleon I. For surcharges, see Benin Nos. C599, C605.

Arms Type of Regular Issue, 1969
1969, June 30 **Litho.** *Perf. 13½x13*
C101 A49 50fr multi .55 .30
For overprint and surcharge see Benin Nos. C417, C596.

Apollo 8 Trip Around the Moon — AP37

Embossed on Gold Foil
1969, July *Die-cut Perf. 10½*
C102 AP37 1000fr gold 20.00 20.00
US Apollo 8 mission, which put the 1st men into orbit around the moon, Dec. 21-27, 1968.

Nos. C67-C68 Surcharged

1969, Aug. 1 **Photo.** *Perf. 13*
C103 AP28 125fr on 70fr, #C67 2.00 1.75
C104 AP28 125fr on 70fr, #C68 2.00 1.75
Man's 1st landing on the moon, July 20, 1969; US astronauts Neil A. Armstrong, Col. Edwin E. Aldrin, Jr., with Lieut. Col. Michael Collins piloting Apollo 11.

Europafrica Issue
Type of Regular Issue, 1969
Design: 100fr, Oil palm industry, Cotonou.

1969, Sept. 22 **Litho.** *Perf. 14*
C105 A51 100fr multi 2.25 .35
a. Souv. sheet of 3, #262-263, C105 4.25 4.25
For surcharge see No. C523.

Dahomey Rotary Emblem — AP38

1969, Sept. 25 *Perf. 14x13½*
C106 AP38 50fr multi 1.00 .75
For surcharge see Benin No. C468.

No. C33 Surcharged

1969, Nov. 15 **Photo.** *Perf. 12½*
C107 AP14 10fr on 50fr multi .45 .20

Dance Type of Regular Issue
Design: Teke dance and Tourist Year emblem.

1969, Dec. 15 **Litho.** *Perf. 14*
C108 A52 70fr multi 2.50 1.50
For surcharge see Benin No. C398.

Painting Type of 1966

Christmas: 30fr, Annunciation, by Vrancke van der Stockt. 45fr, Nativity, Swabian School, horiz. 110fr, Madonna and Child, by the Master of the Gold Brocade. 200fr, Adoration of the Kings, Antwerp School.

1969, Dec. 20   Perf. 12½x12, 12x12½

C109	AP21	30fr multi	.45 .40
C110	AP21	45fr red & multi	.80 .65
C111	AP21	110fr multi	2.00 1.25
C112	AP21	200fr multi	3.50 2.25
		Nos. C109-C112 (4)	6.75 4.55

For surcharges see Benin #C425, C463, C475, C532, C595.

1969, Dec. 27   Perf. 12½x12

Paintings: No. C113, The Artist's Studio (detail), by Gustave Courbet. No. C114, Self-portrait with Gold Chain, by Rembrandt. 150fr, Hendrickje Stoffels, by Rembrandt.

C113	AP21	100fr red & multi	2.25 1.25
C114	AP21	100fr grn & multi	2.25 1.25
C115	AP21	150fr multi	3.50 1.75
		Nos. C113-C115 (3)	8.00 4.25

For overprint and surcharge see Benin Nos. C458, C472.

Franklin D. Roosevelt AP39

Astronauts, Rocket, US Flag — AP40

1970, Feb.   Photo.   Perf. 12½

C116 AP39 100fr ultra, yel grn & blk   1.60 .60

25th anniversary of the death of Pres. Franklin Delano Roosevelt (1882-1945). For surcharge, see No. C637.

1970, Mar. 9   Photo.   Perf. 12½

Astronauts: 50fr, Riding rocket through space. 70fr, In landing module approaching moon. 110fr, Planting US flag on moon.

C117 AP40 30fr multi   .65 .25

Souvenir Sheet

C118		Sheet of 4	8.00 8.00
a.		AP40 50fr violet blue & multi	.75 .75
b.		AP40 70fr violet blue & multi	1.00 1.00
c.		AP40 110fr violet blue & multi	1.25 1.25

See note after No. C104. No. C118 contains Nos. C117, C118a, C118b and C118c. For surcharge see No. C120.

Walt Whitman and Dahoman Huts — AP41

1970, Apr. 30   Engr.   Perf. 13

C119 AP41 100fr Prus bl, brn & emer   1.25 .60

Walt Whitman (1818-92), American poet.

No. C117 Surcharged in Silver with New Value, Heavy Bar and: "APOLLO XIII / SOLIDARITE / SPATIALE / INTERNATIONALE"

1970, May 15   Photo.   Perf. 12½

C120 AP40 40fr on 30fr multi   1.20 .75

The flight of Apollo 13. For surcharge see Benin No. C464.

Soccer Players and Globe — AP42

Designs: 50fr, Goalkeeper catching ball. 200fr, Players kicking ball.

1970, May 19

C121	AP42	40fr multi	.75 .40
C122	AP42	50fr multi	.95 .50
C123	AP42	200fr multi	3.50 1.25
		Nos. C121-C123 (3)	5.20 2.15

9th World Soccer Championships for the Jules Rimet Cup, Mexico City, May 30-June 21, 1970. For surcharge see No. C126.

EXPO '70 Type of Regular Issue

EXPO '70 Emblems and: 70fr, Dahomey pavilion. 120fr, Mt. Fuji, temple and torii.

1970, June 15   Litho.   Perf. 13½x14

C124	A54	70fr yel, red & dk vio	1.25 .60
C125	A54	120fr yel, red & grn	2.25 1.00

For surcharges see Benin Nos. C470, C477.

No. C123 Surcharged with New Value and Overprinted: "Bresil-Italie / 4-1"

1970, July 13   Photo.   Perf. 12½

C126 AP42 100fr on 200fr multi   2.10 1.00

Brazil's victory in the 9th World Soccer Championships, Mexico City. For surcharge see Benin No. C515.

Mercury, Map of Africa and Europe — AP43

Ludwig van Beethoven AP44

Europafrica Issue, 1970

1970, July 20   Photo.   Perf. 12x13

C127	AP43	40fr multi	.80 .40
C128	AP43	70fr multi	1.25 .60

For surcharges see Benin Nos. C429, C488, C566.

1970, Sept. 21   Litho.   Perf. 14x13½

C129	AP44	90fr brt bl & vio blk	1.40 .45
C130	AP44	110fr yel grn & dk brn	1.75 .65

Bicentenary of the birth of Ludwig van Beethoven (1770-1827), composer. For surcharges, see Benin Nos. C476, C608.

Symbols of Learning — AP45

1970, Nov. 6   Photo.   Perf. 12½

C131 AP45 100fr multi   1.75 .75

Laying of the foundation stone for the University at Calavi. For overprint and surcharge see Benin Nos. C356, C616.

Annunciation, Rhenish School, c.1340 — AP46

Paintings of Rhenish School, circa 1340: 70fr, Nativity. 110fr, Adoration of the Kings. 200fr, Presentation at the Temple.

1970, Nov. 9   Perf. 12½x12

C132	AP46	40fr gold & multi	.55 .40
C133	AP46	70fr gold & multi	1.00 .55
C134	AP46	110fr gold & multi	2.40 1.25
C135	AP46	200fr gold & multi	4.00 2.00
		Nos. C132-C135 (4)	7.95 4.20

Christmas 1970. For surcharge see Benin No. C479.

Charles de Gaulle, Arc de Triomphe and Flag — AP47

Design: 500fr, de Gaulle as old man and Notre Dame Cathedral, Paris.

1971, Mar. 15   Photo.   Perf. 12½

C136	AP47	40fr multi	.80 .45
C137	AP47	500fr multi	6.50 3.25

Gen. Charles de Gaulle (1890-1970), President of France. For surcharges see Benin Nos. C465, C567.

L'Indifférent, by Watteau — AP48

Painting: No. C139, Woman playing stringed instrument, by Watteau.

1971, May 3   Photo.   Perf. 13

C138	AP48	100fr red brn & multi	3.25 1.75
C139	AP48	100fr red brn & multi	3.25 1.75

For overprints and surcharge see Nos. C151-C152, Benin Nos. C357D, C456, C526, C617, C638.

1971, May 29   Photo.   Perf. 13

Dürer Paintings: 100fr, Self-portrait, 1498. 200fr, Self-portrait, 1500.

C140	AP48	100fr bl grn & multi	2.25 1.25
C141	AP48	200fr dk grn & multi	4.50 2.25

Albrecht Dürer (1471-1528), German painter and engraver. See Nos. C151-C152, C174-C175. For surcharges and overprints see Benin Nos. C357B, C381, C545, C618.

Johannes Kepler and Diagram — AP49

200fr, Kepler, trajectories, satellite and rocket.

1971, July 12   Engr.   Perf. 13

C142	AP49	40fr brt rose lil, blk & vio bl	.90 .55
C143	AP49	200fr red, blk & dk bl	3.25 1.75

Kepler (1571-1630), German astronomer. For overprint and surcharges see Benin Nos. C342, C348, C466, C480, C568.

Europafrica Issue

Jet Plane, Maps of Europe and Africa — AP50

100fr, Ocean liner, maps of Europe and Africa.

1971, July 19   Photo.   Perf. 12½x12

C144	AP50	50fr blk, lt bl & org	1.00 .60
C145	AP50	100fr multi	1.60 1.00

For surcharges see Benin Nos. C374, C404, C421, C585, C630.

African Postal Union Issue, 1971
Common Design Type

Design: 100fr, Dahomey coat of arms and UAMPT building, Brazzaville, Congo.

1971, Nov. 13   Perf. 13x13½

C146 CD135 100fr bl & multi   1.40 .60

For overprint and surcharge see Benin Nos. C357E, C619.

Flight into Egypt, by Van Dyck — AP51

Paintings: 40fr, Adoration of the Shepherds, by the Master of the Hausbuch, c. 1500, vert. 70fr, Adoration of the Kings, by Holbein the Elder, vert. 200fr, The Birth of Christ, by Dürer.

1971, Nov. 22   Perf. 13

C147	AP51	40fr gold & multi	.80 .45
C148	AP51	70fr gold & multi	1.25 .55
C149	AP51	100fr gold & multi	2.00 .80
C150	AP51	200fr gold & multi	4.75 1.75
		Nos. C147-C150 (4)	8.80 3.55

Christmas 1971

For overprint and surcharges see Benin Nos. C394, C394A, C397, C403, C405, C481, C503, C546, C581, C604, C631.

Painting Type of 1971 Inscribed: "25e ANNIVERSAIRE DE L'UNICEF"

Paintings: 40fr, Prince Balthazar, by Velasquez. 100fr, Infanta Margarita Maria, by Velázquez.

1971, Dec. 11
C151 AP48 40fr gold & multi   1.00 .55
C152 AP48 100fr gold & multi   2.00 .85
25th anniv. of UNICEF.
For surcharges see Benin Nos. C366, C418, C437, C592, C639.

Olympic Games Type

Design: 150fr, Sapporo '72 emblem, ski jump and stork flying.

1972, Feb.   **Engr.**   **Perf. 13**
C153 A61 150fr brn, dp rose lil &
     bl   3.00 1.25
11th Winter Olympic Games, Sapporo, Japan, Feb. 3-13.
For overprint and surcharge see Benin Nos. C347, C433, C645.

Boy Scout and Scout Flag — AP52

Designs: 40fr, Scout playing marimba. 100fr, Scouts doing farm work.

1972, Mar. 19   **Photo.**   **Perf. 13**
Size: 26x35mm
C154 AP52 35fr multi   .50 .25
C155 AP52 40fr multi   .85 .40
Size: 26x46mm
C156 AP52 100fr yel & multi   1.75 .85
   a.   Souvenir sheet of 3, #C154-
     C156, perf. 12½   4.25 4.25
   Nos. C154-C156 (3)   3.10 1.50
World Boy Scout Seminar, Cotonou, Mar. 1972.
For overprint and surcharges see Benin Nos. C373, C414, C569.

Workers Training Institute and Friedrich Naumann — AP53

Design: 250fr, Workers Training Institute and Pres. Theodor Heuss of Germany.

1972, Mar. 29   **Photo.**   **Perf. 13x12**
C157 AP53 100fr brt rose, blk &
     vio   1.25 .65
C158 AP53 250fr bl, blk & vio   2.75 1.25
Laying of foundation stone for National Workers Training Institute.
For surcharges see Benin Nos. C380, C473, C640, C649, Q25A.

Mosaic Floor, St. Mark's, Venice — AP54

12th Century Mosaics from St. Mark's Basilica: 40fr, Roosters carrying fox on a pole. 65fr, Noah sending out dove.

1972, Apr. 10   **Perf. 13**
C159 AP54 35fr gold & multi   1.10 .75
C160 AP54 40fr gold & multi   1.25 .90
C161 AP54 65fr gold & multi   2.10 1.50
   Nos. C159-C161 (3)   4.45 3.15
UNESCO campaign to save Venice.
For surcharges see Benin Nos. 690G, C600.

Neapolitan and Dahoman Dancers — AP55

1972, May 3   **Perf. 13½x13**
C162 AP55 100fr multi   1.50 .65
12th Philatelic Exhibition, Naples.
For surcharges, see Benin Nos. C395, C620.

Running, German Eagle, Olympic Rings — AP56

85fr, High jump and Glyptothek, Munich. 150fr, Shot put and Propylaeum, Munich.

1972, June 12   **Engr.**   **Perf. 13**
C163 AP56 20fr ultra, grn & brn   .40 .25
C164 AP56 85fr brn, grn & ultra   .95 .60
C165 AP56 150fr grn, brn & ultra   2.00 1.00
   a.   Min. sheet of 3, #C163-C165   4.00 4.00
   Nos. C163-C165 (3)   3.35 1.85
20th Olympic Games, Munich, 8/26-9/10.
For overprints and surcharges see Nos. C170-C172, Benin C343, C346, C370, C404A, C559, C651A.

Louis Blériot and his Plane — AP57

1972, June 26
C166 AP57 100fr vio, cl & brt bl   3.00 1.75
Birth centenary of Louis Blériot (1872-1936), French aviation pioneer.
For surcharges see Benin Nos. C386, C621.

Adam, by Lucas Cranach — AP58

Design: 200fr, Eve, by Lucas Cranach.

1972, Oct. 24   **Photo.**
C167 AP58 150fr multi   1.90 .65
C168 AP58 200fr multi   3.25 1.25
Cranach (1472-1553), German painter.
For surcharges see Benin Nos. C402, C537, C643.

Pauline Borghese, by Canova — AP59

1972, Nov. 8
C169 AP59 250fr multi   4.00 1.75
Antonio Canova (1757-1822), Italian sculptor.
For surcharge, see Benin No. 1366.

Nos. C163-C165 Overprinted:
a. 5.000m-10.000m. / VIREN / 2 MEDAILLES D'OR
b. HAUTEUR DAMES / MEYFARTH / MEDAILLE D'OR
c. POIDS / KOMAR / MEDAILLE D'OR

1972, Nov. 13   **Engr.**   **Perf. 13**
C170 AP56(a) 20fr multi   .45 .25
C171 AP56(b) 85fr multi   1.25 .60
C172 AP56(c) 150fr multi   2.25 1.25
   a.   Miniature sheet of 3   5.25 5.25
   Nos. C170-C172 (3)   3.95 2.10
Gold medal winners in 20th Olympic Games: Lasse Viren, Finland, 5,000m. and 10,000m. races (20fr); Ulrike Meyfarth, Germany, women's high jump (85fr); Wladyslaw Komar, Poland, shot put (150fr).
For surcharges, see Benin Nos. C343A, C538, C607.

Louis Pasteur — AP60

1972, Nov. 30
C173 AP60 100fr brt grn, lil & brn   2.25 1.00
Pasteur (1822-95), chemist and bacteriologist.
For surcharges see Benin Nos. C344, C622.

Painting Type of 1971

Paintings by Georges de La Tour (1593-1652), French painter: 35fr, Vielle player. 150fr, The Newborn, horiz.

1972, Dec. 11   **Photo.**
C174 AP48 35fr multi   .80 .40
C175 AP48 150fr multi   2.25 1.25
For surcharges see Benin Nos. C364, C490, C578.

Annunciation, School of Agnolo Gaddi — AP61

Paintings: 125fr, Nativity, by Simone dei Crocifissi. 140fr, Adoration of the Shepherds, by Giovanni di Pietro. 250fr, Adoration of the Kings, by Giotto.

1972, Dec. 15
C176 AP61 35fr gold & multi   .55 .25
C177 AP61 125fr gold & multi   1.50 .65
C178 AP61 140fr gold & multi   2.00 1.00
C179 AP61 250fr gold & multi   3.25 1.50
   Nos. C176-C179 (4)   7.30 3.40
Christmas 1972. See Nos. C195-C198, C234, C251, C253-C254. For overprint and

---

surcharges see Benin Nos. C384, C392, C401, C444, C628, C652.

Statue of St. Teresa, Basilica of Lisieux — AP62

100fr, St. Teresa, roses, and globe, vert.

1973, May 14   **Photo.**   **Perf. 13**
C180 AP62 40fr blk, gold & lt ultra   .75 .45
C181 AP62 100fr gold & multi   2.00 1.00
St. Teresa of Lisieux (Therese Martin, 1873-97), Carmelite nun.
For surcharges see Benin Nos. C390, C570, C623.

Scouts, African Scout Emblem — AP63

Designs (African Scout Emblem and): 20fr, Lord Baden-Powell, vert. 40fr, Scouts building bridge.

1973, July 2   **Engr.**   **Perf. 13**
C182 AP63 15fr bl, grn & choc   .45 .20
C183 AP63 20fr ol & Prus bl   .75 .25
C184 AP63 40fr grn, Prus bl & brn   .90 .35
   a.   Souvenir sheet of 3   3.00 3.00
   Nos. C182-C184 (3)   2.10 .80
24th Boy Scout World Conference, Nairobi, Kenya, July 16-21. No. C184a contains 3 stamps similar to Nos. C182-C184 in changed colors (15fr in ultramarine, slate green and chocolate; 20fr in chocolate, ultramarine and indigo; 40fr in slate green, indigo and chocolate).
For surcharges see Nos. C217-C218, Benin C365, C409, C558, C560, C571.

Copernicus, Venera and Mariner Satellites — AP64

125fr, Copernicus, sun, earth & moon, vert.

1973, Aug. 20   **Engr.**   **Perf. 13**
C185 AP64 65fr blk, dk brn & org   1.25 .55
C186 AP64 125fr bl, slate grn & pur   2.00 1.00
For surcharges see Benin Nos. C345, C375, C601, C642.

Head and City Hall, Brussels AP64a

1973, Sept. 17   **Engr.**   **Perf. 13**
C187 AP64a 100fr blk, Prus bl & dk grn   1.10 .60
African Weeks, Brussels, Sept. 15-30, 1973.

For surcharge see Benin No. C400.

WMO Emblem, World Weather Map — AP65

1973, Sept. 25

C188   AP65   100fr ol grn & lt brn   1.25   .75

Cent. of intl. meteorological cooperation. For surcharges and overprint see Nos. C199, Benin Nos. C382, C624.

Europafrica Issue

AP66

Design: 40fr, similar to 35fr.

1973, Oct. 1   Engr.   Perf. 13

C189   AP66   35fr multi   .55   .35
C190   AP66   40fr bl, sepia & ultra   .70   .40

For overprint and surcharges, see Benin Nos. C411, C564, C593.

John F. Kennedy — AP67

1973, Oct. 18

C191   AP67   200fr bl grn, vio & sl   grn   2.75   2.75
   a.   Souvenir sheet   5.00   5.00

Pres. John F. Kennedy (1917-63). No. C191a contains one stamp in changed colors (bright blue, magenta & brown). For surcharge and overprint, see Benin Nos. C377, C441, C547.

Soccer — AP68

40fr, 2 soccer players. 100fr, 3 soccer players.

1973, Nov. 19   Engr.   Perf. 13

C192   AP68   35fr multi   .55   .25
C193   AP68   40fr multi   .65   .25
C194   AP68   100fr multi   1.25   .65
   Nos. C192-C194 (3)   2.45   1.15

World Soccer Cup, Munich 1974. For surcharges and overprint see Nos. C219-C220, Benin Nos. C396, C591, C644.

Painting Type of 1972

Christmas: 35fr, Annunciation, by Dirk Bouts. 100fr, Nativity, by Giotto. 150fr, Adoration of the Kings, by Botticelli. 200fr, Adoration of the Shepherds, by Jacopo Bassano, horiz.

1973, Dec. 20   Photo.   Perf. 13

C195   AP61   35fr gold & multi   .65   .40
C196   AP61   100fr gold & multi   1.25   .65
C197   AP61   150fr gold & multi   2.40   1.10
C198   AP61   200fr gold & multi   2.75   1.75
   Nos. C195-C198 (4)   7.05   3.90

For surcharges see Benin Nos. C378, C388, C410, C434, C442, C565, C646.

No C188 Surcharged in Violet with New Value and: "OPERATION SKYLAB / 1973-1974"

1974, Feb. 4   Engr.   Perf. 13

C199   AP65   200fr on 100fr multi   2.10   1.25

Skylab US space missions, 1973-74.

Skiers, Snowflake, Olympic Rings — AP69

1974, Feb. 25   Engr.   Perf. 13

C200   AP69   100fr vio bl, brn & brt   bl   1.75   1.10

50th anniversary of first Winter Olympic Games, Chamonix, France. For surcharge, see Benin No. C625.

Marie Curie AP70

1974, June 7   Engr.   Perf. 13

C201   AP70   50fr Lenin   1.40   .65
C202   AP70   125fr shown   1.75   .90
C203   AP70   150fr Churchill   2.00   1.40
   Nos. C201-C203 (3)   5.15   2.95

50th anniv. of the death of Lenin; 40th anniv. of the death of Marie Sklodowska Curie; cent. of the birth of Winston Churchill. For surcharges see Benin Nos. C391A, C489, C597, C632, C634.

Bishop, Persian, 18th Century — AP71

Frederic Chopin — AP72

200fr, Queen, Siamese chess piece, 19th cent.

1974, June 14   Photo.   Perf. 12½x13

C204   AP71   50fr org & multi   2.50   1.00
C205   AP71   200fr brt grn & multi   6.00   2.50

21st Chess Olympiad, Nice, 6/6-30/74.

For surcharges and overprint see Benin Nos. C469, C482, C598, Q11.

1974, June 24   Engr.   Perf. 13

Design: No. C207, Ludwig van Beethoven.

C206   AP72   150fr blk & copper   red   2.50   1.10
C207   AP72   150fr blk & copper   red   2.50   1.10

Famous musicians: Frederic Chopin and Ludwig van Beethoven. For surcharges see Benin Nos. C376, C452, C459, C539, C579, C647.

Astronaut on Moon, and Earth AP73

1974, July 10   Engr.   Perf. 13

C208   AP73   150fr multi   2.75   1.50

5th anniversary of the first moon walk. For surcharges and overprint see Benin Nos. C391, C460, C635.

Litho. & Embossed 'Gold Foil' Stamps
These stamps generally are of a different design format than the rest of the issue. Since there is a commemorative inscription tying them to the issue a separate illustration is not being shown.

There is some question as to the status of 4 sets, Nos. C209-C216, C225-C232, C238-C249.

World Cup Soccer Championships, Munich — AP74

World Cup trophy and players and flags of: 35fr, West Germany, Chile, Australia, DDR. 40fr, Zaire, Scotland, Brazil, Yugoslavia. 100fr, Sweden, Bulgaria, Uruguay, Netherlands. 200fr, Italy, Haiti, Poland, Argentina. 300fr, Stadium. 500fr, Trophy and flags.

Perf. 14x13, 13x14   Litho.

C209   AP74   35fr multicolored   .30   .20
C210   AP74   40fr multicolored   .40   .25
C211   AP74   100fr multicolored   .80   .70
C212   AP74   200fr multicolored   1.50   1.25
C213   AP74   300fr multi, horiz.   2.00   1.50

Souvenir Sheet

C215   AP74   500fr multi, horiz.   4.00   4.00

It is uncertain if this issue was valid for postage or recognized by the Dahomey government.

Nos. C182-C183 Surcharged and Overprinted in Black or Red: "XIe JAMBOREE PANARABE DE BATROUN-LIBAN"

1974, July 19

C217   AP63   100fr on 15fr multi   1.25   .60
C218   AP63   140fr on 20fr multi (R)   1.75   .90

11th Pan-Arab Jamboree, Batrun, Lebanon, Aug. 1974. Overprint includes 2 bars over old denomination; 2-line overprint on No. C217, 3 lines on No. C218.

Nos. C193-C194 Overprinted and Surcharged with New Value and Two Bars: "R F A 2 / HOLLANDE 1"

1974, July 26   Engr.   Perf. 13

C219   AP68   100fr on 40fr   1.10   .65
C220   AP68   150fr on 100fr   1.60   1.00

World Cup Soccer Championship, 1974, victory of German Federal Republic.

Earth and UPU Emblem — AP75

Designs (UPU Emblem and): 65fr, Concorde in flight. 125fr, French railroad car, c. 1860. 200fr, African drummer and Renault mail truck, pre-1939.

1974, Aug. 5   Engr.   Perf. 13

C221   AP75   35fr rose cl & vio   .55   .40
C222   AP75   65fr Prus grn & cl   1.10   .95
C223   AP75   125fr multi   2.50   1.50
C224   AP75   200fr multi   2.50   2.00
   Nos. C221-C224 (4)   6.65   4.85

Centenary of Universal Postal Union. For surcharges, see Benin Nos. C422, C530, C540, C586, C653, Q17B.

UPU, Cent. — AP76

Communications and transportation: 50fr, Rocket, Indian shooting arrow. 100fr, Airplane, dog sled, vert. 125fr, Rocket launch, balloon. 150fr, Rocket re-entry into Earth's atmosphere, drum. 200fr, Locomotive, Pony Express rider. 500fr, UPU headquarters. No. C230, Train, 1829. No. C232, Astronaut canceling envelope on moon.

1974   Litho.   Perf. 13x14, 14x13

C225   AP76   50fr multicolored   .50   .30
C226   AP76   100fr multicolored   .75   .60
C227   AP76   125fr multicolored   1.00   .85
C228   AP76   150fr multicolored   1.75   1.00
C229   AP76   200fr multicolored   2.00   1.25

Litho. & Embossed
Perf. 13½
Size: 48x60mm

C230   AP76   1000fr gold & multi   12.00   12.00

Souvenir Sheets
Litho.
Perf. 13x14

C231   AP76   500fr multicolored   4.50   4.50

Litho. & Embossed
Perf. 13½

C232   AP76   1000fr gold & multi   6.50   6.50

Issued: #C230, C232, Oct. 9; others, Aug. 5. It is uncertain if this issue was valid for postage or recognized by the Dahomey government.

Painting Type of 1972 and

Lion of Belfort by Frederic A. Bartholdi — AP77

Painting: 250fr, Girl with Falcon, by Philippe de Champaigne.

1974, Aug. 20 Engr. Perf. 13
C233 AP77 100fr rose brn 2.50 1.00
C234 AP61 250fr multi 4.00 2.40
For surcharges see Benin Nos. C363, C387, C445, C626.

Prehistoric Animals — AP78

1974, Sept. 23 Photo.
C235 AP78 35fr Rhamphorhynchus 1.50 .80
C236 AP78 150fr Stegosaurus 5.00 2.25
C237 AP78 200fr Tyrannosaurus 7.00 2.75
  Nos. C235-C237 (3) 13.50 5.80
For surcharges and overprint, see Benin Nos. C349, C350, C440, C548, C636.

Conquest of Space — AP79

Various spacecraft and: 50fr, Mercury. 100fr, Venus. 150fr, Mars. 200fr, Jupiter. 400fr, Sun.

1974, Oct. 31 Litho. Perf. 13x14
C238 AP79 50fr multicolored .40 .30
C239 AP79 100fr multicolored 1.00 .50
C240 AP79 150fr multicolored 1.50 .90
C241 AP79 200fr multicolored 2.00 1.25
  Nos. C238-C241 (4) 4.90 2.95
Souvenir Sheet
C242 AP79 400fr multicolored 4.00 4.00

West Germany, World Cup Soccer Champions — AP80

Designs: 100fr, Team. 125fr, Paul Breitner. 150fr, Gerd Muller. 300fr, Presentation of trophy. 500fr, German team positioned on field.

1974, Nov. Litho. Perf. 13x14
C243 AP80 100fr multicolored .75 .50
C244 AP80 125fr multicolored 1.00 .75
C245 AP80 150fr multicolored 1.50 1.00
C246 AP80 300fr multicolored 3.25 2.00
  Nos. C243-C246 (4) 6.50 4.25
Souvenir Sheet
C248 AP80 500fr multicolored 4.50 4.50

Europafrica Issue

Globe, Cogwheel, Emblem — AP81

1974, Dec. 20 Typo. Perf. 13
C250 AP81 250fr red & multi 3.25 2.75
  Printed tête bêche in sheets of 10.
  For surcharges see Benin Nos. C430, C509, C650.

Christmas Type of 1972 and

Nativity, by Martin Schongauer — AP82

Paintings: 35fr, Annunciation, by Schongauer. 100fr, Virgin in Rose Arbor, by Schongauer. 250fr, Virgin and Child, with St. John the Baptist, by Botticelli.

1974, Dec. 23 Photo. Perf. 13
C251 AP61 35fr gold & multi .45 .30
C252 AP82 40fr gold & multi .45 .40
C253 AP61 100fr gold & multi 1.25 .55
C254 AP61 250fr gold & multi 3.25 1.75
  Nos. C251-C254 (4) 5.40 3.00
For surcharges, see Benin Nos. C413, C431, C439, C446, C641.

Apollo and Soyuz Spacecraft AP83

200fr, American and Russian flags, rocket take-off. 500fr, Apollo-Soyuz link-up.

1975, July 16 Litho. Perf. 12½
C255 AP83 35fr multi .50 .30
C256 AP83 200fr vio bl, red & bl 2.40 1.25
C257 AP83 500fr vio bl, ind & red 5.00 3.00
  Nos. C255-C257 (3) 7.90 4.55
Apollo Soyuz space test project (Russo-American cooperation); launching July 15; link-up, July 17.
For surcharges and overprints, see Benin Nos. C406, C415-C416, C451, C542-C543, C549, C580.

Nos. C255-C256 Surcharged in Silver or Black:
"RENCONTRE / APOLLO-SOYOUZ / 17 Juil. 1975"

1975, July 17 Litho. Perf. 12½
C258 AP83 100fr on 35fr (S) 1.25 .60
C259 AP83 300fr on 200fr 3.25 1.40
Apollo-Soyuz link-up in space, July 17, 1975.

ARPHILA Emblem, "Stamps" and Head of Ceres — AP84

1975, Aug. 22 Engr. Perf. 13
C260 AP84 100fr blk, bl & lilac 1.25 .75
  ARPHILA 75, International Philatelic Exhibition, Paris, June 6-16.
  For surcharges see Benin Nos. C383, C474.

Holy Family, by Michelangelo AP85

Infantry and Stars — AP86

Europafrica Issue

1975, Sept. 29 Litho. Perf. 12
C261 AP85 300fr gold & multi 3.50 1.50
For surcharge and overprint, see Benin Nos. C447, C554.

1975, Nov. 18 Engr. Perf. 13
American bicentennial (Stars and): 135fr, Drummers and fifer. 300fr, Artillery with cannon. 500fr, Cavalry.
C262 AP86 75fr grn car & pur .85 .45
C263 AP86 135fr bl, mag & sep 1.50 .90
C264 AP86 300fr vio bl, ver & choc 2.75 1.75
C265 AP86 500fr ver, dk grn & brn 5.00 2.50
  Nos. C262-C265 (4) 10.10 5.60
For overprints and surcharges see Benin Nos. C247-C249, C385, C412, C453, C478, C555, C557, C576, C588.

Diving and Olympic Rings AP87

Design: 250fr, Soccer and Olympic rings.

1975, Nov. 24
C266 AP87 40fr vio, grnsh bl & ol brn .55 .25
C267 AP87 250fr red, emer & brn 2.25 1.25
  Pre-Olympic Year 1975.
  For surcharges see Benin Nos. C341, C393, C582.

AIR POST SEMI-POSTAL STAMPS

Maternity Hospital, Dakar — SPAP1

Dispensary, Mopti — SPAP2

Nurse Weighing Baby — SPAP3

Perf. 13½x12½, 13 (#CB3)
Photo., Engr. (#CB3)
1942, June 22
CB1 SPAP1 1.50fr + 3.50fr green .80 5.50
CB2 SPAP2 2fr + 6fr brown .80 5.50
CB3 SPAP3 3fr + 9fr car red .80 5.50
  Nos. CB1-CB3 (3) 2.40 16.50
  Native children's welfare fund.

Colonial Education Fund
Common Design Type
Perf. 12½x13½
1942, June 22 Engr.
CB4 CD86a 1.20fr + 1.80fr blue & red .80 5.50

AIR POST PARCEL POST STAMPS

Catalogue values for unused stamps in this section are for Never Hinged items.

Nos. C20-C23, C14 Surcharged in Black or Red

1967-69 Engr. Perf. 13
CQ1 AP6 200fr on 200fr 4.75 3.50
CQ2 AP6 300fr on 100fr 5.25 4.25
CQ3 AP6 500fr on 300fr 10.00 8.00
CQ4 AP6 1000fr on 500fr 21.00 16.00
CQ5 AP4 5000fr on 100fr
  (R) ('69) 80.00 80.00
  Nos. CQ1-CQ5 (5) 121.00 111.75
On No. CQ5, "Colis Postaux" is at top, bar at right.

POSTAGE DUE STAMPS

Dahomey Natives — D1   D2

1906 Unwmk. Typo. Perf. 14x13½
J1 D1 5c grn, grnsh 3.25 3.25
J2 D1 10c red brn 4.00 4.00
J3 D1 15c dark blue 8.00 8.00
J4 D1 20c blk, yellow 5.50 5.50
J5 D1 30c red, straw 8.75 8.75
J6 D1 50c violet 24.00 24.00
J7 D1 60c blk, buff 14.50 14.50
J8 D1 1fr blk, pinkish 45.00 40.00
  Nos. J1-J8 (8) 113.00 108.00

1914

J9	D2	5c green	.25	.25
J10	D2	10c rose	.55	.55
J11	D2	15c gray	.55	.55
J12	D2	20c brown	1.10	1.10
J13	D2	30c blue	1.40	1.40
J14	D2	50c black	1.60	1.60
J15	D2	60c orange	2.00	2.00
J16	D2	1fr violet	2.10	2.10
		Nos. J9-J16 (8)	9.55	9.55

Type of 1914 Issue
Surcharged

2 F.

1927

J17	D2	2fr on 1fr lilac rose	5.50	5.50
J18	D2	3fr on 1fr org brn	5.50	5.50

Carved Mask — D3

1941   Engr.   Perf. 14x13

J19	D3	5c black	.25	.25
J20	D3	10c lilac rose	.25	.25
J21	D3	15c dark blue	.25	.25
J22	D3	20c bright yel green	.30	.30
J23	D3	30c orange	.50	.50
J24	D3	50c violet brown	.70	.70
J25	D3	60c slate green	1.10	1.10
J26	D3	1fr rose red	1.40	1.40
J27	D3	2fr yellow	1.50	1.50
J28	D3	3fr dark purple	1.90	1.90
		Nos. J19-J28 (10)	8.15	8.15

Type D3 without "RF"

1944

J28A	D3	10c lilac rose	.50
J28B	D3	15c dark blue	.55
J28C	D3	20c bright yel green	.55
		Nos. J28A-J28C (3)	1.60

Nos. J28A-J28C were issued by the Vichy government in France, but were not placed on sale in Dahomey.

Catalogue values for unused stamps in this section, from this point to the end of the section, are for Never Hinged items.

Republic

Panther and Man — D4

Perf. 14x13½

1963, July 22   Typo.   Unwmk.

J29	D4	1fr green & rose	.20	.20
J30	D4	2fr brn & emerald	.20	.20
J31	D4	5fr org & vio bl	.20	.20
J32	D4	10fr magenta & blk	.50	.50
J33	D4	20fr vio bl & org	.75	.75
		Nos. J29-J33 (5)	1.85	1.85

Mail Boat — D5

No. J35, Heliograph. No. J36, Morse receiver. No. J37, Mailman on bicycle. No. J38, Early telephone. No. J39, Autorail. No. J40, Mail truck. No. J41, Radio tower. No. J42, DC-8F jet plane. No. J43, Early Bird communications satellite.

1967, Oct. 24   Engr.   Perf. 11

J34	D5	1fr brn, dl pur & bl	.20	.20
J35	D5	1fr dl pur, brn & bl	.20	.20
a.		Pair, #J34-J35	.25	
J36	D5	3fr dk brn, dk grn & org	.20	.20
J37	D5	3fr dk grn, dk brn & org	.20	.20
a.		Pair, #J36-J37	.25	

J38	D5	5fr ol bis, lil & bl	.35	.35
J39	D5	5fr lil, ol bis & bl	.35	.35
a.		Pair, #J38-J39	.75	
J40	D5	10fr brn org, vio & grn	.50	.50
J41	D5	10fr vio, brn org & grn	.50	.50
a.		Pair, #J40-J41	1.10	
J42	D5	30fr Prus bl, mar & vio	1.00	1.00
J43	D5	30fr vio, Prus bl & mar	1.00	1.00
a.		Pair, #J42-J43	2.25	
		Nos. J34-J43 (10)	4.50	4.50

Pairs printed tete beche, se-tenant at the base.

PARCEL POST STAMPS

Catalogue values for unused stamps in this section are for Never Hinged items.

Nos. 141-146 and 148 Surcharged

1967, Jan.   Unwmk.   Engr.   Perf. 13

Q1	A15	5fr on 1fr multi	.25	.25
Q2	A15	10fr on 2fr multi	.35	.35
Q3	A15	20fr on 6fr multi	.60	.60
Q4	A15	25fr on 3fr multi	.70	.70
Q5	A15	30fr on 4fr multi	.80	.80
a.		"20" instead of "50"	100.00	
Q6	A15	50fr on 10fr multi	1.25	1.25
Q7	A15	100fr on 20fr multi	2.50	2.50
		Nos. Q1-Q7 (7)	6.45	6.45

The surcharge is arranged to fit the shape of the stamp.
No. Q6a occurred once on the sheet.

DALMATIA

dal-'mă-sh e̅-ə

LOCATION — A promontory in the northwestern part of the Balkan Peninsula, together with several small islands in the Adriatic Sea.
GOVT. — Part of the former Austro-Hungarian crownland of the same name.
AREA — 113 sq. mi.
POP. — 18,719 (1921)
CAPITAL — Zara.

Stamps were issued during Italian occupation. This territory was subsequently annexed by Italy.

100 Centesimi = 1 Corona = 1 Lira

Used values are for postally used stamps.

Issued under Italian Occupation

Italy No. 87 Surcharged

1919, May 1   Wmk. 140   Perf. 14

1	A46	1cor on 1 l brn & grn	3.50	17.00
a.		Pair, one without surcharge	1,000.	1,000.

Italian Stamps of 1906-08 Surcharged — a

1921-22

2	A48	5c on 5c green	2.40	3.25
3	A48	10c on 10c claret	2.40	3.25
4	A49	25c on 25c blue ('22)	4.00	6.75
5	A49	50c on 50c vio ('22)	4.00	6.75
a.		Double surcharge		250.00
b.		Pair, one without surcharge	1,000.	

Italian Stamps of 1901-10 Surcharged — b

6	A46	1cor on 1 l brn & grn ('22)	6.50	21.00
7	A46	5cor on 5 l bl & rose ('22)	47.50	140.00
8	A51	10cor on 10 l gray grn & red ('22)	47.50	140.00
		Nos. 2-8 (7)	114.30	321.00

Surcharges similar to these but differing in style or arrangement of type were used in Austria under Italian occupation.

SPECIAL DELIVERY STAMPS

Italian Special Delivery Stamp No. E1 Surcharged type "a"

1921   Wmk. 140   Perf. 14

E1	SD1	25c on 25c rose red	3.50	15.00
a.		Double surcharge	425.00	675.00

Italian Special Delivery Stamp Surcharged

1922

E2	SD2	1.20 l on 1.20 l	210.00

No. E2 was not placed in use.

POSTAGE DUE STAMPS

Italian Postage Due Stamps and Type Surcharged types "a" or "b"

1922   Wmk. 140   Perf. 14

J1	D3 (a)	50c on 50c buff & mag	2.40	6.75
J2	D3 (b)	1cor on 1 l bl & red	6.50	21.00
J3	D3 (b)	2cor on 2 l bl & red	52.50	130.00
J4	D3 (b)	5cor on 5 l bl & red	52.50	130.00
		Nos. J1-J4 (4)	113.90	287.75

DANISH WEST INDIES

'dā-nish 'west 'in-dēs

LOCATION — Group of islands in the West Indies, lying east of Puerto Rico
GOVT. — Danish colony
AREA — 132 sq. mi.
POP. — 27,086 (1911)
CAPITAL — Charlotte Amalie

The US bought these islands in 1917 and they became the US Virgin Islands, using US stamps and currency.

100 Cents = 1 Dollar
100 Bit = 1 Franc (1905)

Wmk. 111 — Small Crown   Wmk. 112 — Crown

Wmk. 113 — Crown   Wmk. 114 — Multiple Crosses

Coat of Arms — A1

Yellowish Paper
Yellow Wavy-line Burelage, UL to LR

1856   Typo.   Wmk. 111   Imperf.

1	A1	3c dark carmine, brown gum	200.	275.
a.		3c dark carmine, yellow gum	225.	275.
b.		3c carmine, white gum	4,250.	—

The brown and yellow gums were applied locally.
Reprint: 1981, carmine, back-printed across two stamps ("Reprint by Dansk Post og Telegrafmuseum 1978"), value, pair, $10.

White Paper
Yellow Wavy-line Burelage UR to LL

1866

2	A1	3c rose	42.50	75.

No. 2 reprints, unwatermarked: 1930, carmine, value $100. 1942, rose carmine, back-printed across each row ("Nytryk 1942 G. A. Hagemann Danmark og Dansk Vestindiens Frimaerker Bind 2"), value $50.

1872   Perf. 12½

3	A1	3c rose	100.	275.

Without Burelage

1873

4	A1	4c dull blue	250.	475.
a.		Imperf., pair	775.	
b.		Horiz. pair, imperf. vert.	575.	

The 1930 reprint of No. 4 is ultramarine, unwatermarked and imperf., value $100. The 1942 4c reprint is blue, unwatermarked, imperf. and has printing on back (see note below No. 2), value $60.

A2

Normal Frame   Inverted Frame

The arabesques in the corners have a main stem and a branch. When the frame is in normal position, in the upper left corner the branch leaves the main stem half way between two little leaflets. In the lower right corner the branch starts at the foot of the second leaflet. When the frame is inverted the corner designs are, of course, transposed.

White Wove Paper
Varying from Thin to Thick
1874-79   Wmk. 112   Perf. 14x13½

Values for inverted frames, covers and blocks are for the cheapest variety.

5	A2	1c green & brown red	22.50	30.00
a.		1c green & rose lilac, thin paper	80.00	125.00
b.		1c green & red violet, medium paper	45.00	65.00
c.		1c green & claret, thick paper	20.00	30.00
e.		As "c," inverted frame	25.00	32.50
f.		As "a," inverted frame	475.00	

No. 5 exists with "b" surcharge, "10 CENTS 1895." See note below No. 15.

6	A2	3c blue & carmine	27.50	20.00
a.		3c light blue & rose carmine, thin paper	65.00	50.00
b.		3c deep blue & dark carmine, medium paper	40.00	17.00
c.		3c greenish blue & lake, thick paper	32.50	17.00
d.		Imperf., pair	375.00	—
e.		Inverted frame, thick paper	30.00	20.00
f.		As "a," inverted frame	350.00	
7	A2	4c brown & dull blue	16.00	19.00
b.		4c brown & ultramarine, thin paper	225.00	225.00
c.		Diagonal half used as 2c on cover		140.00
d.		As "b," inverted frame	900.00	1,400.
8	A2	5c grn & gray ('76)	30.00	25.00
a.		5c yellow green & dark gray, thin paper	55.00	37.50
b.		Inverted frame, thick paper	30.00	25.00
9	A2	7c lilac & orange	35.00	95.00
a.		7c lilac & yellow	90.00	100.00
b.		Inverted frame	65.00	150.00
10	A2	10c blue & brn ('76)	30.00	30.00
a.		10c dark blue & black brown, thin paper	70.00	45.00
b.		Period between "t" & "s" of "cents"	35.00	30.00
c.		Inverted frame	27.50	32.50
11	A2	12c red lil & yel grn ('77)	42.50	175.00
a.		12c lilac & deep green	160.00	200.00
12	A2	14c lilac & green	650.00	1,250.
a.		Inverted frame	2,500.	3,500.
13	A2	50c vio, thin paper ('79)	190.00	300.00
a.		50c gray violet, thick paper	250.00	375.00
		Nos. 5-13 (9)	1,043.	1,944.

The central element in the fan-shaped scrollwork at the outside of the lower left corner of Nos. 5a and 7b looks like an elongated diamond.

See Nos. 16-20. For surcharges see Nos. 14-15, 23-28, 40.

Nos. 9 and 13 Surcharged in Black

a   b

1887

14	A2 (a)	1c on 7c lilac & orange	100.00	200.00
a.		1c on 7c lilac & yellow	120.00	225.00
b.		Double surcharge	250.00	500.00
c.		Inverted frame	110.00	350.00

1895

15	A2 (b)	10c on 50c violet, thin paper	42.50	67.50

The "b" surcharge also exists on No. 5, with "10" found in two sizes. These are essays.

Type of 1874-79
1896-1901   Perf. 13

16	A2	1c green & red violet, inverted frame ('98)	15.00	22.50
a.		Normal frame	300.00	450.00
17	A2	3c blue & lake, inverted frame ('98)	12.00	17.50
a.		Normal frame	250.00	425.00
18	A2	4c bister & dull blue ('01)	17.50	15.00
a.		Diagonal half used as 2c on cover		100.00
b.		Inverted frame	60.00	85.00
c.		As "b," diagonal half used as 2c on cover		350.00
19	A2	5c green & gray, inverted frame	35.00	35.00
a.		Normal frame	800.00	1,200.
20	A2	10c blue & brown ('01)	80.00	150.00
a.		Inverted frame	1,000.	2,000.
b.		Period between "t" and "s" of "cents"	170.00	160.00
		Nos. 16-20 (5)	159.50	240.00

Arms — A5

1900

21	A5	1c light green	3.00	3.00
22	A5	5c light blue	17.50	25.00

See Nos. 29-30. For surcharges see Nos. 41-42.

Nos. 6, 17, 20 Surcharged

c

Surcharge "c" in Black
1902   Perf. 14x13½

23	A2	2c on 3c blue & carmine, inverted frame	600.00	725.00
a.		"2" in date with straight tail	675.00	800.00
b.		Normal frame		—

Perf. 13

24	A2	2c on 3c blue & lake, inverted frame	10.00	27.50
a.		"2" in date with straight tail	12.00	32.50
b.		Dated "1901"	650.00	650.00
c.		Normal frame	175.00	300.00
d.		Dark green surcharge	2,000.	
e.		As "d" & "a"		—
f.		As "d" & "c"		—

Only one example of No. 24f can exist.

25	A2	8c on 10c blue & brown	25.00	42.50
a.		"2" with straight tail	30.00	45.00
b.		On No. 20b	32.50	45.00
c.		Inverted frame	250.00	425.00

d

Surcharge "d" in Black
1902   Perf. 13

27	A2	2c on 3c blue & lake, inverted frame	12.00	32.50
a.		Normal frame	240.00	425.00
28	A2	8c on 10c blue & brown	12.00	14.00
a.		On No. 20b	18.50	25.00
b.		Inverted frame	225.00	400.00
		Nos. 23-28 (5)	659.00	841.50

1903   Wmk. 113

29	A5	2c carmine	8.00	22.50
30	A5	8c brown	27.50	35.00

King   St. Thomas
Christian   Harbor — A9
IX — A8

1905		**Typo.**	**Perf. 13**	
31	A8	5b green	3.75	3.25
32	A8	10b red	3.75	3.25
33	A8	20b green & blue	8.75	8.25
34	A8	25b ultramarine	8.75	10.50
35	A8	40b red & gray	8.25	8.25
36	A8	50b yellow & gray	10.00	12.00

Perf. 12
Wmk. Two Crowns (113)
Frame Typographed, Center Engraved

37	A9	1fr green & blue	17.50	45.00
38	A9	2fr orange red & brown	30.00	60.00
39	A9	5fr yellow & brown	77.50	275.00
		Nos. 31-39 (9)	168.25	425.50

Favor cancels exist on Nos. 37-39. Value 25% less.

Nos. 18, 22 and 30
Surcharged in Black

1905   Wmk. 112

40	A2	5b on 4c bister & dull blue	16.00	50.00
a.		Inverted frame	45.00	90.00
41	A5	5b on 5c light blue	14.00	47.50

Wmk. 113

42	A5	5b on 8c brown	14.00	50.00
		Nos. 40-42 (3)	44.00	147.50

Favor cancels exist on Nos. 40-42. Value 25% less.

Frederik VIII — A10

Frame Typographed, Center Engraved
1908

43	A10	5b green	1.90	1.90
44	A10	10b red	1.90	1.90
45	A10	15b violet & brown	3.75	4.50
46	A10	20b green & blue	30.00	27.50
47	A10	25b blue & dark blue	1.90	2.50
48	A10	30b claret & slate	50.00	52.50

49	A10	40b vermilion & gray	5.75	9.50
50	A10	50b yellow & brown	5.75	14.00
		Nos. 43-50 (8)	100.95	114.30

Christian X — A11

1915   Wmk. 114   Perf. 14x14½

51	A11	5b yellow green	4.00	5.00
52	A11	10b red	4.00	55.00
53	A11	15b lilac & red brown	4.00	55.00
54	A11	20b green & blue	4.00	55.00
55	A11	25b blue & dark blue	4.00	17.50
56	A11	30b claret & black	4.00	100.00
57	A11	40b orange & black	4.00	100.00
58	A11	50b yellow & brown	4.00	100.00
		Nos. 51-58 (8)	32.00	487.50

Forged and favor cancellations exist.

POSTAGE DUE STAMPS

Royal Cipher,
"Christian 9 Rex"
D1

1902   Litho.   Unwmk.   Perf. 11½

J1	D1	1c dark blue	5.00	17.50
J2	D1	4c dark blue	12.50	22.50
J3	D1	6c dark blue	22.50	60.00
J4	D1	10c dark blue	20.00	65.00
		Nos. J1-J4 (4)	60.00	165.00

There are five types of each value. On the 4c they may be distinguished by differences in the figure "4"; on the other values differences are minute.

Used values of Nos. J1-J8 are for canceled stamps. Uncanceled stamps without gum have probably been used. Value 60% of unused.

Excellent counterfeits of Nos. J1-J4 exist.

Numeral of value — D2

1905-13   Perf. 13

J5	D2	5b red & gray	4.50	6.75
J6	D2	20b red & gray	7.50	14.00
J7	D2	30b red & gray	6.75	14.00
J8	D2	50b red & gray	6.00	35.00
a.		Perf. 14x14½ ('13)	37.50	140.00
b.		Perf. 11½	325.00	
		Nos. J5-J8 (4)	24.75	69.75

All values of this issue are known imperforate, but were not regularly issued.

Used values of Nos. J5-J8 are for canceled stamps. Uncanceled examples without gum have probably been used. Value 60% of unused.

Counterfeits of Nos. J5-J8 exist.

Danish West Indies stamps were replaced by those of the U.S. in 1917, after the U.S. bought the islands.

DANZIG

'dan͜t͜ sig

LOCATION — In northern Europe bordering on the Baltic Sea
AREA — 754 sq. mi.
POP. — 407,000 (approx. 1939)
CAPITAL — Danzig

Established as a "Free City and State" under the protection of the League of Nations in 1920, Danzig was seized by Germany in 1939. It became a Polish province in 1945.

100 Pfennig = 1 Gulden (1923)
100 Pfennig = 1 Mark

Watermarks

Wmk. 108 — Honeycomb

Wmk. 109 — Webbing

Wmk. 110 — Octagons

Wmk. 125 — Lozenges

Wmk. 237 — Swastikas

Used Values of 1920-23 are for favor-canceled stamps unless otherwise noted. Postally used examples bring much higher prices.

For additional varieties, see the *Scott Classic Catalogue*.

German Stamps of 1906-20 Overprinted in Black

Perf. 14, 14½, 15x14½
1920   **Wmk. 125**

1	A16	5pf green	.30	.50
2	A16	10pf car rose	.30	.30
3	A22	15pf violet brown	.30	.30
4	A16	20pf blue violet	.30	1.10
5	A16	30pf org & blk, *buff*	.30	.30
6	A16	40pf car rose	.30	.30
7	A16	50pf pur & blk, *buff*	.50	.30
8	A17	1m red	.50	.60
9	A17	1.25m green	.50	.60
10	A17	1.50m yellow brn	.90	1.60
11	A21	2m blue	3.25	7.25
a.		Double overprint	375.00	
		Never hinged	825.00	
12	A21	2.50m lilac rose	3.00	4.50
13	A19	3m black violet	7.00	10.00
14	A16	4m black & rose	4.75	6.00

15	A20	5m slate & car (25x17 holes)	2.50	3.75
a.		Center & "Danzig" invtd.	15,000.	
		Never hinged	—	
b.		Inverted overprint		20,000.
		Nos. 1-15 (15)	24.70	37.40
		Set, never hinged	100.00	

The 5pf brown, 10pf orange and 40pf lake and black with this overprint were not regularly issued. Value for trio, $450.
For surcharges see Nos. 19-23, C1-C3.
Issued: 40pf, 9/13; 1.50m, 3m 7/20; 4m, 12/21; others 6/14.

Nos. 5, 4 Surcharged in Various Sizes

1920

19	A16	5pf on 30pf (V)	.25	.25
20	A16	10pf on 20pf (R)	.25	.25
a.		Double surcharge	110.00	—
		Never hinged	250.00	
21	A16	25pf on 30pf (G)	.25	.25
a.		Inverted surcharge	85.00	—
		Never hinged	250.00	
22	A16	60pf on 30pf (Br)	.70	1.00
a.		Double surcharge	85.00	290.00
		Never hinged	250.00	
23	A16	80pf on 30pf (V)	.70	1.00

Issued: No. 21, 8/10. No. 20, 8/17. Nos. 19, 22-23, 11/1.

German Stamps Surcharged in Various Styles

Gray Burelage with Points Up

25	A16	1m on 30pf org & blk, *buff* (Bk)	.85	1.50
a.		Pair, one without surcharge		
26	A16	1¼m on 3pf brn (R)	1.00	1.50
27	A22	2m on 35pf red brn (Bl)	1.50	1.50
d.		Surcharge omitted	70.00	—
		Never hinged	260.00	
28	A22	3m on 7½pf org (G)	1.00	1.50
29	A22	5m on 2pf gray (R)	1.00	2.00
30	A22	10m on 7½pf org (Bk)	3.00	7.00
		Nos. 19-30 (11)	10.50	17.75
		Set, never hinged	50.00	

Gray Burelage with Points Down

26a	A16	1¼m on 3pf brown	36.00	42.50
27a	A22	2m on 35pf red brn	400.00	325.00
28a	A22	3m on 7½pf orange	25.00	17.00
29a	A22	5m on 2pf gray	25.00	30.00
30a	A22	10m on 7½pf orange	5.75	11.00
		Nos. 26a-30a (5)	491.75	425.50
		Set, never hinged	1,525.	

Violet Burelage with Points Up

25b	A16	1m on 30pf org & blk, *buff*	85.00	30.00
26b	A16	1¼m on 3pf brown	4.50	6.50
27b	A22	2m on 35pf red brn	11.50	37.50
28b	A22	3m on 7½pf orange	2.25	2.50
29b	A22	5m on 2pf gray	1.25	2.50
30b	A22	10m on 7½pf orange	1.25	2.50
		Nos. 25b-30b (6)	105.75	81.50
		Set, never hinged	430.00	

Violet Burelage with Points Down

25c	A16	1m on 30pf org & blk, *buff*	1.25	2.50
26c	A16	1¼m on 3pf brown	6.50	11.00
27c	A22	2m on 35pf red brn	30.00	50.00
28c	A22	3m on 7½pf orange	40.00	85.00

29c	A22	5m on 2pf gray	6.50	8.50
30c	A22	10m on 7½pf orange	13.50	29.00
		Nos. 25c-30c (6)	97.75	186.00
		Set, never hinged	375.00	

Excellent counterfeits of the surcharges are known.

German Stamps of 1906-20 Overprinted in Blue

1920

31	A22	2pf gray	110.00	200.00
32	A22	2½pf gray	150.00	300.00
33	A16	3pf brown	11.00	17.00
a.		Double overprint	75.00	
		Never hinged	180.00	
34	A16	5pf green	.55	.65
a.		Double overprint	85.00	
		Never hinged	200.00	
35	A22	7½pf orange	40.00	57.50
36	A16	10pf carmine	3.75	7.00
37	A22	15pf dk violet	.60	.65
b.		Double overprint	85.00	
		Never hinged	200.00	
38	A16	20pf blue violet	.55	.65

Overprinted in Carmine or Blue

39	A16	25pf org & blk, *yel*	.55	.65
40	A16	30pf org & blk, *buff*	50.00	92.50
42	A16	40pf lake & blk	2.25	2.50
a.		Inverted overprint	210.00	
b.		Double overprint	425.00	
43	A16	50pf pur & blk, *buff*	175.00	300.00
44	A16	60pf mag (Bl)	1,250.	2,100.
45	A16	75pf green & blk	.55	.60
46	A16	80pf lake & blk, *rose*	2.40	4.25
47	A17	1m carmine	1,200.	2,100.
a.		Double overprint	4,250.	

Overprinted in Carmine

48	A21	2m gray blue	1,200.	2,100.

Counterfeit overprints of Nos. 31-48 exist. Nos. 44, 47 and 48 were issued in small quantities and usually affixed directly to the mail by the postal clerk.
For surcharge see No. 62.

A8

Hanseatic Trading Ship — A9

Serrate Roulette 13½
1921, Jan. 31   Typo.   Wmk. 108

49	A8	5pf brown & violet	.20	.20
50	A8	10pf orange & dk vio	.20	.20
51	A8	25pf green & car rose	.50	.65
52	A8	40pf carmine rose	3.75	3.25
53	A8	80pf ultra	.50	.50
54	A9	1m car rose & blk	1.60	1.60
55	A9	2m dk blue & dk grn	5.00	4.75
56	A9	3m blk & grnsh bl	1.75	2.25
57	A9	5m indigo & rose red	1.75	2.25
58	A9	10m dk grn & brn org	2.50	4.50
		Nos. 49-58 (10)	17.75	20.15
		Set, never hinged	82.50	

Issued in honor of the Constitution.
Nos. 49 and 50 with center in red instead of violet and Nos. 49-51, 54-58 with center inverted are probably proofs. All values of this issue exist imperforate but are not known to have been regularly issued in that condition.

1921, Mar. 11   **Perf. 14**

59	A8	25pf green & car rose	.50	.85
60	A8	40pf carmine rose	.50	.85
61	A8	80pf ultra	5.00	10.00
		Nos. 59-61 (3)	6.00	11.70
		Set, never hinged	34.00	

No. 45 Surcharged in Black

1921, May 6   **Wmk. 125**

62	A16	60pf on 75pf	.95	.90
		Never hinged	5.50	
a.		Double surcharge	100.00	110.00
		Never hinged	250.00	

Surcharge on #62 normally appears at top of design.

Arms — A11   Coat of Arms — A12

Wmk. 108 (Upright or Sideways)
1921-22   **Perf. 14**

63	A11	5(pf) orange	.20	.20
64	A11	10(pf) dark brown	.20	.20
65	A11	15(pf) green	.20	.20
66	A11	20(pf) slate	.20	.20
67	A11	25(pf) dark green	.20	.20
68	A11	30(pf) blue & car	.25	.20
		Never hinged	.85	
a.		Center inverted	67.50	150.00
		Never hinged	160.00	
69	A11	40pf green & car	.20	.20
		Never hinged	.85	
a.		Center inverted	50.00	150.00
		Never hinged	160.00	
70	A11	50pf dk grn & car	.20	.20
71	A11	60pf carmine	.45	.45
72	A11	80pf black & car	.35	.45

Paper With Faint Gray Network

73	A11	1m org & car	.50	.40
a.		Center inverted	67.50	150.00
		Never hinged	210.00	
74	A11	1.20m blue violet	1.25	1.25
75	A11	2m gray & car	3.25	4.25
76	A11	3m violet & car	9.00	10.00

Serrate Roulette 13½
Wmk. 108 Upright

77	A12	5m grn, red & blk	1.25	3.00
78	A12	9m rose, red & org ('22)	3.00	8.50
79	A12	10m ultra, red & blk	1.25	3.00
80	A12	20m red & black	1.25	3.00
		Nos. 63-80 (18)	23.20	35.90
		Set, never hinged	85.00	

In this and succeeding issues the mark values usually have the face of the paper covered with a gray network. This network is often very faint and occasionally is omitted.
Nos. 64-76 exist imperf. Value, each $16-$50 unused, $50-$150 never hinged.
See Nos. 81-93, 99-105. For surcharges and overprints see Nos. 96-98, O1-O33.

Type of 1921 and

A13

Coat of Arms — A13a

1922 Wmk. 108 Upright *Perf. 14*

81	A11	75(pf) deep vio	.20	.25
82	A11	80(pf) green	.20	.25
83	A11	1.25m vio & car	.20	.25
84	A11	1.50m slate gray	.20	.40
85	A11	2m car rose	.20	.25
86	A11	2.40m dk brn & car	1.00	2.00
87	A11	3m car lake	.20	.40
88	A11	4m dark blue	1.00	2.00
89	A11	5m deep grn	.20	.35
90	A11	6m car lake	.20	.35
a.		6m car rose, wmk. 109 sideways	1,800.	
		Never hinged	3,900.	
91	A11	8m light blue	.45	1.60
92	A11	10m orange	.20	.35
93	A11	20m org brn	.20	.35
94	A13	50m gold & car	2.00	6.50
a.		50m gold & red	57.50	120.00
		Never hinged	220.00	
95	A13a	100m on metallic grn & red	3.25	6.00
		Nos. 81-95 (15)	9.70	21.30
		Set, never hinged	42.50	

No. 95 has buff instead of gray network.
Nos. 81-83, 85-86, 88 exist imperf. Value, each $12.50.
Nos. 94-95 exist imperf. Value, each $50

Nos. 87, 88 and 91 Surcharged in Black or Carmine

1922

96	A11	6m on 3m car lake	.25	.60
a.		Double surcharge		
97	A11	8m on 4m dk blue	.30	.85
a.		Double surcharge	60.00	145.00
		Never hinged	140.00	
b.		Pair, one without surcharge	120.00	
98	A11	20m on 8m lt bl (C)	.30	.60
		Nos. 96-98 (3)	.85	2.05
		Set, never hinged	4.00	

Wmk. 109 Sideways

1922-23 *Perf. 14*

99	A11	4m dark blue	.20	.40
100	A11	5m dark green	.20	.40
102	A11	10m orange	.20	.40
103	A11	20m orange brn	.20	.40

Paper Without Network
Wmk. 109 Upright

104	A11	40m pale blue	.20	.60
105	A11	80m red	.20	.60
		Nos. 99-105 (6)	1.20	2.80
		Set, never hinged	5.40	

Nos. 100, 102 and 103 also exist with watermark vertical. Values slightly higher.

Nos. 104-105 exist imperf. Value, each $12.50 unused, $32.50 never hinged.

A15   A15a

Coat of Arms A16

1922-23 Wmk. 109 Upright *Perf. 14*
Paper With Gray Network

106	A15	50m pale bl & red	.20	.40
107	A15a	100m dk grn & red	.20	.40
108	A15a	150m violet & red	.20	.40
109	A16	250m violet & red	.35	.40
110	A16	500m gray blk & red	.35	.40
111	A16	1000m brn & red	.35	.40
112	A16	5000m silver & red	1.50	6.00

Paper Without Network

113	A15	50m pale blue	.40	.60
114	A15a	100m deep green	.40	.60
115	A15a	200m orange	.40	.60
		Nos. 106-115 (10)	4.35	10.20
		Set, never hinged	19.00	

Nos. 108-112 exist imperf. Value, each $50 unused; $125 never hinged.
Nos. 113-115 exist imperf. Value, each $35 unused; $92.50 never hinged.
See Nos. 123-125. For surcharges and overprints see Nos. 126, 137-140, 143, 156-167, O35-O38.

 A17

1923 *Perf. 14*
Paper With Gray Network

117	A17	250m violet & red	.20	.50
118	A17	300m bl grn & red	.20	.50
119	A17	500m gray & red	.20	.50
120	A17	1000m brown & red	.20	.50
121	A17	3000m violet & red	.20	.50
123	A16	10,000m orange & red	.60	.60
124	A16	20,000m pale bl & red	.60	1.00
125	A16	50,000m green & red	.60	1.00
		Nos. 117-125 (8)	2.80	5.10
		Set, never hinged	12.50	

Nos. 117, 119-121 exist imperf. Value, each $19 unused; $45 never hinged; Nos. 123-125 also exist imperf. Values each, $25 unused, $85 never hinged.
See Nos. 127-135. For surcharges & overprints see Nos. 141-142, 144-155, O39-O41.

No. 124 Surcharged in Red

1923, Aug. 14

126	A16	100,000m on #124	.65	6.00
		Never hinged	4.50	

No. 126 exists imperf. Value $50 unused, $125 never hinged.

1923 *Perf. 14*
Paper Without Network

127	A17	1000m brown	.20	.40
129	A17	5000m rose	.20	.40
131	A17	20,000m pale blue	.20	.40
132	A17	50,000m green	.20	.40

Paper With Gray Network

133	A17	100,000m deep blue	.20	.40
134	A17	250,000m violet	.20	.40
135	A17	500,000m slate	.20	.40
		Nos. 127-135 (7)	1.40	2.80
		Set, never hinged	5.00	

Nos. 127, 129, 131-135 exist imperf. Value each, $40 unused, $100 never hinged.
Issued: #127, 7/24. #129, 131, 8/25. #132, 9/1. #133, 9/11. #135, 9/16.

Abbreviations:
th=(tausend) thousand
mil=million

Nos. 115, 114, 132, and Type of 1923 Surcharged

1923 *Perf. 14*
Paper Without Network

137	A15	40th m on 200m	.85	2.00
a.		Double surcharge	85.00	
		Never hinged	160.00	
138	A15	100th m on 200m	.85	2.00
139	A15	250th m on 200m	6.25	13.00
140	A15a	400th m on 100m	.60	.40
141	A17	500th m on #132	.40	.40

On 10,000m

142	A17	1mil m org	3.75	6.25

The surcharges on Nos. 140-142 differ in details from those on Nos. 137-139.

Type of 1923 Surcharged

Paper With Gray Network
On 1,000,000m

143	A16	10mil m org	.40	1.25
		Nos. 137-143 (7)	13.10	25.30
		Set, never hinged	55.00	

Nos. 142-143 exist imperf. Values: No. 142 unused $50, never hinged $125; No. 143 unused $25, never hinged $85.

Type of 1923 Surcharged

Wmk. 109 Upright
Perf. 14
10,000m rose on paper without Network

144	A17	1mil m on 10,000m	.25	.40
145	A17	2mil m on 10,000m	.25	.40
146	A17	3mil m on 10,000m	.25	.40
147	A17	5mil m on 10,000m	.35	.40
b.		Double surcharge	85.00	

10,000m gray lilac on paper without Network

148	A17	10mil m on 10,000m	.40	.75
149	A17	20mil m on 10,000m	.40	.75
150	A17	25mil m on 10,000m	.20	.75
151	A17	40mil m on 10,000m	.20	.75
a.		Double surcharge	52.50	
		Never hinged	160.00	
152	A17	50mil m on 10,000m	.20	.75

Type of 1923 Surcharged in Red

10,000m gray lilac on paper without Network

153	A17	100mil m on 10,000m	.20	.75
154	A17	300mil m on 10,000m	.20	.75
155	A17	500mil m on 10,000m	.20	.75
		Nos. 144-155 (12)	3.10	7.60
		Set, never hinged	15.00	

Nos. 144-147 exist imperf. Value, each $25 unused, $85 never hinged. Nos. 148-155 exist imperf. Value, each $32.50 unused, $85 never hinged.

Types of 1923 Surcharged

1923, Oct. 31 Wmk. 110 *Perf. 14*

156	A15	5pf on 50m	.40	.40
157	A15	10pf on 50m	.40	.40
158	A15a	20pf on 100m	.40	.40
159	A15	25pf on 50m	3.50	9.00
160	A15	30pf on 50m	3.50	2.00
161	A15a	40pf on 100m	2.00	2.00
162	A15a	50pf on 100m	2.00	3.00
163	A15a	75pf on 100m	8.00	16.00

Type of 1923 Surcharged

1923, Nov. 5

164	A16	1g on 1mil m rose	4.50	6.25
165	A16	2g on 1mil m rose	12.00	17.50
166	A16	3g on 1mil m rose	20.00	62.50
167	A16	5g on 1mil m rose	25.00	67.50
		Nos. 156-167 (12)	81.70	186.95
		Set, never hinged	385.00	

Coat of Arms — A19

1924-37 Wmk. 109 *Perf. 14*

168	A19	3pf brn, *yelsh*	1.25	*1.50*
a.		3pf dp brn, *white*	2.10	1.90
		Never hinged	7.25	
170	A19	5pf org, *yelsh*	3.25	.55
a.		White paper	8.50	2.00
		Never hinged	45.00	
c.		Tête bêche pair	375.00	
		Never hinged	725.00	
d.		Syncopated perf., #170	10.50	9.25
		Never hinged	30.00	
e.		Syncopated perf., #170a	210.00	22.50
		Never hinged	110.00	
171	A19	7pf yel grn	1.60	*3.00*
172	A19	8pf yel grn	1.60	*6.00*
173	A19	10pf grn, *yelsh*	5.50	.50
a.		White paper	8.50	2.50
		Never hinged	32.50	
c.		10pf blue grn, *yellowish*	5.00	1.10
		Never hinged	13.00	
d.		Tête bêche pair	325.00	
		Never hinged	750.00	
e.		Syncopated perf., #173	18.00	11.00
		Never hinged	55.00	
f.		Syncopated perf., #173a	27.50	13.00
		Never hinged	100.00	
g.		Syncopated perf., #173c	11.00	14.50
		Never hinged	37.50	
175	A19	15pf gray	3.75	.65
176	A19	15pf red, *yelsh*	2.10	1.10
a.		White paper	4.50	1.10
		Never hinged	25.00	
177	A19	20pf carmine & red	13.50	.65
178	A19	20pf gray	1.75	*2.50*
179	A19	25pf slate & red	22.50	3.75
180	A19	25pf carmine	17.00	1.60
181	A19	30pf green & red	12.50	.85
182	A19	30pf dk violet	1.60	*4.25*
183	A19	35pf ultra	4.50	1.50
184	A19	40pf dk blue & blue	12.00	1.00
185	A19	40pf yel brn & red	6.50	*12.50*
186	A19	40pf dk blue	1.60	*3.75*
a.		Imperf.	60.00	
		Never hinged	170.00	
187	A19	50pf blue & red	16.00	8.50
a.		Yellowish paper	25.00	11.50
		Never hinged	57.50	
188	A19	55pf plum & scar	5.00	*14.50*
189	A19	60pf dk grn & red	6.25	*19.00*
190	A19	70pf yel grn & red	2.10	*7.50*
191	A19	75pf violet & red, *yellowish*	7.50	*29.00*
a.		White paper	10.00	8.50
		Never hinged	32.50	
192	A19	80pf dk grn brn & red	2.10	*7.50*
		Nos. 168-192 (23)	151.45	131.65
		Set, never hinged	625.00	

The 5pf and 10pf with syncopated perforations (Netherlands type C) are coils.
See Nos. 225-232. For overprints and surcharges see Nos. 200-209, 211-215, 241-252, B9-B11, O42-O52.

Oliva Castle and Cathedral A20

St. Mary's Church A23

Council Chamber on the Langenmarkt A24

2g, Mottlau River & Krantor. 3g, View of Zoppot.

1924-32 Engr. Wmk. 125

193	A20	1g yel grn & blk	21.00	*45.00*
		Parcel post cancel		20.00
194	A20	1g org & gray blk	17.00	3.75
		Parcel post cancel		1.00
a.		1g red orange & blk	17.00	11.00

	Never hinged	67.50	
	Parcel post cancel		1.00
195	A20 2g red vio & blk	45.00	110.00
	Parcel post cancel		40.00
196	A20 2g rose & blk	3.75	8.00
	Parcel post cancel		1.75
197	A20 3g dk blue & blk	4.25	5.00
	Parcel post cancel		2.25
198	A23 5g brn red & blk	4.25	8.50
	Parcel post cancel		1.90
199	A24 10g dk brn & blk	21.00	110.00
	Parcel post cancel		18.00
	Nos. 193-199 (7)	116.25	290.25
	Set, never hinged	525.00	

See No. 233. For overprints and surcharges see Nos. 210, 253-254, C31-C35.

Stamps of 1924-25 Overprinted in Black, Violet or Red

1920 15. November 1930

1930, Nov. 15   Typo.   Wmk. 109

200	A19 5pf orange	2.50	3.75
201	A19 10pf yellow grn (V)	3.50	4.50
202	A19 15pf red	6.00	11.00
203	A19 20pf carmine & red	3.00	6.00
204	A19 25pf slate & red	4.25	11.00
205	A19 30pf green & red	8.50	25.00
206	A19 35pf ultra (R)	32.50	100.00
207	A19 40pf dk bl & bl (R)	11.50	45.00
208	A19 50pf dp blue & red	32.50	85.00
209	A19 75pf violet & red	32.50	92.50

Engr.   Wmk. (125)

210	A20 1g orange & blk (R)	32.50	85.00
	Nos. 200-210 (11)	169.25	468.75
	Set, never hinged	675.00	

10th anniv. of the Free State. Counterfeits exist.

Nos. 171 and 183 Surcharged in Red Blue or Green:

Nos. 211-214   No. 215

1934-36

211	A19 6pf on 7pf (R)	.85	1.60
212	A19 8pf on 7pf (Bl)	2.10	2.40
213	A19 8pf on 7pf (R)	1.25	2.50
214	A19 8pf on 7pf (G)	.85	2.50
215	A19 30pf on 35pf (Bl)	12.00	25.00
	Nos. 211-215 (5)	17.05	34.00
	Set, never hinged	60.00	

Bathing Beach, Brösen A25

View of Brösen Beach A26

War Memorial at Brösen — A27

Skyline of Danzig — A28

1936, June 23   Typo.   Wmk. 109

216	A25 10pf deep green	.70	.70
217	A26 25pf rose red	1.25	2.40
218	A27 40pf bright blue	2.25	4.50
	Nos. 216-218 (3)	4.20	7.60
	Set, never hinged	15.00	

Village of Brösen, 125th anniversary.

Exist imperf. Value each, $40 unused, $110 never hinged.

1937, Mar. 27

219	A28 10pf dark blue	.50	1.40
220	A28 15pf violet brown	1.60	2.00
	Set, never hinged	11.25	

Air Defense League.

Danzig Philatelic Exhibition Issue
Souvenir Sheet

DAPOSTA 1937

1. DANZIGER LANDESPOSTWERTZEICHEN AUSSTELLUNG

St. Mary's Church — A29

1937, June 6   Wmk. 109   Perf. 14

221	A29 50pf dark opal green	3.25	21.00
	Never hinged	11.00	

Danzig Philatelic Exhib., June 6-8, 1937.

Arthur Schopenhauer
A30   A31

Design: 40pf, Full-face portrait, white hair.

Unwmk.

1938, Feb. 22   Photo.   Perf. 14

222	A30 15pf dull blue	1.45	2.40
223	A31 25pf sepia	3.50	8.00
224	A31 40pf orange ver	1.50	3.25
	Nos. 222-224 (3)	6.45	13.65
	Set, never hinged	20.00	

150th anniv. of the birth of Schopenhauer.

Type of 1924-35

1938-39   Typo.   Wmk. 237   Perf. 14

225	A19 3pf brown	.90	7.50
226	A19 5pf orange	.90	2.10
b.	Syncopated perf.	1.40	7.50
	Never hinged	5.25	
227	A19 8pf yellow grn	4.00	35.00
228	A19 10pf blue green	.90	2.10
b.	Syncopated perf.	3.00	10.00
	Never hinged	13.50	
229	A19 15pf scarlet	1.60	8.50
230	A19 25pf carmine	2.10	12.50
231	A19 40pf dark blue	2.10	29.00
232	A19 50pf brt bl & red	2.10	135.00

Engr.

233	A20 1g red org & blk	6.75	120.00
	Nos. 225-233 (9)	21.35	351.70
	Set, never hinged	90.00	

Sizes: No. 233, 32½x21¼mm; No. 194, 31x21mm.

Nos. 226b and 228b are coils with Netherlands type C perforation.

Knights in Tournament, 1500 — A33

French Leaving Danzig, 1814 — A35

Stamp Day: 10pf, Signing of Danzig-Sweden neutrality treaty, 1630. 25pf, Battle of Weichselmünde, 1577.

Unwmk.

1939, Jan. 7   Photo.   Perf. 14

234	A33 5pf dark green	.40	2.10
235	A33 10pf copper brown	.85	2.50
236	A35 15pf slate black	1.25	3.00
237	A35 25pf brown violet	1.60	4.25
	Nos. 234-237 (4)	4.10	11.85
	Set, never hinged	13.00	

GESUNDE KINDER FROHE ZUKUNFT
GREGOR MENDEL
FREIE STADT DANZIG

Gregor Mendel — A37

15pf, Dr. Robert Koch. 25pf, Wilhelm Roentgen.

1939, Apr. 29   Photo.   Perf. 13x14

238	A37 10pf copper brown	.65	.85
239	A37 15pf indigo	.65	2.75
240	A37 25pf dark olive green	1.25	2.75
	Nos. 238-240 (3)	2.55	6.35
	Set, never hinged	7.25	

Issued in honor of the achievements of Mendel, Koch and Roentgen.

Issued under German Administration
Stamps of Danzig, 1925-39, Surcharged in Black:

a   b

c

1939   Wmk. 109   Perf. 14

241	A19(b) 4rpf on 35pf ultra	.75	2.50
242	A19(b) 12rpf on 7pf yel grn	1.50	2.25
243	A19(a) 20rpf gray	3.00	8.50

Wmk. 237

244	A19(a) 3rpf brown	.75	2.40
245	A19(a) 5rpf orange	.65	3.00
246	A19(a) 8rpf yellow grn	1.10	4.25
247	A19(a) 10rpf blue grn	2.25	4.25
248	A19(a) 15rpf scarlet	6.00	12.00
249	A19(a) 25rpf carmine	4.50	11.00
250	A19(a) 30rpf dk violet	2.00	4.50
251	A19(a) 40rpf dk blue	2.75	6.00
252	A19(a) 50rpf brt bl & red	4.00	7.00

Thick Paper

253	A20(c) 1rm on 1g red org & blk	14.00	60.00

Wmk. 125
Thin White Paper

254	A20(c) 2rm on 2g rose & blk	20.00	65.00
	Nos. 241-254 (14)	63.25	192.65
	Set, never hinged	190.00	

#241-254 were valid throughout Germany.

SEMI-POSTAL STAMPS

St. George and Dragon — SP1

Wmk. 108

1921, Oct. 16   Typo.   Perf. 14

Size: 19x22mm

B1	SP1 30pf + 30pf grn & org	.45	.85
B2	SP1 60pf + 60pf rose & org	1.25	1.60

Size: 25x30mm
Serrate Roulette 13½

B3	SP1 1.20m + 1.20m dk bl & org	2.00	2.25
	Nos. B1-B3 (3)	3.70	4.70
	Set, never hinged	15.00	

Nos. B1-B3 exist imperf. Value each, $45 unused, $125 never hinged.

Aged Pensioner SP2

1923, Mar.   Wmk. 109   Perf. 14
Paper With Gray Network

B4	SP2 50m + 20m lake	.20	.60
B5	SP2 100m + 30m red vio	.20	.60
	Set, never hinged	2.20	

Nos. B4-B5 exist imperf. Value each, $50 unused, $210 never hinged.

Philatelic Exhibition Issue

FREIE STADT DANZIG

Neptune Fountain — SP3

Various Frames.

1929, July 7   Engr.   Unwmk.

B6	SP3 10pf yel grn & gray	2.40	1.60
B7	SP3 15pf car & gray	2.40	1.60
B8	SP3 25pf ultra & gray	8.50	13.00
a.	25pf violet blue & black	25.00	62.50
	Never hinged	92.50	
	Nos. B6-B8 (3)	13.30	16.20
	Set, never hinged	45.00	

These stamps were sold exclusively at the Danzig Philatelic Exhibition, June 7-14, 1929, at double their face values, the excess being for the aid of the exhibition.

5 W. H. W.

Regular Issue of 1924-25 Surcharged in Black

1934, Jan. 15   Wmk. 109

B9	A19 5pf + 5pf orange	8.50	21.00
B10	A19 10pf + 5pf yel grn	21.00	50.00
B11	A19 15pf + 5pf carmine	12.50	37.50
	Nos. B9-B11 (3)	42.00	108.50
	Set, never hinged	210.00	

Surtax for winter welfare. Counterfeits exist.

Stock Tower — SP4

George Hall — SP6

City Gate, 16th Century SP5

1935, Dec. 16   **Typo.**   *Perf. 14*
B12	SP4	5pf + 5pf orange	.60	1.60
B13	SP5	10pf + 5pf green	1.10	2.50
B14	SP6	15pf + 10pf scarlet	2.50	3.75
	Nos. B12-B14 (3)	4.20	7.85
	Set, never hinged	14.00	

Surtax for winter welfare.

Milk Can Tower SP7   Frauentor SP8

Krantor — SP9

Langgarter Gate — SP10

High Gate SP11

1936, Nov. 25
B15	SP7	10pf + 5pf dk bl	1.50	4.50
a.	Imperf.		75.00	
	Never hinged		180.00	
B16	SP8	15pf + 5pf dull grn	1.50	6.00
B17	SP9	25pf + 10pf red brn	2.25	9.00
B18	SP10	40pf + 20pf brn & red brn	3.00	11.00
B19	SP11	50pf + 20pf bl & dk bl	5.00	17.00
	Nos. B15-B19 (5)	13.25	47.50
	Set, never hinged	62.50	

Surtax for winter welfare.

SP12   SP13

1937, Oct. 30   **Wmk. 109 Sideways**
B20	SP12	25pf + 25pf dk car	2.50	5.25

Wmk. 109 Upright
B21	SP13	40pf + 40pf blue & red	2.50	5.25
a.	Souvenir sheet of 2, #B20a-B21	60.00	100.00
	Never hinged	110.00	
	Set, never hinged	22.00	

Founding of Danzig community at Magdeburg.

Madonna SP14   Mercury SP15

Weather Vane, Town Hall SP16   Neptune Fountain SP17

St. George and Dragon — SP18

1937, Dec. 13
B23	SP14	5pf + 5pf brt violet	2.50	7.50
B24	SP15	10pf + 10pf dk brn	2.50	6.25
B25	SP16	15pf + 5pf bl & yel brn	2.50	8.25
B26	SP17	25pf + 10pf bl grn & grn	3.25	11.00
B27	SP18	40pf + 25pf brt car & bl	5.75	17.50
	Nos. B23-B27 (5)	16.50	50.50
	Set, never hinged	55.00	

Surtax for winter welfare. Designs are from frieze of the Artushof.

"Peter von Danzig" Yacht Race — SP19

Ships: 10pf+5pf, Dredger Fu Shing. 15pf+10pf, S. S. Columbus. 25pf+10pf, S. S. City of Danzig. 40pf+15pf, Peter von Danzig, 1472.

1938, Nov. 28   **Photo.**   **Unwmk.**
B28	SP19	5pf + 5pf dk bl grn	1.10	1.60
B29	SP19	10pf + 5pf gldn brn	1.40	3.00
B30	SP19	15pf + 10pf ol grn	1.60	3.00
B31	SP19	25pf + 10pf indigo	2.50	4.25
B32	SP19	40pf + 15pf vio brn	3.00	7.25
	Nos. B28-B32 (5)	9.60	19.10
	Set, never hinged	40.00	

Surtax for winter welfare.

AIR POST STAMPS

No. 6 Surcharged in Blue or Carmine

1920, Sept. 29   **Wmk. 125**   *Perf. 14*
C1	A16	40pf on 40pf	1.10	2.90
a.	Double surcharge		125.00	250.00
	Never hinged		340.00	
C2	A16	60pf on 40pf (C)	1.10	2.90
a.	Double surcharge		125.00	250.00
	Never hinged		340.00	
C3	A16	1m on 40pf	1.10	2.90
	Nos. C1-C3 (3)	3.30	8.70
	Set, never hinged	13.50	

Plane faces left on No. C2.

AP3

Plane over Danzig AP4

1921-22   **Typo.**   *Perf. 14*
C4	AP3	40(pf) blue green	.25	.45
C5	AP3	60(pf) dk violet	.25	.45
C6	AP3	1m carmine	.25	.45
C7	AP3	2m org brn	.25	.45

Serrate Roulette 13½
Size: 34½x23mm
C8	AP4	5m violet blue	1.25	2.25
C9	AP4	10m dp grn	2.00	4.50
	Nos. C4-C9 (6)	4.25	8.55
	Set, never hinged	18.00	

Nos. C4-C9 exist imperf. Value, each $32.50 unused, $125 never hinged.

1923   **Wmk. (109) Upright**   *Perf. 14*
C10	AP3	40(pf) blue green	.40	2.10
C11	AP3	60(pf) dk violet	.40	2.10
a.	Double impression		—	
C12	AP3	1m carmine	.40	2.10
C13	AP3	2m org brown	.40	2.10
C14	AP3	25m pale blue	.30	.60

Serrate Roulette 13½
Size: 34½x23mm
C15	AP4	5m violet blue	.40	1.00
C16	AP4	10m deep green	.40	1.00

Paper With Gray Network
C17	AP4	20m org brn	.40	1.00

Size: 40x23mm
C18	AP4	50m orange	.30	.60
C19	AP4	100m red	.30	.60
C20	AP4	250m dark brown	.30	.60
C21	AP4	500m car rose	.30	.60
	Nos. C10-C21 (12)	4.30	14.40
	Set, never hinged	17.00	

Nos. C11, C12, C14-C21 exist imperf. Value, Nos. C11, C12, C15-C17, each $8.50 unused, $32.50 never hinged. Value, No. C14, C18-C21, each $40 unused, $125 never hinged.

Nos. C18, C19 and C21 exist with wmk. sideways, both perf and imperf. Value each, $60 unused, $160 never hinged.

Post Horn and Airplanes — AP5

1923, Oct. 18   *Perf. 14*
Paper Without Network
C22	AP5	250,000m scarlet	.25	1.25
C23	AP5	500,000m scarlet	.25	1.25

Exist imperf. Value, each: $50 unused; $125 never hinged.

Surcharged

On 100,000m
C24	AP5	2mil m scarlet	.25	1.25

On 50,000m
C25	AP5	5mil m scarlet	.25	1.25
b.	Cliché of 10,000m in sheet of 50,000m	32.50	160.00
	Never hinged	110.00	

Exist imperf. Value, each $125 unused, $290 never hinged.

Nos. C24 and C25 were not regularly issued without surcharge, although copies have been passed through the post. Values: C24 unused $8.50, never hinged $32.50; C25 unused $12, never hinged $21.

AP6   Plane over Danzig — AP7

1924
C26	AP6	10(pf) vermilion	22.50	3.75
C27	AP6	20(pf) carmine rose	2.10	1.50
C28	AP6	40(pf) olive brown	3.00	12.00
C29	AP6	1g deep green	3.00	3.00
C30	AP7	2½g violet brown	17.50	35.00
	Nos. C26-C30 (5)	48.10	55.25
	Set, never hinged	165.00	

Exist imperf. Value #C26, C30, $85 unused, $200 never hinged; others, each $40 unused, $110 never hinged.

Nos. 193, 195, 197-199 Surcharged in Various Colors

1932   **Wmk. 125**
C31	A20	10pf on 1g (G)	8.50	23.00
C32	A20	15pf on 2g (V)	8.50	23.00
C33	A20	20pf on 3g (Bl)	8.50	23.00
C34	A23	25pf on 5g (R)	8.50	23.00
C35	A24	30pf on 10g (Br)	8.50	23.00
	Nos. C31-C35 (5)	42.50	115.00
	Set, never hinged	200.00	

Intl. Air Post Exhib. of 1932. The surcharges were variously arranged to suit the shapes and designs of the stamps. The stamps were sold at double their surcharged values, the excess being donated to the exhibition funds.

No. C31 exists with inverted surcharge and with double surcharge. Value each, $85 unused, $210 never hinged.

Airplane
AP8   AP9

1935, Oct. 24   **Wmk. 109**
C36	AP8	10pf scarlet	1.60	.85
C37	AP8	15pf yellow	1.60	1.25
C38	AP8	25pf dark green	1.60	1.60
C39	AP8	50pf gray blue	8.00	10.00
C40	AP9	1g magenta	3.25	13.50
	Nos. C36-C40 (5)	16.05	27.20
	Set, never hinged	59.50	

Nos. C36 and C40 exist imperf. Values: C36 unused $20, never hinged $62.50; C40 unused $29, never hinged $85.
See Nos. C42-C45.

Souvenir Sheet

St. Mary's Church — AP10

1937, June 6   *Perf. 14*
C41 AP10 50pf dark grayish
               blue   3.50   21.00
      Never hinged   10.50

Danzig Phil. Exhib., June 6-8, 1937.

Type of 1935

1938-39   **Wmk. 237**
C42 AP8 10pf scarlet   1.25   4.25
C43 AP8 15pf yellow ('39)   2.25   13.00
C44 AP8 25pf dark green   1.60   7.25
C45 AP8 50pf gray blue ('39)   4.25   62.50
      Nos. C42-C45 (4)   9.35   87.00
      Set, never hinged   38.75

POSTAGE DUE STAMPS

Danzig Coat of Arms
        D1   D2

1921-22 Typo. Wmk. (108) *Perf. 14*
Paper Without Network
J1 D1 10(pf) deep violet   .25   .50
J2 D1 20(pf) deep violet   .25   .50
J3 D1 40(pf) deep violet   .25   .50
J4 D1 60(pf) deep violet   .25   .50
J5 D1 75(pf) dp violet ('22)   .25   .50
J6 D1 80(pf) deep violet   .25   .50
J7 D1 120(pf) deep violet   .25   .50
J8 D1 200(pf) dp violet ('22)   .85   1.10
J9 D1 240(pf) deep violet   .25   1.10
J10 D1 300(pf) dp violet ('22)   .85   1.10
J11 D1 400(pf) deep violet   .85   1.10
J12 D1 500(pf) deep violet   .85   1.10
J13 D1 800(pf) deep violet
                       ('22)   .85   1.10
J14 D1 20m dp violet ('22)   .85   1.10
      Nos. J1-J14 (14)   7.10 11.20
      Set, never hinged   27.50

Nos. J1-J14 exist imperf. Value, each $30
unused, $75 never hinged.

1923   **Wmk. 109 Sideways**
J15 D1 100(pf) deep violet   .65   .85
J16 D1 200(pf) deep violet   2.50   4.25
J17 D1 300(pf) deep violet   .65   .85
J18 D1 400(pf) deep violet   .65   .85
J19 D1 500(pf) deep violet   .65   .85
J20 D1 800(pf) deep violet   1.40   4.25
J21 D1 10m deep violet   .65   1.10
J22 D1 20m deep violet   .65   .85
J23 D1 50m deep violet   .65   .85
Paper With Gray Network
J24 D1 100m deep violet   .65   1.10
J25 D1 500m deep violet   .65   1.10
      Nos. J15-J25 (11)   9.75 16.90
      Set, never hinged   38.50

Nos. J15, J17, J22-J25 exist imperf. Value
each, $12.50 unused, $40 never hinged.

Nos. J22-J23 and Type
of 1923 Surcharged

1923, Oct. 1
Paper without Network
J26 D1   5000m on 50m   .40   .85
J27 D1 10,000m on 20m   .40   .85
J28 D1 50,000m on 500m   .40   .85
J29 D1 100,000m on 20m   .85   1.25
      Nos. J26-J29 (4)   2.05   3.80
      Set, never hinged   8.50

On No. J26 the numerals of the surcharge
are all of the larger size.
A 1000(m) on 100m deep violet was prepared but not issued. Value, $145, never
hinged $350.
Nos. J26-J28 exist imperf. Value each, $18
unused, $45 never hinged.

1923-28   **Wmk. 110**
J30 D2   5(pf) blue &
                       blk   .85   .85
J31 D2 10(pf) blue &
                       blk   .40   .85
J32 D2 15(pf) blue &
                       blk   1.25   1.25
J33 D2 20(pf) blue &
                       blk   1.25   2.10
J34 D2 30(pf) blue &
                       blk   8.50   2.10
J35 D2 40(pf) blue &
                       blk   2.10   3.25
J36 D2 50(pf) blue &
                       blk   2.10   2.50
J37 D2 60(pf) blue &
                       blk   13.00 20.00
J38 D2 100(pf) blue &
                       blk   16.50 11.00
J39 D2   3g blue &
                       car   7.50 45.00
    a. "Guldeu" instead of
        "Gulden"   325.00 1,050.
        Never hinged   1,050.
      Nos. J30-J39 (10)   53.45 88.90
      Set, never hinged   180.00

Used values of Nos. J30-J39 are for
postally used stamps.
See Nos. J43-J47.

Postage Due Stamps
of 1923 Issue
Surcharged in Red

1932, Dec. 20
J40 D2 5pf on 40(pf)   2.50   7.50
J41 D2 10pf on 60(pf)   30.00 10.00
J42 D2 20pf on 100(pf)   2.50   7.50
      Nos. J40-J42 (3) 35.00 25.00
      Set, never hinged 133.00

Type of 1923

1938-39   **Wmk. 237**   *Perf. 14*
J43 D2 10(pf) bl & blk
                  ('39)   1.25 62.50
J44 D2 30(pf) bl & blk
                          2.10 50.00
J45 D2 40(pf) bl & blk
                  ('39)   6.25 100.00
J46 D2 60(pf) bl & blk
                  ('39)   6.25 100.00
J47 D2 100(pf) bl & blk   10.00 72.50
      Nos. J43-J47 (5) 25.85 385.00
      Set, never hinged 120.00

OFFICIAL STAMPS

Regular Issues of 1921-22 Overprinted

                          a

1921-22   Wmk. 108   *Perf. 14x14½*
O1 A11   5(pf) orange   .25   .20
O2 A11 10(pf) dark brown   .25   .20
    a. Inverted overprint   60.00
        Never hinged   170.00
O3 A11 15(pf) green   .25   .20
O4 A11 20(pf) slate   .25   .20
O5 A11 25(pf) dark green   .25   .20
O6 A11 30(pf) blue & car   .60   .60
O7 A11 40(pf) grn & car   .25   .20
O8 A11 50(pf) dk grn &
                       car   .25   .20
O9 A11 60(pf) carmine   .25   .20
O10 A11 75(pf) dp vio   .20   .40
O11 A11 80(pf) black & car   .85   .85
O12 A11 80(pf) green   .25   2.50

Paper With Faint Gray Network
O14 A11   1m org & car   .25   .20
O15 A11 1.20m blue violet 1.25   1.25
O16 A11 1.25m vio & car   .20   .40
O17 A11 1.50m slate gray .20   .40
O18 A11   2m gray & car   14.00 12.00
    a. Inverted overprint 110.00
        Never hinged   250.00
O19 A11   2m car rose   .20   .40
O20 A11 2.40m dk brn &
                    car   1.25   2.50
O21 A11   3m violet & car 8.50 12.00
O22 A11   3m car lake   .20   .40
O23 A11   4m dk blue   1.25   .85
O24 A11   5m dp grn   .20   .40
O25 A11   6m car lake   .20   .40
O26 A11 10m orange   .20   .40
O27 A11 20m org brn   .20   .40
      Nos. O1-O27 (26) 32.00 37.95
      Set, never hinged 140.00

Double overprints exist on Nos. O1-O2, O5-
O7, O10 and O12.

Same Overprint on No. 96
O28 A11   6m on 3m   .20   .75
      Never hinged   .90
    a. Inverted overprint 30.00
        Never hinged   85.00

No. 77
Overprinted

Serrate Roulette 13½
1922   **Wmk. 108 Sideways**
O29 A12 5m grn, red & blk 4.00 11.00
        Never hinged   18.00

Nos. 99-103, 106-107 Overprinted
Type "a"

1922-23   Wmk. 109   *Perf. 14*
O30 A11   4m dark blue   .25   .50
O31 A11   5m dark
                    green   .25   .50
O32 A11 10m orange   .25   .50
O33 A11 20m orange
                    brn   .25   .50
O34 A15 50m pale blue
                    & red   .25   .50
O35 A15a 100m dk grn &
                    red   .25   .50

Nos. 113-115, 118-120 Overprinted
Type "a"
O36 A15 50m pale blue   .25   .50
    a. Inverted overprint 25.00
        Never hinged   62.50
O37 A15a 100m dark
                    green   .25   .50
O38 A15 200m orange   .25   .50
    a. Inverted overprint 25.00
        Never hinged   62.50

Paper With Gray Network
O39 A17 300m bl grn &
                    red   .25   .50
O40 A17 500m gray & red   .25   .50
O41 A17 1000m brn & red   .25   .50
      Nos. O30-O41 (12) 3.00   6.00
      Set, never hinged   16.80

Regular Issue of 1924-
25 Overprinted

1924-25   *Perf. 14x14½*
O42 A19 5pf red orange   2.10   3.25
O43 A19 10pf green   6.00   9.00
O44 A19 15pf gray   2.10   3.25
O45 A19 15pf red   18.00 10.00
O46 A19 20pf car & red   2.10   2.10
O47 A19 25pf slate & red 18.00 27.50
O48 A19 30pf green & red   3.00   3.75
O49 A19 35pf ultra   42.50 50.00
O50 A19 40pf dk bl & dull bl 6.50 8.50
O51 A19 50pf dp blue & red 21.00 42.50
O52 A19 75pf violet & red 32.50 120.00
      Nos. O42-O52 (11) 153.80 279.85
      Set, never hinged 575.00

Double overprints exist on Nos. O42-O44,
O47, O50-O52.

DENMARK

'den-,märk

LOCATION — Northern part of a penin-
sula which separates the North and
Baltic Seas, and includes the sur-
rounding islands
GOVT. — Kingdom
AREA — 16,631 sq. mi.
POP. — 5,294,860 (1/1/1999)
CAPITAL — Copenhagen

96 Skilling = 1 Rigsbank Daler
100 Ore = 1 Krone (1875)

> Catalogue values for unused
> stamps in this country are for
> Never Hinged items, beginning
> with Scott 297 in the regular post-
> age section, Scott B15 in the semi-
> postal section, and Scott Q28 in
> the parcel post section.

Values for unused stamps are for
examples with original gum as defined
in the catalogue introduction. Very fine
examples of Nos. 9-37 and O1-O9 will
have perforations clear of the framelines but with the design noticeably off
center. Well centered stamps are quite
scarce and will command substantial
premiums.

Watermarks

Wmk. 111 —   Wmk. 112 —
Small Crown   Crown

Wmk. 113 —   Wmk. 114 —
Crown   Multiple Crosses

                              A1

Royal Emblems — A2

1851   Typo.   Wmk. 111   *Imperf.*
With Yellow Brown Burelage
1   A1 2rs blue   3,000. 2,250.
    a. First printing   8,250. 2,250.
2   A2 4rs brown   500.00 40.00
    a. First printing   600.00 65.00
    b. 4rs yellow brown 875.00 55.00

The first printing of Nos. 1 and 2 had the
burelage printed from a copper plate, giving a
clear impression with the lines in slight relief.
The subsequent impressions had the burelage
typographed, with the lines fainter and not rising above the surface of the paper.
Nos. 1-2 were reprinted in 1885 and 1901
on heavy yellowish paper, unwatermarked and
imperforate, with a brown burelage. No. 1 was
also reprinted without burelage, on both yellowish and white paper. Value for least costly
reprint of No. 1, $50.
No. 2 was reprinted in 1951 in 10 shades
with "Colour Specimen 1951" printed on the
back. It was also reprinted in 1961 in 2 shades
without burelage and with "Farve Nytryk 1961"
printed on the back. Value for least costly
reprint of No. 2, $8.50.

Dotting in Spandrels
A3

Wavy Lines in Spandrels
A4

1854-57

3	A3	2s blue ('55)	75.00	60.00
4	A3	4s brown	325.00	15.00
a.		4s yellow brown	350.00	15.00
5	A3	8s green ('57)	300.00	67.50
a.		8s yellow green		72.50
6	A3	16s gray lilac ('57)	525.00	190.00
		Nos. 3-6 (4)	1,225.	332.50

See No. 10. For denominations in cents see Danish West Indies Nos. 1-4.

1858-62

7	A4	4s yellow brown	65.00	9.00
a.		4s brown	67.50	9.50
b.		Wmk. 112 ('62)	62.50	10.00
8	A4	8s green	800.00	95.00

Nos. 2 to 8 inclusive are known with unofficial perforation 12 or 13, and Nos. 4, 5, 7 and 8 with unofficial roulette 9½.

Nos. 3, 6-8 were reprinted in 1885 on heavy yellowish paper, unwatermarked, imperforate and without burelage. Nos. 4-5 were reprinted in 1924 on white paper, unwatermarked, imperforate, gummed and without burelage. Value for No. 3, $15; Nos. 4-5, each $110; No. 6, $20; Nos. 7-8, each $15.

1863   Wmk. 112   Rouletted 11

9	A4	4s brown	100.00	15.00
a.		4s deep brown	100.00	15.00
10	A3	16s violet	1,400.	650.00

Royal Emblems — A5

1864-68   Perf. 13

11	A5	2s blue ('65)	65.00	35.00
12	A5	3s red vio ('65)	80.00	75.00
13	A5	4s red	40.00	8.00
14	A5	8s bister ('68)	275.00	95.00
15	A5	16s olive green	475.00	175.00
		Nos. 11-15 (5)	935.00	388.00

Nos. 11-15 were reprinted in 1886 on heavy yellowish paper, unwatermarked, imperforate and without gum. The reprints of all values except the 4s were printed in two vertical rows of six, inverted with respect to each other, so that horizontal pairs are always tête bêche. Value $12 each.

Nos. 13 and 15 were reprinted in 1942 with printing on the back across each horizontal row: "Nytryk 1942. G. A. Hagemann: Danmarks og Vestindiens Frimaerker, Bind 2." Value, $70 each.

Imperf, single

11a	A5	2s blue	95.00	95.00
12a	A5	3s red violet	140.00	
13a	A5	4s red	77.50	90.00
14a	A5	8s bister	375.00	
15a	A5	16s olive green	450.00	

1870   Perf. 12½

11b	A5	2s blue	275.00	350.00
12b	A5	3s red violet	475.00	650.00
14b	A5	8s bister	475.00	475.00
15b	A5	16s olive green	725.00	1,450.
		Nos. 11b-15b (4)	1,950.	2,925.

A6

NORMAL FRAME

INVERTED FRAME

The arabesques in the corners have a main stem and a branch. When the frame is in normal position, in the upper left corner the branch leaves the main stem half way between two little leaflets. In the lower right corner the branch starts at the foot of the second leaflet. When the frame is inverted the corner designs are, of course, transposed.

1870-71   Wmk. 112   Perf. 14x13½
Paper Varying from Thin to Thick

16	A6	2s gray & ultra ('71)	70.00	27.50
a.		2s gray & blue	70.00	27.50
17	A6	3s gray & brt lil ('71)	100.00	110.00
18	A6	4s gray & car	40.00	10.00
19	A6	8s gray & brn ('71)	200.00	75.00
20	A6	16s gray & grn ('71)	275.00	175.00

Perf. 12½

21	A6	2s gray & bl ('71)	2,000.	3,250.
22	A6	4s gray & car	150.00	125.00
24	A6	48s brn & lilac	450.00	275.00

Nos. 16-20, 24 were reprinted in 1886 on thin white paper, unwatermarked, imperforate and without gum. These were printed in sheets of 10 in which 1 stamp has the normal frame (value $32.50 each) and 9 the inverted (value $11 each).

Imperf, single

16b	A6	2s	250.
17a	A6	3s	240.
18a	A6	4s	200.
19a	A6	8s	250.
20a	A6	16s	400.
24a	A6	48s	425.

Inverted Frame

16c	A6	2s	1,000.	775.
17b	A6	3s	2,500.	2,000.
18b	A6	4s	775.	87.50
19b	A6	8s	1,750.	900.
20b	A6	16s	2,000.	1,750.
24b	A6	48s	2,750.	1,900.

1875-79   Perf. 14x13½

25	A6	3o gray blue & gray	18.00	15.00
a.		1st "A" of "DANMARK" missing	60.00	150.00
b.		Imperf	750.00	
c.		Inverted frame	18.00	16.00
26	A6	4o slate & blue	25.00	.50
a.		4o gray & blue	25.00	1.10
b.		4o slate & ultra	90.00	17.00
c.		4o gray & ultra	75.00	16.00
d.		Imperf	75.00	
e.		As #26, inverted frame	25.00	.50
27	A6	5o rose & blue ('79)	30.00	72.50
a.		Ball of lower curve of large "5" missing	125.00	300.00
b.		Inverted frame	1,000.	2,250.
28	A6	8o slate & car	22.50	.50
a.		8o gray & carmine	75.00	5.00
b.		Imperf	150.00	—
c.		Inverted frame	22.50	.50
29	A6	12o sl & dull lake	10.00	4.00
a.		12o gray & bright lilac	65.00	8.00
b.		12o gray & dull magenta	72.50	10.00
c.		Inverted frame	14.00	4.00
30	A6	16o slate & brn	40.00	3.50
a.		16o light gray & brown	70.00	5.00
b.		Inverted frame	32.50	4.25
31	A6	20o rose & gray	90.00	32.50
a.		20o carmine & gray	90.00	32.50
b.		Inverted frame	90.00	32.50
32	A6	25o gray & green	65.00	40.00
		On parcel post receipt card		240.00
a.		Inverted frame	77.50	62.50
33	A6	50o brown & vio	70.00	37.50
		On parcel post receipt card		190.00
a.		50o brown & blue violet	400.00	175.00
b.		Inverted frame	70.00	32.50
34	A6	100o gray & org ('77)	110.00	60.00
		On parcel post receipt card		300.00
a.		Imperf, single	375.00	
b.		Inverted frame	150.00	60.00
		Nos. 25-34 (10)	480.50	266.00
		Set, never hinged	1,625.	

The stamps of this issue on thin semi-transparent paper are far scarcer than those on thicker paper.

See Nos. 41-42, 44, 46-47, 50-52. For surcharges see Nos. 55, 79-80, 136.

Arms — A7

Two types of numerals in corners:

Small Numerals

Large Numerals

1882
Small Corner Numerals

35	A7	5o green	240.00	100.00
		Never hinged	725.00	
37	A7	20o blue	190.00	70.00
		Never hinged	650.00	

1884-88
Larger Corner Numerals

38	A7	5o green	15.00	3.50
a.		Imperf		
39	A7	10o carmine ('85)	16.00	2.50
a.		Small numerals in corners ('88)	550.00	725.00
b.		Imperf, single	175.00	
c.		Pair, Nos. 39, 39a	600.00	875.00
40	A7	20o blue	30.00	5.00
a.		Pair, Nos. 37, 40	400.00	875.00
b.		Imperf		
		Nos. 38-40 (3)	61.00	11.00
		Set, never hinged	285.00	

Stamps with large corner numerals have white line around crown and lower oval touches frame.

The plate for No. 39, was damaged and 3 clichés in the bottom row were replaced by clichés for post cards, which had small numerals in the corners.

Two clichés with small numerals were inserted in the plate of No. 40.

See Nos. 43, 45, 48-49, 53-54. For surcharge see No. 56.

1895-1901   Wmk. 112   Perf. 13

41	A6	3o blue & gray	10.00	7.25
42	A6	4o slate & bl ('96)	4.50	.40
43	A7	5o green	12.00	.75
44	A6	8o slate & car	4.50	.45
45	A7	10o rose car	24.00	.65
46	A6	12o sl & dull lake	7.00	4.00
47	A6	16o slate & brown	19.00	4.50
48	A7	20o blue	30.00	2.40
49	A6	24o brown ('01)	7.00	6.00
50	A6	25o gray & grn ('98)	110.00	19.50
51	A6	50o brown & vio ('97)	60.00	24.00
52	A6	100o slate & org	90.00	35.00
		Nos. 41-52 (12)	378.00	104.90
		Set, never hinged	875.00	

Inverted Frame

41b	A6	3o	12.00	7.00
42a	A6	4o	4.50	.45
44a	A6	8o	4.50	.50
46a	A6	12o	14.00	4.50
47a	A6	16o	30.00	5.00
50a	A6	25o	60.00	27.50

51a	A6	50o	95.00	32.50
52a	A6	100o	90.00	57.50
		Nos. 41b-52a (8)	310.00	134.95
		Set, never hinged	635.00	

1902-04   Wmk. 113

41c	A6	3o blue & gray	2.75	3.00
42b	A6	4o slate & blue	17.00	20.00
43a	A7	5o green	2.00	.25
44d	A6	8o slate & carmine	525.00	425.00
45a	A7	10o rose carmine	3.00	.25
48a	A7	20o blue	20.00	4.75
50b	A6	25o gray & green	10.50	4.50
51b	A6	50o brown & violet	27.50	20.00
52b	A6	100o slate & orange	30.00	15.00
		Nos. 41c-52b (9)	637.75	492.75
		Set, never hinged	1,325.	

Inverted Frame

41d	A6	3o	75.00	130.00
42c	A6	4o	140.00	130.00
50c	A6	25o	210.00	60.00
51c	A6	50o	260.00	240.00
52c	A6	100o	225.00	240.00
		Nos. 41d-52c (5)	910.00	800.00
		Set, never hinged	2,500.	

1902   Wmk. 113

53	A7	1o orange	.75	.65
a.		Imperf		
54	A7	15o lilac	11.00	.75
a.		Imperf, single		4,250.

Nos. 44d, 44, 49 Surcharged:

a   b

1904-12   Wmk. 113

55	A6(a)	4o on 8o sl & car	3.50	4.00
a.		Wmk. 112 ('12)	21.00	60.00
		Never hinged	42.50	—
b.		As "a," inverted frame		6,000.

Wmk. 112

56	A7(b)	15o on 24o brown	5.75	17.50
a.		Short "15" at right	27.50	105.00
		Never hinged	60.00	
		Set, never hinged	16.00	

A10

King Christian IX
A11

King Frederik VIII
A12

1905-17   Wmk. 113   Perf. 13

57	A10	1o orange ('06)	2.00	.90
58	A10	2o carmine	4.00	.65
a.		Perf. 14x14½ ('17)	3.25	16.00
59	A10	3o gray	7.75	.65
60	A10	4o dull blue	10.00	1.00
a.		Perf. 14x14½ ('17)	9.75	37.50
61	A10	5o dp green ('12)	4.00	.50
62	A10	10o dp rose ('12)	5.25	.30
63	A10	15o lilac	19.00	2.50
64	A10	20o dk blue ('12)	35.00	.90
		Nos. 57-64 (8)	87.00	7.40
		Set, never hinged	240.00	

The three wavy lines in design A10 are symbolical of the three waters which separate the principal Danish islands.

See Nos. 85-96, 1338-1342A. For surcharges and overprints see Nos. 163, 181, J1, J38, Q1-Q2.

1904-05   Engr.

65	A11	10o scarlet	2.75	.65
66	A11	20o blue	20.00	2.50
67	A11	25o brown ('05)	24.00	7.00
68	A11	50o dull vio ('05)	100.00	120.00
69	A11	100o ocher ('05)	13.00	60.00
		Nos. 65-69 (5)	159.75	190.15
		Set, never hinged	435.00	

1905-06   Re-engraved

70	A11	5o green	4.00	.50
71	A11	10o scarlet ('06)	14.00	.55
		Set, never hinged	44.00	

The re-engraved stamps are much clearer than the originals, and the decoration on the king's left breast has been removed.

1907-12

72	A12	5o green	1.25	.40
a.		Imperf.	—	
73	A12	10o red	3.25	.30
a.		Imperf.	—	
74	A12	20o indigo	14.00	.65
a.		20o bright blue ('11)	14.00	2.50
75	A12	25o olive brn	27.50	1.25
76	A12	35o dp org ('12)	6.00	7.00
77	A12	50o claret	32.50	6.75
78	A12	100o bister brn	90.00	5.00
		Nos. 72-78 (7)	174.50	21.35
		Set, never hinged	450.00	

Nos. 47, 31 and O9 Surcharged:

c   d

Dark Blue Surcharge

1912		**Wmk. 112**		**Perf. 13**
79	A6(c)	35o on 16o	14.00	65.00
a.		Inverted frame	250.00	500.00
			Perf. 14x13½	
80	A6(c)	35o on 20o	30.00	80.00
a.		Inverted frame	115.00	275.00

Black Surcharge

81	O1(d)	35o on 32o	42.50	120.00
		Nos. 79-81 (3)	86.50	265.00
		Set, never hinged	180.00	

General Post Office,
Copenhagen — A15

1912   Engr.   Wmk. 113   Perf. 13

82	A15	5k dark red	425.00	175.00
		Never hinged	1,300.	

See Nos. 135, 843.

Perf. 14x14½

1913-30		**Typo.**		**Wmk. 114**
85	A10	1o dp orange ('14)	.30	.25
a.		Bklt. pane, 2 ea #85, 91 + 2 labels	20.00	
86	A10	2o car ('13)	3.25	.50
a.		Imperf	125.00	250.00
b.		Booklet pane, 4 + 2 labels	27.50	
87	A10	3o gray ('13)	5.25	.50
88	A10	4o blue ('13)	6.50	.65
a.		Half used as 2o on cover		1,250.
89	A10	5o dk brown ('21)	.65	.50
a.		Imperf	175.00	
b.		Booklet pane, 4 + 2 labels	14.00	
90	A10	5o lt green ('30)	1.40	.50
a.		Booklet pane, 4 + 2 labels	16.00	
b.		Booklet pane of 50		
91	A10	7o apple grn ('26)	5.00	7.75
a.		Booklet pane, 4 + 2 labels	20.00	
92	A10	7o dk violet ('30)	14.00	6.50
93	A10	8o gray ('21)	7.00	3.25
94	A10	10o green ('21)	.85	.50
a.		Imperf	200.00	
b.		Booklet pane, 4 + 2 labels	37.50	
95	A10	10o bister brn ('30)	2.00	.50
a.		Booklet pane, 4 + 2 labels	16.00	
b.		Booklet pane of 50		
96	A10	12o violet ('26)	22.50	9.75
		Nos. 85-96 (12)	68.70	31.15
		Set, never hinged	160.00	

No. 88a was used with No. 97 in Faroe Islands, Jan. 3-23, 1919.
See surcharge and overprint note following No. 64.

King Christian X
A16   A17

1913-28   Typo.   Perf. 14x14½

97	A16	5o green	1.10	.50
a.		Booklet pane of 4	11.00	
98	A16	7o orange ('18)	2.25	2.50
99	A16	8o dk gray ('20)	9.75	6.50
100	A16	10o red	1.50	.25
a.		Imperf	200.00	
b.		Booklet pane of 4	11.00	
101	A16	12o gray grn ('18)	6.50	10.00
102	A16	15o violet	2.00	.30
103	A16	20o dp blue	11.50	.50
104	A16	20o brown ('21)	1.00	.25
105	A16	20o red ('26)	1.25	.50
106	A16	25o dk brown	11.50	.50
107	A16	25o brn & blk ('20)	75.00	8.00
108	A16	25o red ('22)	3.25	2.00
109	A16	25o yel grn ('25)	3.00	.50
110	A16	27o ver & blk ('18)	27.50	65.00
111	A16	30o green & blk ('18)	35.00	3.25
112	A16	30o orange ('21)	2.50	2.50
113	A16	30o dk blue ('25)	1.50	1.00
114	A16	35o orange	20.00	7.00
115	A16	35o yel & blk ('19)	7.50	7.25
116	A16	40o vio & blk ('18)	15.00	4.50
117	A16	40o gray bl & blk ('20)	32.50	8.50
118	A16	40o dk blue ('22)	4.50	1.60
119	A16	40o orange ('25)	1.50	2.00
120	A16	50o claret	32.50	5.75
121	A16	50o claret & blk ('19)	57.50	2.00
122	A16	50o lt gray ('22)	7.75	.50
a.		50o olive gray ('21)	65.00	7.75
		Never hinged	175.00	
123	A16	60o brn & bl ('19)	52.50	6.50
a.		60o brown & ultra ('19)	190.00	19.00
		Never hinged	650.00	
124	A16	60o grn bl ('21)	8.00	1.00
125	A16	70o brn & grn ('20)	20.00	4.50
126	A16	80o bl grn ('15)	40.00	20.00
127	A16	90o brn & red ('20)	15.00	5.25
128	A16	1k brn & blk ('22)	45.00	5.00
129	A16	2k gray & cl ('25)	57.50	26.00
130	A16	5k vio & brn ('27)	5.25	7.75
131	A16	10k ver & yel grn ('28)	250.00	55.00
		Nos. 97-131 (35)	868.10	271.65
		Set, never hinged	2,350.	

No. 97 surcharged "2 ORE" is Faroe Islands No. 1.

Nos. 87 and 98, 89 and 94, 89 and 104, 90 and 95, 97 and 103, 100 and 102 exist setenant in coils for use in vending machines.

For surcharges and overprints see Nos. 161-162, 176-177, 182-184, J2-J8, M1-M2, Q3-Q10.

1913-20   Engr.

132	A17	1k yellow brown	77.50	1.25
133	A17	2k gray	110.00	7.00
134	A17	5k purple ('20)	13.00	10.00
		Nos. 132-134 (3)	200.50	18.25
		Set, never hinged	807.50	

For overprint see No. Q11.

G.P.O. Type of 1912
Perf. 14x14½

1915		**Wmk. 114**		**Engr.**
135	A15	5k dark red ('15)	425.00	175.00
		Never hinged	1,300.	

Nos. 46 and O10 Surcharged in Black type "c" and:

e

No. 87 Surcharged

Newspaper Stamps Surcharged

On Issue of 1907

1918		**Wmk. 113**		**Perf. 13**
138	N1	27o on 1o olive	90.00	250.00
139	N1	27o on 5o blue	90.00	250.00
140	N1	27o on 7o car	90.00	250.00
141	N1	27o on 10o dp lil	90.00	250.00
142	N1	27o on 68o yel brn	7.00	35.00
143	N1	27o on 5k rose & yel grn	5.75	22.50
144	N1	27o on 10k bis & bl	7.00	30.00
		Nos. 138-144 (7)	379.75	1,087.
		Set, never hinged	750.00	

On Issue of 1914-15
Wmk. Multiple Crosses (114)
Perf. 14x14½

145	N1	27o on 1o ol gray	3.25	14.50
146	N1	27o on 5o blue	8.00	26.00
147	N1	27o on 7o rose	3.25	9.75
148	N1	27o on 8o green	5.00	15.50
149	N1	27o on 10o dp lil	3.25	12.00
150	N1	27o on 20o green	4.50	13.00
151	N1	27o on 29o org yel	3.25	12.00
152	N1	27o on 38o orange	32.50	97.50
153	N1	27o on 41o ver ('18)	8.00	50.00
154	N1	27o on 1k bl grn & mar	3.25	13.00
		Nos. 145-154 (10)	74.25	263.25
		Set, never hinged	110.00	

Kronborg Castle — A20   Sonderborg Castle — A21

Roskilde Cathedral — A22

Perf. 14½x14, 14x14½

1920, Oct. 5				**Typo.**
156	A20	10o red	3.75	.35
157	A21	20o slate	3.00	.50
158	A22	40o dark brown	12.50	4.50
		Nos. 156-158 (3)	19.25	5.35
		Set, never hinged	35.00	

Reunion of Northern Schleswig with Denmark.
See Nos. 159-160. For surcharges see Nos. B1-B2.

1921

159	A20	10o green	7.75	.50
160	A22	40o dark blue	57.50	13.00
		Set, never hinged	155.00	

Stamps of 1918 Surcharged in Blue

1921-22

161	A16	8o on 7o org ('22)	2.00	5.00
162	A16	8o on 12o gray grn	2.00	15.00
		Set, never hinged	13.50	

No. 87 Surcharged

1921

163	A10	8o on 3o gray	3.75	5.25
		Never hinged	7.50	

Christian X
A23

Christian IV
A24

A25

A26

1924, Dec. 1   Perf. 14x14½

164	A23	10o green	7.00	7.75
165	A24	10o green	7.00	7.75
166	A25	10o green	7.00	7.75
167	A26	10o green	7.00	7.75
a.		Block of 4, #164-167	37.50	60.00
168	A23	15o violet	7.00	7.75
169	A24	15o violet	7.00	7.75
170	A25	15o violet	7.00	7.75
171	A26	15o violet	7.00	7.75
a.		Block of 4, #168-171	37.50	60.00
172	A23	20o dark brown	7.00	7.75
173	A24	20o dark brown	7.00	7.75
174	A25	20o dark brown	7.00	7.75
175	A26	20o dark brown	7.00	7.75
a.		Block of 4, #172-175	37.50	60.00
		Nos. 164-175 (12)	84.00	93.00
		Set, never hinged	168.00	

#167a, 171a, 175a, never hinged   225.00

300th anniv. of the Danish postal service.

Stamps of 1921-22 Surcharged:

k   l

1926

176	A16	(k) 20o on 30o org	4.75	16.00
177	A16	(l) 20o on 40o dk bl	7.50	18.00
		Set, never hinged	22.50	

A27   A28

1926, Mar. 11   Perf. 14x14½

178	A27	10o dull green	1.10	.45
179	A28	20o dark red	1.50	.45
180	A28	30o dark blue	7.00	2.00
		Nos. 178-180 (3)	9.60	2.90
		Set, never hinged	19.00	

75th anniv. of the introduction of postage stamps in Denmark.

Stamps of 1913-26 Surcharged in Blue or Black

No. 181 | Nos. 182-184

1926-27   *Perf. 14x14½*

181	A10	7o on 8o gray (Bl)	1.40	5.75
182	A16	7o on 27o ver & blk	4.25	15.00
183	A16	7o on 20o red ('27)	.65	2.00
184	A16	12o on 15o violet	2.75	7.75

Surcharged on Official Stamps of 1914-23

185	O1 (e)	7o on 1o org	4.00	16.00
186	O1 (e)	7o on 3o gray	7.75	29.00
187	O1 (e)	7o on 4o blue	3.25	14.00
188	O1 (e)	7o on 5o grn	52.50	125.00
189	O1 (e)	7o on 10o grn	4.00	15.50
190	O1 (e)	7o on 15o vio	4.00	15.50
191	O1 (e)	7o on 20o ind	19.00	77.50
a.		Double surcharge	650.00	850.00
		Nos. 181-191 (11)	103.55	323.00
		Set, never hinged	155.00	

Caravel A30 | Christian X A31

1927   *Typo.*   *Perf. 14x14½*

192	A30	15o red	5.75	.25
193	A30	20o gray	10.50	2.25
194	A30	25o light blue	1.10	.40
195	A30	30o ocher	1.25	.40
196	A30	35o red brown	20.00	1.50
197	A30	40o yel green	19.00	.40
		Nos. 192-197 (6)	57.60	5.25
		Set, never hinged	170.00	

See Nos. 232-238J. For surcharges & overprints see Nos. 244-245, 269-272, Q12-Q14, Q19-Q25.

1930, Sept. 26

210	A31	5o apple grn	2.25	.25
a.		Booklet pane, 4 + 2 labels	18.00	
211	A31	7o violet	6.50	4.00
212	A31	8o dk gray	22.50	32.50
213	A31	10o yel brn	4.25	.25
a.		Booklet pane, 4 + 2 labels	29.00	
214	A31	15o red	9.50	.25
215	A31	20o lt gray	25.00	9.75
216	A31	25o lt blue	8.25	1.25
217	A31	30o yel buff	8.75	1.75
218	A31	35o red brown	11.00	4.50
219	A31	40o dp green	9.50	1.25
		Nos. 210-219 (10)	107.50	55.75
		Set, never hinged	280.00	

60th birthday of King Christian X.

Wavy Lines and Numeral of Value — A32

Type A10 Redrawn

1933-40   *Unwmk.*   *Engr.*   *Perf. 13*

220	A32	1o gray blk	.20	.20
221	A32	2o scarlet	.20	.20
222	A32	4o blue	.30	.25
223	A32	5o yel grn	1.00	.25
a.		5o gray green	32.50	65.00
b.		Tête bêche gutter pair	8.00	15.50
c.		Booklet pane of 4	11.00	
d.		Bklt. pane, 1 #223a, 3 #B6	37.50	
e.		As "b," without gutter	13.00	26.00
224	A32	5o rose lake ('38)	.20	.20
a.		Booklet pane of 4	.40	
b.		Booklet pane of 10	.90	
224C	A32	6o orange ('40)	.30	.25
225	A32	7o violet	2.00	.50
226	A32	7o yel grn ('38)	1.10	.75
226A	A32	7o lt brown ('40)	.25	.50
227	A32	8o gray	.45	.50
227A	A32	8o yellow grn ('40)	.25	.50
228	A32	10o orange org	10.00	.25
a.		Tête bêche gutter pair	35.00	52.50
b.		Booklet pane of 4	110.00	
c.		As "a," without gutter	40.00	65.00
		Never hinged	100.00	
229	A32	10o lt brown ('37)	9.50	.50
a.		Booklet pane of 4	100.00	
b.		Booklet pane of 4, 1 #229, 3 #B7	32.50	

230	A32	10o violet ('38)	.60	.25
a.		Booklet pane of 4	2.75	
b.		Bklt. pane, 2 #230, 2 #B10	4.50	
		Nos. 220-230 (14)	26.35	5.10
		Set, never hinged	50.00	

Design A10 was typographed. They had a solid background with groups of small hearts below the heraldic lions in the upper corners and below "DA" and "RK" of "DANMARK." The numerals of value were enclosed in single-lined ovals.

Design A32 is line-engraved and has a background of crossed lines. The hearts have been removed and the numerals of value are now in double-lined ovals. Two types exist of some values.

The 1ö, No. 220, was issued on fluorescent paper in 1969.

No. 230 with wide margins is from booklet pane No. 230b.

Surcharges on 20, 50 & 60öre on #220, 224 and 224C are listed as Faroe Islands #2-3, 5-6.

See Nos. 318, 333, 382, 416, 437-437A, 493-498, 629, 631, 688-695, 793-795, 883-886, 1111-1113, 1116. For overprints and surcharges see Nos. 257, 263, 267-268, 355-356, Q15-Q17, Q31, Q43.

Certain Tête Bêche

Pairs of 1938-55 issues which reached the market in 1971, and were not regularly issued, are not listed. This group comprises 24 different major-number vertical pairs of types A32, A47, A61 and SP3 (13 with gutters, 11 without), and pairs of some minor numbers and shades. They were removed from booklet pane sheets.

Type of 1927 Issue
Type I

Type I — Two columns of squares between sail and left frame line.

1933-34   *Engr.*   *Perf. 13*

232	A30	20o gray	13.50	.50
233	A30	25o blue	77.50	29.00
234	A30	25o brown ('34)	20.00	.25
235	A30	30o orange yel	1.25	1.60
236	A30	30o blue ('34)	1.00	.50
237	A30	35o violet	.50	.50
238	A30	40o yellow grn	5.00	.25
		Nos. 232-238 (7)	118.75	32.60
		Set, never hinged	265.00	

Type II

Type II — One column of squares between sail and left frame line.

1933-40

238A	A30	15o deep red	2.50	.50
k.		Booklet pane of 4	26.00	
l.		Bklt. pane, 1 #238A, 3 #B8	42.50	
238B	A30	15o yel grn ('40)	7.75	.25
238C	A30	20o gray blk ('39)	4.50	.65
238D	A30	20o red ('40)	.50	.25
238E	A30	25o dp brown ('39)	.80	.50
238F	A30	30o blue ('39)	2.00	.65
238G	A30	30o orange ('40)	.50	.50
238H	A30	35o violet ('40)	.90	.75
238I	A30	40o yel grn ('39)	13.00	.50
238J	A30	40o blue ('40)	1.00	.25
		Nos. 238A-238J (10)	33.45	4.80
		Set, never hinged	62.50	

Nos. 232-238J, engraved, have crosshatched background. Nos. 192-197, typographed, have solid background.

No. 238A surcharged 20 ore is listed as Faroe Islands No. 4.

See note on surcharges and overprints following No. 197.

King Christian X — A33

1934-41   *Perf. 13*

239	A33	50o gray	1.00	.25
240	A33	60o blue grn	2.10	.50
240A	A33	75o dk blue ('41)	.45	.50
241	A33	1k lt brown	3.25	.25
242	A33	2k dull red	6.00	1.00
243	A33	5k violet	8.00	3.25
		Nos. 239-243 (6)	20.80	5.75
		Set, never hinged	60.00	

For overprints see Nos. Q26-Q27.

Nos. 233, 235 Surcharged in Black

1934, June 9

244	A30	4o on 25o blue	.50	.50
245	A30	10o on 30o org yel	2.00	3.25
		Set, never hinged	6.25	

"The Ugly Duckling" A34 | Andersen A35

"The Little Mermaid" — A36

1935, Oct. 1   *Perf. 13*

246	A34	5o lt green	4.00	.25
a.		Tête bêche gutter pair	10.00	15.00
b.		Booklet pane of 4	40.00	
c.		As "a," without gutter	15.00	20.00
		Never hinged	45.00	
247	A35	7o dull vio	2.50	4.00
248	A36	10o orange	6.50	.25
a.		Tête bêche gutter pair	13.00	29.00
b.		Booklet pane of 4	65.00	
c.		As "a," without gutter	20.00	40.00
		Never hinged	65.00	
249	A35	15o red	16.00	.25
a.		Tête bêche gutter pair	32.50	45.00
b.		Booklet pane of 4	160.00	
c.		As "a," without gutter	40.00	65.00
		Never hinged	110.00	
250	A35	20o gray	16.00	1.25
251	A35	30o dl bl	2.50	.50
		Nos. 246-251 (6)	47.50	6.50
		Set, never hinged	124.00	

Centenary of the publication of the earliest installment of Hans Christian Andersen's "Fairy Tales."

Nikolai Church A37 | Hans Tausen A38

Ribe Cathedral — A39

1936   *Perf. 13*

252	A37	5o green	1.10	.25
a.		Booklet pane of 4	21.00	
253	A37	7o violet	1.25	5.25
254	A38	10o lt brown	1.60	.25
a.		Booklet pane of 4	25.00	
255	A38	15o dull rose	2.50	.25
256	A39	30o blue	16.00	1.25
		Nos. 252-256 (5)	22.45	7.25
		Set, never hinged	60.00	

Church Reformation in Denmark, 400th anniv.

No. 229 Overprinted in Blue

1937, Sept. 17

257	A32	10o lt brown	1.40	2.50
		Never hinged	2.00	

Jubilee Exhib. held by the Copenhagen Phil. Club on their 50th anniv. The stamps were on sale at the Exhib. only, each holder of a ticket of admission (1k) being entitled to purchase 20 stamps at face value; of a season ticket (5k), 100 stamps.

Yacht and Summer Palace, Marselisborg A40 | Christian X in Streets of Copenhagen A41

Equestrian Statue of Frederik V and Amalienborg Palace — A42

1937, May 15   *Perf. 13*

258	A40	5o green	1.10	.25
a.		Booklet pane of 4	15.00	
259	A41	10o brown	1.10	.25
a.		Booklet pane of 4	15.00	
260	A42	15o scarlet	1.10	.25
a.		Booklet pane of 4	17.00	
261	A41	30o blue	19.00	2.75
		Nos. 258-261 (4)	22.30	3.50
		Set, never hinged	50.00	

25th anniv. of the accession to the throne of King Christian X.

Emancipation Column, Copenhagen — A43

1938, June 20   *Perf. 13*

262	A43	15o scarlet	.50	.50
		Never hinged	1.25	

Abolition of serfdom in Denmark, 150th anniv.

No. 223 Overprinted in Red on Alternate Stamps

1938, Sept. 2

263	A32	5o yellow grn, pair	3.25	13.00
		Never hinged	5.25	

10th Danish Philatelic Exhibition.

Bertel Thorvaldsen A44 | Statue of Jason A45

1938, Nov. 17   *Engr.*   *Perf. 13*

264	A44	5o rose lake	.35	.35
265	A45	10o purple	.50	.25
266	A44	30o dark blue	1.40	.50
		Nos. 264-266 (3)	2.25	1.10
		Set, never hinged	5.25	

The return to Denmark in 1838 of Bertel Thorvaldsen, Danish sculptor.

Stamps of 1933-39 Surcharged with New Values in Black:

a | b

1940
267 A32 (a) 6o on 7o yel grn .30 .50
268 A32 (a) 6o on 8o gray .30 .50
269 A30 (b) 15o on 40o #238 .90 5.25
270 A30 (b) 15o on 40o #238I .90 1.60
271 A30 (c) 20o on 15o dp red 1.10 .25
272 A30 (b) 40o on 30o #238F .90 .25
Nos. 267-272 (6) 4.40 8.35
Set, never hinged 8.00

Bering's Ship — A46

1941, Nov. 27 Engr. Perf. 13
277 A46 10o dk violet .30 .20
278 A46 20o red brown .60 .25
279 A46 40o dk blue .35 .50
Nos. 277-279 (3) 1.25 .95
Set, never hinged 3.00

Death of Vitus Bering, explorer, 200th anniv.

King Christian X — A47

1942-46 Unwmk. Perf. 13
280 A47 10o violet .25 .20
281 A47 15o yel grn .35 .20
282 A47 20o red .35 .20
283 A47 25o brown ('43) .35 .20
284 A47 30o orange ('43) .45 .20
285 A47 35o brt red vio ('44) .40 .50
286 A47 40o blue ('43) .45 .20
286A A47 45o ol brn ('46) .35 .50
286B A47 50o gray ('45) .45 .20
287 A47 60o bluish grn ('44) .45 .20
287A A47 75o dk blue ('46) .40 .20
Nos. 280-287A (11) 4.25 3.10
Set, never hinged 8.00

For overprints see Nos. Q28-Q30.

Round Tower — A48   Condor Plane — A49

1942, Nov. 27
288 A48 10o violet .25 .20
Never hinged .40

300th anniv. of the Round Tower, Copenhagen.
For surcharge see No. B14.

1943, Oct. 29
289 A49 20o red .25 .20
Never hinged .35

25th anniv. of the Danish Aviation Company (Det Danske Luftfartsselskab).

Ejby Church — A50

15ö, Oesterlars Church. 20ö, Hvidbjerg Church.

1944 Engr. Perf. 13
290 A50 10o violet .25 .20
291 A50 15o yellow grn .30 .35
292 A50 20o red .25 .20
Nos. 290-292 (3) .80 .75
Set, never hinged 1.60

Ole Roemer A53   Christian X A54

1944, Sept. 25
293 A53 20o henna brown .30 .50
Never hinged .65

Birth of Ole Roemer, astronomer, 300th anniv.

1945, Sept. 26
294 A54 10o lilac .20 .20
295 A54 20o red .20 .20
296 A54 40o deep blue .40 .25
Nos. 294-296 (3) .80 .65
Set, never hinged 1.75

75th birthday of King Christian X.

Catalogue values for unused stamps in this section, from this point to the end of the section, are for Never Hinged items.

Small State Seal — A55   Tycho Brahe — A56

1946-47 Unwmk. Perf. 13
297 A55 1k brown .85 .20
298 A55 2k red ('47) .70 .20
299 A55 5k dull blue 1.25 .20
Nos. 297-299 (3) 2.80 .60

Nos. 297-299 issued on ordinary and fluorescent paper. Values for ordinary paper are much higher.
See Nos. 395-400, 441A-444D, 499-506, 643-650, 716-720A, 804-815, 909, 1134-1138, 1304-1313, 1474-1478, 1508. For overprints see Nos. Q35, Q40, Q46-Q48.

1946, Dec. 14 Engr.
300 A56 20o dark red .50 .50

Birth of Tycho Brahe, astronomer, 400th anniv.

First Danish Locomotive A57   Modern Steam Locomotive A58

Diesel Locomotive A59

1947, June 27
301 A57 15o steel blue .50 .35
302 A58 20o red .90 .30
303 A59 40o deep blue 3.50 1.90
Nos. 301-303 (3) 4.90 2.55

Inauguration of the Danish State Railways, cent.

Jacobsen A60   Frederik IX A61

1947, Nov. 10 Perf. 13
304 A60 20o dark red .30 .50

60th anniv. of the death of Jacob Christian Jacobsen, founder of the Glyptothek Art Museum, Copenhagen.

1948-50 Unwmk. Perf. 13
Three types among 15ö, 20ö, 30ö:
I — Background of horizontal lines. No outline at left for cheek and ear. King's uniform textured in strong lines.
II — Background of vertical and horizontal lines. Contour of cheek and ear at left. Uniform same.
III — Background and facial contour lines as in II. Uniform lines double and thinner.
306 A61 15(o) green (II) 2.50 .50
a. Type III ('49) 1.60 .50
307 A61 20(o) dk red (I) .85 .20
a. Type III ('49) 1.00 .20
308 A61 25(o) lt brown 1.25 .50
309 A61 30(o) org (II) 13.00 .80
a. Type III ('50) 20.00 .50
310 A61 40(o) dl blue ('49) 4.50 .80
311 A61 45(o) olive ('50) 1.75 .20
312 A61 50(o) gray ('49) 1.75 .20
313 A61 60(o) grnsh bl ('50) 2.50 .20
314 A61 75(o) lil rose ('50) 1.40 .20
Nos. 306-314 (9) 29.50 3.60

See Nos. 319-326, 334-341, 354. For surcharges see Nos. 357-358, 370, B20, B24-B25, Q32-Q34, Q36-Q39.

Legislative Assembly, 1849 — A62

Symbol of UPU — A63

1949, June 5
315 A62 20o red brown .50 .50
Adoption of the Danish constitution, cent.

1949, Oct. 9
316 A63 40o dull blue .65 .50
75th anniv. of the UPU.

Kalundborg Radio Station and Masts — A64

1950, Apr. 1 Engr. Perf. 13
317 A64 20o brown red .50 .50
Radio broadcasting in Denmark, 25th anniv.

Types of 1933-50
1950-51 Unwmk. Perf. 13
318 A32 10o green .30 .20
319 A61 15(o) lilac .75 .20
b. 15(o) gray lilac 4.00 .25
320 A61 20(o) lt brown .55 .20
321 A61 25(o) dark red 3.75 .20
322 A61 35(o) gray grn ('51) .75 .50
323 A61 40(o) gray .90 .20
324 A61 50(o) dark blue 3.00 .20
325 A61 55(o) brown ('51) 29.00 2.25
326 A61 70(o) deep green 2.75 .20
Nos. 318-326 (9) 41.75 4.15

Warship of 1701 — A65   Oersted — A66

1951, Feb. 26 Engr. Perf. 13
327 A65 25o dark red .50 .50
328 A65 50o deep blue 4.00 1.10
250th anniv. of the foundation of the Naval Officers' College.

1951, Mar. 9 Unwmk.
329 A66 50o blue 1.40 .75
Cent. of the death of Hans Christian Oersted, physicist.

Post Chaise ("Ball Post") — A67   Marine Rescue — A68

1951, Apr. 1 Perf. 13
330 A67 15o purple .65 .30
331 A67 25o henna brown .65 .30
Cent. of Denmark's 1st postage stamp.

1952, Mar. 26
332 A68 25o red brown .50 .50
Cent. of the foundation of the Danish Lifesaving Service.

Types of 1933-50
1952-53 Perf. 13
333 A32 12o lt yel grn .30 .20
334 A61 25(o) lt blue 1.00 .20
335 A61 30(o) brown red .55 .50
336 A61 50(o) aqua ('53) .55 .50
337 A61 60(o) dp blue ('53) .75 .50
338 A61 65(o) gray ('53) .55 .50
339 A61 80(o) orange ('53) .85 .20
340 A61 90(o) olive ('53) 3.00 .50
341 A61 95(o) red org ('53) 1.00 .50
Nos. 333-341 (9) 8.55 3.30

Jelling Runic Stone — A69

Designs: 15o, Vikings' camp, Trelleborg. 20o, Church of Kalundborg. 30o, Nyborg castle. 60o, Goose tower, Vordinborg.

1953-56 Perf. 13
342 A69 10o dp green .20 .20
343 A69 15o lt rose vio .20 .20
344 A69 20o brown .20 .20
345 A69 30o red ('54) .25 .20
346 A69 60o dp blue ('54) .50 .20

Designs: 10o, Manor house, Spottrup. 15o, Hammershus castle ruins. 20o, Copenhagen stock exchange. 30o, Statue of Frederik V, Amalienborg. 60o, Soldier statue at Fredericia.

347 A69 10o green ('54) .20 .20
348 A69 15o lilac ('55) .20 .20
349 A69 20o brown ('55) .20 .20
350 A69 30o red ('55) .25 .20
351 A69 60o deep blue ('56) .80 .20
Nos. 342-351 (10) 3.00 2.00

1000th anniv. of the Kingdom of Denmark. Each stamp represents a different century.

Telegraph
Equipment of 1854
A70

Frederik V
A71

1954, Feb. 2 *Perf. 13*
352 A70 30o red brown .50 .50
Cent. of the telegraph in Denmark.

1954, Mar. 31
353 A71 30o dark red .55 .50
200th anniv. of the founding of the Royal Academy of Fine Arts.

Type of 1948-50
1955, Apr. 27
354 A61 25o lilac .50 .50

Nos. 224C and 226A Surcharged with New Value in Black. Nos. 307 and 321 Surcharged with New Value and 4 Bars
1955-56
355 A32 5o on 6o org .25 .20
356 A32 5o on 7o lt brn .25 .20
357 A61 30(o) on 20(o) dk red (I) .30 .50
  a. Type III .35 .50
  b. Double surcharge 1,150. 1,150.
  c. Inverted surcharge 650.00
358 A61 30(o) on 25(o) dk red ('56) .60 .20
  a. Double surcharge —
  Nos. 355-358 (4) 1.40 1.10

A72

A73

1955, Nov. 11 **Unwmk.**
359 A72 30o dark red .50 .50
100th anniv. of the death of Sören Kierkegaard, philosopher and theologian.

1956, Sept. 12 **Engr.**
360 A73 30o Ellehammer's plane .50 .50
50th anniv. of the 1st flight made by Jacob Christian Hansen Ellehammer in a heavier-than-air craft.

Northern Countries Issue

Whooper
Swans — A74

1956, Oct. 30 *Perf. 13*
361 A74 30o rose red 1.60 .20
362 A74 60o ultramarine 1.40 .80
Issued to emphasize the close bonds among the northern countries: Denmark, Finland, Iceland, Norway and Sweden.

Prince's Palace
A75

Harvester
A76

Design: 60ö, Sun God's Chariot.

1957, May 15 **Unwmk.**
363 A75 30o dull red .85 .20
364 A75 60o dark blue .85 .75
150th anniv. of the National Museum.

1958, Sept. 4 **Engr.** *Perf. 13*
365 A76 30o fawn .50 .20
Centenary of the Royal Veterinary and Agricultural College.

Frederik IX
A77

Ballet Dancer
A78

1959, Mar. 11
366 A77 30o rose red .40 .20
367 A77 35o rose lilac .50 .35
368 A77 60o ultra .50 .20
  Nos. 366-368 (3) 1.40 .75
King Frederik's 60th birthday.

1959, May 16
369 A78 35o rose lilac .30 .20
Danish Ballet and Music Festival, May 17-31. See Nos. 401, 422.

No. 319 Surcharged

1960, Apr. 7
370 A61 30o on 15o lilac .30 .20
World Refugee Year, 7/1/59-6/30/60.

Seeder
and Farm
A79

30ö, Harvester combine. 60ö, Plow.

1960, Apr. 28 **Engr.** *Perf. 13*
371 A79 12o green .20 .20
372 A79 30o dull red .30 .20
373 A79 60o dk blue .65 .50
  Nos. 371-373 (3) 1.15 .90

King Frederik IX
and Queen
Ingrid — A80

1960, May 24 **Unwmk.**
374 A80 30o dull red .45 .20
375 A80 60o blue .65 .50
25th anniversary of the marriage of King Frederik IX and Queen Ingrid.

Bascule
Light — A81

Finsen — A82

1960, June 8 **Engr.**
376 A81 30o dull red .50 .50
400th anniv. of the Lighthouse Service.

1960, Aug. 1 *Perf. 13*
377 A82 30o dark red .50 .50
Centenary of the birth of Dr. Niels R. Finsen, physician and scientist.

Nursing
Mother — A83

DC-8 Airliner — A84

1960, Aug. 16 **Unwmk.**
378 A83 60o ultra .55 .20
10th meeting of the regional committee for Europe of WHO, Copenhagen, Aug. 16-20.

Europa Issue, 1960
Common Design Type
1960, Sept. 19 *Perf. 13*
Size: 28x21mm
379 CD3 60o ultra .65 .65

1961, Feb. 24
380 A84 60o ultra .75 .50
10th anniv. of the Scandinavian Airlines System, SAS.

Landscape
A85

Frederik IX
A86

1961, Apr. 21 *Perf. 13*
381 A85 30o copper brown .50 .50
Denmark's Soc. of Nature Lovers, 50th anniv.

Fluorescent Paper
as well as ordinary paper, was used in printing many definitive and commemorative stamps, starting in 1962. These include No. 220, 224; the 15, 20, 25, 30, 35 (Nos. 386 and 387), 50 and 60ö, 1.20k, 1.50k and 25k definitives of following set, and Nos. 297-299, 318, 333, 380, 401-427, 429-435, 438-439, 493, 543, 548, B30.
Only fluorescent paper was used for Nos. 436-437, 437A and 440 onward; in semipostals from B31 onward.

1961-63 **Engr.** *Perf. 13*
382 A32 15o green ('63) .50 .50
383 A86 20o brown .50 .20
384 A86 25o brown ('63) .50 .50
385 A86 30o rose red .65 .50
386 A86 35o olive grn .65 .75
387 A86 35o rose red ('63) .50 .20
388 A86 40o gray 1.00 .20
389 A86 50o aqua .65 .65
390 A86 60o ultra .90 .65
391 A86 70o green 1.60 .50
392 A86 80o red orange 1.60 .50
393 A86 90o olive bister 4.25 .65
394 A86 95o claret ('63) 1.00 .90
  Nos. 382-394 (13) 14.30 6.70
See Nos. 417-419, 438-441. For overprints see Nos. Q41-Q42, Q44-Q45.

State Seal Type of 1946-47
1962-65
395 A55 1.10k lilac ('65) 5.25 2.00
396 A55 1.20k gray 3.00 .20
397 A55 1.25k orange 3.00 .20
398 A55 1.30k green ('65) 5.25 2.00
399 A55 1.50k red lilac 2.40 .40
400 A55 25k yellow grn 8.00 .30
  Nos. 395-400 (6) 26.90 5.50

Dancer Type of 1959 Inscribed "15-31 MAJ"
1962, Apr. 26
401 A78 60o ultra .50 .50
Issued to publicize the Danish Ballet and Music Festival, May 15-31.

Old Mill — A87

M.S.
Selandia — A88

1962, May 10 **Unwmk.** *Perf. 13*
402 A87 10o red brown .30 .50
Cent. of the abolition of mill monopolies.

1962, June 14 **Engr.**
403 A88 60o dark blue 1.60 1.40
M.S. Selandia, the 1st Diesel ship, 50th anniv.

Violin
Scroll,
Leaves,
Lights and
Balloon
A89

1962, Aug. 31
404 A89 35o rose violet .50 .50
150th anniv. of the birth of Georg Carstensen, founder of Tivoli amusement park, Copenhagen.

Cliffs on Moen
Island — A90

Germinating
Wheat — A91

1962, Nov. 22
405 A90 20o pale brown .50 .50
Issued to publicize preservation of natural treasures and landmarks.

1963, Mar. 21 **Engr.**
406 A91 35o fawn .50 .50
FAO "Freedom from Hunger" campaign.

Railroad Wheel,
Tire Tracks,
Waves and
Swallow — A92

Sailing Vessel, Coach, Postilions and Globe — A93

1963, May 14   **Unwmk.**   *Perf. 13*
407 A92 15o green   .50 .50

Inauguration of the "Bird Flight Line" railroad link between Denmark and Germany.

1963, May 27
408 A93 60o dark blue   .50 .65

Cent. of the 1st Intl. Postal Conf., Paris, 1863.

Niels Bohr and Atom Diagram — A94

Early Public School Drawn on Slate — A95

1963, Nov. 21   **Engr.**
409 A94 35o red brown   .50 .50
410 A94 60o dark blue   .65 .50

50th anniv. of Prof. Niels Bohr's (1885-1962) atom theory.

1964, June 19   **Unwmk.**   *Perf. 13*
411 A95 35o red brown   .30 .50

150th anniversary of the royal decrees for the public school system.

Fish and Chart — A96

Danish Watermarks and Perforations A97

1964, Sept. 7   **Engr.**
412 A96 60o violet blue   .50 .65

Conference of the International Council for the Exploration of the Sea, Copenhagen.

1964, Oct. 10   *Perf. 13*
413 A97 35o pink   .50 .50

25th anniv. of Stamp Day and to publicize the Odense Stamp Exhibition, Oct. 10-11.

Landscape A98

Calculator, Ledger and Inkwell — A99

1964, Nov. 12   **Engr.**
414 A98 25o brown   .50 .50

Issued to publicize preservation of natural treasures and landmarks.

1965, Mar. 8   **Unwmk.**
415 A99 15o light olive green   .50 .50

First Business School in Denmark, cent.

Types of 1933 and 1961
1965, May 15   **Engr.**   *Perf. 13*
416 A32 25o apple green   .50 .50
417 A86 40o brown   .50 .50
418 A86 50o rose red   .75 .50
419 A86 80o ultra   2.00 .50
   Nos. 416-419 (4)   3.75 2.00

For overprints see Nos. Q41-Q42.

ITU Emblem, Telegraph Key, Teletype Paper A100

Carl Nielsen (1865-1931), Composer A101

1965, May 17
420 A100 80o dark blue   .50 .50

Cent. of the ITU.

1965, June 9   **Engr.**
421 A101 50o brown red   .50 .50

Dancer Type of 1959 Inscribed "15-31 MAJ"

1965, Sept. 23
422 A78 50o rose red   .50 .50

Issued to publicize the Danish Ballet and Music Festival, May 15-31.

Bogo Windmill A102

Mylius Dalgas Surveying Wasteland A103

1965, Nov. 10   **Engr.**   *Perf. 13*
423 A102 40o brown   .50 .50

Issued to publicize the preservation of natural treasures and landmarks.

1966, Feb. 24
424 A103 25o olive green   .50 .50

Cent. of the Danish Heath Soc. (reclamation of wastelands), founded by Enrico Mylius Dalgas.

Christen Kold (1816-70), Educator — A104

1966, Mar. 29   *Perf. 13*
425 A104 50o dull red   .50 .50

Poorhouse, Copenhagen A105

Holte Allée, Bregentved A106

Dolmen (Grave) in Jutland — A107

1966   **Unwmk.**
426 A105 50o dull red   .50 .50
427 A106 80o dk blue   .75 .75
428 A107 1.50k dk slate grn   .80 .50
   Nos. 426-428 (3)   2.05 1.75

Publicizing preservation of national treasures and ancient monuments. Issued: 50o, May 12; 80o, June 16; 1.50k, Nov. 24.

George Jensen by Ejnar Nielsen A108

Music Bar and Instruments A109

1966, Aug. 31   **Engr.**   *Perf. 13*
429 A108 80o dark blue   .85 .60

George Jensen, silversmith, birth cent.

1967, Jan. 9
430 A109 50o dark red   .50 .50

Royal Danish Academy of Music, cent.

Cogwheels, and Broken Customs Duty Ribbon — A110

1967, Mar. 2
431 A110 80o dark blue   .80 .50

European Free Trade Association. Industrial tariffs were abolished Dec. 31, 1966, among EFTA members: Austria, Denmark, Finland, Great Britain, Norway, Portugal, Sweden and Switzerland.

Windmill and Medieval Fortress — A111

Designs: 40ö, Ship's rigging and baroque house front. 50ö, Old Town Hall. 80ö, New building construction.

1967   **Engr.**   *Perf. 13*
432 A111 25o green   .40 .20
433 A111 40o sepia   .50 .20
434 A111 50o red brown   .50 .20
435 A111 80o dk blue   1.00 .80
   Nos. 432-435 (4)   2.40 1.40

The 800th anniversary of Copenhagen. Issued: #432-433, 4/6; #434-435, 5/11.

Princess Margrethe and Prince Henri — A112

1967, June 10
436 A112 50o red   .30 .50

Marriage of Crown Princess Margrethe and Prince Henri de Monpezat.

Types of 1933-1961
1967-71   **Engr.**   *Perf. 13*
437 A32 30o dk green   .35 .25
437A A32 40o orange ('71)   .35 .25
438 A86 50o brown   .60 .25
439 A86 60o rose red   .60 .25
440 A86 80o green   .60 .25
441 A86 90o ultra   .60 .25
441A A55 1.20k Prus grn ('71)   1.75 .65
442 A55 2.20k orange   2.50 .50
443 A55 2.80k gray   2.50 .65
444 A55 2.90k rose vio   5.25 .50
444A A55 3k dk sl grn ('69)   1.25 .65
444B A55 3.10k plum ('70)   7.75 .65

444C A55 4k gray ('69)   1.60 .25
444D A55 4.10k olive ('70)   7.75 .25
   Nos. 437-444D (14)   33.45 5.60

Issued: #437-441, 6/30/67; #442-443, 7/8/67; #444, 4/29/68; #444A, 444C, 8/28/69; #444B, 444D, 8/27/70; #437A, 441A, 6/24/71.
For overprints see Nos. Q44-Q45.

Sonne — A113

Cross-anchor and Porpoise — A114

1967, Sept. 21
445 A113 60o red   .50 .20

150th anniv. of the birth of Hans Christian Sonne, pioneer of the cooperative movement in Denmark.

1967, Nov. 9   **Engr.**   *Perf. 13*
446 A114 90o dk blue   .50 .50

Centenary of the Danish Seamen's Church in Foreign Ports.

Esbjerg Harbor — A115

Koldinghus A116

1968, Apr. 24
447 A115 30o dk yellow grn   .30 .50

Centenary of Esbjerg Harbor.

1968, June 13
448 A116 60o copper red   .50 .50

700th anniversary of Koldinghus Castle.

Shipbuilding Industry A117

Sower A118

Designs: 50o, Chemical industry. 60o, Electric power. 90o, Engineering.

1968, Oct. 24   **Engr.**   *Perf. 13*
449 A117 30o green   .25 .20
450 A117 50o brown   .25 .20
451 A117 60o red brown   .25 .20
452 A117 90o dark blue   1.00 1.00
   Nos. 449-452 (4)   1.75 1.60

Issued to publicize Danish industries.

1969, Jan. 29
453 A118 30o gray green   .30 .50

Royal Agricultural Soc. of Denmark, 200th anniv.

Five Ancient Ships A119

Frederik IX A120

Nordic Cooperation Issue
1969, Feb. 28   Engr.   *Perf. 13*
454 A119 60o brown red   .80 .20
455 A119 90o blue   1.60 1.60

50th anniv. of the Nordic Soc. and cent. of postal cooperation among the northern countries. The design is taken from a coin found at the site of Birka, an ancient Swedish town. See also Finland No. 481, Iceland Nos. 404-405, Norway Nos. 523-524 and Sweden Nos. 808-810.

1969, Mar. 11
456 A120 50o sepia   .50 .50
457 A120 60o dull red   .50 .50

70th birthday of King Frederik IX.

Common Design Types pictured following the introduction.

Europa Issue, 1969
Common Design Type
1969, Apr. 28
Size: 28x20mm
458 CD12 90o chalky blue   1.10 .75

Kronborg Castle — A121   Danish Flag — A122

1969, May 22   Engr.   *Perf. 13*
459 A121 50o brown   .50 .20

Association of Danes living abroad, 50th anniv.

1969, June 12
460 A122 60o bluish blk, red & gray .50 .50

750th anniversary of the fall of the Dannebrog (Danish flag) from heaven.

Nexo A123   Stensen A124

1969, Aug. 28
461 A123 80o deep green   .50 .20

Centenary of the birth of Martin Andersen Nexo (1869-1954), novelist.

1969, Sept. 25
462 A124 1k deep brown   .50 .20

300th anniv. of the publication of Niels Stensen's geological work "On Solid Bodies."

Abstract Design — A125   Symbolic Design — A126

1969, Nov. 10   Engr.   *Perf. 13*
463 A125 60o rose, red & ultra   .50 .50

1969, Nov. 20
464 A126 30o olive green   .50 .20

Valdemar Poulsen (1869-1942), electrical engineer and inventor.

Post Office Bank — A127   School Safety Patrol — A128

1970, Jan. 15   Engr.   *Perf. 13*
465 A127 60o dk red & org   .50 .20

50th anniv. of post office banking service.

1970, Feb. 19
466 A128 50o brown   .50 .20

Issued to publicize road safety.

Candle in Window A129   Deer A130

1970, May 4   Engr.   *Perf. 13*
467 A129 50o slate, dull bl & yel   .30 .20

25th anniv. of liberation from the Germans.

1970, May 28
468 A130 60o yel grn, red & brn   .50 .50

Tercentenary of Jaegersborg Deer Park.

Elephant Figurehead, 1741 A131   "The Homecoming" by Povl Christensen A132

1970, June 15   *Perf. 11½*
469 A131 30o multicolored   .30 .20

Royal Naval Museum, tercentenary.

1970, June 15   *Perf. 13*
470 A132 60o org, dl vio & ol grn   .50 .20

Union of North Schleswig and Denmark, 50th anniv.

Electromagnet A133

1970, Aug. 13   Engr.
471 A133 80o gray green   .50 .50

150th anniversary of Hans Christian Oersted's discovery of electromagnetism.

Bronze Age Ship A134

Ships: 50o, Viking shipbuilding, from Bayeux tapestry. 60o, Thuroe schooner with topgallant. 90o, Tanker.

1970, Sept. 24
472 A134 30o ocher & brown   .30 .20
473 A134 50o brn red & rose brn   .30 .20
474 A134 60o gray ol & red brn   .55 .20
475 A134 90o blue grn & ultra   1.25 1.25
   Nos. 472-475 (4)   2.40 1.85

UN Emblem A135

1970, Oct. 22   Engr.   *Perf. 13*
476 A135 90o blue, grn & red   1.00 1.00

25th anniversary of the United Nations.

Bertel Thorvaldsen A136   Mathide Fibiger A137

1970, Nov. 19
477 A136 2k slate blue   .70 .70

Bicentenary of the birth of Bertel Thorvaldsen (1768-1844), sculptor.

1971, Feb. 25
478 A137 80o olive green   .50 .50

Danish Women's Association centenary.

Refugees A138   Hans Egede A139

1971, Mar. 26   Engr.   *Perf. 13*
479 A138 50o brown   .25 .20
480 A138 60o brown red   .35 .20

Joint northern campaign for the benefit of refugees.

1971, May 27
481 A139 1k brown   .50 .50

250th anniversary of arrival of Hans Egede in Greenland and beginning of its colonization.

A140

A141

1971, Oct. 14
482 A140 30o Swimming   .25 .20
483 A140 50o Gymnastics   .50 .20
484 A140 60o Soccer   .75 .20
485 A140 90o Sailing   1.00 .80
   Nos. 482-485 (4)   2.50 1.40

1971, Nov. 11   Engr.   *Perf. 13*
486 A141 90o dark blue   .50 .50

Centenary of first lectures given by Georg Brandes (1842-1927), writer and literary critic.

A142

A143

1972, Jan. 27
487 A142 80o slate green   .50 .50

Centenary of Danish sugar production.

1972, Mar. 11   Engr.   *Perf. 13*
488 A143 60o red brown   .65 .20

Frederik IX (1899-1972).

Abstract Design A144

1972, Mar. 11
489 A144 1.20k brt rose lil, bl gray & brn   .65 .65

Danish Meteorological Institute, cent.

Nikolai F. S. Grundtvig A145   Locomotive, 1847, Ferry, Travelers A146

1972, May 4   Engr.   *Perf. 13*
490 A145 1k sepia   .50 .50

Nikolai Frederik Severin Grundtvig (1783-1872), theologian and poet.

1972, June 26
491 A146 70o rose red   .50 .50

125th anniversary of Danish State Railways.

Rebild Hills A147   "Tinker Turned Politician" A148

1972, June 26
492 A147 1k bl, sl grn & mar   .50 .20

125th anniversary of Danish State Railways.

Types of 1933-46
1972-78   Engr.   *Perf. 13*
493 A32 20o slate bl ('74)   .35 .20
494 A32 50o sepia ('74)   .35 .20
a.   Bklt. pane of 12 (4 #318, 4 #493, 4 #494) ('85)   3.50
495 A32 60o apple grn ('76)   1.75 .65
496 A32 60o gray ('78)   .70 .60
497 A32 70o red   .90 .50
498 A32 80o apple grn ('77)   .50 .50
499 A55 2.50k orange   1.75 .50
500 A55 2.80k olive ('75)   1.25 1.25
501 A55 3.50k lilac   2.00 .20
502 A55 4.5k olive   5.25 .50
503 A55 6k vio blk ('76)   2.40 .20
504 A55 7k red lilac ('78)   2.50 .20

505	A55	9k brown ol ('77)	3.25 .20
506	A55	10k lemon ('76)	3.25 .20
		Nos. 493-506 (14)	26.20 5.90

1972, Sept. 14

507	A148	70o dark red	.50 .20

250th anniv. of the comedies of Ludvig Holberg (1684-1754) on the Danish stage.

WHO Building, Copenhagen — A149

1972, Sept. 14

508	A149	2k bl, blk & lt red brn	.70 .70

Opening of WHO Building, Copenhagen.

Bridge Across Little Belt A150

Aeroskobing House c. 1740 A151

Highway engineering (Diagrams): 60o, Hanstholm Harbor. 70o, Lim Fjord Tunnel. 90o, Knudshoved Harbor.

1972, Oct. 19   Engr.   Perf. 13

509	A150	40o dk green	.20 .20
510	A150	60o dk brown	.30 .20
511	A150	70o dk red	.30 .20
512	A150	90o dk blue grn	.50 .50
		Nos. 509-512 (4)	1.30 1.10

1972, Nov. 23

Danish Architecture: 60o, East Bornholm farmhouse, 17th century, horiz. 70o, House, Christianshavn, c. 1710. 1.20k, Hvide Sande Farmhouse, c. 1810, horiz.

Size: 20x28mm, 27x20mm

513	A151	40o red, brn & blk	.35 .25
514	A151	60o blk, vio bl & grn	.35 .25

Size: 18x37mm, 36x20mm

515	A151	70o red, dk red & blk	.45 .20
516	A151	1.20k dk brn, red & grn	1.00 1.00
		Nos. 513-516 (4)	2.15 1.70

Jensen A152

Guard Rails, Cogwheels A153

1973, Feb. 22   Engr.   Perf. 13

517	A152	90o green	.50 .50

Centenary of the birth of Johannes Vilhelm Jensen (1873-1950), lyric poet and novelist.

1973, Mar. 22

518	A153	50o sepia	.50 .20

Centenary of first Danish Factory Act for labor protection.

Abildgaard A154

Rhododendron A155

1973, Mar. 22

519	A154	1k dull blue	.60 .60

Bicentenary of Royal Veterinary College, Christianshaven, founded by Prof. P. C. Abildgaard.

1973, Apr. 26

Design: 70o, Dronningen of Denmark rose.

520	A155	60o brn, grn & vio	.65 .25
521	A155	70o dk red, rose & grn	.65 .25

Centenary of the founding of the Horticultural Society of Denmark.

Nordic Cooperation Issue 1973

Nordic House, Reykjavik A156

1973, June 26   Engr.   Perf. 13

522	A156	70o multicolored	.50 .20
523	A156	1k multicolored	1.50 1.25

A century of postal cooperation among Denmark, Finland, Iceland, Norway and Sweden, and in connection with the Nordic Postal Conference, Reykjavik.

Sextant, Stella Nova, Cassiopeia A157

St. Mark, from 11th Cent. Book of Dalby A158

1973, Oct. 18   Engr.   Perf. 13

524	A157	2k dark brown	.75 .60

400th anniversary of the publication of "De Nova Stella," by Tycho Brahe.

1973, Oct. 18   Photo.   Perf. 14x14½

525	A158	120o buff & multi	1.00 .65

300th anniversary of Royal Library.

Devil and Gossips, Fanefjord Church, 1480 — A159

Frescoes: No. 527, Queen Esther and King Ahasuerus, Tirsted Church, c.1400. No. 528, Miraculous Harvest, Jetsmark Church, c.1474. No. 529, Jesus carrying cross, and wearing crown of thorns, Biersted Church, c.1400. No. 530, Creation of Eve, Fanefjord Church, c.1480.

1973, Nov. 28   Engr.   Perf. 13
Cream Paper

526	A159	70o dk red, yel & grn	1.25 .30
527	A159	70o dk red, yel & grn	1.25 .30
528	A159	70o dk red, yel & grn	1.25 .30
529	A159	70o dk red, yel & grn	1.25 .30
530	A159	70o dk red, yel & grn	1.25 .30
a.		Bklt. pane, 2 each #526-530	35.00
b.		Strip of 5, #526-530	6.25

Blood Donors A160

Queen Margrethe A161

1974, Jan. 24

531	A160	90o purple & red	.50 .50

"Blood Saves Lives."

1974-81   Engr.   Perf. 13

532	A161	60o brown	.50 .50
533	A161	60o orange	.50 .50
534	A161	70o red	.50 .50
535	A161	70o dk brown	.50 .20
536	A161	80o green	.50 .20
537	A161	80o dp brn ('76)	.50 .20
538	A161	90o red lilac	.50 .50
539	A161	90o dull red	.50 .20
540	A161	90o slate grn ('76)	.50 .20
541	A161	100o dp ultra	.50 .20
542	A161	100o gray ('75)	.50 .20
543	A161	100o red ('76)	.50 .20
544	A161	100o brown ('77)	.50 .20
a.		Bklt. pane of 5 (#544, #494, 2 #493, #318)	1.75
545	A161	110o orange ('78)	.75 .75
546	A161	120o slate	.75 .50
547	A161	120o red ('77)	.50 .50
548	A161	130o ultra ('75)	2.00 2.50
549	A161	150o vio bl ('78)	.75 .75
550	A161	180o slate grn ('77)	.65 .60
551	A161	200o blue ('81)	.90 .90
		Nos. 532-551 (20)	12.80 10.55

See #630, 632-642. For overprint see #Q49.

Pantomime Theater — A162

Hverringe A163

1974, May 16

552	A162	100o indigo	.50 .20

Cent. of the Pantomime Theater, Tivoli.

1974, June 20   Engr.   Perf. 13

Views: 60o, Norre Lyndelse, Carl Nielsen's childhood home. 70o, Odense, Hans Chr. Andersen's childhood home. 90o, Hesselagergaard, vert. 120o, Hindsholm.

553	A163	50o brown & multi	.50 .50
554	A163	60o sl grn & multi	.65 .65
555	A163	70o red brn & multi	.50 .50
556	A163	90o dk green & mar	.55 .20
557	A163	120o red org & dk grn	.70 .50
		Nos. 553-557 (5)	2.90 2.35

Emblem, Runner with Map — A164

Iris — A165

1974, Aug. 22   Engr.   Perf. 13

558	A164	70o shown	.65 .65
559	A164	80o Compass	.45 .30

World Orienteering Championships 1974.

1974, Sept. 19

560	A165	90o shown	.50 .20
561	A165	120o Purple orchid	.75 .60

Copenhagen Botanical Garden centenary.

Mailman, 1624, and Postilion, 1780 — A166

Carrier Pigeon — A167

Design: 90o, Balloon and sailing ships.

1974, Oct. 9   Engr.   Perf. 13

562	A166	70o lemon & dk brn	.50 .35
563	A166	90o dull grn & sepia	.50 .20
564	A167	120o dark blue	.65 .65
		Nos. 562-564 (3)	1.65 1.20

350th anniv. of Danish PO (70o, 90o) and cent. of UPU (120o).

Souvenir Sheet

Ferslew's Essays, 1849 and 1852 — A168

Engraved and Photogravure

1975, Feb. 27   Perf. 13

565	A168	Sheet of 4	7.25 8.50
a.		70o Coat of arms	1.75 2.00
b.		80o King Frederik VII	1.75 2.00
c.		90o King Frederik VII	1.75 2.00
d.		100o Mercury	1.75 2.00

HAFNIA 76 Intl. Stamp Exhib., Copenhagen, Aug. 20-29, 1976. Sold for 5k. See No. 585.

Early Radio Equipment A169

Flora Danica Plate A170

1975, Mar. 20   Engr.   Perf. 13

566	A169	90o dull red	.50 .20

Danish broadcasting, 50th anniversary.

1975, May 22

Danish China: 90o, Flora Danica tureen. 130o, Vase and tea caddy, blue fluted china.

567	A170	50o slate grn	.30 .20
568	A170	90o brown red	.65 .65
569	A170	130o violet bl	1.10 1.10
		Nos. 567-569 (3)	2.05 1.95

Church of Moravian Brethren, Christiansfeld A171

120o, Kongsgaard farmhouse, Lejre. 150o, Anna Queenstraede, Helsingor, vert.

1975, June 19
570	A171	70o sepia	.65	.65
571	A171	120o olive green	.80	.80
572	A171	150o violet black	.65	.20
		Nos. 570-572 (3)	2.10	1.65

European Architectural Heritage Year 1975.

Andersen
A172

Watchman's Square, Abenra
A173

Designs: 70o, Numbskull Jack, drawing by Vilh. Pedersen. 130o, The Marshking's Daughter, drawing by L. Frohlich.

1975, Aug. 28 Engr. Perf. 13
573	A172	70o brown & blk	.80	.80
574	A172	90o brn red & dk brn	1.10	.30
575	A172	130o blue blk & sepia	2.40	2.40
		Nos. 573-575 (3)	4.30	3.50

Hans Christian Andersen (1805-75), writer.

1975, Sept. 25
Designs: 90o, Haderslev Cathedral, vert. 100o, Mögeltönder Polder. 120o, Mouth of Vidaaen at Höjer Floodgates.

576	A173	70o multicolored	.50	.50
577	A173	90o multicolored	.40	.20
578	A173	100o multicolored	.50	.25
579	A173	120o multicolored	.65	.50
		Nos. 576-579 (4)	2.05	1.45

European Kingfisher
A174

1975, Oct. 23 Engr. Perf. 13
580	A174	50o shown	.50	.50
581	A174	70o Hedgehog	.50	.50
582	A174	90o Cats	.50	.50
583	A174	130o Avocets	1.40	1.40
584	A174	200o Otter	.80	.20
		Nos. 580-584 (5)	3.70	3.10

Protected animals, and for the centenary of the Danish Society for the Prevention of Cruelty to Animals (90ö).

HAFNIA Type of 1974
Souvenir Sheet
1975, Nov. 20 Engr. & Photo.
585	A168	Sheet of 4	4.50	6.00
a.		50o buff & brown, No. 2	1.10	1.40
b.		70o buff, brown & blue, No. 1	1.10	1.40
c.		90o buff, blue & brown, No. 11	1.10	1.40
d.		130o olive, brown & buff, No. 19	1.10	1.40

HAFNIA 76 Intl. Stamp Exhib., Copenhagen, Aug. 20-29, 1976. Sold for 5k.

Copenhagen, Center — A175

View from Round Tower — A176

Copenhagen, Views: 100o, Central Station, interior. 130o, Harbor.

1976, Mar. 25 Engr. Perf. 12½
586	A175	60o multicolored	.50	.50
587	A176	80o multicolored	.50	.50
588	A176	100o multicolored	.50	.20
589	A175	130o multicolored	1.60	1.60
		Nos. 586-589 (4)	3.10	2.80

Postilion, by Otto Bache
A177

Emil Chr. Hansen, Physiologist, in Laboratory
A178

1976, June 17 Engr. Perf. 12½
590	A177	130o multicolored	1.25	1.25

Souvenir Sheet
591	A177	130o multicolored	9.25	16.00

HAFNIA 76 Intl. Stamp Exhib., Copenhagen, Aug. 20-29. No. 591 contains one stamp similar to No. 590 with design continuous into sheet margin. Sheet shows painting "A String of Horses Outside an Inn" of which No. 590 shows a detail. Sheet sold for 15k including exhibition ticket.

1976, Sept. 23 Engr. Perf. 13
592	A178	100o orange red	.50	.20

Carlsberg Foundation (art and science), centenary.

Glass Blower Molding Glass — A179

Five Water Lilies — A180

Danish Glass Production: 80o, Finished glass removed from pipe. 130o, Glass cut off from foot. 150o, Glass blown up in mold.

1976, Nov. 18 Engr. Perf. 13
593	A179	60o slate	.50	.50
594	A179	80o dk brown	.50	.25
595	A179	130o dk blue	1.00	1.00
596	A179	150o red brown	.60	.25
		Nos. 593-596 (4)	2.60	2.00

Photogravure and Engraved
1977, Feb. 2 Perf. 12½
597	A180	100o brt green & multi	.50	.50
598	A180	130o ultra & multi	1.60	1.60

Nordic countries cooperation for protection of the environment and 25th Session of Nordic Council, Helsinki, Feb. 19.

Road Accident — A181

Europa — A182

1977, Mar. 24 Engr. Perf. 12½
599	A181	100o brown red	.50	.20

Road Safety Traffic Act, May 1, 1977.

1977, May 2 Engr. Perf. 12½
600	A182	1k Allinge	.65	.50
601	A182	1.30k View, Ringsted	4.00	4.00

Kongeaen
A183

Hammers and Horseshoes
A184

Landscapes, Southern Jutland: 90o, Skallingen. 150o, Torskind. 200o, Jelling.

1977, June 30 Engr. Perf. 12½
602	A183	60o multicolored	1.25	1.25
603	A183	90o multicolored	.65	.65
604	A183	150o multicolored	.60	.50
605	A183	200o multicolored	.75	.50
		Nos. 602-605 (4)	3.25	2.90

See Nos. 616-619, 655-658, 666-669.

1977, Sept. 22 Engr. Perf. 12½
Designs: 1k, Chisel, square and plane. 1.30k, Trowel, ceiling brush and folding ruler.

606	A184	80o dk brown	.30	.25
607	A184	1k red	.50	.20
608	A184	1.30k violet bl	.90	.60
		Nos. 606-608 (3)	1.70	1.05

Danish crafts.

Globe Flower — A185

Handball — A186

Endangered Flora: 1.50k, Cnidium dubium.

1977, Nov. 17 Engr. Perf. 12½
609	A185	1k multicolored	.50	.25
610	A185	1.50k multicolored	1.60	1.25

1978, Jan. 19 Perf. 12½
611	A186	1.20k red	.50	.50

Men's World Handball Championships.

Christian IV, Frederiksborg Castle
A187

Frederiksborg Museum
A188

1978, Mar. 16
612	A187	1.20k brown red	.50	.50
613	A188	1.80k black	.60	.30

Frederiksborg Museum, centenary.

Europa Issue

Jens Bang's House, Aalborg
A189

Frederiksborg Castle, Ground Plan and Elevation
A190

1978, May 11 Engr. Perf. 12½
614	A189	1.20k red	.65	.20
615	A190	1.50k dk bl & vio bl	3.00	1.25

Landscape Type of 1977
Landscapes, Central Jutland: 70o, Kongenshus Memorial Park. 120o, Post Office, Old Town in Aarhus. 150o, Lignite fields, Soby. 180o, Church wall, Stadil Church.

1978, June 15 Engr. Perf. 12½
616	A183	70o multicolored	.50	.50
617	A183	120o multicolored	.55	.20
618	A183	150o multicolored	1.00	1.00
619	A183	180o multicolored	.85	.60
		Nos. 616-619 (4)	2.90	2.30

Boats in Harbor — A191

Edible Morel — A192

Danish fishing industry: 1k, Eel traps. 1.80k, Boats in berth. 2.50k, Drying nets.

1978, Sept. 7 Engr. Perf. 12½
620	A191	70o olive gray	.50	.50
621	A191	1k redsh brown	.50	.20
622	A191	1.80k slate	.65	.50
623	A191	2.50k sepia	1.00	.60
		Nos. 620-623 (4)	2.65	1.80

1978, Nov. 16 Engr. Perf. 12½
Design: 1.20k, Satan's mushroom.

624	A192	1k sepia	.80	.65
625	A192	1.20k dull red	.90	.30

Telephones — A193

1979, Jan. 25 Engr. Perf. 12½
626	A193	1.20k dull red	.50	.50

Centenary of Danish telephone.

University Seal
A194

Pentagram: University Faculties
A195

1979, Apr. 5 Engr. Perf. 12½
627	A194	1.30k vermilion	.50	.20
628	A195	1.60k dk vio blue	.65	.65

University of Copenhagen, 500th anniv.

Types of 1933-1974
1979-82 Engr. Perf. 13
629	A32	80o green	.50	.50
630	A161	90o slate	2.50	3.25
631	A32	100o dp green ('81)	.50	.50
632	A161	110o brown	.65	.50
a.		Bklt. pane, #493-494, 632, 2 #318 ('79)	1.50	
633	A161	130o red	.55	.20
a.		Bklt. pane, 2 ea #494, 629, 632, 4 #633 ('79)	6.50	
634	A161	130o brown ('81)	.65	.50
635	A161	140o red org ('80)	2.00	2.50
636	A161	150o red org ('81)	.80	.80
637	A161	160o ultra	1.25	1.25
638	A161	160o red ('81)	.65	.20
a.		Bklt. pane, 2 ea #318, 634, 638, 8 #494	12.00	
639	A161	180o ultra ('80)	1.25	1.25
640	A161	210o gray ('80)	2.00	2.50
641	A161	230o ol grn ('81)	1.25	.65
642	A161	250o blue grn ('81)	1.25	.90
643	A55	2.80k dull grn	1.10	1.10
644	A55	3.30k brn red ('81)	1.25	1.25
645	A55	3.50k grnsh bl ('82)	2.00	2.50
646	A55	4.30k brn red ('80)	4.00	5.25
647	A55	4.70k rose lil ('81)	4.00	5.25
648	A55	8k orange	2.50	.50
649	A55	12k red brn ('81)	4.00	1.00

650 A55 14k dk red brn ('82) 5.75 .70
Nos. 629-650 (22) 40.40 32.70

A196   A197

Europa: 1.30k, Mail cart, 1785. 1.60k, Morse key and amplifier.

1979, May 10   **Perf. 12½**
651 A196 1.30k red 1.00 .20
652 A196 1.60k dark blue 2.25 1.10

1979, June 14   **Engr.**   **Perf. 13**
Viking Art: 1.10k, Gripping beast pendant. 2k, Key with gripping beast design.
653 A197 1.10k sepia .50 .50
654 A197 2k grnsh gray .90 .50

Landscape Type of 1977
Landscapes, Northern Jutland: 80o, Mols Bjerge. 90o, Orslev Kloster. 200o, Trans. 280o, Bovbjerg.

1979, Sept. 6   **Perf. 12½**
655 A183 80o multicolored .50 .50
656 A183 90o multicolored 1.60 1.60
657 A183 200o multicolored .90 .35
658 A183 280o multicolored 1.10 .30
Nos. 655-658 (4) 4.10 3.25

Adam Oehlenschläger (1799-1850), Poet and Dramatist A198

1979, Oct. 4   **Engr.**   **Perf. 13**
659 A198 1.30k dk carmine .50 .25

Score, Violin, Dancing Couple — A199

Ballerina — A200

1979, Nov. 8   **Engr.**   **Perf. 13x12½**
660 A199 1.10k brown .65 .50
661 A200 1.60k ultra .80 .65
Jacob Gade (1879-63), composer; August Bournonville (1805-79), ballet master.

Royal Mail Guards' Office, Copenhagen, 1779 — A201

1980, Feb. 14   **Engr.**   **Perf. 13**
662 A201 1.30k brown red .50 .25
National Postal Service, 200th anniversary.

Symbols of Occupation, Health and Education A202

1980, May 5   **Engr.**   **Perf. 13**
663 A202 1.60k dark blue .80 .80
World Conference of the UN Decade for Women, Copenhagen, July 14-30.

Karen Blixen (1885-1962), Writer (Pen Name Isak Dinesen) — A203

Europa: 1.60k, August Krogh (1874-1949), physiologist.

1980, May 5
664 A203 1.30k red .65 .20
665 A203 1.60k blue 1.25 1.25

Landscape Type of 1977
Northern Jutland: 80o, Viking ship burial grounds, Lindholm Hoje. 110o, Lighthouse, Skagen, vert. 200o, Boreglum Monastery. 280o, Fishing boats, Vorupor Beach.

1980, June 19   **Engr.**   **Perf. 13**
666 A183 80o multicolored .50 .50
667 A183 110o multicolored .50 .50
668 A183 200o multicolored .70 .30
669 A183 280o multicolored 2.00 2.00
Nos. 666-669 (4) 3.70 3.30

Nordic Cooperation Issue

Silver Tankard, by Borchardt Rollufse, 1641 — A204

1980, Sept. 9   **Engr.**   **Perf. 13**
670 A204 1.30k shown .50 .35
671 A204 1.80k Bishop's bowl, Copenhagen faience, 18th cent. 1.10 1.10

Frisian Sceat Facsimile, Obverse and Reverse, 9th Century A205

Coins: 1.40k Silver coin of Valdemar the Great and Absalom, 1157-1182, 1.80k, Gold 12-mark coin of Christian VII, 1781.

1980, Oct. 9   **Engr.**   **Perf. 13**
672 A205 1.30k red & redsh brn .50 .45
673 A205 1.40k ol gray & sl grn 1.60 1.25
674 A205 1.80k dk bl & sl bl 1.25 1.25
Nos. 672-674 (3) 3.35 2.95

Tonder Lace Pattern, North Schleswig — A206

Designs: Tonder lace patterns.

1980, Nov. 13   **Engr.**   **Perf. 13**
675 A206 1.10k brown .65 .65
676 A206 1.30k brown red .50 .30
677 A206 2k olive gray .70 .30
Nos. 675-677 (3) 1.85 1.25

Nyboder Development, Copenhagen, 350th Anniversary A207

Design: 1.30k, View of Nyboder, diff.

1981, Mar. 19
678 A207 1.30k dp org & ocher .70 .70
679 A207 1.60k dp org & ocher .55 .30

Tilting at a Barrel on Shrovetide A208

Design: 2k, Midsummer's Eve bonfire.

1981, May 4   **Engr.**   **Perf. 13**
680 A208 1.60k brown red .65 .20
681 A208 2k dk blue 1.60 .90

Soro Lake and Academy, Zealand — A209

Designs: Views of Zealand.

1981, June 18   **Engr.**   **Perf. 13**
682 A209 100o shown .50 .50
683 A209 150o Poet N.F.S. Grundtvig's home, Udby .65 .65
684 A209 160o Kaj Munk's home, Opager .65 .30
685 A209 200o Gronsund .80 .80
686 A209 230o Bornholm Isld. .85 .80
Nos. 682-686 (5) 3.45 3.05

European Urban Renaissance Year — A210

1981, Sept. 10   **Engr.**   **Perf. 12½x13**
687 A210 1.60k dull red .65 .25

Type of 1933
1981-85   **Engr.**   **Perf. 13**
688 A32 30o orange .35 .35
a.   Bklt. pane 10 (2 #318, 2 #688, 6 #494)('84) 2.75
689 A32 40o purple .35 .35
a.   Bklt. pane of 10 (4 #318, 2 #689, 4 #494) ('89) 2.25
690 A32 80o ol bis ('85) .50 .50
691 A32 100o blue ('83) .70 .35
b.   Bklt. pane of 8 (2 #494, 4 #691, 2 #706) ('83) 8.50
692 A32 150o dk green ('82) .50 .35
693 A32 200o green ('83) .70 .70
694 A32 230o brt yel grn ('84) .85 .35
695 A32 250o brt yel grn ('85) 1.10 .70
Nos. 688-695 (8) 5.05 3.65

Ellehammer's 18-horsepower Biplane, 1906 — A211

1981, Oct. 8   **Engr.**   **Perf. 13**
696 A211 1k shown .65 .65
697 A211 1.30k R-1 Fokker CV reconnaissance plane, 1926 1.10 1.10
698 A211 1.60k Bellanca J-300, 1931 .65 .30
699 A211 2.30k DC-7C, 1957 .90 .70
Nos. 696-699 (4) 3.30 2.75

Arms Type of 1946 and

Queen Margrethe II, 10th Anniv. of Accession — A212

1982-85   **Engr.**   **Perf. 13**
700 A212 1.60k dull red .65 .25
701 A212 1.60k dk ol grn 3.25 4.00
702 A212 1.80k sepia .65 .50
703 A212 2k dull red .90 .25
b.   Bklt. pane, 4 #494, 2 ea #493, 702, 703 12.00
704 A212 2.20k ol grn ('83) 2.50 3.25
705 A212 2.30k violet .90 .30
706 A212 2.50k org red ('83) 1.00 .90
707 A212 2.70k dk blue 1.00 .65
708 A212 2.70k cop red ('84) 1.25 .25
c.   Booklet pane, 3 #688, 2 #494, 3 #708 ('84) 6.00

709 A212 2.80k cop red ('85) 1.00 .25
b.   Booklet pane, 3 #493, 2 #494, 3 #709 ('85) 4.50
710 A212 3k violet ('83) 1.00 .50
711 A212 3.30k bluish blk ('84) 1.60 1.00
712 A212 3.50k blue ('83) 1.75 .65
713 A212 3.50k dk vio ('85) 1.75 .75
714 A212 3.70k dp blue ('84) 1.60 .65
715 A212 3.80k dk blue ('85) 1.60 .50
716 A55 4.30k dk ol grn ('84) 5.25 6.50
717 A55 5.50k dk bl grn ('84) 2.50 1.50
718 A55 16k cop red ('83) 5.25 .80
719 A55 17k cop red ('84) 7.75 1.10
720 A55 18k brn vio ('85) 8.50 1.10
720A A55 50k dk red ('85) 16.00 2.00
Nos. 700-720A (22) 67.65 27.65
See Nos. 796-803, 887, 889, 896, 899.

World Figure Skating Championships A213

1982, Feb. 25
721 A213 2k dark blue .80 .60

A214

A215

1982, Feb. 25   **Engr.**   **Perf. 12½**
722 A214 1.60k Revenue schooner Argus .65 .45
Customs Service centenary

1982, May 3   **Engr.**   **Perf. 12½**
723 A215 2k Abolition of adscription, 1788 1.10 .20
724 A215 2.70k Women's voting right, 1915 2.50 1.00
Europa.

Butter Churn, Barn, Hjedding — A216

Records Office, 400th Anniv. — A217

1982, June 10   **Engr.**   **Perf. 13**
725 A216 1.80k brown .75 .60
Cooperative dairy farming centenary.

1982, June 10
726 A217 2.70k green 1.10 .50

Steen Steensen Blicher (1782-1848), Poet, by J.V. Gertner — A218

1982, Aug. 26   **Engr.**   **Perf. 13**
727 A218 2k brown red .80 .30

Robert Storm
Petersen
(1882-1949),
Cartoonist
A219

Printing in
Denmark, 500th
Anniv.
A220

Characters: 1.50k, Three little men and the
number man. 2k, Peter and Ping the penguin,
horiz.

1982, Sept. 23   Engr.   Perf. 12½
728 A219 1.50k dk bl & red   .70 .50
729 A219 2k red & ol grn   .90 .40

1982, Sept. 23
730 A220 1.80k Press, text, ink
balls   .75 .90

A221   A222

1982, Nov. 4
731 A221 2.70k Library seal   1.00 .50

500th anniv. of University Library.

1983, Jan. 27   Engr.   Perf. 13
732 A222 2k multicolored   .90 .50

World Communications Year.

Amusement
Park, 400th
Anniv.
A223

Badminton
Championship
A224

1983, Feb. 24
733 A223 2k multicolored   .90 .50

1983, Feb. 24
734 A224 2.70k multicolored   1.10 .50

Nordic
Cooperation
Issue — A225

1983, Mar. 24
735 A225 2.50k Egeskov Castle   .90 .40
736 A225 3.50k Troll Church,
North Jutland   1.25 .75

50th Anniv. of
Steel Plate
Printed
Stamps — A226

1983, Mar. 24   Engr.   Perf. 13
737 A226 2.50k car rose   1.00 .50

Europa
1983 — A227

Weights and
Measures
Ordinance,
300th
Anniv. — A228

2.50k, Kildekovshallen Recreation Center,
Copenhagen. 3.50k, Salling Sound Bridge.

1983, May 5   Engr.   Perf. 13
738 A227 2.50k multicolored   *1.25 .20*
739 A227 3.50k multicolored   *2.25 1.00*

1983, June 16
740 A228 2.50k red   1.00 .30

A229   A230

1983, Sept. 8   Engr.
741 A229 5k Codex titlepage   1.75 .75

Christian V Danish law, 300th anniv.

1983, Oct. 6   Engr.   Perf. 13
742 A230 1k Car crash, police   .50 .70
743 A230 2.50k Fire, ambulance
service   1.00 .35
744 A230 3.50k Sea rescue   1.25 .85
Nos. 742-744 (3)   2.75 1.70

Life saving and salvage services.

Elderly in
Society — A231

1983, Oct. 6
745 A231 2k Stages of life   .80 .80
746 A231 2.50k Train passengers 1.00 .30

N.F.S.
Grundtvig
(1783-1872),
Poet — A232

Street Scene, by
C.W. Eckersberg
(1783-1853) — A233

1983, Nov. 3   Engr.
747 A232 2.50k brown red   1.00 .50
748 A233 2.50k brown red   1.00 .30

A234   A235

1984, Jan. 26   Litho. & Engr.
749 A234 2.70k Shovel, sapling   1.10 .50

Plant a tree campaign.

1984, Jan. 26   Engr.
750 A235 3.70k Game   1.60 .65

1984 Billiards World Championships,
Copenhagen, May 10-13.

Hydrographic
Dept.
Bicentenary
A236

Pilotage Service,
300th
Anniv. — A237

1984, Mar. 22   Engr.   Perf. 13
751 A236 2.30k Compass   1.00 .90
752 A237 2.70k Boat   1.10 .50

2nd European
Parliament
Elections
A238

Scouts Around
Campfire, Emblems
A239

Litho. & Engr.
1984, Apr. 12   Perf. 13
753 A238 2.70k org & dk bl   1.25 .30
754 A239 2.70k multi   1.10 .50

Europa (1959-
84)
A240

1984, May 3   Engr.   Perf. 12½
755 A240 2.70k red   *1.75 .20*
756 A240 3.70k blue   *2.25 1.60*

Prince Henrik,
50th Birthday
A241

D Day, 40th
Anniv.
A242

1984, June 6   Engr.
757 A241 2.70k brown red   1.10 .30
758 A242 2.70k War Memorial,
Copenhagen   1.10 .50

See Greenland No. 160.

17th Cent.
Inn — A243

1984, June 6
759 A243 3k multicolored   1.25 1.00

Fishing
and
Shipping
A244

1984, Sept. 6   Engr.
760 A244 2.30k Research (Herring)   1.60 2.00
761 A244 2.70k Sea transport   1.10 .60
762 A244 3.30k Deep-sea fishing 1.60 2.00
763 A244 3.70k Deep-sea, diff.   1.50 2.00
Nos. 760-763 (4)   5.80 6.60

A245   A246

1984, Oct. 5   Litho. & Engr.
764 A245 1k Post bird   .50 .25

1984, Oct. 5
Holberg Meets with an Officer, by Wilhelm
Marstrand (1810-73).

765 A246 2.70k multicolored   1.10 .50

Ludvig Holberg (1684-1754), writer.

Jewish
Community in
Copenhagen,
300th
Anniv. — A247

1984, Oct. 5
766 A247 3.70k Woman blessing
Sabbath can-
dles   1.50 1.25

Carnival in Rome, by Christoffer W.
Eckersberg (1783-1853) — A248

Paintings: 10k, Ymer and Odhumble (Nordic
mythology figures), by Nicolai A. Abildgaard
(1743-1809), vert.

Perf. 12½x13, 13x12½
1984, Nov. 22   Litho. & Engr.
767 A248 5k multicolored   2.75 2.75
768 A248 10k multicolored   5.25 5.25

German and
French Reform
Church, 300th
Anniv. — A249

1985, Jan. 24   Engr.   Perf. 13
769 A249 2.80k magenta   1.10 .50

A250

Bonn-Copenhagen Declaration, 30th
Anniv. — A250

1985, Feb. 21   Litho.   Perf. 14
770 A250 2.80k Map, flags   1.40 .65

A251   A252

1985, Mar. 14   Perf. 13
771 A251 3.80k multicolored   1.50 .90

Intl. Youth Year.

Souvenir Sheet

Early postal ordinances.

1985, Mar. 14   Litho. & Engr.
772   Sheet of 4   6.00 6.50
a.   A252 1k Christian IV's Ordinance
      on Postmen, 1624   1.40 1.60
b.   A252 2.50k Plague Mandate, 1711   1.40 1.60
c.   A252 2.80k Ordinance on Prohibi-
      tion of Mail by Means other than
      the Post, 1775   1.40 1.60
d.   A252 3.80k Act on Postal Articles,
      1831   1.40 1.60

HAFNIA '87 phil. exhib. Sold for 15k.

Europa
1985 — A253

1985, May 2
773 A253 2.80k Musical staff   *1.90   .50*
774 A253 3.80k Musical staff,
           diff.   2.25 1.25

Arrival of Queen
Ingrid in
Denmark, 50th
Anniv. — A254

1985, May 21
775 A254 2.80k Queen Mother,
           chrysanthemums   1.10 .50

See Greenland No. 163.

Opening of the
Faro
Bridges — A255

1985, May 21   Litho.   Perf. 13
776 A255 2.80k Faro-Falster
           Bridge   1.10   .25

St. Cnut's Land
Grant to Lund
Cathedral, 900th
Anniv. — A256

Seal of King Cnut and: 2.80k, Lund Cathedral. 3k, City of Helsingdorg, Sweden.

1985, May 21   Engr.
777 A256 2.80k multi   1.10   .45
778 A256 3k multi   2.00 2.00

See Sweden Nos. 1538-1539.

UN Decade for   Sports
Women   A258
A257

1985, June 27   Litho. & Engr.
779 A257 3.80k Cyclist   1.50 1.00

1985, June 27
780 A258 2.80k Women's floor
           exercise   1.10   .30
781 A258 3.80k Canoe & kayak   1.50   .90
782 A258 6k Cycling   2.40 1.75
      Nos. 780-782 (3)   5.00 2.95

Kronborg Castle,   UN 40th
Elsinore, 400th   Anniv. — A260
Anniv. — A259

1985, Sept. 5
783 A259 2.80k multi   1.10   .50

1985, Sept. 5
784 A260 3.80k Dove, emblem   1.60   .90

Niels Bohr (1885-1962),
Physicist — A261

1985, Oct. 3   Perf. 13x12½
785 A261 2.80k With wife Mar-
           grethe   1.25 2.00

Winner of 1922 Nobel Prize in Physics for
theory of atomic structure.

Hand Signing   Boat, by Helge
"D" — A262   Refn — A263

1985, Nov. 7   Engr.   Perf. 13
786 A262 2.80k multicolored   1.10   .25

Danish Assoc. for the Deaf, 50th anniv.

1985, Nov. 7   Litho.
787 A263 2.80k multicolored   1.25   .50

Abstract
Iron
Sculpture
by
Robert
Jacobsen
A264

Lithographed and Engraved
1985, Nov. 7   Perf. 13x12½
788 A264 3.80k multicolored   3.25 4.50

Painting
by Bjørn
Wiinblad
A265

1986, Jan. 23   Litho.   Perf. 13x12½
789 A265 2.80k multicolored   1.25 2.00

Amnesty
Intl., 25th
Anniv.
A266

Lithographed and Engraved
1986, Jan. 23   Perf. 13
790 A266 2.80k multicolored   1.10   .50

Miniature Sheet

HAFNIA '87 — A267

1986, Feb. 20
791   Sheet of 4   8.00 11.00
a.   A267 100o Holstein carriage, c.
      1840   1.75 2.50
b.   A267 250o Iceboat, c. 1880   1.75 2.50
c.   A267 280o 1st mail van, 1908   1.75 2.50
d.   A267 380o Airmail service 1919 1.75 2.50

      Sold for 15k.

Changing of the
Guard — A268

1986, Mar. 20   Perf. 13
792 A268 2.80k multicolored   1.10   .50

Royal Danish Life Guards barracks and
Rosenborg Drilling Ground, bicent.

Types of 1933-82

1986-90		Engr.	Perf. 13	
793	A32	5o brn org ('89)	.25	.25
794	A32	270o brt yel grn	1.00	.40
b.		Bklt. pane, 6 #318, 2 #691, 2		
		#794	4.75	
795	A32	300o brt yel grn	1.10	.35
796	A212	3k cop red	1.10	.25
797	A212	3.20k deep vio	1.25	.80
798	A212	3.20k carmine	1.25	.25
c.		Bklt. pane, 2 #693, 4 #798	7.00	
799	A212	3.40k dk grn	2.40	2.40
800	A212	3.80k dark vio	1.60	1.60
801	A212	4.10k dark blue	1.60	.40
802	A212	4.20k dk pur	2.40	2.00
803	A212	4.40k dp bl	1.60	.35
804	A55	4.60k gray	4.00	4.00
805	A55	6.50k dp grn	2.50	.80
806	A55	6.60k green	4.00	5.25
807	A55	7.10k brn vio	3.25	3.25
808	A55	7.30k green	4.50	5.25
809	A55	7.70k dk brn vio	4.00	1.50
810	A55	11k brown	4.75	2.75
811	A55	20k dp ultra	7.25	.70
812	A55	22k henna brn	7.25	1.60
813	A55	23k dark olive grn	9.00	2.00
814	A55	24k dark olive grn	8.50	1.00
815	A55	26k dark olive grn	11.00	2.00
		Nos. 793-815 (23)	85.55	39.15

Issued: 6.50k, 20k, 1/9/86; 22k, 1/3/87;
270o, 3k, #797, 3.80k, 4.10k, 4.60k, 6.60k,
7.10k, 24k, 1/7/88; #794b, 1/28/88; 300o,
#798, 3.40k, 4.20k, 4.40k, 7.30k, 7.70k, 11k,
26k, 1/26/89; 5o, 1989; 23k, 1/11/90.

No. 793 issued for use in lieu of currency of
the same face value.

Soro Academy,
400th
Anniv. — A269

1986, Apr. 28   Litho. & Engr.
816 A269 2.80k multi   1.10   .50

A270   A271

1986, Apr. 28
817 A270 3.80k multi   1.50 1.00

Intl. Peace Year.

1986, May 26   Litho.
818 A271 2.80k multi   1.50   .50

Crown Prince Frederik, 18th birthday.

Nordic Cooperation Issue
1986 — A272

Sister towns.

1986, May 27   Engr.
819 A272 2.80k Aalborg Harbor   1.00   .35
820 A272 3.80k Thisted Church
           and Town Hall   1.50   .90

Hoje Tastrup
Train Station
Opening, May
31 — A273

1986, May 27   Litho.
821 A273 2.80k multi   1.10   .50

Mailbox,   Natl. Bird
Telegraph   Candidates
Lines,   A275
Telephone
A274

1986, June 19   Litho.   Perf. 13
822 A274 2.80k multi   1.10   .50

19th European Intl. PTT Congress, Copenhagen, Aug. 12-16.

1986, June 19   Litho. & Engr.

Finalists: a, Corvus corax. b, Sturnus vulgaris. c, Cygnus olor (winner). d, Vanellus
vanellus. e, Alauda arvensis.

823   Strip of 5   9.00 10.00
a.-e. A275 2.80k any single   1.75 1.00

A276

HAFNIA '87 — A277

1986, June 19
824 A276 2.80k multi   1.10 .50

Danish Rifle, Gymnastics and Sports Club, 125th anniv.

Souvenir Sheet

1986, Sept. 4
825   Sheet of 4   8.75 12.50
  a. A277 100o Mailcoach, c. 1841   1.75 2.50
  b. A277 250o Postmaster, c. 1840   1.75 2.50
  c. A277 280o Postman, c. 1851   1.75 2.50
  d. A277 380o Rural postman, c.
         1893   1.75 2.50

Sold for 15k.

Europa
1986 — A278

Cupid — A279

1986, Sept. 4   **Engr.**
826 A278 2.80k Street sweeper   2.10 .20
827 A278 3.80k Garbage truck   2.50 1.50

1986, Oct. 9   **Litho.**
828 A279 3.80k multi   1.50 .90

Premiere of The Whims of Cupid and the Ballet Master, by Vincenzo Galeotti, bicent.

Refugee — A280   A281

1986, Oct. 9   **Litho. & Engr.**
829 A280 2.80k multi   1.10 .50

Danish Refugee Council Relief Campaign.

1986, Oct. 9   Litho.   Perf. 13

Protestant Reformation in Denmark, 450th Anniv.: Sermon, altarpiece detail, 1561, Thorslunde Church, Copenhagen.

830 A281 6.50k multi   2.50 1.25

A282

Abstract by Lin Utzon — A283

1986, Nov. 6   **Litho. & Engr.**
831 A282 3.80k multi   2.40 2.40

Organization for Economic Cooperation and Development, 25th anniv.

1987, Jan. 22   Litho.   Perf. 13
832 A283 2.80k multi   1.10 .50

Art appreciation.

A284

A285

1987, Feb. 26   Engr.   Perf. 13
833 A284 2.80k lake & black   1.10 .50

Danish Consumer Council, 40th anniv.

1987, Apr. 9   Litho.   Perf. 13

Religious art (details) from Ribe Cathedral.

834 A285   3k Fresco   1.25 .60
835 A285 3.80k Stained-glass
                 window   1.75 1.50
836 A285 6.50k Mosaic   2.75 2.75
      Nos. 834-836 (3)   5.75 4.85

Ribe Cathedral redecoration, 1982-1987, by Carl-Henning Pedersen.

A286   A287

Europa (Modern architecture): 2.80k, Central Library, Gentofte, 1985. 3.80k, Hoje Tastrup High School, 1985, horiz.

1987, May 4   Engr.   Perf. 13
837 A286 2.80k rose claret   1.90 .50
838 A286 3.80k bright ultra   2.50 1.50

1987, May 4
839 A287 2.50k dk red & bl blk 1.40 1.25

Danish Academy of Technical Sciences (ATV), 50th anniv.

8th
Gymnaestrada,
Herning, July 7-
11 — A288

1987, June 18   **Litho. & Engr.**
840 A288 2.80k multi   1.10 .50

A289   A290

1987, June 18
841 A289 3.80k multi   1.50 1.00

Danish Cooperative Bacon Factories, cent.

1987, Aug. 27   **Litho.**
842 A290 3.80k Single-sculler   1.50 .90

World Rowing Championships, Aug. 23-30.

HAFNIA '87, Bella Center,
Copenhagen, Oct. 16-25 — A291

Litho. & Engr.

1987, Aug. 27   Perf. 13x12½
843 A291 280o Type A15,
               mail train c.
               1912   1.40 1.40

Souvenir Sheet

843A A291 280o like No. 843,
               green lawn
               and loco-
               motive   24.00 26.00

Purchase of No. 843A included admission to the exhibition. Sold for 45k.

Abstact by Ejler
Bille — A292

1987, Sept. 24   Litho.   Perf. 13
844 A292 2.80k multi   1.10 .25

Rasmus Rask (1787-1832),
Linguist — A293

1987, Oct. 15   Engr.   Perf. 13x12½
845 A293 2.80k dark henna
               brown   1.10 .50

A294

A295

Emblem: Miraculous Catch (Luke 5:4-7),
New Testament.

1987, Oct. 15   Perf. 13
846 A294   3k carmine lake   1.25 .50

Clerical Assoc. for the Home Mission in Denmark, 125th anniv.

Photo. & Engr., Litho. (4.10k)
1988, Feb. 18   Perf. 13

Designs: 3k, Two lions from the gate of Rosenburg Castle around the monogram of Christian IV. 4.10k, Portrait of the monarch painted by P. Isaacsz, vert.

847 A295   3k blue gray & gold 1.25 .30
848 A295 4.10k multi   1.60 .75

Accession of Christian IV (1577-1648), King of Denmark and Norway (1588-1648), 400th anniv.

Ole Worm (1588-
1654),
Archaeologist,
and Runic
Artifacts — A296

1988, Feb. 18   **Engr.**
849 A296 7.10k chocolate   2.75 2.75

A298

Odense,
1000th
Anniv. — A297

Design: St. Cnut's Church and statue of Hans Christian Andersen, Odense.

1988, Mar. 10   **Engr.**
850 A297 3k multi   1.25 .50

1988, Apr. 7   **Litho.**
851 A298 2.70k multi   1.10 .80

Danish Civil Defense and Emergency Planning Agency, 50th Anniv.

WHO, 40th
Anniv. — A299

Abolition of
Stavnsbaand,
200th
Anniv. — A300

1988, Apr. 7   **Litho. & Engr.**
852 A299 4.10k multi   1.60 1.00

1988, May 5   **Litho.**

Painting: King Christian VII riding past the Liberty Memorial, Copenhagen, by C.W. Eckersberg (1783-1853).

853 A300 3.20k multi   1.25 1.00

Stavnsbaand (adscription) provided that all Danish farmers' sons from age 4 to 40 would be bound as villeins to the estates on which they were born, thus providing landowners with free labor.

A301

A302

Europa: Transport and communication.

1988, May 5
854 A301   3k Postwoman on
               bicycle   1.75 .20
855 A301 4.10k Mobile telephone 2.50 1.00

1988, June 16   **Litho.**
856 A302 4.10k multi   1.60 .75

1988 Individual Speedway World Motorcycle Championships, Denmark, Sept. 3.

Federation of
Danish Industries,
150th
Anniv. — A303

Painting (detail): *The Industrialists,* by P.S. Kroyer.

1988, June 16   *Perf. 13½x13*
857 A303 3k multi   1.25 .55

Danish Metalworkers' Union, Cent. — A304

1988, Aug. 18   Litho.   *Perf. 13*
858 A304 3k Glass mosaic by Niels Winkel   1.25 .50

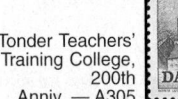

Tonder Teachers' Training College, 200th Anniv. — A305

1988, Aug. 18   Engr.   *Perf. 13x12½*
859 A305 3k lake   1.25 .30

Homage to Leon Degand, Sculpture by Robert Jacobsen A306

1988, Sept. 22   *Perf. 11½x13*
860 A306 4.10k blk, lake & gray   2.50 *4.50*
Danish-French cultural exchange program, 10th anniv. See France No. 2130.

Preservation of Historic Sites — A307

1988, Oct. 13   Engr.   *Perf. 13x12½*
861 A307   3k Lumby Windmill, 1818   1.40 .50
862 A307 7.10k Vejstrup Water Mill, 1837   2.75 2.25

Paintings in the State Museum of Art, Copenhagen — A308

4.10k, *Bathing Boys,* 1902, by Peter Hansen (1868-1928). 10k, *The Hill at Overkaerby,* 1917, by Fritz Syberg (1862-1939).

         Litho. & Engr.
1988, Nov. 3   *Perf. 13*
863 A308 4.10k multi   3.25 4.00
864 A308 10k multi   6.50 7.25
   See #881-882, 951-952, 972-973, 1018-1019.

The Little Mermaid, Sculpture by Edvard Eriksen — A309

1989, Feb. 16   **Engr.**
865 A309 3.20k dark green   1.25 .50
   Tourism industry, cent.

Danish Soccer Assoc., Cent. — A310

NATO Membership, 40th Anniv. — A311

1989, Mar. 16   **Litho.**
866 A310 3.20k multi   1.25 .50

1989, Mar. 16   **Litho.**
867 A311 4.40k dk blue, gold & lt blue   1.75 1.00

Nordic Cooperation Issue — A312

Folk costumes.

1989, Apr. 20   **Litho. & Engr.**
868 A312 3.20k Woman from Valby   1.25 .40
869 A312 4.40k Pork butcher   1.75 1.25

European Parliament 3rd Elections A313

1989, May 11   **Litho.**
870 A313 3k blue & yellow   1.25 1.25

Europa 1989 — A314

Children's toys.

1989, May 11   **Litho. & Engr.**
871 A314 3.20k Lego blocks   *1.90* .20
872 A314 4.40k Wooden soldiers, by Kay Bojesen   3.00 .90

Agricultural Museum, Cent. — A315

1989, June 15   Engr.   *Perf. 13*
873 A315 3.20k Tractor, 1889   1.25 .50

Interparliamentary Union, Cent. — A316

1989, June 15   **Litho. & Engr.**
874 A316 3.40k Folketing Chamber layout   2.50 2.50

Danish Fishery and Marine Research Institute, Cent. A317

1989, Aug. 24   **Litho. & Engr.**
875 A317 3.20k multi   1.10 .50

Bernhard Severin Ingemann (1789-1862), Poet and Novelist — A318

1989, Aug. 24   **Engr.**
876 A318 7.70k dark green   2.75 1.50

A319   A320

Danish Film Office, 50th Anniv.: 3k, Scene from the short feature film *They Reached the Ferry,* 1948. 3.20k, Bodil Ipsen (d. 1964), actress. 4.40k, Carl Th. Dreyer (1889-1968), screenwriter and director.

1989, Sept. 28   **Litho.**
877 A319   3k multi   1.10 1.10
878 A319 3.20k multi   1.10 .50
879 A319 4.40k multi   1.60 .90
    Nos. 877-879 (3)   3.80 2.50

1989, Nov. 10   **Litho. & Engr.**
880 A320 3.20k multi   1.25 .50
   Stamp Day, 50th anniv.

Art Type of 1988

Paintings: 4.40k, *Part of the Northern Gate of the Citadel Bridge,* c. 1837, by Christen Kobke (1810-1848). 10k, *A Little Girl, Elise Kobke, With a Cup in Front of Her,* c. 1850, by Constantin Hansen (1804-1880).

1989, Nov. 10   *Perf. 12½x13*
881 A308 4.40k multi   2.50 2.50
882 A308 10k multi   5.75 5.75

Types of 1933-82 and:

A321a
Queen
A321   Margrethe II
Perf. 12½, 13 (A321a)

1990-98   **Engr.**
883 A32   25o bluish black   .25 .25
  a.   Bklt. pane, 4 #691, 2 #883   1.90
884 A32   125o carmine lake   .50 .25
885 A32   325o lt yel grn   1.25 1.25
886 A32   350o yellow green   1.40 .75
887 A212 3.50k dark red   1.60 .25
  a.   Bklt. pane, 2 each #691, 885, 887   6.75
888 A321 3.50k henna brown   1.40 .25
  b.   Bklt. pane, 4 each #883, #884, #888 ('91)   8.50
889 A212 3.75k dark green   1.60 1.90
890 A321 3.75k green   3.25 4.00
891 A321 3.75k red   1.60 .50
  a.   Bklt. pane, 4 each #884, #891   9.00
  b.   Booklet pane, 2 each #691, 883, 891   4.75
    Complete booklet, #891b   4.75
892 A321a 3.75k red   1.60 .25
  a.   Booklet pane, 2 each #691, 883, 892   4.50
    Complete booklet, #892a   4.50

  b.   Booklet pane, 2 #883, 4 #494, 2 #892   4.50
    Complete booklet, #892b   4.50
893 A321   4k brown   1.60 .65
894 A321a   4k deep bl grn   1.75 .65
895 A321 4.25k olive brown   1.75 1.90
896 A212 4.50k brown violet   2.40 3.25
897 A321 4.50k violet   1.75 2.00
898 A321a 4.50k deep bl blk   1.75 .75
899 A212 4.75k dark blue   1.90 .50
900 A321 4.75k blue   1.90 .50
901 A321 4.75k violet   1.75 2.00
902 A321a 4.75k brown   1.90 2.10
903 A321a   5k violet   2.00 .50
904 A321   5k blue   1.75 .50
905 A321 5.25k black   2.10 1.50
906 A321a 5.25k deep blue   2.10 .75
907 A321 5.50k green   2.50 3.25
908 A321a 5.50k henna brown   2.25 2.10
909 A55   7.50k dark bl grn   3.00 2.75
    Nos. 883-909 (27)   48.60 35.20

   Queen Margrethe II's 50th birthday (No. 888).
   Issued: #888, 4/5; #890, 897, 900, 1990; #888a, 2/14/91; #886, 891, 891a, 901, 904, 6/10/92; 5.50k, 1/13/94; 4k, 5.25k, 6/27/96; #892, 892a, 1/14/97; #894, 902, 903, 906, 8/28/97; #895, 898, 908, 909, 3/26/98; others, 1/11/90.
   See Nos. 1120, 1127, 1135.

A322   A323

Design: Silver coffee pot designed by Axel Johannes Kroyer, Copenhagen, 1726.

1990, Feb. 15   Engr.   *Perf. 13*
911 A322 3.50k dark blue & blk   1.40 .50
   Museum of Decorative Art, cent.

1990, Feb. 15
   Steam engine, 200th anniv.: Steam engine built by Andrew Mitchell, 1790.
912 A323 8.25k dull red brown   3.25 1.75

Nyholm, 300th Anniv. A324

1990, Apr. 5   **Engr.**
913 A324 4.75k black   1.90 .75

Europa 1990 — A325

1990, Apr. 5   **Litho.**
914 A325 3.50k Royal Monogram, Haderslev P.O.   2.50 .20
915 A325 4.75k Odense P.O.   3.75 .75

A326   A327

Pieces from the Flora Danica Banquet Service produced for King Christian VII.

1990, May 3   **Litho.**
916 A326 3.50k Bell-shaped lid, dish   1.90 1.90
917 A326 3.50k Gravy boat, dish   1.90 1.90
918 A326 3.50k Ice pot, casserole, lid   1.90 1.90
919 A326 3.50k Serving dish   1.90 1.90
  a.   Strip of 4, #916-919   8.00 8.00
   Flora Danica porcelain, 200th anniv.

1990, June 14

Endangered plant species.

920	A327	3.25k Marshmallow	1.25	1.25
921	A327	3.50k Red helleborine	2.40	.40
922	A327	3.75k Purple orchis	1.60	1.60
923	A327	4.75k Lady's slipper	2.00	.95
		Nos. 920-923 (4)	7.25	4.20

Village Churches,
Jutland — A328

Perf. 13x12½, 12½x13

1990, Aug. 30   **Engr.**

924	A328	3.50k Gjellerup	1.40	.40
925	A328	4.75k Veng	1.90	.90
926	A328	8.25k Bredsten, vert.	3.25	2.10
		Nos. 924-926 (3)	6.55	3.40

Fredericia,
"The Town
for
Everybody"
A329

Engr. & Embossed

1990, Oct. 5   **Perf. 13**

927	A329	3.50k black & red	1.40	.55

Tordenskiold (Peter
Wessel, 1690-
1720),
Admiral — A330

1990, Oct. 5   **Litho.**   **Perf. 13½x13**

928	A330	3.50k multicolored	1.40	.55

Prevent Bicycle
Thefts — A331

Design: 3.50k, Stop drunk driving.

1990, Nov. 8   **Litho.**   **Perf. 13x12½**

930	A331	3.50k shown	1.40	1.25
931	A331	3.50k Automobile, wine glass	1.40	.30

Locomotives — A332

1991, Mar. 14   **Engr.**   **Perf. 13**

932	A332	3.25k IC3 1990	1.90	1.90
933	A332	3.50k Class A 1882	1.60	.70
934	A332	3.75k Class MY 1954	1.90	1.60
935	A332	4.75k Class P 1907	2.40	1.25
		Nos. 932-935 (4)	7.80	5.45

Europa — A333   Jutland Law,
750th
Anniv. — A334

Satellite photographs showing temperatures
of Danish: 3.50k, Waters. 4.75k, Land.

1991, May 2   **Litho.**   **Perf. 13**

936	A333	3.50k multicolored	2.00	.25
937	A333	4.75k multicolored	2.75	1.00

1991, May 2

938	A334	8.25k multicolored	3.25	2.75

Danish
Islands — A335

1991, June 6

939	A335	3.50k Fano	1.60	.30
940	A335	4.75k Christianso	2.00	.90

Decorative   Keep Denmark
Art — A336   Clean — A337

Designs: 3.25k, Earthenware bowl and jars
by Christian Poulsen. 3.50k, Chair by Hans
Wegner, vert. 4.75k, Silver cutlery by Kay
Bojesen, vert. 8k, Lamp by Poul Henningsen.

1991, Aug. 22   **Litho.**   **Perf. 13**

941	A336	3.25k multicolored	1.25	1.25
942	A336	3.50k multicolored	1.25	.40
943	A336	4.75k multicolored	1.60	1.00
944	A336	8.25k multicolored	3.75	4.00
		Nos. 941-944 (4)	7.85	6.65

1991, Sept. 19   **Engr.**   **Perf. 13**

Designs: 3.50k, Cleaning up after dog.
4.75k, Picking up litter.

945	A337	3.50k red	1.50	.30
946	A337	4.75k blue	2.00	1.00

Posters from
Danish Museum of
Decorative
Arts — A338

Posters for: 3.50k, Nordic Advertising Congress, by Arne Ungermann (1902-1981).
4.50k, Poster Exhibition at Copenhagen Zoo
(baboon), by Valdemar Andersen (1875-
1928). 4.75k, Danish Air Lines, by Ib Andersen
(1907-1969). 12k, The Sinner, by Sven Brasch
(1886-1970).

1991, Sept. 19   **Litho.**

947	A338	3.50k multicolored	1.25	.40
948	A338	4.50k multicolored	2.40	3.25
949	A338	4.75k multicolored	1.75	2.00
950	A338	12k multicolored	5.25	4.50
		Nos. 947-950 (4)	10.65	10.15

Art Type of 1988

Designs: 4.75k, Lady at her Toilet by Harald
Giersing (1881-1927), vert. 14k, Road through
a Wood by Edvard Weie (1879-1943), vert.

1991, Nov. 7   **Litho. & Engr.**   **Perf. 13x12½**

951	A308	4.75k multicolored	2.50	3.25
952	A308	14k multicolored	6.50	7.75

A339   A340

Treasures of Natl. Museum: 3.50k, Earthenware bowl, Skarpsalling. 4.50k, Bronze
dancer, Grevensvaenge. 4.75k, Bottom plate

of silver cauldron, Gundestrup. 8.25k, Flint
knife, Hindsgavl.

1992, Feb. 13   **Engr.**   **Perf. 13**

953	A339	3.50k dk vio & brown	1.40	.40
954	A339	4.50k dk bl & dk ol green	2.75	2.75
955	A339	4.75k brown & black	1.60	1.25
956	A339	8.25k dk ol grn & vio brown	3.25	3.25
		Nos. 953-956 (4)	9.00	7.65

1992, Mar. 12   **Perf. 13½x13**

957	A340	3.50k rose carmine	1.60	.65

Danish Society of Chemical, Civil, Electrical,
and Mechanical Engineers, cent.

Souvenir Sheet

Queen Margaret I (1353-
1412) — A341

Litho. & Engr.

1992, Mar. 12   **Perf. 12½**

958	A341	Sheet of 2	5.25	6.75
a.		3.50k Fresco	2.50	3.25
b.		4.75k Alabaster bust	2.50	3.25

Nordia '94, Scandinavian Philatelic Exhibition. No. 958 sold for 12k to benefit the
exhibition.

Discovery of America,
500th Anniv. — A342

1992, May 7   **Engr.**   **Perf. 12½**

959	A342	3.50k Potato plant	2.00	.40
960	A342	4.75k Ear of corn	3.75	1.75

Europa.

Protect the Environment — A343

Litho. & Engr.

1992, June 10   **Perf. 13**

961	A343	3.75k Hare beside road	1.50	.30
962	A343	5k Fish, water pollution	2.00	.70
963	A343	8.75k Cut trees, vert.	3.50	2.00
		Nos. 961-963 (3)	7.00	3.00

Queen Margrethe II and Prince Henrik,
25th Wedding Anniv. — A344

1992, June 10   **Litho.**   **Perf. 12½x13**

964	A344	3.75k multicolored	1.40	1.60

See Greenland No. 253.

A345   A346

1992, July 16   **Perf. 13**

965	A345	3.75k multicolored	2.00	.50

Denmark, European soccer champions.

1992, Aug. 27   **Engr.**   **Perf. 13**

966	A346	3.75k blue	1.50	.50

Danish Pavilion, Expo '92, Seville.

A347   A348

1992, Oct. 8   **Litho. & Engr.**   **Perf. 13**

967	A347	3.75k blue & org	1.50	.65

Single European market.

Litho. & Engr.

1992, Oct. 8   **Perf. 12½**

Cartoon characters: 3.50k, A Hug, by Ivar
Gjorup. 3.75k, Love Letter, by Phillip Stein
Jonsson. 4.75k, Domestic Triangle, by
Nikoline Werdelin. 5k, Poet and His Little Wife,
by Jorgen Mogensen.

968	A348	3.50k multicolored	1.75	1.00

Engr.

969	A348	3.75k red & purple	1.40	.30
970	A348	4.75k blk & red brn	2.50	2.50
971	A348	5k blue & red brn	1.75	.70
		Nos. 968-971 (4)	7.40	4.50

Art Type of 1988

5k, Landscape from Vejby, 1843, by John
Thomas Lundbye. 10k, Motif from Halleby
Brook, 1847, by Peter Christian Skovgaard.

Litho. & Engr.

1992, Nov. 12   **Perf. 12½x13**

972	A308	5k multicolored	2.25	2.50
973	A308	10k multicolored	4.50	5.25

A349   A350

1992, Nov. 12   *Perf. 13*
974 A349 3.75k Jacob's fight with
       angel   1.50   .50

Publication of new Danish bible.

Litho. & Engr.
1993, Feb. 4   *Perf. 13*

Archaeological Treasures. Anthropomorphic
gold foil figures found in: 3.75k, Lundeborg,
horiz. 5k, Bornholm.

975 A350 3.75k multicolored   1.40   .30
976 A350 5k multicolored   1.90   .70

A351

A352

Butterflies.

1993, Mar. 11   **Litho.**
977 A351 3.75k Small tortoise-
       shell   1.40   .40
978 A351 5k Large blue   2.10   .80
979 A351 8.75k Marsh fritillary   4.00   4.00
980 A351 12k Red admiral   4.50   4.50
     Nos. 977-980 (4)   12.00   9.70

1993, May 6   **Litho.**   *Perf. 12½*

Posters: 3.75k, Pierrot, by Thor Bogelund,
1947, horiz. 5k, Balloons, by Wilhelm Freddie,
1987.

981 A352 3.75k multicolored   1.40   .30
982 A352 5k multicolored   1.75   .80

Tivoli Gardens, 150th anniv.

A353

A354

Europa (Contemporary paintings by): 3.75k,
Troels Worsel, horiz. 5k, Stig Brogger.

1993, May 6   *Perf. 13*
983 A353 3.75k multicolored   1.40   1.10
984 A353 5k multicolored   1.90   .90

1993, June 17   **Engr.**   *Perf. 13*
985 A354 5k dark blue green   1.75   .90

Danish-Russian relations, 500th anniv. See
Russia No. 6154.

Training Ships
A355   A356

Perf. 13, 13½x13 (#987)
1993, June 17   **Litho. & Engr.**
986 A355 3.75k Danmark   1.25   .30
987 A356 4.75k Jens Krogh   2.25   3.00
988 A355 5k Georg Stage,
       horiz.   2.00   1.10

Size: 39x28mm
Perf. 13x13½
989 A356 9.50k Marilyn
       Anne, horiz.   4.00   4.50
     Nos. 986-989 (4)   9.50   8.90

Child's Drawing
of Viking
Ships — A357

Letter Writing
Campaign — A358

1993, Aug. 19   **Litho.**   *Perf. 13*
990 A357 3.75k multicolored   1.50   .50
991 A358 5k lt & dk bl & blk   2.00   1.25

Ethnic
Jewelry — A359

1993, Sept. 16   **Litho.**   *Perf. 13*
992 A359 3.50k Falster   1.40   .70
993 A359 3.75k Amager   1.50   .30
994 A359 5k Laeso   2.00   .60
995 A359 8.75k Romo   3.50   2.00
     Nos. 992-995 (4)   8.40   3.60

Cubist
Paintings
A360

5k, Assemblage, by Vilhelm Lundstrom,
1929. 15k, Composition, by Franciska Clau-
sen, 1929.

Litho. & Engr.
1993, Nov. 11   *Perf. 12½*
996 A360 5k multicolored   2.50   2.50
997 A360 15k multicolored   6.00   6.50

    See Nos. 1033-1034, 1080-1081.

Conservation — A361

1994, Jan. 27   **Litho.**   *Perf. 13*
998 A361 3.75k Save water   1.25   .30
999 A361 5k CO2   1.75   .65

Castles
A362

Castles: 3.50k, Marselisborg, Aarhus.
3.75k, Amalienborg, Copenhagen. 5k, Fredensborg, North Zealand. 8.75k, Graasten, South
Jutland.

Litho. & Engr.
1994, Mar. 17   *Perf. 13x12½*
1000 A362 3.50k multicolored   1.25   .70
1001 A362 3.75k multicolored   1.40   .30
1002 A362 5k multicolored   1.75   .50
1003 A362 8.75k multicolored   3.00   3.00
   a.   Bklt. pane, #1000-1003   10.00   10.00

No. 1003a printed with 2 different labels.
One shows a marching band, the other shows
a ship.

Danmark
Expedition, 1906-
08 — A363

Europa: 3.75k, Expedition ship, Danmark,
Alfred Wegener's weather balloon. 5k, Theodolite, Johan Peter Koch, cartographer.

1994, May 5   **Engr.**   *Perf. 13*
1004 A363 3.75k deep brn vio   *1.40*   .20
1005 A363 5k dp slate grn   *2.00*   .90

Trams — A364

Designs: 3.75k, Copenhagen tram (Engel-
hardt). 4.75k, Aarhus car. 5k, Odense tram,
vert. 12k, Horse-drawn tram.

Litho. & Engr.
1994, June 9   *Perf. 13*
1006 A364 3.75k multicolored   1.25   .30
1007 A364 4.75k multicolored   2.25   2.75
1008 A364 5k multicolored   1.75   1.40
     Size: 38x21mm
1009 A364 12k multicolored   5.25   5.25
    Nos. 1006-1009 (4)   10.50   9.70

Children's
Stamp
Competition
A365

ILO, 75th Anniv.
A366

1994, Aug. 25   **Litho.**   *Perf. 12½*
1010 A365 3.75k multicolored   1.25   .50

1994, Aug. 25   *Perf. 13*
1011 A366 5k multicolored   1.75   .90

A367

A368

Wild animals.

Litho. & Engr.
1994, Oct. 20   *Perf. 12½*
1012 A367 3.75k House spar-
        rows   1.25   .35
1013 A367 4.75k Badger   1.90   1.75
1014 A367 5k Squirrel, vert.   1.75   .90
1015 A367 9.50k Black grouse   3.25   4.00
     Size: 36x26mm
       Perf. 13
1016 A367 12k Grass snake   4.00   4.50
    Nos. 1012-1016 (5)   12.15   11.50

1994, Nov. 10   **Litho.**   *Perf. 13*
1017 A368 3.75k multicolored   1.25   .50

Folk High Schools, 150th anniv.

Painting Type of 1988
Designs: 5k, Study of Italian Woman and
Sleeping Child, by Wilhelm Marstrand. 15k,

Interior from Amaliegade with the Artist's
Brothers, by Wilhelm Bendz.

Litho. & Engr.
1994, Nov. 10   *Perf. 12½x13*
1018 A308 5k multicolored   2.00   2.40
1019 A308 15k multicolored   6.00   6.00

Aarhus
Cathedral
School, 800th
Anniv. — A369

Litho. & Engr.
1995, Jan. 26   *Perf. 13*
1020 A369 3.75k multicolored   1.50   .50

UN, 50th
Anniv. — A370

Litho. & Engr.
1995, Jan. 26   *Perf. 13*
1021 A370 5k multicolored   2.00   .45
    Complete booklet, 10 #1021   30.00

Danish
Islands
A371

1995, Mar. 16   **Engr.**   *Perf. 13*
1022 A371 3.75k Avernako   1.50   .30
    Complete booklet, 10 #1022   15.00
1023 A371 4.75k Fejo   1.90   1.90
1024 A371 5k Fur   2.00   .75
1025 A371 9.50k Endelave   3.00   3.50
   a.   Booklet pane, #1022-1025 +
       2 labels   10.00
    Complete booklet, 2 #1025a   21.00
    Nos. 1022-1025 (4)   8.40   6.45

No. 1025a printed with four different large
labels. Labels with one pane are MF Faaborg
II and MF Endelave. The other pane has MF
Bukken-bruse and MF Fursund.

Liberation
of
Denmark,
50th Anniv.
A372

Designs: 3.75k, Gen. Montgomery, Town
Hall Square, vert. 5k, White busses returning
from concentration camps. 8.75k, Airplane
dropping supplies to resistance. 12k, Jews
escape across the Sound to Sweden.

1995, May 4   **Litho.**   *Perf. 13*
1026 A372 3.75k multicolored   *1.50*   .20
    Complete booklet, 10 #1026   15.00
1027 A372 5k multicolored   *1.90*   .75
1028 A372 8.75k multicolored   *3.00*   3.00
1029 A372 12k multicolored   *4.00*   4.00
    Nos. 1026-1029 (4)   10.40   7.95

Europa (Nos. 1026-1027).

A373

A374

1995, June 8   **Litho.**   *Perf. 13*
1030 A373 3.50k multicolored   1.40   1.00

Danish Rhymed Chronicle, 500th anniv.

1995, June 8

3.75k, Roskilde Festival. 5k, Tonder Festival.

1031	A374	3.75k multi, horiz.	1.50	1.25
	Complete booklet, 10 #1031		14.00	
1032	A374	5k multi	1.75	.50

No. 1031 is 28x21mm.

DANMARK 10.00 — Paintings A375

Designs: 10k, "Sct. Hans Aften, 1955," by Jens Sondergaard. 15k, "Landskab-Gudhjem, 1939," by Niels Lergaard.

Litho. & Engr. — Perf. 13x12½

1033	A375	10k multicolored	4.00	4.50
1034	A375	15k multicolored	6.00	6.50

Tycho Brahe (1546-1601), Astronomer A376

3.75k, Uranienborg Observatory. 5.50k, Sextant.

Litho. & Engr. — Perf. 13

1035	A376	3.75k multicolored	1.50	.50
1036	A376	5.50k multicolored	2.00	2.00

See Sweden Nos. 2149-2150.

Toys A377

Designs: 3.75k, Tekno cars. 5k, Dolls, teddy bear. 8.75k, Model trains. 12k, Glud & Marstrand tin horse-drawn carriage & fire pumper.

1995, Nov. 9 — Perf. 13x12½

1037	A377	3.75k multicolored	1.25	.30
	Complete booklet, 10 #1037		13.00	
1038	A377	5k multicolored	1.75	.75
1039	A377	8.75k multicolored	3.00	3.00
1040	A377	12k multicolored	4.00	4.00
	Nos. 1037-1040 (4)		10.00	8.05

A378 — A379

Cartoonlike views of Copenhagen: 3.75k, Round Tower as music box. 5k, Christiansborg Castle. 8.75k, Marble Church as top of balloon. 12k, The Little Mermaid statue on stage.

1996, Jan. 25 — Litho. — Perf. 13

1041	A378	3.75k multicolored	1.25	.30
	Complete booklet, 10 #1041		13.00	
1042	A378	5k multicolored	1.75	.70
1043	A378	8.75k multicolored	3.00	3.00
1044	A378	12k multicolored	4.00	4.50
	Nos. 1041-1044 (4)		10.00	8.50

Copenhagen, 1996 cultural capital of Europe.

1996, Mar. 21 — Litho. — Perf. 13

1045	A379	3.75k Sports for disabled	1.25	.30
	Complete booklet, 10 #1045		13.00	
1046	A379	4.75k Swimming	1.60	1.60
1047	A379	5k Sailing	1.75	.50
1048	A379	9.50k Cycling	3.25	3.25
a.	Bklt. pane of 4, #1045-1048 + 2 labels		9.00	
	Complete booklet, 2 #1048a		17.50	

No. 1048a printed with two different large labels. One shows hands and soccer ball, second shows tennis racket and tennis balls. Danish Federation for Sports for the Disabled (No. 1045). Modern Olympic Games, cent., Sports Confederation of Denmark, cent., 1996 Summer Olympics, Atlanta (Nos. 1046-1048).

A380 — A381

1996, May 9 — Litho. — Perf. 13

1049	A380	3.75k multicolored	1.50	.50

Danish Employers' Confederation, cent.

1996, May 9

Famous Danish Women (Europa): 3.75k, Karen Blixen (1885-1962), writer. 5k, Asta Nielsen (1881-1972), silent screen actress.

1050	A381	3.75k lt brn & dk brn	1.50	.50
1051	A381	5k gray & dk blue	1.75	.75
	Complete booklet, 10 #1051		20.00	

A382 — A383

Wooden Dinghies: 3.50k, Roskilde Fjord sail boat. 3.75k, Limfjorden skiff. 12.25k, Two-masted smack, South Funen Archipelago.

Perf. 13, 12½ (#1053) — Engr.

1052	A382	3.50k multicolored	1.25	1.00
1053	A382	3.75k multicolored	1.50	.50
	Complete booklet, 10 #1053		16.00	
1054	A382	12.25k multicolored	4.50	5.25
	Nos. 1052-1054 (3)		7.25	6.75

No. 1053 is 20x39mm.

1996, Sept. 12 — Litho. & Engr. — Perf. 13x12½

Lighthouses.

1055	A383	3.75k Fornaes	1.50	.30
	Complete booklet, 10 #1055		16.00	
1056	A383	5k Blavandshuk	1.75	.50
a.	Bklt. pane, 8 #1055, 2 #1056		15.00	
	Complete booklet, #1056a		17.50	
1057	A383	5.25k Bovbjerg	2.00	2.00
1058	A383	8.75k Mon	3.00	3.00
	Nos. 1055-1058 (4)		8.25	5.80

Art Works of Thorvald Bindesboll (1846-1908) — A384

Litho. & Engr. — Perf. 13

1059	A384	3.75k Pitcher	1.50	.30
	Complete booklet, 10 #1059		16.00	

Litho.

1060	A384	4k Portfolio cover	1.60	1.10

Paintings A385

Designs: 10k, "At Lunch," by P.S. Kroyer, 1893. 15k, "The Girl with Sunflowers," by Michael Ancher, 1889.

1996, Nov. 7 — Litho. & Engr. — Perf. 13x12½

1061	A385	10k multicolored	4.00	4.00
1062	A385	15k multicolored	5.25	5.25

A386 — A387

Queen Margrethe II: 3.50k, With Prince Henrik. 3.75k, With Crown Prince Frederik. 4k, Delivering New Year speech. 5.25k, Waving to crowd.

1997, Jan. 14 — Litho. — Perf. 13

1063	A386	3.50k multicolored	1.25	1.25
1064	A386	3.75k multicolored	1.50	.30
	Complete booklet, 10 #1064		16.00	
1065	A386	4k multicolored	1.40	.70
1066	A386	5.25k multicolored	2.00	1.50
a.	Sheet of 4, #1063-1066 + 2 labels		6.50	6.50
	Nos. 1063-1066 (4)		6.15	3.75

Queen Margrethe II, 25th anniv. of coronation.

1997, Mar. 13 — Engr. — Perf. 13

Open Air Museum, Copenhagen, Cent.: 3.50k, Kalstrup post mill. 3.75k, Ellested water mill. 5k, Fjellerup manor barn. 8.75k, Romo farm.

1067	A387	3.50k multicolored	1.25	1.00
1068	A387	3.75k multicolored	1.25	.30
	Complete booklet, 10 #1068		12.50	
1069	A387	5k multicolored	1.75	.75
	Complete booklet, 10 #1069		17.50	
1070	A387	8.75k multicolored	3.00	2.50
a.	Booklet pane, #1067-1070 + label		7.50	
	Complete booklet, 2 #1070a		14.00	
	Nos. 1067-1070 (4)		7.25	4.55

No. 1070a printed with two different large labels. One shows a view of Ellested water mill, the other shows a farm in Ejersted.

Great Belt Railway Link — A388

A389

1997, May 15 — Litho. — Perf. 13

1071	A388	3.75k East Tunnel	1.50	.50
	Complete booklet, 10 #1071		15.00	
1072	A388	4.75k West Bridge	1.75	1.75

1997, June 12 — Litho. — Perf. 13

Kalmar Union, 600th Anniv.: No. 1073, Margrete I and Eric of Pomerania. No. 1074, The Three Graces symbolizing Denmark, Norway and Sweden.

1073	A389	4k multicolored	1.25	1.25
1074	A389	4k multicolored	1.25	1.25
a.	Pair, #1073-1074		3.00	4.00

No. 1074a is a continuous design.

Copenhagen-Roskilde Railway, 150th Anniv. — A390

Designs: 3.75k, Two modern trains under Carlsberg Bridge. 8.75k, Early steam train going under Carlsberg Bridge.

1997, June 12 — Litho. & Engr. — Perf. 13

1075	A390	3.75k multicolored	1.50	.30
	Complete booklet, 10 #1075		15.00	
1076	A390	8.75k multicolored	3.00	2.50

End of Railway Mail Service A391

1997, June 12 — Litho.

1077	A391	5k multicolored	1.75	.70

Stories and Legends A392

Europa: 3.75k, Large cat on top of treasure chest, from "The Tinder Box." 5.25k, Butterfly, pond, frog, from "Thumbelina."

1997, Aug. 28 — Engr. — Perf. 13

1078	A392	3.75k multicolored	1.75	.50
1079	A392	5.25k multicolored	2.25	1.50

Painting Type of 1993

Designs: 9.75k, "Dust Dancing in the Sun," by Vilhelm Hammershoi (1864-1916). 13k, "Woman Mountaineer," by J.F. Willumsen (1863-1958).

Litho. & Engr. — Perf. 13x12½

1080	A360	9.75k multicolored	3.75	4.50
1081	A360	13k multicolored	5.00	5.75

A393

Danish Design: 3.75k, Faaborg chair, vert. 4k, Margrethe bowl, vert. 5k, The Ant (chair). 12.25k, Georg Jensen silver bowl, vert.

1997, Nov. 6 — Litho. — Perf. 13

1082	A393	3.75k multicolored	1.25	.30
	Complete booklet, 10 #1082		12.50	
1083	A393	4k multicolored	1.25	.75
1084	A393	5k multicolored	2.00	.45
1085	A393	12.25k multicolored	4.50	5.25
	Nos. 1082-1085 (4)		9.00	6.75

A394   A395

Danish Confederation of Trade Unions, Cent.: 3.50k, General Workers Union in Denmark (SiD). 3.75k, Danish Confederation of Trade Unions (LO). 4.75k, Danish Nurse's Organization. 5k, Union of Commercial and Clerical Employees in Denmark (HK).

1998, Jan. 22   Litho.   Perf. 13

1086	A394	3.50k multicolored	1.10	.90
1087	A394	3.75k multicolored	1.25	.30
		Complete booklet, 10 #1087	12.50	
1088	A394	4.75k multicolored	1.90	2.50
1089	A394	5k multicolored	1.25	.65
		Complete booklet, 10 #1089	20.00	
		Nos. 1086-1089 (4)	6.25	4.35

Litho. & Engr.

1998, Mar. 26   Perf. 13

1090	A395	3.75k multicolored	1.50	.65
		Complete booklet, 10 #1090	15.00	

City of Roskilde, 1000th anniv.

A396   A397

1998, Mar. 26   Litho.   Perf. 13

1091	A396	5k Ladybug	2.25	.50

Reduce poison.

1998, May 28   Litho.   Perf. 13

New Post & Tele Museum, Copenhagen: 3.75k, Postman, 1922. 4.50k, Morse code operator, c. 1910. 5.50k, Telephone operator, 1910. 8.75k, Modern postman.

1092	A397	3.75k multicolored	1.25	.30
		Complete booklet, 10 #1092	12.50	
a.		Booklet pane, 2 each #1087, 1089, 3 ea. 1090, 1092	17.50	
		Complete booklet, #1092a	17.50	
1093	A397	4.50k multicolored	1.50	1.50
1094	A397	5.50k multicolored	2.00	2.00
1095	A397	8.75k multicolored	2.75	2.75
a.		Booklet pane, 2 #1092-1095	7.50	
		Complete booklet, 2 #1095a	15.00	
		Nos. 1092-1095 (4)	7.50	6.55

No. 1095a is printed with two backgrounds. One shows part of King Christian IV's "Order Concerning Postmen," 1624. The other shows part of Copenhagen c. 1923. Complete booklets contain panes with each background.

Bridges over Great Belt A398

1998, May 28   Engr.   Perf. 13

1096	A398	5k West Bridge (shown)	2.00	1.10
1097	A398	5k East Bridge (suspension)	2.00	1.10
a.		Pair, #1096-1097 + label	4.00	4.25

Nordic Stamps — A399

Shipping: No. 1098, Signal flags, harbor master with binoculars. No. 1099, Radar

image of entrance to Copenhagen harbor, sextant.

1998, May 28   Litho.   Perf. 13

1098	A399	6.50k multicolored	2.50	2.50
1099	A399	6.50k multicolored	2.50	2.50
a.		Pair, #1098-1099	5.00	5.75
b.		Souvenir sheet, #1099a	5.75	7.00

National Festivals — A400

Europa: 3.75k, Horse at Danish agricultural show. 4.50k, Theater, tents at Arhus Festival Week, Arhus.

Litho. & Engr.

1998, Sept. 3   Perf. 13

1100	A400	3.75k multicolored	*1.50*	*.60*
		Complete booklet, 10 #1100	15.00	
1101	A400	4.50k multicolored	*1.75*	*1.00*

Contemporary Art — A401

Paintings: 3.75k, Danish Autumn, by Per Kirkeby. 5k, Alpha, by Mogens Andersen, vert. 8.75k, Imagery, by Ejler Bille, vert. 19k, Celestial Horse, by Carl-Henning Pedersen.

Perf. 12½x13, 13x12½

1998, Oct. 15   Litho. & Engr.

1102	A401	3.75k multicolored	1.25	1.25

Litho.

1103	A401	5k multicolored	2.00	1.50
1104	A401	8.75k multicolored	3.25	3.25
1105	A401	19k multicolored	6.50	7.75
		Nos. 1102-1105 (4)	13.00	13.75

See Nos. 1160-1161, 1190-1191, 1204-1205, 1235-1236, 1255-1256, 1282-1283, 1333-1336.

A402

Fossil, name of Danish geologist: 3.75k, Ammonite, Ole Worm (1588-1654). 4.50k, Shark's teeth, Niels Stensen (1638-86). 5.50k, Sea Urchin, Soren Abildgaard (1718-91). 15k, Slit-shell snail, Erich Pontoppidan (1698-1764).

1998, Nov. 5   Engr.   Perf. 13

1106	A402	3.75k multicolored	1.25	.30
		Complete booklet, 10 #1106	12.50	
1107	A402	4.50k multicolored	1.75	1.75
1108	A402	5.50k multicolored	1.75	1.75
1109	A402	15k multicolored	5.00	4.50
a.		Souvenir sheet, #1106-1109	10.00	11.00

Wavy Lines and Queen Types of 1933, 1997 and:

Queen Margrethe II — A402a

1999-2004   Engr.   Perf. 12¾

1111	A32	150o purple	.60	.25
1112	A32	375o green	1.50	.70
1113	A32	400o green	1.25	.65
1114	A321a	4k red	1.60	.50
a.		Booklet pane, 4 #883, 2 #494, 2 #1114	4.00	

		Complete booklet, #1114a	4.00	
1115	A402a	4k red	1.60	.50
b.		Booklet pane, 4 #883, 2 #494, 2 #1115	2.50	
		Complete booklet, #1115b	2.50	
c.		Sheet of 8 + label	13.00	
1116	A32	425o green	1.60	.65
1117	A402a	4.25k blue	1.75	1.00
1118	A402a	4.25k red	1.50	.70
b.		Booklet pane, 6 #883, 2 #1118	3.50	
c.		Sheet of 8 + central label	12.50	—
1119	A402a	4.50k orange	1.75	1.50
a.		Vert. strip of 10 + 10 etiquettes	17.50	
1120	A402a	4.50k red	1.75	1.10
a.		Booklet pane, 2 #494, 2 #1120	4.00	—
		Complete booklet, #1120a	4.00	
b.		Sheet of 8 + central label	14.50	—
1121	A402a	4.75k sepia	1.75	1.75
1122	A402a	5k dk green	2.00	1.00
a.		Sheet of 8 + 8 etiquettes	55.00	—
1123	A402a	5.25k ultra	2.10	1.00
1124	A402a	5.50k violet	2.25	.90
a.		Sheet of 8 + label	19.00	
b.		Sheet of 8 + 8 etiquettes	20.00	15.00
1125	A321a	5.75k blue	2.25	1.25
1126	A402a	5.75k emerald	2.25	1.25
1127	A402a	6k bister	2.40	.75
a.		Sheet of 10 + 10 etiquettes	25.00	—
1128	A402a	6.25k green	2.25	2.00
1129	A402a	6.50k slate grn	2.50	.90
a.		Sheet of 8 + 8 etiquettes	20.00	20.00
b.		Sheet of 8 + central label	20.00	—
1130	A321a	6.75k slate green	2.75	2.75
1131	A402a	6.75k henna brn	2.75	2.50
1132	A402a	7k rose lilac	2.75	2.50
1133	A402a	8.50k bright blue	3.00	3.00
1134	A55	10.50k dk bl gray	4.00	2.50
1135	A55	11.50k dk bl gray	4.00	4.00
1136	A55	12.50k gray	4.50	4.50
1137	A55	13k orange	4.50	4.50
1138	A55	15k blue	5.25	5.25
		Nos. 1111-1138 (28)	68.15	49.85

Issued: 375o, #1118, 1130, 1/13/99; #1125, 1/3/00; #1119, 1119a, 4.25k, 4.50k, 5k, 5.25k, 5.50k, #1126, 1131, 4/12/00; No. 1119b, 6k, 7k, 5/9/01; Nos. 1119c, 1121a, 1124a, 4/17/01; 150o, 4.75k, 6.50k, 10.50k, 1/2/02. 400o, No. 1120, 6.25k, 8.50k, 11.50k, 1/2/03. No. 1120b, 3/12. Nos. 1124b, 1129a, 3/12/03. Nos. 1128b, 1/2/03; No. 1122a, 4/2/02; 425o, No. 1120, 12.50k, 13k, 15k, 1/2/04. Nos. 1120b, 1127a, 1/2/04.

See Nos. 1295, 1296-1303.

A403

1999, Jan. 13   Litho.   Perf. 13

1143	A403	4k Oersted Satellite	1.50	.55

Deciduous Trees A404

4k, Fagus sylvatica. 5k, Fraxinus excelsior, vert. 5.25k, Tilia cordata, vert. 9.25k, Quercus robur.

1999, Jan. 13   Litho. & Engr.

1144	A404	4k multicolored	1.25	.30
		Complete booklet, 10 #1144	12.50	
1145	A404	5k multicolored	1.75	1.00
1146	A404	5.25k multicolored	1.75	.65
1147	A404	9.25k multicolored	3.00	3.00
		Nos. 1144-1147 (4)	7.75	4.95

50th Anniversaries — A405

Litho. & Engr.

1999, Feb. 24   Perf. 13

1148	A405	3.75k Home Guard	1.50	.90
1149	A405	4.25k NATO	1.60	1.00

A406   A407

Harbingers of spring.

1999, Feb. 24   Litho.

1150	A406	4k Lapwing in flight	1.60	.30
		Complete booklet, 10 #1150	16.00	
1151	A406	5.25k Geese	1.75	.90
a.		Souvenir sheet, #1150-1151	5.50	4.50

Litho. & Engr.

1999, Apr. 28   Perf. 13

Nature Reserves.

1152	A407	4.50k Vejlerne	*1.75*	*1.00*
1153	A407	5.50k Langli	*2.00*	*1.25*

Europa.

Council of Europe, 50th Anniv. A408

1999, Apr. 28   Engr.

1154	A408	9.75k blue	3.25	2.25

Danish Constitution, 150th Anniv. — A409

1999, June 2   Litho.   Perf. 13

1155	A409	4k red & black	1.60	.50

Danish Revue, 150th Anniv. A410

Performers: 4k, Kjeld Petersen and Dirch Passer, comedians. 4.50k, Osvald Helmuth, singer. 5.25k, Preben Kaas and Jorgen Ryg, comedians, singers. 6.75k, Liva Weel, singer.

1999, June 2   Perf. 13

1156	A410	4k deep red	1.60	.50
		Complete booklet, 10 #1156	16.00	
1157	A410	4.50k slate	1.75	1.40
1158	A410	5.25k deep blue	1.75	.85
		Complete booklet, 10 #1158	17.50	
1159	A410	6.75k deep claret	2.25	1.60
a.		Bklt. pane, #1156-1159 + 2 labels	7.50	
		Complete booklet, 2 #1159a	15.00	
		Nos. 1156-1159 (4)	7.35	4.35

No. 1159a printed with two different pairs of labels. One version has showgirl label at left, the second version has showgirl label at right. Complete booklets contain one of each pane.

Contemporary Paintings Type

9.25k, Fire Farver, by Thomas Kluge. 16k, Dreng, by Lise Malinovsky.

1999, Aug. 25   Litho.   Perf. 12¾

1160	A401	9.25k multi, vert.	3.25	4.00
1161	A401	16k multi, vert.	5.25	5.25

Opening of New Extension of the Royal Library, "The Black Diamond" A411

1999, Aug. 25   **Engr.**   **Perf. 13¾**
1162 A411 8.75k black   3.00 3.00

Migratory Birds — A412

Litho. & Engr.
1999, Sept. 29   **Perf. 12¾**
1163 A412 4k Swallows   1.60 .30
   Complete booklet, 10 #1163   16.00
1164 A412 5.25k Gray-lag geese   1.75 1.00
   a. Souvenir sheet, #1163-1164   5.25 6.50
1165 A412 5.50k Common eider   1.75 .90
1166 A412 12.25k Arctic tern   4.50 5.25
   a. Souvenir sheet, #1165-1166   9.00 10.00
   Nos. 1163-1166 (4)   9.60 7.45

Stamps from Nos. 1164a and 1166a lack white border found on Nos. 1163-1166.

New Year 2000 — A413

1999, Nov. 10   **Litho.**   **Perf. 13¼**
1167 A413 4k Hearts   1.25 .50
1168 A413 4k Wavy lines   1.25 .50
   a. Bklt. pane, 5 ea #1167-1168   32.50
   Complete booklet, #1168a   32.50

The 20th Century — A414

4k, Prof. J.H. Deuntzer on front page of newspaper, 1901. 4.50k, Newspaper illustration, 1903. 5.25k, Asta Nielsen and Poul Reumert in the film "The Abyss," 1910. 5.75k, Advertising sticker showing woman on telephone, 1914.
See sheet of 16, #1184a.

2000, Jan. 12   **Litho. & Engr.**
1169 A414 4k buff & blk   1.40 .50
   Complete booklet, 10 #1169   14.00
1170 A414 4.50k multicolored   1.75 1.00
1171 A414 5.25k multicolored   1.75 1.00
   Complete booklet, 10 #1171   17.50
1172 A414 5.75k multicolored   1.75 1.25
   Nos. 1169-1172 (4)   6.65 3.75

2000, May 9
4k, Allegory of women suffrage on front page of newspaper, 1915. 5k, Newspaper caricature of the Kanslergade Agreement, 1933. 5.50k, Film "Long and Short," 1927. 6.75k, Front page of Radio Weekly Review, 1925.

1173 A414 4k multi   1.40 .55
   Booklet, 10 #1173   14.00
1174 A414 5k multi   1.75 1.00
1175 A414 5.50k multi   2.00 1.60
1176 A414 6.75k multi   2.25 2.50
   Nos. 1173-1176 (4)   7.40 5.65

2000, Aug. 23
4k, Liberation of Denmark on front page of newspaper, 1945. 5.75k, Newspaper caricature of new constitution, 1953. 6.75k, Poster for film "Café Paradise," 1950. 12.25k, Advertisement for Arena television, 1957.

1177 A414 4k multi   1.40 .90
   Booklet, 10 #1177   14.00

1178 A414 5.75k multi   2.00 1.60
1179 A414 6.75k multi   2.25 2.50
1180 A414 12.25k multi   4.00 4.25
   Nos. 1177-1180 (4)   9.65 9.25

2000, Nov. 8
4k, Entry of Denmark into European Community on front page of newspaper, 1972. 4.50k, Newspaper caricature of youth revolt, 1969. 5.25k, Poster for film "The Ölsen Gang," 1968. 5.50k, Denmark Post website on Internet, 1999.

1181 A414 4k multi   1.40 .90
   Booklet, 10 #1181   14.00
1182 A414 4.50k multi   1.60 1.60
1183 A414 5.25k multi   1.75 1.00
   Booklet, 10 #1183   17.50
   a. Booklet pane, #1171, 1175, 1179, 1183 + label   8.00
   Booklet, 2 #1183a   16.00
1184 A414 5.50k multi   2.00 1.25
   a. Sheet of 16, #1169-1184   42.50 42.50
   Nos. 1181-1184 (4)   6.75 4.75

No. 1183a comes with two different labels. Booklet contains one of each.

60th Birthday of Queen Margrethe II — A415

2000, Apr. 12   **Litho.**   **Perf. 12¾**
1185 A415 4k blk & car   1.60 .60
   Complete booklet, 10 #1185   16.00
1186 A415 5.25k blk & blue   1.75 .90
   a. Souvenir sheet, #1185-1186   4.00 4.25

Oresund Bridge, Sweden-Denmark — A416

Litho. & Engr.
2000, May 9   **Perf. 12¾**
1187 A416 4.50k shown   1.75 1.90
   Nos. 1187-1188   (4)

Litho.
1188 A416 4.50k Map   1.75 1.90
   a. Pair, #1187-1188   3.50 3.75

See Sweden Nos. 2391-2393.

Europa, 2000
Common Design Type
2000, May 9   **Litho.**   **Perf. 13**
1189 CD17 9.75k multi   3.50 2.25

Contemporary Art Type of 1998
Designs: 4k, Pegasus, by Kurt Trampedach. 5.25k, Landscape, by Nina Sten-Knudsen.

2000, Sept. 27   **Perf. 12¾**
1190 A401 4k multi   1.75 1.75
1191 A401 5.25k multi   1.75 1.90

Royal Danish Air Force, 50th Anniv. A417

2000, Sept. 27   **Engr.**
1192 A417 9.75k black & red   4.00 3.25
   a. Souvenir sheet of 1   4.00 4.50

Botanical Gardens, Copenhagen — A418

Litho. & Engr.
2001, Jan. 24   **Perf. 12¾**
1193 A418 4k Palm House   1.40 .60
   Booklet, 10 #1193   14.00
   Size: 28x21mm
1194 A418 6k Lake   2.00 .85
1195 A418 12.25k Water lilies   4.00 4.50
   Nos. 1193-1195 (3)   7.40 5.95

"Use the Language" A419

2001, Mar. 28   **Litho.**   **Perf. 13**
1196 A419 4k "A," text   1.40 .55
   Booklet, 10 #1196   14.00
1197 A419 7k "Z," text   2.75 .90

Danish Postage Stamps, 150th Anniv. — A420

Portion of #2 and: 4k, Engraver Martinus Willam Ferslew. 5.50k, Printer Andreas Thiele. 6k, Head Copenhagen postmaster Frantz Christopher von Jessen. 10.25k, Postmaster General Magrius Otto Spohus Count Danneskjold-Samsoe.

Litho. & Engr.
2001, Apr. 1   **Perf. 13¼x13**
1198 A420 4k multi   1.50 1.00
1199 A420 5.50k multi   1.90 1.25
   Booklet, 10 #1199   19.00
1200 A420 6k multi   2.00 1.25
1201 A420 10.25k multi   4.00 2.50
   a. Booklet pane, #1198-1201 + label   9.50
   Booklet, 2 #1201a   19.00
   Nos. 1198-1201 (4)   9.40 6.00

No. 1201a printed with two different labels. One version has proof of stamp design, sketch of proposed design and Ferslew's letter to Danneskjold-Samsoe, and other shows two essays and letter from M. T. C. Bartholdy.

Europa — A421

Designs: 4.50k, Hands in water. 9.75k, Woman's head, water.

2001, May 9   **Litho.**   **Perf. 13¼x13**
1202 A421 4.50k multi   1.50 .90
   a. Booklet pane of 5 + 5 etiquettes   7.50
   Booklet, 2 #1202a   15.00
1203 A421 9.75k multi   4.00 4.50

Contemporary Paintings Type of 1998
Designs: 18k, Missus, by Jorn Larsen, horiz. 22k, Postbillede, by Henning Damgaard-Sorensen.

Perf. 13x12½, 12½x13
2001, Aug. 22   **Litho.**
1204 A401 18k multi   6.00 6.50
1205 A401 22k multi   7.25 7.75

Youth Culture A422

Designs: 4k, Skateboarding. 5.50k, Kissing. 6k, Creating music. 10.25k, Tongue piercing.

2001, Aug. 22   **Perf. 13**
1206 A422 4k multi   1.60 .60
   Booklet, 10 #1206   16.00
1207 A422 5.50k multi   1.75 1.10
   Booklet, 10 #1207   17.50
1208 A422 6k multi   1.90 1.90
1209 A422 10.25k multi   4.00 4.00
   a. Souvenir sheet, #1206-1209   9.00 9.75
   Nos. 1206-1209 (4)   9.25 7.60

Hafnia 01 Philatelic Exhibition, Copenhagen A423

Monarch and stamps: 4k, Queen Margrethe II, #757, 1000. 4.50k, King Frederik IX, #775, 1003. 5.50k, King Christian X, #1001, B10. 7k, King Christian IX, #1002, 66.

Litho. & Engr.
2001, Oct. 16   **Perf. 13x13¼**
1210 A423 4k multi   1.60 .75
1211 A423 4.50k multi   1.75 1.75
1212 A423 5.50k multi   1.75 1.75
1213 A423 7k multi   2.50 2.75
   a. Souvenir sheet, #1210-1213   9.00 10.00
   b. Strip, #1210-1213 + central label   10.00 11.50
   Nos. 1210-1213 (4)   7.60 7.00

Island Ferries A424

Designs: 3.75k, Bukken-Bruse. 4k, Ouro. 4.25k, Hjarno. 6k, Barsofaergen.

2001, Nov. 7   **Perf. 12¾**
1214 A424 3.75k multi   1.25 1.60
1215 A424 4k multi   1.60 .60
   Booklet, 10 #1215   16.00
1216 A424 4.25k multi   1.60 1.60
1217 A424 6k multi   2.00 2.25
   Nos. 1214-1217 (4)   6.45 6.05

Comics and Cartoons — A425

Designs: 4k, Rasmus Klump, by Vilhelm Hansen. 5.50k, Valhalla, by Peter Madsen. 6.50k, Jungledyret Hugo, by Flemming Quist Moller. 10.50k, Cirkeline, by Hanne Hastrup.

2002, Jan. 16   **Litho.**   **Perf. 13¼x13**
1218 A425 4k multi   1.50 .55
   Booklet, 10 #1218   15.00
   a. Sheet of 8 + label   15.00 4.00
1219 A425 5.50k multi   1.75 1.00
   Booklet, 10 #1219   17.50
   a. Sheet of 8 + label   21.00 5.50
1220 A425 6.50k multi   2.10 1.75
1221 A425 10.50k multi   4.00 4.50
   a. Souvenir sheet, #1218-1221   10.50 11.00
   Nos. 1218-1221 (4)   9.35 7.80

The Girls in the Airport, Sculpture by Hanne Varming — A426

Designs: 4k, Rear view. 5k, Front view.

Photo. & Engr.

2002, Mar. 13		Perf. 12¾	
1222 A426	4k multi, cream	1.60	.55
	Booklet, 10 #1222	16.00	
1223 A426	5k multi, cream	1.75	1.60

Europa — A427

Winning drawings in children's stamp design contest: 4k, Clown, by Luna Ostergard. 5k, Clown, by Camille Wagner Larsen.

2002, May 15	Litho.	Perf. 13	
1224 A427	4k multi	1.50	.90
	Booklet, 10 #1224	15.00	
1225 A427	5k multi	1.75	1.75
a.	Booklet pane of 5 + 5 etiquettes	8.75	—
	Booklet, 2 #1225a	17.50	

Landscapes A428

2002, May 15		Engr.	
1226 A428	4k Bornholm	1.60	.90
1227 A428	6k West Jutland	1.90	1.90
1228 A428	6.50k Langeland	1.75	2.25
1229 A428	12.50k Thy	4.50	4.50
	Nos. 1226-1229 (4)	9.75	9.55

Historic Postal Vehicles A429

Designs: 4k, 1953 Nimbus motorcycle. 5.50k, 1962 Bedford van. 10k, 1984 Renault 4 van. 19k, 1998 Volvo FH12 tractor trailer.

Litho. & Engr.

2002, Aug. 21		Perf. 13x13¼	
1230 A429	4k multi	1.60	.65
	Booklet, 10 #1230	16.00	
a.	Sheet of 8 + central label	14.00	—
1231 A429	5.50k multi	1.90	1.50
	Booklet, 10 #1231	19.00	
1232 A429	10k multi	4.00	4.00
1233 A429	19k multi	7.00	7.00
a.	Booklet pane of 4, #1230-1233	16.00	
	Booklet, 2 #1233a	32.50	
	Nos. 1230-1233 (4)	14.50	13.15

No. 1233a is printed with two different labels. One shows a 1908 Berliet van and the other a 2002 Peugeot Partner. Both are included in the booklet.

Opening of Copenhagen Metro — A430

2002, Sept. 25	Engr.	Perf. 12¾	
1234 A430	5.50k multi, tan	1.90	.90

Contemporary Paintngs Type of 1998

Designs: 5k, Children's Corner, by Jens Birkemose, vert. 6.50k, Maleren og Modellen, by Frans Kannik, vert.

2002, Sept. 25		Perf. 13x12½	
1235 A401	5k red & blue	1.75	1.75
1236 A401	6.50k multi	2.25	2.25

Intl. Council for the Exploration of the Sea, Cent. — A431

Atlantic cod and: 4k, Exploration ship Dana. 10.50k, Hirtshals lighthouse.

Litho. & Engr.

2002, Sept. 25		Perf. 13¼x13	
1237 A431	4k multi	1.60	.65
1238 A431	10.50k multi	4.00	4.00
a.	Souvenir sheet, #1237-1238	6.50	6.50

See Faroe Islands No. 426, Greenland Nos. 401-402.

Danish House Architecture A432

Designs: 4k, Dianas Have, Horsholm, by Vandkusten Design Studio, 1992. 4.25k, Blangstedgard, Odense, by Poul Ingemann, 1988. 5.50k, Dansk Folkeferie, Karrebaeksminde, by Stephan Kappel, 1979. 6.50k, Fredensborg Terraces, Fredensborg, by Jorn Utzon, 1963. 9k, Soholm, Klampenborg, by Arne Jacobsen, 1950.

Litho. & Engr.

2002, Nov. 8		Perf. 12¾	
1239 A432	4k multi	1.60	1.00
	Booklet, 10 #1239	16.00	
1240 A432	4.25k multi	1.60	.70
1241 A432	5.50k multi	1.90	1.50
1242 A432	6.50k multi	2.25	1.75
1243 A432	9k multi	3.00	3.00
	Nos. 1239-1243 (5)	10.35	7.95

See Nos. 1257-1261, 1267-1271, 1317-1321.

Youth Sports — A433

2003, Jan. 15	Litho.	Perf. 12¾	
1244 A433	4.25k Soccer	1.50	.70
	Booklet, 10 #1244	16.00	
a.	Sheet of 8 + central label	13.00	13.00
1245 A433	5.50k Swimming	1.75	1.50
	Booklet, 10 #1245	17.50	
1246 A433	8.50k Gymnastics	3.25	3.25
1247 A433	11.50k Handball	4.00	4.25
	Nos. 1244-1247 (4)	10.50	9.70

Danish Literary Greenland Expedition, Cent. — A434

Designs: 4.25k, Expedition members Harald Moltke, Knud Rasmussen, Jorgen Bronlund, Ludvig Mylius-Erichsen and Gabriel Olsen. 7k, Campsite.

2003, Mar. 12	Engr.	Perf. 12¾	
1248 A434	4.25k blue gray	1.60	.70

		Size: 61x22mm	
1249 A434	7k multi	2.75	2.75
a.	Souvenir sheet, #1248-1249 + label	5.00	5.00

See Greenland Nos. 407-408.

Europa A435

Insects A436

Poster art: 4.25k, Poster for Copenhagen International Theater Festival, by Ole Fick, 1985. 5.50k, Poster for Bertel Thorvaldsen Museum, by Ole Woldbye, 1970.

2003, May 14	Litho.	Perf. 12¾	
1250 A435	4.25k multi	1.50	.60
	Booklet, 10 #1250	15.00	

Engr.

1251 A435	5.50k black	1.75	1.40
	Booklet, 10 #1251	17.50	
a.	Sheet of 8 + central label	14.00	14.00

2003, May 14		Litho. & Engr.	

Designs: 4.25k, Ephemera danica. 6.50k, Dytiscus latissimus. 12k, Cordulegaster boltoni, vert.

1252 A436	4.25k multi	1.60	.80
a.	Sheet of 8 + central label	17.50	
1253 A436	6.50k multi	2.50	2.25
a.	Sheet of 8 + central label	27.50	—

		Size: 21x39mm	
1254 A436	12k multi	4.75	2.40
a.	Souvenir sheet, #1252-1254	8.00	8.50
	Nos. 1252-1254 (3)	8.85	5.45

Contemporary Art Type of 1998

Designs: 5.50k, Baering, by Sys Hindsbo. 19k, Det Forjaettede Land, by Poul Anker Bech.

2003, Aug. 27		Litho. & Engr.	
		Perf. 12½x13	
1255 A401	5.50k multi	1.75	1.75

Litho.

1256 A401	19k multi	6.50	6.50

Danish House Architecture Type of 2002

Designs: 4k, Bellahoj Apartment Complex, Copenhagen, by Tage Nielsen and Mogens Irming, 1944-58. 4.25k, Anchersvej, Klampenborg, by Mogens Lassen, 1935. 5.25k, Gerthasminde, Odense, by Anton Rosen, 1912-35. 9k, Solvang, Vallekilde College, by Andreas Bentsen and Martin Nyrop, 1889. 15k, Stenbrogard, Brorup, by Peter Holdensen, 1868.

2003, Aug. 27		Litho. & Engr.	
		Perf. 12¾	
1257 A432	4k multi	1.60	1.60
1258 A432	4.25k multi	1.60	.90
	Complete booklet, 10 #1258	16.00	
1259 A432	5.25k multi	1.75	1.75
1260 A432	9k multi	3.25	3.25
1261 A432	15k multi	4.50	4.50
	Nos. 1257-1261 (5)	12.70	12.00

A437

A438

2003, Nov. 7	Engr.	Perf. 12¾	
1262 A437	6.50k gray blue	2.50	1.90

Awarding of first Nobel Prize to a Dane (Niels Finsen for Physiology and Medicine), cent.

2003, Nov. 7		Litho. & Engr.	

Artifacts from Royal Jelling World Heritage Site: 4.25k, Queen Thyra's stone. 5.50k, King Gorm's cup. 8.50k, King Harald's stone. 11.50k, Wall paintings, Jelling Church.

1263 A438	4.25k multi	1.60	1.25
	Booklet, 10 #1263	16.00	
1264 A438	5.50k multi	1.75	1.50
	Booklet, 10 #1264	17.50	

1265 A438	8.50k multi	3.00	3.00
1266 A438	11.50k multi	4.00	4.00
	Nos. 1263-1266 (4)	10.35	9.75

A spiral-bound booklet, enclosed in a slipcase, with four booklet panes containing single stamps of Nos. 1263-1266, and a booklet pane containing a strip of Nos. 1263-1266, sold for 99k. Value, $35.

Danish House Architecture Type of 2002

Designs: 4.50k, Spurveskjul, Virum, by Nicolai Abildgaard, 1805. 6k, Liselund, Mon, by Andreas Kirkerup, 1792. 7k, Kampmann's Yard, Varde, by Hans Wolff Ollgaard, Hack Kampmann and Mikkel Stobberup, 1781. 12.50k, Harsdorff's House, Copenhagen, by Caspar Frederik Harsdorff, 1780. 15k, Nyso Manor, Praesto, by Jens Lauridsen.

2004, Jan.14		Litho. & Engr.	
		Perf. 12¾	
1267 A432	4.50k multi	1.60	1.00
	Booklet, 10 #1267	16.00	
1268 A432	6k multi	2.40	1.60
1269 A432	7k multi	2.50	2.50
1270 A432	12.50k multi	4.00	4.00
1271 A432	15k multi	5.25	5.25
	Nos. 1267-1271 (5)	15.75	14.35

Academy of Fine Arts, Copenhagen, 250th Anniv. — A439

2004, Mar. 26		Litho. & Engr.	
		Perf. 13¼x13	
1272 A439	5.50k multi	2.10	1.25
	Booklet, 10 #1272	21.00	

Norse Gods — A440

Designs: 4.50k, Heimdal guarding Bifrost bridge. 6k, Gefion plowing Sjaelland out of Sweden.

2004, Mar. 26			
1273 A440	4.50k multi	1.75	.85
a.	Sheet of 8 + central label	18.00	18.00
1274 A440	4.25k multi	2.40	1.10
a.	Souvenir sheet, #1273-1274	4.50	4.50
b.	Sheet of 8 + central label	26.00	26.00

Wedding of Crown Prince Frederik and Mary Donaldson — A441

No. 1275: a, Couple facing right. b, Couple facing left.

2004, May 14		Litho. & Photo.	
		Perf. 13x13¼	
1275 A441	Horiz. pair	4.00	1.25
	Booklet, 5 #1275	20.00	
a.-b.	4.50k Either single, denomination 9 mm wide	2.00	1.25
c.-d.	4.50k Either single, denomination 7½ mm wide	2.00	1.25
e.	Souvenir sheet, #1275c-1275d + central label	4.00	4.00

Frederiksberg Palace, 300th Anniv. — A442

Designs: 4.25k, Doorway overlooking Sondermarken Park. 4.50k, Gatehouse archway, castle yard. 6.50k, Aerial view.

Litho. & Engr.

2004, May 14			**Perf. 13**	
1276	A442	4.25k multi	1.60	1.60
1277	A442	4.75k multi	1.75	1.00
		Size: 55x32mm		
1278	A442	6.50k multi	2.50	2.00
a.		Souvenir sheet, #1276-1278	6.00	7.00
		Nos. 1276-1278 (3)	5.85	4.60

Prince Henrik, 70th Birthday — A443

2004, June 9		**Litho.**	**Perf. 12¾**	
1279	A443	4.50k multi	1.60	1.00

Europa
A444

2004, June 9			**Perf. 13**	
1280	A444	6k Cyclists	2.00	1.60
1281	A444	9k Sailboats	3.00	3.00

Contemporary Paintings Type of 1998

Designs: 13k, Senses the Body Landscape, by Lars Ravn, vert. 21k, The Dog Bites, by Lars Norgard, vert.

Litho. & Engr.

2004, Aug. 25			**Perf. 13x12½**	
1282	A401	13k multi	4.50	4.50
		Litho.		
1283	A401	21k multi	7.00	7.00

Viking Ship Museum, Roskilde
A445

Designs: 4.50k, Skuldelev 1 on Roskilde Fjord. 5.50k, Reconstruction of Skuldelev 2. 6.50k, Cross-section of ship. 12.50k, Excavation of archaelogical site where ships were found.

Litho. & Engr.

2004, Aug. 25			**Perf. 13x13¼**	
1284	A445	4.50k multi	1.60	1.00
		Complete booklet, 10 #1284	16.00	
1285	A445	5.50k multi	2.00	1.60
		Complete booklet, 10 #1285	20.00	
1286	A445	6.50k multi	2.40	2.00
1287	A445	12.50k multi	4.50	4.50
		Nos. 1284-1287 (4)	10.50	9.10

A spiral-bound booklet, enclosed in a slipcase, with four booklet panes containing single stamps of Nos. 1284-1287 and a booklet pane containing a strip of Nos. 1284-1287, sold for 99k. Value, $40.

Birds of Prey
A446

Designs: 4.50k, Falco tinnunculus. 5.50k, Accipiter nisus. 6k, Buteo buteo. 7k, Circus aeruginosus.

Litho. & Engr.

2004, Nov. 5			**Perf. 13**	
1288	A446	4.50k multi	1.75	.90
		Complete booklet, 10 #1288	17.50	
a.		Sheet of 8 + central label	14.00	14.00
1289	A446	5.50k multi	2.10	1.40
a.		Sheet of 8 + central label	17.00	17.00
1290	A446	6k multi	2.40	2.00
1291	A446	7k multi	2.75	2.25
		Nos. 1288-1291 (4)	9.00	6.15

Queen and Small State Seal Types of 1946-2000

2005-09		**Engr.**	**Perf. 12¾**	
1295	A402a	4.75k red	1.60	1.00
a.		Sheet of 8 + central label	15.00	
1296	A402a	5.50k red	2.00	.50
b.		Sheet of 8 #1296 + central label	18.00	—
1296A	A402a	6.50k blue	2.60	.50
1297	A402a	7.25k black violet	2.50	2.50
1298	A402a	7.50k blue	2.50	2.50
1299	A402a	7.75k vio blk	2.40	.90
1300	A402a	8k indigo	2.50	2.50
1301	A402a	8.25k Prussian blue	2.50	2.50
1302	A402a	8.75k Prus blue	3.00	1.00
1303	A402a	9k blue	3.25	3.25
1304	A55	10k lemon	3.25	1.25
1304A	A55	10.50k car rose	3.75	3.25
1305	A55	13.50k green	4.25	4.25
1308	A55	16k Prus grn	6.00	1.25
1309	A55	16.50k red brown	5.25	5.25
1310	A55	17k slate green	5.25	5.25
1311	A55	17.50k purple	5.25	5.25
1312	A55	20k blue	7.00	1.75
1312A	A55	20.50k purple	8.25	1.75
1313	A55	22k brown violet	7.00	6.00
		Nos. 1295-1313 (20)	80.10	52.40

Issued: 7.50k, 16.50k, 22k, 1/3. 4.75k, 8k, 11/11. 4.75k, 10k, 17k, 1/2/06. 7.25k, 8.25k, 11/10/06. 13.50k, 17.50k, 1/2/07. 20k, 11/8/07. 5.50k, 6.50k, 7.75k, 8.75k, 1/2/08. Nos. 1296b, 1308, 1312, 3/27/08. Nos. 1303, 1304A, 1/2/09. This is an expanding set. Numbers may change.

Danish House Architecture Type of 2002

Designs: 4.25k, Hjarup Manse, Vamdrup, c. 1665. 4.50k, Ejdersted Farm, Southwest Schleswig, 1653. 7.50k, Provstegade, Randers, c. 1650. 9.50k, Smith's Yard, Koge, c. 1550. 16.50k, Carmelite Monastery, Elsinore, c. 1500.

Litho. & Engr.

2005, Jan. 12			**Perf. 12¾**	
1317	A432	4.25k multi	1.60	1.60
1318	A432	4.50k multi	1.60	.65
		Complete booklet, 10 #1318	16.00	
a.		Booklet pane, 4 #691, 8 #1318	15.00	—
		Complete booklet, #1318a	15.00	
1319	A432	7.50k multi	2.50	2.50
1320	A432	9.50k multi	3.25	3.25
1321	A432	16.50k multi	6.00	6.00
		Nos. 1317-1321 (5)	14.95	14.00

Bonn-Copenhagen Declaration, 50th Anniv. — A447

2005, Mar. 2			**Litho.**	
1322	A447	6.50k multi	2.50	2.00
		See Germany No. 2330.		

Hans Christian Andersen (1805-75), Author — A448

Paper Cutting by Andersen, Scissors — A449

Designs: 6.50k, Pen, inkwell, illustration of duckling, manuscript handwritten by Andersen. 7.50k, Andersen's drawing of Casino dell'Orlogio, Rome, and boots.

2005, Mar. 2			**Engr.**	
1323	A448	4.50k black	1.60	1.60
a.		Sheet of 8 + central label	17.50	17.50
		Litho. & Engr.		
1324	A449	5.50k multi	2.00	2.00
		Complete booklet, 10 #1324	20.00	
a.		Sheet of 8 + central label	22.50	22.50
1325	A449	6.50k multi	2.25	2.00
1326	A449	7.50k multi	3.00	2.50
		Nos. 1323-1326 (4)	8.85	8.10

A spiral-bound booklet, enclosed in a slipcase, with four booklet panes containing single stamps of Nos. 1323-1326, and a booklet pane containing a strip of Nos. 1323-1326, sold for 99k. Value, $37.50.
See Malta Nos. 1196-1199.

August Bournonville (1805-79), Choreographer
A450

Bournonville and: 4.50k, Dancer. 5.50k, Dancers.

Litho. & Engr.

2005, May 4			**Perf. 13¼x13**	
1327	A450	4.50k multi	1.60	1.60
		Complete booklet, 10 #1327	16.00	
a.		Sheet of 8 + central label	14.00	—
1328	A450	5.50k multi	1.90	1.90
a.		Sheet of 8 + central label	17.00	
b.		Souvenir sheet, #1327-1328	4.00	4.00

Sailors in World War II — A451

Designs: 4.50k, Ship convoy. 7.50k, Unloading of ship's cargo.

2005, May 4		**Litho.**	**Perf. 13**	
1329	A451	4.50k multi	1.60	1.60
1330	A451	7.50k multi	2.75	2.75

Europa — A452

2005, May 4			**Perf. 12¾**	
1331	A452	6.50k Hot dog	2.40	1.90
1332	A452	9.50k Fish	3.50	3.75

Contemporary Art Type of 1998

Designs: 5.50k, Telepathy, by Anna Fro Vodder, vert. 6.50k, Home Again, by Kaspar Bonnén, vert. 7.50k, Unrest, by John Korner, vert. 12.50k, Palace in the Morning, by Tal Rosenzweig.

2005, Aug. 24			**Litho.**	
1333	A401	5.50k multi	1.90	1.90
1334	A401	6.50k multi	2.00	2.00
1335	A401	7.50k multi	2.40	2.40
1336	A401	12.50k multi	4.50	4.50
		Nos. 1333-1336 (4)	10.80	10.80

Perf. 13x12½, 12½x13

INDEX:2005 Intl. Design Exhibition, Copenhagen
A453

2005, Aug. 24		**Engr.**	**Perf. 13¼**	
1337	A453	4.50k black	1.75	1.25
		Complete booklet, 10 #1337	17.50	

Wavy Lines Type of 1905-17

2005-08		**Engr.**	**Perf. 12¾**	
1338	A10	25o indigo	.25	.20
a.		Booklet pane, 2 each #1295, 1338 ('06)	3.50	—
		Complete booklet, #1338a	3.50	
1339	A10	50o brown	.25	.20
1340	A10	100o bright blue	.35	.20
1341	A10	200o dark green	.60	.20
1342	A10	450o green	1.60	.65
1342A	A10	500o brt yel grn	1.90	.65
		Nos. 1338-1342A (6)	4.95	2.10

Wavy Line stamps, cent.
Issued: Nos. 1338-1342, 10/28/05. No. 1338a, 1/2/06. No. 1342A, 3/27/08.

Seals
A454

Designs: 4.50k, Phoca vitulina. 5.50k, Halichoerus grypus.

2005, Nov. 11		**Engr.**	**Perf. 13x13¼**	
1343	A454	4.50k multi	1.60	1.25
		Complete booklet, 10 #1343	16.00	
1344	A454	5.50k indigo	1.90	1.50
a.		Souvenir sheet, #1343-1344	4.00	4.00

Flowers — A455

Designs: 4.75k, Calanthus nivalis. 5.50k, Eranthis hyemalis. 7k, Crocus venus hybrid. 8k, Anemone nemorosa.

2006, Jan. 11		**Engr.**	**Perf. 12¾**	
1345	A455	4.75k multi	1.60	.90
		Complete booklet, 10 #1345	16.00	
a.		Sheet of 8 + central label	15.00	—
1346	A455	5.50k multi	1.75	1.75
		Complete booklet, 10 #1346	17.50	
a.		Sheet of 8 + central label	17.00	—
1347	A455	7k multi	2.25	2.25
1348	A455	8k multi	2.50	2.50
		Nos. 1345-1348 (4)	8.10	7.40

Creatures in Norse Mythology — A456

Designs: 4.75k, Elf king and elf girls. 7k, Incubi, werewolves, hel-horse, gnome and troll.

Litho. & Engr.

2006, Mar. 29   *Perf. 13¼x13*
1349	A456	4.75k multi	1.60 1.60
1350	A456	7k multi	2.40 2.40
a.		Souvenir sheet, #1349-1350	4.50 7.00

Rosenborg Castle, 400th Anniv. — A457

Designs: 4.75k, Castle exterior. 5.50k, Silver lion, thrones of king and queen. 13k, Royal coat of arms ceiling decoration.

2006, Mar. 29
1351	A457	4.75k multi	1.60 1.60
		Complete booklet, 10 #1351	16.00
1352	A457	5.50k multi	2.00 2.00
1353	A457	13k multi	4.50 4.50
		Nos. 1351-1353 (3)	8.10 8.10

A spiral-bound booklet, enclosed in a slip-case, with four booklet panes containing single stamps of Nos. 1351-1353 and a booklet pane containing a strip of Nos. 1351-1353, sold for 99k. Value, $35.

New Carlsberg Glyptotek, Cent. — A458

Designs: 4.75k, Marble relief from Athenian graveyard. 5.50k, Conservatory dome. 8k, Dancer Looking at the Sole of Her Right Foot, sculpture by Edgar Degas.

2006, June 7
1354	A458	4.75k multi	1.60 1.60
		Complete booklet, 10 #1354	16.00
1355	A458	5.50k multi	1.90 1.90
1356	A458	8k multi	2.50 2.50
a.		Souvenir sheet, #1354-1356	6.50 6.50
		Nos. 1354-1356 (3)	6.00 6.00

Race Cars A459

Designs: 4.75k, 1958 Alfa Dana Midget, Swebe Jap. 5.50k, 1965 Austin Mini Cooper S, 1965 Ford Cortina GT, 1965 Alfa Romeo 1600 GTA. 10k, 1963 Jaguar E Type, 1967 Volvo P 1800. 17k, 1965 Lotus Elan, Renault Alpine A 110.

2006, June 7   *Perf. 13x13¼*
1357	A459	4.75k multi	1.60 1.60
		Complete booklet, 10 #1357	16.00
1358	A459	5.50k multi	1.90 1.90
		Complete booklet, 10 #1358	19.00
1359	A459	10k multi	3.25 3.25
1360	A459	17k multi	5.25 5.25
		Nos. 1357-1360 (4)	12.00 12.00

Europa — A460

Winning designs in children's stamp design contest: 4.75k, Smiling children, by Rikke Veber Rasmussen. 7k, Two smiling children, by Anette Bertram Nielsen.

2006, Aug. 23   Litho.   *Perf. 13¼x13*
1361	A460	4.75k multi	1.90 .90
		Booklet, 10 #1361	19.00
1362	A460	7k blk & dull grn	2.75 1.25

Airplanes A461

Designs: 4.50k, J. C. H. Ellehammer's 1906 biplane. 4.75k, KZ II, 1946. 5.50k, KZ IV, 1944. 13k, KZ VII, 1947.

Litho. & Engr.

2006, Aug. 23   *Perf. 12¾*
1363	A461	4.50k multi	1.60 1.60
1364	A461	4.75k multi	1.60 1.60
a.		Miniature sheet of 8 + central label	14.00 14.00
1365	A461	5.50k multi	1.90 1.90
a.		Miniature sheet of 8 + central label	16.00 16.00
1366	A461	13k multi	4.25 4.25
		Nos. 1363-1366 (4)	9.35 9.35

Paintings by COBRA Group Artists A462

Designs: 4.75k, Untitled, by Asger Jorn. 5.50k, Landscape of the Night, by Else Alfelt, vert. 7k, New Skin, by Pierre Alechinsky. 8k, The Olive Eater, by Egill Jacobsen, vert.

Perf. 13x13¼, 13¼x13

2006, Nov. 10   Litho.
1367	A462	4.75k multi	1.60 1.60
		Booklet, 10 #1367	16.00
1368	A462	5.50k multi	1.90 1.90
1369	A462	7k multi	2.25 2.25
1370	A462	8k multi	2.50 2.50
		Nos. 1367-1370 (4)	8.25 8.25

See Belgium Nos. 2168-2169.

Danish Soldiers in United Nations Peace-keeping Forces, 50th Anniv. — A463

Litho. & Engr.

2007, Jan. 10   *Perf. 13*
1371	A463	4.75k multi	1.75 1.75

Intl. Polar Year A464

Designs: 7.25k, Wooden and walrus tusk carvings of Norse, Late Dorset and Thule cultures of Greenland. 13.50k, Research airplane used for measuring thickness of polar ice.

2007, Jan. 10   *Perf. 13¼*
1372	A464	7.25k multi	2.50 2.50
1373	A464	13.50k multi	4.75 4.75
a.		Souvenir sheet, #1372-1373	7.50 7.50

Windmills — A465

Designs: 4.50k, Askov Mill, 1891. 4.75k, Gedser Mil, 1957. 6k, Bogo Mill, 1989. 8.25k, Middelgrunden, 2000.

2007, Jan. 10   Engr.
1374	A465	4.50k brown	1.60 1.60
1375	A465	4.75k red	1.60 1.60
		Complete booklet, 10 #1375	16.00
a.		Sheet of 8 + central label	15.00 15.00
1376	A465	6k green	1.90 1.90
		Complete booklet, 10 #1376	19.00
a.		Sheet of 8 + central label	19.00 19.00
1377	A465	8.25k blue	2.50 2.50
		Nos. 1374-1377 (4)	7.60 7.60

Galathea 3 Scientific Expedition — A466

Satellite, ship and: 4.75k, Marine life. 7.25k, Globe showing route of expedition.

Litho. & Engr.

2007, Mar. 28   *Perf. 12¾*
1378	A466	4.75k multi	1.60 1.60
1379	A466	7.25k multi	2.40 2.40
a.		Souvenir sheet, #1378-1379	4.25 4.25

National Museum, Bicent. — A467

Designs: 4.75k, Ceremonial axes. 6k, Funen aquaemanale. 8.25k, Armillary sphere. 10.25k, Wooden mask, Borneo.

2007, Mar. 28   *Perf. 13¼*
1380	A467	4.75k Prus bl & blk	1.60 1.60
		Complete booklet, 10 #1380	16.00
1381	A467	6k brn lake & blk	2.00 2.00
1382	A467	8.25k orange & blk	2.50 2.50
1383	A467	10.25k bl gray & blk	3.25 3.25
		Nos. 1380-1383 (4)	9.35 9.35

A spiral-bound booklet, enclosed in a slip-case, with four booklet panes containing single stamps of Nos. 1380-1383 and a booklet pane containing a strip of Nos. 1380-1383, sold for 109k. Value, $35.

Europa A468

Scouts: 4.75k, On hike. 7.25k, Around campfire.

2007, June 6   *Perf. 13x13¼*
1384	A468	4.75k multi	1.75 1.75
		Complete booklet, 10 #1384	17.50
1385	A468	7.25k multi	2.60 2.60

Scouting, cent.

Modern Art A469

Designs: 4.75k, The Traveler, by Arne Haugen Sorensen. 8.25k, Trionfale, by Seppo Mattinen.

2007, June 6   Litho.   *Perf. 13x12½*
1386	A469	4.75k multi	1.75 1.60
a.		Miniature sheet of 8 + central label	14.00 14.00
1387	A469	8.25k multi	3.00 2.50

Mandatory Use of Metric System in Denmark, Cent. A470

Litho. & Engr.

2007, Aug. 22   *Perf. 12¾*
1388	A470	4.75k black & red	1.75 .85

Nature of Denmark A471

Flora and fauna of Rabjerg Dune: 4.75k, Niobe fritillary butterfly (klitperlemorsommerfugl). 6k, Northern dune tiger beetle (sandspringer). 7.25k, Sand lizard (markfirben). 13.50k, Seaside pansy (klitstedmoderblomst).

2007, Aug. 22
1389	A471	4.75k multi	1.75 .70
		Complete booklet, 10 #1389	17.50
1390	A471	6k multi	2.25 .90
		Complete booklet, 10 #1390	22.50
1391	A471	7.25k multi	2.75 1.00
1392	A471	13.50k multi	5.00 1.75
a.		Souvenir sheet, #1389-1392	12.00 12.00
		Nos. 1389-1392 (4)	11.75 4.35

Famous Men — A472

Designs: 4.75k, Poul Henningsen (1894-1967), designer, and Artichoke lamp. 6k, Victor Borge (1909-2000), comedian, and piano keys. 7.25k, Arne Jacobsen (1902-71), architect, and Egg chair. 8.25k, Piet Hein (1905-96), inventor, and superellipse.

2007, Nov. 8   Engr.   *Perf. 12¾*
1393	A472	4.75k multi	1.75 .85
		Complete booklet, 10 #1393	17.50
1394	A472	6k blk & blue	2.00 1.00
1395	A472	7.25k multi	2.75 1.25
1396	A472	8.25k blk & purple	3.00 1.60
		Nos. 1393-1396 (4)	9.50 4.70

See Nos. 1412-1415.

Danish National Theater A473

Designs: 5.50k, Old Stage. 6.50k, Playhouse. 7.75k, Copenhagen Opera House.

Litho. & Engr.

2008, Jan. 9   *Perf. 13x13¼*
1397	A473	5.50k multi	2.25 1.10
		Complete booklet, 10 #1397	22.50
a.		Sheet of 8 + central label	18.00
1398	A473	6.50k multi	2.60 1.25
		Complete booklet, 10 #1398	26.00
1399	A473	7.75k multi	3.25 1.60
		Nos. 1397-1399 (3)	8.10 3.95

Royal Life Guards, 350th Anniv. — A474

Guards in: 5.50k, Red dress uniforms. 10k, Camouflage uniforms.

Litho. & Engr.
2008, Mar. 27   *Perf. 13¼x13*

1400	A474	5.50k multi	2.40	1.25
	Complete booklet, 10 #1400		24.00	
1401	A474	10k multi	4.25	2.10
a.	Souvenir sheet, #1400-1401		6.25	6.25

Nordic Mythology A475

Places associated with mythology: 5.50k, Lindholm Hoje burial grounds. 7.75k, Feggeklit.

2008, Mar. 27   **Litho.**

1402	A475	5.50k black	2.40	1.25
1403	A475	7.75k black	3.25	1.60
a.	Souvenir sheet, #1402-1403		5.25	5.25

Europa — A476

Designs: 5.50k, Boy writing letter. 7.75k, Girl reading letter.

2008, June 4   **Litho.**   *Perf. 13*

1404	A476	5.50k multi	2.40	1.25
	Complete booklet, 10 #1404		24.00	
1405	A476	7.75k multi	3.25	1.60

Allotment Gardens A477

Designs: 5.50k, Man tending Hjelm Allotment Association garden. 6.50k, Men sitting in Vennelyst Allotment Association garden.

Litho. & Engr.
2008, June 4   *Perf. 13x13¼*

1406	A477	5.50k multi	2.40	1.25
	Complete booklet, 10 #1406		24.00	
a.	Miniature sheet of 8 + central label		19.50	
1407	A477	6.50k multi	2.75	1.40
a.	Miniature sheet of 8 + central label		22.00	

Louisiana Museum of Art, Humlebaek, 50th Anniv. — A478

Designs: 5.50k, Original Museum building, Figures in Landscape, by Roy Lichtenstein, I Am in You, by Doug Aitken. 7.75k, I Am in You, glass corridor, A Closer Grand Canyon, by David Hockney. 8.75k, Reclining Figure No. 5, by Henry Moore, Walking Man, by Albert Giacometti, Big Head, by Giacometti, Slender Ribs, by Alexander Calder. 16k, Slender Ribs, people in concert hall, Untitled, by Sam Francis, seat designed by Poul Kjaerholm.

2008, June 4

1408	A478	5.50k multi	2.40	1.25
1409	A478	7.75k multi	3.25	1.60
a.	Booklet pane, #1408-1409		8.00	—
1410	A478	8.75k multi	3.75	1.90
1411	A478	16k multi	6.75	3.50
a.	Booklet pane, #1410-1411		14.50	—
b.	Booklet pane, #1408-1411		22.00	—
c.	Horiz. strip of 4, #1408-1411		16.50	16.50
	Complete booklet, #1409a, 1411a,1411b		45.00	
	Nos. 1408-1411 (4)		16.15	8.25

Complete booklet sold for 102.40k.

Famous Men Type of 2007

Designs: 5k, Halfdan Rasmussen (1915-2002), poet, and line from poem. 5.50k, Erik Balling (1924-2005), film and television director, and actors in movie. 6.50k, Bodil Kjer (1917-2003), actress. 10k, Niels-Henning Orsted Pedersen (1946-2005), jazz musician, and bass.

2008, Aug. 27   **Engr.**   *Perf. 12¾*

1412	A472	5k blk & claret	1.75	.90
1413	A472	5.50k multi	2.00	1.10
	Complete booklet, 10 #1413		20.00	
1414	A472	6.50k multi	2.25	1.10
	Complete booklet, 10 #1414		22.50	
1415	A472	10k multi	3.50	1.75
	Nos. 1412-1415 (4)		9.50	4.85

Art Photography — A479

Designs: 5.50k, Trappe, by Viggo Rivad. 7.75k, Berlin, by Krass Clement, horiz.

2008, Aug. 27   **Litho.**   *Perf. 13x12¾*

1416	A479	5.50k black	2.00	1.60

Perf. 12¾x13

1417	A479	7.75k black	2.50	2.00

Winter Berries and Flowers — A480

Designs: 5.50k, Ilex aquifolium berries. 6.50k, Helleborus niger flower. 7.75k, Taxus baccata berries. 8.75k, Symphoricarpos rivularis berries.

Litho. & Engr.
2008, Nov. 7   *Perf. 13*

1418	A480	5.50k multi	1.90	.95
	Complete booklet, 10 #1418		19.00	
a.	Booklet pane of 4		7.75	—
1419	A480	6.50k multi	2.25	1.10
1420	A480	7.75k multi	2.75	1.40
1421	A480	8.75k multi	3.00	1.50
a.	Souvenir sheet, #1418-1421		10.00	5.00
b.	Booklet pane of 4, #1418-1421		10.00	—
	Complete booklet, #1418a, 1421b		18.00	
	Nos. 1418-1421 (4)		9.90	4.95

No. 1421b is No. 1421a sewn into the booklet.

COP15 Climate Change Conference, Copenhagen — A481

Designs: 5.50k, Bioenergy. 9k, Low-energy building.

2009, Jan. 7   **Engr.**   *Perf. 13x13¼*

1422	A481	5.50k blue	2.00	1.00
1423	A481	9k blue	3.25	1.75

Old Town Open-Air Museum, Aarhus, Cent. A482

Designs: 5.50k, Mintmaster's Mansion, drummer. 6.50k, Mayor's House, woman in period costume. 8k, Museum of Clocks and Watches and Danish Poster Museum, painter. 10.50k, Steps to Kerteminde School, farm hand.

Litho. & Engr.
2009, Jan. 7   *Perf. 13x13¼*

1424	A482	5.50k multi	2.00	1.00
	Complete booklet, 10 #1424		20.00	
1425	A482	6.50k multi	2.40	1.25
	Complete booklet, 10 #1425		24.00	
1426	A482	8k multi	3.00	1.50
1427	A482	10.50k multi	3.75	1.90
a.	Souvenir sheet, #1424-1427		10.50	10.50
	Nos. 1424-1427 (4)		11.15	5.65

Europa — A483

Designs: 5.50k, Round Tower, Copenhagen. 8k, Tycho Brahe Planetarium.

2009, Mar. 25   **Litho.**   *Perf. 13¼*

1428	A483	5.50k multi	1.90	.95
	Complete booklet, 10 #1428		19.00	
1429	A483	8k multi	2.75	1.40

Flora and Fauna — A484

Designs: 5k, Anacamptus pyramidalis. 5.50k, Falco peregrinus. 8k, Zygaena purpuralis. 17k, Tooth of Mosasaurus lemonnieri.

2009, Mar. 25   **Litho.**   *Perf. 12¾*

1430	A484	5k multi	1.75	.85
1431	A484	5.50k multi	1.90	.95
	Complete booklet, 10 #1431		19.00	
a.	Miniature sheet of 8 + central label		15.50	15.50
1432	A484	8k multi	2.75	1.40
1433	A484	17k multi	5.75	3.00
a.	Souvenir sheet, #1430-1433		12.50	12.50
	Nos. 1430-1433 (4)		12.15	6.20

Copenhagen Zoo, 150th Anniv. — A485

Designs: 5.50k, Zoo Tower, rhinoceros. 6.50k, Elephants. 8k, Red-eyed tree frog, flamingos. 9k, Tiger python, golden lion tamarin.

2009, June 10   **Litho.**   *Perf. 13¼x13*

1434	A485	5.50k multi	2.10	1.10
	Complete booklet, 10 #1434		21.00	
a.	Miniature sheet of 8 + central label		17.00	17.00
1435	A485	6.50k multi	2.50	1.25
a.	Miniature sheet of 8 + central label		20.00	20.00
b.	Booklet pane of 2, #1434-1435		8.00	—
1436	A485	8k multi	3.00	1.50
1437	A485	9k multi	3.50	1.75
a.	Booklet pane of 2, #1436-1437		12.00	—
b.	Booklet pane of 4, #1434-1437		20.00	—
	Complete booklet, #1435b, 1437a, 1437b		40.00	
	Nos. 1434-1437 (4)		11.10	5.60

Complete booklet containing #1435b, 1437a, 1437b sold for 109k.

Historic Maps A486

Maps of Denmark by: 5.50k, Royal Danish Academy of Sciences and Letters, 1841. 6.50k, Johannes Mejer, 1650. 12k, Marcus Jordan, 1585. 18k, Abraham Ortelius, 1570.

2009, July 15   **Litho.**   *Perf. 12½*

1438	A486	5.50k multi	2.10	1.10

Size: 41x24mm
Perf. 12¾

1439	A486	6.50k multi	2.50	1.25
1440	A486	12k multi	4.75	2.40
1441	A486	18k multi	7.00	3.50
	Nos. 1438-1441 (4)		16.35	8.25

Intl. Conference on the History of Cartography, Copenhagen.

Metropolitanskole, 800th Anniv. — A487

Designs: 5.50k, Author Hans Scherfig as boy and Metropolitanskole building, Copenhagen. 6.50k, Two students and current school building, Norrebro.

2009, Sept. 9   **Engr.**   *Perf. 13x13¼*

1442	A487	5.50k red & black	2.25	1.10
1443	A487	6.50k black & grn	2.60	1.40

COP15, United Nations Climate Conference, Copenhagen — A488

Designs: 5.50k, Fuel cell technology. 8k, Wind turbine.

2009, Sept. 9

1444	A488	5.50k blue	2.25	1.10
	Complete booklet, 10 #1444		22.50	
1445	A448	8k gray	3.25	1.60

Modern Art — A489

Designs: 5.50k, Houses in Motion, by Jes Fomsgaard. 12k, Garlic, by Karin Birgitte Lund, vert.

2009   **Litho.**   *Perf. 12¾x13*

1446	A489	5.50k multi	2.25	1.10
a.	Sheet of 8 + central label		18.00	18.00

Perf. 12½x12¾

1447	A489	12k multi	4.75	2.40

Issued: 5.50k, 9/9; 12k, 10/27.

Children Playing in Snow — A490

Designs: 5.50k, Child rolling snow into large ball, snowman. 6.50k, Child in snow, child sledding. 8k, Child throwing snowball at two children. 9k, Two children making snow angels.

2009, Oct. 27　Litho.　Perf. 12½x12¾
1448	A490	Sheet of 4	12.00	12.00
a.		5.50k multi	2.25	1.10
b.		6.50k multi	2.60	1.40
c.		8k multi	3.25	1.60
d.		9k multi	3.75	1.90

Self-Adhesive
Die Cut Perf. 13x13½
1449	A490	5.50k multi	2.25	1.10
a.		Booklet pane of 12	27.00	
1450	A490	6.50k multi	2.60	1.40
a.		Booklet pane of 12	32.00	
1451	A490	8k multi	3.25	1.60
1452	A490	9k multi	3.75	1.90
a.		Sheet of 8, 2 each #1449-1452	24.00	
		Nos. 1449-1452 (4)	11.85	6.00

Nos. 1449a and 1450a each exist with six different booklet covers.

Flora and Fauna — A491

Designs: 8.50k, Bufo calamita. 9.50k, Lycaena phlaeas. 12.50k, Alauda arvensis. 18.50k, Astragalus danicus.

2010, Jan. 2　Litho.　Perf. 12¼
1453		Souvenir sheet of 4	18.50	18.50
a.	A491	8.50k multi	3.25	1.60
b.	A491	9.50k multi	3.50	1.75
c.	A491	12.50k multi	4.75	2.40
d.	A491	18.50k multi	7.00	3.50

Self-Adhesive
Die Cut Perf. 13x13½
1454	A491	8.50k multi	3.25	1.60
1455	A491	9.50k multi	3.50	1.75
1456	A491	12.50k multi	4.75	2.40
1457	A491	18.50k multi	7.00	3.50
		Nos. 1454-1457 (4)	18.50	9.25

Queen Margrethe II — A492

Die Cut Perf. 13
2010, Feb. 10　Litho. & Engr.
Self-Adhesive
Panel Color
1458	A492	5.50k red	2.00	1.00
1459	A492	6.50k Prus blue	2.40	1.25
1460	A492	8.50k yel green	3.25	1.60
1461	A492	9.50k dark blue	3.50	1.75
a.		Miniature sheet of 8, 2 each #1458-1461	36.00	
		Nos. 1458-1461 (4)	11.15	5.60

No. 1461a sold for 99k.

Queen Margrethe II and Family A493

Die Cut Perf. 13¼
2010, Mar. 24　Litho. & Engr.
Self-Adhesive
1462	A493	5.50k multi	2.00	1.00
a.		Booklet pane of 12	24.00	

Queen Margrethe II, 70th birthday.

Ribe, 1300th Anniv. — A494

Designs: 5.50k, Ribe Cathedral. 6.50k, Statue of Queen Dagmar.

2010, Mar. 24　　　　Engr.
Self-Adhesive
1463	A494	5.50k black	2.00	1.00
1464	A494	6.50k black	2.40	1.25
a.		Booklet pane of 12	29.00	
b.		Miniature sheet of 6, 3 each #1463-1464	16.00	

Nordic Coastlines A495

Designs: 5.50k, Ship at Lindo Shipyard. 8.50k, Crane, Port of Aarhus.

Perf. 12¼x12½
2010, Mar. 24　　　　Litho.
1465		Sheet of 2	5.25	5.25
a.	A495	5.50k multi	2.00	1.00
b.	A495	8.50k multi	3.25	1.60

Self-Adhesive
Die Cut Perf. 13¼
1466	A495	5.50k multi	2.00	1.00
1467	A495	8.50k multi	3.25	1.60

Wavy Lines Type of 1905 and Small State Seal Type of 1946
2010　　Engr.　　Die Cut Perf. 13
Self-Adhesive
1468	A10	50o brown	.20	.20
1469	A10	100o blue	.35	.20
1470	A10	200o dark green	.75	.20
1471	A10	300o orange	1.10	.25
1472	A10	400o purple	1.50	.35
1473	A10	500o green	1.90	.45
1474	A55	10k lemon	3.25	.80
1475	A55	15k blue	5.00	1.25
1476	A55	20k dark blue	6.50	1.60
1477	A55	30k red brown	11.00	2.75
1478	A55	50k red	16.00	4.00
		Nos. 1468-1478 (11)	47.55	12.05

Issued: 50o, 100o, 200o, 500o, 4/28; 300o, 400o, 30k, 3/24; 10k, 15k, 20k, 50k, 6/1.

Album Cover for Gasolin' 3, by Gasolin' A496

Die Cut Perf. 13½x13¼
2010, Apr. 28　　　　Litho.
Self-Adhesive
1479	A496	5.50k multi	2.00	1.00
a.		Booklet pane of 12	24.00	
b.		Sheet of 4	8.00	

Klampenborg Racetrack, Cent. — A497

Designs: 5.50k, Horses at finish line. 24k, Spectators watching race.

2010, June 1
Self-Adhesive
1480	A497	5.50k multi	1.75	.90
1481	A497	24k multi	7.75	4.00

Europa — A498

Children's book characters: 5.50k, Sporge-Jorgen. 8.50k, Orla Fro-Snapper, horiz.

Die Cut Perf. 13¼x13½
2010, June 1
Self-Adhesive
1482	A498	5.50k multi	1.75	.90
a.		Sheet of 8	14.00	

Die Cut Perf. 13½x13¼
1483	A498	8.50k multi	2.75	1.40

Booklet Stamp
Serpentine Die Cut 13½
1484	A498	5.50k multi	1.75	.90
a.		Booklet pane of 12	21.00	
b.		Serpentine Die Cut 10	1.75	.90
c.		Booklet pane of 12 #1484b	21.00	

Royal Danish Navy, 500th Anniv. A499

Designs: 5.50k, Frigate Iver Huitfeldt. 6.50k, Artillery ship Niels Iuel. 8.50k, Ironclad warship Todenskjold. 9.50k, Screw frigate Jylland. 16k, Caravel Maria.

Die Cut Perf. 13¼x13
2010, June 1　　　Litho. & Engr.
Self-Adhesive (#1485-1489, 1491-1495)
1485	A499	5.50k red & black	1.75	.90
1486	A499	6.50k red & black	2.10	1.10
a.		Booklet pane of 12	22.00	
1487	A499	8.50k red & black	2.75	1.40
1488	A499	9.50k red & black	3.25	1.60
1489	A499	16k red & black	5.25	2.60
		Nos. 1485-1489 (5)	15.10	7.60

Booklet Stamps
Perf. 12¼x12½
1490		Booklet pane of 5	22.50	—
a.	A499	5.50k red & black	2.60	2.60
b.	A499	6.50k red & black	3.00	3.00
c.	A499	8.50k red & black	4.25	4.25
d.	A499	9.50k red & black	4.75	4.75
e.	A499	16k red & black	7.75	7.75

Booklet Panes of 1
Serpentine Die Cut 13¼x13½
1491	A499	5.50k red & black	2.60	2.60
1492	A499	6.50k red & black	3.00	3.00
1493	A499	8.50k red & black	4.25	4.25
1494	A499	9.50k red & black	4.75	4.75
1495	A499	16k red & black	7.75	7.75
		Complete booklet, #1490-1495	45.00	
		Nos. 1491-1495 (5)	22.35	22.35

Complete booklet sold for 139k.

Greetings — A500

Die Cut Perf. 13x13¼
2010, June 1　　　　Litho.
Self-Adhesive
1496	A500	5.50k Heart	1.75	.90
1497	A500	5.50k Danish Flag	1.75	.90
1498	A500	5.50k "Tillykke"	1.75	.90
1499	A500	5.50k Gift	1.75	.90
1500	A500	5.50k Flower	1.75	.90
a.		Sheet of 10, 2 each #1496-1500	17.50	
		Nos. 1496-1500 (5)	8.75	4.50

The right third of Nos. 1496-1500 has straight-edged die cutting.

A501

A502

A503

A504

A505

A506

A507

A508

A509

A510

Post Danmark Rundt Bicycle Race — A510

2010, Aug. 4　　Die Cut Perf. 13x13¼
1501		Sheet of 10	65.00	
a.	A501	5.50k multi	6.50	3.25
b.	A502	5.50k multi	6.50	3.25
c.	A503	5.50k multi	6.50	3.25
d.	A504	5.50k multi	6.50	3.25
e.	A505	5.50k multi	6.50	3.25
f.	A506	5.50k multi	6.50	3.25
g.	A507	5.50k multi	6.50	3.25
h.	A508	5.50k multi	6.50	3.25
i.	A509	5.50k multi	6.50	3.25
j.	A510	5.50k multi	6.50	3.25

The right third of Nos. 1501a-1501j has straight-edged die cutting.

Famous Men Type of 2007

Designs: 5.50k, Dan Turèll (1946-93), writer, and lines from poem. 6.50k, Tove Ditlevsen (1917-76), poet, and her childhood home. 9.50k, Henry Heerup (1907-93), and "Love in the Coffee Pot." 12.50k, Dea Trier Morch (1941-2001), writer and artist, and illustation from her novel, *Winter's Child*.

Die Cut Perf. 13½x12¾
2010, Aug. 25   Litho. & Engr.
Self-Adhesive

1502	A472	5.50k multi	1.90	.95
a.		Souvenir sheet of 8	15.50	
b.		Booklet pane of 12	23.00	
1503	A472	6.50k multi	2.25	1.10
1504	A472	9.50k multi	3.25	1.60
1505	A472	12.50k multi	4.50	2.25
		Nos. 1502-1505 (4)	11.90	5.90

Art — A511

Designs: 5.50k, Two Roses, by Inge Ellegaard. 18.50k, Night Flower, by Kirstine Roepstorff, vert.

Die Cut Perf. 13¼x13½
2010, Aug. 25   Litho.
Self-Adhesive

1506	A511	5.50k multi	1.90	.95

Die Cut Perf. 13½x13¼

1507	A511	18.50k multi	6.50	3.25

Small State Seal Type of 1946
Die Cut Perf. 13
2010, Oct. 26   Engr.

1508	A55	25k green	9.50	4.75

"Winter Tales" — A512

Designs: 5.50k, Woman on park bench, ducks. 6.50k, Woman on park bench hugging snowman. 8.50k, Woman kissing snowman. 12.50k, Snowman coming to life, dog.

2010, Oct. 26   Litho.   Perf. 12¼x13

1509		Sheet of 4	13.00	6.50
a.	A512	5.50k multi	2.10	1.10
b.	A512	6.50k multi	2.50	1.25
c.	A512	8.50k multi	3.25	1.60
d.	A512	12.50k multi	4.75	2.40

Self-Adhesive
Die Cut Perf. 13¼

1510	A512	5.50k multi	2.10	1.10
1511	A512	6.50k multi	2.50	1.25
1512	A512	8.50k multi	3.25	1.60
1513	A512	12.50k multi	4.75	2.40
		Nos. 1510-1513 (4)	12.60	6.35

Booklet Stamps
Serpentine Die Cut 13½

1514	A512	5.50k multi	2.10	1.10
a.		Booklet pane of 12	26.00	
1515	A512	6.50k multi	2.50	1.25
a.		Booklet pane of 12	30.00	

SEMI-POSTAL STAMPS

Nos. 159, 157 Surcharged in Red

Famous Men Type of 2007 / Wmk. Multiple Crosses (114)

1921, June 17   Perf. 14½x14

B1	A20	10o + 5o green	15.00	65.00
B2	A21	20o + 10o slate	19.00	77.50
		Set, never hinged	97.50	

 Crown and Staff of Aesculapius SP1
 Dybbol Mill SP2

1929, Aug. 1   Engr.

B3	SP1	10o yellow green	4.25	7.75
a.		Booklet pane of 2	27.50	
B4	SP1	15o brick red	6.25	15.00
a.		Booklet pane of 2	32.50	
B5	SP1	25o deep blue	26.50	57.50
a.		Booklet pane of 2	135.00	
		Nos. B3-B5 (3)	37.00	80.25
		Set, never hinged	75.00	

These stamps were sold at a premium of 5 öre each for benefit of the Danish Cancer Committee.

1937, Jan. 20   Unwmk.   Perf. 13

B6	SP2	5o + 5o green	.55	1.25
B7	SP2	10o + 5o lt brown	3.25	9.00
B8	SP2	15o + 5o carmine	3.25	9.00
		Nos. B6-B8 (3)	7.05	19.25
		Set, never hinged	14.00	

The surtax was for a fund in memory of H. P. Hanssen, statesman.

Nos. 223a and B6, Nos. 229 and B7, Nos. 238A and B8 are found se-tenant in booklets. For booklet panes, see Nos. 223d, 229b and 238AI.

Queen Alexandrine — SP3

1939-40   Perf. 13

B9	SP3	5o + 3o rose lake & red ('40)	.20	.20
a.		Booklet pane of 4	2.00	2.00
B10	SP3	10o + 5o dk violet & red	.20	.20
B11	SP3	15o + 5o scarlet & red	.30	.75
		Nos. B9-B11 (3)	.70	1.15
		Set, never hinged	1.65	

The surtax was for the Danish Red Cross.

Nos. 230 and B10 have been issued se-tenant in booklets. See No. 230b. In this pane No. 230 measures 23½x31mm from perf. to perf.

Crown Princess Ingrid and Princess Margrethe — SP4

1941-43

B12	SP4	10o + 5o dk violet	.20	.25
a.		Booklet pane of 10	32.50	
B13	SP4	20o + 5o red ('43)	.20	.25
		Set, never hinged	.60	

Surtax for the Children's Charity Fund.

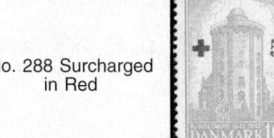
No. 288 Surcharged in Red

1944, May 11

B14	A48	10o + 5o violet	.25	.25
		Never hinged	.30	
a.		Booklet pane of 10	27.50	

The surtax was for the Danish Red Cross.

> Catalogue values for unused stamps in this section, from this point to the end of the section, are for Never Hinged items.

 Symbols of Freedom SP5
 Explosions at Rail Junction SP6
 Danish Flag SP7
 Princess Anne-Marie SP8

1947, May 4   Engr.   Perf. 13

B15	SP5	15o + 5o green	.50	.50
B16	SP6	20o + 5o dark red	.50	.50
B17	SP7	40o + 5o deep blue	1.25	1.25
		Nos. B15-B17 (3)	2.25	2.25

Issued in memory of the Danish struggle for liberty and the liberation of Denmark. The surtax was for the Liberty Fund.

For surcharges see Nos. B22-B23.

1950, Oct. 19   Unwmk.

B18	SP8	25o + 5o rose brown	.55	.50

The surtax was for the National Children's Welfare Association.

S. S. Jutlandia — SP9

1951, Sept. 13   Perf. 13

B19	SP9	25o + 5o red	.75	.75

The surtax was for the Red Cross.

No. 335 Surcharged in Black

1953, Feb. 13

B20	A61	30o + 10o brown red	1.25	1.60

The surtax was for flood relief in the Netherlands.

Stone Memorial — SP10

1953, Mar. 26   Perf. 13

B21	SP10	30o + 5o dark red	1.25	1.60

The surtax was for cultural work of the Danish Border Union.

Nos. B15 and B16 Surcharged with New Value and Ornamental Screen in Black

1955, Feb. 17

B22	SP5	20o + 5o on No. B15	1.25	1.60
B23	SP6	30o + 5o on No. B16	1.25	1.60

The surtax was for the Liberty Fund.

No. 341 Surcharged

1957, Mar. 25

B24	A61	30o + 5o on 95o red org	.65	.65

The surtax went to the Danish Red Cross for aid to Hungary.

#335 Surcharged: "Gronlandsfonden + 10"

1959, Feb. 23

B25	A61	30o + 10o brown red	.80	.90

The surtax was for the Greenland Fund.

 Globe Encircled by Red Cross Flags — SP11
 Queen Ingrid — SP12

1959, June 24   Engr.   Perf. 13

B26	SP11	30o + 5o rose red	.50	.50
B27	SP11	60o + 5o lt ultra & car	.75	.75

Centenary of the Intl. Red Cross idea. The surtax was for the Red Cross. Crosses photogravure on No. B27.

1960, Oct. 25   Unwmk.

B28	SP12	30o + 10o dark red	1.00	1.25

Queen Ingrid's 25th anniv. as a Girl Scout. The surtax was for the Scouts' fund for needy and sick children.

African Mother, Child — SP13
Healthy and Crippled Hands — SP14

1962, May 24

B29	SP13	30o + 10o dark red	.90	1.00

Issued to aid underdeveloped countries.

1963, June 24   Perf. 13

B30	SP14	35o + 10o dark red	1.00	1.25

The surtax was for the benefit of the Cripples' Foundation.

Old Bridge at Danish-German Border — SP15

1964, May 28   Engr.

B31	SP15	35o + 10o henna brn	.75	.75

Surtax for the Danish Border Union.

Princesses Margrethe, Benedikte, Anne-Marie — SP16

Happy Child — SP17

1964, Aug. 24
B32 SP16 35o + 10o dull red   .75 .75
B33 SP16 60o + 10o dk bl & red .95 .95
   The surtax was for the Red Cross.

1965, Oct. 21   **Engr.**   *Perf. 13*
B34 SP17 50o + 10o brick red   .65 .65
   The surtax was for the National Children's Welfare Association.

"Red Cross" in 32 Languages and Red Cross, Red Lion and Sun, and Red Crescent Emblems SP18

1966, Jan. 20   **Engr.**   *Perf. 13*
B35 SP18 50o + 10o red   .65 1.00
   Engraved and Photogravure
B36 SP18 80o + 10o dk bl & red .90 1.25
   The surtax was for the Red Cross.

"Refugees 66" — SP19

Symbolic Rose — SP20

1966, Oct. 24   **Engr.**   *Perf. 13*
B37 SP19 40o + 10o sepia   .70 .70
B38 SP19 50o + 10o rose red .70 .70
B39 SP19 80o + 10o blue   1.25 1.25
   Nos. B37-B39 (3)   2.65 2.65
   The surtax was for aid to refugees.

1967, Oct. 12
B40 SP20 60o + 10o brown red .50 .75
   The surcharge was for the Salvation Army.

Two Greenland Boys in Round Tower — SP21

1968, Sept. 12   **Engr.**   *Perf. 13*
B41 SP21 60o + 10o dark red .65 .90
   The surtax was for child welfare work in Greenland.

Princess Margrethe and Prince Henrik with Prince Frederik — SP22

1969, Dec. 11
B42 SP22 50o + 10o brn & red   .65 .90
B43 SP22 60o + 10o brn red & red   .65 1.00
   The surtax was for the Danish Red Cross.

Child Seeking Help — SP23

1970, Mar. 13
B44 SP23 60o + 10o brown red .65 .90
   Surtax for "Save the Children Fund."

Child — SP24

Marsh Marigold — SP25

1971, Apr. 29   **Engr.**   *Perf. 13*
B45 SP24 60o + 10o copper red .65 .65
   Surtax was for the National Children's Welfare Association.

1972, Aug. 17
B46 SP25 70o + 10o green & yel .50 1.25
   Soc. and Home for the Disabled, cent.

Heimaey Town and Volcano — SP26

1973, Oct. 17   **Engr.**   *Perf. 13*
B47 SP26 70o + 20o vio blue & red   .65 .90
   The surtax was for the victims of the eruption of Heimaey Volcano, Jan. 23, 1973.

Queen Margrethe, IWY Emblem — SP27

1975, Mar. 20   **Engr.**   *Perf. 13*
B48 SP27 90o + 20o red & buff .85 1.25
   International Women's Year 1975. Surtax was for a foundation to benefit women primarily in Greenland and Faroe Islands.

Skuldelev I SP28

   Ships: 90o+20o, Thingvalla, emigrant steamer. 100o+20o, Liner Frederick VIII, c. 1930. 130o+20o, Three-master Danmark.

1976, Jan. 22   **Engr.**   *Perf. 13*
B49 SP28 70 + 20o olive brown .75 .85
B50 SP28 90 + 20o brick red   .75 .85
B51 SP28 100 + 20o olive green .85 1.10
B52 SP28 130 + 20o violet blue .90 1.60
   Nos. B49-B52 (4)   3.25 4.40
   American Declaration of Independence, 200th anniv.

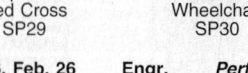

People and Red Cross SP29

Invalid in Wheelchair SP30

1976, Feb. 26   **Engr.**   *Perf. 13*
B53 SP29 100o + 20o red & black   .65 .75
B54 SP29 130o + 20o bl, red & blk   .80 1.00
   Centenary of Danish Red Cross.

1976, May 6   **Engr.**   *Perf. 13*
B55 SP30 100o + 20o ver & blk .65 .75
   The surtax was for the Foundation to Aid the Disabled.

Mother and Child — SP31

Anti-Cancer Campaign — SP32

1977, Mar. 24   **Engr.**   *Perf. 12½*
B56 SP31 1k + 20o multicolored .75 .90
   Danish Society for the Mentally Handicapped, 25th anniv. Surtax was for the Society.

1978, Oct. 12   **Engr.**   *Perf. 13*
B57 SP32 120o + 20o red   .65 1.00
   Danish Anti-Cancer Campaign, 50th anniversary. Surtax was for campaign.

Child and IYC Emblem — SP33

1979, Jan. 25   **Engr.**   *Perf. 12½*
B58 SP33 1.20k + 20o red & brown   .65 1.00
   International Year of the Child.

Foundation for the Disabled, 25th Anniversary SP34

1980, Apr. 10   **Engr.**   *Perf. 13*
B59 SP34 130o + 20o brown red .65 .65

Children Playing Ball SP35

Intl. Year of the Disabled SP36

1981, Feb. 5   **Engr.**   *Perf. 12½x13*
B60 SP35 1.60k + 20o brown red .70 .90
   Surtax was for child welfare.

1981, Sept. 10   **Engr.**   *Perf. 12½x13*
B61 SP36 2k + 20o dark blue   .90 1.60

Stem and Broken Line — SP37

1982, May 3   **Engr.**   *Perf. 13*
B62 SP37 2k + 40o dull red 1.40 2.40
   Surtax was for Danish Multiple Sclerosis Society.

Nurse with Patient SP38

1984 Olympic Games SP39

1983, Jan. 27   **Engr.**
B63 SP38 2k + 40o multicolored 1.75 2.40

1984, Feb. 23   **Litho. & Engr.**
B64 SP39 2.70k + 40o multi 1.50 2.40

Electrocardiogram Reading, Heart — SP40

1984, Sept. 6   **Engr.**   *Perf. 12½*
B65 SP40 2.70k + 40o red 1.75 2.75
   Surtax was for Heart Foundation.

SP41   SP42

1985, May 2   **Litho.**   *Perf. 13*
B66 SP41 2.80k + 50o multi 1.75 2.40
   Liberation from German Occupation, 40th Anniv. Surtax for benefit of World War II veterans.

1985, Oct. 3   **Litho. & Engr.**
   Design: Tapestry detail, by Caroline Ebbeson (1852-1936), former patient, St. Hans Hospital, Roskilade.
B67 SP42 2.80k + 40o multi 1.25 1.75
   Natl. Soc. for the Welfare of the Mentally Ill, 25th Anniv. Surtax benefited the mentally ill.

Danish Arthritis Assoc., 50th Anniv. — SP43

1986, Mar. 20   **Litho.**   *Perf. 13*
B68 SP43 2.80k + 50o multicolored   1.50 2.40
   Surtax for the Arthritis Assoc.

Poul Reichhart (1913-1985), as Papageno in The Magic Flute — SP44

1986, Feb. 6   Litho.   Perf. 13
B69 SP44 2.80k + 50o multi-
ticolored   1.50 2.40
Surtax for the physically handicapped.

Danish Society
for the Blind,
75th
Anniv. — SP45

Litho. & Engr.
1986, Feb. 20   Perf. 13
B70 SP45 2.80k +50o blk, vio brn
& dk red   1.50 2.40

Danish Assoc. of
Epileptics,
25th Anniv.
SP46

1987, Sept. 24   Engr.   Perf. 13
B71 SP46 2.80k +50o dk red, brt
ultra & dk grn   1.60 2.40

Folkekirkens
Nodhjaelp Relief
Organization — SP47

1988, Mar. 10   Engr.
B72 SP47 3k +50o multicolored   1.60 1.90
Surtax for the relief organization.

Natl. Council for
Unwed Mothers,
5th
Anniv. — SP48

1988, Sept. 22   Photo.
B73 SP48 3k +50o dk rose brn   1.75 2.75

SP49   SP50

1989, Feb. 16   Litho.
B74 SP49 3.20k +50o multi   2.00 2.75
Salvation Army.

1990, Aug. 30   Litho.   Perf. 13
B75 SP50 3.50k +50o Insulin
crystal   2.25 3.50
Danish Diabetes Assoc., 50th anniv.

Children's
Telephone
SP51

1991, June 6   Engr.   Perf. 13
B76 SP51 3.50k +50o dark blue   1.75 2.25
Surtax benefits Borns Vilkar, children's wel-
fare organization.

Danish
Dyslexia
Assoc.,
50th Anniv.
SP52

Litho. & Engr.
1992, Aug. 27   Perf. 13
B77 SP52 3.75k +50o multi   1.75 2.50

SP53   SP54

1993, Aug. 19   Litho.   Perf. 13
B78 SP53 3.75k +50o multi   1.60 2.00
YMCA Social Work, 75th anniv.

Litho. & Engr.
1994, June 9   Perf. 13
B79 SP54 3.75k +50o multi   1.50 1.75
Prince Henrik, 60th birthday. Surtax for
Danish Red Cross.

Natl.
Society of
Polio and
Accident
Victims,
50th Anniv.
SP55

1995, June 8   Litho.   Perf. 13
B80 SP55 3.75k +50o red   1.50 1.75

SP56   SP57

1996, Oct. 10   Litho.   Perf. 13
B81 SP56 3.75k +50o red &
black   1.50 1.75
The AIDS Foundation.

1997, May 15   Litho.   Perf. 13
B82 SP57 3.75k +50o multi   1.75 1.90
Asthma-Allergy Assoc.

Danish
Cancer
Society
SP58

1998, Sept. 3   Litho.   Perf. 13
B83 SP58 3.75k +50o multi   1.50 1.75

Danish
Refugee
Council,
50th Anniv.
SP59

SP60

1999, Aug. 25   Litho.   Perf. 13
B84 SP59 4k +50o blue & red   1.60 1.90
For the Alzheimer's Association.

2000, Sept. 27   Engr.   Perf. 13
B85 SP60 4k +50o red & blue   1.50 1.90
For the Cerebral Palsy Association.

Amnesty International — SP61

2001, Jan. 24   Engr.   Perf. 12¾
B86 SP61 4k +50o blk & red   1.60 1.60

LEV
National
Association
SP62

2002, Mar. 13   Engr.   Perf. 12¾
B87 SP62 4k + 50o multi, greenish   1.60 1.60

Doctors
Without
Borders
SP63

2003, Mar. 12   Litho.   Perf. 12¾
B88 SP63 4.25k +50o multi   1.60 1.60
Booklet, 10 #B88   16.00

Children's Aid
Day — SP64

2004, Jan. 14   Litho.   Perf. 12¾
B89 SP64 4.50k +50o multi   1.75 1.75
Booklet, 10 #B89   17.50

SOS
Children's
Villages
SP65

2005, Jan. 12   Litho.   Perf. 12¾
B90 SP65 4.50k +50o multi   1.75 1.75
Complete booklet, 10 #B90   17.50
Surtax was originally intended for an SOS
Children's Village in Burundi, but surtax went
to the relief fund for Dec. 26, 2004 tsunami
victims. A sticker noting this change was to be
applied to the front covers of the booklets.

Danish
Refugee
Council,
50th Anniv.
SP66

2006, Jan. 11   Engr.   Perf. 12¾
B91 SP66 4.75k +50o blk & red,
tan   1.90 1.90
Complete booklet, 10 #B91   19.00

Crown Prince Frederik, Crown
Princess Mary, and Prince Christian
SP67

2007, Jan. 10   Engr.   Perf. 13x13¼
B92 SP67 4.75k +50o multi   1.90 1.90
Complete booklet, 10 #B92   19.00
Surtax for Crown Prince Frederik and Crown
Princess Mary's Fund for Charitable and
Humanitarian Purposes.

Danish Cancer
Society, 80th
Anniv. — SP68

2008, Jan. 9   Engr.   Perf. 12¾
B93 SP68 5.50k +50o blk & red   2.40 2.40
Complete booklet, 10 #B93   24.00

Prince Henrik, Farm Field, Viet Nam,
Emblem of Worldwide Fund for Nature
(WWF)
SP69

2009, Jan. 7   Litho.   Perf. 13x13¼
B94 SP69 5.50k + 50o multi   2.25 2.25
Complete booklet, 10 #B94   22.50
Surtax for Worldwide Fund for Nature.

Danish Children's
Cancer
Foundation
SP70

Die Cut Perf. 13¼x13½
2010, Jan. 6   Litho.
Self-Adhesive
B95 SP70 5.50k +50o multi   2.25 2.25
a.   Souvenir sheet of 4   9.00
Booklet Stamp
Serpentine Die Cut 10
B96 SP70 5.50k +50o multi   2.25 2.25
a.   Booklet pane of 12   27.00
Issued: No. B95a, 8/4.

AIR POST STAMPS

Airplane and
Plowman
AP1

Towers of
Copenhagen
AP2

Wmk. Multiple Crosses (114)
1925-29   Typo.   Perf. 12x12½
C1 AP1 10o yellow green   26.00 45.00
C2 AP1 15o violet ('26)   52.50 90.00
C3 AP1 25o scarlet   40.00 72.50

C4	AP1	50o lt gray ('29)	100.00 300.00
C5	AP1	1k choc ('29)	90.00 275.00
		Nos. C1-C5 (5)	308.50 782.50
		Set, never hinged	785.00

Unwmk.

1934, June 9   Engr.   Perf. 13

C6	AP2	10o orange	.70 1.40
C7	AP2	15o red	3.25 6.50
C8	AP2	20o Prus blue	3.25 6.50
C9	AP2	50o olive black	3.25 6.50
C10	AP2	1k brown	16.00 26.00
		Nos. C6-C10 (5)	26.45 46.90
		Set, never hinged	47.00

LATE FEE STAMPS

LF1

Coat of Arms — LF2

Perf. 14x14½

1923   Typo.   Wmk. 114

I1	LF1	10o green	13.00 5.25
		Never hinged	40.00
a.		Double overprint	2,600.

No. I1 was, at first, not a postage stamp but represented a tax for the services of the post office clerks in filling out postal forms and writing addresses. In 1923 it was put into use as a Late Fee stamp.

1926-31

I2	LF2	10o green	9.00 1.25
I3	LF2	10o brown ('31)	8.25 .50
		Set, never hinged	45.00

1934   Unwmk.   Engr.   Perf. 13

I4	LF2	5o green	.25 .20
I5	LF2	10o orange	.20 .20
		Set, never hinged	1.00

POSTAGE DUE STAMPS

Regular Issues of 1913-20 Overprinted

Perf. 14x14½

1921, May 1   Wmk. 114

J1	A10	1o deep orange	2.00 5.25
J2	A16	5o green	5.25 5.25
J3	A16	7o orange	4.00 6.50
J4	A16	10o red	26.00 16.00
J5	A16	20o deep blue	19.00 11.50
J6	A16	25o brown & blk	26.00 7.75
J7	A16	50o claret & blk	10.00 6.50
		Nos. J1-J7 (7)	92.25 58.75
		Set, never hinged	260.00

Same Overprint in Dark Blue On Military Stamp of 1917

1921, Nov. 23

J8	A16	10o red	10.00 16.00
		Never hinged	30.00
a.		"S" inverted	160.00 210.00
		Never hinged	300.00

Numeral of Value — D1

Typographed (Solid Panel)

1921-30   Perf. 14x14½

J9	D1	1o orange ('22)	1.25 2.50
J10	D1	4o blue ('25)	2.50 3.25
J11	D1	5o brown ('22)	2.75 2.50
J12	D1	5o lt green ('30)	2.50 2.50
J13	D1	7o apple grn ('27)	15.00 26.00
J14	D1	7o dk violet ('30)	40.00 52.50
J15	D1	10o yellow grn ('22)	3.25 2.50
J16	D1	10o lt brown ('30)	1.90 2.50
J17	D1	20o grnsh blue ('21)	1.60 2.50
a.		Double impression	2,500.
J18	D1	20o gray ('30)	3.25 4.50
J19	D1	25o scarlet ('23)	3.25 5.25

J20	D1	25o violet ('26)	3.25 5.25
J21	D1	25o lt blue ('30)	5.25 7.75
J22	D1	1k dk blue ('21)	77.50 15.00
J23	D1	1k brn & dk bl ('25)	9.00 13.00
J24	D1	5k purple ('25)	20.00 13.00
		Nos. J9-J24 (16)	193.00 160.50
		Set, never hinged	535.00

Engraved (Lined Panel)

1934-55   Unwmk.   Perf. 13

J25	D1	1o slate	.20 .20
J26	D1	2o carmine	.20 .50
J27	D1	5o yellow green	.20 .50
J28	D1	6o dk olive ('41)	.40 .65
J29	D1	8o magenta ('50)	2.00 4.00
J30	D1	10o orange	.20 .20
J31	D1	12o dp ultra ('55)	.40 1.25
J32	D1	15o lt violet ('54)	.50 .65
J33	D1	20o gray	.35 .25
J34	D1	25o blue	.50 .65
J35	D1	30o green ('53)	.50 .65
J36	D1	40o claret ('49)	.50 .65
J37	D1	1k brown	.50 .65
		Nos. J25-J37 (13)	6.45 10.80
		Set, never hinged	11.00

No. 96 Surcharged in Black

1934   Wmk. 114   Perf. 14x14½

J38	A10	15o on 12o violet	5.25 6.50
		Never hinged	16.00

MILITARY STAMPS

Nos. 97 and 100 Overprinted in Blue

1917   Wmk. 114   Perf. 14x14½

M1	A16	5o green	16.00 52.50
a.		"S" inverted	250.00 350.00
M2	A16	10o red	16.00 26.00
a.		"S" inverted	250.00 400.00
		Set, never hinged	75.00
#M1a, M2a, never hinged			850.00

The letters "S F" are the initials of "Soldater Frimaerke" (Soldier's Stamp). For overprint see No. J8.

OFFICIAL STAMPS

Small State Seal — O1

Wmk. Crown (112)

1871   Typo.   Perf. 14x13½

O1	O1	2s blue	190.00 160.00
a.		2s ultra	190.00 160.00
b.		Imperf	400.00
O2	O1	4s carmine	77.50 32.50
a.		Imperf	400.00
O3	O1	16s green	450.00 325.00
a.		Imperf	450.00

Perf. 12½

O4	O1	4s carmine	5,750. 575.00
O5	O1	16s green	400.00 550.00
		#O1-O3, O5, never hinged	3,200.

Nos. O4-O5 values are for stamps with defective perfs.
Nos. O1-O3 were reprinted in 1886 upon white wove paper, unwatermarked and imperforate. Value $10 each.

1875   Perf. 14x13½

O6	O1	3o violet	13.00 40.00
O7	O1	4o grnsh blue	12.00 9.00
O8	O1	8o carmine	12.00 2.50
a.		Imperf	—
O9	O1	32o brown	29.00 32.50
		Nos. O6-O9 (4)	66.00 84.00
		Set, never hinged	200.00

For surcharge see No. 81.

1899-02   Perf. 13

O9A	O1	3o red lilac ('02)	4.00 13.00
c.		Imperf	350.00
		As "c," pair	950.00
O9B	O1	4o blue	3.25 4.00
O10	O1	8o carmine	20.00 26.00
		Nos. O9A-O10 (3)	27.25 43.00
		Set, never hinged	85.00

For surcharge see No. 137.

1902-06   Wmk. 113

O11	O1	1o orange	1.75 4.00
O12	O1	3o red lilac ('06)	1.25 1.60
O13	O1	4o blue ('03)	2.50 5.75
O14	O1	5o green	2.50 .65
O15	O1	10o carmine	4.00 2.50
		Nos. O11-O15 (5)	12.00 14.50
		Set, never hinged	30.00

1914-23   Wmk. 114   Perf. 14x14½

O16	O1	1o orange	1.40 2.50
O17	O1	3o gray ('18)	4.00 17.00
O18	O1	4o blue ('16)	30.00 65.00
O19	O1	5o green ('15)	2.50 1.90
O20	O1	5o choc ('23)	5.25 26.00
O21	O1	10o red ('17)	13.00 7.00
O22	O1	10o green ('21)	4.50 7.75
O23	O1	15o violet ('19)	14.00 40.00
O24	O1	20o indigo ('20)	20.00 17.00
		Nos. O16-O24 (9)	94.65 184.15
		Set, never hinged	220.00

For surcharges see Nos. 185-191.
No. O20 is valued CTO.
Official stamps were discontinued Apr. 1, 1924.

NEWSPAPER STAMPS

Numeral of Value — N1

1907   Typo.   Wmk. 113   Perf. 13

P1	N1	1o olive	13.00 4.00
P2	N1	5o blue	26.00 13.00
P3	N1	7o carmine	15.00 2.50
P4	N1	10o deep lilac	45.00 4.50
P5	N1	20o green	40.00 2.50
P6	N1	38o orange	45.00 2.00
P7	N1	68o yellow brown	110.00 40.00
P8	N1	1k bl grn & claret	32.50 4.50
P9	N1	5k rose & yel grn	190.00 45.00
P10	N1	10k bister & blue	190.00 45.00
		Nos. P1-P10 (10)	706.50 163.00
		Set, never hinged	2,650.

For surcharges see Nos. 138-144.

1914-15   Wmk. 114   Perf. 14x14½

P11	N1	1o olive gray	15.00 3.25
P12	N1	5o blue	40.00 13.00
P13	N1	7o rose	40.00 4.50
P14	N1	8o green ('15)	40.00 4.50
P15	N1	10o deep lilac	65.00 4.50
P16	N1	20o green	260.00 5.25
a.		Imperf., pair	1,100.
P17	N1	29o orange yel ('15)	65.00 5.75
P18	N1	38o orange	2,000. 175.00
P19	N1	41o yellow brn ('15)	85.00 4.50
P20	N1	1k blue grn & mar	110.00 5.25
		Nos. P11-P17, P19-P20 (9)	720.00 50.50
		Set, never hinged	2,825.

For surcharges see Nos. 145-154.

PARCEL POST STAMPS

These stamps were for use on postal packets sent by the Esbjerg-Fano Ferry Service.

Regular Issues of 1913-30 Overprinted

1919-41   Wmk. 114   Perf. 14x14½

Q1	A10	10o green ('22)	20.00 20.00
Q2	A10	10o bister brn ('30)	24.00 13.00
Q3	A16	10o red	45.00 90.00
a.		"POSSFAERGE"	200.00 450.00
Q4	A16	15o violet	20.00 40.00
a.		"POSFFAERGE"	240.00 525.00

Q5	A16	30o orange ('22)	20.00 40.00
Q6	A16	30o dk blue ('26)	4.00 7.00
Q7	A16	50o cl & blk ('20)	260.00 325.00
Q8	A16	50o lt gray ('22)	26.00 26.00
a.		50o olive gray ('24)	200.00 400.00
Q9	A16	1k brn & bl ('24)	52.50 26.00
Q9A	A16	5k vio & brn ('41)	1.75 2.75
Q10	A16	10k ver & grn ('30)	72.50 110.00

Engr.

Q11	A17	1k yellow brn	100.00 190.00
a.		"POSSFAERGE"	1,300. 2,350.
		Nos. Q1-Q11 (12)	645.75 889.75
		Set, never hinged	1,540.

1927-30

Q12	A30	15o red ('27)	20.00 14.00
Q13	A30	30o ocher ('27)	13.00 24.00
Q14	A30	40o vel grn ('30)	24.00 14.00
		Nos. Q12-Q14 (3)	57.00 52.00
		Set, never hinged	157.50

Overprinted on Regular Issues of 1933-40

1936-42   Unwmk.   Perf. 13

Q15	A32	5o rose lake ('42)	.30 .30
Q16	A32	10o yellow org	20.00 20.00
Q17	A32	10o lt brown ('38)	1.40 1.90
Q18	A32	10o purple ('39)	.30 .30
Q19	A30	15o deep red	.75 1.50
Q20	A30	30o blue, I	4.50 6.00
Q21	A30	30o blue, II ('40)	12.00 29.00
Q22	A30	30o org, II ('42)	.50 .75
Q23	A30	40o yel grn, I	4.50 7.75
Q24	A30	40o yel grn, II ('40)	13.00 29.00
Q25	A30	40o blue, II ('42)	.75 1.50
Q26	A33	50o gray	1.00 1.50
Q27	A33	1k lt brown	1.00 1.50
		Nos. Q15-Q27 (13)	60.00 101.00
		Set, never hinged	132.50

Catalogue values for unused stamps in this section, from this point to the end of the section, are for Never Hinged items.

Overprinted on Nos. 284, 286, 286B

1945

Q28	A47	30o orange	2.50 2.10
Q29	A47	50o blue	1.60 1.60
Q30	A47	50o gray	2.00 2.00
		Nos. Q28-Q30 (3)	6.10 5.70

Ovptd. on #318, 309, 310, 312, 297

1949-53

Q31	A32	10o green ('53)	.65 .50
Q32	A61	30o orange	4.50 1.60
Q33	A61	40o dull blue	4.00 2.00
Q34	A61	50o gray ('50)	21.00 4.00
Q35	A55	1k brown ('50)	2.00 1.50
		Nos. Q31-Q35 (5)	32.15 9.60

Ovptd. on #335, 323, 336, 326, 397

1955-65

Q36	A61	30o brown red	2.00 2.00
Q37	A61	40o gray	2.00 2.00
Q38	A61	50o aqua	2.00 2.00
Q39	A61	70o deep green	2.00 2.25
Q40	A55	1.25k orange ('65)	9.00 12.00
		Nos. Q36-Q40 (5)	17.00 20.25

Overprinted on Nos. 417 and 419

1967   Engr.   Perf. 13

Q41	A86	40o brown	.65 1.25
Q42	A86	80o ultra	.65 1.25

Nos. 224, 438, 441, 297-299 Overprinted

1967-74   Engr.   Perf. 13

Q43	A32	5o rose lake	.50 .50
Q44	A86	50o brown ('74)	.65 .90
Q45	A86	90o ultra ('70)	1.10 1.60
Q46	A55	1k brown	2.50 3.25
Q47	A55	2k red ('72)	2.25 4.00
Q48	A55	5k dull bl ('72)	6.50 9.00
		Nos. Q43-Q48 (6)	13.50 19.25

Nos. Q44-Q45, Q47-Q48 are on fluorescent paper.

Overprinted on No. 541

1975, Feb. 27

Q49	A161	100o deep ultra	1.60 2.40

DIEGO SUAREZ

dē-ˌā-gō ˈswär-əs

LOCATION — A town at the northern
end of Madagascar
GOVT. — French colony
POP. — 12,237

From 1885 to 1896 Diego-Suarez,
(Antsirane), a French naval base, was a
separate colony and issued its own
stamps. These were succeeded by
stamps of Madagascar.

100 Centimes = 1 Franc

Values for unused stamps are for
examples with original gum as defined
in the catalogue introduction except for
Nos. 6-10 and J1-J2 which are valued
without gum.

Stamps of French
Colonies Handstamp
Surcharged in Violet

1890		Unwmk.	Perf. 14x13½	
1	A9	15c on 1c blk, *bl*	300.00	100.00
2	A9	15c on 5c grn, *grnsh*	650.00	100.00
3	A9	15c on 10c blk, *lav*	300.00	92.50
4	A9	15c on 20c red, *grn*	650.00	80.00
5	A9	15c on 25c blk, *rose*	130.00	52.50

This surcharge is found inverted, double,
etc. See the *Scott Classic Catalogue*. Counterfeits exist.

Ship Flying French
Flag — A2

France — A5

Symbolical of Union of France
and Madagascar
A3   A4

1890		Litho.	Imperf.	
6	A2	1c black	1,150.	225.00
7	A3	5c black	1,100.	200.00
8	A4	15c black	210.00	95.00
9	A5	25c black	225.00	110.00

Counterfeits exist of Nos. 6-9.

A6

1891

10	A6	5c black	350.00	100.00

Excellent counterfeits exist of No. 10.

Stamps of French Colonies
Surcharged in Red or Black

No. 11   No. 12

1892			Perf. 14x13½	
11	A9	5c on 10c blk, *lav* (R)	210.00	105.00
a.		Inverted surcharge	475.00	400.00
12	A9	5c on 20c red, *grn*	190.00	72.50
a.		Inverted surcharge	450.00	400.00

Stamps of French
Colonies Overprinted in
Black or Red

1892

13	A9	1c blue (R)	32.50	20.00
14	A9	2c brown, *buff*	32.50	20.00
15	A9	4c claret, *lav*	52.50	45.00
16	A9	5c green, *grnsh*	110.00	80.00
17	A9	10c black, *lavender*	40.00	32.50
b.		Double overprint	240.00	180.00
18	A9	15c blue, *pale blue*	32.50	20.00
19	A9	20c red, *grn*	40.00	32.50
20	A9	25c black, *rose*	36.00	20.00
21	A9	30c brown, *bis* (R)	1,300.	925.00
22	A9	35c black, *yellow*	1,300.	925.00
23	A9	75c carmine, *rose*	72.50	52.50
a.		Double overprint		400.00
24	A9	1fr brnz grn, *straw* (R)	80.00	52.50
a.		Double overprint	240.00	210.00

Inverted Overprint

13a	A9	1c	225.00	190.00
14a	A9	2c	225.00	190.00
15a	A9	4c		325.00
16a	A9	5c	240.00	200.00
17a	A9	10c	240.00	200.00
20a	A9	25c	200.00	200.00
21a	A9	30c		1,700.
22a	A9	35c		1,700.

Navigation and Commerce
A10   A11

1892		Typo.	Perf. 14x13½	

Name of Colony in Blue or Carmine

25	A10	1c black, *blue*	2.00	2.00
26	A10	2c brown, *buff*	2.75	2.75
27	A10	4c claret, *lav*	3.25	3.25
28	A10	5c green, *grnsh*	6.50	6.50
29	A10	10c black, *lavender*	8.75	7.25
30	A10	15c bl, quadrille paper	15.00	10.50
31	A10	20c red, *green*	21.00	16.00
32	A10	25c black, *rose*	17.50	14.50
33	A10	30c brown, *bister*	22.50	16.00
34	A10	40c red, *straw*	28.00	21.50
35	A10	50c carmine, *rose*	45.00	36.00
36	A10	75c violet, *org*	52.50	45.00
37	A10	1fr brnz grn, *straw*	75.00	60.00
		Nos. 25-37 (13)	299.75	241.25

Perf. 13½x14 stamps are counterfeits.

1894			Perf. 14x13½	
38	A11	1c black, *blue*	2.00	2.00
39	A11	2c brown, *buff*	2.75	2.40
40	A11	4c claret, *lav*	3.25	2.75
41	A11	5c green, *grnsh*	5.50	4.75
42	A11	10c black, *lavender*	7.25	7.25
43	A11	15c blue, quadrille paper	12.00	6.50
44	A11	20c red, *grn*	20.00	14.00
45	A11	25c black, *rose*	12.00	9.50
46	A11	30c brown, *bister*	13.50	6.50
47	A11	40c red, *straw*	13.50	6.50
48	A11	50c carmine, *rose*	20.00	13.50
49	A11	75c violet, *org*	12.00	9.00
50	A11	1fr brnz grn, *straw*	28.00	24.00
		Nos. 38-50 (13)	151.75	108.65

Bisected stamps of type A11 are mentioned
in note after Madagascar No. 62.
For surcharges see Madagascar #56-57,
61-62.
Perf. 13½x14 stamps are counterfeits.

POSTAGE DUE STAMPS

D1   D2

1891		Unwmk.	Litho.	Imperf.	
J1	D1	5c violet		300.00	87.50
J2	D2	50c black		250.00	110.00

Excellent counterfeits exist of Nos. J1-J2.

Postage Due Stamps of French
Colonies Overprinted Like Nos. 13-24

1892

J3	D1	1c black	130.00	72.50
J4	D1	2c black	130.00	65.00
a.		Inverted overprint	450.00	300.00
J5	D1	3c black	130.00	65.00
J6	D1	4c black	130.00	60.00
J7	D1	5c black	130.00	72.50
J8	D1	10c black	36.00	32.50
a.		Inverted overprint	450.00	450.00
J9	D1	15c black	36.00	32.50
a.		Double overprint	575.00	500.00
J10	D1	20c black	200.00	135.00
a.		Double overprint	600.00	500.00
J11	D1	30c black	120.00	60.00
a.		Inverted overprint	450.00	300.00
J12	D1	60c black	1,200.	775.00
J13	D1	1fr brown	2,800.	1,500.

DJIBOUTI

jə-ˈbü-tē

LOCATION — East Africa
GOVT. — Republic
AREA — 8,958 sq. mi.
POP. — 447,439 (1999 est.)
CAPITAL — Djibouti

The French territory of Afars and
Issas became the Republic of Djibouti
June 27, 1977. For 1894-1902 issues
with "Djibouti" or "DJ," see Somali
Coast.

> **Catalogue values for all unused
> stamps in this country are for
> Never Hinged items.**

Afars and Issas Issues of 1972-1977
Overprinted and Surcharged in
Black, Dark Green, Blue or Brown

No. 452

Printing and Perforations as Before

1977				
439	A63	1fr on 4fr (#358;B)	2.00	.25
440	A81	2fr on 5fr (#433;B)	2.00	.25
441	A75	5fr on 20fr (#421;B)	.25	.20
442	A70	8fr (#380;B)	.35	.25
443	A71	20fr (#387;DG)	3.50	.65
444	A81	30fr (#434;B)	3.75	.80
445	A71	40fr (#388;DG)	4.50	1.10
446	A71	45fr (#389;Bl)	5.00	1.25

447	A78	45fr (#428;B)	7.50	1.25
448	A72	50fr (#394;B)	8.00	1.60
449	A71	60fr (#391;Br)	7.00	1.60
450	A79	70fr (#430;B)	8.00	1.90
451	A81	70fr (#435;B)	5.50	2.25
452	A74	100fr (#418;B)	11.00	3.00
453	A72	150fr (#399;B)	11.50	3.50
454	A76	200fr (#432;B)	5.00	3.50
455	A80	200fr (#432;B)	5.75	4.00
456	A74	300fr (#419;B)	9.25	6.50
		Nos. 439-456,C106-C108 (21)	122.10	52.10

Map and Flag of
Djibouti — A83

A84

Design: 65fr, Map and flag of Djibouti, map
of Africa, horiz.

1977, June 27		Litho.	Perf. 12½	
457	A83	45fr multicolored	1.50	.50
458	A83	65fr multicolored	1.90	.75

Independence, June 27.

1977, July 4

459	A84	10fr Headrest, horiz.	.35	.20
460	A84	20fr Water Pipe	.65	.20
461	A84	25fr Pitcher	.90	.45
		Nos. 459-461 (3)	1.90	.85

Ostrich — A85

1977, Aug. 11		Litho.	Perf. 12½	
462	A85	90fr shown	2.75	.80
463	A85	100fr Weaver	4.00	1.10

Snail
A86

Designs: 15fr, Fiddler crab. 50fr, Klipspr-
ingers. 70fr, Green turtle. 80fr, Priacanthus
hamrur (fish). 150fr, Dolphinfish.

1977		Litho.	Perf. 12½	
464	A86	15fr multicolored	.75	.20
465	A86	45fr multicolored	1.50	.40
466	A86	50fr multicolored	2.00	.50
467	A86	70fr multicolored	2.25	.60
468	A86	80fr multicolored	2.75	.75
469	A86	150fr multicolored	4.50	2.00
		Nos. 464-469 (6)	13.75	4.45

Issued: 45fr, 70fr, 80fr, 9/14; others, 12/5.

Pres. Hassan Gouled Aptidon and Djibouti Flag — A87

1978, Feb. 12   Litho.   Perf. 13
470 A87 65fr multicolored   1.25   .45

Charaxes Hansali — A88

Necklace — A89

Butterflies: 20fr, Colias electo. 25fr, Acraea chilo. 150fr, Junonia hierta.

1978, Mar. 13   Litho.   Perf. 12½x13
471 A88 5fr multicolored   .50   .20
472 A88 20fr multicolored   1.25   .25
473 A88 25fr multicolored   1.75   .50
474 A88 150fr multicolored   7.00 1.75
    Nos. 471-474 (4)   10.50 2.70

1978, May 29   Litho.   Perf. 12½x13
Design: 55fr, Necklace, diff.
475 A89 45fr pink & multi   1.00   .35
476 A89 55fr blue & multi   1.50   .45

Bougainvillea A90

Flowers: 35fr, Hibiscus schizopetalus. 250fr, Caesalpinia pulcherrima.

1978, July 10   Photo.   Perf. 12½x13
477 A90 15fr multicolored   .45   .20
478 A90 35fr multicolored   .90   .25
479 A90 250fr multicolored   5.25   .90
    Nos. 477-479 (3)   6.60 1.35

Charonia Nodifera — A91

Sea Shell: 80fr, Charonia variegata.

1978, Oct. 9   Litho.   Perf. 13
480 A91 10fr multicolored   1.10   .35
481 A91 80fr multicolored   4.00   .95

Chaetodon A92

30fr, Yellow surgeonfish. 40fr, Harlequinfish.

1978, Nov. 20   Litho.   Perf. 13x12½
482 A92 8fr multicolored   .75   .25
483 A92 30fr multicolored   1.40   .35
484 A92 40fr multicolored   2.75   .65
    Nos. 482-484 (3)   4.90 1.25

Alsthom BB 1201 at Dock — A93

55fr, Steam locomotive 231. 60fr, Steam locomotive 130 and map of route. 75fr, Diesel.

1979, Jan. 29   Litho.   Perf. 13
485 A93 40fr multicolored   1.25   .20
486 A93 55fr multicolored   1.40   .30
487 A93 60fr multicolored   1.75   .30
488 A93 75fr multicolored   2.25   .40
    Nos. 485-488 (4)   6.65 1.20

Djibouti-Addis Ababa railroad.

Children and IYC Emblem — A94

Design: 200fr, Mother, child, IYC emblem.

1979, Feb. 26   Litho.   Perf. 13
489 A94 20fr multicolored   .45   .20
490 A94 200fr multicolored   3.50 1.10

International Year of the Child.

Plane over Ardoukoba Volcano — A95

30fr, Helicopter over Ardoukoba Volcano.

1979, Mar. 19
491 A95 30fr multi, vert.   .90   .35
492 A95 90fr multi   2.75   .65

Rowland Hill, Postal Clerks, No. C109 — A96

100fr, Somali Coast #22, Djibouti #457, letters, Rowland Hill. 150fr, Letters hoisted onto ship, smoke signals, Rowland Hill.

1979, Apr. 17   Litho.   Perf. 13x12½
493 A96 25fr multicolored   .35   .20
494 A96 40fr multicolored   1.75   .45
495 A96 150fr multicolored   2.75   .70
    Nos. 493-495 (3)   4.85 1.35

Sir Rowland Hill (1795-1879), originator of penny postage.

View of Djibouti, Bird and Local Woman — A97

Design: 80fr, Map and flag of Djibouti, UPU emblem, Concorde, train and mail runner.

1979, June 8   Litho.   Perf. 13x12½
496 A97 55fr multicolored   2.75   .85
497 A97 80fr multicolored   3.25 1.10

Philexafrique II, Libreville, Gabon, June 8-17. Nos. 496, 497 each printed in sheets of 10 with 5 labels showing exhibition emblem.

Solanacea A98

Flowers: 2fr, Opuntia, vert. 15fr, Trichodesma. 45fr, Acacia etbaica. 50fr, Thunbergia alata, vert.

Perf. 13x13½, 13½x13
1979, June 18
498 A98 2fr multicolored   .20   .20
499 A98 8fr multicolored   .25   .20
500 A98 15fr multicolored   .50   .20
501 A98 45fr multicolored   1.00   .20
502 A98 50fr multicolored   1.25   .25
    Nos. 498-502 (5)   3.20 1.05

Running — A99

Olympic Emblem and: 70fr, Basketball, vert. 200fr, Soccer.

Perf. 12½x13, 13x12½
1979, Oct. 22   Litho.
503 A99 70fr multicolored   1.40   .25
504 A99 120fr multicolored   2.10   .50
505 A99 200fr multicolored   3.50   .75
    Nos. 503-505 (3)   7.00 1.50

Pre-Olympic Year.

Cypraecassis Rufa — A100

Shells: 40fr, Lambis chiragra arthritica. 300fr, Harpa connaidalis.

1979, Dec. 22   Litho.   Perf. 13
506 A100 10fr multicolored   .25   .20
507 A100 40fr multicolored   1.25   .20
508 A100 300fr multicolored 6.50 1.50
    Nos. 506-508 (3)   8.00 1.90

Rotary International, 75th Anniversary — A101

1980, Feb. 19   Litho.   Perf. 13x12½
509 A101 90fr multicolored   2.10   .60
  a. Souvenir sheet of 1 #509   5.00 5.00

Lions Club of Djibouti — A102

1980, Feb. 19
510 A102 100fr multicolored 2.25   .75

Colotis Danae — A103

1980, Mar. 17   Perf. 13x13½
511 A103 5fr shown   .75   .50
512 A103 55fr Danaus chrysippus   3.50 1.50

Chess Players, Knight — A104

Chess Federation Creation: 75fr, Chess Game, Florence, 1493.

1980, June 9   Litho.   Perf. 13
513 A104 20fr multicolored   1.00   .20
514 A104 75fr multicolored   2.75   .35

Cribraria A105

1980, Aug. 12   Litho.   Perf. 13
515 A105 15fr shown   .75   .20
516 A105 85fr Nautilius pompilius 2.50   .50

Alexander Fleming, Discoverer of Penicillin — A106

Design: 130fr, Jules Verne, French science fiction writer; earth, moon and spacecraft.

1980, Sept. 1
517	A106	20fr multicolored	1.10	.35
518	A106	130fr multicolored	3.00	.60

Capt. Cook and Endeavor — A107

Capt. James Cook Death Bicentenary: 90fr, Ships and Maps of voyages.

1980, Nov. 20   Litho.   Perf. 13
519	A107	55fr multicolored	1.25	.30
520	A107	90fr multicolored	2.10	.45

Souvenir sheets of 1 exist, perf. 12½x12.

Angel Fish A108

1981, Apr. 13   Litho.   Perf. 12½
521	A108	25fr shown	1.75	.20
522	A108	55fr Moorish idol	3.25	.50
523	A108	70fr Scad	3.75	1.50
	Nos. 521-523 (3)		8.75	2.20

13th World Telecommunications Day — A109

1981, May 17   Litho.   Perf. 13
524	A109	140fr multicolored	2.50	.70

Type 231 Steam Locomotive, Germany, 1958 and Amtrak, US, 1980 — A110

Locomotives: 55fr, Stephenson and his Rocket, Djibouti Railways 230 engine. 65fr, Type TGV, France, Type 962, Japan.

1981, June 9   Litho.   Perf. 13
525	A110	40fr multicolored	1.50	.30
526	A110	55fr multicolored	2.00	.35
527	A110	65fr multicolored	2.50	.40
	Nos. 525-527 (3)		6.00	1.05

Radio Amateurs Club — A111

1981, June 25
528	A111	250fr multicolored	4.50	1.00

Prince Charles and Lady Diana — A112

1981, June 29
529	A112	180fr shown	3.50	.90
530	A112	200fr Couple, diff.	4.00	1.00

Royal Wedding.

Lord Nelson and Victory — A113

1981, July 6   Litho.   Perf. 13x12½
531	A113	100fr multicolored	1.75	.45
532	A113	175fr multicolored	3.00	.90

Lord Horatio Nelson (1758-1805).

Scout Tending Campfire — A114

1981, July 16   Litho.   Perf. 13
533	A114	60fr shown	3.00	.70
534	A114	105fr Scout giving sign	3.75	.80

28th World Scouting Conference, Dakar, Aug. (60fr); 4th Pan-African Scouting Conference, Abidjan, Aug. (105fr).

Pawn and Queen, Swedish Bone Chess Pieces, 13th Cent. — A115

1981, Oct. 15   Litho.   Perf. 13
535	A115	50fr shown	1.50	.35
536	A115	130fr Pawn, knight, Chinese, 19th cent., vert.	2.75	.85

For overprints see Nos. 542-543.

Sheraton Hotel Opening — A116

1981, Nov. 15   Litho.   Perf. 13x12½
537	A116	75fr multicolored	1.50	.45

For surcharge see No. 623.

Acacia Mellifera A117

1981, Dec. 21   Perf. 13
538	A117	10fr Clitoria ternatea, vert.	.35	.20
539	A117	30fr shown	.70	.20
540	A117	35fr Punica granatum	1.00	.20
541	A117	45fr Malvaceous plant, vert.	1.25	.30
	Nos. 538-541 (4)		3.30	.90

See Nos. 558-560.

Nos. 535-536 Overprinted with Winners' Names

1981, Dec.   Litho.   Perf. 13
542	A115	50fr multicolored	1.25	.45
543	A115	130fr multicolored	3.00	.85

World Chess Championship.

TB Bacillus Centenary A117a

1982, Mar. 24   Litho.   Perf. 13
544	A117a	305fr Koch, slide, microscope	5.75	1.50

A117b

1982, Apr. 8   Litho.   Perf. 13
545	A117b	125fr Ivory bishop	3.00	.75
546	A117b	175fr Queen, pawn, 19th cent.	4.25	1.25

1982 World Chess Championship.

A118

1982, May 17   Litho.   Perf. 13
547	A118	150fr multicolored	3.00	.85

14th World Telecommunications Day. For surcharge see No. 647.

Bus and Jeep — A119

1982, July 27   Litho.   Perf. 13
548	A119	20fr shown	.55	.20
549	A119	25fr Dhow, ferry	.70	.20
550	A119	55fr Train, jet	1.50	.45
	Nos. 548-550 (3)		2.75	.85

Shells from the Red Sea A120

1982, Nov. 20   Litho.   Perf. 12½
551	A120	10fr Cypraea erythraeensis	.45	.20
552	A120	15fr Conus sumatrensis	.75	.30
553	A120	25fr Cypraea pulchra	.90	.35
554	A120	30fr Conus inscriptus	1.10	.40
555	A120	70fr Casmaria ponderosa	2.25	.50
556	A120	150fr Cypraea exusta	4.50	1.50
	Nos. 551-556 (6)		9.95	3.25

See Nos. 563-567.

Intl. Palestinian Solidarity Day — A121

1982, Nov. 29   Litho.   Perf. 13
557	A121	40fr multicolored	1.00	.20

Local Flowers type of 1981

Various flowers. 5fr, 55fr, vert.

1983, Apr. 14   Litho.   Perf. 13
558	A117	5fr multicolored	.20	.20
559	A117	50fr multicolored	1.10	.40
560	A117	55fr multicolored	1.25	.40
	Nos. 558-560 (3)		2.55	1.00

World Communications Year — A123

1983, June 20   Litho.   Perf. 13
561	A123	500fr multicolored	8.50	2.25

Conference of Donors, Nov. 21-23 — A124

1983, Nov. 21   Litho.   Perf. 13x12½
562	A124	75fr multicolored	1.25	.40

Shell Type of 1982

1983, Dec. 20   Litho.   Perf. 12½
563	A120	15fr Marginella obtusa	.75	.20
564	A120	30fr Conus jickelli	1.25	.20
565	A120	55fr Cypraea macandrewi	1.75	.40
566	A120	80fr Conus cuvieri	2.25	.50
567	A120	100fr Turbo petholatus	2.50	.65
	Nos. 563-567 (5)		8.50	1.95

Local Butterflies
A125

1984, Jan. 24   Litho.   Perf. 13½x13
568 A125   5fr Colotis chryso-
              nome   .50   .20
569 A125   20fr Colias erate   1.00   .25
570 A125   30fr Junonia orithyia   1.50   .35
571 A125   75fr Acraea
              doubledayi   4.25 1.00
572 A125   110fr Byblia ilithya   5.50 1.50
       Nos. 568-572 (5)   12.75 3.30

Landscapes and Animals — A126

1984, Apr. 29   Litho.   Perf. 13
573 A126   2fr Randa Klip-
              springer   .20   .20
574 A126   8fr Ali Sabieh, gazel-
              les   .20   .20
575 A126   10fr Lake Assal, oryx   .20   .20
576 A126   15fr Tadjoura, gazelle   .25   .20
577 A126   40fr Alaila Dada, jack-
              al, vert.   .75   .20
578 A126   45fr Lake Abbe, wart-
              hog   .75   .30
579 A126   55fr Obock, seagull   1.90   .75
580 A126   125fr Presidential Pal-
              ace, bird   3.75 1.25
       Nos. 573-580 (8)   8.00 3.30

For surcharges see #646, 657-658, 660.

Fire Prevention — A127

1984, Sept. 9   Litho.   Perf. 13
581 A127   25fr Fire truck   .80   .20
582 A127   95fr Hook & ladder   2.75   .50
583 A127   100fr Fire plane   3.00 1.00
       Nos. 581-583 (3)   6.55 1.70

International
Olympic
Committee
Membership
A128

1984, July 22   Litho.   Perf. 13
584 A128   45fr Runners   .90   .35

Motor
Carriage,
1886
A128a

1984, Nov. 11   Litho.   Perf. 12½
585 A128a   35fr shown   .70   .30
586 A128a   65fr Cabriolet, 1896   1.40   .65
587 A128a   90fr Phoenix, 1900   2.00   .95
       Nos. 585-587 (3)   4.10 1.90

Gottlieb Daimler (1834-1900), pioneer automobile manufacturer.

Marie and Pierre
Curie — A129

1984, Dec. 3   Litho.   Perf. 12½
588 A129   150fr Pierre Curie   2.75 1.10
589 A129   150fr Marie Curie   2.75 1.10

A130

Audubon Bicentenary — A130a

Illustration A130a reduced.

1985, Jan. 27   Litho.   Perf. 13
590   A130   5fr Merops al-
              bicollis   .75   .35
591   A130   15fr Pterocles
              exustus   3.25   .85
592   A130   20fr Trachyphonus
              mar-
              garitatus
              somalicus   3.75 1.00
593   A130   25fr Coracias
              garrulus   4.50 1.10
       Nos. 590-593 (4)   12.25 3.30

Souvenir Sheet
Self-Adhesive
Perf. 12½
593A A130a 200fr Pandion
              haliaetus,
              vert.   26.00 26.00

No. 593A is airmail and printed on wood.

Intl. Youth
Year — A131

1985, Mar. 26   Litho.   Perf. 13
594 A131   10fr multicolored   .20   .20
595 A131   30fr multicolored   .50   .30
596 A131   40fr multicolored   .70   .40
       Nos. 594-596 (3)   1.40   .90

German Railways, 150th
Anniv. — A132

Designs: 55fr, Engine No. 29, Addis Ababa-
Djibouti Railways. 75fr, Adler, museum facsimile of the first German locomotive.

1985, Apr. 22   Litho.   Perf. 13
597 A132   55fr multicolored   2.00   .65
598 A132   75fr multicolored   3.00   .90

A133

1985, May 23
599 A133   35fr Planting saplings 1.00   .45
600 A133   65fr Hygiene, family
              health care   1.75   .75
       Scouting.

A134

1985, June 24   Litho.
80fr, Victor Hugo (1802-1885), Novelist.
100fr, Arthur Rimbaud (1854-1891), poet.

601 A134   80fr brt blue & slate   1.40   .80
602 A134   100fr multicolored   1.60 1.00

Sea Shells
A135

1985, July 15   Litho.   Perf. 12½
603 A135   10fr Cypraea nebrites   .25   .20
604 A135   15fr Cypraea turdus   .50   .20
605 A135   30fr Conus acuminatus   1.25   .30
606 A135   40fr Cypraea camelo-
              pardalis   1.50   .55
607 A135   55fr Conus terebra   2.50   .70
       Nos. 603-607 (5)   6.00 1.95

1st World
Cup
Marathon
'85,
Hiroshima
A136

1985, Sept. 2   Perf. 12½x13
608 A136   75fr Winners   1.25   .75
609 A136   100fr Approaching fin-
              ish   2.00 1.00

Halley's Comet — A137

Designs: 85fr, Bayeux Tapestry, Comet and
Halley. 90fr, Vega I, Giotto space probes, map
of planets, comet trajectory.

1986, Jan. 27   Litho.   Perf. 13
610 A137   85fr multicolored   1.50   .50
611 A137   90fr multicolored   1.75   .85

ISERST Solar Energy
Installation — A138

Designs: 50fr, Runners on beach. 150fr,
Windmill, headquarters, power control station.

1986, Mar. 20
612 A138   50fr multicolored   .80   .40
613 A138   150fr multicolored   2.25 1.25

Ships from Columbus's Fleet,
1492 — A139

1986, Apr. 14
614 A139   60fr Santa Maria   1.75   .55
615 A139   90fr Nina, Pinta   3.00   .95

Fish, Red
Sea — A140

1986, June 16   Litho.   Perf. 13½x13
616 A140   20fr Elagatis bipinnu-
              latus   .65   .30
617 A140   25fr Valamugil seheli   .75   .45
618 A140   55fr Lutjanus rivulatus 2.00   .75
       Nos. 616-618 (3)   3.40 1.50

Public Buildings — A141

105fr, People's Palace. 115fr, Ministry of the Interior, Posts & Telecommunications.

1986, July 21   Litho.   Perf. 13
619 A141 105fr multicolored   1.50 .90
620 A141 115fr multicolored   1.75 1.00

Sea-Me-We Building, Keyboard — A142

1986, Sept. 8   Litho.   Perf. 13
621 A142 100fr multicolored   2.00 .70

Souvenir Sheet
Perf. 12½
622 A142 250fr multicolored   13.50 13.50

Southeast Asia, Middle East, Western Europe Submarine Cable System inauguration.

No. 537 Surcharged
"5e ANNIVERSAIRE."
1986, Nov. 15   Perf. 13x12½
623 A116 55fr on 75fr multi   1.00 .40

Pasteur Institute, Cent. — A143

1987, Feb. 19   Litho.   Perf. 13
624 A143 220fr multicolored   4.25 1.60

Natl. Vaccination Campaign.

Edible Mushrooms A144

1987, Apr. 16   Litho.   Perf. 13x12½
625 A144 35fr Macrolepiota imbricata   1.50 .65
626 A144 50fr Lentinus squarrosulus   2.25 .85
627 A144 95fr Terfezia boudieri   3.00 1.50
Nos. 625-627 (3)   6.75 3.00

Wildlife A145

1987, May 14   Perf. 12½x13
628 A145   5fr Hare   .50 .20
629 A145 30fr Dromedary   1.25 .30
630 A145 140fr Cheetah   5.00 1.00
Nos. 628-630 (3)   6.75 1.50

1988 Olympics, Seoul and Calgary — A146

85fr, Pierre de Coubertin (1863-1937), founder of the modern Olympics, & lighting of the flame. 135fr, Ski jumping. 140fr, Running.

1987, July 16   Perf. 13
631 A146 85fr multicolored   1.50 .55
632 A146 135fr multicolored   2.50 .95
633 A146 140fr multicolored   2.75 1.00
Nos. 631-633 (3)   6.75 2.50

Traditional Art — A147

UN Universal Immunization by 1990 Campaign A148

1988, Jan. 20   Litho.   Perf. 13
634 A147 30fr Nomad's comb   .60 .30
635 A147 70fr Wash jug   1.25 .60

1988, Apr. 10   Perf. 12½
636 A148 125fr multicolored   2.25 1.00

16th Africa Cup Soccer Championships, Morocco — A149

1988, Mar. 13   Perf. 13
637 A149 55fr Athletes, view of Rabat   1.10 .50

1988 Winter Olympics, Calgary — A150

1988, May 7   Litho.   Perf. 13
638 A150 45fr Ski jump   1.00 .40

Campaign Against Thirst A151

1988, Sept. 10   Litho.   Perf. 12½x13
639 A151 50fr multicolored   1.25 .45

Intl. Fund for Agricultural Development, 10th Anniv. — A152

1988, Nov. 14   Perf. 13
640 A152 135fr multicolored   2.25 1.00

Michel Lafoux Air Club, 40th Anniv. — A153

1988, Dec. 6
641 A153 145fr 1948 Tiger Moth, 1988 Tobago-10   2.75 1.00

Marine Life A154

1989, Jan. 20   Litho.   Perf. 12½
642 A154 90fr *Lobophyllia costata*   2.25 .30
643 A154 160fr *Lambis truncata*   4.25 1.40

Colotis protomedia A155

1989, Feb. 15
644 A155 70fr multicolored   4.25 2.10

Nos. 573 and 547 Surcharged
1989   Perf. 13
646 A126 70fr on 2fr No. 573   2.25 .50
647 A118 70fr on 150fr No. 547   2.25 .50
Issued: 646, 12/20; 647, 12/29.

Folk Dances — A157

Francolin of Djibouti — A159

1989, Mar. 20
648 A157 30fr shown   .50 .25
649 A157 70fr multicolored, diff. 1.40 .50

1989, Apr. 10   Litho.   Perf. 12½
651 A159 35fr multicolored   1.90 .45

Rare Flora A160

1989, June 12
652 A160 25fr *Calotropis procera*   .50 .20

A161

A162

1989, Aug. 10   Litho.   Perf. 13
653 A161 70fr multicolored   1.25 .50

Interparliamentary Union, cent.

1989, Oct. 1
654 A162 145fr multicolored   2.75 1.10

Intl. Literacy Year.

Petroglyph — A163

1989, Nov. 18   Litho.   Perf. 13
655 A163 5fr multicolored   .35   .20

Girl — A164

1989, Dec. 6
656 A164 55fr multicolored   1.00   .40

Nos. 574, 576-577 Surcharged
1989-1990   Litho.   Perf. 13
657 A126 30fr on 8fr multi   .50   .30
658 A126 50fr on 40fr multi   2.00   .55
660 A126 120fr on 15fr multi   2.00   .80
     Nos. 657-660 (3)   4.50 1.65
Issue dates: 30fr, 12/20/89; 50fr, 7/3/90; 120fr, 3/17/90.

Water Conservation — A165

1990, May 5   Litho.   Perf. 11½
665 A165 120fr multicolored   2.25   .90

Traditional
Jewelry
A166

1990, Mar. 10
666 A166 70fr multicolored   1.25   .45

Commiphora — A167

1990, Feb. 20   Perf. 12
667 A167 30fr multicolored   .60   .35

Baskets — A168

1990, July 3
668 A168 30fr multicolored   .50   .20

A169   A170

1990, June 12   Perf. 11½
669 A169 100fr multicolored   2.00   .80
World Cup Soccer Championships, Italy.

1990, Apr. 16   Perf. 11½
670 A170 55fr shown   1.00   .40
20 kilometer race of Djibouti.

Vaccination
Campaign
A171

1990, Aug. 22   Litho.   Perf. 11½
Granite Paper
671 A171 300fr multicolored   4.50 1.75

Charles de   African Tourism
Gaulle — A172   Year — A173

1990, Sept. 16
Granite Paper
672 A172 200fr multicolored   3.50 1.25

1991, Jan. 23   Litho.   Perf. 13
673 A173 115fr multicolored   2.00   .80

Corals — A174

1991, Jan. 28   Perf. 12½
674 A174 40fr Acropora   .90   .50
675 A174 45fr Seriatopora hytrise 1.25   .50

Aquatic
Birds — A175

1991, Feb. 12
676 A175 10fr Pelecanus rufes-
            cens   .75   .20
677 A175 15fr Egretta gularis   1.50   .25
678 A175 20fr Ardea goliath,
            horiz.   1.75   .30
679 A175 25fr Platalea
            leucorodia, horiz.   2.00   .35
     Nos. 676-679 (4)   6.00 1.10

UNO   Fossils
Development   A177
Conference
A176

1990, Oct. 9   Litho.   Perf. 11½x12
Granite Paper
680 A176 45fr multicolored   1.10   .45

1990, Nov. 1
Granite Paper
681 A177 90fr pur, org & blk   5.25 1.75

Papio
Hamadryas — A178

1990, Dec. 6
Granite Paper
682 A178 50fr multicolored   1.75   .55

Pandion
Haliaetus
A179

1991, Mar. 20   Litho.   Perf. 12x11½
683 A179 200fr multicolored   5.00 1.60

Traditional
Game
A180

1991, Apr. 4
684 A180 250fr multicolored   5.25 3.25
See No. 696.

Djibouti-Ethiopia Railroad — A181

1991, May 25   Litho.   Perf. 11½
685 A181 85fr multicolored   4.00 2.25

World
Environment
Day — A182

1991, June 10
686 A182 110fr multicolored   2.75   .65

Philexafrique — A183

1991, Jul. 16   Litho.   Perf. 11½
687 A183 120fr Islands   3.25 1.75

A184

A185

1991, Sept. 25
688 A184 175fr Handball   4.50 3.00
Pre-Olympic year.

1991, Oct. 16   Litho.   Perf. 11½x12
689 A185 105fr multicolored   2.10 1.10
World Food Day.

Underwater Cable Network — A186

1991, Nov. 28   Perf. 12x11½
690 A186 130fr multicolored   2.75 1.00

Discovery of America, 500th Anniv. A187

1991, Dec. 19   Litho.   Perf. 11½
691 A187 145fr multicolored   3.25 1.60

Arthur Rimbaud (1854-1891) Poet and Merchant — A188

1991-92   Perf. 11½
692 A188 90fr Young man, ship   2.50 .90
693 A188 150fr Old man, camels 2.75 .90

Issued: 90fr, 2/5/92; 150fr, 12/23/91.

Djibouti-Ethiopia Railroad — A189

Design: 250fr, Locomotive, map.

1992   Litho.   Perf. 12x11½
694 A189 70fr multicolored   2.75 1.10

Souvenir Sheet
Perf. 13x12½
695 A189 250fr multicolored   5.25 5.25

Issue dates: 70fr, Feb. 2; 250fr, Jan. 30.

Traditional Game Type of 1991
1992, Feb. 10   Perf. 11½
696 A180 100fr Boys playing Go   2.10 .85

A190

A191

1992, June 9   Litho.   Perf. 14
697 A190 80fr multicolored   2.10 1.25

1992 Summer Olympics, Barcelona.

1992   Litho.   Perf. 14x13½
Traditional food preparation.

698   A191 30fr Pounding grain   1.25 .50
698A A191 45fr Preparing mofo
699   A191 70fr Winnowing grain   1.25 .65
699A A191 75fr Cooking mofo

Issued: Nos. 698, 699, 4/20; No. 698A, 12/6.

Discovery of America, 500th Anniv. A192

1992, May 16   Litho.   Perf. 11½
700 A192 125fr multicolored   2.75 .95

African Soccer Championships A193

Intl. Space Year — A194

1992, July 22   Perf. 14
701 A193 15fr multicolored   .45 .20

Perf. 14x13½, 13½x14
1992, Sept. 28
702 A194 120fr Rocket, satellite 2.50 .85
703 A194 135fr Astronaut, satel-
           lite, horiz.   2.75 .95

Wildlife — 704

1992, Nov. 11   Perf. 14
704 A195 5fr Dik-dik   1.25 .20
705 A195 200fr Caretta caretta 4.00 1.40

Taeniura Lymma — A195a

Perf. 11½x11¾
1990, Mar. 24   Litho.

Panel Color
705A A195a 70fr yellow   — —
705B A195a 100fr green   — —
705C A195a 120fr lilac   — —

A 30fr stamp is believed to exist for this issue. The editors would like to examine an example.

Nomad Girls in Traditional Costumes A196

1993, Jan. 26   Litho.   Perf. 13
706 A196 70fr Girl beside hut 1.60 .45
707 A196 120fr shown   2.75 .75

White-eyed Seagull A197

1993, Feb. 28   Litho.   Perf. 12½
708 A197 300fr multicolored   4.50 1.75

Amin Salman Mosque — A198

1993, Feb. 17   Litho.   Perf. 13¾x14
709 A198 500fr multicolored   52.50 4.25

Handcrafts — A199

Handicrafts Type of 1993
1993, Apr. 23   Litho.   Perf. 13¾x14
710 A199 100fr Neck rest   — —

1993, Apr. 23   Litho.   Perf. 13¾x14
711 A199 125fr Sword   — —

A number has been reserved for a 100fr stamp in this set. The editors would like to examine it.

Cercopithecus Aethiops — A200

1993, May 29   Litho.   Perf. 14¼x13½
712 A200 150fr multi   100.00 —

Organization of African Unity, 30th Anniv. — A201

Perf. 14¼x13½
1993, June 20   Litho.
713 A201 200fr multi   100.00 —

Water Carriers — A202

1993, July 6   Litho.   Perf. 14x13¾
714 A202 30fr Woman   — —
715 A202 50fr Man   — —

Conquest of Space — A203

1993, Sept. 30   Litho.   Perf. 14x13¾
716 A203 90fr multicolored   — —

A204

A205

Traditional utensils.

1993, Sept. 30   Litho.   Perf. 13½
717 A204 15fr Weyso   .45 .20
718 A204 20fr Hangol   .90 .20
719 A204 25fr Saqaf   1.00 .20
720 A204 30fr Subrar   1.40 .45
         Nos. 717-720 (4)   3.75 1.05

1993, Nov. 10   Litho.   Perf. 14
Traditional musical instruments.

721 A205 5fr Flute   .60 .60
722 A205 10fr Drum   .60 .60

Souvenir Sheet

REPUBLIQUE DE DJIBOUTI
Mariage Impérial

Wedding of Japan's Crown Prince
Naruhito and Masako Owada — A206

1994, Jan. 10   Litho.   Perf. 13x12½
Self-Adhesive
723 A206 500fr multicolored   22.50 22.50
No. 723 printed on wood.

20 Kilometer
Race of Djibouti
A207

Promotion of
Breastfeeding
A208

1994   Litho.   Perf. 11½
724 A207 50fr multicolored   2.50 1.00

1994
725 A208 40fr shown   1.25 .40
726 A208 45fr Mother, infant   1.40 .40

Hassan
Gouled
Aptidon
Stadium
A209

1994
727 A209 70fr multicolored   2.50 1.10

Stenella
Longirostris
A210

1994, May 1   Litho.   Perf. 11¾x11½
728 A210 120fr multicolored   6.25 6.25

World Housing
Day — A211

1994, May 9   Litho.   Perf. 11½x11¾
729 A211 30fr multi   —

Eupodotis Senegalensis — A212

Perf. 11¾x11½
1994, June 16   Litho.
730 A212 10fr multicolored   180.00 —

1994 World Cup Soccer
Tournament — A213

1994, Sept. 7
731 A213 200fr multicolored   180.00 —

Traditional Nomad
Costume — A214

Design: 150fr, Dress of a village leader.

Perf. 11½x11¾
1994, Sept. 18   Litho.
732 A214 100fr multicolored   2.00 2.00
Perf. 11¾
733 A214 150fr multicolored   3.25 3.25

Canis
Aureus
A215

Perf. 11¾x11½
1994, Sept. 28   Litho.
734 A215 400fr multi   135.00 —

World
Walking
Day
A216

1994, Oct. 19   Litho.   Perf. 11¾x11½
735 A216 75fr multicolored   —

A217

1994, Nov. 26   Litho.   Perf. 11¾
736 A217 55fr Book stand   —

A218

1994, Dec. 6   Litho.   Perf. 11½x11¾
737 A218 35fr Traditional dance   60.00 —

A219

A220

1995, Feb. 25   Litho.   Perf. 11¾
738 A219 70fr multicolored
Volleyball, cent.

1995, Feb. 25
739 A220 120fr multicolored
United Nations, 50th anniv.

Fight
Against
Thirst
A221

Perf. 11¾x11½
1995, Mar. 29   Litho.
740 A221 100fr multicolored

Threskiornis
Aethiopica — A222

1995, Apr. 5   Litho.   Perf. 11¾
742 A222 50fr multicolored
A number has been reserved for a 30fr
stamp in this set. The editors would like to
examine it.

World Telecommunications
Day — A223

Perf. 11¾x11½
1995, June 10   Litho.
743 A223 125fr multicolored   70.00 —

Crocuta
Crocuta
A224

1995, June 12   Litho.   Perf. 11¾
744 A224 200fr multi   105.00 —

People
Meeting
Under Tree
A225

1995, July 3   Litho.   Perf. 11¾x11½
745 A225 150fr multi   65.00 —

A226

A227

1995, Aug. 9   Perf. 11¾
746 A226 45fr Nomads around
fire   60.00 —

1995, Sept. 27   Perf. 11½x11¾
747 A227 250fr multi   70.00 —
FAO, 50th anniv.

Traditional
Costume — A228

1995, Dec. 6   Litho.   Perf. 11¾
748 A228 90fr multicolored

African Development Bank, 30th
Anniv. — A229

Perf. 11¾x11½
1995. Dec. 18   Litho.
749 A229 300fr multi   60.00 —

African Soccer
Cup — A230

1996, Feb. 28   Litho.   Perf. 11¾
750 A230 70fr multicolored   180.00 —

Leopard
A232

1996, May 6   Litho.   Perf. 11¾
752 A232 70fr multi   105.00 —

Amber
Necklace — A233

1996, June 13   Litho.   Perf. 11¾
753 A233 30fr multi   —

1996 Summer
Olympic Games,
Atlanta — A234

Perf. 11½x11¾
1996, Sept. 21 **Litho.**
754 A234 105fr multicolored   *125.00* —

Commicarpus
Grandiflorus
A236

1996, Oct. 6 **Litho.** **Perf. 11½x11¾**
756 A236 350fr multi   *60.00* —

Djibouti
Folklore — A237

1996, Nov. 28 **Litho.** **Perf. 11¾**
757 A237 95fr multi   — —

Legend of
the Lion
and Three
Bulls
A238

1996, Nov. 28 **Perf. 11¾**
758 A238 95fr multi   *135.00* —

Children's
Day
A239

1996, Dec. 17 **Perf. 11¾x11½**
759 A239 130fr multi   *60.00* —

A240   A241

Legend of the Tortoise and the Fox: No.
760, Tortoise and fox at starting line. No. 761,
Fox leaves tortoise behind. No. 762, Tortoise
passes sleeping fox.

1997, Jan. 17 **Perf. 11¾**
760 A240 60fr multi   — —
761 A240 60fr multi   — —
762 A240 60fr multi   — —
 a.   Horiz. strip, #760-762   *135.00*

1997, Feb. 9 **Litho.** **Perf. 11¾**
763 A241 80fr Mother, child   *52.50*
764 A241 90fr Hands around
       globe   *52.50*
    UNICEF, 50th anniv.

Dancers — A242

1997, May 14 **Litho.** **Perf. 11¾**
765 A242 70fr multi   *70.00* —

Fortune
Teller
A243

Designs: 200fr, Fortune teller and woman.
300fr, Fortune teller, camel.

1997, May 29 **Litho.** **Perf. 11¾**
766 A243 200fr multi   *70.00* —
767 A243 300fr multi   *70.00* —

Woman's
Day — A244

1997, May 30 **Litho.** **Perf. 11¾**
768 A244 250fr multi   *180.00* —

Traditional
Objects — A245

Design: 30fr, Writing board, horiz. 400fr,
Bowl and spoon.

1997, June 5 **Litho.** **Perf. 11¾**
769 A245 30fr multi   *57.50* —
770 A245 400fr multi   *57.50* —

Telecommunications — A246

Designs: 30fr, Arta post office. 100fr, Map,
building with antenna and satellite dishes.
120fr, Ships, map showing submarine cable
route, horiz.

1997, June 27 **Litho.** **Perf. 11¾**
771 A246 30fr multi   — —
772 A246 100fr multi   — —
773 A246 120fr multi   — —

Goats in
Tree
A247

1997, July 26 **Litho.** **Perf. 11¾**
774 A247 120fr multi   *80.00* —

A248

A249

Portrait of Diana: a, 125fr. b, 130fr. c, 150fr.

1998, Mar. 25 **Litho.** **Perf. 13½**
775 A248 Strip of 3, #a.-c.   *5.75* *5.75*
    Diana, Princess of Wales (1961-97).
No. 775 was isssued in sheets of 6 stamps.

1998 **Litho.** **Perf. 13½**
776 A249 130fr multicolored   *2.00* *1.40*
    Mother Teresa (1910-97). No. 776 was
issued in sheets of 4.

Intl. Year
of the
Ocean
A250

a, Tangara chilensis. b, Agalychnis cal-
lidryas. c, Delphinus delphis, megaptera
novaeangliae. d, Cercopithecus aethiops (h).
e, Laticaudia colubrina (i), sphyrna mokarran.
f, Lactoria cornuta, delphinus delphis (g). g,
Delphinus delphis (k). h, Aspidontus taeniatus,
lo vulpinus. i, Sepioteuthis lessoniana. j, Prionace glauca (i), chaetodon ornatissimus. k,
Eupagurus bernherdus. l, Octopus vulgaris
(k).

1998, Apr. 20 **Litho.** **Perf. 13½**
777 A250 75fr Sheet of 12,
       #a.-l.   *16.00* *16.00*

Mahatma Gandhi
(1869-1948)
A251

1998, Apr. 20 **Litho.** **Perf. 11¾**
778 A251 250fr multi   *80.00* —

Traditional
Art — A252

1998, Apr. 25 **Litho.** **Perf. 11½x11¾**
779 A252 30fr multicolored   *135.00* —

Women's Rights and International
Peace — A253

1998, May 3 **Perf. 11¾x11½**
780 A253 70fr multicolored   *60.00* —

World
Water Day
A254

1998, May 10 **Litho.** **Perf. 11¾**
781 A254 45fr multi   *60.00* —

1998 World Cup
Soccer
Championships,
France — A255

1998, June 10 **Litho.** **Perf. 11¾**
782 A255 200fr multi   *160.00* —

Marine
Life — A256

Cats and
Bush — A257

Perf. 11½x11¾, 11¾x11½
1998, July 2 **Litho.**
783 A256 20fr Octopus   *135.00* —
784 A256 25fr Shark, horiz.   *135.00* —

1998, Aug. 30 **Perf. 11½x11¾**
785 A257 120fr multi   *135.00* —

World Telecommunications
Day — A258

1996, Sept. 27   Litho.   Perf. 11¾
786 A258 150fr multi   100.00 —

National
Bank — A259

1998, Sept. 30   Litho.   Perf. 11¾
787 A259 100fr multi   135.00 —

Flags and IGAD
Emblem — A260

Perf. 11½x11¾
1998, Sept. 30   Litho.
788 A260 85fr multi   60.00 —

Traditional
Game
Goos
A261

1998, Oct. 1   Perf. 11¾x11½
789 A261 110fr multi   60.00 —

Fishing
Port
A262

1998
790 A262 100fr multi   115.00 —

Maskali
Island
A263

1998
791 A263 500fr multi   140.00 —

Fish
A264

1999   Litho.   Perf. 13¼x13½
792 A264 70fr multi   115.00 —

Antelope
— A264a

Perf. 13¼x13½
1999, Mar. 16   Litho.
792A A264a 120fr multi   105.00 —

Djibouti
Franc,
50th
Anniv.
A265

1999
793 A265 100fr multi   60.00 —

World Telecommunications
Day — A266

1999
794 A266 125fr multi   55.00 —

Worldwide Fund for Nature
(WWF) — A267

Phacochoerus africanus aeliani: a, Adult
and young. b, Adult standing. c, Head. d, Adult
walking.

2000, Apr. 13   Litho.   Perf. 14
795 A267 100fr Block of 4, #a-d 7.25 7.25

Wild Animals — A268

No. 796: a, Flamingo. b, Ostrich. c, Sifaka.
d, Yellow-billed stork. e, Scarlet macaw. f,
Dwarf puff adder. g, Toucan. h, Whooping
crane.

2000, Apr. 13
796 A268 100fr Sheet of 8, #a-
           h   18.00 18.00

Butterflies — A269

No. 797: a, Doxocopa cherubina. b,
Heliconius charitonius. c, Cantonephele
numili. d, Danaus gilippus. e, Morpho
peleides. f, Heliconius doris.
No. 798, 250fr, Agraulis vanillae. No. 799,
250fr, Strymon melinus.

2000, Apr. 13
797 A269 100fr Sheet of 6, #a-
           f   12.00 12.00
           Souvenir Sheets
798-799 A269 Set of 2   11.00 11.00

No. 797 contains six 28x42mm stamps.

Water
Resources — A270

2000, Apr. 13
800 A270 500fr multi   8.00 8.00

Trains and Landmarks — A271

No. 801: a, 5fr, Class OJ 2-10-2, China. b,
25fr, Eurostar, France-England. c, 15fr, Gla-
cier Express, Switzerland. d, 40fr, Unidentified
train. e, 35fr, Class WP 4-6-2, India.
No. 802, 110fr: a, Nord Chapelon Pacific,
France. b, Class 23 2-6-2, Germany. c, Class
GS-4 4-8-4, US. d, Class A4 4-6-2, Great Brit-
ain. e, Pacific 4-6-2, South Africa. f, Class HP,
India.
No. 803, 120fr: a, VT601, Germany. b, ICIII
Bo-Bo EMU, Netherlands. c, TGV, France. d,
ETR 450, Italy. e, AVE, Spain. f, Bullet Train,
Japan.
No. 804, 250fr, GM War Bonnet, US. No.
805, 250fr, Class 8 Pacific, Great Britain.

2000, Apr. 28
801 A271   Horiz. strip of 5,
             #a-e   1.75 1.75
           Sheets of 6, #a-f
802-803 A271 Set of 2   20.00 20.00
           Souvenir Sheets
804-805 A271 Set of 2   7.00 7.00

Dancers
A272

2000, Apr. 28
806 A272 75fr multi   5.25 5.25

Blacksmith — A273

2000, May 14
807 A273 100fr multi   1.50 1.50

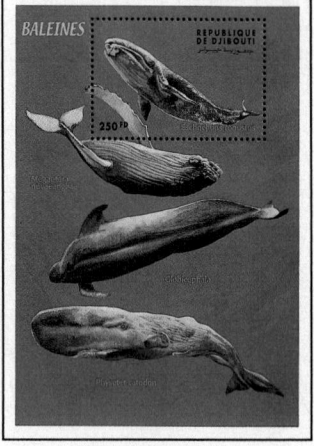

Marine Life — A274

No. 808, vert.: a, Dendrochirus biocellatus.
b, Hippocampus. c, Amphiprion ocellaris,
Amphiprion percula. d, Periclimenes impera-
tor. e, Pomacnetridae. f, Octopus vulgaris.
No. 809, 50fr: a, Cephalopholis miniata. b,
Ptereleotris hanae. c, Sphyraena genie. d,
Tripterygion segmentatum. e, Odontaspididae.
f, Cirrhitidae. g, Amphiprion. h, Capros aper. i,
Balistidae. j, Trygonorhina fasciata. k,
Cephalopholis. l, Corythoichthys ocellatus.
No. 810, 60fr: a, Lutjanus kasmira. b, Chae-
todon fasciatus. c, Epinephelinae. d,
Hypoplectrus gutavarius. e, Loligo opales-
cens. f, Diodontinae. g, Coelenterata. h,
Sargocentron xantherythrum. i, Thalassoma
lunare. j, Hemichromis bimaculatus. k, Dasy-
atis. l, Fromia monilis.
No. 811, 250fr, Eschrichtis robustus. No.
812, 250fr, Cheloniidae.

2000, May 14
808 A274 55fr Sheet of 6, #a-f 5.50 5.50
           Sheets of 12, #a-l
809-810 A274 Set of 2   24.00 24.00
           Souvenir Sheets
811-812 A274 Set of 2   8.00 8.00

Camels
and
Tender
A275

2000, June 26
813 A275 35fr multi   5.25 5.25

Ships
A276

Designs: 10fr, Thomas W. Lawson, 1902. 15fr, BT Global Challenge, 2000. 20fr, Reliance and Shamrock III, 1903. 25fr, Archibald Russell, 1905. 50fr, Greek merchantman, 8th cent. B.C.

No. 819, 130fr: a, Norman warship, 1066. b, Hanseatic cog, c. 1300. c, Santa Maria, 1492. d, Mary Rose, 1510. e, Golden Hind, 1577. f, Sovereign of the Seas, 1637.

No. 820:, 135fr: a, HMS Endeavour, 1768. b, USS Constitution, 1797. c, Chasse-Maree, 1800. d, Baltimore clipper, 1812. e, Lightning, 1853. f, Bluenose, 1921.

No. 821, 250fr, HM Yacht Britannia, 1893. No. 822, 250fr, Herzogin Cecilie, 1902.

2000, June 26
814-818	A276	Set of 5	2.00	2.00

Sheets of 6, #a-f
819-820	A276	Set of 2	25.00	25.00

Souvenir Sheets
821-822	A276	Set of 2	8.00	8.00

Millennium
A277

2000, July 18
823	A277	125fr multi		2.00	2.00

Birds
A278

2000, Aug. 23
824		Horiz. strip of 5	2.00	2.00
a.	A278	5fr Lanius excubitor	.20	.20
b.	A278	10fr Phoenicopterus minor	.20	.20
c.	A278	15fr Eupodatis senegalensis	.20	.20
d.	A278	40fr Noephron perchopterus	.45	.45
e.	A278	50fr Pterocles lichtensteinii	.55	.55

Space Exploration — A279

No. 825, 100fr, vert.: a, John Glenn and Mercury capsule, 1962. b, Soyuz capsule, Apollo-Soyuz mission, 1975. c, Hubble Telescope, 1990. d, Apollo capsule, Apollo-Soyuz mission. e, Glenn at speaker's stand, 1974. f, Space Shuttle Columbia, 1981.

No. 826, 100fr, vert.: a, Apollo 11 service module, 1969. b, Telstar, 1962. c, Ariane 4, 1988. d, Apollo 11 lunar module. e, Neil Armstrong, 1969. f, Splashdown of Apollo 11, 1969.

No. 827, 200fr, Astronaut on moon saluting. No. 828, 250fr, Astronauts conducting experiments on moon. No. 829, 250fr, Space Shuttle Challenger.

2000, Aug. 23   **Sheets of 6, #a-f**
825-826	A279	Set of 2	20.00	20.00

Souvenir Sheets
827-829	A279	Set of 3	12.00	12.00

2000
Summer
Olympics,
Sydney
A280

Olympic flame, flag and: 80fr, Runner. 90fr, Tennis player.

2000   **Perf. 14**
830-831	A280	Set of 2	2.75	2.75

Unknown Soldier
Monument

2004, Apr. 18   Litho.   *Perf. 13x12¾*
832	A280a	175fr multi	—	—

Independence, 27th Anniv. — A281

2004, June 27   Litho.   *Perf. 13*
833	A281	45fr multi	—	—

Dragon
Tree
A282

Pregnant Woman
at
Hospital — A283

Camel
Caravan
A284

Natl. Union of
Djibouti
Women — A285

National
Arms
A286

Perf. 12¾x13, 13x12¾
2004, Dec. 18   Litho.
834	A282	15fr multi	—	—
835	A283	25fr multi	—	—
836	A284	45fr multi	—	—
837	A285	70fr multi	—	—
838	A286	100fr multi	—	—

Friendship
Between
Djibouti
and
People's
Republic of
China,
25th Anniv.

Designs: 5fr, Djibouti Electricity Building. 10fr, Hassan Gouled Stadium. 15fr, Djibouti Central Bank. 30fr, People's Palace. 45fr, Ministry of Foreign Affairs Building.

2004, Dec. 27   **Perf. 12**
839-843	A286a	Set of 5	—	—

Items commemorating the death of Pope John Paul II were declared as "fraudulent" by Djibouti Post.

2006 World Cup Soccer
Championships, Germany — A287

2006   Litho.   *Perf. 13*
844	A287	100fr multi	40.00	40.00

Tanker in Port of Doraleh — A288

2006   Litho.   *Perf. 13*
845	A288	120fr multi	8.25	8.25

Printed in sheets of 4.

Common Market for Eastern and
Southern Africa Summit,
Djibouti — A289

2006   Litho.   *Perf. 13¼x13*
846	A289	150fr multi	5.25	5.25

Djibouti Chamber
of Commerce,
Cent. — A290

2007   Litho.   *Perf. 12¾*
847	A290	50fr multi	—	—
a.		Souvenir sheet of 2	—	—

Independence, 30th Anniv. — A291

2007   Litho.   *Perf. 13*
848	A291	75fr multi	—	—
a.		Souvenir sheet of 2	—	—

Mahamoud Harbi
(1921-60),
Politician — A292

2007   Litho.   *Perf. 13x12¾*
849	A292	165fr multi	11.50	11.50

Indo-Suez Red Sea Bank — A293

2008, Oct. 19   Litho.   *Perf. 13x13½*
850	A293	220fr multi	—	—

Djibouti postal authorities have declared "illegal" the following items:
Sheets of 8 stamps of various values: Mushrooms
Sheets of 6 stamps of various values: Fire trucks and Scouts (3 different)
Sheets of 6 700f stamps: Butterflies and Orchids, Butterflies and Scouts, Trains
Sheets of 6 300f stamps: Birds
Sheets of 4 800f stamps: Bonsai
Sheets of 4 700f stamps: Dogs (4 different), Cats (4 different), Babe Ruth and Tiger Woods, Dinosaurs
Sheets of 2 stamps of various values: Fire trucks (2 different).

AIR POST STAMPS

Afars and Issas Nos. C104-C105, C103 Overprinted with Bars and "REPUBLIQUE DE DJIBOUTI" in Brown or Black

1977   Engr.   *Perf. 13*
C106	AP37	55fr multi (Br)	1.75	1.75
C107	AP37	75fr multi	7.00	3.00

     Litho.   *Perf. 12*
C108	AP36	500fr multi	13.50	13.50
	Nos. C106-C108 (3)		22.25	18.25

Map of Djibouti, Dove, UN
Emblem — AP38

1977, Oct. 19   Photo.   *Perf. 13*
C109	AP38	300fr multi	6.50	4.25

Djibouti's admission to the United Nations.

Marcel Brochet MB 101, 1955 — AP39

Djibouti Aero Club: 85fr, Tiger Moth, 1960. 200fr, Rallye-Commodore, 1973.

1978, Feb. 27 Litho. Perf. 13
C110 AP39 60fr multi   1.25 .40
C111 AP39 85fr multi   1.75 .65
C112 AP39 200fr multi   4.00 1.10
  Nos. C110-C112 (3)   7.00 2.15

Old Man,
by Rubens
AP40

500fr, Hippopotamus Hunt, by Rubens.

1978, Apr. 24 Photo. Perf. 13
C113 AP40 50fr multi   1.00 .35
C114 AP40 500fr multi, horiz.   10.00 3.25

Peter Paul Rubens (1577-1640).

Player Holding
Soccer
Cup — AP41

Design: 300fr, Soccer player, map of South America with Argentina, Cup and emblem.

1978, June 20 Litho. Perf. 13
C115 AP41 100fr multi   1.75 .35
C116 AP41 300fr multi   5.25 1.00

11th World Cup Soccer Championship, Argentina, June 1-25.
For overprints see Nos. C117-C118.

Nos. C115-C116 Overprinted:
  a. ARGENTINE/CHAMPION 1978
  b. ARGENTINE/HOLLANDE/3-1

1978, Aug. 20 Litho. Perf. 13
C117 AP41 (a) 100fr multi   1.75 .40
C118 AP41 (b) 300fr multi   5.25 1.25

Argentina's victory in 1978 Soccer Championship.

Tahitian Women, by Gauguin — AP42

Young
Hare, by
Dürer
AP43

Perf. 13x12½, 12½x13
1978, Sept. 25 Litho.
C119 AP42 100fr multi   2.25 .40
C120 AP43 250fr multi   5.25 1.50

Paul Gauguin (1848-1903) and Albrecht Dürer (1471-1528), painters.

Common Design Types
pictured following the introduction.

Philexafrique II-Essen Issue
Common Design Types

Designs: No. C121, Lynx and Djibouti No. 456. No. C122, Jay and Brunswick No. 3.

1978, Dec. 13 Litho. Perf. 13x12½
C121 CD138 90fr multi   3.00 1.25
C122 CD139 90fr multi   3.00 1.25
  a. Pair, Nos. C121-C122 + label 6.25 6.25

UPU Emblem,
Map of Djibouti,
Dove — AP44

1978, Dec. 18 Engr. Perf. 13
C123 AP44 200fr multi   3.00 1.10

Centenary of Congress of Paris.

Junkers JU-52 and Dewoitine D-338 — AP45

Powered Flight, 75th Anniversary: 250fr, Potez P63-11, 1941 and Supermarine Spitfire HF-VII, 1942. 500fr, Concorde, 1969 and Sikorsky S-40 "American Clipper," 1931.

1979, May 21 Litho. Perf. 13x12½
C124 AP45 140fr multi   2.75 .60
C125 AP45 250fr multi   4.00 1.00
C126 AP45 500fr multi   8.50 1.75
  Nos. C124-C126 (3)   15.25 3.35

The
Laundress,
by Honore
Daumier
AP46

1979, July 10 Litho. Perf. 12½x13
C127 AP46 500fr multi   12.00 3.00

Olympic Emblem, Skis, Sleds — AP47

1980, Jan. 21 Litho. Perf. 13
C128 AP47 150fr multi   2.75 .60

13th Winter Olympic Games, Lake Placid, N.Y., Feb. 12-24.
For surcharges see Nos. C133-C134.

Cathedral of the
Archangel,
Moscow '80
Emblem — AP48

120fr, Lomonossov Univ., Moscow, soccer. 250fr, Cathedral of the Annunciation, running.

1980, Apr. 10 Litho. Perf. 13
C129 AP48 60fr multi   1.00 .25
C130 AP48 120fr multi   2.00 .40
C131 AP48 250fr multi   4.00 1.00
  Nos. C129-C131 (3)   7.00 1.65

22nd Summer Olympic Games, Moscow, July 18-Aug. 3.

Air Djibouti, 1st Anniversary — AP49

1980, Mar. 29 Litho. Perf. 13x12½
C132 AP49 400fr multi   8.50 2.25

No. C128 Surcharged in Black and Blue or Purple:
  80fr.   A.M.   MOSER-PROEL/ AUTRICHE / DESCENTE DAMES/ MEDAILLE D'OR
  200fr. HEIDEN / USA / 5 MEDAIL-LES D'OR / PATINAGE DE VITESSE

1980, Apr. 5 Litho. Perf. 13
C133 AP47 80fr on 150fr   1.75 .50
C134 AP47 200fr on 150fr (P)   3.75 1.50

Apollo 11 Moon Landing, 10th
Anniversary — AP50

Space Conquests: 300fr, Apollo-Soyuz space project, 5th anniversary.

1980, May 8
C135 AP50 200fr multi   4.00 .75
C136 AP50 300fr multi   6.00 1.25

Satellite Earth Station
Inauguration — AP51

1980, July 3 Litho. Perf. 13
C137 AP51 500fr multi   9.00 1.75

Graf Zeppelin — AP52

1980, Oct. 2 Litho. Perf. 13
C138 AP52 100fr shown   2.25 .40
C139 AP52 150fr Ferdinand von
            Zeppelin, blimp   2.75 .60

Zeppelin flight, 80th anniversary.

Voyager Passing Saturn — AP53

1980, Dec. 21 Litho. Perf. 13
C140 AP53 250fr multi   5.00 1.00

AP54

AP55

World Cup Soccer Preliminary Games: 200fr, Players, diff.

1981, Jan. 14
C141 AP54 80fr multi   1.40 .30
C142 AP54 200fr multi   3.50 .65

1981, Feb. 10   Litho.   *Perf. 13*
C143 AP55 100fr multi   2.50 .50

European-African Economic Convention.

5th Anniversary of Viking I Take-off to Mars — AP56

20th Anniversary of Various Space Flights: 75fr, Vostok I, Yuri Gagarin, vert. 150fr, Freedom 7, Alan B. Shepard, vert.

1981, Mar. 9   Litho.   *Perf. 13*
C144 AP56 75fr multi   1.75 .35
C145 AP56 120fr multi   2.25 .45
C146 AP56 150fr multi   3.00 .65
  Nos. C144-C146 (3)   7.00 1.45

Football Players, by Picasso (1881-1973) — AP57

Design: 400fr Man Wearing a Turban, by Rembrandt (1606-1669), vert.

Perf. 13x12½, 12½x13
  Litho.
C147 AP57 300fr multi   6.25 1.40
C148 AP57 400fr multi   7.00 1.75

Columbia Space Shuttle — AP58

1981, Sept. 24   Litho.   *Perf. 13*
C149 AP58 90fr Shuttle, diff., vert.   1.75 .40
C150 AP58 120fr shown   2.25 .60

Nos. C149-C150 Overprinted in Brown with Astronauts' Names and Dates

1981, Nov. 12   Litho.   *Perf. 13*
C151 AP58 90fr multi   1.75 .50
C152 AP58 120fr multi   2.25 .75

1982 World Cup Soccer — AP59

Designs: Various soccer players.

1982, Jan. 20
C153 AP59 110fr multi   2.10 .60
C154 AP59 220fr multi   4.00 1.25

For overprints see Nos. C166-C167.

Space Anniversaries — AP60

Designs: 40fr, Luna 9 moon landing, 15th, vert. 60fr, John Glenn's flight, 20th, vert. 180fr, Viking I Mars landing, 5th.

1982, Feb. 15
C155 AP60 40fr multi   .70 .20
C156 AP60 60fr multi   1.10 .30
C157 AP60 180fr multi   3.00 1.00
  Nos. C155-C157 (3)   4.80 1.50

21st Birthday of Princess Diana of Wales AP61

1982, Apr. 29   Litho.   *Perf. 12½x13*
C158 AP61 120fr Portrait   2.00 .75
C159 AP61 180fr Portrait, diff.   3.00 1.00

For overprints see Nos. C168-C169.

No. 489, Boy Examining Collection — AP62

1982, May 10   *Perf. 13x12½*
C160 AP62 80fr shown   1.75 .55
C161 AP62 140fr No. 495   3.25 1.00
  a. Pair, Nos. C160-C161 + label 6.50 6.50

PHILEXFRANCE '82 Stamp Exhibition, Paris, June 11-21.

1350th Anniv. of Mohammed's Death at Medina — AP63

1982, June 8   Litho.   *Perf. 13*
C162 AP63 500fr Medina Mosque   7.50 2.00

Scouting Year — AP64

1982, June 28
C163 AP64 95fr Baden-Powell   1.50 .50
C164 AP64 200fr Camp, scouts   3.50 1.25

2nd UN Conference on Peaceful Uses of Outer Space, Vienna, Aug. 9-21 — AP65

1982, Aug. 19
C165 AP65 350fr multi   6.50 3.00

Nos. C153-C154 Overprinted with Winner's Name and Scores

1982, July 21   Litho.   *Perf. 13*
C166 AP59 110fr multi   2.00 .60
C167 AP59 220fr multi   4.00 1.10

Italy's victory in 1982 World Cup.

Nos. C158-C159 Overprinted in Blue or Red with Date, Name and Title

1982, Aug. 9   *Perf. 12½x13*
C168 AP61 120fr multi   2.25 .75
C169 AP61 180fr multi (R)   3.25 1.00

Birth of Prince William of Wales, June 21.

Franklin D. Roosevelt (1882-1945) AP66

1982, Oct. 7   Litho.   *Perf. 13*
C170 AP66 115fr shown   1.75 .50
C171 AP66 250fr George Washington   4.50 1.00

Manned Flight Bicentenary AP67

Pre-olympic Year — AP68

1983, Jan. 20   Litho.
C172 AP67 35fr Montgolfiere, 1783   .65 .25
C173 AP67 45fr Giffard, Paris Exposition, 1878   1.10 .30
C174 AP67 120fr Double Eagle II, 1978   2.75 .80
  Nos. C172-C174 (3)   4.50 1.35

1983, Feb. 15
C175 AP68 75fr Volleyball   1.50 .55
C176 AP68 125fr Wind surfing   2.75 .85

50th Anniv. of Air France — AP69

1983, Mar. 20   Litho.   *Perf. 13*
C177 AP69 25fr Bloch 220   .40 .20
C178 AP69 100fr DC-4   1.75 .70
C179 AP69 175fr Boeing 747   3.25 1.10
  Nos. C177-C179 (3)   5.40 2.00

AP70

AP71

180fr, Martin Luther King, Jr. (1929-68), civil rights leader. 250fr, Alfred Nobel (1833-96)

1983, May 18   Litho.   *Perf. 13*
C180 AP70 180fr multi   2.75 1.25
C181 AP70 250fr multi   3.75 2.00

1983, July 18   Litho.   *Perf. 13*

Service Clubs: 90fr, Rotary Club Intl., Sailing Show, Toronto, June 5-9. 150fr, Lions Club Intl., Honolulu Meeting, June 22-24, Djibouti lighthouse.

C182 AP71 90fr multi   1.40 .60
C183 AP71 150fr multi   2.25 1.00
  a. Pair, Nos. C182-C183 + label 5.00 1.75

Vintage Motor Cars — AP72

1983, Sep. 20   Litho.   *Perf. 13x12½*
C184 AP72 60fr Renault, 1904   1.75 .50
C185 AP72 80fr Mercedes, 1910, vert.   2.25 .65
C186 AP72 110fr Lorraine-Dietrich, 1912   2.75 .85
  Nos. C184-C186 (3)   6.75 2.00

Souvenir Sheet

Air France, 50th Anniv. — AP73

Illustration reduced.

1983, Oct. 7   Litho.   Perf. 12½
Self-Adhesive
C187 AP73 250fr multicolored   25.00 2.10
Printed on wood.

Vostok VI AP74

1983, Oct. 20   Litho.   Perf. 12
C188 AP74 120fr shown   2.00 .80
C189 AP74 200fr Explorer I   3.50 1.10

1984 Winter Olympics — AP75

1984, Feb. 14   Litho.   Perf. 13
C190 AP75 70fr Speed skating   1.50 .55
C191 AP75 130fr Figure skating   2.50 1.10

For overprints see Nos. C196-C197.

Souvenir Sheet

Ship — AP76

1984, Feb. 14   Litho.   Perf. 12½
C192 AP76 250fr multi   11.00 1.75
Sea-Me-We (South-east Asia-Middle East-Western Europe) submarine cable construction agreement.

Motorized Hang Gliders — AP77

Various hang gliders.

1984, Mar. 12   Perf. 13x12½
C193 AP77 65fr multi   1.25 .50
C194 AP77 85fr multi   1.60 .60
C195 AP77 100fr multi   2.10 .75
     Nos. C193-C195 (3)   4.95 1.85

Nos. C190-C191 Overprinted with Winners' Names and Country

1984, Mar. 28   Perf. 13
C196 AP75 70fr multi   1.25 .50
C197 AP75 130fr multi   2.40 1.00

Portrait of Marguerite Matisse, 1910, by Henri Matisse AP78

Design: 200fr, Portrait of Mario Varvogli, by Amedeo Modigliani.

1984, Apr. 15   Litho.   Perf. 12½x13
C198 AP78 150fr multi   3.25 1.00
C199 AP78 200fr multi   4.00 1.40

1984 Summer Olympics — AP79

1984, May 24   Perf. 13
C200 AP79 50fr Running   1.00 .40
C201 AP79 60fr High jump   1.25 .40
C202 AP79 80fr Swimming   1.50 .60
     Nos. C200-C202 (3)   3.75 1.40

Battle Scene — AP80

1984, June 16   Litho.   Perf. 13x12½
C203 AP80 300fr multi   6.00 2.75
125th anniv. of Battle of Solferino and 120th anniv. of Red Cross.

Bleriot's Flight over English Channel, 75th Anniv. — AP81

1984, July 8
C204 AP81 40fr 14-Bis plans   .80 .30
C205 AP81 75fr Britten-Norman
          Islander   1.40 .55
C206 AP81 90fr Air Djibouti jet   1.50 .65
     Nos. C204-C206 (3)   3.70 1.50

375th Anniv., Galileo's Telescope AP82

1984, Oct. 7   Litho.   Perf. 13
C207 AP82 120fr Telescopes,
          spacecraft   2.25 .80
C208 AP82 180fr Galileo,
          telescopes   3.25 1.10

1984 Soccer Events — AP83

1984, Oct. 20   Litho.   Perf. 13
C209 AP83 80fr Euro Cup   1.75 .60
C210 AP83 80fr Los Angeles
          Olympics   1.75 .60
a.   Pair, Nos. C209-C210 + label   4.25 1.25

Service Clubs — AP84

1985, Feb. 23   Litho.   Perf. 13
C211 AP84 50fr Lions, World Lep-
          rosy Day   1.40 .50
C212 AP84 60fr Rotary, chess
          board, pieces   1.60 .55
#C211-C212 exist in souvenir sheets of 1.

Telecommunications Technology — AP85

No. C213, Technician, researchist, operator. No. C214, Offshore oil rig, transmission tower, government building.

1985, July 2   Perf. 13x12½
C213 AP85 80fr multi   2.00 .55
C214 AP85 80fr multi   2.00 .55
a.   Pair, Nos. C213-C214 + label   5.00 1.25
PHILEXAFRICA '85, Lome.

Telecommunications Development — AP86

1985, Oct. 2   Perf. 13
C215 AP86 50fr Intl. transmis-
          sion center   .90 .35
C216 AP86 90fr Ariane rocket,
          vert.   1.60 .65
C217 AP86 120fr ARABSAT sat-
          ellite   2.00 .90
     Nos. C215-C217 (3)   4.50 1.90

Youths Windsurfing, Playing Tennis — AP87

No. C219, Tadjoura Highway construction.

1985, Nov. 13   Perf. 13x12½
C218 AP87 100fr multi   2.00 .70
C219 AP87 100fr multi   2.00 .70
a.   Pair, Nos. C218-C219 + label   4.50 1.50
PHILEXAFRICA '85, Lome, Togo, 11/16-24.

1986 World Cup Soccer Championships, Mexico — AP88

1986, Feb. 24   Litho.   Perf. 13
C220 AP88 75fr shown   1.50 .50
C221 AP88 100fr Players, stadi-
          um   2.00 .70

For overprints see Nos. C223-C224.

Statue of Liberty, Cent. — AP89

1986, May 21
C222 AP89 250fr multi   4.00 1.75

Nos. C220-C221 Ovptd. with Winners

1986, Sept. 15   Litho.   Perf. 13
C223   75fr "FRANCE -
               BELGIQUE / 4-2"   1.25 .65
C224   100fr "3-2 ARGENTINE-
               RFA"   1.75 .80

1986 World Chess Championships, May 1-19 — AP89a

Malayan animal chess pieces.

1986, Oct. 13   Litho.   Perf. 13
C225 AP89a 80fr Knight, bish-
          ops   1.75 .60
C226 AP89a 120fr Rook, king,
          pawn   2.75 .90

Yuri Gagarin, Sputnik
Spacecraft — AP90

1986, Nov. 27 **Litho.** *Perf. 13*
C227 AP90 150fr shown   3.00 1.10
C228 AP90 200fr Space rendez-
          vous, 1966   3.25 1.25
First man in space, 25th anniv.; Gemini 8-
Agena link-up, 20th anniv.

Historic Flights — AP91

1987, Jan. 22 **Litho.** *Perf. 13*
C229 AP91 55fr Amiot 370   1.25 .40
C230 AP91 80fr Spirit of St.
          Louis   1.75 .55
C231 AP91 120fr Voyager   2.50 .90
     Nos. C229-C231 (3)   5.50 1.85
First flight from Istria to Djibouti, 1942;
Lindbergh's Transatlantic flight, 1927; nonstop
world circumnavigation without refueling.
For surcharge see No. C240.

Souvenir Sheet

Fight Against Leprosy — AP91a

Design: Raoul Follereau (b. 1903), care
giver to lepers, Gerhard Hansen (1841-1912),
discoverer of bacillus of leprosy.
Illustration reduced.

1987, Mar. 23 **Litho.** *Perf. 13x12½*
Self-Adhesive
C231A AP91a 500fr multi   17.00 4.25
No. C231A printed on wood.

Pres.
Aptidon,
Natl. Crest
and Flag
AP92

1987, June 27 **Litho.** *Perf. 12½x13*
C232 AP92 250fr multi   4.00 1.50
Natl. independence, 10th anniv.

Telstar, 25th Anniv. — AP93

1987, Oct. 1 *Perf. 13*
C233 AP93 190fr shown   3.00 1.25
  a. Souvenir sheet, 1 #C233   12.00
C234 AP93 250fr Samuel
          Morse, tele-
          graph key   3.75 1.50
  a. Souvenir sheet, 1 #C234   12.00
Invention of the telegraph, 150th anniv.
(250fr).
Nos. C233a and C234a also exist imperf.
Value, set of 2, $40.

City of Djibouti, Cent. — AP94

100fr, Djibouti Creek & quay, 1887. 150fr,
Aerial view of city, 1987. 250fr, Somali Coast
#6, 20, postmarks of 1898 & 1903.

1987, Nov. 15 **Litho.** *Perf. 13x12½*
C235 AP94 100fr blk & buff   2.00 1.10
C236 AP94 150fr multi   3.00 1.60
  a. Pair, Nos. C235-C236 + label   6.00 2.75

Souvenir Sheet

237 AP94 250fr multi   5.50 2.75
No. C237 has decorative margin like design
of 100fr.

Intl. Red Cross
and Red
Crescent
Organizations,
125th
Anniv. — AP95

1988, Feb. 17 **Litho.** *Perf. 13*
C238 AP95 300fr multi   6.00 3.25

1988 Summer Olympics,
Seoul — AP96

1988, June 15 **Litho.** *Perf. 13*
C239 AP96 105fr multi   2.50 1.00
For overprint see No. C242.

No. C229 Surcharged in Black

1988, June 28
C240 AP91 70fr on 55fr multi   1.75 .70
Air race in memory of the Paris-Djibouti-St.
Denis flight of French aviator Roland Garros
(1888-1913).

World Post Day — AP97

1988, Oct. 9 **Litho.** *Perf. 13*
C241 AP97 1000fr multi   15.00 10.00

No. C239 Overprinted

1988, Dec. 15 **Litho.** *Perf. 13*
C242 AP96 105fr multi   2.00 1.50

World Telecommunications
Day — AP98

1989, May 17 **Litho.** *Perf. 12½*
C243 AP98 150fr multi   2.75 1.50

PHILEXFRANCE '89, Declaration of
Human Rights and Citizenship
Bicent. — AP99

1989, July 14 **Litho.** *Perf. 12½x13*
C244 AP99 120fr multi   2.25 1.25

Salt, Lake Assal — AP100

1989, Sept. 15 **Litho.** *Perf. 13*
C245 AP100 300fr multicolored   5.50 3.50

POSTAGE DUE STAMP

Urn for Milking
Camel — D1

1988, Jan. 20 **Litho.** *Perf. 13*
J1 D1 60fr multi   .90 .65

DOMINICA

,dä-mə-'nē-kə

LOCATION — The largest island of the Windward group in the West Indies. Southeast of Puerto Rico.
GOVT. — Republic in British Commonwealth
AREA — 290 sq. mi.
POP. — 64,881 (1999 est.)
CAPITAL — Roseau

Formerly a Presidency of the Leeward Islands, Dominica became a separate colony under the governor of the Windward Islands on January 1, 1940. Dominica joined the West Indies federation April 22, 1958. In 1968, Dominica became an associate state of Britain; in 1978, an independent nation.

12 Pence = 1 Shilling
20 Shillings = 1 Pound
100 Cents = 1 Dollar (1949)

Catalogue values for unused stamps in this country are for Never Hinged items, beginning with Scott 112.

Watermark

Wmk. 334 — Rectangles

Queen Victoria — A1

1874, May 4 Typo. Wmk. 1

Perf. 12½

1	A1	1p violet	170.00	55.00
a.		Vertical half used as ½p on cover		8,500.
2	A1	6p green	625.00	115.00
3	A1	1sh deep lilac rose	375.00	80.00
		Nos. 1-3 (3)	1,170.	250.00

During 1875-87 some issues were manuscript dated with village names. These are considered postally used. Stamps with entire village names sell for much more, starting at $100.

1877-79 Perf. 14

4	A1	½p bister ('79)	16.00	60.00
5	A1	1p violet	9.00	2.75
a.		Diagonal or vertical half used as ½p on cover		2,500.
6	A1	2½p red brown ('79)	260.00	32.50
7	A1	4p blue ('79)	125.00	4.00
8	A1	6p green	170.00	22.50
9	A1	1sh dp lilac rose	140.00	57.50
		Nos. 4-9 (6)	720.00	179.25

For surcharges see Nos. 10-15.

No. 5 Bisected and Surcharged in Black or Red:

a	b	c

1882

10	A1(a)	½p on half of 1p	225.00	55.00
a.		Inverted surcharge	1,150.	900.00
b.		Surcharge tete beche pair	2,500.	2,000.

11	A1(b)	½p on half of 1p	72.50	29.00
a.		Surch. reading downward	72.50	29.00
b.		Double surcharge	900.00	
12	A1(c)	½p on half of 1p (R)	35.00	19.00
a.		Inverted surcharge	1,150.	550.00
b.		Double surcharge	1,850.	750.00
		Nos. 10-12 (3)	332.50	103.00

The existence of genuine examples of No. 10b has been questioned.

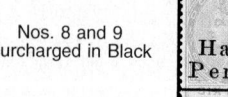

Nos. 8 and 9 Surcharged in Black

1886

13	A1	½p on 6p green	7.00	7.00
14	A1	1p on 6p green	45,000.	12,500.
15	A1	1p on 1sh	17.00	20.00
a.		Double surcharge	11,000.	4,000.

All examples of No. 14 may have small pin marks which may have been part of the surcharging process.

1883-89 Wmk. 2

16	A1	½p bister ('83)	4.50	11.50
17	A1	½p green ('86)	2.50	6.25
18	A1	1p violet ('86)	42.50	15.00
a.		Half used as ½p on cover		2,250.
19	A1	1p dp carmine ('89)	3.50	9.00
a.		1p rose ('87)	19.00	20.00
b.		Vert. half used as ½p on cover		2,100.
20	A1	2½p red brn ('84)	160.00	3.00
21	A1	2½p ultra ('88)	4.25	6.00
22	A1	4p gray ('86)	5.00	7.50
23	A1	6p orange ('88)	16.00	70.00
24	A1	1sh dp lil rose ('88)	200.00	425.00
		Nos. 16-24 (9)	438.25	553.25

Roseau, Capital of Dominica — A6

King Edward VII — A7

1903 Wmk. 1 Perf. 14
Ordinary Paper

25	A6	½p gray green	5.25	3.25
26	A6	1p car & black	10.50	1.00
27	A6	2p brn & gray grn	3.25	5.75
28	A6	2½p ultra & blk	6.50	5.25
29	A6	3p black & vio	10.50	4.50
30	A6	6p org brn & blk	6.75	23.00
31	A6	1sh gray grn & red vio	35.00	52.50
32	A6	2sh red vio & blk	32.50	35.00
33	A6	2sh6p ocher & gray grn	23.00	92.50
34	A7	5sh brown & blk	23.00	175.00
		Nos. 25-34 (10)	258.25	397.75

Nos. 25 to 29 and 31 are on both ordinary and chalky paper. For detailed listings, see the *Scott Classic Specialized Catalogue of Stamps & Covers.*

1907-20 Wmk. 3
Chalky Paper

35	A6	½p gray green	7.50	5.00
36	A6	1p car & black	2.50	.55
37	A6	2p brn & gray grn	8.00	20.00
38	A6	2½p ultra & black	5.50	27.50
39	A6	3p black & vio	5.00	17.00
40	A6	3p vio, yel, chalky paper ('09)	3.75	5.25
41	A6	6p org brn & blk ('08)	65.00	100.00
42	A6	6p vio & dl vio, chalky paper ('09)	12.50	19.00
43	A6	1sh gray grn & red vio	4.75	67.50

44	A6	1sh blk, green, chalky paper ('10)	3.75	3.50
45	A6	2sh red vio & blk ('08)	30.00	40.00
46	A6	2sh ultra & vio, bl ('19)	32.50	110.00
47	A6	2sh6p ocher & gray grn ('08)	27.50	75.00
48	A6	2sh6p red & blk, bl ('20)	32.50	125.00
49	A7	5sh brn & blk ('08)	75.00	75.00
		Nos. 35-49 (15)	315.75	690.30

Nos. 40, 42 and 44 are on both ordinary and chalky paper. For detailed listings, see the *Scott Classic Specialized Catalogue of Stamps & Covers.*
For type surcharged see No. 55.

1908-09 Ordinary Paper

50	A6	½p green	8.00	5.50
51	A6	1p scarlet	1.75	.55
a.		1p carmine	3.50	.35
52	A6	2p gray ('09)	4.50	14.00
53	A6	2½p ultramarine	9.50	7.00
a.		2½p bright blue ('18)	5.75	10.50
		Nos. 50-53 (4)	23.75	27.05

King George V — A8

1914 Chalky Paper Perf. 14

54	A8	5sh grn & scar, yel	70.00	92.50

Type of 1903 Surcharged

1920

55	A6	1½p on 2½p orange	5.50	5.25

1921 Wmk. 4
Ordinary Paper

56	A6	½p green	3.50	21.00
57	A6	1p rose red	2.75	5.50
58	A6	1½p orange	4.75	15.00
59	A6	2p gray	4.25	4.75
60	A6	2½p ultra	2.75	12.00
61	A6	6p vio & dl vio	3.50	50.00
62	A6	2sh ultra & vio, bl	45.00	125.00
63	A6	2sh6p red & blk, bl	45.00	140.00
		Nos. 56-63 (8)	111.50	373.25

No. 61 is on chalky paper.

1923-33 Chalky Paper Wmk. 4

65	A9	½p green & blk	2.50	.85
66	A9	1p violet & blk	4.50	2.25
67	A9	1p scar & black	15.00	1.40
68	A9	1½p car & black	5.00	.90
69	A9	1½p dp brn & blk	15.00	.95
70	A9	2p gray & black	3.00	.65
71	A9	2½p org & black	3.00	12.00
72	A9	2½p ultra & black	7.50	2.75
73	A9	3p ultra & black	3.00	16.00
74	A9	3p red & blk, yel	3.25	1.40
75	A9	4p brown & blk	3.75	7.25
76	A9	6p red vio & blk	4.75	9.00
77	A9	1sh blk, emerald	3.00	3.75
78	A9	2sh ultra & blk, bl	14.00	27.50
79	A9	2sh6p red & blk, bl	25.00	27.50
80	A9	3sh vio & blk, yel	4.50	17.50
81	A9	4sh red & blk, emer	17.00	30.00
82	A9	5sh grn & blk, yel	30.00	62.50
		Nos. 65-82 (18)	163.75	224.15

Issue years: Nos. 80, 82, 1927; Nos. 72, 74, 1928; Nos. 67, 69, 1933; others, 1923.

1923 Wmk. 3

83	A9	3sh vio & blk, yel	5.75	80.00
84	A9	5sh grn & blk, yel	13.50	65.00
85	A9	£1 vio & blk, red	300.00	450.00
		Nos. 83-85 (3)	319.25	595.00

Common Design Types pictured following the introduction.

Silver Jubilee Issue
Common Design Type
Perf. 13½x14

1935, May 6 Wmk. 4 Engr.

90	CD301	1p car & blue	.60	.35
91	CD301	1½p gray blk & ultra	2.00	2.00
92	CD301	2½p blue & brn	3.75	4.50
93	CD301	1sh brt vio & ind	3.75	7.00
		Nos. 90-93 (4)	10.10	13.85
		Set, never hinged	19.00	

Coronation Issue
Common Design Type

1937, May 12 Perf. 11x11½

94	CD302	1p dark carmine	.20	.20
95	CD302	1½p brown	.20	.20
96	CD302	2½p deep ultra	.35	.75
		Nos. 94-96 (3)	.75	1.15
		Set, never hinged	1.50	

Fresh-Water Lake — A10

Layou River — A11

Picking Limes — A12

Boiling Lake — A13

1938-47 Wmk. 4 Perf. 12½

97	A10	½p grn & red brn	.20	.20
98	A11	1p car & gray	.20	.20
99	A12	1½p rose vio & grn	.20	1.10
100	A13	2p brn blk & dp rose	.55	1.50
101	A12	2½p ultra & rose vio	4.00	3.00
102	A11	3p red brn & ol	.20	.60
103	A12	3½p red vio & brt ultra	1.40	2.50
104	A10	6p vio & yel grn	.70	1.90
105	A10	7p org brn & grn	1.25	2.10
106	A13	1sh olive & vio	2.40	1.90
107	A11	2sh red vio & blk	5.50	12.00
108	A10	2sh6p scar ver & blk	12.00	7.75
109	A11	5sh dk brn & bl	6.75	12.00
110	A13	10sh dl org & blk	13.50	22.50
		Nos. 97-110 (14)	48.85	69.25
		Set, never hinged	70.00	

Issued: 3½p, 7p, 2sh, 10sh, 10/15/47; others, 8/15/38.

King George VI — A14

1940, Apr. 15 Photo. Perf. 14½x14

111	A14	¼p brown violet	.40	.55

Catalogue values for unused stamps in this section, from this point to the end of the section, are for Never Hinged items.

Peace Issue
Common Design Type
1946, Oct. 14 Engr. Perf. 13½x14

112	CD303	1p carmine	.25	.25
113	CD303	3½p deep blue	.25	.25

Silver Wedding Issue
Common Design Types
1948, Dec. 1 Photo. Perf. 14x14½

114	CD304	1p scarlet	.25	.25

Engraved; Name Typographed
Perf. 11½x11

115	CD305	10sh orange brn	22.50	32.50

UPU Issue
Common Design Types
Engr.: Name Typo. on 6c and 12c
1949, Oct. 10 Perf. 13½, 11x11½

116	CD306	5c blue	.20	.20
117	CD307	6c chocolate	1.25	1.25
118	CD308	12c rose violet	.70	.70
119	CD309	24c olive	.45	.45
		Nos. 116-119 (4)	2.60	2.60

University Issue
Common Design Types
1951, Feb. 16 Engr. Perf. 14x14½

120	CD310	3c purple & green	.70	.45
121	CD311	12c dp car & dk bl grn	.90	.70

George VI
A15

Drying Cocoa
A16

Picking
Oranges — A17

Designs: 2c and 60c, Carib Baskets. 3c and 48c, Lime Plantation. 4c, Picking Oranges. 5c, Bananas. 6c, Botanical Gardens. 8c, Drying Vanilla Beans. 12c and $1.20, Fresh Water Lake. 14c, Layou River. 24c, Boiling Lake.

Perf. 14½x14
1951, July 1 Photo. Wmk. 4

122	A15	½c brown	.20	.20

Perf. 13x13½
Engr.

123	A16	1c red org & blk	.20	.30
124	A16	2c dp grn & red brn	.20	.20
125	A16	3c red vio & bl grn	.20	.70
126	A16	4c dk brn & brn org	.45	.80
127	A16	5c rose red & blk	1.10	.30
128	A16	6c org brn & ol grn	1.10	.30
129	A16	8c dp bl & dp grn	.75	.70
130	A16	12c emer & gray	.60	1.90
131	A16	14c pur & blue	1.25	1.90
132	A16	24c rose car & red vio	1.00	.30
133	A16	48c red org & bl grn	3.50	8.25
134	A16	60c gray & car	3.50	7.00
135	A16	$1.20 gray & emer	5.50	7.00

Perf. 13½x13

136	A17	$2.40 gray & org	30.00	40.00
		Nos. 122-136 (15)	49.55	69.85

Nos. 125, 127, 129 and 131 Overprinted in Black or Carmine

1951, Oct. 15 Perf. 13x13½

137	A16	3c red vio & bl green	.25	.25
138	A16	5c rose red & black	.50	.50
139	A16	8c dp blue & dp grn (C)	.65	.65
140	A16	14c purple & blue (C)	1.10	1.10
		Nos. 137-140 (4)	2.50	2.50

Adoption of a new constitution for the Windward Islands, 1951.

Coronation Issue
Common Design Type
1953, June 2 Engr. Perf. 13½x13

141	CD312	2c dk green & black	.40	.40

Types of 1951 with Portrait of Queen Elizabeth II
1954, Oct. 1 Photo. Perf. 14½x14

142	A15	½c brown	.20	.20

Perf. 13x13½
Engr.

143	A16	1c red org & blk	.20	.30
144	A16	2c dp grn & red brn	.90	.30
145	A16	3c red vio & bl grn	1.90	.70
146	A16	4c dk brn & brn org	.20	.30
147	A16	5c rose red & blk	1.90	.95
148	A16	6c org brn & ol grn	.55	.30
149	A16	8c dp bl & dp grn	1.25	.30
150	A16	12c emer & gray	.75	.30
151	A16	14c pur & bl	.30	.45
152	A16	24c rose car & red vio	.55	.70
153	A16	48c red org & bl grn	2.40	3.25
154	A16	60c gray & car	1.60	2.75
155	A16	$1.20 gray & emer	24.00	6.25

Perf. 13½x13

156	A17	$2.40 gray & org	24.00	14.00
		Nos. 142-156 (15)	60.70	31.05

Mat
Making — A18

5c, Canoe making. 10c, Bananas.

1957, Oct. 15 Wmk. 4 Perf. 13x13½

157	A18	3c car rose & black	2.40	2.50
158	A18	5c brown & blue	7.50	1.10
159	A18	10c redsh brn & brt grn	4.00	2.25
160	A18	48c violet & brown	1.00	1.10
		Nos. 157-160 (4)	14.90	6.95

West Indies Federation
Common Design Type
Perf. 11½x11
1958, Apr. 22 Wmk. 314

161	CD313	3c green	.50	.50
162	CD313	6c blue	.50	.50
163	CD313	12c car rose	1.00	1.00
		Nos. 161-163 (3)	2.00	2.00

Sailing
Canoe — A19

Traditional
Costume — A20

Designs: 1c, Seashore, Rosalie. 2c, 5c, Queen Elizabeth II by Annigoni. 4c, Sulphur Springs. 6c, Road making. 8c, Dugout canoe. 10c, Frog (mountain chicken). 12c, Boats and Scotts Head. 15c, Bananas. 24c, Imperial parrot. 48c, View of Goodwill. 60c, Cacao tree. $1.20, Coat of Arms. $2.40, Trafalgar Falls. $4.80, Coconut palm.

Two types of 14c:
I — Mountain light violet. Girl's eyes look straight out.
II — Mountain blue. Eyes look sideways.

Perf. 14½x14, 14x14½
1963, May 16 Photo. Wmk. 314

164	A19	1c bl, brn & grn	.20	1.10
165	A20	2c ultramarine	.20	.20
166	A19	3c lt ultra & blk	1.10	1.40
167	A19	4c sl, grn & brn	.20	.20
168	A20	5c magenta	.20	.20
169	A19	6c lt grn, vio & buff	.20	.20
170	A19	8c tan, blk & lt grn	.20	.20
171	A19	10c pink & brn	.20	.20
172	A19	12c bl, blk, grn & brn	.70	.20
173	A20	14c multi (II)	2.75	2.50
a.		Type I	.55	.75
174	A19	15c grn, yel & brn	1.10	.20
175	A20	24c multicolored	9.00	.20
176	A19	48c bl, blk & grn	.75	.55
177	A19	60c blk, grn, org & brn	1.10	.95
178	A19	$1.20 multicolored	7.00	1.40
179	A20	$2.40 grn, bl, brn & blk	3.25	3.25
180	A20	$4.80 bl, brn & grn	13.00	25.00
		Nos. 164-180 (17)	41.15	37.95

For overprints see Nos. 211-232.

1966-67 Wmk. 314 Sideways

167a	A19	4c ('67)	1.25	.90
169a	A19	6c	.25	.80
170a	A19	8c	.65	.90
171a	A19	10c ('67)	.70	.95
174a	A19	15c ('67)	1.25	1.50
		Nos. 167a-174a (5)	4.10	5.05

Freedom from Hunger Issue
Common Design Type
1963, June 4 Perf. 14x14½

181	CD314	15c lilac	.30	.30

Red Cross Centenary Issue
Common Design Type
Wmk. 314
1963, Sept. 2 Litho. Perf. 13

182	CD315	5c black & red	.20	.20
183	CD315	15c ultra & red	.70	.90

Shakespeare Issue
Common Design Type
1964, Apr. 23 Photo. Perf. 14x14½

184	CD316	15c lilac rose	.35	.35

ITU Issue
Common Design Type
1965, May 17 Litho. Perf. 11x11½

185	CD317	2c emerald & blue	.20	.20
186	CD317	48c grnsh blue & slate	.60	.60

Intl. Cooperation Year Issue
Common Design Type
1965, Oct. 25 Perf. 14½

187	CD318	1c blue grn & claret	.20	.20
188	CD318	15c lt violet & grn	.40	.40

Churchill Memorial Issue
Common Design Type
1966, Jan. 24 Photo. Perf. 14
Design in Black, Gold and Carmine Rose

189	CD319	1c bright blue	.20	.20
a.		Gold omitted	2,000.	
190	CD319	5c green	.40	.20
191	CD319	15c brown	.45	.45
192	CD319	24c violet	.65	.65
		Nos. 189-192 (4)	1.70	1.50

Royal Visit Issue
Common Design Type
1966, Feb. 4 Litho. Perf. 11x12

193	CD320	5c violet blue	.85	.12
194	CD320	15c dk car rose	2.40	.45

World Cup Soccer Issue
Common Design Type
1966, July 1 Litho. Perf. 14

195	CD321	5c multicolored	.40	.20
196	CD321	24c multicolored	1.00	.60

WHO Headquarters Issue
Common Design Type
1966, Sept. 20 Litho. Perf. 14

197	CD322	5c multicolored	.20	.20
198	CD322	24c multicolored	.60	.60

UNESCO Anniversary Issue
Common Design Type
1966, Dec. 1 Litho. Perf. 14

199	CD323	5c "Education"	.35	.20
200	CD323	15c "Science"	.50	.20
201	CD323	24c "Culture"	.90	.20
		Nos. 199-201 (3)	1.75	.60

Carib, Negro and Caucasian
Children — A21

10c, Columbus' ship Santa Maria & banderol. 15c, Hands with banderol. 24c, Belaire dancers.

Perf. 14½x14
1967, Nov. 3 Photo. Wmk. 314

202	A21	5c multicolored	.20	.20
203	A21	10c multicolored	.30	.20
204	A21	15c multicolored	.20	.20
205	A21	24c multicolored	.90	.80
		Nos. 202-205 (4)		

Issued for National Day, Nov. 3.

John F. Kennedy and Human Rights
Flame — A22

Human Rights Flame and: 10c, Cecil E. A. Rawle (1891-1938), Dominican crusader for human rights. 12c, Pope John XXIII. 48c, Florence Nightingale. 60c, Dr. Albert Schweitzer.

Wmk. 314 Sideways
1968, Apr. 20 Litho. Perf. 14

206	A22	1c multicolored	.20	.20
207	A22	10c multicolored	.20	.20
208	A22	12c multicolored	.45	.20
209	A22	48c multicolored	.30	.25
210	A22	60c multicolored	.30	.25
		Nos. 206-210 (5)	1.45	1.10

International Human Rights Year.

Stamps and Types of 1963-67 Overprinted in Silver or Black: "ASSOCIATED / STATEHOOD"
Perf. 14½x14, 14x14½
1968, July 8 Photo. Wmk. 314

211	A19	1c multi	.20	.20
212	A20	2c ultra	.20	.20
213	A19	3c lt ultra & blk	.20	.20
214	A19	4c multi	.20	.20
215	A20	5c magenta	.20	.20
216	A19	6c multi (B)	.20	.20
217	A19	8c multi (B)	.20	.20
218	A19	10c pink & brn	.55	1.40
219	A19	12c multi	.20	.20
a.		Watermark upright	.20	.20
220	A20	14c multi (II)	.20	.20
221	A19	15c multi	.20	.20
222	A19	24c multi	4.25	.20
223	A19	48c multi	.55	2.25
a.		Watermark upright	.50	1.25
224	A19	60c multi (B)	.90	2.10
225	A19	$1.20 multi (B)	1.00	3.25
226	A20	$2.40 multi	1.00	2.50
227	A20	$4.80 multi	1.25	8.00
		Nos. 211-227 (17)	11.50	21.70

In this set, overprint was applied to 2c, 3c, 12c, 14c, 24c, 48c, $1.20, $2.40 and $4.80 with watermark upright. A reprinting of the 1c, 4c, 6c, 8c, 10c, 12c, No. 219, 15c and 48c, No. 223 on paper with watermark sideways was made. Same value.

Nos. 164-166, 173 and 178 Overprinted: "NATIONAL DAY / 3 NOVEMBER 1968"
Perf. 14½x14, 14x14½
1968, Nov. 3 Photo. Wmk. 314

228	A19	1c blue, brn & grn	.20	.20
229	A20	2c ultra	.20	.20
230	A19	3c lt ultra & blk	.20	.20
231	A20	14c multi (I)	.20	.20
232	A19	$1.20 multicolored	.70	.70
		Nos. 228-232 (5)	1.50	1.50

A23

#233a, 3 soccer players. #233b, Soccer player, goalie. #234a, Swimmers at start. #234b, Divers. #235a, Javelin thrower, hurdlers. #235b, Hurdlers. #236a, Basketball. #236b, 3 basketball players.

Perf. 11½
1968, Nov. 23 Unwmk. Litho.

233	A23	1c Pair, #a-b	.20	.20
234	A23	5c Pair, #a-b	.20	.20
235	A23	48c Pair, #a-b	.60	.60
236	A23	60c Pair, #a-b	1.75	1.75
		Nos. 233-236 (4)	2.75	2.75

19th Olympic Games, Mexico City, 10/12-27.

The Small Cowper Madonna, by Raphael A24

Perf. 12½x12

1968, Dec. 23   Photo.   Unwmk.
241 A24 5c multicolored .30 .30

Christmas. No. 241 printed in sheets of 20. Sheets of 6 (3x2) exist containing two each of 12c, 24c, and $1.20 stamps, each picturing a different madonna painting. Value $6.

Venus and Adonis, by Rubens — A25

Citrus Fruit Picker — A26

Paintings: 15c, The Death of Socrates, by Louis Jacques David. 24c, Christ at Emmaus, by Velazquez. 50c, Pilate Washing his Hands, by Rembrandt.

Perf. 14½x15

1969, Jan. 30   Litho.   Wmk. 314
242 A25 5c lilac & multi .25 .25
243 A25 15c emerald & multi .35 .35
244 A25 24c lt blue & multi .35 .35
245 A25 50c crimson & multi .55 .55
    Nos. 242-245 (4) 1.50 1.50

20th anniv. (in 1968) of the WHO.

1969, Mar. 10   Perf. 14½

#247, Woman and child. #248, Hotel. #249, Red-necked parrots. #250, Calypso band. #251, Women dancers. #252, Tropical fish and coelenterates. #253, Diver and turtle.

246 A26 10c multicolored .20 .20
247 A26 10c multicolored .20 .20
a.   Pair, #246-247 .25
248 A26 12c multicolored .20 .20
249 A26 12c multicolored .20 .20
a.   Pair, #248-249 .25
250 A26 24c multicolored .35 .35
251 A26 24c multicolored .35 .35
a.   Pair, #250-251 .70
252 A26 48c multicolored 1.00 1.00
253 A26 48c multicolored 1.00 1.00
a.   Pair, #252-253 2.00
    Nos. 246-253 (8) 3.50 3.50

Tourist publicity.

Spinning, by Millet, Flags and ILO Emblem — A27

50th anniv. of the ILO (Etchings by Jean F. Millet, Flags and ILO Emblem): 30c, Threshing. 30c, Flax pulling.

1969, July   Unwmk.   Perf. 13½
254 A27 15c multicolored .20 .20
255 A27 30c multicolored .30 .30
256 A27 38c multicolored .30 .30
    Nos. 254-256 (3) .80 .80

"Strength in Unity," Bananas and Cacao A28

"Strength in Unity" Emblem and: 8c, Map of Dominica and Hawker Siddeley 748. 12c, Map of Caribbean. 24c, Ships in harbor.

1969, July   Litho.
257 A28 5c orange & multi .30 .30
258 A28 8c gray & multi .30 .30
259 A28 12c lilac & multi .30 .30
260 A28 24c lt blue & multi .60 .60
    Nos. 257-260 (4) 1.50 1.50

Caribbean Free Trade Area (CARIFTA).

Gandhi at Spinning Wheel and Big Ben, London A29

38c, Gandhi, Nehru and Fatehpur Sikri Mausoleum. $1.20, Gandhi & Taj Mahal.

1969, Oct.   Litho.   Perf. 14½
261 A29 6c multicolored .55 .20
262 A29 38c multicolored .90 .25
263 A29 $1.20 multicolored 1.00 1.00
    Nos. 261-263 (3) 2.45 1.45

Mohandas K. Gandhi (1869-1948), leader in India's fight for independence. "Gandhi" is misspelled "Ghandi" on Nos. 261-263.

St. Joseph — A30

Stained Glass Windows, from 17th Century French Churches: 8c, St. John. 12c, St. Peter. 60c, St. Paul.

1969, Nov. 10   Litho.   Perf. 14
264 A30 6c black & multi .20 .20
265 A30 8c black & multi .20 .20
266 A30 12c black & multi .20 .20
267 A30 60c black & multi .40 .40
    Nos. 264-267 (4) 1.00 1.00

National Day, Nov. 3. Issued in sheets of 16 (4x4) with control numbers and 4 tabs with a patriotic poem by W. O. M. Pond.

Queen Elizabeth II — A31

Purplethroated Carib (Hummingbird) — A32

2c, Poinsettia. 3c, Red-necked pigeon. 4c, Imperial parrot. 5c, Swallowtail butterfly. 6c,

Brown Julia butterfly. 8c, Banana shipment. 10c, Portsmouth Harbor. 12c, Copra processing plant. 15c, Women with straw work. 25c, Timber plant. 30c, Mining pumice. 38c, Cricket, Grammar School. 50c, Roman Catholic Cathedral. 60c, Government headquarters. $1.20, Melville Hall Airport. $2.40, Coat of Arms. $4.80, Queen Elizabeth II.

Perf. 13½

1969, Nov. 26   Unwmk.   Photo.
Chalky Paper
268 A31 ½c silver & multi .20 .20
269 A32 1c yellow & multi .20 .20
270 A32 2c yellow & multi .20 .20
271 A32 3c yellow & multi .20 .20
272 A32 4c yellow & multi .20 .20
273 A32 5c yellow & multi .20 .20
274 A32 6c brown & multi .20 .20
275 A32 8c brown & multi .20 .20
276 A32 10c yellow & multi .20 .20
277 A32 12c citron & multi .20 .20
278 A32 15c blue & multi .30 .30
279 A32 25c pink & multi .65 .65
280 A32 30c olive & multi .80 .75
281 A32 38c multicolored 1.00 1.10
282 A32 50c brown & multi 1.10 1.25

Wmk. Rectangles (334)
Perf. 14
Size: 38x26mm, 26x38mm
283 A32 60c yel & multi 1.60 1.40
284 A32 $1.20 yel & multi 3.25 3.25
285 A32 $2.40 gold & multi 7.25 7.00
286 A31 $4.80 gold & multi 14.00 13.50
    Nos. 268-286 (19) 31.95 31.20

1972
On glazed Paper
268a A31 ½c silver & multi .30 2.00
269a A32 1c yellow & multi 1.60 1.75
270a A32 2c yellow & multi .55 .50
271a A32 3c yellow & multi 3.00 2.00
272a A32 4c yellow & multi 3.00 2.00
273a A32 5c yellow & multi 3.00 2.25
274a A32 6c brown & multi 3.00 3.00
275a A32 8c brown & multi .45 .60
276a A32 10c yellow & multi .40 .20
277a A32 12c citron & multi .40 .20
278a A32 15c blue & multi .40 .20
279a A32 25c pink & multi .45 .30
280a A32 30c olive & multi 1.60 .90
281a A32 38c multicolored 9.00 17.50
282a A32 50c brown & multi .85 1.25
    Nos. 268a-282a (15) 28.00 34.75

Madonna and Child, by Filippino Lippi — A33

Paintings: 10c, Holy Family with Lamb, by Raphael. 15c, Virgin and Child, by Perugino. $1.20, Madonna of the Rose Hedge, by Botticelli.

Perf. 14½

1969, Dec.   Unwmk.   Litho.
287 A33 6c lt blue & multi .20 .20
288 A33 10c multicolored .20 .20
289 A33 15c lilac & multi .20 .20
290 A33 $1.20 lt grn & multi .60 .60
a.   Souvenir sheet of 2 1.50 1.50
    Nos. 287-290 (4) 1.20 1.20

Christmas. No. 290a contains 2 imperf. stamps with simulated perforations similar to Nos. 289-290.

Neil A. Armstrong, First Man on the Moon — A34

Designs: 5c, American flag and astronauts on moon. 8c, Astronauts collecting moon rocks. 30c, Landing module and earth. 50c, Memorial tablet left on moon. 60c, Astronauts Armstrong, Aldrin and Collins.

1970, Feb. 2   Litho.   Perf. 12½
291 A34 ½c lilac & multi .20 .20
292 A34 5c lt blue & multi .20 .20
293 A34 8c orange & multi .20 .20
294 A34 30c blue & multi .25 .25
295 A34 50c red brn & multi .60 .60

296 A34 60c rose & multi .80 .80
a.   Souvenir sheet of 4 3.00 3.00
    Nos. 291-296 (6) 2.25 2.25

See note after US No. C76. No. 296a contains 4 stamps similar to Nos. 293-296, but imperf. with simulated perforations.

Giant Green Turtle — A35

Designs: 24c, Flying fish. 38c, Anthurium lily. 60c, Imperial and red-necked parrots.

1970, Sept. 6   Litho.   Perf. 13½x13
297 A35 6c lt green & multi .65 .65
298 A35 24c multicolored .85 .85
299 A35 38c green & multi 1.00 1.00
300 A35 60c yellow & multi 4.00 4.00
a.   Souvenir sheet of 4, #297-300 10.00 10.00
    Nos. 297-300 (4) 6.50 6.50

Women in 18th Century Dress A36

Natl. Day: 8c, Carib mace & wife leader, 18th cent. $1, Map & flag of Dominica.

1970, Nov. 3   Litho.   Perf. 14
301 A36 5c yellow & multi .20 .20
302 A36 8c green & multi .20 .20
303 A36 $1 lt blue & multi .60 .60
a.   Souv. sheet of 3, #301-303 + 3 labels 1.75 2.00
    Nos. 301-303 (3) 1.00 1.00

Marley's Ghost — A37

Designs (from A Christmas Carol, by Dickens): 15c, Fezziwig's Ball. 24c, Scrooge and his Nephew's Christmas Party. $1.20, The Ghost of Christmas Present.

1970, Nov. 23   Litho.   Perf. 14x14½
304 A37 2c blue & multi .20 .20
305 A37 15c multicolored .30 .30
306 A37 24c red & multi .30 .30
307 A37 $1.20 multicolored 1.00 1.00
a.   Souvenir sheet of 4, #304-307 3.25 3.25
    Nos. 304-307 (4) 1.80 1.80

Christmas; Charles Dickens (1812-1870).

Hands and Red Cross A38

Designs: 8c, The Doctor, by Sir Luke Fildes. 15c, Dominica flag and Red Cross. 50c, The Sick Child, by Edvard Munch.

1970, Dec. 28   Perf. 14½x14
308 A38 8c multicolored .20 .20
309 A38 10c multicolored .20 .20
310 A38 15c multicolored .20 .20
311 A38 50c multicolored .75 .75
a.   Souvenir sheet of 4, #308-311 2.25 2.50
    Nos. 308-311 (4) 1.35 1.35

Centenary of the British Red Cross Society.

Marigot Primary School — A39

Education Year Emblem and: 8c, Goodwill Junior High School. 14c, University of the West Indies. $1, Trinity College, Cambridge, England.

1971, Mar. 1   Litho.   Perf. 13½
312	A39	5c multicolored	.20	.20
313	A39	8c multicolored	.20	.20
314	A39	14c multicolored	.20	.20
315	A39	$1 multicolored	.65	.65
a.		Souvenir sheet of 2, #314-315	3.50	3.50
		Nos. 312-315 (4)	1.25	1.25

International Education Year.

Waterfall and Bird-of-Paradise Flower — A40

Tourist Publicity: 10c, Boat building. 30c, Sailboat along North Coast. 50c, Speed boat and steamer.

1971, Mar. 22   Perf. 13½x14
316	A40	5c multicolored	.20	.20
317	A40	10c multicolored	.20	.20
318	A40	30c multicolored	.25	.25
319	A40	50c multicolored	.60	.60
a.		Souvenir sheet of 4, #316-319	1.25	1.25
		Nos. 316-319 (4)	1.25	1.25

UNICEF Emblem, Letter "D" A41

1971, June 14   Litho.   Perf. 14
320	A41	5c multicolored	.20	.20
321	A41	10c multicolored	.20	.20
322	A41	38c multicolored	.20	.20
323	A41	$1.20 multicolored	.50	.50
a.		Souvenir sheet of 2, #321, 323	1.00	1.00
		Nos. 320-323 (4)	1.10	1.10

25th anniv. of UNICEF.

Boy Scout, Jamboree Emblem, Torii, Camp and Mt. Fuji — A42

24c, British Scout, flag. 30c, Japanese Scout, flag. $1, Dominican Scout, flag.

1971, Oct. 18   Unwmk.   Perf. 11
324	A42	20c bister & multi	.25	.25
325	A42	24c green & multi	.30	.30
326	A42	30c red lilac & multi	.45	.45
327	A42	$1 blue & multi	1.75	1.75
a.		Souvenir sheet of 2, #326-327	2.75	2.75
		Nos. 324-327 (4)	2.75	2.75

13th Boy Scout World Jamboree, Asagiri Plain, Japan, Aug. 2-10.

Boats at Portsmouth — A43

15c, Carnival street scene. 20c, $1.20, Anthea Mondesire, Carifta Queen. 50c, Rock of Atkinson.

Perf. 13½x14, 14x13½
1971, Nov. 15   Litho.
328	A43	8c multi	.20	.20
329	A43	15c multi	.20	.20
330	A43	20c multi, vert.	.20	.20
331	A43	50c multi, vert.	.30	.30
		Nos. 328-331 (4)	.90	.90

Souvenir Sheet
Perf. 15
| 332 | A43 | $1.20 multi, vert. | 1.00 | 1.00 |

National Day.

First Dominica Coin, 8 Reals, 1761 — A44

Early Dominica Coins: 30c, Eleven and 3-bit pieces, 1798. 35c, Two-real coin, 1770, vert. 50c, Three "mocos" and piece of 8, 1798.

1972, Feb. 7   Litho.   Perf. 14
333	A44	10c violet, silver & blk	.20	.20
334	A44	30c green, silver & blk	.20	.20
335	A44	35c ultra, silver & blk	.25	.25
336	A44	50c red, silver & blk	.35	.35
a.		Souvenir sheet of 2, #335-336	1.40	1.40
		Nos. 333-336 (4)	1.00	1.00

Margin of #336a inscribed "Christmas 1971."

Common Opossum, Environment Emblem — A45

Environment Emblem and: 35c, Agouti. 60c, Oncidium papillo (orchid). $1.20, Hibiscus.

1972, June 5
337	A45	½c yel grn & multi	.20	.20
338	A45	35c org brn & multi	.35	.35
339	A45	60c lt blue & multi	3.00	3.00
340	A45	$1.20 yellow & multi	2.50	2.50
a.		Souvenir sheet of 4, #337-340	8.25	8.25
		Nos. 337-340 (4)	6.05	6.05

UN Conf. on Human Environment, Stockholm, June 5-16.

100-meter Sprint, Olympic Rings — A46

Olympic Rings and: 35m, 400-meter hurdles. 58c, Hammer throw, vert. 72c, Broad jump, vert.

1972, Oct. 9   Litho.   Perf. 14
341	A46	30c dp org & multi	.20	.20
342	A46	35c blue & multi	.30	.30
343	A46	58c lilac rose & multi	.40	.40
344	A46	72c yel green & multi	.85	.85
a.		Souv. sheet, #343-344, perf. 15	1.50	1.50
		Nos. 341-344 (4)	1.75	1.75

20th Olympic Games, Munich, Aug. 26-Sept. 11.

General Post Office — A47

1972, Nov. 1   Perf. 13½
345	A47	10c shown	.20	.20
346	A47	20c Morne Diablotin Mountain	.20	.20
347	A47	30c Rodney's Rock	.20	.20
a.		Souv. sheet, #346-347, perf. 15	.75	.75
		Nos. 345-347 (3)	.60	.60

National Day.

Adoration of the Shepherds, by Caravaggio A48

Paintings: 14c, Madonna and Child, by Rubens. 30c, Madonna and Child, with St. Anne by Orazio Gentileschi. $1, Adoration of the Kings, by Jan Mostaert. (On 8c, painting is mistakenly attributed to Boccaccino, according to Fine Arts Philatelist.)

1972, Dec. 4.
348	A48	8c gold & multi	.20	.20
349	A48	14c gold & multi	.20	.20
350	A48	30c gold & multi	.20	.20
351	A48	$1 gold & multi	.65	.65
a.		Souvenir sheet of 2	1.50	1.50
		Nos. 348-351 (4)	1.25	1.25

Christmas. No. 351a contains one each of Nos. 350-351 with simulated perforations.

Silver Wedding Issue, 1972
Common Design Type

Design: Queen Elizabeth II, Prince Philip, bananas, sisseron parrot.

Perf. 14x14½
1972, Nov. 13   Photo.   Wmk. 314
| 352 | CD324 | 5c olive & multi | .20 | .20 |
| 353 | CD324 | $1 multicolored | .40 | .40 |

See note after Antigua No. 296.

Launching of Tiros Weather Satellite — A49

1c, Nimbus satellite. 2c, Radiosonde balloon & equipment. 30c, Radarscope. 35c, General circulation of atmosphere. 50c, Picture of hurricane transmitted by satellite. $1, Computer weather map. 30c, 35c, 50c, $1, horiz.

Perf. 14½
1973, July 16   Unwmk.   Litho.
354	A49	½c black & multi	.20	.20
355	A49	1c black & multi	.20	.20
356	A49	2c black & multi	.20	.20
357	A49	30c black & multi	.20	.20
358	A49	35c black & multi	.20	.20
359	A49	50c black & multi	.40	.40
360	A49	$1 black & multi	.80	.80
a.		Souvenir sheet of 2, #359-360	2.00	2.00
		Nos. 354-360 (7)	2.20	2.20

Intl. meteorological cooperation, cent.

Going to the Hospital A50

WHO Emblem and: 1c, Maternity and infant care. 2c, Inoculation against smallpox. 30c, Emergency service. 35c, Waiting patients. 50c, Examination. $1, Traveling physician.

1973, Aug. 20   Unwmk.   Perf. 14½
361	A50	½c lt blue & multi	.20	.20
362	A50	1c gray grn & multi	.20	.20
363	A50	2c yellow & multi	.20	.20
364	A50	30c lt vio & multi	.25	.25
365	A50	35c yel grn & multi	.30	.30
366	A50	50c multicolored	.40	.40
367	A50	$1 bister & multi	.70	.70
a.		Souvenir sheet of 2, #366-367, perf. 14x14½	1.50	1.50
		Nos. 361-367 (7)	2.25	2.25

WHO, 25th anniv. #367a exists perf. 14½.

Cyrique Crab — A51

1973, Oct.
368	A51	½c shown	.20	.20
369	A51	22c Blue land crab	.35	.35
370	A51	25c Breadfruit	.45	.45
371	A51	$1.20 Sunflower	2.00	2.00
a.		Souvenir sheet of 4, #368-371	4.00	4.00
		Nos. 368-371 (4)	3.00	3.00

Princess Anne and Mark Phillips — A52

1973, Nov. 14   Perf. 13½
372	A52	25c salmon & multi	.20	.20
373	A52	$2 blue & multi	.70	.70
a.		Souv. sheet of 2 (75c, $1.20)	.80	.80

Wedding of Princess Anne and Capt. Mark Phillips.

Nos. 372-373 were issued in sheets of 5 + label. No. 373a contains 2 stamps of type A52: 75c in colors of the 25c, and $1.20 in colors of the $2.

Nativity, by Brueghel A53

Paintings of the Nativity by: 1c, Botticelli. 2c, Dürer. 12c, Botticelli. 22c, Rubens. 35c, Dürer. $1, Giorgione (inscribed "Giorgeone").

1973   Unwmk.   Perf. 14½x15
374	A53	½c gray & multi	.20	.20
375	A53	1c gray & multi	.20	.20
376	A53	2c gray & multi	.20	.20
377	A53	12c gray & multi	.20	.20
378	A53	22c gray & multi	.20	.20
379	A53	35c gray & multi	.40	.40
380	A53	$1 gray & multi	1.10	1.10
a.		Souvenir sheet of 2	1.75	1.75
		Nos. 374-380 (7)	2.50	2.50

Christmas. No. 380a contains one each of Nos. 379-380 in changed colors.

Carib Basket Weaving — A54

Designs: 10c, Staircase of the Snake. 50c, Miss Caribbean Queen, Kathleen Telemacque, vert. 60c, Miss Carifta Queen, Esther Fadelle, vert. $1, La Jeune Etoille Dancers.

1973, Dec. 17   Perf. 13½x14, 14x13½
381	A54	5c buff & multi	.20	.20
382	A54	10c multicolored	.20	.20
383	A54	50c multicolored	.25	.25
384	A54	60c multicolored	.25	.25
385	A54	$1 multicolored	.25	.25
a.		Souv. sheet of 3, #381-382, 385	.90	.90
		Nos. 381-385 (5)	1.15	1.15

National Day.

U.W.I. Center, Dominica — A55

30c, Graduation. $1, University coat of arms.

1974, Jan. 21   Litho.   Perf. 13½x14
386	A55	12c dp orange & multi	.20	.20
387	A55	30c violet & multi	.20	.20
388	A55	$1 multicolored	.50	.50
a.		Souvenir sheet of 3, #386-388	.85	1.25
		Nos. 386-388 (3)	.90	.90

University of the West Indies, 25th anniv.

Dominica No. 1 and Map of Island A56

Designs: 1c, 50c, No. 8 and post horn. 2c, $1.20, No. 9 and coat of arms. 10c, Like ½c.

1974, May 4   Litho.   Perf. 14½
389	A56	½c brt pur & multi	.20	.20
390	A56	1c salmon & multi	.20	.20
391	A56	2c ultra & multi	.20	.20
392	A56	10c violet & multi	.20	.20
393	A56	50c yel grn & multi	.55	.55
394	A56	$1.20 rose & multi	1.40	1.40
a.		Souv. sheet, #392-394, perf. 15	2.10	2.10
		Nos. 389-394 (6)	2.75	2.75

Centenary of Dominican postage stamps.

Soccer Player and Cup, Brazilian Flag — A57

Soccer cup, various players and flags.

1974, July   Litho.   Perf. 14½
395	A57	½c shown	.20	.20
396	A57	1c Germany, Fed. Rep.	.20	.20
397	A57	2c Italy	.20	.20
398	A57	30c Scotland	.65	.65
399	A57	40c Sweden	.65	.65
400	A57	50c Netherlands	.85	.85
401	A57	$1 Yugoslavia	1.25	1.25
a.		Souvenir sheet of 2, #400-401, perf. 13½	1.60	1.60
		Nos. 395-401 (7)	4.00	4.00

World Cup Soccer Championship, Munich, June 13-July 7.

Indian Hole A58

40c, Teachers' Training College. $1, Petite Savane Co-operative Bay Oil Distillery.

1974, Nov. 1   Litho.   Perf. 13½x14
402	A58	10c multicolored	.20	.20
403	A58	40c multicolored	.35	.35
404	A58	$1 multicolored	.75	.75
a.		Souvenir sheet of 3, #402-404	1.00	1.00
		Nos. 402-404 (3)	1.30	1.30

Churchill at Race Track A59

Sir Winston Churchill (1874-1965): 1c, with Gen. Eisenhower. 2c, with Franklin D. Roosevelt. 20c, as First Lord of the Admiralty. 45c, painting outdoors. $2, giving "V" sign.

1974, Nov. 25   Litho.   Perf. 14½
405	A59	½c multicolored	.20	.20
406	A59	1c multicolored	.20	.20
407	A59	2c multicolored	.20	.20
408	A59	20c multicolored	.20	.20
409	A59	45c multicolored	.30	.30
410	A59	$2 multicolored	.75	.75
a.		Souvenir sheet of 2, #409-410, perf. 13½	1.75	1.75
		Nos. 405-410 (6)	1.85	1.85

Virgin and Child, by Oronzo Tiso — A60

Paintings (Virgin and Child): 1c, by Lorenzo Costa. 2c, by unknown Master. 10c, by G. F. Romanelli. 25c, Holy Family, by G. S. da Sermoneta. 45c, Adoration of the Shepherds, by Guido Reni. $1, Adoration of the Kings, by Cristoforo Caselli.

1974, Dec. 16   Litho.   Perf. 14
411	A60	½c multicolored	.20	.20
412	A60	1c multicolored	.20	.20
413	A60	2c multicolored	.20	.20
414	A60	10c multicolored	.35	.20
415	A60	25c multicolored	.50	.40
416	A60	45c multicolored	.65	.20
417	A60	$1 multicolored	.90	.50
a.		Souvenir sheet of 2, #416-417	2.00	2.00
		Nos. 411-417 (7)	3.00	1.90

Christmas.

Seamail, "Orinoco," 1851, and "Geesthaven," 1966 — A61

Cent. of UPU: $2, $2.40, Airmail, De Havilland 4, 1918, and Boeing 747, 1974.

1974, Dec. 4   Litho.   Perf. 13½
| 418 | A61 | 10c multicolored | .20 | .20 |
| 419 | A61 | $2 multicolored | 1.50 | 1.50 |

Souvenir Sheet
419A		Sheet of 2	2.00	2.00
b.		A61 $1.20 multicolored	.60	.60
c.		A61 $2.40 multicolored	1.40	1.40

Oldwife A62

1975, June 2   Litho.   Perf. 14½
421	A62	½c shown	.20	.20
422	A62	1c Ocyurus chrysurus	.20	.20
423	A62	2c Blue marlin	.20	.20
424	A62	3c Swordfish	.20	.20
425	A62	20c Great barracuda	1.50	1.00
426	A62	$2 Grouper	5.25	2.75
a.		Souvenir sheet, perf. 13½	5.50	5.25
		Nos. 421-426 (6)	7.55	4.55

Myscelia Antholia A63

Designs: Butterflies.

1975, July 28   Litho.   Perf. 14½
427	A63	½c shown	.20	.20
428	A63	1c Lycorea ceres	.20	.20
429	A63	2c Siderone nemesis	.25	.25
430	A63	6c Battus polydamas	1.10	.95
431	A63	30c Anartia lytrea	3.00	1.00
432	A63	40c Morpho peleides	3.00	1.00
433	A63	$2 Dryas julia	4.25	6.75
a.		Souvenir sheet, perf. 13½	6.50	6.50
		Nos. 427-433 (7)	12.00	10.35

Royal Mail Ship Yare A64

Ships Tied in with Dominican History: 1c, Royal mail ship Thames. 2c, Canadian National S.S. Lady Nelson. 20c, C.N. S.S. Lady Rodney. 45c, Harrison Line M.V. Statesman. 50c, Geest Line M.V. Geestcape. $2, Geest Line M.V. Geeststar.

1975, Sept. 1   Perf. 14
434	A64	½c black & multi	.45	.35
435	A64	1c black & multi	.45	.35
436	A64	2c black & multi	.50	.40
437	A64	20c black & multi	1.90	.85
438	A64	45c black & multi	2.25	1.00
439	A64	50c black & multi	2.25	1.25
440	A64	$2 black & multi	4.25	4.75
a.		Souvenir sheet of 2, #439-440	6.75	4.25
		Nos. 434-440 (7)	12.05	8.95

IWY Emblem, Farm Women A65

$2, IWY emblem, dressmaker & saleswoman.

1975, Oct. 30   Litho.   Perf. 14
| 441 | A65 | 10c pink & multi | .20 | .20 |
| 442 | A65 | $2 yellow & multi | .80 | .80 |

International Women's Year.

Public Library — A66

5c, Miss Caribbean Queen 1975. 30c, Citrus factory. $1, National Day Cup.

1975, Nov. 6
443	A66	5c multi, vert.	.30	.30
444	A66	10c multi	.30	.30
445	A66	30c multi	.30	.30
446	A66	$1 multi, vert.	.85	.85
a.		Souvenir sheet of 3	1.00	1.50
		Nos. 443-446 (4)	1.75	1.75

National Day. No. 446a contains 3 stamps similar to Nos. 444-446 with simulated perforations.

Virgin and Child, by Mantegna — A67

Christmas: Paintings of the Virgin and Child.

1975, Nov. 24
447	A67	½c shown	.20	.20
448	A67	1c Fra Filippo Lippi	.20	.20
449	A67	2c Bellini	.20	.20
450	A67	10c Botticelli	.20	.20
451	A67	25c Bellini	.25	.25
452	A67	45c Correggio	.30	.30
453	A67	$1 Durer	.65	.65
a.		Souvenir sheet of 2, #452-453	1.75	1.75
		Nos. 447-453 (7)	2.00	2.00

Hibiscus A68

Queen Elizabeth II — A69

Designs: 1c, African tulip. 2c, Castor oil tree. 3c, White cedar flower. 4c, Eggplant. 5c, Garfish. 6c, Okra. 8c, Zenaida doves. 10c, Screw pine. 20c, Mangoes. 25c, Crayfish. 30c, Manicou. 40c, Bay leaf groves. 50c, Tomatoes. $1, Lime factory. $2, Rum distillery. $5, Bay oil distillery.

1975, Dec. 8   Litho.   Perf. 14½
454	A68	½c ultra & multi	.20	.50
455	A68	1c lilac & multi	.25	.50
456	A68	2c orange & multi	.25	.50
457	A68	3c multicolored	.25	.50
458	A68	4c pink & multi	.25	.50
459	A68	5c multicolored	.30	.50
460	A68	6c gray & multi	.30	.65
461	A68	8c multicolored	4.00	.65
462	A68	10c violet & multi	.25	.20
463	A68	20c yellow & multi	.50	.20
464	A68	25c lemon & multi	.55	.20
465	A68	30c salmon & multi	1.50	.95
466	A68	40c multicolored	1.50	.95
467	A68	50c red & multi	.65	.55
468	A68	$1 citron & multi	.90	.65
469	A68	$2 multicolored	1.60	3.75
470	A68	$5 multicolored	2.00	5.50

Perf. 14
| 471 | A69 | $10 blue & multi | 2.75 | 16.00 |
| | | Nos. 454-471 (18) | 18.00 | 33.25 |

For overprints see Nos. 584-601, 640-643.

American Infantry — A70

Rowing — A71

Designs: 1c, English three-decker, 1782. 2c, George Washington. 45c, English sailors. 75c, English ensign with regimental flag. $2, Admiral Hood. All designs have old maps in background.

1976, Apr. 12   Litho.   Perf. 14½
472	A70	½c green & multi	.20	.20
473	A70	1c purple & multi	.20	.20
474	A70	2c orange & multi	.20	.20
475	A70	45c brown & multi	.90	.90
476	A70	75c ultra & multi	1.50	1.00
477	A70	$2 red & multi	1.75	3.00
a.		Souvenir sheet of 2	4.50	6.00
		Nos. 472-477 (6)	4.75	4.80

American Bicentennial. No. 477a contains 2 stamps similar to Nos. 476-477, perf. 13.

1976, May 24   Litho.   Perf. 14½

1c, Shot put. 2c, Swimming. 40c, Relay race. 45c, Gymnastics. 60c, Sailing. $2, Archery.

478	A71	½c ocher & multi	.20	.20
479	A71	1c ocher & multi	.20	.20
480	A71	2c ocher & multi	.20	.20
481	A71	40c ocher & multi	.20	.20
482	A71	45c ocher & multi	.20	.20
483	A71	60c ocher & multi	.30	.30
484	A71	$2 ocher & multi	.80	.80
a.		Souv. sheet, #483-484, perf 13	2.00	2.00
		Nos. 478-484 (7)	2.10	2.10

21st Olympic Games, Montreal, Canada, July 17-Aug. 1.

Ringed Kingfisher A72

Birds: 1c, Mourning dove. 2c, Green heron. 15c, Broad-winged hawk. 30c, Blue-headed hummingbird. 45c, Banana-quit. $2, Imperial parrot. 15c, 30c, 45c, $2, vert.

1976, June 28
485	A72	½c multicolored	.25	.25
486	A72	1c multicolored	.25	.25
487	A72	2c multicolored	.25	.25
488	A72	15c multicolored	1.25	1.25
489	A72	30c multicolored	2.00	2.00
490	A72	45c multicolored	2.25	2.25
491	A72	$2 multicolored	5.00	5.00
a.		Souv. sheet of 3, #489-491, perf. 13	9.50	9.50
		Nos. 485-491 (7)	11.25	11.25

Map of West Indies, Bats, Wicket and Ball A72a

Prudential Cup — A72b

1976, July 26   Litho.   Perf. 14
492	A72a	15c lt blue & multi	.50	.50
493	A72b	25c lilac rose & black	1.00	1.00

World Cricket Cup, won by West Indies Team, 1975.

Viking Spacecraft — A73

Virgin and Child, by Giorgione — A74

1c, Titan launch center, horiz. 2c, Titan 3-D & Centaur D-IT. 3c, Orbiter & landing capsule. 45c, Capsule with closed parachute. 75c, Capsule with open parachute. $1, Landing capsule descending on Mars, horiz. $2, Viking on Mars, horiz.

1976, Sept. 20   Litho.   Perf. 15
494	A73	½c multicolored	.20	.20
495	A73	1c multicolored	.20	.20
496	A73	2c multicolored	.20	.20
497	A73	3c multicolored	.20	.20
498	A73	45c multicolored	.35	.35
499	A73	75c multicolored	.45	.45
500	A73	$1 multicolored	.55	.55
501	A73	$2 multicolored	.85	.85
a.		Souvenir sheet of 2, #500, 501, perf. 13½	2.00	2.00
		Nos. 494-501 (8)	3.00	3.00

Viking mission to Mars.

1976, Nov. 1   Litho.   Perf. 14

Virgin and Child by: 1c, Bellini. 2c, Mantegna. 6c, Mantegna. 25c, Memling. 45c, 50c, Correggio. $1, $3, Raphael.

502	A74	½c multicolored	.20	.20
503	A74	1c multicolored	.20	.20
504	A74	2c multicolored	.20	.20
505	A74	6c multicolored	.20	.20
506	A74	25c multicolored	.20	.20
507	A74	45c multicolored	.25	.25
508	A74	$3 multicolored	1.25	1.25
		Nos. 502-508 (7)	2.50	2.50

Souvenir Sheet
509		Sheet of 2	1.60	1.60
a.	A74	50c multicolored	.40	.40
b.	A74	$1 multicolored	.80	.80

Christmas.

Island Craft Co-operative — A75

National Day: 50c, Banana harvest, Castle Bruce Co-operative. $1, Banana shipping plant, Bourne Farmers' Co-operative.

1976, Nov. 22   Litho.   Perf. 13½x14
510	A75	10c multicolored	.20	.20
511	A75	50c multicolored	.25	.25
512	A75	$1 multicolored	.45	.45
a.		Souvenir sheet of 3, #510-512	1.00	1.00
		Nos. 510-512 (3)	.90	.90

Common Sundial — A76

Sea Shells: 1c, Flame helmet. 2c, Mouse cone. 20c, Caribbean vase. 40c, West Indian fighting conch. 50c, Short coral shell. $2, Long-spined star shell. $3, Apple murex.

1976, Dec. 20   Litho.   Perf. 14
513	A76	½c black & multi	.20	.20
514	A76	1c black & multi	.20	.20
515	A76	2c black & multi	.20	.20
516	A76	20c black & multi	.35	.20
517	A76	40c black & multi	.75	.55
518	A76	50c black & multi	.80	.65
519	A76	$3 black & multi	5.50	3.50
		Nos. 513-519 (7)	8.00	5.50

Souvenir Sheet
520	A76	$2 black & multi	3.00	3.00

Queen Enthroned — A77

Designs: 1c, Imperial crown. 45c, Elizabeth II and Princess Anne. $2, Coronation ring. $2.50, Ampulla and spoon. $5, Royal visit to Dominica.

1977, Feb. 7   Perf. 14
521	A77	½c multicolored	.20	.20
522	A77	1c multicolored	.20	.20
523	A77	45c multicolored	.25	.25
524	A77	$2 multicolored	.70	.70
525	A77	$2.50 multicolored	.90	.90
		Nos. 521-525 (5)	2.25	2.25

Souvenir Sheet
526	A77	$5 multicolored	2.00	2.00

25th anniv. of the reign of Elizabeth II.
Nos. 521-525 were printed in sheets of 40 (4x10), perf. 14, and sheets of 5 plus label, perf. 12, in changed colors.
For overprints see Nos. 549-554.

Joseph Haydn — A78

Designs: 1c, Fidelio, act I, scene IV. 2c, Dancer Maria Casentini. 15c, Beethoven working on Pastoral Symphony. 30c, "Wellington's Victory." 40c, Soprano Henriette Sontag. $2, Young Beethoven.

1977, Apr. 25   Litho.   Perf. 14
527	A78	½c multicolored	.20	.20
528	A78	1c multicolored	.20	.20
529	A78	2c multicolored	.20	.20
530	A78	15c multicolored	.45	.45
531	A78	30c multicolored	.45	.45
532	A78	40c multicolored	.45	.45
533	A78	$2 multicolored	2.75	2.75
a.		Souvenir sheet of 3, #531-533	3.75	3.75
		Nos. 527-533 (7)	4.70	4.70

Ludwig van Beethoven (1770-1827), composer.

Boy Scouts on Hike A79

Saluting Boy Scout and: 1c, First aid. 2c, Scouts setting up camp. 45c, Rock climbing. 50c, Kayaking. 75c, Map reading. $2, Campfire. $3, Sailing.

1977, Aug. 8   Litho.   Perf. 14
534	A79	½c multicolored	.20	.20
535	A79	1c multicolored	.20	.20
536	A79	2c multicolored	.20	.20
537	A79	45c multicolored	.50	.50
538	A79	50c multicolored	.60	.60
539	A79	$3 multicolored	2.50	2.50
		Nos. 534-539 (6)	4.20	4.20

Souvenir Sheet
540		Sheet of 2	2.50	2.50
a.	A79	75c multicolored		.75
b.	A79	$2 multicolored		1.75

6th Caribbean Jamboree, Kingston, Jamaica, Aug. 5-14.

Nativity A80

Christmas: 1c, Annunciation to the Shepherds. 2c, 45c, Presentation at the Temple (different). 6c, $2, $3, Flight into Egypt (different). 15c, Adoration of the Kings. 50c, Virgin and Child with Angels. ½c to 45c are illustrations from De Lisle Psalter, 14th century. 50c, $2, $3 are from other Psalters.

1977, Nov. 14   Litho.   Perf. 14
541	A80	½c multicolored	.20	.20
542	A80	1c multicolored	.20	.20
543	A80	2c multicolored	.20	.20
544	A80	6c multicolored	.20	.20
545	A80	15c multicolored	.20	.20
546	A80	45c multicolored	.40	.40
547	A80	$3 multicolored	1.10	1.10
		Nos. 541-547 (7)	2.50	2.50

Souvenir Sheet
548		Sheet of 2	1.75	1.75
a.	A80	50c multicolored	.25	.25
b.	A80	$2 multicolored	1.50	1.50

Nos. 521-526 Overprinted "ROYAL VISIT / W.I. 1977"

1977, Nov. 24   Litho.   Perf. 12, 14
549	A77	½c multicolored	.20	.20
550	A77	1c multicolored	.20	.20
551	A77	45c multicolored	.20	.20
552	A77	$2 multicolored	.60	.60
553	A77	$2.50 multicolored	.65	.65
		Nos. 549-553 (5)	1.85	1.85

Souvenir Sheet
Perf. 14
554	A77	$5 multicolored	1.50	1.50

Caribbean visit of Queen Elizabeth II. #549-550 are perf. 12, others perf. 12 and 14.
Two types of No. 554: I. Overprinted only on stamp. II. Overprinted "W.I. 1977" on stamp and "Royal Visit W.I. 1977" on margin.

Masqueraders — A81

Designs: 1c, Sensay costume. 2c, Street musicians. 45c, Douiette band. 50c, Pappy Show wedding. $2, $2.50, Masquerade band.

1978, Jan. 9   Perf. 14
555	A81	½c multicolored	.20	.20
556	A81	1c multicolored	.20	.20
557	A81	2c multicolored	.20	.20
558	A81	45c multicolored	.30	.30
559	A81	50c multicolored	.35	.35
560	A81	$2 multicolored	1.40	1.40
		Nos. 555-560 (6)	2.65	2.65

Souvenir Sheet
561	A81	$2.50 multicolored	1.75	1.75

History of Carnival.

Lindbergh
and Spirit
of St.
Louis
A82

Designs: 10c, Spirit of St. Louis take-off, Long Island, May 20, 1927. 15c, Lindbergh and map of route New York to Paris. 20c, Lindbergh and plane in Paris. 40c, 1st Zeppelin, trial over Lake Constance. 50c, Spirit of St. Louis. 60c, Count Zeppelin and Zeppelin LZ-2, 1906. $2, Graf Zeppelin, 1928. $3, LZ-127, 1928.

1978, Mar. 13   **Litho.**   **Perf. 14½**

562	A82	6c multicolored	.20	.20
563	A82	10c multicolored	.20	.20
564	A82	15c multicolored	.20	.20
565	A82	20c multicolored	.20	.20
566	A82	40c multicolored	.60	.60
567	A82	60c multicolored	.85	.85
568	A82	$3 multicolored	3.75	3.75
		Nos. 562-568 (7)	6.00	6.00

Souvenir Sheet

569		Sheet of 2	2.75	2.75
a.		A82 50c multicolored	.50	.50
b.		A82 $2 multicolored	2.00	2.00

Charles A. Lindbergh's solo transatlantic flight from New York to Paris, 50th anniv., and flights of Graf Zeppelin.

Royal Family on Balcony — A83

Designs: 45c, Coronation. $2.50, Elizabeth II and Prince Philip. $5, Elizabeth II.

1978, June 2   **Litho.**   **Perf. 14**

570	A83	45c multicolored	.20	.20
571	A83	$2 multicolored	.95	.95
572	A83	$2.50 multicolored	1.10	1.10
		Nos. 570-572 (3)	2.25	2.25

Souvenir Sheet

| 573 | A83 | $5 multicolored | 2.00 | 2.00 |

Coronation of Queen Elizabeth II, 25th anniv. Nos. 570-572 were issued in sheets of 50, and in sheets of 3 stamps and label, in changed colors, perf. 12.

Wright Plane Coming out of Hangar A84

Designs: 40c, 1908 plane. 60c, Flyer I gliding. $2, Flyer I taking off. $3, Wilbur and Orville Wright and Flyer I.

1978, July 10   **Litho.**   **Perf. 14½**

574	A84	30c multicolored	.20	.20
575	A84	40c multicolored	.30	.30
576	A84	60c multicolored	.40	.40
577	A84	$2 multicolored	1.60	1.60
		Nos. 574-577 (4)	2.50	2.50

Souvenir Sheet

| 578 | A84 | $3 multicolored | 2.50 | 2.50 |

75th anniv. of first powered flight.

Two Apostles, by Rubens — A85

Rubens Paintings: 45c, Descent from the Cross. 50c, St. Ildefonso Receiving Chasuble. $2, Holy Family. $3, Assumption of the Virgin.

1978, Oct. 16   **Litho.**   **Perf. 14**

579	A85	20c multicolored	.20	.20
580	A85	45c multicolored	.30	.30
581	A85	50c multicolored	.35	.35
582	A85	$3 multicolored	2.00	2.00
		Nos. 579-582 (4)	2.85	2.85

Souvenir Sheet

| 583 | A85 | $2 multicolored | 1.50 | 1.50 |

Christmas.

Nos. 454-471 Overprinted:
"INDEPENDENCE/ 3rd NOVEMBER 1978"

1978 Nov. 1   **Litho.**   **Perf. 14½**

584	A68	½c ultra & multi	.20	.20
585	A68	1c lilac & multi	.20	.20
586	A68	2c orange & multi	.20	.20
587	A68	3c multicolored	.20	.20
588	A68	4c pink & multi	.20	.20
589	A68	5c multicolored	.20	.20
590	A68	6c gray & multi	.20	.20
591	A68	8c multicolored	.20	.20
592	A68	10c violet & multi	.20	.20
a.		Perf. 13½ ('79)		
593	A68	20c yellow & multi	.20	.20
594	A68	25c lemon & multi	.20	.20
595	A68	30c salmon & multi	.30	.30
596	A68	40c multicolored	.40	.55
597	A68	50c red & multi	.55	.75
598	A68	$1 citron & multi	.95	1.40
599	A68	$2 multicolored	2.10	2.75
600	A68	$5 multicolored	4.25	5.50

Perf. 14

601	A69	$10 blue & multi	8.75	12.50
		Nos. 584-601 (18)	19.50	25.95

Map of Dominica with Parishes — A86   Rowland Hill — A87

25c, Sabinea carinalis, natl. flower, & map. 45c, New flag & map. 50c, Coat of arms & map. $2, Prime Minister Patrick John.

1978, Nov. 1   **Perf. 14**

602	A86	10c multicolored	.20	.20
603	A86	25c multicolored	.20	.20
604	A86	45c multicolored	.65	.65
605	A86	50c multicolored	.75	.75
606	A86	$2 multicolored	3.25	3.25
		Nos. 602-606 (5)	5.05	5.05

Souvenir Sheet

| 607 | A86 | $2.50 multicolored | 3.00 | 3.00 |

Dominican independence.

1979, Mar. 19

45c, Great Britain #2. 50c, Dominica #1. $2, Maltese Cross handstamps. $5, Penny Black.

608	A87	25c multicolored	.20	.20
609	A87	45c multicolored	.20	.20
610	A87	50c multicolored	.25	.25
611	A87	$2 multicolored	.95	.95
		Nos. 608-611 (4)	1.60	1.60

Souvenir Sheet

| 612 | A87 | $5 multicolored | 2.00 | 2.00 |

Sir Rowland Hill (1795-1879), originator of penny postage.

Nos. 608-611 printed in sheets of 5 plus label, perf. 12x12½, in changed colors.
For overprints see Nos. 663A-663D.

Boys and Dugout Canoe A88

IYC Emblem and: 40c, Children carrying bananas. 50c, Boys playing cricket. $3, Child feeding rabbits. $5, Boy showing catch of fish.

1979, Apr. 23   **Litho.**   **Perf. 14**

613	A88	30c multicolored	.30	.30
614	A88	40c multicolored	.45	.45
615	A88	50c multicolored	.50	.50
616	A88	$3 multicolored	2.75	2.75
		Nos. 613-616 (4)	4.00	4.00

Souvenir Sheet

| 617 | A88 | $5 multicolored | 3.25 | 3.25 |

Grouper A89

30c, Striped dolphin. 50c, White-tailed tropic birds. 60c, Brown pelicans. $1, Pilot whale. $2, Brown booby. $3, Elkhorn coral.

1979, May 21   **Litho.**   **Perf. 14**

618	A89	20c multicolored	.20	.20
619	A89	30c multicolored	1.00	1.00
620	A89	50c multicolored	1.75	1.75
621	A89	60c multicolored	2.10	2.10
622	A89	$1 multicolored	3.50	3.50
623	A89	$2 multicolored	7.00	7.00
		Nos. 618-623 (6)	15.55	15.55

Souvenir Sheet

| 624 | A89 | $3 multicolored | 3.50 | 3.50 |

Wildlife protection.

Capt. Cook, Bark Endeavour — A90

Capt. Cook and: 50c, Resolution, map of 2nd voyage. 60c, Discovery, map of 3rd voyage. $2, Cook's map of New Zealand, 1770. $5, Portrait.

1979, July 16   **Litho.**   **Perf. 14**

625	A90	10c multicolored	.20	.20
626	A90	50c multicolored	1.00	1.00
627	A90	60c multicolored	1.25	1.25
628	A90	$2 multicolored	3.75	3.75
		Nos. 625-628 (4)	6.20	6.20

Souvenir Sheet

| 629 | A90 | $5 multicolored | 3.00 | 3.00 |

200th death anniv. of Capt. James Cook (1728-1779).

Girl Guides Cooking A91

Girl Guides: 20c, Setting up emergency rain tent. 50c, Raising flag of independent Dominica. $2.50, Playing accordion and singing. $3, Leader and Guides of different ages.

1979, July 30

630	A91	10c multicolored	.20	.20
631	A91	20c multicolored	.20	.20
632	A91	50c multicolored	.40	.40
633	A91	$2.50 multicolored	2.00	2.00
		Nos. 630-633 (4)	2.80	2.80

Souvenir Sheet

| 634 | A91 | $3 multicolored | 2.25 | 2.25 |

50th anniv. of Dominican Girl Guides.

Colvillea — A92

Flowering Trees: 40c, Lignum vitae. 60c, Dwarf poinciana. $2, Fern tree. $3, Perfume tree.

1979, Sept. 3   **Litho.**   **Perf. 14**

635	A92	20c multicolored	.20	.20
636	A92	40c multicolored	.25	.25
637	A92	60c multicolored	.40	.40
638	A92	$2 multicolored	1.40	1.40
		Nos. 635-638 (4)	2.25	2.25

Souvenir Sheet

| 639 | A92 | $3 multicolored | 2.40 | 2.40 |

Nos. 459, 466, 470-471 Overprinted: "HURRICANE / RELIEF"

Perf. 14½, 13½, 13½x14, 14

1979, Oct. 29   **Litho.**

640	A68	5c multicolored	.20	.20
641	A68	40c multicolored	.40	.40
642	A68	$5 multicolored	4.00	4.00
643	A68	$10 multicolored	8.00	8.00
		Nos. 640-643 (4)	12.60	12.60

Hurricane devastation, Aug. 29. Vertical overprint on No. 643, others horizontal.

Music Scenes A92a

1979, Nov. 2   **Litho.**   **Perf. 11**

644	A92a	½c Mickey Mouse	.20	.20
645	A92a	1c Goofy playing guitar	.20	.20
646	A92a	2c Mickey Mouse and Goofy	.20	.20
647	A92a	3c Donald Duck	.20	.20
648	A92a	4c Minnie Mouse	.20	.20
649	A92a	5c Goofy playing accordion	.20	.20
650	A92a	10c Horace Horsecollar and Dale	.20	.20
651	A92a	$2 Huey, Dewey, Louie	3.00	3.00
652	A92a	$2.50 Donald and Huey	3.50	3.50
		Nos. 644-652 (9)	7.90	7.90

Souvenir Sheet
Perf. 13

| 653 | A92a | $3 Mickey Mouse playing piano | 4.50 | 4.50 |

Cathedral of the Assumption — A93

Cathedrals: 40c, St. Patrick's, New York. 45c, St. Paul's, London, vert. 60c, St. Peter's, Rome. $2, Cologne Cathedral. $3, Notre Dame, Paris, vert.

1979, Nov. 26   **Litho.**   **Perf. 14**

654	A93	6c multicolored	.20	.20
655	A93	45c multicolored	.30	.30
656	A93	60c multicolored	.40	.40
657	A93	$3 multicolored	2.00	2.00
		Nos. 654-657 (4)	2.90	2.90

Souvenir Sheet

658		Sheet of 2	1.00	1.00
a.		A93 40c multicolored	.25	.25
b.		A93 $2 multicolored	.75	.75

Christmas.

Nurse and Patients, Rotary Emblem A94

1980, Mar. 31   Litho.   Perf. 14
659	A94	10c shown	.20	.20
660	A94	20c Electrocardiogram machine	.20	.20
661	A94	40c Mental hospital	.30	.30
662	A94	$2.50 Paul Harris, founder	1.40	1.40
		Nos. 659-662 (4)	2.10	2.10

Souvenir Sheet
663	A94	$3 Map of Africa and Europe	2.00	2.00

Rotary International, 75th anniv. Nos. 659-662 each contain quadrant of Rotary emblem.

Nos. 608-611 Overprinted "LONDON 1980"

1980, May 6   Litho.   Perf. 12
663A	A87	25c multicolored	.35	.35
663B	A87	45c multicolored	.55	.55
663C	A87	50c multicolored	.60	.60
663D	A87	$2 multicolored	2.25	2.25
		Nos. 663A-663D (4)	3.75	3.75

London 80 Intl. Stamp Exhib., May 6-14.

Shot Put, Moscow '80 Emblem A95

1980, May 27   Litho.   Perf. 14
664	A95	30c shown	.20	.20
665	A95	40c Basketball	.30	.30
666	A95	60c Swimming	.40	.40
667	A95	$2 Gymnast	1.40	1.40
		Nos. 664-667 (4)	2.30	2.30

Souvenir Sheet
668	A95	$3 Running	2.00	2.00

22nd Summer Olympic Games, Moscow, July 19-Aug. 3.

Embarkation for Cythera, by Watteau — A96

Paintings: 20c, Supper at Emmaus, by Caravaggio. 25c, Charles I Hunting, by Van Dyck, vert. 30c, The Maids of Honor, by Velazquez, vert. 45c, Rape of the Sabine Women, by Poussin. $1, Embarkation for Cythera, by Watteau. $3, Holy Family, by Rembrandt. $5, Girl before a Mirror, by Picasso, vert.

Perf. 14x13½, 13½x14
1980, July 22   Litho.
669	A96	20c multicolored	.20	.20
670	A96	25c multicolored	.20	.20
671	A96	30c multicolored	.20	.20
672	A96	45c multicolored	.25	.25
673	A96	$1 multicolored	.65	.65
674	A96	$5 multicolored	2.40	2.40
		Nos. 669-674 (6)	3.90	3.90

Souvenir Sheet
675	A96	$3 multicolored	1.50	1.50

Queen Mother Elizabeth, 80th Birthday A97

1980, Aug. 4   Perf. 12, 14
676	A97	40c multicolored	.25	.25
677	A97	$2.50 multicolored	.85	.85

Souvenir Sheet
678	A97	$3 multicolored	1.00	1.00

Tinkerbell — A98

Designs: Scenes from Disney's Peter Pan.

1980, Oct. 1   Litho.   Perf. 11
679	A98	½c multicolored	.20	.20
680	A98	1c multicolored	.20	.20
681	A98	2c multicolored	.20	.20
682	A98	3c multicolored	.20	.20
683	A98	4c multicolored	.20	.20
684	A98	5c multicolored	.20	.20
685	A98	10c multicolored	.20	.20
686	A98	$2 multicolored	3.25	1.60
687	A98	$2.50 multicolored	3.25	1.90
		Nos. 679-687 (9)	7.90	4.90

Souvenir Sheet
688	A98	$4 multicolored	6.00	6.00

Christmas.

Douglas Bay A99

1981, Feb. 12   Litho.   Perf. 14
689	A99	20c shown	.20	.20
690	A99	30c Valley of Desolation	.20	.20
691	A99	40c Emerald Pool, vert.	.20	.20
692	A99	$3 Indian River, vert.	1.50	1.50
		Nos. 689-692 (4)	2.10	2.10

Souvenir Sheet
693	A99	$4 Trafalgar Falls	2.00	2.00

Pluto and Fifi — A100

$4, Pluto in Blue Note (1947 cartoon).

1981, Apr. 30   Litho.   Perf. 13½x14
694	A100	$2 multicolored	2.50	2.50

Souvenir Sheet
695	A100	$4 multicolored	4.00	4.00

50th anniversary of Walt Disney's Pluto.

Forest Thrush A101

1981, Apr. 30   Perf. 14
696	A101	20c shown	.20	.20
697	A101	30c Stolid flycatcher	.40	.40
698	A101	40c Blue-hooded euphonia	.55	.55
699	A101	$5 Lesser antillean peewee	7.00	7.00
		Nos. 696-699 (4)	8.15	8.15

Souvenir Sheet
700	A101	$3 Sisserou parrot	4.50	4.50

Royal Wedding Issue
Common Design Type

1981, June 16   Litho.   Perf. 14
701	CD331a	45c Couple	.25	.25
702	CD331a	60c Windsor Castle	.30	.30
703	CD331a	$4 Charles	1.60	1.60
		Nos. 701-703 (3)	2.15	2.15

Souvenir Sheet
704	CD331	$5 Helicopter	2.00	2.00

Booklet
705	CD331		8.25
a.		Pane of 6 (3x25c, Lady Diana, 3x$2, Charles)	4.75
b.		Pane of 1, $5, Couple	3.50

No. 705 contains imperf., self-adhesive stamps.
Nos. 701-703 also printed in sheets of 5 plus label, perf. 12, in changed colors. Value, set of three sheets $10.

Elves Repairing Santa's Sleigh — A102

Christmas: Scenes from Walt Disney's Santa's Workshop.

1981, Nov. 2   Litho.   Perf. 14
706	A102	½c multicolored	.20	.20
707	A102	1c multicolored	.20	.20
708	A102	2c multicolored	.20	.20
709	A102	3c multicolored	.20	.20
710	A102	4c multicolored	.20	.20
711	A102	5c multicolored	.20	.20
712	A102	10c multicolored	.20	.20
713	A102	45c multicolored	.60	.60
714	A102	$5 multicolored	7.50	7.50
		Nos. 706-714 (9)	9.50	9.50

Souvenir Sheet
715	A102	$4 multicolored	6.50	6.50

Ixora A103

1981, Dec. 1   Litho.   Perf. 14
716	A103	1c shown	.20	.20
717	A103	2c Flamboyant	.20	.20
718	A103	4c Poinsettia	.20	.20
719	A103	5c Sabinea carinalis	.20	.20
720	A103	8c Annatto roucou	.20	.20
721	A103	10c Passion fruit	.20	.20
722	A103	15c Breadfruit	.20	.20
723	A103	20c Allamanda buttercup	.20	.20
724	A103	25c Cashew	.20	.20
725	A103	35c Soursop	.25	.25
726	A103	40c Bougainvillea	.30	.65
727	A103	45c Anthurium	.35	.70
728	A103	60c Cacao	.45	.95
729	A103	90c Pawpaw tree	.65	1.40
730	A103	$1 Coconut palm	.70	1.50
731	A103	$2 Coffee tree	1.40	2.75
732	A103	$5 Lobster claw	3.50	7.00
c.		Perf. 12½x12 ('85)	2.25	2.40
733	A103	$10 Banana fig	7.00	14.50
		Nos. 716-733 (18)	16.40	31.50

For overprints see Nos. 852-853.

1984   Perf. 12
Inscribed "1984"
721a	A103	10c	.80	.80
730a	A103	$1	1.00	1.00
732a	A103	$5	3.50	3.50
733a	A103	$10	7.50	7.50
		Nos. 721a-733a (4)	12.80	12.80

1985   Inscribed "1985"   Perf. 14
721b	A103	10c	1.20	.80
722b	A103	15c Breadfruit	3.75	1.50
728b	A103	60c Cacao	5.25	3.25
732b	A103	$5 Lobster claw	4.00	4.00
		Nos. 721b-732b (4)	14.20	9.55

Intl. Year for the Disabled — A104

Bathers, by Picasso — A105

1981, Dec. 22   Litho.   Perf. 14
734	A104	45c Ramp curb	.35	.35
735	A104	60c Bus steps	.50	.50
736	A104	75c Hand-operated car	.65	.65
737	A104	$4 Bus lift	3.00	3.00
		Nos. 734-737 (4)	4.50	4.50

Souvenir Sheet
738	A104	$5 Elevator buttons	6.00	6.00

1981, Dec. 30   Perf. 14½
739	A105	45c Olga in Armchair	.35	.35
740	A105	60c shown	.50	.50
741	A105	75c Woman in Spanish Costume	.65	.65
742	A105	$4 Dog and Cock	3.00	3.00
		Nos. 739-742 (4)	4.50	4.50

Souvenir Sheet
743	A105	$5 Sleeping Peasants	6.00	6.00

1982 World Cup Soccer — A106

Various Disney characters playing soccer.

1982, Jan. 29   Perf. 14
744	A106	½c multicolored	.20	.20
745	A106	1c multicolored	.20	.20
746	A106	2c multicolored	.20	.20
747	A106	3c multicolored	.20	.20
748	A106	4c multicolored	.20	.20
749	A106	5c multicolored	.20	.20
750	A106	10c multicolored	.20	.20
751	A106	60c multicolored	1.10	1.10
752	A106	$5 multicolored	8.50	8.50
		Nos. 744-752 (9)	11.00	11.00

Souvenir Sheet
753	A106	$4 multicolored	6.50	6.50

Golden Days, by Norman Rockwell A107

1982, Mar. 10   Litho.   Perf. 14x13½
754	A107	10c shown	.20	.20
755	A107	25c The Morning News	.20	.20
756	A107	45c The Marbles Champ	.35	.35
757	A107	$1 Speeding Along	.75	.75
		Nos. 754-757 (4)	1.50	1.50

Intl. Decade for Women (1975-85) A108

Famous Women: 10c, Elma Napier (1890-1973), first woman elected to Legislative Council in British West Indies, 1940. 45c, Margaret Mead (1901-1978), anthropologist. $1, Mabel Caudiron (1909-1968), musician and folk historian. $3, Florence Nightingale, founder of modern nursing. $4, Eleanor Roosevelt.

1982, Apr. 15   Litho.   Perf. 14
758 A108 10c multicolored   .20 .20
759 A108 45c multicolored   .35 .35
760 A108 $1 multicolored   .75 .75
761 A108 $4 multicolored   3.25 3.25
      Nos. 758-761 (4)   4.55 4.55
Souvenir Sheet
762 A108 $3 multicolored   3.50 3.50

George Washington and Independence Hall, Philadelphia — A109

Washington or Roosevelt and: 60c, Capitol Building. 90c, The Surrender of Cornwallis, by John Trumbull. $2, Dam construction during New Deal (mural by William Gropper). $5, Washington, Roosevelt.

1982, May 1   Perf. 14½
763 A109 45c multicolored   .35 .35
764 A109 60c multicolored   .45 .45
765 A109 90c multicolored   .70 .70
766 A109 $2 multicolored   1.75 1.75
      Nos. 763-766 (4)   3.25 3.25
Souvenir Sheet
767 A109 $5 multicolored   3.50 3.50

George Washington's 250th birth anniv. and Franklin D. Roosevelt's birth cent.

Godman's Leaf Butterfly — A110

1982, June 1   Litho.   Perf. 14
768 A110 15c shown   .50 .50
769 A110 45c Zebra   2.25 2.25
770 A110 60c Mimic   2.50 2.50
771 A110 $3 Red rim   10.50 10.50
      Nos. 768-771 (4)   15.75 15.75
Souvenir Sheet
772 A110 $5 Southern dagger
             tail   8.00 8.00

Princess Diana Issue
Common Design Type
1982, July 1   Litho.   Perf. 14½x14
773 CD332 45c Buckingham
              Palace   .35 .35
774 CD332 $2 Engagement
              portrait   1.50 1.50
775 CD332 $4 Wedding   3.00 3.00
      Nos. 773-775 (3)   4.85 4.85
Souvenir Sheet
776 CD332 $5 Diana, diff.   4.25 4.25

Also issued in sheet of 5 plus label.
For overprints see Nos. 782-785.

Scouting Year A111

1982, July 1   Litho.   Perf. 14
777 A111 45c Cooking   .95 .95
778 A111 60c Meteorological
              study   1.50 1.50
779 A111 75c Sisserou parrot,
              cub scouts   1.75 1.75
780 A111 $3 Canoeing, Indi-
              an River   6.50 6.50
      Nos. 777-780 (4)   10.70 10.70
Souvenir Sheet
781 A111 $5 Flagbearer   4.50 4.50

Nos. 773-776 Overprinted: "ROYAL BABY / 21.6.82"

1982, Sept. 1   Litho.   Perf. 14½x14
782 CD332 45c multicolored   .35 .35
783 CD332 $2 multicolored   1.50 1.50
784 CD332 $4 multicolored   3.00 3.00
      Nos. 782-784 (3)   4.85 4.85
Souvenir Sheet
785 CD332 $5 multicolored   4.00 4.00

Birth of Prince William of Wales, June 21. Also issued in sheet of 5 plus label.

Christmas — A112

Holy Family Paintings by Raphael.

1982, Oct. 18   Litho.   Perf. 14
786 A112 25c multicolored   .20 .20
787 A112 30c multicolored   .20 .20
788 A112 90c multicolored   .60 .60
789 A112 $4 multicolored   2.75 2.75
      Nos. 786-789 (4)   3.75 3.75
Souvenir Sheet
790 A112 $5 multicolored   4.25 4.25

Goosebeak Whale Eating Squid — A113

1983, Feb. 15   Litho.   Perf. 14
791 A113 45c shown   1.25 1.25
792 A113 60c Humpback
              whale   1.75 1.75
793 A113 75c Great right
              whale   2.25 2.25
794 A113 $3 Melonhead
              whale   9.25 9.25
      Nos. 791-794 (4)   14.50 14.50
Souvenir Sheet
795 A113 $5 Pygmy sperm
              whale   7.00 7.00

A113a

1983, Mar. 14
796 A113a 25c Banana industry   .20 .20
797 A113a 30c Road construc-
               tion   .20 .20
798 A113a 90c Community nurs-
               ing   .55 .55
799 A113a $3 Basket weavers 1.75 1.75
      Nos. 796-799 (4)   2.70 2.70

Commonwealth Day.

World Communications Year — A114

1983, Apr. 18   Litho.   Perf. 14
800 A114 45c Hurricane pattern,
              map   .35 .35
801 A114 60c Air-to-ship commu-
              nication   .45 .45

802 A114 90c Columbia shuttle,
              dish antenna   .70 .70
803 A114 $2 Walkie-talkie   1.50 1.50
      Nos. 800-803 (4)   3.00 3.00
Souvenir Sheet
804 A114 $5 Satellite   3.50 3.50

Manned Flight Bicentenary — A115

1983, July 19   Litho.   Perf. 15
805 A115 45c Mayo Composite   .50 .50
806 A115 60c Macchi M-39   .65 .65
807 A115 90c Fairey Swordfish 1.00 1.00
808 A115 $4 Zeppelin LZ-3   4.25 4.25
      Nos. 805-808 (4)   6.40 6.40
Souvenir Sheet
809 A115 $5 Double Eagle II,
              vert.   4.00 4.00

Duesenberg SJ, 1935 — A116

1983, Sept. 1   Litho.   Perf. 14
810 A116 10c shown   .20 .20
811 A116 45c Studebaker Avanti,
              1962   .35 .35
812 A116 60c Cord 812, 1936   .45 .45
813 A116 75c MG-TC, 1945   .55 .55
814 A116 90c Camaro 350-SS,
              1967   .70 .70
815 A116 $3 Porsche 356, 1948 2.25 2.25
      Nos. 810-815 (6)   4.50 4.50
Souvenir Sheet
816 A116 $5 Ferrari 312-T,
              1975   4.00 4.00

Christmas — A117

Raphael Paintings.

1983, Oct. 4   Litho.   Perf. 13½
817 A117 45c multicolored   .35 .35
818 A117 60c multicolored   .50 .50
819 A117 90c multicolored   .75 .75
820 A117 $4 multicolored   3.25 3.25
      Nos. 817-820 (4)   4.85 4.85
Souvenir Sheet
821 A117 $5 multicolored   4.00 4.00

23rd Olympic Games, Los Angeles, July 28-Aug. 12 — A118

1984, Mar.   Litho.   Perf. 14
822 A118 30c Gymnastics   .25 .25
823 A118 45c Javelin   .35 .35
824 A118 60c Diving   .50 .50
825 A118 $4 Fencing   3.25 3.25
      Nos. 822-825 (4)   4.35 4.35
Souvenir Sheet
826 A118 $5 Equestrian   4.25 4.25

Local Birds A119

1984, May   Litho.
827 A119 5c Plumbeous war-
             bler   3.25 3.25
828 A119 45c Imperial parrot 8.50 8.50
829 A119 60c Blue-headed
             hummingbird   12.50 12.50
830 A119 90c Red-necked par-
             rot   18.00 18.00
      Nos. 827-830 (4)   42.25 42.25
Souvenir Sheet
831 A119 $5 Roseate flamin-
             goes   11.00 11.00

Easter A120

Various Disney characters and Easter bunnies.

1984, Apr. 15   Litho.   Perf. 11
832 A120 ½c multicolored   .20 .20
833 A120 1c multicolored   .20 .20
834 A120 2c multicolored   .20 .20
835 A120 3c multicolored   .20 .20
836 A120 4c multicolored   .20 .20
837 A120 5c multicolored   .20 .20
838 A120 10c multicolored   .20 .20
839 A120 $2 multicolored   4.00 4.00
840 A120 $4 multicolored   8.00 8.00
      Nos. 832-840 (9)   13.40 13.40
Souvenir Sheet
Perf. 14
841 A120 $5 multicolored   7.00 7.00

Ships A121

1984, June 14   Litho.   Perf. 14
842 A121 45c Atlantic Star   1.10 1.10
843 A121 60c Atlantic   1.40 1.40
844 A121 90c Carib fishing pi-
              rogue   2.50 2.50
845 A121 $4 Norway   10.50 10.50
      Nos. 842-845 (4)   15.50 15.50
Souvenir Sheet
846 A121 $5 Santa Maria   6.00 6.00

Local Plants — A122   Correggio & Degas — A122a

1984, Aug. 13
847 A122 45c Guzmania lingulata .45 .45
848 A122 60c Pitcairnia angus-
              tifolia   .55 .55
849 A122 75c Tillandsia fascicu-
              lata   .75 .75

850 A122 $3 Aechmea smithi-
orum   3.25 3.25
Nos. 847-850 (4)   5.00 5.00

Souvenir Sheet

851 A122 $5 Tillandsia utriculata   4.00 4.00

Ausipex Intl. Stamp Exhibition.

Nos. 721, 732 Overprinted: "19th UPU
/ CONGRESS HAMBURG"

1984			**Litho.**	**Perf. 14**
852	A103	10c multicolored	.20	.20
853	A103	$5 multicolored	5.00	5.00

1984, Nov.   **Litho.**   **Perf. 15**

Correggio: 25c, Virgin and Child with Young
St. John. 60c, Christ Bids Farewell to the Virgin Mary. 90c, Do Not Touch Me. $4, The Mys-
tical Marriage of St. Catherine. No. 862, Adoration of the Magi.

Degas, horiz.: 30c, Before the Start. 45c,
On the Racecourse. $1, Jockeys at the Flag-
pole. $3, Racehorses at Longchamp. No. 863,
Self-portrait.

854	A122a	25c multicolored	.20	.20
855	A122a	30c multicolored	.20	.20
856	A122a	45c multicolored	.40	.40
857	A122a	60c multicolored	.55	.55
858	A122a	90c multicolored	.75	.75
859	A122a	$1 multicolored	.90	.90
860	A122a	$3 multicolored	2.50	2.50
861	A122a	$4 multicolored	3.50	3.50
		Nos. 854-861 (8)	9.00	9.00

Souvenir Sheets

862	A122a	$5 multicolored	3.75	3.75
863	A122a	$5 multicolored	3.75	3.75

A123

A124

1984, Dec.				**Perf. 14**
864	A123	30c Avro 748	.20	.20
865	A123	60c Twin Otter	1.40	1.40
866	A123	$1 Islander	2.40	2.40
867	A123	$3 Casa	7.00	7.00
		Nos. 864-867 (4)	11.00	11.00

Souvenir Sheet

868 A123 $5 Boeing 747   7.50 7.50

Intl. Civil Aviation Org., 40th anniv.

1984, Nov.   **Litho.**

Scenes from various Donald Duck movies.

869	A124	45c multicolored	.95	.95
870	A124	60c multicolored	1.25	1.25
871	A124	90c multicolored	2.00	2.00
872	A124	$2 multicolored, perf. 12x12½	4.00	4.00
873	A124	$4 multicolored	7.75	7.75
		Nos. 869-873 (5)	15.95	15.95

Souvenir Sheet
Perf. 13½x14

874 A124 $5 multicolored   6.75 6.75

Christmas and 50th anniv. of Donald Duck.

Cats
A125

1984, Nov. 12   **Litho.**   **Perf. 15**

875	A125	10c Tabby	.20	.20
876	A125	15c Calico shorthair	.20	.20
877	A125	20c Siamese	.20	.20
878	A125	25c Manx	.20	.20
879	A125	45c Abyssinian	.45	.45
880	A125	60c Tortoise shell	.55	.55
881	A125	$1 Rex	.90	.90
882	A125	$2 Persian	2.10	2.10
883	A125	$3 Himalayan	3.25	3.25
884	A125	$5 Burmese	5.00	5.00
		Nos. 875-884 (10)	13.05	13.05

Souvenir Sheet

885 A125 $5 Gray Burmese,
Persian, Ameri-
can shorthair   6.25 6.25

Girl
Guides,
75th
Anniv.
A126

1985, Feb. 18   **Perf. 14**

886	A126	35c Lady Baden-Powell	.50	.50
887	A126	45c Inspecting Domini-can troop	.75	.75
888	A126	60c With Dominican troop leaders	1.00	1.00
889	A126	$3 Lord and Lady Ba-den-Powell, vert.	4.50	4.50
		Nos. 886-889 (4)	6.75	6.75

Souvenir Sheet

890 A126 $5 Flag ceremony   6.75 6.75

John
James
Audubon
A127

1985, Apr. 4

891	A127	45c King rails	1.00	1.00
892	A127	$1 Black & white warbler, vert.	2.10	2.10
893	A127	$2 Broad-winged hawks, vert.	4.00	4.00
894	A127	$3 Ring-necked ducks	6.25	6.25
		Nos. 891-894 (4)	13.35	13.35

Souvenir Sheet

895 A127 $5 Reddish egrets,
vert.   6.25 6.25

Nos. 891-894 exist vertically se-tenant with
labels showing additional bird species.
See Nos. 965-969.

Duke of Edinburgh
Awards,
1984 — A128

1985, Apr. 30

896	A128	45c Woman at com-puter terminal	.65	.65
897	A128	60c Medical staff, patient	.85	.85
898	A128	90c Runners	1.25	1.25
899	A128	$4 Family jogging	5.25	5.25
		Nos. 896-899 (4)	8.00	8.00

Souvenir Sheet

900 A128 $5 Duke of Edin-
burgh   4.50 4.50

Intl. Youth
Year
A129

1985, July 8   **Litho.**   **Perf. 14**

901	A129	45c Cricket match	1.75	1.75
902	A129	60c Environmental study, parrot	2.25	2.25
903	A129	$1 Stamp collecting	3.25	3.25
904	A129	$3 Boating, leisure	11.50	11.50
		Nos. 901-904 (4)	18.75	18.75

Souvenir Sheet

905 A129 $5 Youths join
hands   4.75 4.75

Queen Mother,   Johann Sebastian
85th   Bach — A131
Birthday — A130

1985, July 15

906	A130	60c Visiting Sadlers Wells	.55	.55
907	A130	$1 Fishing	1.25	1.25
908	A130	$3 At Clarence House, 1984	3.75	3.75
		Nos. 906-908 (3)	5.55	5.55

Souvenir Sheet

909 A130 $5 Attending Windsor
Castle Garter
Ceremony   4.50 4.50

1985, Sept. 2

Portrait, signature, music from Explication
and: 45c, Cornett 60c, Coiled trumpet. $1, Pic-
colo. $3, Violoncello piccolo.

910	A131	45c multicolored	.85	.85
911	A131	60c multicolored	1.10	1.10
912	A131	$1 multicolored	1.75	1.75
913	A131	$3 multicolored	6.75	6.75
		Nos. 910-913 (4)	10.45	10.45

Souvenir Sheet

914 A131 $5 Portrait   5.00 5.00

State Visit of Elizabeth II,
Oct. 25 — A132

1985, Oct. 25   **Perf. 14½**

915	A132	60c Flags of UK, Domi-nica	.55	.55
916	A132	$1 Elizabeth II, vert.	.95	.95
917	A132	$4 HMS Britannia	4.50	4.50
		Nos. 915-917 (3)	6.00	6.00

Souvenir Sheet

918 A132 $5 Map   4.50 4.50

Mark Twain — A133

Disney characters in Tom Sawyer.

1985, Nov. 11   **Litho.**   **Perf. 14**

919	A133	20c multicolored	.45	.45
920	A133	60c multicolored	1.10	1.10
921	A133	$1 multicolored	1.90	1.90
922	A133	$1.50 multicolored	3.50	3.50
923	A133	$2 multicolored	5.00	5.00
		Nos. 919-923 (5)	11.95	11.95

Souvenir Sheet

924 A133 $5 multicolored   7.75 7.75

Christmas.

The Brothers Grimm — A134

Disney characters in Little Red Cap (Little
Red Riding Hood).

1985, Nov. 11

925	A134	10c multicolored	.45	.45
926	A134	45c multicolored	.95	.95
927	A134	90c multicolored	1.75	1.75
928	A134	$1 multicolored	2.10	2.10
929	A134	$3 multicolored	6.25	6.25
		Nos. 925-929 (5)	11.50	11.50

Souvenir Sheet

930 A134 $5 multicolored   9.25 9.25

Christmas.

UN,
40th
Anniv.
A135

Stamps of UN, famous men and events:
45c, No. 442 and Lord Baden-Powell. $2, No.
157 and Maimonides (1135-1204) Judaic
scholar. $3, No. 278 and Sir Rowland Hill. $5,
Apollo-Soyuz Mission, 10th anniv.

1985, Nov. 22   **Perf. 14½**

931	A135	45c multicolored	.50	.50
932	A135	$2 multicolored	3.00	3.00
933	A135	$3 multicolored	4.50	4.50
		Nos. 931-933 (3)	8.00	8.00

Souvenir Sheet

934 A135 $5 multicolored   4.50 4.50

1986 World Cup
Soccer
Championships,
Mexico — A136

Various soccer plays.

1986, Mar. 26   **Perf. 14**

935	A136	45c multicolored	1.00	1.00
936	A136	60c multicolored	1.40	1.40
937	A136	$1 multicolored	2.50	2.50
938	A136	$3 multicolored	7.50	7.50
		Nos. 935-938 (4)	12.40	12.40

Souvenir Sheet

939 A136 $5 multicolored   10.00 10.00

For overprints see Nos. 974-978.

Statue of
Liberty,
Cent.
A137

Statue and: 15c, New York police pursuing
river pirates, c. 1890. 25c, Police patrol boat.
45c, Hoboken Ferry Terminal, c. 1890. $4,
Holland Tunnel.

1986, Mar. 26

940	A137	15c multicolored	.60	.60
941	A137	25c multicolored	.60	.60
942	A137	45c multicolored	.85	.85
943	A137	$4 multicolored	8.50	8.50
		Nos. 940-943 (4)	10.55	10.55

Souvenir Sheet

944 A137 $5 Statue, vert.   6.50 6.50

Halley's Comet A138

5c, Jantal Mantar Observatory, Delhi, India, Nasir al Din al Tusi (1201-1274), astronomer. 10c, US Bell X-1 rocket plane breaking sound barrier. 45c, Astronomicum Caesareum, 1540, manuscript diagram of comet's trajectory, 1531. $4, Mark Twain, comet appeared at birth and death. $5, Comet.

1986, Apr. 17
945	A138	5c multicolored	.20	.20
946	A138	10c multicolored	.20	.20
947	A138	45c multicolored	.60	.60
948	A138	$4 multicolored	5.00	5.00
		Nos. 945-948 (4)	6.00	6.00

Souvenir Sheet
949	A138	$5 multicolored	4.50	4.50

For overprints see Nos. 984-988.

Queen Elizabeth II, 60th Birthday
Common Design Type
			Perf. 14
1986, Apr. 21		Litho.	
950	CD339	2c Wedding, 1947	.25 .25
951	CD339	$1 With Pope John Paul II, 1982	.75 .75
952	CD339	$4 Royal visit, 1971	3.00 3.00
		Nos. 950-952 (3)	4.00 4.00

Souvenir Sheet
953	CD339	$5 Age 10	4.25	4.25

AMERIPEX '86 — A139

Walt Disney characters involved in stamp collecting.

1986, May 22 — Perf. 11
954	A139	25c Mickey Mouse and Pluto	.25	.25
955	A139	45c Donald Duck	.80	.80
956	A139	60c Chip-n-Dale	.95	.95
957	A139	$4 Donald, nephews	6.50	6.50
		Nos. 954-957 (4)	8.50	8.50

Souvenir Sheet
Perf. 14
958	A139	$5 Uncle Scrooge	7.25	7.25

British Monarchs — A140

1986, June 9 — Perf. 14
959	A140	10c William I	.20	.20
960	A140	40c Richard II	.40	.40
961	A140	50c Henry VIII	.50	.50
962	A140	$1 Charles II	1.00	1.00
963	A140	$2 Queen Anne	2.10	2.10
964	A140	$4 Queen Victoria	4.50	4.50
		Nos. 959-964 (6)	8.70	8.70

Audubon Type of 1985
Perf. 12½x12, 12x12½
1986, June 18
965	A127	25c Black-throated diver	.45	.45
966	A127	60c Great blue heron	1.10	1.10
967	A127	90c Yellow-crowned night heron	1.75	1.75
968	A127	$4 Shoveler duck	8.00	8.00
		Nos. 965-968 (4)	11.30	11.30

Souvenir Sheet
Perf. 14
969	A127	$5 Goose	12.00	12.00
		Nos. 966-967 vert.		

Royal Wedding Issue, 1986
Common Design Type
1986, July 23 — Perf. 14
970	CD340	45c Couple	.40	.40
971	CD340	60c Prince Andrew	.60	.60
972	CD340	$4 Prince, aircraft	3.00	3.00
		Nos. 970-972 (3)	4.00	4.00

Souvenir Sheet
973	CD340	$5 Couple, diff.	4.50	4.50

Nos. 935-939 Ovptd. "WINNERS / Argentina 3 / W. Germany 2" in Gold
1986, Sept. 15 — Litho. — Perf. 14
974	A136	45c multicolored	.80	.80
975	A136	60c multicolored	1.25	1.25
976	A136	$1 multicolored	2.10	2.10
977	A136	$3 multicolored	6.75	6.75
		Nos. 974-977 (4)	10.90	10.90

Souvenir Sheet
978	A136	$5 multicolored	10.50	10.50

Paintings by Albrecht Durer — A141

A142

1986, Dec. 2 — Litho. — Perf. 14
979	A141	45c Virgin in Prayer	1.00	1.00
980	A141	60c Madonna and Child	1.25	1.25
981	A141	$1 Madonna and Child, diff.	2.25	2.25
982	A141	$3 Madonna and Child with St. Anne	6.50	6.50
		Nos. 979-982 (4)	11.00	11.00

Souvenir Sheet
983	A142	$5 Nativity	10.50	10.50

Nos. 945-949 Printed with Halley's Comet Logo in Black or Silver

1986, Dec. 16
984	A138	5c multicolored	.20	.20
985	A138	10c multicolored	.20	.20
986	A138	45c multicolored	.60	.60
987	A138	$4 multicolored	4.75	4.75
		Nos. 984-987 (4)	5.75	5.75

Souvenir Sheet
988	A138	$5 multi (S)	5.25	5.25

Birds — A143

1987, Jan. 20 — Litho. — Perf. 15
989	A143	1c Broad-winged hawk	.20	.20
990	A143	2c Ruddy quail dove	.20	.20
991	A143	5c Red-necked pigeon	.20	.20
992	A143	10c Green heron	.20	.20
993	A143	15c Common gallinule	.20	.20
994	A143	20c Ringed kingfisher	.20	.20
995	A143	25c Brown pelican	.20	.20
996	A143	35c White-tailed tropicbird	.30	.30
997	A143	45c Red-legged thrush	.40	.40
998	A143	60c Purple throated carib	.55	.55
999	A143	90c Magnificent frigatebird	.75	.75
1000	A143	$1 Trembler	.85	.85
1001	A143	$2 Black-capped petrel	1.75	1.75
1002	A143	$5 Barn owl	4.25	4.25
1003	A143	$10 Imperial parrot	8.75	8.75
		Nos. 989-1003 (15)	19.00	19.00

Inscribed "1989" and "Questa"
1989, Aug. 31 — Litho. — Perf. 14
990a	A143	2c	.20	.20
991a	A143	5c	.20	.20
992a	A143	10c	.20	.20
993a	A143	15c	.20	.20
994a	A143	20c	.20	.20
995a	A143	25c	.30	.30
996a	A143	35c	.50	.50
997a	A143	45c	.60	.60
998a	A143	60c	.85	.85
1000a	A143	$1	1.40	1.40
1001a	A143	$2	2.75	2.75
1002a	A143	$5	6.75	6.75
1003a	A143	$10	14.00	14.00
		Nos. 990a-1003a (13)	28.15	28.15

Inscribed "1990" and "Questa"
1990 — Litho. — Perf. 12
990b	A143	2c	.20	.20
991b	A143	5c	.20	.20
992b	A143	10c	.20	.20
993b	A143	15c	.20	.20
994b	A143	20c	.20	.20
995b	A143	25c	.30	.30
996b	A143	35c	.50	.50
997b	A143	45c	.60	.60
998b	A143	60c	.85	.85
1000b	A143	$1	1.40	1.40
1001b	A143	$2	2.75	2.75
1002b	A143	$5	6.75	6.75
1003b	A143	$10	14.00	14.00
		Nos. 990b-1003b (13)	28.15	28.15

Inscribed "1991" and "Questa"
1991 — Litho. — Perf. 13x11½
990c	A143	2c	.20	.20
991c	A143	5c	.20	.20
992c	A143	10c	.20	.20
993c	A143	15c	.20	.20
994c	A143	20c	.20	.20
995c	A143	25c	.35	.35
996c	A143	35c	.55	.55
997c	A143	45c	.65	.65
998c	A143	60c	.95	.95
1000c	A143	$1	1.60	1.60
1001c	A143	$2	3.00	3.00
1002c	A143	$5	7.50	7.50
1003c	A143	$10	15.00	15.00
		Nos. 990c-1003c (13)	30.60	30.60

Paintings by Marc Chagall (1887-1985) A144

Designs: 25c, Artist and His Model. 35c, Midsummer Night's Dream. 45c, Joseph the Shepherd. 60c, the Cellist. 90c, Woman with Pigs. $1, the Blue Circus. $3, For Vava. $4, the Rider. No. 1012, Purim. No. 1013, Firebird design for the curtain of the Stravinsky Ballet production.

1987, Mar. 2 — Perf. 14
1004	A144	25c multicolored	.25	.25
1005	A144	35c multicolored	.40	.40
1006	A144	45c multicolored	.45	.45
1007	A144	60c multicolored	.65	.65
1008	A144	90c multicolored	.90	.90
1009	A144	$1 multicolored	1.00	1.00
1010	A144	$3 multicolored	3.00	3.00
1011	A144	$4 multicolored	4.25	4.25

Size: 110x95mm
Imperf
1012	A144	$5 multicolored	4.00	4.00
1013	A144	$5 multicolored	4.00	4.00
		Nos. 1004-1013 (10)	18.90	18.90

A145   Conch Shells — A147

America's Cup — A146

1987, Feb. 5 — Perf. 15
1014	A145	45c Reliance, 1903	.50	.45
1015	A145	60c Freedom, 1980	.60	.55
1016	A145	$1 Mischief, 1881	1.10	1.00
1017	A145	$3 Australia, 1977	3.25	2.00
		Nos. 1014-1017 (4)	5.45	4.00

Souvenir Sheet
1018	A146	$5 Courageous, Australia, 1977	4.50	4.50

1987, Apr. 13 — Litho.

Designs: 35c, Morch Poulsen's triton. 45c, Swainson globe purple sea snail. 60c, Banded tulip. No. 1022, Lamarck deltoid rock shell. No. 1023, Junoia volute.
1019	A147	35c multicolored	.35	.35
1020	A147	45c multicolored	.50	.50
1021	A147	60c multicolored	.65	.65
1022	A147	$5 multicolored	4.25	4.25
		Nos. 1019-1022 (4)	5.75	5.75

Souvenir Sheet
1023	A147	$5 multicolored	5.25	5.25

CAPEX '87 A148

Mushrooms.

1987, June 15 — Litho. — Perf. 14
1024	A148	45c Cantharellus cinnabarinus	.85	.85
1025	A148	60c Boletellus cubensis	1.25	1.25
1026	A148	$2 Eccilia cystiophorus	4.50	4.50
1027	A148	$3 Xerocomus guadelupae	6.75	6.75
		Nos. 1024-1027 (4)	13.35	13.35

Souvenir Sheet
1028	A148	$5 Gymnopilus chrysopellus	12.00	12.00

A149

Discovery of America, 500th Anniv. (in 1992) — A150

Explorations of Christopher Columbus: 10c, Discovery of Dominica. 15c, Ships greeted by Carib Indians. 45c, Claiming New World for Spain. 60c, Wrecking of the Santa Maria. 90c, Fleet setting sail. $1, Sighting land. $3, Trading with the Indians. No. 1036, First settlement. No. 1037, Arrival of Second Fleet at Dominica, Nov. 3, 1493. No. 1038, Map of exploration of the Leeward Islands.

1987, July 27   *Perf. 15*

1029	A149	10c multicolored	.25	.25
1030	A149	15c multicolored	.25	.25
1031	A149	45c multicolored	.50	.50
1032	A149	60c multicolored	.65	.65
1033	A149	90c multicolored	1.00	1.00
1034	A149	$1 multicolored	1.10	1.10
1035	A149	$3 multicolored	3.25	3.25
1036	A149	$5 multicolored	5.50	5.50
		Nos. 1029-1036 (8)	12.50	12.50

Souvenir Sheets

1037	A150	$5 multicolored	4.50	4.50
1038	A150	$5 multicolored	4.50	4.50

For overprints see Nos. 1083-1084.

Transportation — A151

10c, Warrior, 1st iron-clad warship. 15c, Maglev-MLU 001, fastest passenger train. 25c, Clipper Flying Cloud, fastest NYC-San Francisco voyage, 1852. 35c, 1st elevated railway, NYC. 45c, Tom Thumb, 1st US passenger train locomotive. 60c, Joshua Slocum, 1st solo circumnavigation of the world in a sloop. 90c, Se-Land Commerce, fastest Pacific crossing. $1, 1st cable car, San Francisco. $3, Orient Express. $4, The North River Steamboat of Clermont, invented by Robert Fulton, 1st successful commercial steamboat.

1987   *Litho.*   *Perf. 14*

1039	A151	10c multicolored	.20	.20
1040	A151	15c multicolored	.20	.20
1041	A151	25c multi, vert.	.45	.45
1042	A151	35c multi, vert.	.55	.55
1043	A151	45c multicolored	.70	.70
1044	A151	60c multi, vert.	1.00	1.00
1045	A151	90c multi, vert.	1.40	1.40
1046	A151	$1 multicolored	1.75	1.75
1047	A151	$3 multicolored	4.75	4.75
1048	A151	$4 multicolored	6.00	6.00
		Nos. 1039-1048 (10)	17.00	17.00

Issued: 10c, 15c, 45c, 60c, $4, 9/28; others 8/1.

For overprints see Nos. 1081-1082.

Christmas — A152

Paintings (details): 20c, Virgin and Child with St. Anne, by Durer. 25c, The Virgin and Child, by Murillo. $2, Madonna and Child, by Vincenzo Foppa (c. 1427-1516). $4, Madonna and Child, by Paolo Veronese (1528-1588). $5, Angel of the Annunciation, anonymous.

1987, Nov. 16

1049	A152	20c multicolored	.30	.30
1050	A152	25c multicolored	.30	.30
1051	A152	$2 multicolored	2.40	2.40
1052	A152	$4 multicolored	4.75	4.75
		Nos. 1049-1052 (4)	7.75	7.75

Souvenir Sheet

1053	A152	$5 multicolored	4.50	4.50

Mickey Mouse, 60th Anniv. A153

Disney theme parks and trains: 20c, People Mover, Disney World. 25c, Horse-drawn Trolley, Disneyland. 45c, Roger E. Broggie, Disney World. 60c, Big Thunder Mountain, Disneyland. 90c, Walter E. Disney, Disneyland. $1, Monorail, Disney World. $3, Casey Jr. from Dumbo. $4, Lilly Belle, Disney World. No. 1062, Rainbow Caverns Mine Train, Disneyland, horiz. No. 1063, Toy train from movie Out of Scale, horiz.

1987, Dec. 7   *Litho.*   *Perf. 14*

1054	A153	20c multicolored	.45	.45
1055	A153	25c multicolored	.45	.45
1056	A153	45c multicolored	.80	.80
1057	A153	60c multicolored	1.10	1.10
1058	A153	90c multicolored	1.40	1.40
1059	A153	$1 multicolored	1.75	1.75
1060	A153	$3 multicolored	5.00	5.00
1061	A153	$4 multicolored	6.75	6.75
		Nos. 1054-1061 (8)	17.70	17.70

Souvenir Sheets

1062	A153	$5 multicolored	4.75	4.75
1063	A153	$5 multicolored	4.75	4.75

40th Wedding Anniv. of Queen Elizabeth II and Prince Philip — A154

1988 Summer Olympics, Seoul — A155

1988, Feb. 15   *Litho.*   *Perf. 14*

1064	A154	45c Couple, wedding party, 1947	.55	.55
1065	A154	60c Elizabeth, Charles, c. 1952	.70	.70
1066	A154	$1 Royal Family, c. 1952	1.25	1.25
1067	A154	$3 Queen with tiara, c. 1960	3.25	3.25
		Nos. 1064-1067 (4)	5.75	5.75

Souvenir Sheet

1068	A154	$5 Elizabeth, 1947	4.00	4.00

1988, Mar. 15

1069	A155	45c Kayaking	.75	.75
1070	A155	60c Tae kwon-do	1.00	1.00
1071	A155	$1 Diving	1.75	1.75
1072	A155	$3 Parallel bars	4.50	4.50
		Nos. 1069-1072 (4)	8.00	8.00

Souvenir Sheet

1073	A155	$5 Soccer	4.00	4.00

For overprints see Nos. 1151-1155.

Reunion '88 Tourism Campaign A156

1988, Apr. 13   *Litho.*   *Perf. 15*

1074	A156	10c Carib Indian, vert.	.20	.20
1075	A156	25c Mountainous interior	.20	.20
1076	A156	35c Indian River, vert.	.25	.25
1077	A156	60c Belaire dancer, vert.	.40	.40
1078	A156	90c The Boiling Lake, vert.	.60	.60
1079	A156	$3 Coral reef	2.00	2.00
		Nos. 1074-1079 (6)	3.65	3.65

Souvenir Sheet

1080	A156	$5 Belaire dancer, diff., vert.	3.50	3.50

Independence, 10th anniv.

Nos. 1046-1047, 1037-1038 Ovptd. for Philatelic Exhibitions in Black

a

b

c

d

1988, June 1   *Litho.*   *Perf. 14*

1081	A151(a)	$1 multi	1.25	1.25
1082	A151(b)	$3 multi	4.50	4.50

Souvenir Sheets
Perf. 15

1083	A150(c)	$5 multi	4.75	4.75
1084	A150(d)	$5 multi	4.75	4.75

Miniature Sheet

Rain Forest Flora and Fauna — A157

Designs: a, White-tailed tropicbirds. b, Blue-throated euphonia. c, Smooth-billed ani. d, Scaly-breasted thrasher. e, Purple-throated carib. f, Southern daggertail and Clench's hairstreak. g, Trembler. h, Imperial parrot. i, Mangrove cuckoo. j, Hercules beetle. k, Orion. l, Red-necked parrot. m, Tillandsia. n, Polystacha luteola and bananaquit. o, False chameleon. p, Iguana. q, Hypolimnas. r, Green-throated carib. s, Heliconia. t, Agouti.

1988, July 25   *Perf. 14½*

1085		Sheet of 20	17.50	17.50
	a.-t.	A157 45c any single	.75	.75

Intl. Fund for Agricultural Development (IFAD), 10th Anniv. — A158

1988, Sept. 5   *Litho.*   *Perf. 14*

1086	A158	45c Hen house	.65	.65
1087	A158	60c Pig farm	.80	.80
1088	A158	90c Cattle	1.25	1.25
1089	A158	$3 Black-belly sheep	4.25	4.25
		Nos. 1086-1089 (4)	6.95	6.95

Souvenir Sheet

1090	A158	$5 Mixed crops, vert.	4.50	4.50

Entertainers A159

1988, Sept. 8

1091	A159	10c Gary Cooper	.20	.20
1092	A159	35c Josephine Baker	.40	.40
1093	A159	45c Maurice Chevalier	.45	.45
1094	A159	60c James Cagney	.55	.55
1095	A159	$1 Clark Gable	.95	.95
1096	A159	$2 Louis Armstrong	2.00	2.00
1097	A159	$3 Liberace	2.75	2.75
1098	A159	$4 Spencer Tracy	3.75	3.75
		Nos. 1091-1098 (8)	11.05	11.05

Souvenir Sheets

1099	A159	$5 Elvis Presley	5.00	5.00
1100	A159	$5 Humphrey Bogart	5.00	5.00

Flowering Trees and Shrubs A160

1988, Sept. 29   *Litho.*   *Perf. 14*

1101	A160	15c Sapodilla	.20	.20
1102	A160	20c Tangerine	.20	.20
1103	A160	25c Avocado pear	.20	.20
1104	A160	45c Amherstia	.30	.30
1105	A160	90c Lipstick tree	.60	.60
1106	A160	$1 Cannonball tree	.65	.65
1107	A160	$3 Saman	2.10	2.10
1108	A160	$4 Pineapple	2.75	2.75
		Nos. 1101-1108 (8)	7.00	7.00

Souvenir Sheets

1109	A160	$5 Lignum vitae	4.25	4.25
1110	A160	$5 Sea grape	4.25	4.25

Paintings by Titian A161

Designs: 25c, Jacopo Strada, c. 1567. 35c, Titian's Daughter Lavinia, c. 1565. 45c, Andrea Navagero, c. 1515. 60c, Judith with Head of Holoferenes, c. 1570. $1, Emilia di Spilimbergo, c. 1560. $2, Martyrdom of St. Lawrence, c. 1548. $3, Salome With the Head of St. John the Baptist, 1560. $4, St. John the

Baptist, c. 1540. No. 1119, Self-portrait, c. 1555. No. 1120, Sisyphus, 1549.

1988, Oct. 10   Litho.   Perf. 13½x14
1111 A161 25c multicolored .20 .20
1112 A161 35c multicolored .30 .30
1113 A161 45c multicolored .45 .45
1114 A161 60c multicolored .55 .55
1115 A161 $1 multicolored 1.50 1.50
1116 A161 $2 multicolored 1.75 1.75
1117 A161 $3 multicolored 2.75 2.75
1118 A161 $4 multicolored 3.50 3.50
Nos. 1111-1118 (8) 11.00 11.00
Souvenir Sheets
1119 A161 $5 multicolored 4.00 4.00
1120 A161 $5 multicolored 4.00 4.00

A162   A163

1988, Oct. 31   Litho.   Perf. 14
1121 A162 20c Imperial parrot .40 .40
1122 A162 45c No. 1, landscape .60 .60
1123 A162 $2 No. 602, water-
fall 2.50 2.50
1124 A162 $3 Carib wood 4.00 4.00
Nos. 1121-1124 (4) 7.50 7.50
Souvenir Sheet
1125 A162 $5 Natl. band per-
forming 4.50 4.50

Independence, 10th Anniv. Nos. 1122-1123 horiz.

1988, Nov. 22
1126 A163 20c With Jackie .20 .20
1127 A163 25c Sailing Vicuna .20 .20
1128 A163 $2 Walking in Hyan-
nis Port 1.10 1.10
1129 A163 $4 Berlin Wall
speech 2.75 2.75
Nos. 1126-1129 (4) 4.25 4.25
Souvenir Sheet
1130 A163 $5 Portrait 4.25 4.25

John F. Kennedy. #1126-1128 horiz.

Miniature Sheet

Christmas, Mickey Mouse 60th Anniv. — A164

#1131: a, Huey, Dewey, Louie. b, Daisy Duck. c, Winnie-the-Pooh. d, Goofy. e, Donald Duck. f, Mickey Mouse. g, Minnie Mouse. h, Chip-n-Dale.
#1132, Mickey, Morty and Ferdy. #1133, Characters visiting shopping mall Santa.

1988, Dec. 1   Perf. 13½x14
1131 A164 Sheet of 8 7.75 7.75
a.-h. 60c any single .95 .95
Souvenir Sheets
1132 A164 $6 multi 6.00 6.00
1133 A164 $6 multi, horiz. 6.00 6.00

UN Declaration of Human Rights, 40th Anniv. — A165

Designs: $3, Flag of Sweden and Raoul Wallenberg, who helped save 100,000 Jews in Budapest from deportation to Nazi concentration camps. $5, Human Rights Flame.

1988, Dec. 12   Perf. 14
1134 A165 $3 multicolored 3.50 3.50
Souvenir Sheet
1135 A165 $5 multi, vert. 4.75 4.75

Coastal Game Fish A166

1988, Dec. 22   Litho.   Perf. 14
1136 A166 10c Greater
amberjack .30 .30
1137 A166 15c Blue marlin .30 .30
1138 A166 35c Cobia .50 .50
1139 A166 45c Dolphin .55 .55
1140 A166 60c Cero .75 .75
1141 A166 90c Mahogany
snapper 1.10 1.10
1142 A166 $3 Yellowfin tuna 3.75 3.75
1143 A166 $4 Rainbow par-
rotfish 5.25 5.25
Nos. 1136-1143 (8) 12.50 12.50
Souvenir Sheets
1144 A166 $5 Manta ray 6.00 6.00
1145 A166 $5 Tarpon 6.00 6.00

Caribbean Insects and Reptiles A167

1988, Dec. 29
1146 A167 10c Leatherback
turtle .30 .30
1147 A167 25c Monarch butterfly .70 .70
1148 A167 60c Green anole 1.75 1.75
1149 A167 $3 Praying mantis 9.25 9.25
Nos. 1146-1149 (4) 12.00 12.00
Souvenir Sheet
1150 A167 $5 Hercules bee-
tle 6.25 6.25

Nos. 1069-1072 Ovptd. for Olympic Winners

a. "Men's c-1,500m O. Heukrodt DDR"
b. "Women's Flyweight N.Y. Choo S. Korea"
c. "Women's Platform Y. Xu China"
d. "V. Artemov USSR"
e. "USSR defeated Brazil 3-2 on penalty kicks after a 1-1 tie"

1989, Mar. 20   Litho.   Perf. 14
1151 A155(a) 45c multi .40 .40
1152 A155(b) 60c multi .50 .50
1153 A155(c) $1 multi .95 .95
1154 A155(d) $3 multi 2.40 2.40
Nos. 1151-1154 (4) 4.25 4.25
Souvenir Sheet
1155 A155(e) $5 multi 4.50 4.50

Pre-Columbian Societies and Their Customs — A168

UPAE and discovery of America anniv. emblems and: 20c, Carib Indians canoeing. 35c, Bow hunting. $1, Canoe making. $3, Shield wrestling. $6, Dancing.

1989, May 8   Litho.   Perf. 14
1156 A168 20c multicolored .30 .30
1157 A168 35c multicolored .45 .45
1158 A168 $1 multicolored 1.25 1.25
1159 A168 $3 multicolored 3.50 3.50
Nos. 1156-1159 (4) 5.50 5.50
Souvenir Sheet
1160 A168 $6 multicolored 5.50 5.50
Discovery of America 500th anniv. (in 1992).

Paintings by Yokoyama Taikan (1868-1958) A169

Designs: 10c, Lao-tzu. 20c, Red Maple Leaves (panels 1-2). 45c, King Wen Learns a Lesson from His Cook. 60c, Red Maple Leaves (panels 3-4). $1, Wild Flowers. $2, Red Maple Leaves (panels 5-6). $3, Red Maple Leaves (panels 7-8). $4, The Indian Ceremony of Floating Lamps on the River. No. 1169, Innocence. No. 1170, Red Maple Leaves (4 panels).

1989, Aug. 8   Litho.   Perf. 13½x14
1161 A169 10c multicolored .20 .20
1162 A169 20c multicolored .20 .20
1163 A169 45c multicolored .40 .40
1164 A169 60c multicolored .55 .55
1165 A169 $1 multicolored .90 .90
1166 A169 $2 multicolored 1.60 1.60
1167 A169 $3 multicolored 2.40 2.40
1168 A169 $4 multicolored 3.25 3.25
Nos. 1161-1168 (8) 9.50 9.50
Souvenir Sheets
1169 A169 $5 multicolored 4.25 4.25
1170 A169 $5 multicolored 4.25 4.25

Hirohito (1901-89) and enthronement of Akihito as emperor of Japan.

PHILEXFRANCE '89, July 7-17, Paris — A170

Designs: 10c, Map of Dominica with French place names, 1766. 35c, French coin, 1688. $1, French ship, 1720. $4, Introduction of coffee to Dominica by the French, 1772. $5, Text.

1989, July 17   Litho.   Perf. 14
1171 A170 10c multi, vert. .20 .20
1172 A170 35c shown .55 .55
1173 A170 $1 multicolored 1.25 1.25
1174 A170 $4 multicolored 4.50 4.50
Nos. 1171-1174 (4) 6.50 6.50
Souvenir Sheet
1175 A170 $5 multicolored 6.25 6.25

Butterflies A171

Designs: 10c, Homerus swallowtail. 15c, Morpho peleides. 25c, Julia. 35c, Gundlach's swallowtail. 60c, Monarch. $1, Gulf fritillary. $3, Red-splashed sulphur. $5, Papilio andraemon. No. 1184, Heliconius doris, Adelpha cytherea, Calliona argenissa, Eurema proterpia. No. 1185, Adelpha iphicla, Dismorphia spio, Lucinia sida.

1989, Sept. 11   Litho.   Perf. 14
1176 A171 10c multicolored .20 .20
1177 A171 15c multicolored .20 .20
1178 A171 25c multicolored .45 .45
1179 A171 35c multicolored .65 .65
1180 A171 60c multicolored 1.10 1.10
1181 A171 $1 multicolored 1.75 1.75
1182 A171 $3 multicolored 4.50 4.50
1183 A171 $5 multicolored 8.00 8.00
Nos. 1176-1183 (8) 16.85 16.85
Souvenir Sheets
1184 A171 $6 multicolored 7.00 7.00
1185 A171 $6 multicolored 7.00 7.00

Misspellings: No. 1181, "Frittillary"; No. 1182, "Sulper."

Orchids — A172

1989, Sept. 28
1186 A172 10c Oncidium pusil-
lum .20 .20
1187 A172 35c Epidendrum
cochleata .55 .55
1188 A172 45c Epidendrum
ciliare .60 .60
1189 A172 60c Cyrtopodium
andersonii .90 .90
1190 A172 $1 Habenaria
pauciflora 1.50 1.50
1191 A172 $2 Maxillaria alba 3.00 3.00
1192 A172 $3 Selenipedium
palmifolium 4.50 4.50
1193 A172 $4 Brassavola
cucullata 6.00 6.00
Nos. 1186-1193 (8) 17.25 17.25
Souvenir Sheets
1194 A172 $5 Oncidium
lanceanum 7.00 7.00
1195 A172 $5 Comparettia
falcata 7.00 7.00

1st Moon Landing, 20th Anniv. A173

1989, Oct. 31   Litho.   Perf. 14
1196 A173 10c Columbia in lu-
nar orbit .20 .20
1197 A173 60c Aldrin de-
scending lad-
der .85 .85
1198 A173 $2 Aldrin, Sea of
Tranquillity 2.75 2.75
1199 A173 $3 Flag raising 4.00 4.00
Nos. 1196-1199 (4) 7.80 7.80
Souvenir Sheet
1200 A173 $6 Liftoff 8.00 8.00

Souvenir Sheets

A174

1990 World Cup Soccer Championships, Italy — A175

Past championship match scenes, flags and soccer ball: a, Brazil vs. Italy, Mexico, 1970. b, England vs. West Germany, England, 1966. c, West Germany vs. Netherlands, West Germany, 1974. d, Italy vs. West Germany, Spain, 1982.

1989, Nov. 7   Perf. 14
1201 A174 Sheet of 4 9.50 9.50
a.-d. $1 any single 2.25 2.25
Perf. 14
1202 A175 $6 shown 7.00 7.00

Souvenir Sheet

The Capitol, Washington, DC — A176

1989, Nov. 17   Litho.   Perf. 14
1203 A176 $4 multicolored   4.50 4.50
World Stamp Expo '89.

Miniature Sheets

American Presidency, 200th
Anniv. — A177

US presidents, historic events and monuments.

No. 1204: a, Washington, 1st inauguration. b, John Adams, presidential mansion, 1800. c, Jefferson, Graff House in Philadelphia, excerpt from the 1st draft of the Declaration of Independence. d, Madison, USS *Constitution* at the defeat of HMS *Guerriere*, 1812. e, Monroe, freed slaves settle Liberia, 1822. f, John Quincy Adams, opening of the Erie Canal, 1825.

No. 1205: a, Fillmore, Commodore Perry laying groundwork for US trade agreement with Japan. b, Pierce, Jefferson Davis and San Xavier del Bac mission, Tucson, AZ, Gadsden Purchase, 1853. c, Buchanan, Pony Express stamp, Buffalo Bill Cody as express rider. d, Lincoln, UPU emblem, Intl. Postal Congress, Paris, 1863. e, Andrew Johnson, polar bear, purchase of Alaska from Russia, 1867. f, Grant, 1st transcontinental railway link, Promontory Point, Utah, 1869.

No. 1206: a, Theodore Roosevelt, construction of the Panama Canal, 1904. b, Taft, Adm. Peary becomes 1st man to reach the North Pole, 1909. c, Wilson, US #C3, cancel commemorating 1st scheduled airmail service, 1918. d, Harding, airship USS *Shenandoah* at Lakehurst, NJ. e, Coolidge, Lindbergh's solo transatlantic flight, 1927. f, Mt. Rushmore, by Gutzon Borglum, 1927.

No. 1207: a, Lyndon B. Johnson, space exploration. b, Nixon visiting PRChina, 1971. c, Ford, tall ship in NY Harbor for Operation Sail, 1976, US bicentennial celebrations. d, Carter, Sadat of Egypt and Begin of Israel during the Camp David Accords, 1979. e, Reagan, European Space Agency emblem, flags and *Columbia* space shuttle. f, Bush, Grumman Avenger bomber he piloted during WWII.

1989, Nov. 17   Perf. 14
1204   Sheet of 6   6.00 6.00
 a.-f. A177 60c any single   .95 .95
1205   Sheet of 6   6.00 6.00
 a.-f. A177 60c any single   .95 .95
1206   Sheet of 6   6.00 6.00
 a.-f. A177 60c any single   .95 .95
1207   Sheet of 6   6.00 6.00
 a.-f. A177 60c any single   .95 .95

Mickey Mouse as a Hollywood
Star — A178

Walt Disney characters: 20c, Reading script. 35c, Television interview. 45c, Named a star in tabloid headline. 60c, Signing autographs. $1, In dressing room, holding fans at bay. $2, Riding in limousine. $3, With Minnie in the limelight. $4, Accepting award. No. 1216, Giving interview during celebrity tennis tournament. No. 1217, Footprint impression in cement outside theater.

1989, Nov. 30   Litho.   Perf. 14x13½
1208 A178 20c multicolored   .35 .35
1209 A178 35c multicolored   .50 .50
1210 A178 45c multicolored   .60 .60
1211 A178 60c multicolored   .80 .80
1212 A178 $1 multicolored   1.40 1.40
1213 A178 $2 multicolored   2.75 2.75
1214 A178 $3 multicolored   4.00 4.00
1215 A178 $4 multicolored   5.25 5.25
  Nos. 1208-1215 (8)   15.65 15.65

Souvenir Sheets
1216 A178 $5 multicolored   6.75 6.75
1217 A178 $5 multicolored   6.75 6.75

Christmas — A179

Religious paintings by Botticelli: 20c, *Madonna in Glory with Seraphim.* 25c, *The Annunciation.* 35c, *Madonna of the Pomegranate.* 45c, *Madonna of the Rose Garden.* 60c, *Madonna of the Book.* $1, *Madonna and Child Under a Baldachin with Three Angels.* $4, *Madonna and Child with Angels.* No. 1225, *Bardi Madonna.* No. 1226, *The Mystic Nativity.* No. 1227, *The Adoration of the Magi.*

1989, Dec. 4   Perf. 14
1218 A179 20c multicolored   .35 .35
1219 A179 25c multicolored   .35 .35
1220 A179 35c multicolored   .55 .55
1221 A179 45c multicolored   .65 .65
1222 A179 60c multicolored   .85 .85
1223 A179 $1 multicolored   1.25 1.25
1224 A179 $4 multicolored   5.00 5.00
1225 A179 $5 multicolored   6.00 6.00
  Nos. 1218-1225 (8)   15.00 15.00

Souvenir Sheets
1226 A179 $5 multicolored   6.00 6.00
1227 A179 $5 multicolored   6.00 6.00

Nehru — A180   Girl
                    Guides — A181

1989, Dec. 27   Litho.   Perf. 14
1228 A180 60c shown   2.40 2.40

Souvenir Sheet
1229 A180 $5 Parliament
           House, New
           Delhi, horiz.   7.50 7.50

Jawaharlal Nehru (1889-1964), 1st prime minister of independent India.

1989, Dec. 29

Guide movement in Dominica, 60th anniv.: 60c, Lady Baden-Powell and Agatha Robinson, former Guide leader on Dominica. $5, Dorris Stockmann, chairman of the world committee of the World Assoc. of Girl Guides and Girl Scouts, and Judith Pestaina, chief commissioner of the Dominica Girl Guides Assoc., horiz.

1230 A181 60c multicolored   1.50 1.50

Souvenir Sheet
1231 A181 $5 multi, horiz.   6.50 6.50

Miniature Sheet

Marine
Life
A182

Designs: a, Cocoa damselfish. b, Stinging jellyfish. c, Dolphin. d, Queen angelfish. e, French angelfish. f, Blue striped grunt. g, Pork

---

fish. h, Hammerhead shark. i, Spadefish. j, Great barracuda. k, Stingray. l, Black grunt. m, Two-spotted butterflyfish. n, Dog snapper. o, Southern puffer. p, Four-eyed butterflyfish. q, Lane snapper. r, Green moray.

1990   Litho.   Perf. 14
1232   Sheet of 18   11.00 11.00
 a.-r. A182 45c any single   .55 .55

Penny Black,
150th Anniv.
A183

Stamp World London '90: 50c, Post Office accelerator, 1830. 60c, $4, No. 1239, London skyline, 1830. $1, Mailcoach. 90c, Railway post car, 1838. $3, Center cycle, 1883. No. 1240, Mail truck, 1899.

1990, May 3   Litho.   Perf. 13½
1233 A183 45c green & black   .45 .45
1234 A183 50c blk & slate blue .55 .55
1235 A183 60c dk blue & blk   .60 .60
1236 A183 90c black & green   .90 .90
1237 A183 $3 blk & dk bl vio 3.50 3.50
1238 A183 $4 dk bl vio & blk 4.50 4.50
  Nos. 1233-1238 (6)   10.50 10.50

Souvenir Sheet
1239 A183 $5 beige & black   5.00 5.00
1240 A183 $5 gray & red brn 5.00 5.00

A184   A185

Birds: 10c, Blue-headed hummingbird. 20c, Black-capped petrel. 45c, Red-necked parrot. 60c, Black swift. $1, Troupial. $2, Brown noddy. $4, Lesser Antillean pewee. $5, Little blue heron. No. 1249, House wren. No. 1250, Imperial parrot.

1990, July 16   Litho.   Perf. 14
1241 A184 10c multicolored   .45 .45
1242 A184 20c multicolored   .60 .60
1243 A184 45c multicolored   .90 .90
1244 A184 60c multicolored   1.10 1.10
1245 A184 $1 multicolored   2.00 2.00
1246 A184 $2 multicolored   3.00 3.00
1247 A184 $4 multicolored   4.75 4.75
1248 A184 $5 multicolored   5.25 5.25
  Nos. 1241-1248 (8)   18.05 18.05

Souvenir Sheets
1249 A184 $6 multicolored   7.75 7.75
1250 A184 $6 multicolored   7.75 7.75

1990, July 19

Shells: 10c, Reticulated cowrie-helmet. 20c, West Indian chank. 35c, West Indian fighting conch. 60c, True tulip. $1, Sunrise tellin. $2, Crown cone. $3, Common dove shell. $4, Atlantic fig shell. No. 1259, Giant tun. No. 1260, King helmet.

1251 A185 10c multicolored   .45 .45
1252 A185 20c multicolored   .60 .60
1253 A185 35c multicolored   .75 .75
1254 A185 60c multicolored   1.10 1.10
1255 A185 $1 multicolored   1.50 1.50
1256 A185 $2 multicolored   2.75 2.75
1257 A185 $3 multicolored   3.50 3.50
1258 A185 $4 multicolored   4.00 4.00
  Nos. 1251-1258 (8)   14.65 14.65

Souvenir Sheets
1259 A185 $5 multicolored   5.00 5.00
1260 A185 $5 multicolored   5.00 5.00

A186   A187

Queen Mother, 90th Birthday: various photos.

1990, Sept. 10
1261 A186 20c multicolored   .30 .30
1262 A186 45c multicolored   .50 .50
1263 A186 60c multicolored   .70 .70
1264 A186 $3 multicolored   3.00 3.00
  Nos. 1261-1264 (4)   4.50 4.50

Souvenir Sheet
1265 A186 $5 multicolored   4.00 4.00

1990, Nov. 5   Litho.   Perf. 14
1266 A187 45c Men's singles,
           tennis   .95 .95
1267 A187 60c Men's foil fencing 1.40 1.40
1268 A187 $2 100m freestyle
           swimming   2.75 2.75
1269 A187 $3 Star class
           yachting   4.25 4.25
  Nos. 1266-1269 (4)   9.35 9.35

Souvenir Sheet
1270 A187 $5 Coxless pairs,
           rowing   8.00 8.00

1992 Summer Olympics, Barcelona.

Christmas
A188

Walt Disney characters on carousel animals: 10c, Mickey, frog. 15c, Huey, Dewey & Louie, white elephant. 25c, Donald, polar bear. 45c, Goofy, goat. $1, Donald, giraffe. $2, Daisy, stork. $4, Goofy, lion. $5, Daisy, horse. No. 1279, Donald, swan chariot, horiz. No. 1280, Mickey, Minnie & Goofy, griffin chariot.

1990, Dec. 13   Perf. 13½x14
1271 A188 10c multicolored   .20 .20
1272 A188 15c multicolored   .20 .20
1273 A188 25c multicolored   .35 .35
1274 A188 45c multicolored   .65 .65
1275 A188 $1 multicolored   1.25 1.25
1276 A188 $2 multicolored   2.40 2.40
1277 A188 $4 multicolored   4.75 4.75
1278 A188 $5 multicolored   6.00 6.00
  Nos. 1271-1278 (8)   15.80 15.80

Souvenir Sheets
                       Perf. 14x13½
1279 A188 $6 multicolored   8.00 8.00
1280 A188 $6 multicolored   8.00 8.00

World Cup Soccer Championships,
Italy — A189

Players and coaches from participating countries.

1990, Dec. 28   Litho.   Perf. 14
1281 A189 15c England   .40 .40
1282 A189 45c Brazil   .60 .60
1283 A189 60c West Germany   1.00 1.00
1284 A189 $4 Austria   5.75 5.75
  Nos. 1281-1284 (4)   7.75 7.75

Souvenir Sheets
1285 A189 $6 Ireland, vert. 5.75 5.75
1286 A189 $6 USSR, vert.   5.75 5.75

Cog Trains of Switzerland — A190

Designs: 10c, Glion-Roches de Naye, 1890. 35c, Electric cog rail car ascending Mt. Pilatus. 45c, Cog railway to Schynige Platte, view of Eiger, Monch and Jungfrau Mountains. 60c, Furka-Oberalp train on Bugnli Viaduct, vert. $1, 1910 Jungfraubahn Cog Railway, Jungfrau Mountain, 1910. $2, Testing Swiss rail cars built for Pike's Peak on Arth-Rigibahn, 1963. $4, Brienz-Rothorn Bahn, 1991. $5, Private 1870 Rigi-Scheideck Hotel post stamp, 1890 Arth-Rigi Railway Engine. No. 1295, Sherlock Holmes watching Brunigline train descending from Brunig Pass. No. 1296, Switzerland #738 and first passenger train to ascend Mt. Rigi, 1871.

1991, Mar. 26   Litho.   Perf. 14

1287	A190	10c multicolored	.40	.40
1288	A190	35c multicolored	.50	.50
1289	A190	45c multicolored	.55	.55
1290	A190	60c multicolored	.70	.70
1291	A190	$1 multicolored	1.25	1.25
1292	A190	$2 multicolored	2.40	2.40
1293	A190	$4 multicolored	5.00	5.00
1294	A190	$5 multicolored	6.25	6.25
		Nos. 1287-1294 (8)	17.05	17.05

Souvenir Sheets
Perf. 13½

| 1295 | A190 | $6 multicolored | 7.50 | 7.50 |
| 1296 | A190 | $6 multicolored | 7.50 | 7.50 |

Nos. 1295-1296 each contain one 50x37mm stamp.

Voyages of Discovery A191

Explorer's ships: 10c, Gil Eannes, 1433-1434. 25c, Alfonso Gonclaves Baldaya, 1436. 45c, Bartolomeu Dias, 1487. 60c, Vasco da Gama, 1497-1499. $1, Vallarte the Dane. $2, Aloisio Cadamosto, 1456-1458. $4, Diogo Gomes, 1457. $5, Diogo Cao, 1482-1485.

1991, Apr. 8   Litho.   Perf. 14

1297	A191	10c multicolored	.30	.30
1298	A191	25c multicolored	.45	.45
1299	A191	45c multicolored	.60	.60
1300	A191	60c multicolored	.75	.75
1301	A191	$1 multicolored	1.10	1.10
1302	A191	$2 multicolored	1.90	1.90
1303	A191	$4 multicolored	3.75	3.75
1304	A191	$5 multicolored	4.50	4.50
		Nos. 1297-1304 (8)	13.35	13.35

Souvenir Sheets

| 1305 | A191 | $6 Blue and yellow macaw | 6.00 | 6.00 |
| 1306 | A191 | $6 Red and yellow macaw | 6.00 | 6.00 |

Discovery of America, 500th anniv. (in 1992).

Japanese Costumes — A192

Walt Disney characters wearing Japanese costumes: 10c, Donald as soldier. 15c, Mickey as Kabuki actor. 25c, Mickey, Minnie in traditional wedding clothes. 45c, Daisy as Geisha girl, vert. $1, Mickey in sokutai dress of high government official, vert. $2, Goofy as mino farmer, vert. $4, Pete as shogun, vert. $5, Donald as warlord. No. 1315, Mickey, as Noh player, vert. No. 1316, Goofy as Kabubei-Jishi street performer, vert.

1991, May 22   Litho.   Perf. 14

1307	A192	10c multicolored	.25	.25
1308	A192	15c multicolored	.25	.25
1309	A192	25c multicolored	.40	.40
1310	A192	45c multicolored	.70	.70
1311	A192	$1 multicolored	1.40	1.40
1312	A192	$2 multicolored	3.00	3.00
1313	A192	$4 multicolored	5.50	5.50
1314	A192	$5 multicolored	7.25	7.25
		Nos. 1307-1314 (8)	18.75	18.75

Souvenir Sheets

| 1315 | A192 | $6 multicolored | 8.50 | 8.50 |
| 1316 | A192 | $6 multicolored | 8.50 | 8.50 |

Phila Nippon '91.

Mushrooms A193

1991, June 3   Litho.   Perf. 14

1318	A193	10c Horn of plenty	.20	.20
1319	A193	15c Shaggy mane	.30	.30
1320	A193	45c Yellow morel	.40	.40
1321	A193	60c Chanterelle	.60	.60
1322	A193	$1 Blewit	1.00	1.00
1323	A193	$2 Slippery jack	2.10	2.10
1324	A193	$4 Emetic russula	4.25	4.25
1325	A193	$5 Honey mushroom	5.00	5.00
		Nos. 1318-1325 (8)	13.85	13.85

Souvenir Sheets

| 1326 | A193 | $6 Beefsteak polypore | 6.00 | 6.00 |
| 1327 | A193 | $6 Voluminous-latex milky | 6.00 | 6.00 |

Royal Family Birthday, Anniversary
Common Design Type

1991, June 17   Litho.   Perf. 14

1328	CD347	10c multicolored	.50	.50
1329	CD347	15c multicolored	.40	.40
1330	CD347	40c multicolored	.55	.55
1331	CD347	60c multicolored	1.10	1.10
1332	CD347	$1 multicolored	1.40	1.40
1333	CD347	$2 multicolored	3.75	3.75
1334	CD347	$4 multicolored	5.75	5.75
1335	CD347	$5 multicolored	9.75	9.75
		Nos. 1328-1335 (8)	23.20	23.20

Souvenir Sheets

| 1336 | CD347 | $5 Elizabeth, Philip | 5.00 | 5.00 |
| 1337 | CD347 | $5 Charles, Diana, sons | 6.50 | 6.50 |

10c, 60c, $2, $4, No. 1336, Queen Elizabeth II, 65th birthday. Others, Charles and Diana, 10th wedding anniversary.

Vincent Van Gogh (1853-1890), Painter — A194

Paintings: 10c, Thatched Cottages. 25c, The House of Pere Eloi. 45c, The Midday Siesta. 60c, Portrait of a Young Peasant, vert. $1, Still Life: Vase with Irises Against a Yellow Background, vert. $2, Still Life Vase with Irises. $4, Blossoming Almond Tree. $5, Irises. No. 1346, A Meadow in the Mountains: Le Mas De Saint-Paul. No. 1347, Doctor Gachet's Garden in Auvers, vert.

1991, July 8   Litho.   Perf. 13½

1338	A194	10c multicolored	.30	.30
1339	A194	25c multicolored	.30	.30
1340	A194	45c multicolored	.55	.55
1341	A194	60c multicolored	.85	.85
1342	A194	$1 multicolored	1.25	1.25
1343	A194	$2 multicolored	2.75	2.75
1344	A194	$4 multicolored	5.00	5.00
1345	A194	$5 multicolored	6.00	6.00
		Nos. 1338-1345 (8)	17.00	17.00

Size: 101x75mm
Imperf

| 1346 | A194 | $6 multicolored | 6.50 | 6.50 |
| 1347 | A194 | $6 multicolored | 6.50 | 6.50 |

Intl. Literacy Year — A195

Scenes from Walt Disney's "The Little Mermaid": 10c, Ariel with Flounder and Sebastian. 25c, King Triton. 45c, Sebastian drums in "Kiss De Girl" concert. 60c, Flotsam and Jetsam taunt Ariel. $1, Scuttle, Flounder and Ariel. $2, Ariel and Flounder discover a book. $4, Prince Eric, dog Max, manservant Grimsby, and crew. $5, Ursula the sea witch. No. 1356, Ariel transformed into human being. No. 1357, Ariel and Prince Eric dancing in town, vert.

1991, Aug. 6   Litho.   Perf. 14

1348	A195	10c multicolored	.20	.20
1349	A195	25c multicolored	.35	.35
1350	A195	45c multicolored	.55	.55
1351	A195	60c multicolored	.80	.80
1352	A195	$1 multicolored	1.40	1.40
1353	A195	$2 multicolored	2.75	2.75
1354	A195	$4 multicolored	5.25	5.25
1355	A195	$5 multicolored	6.75	6.75
		Nos. 1348-1355 (8)	18.05	18.05

Souvenir Sheets

| 1356 | A195 | $6 multicolored | 6.75 | 6.75 |
| 1357 | A195 | $6 multicolored | 6.75 | 6.75 |

World Landmarks — A196

Designs: 10c, Empire State Building, US, vert. 25c, Kremlin, USSR. 45c, Buckingham Palace, United Kingdom. 60c, Eiffel Tower, France, vert. $1, Taj Mahal, India. $2, Sydney Opera House, Australia. $4, Colosseum, Italy. $5, Pyramids, Egypt. No. 1366, Galileo demonstrating laws of physics from Tower of Pisa, Italy. No. 1367, Great Wall of China and Emperor Shi Huang Ti.

1991, Aug. 12   Litho.   Perf. 14

1358	A196	10c multicolored	.20	.20
1359	A196	25c multicolored	.35	.35
1360	A196	45c multicolored	.55	.55
1361	A196	60c multicolored	.80	.80
1362	A196	$1 multicolored	1.40	1.40
1363	A196	$2 multicolored	2.75	2.75
1364	A196	$4 multicolored	5.25	5.25
1365	A196	$5 multicolored	6.75	6.75
		Nos. 1358-1365 (8)	18.05	18.05

Souvenir Sheets

| 1366 | A196 | $6 multicolored | 8.50 | 8.50 |
| 1367 | A196 | $6 multicolored | 8.50 | 8.50 |

Japanese Attack on Pearl Harbor, 50th Anniv. A197

Designs: 10c, 6:00am, First wave of Japanese planes leave carrier Akagi. 15c, 6:40am, Destroyer Ward and PBY attack midget submarine. 45c, 7:00am, Second wave of Japanese planes leave carriers. 60c, 7:48am, Japanese Zeros attack on Kaneohe Air Station. $1, 8:30am, Destroyers Breeze, Medusa and Curtiss sink midget submarine. $2, 8:45am, Damaged battleship Nevada sorties. $4, 8:10am, Battleship Arizona explodes, killing 1,177 men. $5, 9:45am, Japanese attack ends. No. 1376, 8:00am, Japanese fighters and bombers attack Hickam Air Base. No. 1377, 7:55am, Pearl Harbor attack begins.

1991, Sept. 2

1368	A197	10c multicolored	.20	.20
1369	A197	15c multicolored	.30	.30
1370	A197	45c multicolored	.40	.40
1371	A197	60c multicolored	.60	.60
1372	A197	$1 multicolored	1.00	1.00
1373	A197	$2 multicolored	2.10	2.10
1374	A197	$4 multicolored	4.00	4.00
1375	A197	$5 multicolored	5.00	5.00
		Nos. 1368-1375 (8)	13.60	13.60

Souvenir Sheets

| 1376 | A197 | $6 multicolored | 5.75 | 5.75 |
| 1377 | A197 | $6 multicolored | 5.75 | 5.75 |

Butterflies — A198   A199

Perf. 13½x13, 13½x14 (2c, 10c, 15c, 25c, 45c, 90c, $1, $20)

1991-93

1378	A198	1c Little yellow	.25	.25
1379	A198	2c Gulf fritillary	.25	.25
1380	A198	5c Monarch	.25	.25
1381	A198	10c Red rim	.25	.25
1382	A198	15c Flambeau	.25	.25
1383	A198	20c Large orange sulphur	.25	.25
1384	A198	25c Caribbean buckeye	.25	.25
1385	A198	35c Polydamas swallowtail	.30	.30
1386	A198	45c Cassius blue	.40	.40
1386A	A198	55c Great southern white	.50	.50
1387	A198	60c Godman's leaf	.55	.55
1387A	A198	65c Hanno blue	.65	.65
1388	A198	90c Mimic	.90	.90
1389	A198	$1 Long-tailed skipper	1.00	1.00
1389A	A198	$1.20 Orion	1.25	1.25
1390	A198	$2 Cloudless sulphur	2.10	2.10
1391	A198	$5 Painted lady	5.00	5.00
1391A	A198	$10 Southern daggertail	11.50	11.50
1391B	A198	$20 White peacock	21.00	21.00
		Nos. 1379-1391B (18)	46.65	46.65

Issued: 55c, 65c, $1.20, 1/11/93; others, 10/14/91.

1991, Nov. 1

| 1392 | A199 | 45c shown | 2.00 | 2.00 |

Souvenir Sheet

| 1393 | A199 | $5 blk & bl, horiz. | 6.25 | 6.25 |

Charles de Gaulle, birth cent.

Creole Week — A200   Credit Union, 40th Anniv. — A201

45c, Man in 18th cent. costume. 60c, Accordion player. $1, Dancers. $5, Stick fight c. 1785.

1991, Nov. 1   Perf. 14

1394	A200	45c multicolored	.70	.70
1395	A200	60c multicolored	1.00	1.00
1396	A200	$1 multicolored	1.75	1.75
		Nos. 1394-1396 (3)	3.45	3.45

Souvenir Sheet

| 1397 | A200 | $5 multicolored | 7.75 | 7.75 |

1991, Nov. 1

| 1398 | A201 | 10c black | .65 | .65 |
| 1399 | A201 | 60c Emblem, founder, horiz. | 1.60 | 1.60 |

Year of the Environment and Shelter — A202

15c, Keep the beaches clean. 60c, No. 1402, Amazona imperalis. No. 1403, Lagoon outlet.

1991, Nov. 18
1400	A202	15c multicolored	1.10	1.10
1401	A202	60c multicolored	2.40	2.40

Souvenir Sheets
1402	A202	$5 multicolored	7.50	7.50
1403	A202	$5 multicolored	7.50	7.50

Christmas A203

Paintings by Jan van Eyck: 10c, The Virgin Enthroned with Child (detail). 20c, The Madonna at the Fountain. 35c, The Virgin in a Church. 45c, The Madonna with Canon van der Paele. 60c, The Madonna with Canon van der Paele (detail). $1, The Madonna in an Interior. $3, The Annunciation. $5, The Annunciation, diff. No. 1412, The Madonna with Chancellor Rolin. No. 1413, Virgin and Child with Saints and Donor.

1991, Dec. 2 — **Perf. 12**
1404	A203	10c multicolored	.20	.20
1405	A203	20c multicolored	.35	.35
1406	A203	35c multicolored	.45	.45
1407	A203	45c multicolored	.55	.55
1408	A203	60c multicolored	.80	.80
1409	A203	$1 multicolored	1.40	1.40
1410	A203	$3 multicolored	4.00	4.00
1411	A203	$5 multicolored	6.75	6.75
		Nos. 1404-1411 (8)	14.50	14.50

Souvenir Sheets
Perf. 14x14½
1412	A203	$6 multicolored	6.75	6.75
1413	A203	$6 multicolored	6.75	6.75

Queen Elizabeth II's Accession to the Throne, 40th Anniv.
Common Design Type

1992, Feb. 6 — **Litho.** — **Perf. 14**
1414	CD348	10c multicolored	.20	.20
1415	CD348	15c multicolored	.20	.20
1416	CD348	$1 multicolored	.85	.85
1417	CD348	$5 multicolored	4.00	4.00
		Nos. 1414-1417 (4)	5.25	5.25

Souvenir Sheets
1418	CD348	$6 River scene	4.00	4.00
1419	CD348	$6 Seaside village	4.00	4.00

Botanical Gardens, Cent. — A204

Designs: 10c, Cricket match. 15c, Scenic entrance. 45c, Traveller's tree. 60c, Bamboo house. $1, Old pavilion. $2, Ficus benjamina. $4, Cricket ground. $5, Thirty-five steps. No. 1428, Fountain. No. 1429, Cricket masters.

1992, Mar. 30 — **Litho.** — **Perf. 14**
1420	A204	10c multicolored	.20	.20
1421	A204	15c multicolored	.20	.20
1422	A204	45c multicolored	.35	.35
1423	A204	60c multicolored	.55	.55
1424	A204	$1 multicolored	.95	.95
1425	A204	$2 multicolored	2.00	2.00
1426	A204	$4 multicolored	4.00	4.00
1427	A204	$5 multicolored	4.75	4.75
		Nos. 1420-1427 (8)	13.00	13.00

Souvenir Sheets
1428	A204	$6 multicolored	5.00	5.00
1429	A204	$6 multicolored	5.00	5.00

Spanish Art — A205

Paintings or details from paintings by Velazquez: 10c, Pope Innocent X. 15c, 45c The Forge of Vulcan (different details). 60c, Queen Mariana of Austria. $1, Pablo de Valladolid. $2, Sebastian de Morra. $3, Felipe IV (detail). $4, Felipe IV. No. 1438, Surrender of Breda. No. 1439, The Drunkards.

1992, May 4 — **Perf. 13**
1430	A205	10c multicolored	.20	.20
1431	A205	15c multicolored	.20	.20
1432	A205	45c multicolored	.45	.45
1433	A205	60c multicolored	.55	.55
1434	A205	$1 multicolored	.85	.85
1435	A205	$2 multicolored	1.75	1.75
1436	A205	$3 multicolored	2.75	2.75
1437	A205	$4 multicolored	3.75	3.75

Size: 120x95mm
Imperf
1438	A205	$6 multicolored	6.00	6.00
1439	A205	$6 multicolored	6.00	6.00
		Nos. 1430-1439 (10)	22.50	22.50

Granada '92.

Easter — A206

Paintings: 10c, The Supper at Emmaus, studio of Gerrit Van Honthorst. 15c, Christ before Caiaphas, by Van Honthorst, vert. 45c, The Taking of Christ, by Valentin de Boulogne. 60c, Pilate Washing his Hands, by Mattia Preti, vert. $1, The Last Supper (detail), by Master of the Reredos of The Chapel of the Church of S. Francisco D'Evora. $2, The Three Marys at the Tomb (detail), by Adolphe William Bouguereau, vert. $3, Denial of St. Peter, by Hendrik Terbrugghen, vert. $5, Doubting Thomas, by Bernardo Strozzi, vert. No. 1448, The Crucifixion (detail), by Mathias Grunewald, vert. No. 1449, The Resurrection (detail), by Caravaggio, vert.

1992 — **Perf. 14**
1440	A206	10c multicolored	.20	.20
1441	A206	15c multicolored	.20	.20
1442	A206	45c multicolored	.35	.35
1443	A206	60c multicolored	.55	.55
1444	A206	$1 multicolored	.95	.95
1445	A206	$2 multicolored	2.00	2.00
1446	A206	$3 multicolored	2.75	2.75
1447	A206	$4 multicolored	4.75	4.75
		Nos. 1440-1447 (8)	11.75	11.75

Souvenir Sheets
1448	A206	$6 multicolored	5.75	5.75
1449	A206	$6 multicolored	5.75	5.75

Columbus and New World Flora and Fauna — A207

1992, May 18
1450	A207	10c Hercules beetle	.20	.20
1451	A207	25c Crapaud frog	.25	.25
1452	A207	75c Parrot	.70	.70
1453	A207	$2 Anole	2.10	2.10
1454	A207	$4 Royal gramma	4.25	4.25
1455	A207	$5 Hibiscus	5.25	5.25
		Nos. 1450-1455 (6)	12.75	12.75

Souvenir Sheets
1456	A207	$6 Giant katydid	6.00	6.00
1457	A207	$6 Columbus' fleet	6.00	6.00

Nos. 1456-1457 are horiz.

Hummingbirds — A208

10c, Purple throated carib. 15c, Rufous breasted hermit. 45c, Puerto Rican emerald. 60c, Antillean mango. $1, Green throated carib. $2, Blue headed. $4, Eastern streamertail. $5, Antillean crested. #1466, Green mango. #1467, Vervain hummingbird.

1992, May 28
1458	A208	10c multicolored	.20	.20
1459	A208	15c multicolored	.20	.20
1460	A208	45c multicolored	.40	.40
1461	A208	60c multicolored	.60	.60
1462	A208	$1 multicolored	1.00	1.00
1463	A208	$2 multicolored	2.10	2.10
1464	A208	$4 multicolored	4.25	4.25
1465	A208	$5 multicolored	5.25	5.25
		Nos. 1458-1465 (8)	14.00	14.00

Souvenir Sheets
1466	A208	$6 multicolored	7.75	7.75
1467	A208	$6 multicolored	7.75	7.75

Genoa '92.

Dinosaurs A209

1992, June 23 — **Litho.** — **Perf. 14**
1468	A209	10c Camptosaurus	.20	.20
1469	A209	15c Edmontosaurus	.20	.20
1470	A209	25c Corythosaurus	.30	.30
1471	A209	60c Stegosaurus	.60	.60
1472	A209	$1 Torosaurus	1.00	1.00
1473	A209	$3 Euoplocephalus	3.25	3.25
1474	A209	$4 Tyrannosaurus	4.00	4.00
1475	A209	$5 Parasaurolophus	5.50	5.50
		Nos. 1468-1475 (8)	15.05	15.05

Souvenir Sheets
1476	A209	$6 like #1472	6.00	6.00
1477	A209	$6 like #1470	6.00	6.00

Marine Life A210

No. 1478: a, Copper sweeper (b). b, Sea wasp (c). c, Nassau grouper. d, Glasseye snapper, margate. e, Green moray (f). f, Reef squid. g, Octopus. h, Porkfish (g, i). i, Reef squirrelfish (h). j, Coral crab, flower coral. k, Red coral shrimp, sea star, pillar coral (l, n). l, Cubbyu, brain coral (o). m, Basket starfish, thick finger coral. n, Belted cardinal fish, boulder coral (k, m). o, Fire worm, crenelated fire coral.
No. 1479: a, Trumpetfish, blue chromis. b, Queen triggerfish. c, Hawksbill turtle. d, Sergeant major, rock beauty. e, Sharksucker. f, Lemon shark. g, Spotted trunkfish, bluehead. h, Blue tang, yellowtail damselfish. i, Queen angelfish, banded butterflyfish. j, Spotted seahorse, flower coral. k, Stoplight parrotfish, pillar coral. l, Smallmouth grunt, brain coral. m, Flamingo tongue, thick finger coral. n, Arrow crab, boulder coral. o, Sharknose goby, crenelated fire coral.
No. 1480, Harlequin bass. No. 1481, Flamefish.

1992, July 20 — **Litho.** — **Perf. 14**
1478	A210	65c Sheet of 15, #a.-o.	9.50	9.50
1479	A210	65c Sheet of 15, #a.-o.	9.50	9.50

Souvenir Sheets
1480	A210	$6 multicolored	7.75	7.75
1481	A210	$6 multicolored	7.75	7.75

A211

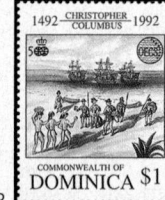

A212

1992, Aug. 10 — **Litho.** — **Perf. 14**
1482	A211	10c Archery	.20	.20
1483	A211	15c Two-man canoeing	.20	.20
1484	A211	25c 110-meter hurdles	.35	.35
1485	A211	60c Men's high jump	.60	.60
1486	A211	$1 Greco-Roman wrestling	.90	.90
1487	A211	$2 Men's rings	1.75	1.75
1488	A211	$4 Men's parallel bars	3.75	3.75
1489	A211	$5 Equestrian	4.75	4.75
		Nos. 1482-1489 (8)	12.50	12.50

Souvenir Sheets
1490	A211	$6 Field hockey	6.25	6.25
1491	A211	$6 Women's platform diving	6.25	6.25

1992 Summer Olympics, Barcelona.

1992 — **Litho.** — **Perf. 14½**
1492	A212	$1 Coming ashore	1.10	1.10
1493	A212	$2 Natives, ships	2.25	2.25

Discovery of America, 500th anniv. Organization of East Caribbean States.

Walt Disney's Goofy, 60th Anniv. — A213

Scenes from Disney cartoon films: 10c, Two Weeks Vacation, 1952. 15c, Aquamania, 1961. 25c, Goofy Gymnastics, 1949. 45c, How to Ride a Horse, 1941. $1, Foul Hunting, 1947. $2, For Whom the Bulls Toil, 1953. $4, Tennis Racquet, 1949. $5, Double Dribble, 1946. No. 1502, Aquamania, 1961, vert. No. 1503, The Goofy Sports Story, 1956, vert.

1992, Nov. 11 — **Litho.** — **Perf. 14x13½**
1494	A213	10c multicolored	.20	.20
1495	A213	15c multicolored	.20	.20
1496	A213	25c multicolored	.35	.35
1497	A213	45c multicolored	.65	.65
1498	A213	$1 multicolored	1.40	1.40
1499	A213	$2 multicolored	2.75	2.75
1500	A213	$4 multicolored	5.50	5.50
1501	A213	$5 multicolored	6.50	6.50
		Nos. 1494-1501 (8)	17.55	17.55

Souvenir Sheets
Perf. 13½x14
1502	A213	$6 multicolored	8.75	8.75
1503	A213	$6 multicolored	8.75	8.75

Model Trains A214

15c, Brass Reno 4-4-0, HO scale, c. 1963. 25c, Union Pacific Golden Classic, G gauge, 1992. 55c, LMS 3rd class brake coach, OO scale, 1970s. 65c, Brass Wabash 2-6-0, HO scale, c. 1958. 75c, Pennsylvania RR T-1 duplex, O gauge, 1991. $1, Streamline engine 2-6-0, O gauge, post World War II. $3, Japanese Natl. Railways class C62, HO scale, c. 1960. $5, Tinplate friction-drive floor trains, 1960s. No. 1512, 1st "toy" train in Japan, 1854. No. 1513, Stephenson's Rocket, 1:26 scale, c. 1972, vert.

1992, Nov. 11			**Perf. 14**	
1504	A214	15c multicolored	.25	.25
1505	A214	25c multicolored	.30	.30
1506	A214	55c multicolored	.55	.55
1507	A214	65c multicolored	.75	.75
1508	A214	75c multicolored	.90	.90
1509	A214	$1 multicolored	1.25	1.25
1510	A214	$3 multicolored	3.50	3.50
1511	A214	$5 multicolored	5.75	5.75
	Nos. 1504-1511 (8)		13.25	13.25

Souvenir Sheets
Perf. 13

1512	A214	$6 multicolored	6.00	6.00
1513	A214	$6 multicolored	6.00	6.00

No. 1512 contains one 52x40mm stamp, No. 1513 one 39x51mm stamp.

Hummel Figurines — A215

Angel: 20c, Playing violin. 25c, Playing horn. 55c, Playing mandolin. 65c, Seated, playing trumpet. 90c, On cloud with lantern. $1, Holding candle. $1.20, Flying. $6, On cloud with candle.

1992, Nov. 2			**Perf. 14**	
1514	A215	20c multicolored	.20	.20
1515	A215	25c multicolored	.25	.25
1516	A215	55c multicolored	.45	.45
1517	A215	65c multicolored	.55	.55
a.		Sheet of 4, #1514-1517	2.25	2.25
1518	A215	90c multicolored	.70	.70
1519	A215	$1 multicolored	.85	.85
1520	A215	$1.20 multicolored	1.00	1.00
1521	A215	$6 multicolored	5.00	5.00
a.		Sheet of 4, #1518-1521	8.00	8.00
	Nos. 1514-1521 (8)		9.00	9.00

Anniversaries and Events
A216   A217

Designs: 25c, Graf Zeppelin, 1929. No. 1523, Elderly man, plant. No. 1524, Elderly man on bicycle. No. 1525, Elderly man helping boy bait hook. No. 1526, Konrad Adenauer. No. 1527, Space shuttle. No. 1528, Wolfgang Amadeus Mozart. No. 1529, Snowy egret. No. 1530, Sir Thomas Lipton, Shamrock V, 1930. $2, Men pulling fishing net toward beach. $3, Helen Keller. No. 1533, Earth Resources Satellite. No. 1534, Map of Germany, 1949. No. 1535, Eland. $5, Count Ferdinand von Zeppelin. No. 1537, Cologne Cathedral, Germany. No. 1538, Scene from the Magic Flute. No. 1539, Mir Space Station. No. 1540, Engine of Graf Zeppelin. No. 1541, Rhinoceros hornbill.

1992			**Litho.**	**Perf. 14**
1522	A216	25c multicolored	.25	.25
1523	A216	45c multicolored	.35	.35
1524	A216	45c multicolored	.35	.35

1525	A216	45c multicolored	.35	.35
1526	A216	90c multicolored	.95	.95
1527	A216	90c multicolored	.65	.65
1528	A217	$1.20 multicolored	2.25	2.25
1529	A216	$1.20 multicolored	1.25	1.25
1530	A216	$1.20 multicolored	1.25	1.25
1531	A216	$2 multicolored	2.00	2.00
1532	A216	$3 multicolored	2.75	2.75
1533	A216	$4 multicolored	3.00	3.00
1534	A216	$4 multicolored	4.50	4.50
1535	A216	$4 multicolored	4.25	4.25
1536	A216	$5 multicolored	5.25	5.25
	Nos. 1522-1536 (15)		29.40	29.40

Souvenir Sheets

1537	A216	$6 multicolored	7.00	7.00
1538	A217	$6 multicolored	7.50	7.50
1539	A216	$6 multicolored	7.00	7.00
1540	A216	$6 multicolored	7.00	7.00
1541	A216	$6 multicolored	6.50	6.50

Konrad Adenauer, 25th anniv. of death (#1526, 1534, 1537). Intl. Space Year (#1527, 1533, 1539). Mozart, 200th anniv. of death (in 1991) (#1528, 1538). Count Zeppelin, 75th anniv. of death (#1522, 1536, 1540). Intl. Day of the Elderly (#1523-1525). Intl. Earth Summit, Rio (#1529, 1535, 1541). America's Cup yacht race (#1530). WHO Intl. Conference on Nutrition, Rome (#1531). Lions Intl., 75th anniv. (#1532).
Issued: #1528, 1539, Oct.; #1523-1527, 1533-1534, 1537-1538, Nov.; #1522, 1529, 1535-1536, 1540-1541, Dec.

Miniature Sheet

PAINTINGS FROM THE LOUVRE
BICENTENNIAL 1793 - 1993

Louvre Museum, Bicent. — A218

Details or entire paintings by Titian: a-b, Madonna and Child with St. Catherine and a Rabbit (diff. details). c, A Woman at Her Toilet. d-e, The Supper at Emmaus (diff. details). f, The Pastoral Concert. g-h, An Allegory, Perhaps of Marriage (diff. details).
Painting by Hieronymus Bosch: $6, The Ship of Fools.

1993, Mar. 24		**Litho.**	**Perf. 12**	
1542	A218	$1 Sheet of 8, #a.-h. + label	11.00	11.00

Souvenir Sheet
Perf. 14½

1543	A218	$6 multicolored	6.50	6.50

No. 1543 contains one 55x88mm stamp.

Elvis Presley, 15th Anniv. of Death (in 1992) A219

a, Portrait. b, With guitar. c, Holding microphone.

1993, Feb.			**Perf. 14**	
1544	A219	$1 Strip of 3, #a.-c.	3.75	3.75

Miniature Sheet

Birds of the Commonwealth of DOMINICA

Birds of Dominica — A220

a, Plumbeous warbler. b, Black swift. c, Blue-hooded euphonia. d, Rufous-throated solitaire. e, Ringed kingfisher. f, Blue-headed hummingbird. g, Bananaquit. h, Trembler. i, Forest thrush. j, Purple-throated carib. k, Ruddy quail dove. l, Least bittern.
No. 1546, Imperial parrot. No. 1547, Red-necked parrot (Amazona arausiaca).

1993, Apr. 30				
1545	A220	90c Sheet of 12, #a.-l.	18.00	18.00

Souvenir Sheet

1546	A220	$6 multicolored	6.50	6.50
1547	A220	$6 multicolored	6.50	6.50

Turtles A221

25c, Leatherback laying eggs. 55c, Hawksbill. 65c, Atlantic Ridley. 90c, Green turtle laying eggs. $1, Green turtle at sea. $2, Hawksbill, diff. $4, Loggerhead. $5, Leatherback at sea. #1556, Green turtle hatchling. #1557, Head of hawksbill.

1993, May 26		**Litho.**	**Perf. 14**	
1548	A221	25c multicolored	.25	.25
1549	A221	55c multicolored	.50	.50
1550	A221	65c multicolored	.70	.70
1551	A221	90c multicolored	.95	.95
1552	A221	$1 multicolored	1.10	1.10
1553	A221	$2 multicolored	2.10	2.10
1554	A221	$4 multicolored	4.00	4.00
1555	A221	$5 multicolored	5.25	5.25
	Nos. 1548-1555 (8)		14.85	14.85

Souvenir Sheets

1556	A221	$6 multicolored	6.75	6.75
1557	A221	$6 multicolored	6.75	6.75

For overprints see Nos. 2103-2107.

Automobiles — A222

Designs: 90c, 1928 Model A Ford. $1.20, Mercedes-Benz winning Swiss Grand Prix, 1936. $4, Mercedes-Benz winning German Grand Prix, 1935. $5, 1915 Model T Ford.
#1562: a, 1993 Mercedes-Benz coupe/roadster. b, 1893 Benz Viktoria.
No. 1563, Ford GT-40.

1993, May		**Litho.**	**Perf. 14**	
1558	A222	90c multicolored	.80	.80
1559	A222	$1.20 multicolored	1.25	1.25
1560	A222	$4 multicolored	3.75	3.75
1561	A222	$5 multicolored	4.75	4.75
	Nos. 1558-1561 (4)		10.55	10.55

Souvenir Sheets

1562	A222	$3 Sheet of 2, #a.-b.	5.50	5.50
1563	A222	$6 multicolored	5.50	5.50

No. 1563 contains one 57x42mm stamp.
First Ford gasoline engine, cent. (#1558, 1561, 1563). Benz's first four-wheeled vehicle, cent. (#1559-1560, 1562).

Dominica Grammar School, Cent. A223

Designs: 25c, School crest. 30c, V. A. A. Archer, first West Indian headmaster. 65c, Hubert A. Charles, first Dominican headmaster. 90c, Present school building.

1993, May				
1564	A223	25c multicolored	.25	.25
1565	A223	30c multicolored	.35	.35
1566	A223	65c multicolored	.70	.70
1567	A223	90c multicolored	.95	.95
	Nos. 1564-1567 (4)		2.25	2.25

Aviation Anniversaries — A224

Designs: 25c, New York ticker tape parade, 1928. 55c, BAC Lightning F2. 65c, Graf Zeppelin over Sphinx, pyramids, 1929. $1, Boeing 314 flying boat. $2, Astronaut stepping onto moon. $4, Viktoria Louise over Kiel harbor, 1912. $5, Supermarine Spitfire, vert. No. 1575, Royal Air Force Crest, vert. No. 1576, Hugo Eckener in airship cockpit, vert. No. 1577, Jean-Pierre Blanchard's hot air balloon, 1793, vert.

1993, May 28		**Litho.**	**Perf. 14**	
1568	A224	25c multicolored	.55	.55
1569	A224	55c multicolored	.65	.65
1570	A224	65c multicolored	1.25	1.25
1571	A224	$1 multicolored	1.40	1.40
1572	A224	$2 multicolored	3.25	3.25
1573	A224	$4 multicolored	8.00	8.00
1574	A224	$5 multicolored	6.25	6.25
	Nos. 1568-1574 (7)		21.35	21.35

Souvenir Sheets

1575	A224	$6 multicolored	7.00	7.00
1576	A224	$6 multicolored	7.00	7.00
1577	A224	$6 multicolored	6.50	6.50

Zeppelin Capt. Hugo Eckener, 125th anniv. of birth (#1568, 1570, 1573, 1576). Royal Air Force, 75th anniv. (#1569, 1574-1575).
Nos. 1575-1576 each contain one 42x57mm stamp.

Miniature Sheet

Coronation Anniversary 1953-1993

Coronation of Queen Elizabeth II, 40th Anniv. A225

Designs: No. 1578a, 20c, Official coronation photograph. b, 25c, Ceremony. c, 65c, Gold State Coach. d, $5, Queen Elizabeth II, Queen Mother.
$6, Portrait, by Norman Hutchinson, 1969.

1993, June 2		**Litho.**	**Perf. 13½x14**	
1578	A225	Sheet, 2 each #a.-d.	15.00	15.00

Souvenir Sheet
Perf. 14

1579	A225	$6 multicolored	7.50	7.50

No. 1579 contains one 28x42mm stamp.
For overprints see Nos. 1688-1689.

Wedding of Japan's Crown Prince
Naruhito and Masako Owada
A226

Cameo photos of couple and: 90c, Crown
Prince holding flowers. $5, Princess wearing
full-length coat.
$6, Princess riding in limousine.

1993, June 14   Litho.   Perf. 14
1580 A226 90c multicolored   1.00 1.00
1581 A226 $5 multicolored   5.50 5.50
Souvenir Sheet
1582 A226 $6 multicolored   7.00 7.00

Inauguration of Pres. William J.
Clinton — A227

$5, Bill, Hillary Clinton. $6, Bill Clinton, vert.

1993, July 30   Litho.   Perf. 14
1583 A227 $5 multicolored   5.00 5.00
Souvenir Sheet
1584 A227 $6 multicolored   7.00 7.00

Willy Brandt (1913-92), German
Chancellor — A228

Brandt and: 65c, Pres. Eisenhower, 1959.
$5, N.K. Winston, 1964. $6, Portrait.

1993, July 30
1585 A228 65c black & brown   .75 .75
1586 A228 $5 black & brown   5.75 5.75
Souvenir Sheet
1587 A228 $6 black & brown   7.00 7.00

Picasso (1881-   Polska '93
1973)   A230
A229

Paintings: 25c, Bather with Beach Ball,
1929. 90c, Portrait of Leo Stein, 1906. $5, Por-
trait of Wilhelm Unde, 1910. $6, Man with a
Pipe, 1915.

1993, July 30
1588 A229 25c multicolored   .25 .25
1589 A229 90c multicolored   1.00 1.00
1590 A229 $5 multicolored   5.75 5.75
     Nos. 1588-1590 (3)   7.00 7.00
Souvenir Sheet
1591 A229 $6 multicolored   7.00 7.00

1993, July 30
Paintings: 90c, Self-portrait, by Marian
Szczyrbula, 1921. $3, Portrait of Bruno Jasien-
ski, by Tytus Czyzewski, 1921. $6, Miser, by
Tadeusz Makowski, 1973.
1592 A230 90c multicolored   1.25 1.25

1593 A230 $3 multicolored   4.25 4.25
Souvenir Sheet
1594 A230 $6 multicolored   7.00 7.00

A231   A232

90c, Monika Holzner, speedskating, 1984.
$4, US hockey players, Ray Leblanc, Tim
Sweeney, 1992. $6, Men's ski jump.

1993, July 30
1595 A231 90c multicolored   1.25 1.25
1596 A231 $4 multicolored   5.25 5.25
Souvenir Sheet
1597 A231 $6 multicolored   6.50 6.50

1994 Winter Olympics, Lillehammer, Norway.

1993, July 30
Designs: $1.20, Astronomer using quadrant.
$3, Observatory. $5, Copernicus.
1598 A232 $1.20 multicolored   2.00 2.00
1599 A232 $3 multicolored   4.50 4.50
Souvenir Sheet
1600 A232 $5 multicolored   7.00 7.00

Copernicus (1473-1543).

Opening
of New
General
Post
Office
A233

New General Post Office and: 25c, Prince
Philip. 90c, Queen Elizabeth II.

1993, July 30
1601 A233 25c multicolored   .25 .25
1602 A233 90c multicolored   1.10 1.10

1994 World Cup
Soccer
Championships,
US — A234

1993, Sept. 8   Litho.   Perf. 14
1603 A234 25c Maradona,
               Buchwald   .30 .30
1604 A234 55c Gullit   .55 .55
1605 A234 65c Chavarria,
               Bliss   .70 .70
1606 A234 90c Maradona   1.00 1.00
1607 A234 90c Alvares   1.00 1.00
1608 A234 $1 Altobelli, Yong-
               hwang   1.25 1.25
1609 A234 $2 Referee,
               Stopyra   2.50 2.50
1610 A234 $5 Renquin,
               Yaremchuk   5.75 5.75
     Nos. 1603-1610 (8)   13.05 13.05
Souvenir Sheets
1611 A234 $6 Brehme   5.75 5.75
1612 A234 $6 Fabbri   5.75 5.75

Taipei
'93 — A235

Chinese kites: No. 1617a, Chang E Rising
up to the Moon. b, Red Phoenix and Rising
Sun. c, Heavenly Judge. d, Monkey King. e,
Goddess of the Luo River. f, Heavenly Maiden
Scatters Flowers.

1993, Oct. 4   Litho.   Perf. 13½x14
1613 A235 25c Tiger Balm
               Gardens   .25 .25
1614 A235 65c Building,
               Kenting
               Park   .65 .65
1615 A235 90c Tzu-en Tower   1.00 1.00
1616 A235 $5 Villa, Lan
               Tao Island   5.00 5.00
     Nos. 1613-1616 (4)   6.90 6.90
Miniature Sheet
1617 A235 $1.65 Sheet of 6,
               #a.-f.   11.50 11.50
Souvenir Sheet
1618 A235 $6 Jade Girl,
               Liao Dynas-
               ty   6.00 6.00

With Bangkok '93 Emblem

Puppets: No. 1623a, Thai, Rama and Sita.
b, Burmese, Tha Khi Lek. c, Burmese, diff. d,
Thai, Demons, Wat Phra Kaew. e, Thai, Hun
Lek performing Khun Chang, Khun Phaen. f,
Thai, Hun Lek performing Ramakien.

1993
1619 A235 25c Tugu Monu-
               ment, Java   .25 .25
1620 A235 55c Candi
               Cangkuang,
               West Java   .65 .65
1621 A235 90c Pura Taman
               Ayun,
               Mengwi   1.00 1.00
1622 A235 $5 Stone mosa-
               ics, Ceto   5.00 5.00
     Nos. 1619-1622 (4)   6.90 6.90
Miniature Sheet
1623 A235 $1.65 Sheet of 6,
               #a.-f.   11.50 11.50
Souvenir Sheet
1624 A235 $6 Stone carv-
               ing, Thai-
               land   6.00 6.00

With Indopex '93 Emblem

Designs: 25c, Ornate Chedi, Wat Phra
Boromathat Chaiya. 55c, Preserved temple
ruins, Sukhothai Historical Park. 90c, Prasat
Hin Phimai, Thailand. $5, Main sanctuary,
Prasat Phanom Rung, Thailand.
Indonesian puppets — #1629: a, Arjuna &
Prabu Gilling Wesi. b, Loro Blonyo. c, Yogy-
anese puppets, Menak cycle. d, Wayang
gedog, Ng Setro. e, Wayang golek, Kencana
Wungu. f, Wayang gedog, Raden Damar
Wulan.
$6, Sculpture of Majapahit noble, Pura
Sada, Kapel.

1993, Oct. 4   Litho.   Perf. 13½x14
1625 A235 25c multicolored   .25 .25
1626 A235 55c multicolored   .65 .65
1627 A235 90c multicolored   1.00 1.00
1628 A235 $5 multicolored   5.00 5.00
     Nos. 1625-1628 (4)   6.90 6.90
Miniature Sheet
1629 A235 $1.65 Sheet of 6,
               #a.-f.   11.50 11.50
Souvenir Sheet
1630 A235 $6 multicolored   6.00 6.00

Miniature Sheet

Willie the Operatic Whale — A236

Nos. 1631-1633, Characters and scenes
from Disney's animated film Willie the Operatic
Whale.

1993, Nov. 1   Litho.   Perf. 14x13½
1631 A236 $1 Sheet of 9, #a.-
               i.   15.00 15.00
Souvenir Sheets
1632 A236 $6 multicolored   5.50 5.50
Perf. 13½x14
1633 A236 $6 multi, vert.   5.50 5.50

Christmas
A237

25c, 55c, 65c, 90c (#1637), Details or entire
woodcut, The Adoration of the Magi, by Durer.
90c (#1638), $1, $3, $5, Details or entire
painting, The Foligni Madonna, by Raphael.
Souvenir Sheets: #1642, $6, The Adoration
of the Magi, by Durer. #1643, $6, The Foligni
Madonna, by Raphael.

1993, Nov. 8   Litho.   Perf. 13
1634-1643 A237 Set of 10   24.00 24.00

A238

Hong Kong
'94 — A239

Stamps, scene from Peak Tram: No. 1644,
Hong Kong #527, city buildings, trees. No.
1645, Trees, tram, #1292.
Chinese jade: No. 1646a, Horse. b, Cup
with handle. c, Vase with birthday peaches. d,
Vase. e, Fu dog and puppy. f, Drinking vessel.

1994, Feb. 18   Litho.   Perf. 14
1644 A238 65c multicolored   .60 .60
1645 A238 65c multicolored   .60 .60
     a. Pair, #1644-1645   1.25 1.25
Miniature Sheet
1646 A239 65c Sheet of 6, #a.-f.   6.00 6.00

Nos. 1644-1645 issued in sheets of 5 pairs.
No. 1645a is a continuous design.
New Year 1994 (Year of the Dog) (#1646e).

Insects, Butterflies, & Birds — A240

Various Hercules beetles: 20c, 25c, 65c, Male. 90c, Female.
$1, Imperial parrot. $2, Southern dagger tail. $3, The mimic. $5, Purple-throated carib.
Each $6: No. 1655, Snout butterfly. No. 1656, Blue-headed hummingbird.

1994, Mar. 15   Litho.   Perf. 14
1647-1654	A240	Set of 8	13.00	13.00
1650a		Min. sheet, 3 each #1647-1650	10.00	10.00
Souvenir Sheets				
1655-1656	A240	Set of 2	12.00	12.00

World Wildlife Fund (#1647-1650).

Mushrooms A241   Orchids A242

Designs: 20c, Russula matoubenis. 25c, Leptonia caeruleocapita. 65c, Inocybe littoralis. 90c, Russula hygrophytica. $1, Pyrrhoglossum lilaceipes. $2, Hygrocybe konradii. $3, Inopilus magnificus. $5, Boletellus cubensis.
No. 1665, Gerronema citrinum. No. 1666, Lentinus strigosus.

1994, Apr. 18
1657	A241	20c multicolored	.20	.20
1658	A241	25c multicolored	.20	.20
1659	A241	65c multicolored	.55	.55
1660	A241	90c multicolored	.85	.85
1661	A241	$1 multicolored	.95	.95
1662	A241	$2 multicolored	2.00	2.00
1663	A241	$3 multicolored	2.75	2.75
1664	A241	$5 multicolored	4.50	4.50
		Nos. 1657-1664 (8)	12.00	12.00
Souvenir Sheets				
1665	A241	$6 multicolored	6.00	6.00
1666	A241	$6 multicolored	6.00	6.00

1994, May 3
Designs: 20c, Laeliocattleya. 25c, Sophrolaeliocattleya. 65c, Odontocidium. 90c, Laeliocattleya, diff. $1, Cattleya. $2, Odontocidium, diff. $3, Epiphronitis. $4, Oncidium.
Each $6: #1675, Schombocattleya. #1676, Cattleya, diff.

1667-1674	A242	Set of 8	12.00	12.00
Souvenir Sheets				
1675-1676	A242	Set of 2	12.50	12.50

New Year 1994 (Year of the Dog) — A243

Designs: 20c, Dachshund. 25c, Beagle. 55c, Greyhound. 90c, Jack Russell terrier. $1, Pekingese. $2, White fox terrier. $4, English toy spaniel. $5, Irish setter.
#1686, Welsh corgi. #1687, Labrador retriever.

1994, May 17
1678	A243	20c multicolored	.20	.20
1679	A243	25c multicolored	.20	.20
1680	A243	65c multicolored	.45	.45
1681	A243	90c multicolored	.75	.75
1682	A243	$1 multicolored	.90	.90
1683	A243	$2 multicolored	1.75	1.75
1684	A243	$4 multicolored	3.50	3.50
1685	A243	$5 multicolored	4.25	4.25
		Nos. 1678-1685 (8)	12.00	12.00
Souvenir Sheets				
1686	A243	$6 multicolored	6.00	6.00
1687	A243	$6 multicolored	6.00	6.00

Nos. 1578-1579 Ovptd. "ROYAL VISIT / FEBRUARY 19, 1994" in Black or Silver

1994, June 27   Litho.   Perf. 13½x14
1688	A225	Sheet, 2 ea #a-d	16.00	16.00
Souvenir Sheet				
1689	A225	$6 multicolored (S)	8.00	8.00

Overprint on No. 1689 appears in sheet margin.

Miniature Sheet

1994 World Cup Soccer Championships, US — A244

No. 1690: a, Dos Armstrong, US. b, Dennis Bergkamp, Netherlands. c, Roberto Baggio, Italy. d, Rai, Brazil. e, Cafu, Brazil. f, Marco Van Baston, Netherlands.
Each $6: No. 1691, Roberto Mancini, Italy. No. 1692, Stanford Stadium, Palo Alto.

1994, July 5   Perf. 14
1690	A244	$1 Sheet of 6, #a.-f.	6.75	6.75
Souvenir Sheets				
1691-1692	A244	Set of 2	12.50	12.50

Butterflies A245

1994, May 3   Litho.   Perf. 14
1693	A245	20c Florida white	.20	.20
1694	A245	25c Red rim	.20	.20
1695	A245	55c Barred sulphur	.50	.50
1696	A245	65c Mimic	.60	.60
1697	A245	$1 Large orange sulphur	1.00	1.00
1698	A245	$2 Southern dagger tail	2.00	2.00
1698A	A245	$3 Dominican snout butterfly	2.75	2.75
1699	A245	$5 Caribbean buckeye	4.75	4.75
		Nos. 1693-1699 (8)	12.00	12.00
Souvenir Sheets				
1700	A245	$6 Clench's hairstreak	6.00	6.00
1701	A245	$6 Painted lady	6.00	6.00

10th Caribbean Scout Jamboree A246

Designs: 20c, Backpacking. 25c, Cooking over campfire. 55c, Making camp. 65c, Camping. $1, Scout drum unit. $2, Planting trees. $4, Sailing. $5, Scout salute.
Each $6: No. 1710, Early Scout troop. No. 1711, Pres. C.A. Sorhaindo, vert.

1994, July 18   Litho.   Perf. 14
1702-1709	A246	Set of 8	13.00	13.00
Souvenir Sheets				
1710-1711	A246	Set of 2	13.00	13.00

For overprints see Nos. 1762-1766.

D-Day, 50th Anniv. A247

Designs: 65c, US Waco glider brings reinforcements. $2, British Horsa gliders land more troops. $3, Glider troops take Pegasus Bridge.
$6, Hadrian glider.

1994, July 26
1712-1714	A247	Set of 3	6.00	6.00
Souvenir Sheet				
1715	A247	$6 multicolored	5.50	5.50

A248

Intl. Olympic Committee, Cent. — A249

Designs: 55c, Ulrike Meyfarth, Germany, high jump, 1984. $1.45, Dieter Baumann, Germany, 5000-meter run, 1992.
$6, Ji Hoon Chae, South Korea, 500-meter short track speed skating, 1994.

1994, July 26
1716	A248	55c multicolored	.60	.60
1717	A248	$1.45 multicolored	1.60	1.60
Souvenir Sheet				
1718	A249	$6 multicolored	6.50	6.50

English Touring Cricket, Cent. A250

Designs: 55c, D.I. Goweer Leics, England, vert. 90c, E.C.L. Ambrose, Leeward Islands. $1, G.A. Gooch, England, vert. $3, First English team, 1895.

1994, July 26
1719-1721	A250	Set of 3	3.50	3.50
Souvenir Sheet				
1722	A250	$3 multicolored	6.00	6.00

Miniature Sheet of 6

First Manned Moon Landing, 25th Anniv. A251

#1723: a, Apollo 14 crew. b, Apollo 14 patch. c, Apollo 14 lunar module Antares at Fra Mauro Crater. d, Apollo 15 crew. e, Apollo 15 patch. f, Apollo 15 mission, Mount Hadley from rover.
$6, 25th anniv. emblem, lunar surface.

1994, July 26
1723	A251	$1 #a.-f.	5.75	5.75
Souvenir Sheet				
1724	A251	$6 multicolored	6.50	6.50

A252

PHILAKOREA '94 — A253

Designs: 65c, P'alsang-jon Hall, Korea. 90c, Popchu-sa Temple. $2, Uhwajong Pavillion, Korea.
Screen, Late Choson Dynasty showing flowers and: No. 1728a, c, e, Birds. b, g, Butterfly. d, Roosters. f, Duck. h, Pheasant. i, Cranes. j, Deer.
$4, Stylized "spirit post" guardian.

1994, July 26   Perf. 14, 13 (#1728)
1725-1727	A252	Set of 3	4.00	4.00
Miniature Sheet of 10				
1728	A253	55c #a.-j.	7.50	7.50
Souvenir Sheet				
1729	A252	$4 multicolored	3.50	3.50

Mickey Mouse, 65th Birthday A254

Disney characters: 20c, Dippy dawg. 25c, Clarabelle Cow. 55c, Horace Horsecollar. 65c, Mortimer Mouse. $1, Joe Piper. $3, Mr. Casey. $4, Chief O'Hara. $5, Mickey and the Blot.
Each $6: No. 1738, Minnie, Tanglefoot. No. 1739, Pluto, Minnie, horiz.

Perf. 13½x14, 14x13½ (#1739)
1994, Oct. 3
1730-1737	A254	Set of 8	15.00	15.00
Souvenir Sheets				
1738-1739	A254	Set of 2	15.00	15.00

A255   A256

Local Entertainers: 20c, Sonia Llyod, folk singer. 25c, Ophelia Marie, singer. 55c, Edney Francis, accordionist. 65c, Norman Letang, saxophonist. 90c, Edie Andre, steel drummer

1994, Dec. 1   Litho.   Perf. 14
1740-1744	A255	Set of 5	2.10	2.10

Miniature Sheet of 9
1994, Dec. 1

Marilyn Monroe (1926-62), Actress: #1745a-1745i, Various portraits. $6, Hands above head. #1746, $6, Holding hat.
1745	A256	90c #a.-i.	12.50	12.50
Souvenir Sheets				
1746-1747	A256	Set of 2	12.00	12.00

Christmas
A257

Details or entire Spanish paintings: 20c, Madonna and child, by Luis de Morales. 25c, Madonna and Child with Yarn Winder, by Morales. 55c, Our Lady of the Rosary, by Zurbaran. 65c, Dream of the Patrician, by Bartolome Murillo. 90c, Madonna of Charity, by El Greco. $1, The Annunciation, by Zurbaran. $2, Mystical Marriage of St. Catherine, by Jusepe de Ribera. $3, The Holy Family with St. Bruno and Other Saints, by Ribera. Each $6: No. 1756, Vision of the Virgin to St. Bernard, by Murillo. No. 1757, Adoration of the Shepherds, by Murillo.

1994, Dec. 2   *Perf. 13½x14*
1748-1755 A257   Set of 8   8.50   8.50
         Souvenir Sheets
1756-1757 A257   Set of 2   12.00   12.00

Order of the Caribbean
Community — A258

First award recipients: 25c, Sir Shridath Ramphal, statesman, Guyana. 65c, William Gilbert Demas, economist, Trinidad & Tobago. 90c, Derek Walcott, writer, St. Lucia.

1994, Dec. 16   *Perf. 14*
1758-1760 A258   Set of 3   2.25   2.25

Jeffrey Edmund, 1994 World Cup Soccer Player A259

1994, Dec. 28
1761 A259   25c multicolored   .20   .20

Nos. 1705, 1708-1711 Ovptd.

18th World Scout Jamboree
Mondial, Holland, May 6, 1995

1995, Mar. 21   **Litho.**   *Perf. 14*
1762-1764 A246   Set of 3   8.50   8.50
        Souvenir Sheets
1765-1766 A246   Set of 2   12.50   12.50
Location of overprint varies.

New Year 1995 (Year of the Boar) — A260

Stylized boars: a, 25c, Facing right. b, 65c, Facing forward. c, $1, Facing left. $2, Two facing each other, horiz.

1995, Apr. 15   **Litho.**   *Perf. 14½*
1767 A260   Strip of 3, #a.-c.   1.75   1.75
   d.   Souv. sheet of 3, #1767a-
        1767c   1.75   1.75
        Souvenir Sheet
1768 A260 $2 multicolored   1.60   1.60
No. 1767 was issued in sheets of 4 strips.

Birds
A261

Designs: 25c, Wood duck. 55c, Mallard. 65c, Blue-winged teal. $5, Blood eared parakeet.
No. 1773, vert.: a, Cattle egret. b, Snow goose (a, c). c, Peregrine falcon. d, Barn owl. e, Black-crowned night heron. f, Common grackle. g, Brown pelican. h, Great egret. i, Ruby-throated hummingbird. j, Laughing gull. k, Greater flamingo. l, Common moorhen.
No. 1774, Trumpeter swan, vert. No. 1775, White-eyed vireo.

1995, Apr. 15   **Litho.**   *Perf. 14*
1769-1772 A261   Set of 4   5.00   5.00
     Miniature Sheet of 12
1773 A261   65c #a.-l.   16.00   16.00
        Souvenir Sheets
1774 A261 $5 multicolored   5.00   5.00
1775 A261 $6 multicolored   6.00   6.00

    Miniature Sheets of 6 or 8

End of World War II, 50th Anniv. A262

No. 1776: a, Mitsubishi A6M2 Zero. b, Aichi D3A1 Type 99 "Val." c, Nakajima 97-B5N "Kate." d, Zuikaku. e, Akagi. f, Ryuho.
No. 1777: a, German Panther tank, Ardennes. b, Allied fighter bomber. c, Patton's army crosses the Rhine. d, Rocket-powered ME 163. e, V-2 rocket on launcher. f, German U-boat surrenders in North Atlantic. g, Round the clock bombardment of Berlin. h, Soviet soldiers reach center of Berlin.
Each $6: No. 1778, Statue atop Dresden's town hall after Allied bombing. No. 1779, Japanese attack plane.

1995   **Litho.**   *Perf. 14*
1776 A262 $2 #a.-f. + label   10.50   10.50
1777 A262 $2 #a.-h. + label   15.00   15.00
        Souvenir Sheets
1778-1779 A262   Set of 2   16.00   16.00
   Issued: #1777-1778, 5/18; others, 7/21.

1996 Summer Olympics, Atlanta A263

Designs: 15c, Mark Breland, boxing. 20c, Lou Banach, Joseph Atiyeh, freestyle wrestling. 25c, Judo. 55c, Fencing. 65c, Matt Biondi, swimming. $1, Gushiken on rings, vert. $2, Cycling, vert. $5, Volleyball.
Each $6: No. 1788, Joe Cargis on Touch of Class, equestrian. No. 1789, Soccer, vert.

1995, July 21
1780-1787 A263   Set of 8   9.75   9.75
        Souvenir Sheets
1788-1789 A263   Set of 2   12.00   12.00

UN, 50th Anniv. — A264

No. 1790: a, 65c, Signatures on UN charter, attendee. b, $1, Attendee. $2, Attendees. $6, Winston Churchill.

1995, Aug. 16   **Litho.**   *Perf. 14*
1790 A264   Strip of 3, #a.-c.   2.75   2.75
        Souvenir Sheet
1791 A264 $6 multicolored   6.00   6.00
No. 1790 is a continuous design.

        Souvenir Sheets

FAO, 50th
Anniv. — A265

Street market scene: a, 90c, Woman in red dress. b, $1, Woman seated. c, $2, Vendors, women.
$6, Woman in field, woman holding water cans, vert.

1995, Aug. 16
1792 A265   Sheet of 3, #a.-c.   2.75   2.75
1793 A265 $6 multicolored   4.75   4.75
No. 1792 is a continuous design.

Queen Mother, 95th Birthday A266

No. 1794: a, Drawing. b, Wearing crown, green dress. c, Formal portrait. d, Blue dress. $6, Portrait as younger woman.

1995, Aug. 16   *Perf. 13½x14*
1794 A266 $1.65 Strip or block of
         4, #a.-d.   5.50   5.50
        Souvenir Sheet
1795 A266 $6 multicolored   6.50   6.50
No. 1794 was issued in sheets of 8 stamps. Sheet margins of Nos. 1794-1795 exist with black frame and text "In Memoriam — 1900-2002" overprinted in sheet margins.

Rotary, 90th Anniv. A267

1995   *Perf. 14*
1796 A267 $1 Paul Harris, em-
         blem   1.00   1.00
        Souvenir Sheet
1797 A267 $6 Rotary emblems   5.25   5.25

Dinosaurs
A268

20c, Monoclonius. 25c, Euoplocephalus. 55c, Coelophysis. 65c, Compsognathus.
No. 1802: a, Dimorphodon. b, Ramphorynchus. c, Giant alligator. d, Pentaceratops.
No. 1803, vert: a, Ceratosaurus. b, Comptosaurus (a). c, Stegosaur. d, Camarasaurs. e, Baronyx. f, Dilophosaurus. g, Dromaeosaurids (f). h, Deinonychus. i, Dinicthys. j, Carcharodon (k). k, Nautiloid. l, Trilobite.
$5, Sauropelta. $6, Triceratops, vert.

1995, Sept. 8
1798-1801 A268   Set of 4   1.50   1.50
1802 A268   90c Strip of 4, #a.-
          b.   3.00   3.00
       Miniature Sheet of 12
1803 A268 $1 #a.-l.   10.00   10.00
        Souvenir Sheets
1804 A268 $5 multicolored   5.50   5.50
1805 A268 $6 multicolored   6.50   6.50
   Singapore '95 (#1798-1801, #1803-1805).

      Miniature Sheets of 6

Nobel Prize Fund Established, Cent. — A269

Recipients, each $2: No. 1806a, Oscar A. Sanchez, peace, 1987. b, Ernst B. Chain, medicine, 1945. c, Aage Bohr, physics, 1975. d, Jaroslav Seifert, literature, 1984. e, Joseph E. Murray, medicine, 1990. f, Jaroslav Heyrovsky, chemistry, 1959.
No. 1807, each $2: a, Adolf von Baeyer, chemistry, 1905. b, Edward Buchner, chemistry, 1907. c, Carl Bosch, chemistry, 1931. d, Otto Hahn, chemistry, 1944. e, Otto Paul Herman Diels, chemistry, 1950. f, Kurt Alder, chemistry, 1950.
No. 1808, Emil A. von Behring, medicine, 1901.

1995, Oct. 24   **Litho.**   *Perf. 14*
1806-1807 A269   Set of 2   19.00   19.00
        Souvenir Sheet
1808 A269 $2 multicolored   1.90   1.90

Christmas
A270

Details or entire paintings: 20c, Madonna and Child, by Pontormo. 25c, The Immaculate Conception, by Murillo. 55c, The Adoration of the Magi, by Filippino Lippi. 65c, Rest on the Flight into Egypt, by Van Dyck. 90c, Sacred Family, by Van Dyck. $5, The Annunciation, by Van Eyck.
No. 1815, The Virgin and the Infant, by Van Eyck. No. 1816, The Holy Family, by Ribera.

1995, Nov. 30   **Litho.**   *Perf. 13½x14*
1809-1814 A270   Set of 6   7.00   7.00
        Souvenir Sheets
1815 A270 $5 multicolored   4.50   4.50
1816 A270 $6 multicolored   5.50   5.50

      Miniature Sheets of 9

Sierra Club, Cent. A271

Designs: No. 1817, each $1: a, Florida panther with mouth open. b, Florida panther looking right. c, Manatee. d, Two manatees. e, Three sockeye salmon. f, Group of sockeye salmon. g, Two southern sea otters. h, Southern sea otter. i, Southern sea otter showing both front paws.
No. 1818, vert, each $1: a, Florida panther. b, Manatee. c, Sockeye salmon. d, Key deer facing left. e, Key deer. f, Key deer with antlers, up close. g, Wallaby with young in pouch. h, Wallaby. i, Wallaby with young.

1995, Dec. 10   *Perf. 14*
1817-1818 A271   Set of 2   15.00   15.00

Chinese Paintings, A City of Cathay A272

No. 1819, brown lettering, each 90c: a, Boats docked, people on shore. b, River, bridge. c, Two boats on river. d, River, pavilion along shore. e, Open sea, people in courtyard.

No. 1820, black lettering, each 90c: a, City scene. b, City scene, wall. c, Outside wall, river. d, Large boat on river. e, People crossing over bridge.

No. 1821, $2: a, Boat on river, city above. b, People walking across bridge.

No. 1822, $2: a, Lifting ramp to another boat, vert. b, Holding lines in water, tree, vert.

1995, Dec. 27   Litho.   Perf. 14½
Strips of 5
1819-1820 A272 Set of 2 9.00 9.00
Souvenir Sheets of 2
1821-1822 A272 Set of 2 7.00 7.00

Nos. 1819-1822 are each continuous designs.

Classic Western Art — A273

Paintings by Raphael: No. 1823, Agony in the Garden. No. 1824, Pope Leo with Nephews. No. 1825, Bindo Altoviti.

$6, Triumphant entry of Constantine into Rome, by Rubens.

1995, Dec. 27   Perf. 14
1823-1825 A273 $2 Set of 3 6.00 6.00
Souvenir Sheet
1826 A273 $6 multicolored 6.00 6.00

New Year 1996 (Year of the Rat) — A274

Stylized rats, Chinese inscriptions: No. 1827a, 25c, purple & brown. b, 65c, orange & green. c. $1, red lilac & blue.
$2, Two rats, horiz.

1996, Jan. 16   Perf. 14½
1827 A274 Strip of 3, #a.-c. 1.90 1.90
Miniature Sheet
1828 A274 Sheet of 1 #1827 1.75 1.75
Souvenir Sheet
1829 A274 $2 multicolored 2.00 2.00
No. 1827 was issued in sheets of 12 stamps.

Miniature Sheet

Disney Lunar New Year — A275

Disney characters representing year of the: No. 1830a, Rat. b, Ox. c, Tiger. d, Hare. e, Dragon. f, Snake. g, Horse. h, Sheep. i, Monkey. j, Rooster. k, Dog. l, Pig.

$3, Rat character. $6, Pig, rat, ox characters on lunar calendar wheel.

1996, Jan. 16   Perf. 14x13½
1830 A275 55c Sheet of 12, #a.-l. 15.00 15.00
Souvenir Sheets
1831 A275 $3 multicolored 5.00 5.00
1832 A275 $6 multicolored 10.00 10.00

Methods of Transportation — A276

Designs: 65c, Donkey cart, 1965. 90c, 1910 Car. $2, 1950 Taxi. $3, 1955 Bus.

1996, Jan. 29   Litho.   Perf. 14
1833-1836 A276 Set of 4 7.50 7.50

Miniature Sheets

Locomotives — A277

No. 1837, each $2: a, "Dragon," Hawaii. b, "Regina," Italy. c, Calazo to Padua, Italy. d, "Mogul," Philippines. e, Nuremberg, Germany. f, "Stanislas," French Natl. Railway. g, "Black Five," Scotland. h, SNCF diesel electric, France. i, "Sir Nigel Gresley," England.

No. 1838, each $2: a, Hohi Line 9600 class, Japan. b, Peloponnese Express, Greece. c, Porter 2-4-0S, Hawaii. d, Norway-Swedish Jodemans Railway. e, 220 Diesel, Federal German Railway. f, 2-8-4T Indian Railways. g, East African Railways. h, Electrical trains, USSR. i, 0-8-0, Austria.

$5, "Duchess of Hamilton," England. $6, Diesel engine, China.

1996, Jan. 29
1837-1838 A277 Set of 2 30.00 30.00
Souvenir Sheets
1839 A277 $5 multicolored 5.50 5.50
1840 A277 $6 multicolored 6.25 6.25

No. 1837h has a face value of $1.

Giant Panda A278

Designs: a, With right leg up on rock. b, Front legs up on rock. c, Seated. d, Holding head down.

1996, May 15   Litho.   Perf. 13½x14
1841 A278 55c Block of 4, #a.-d. 3.75 3.75
Souvenir Sheet
Perf. 14x13½
1842 A278 $3 Panda, horiz. 3.25 3.25
CHINA '96, 9th Asian Intl. Philatelic Exhibition. No. 1841 was issued in sheets of 8 stamps.
See No. 1911.

Queen Elizabeth II, 70th Birthday A279

No. 1843: a, Portrait. b, Wearing regalia of Order of the Garter. c, Wearing bright blue dress, pearls.
$6, In uniform.

1996, May 16   Litho.   Perf. 13½x14
1843 A279 $2 Strip of 3, #a.-c. 5.00 5.00
Souvenir Sheet
1844 A279 $6 multicolored 5.00 5.00
No. 1843 was issued in sheets of 9 stamps.

Legendary Film Detectives A280

Designs: a, Humphrey Bogart as Sam Spade. b, Sean Connery as James Bond. c, Warren Beatty as Dick Tracy. d, Basil Rathbone as Sherlock Holmes. e, William Powell as the Thin Man. f, Sidney Toler as Charlie Chan. g, Peter Sellers as Inspector Clouseau. h, Robert Mitchum as Philip Marlowe. i, Peter Ustinov as Inspector Poirot.
$6, Margaret Rutherford as Miss Marple.

1996, July
1845 A280 $1 Sheet of 9, #a.-i. 9.75 9.75
Souvenir Sheet
1846 A280 $6 multicolored 6.50 6.50

1996 Summer Olympics, Atlanta A281

Designs: 20c, Olympic Stadium, Moscow, 1980. 25c, Hermine Joseph, vert. 55c, Women's field hockey, Zimbabwe, 1980. 90c, Jerome Romain, vert. $1, Polo, discontinued sport, vert. $2, Greg Louganis, diving.

1996   Perf. 14
1847-1852 A281 Set of 6 4.50 4.50

Local Entertainers A282

Designs: 25c, Irene Peltier, national dress of Dominica. 55c, Rupert Bartley, street band player. 65c, Rosemary Cools-Lartigue, pianist. 90c, Celestine "Orion" Theophile, belle queen, Grand Bay. $1, Cecil Bellot, former government band master.

1996, July 31   Litho.   Perf. 14
1853-1857 A282 Set of 5 3.00 3.00

Jerusalem, 3000th Anniv. — A283

Designs: a, 90c, Shrine of the Book, Israel Museum. b, $1, Church of All Nations. c, $2, The Great Synagogue.
$5, Hebrew University, Mount Scopus.

1996, July 31
1858 A283 Sheet of 3, #a.-c. 3.50 3.50
Souvenir Sheet
1859 A283 $5 multicolored 4.50 4.50

Radio, Cent. A284

Entertainers: 90c, Artie Shaw. $1, Benny Goodman. $2, Duke Ellington. $4, Harry James.
$6, Tommy Dorsey, Jimmy Dorsey, horiz.

1996, July 31
1860-1863 A284 Set of 4 6.50 6.50
Souvenir Sheet
1864 A284 $6 multicolored 5.75 5.75

UNICEF, 50th Anniv. A285

20c, Girl looking at globe. 55c, Boy with stethoscope, syringe. $5, Doctor examining child.
No. 1868, Girl, vert.

1996, July 31
1865-1867 A285 Set of 3 4.75 4.75
Souvenir Sheet
1868 A285 $5 multicolored 5.00 5.00

World Post Day — A286

Scenes of 18th cent. life in Dominica: 10c, Captain of ship taking letters by hand. 25c, Anthony Trollope vists Dominica to organize postal service. 55c, Steam vessel "Yare" carries mail around island. 65c, Post offices and agencies. 90c, Country postman carrying mail around mountain tracks. $1, West Indies Federation stamp, first airmail sent on German "goose" seaplane. $2, #602, General Post Office, old and new.
$5, Captain of ship.

1996, Oct. 1   Litho.   Perf. 14
1869-1875 A286 Set of 7 5.25 5.25
Souvenir Sheet
1876 A286 $5 multicolored 5.25 5.25

Fish — A287

Designs: 1c, Scrawled filefish. 2c, Lion fish. 5c, Porcupine fish. 10c, Powder blue surgeonfish. 15c, Red hind. 20c, Golden butterfly fish. 25c, Long-nosed butterfly fish. 35c, Pennant butterfly fish. 45c, Spotted drum. 55c, Blue-girdled angelfish. 60c, Scorpion fish. 65c, Harlequin sweetlips. 90c, Flame angelfish. $1, Queen trigger. $1.20, Stoplight parrot. $1.45, Black durgon. $2, Glasseye snapper. $5, Balloon fish. $10, Creole wrasse. $20, Seabass.

1996, Oct. 1		Litho.	Perf. 14	
1877	A287	1c multicolored	.20	.20
1878	A287	2c multicolored	.20	.20
1879	A287	5c multicolored	.20	.20
1880	A287	10c multicolored	.20	.20
1881	A287	15c multicolored	.20	.20
1882	A287	20c multicolored	.20	.20
1883	A287	25c multicolored	.20	.20
1884	A287	35c multicolored	.35	.35
1885	A287	45c multicolored	.40	.40
1886	A287	55c multicolored	.50	.50
1887	A287	60c multicolored	.60	.60
1888	A287	65c multicolored	.65	.65
1889	A287	90c multicolored	.90	.90
1890	A287	$1 multicolored	.95	.95
1891	A287	$1.20 multicolored	1.25	1.25
1892	A287	$1.45 multicolored	1.40	1.40
1893	A287	$2 multicolored	1.90	1.90
1894	A287	$5 multicolored	4.75	4.75
1895	A287	$10 multicolored	9.75	9.75
1896	A287	$20 multicolored	19.00	19.00
		Nos. 1877-1896 (20)	43.80	43.80

See Nos. 2024-2039B for size 20x18mm stamps.

1996 Summer Olympic Games Type

Past Olympic medalists, vert, each 90c: No. 1897a, Ulrike Meyfarth, high jump. b, Pat McCormick, diving. c, Takeichi Nishi, equestrian. d, Peter Farkas, Greco-Roman wrestling. e, Carl Lewis, track & field. f, Agnes Keleti, gymnastics. g, Yasuhiro Yamashita, judo. h, John Kelly, single sculls. i, Naim Suleymanoglu, weight lifting.
No. 1898, vert, each 90c: a, Sammy Lee, diving. b, Bruce Jenner, decathlon. c, Olga Korbut, gymnastics. d, Steffi Graf, tennis. e, Florence Griffith-Joyner, track and field. f, Mark Spitz, swimming. g, Li Ning, gymnastics. h, Erika Salumae, cycling. i, Abebe Bikila, marathon.
#1899, $5, Joan Benoit, 1st women's marathon, vert.
#1900, $5, Milt Campbell, discus.

1996, June 7		Litho.	Perf. 14	
		Sheets of 9		
1897-1898	A281	Set of 2	14.50	14.50
		Souvenir Sheets		
1899-1900	A281	Set of 2	8.50	8.50

A288   A289

Christmas (Details or entire paintings): 25c, Enthroned Madonna and Child, by Stefano Veneziano. 55c, Noli Me Tangere, by Beato Angelico. 65c, Madonna and Child, by Angelico. 90c, Madonna of Corneta Tarquinia, by Filippo Lippi. $2, Annunciation, by Angelico. $5, Madonna with Child, by Angelico, diff.
Each $6: No. 1907, Coronation of the Virgin, by Beato Angelico. No. 1908, Holy Family with St. Barbara, by Veronese, horiz.

1996, Nov. 25				
1901-1906	A288	Set of 6	8.50	8.50
		Souvenir Sheet		
1907-1908	A288	Set of 2	11.50	11.50

1997		Litho.	Perf. 14	

Paintings of "Herdboy and Buffalo," by Li Keran (1907-89): No. 1909: a, f, Herdboy Plays the Flute. b, g, Playing Cricket in the Autumn. c, h, Listen to the Summer Cicada. d, i, Grazing in the Spring.
$2, Return in Wind and Rain.

1909	A289	90c Strip of 4, #a.-d.	3.50	3.50
		Souvenir Sheets		
1909E	A289	55c Sheet of 4, #f.-i.	2.25	2.25
		Perf. 15x14½		
1910	A289	$2 multicolored	2.25	2.25

New Year 1997 (Year of the Ox).
No. 1909 was printed in sheets of 8 stamps.
No. 1910 contains one 34x52mm stamp.

Souvenir Sheet

Huangshan Mountain, China — A290

1996, May 15		Litho.	Perf. 12	
1911	A290	$2 multicolored	2.50	2.50

China '96. No. 1911 was not available until March 1997.

A291

Lee Lai-Shan, 1996 Olympic Gold Medalist in Wind Surfing — A291a

1997		Litho.	Perf. 15x14	
1912	A291	$2 multicolored	1.90	1.90
		Souvenir Sheet		
		Perf. 14		
1913	A291	$5 multicolored	4.50	4.50

No. 1912 was issued in sheets of 3.
No. 1913 contains one 38x51mm stamp.

Litho. & Embossed
Perf. 9
Without Gum

1913A	A291a	$35 gold & multi, like #1913		

Butterflies
A292

No. 1914: a, Meticalla metis. b, Coeliades forestan. c, Papilio dardanus. d, Mylothris chloris. e, Poecilmitis thyshe. f, Myrina silenus. g, Bematistes aganice. h, Euphaedra neophron. i, Precis hierta.
No. 1915, vert: a, Striped policeman. b, Mountain sandman. c, Brown-veined white. d, Bowker's widow. e, Foxy charaxes. f, Pirate. g, African clouded yellow. h, Garden inspector.
Each $6: No. 1916, Acraea natalica. No. 1917, Eurytela dryope.

1997, Apr. 1		Litho.	Perf. 14	
1914	A292	55c Sheet of 9, #a.-i.	5.00	5.00
1915	A292	90c Sheet of 8, #a.-h.	7.00	7.00
		Souvenir Sheets		
1916-1917	A292	Set of 2	13.00	13.00

UNESCO, 50th Anniv. A293

55c, View from temple, China. 65c, Palace of Diocletian, Croatia. 90c, St. Mary's Cathedral, Hildesheim, Germany. $1, Monastery of Rossanou, Mount Athos, Greece. $2, Scandola Nature Reserve, France. $4, Church of San Antao, Portugal.
No. 1924: a, Ruins of Copan, Honduras. b, Cuzco Cathedral, Peru. c, Olinda, Brazil, d, Canaima Natl. Park, Venezuela. e, Galapagos Islands Natl. Park, Ecuador. f, Ruins of Church, Jesuit missions of Santisima, Paraguay. g, Fortress, San Lorenzo, Panama. h, Natl. Park, Fortress, Haiti.
Each $6: No. 1925, Chengde Lakes, China. No. 1926, Kyoto, Japan.

1997, Apr. 7			Perf. 13½x14	
1918-1923	A293	Set of 6	10.00	10.00
1924	A293	$1 Sheet of 8, #a.-h. + label	9.00	9.00
		Souvenir Sheets		
1925-1926	A293	Set of 2	12.00	12.00

Disney Scenes "Sealed with a Kiss" A294

Cartoon film, year released: 25c, Mickey's Horse, Tanglefoot, 1933. 35c, Shanghaied, 1935. 55c, Pluto's Judgment Day, 1935. 65c, Race for Riches, 1935. 90c, Elmer Elephant, 1936. $1, Brave Little Tailor, 1938. $2, Donald's Crime, 1945. $4, In Dutch, 1946.
Each $6: No. 1935, Nifty Nineties, 1941. No. 1936, Mickey's Surprise Party, 1939.

1997, Apr. 15			Perf. 13½x14	
1927-1934	A294	Set of 8	13.00	13.00
		Souvenir Sheets		
1935-1936	A294	Set of 2	10.00	10.00

Cats — A295   Dogs — A296

25c, Cream Burmese. $1, Snowshoe. $2, Sorrell Abyssinian. $5, Torbie Persian.
No. 1941: a, British bicolor shorthair (d, e). b, Maine coon kitten, Somali kitten (c). c, Maine coon kitten, diff. d, Lynx point Siamese (e). e, Blue Burmese kitten, white Persian (odd-eyed) (f). f, Persian kitten.
No. 1942, Silver tabby.

1997, Apr. 24			Perf. 14	
1937-1940	A295	Set of 4	7.50	7.50
1941	A295	$2 Sheet of 6, #a.-f.	11.50	11.50
		Souvenir Sheet		
1942	A295	$6 multicolored	6.00	6.00

1997, Apr. 24

Designs: 20c, Afghan hound. 55c, Cocker spaniel. 65c, Smooth fox terrier. 90c, West Highland white terrier.
No. 1947a, St. Bernard. b, Boy with grand basset. c, Rough collie. d, Golden retriever. e, Golden retriever, Tibetan spaniel, smooth fox terrier. f, Smooth fox terrier, diff.
$6, Shetland sheepdog.

1943-1946	A296	Set of 4	2.25	2.25
1947	A296	90c Sheet of 6, #a.-f.	5.75	5.75
		Souvenir Sheet		
1948	A296	$6 multicolored	6.00	6.00

Queen Elizabeth II and Prince Philip, 50th Wedding Anniv. A297

No. 1949: a, Queen Elizabeth II. b, Royal Arms. c, Prince, Queen walking among crowd. d, Queen, Prince in military attire. e, Buckingham Palace. f, Prince Philip.
$6, Portrait of Queen and Prince on balcony.

1997, May 29		Litho.	Perf. 14	
1949	A297	$1 Sheet of 6, #a.-f.	6.50	6.50
		Souvenir Sheet		
1950	A297	$6 multicolored	6.00	6.00

Paintings by Hiroshige (1797-1858) A298

#1951: a, Ichigaya Hachiman Shrine. b, Blossoms on the Tama River Embankment. c, Kumano Junisha Shrine, Tsunohazu ("Juniso"). d, Benkei Moat from Soto-Sakurada to Kojimachi. e, Kinokuni Hill & View of Akasak Tameike. f, Naito Shinjuku, Yotsuya.
Each $6: No. 1952, Kasumigaseki. No. 1952A, Sanno Festival Procession at Kojimachi I-chome.

1997, May 29

1951	A298	$1.55 Sheet of 6, #a.-f.	10.00	10.00
		Souvenir Sheets		
1952-1952A	A298	Set of 2	14.00	14.00

Orchids
A299

Designs, vert: 20c, Oncidium altissimum. 25c, Oncidium papilio. 55c, Epidendrum fragrans. 65c, Oncidium lanceanum. 90c, Campylocentrum micranthum. $4, Pogonia rosea.
No. 1959: a, Brassavola cucculata. b, Epidendrum ibaguense. c, Ionopsis utricularioides. d, Rodriguezia lanceolata. e, Oncidium cebolleta. f, Epidendrum ciliare.
Each $5: No. 1960, Stanhopea grandiflora. No. 1961, Oncidium ampliatum.

1997, May 10		Litho.	Perf. 14	
1953-1958	A299	Set of 6	8.00	8.00

1959 A299 $1 Sheet of 6, #a.-
f. 7.00 7.00

Souvenir Sheets

1960-1961 A299 Set of 2 10.50 10.50

Paul P. Harris (1868-1947), Founder
of Rotary, Intl. — A300

Portrait of Harris and: $2, Rotary Village
Corps, irrigation project, Honduras. $6,
Emblems, world community service.

1997, May 29
1962 A300 $2 multicolored 1.75 1.75

Souvenir Sheet
1963 A300 $6 multicolored 7.00 7.00

Heinrich
von
Stephan
(1831-97)
A301

Portraits of Von Stephan and: No. 1964 a,
Kaiser Wilhelm II. b, UPU emblem. c, Postal
messenger, ancient Japan.
$6, Von Stephan, Russian dog team carry-
ing post, 1859.

1997, May 29
1964 A301 $2 Sheet of 3, #a.-c. 5.25 5.25

Souvenir Sheet
1965 A301 $6 multicolored 5.25 5.25

PACIFIC 97.

Chernobyl
Disaster,
10th Anniv.
A302

Designs: No. 1966, Chabad's Children of
Chernobyl. No. 1967, UNESCO.

1997, May 29 **Perf. 13½x14**
1966 A302 $2 multicolored 2.75 2.75
1967 A302 $2 multicolored 2.75 2.75

Grimm's
Fairy Tales
A303

Mother Goose Rhymes — A304

The Goose Girl: No. 1968: a, Girl with
horse. b, Geese, pond, castle. c, Girl. No.
1969, Girl, horiz.
No. 1970: Mary, Mary, Quite Contrary.

1997, May 29 **Perf. 13½x14**
1968 A303 $2 Sheet of 3, #a.-c. 7.00 7.00

Souvenir Sheets
Perf. 14x13½
1969 A303 $6 multicolored 7.00 7.00

Perf. 14
1970 A304 $6 multicolored 7.00 7.00

Return of Hong
Kong to
China — A305

Designs: $1, View of Hong Kong at night.
$1.45, View of Hong Kong in daytime. $2,
View of Hong Kong at night, diff.
Hong Kong skyline at dusk: No. 1974: a,
65c. b, 90c. c, $1. d, $3.

1997, July 1 **Perf. 14**
1971-1973 A305 Set of 3 4.25 4.25
1974 A305 Sheet of 4, #a.-d. 5.50 5.50

#1971-1973 were issued in sheets of 4.

1998 Winter
Olympics,
Nagano — A306

Medal winners: 20c, Yukio Kasaya, 1972 ski
jump. 25c, Jens Weissflog, 1994 ski jump. No.
1977, 55c, Anton Maier, 1968 men's speed
skating. No. 1978, 55c, Ljubov Egorova, 1994
women's cross-country skiing. 65c, 1994 Ice
hockey, Sweden. 90c, Bernhard Glass, 1980
men's luge. $4, Frank-Peter Roetsch, 1988
men's biathlon.
No. 1982: a, like #1975. b, like #1976. c, like
#1977. d, Christa Rothenburger, 1988
women's speed skating.
Each $5: No. 1983, Jacob Tullin Thams,
1924 ski jumping. No. 1984, Charles Jewtraw,
1924 men's speed skating.

1997, July 15
1975-1981 A306 Set of 7 8.75 8.75
1982 A306 $1 Strip or block of
4, #a.-d. 5.00 5.00

Souvenir Sheets
1983-1984 A306 Set of 2 8.50 8.50

No. 1982 issued in sheets of 8 stamps.

1998 World Cup Soccer
Championships, France — A307

Players, vert: 20c, Klinsmann, Germany.
55c, Bergkamp, Holland. 65c, Ravanelli, Italy.
90c, Kinkladze, Georgia. $2, Shearer,
England. $4, Dani, Portugal.
Stadiums: No. 1991, each 65c: a, Wembley,
England. b, Bernabeu, Spain. c, Maracana,
Brazil. d, Torino, Italy. e, Centenary, Uruguay.
f, Olympic, Germany. g, Rose Bowl, US. h,
Azteca, Mexico.
Team Captains: No. 1992, each 65c: a,
Meazza, Italy, 1934. b, Matthaus, Germany,
1990. c, Walter, W. Germany, 1954. d,
Maradona, Argentina, 1986. e, Beckenbauer,
Germany, 1974. f, Moore, England, 1966. g,
Dunga, Brazil, 1994. h, Zoff, Italy, 1982.
$5, Mario Kempes, Argentina, vert. $6, Ally
McCoist, Scotland, vert.

1997, July 21 **Litho.** **Perf. 14**
1985-1990 A307 Set of 6 9.00 9.00

Sheets of 8 + Label
1991-1992 A307 Set of 2 10.00 10.00

Souvenir Sheets
1993 A307 $5 multicolored 4.50 4.50
1994 A307 $6 multicolored 5.50 5.50

Dominica
Credit
Union — A308

25c, Joffre Robinson, former Credit Union
president. 55c, Sister Alicia, founder credit
union movement in Dominica. 65c, Lorrel
Bruce, 1st Cooperative Credit Union president. 90c, Roseau Credit Union Building.
$5, Bruce, Robinson, Sister Alicia.

1997, Aug. 15 **Litho.** **Perf. 14x13½**
1995-1998 A308 Set of 4 2.40 2.40

Souvenir Sheet
Perf. 14
1999 A308 $5 multicolored 5.00 5.00

No. 1999 contains one 28x60mm stamp.

A309 A310

Medical Pioneers: 20c, Louis Pasteur, father
of bacteriology. 25c, Christiaan Barnard, performed first heart transplant. 55c, Sir Alexander Fleming, developer of penicillin. 65c,
Camillo Golgi, neurologist. 90c, Jonas Salk,
developer of polio vaccine. $1, Har Ghobind
Khorana, geneticist. $2, Elizabeth Blackwell,
first woman physician. $3, Sir Frank Macfar-
lane Burnet, immunologist.
$5, Fleming, diff. $6, Pasteur, diff.

1997, Sept. 1 **Litho.** **Perf. 14**
2000-2007 A309 Set of 8 9.00 9.00

Souvenir Sheets
2008 A309 $5 multicolored 5.25 5.25
2009 A309 $6 multicolored 6.25 6.25

1997, Oct. 20 **Litho.** **Perf. 14**
Diana, Princess of Wales (1961-97): Various portraits.

2010 A310 $2 Sheet of 4, #a.-d. 8.00 8.00

Souvenir Sheet
2011 A310 $5 multicolored 6.00 6.00

Christmas — A311

Entire paintings or details: 20c, Echo and
Narcissus, by Poussin. 55c, Angel Departing
from the Family of Tobias, by Rembrandt. 65c,
Seated Nymphs with Flute, by Francois
Boucher. 90c, Angel, by Rembrandt. $2, Dis-
pute of the Holy Sacrament, by Raphael. $4,
Garden of Love, by Rubens.
Each $6: No. 2018, Annunciation, by Botti-
celli. No. 2019, Christ on the Mount of Olives,
by El Greco.

1997, Nov. 10 **Litho.** **Perf. 14**
2012-2017 A311 Set of 6 8.00 8.00

Souvenir Sheets
2018-2019 A311 Set of 2 12.00 12.00

The $4 is incorrectly inscribed Holy Trinity,
by Raphael. No. 2018 is incorrectly inscribed
Study of a Muse, by Raphael.

A312

A313

Paintings of tigers, by Ling-Nan School: No.
2020: a, 55c, Gao Qifeng. b, 65c, Zhao
Shao'ang. c, 90c, Gao Jianfu. d, $1.20, Gao
Jianfu, diff.
$3, Tiger running down mountain, by Gao
Jianfu.

1998, Jan. 5 **Litho.** **Perf. 14½**
2020 A312 Sheet of 4, #a.-d. 3.25 3.25

Souvenir Sheet
Perf. 14x14½
2021 A312 $3 multicolored 2.50 2.50

New Year 1998 (Year of the Tiger). No. 2021
contains one 44x36mm stamp.

Fish Type of 1996
1998 **Perf. 13x13½**
Size: 20x18mm

2024	A287	5c Porcupine fish	.20	.20
2025	A287	10c Powder-blue surge-onfish	.20	.20
2026	A287	15c Red hind	.20	.20
2027	A287	20c Golden but-terflyfish	.20	.20
2028	A287	25c Long-nosed butterf-lyfish	.20	.20
2029	A287	35c Pennant butterf-lyfish	.35	.35
2030	A287	45c Spotted drum	.50	.50
2031	A287	55c Blue-girdled angelfish	.55	.55

2032	A287	60c	Scorpion fish	.60 .60
2033	A287	65c	Harlequin sweetlips	.75 .75
2034	A287	90c	Flame angelfish	.90 .90
2035	A287	$1	Queen trigger	1.10 1.10
2036	A287	$1.20	Stoplight parrot	1.25 1.25
2037	A287	$1.45	Black durgon	1.40 1.40
2038	A287	$2	Glasseye snapper	2.10 2.10
2039	A287	$5	Balloon fish	5.25 5.25
2039A	A287	$10	Creole wrasse	11.00 11.00
2039B	A287	$20	Seabass	21.00 21.00
		Nos. 2024-2039B (18)		47.75 47.75

Numbers have been reserved for additional values in this set.

1998, Feb. 9   Litho.   Perf. 14

Famous 20th cent. athletes — #2040: a, Jesse Owens. b, Owens jumping in 1936 Summer Olympic Games, Berlin. c, Isaac Berger lifting weights. d, Berger. e, Boris Becker. f, Becker playing tennis. g, Arthur Ashe playing tennis, holding Wimbledon trophy. h, Ashe.
No. 2041, Franz Beckenbauer, soccer player, horiz.

Sheet of 8

2040	A313	$1 #a.-h.	8.50 8.50
		Souvenir Sheet	
2041	A313	$6 multi	7.00 7.00

Nos. 2040b-2040c, 2040f-2040g are each 53x38mm.

A314   A315

Japanese Cinema Stars — No. 2042: a, Akira Kurosawa. b, Kurosawa's 1950 film, "Rashomon." c, Toshiro Mifune in 1954 film, "Seven Samurai." d, Mifune. e, Yasujiro Ozu. f, Ozu's 1949 film, "Late Spring." g, Sessue Hayakawa in 1957 film, "Bridge on the River Kwai." h, Hayakawa.
No. 2043, Akira Kurosawa, director.

1998, Feb. 9   Litho.   Perf. 14
Sheet of 8

2042	A314	$1 #a.-h.	8.50 8.50
		Souvenir Sheet	
2043	A314	$6 multi	7.00 7.00

Nos. 2042b-2042c, 2042f-2042g are each 53x38mm.

1998, Mar. 2   Litho.   Perf. 14

Mushrooms: 10c, Omphalotus illudens. 15c, Inocybe fastigiata. 20c, Marasmius plicatulus. 50c, Mycena lilacifolia. 55c, Armillaria straminea. 90c, Tricholomopsis rutilans.
No. 2050, each $1: a, Lepiota naucina. b, Cortinarius violaceus. c, Boletus aereus. d, Tricholoma aurantium. e, Lepiota procera. f, Clitocybe geotropa. g, Lepiota acutesquamosa. h, Tricholoma saponaceum. i, Lycoperdon gemmatum.
No. 2051, each $1: a, Boletus ornatipes. b, Russula xerampelina. c, Cortinarius collinitus. d, Agaricus meleagris. e, Coprinus comatus. f, Amanita caesarea. g, Amanita brunnescens. h, Amanita muscaria. i, Morchella esculenta.
$6, Cortinarius violaceus.

2044-2049	A315	Set of 6	3.00 3.00
		Sheets of 9	
2050-2051	A315	Set of 2	21.00 21.00
		Souvenir Sheet	
2052	A315	$6 multicolored	6.00 6.00

Sailing Ships A316

Designs: 65c, Greek bireme. 90c, Egyptian felucca. $1, Viking longboat. $2, Chinese junk.
No. 2057: a, Two-masted topsail schooner. b, The Golden Hinde. c, Roman merchant ship. d, Gazela Primeriro. e, Moshulu. f, Bluenose.
Each $5: No. 2058, Pinta. No. 2059, Chesapeake Bay skipjack.

1998, Mar. 16   Litho.   Perf. 14

2053-2056	A316	Set of 4	5.00 5.00
2057	A316	55c Block of 6, #a.-f.	3.50 3.50
		Souvenir Sheets	
2058-2059	A316	Set of 2	11.00 11.00

No. 2053 incorrectly inscribed "Egyptian felucca."
No. 2057 was issued in sheets of 12 stamps.

Mickey & Minnie Mouse's 70th Anniv. — A317

25c, Steamboat Willie, 1928. 55c, The Brave Little Tailor, 1938. 65c, Nifty Nineties, 1941. 90c, Mickey Mouse Club, 1955. $1, Mickey, Minnie at the opening of Walt Disney World, 1971. $1.45, Mousercise Mickey & Minnie, 1980.
Each $5: No. 2061, Walt Disney, Mickey, Minnie. No. 2062, Surprise Party for Mickey & Minnie.

1998, June 16   Litho.   Perf. 14x13½

2060A	A317	25c black	.30 .30
2060B	A317	55c multi	.60 .60
2060C	A317	65c multi	.75 .75
2060D	A317	90c multi	1.00 1.00
2060E	A317	$1 multi	1.10 1.10
2060F	A317	$1.45 multi	1.60 1.60
		Nos. 2060A-2060F (6)	5.35 5.35
		Souvenir Sheet of 7	
2060G		#2060A-2060F, 2060h	13.00 13.00
	h.	$5 Runaway brain, perf 13½ at left	4.00 4.00

Size: 130x104mm
Imperf

2061-2062	A317	Set of 2	11.00 11.00

Souvenir Sheet

Disney's The Lion King — A318

1998, June 16   Litho.   Perf. 13½x14

2063	A318	$5 multicolored	7.00 7.00

Sea Birds A319

25c, Erect crested penguin. 65c, Humboldt penguin. 90c, Red knot. $1, Audubon's shearwater.
No. 2068: a, Crested tern. b, Franklin's gull. c, Australian pelican. d, Fairy prion. e, Andean gull. f, Imperial shag. g, Red phalarope. h, Hooded grebe. i, Least auklet. j, Little grebe. k, Cape petrel. l, Horned grebe.
Each $5: No. 2069, Sula nebouxii. No. 2070, Fulmarus glacialis.

1998, Aug. 4   Perf. 14

2064-2067	A319	Set of 4	3.00 3.00

2068	A319	90c Sheet of 12, #a.-l.	11.00 11.00
		Souvenir Sheets	
2069-2070	A319	Set of 2	12.00 12.00

Airplanes A320

20c, Jetstar II. 25c, AN 225. 55c, Dash-8. 65c, Beech-99. 90c, American Eagle. $2, HFB 320 Itansa Jet.
No. 2077, each $1: a, SR 71 "Blackbird." b, Stealth bomber. c, Northrop YF23. d, F-14 A "Tomcat." e, F-15 "Eagle S." f, MiG 29 "Fulcrum." g, Europa X5. h, Camion.
No. 2078, each $1: a, E400. b, CL-215 C-GKDN Amphibian. c, Piper jet. d, Beech Hawker. e, Lockheed YF22. f, Piper Seneca V. g, CL-215 Amphibian. h, Vantase.
Each $6: No. 2079, F-1 Fighter. No. 2080, Sea Hopper.

1998, Aug. 17

2071-2076	A320	Set of 6	5.50 5.50
		Sheets of 8	
2077-2078	A320	Set of 2	19.00 19.00
		Souvenir Sheets	
2079-2080	A320	Set of 2	13.00 13.00

Intl. Year of the Ocean A321

Marine life: 25c, Fridman fish. 55c, Hydrocoral. 65c, Feather star. 90c, Royal angelfish.
No. 2085, each $1: a, Monk seal. b, Galapagos penguin. c, Manta ray. d, Hawksbill turtle. e, Moorish idol. f, Nautilus. g, Giant clam. h, Tubeworms. i, Nudibranch.
No. 2086, each $1: a, Spotted dolphin. b, Atlantic sailfish. c, Sailfin flying fish. d, Fairy basslet. e, Atlantic spadefish. f, Leatherback turtle. g, Blue tang. h, Coral banded shrimp. i, Rock beauty.
No. 2087, Humpback whale. No. 2088, Leafy sea dragon.

1998, Sept. 7   Litho.   Perf. 14

2081-2084	A321	Set of 4	3.00 3.00
		Sheets of 9	
2085-2086	A321	Set of 2	18.00 18.00
		Souvenir Sheets	
2087	A321	$5 multicolored	5.25 5.25
2088	A321	$6 multicolored	6.25 6.25

Organization of American States, 50th Anniv. A322

1998, Sept. 1   Litho.   Perf. 14

2089	A322	$1 multicolored	1.50 1.50

Ferrari Sports Cars A323

55c, 365 GT 2+2. 90c, Boano/Ellena 250 GT. $1, 375 MM coupe. $5, 212.

1998, Sept. 1

2090-2092	A323	Set of 3	4.25 4.25
		Souvenir Sheet	
2093	A323	$5 multicolored	6.00 6.00

No. 2093 contains one 91x35mm stamp.

Gandhi — A324

1998, Sept. 1

2094	A324	90c shown	1.00 1.00
		Souvenir Sheet	
2095	A324	$6 Seated	6.00 6.00

No. 2094 was issued in sheets of 4.

Pablo Picasso A325

Paintings: 90c, The Painter and His Model, 1926. $1, The Crucifixion, 1930. $2, Nude with Raised Arms, 1908, vert.
$6, Cafe at Royan, 1940.

1998, Sept. 1   Perf. 14½

2096-2098	A325	Set of 3	5.00 5.00
		Souvenir Sheet	
2099	A325	$6 multicolored	6.50 6.50

Royal Air Force, 80th Anniv. A326

No. 2100: a, Nimrod MR2P. b, C-130 Hercules Mk3. c, Panavia Tornado GR1. d, C-130 Hercules landing.
$5, Biplane, hawk. $6, Hawker Hart, jet.

1998, Sept. 1   Perf. 14

2100	A326	$2 Sheet of 4, #a.-d.	8.00 8.00
		Souvenir Sheets	
2101	A326	$5 multicolored	5.25 5.25
2102	A326	$6 multicolored	6.25 6.25

No. 2100d incorrectly inscribed Panavia Tornado GR1.

Nos. 1548-1549, 1551-1552, 1554 Ovptd. "Save the Turtles"

1998, Sept. 14

2103-2107	A221	Set of 5	7.00 7.00

A327   A328

1998 World Scouting Jamboree, Chile: 65c, Scout sign. $1, Scout handshake. $2, World Scout flag.
$5, Lord Baden-Powell.

1998

2108-2110	A327	Set of 3	3.50 3.50
		Souvenir Sheet	
2111	A327	$5 multicolored	6.00 6.00

1998, Dec. 1   Litho.   *Perf. 14*

Birds: 25c, Northern cardinal. 55c, Eastern bluebird. 65c, Carolina wren. 90c, Blue jay. $1, Evening grosbeak. $2, Bohemian waxwing. $5, Northern parula. $6, Painted bunting.

2112-2117	A328	Set of 6	5.00 5.00

Souvenir Sheets

2118	A328	$5 multicolored	5.25 5.25
2119	A328	$6 multicolored	6.25 6.25

Christmas.

New Year 1999 (Year of the Rabbit) A329

1999, Jan. 4   Litho.   *Perf. 14*

2120	A329	$1.50 multicolored	2.25 2.25

No. 2120 was issued in sheets of 4.

Orchids — A330

55c, Broughtonia sanguinea. 65c, Cattleyonia Keith Roth "Roma." 90c, Comparettia falcata. $2, Cochleanthes discolor.

No. 2125, each $1: a, Dracula erythiochaete. b, Lycaste aromatica. c, Masdevallia marguerile. d, Encyclia marfae. e, Laelia gouldiana. f, Huntleya meleagris. g, Galeandria baueri. h, Lycale deppei.

No. 2126, each $1: a, Anguloa clowesii. b, Lemboglossum cervantesii. c, Oncidium cebolleta. d, Millonia. e, Pescatorea lehmannll. f, Sophronitis coccinea. g, Pescatorea cerina. h, Encyclia vitellina.

Each $5: No. 2127, Lepanthes ovalis. No. 2128, Encyclia cochleata.

1999, Apr. 26   Litho.   *Perf. 14*

2121-2124	A330	Set of 4	4.50 4.50

Sheets of 8

2125-2126	A330	Set of 2	17.50 17.50

Souvenir Sheets

2127-2128	A330	Set of 2	11.00 11.00

Trains A331

No. 2129, each $1: a, Class 103.1 Co-Co, Germany. b, Class .24, "Trans Pennine," UK. c, GG1 2-Co-Co-2, US. d, LRC Bo-Bo, Canada. e, Class EW, New Zealand. f, Class SS1 "Shao-Shani," China. g, Gulf, Mobile Ohio, US. h, Class 9100 2-Do-2, France.

No. 2130, each $1: a, County Donegal Petrol Rail Car No. 10, Ireland. b, RDC Single Rail Car, US. c, WDM Class Co-Co, India. d, Bi-Polar No. E-2, US. e, Class X Co-Co, Australia. f, Beijing Bo-Bo, China. g, Class E428 2-Bo-Bo-2, Italy. h, Class 581 Twelve-Car Train, Japan.

$5, X-2000 Tilting Express Train, Sweden, vert. $6, Class 87 Bo-Bo, Great Britain, vert.

1999, May 10   Litho.   *Perf. 14*

Sheets of 8

2129-2130	A331	Set of 2	15.00 15.00

Souvenir Sheets

2131	A331	$5 multicolored	4.50 4.50
2132	A331	$6 multicolored	5.50 5.50

Australia '99, World Stamp Expo.

Prehistoric Animals — A332

25c, Tyrannosaurus, vert. 65c, Hypacrosaurus. 90c, Sauropelta. $2, Zalambdalestes.

No. 2137, each $1: a, Barosaurus. b, Rhamphorhynchus. c, Apatosaurus. d, Archaeopteryx. e, Diplodocus. f, Ceratosaurus. g, Stegosaurus. h, Elaphrosaurus. i, Vulcanodon.

No. 2138, each $1: a, Psittacosaurus. b, Pteranodon. c, Ichthyornis. d, Spinosaurus. e, Parasaurolophus. f, Ornithomimus. g, Anatosaurus. h, Triceratops. i, Baronyx.

$5, Yangchuanosaurus. $6, Brachiosaurus.

1999, June 1   Litho.   *Perf. 14*

2133-2136	A332	Set of 4	3.50 3.50

Sheets of 9

2137-2138	A332	Set of 2	18.00 18.00

Souvenir Sheets

2139	A332	$5 multicolored	5.25 5.25
2140	A332	$6 multicolored	6.25 6.25

Wedding of Prince Edward and Sophie Rhys-Jones A333

No. 2141: a, Sophie. b, Sophie, Edward. c, Edward.
$6, like No. 2141b.

1999, June 19   Litho.   *Perf. 13½*

2141	A333	$3 Sheet of 3, #a.-c.	7.75 7.75

Souvenir Sheet

2142	A333	$6 multicolored	5.50 5.50

IBRA '99, World Philatelic Exhibition, Nuremberg — A334

Exhibition emblem, sailing ship Eendraght and: 65c, Cameroun #58, #56. 90c, Cameroun #11, #9.

Emblem, early German train and: $1, Cameroun #19. $2, Cameroun #6.
$6, Cover with Cameroun #19.

1999, June 22   *Perf. 14*

2143-2146	A334	Set of 4	4.50 4.50

Souvenir Sheet

2147	A334	$6 multicolored	7.00 7.00

Souvenir Sheets

PhilexFrance '99 — A335

Trains: $5, L'Aigle, 1855. $6, Mainline diesel locomotive, 1963.

2148	A335	$5 multicolored	5.00 5.00
2149	A335	$6 multicolored	6.00 6.00

Apollo 11 Moon Landing, 30th Anniv. A336

No. 2150: a, Command Module separation b, Service Module separation. c, 3rd Stage Booster separation. d, Landing, Command Modules go to the moon. e, Apollo Ground Tracker. f, Goldstone Radio Telescope.
$6, Apollo 11 after splashdown.

1999, June 22   *Perf. 14*

2150	A336	$1.45 Sheet of 6, #a.-f.	9.00 9.00

Souvenir Sheet

2151	A336	$6 multicolored	6.00 6.00

Paintings by Hokusai (1760-1849) A337

Details or entire paintings — No. 2152:, each $2 a, Pilgrims at Kirifuri Waterfall. b, Kakura-Sato (rats looking at book, pulling on rope). c, Travelers on the Bridge by Ono Waterfall. d, Fast Cargo Boat Battling the Waves. e, Kakura-Sato (rats working with bales). f, Buufinfinh and Weeping cherry.

No. 2153, each $2: a, Cuckoo and Azalea. b, Soldiers (spear in left hand). c, Lover in the snow. d, Ghost of Koheiji. e, Soldiers (spear in right hand). f, Chinese Poet in Snow.

$5, Empress Jitó. $6, One Hundred Poems by One Hundred Poets.

Perf. 13½x13¾

1999, June 22   Litho.

Sheets of 6

2152-2153	A337	Set of 2	19.00 19.00

Souvenir Sheets

2154	A337	$5 multicolored	4.50 4.50
2155	A337	$6 multicolored	5.50 5.50

Johann Wolfgang von Goethe (1749-1832), Poet — A338

No. 2156: a, Faust perceives an astrological sign. b, Portrait of Goethe and Friedrich von Schiller (1759-1805). c, Faust tempted by Mephistopheles.
$6, Profile portrait of Goethe.

1999, June 22   *Perf. 14*

2156	A338	$2 Sheet of 3, #a.-c.	5.00 5.00

Souvenir Sheet

2157	A338	$6 multicolored	5.00 5.00

Rights of the Child — A339

No. 2158: a, Woman, child. b, Child in blue sweater. c, Two children.
$6, Dove, horiz.

1999, June 22   Litho.   *Perf. 14*

2158	A339	$3 Sheet of 3, #a.-c.	7.50 7.50

Souvenir Sheet

2159	A339	$6 multicolored	5.00 5.00

Queen Mother (b. 1900) — A340

A340a

Gold Frames

No. 2160: a, In 1939. b, In Australia, 1958. c, At Badminton, 1982. d, Hatless, in 1982. $6, In 1953.

1999, Aug. 4   *Perf. 14*

2160	A340	$2 Sheet of 4, #a.-d. + label	7.50 7.50

Souvenir Sheet
Perf. 13¾

2161	A340	$6 multicolored	5.00 5.00

No. 2161 contains one 38x51mm stamp. Compare with Nos. 2345-2346. Backdrop of photo is more pink on No. 2161 than on No. 2346. No. 2161 has embossed arms in margin, while No. 2346 does not.

Litho. & Embossed
Die Cut Perf. 8¾
Without Gum

2161A	A340a	$20 gold & multi	20.00 20.00

Flora & Fauna A341

Designs: 25c, Heliconia lobster claw. 65c, Broad winged hawk. $1, Anthurium. $1.55, Blue-headed hummingbird. $2, Bananaquit. $4 Agouti.

No. 2168: a, White-throated sparrow. b, Blue-winged teal. c, Raccoon. d, Alfalf butterfly. e, Bridge. f, Whitetail deer. g, Gray squirrel. h, Banded purple butterfly. i, Snowdrop. j, Bullfrog. k, Mushrooms. l, Large-blotched ensatina.

$5, Eastern chipmunk. $6, Black-footed ferret.

1999

2162-2167	A341	Set of 6	9.00 9.00

Sheet of 12

2168	A341	90c #a.-l.	10.00 10.00

Souvenir Sheets

2169	A341	$5 multicolored	5.00 5.00
2170	A341	$6 multicolored	6.00 6.00

A342 A343

Dominica Festival Commission: 25c, Domfesta. 55c, $5, Dominica's 21st anniv. as a republic. 65c, Carnival development committee. 90c, World Creole Music Festival.

1999 *Perf. 12½*
2171-2174 A342 Set of 4 .... 2.00 2.00
Souvenir Sheet
Perf. 13¼
2175 A342 $5 multicolored 4.50 4.50
No. 2175 contains one 38x51mm stamp.

1999, Aug. 4 *Perf. 14*
Intl. Year of the Elderly: 25c, Family. 65c, Four people. 90c, Four people, one in chair.
2176 A343 Sheet of 3, #a.-c. 1.40 1.40

A345

A346

Christmas: 25c, Yellow-crowned parrot. 55c, Red bishop. 65c, Troupial. 90c, Puerto Rican woodpecker. $2, Mangrove cuckoo. $3, American robin.
$6, Mary with Child Beside the Wall, by Albrecht Dürer.

1999, Dec. 7 *Litho. Perf. 14*
2178-2183 A345 Set of 6 ...... 6.75 6.75
Souvenir Sheet
2184 A345 $6 multi 5.25 5.25
Inscription on No. 2181 is misspelled.

Perf. 12¾x12½
1999, Dec. 31 *Litho.*
Millennium (Highlights of the early 13th Cent.) — #2185: a, Leonardo Fibonacci publishes "Liber Abaci," 1202. b, St. Francis of Assisi. c, Mongols conquer China. d, Children's Crusade begins, 1212. e, Magna Carta signed, 1215. f, Founding of Salamanca University, 1218. g, Snorri Sturluson writes "Prose Edda". h, Chinese painter Ma Yuan dies, 1225. i, Genghis Khan dies, 1227. j, Zen Buddhism in Japan. k, Sixth Crusade. l, Lubeck-Hamburg League. m, Inquisitions begin, 1231. n, Cordoba conquered by Castilians, 1236. o, Democracy in San Marino. p, Maimonides (60x40mm). q, Notre Dame Cathedral, Paris.
Highlights of the 1940s — No. 2186: a, Japan bombs Pearl Harbor. b, Churchill becomes Prime Minister of Great Britain. c, Regular television broadcasting begins in the US. d, Anne Frank hid in Amsterdam. e, D-Day Invasion. f, Yalta Conference. g, Establishment of the UN. h, Germany surrenders, concentration camps exposed. i, Russians hoist flag over gutted Reichstag building. j, Eniac computer. k, Independence for India. l, Bell Laboratories produce 1st transistor. m, Gandhi assassinated. n, Israel achieves statehood. o, Blockade of West Berlin, Berlin Airlift. p, Atomic bomb tested in New Mexico (60x40mm). q, Establishment of People's Republic of China.

Sheets of 17
2185 A346 55c #a.-q. + label ... 8.50 8.50
2186 A346 55c #a.-q. + label ... 8.50 8.50
See Nos. 2249-2252.

New Year 2000 (Year of the Dragon) A347

2000, Feb. 5 *Perf. 13¾*
2187 A347 $1.50 shown 1.50 1.50
Souvenir Sheet
2188 A347 $4 Dragon, horiz. 3.75 3.75
No. 2187 printed in sheets of 4.

Cats — A348

No. 2189, each $1: a, European Shorthair. b, Devon Rex. c, Chartreux. d, Bengal. e, American Wirehair. f, Siberian. g, Burmese. h, American Shorthair.
No. 2190, each $1: a, Asian Longhair. b, Burmilla. c, Snowshoe. d, Pekeface Persian. e, Himalayan Persian. f, Japanese Bobtail. g, Seychelles Longhair. h, Exotic Shorthair.
Each $6: No. 2191, Awake cat. No. 2192, Sleeping cat.

2000, Feb. 21 *Perf. 14¼*
Sheets of 8, #a.-h.
2189-2190 A348 Set of 2 ...... 16.00 16.00
Souvenir Sheets
2191-2192 A348 Set of 2 ...... 12.00 12.00

Puppies — A349

No. 2193: a, Jack Russell Terrier. b, Shar Peis. c, Basset Hound. d, Boxers. e, Wirehaired Terrier. f, Golden Retrievers.
No. 2194, Beagle.

2000, Feb. 21 *Perf. 14½x14¼*
2193 A349 $1 Sheet of 6, #a.-f. .. 6.00 6.00
Souvenir Sheet
2194 A349 $6 multi 6.00 6.00

Flowers A350

Various flowers making up a photomosaic of Princess Diana.

2000, Apr. 3 *Perf. 13¾*
2195 A350 $1 Sheet of 8, #a.-h. .. 7.50 7.50
See No. 2225.

Butterflies A351

No. 2196, each $1.50: a, Giant swallowtail. b, Tiger pierid. c, Orange theope. d, White peacock. e, Blue tharops. f, Mosaic.
No. 2197, each $1.50: a, Banded king shoemaker. b, Figure-of-eight. c, Grecian shoemaker. d, Blue night. e, Monarch. f, Common morpho.
No. 2198, each $1.50: a, Orange-barred sulphur. b, Clorinde. c, Small flambeau. d, Small lace-wing. e, Polydamas swallowtail. f, Atala.
Each $6: No. 2199, Polydamas swallowtail, vert. No. 2200, Sloane's urania, vert. No. 2201, Blue-green reflector, vert.

2000, Apr. 10 *Perf. 14*
Sheets of 6, #a.-f.
2196-2198 A351 Set of 3 ...... 26.00 26.00
Souvenir Sheets
2199-2201 A351 Set of 3 ...... 17.50 17.50

Flowers — A352

Designs: 65c, Passion flower. 90c, Spray orchid. $1, Peach angel's trumpet. $4, Allamanda.
No. 2206, each $1.65: a, Bird of paradise. b, Lobster claw heliconia. c, Candle bush. d, Flor de San Miguel. e, Hibiscus. f, Oleander.
No. 2207, each $1.65: a, Anthurium. b, Fire ginger. c, Shrimp plant. d, Sky vine thunbergia. e, Ceriman. f, Morning glory.
Each $6: No. 2208, Bird of paradise, diff. No. 2109, Hibiscus, diff.

2000, Apr. 25 *Litho. Perf. 14*
2202-2205 A352 Set of 4 ...... 6.00 6.00
Sheets of 6, #a-f
Perf. 13¾
2206-2207 A352 Set of 2 ...... 19.00 19.00
Souvenir Sheets
Perf. 13½x 13¾
2208-2209 A352 Set of 2 ...... 12.00 12.00
Size of stamps: Nos. 2106-2107, 32x48mm; Nos. 2108-2109, 38x51mm.

Paintings of Anthony Van Dyck — A353

No. 2210, each $1.65: a, Lady Jane Goodwin. b, Philip Herbert, 4th Earl of Pembroke. c, Philip, Lord Wharton. d, Sir Thomas Hammer. e, Olivia Porter, Wife of Enymion Porter. f, Sir Thomas Chaloner.
No. 2211, horiz., each $1.65: a, Ladies in Waiting. b, Thomas Wentworth, Earl of Strafford, with Sir Philip Mainwaring. c, Dorothy Rivers Savage, Viscountess Andover and Her Sister Lady Elizabeth Thimbleby. d, Mountjoy Blount, Earl of Newport, and Lord George Goring with a Page. e, Thomas Killigrew and

an Unidentified Man. f, Elizabeth Villiers, Lady Dalkeith, and Cecilia Killigrew.
No. 2212, horiz, each $1.65: a, The Ages of Man. b, Portrait of a Girl as Erminia Accompanied by Cupid. c, Cupid and Psyche. d, Vertumnus and Pomona. e, The Continence of Scipio. f, Diana and Endymion Surprised by a Satyr.
No. 2213, $5, Achilles and the Daughters of Lycomedes. No. 2214, $5, Amaryllis and Mirtillo. No. 2215, $6, Thomas Howard, 2nd Earl of Arundel, with Alathea, Countess of Arundel.

2000, May 29 *Perf. 13¾*
Sheets of 6, #a-f
2210-2212 A353 Set of 3 ...... 27.00 27.00
Souvenir Sheets
2213-2214 A353 Set of 2 ...... 9.00 9.00
2215 A353 $6 multi 5.50 5.50

First Zeppelin Flight, Cent. — A354

No. 2216: a, Count Ferdinand von Zeppelin (1838-1917). b, First takeoff of LZ-1. c, LZ-10 over field. d, LZ-6 and Deutschland in hangar. e, Arrival of Z-4 at Luneville. f, Victoria Luise.
No. 2217, LZ-1, diff.

2000, June 21 *Litho. Perf. 14*
2216 A354 $1.65 Sheet of 6, #a-f 9.00 9.00
Souvenir Sheet
2217 A354 $6 multi 5.50 5.50

Berlin Film Festival, 50th Anniv. — A355

No. 2218: a, Director Satyajit Ray. b, Mahangar. c, Fanfan La Tulipe. d, Le Salaire de la Peur. e, Les Cousins. f, Hon Dansade en Sommar.
No. 2219, Buffalo Bill and the Indians.

2000, June 21
2218 A355 $1.65 Sheet of 6, #a-f 9.00 9.00
Souvenir Sheet
2219 A355 $6 multi 5.50 5.50

100th Test Match at Lord's Ground — A356

2000, June 21
2220 A356 $4 Norbert Philip 3.50 3.50

Souvenir Sheet
2221 A356 $6 Lord's Ground 5.50 5.50

Souvenir Sheets

2000 Summer Olympics, Sydney — A357

a, Jesse Owens. b, Pole vault. c, Lenin Stadium Moscow, Soviet Union flag. d, Ancient Greek discus thrower.

2000, June 21
2222 A357 $2 Sheet of 4, #a-d 8.00 8.00

Public Railways, 175th Anniv. — A358

No. 2223: a, Locomotion No. 1, George Stephenson. b, Brother Jonathon.

2000, June 21
2223 A358 $3 Sheet of 2, #a-b 6.25 6.25
The Stamp Show 2000, London.

Johann Sebastian Bach — A359

2000, June 21
2224 A359 $6 multi 5.50 5.50

Flower Type of 2000
Various pictures of religious sites making up a photomosaic of Pope John Paul II.

2000, June 21   **Litho.**   **Perf. 13¾**
2225 A350 $1 Sheet of 8, #a-h 8.00 8.00

Apollo-Soyuz Mission, 25th Anniv. — A360

No. 2226, vert.: a, Saturn IB launch vehicle. b, Apollo 18. c, Donald K. Slayton. $6, Apollo and Soyuz docking.

2000, June 21   **Perf. 14**
2226 A360 $3 Sheet of 3, #a-c 9.50 9.50

Souvenir Sheet
2227 A360 $6 multi 6.00 6.00

Souvenir Sheet

Albert Einstein (1879-1955) — A361

2000, June 21   **Perf. 14¼**
2228 A361 $6 multi 5.50 5.50

Prince William, 18th Birthday — A362

No. 2229: a, In ski gear. b, In jacket and red sweater. c, In suit and tie. d, In plaid shirt. $6, With Prince Harry.

2000, June 22   **Perf. 14**
2229 A362 $1.65 Sheet of 4, #a-d 6.25 6.25

Souvenir Sheet
Perf. 13¾
2230 A362 $6 multi 5.50 5.50
No. 2229 contains four 28x42mm stamps.

Bob Hope — A363

No. 2231: a, Microphone at right. b, Entertaining troops. c, Wearing bowler. d, Standing in cake. e, Microphone at left. f, With moon.

2000, Aug. 7   **Perf. 14**
2231 A363 $1.65 Sheet of 6, #a-f 10.00 10.00

Monty Python and the Holy Grail, 25th Anniv. — A364

No. 2232: a, Close-up of Eric Idle. b, Terry Jones, Graham Chapman and John Cleese as three-headed giant, horiz. c, Knights facing castle wall. d, Chapman as King Arthur, with helmeted knight. e, Beheaded knight. f, Armless and legless Black Knight and King Arthur.

2000, Aug. 7   **Perf. 13¾**
2232 A364 90c Sheet of 6, #a-f 5.25 5.25

Popes — A365

No. 2233: a, Clement X, 1670-76. b, Innocent X, 1644-55. c, Nicholas V, 1447-55. d, Martin V, 1417-31. e, Julius III, 1550-55. f, Innocent XII, 1691-1700. $6, Clement XIV, 1769-74.

2000, Sept. 5
2233 A365 $1.65 Sheet of 6, #a-f 10.00 10.00

Souvenir Sheet
2234 A365 $6 multi 5.50 5.50

Monarchs — A366

No. 2235: a, Edward IV of England, 1461-83. b, Peter the Great of Russia, 1682-1725. c, Henry VI of England, 1422-61. d, Henry III of England, 1216-72. e, Richard III of England, 1483-85. f, Edward I of England, 1272-1307. $6, Henry VIII of England, 1509-47.

2000, Sept. 5
2235 A366 $1.65 Sheet of 6, #a-f 10.00 10.00

Souvenir Sheet
2236 A366 $6 multi 5.50 5.50

World Stamp Expo 2000, Anaheim — A367

Spacecraft — No. 2237, $1.65: a, Explorer 14. b, Luna 16. c, Copernicus. d, Explorer 16. e, Luna 10. f, Arybhattan.
No. 2238, $1.65: a, ESSA 8. b, Echo 1. c, Topex Poseidon. d, Diademe. e, Early Bird. f, Molniya.
#2239, $6, Hipparcos. #2240, $6, Eole.

2000, June 21   **Litho.**   **Perf. 14¼x14**
Sheets of 6, #a-f
2237-2238 A367 Set of 2 20.00 20.00

Souvenir Sheets
2239-2240 A367 Set of 2 11.00 11.00

David Copperfield, Magician — A368

2000, Aug. 8   **Perf. 14**
2241 A368 $2 multi 1.75 1.75
Printed in sheets of 4.

Souvenir Sheet

Female Recording Groups of the 1960s — A369

No. 2242 — The Crystals, yellow spotlight covering: a, UR, LL and LR corners. b, UL and LL corners. c, UR and LR corners. d, UL, LL and LR corners.

2000, Aug. 8
2242 A369 90c Sheet of 4, #a-d 3.50 3.50

Christmas — A370

Angel: 25c, No. 2247a, Looking right, purple and yellow green background. 65c, No. 2247b, At left, looking left, purple background. 90c, No. 2247c, At right, purple and orange background. $5, No. 2247d, At center, blue and purple background.

2000, Dec. 4
2243-2246 A370 Set of 4 6.25 6.25
Sheet of 4
2247 A370 $1.90 #a-d 7.00 7.00
Souvenir Sheet
2248 A370 $6 Angel 5.50 5.50

Millennium Type of 1999

Chinese Art — No. 2249, 55c: a, Eight Prize Steeds, by Giuseppe Castiglione. b, Oleanders, by Wu Hsi Tsai. c, Mynah and Autumn Flowers, by Chang Hsiung. d, Hen and Chicks Beneath Chrysanthemums, by Chu Ch'ao. e, Long Living Pine and Crane, by Xugu. f, Flowers and Fruits, by Chu Lien. g, Lotus and Willow, by Pu Hua. h, Kuan-Yin, by Ch'ien Hui-An. i, Human Figures, by Jen hsun. j, Han-Shan and Shih-Te, by Ren Yi. k, Landscape and Human Figure, by Jen Yu. l, Poetic Thoughts While Walking With a Staff, by Wangchen. m, Peony, by Chen Heng-Ko. n, Plum and Orchids, by Wu Chang-Shih. o, Monkey, by Kao Chi-Feng. p, Grapes and Locust, by Ch'i Pai-Shih and Galloping Horse, by Xu Beihong (60x40mm). q, The Beauty, by Lin Fengmian.

History of Change — No. 2250, 55c: a, Star charts. b, Precision tools. c, Science of the stars. d, Investigation into healing a human being. e, Sharing of medical information. f, Church. g, Water alarm clock. h, Weighted clock. i, Spring-loaded miniature clock. j, New technology of glass blowing. k, First screws. l, Wood lathe. m, New systems for assembly blocks for ships. n, Interchangeable parts for rifles. o, Study of movement. p, Efficiency and the Industrial Revolution (60x40mm). q, Concept of efficiency.

Highlights of the 1960s — No. 2251, 55c: a, First birth control pill developed. b, Yuri Gagarin becomes first man in space. c, The first hit for the Beatles in Britain. d, Assassination of John F. Kennedy. e, Dr. Martin Luther King's "I Have a Dream" speech. f, Betty Friedan writes "The Feminine Mystique." g, Kenya gains independence. h, U.S. Surgeon General warns about smoking-related health hazards. i, U.S. Congress passes Civil Rights Act. j, U.S. increases military presence in South Viet Nam. k, Ernesto "Che" Guevara. l, First heart transplant. m, Israel wins Six-day War. n, Ho Chi Minh dies. o, First man on the Moon. p, Communists build wall to divide East and West Berlin (60x40mm). q, Woodstock rock concert.

Highlights of the late 14th Century — No. 2252: a, Minnesingers. b, Acampitzin, King of the Aztecs. c, Black Death eases. d, Giotto's campanile built. e, First French franc. f, Ming Dynasty in China. g, Tamerlane begins conquest of Asia. h, Triumph of Death painted by Francesco Traini. i, Robin Hood. j, Geoffrey Chaucer writes "The Canterbury Tales." k, Succession dispute in Japan. l, Jewish exodus from France. m, Temple of the Golden Pavilion built . n, Strasbourg Cathedral built. o, Alhambra Palace (60x40mm). p, Ife bronzes in Nigeria.

2000, Dec. 31   *Perf. 12¾x12½*
Sheets of 17, #a-q
2249-2251 A346 Set of 3   26.00 26.00
2252 A347 65c Sheet of 17,
    #a-h, j-p, 2 #i   10.00 10.00

Hummingbirds — A371

No. 2253, $1.25: a, Green-throated carib. b, Bee, on branch. c, Bee, in flight. d, Bahama woodstar. e, Antillean mango. f, Blue-headed.
No. 2254, $1.65: a, Eastern streamertail. b, Purple-throated carib. c, Vervain. d, Bahama woodstar. e, Puerto Rican emerald. f, Antillean crested.
No. 2255, $5, Feeders. No. 2256, $6, Hispaniolan.

2000, Dec. 18   **Litho.**   *Perf. 14*
Sheets of 6, #a-f
2253-2254 A371 Set of 2   17.00 17.00
Souvenir Sheets
2255-2256 A371 Set of 2   11.00 11.00
Misspellings abound on Nos. 2253-2254.

New Year 2001 (Year of the Snake) A372

2001, Jan. 2   *Perf. 12x12¼*
2257 A372 $1.20 multi   1.00 1.00
Printed in sheets of 4.

Fauna A373

Designs: 15c, Puerto Rican crested toad. 20c, Axolotl. $1.90, Panamanian golden frog. $2.20, Manatee.
No. 2262, $1.45: a, St. Vincent parrot. b, Indigo macaw. c, Cock of the rock. d, Cuban solenodon. e, Cuban hutia. f, Chinchilla.
No. 2263, $1.45: a, South American flamingo. b, Golden conure. c, Ocelot. d, Giant armadillo. e, Margay. f, Maned wolf.
No. 2264, $6, Anteater. No. 2265, $6, Hawksbill turtle.

2000, Dec. 18   **Litho.**   *Perf. 14*
2258-2261 A373 Set of 4   5.00 5.00
Sheets of 6, #a-f
2262-2263 A373 Set of 2   17.00 17.00
Souvenir Sheets
2264-2265 A373 Set of 2   12.00 12.00

Pokémon — A374

No. 2266, horiz.: a, Butterfree. b, Bulbasaur. c, Caterpie. d, Charmander. e, Squirtle. f, Pidgeotto.

2001, Feb.   *Perf. 13¾*
2266 A374 $1.65 Sheet of 6, #a-f 9.00 9.00
Souvenir Sheet
2267 A374 $6 Nidoking   5.50 5.50

A375

Marine Life A376

Designs: No. 2268, 15c, Banded sea snake. 25c, Soldier fish. 55c, Banner fish. No. 2271, 90c, Crown of thorns starfish.
No. 2272, 15c, Fish. 65c, Ray. No. 2274, 90c, Octopus. $3, Fish, diff.
No. 2276, $1.65: a, White-tip reef shark, lionfish, sergeant major. b, Blue-striped snappers. c, Great hammerhead shark, stovepipe sponge, pink vase sponge. d, Hawaiian monk seal, blue tube coral. e, Seahorse, common clownfish, red feather star coral. f, Bat starfish, brown octopus.
No. 2277, $1.65: a, Red sponge, shoal of Anthias. b, Orange-striped triggerfish. c, Coral grouper, soft tree coral. d, Peacock fan worms, gorgonian sea fan. e, Sweetlips, sea fan. f, Giant clam, golden cup coral.
No. 2278: a, Shark. b, Starfish. c, Seahorse. d, Fish. e, Crab. f, Eel.
No. 2279, $5, Royal angelfish. No. 2280, $5, Pink anemone fish. No. 2281, Turtle.

2001, Feb. 27   *Perf. 14*
2268-2271 A375 Set of 4   2.00 2.00
2272-2275 A376 Set of 4   5.00 5.00
Sheets of 6, #a-f
2276-2277 A375 Set of 2   19.00 19.00
2278 A376 $2 Sheet of 6, #a-f   11.00 11.00
Souvenir Sheets
2279-2280 A375 Set of 2   10.00 10.00
2281 A376 $5 multi   5.00 5.00

Phila Nippon '01, Japan — A377

Art: 25c, Gathering of Chinese Women, by Tsuji Kako. 55c, Village by Bamboo Grove, by Takeuchi Seiho. 65c, Mountain Village in Spring, by Suzuki Hyakunen. 90c, Gentleman Amusing Himself, by Domoto Insho. $1, Calmness of Spring Light, by Seiho. $2, Su's Embankment on a Spring Morning, by Tomioka Tessai.
No. 2288, $1.65: a, Thatched Cottages in the Willows, by Kako. b, Joy in the Garden, by Kako. c, Azalea and butterfly, by Kikuchi Hobun. d, Pine Grove, by Kako. e, Woodcutters Talking in Autumn Valley, by Kubota Beisen.
No. 2289, $1.65: a, Waterfowl in Snow, by Kako. b, Heron and Willow, by Kako. c, Crow and Cherry Blossoms, by Hobun. d, Chrysanthemum Immortal, by Yamamoto Shunkyo. e, Cranes of Immortality, by Kako.
No. 2290, $6, Kamo Riverbank in the Misty Rain, by Kako. No. 2291, $6, Diamond Gate, by Kako. No. 2292, $6, Woman, by Suzuki Harunobu.

2001, May 15   **Litho.**   *Perf. 14*
2282-2287 A377 Set of 6   5.25 5.25
Sheets of 5, #a-e
2288-2289 A377 Set of 2   15.00 15.00
Souvenir Sheets
Perf. 13¾
2290-2292 A377 Set of 3   16.00 16.00
Nos. 2290-2292 each contain one 38x51mm stamp.

Queen Victoria (1819-1901) — A378

No. 2293: a, Prince Albert in uniform. b, Victoria with silver crown. c, Victoria with gold crown. d, Albert in suit.
$6, Victoria as old woman.

2001, May 15   *Perf. 14*
2293 A378 $2 Sheet of 4, #a-d   7.25 7.25
Souvenir Sheet
Perf. 13¾
2294 A378 $6 multi   5.50 5.50
No. 2294 contains one 38x51mm stamp.

Queen Elizabeth II, 75th Birthday — A379

No. 2295: a, With crown. b, With white dress. c, Formal portrait by Pietro Annigoni. d, With orange coat. e, With child. f, With green dress.
$6, In uniform.

2001, May 15   *Perf. 14*
2295 A379 $1.20 Sheet of 6, #a-f 6.25 6.25
Souvenir Sheet
2296 A379 $6 multi   5.50 5.50

Toulouse-Lautrec Paintings — A380

No. 2297: a, Two Women Waltzing. b, The Medical Inspection. c, The Two Girlfriends. d, Woman Pulling Up Her Stocking.

2001, May 15   Litho.   Perf. 13¾
2297 A380 $2 Sheet of 4, #a-d   7.25 7.25
Souvenir Sheet
2298 A380 $6 Self-portrait   5.50 5.50

Giuseppe Verdi (1813-1901), Opera Composer — A381

No. 2299: a, Verdi. b, Lady Macbeth. c, Orchestra. d, Score.

2001, May 15   Perf. 14
2299 A381 $2 Sheet of 4, #a-d   7.25 7.25
Souvenir Sheet
2300 A381 $6 Verdi, score   5.50 5.50

Mushrooms A382

Designs: 15c, Cantharellus cibarius. 25c, Hygrocybe pratensis. 55c, Leccinum aurantiacum. $3, Mycena haematopus.
No. 2305, 90c, horiz.: a, Caesar's amanita. b, Agaricus augustus. c, Clitocybe nuda. d, Hygrocybe plavescens. e, Stropharia kaufmanii. f, Hygrophorus speciosus.
No. 2306, $2: a, Marasmiellus candidus. b, Calostoma cinnabarina. c, Cantharellus infundibuliformis. d, Hygrocybe punicea. e, Basket stinkhorn. f, Agrocybe praecox.
No. 2307, $5, Fly agaric, horiz. No. 2308, $5, Gymnopilus spectabilis, horiz.

2001, June 18
2301-2304 A382 Set of 4   4.50 4.50
Sheets of 6, #a-f
2305-2306 A382 Set of 2   18.00 18.00
Souvenir Sheets
2307-2308 A382 Set of 2   10.00 10.00

Mao Zedong (1893-1976) — A383

No. 2309 — Picture from: a, 1945. b, 1926. c, 1949.
$3, 1930.

2001, May 15   Litho.   Perf. 14
2309 A383 $2 Sheet of 3, #a-c   5.25 5.25
Souvenir Sheet
2310 A383 $3 multi   2.75 2.75

Monet Paintings — A384

No. 2311, horiz.: a, The Basin of Argenteuil. b, The Bridge at Argenteuil. c, The Railway Bridge, Argenteuil. d, The Seine Bridge at Argenteuil.
$6, Woman with a Parasol — Madame Monet and Her Son.

2001, May 15   Perf. 13¾
2311 A384 $2 Sheet of 4, #a-d   7.25 7.25
Souvenir Sheet
2312 A384 $6 multi   5.25 5.25

Fauna — A385

No. 2313: a, St. Vincent parrot. b, Painted bunting. c, Jamaican giant anole. d, White-fronted capuchin. e, Strand racerunner. f, Agouti.
No. 2314: a, Cook's tree boa. b, Tamandua. c, Common iguana. d, Solenodon.
No. 2315, $5, Purple gallinule. No. 2316, $5, Rufous-tailed jacamar. No. 2317, $5, Ruby-throated hummingbird, horiz. No. 2318, $5, Bottlenose dolphins, horiz.

2001, Sept. 3   Perf. 14
2313 A385 $1.45 Sheet of 6, #a-f   8.75 8.75
2314 A385 $2 Sheet of 4, #a-d   8.25 8.25
Souvenir Sheets
2315-2318 A385 Set of 4   19.00 19.00

Birds — A386

Designs: 5c, Yellow warbler. 10c, Palmchat. 15c, Snowy cotinga. 20c, Blue-gray gnatcatcher. 25c, Belted kingfisher. 55c, Red-legged thrush. 65c, Bananaquit. 90c, Yellow-bellied sapsucker. $1, White-tailed tropicbird. $1.45, Ruby-throated hummingbird. $1.90, Painted bunting. $2, Great frigatebird. $5, Brown trembler. $10, Red-footed booby. $20, Sooty tern.

2001, Sept. 3   Litho.   Perf. 14¾x14
2319 A386 5c multi   .20 .20
2320 A386 10c multi   .20 .20
2321 A386 15c multi   .20 .20
2322 A386 20c multi   .20 .20
2323 A386 25c multi   .20 .20
2324 A386 55c multi   .50 .50
2325 A386 65c multi   .55 .55

2326 A386 90c multi   .85 .85
2327 A386 $1 multi   1.00 1.00
2328 A386 $1.45 multi   1.40 1.40
2329 A386 $1.90 multi   1.75 1.75
2330 A386 $2 multi   2.00 2.00
2331 A386 $5 multi   5.00 5.00
2332 A386 $10 multi   10.00 10.00
2333 A386 $20 multi   19.00 19.00
Nos. 2319-2333 (15)   43.05 43.05

No. 2323 exists dated "2005."
See No. 2513.

Photomosaic of Queen Elizabeth II — A387

2001, Nov. 15   Perf. 14
2334 A387 $1 multi   1.00 1.00
Issued in sheets of 8.

Christmas — A388

Paintings by Giovanni Bellini: 25c, Madonna and Child. 65c, Madonna and Child, diff. 90c, Baptism of Christ. $1.20, Madonna and Child, diff. $4, Madonna and Child, diff.
$6, Madonna and Child with Sts. Catherine and Mary Magdalene.

2001, Dec. 3
2335-2339 A388 Set of 5   6.75 6.75
Souvenir Sheet
2340 A388 $6 multi   5.50 5.50

2002 World Cup Soccer Championships, Japan and Korea — A389

No. 2341, $2: a, US team, 1950. b, Poster, 1954. c, Poster, 1958. d, Zozimo, 1962. e, Gordon Banks, 1966. f, Pelé, 1970.
No. 2342, $2: a, Daniel Passarella, 1978. b, Paolo Rossi, 1982. c, Diego Maradona, 1986. d, Poster, 1990. e, Seo Jungulon, 1994. f, Jürgen Klinsmann, 1998.
No. 2343, $5, Face on World Cup, 1930. No. 2344, $5, Face and globe on Jules Rimet Trophy, 2002.

2001, Dec. 13   Perf. 13¾x14¼
Sheets of 6, #a-f
2341-2342 A389 Set of 2   21.00 21.00
Souvenir Sheets
Perf. 14¼
2343-2344 A389 Set of 2   10.00 10.00

Queen Mother Type of 1999 Redrawn

No. 2345: a, In 1939. b, In Australia, 1958. c, At Badminton, 1982. d, Hatless, in 1982. $6, In 1953.

2001, Dec.   Perf. 14
Yellow Orange Frames
2345 A340 $2 Sheet of 4, #a-d, + label   7.00 7.00

Souvenir Sheet
Perf. 13¾
2346 A340 $6 multi   5.25 5.25

Queen Mother's 101st birthday. No. 2346 contains one 38x51mm stamp with a bluer backdrop than that found on No. 2161. Sheet margins of Nos. 2345-2346 lack embossing and gold arms and frames found on Nos. 2160-2161.

Souvenir Sheets

Betty Boop — A390

Betty Boop: No. 2347, $5, In chair, pink rose background. No. 2348, $5, Wearing blue blouse, in jungle. No. 2349, $5, With heart and stars, cat with film reel. No. 2350, $5, Wearing nurse's cap.

2001, Oct. 1   Litho.   Perf. 13¾
2347-2350 A390 Set of 4   18.00 18.00

The Three Stooges — A391

No. 2351: a, Man, Larry, Moe with sledgehammer, Joe Besser. b, Larry, woman, Joe Besser, Moe. c, Joe Besser, Larry and Moe on hands and knees. d, Larry grabbing throat of woman holding Joe Besser and Moe. e, Joe Besser drinking from baby bottle, pony, Moe and Larry. f, Military policeman, Joe Besser, Larry, woman. g, Larry. h, Joe Besser. i, Moe.
No. 2352, $5, Moe and Larry, "On the air" sign. No. 2353, $5, Larry and pony.

2001, Oct. 1   Litho.   Perf. 13¾
2351 A391 $1 Sheet of 9, #a-i   8.00 8.00
Souvenir Sheets
2352-2353 A391 Set of 2   9.00 9.00

Souvenir Sheet

New Year 2002 (Year of the Horse) — A392

No. 2354: a, Man with pole, horse. b, Horses grazing. c, Man currying horse. d, Horses with heads up.

2001, Dec. 17   *Perf. 14*
2354 A392 $1.65 Sheet of 4, #a-
       d   6.00 6.00

Reign of Queen Elizabeth II, 50th Anniv. — A393

No. 2355: a, Wearing blue coat. b, With Prince Philip. c, Wearing tiara. d, Wearing flowered hat.
$6, With Prince Philip, diff.

2002, Feb. 6   *Perf. 14¼*
2355 A393 $2 Sheet of 4, #a-d   7.00 7.00
     Souvenir Sheet
2356 A393 $6 multi   5.00 5.00

United We Stand — A394

2002, Feb.   *Perf. 13½x13¼*
2357 A394 $2 multi   1.50 1.50
     Printed in sheets of 4.

Shirley Temple in "Just Around the Corner" — A395

No. 2358, horiz.: a, Temple, woman with dogs. b, Temple, man and woman. c, Temple and man. d, Boy eating turkey leg, Temple carving turkey. e, Temple with old man. f, Temple with group of boys.

No. 2359: a, Boy, Temple with purse. b, Man and Temple using fingers as guns. c, Temple and man. d, Temple cutting boy's hair.
$6, Temple with black man on toadstool.

2002, Apr. 8   *Perf. 12¼*
2358 A395 $1.90 Sheet of 6,
       #a-f   10.00 10.00
2359 A395 $2 Sheet of 4,
       #a-d   7.25 7.25
     Souvenir Sheet
2360 A395 $6 multi   5.25 5.25

Japanese Art — A396

No. 2361, $1.20: a, The Courtesan Tsukioka of the Teahouse Hyogo-Ya, by Eisui Ichirakutei. b, Woman and Servant in the Snow, by Choki Eishosai. c, The Courtesan Shiratsuyu of the Teahouse Wakana-Ya, by Eisho Chokosai. d, Ohisa of the Takashima-Ya, by Toyokuni Utagawa. e, Woman and a Cat, by Kunimasa Utagawa. f, One of "Genre Scenes of Beauties," by Eisen Keisai.
No. 2362, $1.65: a, Women Inside and Outside a Mosquito Net, by Harushige Suzuki. b, Komachi at Shimizu, by Harushige Suzuki. c, Women Viewing Plum Blossoms, by Harunobu Suzuki. d, Women Cooling Themselves at Shijogawara in Kyoto, by Toyohiro Utagawa. e, Woman Reading a Letter, by Utamaro Kitagawa. f, Women Dressed for the Kashima Dance at the Niwaka Festival, by Utamaro Kitagawa.
No. 2363, $1.90: a, Actor Kiyotaro Iwai, by Kunimasa Utagawa. b, Actors Hiriji Otani III and Ryuzo Arashi, by Sharaku Toshusai. c, Actor Komazo Ichikawa II, by Shunko Katsukawa. d, Actors Yaozo Ichikawa and Hangoro Sakata III, by Sharaku Toshusai. e, Actor Torazo Tanimura, by Sharaku Toshusai. f, Actor Kiyotaro Iwai as Oishi, by Toyokuni Utagawa.
No. 2464, $5, Actor Riko Nakamura, by Shunsho Katsukawa. No. 2365, $5, Actors Hanshiro Iwai IV and Sojuro Sawamura III, by Kiyonaga Torii, horiz. No. 2366, $6, Ofuji, Daughter of the Motoyanagi-Ya, by Harunobu Suzuki.

2002, June 17   *Perf. 14¼*
     Sheets of 6, #a-f
2361-2363 A396   Set of 3   24.00 24.00
     Souvenir Sheets
2364-2366 A396   Set of 3   12.00 12.00

Souvenir Sheet

Intl. Year of Mountains — A397

No. 2367: a, Mt. Everest. b, Mt. Kilimanjaro. c, Mt. McKinley.

2002, July 15   *Perf. 14*
2367 A397 $2 Sheet of 3, #a-c   5.00 5.00

2002 Winter Olympics, Salt Lake City A398

Designs: No. 2368, $2, Skiing. No. 2369, $2, Bobsled.

2002, July 15   *Perf. 13½*
2368-2369 A398   Set of 2   3.50 3.50
   a.   Souvenir sheet, #2368-2369   3.50 3.50

First Solo Trans-Atlantic Flight, 75th Anniv. — A399

No. 2370: a, Charles Lindbergh and Spirit of St. Louis. b, Charles and Anne Morrow Lindbergh.
$6, Charles Lindbergh and Spirit of St. Louis, diff.

2002, July 15   *Perf. 14*
2370 A399 $3 Sheet of 2, #a-b   5.00 5.00
     Souvenir Sheet
2371 A399 $6 multi   5.00 5.00

Popeye in New York — A400

No. 2372, $1: a, Olive Oyl. b, Brutus. c, Sweet Pea. d, Wimpy. e, Jeep. f, Popeye.
No. 2373, $1.90: a, Popeye and Olive Oyl, giraffe at Bronx Zoo. b, Popeye and Olive Oyl, Statue of Liberty. c, Popeye, Olive Oyl, Empire State Building. d, Popeye skating at Rockefeller Center. e, Popeye at Yankee Stadium. f, Popeye helping firefighters.
No. 2374, $6, Popeye, Atlas Statue, Rockefeller Center. No. 2375, $6, Popeye, Olive Oyl and Radio City Music Hall Rockettes, horiz.

2002, July 22
     Sheets of 6, #a-f
2372-2373 A400   Set of 2   15.00 15.00
     Souvenir Sheets
2374-2375 A400   Set of 2   10.50 10.50

20th World Scout Jamboree, Thailand — A401

No. 2376: a, Lord Robert Baden-Powell (facing forward). b, Lady Olave Baden-Powell. c, Maceo Johnson.
$6, Lord Baden-Powell (profile).

2002, July 15   **Litho.**   *Perf. 14¼x14*
2376 A401 $3 Sheet of 3, #a-c   8.00 8.00
     Souvenir Sheet
2377 A401 $6 multi   5.25 5.25

Birds, Insects, Moths and Whales — A402

No. 2378, $1.50, vert. — Birds: a, Brown trembler. b, Snowy ctinga. c, Bananaquit. d, Painted bunting. e, Belted kingfisher. f, Ruby-throated hummingbird.
No. 2379, $1.50, vert. — Insects: a, Field cricket. b, Migratory grasshopper. c, Honey bee. d, Hercules beetle. e, Black ant. f, Cicada.
No. 2380, $1.50, vert. — Moths: a, Carolina sphinx. b, White-lined sphinx. c, Orizaba silkmoth. d, Hieroglyphic moth. e, Hickory tussock moth. f, Diva moth.
No. 2381, $1.50, vert. — Whales: a, Sei. b, Killer. c, Blue. d, White. e, Pygmy. f, Sperm.
No. 2382, $6, Yellow-bellied sapsucker. No. 2383, $6, Bumble bee. No. 2384, $6, Ornate moth. No. 2385, $6, Gray whale.

2002, July 29   *Perf. 14*
     Sheets of 6, #a-f
2378-2381 A402   Set of 4   32.50 32.50
     Souvenir Sheets
2382-2385 A402   Set of 4   20.00 20.00

A403

A404

Amphilex 2002 Intl. Stamp Exhibition, Amsterdam — A405

No. 2386 — Dutch Nobel Prize winners: a, Willem Einthoven, Medicine, 1924. b, Nobel Economics medal. c, Peter J. W. Debye, Chemistry, 1936. d, Frits Zernike, Physics, 1953. e, Jan Tinbergen, Economics, 1969. f, Simon van der Meer, Physics, 1984.

No. 2387 — Dutch lighthouses: a, Marken. b, Harlingen. c, Den Oever. d, De Ven. e, Urk. f, Oosterleek.

No. 2388 — Traditional women's costumes: a, South Holland woman with small white head covering (facing forward). b, Zeeland woman with large white head covering (facing backwards). c, Limburg woman with black scarf.

2002, Aug. 30   **Perf. 13½x13¼**
2386 A403 $1.50 Sheet of 6, #a-f   8.00 8.00
2387 A404 $1.50 Sheet of 6, #a-f   8.00 8.00
     Perf. 13½
2388 A405 $3 Sheet of 3, #a-c   8.00 8.00

Intl. Year of Ecotourism A406

Island scenes and cartoon characters: 45c, Detective H2O. 50c, Factman. 55c, B.B. 60c, Stanley the Starfish. 90c, Toxi. $1.20, Adopt. $6, Litterbit.

2002, Oct. 16   **Perf. 14¼**
2389-2394 A406   Set of 6   3.25 3.25
     Souvenir Sheet
2395 A406 $6 multi   5.00 5.00

Elvis Presley (1935-77) A407

2002, Oct. 28   **Perf. 13¾**
2396 A407 $1.50 multi   1.10 1.10
   Printed in sheets of 6 stamps with slightly differing frames.

Amerigo Vespucci (1454-1512), Explorer — A408

No. 2397: a, Compass rose. b, Vespucci with map. c, Map scroll.
$5, Two men.

2002, Nov. 28   **Perf. 13¾**
2397 A409 $3 Sheet of 3, #a-c   8.00 8.00
     Souvenir Sheet
     Perf. 14
2398 A409 $5 multi   4.50 4.50
No. 2397 contains three 50x38mm stamps.

Pres. John F. Kennedy (1917-63) — A409

No. 2399, $1.90: a, Wearing military uniform. b, With red denomination at UL. c, With blue denomination at UR. d, Wearing tan suit.
No. 2400, $1.90 (denominations at UL in blue): a, Wearing red tie. b, Wearing blue tie (profile). c, Wearing black tie. d, With hand on chin.

2002, Dec. 16   **Perf. 14**
     Sheets of 4, #a-d
2399-2400 A409   Set of 2   13.50 13.50

Pres. Ronald Reagan — A410

No. 2401, $1.90: a, Wearing cowboy hat. b, Wearing blue green sweater. c, Wearing red sweater. d, Wearing blue sweater.
No. 2402, $1.90, horiz.: a, Wearing blue shirt, and with wife, Nancy. b, Nancy and US flag. c, Ronald. d, Wearing pink shirt, and with wife.

2002, Dec. 16   **Litho.**   **Perf. 14**
     Sheets of 4, #a-d
2401-2402 A410   Set of 2   13.50 13.50

Princess Diana (1961-97) — A411

2002, Dec. 16
2403 A411 $1.90 Sheet of 4, #a-d   7.00 7.00
     Souvenir Sheet
2404 A411 $5 multi   4.50 4.50

Elizabeth "Ma Pampo" Israel, 128th Birthday — A412

2003, Jan. 27   **Perf. 13½x13¼**
2405 A412 90c multi   .70 .70

New Year 2003 (Year of the Ram) — A413

2003, Feb. 10   **Perf. 13¾**
2406 A413 $1.65 multi   1.25 1.25
   Printed in sheets of 4.

     Souvenir Sheets

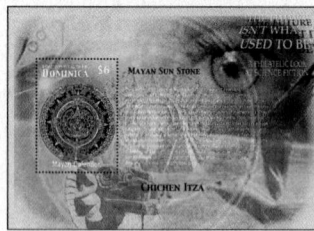

Science Fiction — A414

Designs: No. 2407, $6, Mayan calendar. No. 2408, $6, Atlas. No. 2409, $6, Confucius. No. 2410, $6, Nazca Lines. No. 2411, $6, Pres. Franklin D. Roosevelt and Pres. John F. Kennedy. No. 2412, $6, Zoroaster.

2003, Feb. 10   **Perf. 13¼**
2407-2412 A414   Set of 6   27.50 27.50

A415

Coronation of Queen Elizabeth II, 50th Anniv. — A416

No. 2413: a, Wearing white dress, no crown. b, Wearing black robe. c, Wearing crown.
$6, Wearing crown, diff. $20, Wearing red robe.

2003   **Litho.**   **Perf. 14**
2413 A415 $3 Sheet of 3, #a-c   6.75 6.75
     Souvenir Sheet
2414 A415 $6 multi   4.50 4.50
     Miniature Sheet
     Litho. & Embossed
     Perf. 13¼x13
2415 A416 $20 gold & multi   15.00 15.00
   Issued: Nos. 2413-2414, 5/13; No. 2415, 2/24.

Prince William, 21st Birthday — A417

No. 2416: a, Wearing dark blue shirt. b, Wearing blue suit, holding flowers. c, In polo uniform.
$6, Wearing black suit.

2003, June 21   Litho.   **Perf. 14**
2416 A417 $3 Sheet of 3, #a-c   6.75 6.75
    Souvenir Sheet
2417 A417 $6 multi   4.50 4.50

Intl. Year of Fresh Water — A418

No. 2418: a, Trafalgar Falls. b, YS Falls. c, Dunn's River.
$6, Annandale Falls.

2003, June 21   **Perf. 13½**
2418 A418 $3 Sheet of 3, #a-c   6.75 6.75
    Souvenir Sheet
2419 A418 $6 multi   4.50 4.50

Teddy Bears, Cent. — A419

No. 2420 — Bear with: a, Purple shirt. b, Pink shirt and party favor. c, Green shirt and party favor. d, Black hat. e, Purple hat. f, Pink shirt and birthday cake.
No. 2421 — Bear with: a, Reindeer sweater, text at top. b, Santa Claus costume, text at top. c, Santa Claus costume, text at bottom. d, Reindeer sweater, text at bottom.

2003, June 21   **Perf. 13½**
2420 A419 $1.65 Sheet of 6, #a-f   7.50 7.50
2421 A419 $2 Sheet of 4, #a-d   6.00 6.00
No. 2421 contains four 37x51mm stamps.

No. 2422, $2 — Cadillacs: a, 1903 Model A Runabout. b, 1912 Model 30. c, 1918 Type 57 Victoria Coupe. d, 1927 Lasalle Convertible Coupe.
No. 2423, $2 — Corvettes: a, 1953. b, 1956. c, 1957. d, 1962.
No. 2424, $5, 1933 Cadillac 355-C V8 sedan. No. 2425, $5, 1959 Corvette.

2003, June 21   **Perf. 13¼**
    Sheets of 4, #a-d
2422-2423 A420   Set of 2   12.00 12.00
    Souvenir Sheets
2424-2425 A420   Set of 2   7.50 7.50

Tour de France Bicycle Race, Cent. — A421

No. 2426 — Champions: a, Firmin Lambot, 1919. b, Phillippe Thys, 1920. c, Léon Scieur, 1921. d, Lambot, 1922.
$5, François Faber.

2003, June 21
2426 A421 $2 Sheet of 4, #a-d   6.00 6.00
    Souvenir Sheet
2427 A421 $5 multi   3.75 3.75

History of Aviation — A422

No. 2428: a, Sputnik, first orbiting satellite, 1957. b, Yuri Gagarin, first man in space, 1961. c, Neil Armstrong, first man on the Moon, 1969. d, Skylab 1, 1973.
$6, Flight over Mt. Everest, 1933.

2003, June 21   **Perf. 14**
2428 A422 $2 Sheet of 4, #a-d   6.50 6.50
    Souvenir Sheet
2429 A422 $6 multi   5.00 5.00

Lewis & Clark Expedition A423

Designs: 20c, Dealing with the Chinook Indians. 50c, Compass used in expedition. 55c, Rocky Mountains. 65c, Medals presented to the Indians, vert. 90c, First encounter with grizzly bear. $1, Befriending Shoshone Indians. $2, Lewis after the expedition, vert. $4, Lewis & Clark, vert.
No. 2438, $5, Meriwether Lewis, vert. No. 2439, $5, William Clark, vert.

2003, June 21
2430-2437 A423   Set of 8   7.50 7.50
    Souvenir Sheets
2438-2439 A423   Set of 2   7.50 7.50

2002 World Cup Soccer Championships, Japan and Korea — A424

No. 2440, $1.45: a, Danny Mills. b, Paul Scholes. c, Darius Vassell. d, Michael Owen. e, Emile Heskey. f, Rio Ferdinand.
No. 2441, $1.45: a, Bobby Moore. b, Roger Hunt. c, Gordon Banks. d, Bobby Charlton. e, Alan Ball. f, Geoff Hurst.
No. 2442, $3: a, Ashley Cole. b, David Seaman.
No. 2443, $3: a, Sven-Goran Eriksson. b, Nikki Butt.
No. 2444, $3: a, Robbie Fowler. b, Sol Campbell.
No. 2445, $3: a, Charlton, Ball and Hunt. b, Nobby Stiles.
No. 2446, $3: a, Franz Beckenbauer. b, Oliver Kahn.

2003, June 21   **Perf. 13¼**
    Sheets of 6, #a-f
2440-2441 A424   Set of 2   13.00 13.00
    Souvenir Sheets of 2, #a-b
2442-2446 A424   Set of 5   22.50 22.50

CARICOM, 30th Anniv. — A425

2003, July 25   **Perf. 13½**
2447 A425 $1 multi   .75 .75

Christmas A426

Painting details: 50c, Madonna and Child with the Young St. John, by Correggio. 90c, Madonna in Glory with the Christ Child and Sts. Frances and Alvise with the Donor, by Titian. $1.45, Madonna and Child with Angels Playing Musical Instruments, by Correggio. $3, Madonna of the Cherries, by Titian.
$6, Holy Family with John the Baptist, by Andrea del Sarto.

2003, Nov. 17   Litho.   **Perf. 14¼**
2448-2451 A426   Set of 4   4.50 4.50
    Souvenir Sheet
2452 A426 $6 multi   4.50 4.50

New Year 2004 (Year of the Monkey) — A427

No. 2453: a, Orange monkey, hindquarters of brown monkey. b, Monkey with brown face. c, Brown monkey drinking water. d, Monkey with blue face.

2004, Jan. 5   Litho.   **Perf. 14**
2453 A427 $1.50 Sheet of 4, #a.-d.   4.50 4.50

Paintings of Pablo Picasso — A428

No. 2454, vert.: a, Portrait of Manuel Pallarés. b, Woman with Vase of Flowers. c, Woman with a Fan (Fernande). d, Portrait of Clovis Sagot.
$5, Brick Factory at Torosa (The Factory).

2004, Mar. 8   **Perf. 14¼**
2454 A428 $1 Sheet of 4, #a.-d.   3.00 3.00
    Imperf
2455 A428 $5 multi   3.75 3.75
No. 2454 contains four 38x50mm stamps.

Paintings of Paul Gauguin — A429

No. 2456: a, Village Tahitien avec la Femme en Marche. b, La Barriere. c, Bonjour, Monsieur Gauguin. d, Vegetation Tropicale.
$5, Petites Bretonnes Devant la Mer.

2004, Mar. 8   **Perf. 14¼**
2456 A429 $2 Sheet of 4, #a.-d.   6.00 6.00
    Imperf
2457 A429 $5 multi   3.75 3.75
No. 2456 contains four 38x50mm stamps.

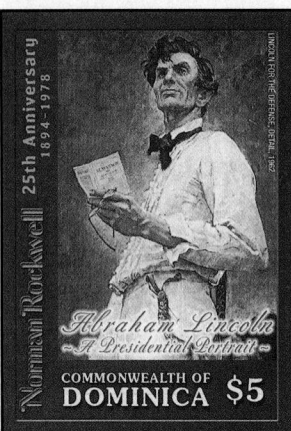

Paintings of Presidents by Norman Rockwell — A430

No. 2458: a, Dwight D. Eisenhower. b, John F. Kennedy. c, Lyndon B. Johnson. d, Richard M. Nixon.
$5, Abraham Lincoln.

2004, Mar. 8   **Perf. 14¼**
2458 A430 $2 Sheet of 4, #a.-d. 6.00 6.00
Imperf
2459 A430 $5 multi 3.75 3.75
No. 2458 contains four 38x50mm stamps.

Paintings of James McNeill Whistler — A431

Designs: 50c, Symphony in White No. 3. $1, The Artist's Studio, vert. $1.65, The Thames in Ice, vert. No. 2463, $2, Arrangement in Black: Portrait of F. R. Leyland, vert.
No. 2464, $2, vert.: a, Arrangement in Brown & Black: Portrait of Miss Rosa Corder. b, Harmony in Red: Lamplight. c, Symphony in Flesh Color & Pink: Portrait of Mrs. Frances Leyland. d, Arrangement in Yellow & Gray: Effie Deans.
$5, Harmony in Gray and Green: Miss Cicely Alexander, vert.

2004, Mar. 8   **Perf. 14¼**
2460-2463 A431 Set of 4 4.00 4.00
Perf. 13½
2464 A431 $2 Sheet of 4, #a-d 6.00 6.00
Imperf
Size: 71x103mm
2465 A431 $5 multi 3.75 3.75
No. 2464 contains four 35x70mm stamps.

Fish A432

Designs: 20c, Banded butterflyfish. 25c, Queen angelfish. 55c, Porkfish. No. 2469, $5, Redband parrotfish.
No. 2470: a, Beaugregory. b, Porkfish, diff. c, Bicolor cherubfish. d, Rock beauty. e, Blackfin snapper. f, Blue tang.
No. 2471, $5, Indigo hamlet.

2004, Mar. 8   **Perf. 14¼x14¾**
2466-2469 A432 Set of 4 4.50 4.50
Perf. 14
2470 A432 $2 Sheet of 6, #a-f 9.00 9.00
Souvenir Sheet
2471 A432 $5 multi 3.75 3.75
Nos. 2470-2471 each contain 42x28mm stamps.

Shells A433

Designs: 20c, Siratus perelegans. 90c, Polystira albida. $1.45, Cypraea cervus. $2, Strombus gallus.
No. 2476: a, Strombus pugilis. b, Cittarium pica. c, Distorsio clathrata. d, Melongena morio. e, Prunum labiata. f, Chione paphia.
$5, Strombus alatus, vert.

2004, Mar. 8   **Perf. 14¼x14¾**
2472-2475 A433 Set of 4 3.50 3.50
Perf. 14
2476 A433 $1.90 Sheet of 6, #a-f 8.50 8.50
Souvenir Sheet
2477 A433 $5 multi 3.75 3.75
No. 2476 contain six 42x28mm stamps; No. 2477 contains one 28x42mm stamp.

Orchids — A434

Designs: 25c, Epidendrum pseudepidendrum. 55c, Aspasia epidendroides. $1.50, Cochleanthes discolor. $4, Brassavola nodosa.
No. 2482: a, Laelia anceps. b, Caularthron bicornutum. c, Cattleya velutina. d, Cattleya warneri. e, Oncidium splendidum. f, Psychlis atropurpurea.
$5, Maxillaria cuculata, vert.

2004, Mar. 8   **Perf. 14¼x14¾**
2478-2481 A434 Set of 4 4.75 4.75
Perf. 14
2482 A434 $1.90 Sheet of 6, #a-f 8.50 8.50
Souvenir Sheet
2483 A434 $5 multi 3.75 3.75
No. 2482 contains six 42x28mm stamps; No. 2483 contains one 28x42mm stamp.

Butterflies — A435

Designs: 50c, Small flambeau. 90c, Tiger pierid. $1, White peacock. No. 2469, $2, Cramer's mesene.
No. 2488, $2: a, Figure-of-eight. b, Orange theope. c, Clorinde. d, Grecian shoemaker. e, Orange-barred sulphur. f, Common morpho.
$5, Giant swallowtail, vert.

2004, Mar. 8   **Perf. 14¼x14¾**
2484-2487 A435 Set of 4 3.25 3.25
Perf. 14
2488 A435 $2 Sheet of 6, #a-f 9.00 9.00
Souvenir Sheets
2489 A435 $5 multi 3.75 3.75
No. 2488 contains six 42x28mm stamps; No. 2489 contains one 28x42mm stamp.

Olympic Gold Medalists A436

Designs: 20c, Elizabeth Robinson, Amsterdam, 1928. 25c, Károly Takács, London, 1948. 55c, Bob Beamon, Mexico City, 1968. 65c, Mildred Didrikson, Los Angeles, 1932. $1, Ville Ritola, Paris, 1924. $1.65, Alfred Hajós (Guttman), Athens, 1896. $2, Paavo Nurmi, Antwerp, 1920. $4, Nedo Nadi, Antwerp, 1920.

2004, Apr. 12   **Perf. 13¼**
2490-2497 A436 Set of 8 7.75 7.75

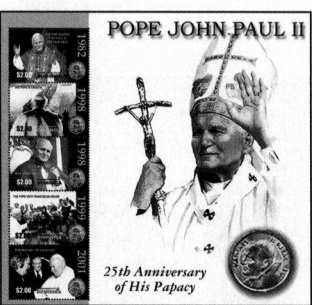

Election of Pope John Paul II, 25th Anniv. (in 2003) — A437

No. 2498: a, Praying for peace in Falkland Islands, 1982. b, In Croatia, 1998. c, Seated, 1998. d, With Franciscan monks, 1999. e, Remembering the Holocaust, 2001.

2004, June 21   **Litho.**   **Perf. 14**
2498 A437 $2 Sheet of 5, #a-e 7.50 7.50

European Soccer Championships, Portugal — A438

No. 2499, vert.: a, Jose Luis Villalonga. b, Lev Yashin. c, Marcelino Martinez. d, Santiago Bernabeu Stadium.
$6, 1964 Spain team.

2004, June 21   **Perf. 14**
2499 A438 $2 Sheet of 4, #a-d 6.00 6.00
Souvenir Sheet
Perf. 14¼
2500 A438 $6 multi 4.50 4.50
No. 2499 contains four 28x42mm stamps.

Trains — A439

No. 2501, $1: a, Engine #22, V7 T4-4-0, V7T4-6-0. b, Don J12. c, Baldwin 2-D-D. d,

Southern Engine #20. e, 143-890 2DB class electric locomotive. f, Engine #1.
No. 2502, $1: a, Canadian Pacific freight train. b, Queensland Rail IM U railroad. c, Green and white Shinkansen locomotive. d, Amtrak locomotive. e, Shinkansen locomotive in station. f, YPDMU rail cars.
No. 2503, $1: a, Santa Fe Railroad locomotive. b, Via Rail train, Canada. c, Two Conrail road switchers. d, Strasburg Railroad #90. e, Deltic diesel-electric engine. f, Brighton Belle.
No. 2504, $6, Golsdorf two cylinder compound locomotive 4-4-0. No. 2505, $6, Southern Pacific 4449 4-8-4. No. 2506, $6, White, yellow and blue Shinkansen.

2004, July 12   **Perf. 13¼x13½**
Sheets of 6, #a-f
2501-2503 A439 Set of 3 13.50 13.50
Souvenir Sheets
2504-2506 A439 Set of 3 13.50 13.50

D-Day, 60th Anniv. A440

Designs: $1, Eddie Hannath. $4, Pres. Franklin D. Roosevelt.
No. 2509: a, Rangers make their way towards the cliffs of Pointe du Hoc. b, Rangers begin scaling the cliffs of Pointe du Hoc. c, British troops advance on Sword Beach. d, An AVRE Petard heads inland off Sword Beach.
$6, British troops landing on Sword Beach.

2004, July 22   **Perf. 14**
Stamp + Label (#2507-2508)
2507-2508 A440 Set of 2 3.75 3.75
2509 A440 $2 Sheet of 4, #a-d 6.00 6.00
Souvenir Sheet
2510 A440 $6 multi 4.50 4.50

George Herman "Babe" Ruth (1895-1948), Baseball Player — A441

No. 2511: a, Swinging bat. b, Swinging bat, looking up. c, Holding three bats. d, Hand on knee.

2004, Aug. 18   **Perf. 13½x13¼**
2511 A441 $2 Sheet of 4, #a-d 6.00 6.00

Marilyn Monroe (1926-62),
Actress — A442

No. 2512: a, Wearing earrings and necklace. b, Wearing earrings. c, Wearing no earrings or necklace. d, Wearing necklace.

2004, Aug. 18
2512 A442 $2 Sheet of 4, #a-d   6.00 6.00

Bird Type of 2001
2004, Sept. 3   Perf. 14¾x14
2513 A386 50c Baltimore oriole   .40 .40
Exists dated "2005."

Queen
Juliana of the
Netherlands
(1909-2004)
A443

2004, Sept. 21   Perf. 13¼
2514 A443 $2 multi   1.50 1.50
Printed in sheets of 6.

Intl. Year of Peace — A444

No. 2515: a, Mother Teresa, UN emblem. b, Mother Teresa feeding poor. c, Dove.

2004, Sept. 21   Perf. 14
2515 A444 $2 Sheet of 3, #a-c   4.50 4.50

Souvenir Sheet

Deng Xiaoping (1904-97) and Mao
Zedong (1893-1976), Chinese
Leaders — A445

2004, Sept. 21   Perf. 14
2516 A445 $6 multi   4.50 4.50

National Soccer Team — A446

2004, Nov. 8   Litho.   Perf. 12
2517 A446 90c multi   .70 .70

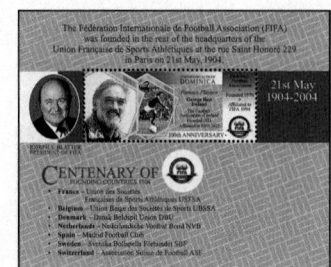

FIFA (Fédération Internationale de
Football Association), Cent. — A447

No. 2518: a, Ferenc Puskas. b, Rivaldo. c, Carsten Jancker. d, Johan Cruyff.
$6, George Best.

2004, Nov. 8   Perf. 12¾x12½
2518 A447 $2 Sheet of 4, #a-d   6.00 6.00
Souvenir Sheet
2519 A447 $6 multi   4.50 4.50

Worldwide Fund for Nature
(WWF) — A448

No. 2520: a, Green-throated Carib (denomination in blue). b, Purple-throated Carib (denomination in white). c, Green-throated Carib (denomination in white). d, Purple-throated Carib (denomination in red).

2005, Jan. 10   Perf. 14
2520 A448 $2 Block of 4, #a-d   6.00 6.00
  e.   Miniature sheet, 2 each
        #2520a-2520d   12.00 12.00

Prehistoric Animals — A449

No. 2521, $2: a, Tyrannosaurus rex. b, Velociraptor. c, Stegosaurus. d, Psittacosaurus.
No. 2522, $2: a, Mammuthus columbi. b, Spinosaurus. c, Ankylosaurus. d, Mammuthus primigenius.
No. 2523, $2: a, Pterodactylus. b, Pteranodon. c, Sordes. d, Caudiptheryx zoui.
$3, Compsognathus. $5, Archaeopteryx. $6, Mammuthus primigenius, diff.

2005, Jan. 10   Perf. 12¾
Sheets of 4, #a-d
2521-2523 A449   Set of 3   18.00 18.00
Souvenir Sheets
2524-2526 A449   Set of 3   10.50 10.50

Birds
A450

Designs: 25c, Brown booby. 90c, Brown pelican. $1, Red-billed tropicbird. $4, Northern gannet.
No. 2531: a, Great egret. b, Black-necked grebe. c, Turkey vulture. d, Snail kite.
$6, Red knot.

2005, Jan. 10   Perf. 14
2527-2530 A450   Set of 4   4.75 4.75
2531 A450 $2 Sheet of 4, #a-d   6.00 6.00
Souvenir Sheet
2532 A450 $6 multi   4.50 4.50

Mushrooms — A451

No. 2533: a, Cortinarius mucosus. b, Cortinarius splendens. c, Cortinarius rufoolivaceus. d, Inocybe erubescens.
$6, Split fibercap.

2005, Jan. 10
2533 A451 $2 Sheet of 4, #a-d   6.00 6.00
Souvenir Sheet
2534 A451 $6 multi   4.50 4.50

Miniature Sheet

Flowers — A452

No. 2535: a, Sweetshrub. b, Pink turtleheads. c, Flowering quince. d, Water lily.
$6, Glory of the snow, vert.

2005, Jan. 10   Litho.   Perf. 14
2535 A452 $2 Sheet of 4, #a-d   6.00 6.00
Souvenir Sheet
2535E A452 $6 multi   4.50 4.50

New Year 2005
(Year of the
Rooster) — A453

2005, Jan. 24   Perf. 12¾x12½
2536 A453 $1 shown   .75 .75
Souvenir Sheet
Perf. 12
2537 A453 $4 Roosters   3.00 3.00
No. 2537 contains one 56x36mm stamp.

A454

Elvis Presley (1935-77) — A455

Elvis Presley (1935-77) — A455a

No. 2538: a, Green background under country name and near shirt collar. b, Guitar. c, Large red violet areas at side of head. d, Dark green background under country name, blue background near shirt collar. e, Purple background near shirt collar. f, Small red violet areas at side of head.
No. 2539: a, Country name in white, blue background at UR. b, Country name in white, pink background at UR. c, Country name in white, orange background at UR. d, Country name in blue, green background at UR. e, Presley and guitar. f, Country name in blue, yellow background at UR. g, Country name in blue, blue background at UR.
No. 2539H illustration reduced.

2005, Apr. 5   Perf. 13½
2538 A454 $1 Sheet of 9, #a-
        c, 2 each #d-f   6.75 6.75
2539 A455 $1 Sheet of 9, #a,
        c, e-g, 2 each
        #b, d   6.75 6.75
Litho. & Embossed
Variable Serpentine Die Cut
Without Gum
2539H A455a $20 gold & multi 15.00 15.00
No. 2539H was not available in the marketplace until 2006.

Miniature Sheet

Rotary International, Cent. — A456

No. 2540: a, Globe and Rotary emblem. b, Rotary emblem. c, Women and children.

2005, Sept. 7   Perf. 12½x12¾
2540 A456 $3 Sheet of 3, #a-c   6.75 6.75

Battle of Trafalgar, Bicent. — A457

Designs: 55c, Admiral Horatio Nelson explaining plan of attack before battle. 65c, Orient explodes during the Battle of the Nile, vert. $1, Nelson and his men board San Nicolas during the Battle of Cape St. Vincent, vert. $2, Ships Agamemnon and Ca Ira in battle. $6, HMS Victory.

2005, Sept. 7   **Perf. 13¼**
2541-2544 A457   Set of 4   3.25 3.25
Souvenir Sheet
Perf. 12
2545 A457 $6 multi   4.50 4.50

Hans Christian Andersen (1805-75), Author — A458

No. 2546: a, The Swineherd. b, The Nightingale. c, The Fir Tree. $6, The Ugly Duckling.

2005, Sept. 7   **Perf. 12¾**
2546 A458 $2 Sheet of 3, #a-c   4.50 4.50
Souvenir Sheet
Perf. 12
2547 A458 $6 multi   4.50 4.50
No. 2546 contains three 42x28mm stamps.

Friedrich von Schiller (1759-1805), Writer — A459

No. 2548, vert. — Schiller and German Democratic Republic stamps: a, #241. b, #242. c, #243. $6, Statue of Schiller.

2005, Sept. 7   **Perf. 12¾**
2548 A459 $3 Sheet of 3, #a-c   6.75 6.75
Souvenir Sheet
2549 A459 $6 multi   4.50 4.50

Jules Verne (1828-1905), Writer — A460

No. 2550: a, Men, dog and rooster in space. b, Astronauts. c, Men looking at undersea creature. d, Submarine. $6, Portrait of Verne.

2005, Sept. 7
2550 A460 $2 Sheet of 4, #a-d   6.00 6.00
Souvenir Sheet
2551 A460 $6 multi   4.50 4.50

World Cup Soccer Championships, 75th Anniv. — A461

No. 2552: a, 1934 Italy team. b, Scene from 1934 Italy victory over Czechoslovakia. c, Flaminio Stadium. d, Angelos Schiavo. $6, Italian team celebrating.

2005, Sept. 7   **Perf. 12**
2552 A461 $2 Sheet of 4, #a-d   6.00 6.00
Souvenir Sheet
2553 A461 $6 multi   4.50 4.50

Christmas — A462

Painting details: 25c, Madonna and Child with Two Angels, by Sandro Botticelli. 50c, Madonna and Child with Angels, by Botticelli. 65c, Madonna and Child, by Pietro Lorenzetti. 90c, Madonna del Roseto, by Botticelli. $1.20, Adoration of the Magi, by Lorenzetti. $3, Madonna in Glory with the Seraphim, by Botticelli. $5, Madonna of Frari, by Titian, horiz.

2005, Nov. 15   **Perf. 12¾**
2554-2559 A462   Set of 6   5.00 5.00
Souvenir Sheet
2560 A462 $5 multi   3.75 3.75

Pope John Paul II (1920-2005) and Princess Diana (1961-97) — A463

2005   **Perf. 13½x13¼**
2561 A463 $3 multi   2.25 2.25

Pope Benedict XVI — A464

2005   **Litho.**   **Perf. 13½x13¼**
2562 A464 $2 multi   1.50 1.50
Printed in sheets of 4.

Souvenir Sheet

New Year 2006 (Year of the Dog) — A465

No. 2563 — Dog figurines with background colors of: a, Pale green and green. b, Orange and pink. c, Rose pink and yellow.

2006, Jan. 3   **Perf. 13¼x13½**
2563 A465 $1 Sheet of 3, #a-c   2.25 2.25

Miniature Sheets

National Basketball Association Players and Team Emblems — A466

No. 2564, 90c: a, Orlando Magic emblem. b, Hedo Turkoglu.
No. 2565, 90c: a, Denver Nuggets emblem. b, Kenyon Martin.
No. 2566, 90c: a, Miami Heat emblem. b, Antoine Walker.
No. 2567, 90c: a, Golden State Warriors emblem. b, Jason Richardson.
No. 2568, 90c: a, Phoenix Suns emblem. b, Amaré Stoudemire.
No. 2569, 90c: a, Los Angeles Clippers emblem. b, Elton Brand.

2006, Feb. 14   **Perf. 14**
Sheets of 12, 2 each #a, 10 each #b
2564-2569 A466   Set of 6   50.00 50.00

Léopold Sédar Senghor (1906-2001), First President of Senegal — A467

2006, Mar. 20   **Perf. 13¼**
2570 A467 $2 multi   1.50 1.50

2006 Winter Olympics, Turin — A468

Designs: 75c, Yugoslavia #1670. 90c, 1984 Sarajevo Winter Olympics poster, vert. $2, Japan #2607g, vert. $3, 1998 Nagano Winter Olympics poster, vert.

2006, Mar. 29
2571-2574 A468   Set of 4   5.00 5.00
Each stamp printed in sheets of 4.

Queen Elizabeth II, 80th Birthday — A469

No. 2575: a, As infant, with mother. b, As young child. c, As baby, wearing bonnet. d, As young girl, wearing jacket. $5, Wearing tiara and sash.

2006, Mar. 29
2575 A469 $2 Sheet of 4, #a-d   6.00 6.00
Souvenir Sheet
2576 A469 $5 multi   3.75 3.75

Marilyn Monroe (1926-62), Actress — A470

2006, Apr. 7
2577 A470 $3 multi   2.25 2.25
Printed in sheets of 4.

Space Achievements — A471

No. 2578 — Viking I: a, Trenches dug by Viking I. b, Sunset at Viking I landing site. c, Chryse Planitia looking northwest over Viking I. d, First panoramic image of Chryse Planitia, country name and denomination in white. e, As "d," country name in black, denomination in white. f, As "d," country name and denomination in black.

No. 2579, $3, vert. — Luna 9: a, Flight apparatus. b, Modified SS-6 Sapwood rocket. c, Luna 9 Soft Lander. d, Tyuratam.

No. 2580, $3, vert. — Giotto Comet Probe: a, Launch of Giotto. b, Giotto during solar simulation test. c, Halley's Comet develops seven tails. d, Giotto and Comet Grigg-Skjellerup approach trajectories.

No. 2581, $6, Intl. Space Station. No. 2582, $6, Mars Reconnaissance Orbiter. No. 2583, $6, Venus Express Orbiter.

2006, June 6   Litho.   Perf. 14
2578 A471 $2 Sheet of 6, #a-f 9.00 9.00
Sheets of 4, #a-d
2579-2580 A471 Set of 2 18.00 18.00
Souvenir Sheets
2581-2583 A471 Set of 3 13.50 13.50

Miniature Sheet

Wolfgang Amadeus Mozart (1756-91), Composer — A472

No. 2584: a, Oval portrait. b, Playing harpsichord. c, Wearing red coat. d, Head of Mozart.

2006, Sept. 1   Perf. 13¼
2584 A472 $3 Sheet of 4, #a-d 9.00 9.00

Miniature Sheet

Purchase of Graceland by Elvis Presley, 50th Anniv. — A473

No. 2585: a, View of path leading to front door. b, Graceland, columns at right. c, Graceland, columns at left. d, Room with Presley's costumes.

2006, Sept. 1   Perf. 13¼
2585 A473 $3 Sheet of 4, #a-d 9.00 9.00

Miniature Sheets

Pres. John F. Kennedy (1917-63) — A474

No. 2586, $3: a, Supporters holding campaign sign. b, Kennedy campaigning. c, Kennedy waiting for concession. d, Kennedy addressing the nation.

No. 2587, $3: a, Kennedy on crutches from war injuries. b, Kennedy on stretcher. c, Dust jacket of *Profiles in Courage*. d, Kennedy as senator.

2006, Oct. 1   Perf. 13¼
Sheets of 4, #a-d
2586-2587 A474 Set of 2 18.00 18.00

Shells — A475

Designs: 5c, Turbinella angulata. 10c, Vasum muricatum. 15c, Fusinus closter. 20c, Crasispira gibbosa. 25c, Terebra strigata. 50c, Prunum carneum. 65c, Purpura patula. 90c, C. chrysostoma. $1, M. nodulosa. $2, Conus regius. $3.50, Conus hieroglyphus. $5, Anodontia alba, vert. $10, C. cassidiformis. $20, Strigilla carnaria, vert.

2006, Oct. 1   Perf. 14x15, 15x14
2588 A475   5c multi   .20   .20
2589 A475 10c multi   .20   .20
2590 A475 15c multi   .20   .20
2591 A475 20c multi   .20   .20
2592 A475 25c multi   .20   .20
2593 A475 50c multi   .35   .35
2594 A475 65c multi   .50   .50
2595 A475 90c multi   .65   .65
2596 A475 $1 multi   .75   .75
2597 A475 $2 multi 1.50 1.50
2598 A475 $3.50 multi 2.60 2.60
2599 A475 $5 multi 3.75 3.75
2600 A475 $10 multi 7.50 7.50
2601 A475 $20 multi 15.00 15.00
  Nos. 2588-2601 (14) 33.60 33.60

Souvenir Sheet

Ludwig Durr (1878-1956), Engineer — A476

2006, Nov. 15   Litho.   Perf. 12¾
2602 A476 $5 multi 3.75 3.75

Betty Boop — A477

No. 2603, vert.: a, Betty Boop with black background and leg raised. b, Lips. c, Betty Boop with black background. d, Dog on leash, star. e, Betty Boop, white background. f, Dog, two stars.

No. 2604 — Betty Boop with: a, Light blue panel at top. b, Light yellow panel at top.

2006, Nov. 15
2603 A477 $2 Sheet of 6, #a-f 9.00 9.00
Souvenir Sheet
2604 A477 $3.50 Sheet of 2, #a-b 5.25 5.25

Christmas A478

Christmas stocking showing: No. 2605, 25c, No. 2609a, $2, Christmas tree. No. 2606, 50c, No. 2609b, $2, Bell. No. 2607, 90c, No. 2609c, $2, Candy canes. No. 2608, $1, No. 2609d, $2, Stars.

2006, Dec. 1   Perf. 14¼
2605-2608 A478 Set of 4 2.00 2.00
Souvenir Sheet
2609 A478 $2 Sheet of 4, #a-d 6.00 6.00

Souvenir Sheet

Christopher Columbus (1451-1506), Explorer — A479

2007, Jan. 10   Perf. 12
2610 A479 $5 brn & black 3.75 3.75

Scouting, Cent. — A480

2007, Jan. 10
2611 A480 $3.50 blue & multi 2.60 2.60
Souvenir Sheet
2612 A480 $5 org & multi 3.75 3.75
  No. 2611 was printed in sheets of 3.

Concorde Prototype 001 F-WTSS — A481

No. 2613: a, $1, Airplane in hangar. b, $2, Airplane out of hangar.

2007, Jan. 23   Perf. 13¼
2613 A481 Pair, #a-b 2.25 2.25
Printed in sheets containing 3 of each stamp.

Rembrandt (1606-69), Painter — A482

No. 2614, vert. — Details from Christ Driving the Money Changers from the Temple: a, Christ. b, Man with moustache looking up. c, Man with striped headdress. d, Man protecting face with hands.
  $5, Jesus and His Disciples.

2007, Jan. 23   Perf. 13¼
2614 A482 $2 Sheet of 4, #a-d 6.00 6.00
Imperf
2615 A482 $5 shown 3.75 3.75
  No. 2614 contains four 38x50mm stamps.

Cricket World Cup — A483

Designs: 90c, Cricket bats, ball and wicket, map and flag of Dominica. $1, Umpire Billy Doctrove.
  $5, Cricket bats, ball and wicket.

2007, Apr. 11   Perf. 14
2616-2617 A483 Set of 2 1.50 1.50
Souvenir Sheet
2618 A483 $5 multi 3.75 3.75

Birds A484

Designs: 10c, Great frigatebird. 25c, Peruvian booby. 90c, Black stork, vert. No. 2622, $5, Lipkin, vert.
  No. 2623: a, Antillean crested hummingbird. b, Rufous-breasted hermit. c, Cuban hummingbird. d, Blue-headed hummingbird.
  No. 2624, $5, Red-capped manakin, vert.

2007, Apr. 11   Perf. 12¾
2619-2622 A484 Set of 4 4.75 4.75
2623 A484 $2 Sheet of 4, #a-d 7.00 7.00
Souvenir Sheet
2624 A484 $5 multi 4.75 4.75

Flowers — A485

Designs: 10c, Red jasmine. 25c, Bougainvillea. 90c, Portia tree. No. 2628, $5, Rose bay.
  No. 2629 — Orchids: a, $1, Tolumnia urophylla. b, $1, Brassavola cucullata. c, $2, Isochilus linearis. d, Spathoglottis plicata.

No. 2630, horiz.: a, Red ginger. b, Baobab. c, Purple wreath. d, Thunbergia.
No. 2631, $5, Flamboyant. No. 2632, $5, Oncidium altissimum.

2007, Apr. 11   Litho.   Perf. 12¾
2625-2628	A485	Set of 4	4.75	4.75
2629	A485	Sheet of 4, #a-d	4.50	4.50
2630	A485	$2 Sheet of 4, #a-d	6.00	6.00
		Souvenir Sheets		
2631-2632	A485	Set of 2	7.50	7.50

Princess Diana (1961-97) — A486

No. 2633: a, Holding flowers, wearing purple hat. b, Without hat. c, Not holding flowers, wearing purple hat. d, Close-up of #2633a, lines on face. e, Close-up of #2633b, lines on face. f, Close-up of #2633c, lines on face.
$5, Wearing purple sweater.

2007, June 11   Perf. 13½
2633	A486	$1 Sheet of 6, #a-f	4.50	4.50
		Souvenir Sheet		
2634	A486	$5 multi	3.75	3.75

No. 2633 contains six 28x42mm stamps.

Texas Rangers — A487

No. 2635, horiz.: a, Two Rangers on horses. b, Seven Rangers in front of building with pillars. c, Ten rangers showing rifles. d, Rangers on horses. e, Rangers around still. f, Three Rangers at Justice of the Peace office. g, Rangers and tents. h, Rangers and locomotive. i, Five Rangers on horses near house.
$5, Statue of Charles Goodnight.

2007, June 15   Perf. 13½
2635	A487	$1 Sheet of 9, #a-i	6.75	6.75
		Souvenir Sheet		
2636	A487	$5 multi	3.75	3.75

American Topical Association National Topical Stamp Show, Irving, TX.

Miniature Sheet

New Year 2007 (Year of the Pig) — A488

No. 2637 — Text in: a, Red. b, Green. c, Blue green. d, Purple.

2007, July 2
2637	A488	$2 Sheet of 4, #a-d	6.00	6.00

A489

A490

A491

Christmas
A492

2007, Nov. 19   Litho.   Perf. 14¾x14
2638	A489	25c multi	.20	.20
2639	A490	50c multi	.40	.40
2640	A491	90c multi	.70	.70
2641	A492	$1 multi	.75	.75
		Nos. 2638-2641 (4)	2.05	2.05

New Year 2008 (Year of the Rat) — A493

2008, Feb. 28   Perf. 12
2642	A493	$1 multi	.75	.75

Printed in sheets of 4.

University of the West Indies, 60th Anniv.
A494

University crest, Dr. Bernard A. Sorhaindo and denomination in: 50c, Red brown. 65c, Green. 90c, Brown.
No. 2646, $5, Crest, Sorhaindo, denomination in black. No. 2647, $5, Crest, Sorhaindo, denomination in blue. No. 2648, $5, Crest, diploma, 60th anniversary emblem.

2008, Apr. 8   Perf. 13¼
2643-2645	A494	Set of 3	1.60	1.60
		Souvenir Sheets		
2646-2648	A494	Set of 3	11.50	11.50

Miniature Sheet

2008 Summer Olympics, Beijing — A495

No. 2649: a, Archery. b, Men's gymnastics. c, Badminton. d, Boxing.

2008, Apr. 8   Perf. 13¼x13
2649	A495	$1.40 Sheet of 4, #a-d	4.25	4.25

Miniature Sheet

Visit of Pope Benedict XVI to New York — A496

No. 2650 — Pope and part of St. Patrick's Cathedral in background: a, Small circular window under spire. b, Large central circular window. c, Archway below spire. d, Archway above main door.

2008, June 16   Litho.   Perf. 13½
2650	A496	$1.40 Sheet of 4, #a-d	4.25	4.25

Miniature Sheet

Wedding of Queen Elizabeth II and Prince Philip, 60th Anniv. — A497

No. 2651: a, Couple, denomination in white. b, Queen, denomination in red violet. c, Couple, denomination in black. d, Queen, denomination in white. e, Couple, denomination in red violet. f, Queen, denomination in black.

2008, June 16
2651	A497	$1 Sheet of 6, #a-f	4.50	4.50

Miniature Sheet

Elvis Presley (1935-77) — A498

No. 2652 — Presley and: a, Black and red background, Prussian blue denomination. b, Gray and black background, purple denomination. c, Blue and black background, Prussian blue denomination. d, Purple and black background, purple denomination. e, Gray and black background, Prussian blue denomination. f, Brown and black background, purple denomination.

2008, June 16
2652	A498	$1.50 Sheet of 6 #a-f	6.75	6.75

A499

Muhammad Ali, Boxer — A500

No. 2653 — Ali: a, Sweating, denomination in white. b, Smiling, denomination in black. c, Wearing headgear. d, With arms raised.
No. 2654 — Ali: a, Seated in corner of boxing ring. b, Speaking to the press. c, Punching bag. d, Wearing headgear and mouth guard.

2008, July 7
2653	A499	$2 Sheet of 4, #a-d	6.25	6.25
2654	A500	$2 Sheet of 4, #a-d	6.25	6.25

Convent High School, 150th Anniv.
A501

Panel color: 50c, Red violet. 65c, Yellow orange. 90c, Blue. $1, Red.
$5, Denomination in LR corner.

2008, Oct. 1   Perf. 12½
2655-2658	A501	Set of 4	2.40	2.40
		Souvenir Sheet		
2659	A501	$5 multi	4.00	4.00

Dogs — A502

Designs: 25c, Dandie Dinmont terrier. 50c, Alaskan malamute. 90c, Welsh Springer spaniel. $1, Pug. $2, Norfolk terrier. $5, Vizsla.

No. 2666: a, Akita. b, Australian cattle dog. c, Border collie. d, Staffordshire bull terrier cross.

Perf. 14¼x14¾

2008, Dec. 11			**Litho.**
2660-2665	A502	Set of 6	8.25 8.25
2666	A502 $2.50 Sheet of 4, #a-d		8.50 8.50

Miniature Sheet

Marilyn Monroe (1926-62), Actress — A503

No. 2667 — Monroe wearing: a, Purple sweater, hand on arm. b, Orange sweater, looking in mirror. c, Purple sweater, holding post. d, Orange sweater, holding wine glass.

2008, Dec. 11		**Perf. 14**
2667	A503 $2 Sheet of 4, #a-d	6.00 6.00

Christmas
A504

Designs: 25c, Santa Claus. 50c, Palm tree with Christmas ornaments. 90c, Christmas stocking. $1, Poinsettias.

2008, Dec. 15		**Perf. 12**
2668-2671	A504 Set of 4	2.00 2.00

New Year 2009 (Year of the Ox)
A505

2009, Jan. 5		**Perf. 14¾x14¼**
2672	A505 $2 multi	1.50 1.50

Printed in sheets of 4.

Inauguration of Barack Obama as US President
A506

Pres. Obama: 65c, With raised hand. 90c, Hand not showing.

No. 2675: a, $2.25, Like 65c. b, $2.25, Looking over shoulder. c, $2.25, Like 90c. d, $2.50,

Like 90c. e, $2.50, Looking over shoulder. f, $2.50, Like 65c.

2009, Jan. 20			**Perf. 11½**
2673-2674	A506	Set of 2	1.25 1.25
2675	A506	Sheet of 6, #a-f	11.00 11.00

Diplomatic Relations Between Dominica and People's Republic of China, 5th Anniv.
A507

Denominations: 50c, 65c, 90c, $1.

2009, Mar. 23			**Perf. 14¾x14¼**
2676-2679	A507	Set of 4	2.40 2.40
Souvenir Sheet			
2680	A507 $5 multi		3.75 3.75

Peony
A508

2009, Apr. 10		**Perf. 13¼**
2681	A508 75c shown	.55 .55
Souvenir Sheet		
2682	A508 $5 Peonies	3.75 3.75

No. 2682 contains one 44x44mm stamp.

Miniature Sheet

Elvis Presley (1935-77) — A509

No. 2683 — Various photos of Presley with background colors of: a, Yellow orange. b, Gray and blue. c, Blue. d, Gray.

2009, May 23		**Perf. 13¼**
2683	A509 $2.50 Sheet of 4, #a-d	7.75 7.75

Miniature Sheet

Joseph Haydn (1732-1809), Composer — A510

No. 2684: a, Haydn. b, Haydn's birthplace, Rohrau, Austria. c, Wolfgang Amadeus Mozart. d, St. Stephen's Cathedral, Vienna. e, Nikolaus Esterházy, sponsor of Haydn. f, Esterházy Palace, Fertod, Hungary.

2009, June 10		**Perf. 11½**
2684	A510 $2.25 Sheet of 6, #a-f	10.00 10.00

Mushrooms
A511

Designs: 50c, Leucopaxillus gracillimus. 65c, Calvatia cyathiformis. 90c, Hygrocybe viridiphylla. $1, Boletellus coccineus.

No. 2689, $2: a, Hygrocybe acutoconica. b, Lepiota sulphureocyanescens. c, Lactarius rubrilacteus. d, Lactarius ferrugineus. e, Asterophera lycoperdoides. f, Amanita polypyramis.

2009, Sept. 8		**Litho.**	**Perf. 14x14¾**
2685-2688	A511	Set of 4	2.25 2.25
2689	A511 $2 Sheet of 6, #a-f		9.00 9.00

A512

Corals and Marine Life — A513

Designs: 50c, Lobed star coral and shark. 65c, Orange cup coral and fish. 90c, Grooved brain coral and turtle. $1, Elkhorn coral and fish.

No. 2694, $2: a, Rough star coral and fish. b, Branched finger coral and fish. c, Wire coral and ray. d, Great star coral and fish. e, Pillar coral and fish. f, Rose lace coral and fish.

2009, Sept. 8			**Perf. 14¾x14**
2690-2693	A512	Set of 4	2.25 2.25
2694	A513 $2 Sheet of 6, #a-f		9.00 9.00

Butterflies
A514

Designs: 90c, Banded orange heliconian. $1, Gulf fritillary. $2, Julia longwing. $5, Zebra longwing.

No. 2699: a, Cuban cattleheart. b, White peacock. c, Bahamian swallowtail. d, Tropical buckeye.

No. 2700, $6, Purple emperor. No. 2701, $6, Atala black.

2009, Sept. 8			**Perf. 14¾x14**
2695-2698	A514	Set of 4	6.75 6.75
2699	A514 $2.50 Sheet of 4, #a-d		7.50 7.50
Souvenir Sheets			
Perf. 14¼			
2700-2701	A514	Set of 2	9.00 9.00

Nos. 2700-2701 each contain one 50x38mm stamp.

Dolphins and Whales
A515

Designs: 50c, Irawaddy dolphin. 65c, Pantropical spotted dolphin. 90c, Atlantic humpback dolphin. $1, Indian humpback dolphin.

No. 2706: a, Melon-headed whale. b, Striped dolphin. c, Atlantic spotted dolphin. d, Clymene dolphin. e, Pantropical spotted dolphin (Stenella attenuata graffmani). f, Pantropical spotted dolphin (Stenella attenuata).

2009, Sept. 8		**Litho.**	**Perf. 14¾x14**
2702-2705	A515	Set of 4	2.25 2.25
2706	A515 $2 Sheet of 6, #a-f		9.00 9.00

See No. 2732.

Shells
A516

Designs: 50c, Oliva reticularis. 65c, Vasum muricatum. 90c, Olivella nivea. $1, Olivella mutica.

No. 2711: a, Hyalina avena. b, Persicula fluctuata. c, Agatrix agassizi. d, Trigonostoma rugosum. e, Olivella floralia. f, Marginella eburneola.

2009, Sept. 8			
2707-2710	A516	Set of 4	2.25 2.25
2711	A516 $2 Sheet of 6, #a-f		9.00 9.00

Miniature Sheet

Expo 2010, Shanghai — A517

No. 2712: a, Bund. b, Shanghai Museum. c, Yangpu Bridge. d, Shanghai Theater.

2009, Oct. 16		**Perf. 13x12¾**
2712	A517 $1.50 Sheet of 4, #a-d	4.50 4.50

Discovery of Manhattan Island by Henry Hudson, 400th Anniv. — A518

No. 2713, horiz.: a, Panoramic view of New York City, 1913. b, Hudson, the Dreamer, by Jean L.G. Ferris. c, Henry Hudson. d, Hudson's ship, Half Moon. e, Map of Hudson River, c. 1600. f, Henry Hudson Memorial Column, Bronx, NY.

$6, Hudson, aerial view of New York City.

2009, Oct. 16　　　*Perf. 13x12¾*
2713 A518 $2.25 Sheet of 6,
　　　　#a-f　　　　　　10.00 10.00
Souvenir Sheet
Perf. 12¾x13
2714 A518　$6 multi　　　　4.50 4.50

Miniature Sheet

Pres. John F. Kennedy (1917-63) — A519

No. 2715 — Pres. Kennedy: a, On telephone. b, With family. c, With Vice-president Lyndon B. Johnson. d, Pointing.

2009, Oct. 30　　　*Perf. 11½x12*
2715 A519 $2.50 Sheet of 4, #a-
　　　　d　　　　　　　　7.50 7.50

Miniature Sheet

First Man on the Moon, 40th Anniv. — A520

No. 2716: a, Apollo 11 crew. b, Moon landing on television. c, Apollo 11 capsule with parachutes. d, Earth, Apollo 11 modules and patch. e, Command Module in Moon orbit. f, Project Orion.

2009, Nov. 2　　　*Perf. 11½*
2716 A520 $2 Sheet of 6, #a-f 9.00 9.00

Chinese Aviation, Cent. — A521

No. 2717: a, H-5. b, H-6. c, H-6H. d, H-6L. $6, H-6U.

2009, Nov. 12　　　*Perf. 14*
2717 A521 $2 Sheet of 4, #a-d　6.50 6.50
Souvenir Sheet
Perf. 14¼
2718 A521　$6 multi　　　　4.75 4.75
Aeropex 2009 Intl. Philatelic Exhibition, Beijing. No. 2717 contains four 42x28mm stamps.

Christmas
A522

Designs: 50c, Bell-shaped Christmas tree ornament. 65c, Candles and poinsettia. 90c, Gingerbread man. $1.10, Decorated palm tree. $2.25, Christmas tree ornaments. $2.75, Women dancers.

2009, Nov. 16　　　*Perf. 11½*
2719-2724 A522　Set of 6　　6.25 6.25

Personalized
Stamp — A523

2009, Dec. 18　　　*Perf. 14x14¾*
2725 A523 $3 gray　　　　2.25 2.25
The vignette on the stamp shown is a generic image. Stamps without a vignette were also made available. Printed in sheets of 12.

Pope John Paul II (1920-2005) A524

2010, Jan. 4　　　*Perf. 12x11½*
2726 A524 $2.75 multi　　2.10 2.10
Printed in sheets of 4.

Miniature Sheet

Chinese Zodiac Animals — A524a

No. 2726A — Various stamps of People's Republic of China depicting Zodiac animals: b, Monkey. c, Rooster. d, Dog. e, Pig. f, Rat. g, Ox. h, Tiger. i, Rabbit. j, Dragon. k, Snake. l, Horse. m, Ram.

2010, Jan. 4　　　*Litho.*　*Perf. 12¾*
2726A A524a 60c Sheet of 12,
　　　　#b-m　　　　　　5.50 5.50

Souvenir Sheet

New Year 2010 (Year of the Tiger) — A525

2010, Jan. 4　　　*Perf. 12¾*
2727 A525 $5 multi　　　　4.00 4.00

Miniature Sheet

Elvis Presley (1935-77) — A526

Various drawings of Presley.

2010, Jan. 8　　　*Perf. 11½*
2728 A526 $2.50 Sheet of 4, #a-
　　　　d　　　　　　　　7.75 7.75

Miniature Sheet

NASCAR Drivers and Their Cars — A527

No. 2729: a, Denny Hamlin. b, Kyle Busch. c, Joey Logano. d, Hamlin's car (#11). e, Busch's car (#18). f, Logano's car (#20).

2010, Jan. 19　　　*Litho.*
2729 A527 $3.25 Sheet of 6,
　　　　#a-f　　　　　　15.00 15.00

Miniature Sheets

Dogs — A528

No. 2730, $2.50 — Dalmatian and: a, Books. b, Stone wall. c, Swimming pool. d, Stack of logs.
No. 2731, $2.50 — Boxer and: a, Brick wall. b, Bush. c, Window. d, Fence.

2010, Jan. 19　　　*Perf. 11½x11¾*
Sheets of 4, #a-d
2730-2731 A528　Set of 2　15.50 15.50

No. 2706 With "Haiti Earthquake Relief Fund" and Map of Haiti Added to Stamps and Sheet Margin
Miniature Sheet
Designs as before.

2010, Feb. 4　　　*Perf. 14¾x14*
2732 A515 $2 Sheet of 6, #a-f　9.25 9.25
Position of added text varies on each stamp.

Ferraris and Their Parts A529

No. 2733, $1.25: a, Engine of 1982 208 GTB Turbo. b, 1982 208 GTB Turbo.
No. 2734, $1.25: a, Engine of 1983 126 C3. b, 1983 126 C3.
No. 2735, $1.25: a, Side panel and rear wheel of 1984 Testarossa. b, 1984 Testarossa.
No. 2736, $1.25: a, Suspension of 1987 408 4RM. b, 1987 408 4RM.

2010, Feb. 17　　　*Perf. 12*
Vert. Pairs, #a-b
2733-2736 A529　Set of 4　　8.00 8.00
Nos. 2733-2736 each were printed in sheets containing four pairs.

Miniature Sheet

Mother Teresa (1910-97), Humanitarian — A530

No. 2737 - Mother Teresa: a, Denomination in black. b, Holding rosary. c, Wearing white habit. d, Kissing hand of Pope John Paul II.

2010, Feb. 24　　　*Perf. 11¼x11½*
2737 A530 $2.50 Sheet of 4, #a-
　　　　d　　　　　　　　8.00 8.00

Boy Scouts of America, Cent. — A531

No. 2738, $2.50: a, Outdoor skills. b, Campfire inspirations.
No. 2739, $2.50: a, Emergency one-man carry. b, Swimming fun with safety.

2010, Feb. 24   **Perf. 13¼**
Pairs, #a-b
2738-2739 A531   Set of 2   8.00 8.00
Nos. 2738-2739 each were printed in sheets containing two pairs.

Miniature Sheet

Pope Benedict XVI — A532

No. 2740 — Pope Benedict XVI: a, Wearing red, holding candle. b, Wearing white, hands clasped. c, Wearing red, not holding candle. d, Wearing white, hands not clasped.

2010, Mar. 23   **Perf. 11½x12**
2740 A532 $2.50 Sheet of 4, #a-
   d   7.50 7.50

Caravaggio Paintings — A533

No. 2741, vert.: a, Mary Magdalene. b, Sick Bacchus. c, Bacchus. d, The Inspiration of Saint Matthew.
$6, Saint Gerolamo.

2010, Mar. 23   **Perf. 12x11½**
2741 A533 $2.50 Sheet of 4, #a-
   d   7.50 7.50
Souvenir Sheet
Perf. 11½
2742 A533 $6 multi   4.50 4.50

Miniature Sheet

Girl Guides, Cent. — A534

No. 2743: a, Rainbows. b, Brownies. c, Guides. d, Senior Section. $6, Girl Guide, vert.

2010, Apr. 19   **Perf. 11½x12**
2743 A534 $2.75 Sheet of 4, #a-
   d   8.25 8.25
Souvenir Sheet
Perf. 11¼x11½
2743E A534 $6 multi   4.50 4.50

Souvenir Sheets

A535

A536

A537

Elvis Presley (1935-77) — A538

2010, May 12   **Perf. 13½**
2744 A535 $6 multi   4.50 4.50
2745 A536 $6 multi   4.50 4.50
2746 A537 $6 multi   4.50 4.50
2747 A538 $6 multi   4.50 4.50
   Nos. 2744-2747 (4)   18.00 18.00

Miniature Sheets

Pres. Abraham Lincoln (1809-65) — A539

No. 2748, $2.50 — Photographs of Lincoln: a, Without beard. b, Without beard, arms crossed. c, Reading to son, Tad. d, With beard.
No. 2749, $2.50: a, Statue of Lincoln, Bascom Hill, University of Wisconsin. b, Aerial view of Lincoln Memorial. c, Statue of Lincoln in Lincoln Memorial. d, Sculpture of Lincoln, Mount Rushmore.

2010, June 22   **Litho.**   **Perf. 11½**
Sheets of 4, #a-d
2748-2749 A539   Set of 2   15.00 15.00

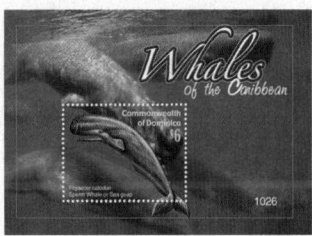

Whales — A540

No. 2750: a, Sowerby's beaked whale. b, Blainville's beaked whale. c, Short-finned pilot whale. d, True's beaked whale. e, False killer whale. f, Dwarf sperm whale.
$6, Sperm whale.

2010, June 22   Litho.   Perf. 13x13½
2750 A540 $2 Sheet of 6, #a-f   9.00 9.00
Souvenir Sheet
2751 A540 $6 multi   4.50 4.50

No. 50
Surcharged in
Red

1916   **Wmk. 3**   **Perf. 14**
MR1   A6   ½p on ½p green   2.75 .85

No. 50
Overprinted in
Black

1918
MR2   A6   ½p green   5.00 *7.00*

Nos. 50, 40 in
Black or Red

1918
MR3   A6   ½p green   .20 *.55*
MR4   A6   3p violet, *yel* (R)   3.75 *5.00*

Type of 1908-
09 Surcharged
in Red

1919
MR5   A6   1½p on 2½p orange   .20 *.60*

DOMINICAN REPUBLIC

də-'mi-ni-kən ri-'pə-blik

LOCATION — Comprises about two-thirds of the island of Hispaniola in the West Indies
GOVT. — Republic
AREA — 18,700 sq. mi.
POP. — 8,129,734 (1999 est.)
CAPITAL — Santo Domingo

8 Reales = 1 Peso
100 Centavos = 1 Peso (1880)
100 Centimos = 1 Franco (1883)
100 Centavos = 1 Peso (1885)

Catalogue values for unused stamps in this country are for Never Hinged items, beginning with Scott 437 in the regular postage section, Scott B1 in the semipostal section, Scott C75 in the airpost section, Scott CB1 in the airpost semi-postal section, Scott E7 in the special delivery section, Scott G13 in the insured letter section, Scott J14 in the postage due section, Scott O26 in the officials section, and Scott RA20 in the postal tax section.

Watermarks

Wmk. 115 — Diamonds   Wmk. 116 — Crosses and Circles

Coat of Arms
A1   A2

1865   Unwmk.   Typo.   Imperf.
Wove Paper

| 1 | A1 | ½r black, *rose* | 600.00 | 600. |
| 2 | A1 | 1r black, *dp green* | 975.00 | 950. |

Twelve varieties of each.

Laid Paper

| 3 | A2 | ½r black, *pale green* | 550.00 | 475. |
| 4 | A2 | 1r black, *straw* | 1,700.00 | 1,100. |

Twelve varieties of the ½r, ten of the 1r.

A3   A4

1866   Laid Paper   Unwmk.

5	A3	½r black, *straw*	200.00	150.00
6	A3	1r black, *pale green*	2,500.00	2,000.
7	A4	1r black, *pale green*	175.00	125.00

Nos. 5-8 have 21 varieties (sheets of 21).

Wmk. 115

| 8 | A3 | 1r black, *pale green* | 13,000.00 | 13,000. |
| a. | | "CORREOS" and "Un Real" doubled | 21,000. | |

The unique example of No. 8a is centered in the grade of fine, has a shallow thin spot and pinhole.

1866-67   Wove Paper   Unwmk.

9	A3	½r black, *rose* ('67)	47.50	47.50
10	A3	1r blk, *pale green* ('67)	85.00	75.00
a.		Inscription dbl., top & bottom	400.00	400.00
11	A3	1r black, *blue* ('67)	50.00	30.00
a.		1r black, *light blue* ('67)	50.00	30.00
b.		No space btwn. "Un" and "real"	600.00	500.00
c.		Without inscription at top & bottom	1,500.	1,000.
d.		Inscription invtd., top & bottom	—	
		Nos. 9-11 (3)	182.50	152.50

1867-71

Pelure Paper

13	A3	½r black, *rose*	150.00	75.00
15	A3	½r black, *lav* ('68)	250.00	210.00
a.		Without inscription at top and bottom		525.00
b.		Dbl. inscriptions, one invtd.		425.00
16	A3	½r black, *grnsh gray* ('68)	260.00	225.00
17	A3	½r black, *yellow* ('68)	12,000.	
18	A3	½r black, *ol* ('69)	3,000.	5,500.
22	A3	1r black, *blue*	4,000.	
23	A3	1r black, *lavender*	225.00	200.00
24	A4	1r black, *rose* ('68)	225.00	225.00
25	A4	1r black, *mag* ('69)	2,250.	1,300.
26	A4	1r black, *sal* ('71)	300.00	225.00

Value for No. 17 is for an example with very fine centering and small faults. Value for No. 22 is for a faulty example with very fine centering and appearance.

1870-73

Ordinary Paper

27	A3	½r black, *magenta*	2,500.	4,750.
28	A3	½r blue, *rose* (blk inscription) ('71)	50.00	42.50
a.		Blue inscription	500.00	500.00
b.		Without inscription at top and bottom		
29	A3	½r black, *yel* ('73)	30.00	21.00
a.		Without inscription at top and bottom	700.00	700.00
30	A4	1r black, *vio* ('73)	30.00	21.00
a.		Without inscription at top and bottom	700.00	700.00
31	A4	1r black, *dk grn*	60.00	50.00

Nos. 9-31 have 21 varieties (sheets of 21). Nos. 29 and 30 are known pin-perforated, unofficially.
Bisects are known of several of the early 1r stamps.

A5   A6

1879   Perf. 12½x13

32	A5	½r violet	2.50	1.50
a.		Imperf., pair	9.00	9.00
b.		Horiz. pair, imperf. vert.	17.00	
33	A5	½r violet, *bluish*	2.50	1.50
a.		Imperf., pair	9.00	7.50
34	A6	1r carmine	3.50	1.50
a.		Imperf., pair	11.50	9.00
b.		Perf. 13	11.50	7.50
c.		Perf. 13x12½	11.50	7.50
35	A6	1r carmine, *sal*	2.50	1.50
a.		Imperf., pair	8.25	8.25
		Nos. 32-35 (4)	11.00	6.00

In 1891 15 stamps of 1879-83 were surcharged "U P U," new values and crossed diagonal lines.

1880   Typo.   Rouletted in Color

36	A6	1c green	1.25	.90
b.		Laid paper	50.00	50.00
37	A6	2c red	1.00	.75
a.		Pelure paper	40.00	40.00
b.		Laid paper	40.00	40.00
38	A6	5c blue	1.25	.60
39	A6	10c rose	3.25	.90
40	A6	20c brown	2.00	.75
41	A6	25c violet	2.25	1.10
42	A6	50c orange	2.50	1.50
43	A6	75c ultra	5.00	2.50
a.		Laid paper	40.00	40.00
44	A6	1p gold	6.50	4.00
a.		Laid paper	50.00	50.00
b.		Double impression	42.50	42.50
		Nos. 36-44 (9)	25.00	13.00

1881

Network Covering Stamp

45	A6	1c green	.90	.45
46	A6	2c red	.90	.45
47	A6	5c blue	1.25	.45
48	A6	10c rose	1.50	.60
49	A6	20c brown	1.50	.80
50	A6	25c violet	1.75	.90
51	A6	50c orange	2.00	1.25
52	A6	75c ultra	6.00	4.00
53	A6	1p gold	8.00	6.50
		Nos. 45-53 (9)	23.80	15.40

Preceding Issues (Type A6) Surch. with Value in New Currency:

a   b

c   d

e   f

g   h

i

1883

Without Network

54	(a)	5c on 1c green	1.40	1.50
b.		Inverted surcharge	21.00	21.00
c.		Surcharged "25 céntimos"	50.00	50.00
d.		Surcharged "10 céntimos"	27.50	27.50
55	(b)	5c on 1c green	25.00	9.00
b.		Double surcharge	100.00	
c.		Laid paper	65.00	65.00
56	(c)	5c on 1c green	17.00	9.50
b.		Surcharged "10 céntimos"	35.00	35.00
c.		Surcharged "25 céntimos"	37.50	37.50
57	(a)	10c on 2c red	5.00	3.00
a.		Inverted surcharge	27.50	27.50
d.		Surcharged "5 céntimos"	52.50	52.50
e.		Surcharged "25 céntimos"	75.00	75.00
58	(c)	10c on 2c red	4.50	3.50
a.		"Céntimo"		
b.		Inverted surcharge	37.50	37.50
c.		Surcharged "25 céntimos"	60.00	60.00
d.		"10" omitted	60.00	
59	(a)	25c on 5c blue	6.50	4.00
a.		Surcharged "5 céntimos"	52.50	
b.		Surcharged "10 céntimos"	52.50	52.50
c.		Surcharged "50 céntimos"	75.00	75.00
d.		Inverted surcharge	50.00	50.00
60	(c)	25c on 5c blue	7.50	3.50
a.		Inverted surcharge	45.00	37.50
b.		Surcharged "10 céntimos"	45.00	37.50
e.		"25" omitted	75.00	
f.		Surcharged on back		75.00
61	(a)	50c on 10c rose	25.00	11.50
a.		Inverted surcharge	50.00	45.00
62	(c)	50c on 10c rose	35.00	17.50
a.		Inverted surcharge	52.50	52.50
63	(d)	1fr on 20c brown	15.00	9.75
64	(e)	1fr on 20c brown	17.50	9.75
a.		Comma after "Franco,"	27.50	27.50
65	(f)	1fr on 20c brown	25.00	17.50
a.		Inverted surcharge		75.00
66	(g)	1fr25c on 25c violet	21.00	15.00
a.		Inverted surcharge	65.00	65.00
67	(g)	2fr50c on 50c orange	15.00	10.50
68	(g)	3fr75c on 75c ultra	27.50	25.00
b.		Inverted surcharge	60.00	60.00
c.		Laid paper	75.00	75.00

| 70 | (i) | 5fr on 1p gold | 550.00 | 500.00 |
| a. | | "s" of "francos" inverted | 700.00 | 700.00 |

With Network

71	(a)	5c on 1c green	3.00	2.50
b.		Inverted surcharge	22.50	22.50
c.		Double surcharge	22.50	22.50
d.		Surcharged "25 céntimos"	42.50	42.50
e.		"5" omitted	75.00	75.00
72	(b)	5c on 1c green	21.00	9.00
b.		Inverted surcharge	60.00	60.00
73	(c)	5c on 1c green	27.50	11.50
b.		Surcharged "10 céntimos"	50.00	42.50
c.		Surcharged "25 céntimos"	60.00	
74	(a)	10c on 2c red	3.75	2.25
a.		Surcharged "5 céntimos"	52.50	45.00
b.		Surcharged "25 céntimos"	67.50	67.50
c.		"10" omitted	57.50	
75	(c)	10c on 2c red	3.00	2.00
a.		Inverted surcharge	30.00	17.00
76	(a)	25c on 5c blue	7.50	3.50
a.		Surcharged "10 céntimos"	75.00	
b.		Surcharged "5 céntimos"	60.00	
c.		Surcharged "50 céntimos"	67.50	
77	(c)	25c on 5c blue	60.00	30.00
a.		Inverted surcharge		
b.		Surcharged on back		
78	(a)	50c on 10c rose	25.00	7.50
a.		Inverted surcharge	50.00	30.00
b.		Surcharged "25 céntimos"	60.00	
79	(c)	50c on 10c rose	30.00	9.50
a.		Inverted surcharge	60.00	
80	(d)	1fr on 20c brown	12.00	9.75
81	(e)	1fr on 20c brown	14.50	12.50
a.		Comma after "Franco"	35.00	35.00
b.		Inverted surcharge	75.00	
82	(f)	1fr on 20c brown	25.00	20.00
a.		Inverted surcharge	75.00	
83	(g)	1fr25c on 25c violet	45.00	30.00
a.		Inverted surcharge	75.00	
84	(g)	2fr50c on 50c orange	19.00	12.50
a.		Inverted surcharge	35.00	27.50
85	(g)	3fr75c on 75c ultra	45.00	42.50
86	(h)	5fr on 1p gold	140.00	140.00
a.		Inverted surcharge		
87	(i)	5fr on 1p gold	190.00	190.00

Many minor varieties exist in Nos. 54-87: accent on "i" of "centimos"; "5" with straight top; "1" with straight serif.

A7   A7a

1885-91   Engr.   Perf. 12

88	A7	1c green	.90	.45
89	A7	2c vermilion	.90	.45
90	A7	5c blue	1.25	.45
91	A7a	10c orange	2.00	.60
92	A7a	20c dark brown	2.00	.75
93	A7a	50c violet ('91)	7.00	6.00
94	A7	1p carmine ('91)	18.00	12.00
95	A7	2p red brown ('91)	22.50	14.00
		Nos. 88-95 (8)	54.55	34.70

Nos. 93, 94, 95 were issued without gum. Imperf. varieties are proofs.
For surcharges see Nos. 166-168.

Coat of Arms — A8

1895   Perf. 12½x14

96	A8	1c green	1.10	.45
97	A8	2c orange red	1.10	.45
98	A8	5c blue	1.25	.45
99	A8	10c orange	2.75	1.40
		Nos. 96-99 (4)	6.20	2.75

Exist imperforate but were not issued.

1897   Perf. 14

96a	A8	1c green	1.40	.50
97a	A8	2c orange red	8.00	.75
98a	A8	5c blue	1.40	.75
99a	A8	10c orange	2.75	1.50
		Nos. 96a-99a (4)	13.55	3.50

Voyage of Diego Méndez from Jamaica — A9

Enriquillo's
Revolt — A10

Sarcophagus
of Columbus
A11

"Española"
Guarding
Remains of
Columbus
A12

Toscanelli
Replying to
Columbus
A13

Bartolomé de
las Casas
Defending
Indians — A14

Columbus at
Salamanca
A15

Columbus'
Mausoleum
A16

1899, Feb. 27   Litho.   Perf. 11½

100	A9	1c brown violet	6.25	4.25
102	A10	2c rose red	1.75	.70
103	A11	5c blue	2.00	.70
104	A12	10c orange	4.25	1.25
a.		Tête bêche pair	42.50	42.50
105	A13	20c brown	9.00	7.00
106	A14	50c yellow green	9.75	8.25
a.		Tête bêche pair	60.00	60.00
107	A15	1p black, *gray bl*	22.50	17.50
108	A16	2p bister brown	40.00	40.00

1900, Jan.

109	A11	¼c black	.70	1.25
110	A15	½c black	.70	1.25
110A	A9	1c gray green	.70	.50
		Nos. 100-110A (11)	97.60	82.65

Nos. 100-110A were issued to raise funds for a Columbus mausoleum.

Imperf., Pairs

100a	A9	1c brown violet	16.50	16.50
102a	A10	2c rose red	5.00	
103a	A11	5c blue	5.75	
104b	A12	10c orange	8.75	
105a	A13	20c brown	15.00	
106b	A14	50c yellow green	17.50	
c.		As "b," tête bêche pair	125.00	
107a	A15	1p black, *gray blue*	42.50	
108a	A16	2p bister brown	70.00	
109a	A11	¼c black	3.75	4.25
110b	A15	½c black	3.75	4.25
110c	A9	1c gray green	3.50	

Map of
Hispaniola — A17

A18

1900, Oct. 21   Unwmk.   Perf. 14

111	A17	¼c dark blue	.65	.40
112	A17	½c rose	.65	.40
113	A17	1c olive green	.65	.40
114	A17	2c deep green	.65	.40

115	A17	5c red brown	.65	.40
a.		Vertical pair, imperf. between	17.50	

Perf. 12

116	A17	10c orange	.65	.40
117	A17	20c lilac	2.75	2.10
a.		20c rose (error)	6.00	6.00
118	A17	50c black	2.50	2.25
119	A17	1p brown	2.75	2.25
		Nos. 111-119 (9)	11.90	9.00

Several varieties in design are known in this issue. They were deliberately made. Counterfeits of Nos. 111-119 abound.

1901-06   Typo.   Perf. 14

120	A18	½c carmine & vio	.65	.35
121	A18	½c blk & org ('05)	1.50	.85
122	A18	½c grn & blk ('06)	.80	.30
123	A18	1c ol grn & vio	.65	.20
124	A18	1c blk & ultra ('05)	1.50	.70
125	A18	1c car & blk ('06)	1.00	.45
126	A18	2c dp grn & vio	.70	.20
127	A18	2c blk & vio ('05)	2.00	.60
128	A18	2c org brn & blk ('06)	1.00	.20
129	A18	5c org brn & vio	.75	.25
130	A18	5c black & cl ('05)	2.25	1.00
131	A18	5c blue & blk ('06)	1.25	.30
132	A18	10c orange & vio	1.25	.35
133	A18	10c blk & grn ('05)	3.75	2.00
134	A18	10c red vio & blk ('06)	1.25	.35
135	A18	20c brn vio & vio	2.25	.70
136	A18	20c blk & ol ('05)	11.50	7.50
137	A18	20c ol grn & blk ('06)	6.50	2.50
138	A18	50c gray blk & vio	7.00	5.00
139	A18	50c blk & red brn ('05)	40.00	30.00
140	A18	50c brn & blk ('06)	7.50	7.00
141	A18	1p brn & vio	16.00	9.50
142	A18	1p blk & gray ('05)	175.00	200.00
143	A18	1p violet & blk	17.50	12.00
		Nos. 120-143 (24)	303.55	282.30

Issued: 11/15/01; 5/11/05; 8/17/06.
See #172-176. For surcharges see #151-156.

Francisco
Sánchez — A19

Juan Pablo
Duarte — A20

Ramón
Mella — A21

Ft. Santo
Domingo — A22

1902, Feb. 25   Engr.   Perf. 12

144	A19	1c dk green & blk	.25	.25
145	A20	2c scarlet & blk	.25	.25
146	A20	5c blue & blk	.25	.25
147	A19	10c orange & blk	.25	.25
148	A21	12c purple & blk	.25	.25
149	A21	20c rose & blk	.35	.35
150	A22	50c brown & blk	.50	.50
		Nos. 144-150 (7)	2.10	2.10

Center Inverted

144a	A19	1c	6.00	3.50
145a	A20	2c	6.00	3.50
146a	A20	5c	6.00	3.50
148a	A21	12c	6.00	3.50
149a	A21	20c	6.00	3.50
150a	A22	50c	6.00	3.50
		Nos. 144a-150a (6)	36.00	21.00

400th anniversary of Santo Domingo. Imperforate varieties of Nos. 144 to 150 were never sold to the public.

Nos. 138, 141
Surcharged in Black

1904, Aug.

151	A18	2c on 50c	7.00	6.00
152	A18	2c on 1p	10.50	7.00
b.		"2" omitted	50.00	50.00
153	A18	5c on 50c	3.75	2.10
154	A18	5c on 1p	4.00	3.50
155	A18	10c on 50c	7.00	6.50
156	A18	10c on 1p	7.00	6.50
		Nos. 151-156 (6)	39.25	31.60

Inverted Surcharge

151a	A18	2c on 50c	15.00	15.00
152a	A18	2c on 1p	15.00	15.00
c.		As "a," "2" omitted	85.00	85.00
153a	A18	5c on 50c	5.50	5.50
154a	A18	5c on 1p	7.00	6.50
155a	A18	10c on 50c	14.00	14.00
156a	A18	10c on 1p	10.00	10.00
		Nos. 151a-156a (6)	66.50	66.00

Official Stamps
of 1902
Overprinted

Red Overprint

1904, Aug. 16

157	O1	5c dk blue & blk	5.00	2.75
a.		Inverted overprint	6.50	5.50

Black Overprint

158	O1	2c scarlet & blk	12.50	4.00
a.		Inverted overprint	15.00	5.00
159	O1	5c dk blue & blk	3,500.	3,500.
160	O1	10c yellow grn & blk	9.25	9.00
a.		Inverted overprint	12.50	12.50

Surcharged

161	O1	1c on 20c yellow & blk	4.00	2.75
a.		Inverted surcharge	6.50	5.00

Nos. J1-J2
Surcharged or
Overprinted

Surcharged "CENTAVOS"

1904-05

Black Surcharge

162	D1	1c on 2c olive gray	250.00	200.00
a.		"entavos"	—	—
b.		"Dominican"	350.00	300.00
c.		"Centavo"	350.00	300.00

Carmine Surcharge or Overprint

163	D1	1c on 2c olive gray	2.50	1.00
a.		Inverted surcharge	3.50	2.50
b.		"Domihicana"	15.00	15.00
c.		As "b," inverted	40.00	40.00
d.		"Dominican"	10.50	10.50
e.		"Centavos" omitted	30.00	
g.		"entavos"	30.00	
163F	D1	1c on 4c olive gray	35.00	7.00
164	D1	2c olive gray	.80	.50
a.		"Domihicana"	11.00	11.00
b.		Inverted overprint	1.90	1.90
c.		As "a," inverted	25.00	25.00
d.		"Dominican"	5.75	5.75
e.		"Centavo" omitted	12.50	10.00
f.		"entavos"	12.50	12.50
g.		As "f," inverted	40.00	40.00
h.		As "d," inverted	40.00	40.00

Surcharged "CENTAVO"

165	D1	1c on 4c olive gray	.80	.65
a.		"Domihicana"	10.00	10.00
c.		Inverted surcharge	1.75	1.75
d.		"1" omitted	3.50	3.50
e.		As "a," inverted	32.50	32.50
f.		As "d," inverted	40.00	40.00
g.		Double surcharge	30.00	30.00

No. 92 Surcharged in
Red

1905, Apr. 4

166	A7a	2c on 20c dk brown	7.00	5.00
a.		Inverted surcharge	15.00	15.00
167	A7a	5c on 20c dk brown	4.00	1.75
a.		Inverted surcharge	16.00	16.00
b.		Double surcharge	25.00	25.00
168	A7a	10c on 20c dk brown	7.00	6.50
		Nos. 166-168 (3)	18.00	11.75

Nos. 166-168 exist with inverted "A" for "V" in "CENTAVOS" in surcharge.

Nos. J2, J4, J3 Surcharged:

1906, Jan. 16   Perf. 14

Red Surcharge

169	D1	1c on 4c olive gray	.85	.50
a.		Inverted surcharge	10.50	10.50
b.		Double surcharge	25.00	

1906, May 1

Black Surcharge

170	D1	1c on 10c olive gray	1.00	.40
a.		Inverted surcharge	10.50	10.50
b.		Double surcharge	14.00	14.00
c.		"OMINICANA"	20.00	20.00
d.		As "c," inverted	150.00	
171	D2	2c on 5c olive gray	1.00	.40
a.		Inverted surcharge	10.50	10.50
b.		Double surcharge	35.00	

The varieties small "C" or small "A" in "REPUBLICA" are found on #169, 170, 171.

Arms Type of 1901-06

1907-10   Wmk. 116

172	A18	½c grn & blk ('08)	.75	.20
173	A18	1c carmine & blk	.75	.20
174	A18	2c orange brn & blk	.75	.20
175	A18	5c blue & blk	.75	.25
176	A18	10c red vio & blk ('10)	8.00	1.00
		Nos. 172-176 (5)	11.00	1.85

No. O6
Overprinted in
Red

1911, July 11   Perf. 13½x14, 13½x13

177	O2	2c scarlet & black	1.25	.50
a.		"HABILITAOO"	8.75	6.00
b.		Inverted overprint	21.00	
c.		Double overprint	21.00	

A23

Juan Pablo
Duarte — A24

1911-13   Perf. 14

Center in Black

178	A23	½c orange ('13)	.25	.20
179	A23	1c green	.25	.20
180	A23	2c carmine	.25	.20
181	A23	5c gray blue ('13)	.75	.20
182	A23	10c red violet	1.25	.45
183	A23	20c olive green	8.25	7.75
184	A23	50c yellow brn ('12)	3.25	3.25
185	A23	1p violet ('12)	5.50	3.50
		Nos. 178-185 (8)	19.75	15.75

See Nos. 230-232.

1914, Apr. 13   Perf. 13x14

Background Red, White and Blue

186	A24	½c orange & blk	.55	.30
187	A24	1c green & blk	.55	.30
188	A24	2c rose & blk	.55	.30
189	A24	5c slate & blk	.55	.40

190	A24	10c magenta & blk	1.25	.70
191	A24	20c olive grn & blk	2.25	1.90
192	A24	50c brown & blk	3.00	2.75
193	A24	1p dull lilac & blk	5.00	4.00
		Nos. 186-193 (8)	13.70	10.65

Cent. of the birth of Juan Pablo Duarte (1813-1876), patriot and revolutionary.

Official Stamps of 1909-12 Surcharged in Violet or Overprinted in Red:

a

b

1915, Feb.   Perf. 13½x13, 13½x14

194	O2 (a)	½c on 20c orange & blk	.50	.35
a.		Inverted surcharge	6.00	6.00
b.		Double surcharge	8.75	8.75
c.		"Habilitado" omitted	5.25	5.25
195	O2 (b)	1c blue grn & blk	.80	.25
a.		Inverted overprint	6.00	6.00
b.		Double overprint	7.00	
c.		Overprinted "1915" only	12.50	
196	O2 (b)	2c scarlet & blk	.80	.25
a.		Inverted overprint	5.25	5.25
b.		Double overprint	7.75	7.75
c.		Overprinted "1915" only	8.75	
d.		"1915" double		
197	O2 (b)	5c dk blue & blk	1.00	.25
a.		Inverted overprint	7.00	7.00
b.		Double overprint	8.75	8.75
c.		Double ovpt., one invtd.	27.50	
d.		Overprinted "1915" only	8.50	
198	O2 (b)	10c yel grn & blk	2.75	2.40
a.		Inverted overprint	15.00	
199	O2 (b)	20c orange & blk	9.00	6.50
a.		"Habilitado" omitted		
		Nos. 194-199 (6)	14.85	10.00

Nos. 194, 196-198 are known with both perforations. Nos. 195, 199 are only perf. 13½x13.

The variety capital "I" for "1" in "Habilitado" occurs once in each sheet in all denominations.

A25

Type of 1911-13 Redrawn Overprinted "1915" in Red

TWO CENTAVOS:
Type I — "DOS" in small letters.
Type II — "DOS" in larger letters with white dot at each end of the word.

1915   Unwmk.   Litho.   Perf. 11½

200	A25	½c violet & blk	.75	.20
a.		Imperf., pair	5.75	
201	A25	1c yel brn & blk	.75	.20
a.		Imperf., pair	6.50	
b.		Vert. pair, imperf. horiz.	10.50	
c.		Horiz. pair, imperf. vert.	10.50	
202	A25	2c ol grn & blk (I)	3.75	.25
a.		Imperf., pair	10.00	
203	A25	2c ol grn & blk (II)	6.00	.20
a.		Center omitted	87.50	
b.		Frame omitted	87.50	
c.		Imperf., pair	15.00	
d.		Horiz. pair, imperf. vert.	15.00	
204	A25	5c magenta & blk	3.25	.25
a.		Pair, one without overprint	65.00	
b.		Imperf., pair	6.50	
205	A25	10c gray blue & blk	3.75	.50
a.		Imperf., pair	7.75	
b.		Horiz. pair, imperf. vert.	35.00	
206	A25	20c rose red & blk	6.50	1.40
a.		Imperf., pair	12.50	
207	A25	50c green & blk	8.50	4.00
a.		Imperf., pair	25.00	
208	A25	1p orange & blk	17.50	7.00
a.		Imperf., pair	52.50	
		Nos. 200-208 (9)	50.75	14.00

Type of 1915 Overprinted "1916" in Red

1916

209	A25	½c violet & blk	1.60	.20
a.		Imperf., pair	21.00	
210	A25	1c green & blk	2.40	.20
a.		Imperf., pair	21.00	

Type of 1915 Overprinted "1917" in Red

1917-19

213	A25	½c red lilac & blk	2.50	.30
a.		Horiz. pair, imperf. btwn.	47.50	47.50
214	A25	1c yellow grn & blk	1.50	.20
a.		Vert. pair, imperf. btwn.	50.00	
215	A25	2c olive grn & blk	1.60	.20
a.		Imperf., pair	35.00	
216	A25	5c magenta & blk	16.00	.70
		Nos. 213-216 (4)	21.60	1.40

Type of 1915 Overprinted "1919" in Red

1919

219	A25	2c olive grn & blk	10.00	.20

Type of 1915 Overprinted "1920" in Red

1920-27

220	A25	½c lilac rose & blk	.50	.25
a.		Horiz. pair, imperf. btwn.	25.00	25.00
b.		Inverted overprint		
c.		Double overprint		
d.		Double overprint, one invtd.		
221	A25	1c yellow grn & blk	.75	.20
a.		Overprint omitted	70.00	
b.		Horiz. pair, imperf. btwn.	40.00	
222	A25	2c olive grn & blk	.75	.20
a.		Vertical pair, imperf. between	27.50	
223	A25	5c dp rose & blk	9.00	.50
224	A25	10c blue & black	5.00	.25
225	A25	20c rose red & blk ('27)	7.00	.50
226	A25	50c green & blk ('27)	52.50	17.50
		Nos. 220-226 (7)	75.50	19.40

Type of 1915 Overprinted "1921" in Red

1921

227	A25	1c yellow grn & blk	3.75	.30
a.		Horiz. pair, imperf. btwn.	45.00	45.00
b.		Imperf., pair	45.00	45.00
228	A25	2c olive grn & blk	5.00	.30
a.		Vert. pair, imperf. btwn.	45.00	

Redrawn Design of 1915 without Overprint

1922

230	A25	1c green	2.75	.20
231	A25	2c carmine (II)	2.75	.20
232	A25	5c blue	4.25	.25
		Nos. 230-232 (3)	9.75	.65

Nos. 230-232 exist imperf.

A26   A27

Second Redrawing

TEN CENTAVOS:
Type I — Numerals 2mm high. "DIEZ" in thick letters with large white dot at each end.
Type II — Numerals 3mm high. "DIEZ" in thin letters with white dot with colored center at each end.

1924-27

233	A26	1c green	1.10	.20
a.		Vert. pair, imperf. btwn.	35.00	35.00
234	A26	2c red	.70	.20
235	A26	5c blue	1.60	.20
236	A26	10c pale bl & blk (I) ('26)	12.00	3.00
236A	A26	10c pale bl & blk (II)	22.50	1.10
236B	A26	50c gray grn & blk ('26)	45.00	27.50
237	A26	1p orange & blk ('27)	16.00	10.50
		Nos. 233-237 (7)	98.90	42.70

In the second redrawing the shield has a flat top and the design differs in many details from the stamps of 1911-13 and 1915-22.

1927

238	A27	½c lilac rose & blk	.30	.20

Exhibition
Pavilion — A28

1927   Unwmk.   Perf. 12

239	A28	2c carmine	.80	.50
240	A28	5c ultra	1.75	.50

Natl. and West Indian Exhib. at Santiago de los Caballeros.

Ruins of Columbus' Fortress A29

1928

241	A29	½c lilac rose	.65	.35
242	A29	1c deep green	.50	.20
a.		Horiz. pair, imperf. btwn.	25.00	
243	A29	2c red	.65	.20
244	A29	5c dark blue	1.90	.35
245	A29	10c light blue	1.90	.30
246	A29	20c rose	3.25	.40
247	A29	50c yellow green	10.50	6.50
248	A29	1p orange yellow	27.50	20.00
		Nos. 241-248 (8)	46.85	28.30

Reprints exist of 1c, 2c and 10c.
Issued: 1c, 2c, 10c, Oct. 1; others, Dec.

Horacio Vasquez — A30   Convent of San Ignacio de Loyola — A31

1929, May-June

249	A30	½c dull rose	.50	.30
250	A30	1c gray green	.50	.20
251	A30	2c red	.60	.20
252	A30	5c dark ultra	1.25	.35
253	A30	10c pale blue	1.75	.50
		Nos. 249-253 (5)	4.60	1.55

Signing of the "Frontier" treaty with Haiti.
Issue dates: 2c, May; others, June.

Imperf., Pairs

249a	A30	½c	12.50
250a	A30	1c	12.50
251a	A30	2c	12.50
252a	A30	5c	14.00

1930, May 1   Perf. 11½

254	A31	½c red brown	.65	.45
a.		Imperf., pair	55.00	55.00
255	A31	1c deep green	.50	.20
256	A31	2c vermilion	.50	.20
a.		Imperf., pair	60.00	
257	A31	5c deep blue	1.25	.35
258	A31	10c light blue	3.00	1.00
		Nos. 254-258 (5)	5.90	2.20

Cathedral of Santo Domingo, First Church in America A32

1931   Perf. 12

260	A32	1c deep green	.65	.20
a.		Imperf., pair	50.00	
261	A32	2c scarlet	.45	.20
a.		Imperf., pair	50.00	
262	A32	3c violet	.65	.20
263	A32	7c dark blue	2.00	.25
264	A32	8c bister	2.75	.85
265	A32	10c light blue	4.50	1.00
a.		Imperf., pair	35.00	
		Nos. 260-265 (6)	11.00	2.70

Issued: 3c-7c, Aug. 1; others, July 11.
For overprint see No. RAC8.

A33

Overprinted or Surcharged in Black

1932, Dec. 20   Perf. 12

Cross in Red

265B	A33	1c yellow green	.50	.45
265C	A33	3c on 2c violet	.70	.55
265D	A33	5c blue	4.00	4.25
265E	A33	7c on 10c turq bl	5.50	5.75
		Nos. 265B-265E (4)	10.70	11.00

Proceeds of sale given to Red Cross. Valid Dec. 20 to Jan. 5, 1933.
Inverted and pairs, one without surcharge or overprint, exist on Nos. 265B-265D, as well as missing letters.

Fernando Arturo de Merino (1833-1906) as President — A35

Cathedral of Santo Domingo A36

Designs: ½c, 5c, 8c, Tomb of Merino. 1c, 3c, 10c, as Archbishop.

1933, Feb. 27   Engr.   Perf. 14

266	A35	½c lt violet	.45	.35
267	A35	1c yellow green	.60	.25
268	A35	2c lt red	1.00	.75
269	A35	3c deep violet	.70	.30
270	A35	5c dark blue	.80	.35
271	A35	7c ultra	1.40	.50
272	A35	8c dark green	1.75	.75
273	A35	10c orange yel	1.50	.50
274	A35	20c carmine rose	3.00	1.25
275	A36	50c lemon	11.25	6.00
276	A36	1p dark brown	24.75	14.00
		Nos. 266-276 (11)	47.20	25.00

For surcharges see Nos. G1-G7.

Tower of Homage, Ozama Fortress — A37

1932   Litho.   Perf. 12

278	A37	1c green	1.25	.20
279	A37	3c violet	.80	.20

Issue dates: 1c, July 2; 3c, June 22.

"CORREOS" added at left

1933, May 28

283	A37	1c dark green	.40	.20

President Rafael L. Trujillo
A38   A39

1933, Aug. 16   Engr.   Perf. 14

286	A38	1c yellow grn & blk	.75	.35
287	A39	3c dp violet & blk	.90	.35
288	A38	7c ultra & blk	2.00	.75
		Nos. 286-288 (3)	3.65	1.45

42nd birthday of President Rafael Leonidas Trujillo Molina.

San Rafael Bridge — A40

1934   Litho.   Perf. 12
289	A40	½c dull violet	.70 .35
290	A40	1c dark green	.90 .20
291	A40	3c violet	1.40 .20
		Nos. 289-291 (3)	3.00 .75

Opening of San Rafael Bridge.
Issue dates: ½c, 3c, Mar. 3; 1c, Feb. 17.

Trujillo
Bridge
A41

1934
292	A41	½c red brown	.50 .25
293	A41	1c green	.75 .20
294	A41	3c purple	1.10 .20
		Nos. 292-294 (3)	2.35 .65

Opening of the General Trujillo Bridge near Ciudad Trujillo.
Issue dates: 1c, Aug. 24. Others, Sept. 7.

Ramfis
Bridge
A42

1935, Apr. 6
295	A42	1c green	.45 .20
296	A42	3c yellow brown	.50 .20
297	A42	5c brown violet	1.60 1.00
298	A42	10c rose	3.25 1.40
		Nos. 295-298 (4)	5.80 2.80

Opening of the Ramfis Bridge over the Higuamo River.

President Trujillo — A43

A44

A45

1935   Perf. 11
299	A43	3c yellow & brown	.25 .20
300	A44	5c org red, bl, red & bis	
			.35 .20
301	A45	7c ultra, bl, red & brn	.50 .20
302	A44	10c red vio, bl, red & bis	.75 .20
		Nos. 299-302 (4)	1.85 .80

Ratification of a treaty setting the frontier between Dominican Republic and Haiti.
Issued: 3c, 10/29; 5c, 10c, 11/25; 7c, 11/8.

National
Palace
A46

1935, Apr. 1   Perf. 11½
303	A46	25c yellow orange	2.75 .30

Obligatory for all mail addressed to the president and cabinet ministers.

Post Office,
Santiago
A47

1936
304	A47	½c bright violet	.30 .35
305	A47	1c green	.30 .20

Issue dates: ½c, Jan. 14; 1c, Jan. 4.

George Washington Ave., Ciudad
Trujillo — A48

1936, Feb. 22
306	A48	½c brn & vio brn	.40 .45
a.		Imperf., pair	52.50
307	A48	2c carmine & brn	.40 .30
308	A48	3c yellow org & red brn	.65 .20
309	A48	7c ultra, blue & brn	1.25 1.25
a.		Imperf., pair	52.50
		Nos. 306-309 (4)	2.70 2.20

Dedication of George Washington Avenue, Ciudad Trujillo.

José Nuñez de
Cáceres — A49

Felix M. del
Monte — A55

Proposed National Library — A56

1936   Unwmk. Engr.   Perf. 13½, 14
310	A49	½c dull violet	.30 .20
311	A49	1c dark green	.25 .20
312	A49	2c carmine	.30 .20
313	A49	3c violet	.30 .20
314	A49	5c deep ultra	.55 .30
315	A49	7c slate blue	1.00 .55
316	A55	10c orange	1.00 .30
317	A56	20c olive green	3.75 2.75
318	A55	25c gray violet	6.00 8.00
319	A55	30c scarlet	7.50 10.00
320	A55	50c black brown	8.00 5.50
321	A55	1p black	27.50 32.50
322	A55	2p yellow brown	65.00 80.00
		Nos. 310-322 (13)	121.45 140.70

The funds derived from the sale of these stamps were returned to the National Treasury Fund for the erection of a building for the National Library and Archives.
Issued: 3c, 7c, Mar. 18; others, May 22.

1c, Gen. Gregorio Luperon. 2c, Emiliano Tejera. 3c, Pres. Trujillo. 5c, Jose Reyes. 7c, Gen. Antonio Duverge. 25c, Francisco J. Peynado. 30c, Salome Urena. 50c, Gen. Jose M. Cabral. 1p, Manuel de Jesus Galvan. 2p, Gaston F. Deligne.

President Trujillo and Obelisk — A62

1937, Jan. 11   Litho.   Perf. 11½
323	A62	1c green	.20 .20
324	A62	3c violet	.40 .20
325	A62	7c blue & turq blue	1.00 1.00
		Nos. 323-325 (3)	1.60 1.40

1st anniv. of naming Ciudad Trujillo.

Discus Thrower
and Flag — A63

1937, Aug. 14
Flag in Red and Blue
326	A63	1c dark green	8.00 .75
327	A63	3c violet	12.00 .75
328	A63	7c dark blue	20.00 3.75
		Nos. 326-328 (3)	40.00 5.25

1st Natl. Olympic Games, Aug. 16, 1937.

Symbolical of Peace, Labor and
Progress — A64

1937, Sept. 18   Perf. 12
329	A64	3c purple	.35 .20

"8th Year of the Benefactor."

Monument to
Father Francisco
Xavier Billini (1837-
90) — A65

1937, Dec. 29
330	A65	½c deep orange	.20 .20
331	A65	5c purple	.45 .20

Globe and
Torch of
Liberty — A66

1938, Feb. 22   Perf. 11½
332	A66	1c green	.40 .20
333	A66	3c purple	.55 .20
334	A66	10c orange	1.10 .20
		Nos. 332-334 (3)	2.05 .60

150th anniv. of the Constitution of the US.

Pledge of Trinitarians, City Gate and
National Flag — A67

1938, July 16   Perf. 12
335	A67	1c green, red & dk bl	.40 .20
336	A67	3c purple, red & bl	.45 .20
337	A67	10c orange, red & bl	1.00 .40
		Nos. 335-337 (3)	1.85 .80

Trinitarians and patriots, Francisco Del Rosario Sanchez, Ramon Matias Mella and Juan Pablo Duarte, who helped free their country from foreign domination.

Seal of the
University of Santo
Domingo — A68

1938, Oct. 28
338	A68	½c orange	.30 .25
339	A68	1c dp green & lt green	.30 .20
340	A68	3c purple & pale vio	.40 .20
341	A68	7c dp blue & lt blue	.75 .35
		Nos. 338-341 (4)	1.75 1.00

Founding of the University of Santo Domingo, on Oct. 28, 1538.

Trylon and Perisphere, Flag and
Proposed Columbus
Lighthouse — A69

1939, Apr. 30   Litho.   Perf. 12
Flag in Blue and Red
342	A69	½c red org & org	.35 .20
343	A69	1c green & lt green	.40 .20
344	A69	3c purple & pale vio	.40 .20
345	A69	10c orange & yellow	1.40 .65
		Nos. 342-345, C33 (5)	3.95 1.85

New York World's Fair.

A70

A71

1939, Sept.   Typo.
346	A70	½c black & pale gray	.30 .20
347	A70	1c black & yel grn	.40 .20
348	A70	3c black & yel brn	.40 .20
349	A70	7c black & dp ultra	1.00 .90
350	A70	10c black & brt red vio	1.50 .40
		Nos. 346-350 (5)	3.60 1.90

José Trujillo Valdez (1863-1935), father of President Trujillo Molina.

1940, Apr. 14   Litho.   Perf. 11½
Map of the Americas and flags of 21 American republics.

Flags in National Colors
351	A71	1c deep green	.35 .20
352	A71	2c carmine	.45 .20
353	A71	3c red violet	.60 .20
354	A71	10c orange	1.25 .20
355	A71	1p chestnut	15.00 9.50
		Nos. 351-355 (5)	17.65 10.30

Pan American Union, 50th anniv.

Sir Rowland
Hill — A72

1940, May 6   Perf. 12
356	A72	3c brt red vio & rose lil	3.00 .40
357	A72	7c dk blue & lt blue	6.00 1.40

Centenary of first postage stamp.

Julia Molina Trujillo A73

1940, May 26
358 A73 1c grn, lt grn & dk grn .35 .20
359 A73 2c brt red, buff & dp rose .35 .25
360 A73 3c org, dl org & brn org .50 .20
361 A73 7c bl, pale bl & dk bl 1.00 .35
    Nos. 358-361 (4) 2.20 1.00

Issued in commemoration of Mother's Day.

Map of Caribbean A74

1940, June 6   **Perf. 11½**
362 A74 3c brt car & pale rose .40 .20
363 A74 7c dk blue & lt blue .75 .20
364 A74 1p yel grn & pale grn 7.50 6.50
    Nos. 362-364 (3) 8.65 6.90

2nd Inter-American Caribbean Conf. held at Ciudad Trujillo, May 31 to June 6.

Marion Military Hospital — A75

1940, Dec. 24
365 A75 ½c chestnut & fawn .25 .20

Fortress, Ciudad Trujillo A76

Statue of Columbus, Ciudad Trujillo — A77

1941
366 A76 1c dk green & lt green .20 .20
367 A77 2c brt red & rose .20 .20
368 A77 10c orange brn & buff .55 .25
    Nos. 366-368 (3) .95 .65

Issue dates: 1c, Mar. 27; others, Apr. 7.

Sánchez, Duarte, Mella and Trujillo — A78

1941, May 16
369 A78 3c brt red lil & red vio .25 .20
370 A78 4c brt red, crim & pale rose .40 .20
371 A78 13c dk blue & lt blue .60 .35
372 A78 15c orange brn & buff 2.00 1.50
373 A78 17c lt bl, bl & pale bl 2.00 1.50
374 A78 1p org, yel brn & pale org 8.25 7.00

375 A78 2p lt gray & pale gray 18.00 7.25
    Nos. 369-375 (7) 31.50 18.00

Trujillo-Hull Treaty signed Sept. 24, 1940 and effective Apr. 1, 1941.

Bastion of February 27 — A79

1941, Oct. 20
376 A79 5c brt blue & lt blue .50 .20

School, Torch of Knowledge, Pres. Trujillo — A80

1941
377 A80 ½c chestnut & fawn .20 .20
378 A80 1c dk green & lt green .25 .20

Education campaign.
Issue dates: ½c, Dec. 12, 1c, Dec. 2.

Reserve Bank of Dominican Republic A81

1942   **Unwmk.**
379 A81 5c lt brown & buff .40 .20
380 A81 17c dp blue & lt blue .75 .45

Founding of the Reserve Bank, 10/24/41.

Representation of Transportation A82

Virgin of Altagracia A83

1942, Aug. 15
381 A82 3c dk brn, grn yel & lt 3.75 .50
382 A82 15c pur, grn, yel & lt bl 8.25 3.75

Day of Posts and Telegraph, 8th anniv.

1942, Aug. 15
383 A83 ½c gray & pale gray .75 .20
384 A83 1c dp grn & lt grn 1.50 .20
385 A83 3c brt red lil & lil 9.75 .20
386 A83 5c dk vio brn & vio brn 2.00 .20
387 A83 10c rose pink & pink 7.00 .25
388 A83 15c dp blue & lt blue 7.50 .30
    Nos. 383-388 (6) 28.50 1.35

20th anniv. of the coronation of Our Lady of Altagracia.

Bananas — A84

Cows — A85

1942-43
389 A84 3c dk brn & grn ('43) .50 .20
390 A84 4c vermilion & blk ('43) .50 .30
391 A85 5c dp blue & cop brn .50 .20
392 A85 15c dk pur & blue grn .75 .40
    Nos. 389-392 (4) 2.25 1.10

Issue date: 5c, 15c, Aug. 18.

Emblems of Dominican and Trujillista Parties A86

1943, Jan. 15
393 A86 3c orange .40 .20
394 A86 4c dark red .50 .20
395 A86 13c brt red lilac 1.10 .20
396 A86 1p lt blue 5.00 1.60
    Nos. 393-396 (4) 7.00 2.20

Re-election of President Rafael Trujillo Molina, May 16, 1942.

Model Market, Ciudad Trujillo A87

1944
397 A87 2c dk brown & buff .20 .20

Bastion of Feb. 27 and National Flag — A88

1944, Feb. 27   **Unwmk.**
Flag in Dark Blue and Carmine
398 A88 ½c ocher .20 .20
399 A88 1c yellow green .20 .20
400 A88 2c scarlet .20 .20
401 A88 3c brt red vio .20 .20
402 A88 5c yellow orange .20 .20
403 A88 7c brt blue .25 .25
404 A88 10c orange brown .40 .30
405 A88 20c olive green .65 .60
406 A88 50c lt blue 1.90 1.75
    Nos. 398-406,C46-C48 (12) 7.00 5.80

Souvenir Sheet
Imperf
407 A88 Sheet of 12 110.00 110.00
  a.-l. Single stamp 3.00 3.00

Centenary of Independence.
No. 407 contains 1 each of Nos. 398-406 and C46-C48 with simulated perforations. Size: 141x205mm.

Battlefield and Nurse with Child A90

1944, Aug. 1
408 A90 1c dk bl grn, buff & car .20 .20
  a. Vertical pair, imperf. btwn. 15.00
  b. Horiz. pair, imperf. vert. 15.00
409 A90 2c dk brn, buff & car .30 .20
410 A90 3c brt bl, buff & car .30 .20
411 A90 10c rose car, buff & car .60 .20
    Nos. 408-411 (4) 1.40 .80

80th anniv. of the Intl. Red Cross.

Municipal Building, San Cristóbal A91

Emblem of Communications A92

Unwmk.
1945, Jan. 10   **Litho.**   **Perf. 12**
412 A91 ½c blue & lt blue .20 .20
413 A91 1c dk green & green .20 .20
414 A91 2c red org & org .20 .20
415 A91 3c dk brown & brown .20 .20
416 A91 10c ultra & gray blue .60 .20
    Nos. 412-416 (5) 1.40 1.00

Centenary of the constitution.

1945, Sept. 1
Center in Dark Blue and Carmine
417 A92 3c orange .20 .20
418 A92 20c yellow green .75 .20
419 A92 50c light blue 1.50 .55
    Nos. 417-419,C53-C56 (7) 4.35 1.80

Palace of Justice, Ciudad Trujillo A93

1946   **Perf. 11½**
420 A93 3c dk red brown & buff .20 .20

Map of Hispaniola — A94

1946, Aug. 4   **Perf. 12**
421 A94 10c multicolored .45 .20
    Nos. 421,C62-C63 (3) 2.15 .60

450th anniv. of the founding of Santo Domingo.

Waterfall of Jimenoa — A95

1946-47
Center Multicolored
422 A95 1c yellow grn ('47) .20 .20
423 A95 2c carmine ('47) .20 .20
424 A95 3c deep blue .20 .20
425 A95 13c red violet ('47) .40 .30
426 A95 20c chocolate ('47) .75 .20
427 A95 50c orange ('47) 1.50 1.10
    Nos. 422-427,C64-C67 (10) 8.70 4.70

Nos. 422-423, 425-427 issued Mar. 18.
For surcharge see No. 540.

Executive Palace A96

1948, Feb. 27
428 A96 1c yellow green .20 .20
429 A96 3c deep blue .20 .20
Nos. 428-429,C68-C69 (4) 5.90 2.65

Church of San Francisco Ruins — A97

1949, Apr. 13 *Perf. 11½*
430 A97 1c dk grn & pale grn .20 .20
431 A97 3c dp bl & pale bl .20 .20
Nos. 430-431,C70-C73 (6) 3.15 1.50

Gen. Pedro Santano — A98

Pigeon and Globe — A99

1949, Aug. 10
432 A98 3c deep blue & blue .20 .20

Battle of Las Carreras, cent. See #C74.

1950, Mar. 23
Center and Inscriptions in Brown
433 A99 1c green & pale green .20 .20
434 A99 2c yel grn & yel .20 .20
435 A99 5c blue & pale blue .20 .20
436 A99 7c dk vio bl & pale bl .40 .20
Nos. 433-436 (4) 1.00 .80

75th anniv. of the UPU.

Catalogue values for unused stamps in this section, from this point to the end of the section, are for Never Hinged items.

Hotel Jimani A100

Hotels: 1c, 2c, Hamaca. 5c, Montana. 15c, San Cristobal. 20c, Maguana.

1950-52
437 A100 ½c org brn & buff .20 .20
438 A100 1c dp grn & grn ('51) .20 .20
439 A100 2c red org & sal ('52) .20 .20
440 A100 5c blue & lt blue .30 .20
441 A100 15c dp orange & yel .55 .20
442 A100 20c lilac & rose lilac 1.00 .20
443 A100 1p chocolate & yel 4.00 1.60
Nos. 437-443,C75-C76 (9) 9.95 5.00

Issue dates: 1c, Dec. 1, 1951; 2c, Jan. 11, 1952; others, Sept. 8, 1950.
The ½c, 15c and 20c exist imperf.

Ruins of Church and Hospital of San Nicolas de Bari A101

School of Medicine — A102

Queen Isabella I — A103

1950, Oct. 2
444 A101 2c dk green & rose brn .20 .20
445 A102 5c vio blue & org brn .40 .20
Nos. 444-445,C77 (3) 1.20 .60

13th Pan-American Health Conference. Nos. 444-445 and C77 exist imperf.

1951, Oct. 12
446 A103 5c dk blue & red brn .50 .20

500th anniversary of the birth of Queen Isabella I of Spain. Exists imperf.

Dr. Salvador B. Gautier Hospital A104

1952, Aug.
447 A104 1c dark green .20 .20
448 A104 2c red .20 .20
449 A104 5c violet blue .40 .20
Nos. 447-449,C78-C79 (5) 3.90 2.95

Columbus Lighthouse and Flags of 21 Republics A105

1953, Jan. 6 **Engr.** *Perf. 13*
450 A105 2c dark green .25 .20
451 A105 5c deep blue .35 .20
452 A105 10c deep carmine .60 .25
Nos. 450-452,C80-C86 (10) 5.35 3.65

Treasury Building, Ciudad Trujillo A106

Sugar Industry, "Central Rio Haina" A107

1953 **Litho.** *Perf. 11½*
453 A106 ½c brown .20 .20
454 A106 2c dark blue .20 .20
455 A107 5c blue & vio brn .20 .20
456 A106 15c orange .75 .25
Nos. 453-456 (4) 1.35 .85

For surcharge see No. 539.

José Marti — A108

Monument to the Peace of Trujillo — A109

1954 *Perf. 12½*
457 A108 10c dp blue & dk brown .45 .20
Centenary of the birth of Jose Marti (1853-1895), Cuban patriot.

1954, May 25
458 A109 2c green .20 .20
459 A109 7c blue .25 .20
460 A109 20c orange .80 .20
Nos. 458-460 (3) 1.25 .60

See No. 493.

Rotary Emblem A110

1955, Feb. 23 *Perf. 12*
461 A110 7c deep blue .60 .20

50th anniv., Rotary Intl. See No. C90.

Gen. Rafael L. Trujillo — A111

4c, Trujillo in civilian clothes. 7c, Trujillo statue. 10c, Symbols of culture & prosperity.

1955, May 16 **Engr.** *Perf. 13½x13*
462 A111 2c red .30 .20
463 A111 4c lt olive green .30 .20
464 A111 7c indigo .35 .20
465 A111 10c brown .85 .20
Nos. 462-465,C91-C93 (7) 4.50 1.80

25th anniversary of the Trujillo era.

General Rafael L. Trujillo — A112

Angelita Trujillo — A113

1955, Dec. 20 **Unwmk.** *Perf. 13*
466 A112 7c deep claret .35 .20
467 A112 10c dark blue .50 .20
Nos. 466-467,C94 (3) 1.20 .60

1955, Dec. 20 **Litho.** *Perf. 12½*
468 A113 10c blue & ultra .45 .20

Nos. 466-468 were issued to publicize the International Fair of Peace and Brotherhood in Ciudad Trujillo, Dec. 1955.

Airport A114

Cedar — A115

1956, Apr. 6 *Perf. 12½*
469 A114 1c brown .20 .20
470 A114 2c red orange .20 .20
Nos. 469-470,C95 (3) .80 .60

3rd Caribbean conf. of the ICAO.

1956, Dec. 8 *Perf. 11½x12*
471 A115 5c car rose & grn 1.10 .20
472 A115 6c red vio & grn 1.40 .20
Nos. 471-472,C96 (3) 4.10 .60

Reforestation program.

Fair Emblem A116

Fanny Blankers-Koen, Netherlands A117

1957, Jan. 10 *Perf. 12½*
473 A116 7c blue, lt brn & ver .35 .20

2nd International Livestock Show, Ciudad Trujillo, Jan. 10-20, 1957. Exists imperf.

Engraved & Lithographed
1957, Jan. 24 *Perf. 11½, Imperf.*
Olympic Winners and Flags: 2c, Jesse Owens, US. 3c, Kee Chung Sohn, Japan. 5c, Lord Burghley, England. 7c, Bob Mathias, US.

Flags in National Colors
474 A117 1c brn, lt bl, vio & mar .20 .20
475 A117 2c dk brn, lt bl & vio .20 .20
476 A117 3c red lilac & red .20 .20
477 A117 5c red org & vio .20 .20
478 A117 7c green & violet .20 .20
Nos. 474-478,C97-C99 (8) 1.75 1.75

16th Olympic Games, Melbourne, Nov. 22-Dec. 8, 1956.
Miniature sheets of 5 exist, perf. and imperf., containing Nos. 474-478. Value, 2 sheets, perf. and imperf., $15.
For surcharges see Nos. B1-B5, B26-B30, CB1-CB3, CB16-CB18.

Lars Hall, Sweden, Pentathlon — A118

Olympic Winners and Flags: 2c, Betty Cuthbert, Australia, 100 & 200 meter dash. 3c, Egil Danielsen, Norway, javelin. 5c, Alain Mimoun, France, marathon. 7c, Norman Read, New Zealand, 50 km. walk.

Perf. 13½, Imperf.
1957, July 18   Photo.   Unwmk.
Flags in National Colors

479	A118	1c brn & brt bl	.20 .20
480	A118	2c org ver & dk bl	.20 .20
481	A118	3c dark blue	.20 .20
482	A118	5c ol & dk bl	.20 .20
483	A118	7c rose brn & dk bl	.20 .20
		Nos. 479-483,C100-C102 (8)	1.75 1.75

1956 Olympic winners.

Miniature sheets of 8 exist, perf. and imperf., containing Nos. 479-483 and C100-C102. The center label in these sheets is printed in two forms: Olympic gold medal or Olympic flag. Sheets measure 140x140mm. Value, 4 sheets, perf. and imperf., medal and flag, $18.

A third set of similar miniature sheets (perf. and imperf.) with center label showing an incorrect version of the Dominican Republic flag (colors transposed) was printed. These sheets are said to have been briefly sold on the first day, then withdrawn as the misprint was discovered. Value, 2 sheets, perf. & imperf., $150.

For surcharges see Nos. B6-B10, CB4-CB6.

Gerald Ouellette, Canada, Small Bore Rifle, Prone — A119

Ron Delaney, Ireland, 1,500 Meter Run — A120

Olympic Winners and Flags: 3c, Tenley Albright, US, figure skating. 5c, Joaquin Capilla, Mexico, platform diving. 7c, Ercole Baldini, Italy, individual road race (cycling).

Engraved and Lithographed
1957, Nov. 12   Perf. 13½, Imperf.
Flags in National Colors

484	A119	1c red brown	.20 .20
485	A120	2c gray brown	.20 .20
486	A119	3c violet	.20 .20
487	A120	5c red orange	.20 .20
488	A119	7c Prus green	.20 .20
		Nos. 484-488,C103-C105 (8)	1.75 1.75

1956 Olympic winners.

Miniature sheets of 5 exist, perf. and imperf., containing Nos. 484-488. Value, 2 sheets, perf. and imperf., $5.50.

For surcharges see Nos. B11-B20, CB7-CB12.

Mahogany Flower — A121   Cervantes, Globe, Book — A122

1957-58   Litho.   Perf. 12½
489	A121	2c green & maroon	.20 .20

Perf. 12
490	A121	4c lilac & rose ('58)	.20 .20
491	A121	7c ultra & gray grn	.35 .20
492	A121	25c brown & org ('58)	1.00 .35
		Nos. 489-492 (4)	1.75 .95

Sizes: No. 489, 25x29¼mm; No. 490-492, 24x28¾mm. In 1959, the 2c was reissued in size 24¼x28½mm with slightly different tones of green and maroon.

Issued: 2c, 10/24; 7c, 11/6; 4c, 25c, 4/7/58.

For surcharges see Nos. 537-538.

Type of 1954, Redrawn
Perf. 12x11½
1957, June 12   Unwmk.
493	A109	7c bright blue	.55 .20

On No. 493 the cent symbol is smaller, the shading of the sky and steps stronger and the letters in "Correos" shorter and bolder.

1958, Apr. 23   Litho.   Perf. 12½
494	A122	4c yellow green	.20 .20
495	A122	7c red lilac	.20 .20
496	A122	10c lt olive brown	.35 .20
		Nos. 494-496 (3)	.75 .60

4th Book Fair, Apr. 23-28. Exist imperf.

Gen. Rafael L. Trujillo — A123

1958, Aug. 16   Perf. 12
497	A123	2c red lilac & yel	.25 .20
498	A123	4c green & yel	.25 .20
499	A123	7c brown & yel	.25 .20
a.		Souv. sheet of 3, #497-499, imperf.	1.00 .80
		Nos. 497-499 (3)	.75 .60

25th anniv. of Gen. Trujillo's designation as "Benefactor of his country."

S. S. Rhadames A124

1958, Oct. 27   Perf. 12½
500	A124	7c bright blue	1.00 .30

Day of the Dominican Merchant Marine. Exists imperf.

Shozo Sasahara, Japan, Featherweight Wrestling — A125

Olympic Winners and Flags: 1c, Gillian Sheen, England, fencing, vert. 2c, Milton Campbell, US, decathlon, vert. 5c, Madeleine Berthod, Switzerland, downhill skiing. 7c, Murray Rose, Australia, 400 & 1,500 meter freestyle.

Perf. 13½, Imperf.
1958, Oct. 30   Photo.
Flags in National Colors

501	A125	1c rose, ind & ultra	.30 .20
502	A125	2c brown & blue	.30 .20
503	A125	3c gray, vio, blk & buff	.30 .20
504	A125	5c rose, dk bl, brn & red	.30 .20
505	A125	7c lt brn, dk bl & red	.30 .20
		Nos. 501-505,C106-C108 (8)	2.25 1.75

1956 Olympic winners.

Miniature sheets of 5 exist, perf. and imperf., containing Nos. 501-505. Value, 2 sheets, perf. and imperf., $5.

For surcharges see Nos. B21-B25, CB13-CB15.

Globe and Symbolic Fire — A126

1958, Nov. 3   Litho.   Perf. 11½
506	A126	7c blue & dp carmine	.30 .20

UNESCO Headquarters in Paris opening, Nov. 3.

Dominican Republic Pavilion, Brussels Fair — A127

1958, Dec. 9   Unwmk.   Perf. 12½
507	A127	7c blue green	.25 .20
		Nos. 507,C109-C110 (3)	1.20 .80

Universal & Intl. Exposition at Brussels.

Gen. Trujillo Placing Wreath on Altar of the Nation — A128

1959, July 10   Perf. 12
508	A128	9c brn, grn, red & gold	.25 .20
a.		Souv. sheet of 1, imperf.	1.00 .75

29th anniversary of the Trujillo regime.

Lt. Leonidas Rhadames Trujillo, Team Captain — A129

Jamaican Polo Team — A130

Design: 10c, Lt. Trujillo on polo pony.

1959, May 15
509	A129	2c violet	.20 .20
510	A130	7c yellow brown	.35 .25
511	A130	10c green	.45 .25
		Nos. 509-511,C111 (4)	1.35 1.00

Jamaica-Dominican Republic polo match at Ciudad Trujillo.

Symbolical of Census A131

1959, Aug. 15   Litho.   Perf. 12½
Flag in Ultramarine and Red

512	A131	1c blue & black	.20 .20
513	A131	9c green & black	.25 .20
514	A131	13c orange & black	.50 .25
		Nos. 512-514 (3)	.95 .65

Issued to publicize the 1960 census.

Trujillo Stadium — A132

1959, Aug. 27
515	A132	9c green & gray	.40 .25

Issued to publicize the 3rd Pan American Games, Chicago, Aug. 27-Sept. 7.

Charles V A133

1959, Oct. 12   Unwmk.   Perf. 12
516	A133	5c bright pink	.25 .20
517	A133	9c violet blue	.40 .20

400th anniv. of the death of Charles V (1500-1558), Holy Roman Emperor.

Rhadames Bridge — A134

1959-60   Litho.   Perf. 12
1c and No. 520, Different view of bridge.

518	A134	1c green & gray ('60)	.30 .20
519	A134	2c ultra & gray	.30 .20
520	A134	2c red & gray ('60)	.30 .20
521	A134	5c brn & dull red brn	.30 .20
		Nos. 518-521 (4)	1.20 .80

Issued: No. 519, 10/22; 5c, 11/30; 1c, No. 520, 2/6.

For surcharge see No. 536.

Sosua Refugee Settlement and WRY Emblem — A135

1960, Apr. 7   Perf. 12½
Center in Gray

522	A135	5c red brn & yel grn	.20 .20
523	A135	9c carmine & lt blue	.20 .20
524	A135	13c orange & green	.50 .20
		Nos. 522-524,C113-C114 (5)	2.30 1.20

World Refugee Year, 7/1/59-6/30/60.
For surcharges see Nos. B31-B33.

Sholam Takhti, Iran, Lightweight Wrestling — A136

Olympic Winners: 2c, Masaru Furukawa, Japan, 200 meter breast stroke. 3c, Mildred McDaniel, US, high jump. 5c, Terence Spinks,

England, featherweight boxing. 7c, Carlo Pavesi, Italy, fencing.

Perf. 13½, Imperf.

1960, Sept. 14   Photo.

Flags in National Colors

525 A136 1c red, yel grn & blk   .20 .20
526 A136 2c org, grnsh bl & brn   .20 .20
527 A136 3c henna brn & bl   .20 .20
528 A136 5c brown & ultra   .20 .20
529 A136 7c grn, bl & rose brn   .20 .20
  Nos. 525-529,C115-C117 (8)   1.70 1.70

17th Olympic Games, Rome, 8/25-9/11. Miniature sheets of 5 exist, perf. and imperf., containing Nos. 525-529. Value, 2 sheets, perf. & imperf., $5.

For surcharges see Nos. B34-B38, CB21-CB23.

Post Office, Ciudad Trujillo A137

1960, Aug. 26   Litho.   Perf. 11½x12
530 A137 2c ultra & gray   .25 .20
  Exists imperf.

Cattle A138

1960, Aug. 30
531 A138 9c carmine & gray   .25 .20

Issued to publicize the Agricultural and Industrial Fair, San Juan de la Maguana.

Nos. 518, 490-491, 453, 427 Surcharged in Red, Black or Blue

1960-61   Perf. 12
536 A134 2c on 1c grn & gray (R)   .20 .20
537 A121 9c on 4c lilac & rose   .50 .20
  a. Inverted surcharge   21.00
538 A121 9c on 7c ultra & gray grn (R)   .50 .20
539 A106 36c on ½c brown   1.40 1.25
  a. Inverted surcharge   18.00
540 A95 1p on 50c multi (Bl)   3.25 2.40
  Nos. 536-540 (5)   5.85 4.25

Issue dates: No. 536, Dec. 30, 1960; No. 537, Dec. 20, 1960; others, Feb. 4, 1961.

Trujillo Memorial A139   Coffee, Cacao A140

1961   Unwmk.   Perf. 11½
548 A139 1c brown   .20 .20
549 A139 2c green   .20 .20
550 A139 4c rose lilac   .40 .30
551 A139 5c light blue   .40 .20
552 A139 9c red orange   .40 .20
  Nos. 548-552 (5)   1.60 1.10

Gen. Rafael L. Trujillo (1891-1961). Issued: 2c, 8/7; 4c, 10/24; others 8/30.

1961, Dec. 30   Litho.   Perf. 12½
553 A140 1c blue green   .20 .20
554 A140 2c orange brown   .20 .20
555 A140 4c violet   .20 .20
556 A140 5c blue   .20 .20
557 A140 9c gray   .35 .20
  Nos. 553-557,C118-C119 (7)   1.90 1.75
  Nos. 553-557 exist imperf.

Dagger Pointing at Mosquito — A141

1962, Apr. 29   Photo.   Perf. 12
558 A141 10c brt pink & red lilac   .30 .20
559 A141 20c pale brn & brn   .45 .25
560 A141 25c pale grn & yel grn   .60 .30
  Nos. 558-560,B39-B40,C120-C121,CB24-CB25 (9)   4.10 2.80

WHO drive to eradicate malaria.

Broken Fetters and Laurel A142

"Justice," Map of Dominican Republic — A143   Farm, Factory and Flag — A144

Design: 20c, Flag, torch and inscription.

1962, May 30   Litho.   Perf. 12½
561 A142 1c grn, yel, ultra & red   .20 .20
562 A143 9c bister ultra & red   .30 .20
563 A142 20c lt blue, ultra & red   .60 .25
  a. Souvenir sheet of 3, #561-563   1.50 1.50
564 A143 1p lilac, ultra & red   3.00 1.40
  Nos. 561-564,C122-C123 (6)   5.50 3.05

1st anniv. of end of Trujillo era. Nos. 561-564 exist imperf.

1962, May 22
565 A144 1c ultra, red & green   .20 .20
566 A144 2c ultra & red   .20 .20
567 A144 3c ultra, red & brown   .20 .20
568 A144 5c ultra, red & blue   .20 .20
569 A144 15c ultra, red & orange   .30 .30
  Nos. 565-569 (5)   1.10 1.10

Map and Laurel A145

1962, June 14   Litho.
570 A145 1c black   .30 .20

Honoring the martyrs of June 1959 revolution.

Western Hemisphere and Carrier Pigeon — A146   Archbishop Adolfo Alejandro Nouel — A147

1962, Oct. 23   Unwmk.   Perf. 12½
571 A146 2c rose red   .20 .20
572 A146 9c orange   .20 .20
573 A146 14c blue green   .35 .20
  Nos. 571-573,C124-C125 (5)   1.40 1.20

50th anniv. of the founding of the Postal Union of the Americas and Spain, UPAE.

1962, Dec. 18
574 A147 2c bl grn & dull bl   .20 .20
575 A147 9c orange & red brn   .25 .20
576 A147 13c maroon & vio brn   .30 .20
  Nos. 574-576,C126-C127 (5)   1.60 1.30

Cent. of the birth of Archbishop Adolfo Alejandro Nouel, President of Dominican Republic in 1911.

Globe, Banner and Emblems A148

1963, Apr. 15   Unwmk.   Perf. 11½
Banner in Dark Blue & Red
577 A148 2c green   .20 .20
578 A148 5c brt rose lilac   .20 .20
579 A148 9c red orange   .35 .20
  Nos. 577-579,B41-B43 (6)   1.45 1.30

FAO "Freedom from Hunger" campaign.

Juan Pablo Duarte — A149

1963, July 7   Litho.   Perf. 12x11½
580 A149 2c shown   .25 .20
581 A149 7c Francisco Sanchez   .25 .20
582 A149 9c Ramon Mella   .25 .20
  Nos. 580-582 (3)   .75 .60

120th anniv. of separation from Haiti. See #C128.

Ulises F. Espaillat, Benigno F. de Rojas and Pedro F. Bono — A150

Designs: 4c, Generals Santiago Rodriguez, Jose Cabrera and Benito Moncion. 5c, Capotillo monument. 9c, Generals Gaspar Polanco, Gregorio Luperon and Jose A. Salcedo.

1963, Aug. 16   Unwmk.   Perf. 11½
583 A150 2c green   .20 .20
584 A150 4c red orange   .20 .20
585 A150 5c brown   .20 .20
586 A150 9c bright blue   .20 .20
  a. Souvenir sheet of 4   1.00 1.00
  Nos. 583-586 (4)   .80 .80

Cent. of the Restoration. No. 586a contains 4 imperf. stamps similar to Nos. 583-586.

Patient and Nurse — A151

Scales, Globe, UNESCO Emblem A152

1963, Oct. 25   Unwmk.   Perf. 12½
587 A151 3c gray & carmine   .20 .20
588 A151 6c emerald & red   .20 .20
  Nos. 587-588,C129 (3)   .70 .65

Centenary of International Red Cross. Nos. 587-588 exist imperf. See No. C129.

1963, Dec. 10   Litho.
589 A152 6c pink & deep pink   .20 .20
590 A152 50c lt green & green   .65 .65
  Nos. 589-590,C130-C131 (4)   1.35 1.25

Universal Declaration of Human Rights, 15th anniv. Nos. 589-590 exist imperf.

Ramses II Battling the Hittites (from Abu Simbel) — A153

Design: 6c, Two heads of Ramses II.

1964, Mar. 8   Unwmk.   Perf. 12½
591 A153 3c pale pink & ver   .25 .20
592 A153 6c pale blue & ultra   .25 .20
593 A153 9c pale rose & red brn   .25 .20
  Nos. 591-593,C132-C133 (5)   1.25 1.00

UNESCO world campaign to save historic monuments in Nubia.

For surcharges see Nos. B44-B46.

Maximo Gomez — A154   Palm Chat — A155

1964, Apr. 30   Litho.
594 A154 2c lt blue & blue   .25 .20
595 A154 6c dull pink & dull claret   .25 .20

Bicent. of the founding of the town of Bani.

1964, June 8   Unwmk.   Perf. 12½

Design: 6c, Hispaniolan parrot.

Size: 27x37½mm
596 A155 3c ultra, brn & yel   1.90 .20
597 A155 6c gray & multi   3.00 .20
  Nos. 596-597,C134 (3)   9.65 .60

See Nos. 602-604.

Rocket Leaving Earth A156

Designs: 1c, Launching of rocket, vert. 3c, Space capsule orbiting earth. 6c, As 2c.

1964, July 28   **Litho.**
598 A156 1c sky blue .20 .20
599 A156 2c emerald .20 .20
600 A156 3c blue .20 .20
601 A156 6c sky blue .35 .20
    Nos. 598-601,C135-C136 (6) 1.50 1.25

Conquest of space.

Bird Type of 1964

Designs: 1c, Narrow-billed tody. 2c, His-paniolan emerald hummingbird. 6c, Hispaniolan trogon.

1964, Nov. 7   **Perf. 11½**
Size: 26x37mm
Birds in Natural Colors
602 A155 1c bright pink 1.90 .20
603 A155 2c dark brown 1.90 .20
604 A155 6c blue 3.00 .20
    Nos. 602-604 (3) 6.80 .60

Universal Postal Union and United Nations Emblems A157

1964, Dec. 5   **Litho.**   **Perf. 12½**
605 A157 1c red .20 .20
606 A157 4c green .20 .20
607 A157 5c orange .20 .20
    Nos. 605-607,C138 (4) .85 .80

15th UPU Cong., Vienna, May-June 1964.

International Cooperation Year Emblem A158

1965, Feb. 16   **Unwmk.**   **Perf. 12½**
608 A158 2c lt blue & ultra .25 .20
609 A158 3c emerald & dk grn .25 .20
610 A158 6c salmon pink & red .25 .20
    Nos. 608-610,C139 (4) 1.05 .85

UN Intl. Cooperation Year.

Virgin of Altagracia A159

Flags of 21 American Nations — A160

Design: 2c, Hands holding lily.

1965, Mar. 18   **Unwmk.**   **Perf. 12½**
611 A159 2c grn, emer & dp rose .20 .20
612 A159 6c multicolored .30 .25
    Nos. 611-612,C140 (3) .80 .70

4th Mariological Cong. and 11th Intl. Marian Cong. No. 612 exists imperf.

1965, Apr. 14   **Litho.**   **Perf. 11½**
613 A160 2c brown, yel & multi .20 .20
614 A160 6c red lilac & multi .30 .20

Organization of American States.

Stamp of 1865 (No. 1) — A161

1965, Dec. 28   **Litho.**   **Perf. 12½**
615 A161 1c pink, buff & blk .25 .20
616 A161 2c blue, buff & blk .25 .20
617 A161 6c emerald, buff & blk .25 .20
    a. Souvenir sheet of 2 1.00 1.00
    Nos. 615-617,C142-C143 (5) 1.25 1.00

Cent. of 1st Dominican postage stamps. No. 617a shows replicas of Nos. 1-2. Sold for 50c.

WHO Headquarters, Geneva — A162

1966, May 21   **Litho.**   **Perf. 12½**
618 A162 6c blue .20 .20
619 A162 10c red lilac .30 .20

New WHO Headquarters, Geneva.

Man Holding Map of Republic — A163

1966, May 23
620 A163 2c black & brt green .20 .20
621 A163 6c black & dp orange .35 .20

General elections, June 1, 1966.

Ascia Monuste — A164

Natl. Altar — A165

1966   **Litho.**   **Perf. 12½**
Various Butterflies in Natural Colors
Size: 31x21mm
622 A164 1c blue & vio bl 1.50 .20
623 A164 2c lt grn & brt grn 1.40 .20
624 A164 3c lt gray & gray 1.40 .20
625 A164 6c pink & magenta 2.25 1.00
626 A164 8c buff & brown 3.50 1.40
    Nos. 622-626,C146-C148 (8) 35.05 7.75

Issued: 1c, 9/7; 3c, 9/11; others, 11/8.
For surcharges see Nos. B47-B51, CB28-CB30.

1967, Jan. 18   **Litho.**   **Perf. 11½**
627 A165 1c bright blue .20 .20
628 A165 2c carmine rose .20 .20
629 A165 3c emerald .20 .20
630 A165 4c gray .20 .20
631 A165 5c orange yellow .20 .20
632 A165 6c orange .20 .20
    Nos. 627-632,C149-C151 (9) 1.90 1.85

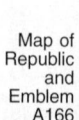

Map of Republic and Emblem A166

Rook and Knight A167

1967, Mar. 30   **Litho.**   **Perf. 12½**
633 A166 2c yellow, blue & blk .20 .20
634 A166 6c orange, blue & blk .20 .20
635 A166 10c emerald, blue & blk .60 .45
    Nos. 633-635 (3) 1.00 .85

Development Year, 1967.

1967, June 23   **Litho.**   **Perf. 12½**
636 A167 25c multicolored 2.25 .40

5th Central American Chess Championships, Santo Domingo. See Nos. C152-C152a.

Alliance for Progress A168

Institute Emblem A169

1967, Sept. 16   **Litho.**   **Perf. 12½**
637 A168 1c bright green .20 .20
    Nos. 637,C153-C154 (3) .85 .70

6th anniv. of the Alliance for Progress.

1967, Oct. 7
638 A169 3c bright green .25 .20
639 A169 6c salmon pink .25 .20
    Nos. 638-639,C155 (3) .95 .65

25th anniversary of the Inter-American Agriculture Institute.

Globe and Satellite A170

1968, June 15   **Typo.**   **Perf. 12**
640 A170 6c black & multi .25 .20
    Nos. 640,C156-C157 (3) .85 .70

World Meteorological Day, Mar. 23.

Boxers A171

1968, June 29
641 A171 6c rose red & dp claret .25 .20
    Nos. 641,C158-C159 (3) .80 .60

Fight between Carlos Ortiz, Puerto Rico, and Teo Cruz, Dominican Republic, for the World Lightweight Boxing Championship.

Lions Emblem — A172

1968, Aug. 9   **Litho.**   **Perf. 11½**
642 A172 6c brown & multi .25 .20

Lions Intl., 50th anniv. (in 1967). See No. C160.

Wrestling and Olympic Emblem A173

1968, Nov. 12   **Litho.**   **Perf. 11½**
643 A173 1c shown .20 .20
644 A173 6c Running .25 .20
645 A173 25c Boxing .75 .40
    Nos. 643-645,C161-C162 (5) 2.20 1.65

19th Olympic Games, Mexico City, 10/12-27.

Map of Americas and House — A174

Stool in Human Form A175

1969, Jan. 25   **Litho.**   **Perf. 12½**
646 A174 6c brt bl, lt bl & grn .20 .20

7th Inter-American Conference for Savings and Loans, Santo Domingo, Jan. 25-31. See No. C163.

1969, Jan. 31   **Litho.**   **Perf. 12½**

Taino Art: 2c, Wood carved mother figure, vert. 3c, Face carved on 3-cornered stone. 4c, Stone hatchet, vert. 5c, Clay pot.

647 A175 1c yellow, org & blk .30 .20
648 A175 2c lt grn, grn & blk .30 .20
649 A175 3c citron, ol & brt grn .30 .20
650 A175 4c lt lil, lil & brt grn .30 .20
651 A175 5c yellow, org & brn .30 .20
    Nos. 647-651,C164-C166 (8) 2.25 1.70

Taino art flourished in the West Indies at the time of Columbus.

Community Day Emblem — A176

COTAL Emblem — A177

Headquarters Building and COTAL Emblem — A178

1969, Mar. 25   Litho.   Perf. 12½
652 A176 6c dull green & gold   .25 .20

Community Development Day, Mar. 22.

1969, May 25   Litho.   Perf. 12½

Design: 2c, Boy and COTAL emblem.

653 A177 1c lt & dk blue & red   .25 .20
654 A177 2c emerald & dk grn   .25 .20
655 A178 6c vermilion & pink   .25 .20
   Nos. 653-655,C167 (4)   1.00 .80

12th Congress of the Confederation of Latin American Tourist Organizations (COTAL), Santo Domingo, May 25-29.

ILO Emblem — A179

Sliding into Base — A180

1969, June 27   Litho.   Perf. 12½
656 A179 6c lt grnsh bl, grnsh bl & blk   .25 .20

50th anniv. of the ILO. See No. C168.

1969, Aug. 15   Litho.   Perf. 12½

Designs: 1c, Catching a fly ball. 2c, View of Cibao Stadium, horiz.

Size: 21x31mm (1c, 3c); 43x30mm (2c)

657 A180 1c green & gray   .30 .20
658 A180 2c green & lt green   .30 .20
659 A180 3c purple & red brown   .30 .20
   Nos. 657-659,C169-C171 (6)   6.20 4.20

17th World Amateur Baseball Championships, Santo Domingo.

Las Damas Dam A181

Tavera Dam — A182

Designs: 2c, Las Damas hydroelectric station, vert. 6c, Arroyo Hondo substation.

1969   Litho.   Perf. 12
660 A181 2c green & multi   .30 .20
661 A181 3c dk blue & multi   .30 .20
662 A181 6c brt rose lilac   .30 .20
663 A182 6c multicolored   .50 .20
   Nos. 660-663,C172-C173 (6)   2.15 1.20

National electrification plan.
   Issued: Nos. 660-662, Sept. 15; No. 663, Oct. 15.

Juan Pablo Duarte — A183

Map of Republic, People, Census Emblem A184

1970, Jan. 26   Litho.   Perf. 12
664 A183 1c emerald & dk grn   .25 .20
665 A183 2c sal pink & dp car   .25 .20
666 A183 3c brt pink & plum   .25 .20
667 A183 6c blue & violet blue   .25 .20
   Nos. 664-667,C174 (5)   1.45 1.05

Issued for Duarte Day in memory of Juan Pablo Duarte (1813-1876), liberator.

1970, Feb. 6   Perf. 11

Design: 6c, Census emblem and inscription.

668 A184 5c emerald & blk   .25 .20
669 A184 6c ultra & blue   .25 .20
   Nos. 668-669,C175 (3)   .95 .65

Census of 1970.

Abelardo Rodriguez Urdaneta — A185

"One of Many" A186

1970, Feb. 20   Litho.   Perf. 12½
670 A185 3c ultramarine   .25 .20
671 A186 6c green & yel grn   .25 .20
   Nos. 670-671,C176 (3)   .80 .60

Issued to honor Abelardo Rodriguez Urdaneta, sculptor.

Masonic Symbols — A187

1970, Mar. 2
672 A187 6c green   .25 .20

8th Inter-American Masonic Conference, Santo Domingo, Mar. 1-7. See No. C177.

Communications Satellite — A188

1970, May 25   Litho.   Perf. 12½
673 A188 20c olive & gray   .50 .30

World Telecommunications Day. See #C178.

UPU Headquarters, Bern — A189

1970, June 5   Perf. 11
674 A189 6c gray & brown   .25 .20

Inauguration of the new UPU headquarters in Bern. See No. C179.

Education Year Emblem — A190   Pedro Alejandrino Pina — A191

1970, June 26   Litho.   Perf. 12½
675 A190 4c rose lilac   .25 .20

Issued for International Education Year, 1970. See No. C180.

1970, Aug. 24   Litho.   Perf. 12½
676 A191 6c lt red brn & blk   .25 .20

Pedro Alejandrino Pina (1820-70), author.

Children Reading A192

1970, Oct. 12   Litho.   Perf. 12½
677 A192 5c dull green   .25 .20
   Nos. 677,C181-C182 (3)   .80 .60

1st World Exhibition of Books and Culture Festival, Santo Domingo, Oct. 11-Dec. 11.

Virgin of Altagracia — A193   Rodriguez Objio — A194

1971, Jan. 20   Litho.   Perf. 12½
678 A193 3c multicolored   .25 .20

Inauguration of the Basilica of Our Lady of Altagracia. See No. C184.

1971, June 18   Litho.   Perf. 11
679 A194 6c light blue   .25 .20

Manuel Rodriguez Objio (1838-1871), poet.

Boxing and Canoeing — A195

1971, Sept. 10
680 A195 2c shown   .25 .20
681 A195 5c Basketball   .25 .20
   Nos. 680-681,C186 (3)   .75 .60

2nd National Games.

Goat and Fruit A196

Designs: 2c, Cow and goose. 3c, Cacao and horse. 6c, Bananas, coffee and pig.

1971, Sept. 29   Perf. 12½
682 A196 1c brown & multi   .25 .20
683 A196 2c plum & multi   .25 .20
684 A196 3c green & multi   .25 .20
685 A196 6c blue & multi   .25 .20
   Nos. 682-685,C187 (5)   1.50 1.10

6th Natl. agriculture and livestock census.

José Nuñez de Cáceres — A197

Shepherds and Star — A198

1971, Dec. 1   Perf. 11
686 A197 6c lt bl, lil & dk bl   .25 .20

Sesquicentennial of first national independence. See No. C188.

1971, Dec. 10   Perf. 12½
687 A198 6c blue, brown & yel   .25 .20

Christmas 1971. See No. C189.

UNICEF Emblem, Child on Beach — A199

1971, Dec. 14   Litho.   Perf. 11
688 A199 6c gray blue & multi   .25 .20
UNICEF, 25th anniv. See No. C190.

Book Year Emblem A200

Taino Mask — A201

1972, Jan. 25   Perf. 12½
689 A200 1c green, ultra & red   .25 .20
690 A200 2c brown, ultra & red   .25 .20
   Nos. 689-690,C191 (3)   .80 .65
Intl. Book Year 1972.

1972, May 10   Litho.   Perf. 11
4c, Ladle and amulet. 6c, Human figure.
691 A201 2c pink & multi   .40 .20
692 A201 4c black, bl & ocher   .40 .20
693 A201 6c gray & multi   .40 .20
   Nos. 691-693,C194-C196 (6)   3.70 1.45
Taino art. See note after No. 651.

Globe A202

1972, May 17   Perf. 12½
694 A202 6c blue & multi   .25 .20
4th World Telecommunications Day. See No. C197.

"1972," Stamps and Map of Dominican Republic A203

1972, June 3
695 A203 2c green & multi   .25 .20
First National Philatelic Exhibition, Santo Domingo, June 3-17. See No. C198.

Basketball — A204

1972, Aug. 25   Litho.   Perf. 12½
696 A204 2c blue & multi   .25 .20
20th Olympic Games, Munich, Aug. 26-Sept. 11. See No. C199.

Club Emblem A205

1972, Sept. 29   Litho.   Perf. 10½
697 A205 1c lt green & multi   .25 .20
50th anniversary of the Club Activo 20-30 International. See No. C200.

Emilio A. Morel A206

1972, Oct. 20   Perf. 12½
698 A206 6c brt pink & multi   .25 .20
Emilio A. Morel (1884-1958), poet and journalist. See No. C201.

Central Bank Building A207

1972, Oct. 23
699 A207 1c shown   .25 .20
700 A207 5c 1-peso note   .25 .20
   Nos. 699-700,C202 (3)   1.15 .85
25th anniv. of Central Bank.

Holy Family — A208

Poinsettia A209

1972, Nov. 21
701 A208 2c rose lil, pur & gold   .25 .20
702 A209 6c red & multi   .25 .20
   Nos. 701-702,C203 (3)   .95 .60
Christmas 1972.

Mail Box and Student A210

1972, Dec. 15
703 A210 2c rose red   .20 .20
704 A210 6c blue   .20 .20
705 A210 10c emerald   .35 .20
   Nos. 703-705 (3)   .75 .60
Publicity for correspondence schools.

Tavera Dam A211

1973, Feb. 26   Litho.   Perf. 12½
706 A211 10c multicolored   .30 .20
Inauguration of the Tavera Dam.

Various Sports — A212

Designs: a, UL. b, UR. c, LL. d, LR.

1973, Mar. 30   Perf. 13½x13
707 A212   Block of 4   .40 .50
 a.-d.   2c, any single   .20 .20
708 A212   Block of 4   4.50 4.50
 a.-d.   25c, any single   .90 .35
   Nos. 707-708,C204-C205 (4)   8.90 9.00
12th Central American and Caribbean Games, Santo Domingo, Summer 1974.

Christ Carrying the Cross A213

6c, Belfry of Church of Our Lady of Carmen.

1973, Apr. 18   Litho.   Perf. 10½
709 A213 2c multicolored   .25 .20
710 A213 6c multicolored, vert.   .25 .20
   Nos. 709-710,C206 (3)   .90 .60
Holy Week, 1973.

WMO Emblem, Weather Satellite, "Weather" A214

Mask, Cibao — A215

1973, Aug. 10   Litho.   Perf. 13½x13
711 A214 6c magenta & multi   .25 .20
Centenary of international meteorological cooperation. See No. C208.

1973, Oct. 12   Litho.   Perf. 10½
712 A215 1c Maguey drum, horiz   .25 .20
713 A215 2c Carved amber, horiz   .25 .20
714 A215 4c shown   .25 .20
715 A215 6c Pottery   .25 .20
   Nos. 712-715,C210-C211 (6)   1.50 1.20
Opening of Museum of Mankind in Santo Domingo.

Nativity A216

Christmas: 6c, Stained glass window, vert.

Perf. 13½x13, 13x13½
1973, Nov. 26
716 A216   2c black, bl & yel   .25 .20
717 A216   6c rose & multi   .25 .20
   Nos. 716-717,C212 (3)   .75 .60
No. 717 exists imperf.

Dominican Scout Emblem A217

Design: 5c, Scouts and flag.

1973, Dec. 7   Litho.   Perf. 12
Size: 35x35mm
718 A217 1c ultra & multi   .25 .20
Size: 26x36mm
719 A217 5c black & multi   .25 .20
   Nos. 718-719,C213 (3)   1.15 .95
Dominican Republic Boy Scouts, 50th anniv.

Sports Palace, Basketball Players A218

Design: 6c, Bicyclist and race track.

1974, Feb. 25   Litho.   Perf. 13½
720 A218 2c red brown & multi   .25 .20
721 A218 6c yellow & multi   .25 .20
   Nos. 720-721,C214-C215 (4)   1.10 .80
12th Central American and Caribbean Games, Santo Domingo, 1974.

Bell Tower, Cathedral of Santo Domingo — A219

Mater Dolorosa — A220

1974, June 27   Litho.   Perf. 13½
722 A219 2c multicolored   .25 .20
723 A220 6c multicolored   .30 .20
   Nos. 722-723,C216 (3)   .85 .60
Holy Week 1974.

Francisco del Rosario Sanchez Bridge — A221

1974, July 12   Perf. 12
724 A221 6c multicolored   .35 .20
See No. C217.

Map, Emblem and Patient — A222

Design: 5c, Map of Dominican Republic, diabetics' emblem and pancreas.

1974, Aug. 22   Litho.   Perf. 13
725 A222 4c blue & multi   .25 .20
726 A222 5c yellow grn & multi   .25 .20
   Nos. 725-726,C218-C219 (4) 2.00 1.40
Fight against diabetes.

Train and UPU Emblem A223

Design: 6c, Mail coach and UPU emblem.

1974, Oct. 9   Litho.   Perf. 13½
727 A223 2c blue & multi   .60 .60
728 A223 6c brown & multi   .25 .20
   Nos. 727-728,C220-C221 (4) 4.85 1.90
Cent. of UPU.

Golfers — A224

Design: 2c, Championship emblem and badge of Dominican Golf Association, horiz.

1974, Oct. 24   Perf. 13x13½, 13½x13
729 A224 2c yellow & blk   1.00 .25
730 A224 6c blue & multi   1.25 .25
   Nos. 729-730,C222-C223 (4) 3.40 1.10
World Amateur Golf Championships.

Christmas Decorations A225

Virgin and Child — A226

1974, Dec. 3   Litho.   Perf. 12
731 A225 2c multicolored   .25 .20
732 A226 6c multicolored   .25 .20
   Nos. 731-732,C224 (3)   .80 .60
Christmas 1974.

Tomatoes, FAO Emblem — A227

1974, Dec. 5
733 A227 2c shown   .70 .20
734 A227 3c Avocados   .70 .20
735 A227 5c Coconuts   .70 .20
   Nos. 733-735,C225 (4)   3.20 .80
World Food Program, 10th anniv.

Fernando A. Defillo A228

Tower, Our Lady of the Rosary Convent A229

1975, Feb. 14   Litho.   Perf. 13½x13
736 A228 1c dull brown   .25 .20
737 A228 6c dull green   .25 .20
Dr. Defillo (1874-1949), physician.

1975, Mar. 26   Litho.   Perf. 13½
Design: 2c, Jesus saying "I am the Resurrection and the Life."
738 A229 2c brown & multi   .25 .20
739 A229 6c multicolored   .25 .20
   Nos. 738-739,C226 (3)   .80 .60
Holy Week 1975.

Hands (Steel Beams) with Symbols of Agriculture, Industry A230

1975, May 19   Litho.   Perf. 10½x10
740 A230 6c dull blue & multi   .25 .20
16th Assembly of the Governors of the International Development Bank, Santo Domingo, May 1975. See No. C228.

Satellite Tracking Station — A231

1975, June 21   Litho.   Perf. 13½
741 A231 5c multicolored   .25 .20
Opening of first earth satellite tracking station in Dominican Republic. See No. C229.

Apollo A232

1975, July 24
   Size: 35x25mm
742 A232 1c shown   .25 .20
743 A232 4c Soyuz   .25 .20
   Nos. 742-743,C230 (3)   5.75 3.65
Apollo Soyuz space test project (Russo-American cooperation), launching July 15; link-up, July 17.

Father Rafael C. Castellanos A233

1975, Aug. 6   Litho.   Perf. 12
744 A233 6c brown & buff   .25 .20
Castellanos (1875-1934), 1st Apostolic Administrator in Dominican Republic.

Women and Men Around IWY Emblem — A234

1975, Aug. 6   Perf. 13
745 A234 3c orange & multi   .25 .20
International Women's Year 1975.

Guacanagarix A235

Basketball A236

Indian Chiefs: 2c, Guarionex. 3c, Caonabo. 4c, Bohechio. 5c, Cayacoa. 6c, Anacona (woman). 9c, Hatuey.

1975, Sept. 27   Litho.   Perf. 12
746 A235 1c yellow & multi   .25 .20
747 A235 2c salmon & multi   .25 .20
748 A235 3c violet bl & multi   .25 .20
749 A235 4c green & multi   .25 .20
750 A235 5c blue & multi   .25 .20
751 A235 6c violet & multi   .25 .20
752 A235 9c rose & multi   .30 .25
   Nos. 746-752,C231-C233 (10) 2.65 2.20

1975, Oct. 24   Litho.   Perf. 12
Design: 6c, Baseball and Games' emblem.
753 A236 2c pink & multi   .30 .20
754 A236 6c orange & multi   .30 .20
   Nos. 753-754,C234-C235 (4) 1.20 .85
7th Pan-American Games, Mexico City, Oct. 13-26.

Carolers — A237

6c, Dominican nativity with farmers & shepherds.

1975, Dec. 12   Litho.   Perf. 13x13½
755 A237 2c yellow & multi   .25 .20
756 A237 6c blue & multi   .25 .20
   Nos. 755-756,C236 (3)   .75 .60
Christmas 1975.

Abudefdul Marginatus — A238

1976, Jan. 23   Litho.   Perf. 13
757 A238 10c shown   .45 .25
758 A238 10c Doncella   .45 .25
759 A238 10c Carajuelo   .45 .25
760 A238 10c Reina de los Angeles .45 .25
761 A238 10c Pargo Colorado   .45 .25
  a. Strip of 5, #757-761   5.75 5.75

Ascension, by J. Priego — A239

"Separacion Dominicana" and Adm. Cambiaso A240

2c, Mary Magdalene, by Enrique Godoy.

1976, Apr. 14   Litho.   Perf. 13½
762 A239 2c blue & multi   .25 .20
763 A239 6c yellow & multi   .25 .20
    Nos. 762-763,C238 (3)   .80 .65
    Holy Week 1976.

1976, Apr. 15   Perf. 13½x13
764 A240 20c multicolored   .85 .45
Naval Battle off Tortuga, Apr. 15, 1844.

Maps of US and Dominican Republic — A241

Design: 9c, Maps within cogwheels.

1976, May 29   Litho.   Perf. 13½
765 A241 6c violet bl & multi   .25 .20
766 A241 9c violet bl & multi   .25 .20
    Nos. 765-766,C239-C240 (4)   1.95 1.70
    American Bicentennial.

Flags of Dominican Republic and Spain A242

1976, May 31
767 A242 6c multicolored   .35 .20
Visit of King Juan Carlos I and Queen Sofia of Spain. See No. C241.

Various Telephones A243

1976, July 15   Perf. 12x12½
768 A243 6c multicolored   .25 .20
Cent. of 1st telephone call by Alexander Graham Bell, Mar. 10, 1876. See No. C242.

Vision of Duarte, by Luis Desangles — A244

Juan Pablo Duarte, by Rhadames Mejia — A245

1976, July 20   Litho.   Perf. 13x13½
769 A244 2c multicolored   .25 .20
Perf. 13½
770 A245 6c multicolored   .25 .20
    Nos. 769-770,C243-C244 (4)   1.90 1.35
Juan Pablo Duarte, liberation hero, death centenary.

Fire Hydrant — A246

Design: 6c, Firemen's emblem.

1976, Sept. 13   Litho.   Perf. 12
771 A246 4c multicolored   .25 .20
772 A246 6c multicolored   .25 .20
    Nos. 771-772,C245 (3)   .90 .60
Honoring firemen. Nos. 771-772 inscribed "Correos."

Radio and Atom Symbols A247

1976, Oct. 8   Litho.   Perf. 13½
773 A247 6c red & black   .25 .20
Dominican Radio Club, 50th anniv. See #C246.

Spain, Central and South America, Galleon A248

1976, Oct. 22   Litho.   Perf. 13½
774 A248 6c multicolored   .25 .20
Spanish heritage. See No. C247.

Boxing and Montreal Emblem A249

Design: 3c, Weight lifting.

1976, Oct. 22   Perf. 12
775 A249 2c blue & multi   .25 .20
776 A249 3c multicolored   .25 .20
    Nos. 775-776,C248-C249 (4)   1.65 1.10
21st Olympic Games, Montreal, Canada, July 17-Aug. 1.

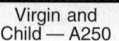

Virgin and Child — A250

Three Kings — A251

1976, Dec. 8   Litho.   Perf. 13½
777 A250 2c multicolored   .25 .20
778 A251 6c multicolored   .25 .20
    Nos. 777-778,C250 (3)   .80 .65
    Christmas 1976.

Cable Car and Beach Scenes A252

1977, Jan. 7
779 A252 6c multicolored   .25 .20
    Nos. 779,C251-C253 (4)   1.25 .90
    Tourist publicity.

Championship Emblem — A253

1977, Mar. 4   Litho.   Perf. 13½
780 A253 3c rose & multi   .25 .20
781 A253 5c yellow & multi   .25 .20
    Nos. 780-781,C254-C255 (4)   1.65 1.10
10th Central American and Caribbean Children's and Young People's Swimming Championships, Santo Domingo.

Christ Carrying Cross — A254

Design: 6c, Head with crown of thorns.

1977, Apr. 18   Litho.   Perf. 13½x13
782 A254 2c multicolored   .25 .20
783 A254 6c black & rose   .25 .20
    Nos. 782-783,C256 (3)   .80 .60
    Holy Week 1977.

Doves, Lions Emblem A255

1977, May 6   Perf. 13½x13
784 A255 2c lt blue & multi   .25 .20
785 A255 6c salmon & multi   .25 .20
    Nos. 784-785,C257 (3)   .75 .60
12th annual Dominican Republic Lions Convention.

Battle Scene A256

1977, June 15   Litho.   Perf. 13x13½
786 A256 20c multicolored   .70 .35
    Dominican Navy.

Water Lily — A257

National Botanical Garden: 4c, "Flor de Mayo" (orchid). 6c, Sebesten.

1977, Aug. 19   Litho.   Perf. 12
787 A257 2c multicolored   .35 .20
788 A257 4c multicolored   .35 .20
789 A257 6c multicolored   .35 .20
    Nos. 787-789,C259-C260 (5)   2.45 1.60

Chart and Computers — A258

1977, Nov. 30   Litho.   Perf. 13
790 A258 6c multicolored   .25 .20
7th Interamerican Statistics Conf. See No. C261.

Solenodon Paradoxus — A259

Design: 20c, Iguana and Congress emblem.

1977, Dec. 29   Litho.   Perf. 13
791 A259 6c multicolored   1.75 .20
792 A259 20c multicolored   3.25 .30
    Nos. 791-792,C262-C263 (4)   10.50 1.30
8th Pan-American Veterinary and Zoo-technical Congress.

Main Gate, Casa del Cordon, 1503 — A260

Crown of Thorns, Tools at the Cross — A261

1978, Jan. 19   Perf. 13x13½
Size: 26x36mm
793 A260 6c multicolored   .25 .20
Spanish heritage. See No. C264.

1978, Mar. 21   Litho.   Perf. 12
6c, Head of Jesus with crown of thorns.

Size: 22x33mm

794	A261	2c multicolored	.20 .20
795	A261	6c slate	.35 .20
		Nos. 794-795,C265-C266 (4)	1.20 .90

Holy Week 1978.

Cardinal Octavio A. Beras Rojas — A262

Pres. Manuel de Troncoso — A263

1978, May 5   Litho.   Perf. 13

796	A262	6c multicolored	.25 .20

First Cardinal from Dominican Republic, consecrated May 24, 1976. See No. C268.

1978, June 12   Litho.   Perf. 13½

797	A263	2c black, rose & brn	.20 .20
798	A263	6c black, gray & brn	.35 .25

Manuel de Jesus Troncoso de la Concha (1878-1955), pres. of Dominican Republic, 1940-42.

Father Juan N. Zegri y Moreno — A264

1978, July 11   Litho.   Perf. 13x13½

799	A264	6c multicolored	.25 .20

Congregation of the Merciful Sisters of Charity, centenary. See No. C273.

Boxing and Games' Emblem A265

1978, July 21   Perf. 12

800	A265	2c shown	.25 .20
801	A265	6c Weight lifting	.30 .20
		Nos. 800-801,C274-C275 (4)	1.40 .90

13th Central American & Caribbean Games, Medellin, Colombia.

Sun over Landscape A266

Ships of Columbus, Map of Dominican Republic — A267

Design: 6c, Sun over beach and boat.

1978, Sept. 12   Litho.   Perf. 12

802	A266	2c multicolored	.30 .20
803	A266	6c multicolored	.30 .20
		Nos. 802-803,C280-C281 (4)	1.25 .80

Tourist publicity.

1978, Oct. 12   Litho.   Perf. 13½

804	A267	2c multicolored	.25 .20

Spanish heritage. See No. C282.

Dove, Lamp, Poinsettia A268

Design: 6c, Dominican family and star, vert.

1978, Dec. 5   Litho.   Perf. 12

805	A268	2c multicolored	.30 .20
806	A268	6c multicolored	.40 .20
		Nos. 805-806,C284 (3)	1.00 .65

Christmas 1978.

Starving Child, IYC Emblem — A269

Crucifixion A270

1979, Feb. 26   Litho.   Perf. 12

807	A269	2c orange & black	.25 .20
		Nos. 807,C287-C289 (4)	1.85 1.35

Intl. Year of the Child.

1979, Apr. 9   Litho.   Perf. 13½

Design: 3c, Jesus carrying cross, horiz.

808	A270	2c multicolored	.25 .20
809	A270	3c multicolored	.35 .20
		Nos. 808-809,C290 (3)	2.00 1.40

Holy Week.

Stigmaphyllon Periplocifolium — A271

1979, May 17   Litho.   Perf. 12

810	A271	50c multicolored	1.00 .50
		Nos. 810,C293-C295 (4)	2.25 1.50

Dr. Rafael M. Moscoso National Botanical Garden.

Heart, Diseased Blood Vessel A272

Design: 1p, Cardiology Institute and heart.

1979, June 2   Litho.   Perf. 13½

811	A272	3c multicolored	.20 .20
812	A272	1p multicolored	1.75 .75
		Nos. 811-812,C296 (3)	2.55 1.35

Dominican Cardiology Institute.

Baseball, Games' Emblem A273

3c, Bicycling and Games' emblem, vert.

1979, June 20

813	A273	2c multicolored	.25 .20
814	A273	3c multicolored	.25 .20
		Nos. 813-814,C297 (3)	.90 .70

8th Pan American Games, Puerto Rico, June 30-July 15.

Soccer — A274

Thomas A. Edison — A275

Design: 25c, Swimming, horiz.

1979, Aug. 9   Litho.   Perf. 12

815	A274	2c multicolored	.25 .20
816	A274	25c multicolored	.35 .25
		Nos. 815-816,C298 (3)	.90 .70

Third National Games.

1979, Aug. 27   Perf. 13½

817	A275	25c multicolored	.60 .45

Cent. of invention of electric light. See No. C300.

Hand Holding Electric Plug A276

Design: 6c, Filling automobile gas tank.

1979, Aug. 30

818	A276	2c multicolored	.25 .20
819	A276	6c multicolored	.30 .25

Energy conservation.

Parrot A277

Birds: 6c, Temnotrogon roseigaster.

1979, Sept. 12   Litho.   Perf. 12

820	A277	2c multicolored	1.50 .20
821	A277	6c multicolored	1.50 .20
		Nos. 820-821,C301-C303 (5)	15.60 2.00

A278

A279

Lions Emblem, Map of Dominican Republic.

1979, Nov. 13   Litho.   Perf. 12

822	A278	20c multicolored	.45 .35

Lions International Club of Dominican Republic, 10th anniversary. See No. C304.

1979, Dec. 18   Litho.   Perf. 12

823	A279	2c Holy Family	.25 .20

Christmas 1979. See No. C305.

A280

A281

Design: Jesus Carrying Cross.

1980, Mar. 27   Litho.   Perf. 12

824	A280	3c multicolored	.25 .20
		Nos. 824,C306-C307 (3)	.75 .65

Holy Week.

1980, May 15   Litho.   Perf. 13½

825	A281	1c shown	.40 .20
826	A281	2c Coffee	.40 .20
827	A281	3c Plantain	.40 .20
828	A281	4c Sugar cane	.40 .20
829	A281	5c Corn	.40 .20
		Nos. 825-829 (5)	2.00 1.00

Cacao Harvest (Agriculture Year)

Cotuf Gold Mine, Pueblo Viejo, Flag of Dominican Republic A282

1980, July 8   Litho.   Perf. 13½
830 A282 6c multicolored   .25   .20
    Nos. 830,C310-C311 (3)   1.55 1.10
    Nationalization of gold mining.

Blind Man's Buff A283

1980, July 21   Perf. 12
831 A283 3c shown   .25   .20
832 A283 4c Marbles   .25   .20
833 A283 5c Drawing in sand   .30   .25
834 A283 6c Hopscotch   .30   .25
    Nos. 831-834 (4)   1.10   .90

Iguana A284

1980, Aug. 30   Litho.   Perf. 12
835 A284 20c multicolored   2.00   .45
    Nos. 835,C314-C317 (5)   12.90 2.80

Dance, by Jaime Colson A285

Perf. 13x13½, 13½x13
1980, Sept. 23   Litho.
836 A285 3c shown   .25   .20
837 A285 50c Woman, by Gilberto Hernandez Ortega, vert.   .90   .60
    Nos. 836-837,C318-C319 (4)   1.95 1.40

Three Kings — A286

Salcedo Province Cent. — A287

1980, Dec. 5   Litho.   Perf. 13½
838 A286 3c shown   .25   .20
839 A286 6c Carolers   .25   .20
    Nos. 838-839,C327 (3)   .80   .65
    Christmas 1980.

1981, Jan. 14   Litho.   Perf. 13½
840 A287 6c multicolored   .25   .20
    See No. C328.

Juan Pablo Duarte, Liberation Hero, 105th Anniv. of Death — A288

1981, Feb. 6   Litho.   Perf. 12
841 A288 2c sepia & deep bister   .30   .20

Gymnast — A289

Mother Mazzarello A290

1981, Mar. 31   Litho.   Perf. 13½
842 A289 1c shown   .30   .20
843 A289 2c Running   .30   .20
844 A289 3c Pole vault   .30   .20
845 A289 6c Boxing   .30   .20
    Nos. 842-845,C331 (5)   1.75 1.15
    5th National Games.

1981, Apr. 14   Perf. 12
846 A290 6c multicolored   .30   .20
    Mother Maria Mazzarello (1837-1881), founder of Daughters of Mary.

A291

A292

1981, May 18   Litho.   Perf. 13½
847 A291 6c gray vio & lt gray   .25   .20
    Pedro Henriquez Urena, Historian (1884-1946)

1981, June 30   Litho.   Perf. 12
848 A292 2c shown   .20   .20
849 A292 6c River, forest   .30   .20
    Forest conservation.

Family in House, Census Emblem A293

1981, Aug. 14   Litho.   Perf. 12
850 A293 3c shown   .20   .20
851 A293 6c Farmer   .30   .20
    1981 natl. population and housing census.

A294

A295

1981, Dec. 23   Litho.   Perf. 13½
852 A294 2c Bells   .25   .20
853 A294 3c Poinsettia   .25   .20
    Nos. 852-853,C353 (3)   1.00   .70
    Christmas.

1982, Jan. 29   Litho.   Perf. 13½
854 A295 2c Juan Pablo Duarte   .25   .20

National Elections A296

Designs: Voters casting votes. 3c, 6c vert.

1982, Mar. 30   Litho.   Perf. 13½
855 A296 2c multicolored   .20   .20
856 A296 3c multicolored   .20   .20
857 A296 6c multicolored   .30   .25
    Nos. 855-857 (3)   .70   .65

A297

A298

Energy Conservation: Various forms of energy.

1982, May 10   Litho.   Perf. 12
858 A297 1c multicolored   .25   .20
859 A297 2c multicolored   .25   .20
860 A297 3c multicolored   .25   .20
861 A297 4c multicolored   .35   .25
862 A297 6c multicolored   .35   .25
863 A297 6c multicolored   .35   .25
    Nos. 858-863 (6)   1.80 1.35

1982, Aug. 2   Perf. 12x12½
864 A298 6c multicolored   .25   .20
    Emilio Prud'Homme (1856-1932), composer.

Pres. Antonio Guzman Fernandez (1911-1982) A299

1982, Aug. 4   Perf. 13x13½
865 A299 6c multicolored   .25   .20

14th Central American and Caribbean Games A300

1982, Aug. 13   Perf. 12, Imperf.
866 A300 3c Baseball   .50   .20
    See Nos. C368-C370.

San Pedro de Macoris Province Centenary — A301

1982, Aug. 26   Perf. 13
867 A301 1c Wagon   .30   .20
868 A301 2c Stained-glass window   .30   .20
869 A301 5c Views   .40   .25
    Nos. 867-869,C375 (4)   1.40   .95
    Size of 2c, 25x35mm.

St. Teresa of Jesus of Avila (1515-1582) A302

1982, Nov. 17   Litho.   Perf. 13½
870 A302 6c multicolored   .45   .20

Christmas 1982 — A303

Environmental Protection A304

Various Christmas balls.

1982, Dec. 8
871 A303 6c multicolored   .25   .20
    See No. C380.

1982, Dec. 15   *Perf. 12*
872 A304 2c Bird .20 .20
873 A304 3c Water .20 .20
874 A304 6c Forest .20 .20
875 A304 20c Fish .50 .35
   Nos. 872-875 (4) 1.10 .95

Natl. Literacy Campaign A305

1983, Mar. 9   **Litho.**   *Perf. 13½*
876 A305 2c Vowels on blackboard .20 .20
877 A305 3c Writing, reading .20 .20
878 A305 6c Children, pencil .35 .20
   Nos. 876-878 (3) .75 .60

A306

A307

5c, similar arms, incorporating stylized centenary monument.

1983, Apr. 4   *Perf. 12*
879 A306 1c multicolored .25 .20
880 A306 5c multicolored .30 .20

Mao City centenary.

1983, Apr. 25   **Litho.**   *Perf. 12*

Dominican Historians: 2c, Antonio del Monte y Tejada (1780-1861). 3c, Manuel Ubaldo Gomez (1857-1941). 5c, Emiliano Tejera (1841-1923). 6c, Bernardo Pichardo (1877-1924). 7c, Americo Lugo (1870-1952). 10c, José Gabriel Garcia (1834-1910). 7c, 10c airmail.
881 A307 2c multicolored .25 .20
882 A307 3c multicolored .25 .20
883 A307 5c multicolored .25 .20
884 A307 6c multicolored .25 .20
885 A307 7c multicolored .25 .25
886 A307 10c multicolored .30 .30
   Nos. 881-886 (6) 1.55 1.35

National Anthem, 100th Anniv. A308

Emilio Prud'Homme, & Jose Reyes, composer.

1983, Sept. 13   **Litho.**   *Perf. 13½*
887 A308 6c copper red & blk .30 .20

Free Masons, 125th Anniv. — A309

Church of Our Lady of Regla, 300th Anniv. — A310

1983, Oct. 24   **Litho.**   *Perf. 12*
888 A309 4c Emblem .25 .20

1983, Nov. 5   *Perf. 13½*
889 A310 3c Church .25 .20
890 A310 6c Statue .30 .20

450th Anniv. of Monte Cristi Province — A311

6th Natl. Games — A312

1983, Nov. 25   *Perf. 12*
891 A311 1c Tower .25 .20
892 A311 2c Arms .25 .20
893 A311 5c Cuban independence site, horiz. .30 .20
894 A311 7c Workers, horiz. .30 .20
   Nos. 891-894 (4) 1.10 .80

1983, Dec. 9
895 A312 6c Bicycling, boxing, baseball .25 .20
896 A312 10c Gymnast, weight lifting, swimming .30 .20

10c airmail.

Restoration of the Republic, 120th Anniv. — A313

1983, Dec. 30   **Litho.**   *Perf. 13½*
897 A313 1c Capotillo Heroes Monument .30 .20

140th Anniv. of Independence — A314

Designs: 6c, Matia Ramon Mella (Patriot), flag. 25c, Mella's Blunderbuss rifle, Gate of Deliverance (independence declaration site).

1984, Feb. 24   **Litho.**   *Perf. 13½*
898 A314 6c multicolored .20 .20
899 A314 25c multicolored .60 .35

Heriberto Pieter (1884-1972), Physician, First Negro Graduate — A315

1984, Mar. 16
900 A315 3c multicolored .25 .20

Battle of Barranquita, 67th Anniv. — A316

1983, Dec. 30   *Perf. 12*
901 A316 5c multicolored .30 .20

Battle of Santiago, 140th Anniv. A317

1984, Mar. 29   *Perf. 13½*
902 A317 7c multicolored .35 .25

Coast Guard Ship DC-1, 1934 A318

1984, Apr. 13   **Litho.**
903 A318 10c multicolored .40 .20

Navy Day and 140th anniv. of Battle of Tortuguero.

Birth Centenary of Pedro Henriquez Urena — A319

1984, June 29   **Litho.**   *Perf. 12*
904 A319 7c Salome Urena .20 .20
905 A319 10c Text .25 .25
906 A319 22c Urena .30 .25
   Nos. 904-906 (3) .75 .70

Monument to Heroes of June 1959 A320

1984, June 20   *Perf. 13½*
907 A320 6c silver & blue .40 .25

The feat of Constanza Maimon and Estero Hondo, 25th anniv.

1984 Summer Olympics A321

1984, Aug. 1
908 A321 1p Hurdles 1.75 1.75
909 A321 1p Weightlifting 1.75 1.75
910 A321 1p Boxing 1.75 1.75
911 A321 1p Baseball 1.75 1.75
  a. Block of 4, #908-911 13.50 13.50
   Nos. 908-911 (4) 7.00 7.00

Protection of Fauna — A322

1984, Oct. 3   **Litho.**   *Perf. 12*
912 A322 10c Owl 2.25 .25
913 A322 15c Flamingo 3.50 .35
914 A322 25c Wild Pig 4.50 .40
915 A322 35c Solenodon 6.25 .65
   Nos. 912-915 (4) 16.50 1.65

500th Anniv. of Discovery of America A323

1984, Oct. 10   **Litho.**   *Perf. 13½x13*
916 A323 10c Landing on Hispaniola .20 .20
917 A323 35c Destruction of Ft. Navidad .55 .35
918 A323 65c First Mass in America .95 .65
919 A323 1p Battle of Santo Cerro 1.40 .90
   Nos. 916-919 (4) 3.10 2.10

Visit of Pope John Paul II — A324

1984, Oct. 11   **Litho.**   *Perf. 13x13½*
920   Block of 4 8.50 8.50
  a. A324 75c shown 1.75 1.75
  b. A324 75c Pope, map of Caribbean 1.75 1.75
  c. A324 75c Pope, globe 1.75 1.75
  d. A324 75c Bishop's crozier 1.75 1.75

150th Anniv. of Birth of Maximo Gomez (1986) A325

1984, Dec. 6   **Litho.**   *Perf. 13½*
921 A325 10c Gomez on horseback .25 .20
922 A325 20c Maximo Gomez .25 .20

Christmas
1984
A326

Perf. 13½x13, 13x13½

1984, Dec. 14 Litho.
923 A326 5c multicolored .25 .20
924 A326 10c multicolored, vert. .25 .25

Sacrifice of
the Child,
by Eligio
Pichardo
A327

Paintings and sculpture: 10c, The Pumpkin
Sellers, by Gaspar Mario Cruz; 25c, The Market, by Celeste Woss y Gil; 50c, Horses in the
Rain, by Dario Suro.

1984, Dec. 19 Litho. **Perf. 13½**
925 A327 5c multi .45 .20
926 A327 10c multi, vert. .45 .20
927 A327 25c multi .50 .25
928 A327 50c multi 1.10 .35
Nos. 925-928 (4) 2.50 1.00

Day of Our
Lady of
Altagracia
A328

1985, Jan. 21
929 A328 5c Old church at
Higuey, 1572 .25 .20
930 A328 10c Our Lady of Altagracia 1514, vert. .25 .20
931 A328 25c Basilica of the Protector, Higuey
1971, vert. .50 .30
Nos. 929-931 (3) 1.00 .70

Independence, 141st Anniv. — A329

Painting: The Fathers of Our Country
(Duarte, Sanchez and Mella).

1985, Mar. 8 **Perf. 12½**
932 A329 5c multicolored .25 .20
933 A329 10c multicolored .30 .20
934 A329 25c multicolored .50 .25
Nos. 932-934 (3) 1.05 .65

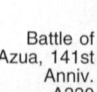

Battle of
Azua, 141st
Anniv.
A330

1985, Apr. 8 Litho. **Perf. 13½**
935 A330 10c Gen. Antonio
Duverge, Statue .35 .20

A331

A332

1985, Apr. 15 Litho.
936 A331 25c Santo Domingo
Lighthouse, 1853 .50 .25

Battle of Tortuguero, 141st anniv.

1985, Apr. 15 Litho. **Perf. 12**
937 A332 35c multicolored .85 .30

American Airforces Cooperation System,
25th anniv.

A333

A334

1985, May 24 Litho. **Perf. 13½**
938 A333 10c Don Carlos M.
Rojas, 1st gov. .40 .30

Espaillat Province cent.

1985, July 5 Litho. **Perf. 12**
939 A334 5c Table tennis .25 .20
940 A334 10c Walking race .30 .30

MOCA '85, 7th Natl. Games.

Intl. Youth
Year
A335

1985, July 29 **Perf. 13½**
941 A335 5c Youth .30 .20
942 A335 25c The Haitises .85 .30
943 A335 35c Mt. Duarte summit .90 .30
944 A335 2p Mt. Duarte 7.00 2.75
Nos. 941-944 (4) 9.05 3.55

Interamerican Development Bank, 25th
Anniv. — A336

10c, Haina Harbor. 25c, Map of development sites. 1p, Tavera-Bao-Lopez Hydroelectric Complex.

1985, Aug. 23
945 A336 10c multicolored .25 .20
946 A336 25c multicolored .75 .40
947 A336 1p multicolored 2.75 1.75
Nos. 945-947 (3) 3.75 2.35

Intl. Decade for
Women — A337

Design: Evangelina Rodriguez (1879-1947),
first Dominican woman doctor.

1985, Sept. 26
948 A337 10c multicolored .30 .20

1985, Oct. 9 **Perf. 12**
949 A338 5c multicolored .40 .25
950 A338 25c multicolored 1.10 .35

15th Central
American and
Caribbean
Games,
Santiago — A338

4th Adm.
Christopher
Columbus
Regatta,
Casa de
Espana
A339

Designs: 50c, Founding of Santo Domingo,
1496. 65c, Chapel of Our Lady of the Rosary,
1496, Santo Domingo. 1p, Columbus, American Indian and old Spanish coat of arms.

1985, Oct. 10 **Perf. 13½**
951 A339 35c multicolored 1.10 .60
952 A339 50c multicolored 1.60 1.10
953 A339 65c multicolored 2.25 1.25
954 A339 1p multicolored 4.00 2.25
Nos. 951-954 (4) 8.95 5.20

Discovery of America, 500th anniv. (in 1992).

Cacique
Enriquillo — A340

Designs: 5c, Enriquillo in the Bahuroco
Mountains, mural detail.

1985, Oct. 31
955 A340 5c multicolored .20 .20
956 A340 10c multicolored .45 .25

Enriquillo (d. 1536), leader of revolution
against Spain. Size of No. 955: 47x33mm.

Archbishop
Fernando Arturo
de
Merino — A341

1985, Dec. 3 **Perf. 12**
957 A341 25c multicolored .50 .35

Cent. of holy orders granted to Merino
(1833-1906), pres. of the republic 1880-82.

Mirabal
Sisters,
Political
Martyrs
1960
A342

1985, Dec. 18 **Perf. 13½**
958 A342 10c multicolored .30 .20

Christmas
A343

1985, Dec. 18
959 A343 10c multicolored .30 .20
960 A343 25c multicolored .70 .35

Day of Independence, Feb. 27 — A344

Design: Mausoleum of founding fathers
Duarte, Sanchez and Mella.

1986, Feb. 26 Litho. **Perf. 13½**
961 A344 5c multicolored .25 .20
962 A344 10c multicolored .25 .25

Holy Week
A345

Colonial churches.

1986, Apr. 10
963 A345 5c San Miguel .40 .25
964 A345 5c San Andres .40 .25
965 A345 10c Santa Barbara .40 .25
966 A345 10c San Lazaro .40 .25
967 A345 10c San Carlos .40 .25
Nos. 963-967 (5) 2.00 1.25

Navy Day
A346

Design: Juan Bautista Cambiaso, Juan Bautista Maggiolo and Juan Alejandro Acosta,
1884 independence battle heroes.

1986, Apr. 15
968 A346 10c multicolored .30 .20

Natl.
Elections — A347

Natl. Postal
Institute
Inauguration
A348

1986, Apr. 29
969 A347 5c Voters, map .25 .20
970 A347 10c Ballot box .30 .25

1986, June 10
971 A348 10c gold, blue & red .30 .20
972 A348 25c silver, blue & red .70 .30
973 A348 50c black, blue & red 1.40 .50
Nos. 971-973 (3) 2.40 1.00

Central America
and Caribbean
Games,
Santiago — A349

1986, July 17   Litho.   Perf. 13½
974 A349 10c Weight lifting .30 .20
975 A349 25c Gymnastics .60 .30
976 A349 35c Diving .90 .35
977 A349 50c Equestrian 1.10 .55
Nos. 974-977 (4) 2.90 1.40

Historians
A350

Designs: 5c, Ercilia Pepin (b. 1886), vert. 10c, Ramon Emilio Jimenez (b. 1886) and Victor Garrido (1886-1972).

1986, Aug. 1   Litho.   Perf. 13½
978 A350 5c silver & dull brn .25 .20
979 A350 10c silver & dull brn .25 .20

A351

A352

Discovery of America, 500th Anniv. (in 1992) — A353

Designs: 25c, Yachts racing, 5th Adm. Christopher Columbus Regatta, Casa de Espana. 50c, Columbus founding La Isabela

City. 65c, Exploration of the hidalgos. 1p, Columbus returning to the Court of Ferdinand and Isabella. 1.50p, Emblems.

1986, Oct. 10   Litho.   Perf. 13½
980 A351 25c multicolored .60 .35
981 A352 50c multicolored 1.40 .55
982 A352 65c multicolored 1.75 .90
983 A352 1p multicolored 2.75 1.25

Textured Paper
Size: 86x58mm
Imperf
984 A353 1.50p multicolored 5.50 5.50
Nos. 980-984 (5) 12.00 8.55

1986 World Cup
Soccer
Championships,
Mexico — A354

Medicinal
Plants — A355

Various soccer plays.

1986, Oct. 21   Perf. 13½
985 A354 50c multicolored 1.25 .60
986 A354 75c multicolored 2.75 1.00

1986, Dec. 5
987 A355 5c Zea mays .20 .20
988 A355 10c Bixa orellana .20 .20
989 A355 25c Momordica charantia .60 .20
990 A355 50c Annona muricata 1.25 .50
Nos. 987-990 (4) 2.25 1.10

Second Caribbean Pharmacopeia Seminar.

Christmas
A356

1986, Dec. 19
991 A356 5c Urban scene .40 .25
992 A356 25c Rural scene 1.00 .30

A357

A358

1986, Dec. 31   Litho.   Perf. 13½
993 A357 10c shown .40 .20
994 A357 25c Portrait, c. 1900 .70 .40

Maximo Gomez (1836-1905), revolutionary, statesman.

1987, Mar. 30   Litho.   Perf. 13½
995 A358 50c brt blue, blk & red 1.25 .60

16th Pan American Ophthalmological Conf., Apr. 5-10.

A359

A360

Stained-glass window, San Juan Bosco church, Santo Domingo: Ascension of Christ to Heaven.

1987, May 28
996 A359 35c multicolored 1.25 .45

1987, Aug. 21
Edible plants.
997 A360 5c Sorghum bicolor .20 .20
998 A360 25c Martanta arundinacea .55 .30
999 A360 65c Calathaea allouia 1.75 .90
1000 A360 1p Voandzeia subter-ranea 2.75 1.25
Nos. 997-1000 (4) 5.25 2.65

Activo 20-
30 Intl.,
25th Anniv.
A361

1987, Aug. 26
1001 A361 35c multicolored 1.00 .35

Adm.
Christopher
Columbus
Regatta
A362

A363

Columbus Memorial, Santo
Domingo — A364

1987, Oct. 14
1002 A362 50c shown 1.25 .45
1003 A363 75c shown 1.75 .65
1004 A363 1p Building Ft. Santiago 2.40 .90
1005 A363 1.50p Columbus im-prisoned by Bombadilla 3.75 1.40

Size: 82x70mm
Imperf
1006 A364 2.50p shown 8.00 5.00
Nos. 1002-1006 (5) 17.15 8.40

Discovery of America, 500th anniv. in 1992.

A365

A366

1987, Sept. 28
1007 A365 40c multicolored 1.00 .45

Junior Olympics, La Vega, 50th anniv.

1987, Nov. 10   Litho.   Perf. 13½
Historians and authors: 10c, Jose Antonio Hungria. 25c, Joaquin Sergio Inchaustegui.
1008 A366 10c buff & brown .25 .20
1009 A366 25c pale grn & grn .60 .25

SAN CRISTOBAL '87, 8th Natl.
Games — A367

1987, Nov. 19
1010 A367 5c Baseball .60 .20
1011 A367 10c Boxing .30 .20
1012 A367 50c Judo 1.40 .65
Nos. 1010-1012 (3) 2.30 1.05

Christmas
1987
A368

1987, Dec. 9   Litho.   Perf. 13½
1013 A368 10c Roasting pig .50 .20
1014 A368 50c Arriving at airport 1.50 .55

Fr. Xavier Billini
(b. 1837) — A369

1987, Dec. 18　Litho.　Perf. 13½
1015	A369	10c Statue	.25	.20
1016	A369	25c Portrait	.55	.30
1017	A369	75c Ana Hernandez de Billini, his mother	1.60	.90
		Nos. 1015-1017 (3)	2.40	1.40

Frank Feliz, Sr., and Aircraft A370

1987, Dec. 22
1018 A370 25c shown　　　　.45　.25

Size: 86x106mm
Imperf
1019 A370　2p No. C30, map　6.50 6.00

Pan-American goodwill flight to South American countries by the planes Colon, Pinta, Nina and Santa Maria, 50th anniv.

Flora
A371

1988, Feb. 3　Litho.　Perf. 13½
1020	A371	50c Bromelia pinguin	1.60	.60
1021	A371	50c Tillandsia fasciculata	1.60	.60
1022	A371	50c Tillandsia hotteana, vert.	1.60	.60
1023	A371	50c Tillandsia compacta, vert.	1.60	.60
		Nos. 1020-1023 (4)	6.40	2.40

St. John Bosco (1815-1888) A372

1988, Feb. 23　Litho.　Perf. 13½
1024	A372	10c shown	.35	.20
1025	A372	70c Stained-glass window	1.25	.90

Dominican Rehabilitation Assoc., 25th Anniv. — A373

1988, Mar. 1
1026 A373 20c multicolored　　.55　.30

A374

A375

1988, Apr. 6　Litho.　Perf. 13½
1027 A374 20c dk red brn & lt fawn　　　　.55　.30

Dr. Manuel Emilio Perdomo (b.1886).

1988, Apr. 29　Litho.　Perf. 13½
1028 A375 20c multicolored　　.55　.30

Dominican College of Engineers, Architects and Surveyors (CODIA), 25th Anniv.

Independence Day, Mexico — A376

Flags and: No. 1029, Fr. Miguel Hidalgo y Costilla (1753-1811), Mexican revolutionary. No. 1030, Juan Pablo Duarte (1813-1876), father of Dominican independence.

1988, Sept. 12　Litho.　Perf. 13½
1029	A376	50c multicolored	1.10	.50
1030	A376	50c multicolored	1.10	.50

1988 Summer Olympics, Seoul A377

1988, Sept. 21　Litho.　Perf. 13½
1031	A377	50c Running, vert.	.95	.20
1032	A377	70c Table tennis, vert.	1.50	.35
1033	A377	1p Judo, vert.	2.40	.40
1034	A377	1.50p Mural by Tete Marella	3.50	.75
		Nos. 1031-1034 (4)	8.35	1.70

A378

Discovery of America, 500th Anniv. (in 1992) — A379

Designs: 50c, 7th Adm. Christopher Columbus Regatta, Casa de Espana, 1988. 70c, La Concepcion Fortress, La Vega Real, 1494. 1.50p, Ft. Bonao. 2p, Nicolas de Ovando (c. 1451-1511), governor of Spanish possessions in America from 1502 to 1509. 3p, Mausoleum of Christopher Columbus, Santo Domingo Cathedral.

1988, Oct. 14　　　　Perf. 13½
1035	A378	50c multicolored	.95	.50
1036	A378	70c multicolored	1.60	.75
1037	A378	1.50p multicolored	3.25	1.50
1038	A378	2p multicolored	4.75	1.90

Size: 78x109mm
Imperf
1039	A379	3p multicolored	5.00	5.00
		Nos. 1035-1039 (5)	15.55	9.65

Discovery of America, 500th anniv. (in 1992). No. 1038 inscribed "1501-1509."

Duverge Parish, Cent. — A380

1988, July 13　Litho.　Perf. 13½
1040 A380 50c multicolored　　1.25　.40

A381

Trinitarians, 150th Anniv. — A382

1988, Nov. 11
1041	A381	10c shown	.40	.20
1042	A382	1p Trinitarian Plaza	1.90	.40
1043	A382	5p Independence Plaza	11.50	3.00
		Nos. 1041-1043 (3)	13.80	3.60

See footnote after No. 337.

Pharmacology and Biochemistry A383

The Holy Family, 1504, by Miguel Angel — A384

1988, Nov. 28　Litho.　Perf. 13½
1044 A383 1p multicolored　　1.50 1.25

13th Pan American and 16th Central American Congresses.

1988, Dec. 12
1045	A384	10c shown	.25	.20
1046	A384	20c Stained-glass window	.45	.30

Christmas.

Municipal Technical Advisory Organization (LIGA), 50th Anniv. — A385

Ana Teresa Paradas (1890-1960), 1st Female Lawyer of the Republic, 1913 — A386

1988, Dec. 23
1047 A385 20c multicolored　　　.55　.35

1988, Dec. 26
1048 A386 20c deep claret　　　.55　.35

French Revolution Bicent. A387

1989, Mar. 10　Litho.　Perf. 13½
1049 A387 3p red & violet blue　2.50 2.50

Battle of Tortuga, Apr. 15, 1844 A388

1989, Apr. 14　Litho.　Perf. 13½
1050 A388 40c multicolored　　　.80　.50

Natl. Anti-
drug
Campaign
A389

1989, May 15
1051	A389	10c multicolored	.30	.20
1052	A389	20c multicolored	.35	.20
1053	A389	50c multicolored	.60	.20
1054	A389	70c multicolored	.85	.30
1055	A389	1p multicolored	1.25	.30
1056	A389	1.50p multicolored	1.75	.40
1057	A389	2p multicolored	2.40	.60
1058	A389	5p multicolored	6.00	1.25
1059	A389	10p multicolored	11.50	3.00
	Nos. 1051-1059 (9)		25.00	6.45

Mother's
Day
A390

1989, May 30   Litho.   Perf. 13½
1060	A390	20c multicolored	.25	.20

Eugenio Maria de
Hostos (b.
1839) — A391

Gen. Gregorio
Luperon (b.
1839) — A392

1989, Aug. 22   Litho.   Perf. 13½
1061	A391	20c multicolored	.45	.20

1989, Aug. 28
1062	A392	20c multicolored	.45	.20

Little
League
Baseball,
50th Anniv.
A393

1989, Sept. 29
1063	A393	1p multicolored	1.50	.75

Diabetes
'89, 7th
Latin
American
Congress
A394

1989, Oct. 9   Litho.   Perf. 13½
1064	A394	1p multicolored	1.50	.60

America
Issue
A395

UPAE emblem, pre-Columbian artifacts and customs: 20c, Cohoba silver statue and ritual dance. 1p, Taina mortar, pestle and family preparing cazabe.

1989, Oct. 12
1065	A395	20c multicolored	.75	.20
1066	A395	1p multicolored	3.75	2.10

8th Adm.
Christopher
Columbus
Regatta, Casa de
Espana — A396

European Colonization of the
Americas — A397

Designs: 70c, Fr. Pedro de Cordoba converting the Indians to Catholicism. 1p, Christopher Columbus trading with the Indians. 3p, Sermon of Pedro de Cordoba.

1989, Oct. 13
1067	A396	50c shown	.50	.30
1068	A397	70c multicolored	.70	.45
1069	A397	1p multicolored	.95	.65
1070	A397	3p multicolored	3.25	1.90
	Nos. 1067-1070 (4)		5.40	3.30

Discovery of America, 500th anniv. (in 1992).

Natl. Afforestation
A398

1989, Oct. 30   Litho.   Perf. 13½
1071	A398	10c shown	.20	.20
1072	A398	20c Tree	.25	.20
1073	A398	50c Forest	.70	.45
1074	A398	1p Sapling, mature trees	1.60	.90
	Nos. 1071-1074 (4)		2.75	1.75

9th Natl. Games,
La Vega — A399

Holy Week
(Easter) — A400

1990, Mar. 20   Litho.   Perf. 13½
1075	A399	10c Cycling	.20	.20
1076	A399	20c Running	.35	.30
1077	A399	50c Basketball	.95	.65
	Nos. 1075-1077 (3)		1.50	1.15

1990, Apr. 5
1078	A400	20c shown	.35	.30
1079	A400	50c Jesus carrying cross	1.00	.70

Labor Day,
Cent.
A401

1990, Apr. 30   Litho.   Perf. 13½
1080	A401	1p multicolored	1.50	.65

Urban
Renewal
A402

1990, May 10
1081	A402	10c shown	.20	.20
1082	A402	20c Highway underpass	.20	.20
1083	A402	50c Library	.70	.25
1084	A402	1p City street	1.60	.65
	Nos. 1081-1084 (4)		2.70	1.30

No. 1084 inscribed $100 instead of $1.00.

Penny Black,
150th
Anniv. — A403

1990, May 29
1085	A403	1p multicolored	2.00	1.50

Size: 62x80mm
Imperf
1086	A403	3p Sir Rowland Hill, Penny Black	5.75	5.75

Organization of American States,
Cent. — A404

1990, Oct. 5   Litho.   Perf. 13½
1087	A404	2p Flags	4.00	2.40

Children's
Drawings
A405

1990, Aug. 7
1088	A405	50c House of Tostado	1.00	.65
1089	A405	50c Ruins of St. Nicolas of Bari	1.00	.65

Discovery
of America,
500th
Anniv. (in
1992)
A406

Designs: 1p, Fight at the Gulf of Arrows. 2p, Columbus talking with Guacanagari Indians. 5p, Columbus and Caonabo Indian prisoner.

1990, Oct. 12
1090	A406	1p multicolored	2.00	1.25
1091	A406	2p multicolored	4.00	2.75
1092	A406	5p multicolored	10.00	7.00
	Nos. 1090-1092 (3)		16.00	11.00

9th Adm.
Christopher
Columbus
Regatta — A407

1990, Oct. 12
1093	A407	50c multicolored	1.00	.70

America
Issue
A408

UPAE emblem and: 50c, Men in canoe. 3p, Man on hammock.

1990, Nov. 7   Litho.   Perf. 13½
1094	A408	50c multicolored	1.75	.70
1095	A408	3p multicolored	7.25	4.50

A409

A410

Discovery of Hispaniola: 50c, 1st official mass in Americas. 1p, Arms of 1st religious order in Americas. 3p, Map of island, horiz. 4p, Christopher Columbus, 1st viceroy and governor in Americas.

1991, July 17   Litho.   Perf. 13½
1096	A409	50c multicolored	.75	.40
1097	A409	1p multicolored	1.50	.85
1098	A409	3p multicolored	3.00	1.50
1099	A409	4p multicolored	8.25	4.50
	Nos. 1096-1099 (4)		13.50	7.25

1991
1100	A410	30c Boxing	.40	.20
1101	A410	50c Cycling	1.25	.50
1102	A410	1p Bowling	2.50	1.00
	Nos. 1100-1102 (3)		4.15	1.70

11th Pan American Games, Havana.

Dr. Tomas Eudoro Perez Rancier, Birth Cent. — A411

1991, July 3
1103 A411 2p yellow & black　4.25 1.50

10th Columbus Regatta, Casa de Espana — A412

Discovery of America, 500th Anniv. (in 1992) A413

Designs: 50c, Encounter of three cultures. 3p, Columbus and Dr. Alvarez Chanca caring for sick. 4p, Rebellion of Enriquillo.

1991, Oct. 15　Litho.　Perf. 13½
1104 A412 30c multicolored　.60 .20
1105 A413 50c multicolored　.75 .30
1106 A413 3p multicolored　4.75 1.90
1107 A413 4p multicolored　6.50 2.75
　Nos. 1104-1107 (4)　12.60 5.15
　See No. 1116.

A414

A415

1991, Nov. 18
1108 A414 3p black & red　4.25 1.75
　Cornea Bank.

1991　Litho.　Perf. 13½
1109 A415 1p Santa Maria　2.75 .85
1110 A415 3p Christopher Columbus　6.25 3.50
　America issue.

33rd Meeting of Inter-American Development Bank Governors, Santo Domingo — A416

1992　Litho.　Perf. 13½
1111 A416 1p multicolored　1.50 .75

A417

A418

1992　Litho.　Perf. 13½
1112 A417 3p multicolored　4.50 1.75
　Espanola '92 Philatelic Exposition.

1992　Litho.　Perf. 13½
　Valentin Salinero, Order of the Apostles founder.
1113 A418 1p blue & brown　1.50 .75
　Order of the Apostles, cent.

Ruins of Monastery of San Francisco A419

Designs: 3p, Ruins of San Nicolas hospital, first in the Americas.

1992, July 28
1114 A419 50c multicolored　.60 .35
1115 A419 3p multicolored　4.75 2.50

Type of 1991 and

A420

Designs: 50c, Racing yacht. 1p, Native women, Columbus. 2p, Natives offering Columbus tobacco. 3p, Native woman, Columbus, corn.

1992, Oct. 6　Litho.　Perf. 13½
1116 A412 50c multicolored　.70 .35
1117 A420 1p multicolored　1.60 .75
1118 A420 2p multicolored　3.25 1.50
1119 A420 3p multicolored　4.25 1.75
　Nos. 1116-1119 (4)　9.80 4.35
　11th Columbus Regatta (No. 1116), Discovery of America, 500th anniv. (Nos. 1117-1119).

23rd Convention of the Alliance of Panamerican Round Tables, Santo Domingo — A421

1992, Oct. 14
1120 A421 1p multicolored　1.50 .60

Visit by Pope John Paul II A422

Cathedrals: 50c, Vega. 3p, Santo Domingo.

1992, Oct. 1　Photo.
1121 A422 50c multicolored　1.40 .60
1122 A422 3p multicolored　4.00 1.75

Columbus Lighthouse A423

1992, Oct. 12　Litho.
1123 A423 30c multicolored　.85 .35
1124 A423 1p multicolored　1.75 .60

Size: 70x133mm
Imperf
1125 A423 3p Lighthouse at night　5.00 5.00

America Issue A424

Designs: 50c, First royal residence in America, Santo Domingo. 3p, First viceregal residence in America, Royal Palace, Colon.

1992, Nov. 13　Litho.　Perf. 13½
1126 A424 50c multicolored　.75 .40
1127 A424 3p multicolored　3.75 2.50

A425

Natl. Census — A426

1992, Dec. 2　Litho.　Perf. 13½
1128 A425 30c Torch bearer　.40 .20
1129 A425 1p Emblems　1.25 .50
1130 A425 4p Judo　6.50 2.50
　Nos. 1128-1130 (3)　8.15 3.20
　1992 Natl. Sports Games, San Juan. Secretary of Sports, Education, Exercise and Recreation (No. 1129).

1992-93　Litho.　Perf. 13½
1131 A426 50c black, buff & blue　.70 .25
1132 A426 1p blk, brn & blue　1.40 .50
1133 A426 3p blk, gray & bl　4.75 1.75
1134 A426 4p blk, yel grn & bl　6.00 2.00
　Nos. 1131-1134 (4)　12.85 4.50
　Issued: 50c, 1p, 5/12/92; 3p, 4p, 9/9/93.

A427

A428

1993, May 30
1135 A427 30c multicolored　.45 .20
1136 A427 50c multicolored　.75 .30
1137 A427 1p multicolored　1.60 .60
　Nos. 1135-1137 (3)　2.80 1.10
　Ema Balaguer, humanitarian.

1993, Oct. 7　Litho.　Perf. 13½
1138 A428 30c shown　.90 .45
1139 A428 1p Emblem, flags　2.75 1.00
　Rotary Club of Santo Domingo, 50th anniv.

17th Central American & Caribbean Games, Ponce A429

1993, Dec. 21　Litho.　Perf. 13½
1140 A429 50c Tennis　.60 .20
1141 A429 4p Swimming　6.25 1.50

Natl. Education Plan — A430

Spanish America — A431

1993, Dec. 8
1142 A430 1.50p multicolored　2.25 .75

1993, Dec. 28
1143 A431 50c First university
lecturn .70 .25
1144 A431 3p First city coat of
arms 4.75 1.25

America
Issue
A432

1993, Dec. 30
1145 A432 1p Aratinga
chloroptera 1.25 .50
1146 A432 3p Cyclura cornuta 4.75 2.00

Opening of
New Natl.
Post Office
A433

1993, Nov. 12
Color of Inscription
1147 A433 1p olive .75 .50
1148 A433 3p red 2.25 1.40
1149 A433 4p blue 3.00 1.75
1150 A433 5p green 3.75 2.00
1151 A433 10p black 7.50 4.00

Size: 105x96mm
Imperf
1152 A433 5p black 8.75 8.75
Nos. 1147-1152 (6) 26.00 18.40

First Mass in
America, 500th
Anniv. — A434

1994, Feb. 3 Litho. Perf. 13½
1153 A434 2p multicolored 3.00 1.00

5th Natl.
Philatelic
Exhibition
A435

1994, Feb. 25
1154 A435 3p multicolored 4.50 1.40

Natl. Independence, 150th
Anniv. — A436

No. 1155: a, Men with document, left side of
table. b, Document on right side of table, men.
c, Flag. d, Couple at window. e, Child holding
material, mother making flag.
No. 1156: a, Men looking upward, shooting
muskets. b, Men with guns, swords looking
backwards. c, Natl. coat of arms. d, Men with
guns, swords, one pointing upward. e, Men
with weapons, one with flag.
10p, Three men, angel carrying musket,
flag.

1994, Feb. 26
Strips of 5
1155 A436 2p #a.-e. 8.25 4.00
1156 A436 3p #a.-e. 12.50 6.00

Size: 161x104mm
Imperf
1157 A436 10p multicolored 11.50 11.50
Nos. 1155-1157 (3) 32.25 21.50

Nos. 1155a-1155b, 1155d-1155e, 1156a-
1156b, 1156d-1156e have a continuous
design.

Solenodon
Paradoxus
A437

Designs: a, Crawling on rock. b, Walking in
leaves. c, Looking up. d, With food in mouth.

1994, Mar. 15 Litho. Perf. 13½
1158 A437 1p Block of 4, #a.-d. 6.00 3.00
World Wildlife Fund.

Battle of
March 19,
150th
Anniv.
A438

No. 1160, Soldiers advancing uphill toward
fort.

1994
1159 A438 2p multicolored 3.00 1.00
1160 A438 2p multicolored 3.00 1.00
Issued: No. 1159, Mar. 18; No. 1160, Mar.
29.

Virgin of
Amparo — A439

Natl. Elections,
May 16 — A440

1994, Apr. 15 Litho. Perf. 13½
1161 A439 3p multicolored 4.50 1.40
Battle of Puerto Tortuguero, 150th anniv.

1994, Apr. 4
1162 A440 2p multicolored 3.00 1.00

1994 World Cup
Soccer
Championships,
US — A441

1994, June 24 Litho. Perf. 13½
1163 A441 4p multicolored 4.75 1.50
1164 A441 6p multicolored 6.75 2.00

Ema
Balaguer
City of
Children
A442

1994, July 20 Litho. Perf. 13½
1165 A442 1p magenta & brown 2.75 .40

Stamp
Day
A443

1994, Oct. 18 Litho. Perf. 13½
1166 A443 5p Type A3 7.25 2.00

America
Issue — A444

1994, Oct. 28
1167 A444 2p Pony Express 2.75 1.00
1168 A444 6p Sailing ship 9.00 3.00

Province of
LaVega,
500th
Anniv.
A445

3p, Ruins of San Francisco Monastery.

1994, Nov. 24 Litho. Perf. 13½
1169 A445 3p multicolored 6.75 1.40

First Church the New World, 500th
Anniv. — A446

a, "La Isabela," cradle of evangelization. b,
"Temple of the Americas," first mission.

1994, Dec. 5 Perf. 11½
1170 A446 3p Pair, #a.-b. 9.00 2.50

A447

A448

1994, Nov. 6 Perf. 13½
1171 A447 3p multicolored 4.50 1.40
Constitution, 150th anniv.

1994, Nov. 18
Christmas: 2p, Holy family's flight into
Egypt. 3p, Modern family of three standing at
river's edge.
1172 A448 2p multicolored 3.25 1.00
1173 A448 3p multicolored 4.25 1.40
Intl. Year of the Family.

Firsts in
America — A449

1994, Dec. 21 Litho. Perf. 13½
1174 A449 2p Circulating coins 3.00 .75
1175 A449 5p Sermon for Justice 7.00 2.00

Snakes
A450

No. 1176, Hypsirhynchus ferox. No. 1177,
Antillophis parvifrons. No. 1178, Uromacer
catesbyi. No. 1179, Epicrates striatus.

1994, Dec. 26
1176 A450 2p multicolored 3.00 .75
1177 A450 2p multicolored 3.00 .75
a. Pair, #1176-1177 6.00 5.50
1178 A450 2p multicolored 3.00 .75
1179 A450 2p multicolored 3.00 .75
a. Pair, #1178-1179 6.00 5.50
Nos. 1177a, 1179a are continuous designs.

Pan
American
Games,
Mar Del
Plata,
Argentina
A451

1995, Apr. 20 Perf. 13½
1180 A451 4p Tae kwon do 4.50 1.50
1181 A451 13p Tennis 13.50 4.50

FAO, 50th Anniv. — A452

1995, Apr. 21 Litho. Perf. 11½
1182 A452 4p multicolored 4.50 1.50

A453

A454

Designs: 2p, Jose Marti, Maximo Gomez. 3p, Marti. 4p, Marti seated at desk, Gomez.

1995, May 19	**Litho.**	**Perf. 13½**	
1183	A453	2p multicolored	1.90	.20
1184	A453	3p multicolored	2.50	.40
1185	A453	4p multicolored	3.50	.50
		Nos. 1183-1185 (3)	7.90	1.10

Jose Marti (1853-95), Montecristi Manifesto, cent.

1995, May 22

1186	A454	3p multicolored	2.75	.45

Basketball, cent.

Medicinal Plants — A455

1995, May 26

1187	A455	2p Pimenta ozua	2.00	.20
1188	A455	2p Melocactus communis	2.00	.20
1189	A455	3p Smilax	3.00	.30
1190	A455	3p Zamia	3.00	.30
		Nos. 1187-1190 (4)	10.00	1.00

Tourism A456

4p, San Souci Port. 5p, Barahona Airport. 6p, G. Luperon Airport. 13p, Airport of the Americas.

1995, June 21

1191	A456	4p multicolored	2.50	.40
1192	A456	5p multicolored	3.25	.60
1193	A456	6p multicolored	4.00	.70
1194	A456	13p multicolored	8.25	1.50
		Nos. 1191-1194 (4)	18.00	3.20

Santiago de Los Caballeros, 500th Anniv. A457

1995, July 29	**Litho.**	**Perf. 13½**	
1195	A457	3p Jacagua ruins	4.50	.70

Whales A458

Designs: No. 1196, Physeter macrocephalus. No. 1197, Balaenoptera borealis. No. 1198, Ziphius cavirostris. No. 1199, Megaptera novaeangliae.

1995, Aug. 14

1196	A458	3p multicolored	2.75	.40
1197	A458	3p multicolored	2.75	.40
1198	A458	3p multicolored	2.75	.40
1199	A458	3p multicolored	2.75	.40
		Nos. 1196-1199 (4)	11.00	1.60

Stamp Day A459

1995, Oct. 18	**Litho.**	**Perf. 13½**	
1200	A459	4p No. 37	3.00	.40

Popular Singers — A460

1995, Oct. 8

1201	A460	2p Rafael Colon	1.50	.20
1202	A460	3p Casandra Damiron	2.00	.30

Cathedral of Santiago, Cent. A461

1995, Dec. 28	**Litho.**	**Perf. 13½**	
1203	A461	3p multicolored	2.25	.30

4th World Conference of Women, Beijing — A462

1995, Nov. 23

1204	A462	2p multicolored	5.25	.20

Volleyball, Cent. — A463

Norceca '95 — A464

Singers — A465

1995, Oct. 19		**Imperf.**	
1205	A463	5p multicolored	3.75	.60
		Perf. 13½	
1206	A464	6p multicolored	4.25	.70

1995, Dec. 27		**Perf. 13½**	
1207	A465	2p Antonio Mesa	1.60	.20
1208	A465	2p Julieta Otero	1.60	.20
1209	A465	2p Susano Polanco	1.60	.20
		Nos. 1207-1209 (3)	4.80	.60

Columbus Lighthouse A466

1995, Dec. 5

1210	A466	10p dk bl, bl & gray	10.00	1.25

See Nos. 1241, 1265, 1299, 1337, 1371, 1375, 1382.

A467

UN, 50th Anniv. A468

1995, Oct. 24

1211	A467	2p multicolored	1.50	.20
		Perf. 11½	
1212	A468	6p multicolored	4.50	.70

Environmental Protection — A469

America issue: 2p, Flamingos, sea gull. 6p, Manglar.

1995, Dec. 19	**Litho.**	**Perf. 13½**	
1213	A469	2p multicolored	1.40	.25
1214	A469	6p multicolored	4.50	.75

Dominican Republic Air Force, 50th Anniv. A470

Aircraft: a, O2U-35D Corsair. b, PT-17 Stearman. c, AT-6 Texan. d, PBY-5A Catalina. e, TF-10 Beaufighter. f, FB-6 Mosquito. g, P-38 Lightning. h, P-51D Mustang. i, B-17G Flying Fortress. j, P-47D Thunderbolt. k, FB-5 Vampire. l, C-46 Commander. m, B-26 Invader. n, C-47 Skytrain. o, T-28D Trojan. p, T-33A Silverstar. q, Cessna T-41D. r, T-34 Mentor. s, Cessna O-2A. t, A-37B Dragonfly.

1995, Dec. 30

1215	A470	2p Sheet of 20, #a-t	22.50	11.50

See No. 1228.

UNICEF, 50th Anniv. — A471

1996, Feb. 23

1216	A471	2p shown	1.25	.25
1217	A471	4p Mirror image of #1216	2.25	.50

Intl. Sailing Competition A472

1996, Mar. 8

1218	A472	5p multicolored	3.00	.70

Eduardo Brito, Singer, 50th Death Anniv. — A473

1996, Jan. 15
1219	A473	1p shown	.60	.20
1220	A473	2p With maracas	1.25	.30
1221	A473	3p Portrait	1.90	.50
		Nos. 1219-1221 (3)	3.75	1.00

No. 1220 is 54x35mm.

Natl. Journalist Day — A474

Design: Arturo J. Pellerano Alfau, Dr. Freddy Gaton Arce, Rafael Herrera Cabral.

1996, Apr. 17   Litho.   Perf. 13½
1222	A474	5p multicolored	3.50	.70

ESPAMER '96, Seville — A475

1996, June 7   Litho.   Perf. 13½
1223	A475	15p multicolored	9.00	1.50

1996 Summer Olympic Games, Atlanta — A476

1996, July 5
1224	A476	5p Judo	3.75	.70
1225	A476	15p Torch	9.75	1.75

Modern Olympic Games, Cent. — A477

1996, July 5
1226	A477	6p Greece No. 118	3.50	.70
1227	A477	15p No. 328	8.50	1.50

Dominican Republic Air Force, 50th Anniv. Type of 1995

Helicopters: a, Sikorsky S-55. b, Alouette II. c, Alouette III. d, OH-6A Cayuse. e, Bell 205 A-1. f, Dauphin II SA.365C.

1996, July 31   Litho.   Perf. 13½
1228	A470	3p Sheet of 6, #a.-f.	8.00	8.00

World Day Against Illegal Drugs — A478

1996, Sept. 23   Litho.   Perf. 13½
1229	A478	15p multicolored	8.50	1.50

Mail Delivery A479

No. 1230, World delivery, putting mail in letter box, mailman receiving mail on motorcycle. No. 1231, Woman giving mail to man on horseback, vert. No. 1232, Child holding letter beside mailbox.

1996, July 17   Litho.   Perf. 13½
1230	A479	3p multicolored	2.25	.75
1231	A479	3p multicolored	2.25	.75
1232	A479	3p multicolored	2.25	.75
		Nos. 1230-1232 (3)	6.75	2.25

America Issue — A480

1996, Oct. 15   Litho.   Perf. 13½
1233	A480	2p Men's costume	1.25	.25
1234	A480	6p Women's costume	3.50	.75

Stamp Day A481

1996, Oct. 18
1235	A481	5p No. 142	3.00	.70

26th Intl. Sunfish Championships — A482

6p, Sun, natl. flag, sailboat, vert. 10p, Man sailing boat.

1996, Oct. 16
1236	A482	6p multicolored	3.50	.90
1237	A482	10p multicolored	5.75	1.40

A483

Buteo ridgwayi -GAVILAN- $2 — A484

1996, Nov. 25   Litho.   Perf. 13½
1238	A483	5p green & multi	3.00	.65
1239	A483	10p pink & multi	5.75	1.25

Intl. Day to End Violence Against Women.

1996, Nov. 11

Birds: a, Buteo ridgwayi. b, Aratinga chloroptera. c, Amazona ventralis. d, Hyetornis rufigularis. e, Saurothera longirostris. f, Siphonorhis brewsteri. g, Chlorostilbon swainsonii. h, Todus angustirostris. i, Todus subulatus. j, Temnotrogon roseigaster. k, Nesoctites micromegas. l, Melanerpes striatus. m, Turdus swalesi. n, Carduelis dominicensis. o, Dulus dominicus. p, Microligea palustris. q, Vireo nanus. r, Xenoligea montanta. s, Turdus swalesi dodae. t, Calyptophilus frugivorus tertius. u, Corvus leucognaphalus. v, Calyptophilus frugivorus neibae.

1240	A484	2p Sheet of 22, #a-		
		v	40.00	30.00

Lighthouse Type of 1995

1996, Dec. 27   Litho.   Perf. 13½
1241	A466	10p grn, sil & gray	6.50	1.40

Turtles A485

a, Dermochelys coriacea. b, Caretta caretta. c, Chelonia mydas. d, Eretmochelys imbricata.

1996, Dec. 30
1242	A485	5p Block of 4, #a.-		
		d.	12.00	10.00

Natl. Youth Day — A486

National Anthem — A487

1997, Jan. 31
1243	A486	3p multicolored	1.75	.45

1997, Feb. 26

Designs: 2p, Lyrics, by Emilio Prudhome. 3p, Music, by Jose Reyes.

1244	A487	2p multicolored	1.25	.25
1245	A487	3p multicolored	1.75	.40

Salomé Urena (1850-97), Poet — A488

Comet Hale-Bopp A489

1997, Mar. 6   Perf. 13½
1246	A488	3p multicolored	1.75	.40

1997, Apr. 1
1247	A489	5p multicolored	4.25	.65

Size: 72x47mm
Imperf
1248	A489	10p multicolored	11.00	11.00

A490

11th Natl. Sports Games, Mao '97 — A491

2p, Mascot running with torch. 3p, Mascot in batting stance, vert. 5p, Runner breaking finish line.

1997, Apr. 3
1249	A490	2p multicolored	1.75	.25
1250	A491	3p multicolored	2.75	.40
1251	A491	5p multicolored	4.25	.65
		Nos. 1249-1251 (3)	8.75	1.30

A492

A493

Design: 10p, 5p, Heinrich von Stephan (1831-97), founder of UPU.

1997, Apr. 8   Litho.   Perf. 13½
1252	A492	10p multicolored	5.75	1.25

Souvenir Sheet
Imperf

1253 A492   5p like #1252   3.00   .65

No. 1253 has simulated perforations.

1997, Apr. 29   *Perf. 13½*

1254 A493 10p multicolored   8.75 1.25

25th Intl. Congress of CLAHT (Caracas and Latin American Group of Hemostasis and Thrombosis).

Gregorio Luperón (1839-1897), Politician — A494

House of Spain, 80th Anniv. — A495

1997, May 21

1255 A494 3p multicolored   1.75   .40

1997, July 4

1256 A495 5p multicolored   3.00   .65

First Peso Coin, Cent. A496

1997, Aug. 6   Litho.   *Perf. 13½*

1257 A496 2p multicolored   1.50   .20

A497

Coronation of the Image of Our Lady of Alta Gracia, 75th Anniv. — A498

1997, Aug. 12

1258 A497 3p multicolored   1.75   .20
1259 A498 5p multicolored   3.00   .35

America Issue A499

Life of a postman: 2p, Dog grabbing pants leg of postman on motorcycle. 6p, Dog tearing pants leg of postman with letter.

1997, Oct. 9   Litho.   *Perf. 13½*

1260 A499 2p multicolored   1.25   .30

Size: 35½x35½mm

1261 A499 6p multicolored   3.25   .70

Mother Teresa (1910-97) A500

1997, Oct. 17

1262 A500 5p multicolored   3.00   .65

Stamp Day — A501

1997, Oct. 18

1263 A501 5p Nos. 108, 322   2.50   .55

Central Bank of the Dominican Republic, 50th Anniv. — A502

1997, Oct. 30   *Perf. 11½*

1264 A502 10p multicolored   5.00 1.10

Lighthouse Type of 1995

1997, Dec. 15   Litho.   *Perf. 13½*

1265 A466 10p bright rose & gray   6.50 1.75

Bats A503

a, Erophylius bombifrons. b, Brachyphylla nana. c, Molossus molossus. d, Lasiurus borealis.

1997, Nov. 11

1266 A503 5p Block of 4, #a.-
      d.   10.00 10.00

Dominican Air Force, 50th Anniv. — A504

Insignias: a, Air Force, red, white, and blue target. b, Northern Air Command, "shark plane." c, Air Command, eagle's wings over

---

target. d, Rescue Force, eagle. e, Maintenance Command. f, Combat Force, dragon, target.

1997, Dec. 19

1267 A504 3p Sheet of 6, #a.-
      f.   11.00 11.00

Construction of the National Palace, 50th Anniv. — A505

1997, Dec. 30   Litho.   *Perf. 13½*

1268 A505 10p multicolored   5.75 1.50

First Regional Symposium on Pre-Columbian Culture and Caribbean Contemporary Art — A506

1998, Jan. 28

1269 A506 6p multicolored   3.50   .85

A507

A508

1998, Apr. 2   Litho.   *Perf. 13½*

1270 A507 10p multicolored   5.75   .65

American Chamber of Commerce of the Dominican Republic, 75th anniv.

1998, Apr. 26

Book Fair: 3p, Natl. Book Fair, 25th anniv. 5p, Intl. Book Fair, Santo Domingo '98.

1271 A508 3p black, blue & red   1.75   .20

Size: 35x33mm

1272 A508 5p black, blue & red   3.00   .35

Organization of American States, 50th Anniv. — A509

1998, Apr. 30

1273 A509 5p blue & multi   3.00   .35
1274 A509 5p pink & multi   3.00   .35

Establishment of the State of Israel, 50th Anniv. — A510

1998, Apr. 30

1275 A510 10p multicolored   8.00   .90

Dominican Air Force, 50th Anniv. — A511

a, Gen. Frank Felix Miranda, portrait at left. b, Early aircraft. c, Col. Ernesto Tejeda, portrait at right. d, As "c," portrait at left. e, As "a," portrait at right.

1998, June 26

Sheet of 6

1276 A511 3p #a, c-e, 2 b   10.00 10.00

City of Santo Domingo, 500th Anniv. A512

2p, Sun clock. 3p, St. Lazaro Church & Hospital. 4p, First Cathedral in America. 5p, Royal Palace. 6p, Tower of Honor. 10p, St. Nicolas of Bari Church & Hospital.

1998, Aug. 6   Litho.   *Perf. 13½*

1277 A512 2p multi, vert.   1.10   .20
1278 A512 3p multi   1.75   .20
1279 A512 4p multi   2.25   .25
1280 A512 5p multi   3.00   .35
1281 A512 6p multi   3.50   .40
1282 A512 10p multi, vert.   5.75   .60
    Nos. 1277-1282 (6)   17.35 2.00

National Theater, 25th Anniv. — A513

1998, Aug. 14   *Perf. 13x13½*

1283 A513 10p multicolored   5.75   .65

Latin Union, 44th Anniv. A514

1998, Aug. 26   *Perf. 13½*

1284 A514 10p multicolored   5.75   .65

ICCO (Intl. Cocoa Organization of America & Europe), 25th Anniv. — A515

1998, Sept. 3
1285 A515 10p multicolored 7.00 .80

Nino Ferrua (1909-79), Stamp Designer A516

1998, Oct. 18   Litho.   Perf. 13½x13
1286 A516 5p multicolored 3.00 .35
Stamp Day.

Pontificate of John Paul II, 20th Anniv. A517

1998, Oct. 22   Perf. 13½
1287 A517 5p shown 3.25 .40
1288 A517 10p Portrait, diff. 6.75 .75

Medicinal Plants — A518

a, Pimenta racemosa. b, Pimenta haitiensis. c, Cymbopogon citratus. d, Citrus aurantium.

1998, Nov. 2
1289 A518 3p Block of 4, #a.-d. 6.50 .75

Famous Women A519

America Issue: 2p, Juana Saltitopa standing with cannon. 6p, Anacaona, Indian maiden, group of Indians.

1998, Nov. 5
1290 A519 2p multicolored 1.75 .30
1291 A519 6p multicolored 4.25 .50

A520

A521

1998, Nov. 20
1292 A520 5p multicolored 4.00 .90
Intl. Year of the Ocean.

1998, Nov. 23
1293 A521 5p multicolored 2.25 .50
Expofila '98, Santo Domingo. Santo Domingo, 500th anniv.

National Military Heroes — A522

Designs: a, Fernando Valerio. b, Benito Moncion. c, Jose Maria Cabral. d, Antonio Duverge. e, Gregorio Luperon. f, Jose A. Salcedo. g, Fco. A. Salcedo. h, Gaspar Polanco. i, Santiago Rodriguez. j, Juan Bta. Cambiaso. k, Jose J. Puello. l, Jose Ma. Imbert. m, Juan A. Acosta. n, Marcos Adon. o, Matias R. Mella. p, Francisco R. Sanchez. q, Juan Pablo Duarte. r, Olegario Tenares. s, Pedro Santana. t, Juan Sanchez Ramirez.

1998, Nov. 29
1294 A522 3p Sheet of 20, #a.-t. 26.50 24.50

1st Natl. Paper Money, 150th Anniv. — A523

1998, Nov. 30   Perf. 11½
1295 A523 10p multicolored 4.50 .90

Christmas A524

1998, Dec. 7   Perf. 13½
1296 A524 2p Roasting hog .75 .20
1297 A524 5p Magi 2.25 .45

Universal Declaration of Human Rights, 50th Anniv. A525

1998, Dec. 10
1298 A525 10p multicolored 4.00 .80

Columbus Lighthouse Type of 1995
1998, Dec. 11
1299 A466 10p orange & black 5.00 1.00

Shells A526

Designs: a, Lyria vegai. b, Strombus gigas. c, Cittarium pica. d, Nerita peloronta.

1998, Dec. 16
1300 A526 5p Block of 4, #a.-d. 11.00 2.10

Gaspar Hernández (1798-1858), Priest — A527

1998, Dec. 18
1301 A527 3p multicolored 1.25 .20

Dominican Society of Endocrinology and Nutrition, 25th Anniv. — A528

1999, Feb. 24   Litho.   Perf. 13¼
1302 A528 10p multicolored 3.25 .65

Office of Comptroller General — A529

1999, May 4   Litho.   Perf. 13¼
1303 A529 2p multicolored .80 .20

Export Industries A530

Perf. 13½x13¼, 13¼x13½
1999, Apr. 30   Litho.
1304 A530 6p Tobacco 2.00 .40
1305 A530 10p Textiles, vert. 3.25 .65

Pan American Games, Winnipeg - A530a

1999, July 29   Litho.   Perf. 13¼x13½
1306 A530a 5p Baseball 2.00 .50
1307 A530a 6p Weight lifting 3.00 .55

Native Plants — A531

Designs: a, Pseudophoenix ekmanii. b, Murtigia calabura. c, Pouteria dominguensis. d, Rubus dominguensis focke.

1999, July 13
1308 A531 5p Block of 4, #a.-d. 9.00 9.00

Presidents of the Dominican Republic A532

Designs: a, Tomas Bobadilla y Briones. b, Pedro Santana. c, Manuel Jimenez. d, Buenaventura Baez. e, Manuel de Regla Mota. f, José Desiderio Valverde. g, José A. Salcedo. h, Gaspar Polanco.

1999, Aug. 31   Perf. 13½x13¼
1309 A532 3p Sheet of 8, #a.-h. + label 10.00 10.00

A533

Sovereign Military Order of Malta A534

Perf. 13¼x13½
1999, Sept. 20   Litho.
1310 A533 2p multicolored .75 .20
Perf. 13½
1311 A534 10p multicolored 4.00 .75

Paintings by José Vela Zanetti (1913-99) — A535

Various paintings.

Perf. 13½x13¼, 13¼x 13½
1999, Sept. 8
1312 A535 2p multi, vert. .70 .20
1313 A535 3p multi, vert. 1.25 .20
1314 A535 5p multi 1.90 .30
1315 A535 6p multi, vert. 2.40 .55
1316 A535 10p multi, vert. 3.75 1.10
  Nos. 1312-1316 (5) 10.00 2.35

Insects
A536

Designs: a, Strataegus quadrifoveatus. b, Anetia jaegeri. c, Polyancistroydes tettigonidae. d, Aploppus phasmidae.

1999, Sept. 10   **Perf. 13½x13¼**
1317 A536 5p Block of 4, #a.-d.   8.00 8.00

SOS Children's Villages, 50th Anniv. — A537

Intl. Year of the Elderly — A538

1999, Sept. 29   **Perf. 13¼x13½**
1318 A537 10p multicolored   4.00 1.60

1999, Oct. 1
1319 A538 2p Man   .75 .20
1320 A538 5p Woman   2.00 1.00

A539

1999, Oct. 5
1321 A539 5p multicolored   2.00 .90
World Education Day.

A540

1999, Oct. 18
Designs: 2p, Skull and crossbones, land mines, shattered gun. 6p, Mushroom cloud.
1322 A540 2p multicolored   .75 .50
1323 A540 6p multicolored   2.50 1.25
America Issue, a new millennium without arms.

Stamp Day — A541

1999, Oct. 22
1324 A541 5p Luis F. Thomen   2.00 .90

Account of Gen. Juan Pablo Duarte A542

1999, July 16   **Perf. 13½**
1325 A542 3p multicolored   1.25 .20

A543

Contemporary Writers — A544

Perf. 13¼x13½, 13½x13¼
1999, June 23
1326 A543 2p multicolored   .65 .20
1327 A544 10p multicolored   4.75 2.25

Dermatological Society, 50th Anniv. — A545

1999, Sept. 15   **Litho.**   **Perf. 13¼**
1328 A545 3p multi   1.25 .20

Millennium — A546

3p, Earth, trees. 5p, Scientific achievements.

Perf. 13¼x13½
1999, Nov. 10   **Litho.**
1329 A546 3p multi   1.25 .75
1330 A546 5p multi   2.25 1.10

2nd Summit of African, Caribbean and Pacific Heads of State — A547

Emblem and: 5p, Map of Caribbean area, whale. 6p, Map of Pacific area, Easter Island statues. 10p, Map of Africa, lion.

1999, Nov. 23
1331 A547 5p multi   2.00 1.00
1332 A547 6p multi   2.50 1.10
1333 A547 10p multi   4.00 2.00
   Nos. 1331-1333 (3)   8.50 4.10

UPU, 125th Anniv. A548

6p, Globe, envelope, computer, electronic circuits. 10p, Envelope, electronic circuits.

1999, Nov. 29
1334 A548 6p multi   2.25 1.00
   Size: 50x75mm
   Imperf
1335 A548 10p multi   4.50 2.10

Union of Latin American Universities, 50th Anniv. — A549

1999, Dec. 3   **Perf. 13½x13¼**
1336 A549 6p multi   2.25 1.00

Lighthouse Type of 1995
1999, Dec. 14   **Perf. 13¼x13½**
1337 A466 10p brown & silver   4.00 1.75

Classical Musicians A550

No. 1338, José de Jésus Ravelo (1876-1951), clarinet. No. 1339, Juan Francisco Garcia (1892-1974), cornet. No. 1340, Manuel Simo (1916-88), saxophone.

1999, Dec. 17
1338 A550 5p multi   2.00 1.00
1339 A550 5p multi   2.00 1.00
1340 A550 5p multi   2.00 1.00
   Nos. 1338-1340 (3)   6.00 3.00

Municipal Notes, Cent. — A551

Notes and background colors — No. 1341: a, Santo Domingo, San Pedro de Macorís, deep purple. b, Puerto Plata, Moca, purple. No. 1342, vert.: a, Santiago, Cotui, blue green. b, San Francisco de Macorís, La Vega,

golden brown. c, San Cristobal, Samana, peacock blue.
   No. 1343: a, As No. 1342a, green background. b, As No. 1342b, brown background. c, As No. 1342c, Prussian blue background.

1999, Dec. 30   **Perf. 13¼**
1341 A551 2p Pair, #a.-b.   2.00 1.00
1342 A551 2p Strip of 3, #a.-c.   2.50 1.10
   Souvenir Sheet
   Imperf
1343 A551 2p Sheet of 5, Nos. 1341a-1341b, 1343a-1343c   4.50 2.25

Chamber of Spanish Commerce and Industry, 75th Anniv. — A552

1999, Dec. 30   **Perf. 13¼x13½**
1344 A552 10p multi   4.50 2.10

Fight Against Drugs A553

2000, Feb. 17   **Litho.**   **Perf. 13½**
1345 A553 5p multi   2.25 .60
Hogar Crea Dominicana Inc., 25th anniv.

Duarte Institute — A554

2000, Feb. 25   **Perf. 13¼**
1346 A554 2p multi   .90 .20

Prevention of Child Abuse — A555

2000, Mar. 31
1347 A555 2p multi   .90 .20

National Police A556

2000, Apr. 6   **Perf. 13½**
1348 A556 2p shown   .90 .20
   Size: 37x28mm
   Perf. 13½x13¼
1349 A556 5p Crest   2.25 1.10

Dominican Institute of Industrial Technology, 25th Anniv. A557

2000, Apr. 11   *Perf. 13½*
1350 A557 2p multi   .90 .20

Independencia Province, 50th Anniv. — A558

2000, Apr. 15
1351 A558 3p multi   1.25 .20

A559

12th Natl. Games, La Romana A560

2000, Apr. 27   *Perf. 13½x13¼*
1352 A559 2p Baseball   .75 .20
1353 A559 3p Boxing   1.50 .20
     Perf. 13½
1354 A560 5p Emblem   2.25 1.00
     Nos. 1352-1354 (3)   4.50 1.40

Paintings A561

Designs: 5p, The Violinist, by Darío Suro. 10p, Self-portrait, by Théodore Chassériau.

2000, May 5   *Perf. 13¼*
1355 A561 5p multi   2.50 1.10
1356 A561 10p multi   4.25 2.50

Presidential Elections A562

2000, May 12
1357 A562 2p multi   .90 .20

Classical Musicians A563

#1358, Julio Alberto Hernandez Camejo (1900-99), pianist. #1359, Ramon Diaz (1901-76), bassoonist. #1360, Enrique de Marchena Dujarric (1908-88), pianist.

2000, May 31   *Perf. 13½*
1358 A563 5p multi   2.25 .95
1359 A563 5p multi   2.25 .95
1360 A563 5p multi   2.25 .95
     Nos. 1358-1360 (3)   6.75 2.85

Expo 2000, Hanover A564

2000, June 1
1361 A564 5p shown   2.25 .70
1362 A564 10p Emblem, diff.   4.50 2.10

Art by Jaime Colson — A565

Designs: 2p, Woman on horseback. 3p, Abstract. 5p, Musicians and dancers, horiz. 6p, Nudes. 10p, Colson.

2000   **Litho.**   *Perf. 13¼*
1363-1367 A565   Set of 5   13.50 6.75

Holy Year 2000 A566

Churches: 2p, Santo Cristo de los Milagros de Bayaguana Sanctuary. 5p, Santa Maria la Menor Cathedral, first in the Americas, vert. 10p, Nuestra Señora de la Altagracia Basilica, vert.

2000   *Perf. 13½x13¼, 13¼x13½*
1368-1370 A566   Set of 3   8.00 4.00

Lighthouse Type of 1995
2000   *Perf. 13¼x13½*
1371 A466 10p buff, brn & sil   5.25 2.75

Dominican Republic — Republic of China Diplomatic Relations A566a

Flags of Dominican Republic and Republic of China and: 5p, Illustration of dragon. 10p, Carved dragon.

Serpentine Die Cut 11¼
2000, Dec. 15   **Litho.**
     Self-Adhesive
1371A-1371B A566a   Set of 2   7.25 3.50

America Issue — Campaign Against AIDS — A566b

Designs: 2p, Child. 6p, AIDS patient (38x38mm).

2000, Dec. 21   **Self-Adhesive**
1371C-1371D A566b   Set of 2   4.00 2.00

UN High Commissioner for Refugees, 50th Anniv. — A566c

2000, Dec. 29   **Self-Adhesive**
1371E A566c 10p multi   4.50 2.25

Environmental Protection — A567

Designs: 2p, Lizard on leaf, vert. $3, House. $5, River rapids, vert.

Serpentine Die Cut 11¼
2000   **Litho.**
     Self-Adhesive
1372-1374 A567   Set of 3   5.00 2.50

Lighthouse Type of 1995
2001   **Litho.**   *Perf. 13¼x13½*
1375 A466 15p lt bl, dk bl & sil   7.25 3.50

Concepcion Bona, Seamstress of First Dominican Republic Flag, Cent. of Death — A568

2001   *Perf. 13½x13¼*
1376 A568 10p multi   4.50 2.10

Stamp Day — A569

2001
1377 A569 5p multi   2.25 1.10

Year of Dialogue Among Civilizations A570

2001   *Perf. 13¼x13½*
1378 A570 12p multi   5.50 2.50

America Issue — UNESCO World Heritage A571

Designs: 4p, San Felipe Fort. 15p, Ruins of San Nicolas de Bari Hospital (27x37mm).

2001   *Perf. 13½, 13¼x13½ (15p)*
1379-1380 A571   Set of 2   8.50 4.25

Lighthouse Type of 1995
2002, Oct. 17   Litho.   *Perf. 13½x13¾*
1382 A466 15p yel & multi   4.00 2.00

Mushrooms — A572

No. 1383: a, Pycnoporus sanguineus. b, Morchella elata. c, Mycena epipterygia. d, Coriolopsis polyzona.

     Perf. 13¼x13½
2001, Sept. 13   **Litho.**
1383 A572 6p Block of 4, #a-d   13.00 6.50

National Botanical Gardens, 25th Anniv. — A573

No. 1384: a, Isidorea pungens. b, Pereskia quisqueyana. c, Goetzea ekmanii. d, Cubanola domingensis.

Perf. 13¼x13½

2001, Sept. 20   **Litho.**
1384 A573 4p Block of 4, #a-d   8.00 8.00

Presidents of the Dominican Republic — A574

No. 1385: a, Gen. José María Cabral. b, Gen. Gregório Luperón. c, Gen. Ignacio María González. d, Ulises Espaillat. e, Pedro A. Pimentel. f, Federico de Jesús García. g, Frenando Arturo de Mariño. h, Gen. Ulises Heureaux.

2001, Sept. 27   **Litho.**   **Perf. 13¼**
1385 A574 6p Sheet of 8, #a-h, + label   22.50 11.00

Blessed Josemaría Escrivá de Balaguer (1902-75), Founder of Opus Dei — A575

2002, Aug. 29   **Perf. 13½x13¼**
1386 A575 10p multi   4.00 1.90

Loyola Polytechnic Institute, 50th Anniv. — A576

2002, Oct. 24   **Perf. 13¼x13½**
1387 A576 6p multi   2.00 .95

12th Iberoamerican Heads of State Summit — A577

Designs: 12p, Flags below map. 15p, Flags above map.

Perf. 13¾x13½
2002, Nov. 14   **Litho.**
1388-1389 A577   Set of 2   7.25 3.50

America Issue — Youth Education and Literacy — A578

Designs: 4p, Teacher helping child write. 15p, Child writing on blackboard.

2002, Dec. 20   **Perf. 13¼x13½**
1390-1391 A578   Set of 2   5.00 2.50

Coccothrinax Spissa — A579

Perf. 13¼x13½
2002, Dec. 20   **Litho.**
1392 A579 10p multi   2.75 1.40

2003 Pan American Games, Santo Domingo — A580

Color of "2003" in design: 4p, Light green blue. 6p, Blue. 12p, Red.

2003, Feb. 25
1393-1395 A580   Set of 3   6.25 3.00

Medicinal Plants — A581

No. 1396: a, Hymenaea courbaril. b, Spondias mombin. c, Genipa americana. d, Guazuma ulmifonia.

2003, June 17
1396 A581 5p Block of 4, #a-d   5.50 2.75

Dr. José Francisco Peña Gomez (1937-98), Politician A582

Litho. & Engr.
2003, Dec. 17   **Perf. 11½**
1397 A582 10p multi   2.75 1.40

José Marti (1853-95), Cuban Patriot — A583

2003, Nov. 5   **Litho.**   **Perf. 13x13¼**
1398 A583 15p multi   4.00 2.00

Pan American Health Organization, Cent. (in 2002) — A583a

Perf. 13½x13¼
2003, Sept. 12   **Litho.**
1398A A583a 20p multi   3.75 1.90

America Issue — Flora and Fauna — A584

Designs: 5p, Aristelliger lar. 15p, Corpernicia berteroana, vert.

Perf. 13½x13¼, 13¼x13½
2004, Jan. 19
1399-1400 A584   Set of 2   5.00 2.50
   Nos. 1399-1400 are dated "2003."

Election of Pope John Paul II, 25th Anniv. — A585

Pope John Paul II: 10p, With hand touching face. 15p, Blessing crowd, horiz. 25p, Vignettes of 10p and 15p stamps.

Perf. 13¼x13½, 13½x13¼
2005, Nov. 26
1401-1402 A585   Set of 2   6.75 3.25
Size: 57x85mm
Imperf
1403 A585 25p multi   7.25 3.50

National Council for Children A586

2004, Mar. 10   **Perf. 13½x13¼**
1404 A586 7p multi   1.25 .60

Exfilna National Philatelic Exhibition A587

2004, Dec. 8   Litho.   Perf. 13½x13¼
1405 A587 7p multi   2.25 1.10

America Issue — Fight Against Poverty A588

Design: 10p, Shack. 20p, Poor man.

2004, Dec. 23
1406-1407 A588   Set of 2   6.75 3.50

Dominican Republic - Canada Diplomatic Relations, 50th Anniv. A589

2004, Dec. 31
1408 A589 20p multi   4.50 2.25

Interexpo '05 Intl. Philatelic Exhibition A590

Designs: 7p, Dove and stamp. 20p, Map highlighting Dominican Republic, vert.

Perf. 13½x13¼, 13¼x13½

2005 Litho.
1409-1410 A590 Set of 2 6.50 3.25
Souvenir Sheet

Design: 10p, Similar to 7p.

1410A A590 10p multi 2.00 2.00

Dominican Republic Philatelic Society, 50th anniv.
Issued: 20p, 10/16; 7p, 10/17; 10p, 2005.

America Issue — Environmental Protection A591

Prevention of: 10p, Water pollution. 20p, Air pollution.

2005 **Perf. 13¼x13½**
1411-1412 A591 Set of 2 5.50 2.75

Monte Plata Maternity Clinic A592

Perf. 13½x13¼

2005, Nov. 14 Litho.
1413 A592 15p multi 2.75 1.40

Proclamation of Sister City Status of Santo Domingo and La Guardia, Spain — A593

2005, Nov. 11
1414 A593 10p multi 1.90 .95

Stamp Day A594

2005 Litho. **Perf. 13½x13¼**
1415 A594 10p multi 1.90 .95

Palace of Fine Arts, 50th Anniv. A595

2006, Oct. 10 Litho. **Perf. 13¾x13¼**
1416 A595 7p multi 1.40 .70

Dominican History Academy, 75th Anniv. — A596

2006, Oct. 30 **Perf. 13¼**
1417 A596 10p multi 1.60 .80

16th Intl. Boxing Congress, Santo Domingo — A597

2006, Nov. 2 **Perf. 13¼x13½**
1418 A597 20p multi 3.25 1.60

Pope John Paul II (1920-2005) A598

Pope and: 10p, Crucifix. 20p, Dove, horiz.

2006, Nov. 4 **Perf. 13½**
1419-1420 A598 Set of 2 4.75 2.40

Blessing of Natl. Sacred Heart of Jesus Sanctuary, 50th Anniv. — A599

2006, Nov. 24 **Perf. 13½x13¼**
1421 A599 10p multi 1.60 .80

Ninth Latin American Botanical Congress A600

2006 **Perf. 13¼x13½**
1422 A600 20p multi 3.25 1.60

America Issue, Energy Conservation — A601

Designs: 10p, Light bulb in hands. 20p, Transmission lines and tower.

2006 **Perf. 13x13¼**
1423-1424 A601 Set of 2 4.75 2.40

Pres. Joaquin Balaguer (1906-2002) A602

Balaguer: 7p, Wearing bow tie. 10p, Holding book.

2006, Sept. 1 **Perf. 13¼x13½**
1425-1426 A602 Set of 2 3.00 1.50

Office of the First Lady A603

Emblem and: 10p, Tree. 25p, Computer and keyboard.

2007, Mar. 1 **Perf. 13½x13¼**
1427-1428 A603 Set of 2 5.50 2.75

Selection of Nicolás de Jesus Cardinal López Rodríguez as Archbishop of Santo Domingo, 25th Anniv. — A604

López Rodríguez: 10p, Standing next to chair. 15p, With Pope John Paul II. 25p, Holding crucifix.

2007, May 25 **Perf. 13¼x13½**
1429-1431 A604 Set of 3 8.00 4.00

2007 Pan American Games, Rio de Janeiro — A605

Designs: 15p, High jump. 20p, Weight lifting.

2007, July 6 Litho.
1432-1433 A605 Set of 2 5.50 2.75

Podilymbus Podiceps A606

2007 Litho. **Perf. 13½x13¼**
1434 A606 20p multi 3.25 1.60
Dated 2006.

Stamp Day — A607

2007, Oct. **Perf. 13¼x13½**
1435 A607 15p multi 2.50 1.25

America Issue, Education For All — A608

Top panel in: 10p, Red. 20p, Blue.

2007, Oct.
1436-1437 A608 Set of 2 5.00 2.50

Treaty of Friendship With the Netherlands, 150th Anniv. — A609

2007, Nov. **Perf. 13½x13¼**
1438 A609 25p multi 4.00 2.00

Palace of Columbus A610

2007
1439 A610 10p multi 1.60 .80

Barahona Province, Cent. — A611

2007 **Perf. 13¼x13**
1440 A611 10p multi 1.60 .80

Salvaléon de Higuey, 500th Anniv. A612

2007 **Perf. 13½**
1441 A612 15p multi 2.50 1.25

Friendship and Cooperation Between Dominican Republic and Republic of China — A613

Designs: 10p, Prunus mume, Swietenia mahagonni. 15p, Urocissa caeruela, Dulus dominicus. 35p, Buildings from China and Dominican Republic.

2007
1442-1444 A613 Set of 3   9.75 5.00

Children's Book Illustrations by Dr. Sophie Jakowska A614

Initials of Dr. Jakowska and: No. 1445, 7p, Trichechus manatus manatus. No. 1446, 7p, Eretmochelys imbricata, horiz. No. 1447, 10p, Photograph of Jakowska. No. 1448, 10p, Amazona ventralis. 15p, Crocodylus acutus, horiz.

2007   *Perf. 13¼x13, 13x13¼*
1445-1449 A614 Set of 5   8.00 4.00

Scouting, Cent. — A615

Designs: 10p, Dominican Republic Scouting emblem. 15p, Scouts, knotted rope.

2007   Litho.   *Perf. 13½*
1450-1451 A615 Set of 2   4.25 2.10

Dominican Diaspora — A616

2008   *Perf. 13¼x13*
1452 A616 15p multi   2.60 1.25

Freemasonry in Dominican Republic, 150th Anniv. — A617

2008   *Perf. 13¼x13½*
1453 A617 25p multi   4.25 2.10

Stamp Day A618

2008   *Perf. 13¼*
1454 A618 20p brown   3.50 1.75

2008 Summer Olympics, Beijing — A619

No. 1455: a, Taekwondo. b, Boxing. c, Table tennis. d, Judo.

2008   *Perf. 13x13¼*
1455 A619 10p Block of 4, #a-d   7.00 3.50

Women Involved in Fight for Independence A620

No. 1456: a, Juana de la Merced Trinidad (d. 1860). b, Joaquina Filomena Gomez de la Cova (1800-93). c, Maria Baltasara de los Reyes (1789-1867). d, Rosa Protomartir Duarte y Diaz (1820-88). e, Manuela Diaz y Jimenez (1786-1858). f, Petronila Abreu y Delgado (1815-1904). g, Micaela de Rivera de Santana (1785-1854). h, Froilana Febles de Santana (1814-88). i, Rosa Montas de Duvergé (1813-95). j, Josefa Antonia Perez de la Paz (1788-1855). k, Ana Valverde (1798-1864). l, Maria de la Concepción Bona y Hernandez (1824-1901). m, Maria de Jesus Pina y Benitez (1825-58). n, Maria Trinidad Sanchez y Ramona (1794-1845).

2008   *Perf. 13¼x13½*
1456   Sheet of 14 + 31 labels 22.50 11.50
   a.-n. A620 10p Any single   1.60 .80

Arms of Santiago, 500th Anniv. A621

2008   Litho.   *Perf. 13x13¼*
1457 A621 10p multi   .90 .30

Discovery of Quisqueya (Hispaniola) by Christopher Columbus, 1492 — A622

2008
1458 A622 10p multi   .90 .30

General Timoteo Ogando Encarnación (1818-1908) A623

2008   *Perf. 13¼x13*
1459 A623 10p multi   .90 .30

Campaign Against Commercial Sexual Exploitation A624

2008
1460 A624 10p multi   .90 .30

Intl. Swimming Federation, Cent. — A625

2008   *Perf. 13½*
1461 A625 15p multi   .90 .40

America Issue, National Festivals — A626

No. 1462: a, 15p, Shot of Independence. b, 25p, Sword of the Restoration.

2008   *Perf. 13¼x13*
1462 A626   Horiz. pair, #a-b   3.25 1.10

Duarte y Díez Family Tree — A627

No. 1463: a, Juan J. Duarte (1768-1843) and wife, Manuela Díez (1786-1858). b, Juan J. Duarte's sons, Juan Pablo (1813-76), Dominican independence leader, and Vicente (1802-65). c, Juan J. Duarte's son, Manuel (1826-90), and daughter, Rosa (1820-88). d, Juan J. Duarte's daughters, Francisca (1831-99), and Filomena (1818-65).

2009, Feb. 26   *Perf. 13½x13¼*
1463 A627 10p Block of 4, #a-d   3.50 1.10

Chinatown, Santo Domingo A628

Designs: 15p, Confucius Plaza. 20p, Gateway.

2009, Apr. 17
1464-1465 A628 Set of 2   2.50 1.00

De La Salle Schools in Dominican Republic, 75th Anniv. A629

St. Jean Baptiste de la Salle (1651-1719) A630

2009, May 14   *Perf. 13½x13¼*
1466 A629 7p multi   .50 .20
             Perf. 13¼x13½
1467 A630 10p multi   .90 .30

Invasion of Constanza, Maimón and Estero Hondo by Dominican Exiles, 50th Anniv. A631

2009, June 17   *Perf. 13½*
1468 A631 10p multi   .90 .30

Pres. Juan Bosch (1909-2001) A632

2009   *Perf. 13¼x13*
1469 A632 20p multi   1.40 .55

Crabs — A633

No. 1470: a, Epilobocera haytensis. b, Gecarcinus ruricola. c, Coenobita clypeatus. d, Callinectes sapidus.

2009 **Litho.** **Perf. 13½x13¼**
1470 A633 10p Block of 4, #a-d 3.50 2.25

Winning Designs in Children's Christmas Stamp Design Contest — A634

No. 1471: a, Dancers and musicians in front of house. b, Parade. c, Family and livestock. d, Villagers, manger and Christmas tree.

2009, Oct. 5 **Litho.** **Perf. 13x13¼**
1471 A634 10p Block of 4, #a-d 2.25 2.25

Plazas A635

Designs: 15p, Galicia Plaza, Santo Domingo. 25p, Santo Domingo Plaza, La Guardia, Spain.

2009, Oct. 15 **Perf. 13¼**
1472-1473 A635 Set of 2 2.25 2.25

15th American Genealogical Reunion — A636

2009, Nov. 3 **Perf. 13x13¼**
1474 A636 75p multi 4.25 4.25

Natl. School of Judicature A637

2009, Nov. 4 **Perf. 13½**
1475 A637 7p multi .40 .40

America Issue, Toys and Games — A638

Designs: 10p, Fu-fu. 15p, Hopscotch, horiz. 20p, Pañuelo, horiz.

2009 **Perf. 13x13, 13x13¼**
1476-1477 A638 Set of 2 1.40 1.40
Imperf
Size: 76x50mm
1478 A638 20p multi 1.10 1.10

Miniature Sheet

Dominican Republic Presidents — A639

No. 1479: a, Benigno Filomeno De Rojas. b, Jacinto B. De Castro. c, Mactos Cabral. d, Gen. Cesáreo Guillermo. e, Francisco G. Billini. f, Alejandro Woss y Gil. g, Carlos Felipe Morales Languasco. h, Ramón Cáceres.

2009 **Perf. 13¼**
1479 A639 7p Sheet of 8, #a-h, + central label 3.25 3.25

National Coat of Arms — A640

2010, Feb. 10 **Perf. 13¼x13½**
1480 A640 50p multi 2.75 2.75

14th Ibero-American Notaries Meeting — A641

2010, June 3 **Litho.** **Perf. 13¼x13**
1481 A641 26p multi 1.40 1.40

Preservation of Polar Regions — A642

2010, July 7 **Perf. 13½x13¼**
1482 A642 20p multi 1.10 1.10

Solenodon Parodoxus A643

2010, July 28
1483 A643 25p multi 1.40 1.40

Biodiversity protection.

National Philatelic and Numismatic Museum, 25th Anniv. — A644

2010, Aug. 10 **Perf. 13¼x13**
1484 A644 33p ocher & black 1.90 1.90

Juan Pablo Duarte (1813-76), Independence Leader, and Birthplace, Santo Domingo — A645

2010, Aug. 30 **Perf. 11½x13¼**
1485 A645 25p multi 1.40 1.40

SEMI-POSTAL STAMPS

Catalogue values for unused stamps in this section are for Never Hinged items.

Nos. 474-478 Surcharged in Red

Engraved and Lithographed
1957, Feb. 8 **Unwmk.** **Perf. 11½**
Flags in National Colors
B1 A117 1c + 2c brn, lt bl, vio & mar .20 .20
B2 A117 2c + 2c dk brn, lt bl & vio .20 .20
B3 A117 3c + 2c red lilac & red .20 .20

B4 A117 5c + 2c red orange & vio .20 .20
B5 A117 7c + 2c green & violet .30 .30
Nos. B1-B5,CB1-CB3 (8) 2.20 2.20

The surtax was to aid Hungarian refugees. A similar 25c surcharge was applied to the miniature sheets described in the footnote following No. 478. Value, 2 sheets, perf. and imperf., $32.50

Nos. 479-483 Surcharged in Red Orange

1957, Sept. 9 **Photo.** **Perf. 13½**
Flags in National Colors
B6 A118 1c + 2c brown & brt bl .20 .20
B7 A118 2c + 2c org ver & dk bl .30 .30
B8 A118 3c + 2c dark blue .35 .35
B9 A118 5c + 2c olive & dk bl .45 .45
B10 A118 7c + 2c rose brn & dk bl .50 .50
Nos. B6-B10,CB4-CB6 (8) 3.55 3.50

Cent. of the birth of Lord Baden Powell and the 50th anniv. of the Scout Movement. The surtax was for the Dominican Republic Boy Scouts.

A similar 5c surcharge was applied to the miniature sheets described in the footnote following No. 483. Value 4 sheets, perf. and imperf., medal and flag, $62.50

Types of Olympic Regular Issue, 1957, Surcharged in Carmine

a

b

1958, May 26 **Engr. & Litho.**
Flags in National Colors
Pink Paper
B11 A119(a) 1c + 2c red brown .20 .20
B12 A119(b) 1c + 2c red brown .20 .20
B13 A120(a) 2c + 2c gray brown .25 .25
B14 A120(b) 2c + 2c gray brown .25 .25
B15 A119(a) 3c + 2c violet .25 .25
B16 A119(b) 3c + 2c violet .25 .25
B17 A120(a) 5c + 2c red orange .35 .35
B18 A120(b) 5c + 2c red orange .35 .35
B19 A119(a) 7c + 2c Prus green .40 .40
B20 A119(b) 7c + 2c Prus green .40 .40
Nos. B11-B20,CB7-CB12 (16) 5.00 5.00

Surtax for the UN Relief and Works Agency for Palestine Refugees.

A similar 5c surcharge, plus marginal United Nations emblem and "UNRWA," was applied to the miniature sheets described in the footnote following No. 488. Value, 4 sheets, perf. and imperf., $20.

Nos. 501-505
Surcharged

Perf. 13½

1959, Apr. 13   Photo.   Unwmk.
Flags in National Colors

B21	A125	1c + 2c rose, indigo & ultra	.30	.30
B22	A125	1c + 2c brown & blue	.35	.35
B23	A125	3c + 2c gray, vio, blk & buff	.40	.40
B24	A125	5c + 2c rose, dk bl, brn & red	.50	.50
B25	A125	7c + 2c lt brn, dk bl & red	.55	.55
		Nos. B21-B25,CB13-CB15 (8)	4.30	4.30

International Geophysical Year, 1957-58.
A similar 5c surcharge was applied to the miniature sheets described in the footnote following No. 505. Value, 2 sheets, perf. and imperf., $40.

Type of 1957
Surcharged in Red

Engraved and Lithographed
1959, Sept. 10   Unwmk.   *Imperf.*
Flags in National Colors

B26	A117	1c + 2c brn, lt bl, vio & mar	.30	.30
B27	A117	2c + 2c dk brn, lt bl & vio	.30	.30
B28	A117	3c + 2c red lilac & red	.35	.35
B29	A117	5c + 2c red org & vio	.35	.35
B30	A117	7c + 2c green & violet	.45	.45
		Nos. B26-B30,CB16-CB18 (8)	3.25	3.25

3rd Pan American Games, Chicago, Aug. 27-Sept. 7, 1959.

Nos. 522-524 Surcharged in Red

1960, Apr. 7   Litho.   *Perf. 12½*
Center in Gray

B31	A135	5c + 5c red brn & yel grn	.30	.30
B32	A135	9c + 5c car & lt bl	.30	.30
B33	A135	13c + 5c grn & grn	.65	.65
		Nos. B31-B33,CB19-CB20 (5)	2.00	2.00

World Refugee Year, July 1, 1959-June 30, 1960. The surtax was for aid to refugees.
Souvenir sheets exist perf. and imperf., containing one each of Nos. B31-B33 and CB19-CB20. Value, 2 sheets, perf. and imperf., $12.50

Nos. 525-529 Surcharged: "XV ANIVERSARIO DE LA UNESCO +2c"

1962, Jan. 8   Photo.   *Perf. 13½*
Flags in National Colors

B34	A136	1c + 2c red, yel grn & blk	.25	.25
B35	A136	2c + 2c org, grnsh bl & brn	.25	.25
B36	A136	3c + 2c henna brn & bl	.25	.25

B37	A136	5c + 2c brown & ultra	.25	.25
B38	A136	7c + 2c grn, bl & rose brn	.25	.25
		Nos. B34-B38,CB21-CB23 (8)	2.10	2.10

15th anniv. (in 1961) of UNESCO.
A similar 5c surcharge was applied to the miniature sheets described in the footnote following No. 529. Value, 2 sheets, perf. and imperf., $16.

Anti-Malaria Type of 1962
1962, Apr. 29   Litho.   *Perf. 12*

B39	A141	10c + 2c brt pink & red lil	.30	.30
B40	A141	20c + 2c pale brn & brn	.45	.45

Freedom from Hunger Type of 1963
1963, Apr. 15   Unwmk.   *Perf. 11½*
Banner in Dark Blue & Red

B41	A148	2c + 1c green	.20	.20
B42	A148	5c + 2c brt rose lil	.25	.25
B43	A148	9c + 2c orange	.25	.25
		Nos. B41-B43 (3)	.70	.70

A souvenir sheet contains three imperf. stamps similar to Nos. B41-B43. Value, $1.50.

Nos. 591-593 Surcharged

1964, Mar. 8   *Perf. 12½*

B44	A153	3c + 2c pale pink & ver	.20	.20
B45	A153	6c + 2c pale bl & ultra	.20	.20
B46	A153	9c + 2c pale rose & red brn	.25	.25
		Nos. B44-B46,CB26-CB27 (5)	1.15	1.05

UNESCO world campaign to save historic monuments in Nubia.

Nos. 622-626
Surcharged

1966, Dec. 9   Litho.   *Perf. 12½*
Size: 31x21mm

B47	A164	1c + 2c multi	8.50	1.25
B48	A164	2c + 2c multi	8.50	1.25
B49	A164	3c + 2c multi	8.50	1.25
B50	A164	5c + 4c multi	8.50	1.25
B51	A164	8c + 4c multi	8.50	1.25
		Nos. B47-B51,CB28-CB30 (8)	56.00	14.00

Surtax for victims of Hurricane Inez.

AIR POST STAMPS

Map of Hispaniola — AP1

Perf. 11½
1928, May 31   Litho.   Unwmk.

C1	AP1	10c deep ultra	4.50	2.00

1930

C2	AP1	10c ocher	3.00	2.00
a.		Vert. pair, imperf. btwn.	600.00	
C3	AP1	15c scarlet	6.00	3.00
C4	AP1	20c dull green	2.75	.50
C5	AP1	30c violet	6.00	3.25
		Nos. C2-C5 (4)	17.75	8.75

#C2-C5 have only "CENTAVOS" in lower panel. Issued: 10c, 20c, 1/24; 15c, 30c, 2/14.

1930

C6	AP1	10c light blue	1.50	.60
C7	AP1	15c blue green	3.00	.90
C8	AP1	20c yellow brown	3.25	.45
a.		Horiz. pair, imperf. vert.	450.00	450.00
C9	AP1	30c chocolate	5.50	1.50
		Nos. C6-C9 (4)	13.25	3.45

Issue dates: 10c, 15c, 20c, Sept.; 30c, Oct.

Batwing Sundial Erected in 1753 — AP2

1931-33   *Perf. 12*

C10	AP2	10c carmine	3.25	.50
C11	AP2	10c light blue	1.40	.50
C12	AP2	10c dark green	5.50	2.50
C13	AP2	15c rose lilac	2.50	.50
C14	AP2	20c dark blue	5.50	2.10
a.		Numerals reading up at left and down at right	5.00	2.50
b.		Imperf., pair	250.00	
C15	AP2	30c green	2.25	.25
C16	AP2	50c red brown	5.50	.50
C17	AP2	1p deep orange	7.50	2.50
		Nos. C10-C17 (8)	33.40	9.35

Issued: #C11, 7/2/32; #C12, 5/28/33; others 8/16.

Airplane and Ozama Fortress AP3

1933, Nov. 20

C18	AP3	10c dark blue	3.00	.50

Airplane and Trujillo Bridge AP4

1934, Sept. 20

C19	AP4	10c dark blue	3.00	.50

Symbolic of Flight AP5

1935, Apr. 29

C20	AP5	10c lt blue & dk blue	1.40	.40

AP6

1936, Feb. 11   *Perf. 11½*

C21	AP6	10c dk bl & turq bl	2.25	.40

Allegory of Flight AP7

1936, Oct. 17

C22	AP7	10c dk bl, bl & turq bl	2.00	.30

Macoris Airport AP8

1937, Oct. 22

C23	AP8	10c green	.90	.20

Fleet of Columbus AP9

Air Fleet AP10

Proposed Columbus Lighthouse — AP11

1937, Nov. 9   *Perf. 12*

C24	AP9	10c rose red	1.50	1.25
C25	AP10	15c purple	1.25	.85
C26	AP11	20c dk bl & lt bl	1.25	.90
C27	AP10	25c red violet	1.75	1.00
C28	AP11	30c yellow green	1.50	1.00
C29	AP10	50c brown	3.25	1.25
C30	AP11	75c dk olive grn	9.00	9.00
C31	AP9	1p orange	5.50	1.75
		Nos. C24-C31 (8)	25.00	17.00

Goodwill flight to all American countries by the planes "Colon", "Pinta," "Nina" and "Santa Maria."
#C30 was reproduced imperf. on #1019.

Pan American Clipper AP12

1938, July 30

C32	AP12	10c green	1.00	.20

Trylon and Perisphere, Plane and Proposed Columbus Lighthouse — AP13

1939, Apr. 30

C33	AP13	10c green & lt green	1.40	.60

New York World's Fair.

Airplane AP14

1939, Oct. 18
C34 AP14 10c green & dp green 1.40 .20
a.   Pair, imperf. btwn. 450.00

Proposed Columbus Lighthouse, Plane and Caravels — AP15

Christopher Columbus and Proposed Lighthouse — AP16

Proposed Lighthouse — AP17

Christopher Columbus — AP18

Caravel — AP19

1940, Oct. 12
C35 AP15 10c sapphire & lt bl .85 .45
C36 AP16 15c org brn & brn 1.10 .75
C37 AP17 20c rose red & red 1.10 .75
C38 AP18 25c brt red lil & red vio 1.10 .35
C39 AP19 50c green & lt green 2.25 1.25
    Nos. C35-C39 (5) 6.40 3.55

Discovery of America by Columbus and proposed Columbus memorial lighthouse in Dominican Republic.

Posts and Telegraph Building, San Cristobal AP20

1941, Feb. 21
C40 AP20 10c brt red lil & pale lil rose .40 .20

Globe, Wing and Letter AP21

1942, Feb. 13
C41 AP21 10c dark violet brn .50 .25
C42 AP21 75c deep orange 2.75 1.75

Plane AP22

1943, Sept. 1
C43 AP22 10c brt red lilac .30 .20
C44 AP22 20c dp blue & blue .35 .20
C45 AP22 25c yellow olive 5.00 2.40
    Nos. C43-C45 (3) 5.65 2.80

Plane, Flag, Coat of Arms and Torch of Liberty — AP23

1944, Feb. 27 Perf. 11½
Flag in Gray, Dark Blue, Carmine
C46 AP23 10c multicolored .35 .20
C47 AP23 20c multicolored .45 .20
C48 AP23 1p multicolored 2.00 1.50
    Nos. C46-C48 (3) 2.80 1.90

Centenary of Independence. See No. 407 for souvenir sheet listing.

Communications Building, Ciudad Trujillo — AP24

1944, Nov. 12 Litho. Perf. 12
C49 AP24 9c yel grn & blue .20 .20
C50 AP24 13c dull brn & rose car .25 .20
C51 AP24 25c org & dull red .35 .20
b.   Vert. pair, imperf. btwn. 45.00
C52 AP24 30c black & ultra .75 .65
    Nos. C49-C52 (4) 1.55 1.25

Twenty booklets of 100 (25 panes of 4) of the 25c were issued. All booklets are still intact.

Communications Type
1945, Sept. 1
Center in Dark Blue and Carmine
C53 A92 7c deep yellow green .30 .25
C54 A92 12c red orange .35 .20
C55 A92 13c deep blue .45 .20
C56 A92 25c orange brown .80 .20
    Nos. C53-C56 (4) 1.90 .85

AP26

Flags and National Anthem AP27

Unwmk.
1946, Feb. 27 Litho. Perf. 12
Center in Dark Blue, Deep Carmine and Black
C57 AP26 10c carmine .65 .30
C58 AP26 15c blue 1.50 .75
C59 AP26 20c chocolate 1.75 .75
C60 AP26 35c orange 2.10 .85
C61 AP27 1p grn, yel grn & cit 19.00 8.75
    Nos. C57-C61 (5) 25.00 11.40

Nos. C57-C61 exist imperf.

Map Type of Regular Issue
1946, Aug. 4
C62 A94 10c multicolored .60 .20
C63 A94 13c multicolored 1.10 .20

Waterfall Type of Regular Issue
1947, Mar. 18 Litho.
Center Multicolored
C64 A95 18c light blue .75 .35
C65 A95 23c carmine 1.10 .55
C66 A95 50c red violet 1.50 .50
C67 A95 75c chocolate 2.10 1.00
    Nos. C64-C67 (4) 5.45 2.40

Palace Type of Regular Issue
1948, Feb. 27
C68 A96 37c orange brown 1.50 .75
C69 A96 1p orange yellow 4.00 1.50

Ruins Type of Regular Issue
1949 Unwmk. Perf. 11½
C70 A97 7c ol grn & pale ol grn .30 .20
C71 A97 10c orange brn & buff .30 .20
C72 A97 15c brt rose & pale pink .90 .25
C73 A97 20c green & pale green 1.25 .45
    Nos. C70-C73 (4) 2.75 1.10

Issue dates: 10c, Apr. 4; others, Apr. 13.

Las Carreras Monument — AP32

1949, Aug. 10
C74 AP32 10c red & pink .45 .20

Cent. of the Battle of Las Carreras.

Catalogue values for unused stamps in this section, from this point to the end of the section, are for Never Hinged items.

Hotel Type of Regular Issue
Hotels: 12c, Montana. 37c, San Cristobal.

1950, Sept. 8
C75 A100 12c dk blue & blue .50 .20
C76 A100 37c carmine & pink 3.00 2.00

Map, Plane and Caduceus AP34

1950, Oct. 2
C77 AP34 12c orange brn & yel .60 .20

13th Pan-American Health Conf. Exists imperf.

Hospital Type of Regular Issue
1952, Aug.
C78 A104 23c deep blue .85 .85
C79 A104 29c carmine 2.25 1.50

Columbus Lighthouse and Plane — AP36

Ano Mariano Initials in Monogram — AP37

1953, Jan. 6 Engr. Perf. 13
C80 AP36 12c ocher .30 .20
C81 AP36 14c dark blue .20 .20
C82 AP36 20c black brown .60 .45
C83 AP36 23c deep plum .35 .30
C84 AP36 25c dark blue .70 .55
C85 AP36 29c deep green .60 .50
C86 AP36 1p red brown 1.40 .80
a.   Miniature sheet of 10 15.00 15.00
    Nos. C80-C86 (7) 4.15 3.00

No. C86a is lithographed and contains Nos. 450-452 and C80-C86, in slightly different shades. Sheet measures 190x130mm and is imperf. with simulated perforations.
A miniature sheet similar to No. C86a, but measuring 200x163mm and in folder, exists. Value $100.

1954, Aug. 5 Litho. Perf. 11½
C87 AP37 8c claret .20 .20
C88 AP37 11c blue .20 .20
C89 AP37 33c brown orange .80 .50
    Nos. C87-C89 (3) 1.20 .90

Marian Year. Nos. C87-C89 exist imperf.

Rotary Type of Regular Issue
1955, Feb. 23 Perf. 12
C90 A110 11c rose red .35 .20

Flags — AP39

Portraits of General Hector B. Trujillo: 25c, In civilian clothes. 33c, In uniform.

1955, May 16 Engr. Perf. 13½x13
C91 AP39 11c blue, yel & car .55 .20
C92 AP39 25c rose violet .90 .30
C93 AP39 33c orange brown 1.25 .50
    Nos. C91-C93 (3) 2.70 1.00

The center of No. C91 is litho. 25th anniv. of the inauguration of the Trujillo era.

Fair Type of Regular Issue
1955, Dec. 20 Unwmk. Perf. 13
C94 A112 11c vermilion .35 .20

ICAO Type of Regular Issue
1956, Apr. 6 Litho. Perf. 12½
C95 A114 11c ultra .40 .20

Tree Type of Regular Issue
Design: 13c, Mahogany tree.

1956, Dec. 8 Litho. Perf. 11½x12
C96 A115 13c orange & green 1.60 .20

Type of Regular Issue, 1957
Olympic Winners and Flags: 11c, Paavo Nurmi, Finland. 16c, Ugo Frigerio, Italy. 17c, Mildred Didrikson ("Didrickson" on stamp), US.

Engraved and Lithographed
Perf. 11½, Imperf.
1957, Jan. 24 Unwmk.
Flags in National Colors
C97 A117 11c ultra & red org .25 .25
C98 A117 16c carmine & lt grn .25 .25
C99 A117 17c black, vio & red .25 .25
    Nos. C97-C99 (3) .75 .75

16th Olympic Games, Melbourne, Nov. 22-Dec. 8, 1956.
Souvenir sheets of 3 exist, perf. and imperf., containing Nos. C97-C99. Value, 2 sheets, perf. & imperf., $15.
For surcharges see Nos. CB1-CB3, CB16-CB18.

Type of Regular Issue
Olympic Winners and Flags: 11c, Robert Morrow, US, 100 & 200 meter dash. 16c, Chris Brasher, England, steeplechase. 17c, A. Ferreira Da Silva, Brazil, hop, step and jump.

Perf. 13½, Imperf.
1957, July 18 Photo.
Flags in National Colors
C100 A118 11c yellow grn & dk bl .25 .25
C101 A118 16c lilac & dk blue .25 .25
C102 A118 17c brown & blue grn .25 .25
    Nos. C100-C102 (3) .75 .75

1956 Olympic winners.
See note on miniature sheets following No. 483.

For surcharges see Nos. CB4-CB6.

Types of Regular Issue

Olympic Winners and Flags: 11c, Hans Winkler, Germany, individual jumping. 16c, Alfred Oerter, US, discus throw. 17c, Shirley Strickland, Australia, 800 meter hurdles.

Engraved and Lithographed
Perf. 13½, Imperf.

1957, Nov. 12   **Unwmk.**

Flags in National Colors

C103	A119	11c ultra	.25	.25
C104	A120	16c rose carmine	.25	.25
C105	A119	17c claret	.25	.25
	Nos. C103-C105 (3)		.75	.75

1956 Olympic winners.
Miniature sheets of 3 exist, perf. and imperf., containing Nos. C103-C105. Value, 2 sheets, perf. and imperf., $5.50.
For surcharges see Nos. CB7-CB12.

Type of Regular Issue

Olympic Winners and Flags: 11c, Charles Jenkins, 400 & 800 meter run, and Thomas Courtney, 1,600 meter relay, US. 16c, Field hockey team, India. 17c, Yachting team, Sweden.

Perf. 13½, Imperf.

1958, Oct. 30   **Unwmk.**   **Photo.**

Flags in National Colors

C106	A125	11c blue, olive & brn	.25	.25
C107	A125	16c lt grn, org & dk bl	.25	.25
C108	A125	17c ver, blue & yel	.25	.25
	Nos. C106-C108 (3)		.75	.75

1956 Olympic winners.
Miniature sheets of 3 exist, perf. and imperf., containing Nos. C106-C108. Value, 2 sheets, perf. and imperf., $3.
For surcharges see Nos. CB13-CB15.

Fair Type of Regular Issue

1958, Dec. 9   **Litho.**   *Perf. 12½*

C109	A127	9c gray	.25	.20
C110	A127	25c lt violet	.70	.40
a.		Souv. sheet of 3, #C109-C110, 507, imperf.	1.75	1.75

Polo Type of Regular Issue

1959, May 15   *Perf. 12*

C111	A130	11c Dominican polo team	.35	.30

"San Cristobal" Plane — AP42

Perf. 11½

1960, Feb. 25   **Unwmk.**   **Litho.**

C112	AP42	13c org, bl, grn & gray	.30	.20

Dominican Civil Aviation.

Children and WRY Emblem AP43

1960, Apr. 7   *Perf. 12½*

C113	AP43	10c plum, gray & grn	.60	.30
C114	AP43	13c gray & green	.80	.30

World Refugee Year, 7/1/59-6/30/60.
For surcharges see Nos. CB19-CB20.

Olympic Type of Regular Issue

Olympic Winners: 11c, Pat McCormick, US, diving. 16c, Mithat Bayrack, Turkey, welterweight wrestling. 17c, Ursula Happe, Germany, 200 meter breast stroke.

Perf. 13½, Imperf.

1960, Sept. 14   **Photo.**

Flags in National Colors

C115	A136	11c blue, gray & brn	.20	.20
C116	A136	16c red, brown & ol	.25	.25
C117	A136	17c black, blue & ocher	.25	.25
	Nos. C115-C117 (3)		.70	.70

17th Olympic Games, Rome, 8/25-9/11.
Miniature sheets of 3 exist, perf. and imperf., containing Nos. C115-C117. Value, 2 sheets, perf. and imperf., $3.75.
For surcharges see Nos. CB21-CB23.

Coffee-Cacao Type of Regular Issue

1961, Dec. 30   **Litho.**   *Perf. 12½*

C118	A140	13c orange ver	.25	.25
C119	A140	33c brt yellow	.50	.50

Nos. C118-C119 exist imperf.

Anti-Malaria Type of Regular Issue

1962, Apr. 29   **Unwmk.**   *Perf. 12*

C120	A141	13c pink & red	.40	.20
C121	A141	33c org & dp org	.70	.45

See Nos. CB24-CB25.

Type of Regular Issue

Designs: 13c, Broken fetters and laurel. 50c, Flag, torch and inscription.

1962, May 30   *Perf. 12½*

C122	A142	13c brn, yel, ol, ultra & red	.30	.20
C123	A142	50c rose lilac, ultra & red	1.10	.75

No. C122 exists imperf.

UPAE Type of Regular Issue

1962, Oct. 23   *Perf. 12½*

C124	A146	13c bright blue	.25	.20
C125	A146	22c dull red brown	.40	.40

Nos. C124-C125 exist imperf.

Nouel Type of Regular Issue

Design: Frame altered with rosary and cross surrounding portrait.

1962, Dec. 18

C126	A147	13c blue & pale blue	.35	.20
C127	A147	25c vio & pale vio	.50	.50
a.		Souv. sheet, #C126-C127, imperf	1.00	1.00

Nos. C126-C127 exist imperf.

Sanchez, Duarte, Mella AP44

1963, July 7   **Litho.**   *Perf. 11½x12*

C128	A44	15c orange	.30	.25

120th anniv. of separation from Haiti.

World Map AP45

1963, Oct. 25   **Unwmk.**   *Perf. 12½*

C129	AP45	10c gray & carmine	.30	.25

Cent. of Intl. Red Cross. Exists imperf.

Human Rights Type

1963, Dec. 10   **Litho.**

C130	A152	7c fawn & red brn	.25	.20
C131	A152	10c lt blue & blue	.25	.20

Nos. C130-C131 exist imperf.

Ramses II Battling the Hittites (from Abu Simbel) — AP46

1964, Mar. 8   *Perf. 12½*

C132	AP46	10c brt violet	.25	.20
C133	AP46	13c yellow	.25	.20

UNESCO world campaign to save historic monuments in Nubia.
Nos. C132-C133 exist imperf.
For surcharges see Nos. CB26-CB27.

Striated Woodpecker — AP47

1964, June 8   **Litho.**

C134	AP47	10c multicolored	4.75	.20

Type of Space Issue

Designs: 7c, Rocket leaving earth. 10c, Space capsule orbiting earth.

1964, July 28   **Unwmk.**   *Perf. 12½*

C135	A156	7c brt green	.25	.20
C136	A156	10c violet blue	.30	.25
a.		Souvenir sheet	3.50	3.50

No. C136a contains 7c and 10c stamps similar to Nos. C135-C136 with simulated perforations.

Pres. John F. Kennedy — AP48

1964, Nov. 22   *Perf. 11½*

C137	AP48	10c buff & dk brown	.45	.25

President John F. Kennedy (1917-63). Sheets of 10 (5x2) and sheets of 50.

UPU Type of Regular Issue

1964, Dec. 5   **Litho.**   *Perf. 12½*

C138	A157	7c blue	.25	.20

ICY Type of Regular Issue

1965, Feb. 16   **Unwmk.**   *Perf. 12½*

C139	A158	10c lilac & violet	.30	.25

Basilica of Our Lady of Altagracia — AP49

1965, Mar. 18   **Unwmk.**   *Perf. 12½*

C140	AP49	10c multicolored	.30	.25

Fourth Mariological Congress and the Eleventh International Marian Congress.

Abraham Lincoln — AP50

1965, Apr. 15   **Litho.**   *Perf. 12½*

C141	AP50	17c bright blue	.45	.35

Cent. of the death of Abraham Lincoln.

Stamp Centenary Type of 1965

Design: Stamp of 1865, (No. 2).

1965, Dec. 28   **Litho.**   *Perf. 12½*

C142	A161	7c violet, lt grn & blk	.25	.20
C143	A161	10c yellow, lt grn & blk	.25	.20

ITU Emblem, Old and New Communication Equipment — AP51

1966, Apr. 6   **Litho.**   *Perf. 12½*

C144	AP51	28c pink & carmine	.65	.65
C145	AP51	45c brt grn & grn	1.00	1.00

Cent. (in 1965) of the ITU.

Butterfly Type of Regular Issue

1966, Nov. 8   **Litho.**   *Perf. 12½*
Various Butterflies in Natural Colors
Size: 35x24mm

C146	A164	10c lt violet & violet	5.75	.75
C147	A164	50c org & dp org	8.25	1.50
C148	A164	75c pink & rose red	11.00	2.50
	Nos. C146-C148 (3)		25.00	4.75

For surcharges see Nos. CB28-CB30.

Altar Type of Regular Issue

1967, Jan. 18   **Litho.**   *Perf. 11½*

C149	A165	7c lt olive green	.20	.20
C150	A165	10c lilac	.20	.20
C151	A165	20c yellow brown	.30	.25
	Nos. C149-C151 (3)		.70	.65

Chess Type of Regular Issue

Design: 10c, Pawn and Bishop.

1967, June 23   **Litho.**   *Perf. 12½*

C152	A167	10c ol, lt ol & blk	1.25	.30
a.		Souvenir sheet	10.00	1.90

No. C152a contains 2 imperf. stamps similar to Nos. 636 and C152.

Alliance for Progress Type

1967, Sept. 16   **Litho.**   *Perf. 12½*

C153	A168	8c gray	.30	.25
C154	A168	10c blue	.35	.25

Cornucopia and Emblem — AP52   Latin American Flags — AP53

1967, Oct. 7

C155	AP52	12c multicolored	.45	.25

25th anniversary of the Inter-American Agriculture Institute.

Satellite Type of Regular Issue

1968, June 15   **Typo.**   *Perf. 12*

C156	A170	10c dp blue & multi	.25	.20
C157	A170	15c purple & multi	.35	.30

Boxing Type of Regular Issue

Designs: Two views of boxing match.

1968, June 29
C158 A171 7c orange yel & grn .25 .20
C159 A171 10c gray & blue .30 .20
See note after No. 641.

Lions Type of Regular Issue
1968, Aug. 9 **Litho.** *Perf. 11½*
C160 A172 10c ultra & multi .25 .20

Olympic Type of Regular Issue
Designs (Olympic Emblem and): 10c, Weight lifting. 33c, Pistol shooting.
1968, Nov. 12 **Litho.** *Perf. 11½*
C161 A173 10c buff & multi .25 .25
C162 A173 33c pink & multi .75 .60

1969, Jan. 25 **Litho.** *Perf. 12½*
C163 AP53 10c pink & multi .25 .20
7th Inter-American Savings and Loan Conference, Santo Domingo, Jan. 25-31.

Taino Art Type of Regular Issue
7c, Various vomiting spoons with human heads, vert. 10c, Female torso forming drinking vessel. 20c, Vase with human head, vert.
1969, Jan. 31 **Litho.** *Perf. 12½*
C164 A175 7c lt bl, bl & lem .20 .20
C165 A175 10c pink, ver & brn .25 .20
C166 A175 20c yellow, org & brn .30 .30
Nos. C164-C166 (3) .75 .70

COTAL Type of Regular Issue
10c, Airport of the Americas and COTAL emblem.
1969, May 25 **Litho.** *Perf. 12½*
C167 A178 10c brown & pale fawn .25 .20

ILO Type of Regular Issue
1969, June 27 **Litho.** *Perf. 12½*
C168 A179 10c rose, red & black .25 .20

Baseball Type of Regular Issue
Designs: 7c, Bleachers, Tetelo Vargas Stadium, horiz. 10c, Batter, catcher and umpire. 1p, Quisqueya Stadium, horiz.
1969, Aug. 15 **Litho.** *Perf. 12½*
Size: 43x30mm (7c, 1p); 21x31mm (10c)
C169 A180 7c magenta & org .50 .30
C170 A180 10c mar & rose red .55 .30
C171 A180 1p violet blue & brn 4.25 3.00
Nos. C169-C171 (3) 5.30 3.60

Electrification Types of Regular Issue
Design: No. C172, Rio Haina steam plant. No. C173, Valdesa Dam.
1969 **Litho.** *Perf. 12*
C172 A181 10c orange ver .35 .20
C173 A182 10c multicolored .40 .20
Issued: #C172, Sept. 15; #C173, Oct. 15.

Duarte Type of Regular Issue
1970, Jan. 26 **Litho.** *Perf. 12*
C174 A183 10c brown & dk brown .45 .25

Census Type of Regular Issue
Design: 10c, Buildings and census emblem.
1970, Feb. 6 *Perf. 11*
C175 A184 10c lt blue & multi .45 .25

Sculpture Type of Regular Issue
Design: 10c, The Prisoner, by Abelardo Rodriguez Urdaneta, vert.
1970, Feb. 20 **Litho.** *Perf. 12½*
C176 A186 10c bluish gray .30 .20

Masonic Type of Regular Issue
1970, Mar. 2
C177 A187 10c brown .25 .20

Satellite Type of Regular Issue
1970, May 25 **Litho.** *Perf. 12½*
C178 A188 7c blue & gray .25 .20

UPU Type of Regular Issue
1970, June 5 *Perf. 11*
C179 A189 10c yellow & brown .25 .20

Education Year Type of Regular Issue
1970, June 26 **Litho.** *Perf. 12½*
C180 A190 15c bright pink .45 .25

Dancers AP54

Album, Globe and Emblem — AP55

Design: 10c, UN emblem and wheel.
1970, Oct. 12 **Litho.** *Perf. 12½*
C181 AP54 7c blue & multi .25 .20
C182 AP54 10c pink & multi .30 .20
1st World Exhib. of Books and Culture Festival, Santo Domingo, Oct. 11-Dec. 11.

1970, Oct. 26 **Litho.** *Perf. 11*
C183 AP55 10c multicolored .30 .25
EXFILCA 70, 2nd Interamerican Philatelic Exhibition, Caracas, Venezuela, 11/27-12/6.

Basilica of Our Lady of Altagracia — AP56

1971, Jan. 20 **Litho.** *Perf. 12½*
C184 AP56 17c multicolored .65 .35
Inauguration of the Basilica of Our Lady of Altagracia.

Map of Dominican Republic, CARE Package AP57

1971, May 28 **Litho.** *Perf. 12½*
C185 AP57 10c blue & green .25 .20
25th anniversary of CARE, a US-Canadian Cooperative for American Relief Everywhere.

Sports Type of Regular Issue
1971, Sept. 10 *Perf. 11*
C186 A195 7c Volleyball .25 .20

Animal Type of Regular Issue
Design: 25c, Cock and grain.
1971, Sept. 29 *Perf. 12½*
C187 A196 25c black & multi .50 .30

Independence Type
10c, Dominican-Colombian flag of 1821.
1971, Dec. 1 *Perf. 11*
C188 A197 10c vio bl, yel & red .50 .30

Christmas Type of Regular Issue
1971, Dec. 10 *Perf. 12½*
C189 A198 10c Bell, 1493 .25 .20

UNICEF Type of Regular Issue
Design: UNICEF emblem & child on beach.
1971, Dec. 14 *Perf. 11*
C190 A199 15c multicolored .45 .30

Book Year Type of Regular Issue
1972, Jan. 25 **Litho.** *Perf. 12½*
C191 A200 12c lilac, dk bl & red .30 .25

Magnifying Glass over Peru on Map of Americas — AP58

"Your Heart is your Health" — AP59

1972, Mar. 7 **Litho.** *Perf. 12*
C192 AP58 10c blue & multi .30 .25
EXFILIMA '71, 3rd Inter-American Philatelic Exposition, Lima, Peru, Nov. 6-14, 1971.

1972, Apr. 27 **Litho.** *Perf. 11*
C193 AP59 7c red & multi .25 .20
World Health Day.

Taino Art Type of 1972
Taino Art: 8c, Ritual vessel showing human figures. 10c, Trumpet (shell). 25c, Carved vomiting spoons. All horiz.
1972, May 10 **Litho.** *Perf. 11*
C194 A201 8c multicolored .40 .20
C195 A201 10c lt blue & multi .60 .20
C196 A201 25c multicolored 1.50 .45
Nos. C194-C196 (3) 2.50 .85

Telecommunications Type of Regular Issue
1972, May 17 *Perf. 12½*
C197 A202 21c yellow & multi .60 .30

Exhibition Type of Regular Issue
1972, June 3
C198 A203 33c orange & multi .60 .40

Olympic Type of Regular Issue
1972, Aug. 25 **Litho.** *Perf. 12½*
C199 A204 33c Running .75 .50

Club Type of Regular Issue
1972, Sept. 29 **Litho.** *Perf. 10½*
C200 A205 20c blue & multi .40 .25

Morel Type of Regular Issue
1972, Oct. 20 **Litho.** *Perf. 12½*
C201 A206 10c multicolored .25 .20

Bank Type of Regular Issue
25c, 1947 silver coin, entrance to the Mint.
1972, Oct. 23
C202 A207 25c ocher & multi .65 .45

"La Navidad" Fortress, 1492 AP60

1972, Nov. 21 **Litho.** *Perf. 12½*
C203 AP60 10c multicolored .45 .20
Christmas 1972.

Sports Type of Regular Issue
Various sports; a, UL. b, UR. c, LL. d, LR.
1973, Mar. 30 **Litho.** *Perf. 13½x13*
C204 A212 Block of 4 1.50 1.50
a.-d. 8c, any single .25 .25
C205 A212 Block of 4 2.50 2.50
a.-d. 10c, any single .50 .30

Easter Type 1973
10c, Belfry of Church of Our Lady of Help.
1973, Apr. 18 **Litho.** *Perf. 10½*
C206 A213 10c multicolored .40 .20

North and South America on Globe — AP61

1973, May 29 **Litho.** *Perf. 12*
C207 AP61 7c multicolored .25 .20
Pan-American Health Organization, 70th anniversary (in 1972).

WMO Type of Regular Issue
1973, Aug. 10 **Litho.** *Perf. 13½x13*
C208 A214 7c green & multi .25 .20

INTERPOL Emblem Police Scientist AP62

1973, Sept. 28 **Litho.** *Perf. 10½*
C209 AP62 10c vio bl, bl & emer .35 .20
50th anniversary of International Criminal Police Organization.

Handicraft Type of Regular Issue
1973, Oct. 12
C210 A215 7c Sailing ship, mosaic .20 .20
C211 A215 10c Maracas rattles, horiz. .30 .20

Christmas Type of Regular Issue
Design: 10c, Angels adoring Christ Child.
1973, Nov. 26 **Litho.** *Perf. 13½x13*
C212 A216 10c multicolored .25 .20

Scout Type of Regular Issue
21c, Scouts cooking, Lord Baden-Powell.
1973, Dec. 7 **Litho.** *Perf. 12*
C213 A217 21c red & multi .65 .55

Sport Type of Regular Issue
10c, Olympic swimming pool and diver. 25c, Olympic Stadium, soccer and discus.
1974, Feb. 25 **Litho.** *Perf. 13½*
C214 A218 10c blue & multi .20 .20
C215 A218 25c multicolored .40 .20

The Last Supper AP63

1974, June 27 **Litho.** *Perf. 13½*
C216 AP63 10c multicolored .30 .20
Holy Week 1974.

Bridge Type
Design: 10c, Higuamo Bridge.
1974, July 12 *Perf. 12*
C217 A221 10c multicolored .40 .20

Diabetes Type
Map of Dominican Republic, Diabetics' Emblem and: 7c, Kidney. 33c, Eye & heart.
1974, Aug. 22 **Litho.** *Perf. 13*
C218 A222 7c yellow & multi .25 .25
C219 A222 33c lt blue & multi 1.25 .75

UPU Type

1974, Oct. 9 **Litho.** **Perf. 13½**
C220 A223 7c Ships 1.50 .35
C221 A223 33c Jet 2.50 .75
a. Souvenir sheet of 4 7.50 7.50

No. C221a contains Nos. 727-728, C220-C221 forming continuous design.

Golfers and Championship
Emblem — AP64

20c, Golfer and Golf Association emblem.

1974, Oct. 24 **Litho.** **Perf. 13x13½**
C222 AP64 10c green & multi .40 .20
C223 AP64 20c green & multi .75 .40

World Amateur Golf Championships.

Hand
Holding
Dove
AP65

1974, Dec. 3 **Litho.** **Perf. 12**
C224 AP65 10c multicolored .30 .20

Christmas 1974.

FAO Type

10c, Bee, beehive and barrel of honey.

1974, Dec. 5
C225 A227 10c multicolored 1.10 .20

Chrismon,
Lamb, Candle
and
Palm — AP66

Spain No. 1,
España 75
Emblem — AP67

1975, Mar. 26 **Litho.** **Perf. 13½**
C226 AP66 10c gold & multi .30 .20

Holy Week 1975.

1975, Apr. 10
C227 AP67 12c red, yel & blk .40 .25

Espana 75, International Philatelic Exhibition, Madrid, Apr. 4-13.

Development Bank Type

1975, May 19 **Litho.** **Perf. 10½x10**
C228 A230 10c rose car & multi .30 .20

Three
Satellites
and Globe
AP68

1975, June 21 **Litho.** **Perf. 13½**
C229 AP68 15c multicolored .45 .35

Opening of first earth satellite tracking station in Dominican Republic.

Apollo Type

Design: 2p, Apollo-Soyuz link-up over earth.

1975, July 24 **Perf. 13**
Size: 42x28mm
C230 A232 2p multicolored 5.25 3.25

Indian Chief Type

7c, Mayobanex. 8c, Cotubanama & Juan de Esquivel. 10c, Enriquillo & Mencia.

1975, Sept. 27 **Litho.** **Perf. 12**
C231 A235 7c lt green & multi .25 .25
C232 A235 8c orange & multi .30 .25
C233 A235 10c gray & multi .30 .25
Nos. C231-C233 (3) .85 .75

Volleyball
AP69

10c, Weight lifting and Games' emblem.

1975, Oct. 24 **Litho.** **Perf. 12**
C234 AP69 7c blue & multi .25 .20
C235 AP69 10c multicolored .35 .25

7th Pan-American Games, Mexico City, Oct. 13-26.

Christmas Type

Design: 10c, Dove and peace message.

1975, Dec. 12 **Litho.** **Perf. 13x13½**
C236 A237 10c yellow & multi .25 .20

Valdesia Dam — AP70

1976, Jan. 26 **Litho.** **Perf. 13**
C237 AP70 10c multicolored .35 .20

Holy Week Type 1976

Design: 10c, Crucifixion, by Eliezer Castillo.

1976, Apr. 14 **Litho.** **Perf. 13½**
C238 A239 10c multicolored .30 .25

Bicentennial Type and

George
Washington,
Independence
Hall — AP71

Design: 10c, Hands holding maps of US and Dominican Republic.

1976, May 29 **Litho.** **Perf. 13½**
C239 A241 10c vio bl, grn & blk .35 .20
C240 AP71 75c black & orange 1.10 1.10

American Bicentennial; No. C240 also for Interphil 76 International Philatelic Exhibition, Philadelphia, Pa., May 29-June 6.

King Juan
Carlos I and
Queen
Sofia — AP72

1976, May 31
C241 AP72 21c multicolored .60 .60

Visit of King Juan Carlos I and Queen Sofia of Spain.

Telephone Type

Design: 10c, Alexander Graham Bell and telephones, 1876 and 1976.

1976, July 15
C242 A243 10c multicolored .30 .20

Duarte Types

10c, Scroll with Duarte letter and Dominican flag. 33c, Duarte return from Exile, by E. Godoy.

1976, July 20 **Litho.** **Perf. 13½**
C243 A245 10c blue & multi .30 .20
Perf. 13x13½
C244 A244 33c brown & multi 1.10 .75

Fire Engine
AP73

1976, Sept. 13 **Litho.** **Perf. 12**
C245 AP73 10c multicolored .40 .20

Honoring firemen.

Radio Club Type

1976, Oct. 8 **Litho.** **Perf. 13½**
C246 A247 10c blue & black .30 .20

Various
People — AP74

1976, Oct. 22 **Litho.** **Perf. 13½**
C247 AP74 21c multicolored .35 .35

Spanish heritage.

Olympic Games Type

1976, Oct. 22 **Perf. 12**
C248 A249 10c Running .30 .20
C249 A249 25c Basketball .85 .50

Christmas Type

Design: 10c, Angel with bells.

1976, Dec. 8 **Litho.** **Perf. 13½**
C250 A251 10c multicolored .30 .25

Tourist
Activities
AP75

Tourist publicity: 12c, Angling and hotel. 25c, Horseback riding and waterfall, vert.

1977, Jan. 7
Size: 36x36mm
C251 AP75 10c multicolored .25 .20
Size: 34x25½mm, 25½x34mm
C252 AP75 12c multicolored .25 .20
C253 AP75 25c multicolored .50 .30
Nos. C251-C253 (3) 1.00 .70

Championship Type

1977, Mar. 4 **Litho.** **Perf. 13½**
C254 A253 10c yel grn & multi .30 .20
C255 A253 25c lt brown & multi .85 .50

Holy Week Type 1977

Design: 10c, Belfry and open book.

1977, Apr. 18 **Litho.** **Perf. 13½x13**
C256 A254 10c multicolored .30 .20

Lions Type

1977, May 6 **Perf. 13½x13**
C257 A255 7c lt green & multi .25 .20

Caravel under
Sail — AP76

Melon
Cactus — AP77

1977, July 16 **Litho.** **Perf. 13**
C258 AP76 10c multicolored .45 .30

Miss Universe Contest, held in Dominican Republic.

1977, Aug. 19 **Litho.** **Perf. 12**
Design: 33c, Coccothrinax (tree).
C259 AP77 7c multicolored .30 .25
C260 AP77 33c multicolored 1.10 .75

National Botanical Garden.

Chart and
Factories — AP78

1977, Nov. 30 **Litho.** **Perf. 13x13½**
C261 AP78 28c multicolored .50 .50

7th Interamerican Statistics Conference.

Animal Type

Congress Emblem and: 10c, "Dorado," red Roman stud bull. 25c, Flamingo, vert.

1977, Dec. 29 **Litho.** **Perf. 13**
C262 A259 10c multicolored 2.00 .30
C263 A259 25c multicolored 3.50 .50

Spanish Heritage Type

21c, Window, Casa del Tostado, 16th cent.

1978, Jan. 19 **Perf. 13x13½**
Size: 28x41mm
C264 A260 21c multicolored .45 .35

Holy Week Type, 1978

7c, Facade, Santo Domingo Cathedral. 10c, Facade of Dominican Convent.

1978, Mar. 21 Litho. *Perf. 12*
Size: 27x36mm
C265 A261 7c multicolored .25 .25
C266 A261 10c multicolored .40 .25

Schooner
Duarte
AP79

1978, Apr. 15 Litho. *Perf. 13½*
C267 AP79 7c multicolored .35 .20
Dominican naval forces training ship.

Cardinal Type

1978, May 5 Litho. *Perf. 13*
C268 A262 10c multicolored .30 .20

Antenna
AP80

1978, May 17 Litho. *Perf. 13½*
C269 AP80 25c silver & multi .55 .35
10th World Telecommunications Day.

No. C1 and
Map
AP81

1978, June 6
C270 AP81 10c multicolored .30 .20
1st Dominican Rep. airmail stamp, 50th anniv.

Globe, Soccer
Ball,
Emblem — AP82

Crown, Cross and
Rosary
Emblem — AP83

33c, Soccer field, Argentina '78 emblem, globe.
1978, June 29
C271 AP82 12c multicolored .50 .35
C272 AP82 33c multicolored 1.00 1.00
11th World Cup Soccer Championship, Argentina, June 1-25.

1978, July 11 *Perf. 13x13½*
C273 AP83 21c multicolored .65 .65
Congregation of the Merciful Sisters of Charity, centenary.

Sports Type

1978, July 21 Litho. *Perf. 13½*
C274 A265 7c Baseball, vert. .40 .25
C275 A265 10c Basketball, vert. .45 .25

Wright
Brothers
and Glider,
1902
AP84

Designs: 7c, Diagrams of Flyer I and jet, vert. 13c, Diagram of air flow over wing. 45c, Flyer I over world map.

1978, Aug. 8 *Perf. 12*
C276 AP84 7c multicolored .25 .20
C277 AP84 10c multicolored .35 .20
C278 AP84 13c multicolored .55 .25
C279 AP84 45c multicolored 1.50 .95
Nos. C276-C279 (4) 2.65 1.60
75th anniversary of first powered flight.

Tourist Type

Designs: 7c, Sun and musical instruments. 10c, Sun and plane over Santo Domingo.

1978, Sept. 12 Litho. *Perf. 12*
C280 A266 7c multicolored .30 .20
C281 A266 10c multicolored .35 .20

People and
Globe
AP85

1978, Oct. 12 Litho. *Perf. 13½*
C282 AP85 21c multicolored .70 .70
Spanish heritage.

Dominican
Republic
and UN
Flags
AP86

1978, Oct. 23 *Perf. 12*
C283 AP86 33c multicolored .75 .75
33rd anniversary of the United Nations.

Statue of the
Virgin — AP87

Pope John Paul
II — AP88

1978, Dec. 5 Litho. *Perf. 12*
C284 AP87 10c multicolored .30 .25
Christmas 1978.

1979, Jan. 25 Litho. *Perf. 13½*
C285 AP88 10c multicolored 3.00 3.00
Visit of Pope John Paul II to the Dominican Republic, Jan. 25-26.

Map of
Beata
Island
AP89

1979, Jan. 25 *Perf. 12*
C286 AP89 10c multicolored .50 .30
1st expedition of radio amateurs to Beata Is.

Year of the Child Type, 1979

Designs (ICY Emblem and): 7c, Children reading book. 10c, Symbolic head and protective hands. 33c, Hands and jars.

1979, Feb. 26
C287 A269 7c multicolored .20 .20
C288 A269 10c multicolored .30 .20
C289 A269 33c multicolored 1.10 .75
Nos. C287-C289 (3) 1.60 1.15

Pope John Paul II
Giving
Benediction
AP90

Adm. Juan
Bautista
Cambiaso
AP91

1979, Apr. 9 Litho. *Perf. 13½*
C290 AP90 10c multicolored 1.40 1.00
Holy Week.

1979, Apr. 14 *Perf. 12*
C291 AP91 10c multicolored .30 .20
135th anniv. of the Battle of Tortuguero.

Map of
Dominican
Rep.,
Album,
Magnifier
AP92

1979, Apr. 18
C292 AP92 33c multicolored .75 .75
EXFILNA, 3rd National Philatelic Exhibition, Apr. 18-22.

Flower Type

Designs: 7c, Passionflower. 10c, Isidorea pungens. 13c, Calotropis procera.

1979, May 17 Litho. *Perf. 12*
C293 A271 7c multicolored .30 .30
C294 A271 10c multicolored .40 .25
C295 A271 13c multicolored .55 .45
Nos. C293-C295 (3) 1.25 1.00

Cardiology Type, 1979

10c, Figure of man showing blood circulation.

1979, June 2 Litho. *Perf. 13½*
C296 A272 10c multicolored,
vert. .60 .40

Sports Type

7c, Runner and Games' emblem, vert.

1979, June 20
C297 A273 7c multicolored .40 .30

Soccer Type

1979, Aug. 9 Litho. *Perf. 12*
C298 A273 10c Tennis, vert. .30 .25

Rowland Hill,
Dominican
Republic No.
1 — AP93

1979, Aug. 21 *Perf. 13½*
C299 AP93 2p multicolored 3.00 2.50
Sir Rowland Hill (1795-1879), originator of penny postage.

Electric Light Type

Design: 10c, "100" and light bulb, horiz.

1979, Aug. 27 *Perf. 13½*
C300 A275 10c multicolored .40 .30

Bird Type

Birds: 7c, Phaenicophilus palmarum. 10c, Calyptophilus frugivorus tertius. 45c, Icterus dominicensis.

1979, Sept. 12 Litho. *Perf. 12*
C301 A277 7c multicolored 2.10 .30
C302 A277 10c multicolored 3.00 .30
C303 A277 45c multicolored 7.50 1.00
Nos. C301-C303 (3) 12.60 1.60

Lions Type

10c, Melvin Jones, organization founder.

1979, Nov. 13 Litho. *Perf. 12*
C304 A278 10c multicolored .50 .30

Christmas Type

Christmas: 10c, Three Kings riding camels.

1979, Dec. 18 Litho. *Perf. 12*
C305 A279 10c multicolored .25 .25

Holy Week Type

1980, Mar. 27 Litho. *Perf. 12*
C306 A280 7c Crucifixion .20 .20
C307 A280 10c Resurrection .30 .25

Navy
Day — AP94

1980, Apr. 15 Litho. *Perf. 13½*
C308 AP94 21c multicolored .45 .40

Dominican
Philatelic
Society,
25th
Anniversary
AP95

1980, Apr. 18
C309 AP95 10c multicolored .30 .25

Gold Type

1980, July 8 Litho. *Perf. 13½*
C310 A282 10c Drag line mining .45 .35
C311 A282 33c Mine .85 .55

Tourism
Secretariat
Emblem — AP96

1980, Aug. 26   Litho.   Perf. 13½
C312 AP96 10c shown   .30 .25
C313 AP96 33c Conf. emblem   1.10 .75
World Tourism Conf., Manila, Sept. 27.

Iguana Type

1980, Aug. 30   Perf. 12
C314 A284 7c American croco-
                  dile   1.75 .35
C315 A284 10c Cuban rat   1.90 .40
C316 A284 25c Manatee   3.00 .65
C317 A284 45c Turtle   4.25 .95
    Nos. C314-C317 (4)   10.90 2.35

Painting Type

1980, Sept. 23   Litho.   Perf. 13½x13
C318 A285 10c Abstract, by Paul
                  Guidicelli, vert.   .30 .25
C319 A285 17c Farmer, by Yoryi
                  Morel, vert.   .50 .35

Visit of
Radio
Amateurs
to Catalina
Island
AP97

1980, Oct. 3
C320 AP97 7c multicolored   .50 .50

Rotary International, 75th
Anniversary — AP98

1980, Oct. 23   Litho.   Perf. 12
C321 AP98 10c Globe, emblem,
                  vert.   .40 .30
C322 AP98 33c shown   .75 .75

Carrier
Pigeons,
UPU
Emblem
AP99

1980, Oct. 31   Perf. 13½
C323 AP99 33c shown   .40 .35
C324 AP99 45c Pigeons, diff.   .50 .40
C325 AP99 50c Pigeon, stamp   1.00 .50
    Nos. C323-C325 (3)   1.90 1.25

Souvenir Sheet
Imperf

C326 AP99 1.10p UPU emblem   1.50 1.50
    UPU cent. No. C326 contains one
48½x31mm stamp.

Christmas Type

1980, Dec. 5   Litho.   Perf. 13½
C327 A286 10c Holy Family   .30 .25
    Christmas 1980.

Salcedo Type
Design: Map and arms of Salcedo.

1981, Jan. 14   Litho.   Perf. 13½
C328 A287 10c multicolored   .25 .25

AP100

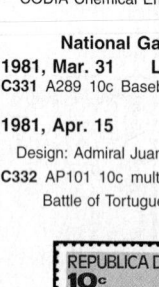

AP101

Industrial Symbols, Seminar Emblem.

1981, Feb. 18   Litho.   Perf. 13½
C329 AP100 10c shown   .30 .25
C330 AP100 33c Seminar em-
                  blem   .55 .25
CODIA Chemical Engineering Seminar.

National Games Type

1981, Mar. 31   Litho.   Perf. 13½
C331 A289 10c Baseball   .55 .35

1981, Apr. 15
    Design: Admiral Juan Alejandro Acosta.
C332 AP101 10c multicolored   .25 .20
    Battle of Tortuguero anniversary.

13th World Telecommunications
Day — AP102

1981, May 16   Litho.   Perf. 12
C333 AP102 10c multicolored   .25 .20

Heinrich von
Stephan
AP103

1981, July 15   Litho.   Perf. 13½
C334 AP103 33c tan & lt red brn .75 .75
    Birth sesquicentennial of UPU founder.

1981, July 24
C335 AP104 7c Stylized people .30 .30
C336 AP104 33c shown   .75 .75
    Intl. Year of the Disabled.

EXPURIDOM '81 Intl. Stamp Show,
Santo Domingo, July 31-Aug.
2 — AP105

1981, July 31
C337 AP105 7c multicolored   .50 .35

Bullet
Holes in
Target,
Competition
Emblem
AP106

1981, Aug. 12
C338 AP106 10c shown   .20 .20
C339 AP106 15c Riflemen   .30 .25
C340 AP106 25c Pistol shooting .50 .40
    Nos. C338-C340 (3)   1.00 .85
2nd World Sharpshooting Championship.

Exports — AP107

World Food
Day — AP108

1981, Oct. 16   Litho.   Perf. 12
C341 AP107 7c Jewelry   .35 .25
C342 AP107 10c Handicrafts   .45 .25
C343 AP107 11c Fruit   .35 .30
C344 AP107 17c Vegetables   .60 .40
    Nos. C341-C344 (4)   1.75 1.20

1981, Oct. 16   Litho.   Perf. 13½
C345 AP108 10c Fruits   .50 .30
C346 AP108 50c Vegetables   1.25 1.10

5th Natl.
Games
AP109

1981, Dec. 5   Litho.   Perf. 13½
C347 AP109 10c Javelin, vert.   .40 .35
C348 AP109 50c Cycling   1.75 1.75

Orchids
AP110

1981, Dec. 14
C349 AP110 7c Encyclia
                  cochleata   .55 .20
C350 AP110 10c Broughtonia
                  domingensis   .75 .25
C351 AP110 25c Encyclia trun-
                  cata   1.10 .55
C352 AP110 75c Elleanthus
                  capitatus   2.50 1.50
    Nos. C349-C352 (4)   4.90 2.50

Christmas Type

1981, Dec. 23
C353 A294 10c Dove, sun   .50 .30

Battle of
Tortuguero
Anniv.
AP111

1982, Apr. 15   Litho.   Perf. 13½
C354 AP111 10c Naval Academy,
                  cadets   .30 .25

1982 World Cup
Soccer — AP112

American Air
Forces
Cooperation
System — AP113

Designs: Various soccer players.

1982, Apr. 19
C355 AP112 10c multicolored   .45 .35
C356 AP112 21c multicolored   .45 .30
C357 AP112 33c multicolored   .90 .90
    Nos. C355-C357 (3)   1.80 1.55

1982, Apr. 12   Perf. 12
C358 AP113 10c multicolored   .30 .25

Scouting
Year
AP114

1982, Apr. 30   Litho.   Perf. 13½
C359 AP114 10c Baden-Powell,
                  vert.   .25 .20
C360 AP114 15c Globe   .35 .25
C361 AP114 25c Baden-Powell,
                  scout, vert.   .50 .30
    Nos. C359-C361 (3)   1.10 .75

Dancers — AP115

Espamer '82
Emblem — AP116

1982, June 1   Litho.   Perf. 13½
C362 AP115 7c Emblem   .20 .20
C363 AP115 10c Cathedral, Ca-
                  sa del Tos-
                  tado, Santo
                  Domingo   .25 .20
C364 AP115 33c shown   .85 .85
    Nos. C362-C364 (3)   1.30 1.25
    Tourist Org. of the Americas, 25th Congress
(COTAL '82), Santo Domingo.

1982, July 5
    Espamer '82 Intl. Stamp Exhibition, San
Juan, Oct. 12-17: Symbolic stamps.
C365 AP116 7c multi   .20 .20
C366 AP116 13c multi, horiz.   .35 .30
C367 AP116 50c multi, horiz.   1.60 1.25
    Nos. C365-C367 (3)   2.15 1.75

Sports Type

1982, Aug. 13   *Perf. 12, Imperf.*

C368	A300	10c Basketball	.30 .20
C369	A300	13c Boxing	.50 .25
C370	A300	25c Gymnast	.65 .30
		Nos. C368-C370 (3)	1.45 .75

Harbor, by Alejandro Bonilla — AP117

Paintings: 10c, Portrait of a Woman, by Leopoldo Navarro. 45c, Amelia Francasci, by Luis Desangles. 2p, Portrait, by Abelardo Rodriguez Urdaneta. 10c, 45c, 2p vert.

1982, Aug. 20   *Perf. 13, Imperf.*

C371	AP117	7c multicolored	.30 .20
C372	AP117	10c multicolored	.40 .30
C373	AP117	45c multicolored	1.75 1.10
C374	AP117	2p multicolored	7.50 4.50
		Nos. C371-C374 (4)	9.95 6.10

San Pedro de Macoris Type

1982, Aug. 26

Size: 42x29mm

C375	A301	7c Lake	.40 .30

35th Anniv. of Central Bank AP118

1982, Oct. 22   *Perf. 13½x13*

C376	AP118	10c multicolored	.50 .35

490th Anniv. of Discovery of America AP119

1982, Oct. 7   *Perf. 13½*

C377	AP119	7c Map	1.25 .95
C378	AP119	10c Santa Maria, vert.	1.50 1.10
C379	AP119	21c Columbus, vert.	1.75 1.10
		Nos. C377-C379 (3)	4.50 3.15

Christmas Type

1982, Dec. 8

C380	A303	10c multicolored	.50 .35

French Alliance Centenary AP120

1983, Mar. 31   *Litho.*   *Perf. 13½*

C381	AP120	33c multicolored	.60 .55

Battle of Tortuguero Anniv. AP121

1983, Apr. 15   *Litho.*   *Perf. 13½*

C382	AP121	15c Frigate Mella-451	.70 .35

World Communications Year — AP122

1983, May 6   *Litho.*   *Perf. 13½*

C383	AP122	10c dk blue & blue	.30 .25

AP123

AP124

1983, July 5   *Litho.*   *Perf. 13½*

C384	AP123	9c multicolored	.50 .35

Simon Bolivar (1783-1830).

1983, Aug. 22   *Litho.*   *Perf. 12*

C385	AP124	7c Gymnast, basketball	.40 .20
C386	AP124	10c Highjump, boxing	.55 .20
C387	AP124	15c Baseball, weight lifting, bicycling	.65 .30
		Nos. C385-C387 (3)	1.60 .70

9th Pan American Games, Caracas, Aug. 13-28.

491st Anniv. of Discovery of America AP125

1983, Oct. 11   *Litho.*   *Perf. 13½*

C388	AP125	10c Columbus' ships, map	1.25 .45
C389	AP125	21c Santa Maria (trophy)	1.75 .65
C390	AP125	33c Yacht Sotavento, vert.	2.00 .70
		Nos. C388-C390 (3)	5.00 1.80

Size: 103x103mm

Imperf

C391	AP125	50c Ship models	10.00 10.00

10th Anniv. of Latin American Civil Aviation Commission AP126

1983, Dec. 7

C392	AP126	10c dark blue	.50 .35

Funeral Procession, by Juan Bautista Gomez — AP127

Designs: 15c, Meeting of Maximo Gomez and Jose Marti in Guayubin, by Enrique Garcia Godoy. 21c, St. Francis, by Angel Perdomo, vert. 33c, Portrait of a Girl, by Adriana Billini, vert.

1983, Dec. 26   *Perf. 13½*

C393	AP127	10c multicolored	.35 .20
C394	AP127	15c multicolored	.35 .20
C395	AP127	21c multicolored	.45 .25
C396	AP127	33c multicolored	.70 .25
		Nos. C393-C396 (4)	1.85 .90

Christmas 1983 — AP128

1983, Dec. 13   *Litho.*   *Perf. 13½*

C397	AP128	10c Bells, ornaments	.30 .20

AIR POST SEMI-POSTAL STAMPS

> Catalogue values for unused stamps in this section are for Never Hinged items.

Nos. C97-C99 Surcharged in Red like Nos. B1-B5

Engraved and Lithographed

1957, Feb. 8   *Unwmk.*   *Perf. 11½*

Flags in National Colors

CB1	A117	11c + 2c ultra & red org	.30 .30
CB2	A117	16c + 2c car & lt grn	.40 .40
CB3	A117	17c + 2c blk, vio & red	.40 .40
		Nos. CB1-CB3 (3)	1.10 1.10

The surtax was to aid Hungarian refugees. A similar 25c surcharge was applied to the souvenir sheets described in the footnote following No. C99. Value, 2 sheets, perf. and imperf., $17.50.

Nos. C100-C102 Surcharged in Red Orange like Nos. B6-B10

1957, Sept. 9   *Photo.*   *Perf. 13½*

Flags in National Colors

CB4	A118	11c + 2c yel grn & dk bl	.50 .45
CB5	A118	16c + 2c lilac & dk bl	.60 .60
CB6	A118	17c + 2c brn & bl grn	.65 .65
		Nos. CB4-CB6 (3)	1.75 1.70

See note after No. B10.
A similar 5c surcharge was applied to the miniature sheets described in the footnote following No. 483. Value, 4 sheets, perf. & imperf., medal and flag, $40.

Types of Olympic Air Post Stamps, 1957, Surcharged in Carmine like Nos. B11-B20

1958, May 26   *Engr. & Litho.*

Flags in National Colors

Pink Paper

CB7	A119(a)	11c + 2c ultra	.30 .30
CB8	A119(b)	11c + 2c ultra	.30 .30
CB9	A120(a)	16c + 2c rose car	.35 .35
CB10	A120(b)	16c + 2c rose car	.35 .35
CB11	A119(a)	17c + 2c claret	.40 .40
CB12	A119(b)	17c + 2c claret	.40 .40
		Nos. CB7-CB12 (6)	2.10 2.10

A similar 5c surcharge, plus marginal UN emblem and "UNRWA," was applied to the miniature sheets described in the footnote following No. C105. Value, 4 sheets, perf. and imperf., $20.

Nos. C106-C108 Surcharged like Nos. B21-B25

1959, Apr. 13   *Photo.*   *Perf. 13½*

Flags in National Colors

CB13	A125	11c + 2c blue, ol & brn	.50 .50
CB14	A125	16c + 2c lt grn, org & dk bl	.70 .70
CB15	A125	17c + 2c ver bl & yel	1.00 1.00
		Nos. CB13-CB15 (3)	2.20 2.20

A similar 5c surcharge was applied to the miniature sheets described in the footnote following No. C108. Value, 2 sheets, perf. and imperf., $25.

Type of Regular Issue 1957 Surcharged in Red like Nos. B26-B30

Engraved and Lithographed

1959, Sept. 10   *Imperf.*

Flags in National Colors

CB16	A117	11c + 2c ultra & red org	.45 .45
CB17	A117	16c + 2c carmine & lt grn	.50 .50
CB18	A117	17c + 2c black, vio & red	.55 .55
		Nos. CB16-CB18 (3)	1.50 1.50

Nos. C113-C114 Surcharged in Red like Nos. B31-B33

1960, Apr. 7   *Litho.*   *Perf. 12½*

CB19	AP43	10c + 5c plum, gray & grn	.30 .30
CB20	AP43	13c + 5c gray & green	.45 .45

World Refugee Year.
For souvenir sheets see note after No. B33.

Nos. C115-C117 Surcharged: "XV ANIVERSARIO DE LA UNESCO + 2c"

Perf. 13½

1962, Jan. 8   *Unwmk.*   *Photo.*

Flags in National Colors

CB21	A136	11c + 2c blue, gray & brn	.25 .25
CB22	A136	16c + 2c red, brn & ol	.30 .30
CB23	A136	17c + 2c blk, bl & ocher	.30 .30
		Nos. CB21-CB23 (3)	.85 .85

See note after No. B38.
A similar 5c surcharge was applied to the miniature sheets described in the footnote following No. C117. Value, 2 sheets, perf. and imperf., $7.50.

Anti-Malaria Type of 1962

1962, Apr. 29   *Litho.*   *Perf. 12*

CB24	A141	13c + 2c pink & red	.30 .25
CB25	A141	33c + 2c org & dp org	.60 .40

Souvenir sheets exist, perf. and imperf. containing one each of Nos. B39-B40, CB24-CB25 and a 25c+2c pale grn and yel grn. Value, 2 sheets, perf. and imperf., $7.50.

Nos. C132-C133 Surcharged like Nos. B44-B46

1964, Mar. 8

CB26	AP46	10c + 2c brt violet	.25 .20
CB27	AP46	13c + 2c yellow	.25 .20

Nos. C146-C148 Surcharged like Nos. B47-B51

1966, Dec. 9   *Litho.*   *Perf. 12½*

Size: 35x24mm

CB28	A164	10c + 5c multi	3.00 1.00
CB29	A164	50c + 10c multi	4.50 3.00
CB30	A164	75c + 10c multi	6.00 3.75
		Nos. CB28-CB30 (3)	13.50 7.75

AIR POST OFFICIAL STAMPS

Nos. O13-O14 Overprinted in Blue

Unwmk.

1930, Dec. 3   *Typo.*   *Perf. 12*

CO1	O3	10c light blue	10.50 11.00
a.		Pair, one without ovpt.	900.00
CO2	O3	20c orange	10.50 11.00

SPECIAL DELIVERY STAMPS

Biplane
SD1

Perf. 11½

1920, Apr.		**Unwmk.**	**Litho.**
E1	SD1 10c deep ultra	5.50	1.25
a.	Imperf., pair		

Special Delivery Messenger — SD2

1925
E2	SD2 10c dark blue	16.00	4.50

SD3

1927
E3	SD3 10c red brown	5.00	1.25
a.	"E EXPRESO" at top	55.00	55.00

Type of 1927

1941   **Redrawn**
E4	SD3 10c yellow green	2.75	3.00
E5	SD3 10c dark blue green	2.40	.60

The redrawn design differs slightly from SD3.
Issue dates: No. E4, Mar. 27; No. E5, Aug. 7.

Emblem of Communications — SD4

1945, Sept. 1   **Perf. 12**
E6	SD4 10c rose car, car & dk bl	.90	.20

Catalogue values for unused stamps in this section, from this point to the end of the section, are for Never Hinged items.

SD5

1950   **Litho.**   **Unwmk.**
E7	SD5 10c multicolored	.50	.20

Exists imperf.

Modern Communications
System — SD6

1956, Aug. 18   **Perf. 11½**
E8	SD6 25c green	1.00	.30

Carrier
Pigeon
SD7

1967   **Litho.**   **Perf. 11½**
E9	SD7 25c light blue	.55	.25

Carrier Pigeon,
Globe — SD8

Messenger,
Plane — SD9

1978, Aug. 2   **Litho.**   **Perf. 13½**
E10	SD8 25c multicolored	.75	.30

1979, Nov. 30   **Perf. 13½**
E11	SD9 25c multicolored	.45	.25

Motorcycling — SD10

1989, May   **Litho.**   **Perf. 13½**
E12	SD10 1p multicolored	2.50	1.10

Postman
SD11

1999   **Litho.**   **Perf. 13½x13¼**
E13	SD11 8p multicolored	2.75	2.75

INSURED LETTER STAMPS

Merino Issue of
1933 Surcharged
in Red or Black

1935, Feb. 1   **Unwmk.**   **Perf. 14**
G1	A35 8c on 7c ultra	.60	.20
a.	Inverted surcharge	18.00	
G2	A35 15c on 10c org yel	.65	.20
a.	Inverted surcharge	18.00	
G3	A35 30c on 8c dk green	1.75	.90
G4	A35 45c on 20c car rose (Bk)	3.00	1.00
G5	A36 70c on 50c lemon	6.00	1.25
	Nos. G1-G5 (5)	12.00	3.55

Merino Issue of
1933 Surcharged
in Red

1940
G6	A35 8c on ½c lt vio	2.00	2.00
G7	A35 8c on 7c ultra	3.25	3.25

Coat of
Arms — IL1

1940-45   **Litho.**   **Perf. 11½**
Arms in Black
G8	IL1 8c brown red	.60	.25
a.	8c dk red, no shading on inner frame	1.00	.20
G9	IL1 15c dp orange ('45)	1.25	.20
G10	IL1 30c dk green ('41)	1.50	.20
a.	30c yellow green	1.50	.20
G11	IL1 45c ultra ('44)	1.50	.30
G12	IL1 70c olive brn ('44)	1.75	.30
	Nos. G8-G12 (5)	6.60	1.25

See Nos. G13-G16, G24-G27.

Catalogue values for unused stamps in this section, from this point to the end of the section, are for Never Hinged items.

Redrawn Type of 1940-45

1952-53
Arms in Black
G13	IL1 8c car lake ('53)	2.40	.50
G14	IL1 15c red orange ('53)	1.75	.75
G15	IL1 70c dp brown car	5.25	1.50
	Nos. G13-G15 (3)	9.40	2.75

Larger and bolder numerals on 8c and 15c. Smaller and bolder "70." There are many other minor differences in the design.

Type of 1940-45

1954
Arms in Black, 15x16mm
G16	IL1 10c carmine	.75	.25

Coat of
Arms — IL2

1955-69   **Unwmk.**   **Litho.**   **Perf. 11½**
Arms in Black, 13½x11½mm
G17	IL2 10c carmine rose	.35	.20
G18	IL2 15c red orange ('56)	3.75	1.50
G19	IL2 20c red orange ('58)	.90	.30
a.	20c orange ('69)	.90	.30
b.	20c orange, retouched ('69)	3.50	1.25
G20	IL2 30c dark green ('55)	1.40	.30
G21	IL2 40c dark green ('58)	1.50	.90
a.	40c lt yellow grn ('62)	1.50	.45
G22	IL2 45c ultra ('56)	4.00	3.75
G23	IL2 70c dp brn car ('56)	5.00	2.00
	Nos. G17-G23 (7)	16.90	8.95

On No. G19b the horizontal shading lines of shield are omitted.
See Nos. G28-G37.

Type of 1940-45
Second Redrawing

1963   **Perf. 12½**
Arms in Black, 17x16mm
G24	IL1 10c red orange	1.25	.30
G25	IL1 20c orange	1.50	.50

Third Redrawing

1966   **Litho.**   **Perf. 12½**
Arms in Black, 14x14mm
G26	IL1 10c violet	.40	.20
G27	IL1 40c orange	1.50	1.00

Type of 1955-62

1968   **Litho.**   **Perf. 11½**
Arms in Black, 13½x11½mm
G28	IL2 20c red	2.00	.75
G29	IL2 60c yellow	1.50	1.50

1973-76   **Litho.**   **Perf. 12½**
Arms in Black, 11x11mm
G30	IL2 10c car rose ('76)	.50	.35
G31	IL2 20c yellow	1.40	.90
G32	IL2 20c orange ('76)	1.75	.50
G33	IL2 40c yel grn	1.60	1.00
a.	40c green ('76)	3.00	3.00
G34	IL2 70c blue	1.75	1.90
	Nos. G30-G34 (5)	7.00	4.65

1973   **Perf. 11½**
Arms in Black, 13½x11½mm
G35	IL2 10c dark violet	.90	.30

1978, Aug. 9   **Perf. 10½**
Arms in Black, 11x11mm
G36	IL2 10c rose magenta	.35	.20
G37	IL2 40c bright green	1.50	1.50

IL3

1982-83   **Litho.**   **Perf. 10½**
Arms in Black
G38	IL3 10c deep magenta	.20	.20
G39	IL3 20c deep orange	.35	.30
G40	IL3 40c bluish green	.75	.50
	Nos. G38-G40 (3)	1.30	1.00

IL4

1986   **Litho.**   **Perf. 10½**
Arms in Black
G41	IL4 20c brt rose lilac	.30	.25
G42	IL4 60c orange	1.00	.70
G43	IL4 1p light blue	1.60	1.10
G44	IL4 1.25p pink	2.10	1.40
G45	IL4 1.50p vermilion	2.50	1.50
G46	IL4 3p light green	5.00	3.25
G47	IL4 3.50p olive bister	6.00	3.75
G48	IL4 4p yellow	6.75	4.50
G49	IL4 4.50p lt blue grn	7.50	5.00
G50	IL4 5p brown olive	8.25	5.50
G51	IL4 6p gray	9.75	6.75
G52	IL4 6.50p lt ultra	11.00	7.50
	Nos. G41-G52 (12)	61.75	41.20

Issue dates: Nos. G42-G43, G45, July 16. Nos. G46-G52, Sept. 2. Nos. G41, G44, Nov. 6.

Coat of
Arms — IL5

1989-90   **Litho.**   **Perf. 13½**
Arms in Black
G53	IL5 20c brt lilac rose	.25	.20
G54	IL5 60c orange ('90)	.75	.45
G55	IL5 1p sky blue	1.25	.75
G56	IL5 1.25p lt salmon pink	1.50	.90
G57	IL5 1.50p dark red	1.90	1.10
	Nos. G53-G57 (5)	5.65	3.40

"RD$" in lower left square on Nos. G55-G57.

IL6

1994, Oct.   **Litho.**   **Perf. 13½**
Arms in Black
G58	IL6 50c lilac rose	.20	.20
G59	IL6 1p sky blue	.25	.25
G60	IL6 1.50p red	.30	.30
G61	IL6 2p pink	.50	.50

G62	IL6	3p violet blue	.60 .60
G63	IL6	5p yellow	.90 .90
G64	IL6	6p apple green	1.25 1.25
G65	IL6	8p green	1.40 1.40
G66	IL6	10p silver gray	1.90 1.90
		Nos. G58-G66 (9)	7.30 7.30

POSTAGE DUE STAMPS

D1

1901   Unwmk.   Typo.   *Perf. 14*

J1	D1	2c olive gray	.70 .20
J2	D1	4c olive gray	.90 .20
J3	D1	5c olive gray	1.50 .30
J4	D1	10c olive gray	2.75 .75
		Nos. J1-J4 (4)	5.85 1.45

For surcharges and overprint see Nos. 162-165, 169-171.

1909   Wmk. 116

J5	D1	2c olive gray	1.50 .50
J6	D1	4c olive gray	1.50 .50
J7	D1	6c olive gray	2.00 .75
J8	D1	10c olive gray	4.00 2.50
		Nos. J5-J8 (4)	9.00 4.25

1913

J9	D1	2c olive green	.45 .20
J10	D1	4c olive green	.50 .20
J11	D1	6c olive green	.80 .35
J12	D1	10c olive green	.90 .40
		Nos. J9-J12 (4)	2.65 1.15

1922   Unwmk.   Litho.   *Perf. 11½*

J13	D1	1c olive green	.55 .55

Catalogue values for unused stamps in this section, from this point to the end of the section, are for Never Hinged items.

D2   D3

1942

J14	D2	1c dk red & pale pink	.25 .20
J15	D2	2c dk bl & pale bl	.25 .20
J16	D2	4c dk grn & pale grn	.25 .25
J17	D2	6c green & buff	.35 .25
J18	D2	8c yel org & pale yel	.35 .30
J19	D2	10c mag & pale pink	.45 .40
		Nos. J14-J19 (6)	1.90 1.60

1955

Size: 20½x25mm

J20	D2	2c dark blue	1.40 1.00

1959   Litho.   *Perf. 11½*

Size: 21x25½mm

J21	D3	1c dark car rose	1.25 1.25
J22	D3	2c dark blue	1.25 1.25
J23	D3	4c green	3.00 3.00
		Nos. J21-J23 (3)	5.50 5.50

OFFICIAL STAMPS

Bastion of February 27
O1

Unwmk.

1902, Feb. 25   Litho.   *Perf. 12*

O1	O1	2c scarlet & blk	.50 .30
O2	O1	5c dk blue & blk	.65 .25
O3	O1	10c yel grn & blk	.75 .45

O4	O1	20c yellow & blk	1.00 .40
a.		Imperf., pair	11.00
		Nos. O1-O4 (4)	2.90 1.40

For overprints and surcharge see #157-161.

Bastion of Feb. 27   Columbus
O2   Lighthouse O3

Perf. 13½x13, 13½x14

1909-12   Wmk. 116   Typo.

O5	O2	1c blue grn & blk	.30 .20
O6	O2	2c scarlet & blk	.35 .20
O7	O2	5c dk blue & blk	.75 .20
O8	O2	10c yel grn & blk ('12)	1.10 .70
O9	O2	20c orange & blk ('12)	2.00 1.60
		Nos. O5-O9 (5)	4.50 3.00

The 2c, 5c are found in both perforations; 1c, 20c perf. 13½x13; 10c perf. 13½x14. For overprints and surcharge see #177, 194-199.

1928   Unwmk.   *Perf. 12*

O10	O3	1c green	.20 .20
O11	O3	2c red	.20 .20
O12	O3	5c ultramarine	.25 .25
O13	O3	10c light blue	.30 .30
O14	O3	20c orange	.45 .45
		Nos. O10-O14 (5)	1.40 1.40

For overprints see Nos. CO1-CO2.

Proposed Columbus Lighthouse O4

1937   Litho.   *Perf. 11½*

O15	O4	3c dark purple	.85 .20
O16	O4	7c indigo & blue	.90 .30
O17	O4	10c orange yellow	1.00 .45
		Nos. O15-O17 (3)	2.75 .95

Proposed Columbus Lighthouse O5

1939-41

O18	O5	1c dp grn & lt grn	.35 .20
O19	O5	2c crim & pale pink	.35 .20
O20	O5	3c purple & lt vio	.35 .20
O21	O5	5c dk bl & lt bl ('40)	.60 .30
O21A	O5	5c lt blue ('41)	1.50 1.00
O22	O5	7c brt bl & lt bl ('41)	1.10 .20
O23	O5	10c yel org & pale org ('41)	1.10 .35
O24	O5	20c brn org & buff ('41)	3.00 .50
O25	O5	50c brt red lil & pale lil ('41)	3.50 1.50
		Nos. O18-O25 (9)	11.85 4.45

Catalogue values for unused stamps in this section, from this point to the end of the section, are for Never Hinged items.

Type of 1939

1950   Redrawn

O26	O5	50c dp car & rose	6.25 1.25

The numerals "50" measure 3mm, and are close to left and right frames; numerals measure 4mm on No. O25. There are minor differences.

Denominations in "Centavos Oro"

1950

O27	O5	5c light blue	.55 .20
O28	O5	10c yel & pale yel	.65 .30
O29	O5	20c dl org brn & buff	.70 .50
		Nos. O27-O29 (3)	1.90 1.00

Letters of top inscription are 1½mm high.

Type of 1939-41
Second Redrawing
Denominations in "Centavos Oro"

1956   Unwmk.   *Perf. 11½*

O30	O5	7c blue & lt blue	.50 .50
O31	O5	20c yellow brn & buff	1.25 1.25
O32	O5	50c red lil & brt pink	3.25 3.25
		Nos. O30-O32 (3)	5.00 5.00

The letters of top inscription are 2mm high, the trees at base of monument have been redrawn, etc. On No. O32 the numerals are similar to No. O26.

POSTAL TAX STAMPS

Santo Domingo after Hurricane PT1

Hurricane's Effect on Capital PT2

1930, Dec.   Unwmk.   Litho.   *Perf. 12*

RA1	PT1	1c green & rose	.20 .20
RA2	PT1	2c red rose	.20 .20
RA3	PT2	5c ultra & rose	.30 .20
RA4	PT2	10c yellow & rose	.35 .30

Imperf

RA5	PT1	1c green & rose	.40 .30
RA6	PT1	2c red & rose	.50 .30
RA7	PT2	5c ultra & rose	.60 .50
RA8	PT2	10c yellow & rose	.90 .75
		Nos. RA1-RA8 (8)	3.45 2.75

For surcharges see Nos. RAC1-RAC7.

Tête bêche Pairs

RA1a	PT1	1c green & rose	1.75 1.75
RA2a	PT1	2c red rose	1.75 1.50
RA3a	PT1	5c ultra & rose	1.75 2.10
RA4a	PT1	10c yellow & rose	2.10 2.10
RA5a	PT1	1c green & rose	1.75 1.75
RA6a	PT1	2c red & rose	1.75 1.75
RA7a	PT1	5c ultra & rose	2.10 2.10
RA8a	PT1	10c yellow & rose	2.10 2.10
		Nos. RA1a-RA8a (8)	15.05 15.15

Dr. Martos   Nurse and
Sanatorium — PT3   Child — PT4

1944, Apr. 1   Litho.   *Perf. 11½*

RA9	PT3	1c dp bl, sl bl & red	.30 .25

1947, Apr. 1   Unwmk.

RA10	PT4	1c dp bl, pale bl & car	.45 .25

Sanatorium of the Holy Help — PT5

1949, Apr. 1

RA11	PT5	1c dp bl, pale bl & car	.35 .25

Youth Holding   "Suffer Little
Banner   Children to
PT6   Come Unto Me" PT7

1950, Apr. 1   *Perf. 11½*

RA12	PT6	1c dp bl, pale bl & car	.25 .25

1950, Dec. 1   *Perf. 12*

Size: 22½x32mm

RA13	PT7	1c lt bl & pale bl	.90 .25
b.		Perf. 12½ ('52)	4.50 .25

Vertical line centering side borders merges into dots toward the bottom. See Nos. RA13A, RA17, RA19, RA26, RA32, RA35. The tax was for child welfare.

1951, Dec. 1   Redrawn

RA13A	PT7	1c lt blue & pale blue	4.50 .25

In the redrawn stamp, the standing child, a blonde in No. RA13, is changed to a brunette; more foliage has been added above child's head and to branches showing in upper right corner. Vertical dashes in side borders.

Tuberculosis Sanatorium, Santiago — PT8

1952, Apr. 1   Litho.   *Perf. 11½*

RA14	PT8	1c lt blue & car	.25 .25

Sword, Serpent and Crab — PT9

1953, Feb. 1   Unwmk.   *Perf. 12*

RA15	PT9	1c carmine	.35 .25

The tax was for the Dominican League Against Cancer. See Nos. RA18, RA21, RA43, RA46, RA51, RA56, RA61, RA67, RA72, RA76, RA82, RA88, RA93, RA96.

Tuberculosis Dispensary for Children — PT10

1953, Apr. 1   Litho.   Perf. 12½
RA16 PT10 1c dp bl, pale bl & red   .25 .25
See No. RA22.

Jesus Type of 1950
Second Redrawing
1953, Dec. 1   Perf. 11½
Size: 22x31mm
RA17 PT7 1c blue   .35 .20

Solid shading in sky reduced to a few scattered dots. Girl's left arm indicated. Rough white dots in side borders.

Cancer Type of 1952
1954, Oct. 1   Redrawn   Perf. 12½
RA18 PT9 1c rose carmine   .25 .20
  a.   1c red orange ('58)   .30 .20
  b.   1c carmine ('70)   1.25 .20

Upper right serif of numeral "1" eliminated; diagonal line added through "C" and period removed; sword extended, placing top on a line with top of "1." Dots of background screen arranged diagonally. Many other differences.
The tax was for the Dominican League Against Cancer. No. RA18a exists imperf.
On No. RA18b background screen eliminates white outline of crab.

Jesus Type of 1950
1954, Dec. 1   Third Redrawing
Size: 23x32¾mm
RA19 PT7 1c bright blue   .25 .20
  a.   1c pale blue ('59)   .20 .20

Center completely screened. Tiny white horizontal rectangles in side borders.

> Catalogue values for unused stamps in this section, from this point to the end of the section, are for Never Hinged items.

Lorraine Cross as Bell Clapper — PT11

1955, Apr. 1   Litho.   Perf. 11½x12
RA20 PT11 1c black, yel & red   .30 .25

Cancer Type of 1952
Second Redrawing
1956, Oct. 1   Perf. 12½
RA21 PT9 1c carmine   .35 .20
  a.   1c red orange ('64)   1.00 .50

Similar to No. RA18, but dots of background screen arranged in vertical and horizontal rows. Outlines of central device, lettering and frame clearly delineated. "C" of cent-sign smaller. Upper claw in solid color.

TB Dispensary Type of 1953
Redrawn
1954, Apr. 1
RA22 PT10 1c blue & red   .70 .25
  a.   Red (cross) omitted   55.00

No. RA22 has third color omitted; clouds added; bolder letters and numerals.

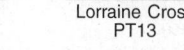

Angelita Trujillo PT12

Lorraine Cross PT13

1955, Dec. 1   Unwmk.   Perf. 12½
RA23 PT12 1c violet   .60 .25
The tax was for child welfare.

1956, Apr. 1   Litho.   Perf. 11½
RA24 PT13 1c blk, grn, lem & red   .30 .25

The tax was for the Anti-Tuberculosis League. Inscribed: B.C.G. (Bacillus Calmette-Guerin).

PT14

PT15

1957, Apr. 1
RA25 PT14 1c red, blk, yel, grn & bl .30 .25

Jesus Type of 1950
Fourth Redrawing
1956, Dec. 1   Unwmk.   Perf. 12
Size: 21¾x31¼mm
RA26 PT7 1c blue   .30 .20

Thin white lines around numeral boxes. Girl's bouquet touches Jesus' sleeve. Tiny white squares or rectangles in side borders. Foliage at either side of "Era de Trujillo" panel.

1958, Apr. 1   Litho.   Perf. 12½
RA27 PT15 1c brown car & red   .25 .20

Inscribed "1959"
1959, Apr. 1
RA28 PT15 1c brown car & red   .25 .20

PT16

PT17

1960, Apr. 1   Perf. 12
RA29 PT16 1c bl, pale yel & red   .30 .25

1961, Apr. 1   Unwmk.   Perf. 11½
RA30 PT17 1c blue & red   .25 .20
Nos. RA29-RA30: tax was for the Anti-Tuberculosis League.
See No. RA33.

Maria de los Angeles M. de Trujillo and Housing Project
PT18

1961, Aug. 1   Litho.   Perf. 12
RA31 PT18 1c carmine rose   .30 .25
The tax was for aid to the needy.
Nos. RA31-RA33 exist imperf.

Jesus Type of 1950
Fifth Redrawing
1961, Dec. 1   Unwmk.   Perf. 12½
RA32 PT7 1c blue   .30 .25

No. RA32 is similar to No. RA19, but "Era de Trujillo" has been replaced by a solid color panel.

Type of 1961 Dated "1962"
1962, Apr. 2   Perf. 12½
RA33 PT17 1c blue & red   .60 .25
Tax for the Anti-Tuberculosis League.

Man's Chest PT19

Hibiscus PT20

1963, Apr. 1   Perf. 12x11½
RA34 PT19 1c ultra & red   .30 .25

Jesus Type of 1950
Sixth Redrawing
1963, Dec. 1   Perf. 11½
Size: 21¾x32mm
RA35 PT7 1c blue   .30 .25
  a.   1c deep blue ('64)   .30 .25

No. RA35 is similar to No. RA26, but "Era de Trujillo" panel has been omitted.

1966, Apr. 1   Litho.   Perf. 11½
RA36 PT20 1c emerald & car   .25 .20
Tax for the Anti-Tuberculosis League.

Domingoa Nodosa — PT21

Civil Defense Emblem — PT22

1967, Apr. 1   Litho.   Perf. 12½
RA37 PT21 1c lilac & red   .75 .25
Tax for the Anti-Tuberculosis League.

1967, July 1   Litho.   Rouletted 13
RA38 PT22 1c multicolored   .25 .20
Tax for the Civil Defense Organization.

Boy, School and Yule Bells — PT23

Hand Holding Invalid — PT24

1967, Dec. 1   Litho.   Perf. 12½
RA39 PT23 1c rose red & pink   .35 .25

1968   Perf. 11
RA40 PT23 1c vermilion   .30 .25

No. RA40 has screened background; No. RA39, smooth background.
The tax was for child welfare.
See Nos. RA49A, RA52, RA57, RA62, RA68, RA73, RA77, RA81.

1968, Mar. 19   Litho.   Perf. 12½
RA41 PT24 1c green & yellow   .25 .20
  a.   1c olive green & deep yellow,
          perf. 11½x12 ('69)   .25 .25

The tax was for the rehabilitation of the handicapped. See Nos. RA47, RA50, RA54.

Dogbane PT25

Schoolyard, Torch PT26

1968, Apr. 25   Litho.   Perf. 12½
RA42 PT25 1c emerald, yel & red   .25 .20
The tax was for the Anti-Tuberculosis League. See Nos. RA45, RA49.

Redrawn Cancer Type of 1955
1968, Oct. 1   Litho.   Perf. 12
RA43 PT9 1c emerald   .25 .20
The tax was for the Dominican League against Cancer.

1969, Feb. 1   Litho.   Perf. 12½
RA44 PT26 1c light blue   .30 .25
Issued for Education Year 1969.

Flower Type of 1968
Design: No. RA45, Violets.
1969, Apr. 25   Litho.   Perf. 12½
RA45 PT25 1c emerald, lil & red   .45 .25
Tax for the Anti-Tuberculosis League.

Redrawn Cancer Type of 1955
1969, Oct. 1   Litho.   Perf. 11
RA46 PT9 1c brt rose lilac   .25 .20
Tax for Dominican League against Cancer.

Invalid Type of 1968
1970, Mar. 2   Perf. 12½
RA47 PT24 1c blue   .25 .20
The tax was for the rehabilitation of the handicapped.

Book, Sun and
Education Year
Emblem
PT27

Communications
Emblem
PT28

1970, Feb. 6   *Perf. 11*
RA48 PT27 1c bright pink   .25 .20
International Education Year.

Flower Type of 1968

Design: 1c, Eleanthus capitatus; cross in upper left corner, denomination in lower right.

1970, Apr. 30   *Perf. 11*
RA49 PT25 1c emerald, red & yel   .75 .25
Tax for Anti-Tuberculosis League.

Boy Type of 1967

1970, Dec. 1   *Perf. 12½*
RA49A PT23 1c orange   .30 .25

1971, Jan. 2   **Litho.**   *Perf. 11*
Size: 17½x20½mm
RA49B PT28 1c vio bl & red (white frame)   .30 .25
Tax was for Postal and Telegraph Communications School.
See Nos. RA53, RA58, RA63, RA69, RA78, RA91.

Invalid Type of 1968

1971, Mar. 1   **Litho.**   *Perf. 11*
RA50 PT24 1c brt rose lilac   .30 .25
Tax for rehabilitation of the handicapped.

Cancer Type of 1952
Third Redrawing

1971, Oct. 1   *Perf. 11½*
RA51 PT9 1c dp yellow green   .30 .25
Background of No. RA51 appears white and design stands out. No. RA43 has greenish background and design appears faint. Numeral "1" on No. RA51 is 3½mm high, on No. RA43 it is 3mm.

Boy Type of 1967

1971, Dec. 1   **Litho.**   *Perf. 11*
RA52 PT23 1c green   .30 .25

Communications Type of 1971

1972, Jan. 3   **Litho.**   *Perf. 12½*
Size: 19x22mm
RA53 PT28 1c dk bl & red (bl frame)   .25 .20
Tax was for the Postal and Telegraph Communications School.

Invalid Type of 1968

1972, Mar. 1   **Litho.**   *Perf. 11½*
RA54 PT24 1c brown   .60 .25

Orchid — PT29

1972, Apr. 2   *Perf. 11*
RA55 PT29 1c lt grn, red & yel   1.10 .30
Tax was for the Anti-Tuberculosis League.

Redrawn Cancer Type of 1954-58
1972, Oct. 2   *Perf. 12½*
RA56 PT9 1c orange   .25 .20
Tax for Dominican League against Cancer.

Boy Type of 1967

1972, Dec. 1   *Perf. 12*
RA57 PT23 1c violet   .25 .20
Tax was for child welfare.

Communications Type of 1971

1973, Jan. 2   *Perf. 10½*
Size: 19x22mm
RA58 PT28 1c dk bl & red (red frame)   .25 .20
Tax was for Postal and Telegraph Communications School.

Invalid
PT30

Hibiscus
PT31

1973, Mar. 1   **Litho.**   *Perf. 12½*
Size: 21x25mm
RA59 PT30 1c olive   .25 .20
Tax was for the Dominican Rehabilitation Association. See Nos. RA66, RA70, RA74, RA79, RA86.

1973, Apr. 17   **Litho.**   *Perf. 10½*
RA60 PT31 1c multicolored   .75 .25
Tax was for Anti-Tuberculosis League. Exists imperf.

Cancer Type of 1952 Redrawn and "1973" Added

1973, Oct. 1   *Perf. 13½*
RA61 PT9 1c olive green   .30 .25
Tax was for Dominican League Against Cancer.

Boy Type of 1967

1973, Dec. 1   **Litho.**   *Perf. 13x13½*
RA62 PT23 1c blue   .60 .25

Communications Type of 1971

1973, Nov. 3   *Perf. 10½*
Size: 19x22mm
RA63 PT28 1c bl & red (lt grn frame)   .25 .20
Tax was for Postal and Telegraph Communications School. Exists imperf.

Invalid Type of 1973

1974, Mar. 1   **Litho.**   *Perf. 10½*
Size: 22x27½mm
RA66 PT30 1c light ultra   .30 .25
See note after No. RA59.

Cancer Type of 1952 Redrawn and "1974" Added

1974, Oct. 1   *Perf. 12*
RA67 PT9 1c orange   .30 .25
Tax for Dominican League Against Cancer.

Boy Type of 1967

1974, Dec. 2   **Litho.**   *Perf. 11½*
RA68 PT23 1c dk brown & buff   .25 .20

Communications Type of 1971

1974, Nov. 13   *Perf. 10½*
RA69 PT28 1c blue & red (yel frame)   .25 .20

Invalid Type of 1973 Dated "1975"

1975, Mar. 1   *Perf. 13½x13*
Size: 21x32mm
RA70 PT30 1c olive brown   .30 .25
See note after No. RA59.

Catteeyopsis
Rosea
PT32

Oncidium
Colochilum
PT33

1975, Apr. 1   *Perf. 12*
RA71 PT32 1c blue & multi   1.10 .75
Tax was for Anti-Tuberculosis League.

Cancer Type of 1952 Redrawn and "1975" Added

1975, Oct. 1   **Litho.**   *Perf. 12*
RA72 PT9 1c violet blue   .30 .25
Tax was for Dominican League Against Cancer. Exists imperf.

Boy Type of 1967

1975, Dec. 1   **Litho.**   *Perf. 12*
RA73 PT23 1c red orange   .25 .20
Tax was for child welfare.

Invalid Type of 1973 Dated "1976"

1976, Mar. 1   **Litho.**   *Perf. 12*
Size: 21x31mm
RA74 PT30 1c ultra   .30 .25
See note after No. RA59.

1976, Apr. 6   *Perf. 13x13½*
RA75 PT33 1c green & multi   .60 .25
Tax was for Anti-Tuberculosis League. See Nos. RA80, RA84.

Cancer Type of 1952 Redrawn and "1976" Added

1976, Oct. 1   **Litho.**   *Perf. 13½*
RA76 PT9 1c green   .30 .25
Tax was for Dominican League Against Cancer.

Boy Type of 1967

1976, Dec. 1   **Litho.**   *Perf. 13½*
RA77 PT23 1c purple   .30 .25
Tax was for child welfare.

Communications Type of 1971

1977, Jan. 7   **Litho.**   *Perf. 10½*
Size: 19x22mm
RA78 PT28 1c blue & red (lil frame) .25 .20
Tax was for Postal and Telegraph Communications School.

Invalid Type of 1973 Dated "1977"

1977, Mar. 11   *Perf. 12*
Size: 21x31mm
RA79 PT30 1c ultra   .30 .25
See note after No. RA59.

Orchid Type of 1976 Dated "1977"

Orchid: Oncidium variegatum.

1977, Apr. 22   **Litho.**   *Perf. 13½*
RA80 PT33 1c multicolored   .75 .25
Tax was for Anti-Tuberculosis League.

Boy Type of 1967

1977, Dec. 27   **Litho.**   *Perf. 12*
RA81 PT23 1c emerald   .25 .20
Tax was for child welfare.

Cancer Type of 1952 Redrawn and "1977" Added

1978, Oct. 2   **Litho.**   *Perf. 13½*
RA82 PT9 1c lilac rose   .30 .25
Tax for Dominican League Against Cancer.

Mother, Child,
Holly — PT34

University
Seal — PT35

1978, Dec. 1   **Litho.**   *Perf. 13½*
RA83 PT34 1c green   .25 .20
Tax was for child welfare.
See Nos. RA89, RA92, RA97.

Orchid Type of 1973 Dated "1978"

Flower: Yellow alder.

1979, Apr.   **Litho.**   *Perf. 13½*
RA84 PT33 1c lt blue & multi   .75 .25
Tax was for Anti-Tuberculosis League.

1979, Feb. 10   **Litho.**   *Perf. 13½*
RA85 PT35 2c ultra & gray   .25 .20
450th anniv. of University of Santo Domingo.

Invalid Type of 1973 Dated "1978"

1979, Mar. 1   **Litho.**   *Perf. 12*
RA86 PT30 1c emerald   .25 .20
See note after No. RA59.

Invalid
PT36

Turnera
Ulmifolia
(Marilope)
PT37

1980, Mar. 28   **Litho.**   *Perf. 13½*
RA87 PT36 1c olive & citron   .60 .25

Cancer Type of 1952 Redrawn and "1980" Added

1980, Oct. 1
RA88 PT9 1c violet & dk pur   .25 .20

Mother and Child Type of 1978

1980, Dec. 1   **Litho.**   *Perf. 13½*
RA89 PT34 1c bright blue   .25 .20

1981, Apr. 27   **Litho.**   *Perf. 12*
RA90 PT37 1c multicolored   .25 .20
Tax was for Anti-Tuberculosis League.
See Nos. RA98-RA99.

Communications Type of 1971

1981, Feb.   **Litho.**   *Perf. 10½*
RA91 PT28 1c blue & red (lt bl frame)   .60 .25

Mother and Child Type of 1978

1982, Dec. 1   **Litho.**   *Perf. 12x12½*
RA92 PT34 1c lt bluish green   .25 .20
Inscribed 1981.

Cancer Type of 1952 Redrawn and "1981" Added

1982   **Litho.**   *Perf. 13½*
RA93 PT9 1c blue & dp blue   .60 .25

PT38

Disabled — PT39

1983, Apr. 29   Litho.   Perf. 12
RA94 PT38 1c multicolored   .25 .20
Tax was for Red Cross.

1984   Litho.   Perf. 13½
RA95 PT39 1c sky blue   .25 .20

Cancer Type of 1952 Redrawn and "1983" Added
1983, Oct. 1   Litho.   Perf. 13½
RA96 PT9 1c lt bluish grn & dk grn   .25 .20

Mother and Child Type of 1978
1983, Dec. 1   Litho.   Perf. 12
RA97 PT34 1c light green   .25 .20
Inscribed 1983.

Flower Type of 1981 Dated "1983" or "1984"
1983-85   Litho.   Perf. 12x12½
RA98 PT37 1c 1983   .25 .20
RA99 PT37 1c 1984   .25 .20
Issued: #RA98, 4/19/83; #RA99, 4/1/85.

POSTAL TAX AIR POST STAMPS

Postal Tax Stamps Surcharged in Red or Gold

1930, Dec. 3   Unwmk.   Perf. 12
RAC1 PT2 5c + 5c blk & rose (R)   25.00 25.00
   a.   Tête bêche pair   125.00
   b.   "Habilitado Para" missing   52.50
RAC2 PT2 10c + 10c blk & rose (R)   25.00 25.00
   a.   Tête bêche pair   125.00
   b.   "Habilitado Para" missing   52.50
   c.   Gold surcharge   95.00 95.00
   d.   As "c," tête bêche pair   450.00
   e.   As "c" and "b"   250.00
Nos. RAC1-RAC2 were on sale one day.

RAC4 PT2 5c + 5c ultra & rose (R)   6.00 6.00
   a.   Tête bêche pair   45.00
   b.   Inverted surcharge   42.50
   c.   Tête bêche pair, inverted surcharge   600.00
   d.   Pair, one without surcharge   190.00
   e.   "Habilitado Para" missing   15.00
RAC5 PT2 10c + 10c yel & rose (G)   4.50 4.50
   a.   Tête bêche pair   42.50
   b.   "Habilitado Para" missing   18.00

Imperf
RAC6 PT2 5c + 5c ultra & rose (R)   6.00 6.00
   a.   Tête bêche pair   52.50
   b.   "Habilitado Para" missing   18.00
RAC7 PT2 10c + 10c yel & rose (G)   6.00 6.00
   a.   Tête bêche pair   52.50
   b.   "Habilitado Para" missing   18.00
Nos. RAC1-RAC7 (6)   72.50 72.50

It was obligatory to use Nos. RA1-RA8 and RAC1-RAC7 on all postal matter, in amounts equal to the ordinary postage.
This surtax was for the aid of sufferers from the hurricane of Sept. 3, 1930.

No. 261 Overprinted in Green

CORREO AEREO INTERNO

1933, Oct. 11
RAC8 A32 2c scarlet   .35 .30
   a.   Double overprint   9.00
   b.   Pair, one without overprint   375.00
By official decree this stamp, in addition to the regular postage, had to be used on every letter, etc., sent by the internal air post service.

DUBAI

دبي dü-ˈbī

LOCATION — Oman Peninsula, Arabia, on Persian Gulf
GOVT. — Sheikdom under British protection
AREA — 1,500 sq. mi.
POP. — 60,000
CAPITAL — Dubai

Dubai is one of six Persian Gulf sheikdoms to join the United Arab Emirates which proclaimed its independence Dec. 2, 1971. See United Arab Emirates.

100 Naye Paise = 1 Rupee
100 Dirhams = 1 Riyal (1966)

Imperforate
Many issues were accompanied by smaller quantities of imperforate stamps.

Catalogue values for all unused stamps in this country are for Never Hinged items.

Hermit Crab — A1

Sheik Rashid bin Said al Maktum — A2

2np, 20np, Cuttlefish. 3np, 25np, Snail. 4np, 30np, Crab. 5np, 35np, Sea urchin. 10np, 50np, Sea shell. 1r, Fortress wall. 2r, View of Dubai. 3r, Fortress wall. 5r, View of Dubai.

Perf. 12x11½
1963, June 15   Litho.   Unwmk.
1   A1   1np dl bl & car rose   .30 .20
2   A1   2np lt bl & bis brn   .35 .20
3   A1   3np green & sepia   .35 .20
4   A1   4np pink & orange   .35 .20
5   A1   5np violet & blk   .35 .20
6   A1   10np brn org & blk   .35 .25
7   A1   15np gray ol & dp car   .70 .25
8   A1   20np rose red & org brn   .75 .40
9   A1   25np ap grn & red brn   .90 .40
10   A1   30np gray & red   1.00 .40
11   A1   35np dl lil & dl vio   1.00 .40
12   A1   50np org & sepia   1.75 .75
13   A1   1r brt bl & red org   4.00 1.25
14   A1   2r dull yel & brn   8.00 3.00
15   A1   3r rose car & blk   14.00 4.50
16   A1   5r grn & dl red brn   25.00 8.50

Perf. 12
17   A2   10r rose lake, grnsh bl & blk   55.00 17.50
Nos. 1-17 (17)   114.15 38.60

Nos. 13-17 exist perf 10½. Values are much higher.

Dhows A3

Designs: 2np, First-aid tent. 3np, Camel caravan. 4np, Butterfly.

1963, Sept. 1   Unwmk.   Perf. 12
18   A3   1np ultra, yel & red   .70 .35
19   A3   2np brn, yel & red   .70 .35
20   A3   3np red brn, org & red   .70 .35
21   A3   4np brn, brt grn & red   .70 .35
Nos. 18-21,C9-C12 (8)   9.90 4.10

Intl. Red Cross, cent. Exist perf. 10½. Values, each $1.75.
Four imperf. souvenir sheets exist in the denominations and designs of Nos. C9-C12, with "Air-Mail" omitted and colors changed. Size: 119x99mm. Value $50.
For overprints see Nos. C52-C54.

A4

Anopheles Mosquito: 2np, Mosquito and entwined snakes. 3np, Mosquitoes over swamp.

1963, Dec. 20   Unwmk.   Perf. 12
22   A4   1np emer & red brn   .25 .20
23   A4   1np red & dark brn   .25 .20
24   A4   1np blue & carmine   .25 .20
25   A4   2np brn & orange   .25 .20
26   A4   2np carmine & blue   .25 .20
27   A4   3np org brn & blue   .25 .20
Nos. 22-27,C13-C15 (9)   3.50 2.00

WHO drive to eradicate malaria.

Designs: 1np, Scouts forming pyramid. 2np, Bugler. 3np, Cub Scouts. 4np, Scouts and bugler. 5np, Scouts presenting flag.

1964   Unwmk.
28   A5   1np dk brn & ocher   .20 .20
29   A5   2np car rose & sep   .20 .20
30   A5   3np blue & red org   .20 .20
31   A5   4np carmine & blue   .20 .20
32   A5   5np ind & bluish grn   .35 .20
Nos. 28-32,C20-C24 (10)   6.30 2.90

11th Boy Scout Jamboree, Marathon, Greece, Aug., 1963.
For overprints see Nos. C47-C51.

Unisphere, New York Skyline and Dubai Harbor — A6

2np, 4np, 10np, Views of NYC and Dubai.

1964, Apr. 22   Litho.   Perf. 12
33   A6   1np dk bl & rose red   .20 .20
34   A6   2np dl red, lil rose & bl   .20 .20
35   A6   3np brown & green   .20 .20
36   A6   4np emer, brt grn & red   .20 .20
37   A6   5np ol, sl grn & lil   .20 .20

---

38   A6   10np brn org, red org & blk   .80 .50
Nos. 33-38,C36-C38 (9)   6.55 3.80
New York World's Fair, 1964-65.

Gymnast — A8

Designs: 2np, 5np, 20np, 40np, Various exercises on bar. 3np, 30np, Various exercises on vaulting horse. 4np, 10np, 1r, Various exercises on rings.

1964   Photo.   Perf. 14
43   A8   1np org brn & yel grn   .20 .20
44   A8   2np dk brn & grnsh bl   .20 .20
45   A8   3np ultra & org brn   .20 .20
46   A8   4np dk pur & yel   .25 .20
47   A8   5np ocher & dk bl   .25 .20
48   A8   10np brt bl & ocher   .30 .20
49   A8   20np ol & lil rose   .50 .20
50   A8   30np dk bl & yel   1.10 .25
51   A8   40np Prus grn & dl org   1.90 .50
52   A8   1r rose vio & grnsh bl   5.00 1.25
Nos. 43-52 (10)   9.90 3.40

18th Olympic Games, Tokyo, Oct. 10-25, 1964. An imperf. miniature sheet contains a 67x67mm stamp similar to No. 52. Value $11.

Palace — A9

Sheik Rashid bin Said — A10

Designs: 20np, 25np, View of new Dubai. 35np, 40np, Bridge and dhow. 60np, 1r, Bridge. 1.25r, Minaret. 1.50r, 3r, Old Dubai.

1966, May 30   Photo.   Perf. 14x14½
Size: 23x18mm
53   A9   5np brown & indigo   .20 .20
54   A9   10np black & orange   .20 .20
55   A9   15np ultra & brown   .35 .25

Perf. 13
Size: 27½x20½mm
56   A9   20np blue & red brn   .45 .30
57   A9   25np org ver & ultra   .45 .40
58   A9   35np violet & emer   .70 .50
59   A9   40np grnsh bl & bl   1.10 .50

Perf. 14½
Size: 31½x24mm
60   A9   60np yel grn & org ver   1.75 1.00
61   A9   1r ultra & blue   2.75 1.50
62   A9   1.25r brn org & blk   3.25 2.00
63   A9   1.50r rose lil & yel grn   5.50 2.10
64   A9   3r dk ol bis & vio   10.00 4.00

Engr.
Perf. 14
65   A10   5r rose carmine   18.50 7.50
66   A10   10r dark blue   37.50 16.00
Nos. 53-66 (14)   82.70 36.45

Nos. 53-62, 64-66 Overprinted with New Currency Names and Bars
1967
67   A9   5d on 5np   .25 .20
68   A9   10d on 10np   .25 .20
69   A9   15d on 15np   .45 .20
70   A9   20d on 20np   .90 .25
71   A9   25d on 25np   1.00 .25
72   A9   35d on 35np   1.10 .25

73	A9	40d on 40np	1.50	.30
74	A9	60d on 60np	2.50	.40
75	A9	1r on 1r	3.50	.65
76	A9	1.25r on 1.25r	6.75	1.25
77	A9	3r on 3r	13.50	3.50
78	A10	5r on 5r	24.00	7.00
79	A10	10r on 10r	37.50	13.50
		Nos. 67-79 (13)	93.20	27.95

Sheik and Falcon — A11

Dhow — A12

Litho. & Engr.
1967, Aug. 21   Perf. 13½

80	A11	5d dp car & org	1.25	.30
81	A11	10d sepia & green	1.40	.20
82	A11	20d dp cl & bl gray	1.50	.30
83	A11	35d slate & car	2.00	.30
84	A11	60d vio bl & emer	3.50	.50
85	A11	1r green & lilac	5.00	.50
86	A12	1.25r lt bl & claret	5.50	.65
87	A12	3r dull vio & claret	9.50	1.75
88	A12	5r brt grn & vio	20.00	3.75
89	A12	10r lil rose & grn	29.00	6.75
		Nos. 80-89 (10)	78.65	15.00

S. S. Bamora, 1914 — A13

35d, De Havilland 66 plane, 1930. 60d, S. S. Sirdhana, 1947. 1r, Armstrong Whitworth 15 "Atlanta," 1938. 1.25r, S. S. Chandpara, 1949. 3r, BOAC Sunderland amphibian plane, 1943. No. 96, Freighter Bombala, 1961, and BOAC Super VC10, 1967.

1969, Feb. 12   Litho.   Perf. 14x13½

90	A13	25d lt grn, bl & blk	.25	.20
91	A13	35d multicolored	.25	.20
92	A13	60d multicolored	.80	.20
93	A13	1r lil, blk & dl yel	1.00	.20
94	A13	1.25r gray, blk & dp org	1.25	.20
95	A13	3r pink, blk & bl grn	2.10	.35
		Nos. 90-95 (6)	5.65	1.35

Miniature Sheet
Imperf

96	A13	1.25r pink, blk & bl grn	7.50	7.50

60 years of postal service.

Mother and Children, by Rubens A14

Arab Mother's Day: 60d, Madonna and Child, by Murillo. 1r, Mother and Child, by Francesco Mazzuoli. 3r, Madonna and Child, by Correggio.

1969, Mar. 21   Litho.   Perf. 13½

97	A14	60d silver & multi	.75	.20
98	A14	1r silver & multi	1.50	.20
99	A14	1.25r silver & multi	1.75	.20
100	A14	3r silver & multi	3.50	.45
		Nos. 97-100 (4)	7.50	1.05

Porkfish — A15

1969, May 26   Litho.   Perf. 11

101	A15	60d shown	1.75	.35
102	A15	60d Spotted grouper	1.75	.35
103	A15	60d Moonfish	1.75	.35
104	A15	60d Sweetlips	1.75	.35
105	A15	60d Blue angel	1.75	.35
106	A15	60d Texas skate	1.75	.35
107	A15	60d Striped butter- lyfish	1.75	.35
108	A15	60d Imperial angelfish	1.75	.35
a.		Block of 8, #101-108	25.00	
		Nos. 101-108 (8)	14.00	2.80

Nos. 101-108 printed in se-tenant blocks of 8, each sheet containing two such blocks.

Explorers and Map of Arabia — A16

1969, July 21   Litho.   Perf. 13½x13

109	A16	35d brown & green	.95	.20
110	A16	60d vio & sepia	1.40	.20
111	A16	1r green & dl bl	4.25	.20
112	A16	1.25r gray & rose car	5.25	.20
		Nos. 109-112 (4)	11.85	.80

European explorers of Arabia: Sir Richard Francis Burton (1821-1890), Charles Montagu Doughty (1843-1926), Johann Ludwig Burckhardt (1784-1817) and Wilfred Patrick Thesiger (1910-).

Construction of World's First Underwater Oil Storage Tank — A17

Designs: 20d, Launching of oil storage tank. 35d, Oil storage tank in place on ocean ground. 60d, Sheik Rashid bin Said, offshore drilling platform and monument commemorating first oil export. 1r, Offshore production platform and helicopter port.

1969, Oct. 13   Litho.   Perf. 11

113	A17	5d blue & multi	.25	.20
114	A17	20d blue & multi	.85	.20
115	A17	35d blue & multi	1.60	.20
116	A17	60d blue & multi	2.50	.20
117	A17	1r blue & multi	3.50	.20
		Nos. 113-117 (5)	8.70	1.00

Astronauts Collecting Moon Rocks — A18

Designs: 1r, Astronaut at foot of ladder. 1.25r, Astronauts planting American flag.

1969, Dec. 15   Litho.   Perf. 14½

118		Strip of 3	4.50	.30
a.		A18 60d multicolored	.45	.20
b.		A18 1r multicolored	.90	.20
c.		A18 1.25r multicolored (airmail)	1.90	.20

The 1.25r is inscribed "AIRMAIL."

Sizes: 60d and 1r, 28½x41mm; 1.25r, 60½x41mm.
See note after US No. C76.

Ocean Weather Ship Launching Radio Sonde, and Hastings Plane — A19

WMO Emblem and: 1r, Kew-type radio sonde, weather balloon and radar antenna. 1.25r, Tiros satellite and weather sounding rocket. 3r, Ariel satellite and rocket launching.

1970, Mar. 23   Litho.   Perf. 11

121	A19	60d dl grn, brn & blk	.45	.20
122	A19	1r brown & multi	.85	.20
123	A19	1.25r dk blue & multi	.95	.20
124	A19	3r multicolored	2.25	.30
		Nos. 121-124 (4)	4.50	.90

10th World Meteorological Day.

UPU Headquarters and Monument, Bern — A20

60d, UPU monument, Bern, telecommunications satellite and London PO tower.

1970, May 20   Litho.   Perf. 13½x14

125	A20	5d lt green & multi	.65	.20
126	A20	60d dp blue & multi	1.60	.20

UPU Headquarters opening, May 20.

Charles Dickens, London Skyline — A21

60d, Dickens' portrait, vert. 1.25r, Dickens & "Old Curiosity Shop." 3r, Bound volumes.

1970, July 23   Litho.   Perf. 13½

127	A21	60d olive & multi	.70	.20
128	A21	1r multicolored	.85	.20
129	A21	1.25r buff & multi	1.00	.20
130	A21	3r multicolored	3.25	.50
		Nos. 127-130 (4)	5.80	1.10

Dickens (1812-70), English novelist.

The Graham Children, by William Hogarth — A22

Paintings: 60d, Caroline Murat and her Children, by François Pascal Gerard, vert. 1r, Napoleon with the Children on the Terrace in St. Cloud, by Louis Ducis.

1970, Oct. 1   Litho.   Perf. 13½

131	A22	35d multicolored	.75	.20
132	A22	60d multicolored	1.25	.20
133	A22	1r multicolored	2.00	.20
		Nos. 131-133 (3)	4.00	.60

Issued for Children's Day.

National Bank of Dubai A24

Sheik Rashid bin Said — A23   Television Station — A25

Designs: 10d, Boat building. 20d, Al Maktum Bascule Bridge. 35d, Great Mosque, Dubai, vert. 1r, Dubai International Airport, horiz. 1.25r, Port Rashid harbor project, horiz. 3r, Rashid Hospital, horiz. 5r, Dubai Trade School, horiz.

Perf. 14x14½, 14½x14

1970-71			**Litho.**
134	A23	5d multi ('71)	.30	.20
135	A24	10d multi ('71)	.30	.20
136	A24	20d multi ('71)	.50	.20
137	A24	35d multi ('71)	.65	.20
138	A24	60d multicolored	1.00	.20

Perf. 14

139	A25	1r multicolored	1.50	.20
140	A25	1.25r multicolored	1.50	.20
141	A25	3r multicolored	4.50	.25
142	A25	5r multicolored	7.25	.40
143	A25	10r multicolored ('71)	17.50	.85
		Nos. 134-143 (10)	35.00	2.90

Dubai Airport A26

Designs: 1.25r, Airport entrance.

1971, May 15   Litho.   Perf. 13½x14

144	A26	1r multicolored	3.25	.20
145	A26	1.25r multicolored	4.00	.20

Opening of Dubai International Airport.

Map With Tracking Stations, Satellites A27

1971, June 21   Litho.   Perf. 14½

146	A27	60d multicolored	.60	.30

Outer Space Telecommunications Cong., Paris, Mar. 29-Apr. 2. See Nos. C55-C56.

Fan, Scout Emblem, Map of Japan — A28

Designs: 1r, Boy Scouts in kayaks. 1.25r, Mountaineering. 3r, Campfire, horiz.

Perf. 14x13½, 13½x14

1971, Aug. 30   **Litho.**
147	A28	60d multicolored	.50	.20
148	A28	1r multicolored	1.00	.20
149	A28	1.25r multicolored	1.25	.20
150	A28	3r multicolored	2.75	.30
		Nos. 147-150 (4)	5.50	.90

13th Boy Scout World Jamboree, Asagiri Plain, Japan, Aug. 2-10.

Albrecht Dürer, Self-portrait
A29

1971, Oct. 18   **Perf. 14x13½**
| 151 | A29 | 60d gold & multi | .80 | .20 |

See Nos. C57-C59.

Boy in Meadow
A30

5r, Boys playing and UNICEF emblem.

1971, Dec. 11   **Perf. 13½**
| 152 | A30 | 60d multi | .45 | .20 |
| 153 | A30 | 5r multi, horiz. | 3.50 | .50 |

25th anniv. of UNICEF. See No. C60.

Ludwig van Beethoven
A31

Portrait: 10d, Leonardo da Vinci.

1972, Feb. 7
| 154 | A31 | 10d lt tan & multi | .30 | .20 |
| 155 | A31 | 35d lt tan & multi | .45 | .20 |

See Nos. C61-C62.

Olympic Emblems, Gymnast on Rings — A32

1972, July 31   **Litho.**   **Perf. 13½**
156	A32	35d shown	.55	.20
157	A32	40d Fencing	.65	.20
158	A32	65d Hockey	.80	.20
		Nos. 156-158,C65-C67 (6)	7.50	1.20

20th Olympic Games, Munich, 8/26-9/11. Stamps of Dubai were replaced in 1972 by those of United Arab Emirates.

AIR POST STAMPS

Type of Regular Issue and

Peregrine Falcon — AP1

Wheat — AP2

Design: A1, Falcon over bridge.

Perf. 12x11½, 11½x12

1963, June 15   **Litho.**   **Unwmk.**
C1	A1	20np dk red brn & lt blue	2.00	.25
C2	AP1	25np ol & blk brn	2.25	.35
C3	A1	30np red org & blk	2.75	.40
C4	AP1	40np grayish brn & dk violet	3.00	.50
C5	A1	50np emer & rose cl	3.75	.65
C6	AP1	60np brn org & blk	4.50	.65
C7	A1	75np vio & dp grn	6.50	.75
C8	AP1	1r org & red brn	8.00	.90
		Nos. C1-C8 (8)	32.75	4.45

Red Cross Type

Designs: 20np, Dhows. 30np, First-aid tent. 40np, Camel caravan. 50np, Butterfly.

1963, Sept. 1   **Unwmk.**   **Perf. 12**
C9	A3	20np brown, yel & red	1.25	.50
C10	A3	30np dk bl, buff & red	1.25	.50
C11	A3	40np black, yel & red	1.60	.60
C12	A3	50np vio, lt bl & red	3.00	1.10
		Nos. C9-C12 (4)	7.10	2.70

Malaria Type

Designs: 30np, Anopheles mosquito. 40np, Mosquito and coiled arrows. 70np, Mosquitoes over swamp.

1963, Dec. 20   **Unwmk.**   **Perf. 12**
C13	A4	30np purple & emer	.50	.20
C14	A4	40np red & dull grn	.60	.25
C15	A4	70np slate & citron	.90	.35
		Nos. C13-C15 (3)	2.00	.80

Three imperf. souv. sheets exist containing 4 stamps each in changed colors similar to #C13-C15. Value $30.

1963, Dec. 30   **Litho.**

40np, Wheat and palm tree. 70np, Hands holding wheat. 1r, Woman carrying basket.
C16	AP2	30np vio bl & ocher	.55	.30
C17	AP2	40np red & olive	.80	.45
C18	AP2	70np green & orange	1.25	.65
C19	AP2	1r org brn & Prus bl	1.90	1.00
		Nos. C16-C19 (4)	4.50	2.40

Boy Scout Type

Designs: 20np, Human pyramid. 30np, Bugler. 40np, Cub Scouts. 70np, Scouts and bugler. 1r, Scouts presenting flag.

1964, Jan. 20
C20	A5	20np green & dk brn	.30	.20
C21	A5	30np lilac & ocher	.65	.25
C22	A5	40np vio bl & yel grn	.80	.30
C23	A5	70np dk grn & gray	1.40	.45
C24	A5	1r vio bl & red org	2.00	.70
		Nos. C20-C24 (5)	5.15	1.90

Five imperf. souv. sheets exist containing 4 stamps each in changed colors similar to #C20-C24. Value $60.
For overprints see Nos. C47-C51.

John F. Kennedy and US Seal AP3

1964, Jan. 15   **Litho.**
C25	AP3	75np grn & blk, *lt grn*	.90	.55
C26	AP3	1r ocher & blk, *tan*	1.25	.60
C27	AP3	1.25r mag & blk, *gray*	1.60	.85
		Nos. C25-C27 (3)	3.75	2.00

Pres. John F. Kennedy (1917-1963). A souvenir sheet contains one imperf. 1.25r in buff and black with simulated perforations. Value $6.
For overprints see Nos. C52-C54.

Spacecraft — AP4

Designs: 1np, 5np, Ascending rocket, vert. 2np, 1r, Mercury capsule, vert. 4np, 2r, Twin spacecraft.

1964, Jan. 25   **Unwmk.**   **Perf. 12**
C28	AP4	1np emerald & org	.25	.20
C29	AP4	2np multicolored	.30	.20
C30	AP4	3np multicolored	.35	.20
C31	AP4	4np multicolored	.40	.20
C32	AP4	5np blue & orange	.45	.20
C33	AP4	1r vio bl, dp car & buff	1.25	.70
C34	AP4	1.50r vio bl, dp car & buff	2.00	1.25
C35	AP4	2r blue, yel & red	2.75	1.50
		Nos. C28-C35 (8)	7.75	4.45

Issued to honor the astronauts. An imperf. souvenir sheet contains one stamp similar to No. C35. Value $7.

New York World's Fair Type

Statue of Liberty and ships in Dubai harbor.

1964, Apr. 22   **Litho.**
C36	A6	75np gray bl, ultra & blk	.90	.40
C37	A6	2r gray grn, dk brn & bis	1.60	.80
C38	A6	3r dl grn, gray ol & dp org	2.25	1.10
		Nos. C36-C38 (3)	4.75	2.30

An imperf. souvenir sheet contains 2 stamps in Statue of Liberty design: 2r dark brown and rose carmine, and 3r ultramarine and gold. Value $10.

Scales and Flame
AP5

1964, Apr. 30   **Litho.**   **Perf. 12**
C39	AP5	35np bl, brn & scar	.60	.30
C40	AP5	50np lt bl, dk grn & scar	.75	.35
C41	AP5	1r grnsh bl, blk & scar	1.40	.60
C42	AP5	3r lt ultra, ultra, & scar	4.00	2.00
		Nos. C39-C42 (4)	6.75	3.25

15th anniv. of the Universal Declaration of Human Rights. An imperf. souvenir sheet contains one 3r light green, ultramarine and scarlet stamp. Value $7.50.

Nos. C20-C24 Overprinted in Red and Black (Shield in Red)

1964, June 20
C47	A5	20np green & dk brn	1.00	.40
C48	A5	30np lilac & ocher	1.25	.50
C49	A5	40np vio bl & yel grn	2.00	.75
C50	A5	70np dk grn & gray	3.25	1.50
C51	A5	1r vio bl & red org	4.50	2.00
		Nos. C47-C51 (5)	12.00	5.15

9th Winter Olympic Games, Innsbruck, Austria, Jan. 29-Feb. 9, 1964.
A similar but unauthorized overprint, with shield in black, exists on Nos. 28-32, C20-C24, and the five souvenir sheets mentioned below No. C24. The Dubai G.P.O. calls this black-shield overprint "bogus."

Nos. C25-C27 Overprinted in Brown or Green

1964, Sept. 15
C52	AP3	75np (Br)	2.00	2.00
C53	AP3	1r (G)	2.40	2.40
C54	AP3	1.25r (G)	3.00	3.00
		Nos. C52-C54 (3)	7.40	7.40

Pres. John F. Kennedy 48th birth anniv. The same overprint in black was applied to the souv. sheet noted after No. C27.

Communications Type

Designs: 1r, Intelsat 4, tracking station on globe and rocket. 5r, Eiffel Tower, Syncom 3 and Goonhilly radar station.

1971, June 21   **Litho.**   **Perf. 14½**
| C55 | A27 | 1r lt brown & multi | .60 | .20 |
| C56 | A27 | 5r multicolored | 3.00 | .45 |

Portrait Type

1r, Newton. 1.25r, Avicenna. 3r, Voltaire.

1971, Oct. 18   **Litho.**   **Perf. 14x13½**
C57	A29	1r gold & multi	1.10	.20
C58	A29	1.25r gold & multi	1.40	.20
C59	A29	3r gold & multi	4.00	.50
		Nos. C57-C59 (3)	6.50	.90

UNICEF Type

1r, Mother, children, UNICEF emblem.

1971, Dec. 11   **Perf. 13½**
| C60 | A30 | 1r gold & multi | 1.00 | .20 |

Portrait Type

75d, Khalil Gibran. 5r, Charles de Gaulle.

1972, Feb. 7   **Litho.**   **Perf. 13½**
| C61 | A31 | 75d lt tan & multi | .75 | .20 |
| C62 | A31 | 5r lt tan & multi | 5.25 | .35 |

Infant Health Care AP6

Design: 75d, Nurse supervising children at meal, and WHO emblem, vert.

1972, Apr. 7   **Litho.**   **Perf. 14x13½**
| C63 | AP6 | 75d multicolored | 1.60 | .20 |
| C64 | AP6 | 1.25r multicolored | 2.40 | .25 |

World Health Day.

Olympic Type

1972, July 31   **Litho.**   **Perf. 13½**
C65	A32	75d Water polo	1.50	.20
C66	A32	1r Steeplechase	1.75	.20
C67	A32	1.25r Running	2.25	.20
		Nos. C65-C67 (3)	5.50	.60

POSTAGE DUE STAMPS

Type of Regular Issue

Designs: 1np, 4np, 15np, Clam. 2np, 5np, 25np, Mussel. 3np, 10np, 35np, Oyster.

Perf. 12x11½

1963, June 15   **Litho.**   **Unwmk.**
J1	A1	1np gray grn & ver	.85	.35
J2	A1	2np lemon & brt bl	1.00	.45
J3	A1	3np dl rose & green	1.50	.75
J4	A1	4np light grn & mag	2.00	1.00
J5	A1	5np vermilion & blk	2.50	1.25
J6	A1	10np citron & violet	3.00	1.50
J7	A1	15np brt ultra & ver	4.00	1.90
J8	A1	25np buff & olive grn	4.75	2.00
J9	A1	35np turq bl & dp org	5.50	2.75
		Nos. J1-J9 (9)	25.10	11.95

Sheik Rashid bin
Said — D1

1972, May 22 Litho.   Perf. 14x14½

J10	D1	5d blk & gray grn	1.50	.75
J11	D1	10d vio bl, blk & bis	2.00	.85
J12	D1	20d sl grn, blk & brick red	4.00	1.50
J13	D1	30d grnsh gray, blk & lil	5.25	2.25
J14	D1	50d lilac, brn & bis	9.50	4.50
		Nos. J10-J14 (5)	22.25	9.85

EAST AFRICA & UGANDA PROTECTORATES

ˈēst ˈä-fri-kə and ü-ˈgan-də
prə-ˈtek-t̯ə-ˌrəts

LOCATION — Central East Africa, bordering on the Indian Ocean
GOVT. — British Protectorate
AREA — 350,000 sq. mi. (approx.)
POP. — 6,503,507 (approx.)
CAPITAL — Mombasa

This territory, formerly administered by the British East Africa Colony, was divided between Kenya Colony and the Uganda Protectorate. See Kenya, Uganda and Tanzania.

16 Annas = 1 Rupee
100 Cents = 1 Rupee (1907)

Altered high value stamps of East Africa and Uganda are plentiful. Expertization by competent authorities is recommended.

A1   A2

King Edward VII

1903   Typo.   Wmk. 2   Perf. 14

1	A1	½a gray green	5.00	16.50
2	A1	1a car & black	2.25	1.50
3	A1	2a vio & dull vio	10.50	3.00
4	A1	2½a ultramarine	14.50	60.00
5	A1	3a gray grn & brn	22.50	67.50
6	A1	4a blk & gray grn	13.50	27.50
7	A1	5a org brn & blk	22.50	60.00
8	A1	8a pale blue & blk	26.00	50.00

Wmk. 1

9	A2	1r gray green	20.00	67.50
10	A2	2r vio & dull vio	87.50	100.00
11	A2	3r blk & gray grn	120.00	225.00
12	A2	4r lt green & blk	125.00	225.00
13	A2	5r car & black	140.00	225.00
14	A2	10r ultra & black	275.00	450.00
15	A2	20r ol gray & blk	675.00	1,600.
16	A2	50r org brn & blk	1,900.	3,750.
		Nos. 1-14 (14)	884.25	1,578.

Nos. 9 and 14 are on both ordinary and chalky paper. Values are for examples on ordinary paper. Values are for the least expensive varieties. See "Scott Classic Specialized Catalogue of Stamps & Covers" for detailed listings.

1904-07   Wmk. 3   Chalky Paper

17	A1	½a gray green	10.50	3.75
18a	A1	1a car & black	4.50	1.00
19	A1	2a vio & dull vio	3.50	3.25
20	A1	2½a blue	10.00	37.50
a.		2½a blue & ultramarine	9.50	21.00
21	A1	3a gray grn & brn	4.75	35.00
22	A1	4a blk & gray grn	9.25	22.50

23	A1	5a org brn & blk	8.00	18.50
24a	A1	8a pale blue & blk	8.75	10.50
25	A2	1r gray green	35.00	75.00
26	A2	2r vio & dl vio	47.50	67.50
27	A2	3r blk & gray grn	67.50	125.00
28	A2	4r lt green & blk	100.00	180.00
29	A2	5r car & black	115.00	150.00
29A	A2	10r ultra & black	225.00	300.00
30	A2	20r ol gray & blk	675.00	1,250.
30A	A2	50r org brn & blk	2,100.	3,750.
		Nos. 17-29 (13)	424.25	729.50

Nos. 17-19, 21-24 are on both ordinary and chalky paper. No. 20 is on ordinary paper. Values are for the least expensive varieties. See "Scott Classic Specialized Catalogue of Stamps & Covers" for detailed listings.

1907-08

31	A1	1c brown ('08)	3.00	.20
32	A1	3c gray green	17.50	.80
33	A1	6c carmine	3.25	.20
34	A1	10c citron & violet	11.00	10.00
35	A1	12c red vio & dl vio	12.00	3.50
36	A1	15c ultramarine	30.00	11.00
37	A1	25c blk & blue green	14.50	8.50
38	A1	50c org brn & green	14.50	14.50
39	A1	75c pale bl & gray blk ('08)	5.50	40.00
		Nos. 31-39 (9)	111.25	88.70

Nos. 31-33, 36 are on ordinary paper. There are two dies of the 6c differing very slightly in many details.

King George V

A3   A4

1912-18   Ordinary Paper   Wmk. 3

40	A3	1c black	.40	2.10
41	A3	3c green	2.50	.75
a.		Booklet pane of 6		
42	A3	6c carmine	1.50	.70
a.		Booklet pane of 6		
43	A3	10c yel orange	2.50	.65
44	A3	12c gray	3.25	.65
45	A3	15c ultramarine	3.25	1.00

Chalky Paper

46	A3	25c scar & blk, yel	.65	1.60
47	A3	50c violet & black	1.90	1.60
48	A3	75c black, *green*	1.90	21.00
a.		75c black, emerald	13.50	65.00
b.		75c blk, *bl grn*, olive back	7.25	9.25
c.		75c blk, *emer*, olive back	50.00	175.00
49	A4	1r black, *green*	2.25	5.25
a.		1r black, emerald	6.00	60.00
50	A4	2r blk & red, *bl*	24.50	45.00
51	A4	3r gray grn & vio	24.50	110.00
52	A4	4r grn & red, yel	55.00	125.00
53	A4	5r dl vio & ultra	60.00	175.00
54	A4	10r grn & red, *grn*	175.00	275.00
55	A4	20r vio & blk, *red*	425.00	425.00
56	A4	20r bl & violet, *blue* ('18)	500.00	550.00
57	A4	50r gray grn & rose red	900.00	975.00
58	A4	100r blk & vio, *red*	6,000.	3,000.
59	A4	500r red & grn, *grn*	23,000.	
		Nos. 40-54 (15)	359.10	765.30

1914   Surface-colored Paper

60	A3	25c scarlet & blk, *yel*	.65	5.50
61	A3	75c black, *green*	1.25	19.50

Stamps of types A3 and A4 with watermark 4 are listed under Kenya, Uganda and Tanzania.

The 1r through 50r with revenue cancellations sell for minimal prices. The 100r and 500r were available for postage but were nearly always used fiscally.

For surcharge see No. 62.

No. 42 Surcharged

1919

62	A3	4c on 6c carmine	1.50	.20
a.		Double surcharge	150.00	240.00
b.		Without squares over old value	50.00	85.00
c.		Pair, one without surcharge	2,000.	2,250.
d.		Inverted surcharge	325.00	475.00

For later issues see Kenya, Uganda and Tanzania.

For stamps of East Africa and Uganda overprinted "G. E. A." see German East Africa.

EASTERN RUMELIA

ˈē-stərn rü-ˈmēl-yə

(South Bulgaria)

LOCATION — In southern Bulgaria
GOVT. — An autonomous unit of the Turkish Empire.
CAPITAL — Philippopolis (Plovdiv)

In 1885 the province of Eastern Rumelia revolted against Turkish rule and united with Bulgaria, adopting the new name of South Bulgaria. This union was assured by the Treaty of Bucharest in 1886, following the war between Serbia and Bulgaria.

40 Paras = 1 Piaster

Counterfeits of all overprints are plentiful.

No. 1

A2   A3

Stamps of Turkey, 1876-84,
Overprinted in Blue

1880   Unwmk.   Perf. 13½

1	A5	½pi on 20pa yel grn	67.50	57.50
a.		Horiz. pair, one without overprint		400.00
3	A2	10pa blk & rose	55.00	
4	A2	20pa vio & grn	87.50	67.50
6	A2	2pi blk & buff	115.00	100.00
7	A2	5pi red & bl	450.00	500.00
8	A3	10pa blk & red lil	57.50	

Nos. 3 & 8 were not placed in use. Inverted and double overprints of all values exist.

Same, with Extra Overprint "R. O."

9	A3	10pa blk & red lil	97.50	95.00

Crescent and Turkish
Inscriptions of
Value — A4

1881   Typo.   Perf. 13½

10	A4	5pa blk & olive	17.00	1.35
11	A4	10pa blk & green	34.00	1.35
12	A4	20pa blk & rose	1.75	1.25
13	A4	1pi blk & blue	5.75	4.50
14	A4	5pi rose & blue	57.50	82.50

Tête bêche pairs, imperforates and all perf. 11½ examples of Nos. 10-14 were not placed in use, and were found only in the remainder

---

stock. This is true also of a 10pa cliché in the 20pa plate, and of a cliché of Turkey No. 63 in the 1pi plate. See the *Scott Classic Catalogue.*

Perf. 11½

1884   Perf. 11½

15	A4	5pa lil & pale lil	.55	.45
16	A4	10pa grn & pale grn	.20	.45
17	A4	20pa car & pale rose	.55	
18	A4	1pi bl & pale bl	1.15	
19	A4	5pi brn & pale brn	400.00	

Nos. 17-19 were not placed in use, and were found only in the remainder stock.
Nos. 15-19 imperf. are from remainders.
See the *Scott Classic Catalogue* for perf 13½ listings.
For overprints see Turkey Nos. 542-545.

South Bulgaria

Counterfeits of all overprints are plentiful.

Nos. 10-14 Overprinted in Two Types:

a   b

Type a — Four toes on each foot.
Type b — Three toes on each foot.

1885   Unwmk.   Perf. 13½
Blue Overprint

20	A4 (a)	5pa blk & olive	325.00	375.00
21	A4 (a)	10pa blk & grn	875.00	825.00
22	A4 (a)	20pa blk & rose	325.00	
23	A4 (a)	1pi blk & blue	37.50	72.50
24	A4 (b)	5pi rose & blue	1,100.	

See the *Scott Classic Catalogue* for #22-23, type b, #24, type a, and #22, perf 11 ½, types a and b.

Black Overprint

24B	A4 (a)	20pa blk & rose	275.00	
25	A4 (a)	1pi blk & bl	55.00	115.00
26	A4 (b)	5pi rose & bl	675.00	

See the *Scott Classic Catalogue* for #25 type b.

Same Overprint on Nos. 15-17
Perf. 11½
Blue Overprint

27	A4 (a)	5pa lil & pale lil, type "b"	22.50	57.50
28	A4 (b)	10pa grn & pale grn	40.00	75.00
29	A4 (b)	20pa car & pale rose	275.00	375.00

Black Overprint
Perf. 13½

30	A4 (b)	5pa lil & pale lil	40.00	67.50

Perf. 11½

31	A4 (a)	10pa grn & pale grn	42.50	85.00
32	A4 (b)	20pa car & pale rose	55.00	82.50

See the *Scott Classic Catalogue* for detailed listings of #27-32.

Nos. 10-17 Handstamped in Black in Two Types:

a   b

Type a — First letter at top circular.
Type b — First letter at top oval.

1885   Perf. 13½

33	A4 (b)	5pa blk & olive	300.00	250.00
34	A4 (b)	10pa blk & grn	225.00	250.00
35	A4 (b)	20pa blk & rose	72.50	85.00
36	A4 (a)	1pi blk & bl	87.50	115.00
37	A4 (a)	5pi rose & blue, type "a"	2,500.	

Perf. 13½

38	A4 (a)	5pa lil & pale lil	26.00	44.00

Perf. 11½

39	A4 (a)	10pa grn & pale grn	29.00	35.00
40	A4 (a)	20pa car & pale rose	29.00	50.00

See the *Scott Classic Catalogue* for #38-40, type b, and #38, perf 11½, types a and b.

Nos. 20-40 exist with inverted and double handstamps. Overprints in unlisted colors are proofs.

The stamps of South Bulgaria were superseded in 1886 by those of Bulgaria.

EASTERN SILESIA

ˈē-stərn sī-ˈlē-zhˌē-ə

LOCATION — In central Europe
GOVT. — Austrian crownland
AREA — 1,987 sq. mi.
POP. — 680,422 (estimated 1920)
CAPITAL — Troppau

After World War I, this territory was occupied by Czechoslovakia and eventually was divided between Poland and Czechoslovakia, the dividing line running through Teschen.

100 Heller = 1 Krone
100 Fennigi = 1 Marka

Plebiscite Issues

Stamps of Czechoslovakia 1918-20, Overprinted in Black, Blue, Violet or Red

1920		Unwmk.		Imperf.
1	A2	1h dark brown	.20	.30
2	A1	3h red violet	.20	.20
3	A2	5h blue green	23.50	22.50
4	A2	15h red	11.50	11.00
5	A1	20h blue green	.20	.20
6	A2	25h dull violet	.75	.75
7	A1	30h bister (R)	.20	.20
8	A1	40h red orange	.30	.30
9	A2	50h dull violet	.60	.45
10	A2	50h dark blue	2.60	1.50
11	A2	60h orange (Bl)	.75	.75
12	A2	75h slate (R)	.50	.75
13	A2	80h olive grn (R)	.50	.75
14	A1	100h brown	1.10	1.10
15	A2	120h gray blk (R)	1.60	2.25
16	A1	200h ultra (R)	1.60	2.00
17	A2	300h green (R)	6.25	7.50
18	A1	400h purple (R)	2.60	3.00
20	A2	500h red brn (Bl)	5.25	6.00
a.		Black overprint	6.25	9.00
21	A2	1000h violet (Bl)	13.00	13.50
a.		Black overprint	62.50	75.00
		Nos. 1-21 (20)	73.20	75.00

Perf. 11½, 13¾

22	A2	1h dark brown	.20	.20
23	A2	5h blue green	.30	.25
24	A2	10h yellow green	.30	.25
a.		Imperf.	260.00	210.00
25	A2	15h red	.50	.20
26	A2	20h rose	.50	.35
a.		Imperf.	300.00	250.00
27	A2	25h dull violet	.50	.35
28	A2	30h red violet (Bl)	.35	.35
29	A2	60h orange (Bl)	.50	.50
30	A1	200h ultra (R)	3.00	3.00
		Nos. 22-30 (9)	6.15	5.45

The letters "S. O." are the initials of "Silésie Orientale."

Forged cancellations are found on #1-30.

Overprinted in Carmine or Violet

31	A4	500h sl, *grysh* (C)	40.00
32	A4	1000h blk brn, *brnsh*	40.00

Excellent counterfeits of this overprint exist.

Stamps of Poland, 1919, Overprinted

1920			Perf. 11½	
41	A10	5f green	.20	.20
42	A10	10f red brown	.20	.20
43	A10	15f light red	.20	.20
44	A11	25f olive green	.20	.20
45	A11	50f blue green	.20	.20

Overprinted

46	A12	1k deep green	.20	.20
47	A12	1.50k brown	.20	.20
48	A12	2k dark blue	.20	.20
49	A13	2.50k dull violet	.30	.20
50	A14	5k slate blue	.50	.20
		Nos. 41-50 (10)	2.40	2.00

SPECIAL DELIVERY STAMPS

Czechoslovakia Special Delivery Stamps Overprinted in Blue

1920		Unwmk.		Imperf.
E1	SD1	2h red violet, *yel*	.20	.20
a.		Black overprint	4.75	.80
E2	SD1	5h yellow green, *yel*	.20	.20
a.		Black overprint	8.00	5.00

Nos. E1-E2a exist on white paper.

POSTAGE DUE STAMPS

Czechoslovakia Postage Due Stamps Overprinted In Blue or Red

1920		Unwmk.		Imperf.
J1	D1	5h deep bis (Bl)	.25	.20
a.		Black overprint	72.50	62.50
J2	D1	10h deep bister	.25	.20
J3	D1	15h deep bister	.25	.20
J4	D1	20h deep bister	.25	.20
J5	D1	25h deep bister	.25	.20
J6	D1	30h deep bister	.25	.20
J7	D1	40h deep bister	.50	.25
J8	D1	50h deep bister	2.60	3.00
J9	D1	100h blk brn (R)	2.60	3.00
J10	D1	500h gray grn (R)	5.75	4.50
J11	D1	1000h purple (R)	8.50	11.50
		Nos. J1-J11 (11)	21.45	23.45

Forged cancellations exist.

NEWSPAPER STAMPS

Czechoslovakia Newspaper Stamps Overprinted in Black like Nos. 1-30

1920		Unwmk.		Imperf.
P1	N1	2h gray green	.30	.30
P2	N1	6h red	.20	.20
P3	N1	10h dull violet	.40	.20
P4	N1	20h blue	.65	.25
P5	N1	30h gray brown	.65	.25
		Nos. P1-P5 (5)	2.20	1.20

ECUADOR

'e-kwə-,dor

LOCATION — Northwest coast of South America, bordering on the Pacific Ocean
GOVT. — Republic
AREA — 116,270 (?) sq. mi.
POP. — 12,562,496 (1999 est.)
CAPITAL — Quito

The Republic of Ecuador was so constituted on May 11, 1830, after the Civil War which separated the original members of the Republic of Colombia, founded by Simon Bolivar by uniting the Presidency of Quito with the Viceroyalty of New Grenada and the Captaincy of Venezuela. The Presidency of Quito became the Republic of Ecuador.

8 Reales = 1 Peso
100 Centavos = 1 Sucre (1881)
100 Cents = 1 Dollar (2000)

Catalogue values for unused stamps in this country are for Never Hinged items, beginning with Scott 453 in the regular postage section, Scott C147 in the airpost section, Scott CO19 in the airpost officials section, Scott O201 in the officials section, Scott RA60 in the postal tax section, and all entries in the Galapagos section.

Watermarks

Wmk. 117 — Liberty Cap

Wmk. 127 Quatrefoils

Wmk. 233 — "Harrison & Sons, London" in Script Letters

Wmk. 340 — Alternating Interlaced Wavy Lines

Wmk. 367 — Liberty Cap, Emblem, Inscription

Wmk. 395 — Emblem, Inscription

Coat of Arms
A1   A2

1865-72   Unwmk.   Typo.   Imperf.
Quadrille Paper

| 1 | A1 | 1r yellow ('72) | 60.00 | 55.00 |

Wove Paper

2	A1	½r ultra	40.00	15.00
a.		½r gray blue ('67)	40.00	15.00
b.		Batonne paper ('70)	50.00	25.00
c.		Blue paper ('72)	250.00	100.00
3	A1	1r buff	25.00	18.00
a.		1r orange buff	30.00	20.00
4	A1	1r yellow	25.00	15.00
a.		1r olive yellow ('66)	32.50	22.50
b.		Laid paper	175.00	110.00
c.		Half used as ½r on cover		900.00
d.		Batonne paper	40.00	30.00
5	A1	1r green	300.00	50.00
a.		Half used as ½r on cover		900.00
6	A2	4r red ('66)	500.00	200.00
a.		4r red brown ('66)	700.00	200.00
b.		Arms in circle	500.00	250.00
c.		Printed on both sides	550.00	
d.		Half used as 2r on cover		1,600.
		Nos. 1-6 (6)	950.00	353.00

Letter paper embossed with arms of Ecuador was used in printing a number of sheets of Nos. 2, 4-6.
Papermakers' watermarks on No. 2e, 4f, 5c and 6f reads "Rolland Freres".
On the 4r the oval holding the coat of arms is usually 13½-14mm wide, but on about one-fifth of the stamps in the sheet it is 15-15½mm wide, almost a circle.
The 2r, 8r and 12r, type A1, are bogus.
Proofs of the ½r, type A1, are known in black and green.
An essay of type A2 shows the condor's head facing right.

1871-72
Blue-surface Paper

| 7 | A1 | ½r ultra | 50.00 | 25.00 |
| 8 | A1 | 1r yellow | 300.00 | 100.00 |

Unofficial reprints of types A1-A2 differ in color, have a different sheet makeup and lack gum. Type A1 reprints usually have a double frameline at left. All stamps on blue paper with horiz. blue lines are reprints.

A3

A4

1872   White Paper   Litho.   Perf. 11

9	A3	½r blue	30.00	5.00
10	A4	1r yellow	40.00	7.00
11	A3	1p rose	5.00	25.00
		Nos. 9-11 (3)	75.00	37.00

The 1r surcharged 4c is fraudulent.

A5   A6

A7   A8

A9   A10

1881, Nov. 1   Engr.   Perf. 12

12	A5	1c yellow brn	.40	.20
13	A6	2c lake	.40	.20
14	A7	5c blue	10.00	.40
15	A8	10c orange	.40	.20
16	A9	20c gray violet	.40	.20
17	A10	50c blue green	2.00	2.00
		Nos. 12-17 (6)	13.60	3.20

The 1c surcharged 3c, and 20c surcharged 5c are fraudulent.
For overprints see Nos. O1-O6.

DIEZ

CENTAVOS

No. 17 Surcharged in Black

1883, Apr.

| 18 | A10 | 10c on 50c blue grn | 50.00 | 30.00 |
| a. | | Double surcharge | | |

Dangerous forgeries exist.

A12

A13

A14   A15

1887

19	A12	1c blue green	.50	.40
20	A13	2c vermilion	1.00	.40
21	A14	5c blue	3.00	.50
22	A15	80c olive green	6.00	15.00
		Nos. 19-22 (4)	10.50	16.30

For overprints see Nos. O7-O10.

President Juan Flores — A16

1892

23	A16	1c orange	.30	1.00
24	A16	2c dk brown	.30	1.00
25	A16	5c vermilion	.30	1.00
26	A16	10c green	.30	1.00
27	A16	20c red brown	.30	1.00
28	A16	50c maroon	.30	2.00
29	A16	1s blue	.30	4.00
30	A16	5s purple	1.00	8.00
		Nos. 23-30 (8)	3.10	19.00

The issues of 1892, 1894, 1895 and 1896 were printed by the Hamilton Bank Note Co., New York, to the order of N. F. Seebeck, who held a contract for stamps with the government of Ecuador.
No. 30 in green is said to be an essay or color trial.
For surcharges and overprints see Nos. 31-37, O11-O17.

Nos. 29 and 30 Surcharged in Black

1893
Surcharge Measures 25½x2½mm

31	A16	5c on 1s blue	6.00	6.00
32	A16	5c on 5s purple	10.00	9.00
a.		Double surcharge		

Surcharge Measures 24x2¼mm

33	A16	5c on 1s blue	3.00	3.00
a.		Double surcharge, one inverted		
34	A16	5c on 5s purple	12.00	10.00
a.		Double surcharge, one invtd.		

Nos. 28-30 Surcharged in Black

35	A16	5c on 50c maroon	2.00	2.00
a.		Inverted surcharge	5.00	
36	A16	5c on 1s blue	2.50	2.00
37	A16	5c on 5s purple	10.00	10.00
		Nos. 31-37 (7)	45.50	42.00

Pres. Juan Flores   Pres. Vicente Rocafuerte
A19   A20

| 38 | A19 | 5c on 5s lake | 4.00 | 4.00 |

It is stated that No. 38 was used exclusively as a postage stamp and not for telegrams.

1894   Dated 1894   Perf. 12
Various Frames

39	A20	1c blue	.40	.40
40	A20	2c yellow brn	.40	.40
41	A20	5c green	.40	.40
b.		Perf. 14	6.00	2.00
42	A20	10c vermilion	.70	.60
43	A20	20c black	1.10	.70
44	A20	50c orange	6.00	2.00
45	A20	1s carmine	9.50	4.00
46	A20	5s dark blue	12.00	6.00
		Nos. 39-46 (8)	30.50	14.50

1895
Same, Dated "1895"

47	A20	1c blue	.90	.70
48	A20	2c yellow brn	.90	.70
49	A20	5c green	.70	.50
50	A20	10c vermilion	.70	.40
51	A20	20c black	1.00	1.00
52	A20	50c orange	3.50	2.25
53	A20	1s carmine	21.00	8.00
54	A20	5s dark blue	8.50	4.00
		Nos. 47-54 (8)	37.20	17.55

Reprints of the 2c, 10c, 50c, 1s and 5s of the 1894-95 issues are generally on thick paper. Original issues are on thin to medium thick paper. To distinguish reprints from originals, a comparison of paper thickness, paper color, gum, printing clarity and direction of paper weave is necessary. Value 20 cents each.
For overprints see #77-112, O20-O33, O50-O91.

A21

A22

A23

A24

A25

A26

A27

A28

1896 — Wmk. 117

55	A21	1c dk green	.70	.60
56	A22	2c red	.70	.40
57	A23	5c blue	.70	.40
58	A24	10c bister brn	.60	.90
59	A25	20c orange	1.40	2.00
60	A26	50c dark blue	5.00	3.00
61	A27	1s yellow brn	4.00	4.00
62	A28	5s violet	14.00	5.50
		Nos. 55-62 (8)	27.10	16.80

Unwmk.

62A	A21	1c dk green	1.00	.40
62B	A22	2c red	1.10	.40
62C	A23	5c blue	1.10	.70
62D	A24	10c bister brn	.70	1.40
62E	A25	20c orange	6.00	5.50
62F	A26	50c dark blue	2.00	2.75
62G	A27	1s yellow brn	6.00	8.00
62H	A28	5s violet	15.00	6.00
		Nos. 62A-62H (8)	32.90	25.15

Reprints of Nos. 55-62H are on very thick paper, with paper weave direction vertical. Value 20 cents each.

For surcharges and overprints see Nos. 74, 76, 113-114, O34-O49.

Vicente Roca, Diego Noboa and José Olmedo — A28a

General Juan Francisco Elizalde — A28b

Perf. 11½

1896, Oct. 9		Unwmk.		Litho.
63	A28a	1c rose	.35	.40
64	A28b	2c blue	.35	.45
65	A28a	5c green	.55	.55
66	A28b	10c ocher	.55	.55
67	A28a	20c red	.80	2.50
68	A28b	50c violet	1.25	3.50
69	A28a	1s orange	2.50	6.00
		Nos. 63-69 (7)	6.35	13.95

Success of the Liberal Party in 1845 & 1895.
For overprints see Nos. 115-125.

A29

Black Surcharge

1896, Nov.			Perf. 12	
70	A29	1c on 1c ver, "1893-1894"	1.00	.60
	a.	Inverted surcharge	2.50	2.00
	b.	Double surcharge	8.00	7.00
71	A29	2c on 2c bl, "1893-1894"	2.00	1.75
	a.	Inverted surcharge	4.00	3.50
72	A29	5c on 10c org, "1887-1888"	2.00	.60
	a.	Inverted surcharge	4.00	1.75
	b.	Double surcharge	7.00	4.00
	c.	Surcharged "2cts"	1.00	.80
	d.	"1893-1894"	6.00	5.00
73	A29	10c on 4c brn, "1887-1888"	2.00	1.10
	a.	Inverted surcharge	4.00	1.75
	b.	Double surcharge	6.00	3.50
	c.	Double surcharge, one inverted		
	d.	Surcharged "1 cto"	2.00	2.75
	e.	"1891-1892"	17.00	13.50
		Nos. 70-73 (4)	7.00	4.05

Similar surcharges of type A29 include:
Dated "1887-1888" — 1c on 1c blue green, 1c on 2c red, 1c on 4c brown, 1c on 10c yellow; 2c on 2c red, 2c on 10c yellow; 10c on 1c green.
Dated "1891-1892" — 1c on 1c blue green, 1c on 4c brown.
Dated "1893-1894" — 2c on 10c yellow; 10c on 1c vermilion, 10c on 10s black.
For overprints see Nos. O18-O19.

Nos. 59-60 Surcharged in Black or Red

1896, Oct.			Wmk. 117	
74	A25	5c on 20c orange	40.00	40.00
76	A26	10c on 50c dk bl (R)	50.00	50.00
	a.	Double surcharge		

The surcharge is diag., horiz. or vert.

Overprinted

On Issue of 1894

1897			Unwmk.	
77	A20	1c blue	2.25	2.25
78	A20	2c yellow brn	1.90	1.30
79	A20	5c green	.90	.90
80	A20	10c vermilion	2.75	2.25
81	A20	20c black	3.00	2.75
82	A20	50c orange	6.50	3.25
83	A20	1s carmine	19.00	6.50
84	A20	5s dark blue	110.00	90.00
		Nos. 77-84 (8)	146.30	109.20

On Issue of 1895

85	A20	1c blue	6.00	5.50
86	A20	2c yellow brn	2.25	2.25
87	A20	5c green	1.90	1.60
88	A20	10c vermilion	7.00	6.00
89	A20	20c black	1.90	1.75
90	A20	50c orange	32.50	13.00
91	A20	1s carmine	14.50	7.50
92	A20	5s dark blue	14.50	14.50
		Nos. 85-92 (8)	80.55	52.10

Overprinted

On Issue of 1894

93	A20	1c blue	1.40	.90
94	A20	2c yellow brn	1.20	.75
95	A20	5c green	.60	.50
96	A20	10c vermilion	3.50	1.75
97	A20	20c black	3.75	2.50
98	A20	50c orange	7.00	2.75
99	A20	1s carmine	13.00	8.50
100	A20	5s dark blue	115.00	85.00
		Nos. 93-100 (8)	145.45	102.65

On Issue of 1895

101	A20	1c blue	3.25	1.60
102	A20	2c yellow brn	1.60	1.60
103	A20	5c green	1.75	1.00
104	A20	10c vermilion	5.50	4.50
105	A20	20c black	5.00	1.20
106	A20	50c orange	1.75	1.75
107	A20	1s carmine	8.00	7.00
108	A20	5s dark blue	9.50	9.50
		Nos. 101-108 (8)	36.35	28.15

Overprints on Nos. 77-108 are to be found reading upward from left to right and downward from left to right, as well as inverted.

Overprinted 1897 y 1898

On Issue of 1894

1897				
109	A20	10c vermilion	—	—

On Issue of 1895

110	A20	2c yellow brn	—	—
111	A20	1s carmine	—	—
112	A20	5s dark blue	—	—

Nos. 56, 59 Overprinted like Nos. 93-108

1897, June			Wmk. 117	
113	A22	2c red	—	—
114	A25	20c orange	—	—

Many forged overprints on Nos. 77-114 exist, made on original stamps and reprints.

Stamps or Types of 1896 Overprinted like Nos. 93-108

1897			Perf. 11½	
115	A28b	1c rose	3.75	3.75
116	A28b	2c blue	3.00	3.00
117	A28b	5c green	3.00	3.00
118	A28a	1s yellow	15.00	15.00
		Nos. 115-118 (4)	24.75	24.75

No. 63 Overprinted like Nos. 77-92

1897				
119	A28a	1c rose	.60	.50

Nos. 63-66 Overprinted in Black

1897				
122	A28a	1c rose	4.50	4.00
123	A28b	2c blue	4.50	4.00
124	A28a	5c green	4.50	4.00
125	A28b	10c ocher	4.50	4.00
	a.	Double overprint	10.50	9.50
		Nos. 122-125 (4)	18.00	16.00

The 20c, 50c and 1s with this overprint in black and all values of the issue overprinted in blue are reprints.

Overprint Inverted

122a	A28a	1c	6.00	5.50
123a	A28b	2c	6.00	5.50
124a	A28a	5c	6.00	5.50
125b	A28b	10c	6.00	5.50

Coat of Arms — A33

1897, June 23		Engr.	Perf. 14-16	
127	A33	1c dk yellow grn	.30	.20
128	A33	2c orange red	.30	.20
129	A33	5c lake	.30	.20
130	A33	10c dk brown	.30	.20
131	A33	20c yellow	.45	.40
132	A33	50c dull blue	.45	.65
133	A33	1s gray	.85	.80
134	A33	5s dark lilac	1.50	1.10
		Nos. 127-134 (8)	4.45	3.75

No. 135

No. 136

1899, May

135	A33	1c on 2c orange red	3.00	1.50
136	A33	5c on 10c brown	2.50	1.00
	a.	Double surcharge		

Luis Vargas Torres
A36

Abdón Calderón
A37

Juan Montalvo
A38

José Mejia
A39

Santa Cruz y Espejo — A40

Pedro Carbo — A41

José Joaquin Olmedo
A42

Pedro Moncayo
A43

1899 — Perf. 12½-16

137	A36	1c gray blue & blk	.40	.20
	a.	Horiz. pair, imperf. vert.		
138	A37	2c brown lil & blk	.40	.20
139	A38	5c lake & blk	.70	.20
140	A39	10c violet & blk	.70	.20
141	A40	20c green & blk	.70	.20
142	A41	50c lil rose & blk	1.75	.55
143	A42	1s ocher & blk	8.00	1.75
144	A43	5s lilac & blk	14.50	5.00
		Nos. 137-144 (8)	27.15	8.30

1901

145	A36	1c scarlet & blk	.45	.20
146	A37	2c green & blk	.45	.20
147	A38	5c gray lil & blk	.45	.20
148	A39	10c dp blue & blk	.50	.25
149	A40	20c gray & blk	.50	.25
150	A41	50c lt blue & blk	1.60	.65
151	A42	1s brown & blk	6.00	1.75
152	A43	5s gray blk & blk	9.00	4.00
		Nos. 145-152 (8)	18.95	7.50

In July, 1902, following the theft of a quantity of stamps during a fire at Guayaquil, the Government authorized the governors of the provinces to handstamp their stocks. Many varieties of these handstamps exist.

Other control marks were used in 1907.
For overprints see Nos. O103-O106, O167.

A44

Surcharged on Revenue Stamp
Dated 1901-1902

1903-06 — **Perf. 14, 15**

153	A44	1c on 5c gray lil ('06)	.75	.40
154	A44	1c on 20c gray ('06)	10.00	4.50
155	A44	1c on 25c yellow	1.50	.40
a.		Double surcharge		
156	A44	1c on 1s bl ('06)	77.50	50.00
157	A44	3c on 5c gray lil ('06)	10.00	4.00
158	A44	3c on 20c gray ('06)	25.00	15.00
159	A44	3c on 25c yel ('06)	24.00	15.00
159A	A44	3c on 1s blue ('06)	3.75	2.25
		Nos. 153-159A (8)	152.50	91.55

Counterfeits are plentiful.
See #191-197.

Capt. Abdón Calderón
A45   A46

1904, July 31 — **Perf. 12**

160	A45	1c red & blk	.40	.30
161	A45	2c blue & blk	.50	.35
162	A46	5c yellow & blk	1.50	1.00
163	A45	10c red & blk	6.00	1.00
164	A45	20c blue & blk	10.00	2.50
165	A46	50c yellow & blk	65.00	35.00
		Nos. 160-165 (6)	83.40	40.15

Centenary of the birth of Calderón.

Presidents

Vicente   Diego
Roca — A47   Noboa — A48

Francisco   José M.
Robles — A49   Urvina — A50

García   Jerónimo
Moreno — A51   Carrión — A52

Javier   Antonio
Espinoza   Borrero
A53   A54

1907, July — **Perf. 14, 15**

166	A47	1c red & blk	1.00	.20
167	A48	2c pale blue & blk	2.00	.20
168	A49	3c orange & blk	3.00	.20
169	A50	5c lilac rose & blk	3.75	.20
170	A51	10c dp blue & blk	7.50	.20
171	A52	20c yellow grn & blk	10.00	.20
172	A53	50c violet & blk	22.50	.70
173	A54	1s green & blk	30.00	2.00
		Nos. 166-173 (8)	79.75	4.05

The stamps of the 1907 issue frequently have control marks similar to those found on the 1899 and 1901 issues. These marks were applied to distinguish the stamps issued in the various provinces and to serve as a check on local officials.

Locomotive — A55

García Moreno — A56

Gen. Eloy Alfaro — A57

Abelardo Moncayo — A58

Archer Harman — A59

James Sivewright — A60

Mt. Chimborazo
A61

1908, June 25

174	A55	1c red brown	.80	1.50
175	A56	2c blue & blk	1.00	1.60
176	A57	5c claret & blk	2.00	3.75
177	A58	10c ocher & blk	1.40	2.10
178	A59	20c green & blk	1.40	2.75
179	A60	50c gray & blk	1.40	2.75
180	A61	1s black	2.75	5.50
		Nos. 174-180 (7)	10.75	19.95

Opening of the Guayaquil-Quito Railway.

José Mejía   Principal
Vallejo — A62   Exposition
                    Building — A70

Designs: 2c, Francisco J. E. Santa Cruz y Espejo. 3c, Francisco Ascásubi. 5c, Juan Salinas. 10c, Juan Pio de Montúfar, el Marques de Selva Alegre. 20c, Carlos de Montúfar. 50c, Juan de Dios Morales. 1s, Manuel R. de Quiroga.

1909, Aug. 10 — **Perf. 12**

181	A62	1c green	.25	.45
182	A62	2c blue	.25	.45
183	A62	3c orange	.25	.55
184	A62	5c claret	.25	.55
185	A62	10c yellow brn	.35	.55
186	A62	20c gray	.35	.80
187	A62	50c vermilion	.35	.80
188	A62	1s olive grn	.40	1.00
189	A70	5s violet	.90	2.00
		Nos. 181-189 (9)	3.35	7.15

National Exposition of 1909.

Surcharged

CINCO
CENTAVOS

1909

190	A68	5c on 50c vermilion	.80	.50

Revenue Stamps Surcharged as in 1903

1910 — **Perf. 14, 15**

Stamps Dated 1905-1906

191	A44	1c on 5c green	2.25	1.75
192	A44	5c on 20c blue	9.50	2.00
193	A44	5c on 25c violet	18.00	3.50

Stamps Dated 1907-1908

194	A44	1c on 5c green	.40	.40
195	A44	5c on 20c blue	14.00	9.50
196	A44	5c on 25c violet	1.20	.40

Stamp Dated 1909-1910

197	A44	5c on 20c blue	80.00	60.00
		Nos. 191-197 (7)	125.35	77.55

Presidents

Roca — A71   Noboa — A72

Robles — A73   Urvina — A74

Moreno — A75   Borrero — A76

1911-28 — **Perf. 12**

198	A71	1c scarlet & blk	.80	.20
199	A71	1c orange ('16)	.80	.20
200	A71	1c lt blue ('25)	.40	.20
201	A72	2c blue & blk	1.10	.20
202	A72	2c green ('16)	1.10	.20
203	A72	2c dk violet ('25)	1.10	.20
204	A73	3c orange & blk ('13)	2.25	.30
205	A73	3c black ('15)	1.50	.20
206	A74	5c scarlet & blk	1.90	.20
207	A74	5c violet ('15)	1.90	.20
208	A74	5c rose ('25)	.70	.20
209	A74	5c dk brown ('28)	.70	.20
210	A75	10c dp blue & blk	2.25	.20
211	A75	10c dp blue ('15)	2.25	.20
212	A75	10c yellow grn ('25)	.70	.20
213	A75	10c black ('28)	1.25	.20
214	A76	1s green & blk	12.00	1.10
215	A76	1s orange & blk ('27)	8.00	.20
		Nos. 198-215 (18)	41.05	4.60

For overprints see Nos. 260-262, O107-O122, O124-O134, O156-O157, O160-O162, O164-O166, O168-O173, O175-O178, O183-O184, O189, RA1.

A77

1912 — **Perf. 14, 15**

216	A77	1c on 1s green	1.00	1.00
217	A77	2c on 2s carmine	2.50	1.50
218	A77	2c on 5s dull blue	1.50	1.50
219	A77	2c on 10s yellow	5.00	5.00
a.		Inverted surcharge	16.00	12.00
		Nos. 216-219 (4)	10.00	9.00

No. 216 exists with narrow "V" and small "U" in "UN" and Nos. 217, 218 and 219 with "D" with serifs or small "O" in "DOS."

Enrique   Jerónimo
Váldez — A78   Carrión — A79

Javier
Espinoza — A80

1915-17 — **Perf. 12**

220	A78	4c red & blk	.40	.20
221	A79	20c green & blk ('17)	3.50	.20
222	A80	50c dp violet & blk	6.00	.45
		Nos. 220-222 (3)	9.90	.85

For overprints see #O123, O135, O163, O174.

Olmedo — A86   Monument to
                 "Fathers of the
                 Country" — A95

Laurel Wreath and
Star — A104

Designs: 2c, Rafael Ximena. 3c, Roca. 4c, Luis F. Vivero. 5c, Luis Febres Cordero. 6c, Francisco Lavayen. 7c, Jorge Antonio de Elizalde. 8c, Baltazar Garcia. 9c, Jose de Antepara. 15c, Luis Urdaneta. 20c, Jose M. Villamil. 30c, Miguel Letamendi. 40c, Gregorio Escobedo. 50c, Gen. Antonio Jose de Sucre. 60c, Juan Illingworth. 70c, Roca. 80c, Rocafuerte. 1s, Simon Bolivar.

1920

223	A86	1c yellow grn	.30	.20
224	A86	2c carmine	.30	.20
225	A86	3c yellow brn	.30	.20
226	A86	4c myrtle green	.45	.20
227	A86	5c pale blue	.45	.20
228	A86	6c red orange	.80	.30
229	A86	7c brown	2.25	.75
230	A86	8c apple green	1.10	.35
231	A86	9c lake	4.25	1.25
232	A95	10c lt blue	1.50	.20
233	A86	15c dk gray	2.25	.35
234	A86	20c dk violet	2.25	.20
235	A86	30c brt violet	4.25	1.00
236	A86	40c dk brown	7.50	1.75
237	A86	50c dk gray	5.25	.35
238	A86	60c dk blue	9.50	1.90
239	A86	70c gray	16.00	4.25
240	A86	80c orange yel	16.50	4.25

241	A104	90c green	17.00 4.25
242	A86	1s pale blue	24.00 7.00
		Nos. 223-242 (20)	116.20 29.15

Cent. of the independence of Guayaquil.
For overprints and surcharges see Nos. 263, 274-292, O136-O155, O179-O182, O185-O188.

Postal Tax Stamp of 1924 Overprinted

1925

259	PT6	20c bister brown	4.00 1.50

Stamps of 1915-25 Overprinted in Black or Red Upright (1c, 3c, 5c) or Inverted (2c, 4c, 10c)

1926

260	A71	1c lt blue	11.00 9.50
261	A72	2c dk violet	11.00 9.50
262	A73	3c black (R)	11.00 9.50
263	A86	4c myrtle green	11.00 9.50
264	A74	5c rose	16.00 9.50
265	A75	10c yellow grn	16.00 9.50
		Nos. 260-265 (6)	76.00 57.00

Quito-Esmeraldas railway opening.
Upright overprints on 2c, 4c, 10c and inverted overprints on 1c, 3c, 5c sell for more.

Postal Tax Stamps of 1920-24 Overprinted

1927

266	PT6	1c olive green	.50 .20
a.		"POSTAI"	1.40 .85
b.		Double overprint	2.00 .85
c.		Inverted overprint	2.00 .85
267	PT6	2c deep green	.50 .20
a.		"POSTAI"	1.40 .85
b.		Double overprint	2.00 .85
268	PT6	20c bister brown	1.00 .20
a.		"POSTAI"	8.50 5.00
		Nos. 266-268 (3)	2.00 .60

Quito Post Office — A109

1927, June

269	A109	5c orange	.50 .20
270	A109	10c dark green	.70 .20
271	A109	20c violet	.80 .20
		Nos. 269-271 (3)	2.00 .60

Opening of new Quito P.O.
For overprint see No. O190.

Postal Tax Stamp of 1924 Overprinted in Dark Blue

POSTAL

1928

273	PT6	20c bister brown	.50 .20
a.		Double overprint, one inverted	2.00 .70

See No. 339 for 10c with same overprint.

Nos. 235, 239-240 Overprinted in Red Brown and Surcharged in Dark Blue

---

1928, July 8

274	A86	10c on 30c violet	15.00 15.00
275	A86	50c on 70c gray	18.00 18.00
276	A86	1s on 80c org yel	21.00 21.00
		Nos. 274-276 (3)	54.00 54.00

Quito-Cayambe railway opening.

Stamps of 1920 Surcharged

1928, Oct. 9

277	A86	1c on 1c yel grn	15.00 15.00
278	A86	1c on 2c car	.30 .30
279	A86	2c on 3c yel brn	2.25 2.25
a.		Dbl. surch., one reading up	30.00 30.00
280	A86	2c on 4c myr grn	1.50 1.50
281	A86	2c on 5c lt blue	.60 .45
a.		Dbl. surch., one reading up	30.00 30.00
282	A86	2c on 7c brown	75.00 75.00
283	A86	5c on 6c red org	.40 .30
a.		"5 ctvos." omitted	37.50 37.50
284	A86	10c on 7c brown	1.25 1.25
285	A86	20c on 8c apple grn	.35 .30
a.		Double surcharge	
286	A95	40c on 10c blue	4.25 4.25
287	A86	40c on 15c dk gray	1.25 1.25
288	A86	50c on 20c dk vio	13.25 13.25
289	A86	1s on 40c dk brown	4.50 4.50
290	A86	5s on 50c dk green	5.25 5.25
291	A86	10s on 60c dk blue	19.50 19.50

With Additional Surcharge in Red

292	A86	10c on 2c on 7c brn	.50 .50
a.		Red surcharge double	30.00 30.00
		Nos. 277-292 (16)	145.15 144.85

National Assembly of 1928.
Counterfeit overprints exist of #277-291.

A111   A112

Surcharged in Various Colors

1928, Oct. 31   *Perf. 14*

293	A111	5c on 20c gray lil (Bk)	3.00 1.75
294	A111	10c on 20c gray lil (R)	3.00 1.75
295	A111	20c on 1s grn (O)	3.00 1.75
296	A111	50c on 1s grn (Bl)	3.75 1.40
297	A111	1s on 1s grn (V)	4.75 1.75
298	A111	5s on 2s red (G)	15.00 9.00
299	A111	10s on 2s red (Br)	18.00 12.00
a.		Black surcharge	15.00 10.00
		Nos. 293-299 (7)	50.50 29.40

Quito-Otavalo railway opening.
See Nos. 586-587.

Postal Tax Stamp of 1924 Overprinted in Red

1929   *Perf. 12*

302	PT6	2c deep green	.50 .20

There are two types of overprint on No. 302 differing slightly.

1929

Red Overprint

303	A112	1c dark blue	.50 .20
a.		Overprint reading down	.75 .50

See Nos. 586-587.

Plowing — A113

Cultivating Cacao — A114

Cacao Pod — A115

Loading Sugar Cane — A119

Growing Tobacco — A116

Exportation of Fruits — A117

Landscape — A118

Scene in Quito A120

Scene in Quito A121

Olmedo — A122

Monument to Simón Bolívar — A125

Designs: 2s, Sucre. 5s, Bolivar.

1930, Aug. 1   *Perf. 12½*

304	A113	1c yellow & car	.30 .20
305	A114	2c yellow & grn	.30 .20
306	A115	5c dp grn & vio brn	.35 .20
307	A116	6c yellow & red	.40 .20
308	A117	10c orange & ol grn	.40 .20
309	A118	16c red & yel grn	.50 .25
310	A119	20c ultra & yel	.80 .20
311	A120	40c orange & sepia	1.10 .35
312	A121	50c orange & sepia	1.10 .40
313	A122	1s dp green & blk	4.25 .45
314	A122	2s dk blue & blk	6.50 2.00
315	A122	5s dk violet & blk	11.50 3.00
316	A125	10s car rose & blk	40.00 6.00
		Nos. 304-316 (13)	67.50 13.65

Centenary of founding of republic.
For surcharges and overprints see Nos. 319-320, 331-338, RA25, RA33, RA43.

A126   A127

Red Overprint

1933   *Perf. 15*

317	A126	10c olive brown	1.15 .20

Blue Overprint

318	A127	10c olive brown	.70 .20
a.		Inverted overprint	5.00 5.00

For overprint see No. 339.

Nos. 307, 309 Surcharged in Black

1933   *Perf. 12½*

319	A116	5c on 6c yellow & red	1.00 .20
320	A118	10c on 16c red & yel grn	2.00 .20
a.		Inverted overprint	4.00 4.00

Landscape A128   Mt. Chimborazo A129

1934-45   *Perf. 12*

321	A128	5c violet	1.40 .45
322	A128	5c blue	1.40 .45
323	A128	5c dark brown	1.40 .45

323A	A128	5c slate blk ('45)	1.40	.45
324	A128	10c rose	1.40	.45
325	A128	10c dark green	1.40	.45
326	A128	10c brown	1.40	.45
327	A128	10c orange	1.40	.45
328	A128	10c olive green	1.40	.45
329	A128	10c gray blk ('35)	1.40	.45
329A	A128	10c red lilac ('44)	1.40	.45

Perf. 14

330	A129	1s carmine rose	1.60	.50
	Nos. 321-330 (12)		17.00	5.45

Stamps of 1930 Surcharged or Ovptd. in various colors similar to:

INAUGURACION MONUMENTO A BOLIVAR 5 ctvs. QUITO, 24 DE JULIO DE 1935

1935   **Perf. 12½**

331	A116	5c on 6c (Bl)	.90	.35
332	A116	10c on 6c (G)	1.25	.35
333	A119	20c (R)	1.75	.35
334	A120	40c (G)	2.50	.35
335	A121	50c (G)	3.00	.40
336	A122	1s on 5s (Gold)	7.00	1.00
337	A122	2s on 5s (Gold)	9.50	1.60
338	A125	5s on 10s (Bl)	12.00	4.25
	Nos. 331-338,C35-C38 (12)		87.90	28.65

Unveiling of a monument to Bolivar at Quito, July 24, 1935.

A129a

1935, Oct. 13   Photo.   Perf. 11½x11

338A	A129a	5c ultra & black	.20	.20
338B	A129a	10c orange & blue	.20	.20
338C	A129a	40c dk carmine & red	.20	30
338D	A129a	1S blue green & red	.30	70
338E	A129a	2S violet & red	.55	1.20
	Nos. 338A-338E,C38A-C38E (10)		4.05	6.50

Columbus Day. Nos. 338A-338E and C38A-C38E were prepared by the Sociedad Colombista Panamericana and were sold by the Ecuadorian post office through Oct. 30.

Telegraph Stamp Overprinted Diagonally in Red like No. 273

1935   **Perf. 14½**

339	A126	10c olive brown	.75	.25

Map of Galápagos Islands A130   Galápagos Land Iguana A131

Galápagos Tortoise — A132   Charles R. Darwin — A133

Columbus A134   Island Scene A135

1936   **Perf. 14**

340	A130	2c black	1.00	.25
341	A131	5c olive grn	1.25	.25
342	A132	10c brown	2.25	.30
343	A133	20c dk violet	2.50	.40
344	A134	1s dk carmine	4.00	.75
345	A135	2s dark blue	6.00	1.25
	Nos. 340-345 (6)		17.00	3.20

Cent. of the visit of Charles Darwin to the Galápagos Islands, Sept. 17, 1835.
For overprints see Nos. O191-O195.

Tobacco Stamp Overprinted in Black

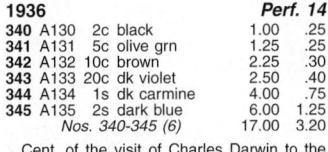

REPUBLICA EL ECUADOR POSTAL UN

1936   **Rouletted 7**

346	PT7	1c rose red	.50	.25
	a.	Horiz. pair, imperf. vert.		
	b.	Double surcharge		

No. 346 is similar to type PT7 but does not include "CASA CORREOS."

Louis Godin, Charles M. de la Condamine and Pierre Bouguer A136

Portraits: 5c, 20c, Antonio Ulloa, La Condamine and Jorge Juan.

1936   **Engr.   Perf. 12½**

347	A1362c	deep blue	.50	.30
348	A1365c	dark green	.50	.30
349	A13610c	deep orange	.50	.30
350	A13620c	violet	.80	.30
351	A13650c	dark red	1.25	.30
	Nos. 347-351,C39-C42 (9)		6.60	2.45

Bicentenary of Geodesical Mission to Quito.

Independence Monument — A137

1936   **Perf. 13½x14**

352	A137	2c green	2.00	1.10
353	A137	5c dark violet	2.00	1.10
354	A137	10c carmine rose	2.00	1.10
355	A137	20c black	2.00	1.10
356	A137	50c brown	2.75	1.75
357	A137	1s dark red	3.75	3.25
	Nos. 352-357,C43-C50 (14)		45.50	37.40

1st Intl. Philatelic Exhibition at Quito.

Coat of Arms — A138

Overprint in Black or Red

1937   **Perf. 12½**

359	A138	5c olive green	2.00	.30
360	A138	10c dark blue (R)	2.00	.25

For overprint see No. 562.

Andean Landscape A139

Atahualpa, the Last Inca A140

Hat Weavers — A141

Coast Landscape A142   Gold Washing A143

1937, Aug. 19   **Perf. 11½**

361	A139	2c green	.50	.25
362	A140	5c deep rose	.50	.25
363	A141	10c blue	.50	.25
364	A142	20c deep rose	1.50	.30
365	A143	1s olive green	2.00	.35
	Nos. 361-365 (5)		5.00	1.40

For overprints see Nos. O196-O200.

"Liberty" Carrying Flag of Ecuador — A144

Engraved and Lithographed

1938, Feb. 22   **Perf. 12**

Center Multicolored

366	A144	2c blue	.25	.20
367	A144	5c violet	.30	.20
368	A144	10c black	.40	.20
369	A144	20c brown	.55	.20
370	A144	50c black	.85	.20
371	A144	1s olive blk	1.25	.30
372	A144	2s dk brn	2.50	.40
	Nos. 366-372,C57-C63 (14)		20.60	3.80

US Constitution, 150th anniversary.
For overprints and surcharges see Nos. 413-415, 444-446, RA46, RA52.

 A145   A146

 A147   A148

Designs: 10c, Winged figure holding globe. 50c, Cactus, winged wheel. 1s, "Communications." 2s, "Construction."

Perf. 13, 13x13½

1938, Oct. 30   **Engr.**

373	A145	10c bright ultra	.40	.20
374	A146	50c deep red violet	.40	.20
375	A147	1s copper red	.70	.20
376	A148	2s dark green	1.10	.20
	Nos. 373-376 (4)		2.60	.80

Progress of Ecuador Exhibition.
For overprints see Nos. C105-C113.

Parade of Athletes — A149

Runner — A150

Basketball — A151

Wrestlers A152

Diver A153

1939, Mar.   **Perf. 12**

377	A149	5c carmine rose	2.75	.45
378	A150	10c deep blue	3.25	.55
379	A151	50c gray olive	5.25	.75
380	A152	1s dull violet	7.50	.75
381	A153	2s dull olive green	11.00	.95
	Nos. 377-381,C65-C69 (10)		71.25	5.60

First Bolivarian Games (1938), Bogota.

Dolores Mission A154

Trylon and Perisphere A155

1939, June 16   **Perf. 12½x13**

382	A154	2c blue green	.50	.25
383	A154	5c rose red	.50	.25
384	A154	10c ultra	.50	.25
385	A154	50c yellow brown	1.20	.25
386	A154	1s black	1.90	.25
387	A154	2s purple	1.25	.40
	Nos. 382-387,C73-C79 (13)		11.25	3.05

Golden Gate International Exposition.
For surcharges see Nos. 429, 436.

1939, June 30

388	A155	2c lt olive green	.70	.35
389	A155	5c red orange	.70	.35
390	A155	10c ultra	.70	.35
391	A155	50c slate gray	1.00	.35
392	A155	1s rose carmine	1.75	.35
393	A155	2s black brown	2.00	.40
	Nos. 388-393,C80-C86 (13)		15.10	3.55

New York World's Fair.
For surcharge see No. 437.

Flags of the 21 American Republics — A156

1940   **Perf. 12**

394	A156	5c dp rose & blk	1.00	.20
395	A156	10c dk blue & blk	.40	.20
396	A156	50c Prus green & blk	.60	.20
397	A156	1s dp violet & blk	1.00	.30
	Nos. 394-397,C87-C90 (8)		7.85	2.35

Pan American Union, 50th anniversary.

Coat of Arms — A138

Francisco J. E. Santa
Cruz y
Espejo — A157

1941, Dec. 15
398 A157 30c blue 1.25 .20
399 A157 1s red orange 2.50 .35
 Nos. 398-399,C91-C92 (4) 20.00 1.20

Exposition of Journalism held under the
auspices of the Natl. Newspaper Men's Union.

Francisco de
Orellana
A158

Gonzalo Pizarro
A159

View of
Guayaquil
A160

View of
Quito — A161

1942, Jan. 30
400 A158 10c sepia .90 .35
401 A159 40c deep rose 2.50 .35
402 A160 1s violet 3.50 .35
403 A161 2s dark blue 4.50 .45
 Nos. 400-403,C93-C96 (8) 23.45 2.75

400th anniv. of the discovery and exploration of the Amazon River by Orellana.

Remigio
Crespo Toral
A162

Alfredo
Baquerizo
Moreno
A163

1942 *Perf. 13½*
404 A162 10c green .60 .20
405 A162 50c brown 1.00 .20
 Nos. 404-405,C97 (3) 2.85 .85

1942
406 A163 10c green .25 .25

Mt.
Chimborazo
A164

1942-47 *Perf. 12*
407 A164 30c red brown .60 .25
407A A164 30c lt blue ('43) .60 .25
407B A164 30c red orange ('44) .60 .25
407C A164 30c green ('47) .60 .25
 Nos. 407-407C (4) 2.40 1.00

View of
Guayaquil
A165

1942-44
408 A165 20c red .45 .20
408A A165 20c deep blue ('44) .45 .20

Gen. Eloy
Alfaro — A166

Devil's
Nose — A167

President Alfaro (1842-1912): 30c, Military
College. 1s, Montecristi, Alfaro's birthplace.

1942
409 A166 10c dk rose & blk .60 .20
410 A167 20c ol blk & red brn .60 .20
411 A167 30c ol gray & grn .75 .20
412 A167 1s slate & salmon 1.80 .25
 Nos. 409-412,C98-C101 (8) 20.15 3.70

Nos. 370-372 Overprinted in Red
Brown

1943, Apr. 15 *Perf. 11½*
413 A144 50c multicolored .60 .60
414 A144 1s multicolored 1.10 1.10
415 A144 2s multicolored 2.40 2.40
 Nos. 413-415,C102-C104 (6) 14.10 9.70

Visit of US Vice-Pres. Henry A. Wallace.

"30 Centavos" — A170

Black Surcharge

1943 *Perf. 12½*
416 A170 30c on 50c red brn 1.00 .25
 a. Without bars 1.00 .25

Map Showing US and
Ecuador — A171

1943, Oct. 9 *Perf. 12*
417 A171 10c dull violet .70 .50
418 A171 20c red brown .70 .50
419 A171 30c orange .70 .50
420 A171 50c olive green .80 .60

421 A171 1s deep violet .90 .65
422 A171 10s olive bister 7.50 5.25
 Nos. 417-422,C114-C118 (11) 29.80 15.10

Good will tour of Pres. Arroyo del Rio in
1942.

1944, Feb. 7
423 A171 10c yellow green .60 .45
424 A171 20c rose pink .60 .45
425 A171 30c dark gray brown .60 .45
426 A171 50c deep red lilac .60 .45
427 A171 1s olive gray .90 .65
428 A171 10s red orange 9.50 6.00
 Nos. 423-428,C119-C123 (11) 23.60 13.40

For surcharges see Nos. B1-B6.

No. 385 Surcharged
in Black

1944 *Unwmk.* *Perf. 12½x13*
429 A154 30c on 50c yel brn 2.00 .20

Archbishop Federico
González Suárez,
Birth Cent. — A172

1944 *Perf. 12*
430 A172 10c deep blue .40 .20
431 A172 20c green .40 .20
432 A172 30c dk violet brn .50 .20
433 A172 1s dull violet .90 .25
 Nos. 430-433,C124-C127 (8) 15.50 3.75

Air Post Stamps
Nos. C76 and C83
Surcharged in Black

1944 *Perf. 12½x13*
434 AP15 30c on 50c rose vio .40 .20
435 AP16 30c on 50c sl grn .40 .20

Nos. 382 and 388
Surcharged in Black

1944-45
436 A154 5c on 2c bl grn .50 .20
 a. Double surcharge 4.00
437 A155 5c on 2c lt ol grn ('45) .50 .20

Government
Palace,
Quito — A173

1944 *Engr.* *Perf. 11*
438 A173 10c dark green .50 .20
439 A173 30c blue .50 .20

For surcharges see Nos. 452, RAC1-RAC2.

Symbol of
the Red
Cross
A174

1945, Apr. 25 *Perf. 12*
Cross in Rose
440 A174 30c bister brown 1.75 .35
441 A174 1s red brown 2.40 .45
442 A174 5s turq green 4.25 1.10
443 A174 10s scarlet 11.50 3.00
 Nos. 440-443,C131-C134 (8) 55.90 11.30

International Red Cross, 80th anniversary.

Nos. 370 to 372 Overprinted in Dark
Blue and Gold

1945, Oct. 2 *Perf. 11½*
Center Multicolored
444 A144 50c black .80 .70
 a. Double overprint
445 A144 1s olive black 1.40 1.40
446 A144 2s dark brown 2.75 2.50
 Nos. 444-446,C139-C141 (6) 9.95 8.25

Visit of Pres. Juan Antonio Rios of Chile.

General Antonio
José de Sucre,
150th Birth
Anniv. — A175

1945, Nov. 14 *Engr.* *Perf. 12*
447 A175 10c olive .50 .25
448 A175 20c red brown .50 .20
449 A175 40c olive gray .50 .20
450 A175 1s dark green 1.00 .25
451 A175 2s sepia 2.00 .75
 Nos. 447-451,C142-C146 (10) 12.00 5.20

No. 438 Surcharged in Blue

1945 *Perf. 11*
452 A173 20c on 10c dark green .50 .20
 a. Fancy bar omitted

Catalogue values for unused
stamps in this section, from this
point to the end of the section, are
for Never Hinged items.

Map of Pan-
American Highway
and Arms of
Loja — A176

1946, Apr. 22 *Engr.* *Perf. 12*
453 A176 20c red brown .75 .50
454 A176 30c bright green .75 .50
455 A176 1s bright ultra .75 .50
456 A176 5s deep red lilac 2.25 1.50
457 A176 10s scarlet 6.00 4.75
 Nos. 453-457,C147-C151 (10) 21.60 12.05

Torch of Democracy — A177

Popular Suffrage A178

Flag of Ecuador — A179

Pres. José M. Velasco Ibarra — A180

1946, Aug. 9   Unwmk.   Perf. 12½
458	A177	5c dark blue	.25	.20
459	A178	10c Prus green	.25	.20
460	A179	20c carmine	.30	.20
461	A180	30c chocolate	.55	.20
	Nos. 458-461,C152-C155 (8)		3.75	1.85

Revolution of May 28, 1944, 2nd anniv.

"30 Ctvs." — A181

Black Surcharge

1946
462	A181	30c on 50c red brown	1.00	.20

For overprint see No. 484.

Nos. CO13-CO14 With Additional Overprint in Black

1946   Perf. 11½
463	AP7	10c chestnut	1.00	.20
464	AP7	20c olive black	1.00	.20

Instructor and Student — A182

1946, Sept. 16   Perf. 12½
465	A182	10c deep blue	.60	.60
466	A182	20c chocolate	.60	.60
467	A182	30c dark green	.60	.60
468	A182	50c bluish blk	1.20	1.20
469	A182	1s dark red	1.50	1.40
470	A182	10s dark violet	9.00	2.40
	Nos. 465-470,C156-C160 (11)		29.95	11.95

Campaign for adult education.

Mariana de Jesus Paredes y Flores — A183

Urn — A184

1946, Nov. 28
471	A183	10c black brown	.60	.60
472	A183	20c green	.60	.60
473	A183	30c purple	.60	.60
474	A184	1s rose brown	.80	.60
	Nos. 471-474,C161-C164 (8)		8.00	6.10

300th anniv. of the death of the Blessed Mariana de Jesus Paredes y Flores.

Pres. Vicente Rocafuerte A185

Jesuits' Church Quito A186

45c, 50c, 80c, F.J.E. de Santa Cruz y Espejo.

1947, Nov. 27   Perf. 12
475	A185	5c redsh brown	.30	.20
476	A185	10c sepia	.30	.20
477	A185	15c gray black	.30	.20
478	A186	20c redsh brown	.30	.20
479	A186	30c red violet	.35	.20
480	A186	40c brt ultra	.45	.20
481	A185	45c dk slate grn	.50	.20
482	A185	50c olive black	.50	.20
483	A185	80c orange red	.80	.20
	Nos. 475-483,C165-C171 (16)		7.80	3.20

For overprints and surcharges see Nos. 489, 496, 525-527.

Type of 1946, Overprinted "POSTAL" in Black but Without Additional Surcharge

1948   Engr.
484	A181	10c orange	.75	.25

Andrés Bello A188

Flagship of Columbus A189

1948, Apr. 21   Perf. 13
485	A188	20c lt blue	.50	.25
486	A188	30c rose carmine	.50	.25
487	A188	40c blue green	.50	.25
488	A188	1s black brown	.70	.25
	Nos. 485-488,C172-C174 (7)		3.90	1.65

83rd anniversary of the death of Andrés Bello (1781-1865), educator.

No. 480 Overprinted in Black

1948, May 24   Perf. 12
489	A186	40c bright ultra	1.00	.30

See No. C175.

1948   Perf. 14
490	A189	10c dark blue green	.60	.60
491	A189	20c brown	.60	.60
492	A189	30c dark purple	1.50	.60
493	A189	50c deep claret	1.75	.60
494	A189	1s ultra	3.75	1.50
495	A189	5s carmine	6.75	1.60
	Nos. 490-495,C176-C180 (11)		34.80	17.00

Issued to publicize the proposed Columbus Memorial Lighthouse near Ciudad Trujillo, Dominican Republic.

No. 483 Overprinted in Blue

1948   Perf. 12
"MANANA" Reading Down
496	A185	80c orange red	.50	.25

Issued to publicize the National Fair of Today and Tomorrow, 1948. See No. C181.

Telegrafo I in Flight — A190

Book and Pen — A191

1948   Engr.   Perf. 12½
497	A190	30c red orange	.75	.25
498	A190	40c rose lilac	.75	.25
499	A190	60c violet blue	.75	.25
500	A190	1s brown red	.75	.25
501	A190	3s brown	2.40	.35
502	A190	5s gray black	2.75	.35
	Nos. 497-502,C182-C187 (12)		16.40	3.45

25th anniversary (in 1945) of the first postal flight in Ecuador.

1948, Oct. 12   Unwmk.   Perf. 14
503	A191	10c deep claret	.60	.20
504	A191	20c brown	.60	.20
505	A191	30c dark green	.75	.20
506	A191	50c red	.75	.20
507	A191	1s purple	1.00	.30
508	A191	10s dull blue	10.00	1.00
	Nos. 503-508,C188-C192 (11)		34.70	9.75

Campaign for adult education.

A192

Franklin D. Roosevelt and Two of "Four Freedoms" — A193

1948, Oct. 24   Perf. 12½
509	A192	10c rose brn & gray	.45	.40
510	A192	20c brn ol & bl	.45	.40
511	A193	30c ol bis & car rose	.45	.40
512	A193	40c red vio & sep	.60	.40
513	A193	1s org brn & car	.65	.50
	Nos. 509-513,C193-C197 (10)		7.15	3.35

Maldonado and Map — A194

Riobamba Aqueduct A195

Maldonado on Bank of Riobamba A196

Pedro V. Maldonado A197

1948, Nov. 17   Engr.   Unwmk.
514	A194	5c gray blk & ver	.60	.20
515	A195	10c car & gray blk	.70	.20
516	A196	30c bis brn & ultra	.80	.20
517	A195	40c sage grn & vio	1.10	.20
518	A194	50c grn & car	1.40	.30
519	A197	1s brn & slate bl	1.75	.35
	Nos. 514-519,C198-C201 (10)		10.95	2.25

Bicentenary of the death of Pedro Vicente Maldonado, geographer.

For overprints and surcharges see Nos. 537-540.

A198

Miguel de Cervantes Saavedra A199

1949, May 2   Perf. 12½x12
520	A198	30c dk car rose & dp ultra	1.00	.25
521	A199	60c bis & brn vio	1.50	.40
522	A198	1s grn & rose car	1.60	.25
523	A199	2s gray blk & red brn	3.50	.40
524	A198	5s choc & aqua	6.25	1.10
	Nos. 520-524,C202-C206 (10)		29.85	5.90

400th anniv. of the birth of Miguel de Cervantes Saavedra, novelist, playwright and poet.

No. 480 Surcharged in Carmine

1949, June 15   Perf. 12
525	A186	10c on 40c brt ultra	.50	.20
526	A186	20c on 40c brt ultra	.70	.20
a.	Double surcharge			
527	A186	30c on 40c brt ultra	.70	.20
	Nos. 525-527,C207-C209 (6)		3.30	1.20

2nd Natl. Eucharistic Cong., Quito, 6/49.
No. 526 exists se-tenant with No. 527.

Monument on Equator — A200

1949, June   Engr.   Perf. 12½x12
528 A200 10c deep plum   .50 .20

For overprint see No. 536.

No. 542 Surcharged in Black and Carmine

1949   Perf. 12x12½
529 A203 10c on 50c green   .50 .25
530 A203 20c on 50c green   .50 .25
531 A203 30c on 50c green   .60 .25
   Nos. 529-531,C210-C213 (7)   7.00 2.75

Universal Postal Union, 75th anniversary.

Consular Service Stamps Surcharged in Black

Arms of Ecuador — R1

1949   Perf. 12
532 R1 20c on 25c red brown   .75 .20
533 R1 30c on 50c gray   .75 .20

For other overprints and surcharges on type R1 see Nos. 544-549, 566-570, C245, C249-C252, RA60-RA62, RA72.

Nos. RA49A and RA55 Overprinted in Black

a

1950   Unwmk.   Perf. 12
534 PT18 5c green   .50 .20
535 PT21 5c blue   .50 .20

Overprint 15mm on No. 534.

Nos. 528 and 517 to 519 Overprinted or Surcharged in Black or Carmine

1950, Feb. 10   Perf. 12½x12
536 A200 10c dp plum   .75 .75

Perf. 12½
537 A195 20c on 40c sage grn
   & vio   1.40 1.40
538 A195 30c on 40c sage grn
   & vio   1.50 1.50
539 A194 50c grn & car   2.25 2.25
540 A197 1s brn & slate bl
   (C)   3.00 3.00

No. C220 Overprinted Type "a" in Carmine
Perf. 11
Overprint 15mm long
541 A173 10s violet   7.50 3.75
   Nos. 536-541,C216-C220 (11)   36.15 24.65

Nos. 536-541 publicize adult education.

San Pablo Lake — A203

Perf. 12x12½
1950, May   Engr.   Unwmk.
542 A203 50c green   .75 .20

For surcharges see Nos. 529-531.

Consular Service Stamp Surcharged "CORREOS" and New Value Vertically in Black

1950   Perf. 12
544 R1 30c on 50c gray   .75 .25

Consular Service Stamps Overprinted or Surcharged in Black

b

c

d

e

f

g

1951   Unwmk.   Perf. 12
545 R1 (b)   5c on 10c car rose   .75 .25
546 R1 (c)   10c car rose   .75 .25
547 R1 (d)   10c car rose   .75 .25
548 R1 (e)   20c on 25c red brn   .75 .25
549 R1 (e)   30c on 50c gray   .75 .25
550 R2 (f)   40c on 25c blue   .75 .25
551 R2 (g)   50c on 25c blue   5.25 .25
   Nos. 545-551 (7)   5.25 1.75

See #552-554, C233-C234, C246-C248, RA67.

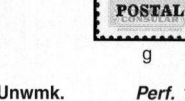

Consular Service Stamps Surcharged in Black

1951
552 R2 20c on 25c blue   .75 .20
553 R2 30c on 25c blue   .75 .20

Adult education. See Nos. C225-C226.

Consular Service Stamp Surcharged in Black

1951
554 R2 $0.30 on 50c car rose   .75 .25

Reliquary of St. Mariana and Vatican — A204

Perf. 12½x12
1952, Feb.   Engr.   Unwmk.
555 A204 10c emer & red brn   .90 .70
556 A204 20c dp bl & pur   .90 .70
557 A204 30c car & bl grn   .90 .70
   Nos. 555-557,C227-C230 (7)   7.90 3.70

Issued to publicize the canonization of Mariana de Jesus Paredes y Flores.

Presidents Galo Plaza and Harry Truman — A205

2s, Pres. Plaza addressing US Congress.

1952, Mar. 26   Perf. 12
558 A205 1s rose car & gray blk   .70 .60
559 A205 2s dl bl & sepia   1.75 .90
   Nos. 558-559,C231-C232 (4)   5.45 4.20

1951 visit of Pres. Galo Plaza y Lasso to the US.

R3

Fiscal Stamps Surcharged or Overprinted Type "c" Horizontally in Carmine or Black

1952   Unwmk.   Engr.   Perf. 12
560 R3 20c on 30c dp bl (C)   .75 .25
561 R3 30c deep blue   .75 .20

Diagonal Overprint
562 A138 50c purple   .75 .20
   Nos. 560-562 (3)   2.25 .65

For overprints and surcharge see Nos. RA68-RA69, RA71.

Pres. José M. Urvina, Slave and "Liberty" A206

Hyphen-hole Perf. 7x6½
1952   Litho.
563 A206 20c red & green   .60 .40
564 A206 30c red & vio bl   .75 .40
565 A206 50c blue & car   1.20 .40
   Nos. 563-565,C236-C239 (7)   26.55 5.00

Centenary of abolition of slavery in Ecuador. Counterfeits exist.

Consular Service Stamps Surcharged in Black — f

1952-53   Unwmk.   Perf. 12
566 R1 10c on 20s blue ('53)   .75 .20
567 R1 20c on 10s gray ('53)   .75 .20
568 R1 20c on 20s blue   .75 .20
569 R1 20c on 10s gray ('53)   .75 .20
570 R1 30c on 20s blue   .75 .20
   Nos. 566-570 (5)   3.75 1.00

Similar surcharges of 60c and 90c on the 20s blue are said to be bogus.

Teacher and Students — A207

New Citizens Voting — A208

Designs: 10c, Instructor with student. 30c, Teaching the alphabet.

1953, Apr. 13   Engr.
571 A207 5c lt bl   .30 .20
572 A207 10c dk car rose   .45 .20
573 A208 20c brt brn org   .50 .20
574 A208 30c dp red lil   .75 .20
   Nos. 571-574,C240-C241 (6)   6.00 1.20

1952 adult education campaign.

A209

Cuicocha Lagoon — A210

Black Surcharge

1953
575 A209 40c on 50c purple   1.00 .25

1953   Engr.   Perf. 13x12½

Designs: 10c, Equatorial Line monument. 20c, Quininde countryside. 30c, Tomebamba river. 40c, La Chilintosa rock. 50c, Iliniza Mountains.

Frames in Black
576 A210 5c brt bl   .50 .50
577 A210 10c brt grn   .50 .50
578 A210 20c purple   .50 .50
579 A210 30c brown   .50 .50
580 A210 40c orange   .50 .50
581 A210 50c dp car   .90 .50
   Nos. 576-581 (6)   3.40 3.00

A211   A212

Carlos Maria Cardinal de la Torre and arches.

1954, Jan.   **Photo.**   **Perf. 8½**
582 A211 30c blk & ver .60 .60
583 A211 50c blk & rose lil .60 .60
    Nos. 582-583,C253-C255 (5) 4.45 3.00

1st anniv. of the elevation of Archbishop de la Torre to Cardinal.

1954, Apr. 22
584 A212 30c blk & gray 1.20 1.20
585 A212 50c blk brn & yel 1.20 1.20
    Nos. 584-585,C256-C260 (7) 8.40 5.40

Queen Isabella I (1451-1504) of Spain, 500th birth anniv.

Type of 1929; "POSTAL" Overprint Larger, No Letterspacing
1954-55   **Unwmk.**   **Perf. 12**
586 A112 5c ol grn ('55) .75 .20
587 A112 10c orange .75 .20

The normal overprint on Nos. 586-587 reads up. It also exists reading down.

Indian Messenger A213   Products of Ecuador A214

1954, Aug. 2   **Litho.**   **Perf. 11**
588 A213 30c dk brn 1.00 .20

Day of the Postal Employee. See No. C263.

1954, Sept. 24   **Photo.**
589 A214 10c orange .40 .20
590 A214 20c vermilion .40 .20
591 A214 30c rose pink .40 .20
592 A214 40c dk gray grn .60 .20
593 A214 50c yel brn .80 .20
    Nos. 589-593 (5) 2.60 1.00

José Abel Castillo — A215   Babahoyo River Los Rios — A216

Perf. 11½x11
1955, Oct. 19   **Engr.**   **Unwmk.**
594 A215 30c olive bister .60 .20
595 A215 50c dk gray .60 .20
    Nos. 594-595,C282-C286 (7) 15.40 2.25

30th anniv. of the 1st flight of the "Telegrafo I" and to honor Castillo, aviation pioneer.

1955-56   **Photo.**   **Perf. 13**

Designs: 5c, Palms, Esmeraldas. 10c, Fishermen, Manabi. 30c, Guayaquil, Guayas. 50c, Pital River, El Oro. 70c, Cactus, Galapagos Isls. 80c, Orchids, Napo-Pastaza. 1s, Aguacate Mission, Zamora-Chinchipe. 2s, Jibaro Indian, Morona-Santiago.

596 A216 5c yel grn ('56) 1.50 .30
597 A216 10c blue ('56) 1.50 .30
598 A216 20c brown 1.50 .30
599 A216 30c dk gray 1.50 .30
600 A216 50c bl grn 1.50 .30
601 A216 70c ol ('56) 1.50 .30
602 A216 80c dp vio ('56) 3.75 .30

603 A216 1s org ('56) 2.00 .30
604 A216 2s rose red ('56) 3.75 .30
    Nos. 596-604 (9) 18.50 2.70

See #620-630, 670, C288-C297, C310-C311.

Brother Juan Adam Schwarz, S. J. — A217

1956, Aug. 27   **Engr.**   **Perf. 13½**
605 A217 5c yel grn .40 .20
606 A217 10c org red .40 .20
607 A217 20c lt vio .40 .20
608 A217 30c dk grn .40 .20
609 A217 40c blue .40 .20
610 A217 50c dp ultra .40 .20
611 A217 70c orange .40 .20
    Nos. 605-611,C302-C305 (11) 5.20 2.20

Bicentennial of printing in Ecuador and honoring Brother Juan Adam Schwarz, S.J.

Andres Hurtado de Mendoza — A218

Gil Ramirez Davalos A219

Designs: 20c, Brother Vincent Solano.

1957, Apr. 7   **Unwmk.**   **Perf. 12**
612 A218 5c dk bl, *pink* .60 .20
613 A219 10c grn, *grnsh* .60 .20
614 A218 20c choc, *buff* .60 .20
    a.   Souvenir sheet of 4, imperf. 3.00 3.00
    Nos. 612-614,C312-C314 (6) 2.55 1.20

4th cent. of the founding of Cuenca.
#614a contains 2 5c gray & 2 20c brown red stamps in designs similar to #612, 614. It was printed on white ungummed paper.

Francisco Marcos, Gen. Pedro Alcantara Herran and Santos Michelena A220

1957, Sept. 5   **Engr.**   **Perf. 14½x14**
615 A220 40c yellow .40 .20
616 A220 50c ultra .40 .20
617 A220 2s dk red 1.00 .20
    Nos. 615-617 (3) 1.80 .60

7th Postal Congress of the Americas and Spain (in 1955).

Souvenir Sheets

Various Railroad Scenes — A221

1957   **Litho.**   **Perf. 10½x11**
618 A221 20c Sheet of 5 7.50 4.25
619 A221 30c Sheet of 5 7.50 4.25

Issued to commemorate the opening of the Quito-Ibarra-San Lorenzo railroad.
Nos. 618-619 contain 2 orange yellow, 1 ultramarine and 2 carmine stamps, each in a different design.

Scenic Type of 1955-56.

Designs as before, except: 40c, as 70c. 90c, as 80c. No. 629, San Pablo, Imbabura.

1957-58   **Photo.**   **Perf. 13**
620 A216 5c light blue 1.75 .20
621 A216 10c brown 1.75 .20
622 A216 20c crimson rose 1.75 .20
623 A216 20c yel green 1.75 .20
624 A216 30c rose red 2.50 .20
625 A216 40c chalky blue 1.75 .20
626 A216 50c lt vio 2.50 .20
627 A216 90c brt ultra 1.75 .20
628 A216 1s dark brown 1.75 .20
629 A216 1s gray blk ('58) 1.75 .20
630 A216 2s brown 2.75 .20
    Nos. 620-630 (11) 21.75 2.20

Blue and Yellow Macaw — A222

Birds: 20c, Red-breasted toucan. 30c, Condor. 40c, Black-tailed and sword-tailed hummingbirds.

Perf. 13½x13
1958, Jan. 7   **Litho.**   **Unwmk.**
Birds in Natural Colors
634 A222 10c red brn 1.25 .20
635 A222 20c dk gray 1.25 .20
636 A222 30c brt yel grn 3.25 .20
637 A222 40c red org 3.25 .20
    Nos. 634-637 (4) 9.00 .80

Carlos Sanz de Santamaria A223

Richard M. Nixon and Flags — A224

#640, Dr. Ramon Villeda Morales, flags. 2.20s, José Carlos de Macedo Soares, horizontal flags.

1958   **Perf. 12**
Flags in Red, Blue, Yellow & Green
638 A223 1.80s dl vio .50 .20
639 A224 2s dk grn .50 .20
640 A224 2s dk brn .50 .20
641 A223 2.20s blk brn .50 .20
    Nos. 638-641 (4) 2.00 .80

Visits: Colombia's Foreign Minister Dr. Carlos Sanz de Santamaria; US Vice Pres. Nixon, May 9-10; Pres. Ramon Villeda Morales of Honduras; Brazil's Foreign Minister José Carlos de Macedo Soares. See Nos. C419-C421. For overprints and surcharges see Nos. 775-775C, C419-C421, C460.

Locomotive of 1908 A225

Garcia Moreno, Jose Caamano, L. Plaza and Eloy Alfaro — A226

Design: 50c, Diesel locomotive.

Perf. 13½x14, 14
1958, Aug. 9   **Photo.**   **Unwmk.**
642 A225 30c brn blk .20 .20
643 A225 50c dk car .30 .20
644 A226 5s dk brn 1.10 .70
    Nos. 642-644 (3) 1.60 1.10

Guayaquil-Quito railroad, 50th anniv.

Cardinal — A227

Birds: 30c, Andean cock-of-the-rock. 50c, Glossy cowbird. 60c, Red-fronted Amazon.

1958   **Litho.**   **Perf. 13½x13**
Birds in Natural Colors
645 A227 20c bluish grn, blk & red 1.25 .20
646 A227 30c buff, blk & brt bl 1.50 .20
647 A227 50c org, blk & grn 1.75 .45
648 A227 60c pale rose, blk & bluish grn 3.50 .45
    Nos. 645-648 (4) 8.00 1.30

UNESCO Building and Eiffel Tower, Paris — A228

1958, Nov. 3   **Engr.**   **Perf. 12½**
649 A228 80c brown .45 .20

UNESCO Headquarters in Paris opening, Nov. 3.

Globe and Satellites — A229

Virgin of Quito — A230

1958, Dec. 20   **Photo.**   **Perf. 14x13½**
650 A229 1.80s dark blue 1.00 .45

International Geophysical Year, 1957-58. For overprints see Nos. 718, C422.

1959, Sept. 8   **Unwmk.**   **Perf. 13**
651 A230 5c ol grn .25 .20
652 A230 10c yel brn .25 .20
653 A230 20c purple .25 .20
654 A230 30c ultra .25 .20
655 A230 80c dk car rose .25 .20
    Nos. 651-655 (5) 1.25 1.00

See No. C290. For surcharges and overprint see Nos. 695-699.

Uprooted Oak
Emblem — A231

1960, Apr. 7   Litho.   Perf. 14x13
656 A231 80c rose car & grn   .25 .20

World Refugee Year, 71/59-630/60.
For overprints see Nos. 709, 719, O205.

Great Anteater
and
Arms — A232

Animals: 40c, Tapir and map. 80c, Specta-
cled bear and arms. 1s, Puma and map.

1960, May 14   Photo.   Perf. 13
657 A232 20c org, grn & blk   .60 .20
658 A232 40c yel grn, bl grn &
         brn   .90 .20
659 A232 80c bl, blk & red brn 1.50 .20
660 A232 1s Prus bl, plum &
         ocher   2.75 .60
    Nos. 657-660 (4)   5.75 1.20

Founding of the city of Baeza, 4th cent.
See Nos. 676-679.

Hotel Quito
A233

#662, Dormitory, Catholic University. #663,
Dormitory, Central University. #664, Airport,
Quito. #665, Overpass on Highway to Quito.
#666, Security Bank. #667, Ministry of For-
eign Affairs. #668, Government Palace. #669,
Legislative Palace.

Perf. 11x11½
1960, Aug. 8   Engr.   Unwmk.
661 A233 1s dk pur & redsh brn .40 .20
662 A233 1s dk bl & brn   .40 .20
663 A233 1s blk & red   .40 .20
664 A233 1s dk bl & ultra   .40 .20
665 A233 1s dk pur & dk car
         rose   .40 .20
666 A233 1s blk & ol bis   .40 .20
667 A233 1s dk pur & turq   .40 .20
668 A233 1s dk bl & grn   .40 .20
669 A233 1s blk & vio   .40 .20
    Nos. 661-669 (9)   3.60 1.80

11th Inter-American Conference, Quito.
For surcharges see Nos. 700-708.

Type of Regular Issue, 1955-56
Souvenir Sheet

Design: Orchids, Napo-Pastaza.

1960   Photo.   Perf. 13
Yellow Paper
670   Sheet of 2   5.75 5.75
  a. A216 80c deep violet   .85 .40
  b. A216 90c deep green   .85 .40

25th anniv. of Asociacion Filatelica Ecuatori-
ana. Marginal inscription in silver. Exists with
silver inscription omitted.

"Freedom of
Expression" — A234

Manabi
Bridge
A235

10c, "Freedom to vote." 20c, "Freedom to
work." 30c, Coins, "Monetary stability."

1960, Aug. 29   Litho.   Perf. 13
671 A234 5c dk bl   .75 .20
672 A234 10c lt vio   .75 .20
673 A234 20c orange   .75 .20
674 A234 30c bluish grn   .75 .20
675 A235 40c brn & bluish grn .75 .20
    Nos. 671-675 (5)   3.75 1.00

Achievements of President Camilo Ponce
Enriquez. See Nos. C370-C374.

Animal Type of 1960.

Animals: 10c, Collared peccary. 20c, Kinka-
jou. 80c, Jaguar. 1s, Mountain coati.

Unwmk.
1961, July 13   Photo.   Perf. 13
676 A232 10c grn, rose red & blk .50 .20
677 A232 20c vio, grnsh bl & brn 1.10 .20
678 A232 80c red org, dl yel &
         blk   1.90 .50
679 A232 1s brn, brt grn & org 3.00 .60
    Nos. 676-679 (4)   6.50 1.50

Founding of the city of Tena, 400th anniv.

Graphium
Pausianus
A236

Butterflies: 30c, Papilio torquatus leptalea.
50c, Graphium molops molops. 80c, Battus
lycidas.

1961, July 13   Litho.   Perf. 13½
680 A236 20c pink & multi   .70 .20
681 A236 30c lt ultra & multi 1.40 .20
682 A236 50c org & multi   1.40 .20
683 A236 80c bl grn & multi   2.50 .20
    Nos. 680-683 (4)   6.00 .80

See Nos. 711-713.

Galapagos Islands Nos. L1-L3
Overprinted in Black or Red

1961, Oct. 31   Photo.   Perf. 12
684 A1 20c dk brn   1.25 .20
685 A2 50c violet   1.25 .20
686 A1 1s dk ol grn (R)   2.75 1.50
    Nos. 684-686, C389-C391 (6) 13.25 6.35

Establishment of maritime biological sta-
tions on Galapagos Islands by UNESCO.
Overprint arranged differently on 20c, 1s.
See Nos. C389-C391.

Daniel
Enrique
Proaño
School
A237

Designs: 60c, Loja-Zamora highway, vert.
80c, Aguirre Abad College, Guayaquil. 1s,
Army quarters, Quito.

Perf. 11x11½, 11½x11
1962, Jan. 10   Engr.   Unwmk.
687 A237 50c dl bl & blk   .45 .20
688 A237 60c ol grn & blk   .45 .20
689 A237 80c org red & blk   .45 .20
690 A237 1s rose lake & blk   .45 .20
    Nos. 687-690 (4)   1.80 .80

Pres.
Arosemena,
Flags of
Ecuador,
US — A238

Protection for The
Family — A239

Designs (Arosemena and): 10c, Flags of
Ecuador. 20c, Flags of Ecuador and Panama.

1963, July 1   Litho.   Perf. 14
691 A238 10c buff & multi   .40 .20
692 A238 20c multi   .50 .20
693 A238 60c multi   .50 .20
    Nos. 691-693, C409-C411 (6) 3.40 1.35

Issued to commemorate Pres. Carlos J.
Arosemena's friendship trip, July 1962.
Imperfs exist. Value $9.

1963, July 9   Unwmk.   Perf. 14
694 A239 10c ultra, red, gray & blk .50 .20

Social Insurance, 25th anniv. See #C413.

No. 655 Overprinted or Surcharged in
Black or Blue

1963   Photo.   Perf. 13
695 A230 10c on 80c dk car rose .50 .20
696 A230 20c on 80c dk car rose .50 .20
697 A230 50c on 80c dk car rose .50 .20
698 A230 60c on 80c dk car rose
         (Bl)   .50 .20
699 A230 80c dk car rose   .50 .20
    Nos. 695-699 (5)   2.50 1.00

Nos. 661-669 Surcharged

1964, Apr. 20   Engr.   Perf. 11x11½
700 A233 10c on 1s dk pur &
         redsh brn   .75 .20
701 A233 10c on 1s dk pur &
         turq   .75 .20
702 A233 20c on 1s dk bl & brn .75 .20
703 A233 20c on 1s dk bl & grn .75 .20
704 A233 30c on 1s dk pur & dk
         car rose   .75 .20
705 A233 40c on 1s blk & ol bis .75 .20
706 A233 60c on 1s blk & red   .75 .20
707 A233 80c on 1s dk bl & ultra .75 .20
708 A233 80c on 1s blk & vio   .75 .20
    Nos. 700-708 (9)   6.75 1.80

No. 656 Overprinted in Black or Light
Ultramarine

1964   Litho.   Perf. 14x13
709 A231 80c rose car & grn   5.25 1.25

Butterfly Type of 1961

Butterflies: Same as on Nos. 680, 682-683.

1964, June   Litho.   Perf. 13½
711 A236 20c brt grn & multi 1.25 .20
712 A236 50c sal pink & multi 1.75 .20
713 A236 80c lt red brn & multi 3.00 .20
    Nos. 711-713 (3)   6.00 .60

Alliance for
Progress
Emblem,
Agriculture
and
Industry
A240

Designs: 50c, Emblem, gear wheels, mountain and seashore. 80c, Emblem, banana
worker, fish, factory and ship.

1964, Aug. 26   Unwmk.   Perf. 12
715 A240 40c bis brn & vio   .20 .20
716 A240 50c red org & blk   .25 .20
717 A240 80c bl & dk brn   .35 .20
    Nos. 715-717 (3)   .80 .60

Issued to publicize the Alliance for Progress
which aims to stimulate economic growth and
raise living standards in Latin America.

No. 650 Overprinted in Red

1964   Photo.   Perf. 14x13½
718 A229 1.80s dark blue   2.75 2.25

No. 656 Overprinted

Illustration reduced.

1964, July   Litho.   Perf. 14x13
719 A231 80c block of 4   3.50 3.50

Organization of American States.

World Map
and Banana
Tree — A241

1964, Oct. 26   Perf. 12½x12
720 A241 50c dk brn, gray & gray
         ol   .25 .20
721 A241 80c blk, org & gray ol .25 .20

Issued to publicize the Banana Conference,
Oct.-Nov. 1964. See Nos. C427-C428a.

King Philip II of Spain and Map of Upper Amazon River A242

Designs (Map and): 20c, Juan de Salinas de Loyola. 30c, Hernando de Santillan.

1964, Dec. 6   Litho.   Perf. 13½
722 A242 1c rose, blk & buff   .25 .25
723 A242 20c bl grn, blk & buff   .25 .25
724 A242 30c bl, blk & buff   .25 .25
    Nos. 722-724 (3)   .75 .75

4th centenary of the establishment of the Royal High Court in Quito.

Pole Vaulting A243

1964, Dec. 16   Perf. 14x13½
725 A243 80c vio bl, yel grn & brn   .25 .20

18th Olympic Games, Tokyo, Oct. 10-25. See Nos. C432-C434.

Peter Fleming and Two-toed Sloth — A244

Designs: 20c, James Elliot and armadillo. 30c, T. Edward McCully, Jr., and squirrel. 40c, Roger Youderian and deer. 60c, Nathaniel (Nate) Saint and plane over Napo River.

1965   Unwmk.   Perf. 13½
726 A244 20c emerald & multi   1.10 .35
727 A244 30c yellow & multi   1.10 .35
728 A244 40c lilac & multi   1.10 .35
729 A244 60c multi   1.10 .35
730 A244 80c multi   1.10 .35
    Nos. 726-730 (5)   5.50 1.75

Issued in memory of five American Protestant missionaries, killed by the Auca Indians, 1/8/56.
Issue dates: 80c, May 11; others, July 8.

Juan B. Vázquez and Benigno Malo College — A245

1965, June 6   Litho.   Perf. 14
731 A245 20c blk, yel & vio bl   .20 .20
732 A245 60c blk, red, yel & vio bl   .20 .20
733 A245 80c blk, emer, yel & vio bl .20 .20
    Nos. 731-733 (3)   .60 .60

Centenary (in 1964) of the founding of Benigno Malo National College.

National Anthem, Juan Leon Mera and Antonio Neumane A246

1965, Aug. 10   Litho.   Perf. 13½
734 A246 50c pink & blk   .20 .20
735 A246 80c lt grn & blk   .35 .20
736 A246 5s bis & blk   .75 .45
737 A246 10s lt ultra & blk   1.40 1.00
    Nos. 734-737 (4)   2.70 1.85

Cent. of the national anthem. The name of the poet Juan Leon Mera is misspelled on the stamps.
For surcharges see Nos. 766C, 766H.

Torch and Athletes (Shot Put, Discus, Javelin and Hammer Throw) — A247

50c, 1s, Runners. 60c, 1.50s, Soccer.

1965, Nov. 20   Perf. 12x12½
738 A247 40c org, gold, & blk   .20 .20
739 A247 50c org ver, gold & blk   .20 .20
740 A247 60c bl, gold & blk   .20 .20
741 A247 80c brt yel grn, gold & blk .30 .20
742 A247 1s lt vio, gold & blk   .30 .20
743 A247 1.50s brt pink, gold & blk   .75 .50
    Nos. 738-743,C435-C440 (12)   5.80 3.30

Issued to publicize the 5th Bolivarian Games, held at Guayaquil and Quito.
For surcharges see #766B, 766D, C449.

Stamps of 1865 A248

1965, Dec. 30   Litho.   Perf. 13½
Stamps of 1865 in Yellow, Ultramarine & Green
744 A248 80c rose red   .20 .20
745 A248 1.30s rose lilac   .40 .20
746 A248 3s chocolate   .55 .20
747 A248 4s black   .85 .20
a.   Souv. sheet, #744-747, imperf.   4.00 4.00
    Nos. 744-747 (4)   2.00 .80

Cent. of Ecuadorian postage stamps.

The postal validity of some of the following sets has been questioned.

ITU Centenary — A248a

1966, Jan. 27   Litho.   Perf. 12x12½
748 A248a 10c Telstar   .20 .20
748A A248a 10c Syncom   .20 .20
748B A248a 80c Relay   .20 .20
748C A248a 1.50s Luna 3   .40 .35
748D A248a 3s Echo II   2.25 1.40
f.   Souv. sheet of 3, #748, 748B, 748D, perf. 14x12½   18.00
748E A248a 4s E. Branly, Marconi, Bell, E. Belin   2.50 2.00
g.   Souv. sheet of 3, #748A, 748C, 748E, perf. 14x12½   18.00
    Nos. 748-748E (6)   5.75 4.35

1.50s, 3s, 4s are airmail.
Nos. 748Df, 748Eg are printed on surface colored paper. Exist imperf. Value, each $18.

Space Exploration — A248b

10c, Edward White's space walk, June 8, 1965. 1s, Gemini 5, Aug. 21, 1965. 1.30s, Solar system. 2s, Charles Conrad, L. Gordon Cooper, Gemini 5, Aug. 21-29, 1965. 2.50s, Gemini 6. 3.50s, Alexei L. Leonov's space walk, Mar. 18, 1965.

1966, Jan. 27   Perf. 12x12½
749 A248b 10c multi   .20 .20
749A A248b 1s multi   .45 .20
749B A248b 1.30s multi   .45 .20
749C A248b 2s multi   1.40 .65
749D A248b 2.50s multi   1.40 .65
749E A248b 3.50s multi   3.00 2.50
f.   Souv. sheet of 3, #749, 749B, 749E, perf. 14x12½   15.00 10.00
    Nos. 749-749E (6)   6.90 4.40

1.30s, 2s, 2.50s, 3.50s are airmail.
No. 749Ef is printed on surface colored paper. Exists imperf. Value $15.

Dante's Dream by Rossetti — A248c

Designs: 80c, Dante and Beatrix by Holliday. 2s, Galileo Galilei, 400th birth cent., vert. 3s, Dante, 700th birth cent., vert.

1966, June   Perf. 13½x14, 14x13½
750 A248c 10c multicolored   .20 .20
750A A248c 80c multicolored   .20 .20
750B A248c 2s multicolored   2.50 1.75
750C A248c 3s multicolored   2.75 2.75
d.   Souv. sheet of 3, #750, 750A, 750C, perf. 12x12½   18.00 18.00
    Nos. 750-750C (4)   5.65 4.90

Nos. 750A-750B are airmail. No. 750Cd exists imperf. Value $18.

Pavonine Quetzal — A249

Birds: 50c, Blue-crowned motmot. 60c, Paradise tanager. 80c, Wire-tailed manakin.

1966, June 17   Litho.   Perf. 13½
Birds in Natural Colors
751 A249 40c dl rose & blk   1.60 .20
751A A249 50c sal & blk   1.60 .20
751B A249 60c lt ocher & blk   1.60 .20
751C A249 80c lt bl & blk   1.60 .20
    Nos. 751-751C,C441-C448 (12)   31.70 5.70

For surcharges see Nos. 766E-766F, C450, C455-C457.

Pope Paul VI — A249a

Pope Paul VI and: 1.30s, Nativity. 3.50s, Virgin of Merced.

1966, June 24   Perf. 12½x12
752 A249a 10c multicolored   .30 .20
752A A249a 1.30s multicolored   .80 .60
752B A249a 3.50s multicolored   2.50 2.50
c.   Souv. sheet of 3, #752, perf. 14x13½, 752A-752B, perf. 12½x12   18.00 18.00
    Nos. 752-752B (3)   3.60 3.30

Nos. 752A-752B are airmail.
No. 752Bc is printed on surface colored paper. Exists imperf. Value $18.

Sir Winston Churchill, (1874-1965) — A249b

Famous Men: 10c, Dag Hammarskjold, vert. 1.50s, Albert Schweitzer, vert. 2.50s, John F. Kennedy, vert. 4s, Churchill, Kennedy.

Perf. 14x13½, 13½x14
1966, June 24
753 A249b 10c vio bl, brn & blk   .20 .20
753A A249b 1s ver, bl & blk   .35 .20
753B A249b 1.50s brn, lil rose & blk .90 .45
753C A249b 2.50s ver, bl & blk   2.25 1.25
753D A249b 4s bl, blk & brn   2.75 2.00
e.   Souv. sheet of 3, #753, 753B, 753D   32.50 32.50
    Nos. 753-753D (5)   6.45 4.10

Nos. 753C-753D are airmail.
No. 753De is printed on surface colored paper. 10c stamp is perf. 14x13½, 1.50s is perf. 14x13½x14x12, 4s is perf. 12x12½x13x12½. Exists imperf. Value $32.50.

History of Summer Olympics — A249c

1966, June 27   Perf. 12x12½
754 A249c 10c Long jump   .20 .20
754A A249c 10c Wrestling   .20 .20
754B A249c 80c Discus, javelin   .55 .20
754C A249c 1.30s Chariot racing   1.25 .45
754D A249c 3s High jump   2.10 1.00
f.   Souv. sheet of 3, #754, 754B, 754D   13.50 8.50
754E A249c 3.50s Discus   3.50 1.25
g.   Souv. sheet of 3, #754A, 754C, 754E   13.50 9.50
    Nos. 754-754E (6)   7.80 3.30

Nos. 754C-754D are airmail.
Nos. 754Df, 754Eg are printed on surface colored paper.
Nos. 754Df and 754Eg exist imperf. Value $13.50.

1968 Winter Olympics, Grenoble — A249d

1966, June 27 — Perf. 14

755	A249d	10c	Speedskating	.20	.20
755A	A249d	1s	Ice hockey	.45	.20
755B	A249d	1.50s	Ski jumping	.70	.35
755C	A249d	2s	Cross country skiing	1.40	.55
755D	A249d	2.50s	Downhill skiing	1.75	1.75
755E	A249d	4s	Figure skating	2.25	2.25
f.	Souv. sheet of 3, #755, 755B, 755E, perf. 14x13½			9.00	7.25
	Nos. 755-755E (6)			6.75	5.30

No. 755Ef is printed on surface colored paper. Exists imperf. Value same as perf.

French-American Cooperation in Space — A249e

Designs: 1.50s, French satellite D-1, Mt. Gros observatory, vert. 4s, John F. Kennedy, satellites.

1966 — Perf. 13½x14, 14x13½

756	A249e	10c multicolored	.50	.30
756A	A249e	1.50s multicolored	2.00	1.40
756B	A249e	4s multicolored	4.25	2.75
c.	Sheet of 3, #756-756B		18.00	14.00
	Nos. 756-756B (3)		6.75	4.45

Nos. 756A-756B are airmail.
No. 756Bc exists imperf. Value same as perf.

Moon Exploration A249f

1966 — Perf. 14

758	A249f	10c Surveyor	.20	.20
758A	A249f	80c Luna 10	.20	.20
758B	A249f	1s Luna 9	.20	.20
758C	A249f	2s Astronaut flight trainer	.80	.55
758D	A249f	2.50s Ranger 7	1.10	.85
758E	A249f	3s Lunar Orbiter 1	1.50	1.50
f.	Sheet of 3, #758, 758A, 758E		13.50	13.50
	Nos. 758-758E (6)		4.00	3.50

Nos. 758C-758E are airmail. Stamps in No. 758f have colored pattern in border.
No. 758f exists imperf. Value same as perf.

1968 Summer Olympics, Mexico City — A249g

Paintings by Mexican artists: 10c, Wanderer by Diego Rivera. 1s, Workers by Jose Orozco. 1.30s, Pres. Juarez by Orozco. 2s, Mother and Child by David Siqueiros. 2.50s, Two Women by Rivera. 3.50s, New Democracy by Siqueiros.

1967, Mar. 13 — Perf. 14

759	A249g	10c multicolored	.20	.20
759A	A249g	1s multicolored	.65	.20
759B	A249g	1.30s multicolored	.90	.40
759C	A249g	2s multicolored	1.10	.65
759D	A249g	2.50s multicolored	1.40	1.40
759E	A249g	3.50s multicolored	2.50	2.25
f.	Sheet of 3, #759, 759B, 759E		18.00	
	Nos. 759-759E (6)		6.75	5.10

Nos. 759B-759E are airmail.

No. 759f is printed on surface colored paper that differs slightly from Nos. 759-759E. Exists imperf. Value same as perf.

1968 Summer Olympics, Mexico City — A249h

1967, Mar. 13

760	A249h	10c Soccer	.20	.20
760A	A249h	10c Hurdles	.20	.20
760B	A249h	80c Track	.20	.20
760C	A249h	1.50s Fencing	.90	.40
760D	A249h	3s High jump	1.75	1.25
f.	Souv. sheet of 3, #760A, 760B, 760D		18.00	11.00
760E	A249h	4s Swimming	3.50	1.75
g.	Souv. sheet of 3, #760, 760C, 760E		13.50	8.50
	Nos. 760-760E (6)		6.75	4.00

Nos. 760C-760E are airmail.
No. 760f-760g are printed on surface colored paper. Exist imperf. Value same as perf.

4th Natl. Eucharistic Congress A249i

Paintings: 10c, Madonna and Child by unknown artist. 60c, Holy Family by Rodriguez. 80c, Madonna and Child by Samaniego. 1s, Good Shepherd by Samaniego. 1.50s, Assumption of the Virgin by Vargas. 2s, Man in Prayer by Santiago.
10s, Chalice, eucharist, church, wheat.

1967, May 10

761	A249i	10c multicolored	.20	.20
761A	A249i	60c multicolored	.75	.35
761B	A249i	80c multicolored	.95	.35
761C	A249i	1s multicolored	1.10	.60
761D	A249i	1.50s multicolored	1.75	.85
761E	A249i	2s multicolored	2.75	.85
	Nos. 761-761E (6)		7.50	3.20

Souvenir Sheet

761F	A249i	10s multi	7.50	7.50

Nos. 761D-761E are airmail. Frames and inscriptions vary greatly.
No. 761F exists imperf. with an orange margin color. Value, same.

Madonna and Child Enthroned by Guido Reni A249j

Paintings of the Madonna and Child by: 40c, van Hemesen. 50c, Memling. 1.30s, Durer. 2.50s, Raphael. 3s, Murillo.

1967, May 25 — Perf. 14x13½

762	A249j	10c multicolored	.20	.20
762A	A249j	40c multicolored	.20	.20
762B	A249j	50c multicolored	.20	.20
762C	A249j	1.30s multicolored	.80	.40
762D	A249j	2.50s multicolored	2.10	1.10
762E	A249j	3s multicolored	3.25	1.40
	Nos. 762-762E (6)		6.75	3.50

Nos. 762C-762E are airmail.

Portrait of a Young Woman by Rogier van der Weyden A249k

Designs: 1s, Helene Fourment by Rubens. 1.50s, Venetian Woman by Durer. 2s, Lady Sheffield by Gainsborough. 2.50s, Suzon by Manet. 4s, Lady with a Unicorn by Raphael.

1967, Sept. 9 — Perf. 14x13½

763	A249k	10c multicolored	.20	.20
763A	A249k	1s multicolored	.65	.40
763B	A249k	1.50s multicolored	1.40	.50
763C	A249k	2s multicolored	1.75	.70
763D	A249k	2.50s multicolored	2.75	.90
763E	A249k	4s multicolored	3.25	1.40
f.	Sheet of 3, #763, 763B, 763E, perf. 14		13.50	9.50
	Nos. 763-763E (6)		10.00	4.10

Stamps in No. 763f have colored pattern in border. Exists imperf. Value same as perf.

John F. Kennedy, 50th Birth Anniv. A249l

JFK and: No. 764A, Dag Hammarskjold. 80c, Pope Paul VI. 1.30s, Konrad Adenauer. 3s, Charles de Gaulle. 3.50s, Winston Churchill.

Perf. 14x13½, 13½x14

1967, Sept. 11

764	A249l	10c lil, brn & bl	.20	.20
764A	A249l	10c yel, brn & sky bl	.20	.20
764B	A249l	80c yel, brn & sal	.20	.20
764C	A249l	1.30s yel, brn & pink	2.40	.90
764D	A249l	3s yel, brn & yel grn	3.25	1.60
764E	A249l	3.50s yel, brn & bl	4.75	2.25
	Nos. 764-764E (6)		11.00	5.35

Souvenir Sheets

764F		Sheet of 3	18.00	10.00
h.	like #764, 35x27mm			
i.	like #764B, 35x27mm			
j.	like #764D, 35x27mm			
764G		Sheet of 3	18.00	10.00
k.	like #764A, 35x27mm			
l.	like #764C, 35x27mm			
m.	like #764E, 35x27mm			

Nos. 764C-764E are airmail. Nos. 764A-764E horiz. Stamps in Nos. 764F-764G have colored pattern in border.
Nos. 764F and 764G exist imperf. Values same as perf.

Christmas — A249m

Designs: No. 765A, Children's procession. 40c, Candlelight procession. 50c, Children singing. 60c, Processional. 2.50s, Christmas celebration.

1967, Dec. 29 — Perf. 13x14

765	A249m	10c multi	.45	.20
765A	A249m	10c multi	.45	.20
765B	A249m	40c multi	.45	.20
765C	A249m	50c multi	.45	.20
765D	A249m	60c multi	.45	.20
765E	A249m	2.50s multi	13.00	10.50
	Nos. 765-765E (6)		15.25	11.00

No. 765E is airmail. See Nos. 768-768F.

Various Surcharges on Issues of 1956-66

1967-68

766	AP72	30c on 1.10s (C337)	.40	.20
766A	AP66	40c on 1.70s (C292)	.40	.20
766B	A247	40c on 3.50s (C438)	.40	.20
766C	A246	50c on 5s (736) ('68)	.40	.20
766D	A247	80c on 1.50s (743)	.45	.20
766E	A249	80c on 2.50s (C445)	.45	.20
766F	A249	1s on 40s (C447)	.55	.20
766G	AP66	1.30s on 1.90s (C293)	.65	.55
766H	A246	2s on 10s (737) ('68)	1.10	1.00
	Nos. 766-766H,C449-C450 (11)		5.50	2.70

The surcharge on Nos. 766B-766C, 766E and 766G-766H includes "Resello." The obliteration of old denomination and arrangement of surcharges differ on each stamp.

Bust of Peñaherrera, Central University, Quito — A250

50c, Law books. 80c, Open book, laurel, horiz.

Perf. 12x12½, 12½x12

1967, Dec. 29 — Litho.

767	A250	50c brt grn & blk	.20	.20
767A	A250	60c rose & blk	.20	.20
767B	A250	80c rose lil & blk	.20	.20
	Nos. 767-767B,C451-C452 (5)		1.10	1.00

Cent. (in 1964) of the birth of Dr. Victor Manuel Peñaherrera (1864-1932), author of the civil and criminal codes of Ecuador.

Christmas Type of 1967

Native Christian Art: 10c, Mourning of the Death of Christ, by Manuel Chili. 80c, Ascension of the Holy Virgin, vert. 1s, The Holy Virgin. 1.30s, Coronation of the Holy Virgin, by Bernardo Rodriguez, vert. 1.50s, Madonna and Child with the Heavenly Host, vert. 2s, Madonna and Child, by Manuel Samaniego, vert. 3s, Immaculate Conception, by Bernardo de Legranda, vert. 3.50s, Passion of Christ, by Chili, vert. 4s, The Holy Virgin of Quito, by de Legranda, vert.

1968 Jan. 19 — Perf. 13½x14, 14x13½

768	A249m	10c multi	.30	.30
768A	A249m	80c multi	.30	.30
768B	A249m	1s multi	.30	.30
768C	A249m	1.30s multi	.30	.30
768D	A249m	1.50s multi	.65	.35
768E	A249m	2s multi	.85	.85
	Nos. 768-768E (6)		2.70	2.40

Souvenir Sheet

Perf. 14

768F		Sheet of 3	18.00	11.00
g.	A249m 3s multicolored			
h.	A249m 3.50s multicolored			
i.	A249m 4s multicolored			

Nos. 768C-768F are airmail. No. 768F exists imperf. Value same.

Tourism Year — A250a

20c, Woman from Otavalo. 30c, Colorado Indian. 40c, Petroglyph of a cat. 50c, Petroglyph of a mythological predator. 60c, Woman in a bazaar. 80c, 1s, 1.30s, Petroglyphs, diff. 1.50s, Colonial street, Quito. 2s, Amulet.

1968, Apr. 1   **Perf. 13½x14**
769	A250a	20c multicolored	.20	.20
769A	A250a	30c multicolored	.20	.20
769B	A250a	40c multicolored	.20	.20
769C	A250a	50c multicolored	.20	.35
769D	A250a	60c multicolored	.20	.20
769E	A250a	80c multicolored	.20	.20
769F	A250a	1s multicolored	.30	.20
769G	A250a	1.30s multicolored	.20	.20
769H	A250a	1.50s multicolored	.30	.20
769I	A250a	2s multicolored	.35	.20
		Nos. 769-769I (10)	2.35	2.00

Eleventh Congress of the Confederation of Latin American Tourist Organizations (COTAL). Nos. 769G-769I are airmail.

Otto Arosemena Gomez — A251

Lions Emblem — A252

Design: 1s, Page from the Constitution.

1968, May 9   **Litho.**   **Perf. 13½x14**
770	A251	80c lil & multi	.20	.20
770A	A251	1s multi	.20	.20
		Nos. 770-770A,C453-C454 (4)	.90	.80

First anniversary of the administration of Pres. Otto Arosemena Gomez.

1968, May 24   **Litho.**   **Perf. 13½x14**
771	A252	80c multi	.20	.20
771A	A252	1.30s multi	.25	.20
771B	A252	2s pink & multi	.30	.20
c.		Souvenir sheet of 1	5.25	5.25
		Nos. 771-771B (3)	.75	.60

50th anniv. (in 1967) of Lions Intl. No. 771c contains one 5s 39x49mm stamp. Exists imperf. Value same as perf.

Pope Paul VI, Visit to Latin America — A252a

39th Intl. Eucharistic Congress, Bogota, Colombia A252b

60c, Pope Paul VI, vert. 1s, Madonna by Botticelli. 1.30s, Pope Paul VI with flags of South American nations. 2s, Madonna and Child by Durer.

1969   **Perf. 13½x14, 14x13½**
772	A252a	40c multicolored	.20	.20
772A	A252a	60c multicolored	.70	.20
772B	A252b	1s multicolored	2.25	.70

772C	A252a	1.30s multicolored	1.60	.75
e.		Souv. sheet of 3, #772, 772A, 772C, imperf.	4.50	2.75
772D	A252b	2s multicolored	2.25	1.00
f.		Souv. sheet of 2, #772B, 772D, imperf.	4.50	2.75
		Nos. 772C-772D (5)	7.00	2.85

Nos. 772C-772D are airmail. Nos. 772-772f overprinted in silver with the national coat of arms.

Madonna with the Angel by Rogier van der Weyden A252c

Paintings by various artists showing the life of the Virgin Mary.

1969   **Perf. 14x13½, 13½x14**
773	A252c	40c shown	.25	.25
773A	A252c	60c Van der Weyden, diff.	.25	.25
773B	A252c	1s Raphael	.35	.25
773C	A252c	1.30s Veronese	1.25	.65
e.		Souv. sheet of 2, #773B-773C, imperf.	6.75	3.25
773D	A252c	2s Van der Weyden, horiz.	2.40	1.10
f.		Souv. sheet of 3, #773-773A, 773D, imperf.	6.75	3.25
		Nos. 773-773D (5)	4.50	2.50

Nos. 773-773Df overprinted in silver with the national coat of arms. Nos. 773C-773D are airmail.

Nos. C331 and C326 Surcharged in Violet and Dark Blue

a

b

1969, Jan. 10   **Perf. 11½, 14x13½**
774	AP79 (a)	40c on 1.30s (V)	.50	.25
774A	AP76 (b)	50c on 1.30s (DBl)	.50	.25

Type of 1958 Surcharged and Overprinted in Plum and Black

Design: Ignacio Luis Arcaya, Foreign Minister of Venezuela.

1969, Mar.   **Litho.**   **Perf. 12**
Flags in Red, Blue and Yellow
775	A223	50c on 2s sepia	.20	.20
775A	A223	80c on 2s sepia	.20	.20
775B	A223	1s on 2s sepia	.20	.20
775C	A223	2s sepia	.20	.20
		Nos. 775-775C,C455-C457 (7)	2.30	1.55

Nos. 775-775C were not issued without overprint. The obliteration of old denomination on No. 775A is a small square around a star.

Overprint is plum, except for the black small coat of arms on right flag.

Map of Ecuador and Oriental Region — A253

Surcharge typographed in Dark Blue, Red Brown, Black or Lilac

1969   **Litho.**   **Perf. 14**
776	A253	20c on 30c (DBl)	.50	.30
776A	A253	40c on 30c (RBr)	.50	.30
777	A253	50c on 30c (DBl)	.50	.30
778	A253	60c on 30c (DBl)	.50	.30
778A	A253	60c on 30c (Bk)	.65	.65
778B	A253	80c on 30c (Bk)	—	25.00
779	A253	80c on 30c (Bk)	.50	.30
780	A253	1s on 30c (L)	.50	.30
780A	A253	1s on 30c (DBl)	2.00	1.25
781	A253	1.30s on 30c (Bk)	.90	.40
782	A253	1.50s on 30c (Bk)	.90	.40
783	A253	2s on 30c (DBl)	1.00	.40
784	A253	3s on 30c (DBl)	1.25	.45
784A	A253	4s on 30c (DBl)	3.25	3.25
785	A253	4s on 30c (Bk)	1.25	.40
786	A253	5s on 30c (Bk)	1.60	.55
		Nos. 776-786 (16)	15.80	34.55

Not issued without surcharge.

M. L. King, John and Robert Kennedy — A254

Thecla Coronata — A255

1969-70   **Typo.**   **Perf. 12½**
787	A254	4s blk, bl, grn & buff	.45	.20

Perf. 13½
788	A254	4s blk, lt bl & grn ('70)	.45	.20

In memory of John F. Kennedy, Robert F. Kennedy and Martin Luther King, Jr.

1970   **Litho.**   **Perf. 12½**

Butterflies: 20c, Papilio zabreus. 30c, Heliconius chestertoni. 40c, Papilio pausanias. 50c, Pereute leucodrosime. 60c, Metamorpha dido. 80c, Morpho cypris. 1s, Catagramma astarte.

789	A255	10c buff & multi	3.25	.45
790	A255	20c lt grn & multi	3.25	.45
791	A255	30c pink & multi	3.25	.45
792	A255	40c lt bl & multi	3.25	.20
793	A255	50c gold & multi	3.25	.20
794	A255	60c salmon & multi	3.25	.20
795	A255	80c silver & multi	3.25	.20
796	A255	1s lt grn & multi	3.25	.20

Same, White Background
Perf. 13½
797	A255	10c multi	3.25	.45
798	A255	20c multi	3.25	.45
799	A255	30c multi	3.25	.45
800	A255	40c multi	3.25	.20
801	A255	50c multi	3.25	.20
802	A255	60c multi	3.25	.20
803	A255	80c multi	3.25	.20
804	A255	1s multi	3.25	.20
		Nos. 789-804,C461-C464 (20)	66.00	5.70

Surcharged Revenue Stamps
A256   A257

1970, June 16   **Litho.**   **Perf. 14**
Red Surcharge
805	A256	1s on 1s light blue	.20	.20
806	A256	1.30s on 1s light blue	.20	.20
807	A256	1.50s on 1s light blue	.30	.30
808	A256	2s on 1s light blue	.35	.20
809	A256	5s on 1s light blue	.75	.35
810	A256	10s on 1s light blue	1.50	.60
		Nos. 805-810 (6)	3.30	1.85

1970   **Typo.**   **Perf. 12**
Black Surcharge
811	A257	60c on 1s violet	.20	.20
812	A257	80c on 1s violet	.20	.20
813	A257	1s on 1s violet	.20	.20
814	A257	1.10s on 1s violet	.20	.20
815	A257	1.30s on 1s violet	.20	.20
816	A257	1.50s on 1s violet	.35	.20
817	A257	2s on 1s violet	.35	.20
818	A257	2.20s on 1s violet	.40	.20
819	A257	3s on 1s violet	.55	.20
		Nos. 811-819 (9)	2.65	1.80

1970
820	A257	1.10s on 2s green	.20	.20
821	A257	1.30s on 2s green	.20	.20
822	A257	1.50s on 2s green	.35	.20
823	A257	2s on 2s green	.35	.20
824	A257	3.40s on 2s green	.55	.20
825	A257	5s on 2s green	.80	.20
826	A257	10s on 2s green	1.25	.20
827	A257	20s on 2s green	2.40	.80
828	A257	50s on 2s green	5.00	2.50
		Nos. 820-828 (9)	11.10	4.70

1970
829	A257	3s on 5s blue	.55	.20
830	A257	5s on 5s blue	.65	.35
831	A257	10s on 40s orange	1.25	.20
		Nos. 829-831 (3)	2.45	1.20

Arms of Zamora Chinchipe — A258   Flags of Ecuador and Chile — A259

Design: 1s, Arms and flag of Esmeraldas.

1971   **Litho.**   **Perf. 10½**
832	A258	50c pale yel & multi	.25	.25
833	A258	1s sal & multi	.25	.20
		Nos. 832-833,C465-C469 (7)	3.70	1.95

1971, Sept.   **Perf. 12½**
840	A259	1.30s blk & multi	.20	.20
		Nos. 840,C481-C482 (3)	.70	.60

Visit of Pres. Salvador Allende of Chile, Aug. 24.

Ismael Pérez Pazmiño — A260

1971, Sept. 16   **Perf. 12x11½**
841	A260	1s grn & multi	.25	.20
		Nos. 841,C485-C486 (3)	.90	.60

"El Universo," newspaper founded by Ismael Pérez Pazmiño, 50th anniv.

CARE Package — A261   Flags of Ecuador and Argentina — A262

1971-72　　　　　　　**Perf. 12½**
842 A261 30c lilac ('72)　　　.20　.20
843 A261 40c emerald ('72)　.20　.20
844 A261 50c blue　　　　　　.20　.20
845 A261 60c carmine　　　　.20　.20
846 A261 80c lt brn ('72)　　.20　.20
　　　Nos. 842-846 (5)　　　1.00　1.00

25th anniversary of CARE, a US-Canadian Cooperative for American Relief Everywhere.

1972　　　　　　　　　**Perf. 11½**
847 A262 1s blk & multi　　　.20　.20
　　　Nos. 847,C491-C492 (3)　.90　.70

Visit of Lt. Gen. Alejandro Agustin Lanusse, president of Argentina, Jan. 25.

Jesus Giving Keys to St. Peter, by Miguel de Santiago A263

Ecuadorian Paintings: 1.10s, Virgin of Mercy, Quito School. 2s, Virgin Mary, by Manuel Samaniego.

1972, Apr. 24　Litho.　Perf. 14x13½
848 A263 50c black & multi　　.25　.25
849 A263 1.10s black & multi　.35　.35
850 A263 2s black & multi　　.60　.60
　a.　Souvenir sheet of 3　　2.50　2.50
　　　Nos. 848-850,C494-C495 (5)　2.80　2.15

No. 850a contains 3 imperf. stamps similar to Nos. 848-850.

1972, May 4
Ecuadorian Statues: 50c, Our Lady of Sorrow, by Caspicara. 1.10s, Nativity, Quito School, horiz. 2s, Virgin of Quito, anonymous.

851 A263 50c blk & multi　　.20　.20
852 A263 1.10s blk & multi　.35　.35
853 A263 2s blk & multi　　.55　.55
　a.　Souv. sheet of 3　　　3.25　2.75
　　　Nos. 851-853,C496-C497 (5)　2.70　2.05

Letters of "Ecuador" 3mm high on Nos. 851-853, 7mm high on Nos. 848-850. No. 853a contains 3 imperf. stamps similar to Nos. 851-853.

A264

A265

Designs: 30c, Gen. Juan Ignacio Pareja. 40c, Juan José Flores. 50c, Leon de Febres Cordero. 60c, Ignacio Torres. 70c, Francisco de Paula Santander. 1s, José M. Cordova.

1972, May 24　　　　　**Perf. 12½**
854 A264 30c blue & multi　　.40　.40
855 A264 40c blue & multi　　.40　.40
856 A264 50c blue & multi　　.40　.40
857 A264 60c blue & multi　　.40　.40

858 A264 70c blue & multi　　.40　.40
859 A264 1s blue & multi　　.40　.40
　　　Nos. 854-859,C498-C503 (12)　10.15　6.95

Sesquicentennial of the Battle of Pichincha and the liberation of Quito.

1972, July　Photo.　Perf. 13
Designs: 2s, Woman Wearing Poncho. 3s, Striped poncho. 5s, Embroidered poncho. 10s, Metal vase.

860 A265 2s multicolored　　.40　.40
861 A265 3s multicolored　　.65　.50
862 A265 5s multicolored　　.90　.85
863 A265 10s dp blue & multi　2.00　1.50
　a.　Souvenir sheet of 4　　6.00　6.00
　　　Nos. 860-863,C504-C507 (8)　8.20　5.85

Handicraft of Ecuador. No. 863a contains 4 imperf. stamps similar to Nos. 860-863.

Sucre Statue, Santo Domingo — A266

Radar Station — A267

1.80s, San Agustin Convent. 2.30s, Plaza de la Independencia. 2.50s, Bolivar statue, La Alameda. 4.75s, Chapel door.

1972, Dec. 6　Litho.　Perf. 11½
864 A266 1.20s yel & multi　　.25　.25
865 A266 1.80s yel & multi　　.25　.25
866 A266 2.30s yel & multi　　.25　.25
867 A266 2.50s yel & multi　　.40　.25
868 A266 4.75s yel & multi　　.55　.30
　　　Nos. 864-868,C518-C524 (12)　5.80　3.50

Sesquicentennial of the Battle of Pichincha.

1973, Apr. 5　　　　　　**Wmk. 367**
869 A267 1s multicolored　　.25　.20

Inauguration of earth telecommunications station, Oct. 19, 1972.

Blue-footed Boobies A268

Wmk. 367, Unwmkd. (#872)
1973　Litho.　Perf. 11½x12
870 A268 30c shown　　　　.40　.20
871 A268 40c Blue-faced booby　.40　.20
872 A268 50c Oyster-catcher　.40　.20
873 A268 60c California sea lions　.85　.20
874 A268 70c Galapagos giant tortoise　1.00　.20
875 A268 1s California sea lion　1.40　.25
　　　Nos. 870-875,C527-C528 (8)　8.65　1.75

Elevation of Galapagos Islands to a province of Ecuador.
Issue dates: 50c, Oct. 3; others Aug. 16.

Black-chinned Mountain Tanager — A269

Birds of Ecuador: 2s, Moriche oriole. 3s, Toucan barbet, vert. 5s, Masked crimson tanager, vert. 10s, Blue-necked tanager, vert.

Perf. 11x11½, 11½x11
1973, Dec. 6　Litho.　Unwmk.
876 A269 1s brick red & multi　.65　.20
877 A269 2s lt blue & multi　　1.10　.20
878 A269 3s lt green & multi　　1.10　.20
879 A269 5s pale lilac & multi　2.40　.65

880 A269 10s pale yel grn & multi　4.75　1.40
　　　Nos. 876-880 (5)　　10.00　2.65

Two souvenir sheets exist: one contains 2 imperf. stamps similar to Nos. 876-877 with yellow margin and black inscription; the other 3 stamps similar to Nos. 878-880; gray margin and black inscription including "Aereo." Both sheets dated "1972." Size: 143x84mm. Value, each $9.

Marco T. Varea, Botanist — A270

Portraits: 60c, Pio Jaramillo Alvarado, writer. 70c, Prof. Luciano Andrade M. No. 883, Marco T. Varea, botanist. No. 884, Dr. Juan Modesto Carbo Noboa, medical researcher. No. 885, Alfredo J. Valenzuela. No. 886, Capt. Edmundo Chiriboga G. 1.20s, Francisco Campos R., scientist. 1.80s, Luis Vernaza Lazarte, philanthropist.

1974　Unwmk.　Perf. 12x11½
881 A270 60c crimson rose　　.20　.20
882 A270 70c lilac　　　　　.20　.20
883 A270 1s ultra　　　　　.20　.20
884 A270 1s orange　　　　.20　.20
885 A270 1s emerald　　　　.20　.20
886 A270 1s brown　　　　.20　.20
887 A270 1.20s apple green　.30　.20
889 A270 1.80s lt blue　　　.40　.25
　　　Nos. 881-889 (8)　　　1.90　1.65

Arcade A271

Designs: 30c, Monastery, entrance. 40c, Church. 50c, View of Church through gate, vert. 60c, Chapel, vert. 70c, Church and cemetery, vert.

Perf. 11½x12, 12x11½
1975, Feb. 4　　　　　　**Litho.**
896 A271 20c yellow & multi　.25　.20
897 A271 30c yellow & multi　.25　.20
898 A271 40c yellow & multi　.25　.20
899 A271 50c yellow & multi　.25　.20
900 A271 60c yellow & multi　.25　.20
901 A271 70c yellow & multi　.25　.20
　　　Nos. 896-901 (6)　　　1.50　1.20

Colonial Monastery, Tilipulo, Cotopaxi Province.

Angel Polibio Chaves, Founder of Bolivar Province — A272

Portrait: No. 903, Emilio Estrada Ycaza (1916-1961), archeologist.

1975　Litho.　Perf. 12x11½
902 A272 80c violet bl & lt bl　.20　.20
903 A272 80c vermilion & pink　.20　.20

Issue dates: #902, Feb. 21; #903, Mar. 25.

R. Rodriguez Palacios and A. Duran Quintero — A273

"Woman of Action" — A274

1975, Apr. 1　Litho.　Perf. 12x11½
910 A273 1s multicolored　　.20　.20
　　　Nos. 910,C547-C548 (3)　.70　.60

Meeting of the Ministers for Public Works of Ecuador and Colombia, July 27, 1973.

1975, June
Design: No. 912, "Woman of Peace."
911 A274 1s yellow & multi　.20　.20
912 A274 1s blue & multi　　.20　.20

International Women's Year 1975.

Planes, Soldier and Ship — A275

1975, July 9　　　　**Perf. 11½x12**
913 A275 2s multicolored　　.30　.25

3 years of Natl. Revolutionary Government.

Hurdling — A276

Designs: Modern sports drawn Inca style.

1975, Sept. 11　Litho.　Perf. 11½
914 A276 20c shown　　　　.45　.35
915 A276 20c Chess　　　　.45　.35
916 A276 30c Basketball　　.45　.35
917 A276 30c Boxing　　　　.45　.35
918 A276 40c Bicycling　　　.45　.35
919 A276 40c Steeplechase　.45　.35
920 A276 50c Soccer　　　　.45　.35
921 A276 50c Fencing　　　.45　.35
922 A276 60c Golf　　　　　.45　.35
923 A276 60c Vaulting　　　.45　.35
924 A276 70c Judo (standing)　.45　.35
925 A276 70c Wrestling　　　.45　.35
926 A276 80c Swimming　　.45　.35
927 A276 80c Weight lifting　.45　.35
928 A276 1s Table Tennis　　.45　.35
929 A276 1s Paddle ball　　.45　.35
　　　Nos. 914-929,C554-C558 (21)　10.00　6.85

3rd Ecuadorian Games.

Genciana A277

Designs: Ecuadorian plants.

Perf. 12x11½, 11½x12
1975, Nov. 18　　　　　　**Litho.**
930 A277 20c Orchid, vert　　.25　.25
931 A277 30c shown　　　　.25　.25
932 A277 40c Bromeliaceae cactaceae, vert　.30　.25
933 A277 50c Orchid　　　　.30　.25
934 A277 60c Orchid　　　　.35　.25
935 A277 80c Flowering cactus　.35　.25
936 A277 1s Orchid　　　　.60　.25
　　　Nos. 930-936,C559-C563 (12)　5.75　3.60

Venus, Chorrera Culture — A278

Female Mask, Tolita Culture — A279

Designs: 30c, Venus, Valdivia Culture. 40c, Seated man, Chorrera Culture. 50c, Man with poncho, Panzaleo Culture (late). 60c, Mythical head, Cashaloma Culture. 80c, Musician, Tolita Culture. No. 943, Chief Priest, Mantefia Culture. No. 945, Ornament, Tolita Culture. No. 946, Angry mask, Tolita Culture.

1976, Feb. 12   Litho.   Perf. 11½
937	A278	20c multicolored	.45 .20
938	A278	30c multicolored	.45 .20
939	A278	40c multicolored	.45 .20
940	A278	50c multicolored	.45 .20
941	A278	60c multicolored	.45 .20
942	A278	80c multicolored	.45 .20
943	A278	1s multicolored	.45 .20
944	A279	1s multicolored	.45 .20
945	A279	1s multicolored	.45 .20
946	A279	1s multicolored	.45 .20
	Nos. 937-946,C568-C572 (15)		8.00 3.30

Archaeological artifacts.

Strawberries A280

Carlos Amable Ortiz (1859-1937) A281

1976, Mar. 30
947	A280	1s blue & multi	.35 .20
	Nos. 947,C573-C574 (3)		1.35 .60

25th Flower and Fruit Festival, Ambato.

1976, Mar. 15   Litho.   Perf. 11½

No. 949, Sixto Maria Duran (1875-1947). No. 950, Segundo Cueva Celi (1901-1969). No. 951, Cristobal Ojeda Davila (1910-1952). No. 952, Luis Alberto Valencia (1918-1970).

948	A281	1s ver & multi	.25 .20
949	A281	1s orange & multi	.25 .20
950	A281	1s lt green & multi	.25 .20
951	A281	1s blue & multi	.25 .20
952	A281	1s lt brn & multi	.25 .20
	Nos. 948-952 (5)		1.25 1.00

Ecuadorian composers and musicians.

Institute Emblem A282

1977, Aug. 15   Litho.   Perf. 11½x12
953	A282	2s multicolored	.25 .20

11th General Assembly of Pan-American Institute of Geography and History, Quito, Aug. 15-30. See Nos. C597-C597a.

Hands Holding Rotary Emblem A283

José Peralta — A284

1977, Aug. 31   Litho.   Perf. 12
954	A283	1s multicolored	.20 .20
955	A283	2s multicolored	.30 .20

Souvenir Sheets
Imperf
956	A283	5s multicolored	1.10 1.10
957	A283	10s multicolored	1.40 1.40

Rotary Club of Guayaquil, 50th anniv.

1977   Litho.   Perf. 11½

Design: 2.40s, Peralta statue.
958	A284	1.80s multi	.20 .20
959	A284	2.40s multi	.25 .20
	Nos. 958-959,C609 (3)		.80 .65

José Peralta (1855-1937), writer.

Blue-faced Booby A285

Galapagos Birds: 1.80s, Red-footed booby. 2.40s, Blue-footed boobies. 3.40s, Gull. 4.40s, Galapagos hawk. 5.40s, Map of Galapagos Islands and boobies, vert.

Perf. 11½x12, 12x11½
1977, Nov. 29   Litho.
960	A285	1.20s multi	.45 .20
961	A285	1.80s multi	.60 .20
962	A285	2.40s multi	1.10 .20
963	A285	3.40s multi	1.60 .20
964	A285	4.40s multi	2.25 .35
965	A285	5.40s multi	3.00 .35
	Nos. 960-965 (6)		9.00 1.50

Dr. Corral Moscoso Hospital, Cuenca A286

1978, Apr. 12   Litho.   Perf. 11½x12
966	A286	3s multicolored	.25 .20
	Nos. 966,C613-C614 (3)		1.75 1.00

Inauguration (in 1977) of Dr. Vicente Corral Moscoso Regional Hospital, Cuenca.

Surveyor Plane over Ecuador — A287

Latin-American Lions Emblem — A288

1978, Apr. 12   Litho.   Perf. 11½
967	A287	6s multicolored	.55 .30
	Nos. 967,C619-C620 (3)		2.85 2.20

Military Geographical Institute, 50th anniv.

1978
968	A288	3s multi	.70 .25
969	A288	4.20s multi	1.00 .25
	Nos. 968-969,C621-C623 (5)		5.85 3.65

7th meeting of Latin American Lions, Jan. 25-29.

70th Anniversary Emblem — A289

1978, Sept.   Litho.   Perf. 11½
970	A289	4.20s gray & multi	.45 .30

70th anniversary of Filanbanco (Philanthropic Bank). See No. C626.

Goalmouth and Net — A290

Designs: 1.80s, "Gauchito" and Games emblem, vert. 4.40s, "Gauchito," vert.

1978, Nov. 1   Litho.   Perf. 12
971	A290	1.20s multi	.20 .20
972	A290	1.80s multi	.20 .20
973	A290	4.40s multi	.55 .20
	Nos. 971-973,C627-C629 (6)		3.15 1.85

11th World Cup Soccer Championship, Argentina, June 1-25.

Symbols for Male and Female — A291

1979, Feb. 15   Litho.   Perf. 12x11½
974	A291	3.40s multi	.45 .30

Inter-American Women's Commission, 50th anniversary.

Emblem A292

1979, June 21   Litho.   Perf. 11½x12
975	A292	4.40s multi	.40 .30
976	A292	5.40s multi	.50 .30

Ecuadorian Mortgage Bank, 16th anniv.

Street Scene, Quito — A293

Perf. 12x11½
1979, Aug. 3   Litho.   Unwmk.
977	A293	3.40s multi	.35 .20
	Nos. 977,C651-C653 (4)		8.00 3.65

Natl. heritage: Quito & Galapagos Islands.

Jose Joaquin de Olmedo (1780-1847), Physician — A294

Chief Enriquillo, Dominican Republic — A295

1980, Apr. 29   Litho.   Perf. 12x11½
978	A294	3s multi	.25 .25
979	A294	5s multi	.45 .40
	Nos. 978-979,C662 (3)		1.70 1.30

First Pres. of Free State of Guayaquil, 1820.

Wmk. 367, Unwmkd. (#981-983)
1980, May 12

Indo-American Tribal Chiefs: 3.40s, Guaycaypuro, Venezuela. No. 982, Abayuba, Uruguay. No. 983, Atlacatl, Salvador.
980	A295	3s multi	.45 .20
981	A295	3.40s multi	.75 .35
982	A295	5s multi	1.75 .55
983	A295	5s multi	1.75 .55
	Nos. 980-983,C663-C678 (20)		40.95 9.90

King Juan Carlos and Queen Sofia, Visit to Ecuador A296

Perf. 11½x12
1980, May 18   Unwmk.
984	A296	3.40s multi	.45 .30

See No. C679.

Cofan Indian, Napo Province — A297

1980, June 10   Litho.   Perf. 12x11½
985	A297	3s shown	.45 .20
986	A297	3.40s Zuleta man, Imbabura	.45 .20
987	A297	5s Chota woman, Imbabura	.65 .20
	Nos. 985-987,C681-C684 (7)		7.25 4.90

Basilica, Our Lady of Mercy Church, Quito A298

1980, July 7   Litho.   Perf. 11½
988	A298	3.40s shown	.45 .20
989	A298	3.40s Balcony	.45 .20
989A	A298	3.40s Dome and cupolas	.45 .20

Sizes: 91x116mm, 116x91mm
Imperf
990	A298	5s multi	1.60 1.60
990A	A298	5s multi, horiz.	1.60 1.60
990B	A298	5s multi	1.60 1.60
	Nos. 988-990B,C685-C691 (13)		14.25 9.40

Virgin of Mercy, patron saint of Ecuadorian armed forces. No. 990 contains designs of Nos. C686, C685, 989. No. 990A contains designs of Nos. C688, C691, C690. No. 990B contains designs of Nos. C689, C687, 989A, 988.

Olympic Torch and Rings — A299

Coronation of Virgin of Cisne, 50th Anniv. — A300

Perf. 12x11½

			1980, July 19		**Wmk. 395**
991	A299	5s multi		.70	.20
992	A299	7.60s multi		1.25	.30
		Nos. 991-992,C695-C696 (4)		3.95	1.80

Souvenir Sheet
Imperf

993	A299	30s multi	6.75	6.75

22nd Summer Olympic Games, Moscow, July 19-Aug. 3.
No. 993 contains vignettes in designs of Nos. 991 and C695.

1980		**Litho.**	**Perf. 11½**	
994	A300	1.20s shown	.30	.30
995	A300	3.40s Different statue	.40	.30

J.J. Olmeda, Father de Velasco, Flags of Ecuador and Riobamba, Constitution A301

1980, Sept. 20		**Litho.**	**Perf. 11½**	
996	A301	3.40s multi	.30	.30
997	A301	5s multi	.70	.45
		Nos. 996-997,C700-C701 (4)	2.70	1.60

Souvenir Sheet
Imperf

998	A301	30s multi	3.25	3.25

Constitutional Assembly of Riobamba sesquicentennial. #998 contains vignettes in designs of #996-997.

Young Indian Girl — A302

Perf. 12x11½

1980, Oct. 9		**Litho.**	**Wmk. 395**	
999	A302	1.20s multi	.20	.20
1000	A302	3.40s multi	.55	.20
		Nos. 999-1000,C703-C704 (4)	3.00	1.55

Democratic government, 1st anniversary.

OPEC Emblem A303

1980, Nov. 8			**Perf. 11½x12**	
1001	A303	3.40s multi	.45	.20

20th anniversary of OPEC. See No. C706.

Decorative Hedges, Capitol Gardens, Carchi A304

1980, Nov. 21			**Perf. 13**	
1002	A304	3s multi	.50	.25
		Nos. 1002,C707-C708 (3)	3.75	1.90

Carchi province centennial.

Cattleya Maxima A305

Designs: Orchids.

1980, Nov. 22			**Perf. 11½x12**	
1003	A305	1.20s *shown*	.55	.20
1004	A305	3s *Comparattia speciosa*	.95	.40
1005	A305	3.40s *Cattleya iricolor*	1.25	.45
		Nos. 1003-1005,C709-C712 (7)	22.50	6.35

Souvenir Sheet
Imperf

1006	A305	30s multi	8.00	6.00

No. 1006 contains vignettes in designs of Nos. 1003-1005.

Pope John Paul II and Children — A306

1980, Dec. 27			**Perf. 12**	
1007	A306	3.40s multi	.60	.30
		Nos. 1007,C715-C716 (3)	2.80	1.40

Christmas and visit of Pope John Paul II.

Carlos and Jorge Mantilla Ortega, Editors of El Comercio — A307

El Comercio Newspaper, 75th Anniv.: 3.40s, Editors Cesar & Carlos Mantilla Jacome.

1981, Jan. 6				
1008	A307	2s multi	.25	.25
1009	A307	3.40s multi	.45	.25

Soldier on Map of Ecuador A308

1981, Mar. 10		**Litho.**	**Perf. 13**	
1010	A308	3.40s shown	.25	.25
1011	A308	3.40s Pres. Roldos	.25	.25

National defense.

Theodore E. Gildred and Ecuador I A309

1981, Mar. 31		**Litho.**	**Perf. 13**	
1012	A309	2s lt bl & blk	.25	.25

Ecuador-US flight, 50th anniv.

A310

A311

1981, Apr. 10				
1013	A310	2s multi	.30	.20

Octavio Cordero Palacios (1870-1930), humanist.

1981		**Litho.**	**Perf. 13**	
1014	A311	2s multi	.30	.30
		Nos. 1014,C721-C722 (3)	2.70	1.55

Radio station HCJB, 50th anniv.

Virgin of Dolorosa A312

1981, Apr. 30		**Litho.**	**Perf. 12**	
1015	A312	2s shown	.20	.20
1016	A312	2s San Gabriel College Church	.20	.20

Miracle of the painting of the Virgin of Dolorosa at San Gabriel College, 75th anniv.

Dr. Rafael Mendoza Aviles Bridge Inauguration A313

1981, July 25			**Perf. 13**	
1017	A313	2s multi	.30	.20

Pablo Picasso (1881-1973), Painter — A313a

1981, Oct. 26		**Litho.**	**Imperf.**	
1017A	A313a	20s multi	2.75	2.75
		Nos. 1017A,C728-C731 (5)	8.05	6.85

No. 1017A contains design of No. C728, additional portrait.

World Food Day — A314

1981, Dec. 31		**Litho.**	**Perf. 13½x13**	
1018	A314	5s multi	.45	.20

See No. C732

Transnave Shipping Co. 10th Anniv. — A315

Intl. Year of the Disabled — A316

1982, Jan. 21		**Litho.**	**Perf. 13**	
1019	A315	3.50s Freighter Isla Salango	.45	.20

1982, Feb. 25				
1020	A316	3.40s Man in wheelchair	.40	.20
		Nos. 1020,C733-C734 (3)	2.00	1.05

Arch — A317

Juan Montalvo Birth Sesqui. — A318

1982, May		**Litho.**	**Perf. 13**	
1021	A317	2s shown	.25	.25
1022	A317	3s Houses	.45	.25

Miniature Sheet
Perf. 12½ on 2 Sides

1023		Sheet of 4, 18th cent. map of Quito	5.00	4.50
a.-d.	A317	6s multi	1.10	.50

QUITEX '82, 4th Natl. Stamp Exhib., Quito, Apr. 16-22. #1023 contains 4 48x31mm stamps.

1982			**Perf. 13**	
1024	A318	2s Portrait	.25	.25
1025	A318	3s Mausoleum	.25	.25
		Nos. 1024-1025,C735 (3)	1.50	1.05

American Air Forces Cooperation System — A319

4th World Swimming Champ., Guayaquil A320

1982				
1026	A319	5s Emblem	.45	.35

1982, July 30				
1027	A320	1.80s Stadium	.20	.20
1028	A320	3.40s Water polo	.35	.20
		Nos. 1027-1028,C736-C737 (4)	2.50	1.25

A321　　A322

1982, Dec.　　Litho.　　Perf. 13
1029　A321　5.40s shown　　.25　.25
1030　A321　6s Statue　　.35　.25

Juan L. Mera (1832-?), Writer, by Victor Mideros.

1983, Mar. 28　　Litho.　　Perf. 13
1031　A322　2s multi　　.35　.25

St. Teresa of Jesus of Avila (1515-82).

Sea Lions　　Flamingoes
A323　　A324

1983, June 17　　Litho.　　Perf. 13
1032　A323　3s multi　　1.40　.20
1033　A324　5s multi　　2.25　.20

Ecuadorian rule over Galapagos Islds., sesqui. (3s); Charles Darwin (1809-1882).

Pres. Rocafuerte　　Simon Bolivar
A325　　A326

Perf. 13x13½
1983, Aug. 26　　Litho.　　Wmk. 395
1034　A325　5s Statue　　.30　.20
1035　A325　20s Portrait　　.85　.35
1036　A326　20s Portrait　　.85　.35
　　Nos. 1034-1036 (3)　　2.00　.90

Vicente Rocafuerte Bejarano, president, 1833-39 (Nos. 1034-1035).

A327　　A328

1983, Sept. 3
1037　A327　5s River　　.70　.20
1038　A327　10s Dam　　1.10　.85
Size: 110x89mm
Imperf
1039　A327　20s Dam, river　　3.50　3.50
　　Nos. 1037-1039 (3)　　5.30　4.55

Paute hydroelectric plant opening. No. 1039 is airmail.

Wmk. 395
1983, Oct. 11　　Litho.　　Perf. 13
1040　A328　2s multi　　.35　.25

World Communication Year.

A329　　A330

1983, Sept.　　Litho.　　Perf. 13
1041　A329　3s multi　　.35　.25

Cent. of Bolivar and El Oro Provinces (1984).

1984, Mar.　　Litho.　　Perf. 13
1042　A330　15s Engraving　　.45　.30

Atahualpa (1497-1529), last Incan ruler.

A331

Christmas
1983 — A331a

Creche figures.

Perf. 13½x13, 13x13½
1984, July 7　　　　Litho.
1043　A331　5s Jesus & the teach-
　　　　ers　　.25　.20
1044　A331　5s Three kings　　.25　.20
1045　A331　5s Holy Family　　.25　.20
1046　A331a　6s Priest　　.25　.20
　　Nos. 1043-1046 (4)　　1.00　.80

Foreign
Policy of
Pres.
Hurtado
A332

State visits.

1984, July 10　　　　Perf. 13½x13
1047　A332　8s Brazil　　.40　.20
1048　A332　9s PRC　　.45　.20
1049　A332　24s UN　　1.25　.90
1050　A332　28s US　　1.60　.95
1051　A332　29s Venezuela　　1.60　1.10
1052　A332　37s Latin American
　　　　Economic Conf.,
　　　　Quito　　2.00　1.40
　　Nos. 1047-1052 (6)　　7.30　4.75

Miguel Diaz
Cueva
(1884-1942),
Lawyer
A333

1984, Aug. 8　　Litho.　　Perf. 13½x13
1053　A333　10s multicolored　　.70　.35

1984 Winter　　Manned Flight
Olympics　　Bicentenary
A334　　A335

Perf. 13x13½, 12x11½ (6s)
1984, Aug. 15
1054　A334　2s Emblem　　.20　.20
1055　A334　4s Ice skating　　.20　.20
1056　A334　6s Skating, diff.　　.20　.20
1057　A334　10s Skiing　　1.25　.20
　　Nos. 1054-1057 (4)　　1.85　.80
Size: 90x100mm
1057A　A334　20s Figure skat-
　　　　ing　　35.00　15.00

1984, Aug. 15　　　　Perf. 13x13½
1058　A335　3s Montgolfier　　.20　.20
1059　A335　6s Charlier's balloon,
　　　　Paris, 1789　　.65　.20
Souvenir Sheet
1060　A335　20s Graf Zeppelin,
　　　　Montgolfier　　2.50　1.50

No. 1060 is airmail and contains one imperf. stamp (50x37mm).

SAN MATEO
'83,
Esmeraldas
A336

1984　　　　Litho.　　Perf. 13
1061　A336　8s La Marimba folk
　　　　dance　　1.75　.25
Size: 89x110mm
Imperf
1061A　A336　15s La Marimba,
　　　　diff.　　2.50　2.50

No. 1061A is airmail.

Jose Maria de
Jesus Yerovi (b.
1824), 4th
Archbishop of
Quito — A337

1984
1062　A337　5s multi　　.35　.25

Canonization
of Brother
Miguel
A338

1984　　　　Litho.　　Perf. 13
1063　A338　9s Academy of Lan-
　　　　guages　　.50　.20
1064　A338　24s Vatican City, vert.　1.00　.70
Imperf
Size: 110x90mm
1065　A338　28s Home of Brother
　　　　Miguel　　3.25　2.10
　　Nos. 1063-1065 (3)　　4.75　3.00

No. 1065, airmail, has black control number.

State Visit of Pope　　Beatification of
John　　Mercedes de
Paul II — A339　　Jesus
　　　　Molina — A340

1985, Jan. 23　　Litho.　　Perf. 13x13½
1066　A339　1.60s Papal arms　　2.00　.25
1067　A339　5s Blessing
　　　　crowd　　2.00　.25
1068　A339　9s World map,
　　　　itinerary　　2.00　.25
1069　A339　28s Pope waving　　4.50　.50
1070　A339　29s Portrait　　5.00　.60
Size: 90x109mm
Imperf
1071　A339　30s Pope holding
　　　　crosier　　10.00　10.00
　　Nos. 1066-1071 (6)　　25.50　11.85

1985, Jan. 23
Paintings, sculpture.
1072　A340　1.60s Portrait　　.30　.20
1073　A340　5s Czestochowa
　　　　Madonna　　.30　.20
1074　A340　9s Alborada Ma-
　　　　donna　　.75　.20
Size: 90x110mm
Imperf
1075　A340　20s Mercedes de
　　　　Jesus, children 5.00　5.00
　　Nos. 1072-1075 (4)　　6.35　5.60

Visit of Pope John Paul II, birth bimillennium of the Virgin Mary.

Samuel Valarezo
Delgado,
Naturalist,
Politician — A341

1985, Feb.
1076　A341　2s Bird　　.20　.20
1077　A341　3s Swordfish, tuna　.20　.20
1078　A341　6s Portrait　　.30　.20
　　Nos. 1076-1078 (3)　　.70　.60

ESPANA '84,
Madrid
A342

1985, Apr. 25　　　　Perf. 13½x13
1079　A342　6s Emblem　　.20　.20
1080　A342　10s Spanish royal
　　　　family　　.70　.20
Size: 110x90mm
Imperf
1081　A342　15s Retiro Park, exhi-
　　　　bition site　　1.50　1.50

Dr. Pio
Jaramillo
Alvarado
(1884-1968),
Historian
A343

1985, May 17
1082　A343　6s multi　　.25　.20

Ingenio Valdez Sugar Refinery — A344

Designs: 50s, Sugar cane, emblem. 100s, Rafael Valdez Cervantes, founder.

1985, June   **Litho.**   **Perf. 13**
1082A	A344	50s multi	1.25	.65
1082B	A344	100s multi	2.75	1.40

Size: 110x90mm
Imperf
1083	A344	30s multi	2.00	2.00
		Nos. 1082A-1083 (3)	6.00	4.05

Chamber of Commerce, 10th Anniv. A345

50s, Natl. and American Statues of Liberty.

1985, Aug. 15   **Perf. 13½x13**
1084	A345	24s multicolored	.80	.45
1085	A345	28s multicolored	1.00	.65

Size: 110x90mm
Imperf
1086	A345	50s multicolored	2.75	2.75
		Nos. 1084-1086 (3)	4.55	3.85

Natl. Philatelic Assoc., AFE, 50th Anniv. — A346

1985, Aug. 25   **Perf. 12**
1087	A346	25s AFE emblem	.60	.40
1088	A346	30s No. 357, horiz.	1.00	.65

Guayaquil Fire Dept., 150th Anniv. A347

1985, Oct. 10   **Perf. 13½x13**
1089	A347	6s Steam fire pump, 1882	.20	.20
1090	A347	10s Fire Wagon, 1899	.50	.20
1091	A347	20s Anniv. emblem, natl. flag	.90	.70
		Nos. 1089-1091 (3)	1.60	1.10

Natl. Infant Survival Campaign A348   1st Natl. Phil. Cong., Quito, Nov. 25-28 A349

1985, Oct.   **Perf. 13x13½**
1092	A348	10s Boy, girl, tree	.45	.30

1985, Nov.   **Perf. 13x13½, 13½x13**

20th cent. illustrations, natl. cultural collection: 5s, Supreme Court, Quito, by J. M. Roura. 10s, Riobamba Cathedral, by O. Munaz. 15s, House of 100 Windows, by J. M. Roura, horiz. 20s, Rural cottage near Cuenca, by J. M. Roura.

No. 1097: a, Stampless cover, 1779, Riobamba. b, Hand press, 1864, Quito. c, Postrider, 1880, Cuenca. d, Monoplane, 1st airmail flight, 1919, Guayaquil.

1093	A349	5s multi	.20	.20
1094	A349	10s multi	.50	.20
1095	A349	15s multi	.65	.50
1096	A349	20s multi	.90	.65
		Nos. 1093-1096 (4)	2.25	1.55

Souvenir Sheet
1097		Sheet of 4	1.00	1.00
a.-d.	A349	5s, any single	.20	.20

AFE, 50th anniv. #1097 contains 53x42mm stamps, perf. 13x12½ on 2 sides.

10th Bolivarian Games, Cuenca A350

1985, Nov.   **Perf. 13½x13**
1098	A350	10s Boxing	.50	.20
1099	A350	25s Women's gymnastics	.65	.35
1100	A350	30s Discus	.85	.40
		Nos. 1098-1100 (3)	2.00	.95

BAE Calderon, Navy Cent. — A351

Military anniv.: #1102, Fighter plane, Air Force 65th anniv. #1103, Army & paratroops emblems, Special Forces 30th anniv.

1985, Dec.   **Perf. 13x13½**
1101	A351	10s multi	.45	.20
1102	A351	10s multi	.45	.20
1103	A351	10s multi	.45	.20
		Nos. 1101-1103 (3)	1.35	.60

UN, 40th Anniv. A352

1985, Oct.   **Litho.**   **Perf. 13**
1104	A352	10s UN flag	.45	.20
1105	A352	20s Natl. flag	.45	.20

Size: 110x90mm
Imperf
1106	A352	50s UN Building	1.25	1.25
		Nos. 1104-1106 (3)	2.15	1.65

Christmas A353   Indigenous Flowers A354

1985, Nov.
1107	A353	5s Child riding donkey	.20	.20
1108	A353	10s Baked goods	.45	.20
1109	A353	15s Riding donkey, diff.	.60	.45

Size: 90x110mm
Imperf
1110	A353	30s like 5s	1.50	1.50
		Nos. 1107-1110 (4)	2.75	2.35

1986, Feb.
1111	A354	24s Embotrium grandiforum	1.00	.45
1112	A354	28s Topobea sp.	1.75	.45
1113	A354	29s Befaria resinosa mutis	2.25	.50

Size: 110x90mm
Imperf
1114	A354	15s multi	7.25	5.00
		Nos. 1111-1114 (4)	12.25	6.40

No. 1114 contains designs of Nos. 1111, 1113, 1112; black control number.

Discovery of the Galapagos Islds., 450th Anniv. A355

Map of the Islands — A356

1986, Feb. 12
1115	A355	10s Land iguana	.45	.20
1116	A355	20s Sea lion	.90	.45
1117	A355	30s Frigate birds	1.40	.70
1118	A355	40s Penguins	1.75	1.00
1119	A355	50s Sea turtle	2.25	1.10
1120	A355	100s Charles Darwin	4.50	2.50
1121	A355	200s Bishop Tomas de Berlenga, discoverer	8.75	4.50

Perf. 12½ on 2 Sides
1122	A356	Sheet of 4	11.00	11.00
a.-d.		50s, any single	1.50	1.50
		Nos. 1115-1122 (8)	31.00	21.45

No. 1122 contains 53x42mm stamps.

Inter-American Development Bank, 25th Anniv. — A357

5s, Antonio Ortiz Mena, pres. 1971-88. 10s, Felipe Herrera, pres. 1960-71. 50s, Emblem.

1986, Mar. 6
1123	A357	5s multi	.40	.20
1124	A357	10s multi	.60	.20
1125	A357	50s multi	1.00	.80
		Nos. 1123-1125 (3)	2.00	1.20

Guayaquil Tennis Club, 75th Anniv. A358

1986, Mar. 7
1126	A358	10s Emblem	.45	.20
1127	A358	10s Francisco Segura Cano, vert.	.45	.20
1128	A358	10s Andres Gomez Santos, vert.	.45	.20
		Nos. 1126-1128 (3)	1.35	.60

1986 World Cup Soccer Championships, Mexico — A359

1986, May 5
1129	A359	5s Shot	.20	.20
1130	A359	10s Block	.80	.20

An imperf. stamp exists picturing flags, player and emblem. Value $8.50.

Meeting of Presidents Cordero and Betancourt of Colombia, Feb. 1985 A360

1986   **Litho.**   **Perf. 13½x13**
1131	A360	20s Presidents	.45	.20
1132	A360	20s Embracing	.45	.20

Exports A361

35s, #1137c, Shrimp. 40s, #1137b, Tuna. 45s, #1137a, Sardines. #1137d, MICIP emblem.

1986, Apr. 12
1133	A361	35s ultra & ver	1.00	.55
1134	A361	40s red & yel grn	1.00	.55
1135	A361	45s car & dk yel	1.15	.75

Perf. 12½ on 2 Sides
1137		Sheet of 4	2.25	2.25
a.-d.	A361	10s, any single	.40	.40
		Nos. 1133-1137 (4)	5.40	4.10

No. 1137 contains 4 53x42mm stamps.

A362

La Condamine's First Geodesic
Mission, 250th Anniv. — A363

#1141a, Triangulation map for determining
equatorial meridian, 1736. #1141b, Partial
map of the Maranon & Amazon Rivers, by
Samuel Fritz, 1743-1744. #1141c, Base of
measurement, Yaruqui plains. #1141d,
Caraburo & Dyambaru Pyramids near Quito.
#1141 has a continuous design.

1986, July 10 Litho. Perf. 13½x13
1138 A362 10s La Condamine .35 .20
1139 A362 15s Maldonado .45 .20
1140 A362 20s Middle of the
World, Quito .55 .20
Nos. 1138-1140 (3) 1.35 .60

Souvenir Sheet
Perf. 12½ on 2 Sides
1141 A363 Sheet of 4 2.75 2.75
a.-d. 10s any single .40 .40

Chambers of
Commerce
A364

1986 Litho. Perf. 13½x13
1142 A364 10s Pichincha .25 .20
1143 A364 10s Cuenca .25 .20
1144 A364 10s Guayaquil .25 .20
Nos. 1142-1144 (3) .75 .60

Civil Service and
Communications
Ministry, 57th
Anniv. — A365

Organization emblems.

1986, Dec. Litho. Perf. 13x13½
1145 A365 5s State railway .20 .20
1146 A365 10s Post office .20 .20
1147 A365 15s Communications .55 .20
1148 A365 20s Ministry of Public
Works .65 .40
Nos. 1145-1148 (4) 1.60 1.00

A366 A367

1987, Feb. 16 Litho. Perf. 13x13½
1149 A366 5s multi .35 .25

Chamber of Agriculture of the 1st Zone,
50th anniv.

Litho. & Typo.
1988, Jan. 6 Perf. 13
Col. Luis Vargas Torres (d. 1887): 50s, Portrait. #1151, Combat unit, c. 1885. #1152a,
Torres & his mother, Delfina. #1152b, Letter to
Delfina written by Torres during imprisonment,
1882. #1152c, Arms of Ecuador & combat
unit.

1150 A367 50s yel grn, blk &
gold 1.00 .80

1151 A367 100s ver, gold & ultra 2.25 1.40

Size: 95x140mm
Perf. 12 on One or Two Sides
1152 Block of 3 6.75 6.75
a.-c. A367 100s any single 1.50 1.50
Nos. 1150-1152 (3) 10.00 8.95

Sizes: #1152a, 1152c, 95x28mm; #1152b,
95x83mm.

Founding of
Guayaquil,
450th Anniv.
A368

15s, Street in Las Penas. 30s, Rafael Mendoza Aviles Bridge. 40s, Francisco de Orellana (c. 1490-1546), Spanish explorer,
founder, & reenactment of landing, 1538.

1988, Feb. 19 Litho. Perf. 13
1153 A368 15s multi, vert. .20 .20
1154 A368 30s multi .45 .20
1155 A368 40s multi .60 .20
Nos. 1153-1155 (3) 1.25 .60

Social
Security
Foundation
(IESS), 60th
Anniv.
A369

1988, Mar. 11
1156 A369 50s shown .75 .40
1157 A369 100s multi, diff. 1.50 1.00

Dr. Pedro
Moncayo y
Esparza
(1807-1888),
Author,
Politician
A370

1988, Apr. 28 Litho. Perf. 14x13½
1158 A370 10s Yaguarcocha
Lake .20 .20
1159 A370 15s shown .20 .20
1160 A370 20s Residence .20 .20

Size: 89x110mm
Imperf
1161 A370 100s Full-length portrait 1.10 1.10
Nos. 1158-1161 (4) 1.70 1.70

A371

Avianca Airlines,
60th
Anniv. — A372

1988, May 12 Litho. Perf. 14x13½
1162 A371 10s Junkers F-13 .20 .20
1163 A371 20s Dornier Wal
seaplane .20 .20
1164 A371 30s Ford 5AT trimotor .45 .20
1165 A371 40s Boeing 247-D .55 .20
1166 A371 50s Boeing 720-
059B .65 .45
1167 A371 100s Douglas DC-3 1.50 .60
1168 A371 200s Boeing 727-
200 2.75 1.50
1169 A371 300s Sikorsky S-38 4.75 2.00

Perf. 13½x14
1170 A372 500s shown 7.25 3.50
Nos. 1162-1170 (9) 18.30 8.85

San Gabriel
College,
125th Anniv.
A373

1988, July 25 Litho. Perf. 14x13½
1171 A373 15s Contemporary facility .20 .20
1172 A373 35s College entrance,
19th cent. .50 .30

A374

Military
Geographical
Institute,
60th Anniv.
A375

1988, July 25 Perf. 12½ on 2 Sides
Size of No. 1173: 110x90mm
1173 A374 Block of 4 1.75 1.75
a.-d. 5s any single .30 .30

Perf. 13½
1174 A375 25s Planetarium .45 .20
1175 A375 50s Zeiss projector .80 .20
1176 A375 60s Anniv. em-
blem 1.00 .35
1177 A375 500s Creation, mural by E.
Kingman 6.25 3.25
Nos. 1173-1177 (5) 10.25 5.75

In 1996 Nos. 1174, 1183, 1265 were
surcharged 800s, 2600s 400s respectively.
Only a few sets were sold to the public. The
balance were sold by postal employees at
greatly inflated prices.

Salesian
Brothers in
Ecuador,
Cent.
A376

Designs: 10s, St. John Bosco (1815-88),
vert. 50s, 1st Salesian Cong. in Ecuador.
100s, Bosco, Salesian Brothers monument
and Andes Mountains.

1988, July 29 Litho. Perf. 13½
1178 A376 10s multi .25 .25
1179 A376 50s multi .75 .40

Size: 89x110mm
Imperf
1180 A376 100s multi 2.25 1.60
Nos. 1178-1180 (3) 3.25 2.25

Francisco Coello,
Founder — A377

Social Services Council, Guayaquil,
Cent. — A378

Flag: a, Emblem (upper left portion). b,
Emblem (upper right portion). c, Emblem
(lower left portion) and "100 AÑOS." d,
Emblem (lower right portion) and "DE TRADI-
CION DE FE, AMPARO Y ESPERANZA."

1988, Nov. 24 Litho. Perf. 13½x14
1181 A377 15s shown .20 .20
1182 A377 20s Eduardo
Arosemena, 1st
Director .20 .20
1183 A377 45s Emblem .45 .20

Size: 110x90mm
Perf. 12½ on 2 Sides
1184 A378 Block of 4 1.25 1.25
a.-d. 10s any single .30 .30
Nos. 1181-1184 (4) 2.10 1.85

For surcharge see note following No. 1177.

A379

Azuay Bank, 75th Anniv. — A380

Perf. 14x13½, 13½x14
1989, Mar. 1 Litho.
1185 A379 20s shown .20 .20
1186 A379 40s multi, vert. .30 .20

Size: 90x110mm
Imperf
1187 A380 500s shown 9.00 2.40
Nos. 1185-1187 (3) 9.50 2.80

1988 Summer
Olympics,
Seoul — A381

Character trademark demonstrating sports.

1989, Mar. 20 Perf. 13½x14
1188 A381 10s Running .20 .20
1189 A381 20s Boxing .20 .20
1190 A381 30s Cycling .40 .20
1191 A381 40s Shooting .40 .20
1192 A381 100s Diving .90 .60
1193 A381 200s Weight lifting 1.75 1.25
1194 A381 300s Tae kwon do 2.75 1.75

Size: 90x110mm

Imperf

1195	A381	200s	Emblems	2.75	2.75
			Nos. 1188-1195 (8)	9.35	7.15

RUMINAHUI '88 — A382

Designs: 50s, *Bird,* by Joaquin Tinta, vert. 70s, Matriz Church, Sangolqui. 300s, Monument to Ruminahui in Sangolqui, Pichincha.

Perf. 14x13½, 13½x14

1989, May 2　　Litho.　　Wmk. 395

1196	A382	50s	multi	.80	.20
1197	A382	70s	multi	1.00	.20

Size: 90x111mm

Imperf

1198	A382	300s	multi	5.75	1.10
			Nos. 1196-1198 (3)	7.55	1.50

Cantonization, 50th anniv.

Benjamin Carrion Mora, Educator A383

Perf. 13½x14, 14x13½

1989, May 10　　　　Litho.

1199	A383	50s	Portrait, vert.	.45	.20
1200	A383	70s	Loja landscape	.55	.20
1201	A383	1000s	University	8.00	3.50

Size: 110x90mm

Imperf

1202	A383	200s	Portrait, diff.	1.50	1.50
			Nos. 1199-1202 (4)	10.50	5.40

2nd Intl. Art Biennial A384

Prize-winning art: 40s, *The Gilded Frame,* by Myrna Baez. 70s, *Paraguay III,* by Carlos Colorabino, vert. 100s, Ordinance establishing the art exhibition. 180s, *Modulation 892,* by Julio Le Parc, vert.

Perf. 14x13½, 13½x14, Imperf. (100s)

1989, June 2　　　　Litho.

Size of No. 1205: 110x90mm

1203	A384	40s	multi	.45	.20
1204	A384	70s	multi	.90	.20
1205	A384	100s	multi	1.75	.75
1206	A384	180s	multi	1.50	.95
			Nos. 1203-1206 (4)	4.60	2.10

Guayaquil Chamber of Commerce, Cent. A385

Perf. 13½x14, 14x13½, Imperf. (No. 1208)

1989, June 20　　　　Litho.

Size of No. 1208: 110x91mm

1207	A385	50s	Founder Ignacio Molestina, vert.	.75	.35
1208	A385	200s	Flags	3.25	2.00
1209	A385	300s	Headquarters	2.25	2.25
1210	A385	500s	Flags, diff.	1.50	1.50
			Nos. 1207-1210 (4)	7.75	6.10

French Revolution, Bicent. A386

20s, French natl. colors, anniv. emblem. 50s, Cathedral fresco. 100s, Rooster. 200s, Symbols of the revolution. 600s, Story board showing events of the revolution.

1989, July 11　　Perf. 13½x14, 14x13½

1211	A386	20s	multi, vert.	.20	.20
1212	A386	50s	multi	.45	.20
1213	A386	100s	multi, vert.	.70	.45

Size: 90x110mm

Imperf

1214	A386	200s	multi, vert.	1.50	1.50
1215	A386	600s	multi, vert.	6.00	6.00
			Nos. 1211-1215 (5)	8.85	8.35

A387

Ministry of Public Works and Communications A388

#1216a, MOP emblem, 2-lane roadway. #1216b, State railway emblem, train. #1216c, Postal service emblem, airmail cover. #1216d, Telecommunications (IETEL) emblem, wall telephone. #1217, MOP, IETEL, postal service & state railway emblems. 100s, IETEL emblem. 200s, MOP emblem.

1989, July 7　　Perf. 12½ on 2 Sides

1216	A387		Block of 4	2.00	2.00
a.-d.			50s any single	.40	.40

Perf. 13½x14

1217	A388	50s	shown	.35	.20
1218	A388	100s	multi	.65	.40
1219	A388	200s	multi	1.50	.85
			Nos. 1216-1219 (4)	4.50	3.45

MOP, 60th anniv.; national communications, 105th anniv. (No. 1216d, 100s).

Natl. Red Cross, Intl. Red Cross and Red Crescent Societies, 125th Annivs. A389

1989, Sept. 14　　Litho.　　Perf. 13½

1220	A389	10s	Medical volunteer, vert.	.20	.20
1221	A389	30s	shown	.20	.20
1222	A389	200s	Two volunteers	1.40	.85
			Nos. 1220-1222 (3)	1.80	1.25

Juan Montalvo (1832-1889), Writer A390

1989, Nov. 11　　Litho.　　Perf. 14x13½

1223	A390	50s	Mausoleum, Ambato	.35	.20
1224	A390	100s	Portrait (detail)	.90	.55
1225	A390	200s	Monument, Ambato	1.60	1.25

Size: 90x110mm

Imperf

1226	A390	200s	Portrait	1.25	1.25
			Nos. 1223-1226 (4)	4.10	3.25

America Issue A391

UPAE emblem and pre-Columbian pottery.

1990, Mar. 6　　Litho.　　Perf. 13½

1227	A391	200s	La Tolita incensory, vert.	1.60	1.10
1228	A391	300s	Warrior (plate)	2.50	1.60

Dated 1989.

Dr. Luis Carlos Jaramillo Leon, Founder A392

#1233a, Dr. Leon. #1230, 1233b, Federico Malo Andrade, honorary president. 130s, #1233c, Roberto Crespo Toral, 1st president. 200s, Alfonso Jaramillo Leon, founder.

1990, Jan. 17　　Litho.　　Perf. 13½

1229	A392	100s	shown	.80	.55
1230	A392	100s	multicolored	.80	.55
1231	A392	130s	multicolored	1.10	.70
1232	A392	200s	multicolored	1.60	1.10

Size: 91x38mm

Perf. 12½ Horiz. on 1 or 2 sides

1233			Block of 3	2.75	2.75
a.-c.			A392 100s any single	.50	.50
			Nos. 1229-1233 (5)	7.05	5.65

Chamber of Commerce, 70th anniversary.

World Cup Soccer, Italy — A393

1990, July 12　　Litho.　　Perf. 13½

1234	A393	100s	shown	.55	.20
1235	A393	200s	Soccer player	1.10	.55
1236	A393	300s	Map of Italy, trophy	1.75	.80

Imperf

Size: 110x90mm

1237	A393	200s	Player, flags	1.50	1.50

Size: 60x90mm

1238	A393	300s	World Cup Trophy	2.25	2.25
			Nos. 1234-1238 (5)	7.15	5.30

Nos. 1235-1236, 1238 vert.

A394　　　　A396

A395

1990, June 12　　　　Perf. 13½

1239	A394	100s	multi	.60	.20
1240	A394	200s	Church tower, book	1.00	.60

College of St. Mariana, cent.

1990, Sept. 7　　Litho.　　Perf. 13½

Tourism: No. 100s, No. 1244c, Iguana. 200s, No. 1244b, La Compania Church, Quito. 300s, No. 1244a, Old man from Vilcabamba. No. 1244d, Locomotive.

1241	A395	100s	multi	.70	.20
1242	A395	200s	multi, vert.	1.40	.45
1243	A395	300s	multi	1.90	.65

Size: 111x90mm

Perf. 12½ on 2 sides

1244			Block of 4	6.75	3.25
a.-d.			A395 100s any single	.35	.20
			Nos. 1241-1244 (4)	10.75	4.55

1990, Sept. 1　　　　Perf. 13½

National Census: 100s, No. 1248a, People and house. 200s, No. 1248b, Map. 300s, No. 1248c, Census breakdown, pencil.

1245	A396	100s	multicolored	.45	.20
1246	A396	200s	multicolored, horiz.	1.00	.45
1247	A396	300s	multicolored	1.40	.65

Size: 109x88mm

Perf. 12½ on 2 sides

1248			Block of 3	1.50	1.50
a.-c.			A396 100s any single	.30	.30
			Nos. 1245-1248 (4)	4.35	2.80

A397　　　　A398

1990, Nov. 2　　Litho.　　Perf. 14

1249	A397	200s	Flags	.95	.35
1250	A397	300s	shown	1.40	.50

Organization of Petroleum Exporting Countries (OPEC), 30th anniv.

1990, Oct. 31　　　　Perf. 13½x14

1251	A398	200s	Emblem	.95	.35
1252	A398	300s	Wooden parrots	1.40	.50

Size: 92x110mm

Imperf

1253	A398	200s	Wooden parrots, diff.	1.60	1.60
			Nos. 1251-1253 (3)	3.95	2.45

Artisans' Organization, 25th anniv.

Flowers — A399

Wmk. 395

1990, Nov. 12 **Litho.** *Perf. 13½*
1254 A399 100s Sobralia .90 .20
1255 A399 100s Blakea, vert. .90 .20
1256 A399 100s Cattleya, vert. .90 .20
1257 A399 100s Loasa, vert. .90 .20
　Nos. 1254-1257 (4) 3.60 .80

Discovery of America, 500th Anniv. (in 1992) A400

1990, Dec. 31 **Litho.** *Perf. 13½*
1258 A400 100s Ancient dwelling .55 .20
1259 A400 200s Mangrove swamp 1.25 .35

Natl. Union of Journalists, 50th Anniv. A401

1991, Feb. 28
1260 A401 200s shown .95 .65
1261 A401 300s Eugenio Espejo, writer 1.60 .70
1262 A401 400s Union emblem 1.75 .95
　Nos. 1260-1262 (3) 4.30 2.30

Radio Quito, 50th Anniv. A402

Designs: 200s, Man with microphone, vert. 500s, Family listening to radio.

1991, Apr. 10
1263 A402 200s multicolored .75 .35
1264 A402 500s multicolored 1.60 .85

Dr. Pablo A. Suarez, Birth Cent. — A403

1991, Sept. 16 **Wmk. 395**
1265 A403 70s multicolored .35 .25
　Dated 1990.
　For surcharge see note following No. 1177.
　Value $20.

America Issue A404

UPAEP emblem and: 200s, Columbus' ships. 500s, Columbus, landing in America.

1991, Oct. 18 **Litho.** *Perf. 13½x13*
1266 A404 200s multicolored 1.00 .65
1267 A404 500s multicolored 1.90 1.25

A405　　　　　A406

Designs: Cultural artifacts.

Wmk. 395

1991, Nov. 14 **Litho.** *Perf. 13½*
1268 A405 100s Cat censer .50 .20
1269 A405 200s Statue of old man's head 1.00 .35
1270 A405 300s Zoomorphic statue 1.75 .60
　Nos. 1268-1270 (3) 3.25 1.15
　Dated 1990. See No. 1291.

1991 *Perf. 13*
Design: 500s, Woman in profile.
1271 A406 300s shown 1.00 .55
1272 A406 500s multicolored 1.90 1.00
　Day of Non-violence Toward Women.

Jacinto Jijon y Caamano, Archaeologist, Birth Cent. — A407

1991, Dec. 11 *Perf. 13½*
1273 A407 200s Portrait, vert. .70 .35
1274 A407 300s shown 1.10 .55

Pres. Rodrigo Borja, Ecuador and Pres. Jaime Paz Zamora, Bolivia — A408

1991, Dec. 10 *Perf. 14x13½*
1275 A408 500s multicolored 1.75 .90

Pres. Rodrigo Borja's Visit to the UN — A409

Wmk. 395

1992, Jan. 24 *Perf. 14*
1276 A409 100s multicolored .40 .20
1277 A409 1000s Flags, world map 3.00 1.60

Battle of Jambeli, 50th Anniv. — A410

#1278, Gunboat Calderon and Capt. Raphael Moran Valverde. #1279, Dispatch

boat Atahualpa and Ens. Victor Naranjo Fiallo. #1280, Valverde, Fiallo and ships.

1992, Apr. 7
1278 A410 300s multicolored .55 .40
1279 A410 500s multicolored 1.25 .90

Size: 110x90mm
Imperf
1280 A410 500s multicolored 2.75 2.40
　Nos. 1278-1280 (3) 4.55 3.70

Galapagos Islands Wildlife — A411

Designs: No. 1281, Giant tortoise. No. 1282, Galapagos penguin, vert. No. 1283, Zalophus californianus, vert. No. 1284, Swallow-tailed gull. No. 1285, Fregata minor. No. 1286, Land iguana.

1992, Apr. 10 **Litho.** *Perf. 13½*
1281 A411 100s multicolored 1.75 .80
1282 A411 100s multicolored 1.75 .80
1283 A411 100s multicolored 1.75 .80
1284 A411 100s multicolored 1.75 .80
1285 A411 100s multicolored 1.75 .80
1286 A411 100s multicolored 1.75 .80
　Nos. 1281-1286 (6) 10.50 4.80

Vicente Rocafuerte National College, 150th Anniv. (in 1991) A412

Perf. 14x13½
1992, Apr. 29 **Litho.** **Wmk. 395**
1287 A412 200s shown .70 .35
1288 A412 400s Vicente Rocafuerte 1.10 .60

Eloy Alfaro (1842-1912), President — A413

Designs: 300s, Portrait, vert.

Perf. 13½x14, 14x13½
1992, Aug. 26 **Litho.** **Wmk. 395**
1289 A413 300s multicolored .90 .70
1290 A413 700s multicolored 1.60 1.00

Cultural Artifacts Type of 1991
1992, Sept. 6 **Litho.** *Perf. 13½*
1291 A405 400s Ceremonial mask 1.40 .75
　Dated 1990.

Discovery of America, 500th Anniv. A414

Wmk. 395

1992, Oct. 15 **Litho.** *Perf. 13½*
1292 A414 200s Sailing ship .75 .50
1293 A414 400s Columbus, map, vert. 1.40 .85

Andres F. Cordova (b. 1892) A415

1992, Nov. 17 **Litho.** *Perf. 13½*
1294 A415 300s multicolored .90 .55

Beatification of Narcisa of Jesus — A416

1992, Nov. 30 *Perf. 13½*
1295 A416 100s multicolored .35 .20

A417　　　　　A418

Christmas: 300s, Infant Jesus of Saqueo, 18th cent. 600s, Stable scene, Infant Jesus asleep on hay.

1992, Dec. 14 *Perf. 13½*
1296 A417 300s multicolored .95 .60
1297 A417 600s multicolored 1.75 1.00

1992, Dec. 29
1298 A418 200s multicolored .70 .45
　Father Juan de Velasco, Death Bicent.

Frogs — A419　　　　A420

Perf. 13½x14
1993, Jan. 28 **Litho.** **Wmk. 395**
1299 A419 300s Agalychnis spurelli .50 .35
1300 A419 300s Atelopus bomolochos .50 .35
1301 A419 600s Gastrotheca plumbea 1.40 .90
1302 A419 600s Hyla picturata 1.40 .90
1303 A419 900s Dendrobates sp. 2.10 1.40
1304 A419 900s Sphaenorhyncus lacteus 2.10 1.40
　Nos. 1299-1304 (6) 8.00 5.30

1993, Feb. 16 **Litho.** *Perf. 13x13½*
1305 A420 300s blue .80 .20
　J. Roberto Paez, (1893-1983), co-founder of social security.

A421   A422

1993, Mar. 16   *Perf. 13½x14*
1306 A421 500s No. 168   1.25   .45
     Francisco Robles (1811-93).

Perf. 13½x14
1993, Mar. 25   Litho.   Wmk. 395
1307 A422 300s Natl. police   .70   .50

Pres. Jose Maria Velasco Ibarra (1893-1979)
A423

Perf. 14x13½
1993, Mar. 31   Litho.   Wmk. 395
1308 A423 500s multicolored   1.25   .45

Insects — A424

Wmk. 395
1993, May 27   Litho.   *Perf. 13½*
1309 A424 150s Fulgora
     laternaria   .55   .20
1310 A424 200s Semiotus
     ligneus   .65   .20
1311 A424 300s Taeniotes
     pulverulenta   1.10   .35
1312 A424 400s Danaus plexip-
     pus   1.25   .40
1313 A424 600s Erotylus onagga   2.10   .65
1314 A424 700s Xylocopa
     darwini   2.25   .75
    Nos. 1309-1314 (6)   7.90 2.55

A425

Wmk. 395
1993, May 31   Litho.   *Perf. 13½*
1315 A425 1000s multicolored   2.25 1.25
    Pedro Fermin Cevallos Villacreces (1812-93), historian and founder of Academy of Language.

First Latin-American Children's Peace Assembly, Quito — A426

1993, June 7
1316 A426 300s multicolored   .70   .45

Juan Benigno Vela Hervas (1843-97), Jurist
A427

Perf. 13x13½
1993, July 8   Litho.   Wmk. 395
1317 A427 2000s multicolored   4.50 2.40

Guillermo Bustamante, Birth Cent.
A428

1993, Sept. 23   *Perf. 13½*
1318 A428 1500s multicolored   4.00 1.75

University of Ecuador School of Medicine, 300th Anniv.
A429

Perf. 14x13½
1993, Sept. 7   Litho.   Wmk. 395
1319 A429 300s multicolored   .70   .45

Maldonado-La Condamine Amazon Expedition, 250th Anniv. — A430

    Designs: 150s, Cinchona cordifolia. 200s, Pedro V. Maldonado, 1500s, Charles La Condamine (1701-74), explorer.

1993, Aug. 20
1320 A430 150s multicolored   .35   .20
1321 A430 200s multicolored   .45   .20
1322 A430 1500s multicolored   3.00 1.75
    Nos. 1320-1322 (3)   3.80 2.15

A431   A432

Wmk. 395
1993, Nov. 27   Litho.   *Perf. 13*
1323 A431 500s multicolored   1.00   .55
    Dr. Carlos A. Arroyo del Rio, birth cent.

1993, Oct. 15   *Perf. 13½x13, 13x13½*
    Endangered species: 400s, Dinomys branickii, horiz. 800s, Ara severa.

1324 A432 400s multicolored   1.25   .60
1325 A432 800s multicolored   2.25 1.10
     America issue.

Christmas
A433

    600s, Holy Family, 18th cent. Tagua miniatures. 900s, Mother and child, vert.

Wmk. 395
1993, Dec. 1   Litho.   *Perf. 13*
1326 A433 600s multicolored   1.25   .80
1327 A433 900s multicolored   2.00 1.25

A434   A435

Wmk. 395
1994, Jan. 18   Litho.   *Perf. 13*
1328 A434 300s grn, blk & org   .30   .30
     Intl. Year of the Family.

1994, Jan. 25
1329 A435 500s multicolored   1.60   .90
    Dr. Julio Tobar Donoso, birth cent.

Orchids — A436

Wmk. 395
1994, Feb. 7   Litho.   *Perf. 13½*
1330 A436 150s Dracula hirtzii   .35   .20
1331 A436 150s Sobralia
     dichotoma   .35   .20
1332 A436 300s Encyclia
     pulcherrima   .70   .30
1333 A436 300s Lepanthes
     delhierroi   .70   .30
1334 A436 600s Masdevallia
     rosea   1.40   .55
1335 A436 600s Telipogon
     andicola   1.40   .55
    Nos. 1330-1335 (6)   4.90 2.10
    First Convention on the Conservation of Andean Orchids.

A437   A438

1994, Apr. 12   *Perf. 13*
1336 A437 200s multicolored   .45   .20
    Federico Gonzalez Suarez (1844-1917).

1994, Jan. 11
1337 A438 400s multicolored   1.00   .55
     Scouting in Ecuador.

Dr. Miguel Egas Cabezas (1823-94)
A439

Wmk. 395
1994, Mar. 10   Litho.   *Perf. 13*
1338 A439 100s multicolored   .45   .20

A440   A441

1994, July 12
1339 A440 200s multicolored   .70   .45
    Fr. Aurelio Espinosa, birth cent.

Wmk. 395
1994, June 10   Litho.   *Perf. 13*
    #1341, 1343d, Mascot. 900s, Player.
    #1343: a, Emblem. b, "COPA MUNDIAL FUTBOL '94," emblem. c, "COPA MUNDIAL, USA 94."
1340 A441 300s shown   .90   .55
1341 A441 600s Mascot   1.75   .90
1342 A441 900s Soccer player   2.75 1.40
    Perf. 12 on 2 Sides
1343 A441 600s Block of 4, #a.-
     d.   7.00 6.00
   Nos. 1340-1343 (4)   12.40 8.85
    1994 World Cup Soccer Championships, US. No. 1343 contains two 50x25mm stamps, two 50x51mm stamps.

Ecuador in Antarctica
A442

1994, July 19   *Perf. 13*
1344 A442 600s Outpost   2.00   .70
1345 A442 900s Ship, B/1 Orion   3.25 1.10

ILO, 75th Anniv.
A443

1994   Litho.   Wmk. 395   *Perf. 13*
1346 A443 100s multicolored   .30   .20

Ecuadorian Culture Center, 50th Anniv.
A444

1994
1347 A444 700s Benjamin Car-
     rion, vert.   2.10 1.40
1348 A444 900s Cultural center   3.25 1.60

Natl. Lottery, Cent.
A445

1994
1349 A445 1000s multicolored   3.60 1.75

Junior World Cycling Championships, Quito — A446

Wmk. 395
1994, June 22 **Litho.** **Perf. 13**
1350 A446 300s shown .50 .35
1351 A446 400s Stylized cyclist,
vert. .75 .40

Postal Transportation
A447

Christmas A448

America Issue: No. 1352, Van, airplane, ship, horiz. No. 1353, Airplane, mail bag.

1994
1352 A447 600s multicolored .70 .35
1353 A447 600s multicolored .90 .45

1994
#1354, Simulated stamp showing globe circled by envelope, horiz. #1355, Nativity.
1354 A448 600s multicolored 1.00 .75
1355 A448 900s multicolored 1.00 .75

Juan Leon Mera, Death Cent.
A449 A450

Wmk. 395
1994, Dec. 21 **Litho.** **Perf. 13**
1356 A449 600s Mera's home .85 .65
1357 A450 900s multicolored 2.00 1.25

Gen. Antonio Jose de Sucre (1795-1830) — A451

Perf. 14x13½
1995, Mar. 14 **Litho.** **Wmk. 395**
1358 A451 1500s shown 2.50 1.50
1359 A451 2000s Portrait at right 3.75 2.00

Size: 80x105
Imperf
1360 A451 3000s In military uniform 4.00 4.00
Nos. 1358-1360 (3) 10.25 7.50

Beatification of Josemaria Escriva, 3rd Anniv. — A452

1995, May 17 **Perf. 13x13½**
1361 A452 900s multicolored 1.10 .80

Gen. Eloy Alfaro (1842-1912), Alfarista Revolution, Cent.
A453

1995, June 5 **Perf. 13½x13**
1362 A453 800s multicolored 1.10 .80

A454

Conflict Between Ecuador & Peru — A455

Designs: 200s, Soldier writing to children. 400s, Hand holding flag of Ecuador. 800s, Soldier in wilderness.

1995, July **Perf. 13½, 13 (#1364)**
1363 A454 200s multicolored .35 .20
1364 A455 400s multicolored .75 .35
1365 A454 800s multicolored 1.25 .65
Nos. 1363-1365 (3) 2.35 1.20

CARE, 50th Anniv. — A456

1995, July 14 **Perf. 13½**
1366 A456 400s Girl, vert. .50 .30
1367 A456 800s shown 1.50 1.00

CAF (Andes Development Corporation), 25th Anniv. — A457

1995, Aug. 22 **Perf. 13**
1368 A457 1000s multicolored 2.10 .85

A458 A459

1995, Sept. 2 **Litho.** **Perf. 13**
1369 A458 500s Virgin of Cisne .60 .45

1995, Sept. 28
1370 A459 400s multicolored .70 .45
Natl. Institute of Children and Families (INNFA), 35th anniv.

UN, 50th Anniv.
A460

Wmk. 395
1995, Oct. 6 **Litho.** **Perf. 13**
1371 A460 1000s bl, blk & bis 1.75 .90

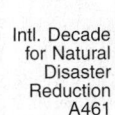

Intl. Decade for Natural Disaster Reduction
A461

Civil defense emblem and: No. 1372, House surrounded by flood waters. No. 1373, Family leaving site of erupting volcano. No. 1374, People under table during earthquake. No. 1375, Couple planting seedlings on hillside. No. 1376, Man reading instruction booklet for natural disaster preparation.

1995, Oct. 11
1372 A461 1000s multicolored 1.60 .85
1373 A461 1000s multicolored 1.60 .85
1374 A461 1000s multicolored 1.60 .85
1375 A461 1000s multicolored 1.60 .85
1376 A461 1000s multicolored 1.60 .85
Nos. 1372-1376 (5) 8.00 4.25

FAO, 50th Anniv.
A462

1995, Oct. 16
1377 A462 1300s multicolored 2.25 1.25

Women's Culture Club, 50th Anniv.
A463

1995, Oct. 20
1378 A463 1500s multicolored 2.00 1.50

29th Assembly of Inter-America Philatelic Federation, Quito — A464

1995, Nov. 11
1379 A464 1000s blue & red 1.25 .85

A465 A466

Christmas: 2000s, Santa, sleigh, reindeer on top of world. 2600s, Man on decorated horse, children.

Wmk. 395
1995, Dec. **Litho.** **Perf. 13**
1380 A465 2000s multicolored 4.00 2.40
1381 A465 2600s multicolored 4.50 2.40

1995, Dec.
Indigenous Birds: #1382, Aglaiocercus kingi.
#1383: a, Coeligena torquata. b, Phaethornis superciliosus. c, Ocreatus underwoodii. d, Oreotrochilus chimborazo. e, Aglaiocercus coelestis.
1382 A466 1000s multicolored 1.75 .85
1383 A466 1000s Strip of 5, #a.-e. 9.25 6.25

Ecuadoran Air Force, 75th Anniv.
A467

1995, Dec.
1384 A467 1000s multicolored 1.75 .95

Year of Folk Music — A468

2000s, Julio Jaramillo (1935-78), musician, composer. 3000s, Jaramillo, wall.

1996, Jan. 16 **Litho.** **Perf. 13**
1385 A468 2000s multicolored 3.50 1.75

Imperf
1386 A468 3000s multicolored 4.50 4.00

Advancement of Ecuador, 4 Year Program
A469

Designs show symbols for: 1500s, Mail delivery. 2000s, Customs crossing. 2600s, Telecommunications. 3000p, Ports.

Wmk. 395
1996, July 23 **Litho.** **Perf. 13**
1387 A469 1000s multicolored 1.60 .70
1388 A469 1500s multicolored 2.40 1.10
1389 A469 2000s multicolored 3.00 1.50
1390 A469 2600s multicolored 4.00 1.75
  a. Pair, #1388, #1390 5.25 5.25
  b. Pair, #1389, #1390 6.00 6.00
1391 A369 3000s multicolored 5.00 2.75
  a. Pair, #1387, #1391 5.50 5.50
  b. Pair, #1389, #1391 6.75 6.75
Nos. 1387-1391 (5) 16.00 7.80

Nos. 1387-1391 were issued in strips of 2 each.

Esmeraldas '96, 8th National Games
A470

Mascot depicting two sports on each stamp: No. 1392, Tennis, boxing. No. 1393, Basketball, soccer. 600s, Racketball, swimming. 800s, Weight lifting, karate. 1000s, Volleyball, gymnastics. 1200s, Athletics, judo. No. 1398, Chess, wrestling.
No. 1399, Mascot holding flag, emblem, surrounded by flags.

1996, July 30
1392 A470 400s multicolored .50 .20
1393 A470 400s multicolored .50 .20
1394 A470 600s multicolored .80 .40
  a. Pair, #1392, #1394 1.25 1.25
1395 A470 800s multicolored 1.10 .55
  a. Pair, #1394-1395 1.75 1.75
1396 A470 1000s multicolored 1.50 .65
  a. Pair, #1393, #1396 1.90 1.90
  b. Pair, #1395-1396 2.40 2.40

1397 A470 1200s multicolored 1.60 .85
1398 A470 2000s multicolored 3.00 1.25
Nos. 1392-1398 (7) 9.00 4.10

Size: 120x100mm

1399 A470 2000s multicolored 3.00 3.00

Nos. 1392-1396 were printed in strips of 2 each.

Civil Aviation, 50th Anniv. A471

1996, Aug. 8
1400 A471 2000s multicolored 3.00 1.25

1996 Summer Olympic Games, Atlanta A472

Atlanta Games emblem and: 1000s, Mascot carrying torch. No. 1402, Emblem of Olympic Committee of Ecuador. 3000s, Jefferson Perez, vert.
No. 1404, Perez, gold medalist, 20-kilometer walk, walking.

1996
1401 A472 1000s multicolored 1.50 .65
1402 A472 2000s multicolored 3.50 2.10
   a. Pair, #1401-1402 4.50 4.50
1403 A472 3000s multicolored 4.25 2.25
Nos. 1401-1403 (3) 9.25 5.00

Size: 100x120mm

Imperf

1404 A472 2000s multicolored 3.00 3.00

Fight Against Drug Abuse — A473

Dr. Eduardo Salazar Gomez, Birth Cent. — A474

1996 Litho. Wmk. 395 Perf. 13
1408 A473 2000s multicolored 3.75 2.00

1996
1409 A474 1000s multicolored 2.00 1.00

Catholic University, Quito, 50th Anniv. A475

Junior League Organization A476

Designs: 400s, Outside view of building, horiz. 800s, Entrance.

1996
1410 A475 400s multicolored .80 .45
1411 A475 800s multicolored 1.60 .85

1996
1412 A476 2000s Children's faces, horiz. 4.00 2.50
1413 A476 2600s shown 5.00 3.00

Catholic University, Quito, 50th Anniv. A477

1996, Nov.
1414 A477 2000s multicolored 3.75 2.00

The Universe Daily Newspaper, 75th Anniv. — A478

1996, Dec.
1415 A478 2000s multicolored 3.75 2.00

Private Technical University, Loja — A479

1996, Dec. 9
1416 A479 4700s multicolored 9.00 4.50

UNICEF, 50th Anniv. A480

1996, Dec. 11
1417 A480 2000s multicolored 3.75 2.00

Christmas A481

Children's paintings: 600s, Merry Christmas All Over the World. 800s, World of Peace and Love. 2000s, Christmas.

1996, Dec. 19
1418 A481 600s multicolored 1.25 .75
1419 A481 800s multicolored 1.50 .90

Size: 51x31mm

Perf. 13½

1420 A481 2000s multicolored 3.50 1.90
Nos. 1418-1420 (3) 6.25 3.55

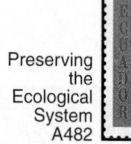

Preserving the Ecological System A482

America '95: 1000s, Voltur grypus. 1500s, Harpia harpyja, vert.

1996, Dec. 30 Perf. 13
1421 A482 1000s multicolored 2.00 1.25
1422 A482 1500s multicolored 3.00 1.75

Typical Children's Costumes — A483

America '96: No. 1423, "Bordando" girl, Zuleta. No. 1424, Girl from Otavalo.

1996, Dec. 30
1423 A483 2600s multicolored 4.50 1.50
1424 A483 2600s multicolored 4.50 4.00
   a. Pair, #1423-1424 11.00 11.00

Mejia Natl. Institute, Cent. A484

Design: Jose Mejia Lequerica, building.

1997, Jan. 10
1425 A484 1000s multicolored 2.00 1.00

Army Polytechnical School, 75th Anniv. A485

Wmk. 395
1997, June 16 Typo. Perf. 13
1426 A485 400s multicolored .90 .50

Natl. Experimental College, Ambato, 50th Anniv. A486

1997, June 20
1427 A486 600s multicolored 1.10 .70

Vicente Rocafuerte (1783-1847), First Constitutional President of Ecuador — A487

1997, July 1
1428 A487 400s multicolored .90 .50

49th Intl. Congress of the Americanists A488

1997, July 3
1429 A488 2000s multicolored 3.75 1.90

Butterflies A489

Designs: 400s, Actinote equatoria. 600s, Dismorphia amphione. 800s, Marpesia corinna. 2000s, Marpesia berania. 2600s, Morpho helenor.

1997, July 21
1430 A489 400s multicolored .70 .30
1431 A489 600s multicolored .95 .35
1432 A489 800s multicolored 1.60 .65
1433 A489 2000s multicolored 3.75 1.60
1434 A489 2600s multicolored 5.50 2.00
Nos. 1430-1434 (5) 12.50 4.90

Air Club of Ecuador, 66th Anniv. A490

1997, July 23
1435 A490 2600s multicolored 5.25 2.10

Orchids — A491

400s, Epidendrum secundum. 600s, Epidendrum. 800s, Oncidium cultratrum. 2000s, Oncidium sp mariposa. 2600s, Pleurothalis corrulensis.

1997, Aug. 14 Litho. Perf. 13
1436 A491 400s multicolored .70 .30
1437 A491 600s multicolored .95 .40
1438 A491 800s multicolored 1.60 .65
1439 A491 2000s multicolored 3.75 1.60
1440 A491 2600s multicolored 5.50 2.00
Nos. 1436-1440 (5) 12.50 4.95

Rocks and Minerals — A492

1997, Oct. 6 Litho. Perf. 13
1441 A492 400s Quartz .70 .30
1442 A492 600s Chalcopyrite .95 .40
1443 A492 800s Gold 1.60 .65
1444 A492 2000s Petrified wood 3.75 1.60
1445 A492 2600s Pyrite 5.50 2.00
Nos. 1441-1445 (5) 12.50 4.95

A493 A494

Christmas (Children's designs): 400s, Santa as postman delivering letters over world. 2600s, Star on Christmas tree reaching for letters, airplane under tree. 3000s, Child dreaming of angels carrying letters.

1997, Dec. 22 Litho. Perf. 13
1446 A493 400s multicolored .70 .30
1447 A493 2600s multicolored 5.25 2.00
1448 A493 3000s multicolored 6.50 2.50
Nos. 1446-1448 (3) 12.45 4.80

1997, Dec. 29
1449 A494 800s Life of a Postman 1.40 .70
1450 A494 2000s On bicycle 4.00 1.60

America issue.

A495 A496

Matilde Hidalgo de Procel (1889-1974), physician, social reformer.

1998, Mar. 6   Litho.   Perf. 13
1451 A495 2000s multicolored   3.50 2.50
Intl. Women's Day.

Wmk. 395
1998, Apr. 22   Litho.   Perf. 13
1452 A496 2000s multicolored   6.25 4.00
Dr. Misael Acosta Solis, botanist.

Organization of American States (OAS), 50th Anniv. A497

1998, Apr. 30
1453 A497 2600s multicolored   4.50 3.25

1998 World Cup Soccer Championships, France — A498

Designs: 2600s, Trophy, mascot, vert. 3000s, Two players, trophy.

1998, May
1454 A498 2000s multicolored   3.50 2.25
1455 A498 2600s multicolored   4.50 2.75
1456 A498 3000s multicolored   5.50 3.25
  Nos. 1454-1456 (3)   13.50 8.25

Flowers — A499   Galapagos Flora — A500

600s, Gypsophila paniculata. 800s, Banana flowers. 2000s, Roses. 2600s, Asters.

1998, June
1457 A499 600s multicolored   1.25 .60
1458 A499 800s multicolored   1.50 .90
1459 A499 2000s multicolored   3.50 2.25
1460 A499 2600s multicolored   4.50 2.75
  Nos. 1457-1460 (4)   10.75 6.50

1998, July
Designs: 600s, Jasminocereus thouarsii. 1000s, Cordia lutea lamarck. 2600s, Momordica charantia.

1461 A500 600s multicolored   1.00 .60
1462 A500 1000s multicolored   1.75 1.00
1463 A500 2600s multicolored   4.50 2.75
  Nos. 1461-1463 (3)   7.25 4.35

Tourism A501

600s, St. Augustine Church, Quito. 800s, Monument to the Heroes of the Independence, Guayaquil. 2000s, Equator Monument, Quito. 2600s, Mojanda Lake.

1998, July
1464 A501 600s multi, vert.   1.25 .60
1465 A501 800s multi, vert.   1.50 .90
1466 A501 2000s multi   3.50 2.25
1467 A501 2600s multi   4.50 2.75
  Nos. 1464-1467 (4)   10.75 6.50

Emiliano Ortega Espinosa (1898-1974), Educator A502

Perf. 13¼x13, 13x13¼
1998   Litho.   Wmk. 395
1468 A502 400s shown   .75 .50
1469 A502 4700s Portrait, vert.   10.00 8.25

A503   A504

Carlos Cueva Tamariz (1898-1991), educator.

Perf. 13x13¼
1998, Nov.   Litho.   Wmk. 395
1470 A503 2600s multicolored   4.50 3.50

Wmk. 395
1998, Nov. 20   Litho.   Perf. 13
1471 A504 600s multicolored   1.10 .90
Radio Club of Guayaquil, 75th anniv.

6th South American Games — A505

Designs: 400s, Mascot. 1000s, Games poster, tennis rackets, hurdles, sailing, hammer throw, bowling, boxing. 2600s, Mascot, parallel bars, wrestling, judo, fencing, running, swimming, shooting, cycling.

1998
1472 A505 400s multicolored   1.00 .50
1473 A505 1000s multicolored   1.75 1.00
1474 A505 2600s multicolored   4.50 2.75
  Nos. 1472-1474 (3)   7.25 4.25

Paintings by Eduardo Kingman (1913-85) A506

Designs: 600s, Ecuadoran Woman, vert. 800s, World Without Answers.

1998, Dec. 10
1475 A506 600s multicolored   1.00 .60
1476 A506 800s multicolored   1.50 .90

Manuela Sáenz (1797-1856), Mistress of Simon Bolívar — A507

1999, Jan. 19
1477 A507 1000s multicolored   1.50 .95
America issue. Exists imperf.

Christmas A508

Children's drawings: 1000s, Santa posting letters on tree. 2600s, People holding up giant letter, vert. 3000s, Santas parachuting with letters, nativity scene, tree, vert.

1998, Dec. 22
1478 A508 1000s multicolored   1.50 .95
1479 A508 2600s multicolored   4.00 2.50
1480 A508 3000s multicolored   4.50 2.75
  Nos. 1478-1480 (3)   10.00 6.20

Los Tayos Caves A509

1999, Feb. 25   Litho.   Perf. 13
1481 A509 1000s Man in cave, vert.   1.40 .90
1482 A509 2600s shown   4.00 2.50

Napal, the Age of Wrath, by Oswaldo Guayasamin (1919-99) — A510

Wmk. 395
1999, May 12   Litho.   Perf. 13
1483 A510 2000s multicolored   3.25 1.10
Iberoamerica art exhibition.

Universal Day of Human Rights A511

1999, May 28
1484 A511 4000s multicolored   6.25 4.00

Eloy Alfaro Superior Military College, Cent. A512

5200s, Cannon, monument, flags, buildings. 9400s, Honor Guard, modern building.

1999, June 4
1485 A512 5200s multicolored   9.00 6.00
1486 A512 9400s multicolored   15.00 9.00

Puyo, 100th Anniv. — A513

Designs: a, Bromeliad. b, Ara chloroptera.

1999, June 2
1487 A513 4000s Pair, #a.-b.   13.00 9.00

Dr. Rafael Barahona Andrade (1827-98) A514

Perf. 13¼x13
1999, June 17   Litho.   Wmk. 395
1488 A514 5200s multi   8.00 4.50

Generals — A515

Designs: 2000s, Manuel Antonio de Luzarraga y Echezurria (1776-1859). 4000s, Tomas Carlos Wright (1799-1868).

1999, Aug. 11   Perf. 13x13¼
1489-1490 A515   Set of 2   9.50 6.00

Galapagos Islands Flora and Fauna A516

No. 1491, vert.: a, Phoenicopterus ruber. b, Buteo galapagoensis. c, Amblyrhynchus cristatus. d, Conolophus subcristatus. e, Opuntia galapageia. f, Pyrocephalus rubinus. g, Sula nebouxii. h, Sula dactylatra. i, Scalesia villosa. j, G. elephantopus abingdoni.
No. 1492: a, Brachycereus nesioticus. b, Dendroica petechia. c, Nannopterum harrisi. d, Tursiops truncatus. e, Pentaceraster cumingi. f, G. elephantopus porteri. g, Microlophus albemarlensis. h, Arctocephalus galapagoensis. i, Spheniscus mendiculus. j, Geospiza scandens.

Perf. 13x13¼, 13¼x13
1999, Sept. 3   Litho.   Wmk. 395
1491   Strip of 10   90.00 75.00
 a.-j. A516 7000s Any single   5.50 1.75
1492   Strip of 10   160.00 125.00
 a.-j. A516 15,000s Any single   12.00 5.00

Intl. Year of Older Persons A517

Designs: No. 1493, 1000s, Hands of child and old person. No. 1494, 1000s, Emblem.

Perf. 13¼x13
1999, Sept. 22   Litho.   Wmk. 395
1493-1494 A517   Set of 2   2.75 1.75

SOS Children's Villages, 50th Anniv. — A518

a, 2000s, Two children. b, 2000s, One child. Illustration reduced.

1999, Sept. 30
1495 A518   Pair, #a-b   4.00 2.50

America Issue, A World Without Arms — A519

No. 1496: a, World map. b, Tree, bird, Earth. Illustration reduced.

Perf. 13¼x13
1999, Dec. 11   Litho.   Wmk. 395
1496 A519 4000s Pair, #a-b   14.50 10.00

UPU, 125th Anniv. A520

Design: 8000s, UPU emblem. 1000s, Ecuadorian Postal Service mascot, vert. 4000s, Dove with letter, vert.

Perf. 13¼x12¾
1999, Dec. 11   Litho.   Wmk. 395
1497 A520 1000s multi   .75   .45
1498 A520 4000s multi   3.00   1.75
1499 A520 8000s multi   6.25   4.00
  Nos. 1497-1499 (3)   10.00   6.20

Ecuador as Secretary General of Permanent South Pacific Commission A521

Perf. 13x13¼
1999, Dec. 21   Litho.   Wmk. 395
1500 A521 7000s multi   6.75   4.50

Machala Tourism A522

Designs: No. 1501, Banana flower and city. No. 1502, vert.: a, Monument to banana plantation workers. b, City Hall.

1999, Dec. 28   Perf. 13¼x13, 13x13¼
1501 A522 3000s multi   2.75   1.60
1502 A522 3000s Pair, #a-b   5.75   3.25

EMELEC Soccer Team — A523

#1503: a, Jorge Bolanos. b, Carlos Raffo. No. 1504, EMELEC team photo, 1957. No. 1505, Player, vert.

Perf. 13x13¼, 13¼x13
2000, Jan. 7   Litho.
1503 A523 1000s Pair, #a-b   2.25   2.25
1504 A523 2000s multi   2.25   1.40
1505 A523 2000s multi   2.25   1.40

Guayas Philanthropic Society, 150th Anniv. A524

Designs: 1000s, Building. 2000s, Founder Juan Maria Martinez Coello. 4000s, Emblem.

Perf. 13¼x13
2000, Jan. 19   Litho.   Wmk. 395
1506-1508 A524   Set of 3   1.75   1.00

Dual Nationality Day — A525

2000, Jan. 24   Perf. 13x13¼
1509 A525 7000s multi   1.75   1.10

Cuenca, World Heritage Site — A526

No. 1510: a, Buildings. b, Puente Roto and Tomebamba River. c, Church bell gable, Concepcion Monastery. d, Cathedral and city skyline. e, San José Church.

2000, Mar. 24   Perf. 13¼x13
1510   4.50   4.50
  a.-e. A526 4000s Any single   .65   .35

Nicolas Lapentti, Tennis Player — A527

2000, Mar. 26   Perf. 13¼x13
1511 A527 8000s multi   2.00   1.25

Birds — A528

No. 1512: a, Diglossa cyanea. b, Oreotrochilus chimborazo. c, Trogon personatus. d, Colibri coruscans. e, Atlapetes rufinucha.

2000, Apr. 7
1512   Horiz. strip of 5   9.00   9.00
  a.-e. A528 8000s Any single   1.40   .95

Relocation of Riobamba, Bicent. A529

Designs: No. 1513, Mt. Chimborazo. No. 1514: a, Riobamba Cathedral. b, Statue of Pedro Vicente Maldonado.

2000, Apr. 13   Perf. 13¼x13, 13x13¼
1513 A529 8000s multi   1.75   1.00
1514 A529 8000s Pair, #a-b   3.50   3.50

Gen. Eloy Alfaro, Founder of Natl. Music Conservatory A530

2000, Apr. 19   Perf. 13x13¼
1515 A530 10,000s multi   2.75   1.60
  Natl. Music Conservatory, cent.

Climbing of Mt. Everest by Ivan Vallejo Ricaurte A531

2000, May 23   Perf. 13¼x13
1516 A531 8000s multi   2.75   1.50

100 Cents=1 Dollar

Dolores Sucre Fiscal College, 50th Anniv. — A532

Perf. 13x13¼
2000   Litho.   Wmk. 395
1517 A532 32c multi   2.10   1.00

Training Ship Guayas — A533

2000, July 5   Perf. 13x13¼
1518 A533 68c multi   1.40   .70
Imperf
Size: 90x110mm
1519 A533 $1 multi   6.00   3.25

Battle of Jambeli, 59th Anniv., Navy Day — A534

2000   Perf. 13¼x13
1520 A534 16c multi   1.10   .20

Guayaquil Civic Renovation A535

2000, July   Perf. 13x13¼
1521 A535 84c multi   5.40   2.50

Megaptera Novaeangliae — A536

2000, Aug. 3   Perf. 13¼x13
1522 A536 84c multi   5.25   2.50
Imperf
Size: 90x110mm
1523 A536 $1 Two whales   7.25   3.50

American and Caribbean Dog Show, Quito A537

2000, Aug.   Perf. 13¼x13
1524 A537 68c multi   4.00   2.00

Guayaquil Tennis Club, 90th Anniv. A538

2000, Aug.   Wmk. 395
1525 A538 84c multi   5.00   2.50

Alberto Spencer, Soccer Player — A539

2000   Perf. 13x13¼
1526 A539 68c multi   4.00   2.00
Imperf
Size: 69x99mm
1527 A539 $1 Spencer, crowd   6.25   3.00

2000 Summer Olympics, Sydney — A540

Ecuadoran team emblem, Games emblem and: 32c Mascots. 68c, Runner Jefferson Perez Marchista. 84c, Weight lifter Boris Burov, Olympic flag, horiz.

2000, Sept.   Perf. 13x13¼, 13¼x13
1528-1530 A540   Set of 3   10.75   5.50

Salinas Yacht Club, 60th Anniv. A541

Designs: No. 1531a, Lighthouse, vert. Nos. 1531b, 1533, Sailboat, vert. 68c, Sailboats, fisherman, waterskier, scuba diver.

2000, Oct.   Perf. 13x13¼
1531 A541 32c Horiz. pair, #a-b   3.75   2.00
Perf. 13¼x13
1532 A541 68c multi   4.25   2.10

Imperf
Size: 69x100mm
1533 A541 $1 multi 6.25 3.00

Inter-American Development Bank, 40th Anniv. — A542

Designs: No. 1534a, 68c, No. 1536a, 25c, Salsipuedes Bridge, Felipe Herrera. No. 1534b, 68c, No. 1536b, 25c, Daule-Peripa Dam, Antonio Ortiz Mena. No. 1535a, 84c, No. 1536c, 25c, Enrique Iglesias, Ucubamba Water Treatment Plant. No. 1535b, 84c, No. 1536d, 25c, Bank emblem, History Museum, Quito.
Illustration reduced.

2000, Oct. 27   Perf. 13¼x13
Horiz. Pairs, #a-b
1534-1535 A542 Set of 2 18.00 9.00
Rouletted 14 on 2 sides
1536 A542 25c Sheet of 4, #a-d 6.25 3.00
Size of Nos. 1536a-1536b, 75x48mm; Nos. 1536c-1536d, 75x42mm.

National Union of Journalists A543

2000, Nov. 1   Perf. 13¼x13
1537 A543 16c multi 1.00 .20

Civil Registry, Cent. — A544

No. 1538: a, People, flag, computer. b, Fingerprint, family.

2000, Oct. 27   Perf. 13x13¼
1538 A544 68c Horiz. pair, #a-b 8.00 3.00

Mama Negra Festival, Latacunga — A545

No. 1539: a, Mama Negra with doll. b, Man in Moor King costume.

2000, Nov.   Perf. 13x13¼
1539 A545 32c Horiz. pair, #a-b 3.75 2.00
Imperf
Size: 100x68mm
1540 A545 $1 Mama Negra, doll, diff. 5.75 2.10

Ministry of Labor, 75th Anniv. — A546

2000, Nov. 15   Perf. 13x13¼
1541 A546 68c multi 3.75 1.40

Intl. Fruits and Flowers Festival, Ambato, 50th Anniv. A547

No. 1542, horiz.: a, Tungurahua Volcano. b, Aerial view of Ambato.
No. 1544, horiz.: a, Flower. b, Fruit.

2000, Nov.   Perf. 13¾
1542 A547 32c Vert. pair, #a-b 3.75 2.00
1543 A547 84c shown 5.25 2.50
1544 A547 84c Vert. pair, #a-b 10.50 5.25
Nos. 1542-1544 (3) 19.50 9.75
Imperf
Size: 68x100mm
1545 A547 $1 Ambato 5.75 2.75

Christmas — A548

Children's art by — No. 1546, 68c: a, Giannina Rhor Isaias. b, Josue Remache Romero. No. 1547, 84c: a, Maria Cedeño Bazurtto. b, Juan Alban Salazar.
$1, Walther Carvache.
Illustration reduced.

2000, Dec. 15   Perf. 13¼x13
Horiz. Pairs, #a-b
1546-1547 A548 Set of 2 18.00 9.00
Imperf
Size: 100x69mm
1548 A548 $1 multi 5.75 2.75

Expoflores Flower Producer and Exporter Association A549

2000   Perf. 13x13¼
1549 A549 68c multi 4.00 2.00

Man's Chapel, Guayasamin A550

2000   Perf. 13¼x13
1550 A550 16c multi 1.10 .20

Spanish Chamber of Commerce in Ecuador, 80th Anniv. — A551

2000, Dec.   Perf. 13x13¼
1551 A551 16c multi 1.10 .20

Intl. Volunteers Year — A552

2000   Wmk. 395
1552 A552 16c multi 1.10 .20

Restoration of Bolivar Theater, Quito — A553

Designs: 16c, Piano, banquet room. 32c, Stage, orchestra, horiz.

2000, Dec.   Perf. 13x13¼, 13¼x13
1553-1554 A553 Set of 2 3.25 1.50

Spondylus Princeps A554

2000, Dec. 16   Perf. 13¾
1555 A554 84c multi 5.00 2.50
Imperf
Size: 69x99mm
1556 A554 $1 multi 5.75 2.75

America Issue, Fight Against AIDS — A555

No. 1557: a, Strands. b, Earth.

2000   Perf. 13x13¼
1557 A555 84c Horiz. pair, #a-b 11.00 5.25

Guayas Province Red Cross, 90th Anniv. A556

2000   Perf. 13¼x13
1558 A556 16c multi 1.10 .55

Guayas Sports Federation, 78th Anniv. — A557

2000, Dec.   Perf. 13x13¼
1559 A557 16c multi 1.10 .55

Landscapes A557a

Designs: No. 1559A, 16c, Andean region. No. 1559B, 16c, Pacific coast. 32c, Tourism emblem. 68c, Amazonia. 84c, Galápagos Islands.

Perf. 13¼x12¾
2001, Jan. 24   Litho.   Wmk. 395
1559A A557a 16c multi 1.25 .60
1559B A557a 16c multi 1.25 .60
1559C A557a 32c multi 2.50 1.10
1559D A557a 68c multi 4.75 2.40
1559E A557a 68c multi 4.75 2.40
Nos. 1559A-1559E (5) 14.50 7.10

Guayas Soccer Team, 50th Anniv. A558

2001, Mar. 8   Perf. 13¼x13
1560 A558 68c multi 4.00 1.90

Census — A558a   Census — A558b

Perf. 12¾x13¼
2001, Mar. 12   Litho.   Wmk. 395
1560A A558a 68c multi 4.00 4.00
1560B A558b 68c multi 4.00 4.00
c. Horiz. pair, #1560A-1560B 8.00 8.00

Dr. Raúl Clemente Huerta A559

2001, Apr. 4   Perf. 13¼x13
1561 A559 68c multi 4.50 2.25

Dr. Antonio J. Quevedo, Birth Cent. A560

2001, Apr. 5 **Litho.**
1562 A560 84c multi 5.50 2.50

Military Geographic Institute A560a

No. 1562A: b, Soldier, building. c, Computer, printing press.

Perf. 13¼x12¾
2001, Apr. 11 **Litho.** **Wmk. 395**
1562A A560a 68c Vert. pair, #b-c 9.00 4.50

Automobile Club of Ecuador, 50th Anniv. A561

2001, May 15 **Wmk. 395**
1563 A561 84c multi 5.50 2.50

San Francisco de Peleusí Church, Azogues — A561a

Perf. 12¾x13¼
2001, May **Litho.** **Wmk. 395**
1563A A561a 84c multi 5.50 2.50

Women's Training Institute — A562

2001, Apr. 10 **Perf. 13x13¼**
1564 A562 84c multi 5.50 2.50

Intl. Women's Day A563

No. 1565: a, Woman, child, corn. b, Woman, emblem.
2001, Apr. 2 **Perf. 13¼x13**
1565 A563 84c Vert. pair, #a-b 11.00 5.25

Secular Education at Manuela Cañizares University, Cent. A564

2001, Mar. 29 **Wmk. 395**
1566 A564 84c multi 5.50 2.50

Ecuador Merchant Marines, Cent. — A565

2001, Jan. 2001 **Perf. 13x13¼**
1567 A565 16c multi 1.10 .55

Ambato Technical University, 32nd Anniv. A566

No. 1568: a, Building. b, Painting.
2001 **Perf. 13¼x13**
1568 A566 32c Vert. pair, #a-b 4.50 2.25

Galapagos Islands Scenes — A567

No. 1569: a, Española Island (shown). b, San Cristobal Island. c, Bartolome Island. d, Española Island, diff. e, Bartolome and Santiago Islands.
$1, Bird on rock, Española Island.
2001, Feb. 17 **Perf. 13¾**
1569 A567 Horiz. strip of 5 5.00 2.25
a.-e. A567 16c Any single .35 .20
Imperf
Size: 100x70mm
1570 A567 $1 multi 6.75 3.25

Alexander von Humboldt (1769-1859), Naturalist — A568

Perf. 13x13¼
2001, June 14 **Litho.** **Wmk. 395**
1571 A568 84c multi 5.00 2.40

Ecuadorian Atomic Energy Commission A568a

2001, Aug. 3 **Litho.** **Perf. 12¾x13¼**
1571A A568a 70c multi 4.50 2.25

Lebanese Union, 80th Anniv. — A569

No. 1572: a, Building and emblem. b, Emblem.
Illustration reduced.
2001, Aug. 30 **Perf. 13¼x13**
1572 A569 16c Horiz. pair, #a-b 2.40 1.25

Manta Port Authority — A570

No. 1573: a, Emblem. b, Ships in port.
Illustration reduced.
2001, Sept. 28
1573 A570 68c Horiz. pair, #a-b 8.00 4.00

Esmereldas Province Tourism — A571

No. 1574: a, Beach. b, Musicians and dancers on beach.
Illustration reduced.
2001
1574 A571 86c Horiz. pair, #a-b 10.00 5.00

Latin American Writers — A572

No. 1575: a, Claudia Lars (1899-1974), Salvadoran poet. b, Federico Proaño (1848-94), Ecuadoran journalist.
2001, Aug. 28 **Perf. 13x13¼**
1575 A572 86c Horiz. pair, #a-b 12.00 5.75

Andean Condor Preservation — A573

No. 1576: a, Condor and chick. b, Condor heads, FRAPZOO emblem.
$1, Condor in flight, FRAPZOO emblem.
2001, July 23 **Perf. 13x13¼**
1576 A573 86c Horiz. pair, #a-b 10.00 5.00

Imperf
Size: 68x99mm
1577 A573 $1 multi 6.25 3.00

Ecuador — Peru Peace Accords A574

No. 1578: a, Map of Ecuador and Peru. b, Soldier. c, Flags of military obeservers. d, Amazon River. e, Men in field.
2001, May 22 **Perf. 13¼x13**
1578 A574 Horiz. strip of 5 22.50 11.00
a.-e. A574 68c Any single 4.00 2.00

Archidona Canton — A575

No. 1579: a, Phragmipedium orchid. b, Saimiri sciureus. c, B. macrophylla. d, Church. e, Kichwa Indian family.
2001, Apr. 28 **Perf. 13¼x13¼**
1579 A575 Vert. strip of 5 27.50 13.50
a.-e. A575 84c Any single 5.00 2.40

Ecotourism in Baños A576

No. 1580: a, Orchid. b, Basilica, Baños. c, Tungurahua Volcano. d, Pailon del Diablo Waterfall. e, Statue of Virgin of Rosario de Agua Santa.
$1, Pailon del Diablo Waterfall, orchid.
2001 **Perf. 13¼x13**
1580 A576 Horiz. strip of 5 24.00 12.00
a.-e. A576 86c Any single 4.50 2.25

Imperf
Size: 68x99mm
1581 A576 $1 multi 6.25 3.00

Guayas Educational Journalists Association, 30th Anniv. A577

Perf. 13¼x13
2001, Oct. 15 **Litho.** **Wmk. 395**
1582 A577 16c multi 1.10 .60

 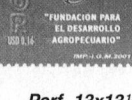

Foundation for Development of Cattle Ranching, 15th Anniv. — A578

2001, Aug. 15 **Perf. 13x13¼**
1583 A578 16c multi 1.10 .60

City Gates, Loja — A579

2001 **Perf. 13¼x13**
1584 A579 32c multi 2.10 .95

Quito Municipal District Directorate of Security A580

2001, Nov. 26
1585 A580 68c multi 4.00 2.00

Salvador Bustamante Celi (1876-1935), Musician A581

2001
1586 A581 68c multi 4.50 2.25

Marcel Laniado de Wind (1927-98), First Pres. of Natl. Modernization Council — A582

2001, Aug. 6 **Perf. 13x13¼**
1587 A582 70c multi 4.50 2.25

Bernardino Cardinal Echeverria (1912-2000) A583

2001, Nov. 14
1588 A583 84c multi 5.50 2.50

José Joaquin Olmedo (1780-1847), Statesman and Poet — A584

2001, Nov. 8
1589 A584 84c multi 5.50 2.50

El Angel Ecological Reserve — A585

No. 1590: a, Paja de Paramo. b, Frailejón. Illustration reduced.

2001 **Perf. 13¼x13**
1590 A585 16c Horiz. pair, #a-b 2.20 1.00

Yahuarcocha Race Track — A586

No. 1591: a, Race track and lake. b, Lake. Illustration reduced.

2001, Nov. 30
1591 A586 68c Horiz. pair, #a-b 8.00 4.00

World Food Day — A587

No. 1592: a, Wheat ears. b, Food baskets. Illustration reduced.

2001, Nov. 5
1592 A587 84c Horiz. pair, #a-b 11.00 5.50

Art of Voroshilov Bazante A588

No. 1593: a, Spatial composition. b, Abstract, artists name at LR. c, Urban landscape. d, Abstract, diff., "Abstracto" at UL, denomination at LL. e, Abstract, denomination at LR.

2001, Nov.
1593 Horiz. strip of 5 27.50 12.50
a.-e. A588 84c Any single 5.00 2.50

Wilson Popenoe Private Foundation A589

2001, Nov. 19 Litho. Perf. 13¼x13
1594 A589 16c multi 1.10 .55

FAO Food Program A590

2001, Aug. 15
1595 A590 84c multi 5.50 2.50

Rotary District 4400, 75th Anniv. — A591

2001, Nov. 30 **Perf. 13x13¼**
1596 A591 84c multi 5.50 2.50

Pres. Camilo Ponce Enriquez (1912-76) A592

Pedro Vicente Maldonado (1702-48), Geographer A593

2001
1597 A592 84c multi 5.50 2.50

2001, Dec. 12
1598 A593 84c multi 5.50 2.50

Otonga Foundation — A595

No. 1599: a, Frog on branch. b, Mustela frenata.

2001, Oct. 31
1599 A595 16c Horiz. pair, #a-b 2.20 1.10

Tourism in Zaruma — A596

No. 1600: a, Virgen del Carmen. b, Orchid. Illustration reduced.

2001, Dec. 12 **Perf. 13¼x13**
1600 A596 68c Horiz. pair, #a-b 8.00 4.00

Radio HCJB, 70th Anniv. — A597

No. 1601: a, Microphone. b, Announcer. Illustration reduced.

2001, Dec. 21
1601 A597 68c Horiz. pair, #a-b 8.00 4.00

Tennis A598

No. 1602: a, Davis Cup. b, K. Lapentti, G. Lapentti, L.A. Morejón, A. Intriago and R. Viver. c, Francisco Guzman and Miguel Olvera. d, Pancho Segura. e, Andres Gomez.

2001, Nov. 1
1602 Horiz. strip of 5 21.00 10.50
a.-e. A598 68c Any single 4.00 2.00

Church Paintings of Wilfrido Martínez — A599

No. 1603: a, San Francisco (artist's name is vert.). b, Guapulo. c, San Francisco (artist's name is horiz.). d, La Compania. e, El Rosario.

2002, Apr. 9 **Perf. 13¾**
1603 Horiz. strip of 5 24.00 12.00
a.-e. A599 90c Any single 4.50 2.25

First Judicial Summit of the Americas, Quito A600

Perf. 13¼x13
2002, Jan. 8 Litho. Wmk. 395
1604 A600 68c multi 4.00 2.00

Union Club, Guayaquil — A601

2002, Apr. 25 **Perf. 13x13¼**
1605 A601 90c multi 5.50 2.75

South American Soccer Confederation A602

Designs: 25c, Confederation Pres. Nicolás Leoz. 40c, Confederation emblem, soccer players. 70c, Emblem of Emelec team.

2002, Jan. 29
1606-1608 A602 Set of 3 8.00 4.00

World Conservation Union — A603

Designs: 70c, Fish, man's head. 85c, Leopard, man, horiz.
$1, Bird, animals, women and children, horiz.

2002, Feb. 21 Perf. 13x13¼, 13¼x13
1609-1610 A603 Set of 2 9.00 4.50
Imperf
Size: 100x70mm
1611 A603 $1 multi 6.25 3.00

UN High Commissioner for Refugees — A604

Designs: 70c, Emblem. 85c, Child. $1, Refugees carrying belongings, horiz.

2002, Feb. 28 **Perf. 13x13¼**
1612-1613 A604 Set of 2 9.00 4.50
Imperf
Size: 100x70mm
1614 A604 $1 multi 6.25 3.00

Ecuadorian Educational Credit and Scholarship Institute — A605

No. 1615: a, Student using microscope. b, Emblem.

2002, Apr. 30 *Perf. 13x13¼*
1615 A605 25c Horiz. pair, #a-b 2.50 1.25

Cuenca Soccer Team — A606

No. 1616: a, Team photo. b, Emblem, player dribbling.
Illustration reduced.

2002, Apr. 19 *Perf. 13¼x13*
1616 A606 25c Horiz. pair, #a-b 2.50 1.25

Imbabura Province History — A607

No. 1617: a, Building. b, Statue.

2002, Mar. 27 *Perf. 13x13¼*
1617 A607 40c Horiz. pair, #a-b 5.00 2.40

Crucita — A608

No. 1618: a, Parachutist with sun on horizon. b, Prachutist above beach.
Illustration reduced.

2002, Mar. 28 *Perf. 13¼x13*
1618 A608 40c Horiz. pair, #a-b 5.00 2.40

Mountains A609

No. 1619: a, Mt. Altar (trees in foreground). b, Mt. Chimborazo. c, Mt. Carihuayrazo. d, Mt. Altar (lake in foreground). e, Mt. Cubillin.

2002, Apr. 19
1619 Horiz. strip of 5 29.00 15.00
a.-e. A609 90c Any single 5.00 2.25

Endangered Frogs A610

No. 1620: a, Atelopus bomolochos. b, Atelopus longirostris. c, Atelopus pachydermus. d, Atelopus arthuri. e, Atelopus sp.
$1, Atelopus ignescens.

2002, Mar. 25 *Perf. 13¼x13*
1620 Horiz. strip of 5 29.00 15.00
a.-e. A610 $1.05 Any single 5.00 2.25
Imperf
1621 A610 $1 multi 8.50 7.00

Size: 100x70mm

National Anti-narcotics Police — A611

No. 1622: a, Policeman and dog. b, Emblem.

Perf. 13x13¼
2002, Apr. 23 *Litho.* *Wmk. 395*
1622 A611 40c Horiz. pair, #a-b 5.00 2.50

2002 World Cup Soccer Championships, Japan and Korea — A612

Designs: 90c, Ecuadorian Soccer Federation emblem, vert. $1.05, $2, Emblem, team photo, players in action.

2002, Apr. 28 *Perf. 13x13¼, 13¼x13*
1623-1624 A612 Set of 2 7.25 3.50
Imperf
Size: 100x70mm
1625 A612 $2 multi 7.25 3.50

Dr. Servio Aguirre Villamagua, Forest Conservationist — A613

No. 1626: a, Aguirre. b, Plant.
Illustration reduced.

2002, May 22 *Perf. 13¼x13*
1626 A613 40c Horiz. pair, #a-b 3.00 1.50

Food and Agriculture Organization in Ecuador, 50th Anniv. A614

2002, May 30
1627 A614 $1.05 multi 4.00 2.00

Galapagos Islands Fauna A615

No. 1628: .a, Grapsus grapsus. b, Conolophus subcristatus.
No. 1629, vert.: a, Sula sula websteri. b, Phoenicopterus ruber.
No. 1630, Amblyrhynchus cristatus.
No. 1631, vert.: a, Pair of Zalophus californianus wollebacki. b, One Zalophus californianus wollebacki.
No. 1632, Sula nebouxxi excisa, vert.
No. 1633, vert.: a, Sula dactylatra granti. b, Emblem of Iberoamerican Summit on Tourism and Environment.
$2, Bird, tourists, tourist ship.

2002, May 31 *Perf. 13¼x13, 13x13¼*
1628 A615 25c Horiz. pair,
#a-b 2.50 1.50
1629 A615 40c Horiz. pair,
#a-b 3.50 2.00
1630 A615 90c multi 4.25 3.00
1631 A615 90c Horiz. pair,
#a-b 8.50 4.50
1632 A615 $1.05 multi 5.00 2.50
1633 A615 $1.05 Horiz. pair,
#a-b 9.50 5.00
Nos. 1628-1633 (6) 33.25 18.50
Imperf
Size: 100x68mm
1634 A615 $2 multi 9.00 7.00

Ministry of Foreign Relations — A616

2002, June 5 *Perf. 13x13¼*
1635 A616 90c multi 3.50 1.60

Army Polytechnic School, 80th Anniv. A617

2002, June 13 *Perf. 13¼x13*
1636 A617 25c multi 1.25 .60

Military Engineers, Cent. A618

Designs: No. 1637, 40c, Castle of Engineering. No. 1638, 40c, Castle of Engineering, Military engineers in action, vert.
$2, Castle of Engineering, engineers in action, emblems of military groups.

Perf. 13¼x13, 13x13¼
2002, June 19
1637-1638 A618 Set of 2 3.20 1.60
Imperf
Size: 100x68mm
1639 A618 $2 multi 7.25 3.50

Dr. Alfredo Pérez Guerrero (1901-66), Academic — A619

2002, July 4 *Perf. 13x13¼*
1640 A619 25c multi 1.25 .60

20th Anniv. of Ecuador's Second Place Finish In World Taekwondo Championships — A620

2002, July 18 *Perf. 13¼x13*
1641 A620 40c multi 1.60 .80

Orellana Province — A621

No. 1642: a, Three native men. b, Man in tree.
Illustration reduced.

2002, July 30 *Wmk. 395*
1642 A621 25c Horiz. pair, #a-b 2.50 1.25

CARE in Ecuador, 40th Anniv. — A622

No. 1643: a, Two children. b, Boy.

2002, July 30 *Perf. 13x13¼*
1643 A622 90c Horiz. pair, #a-b 7.25 3.50

Macará Region A623

2002, Aug. 10 *Perf. 13¼x13*
1644 A623 40c multi 1.60 .80

Intl. Organization for Migration, 50th Anniv. — A624

Quito Philharmonic Society, 50th Anniv. — A625

2002, Aug. 18 *Perf. 13x13¼*
1645 A624 $1.05 multi 4.00 2.00

2002, Aug. 29
1646 A625 25c multi 1.25 .60

Comptroller General, 75th Anniv. — A625a

Perf. 13x13¼
2002, Sept. 26 *Litho.* *Wmk. 395*
1646A A625a 40c multi 1.60 .80

Second World Meeting of Mountain People — A626

No. 1647 — Emblem of World Meeting and: a, Mountain. b, Group of people. c, Houses in valley. d, Town. e, Other emblems.

2002, Sept. 18
1647   Horiz. strip of 5   18.00   9.00
a.-e. A626 90c Any single   3.50   1.60

Pujili
Dancer — A627

Perf. 13x13¼
2002, Oct. 14   **Litho.**   **Wmk. 395**
1648   A627 $1.05 multi   4.00 2.00

Paintings of Milton Estrella
Gavidia — A628

No. 1649 — Various paintings with background colors of: a, Blue violet. b, Brown violet. c, Olive green. d, Blue. e, Gray lilac.

Wmk. 395
2002, May 17   **Litho.**   **Perf. 13¾**
1649   Horiz. strip of 5   18.00   9.00
a.-e. A628 90c Any single   3.50   1.60

Paintings of
Leonardo
Hidalgo
A629

No. 1650: a, La Dolorosa. b, El Hombre Cargando su Fruto. c, Frida Kahlo. d, El Hombre Fuerte del Mar. e, Jesus.

Wmk. 395
2002, Oct. 3   **Litho.**   **Perf. 13¾**
1650   Horiz. strip of 5   18.00   9.00
a.-e. A629 90c Any single   3.50   1.60

Pan-American Health Organization,
Cent. — A630

2002, Dec. 2   **Perf. 13¼x12¾**
1651   A630 $1.05 multi   4.00 2.00

Lo Nuestro Art Exhibition — A631

No. 1652: a, Wall with six works of art. b, Walls with 16 works of art.
Illustration reduced.

2002, Dec. 15
1652   A631 25c Horiz. pair, #a-b   2.00 1.00

Catholic
University,
40th Anniv.
A632

2002, Dec. 18
1653   A632 40c multi   1.60   .80

America Issue — UNESCO World
Heritage Sites — A633

No. 1654: a, Cupola of San Blas Church, Cuenca. b, Society of Jesus Church, Quito.

2002, Dec. 18   **Perf. 12¾x13¼**
1654   A633 25c Horiz. pair, #a-b   2.50 1.25
Dated 2001.

America Issue — Youth, Education
and Literacy — A634

No. 1655: a, Students and blackboard. b, Toddler and books.
Illustration reduced.

2002, Dec. 18   **Perf. 13¼x12¾**
1655   A634 25c Horiz. pair, #a-b   2.50 1.25

Second Meeting of South American
Presidents, Guayaquil — A635

No. 1656: a, Meeting emblem. b, Emblem, presidents and flags.
Illustration reduced.

2003, Jan. 13
1656   A635 $1.05 Horiz. pair, #a-b   7.25 3.50

Papal Benediction
for Ecuadorian
Emigrants — A636

2003, Jan. 24   **Perf. 12¾x13¼**
1657   A636 $1.05 multi   3.60 1.75
Size: 68x100mm
Imperf
1658   A636 $2 multi   7.25 3.50

World
Vison — A637

2003, Feb. 6   **Perf. 12¾x13¼**
1659   A637 40c multi   1.40   .70

Intl. Women's
Day — A638

2003, Mar. 8   **Wmk. 395**
1660   A638 $1.05 multi   3.60 1.75

Agustin Cueva
Vallejo (1820-73),
Physician — A639

2003, Mar. 13   **Litho.**
1661   A639 40c multi   1.40   .70

Blasco Moscoso
Cuesta, Founder of
Pichincha Sports
Writers
Association — A640

2003, Mar. 14
1662   A640 25c multi   .90   .45

Cuenca
Artisan
Products
A641

No. 1663: a, Azuay University domes. b, Tinware. c, Jewelry. d, Fireworks. e, Saddles.
No. 1664: a, Engraving. b, Metallurgy. c, Baskets. d, Embroidery. e, Ceramics.
$2, Assorted products.

2003, Mar. 27   **Perf. 13¼x12¾**
1663   Horiz. strip of 5   4.50   2.10
a.-e. A641 25c Any single   .80   .40
1664   Horiz. strip of 5   18.00   8.75
a.-e. A641 $1.05 Any single   3.25   1.50
Size: 100x68mm
Imperf
1665   A641 $2 multi   7.25 3.50

Flora and
Fauna
A642

No. 1666: a, Curculionidae. b, Lycidae. c, Acridoidea. d, Arachnidae. e, Liliacea.

2003, Apr. 4   **Perf. 13¼x12¾**
1666   Horiz. strip of 5   18.00   8.75
a.-e. A642 $1.05 Any single   3.50   1.60

Military
Geographic
Institute, 75th
Anniv.
A643

Designs: No. 1667, 40c, No. 1669, $2, Painting by Eduardo Kingman. No. 1668, 40c, Institute emblem, vert.

Perf. 13¼x12¾, 12¾x13¼
2003, Apr. 11
1667-1668   A643   Set of 2   2.90 1.40

Size: 100x68mm
Imperf
1669   A643 $2 multi   7.25 3.50

Galápagos Marine
Reserve — A644

Designs: 40c, Stylized butterfly.
No. 1671, $1.05, horiz.: a, Sphyrna lewini. b, Chelonia mydas agassisi.
No. 1672, $1.05, horiz.: a, Xanthichthys mento. b, Zanclus cornutus.
$2, Tubastrea coccinea, horiz.

Perf. 12¾x13¼, 13¼x12¾
2003, May 9
1670   A644 40c multi   1.40   .70
Horiz. Pairs, #a-b
1671-1672   A644   Set of 2   14.50 7.25
Size: 100x68mm
Imperf
1673   A644 $2 multi   7.25 3.50

Intl. Tourism
Trade Fair of
Ecuador
A645

No. 1674: a, Monkey in tree. b, Birds. c, Embroidery. d, Mountain. e, Hat seller on beach.

2003, May 14   **Perf. 13¼x12¾**
1674   Vert. strip of 5   4.50 2.25
a.-e. A645 25c Any single   .80   .40

Artifacts of Pre-Columbian
Cultures — A646

No. 1675, 25c: a, Gold bell with monkey. b, Amphora.
No. 1676, 25c: a, Sculpture of a man. b, Three-footed pot.

Perf. 13x13¼
2003, May 16   **Litho.**   **Wmk. 395**
Horiz. pairs, #a-b
1675-1676   A646   Set of 2   3.50 1.75

Central Bank
of Ecuador
A647

No. 1677, vert.: a, Tolita Culture mask. b, Guayaquil Historic Park.
$1.05, Pumapungo Museum.

Perf. 13x13¼, 13¼x13
2003, June 5   **Litho.**
1677   A647 25c Horiz. pair,
     #a-b   1.00   .50
1678   A647 $1.05 multi   2.10 1.10

Philately and
Guayaquil
A648

No. 1679, horiz.: a, British consular cover to Veracruz with British stamp and cancel. b, Stampless cover.

No. 1680, horiz.: a, SCADTA first flight cover. b, French consular cover to Lima with French stamps and cancels.

$1.05, Philatelic magazines.

$2, Guayaquil Philatelic Club emblem, Ecuadoran stamps, horiz.

2003, July 22   **Perf. 13¾**
1679 A648   40c Vert. pair, #a-b   2.75 1.40
1680 A648   40c Vert. pair, #a-b   2.75 1.40
1681 A648 $1.05 multi   3.50 1.75
    Nos. 1679-1681 (3)   9.00 4.55
Size: 100x69mm
Imperf
1682 A648 $2 multi   7.00 3.50

Guayaquil
Urban
Renewal
A649

No. 1683: a, Punta Cerro Santa Ana. b, Plaza Colón. c, Malecón Gardens. d, Crystal Palace. e, Plaza de San Francisco.

2003, July 26   **Perf. 13¼x13**
1683   Horiz. strip of 5   15.00 7.25
  a.-e.   A649 90c Any single   2.75 1.40

World Bird
Festival
A650

Designs: No. 1684, $1.05, Geranoaetus melanoleucus. No. 1685, $1.05, Harpia harpyja, vert.

2003, Sept. 2   **Perf. 13¼x13, 13x13¼**
1684-1685 A650   Set of 2   7.25 3.50

Zamora-Chinchipe Province, 50th
Anniv. — A651

No. 1686: a, Shown. b, Eira barbara. c, Boa constrictor. d, Tapirus terrestris. e, Psophia crepitans.

2003, Nov. 7   **Perf. 13¼x13**
1686   Vert. strip of 5   4.50 2.25
  a.-e. A651 25c Any single   .80 .40

America Issue — Flora and
Fauna — A652

No. 1687: a, Semnornis ramphastinus. b, Bomarea glaucescens.

Perf. 13x13¼
2003, Nov. 1   **Litho.**   **Wmk. 395**
1687 A652 $1.05 Horiz. pair, #a-b   6.25 3.00

Selection of
Quito as
World
Heritage Site,
25th Anniv.
A653

Churches: 40c, El Sagrario. No. 1689a, La Compañia de Jesus. No. 1689b, Santa Barbara. $1.05, San Francisco, vert.

2003, Nov. 1   **Perf. 13¼x13, 13x13¼**
1688 A653   40c multi   1.00 .50
1689 A653   90c Horiz. pair, #a-b   5.00 2.50
1690 A653 $1.05 multi   3.00 1.40
    Nos. 1688-1690 (3)   9.00 4.40

Christmas
A654

Children's art by: No. 1691a, Stephanie Pacheco. No. 1691b, Sebastián Tejada. 40c, María Claudia Iturralde, vert. 90c, Luis Antonio Ortega. $1.05, Angel Andrés Castro, vert.

2003, Nov. 1
1691 A654   25c Horiz. pair, #a-b   1.50 .70
1692 A654   40c multi   1.25 .55
1693 A654   90c multi   2.75 1.25
1694 A654 $1.05 multi   3.00 1.50
    Nos. 1691-1694 (4)   8.50 4.00

Treasures of
Guayaquil
Municipal
Museum
A655

No. 1695: a, Santiago de Guayaquil Act of Independence. b, Punaes ceremonial stone. c, Proclamation of Mariano Donoso. d, Tzantzas. e, Manteño-Huancavilca totem.

2003, Dec. 1   **Perf. 13¼x13**
1695   Horiz. strip of 5   5.75 2.75
  a.-e. A655 40c Any single   1.10 .55

Selection of
Galapagos Islands
as World Heritage
Site, 25th
Anniv. — A656

No. 1696: a, Zalophus californianus wollebacki. b, Fregata minor palmerstoni. c, Sula nebouxii excisa. d, Isla Bartolomé. e, Two Sula nebouxii excisa shaped as "25."

2003, Nov. 26   **Perf. 13¼x13**
1696   Horiz. strip of 5   5.75 2.75
  a.-e. A656 40c Any single   1.10 .55

Army Aviation Instruction, 50th
Anniv. — A657

No. 1697, 40c: a, Mountain, airplanes, emblem. b, Airplane in flight, men on ground.
No. 1698, 40c, horiz.: a, Helicopter and soldiers. b, Airplanes, mountain, people.

2004, Jan. 21   **Perf. 13x13¼, 13¼x13**
Horiz. pairs, #a-b
1697-1698 A657   Set of 2   4.50 2.25

Military Geographical Institute's Role
in National Development — A658

2004, Apr. 14   **Perf. 13¼x13**
1699 A658 $1.05 multi   3.00 1.50

Commander
Rafael Morán
Valverde, Military
Hero — A659

2004, Apr. 5   **Perf. 13x13¼**
1700 A659 $1.05 multi   3.00 1.50

Intl. Philately Day — A660

No. 1701: a, Ecuador #2, Greece #1. b, Cover with six stamps.

$2, Various stamps, tongs, magnifying glass, stamp catalogues.

Illustration reduced.

2004, May 6   **Perf. 13¼x13**
1701 A660 75c Horiz. pair, #a-b   5.00 2.50
Imperf
Size: 100x68mm
1702 A660 $2 multi   6.25 3.00

Ecuadorian
Volleyball
Federation
A661

Perf. 13x13¼
2004, May 27   **Litho.**   **Wmk. 395**
1703 A661 75c multi   2.50 1.10

2004 Miss
Universe
Pageant
A662

2004, May 29   **Perf. 13¾**
1704 A662 75c multi   2.50 1.25

Sculpture by
Mario Tapia
A663

No. 1705: a, Adolescencia. b, Beato Chaminade. c, Delfin de Galapagos. d, Pelicano. e, Homenaje a Carlo Vidano.

$2, Similar to No. 1705b.

2004, June 1   **Perf. 13¼x13**
1705   Horiz. strip of 5   13.50 6.75
  a.-e. A663 90c Any single   1.80 .90
Imperf
Size: 100x69mm
1706 A663 $2 multi   7.25 3.75

Pedro Vicente
Maldonado (1704-
48), Cartographer
A664

2004, June 25   **Perf. 13x13¼**
1707 A664 90c multi   2.50 1.25

Dr. Agustín Cueva
Tamariz (1903-
79) — A665

2004, June 30   **Litho.**
1708 A665 90c multi   2.50 1.25

34th General
Assembly of the
Organization of
American
States — A666

2004, July 4   **Wmk. 395**
1709 A666 75c multi   2.50 1.25

Dr. Angel
Felicísmo Rojas
(b. 1909),
Writer — A667

2004, July 11
1710 A667 50c multi   1.60 .80

Ecuadoran
and Spanish
Postal
Money
Orders
A668

2004, Aug. 3   **Perf. 13¼x13**
1711 A668 $1.05 multi   3.00 1.50

2004 Summer Olympics,
Athens — A669

No. 1712 — 2004 Summer Olympics emblem, Ecuadoran Olympic Committee emblem and: a, 2004 Olympics mascots. b, Alexandra Escobar Guerrero.

2004, Aug. 3   Perf. 13x13¼
1712 A669 $1.05 Horiz. pair,
      #a-b   6.25 3.25

Ecuador Orchid
Association, 30th
Anniv. — A670

Designs: 25c, Cattleya maxima. $1.05, Epidendrum bracteolatum.

2004, Sept. 30
1713-1714 A670   Set of 2   3.75 1.90

Guayaquil
Symphony
Orchestra — A671

        Perf. 13x13¼
2004, Nov. 19 Litho.   Wmk. 395
1715 A671 90c multi   2.50 1.25

Christmas — A672

Children's art: 40c, Christmas stocking with envelopes. $1.05, Santa Claus giving letter to Christmas tree, horiz.

2004, Dec. 12 Perf. 13x13¼, 13¼x13
1716-1717 A672   Set of 2   4.00 2.00

America Issue -
Environmental
Protection — A673

Designs: 40d, Buddha and trees. $1.05, Mother Earth.

2004, Dec. 23   Perf. 13x13¼
1718-1719 A673   Set of 2   4.00 2.00

Galapagos
Islands
Fauna
A674

Designs: 40c, Chelonoidis abingdonii. 90c, Amblyrhynchus cristatus, vert. $2.15, Sula granti. $3, Fregata magnifiscens. $2, Creagrus furcatus, vert.

2005, Feb. 18 Perf. 13¼x13, 13x13¼
1720-1723 A674   Set of 4   21.00 10.50
        Imperf
        Size: 68x98mm
1724 A674 $2 multi   6.25 3.00

El Mercurio
Newspaper,
80th Anniv.
A675

Designs: $1.25, Masthead. $2, Dr. Nicanor Merchan Bermeo, newspaper co-founder. $2.25, Miguel Merchan Ochoa.

2005, Mar. 4   Perf. 13¼x13, 13x13¼
1725-1727 A675   Set of 3   18.00 9.00

Tourism
A676

2005, Mar. 22   Perf. 13¼x13
1728 A676 $3.75 multi   12.00 6.00

Ecuadorian Chess
Federation, 25th
Anniv. — A677

2005, Apr. 1   Perf. 13x13¼
1729 A677 $1.25 multi   4.00 2.00

Ecuadorian
Olympic Academy,
25th
Anniv. — A678

        Perf. 13x13¼
2005, June 20 Litho.   Wmk. 395
1730 A678 $1.25 shown   4.00 2.00
        Imperf
        Size: 69x100mm
1731 A678 $2 Emblems   7.00 3.50

Rotary International, Cent. — A679

Rotary emblem and: 40c, Man on Mt. Chimborazo. 90c, People on Mt. Cotopaxi. $2, Man on Mt. Shisha Pangma, Nepal.

2005, June 29   Perf. 13¼x13
1732-1734 A679   Set of 3   11.00 5.25

Guayaquil Conference, 183rd
Anniv. — A680

No. 1735 — Guayaquil Philatelic Club emblem and: a, José de San Martín, Argentina #1. b, Simón Bolívar, Venezuela #1. $2, Bolívar, San Martín, monument. Illustration reduced.

2005, July 22   Perf. 13¼x13
1735 A680 90c Horiz. pair, #a-b 6.00 3.00
        Imperf
        Size:98x68mm
1736 A680 $2 multi   7.00 3.50

Intl. Year of Books
and
Reading — A681

        Perf. 13x13¼
2005, July 22 Litho.   Wmk. 395
1737 A681 25c multi   1.00 .50

Dr. Juan Isaac Lovato Vargas (1904-
2001), Judge — A682

        Perf. 13¼x13
2005, July 28 Litho.   Wmk. 395
1738 A682 $1.25 multi   4.50 2.25

Mountain and Eastern Cattleman's
Association — A683

No. 1739 — Emblem and: a, Mountains. b, Head of cow.

2005, Aug. 4   Perf. 13¼x13
1739 A683 40c Horiz. pair, #a-b 2.50 3.00

University
Sports
League of
Quito, 75th
Anniv.
A684

No. 1740: a, University Sports League Stadium. b, 1969 University Sports League soccer team. c, Emblem. d, Children playing at school. e, Statue of emblem, League Country Club.
  $2, Soccer shirt, vert.

2005, Aug. 4   Perf. 13¼x13
1740 Horiz. strip of 5   6.50 3.25
a.-e. A684 40c Any single   1.25 .65
        Size: 68x98mm
1741 A684 $2 multi   7.00 3.50

15th
Bolivarian
Games,
Armenia
and Pereira
A685

2005, Aug. 8   Perf. 13¼x13
1742 A685 25c multi   1.00 .50

1938 South American Swimming
Champions, Trophy and Swimming
Federation Emblem
A686

2005, Aug. 8   Litho.
1743 A686 25c multi   1.00 .50

First Ecuadoran victory in international sports competition.

Virgin of
Cisne — A687

2005, Sept. 6   Perf. 13¾
1744 A687 $1.25 multi   4.50 2.25

History of
the
Ecuadoran
Army
A688

No. 1745: a, Troops in Esmeraldas, 1916. b, Military school cadets, 1928. c, Cayambe Battalion. d, Arms and Grandsons of Gen. Eloy Alfaro. e, Imbabura Battalion. $2, Battle for emancipation of Guayaquil.

2005, Sept. 15   Perf. 13¼x13
1745 Horiz. strip of 5   6.50 3.25
a.-e. A688 40c Any single   .80 .40
        Imperf
        Size: 98x67mm
1746 A688 $2 multi   7.00 3.50

Carchi Province
Arms — A689

No. 1747: a, Tulcán Canton. b, Bolívar Canton.
No. 1748: a, Carchi Province. b, Huaca Canton. c, Mira Canton. d, Espejo Canton. e, Montúfar Canton.

2005, Sept. 26 — Perf. 13x13¼

1747	Horiz. pair	2.50	1.25
a.-b.	A689 40c Either single	1.25	.65
1748	Horiz. strip of 5	6.50	3.25
a.-e.	A689 40c Any single	1.25	.65

Tourism — A690

No. 1749: a, Cerro Santa Ana, Guayaquil. b, Esmereldas. c, Misahualli. d, Tsunki Shuar, Pastaza.
No. 1750: a, Cisne Church, Loja. b, Ingapirca Ruins. c, Seal, Galapagos Islands. d, Sea turtle, Galapagos Islands.
Illustration reduced.

Perf. 13¼x13
2005, Sept. 26 Litho. Wmk. 395

1749	A690 30c Block of 4, #a-d	4.00	2.10
1750	A690 40c Block of 4, #a-d	5.50	2.75

St. Mariana de Jesús Paredes y Flores A691

2005, Oct. 19

1751	A691 25c multi	1.00	.50

Popes Reigning in 2005 — A692

No. 1752: a, $1.25, Pope John Paul II (1920-2005). b, $2, Pope Benedict XVI.
Illustration reduced.

2005, Oct. 19

1752	A692 Horiz. pair, #a-b	11.00	5.50

Cenepa War With Peru, 10th Anniv. — A693

No. 1753: a, Mirage F1-JA airplanes. b, Cessna A-37B airplanes. c, Kfir-C2 airplanes. d, Lt. Col. Carlos Uscategui and airplane.
Illustration reduced.

2005, Oct. 26

1753	A693 $1.25 Block of 4, #a-d	18.00	9.00

First Guayaquil to Cuenca Airmail Flight, 85th Anniv. — A694

No. 1754: a, 25c, Tail of Telegrafo I airplane, flight manager José Abel Castillo. b, $1, Front of Telegrafo I airplane, pilot Elia Liut.

Illustration reduced.

2005, Nov. 12

1754	A694 Horiz. pair, #a-b	4.50	2.25

Ecuadorian Armed Forces in United Nations Peacekeeping Forces — A695

No. 1755: a, Female soldier. b, Two soldiers wearing helmets. c, Soldiers with flags. d, United Nations and Ecuadorian flags, beret of Peacekeeping forces.
Illustration reduced.

2005, Nov. 25 — Perf. 13x13¼

1755	A695 75c Block of 4, #a-d	10.00	5.00

Christmas — A696

No. 1756 — Children's drawings by: a, Pamela Alejandra Castillo Rocha. b, Kira Cedeño. c, Silvia Moran Burgos. d, Carol Garcia.

2005, Nov. 25

1756	A696 $1.25 Block of 4, #a-d	18.00	9.00

18th Cent. Watercolors of Ecuadorians A697

No. 1757: a, Water bearer. b, Indian governor's wife. c, Dancer. d, Cuenca Indian. e, Municipal council piper. f, Indian carrying skyrockets. g, Woman (Mina gigante). h, Majordomo. i, Society woman (Chola pinganilla). j, Street sweeper.

2005, Nov. 30 — Perf. 13¾

1757	Block of 10	10.00	5.00
a.-j.	A697 25c Any single	1.00	.50

Publication of Don Quixote, 400th Anniv. — A698

No. 1758 — Drawings of Don Quixote and: a, Windmills. b, Tree.

2005, Dec. 7 — Perf. 13x13¼

1758	A698 $2 Horiz. pair, #a-b	14.00	7.00

Colonial Religious Art — A699

Colonial Religious Art — A700

No. 1759: a, St. Joseph and Baby Jesus. b, Resurrected Christ. c, Virgin of Quito. d, St. Augustine.
No. 1760: $2, The Divine Shepherd.

2005, Dec. 9

1759	A699 40c Block of 4, #a-d	5.00	2.50

Souvenir Sheet
Imperf

1760	A700 $2 multi	7.00	3.50

El Comercio Newspaper, Cent. (in 2006) A701

"100" and: No. 1761, Statue at LL, newspaper masthead. No. 1762a, Statue at LR. No. 1762b, Statue in "0." No. 1763, Statue in seal. No. 1764, Statue at LL, newspaper masthead, simulated perforations.

Perf. 13¼x13
2006, Jan. 2 Litho. Wmk. 395

1761	A701 40c multi	1.50	.70
1762	A701 40c Horiz. pair, #a-b	2.75	1.50

Size: 55x35mm
Perf. 13¾

1763	A701 50c multi	1.75	.90
	Nos. 1761-1763 (3)	6.00	3.10

Size: 100x69mm
Imperf

1764	A701 $2 multi	6.50	3.25

Dated 2006.

Quito Tourism A702

2006, Jan. 11 — Perf. 13¼x13

1765	A702 25c multi	1.00	.50

Dated 2005.

35th Latin American and Caribbean Lions' Club Forum, Quito — A703

Color of oceans: 90c, White. $2, Orange.

2006, Jan. 19 — Perf. 13x13¼

1766	A703 90c multi	3.25	1.50

Size: 68x99mm
Imperf

1767	A703 $2 multi	6.50	3.25

Biodiversity of Puyo A704

Designs: $1, Cromacris sp. $1.20, Desmodus rotundus.

2006, Mar. 22 — Perf. 13¼x13

1768-1769	A704 Set of 2	8.00	4.00

America Issue, Fight Against Poverty A705

Various Pre-Columbian Guayasamin figurines: 40c, 80c, $1, $1.20.

2006, Feb. 12

1770-1773	A705 Set of 4	12.00	6.00

Benito Juarez (1806-72), President of Mexico — A706

2006, Mar. 21 — Perf. 13x13¼

1774	A706 $1.20 multi	4.25	2.25

Manteña Raft A707

2006, Mar. 23 — Perf. 13¼x13

1775	A707 $1 multi	3.75	1.90

Straw Hat Makers A708

Designs: No. 1776, 40c, Hat maker. No. 1777, 40c, Hat maker wearing hat, vert.

2006, Apr. 8   *Perf. 13¼x13, 13x13¼*
1776-1777 A708   Set of 2   3.00 1.50

Federation of University Students — A709

2006, Apr. 21   *Perf. 13x13¼*
1778 A709 30c multi   1.10 .55

Miracle of Colegio San Gabriel, Cent. — A710

2006, Apr. 21   **Wmk. 395**
1779 A710 80c multi   3.00 1.50

Ibarra, 400th Anniv. A711

2006, Apr. 28   *Perf. 13¼x13*
1780 A711 20c shown   .70 .20

Size: 68x100mm
Imperf
1781 A711 $2.50 Painting, diff.   9.00 4.50

Baltazara Calderon — A712

2005, May 16   *Perf. 13x13¼*
1782 A712 $1 multi   3.75 1.90

18th Cent. Military Uniforms A713

No. 1783: a, Compañia Fija de Quito. b, Dragones de Quito. c, Infanteria de Quito. d, Dragones de Guayaquil (gray horse). e, Dragones de Guayaquil (brown horse).

2006, May 18   *Perf. 13¾*
1783   Horiz. strip of 5   3.50 1.75
   a.-e.   A713 20c Any single   .70 .20

Mushrooms and Fauna of Podocarpus Park — A714

Designs: 20c, Basidiomicetes. 25c, Tremarctus ornatus. 90c, Harpya harpyja, vert.

Perf. 13¼x13, 13x13¼
2006, May 22   **Litho.**   **Wmk. 395**
1784-1786 A714   Set of 3   5.00 2.50

Wolfgang Amadeus Mozart (1756-91), Composer A715

2006, May 31   *Perf. 13¼x13*
1787 A715 20c multi   .70 .20

UNICEF, 60th Anniv. A716

Designs: 75c, Child, butterfly, and sun. $1, Children and books.

Perf. 13¼x13
2006, June 1   **Litho.**   **Wmk. 395**
1788-1789 A716   Set of 2   6.50 3.25

Eloy Alfaro Military School A717

2006, June 5
1790 A717 80c multi   3.00 1.50

Banco Pichincha, Cent. A718

Designs: No. 1791, 1906 1-sucre banknote. No. 1792 — First bank building: a, Denomination at left. b, Denomination at right.

2006, June 8
1791 A718 40c shown   1.50 .75
1792 A718 40c Horiz. pair, #a-b   3.00 1.50

2006 World Cup Soccer Championships, Germany — A719

FIFA emblem and: 40c, World Cup. 80c, 2006 World Cup emblem. $1, Mascot. $1.20, World Cup and flags of competing countries.

Perf. 13¼x13
2006, June 9   **Litho.**   **Wmk. 395**
1793-1796 A719   Set of 4   12.00 6.00

Designs: No. 1797C, Like #1796. No. 1797D, Similar to #1796, but with scores of Ecuador team's first round victories.

2006   **Litho.**   **Wmk. 395**   *Imperf.*
Size: 60x40mm
1797C A719 $2 multi   6.50 3.25
1797D A719 $2 multi   6.50 3.25

A720

Plaza de Mayo Mothers of Argentina — A721

Illustration A721 reduced.

Perf. 13¼x13
2006, June 19   **Litho.**   **Wmk. 395**
1798 A720 80c multi   3.00 1.50
Imperf
1799 A721 $2.50 multi   9.00 4.50

Machala Canton, 182nd Anniv. A722

2006, June 20   *Perf. 13¼x13*
1800 A722 30c multi   1.10 .55

Machala Canton, 182nd Anniv. — A723

Flags of 2006 World Cup Championship participants, FIFA emblem and: No. 1801, Flag of Ecuador. No. 1802, Soccer shoes and ball.

2006   **Litho.**   **Wmk. 395**   *Imperf.*
1801 A723 $2 multi   6.50 3.25
1802 A723 $2 multi   6.50 3.25

2006 World Cup Soccer Championships, Germany.

Garibaldi Italian Assistance Society — A724

2006, July 7   *Perf. 13x13¼*
1803 A724 90c multi   3.25 1.60

Souvenir Sheet

Municipal Railroads — A726

Wmk. 395
2006, July 20   **Litho.**   *Imperf.*
1806 A726 $2 multi   6.50 3.25

Simón Bolívar Experimental College — A727

Bolívar A728

2006, July 25   **Litho.**   *Perf. 13x13¼*
1807 A727 20c multi   .70 .20
Imperf
1808 A728 $10 multi   35.00 17.50

Spondylus Shell Carvings in National Institute of Cultural Heritage A729

Designs: 25c, Necklace. No. 1810, vert.: a, Figurine of trader. b, Figurine of fishermen in boat.

2006, July 26   *Perf. 13¼x13, 13x13¼*
1809 A729 25c multi   1.25 .45
1810 A729 $1 Horiz. pair, #a-b   6.75 6.75

Indian Postal Runner and Ecuador Post Emblem — A730

Background colors: 25c, White. 30c, Dark blue. 40c, Black. 60c, Beige. 80c, Olive green

2006, Aug. 5   **Perf. 13x13¼**
1811-1815 A730   Set of 5   8.50 4.75

Ecuadorian Olympic Committee A731

2006, Aug. 15   **Litho.**
1816 A731 30c multi   1.10 .55

Writers — A732

Designs: $1, Jorge Icaza (1906-78). $1.20, Pablo Palacio (1906-47).

2006, Sept. 18   **Wmk. 395**
1817-1818 A732   Set of 2   8.00 4.00

Ecuadorian Food — A733

No. 1819: a, Bandera Manabi. b, Viche de Manabi. Illustration reduced.

2006, Sept. 23   **Perf. 13¼x13**
1819 A733 $1 Horiz. pair, #a-b   7.00 3.50

Orchids — A734

No. 1820: a, Caucaea olivaceum. b, Cyrtochilum macranthum. c, Miltoniopsis vexillaria. d, Odontoglossum harryanum. e, Cyrtochilum pastasae. f, Cyrtochilum loxense. g, Cyrtochilum eduardii. h, Odontoglossum epidendroides. i, Cyrtochilum retusum. j, Cyrtochilum geniculatum.
$2, Cyrtochilum macranthum, diff.

2006, Sept. 29   **Perf. 13x13¼**
1820   Block of 10   11.00 5.50
a.-j. A734 30c Any single   1.10 .55

Imperf
Size: 66x95mm
1821 A734 $2 multi   7.00 3.50

America Issue, Energy Conservation — A735

Background color: $1, Brown. $1.20, Blue.

2006, Oct. 4   **Perf. 13¼x13**
1822-1823 A735   Set of 2   8.00 4.00

Natural Fiber Art, by Giti Neuman — A736

Designs: No. 1824, En la Ventana.
No. 1825: a, Forma en Movimiento. b, Caminantes.
No. 1826, horiz.: a, Caminando. b, Cabezas Huecas.

2006, Oct. 4   **Perf. 13x13¼, 13¼x13**
1824 A736 30c multi   1.00 .55
1825 A736 30c Vert. pair, #a-b   2.25 1.00
1826 A736 30c Horiz. pair, #a-b   2.25 1.00
   Nos. 1824-1826 (3)   5.50 2.55

Tourism in Otovalo A737

Designs: 25c, El Lechero tree. 30c, El Jordan Church. 75c, Young girl, vert. $1, Costume for El Coraza Festival, vert.

2006, Oct. 18   **Perf. 13¼x13, 13x13¼**
1827-1830 A737   Set of 4   8.50 4.25

Eruption of Tungurahua Volcano — A738

No. 1831: a, Ash cloud above volcano. b, Lava flowing down volcano.

2006, Oct. 20   **Perf. 13x13¼**
1831 A738 $1 Horiz. pair, #a-b   7.00 3.50

Urban Renewal of Guayaquil A739

No. 1832: a, Municipal Palace, denomination at left. b, Municipal Palace, denomination at right. c, Vulcan forge. d, José Joaquín de Olmedo Airport. e, Bus station.

2006, Oct. 24   **Perf. 13¼x13**
1832   Horiz. strip of 5   18.00 9.00
a.-e. A739 $1 Any single   3.50 1.75

Radio Station HCJB, 75th Anniv. A740

2006, Oct. 26   **Wmk. 395**
1833 A740 $1 multi   3.75 1.90

Millennium Development Objectives of the United Nations — A741

2006, Oct. 27   **Perf. 13¾**
1834 A741 $2 multi   7.00 3.50

Pres. Galo Plaza Lasso (1906-87) — A742

Designs: 40c, Photograph. 80c, Tree.

2006, Oct. 27   **Perf. 13x13¼**
1835-1836 A742   Set of 2   4.25 2.25

German Shepherd Breeding Association A743

2006, Oct. 28   **Litho.**   **Perf. 13¼x13**
1837 A743 $1 multi   3.75 1.90

Military Parachuting, 50th Anniv. A744

Designs: 20c, Soldiers. 40c, Soldiers and airplane. 60c, Soldier and troop emblem. 80c, Paratrooper in air.

Perf. 13¼x13, 13x13¼
2006, Oct. 31   **Litho.**   **Wmk. 395**
1838-1841 A744   Set of 4   7.00 3.50

Galapagos Islands Fauna — A745

No. 1842, horiz.: a, Sea turtle. b, Sea gull. c, Marine iguana. d, Blue-footed boobies. e, Sea lion.
80c, Flamingo. $1, Crab. $1.20, Fish.

2006, Nov. 1
1842 A745 30c Horiz. strip of
   5, #a-e   5.50 2.75
1843 A745 80c multi   2.75 1.40
1844 A745 $1 multi   3.50 1.75
1845 A745 $1.20 multi   4.25 2.25
   Nos. 1842-1845 (4)   16.00 8.15

Christmas — A746

2006, Nov. 28   **Perf. 13x13¼**
1846 A746 80c multi   2.75 1.40

Monsignor Juan I. Larrea Holguín (1927-2006) — A747

No. 1847: a, In bishop's robes. b, In judicial robes.

2006, Dec. 8   **Perf. 13¾**
1847 A747 40c Horiz. pair, #a-b   3.00 1.50

Freemasonry A748

Designs: 25c, Masonic altar, beehive. 40c, Compass and square.

2006, Dec. 11   **Perf. 13x13¼**
1848-1849 A748   Set of 2   2.40 1.10

Quito Zoo Animals — A749

No. 1850: a, Parrot. b, Frog.
No. 1851: a, Harpy eagle. b, Jaguar.
$2, Parrot on branch.

2006, Dec. 11   **Perf. 13x13¼**
1850 A749 60c Horiz. pair, #a-b   4.00 2.10
1851 A749 80c Horiz. pair, #a-b   5.50 2.75
Imperf
Size: 40x65mm
1852 A749 $2 multi   7.00 3.50

Erotic and Fertility Figurines — A750

Designs: 10c, Nursing mother. 20c, Copulating couple. $1.20, Pregnant woman. $2, Man with erect penis.

2006, Dec. 12   **Perf. 13x13¼**
1853-1856 A750   Set of 4   13.00 6.50

Admiral Juan Illingworth Naval Museum — A751

Emblem of Ecuador Navy and Illingworth: 20c, On rope ladder, 1880. 25c, As Marine Guard, 1854.

2006, Dec. 15   **Litho.**
1857-1858 A751   Set of 2   1.60   .80

Colors of Ecuador Flag — A752

2006, Dec. 15   **Wmk. 395**
1859 A752 $10 multi   35.00 17.50

Postmen and Bicycles A753

Color of photograph: 20c, Gray brown. 40c, Gray blue. 80c, Red.

2006, Dec. 17   **Perf. 13¼x13**
1860-1862 A753   Set of 3   5.00 2.50

Pets A754

Designs: 25c, Puppy. 40c, Dog, vert. 50c, Cat with brown and blue eyes, vert. 80c, Dog running. $1, Cat with blue eyes, vert.

2006, Dec. 17   **Perf. 13¼x13, 13x13¼**
1863-1867 A754   Set of 5   10.00 5.00

Cuenca Biennale A755

Art by: 5c, Alexander Apóstol. 15c, Ricardo González Elias, vert.

2006, Dec. 20
1868-1869 A755   Set of 2   .40   .20

Independence Monument, 50th Anniv. — A756

No. 1870: a, Head of statue. b, Entire statue.

Illustration reduced.

2006, Dec. 21   **Perf. 13¾**
1870 A756 20c Horiz. pair, #a-b   1.50   .75

Quito Fair — A757

Designs: No. 1871, Matador Manolo Caena. No. 1872 — Matadors: a, Sebastián Castella. b, El Juli. No. 1873, horiz. — Quito Bull Ring: a, At right. b, At left. $3, Sculpture of Jesus, horiz.

Perf. 13x13¼, 13¼x13
2006, Dec. 27   **Litho.**
1871 A757 50c multi   2.00   .90
1872 A757 50c Horiz. pair, #a-b   3.50 2.00
1873 A757 50c Horiz. pair, #a-b   3.50 2.00
   Nos. 1871-1873 (3)   9.00 4.90

Litho. With Foil Application
Imperf
Size: 65x40mm
1874 A757 $3 multi   11.00 5.50

Pirates A758

No. 1875, vert.: a, Jolly Roger flag, ship, sea lions. b, Sea lions, ships. c, Ships, Jolly roger flag. d, Armed pirate on ship. e, Ship, Jolly Roger flag. No. 1876: a, Map of Galapagos Islands, Jolly Roger flag, Sir Francis Drake. b, Ship, map, skull. $1, Ship, map, skull, William Dampier.

Perf. 13x13¼, 13¼x13
2006, Dec. 27   **Litho.**
1875 A758 30c Horiz. strip of 5,
      #a-e   6.00 3.00
1876 A758 40c Horiz. pair, #a-b   3.00 1.50
1877 A758 $1 multi   4.00 2.00
   Nos. 1875-1877 (3)   13.00 6.50

SEK International University, Quito A759

Perf. 13¼x13
2006, Dec. 29   **Wmk. 395**
1878 A759 10c multi   .40   .40

Scouting, Cent. — A760

Scout emblem and: 25c, Circles. $2, Scout and circles.

Perf. 13x13¼
2007, Mar. 29   **Litho.**   **Wmk. 395**
1879-1880 A760   Set of 2   6.75 3.25

Hispanic-American Poetry Festival — A761

2007, Apr. 19
1881 A761 10c multi   .30   .30

Cuenca, 450th Anniv. — A762

Designs: 40c, Casa de los Arcos (Arch House). 75c, Vergel Plaza. 80c, Tomebamba River Gorge, horiz. $3, Cathedral of the Immaculate Conception.

2007, Apr. 27   **Perf. 13x13¼, 13¼x13**
1882-1885 A762   Set of 4   14.50 7.25

Prehistoric Animals — A763

Designs: No. 1886, 80c, Megatherium. No. 1887, 80c, Smilodon, horiz.

2007, May 10
1886-1887 A763   Set of 2   4.75 2.25

Beetles A764

Designs: No. 1888, Golopha eaucus. No. 1889: a, Chrysophora chrysochlora. b, Dynastes hercules.

2007, May 10   **Perf. 13¼x13**
1888 A764 40c multi   1.25   .60
1889 A764 40c Horiz. pair, #a-b   2.40 1.25

Guayaquil Rotary Club, 80th Anniv. A765

2007, June 1   **Wmk. 395**
1890 A765 25c multi   .75   .35

America Issue, Education For All — A766

Designs: 40c, Children on school bus. 80c, Girl doing geometry work. $1, Children flying kites, vert. $1.20, Student in wheelchair, vert. $2, Girl and handprints, vert.

2007, June 6   **Perf. 13¼x13, 13x13¼**
1891-1894 A766   Set of 4   10.00 5.00
Imperf
Size: 40x65mm
1895 A766 $2 multi   6.00 3.00

Naval Institute of Oceanography, 75th Anniv. — A767

Antarctic research: 10c, Penguin, ship. $3, Scientists and scientific equipment, horiz.

2007, July 18   **Perf. 13x13¼**
1896 A767 10c multi   .30   .30
Perf. 12
Size: 52x32mm
1897 A767 $3 multi   9.00 4.50

Central Bank of Ecuador, 80th Anniv. — A768

2007, Aug. 28   **Perf. 12**
1898 A768 $2 multi   6.00 3.00

Guayaquil Firefighters A769

Various firefighers at fires: 5c, 10c, 15c, 25c, $1. 25c and $1 are horiz.

2007, Oct. 10   **Perf. 13x13¼, 13¼x13**
1899-1903 A769   Set of 5   4.50 2.25

Breast Cancer Prevention A770

2007, Oct. 15   **Perf. 13¼x13**
1904 A770 $3 multi   9.00 4.50

Guayaquil Tourism — A771

Designs: 5c, Las Peñas. 10c, Lighthouse, Santa Ana Hill. 15c, El Velero Bridge. 25c, Mercado Sur, horiz. $1, June 5 Bridge, horiz.

2007, Oct. 23   **Perf. 13x13¼, 13¼x13**
1905-1909 A771   Set of 5   4.50 2.25

Cuenca Chamber of Industries, 70th Anniv. A772

2007, Oct. 25   *Perf. 13¼x13*
1910 A772 $1.20 multi   3.50 1.75

Operation Smile A773

2007, Nov. 16   Litho.
1911 A773 $1 multi   3.00 1.50

Vistazo Magazine, 50th Anniv. A774

2007, Nov. 29   *Perf. 12*
1912 A774 20c multi   .60 .20

Galapagos Islands Fauna A775

Designs: 40c, Sea turtle. 80c, Penguin. $1, Dolphin. $1.20, Tropicbird.

2007, Nov. 30   *Perf. 13¼x13*
1913-1916 A775 Set of 4   10.00 5.00
Compare with type A780.

Comptroller General, 80th Anniv. A776

2007, Dec. 3   *Perf. 12*
1917 A776 20c multi   .60 .20

2007 Pan American Games, Rio de Janeiro — A777

No. 1918 — Athletes and text noting gold medalists: a, Alexandra Escobar. b, Seledina Nieve. c, Jefferson Perez. d, Xavier Moreno. e, Under-18 soccer team.

2007, Dec. 18   *Perf. 13x13¼*
1918   Horiz. strip of 5   6.00 3.00
a.-e. A777 40c Any single   1.10 .60

Christmas — A778

No. 1919: a, The Annunciation. b, The Three Magi. c, Nativity. d, Flight into Egypt. Illustration reduced.

2007, Dec. 20   *Perf. 13¼x13*
1919 A778 20c Block of 4, #a-d   2.40 1.25

Guayas Province Transit Commission, 60th Anniv. — A779

     Perf. 13x13¼
2008, Jan. 29   Litho.   **Wmk. 395**
1920 A779 $1 multi   3.00 1.50

Galapagos Islands A780

Map of islands and: 40c, Pelecanus occidentalis. 80c, Aetobatus narinari. $1, Carcharhinus galapagensis. $1.20, San Cristóbal Windmill Project.

2008, Mar. 18   *Perf. 13¼x13*
1921-1924 A780   Set of 4   10.00 5.00
Compare with Type A775.

Free Maternity and Infant Care — A781

2008, Mar. 28   *Perf. 12*
1925 A781 $1 multi   3.00 1.50

Guayaquil Port Authority, 50th Anniv. A782

2008, Apr. 8
1926 A782 20c multi   .60 .20

Tungurahua Chamber of Industry, 80th Anniv. — A783

     Wmk. 395
2008, Apr. 24   Litho.   *Perf. 12*
1927 A783 $3 multi   9.00 4.50

Father Carlos Crespi (1891-1982) — A784

2008, Apr. 30
1928 A784 $2 multi   6.00 3.00

Santiago de Guayaquil Medallion A785

2008, June 3
1929 A785 30c multi   .90 .45
Intl. Philately Day.

Jorge Pérez Concha, Historian and Diplomat, Cent. — A786

2008, June 4
1930 A786 $3 multi   9.00 4.50

Los Pinos College, Quito, 40th Anniv. A787

2008, June 6
1931 A787 20c multi   .60 .20

Guayaquil-Quito Railway, Cent. — A788

Ecuador No. 174 and: 56c, Steam locomotive. $5, Steam locomotives, Gabriel García Moreno and Gen. Eloy Alfaro.

2008, June 23   *Perf. 12*
1932 A788 56c multi   1.75 .85

     Imperf
     Size: 100x70mm
1933 A788 $5 multi   15.00 7.50

Polytechnic School of the Coast, 50th Anniv. — A789

     Wmk. 395
2008, July 28   Litho.   *Perf. 12*
1934 A789 32c multi   .90 .40

Latin American Youth Year — A790

2008, Aug. 20
1935 A790 30c multi   .90 .40

Ecuadorian Cacao — A791

No. 1936: a, Cacao pod, UL corner of #306. b, Cacao flower, UR corner of #306. c, Cacao processing, LL corner of #306. d, Cacao pods and beans, chocolate candy, LR corner of #306.
Illustration reduced.

2008, Oct. 1   *Perf. 13¼x13*
1936 A791 56c Block of 4, #a-d   6.50 3.25

Meridiano Newspaper, 25th Anniv. — A792

2008, Oct. 22   *Perf. 13x13¼*
1937 A792 60c multi   1.75 .85

Intl. Swimming Federation, Cent. A793

No. 1938: a, World Map. b, Ecuadorian swimmer.
30c, Swimmer from underwater.

2008, Oct. 31   *Perf. 13¼x13*
1938 A793 24c Horiz. pair, #a-b   1.00 .50
1939 A793 30c multi   .60 .30

Office of the Procurator General, 80th Anniv. — A794

2008, Nov. 11   *Perf. 13x13¼*
1940 A794 25c multi   .50 .25

Guayaquil Chamber of Construction, 40th Anniv. A795

2008, Nov. 27   *Perf. 13¼x13*
1941 A795 $1 multi   2.00 1.00

New Constitution — A796

Flag and: 32c, Sun behind clouds. $5, People, vert.

2008, Nov. 29   *Perf. 12*
1942 A796 32c multi   .65 .30

Size: 66x95mm
Imperf
1943 A796 $5 multi   10.00 5.00

Santiago de Guayaquil Municipal Museum, Cent. A797

No. 1944: a, Old musuem building. b, New museum building with murals.
$2, Entrance to old musuem building.

2008, Dec. 16   *Perf. 13¼x13*
1944 A797 60c Horiz. pair, #a-b   2.40 1.25
1945 A797 $2 multi   4.00 2.00

Friendship Between Ecuador and Japan, 90th Anniv. — A798

No. 1945: a, Cotopaxi Volcano, Ecuador. b, Mt. Fuji, Japan. Illustration reduced.

2008, Dec. 17
1946 A798 30c Horiz. pair, #a-b   1.25 .60

America Issue, National Festivals — A799

No. 1947 — Festival of Sts. Peter and Paul: a, Dancers. b, Guitarist.
No. 1948, vert. — Diablada Pillareña: a, Figure with red mask. b, Figure with black mask. Illustration reduced.

2008, Dec. 23   *Perf. 13¼x13*
1947 A799 20c Horiz. pair, #a-b   .80 .40

              Perf. 13x13¼
1948 A799 $1 Horiz. pair, #a-b   4.00 2.00

Christmas A800

Various creche figurines of Holy Family and animals with background color of: 30c, Blue.
No. 1949: a, Green. b, Yellow brown.

2008, Dec. 23   *Perf. 13¼x13*
1949 A800 30c multi   .60 .30
1950 A800 80c Horiz. pair, #a-b   3.25 1.60

A801

A802

A803

A804

Jacchigua National Folk Ballet A805

       Perf. 13¼x13
2009, Feb. 18   Litho.   **Wmk. 395**
1951   Horiz. strip of 5   10.00 5.00
  a.   A801 $1 multi   2.00 1.00
  b.   A802 $1 multi   2.00 1.00
  c.   A803 $1 multi   2.00 1.00
  d.   A804 $1 multi   2.00 1.00
  e.   A805 $1 multi   2.00 1.00

Intl. Philately Day — A809

       Perf. 13¼x13
2009, May 6   **Wmk. 395**
1965 A809 75c multi   1.50 .75

Designs: 20c, Feet of polar bear. 80c, Earth in water.

2009, Mar. 31
1952-1953 A806   Set of 2   2.00 1.00

A807

Tourism — A808

Designs: No. 1954, Babahoyo River, Los Ríos Province. No. 1955, Ingapirca Ruins, Cañar Province. No. 1956, Rafters on Quijos River, Napo Province. No. 1957, Marimba group, Esmeraldas Province. $1.25, Tulcán cemetery, Carchi Province. $2, Train and Mt. Chimborazo, Chimborazo Province. $3, Alcea rosea flowers, Morona-Santiago Province. $5, Acrocinus longimanus, Sucumbíos Province.
No. 1962: a, Like #1954. c, Like #1957. c, Like #1958. d, Like #1955. e, Like #1959. f, Like #1956. g, Like #1960. h, Like #1961.
No. 1963: a, Equator Monument, Pichincha Province. b, Colorado Indians, Santo Domingo de los Tsáchilas Province. c, Los Frailes Beach, Manabí Province. d, Banana plantation, El Oro Province. e, Arctocephalus galapagoensis, Galápagos Province. f, Cuicocha Lake, Imbabura Province. g, Harpia harpyja, Pastaza Province. h, Shuar community, Orellana Province.
No. 1964: a, Bolívar and San Martín Monument, Guayas Province. b, The Lovers of Sumpa, Santa Elena Province. c, Pillaro devil, Tungurahua Province. d, Mt. Cotopaxi, Cotopaxi Province. e, Guaranga Indian Monument, Bolívar Province. f, Virgin of Cisne, Loja Province. g, Tomebamba River, Azuay Province. h, Leopardus pardalis, Zamora Province.

       Perf. 13¼x13
2009   Litho.   **Wmk. 395**
1954 A807 25c multi   .50 .25
1955 A807 50c multi   1.00 .50
1956 A807 75c multi   1.50 .75
1957 A807 $1 multi   2.00 1.00
1958 A807 $1.25 multi   2.50 1.25
1959 A807 $2 multi   4.00 2.00
1960 A807 $3 multi   6.00 3.00
1961 A807 $5 multi   10.00 5.00
   Nos. 1954-1961 (8)   27.50 13.75

Booklet Stamps
Self-Adhesive
Die Cut
Unwmk.
1962   Booklet pane of 8 +
     2 labels   10.00
  a.-b.   A808 25c Either single   .50 .25
  c.-d.   A808 50c Either single   1.00 .50
  e.-f.   A808 75c Either single   1.50 .75
  g.-h.   A808 $1 Either single   2.00 1.00
1963   Booklet pane of 8 +
     2 labels   10.00
  a.-b.   A808 25c Either single   .50 .25
  c.-d.   A808 50c Either single   1.00 .50
  e.-f.   A808 75c Either single   1.50 .75
  g.-h.   A808 $1 Either single   2.00 1.00
1964   Booklet pane of 8 +
     2 labels   10.00
  a.-b.   A808 25c Either single   .50 .25
  c.-d.   A808 50c Either single   1.00 .50
  e.-f.   A808 75c Either single   1.50 .75
  g.-h.   A808 $1 Either single   2.00 1.00
   Nos. 1962-1964 (3)   30.00

Issued: Nos. 1954-1961, 4/29; Nos. 1962-1964, July.

Icons of Santa Clara Monastery A810

No. 1966: a, Angel. b, Jesus Christ. c, Pensive child. d, Protective Virgin. e, Virgin of Quito.

2009, June 9   *Perf. 13x13¼*
1966   Horiz. strip of 5   10.00 5.00
  a.-e.   A810 $1 Any single   2.00 1.00

National Finance Corporation, 45th Anniv. A811

2009, June 22   *Perf. 13¼x13*
1967 A811 $1.25 multi   2.50 1.25

Ambato Electric Company, 50th Anniv. A812

2009, June
1968 A812 $1 multi   2.00 1.00

Paute-Molino Dam, 25th Anniv. A813

2009, July 22
1969 A813 $2 multi   4.00 2.00

El Telégrafo Newspaper, 125th Anniv. A814

2009, July 30   *Perf. 12*
1970 A814 $1.75 multi   3.50 1.75

Call for Independence, Bicent. — A815

Nos. 1971 and 1972 — Doves, butterflies, bell and: a, Open mouth. b, Monument. Illustration reduced.

2009, Aug. 14   *Perf. 13¼x13*
1971 A815 $3 Horiz. pair, #a-b   12.00 6.00

Souvenir Sheet
With Horizontal Blue Stripe Added to Middle of Stamps
1972 A815 $3 Sheet of 2, #a-b   12.00 6.00

Call for Independence, Bicent. — A816

Serpentine Die Cut 12½x12¼
2009, Aug. 14   **Litho.**   **Unwmk.**
Self-Adhesive
Printed on Cork
1973 A816 $3.50 multi   7.00 3.50

Chinese Benevolent Society, Cent. — A817

No. 1974: a, Galápagos tortoise. b, Giant panda.
Illustration reduced.

Perf. 13¼x13
2009, Aug. 18   **Wmk. 395**
1974 A817 25c Horiz. pair, #a-b   1.00 .50

Famous People A818

No. 1975: a, Carlos Silva Pareja (1909-68), musician. b, Tránsito Amaguaña (1909-2009), Indian rights advocate. c, Demetrio Aguilera Malta (1909-81), writer, diplomat. d, Carlos Zevallos Menéndez (1909-81), archaeologist. e, Humberto Salvador Guerra (1909-82), writer.

2009, Aug. 28   **Litho.**
1975   Horiz. strip of 5   2.50 1.25
a.-e.   A818 25c Any single   .50 .25

Ecuadorian Olympic Committee, 50th Anniv. A819

Designs: No. 1976, 25c, Shooting, cycling, equestrian, wrestling, archery, and basketball. No. 1977, 25c, Diving, running, weight lifting, tennis, boxing and soccer, vert.

2009, Oct. 17   **Perf. 13¼x13, 13x13¼**
1976-1977 A819   Set of 2   1.00 .50

Exportation of Cooperative Open Banking Information System A820

Perf. 13¼x13
2009, Nov. 5   **Litho.**   **Wmk. 395**
1978 A820 50c multi   1.00 1.00

Loja National University, 150th Anniv. — A821

Wmk. 395
2009, Nov. 27   **Litho.**   **Perf. 12**
1979 A821 $2 multi   4.00 2.00

Independence, Bicent. — A822

No. 1980: a, Juan Pío Montúfar (1758-1818), Chairman of Supreme Council of Government. b, José Mejía Lequerica (1777-1813), representative to Cortes of Cadiz. c, Eugenio Espejo (1747-95), journalist, medical pioneer. d, Manuela Cañizares (1769-1814), patriot. e, Bicentenary emblem.

2009, Nov. 28
1980   Horiz. strip of 5   7.50 3.75
a.-e.   A822 75c Any single   1.50 .75

A823

Charles Darwin (1809-82), Naturalist — A824

No. 1982 — Darwin and: a, Phoenicopterus ruber. b, Ardea herodias. c, Calandria galapagosa. d, Conolopus marthae. e, Sula granti. f, Rhincodon typus. g, Zalophus wollebaeki. h, Phalacrocorax harrisi. i, Geochelone nigra abingdoni. Nos. 1982a-1982h are 35x35mm, No. 1982i is 38mm diameter.

Perf. 13¾x14
2009, Nov. 30   **Unwmk.**
Granite Paper
1981 A823 $5 multi   10.00 5.00
Perf. 13¼ ($1), 13¾ ($2)
1982 A824   Sheet of 9   20.00 10.00
a.-h. $1 Any single   2.00 1.00
i. $2 multi   4.00 2.00

Christmas A825

Perf. 13¼x13
2009, Dec. 10   **Wmk. 395**
1983 A825 $1 multi   2.00 1.00

America Issue, Toys and Games — A826

No. 1984: a, Paddle and ball. b, Go-cart.

2009, Dec. 18
1984 A826 $1 Horiz. pair, #a-b   4.00 2.00

SEMI-POSTAL STAMPS

Nos. 423-428 Surcharged in Carmine or Blue:

1944, May 9   **Unwmk.**   **Perf. 12**
B1 A171 10c + 10c yel grn (C)   .60 .30
B2 A171 20c + 20c rose pink   .60 .30
B3 A171 30c + 20c dk gray brn   .60 .30
B4 A171 50c + 20c dp red lil   1.20 .60
B5 A171 1s + 50c ol gray (C)   2.00 1.00
B6 A171 10s + 2s red orange   7.00 3.50
Nos. B1-B6 (6)   12.00 6.00

The surtax aided Mendez Hospital.

AIR POST STAMPS

In 1928-30, the internal airmail service of Ecuador was handled by the Sociedad Colombo-Alemana de Transportes Aereos ("SCADTA") under government sanction. During this period SCADTA issued stamps which were the only legal franking for airmail service except that handled under contract with Pan American-Grace Airways. SCADTA issues are Nos. C1-C6, C16-C25, CF1-CF2.

Colombia Air Post Stamps of 1923 Surcharged in Carmine

"Provisional" at 45 degree Angle
Perf. 14x14½
1928, Aug. 28   **Wmk. 116**
C1 AP6 50c on 10c green   110.00 70.00
C2 AP6 75c on 15c car   210.00 160.00
C3 AP6 1s on 20c gray   70.00 42.50
C4 AP6 1½s on 30c blue   45.00 35.00
C5 AP6 3s on 60c brown   85.00 52.50
Nos. C1-C5 (5)   520.00 360.00

"Provisional" at 41 degree Angle
1929, Mar. 20
C1a AP6 50c on 10c green   125.00 110.00
C2a AP6 75c on 15c carmine   225.00 175.00
C3a AP6 1s on 20c gray   225.00 175.00
Nos. C1a-C3a (3)   575.00 460.00

C6 AP6 50c on 10c green   700.00 1,700.

A 75c on 15c carmine with "Cts." between the surcharged numerals exists. There is no evidence that it was regularly issued or used. For overprints see Nos. CF1-CF1a.

Plane over River Guayas — AP1

Unwmk.
1929, May 5   **Engr.**   **Perf. 12**
C8 AP1 2c black   .40 .20
C9 AP1 5c carmine rose   .40 .20
C10 AP1 10c deep brown   .40 .20
C11 AP1 20c dark violet   .90 .20
C12 AP1 50c deep green   1.60 .45
C13 AP1 1s dark blue   6.00 2.75
C14 AP1 5s orange yellow   25.00 11.00
C15 AP1 10s orange red   135.00 57.50
Nos. C8-C15 (8)   169.70 72.50

Establishment of commercial air service in Ecuador. The stamps were available for all forms of postal service and were largely used for franking ordinary letters.
Nos. C13-C15 show numerals in color on white background. Counterfeits of No. C15 exist.
See #C26-C31. For overprints and surcharge see #C32-C38, C287, CO1-CO12.

Jesuit Church La Compania AP2   Mount Chimborazo AP3

Wmk. 127
1929, Apr. 1   **Litho.**   **Perf. 14**
C16 AP2 50c red brown   4.50 2.25
C17 AP2 75c green   4.50 2.25
C18 AP2 1s rose   7.00 2.25
C19 AP2 1½s gray blue   7.00 2.25
C20 AP2 2s violet   11.50 4.50
C21 AP2 3s brown   11.50 4.50
C22 AP3 5s lt blue   40.00 14.00
C23 AP3 10s lt red   85.00 30.00
C24 AP3 15s violet   140.00 60.00
C25 AP3 25s olive green   190.00 70.00
Nos. C16-C25 (10)   501.00 192.00

For overprint see No. CF2.

Plane Type of 1929
1930-44   **Unwmk.**   **Engr.**   **Perf. 12**
C26 AP1 1s carmine lake   6.50 .55
C27 AP1 1s green ('44)   1.00 .20
C28 AP1 5s olive green   10.00 3.75
C29 AP1 5s purple ('44)   2.00 .20
C30 AP1 10s black   30.00 5.50
C31 AP1 10s brt ultra ('44)   4.50 .30
Nos. C26-C31 (6)   54.00 10.50

Nos. C26-C31 show numerals in color on white background.
For surcharge see No. C287.

Type of 1929 Overprinted in Various Colors

AP4

1930, June 4
C32 AP4 1s car lake (Bk)   22.50 22.50
a.   Double ovpt. (R Br + Bk)   75.00

C33 AP4 5s olive grn (Bl) 22.50 22.50
C34 AP4 10s black (R Br) 22.50 22.50
Nos. C32-C34 (3) 67.50 67.50

Flight of Capt. Benjamin Mendez from Bogota to Quito, bearing a crown of flowers for the tomb of Grand Marshal Sucre.

Air Post Official Stamps of 1929-30 Overprinted in Various Colors or Surcharged Similarly in Upper & Lower Case

1935, July 24
C35 AP1 50c deep green (Bl) 12.50 5.00
C36 AP1 50c olive brn (R) 12.50 5.00
C37 AP1 1s on 5s ol grn (Bk) 12.50 5.00
  a. Double surcharge 95.00
C38 AP1 2s on 10s black (R) 12.50 5.00
Nos. C35-C38 (4) 50.00 20.00

Unveiling of a monument to Bolívar at Quito, July 24th, 1935.

AP5

1935, Oct. 13 Photo. Perf. 11½x11
C38A AP5 5c ultra & red .20 .30
C38B AP5 10c brown & black .20 .50
C38C AP5 50c green & red .20 .50
C38D AP5 1S carmine & blue .80 1.20
C38E AP5 5S gray grn & red 1.20 2.40
Nos. C38A-C38E (5) 2.60 4.90

Columbus Day. Nos. 338A-338E and C38A-C38E were prepared by the Sociedad Colombista Panamericana and were sold by the Ecuadorian post office through Oct. 30. Nos. C38B-C38E exist imperf.

Geodesical Mission Issue

AÉREO

Nos. 349-351 Overprinted in Blue or Black and Type of Regular issue

1936, July 3 Perf. 12½
C39 A136 10c deep orange (Bl) .60 .20
C40 A136 20c violet (Bk) .60 .20
C41 A136 50c dark red (Bl) .60 .20
C42 A136 70c black 1.25 .35
Nos. C39-C42 (4) 3.05 .95

For surcharge see No. RA42.

Philatelic Exhibition Issue
Type of Regular Issue Overprinted "AEREA"

1936, Oct. 20 Perf. 13½x14
C43 A137 2c rose 4.50 4.50
C44 A137 5c brown orange 4.50 4.50
C45 A137 10c brown 4.50 4.50
C46 A137 20c ultra 4.50 4.50
C47 A137 50c red violet 4.50 4.50
C48 A137 1s green 4.50 4.50
Nos. C43-C48 (6) 27.00 27.00

Condor and Plane — AP6

Perf. 13½
C49 AP6 70c orange brown 2.00 .50
C50 AP6 1s dull violet 2.00 .50
Nos. C43-C50 were issued for the 1st Intl. Phil. Exhib. at Quito.

Condor over "El Altar" — AP7

1937-46 Perf. 11½, 12
C51 AP7 10c chestnut 5.00 .20
C52 AP7 20c olive black 6.50 .20
C53 AP7 40c rose car ('46) 6.50 .20
C54 AP7 70c black brown 9.00 .20
C55 AP7 1s gray black 14.00 .20
C56 AP7 2s dark violet 24.00 .65
Nos. C51-C56 (6) 65.00 1.65

Issue dates: 40c, Oct. 7; others, Aug. 19.
For overprints see #463-464, CO13-CO17.

Portrait of Washington, American Eagle and Flags — AP8

Engraved and Lithographed
1938, Feb. 9 Perf. 12
Center Multicolored
C57 AP8 2c brown .40 .20
C58 AP8 5c black .40 .20
C59 AP8 10c brown .40 .20
C60 AP8 20c dark blue .80 .20
C61 AP8 50c violet 1.75 .20
C62 AP8 1s black 3.25 .20
C63 AP8 2s violet 7.50 .90
Nos. C57-C63 (7) 14.50 2.10

150th anniv. of the US Constitution.
In 1947, Nos. C61-C63 were overprinted in dark blue: "Primero la Patria!" and plane. These revolutionary propaganda stamps were later renounced by decree. Value $20.
For overprints see #C102-C104, C139-C141.

No. RA35 Surcharged in Red

AEREO SEDTA 0,65

1938, Nov. 16 Perf. 13½
C64 PT12 65c on 3c ultra .40 .20

A national airmail concession was given to the Sociedad Ecuatoriano de Transportes Aereos (SEDTA) in July, 1938. No. RA35 was surcharged for SEDTA postal requirements. SEDTA operated through 1940.

Army Horseman — AP9

Woman Runner — AP10

Tennis — AP11   Boxing — AP12

Olympic Fire — AP13

1939, Mar. Engr. Perf. 12
C65 AP9 5c lt green 1.50 .20
C66 AP10 10c salmon 2.00 .20
C67 AP11 50c redsh brown 10.50 .20
C68 AP12 1s black brown 12.50 .45
C69 AP13 2s rose carmine 15.00 1.10
Nos. C65-C69 (5) 41.50 2.15

First Bolivarian Games (1938).

Plane over Chimborazo AP14

1939, May 1 Perf. 13x12½
C70 AP14 1s yellow brown .40 .20
C71 AP14 2s rose violet .70 .20
C72 AP14 5s black 1.90 .20
Nos. C70-C72 (3) 3.00 .60

Golden Gate Bridge and Mountain Peak — AP15   Empire State Building and Mountain Peak — AP16

1939 Perf. 12½x13
C73 AP15 2c black .40 .20
C74 AP15 5c rose red .40 .20
C75 AP15 10c indigo .40 .20
C76 AP15 50c rose violet .40 .20
C77 AP15 1s chocolate .80 .20
C78 AP15 2s yellow brown 1.00 .20
C79 AP15 5s emerald 2.00 .20
Nos. C73-C79 (7) 5.40 1.40

Golden Gate International Exposition.
For surcharge & overprint see #434, CO18.

1939
C80 AP16 2c brown orange .60 .20
C81 AP16 5c dark carmine .60 .20
C82 AP16 10c indigo .60 .20
C83 AP16 50c slate green .60 .20
C84 AP16 1s deep orange 1.20 .20
C85 AP16 2s dk red violet 1.40 .20
C86 AP16 5s dark gray 3.25 .20
Nos. C80-C86 (7) 8.25 1.40

New York World's Fair.
For surcharge see No. 435.

Map of the Americas and Airplane — AP17

1940, July 9
C87 AP17 10c red org & blue .40 .20
C88 AP17 70c sepia & blue .40 .20
C89 AP17 1s copper brn & blue .80 .20
C90 AP17 10s black & blue 3.25 .85
Nos. C87-C90 (4) 4.85 1.45

Pan American Union, 50th anniversary.

Journalism Type
1941, Dec. 15
C91 A157 3s rose carmine 5.25 .20
C92 A157 10s yellow orange 11.00 .45

See note after No. 399.

Old Map of South America Showing Amazon River — AP19   Panoramic View of Amazon River — AP20

Designs: 70c, Gonzalo de Pineda. 5s, Painting of the expedition.

1942, Jan. 30
C93 AP19 40c black & buff 1.90 .20
C94 AP19 70c olive 2.90 .20
C95 AP20 2s dark green 3.25 .20
C96 AP19 5s rose 4.00 .60
Nos. C93-C96 (4) 12.05 1.25

See note after No. 403.

Remigio Crespo Toral Type
1942, Sept. 1 Perf. 13½
C97 A162 10c dull violet 1.25 .45

Alfaro Types
70c, Gen. Eloy Alfaro. 1s, Devils's Nose. 3s, Military College. 5s, Montecristi, Alfaro's birthplace.

1943, Feb. 16 Perf. 12
C98 A166 70c dk rose & blk 1.90 .20
C99 A167 1s ol blk & red brn 3.25 .65
C100 A167 3s ol gray & grn 4.50 .90
C101 A167 5s slate & salmon 6.75 1.10
Nos. C98-C101 (4) 16.40 2.85

Nos. C61-C63 Overprinted in Red Brown

1943, Apr. 15 Perf. 11½
Center Multicolored
C102 AP8 50c violet 2.75 1.50
C103 AP8 1s black 3.25 1.60
C104 AP8 2s violet 4.00 2.50
Nos. C102-C104 (3) 10.00 5.60

Visit of US Vice-Pres. Henry A. Wallace.

Nos. 374-376 Overprinted "AEREO LOOR A BOLIVIA JUNIO 11-1943" (like Nos. C111-C113)

1943, June 11 Perf. 13
C105 A146 50c dp red violet .40 .20
C106 A147 1s copper red .60 .20
C107 A148 2s dark green .70 .20
Nos. C105-C107 (3) 1.70 .60

Visit of Pres. Eurique Penaranda of Bolivia.
Vertical overprints on Nos. C105-C106.

Nos. 374-376 Overprinted "AEREO LOOR A PARAGUAY JULIO 5-1943" (like Nos. C111-C113)

1943, July 5
C108 A146 50c dp red violet .40 .20
  a. Double overprint 75.00
C109 A147 1s copper red 1.00 .50
C110 A148 2s dark green 1.40 .70
Nos. C108-C110 (3) 2.80 1.40

Visit of Pres. Higinio Moringo of Paraguay.
Vertical overprints on Nos. C108-C109.

Nos. 374-376 Overprinted in Black

1943, July 23

C111	A146	50c dp red violet	.40	.20
C112	A147	1s copper red	.60	.20
C113	A148	2s dark green	.70	.20
		Nos. C111-C113 (3)	1.70	.60

Issued to commemorate the visit of President Isaias Medina Angarita of Venezuela. Vertical overprint on Nos. C111-C112. See Nos. C105-C110.

President Arroyo del Rio Addressing US Congress — AP26

1943, Oct. 9   *Perf. 12*

C114	AP26	50c dark brown	.90	.50
C115	AP26	70c brt rose	1.20	.50
C116	AP26	3s dark blue	1.40	.65
C117	AP26	5s dark green	3.00	1.20
C118	AP26	10s olive black	12.00	4.25
		Nos. C114-C118 (5)	18.50	7.10

Good will tour of Pres. Arroyo del Rio in 1942.
For surcharges see Nos. CB1-CB5.

1944, Feb. 7

C119	AP26	50c dp red lilac	.90	.65
C120	AP26	70c red brown	1.75	.65
C121	AP26	3s turq green	1.75	.65
C122	AP26	5s brt ultra	2.90	1.40
C123	AP26	10s scarlet	3.50	1.60
		Nos. C119-C123 (5)	10.80	4.95
		Nos. C114-C123 (10)	29.30	12.05

Church of San Francisco, Quito — AP27

1944, Feb. 13

C124	AP27	70c turq green	1.90	.45
C125	AP27	1s olive	1.90	.45
C126	AP27	3s red orange	4.25	.90
C127	AP27	5s carmine rose	5.25	1.10
		Nos. C124-C127 (4)	13.30	2.90

See note after No. 433.

Palace Type

1944   Engr.   *Perf. 11*

C128	A173	3s orange	1.00	.20
C129	A173	5s dark brown	1.75	.20
C130	A173	10s dark red	4.00	.20
		Nos. C128-C130 (3)	6.75	.60

See No. C221. For overprints and surcharges see Nos. 541, C136-C138, C210-C213, C218-C220, C223-C224, C277-C279.

Red Cross Type

1945, Apr. 25   Unwmk.   *Perf. 12*
Cross in Rose

C131	A174	2s deep blue	4.00	.70
C132	A174	3s green	4.50	.85
C133	A174	5s dark violet	6.50	1.10
C134	A174	10s carmine rose	21.00	3.75
		Nos. C131-C134 (4)	36.00	6.40

No. RA55 Surcharged in Black

1945, June 8

C135	PT21	40c on 5c blue	1.00	.20
a.		Double surcharge		10.00

Counterfeits exist.

Nos. C128-C130 Overprinted in Green

1945, Sept. 6   *Perf. 11*

C136	A173	3s orange	1.00	.50
a.		Inverted overprint	50.00	
b.		Double overprint	50.00	
C137	A173	5s dark brown	1.25	.65
C138	A173	10s dark red	3.25	1.25
		Nos. C136-C138 (3)	5.50	2.40

Nos. C61-C63 Overprinted in Dark Blue and Gold like Nos. 444-446

1945, Oct. 2   *Perf. 12*
Center Multicolored

C139	AP8	50c violet	1.25	.25
C140	AP8	1s black	1.50	1.50
C141	AP8	2s violet	2.25	1.90
		Nos. C139-C141 (3)	5.00	3.65

Visit of Pres. Juan Antonio Rios of Chile.

Monument to Liberty — AP30

1945, Nov. 14   Engr.

C142	AP30	30c blue	.40	.20
C143	AP30	40c rose carmine	.40	.20
C144	AP30	1s dull violet	1.20	.45
C145	AP30	3s gray black	2.25	1.10
C146	AP30	5s purple brown	3.25	1.60
		Nos. C142-C146 (5)	7.50	3.55

Gen. Antonio Jose de Sucre, 150th birth anniv.

> **Catalogue values for unused stamps in this section, from this point to the end of the section, are for Never Hinged items.**

Highway Type

1946, Apr. 22   Unwmk.

C147	A176	1s carmine rose	1.20	.40
C148	A176	2s violet	1.40	.70
C149	A176	3s turq green	2.00	1.00
C150	A176	5s red orange	2.75	1.20
C151	A176	10s dark blue	3.75	1.00
		Nos. C147-C151 (5)	11.10	4.30

Revolution Types

1946, Aug. 9   *Perf. 12½*

C152	A177	40c deep claret	.25	.20
C153	A178	1s sepia	.25	.20
C154	A179	2s indigo	.70	.20
C155	A180	3s olive green	1.20	.45
		Nos. C152-C155 (4)	2.40	1.05

National Union of Periodicals, Initials and Quill Pen — AP36

1946, Sept. 16

C156	AP36	50c dull purple	1.00	.60
C157	AP36	70c dark green	1.20	.60
C158	AP36	3s red	2.25	1.00
C159	AP36	3s indigo	3.00	1.20
C160	AP36	10s chocolate	9.00	1.75
		Nos. C156-C160 (5)	16.45	5.15

Campaign for adult education.

The Blessed Mariana Teaching Children — AP37

"Lily of Quito" — AP38

1946, Nov. 28   Unwmk.

C161	AP37	40c chocolate	.40	.40
C162	AP37	60c deep blue	.70	.70
C163	AP38	3s orange yellow	1.30	1.00
C164	AP38	5s green	3.00	1.50
		Nos. C161-C164 (4)	5.40	3.70

300th anniv. of the death of the Blessed Mariana de Jesus Paredes y Flores.

Rocafuerte Type

60c-1.10s, Jual de Velasco. 1.30s-2s, Riobamba Irrigation Canal.

1947, Nov. 27   *Perf. 12*

C165	A185	60c dark green	.40	.20
C166	A185	70c purple	.40	.20
C167	A185	1s black brown	.40	.20
C168	A185	1.10s car rose	.40	.20
C169	A185	1.30s deep blue	.40	.20
C170	A185	1.90s olive bister	1.00	.20
C171	A185	2s olive green	1.00	.20
		Nos. C165-C171 (7)	4.00	1.40

For overprints & surcharges see #C175, C181, C207-C209, C215, C216-C217, C222, C235.

Bello Type

1948, Apr. 21   *Perf. 13*

C172	A188	60c magenta	.40	.20
C173	A188	1.30s dk blue grn	.70	.20
C174	A188	1.90s dk rose car	.60	.25
		Nos. C172-C174 (3)	1.70	.65

No. C166 Overprinted in Black

1948, May 24   *Perf. 12*

C175	A185	70c purple	1.00	.35

Columbus — AP42

1948, May 26   *Perf. 14*

C176	AP42	50c olive green	.80	.80
C177	AP42	70c rose carmine	.80	.80
C178	AP42	3s ultra	2.75	2.40
C179	AP42	5s brown	3.50	3.50
C180	AP42	10s deep violet	12.00	4.00
		Nos. C176-C180 (5)	19.85	11.50

See note after No. 495.

No. C169 Overprinted in Carmine like No. 496 (MANANA reads up)

1948, Aug. 26   Unwmk.   *Perf. 12*

C181	A185	1.30s deep blue	.80	.25

National Fair of Today and Tomorrow, 1948.

Elia Liut and Telegrafo I AP43

Teacher and Pupils AP44

1948, Sept. 10   *Perf. 12½*

C182	AP43	60c rose red	1.00	.20
C183	AP43	1s green	1.00	.25
C184	AP43	1.30s deep claret	1.00	.25
C185	AP43	1.90s deep violet	1.00	.25
C186	AP43	2s dark brown	1.50	.30
C187	AP43	5s blue	2.75	.50
		Nos. C182-C187 (6)	8.25	1.75

25th anniv. (in 1945) of the 1st postal flight in Ecuador.

1948, Oct. 12   *Perf. 14*

C188	AP44	50c violet	1.75	.60
C189	AP44	70c deep blue	1.75	.60
C190	AP44	3s dark green	3.50	1.60
C191	AP44	5s red	5.00	2.10
C192	AP44	10s brown	9.00	2.75
		Nos. C188-C192 (5)	21.00	7.65

Campaign for adult education.

AP45

Franklin D. Roosevelt and Two of "Four Freedoms" — AP46

1948, Oct. 24   *Perf. 12½*

C193	AP45	60c emer & org brn	.40	.25
C194	AP45	1s car rose & slate	.40	.25
C195	AP46	1.50s grn & red brn	.40	.25
C196	AP46	2s red & black	1.10	.25
C197	AP46	5s ultra & blk	2.25	.25
		Nos. C193-C197 (5)	4.55	1.25

Maldonado Types

1948, Nov. 17

C198	A196	60c dp org & rose car	.80	.20
C199	A197	90c red & gray blk	.80	.20
C200	A196	1.30s pur & dp org	1.50	.20
C201	A197	2s dp bl & dull grn	1.50	.20
		Nos. C198-C201 (4)	4.60	.80

See note after No. 519.

Juan Montalvo and Cervantes AP47

Don Quixote — AP48

1949, May 2   Engr.   *Perf. 12½x12*

C202	AP47	1.30s ol brn & ultra	5.00	2.50
C203	AP48	1.90s grn & rose car	1.20	.30
C204	AP47	3s vio & org brn	1.80	.30
C205	AP48	5s red & gray blk	3.00	.20
C206	AP48	10s red lil & aqua	5.00	.20
		Nos. C202-C206 (5)	16.00	3.50

400th anniv. of the birth of Miguel de Cervantes Saavedra, novelist, playwright and poet, and the 60th anniv. of the death of Juan Montalvo (1832-89), Ecuadorean writer.
For surcharges see Nos. C225-C226.

No. C168
Surcharged in Blue

1949, June 15   *Perf. 12*
C207 A185 50c on 1.10s car rose   .40   .20
C208 A185 60c on 1.10s car rose   .50   .20
C209 A185 90c on 1.10s car rose   .60   .20
    Nos. C207-C209 (3)   1.40   .60

2nd Eucharistic Cong., Quito, June 1949.

No. C128 Surcharged in Black

1949, Oct. 11   *Perf. 11*
C210 A173 60c on 3s orange   .90   .60
   a.   Double surcharge   30.00
C211 A173 90c on 3s orange   .90   .20
C212 A173   1s on 3s orange   1.10   .60
C213 A173   2s on 3s orange   2.50   .60
    Nos. C210-C213 (4)   5.40   2.00

"SUCRE(S)" in capitals on Nos. C212-C213.
75th anniv. of the UPU.

AP49

Black Surcharge

1950   **Unwmk.**   *Perf. 12*
C214 AP49 60c on 50c gray   .75   .20
   a.   Double surcharge   15.00

**No. C170 Surcharged with New
Value in Black**

C215 A185 90c on 1.90s ol bis   .75   .20

Nos. C168, C128-C129 and Type of
1944 Surcharged or Overprinted in
Black or Carmine

1950, Feb. 10   *Perf. 12*
C216 A185 50c on 1.10s   1.75   1.75
C217 A185 70c on 1.10s   2.25   1.75
    Perf. 11
C218 A173   3s orange   3.25   3.00
C219 A173   5s dark brown (C)   5.00   2.50
C220 A173 10s violet (C)   7.50   3.00
    Nos. C216-C220 (5)   19.75   12.00

Issued to publicize adult education.
For overprint see No. 541.

Govt. Palace Type of 1944
1950, May 15   **Engr.**   *Perf. 11*
C221 A173 10s violet   2.25   .20

For surcharges see Nos. C277-C279.

No. C169 Surcharged with New Value
in Black

1950   *Perf. 12*
C222 A185 90c on 1.30s dp blue   .40   .20

See No. C235.

Nos. C128-C129 Overprinted in Black

1951, July 28   **Unwmk.**   *Perf. 11*
C223 A173 3s orange   1.90   .95
C224 A173 5s dark brown   3.75   1.75

20,000th crossing of the equator by Pan
American-Grace Airways planes.

Nos. C202-C203 Surcharged in Black

1951   **Unwmk.**   *Perf. 12½x12*
C225 AP47 60c on 1.30s   .50   .20
C226 AP48   1s on 1.90s   .50   .20
   a.   Inverted surcharge   20.00

Issued to publicize adult education.

St. Mariana de
Jesus — AP50

1952, Feb. 15   **Engr.**
C227 AP50 60c plum & aqua   1.10   .40
C228 AP50 90c dk grn & lt ultra   1.30   .40
C229 AP50   1s car & dk grn   1.40   .40
C230 AP50   2s indigo & rose lil   1.40   .40
    Nos. C227-C230 (4)   5.20   1.60

Canonization of Mariana de Jesus Paredes
y Flores.

Plaza Visit to US Issue

3s, as No. 558. 5s, as No. 559.

1952, Mar. 26   *Perf. 12*
C231 A205 3s lilac & bl grn   1.00   .70
C232 A205 5s red brn & ol gray   2.00   2.00
   a.   Souv. sheet of 2, #C231-C232   4.50   *9.00*

**Consular Service Stamps Surcharged
"AEREO" and New Value in Black**

1952   **Unwmk.**   *Perf. 12*
C233 R2 60c on 1s green   .50   .20
C234 R2   1s on 1s green   .50   .20

Type R2 illustrated above No. 545.

**No. C169 Surcharged with New
Value in Carmine**

C235 A185 90c on 1.30s dp bl   .50   .20
    Nos. C233-C235 (3)   1.50   .60

See No. C222.

Pres. José M.
Urvina and
Allegory of
Freedom
AP52

Torch of
Knowledge
AP53

Hyphen-hole Perf. 7x6½
1952, Nov. 18   *Litho.*
C236 AP52 60c rose red & blue   6.00   1.20
C237 AP52 90c lilac & red   6.00   1.40
C238 AP52   1s orange & green   6.00   .40
C239 AP52   2s red brn & blue   6.00   .80
    Nos. C236-C239 (4)   24.00   3.80

Centenary of abolition of slavery in Ecuador.
Counterfeits exist.

Unwmk.
1953, Apr. 13   **Engr.**   *Perf. 12*
Design: 2s, Aged couple studying alphabet.
C240 AP53 1s dark blue   1.75   .20
C241 AP53 2s red orange   2.25   .20

1952 adult education campaign.

Globe
Showing Part
of Western
Hemisphere
AP54

1953, June 5   *Perf. 12½x12*
C242 AP54 60c orange yellow   .40   .20
C243 AP54 90c dark blue   .70   .35
C244 AP54   3s carmine   1.10   .45
    Nos. C242-C244 (3)   2.20   1.00

Issued to publicize the crossing of the equator by the Pan-American highway.

**Consular Service Stamps Surcharged
in Black**

    a   b

1953-54   *Perf. 12*
C245 R1 (a) 60c on 2s brown   .35   .20
C246 R2 (a) 60c on 5s sep ('54)   .35   .20
C247 R2 (a) 70c on 5s sep ('54)   .35   .20
C248 R2 (a) 90c on 50c car rose
              ('54)   .35   .20
C249 R1 (b)   1s on 2s brown   .35   .20
C250 R1 (a)   1s on 2s brn ('54)   .35   .20
C251 R1 (a)   1s on 2s brn ('54)   .65   .20
C252 R1 (a)   3s on 5s vio ('54)   .90   .20
    Nos. C245-C252 (8)   3.65   1.60

Surcharge is horizontal on Nos. C245, C247
and C248.

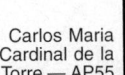

Carlos Maria
Cardinal de la
Torre — AP55

Queen Isabella
I — AP56

1954, Jan. 13   **Photo.**   *Perf. 8½*
    Center in Black
C253 AP55 60c rose lilac   .75   .60
C254 AP55 90c green   1.00   .60
C255 AP55   3s orange   1.50   .60
    Nos. C253-C255 (3)   3.25   1.80

1st anniv. of the elevation of Archbishop de
la Torre to Cardinal.

1954, Apr. 22
C256 AP56 60c dk grn & grn   .60   .60
C257 AP56 90c lil rose   .60   .60
C258 AP56   1s blk & pale lil   .60   .60
C259 AP56   2s blk brn & pale bl   1.20   .60
C260 AP56   5s blk brn & buff   3.00   .60
    Nos. C256-C260 (5)   6.00   3.00

See note with No. 585.

Post Office,
Guayaquil
AP57

1954, May 19   **Engr.**   *Perf. 12½x12*
    Black Surcharge
C261 AP57 80c on 20c red   .30   .20
C262 AP57   1s on 20c red   .30   .20

25th anniversary of Pan American-Grace
Airways' operation in Ecuador.

Plane, Gateway
and
Wheel — AP58

1954, Aug. 2   **Unwmk.**
    Litho.   *Perf. 11*
C263 AP58 80c blue   .35   .20

Day of the Postal Employee.

San Pablo
Lagoon
AP59

1954, Sept. 24   **Photo.**
C264 AP59 60c orange   .30   .20
C265 AP59 70c rose pink   .30   .20
C266 AP59 90c dp grn   .30   .20
C267 AP59   1s dk gray grn   .30   .20
C268 AP59   2s blue   .40   .20
C269 AP59   3s yel brn   .65   .20
    Nos. C264-C269 (6)   2.25   1.20

Glorification
of Abdon
Calderon
Garaicoa
AP60

Capt.
Calderon — AP61

1954, Oct. 1
C270 AP60 80c rose pink   .55   .20
C271 AP61 90c blue   .55   .20

150th anniversary of the birth of Capt.
Abdon Calderon Garaicoa.

El Cebollar
College
AP62

Brother Miguel
Instructing
Boys — AP63

Designs: 90c, Francisco Febres Cordero (Brother Miguel). 2.50s, Tomb of Brother Miguel. 3s, Monument to Brother Miguel.

1954, Dec. 3   **Unwmk.**   *Perf. 11*

C272	AP62	70c dk grn	.25	.20
C273	AP63	80c dk brn	.25	.20
C274	AP63	90c dk gray bl	.25	.20
C275	AP63	2.50s indigo	.45	.20
C276	AP62	3s lil rose	.65	.35
		Nos. C272-C276 (5)	1.85	1.15

Centenary of the birth of Francisco Febres Cordero (Brother Miguel).

No. C221 Surcharged in Various Colors

1955, May 25

C277	A173	1s on 10s vio (Bk)	.30	.20
C278	A173	1.70s on 10s vio (C)	.50	.20
C279	A173	4.20s on 10s vio (Br)	.80	.35
		Nos. C277-C279 (3)	1.60	.75

Denomination in larger type on No. C279. National Exhibition of Daily Periodicals.

"La Rotonda," Guayaquil, and Rotary Emblem AP64

Design: 90c, Eugenio Espejo hospital, Quito, and Rotary emblem.

1955, July 9   **Engr.**   *Perf. 12½*

C280	AP64	80c dark brown	.25	.25
C281	AP64	90c dark grown	.35	.35

50th anniv. of the founding of Rotary Intl.

José Abel Castillo AP65

2s, 5s, José Abel Castillo, Map of Ecuador.

1955, Oct. 19   *Perf. 11x11½*

C282	AP65	60c chocolate	1.60	.20
C283	AP65	90c light olive green	1.60	.20
C284	AP65	1s lilac	2.50	.20
C285	AP65	2s vermilion	2.75	.70
C286	AP65	5s ultra	5.75	.55
		Nos. C282-C286 (5)	14.20	1.85

See note after No. 595.

No. C29 Surcharged in Black

1955, Oct. 24   *Perf. 12*

C287	AP1	1s on 5s purple	1.00	.20

A similar surcharge on No. C29, set in two lines with letters 5mm high and no X's or black-out line of squares, was privately applied.

San Pablo, Imbabura — AP66

50s, Rumichaca Caves. 1.30s, Virgin of Quito. 1.50s, Cotopaxi Volcano. 1.70s, Tungurahua Volcano, Tungurahua. 1.90s, Guanacos. 2.40s, Mat market. 2.50s, Ruins at Incapirca. 4.20s, El Carmen, Cuenca, Azuay. 4.80s, Santo Domingo Church.

1956, Jan. 2   **Photo.**   *Perf. 13*

C288	AP66	50c slate blue	2.75	.20
C289	AP66	1s ultra	2.75	.20
C290	AP66	1.30s crimson	4.25	.20
C291	AP66	1.50s dp grn	2.75	.20
C292	AP66	1.70s yel brn	1.75	.20
C293	AP66	1.90s olive	3.50	.20
C294	AP66	2.40s red org	3.75	.20
C295	AP66	2.50s violet	3.75	.20
C296	AP66	4.20s black	4.75	.20
C297	AP66	4.80s yel org	7.50	.30
		Nos. C288-C297 (10)	37.50	2.10

See Nos. C310-C311. For surcharges see Nos. 766A, 766G.

Honorato Vazquez — AP67

Title Page of First Book — AP68

1956, May 28   **Engr.**

Various Portraits

C298	AP67	1s yellow green	.50	.20
C299	AP67	1.50s red	.50	.20
C300	AP67	1.70s bright blue	.50	.20
C301	AP67	1.90s slate blue	.50	.20
		Nos. C298-C301 (4)	2.00	.80

Birth centenary (in 1955) of Honorato Vazquez, statesman.

1956, Aug. 27   **Unwmk.**   *Perf. 13½*

C302	AP68	1s black	.60	.20
C303	AP68	1.70s slate bl	.60	.20
C304	AP68	2s blk brn	.60	.20
C305	AP68	3s redsh brn	.60	.20
		Nos. C302-C305 (4)	2.40	.80

Bicentenary of printing in Ecuador.

Hands Reaching for UN Emblem AP69

1956, Oct. 24   *Perf. 14*

C307	AP69	1.70s red org	1.00	.20

10th anniv. of the UN (in 1955).
See No. C319. For overprint see No. C426.

Coat of Arms and Basketball Player — AP70

Designs: 1.70s, Map of South America with flags and girl basketball players.

1956, Dec. 28   **Photo.**   *Perf. 14½x14*

C308	AP70	1s red lilac	.50	.20
C309	AP70	1.70s deep green	.75	.20

6th South American Women's Basketball Championship, Aug. 1956.

Scenic Type of 1956

1957, Jan. 2   *Perf. 13*

C310	AP66	50c bl grn	1.75	.20
C311	AP66	1s orange	1.75	.20

Type of Regular Issue, 1957

Designs: 50c, Map of Cuenca, 16th century. 80c, Cathedral of Cuenca. 1s, Modern City Hall.

Unwmk.

1957, Apr. 7   **Photo.**   *Perf. 12*

C312	A219	50c brn, *cr*	.20	.20
a.		Souvenir sheet of 4	1.00	1.00
C313	A219	80c red, *bluish*	.25	.20
C314	A219	1s pur, *yel*	.30	.20
a.		Souvenir sheet of 3	2.00	2.00
		Nos. C312-C314 (3)	.75	.60

No. C312a contains 4 imperf. 50c stamps similar to No. 613, but inscribed "AEREO" and printed in green. The sheet is printed on white ungummed paper.

No. C314a contains 3 imperf. stamps in designs similar to Nos. C312-C314, but with colors changed to orange (50c), brown (80c), violet (1s). The sheet is printed on white ungummed paper.

Gabriela Mistral — AP71

Arms of Espejo, Carchi — AP72

Unwmk.

1957, Sept. 18   **Litho.**   *Perf. 14*

C315	AP71	2s lt bl, blk & red	.40	.20

Issued to honor Gabriela Mistral (1889-1957), Chilean poet and educator.
See Nos. C406-C407.

1957, Nov. 16   *Perf. 14½x13½*

Arms of Cantons: 2s, Montufar. 4.20s, Tulcan.

Coat of Arms Multicolored

C316	AP72	1s carmine	.40	.20
C317	AP72	2s black	.40	.20
C318	AP72	4.20s ultra	.75	.20
		Nos. C316-C318 (3)	1.55	.60

Province of Carchi.
See Nos. C334-C337, C355-C364, C392-C395. For surcharge see No. 766.

Redrawn UN Type of 1956

1957, Dec. 10   **Engr.**   *Perf. 14*

C319	AP69	2s greenish blue	.40	.25

Honoring the UN. Dates, as on No. C307, are omitted; inscribed: "Homenaje a las Naciones Unidas."

Mater Dolorosa, San Gabriel College — AP73

Rafael Maria Arizaga — AP74

#C321, 1s, Door of San Gabriel College, Quito.

1958, Apr. 27   **Engr.**   *Perf. 14*

C320	AP73	30c rose cl, *dp rose*	.25	.20
C321	AP73	30c rose cl, *dp rose*	.25	.20
a.		Pair, #C320-C321	.60	.60
C322	AP73	1s dk bl, *lt bl*	.25	.20
C323	AP73	1.70s dk bl, *lt bl*	.25	.20
a.		Pair, #C322-C323	.60	.60

Miracle of San Gabriel College, Quito, 50th anniv.

1958, July 21   **Litho.**

C324	AP74	1s multi	.30	.20

Rafael Maria Arizaga (1858-1933), writer.
See Nos. C343, C350, C412.

Daule River Bridge AP75

1958, July 25   **Engr.**   *Perf. 13½x14*

C325	AP75	1.30s green	.35	.20

Issued to commemorate the opening of the River Daule bridge in Guayas province.
See Nos. C367-C369.

Basketball Player — AP76

Symbolical of the Eucharist — AP77

1958, Sept. 1   **Photo.**   *Perf. 14x13½*

C326	AP76	1.30s dk grn & lt brn	.35	.30

South American basketball championships.
For surcharge see No. 774A.

1958, Sept. 25   **Litho.**   **Unwmk.**

Design: 60c, Cathedral of Guayaquil.

C327	AP77	10c vio & buff	.35	.20
C328	AP77	60c org & vio brn	.35	.20
C329	AP77	1s brn & lt bl	.35	.20
		Nos. C327-C329 (3)	1.05	.60

Souvenir Sheet

Symbolical of the Eucharist — AP78

Perf. 13½x14

C330	AP78	Sheet of 4	2.50	2.10
a.-d.		40c dark blue, any single	.25	.25

3rd National Eucharistic Congress.

Stamps of 1865 and 1920 — AP79

Designs: 2s, Stamps of 1920 and 1948. 4.20s, Municipal museum and library.

1958, Oct. 8 Photo. Perf. 11½
Granite Paper
C331 AP79 1.30s grn & brn red   .20 .20
C332 AP79 2s bl & vio   .50 .30
C333 AP79 4.20s dk brn   .60 .40
  Nos. C331-C333 (3)   1.30 .90

National Philatelic Exposition (EXFIGUA), Guayaquil, Oct. 4-14.
For surcharge see No. 774.

Coat of Arms Type of 1957
Province of Imbabura
Arms of Cantons: 50c, Cotacachi. 60c, Antonio Ante. 80c, Otavlo. 1.10s, Ibarra.

1958, Nov. 9 Litho. Perf. 14½x13½
Coats of Arms Multicolored
C334 AP72 50c blk & red   .35 .20
C335 AP72 60c blk, bl & red   .35 .20
C336 AP72 80c blk & yel   .35 .20
C337 AP72 1.10s blk & red   .35 .20
  Nos. C334-C337 (4)   1.40 .80

Charles V — AP80   Paul Rivet — AP81

Engr. & Photo.
1958, Dec. 12 Perf. 14x13½
C338 AP80 2s brn red & dk brn   .30 .20
C339 AP80 4.20s dk gray & red brn .40 .30

400th anniv. of the death of Charles V, Holy Roman Emperor.

1958, Dec. 29 Photo. Perf. 11½
Granite Paper
C340 AP81 1s brown   .30 .20

Issued in honor of Paul Rivet (1876-1958), French anthropologist.

1959, May 6
Portrait: 2s, Alexander von Humboldt.
C341 AP81 2s slate   .25 .20

Cent. of the death of Alexander von Humboldt, German naturalist and geographer.

Front Page of "El Telegrafo" — AP82

1959, Feb. Litho. Perf. 13½
C342 AP82 1.30s bl grn & blk   .25 .20

75th anniv. of Ecuador's oldest newspaper.

Portrait Type of 1958
José Luis Tamayo (1858-1947), lawyer.

1959, June 26 Unwmk. Perf. 14
Portrait Multicolored
C343 AP74 1.30s lt grn, bl & sal .30 .20

El Sagrario & House of Manuela Canizares AP83

Condor — AP84

Designs: 80c, Hall at San Agustin. 1s, First words of the constitutional act. 2s, Entrance to Cuartel Real. 4.20s, Allegory of Liberty.

Unwmk.
1959, Aug. 28 Photo. Perf. 14
C344 AP83 20c ultra & lt brn   .25 .20
C345 AP83 80c brt bl & dp org   .25 .20
C346 AP83 1s dk red & dk ol   .25 .20
C347 AP84 1.30s brt bl & org   .25 .20
C348 AP84 2s ultra & org brn   .25 .20
C349 AP84 4.20s scar & brt bl   .40 .30
  Nos. C344-C349 (6)   1.65 1.30

Sesquicentennial of the revolution.

Portrait Type of 1958
1s, Alfredo Baquerizo Moreno (1859-1951), statesman.

1959, Sept. 26 Litho. Perf. 14
C350 AP74 1s gray, red & salmon   .30 .20

Pope Pius XII — AP85

1959, Oct. 9 Unwmk. Perf. 14½
C351 AP85 1.30s multi   .35 .20

Issued in memory of Pope Pius XII.

Flags of Argentina, Bolivia, Brazil, Guatemala, Haiti, Mexico and Peru — AP86

Flags of: 80c, Chile, Costa Rica, Cuba, Dominican Republic, Panama, Paraguay, United States. 1.30s, Colombia, Ecuador, Honduras, Nicaragua, Salvador, Uruguay, Venezuela.

1959, Oct. 12 Perf. 13½.
C352 AP86 50c multi   .20 .20
C353 AP86 80c yel, red & bl   .20 .20
C354 AP86 1.30s multi   .35 .20
  Nos. C352-C354 (3)   .75 .60

Organization of American States.
For overprints see #C423-C425, CO19-CO21.

Arms of the Cantons Type of 1957
Province of Pichincha
10c, Rumiñahui. 40c, Pedro Moncayo. 1s, Mejia. 1.30s, Cayambe. 4.20s, Quito.

Perf. 14½x13½
1959-60 Unwmk. Litho.
Coat of Arms Multicolored
C355 AP72 10c blk & dk red ('60) .35 .20
C356 AP72 40c blk & yel   .35 .20
C357 AP72 1s blk & brn ('60)   .35 .20
C358 AP72 1.30s blk & grn ('60)   .35 .20
C359 AP72 4.20s blk & org   .35 .20
  Nos. C355-C359 (5)   1.75 1.00

Province of Cotopaxi
40c, Pangua. 60c, Pujili. 70c, Saquisili. 1s, Salcedo. 1.30s, Latacunga.

1960
Coat of Arms Multicolored
C360 AP72 40c blk & car   .25 .20
C361 AP72 60c blk & bl   .25 .20
C362 AP72 70c blk & turq   .25 .20
C363 AP72 1s blk & red org   .25 .20
C364 AP72 1.30s blk & org   .30 .20
  Nos. C360-C364 (5)   1.30 1.00

Flags of American Nations — AP87

1960, Feb. 23 Perf. 13x12½
C365 AP87 1.30s multi   .20 .20
C366 AP87 2s multi   .25 .20

11th Inter-American Conference, Feb. 1960.

Bridge Type of 1958
Bridges: No. C367, Juntas. No. C368, Saracay. 2s, Railroad bridge, Ambato.

1960 Litho. Perf. 13½
C367 AP75 1.30s chocolate   .25 .20

Photo. Perf. 12½
C368 AP75 1.30s emerald   .25 .20
C369 AP75 2s brown   .35 .20
  Nos. C367-C369 (3)   .85 .60

Building of three new bridges.

Bahia-Chone Road — AP88

Pres. Camilo Ponce Enriquez AP89

Designs: 4.20s, Public Works Building, Cuenca. 5s, El Coca airport. 10s, New Harbor, Guayaquil.

1960, Aug. Litho. Perf. 14
C370 AP88 1.30s blk & dl yel   .20 .20
C371 AP88 4.20s rose car & lt grn .30 .30
C372 AP88 5s dk brn & yel   .45 .35
C373 AP88 10s dk bl & bl   1.00 .35
Perf. 11x11½
C374 AP89 2s org brn & blk   1.40 .25
  Nos. C370-C374 (5)   3.35 1.45

Nos. C370-C374 publicize the achievements of Pres. Camilo Ponce Enriquez (1956-1960).
Issued: #C370-C373, 8/24; #C374, 8/31.

Red Cross Building, Quito and Henri Dunant AP90

1960, Oct. 5 Unwmk. Perf. 13x14
C375 AP90 2s rose vio & car   .45 .20

Centenary (in 1959) of Red Cross idea.

For overprint see No. C408.

El Belen Church, Quito — AP91

1961, Jan. 14 Perf. 12½
C376 AP91 3s multi   .40 .20

Ecuador's participation in the 1960 Barcelona Philatelic Congress.

Map of Ecuador and Amazon River System AP92

1961, Feb. 27 Litho. Perf. 10½
C377 AP92 80c salmpn, claret & grn .25 .20
C378 AP92 1.30s gray, slate & grn .35 .20
C379 AP92 2s beige, red & grn   .50 .20
  Nos. C377-C379 (3)   1.10 .60

Amazon Week, and the 132nd anniversary of the Battle of Tarqui against Peru.

Juan Montalvo, Juan Leon Mera, Juan Benigno Vela — AP93

Hugo Ortiz G. — AP94

1961, Apr. 13 Unwmk. Perf. 13
C380 AP93 1.30s salmon & blk   .35 .20

Centenary of Tungurahua province.

1961, May 25 Perf. 14x14½
Design: No. C382, Ortiz monument.
C381 AP94 1.30s grnsh bl, blk & yel .25 .20
C382 AP94 1.30s grnsh bl, pur, ol & brn .25 .20

Lt. Hugo Ortiz G., killed in battle 8/2/41.

Condor and Airplane Stamp of 1936 AP95

1.30s, Map of South America and stamp of 1865. 2s, Bolivar monument stamp of 1930.

Perf. 10½
1961, May 25 Litho. Unwmk.
Size: 41x28mm
C383 AP95 80c org & vio   .20 .20
Size: 41x34mm
C384 AP95 1.30s bl, yel, ol & car .40 .35

Size: 40½x37mm

C385	AP95	2s car rose & blk	.60	.35
		Nos. C383-C385 (3)	1.20	.90

Third National Philatelic Exhibition, Quito, May 25-June 3, 1961.

Arms of Los Rios and Egret — AP96

1961, May 27   Perf. 14½x13½
Coat of Arms Multicolored

C386	AP96	2s bl & blk	.35	.30

Centenary (in 1960) of Los Rios province.

Gabriel Garcia Moreno — AP97   Remigio Crespo Toral — AP98

1961, Sept. 24   Unwmk.   Perf. 12

C387	AP97	1s bl, brn & buff	.40	.20

Centenary of the restoration of national integrity.

1961, Nov. 3   Unwmk.   Perf. 14

C388	AP98	50c multi	.30	.20

Centenary of the birth of Remigio Crespo Toral, poet laureate of Ecuador.

Galapagos Islands Nos. LC1-LC3
Overprinted in Black or Red:
"Estacion de Biologia Maritima de
Galapagos" and "UNESCO 1961"
(Similar to #684-686)

1961, Oct. 31   Photo.   Perf. 12

C389	A1	1s dp bl	1.25	.20
a.		"de Galapagos" on top line	6.00	6.00
C390	A1	1.80s rose vio	3.00	1.50
a.		UNESCO emblem omitted	6.00	6.00
C391	A1	4.20s blk (R)	3.75	2.75
		Nos. C389-C391 (3)	8.00	4.45

Establishment of maritime biological stations on Galapagos Islands by UNESCO.

Arms of the Cantons Type of 1957
Province of Tungurahua

50c, Pillaro. 1s, Pelileo. 1.30s, Baños. 2s, Ambato.

Perf. 14½x13½
1962, Mar. 30   Litho.   Unwmk.
Coats of Arms Multicolored

C392	AP72	50c black	.20	.20
C393	AP72	1s black	.20	.20
C394	AP72	1.30s black	.45	.20
C395	AP72	2s black	.75	.20
		Nos. C392-C395 (4)	1.60	.80

Pres. Arosemena and Prince Philip, Arms of Ecuador and Great Britain and Equator Monument AP99

Perf. 14x13½
1962, Feb. 17   Wmk. 340

C396	AP99	1.30s bl, sepia, red & yel	.20	.20
C397	AP99	2s multi	.35	.20

Visit of Prince Philip, Duke of Edinburgh, to Ecuador, Feb. 17-20, 1962.

Mountain Farming — AP100

Perf. 12½
1963, Mar. 21   Unwmk.   Litho.

C398	AP100	30c emer, yel & blk	.20	.20
C399	AP100	3s dl red, grn & org	.50	.20
C400	AP100	4.20s bl, blk & yel	.70	.45
		Nos. C398-C400 (3)	1.40	.85

FAO "Freedom from Hunger" campaign.
Exist imperf. Value $32.50.

Mosquito and Malaria Eradication Emblem AP101

1963, Apr. 17   Unwmk.   Perf. 12½

C401	AP101	50c multi	.20	.20
C402	AP101	80c multi	.20	.20
C403	AP101	2s multi	.30	.20
		Nos. C401-C403 (3)	.70	.60

WHO drive to eradicate malaria.

Stagecoach and Jet Plane AP102

1963, May 7   Litho.

C404	AP102	2s org & car rose	.30	.20
C405	AP102	4.20s claret & ultra	.50	.35

1st Intl. Postal Conference, Paris, 1863.

Type of 1957 Inscribed "Islas
Galapagos," Surcharged with New
Value and Overprinted "Ecuador" in
Black or Red

1963, June 19   Unwmk.   Perf. 14

C406	AP71	5s on 2s gray, dk bl & red	.80	.60
C407	AP71	10s on 2s gray, dk bl & red (R)	1.40	1.40

The basic 2s exists without surcharge and overprint. No. C407 exists with "ECUADOR" omitted, and with both "ECUADOR" and "10 SUCRES" double.

No. C375 Overprinted: "1863-
1963/Centenario/de la Fundación/ de
la Cruz Roja/Internacional"

1963, June 21   Photo.   Perf. 13x14

C408	AP90	2s rose vio & car	.30	.20

Intl. Red Cross, centenary.

Type of Regular Issue, 1963

Arosemena and: 70c, Flags of Ecuador. 2s, Flags of Ecuador, Panama. 4s, Flags of Ecuador, US.

1963, July 1   Litho.   Perf. 14

C409	A238	70c pale bl & multi	.25	.20
C410	A238	2s pink & multi	.50	.20
C411	A238	4s lt bl & multi	1.25	.35
		Nos. C409-C411 (3)	2.00	.75

Imperfs exist. Value $15.

Portrait Type of 1958

Portrait: 2s, Dr. Mariano Cueva (1812-82).

Unwmk.
1963, July 4   Litho.   Perf. 14

C412	AP74	2s lt grn & multi	.35	.20

Social Insurance Symbol — AP103   Mother and Child — AP104

1963, July 9   Litho.

C413	AP103	10s brn, bl, gray & ocher	.90	.70

25th anniversary of Social Insurance.
Exists imperf. Value $9.

1963, July 28   Perf. 12½

C414	AP104	1.30s org, dk bl & blk	.20	.20
C415	AP104	5s gray, red & brn	.45	.45

7th Pan-American and South American Pediatrics Congresses, Quito.

Simon Bolivar Airport, Guayaquil AP105

1963, July 25   Perf. 14

C416	AP105	60c gray	.20	.20
C417	AP105	70c dl grn	.20	.20
C418	AP105	5s brn vio	.50	.35
		Nos. C416-C418 (3)	.90	.75

Opening of Simon Bolivar Airport, Guayaquil, July 15, 1962.
Exist imperf. Value $4.50.

Nos. 638, 640-641 Overprinted
"AEREO"

1964   Perf. 12
Flags in National Colors

C419	A223	1.80s dl vio	.50	.35
C420	A224	2s dk brn	.50	.35
C421	A223	2.20s blk brn	.50	.35
		Nos. C419-C421 (3)	1.50	1.05

On 1.80s and 2.20s, "AEREO" is vertical, reading down.

No. 650 Overprinted in Gold: "FARO
DE COLON / AEREO"

1964   Photo.   Perf. 14x13½

C422	A229	1.80s dk bl	2.50	1.50

Nos. C352-C354 Overprinted

Illustration reduced.

1964   Litho.   Perf. 13½

C423	AP86	50c bl & multi	.65	.45
C424	AP86	80c yel & multi	.65	.45
C425	AP86	1.30s pale grn & multi	.65	.45
		Nos. C423-C425 (3)	1.95	1.35

No. C307 Overprinted:
"DECLARACION / DERECHOS
HUMANOS / 1964 / XV-ANIV"

Unwmk.
1964, Sept. 29   Engr.   Perf. 14

C426	AP69	1.70s red org	.35	.20

15th anniversary (in 1963) of the Universal Declaration of Human Rights.

Banana Type

1964, Oct. 26   Litho.   Perf. 12½x12

C427	A241	4.20s blk, bis & gray ol	.30	.20
C428	A241	10s blk, scar & gray ol	.50	.40
a.		Souv. sheet of 4	2.10	2.10

No. C428a contains imperf. stamps similar to Nos. 720-721 and C427-C428.

John F. Kennedy, Flag-draped Coffin and John Jr. — AP106

1964, Nov. 22   Litho.   Perf. 14

C429	AP106	4.20s multi	1.00	.75
C430	AP106	5s multi	1.25	.90
C431	AP106	10s multi	2.25	1.25
a.		Souv. sheet of 3	8.00	8.00
		Nos. C429-C431 (3)	4.50	2.90

President John F. Kennedy (1917-63).
No. C431a contains stamps similar to Nos.
C429-C431, imperf.

Olympic Type

1.30s, Gymnast, vert. 1.80s, Hurdler. 2s, Basketball.

Perf. 13½x14, 14x13½
1964, Dec. 16   Unwmk.

C432	A243	1.30s vio bl, ver & brn	.45	.20
C433	A243	1.80s vio bl & multi	.45	.20
C434	A243	2s red & multi	.45	.20
a.		Souv. sheet of 4	3.25	3.25
		Nos. C432-C434 (3)	1.35	.60

No. C434a contains stamps similar to Nos.
725 and C432-C434, imperf.

Sports Type

Torch and Athletes: 2s, 3s, Diver, gymnast, wrestlers and weight lifter. 2.50s, 4s, Bicyclists. 3.50s, 5s, Jumpers.

1965, Nov. 20   Litho.   Perf. 12x12½

C435	A247	2s bl, gold & blk	.60	.20
C436	A247	2.50s org, gold & blk	.60	.20
C437	A247	3s brt pink, gold & blk	.60	.20
C438	A247	3.50s lt vio, gold & bl	.65	.65
C439	A247	4s brt yel grn, gold & blk	.65	.20
C440	A247	5s red org, gold & blk	.75	.35
a.		Souv. sheet of 12	12.00	12.00
		Nos. C435-C440 (6)	3.85	1.80

No. C440a contains 12 imperf. stamps similar to Nos. 738-743 and C435-C440.
For surcharges see Nos. 766B, C449.

Bird Type

Birds: 1s, Yellow grosbeak. 1.30s, Black-headed parrot. 1.50s, Scarlet tanager. 2s, Sapphire quail-dove. 2.50s, Violet-tailed sylph. 3s, Lemon-throated barbet. 4s, Yellow-tailed oriole. 10s, Collared puffbird.

1966, June 17   Litho.   Perf. 13½
Birds in Natural Colors

C441	A249	1s lt red brn & blk	1.10	.20
C442	A249	1.30s pink & blk	1.10	.20
C443	A249	1.50s pale grn & blk	1.10	.20
C444	A249	2s sal & blk	2.75	.45
C445	A249	2.50s lt yel grn & blk	2.75	.45
C446	A249	3s sal & blk	3.75	.50
C447	A249	4s gray & blk	5.00	.80
C448	A249	10s beige & blk	7.75	2.10
		Nos. C441-C448 (8)	23.50	4.90

For surcharges see Nos. 766E-766F, C450, C455-C457.

Nos. C436 and C443 Surcharged

1967

C449	A247	80c on 2.50s multi	.45	.35
C450	A249	80c on 1.50s multi	.45	.20

Old denomination on No. C449 is obliterated with heavy bar; the surcharge on No. C450 includes "Resello" and an ornament over old denomination.

Peñaherrera Monument, Quito — AP107

Design: 2s, Peñaherrera statue.

1967, Dec. 29   Litho.   Perf. 12x12½
C451 AP107 1.30s blk & org   .25 .20
C452 AP107   2s blk & lt ultra   .25 .20
See note after No. 767B.

Arosemena Type

1.30s, Inauguration. 2s, Pres. Arosemena speaking in Punta del Este.

1968, May 9   Litho.   Perf. 13½x14
C453 A251 1.30s multi   .25 .20
C454 A251   2s multi   .25 .20

No. C448 Surcharged in Plum, Dark Blue or Green

1969, Jan. 9   Litho.   Perf. 13½
Bird in Natural Colors
C455 A249 80c on 10s beige (P)   .50 .25
C456 A249   1s on 10s beige (DBl)   .50 .25
C457 A249   2s on 10s beige (G)   .50 .25
Nos. C455-C457 (3)   1.50 .75

"Operation Friendship" AP108

1969-70   Typo.   Perf. 13½
C458 AP108 2s yel, blk, red & lt bl   .25 .20
a.   Perf. 12½   .25 .20
C459 AP108 2s bl, blk, car & yel ('70)   .25 .20

Friendship campaign. Medallion background on Nos. C458 and C458a is blue; on No. C459, yellow.
No. C459 exists imperf. Value $5.

No. 639 Surcharged in Gold "S/. 5 AEREO" and Bar

1969, Nov. 25   Litho.   Perf. 12
C460 A224 5s on 2s multi   1.60 .50

Butterfly Type

Butterflies: 1.30s, Morpho peleides. 1.50s, Anartia amathea.

1970   Litho.   Perf. 12½
C461 A255 1.30s multi   3.50 .25
C462 A255 1.50s pink & multi   3.50 .25

Same, White Background

1970   Perf. 13½
C463 A255 1.30s multi   3.50 .25
C464 A255 1.50s multi   3.50 .25

Arms Type

Provincial Arms and Flags: 1.30s, El Oro. 2s, Loja. 3s, Manabi. 5s, Pichincha. 10s, Guayas.

1971   Litho.   Perf. 10½
C465 A258 1.30s pink & multi   .30 .20
C466 A258   2s multi   .35 .20
C467 A258   3s multi   .55 .30
C468 A258   5s multi   .75 .35
C469 A258   10s multi   1.25 .40
Nos. C465-C469 (5)   3.20 1.45

Presentation of the Virgin — AP109

Pres. Allende and Chilean Flag AP110

Art of Quito: 1.50s, Blessed Anne at Prayer. 2s, St. Theresa de Jesus. 2.50s, Altar of Carmen, horiz. 3s, Descent from the Cross. 4s, Christ of St. Mariana de Jesus. 5s, Shrine of St. Anthony. 10s, Cross of San Diego.

1971   Perf. 11½
Inscriptions in Black
C473 AP109 1.30s multi   .20 .20
C474 AP109 1.50s multi   .25 .20
C475 AP109   2s multi   .30 .20
C476 AP109 2.50s multi   .40 .20
C477 AP109   3s multi   .55 .20
C478 AP109   4s multi   .65 .20
C479 AP109   5s multi   .65 .35
C480 AP109   10s multi   1.50 .65
Nos. C473-C480 (8)   4.50 2.20

1971, Aug. 24   Perf. 12½

2.10s, Pres. José M. Velasco Ibarra of Ecuador, Pres. Salvador Allende of Chile, national flags.

C481 AP110   2s multi   .25 .20
C482 AP110 2.10s multi   .25 .20
Visit of Pres. Salvador Allende of Chile, Aug. 24.

Globe and Emblem AP111

1971
C483 AP111   5s black   1.00 .35
C484 AP111 5.50s dl pur & blk   1.00 .35
Opening of Postal Museum, Aug. 24, 1971. Exist imperf. Value $7.50.

Pazmiño Type

1971, Sept. 16   Perf. 12x11½
C485 A260 1.50s grn & multi   .25 .20
C486 A260 2.50s grn & multi   .40 .20

AP112

AP113

Designs: 5s, Map of Americas. 10s, Converging roads and map. 20s, Map of Americas and Equator. 50s, Mountain road and monument on Equator.

1971   Perf. 11½
C487 AP112   5s org & multi   .85 .45
C488 AP112   10s org & blk   1.25 1.00
C489 AP112   20s blk, bl & brt rose   2.40 1.60
C490 AP112 50s bl, blk & gray   3.50 2.50
Nos. C487-C490 (4)   8.00 5.55

11th Pan-American Road Congress. Issued: 5s, 10s, 50s, 11/15; 20s, 11/22. No. C488 exists imperf. Value $8.

1972
Design: 3s, Arms of Ecuador and Argentina. 5s, Presidents José M. Velasco Ibarra and Alejandro Agustin Lanusse.

C491 AP113 3s blk & multi   .25 .20
C492 AP113 5s blk & multi   .45 .30

Visit of Lt. Gen. Alejandro Agustin Lanusse, president of Argentina, Jan. 25.

Flame, Scales, Map of Americas AP114

1972, Apr. 24   Litho.   Perf. 12½
C493 AP114 1.30s bl & red   .30 .20

17th Conference of the Interamerican Federation of Lawyers, Quito, Apr. 24.

Religious Paintings Type of Regular Issue

Ecuadorian Paintings: 3s, Virgin of the Flowers, by Miguel de Santiago. 10s, Virgin of the Rosary, by Quito School.

1972, Apr. 24   Perf. 14x13½
C494 A263   3s blk & multi   .35 .35
C495 A263 10s blk & multi   1.25 .60
a.   Souv. sheet of 2, #C494-C495   1.50 1.50

1972, May 4

Ecuadorian Statues: 3s, St. Dominic, Quito School. 10s, St. Rosa of Lima, by Bernardo de Legarda.

C496 A263   3s blk & multi   .35 .35
C497 A263 10s blk & multi   1.25 .60
a.   Souv. sheet of 2, #C496-C497   2.50 2.10

Letters of "Ecuador" 3mm high on #C496-C497, 7mm high on #C494-C495.

Portrait Type

Designs (Generals, from Paintings): 1.30s, José Maria Saenz. 3s, Tomás Wright. 4s, Antonio Farfan. 5s, Antonio José de Sucre. 10s, Simon Bolivar. 20s, Arms of Ecuador.

1972, May 24
C498 A264 1.30s bl & multi   .40 .40
C499 A264   3s bl & multi   .50 .40
C500 A264   4s bl & multi   .60 .40
C501 A264   5s bl & multi   1.00 .60
C502 A264   10s bl & multi   1.75 1.00
C503 A264   20s bl & multi   3.50 1.75
Nos. C498-C503 (6)   7.75 4.55

Artisan Type

Handicraft of Ecuador: 2s, Woman wearing flowered poncho. 3s, Striped poncho. 5s, Poncho with roses. 10s, Gold sunburst sculpture.

1972, July   Photo.   Perf. 13
C504 A265   2s multi   .45 .40
C505 A265   3s multi   .70 .45
C506 A265   5s multi   1.10 .50
C507 A265 10s org red & multi   2.00 1.25
a.   Souv. sheet of 4, #C504-C507   4.75 4.75
Nos. C504-C507 (4)   4.25 2.60

Epidendrum Orchid — AP115

1972   Photo.   Perf. 12½
C508 AP115   4s shown   1.40 1.25
C509 AP115   6s Canna   1.75 1.50
C510 AP115 10s Jimson weed   3.25 3.00
a.   Souv. sheet of 3, #C508-C510   10.00 8.25
Nos. C508-C510 (3)   6.40 5.75

Exists imperf.

Oil Drilling Towers — AP116

Coat of Arms — AP117

1972, Oct. 17   Litho.   Perf. 11½
C511 AP116 1.30s bl & multi   .25 .20
Ecuadorian oil industry.

1972, Nov. 18   Litho.   Perf. 11½
Arms Multicolored
C512 AP117   2s black   .25 .20
C513 AP117   3s black   .25 .20
C514 AP117   4s black   .30 .20
C515 AP117 4.50s black   .30 .20
C516 AP117 6.30s black   .65 .30
C517 AP117 6.90s black   .65 .30
Nos. C512-C517 (6)   2.40 1.40

Pichincha Type

Designs: 2.40s, Corridor, San Agustin. 4.50s, La Merced Convent. 5.50s, Column base. 6.30s, Chapter Hall, San Agustin. 6.90s, Interior, San Agustin. 7.40s, Crucifixion, Cantuña Chapel. 7.90s, Decorated ceiling, San Agustin.

1972, Dec. 6   Wmk. 367
C518 A266 2.40s yel & multi   .30 .20
C519 A266 4.50s yel & multi   .45 .20
C520 A266 5.50s yel & multi   .55 .20
C521 A266 6.30s yel & multi   .60 .40
C522 A266 6.90s yel & multi   .65 .40
C523 A266 7.40s yel & multi   .75 .40
C524 A266 7.90s yel & multi   .80 .40
Nos. C518-C524 (7)   4.10 2.20

UN Emblem — AP118

OAS Emblem — AP119

1973, Mar. 23   Unwmk.
C525 AP118 1.30s lt bl & blk   .25 .20

25th anniversary of the Economic Committee for Latin America (CEPAL).

1973, Apr. 14   Wmk. 367
C526 AP119 1.50s multi   .30 .20
a.   Unwatermarked   .30 .20

Day of the Americas and "Philately for Peace."

Bird Type

1973   Unwmk.   Perf. 11½x11
C527 A268 1.30s Blue-footed booby   2.10 .20
C528 A268   3s Brown pelican   2.10 .20

Presidents
Lara and
Caldera
AP120

1973, June 15   **Wmk. 367**
C529 AP120 3s multi   .35 .20

Visit of Venezuela Pres. Rafael Caldera, Feb. 5-7.

Silver Coin,
1934 — AP121

Globe, OPEC
Emblem, Oil
Derrick — AP122

Ecuadorian Coins: 10s, Silver coin, obverse. 50s, Gold coin, 1928.

Unwmk.

1973, Dec. 14   **Photo.**   **Perf. 14**
C530 AP121 5s multi   .55 .40
C531 AP121 10s multi   .95 .60
C532 AP121 50s multi   4.50 2.40
   a.   Souvenir sheet of 3   6.50 6.50
   Nos. C530-C532 (3)   6.00 3.40

No. C532a contains one each of Nos. C530-C532; Dated "1972." Exists imperf. Value, same.

A gold marginal overprint was applied in 1974 to No. C532a (perf. and imperf.): "X Campeonato Mundial de Football / Munich - 1974." Value, each $60.

A carmine overprint was applied in 1974 to No. C532a (perf. and imperf.): "Seminario de Telecommunicaciones Rurales / Septiembre-1974 / Quito-Ecuador" and ITU emblem. Value, each $8.50.

1974, June 15   **Litho.**   **Perf. 11½**
C533 AP122 2s multi   .30 .20

Meeting of Organization of Oil Exporting Countries, Quito, June 15-24.

Ecuadorian Flag,
UPU
Emblem — AP123

1974, July 15   **Litho.**   **Perf. 11½**
C534 AP123 1.30s multi   .25 .20

Centenary of Universal Postal Union. Two 25s souvenir sheets exist. These were sold on a restricted basis. Value, each $40.

Teodoro Wolf
AP124

Capt. Edmundo
Chiriboga
AP125

1974   **Litho.**   **Perf. 12x11½**
C535 AP124 1.30s blk & ultra   .20 .20
C536 AP125 1.50s gray   .25 .20

Teodoro Wolf, geographer; Edmundo Chiriboga, national hero.
Issued: #C535, Nov. 29; #C536, Dec. 4.

Congress
Emblem
AP126

1974, Dec. 8   **Litho.**   **Perf. 11½x12**
C537 AP126 5s bl & multi   .35 .20

8th Inter-American Postmasters' Cong., Quito.

Map of Americas
and Coat of Arms
AP127

Prominent
Ecuadorians
AP128

1975, Feb. 1   **Perf. 12x11½**
C538 AP127 3s bl & multi   .35 .20

EXFIGUA Stamp Exhibition and 5th General Assembly of Federation Inter-Americana de Filatelia, Guayaquil, Nov. 1973.

1975   **Perf. 12x11½**

#C539, Manuel J. Calle, Journalist. #C540, Leopoldo Benites V., president of UN General Assembly, 1973-74; #C541, Adofo H. Simmonds G. (1892-1969), journalists; #C542, Juan de Dios Martinez Mera, President of Ecuador, birth centenary.

C539 AP128 5s lilac rose   .45 .20
C540 AP128 5s gray   .45 .20
C541 AP128 5s violet   .45 .30
C542 AP128 5s blk & rose red   .45 .20
   Nos. C539-C542 (4)   1.80 .90

Pres. Guillermo Rodriguez
Lara — AP129

1975   **Unwmk.**   **Perf. 12**
C546 AP129 5s vermilion & blk   .50 .30

State visit of Pres. Guillermo Rodriguez Lara to Algeria, Romania and Venezuela.

Meeting Type of 1975

1.50s, Rafael Rodriguez Palacios & Argelino Duran Quintero meeting at border in Rumichaca. 2s, Signing border agreement.

1975, Apr. 1   **Litho.**   **Perf. 12x11½**
C547 A273 1.50s multi   .25 .20
C548 A273 2s multi   .25 .20

Sacred Heart
(Painting)
AP130

Quito Cathedral
AP131

Design: 2s, Monstrance.

1975, Apr. 28   **Litho.**   **Perf. 12x11½**
C549 AP130 1.30s yel & multi   .20 .20
C550 AP130 2s bl & multi   .20 .20
C551 AP131 3s multi   .30 .20
   Nos. C549-C551 (3)   .70 .60

3rd Bolivarian Eucharistic Congress, Quito, June 9-16, 1974.

J. Delgado
Panchana with
Trophy — AP132

J. Delgado
Panchana
Swimming
AP133

Perf. 12x11½, 11½x12
1975, June 12   **Unwmk.**
C552 AP132 1.30s bl & multi   .20 .20
C553 AP133 3s blk & multi   .30 .20

Jorge Delgado Panchana, South American swimming champion, 1971 and 1974.

Sports Type of 1975

1975, Sept. 11   **Litho.**   **Perf. 11½**
C554 A276 1.30s Tennis   .45 .25
C555 A276 2s Target shooting   .45 .25
C556 A276 2.80s Volleyball   .55 .25
C557 A276 3s Raft with sails   .55 .25
C558 A276 5s Mask   .80 .25
   Nos. C554-C558 (5)   2.80 1.25

Flower Type of 1975

1975, Nov. 18   **Litho.**   **Perf. 11½x12**
C559 A277 1.30s Pitcairnia
       pungens   .25 .25
C560 A277 2s Scarlet sage   .40 .25
C561 A277 3s Amaryllis   .60 .35
C562 A277 4s Opuntia
       quitense   .85 .40
C563 A277 5s Amaryllis   1.25 .60
   Nos. C559-C563 (5)   3.35 1.85

Tail Assemblies
and
Emblem — AP134

Planes over Map
of
Ecuador — AP135

1975, Dec. 17   **Litho.**   **Perf. 11½**
C564 AP134 1.30s bl & multi   .30 .20
C565 AP135 3s multi   .35 .20

TAME, Military Transport Airline, 13th anniv.

Benalcázar
Statue — AP136

1976, Feb. 6   **Litho.**   **Perf. 11½**
C566 AP136 2s multi   .25 .20
C567 AP136 3s multi   .25 .20

Sebastián de Benalcázar (1495-1550), Spanish conquistador, founder of Quito.

Archaeology Type of 1975

1.30s, Seated man, Carchi Culture. 2s, Funerary urn, Tuncahuan Culture. 3s, Priest, Bahia de Caraquez Culture. 4s, Snail's shell, Cuasmal Culture. 5s, Bowl supported by figurines, Guangala Culture.

1976, Feb. 12   **Litho.**   **Perf. 11½**
C568 A278 1.30s multi   .20 .20
C569 A278 2s multi   .45 .20
C570 A278 3s multi   .65 .30
C571 A278 4s multi   .95 .30
C572 A278 5s multi   1.25 .30
   Nos. C568-C572 (5)   3.50 1.30

Fruit Type of 1976

1976, Mar. 30
C573 A280 2s Apples   .40 .20
C574 A280 5s Rose   .60 .20

Lufthansa
Jet — AP137

1976, June 25   **Litho.**   **Perf. 12**
C575 AP137 10s bl & multi   1.50 .35

Lufthansa, 50th anniversary.
An imperf. 20s miniature sheet exists, similar to No. C575 enlarged, with overprinted black bar covering line below "Lufthansa." Size: 90x115mm.

Projected PO,
Quito — AP138

Fruit
Peddler — AP139

1976, Aug. 10   **Litho.**   **Perf. 12**
C576 AP138 5s blk & multi   .30 .20

Design for new General Post Office, Quito.

1976, July 25

#C578, Longshoreman. #C579, Cerros del Carmen & Santa Ana, hills of Guayaquil, horiz. #C580, Sebastián de Belalcázar. #C581, Francisco de Orellana. #C582, Chief Guayas & his wife Quila.

C577 AP139 1.30s red & multi   .20 .20
C578 AP139 1.30s red & multi   .20 .20
C579 AP139 1.30s red & multi   .20 .20
C580 AP139 2s red & multi   .20 .20
C581 AP139 2s red & multi   .20 .20
C582 AP139 2s red & multi   .20 .20
   Nos. C577-C582 (6)   1.20 1.20

Founding of Quayaquil, 441st anniversary.

Emblem and
Laurel
AP140

1976, Aug. 9
C583 AP140 1.30s yel & multi   .25 .20

Bolivarian Soc. of Ecuador, 50th anniv.

Western
Hemisphere and
Equator
Monument
AP141

Congress Emblem
AP142

1976, Sept. 6
C584 AP141 2s multi   .25 .20

Souvenir Sheet
Imperf
C585 AP141 5s multi   3.25 3.25

3rd Conf. of Pan-American Transport Ministers, Quito, Sept. 6-11. No. C585 contains design similar to No. C584 with black denomination and red control number in margin.

1976, Sept. 27   **Litho.**   *Perf. 11½*
C586 AP142 1.30s bl & multi   .30 .20
C587 AP142 3s bl & multi   .40 .30

Souvenir Sheet
Imperf
C588 AP142 10s bl & multi   1.50 1.00

10th Inter-American Congress of the Construction Industry, Quito, Sept. 27-30.

George Washington AP143

American Bicentennial: 5s, Naval battle, Sept. 23, 1779, in which the Bonhomme Richard, commanded by John Paul Jones, defeated and captured the Serapis, British man-of-war, off Yorkshire coast, horiz.

1976, Oct. 18   **Litho.**   *Perf. 12*
C589 AP143 3s blk & multi   .60 .30
C590 AP143 5s red brn & yel   .90 .45

Dr. Hideyo Noguchi — AP144   Luis Cordero — AP145

1976   **Litho.**   *Perf. 11½*
C591 AP144 3s yel & multi   .35 .20

Dr. Hideyo Noguchi (1876-1928), bacteriologist (at Rockefeller Institute). A 10s imperf. miniature sheet in same design exists without "Aereo." Size: 95x114mm. Value $6.

1976, Dec.   **Litho.**   *Perf. 11½*
C592 AP145 2s multi   .25 .20

Luis Cordero (1833-1912), president of Ecuador.

Mariuxi Febres Cordero — AP146

1976, Dec.   *Perf. 11½*
C593 AP146 3s multi   .25 .20

Mariuxi Febres Cordero, South American swimming champion.

Flags and Monument AP147

1976, Nov. 9   *Perf. 12*
C594 AP147 3s multi   .25 .20

Miniature Sheet
Imperf
C595 AP147 5s multi   2.50 1.50

2nd Meeting of the Agriculture Ministers of the Andean Countries, Quito, Nov. 8-10.

Sister Catalina — AP148   Congress Hall, Quito — AP149

1977, June 17   **Litho.**   *Perf. 12x11½*
C596 AP148 1.30s blk & pale salmon   .30 .20

Sister Catalina de Jesus Herrera (1717-1795), writer.

1977, Aug. 15   **Litho.**   *Perf. 12x11½*
C597 AP149 5s multi   .45 .20
   a.   10s souvenir sheet   1.50 1.50

11th General Assembly of Pan-American Institute of Geography and History, Quito, Aug. 15-30. No. C597a contains the designs of types A282 and AP149 without denominations and with simulated perforations.

Pres. Alfonso López Michelsen, Flag of Colombia — AP150

Designs: 5s, Pres. López M. of Colombia, Pres. Alfredo Povedo B. of Ecuador and aide. 7s, as 5s, vert. 9s, 10s, Presidents with aides.

1977   *Perf. 12*
C598 AP150 2.60s multi   .45 .20
C599 AP150 5s multi   .65 .25
C600 AP150 7s multi   .70 .35
C601 AP150 9s multi   1.10 .55

Imperf
C602 AP150 10s multi   .85 .70
   Nos. C598-C602 (5)   3.75 2.05

Meeting of the Presidents of Ecuador and Colombia and Declaration of Putumayo, Feb. 25, 1977. Nos. C598-C602 are overprinted in multiple fluorescent, colorless rows: INSTITUTO GEOGRAFICO MILITAR GOBIERNO DEL ECUADOR.

Ceramic Figure, Tolita Culture AP151

9s, Divine Shepherdess, sculpture by Bernardo de Legarda. 11s, The Fruit Seller, sculpture by Legarda. 20s, Sun God, pre-Columbian gold mask.

1977, Aug. 24   *Perf. 12*
C603 AP151 7s gold & multi   1.25 .40
C604 AP151 9s gold & multi   1.60 .45
C605 AP151 11s gold & multi   2.10 1.00
   Nos. C603-C605 (3)   4.95 1.85

Souvenir Sheet
Gold Embossed
Imperf
C606 AP151 20s vio, bl, blk & gold   8.00 4.25

Central Bank of Ecuador, 50th anniversary. Nos. C603-C605 overprinted like Nos. C598-C602.

Lungs — AP152   Brother Miguel, St. Peter's, Rome — AP153

1977, Oct. 5   **Litho.**   *Perf. 12x11½*
C607 AP152 2.60s multi   .30 .25

3rd Cong. of the Bolivarian Pneumonic Soc. and cent. of the founding of the medical faculty of the University of Guayaquil.

1977
C608 AP153 2.60s multi   .25 .20

Beatification of Brother Miguel.

Peralta Type
2.60s, Titles of works by Peralta & his bookmark.

1977   *Perf. 11½*
C609 A284 2.60s multi   .35 .25

Broadcast Tower — AP154   Remigio Romero y Cordero — AP155

1977, Dec. 2   **Litho.**   *Perf. 12x11½*
C610 AP154 5s multi   .35 .35

9th World Telecommunications Day.

1978, Mar. 2   **Litho.**   *Perf. 12½x11½*
C611 AP155 3s multi   .30 .20
C612 AP155 10.60s multi   .45 .25

Imperf
C612A AP155 10s multi   1.10 1.10
   Nos. C611-C612A (3)   1.85 1.55

Remigio Romero y Cordero (1895-1967), poet.
No. C612A contains a vignette similar to Nos. C611-C612.

Dr. Vicente Corral Moscoso AP156   Faces AP157

5s, Hospital emblem with Caduceus.

1978, Apr. 12   **Litho.**   *Imperf.*
C613 AP156 5s multi   .55 .30
     Perf. 12x11½
C614 AP156 7.60s multi   .95 .50

Inauguration (in 1977) of Dr. Vicente Corral Moscoso Regional Hospital, Cuenca.

1978, Mar. 17

Designs: 9s, Emblems and flags of Ecuador. 10s, 11s, Hands reaching for light.
C615 AP157 7s multicolored   .60 .20
C616 AP157 9s multicolored   .85 .20
C617 AP157 11s multicolored   1.00 .20

Imperf
C618 AP157 10s multicolored   1.00 1.00
   Nos. C615-C618 (4)   3.45 1.60

Ecuadorian Social Security Institute, 50th anniv.

Geographical Institute Type
7.60s, Plane over map of Ecuador with mountains.

1978, Apr. 12   **Litho.**   *Perf. 11½*
C619 A287 7.60s multi   .90 .50

Imperf
C620 A287 10s multi   1.40 1.40

No. C620 contains 2 vignettes with simulated perforations in designs of Nos. 967 and C619.

Lions Type
1978   *Perf. 11½*
C621 A288 5s multi   .65 .25
C622 A288 6.20s multi   1.00 .40

Imperf
C623 A288 10s multi   2.50 2.50
   Nos. C621-C623 (3)   4.15 3.15

No. C623 contains a vignette similar to Nos. C621-C622.

San Martin — AP158

1978, Apr. 13   **Litho.**   *Perf. 12*
C624 AP158 10.60s multi   1.40 .50

Imperf
C625 AP158 10s multi   1.40 1.40

Gen. José de San Martin (1778-1850), soldier and statesman. No. C625 contains a vignette similar to No. C624.

Bank Type
Design: 5s, Bank emblem.

1978, Sept.   **Litho.**   *Perf. 11½*
C626 A289 5s gray & multi   .30 .20

Soccer Type
Designs: 2.60s, "Gauchito" and Games' emblem. 5s, "Gauchito." 7s, Soccer ball. 9s, Games' emblem, vert. 10s, Games' emblem.

1978, Nov. 1   *Perf. 12*
C627 A290 2.60s multi   .30 .20
C628 A290 7s multi   .80 .40
C629 A290 9s multi   1.10 .65

Imperf
C630 A290 5s blk & bl   6.00 6.00
C631 A290 10s blk & bl   6.00 6.00
   Nos. C627-C631 (5)   14.20 13.25

Bernardo
O'Higgins
AP159

Old Men of
Vilcabamba
AP160

1978, Nov. 11   Litho.   Perf. 12x11½
C632 AP159 10.60s multi   .70 .30

Imperf
C633 AP159   10s multi   1.50 .90

Gen. Bernardo O'Higgins (1778-1842), Chilean soldier and statesman. No. C633 contains a vignette similar to No. C632.

1978, Nov. 11   Perf. 12x11½
C634 AP160 5s multi   .50 .30

Vilcabamba, valley of longevity.

Humphrey
AP161

Virgin and Child
AP162

1978, Nov. 27   Litho.   Perf. 12x11½
C635 AP61 5s multi   .50 .30

Hubert H. Humphrey (1911-1978), Vice President of the US.

1978

Children's Drawings: 4.60s, Holy Family. 6.20s, Candle and children.

C636 AP162 2.20s multi   .20 .20
C637 AP162 4.60s multi   .45 .25
C638 AP162 6.20s multi   .75 .35
    Nos. C636-C638 (3)   1.40 .80

Christmas 1978.

Village, by
Anibal Villacis
AP163

Ecuadorian Painters: No. C640, Mountain Village, by Gilberto Almeida. No. C641, Bay, by Roura Oxandaberro. No. C642, Abstract, by Luis Molinari. No. C643, Statue, by Oswaldo Viteri. No. C644, Tools, by Enrique Tabara.

1978, Dec. 9   Perf. 12
C639 AP163 5s multi   .50 .25
C640 AP163 5s multi   .50 .25
C641 AP163 5s multi   .50 .25
C642 AP163 5s multi   .50 .25
C643 AP163 5s multi   .50 .25
C644 AP163 5s multi   .50 .25
    Nos. C639-C644 (6)   3.00 1.50

House and
Monument
AP164

Design: 3.40s, Monument, vert.

1979, Feb. 27   Litho.   Perf. 12
C645 AP164 2.40s multi   .30 .20
C646 AP164 3.40s multi   .30 .20

Imperf
C647 AP164   10s multi   1.00 1.00
    Nos. C645-C647 (3)   1.60 1.40

Sesquicentennial of Battle of Portete and Tarqui. #C647 contains vignettes similar to #C645-C646.

Fish and
Ship — AP165

Flags of Ecuador
and
U.S. — AP166

7s, Map of Ecuador & Galapagos showing territorial waters. 9s, Map of South America with west-coast territorial waters.

Perf. 12x11½, 11½x12
1979, July 23   Litho.   Wmk. 367
C648 AP165 5s multi   .75 .25
C649 AP165 7s multi, horiz.   1.00 .35
C650 AP165 9s multi   1.40 .50
    Nos. C648-C650 (3)   3.15 1.10

Declaration of 200-mile territorial limit, 25th anniversary.

1979, Aug. 3   Perf. 12x11½
Designs: 10.60s, Bells in Quito clock tower, horiz. 13.60s, Aerial view of Galapagos coast.

C651 A293 10.60s multi   1.25 .60
C652 A293 13.60s multi   1.40 .75

Size: 115x91mm
Imperf
Unwmk.
C653 A293   10s multi   5.00 2.10
    Nos. C651-C653 (3)   7.65 3.45

National heritage: Quito and Galapagos Islands. No. C653 contains vignettes similar to Nos. 977, C651-C652.

1979, Aug.   Wmk. 367   Perf. 11½x12
C654 AP166 7.60s multi   .40 .40
C655 AP166 10.60s multi   .60 .60

Size: 115x91mm
Imperf
Unwmk.
C656 AP166   10s multi   1.00 .65
    Nos. C654-C656 (3)   2.00 1.65

5th anniv. of Ecuador-US Chamber of Commerce. No. C656 contains vignettes similar to Nos. C654-C655.

Smiling Girl, IYC
Emblem — AP167

Perf. 12x11½
1979, Sept. 7   Litho.   Wmk. 367
C657 AP167 10s multi   .80 .45

International Year of the Child.

Citizens and
Flag of
Ecuador
AP168

Design: 10.60s, Pres. Jaime Roldas Aguilera, flag of Ecuador, vert.

Perf. 11½
1979, Sept. 27   Litho.   Unwmk.
C658 AP168 7.60s multi   .85 .35

Wmk. 367
C659 AP168 10.60s multi   1.00 .30

Restoration of democracy to Ecuador.

Ecuador Coat of
Arms, Olympic
Rings and
Eagle — AP169

Perf. 12x11½
1979, Nov. 23   Unwmk.
C660 AP169 28s multi   2.00 1.25

5th National Games, Cuenca.

CIESPAL
Building,
Quito
AP170

Perf. 11½x12½
1979, Dec. 26   Wmk. 367
C661 AP170 10.60s multi   .70 .40

Opening of Ecuadorian Institute of Engineers building.

Olmedo Type
Perf. 12x11½
1980, Apr. 29   Litho.   Unwmk.
C662 A294 10s multi   1.00 .65

Tribal Chief Type

Indo-American Tribal Chiefs: #C663, Cuauhtemoc, Mexico. #C664, Lempira, Honduras. #C665, Nicaragua. #C666, Lambaré, Paraguay. #C667, Urraca, Panama. #C668, Anacaona, Haiti. #C669, Caupolican, Chile. #C670, Tacun-Uman, Guatemala. #C671, Calarca, Colombia. #C672, Garabito, Costa Rica. #C673, Hatuey, Cuba. #C674, Cmarao, Brazil. #C675, Tehuelche, Argentina. #C676, Tupaj Katri, Bolivia. 17.80s, Sequoyah, US. 22.80s, Ruminahui, Ecuador.

Wmk. 367 (#C663, C667), Unwmkd.
1980, May 12
C663 A295 7.60s multi   1.75 .35
C664 A295 7.60s multi   1.75 .35
C665 A295 7.60s multi   1.75 .35
C666 A295   10s multi   1.90 .40
C667 A295   10s multi   1.90 .40
C668 A295 10.60s multi   1.90 .40
C669 A295 10.60s multi   1.90 .40
C670 A295 10.60s multi   1.90 .40
C671 A295 12.80s multi   2.50 .55
C672 A295 12.80s multi   2.50 .55
C673 A295 12.80s multi   2.50 .55
C674 A295 13.60s multi   2.50 .55
C675 A295 13.60s multi   2.50 .55
C676 A295 13.60s multi   2.50 .55
C677 A295 17.80s multi   3.00 .65
C678 A295 22.80s multi   3.50 1.25
    Nos. C663-C678 (16)   36.25 8.25

Royal Visit Type
Perf. 11½x12
1980, May 18   Unwmk.
C679 A296 10.60s multi   .65 .40

Pichincha
Provincial
Development
Council
Building — AP171

1980, June 1   Perf. 12x11½
C680 AP171 10.60s multi   1.10 .50

Progress in Pichincha Province.

Indian Type
1980, June 10   Litho.   Perf. 12x11½
C681 A297 7.60s Salasaca boy,
    Tungurahua   1.10 .85
C682 A297   10s Amula woman, Chimborazo   1.25 .95
C683 A297 10.60s Canar woman, Canar   1.60 1.10
C684 A297 13.60s Colorado Indian, Pichincha   1.75 1.40
    Nos. C681-C684 (4)   5.70 4.30

Virgin of Mercy Type
1980, July 7   Litho.   Perf. 11½
C685 A298 7.60s Cupola, cloisters   .90 .50
C686 A298 7.60s Gold screen   .90 .50
C687 A298 7.60s Quito from basilica tower   .90 .50
C688 A298 10.60s Retable   1.10 .50
C689 A298 10.60s Pulpit   1.10 .50
C690 A298 13.60s Cupola   1.60 .75
C691 A298 13.60s Statue of Virgin   1.60 .75
    Nos. C685-C691 (7)   8.10 4.00

UPU Monument
AP172

Marshal Sucre, by
Marco Sales
AP173

Design: 17.80s, Mail box, 1880.

1980, July 7   Perf. 12
C692 AP172 10.60s multi   1.25 .65
C693 AP172 17.80s multi   2.25 1.00

Souvenir Sheet
C694 AP172   25s multi   3.00 2.50

UPU membership cent. No. C694 contains designs of C692 and C693, horiz., perf. 11½.

Olympic Type.

Design: 10.60s, 13.60s, Moscow '80 emblem, Olympic rings.

Perf. 12x11½
1980, July 19   Wmk. 395
C695 A299 10.60s multi   .75 .55
C696 A299 13.60s multi   1.25 .75

Souvenir Sheet
C697 A299   30s multi   6.75 6.75

No. C697 contains vignettes in designs of Nos. 991 and C695.

1980
C698 AP173 10.60s multi   .70 .50

Marshal Antonio Jose de Sucre, death sesquicentennial.

Rotary
International, 75th
Anniversary
AP174

1980, Aug. 4   Perf. 11½
C699 AP174 10s multi   1.25 .55

Riobamba Type

Design: 7.60s, 10.60s, Monstrance, Riobamba Cathedral, vert.

1980, Sept. 20   Litho.   Perf. 11½
C700 A301 7.60s multi   .70 .40
C701 A301 10.60s multi   1.00 .45

Souvenir Sheet
Imperf
C702 A301   30s multi   1.90 1.90

No. C702 contains vignettes in designs of Nos. 996 and C701.

Democracy Type

7.60s, 10.60s, Pres. Aguilera and voter.

Perf. 12x11½
1980, Oct. 9   Litho.   Wmk. 395
C703 A302 7.60s multi   1.00 .55
C704 A302 10.60s multi   1.25 .60

Souvenir Sheet
Imperf
C705 A302 15s multi   1.10 1.10

No. C705 contains vignettes in designs of Nos. 999 and C703.

OPEC Type

20th Anniversary of OPEC: 7.60s, Men holding OPEC emblem, vert.

1980, Nov. 8   Perf. 11½x12
C706 A303 7.60s multi   .55 .45

Carchi Province Type

10.60s, Governor's Palace, vert. 17.80s, Victory Museum, Central Square, vert.

1980, Nov. 21   Perf. 13
C707 A304 10.60c multi   1.25 .65
C708 A304 17.80s multi   2.00 1.00

Orchid Type

Perf. 12x11½, 11½x12
1980, Nov. 22
C709 A305 7.60s *Anguloa uniflora*   2.75 .70
C710 A305 10.60s *Scuticaria salesiana* 3.50 .45
C711 A305 50s *Helcia sanguinolenta*, vert.   5.75 1.40
C712 A305 100s *Anguloa virginalis*   7.75 2.75
Nos. C709-C712 (4)   19.75 5.30

Souvenir Sheets
Imperf
C713 A305 20s multi   7.50 5.25
C714 A305 20s multi   7.50 5.25

Nos. C713-C714 contain vignettes in designs of Nos. C709, C711 and C710, C712 respectively.

Christmas Type

7.60s, Pope blessing crowd. 10.60s, Portrait.

1980, Dec. 27   Perf. 12
C715 A306 7.60s multi, vert.   .95 .50
C716 A306 10.60s multi, vert.   1.25 .60

Isidro Cueva — AP175

Simon Bolivar, by Marco Salas — AP176

1980, Nov. 20   Perf. 13
C717 AP175 18.20s multi   2.25 1.10

Dr. Isidro Ayora Cueva, former president, birth centenary.

1980, Dec. 17   Perf. 11½
C718 AP176 13.60s multi   1.75 .90

Simon Bolivar death sesquicentennial.

Turtle, Galapagos Islands AP177

100s, Oldest Ecuadorian mail box, 1793.

1981, Feb. 12   Litho.   Perf. 13
C719 AP177 50s multi   6.50 4.25
C720 AP177 100s multi, vert. 8.00 5.50

HCJB Type

1981   Litho.   Perf. 13
C721 A311 7.60s Emblem, horiz. 1.00 .55
C722 A311 10.60s Emblem, diff. 1.40 .70

Soccer Players — AP178

1981, July 8
C723 AP178 7.60s Emblem   1.00 .60
C724 AP178 10.60s shown   1.25 .60
C725 AP178 13.60s World Cup 1.60 .90
Nos. C723-C725 (3)   3.85 2.10

Souvenir Sheets
C726 AP178 20s multi   3.25 3.25
C727 AP178 20s multi   3.25 3.25

1982 World Cup Soccer Championship. Nos. C726-C727 contain vignettes in designs of Nos. C723 and C724 respectively.

Picasso Type

1981, Oct. 26   Litho.   Perf. 13
C728 A313a 7.60s Still-life   .75 .40
C729 A313a 10.60s First Communion, vert.   .95 .50
C730 A313a 13.60s Las Meninas, vert.   1.10 .70

Size: 110x90mm
Imperf
C731 A313a 20s multi   2.50 2.50
Nos. C728-C731 (4)   5.30 4.10

No. C731 contains designs of Nos. C730, C729.

World Food Day Type

1981, Dec. 31   Litho.   Perf. 13x13½
C732 A314 10.60s Farming, vert. 1.25 .60

IYD Type

1982, Feb. 25   Litho.   Perf. 13
C733 A316 7.60s Emblem   .70 .40
C734 A316 10.60s Man with crutch .90 .45

Montalvo Type

1982   Litho.   Perf. 13
C735 A318 5s Home, horiz.   1.00 .55

Swimming Type

1982, July 30
C736 A320 10.20s Emblem, vert. .85 .40
C737 A320 14.20s Diving, vert. 1.10 .45

Pres. Jaime Roldos, (1940-81), Mrs. Martha Roldos, Independence Monument, Quito — AP179

1983, May 25   Litho.   Perf. 12
C738 AP179 13.60s multi   .65 .50

Souvenir Sheet
Imperf
C739 AP179 20s multi   2.00 2.00

AIR POST SEMI-POSTAL STAMPS

Nos. C119-C123 Surcharged in Blue or Red:

1944, May 9   Unwmk.   Perf. 12
CB1 AP26 50c + 50c   6.50 3.25
CB2 AP26 70c + 30c   6.50 3.25
CB3 AP26 3s + 50c (R)   6.50 3.25
CB4 AP26 5s + 1s (R)   6.50 3.25
CB5 AP26 10s + 2s   6.50 3.25
Nos. CB1-CB5 (5)   32.50 16.25

The surtax aided Mendez Hospital.

AIR POST REGISTRATION STAMPS

Issued by Sociedad Colombo-Alemana de Transportes Aereos (SCADTA)

Nos. C3 and C3a Overprinted "R" in Carmine

1928-29   Wmk. 116   Perf. 14x14½
CF1 AP6 1s on 20c (#C3)   110.00 100.00
a. 1s on 20c (#C3a) ('29) 140.00 110.00

No. C18 Overprinted "R" in Black

1929, Apr. 1   Wmk. 127   Perf. 14
CF2 AP2 1s rose   75.00 55.00

AIR POST OFFICIAL STAMPS

Nos. C8-C15 Overprinted in Red or Black

1929, May   Unwmk.   Perf. 12
CO1 AP1 2c black (R)   1.00 .50
CO2 AP1 5c carmine rose   1.00 .50
CO3 AP1 10c deep brown   1.00 .50
CO4 AP1 20c dark violet   1.00 .50
CO5 AP1 50c deep green   4.00 2.00
CO6 AP1 1s dark blue   4.00 2.00
a. Inverted overprint   240.00
CO7 AP1 5s orange yellow   18.00 7.75
CO8 AP1 10s orange red   210.00 75.00
Nos. CO1-CO8 (8)   240.00 88.75

Establishment of commercial air service in Ecuador.
Counterfeits of No. CO8 exist.
See Nos. CO9-CO12. For overprints and surcharges see Nos. C35-C38.

1930, Jan. 9
CO9 AP1 50c olive brown   3.50 1.75
CO10 AP1 1s carmine lake   4.50 2.25
CO11 AP1 5s olive green   11.00 5.50
CO12 AP1 10s black   21.00 10.50
Nos. CO9-CO12 (4)   40.00 20.00

For surcharges and overprint see Nos. C36-C38.

Air Post Stamps of 1937 Overprinted in Black

1937, Aug. 19
CO13 AP7 10c chestnut   .50 .20
CO14 AP7 20c olive black   .50 .20
CO15 AP7 70c black brown   .60 .20
CO16 AP7 1s gray black   .70 .20
CO17 AP7 2s dark violet   .70 .30
Nos. CO13-CO17 (5)   3.00 1.10

For overprints see Nos. 463-464.

No. C79 Overprinted in Black

1940, Aug. 1   Perf. 12½x13
CO18 AP15 5s emerald   1.75 .60

> Catalogue values for unused stamps in this section, from this point to the end of the section, are for Never Hinged items.

Nos. C352-C354 Overprinted: "1961 oficial"

1964   Perf. 13½
CO19 AP86 50c multi   1.75 .85
CO20 AP86 80c multi   1.75 .85
CO21 AP86 1.30s multi   1.75 .85
Nos. CO19-CO21 (3)   5.25 2.55

SPECIAL DELIVERY STAMPS

SD1

1928   Unwmk.   Perf. 12
E1 SD1 2c on 2c blue   8.00 9.00
E2 SD1 5c on 2c blue   7.00 9.00
E3 SD1 10c on 2c blue   7.00 6.00
a. "10 CTVOS" inverted   21.00 25.00
E4 SD1 20c on 2c blue   10.00 9.00
E5 SD1 50c on 2c blue   12.00 9.00
Nos. E1-E5 (5)   44.00 42.00

No. RA49A Surcharged in Red

1945
E6 PT18 20c on 5c green   3.00 2.00

LATE FEE STAMP

No. RA49A Surcharged in Black

1945   Unwmk.   Perf. 12
I1 PT18 10c on 5c green   1.00 1.00

POSTAGE DUE STAMPS

Numeral — D1   Coat of Arms — D2

1896   Engr.   Wmk. 117   Perf. 12
J1 D1 1c blue green   6.00 6.50
J2 D1 2c blue green   6.00 6.50
J3 D1 5c blue green   6.00 6.50
J4 D1 10c blue green   6.00 6.50
J5 D1 20c blue green   6.00 8.50

J6	D1	50c blue green	6.00	13.00
J7	D1	100c blue green	6.00	17.00
		Nos. J1-J7 (7)	42.00	64.50

Reprints are on very thick paper with distinct watermark and vertical paper-weave direction. Value 15c each.

Unwmk.

J8	D1	1c blue green	5.00	6.00
J9	D1	2c blue green	5.00	6.00
J10	D1	5c blue green	5.00	6.00
J11	D1	10c blue green	5.00	6.00
J12	D1	20c blue green	5.00	7.50
J13	D1	50c blue green	5.00	10.50
J14	D1	100c blue green	5.00	15.00
		Nos. J8-J14 (7)	35.00	57.00

1929

J15	D2	5c deep blue	.40	.40
J16	D2	10c orange yellow	.40	.40
J17	D2	20c red	.60	.60
		Nos. J15-J17 (3)	1.40	1.40

Numeral — D3

Perf. 13½

1958, Nov. Unwmk. Litho.

J18	D3	10c bright lilac	.50	.40
J19	D3	1s maroon	.50	.40
J20	D3	1s maroon	.60	.40
J21	D3	2s red	.70	.40
		Nos. J18-J21 (4)	2.30	1.60

OFFICIAL STAMPS

Regular Issues of 1881 and 1887 Handstamped in Black

1886 Unwmk. Perf. 12

O1	A5	1c yellow brown	2.50	2.50
O2	A6	2c lake	3.00	3.00
O3	A7	5c blue	6.75	8.75
O4	A8	10c orange	5.25	3.25
O5	A9	20c gray violet	5.25	5.25
O6	A10	50c blue green	15.00	11.50
		Nos. O1-O6 (6)	37.75	34.25

1887

O7	A12	1c green	3.25	2.50
O8	A13	2c vermilion	3.25	3.25
O9	A14	5c blue	5.25	2.50
O10	A15	80c olive green	17.50	10.00
		Nos. O7-O10 (4)	29.25	18.25

Nos. O1-O10 are known with red handstamp but these are believed to be speculative.

The overprint on the 1886-87 issues is handstamped and is found in various positions.

Flores — O1   Arms — O1a

1892

Carmine Overprint

O11	O1	1c ultramarine	.20	.40
O12	O1	2c ultramarine	.20	.40
O13	O1	5c ultramarine	.20	.40
O14	O1	10c ultramarine	.20	.60
O15	O1	20c ultramarine	.20	.90
O16	O1	50c ultramarine	.20	.90
O17	O1	1s ultramarine	.35	1.00
		Nos. O11-O17 (7)	1.55	4.60

1894

O18	O1a	1c slate green (R)	15.00	
O19	O1a	2c lake (Bk)	20.00	

Nos. O18 and O19 were not placed in use.

Rocafuerte

Dated 1894

1894

Carmine Overprint

O20	O2	1c gray black	.60	1.00
O21	O2	2c gray black	.60	.60
O22	O2	5c gray black	.60	.60
O23	O2	10c gray black	.75	1.00
O24	O2	20c gray black	1.00	1.00
O25	O2	50c gray black	3.75	3.75
O26	O2	1s gray black	6.00	6.00
		Nos. O20-O26 (7)	13.30	13.95

Dated 1895

1895

Carmine Overprint

O27	O2	1c gray black	5.25	5.25
O28	O2	2c gray black	7.50	7.50
O29	O2	5c gray black	1.50	1.50
O30	O2	10c gray black	7.50	7.50
O31	O2	20c gray black	11.00	10.50
O32	O2	50c gray black	75.00	75.00
O33	O2	1s gray black	3.75	3.75
		Nos. O27-O33 (7)	111.50	111.00

Reprints of 1894-95 issues are on very thick paper with paper weave found both horizontal and vertical for all denominations. Values: Nos. O20-O26, 35c each; O27-O33, 20c each. Generally they are blacker than originals. For overprints see Nos. O50-O91.

Types of 1896 Overprinted in Carmine

1896 Wmk. 117

O34	A21	1c olive bister	1.00	1.00
O35	A22	2c olive bister	1.00	1.00
O36	A23	5c olive bister	1.00	1.00
O37	A24	10c olive bister	1.00	1.00
O38	A25	20c olive bister	1.00	1.00
O39	A26	50c olive bister	1.00	1.00
O40	A27	1s olive bister	3.00	3.00
O41	A28	5s olive bister	6.00	6.00
		Nos. O34-O41 (8)	15.00	15.00

Reprints of Nos. O34-O41 are on thick paper with vertical paper weave direction.

Unwmk.

O42	A21	1c olive bister	3.00	3.00
O43	A22	2c olive bister	3.00	3.00
O44	A23	5c olive bister	3.00	3.00
O45	A24	10c olive bister	3.00	3.00
O46	A25	20c olive bister	3.00	3.00
O47	A26	50c olive bister	3.00	3.00
O48	A27	1s olive bister	7.50	7.50
O49	A28	5s olive bister	10.50	10.50
		Nos. O42-O49 (8)	36.00	36.00

Reprints of Nos. O42-O49 all have overprint in black. Value 20 cents each.

#O20-O26 Overprinted

1897 1898

1897-98

O50	O2	1c gray black	20.00	20.00
O51	O2	2c gray black	35.00	35.00
O52	O2	5c gray black	200.00	200.00
O53	O2	10c gray black	30.00	30.00
O54	O2	20c gray black	20.00	20.00
O55	O2	50c gray black	35.00	35.00
O56	O2	1s gray black	55.00	55.00
		Nos. O50-O56 (7)	395.00	395.00

#O20-O26 Overprinted

1897 1898

O57	O2	1c gray black	4.00	4.00
O58	O2	2c gray black	9.00	9.00
O59	O2	5c gray black	90.00	90.00
O60	O2	10c gray black	100.00	100.00
O61	O2	20c gray black	25.00	25.00
O62	O2	50c gray black	15.00	15.00
O63	O2	1s gray black	165.00	165.00
		Nos. O57-O63 (7)	408.00	408.00

#O20-O26 Overprinted   **1897 y 1898**

O64	O2	1c gray black	40.00	40.00
O65	O2	2c gray black	40.00	40.00
O66	O2	5c gray black	40.00	40.00
O67	O2	10c gray black	40.00	40.00
O68	O2	20c gray black	40.00	40.00
O69	O2	50c gray black	40.00	40.00
O70	O2	1s gray black	40.00	40.00
		Nos. O64-O70 (7)	280.00	280.00

#O27-O33 Overprinted in Black like Nos. O50-O56

O71	O2	1c gray black	20.00	20.00
O72	O2	2c gray black	20.00	20.00
O73	O2	5c gray black	20.00	20.00
O74	O2	10c gray black	20.00	20.00
O75	O2	20c gray black	30.00	30.00
O76	O2	50c gray black	275.00	275.00
O77	O2	1s gray black	100.00	100.00
		Nos. O71-O77 (7)	485.00	485.00

#O27-O33 Overprinted like #O57-O63

O78	O2	1c gray black	35.00	35.00
O79	O2	2c gray black	30.00	30.00
O80	O2	5c gray black	30.00	30.00
O81	O2	10c gray black	32.50	32.50
O82	O2	20c gray black	42.50	42.50
O83	O2	50c gray black	30.00	30.00
O84	O2	1s gray black	30.00	30.00
		Nos. O78-O84 (7)	230.00	230.00

#O27-O33 Overprinted like #O64-O70

O85	O2	1c gray black	90.00	90.00
O86	O2	2c gray black	20.00	20.00
O87	O2	5c gray black	80.00	80.00
O88	O2	10c gray black	80.00	80.00
O89	O2	20c gray black	140.00	140.00
O90	O2	50c gray black	85.00	85.00
O91	O2	1s gray black	165.00	165.00
		Nos. O85-O91 (7)	660.00	660.00

Many forged overprints of Nos. O50-O91 exist, made on the original stamps and reprints.

O3

Black Surcharge

1898-99 Perf. 15, 16

O92	O3	5c on 50c lilac	10.00	10.00
a.	Inverted surcharge		25.00	25.00
O93	O3	10c on 20s org	15.00	15.00
a.	Double surcharge		40.00	30.00
O94	O3	10c on 50c lilac	140.00	140.00
O95	O3	10c on 50c lilac	30.00	30.00
O96	O3	20c on 50s green	30.00	30.00
		Nos. O92-O96 (5)	225.00	225.00

Green Surcharge

O97	O3	5c on 50c lilac	10.00	10.00
a.	Double surcharge		5.00	
b.	Double surcharge, blk and grn		12.00	
c.	Same as "b," blk surch. invtd.		5.00	

Red Surcharge

1899

O98	O3	5c on 50c lilac	10.00	10.00
a.	Double surcharge		20.00	
b.	Dbl. surch., blk and red		25.00	
O99	O3	20c on 50s green	15.00	15.00
a.	Inverted surcharge		40.00	
b.	Dbl. surch., red and blk		60.00	

Similar Surcharge in Black Value in Words in Two Lines

O100	O3	1c on 5c blue	650.00	

Red Surcharge

O101	O3	2c on 5c blue	1,150.	
O102	O3	4c on 20c blue	800.00	

Types of Regular Issue of 1899 Overprinted in Black

1899 Perf. 14, 15

O103	A37	2c orange & blk	.70	1.60
O104	A39	10c orange & blk	.70	1.60
O105	A40	20c orange & blk	.50	2.50
O106	A41	50c orange & blk	.50	3.25
		Nos. O103-O106 (4)	2.40	8.95

For overprint see No. O167.

The above overprint was applied to remainders of the postage stamps of 1904 with the idea of increasing their salability. They were never regularly in use as official stamps.

Regular Issue of 1911-13 Overprinted in Black

1913 Perf. 12

O107	A71	1c scarlet & blk	3.50	3.50
O108	A72	2c blue & blk	3.50	3.50
O109	A73	3c orange & blk	2.25	2.25
O110	A74	5c scarlet & blk	4.50	4.50
O111	A75	10c blue & blk	4.50	4.50
		Nos. O107-O111 (5)	18.25	18.25

Regular Issue of 1911-13 Overprinted

Overprint 22x3½mm

1916-17

O112	A72	2c blue & blk	25.00	18.00
O113	A74	5c scarlet & blk	25.00	18.00
O114	A75	10c blue & blk	15.00	12.00
		Nos. O112-O114 (3)	65.00	48.00

Overprint 25x4mm

O115	A71	1c scarlet & blk	1.10	1.10
O116	A72	2c blue & blk	1.60	1.60
a.	Inverted overprint		5.00	5.00
O117	A73	3c orange & blk	1.00	1.00
O118	A74	5c scarlet & blk	1.60	1.60
O119	A75	10c blue & blk	1.60	1.60
		Nos. O115-O119 (5)	6.90	6.90

Same Overprint On Regular Issue of 1915-17

O120	A71	1c orange	1.40	1.40
O121	A72	2c green	1.40	1.40
O122	A73	3c black	2.25	2.25
O123	A78	4c red & blk	2.25	2.25
a.	Inverted overprint		15.00	
O124	A74	5c violet	1.40	1.40
O125	A75	10c blue	2.75	2.75
O126	A79	20c green & blk	15.00	15.00
		Nos. O120-O126 (7)	26.45	26.45

Regular Issues of 1911-17 Overprinted in Black or Red

O127	A71	1c orange	.90	.90
O128	A72	2c green	.70	.70
O129	A73	3c black (Bk)	.90	.90
O130	A73	3c black (R)	.90	.70
a.	Inverted overprint			
O131	A78	4c red & blk	.90	.90
O132	A74	5c violet	1.75	.90
O133	A75	10c blue & blk	4.50	1.75
O134	A75	10c blue	.90	.90
O135	A79	20c green & blk	4.50	1.75
		Nos. O127-O135 (9)	15.95	9.40

Regular Issue of
1920 Overprinted

1920

O136	A86	1c green	1.25	1.25
a.		Inverted overprint	17.00	—
O137	A86	2c carmine	1.00	1.00
O138	A86	3c yellow brn	1.25	1.25
O139	A86	4c dark green	2.00	2.00
a.		Inverted overprint	17.00	—
O140	A86	5c blue	2.00	2.00
O141	A86	6c orange	1.25	1.25
O142	A86	7c brown	2.00	2.00
O143	A86	8c yellow green	2.50	2.50
O144	A86	9c red	3.25	3.25
O145	A95	10c blue	2.00	2.00
O146	A86	15c gray	11.00	11.00
O147	A86	20c deep violet	14.50	14.50
O148	A86	30c violet	17.00	17.00
O149	A86	40c dark brown	21.00	21.00
O150	A86	50c dark green	14.50	14.50
O151	A86	60c dark blue	17.00	17.00
O152	A86	70c gray	17.00	17.00
O153	A86	80c yellow	21.00	21.00
O154	A104	90c green	21.00	21.00
O155	A86	1s blue	45.00	45.00
		Nos. O136-O155 (20)	217.50	217.50

Cent. of the independence of Guayaquil.

Stamps of 1911
Overprinted

1922

O156	A71	1c scarlet & blk	9.00	9.00
O157	A72	2c blue & blk	4.50	4.50

Revenue Stamps of 1919-1920
Overprinted like Nos. O156 and O157

1924

O158	PT3	1c dark blue	2.00	2.00
O159	PT3	2c green	12.50	12.50

Regular Issues of
1911-17 Overprinted

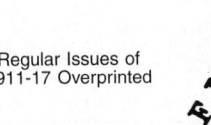

1924

O160	A71	1c orange	7.00	7.00
a.		Inverted overprint	15.00	

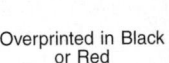

Overprinted in Black
or Red

O161	A72	2c green	.60	.60
O162	A73	3c black (R)	.80	.80
O163	A78	4c red & blk	1.25	1.25
O164	A74	5c violet	1.25	1.25
O165	A75	10c deep blue	1.25	1.25
O166	A76	1s green & blk	7.00	7.00
		Nos. O160-O166 (7)	19.15	19.15

No. O106 with
Additional Overprint

1924 *Perf. 14, 15*

O167	A41	50c orange & blk	2.25	2.25

Nos. O160-O167 exist with inverted
overprint.

No. 199 Overprinted

1924 *Perf. 12*

O168	A71	1c orange	5.50	5.50

Regular Issues of
1911-25 Overprinted

1925

O169	A71	1c scarlet & blk	10.00	4.25
a.		Inverted overprint	15.00	
O170	A71	1c orange	.60	.60
a.		Inverted overprint	4.00	
O171	A72	2c green	.60	.60
a.		Inverted overprint	4.00	
O172	A73	3c black (Bk)	.60	.60
O173	A73	3c black (R)	1.10	1.10
O174	A78	4c red & blk	.60	.60
O175	A74	5c violet	.80	.80
O176	A74	5c rose	.80	.80
O177	A75	10c deep blue	.60	.60
		Nos. O169-O177 (9)	15.70	9.95

Regular Issues of 1916-25 Overprinted
Vertically Up or Down

1927, Oct.

O178	A71	1c orange	2.00	2.00
O179	A86	2c carmine	2.00	2.00
O180	A86	3c yellow brown	2.00	2.00
O181	A86	4c myrtle green	2.00	2.00
O182	A86	5c pale blue	2.00	2.00
O183	A75	10c yellow green	2.00	2.00
		Nos. O178-O183 (6)	12.00	12.00

Regular Issues of
1920-27 Overprinted

1928

O184	A71	1c lt blue	1.25	1.25
O185	A86	2c carmine	1.25	1.25
O186	A86	3c yellow brown	1.25	1.25
a.		Inverted overprint	5.00	
O187	A86	4c myrtle green	1.25	1.25
O188	A86	5c lt blue	1.25	1.25
O189	A75	10c yellow green	1.25	1.25
O190	A109	20c violet	11.00	2.50
a.		Overprint reading up	3.50	2.25
		Nos. O184-O190 (7)	18.50	10.00

The overprint is placed vertically reading
down on No. O190.

Regular Issue of 1936
Overprinted in Black

1936 *Perf. 14*

O191	A131	5c olive green	1.50	1.50
O192	A132	10c brown	1.50	1.50
O193	A133	20c dark violet	1.90	.70
O194	A134	1s dark carmine	2.25	1.10
O195	A135	2s dark blue	2.50	1.75
		Nos. O191-O195 (5)	9.65	6.55

Regular Postage
Stamps of 1937
Overprinted in Black

1937 *Perf. 11½*

O196	A139	2c green	.40	.40
O197	A140	5c deep rose	.40	.40
O198	A141	10c blue	.40	.40
O199	A142	20c deep rose	.40	.40
O200	A143	1s olive green	.40	.40
		Nos. O196-O200 (5)	2.00	2.00

**Catalogue values for unused
stamps in this section, from this
point to the end of the section, are
for Never Hinged items.**

Tobacco Stamp, Overprinted in Black

CORRESPONDENCIA OFICIAL

1946 *Unwmk.* *Rouletted*

O201	PT7	1c rose red	1.75	1.75

Communications Building, Quito — O4

1947 *Unwmk.* *Litho.* *Perf. 11*

O202	O4	30c brown	.60	.40
O203	O4	30c greenish blue	.60	.40
a.		Imperf., pair		
O204	O4	30c purple	.60	.40
		Nos. O202-O204 (3)	1.80	1.20

Nos. O202 to O204 overprinted "Primero la
Patria!" and plane in dark blue were issued in
August, 1947, by a revolutionary group. They
were later repudiated by decree.

No. 719 with Additional Diagonal
Overprint

Illustration reduced.

1964 *Perf. 14x13*

O205	A231	80c block of 4	6.00	6.00

The "OEA" overprint covers four stamps, the
"oficial" overprint is applied to every stamp.

A set of 20 imperforate items in the
above Roosevelt design, some overprinted with the initials of various government ministries, was released in

1949. Later that year a set of 8 miniature sheets, bearing the same design
plus a marginal inscription, "Pre-
sidencia (or Vicepresidencia) de la
Republica," and a frame-line were
released. In the editors' opinion, information justifying the listing of these
issues has not been received.

POSTAL TAX STAMPS

Roca — PT1

1920 *Unwmk.* *Perf. 12*

RA1	PT1	1c orange	.60	.30

PT2   PT3

RA2	PT2	1c red & blue	1.10	.20
a.		"de" inverted	10.50	5.25
b.		Double overprint	10.00	.60
c.		Inverted overprint	10.00	.60
RA3	PT3	1c deep blue	1.25	.20
a.		Inverted overprint	6.00	1.00
b.		Double overprint	6.00	1.00

For overprints see Nos. O158-O159.

PT4   PT5

Red or Black Surcharge or Overprint
Stamp Dated 1911-1912

RA4	PT4	20c deep blue	—	30.00

Stamp Dated 1913-1914

RA5	PT4	20c deep blue (R)	2.25	.35

Stamp Dated 1917-1918

RA6	PT4	20c olive green (R)	6.50	.55
a.		Dated 1919-20	25.00	
RA7	PT5	1c on 2c green	.90	.20

Stamp Dated 1911-1912

RA8	PT5	1c on 5c green	.90	.20
a.		Double surcharge		

Stamp Dated 1913-1914

RA9	PT5	1c on 5c green	8.00	.55
a.		Double surcharge	12.00	4.00

On Nos. RA7, RA8 and RA9 the surcharge
is found reading upward or downward.
For surcharges see Nos. RA15-RA16.

Post Office — PT6

1920-24 *Engr.*

RA10	PT6	1c olive green	.40	.20
RA11	PT6	2c deep green	.40	.20
RA12	PT6	20c bister brn ('24)	1.75	.20
RA13	PT6	2s violet	11.50	3.25
RA14	PT6	5s blue	20.00	5.75
		Nos. RA10-RA14 (5)	34.05	9.60

For overprints and surcharge see Nos. 259,
266-268, 273, 302, RA17.

Revenue Stamps of 1917-18 Surcharged Vertically in Red reading up or down

1921-22
RA15 PT5 20c on 1c dk blue 55.00 6.50
RA16 PT5 20c on 2c green 55.00 6.50

No. RA12 Surcharged in Green

1924
RA17 PT6 2c on 20c bis brn .60 .20
  a. Inverted surcharge 12.00 5.00
  b. Double surcharge 4.00 2.00

PT7

1924 **Rouletted 7**
RA18 PT7 1c rose red .90 .20
  a. Inverted overprint 3.50

Similar Design, Eagle at left
Perf. 12
RA19 PT7 2c blue .90 .20
  a. Inverted overprint 3.50 1.75

For overprints and surcharges see Nos. 346, O201, RA32, RA34, RA37, RA44-RA45, RA47.

PT8

Inscribed "Timbre Fiscal"
1924
RA20 PT8 1c yellow 4.50 .85
RA21 PT8 2c dark blue 1.40 .35

Inscribed "Region Oriental"
RA22 PT8 1c yellow .70 .30
RA23 PT8 2c dark blue 1.40 .35
  Nos. RA20-RA23 (4) 8.00 1.85

Overprint on No. RA22 reads down or up.

Revenue Stamp Overprinted in Blue

1934
RA24 2c green .40 .20
  a. Blue overprint inverted 3.50 1.75
  b. Blue ovpt. dbl., one invtd. 4.00 1.25

Postage Stamp of 1930 Overprinted in Red
Perf. 12½
RA25 A11920c ultra & yel .50 .20

Telegraph Stamp Overprinted in Red, like No. RA24, and Surcharged diagonally in Black

1934 **Perf. 14**
RA26 2c on 10c olive brn .70 .20
  a. Double surcharge 5.50

Overprint Blue, Surcharge Red
RA27 2c on 10c olive brn .70 .20

PT9   PT10

Symbols of Post and Telegraph Service PT11

1934-36 **Perf. 12**
RA28 PT9 2c green .60 .20
  a. Both overprints in red ('36) .60 .20

Postal Tax stamp of 1920-24, overprinted in red "POSTAL" has been again overprinted "CASA de Correos y Teleg. de Guayaquil" in black.

Perf. 14½x14
1934 **Photo.** **Wmk. 233**
RA29 PT10 2c yellow green .40 .20

For the rebuilding of the GPO at Guayaquil. For surcharge see No. RA31.

1935
RA30 PT1120c claret .50 .20

For the rebuilding of the GPO at Guayaquil.

No. RA29 Surcharged in Red and Overprinted in Black

1935
RA31 PT10 3c on 2c yel grn .40 .20
  a. Double surcharge

Social and Rural Workers' Insurance Fund.

Tobacco Stamp Surcharged in Black

1936 **Unwmk.** **Rouletted 7**
RA32 PT7 3c on 1c rose red .60 .20
  a. Lines of words reversed 2.00 .20
  b. Horiz. pair, imperf. vert.

Issued for the Social and Rural Workers' Insurance Fund.

No. 310 Overprinted in Black

1936 **Perf. 12½**
RA33 A11920cultra & yel .60 .20
  a. Double overprint

Tobacco Stamp Surcharged in Black

1936 **Rouletted 7**
RA34 PT7 3c on 1c rose red .60 .20

Social and Rural Workers' Insurance Fund.

Worker — PT12

1936 **Engr.** **Perf. 13½**
RA35 PT123c ultra .40 .20

Social and Rural Workers' Insurance Fund. For surcharges see Nos. C64, RA36, RA53-RA54.

Surcharged in Black

1936
RA36 PT135c on 3c ultra .60 .20

This combines the 2c for the rebuilding of the post office with the 3c for the Social and Rural Workers' Insurance Fund.

National Defense Issue
Tobacco Stamp, Surcharged in Black

1936 **Rouletted 7**
RA37 PT7 10c on 1c rose .90 .20
  a. Double surcharge

Symbolical of Defense — PT14

1937-42 **Perf. 12½**
RA38 PT1410c deep blue .90 .20

A 1s violet and 2s green exist in type PT14. For surcharge see No. RA40.

PT15

Overprinted or Surcharged in Black
1937 **Engr. & Typo.** **Perf. 13½**
RA39 PT15 5c lt brn & red 2.00 .25
  d. Inverted overprint 20.00

1942 **Perf. 12, 11½**
RA39A PT15 20c on 5c rose pink & red 75.00 20.00
RA39B PT15 20c on 1s yel brn & red 75.00 20.00
RA39C PT15 20c on 2s grn & red 75.00 20.00
  Nos. RA39A-RA39C (3) 225.00 60.00

A 50c dark blue and red exists.

No. RA38 Surcharged in Red

1937 **Engr.** **Perf. 12½**
RA40 PT14 5c on 10c dp blue 1.10 .20

Map of Ecuador — PT16

1938 **Perf. 14x13½**
RA41 PT16 5c carmine rose .70 .20

Social and Rural Workers' Insurance Fund.

No. C42 Surcharged in Red

1938 **Perf. 12½**
RA42 AP5 20c on 70c black 1.10 .20

No. 307 Surcharged in Red

1938
RA43 A116 5c on 6c yel & red .40 .20

This stamp was obligatory on all mail from Nov. 23rd to 30th, 1938. The tax was for the Intl. Union for the Control of Cancer.

Tobacco Stamp, Surcharged in Black

1939 **Rouletted**
RA44 PT7 5c on 1c rose .70 .20
  a. Double surcharge
  b. Triple surcharge

Tobacco Stamp, Surcharged in Blue

1940
RA45 PT7 5c on 1c rose red 1.00 .20
  a. Double surcharge 3.50 3.50

No. 370 Surcharged in Carmine

1940   **Perf. 11½**
RA46 A144 20c on 50c blk & multi   .50   .20
   a.   Double surcharge, one inverted

Tobacco Stamp, Surcharged in Black

**TIMBRE PATRIOTICO
VEINTE CENTAVOS**

1940   **Rouletted**
RA47 PT7 20c on 1c rose red   6.00   .50

Farmer Plowing
PT17

Communication Symbols
PT18

1940   **Perf. 13x13½**
RA48 PT17 5c carmine rose   .70   .20

1940-43   **Perf. 12**
RA49 PT18 5c copper brown   .70   .20
RA49A PT18 5c green ('43)   .70   .20

   For overprint and surcharges see #534, E6, I1.

Pursuit Planes
PT19

Warrior
Shielding
Women
PT20

1941   **Perf. 11½x13**
RA50 PT19 20c ultra   1.10   .20

   The tax was used for national defense.

1942-46   **Engr.**   **Perf. 12**
RA51 PT20 20c dark blue   1.10   .20
RA51A PT20 40c black brown ('46)   1.10   .20

   The tax was used for national defense.
   A 20c carmine, 20c brown and 30c gray exist lithographed in type PT20.

No. 370 Surcharged in Carmine

CASA DE
CORREOS y TELEGRAFOS
DE GUAYAQUIL
VEINTE CENTAVOS

1942   **Perf. 11½**
RA52 A144 20c on 50c multi   1.10   .20
   a.   Double surcharge   10.00

No. RA35 Surcharged in Red

1943   **Perf. 13½**
RA53 PT12 5c on 3c ultra   .60   .20

No. RA53 with Additional Surcharge in Black

1943
RA54 PT12 5c on 5c on 3c ultra   1.10   .20

Peons — PT21

1943   **Perf. 12**
RA55 PT21 5c blue   .90   .20
   The tax was for farm workers.
   For overprint & surcharge see #535, C135.

Revenue Stamp (as No. RA64) Overprinted or Surcharged in Black

TIMBRE PATRIOTICO

No. RA56

No. RA57

1943   **Perf. 12½**
RA56 20c red orange   75.00   1.50

1943   **Perf. 12**
RA57 20c on 10c orange   2.25   .25
   a.   Double surcharge

Coat of Arms — PT22

1943   **Perf. 12½**
RA58 PT22 20c orange red   .70   .20
   The tax was for national defense.

No. RA58 Surcharged in Black

1944
RA59 PT22 30c on 20c org red   .70   .20
   a.   Double surcharge

> **Catalogue values for unused stamps in this section, from this point to the end of the section, are for Never Hinged items.**

Consular Service Stamps Surcharged in Black

1951   **Unwmk.**   **Perf. 12**
RA60 R1 20c on 1s red   .60   .20
RA61 R1 20c on 2s brown   .60   .20
RA62 R1 20c on 5s violet   .60   .20
   Nos. RA60-RA62 (3)   1.80   .60

Teacher and Pupils in
Schoolyard — PT23

PT24

1952   **Engr.**   **Perf. 13**
RA63 PT23 20c blue green   .60   .20

Revenue Stamp Overprinted "PATRIOTICO / SANITARIO"

1952   **Perf. 12**
RA64 PT24 40(c) olive green   1.10   .20
   For overprints & surcharges see #RA56-RA57

Woman Holding
Flag — PT25

ESCOLAR
PT26

1953   **Perf. 12½**
RA65 PT25 40c ultra   1.25   .20

Telegraph Stamp Surcharged

1954   **Unwmk.**   **Perf. 13**
RA66 PT26 20c on 30c red brn   1.00   .20

PRO TURISMO 1954 10 ctvs.
PT26a

10 ctvs. 10 PRO TURISMO 1954 Diez Centavos
PT26b

PRO TURISMO 1954
PT26c

Revenue Stamps Surcharged or Overprinted Horizontally in Black

1954   **Unwmk.**   **Perf. 12**
RA67 PT26a 10c on 25c blue   1.25   .20
RA68 PT26b 10c on 50c org red   1.25   .20
RA69 PT26c 10c carmine   1.25   .20
   Nos. RA67-RA69 (3)   3.75   .60

PT27

Telegraph Stamp Surcharged "Pro-Turismo 1954 10 ctvs. 10"

1954   **Perf. 13**
RA70 PT27 10c on 30c red brn   2.25   .20

Revenue Stamp Overprinted in Black

1954   **Perf. 12**
RA71 R3 20c olive black   1.75   .20

Consular Service Stamp Surcharged in Black

1954
RA72 R1 20c on 10s gray   1.75   .20

Young Student at Desk
PT28

Globe, Ship, Plane
PT29

Imprint: "Heraclio Fournier.-Vitoria"

1954   **Photo.**   **Perf. 11**
RA73 PT28 20c rose pink   1.10   .20
   See No. RA76.

1954   **Engr.**   **Perf. 12**
RA74 PT29 10c dp magenta   1.60   .20

Soldier Kissing
Flag — PT30

1955   **Photo.**   **Perf. 11**
RA75 PT30 40c blue   2.25   .20
   See No. RA77.

**Types of 1954-55 Redrawn.
Imprint: "Thomas de la Rue & Co. Ltd."**

1957   **Unwmk.**   **Perf. 13**
RA76 PT28 20c rose pink   1.10   .20
              Perf. 14x14½
RA77 PT30 40c blue   2.25   .20
   No. RA77 is inscribed "Republica del Ecuador."

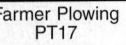

The above stamp is believed to have been used only for fiscal purposes.

AIR POST POSTAL TAX STAMPS

No. 438
Surcharged in
Black or
Carmine
20 Ctvs.

1945 **Unwmk.** **Perf. 11**
RAC1 A173 20c on 10c dk grn .75 .20
a. Pair, one without surcharge 90.00
RAC2 A173 20c on 10c dk grn (C) .75 .20

Obligatory on letters and parcel post carried on planes in the domestic service.

Liberty,
Mercury
and
Planes
PTAP1

1946 **Engr.** **Perf. 12**
RAC3 PTAP1 20c orange brown .75 .20

GALAPAGOS ISLANDS

Issued for use in the Galapagos Islands (Columbus Archipelago), a province of Ecuador, but were commonly used throughout the country.

Catalogue values for unused stamps in this section are for Never Hinged items.

Sea
Lions — A1

Map — A2

Design: 1s, Marine iguana.

Unwmk.
1957, July 15 **Photo.** **Perf. 12**
L1 A1 20c dark brown 1.50 .30
L2 A2 50c violet 1.00 .30
L3 A1 1s dull olive green 4.75 .80
Nos. L1-L3 (3) 7.25 1.40
Nos. L1-L3,LC1-LC3 (3) 7.25 1.40

125th anniv. of Ecuador's possession of the Galapagos Islands, and publicizing the islands.
See Nos. LC1-LC3. For overprints see Nos. 684-686, C389-C391.

GALAPAGOS AIR POST STAMPS

Type of Regular Issue

1s, Santa Cruz Island. 1.80s, Map of Galapagos archipelago. 4.20s, Galapagos giant tortoise.

Unwmk.
1957, July 19 **Photo.** **Perf. 12**
LC1 A1 1s deep blue 1.25 .30
LC2 A1 1.80s rose violet 2.50 .70
LC3 A1 4.20s black 7.50 1.25
Nos. LC1-LC3 (3) 11.25 2.25

For overprints see Nos. C389-C391.

Redrawn Type of Ecuador, 1956
1959, Jan. 3 **Engr.** **Perf. 14**
LC4 AP69 2s lt olive green 1.25 .70
Issued to honor the United Nations.
See note after No. C407.

EGYPT

'ē-jəpt

LOCATION — Northern Africa, bordering on the Mediterranean and the Red Sea
GOVT. — Republic
AREA — 386,900 sq. mi.
POP. — 61,404,000 (1997 est.)
CAPITAL — Cairo

Modern Egypt was a part of Turkey until 1914 when a British protectorate was declared over the country and the Khedive was deposed in favor of Hussein Kamil under the title of sultan. In 1922 the protectorate ended and the reigning sultan was declared king of the new monarchy. Egypt became a republic on June 18, 1953. Egypt merged with Syria in 1958 to form the United Arab Republic. Syria left this union in 1961. In 1971 Egypt took the name of Arab Republic of Egypt.

40 Paras = 1 Piaster
1000 Milliemes = 100 Piasters = 1 Pound (1888)
1000 Milliemes = 1 Pound (1953)
1000 Milliemes = 100 Piasters = 1 Pound (1982)

Catalogue values for unused stamps in this country are for Never Hinged items, beginning with Scott 241 in the regular postage section, Scott B1 in the semi-postal section, Scott C38 in the airpost section, Scott CB1 in the airpost semi-postal section, Scott E5 in the special delivery section, Scott J40 in the postage due section, Scott M16 in the military stamps section, Scott O60 in the officials section, Scott N1 in the occupation section, Scott NC1 in the occupation airpost section, Scott NE1 in the occupation special delivery section, and Scott NJ1 in the occupation postage due section.

Watermarks

Wmk. 118 —
Pyramid and Star

Wmk. 119 —
Crescent and
Star

Wmk. 120 —
Triple Crescent
and Star

Wmk. 195
—
Multiple
Crown
and
Arabic F

"F" in watermark stands for Fuad.

Wmk. 315 — Multiple Eagle

Wmk. 318 —
Multiple
Eagle and
"Misr"

Wmk. 328 — U A R

Wmk. 342 — Coat of Arms, Multiple

Values for unused stamps are for examples with original gum as defined in the catalogue introduction. Very fine examples of Nos. 1-15 will have perforations that are clear of the framelines but with the design noticeably off center. Well centered stamps are extremely scarce and will command substantial premiums.

Turkish Numerals

Turkish Suzerainty

A1	A2
A3	A4
A5	A6
A7	

Surcharged in Black
Wmk. 118
1866, Jan. 1 **Litho.** **Perf. 12½**

					Perf. 12½
1	A1	5pa greenish gray		50.00	30.00
a.		Imperf., pair		225.00	
b.		Pair, imperf. between		350.00	
c.		Perf. 12½x13		60.00	57.50
d.		Perf. 13		300.00	350.00
2	A2	10pa brown		75.00	32.50
a.		Imperf., pair		190.00	
b.		Pair, imperf. between		400.00	
c.		Perf. 13		200.00	210.00
d.		Perf. 12½x15		300.00	325.00
e.		Perf. 12½x13		92.50	55.00
3	A3	20pa blue		105.00	35.00
a.		Imperf., pair		275.00	
b.		Pair, imperf. between		450.00	
c.		Perf. 12½x13		115.00	95.00
d.		Perf. 13		475.00	275.00
4	A4	2pi yellow		125.00	47.50
a.		Imperf.		140.00	125.00
b.		Imperf. vert. or horiz., pair		400.00	400.00
c.		Perf. 12½x15		160.00	
d.		Diagonal half used as 1pi on cover			2,600.
e.		Perf. 12½x13, 13x12½		150.00	55.00
5	A5	5pi rose		300.00	250.00
a.		Imperf.		400.00	375.00
b.		Imperf. vert. or horiz., pair		1,200.	
d.		Inscription of 10pi, imperf.		950.00	850.00
e.		Perf. 12½x13, 13x12½		350.00	275.00
f.		As "d," perf. 12½x15		1,000.	850.00
6	A6	10pi slate bl		350.00	325.00
a.		Imperf.		550.00	450.00
b.		Pair, imperf. between		2,500.	
c.		Perf. 12½x13, 13x12½		550.00	550.00
d.		Perf. 13		1,850.	

Unwmk.
Typo.

7	A7	1pi rose lilac		80.00	5.50
a.		Imperf.		110.00	
b.		Horiz. pair, imperf. vert.		500.00	
c.		Perf. 12½x13, 13x12½		100.00	25.00
d.		Perf. 13		350.00	210.00
e.		Perf. 12½x15		350.00	
		Nos. 1-7 (7)		1,085.	725.50

Single imperforates of types A1-A10 are sometimes simulated by trimming wide-margined examples of perforated stamps.
No. 4d must be dated between July 16 and July 31, 1867.
Proofs of Nos. 1-7 are on smooth white paper, unwatermarked and imperforate. Proofs of No. 7 are on thinner paper than No. 7a.

Sphinx and
Pyramid — A8

Perf. 15x12½
1867 **Litho.** **Wmk. 119**
8	A8	5pa orange		30.00	11.00
a.		Imperf.		250.00	
b.		Horiz. pair, imperf between		175.00	
c.		Vert. pair, imperf between			
9	A8	10pa lilac ('69)		70.00	11.00
a.		10pa violet		82.50	14.00
b.		Half used as 5pa on newspaper piece			850.00
11	A8	20pa yellow green ('69)		110.00	11.00
a.		20pa blue green		125.00	17.00

13	A8	1pi rose red		12.50	1.10
a.		Imperf. pair		150.00	
b.		Pair, imperf. between		300.00	
d.		Rouletted		70.00	
e.		1pi lake red		130.00	32.50
14	A8	2pi blue		150.00	17.00
a.		Imperf.		250.00	
b.		Horiz. pair, imperf. vert.		500.00	
d.		Perf. 12½		250.00	
15	A8	5pi brown		375.00	200.00
		Nos. 8-15 (6)		747.50	251.10

There are 4 types of each value, so placed that any block of 4 contains all types.

A9   A10

Clear Impressions
Thick Opaque Paper
Typographed by the Government at Boulac
Perf. 12½x13½ Clean-cut

1872   **Wmk. 119**

19	A9	5pa brown		10.00	5.00
20	A9	10pa lilac		9.00	3.75
21	A9	20pa blue		50.00	4.00
22	A9	1pi rose red		57.50	2.25
h.		Half used as 20pa on cover			700.00
23	A9	2pi dull yellow		100.00	15.00
j.		Half used as 1p on cover			1,200.
24	A9	2½pi dull violet		85.00	11.00
25	A9	5pi green		325.00	35.00
i.		Tête bêche pair			
		Nos. 19-25 (7)		636.50	76.00

Perf. 13½ Clean-cut

19a	A9	5pa brown		27.50	9.25
20a	A9	10pa dull lilac		9.00	4.25
21a	A9	20pa blue		90.00	20.00
22a	A9	1pi rose red		82.50	8.00
23a	A9	2pi dull yellow		55.00	8.00
24a	A9	2½pi dull violet		1,200.	225.00
25a	A9	5pi green		375.00	75.00

Litho.

21m	A9	20pa blue, perf. 12½x13½		150.00	80.00
21n	A9	20pa blue, perf. 13½		225.00	57.50
21p	A9	20pa blue, imperf.		250.00	
22m	A9	1pi rose red, perf. 12½x13½		550.00	20.00
22n	A9	1pi rose red, perf. 13½		875.00	50.00

Typographed
Blurred Impressions
Thinner Paper
Perf. 12½ Rough

1874-75   **Wmk. 119**

26	A10	5pa brown ('75)		9.50	3.50
f.		Imperf.		200.00	200.00
f.		Vert. pair, imperf. horiz.		1,000.	
g.		Tête bêche pair		45.00	45.00
20b	A9	10pa gray lilac		10.00	3.50
g.		Tête bêche pair		225.00	225.00
21b	A9	20pa gray blue		90.00	4.00
k.		Half used as 10pa on cover			
22b	A9	1pi vermilion		7.50	1.75
f.		Imperf.		—	150.00
f.		Tête bêche pair		150.00	125.00
23b	A9	2pi yellow		75.00	5.75
g.		Tête bêche pair		600.00	600.00
24b	A9	2½pi deep violet		9.25	3.50
e.		Imperf.			
f.		Tête bêche pair		600.00	600.00
25b	A9	5pi yellow green		60.00	22.50
e.		Imperf.		400.00	—

No. 26f normally occurs tête-bêche.

Perf. 13½x12½ Rough

26c	A10	5pa brown		7.50	4.50
i.		Tête bêche pair		62.50	62.50
20c	A9	10pa gray lilac		12.00	3.25
g.		Tête bêche pair		225.00	225.00
21c	A9	20pa gray blue		8.50	3.75
h.		Pair, imperf. between		350.00	
22c	A9	1pi vermilion		55.00	3.25
i.		Tête bêche pair		500.00	500.00
23c	A9	2pi yellow		10.00	6.00
g.		Tête bêche pair		500.00	500.00
k.		Half used as 1pi on cover			2,800.

Perf. 12½x13½ Rough

23d	A9	2pi yellow ('75)		62.50	10.00
h.		Tête bêche pair		1,250.	
24d	A9	2½pi dp violet ('75)		45.00	12.50
i.		Tête bêche pair		1,150.	1,000.
25d	A9	5pi yel green ('75)		350.00	225.00

Nos. 24b, 24d
Surcharged in Black

1879, Jan. 1   **Perf. 12½ Rough**

27	A9	5pa on 2½pi dull vio		10.00	9.00
a.		Imperf.		400.00	400.00
b.		Tête bêche pair		7,500.	

c.		Inverted surcharge		125.00	75.00
d.		Perf. 12½x13½ rough		12.00	12.00
e.		As "d," tête bêche pair		7,500.	
f.		As "d," inverted surcharge		140.00	95.00
28	A9	10pa on 2½pi dull vio		12.50	12.50
a.		Imperf.		400.00	400.00
b.		Tête bêche pair		2,500.	
c.		Inverted surcharge		125.00	82.50
d.		Perf. 12½x13½ rough		17.00	17.00
e.		As "d," tête bêche pair		3,000.	
f.		As "d," inverted surcharge		150.00	125.00

A11   A12

A13   A14

A15   A16

1879-1902   **Typo.**   **Perf. 14x13½**
Ordinary Paper

29	A11	5pa brown		1.50	.60
30	A12	10pa violet		50.00	5.00
31	A12	10pa lilac rose ('81)		70.00	6.25
32	A12	10pa gray ('82)		15.00	1.60
33	A12	10pa green ('84)		.80	.65
34	A13	20pa ultra		67.50	2.25
35	A13	20pa rose ('84)		19.00	1.25
36	A14	1pi rose		27.50	.30
37	A14	1pi ultra ('84)		3.50	.20
38	A15	2pi orange yel		35.00	1.50
39	A15	2pi orange brn		27.50	1.50
40	A16	5pi green		77.50	8.75
41	A16	5pi gray ('84)		25.00	.50
		Nos. 29-41 (13)		419.80	30.35

Nos. 29-31, 35-41 imperf are proofs.
Nos. 37, 39, 41, exist on both ordinary and chalky paper. See *Scott Classic Specialized Catalogue of Stamps & Covers* for detailed listings.
For overprints see Nos. 42, O6-O7.

A17

1884, Feb. 1

42	A17	20pa on 5pi green		17.50	2.25
a.		Inverted surcharge		70.00	62.50

A18   A19

A20   A21

A22   A23

1888-1906
Ordinary Paper

43	A18	1m pale brown ('02)		3.00	.20
44	A19	2m green ('02)		2.25	.20
45	A20	3m maroon ('92)		8.00	1.25
46	A20	3m yel org ('02)		5.75	.20
48	A22	5m carmine rose		3.00	.20
49	A23	10p purple ('89)		40.00	1.00
		Nos. 43-49 (6)		62.00	3.05

Chalky Paper

43a	A18	1m pale brown ('02)		1.00	.20
44a	A19	2m green ('02)		1.25	.20
46a	A20	3m yel org ('02)		3.50	.20
47	A21	4m brown red ('06)		2.25	.20
48b	A22	5m rose ('02)		3.00	.20
49b	A23	10p mauve ('02)		25.00	.55

Nos. 43-44, 47-48 imperf are proofs.
For overprints see Nos. O2-O5, O8-O10, O14-O15.

Boats on Nile   Cleopatra
A24   A25

Ras-el-Tin   Giza
Palace   Pyramids
A26   A27

Sphinx   Colossi of Thebes
A28   A29

Pylon of Karnak   Citadel at
and Temple of   Cairo — A31
Khonsu — A30

Rock Temple of Abu   Aswan
Simbel — A32   Dam — A33

Perf. 13½x14

1914, Jan. 8   **Wmk. 119**
Chalk-surfaced Paper

50	A24	1m olive brown		1.00	.80
51	A25	2m dp green		1.50	.20
52	A26	3m orange		2.00	.50
53	A27	4m red		2.75	.75
54	A28	5m lake		2.00	.20
a.		Booklet pane of 6		225.00	
55	A29	10m dk blue		4.75	.40

Perf. 14

56	A30	20m olive grn		8.00	.70
57	A31	50m red violet		15.00	1.10
58	A32	100m black		40.00	1.40
59	A33	200m plum		47.50	3.75
		Nos. 50-59 (10)		124.50	9.80

All values of this issue exist imperforate on both watermarked and unwatermarked paper but are not known to have been issued in that condition.
See Nos. 61-69, 72-74. For overprints and surcharge see Nos. 60, 78-91, O11-O13, O16-O27, O30.

British Protectorate

No. 52 Surcharged

1915, Oct. 15

60	A26	2m on 3m orange		2.25	2.25
a.		Inverted surcharge		225.00	225.00

Scenic Types of 1914 and

Statue of Ramses II
A34   A35

1921-22   **Wmk. 120**   **Perf. 13½x14**
Chalk-surfaced Paper

61	A24	1m olive brown		1.00	.80
62	A25	2m dp green		3.25	1.75
63	A25	2m red ('22)		2.75	.60
64	A26	3m orange		2.25	.70
65	A27	4m green ('22)		4.50	4.00
66	A28	5m lake		3.00	.20
67	A28	5m pink		3.25	.20
68	A29	10m dp blue		3.75	.20
69	A29	10m lake ('22)		3.00	.50
70	A34	15m indigo ('22)		3.75	.20
71	A35	15m indigo ('22)		17.50	2.50

Perf. 14

72	A30	20m olive green		12.50	.40
73	A31	50m maroon		14.00	.50
74	A32	100m black		60.00	6.75
		Nos. 61-74 (14)		134.50	19.30

For overprints see Nos. O28-O29.

Independent Kingdom

Stamps of 1921-22
Overprinted

1922, Oct. 10

78	A24	1m olive brown		1.50	.70
a.		Inverted overprint		350.00	450.00
b.		Double overprint		200.00	

79	A25	2m red	1.00	.40
a.		Double overprint	200.00	
80	A26	3m orange	2.25	.95
81	A27	4m green	1.50	.60
b.		Inverted overprint	225.00	
82	A28	5m pink	2.75	.20
83	A29	10m lake	2.75	.20
84	A34	15m indigo	5.75	.90
85	A35	15m indigo	4.50	.90

Perf. 14

86	A30	20m olive green	6.00	.60
a.		Inverted overprint	200.00	—
b.		Double overprint	300.00	—
87	A31	50m maroon	9.00	.60
a.		Inverted overprint	400.00	500.00
88	A32	100m black	22.50	1.25
a.		Inverted overprint	500.00	160.00
b.		Double overprint	400.00	150.00
		Nos. 78-88 (11)	59.50	7.30

Same Overprint on Nos. 58-59
Wmk. Crescent and Star (119)

90	A32	100m black	90.00	50.00
91	A33	200m plum	30.00	1.50

Proclamation of the Egyptian monarchy. The overprint signifies "The Egyptian Kingdom, March 15, 1922." It exists in four types, one lithographed and three typographed on Nos. 78-87, but lithographed only on Nos. 88-91.

King Fuad
A36   A37

Wmk. 120
1923-24   Photo.   Perf. 13½
Size 18x22½mm

92	A36	1m orange	.35	.20
93	A36	2m black	.75	.20
94	A36	3m brown	1.00	.40
a.		Imperf., pair	200.00	
95	A36	4m yellow grn	.90	.50
96	A36	5m orange brn	.35	.20
a.		Imperf., pair	50.00	
97	A36	10m rose	1.50	.20
98	A36	15m ultra	3.25	.20

Perf. 14
Size: 22x28mm

99	A36	20m dk green	6.25	.20
100	A36	50m myrtle grn	9.00	.20
101	A36	100m red violet	21.00	.55
102	A36	200m violet ('24)	42.50	1.75
a.		Imperf., pair	300.00	
103	A37	£1 ultra & dk vio ('24)	175.00	25.00
a.		Imperf., pair	1,600.	
		Nos. 92-103 (12)	261.85	29.60

For overprints & surcharge see Nos. 167, O31-O38.

Thoth Carving Name of King Fuad — A38

1925, Apr.   Litho.   Perf. 11

105	A38	5m brown	8.25	4.75
106	A38	10m rose	12.50	8.00
107	A38	15m ultra	15.00	9.50
		Nos. 105-107 (3)	35.75	22.25

International Geographical Congress, Cairo. Nos. 106-107 exist with both white and yellowish gum.

Oxen Plowing A39

1926   Wmk. 195   Perf. 13x13½

108	A39	5m lt brown	3.00	1.00
109	A39	10m brt rose	2.75	.90
110	A39	15m dp blue	3.00	.90
111	A39	50m Prus green	14.00	3.00
112	A39	100m brown vio	20.00	5.00
113	A39	200m brt violet	32.50	15.00
		Nos. 108-113 (6)	75.25	25.80

12th Agricultural and Industrial Exhibition at Gezira.
For surcharges see Nos. 115-117.

King Fuad — A40

Perf. 14x14½
1926, Apr. 2   Photo.   Wmk. 120

114	A40	50p brn vio & red vio	135.00	22.50

58th birthday of King Fuad.
For overprint and surcharge see #124, 166.

Nos. 111-113 Surcharged

Perf. 13x13½
1926, Aug. 24   Wmk. 195

115	A39	5m on 50m Prus green	2.25	2.25
116	A39	10m on 100m brown vio	2.25	2.25
117	A39	15m on 200m brt violet	2.25	2.25
a.		Double surcharge	300.00	
		Nos. 115-117 (3)	6.75	6.75

Ship of Hatshepsut — A41

1926, Dec. 9   Litho.   Perf. 13½

118	A41	5m brown & blk	3.00	1.40
119	A41	10m dp red & blk	3.50	1.50
120	A41	15m dp blue & blk	4.00	1.50
		Nos. 118-120 (3)	10.50	4.40

International Navigation Congress, Cairo.
For overprints see Nos. 121-123.

Nos. 118-120, 114 Overprinted

PORT FOUAD

1926, Dec. 21

121	A41 (a)	5m	250.00	150.00
122	A41 (a)	10m	250.00	150.00
123	A41 (a)	15m	250.00	150.00

Perf. 14x14½
Wmk. 120

124	A40 (b)	50p	1,500.	875.00

Inauguration of Port Fuad opposite Port Said. Nos. 121-123 have a block over "Le Caire" at lower left.
Forgeries of Nos. 121-124 exist.

Branch of Cotton A42

Perf. 13x13½
1927, Jan. 25   Wmk. 195

125	A42	5m dk brown & sl grn	1.75	.80
126	A42	10m dp red & slate grn	2.75	1.50
127	A42	15m dp blue & slate grn	3.50	1.50
		Nos. 125-127 (3)	8.00	3.80

International Cotton Congress, Cairo.

King Fuad
A43   A44

A45

A46

Type I   Type II

Early printings of the seven values indicated were printed from plates with screens of vertical dots in the vignettes (type I). All values were printed later from plates with screens of diagonal dots (type II).

Perf. 13x13½
1927-37   Wmk. 195   Photo.
Type II

128	A43	1m orange	.35	.20
a.		Type I	3.00	.50
129	A43	2m black	.35	.20
a.		Type I	10.00	5.00
130	A43	3m olive brn	.35	.20
a.		Type I	2.00	.50
131	A43	3m dp green ('30)	.65	.20
132	A43	4m yellow grn	.85	.40
a.		Type I	60.00	10.00
133	A43	4m brown ('30)	1.00	.40
134	A43	4m dp green ('34)	.85	.40
135	A43	5m dk red brn ('29)	.95	.40
a.		Type I	3.00	.75
136	A43	10m dk red ('29)	1.25	.20
a.		10m orange red, type I	2.00	.30
137	A43	10m purple ('34)	2.75	.20
138	A43	13m car rose ('32)	1.50	.40
139	A43	15m ultra	2.50	.20
a.		Type I	10.00	.50
140	A43	15m dk violet ('34)	5.25	.20
141	A43	20m ultra ('34)	9.25	.30

Perf. 13½x14

142	A44	20m olive grn	3.25	.40
143	A44	20m ultra ('32)	4.00	.20
144	A44	40m olive brn ('32)	3.25	.20
145	A44	50m Prus green	3.50	.20
a.		50m greenish blue	5.50	.20
146	A44	100m brown vio	6.00	.20
a.		100m claret	9.00	.20
147	A44	200m deep violet	6.00	.50

Printings of Nos. 142, 145 and 146, made in 1929 and later, were from new plates with stronger impressions and darker colors.

Perf. 13x13½

148	A45	500m choc & Prus bl, entirely photo ('32)	100.00	25.00
a.		Frame litho, vignette photo	125.00	11.50
149	A46	£1 dk grn & org brn, entirely photo ('37)	125.00	8.25
a.		Frame litho, vignette photo	160.00	7.00
		Nos. 128-149 (22)	278.85	38.85

Statue of Amenhotep, Son of Hapu — A47

1927, Dec. 29   Photo.   Perf. 13½x13

150	A47	5m orange brown	1.50	.45
151	A47	10m copper red	2.00	.50
152	A47	15m deep blue	3.00	.55
		Nos. 150-152 (3)	6.50	1.50

Statistical Congress, Cairo.

Imhotep — A48   Mohammed Ali Pasha — A49

1928, Dec. 15

153	A48	5m orange brown	1.10	.50
154	A49	10m copper red	1.25	.50

Intl. Congress of Medicine at Cairo and the cent. of the Faculty of Medicine at Cairo.

Prince Farouk — A50

1929, Feb. 11   Litho.

155	A50	5m choc & gray	2.00	1.10
156	A50	10m dull red & gray	3.00	1.25
157	A50	15m ultra & gray	3.00	1.25
158	A50	20m Prus blue & gray	3.50	1.25
		Nos. 155-158 (4)	11.50	4.85

Ninth birthday of Prince Farouk. Nos. 155-158 with black or brown centers are trial color proofs. They were sent to the UPU, but were never placed on sale to the public, although some are known used.

Tomb Fresco at El-Bersheh — A51

1931, Feb. 15   *Perf. 13x13½*
163 A51 5m brown   1.50 .55
164 A51 10m copper red   2.50 1.25
165 A51 15m dark blue   3.50 1.50
  Nos. 163-165 (3)   7.50 3.30

14th Agricultural & Industrial Exhib., Cairo.

Nos. 114 and 103 Surcharged with
Bars and

1932   **Wmk. 120**   *Perf. 14x14½*
166 A40 50m on 50p   20.00 2.75
     Perf. 14
167 A37 100m on £1   250.00 190.00

Locomotive of 1852 — A52

    Perf. 13x13½
1933, Jan. 19   **Litho.**   **Wmk. 195**
168 A52 5m shown   13.00 5.25
169 A52 13m 1859   19.00 9.00
170 A52 15m 1862   19.00 9.00
171 A52 20m 1932   19.00 9.00
  Nos. 168-171 (4)   70.00 32.25

International Railroad Congress, Heliopolis.

Commercial Passenger
Airplane — A56

Dornier
Do-X
A57

Graf
Zeppelin
A58

1933, Dec. 20   **Photo.**
172 A56 5m brown   6.00 2.10
173 A56 10m brt violet   14.00 8.50
174 A57 13m brown car   17.00 11.00
175 A57 15m violet   17.00 10.50
176 A58 20m blue   22.50 19.00
  Nos. 172-176 (5)   76.50 51.10

International Aviation Congress, Cairo.

 A59   Khedive Ismail Pasha — A60

1934, Feb. 1   *Perf. 13½*
177 A59 1m dp orange   .50 1.00
178 A59 2m black   .55 1.00
179 A59 3m brown   .60 1.25
180 A59 4m blue green   .90 .40
181 A59 5m red brown   .95 .20
182 A59 10m violet   2.00 .20
183 A59 13m copper red   3.00 1.25
184 A59 15m dull violet   3.00 1.10
185 A59 20m ultra   2.00 .30
186 A59 50m Prus blue   7.00 .60
187 A59 100m olive grn   16.50 1.00
188 A59 200m dp violet   55.00 5.50
    Perf. 13½x13
189 A60 50p brown   175.00 75.00
190 A60 £1 Prus blue   285.00 125.00
  Nos. 177-190 (14)   552.00 213.80

10th Congress of UPU, Cairo.

King Fuad — A61

1936-37   *Perf. 13½*
191 A61 1m dull orange   .55 .80
192 A61 2m black   1.75 .20
193 A61 4m dk green   2.00 .20
194 A61 5m chestnut   1.40 .20
195 A61 10m purple ('37)   2.50 .20
196 A61 15m brown violet   2.75 .50
197 A61 20m sapphire   3.25 .20
  Nos. 191-197 (7)   14.20 2.30

Entrance to
Agricultural
Building — A62

Agricultural Building — A63

Design: 15m, 20m, Industrial Building.

1936, Feb. 15   *Perf. 13½x13*
198 A62 5m brown   1.25 .85
    Perf. 13x13½
199 A63 10m violet   1.50 .95
200 A63 13m copper red   1.75 2.00
201 A63 15m dark violet   1.25 1.00
202 A63 20m blue   2.50 2.00
  Nos. 198-202 (5)   8.25 6.80

15th Agricultural & Industrial Exhib., Cairo.

Signing of Treaty — A65

1936, Dec. 22   *Perf. 11*
203 A65 5m brown   .90 .60
204 A65 15m dk violet   1.00 .75
205 A65 20m sapphire   2.50 1.00
  Nos. 203-205 (3)   4.40 2.35

Signing of Anglo-Egyptian Treaty, Aug. 26, 1936.

 King Farouk — A66   Medal for Montreux Conf. — A67

1937-44   **Wmk. 195**   *Perf. 13x13½*
206 A66 1m brown org   .30 .20
207 A66 2m vermilion   .30 .20
208 A66 3m brown   .30 .20
209 A66 4m green   .30 .20
210 A66 5m red brown   .50 .20
211 A66 6m lt yel grn ('40)   .60 .20
212 A66 10m purple   .30 .20
213 A66 13m rose car   .60 .35
214 A66 15m dk vio brn   .50 .20
215 A66 20m blue   .75 .35
216 A66 20m lil gray ('44)   .75 .20
  Nos. 206-216 (11)   5.20 2.50

For overprints see Nos. 301, 303, 345, 348, 360E, N3, N6, N8, N22, N25, N27.

1937, Oct. 15   *Perf. 13½x13*
217 A67 5m red brown   1.00 .55
218 A67 15m dk violet   1.50 1.10
219 A67 20m sapphire   1.50 1.25
  Nos. 217-219 (3)   4.00 2.90

Intl. Treaty signed at Montreux, Switzerland, under which foreign privileges in Egypt were to end in 1949.

Eye of Ré — A68

1937, Dec. 8   *Perf. 13x13½*
220 A68 5m brown   1.10 .75
221 A68 15m dk violet   1.25 .75
222 A68 20m sapphire   1.75 1.00
  Nos. 220-222 (3)   4.10 2.50

15th Ophthalmological Congress, Cairo, December, 1937.

King Farouk, Queen Farida — A69

1938, Jan. 20   *Perf. 11*
223 A69 5m red brown   7.50 4.25

Royal wedding of King Farouk and Farida Zulficar.

Inscribed: "11 Fevrier 1938"
1938, Feb. 11
224 A69 £1 green & sepia   250.00 125.00

King Farouk's 18th birthday.

Cotton Picker — A70

1938, Jan. 26   *Perf. 13½x13*
225 A70 5m red brown   .75 .50
226 A70 15m dk violet   2.25 .85
227 A70 20m sapphire   2.00 .75
  Nos. 225-227 (3)   5.00 2.10

18th International Cotton Congress at Cairo.

Pyramids of Giza and Colossus of Thebes A71

1938, Feb. 1   *Perf. 13x13½*
228 A71 5m red brown   1.25 .65
229 A71 15m dk violet   1.75 .80
230 A71 20m sapphire   2.00 .80
  Nos. 228-230 (3)   5.00 2.25

Intl. Telecommunication Conf., Cairo.

Branch of Hydnocarpus — A72

1938, Mar. 21   *Perf. 13x13½*
231 A72 5m red brown   1.25 .50
232 A72 15m dk violet   1.75 .60
233 A72 20m sapphire   1.75 .60
  Nos. 231-233 (3)   4.75 1.70

International Leprosy Congress, Cairo.

King Farouk and Pyramids — A73

King Farouk
A74   A75

Backgrounds: 40m, Hussan Mosque. 50m, Cairo Citadel. 100m, Aswan Dam. 200m, Cairo University.

1939-46   **Photo.**   *Perf. 14x13½*
234 A73 30m gray   .75 .20
  a. 30m slate gray   .75 .20
234B A73 30m ol grn ('46)   .80 .20
235 A73 40m dk brown   .85 .20
236 A73 50m Prus green   1.00 .20
237 A73 100m brown vio   1.40 .20
238 A73 200m dk violet   4.25 .20
    Perf. 13½x13
239 A74 50p green & sep   11.00 3.00
240 A75 £1 dp bl & dk brn   25.00 5.75
  Nos. 234-240 (8)   45.05 9.95

For £1 with A77 portrait, see No. 269D. See Nos. 267-269D. For overprints see Nos. 310-314, 316, 355-358, 360, 363-364, N13-N19, N32-N38.

> **Catalogue values for unused stamps in this section, from this point to the end of the section, are for Never Hinged items.**

King Fuad
A76

King Farouk
A77

1944, Apr. 28 Perf. 13½x13
241 A76 10m dk violet .50 .20
8th anniv. of the death of King Fuad.

1944-50 Wmk. 195 Perf. 13x13½
242 A77 1m yellow brn ('45) .45 .20
243 A77 2m red org ('45) .45 .20
244 A77 3m sepia ('46) 1.00 1.00
245 A77 4m dp green ('45) .45 .20
246 A77 5m red brown ('46) .45 .20
247 A77 10m dp violet .45 .20
247A A77 13m rose red ('50) 12.00 4.25
248 A77 15m dk violet ('45) .45 .20
249 A77 17m olive grn .50 .20
250 A77 20m dk gray ('45) .75 .20
251 A77 22m dp blue ('45) .75 .20
Nos. 242-251 (11) 17.70 7.05

For overprints see Nos. 299-300, 302, 304-309, 343-344, 346-347, 349-354, 360B, 361-362, N1-N2, N4-N5, N7, N9-N12, N20-N21, N23-N24, N26, N28-N31.

King
Farouk — A78

Khedive Ismail
Pasha — A79

1945, Feb. 10 Perf. 13½x13
252 A78 10m deep violet .40 .20
25th birthday of King Farouk.

1945, Mar. 2 Photo.
253 A79 10m dark olive .35 .20
50th anniv. of death of Khedive Ismail Pasha.

Flags of Arab
Nations — A80

1945, July 29
254 A80 10m violet .35 .20
255 A80 22m dp yellow grn .50 .20
League of Arab Nations Conference, Cairo, Mar. 22, 1945.

Flags of
Egypt and
Saudi
Arabia
A81

Perf. 13x13½
1946, Jan. 10 Wmk. 195
256 A81 10m dp yellow grn .35 .20
Visit of King Ibn Saud, Jan. 1946.

Citadel,
Cairo
A82

1946, Aug. 9
257 A82 10m yel brn & dp yel grn .40 .20
Withdrawal of British troops from Cairo Citadel, Aug. 9, 1946.

King
Farouk
and
Inchas
Palace,
Cairo
A83

2m, Prince Abdullah, Yemen. 3m, Pres. Bechara el-Khoury, Lebanon. 4m, King Abdul Aziz ibn Saud, Saudi Arabia. 5m, King Faisal II, Iraq. 10m, Amir Abdullah ibn Hussein, Jordan. 15m, Pres. Shukri el Kouatly, Syria.

1946, Nov. 9
258 A83 1m dp yellow grn .60 .20
259 A83 2m sepia .60 .20
260 A83 3m deep blue .60 .20
261 A83 4m brown orange .60 .20
262 A83 5m brown red .60 .20
263 A83 10m dark gray .75 .20
264 A83 15m deep violet .75 .20
Nos. 258-264 (7) 4.50 1.40
Arab League Cong. at Cairo, May 28, 1946.

Parliament Building, Cairo — A84

1947, Apr. 7 Photo.
265 A84 10m green .35 .20
36th conf. of the Interparliamentary Union, Apr. 1947.

Raising Egyptian
Flag over Kasr-
el-Nil
Barracks — A85

King
Farouk — A85a

1947, May 6 Perf. 13½x13
266 A85 10m dp plum & yel grn .40 .20
Withdrawal of British troops from the Nile Delta.

Farouk Types 1939 Redrawn
1947-51 Wmk. 195 Perf. 14x13½
267 A73 30m olive green .50 .20
268 A73 40m dk brown .60 .20
269 A73 50m Prus grn ('48) .90 .20
269A A73 100m dk brn vio ('49) 5.75 .75
269B A73 200m dk violet ('49) 11.00 1.25

Perf. 13½x13
269C A85a 50p green & sep ('51) 25.00 8.50
269D A75 £1 dp bl & dk brn ('50) 36.00 3.75
Nos. 267-269D (7) 79.75 14.85

The king faces slightly to the left and clouds have been added in the sky on Nos. 267-269B. Backgrounds as in 1939-46 issue. Portrait on £1 as on type A77.

For overprints see Nos. 315, 359.

Field and
Branch of
Cotton — A86

Map and Infantry
Column — A87

Perf. 13½x13
1948, Apr. 1 Wmk. 195
270 A86 10m olive green .40 .20
Intl. Cotton Cong. held at Cairo in Apr. 1948.

1948, June 15 Perf. 11½x11
271 A87 10m green .40 .20
Arrival of Egyptian troops at Gaza, 5/15/48.

Ibrahim Pasha (1789-1848) — A88

1948, Nov. 10 Perf. 13x13½
272 A88 10m brn red & dp grn .40 .20

Statue,
"The Nile"
A89

Protection of
Industry and
Agriculture — A90

Perf. 13x13½
1949, Mar. 1 Photo. Wmk. 195
273 A89 1m dk green .40 .20
274 A89 10m purple 1.00 .20
275 A89 17m crimson 1.00 .20
276 A89 22m deep blue 1.00 .40

Perf. 11½x11
277 A90 30m dk brown 1.50 .50
Nos. 273-277 (5) 4.90 1.50

Souvenir Sheets
Photo. & Litho.
Imperf
278 Sheet of 4 3.25 3.25
a. A89 1m red brown .60 .60
b. A89 10m dark brown .60 .60
c. A89 17m brown orange .60 .60
d. A89 22m dark Prussian green .60 .60
279 Sheet of 2 3.25 3.25
a. A90 10m violet gray 1.50 1.50
b. A90 30m red orange 1.50 1.50

16th Agricultural & Industrial Expo., Cairo.

Mohammed Ali
and Map — A93

Globe — A94

Perf. 11½x11
1949, Aug. 2 Photo. Wmk. 195
280 A93 10m orange brn & grn .60 .20
Centenary of death of Mohammed Ali.

1949, Oct. 9 Perf. 13½x13
281 A94 10m rose brown .85 .60
282 A94 22m violet 1.75 .85
283 A94 30m dull blue 2.40 1.10
Nos. 281-283 (3) 5.00 2.55
75th anniv. of the UPU.

Scales of
Justice
A95

1949, Oct. 14 Perf. 13x13½
284 A95 10m deep olive green .40 .20
End of the Mixed Judiciary System, 10/14/49.

Desert
Scene
A96

1950, Dec. 27
285 A96 10m violet & red brn .45 .20
Opening of the Fuad I Institute of the Desert.

Fuad I
University
A97

1950, Dec. 27
286 A97 22m dp green & claret .60 .25
Founding of Fuad I University, 25th anniv.

Globe and
Khedive
Ismail
Pasha
A98

1950, Dec. 27
287 A98 30m claret & dp grn .55 .25
75th anniv. of Royal Geographic Society of Egypt.

Picking
Cotton — A99

1951, Feb. 24
290 A99 10m olive green .35 .20
International Cotton Congress, 1951.

King Farouk and Queen
Narriman — A100

1951, May 6 Photo. Perf. 11x11½
291 A100 10m green & red brn 3.50 2.75
a. Souvenir sheet 14.00 16.00
Marriage of King Farouk and Narriman
Sadek, May 6, 1951.

Stadium
Entrance
A101

Arms of Alexandria
and Olympic
Emblem — A102

King
Farouk
A103

1951, Oct. 5 Perf. 13x13½, 13½x13
292 A101 10m brown 1.00 .60
293 A102 22m dp green 1.25 .95
294 A103 30m blue & dp grn 1.25 .95
a. Souvenir sheet of 3, #292-
294 14.00 16.00
Nos. 292-294 (3) 3.50 2.50

Issued to publicize the first Mediterranean
Games, Alexandria, Oct. 5-20, 1951.

Winged Figure and
Map — A105

Designs: 22m, King Farouk and Map. 30m,
King Farouk and Flag.

Dated "16 Oct. 1951"
1952, Feb. 11 Perf. 13½x13
296 A105 10m dp green .75 .25
297 A105 22m plum & dp grn 1.00 .45
298 A105 30m green & brown 1.25 .55
a. Souvenir sheet of 3, #296-298 10.00 9.00
Nos. 296-298 (3) 3.00 1.25

Abrogation of the Anglo-Egyptian treaty.

Stamps of 1937-51
Overprinted in Various
Colors

Perf. 13x13½
1952, Jan. 17 Wmk. 195
299 A77 1m yellow brown .35 .20
300 A77 2m red org (Bl) .35 .20
301 A66 3m brown (Bl) .35 .50
302 A77 4m dp green (RV) .35 .20
303 A66 6m lt yel grn (RV) .90 .70
304 A77 10m dp vio (C) .35 .25
305 A77 13m rose red (Bl) 1.75 .75
306 A77 15m dk violet (C) 2.00 .75
307 A77 17m olive grn (C) 1.90 .30
308 A77 20m dk gray (RV) 1.40 .30
309 A77 22m dp blue (C) 2.50 1.50

No. 244, the 3m sepia, exists with this overprint but was not regularly issued or used.

**Same Overprint, 24½mm Wide, on
Nos. 267 to 269B**

Perf. 14x13½
310 A73 30m olive grn
(DkBl) 1.25 .20
a. Black overprint 1.50 .20
311 A73 40m dk brown (G) .90 .20
312 A73 50m Prus grn (C) 1.25 .25
313 A73 100m dk brn vio (C) 2.75 .40
314 A73 200m dk violet (C) 13.00 1.25

**Same Overprint, 19mm Wide, on
Nos. 269C-269D**

Perf. 13½x13
315 A85a 50p grn & sep (C) 25.00 4.75
316 A75 £1 dp bl & dk brn
(Bl) 40.00 5.25
Nos. 299-316 (18) 96.35 17.95

The overprint translates: King of Egypt and
the Sudan, Oct. 16, 1951.
Overprints in colors other than as listed are
color trials.

Egyptian
Flag — A106

Perf. 13½x13
1952, May 6 Photo. Wmk. 195
317 A106 10m org yel, dp bl &
dp grn 1.00 .20
a. Souvenir sheet of 1 7.50 5.25

Issued to commemorate the birth of Crown
Prince Ahmed Fuad, Jan. 16, 1952.

"Dawn of
New Era"
A107

Symbolical of Egypt
Freed — A108

Designs: 10m, "Egypt" with raised sword.
22m, Citizens marching with flag.

Perf. 13x13½, 13½x13
1952, Nov. 23
Dated: "23 Juillet 1952"
318 A107 4m dp grn & org .35 .25
319 A107 10m dp grn & cop brn .35 .50
320 A108 17m brn org & dp grn .75 .60
321 A108 22m choc & dp grn 1.00 .45
Nos. 318-321 (4) 2.45 1.80

Change of government, July 23, 1952.

Republic

Farmer
A109

Soldier
A110

Mosque of
Sultan
Hassan — A111

Queen
Nefertiti — A112

1953-56 Perf. 13x13½
322 A109 1m red brown .35 .20
323 A109 2m dk lilac .35 .20
324 A109 3m brt blue .35 .40
325 A109 4m dk green .35 .20
326 A110 10m dk brown ("Defence") .40 .40
327 A110 10m dk brown ("Defense") .55 .20
328 A110 15m gray .35 .20
329 A110 17m dk grnsh blue .45 .20
330 A110 20m purple .35 .20
Perf. 13½
331 A111 30m dull green .35 .20
332 A111 32m brt blue .70 .20
333 A111 35m violet ('55) .90 .20
334 A111 37m gldn brn ('56) 1.75 .60
335 A111 40m red brown .70 .20
336 A111 50m violet brn 1.20 .20
337 A112 100m henna brn 1.50 .20
338 A112 200m dk grnsh blue 3.75 .50
339 A112 500m purple 11.00 1.00
340 A112 £1 dk grn, blk &
red 25.00 3.25
Nos. 322-340 (19) 50.35 8.75

Nos. 327-330 are inscribed "Defense."
See No. 490. For overprints and surcharges
see Nos. 460, 500, N44-N56, N72.

**Stamps of 1939-51 Overprinted in
Black with Three Bars to Obliterate
Portrait**

1953 Perf. 13x13½, 13½x13
343 A77 1m yellow brn .35 .20
344 A77 2m red orange .35 .20
345 A66 3m brown .50 .50
346 A77 3m sepia .35 .20
347 A77 4m dp green .35 .20
348 A66 6m lt yellow
grn .35 .20
349 A77 10m dp violet .35 .20
350 A77 13m rose red .50 .20
351 A77 15m dk violet .35 .20

352 A77 17m olive grn .35 .20
353 A77 20m dk gray .50 .20
354 A77 22m deep blue .55 .20
355 A73 30m ol grn
(#267) .60 .20
356 A73 50m Prus grn
(#269) 1.00 .25
357 A73 100m dk brn vio
(#269A) 1.50 .40
358 A73 200m dk violet
(#269B) 4.50 1.00
359 A85a 50p grn & sepia 15.00 5.00
360 A75 £1 dp bl & dk
brn
(#269D) 30.00 4.75
Nos. 343-360 (18) 57.45 14.30

No. 206 with this overprint is a forgery.

**Same Overprint on Nos. 300, 303-
305, 311 and 314**
360B A77 2m red orange .40 .20
360E A66 6m lt yel grn 50.00
361 A77 10m dp violet 4.00 4.00
362 A77 13m rose red 1.25 .75
363 A73 40m dk brown 6.00 .75
364 A73 200m dk violet 4.00 .90
Nos. 360B,361-364 (5) 15.65 6.60

Practically all values of Nos. 343-364 exist
with double overprint. Other values of the 1952
overprinted issue are known with counterfeit
bars.

Symbols
of
Electronic
Progress
A113

1953, Nov. 23 Photo. Perf. 13x13½
365 A113 10m brt blue .50 .20

Electronics Exposition, Cairo, Nov. 23.

Crowd
Acclaiming the
Republic
A114

Farmer
A115

Design: 30m, Crowd, flag and eagle.

Perf. 13½x13
1954, June 18 Wmk. 195
366 A114 10m brown .55 .25
367 A114 30m deep blue .90 .60

Proclamation of the republic, 1st anniv.

1954-55 Perf. 13x13½
368 A115 1m red brown .35 .20
369 A115 2m dark lilac .35 .20
370 A115 3m brt blue .35 .20
371 A115 4m dk green ('55) .70 .45
372 A115 5m dp car ('55) .35 .20
Nos. 368-372 (5) 2.10 1.25

For overprints see Nos. N39-N43.

Egyptian Flag,
Map — A116

Globe — A117

Design: 35m, Bugler, soldier and map.

1954, Nov. 4   Perf. 13½x13
373 A116 10m rose vio & grn   .45 .25
374 A116 35m ver, blk & bl grn   .65 .55

Agreement of Oct. 19, 1954, with Great Britain for the evacuation of the Suez Canal zone by British troops.

Arab Postal Union Issue
1955, Jan. 1
375 A117 5m yellow brn   .45 .20
376 A117 10m green   .45 .20
377 A117 37m violet   .90 .80
    Nos. 375-377 (3)   1.80 1.20

Founding of the Arab Postal Union, 7/1/54. For overprints see Nos. 381-383.

Paul P. Harris and Rotary Emblem — A118

35m, Globe, wings and Rotary emblem.

Perf. 13½x13
1955, Feb. 23   Wmk. 195
378 A118 10m claret   .95 .30
379 A118 35m blue   1.25 .40

50th anniv. of the founding of Rotary Intl.

Nos. 375-377 Overprinted

1955, Nov. 1
381 A117 5m yellow brown   .70 .60
382 A117 10m green   .85 .35
383 A117 37m violet   1.00 .80
    Nos. 381-383 (3)   2.55 1.75

Arab Postal Union Congress held at Cairo, Mar. 15, 1955.

Map of Africa and Asia, Olive Branch and Rings A119

Globe, Torch, Dove and Olive Branch — A120

1956, July 29 Perf. 13x13½, 13½x13
384 A119 10m chestnut & green   .40 .25
385 A120 35m org yel & dull pur   .80 .70

Afro-Asian Festival, Cairo, July, 1956.

Map of Suez Canal and Ship — A121

Queen Nefertiti — A122

Perf. 11½x11
1956, Sept. 26   Wmk. 195
386 A121 10m blue & buff   .55 .55

Nationalization of the Suez Canal, July 26, 1956. See No. 393.

1956, Oct. 15   Perf. 13½x13
387 A122 10m dark green   1.25 .90

Intl. Museum Week (UNESCO), Oct. 8-14.

Egyptians Defending Port Said — A123

1956, Dec. 20 Litho. Perf. 11x11½
388 A123 10m brown violet   1.00 .60

Honoring the defenders of Port Said.

No. 388 Overprinted in Carmine Rose

1957, Jan. 14
389 A123 10m brown violet   1.00 .60

Evacuation of Port Said by British and French troops, Dec. 22, 1956.

Old and New Trains A124

1957, Jan. 30 Photo. Perf. 13x13½
390 A124 10m red violet & gray   1.00 .90

100th anniv. of the Egyptian Railway System (in 1956).

Mother and Children A125

1957, Mar. 21
391 A125 10m crimson   .90 .35

Mother's Day, 1957.

Battle Scene A126

Perf. 13x13½
1957, Mar. 28   Wmk. 195
392 A126 10m bright blue   .65 .30

Victory over the British at Rosetta, 150th anniv.

Type of 1956; New Inscriptions in English
1957, Apr. 15   Perf. 11½x11
393 A121 100m blue & yel grn   1.50 1.00

Reopening of the Suez Canal.
No. 393 is inscribed: "Nationalisation of Suez Canal Co. Guarantees Freedom of Navigation" and "Reopening 1957."

Map of Gaza Strip — A127

Perf. 13½x13
1957, May 4   Photo.   Wmk. 195
394 A127 10m Prus blue   1.50 .70

"Gaza Part of Arab Nation."
For overprint see No. N57.

Al Azhar University A128

1957, Apr. 27   Perf. 13x13½
New Arabic Date in Red
395 A128 10m brt violet   .45 .40
396 A128 15m violet brown   .60 .35
397 A128 20m dark gray   1.25 .70
    Nos. 395-397 (3)   2.30 1.45

Millenary of Al Azhar University, Cairo.

Shepheard's Hotel, Cairo — A129

Gate, Palace and Eagle — A130

Perf. 13½x13
1957, July 20   Wmk. 195
398 A129 10m brt violet   .65 .20

Reopening of Shepheard's Hotel, Cairo.

Perf. 11½x11
1957, July 22   Wmk. 315
399 A130 10m yellow & brown   .65 .20

First meeting of New National Assembly.

Amasis I in Battle of Avaris, 1580 B.C. A131

Designs: No. 401, Sultan Saladin, Hitteen, 1187 A. D. No. 402, Louis IX of France in chains, Mansourah, 1250, vert. No. 403, Map of Middle East, Ein Galout, 1260. No. 404, Port Said, 1956.

Inscribed:
"Egypt Tomb of Aggressors 1957"
1957, July 26 Perf. 13x13½, 13½x13
400 A131 10m carmine rose   1.00 1.00
401 A131 10m dk olive grn   1.00 1.00
402 A131 10m brown violet   1.00 1.00
403 A131 10m grnsh blue   1.00 1.00
404 A131 10m yellow brown   1.00 1.00
    Nos. 400-404 (5)   5.00 5.00

No. 400 exists with Wmk. 195.

Ahmed Arabi Speaking to the Khedive A132

Perf. 13x13½
1957, Sept. 16   Wmk. 315
405 A132 10m deep violet   .80 .20

75th anniversary of Arabi Revolution.

Hafez Ibrahim — A133

Portrait: No. 407, Ahmed Shawky.

1957, Oct. 14   Perf. 13½x13
406 A133 10m dull red brn   .30 .20
407 A133 10m olive green   .30 .20
  a. Pair, #406-407   1.00 1.00

25th anniv. of the deaths of Hafez Ibrahim and Ahmed Shawky, poets.

MiG and Ilyushin Planes A134

Design: No. 409, Viscount plane.

1957, Dec. 19   Perf. 13½x13
408 A134 10m ultra   .50 .20
409 A134 10m green   .50 .20
  a. Pair, #408-409   1.20 1.20

25th anniv. of the Egyptian Air Force and of Misrair, the Egyptian airline.

Pyramids, Dove and Globe A135

1957, Dec. 26   Photo.   Wmk. 315
410 A135 5m brown orange   .40 .25
411 A135 10m green   .40 .20
412 A135 15m brt violet   .40 .20
    Nos. 410-412 (3)   1.20 .65

Afro-Asian Peoples Conf., Cairo, 12/26-1/2.

Farmer's Wife
A136

Ramses II
A137

"Industry" — A138

1957-58   Wmk. 315   Perf. 13½
413 A136 1m blue green ('58)   .30 .20
414 A137 10m violet   .30 .20

1958   Wmk. 318
415 A136 1m lt blue green   .30 .20
416 A138 5m brown   .35 .20
417 A137 10m violet   .60 .20
    Nos. 413-417 (5)   1.85 1.00

See Nos. 438-444, 474-488, 535. For overprints see Nos. N58-N63, N66-N68, N75, N77-N78.

Cyclists — A139

Mustafa
Kamel — A140

Perf. 13½x13

1958, Jan. 12   Wmk. 315
418 A139 10m lt red brown   .50 .30

5th Intl. Bicycle Race, Egypt, Jan. 12-26.

1958, Feb. 10   Photo.   Wmk. 318
419 A140 10m blue gray   .80 .20

50th anniversary of the death of Mustafa Kamel, orator and politician.

United Arab Republic

Linked Maps of
Egypt and
Syria — A141

Cotton — A142

Perf. 11½x11

1958, Mar. 22   Wmk. 318
436 A141 10m yellow & green   .75 .20

Birth of United Arab Republic. See No. C90. See also Syria-UAR Nos. 1 and C1.

1958, Apr. 5   Perf. 13½x13
437 A142 10m Prussian blue   .40 .20

Intl. Fair for Egyptian Cotton, Apr., 1958.

Types of 1957-58 Inscribed "U.A.R. EGYPT" and

Princess
Nofret — A143

Designs: 1m, Farmer's wife. 2m, Ibn-Tulun's Mosque. 4m, 14th century glass lamp (design lacks "1963" of A217). 5m, "Industry" (factories and cogwheel). 10m, Ramses II. 35m, "Commerce" (eagle, ship and cargo).

1958   Perf. 13½x14
438 A136 1m crimson   .20 .20
439 A138 2m blue   .20 .20
440 A143 3m dk red brown   .20 .20
441 A217 4m green   .20 .20
442 A138 5m brown   .20 .20
443 A137 10m violet   .55 .30
444 A138 35m lt ultra   2.00 .40
    Nos. 438-444 (7)   3.55 1.70

See Nos. 474-488, 532-533, N62-N68, N75-N78.

Qasim
Amin — A144

Doves, Broken
Chain and
Globe — A145

1958, Apr. 23   Perf. 13½x13
445 A144 10m deep blue   .60 .20

50th anniversary of the death of Qasim Amin, author of "Emancipation of Women."

1958, June 18
446 A145 10m violet   .60 .20

5th anniv. of the republic and to publicize the struggle of peoples and individuals for freedom.
    For overprint see No. N69.

Cement
Industry — A146

UAR Flag — A147

Industries: No. 448, Textile. No. 449, Iron & steel. No. 450, Petroleum (Oil). No. 451, Electricity and fertilizers.

Perf. 13½x13

1958, July 23   Photo.   Wmk. 318
447 A146 10m red brown   .40 .25
448 A146 10m blue green   .40 .25
449 A146 10m bright red   .40 .25
450 A146 10m olive green   .40 .25
451 A146 10m dark blue   .40 .25
  a.   Strip of 5, #447-451   2.75 2.75

Souvenir Sheet
Imperf
452 A147 50m grn, dp car &
          blk   16.00 14.00
    Revolution of July 23, 1952, 6th anniv.

Sayed Darwich
A148

Hand Holding
Torch, Broken
Chain and Flag
A149

1958, Sept. 15   Perf. 13½x13
453 A148 10m violet brown   .40 .20

35th anniv. of the death of Sayed Darwich, Arab composer.

1958, Oct. 14   Photo.   Wmk. 318
454 A149 10m carmine rose   .40 .20

Establishment of the Republic of Iraq.
See Syria-UAR No. 13.

Maps and Cogwheels — A150

1958, Dec. 8   Perf. 13x13½
455 A150 10m blue   .40 .20

Issued to publicize the Economic Conference of Afro-Asian Countries, Cairo, Dec. 8.

Overprinted in Red in English and Arabic in 3 Lines: "Industrial and Agricultural Production Fair"

1958, Dec. 9
456 A150 10m lt red brown   .40 .20

Issued to publicize the Industrial and Agricultural Production Fair, Cairo, Dec. 9.

Dr.
Mahmoud
Azmy and
UN
Emblem
A151

1958, Dec. 10
457 A151 10m dull violet   .35 .20
458 A151 35m green   .75 .40

10th anniv. of the signing of the Universal Declaration of Human Rights.
    For overprints see Nos. N70-N71.

University Building, Sphinx,
"Education" and God Thoth — A152

1958, Dec. 21   Photo.   Wmk. 318
459 A152 10m grnsh black   .40 .20

50th anniversary of Cairo University.

No. 337 Surcharged

1959, Jan. 20   Wmk. 195   Perf. 13½
460 A112 55m on 100m henna
          brn   3.00 .75

For overprint see No. N72.

Emblem
A153

1959, Feb. 2   Perf. 13x13½
461 A153 10m lt olive green   .40 .20

Afro-Asian Youth Conf., Cairo, Feb. 2.

See Syria UAR issues for stamps of designs A141, A149, A154, A156, A157, A162, A170, A172, A173, A179 with denominations in piasters (p).

Arms of
UAR — A154

Perf. 13½x13

1959, Feb. 22   Photo.   Wmk. 318
462 A154 10m green, blk & red .40 .20

First anniversary, United Arab Republic.
See Syria UAR No. 17.

Nile Hilton
Hotel
A155

1959, Feb. 22   Perf. 13x13½
463 A155 10m dark gray   .40 .20

Opening of the Nile Hilton Hotel, Cairo.

Globe,
Radio and
Telegraph
A156

1959, Mar. 1
464 A156 10m violet   .40 .20

Arab Union of Telecommunications.
See Syria-UAR Nos. C20-C21.

United Arab States Issue

Flags of
UAR and
Yemen
A157

1959, Mar. 8
465 A157 10m sl grn, car & blk .40 .20

First anniversary of United Arab States.
See Syria-UAR No. 16.

Oil Derrick and Pipe Line — A158

Perf. 13½x13
1959, Apr. 16   Litho.   Wmk. 318
466 A158 10m lt bl & dk bl   .45   .20
First Arab Petroleum Congress, Cairo.

Railroad A159

Designs: No. 468, Bus on highway. No. 469, River barge. No. 470, Ocean liner. No. 471, Telecommunications on map. No. 472, Stamp printing building, Heliopolis. No. 472A, Ship, train, plane and motorcycle mail carrier.

1959, July 23   Photo.   Perf. 13x13½
Frame in Gray
467 A159 10m maroon   .85   .30
468 A159 10m green   .85   .30
469 A159 10m violet   .85   .30
470 A159 10m dark blue   .85   .30
471 A159 10m dull purple   .85   .30
472 A159 10m scarlet   .85   .30
    Nos. 467-472 (6)   5.10   1.80
Souvenir Sheet
Imperf
472A A159 50m green & red 12.00 12.00
No. 472A for the 7th anniv. of the Egyptian revolution of 1952 and was sold only with 5 sets of Nos. 467-472.

Globe, Swallows and Map — A160

1959, Aug. 8   Perf. 13½x13
473 A160 10m maroon   .40   .20
Convention of the Assoc. of Arab Emigrants in the US.

Types of 1953-58 without "Egypt" and

St. Simon's Gate, Bosra, Syria — A161

Designs: 1m, Farmer's wife. 2m, Ibn-Tulun's Mosque. 3m, Princess Nofret. 4m, 14th century glass lamp (design lacks "1963" of A217). 5m, "Industry" (factories and cogwheel). 10m, Ramses II. 15m, Omayyad Mosque, Damascus. 20m, Lotus vase, Tutankhamen treasure. 35m, Eagle, ship and cargo. 40m, Scribe statue. 45m, Saladin's citadel, Aleppo. 55m, Eagle, cotton and wheat. 60m, Dam and factory. 100m, Eagle, hand, cotton and grain. 200m, Palmyra ruins, Syria. 500m, Queen Nefertiti, inscribed "UAR" (no ovpt.).

Perf. 13½x14, 14x13½
1959-60   Wmk. 328   Photo.
474 A136 1m vermilion   .20   .20
475 A138 2m dp blue ('60) .20   .20
476 A143 3m maroon   .20   .20
477 A217 4m green ('60)   .20   .20
478 A138 5m black ('60)   .20   .20
479 A137 10m dk ol grn   .30   .20
480 A138 15m deep claret   .30   .20
481 A138 20m crimson ('60) .30   .20
482 A161 30m brown vio   .35   .20

483 A138 35m lt vio bl ('60)   .50   .20
484 A143 40m sepia   .55   .20
485 A161 45m lil gray ('60)   .90   .20
486 A138 55m brt blue grn   1.00   .20
487 A138 60m dp purple ('60)   1.25   .20
488 A138 100m org & sl grn
            ('60)   2.25   .30
489 A161 200m lt blue & mar   4.00   .50
490 A112 500m dk gray & red
            ('60)   12.00 1.25
    Nos. 474-490 (17)   24.70 4.85
    See Nos. 532-535.

Shield and Cogwheel — A162

Perf. 13½x13
1959, Oct. 20   Photo.   Wmk. 328
491 A162 10m brt car rose   .40   .20
Issued for Army Day, 1959.
See Syria-UAR No. 32.

Cairo Museum A163

1959, Nov. 18   Perf. 13x13½
492 A163 10m olive gray   .40   .20
Centenary of Cairo museum.

Abu Simbel Temple of Ramses II — A164

1959, Dec. 22   Perf. 11x11½
493 A164 10m lt red brn, pnksh .50   .25
Issued as propaganda to save historic monuments in Nubia threatened by the construction of Aswan High Dam.

Postrider, 12th Century A165

1960, Jan. 2   Perf. 13x13½
494 A165 10m dark blue   .40   .20
Issued for Post Day, Jan. 2.

Hydroelectric Power Station, Aswan Dam — A166

1960, Jan. 9
495 A166 10m violet blk   .40   .20
Inauguration of the Aswan Dam hydroelectric power station, Jan. 9.

A167

10m, Arabic and English Description of Aswan High Dam. 35m, Architect's Drawing of Aswan High Dam.

1960, Jan. 9   Perf. 11x11½
496   10m claret   .60   .30
497   35m claret   .95   .30
a.   A167 Pair, #496-497   1.60   1.60
Start of work on the Aswan High Dam.

Symbols of Agriculture and Industry — A169   Arms and Flag — A170

1960, Jan. 16   Perf. 13½x13
498 A169 10m gray grn & sl grn .35   .20
Industrial and Agricultural Fair, Cairo.

1960, Feb. 22   Photo.   Wmk. 328
499 A170 10m green, blk & red   .35   .20
2nd anniversary of the proclamation of the United Arab Republic.
See Syria-UAR No. 38.

No. 340 Overprinted "UAR" in English and Arabic in Red

1960   Wmk. 195   Perf. 13½
500 A112   £1 dk grn, blk & red 19.00 5.00

"Art" — A171

Perf. 13½x13
1960, Mar. 1   Wmk. 328
501 A171 10m brown   .40   .20
Issued to publicize the 3rd Biennial Exhibition of Fine Arts in Alexandria.

Arab League Center, Cairo A172

1960, Mar. 22   Photo.   Perf. 13x13½
502 A172 10m dull grn & blk   .35   .20
Opening of Arab League Center and Arab Postal Museum, Cairo.
See Syria-UAR No. 40.

Refugees Pointing to Map of Palestine A173

1960, Apr. 7
503 A173 10m orange ver   .40   .20
504 A173 35m Prus blue   .60   .20
World Refugee Year, 7/1/59-6/30/60.
See Nos. N73-N74. See also Syria-UAR Nos. 43-44.

Weight Lifter — A174

Stadium, Cairo — A175

Sports: No. 506, Basketball. No. 507, Soccer. No. 508, Fencing. No. 509, Rowing. 30m, Steeplechase, horiz. 35m, Swimming, horiz.

Perf. 13½x13
1960, July 23   Photo.   Wmk. 328
505 A174 5m gray   .45   .20
506 A174 5m brown   .45   .20
507 A174 5m dp claret   .45   .20
508 A174 10m brt carmine   .45   .20
509 A174 10m gray green   .45   .20
a.   Vert. or horiz. strip of #505-509 2.50
510 A174 30m purple   .60   .20
511 A174 35m dark blue   .70   .20
    Nos. 505-511 (7)   3.55   1.40
Souvenir Sheet
Imperf
512 A175 100m car & brown   3.00   3.00
Nos. 505-511 for the 17th Olympic Games, Rome, Aug. 25-Sept. 11.

Dove and UN Emblem — A176

35m, Lights surrounding UN emblem, horiz.

Perf. 13½x13

1960, Oct. 24   **Wmk. 328**
513 A176 10m purple .25 .20
514 A176 35m brt rose .35 .20

15th anniversary of United Nations.

Abu Simbel Temple of Queen
Nefertari — A177

Perf. 11x11½

1960, Nov. 14   **Photo.**   **Wmk. 328**
515 A177 10m ocher, buff .55 .20

Issued as propaganda to save historic monuments in Nubia and in connection with the UNESCO meeting, Paris, Nov. 14.

Model
Post
Office
A178

1961, Jan. 2   **Perf. 13x13½**
516 A178 10m brt car rose .35 .20

Issued for Post Day, Jan. 2.

Eagle, Fasces
and Victory
Wreath — A179

Wheat and
Globe
Surrounded by
Flags — A180

1961, Feb. 22   **Perf. 13½x13**
517 A179 10m dull violet .35 .20

3rd anniversary of United Arab Republic. See Syria-UAR No. 50.

1961, Mar. 21   **Wmk. 328**
518 A180 10m vermilion .35 .20

Intl. Agricultural Exhib., Cairo, 3/21-4/20.

Patrice
Lumumba and
Map
A181

Reading Braille
and WHO
Emblem
A182

1961, Mar. 30   **Perf. 13½x13**
519 A181 10m black .35 .20

Africa Day, Apr. 15 and 3rd Conf. of Independent African States, Cairo, Mar. 25-31.

1961, Apr. 6   **Photo.**
520 A182 10m red brown .35 .20

WHO Day. See Nos. B21, N80.

Tower of
Cairo — A183

Arab Woman
and Son,
Palestine
Map — A184

1961, Apr. 11   **Perf. 13½x13**
521 A183 10m grnsh blue .35 .20

Opening of the 600-foot Tower of Cairo, on island of Gizireh. See No. C95.

1961, May 15   **Wmk. 328**
522 A184 10m brt green .40 .20

Issued for Palestine Day.
See No. N79.

Symbols
of Industry
and
Electricity
A185

Chart and Workers — A186

#524, New buildings and family. #525, Ship, train, bus and radio. #526, Dam, cotton and field. #527, Hand holding candle and family.

1961, July 23   **Photo.**   **Perf. 13½x13½**
523 A185 10m dp carmine .45 .20
524 A185 10m brt blue .45 .20
525 A185 10m dk vio brown .45 .20
526 A185 35m dk green .55 .20
527 A185 35m brt purple .55 .20
   Nos. 523-527 (5) 2.45 1.00

Souvenir Sheet
Imperf

528 A186 100m red brown 3.00 2.25

9th anniv. of the revolution.

Map of Suez Canal
and Ships — A187

Perf. 11½x11

1961, July 26   **Unwmk.**
529 A187 10m olive .40 .20

Suez Canal Co. nationalization, 5th anniv.

Various Enterprises of Misr
Bank — A188

Perf. 13x13½

1961, Aug. 22   **Wmk. 328**
530 A188 10m red brn, pnksh .35 .20

The 41st anniversary of Misr Bank.

Flag, Ship's Wheel
and
Battleship — A189

1961, Aug. 29   **Photo.**   **Perf. 13½x13**
531 A189 10m deep blue .40 .20

Issued for Navy Day.

Type A136 Redrawn, Type A138, Type A217 and:

Eagle of Saladin
over Cairo — A190

Designs: 1m, Farmer's wife. 4m, 14th cent. glass lamp. 35m, "Commerce."

1961, Aug. 31   **Unwmk.**   **Perf. 11½**
532 A136 1m blue .25 .20
533 A217 4m olive .25 .20
534 A190 10m purple .25 .20
535 A138 35m slate blue .30 .20
   Nos. 532-535 (4) 1.05 .80

Smaller of two Arabic inscriptions in new positions: 1m, at right above Egyptian numeral; 4m, upward to spot beside waist of lamp; 35m, upper left corner below "UAR." On 4m, "UAR" is 2mm deep instead of 1mm. "Egypt" omitted as in 1959-60.

UN Emblem, Book,
Cogwheel,
Corn — A191

Perf. 13½x13½

1961, Oct. 24   **Photo.**   **Wmk. 328**

Design: 35m, Globe and cogwheel, horiz.

536 A191 10m black & ocher .25 .20
537 A191 35m blue grn & brn .45 .20

UN Technical Assistance Program and 16th anniv. of the UN.
See Nos. N81-N82.

Trajan's Kiosk, Philae — A192

1961, Nov. 4   **Unwmk.**   **Perf. 11½**
     Size: 60x27mm
538 A192 10m dp vio blue .75 .30

15th anniv. of UNESCO, and to publicize UNESCO's help in safeguarding the monuments of Nubia.

Palette,
Brushes, Map
of
Mediterranean
A193

Atom and
Educational
Symbols
A194

1961, Dec. 14   **Wmk. 328**   **Perf. 13½**
539 A193 10m dk red brown .35 .20

Issued to publicize the 4th Biennial Exhibition of Fine Arts in Alexandria.

1961, Dec. 18
540 A194 10m dull purple .35 .20

Issued to publicize Education Day.
See No. N83.

Arms of
UAR
A195

1961, Dec. 23   **Unwmk.**   **Perf. 11½**
541 A195 10m brt pink, brt grn & blk .35 .20

Victory Day. See No. N84.

Sphinx at
Giza — A196

1961, Dec. 27   **Perf. 11x11½**
542 A196 10m black .45 .30

Issued to publicize the "Sound and Light" Project, the installation of floodlights and sound equipment at the site of the Pyramids and Sphinx.

Post
Office
Printing
Plant,
Nasser
City
A197

1962, Jan. 2   **Photo.**   **Perf. 11½x11**
543 A197 10m dk brown .35 .20

Issued for Post Day, Jan. 2.

Map of Africa, King Mohammed V of Morocco and Flags — A198

1962, Jan. 4   *Perf. 11x11½*
544 A198 10m indigo   .35   .20

African Charter, Casablanca, 1st anniv.

Girl Scout Saluting and Emblem A199

     Perf. 13x13½
1962, Feb. 22   Wmk. 328
545 A199 10m bright blue   1.25   .30

Egyptian Girl Scouts' 25th anniversary.

Arab Refugees, Flag and Map — A200

Mother and Child — A201

1962, Mar. 7   *Perf. 13½x13*
546 A200 10m dark slate green   .35   .20

5th anniv. of the liberation of the Gaza Strip. See No. N85.

1962, Mar. 21   Photo.
547 A201 10m dk violet brn   1.00   .20

Issued for Arab Mother's Day, Mar. 21.

Map of Africa and Post Horn — A202

1962, Apr. 23   Wmk. 328
548 A202 10m crimson & ocher   .30   .20
549 A202 50m dp blue & ocher   .60   .20

Establishment of African Postal Union.

Cadets on Parade and Academy Emblem A203

1962, June 18   *Perf. 13½x13½*
550 A203 10m green   .35   .20

Egyptian Military Academy, 150th anniv.

Malaria Eradication Emblem — A204

Theodor Bilharz — A205

1962, June 20   *Perf. 13½x13*
551 A204 10m dk brown & red   .25   .20
552 A204 35m dk green & blue   .30   .20

WHO drive to eradicate malaria. See Nos. N87-N88.

1962, June 24   *Perf. 11x11½*
553 A205 10m brown orange   .35   .20

Dr. Theodor Bilharz (1825-1862), German physician who first described bilharziasis, an endemic disease in Egypt.

Patrice Lumumba and Map of Africa — A206

Hand on Charter — A207

1962, July 1   Photo.   Wmk. 342
554 A206 10m rose & red   .35   .20

Issued in memory of Patrice Lumumba (1925-61), Premier of Congo.

1962, July 10   *Perf. 11x11½*
555 A207 10m brt blue & dk brn   .35   .20

Proclamation of the National Charter.

"Birth of the Revolution" A208

Symbolic Designs: #557, Proclamation (Scroll and book). #558, Agricultural Reform (Farm and crescent). #559, Bandung Conference (Dove, globe and olive branch). #560, Birth of UAR (Eagle and flag). #561, Industrialization (cogwheel, factory, ship and bus). #562, Aswan High Dam. #563, Social Revolution (Modern buildings and emblem). 100m, Arms of UAR, emblems of Afro-Asian and African countries and UN.

1962, July 23   *Perf. 11½*
556 A208 10m brn, dk red brn
     & pink   .20   .20
557 A208 10m dk blue & sepia   .20   .20
558 A208 10m sepia & brt bl   .20   .20
559 A208 10m olive & dk ultra   .20   .20
560 A208 10m grn, blk & red   .20   .20
561 A208 10m brn org & indigo   .20   .20
562 A208 10m brn org & vio blk   .20   .20
563 A208 10m orange & blk   .20   .20
     Nos. 556-563 (8)   1.60   1.60

Souvenir Sheets
Perf. 11½
564 A208 100m grn, pink, red &
     blk   2.50   2.25

10th anniv. of the revolution. No. 564 exists imperf. Same value.

Mahmoud Moukhtar, Museum and Sculpture A209

1962, July 24   *Perf. 11½x11*
565 A209 10m lt vio bl & olive   .35   .20

Opening of the Moukhtar Museum, Island of Gezireh. The sculpture is "La Vestale de Secrets" by Moukhtar.

Flag of Algeria and Map of Africa Showing Algeria — A210

1962, Aug. 15   *Perf. 11x11½*
566 A210 10m multicolored   .35   .20

Algeria's independence, July 1, 1962.

Rocket, Arms of UAR and Atom Symbol — A211

1962, Sept. 1   Photo.   Wmk. 342
567 A211 10m brt grn, red & blk   .40   .20

Launching of UAR rockets.

Rifle and Target — A212

Map of Africa, Table Tennis Paddle, Net and Ball — A213

1962, Sept. 18   *Perf. 11½*
568 A212   5m green, blk & red   .45   .25
569 A213   5m green, blk & red   .45   .25
  a.   Pair, #568-569   1.00   1.00
570 A212 10m bister, bl & dk grn   .55   .40
571 A213 10m bister, bl & dk grn   .55   .40
  a.   Pair, #570-571   1.25   1.25
572 A212 35m dp ultra, red & blk   1.25   .85
573 A213 35m dp ultra, red & blk   1.25   .85
  a.   Pair, #572-573   2.75   2.75
     Nos. 568-573 (6)   4.50   3.00

38th World Shooting Championships and the 1st African Table Tennis Tournament. Types A212 and A213 are printed se-tenant at the base.

Dag Hammarskjold and UN Emblem — A214

Queen Nefertari Crowned by Isis and Hathor — A215

1962, Oct. 24   Photo.   Wmk. 342
Portrait in Slate Blue
574 A214   5m deep lilac   .40   .20
575 A214 10m olive   .50   .20
576 A214 35m deep ultra   .65   .20
     Nos. 574-576 (3)   1.55   .60

Dag Hammarskjold, Secretary General of the UN, 1953-61, and 17th anniv. of the UN. See Nos. N89-N91.

1962, Oct. 31   *Perf. 11½*
577 A215 10m blue & ocher   1.00   .40

Issued to publicize the UNESCO campaign to safeguard the monuments of Nubia.

Jet Trainer, Hawker Hart Biplane and College Emblem A216

1962, Nov. 2   *Perf. 11½x11*
578 A216 10m bl, dk bl & crim   .35   .20

25th anniversary of Air Force College.

14th Century Glass Lamp and "1963" — A217

Yemen Flag and Hand with Torch — A218

1963, Feb. 20   *Perf. 11x11½*
579 A217 4m dk brn, grn & car   .35   .20

Issued for use on greeting cards. See Nos. 441, 477, 533, N76, N92. For overprint see No. N65.

1963, Mar. 14   Photo.   Wmk. 342
580 A218 10m olive & brt car   .35   .20

Establishment of Yemen Arab Republic.

Tennis Player, Pyramids and Globe A219

     Perf. 11½x11
1963, Mar. 20   Unwmk.
581 A219 10m gray, blk & brn   .50   .20

Intl. Lawn Tennis Championships, Cairo.

Cow, UN and FAO Emblems A220

Designs: 10m, Corn, wheat and emblems, vert. 35m, Wheat, corn and emblems.

Perf. 11½x11, 11x11½

1963, Mar. 21   **Wmk. 342**
582 A220 5m violet & dp org .40 .25
583 A220 10m ultra & yel .45 .25
584 A220 35m blue, yel & blk .55 .40
    Nos. 582-584 (3) 1.40 .90

FAO "Freedom from Hunger" campaign.
See Nos. N93-N95.

Centenary Emblem — A221

Design: 35m, Globe and emblem.

1963, May 8 Unwmk. Perf. 11x11½
585 A221 10m lt blue, red & mar .30 .20
586 A221 35m lt blue & red .60 .20
    Centenary of the Red Cross.
See Nos. N96-N97.

Arab Socialist Union Emblem A222

50m, Tools, torch & symbol of National Charter.

Wmk. 342
1963, July 23 Photo. Perf. 11½
587 A222 10m slate & rose pink .35 .20

Souvenir Sheets
Perf. 11½
588 A222 50m vio bl & org yel 1.90 1.60

11th anniv. of the revolution and to publicize the Arab Socialist Union.
No. 588 exists imperf. Same value.

Television Station, Cairo, and Screen A223

1963, Aug. 1 Perf. 11½x11
589 A223 10m dk blue & yel .35 .20

2nd Intl. Television Festival, Alexandria, 9/1-10.

Queen Nefertari A224   Swimmer and Map of Suez Canal A225

Designs: 10m, Great Hypostyle Hall, Abu Simbel. 35m, Ramses in moonlight.

Wmk. 342
1963, Oct. 1 Photo. Perf. 11
Size: 25x42mm (5m, 35m);
28x61mm (10m)
590 A224 5m brt vio blue & yel .40 .25
591 A224 10m gray, blk & red org .60 .30
592 A224 35m org yel & blk 1.00 .35
    Nos. 590-592 (3) 2.00 .90

UNESCO world campaign to save historic monuments in Nubia.
See Nos. N98-N100.

1963, Oct. 15
593 A225 10m blue & sal rose .35 .20

Intl. Suez Canal Swimming Championship.

Ministry of Agriculture — A226

Perf. 11½x11
1963, Nov. 20 Wmk. 342
594 A226 10m multicolored .35 .20

50th anniv. of the Ministry of Agriculture.

Modern Building and Map of Africa and Asia A227

1963, Dec. 7
595 A227 10m multicolored .35 .20

Afro-Asian Housing Congress, Dec. 7-12.

Scales, Globe, UN Emblem A228

1963, Dec. 10
596 A228 5m dk green & yel .30 .20
597 A228 10m blue, gray & blk .35 .20
598 A228 35m rose red, pink & red .40 .30
    Nos. 596-598 (3) 1.05 .70

15th anniv. of the Universal Declaration of Human Rights.
See Nos. N101-N103.

Sculpture, Arms of Alexandria and Palette with Flags — A229

1963, Dec. 12 Perf. 11x11½
599 A229 10m pale bl, dk bl & brn .35 .20

Issued to publicize the 5th Biennial Exhibition of Fine Arts in Alexandria.

Lion and Nile Hilton Hotel — A230   Vase, 13th Century — A231

Pharaoh Userkaf (5th Dynasty) A232

Designs: 1m, Vase, 14th century. 2m, Ivory headrest. 3m, Pharaonic calcite boat. 4m, Minaret and gate. 5m, Nile and Aswan High Dam. 10m, Eagle of Saladin over pyramids. 15m, Window, Ibn Tulun's mosque. No. 608, Mitwalli Gate, Cairo. 35m, Nefertari. 40m, Tower Hotel. 55m, Sultan Hassan's Mosque. 60m, Courtyard, Al Azhar University. 200m, Head of Ramses II. 500m, Funerary mask of Tutankhamen.

1964-67 Unwmk. Photo. Perf. 11
Size: Nos. 608, 612, 19x24mm;
others, 24x29mm
600 A231 1m citron & ultra .20 .20
601 A230 2m magenta & bis .20 .20
602 A230 3m sal, org & bl .20 .20
603 A235 4m och, blk & ultra .35 .20
604 A231 5m brn & brt blue .20 .20
    a.   5m brown & dark blue .50 .20
605 A231 10m green, dk brn & lt brn .30 .20
606 A230 15m ultra & yel .30 .20
607 A230 20m brn org & blk .70 .20
608 A231 20m lt olive grn ('67) 1.50 .20
609 A231 30m yellow & brown .70 .20
610 A231 35m sal, och & ultra .60 .20
611 A231 40m ultra & yellow 1.50 .40
612 A231 55m brt red lil ('67) 2.00 .20
613 A231 60m grnsh bl & yel brn .80 .30

Wmk. 342
614 A232 100m dk vio brn & sl 5.00 .85
615 A232 200m bluish blk & yel brn 8.00 1.00
616 A232 500m ultra & dp org 17.50 3.00
    Nos. 600-616 (17) 40.05 7.95

Nos. 603 & N107 lack the vertically arranged dates which appear at lower right on No. 619.
See Nos. N104-N116.

HSN Commission Emblem — A233

Perf. 11x11½
1964, Jan. 10 Wmk. 342
617 A233 10m dull bl, dk bl & yel .35 .20

1st conf. of the Commission of Health, Sanitation and Nutrition.

Arab League Emblem — A234

1964, Jan. 13 Perf. 11
618 A234 10m brt green & blk .35 .20

1st meeting of the Heads of State of the Arab League, Cairo, January.
See No. N117.

Minaret at Night — A235

1964 Unwmk. Perf. 11
619 A235 4m emerald, blk & red .35 .20

Issued for use on greeting cards.
See Nos. 603, N107, N118.

Old and New Dwellings and Map of Nubia A236

Perf. 11½x11
1964, Feb. 27 Photo. Wmk. 342
620 A236 10m dull vio & yel .35 .20

Resettlement of Nubian population.

Map of Africa and Asia and Train A237

1964, Mar. 21
621 A237 10m dull bl, dk bl & yel .90 .50

Asian Railway Conference, Cairo, Mar. 21.

Ikhnaton and Nefertiti with Children — A238

1964, Mar. 21 Perf. 11x11½
622 A238 10m dk brown & ultra .50 .30

Issued for Arab Mother's Day, Mar. 21.

APU Emblem — A239   WHO Emblem — A240

1964, Apr. 1 Photo. Wmk. 342
623 A239 10m org brn & bl, sal .35 .20

Permanent Office of the APU, 10th anniv.
See No. N119.

1964, Apr. 7
624 A240 10m dk blue & red .35 .20

World Health Day (Anti-Tuberculosis).
See No. N120.

Statue of Liberty, World's Fair Pavilion and Pyramids A241

1964, Apr. 22 — Perf. 11½x11
625 A241 10m brt green & ol,
grysh .35 .20

New York World's Fair, 1964-65.

Nile and Aswan High Dam
A242

1964, May 15 — Unwmk. Perf. 11½
626 A242 10m black & blue .35 .20

The diversion of the Nile.

"Land Reclamation" — A243

Design: No. 628, "Electricity," Aswan High Dam hydroelectric station.

1964, July 23 — Perf. 11½
627 A243 10m yellow & emer .35 .20
628 A243 10m green & blk .35 .20

Land reclamation and hydroelectric power due to the Aswan High Dam.

An imperf. souvenir sheet, issued July 23, contains two 50m black and blue stamps showing Aswan High Dam before and after diversion of the Nile. Value $2.

Map of Africa and 34 Flags — A244

1964, July 17 — Photo.
629 A244 10m brn, brt bl & blk .35 .20

Assembly of Heads of State and Government of the Organization for African Unity at Cairo in July.

Jamboree Emblem — A245

Design: No. 631, Emblem of Air Scouts.

1964, Aug. 28 — Unwmk. Perf. 11½
630 A245 10m red, grn & blk .50 .40
631 A245 10m green & red .50 .40
a. Pair, #630-631 1.25 1.25

The 6th Pan Arab Jamboree, Alexandria.

Flag of Algeria
A246

1964, Sept. 5 — Perf. 11½x11
Flags in Original Colors
632 A246 10m Algeria .65 .30
633 A246 10m Iraq .65 .30
634 A246 10m Jordan .65 .30
635 A246 10m Kuwait .65 .30
636 A246 10m Lebanon .65 .30
637 A246 10m Libya .65 .30
638 A246 10m Morocco .65 .30
639 A246 10m Saudi Arabia .65 .30
640 A246 10m Sudan .65 .30
641 A246 10m Syria .65 .30
642 A246 10m Tunisia .65 .30
643 A246 10m UAR .65 .30
644 A246 10m Yemen .65 .30
Nos. 632-644 (13) 8.45 3.90

2nd meeting of the Heads of State of the Arab League, Alexandria, Sept. 1964.

World Map, Dove, Olive Branches and Pyramids — A247

1964, Oct. 5 — Perf. 11½
645 A247 10m slate blue & yel .35 .20

Conference of Heads of State of Non-Aligned Countries, Cairo, Oct. 1964.

Pharaonic Athletes
A248

Designs from ancient decorations: 10m, Four athletes, vert. 35m, Wrestlers, vert. 50m, Pharaoh in chariot hunting.

Perf. 11½x11, 11x11½
1964, Oct. 10 — Photo. Unwmk.
Sizes: 39x22mm, 22x39mm
646 A248 5m lt green & org .25 .20
647 A248 10m slate bl & lt brn .35 .20
648 A248 35m dull vio & lt brn .65 .50
Size: 58x24mm
649 A248 50m ultra & brn org 1.25 .75
Nos. 646-649 (4) 2.50 1.65

18th Olympic Games Tokyo, Oct. 10-25.

Emblem, Map of Africa and Asia
A249

Map of Africa, Communication Symbols
A250

1964, Oct. 10 — Perf. 11x11½
650 A249 10m violet & yellow .35 .20

First Afro-Asian Medical Congress.

1964, Oct. 24
651 A250 10m green & blk .35 .20

Pan-African and Malagasy Posts and Telecommunications Cong., Cairo, Oct. 24-Nov. 6.

Horus and Facade of Nefertari Temple, Abu Simbel
A251

Ramses II — A252

Designs: 35m, A god holding rope of life, Abu Simbel. 50m, Isis of Kalabsha, horiz.

1964, Oct. 24 — Perf. 11½, 11x11½
652 A251 5m grnsh bl & yel
brn .70 .30
653 A252 10m sepia & brt yel 1.00 .30
654 A251 35m brown org & indigo 2.00 .90
Nos. 652-654 (3) 3.70 1.50
Souvenir Sheet
Imperf
655 A252 50m olive & vio blk 15.00 15.00

"Save the Monuments of Nubia" campaign. No. 655 contains one horiz. stamp.

Emblems of Cooperation, Rural Handicraft and Women's Work — A253

1964, Dec. 8 — Photo. Unwmk.
656 A253 10m yellow & dk blue .35 .20

25th anniv. of the Ministry of Social Affairs.

UN, UNESCO Emblems, Pyramids
A254

Minaret, Mardani Mosque
A255

1964, Dec. 24 — Perf. 11x11½
657 A254 10m ultra & yellow .35 .20

Issued for UNESCO Day.

1965, Jan. 20 — Photo. Perf. 11
658 A255 4m blue & dk brown .35 .20

Issued for use on greeting cards.
See No. N121.

Police Emblem over City
A256

Oil Derrick and Emblem
A257

Perf. 11x11½
1965, Jan. 25 — Wmk. 342
659 A256 10m black & yellow .55 .20

Issued for Police Day.

1965, Mar. 16 — Photo.
660 A257 10m dk brown & yellow .45 .20

5th Arab Petroleum Congress and the 2nd Arab Petroleum Exhibition.

Flags and Emblem of the Arab League — A258

Red Crescent and WHO Emblem — A259

Design: 20m, Arab League emblem, horiz.

1965, Mar. 22 — Wmk. 342
661 A258 10m green, red & blk .50 .30
662 A258 20m ultra & brown .85 .40

20th anniversary of the Arab League.
See Nos. N122-N123.

1965, Apr. 7 — Photo.
663 A259 10m blue & crimson .35 .20

World Health Day (Smallpox: Constant Alert).
See No. N124.

Dagger in Map of Palestine — A260

1965, Apr. 9 — Perf. 11x11½
664 A260 10m black & red 1.25 .30

Deir Yassin massacre, Apr. 9, 1948.
See No. N125.

ITU Emblem, Old and New Communication Equipment — A261

1965, May 17 — Perf. 11½x11
665 A261 5m violet blk & yel .30 .25
666 A261 10m red & yellow .35 .25
667 A261 35m dk blue, ultra &
yel 1.10 .80
Nos. 665-667 (3) 1.75 1.30

Cent. of the ITU. See Nos. N126-N128.

Library Aflame and Lamp A262

1965, June 7   Photo.   Wmk. 342
668 A262 10m black, grn & red   .40 .20
Burning of the Library of Algiers, 6/7/62.

Sheik Mohammed Abdo (1850-1905), Mufti of Egypt — A263

1965, July 11   Perf. 11x11½
669 A263 10m Prus blue & bis brn   .35 .20

Pouring Ladle (Heavy Industry) A264

President Gamal Abdel Nasser and Emblems of Arab League, African Unity Organization, Afro-Asian Countries and UN — A265

#670, Search for off-shore oil. #672, Housing, construction in Nasser City (diamond shaped).

1965, July 23   Perf. 11½
670 A264 10m indigo & lt blue   .60 .35
671 A264 10m brown & yellow   .60 .35
672 A264 10m yel brn & blk   .60 .35
673 A265 100m lt green & blk   4.25 3.25
    Nos. 670-673 (4)   6.05 4.30

13th anniversary of the revolution.
The 100m was printed in sheets of six, consisting of two singles and two vertical pairs. Margins and gutters contain multiple UAR coat of arms in light green. Size: 240x330mm.

4th Pan Arab Games Emblem A266

Map and Emblems of Previous Games — A267

#675, Swimmers Zeitun & Abd el Gelil, arms of Alexandria. 35m, Race horse "Saadoon."

Perf. 11½x11; 11½ (#676)
1965, Sept. 2   Photo.   Wmk. 342
674 A266 5m blue & red   .30 .20
675 A266 10m dp blue & dk brn   .45 .40
676 A267 10m org brn & dp bl   .50 .40
677 A266 35m green & brown   1.00 .75
    Nos. 674-677 (4)   2.25 1.75

4th Pan Arab Games, Cairo, Sept. 2-11. No. 675 for the long-distance swimming competition at Alexandria, a part of the Games.

Map of Arab Countries, Emblem of Arab League and Broken Chain A268

1965, Sept. 13   Photo.   Perf. 11½
678 A268 10m brown & yellow   .35 .20
3rd Arab Summit Conf., Casablanca, 9/13.

Land Forces Emblem and Sun — A269

Perf. 11x11½
1965, Oct. 20   Wmk. 342
679 A269 10m bister brn & blk   .40 .20
Issued for Land Forces Day.

Map of Africa, Torch and Olive Branches — A270

1965, Oct. 21   Perf. 11½
680 A270 10m dull pur & car rose   .35 .20
Assembly of Heads of State of the Organization for African Unity.

Ramses II, Abu Simbel, and ICY Emblem A271

Pillars, Philae, and UN Emblem — A272

Designs: 35m, Two Ramses II statues, Abu Simbel and UNESCO emblem. 50m, Cartouche of Ramses II and ICY emblem, horiz.

Wmk. 342
1965, Oct. 24   Photo.   Perf. 11½
681 A271 5m yellow & slate grn   1.00 .35
682 A272 10m blue & black   1.50 .40
683 A271 35m dk violet & yel   3.50 1.25
    Nos. 681-683 (3)   6.00 2.00

Souvenir Sheet
Imperf
684 A272 50m brt ultra & dk brn   5.00 4.00

Intl. cooperation in saving the Nubian monuments. No. 684 also for the 20th anniv. of the UN. No. 684 contains one 42x25mm stamp.

Al-Maqrizi, Buildings and Books A273

Perf. 11½x11
1965, Nov. 20   Photo.   Wmk. 342
685 A273 10m olive & dk slate grn   .35 .20
Ahmed Al-Maqrizi (1365-1442), historian.

Flag of UAR, Arms of Alexandria and Art Symbols — A274

1965, Dec. 16   Perf. 11½x11½
686 A274 10m multicolored   .35 .20
6th Biennial Exhibition of Fine Arts in Alexandria, Dec. 16, 1965-Mar. 31, 1966.

Parchment Letter, Carrier Pigeon and Postrider A275

1966, Jan. 2   Wmk. 342   Perf. 11½
687 A275 10m multicolored   .45 .20
    Nos. 687,CB1-CB2 (3)   5.95 4.45
Post Day, Jan. 2.

Lamp and Arch — A276

Exhibition Poster — A277

1966, Jan. 10   Unwmk.   Perf. 11
688 A276 4m violet & dp org   .30 .20
Issued for use on greeting cards.

Perf. 11x11½
1966, Jan. 27   Wmk. 342
689 A277 10m lt blue & blk   .35 .20
Industrial Exhibition, Jan. 29-Feb.

Arab League Emblem — A278

Printed Page and Torch — A279

1966, Mar. 22   Photo.   Wmk. 342
690 A278 10m brt yellow & pur   .35 .20
Arab Publicity Week, Mar. 22-28.

1966, Mar. 25   Perf. 11x11½
691 A279 10m dp orange & sl blue   .35 .20
Centenary of the national press.

Traffic Signal at Night — A280

Hands Holding Torch, Flags of UAR & Iraq — A281

1966, May 4   Photo.   Wmk. 342
692 A280 10m green & red   .55 .20
Issued for Traffic Day.

1966, May 26   Perf. 11x11½
693 A281 10m dp claret, rose red & brt grn   .35 .20
Friendship between UAR and Iraq.

Workers and UN Emblem A282

Perf. 11½x11
1966, June 1   Photo.   Wmk. 342
694 A282 5m blue grn & blk   .30 .25
695 A282 10m brt rose lil & grn   .35 .25
696 A282 35m orange & black   .90 .70
    Nos. 694-696 (3)   1.55 1.20
50th session of the ILO.

Mobilization Dept. Emblem, People and City — A283

1966, June 30　　　　**Perf. 11x11½**
697 A283 10m dull pur & brn　　.35　.20
Population sample, May 31-June 16.

"Salah el Din," Crane and Cogwheel A284

Present-day Basket Dance and Pharaonic Dance — A285

#699, Transfer of first stones of Abu Simbel. #700, Development of Sinai (map of Red Sea area and Sinai Peninsula). #701, El Maadi Hospital and nurse with patient.

Wmk. 342
1966, July 23　**Photo.**　**Perf. 11½**
698 A284 10m orange & multi　　.45　.30
699 A284 10m brt green & multi　.45　.30
700 A284 10m yellow & multi　　.45　.30
701 A284 10m lt blue & multi　　.45　.30
　Nos. 698-701 (4)　　　　1.80　1.20
Souvenir Sheet
Imperf
702 A285 100m multicolored　　5.00　3.75
14th anniv. of the revolution.

Suez Canal Headquarters, Ships and Map of Canal — A286

1966, July 26　　　　**Perf. 11½**
703 A286 10m blue & crimson　1.00　.40
Suez Canal nationalization, 10th anniv.

Cotton, Farmers with Plow and Tractor A287

Perf. 11½x11
1966, Sept. 9　**Photo.**　**Wmk. 342**
704 A287 5m shown　　　　　.30　.25
705 A287 10m Rice　　　　　.30　.25
706 A287 35m Onions　　　　.80　.50
　Nos. 704-706 (3)　　　　1.40　1.00
Issued for Farmer's Day.

WHO Headquarters, Geneva — A288

Designs: 10m, UN refugee emblem. 35m, UNICEF emblem.

Perf. 11½x11
1966, Oct. 24　　　　　**Wmk. 342**
707 A288 5m olive & brt pur　　.40　.25
708 A288 10m orange & brt pur　.40　.25
709 A288 35m lt blue & brt pur　.70　.45
　Nos. 707-709 (3)　　　　1.50　.95
21st anniversary of the United Nations.
See Nos. N129-N131.

World Map and Festival Emblem A289

1966, Nov. 8　　　　　**Photo.**
710 A289 10m brt purple & yellow　.35　.20
5th Intl. Television Festival, Nov. 1-10.

Arms of UAR, Rocket and Pylon A290

1966, Dec. 23　**Wmk. 342**　**Perf. 11½**
711 A290 10m brt grn & car rose　.40　.20
Issued for Victory Day.
See No. N132.

Jackal A291

35m, Alabaster head from Tutankhamen treasure.

1967, Jan. 2　　　　　**Photo.**
712 A291 10m slate, yel & brn　1.10　.30
713 A291 35m bl, dk vio & ocher　2.25　.55
Issued for Post Day, Jan. 2.

Carnations A292

Workers Planting Tree A293

1967, Jan. 10　**Unwmk.**　**Perf. 11**
714 A292 4m citron & purple　　.35　.20
Issued for use on greeting cards.

Perf. 11x11½
1967, Mar. 15　　　　**Wmk. 342**
715 A293 10m brt green & blk vio　.35　.20
Issued to publicize the Tree Festival.

Gamal el-Dine el-Afaghani and Arab League Emblem — A294

1967, Mar. 22　**Photo.**　**Wmk. 342**
716 A294 10m dp green & dk brn　.35　.20
Arab Publicity Week, Mar. 22-28.
See No. N133.

Census Emblem, Man, Woman and Factory A295

1967, Apr. 23　　　　**Perf. 11½x11**
717 A295 10m black & dp org　　.35　.20
First industrial census.

Brickmaking Fresco, Tomb of Rekhmire, Thebes, 1504-1450 B.C. — A296

1967, May 1　**Photo.**　**Wmk. 342**
718 A296 10m olive & orange　　.35　.20
Issued for Labor Day, 1967.
See No. N134.

Ramses II and Queen Nefertari — A297

Design: 35m, Shooting geese, frieze from tomb of Atet at Meidum, c. 2724 B. C.

Perf. 11½x11
1967, June 7　**Photo.**　**Wmk. 342**
719 A297 10m multicolored　　.75　.40
720 A297 35m dk green & org　3.00　1.00
　Nos. 719-720,C113-C115 (5)　10.75　4.65
Issued for International Tourist Year, 1967.

President Nasser, Crowd and Map of Palestine A298

1967, June 22　　　　**Perf. 11½**
721 A298 10m dp org, yel & ol　2.00　.75
Issued to publicize Arab solidarity for "the defense of Palestine."

Souvenir Sheet

National Products — A299

1967, July 23　　**Wmk. 342**　**Imperf.**
722 A299 100m multicolored　3.50　2.75
15th anniv. of the revolution.

Salama Higazi — A300

Perf. 11x11½
1967, Oct. 14　**Photo.**　**Wmk. 342**
723 A300 20m brown & dk blue　.80　.20
50th anniversary of the death of Salama Higazi, pioneer of Egyptian lyric stage.

Stag on Ceramic Disk A301

Design: 55m, Apse showing Christ in Glory, Madonna and Saints, Coptic Museum, and UNESCO Emblem.

1967, Oct. 24　　　　**Perf. 11½**
724 A301 20m dull rose & dk bl　.65　.35
725 A301 55m dk slate grn & yel　1.30　.60
　Nos. 724-725,C117 (3)　　3.20　1.80
22nd anniv. of the UN.

Savings Bank and Postal Authority Emblems A302

1967, Oct. 31　　　　**Perf. 11½x11**
726 A302 20m sal pink & dk blue　.40　.20
International Savings Day.

Rose — A303

Unwmk.
1967, Dec. 15　**Photo.**　**Perf. 11**
727 A303 5m green & rose lilac　.35　.20
Issued for use on greeting cards.

Pharaonic
Dress — A304

Aswan High
Dam and Power
Lines — A305

Designs: Various pharaonic dresses from temple decorations.

Perf. 11x11½

1968, Jan. 2   **Wmk. 342**
728 A304 20m brown, grn & buff   .90   .30
729 A304 55m lt grn, yel & sepia 1.60   .60
730 A304 80m dk brn, bl & brt
         rose   2.25   .90
    Nos. 728-730 (3)   4.75 1.80

Issued for Post Day, Jan. 2.
See Nos. 752-755.

1968, Jan. 9
731 A305 20m yel, bl & dk brn   .35 .20

1st electricity generated by the Aswan Hydroelectric Station.

Alabaster
Vessel,
Tutankhamen
Treasure
A306

Girl, Moon and
Paint Brushes
A308

Capital of
Coptic
Limestone
Pillar
A307

Perf. 11x11½, 11½

1968, Jan. 20   **Photo.**   **Wmk. 342**
732 A306 20m dk ultra, yel & brn   .60 .25
733 A307 80m lt grn, dk pur & ol
         grn   1.00 .75

2nd International Festival of Museums.

1968, Feb. 15   **Perf. 11x11½**
734 A308 20m brt blue & black   .35 .20

7th Biennial Exhibition of Fine Arts, Alexandria, Feb. 15.

Cattle and Veterinarian — A309

Perf. 11½x11

1968, May 4   **Photo.**   **Wmk. 342**
735 A309 20m brown, yel & grn   .55 .20

8th Arab Veterinary Congress, Cairo.

Human Rights
Flame — A310

Perf. 11x11½
1968, July 1   **Photo.**   **Wmk. 342**
736 A310 20m citron, crim & grn   .40 .25
737 A310 60m sky blue, crim & grn   .65 .50

International Human Rights Year, 1968.

Open Book
with
Symbols of
Science,
Victory
Election
Result
A311

Workers, Cogwheel with Coat of Arms
and Open Book — A312

1968, July 23   **Perf. 11½**
738 A311 20m rose red & sl grn   .35 .20
Souvenir Sheet
Imperf
739 A312 100m lt grn, org & pur 3.00 2.25

16th anniversary of the revolution.

Imhotep
and WHO
Emblem
A313

No. 741, Avicenna and WHO emblem.

Perf. 11½x11
1968, Sept. 1   **Photo.**   **Wmk. 342**
740 A313 20m blue, yel & brn   .80 .30
741 A313 20m yellow, bl & brn   .80 .30
    a.   Pair, #740-741   2.00 1.75

20th anniv. of the WHO. Nos. 740-741 printed in checkerboard sheets of 50 (5x10).

Table Tennis — A314

Perf. 11x11½
1968, Sept. 20   **Photo.**   **Wmk. 342**
742 A314 20m lt green & dk brn 1.00 .35

First Mediterranean Table Tennis Tournament, Alexandria, Sept. 20-27.

Factories
and Fair
Emblem
A315

1968, Oct. 20   **Wmk. 342**   **Perf. 11½**
743 A315 20m bl gray, red & sl bl   .35 .20

Cairo International Industrial Fair.

Temples of Philae — A316

Refugees,
Map of
Palestine,
Refugee
Year
Emblem
A317

55m, Temple at Philae & UNESCO emblem.

1968, Oct. 24   **Photo.**
744 A316 20m multicolored   1.00 .25
745 A317 30m multicolored   1.25 .70
746 A317 55m lt blue, yel & blk   2.25 1.00
    Nos. 744-746 (3)   4.50 1.95

Issued for United Nations Day, Oct. 24.

Egyptian Boy Scout
Emblem — A318

1968, Nov. 1
747 A318 10m dull org & vio bl   .85 .30

50th anniversary of Egyptian Boy Scouts.

Pharaonic
Sports
A319

Design: 30m, Pharaonic sports, diff.

1968, Nov. 1
748 A319 20m pale ol, pale sal &
         blk   .55 .25
749 A319 30m pale blue, buff &
         pur   1.00 .55

19th Olympic Games, Mexico City, 10/12-27.

Aly Moubarak
A320

Lotus
A321

1968, Nov. 9   **Perf. 11½**
750 A320 20m green, brn & bister   .35 .20

Aly Moubarak (1823-93), founder of the modern educational system in Egypt.

1968, Dec. 11   **Photo.**   **Wmk. 342**
751 A321 5m brt blue, grn & yel   .35 .20

Issued for use on greeting cards.

Son of Ramses
III — A322

Hefni
Nassef — A323

Pharaonic Dress: No. 753, Ramses III. No. 754, Girl carrying basket on her head. 55m, Queen of the New Empire in transparent dress.

1969, Jan. 2   **Photo.**   **Perf. 11½**
752 A322   5m blue & multi   .45 .20
753 A322 20m blue & multi   .75 .30
754 A322 20m blue & multi   .90 .35
755 A322 55m blue & multi   2.25 .65
    Nos. 752-755 (4)   4.35 1.50

Issued for Post Day, Jan. 2.

Perf. 11x11½
1969, Mar. 2   **Photo.**   **Wmk. 342**

Portrait: No. 757, Mohammed Farid.

756 A323 20m purple & brown   .50 .20
757 A323 20m emerald & brown   .50 .20
    a.   Pair, #756-757   1.10 1.00

50th anniv. of the death of Hefni Nassef (1860-1919) writer and government worker, and Mohammed Farid (1867-1919), lawyer and Speaker of the Nationalist Party.

Teacher and
Children
A324

ILO Emblem
and Factory
Chimneys
A325

1969, Mar. 2   **Perf. 11x11½**
758 A324 20m multicolored   .35 .20

Arab Teacher's Day.

1969, Apr. 11   **Photo.**   **Wmk. 342**
759 A325 20m brown, ultra & car   .35 .20

50th anniv. of the ILO.

Flag of Algeria, Africa Day and Tourist Year Emblems A326

Perf. 11½x11

1969, May 25   Litho.   Wmk. 342

760	A326	10m Algeria	.75	.35
761	A326	10m Botswana	.75	.35
762	A326	10m Burundi	.75	.35
763	A326	10m Cameroun	.75	.35
764	A326	10m Cent. Afr. Rep.	.75	.35
765	A326	10m Chad	.75	.35
766	A326	10m Congo, ex-Belgian	.75	.35
767	A326	10m Congo, ex-French	.75	.35
768	A326	10m Dahomey	.75	.35
769	A326	10m Equatorial Guinea	.75	.35
770	A326	10m Ethiopia	.75	.35
771	A326	10m Gabon	.75	.35
772	A326	10m Gambia	.75	.35
773	A326	10m Ghana	.75	.35
774	A326	10m Guinea	.75	.35
775	A326	10m Ivory Coast	.75	.35
776	A326	10m Kenya	.75	.35
777	A326	10m Lesotho	.75	.35
778	A326	10m Liberia	.75	.35
779	A326	10m Libya	.75	.35
780	A326	10m Malagasy	.75	.35
781	A326	10m Malawi	.75	.35
782	A326	10m Mali	.75	.35
783	A326	10m Mauritania	.75	.35
784	A326	10m Mauritius	.75	.35
785	A326	10m Morocco	.75	.35
786	A326	10m Niger	.75	.35
787	A326	10m Nigeria	.75	.35
788	A326	10m Rwanda	.75	.35
789	A326	10m Senegal	.75	.35
790	A326	10m Sierra Leone	.75	.35
791	A326	10m Somalia	.75	.35
792	A326	10m Sudan	.75	.35
793	A326	10m Swaziland	.75	.35
794	A326	10m Tanzania	.75	.35
795	A326	10m Togo	.75	.35
796	A326	10m Tunisia	.75	.35
797	A326	10m Uganda	.75	.35
798	A326	10m UAR	.75	.35
799	A326	10m Upper Volta	.75	.35
800	A326	10m Zambia	.75	.35
		Nos. 760-800 (41)	30.75	14.35

El Fetouh Gate, Cairo A327

Sculptures from the Egyptian Museum, Cairo — A328

Millenary of Cairo — A329

#802, Al Azhar University. #803, The Citadel. #805, Sculptures, Coptic Museum. #806, Glass plate and vase, Fatimid dynasty, Islamic Museum. #807a, Islamic coin. #807b, Fatimist era jewelry. #807c, Copper vase. #807d, Coins and plaque.

Perf. 11½x11

1969, July 23   Photo.   Wmk. 342

801	A327	10m dk brown & multi	.50	.20
802	A327	10m green & multi	.50	.20
803	A327	10m blue & multi	.50	.20

Perf. 11½

804	A328	20m yellow grn & multi	.75	.30
805	A328	20m dp ultra & multi	.75	.30
806	A328	20m brown & multi	.75	.30
		Nos. 801-806 (6)	3.75	1.50

Souvenir Sheet

807	A329	Sheet of 4	8.50	7.50
a.		20m dark blue & multi	1.75	1.50
b.		20m lilac & multi	1.75	1.50
c.		20m yellow & multi	1.75	1.50
d.		20m dark green & multi	1.75	1.50

Millenium of the founding of Cairo.

African Development Bank Emblem — A330

Perf. 11x11½

1969, Sept. 10   Photo.   Wmk. 342

808 A330 20m emerald, yel & vio   .35   .20

African Development Bank, 5th anniv.

Pharaonic Boat and UN Emblem A331

Temple of Philae Inundated and UNESCO Emblem A332

Design: 5m, King and Queen from Abu Simbel Temple and UNESCO Emblem (size: 21x38mm).

Perf. 11x11½, 11½x11

1969, Oct. 24   Photo.   Wmk. 342

809	A332	5m brown & multi	.80	.30
810	A331	20m yellow & ultra	1.00	.30

Perf. 11½

811	A332	55m yellow & multi	1.50	.75
		Nos. 809-811 (3)	3.30	1.35

Issued for United Nations Day.

Ships of 1869 and 1967 and Maps of Africa and Suez Canal — A333

1969, Nov. 15   Perf. 11½x11

812 A333 20m lt blue & multi   1.10   .40

Centenary of the Suez Canal.

Cairo Opera House and Performance of Aida — A334

1969, Nov. 15

813 A334 20m multicolored   .75   .35

Centenary of the Cairo Opera House.

Crowd with Egyptian and Revolutionary Flags — A335

1969, Nov. 15   Perf. 11½x11

814 A335 20m brt grn, dull lil & red   .85   .35

Revolution of 1919.

Ancient Arithmetic and Computer Cards A336

Perf. 11½x11

1969, Dec. 17   Photo.   Wmk. 342

815 A336 20m multicolored   .40   .20

Intl. Congress for Scientific Accounting, Cairo, Dec. 17-19.

Poinsettia A337

Sakkara Step Pyramid A338

El Fetouh Gate, Cairo — A339

Fountain, Sultan Hassan Mosque, Cairo — A340

King Khafre (Ruled c. 2850 B.C.) A341

1969, Dec. 24   Unwmk.   Perf. 11

816 A337 5m yellow, grn & car   .30   .20

Issued for use on greeting cards.

**Wmk. 342 (20m, £1), Unwmkd.
Photo.; Engr. (20m, 55m)**

1969-70   Perf. 11

Designs: 5m, Al Azhar Mosque. 10m, Luxor Temple. 50m, Qaitbay Fort, Alexandria.

817	A338	1m multi ('70)	.30	.40
818	A338	5m multi ('70)	.50	.20
819	A338	10m multi ('70)	.50	.20
820	A339	20m dark brown	2.25	.35
821	A338	50m multi ('70)	2.25	.50
822	A340	55m slate green	3.50	.30

Perf. 11½

Photo. & Engr.

823	A341	£1 org & sl grn ('70)	50.00	10.00
		Nos. 817-823 (7)	59.30	11.95

See Nos. 889-891, 893-897, 899, 901-902, 904.

Veiled Women, by Mahmoud Said — A342

Perf. 11x11½

1970, Jan. 2   Photo.   Wmk. 342

824 A342 100m blue & multi   3.00   2.40

Post Day. Sheet of 8 with 2 panes of 4.

Parliament, Scales, Globe and Laurel — A343

1970, Feb. 2   Perf. 11½x11

825 A343 20m blue, vio bl & ocher   .55   .20

Intl. Conf. of Parliamentarians on the Middle East Crisis, Cairo, Feb. 2-5.

Map of Arab League Countries, Flag and Emblem A344

Perf. 11½x11

1970, Mar. 22   Photo.   Wmk. 342

826 A344 30m brn org, grn & dk pur   .45   .20

Arab League, 25th anniv. See No. B42.

Mena House and Sheraton Hotel — A345

1970, Mar. 23

827 A345 20m olive, org & bl   .55   .20

Centenary of Mena House and the inauguration of the Cairo Sheraton Hotel.

Manufacture of Medicine — A346

1970, Apr. 20

828 A346 20m brown, yel & bl   .90   .25

Production of medicines in Egypt, 30th anniv.

Mermaid — A347

1970, Apr. 20   *Perf. 11x11½*
829 A347 20m orange, blk & ultra   .35 .20

8th Biennial Exhibition of Fine Arts, Alexandria, March 12.

Misr Bank and Talaat Harb A348   ITU Emblem A349

1970, May 7   Photo.   Wmk. 342
830 A348 20m multicolored   .35 .20

50th anniversary of Misr Bank.

1970, May 17   *Perf. 11x11½*
831 A349 20m dk brn, yel & dull bl   .45 .20

World Telecommunications Day.

UPU Headquarters, Bern — A350

1970, May 20   *Perf. 11½x11*
832 A350 20m multicolored   .40 .20

Inauguration of the UPU Headquarters in Bern. See No. C128.

Basketball Player and Map of Africa — A351

UPU, UN and U.P.A.F. Emblems A352

No. 834, Soccer player, map of Africa & cup, horiz.

Perf. 11x11½, 11½x11
1970, May 25   Photo.   Wmk. 342
833 A351 20m lt blue, yel & brn   .65 .30
834 A351 20m yellow & multi   .55 .25
835 A352 20m ocher, grn & blk   .45 .20
     Nos. 833-835 (3)   1.65 .75

Africa Day. No. 833 also for the 5th African basketball championship for men; No. 834 the annual African Soccer championship; No. 835 publicizes the African Postal Union seminar.

Fist and Freed Bird — A353

1970, July 23   Photo.   *Perf. 11*
836 A353 20m lt green, org & blk   .50 .20

Souvenir Sheet
Imperf
837 A353 100m lt blue, dp org & blk   3.25 2.40

18th anniv. of the revolution.

Al Aqsa Mosque on Fire — A354

1970, Aug. 21   Wmk. 342   *Perf. 11*
838 A354 20m multicolored   .85 .25
839 A354 60m brt blue & multi   1.90 1.25

1st anniv. of the burning of Al Aqsa Mosque, Jerusalem.

Standardization Emblems — A355

1970, Oct. 14   Wmk. 342   *Perf. 11*
840 A355 20m yellow, ultra & grn   .55 .20

World Standards Day and 25th anniv. of the Intl. Standardization Organization, ISO.

UN Emblem, Scales and Dove — A356

Temple at Philae A357

Child, Education Year and UN Emblems A358

Designs: 10m, UN emblem. No. 845, 2nd Temple at Philae (denomination at left).

Perf. 11 (5m), 11½ (others)
1970, Oct. 24   Photo.   Wmk. 342
841 A356 5m lt bl, rose lil & sl   .20 .20
842 A357 10m yel, brn & lt bl   .25 .20
843 A358 20m slate & multi   .45 .20
844 A357 55m brn, bl & ocher   1.00 .60

845 A357 55m brn, bl & ocher   1.00 .60
 a.   Strip of 3, #842, 844-845   2.50 2.00
     Nos. 841-845,B43 (6)   3.65 2.40

25th anniv. of the UN. #843 also for Intl. Education Year; Nos. 842, 844-845, the work of UNESCO in saving the Temples of Philae. No. 845a printed in sheets of 35 (15 No. 842, 10 each Nos. 844-845). Nos. 844-845 show continuous picture of the Temples at Philae.

Gamal Abdel Nasser — A359

1970, Nov. 6   Wmk. 342   *Perf. 11*
846 A359 5m sky blue & blk   .20 .20
847 A359 20m gray green & blk   .50 .20
     Nos. 846-847,C129-C130 (4)   3.20 1.50

Gamal Abdel Nasser (1918-70), Pres. of Egypt.

Medical Association Building — A360

#849, Old & new National Library. #850, Egyptian Credo (Nasser quotation). #851, Engineering Society, old & new buildings. #852, Government Printing Offices, old & new buildings.

1970, Dec. 20   Photo.   *Perf. 11*
848 A360 20m yel, grn & brn   .55 .30
849 A360 20m green & multi   .55 .30
850 A360 20m lt blue & brn   .55 .30
851 A360 20m blue, yel & brn   .55 .30
852 A360 20m blue, yel & brn   .55 .30
 a.   Strip of 5, #848-852   3.25 3.25

50th anniv. of Egyptian Medical Assoc. (No. 848); cent. of Natl. Library (No. 849); Egyptian Engineering Assoc. (No. 851); sesqui. of Government Printing Offices (No. 852).

Map and Flags of UAR, Libya, Sudan A361

1970, Dec. 27   *Perf. 11½*
853 A361 20m lt grn, car & blk   .55 .20

Signing of the Charter of Tripoli affirming the unity of UAR, Libya & the Sudan, 12/27/70.

Qalawun Minaret — A362

Designs (Minarets): 10m, As Saleh. 20m, Isna. 55m, Al Hakim.

1971, Jan. 2   Wmk. 342   *Perf. 11*
854 A362 5m green & multi   .40 .20
855 A362 10m green & multi   1.00 .40
856 A362 20m green & multi   2.00 .80
857 A362 55m green & multi   3.50 1.60
 a.   Strip of 4, #854-857 + label   8.75 5.75

Post Day, 1971.
See Nos. 905-908, 932-935.

Gamal Abdel Nasser A363

Photogravure and Engraved
1971   Wmk. 342   *Perf. 11½*
858 A363 200m brn vio & dk bl   5.00 .90
859 A363 500m blue & black   12.00 3.00

Souvenir Sheet

Design: Portrait facing right.

Imperf
860   Sheet of 2   11.50 9.50
 a.   A363 100m light green & black   3.50 2.50
 b.   A363 200m blue & black   5.50 4.00

No. 860 commemorates inauguration of the Aswan High Dam, which is shown in margin. Issued: No. 860, 1/15; Nos. 858-859, 2/1. See No. 903.

Cotton and Globe A364

1971, Mar. 6   Photo.   *Perf. 11½x11*
861 A364 20m lt green, blue & brn   .40 .20

Egyptian cotton.

Arab Countries, and Arab Postal Union Emblem A365

1971, Mar. 6   Wmk. 342
862 A365 20m lt bl, org & sl grn   .40 .20

9th Arab Postal Cong., Cairo, 3/6-25. See No. C131.

Cairo Fair Emblem — A366

1971, Mar. 6   *Perf. 11x11½*
863 A366 20m plum, blk & org   .50 .20

Cairo International Fair, March 2-23.

Nesy Ra, Apers Papyrus and WHO Emblem A367

Perf. 11½x11
1971, Apr. 30   Photo.   Wmk. 342
864 A367 20m yellow bis & pur   .70 .20

World Health Organization Day.

Gamal Abdel Nasser — A368

1971, May 1 — Perf. 11

865	A368	20m purple & bl gray	1.00	.35
866	A368	55m blue & purple	3.25	1.10

Map of Africa, Telecommunications Symbols — A369

1971, May 17 — Perf. 11½x11

867	A369	20m blue & multi	.60	.20

Pan-African telecommunications system.

Wheelwright A370

Hand Holding Wheat and Laurel A371

Candle Lighting Africa — A372

1971, July 23 — Perf. 11x11½ — Photo. — Wmk. 342

868	A370	20m yellow & multi	.45	.25
869	A371	20m tan, grn & ocher	.45	.25

Souvenir Sheet
Imperf

870	A372	100m blue & multi	4.75	4.75

19th anniv. of the July Revolution. No. 870 contains one stamp with simulated perforations in gold.

Arab Postal Union Emblem A373

1971, Aug. 3 — Perf. 11½

871	A373	20m black, yel & grn	.35	.20

25th anniv. of the Conf. of Sofar, Lebanon, establishing the APU. See No. C135.

Arab Republic of Egypt

Three Links A374

Perf. 11½x11
1971, Sept. 28 — Photo. — Wmk. 342

872	A374	20m gray, org brn & blk	.50	.25

Confederation of Arab Republics (Egypt, Syria and Libya). See No. C136.

Gamal Abdel Nasser A375

Blood Donation A376

1971, Sept. 28 — Perf. 11x11½

873	A375	5m slate grn & vio brn	.40	.20
874	A375	20m violet brn & ultra	.60	.20
875	A375	30m ultra & brown	1.10	.40
876	A375	55m brown & emerald	1.90	.50
		Nos. 873-876 (4)	4.00	1.30

Death of Pres. Gamal Abdel Nasser, 1st anniv.

1971, Oct. 24

877	A376	20m green & carmine	.70	.20

"Blood Saves Lives."

Princess Nursing Child, UNICEF Emblem A377

Submerged Pillar, Philae, UNESCO Emblem A379

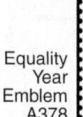

Equality Year Emblem A378

Perf. 11x11½, 11½x11
1971, Oct. 24 — Photo. — Wmk. 342

878	A377	5m buff, blk & org brn	.30	.20
879	A378	20m red brn, grn, yel & blk	.55	.20
880	A379	55m black, lt bl, yel & brn	1.25	.20
		Nos. 878-880,C137 (4)	3.70	1.00

UN Day. No. 878 honors UN Intl. Children's Fund; No. 879 for Intl. Year Against Racial Discrimination; No. 880 honors UNESCO.

Postal Traffic Center, Alexandria A380

1971, Oct. 31 — Perf. 11½x11

881	A380	20m blue & bister	.70	.20

Opening of Postal Traffic Center in Alexandria.

Sunflower A381

Abdalla El Nadim A382

1971, Nov. 13 — Perf. 11

882	A381	5m lt blue & multi	.35	.20

For use on greeting cards.

1971, Nov. 14 — Perf. 11x11½

883	A382	20m green & brown	.50	.20

Abdalla El Nadim (1845-1896), journalist, publisher, connected with Orabi Revolution.

Section of Earth's Crust, Map of Africa on Globe A383

1971, Nov. 27 — Perf. 11½x11

884	A383	20m ultra, yel & brn	.85	.20

75th anniv. of Egyptian Geological Survey and Intl. Conference, Nov. 27-Dec. 1.

Postal Union Emblem, Letter and Dove A384

55m, African Postal Union emblem and letter.

1971, Dec. 2

885	A384	5m multicolored	.45	.20
886	A384	20m olive, blk & org	.90	.20
887	A384	55m red, blk & blue	2.00	.90
		Nos. 885-887,C138 (4)	4.75	1.70

10th anniversary of African Postal Union.

Money and Safe Deposit Box A385

1971, Dec. 23 — Perf. 11½

888	A385	20m rose, brn & grn	.70	.20

70th anniversary of Postal Savings Bank.

Types of 1969-70, 1971
Inscribed "A. R. Egypt" and

Ramses II — A385a

Designs as before and: No. 894, King Citi I. No. 897, View of Alexandria. No. 898, Queen Nefertari. No. 900, Sphinx and Middle Pyramid. 100m, Cairo Mosque. 200m, Head of Pharaoh Userkaf.

Wmk. 342 (892A, 901-904)
1972-76 — Photo. — Unwmk. — Perf. 11

889	A338	1m multi	.25	.25
890	A338	1m dk brn ('73)	.25	.25
891	A338	5m multi	.30	.20
892	A385a	5m olive ('73)	.35	.20
892A	A385a	5m bister ('76)	.40	.20
893	A338	10m multi	.50	.25
894	A338	10m lt brn ('73)	.45	.25
895	A338	20m olive	.90	.25
896	A339	20m purple ('73)	1.00	.25
897	A338	50m multi	2.00	.30
898	A385a	50m dull bl ('73)	2.25	.30
899	A340	55m red lilac	3.25	.75
900	A340	55m green ('74)	1.75	.50
901	A339	100m lt blue, dp org & blk	2.50	.50

Perf. 11½
Photo. & Engr.

902	A341	200m yel grn & brn	6.00	1.25
903	A363	500m bl & choc	16.00	3.25
904	A341	£1 orange & sl grn	35.00	8.00
		Nos. 889-904 (17)	73.15	16.95

Minaret Type of 1971

5m, West Minaret, Nasser Mosque. 20m, East Minaret, Nasser Mosque. 30m, Minaret, Al Gawli Mosque. 55m, Minaret, Ibn Tulun Mosque.

Wmk. 342
1972, Jan. 2 — Photo. — Perf. 11

905	A362	5m dk green & multi	.40	.20
906	A362	20m dk green & multi	1.10	.20
907	A362	30m dk green & multi	2.50	.50
908	A362	55m dk green & multi	3.50	1.40
a.		Strip of 4, #905-908 + label	8.00	2.50

Post Day, 1972.

Police Emblem and Activities — A386

1972, Jan. 25 — Perf. 11½

909	A386	20m dull blue, brn & yel	1.75	.35

Police Day 1972.

UNESCO, UN and Book Year Emblems — A387

1972, Jan. 25 — Perf. 11x11½

910	A387	20m lt yel grn, vio bl & yel	.70	.20

International Book Year 1972.

Alexandria Biennale A388

1972, Feb. 15 — Wmk. 342 — Perf. 11½

911	A388	20m black, brt rose & yel	.70	.20

9th Biennial Exhibition of Fine Arts, Alexandria, Mar., 1972.

Fair Emblem
A389

Abdel Moniem
Riad
A390

1972, Mar. 5   *Perf. 11x11½*
912 A389 20m blue, org & yel grn   .70   .20
International Cairo Fair.

1972, Mar. 21   **Photo.**   **Wmk. 342**
913 A390 20m blue & brown   1.00   .20
In memory of Brig. Gen. Abdel Moniem
Riad (1919-1969), military hero.

Bird
Feeding
Young
A391

1972, Mar. 21   *Perf. 11½*
914 A391 20m yellow & multi   .50   .20
Mother's Day.

Tutankhamen — A392

Design: 55m, Back of chair with king's name
and symbols of eternity.

1972, May 22   **Unwmk.**
915 A392 20m gray, blk &
        ocher   1.75   .50
916 A392 55m purple & yellow   4.75   1.50
Nos. 915-916,C142-C143 (4)   23.50   10.00
Discovery of the tomb of Tutankhamen by
Howard Carter & Lord Carnarvon, 50th anniv.
See No. C144.

Queen
Nefertiti
A393

Wmk. 342
1972, May 22   **Photo.**   *Perf. 11½*
917 A393 20m red, blk & gold   .70   .20
Soc. of the Friends of Art, 50th anniv.

Map of
Africa — A394

1972, May 25   *Perf. 11x11½*
918 A394 20m purple, bl & brn   .40   .20
Africa Day.

Atom
Symbol,
"Faith and
Science"
A395

Design: No. 920, Egyptian coat of arms.

1972, July 23   *Perf. 11½*
919 A395 20m blue, claret & blk   .75   .20
920 A395 20m ol grn, gold & blk   .75   .20
20th anniversary of the revolution.

Boxing, Olympic and Motion
Emblems — A396

Designs (Olympic and Motion Emblems
and): 10m, Wrestling. 20m, Basketball.

1972, Aug. 17   *Perf. 11½x11*
921 A396 5m blue & multi   .30   .20
922 A396 10m yellow & multi   .45   .25
923 A396 20m ver & multi   .50   .30
Nos. 921-923,C149-C152 (7)   6.00   3.15
20th Olympic Games, Munich, 8/26-9/11.

Flag of Confederation of Arab
Republics — A397

1972, Sept. 1   **Wmk. 342**   *Perf. 11½*
924 A397 20m carmine, bis & blk   .60   .20
Confederation of Arab Republics, 1st anniv.

Red Crescent, TB
and UN
Emblems — A398

Heart and
WHO
Emblem
A399

Refugees, UNRWA Emblem, Map of
Palestine — A400

Design: 55m, Inundated Temple of Philae,
UNESCO emblem.

Perf. 11x11½ (#925), 11½ (#926,
928), 11 (#927)
1972, Oct. 24   **Photo.**
925 A398 10m brn org, red & bl   .45   .25
926 A399 20m green, yel & blk   .80   .35
927 A400 30m lt bl, pur & lt brn   2.25   .70
928 A399 55m brn, gold & bluish
         gray   2.50   .90
Nos. 925-927 (3)   3.50   1.30
UN Day. No. 925 is for the 14th Regional
Tuberculosis Conf., Cairo, 1972; No. 926
World Health Month; No. 927 publicizes aid to
refugees and No. 928 the UN campaign to
save the Temples at Philae.

Morning
Glory — A401

1972, Oct. 24   *Perf. 11*
929 A401 10m yel, lilac & grn   .50   .20
For use on greeting cards.

"Seeing
Eye"
A402

1972, Nov. 30   *Perf. 11½*
930 A402 20m multicolored   .70   .20
Social Work Day.

Sculling Race, View of Luxor — A403

1972, Dec. 17   **Wmk. 342**   *Perf. 11*
931 A403 20m blue & brown   1.10   .30
3rd Nile Intl. Rowing Festival, Dec. 1972.

Minaret Type of 1971

10m, Al Maridani, 1338. 20m, Bashtak,
1337. 30m, Qusun, 1330. 55m, Al Gashankir,
1306.

1973, Jan. 2
Frame in Bright Yellow Green
932 A362 10m multicolored   .70   .20
933 A362 20m multicolored   1.20   .30
934 A362 30m multicolored   2.50   .55
935 A362 55m multicolored   3.50   1.25
   a.   Strip of 4, #932-935 + Label   9.50   6.50
Post Day, 1973.

Cairo Fair
Emblem
A404

Perf. 11½x11
1973, Mar. 21   **Photo.**   **Wmk. 342**
936 A404 20m gray & multi   .50   .20
International Cairo Fair.

Family — A405

1973, Mar. 21   *Perf. 11x11½*
937 A405 20m multicolored   .60   .20
Family planning.

Sania
Girls'
School
and Hoda
Sharawi
A406

Perf. 11½x11
1973, July 15   **Photo.**   **Wmk. 342**
938 A406 20m ultra & multi   .60   .20
Centenary of education for girls and 50th
anniversary of the Egyptian Women's Union,
founded by Hoda Sharawi.

Rifaa el
Tahtawi — A407

1973, July 15   *Perf. 11x11½*
939 A407 20m brt green, ol & brn   .60   .20
Centenary of the death of Rifaa el Tahtawi,
champion of democracy and principal of language school.

Omar Makram
A408

Abdel Rahman
al Gabarti,
Historian
A409

"Reconstruction and Battle" — A410

No. 941, Mohamed Korayem, martyr.

1973, July 23
940 A408 20m yel grn, bl & brn .45 .25
941 A408 20m lt grn, bl & brn .45 .25
942 A409 20m ocher & brown .45 .25
Nos. 940-942 (3) 1.35 .75

Souvenir Sheet
Imperf
943 A410 110m gold, bl & blk 3.25 3.00
Revolution establishing the republic, 21st anniv.

Grain, Cow, FAO Emblem A411

Perf. 11½x11
1973, Oct. 24 **Wmk. 342**
944 A411 10m brn, dk bl & yel grn .50 .20
10th anniv. of the World Food Org.

Inundated Temples at Philae A412

1973, Oct. 24 **Perf. 11½**
945 A412 55m blue, pur & org 3.00 1.00
UNESCO campaign to save the temples at Philae.

Bank Building A413

1973, Oct. 24
946 A413 20m brn org, grn & blk .50 .20
75th anniv. of the National Bank of Egypt.

Rose — A414

1973, Oct. 24 **Perf. 11**
947 A414 10m blue & multi .40 .20
For use on greeting cards.

Human Rights Flame A415

Taha Hussein A416

Perf. 11x11½
1973, Dec. 8 **Photo.** **Wmk. 342**
948 A415 20m yel grn, dk bl & car .45 .20
25th anniversary of the Universal Declaration of Human Rights.

1973, Dec. 10
949 A416 20m dk blue, brn & emer .35 .20
Dr. Taha Hussein (1893-1973), "Father of Education" in Egypt, writer, philosopher.

Pres. Sadat, Flag and Battle of Oct. 6 — A417

1973, Dec. 23 **Perf. 11x11½**
950 A417 20m yellow, blk & red 1.50 1.00
October War against Israel (crossing of Suez Canal by Egyptian forces, Oct. 6, 1973). See No. 959.

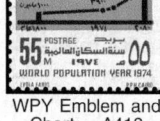

WPY Emblem and Chart — A418

Cairo Fair Emblem — A419

1974, Mar. 21 **Wmk. 342** **Perf. 11**
951 A418 55m org, grn & dk bl .85 .30
World Population Year.

1974, Mar. 21 **Photo.**
952 A419 20m blue & multi .40 .20
Cairo International Fair.

Nurse and Medal of Angels of Ramadan 10 — A420

1974, May 15 **Perf. 11½**
953 A420 55m multicolored 1.40 .35
Nurses' and World Hospital Day.

Workers, Relief Carving from Queen Tee's Tomb, Sakhara — A421

1974, May 15 **Perf. 11**
954 A421 20m yellow, blue & brn .60 .20
Workers' Day.

Pres. Sadat, Troops Crossing Suez Canal — A422

"Reconstruction," Map of Suez Canal and New Building — A423

Sheet of Aluminum A424

Design: 110m, Pres. Sadat's "October Working Paper," symbols of science and development.

1974, July 23 **Photo.** **Perf. 11x11½**
955 A422 20m multicolored .70 .35
956 A423 20m blue, gold & blk .70 .35

Perf. 11½
957 A424 20m plum & silver .70 .35
Nos. 955-957 (3) 2.10 1.05

Souvenir Sheet
Imperf
958 A424 110m green & multi 3.50 3.00
22nd anniv. of the revolution establishing the republic and for the end of the October War. No. 958 contains one 52x59mm stamp.

Pres. Sadat and Flag — A425

Perf. 11x11½
1974, Oct. 6 **Wmk. 342**
959 A425 20m yellow, blk & red 1.25 .60
1st anniv. of Battle. See No. 950.

Palette and Brushes A426

1974, Oct. 6 **Perf. 11½**
960 A426 30m purple, yel & blk .70 .20
6th Exhibition of Plastic Art.

Teachers and Pupils — A427

1974, Oct. 6 **Perf. 11x11½**
961 A427 20m multicolored .55 .20
Teachers' Day.

Souvenir Sheet

UPU Monument, Bern — A428

1974, Oct. 6 **Imperf.**
962 A428 110m gold & multi 5.00 4.25
Cent. of the UPU.

Emblems, Cogwheel and Calipers — A429

Refugee Camp under Attack and UN Refugee Organization Emblem — A430

Child and UNICEF Emblem A431

Temple of Philae — A432

1974, Oct. 24 **Perf. 11½, 11x11½**
963 A429 10m black, bl & yel .40 .20
964 A430 20m dp org, bl & blk .75 .20
965 A431 30m green, bl & brn 1.00 .40
966 A432 55m black, bl & yel 2.40 .85
Nos. 963-966 (4) 4.55 1.65

UN Day. World Standards Day (10m); Palestinian refugee repatriation (20m); Family Planning (30m); Campaign to save Temple of Philae (55m).

Calla Lily — A433

1974, Nov. 7 **Perf. 11**
967 A433 10m ultra & multi .40 .20
For use on greeting cards.

10m-coins, Smokestacks and Grain — A434

1974, Nov. 7 **Perf. 11½x11**
968 A434 20m yel grn, dk bl & sil .40 .20
International Savings Day.

Organization Emblem and Medical Services — A435

1974, Nov. 7 **Perf. 11½**
969 A435 30m vio, red & gold .65 .20
Health Insurance Organization, 10th anniv.

Mustafa Lutfy El Manfalouty A436

Abbas Mahmoud El Akkad A437

Perf. 11x11½
1974, Dec. 8 **Photo.** **Wmk. 342**
970 A436 20m blue blk & brn .40 .25
971 A437 20m brown & bl blk .40 .25
a. Pair, #970-971 1.00 .80

Arab writers; El Manfalouty (1876-1924) and El Akkad (1889-1964).

Goddess Maat Facing God Thoth — A438

Fish-shaped Vase — A439

Pharaonic Golden Vase — A440

Sign of Life, Mirror — A441

Wmk. 342
1975, Jan. 2 **Photo.** **Perf. 11½**
972 A438 20m silver & multi .75 .25
973 A439 30m multicolored 1.00 .25
974 A440 55m multicolored 1.40 .65
975 A441 110m blue & multi 2.25 1.25
Nos. 972-975 (4) 5.40 2.40

Post Day 1975. Egyptian art works from 12th-5th centuries B.C.

Om Kolthoum — A442

Perf. 11½
1975, Mar. 3 **Photo.** **Unwmk.**
976 A442 20m brown .70 .20
In memory of Om Kolthoum, singer.

Crescent, Globe, Al Aqsa and Kaaba — A443

Cairo Fair Emblem — A444

1975, Mar. 25
977 A443 20m multicolored .70 .20
Mohammed's Birthday.

Perf. 11x11½
1975, Mar. 25 **Wmk. 342**
978 A444 20m multicolored .40 .20
International Cairo Fair.

Kasr El Ainy Hospital WHO Emblem A445

Perf. 11½x11
1975, May 7 **Photo.** **Wmk. 342**
979 A445 20m dk brown & blue .60 .20
World Health Organization Day.

Children Reading Book — A446

Children and Line Graph — A447

1975, May 7 **Perf. 11x11½**
980 A446 20m multicolored .70 .20
981 A447 20m multicolored .70 .20
Science Day.

Suez Canal, Globe, Ships, Pres. Sadat — A448

1975, June 5 **Perf. 11½**
982 A448 20m blue, brn & blk 1.00 .30
Nos. 982,C166-C167 (3) 5.00 2.00
Reopening of the Suez Canal, June 5.

Belmabgoknis Flowers — A449

1975, July 30 **Photo.** **Wmk. 342**
983 A449 10m green & blue .40 .20
For use on greeting cards.

Sphinx and Pyramids Illuminated — A450

Rural Electrification — A451

Map of Egypt with Tourist Sites — A452

Illustration A452 is reduced.

1975, July 23
984 A450 20m black, org & grn .55 .25
985 A451 20m dk blue & brown .55 .25
Perf. 11
986 A452 110m multicolored 5.50 4.75
Nos. 984-986 (3) 6.60 5.25

23rd anniversary of the revolution establishing the republic. No. 986 printed in sheets of 6 (2x3). Size: 71x80mm.

Volleyball — A453

1975, Aug. 2 **Photo.** **Perf. 11x11½**
987 A453 20m shown .70 .25
988 A453 20m Running .70 .25
989 A453 20m Torch and flag bearers .70 .25

990	A453	20m	Basketball	.70	.25
991	A453	20m	Soccer	.70	.25
a.			Strip of 5, #987-991	4.00	3.50

6th Arab School Tournament.

Egyptian
Flag and
Tanks
A454

1975 Photo. Unwmk. Perf. 11½
992 A454 20m multicolored   1.25 .40

**Two-line Arabic Inscription
in Bottom Panel, "M" over "20"**

992A A454 20m multicolored   1.25 .40

No. 992 for 2nd anniv. of October War against Israel, "The Spark;" No. 992A, the Intl. Symposium on October War against Israel 1973, Cairo University, Oct. 27-31. Issue dates: No. 992, Oct. 6; No. 992A, Oct. 24.

Arrows Pointing
to Fluke, and
Emblems
A455

Submerged Wall
and Sculpture,
UNESCO Emblem
A456

Perf. 11x11½
1975, Oct. 24 Wmk. 342
993 A455 20m multicolored   .65 .30
994 A456 55m multicolored   1.90 .50

UN Day. 20m for Intl. Conf. on Schistosomiasis (Bilharziasis); 55m for UNESCO help in saving temples at Philae. See Nos. C169-C170.

Pharaonic Gate,
University
Emblem — A457

Al
Biruni — A458

1975, Nov. 15 Photo. Wmk. 342
995 A457 20m multicolored   .35 .20

Ain Shams University, 25th anniversary.

1975, Dec. 23 Photo. Perf. 11x11½

Arab Philosophers: No. 997, Al Farabi and lute. No. 998, Al Kanady, book and compass.

996	A458	20m blue, brn & grn	1.10	.30
997	A458	20m blue, brn & grn	1.10	.30
998	A458	20m blue, brn & grn	1.10	.30
		Nos. 996-998 (3)	3.30	.90

Ibex
(Prow) — A459

Post Day (from Tutankhamen's Tomb): 30m, Lioness. 55m, Cow's head (Goddess Hawthor). 110m, Hippopotamus' head (God Horus).

1976, Jan. 2 Unwmk. Perf. 11½
999 A459 20m multicolored   3.25 1.25

Wmk. 342
1000	A459	30m brown, gold & ultra	5.25	1.50
1001	A459	55m multicolored	9.50	3.25
1002	A459	110m multicolored	13.00	8.00
		Nos. 999-1002 (4)	31.00	14.00

Lake, Aswan Dam, Industry and
Agriculture — A460

Perf. 11½x11
1976, Jan. 27 Photo. Wmk. 342
1003 A460 20m multicolored   .60 .20

Filling of lake formed by Aswan High Dam.

Fair
Emblem — A461

Commemorative
Medal — A462

1976, Mar. 15 Perf. 11x11½
1004 A461 20m orange & purple   .35 .20

9th International Cairo Fair, Mar. 8-27.

1976, Mar. 15 Wmk. 342
1005 A462 20m olive, yel & blk   .35 .20

11th Biennial Exhibition of Fine Arts, Alexandria.

Hands
Shielding
Invalid
A463

1976, Apr. 7 Photo. Perf. 11½
1006 A463 20m dk grn, lt grn & yel   .40 .20

Founding of Faithfulness and Hope Society.

Eye and
WHO
Emblem
A464

1976, Apr. 7
1007 A464 20m dk brn, yel & grn   .60 .20

World Health Day: "Foresight prevents blindness."

Pres. Sadat, Legal Department
Emblem — A465

Perf. 11½x11
1976, May 15 Photo. Wmk. 342
1008 A465 20m olive & multi   .75 .25

Centenary of State Legal Department.

Scales of
Justice — A466

1976, May 15 Perf. 11x11½
1009 A466 20m carmine, blk & grn   .60 .20

5th anniversary of Rectification Movement.

Al-Ahram
Front
Page,
First Issue
A467

Perf. 11½x11
1976, June 25 Photo. Wmk. 342
1010 A467 20m bister & multi   .45 .20

Centenary of Al-Ahram newspaper.

World Map, Pres. Sadat and
Emblems — A468

1976, July 23 Perf. 11x11½
1011 A468 20m bl, blk & yel   .55 .30

Size: 240x216mm
Imperf
1012 A468 110m bl, brn & yel   5.50 4.75

24th anniv. of the revolution. No. 1012 design is similar to No. 1011.

Scarborough
Lily — A469

1976, Sept. 10 Photo. Perf. 11
1013 A469 10m multicolored   .35 .20

For use on greeting cards.

Reconstruction of Sinai by
Irrigation — A470

Abu Redice Oil
Wells and
Refinery — A471

Unknown Soldier, Memorial Pyramid
for October War — A472

1976, Oct. 6 Perf. 11x11½
| 1014 | A470 | 20m multicolored | .65 | .35 |
| 1015 | A471 | 20m multicolored | .65 | .35 |

Size: 65x77mm
1016 A472 110m grn, bl & blk   6.00 5.00

October War against Israel, 3rd anniv.

Papyrus with Children's Animal
Story — A473

Al Aqsa Mosque, Palestinian
Refugees — A474

55m, Isis, from Philae Temple, UNESCO emblem, vert. 110m, UNESCO emblem & "30."

Perf. 11½, 11½x11

1976, Oct. 24   Photo.   Wmk. 342
1017	A473	20m dk bl, bis & brn	.55	.20
1018	A474	30m brn, grn & blk	.75	.30
1019	A473	55m dk blue & bister	1.25	.45
1020	A474	110m lt grn, vio bl & red	2.25	1.25
	Nos. 1017-1020 (4)		4.80	2.20

30th anniversary of UNESCO.

Census Chart
A475

1976, Nov. 22   Photo.   Perf. 11½x11
1021	A475	20m multicolored	.40	.20

10th General Population and Housing Census.

A476   A477

Design: Nile and commemorative medal.

1976, Nov. 22   Perf. 11x11½
1022	A476	20m green & brown	.45	.20

Geographical Soc. of Egypt, cent. (in 1975).

1977, Jan. 2   Photo.   Perf. 11x11½

Post Day: 20m, Ikhnaton. 30m, Ikhnaton's daughter. 55m, Nefertiti, Ikhnaton's wife. 110m, Ikhnaton, front view.
1023	A477	20m multicolored	.30	.20
1024	A477	30m multicolored	.30	.20
1025	A477	55m multicolored	.65	.25
1026	A477	110m multicolored	2.75	.60
	Nos. 1023-1026 (4)		4.00	1.25

Policeman, Emblem and Emergency Car — A478

Perf. 11½x11

1977, Feb. 25   Photo.   Wmk. 342
1027	A478	20m multicolored	.85	.20

Police Day.

Map of Africa, Arab League Emblem — A479

1977, Mar 7   Perf. 11x11½
1028	A479	55m multicolored	.70	.20

First Afro-Arab Summit Conference, Cairo.

Fair Emblem, Pharaonic Ship A480

1977, Mar. 7   Perf. 11½x11
1029	A480	20m green, blk & red	.45	.20

10th International Cairo Fair.

King Faisal — A481   Healthy and Crippled Children — A482

1977, Mar. 22   Photo.   Perf. 11x11½
1030	A481	20m indigo & brown	.45	.20

King Faisal Ben Abdel-Aziz Al Saud of Saudi Arabia (1906-1975).

1977, Apr. 12   Wmk. 342
1031	A482	20m multicolored	.50	.20

National campaign to fight poliomyelitis.

APU Emblem, Members' Flags A483

1977, Apr. 12   Perf. 11½
1032	A483	20m blue & multi	.25	.20
1033	A483	30m gray & multi	.25	.20

25th anniv. of Arab Postal Union (APU).

Children's Village A484

Perf. 11½x11

1977, May 7   Photo.   Wmk. 342
1034	A484	20m multicolored	.25	.20
1035	A484	55m multicolored	.75	.40

Inauguration of Children's Village, Cairo.

Loom, Spindle and Factory A485

1977, May 7
1036	A485	20m multicolored	.35	.20

Egyptian Spinning and Weaving Company, El Mehalla el Kobra, 50th anniv.

Satellite, Globe, ITU Emblem — A486

1977, May 17   Perf. 11x11½
1037	A486	110m dk blue & multi	1.25	.50

World Telecommunications Day.

Flag and "25" A487

Egyptian Flag and Eagle — A488

Perf. 11½x11

1977, July 23   Photo.   Wmk. 342
1038	A487	20m silver, car & blk	.50	.20

Perf. 11x11½
1039	A488	110m multicolored	2.50	1.00

25th anniversary of July 23rd Revolution. No. 1039 printed in sheets of six. Size: 75x83mm.

Saad Zaghloul A489   Archbishop Capucci, Map of Palestine A490

Perf. 11x11½

1977, Aug. 23   Photo.   Wmk. 342
1040	A489	20m dk green & dk brn	.20	.20

Saad Zaghloul, leader of 1919 Revolution, 50th death anniversary.

1977, Sept. 1
1041	A490	45m emerald & blue	1.00	.40

Palestinian Archbishop Hilarion Capucci, jailed by Israel in 1974.

Bird-of-Paradise Flower — A491

1977, Sept. 3
1042	A491	10m multicolored	.20	.20

For use on greeting cards.

Proclamation Greening the Land — A492

Perf. 11x11½

1977, Sept. 25   Photo.   Wmk. 342
1043	A492	20m multicolored	.20	.20

Agrarian Reform Law, 25th anniversary.

Soldier, Tanks, Medal of Oct. 6 A493

Anwar Sadat — A494

1977, Oct. 6   Perf. 11½x11½
1044	A493	20m multicolored	.30	.20

Unwmk.
Perf. 11
1045	A494	140m dk brn, gold & red	4.75	4.75

October War against Israel, 4th anniv. No. 1045 printed in sheets of 16.

Refugees Looking at Al Aqsa Mosque A495

Goddess Taueret and Spirit of Flight (Horus) A496

Mural Relief, Temple of Philae — A497

Wmk. 342
1977, Oct. 24   Photo.   Perf. 11
1046	A495	45m green, red & blk	.40	.20
1047	A496	55m dp blue & yellow	.60	.25
1048	A497	140m ol bis & dk brn	1.50	.80
	Nos. 1046-1048 (3)		2.50	1.25

United Nations Day.

Electric Trains, First Egyptian Locomotive — A498

1977, Oct. 22
1049 A498 20m multicolored   1.00 .20
125th anniversary of Egyptian railroads.

Film and Eye A499

1977, Nov. 16   *Perf. 11½x11*
1050 A499 20m gray, blk & gold   .35 .20
50th anniversary of Egyptian cinema.

Natural Gas Well and Refinery — A500

1977, Nov. 17   **Photo.**
1051 A500 20m multicolored   .40 .20
National Oil Festival, celebrating the acquisition of Sinai oil wells.

Pres. Sadat and Dome of the Rock A501

Perf. 11½x11
1977, Dec. 31 **Photo.** **Wmk. 342**
1052 A501 20m green, brn & blk   .60 .20
1053 A501 140m green, blk & brn   2.25 .80
Pres. Sadat's peace mission to Israel.

Ramses II — A502

Post Day: 45m, Queen Nefertari, bas-relief.

1978, Jan. 2   *Perf. 11½*
1054 A502 20m green, blk & gold   .60 .20
1055 A502 45m orange, blk & ol   1.25 .70
Post Day 1978.

Water Wheels, Fayum — A503

Flying Duck, from Floor in Ikhnaton's Palace A504

5m, Birdhouse, 10m, Statue of Horus. 20m, 30m, Al Rifa'i Mosque, Cairo. 50m, Monastery, Wadi al-Natrun. 55m, Ruins of Edfu Temple. 70m, 80m, Bridge of Oct. 6. 85m, Medum pyramid. 100m, Facade, El Morsi Mosque, Alexandria. 200m, Column, Alexandria, Sphinx. 500m, Arabian stallion.

Wmk. 342, Unwmkd. (30m, 70m, 80m)

1978-85   *Perf. 11½*
1056 A503   1m slate blue   .20 .20
   a.   Unwmkd. ('79)   .20 .20
   b.   1m gray ('83)   .20 .20
   c.   1m gray, unwmkd. ('83)   .20 .20
1057 A503   5m bister brn   .20 .20
   a.   5m dull brn, unwmkd. (79)   .20 .20
1058 A503   10m brt green   .20 .20
   a.   Unwmkd. ('79)   .20 .20
1059 A503   20m dk brown   .20 .20
   b.   Unwmkd. ('79)   .20 .20
1059A A503   30m sepia   .20 .20
1060 A503   50m Prus blue   .25 .25
   a.   Unwmkd. ('79)   .25 .25
   b.   Unwmkd., brt blue ('87)   .25 .25
1061 A503   55m olive   .25 .25
1062 A503   70m olive ('79)   .30 .25
1062A A503   80m olive ('82)   .35 .25
1063 A503   85m dp purple   .40 .25
   a.   Unwmkd. ('85)   .40 .25
1064 A503   100m brown   .45 .25
   a.   Unwmkd. ('85)   .65 .25
1065 A503   200m bl & indigo   2.00 .60
1066 A504   500m multicolored   5.00 1.50
1067 A504   £1 multicolored   7.50 2.00
   Nos. 1056-1067 (14)   17.50 6.30

Issued: 500m, £1, 2/27/78; 70m, 8/22/79; others, 7/23/78.

Fair Emblem and Wheat A505

1978, Mar. 15   *Perf. 11½*
1072 A505 20m multicolored   .20 .20
11th Cairo International Fair, Mar. 11-25.

Emblem, Kasr El Ainy School A506

1978, Mar. 18   *Perf. 11½x11*
1073 A506 20m lt blue, blk & gold   .20 .20
Kasr El Ainy School of Medicine, 150th anniv.

A507

#1074, Soldiers and Emblem. #1075, Youssef El Sebai.

1978, Mar. 30   *Perf. 11x11½*
1074   20m multicolored   .30 .20
1075   20m bister brown   .30 .20
   a.   A507 Pair, #1074-1075   .60 .20
Youssef El Sebai, newspaper editor, assassinated on Cyprus and in memory of the commandos killed in raid on Cyprus.

Biennale Medal, Statue for Entrance to Port Said A509

1978, Apr. 1   *Perf. 11½*
1076 A509 20m blue, grn & blk   .25 .25
12th Biennial Exhibition of Fine Arts, Alexandria.

Child with Smallpox, UN Emblem A510

1978, Apr. 7   **Photo.**   *Perf. 11½*
1077 A510 20m multicolored   .20 .20
Eradication of smallpox.

Heart & Arrow, UN Emblem — A511

Anwar Sadat — A512

1978, Apr. 7   **Wmk. 342**
1078 A511 20m multicolored   .20 .20
Fight against hypertension.

1978, May 15 Photo. *Perf. 11½x11*
1079 A512 20m green, brn & gold   .35 .20
7th anniversary of Rectification Movement.

Social Security Emblem — A513

1978, May 16   *Perf. 11*
1080 A513 20m lt green & dk brn   .20 .20
General Organization of Insurance and Pensions (Social Security), 25th anniversary.

New Cities on Map of Egypt — A514

Map of Egypt and Sudan, Wheat — A515

Wmk. 342
1978, July 23   Photo.   *Perf. 11½*
1081 A514 20m multicolored   .50 .20
1082 A515 45m multicolored   1.00 .20
26th anniversary of July 23rd revolution.

Symbols of Egyptian Ministries — A516

1978, Aug. 28 Photo. *Perf. 11½x11*
1083 A516 20m multicolored   .35 .20
Centenary of Egyptian Ministerial System.

Pres. Sadat and "Spirit of Egypt" Showing Way — A517

1978, Oct. 6   Photo.   *Perf. 11x11½*
1084 A517 20m multicolored   .50 .20
October War against Israel, 5th anniv.

Fight Against Racial Discrimination Emblem — A518

Dove and Human Rights Emblem — A520

Kobet al Sakra Mosque, Refugee Camp A519

UN Day: 55m, Temple at Biga and UNESCO emblem, horiz.

Perf. 11, 11½ (45m)
1978, Oct. 24   Photo.   Wmk. 342
1085	A518	20m multicolored	.30	.20
1086	A519	45m multicolored	.85	.20
1087	A518	55m multicolored	.40	.20
1088	A520	140m multicolored	2.10	.30
		Nos. 1085-1088 (4)	3.65	.90

Pilgrims, Mt. Arafat and Holy Kaaba — A521

1978, Nov. 7   Photo.   Perf. 11
1089 A521 45m multicolored   .80 .20
Pilgrimage to Mecca.

Tahtib Horse Dance — A522

1978, Nov. 7
1090 A522 10m multicolored   .45 .20
1091 A522 20m multicolored   .45 .20

UN Emblem, Globe and Grain A523

1978, Nov. 11   Photo.   Perf. 11½
1092 A523 20m green, dk bl & yel   .30 .20
Technical Cooperation Among Developing Countries Conf., Buenos Aires, Sept. 1978.

Pipes, Map and Emblem of Sumed Pipeline A524

1978, Nov. 11
1093 A524 20m brown, bl & yel   .45 .20
Inauguration of Sumed pipeline from Suez to Alexandria, 1st anniversary.

Mastheads A525

Abu el Walid A526

1978, Dec. 24   Perf. 11x11½
1094 A525 20m brown & black   .45 .20
El Wakea el Masriya newspaper, 150th anniv.

1978, Dec. 24
1095 A526 45m brt green & indigo   .55 .20
800th death anniv. of Abu el Walid ibn Rashid.

Helwan Observatory and Sky — A527

1978, Dec. 30   Wmk. 342
1096 A527 20m multicolored   .60 .20
Helwan Observatory, 75th anniversary.

Second Daughter of Ramses II A528

Ramses Statues, Abu Simbel, and Cartouches — A529

1979, Jan. 2   Photo.   Perf. 11
1097 A528 20m brown & yellow   .50 .25
Perf. 11½x11
1098 A529 140m multicolored   1.75 .35
Post Day 1979.

Book, Reader and Globe A530

Perf. 11½x11
1979, Feb. 1   Photo.   Wmk. 342
1099 A530 20m yellow grn & brown   .35 .20
Cairo 11th International Book Fair.

Wheat, Globe, Fair Emblem — A531

Perf. 11x11½
1979, Mar. 17   Photo.   Unwmk.
1100 A531 20m blue, org & blk   .35 .20
12th Cairo International Fair, Mar.-Apr.

Skull, Poppy, Agency Emblem — A532

1979, Mar. 20   Perf. 11
1101 A532 70m multicolored   1.25 .35
Anti-Narcotics General Administration, 50th anniv.

Isis Holding Horus — A533

1979, Mar. 21
1102 A533 140m multicolored   2.10 .50
Mother's Day.

World Map and Book — A534

Perf. 11x11½
1979, Mar. 22   Wmk. 342
1103 A534 45m yellow, bl & brn   .45 .25
Cultural achievements of the Arabs.

Pres. Sadat's Signature, Peace Doves A535

Wmk. 342
1979, Mar. 31   Photo.   Perf. 11½
1104 A535 70m brt green & red   1.00 .25
1105 A535 140m yellow grn & red   2.00 .60
Signing of Peace Treaty between Egypt and Israel, Mar. 26.

1979, May 26   Photo.   Perf. 11½
1106 A535 20m yellow & dk brn   .40 .20
Return of Al Arish to Egypt.

Honeycomb with Food Symbols A536

1979, May 15
1107 A536 20m multicolored   .30 .20
8th anniversary of movement to establish food security.

Coins, 1959, 1979 A537

Perf. 11½x11
1979, June 1   Wmk. 342   Photo.
1108 A537 20m yellow & gray   .35 .20
25th anniversary of the Egyptian Mint.

Egypt No. 1104 under Magnifying Glass — A538

1979, June 1   Perf. 11
1109 A538 20m green, blk & brn   .40 .20
Philatelic Society of Egypt, 50th anniversary.

Book, Atom Symbol, Rising Sun — A539

"23 July," "Revolution" and "Peace" — A540

Perf. 11½x11
1979, July 23 **Wmk. 342**
1110 A539 20m multicolored .35 .20
Miniature Sheet
Imperf
1111 A540 140m multicolored 3.00 1.50
27th anniversary of July 23rd revolution.

Musicians — A541

1979, Aug. 22 **Perf. 11½**
1112 A541 10m multicolored .20 .20
For use on greeting cards.

Dove over Map of Suez Canal A542

Wmk. 342
1979, Oct. 6 **Photo.** **Perf. 11½**
1113 A542 20m blue & brown .40 .20
October War against Israel, 6th anniv.

Prehistoric Mammal Skeleton, Map of Africa — A543

Perf. 11½x11
1979, Oct. 9 **Photo.** **Wmk. 342**
1114 A543 20m multicolored 1.25 .25
Egyptian Geological Museum, 75th anniv.

T Square on Drawing Board — A544

1979, Oct. 11 **Perf. 11**
1115 A544 20m multicolored .50 .20
Engineers Day.

Human Rights Emblem Over Globe — A545

Boy Balancing IYC Emblem — A546

Perf. 11½
1979, Oct. 24 **Photo.** **Unwmk.**
1116 A545 45m multicolored .50 .25
1117 A546 140m multicolored 1.25 .50
UN Day and Intl. Year of the Child.

International Savings Day — A547

1979, Oct. 31
1118 A547 70m multicolored .75 .30

A548   A549

Design: Shooting championship emblem.

1979, Nov. 16
1119 A548 20m multicolored .40 .20
20th International Military Shooting Championship, Cairo.

1979, Nov. 29 **Perf. 11x11½**
1120 A549 45m multicolored .75 .25
International Palestinian Solidarity Day.

Dove Holding Olive Branch, Rotary Emblem, Globe A550

1979, Dec. 3 **Photo.** **Perf. 11½**
1121 A550 140m multicolored 1.25 .60
Rotary Intl., 75th anniv,; Cairo Rotary Club, 50th anniv.

Arms Factories, 25th Anniversary — A551

Perf. 11½x11
1979, Dec. 23 **Photo.** **Wmk. 342**
1122 A551 20m lt olive grn & brn .35 .20

Aly El Garem (1881-1949) A552

Pharaonic Capital A553

Poets: No. 1124, Mahmoud Samy El Baroudy (1839-1904).

1979, Dec. 25 **Perf. 11x11½**
1123 A552 20m dk brn & yel brn .40 .20
1124 A552 20m brown & dk brown .40 .20
a. Pair, #1123-1124 .80 .80

1980, Jan. 2 **Unwmk.** **Perf. 11½**
Post Day: Various Pharaonic capitals.
1125 A553 20m multicolored .35 .25
1126 A553 45m multicolored .50 .35
1127 A553 70m multicolored .70 .25
1128 A553 140m multicolored 2.00 .40
a. Strip of 4, #1125-1128 4.75 2.40

Golden Goddess of Writing, Fair Emblem — A554

Exhibition Catalogue and Medal — A555

1980, Feb. 2 **Photo.** **Perf. 11½**
1129 A554 20m multicolored .60 .20
12th Cairo Intl. Book Fair, Jan. 24-Feb. 4.

1980, Feb. 2
1130 A555 20m multicolored .45 .20
13th Biennial Exhibition of Fine Arts, Alexandria.

13th Cairo International Fair — A556

1980, Mar. 8 **Photo.** **Perf. 11x11½**
1131 A556 20m multicolored .45 .20

Kiosk of Trajan — A557

a, Kiosk of Tratan. b, Temple of Korasy, entry at right. c, Temple of Ksalabsha, carvings on frame. d, Temple of Philae, 5 columns..

1980, Mar. 10 **Perf. 11½**
1132 Strip of 4 + label 5.00 5.00
a.-d. A557 70m, any single 1.00 .60
UNESCO campaign to save Nubian monuments, 20th anniversary. Shown on stamps are Temples of Philae, Kalabsha, Korasy.

Physicians' Day — A558

1980, Mar. 18 **Perf. 11x11½**
1133 A558 20m multicolored .45 .20

Rectification Movement, 9th Anniversary — A559

Perf. 11½x11
1980, May 15 **Photo.** **Wmk. 342**
1134 A559 20m multicolored .45 .20

Re-opening of Suez Canal, 5th Anniversary — A560

1980, June 5 **Perf. 11½**
1135 A560 140m multicolored 1.40 .50

Prevention of Cruelty to Animals Week A561

1980, June 5
1136 A561 20m lt yel grn & gray .70 .20

Industry Day A562

Perf. 11½x11
1980, July 12 Photo. Wmk. 342
1137 A562 20m multicolored .35 .20

Leaf with Text A563

Family Protection Emblem — A564

1980, July 23 *Perf. 11½*
1138 A563 20m multicolored .45 .20
Souvenir Sheet
Imperf
1139 A564 140m multicolored 2.75 .55
July 23rd Revolution, 28th anniv.; Social Security Year.

Erksous Seller and Nakrazan Player — A565

Perf. 11½
1980, Aug. 8 Unwmk. Photo.
1140 A565 10m multicolored .30 .20
For use on greeting cards.

October War Against Israel, 7th Anniv. — A566

1980, Oct. 6 *Litho.*
1141 A566 20m multicolored .75 .20

Islamic and Coptic Columns A567

International Telecommunications Union Emblem — A568

Wmk. 342
1980, Oct. 24 Photo. *Perf. 11½*
1142 A567 70m multicolored .70 .55
1143 A568 140m multicolored 1.40 .85
UN Day. Campaign to save Egyptian monuments (70m), Intl. Telecommunications Day (140m).

Hegira (Pilgrimage Year) A569

1980, Nov. 9 Litho. *Perf. 11x11½*
1144 A569 45m multicolored .60 .25

Opening of Suez Canal Third Branch A570

Perf. 11½x11
1980, Dec. 16 Photo. Wmk. 342
1145 A570 70m multicolored .80 .30

Mustafa Sadek El-Rafai (1880-1927), Writer — A571

No. 1147, Ali Mustafa Mousharafa (1898-1950), mathematician (with glasses). No. 1148, Ali Ibrahim (1880-1947), surgeon.

1980, Dec. 23 *Perf. 11x11½*
1146 A571 20m green & brown .45 .25
1147 A571 20m green & brown .45 .25
1148 A571 20m green & brown .45 .25
a. Strip of 3, #1146-1148 1.90 .75
See Nos. 1178-1179.

Ladybug Scarab Emblem — A572   von Stephan, UPU — A573

Perf. 11½
1981, Jan. 2 Photo. Unwmk.
1149 A572 70m shown .90 .25
1150 A572 70m Scarab, reverse .90 .25
Post Day.

Perf. 11x11½
1981, Jan. 7 Wmk. 342
1151 A573 140m grnsh bl & dk brn 1.75 .70
Heinrich von Stephan (1831-97), founder of UPU.

13th Cairo International Book Fair — A574

1981, Feb. 1 *Perf. 11½x11*
1152 A574 20m multicolored .40 .20

14th Cairo International Fair, Mar. 14-28 — A575

Perf. 11x11½
1981, Mar. 14 Photo. Wmk. 342
1153 A575 20m multicolored .40 .20

Rural Electrification Authority, 10th Anniversary — A576

1981, Mar. 18
1154 A576 20m multicolored .45 .20

Veterans' Day — A577   Intl. Dentistry Conf., Cairo — A578

1981, Mar. 26
1155 A577 20m multicolored .50 .20

Perf. 11x11½
1981, Apr. 14 Photo. Wmk. 342
1156 A578 20m red & olive .50 .20

Trade Union Emblem — A579   Nurses' Day — A580

Perf. 11x11½
1981, May 1 Photo. Wmk. 342
1157 A579 20m brt blue & dk brn .40 .20
International Confederation of Arab Trade Unions, 25th anniv.

1981, May 12
1158 A580 20m multicolored .40 .20

Irrigation Equipment (Electrification Movement) — A581

1981, May 15 *Perf. 11½*
1159 A581 20m multicolored .40 .20

Air Force Day — A582

Perf. 11x11½
1981, June 30 Photo. Wmk. 342
1160 A582 20m multicolored .50 .20

Flag Surrounding Map of Suez Canal — A583

Wmk. 342
1981, July 23 **Photo.** *Perf. 11½*
1161 A583 20m multicolored .45 .20
1162 A583 20m Emblems .45 .20

July 23rd Revolution, 29th anniv.; Social Defense Year.

1981 Feasts — A584

Wmk. 342
1981, July 29 **Photo.** *Perf. 11*
1163 A584 10m multicolored .40 .20

A585   A586

1981, Aug. 10 *Perf. 11x11½*
1164 A585 140m Kemal Ataturk 2.00 .80

Perf. 11x11½
1981, Sept. 9 **Photo.** **Wmk. 342**
1165 A586 20m Orabi Pasha, Leader of Egyptian Force .40 .20

Orabi Revolution centenary.

A587   A588

1981, Sept. 14
1166 A587 45m Athlete, Pyramids, Sphinx .80 .20

World Muscular Athletics Championships, Cairo.

Perf. 11x11½
1981, Sept. 26 **Photo.** **Wmk. 342**
1167 A588 45m multicolored .60 .20

Ministry of Industry and Mineral Resources, 25th anniv.

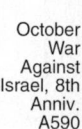

20th Intl. Occupational Health Congress, Cairo — A589

1981, Sept. 28 *Perf. 11½x11*
1168 A589 20m multicolored .50 .20

October War Against Israel, 8th Anniv. A590

1981, Oct. 6
1169 A590 20m multicolored .70 .20

World Food Day A591

13th World Telecommunications Day — A592

Intl. Year of the Disabled — A593

Fight Against Apartheid A594

Perf. 11½x11, 11x11½
1981, Oct. 24 **Photo.** **Wmk. 342**
1170 A591 10m multicolored .30 .20
1171 A592 20m multicolored .30 .20
1172 A593 45m multicolored .50 .25
1173 A594 230m multicolored 3.00 1.10
Nos. 1170-1173 (4) 4.10 1.75

United Nations Day.

Pres. Anwar Sadat (1917-81) — A595

Perf. 11x11½
1981, Nov. 14 **Unwmk.**
1174 A595 30m multicolored 1.40 .65
1175 A595 230m multicolored 3.50 2.50

Establishment of Shura Council — A596

Perf. 11½x11
1981, Dec. 12 **Photo.** **Wmk. 342**
1176 A596 45m purple & yellow .50 .20

Agricultural Credit and Development Bank, 50th Anniv. — A597

1981, Dec. 15 *Perf. 11x11½*
1177 A597 20m multicolored .40 .20

Famous Men Type of 1980

30m, Ali el-Ghayati (1885-1956), journalist. 60m, Omar Ebn sl-Fared (1181-1234), Sufi poet.

Perf. 11x11½
1981, Dec. 21 **Photo.** **Wmk. 342**
1178 A571 30m green & brown .40 .20
1179 A571 60m green & brown .60 .20
a. Pair, #1178-1179 1.00 .50

20th Anniv. of African Postal Union A598

1981, Dec. 21 *Perf. 11½x11*
1180 A598 60m multicolored .90 .30

14th Cairo Intl. Book Fair — A599

Arab Trade Union of Egypt, 25th Anniv. — A600

1982, Jan. 28
1181 A599 3p brown & yellow .60 .20

1982, Jan. 30
1182 A600 3p multicolored .40 .20

Khartoum Branch of Cairo University, 25th Anniv. A601

Perf. 11½x11
1982, Mar. 4 **Wmk. 342**
1183 A601 6p blue & green .80 .35

15th Cairo Intl. Fair — A602

1982, Mar. 13 *Perf. 11x11½*
1184 A602 3p multicolored .40 .20

50th Anniv. of Al-Ghardaka Marine Biological Station — A603

Fish of the Red Sea.

1982, Apr. 24 **Litho.** *Perf. 11½x11*
1185 10m Lined butterfly fish .65 .45
1186 30m Blue-banded sea perch .95 .50
1187 60m Batfish 1.10 .75
1188 230m Blue-spotted boxfish 3.00 1.40
a. A603 Block of 4, #1185-1188 6.00 2.00

Liberation of the Sinai — A604

1982, Apr. 25 **Photo.** *Perf. 11x11½*
1189 A604 3p multicolored .60 .20

50th Anniv. of Egypt Air A605

1982, May 7 **Photo.** *Perf. 11½x11*
1190 A605 23p multicolored 2.50 1.40

Minaret — A606

Al Azhar Mosque — A607

a, shown. b, Two terraces. c, Three terraces. d, Two turrets at top.

Perf. 11x11½
1982, June 28 **Photo.** **Wmk. 342**
1191 Strip of 4 + label 3.50 3.50
a.-d. A606 6p any single, multi .55 .30

Souvenir Sheet
Unwmk. *Imperf.*
1192 A607 23p multicolored 6.00 3.00

Al Azhar Mosque millennium.
No. 1192 airmail.

Dove — A608

Flower in Natl. Colors — A609

Perf. 11x11½
1982, July 23   Photo.   Wmk. 342
1193 A608 3p multicolored   .40   .20

Souvenir Sheet
Imperf
1194 A609 23p multicolored   4.25 2.10
30th anniv. of July 23rd Revolution.

World Tourism Day A610

Design: Sphinx, pyramid of Cheops, St. Catherine's Tower.

Perf. 11½x11
1982, Sept. 27   Photo.   Wmk. 342
1195 A610 23p multicolored   2.75 1.40

October War Against Israel, 9th Anniv. A611

1982, Oct. 6
1196 A611 3p Memorial, map   .60   .20

Biennale of Alexandria Art Exhibition — A612

1982, Oct. 17   Perf. 11x11½
1197 A612 3p multicolored   .45   .20

10th Anniv. of UN Conference on Human Environment — A613

2nd UN Conference on Peaceful Uses of Outer Space, Vienna, Aug. 9-21 — A614

Scouting Year A615

TB Bacillus Centenary A616

Perf. 11½x11, 11½ (A615)
1982, Oct. 24
1198 A613 3p multicolored   .40   .20
1199 A614 6p multicolored   .70   .20
1200 A615 6p multicolored   .70   .20
1201 A616 8p multicolored   .80   .20
    Nos. 1198-1201 (4)   2.60   .80
United Nations Day.

50th Anniv. of Air Force A617

1982, Nov. 2   Perf. 11½x11
1202 A617 3p Jet, plane   .60   .20

Ahmed Chawki (1868-1932) and Hafez Ibrahim (1871-1932), Poets — A618

Perf. 11½x11
1982, Nov. 25   Photo.   Wmk. 342
1203 A618 6p multicolored   .60   .20

Natl. Research Center, 25th Anniv. — A619

1982, Dec. 12   Photo.   Perf. 11x11½
1204 A619 3p red & blue   .65   .20

50th Anniv. of Arab Language Society A620

1982, Dec. 25   Perf. 11½x11
1205 A620 6p multicolored   .65   .20

Year of the Aged — A621

Post Day A622

1982, Dec. 25   Perf. 11x11½
1206 A621 23p multicolored   2.50 1.40

1983, Jan. 2   Perf. 11½
1207 A622 3p multicolored   .50   .20

15th Cairo Intl. Book Fair — A623

Perf. 11x11½
1983, Jan. 25   Photo.   Wmk. 342
1208 A623 3p blue & red   .50   .20

Police Day A624

1983, Jan. 25   Perf. 11½x11
1209 A624 3p multicolored   .60   .20

16th Cairo Intl. Fair — A625

5th UN African Map Conf., Cairo — A626

Perf. 11x11½
1983, Mar. 2   Photo.   Wmk. 342
1210 A625 3p multicolored   .50   .20

1983, Mar. 2
1211 A626 3p lt green & blue   .60   .20

African Ministers of Transport, Communications and Planning, 3rd Conference — A627

1983, Mar. 8   Perf. 11½x11
1212 A627 23p green & blue   1.75 1.00

A628   A629

1983, Mar. 20   Perf. 11x11½
1213 A628 3p Heading   .50   .20
1214 A628 3p Kick   .50   .20
    a. Pair, #1213-1214   1.25 1.25
Victory in African Soccer Cup.

Perf. 11x11½
1983, Apr. 2   Photo.   Wmk. 342
1215 A629 3p olive & red   .70   .20
World Health Day and Natl. Blood Donation Campaign.

Org. of African Trade Union Unity A630

Perf. 11½x11
1983, Apr. 21   Photo.   Wmk. 342
1216 A630 3p multicolored   .50   .20

1st Anniv. of Sinai Liberation A631

75th Anniv. of Entomology Society A632

1983, Apr. 25   Perf. 11x11½
1217 A631 3p multicolored   .75   .20

1983, May 23
1218 A632 3p Emblem (Holy Scarab) .75   .20

Flowers — A633

1983, June 11   Photo.   Perf. 11½x11
1219 A633 20m green & org red   .40   .20

5th African Handball Championship, Cairo — A634

Perf. 11½x11
1983, July 22   Photo.   Wmk. 342
1220 A634 6p brown & dk grn   .60   .20

31st Anniv. of
Revolution
A635

Simon Bolivar
(1783-1830)
A636

1983, July 23   *Perf. 11½*
1221 A635 3p multicolored   .40 .20

1983, Aug.   *Perf. 11x11½*
1222 A636 23p brown & dull grn   1.25 .80

Centenary
of Arrival
of Natl.
Hero
Orabi in
Ceylon
A637

Perf. 11½x11
1983, Aug. 25   **Photo.**   **Wmk. 342**
1223 A637 3p Map, Orabi, El-Zahra
School   .40 .20

Islamic
Vase,
Museum
Building
A638

1983, Sept. 14   **Photo.**   *Perf. 11½x11*
1224 A638 3p yel brn & dk brn   .70 .20
Reopening of Islamic Museum.

October War
Against Israel,
10th
Anniv. — A639

2nd Pharaonic
Race — A640

1983, Oct. 6   *Perf. 11½*
1225 A639 3p multicolored   .70 .20

1983, Oct. 17   *Perf. 11½*
1226 A640 23p multicolored   2.00 1.25

United Nations
Day — A641

1983, Oct. 24   **Photo.**   *Perf. 11*
1227 A641   3p IMO, ships, horiz.   .40 .20
1228 A641   6p ITU, UPU   .40 .20
1229 A641   6p FAO, UN, grain   .40 .20
1230 A641 23p UN, ocean   2.00 .60
    Nos. 1227-1230 (4)   3.20 1.20

4th World Karate Championship,
Cairo — A642

1983, Nov.   **Photo.**   *Perf. 13*
1231 A642 3p multicolored   .60 .20

Intl. Palestinian Cooperation
Day — A643

1983, Nov. 29   **Photo.**   *Perf. 13x13½*
1232 A643 6p Dome of the Rock   1.00 .20

75th Anniv.
of Faculty
of Fine
Arts, Cairo
A644

1983, Nov. 30   *Perf. 13*
1233 A644 3p multicolored   .40 .20

75th Anniv. of Cairo
University — A645

1983, Nov. 30   *Perf. 11x11½*
1234 A645 3p multicolored   .40 .20

Intl.
Egyptian
Society of
Mother
and Child
Care
A646

1983, Nov. 30   *Perf. 11½x11*
1235 A646 3p multicolored   .40 .20

Org. of African
Unity, 20th
Anniv. — A647

World Heritage
Convention, 10th
Anniv. — A648

Perf. 11x11½
1983, Dec. 20   **Photo.**   **Wmk. 342**
1236 A647 3p multicolored   .40 .20

1983, Dec. 24
1237   Strip of 3   2.50 2.50
  a.   A648 3p Wood carving, Islamic   .75 .40
  b.   A648 3p Coptic tapestry   .75 .40
  c.   A648 3p Ramses II Thebes   .75 .40

Post Day
A649

Restored Forts: 6p, Quatbay. 23p, Mosque,
Salah El-Din.

1984, Jan. 2   *Perf. 13*
1238 A649   6p multicolored   .50 .20
1239 A649 23p multicolored   2.00 1.25

Misr
Insurance
Co., 50
Anniv.
A650

1984, Jan. 14   *Perf. 11½x11*
1240 A650 3p multicolored   .35 .20

16th Cairo Intl. Book
Fair — A651

Perf. 13½x13
1984, Jan. 26   **Photo.**   **Wmk. 342**
1241 A651 3p multicolored   .40 .20

17th
Cairo Intl.
Fair
A652

Perf. 11½x11
1984, Mar. 10   **Photo.**   **Wmk. 342**
1242 A652 3p multicolored   .45 .20

25th Anniv. of
Asyut University
A653

75th Anniv. of
Cooperative
Unions
A654

1984, Mar. 10   *Perf. 11x11½*
1243 A653 3p multicolored   .40 .20

1984, Mar. 17
1244 A654 3p multicolored   .40 .20

World Theater
Day — A655

Mahmoud Mokhtar
(1891-1934),
Sculptor — A656

Perf. 11x11½, 11½x11
1984, Mar. 27   **Photo.**   **Unwmk.**
1245 A655 3p Masks   .45 .20
1246 A656 3p Pride of the Nile   .45 .20

World Health Day and Fight Against
Polio — A657

Perf. 11½x11
1984, Apr. 7   **Photo.**   **Wmk. 342**
1247 A657 3p Polio vaccine   .60 .20

2nd Anniv. of Sinai
Liberation — A658

1984, Apr. 25
1248 A658 3p Doves, map   .50 .20

Africa
Day
A659

Perf. 12½x13½
1984, May 25   **Photo.**   **Wmk. 342**
1249 A659 3p Map, UN emblem   .40 .20

Satellite,
Waves — A660

Flower — A661

1984, May 31   *Perf. 11x11½*
1250 A660 3p multicolored   .50 .20
Radio broadcasting in Egypt, 50th anniv.

1984, June 1
1251 A661 2p red & green   .35 .20

Intl. Cairo Arab Arts Biennale — A662

1984, June 1 **Perf. 13½x12½**
1252 A662 3p multicolored .50 .20

July Revolution, 32nd Anniv. — A663

Wmk. 342
1984, July 23 **Photo.** **Perf. 11**
1253 A663 3p Atomic energy, agriculture .50 .20

A664 A665

1984 Summer Olympics: a, Boxing. b, Basketball. c, Volleyball. d, Soccer.

1984, July 28
1254 Strip of 4 + label 4.50 4.50
a.-d. A664 3p any single .40 .40

Size: 130x80mm
Imperf
1255 A664 30p like No. 1254 4.25 4.25

Wmk. 342
1984, Aug. 13 **Photo.** **Perf. 11**
1256 A665 3p bl & multi .45 .20
1257 A665 23p grn & multi 1.90 .90

2nd Genl. Conference of Egyptians Abroad, Aug. 11-15, Cairo.

Youth Hostels, 30th Anniv. — A666 Egypt Tour Co., 50th Anniv. — A667

Perf. 11x11½
1984, Sept. 22 **Photo.** **Wmk. 342**
1258 A666 3p Youths, emblem .40 .20

1984, Sept. 27
1259 A667 3p Emblem, sphinx .50 .20

October War Against Israel, 11th Anniv. — A668 Egypt-Sudan Unity — A669

1984, Oct. 6
1260 A668 3p Map, eagle .40 .20

1984, Oct. 12
1261 A669 3p Map of Nile, arms .50 .20

UN Day — A670 Tanks, Emblem — A671

Perf. 13½x12½
1984, Oct. 24 **Photo.** **Wmk. 342**
1262 A670 3p UNICEF Emblem, child .40 .20

UN campaign for infant survival.

1984, Nov. 10
1263 A671 3p multicolored .50 .20

Military Equipment Exhibition, Cairo, Nov. 10-14.

Tolon Mosque, Egypt A672

1984, Dec. 23 **Photo.** **Perf. 11½x11**
1264 A672 3p multicolored .60 .20

Ahmed Ebn Tolon (A.D. 835-884), Gov. of Egypt, founder of Kataea City.

A673 A674

1984, Dec. 23 **Perf. 11x11½**
1265 A673 3p multicolored .40 .20

Kamel el-Kilany (1897-1959), author.

Perf. 11x11½
1984, Dec. 26 **Photo.** **Wmk. 342**
Globe and congress emblem.
1266 A674 3p lt blue, ver & blk .60 .20

29th Intl. Congress on the History of Medicine, Dec. 27, 1984-Jan. 1, 1985, Cairo.

Academy of the Arts, 25th Anniv. A675

1984, Dec. 31 **Perf. 13**
1267 A675 3p Emblem in spotlights .60 .20

Pharaoh Receiving Message, Natl. Postal Museum, Cairo A676

1985, Jan. 2 **Perf. 11½x11**
1268 A676 3p brown, lt bl & ver .60 .20

Postal Museum, 50th anniv.

Intl. Union of Architects, 15th Conference, Jan. 14-Feb. 15 — A677

1985, Jan. 20
1269 A677 3p multicolored .60 .20

Seated Pharaonic Scribe — A678 Wheat, Cogwheels, Fair Emblem — A679

1985, Jan. 22 **Perf. 11x11½**
1270 A678 3p brt org & dk blue grn .60 .20

17th Intl. Book Fair, Jan. 22-Feb. 3, Cairo.

1985, Mar. 9 **Perf. 13½x13**
1271 A679 3p multicolored .60 .20

18th Intl. Fair, Mar. 9-22, Cairo.

Return of Sinai to Egypt, 3rd Anniv. — A680

1985, Apr. 25 **Wmk. 342** **Litho.**
1272 A680 5p multicolored .60 .20

Ancient Artifacts — A681

A681a

Designs: 1p, God Mout, limestone sculpture, 360-340 B.C. 2p, No. 1281, Five wading birds, bas-relief. 3p, No. 1276, Seated statue, Ramses II, Temple of Luxor. No. 1276A, Vase. 8p, 15p, Slave bearing votive fruit offering, mural. 10p, Double-handled flask. 11p, Sculpted head of woman. No. 1282, Pitcher. 30p, 50p, Decanter. 35p, Temple of Karnak carved capitals. £1, Mosque.

1985-90 Photo. Unwmk. Perf. 11½
1273 A681 1p brown olive .40 .20
1274 A681 2p brt grnsh bl .40 .20
1275 A681 3p yellow brown .40 .20
1276 A681 5p dk violet .40 .20
1276A A681 5p lemon .40 .20
1277 A681 8p pale ol grn, sep & brn .50 .20
1278 A681 10p dk vio & bl .60 .20
1279 A681 11p dk violet .60 .30
1280 A681 15p pale yel, sep & brn .60 .30
1281 A681 20p yellow green .60 .30
1282 A681 20p dk grn & yel .60 .30
1283 A681 30p ol bis & buff .70 .50
1284 A681 35p sep & pale yel 1.00 .60
1285 A681 50p purple & buff 1.40 .80
1285A A681a £1 brown & buff 3.75 3.75
1286 A681a £2 sepia & yel 6.00 6.00
Nos. 1273-1286 (16) 18.35 14.25

Issued: 1p, 2p, 3p, No. 1276, 8p, 11p, 15p, 5/1/85; 35p, 7/7/85; No. 1281, 4/1/86; 10p, 10/1/89; £2, 12/1/89; No. 1282, 2/1/90; 30p, 50p, 2/5/90; £1, 2/8/90; No. 1276A, 12/15/90. Nos. 1276A, 1278 are 18x23mm. No. 1278 exists dated "1990." See Nos. 1467, 1470, 1472.

Helwan University School of Music, 50th Anniv. A682

1985, May 15
1287 A682 5p multicolored .50 .20

El-Moulid Bride, Folk Doll — A683

1985
1288 A683 2p orange & multi .40 .20
1289 A683 5p red & multi .40 .20

Festivals 1985. Issued: 2p, 6/11; 5p, 8/10.

A684 A685

Winning teams: a, b, Cairo Sports Stadium. c, El-Mokawiloon Club, white uniform, 1983. d, Natl. Club, red uniform, 1984. e, El-Zamalek Club, orange uniform, 1984.

1985, June 17 **Perf. 13½x13**
1290 Strip of 5 5.00 5.00
a.-e. A684 5p any single 1.00 1.00

1985 Africa Cup Soccer Championships. Cairo Sports Stadium, 25th anniv. Nos. 1290a-1290b have continuous design.

1985, July 23 **Perf. 11½x11**
1291 A685 5p blue, brn & yel .65 .20

Egyptian Television, 25th anniv. Egyptian Revolution, 33rd anniv.

Suez Canal Reopening, 10th Anniv. — A686

Perf. 13x13½
1985, July 23 **Litho.** **Wmk. 342**
1292 A686 5p multicolored .65 .20

Egyptian Revolution, 33rd anniv.

Ahmed Hamdi Memorial Underwater Tunnel — A687

1985, July 23 **Perf. 13½x13**
1293 A687 5p blue, vio & org .50 .20

Egyptian Revolution, 33rd anniv.

Souvenir Sheet

Aswan High Dam, 25th Anniv. — A688

Wmk. 342
1985, July 23 **Photo.** **Imperf.**
1294 A688 30p multicolored 3.50 2.75

Heart, Map, Olive Laurel, Conference Emblem — A689

1985, Aug. 10 **Litho.** **Perf. 13½x13**
1295 A689 15p multicolored 1.25 .85

Egyptian Emigrants, 3rd general conference, Aug. 10-14, Cairo.

Natl. Tourism Ministry, 50th Anniv. — A690

1985, Sept. 10 **Perf. 13x13½**
1296 A690 5p multicolored .45 .20

October War Against Israel, 12th Anniv. — A691

1985, Oct. 6
1297 A691 5p multicolored .45 .20

Air Scouts Assoc., 30th Anniv. — A692

1985, Oct. 15 **Photo.** **Perf. 11½**
1298 A692 5p Emblem .55 .20

A693

UN, 40th Anniv. — A694

1985, Oct. 24
1299 A693 5p UN emblem, weather map .45 .20

UN Day, Meteorology Day.

1985, Oct. 24
1300 A694 15p multicolored 1.25 .85

Intl. Youth Year — A695

A696

1985, Oct. 24
1301 A695 5p multicolored .45 .20

1985, Oct. 24
1302 A696 15p blue & int blue 1.25 .85

Intl. Communications Development Program.

A697   A698

Emblem, hieroglyphics of Hassi Raa, 1st known dentist.

1985, Oct. 29 **Perf. 11x11½**
1303 A697 5p beige & pale bl vio .75 .25

2nd Intl. Dentistry Conference.

1985, Nov. 18 **Photo.** **Perf. 11½**
1304 A698 5p Emblem, squash player .45 .20

1985 World Squash Championships, Nov. 18-Dec. 4.

A699   A700

1985, Nov. 2 **Litho.** **Perf. 13½x13**
1305 A699 5p multicolored .45 .20

4th Intl. Conference on the Biography and Sunna of Mohammed.

1985, Dec. 1 **Photo.** **Perf. 11x11½**
1306 A700 5p multicolored .45 .20

1st Conference on the Development of Vocational Training.

Natl. Olympic Committee, 75th Anniv. — A701

18th Intl. Book Fair, Cairo — A702

1985, Dec. 28 **Photo.** **Perf. 13x13½**
1307 A701 5p multicolored .50 .20

1986, Jan. 21 **Perf. 11x11½**
1308 A702 5p Pharaonic scribe .45 .20

CODATU III — A703

1986, Jan. 26 **Perf. 11½**
1309 A703 5p lt ol grn, ver & grnsh bl .40 .20

3rd Intl. Conference on Urban Transportation in Developing Countries, Cairo.

Central Bank, 25th Anniv. — A704

1986, Jan. 30 **Perf. 13x13½**
1310 A704 5p multicolored .40 .20

Cairo Postal Traffic Center Inauguration — A705

1986, Jan. 30 **Perf. 11½x11**
1311 A705 5p blue & dk brown .40 .20

Pharaonic Mural, Btah Hotteb's Tomb at Saqqara A706

1986, Feb. 27 **Photo.** **Perf. 11½x11**
1312 A706 5p yel, gldn brn & brn .60 .25

Faculty of Commerce, Cairo Univ., 75th anniv.

Cairo Intl. Fair,
Mar. 8-
21 — A707

1986, Mar. 8   Litho.   Perf. 13½x13
1313 A707 5p multicolored   .40   .20

Queen Nefertiti, Sinai — A708

Perf. 13x13½
1986, Apr. 25   Litho.   Wmk. 342
1314 A708 5p multicolored   .50   .20
Return of the Sinai to Egypt, 4th anniv.

Ministry of
Health, 50th
Anniv. — A709

1986, Apr. 10   Perf. 13½x13
1315 A709 5p multicolored   .45   .20

1986 Census — A710

1986, May 26   Photo.   Perf. 11½
1316 A710 15p brn, grnsh bl &
    yel bis   1.00   1.00

Egypt, Winner of   Festivals,
African Soccer   Roses — A712
Cup — A711

1986, May 31   Perf. 13½x13
1317 A711 5p English inscription
        below cup   .50   .50
1318 A711 5p Arabic   .50   .50
    a.   Pair, #1317-1318   1.00   1.00

1986, June 2   Perf. 11½
1319 A712 5p multicolored   .40   .20

World
Environment
Day — A713

1986, June 5   Perf. 13½x13
1320 A713 15p Emblem, smoke-
    stacks   1.10 1.10

July 23rd
Revolution,
34th Anniv.
A714

1986, July 23   Litho.   Perf. 13
1321 A714 5p gray grn, scar & yel
    bis   .40   .20

6th African
Roads
Conference,
Cairo, Sept. 22-
26 — A715

Perf. 13½x13
1986, Sept. 21   Litho.   Wmk. 342
1322 A715 15p multicolored   1.00 1.00

October
War
Against
Israel, 13th
Anniv.
A716

1986, Oct. 6   Litho.   Perf. 13
1323 A716 5p multicolored   .70   .25

Engineers'
Syndicate,
40th Anniv.
A717

1986, Oct. 11   Photo.   Perf. 11½
1324 A717 5p lt blue, brn & pale
    grn   .40   .20

Workers'   Intl. Peace
Cultural   Year — A719
Education
Assoc., 25th
Anniv. — A718

1986, Oct. 11   Perf. 11x11½
1325 A718 5p orange & rose vio   .40   .20

1986, Oct. 24
1326 A719 5p blue, grn & pale sal   .35   .20

First Oil Well in
Egypt,
Cent. — A720

1986, Nov. 7   Photo.   Perf. 11½
1327 A720 5p dull grn, blk & pale
    yel   .60   .25

UN Child
Survival
Campaign
A721

1986, Nov. 20   Litho.   Perf. 13
1328 A721 5p multicolored   .60   .25

Ahmed Amin,
Philosopher
A722

1986, Dec. 20   Perf. 11½
1329 A722 5p pale grn, pale yel &
    brn   .40   .20

National Theater,
50th
Anniv. — A723

1986, Dec. 20   Perf. 13½x13
1330 A723 5p multicolored   .45   .20

Post
Day
A724

Step Pyramid, Saqqara, King Zoser.

Perf. 13x13½
1987, Jan. 2   Litho.   Wmk. 342
1331 A724 5p multicolored   .60   .25

19th Intl.
Book Fair,
Cairo
A725

1987, Jan. 25   Litho.   Perf. 13
1332 A725 5p multicolored   .40   .20

5th World
Conference
on Islamic
Education
A726

Wmk. 342
1987, Mar. 8   Litho.   Perf. 13
1333 A726 5p multicolored   .45   .20

20th Intl. Fair,
Cairo — A727

1987, Mar. 21   Photo.   Perf. 11½
1334 A727 5p Good workers medal   .40   .20

Veteran's
Day
A728

1987, Mar. 26
1335 A728 5p multicolored   .40   .20

Intl. Gardens Inauguration, Nasser
City — A729

1987, Mar. 30　　Litho.　　Perf. 13
1336　A729　15p multicolored　　　　1.00　1.00

World
Health Day
A730

1987, Apr. 7　　Photo.　　Perf. 11½
1337　A730　5p Mother feeding child .45　.20
Litho.
Perf. 13
1338　A730　5p Oral rehydration
　　　　　　　therapy　　　　　　　　.45　.20

A731

Natl. Team Victory at 1986 Intl. Soccer
Championships — A732

Trophies: No. 1339a, Al Ahly Cup. No.
1339b, National Cup. No. 1339c, Al Zamalek
Cup. No. 1340, Natl. flag, Cairo Stadium and
trophies pictured on No. 1339.

1987, Apr. 19　　Litho.　　Perf. 13½x13
1339　　　　　Strip of 3　　　　　1.50　1.50
　a.-c.　A731 5p any single　　　.50　.50
Size: 115x85mm
Imperf
1340　A732 30p multicolored　　　3.50　3.50

A733　　　　　A734

Salah El Din Citadel, Pharoah's Is., Sinai.

1987, Apr. 25
1341　A733　5p sky blue & lt brown　.50　.20
Return of the Sinai to Egypt, 5th anniv.

1987, May 21　　Photo.　　Perf. 11½
Festivals.
1342　A734　5p Dahlia　　　　　　.40　.20

Cultural Heritage Exhibition — A735

1987, June 17　　Litho.　　Perf. 13x13½
1343　A735　15p multicolored　　　1.00　1.00

Tourism Year — A736

a, Column and Sphinx, Alexandria. b, St.
Catherine's Monastery, Mt. Sinai. c, Colossi of
Thebes. d, Temple of Theban Triad, Luxor.

1987, June 18
1344　　　　　Block of 4　　　　　4.00　4.00
　a.-d.　A736 15p any single　　　1.00　1.00
　　　　　See No. C187.

National
Day
A737

1987, June 26　　　　　　Perf. 13
1345　A737　5p multicolored　　　.40　.20

Industry-Agriculture Exhibition — A738

1987, July 23　　Photo.　　Perf. 11½
1346　A738　5p grn, dull org & blk　.40　.20

Intl. Year of
Shelter for
the
Homeless
A739

1987, Sept. 2　　Litho.　　Perf. 13
1347　A739　5p multicolored　　　.40　.20
World Architects' Day.

Aida,
Performed
at Al
Ahram
Pyramid,
Giza
A740

Radamis and troops returning from
Ethiopia.

1987, Sept. 21
1348　A740　15p multicolored　　　1.25　1.25
Size: 70x70mm
Imperf
1349　A740　30p multicolored　　　5.00　5.00

Greater Cairo Subway
Inauguration — A741

1987, Sept. 27　　　　Perf. 13x13½
1350　A741　5p multicolored　　　.85　.25

Industry
Day
A742

1987, Oct. 1　　　　　　Perf. 13
1351　A742　5p multicolored　　　.40　.20

Battle of Hettin,
700th Anniv. — A743

1987, Oct. 6　　Photo.　　Perf. 11x11½
1352　A743　5p multicolored　　　.50　.20

UPU
Emblem
A744

Perf. 11½
1987, Oct. 24　　Unwmk.　　Photo.
1353　A744　5p multicolored　　　.45　.20
UN Executive Council, 40th anniv.; UPU
Consultative Council, 30th anniv.

16th Art Biennial
of Alexandria
A745

1987, Nov. 7　　Litho.　　Perf. 13½x13
1354　A745　5p multicolored　　　.45　.20

Second Intl. Defense Equipment
Exhibition, Cairo, Nov. 9-13 — A746

Perf. 13x13½
1987, Nov. 9　　Litho.　　Unwmk.
1355　A746　5p multicolored　　　.45　.20

2nd Pan-Arab Congress on
Anaesthesia and Intensive
Care — A747

Unwmk.
1987, Dec. 1　　Litho.　　Perf. 13
1356　A747　5p multicolored　　　.50　.20

Intl. Orthopedic
and Traumatology
Conference
A748

1987, Dec. 1　　　　Perf. 13½x13
1357　A748　5p gray, red brn & bl　.50　.20

Selim Hassan
(1887-1961),
Egyptologist, and
Hieroglyphs
A749

Abdel Hamid Badawi (1887-1965), Jurist, and Scales of Justice — A750

Perf. 13½x13

1987, Dec. 30   Litho.   Unwmk.
1358 A749 5p multicolored   .45 .20
1359 A750 5p multicolored   .45 .20

Stamp Day 1988 — A751

Pyramids of the Pharaohs and: a, Cheops. b, Chefren. c, Mycerinus. No. 1360 has a continuous design.

1988, Jan. 2
1360 A751 Strip of 3   4.00 4.00
a.-c.   15p, any single   1.25 1.25

Afro-Asian Peoples Solidarity Organization, 30th Anniv. — A752

1988, Jan. 10   *Perf. 13x13½*
1361 A752 15p multicolored   1.00 1.00

20th Intl. Book Fair, Cairo — A753

1988, Jan. 26   *Perf. 13½x13*
1362 A753 5p multicolored   .40 .20

Martrans (Natl. Shipping Line), 25th Anniv. A754

Unwmk.
1988, Mar. 3   Litho.   *Perf. 13*
1363 A754 5p multicolored   .60 .25

Cairo Intl. Fair A755

1988, Mar. 12   Photo.   *Perf. 11½x11*
1364 A755 5p multicolored   .40 .20

World Health Day 1988: Diabetes A756

1988 Festivals A757

Perf. 11x11½

1988, Apr. 7   Photo.   Unwmk.
1365 A756 5p multicolored   .45 .20

1988, Apr. 17   *Perf. 11½*
1366 A757 5p grn, brn org & brn   .45 .20

African Postal Union, 25th Anniv. — A758

1988, Apr. 23   Litho.   *Perf. 13x13½*
1367 A758 15p brt blue   1.00 1.00

Oppose Racial Discrimination — A759

1988, May 25   Photo.   *Perf. 11½*
1368 A759 5p multicolored   .40 .20

Taw Fek-Hakem (1902-1987), Playwright, Novelist — A760

1988, Aug. 5   Photo.   *Perf. 11½*
1369 A760 5p brt grn bl & org brn   .60 .25

See Nos. 1383-1384, 1479-1480, 1486, 1500-1502, 1543-1546.

Faculty of Art Education, 50th Anniv. A761

Perf. 11½

1988, Sept. 10   Photo.   Unwmk.
1370 A761 5p multicolored   .50 .20

A762

1988 Summer Olympics, Seoul — A763

1988, Sept. 17   Litho.   *Perf. 13*
1371 A762 15p multicolored   1.25 1.25
Size: 96x91mm
Imperf.
1372 A763 30p multicolored   5.00 5.00

No. 1371 is airmail.

October War Against Israel, 15th Anniv. — A764

Perf. 13x13½

1988, Oct. 6   Litho.   Unwmk.
1373 A764 5p multicolored   .50 .20

A765

Opening of the Opera House — A766

1988, Oct. 10   *Perf. 11½*
1374 A765 5p multicolored   .50 .20
Size: 112x75mm
Imperf
1375 A766 50p multicolored   3.50 3.50

Intl. Red Cross and Red Crescent Organizations, 125th Annivs. — A767

Perf. 11½

1988, Oct. 24   Photo.   Unwmk.
1376 A767 5p green, blk & red   .40 .20

WHO, 40th Anniv. — A768

1988, Oct. 24   *Perf. 11x11½*
1377 A768 20p multicolored   1.10 1.10

Naguib Mahfouz, 1988 Nobel Prize Winner for Literature — A769

1988, Nov. 7   Litho.   *Perf. 13x13½*
1378 A769 5p multicolored   .60 .25

See No. C190.

Arab Scouting Organization, 75th Anniv. — A770

1988, Nov. 10
1379 A770 25p multicolored   1.10 1.10

Return of Taba to Egypt — A771

1988, Nov. 15
1380 A771 5p multicolored   .40 .20

Intl. Conference on Orthopedic Surgery, Cairo, Nov. 15-18 — A772

1988, Nov. 15   Photo.   *Perf. 11½x11*
1381 A772 5p buff, brt yel grn & brn   .40 .20

A773

1988, Dec. 3   **Perf. 11½**
1382 A773 5p multicolored   .40   .20
    Ministry of Agriculture, 75th anniv.

A774

Perf. 13½x13
1988, Dec. 29   **Litho.**   **Unwmk.**
  Famous Men: No. 1383, Mohamed Hussein Hekal (1888-1956), author, politician. No. 1384, Ahmed Lotfi El Sayed (1872-1963), educator, politician.

1383 A774 5p green & red brn   .40   .20
1384 A774 5p green & red brn   .40   .20
   a.   Pair, #1383-1384   .80   .40

A775

A776

  Statues: 5p, Statue of K. Abr, a priest, 5th cent. No. 1386, Queen Nefert, 4th Dynasty. No. 1387, King Ra Hoteb, 4th Dynasty.

1989, Jan. 2
1385 A775   5p multicolored   .40   .20
1386 A775 25p multicolored   1.40   1.40
1387 A775 25p multicolored   1.40   1.40
   a.   Pair, #1386-1387   3.25   3.25
   Nos. 1385-1387 (3)   3.20   3.00
    Stamp Day.

1989, Jan. 10
1388 A776 5p dull green   .50   .20
  Jawaharlal Nehru (1889-1964), 1st Prime Minister of independent India.

Nile Hilton Hotel, 30th Anniv. — A777

1989, Feb. 22   **Litho.**   **Perf. 13x13½**
1389 A777 5p multicolored   .50   .20

Return of
Taba to
Egypt
A778

Unwmk.
1989, Mar. 15   **Litho.**   **Perf. 13**
1390 A778 5p multicolored   .40   .20

2nd Stage
of Cairo
Subway
A779

1989, Apr. 12   **Litho.**   **Perf. 13**
1391 A779 5p multicolored   .50   .20

Festivals — A780

1989, May 4   **Photo.**   **Perf. 11½**
1392 A780 5p multicolored   .40   .20

1st Arab
Olympic
Day
A781

1989, May 24
1393 A781 5p tan, blk & dull grn   .50   .20

Interparliamentary Union,
Cent. — A782

  Pyramids and the Parliament Building, Cairo.

1989, June 29   **Litho.**   **Perf. 13x13½**
1394 A782 25p shown   1.25   1.25
    Size: 87x76mm
    Imperf
1395 A782 25p multi, diff.   2.75   2.75

French Revolution, Bicent. — A783

1989, July 14   **Photo.**   **Perf. 11½**
1396 A783 25p multicolored   1.25   1.25

African
Development
Bank, 25th
Anniv. — A784

Perf. 11½
1989, Oct. 1   **Photo.**   **Unwmk.**
1397 A784 10p multicolored   .40   .20

A785

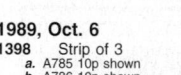

October War Against
Israel, 16th
Anniv. — A786

1989, Oct. 6   **Perf. 13**
1398   Strip of 3   1.50   1.50
   a.   A785 10p shown   .50   .50
   b.   A786 10p shown   .50   .50
   c.   A785 10p Battle scene   .50   .50
    See No. 1424.

Aga Khan Award
for Architecture
A788

Perf. 11½
1989, Oct. 15   **Photo.**   **Unwmk.**
1400 A788 35p multicolored   1.00   1.00

Natl. Health
Insurance
Plan, 25th
Anniv.
A789

1989, Oct. 24
1401 A789 10p blk, gray & ver   .45   .20

World Post
Day — A790

1989, Oct. 24   **Perf. 11x11½**
1402 A790 35p blue, blk & brt yel   .90   .90

Statues of Memnon, Thebes — A791

Perf. 11½
1989, Nov. 12   **Photo.**   **Unwmk.**
1403 A791 10p lt vio, blk & brt
     yel grn   .40   .20
  Intl. Cong. & Convention Assoc. (ICCA) annual convention, Nov. 11-18, Cairo.

Cairo University
School of
Agriculture,
Cent. — A792

1989, Nov. 15
1404 A792 10p pale grn, blk &
     brt yel   .35   .20

Cairo Intl. Conference Center — A793

1989, Nov. 20   **Perf. 11½x11**
1405 A793 5p multicolored   .35   .20

Road Safety Soc., 20th Anniv. — A794

1989, Nov. 20   **Perf. 11½**
1406 A794 10p multicolored   .40   .20

Alexandria
University,
50th
Anniv. — A795

1989, Nov. 30   **Perf. 11x11½**
1407 A795 10p pale blue & tan   .35   .20

Portrait of Pasha, Monument in Opera Square, Cairo
A796

Perf. 11½x11
1989, Dec. 31   Photo.   Unwmk.
1408 A796 10p multicolored   .45   .20

Ibrahim Pasha (d. 1838), army commander from 1825 to 1828.

Famous Men
A797   A798

1989, Dec. 31   Perf. 11x11½
1409 A797 10p grn & dk ol grn   .40   .20
1410 A798 10p golden brown   .40   .20

Abd El-Rahman El-Rafei (b. 1889), historian (No. 1409); Abdel Kader El Mazni (b. 1889), man of letters (No. 1410).
See Nos. 1431-1432.

Statue of Priest Ranofr — A799

Relief Sculpture of Betah Hoteb — A800

1990, Jan. 2   Perf. 13½x13
1411 A799 30p multicolored   .90   .90
1412 A800 30p multicolored   .90   .90
a. Pair, #1411-1412   2.00   2.00
Stamp Day.

Arab Cooperation Council, 1st Anniv. — A801

Perf. 13x13½
1990, Feb. 16   Photo.   Unwmk.
1413 A801 10p multicolored   .40   .20
1414 A801 35p multicolored   1.00   1.00

Emblem, Conference Center
A802

Road Safety Emblems
A803

Perf. 13½x13
1990, Mar. 10   Litho.   Unwmk.
1415 A802 10p brt yel grn, red & blk   .50   .20

Size: 80x59mm
Imperf
1416 A802 30p multicolored   1.25   1.25

African Parliamentary Union 13th general conference, Mar. 10-15.

1990, Mar. 19   Photo.   Perf. 11x11½
1417 A803 10p multicolored   .60   .25

Intl. Conference on Road Safety & Accidents in Developing Countries, Mar. 19-22.

Festivals 1990 — A804

1990, Apr. 24   Perf. 11½
1418 A804 10p multicolored   .40   .20

Sinai Liberation, 8th Anniv. A805

1990, Apr. 25
1419 A805 10p blue, blk & yel grn   .50   .20

World Cup Soccer Championships, Italy — A806

1990, May 26   Litho.   Perf. 13½x13
1420 A806 10p multicolored   .40   .20
Souvenir Sheet
Imperf
1421 A806 50p Flags, trophy   1.75   1.75

World Basketball Championships, Argentina — A807

1990, Aug. 8   Perf. 13x13½
1422 A807 10p multicolored   .50   .20

Natl. Population Council, 5th Anniv. — A808

1990, Sept. 15   Perf. 13½x13
1423 A808 10p brown & yel grn   .50   .20

October War Against Israel Type
1990, Oct. 6   Litho.   Perf. 13x13½
1424   Strip of 3   1.75   1.75
a. A785 10p Bunker, tank   .55   .55
b. A786 10p like #1398b   .55   .55
c. A785 10p Troops with flag, flame thrower   .55   .55

Egyptian Postal Service, 125th Anniv. — A809

1990, Oct. 9
1425 A809 10p lt blue, blk & red   .50   .20

Dar El Eloum Faculty, Cent. A810

1990, Oct. 13   Litho.   Perf. 13
1426 A810 10p multicolored   .40   .20

UN Development Program, 40th Anniv. — A811

ITU, 125th Anniv. — A812

1990, Oct. 24   Perf. 11½
1427 A811 30p yel, bl grn & yel grn   .75   .75
Perf. 13
1428 A812 30p multicolored   .75   .75
UN Day.

Ras Mohammed Natl. Park — A813

Various tropical fish and coral reefs.

1990, Dec. 22   Litho.   Perf. 13
1429 A813 Block of 4   3.50   3.50
a.-b. 10p any single   .75   .75
c.-d. 20p any single   1.00   1.00

Day of the Disabled — A814

1990. Dec. 15   Photo.   Perf. 11
1430 A814 10p multicolored   .60   .25

Mohamed Fahmy Abdel Meguid Bey, Medical Reformer
A815

Nabaweya Moussa (1890-1951), Educator
A816

Perf. 11x11½
1990, Dec. 30   Unwmk.
1431 A815 10p Prus bl, brn & org   .40   .20
1432 A816 10p grn, org brn & blk   .40   .20

Stamp Day — A817

1991, Jan. 1   Litho.   Perf. 13½x13
1433 A817 5p No. 1   .40   .20
1434 A817 10p No. 2   .40   .20
1435 A817 20p No. 3   .60   .60
a. Strip of 3, #1433-1435   1.40   1.40

See Nos. 1443-1446, 1459-1460.

Veterinary Surgeon Syndicate, 50th
Anniv. — A818

1991, Feb. 28　Photo.　Perf. 11½
1436　A818　10p multicolored　.40　.20

Syndicate of Journalists, 50th
Anniv. — A819

1991, Apr.　Photo.　Perf. 11½
1437　A819　10p multicolored　.40　.20

Festivals — A820

1991, Apr. 13
1438　A820　10p multicolored　.40　.20

Giza Zoo, Cent. — A821

1991, June 15　Litho.　Imperf.
Size: 80x63mm
1439　A821　50p multicolored　3.00　3.00

Mahmoud Mokhtar (1891-1934),
Sculptor — A822

Mohamed Nagi
(1888-1956),
Painter — A823

Perf. 13x13½, 13½x13
1991, June 11　　　　Litho.
1440　A822　10p multicolored　.40　.20
1441　A823　10p multicolored　.40　.20

Faculty of Engineering — A824

1991, June 30　　　Perf. 13x13½
1442　A824　10p multicolored　.40　.20

Stamp Day Type
Designs: No. 1443, No. 5. No. 1444, No. 4.
No. 1445, No. 7. No. 1446, Sphinx, pyramid,
No. 6.

1991, July 23　　　　Perf. 13
1443　A817　10p orange & blk　.40　.20
1444　A817　10p yellow & blk　.40　.20
1445　A817　10p lilac & blk　.40　.20
　　a.　Strip of 3, #1443-1445　1.25　1.25
Size: 80x60mm
Imperf
1446　A817　50p multicolored　1.75　1.75
　　Nos. 1443-1446 (4)　2.95　2.35

Mohamed
Abdel el
Wahab,
Musician
A825

1991, Aug. 28　　　Perf. 13
1447　A825　10p multicolored　.40　.20

5th Africa Games, Cairo — A826

No. 1448, Karate, judo. No. 1449, Table tennis, field hockey, tennis. No. 1450, Running,
gymnastics, swimming. No. 1451, Soccer,
basketball, shooting. No. 1452, Boxing, wrestling, weightlifting. No. 1453, Handball, cycling,
volleyball. No. 1454, Games mascot, vert. No.
1455, Mascot, emblem, torch.

Perf. 13x13½
1991, Sept.　　　　　Unwmk.
1448　A826　10p multicolored　.45　.20
1449　A826　10p multicolored　.45　.20
　　a.　Pair, #1448-1449　.90　.90
1450　A826　10p multicolored　.45　.20
1451　A826　10p multicolored　.45　.20
　　a.　Pair, #1450-1451　.90　.90
1452　A826　10p multicolored　.45　.20
1453　A826　10p multicolored　.45　.20
　　a.　Pair, #1452-1453　.90　.90
Perf. 13½x13
1454　A826　10p multicolored　.45　.20
Size: 80x60mm
Imperf
1455　A826　50p multicolored　1.75　1.75
　　Nos. 1448-1455 (8)　4.90　3.15

Intl.
Statistics
Institute,
48th
Session
A827

1991, Sept. 9
1456　A827　10p multicolored　.40　.20

Opening of Dar
Al Eftaa Religious
Center — A828

1991, Oct. 1　Litho.　Perf. 13
1457　A828　10p multicolored　.40　.20

October War Against Israel, 18th
Anniv. — A829

1991, Oct. 6　　　　Perf. 13x13½
1458　A829　10p multicolored　.50　.20

Stamp Day Type
Designs: 10p, No. 6. £1, Stamp exhibition
emblem, hieroglyphics, pyramids, sphinx.

1991, Oct. 7　　　　Perf. 13
1459　A817　10p blue & black　.50　.20
Size: 90x60mm
Imperf
1460　A817　£1 multicolored　5.00　5.00
Natl. Philatelic Exhibition, Cairo, 10/7-12
(No. 1460). No. 1460 sold with £1 at
exhibition.

Ancient Artifacts Type of 1985
Perf. 11½x11
1990-92　　Unwmk.　Photo.
Size: 18x23mm
1467　A681　10p like #1278　.60　.25
1470　A681　30p like #1283　1.00　1.00
1472　A681　50p like #1285　1.75　1.75
　　Nos. 1467-1472 (3)　3.35　3.00
Issued: 10p, 1/20/90; 30p, 9/1/91; 50p,
7/11/92.

United Nations Day — A830

No. 1477, Brick hands housing people. No.
1478, Woman learning to write, fingerprint,
vert.

Perf. 13x13½, 13½x13
1991, Oct. 24　　　　Litho.
1476　A830　10p shown　.40　.20
1477　A830　10p multicolored　.40　.20
1478　A830　10p multicolored　.40　.20
　　Nos. 1476-1478 (3)　1.20　.60

Famous Men Type of 1988
Inscribed "1991"
Designs: No. 1479, Dr. Zaki Mubarak (1891-
1952), writer and poet. No. 1480, Abd El
Kader Hamza (1879-1941), journalist.

1991, Dec. 23　Photo.　Perf. 13½x13
1479　A760　10p olive brown　.40　.20
1480　A760　10p gray　.40　.20

A831

Post Day — A832

1992, Jan. 2　Litho.　Perf. 13
1481　A831　10p shown　.40　.25
1482　A831　45p Bird mosaic　1.00　1.00
Perf. 14
1483　A832　70p shown　1.75　1.75
　　Nos. 1481-1483 (3)　3.15　3.00
Nos. 1482-1483 are airmail.

Police
Day — A833

1992, Jan. 25　　　Perf. 14
1484　A833　10p multicolored　.40　.20

25th
Cairo
Intl.
Fair
A834

1992, Feb. 15　Litho.　Perf. 14
1485　A834　10p multicolored　.40　.20

Famous Men Type of 1988
Inscribed "1992"
10p, Sayed Darwish (1882-1923), musician.

1992, Mar. 17　Photo.　Perf. 14x13½
1486　A760　10p dull org & olive　.40　.20

Festivals — A835

1992, Mar. 18　　　Perf. 11½
1487　A835　10p Egyptian hoopoe　.40　.20

World
Health Day
A836

1992, Apr. 20   Litho.   Perf. 13
1488 A836 10p multicolored   .50   .20

Aswan
Dam, 90th
Anniv.
A837

1992, July   Litho.   Perf. 13
1489 A837 10p No. 487   .50   .20

20th Arab Scout Jamboree — A838

1992, July 10   Perf. 13x13½
1490 A838 10p multicolored   .50   .20

A839

A840

1992, July 20   Perf. 13½x13
1491 A839 10p multicolored   .40   .20
Size: 80x60mm
Imperf
1492 A839 70p Summer Games'
emblem   1.75   1.75
1992 Summer Olympics, Barcelona.

1992, Sept. 14   Litho.   Perf. 13½x13
1493 A840 10p multicolored   .40   .20
El Helal Magazine, cent.

Alexandria World Festival — A841

1992, Sept. 27   Perf. 13x13½
1494 A841 70p multicolored   1.60   1.60

Congress of Federation of World and
American Travel Companies,
Cairo — A842

1992, Sept. 20
1495 A842 70p multicolored   1.50   1.50

World Post
Day
A843

1992, Oct. 9   Litho.   Perf. 13
1496 A843 10p dk bl, lt bl & blk   .40   .20

Children's
Day — A844

1992, Oct. 24   Litho.   Perf. 13½x13
1497 A844 10p multicolored   .50   .20

Intl.
Conference
on Food,
Agriculture
and World
Health
A845

1992, Oct. 24   Perf. 13
1498 A845 70p multicolored   1.50   1.50

A846

A847

1992, Nov. 21   Perf. 13½x13
1499 A846 10p multicolored   .50   .20
20th Arab Scout Conference, Cairo.

Famous Men Type of 1988
Inscribed "1992"

No. 1500, Talaat Harb, economist. No.
1501, Mohamed Taymour, writer. No. 1502,
Dr. Ahmed Zaki Abu Shadi (with glasses), physician & poet.

1992, Dec. 23   Photo.   Perf. 13½x13
1500 A760 10p blue & brown   .40   .20
1501 A760 10p citron & blue gray   .40   .20
1502 A760 10p citron & blue gray   .40   .20
a.   Pair, #1501-1502   .80   .80
Nos. 1500-1502 (3)   1.20   .60

1993, Jan. 2   Litho.   Perf. 13½x13
Pharaohs: 10p, Sesostris I.   45p,
Amenemhet III. 70p, Hur I.

1503 A847 10p brown & yellow   .45   .20
1504 A847 45p brown & yellow   .65   .65
1505 A847 70p brown & yellow   1.00   1.00
a.   Strip of 3, #1503-1505   2.10   2.10
Post Day.

Intl. Book Fair,
Cairo — A848

1993, Jan. 26   Litho.   Perf. 13½x13
1506 A848 15p multicolored   .40   .20

A849

A849b

A849d

A849f

A849g

A849a

A849c

A849e

A849h

Artifacts: A849, Bust. A849a, Sphinx.
A849b, Bust of princess. A849c, Ramses II.
A849d, Queen Ti. A849e, Horemheb. A849f,
As A849b. A849g, Amenhotep III. £1, Head of
a woman. £2, Woman wearing headdress. £5,
Pharaonic capital.

Photo., Litho. (#1511)
1993-99   Unwmk.   Perf. 11½x11,
1507 A849 5p multi   .30   .20
1508 A849a 15p brn & bis   .30   .20
1509 A849a 15p brn & bis   .30   .20
1510 A849b 25p brn & org   .30   .20
brn   .30   .25
1511 A849c 55p blk & bl   .65   .65
Size: 21x25mm
Perf. 11¼
1512 A849 5p dp cl &
brick red   .30   .20
1513 A849d 5p brown   .30   .20
a.   Wmk. 342   .30   .20
1514 A849a 15p brn & bis   .30   .20
1515 A849e 20p blk & gray   .30   .20
a.   Wmk. 342   .30   .20
1516 A849f 25p black brown   .35   .30
brn   .30   .20
1517 A849f 25p black brown   .30   .20
1518 A849c 55p blk & lt bl   .60   .60
1519 A849g 75p blk & brn   .80   .80
Perf. 11½
1520 A849h £1 slate & blk   2.25   2.25
1521 A849h £2 brn & grn   5.00   5.00
1521A A849h £5 brn & gold   10.00   10.00
Nos. 1507-1521A (16)   22.35   21.45

Warning: Avoid using watermark fluid on
Nos. 1513-1513a and 1515-1515a. Images
will be adversely affected.
Body of Sphinx on Nos. 1509, 1514 stops
above value, and extends through value on
No. 1508.
Issued: Nos. 1507-1508, 2/1; No. 1509,
3/10; £1, £2, 4/1; No. 1511, 7/1/93; £5, 8/1/93;
Nos. 1512, 1514, 1518, 10/30/94; No. 1516,
6/25/94; 20p, 2/1/97; 75p, 3/25/97; No. 1517,
1998; Nos. 1513a, 1515a, 1999.
See Nos. C204-C206.

Architects' Association, 75th
Anniv. — A850

1993, Feb. 28   Litho.   Perf. 13x13½
1522 A850 15p multicolored   .40   .20

New
Building for
Ministry of
Foreign
Affairs
A851

1993, Mar. 15   Perf. 13
1523 A851 15p multicolored   .40   .20
1524 A851 80p multicolored   1.10   1.10
Diplomacy Day (No. 1523). No. 1524 is
airmail.

Feasts — A852

1993, Mar. 20   Litho.   Perf. 13x13½
1525 A852 15p Opuntia   .40 .20

Newspaper, Le Progres Egyptien,
Cent. — A853

1993, Apr. 15   Litho.   Perf. 13x13½
1526 A853 15p multicolored   .40 .20

A854   A855

1993, May 15   Litho.   Perf. 13½x13
1527 A854 15p multicolored   .50 .20
World Telecommunications Day.

1993, June 15   Litho.   Perf. 13½x13
1528 A855 15p multicolored   .40 .20
UN Conference on Human Rights, Vienna.

Organization of African Unity — A856

1993, June 26   Perf. 13
1529 A856 15p yel grn & multi   .40 .20
1530 A856 80p red violet & multi   1.10 1.10
No. 1530 is airmail.

World PTT Conference, Cairo — A857

1993, Sept. 4   Litho.   Perf. 13
1531 A857 15p multicolored   .40 .20

Salah El-Din El Ayubi (1137-1193),
Dome of the Rock — A858

1993, Sept. 4
1532 A858 55p multicolored   1.10 1.10

A859

A860

1993, Oct. 6
1533 A859 15p multicolored   .50 .20
October War Against Israel, 20th Anniv.

1993, Oct. 12   Perf. 13½x13
1534 A860 15p cream & multi   .40 .20
1535 A860 55p silver & multi   1.10 1.10
1536 A860 80p gold & multi   1.50 1.50
              Imperf
           Size: 90x70mm
1537 A860 80p multicolored   3.00 3.00
      Nos. 1534-1537 (4)   6.00 5.80
Pres. Mohamed Hosni Mubarak, Third Term.

Reduction
of Natural
Disasters
A861

1993, Oct. 24   Litho.   Perf. 13
1538 A861 80p multicolored   1.10 1.10

Electricity in
Egypt,
Cent. — A862

1993, Oct. 24   Perf. 13½x13
1539 A862 15p multicolored   .40 .20

Intl. Conference on Big Dams,
Cairo — A863

1993, Nov. 19   Litho.   Perf. 13
1540 A863 15p multicolored   .40 .20

35th Military Intl. Soccer
Championship — A864

1993, Dec. 1   Litho.   Perf. 13x13½
1541 A864 15p orange & multi   .40 .20
1542 A864 15p Trophy, emblem   .40 .20
9th Men's Junior World Handball Champion-
ship (No. 1542).

Famous Men Type of 1988
Inscribed "1993"

No. 1543, A. Al. Bishry. No. 1544, M.F. Abu
Hadeed. No. 1545, M.B. Al. Tunisy. No. 1546,
Ali Moubarak.

1993, Dec. 25   Perf. 13½x13
1543 A760 15p blue   .40 .20
1544 A760 15p blue black   .40 .20
1545 A760 15p light violet   .40 .20
1546 A760 15p green   .40 .20
      Nos. 1543-1546 (4)   1.60 .80

Post Day — A865

1994, Jan. 2
1547 A865 15p Amenhotep III   .40 .20
1548 A865 55p Queen Hatshep-
                 sut   1.00 1.00
1549 A865 80p Thutmose III   1.10 1.10
      Nos. 1547-1549 (3)   2.50 2.30

Congress of Egyptian Sedimentary
Geology Society — A866

1994, Jan. 4   Litho.   Perf. 13x13½
1550 A866 15p multicolored   .40 .20

Birds
A867

1994, Mar. 3   Litho.   Perf. 13
1551 A867 Block of 4, #a.-d.   1.60 1.60
  a.   15p Egyptian swallow   .40 .40
  b.   15p Fire crest   .40 .40
  c.   15p Rose-ringed parrot   .40 .40
  d.   15p Goldfinch   .40 .40
      Festivals 1994.

A868

A869

1994, Mar. 25   Perf. 13½x13
1552 A868 15p multicolored   .40 .20
Arab Scouting, 40th anniv.

1994, Apr. 9   Litho.   Perf. 13½x13
1553 A869 15p multicolored   .40 .20
27th Cairo Intl. Fair.

A870

A871

1994, Apr. 15   Litho.   Perf. 13
1554 A870 15p green & brown   .40 .20

1994 African Telecommunications Exhibition, Cairo.

1994, Apr. 30   Litho.   Perf. 13
1555 A871 15p grn, blk & blue   .40 .20

Natl. Afforestation Campaign.

5th Arab Energy Conference, Cairo. — A872

Litho.
Perf. 13
1994, July 5
1556 A872 15p multicolored   .40 .20

Signing of Washington Accord for Palestinian Self-Rule in Gaza and Jericho — A873

1994, May 4   Litho.   Perf. 13
1557 A873 15p multicolored   .60 .25

18th Biennial Art Exhibition, Alexandria — A874

1994, May 21
1558 A874 15p yel, blk & gray   .40 .20

Organization of African Unity — A875

1994, May 25
1559 A875 15p multicolored   .40 .20

Natl. Reading Festival — A876

1994, June 15
1560 A876 15p multicolored   .40 .20

ILO, 75th Anniv. — A877

1994, June 28   Litho.   Perf. 13½x13
1561 A877 15p multicolored   .60 .25

Intl. Conference on Population and Development, Cairo — A878

15p, Conference, UN emblems. 80p, Drawings, hieroglyphics, conference emblem.

1994, Sept. 5   Litho.   Perf. 13
1562 A878 15p multi   .40 .20
1563 A878 80p multi, vert.   1.10 1.10
No. 1563 is airmail.

World Junior Squash Championships — A879

1994, Sept. 14   Litho.   Perf. 13
1564 A879 15p multicolored   .40 .20

World Post Day A880

1994, Oct. 9   Litho.   Perf. 13
1565 A880 15p multicolored   .50 .20

Intl. Red Cross & Red Crescent Societies, 75th Anniv. — A881

1994, Oct. 24
1566 A881 80p multicolored   1.50 1.50

Akhbar El-Yom Newspaper, 50th Anniv. — A882

1994, Nov. 11
1567 A882 15p multicolored   .40 .20

African Field Hockey Club Championships — A883

1994, Nov. 14   Litho.   Perf. 13
1568 A883 15p multicolored   .40 .20

A884

Opera Aida, by Verdi — A885

1994, Nov. 26
1569 A884 15p multicolored   .40 .20
Imperf
Size: 58x69mm
1570 A885 80p multicolored   2.50 2.50
No. 1570 is airmail.

Intl. Olympic Committee, Cent. — A886

Egyptian Youth Hostels Assoc., 40th Anniv. — A887

1994, Dec. 10   Perf. 13
1571 A886 15p multicolored   .40 .20

1994, Dec. 24
1572 A887 15p multicolored   .40 .20

Intl. Speed Ball Federation, 10th Anniv. — A888

1994, Dec. 25
1573 A888 15p multicolored   .40 .20

African Development Bank, 30th Anniv. — A889

1994, Dec. 26
1574 A889 15p multicolored   .40 .20

Opening of Suez Canal, 125th Anniv. — A890

Design: 80p, Map, inaugural ceremony.

1994, Dec. 27
1575 A890 15p multicolored   .40 .20
1576 A890 80p multicolored   1.25 1.25
No. 1576 is airmail.

Famous Men — A891

Post Day — A892

1994, Dec. 29
1577	A891	15p Hassan Fathy, engineer	.40	.20
1578	A891	15p Mahmoud Taimour, writer	.40	.20

1995, Jan. 2   Litho.   Perf. 13½x13
15p, Statue of Akhenaton. 55p, Golden mask of King Tutankhamen. 80p, Statue of Nefertiti.
1579	A892	15p multicolored	.40	.20
1580	A892	55p multicolored	1.00	1.00
1581	A892	80p multicolored	1.25	1.25
		Nos. 1579-1581 (3)	2.65	2.45

World Tourism Organization, 20th Anniv. — A893

1995, Jan. 2   Perf. 13x13½
1582	A893	15p multicolored	.40	.20

Festivals — A894

1995, Feb. 25   Litho.   Perf. 13x13½
1583	A894	15p multicolored	.40	.20

Egyptian Women's Day — A895

1995, Mar. 16   Litho.   Perf. 13x13½
1584	A895	15p multicolored	.40	.20

Arab League, 50th Anniv. — A896

1995, Mar. 22   Perf. 13½x13
1585	A896	15p blue & multi	.40	.20
1586	A896	55p green & multi	.75	.75

Sheraton Hotel, Cairo, 25th Anniv. — A897

1995, Mar. 28   Perf. 13x13½
1587	A897	15p multicolored	.40	.20

Misr Bank, 75th Anniv. — A898

1995, May 7   Litho.   Perf. 13½x13
1588	A898	15p multicolored	.60	.25

World Telecommunications Day — A899

1995, May 31   Perf. 13x13½
1589	A899	80p multicolored	1.00	1.00

Wilhelm Roentgen (1845-1923), Discovery of the X-Ray, Cent. — A900

1995, May   Litho.   Perf. 13½x13
1590	A900	15p multicolored	.60	.25

Membership in World Heritage Committee, 20th Anniv. (in 1994) — A901

Artifacts from the Shaft of Luxor: No. 1591, Goddess Hathor. No. 1592, God Atoum. 80p, God Amon and Horemheb.

1995, July 23   Litho.   Perf. 13½x13
1591		15p multicolored	.40	.20
1592		15p multicolored	.40	.20
a.		A901 Pair, #1591-1592	.80	.80
1593	A901	80p multicolored	1.10	1.10
		Nos. 1591-1593 (3)	1.90	1.50

No. 1592a is a continuous design. No. 1593 is airmail.

21st Intl. Conference on Pediatrics, Cairo A902

1995, Sept. 10   Litho.   Perf. 13
1594	A902	15p multicolored	.60	.25

Intl. Ozone Day — A903

1995, Sept. 16   Litho.   Perf. 13x12½
1595	A903	15p green & multi	.40	.20
1596	A903	55p brown & multi	.85	.85
1597	A903	80p blue & multi	1.10	1.10
		Nos. 1595-1597 (3)	2.35	2.15

See Nos. 1622-1623.

World Tourism Day A904

1995, Sept. 25   Perf. 12½x13
1598	A904	15p multicolored	.40	.20

Government Printing House, 175th Anniv. — A905

1995, Sept. 27
1599	A905	15p multicolored	.40	.20

Sun Verticality on Abu Simbel Temple A906

1995, Oct. 22   Litho.   Perf. 12½x13
1600	A906	15p multicolored	.75	.30

Opening of New Esna Dam — A907

1995, Nov. 25   Perf. 12½
1601	A907	15p multicolored	.75	.30

Egyptian Engineers Assoc., 75th Anniv. A908

1995, Dec. 20   Perf. 13
1602	A908	15p multicolored	.40	.20

A909   A910

Famous entertainers.

1995, Dec. 9   Litho.   Perf. 13x12½
1603	A909	15p A. Hafez	.40	.20
1604	A909	15p Y. Wahby	.40	.20
1605	A909	15p N. El. Rihany	.40	.20
		Nos. 1603-1605 (3)	1.20	.60

1995, Dec. 23   Litho.   Perf. 13x12½
1606	A910	15p multicolored	.40	.20

Motion Pictures, cent.

Post Day A911

Ancient paintings: 55p, Man facing right. 80p, Man facing left. 100p, Playing flute, dancers.

1996, Jan. 2   Litho.   Perf. 13½x13
1607		55p multicolored	.60	.60
1608		80p multicolored	.90	.90
a.		A911 Pair, Nos. 1607-1608	1.50	1.50

Imperf
Size: 88x72mm
1609	A911	100p multicolored	1.25	1.25

Nos. 1607-1608 are airmail.

Feasts — A912

1996, Feb. 15   Perf. 12½
1610	A912	15p blue flowers	.30	.20
1611	A912	15p red flowers	.30	.20
a.		Pair, No. 1610-1611	.60	.60

A913   A914

1996, Mar. 13 Litho.   *Perf. 13x12½*
1612 A913 15p pink & multi   .40 .20
1613 A913 80p brown & multi   .90 .90
  Summit of Peace Makers, Sharm al-Sheikh.
No. 1613 is airmail.

1996, Mar. 16
1614 A914 15p multicolored   .40 .20
  29th Intl. Fair, Cairo.

Egyptian Geological Survey, Cent. A915

1996, Mar. 18   *Perf. 12½x13*
1615 A915 15p multicolored   .40 .20

A916   A917

1996, Apr. 11 Litho.   *Perf. 13x12½*
1616 A916 15p blue & multi   .40 .20
1617 A916 80p pink & multi   .90 .90
  Signing of African Nuclear Weapon-Free
Zone Treaty.

1996, Apr. 20 Litho.   *Perf. 13x12½*
1618 A917 15p multicolored   .40 .20
  Egyptian Society of Accountants and Auditors, 50th anniv.

A918   A919

1996, May 4
1619 A918 15p multicolored   .40 .20
  General census.

1996, July 15 Litho.   *Perf. 13x12½*
  1996 Summer Olympics, Atlanta: 15p,
Atlanta 1996 emblem. £1, Emblem surrounded
by sports pictograms.
1620 A919 15p lilac & multi   .40 .20
  Size: 63x103mm
  Imperf
1621 A919 £1 black & multi   1.60 1.60
  No. 1621 is airmail.

Intl. Ozone Day Type of 1995
1996, Sept. 16 Litho.   *Perf. 13x12½*
1622 A903 15p pink & multi   .40 .20
1623 A903 80p gray & multi   1.10 1.10
  No. 1623 is airmail.

A920   A921

1996, Sept. 19
1624 A920 80p multicolored   1.00 1.00
  2nd Alexandria World Festival.

1996, Sept. 21
1625 A921 15p grn, blk & bl   .50 .20
  Scientific Research and Technology Academy, 25th anniv.

Opening of 2nd Line of Greater Cairo Subway System A922

1996, Oct. 7   *Perf. 12½x13*
1626 A922 15p multicolored   .50 .20

Rowing Festival A923

1996
1627 A923 15p multicolored   .40 .20

Courts of the State Council, 50th Anniv. A924

1996, Nov. 2 Litho.   *Perf. 12½x13*
1628 A924 15p blue & claret   .40 .20

A925   A926

1996, Nov. 4   *Perf. 13x12½*
1629 A925 15p yel, blk & blue   .40 .20
  Intl. Federation of Training and Development
Organizations World Conf.

1996, Nov. 12 Litho.   *Perf. 13x12½*
  Cairo Economic Summit (MENA): £1,
Graph, earth, gear, olive branch, wheat.
1630 A926 15p shown   .75 .30
  Size: 65x45mm
  Imperf
1631 A926 £1 multicolored   1.75 1.75
  No. 1631 is airmail.

A927   A928

1996, Nov. 13   *Perf. 13x12½*
1632 A927 15p multicolored   .40 .20
  1996 World Food Summit, Rome.

1996, Nov. 16
  National Day of El-Gharbia Governorate: Al
Sayd Ahmed El-Badawy mosque, Tanta.
1633 A928 15p multicolored   .40 .20

A929   A930

  Famous artists.

1996, Dec. 28 Litho.   *Perf. 13x12½*
1634 A929 20p Ali El-Kassar   .45 .20
1635 A929 20p George Abyad   .45 .20
1636 A929 20p Mohamed
              Kareem   .45 .20
1637 A929 20p Fatma Roshdi   .45 .20
  Nos. 1634-1637 (4)   1.80 .80
  See Nos. 1666-1669.

1997, Jan. 2
1638 A930 20p multicolored   .45 .20
  Size: 61x80mm
  Imperf
1639 A930 £1 multicolored   2.00 2.00
  Discovery of Tutankhamen's tomb, 75th
anniv.
  No. 1639 is airmail.

Police Day A931

1997, Jan. 25 Litho.   *Perf. 13x13½*
1640 A931 20p multicolored   .40 .20

Feasts — A932

1997, Feb. 1   *Perf. 13*
1641 A932 20p pink flowers   .40 .20
1642 A932 20p white fowers   .40 .20
  a.   Pair, #1641-1642   .80 .80

World Civil Defense Day A933

1997, Mar. 10 Litho.   *Perf. 13x13½*
1643 A933 20p multicolored   .40 .20

30th Cairo Intl. Fair — A934

1997, Mar. 19   *Perf. 13½x13*
1644 A934 20p multicolored   .40 .20

Mahmoud Said, Photographer, Artist, Birth Cent. — A935

The City, By Mahmoud Said — A936

1997, Apr. 12 Litho.   *Perf. 12½*
1645 A935 20p multicolored   .40 .20
  Size: 80x60mm
  Imperf
1646 A936 £1 multicolored   1.25 1.25
  No. 1646 is airmail.

Institute of African Research and Studies, 50th Anniv. — A937

1997, May 27 Litho.   *Perf. 13*
1647 A937 75p multicolored   .65 .65

New Headquarters of State Information Service — A938

1997, Aug. 16 Litho.   *Perf. 12½*
1648 A938 20p multicolored   .40 .20

A939   A940

£1, Mascot, soccer ball, playing field, emblems.

1997, Sept. 4   **Perf. 13x12½**
1649 A939   20p multicolored   .40   .20
1650 AP81   75p multicolored   .65   .65

Size: 75x55mm

Imperf

1651 A939   £1 multicolored   1.75   1.75

Nos. 1650-1651 are airmail. Under 17 FIFA World Soccer Championships, Egypt.

1997, Sept. 16   **Perf. 13**
1652 A940   20p lt bl grn & multi   .40   .20
1653 A940   £1 pink & multi   1.25   1.25

Montreal Protocol on Substances that Deplete the Ozone Layer, 10th anniv. No. 1653 is airmail.

Completion of Second Stage of Metro Line No. 2 — A941

1997, Sept. 27   **Perf. 12½x13**
1654 A941   20p multicolored   .40   .20

Premiere in Egypt of Opera Aida, by Verdi, 125th Anniv. A942

1997, Oct. 12   **Perf. 13**
1655 A942   20p multicolored   .50   .20

Size: 80x75mm

Imperf

1656 A942   £1 like #1655   1.75   1.75

No. 1656 is airmail.

Queen Nefertari — A943

1997, Oct. 25   **Litho.**   **Perf. 13**
1657 A943   £1 multicolored   1.25   1.25

A944   A945

1997, Nov. 17   **Litho.**   **Perf. 13**
1658 A944   20p multicolored   .40   .20

Intl. Congress of Orthopedics, Cairo.

1997, Nov. 22   **Perf. 13x12½**

Designs: 20p, Goddess Selket. £1, Scarab, baboon pendant.

1659 A945   20p black & gold   .40   .20

Size: 73x62mm

Imperf

1660 A945   £1 multicolored   1.25   1.25

No. 1660 is airmail. Discovery of King Tutanhkamen's tomb, 75th anniv.

Inauguration of Nubia Monument Museum — A946

1997, Nov. 23   **Perf. 13**
1661 A946 20p multicolored   .60   .25

Arab Land Bank, 50th Anniv. — A947

1997, Dec. 10   **Perf. 12½**
1662 A947   20p multicolored   .60   .25

5th Pan Arab Congress on Anesthesia and Intensive Care — A948

1997, Dec. 9   **Litho.**   **Perf. 13**
1663 A948 20p multicolored   .60   .25

El Salaam Canal — A949

1997, Dec. 28
1664 A949 20p multicolored   .60   .25
Liberation of Sinai, 15th anniv.

A950   A951

Famous Artists Type of 1996 and A950

1997, Dec. 23   **Litho.**   **Perf. 13x12½**
1665 A950   20p blue   .40   .20
1666 A929   20p Zaky Tolaimat   .40   .20
1667 A929   20p Ismael Yassen   .40   .20
1668 A929   20p Zaky Roustom   .40   .20
1669 A929   20p Soliman Naguib   .40   .20
   a.   Strip of 5, #1665-1669   2.00   2.00

1998, Jan. 2   **Perf. 13**

Stamp Day: 20p, King Tutankhamen's guard. 75p, King Ramses III. £1, Cover of King Tutankhamen's coffin.

1670 A951   20p multicolored   .50   .20
1671 A951   75p multicolored   1.10   1.10

Size: 26x43mm

1672 A951   £1 multicolored   2.25   2.25

Nos. 1671-1672 are airmail.

Feasts — A952

1998, Jan. 20
1673   20p multicolored   .40   .20
1674   20p multicolored   .40   .20
   a.   A952 Pair, #1673-1674   .80   .80

Intl. Cairo Fair — A954

1998, Mar. 11   **Litho.**   **Perf. 13**
1675 A954 20p multicolored   .50   .20

1998, Mar. 12
1676 A955 20p multicolored   .50   .20

Natl. Bank of Egypt, Cent. — A955

Tutankhamen   Thutmose IV
A956   A957

1998   **Litho.**   **Perf. 13½x12½**
1677 A956   £2 multicolored   1.75   1.75
1678 A957   £5 purple & black   4.25   4.25

Issued: £2, 4/23; £5, 3/23.

A958

A959

1998, Apr. 14   **Perf. 13**
1679 A958   20p green & multi   .40   .20
1680 A958   75p blue & multi   1.10   1.10

Size: 70x52mm

Imperf

1681 A958   £1 Natl. flags, map, trophy   2.25   2.25

Egypt, winners of 21st African Cup of Nations soccer competition. Nos. 1680-1681 are airmail.

1998, May 30   **Litho.**   **Perf. 13**
1682 A959 20p Egyptian Satellite "Nile Sat"   .50   .20

World Environment Day — A960

1998, June 5
1683 A960 20p shown   .60   .25

Size: 43x62mm

Imperf

1684 A960   £1 Fauna, emblems   2.00   2.00

No. 1684 is airmail.

A961

A962

1998, June 14
1685 A961 20p blue & black .40 .20
1686 A961 £1 yellow, green & black 1.10 1.10
Dr. Ahmed Zewail, winner of Franklin Institute award.
No. 1686 is airmail.

1998, July 15
Imam Sheikh Mohamed Metwalli Al-Shaarawi.
1687 A962 20p buff & multi .40 .20
1688 A962 £1 green & multi 1.10 1.10
No. 1688 is airmail.

A963

A964

1998, Sept. 12 Litho. Perf. 13
1689 A963 20p multicolored .50 .20
Day of the Nile Flood.

1998, Sept. 30 Litho. Perf. 13
1690 A964 20p multicolored .50 .20
Chemistry Administration, cent.

October War Against Israel, 25th Anniv. — A965

1998, Oct. 6 Litho. Perf. 13
1691 A965 20p multicolored .60 .25
Size: 50x70mm
Imperf
1692 A965 £2 like No. 1691 4.00 4.00
No. 1692 is airmail.

Egyptian Survey Authority, Cent. — A966

1998, Oct. 15 Perf. 13
1693 A966 20p multicolored .50 .20

Cairo University, 90th Anniv. — A967

1998, Dec. 7 Litho. Perf. 13
1694 A967 20p multicolored .50 .20

A968

A970

1998, Dec. 17 Litho. Perf. 13
1695 A968 20p multicolored .40 .20
Egyptian trade unions, cent.

1999, Jan. 2 Litho. Perf. 13
Post Day (19th Dynasty): 20p, Queen Nefertari, Goddess Isis. 125p, God Osiris, Goddess Isis.
1696 A970 20p multicolored .50 .20
Size: 41x61mm
Imperf
1697 A970 125p multicolored 2.00 2.00
No. 1697 is airmail.

Feasts — A971

1999, Jan. 5 Perf. 13
1698 20p multicolored .40 .20
1699 20p multicolored .40 .20
a. A971 Pair, #1698-1699 .80 .80

Intl. Women's Day — A973

1999, Mar. 7 Litho. Perf. 13
1700 A973 20p multicolored .50 .20

Cairo Intl. Fair — A974

1999, Mar. 9
1701 A974 20p multicolored .50 .20

Opening of Metro Line Beneath Nile River — A975

1999, Apr. Litho. Perf. 13
1702 A975 20p multicolored .60 .25

A976

UPU, 125th Anniv. — A977

1999, Apr. 21
1703 A976 20p shown .40 .20
1704 A976 £1 multi 1.00 1.00
1705 A977 125p shown 1.10 1.10
Size: 50x70mm
Imperf
1706 A977 125p multi 2.25 2.25
Nos. 1703-1706 (4) 4.75 4.55
Nos. 1704-1706 are airmail.

A978

A980

1999, May 8 Perf. 13
1707 A978 20p green & multi .40 .20
1708 A978 125p buff, red & multi 1.25 1.25
Geneva Conventions, 50th anniv. No. 1708 is airmail.

1999, May 20 Litho. Perf. 13x12¾
1710 A980 20p green & multi .40 .20
1711 A980 £1 buff & multi 1.10 1.10
African Development Bank, 35th Meeting, Cairo. No. 1711 is airmail.

16th Men's Handball World Championship — A981

20p, Stylized player with ball, pyramids. 1£, Mascot with ball, Sphinx, pyramids, globe. 125p, Mascot with ball, goalie, pyramids.

1999, June 1 Perf. 13
1712 A981 20p multicolored .40 .20
1713 A981 £1 multicolored 1.00 1.00
1714 A981 125p multicolored 1.10 1.10
Nos. 1712-1714 (3) 2.50 2.30
Nos. 1713-1714 are airmail.

Goddess Selket — A982

1999, June 23 Litho. Perf. 13
1715 A982 25p multicolored .60 .25
See Nos. 1750, 1754.

SOS Children's Village, 50th Anniv. — A983

1999, June 23 Perf. 12¾x13¼
1716 A983 20p grn, blk & blue .40 .20
1717 A983 125p buff, blk & bl 1.10 1.10
No. 1717 is airmail.

A984

A985

No. 1718, Sameera Moussa (1917-52), Physicist. No. 1719, Aisha Abdul Rahman (1913-98), writer. No. 1720, Ahmed Eldemerdash Touny (1907-97), member of Intl. Olympic Committee.

1999		Litho.	Perf. 13x12¾	
1718	A984	20p multicolored	.45	.20
1719	A984	20p multicolored	.45	.20
1720	A984	20p multicolored	.45	.20
		Nos. 1718-1720 (3)	1.35	.60

Issued: Nos. 1718-1719, 7/23; No. 1720, 8/13.
See Nos. 1730-1733.

1999, Oct. 5		Litho.	Perf. 13x12¾	
1721	A985	20p org & multi	.40	.20
1722	A985	£1 silver & multi	1.00	1.00
1723	A985	125p gold & multi	1.10	1.10
		Imperf		
1724	A985	125p multicolored	2.25	2.25
		Nos. 1721-1724 (4)	4.75	4.55

Pres. Hosni Mubarak, 4th term.
Nos. 1722-1724 are airmail.

A986

A987

1999, Nov. 15		Litho.	Perf. 13¼x13	
		Background Color		
1725	A986	20p green	.40	.20
1726	A986	£1 red vio	1.00	1.00
1727	A986	125p purple	1.10	1.10
		Nos. 1725-1727 (3)	2.50	2.30

Intl. Year of the Elderly. Nos. 1726-1727 are airmail.

1999, Nov. 20
1728	A987	20p multi	.50	.20
		Children's Day.		

Famous People Type of 1999

No. 1730, Farid El Attrash (1913-76), singer, movie star. No. 1731, Laila Mourad (1918-95), singer, movie star. No. 1732, Anwar Wagdi (1911-55), actor, director. No. 1733, Asia Dagher (1901-86), actor, producer.

1999, Dec. 30		Litho.	Perf. 13x12¾	
1730	A984	20p lt bl & blk	.40	.20
1731	A984	20p lt bl & blk	.40	.20
1732	A984	20p lt bl & blk	.40	.20
1733	A984	20p lt bl & blk	.40	.20
		Nos. 1730-1733 (4)	1.60	.80

Millennium
A989

20p, "1999" & "2000." 125p, Countdown of years. £2, Holy Family, Virgin Tree.

2000, Jan. 1			Perf. 13x12¾	
1734	A989	20p multi	.40	.20
1735	A989	125p multi	1.10	1.10
		Size: 70x50mm		
		Imperf		
1736	A989	£2 multi, horiz.	4.00	4.00
		Nos. 1734-1736 (3)	5.50	5.30

Nos. 1735-1736 are airmail.

A990

Post Day — A991

2000, Jan. 2			Perf. 13¼x12¾	
1737	A990	20p multi	.50	.20
1738	A991	20p multi	.50	.20
a.		Pair, #1737-1738	1.00	1.00
		Size: 70x50mm		
1739	A991	125p Chariot, horiz.	2.00	2.00
		Nos. 1737-1739 (3)	3.00	2.40

Ain Shams University, 50th
Anniv. — A992

2000, Jan. 3			Perf. 13¼x13	
1740	A992	20p multi	.50	.20

Feasts
A993   A994

2000, Jan. 5			Perf. 13x13¼	
1741	A993	20p multi	.35	.20
1742	A994	20p multi	.35	.20
a.		Pair, #1741-1742	.70	.70

A995

A996

2000, Jan. 20			Perf. 13¼x13	
1743	A995	20p multi	.50	.20

Islamic Development Bank, 25th anniv.

2000, Feb. 28			Perf. 13¼x12¾	
1744	A996	125p multi	1.10	1.10

Common Market for Eastern and Southern Africa Economic Conference.

Death of Om
Kolthoum, 25th
Anniv. — A997

Europe-Africa
Summit,
Cairo — A999

8th Intl. Congress of
Egyptologists — A998

2000, Mar. 11			Perf. 13¼x13	
1745	A997	20p multi	.50	.20

2000, Mar. 28			Perf. 13x13¼	
1746	A998	20p multi	.50	.20

2000, Apr. 3			Perf. 13¼x13	
1747	A999	125p multi	1.25	1.25

Group of 15 Developing Nations, 10th
Summit, Cairo — A1000

Perf. 12¾x13¼
2000, June 19			Litho.	
1748	A1000	125p multi	1.25	1.25

Goddess Selket Type of 1999 and

Scene from
20th Dynasty
A1003

King Seostris
A1005

Nofret, Wife of
Rahotep
A1004

20th
Dynasty — A1007

Princess Merit
Aton
A1006

Pyramid at Snefru
A1008

Wife of Sheikh-
el-Balad
A1009

King
Psusennes I
A1010

King
Tutankhamen
A1011

Obelisk of
Ramses II
A1011a

Temple of
Karnak
A1012

Perf. 12¾x13¼, 11¼ (1752-1755, 1757), 11x11½ (1758-1760), 13¼x12¾ (1756, 1761, 1763)
Photo., Litho. (1751, 1761, 1763)

2000-2002

1750	A982	10p multi	.40	.20
1750A	A982	10p multi, Type II	3.00	3.00
1751	A1003	10p multi	.40	.20
1752	A1004	20p multi	.40	.20
1753	A1005	25p multi	.40	.20
1754	A982	30p multi	.50	.20
1755	A1006	30p multi	.40	.20
1756	A1007	50p multi	.40	.20
1757	A1008	£1 multi	.60	.60
1758	A1009	110p multi	.65	.65
1759	A1010	125p multi	.75	.75
1760	A1011	150p multi	.85	.85
1761	A1011a	225p multi	1.50	1.50
1763	A1012	£5 multi	4.25	4.25
		Nos. 1750-1763 (14)	14.50	13.00

Issued: 20p, 6/25; No. 1750, 3/25/01; No. 1750A, 2001 (?); 30p, 6/11/01. Nos. 1751, 1755, 225p, 5/25/02; 110p, 6/4/02; 125p, 6/20/02; 150p, 6/15/02; £5, 6/1/02. 30p, 50p, #1, 6/30/02.

Type I (No. 1750), has "Goddess" in smaller type than "Silakht." Type II (No. 1750A), has "Goddess" and "Silakht" in type the same height.

Intl. Day Against Drug Abuse — A1013

Perf. 12¾x13¼

2000, June 26   Litho.
1764 A1013 20p multi   .50 .20

See No. 1796.

Natl. Insurance
Company,
Cent. — A1014

Perf. 13¼x12¾

2000, Aug. 20   Litho.
1765 A1014 20p multi shown   .50 .20

Imperf
Size: 96x75mm
1766 A1014 125p Emblem, building, horiz.   2.25 2.25

2000 Summer
Olympics,
Sydney
A1015

Background colors: 20p, Light blue. 125p, Pink.

2000, Sept. 9   *Perf. 13¼x12¾*
1767-1768 A1015 Set of 2   1.40 1.40

No. 1768 is airmail.

Productive Cooperative Union, 25th
Anniv. — A1016

2000, Sept. 15   *Perf. 12¾x13¼*
1769 A1016 20p multi   .50 .20

Opening of Fourth Stage of Second
Cairo Subway Line — A1017

2000, Oct. 7
1770 A1017 20p multi   .50 .20

World Post Day — A1018

2000, Oct. 9
1771 A1018 125p multi   1.10 1.10

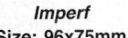

Solidarity with Palestinians — A1019

Palestinian Authority flag and: 20p, Dome of the Rock, Jerusalem, vert. No. 1773, 125p, shown. No. 1774, 125p, Dome of the Rock, father and boy, vert.

Perf. 13¼x12¾, 12¾x13¼
2000, Nov. 29
1772-1774 A1019 Set of 3   2.75 2.75

No. 1774 is airmail.

Opening of El-Ferdan Railway
Bridge — A1020

2000, Dec. 2   *Perf. 12¾x13¼*
1775 A1020 20p multi   .50 .20

Disabled
Person's
Day — A1021

2000, Dec. 9   *Perf. 13¼x12¾*
1776 A1021 20p multi   .50 .20

Opening of Al-Azhar Professorial
Building — A1022

2000, Dec. 10   *Perf. 12¾x13¼*
1777 A1022 20p multi   .50 .20

Famous
Egyptians
A1023

No. 1778: a, Karem Mahmoud, artist (yellow background). b, Mahmoud El-Miligi, artist (green background). c, Mohamed Fawzi, musician (pink background). d, Hussein Riyad, artist (lilac background). e, Abdel Wares Asser, artist (light blue background).

2000, Dec. 24   *Perf. 13¼x12¾*
1778   Horiz. strip of 5   2.00 2.00
a.-e. A1023 20p Any single   .40 .20

Feasts — A1024

a, Red and yellow flowers. b, Purple flowers.

Perf. 12¾x13¼
2000, Dec. 23   Litho.
1779 A1024 20p Pair, #a-b   .80 .80

Jerusalem, City of Peace — A1025

2001, Jan. 1   *Imperf.*
1780 A1025 £2 multi   2.75 2.75

Post Day — A1026

Ancient Egyptian art: 20p, 8 standing figures. No. 1782, 125p, 3 large standing figures.

2001, Jan. 2   *Perf. 12¾x13¼*
1781-1782 A1026 Set of 2   1.40 1.40

Imperf
Size: 80x60mm
1783 A1026 125p Chariot   2.25 2.25

No. 1782 is airmail.

Arab Labor
Organization,
36th
Anniv. — A1027

Perf. 13¼x12¾
2001, Feb. 10   Litho.
1784 A1027 20p multi   .50 .20

Postal Savings
Bank,
Cent. — A1028

2001, Mar. 1
1785 A1028 20p multi   .50 .20

Natl. Council for Women, 1st
Anniv. — A1029

Background colors: 30p, Pink. 125p, Blue.

2001, Mar. 16   *Perf. 12¾x13¼*
1786-1787 A1029 Set of 2   2.00 1.60

No. 1787 is airmail.

Cairo Intl.
Fair — A1030

2001, Mar. 21   *Perf. 13¼x12¾*
1788 A1030 30p multi   .50   .20

Helwan University, 25th
Anniv. — A1031

2001, May 4   *Perf. 12¾x13¼*
1789 A1031 30p multi   .50   .20

Inauguration of Alexandria
Library — A1032

2001, May 20
1790 A1032 125p multi   1.10   1.10

African
Conference on
the Future of
Children
A1033

Background color: 30p, Blue. 125p, Red.

2001, May 28   *Perf. 13¼x12¾*
1791-1792 A1033   Set of 2   2.00   1.60

No. 1792 is airmail.

World
Environment
Day — A1034

2001, June 5   **Litho.**   *Perf. 13¼x12¾*
1793 A1034 125p multi   1.25   1.25

World Military
Soccer
Championships
A1035

Designs: 30p, Emblem. 125p, Emblem and map.

      Perf. 13¼x12¾
2001, June 21   **Litho.**
1794-1795 A1035   Set of 2   2.00   1.60

**Intl. Day Against Drug Abuse Type
of 2000**

2001, June 26   *Perf. 12¾x13¼*
1796 A1013 30p multi   .50   .20

Egypt's Victory in World Military
Soccer Championships — A1036

2001, July 6   **Litho.**   *Imperf.*
1797 A1036 125p multi   2.25   2.25

Egyptian Railways, 150th
Anniv. — A1037

2001, July 12   *Perf. 12¾x13¼*
1798 A1037 30p multi   .60   .25

Poets — A1038

No. 1799: a, Aziz Abaza Pasha (1898-73), blue background. b, Ahmed Rami (1892-1981), pink background.

2001, July 28   *Perf. 13¼x12¾*
1799 A1038 30p Horiz. pair, #a-b   .70   .70

Intl. Volunteers
Year — A1039

2001, Aug. 18
1800 A1039 125p multi   1.10   1.10

Ismailia Folklore
Festival — A1040

2001, Aug. 20
1801 A1040 30p multi   .60   .25

Satellite Telecommunications Ground
Stations, 25th Anniv. — A1041

2001, Sept. 8   *Perf. 12¾x13¼*
1802 A1041 30p multi   .60   .25

Year of Dialogue
Among
Civilizations
A1042

Designs: No. 1803, 125p, Emblem. No. 1804, 125p, UN emblem, globe, symbols of various civilizations, horiz.

   Perf. 13¼x12¾, 12¾x13¼
2001, Oct. 9
1803-1804 A1042   Set of 2   3.00   2.50

Opening of Suez Canal
Bridge — A1043

No. 1805: a, 30p, Bridge, ship. b, 125p, Bridge, road.
No. 1806, Bridge, ship and flags of Egypt and Japan.

2001, Oct. 10   *Perf. 12¾x13¼*
1805 A1043   Horiz. pair, #a-b   1.50   1.50
       Imperf
     Size: 81x60mm
1806 A1043 125p multi   2.25   2.25

Ancient Gold Masks — A1044

Designs: No. 1807, 30p, Mask of San Xing Dui, China, green background. No. 1808, 30p, Funerary mask of King Tutankhamun, brown background.

2001, Oct. 12   *Perf. 12¾x13¼*
1807-1808 A1044   Set of 2   .75   .75
See People's Republic of China 3141-3142.

Opening of Azhar
Tunnels,
Cairo — A1045

2001, Oct. 28   *Perf. 13¼x12¾*
1809 A1045 30p multi   .60   .25

El-Menoufia
University, 25th
Anniv. — A1046

2001, Nov. 25
1810 A1046 30p multi   .60   .25

Feasts — A1047

No.1811: a, Black and white bird on branch. b, Sea gulls. c, Parrot. d, Blue bird on branch.

2001, Dec. 5
1811 A1047 30p Block of 4, #a-d   2.00   1.10

Musicians — A1048

No. 1812: a, Zakaria Ahmed (1896-1961) with scarf around neck (4). b, Riyadh El-Sonbati (1908-81) with glasses with rectangular lenses (3). c, Mahmoud El-Sherif (1912-90) (2). d, Mohamed El-Kasabgi (1898-1966) with glasses with round lenses (1). Stamp numbers, shown in parentheses, are found at the bottom center in Arabian script. Illustration reduced.

2001, Dec.
1812 A1048 30p Horiz. strip of 4   2.00   1.10

Painting From Tomb of Anhur Khawi — A1049

Painting from Tomb of Irinefer — A1050

2002, Jan. 2 Litho. Perf. 12¾x13¼
1813 A1049 30p multi   .60 .25
Imperf
Size: 79x60mm
1814 A1050 125p multi   2.25 2.25
Stamp Day.

Intl. Nephrology Congress A1051

2002, Jan. 16 Litho. Perf. 13¼x12¾
1815 A1051 30p multi   .60 .25

Police Day, 50th Anniv. A1052

2002, Jan. 25   Perf. 12¾x13¼
1816 A1052 30p multi   .60 .25
Imperf
Size: 79x50mm
1817 A1052 30p multi   1.75 1.75

Return of Sinai to Egypt, 20th Anniv. — A1053

2002, Apr. 25   Perf. 13¼x12¾
1818 A1053 30p multi   .60 .25

Cairo Bank, 50th Anniv. — A1054

2002, May 15
1819 A1054 30p multi   .60 .25

Weight Lifters — A1055

No. 1820: a, Ibrahim Shams, 1948 (weights over head). b, Khidre el Touney, 1936 (weights at knees).

2002, June 1
1820 A1055 30p Horiz. pair, #a-b .60 .25

Al Akhbar Newspaper, 50th Anniv. — A1056

2002, June 15   Perf. 12¾x13¼
1821 A1056 30p multi   .60 .25

Nos. 318-321 and Egyptian Arms — A1057

2002, July 23 Litho. Imperf.
1822 A1057 125p multi   1.60 1.60
July 23rd Revolution, 50th anniv.

Aswan Dam, Cent. — A1058

No. 1823: a, Dam. b, Dam and buildings.

2002, Aug. 15   Perf. 12¾x13¼
1823 A1058 30p horiz. pair, #a-b .60 .60

Intl. Day for Preservation of the Ozone Layer — A1059

2002, Sept. 16   Perf. 13¼x12¾
1824 A1059 125p multi   1.25 1.25

18th Intl. Conference on Road Safety, Cairo — A1060

2002, Sept. 22
1825 A1060 30p multi   .60 .25

17th Congress of Intl. Federation of Otorhinolaryngological Societies, Cairo — A1061

2002, Sept. 28
1826 A1061 30p multi   .60 .25

World Post Day — A1062

2002, Oct. 9
1827 A1062 125p multi   1.10 1.10

Opening of Alexandria Library — A1063

Ancient Alexandria Library — A1064

Designs: 30p, Library exterior. 125p, Pillar, sun on horizon, vert.

Perf. 12¾x13¼, 13¼x12¾
2002, Oct. 16
1828-1829 A1063 Set of 2   1.50 1.50
Size: 60x80mm
Imperf
1830 A1064 125p multi   1.60 1.60

Hassan Faek, Actor — A1065

Aziza Amir, Actress — A1066

Farid Shawki, Actor — A1067

Mary Mounib, Actress — A1068

2002, Nov. 23   Perf. 13¼x12¾
1831   Horiz. strip of 4   1.60 1.60
  a. A1065 30p tan & black   .40 .20
  b. A1066 30p tan & black   .40 .20
  c. A1067 30p tan & black   .40 .20
  d. A1068 30p tan & black   .40 .20

A1069

A1070

A1071

Birds — A1072

2002, Dec. 3   **Perf. 13¼x12¾**
1832   Block of 4   1.60 1.60
   a. A1069 30p multi   .40 .20
   b. A1070 30p multi   .40 .20
   c. A1071 30p multi   .40 .20
   d. A1072 30p multi   .40 .20

Egyptian Museum, Cent. — A1073

2002, Dec. 11   **Perf. 12¾x13¼**
1833 A1073 30p shown   .60 .25
Size: 80x60mm
Imperf
1834 A1073 125p Entrance, stat-
    ue of Cheops   1.75 1.75

Opening of Aswan Suspension
Bridge — A1074

No. 1835: a, Bridge and support cables. b,
Bridge towers.

2002, Dec. 17   **Perf. 12¾x13¼**
1835 A1074 30p Horiz. pair, #a-b   .75 .75

Suez Canal
University, 25th
Anniv. — A1075

2002, Dec. 29   **Perf. 13¼x12¾**
1836 A1075 30p multi   .50 .20

Toshka Land Reclamation
Project — A1076

2002, Dec. 31   **Perf. 12¾x13¼**
1837 A1076 30p multi   .50 .20

A1077

A1078

Post Day — A1079

2003, Jan. 2
1838 A1077   30p multi   .40 .20
1839 A1078   30p multi   .40 .20
1840 A1079 125p multi   1.10 1.10
   Nos. 1838-1840 (3)   1.90 1.50

Cairo Intl.
Communications
and Information
Technology
Fair — A1080

2003, Jan. 12   Litho.   Perf. 13¼x12¾
1841 A1080 30p multi   .60 .25

Intl. Nile Children's Song
Festival — A1081

Background color: 30p, Brown. 125p,
Green.

2003, Jan. 28   **Perf. 12¾x13¼**
1842-1843 A1081   Set of 2   1.25 1.25

Intl. Table Tennis
Championships — A1082

Background color: 30p, Blue. 125p, Orange.

2003, Feb. 3
1844-1845 A1082   Set of 2   1.25 1.25

Tenth Intl. Building
and Construction
Conference
A1083

Background color: 30p, Orange. 125p, Blue.

2003, Apr. 1   **Perf. 13¼x12¾**
1846-1847 A1083   Set of 2   1.10 1.10

Arab Lawyer's Union, 60th
Anniv. — A1084

Background color: 30p, Blue. 125p, Lilac.

2003, Apr. 25   **Perf. 12¾x13¼**
1848-1849 A1084   Set of 2   1.10 1.10

Inauguration of First Phase of Smart
Village Project — A1085

Denomination color: 30p, White. 125p, Yellow. £1, White.

2003, July 1   **Perf. 12¾x13¼**
1850-1851 A1085   Set of 2   1.10 1.10
Size: 79x59mm
Imperf
1852 A1085 £1 multi   2.00 2.00

Writers — A1086

No. 1853: a, Ihsan Abdul Qudous (1919-90)
(wearing checked tie). b, Youssef Idris (1927-
91) (wearing solid tie).

2003, July 28   **Perf. 13¼x12¾**
1853 A1086 30p Horiz. pair, #a-b   .75 .75

African Men's
Basketball
Championships
A1087

Background color: 30p, Black. 125p, Blue.

2003, Aug. 12
1854-1855 A1087   Set of 2   1.10 1.10

Natl. Institute of Astronomical and
Geophysical Research, Cent. — A1088

2003, Sept. 7   **Perf. 12¾x13¼**
1856 A1088 30p multi   .75 .30

World Tourism Day — A1089

Denomination color: 30p, White. 125p, Red.

Perf. 12¾x13¼
2003, Sept. 27   **Litho.**
1857-1858 A1089   Set of 2   1.10 1.10

Egypt's Bid for Hosting 2010 World
Cup Soccer Championships — A1090

Designs: 30p, Emblem, vert. 125p, Emblem,
funerary mask of King Tutankhamen.

Perf. 13¼x12¾, 12¾x13¼
2003, Sept. 27
1859-1860 A1090   Set of 2   1.10 1.10

October War
Against Israel,
30th
Anniv. — A1091

2003, Oct. 6   **Perf. 13¼x12¾**
1861 A1091 30p multi   .75 .30

World Post
Day — A1092

2003, Oct. 9
1862 A1092 125p multi   .80 .80

National Bar
Association, 91st
Anniv. — A1093

2003, Oct. 30
1863 A1093 30p multi .50 .20

Festivals — A1094

No. 1864: a, Pink orchids. b, White rose. c,
Red rose. d, Sunflower.

2003, Nov. 23 *Perf. 14*
1864 A1094 30p Block of 4, #a-d 1.25 1.25

Film Directors — A1095

No. 1865: a, Salah Abou Seif (balding man
with open collar). b, Kamal Selim (round eye-
glasses) c, Henri Barakat (square eye-
glasses). d, Hassan El Emam.

2003, Dec. 1 *Perf. 13¼x12¾*
1865 A1095 30p Horiz. strip of 4,
#a-d 1.25 1.25

El Gomhoreya
Newspaper, 50th
Anniv. — A1096

2003, Dec. 7
1866 A1096 30p multi .50 .20

Cairo Bourse, Cent. — A1097

2003, Dec. 7 *Perf. 12¾x13¼*
1867 A1097 30p multi .50 .20

Mrs. Suzanne Mubarak, Emblems of
Fifth E-9 Ministerial Review Meeting
and UNESCO — A1098

Background color: 30p, Blue. 125p, Orange.
£2, Blue.

Perf. 12¾x13¼
2003, Dec. 18 Set of 2 1.10 1.10
1868-1869 A1098
Imperf
Size: 79x60mm
1870 A1098 £2 multi 2.25 2.25

Delta International
Bank, 25th
Anniv. — A1099

Background color: 30p, Green. 125p, Blue.
£2, Green and blue, horiz.

2004, Jan. 1 *Perf. 12¾x13¼*
1871-1872 A1099 Set of 2 1.00 1.00
Imperf
Size: 80x60mm
1873 A1099 £2 multi 2.25 2.25

Post
Day
A1100

Denominations: 30p, 125p.

2004, Jan. 2 *Perf. 12¾x13¼*
1874-1875 A1100 Set of 2 1.00 1.00

Eighth Intl. Telecommunications
Conference — A1101

2004, Jan. 17
1876 A1101 30p multi .70 .30

Treasures
of Egypt
A1102

No. 1877: a, Sinai. b, Pyramids at dusk. c,
Egyptian Bedouin. d, Red Sea corals. e, Suez
Canal, Ferdinand-Marie de Lesseps, Khedive
Ismail. f, Ramadan lanterns. g, Nile felucca. h,
White Western Desert. i, Maydum Pyramid.
No. 1878: a, St. Catherine Monastery, Sinai.
b, Icon of Sts. Paul and Anthony. c, Mosque of
Muhammad Ali. d, Lamp, Old Cairo. e,
Emblem of Sultan Qaytbay. f, Minaret, Cairo.
g, Mosque of al-Azhar. h, Coptic priest and
icon, Cairo. i, Ben Ezra Synagogue.
No. 1879: a, Ankh. b, Rosetta Stone. c, Sar-
cophagus of Ahmes Meritamun. d, Stela of
Amenmhat. e, Sphinx. f, Udjat. g, Canopic jars

of Tutankhamun. h, Cartouche of
Tutankhamun. i, Egyptian scribe.
No. 1880: a, Sphinx, diff. b, Queen Nefertiti.
c, Tutankhamun.

2004, Jan. 22 Litho. *Perf. 13x13¼*
1877 Booklet pane of 9 2.25 —
a.-i. A1102 30p Any single .40 .20
1878 Booklet pane of 9 11.00 —
a.-i. A1102 125p Any single 1.25 1.25

**Litho. & Embossed, Litho. &
Embossed With Foil Application
(£10)**
1879 Booklet pane of 9 17.50 —
a.-i. A1102 £2 Any single 1.90 1.90
Perf. 13¼
1880 Booklet pane of 3 19.00 —
a.-b. A1102 £5 Either single,
38x51mm 4.50 4.50
c. A1102 £10 gold & multi,
38x51mm 9.00 9.00
Complete booklet, #1877-
1880 50.00

Complete booklet sold for £80.

Morkos
Hanna — A1103

Ahmed
Lotfi — A1104

Mahmoud Abu el
Nasr — A1105

Abd el Aziz
Fahmy — A1106

Ibrahim el
Helbawi — A1107

Makram
Ebeid — A1108

Mohammad
Naguib el
Gharabli — A1109

Mohammad
Bassiouni
A1110

Mohammad Hafez
Ramadan
A1111

Mohammad Abu
Shadi — A1112

Mahmoud Fahmi
Goundia — A1113

Kamel Youssof
Saleh — A1114

Abd el Hamid
Abd el
Hakk — A1115

Mohammad Ali
Allouba — A1116

Kamel Sedki
Beck — A1117

Bar Association
Emblem — A1118

Abd el Rahman el
Rafei — A1119

Abd el Fattah el
Shalkany
A1120

Mohammad Sabri
Abu
Alam — A1121

Omar
Omar — A1122

Sameh
Ashour — A1123

Ahmed el
Khawaga
A1124

Abd el Aziz el
Shorgabi
A1125

Mostafa el
Baradei — A1126

2004, Feb. **Litho.** **Perf. 13¼x12¾**
1881	Block of 25	10.00	10.00
a.	A1103 30p bright blue & black	.40	.20
b.	A1104 30p bright blue & black	.40	.20
c.	A1105 30p bright blue & black	.40	.20
d.	A1106 30p bright blue & black	.40	.20
e.	A1107 30p bright blue & black	.40	.20
f.	A1108 30p pink & black	.40	.20
g.	A1109 30p pink & black	.40	.20
h.	A1110 30p pink & black	.40	.20
i.	A1111 30p pink & black	.40	.20
j.	A1112 30p pink & black	.40	.20
k.	A1113 30p orange & black	.40	.20
l.	A1114 30p orange & black	.40	.20
m.	A1115 30p orange & black	.40	.20
n.	A1116 30p orange & black	.40	.20
o.	A1117 30p orange & black	.40	.20
p.	A1118 30p green & multi	.40	.20
q.	A1119 30p green & black	.40	.20
r.	A1120 30p green & black	.40	.20
s.	A1121 30p green & black	.40	.20
t.	A1122 30p green & black	.40	.20
u.	A1118 30p dark blue & multi	.40	.20
v.	A1123 30p dark blue & black	.40	.20
w.	A1124 30p dark blue & black	.40	.20
x.	A1125 30p dark blue & black	.40	.20
y.	A1126 30p dark blue & black	.40	.20

National Bar Association, 92nd anniv.

IBM Corporation
in Egypt, 50th
Anniv. — A1127

2004, Feb. 24
1882 A1127 30p multi .50 .20

Cairo Rotary
Club, 75th
Anniv. — A1128

2004, Mar. 11
1883 A1128 30p multi .50 .20

Egyptian Victory
in Regional
Computer
Programming
and Information
Technology
Competition
A1129

2004, Mar. 15
1884 A1129 30p multi .60 .25

National
Women's
Day — A1130

Background colors: 30p, Blue. 125p, Red
orange.

2004, Mar. 16 **Litho.**
1885-1886 A1130 Set of 2 1.00 1.00

Anti-Narcotics General Administration,
75th Anniv. — A1131

2004, Mar. 20 **Perf. 12¾x13¼**
1887 A1131 30p multi .75 .30
Imperf
Size: 80x60mm
1888 A1131 125p multi 2.00 2.00

Orphan's
Day — A1132

2004, Apr. 2 **Perf. 13¼x12¾**
1889 A1132 30p multi .60 .25
Compare with Types A1169 and A1199.

Telecom Africa Fair and Conference,
Cairo — A1133

2004, May 4 **Perf. 12¾x13¼**
1890 A1133 30p multi .60 .25

Egyptian
Philatelic Society,
75th
Anniv. — A1134

Designs: 30p, Emblem. 125p, Emblem,
stamp, magnifying glass, tongs.

2004, May 20 **Perf. 13¼x12¾**
1891 A1134 30p multi .60 .25

Imperf
Size: 80x60mm
1892 A1134 125p multi   2.00 2.00

State Information Service, 50th
Anniv. — A1135

2004, May 30   ***Perf. 12¾x13¼***
1893 A1135 30p multi   .50 .20

Tenth Radio and
Television
Festival,
Cairo — A1136

Designs: 30p, Festival emblem, green background. £1, Fesitval emblem, brown background. 125p, Sphinx, festival emblem, film, horiz. £2, Like 125p, horiz.

Perf. 13¼x12¾, 12¾x13¼
2004, June 1
1894-1896 A1136 Set of 3   1.75 1.75
Imperf
Size: 80x60mm
1897 A1136 £2 multi   2.25 2.25

Pres. Hosni Mubarak, "Education for
All" Arab Regional Conference
Emblem — A1137

Stylized Children,
Emblems
A1138

Perf. 12¾x13¼, 13¼x12¾
2004, June 1
1898 A1137 30p yel & multi   .35 .20
1899 A1137 125p red org & multi .60 .60
1900 A1138 125p multi   .60 .60
  Nos. 1898-1900 (3)   1.55 1.40
Imperf
Size: 80x60mm
1901 A1137 £2 blue & multi   2.25 2.25

Construction and
Housing Bank,
25th
Anniv. — A1139

2004, June 24   ***Perf. 13¼x12¾***
1902 A1139 30p multi   .60 .25

2004 Summer
Olympics,
Athens — A1140

Background color: 30p, Gray. 150p, Orange yellow.

Perf. 13¼x12¾
2004, Aug. 13   **Litho.**
1903-1904 A1140 Set of 2 1.40 1.40

Scouting in Egypt, 90th
Anniv. — A1141

2004, Aug. 15   ***Perf. 12¾x13¼***
1905 A1141 30p multi   .70 .30

14th Intl. Folklore
Festival,
Ismailia — A1142

2004, Aug. 24   ***Perf. 13¼x12¾***
1906 A1142 30p multi   .60 .25

Administrative
Attorneys, 50th
Anniv. — A1143

2004, Sept. 16   ***Perf. 13¼x12¾***
1907 A1143 30p multi   .60 .25
Imperf
Size: 60x80mm
1908 A1143 £1 multi   3.00 3.00

Egyptian National Archives, 50th
Anniv. — A1144

2004, Sept. 20   ***Perf. 12¾x13¼***
1909 A1144 30p multi   .60 .25

Light and Hope Society, 50th
Anniv. — A1145

2004, Sept. 26
1910 A1145 30p multi   .60 .25

General Arab
Journalists
Union, 10th
Conference
A1146

2004, Oct. 2   ***Perf. 13¼x12¾***
1911 A1146 125p multi   .80 .80

Telecom Egypt, 150th Anniv. A1146a

2004, Oct. 3 **Litho.** ***Perf. 12¾x13¼***
1911A A1146a 30p multi   9.00 9.00

No. 1911A was withdrawn from sale after a few days as anniversary emblem was incorrect.

Military Production Day, 50th
Anniv. — A1147

2004, Oct. 6   ***Perf. 12¾x13¼***
1912 A1147 30p multi   .70 .30

World Post Day — A1148

2004, Oct. 9
1913 A1148 150p multi   1.00 1.00

Egyptian Youth
Hostels
Association, 50th
Anniv. — A1149

2004, Oct. 20   ***Perf. 13¼x12¾***
1914 A1149 30p multi   .60 .25

Rose — A1150

Songbird
A1151

Perf. 12¾x13¼
2004, Nov. 10   **Litho.**
1915 A1150 30p multi   .50 .20
Perf. 13¼x12¾
1916 A1151 30p multi   .50 .20

24th Arab Scouting
Congress — A1152

2004, Nov. 27   ***Perf. 12¾x13¼***
1917 A1152 30p multi   .65 .25

Arab Scouting Organization, 50th
Anniv. — A1153

2004, Dec. 4
1918 A1153 30p multi   .65 .25

Islamic Art
Museum
Foundation,
Cent. — A1154

2004, Dec. 15   ***Perf. 13¼x12¾***
1919 A1154 30p multi   .65 .25

FIFA (Fédération Internationale de Football Association), Cent. — A1155

2004, Dec. 15   *Perf. 12¾x13¼*
1920 A1155 150p multi   1.00 1.00

Fekri Abaza (1896-1979), Journalist A1156

Abd El Rahman El Sharqawi (1920-87), Journalist A1157

2004, Dec. 28   *Perf. 13¼x12¾*
1921 A1156 30p multi   .40 .20
1922 A1157 30p multi   .40 .20

Telecom Egypt, 150th Anniv. — A1158

  Color of central panel: 30p, White. 125p, Gray.

2004, Dec. 30   *Perf. 12¾x13¼*
1923-1924 A1158   Set of 2   1.10 1.10

First Sale of Natural Gas to Jordan — A1159

2005, Jan. 1
1925 A1159 30p multi   .70 .30

Post Day — A1160

2005, Jan. 2   *Perf. 13¼x12¾*
1926 A1160 30p multi   .60 .25

Opening of Om El Massrean — El Moneib Subway Line, Cairo — A1161

2005, Jan. 16   *Perf. 12¾x13¼*
1927 A1161 30p multi   .60 .25
        Imperf
      Size: 80x59mm
1928 A1161 150p multi   1.75 1.75

Police Day — A1162

  Pres. Hosni Mubarak and flag stripes aligned: 30p, Vertically. £1, Horizontally.

2005, Jan. 25   *Perf. 13¼x12¾*
1929 A1162 30p multi   .50 .20
        Imperf
      Size: 80x59mm
1930 A1162 £1 multi   1.50 1.50

El Mohandes Insurance Company, 25th Anniv. — A1163

2005, Jan. 26   *Perf. 13¼x12¾*
1931 A1163 30p multi   .60 .25

9th Intl. Telecommunications and Information Conference, Cairo — A1164

2005, Feb. 1
1932 A1164 30p multi   .60 .25

7th University Youth Week — A1165

2005, Feb. 5
1933 A1165 30p multi   .60 .25

Rotary International, Cent. — A1166

2005, Feb. 23   **Litho.**
1934 A1166 30p multi   .70 .30

38th Intl. Fair, Cairo — A1167

2005, Mar. 15
1935 A1167 30p multi   .40 .20

Arab League, 60th Anniv. — A1168

2005, Mar. 22
1936 A1168 30p multi   .50 .20

Orphan's Day — A1169

2005, Apr. 2
1937 A1169 30p multi   .50 .20

Heliopolis Foundation, Cent. — A1170

2005, May 5   *Perf. 12¾x13¼*
1938 A1170 30p multi   .60 .25

National Center of Social and Criminological Research, 50th Anniv. — A1171

2005, May 22 Litho.   *Perf. 13¼x12¾*
1939 A1171 30p multi   .60 .25

Egyptian-European Association Agreement, 1st Anniv. — A1172

2005, June 1
1940 A1172 150p multi   .80 .80

World Environment Day — A1173

2005, June 5   *Perf. 12¾x13¼*
1941 A1173 30p multi   .75 .30

World Summit on the Information Society, Tunis — A1174

2005, July 31 Litho.   *Perf. 13¼x12¾*
1942 A1174 150p multi   1.25 1.25

Ministry of Youth, 50th Anniv. — A1175

Background colors: 30p, Green. 125p, Olive green.

2005, Aug. 13
1943-1944 A1175   Set of 2   1.00 1.00

Presidential Elections A1176

2005, Sept. 7
1945 A1176 30p multi   .60 .25

13th World Psychiatry Congress, Cairo — A1177

Designs: 30p, Emblem. 150p, Emblem and funerary mask of King Tutankhamen, horiz.

2005, Sept. 10   *Perf. 13¼x12¾*
1946 A1177 30p multi   .60 .25
Imperf
Size: 80x60mm
1947 A1177 150p multi   1.75 1.75

World Literacy Day — A1178

2005, Sept. 24   *Perf. 12¾x13¼*
1948 A1178 30p multi   .50 .20

Re-election of Pres. Hosni Mubarak A1179

2005, Sept. 27   *Perf. 13¼x12¾*
1949 A1179 30p multi   .50 .20

Mohamed El-Baradei, Director General of Intl. Atomic Energy Agency — A1180

Background colors: 30p, Blue green. 150p, Rose lilac.

2005, Oct. 8
1950-1951 A1180   Set of 2   1.50 1.50
Awarding of 2005 Nobel Peace Prize to El-Baradei and IAEA.

World Post Day — A1181

Denominations: 30p, 150p.

2005, Oct. 9
1952-1953 A1181   Set of 2   1.25 1.25

Intl. Year of Sports and Physical Education A1182

2005, Oct. 24
1954 A1182 150p multi   1.00 1.00

United Nations, 60th Anniv. — A1183

2005, Oct. 24   *Perf. 12¾x13¼*
1955 A1183 150p multi   1.00 1.00

Festivals A1184

2005, Nov. 1   *Perf. 13¼x12¾*
1956 A1184 30p multi   .65 .25

Alexandria Biennale, 50th Anniv. — A1185

2005, Dec. 1
1957 A1185 30p multi   .60 .25

K-8 Training Airplane — A1186

Denominations: 30p, 150p.

Perf. 12¾x13¼
2005, Dec. 26   **Litho.**
1958-1959 A1186   Set of 2   1.00 1.00

Saved Mekawi, Musician A1187

Mohamed El Mogi (1923-95), Musician A1188

Kamal El Taweel, Composer A1189

Ali Ismael (1921-75), Composer A1190

Mohamed Roshdi, Folk Singer — A1191

2005, Dec. 31   *Perf. 13¼x12¾*
1960   Horiz. strip of 5   1.25 1.25
  a. A1187 30p green & multi   .25 .20
  b. A1188 30p blue & multi   .25 .20
  c. A1189 30p lilac & black   .25 .20
  d. A1190 30p org & black   .25 .20
  e. A1191 30p brt org & black   .25 .20

Post Day — A1192

2006, Jan. 2
1961 A1192 30p multi   .40 .20

25th Africa Cup of Nations Soccer Tournament A1193

2006, Jan. 20
1962 A1193 30p multi   .40 .20

Arab University Youth Week — A1194

2006, Feb. 4   *Perf. 12¾x13¼*
1963 A1194 30p multi   .40 .20

Intl. Telecommunications, Information and Networking Exhibition, Cairo — A1195

2006, Feb. 5   *Perf. 13¼x12¾*
1964 A1195 30p multi   .40 .20

Pres. Hosni Mubarak Holding African
Cup of Nations — A1196

2006, Feb. 10   *Perf. 12¾x13¼*
1965 A1196   30p multi   .40   .20
      Size: 80x60mm
      Imperf
1966 A1196   150p multi   1.10 1.10

Information and
Decision Support
Center, 20th
Anniv. — A1197

2006, Mar. 27   *Perf. 13¼x12¾*
1967 A1197   30p multi   .40   .20

Total Solar Eclipse of March 29,
2006 — A1198

2006, Mar. 29   *Perf. 12¾x13¼*
1968 A1198   30p multi   .40   .20
      Size: 82x60mm
      Imperf
1969 A1198   150p multi   1.10 1.10

Orphan's
Day — A1199

2006, Apr. 2   *Perf. 13¼x12¾*
1970 A1199   30p multi   .40   .20
  Compare with types A1132 and A1169.

Gamal Hemdan
(1928-93),
Geographical
Historian
A1200

2006, Apr. 16
1971 A1200   30p lilac & black   .40   .20

Abd El-Rahman
ibn Khaldun
(1332-1406),
Historian
A1201

2006, May 27
1972 A1201   30p multi   .40   .20

World Environment Day — A1202

  Designs: 30p, Stone pillar in White Desert.
150p, Trees in desert.

2006, June 5   *Perf. 12¾x13¼*
1973-1974 A1202   Set of 2   1.25 1.25

Diplomatic Relations Between Egypt
and People's Republic of China, 50th
Anniv. — A1203

  No. 1975: a, Abu Simbel Temple, Egypt. b,
South Gate Pavilion, China.

2006, July 13   **Litho.**   *Perf. 12*
1975 A1203   £1.50 Horiz. pair,
        #a-b, + cen-
        tral label   1.40 1.40
  c.   Souvenir sheet, #1975   1.10 1.10

Military Academy Headquarters,
Heliopolis, 50th Anniv. — A1204

2006, July 19   *Perf. 12¾x13¼*
1976 A1204   30p multi   .40   .20

Nationalization of
the Suez Canal,
50th
Anniv. — A1205

2006, July 26   *Perf. 13¼x12¾*
1977 A1205   30p multi   .40   .20

World Post
Day — A1206

  Denominations: 30p, 150p.

2006, Oct. 9
1978-1979 A1206   Set of 2   1.25 1.25

China - Africa Summit — A1206a

  No. 1979A: b, Chinese mask. c, African
mask.

2006, Nov. 5   **Litho.**   *Perf. 12*
1979A   Horiz. pair with central
        label   1.10 1.10
  b.-c.   A1206a £1.50 Either single   .55   .55

National Housing
Census — A1207

2006, Nov. 21   **Litho.**   *Perf. 13¼x13*
1980 A1207   30p multi   .20   .20

Al-Ahram Newspaper — A1208

  No. 1981: a, Newspaper headquarters. b,
Newspaper emblem.
  150p, Headquarters and emblem.

2006, Nov. 26   *Perf. 13x13¼*
1981 A1208   30p Horiz. pair, #a-
        b, + central
        label   .20   .20
      Imperf
      Size: 80x60mm
1982 A1208   150p multi   .55   .55

Natl. Council for Childhood and
Motherhood — A1209

2006, Dec. 27   *Perf. 13x13¼*
1983 A1209   150p multi   .55   .55

Feasts — A1210

2006, Dec. 30
1984 A1210   30p multi   .20   .20

Post Day — A1211

2007, Jan. 2
1985 A1211   30p multi   .20   .20

Ali El Kassar
(1888-1957),
Artist — A1212

2007, Jan. 15   *Perf. 13¼x13*
1986 A1212   30p multi   .20   .20

Automobile and Touring Club of
Egypt — A1213

2007, Jan. 14   **Litho.**   *Perf. 12¾x13¼*
1987 A1213   30p multi   .20   .20
      Imperf
      Size: 80x60mm
1988 A1213   150p multi   .55   .55

Police Day — A1214

2007, Jan. 25   *Perf. 12¾x13¼*
1989 A1214   30p multi   .20   .20
      Imperf
      Size: 80x60mm
1990 A1214   150p multi   .55   .55

Rededication of National
Library — A1215

2007, Feb. 25   *Perf. 12¾x13¼*
1991 A1215   30p multi   .20   .20

Arabic Language
Academy, 75th
Anniv. — A1216

2007, Mar. 17 *Perf. 13¼x12¾*
1992 A1216 30p multi .20 .20

World Health Day — A1217

2007, Apr. 7 Litho. *Perf. 12¾x13¼*
1993 A1217 30p multi .20 .20

Egyptian Trade
Union
Federation, 50th
Anniv. — A1218

2007, May 1 *Perf. 13¼x12¾*
1994 A1218 30p multi .20 .20

Egypt Air, 75th Anniv. — A1219

Anniversary emblem and: 30p, Biplane.
150p, Biplane and jet.

2007, May 7 *Perf. 12¾x13¼*
1995-1996 A1219 Set of 2 .65 .65

Return of Sinai to Egypt, 25th
Anniv. — A1220

No. 1997: a, Monastery of St. Catherine. b,
Salah el Din Castle. c, Sharm el-Sheikh. d,
Oasis of Nabq.

2007, Apr. 25 Litho. *Perf. 12¾x13¼*
1997 A1220 30p Block of 4, #a-d .45 .45

Mevlana Jalal ad-
Din ar-Rumi
(1207-73),
Islamic
Philosopher
A1221

2007, May 8 *Perf. 13¼x12¾*
1998 A1221 150p multi .55 .55

World
Environment
Day — A1222

Designs: 30p, Sinai baton blue butterfly.
150p, Melting ice, horiz.

Perf. 13¼x12¾, 12¾x13¼
2007, June 5
1999-2000 A1222 Set of 2 .65 .65

Scouting, Cent. — A1223

2007, June 6 *Perf. 12¾x13¼*
2001 A1223 150p multi .55 .55

EuroMed Postal Conference, Marseille,
France — A1224

2007, July 9
2002 A1224 150p multi .55 .55

Diplomatic Relations Between Egypt
and Nepal, 50th Anniv. — A1225

2007, July 16
2003 A1225 150p multi .55 .55

Egyptian Air Force, 75th
Anniv. — A1226

2007, Oct. 14 Litho. *Perf. 13x13¼*
2004 A1226 30p multi .20 .20

A1227

11th Arab Games — A1228

2007, Oct. 26 Litho. *Perf. 13¼x12¾*
2005 A1227 150p multi .55 .55
Imperf
Size: 95x75mm
2006 A1228 150p multi .55 .55

Assiut University,
50th
Anniv. — A1229

2007, Nov. 27 *Perf. 13¼x12¾*
2007 A1229 30p brn & blk .20 .20

Hafez Ibrahim
(1872-1932),
Poet — A1230

Ahmed Shawky
(1868-1932),
Poet — A1231

2007, Dec. 16
2008 A1230 30p multi .20 .20
2009 A1231 30p multi .20 .20

Egyptian
Handball
Federation, 50th
Anniv. — A1232

2007, Dec. 30
2010 A1232 30p multi .20 .20

Musicians — A1233

2008, Jan. 1 *Perf. 12¾x13¼*
2011 A1233 30p multi .20 .20

Post Day — A1234

2008, Feb. 7 Litho. *Imperf.*
2012 A1234 150p multi .55 .55

Africa Cup of
Nations Soccer
Championships,
Ghana — A1235

2008, Feb. 10 *Perf. 13¼x13*
2013 A1235 30p multi .20 .20

Wadi El-Hitan UNESCO World
Heritage Site — A1236

No. 2014: a, Whale bones on ground. b,
Whale skeleton.

2008, Feb. 10   *Perf. 13x13¼*
2014   Horiz. pair with central
     label   .25 .25
a.-b.   A1236 30p Either single   .20 .20

Cairo University,
Cent. — A1237

2008, Apr. 14   *Perf. 13¼x13*
2015 A1237 30p multi   .20 .20

Land Mine Clearance in Northwest
Egypt — A1238

No. 2016 — Map and: a, Amputee surrounded by land mines. b, Hand, "no land
mines" symbol, vert.

Perf. 13x13¼, 13¼x13 (#2016b)
2008, Apr. 22
2016 A1238 150p Pair, #a-b   1.10 1.10

Telecom Africa
Conference
A1239

2008, May 12   *Perf. 13¼x13*
2017 A1239 30p multi   .20 .20

World
Environment
Day — A1240

Background colors: 30p, Blue. 150p, Lilac.

2008, June 5
2018-2019 A1240   Set of 2   .70 .70

Faculty of Fine Arts, Cent. — A1241

No. 2020 — Background color: a, 30p, Blue.
b, 150p, Green.

2008, June 21   *Litho.*   *Perf. 13¼x13*
2020 A1241   Horiz. pair, #a-b   .70 .70

Pan African Postal Union
Plenipotentiary Conference,
Cairo — A1242

2008, June 28   *Perf. 13x13¼*
2021 A1242 150p multi   .60 .60

Egypt Air Joining Star
Alliance — A1243

2008, July 11
2022 A1243 150p multi   .60 .60

Alexandria, 2008 Islamic Cultural
Capital — A1244

2008, July 26
2023 A1244 150p multi   .60 .60

Arab Post Day — A1245

No. 2024 — Emblem and: a, World map,
pigeon. b, Camel caravan.

2008, Aug. 3
2024   Horiz. pair   1.25 1.25
a.-b.   A1245 150p Either single   .60 .60

24th Universal Postal Union Congress,
Geneva, Switzerland — A1246

2008, Aug. 4   *Litho.*   *Perf. 12¾x13¼*
2025 A1246 150p multi   .60 .60

Men's Sports
Education
Faculty, 50th
Anniv. — A1247

2008, Oct. 15   *Litho.*   *Perf. 13¼x13*
2026 A1247 30p multi   .20 .20

Postech 2008 Intl. Postal Technology
Conference, Sharm El-
Sheikh — A1248

Map and: 30p, Queen Nefertari holding Postech 2008 emblem. 150p, Statue of King Tutankhamen, hand holding Postech emblem.

Perf. 12¾x13¼
2008, Nov. 17   *Litho.*
2027-2028 A1248   Set of 2   .70 .70

Egyptian
Cooperative
Movement,
Cent. — A1249

2008, Dec. 22   *Perf. 13¼x12¾*
2029 A1249 30p multi   .20 .20

Natl. Telecommunications Institute,
25th Anniv. — A1250

2008, Dec. 31   *Perf. 12¾x13¼*
2030 A1250 30p multi   .20 .20

Natl. Sports
Council — A1251

2009, Mar. 3   *Perf. 13¼x12¾*
2031 A1251 150p multi   .55 .55

Constitutional
Judiciary, 40th
Anniv. — A1252

Designs: 30p, Emblem, text below. 150p,
Emblem, text at right, horiz.

2009, Mar. 7   *Perf. 13¼x12¾*
2032 A1252 30p multi   .20 .20
    Size:80x60mm
      Imperf
2033 A1252 150p multi   .55 .55

Intl. Francophone Day — A1253

2009, Mar. 20   *Perf. 12¾x13¼*
2034 A1253 150p multi   .55 .55

Orphan's
Day — A1254

2009, Apr. 3   *Perf. 13¼x12¾*
2035 A1254 150p multi   .55 .55

Intl. Labor Organization, 90th
Anniv. — A1255

2009, Apr. 21   *Perf. 12¾x13¼*
2036 A1255 150p multi   .55 .55

Suzanne Mubarak Women's International Peace Movement A1256

2009, May 14   *Perf. 13¼x12¾*
2037 A1256 150p multi   .55   .55

Yehia Hakki (1905-92), Writer — A1257

2009, May 11   Litho.   *Perf. 12¾x13¼*
2038 A1257 150p multi   .55   .55

Nobel Laureates From Africa — A1258

No. 2039: a, Ahmed Zemail, Chemistry, 1999. b, Bishop Desmond Tutu, Peace, 1984. c, Wangari Maathai, Peace 2004. d, Anwar al-Sadat, Peace, 1978. e, Naguib Mahfouz, Literature, 1988. f, Allan M. Cormack, Physiology or Medicine, 1979. g, Nelson Mandela, Peace, 1993. h, Wole Soyinka, Literature, 1986. i, Sydney Brenner, Physiology or Medicine, 2002. j, F.W. de Klerk, Peace, 1993. k, Nadine Gordimer, Literature, 1991. l, Max Theiler, Physiology or Medicine, 1951. m, Mohamed El Baradei, Peace, 2005. n, Albert Luthuli, Peace, 1960. o, Kofi Annan, Peace, 2001. p, J.M. Coetzee, Literature, 2003.

2009, June 9
2039   Sheet of 16, #a-p, + 9
     labels   9.00   9.00
   a.-p.   A1258 150p Any single

Fourth Extraordinary Session of the Pan-African Postal Union Plenipotentiary Conference, Cairo.

Fifteenth Non-Aligned Movement Summit, Sharm el-Sheikh A1259

2009, July 15   *Perf. 13¼x12¾*
2040 A1259 150p multi   .55   .55

Opening of Mubarak Public Library, Damanhour — A1260

2009, May 7   Litho.   *Perf. 13x13¼*
2041 A1260 150p multi   .55   .55

Jerusalem, Capital of Arab Culture — A1261

2009, Aug. 3   *Perf. 13¼x13*
2042 A1261 150p multi   .55   .55

FIFA Under-20 World Cup Soccer Championships, Egypt — A1262

No. 2042 — Tournament emblem, trophy and flag of participating team: a, Paraguay. b, Brazil. c, Uruguay. d, Germany. e, Nigeria. f, South Korea. g, Venezuela. h, Ghana. i, United Arab Emirates. j, South Africa. k, Egypt. l, Spain. m, Italy. n, Hungary. o, Czech Republic. p, Costa Rica.

2009, Oct. 5   *Perf. 13x13¼*
2043   Sheet of 16, #a-p, + 9
     labels   9.00   9.00
   a.-p.   A1262 150p Any single   .55   .55

Fourth Ministerial Conference of Forum on China-African Cooperation, Sharm El Sheikh — A1263

2009, Nov. 8
2044 A1263 150p multi   .55   .55

Fourth Meeting of Internet Governance Forum, Sharm El Sheikh — A1264

2009, Nov. 15
2045 A1264 150p multi   .55   .55

Luxor Governate — A1264a

2009, Dec. 9   Litho.   *Perf. 12¾x13¼*
2045A A1264a 250p multi   .95   .95

Egyptian Society of Political Economy, Statistics and Legislation, Cent. — A1265

2009, Dec. 19
2046 A1265 150p multi   .55   .55

Pharmaceutical Industry Drug Holding Company, 75th Anniv. — A1266

Background colors: 30p, Pink, yellow and pale green. 150p, Green.

2009, Dec. 19   *Perf. 13¼x13*
2047-2048 A1266   Set of 2   .65   .65

Egyptian Stock Exchange, 125th Anniv. — A1267

Stock Exchange Building with anniversary emblem at left in: 30p, Gold and white. 150p, Gold (75x30mm).

2009, Dec. 21   *Perf. 13x13¼*
2049-2050 A1267   Set of 2   .65   .65

Pan-African Postal Union, 30th Anniv. — A1268

2010, Jan. 18
2051 A1268 150p multi   .55   .55

National Council for Women, 10th Anniv. — A1269

2010, Mar. 16
2052 A1269 30p multi   .20   .20

Orphan's Day — A1270

2010, Jan. 4   Litho.   *Perf. 13¼x12¾*
2053 A1270 30p multi   .20   .20

Edfo Temple — A1271

2010, Jan. 5   *Perf. 12¾x13¼*
2054 A1271 250p multi   .95   .95

Aswan High Dam, 50th Anniv. — A1272

No. 2055 - Part of dam: a, 30p. b, £1.

2010, Jan. 15
2055 A1272   Horiz. pair, #a-b   .50   .50

Arab League Center, 50th Anniv. — A1273

2010, Mar. 22
2056 A1273 200p multi   .75   .75

SEMI-POSTAL STAMPS

Catalogue values for unused stamps in this section are for Never Hinged items.

Princess Ferial — SP1

Perf. 13½x14
1940, May 17   Photo.   Wmk. 195
B1   SP1 5m + 5m copper brown   3.00   .75

No. B1 Overprinted in Green

1943, Nov. 17
B2	SP1	5m + 5m	10.00	6.00
a.	Arabic date "1493"		200.00	200.00

The surtax on Nos. B1 and B2 was for the children's fund.

First Postage Stamp of Egypt SP2

Khedive Ismail Pasha SP3

No. B5, King Fuad. No. B6, King Farouk.

Perf. 13x13½
1946, Feb. 28   **Wmk. 195**
B3	SP2	1m + 1m gray		.40	.25
B4	SP3	10m + 10m violet		.50	.25
B5	SP3	17m + 17m brown		.50	.25
B6	SP3	22m + 22m yel grn		.50	.25
a.	Souv. sheet, #B3-B6, perf. 8½		40.00	35.00
b.	As "a," imperf.		40.00	35.00
	Nos. B3-B6 (4)		1.90	1.00

80th anniv. of Egypt's 1st postage stamp. Nos. B6a, B6b measure 129x171mm.

Goddess Hathor, King Men-kau-Re (Mycerinus) and Jackalheaded Goddess — SP7

Ramesseum, Thebes — SP8

Queen Nefertiti SP9

Funerary Mask of King Tutankhamen SP10

Perf. 13½x13
1947, Mar. 9   **Wmk. 195**
B9	SP7	5m + 5m slate	2.00	.50
B10	SP8	15m + 15m dp blue	2.00	.70
B11	SP9	30m + 30m henna brn	2.00	1.00
B12	SP10	50m + 50m brown	3.00	1.10
	Nos. B9-B12 (4)		9.00	3.30

Intl. Exposition of Contemporary Art, Cairo.

Boy Scout Emblem — SP11

Scout Emblems: 20m+10m, Sea Scouts. 35m+15m, Air Explorers.

1956, July 25   **Photo.**   **Perf. 13½x13**
B13	SP11	10m + 10m green	1.00	.40
B14	SP11	20m + 10m ultra	1.50	.60
B15	SP11	35m + 15m blue	2.00	.70
	Nos. B13-B15 (3)		4.50	1.70

2nd Arab Scout Jamboree, Alexandria-Aboukir, 1956.

Souvenir sheets, perf. and imperf., contain one each of Nos. B13-B15. Size: 118x158mm. Value $750 each.

Ambulance — SP12

1957, May 13   **Perf. 13x13½**
B16	SP12	10m + 5m rose red	.40	.20

50th anniv. of the Public Aid Society.

United Arab Republic

Eye and Map of Africa, Europe and Asia SP13

Postal Emblem SP14

Perf. 13½x13
1958, Mar. 1   **Photo.**   **Wmk. 318**
B17	SP13	10m + 5m orange	1.00	.40

1st Afro-Asian Cong. of Ophthalmology, Cairo.
The surtax was for centers to aid the blind.

1959, Jan. 2
B18	SP14	10m + 5m bl grn, red & blk	.40	.20

Post Day. The surtax went to the social fund for postal employees.
See Syria UAR issues No. B1 for similar stamp with denominations in piasters (p).

Children and UN Emblem SP15

Arab League Building, Cairo, and Emblem SP16

1959, Oct. 24   **Wmk. 328**
B19	SP15	10m + 5m brown lake	.30	.20
B20	SP15	35m + 10m dk blue	.50	.20

Issued for International Children's Day and to honor UNICEF.

Braille Type of Regular Issue, 1961
1961, Apr. 6   **Perf. 13½x13**
B21	A182	35m + 15m yel & brn	.75	.25

1962, Mar. 22   **Photo.**   **Wmk. 328**
B22	SP16	10m + 5m gray	.40	.20

Arab Publicity Week, Mar. 22-28.
See No. N86.

Postal Emblem — SP17

Stamp of 1866 — SP18

1963, Jan. 2   **Wmk. 342**   **Perf. 11½**
B23	SP17	20m + 10m brt grn, red & blk	.80	.60
B24	SP18	40m + 20m blk & brn org	1.50	.90
B25	SP18	40m + 20m brn org & blk	1.50	.90
a.	Pair, #B24-B25		3.50	3.00
	Nos. B23-B25 (3)		3.80	2.40

Post Day, Jan. 2 and 1966 exhibition of the FIP.

Arms of UAR and Pyramids SP19

1964, Jan. 2   **Wmk. 342**   **Perf. 11**
B26	SP19	10m + 5m org yel & grn	1.40	.80
B27	SP19	80m + 40m grnsh bl & blk	2.75	1.25
B28	SP19	115m + 55m org brn & blk	3.25	1.75
	Nos. B26-B28 (3)		7.40	3.80

Issued for Post Day. Jan. 2.

Type of 1963 and

SP20

Postal Emblem — SP20a

No. B30, Emblem of Postal Secondary School. 80m+40m, Postal emblem, gearwheel, laurel wreath.

Perf. 11½
1965, Jan. 2   **Unwmk.**   **Photo.**
B29	SP20	10m + 5m lt grn & car	.60	.40
B30	SP20	10m + 5m ultra, car & blk	.60	.40
a.	Pair, #B29-B30		1.50	1.25
B31	SP20a	80m + 40m rose, brt grn & blk	2.50	1.50
	Nos. B29-B31 (3)		3.70	2.30

Issued for Post Day, Jan. 2. No. B31 also publicizes the Stamp Centenary Exhibition.

Souvenir Sheet

Stamps of Egypt, 1866 — SP21

1966, Jan. 2   **Wmk. 342**   **Imperf.**
B32	SP21	140m + 60m blk, sl bl & rose	3.75	3.25

Post Day, 1966, and cent. of the 1st Egyptian postage stamps.

Pharaonic "Mediator" — SP22

Design: 115m+40m, Pharaonic guard.

1967, Jan. 2   **Wmk. 342**   **Perf. 11½**
B33	SP22	80m + 20m multi	3.00	2.00
B34	SP22	115m + 40m multi	4.75	3.00

Issued for Post Day, Jan. 2.

Grand Canal, Doges' Palace, Venice, and Santa Maria del Fiore, Florence — SP23

115m+30m, Piazzetta and Campanile, Venice, and Palazzo Vecchio, Florence.

Perf. 11½x11
1967, Dec. 9   **Photo.**   **Wmk. 342**
B35	SP23	80m + 20m grn, yel & brn	1.50	1.00
B36	SP23	115m + 30m ol, yel & sl bl	2.25	1.75

The surtax was to help save the cultural monuments of Venice and Florence, damaged in the 1966 floods.

Boy and Girl — SP24

Emblem and Flags of Arab League — SP25

Design: No. B38, Five children and arch.

Wmk. 342

1968, Dec. 11   **Photo.**   *Perf. 11*
B37 SP24 20m + 10m car, bl & lt
brn .75 .50
B38 SP24 20m + 10m vio bl, sep &
lt grn .75 .50

Children's Day & 22nd anniv. of UNICEF.

1969, Mar. 22   *Perf. 11x11½*
B39 SP25 20m + 10m multi .45 .25

Arab Publicity Week, Mar. 22-28.

Refugee
Family
SP26

1969, Oct. 24   **Photo.**   *Perf. 11½*
B40 SP26 30m + 10m multi .70 .40

Issued for United Nations Day.

Men of
Three
Races,
Human
Rights
Emblem
SP27

1970, Mar. 21   *Perf. 11½x11*
B41 SP27 20m + 10m multi .95 .70

Issued to publicize the International Day for
the Elimination of Racial Discrimination.

Arab League Type

1970, Mar. 22   **Wmk. 342**
B42 A344 20m + 10m bl, grn & brn .70 .55

Map of
Palestine
and
Refugees
SP28

Perf. 11½x11
1970, Oct. 24   **Photo.**   **Wmk. 342**
B43 SP28 20m + 10m multi .75 .60

25th anniv. of the UN and to draw attention
to the plight of the Palestinian refugees.

Arab Republic of Egypt

Blind Girl, WHO and
Society
Emblems — SP29

1973, Oct. 24   **Photo.**   *Perf. 11x11½*
B44 SP29 20m + 10m blue & gold .65 .50

25th anniv. of WHO and for the Light and
Hope Soc., which educates and helps blind
girls.

Map of Africa,
OAU Emblem
SP30

Social Work Day
Emblem
SP31

Perf. 11x11½
1973, Dec. 8   **Photo.**   **Wmk. 342**
B45 SP30 55m + 20m multi 1.75 1.00

Organization for African Unity, 10th anniv.

1973, Dec. 8
B46 SP31 20m + 10m multi .75 .65

Social Work Day.

Jihan al Sadat Consoling Wounded
Man — SP32

1974, Mar. 21   **Wmk. 342**   *Perf. 11*
B47 SP32 20m + 10m multi .90 .70

Faithfulness and Hope Society.

Afghan
Solidarity
SP33

Wmk. 342
1981, July 15   **Photo.**   *Perf. 11½*
B48 SP33 20m + 10m multi 1.25 1.25

Size: 30x25mm
1981   **Photo.**   *Perf. 11½*
B49 SP33 20m + 10m multi 4.00 3.50

Map of Sudan,
Dunes, Dead
Tree — SP34

1986, Mar. 25   **Photo.**   *Perf. 13x13½*
B50 SP34 15p + 5p multi 1.60 1.00

Fight against drought and desertification of
the Sudan. Surtax for drought relief.

Organization of African Unity, 25th
Anniv. — SP35

1988, May 25   **Litho.**   *Perf. 13*
B51 SP35 15p +10p multi .90 .90

AIR POST STAMPS

Mail Plane
in Flight
AP1

Perf. 13x13½
1926, Mar. 10   **Wmk. 195**   **Photo.**
C1 AP1 27m deep violet 24.00 24.00

1929, July 17
C2 AP1 27m orange brown 7.00 2.25

Zeppelin Issue
No. C2 Surcharged in Blue or Violet

1931, Apr. 6
C3 AP1 50m on 27m (Bl) 75.00 75.00
  a. "1951" instead of "1931" 100.00 100.00
C4 AP1 100m on 27m (V) 75.00 *75.00*

Airplane
over Giza
Pyramids
AP2

1933-38   **Litho.**   *Perf. 13x13½*
C5 AP2 1m orange & blk .40 .25
C6 AP2 2m gray & blk .80 .55
C7 AP2 2m org red & blk
  ('38) 2.00 .75
C8 AP2 3m ol brn & blk .60 .20
C9 AP2 4m green & blk .90 .45
C10 AP2 5m dp brown & blk .40 .20
C11 AP2 6m dk green & blk 1.50 .65
C12 AP2 7m dk blue & blk 1.00 .55
C13 AP2 8m violet & blk .60 .20
C14 AP2 9m dp red & blk 2.50 .75
C15 AP2 10m violet & brn .75 .25
C16 AP2 20m dk green & brn .60 .20
C17 AP2 30m dull blue & brn .75 .20
C18 AP2 40m dp red & brn 15.00 .60
C19 AP2 50m orange & brn 12.00 .55
C20 AP2 60m gray & brn 3.75 .55
C21 AP2 70m dk blue & bl
  grn 3.50 .50
C22 AP2 80m ol brn & bl grn 3.50 .50
C23 AP2 90m org & bl grn 4.00 .50
C24 AP2 100m vio & bl grn 7.00 .50
C25 AP2 200m dp red & bl grn 10.00 1.00
  Nos. C5-C25 (21) 71.55 9.60

See #C34-C37. For overprint see #C38.

Type of 1933
1941-43   **Photo.**
C34 AP2 5m copper brn ('43) .25 .25
C35 AP2 10m violet .50 .25
C36 AP2 25m dk vio brn ('43) .50 .25
C37 AP2 30m green .65 .25
  Nos. C34-C37 (4) 1.90 1.00

Catalogue values for unused
stamps in this section, from this
point to the end of the section, are
for Never Hinged items.

No. C37 Overprinted in Black

1946, Oct. 1
C38 AP2 30m green .50 .35
  a. Double overprint 400.00
  b. Inverted overprint 400.00

Middle East Intl. Air Navigation Congress,
Cairo, Oct. 1946.

King
Farouk,
Delta
Dam and
DC-3
Plane
AP3

Perf. 13x13½
1947, Feb. 19   **Photo.**   **Wmk. 195**
C39 AP3 2m red orange .25 *.55*
C40 AP3 3m dk brown .25 *.60*
C41 AP3 5m red brown .25 .20
C42 AP3 7m dp yellow org .45 .20
C43 AP3 8m green .45 *.70*
C44 AP3 10m violet .40 .20
C45 AP3 20m brt blue .50 .20
C46 AP3 30m brown violet .60 .20
C47 AP3 40m carmine rose 1.50 .60
C48 AP3 50m Prus green 1.75 .70
C49 AP3 100m olive green 3.25 .75
C50 AP3 200m dark gray 7.00 2.75
  Nos. C39-C50 (12) 16.65 7.65

For overprints see Nos. C51-C64, C67-C89,
NC1-NC30.

Nos. C49 and C50 Surcharged in
Black

1948, Aug. 23
C51 AP3 13m on 100m .50 .40
C52 AP3 22m on 200m .60 *.75*
  a. Date omitted

Inaugural flights of "Services Aeriens
Internationaux d'Egypte" from Cairo to Athens
and Rome, Aug. 23, 1948.

Nos. C39 to C50 Overprinted in
Various Colors

Overprint 27mm Wide
1952, Jan.   **Wmk. 195**   *Perf. 13x13½*
C53 AP3 2m red orange (Bl) .35 .20
C54 AP3 3m dark brown
  (RV) .80 .80
C55 AP3 5m red brown .35 .35
C56 AP3 7m dp yel org (Bl) .70 .40
C57 AP3 8m green (RV) 1.00 .80
C58 AP3 10m violet (G) .80 .80
C59 AP3 20m brt blue (RV) 3.25 1.00
C60 AP3 30m brown vio (G) 1.00 .40
C61 AP3 40m carmine rose
  (RV) 1.50 1.25
C62 AP3 50m Prus green
  (RV) 4.00 3.00
C63 AP3 100m olive green 5.00 2.00
C64 AP3 200m dark gray (RV) 10.00 4.00
  Nos. C53-C64 (12) 28.75 15.00

See notes after No. 316.

Delta
Dam and
Douglas
DC-3
AP4

1953 Photo.
C65 AP4 5m red brown .50 .50
C66 AP4 15m olive green 1.00 1.00

For overprints see Nos. NC31-NC32.

Nos. C39-C49 Overprinted in Black
with Three Bars to Obliterate Portrait

1953
C67 AP3 2m red orange 1.50 1.50
C68 AP3 3m dk brown 1.20 1.20
C69 AP3 5m red brown .80 .80
C70 AP3 7m dp yellow org .50 .50
C71 AP3 8m green 1.20 1.20
C72 AP3 10m violet 35.00
C73 AP3 20m brt blue 1.50 .30
C74 AP3 30m brown violet 1.75 .60
C75 AP3 40m carmine rose 1.75 1.00
C76 AP3 50m Prus green 3.25 1.75
C77 AP3 100m olive green 4.25 2.75
C77A AP3 200m gray 60.00

Nos. C72 and C77A are in question. They
are not known postally used.

Nos. C53-C64 Overprinted in Black
with Three Bars to Obliterate Portrait

1953
C78 AP3 2m red orange .60 .35
C79 AP3 3m dark brown 1.10 .80
C80 AP3 5m red brown .40 .25
C82 AP3 8m green .80 1.50
C83 AP3 10m violet .70 1.25
C85 AP3 30m brown violet 1.50 1.25
C87 AP3 50m Prus green 4.00 1.00
C88 AP3 100m olive green 6.00 3.00
C89 AP3 200m dark gray 10.00 10.00
Nos. C78-C89 (9) 25.10 20.40

Practically all values of Nos. C67-C89 exist
with double overprint. The 7m, 20m and 40m
with this overprint are forgeries.

**United Arab Republic
Type of Regular Issue**
Perf. 11½x11
1958, Mar. 22 Photo. Wmk. 318
C90 A141 15m ultra & red brn .40 .25

Pyramids
at Giza
AP5

Al Azhar
University
AP6

Designs: 15m, Colossi of Memnon, Thebes.
90m, St. Catherine Monastery, Mt. Sinai.

1959-60 Wmk. 328 *Perf. 13x13½*
C91 AP5 5m bright red .25 .20
C92 AP5 15m dk dull violet .35 .30
C93 AP6 60m dk green .75 .50
C94 AP5 90m brown car ('60) 1.50 1.00
Nos. C91-C94 (4) 2.85 2.00

Nos. C91-C93 exist imperf. See Nos. C101,
C105, NC33.

Tower of Cairo Type, Redrawn
1961, May 1 *Perf. 13½x13*
C95 A183 50m bright blue .90 .45

Top inscription has been replaced by two
airplanes.

Weather Vane, Anemometer and UN
World Meteorological Organization
Emblem — AP7

Perf. 11½x11
1962, Mar. 23 Photo. Unwmk.
C96 AP7 60m yellow & dp blue 1.50 .90

2nd World Meteorological Day, Mar. 23.

Patrice Lumumba
and Map of
Africa — AP8

Perf. 13½x13
1962, July 1 Wmk. 328
C97 AP8 35m multicolored .65 .35

Patrice Lumumba (1925-61), Premier of
Congo.

Maritime Station, Alexandria — AP9

Designs: 30m, International Airport, Cairo.
40m, Railroad Station, Luxor.

1963, Mar. 18 *Perf. 13x13½*
C98 AP9 20m dark brown .60 .20
C99 AP9 30m carmine rose .85 .35
C100 AP9 40m black 1.50 .90
Nos. C98-C100 (3) 2.95 1.45

Type of 1959-60 and

Temple of
Queen
Nefertari,
Abu
Simbel
AP10

Arch and Tower of
Cairo — AP11

Designs: 80m, Al Azhar University seen
through arch. 140m, Ramses II, Abu Simbel.

Perf. 11½x11, 11x11½
1963-65 Photo. Wmk. 342
C101 AP6 80m vio blk & brt
bl 3.75 1.50
C102 AP10 115m brown & yel 2.75 1.25
C103 AP10 140m pale vio, blk
& org red 2.75 1.25

Unwmk.
C104 AP11 50m yel brn & brt
bl 2.25 1.00
C105 AP6 80m vio bl & lt bl 3.50 1.50
Nos. C101-C105 (5) 15.00 6.50

Issued: 50m, 11/2/64; No. C105, 2/13/65;
others, 10/24/63.
See Nos. NC34-NC36.

Weather Vane, Anemometer and
WMO Emblem — AP12

Perf. 11½x11
1965, Mar. 23 Wmk. 342
C106 AP12 80m dk blue & rose
lil 2.50 1.25

Fifth World Meteorological Day.
See No. NC37.

Game Board from Tomb of
Tutankhamen — AP13

1965, July 1 Photo. Unwmk.
C107 AP13 10m yellow & dk blue 1.25 .40

See No. NC38.

Temples at Abu Simbel — AP14

1966, Apr. 28 Wmk. 342 *Perf. 11½*
C108 AP14 20m multicolored 1.00 .40
C109 AP14 80m multicolored 2.00 1.10

Issued to commemorate the transfer of the
temples of Abu Simbel to a hilltop, 1963-66.

Scout
Camp
and
Jamboree
Emblem
AP15

1966, Aug. 10 *Perf. 11½x11*
C110 AP15 20m olive & rose 1.40 .45

7th Pan-Arab Boy Scout Jamboree, Good
Daim, Libya, Aug. 12.

St. Catherine Monastery, Mt.
Sinai — AP16

1966, Nov. 30 Photo. Wmk. 342
C111 AP16 80m multicolored 2.10 1.25

St. Catherine Monastery, Sinai, 1400th
anniv.

Cairo
Airport
AP17

1967, Apr. 26 *Perf. 11½x11*
C112 AP17 20m sky bl, sl grn & lt
brn .85 .35

Hotel El
Alamein and
Map of Nile
Delta
AP18

Intl. Tourist Year: 80m, The Virgin's Tree,
Virgin Mary and Child. 115m, Fishing in the
Red Sea.

1967, June 7 Wmk. 342 *Perf. 11½*
C113 AP18 20m dull pur, sl
grn & dl
org .75 .25
C114 AP18 80m blue & multi 2.25 1.00
C115 AP18 115m brown, org &
bl 4.00 2.00
Nos. C113-C115 (3) 7.00 3.25

Oil
Derricks,
Map of
Egypt
AP19

1967, July 23 Photo.
C116 AP19 50m org & bluish blk 1.10 .75

15th anniversary of the revolution.

Type of Regular Issue, 1967
Design: 80m, Back of Tutankhamen's throne
and UNESCO emblem.

1967, Oct. 24 Wmk. 342 *Perf. 11½*
C117 A301 80m blue & yellow 1.25 .85

Koran — AP20

1968, Mar. 25 Wmk. 342 *Perf. 11½*
C118 AP20 30m lilac, bl & yel .75 .60
C119 AP20 80m lilac, bl & yel 1.50 .80
a. Pair, #C118-C119 + label 3.00 2.50

1400th anniv. of the Koran. Nos. C118-
C119 are printed in miniature sheets of 4 containing 2 each of Nos. C118-C119.

St. Mark and St. Mark's
Cathedral — AP21

1968, June 25 Wmk. 342 *Perf. 11½*
C120 AP21 80m brt grn, dk brn &
dp car 1.50 .70

Martyrdom of St. Mark, 1900th anniv. and
the consecration of St. Mark's Cathedral,
Cairo.

Map of United Arab Airlines and
Boeing 707
AP22

Design: No. C122, Ilyushin 18 and routes of
United Arab Airlines.

1968-69 Photo. Perf. 11½x11
C121 AP22 55m blue, ocher &
car 1.25 .65
C122 AP22 55m bl, yel & vio blk
('69) 1.10 .65
1st flights of a Boeing 707 and an Ilyushin 18 for United Arab Airlines.

Mahatma Gandhi, Arms of India and UAR AP23

Imam El Boukhary AP24

1969, Sept. 10 Perf. 11x11½
C123 AP23 80m lt blue, ocher & brn 3.25 1.50
Mohandas K. Gandhi (1869-1948), leader in India's fight for independence.

1969, Dec. 27 Photo. Wmk. 342
C124 AP24 30m lt olive & dk brown .70 .20
1100th anniv. of the death of the Imam El Boukhary (824-870), philosopher and writer.

Azzahir Beybars Mosque AP25

1969, Dec. 27 Engr. Perf. 11½x11
C125 AP25 30m red lilac .50 .20
700th anniv. of the founding of the Azzahir Beybars Mosque, Cairo.

Lenin (1870-1924) — AP26

Perf. 11x11½
1970, Apr. 22 Photo. Wmk. 342
C126 AP26 80m lt green & brown 1.75 1.00

Phantom Fighters and Destroyed Factory AP27

1970, May 1 Perf. 11½x11
C127 AP27 80m yel, grn & dk vio brn 1.50 .90
Issued to commemorate the destruction of the Abu-Zaabal factory by Israeli planes.

UPU Type of Regular Issue
1970, May 20 Photo. Wmk. 342
C128 A350 80m multicolored 1.20 .85

Nasser and Burial Mosque — AP28

1970, Nov. 6 Wmk. 342 Perf. 11
C129 AP28 30m olive & blk .75 .30
C130 AP28 80m brown & blk 1.75 .80
Gamal Abdel Nasser (1918-70), Pres. of Egypt.

Postal Congress Type
Perf. 11½x11
1971, Mar. 6 Photo. Wmk. 342
C131 A365 30m lt ol, org & sl grn .80 .40

Nasser, El Rifaei and Sultan Hussein Mosques AP29

Designs: 85m, Nasser and Ramses Square, Cairo. 110m, Nasser, Sphinx and pyramids.

Perf. 11½x11
1971, July 1 Photo. Wmk. 342
C132 AP29 30m multicolored 2.50 .75
C133 AP29 85m multicolored 4.00 1.00
C134 AP29 110m multicolored 5.50 1.50
Nos. C132-C134 (3) 12.00 3.25

APU Type of Regular Issue
1971, Aug. 3 Wmk. 342 Perf. 11½
C135 A373 30m brown, yel & bl .85 .40

Arab Republic of Egypt Confederation Type
Perf. 11½x11
1971, Sept. 28 Photo. Wmk. 342
C136 A374 30m gray, sl grn & dk pur .80 .40

Al Aqsa Mosque and Woman AP30

Wmk. 342
1971, Oct. 24 Photo. Perf. 11½
C137 AP30 30m bl, yel, brn & grn 1.60 .40
25th anniv. of the UN (in 1970) and return of Palestinian refugees.

Postal Union Type
30m, African Postal Union emblem & letter.

1971, Dec. 2 Perf. 11½x11
C138 A384 30m green, blk & bl 1.40 .40

Aida, Triumphal March AP31

1971, Dec. 23 Wmk. 342 Perf. 11½
C139 AP31 110m dk brn, yel & sl grn 5.50 2.75
Centenary of the first performance of the opera Aida, by Giuseppe Verdi.

Globe, Glider, Rocket Club Emblem AP32

St. Catherine's Monastery on Fire AP33

1972, Feb. 11 Perf. 11x11½
C140 AP32 30m blue, ocher & yel 1.25 .40
International Aerospace Education Conference, Cairo, Jan. 11-13.

Perf. 11½x11
1972, Feb. 15 Unwmk.
C141 AP33 110m dp car, org & blk 4.25 3.00
The burning of St. Catherine's Monastery in Sinai Desert, Nov. 30, 1971.

Tutankhamen in Garden — AP34

Tutankhamen, from 2nd Sarcophagus — AP35

Design: No. C143, Ankhesenamun.

1972, May 22 Photo. Perf. 11½
C142 AP34 110m brn org, bl & grn 8.50 4.00
C143 AP34 110m brn org, bl & grn 8.50 4.00
a. Pair, #C142-C143 24.00 20.00

Souvenir Sheet
Imperf
C144 AP35 200m gold & multi 30.00 27.50
50th anniv. of the discovery of the tomb of Tutankhamen. No. C143a has continuous design.

Souvenir Sheet

Flag of Confederation of Arab Republics — AP36

1972, July 23 Photo. Imperf.
C145 AP36 110m gold, dp car & blk 4.25 4.00
20th anniversary of the revolution.

Temples at Abu Simbel AP37

Designs: 30m, Al Azhar Mosque and St. George's Church. 110m, Pyramids at Giza.

1972 Wmk. 342 Perf. 11½x11
C146 AP37 30m blue, brn & buff 2.00 .35
C147 AP37 85m bl, brn & ocher 3.00 1.25
C148 AP37 110m multicolored 4.75 1.25
Nos. C146-C148 (3) 9.75 2.85
Issued: Nos. C146, C148, 11/22; No. C147, 8/1.

Olympic Type of Regular Issue
Olympic and Motion Emblems and: No. C149, Handball. No. C150, Weight lifting. 50m, Swimming. 55m, Gymnastics. All vertical.

1972, Aug. 17 Perf. 11x11½
C149 A396 30m multicolored .75 .35
C150 A396 30m yellow & multi .75 .35
C151 A396 50m blue & multi 1.50 .80
C152 A396 55m multicolored 1.75 .90
Nos. C149-C152 (4) 4.75 2.40

Champollion, Rosetta Stone, Hieroglyphics — AP38

1972, Oct. 16
C153 AP38 110m gold, grn & blk 7.50 2.50
Sesquicentennial of the deciphering of Egyptian hieroglyphics by Jean-François Champollion.

World Map, Telephone, Radar, ITU Emblem — AP39

1973, Mar. 21 Photo. Perf. 11
C154 AP39 30m lt bl, dk bl & blk .90 .25
5th World Telecommunications Day.

Karnak Temple, Luxor — AP40

Hand Dripping Blood and Falling Plane — AP41

1973, Mar. 21
C155 AP40 110m dp ultra, blk & rose 4.75 2.25

Sound and light at Karnak.

1973, May 1 *Perf. 11x11½*
C156 AP41 110m multicolored 6.00 1.75

Israeli attack on Libyan civilian plane, Feb. 1973.

WMO Emblem, Weather Vane — AP42

1973, Oct. 24 *Perf. 11x11½*
C157 AP42 110m blue, gold & pur 2.75 1.75

Cent. of intl. meteorological cooperation.

Refugees, Map of Palestine AP43

1973, Oct. 24 *Perf. 11½*
C158 AP43 30m dk brn, yel & bl 1.60 .50

Plight of Palestinian refugees.

INTERPOL Emblem AP44

Postal and UPU Emblems AP45

Perf. 11x11½
1973, Dec. 8 **Photo.** **Wmk. 342**
C159 AP44 110m black & multi 3.50 1.75

Intl. Criminal Police Organization, 50th anniv.

1974, Jan. 2 **Unwmk.** *Perf. 11*

Post Day (UPU Emblems and): 30m, APU emblem. 55m, African Postal Union emblem. 110m, UPU emblem.

Size: 26x46½mm
C160 AP45 20m gray, red & blk .40 .20
C161 AP45 30m sal, blk & pur .60 .20

C162 AP45 55m emerald, blk & brt mag 1.25 .50

Size: 37x37½mm
Perf. 11½
C163 AP45 110m lt bl, blk & gold 1.50 1.00
Nos. C160-C163 (4) 3.75 1.90

Solar Bark of Khufu (Cheops) — AP46

Wmk. 342
1974, Mar. 21 **Photo.** *Perf. 11½*
C164 AP46 110m blue, gold & brn 3.00 2.10

Solar Bark Museum.

Hotel Meridien AP47

1974, Oct. 6 *Perf. 11½x11*
C165 AP47 110m multicolored 2.00 1.10

Opening of Hotel Meridien, Cairo.

Suez Canal Type of 1975
1975, June 5 *Perf. 11½*
C166 A448 30m bl, yel grn & ind 1.50 .45
C167 A448 110m indigo & blue 2.50 1.25

Irrigation Commission Emblem — AP48

1975, July 20
C168 AP48 110m orange & dk grn 2.00 1.00

9th Intl. Congress on Irrigation and Drainage, Moscow, and 25th anniv. of the Intl. Commission on Irrigation and Drainage.

Refugees and UNWRA Emblem — AP49

Woman and IWY Emblem — AP50

Perf. 11x11½
1975, Oct. 24 **Wmk. 342**
C169 AP49 30m multicolored 1.25 .40

Unwmk.
C170 AP50 110m olive, org & blk 3.00 1.75

UN Day. 30m publicizes UN help for refugees; 110m is for Intl. Women's Year 1975.

Step Pyramid, Sakhara, and Entrance Gate AP51

Designs: 45m, 60m, Plane over Giza Pyramids. 140m, Plane over boats on Nile.

Perf. 11½x11
1978-82 **Photo.** **Wmk. 342**
C171 AP51 45m yel & brown .55 .20
C171A AP51 60m olive 1.25 .75
C172 AP51 115m blue & brown .85 .50
C173 AP51 140m blue & purple 1.90 .85
C173A AP51 185m bl, sep & gray brn 4.50 1.75
Nos. C171-C173A (5) 9.05 4.05

Issued: 60m, 1/15/82; 185m, 1982; others, 1/1/78.

Flyer and UN ICAO Emblem — AP52

Perf. 11x11½
1978, Dec. 30 **Photo.** **Wmk. 342**
C174 AP52 140m blue, blk & brn 1.90 .95

75th anniversary of 1st powered flight.

Seeing Eye Medallion AP53

Perf. 11½x11
1981, Oct. 1 **Photo.** **Wmk. 342**
C175 AP53 230m multicolored 2.25 1.00

Hilton Ramses Hotel Opening — AP54

Perf. 11x11½
1982, Mar. 15 **Photo.** **Wmk. 342**
C176 AP54 18½p multi 1.75 .75

Temple of Horus, Edfu AP55

Designs: 15p, like 6p. 18½p, 25p, Statue of Akhnaton, Thebes, hieroglyphics, vert. 23p, 30p, Giza pyramids.

1985 Photo. Perf. 11½x11, 11x11½
C177 AP55 6p lt blue & dk bl grn .75 .30
C178 AP55 15p grnsh bl & brn 1.25 .45
C179 AP55 18½p grn, sep & dp yel 1.60 .90

C180 AP55 23p grnsh bl, sep & yel bis 2.00 1.10
C181 AP55 25p lt bl, sep & yel bis 1.75 .80
a. Unwmkd. ('87) 2.25 1.00
C182 AP55 30p grnsh bl, sep & org yel 1.75 .70
a. Unwmkd. ('87) 2.25 1.00
Nos. C177-C182 (6) 9.10 4.25

Issued: 6p, 18½p, 23p, 3/1; 15p, 25p, 30p, 5/1.
See No. C236.

Post Day — AP56

Narmer Board, oldest known hieroglyphic inscriptions: No. C183a, Tablet obverse. No. C183b, Reverse.

1986, Jan. 2 Photo. Perf. 13½x13
C183 AP56 Pair 2.00 2.00
a.-b. 15p any single 1.00 1.00

Map, Jet, AFRAA Emblem AP57

1986, Apr. 7 Photo. Perf. 11½
C184 AP57 15p blue, yel & blk 1.00 1.00

African Airlines Assoc., 18th General Assembly, Cairo, Apr. 7-10.

World Food Day AP58

UNESCO, 40th Anniv. — AP59

Perf. 13½x13, 13x13½
1986, Oct. 24 **Litho.**
C185 AP58 15p multicolored .80 .80
C186 AP59 15p multicolored .80 .80

UN Day.

Tourism Year — AP60

Design: Column and Sphinx in Alexandria, St. Catherine's Monastery in Mt. Sinai, Colossi of Thebes and Temple of Theban Triad in Luxor.

Unwmk.
1987, Sept. 30 **Litho.** *Imperf.*
Size: 140x90mm
C187 AP60 30p multicolored 4.00 4.00

Palestinian Uprising — AP61

1988, Sept. 28 Litho. *Perf. 12x13½*
C188 AP61 25p multicolored   1.25 1.25

UN
Day
AP62

1988, Oct. 20 Litho. *Perf. 13x13½*
C189 AP62 25p multicolored   1.25 1.25

Nobel Prize Type of 1988
1988, Nov. 7
C190 A769 25p multicolored   1.25 1.25

Arab Cooperation Council — AP63   Architecture and Art — AP64

1989, May 10 Litho. *Perf. 13½x13*
C191 AP63 25p Flags   1.00 1.00
Size: 89x80mm
Imperf
C192 AP63 50p Flags, seal   3.25 3.25

1989-91 Photo. *Perf. 11x11½*
C193 AP64 20p Balcony   .60 .60
C194 AP64 25p Brazier   .80 .80
C195 AP64 35p shown   1.00 1.00
C196 AP64 45p Tapestry   1.40 1.40
C197 AP64 45p like #C195   1.40 1.40
C198 AP64 50p Stag (dish)   1.50 1.50
C199 AP64 55p 4 animals
        (plate)   1.75 1.75
C200 AP64 60p like #C198   2.00 2.00
C201 AP64 65p like #C198   2.25 2.25
C202 AP64 80p like #C198   2.40 2.40
C203 AP64 85p like #C199   2.75 2.75
    Nos. C193-C203 (11)   17.85 17.85

Issued: 35p, 60p, 10/1/89; 55p, 1/1/90; No.
C197, C202, 1/25/91; 65p, 85p, 7/20/91;
others, 4/1/89.

AP65

Funerary Mask of King
Tutankhamen — AP66

King Tutankhamen
AP66a

1993-99 Litho. *Perf. 11½*
C204 AP65 55p multicolored   1.75 .95
C205 AP66 80p multicolored   3.00 1.25
Photo.
Perf. 11x11¼
C206 AP66a £1 black & brown   1.25 1.25
   b.   Wmk. 342   1.25 1.25
    Nos. C204-C206 (3)   6.00 3.45

Issued: 55p, 80p, 3/1/93; £1, 1997; No.
C206b, 1999.
See No. C231.

ICAO, 50th
Anniv. — AP67

1994, Sept. 16 Litho. *Perf. 13*
C207 AP67 80p multicolored   1.00 1.00

Intl. Year of the Family — AP68

1994, Oct. 24 Litho. *Perf. 13*
C208 AP68 80p multicolored   1.00 1.00

Arab League for Education, Culture, &
Science Organization — AP69

1995, July 25 Litho. *Perf. 13x13½*
C209 AP69 55p multicolored   .70 .70

UN Organizations, 50th
Anniv. — AP70

Perf. 12½x13, 13x12½
1995, Oct. 24   Litho.
C210 AP70 80p UN   1.75 1.75
C211 AP70 80p FAO   1.75 1.75
C212 AP70 80p UNESCO, vert.   1.75 1.75
    Nos. C210-C212 (3)   5.25 5.25

Arab Summit,
Cairo — AP71

1996, June 21 Litho. *Perf. 13x12½*
C213 AP71 55p multicolored   .60 .60

16th Intl. Conference on Irrigation and
Drainage, Cairo — AP72

1996, Sept. 15 Litho. *Perf. 12½x13*
C214 AP72 80p multicolored   1.10 1.10

Intl. Tourism Day — AP73

1996, Sept. 27   *Perf. 13*
C215 AP73 80p multicolored   .90 .90

Arabian Horse   World Post
Day — AP74   Day — AP75

1996   *Perf. 13x12½*
C216 AP74 55p grn, blk & gray   .60 .60

1996, Oct. 9 Litho. *Perf. 13x12½*
C217 AP75 80p multicolored   1.10 1.10

AP76   AP77

1996, Oct. 24
C218 AP76 55p multicolored   .60 .60
   Cairo, Arab cultural capital of 1996.

1996, Oct. 24
C219 AP77 80p multicolored   1.00 1.00
   UNICEF, 50th anniv.

World
Meteorological
Day — AP78   Thutmose
III — AP79

1997, Mar. 23 Litho. *Perf. 13x12½*
C220 AP78 £1 multicolored   1.25 1.25

1997, Mar. 25 Photo. *Perf. 11x11½*
C221 AP79 75p blk, bl & gray   1.10 1.10

Heinrich von Stephan (1831-
97) — AP80

1997, Apr. 15 Litho. *Perf. 13*
C222 AP80 £1 multicolored   1.25 1.25

AP81

1997, Sept. 11
C223 AP81 £1 multicolored   .90 .90
   98th Intl. Parliamentary Conference, Cairo.

AP82   AP83

1997, Sept. 10 Litho. *Perf. 13*
C224 AP82 75p multicolored   .90 .90
   1997 Egyptian Team, top medal winners of
   8th Pan Arab Games, Beirut, Lebanon.

1997, Sept. 27   *Perf. 13x12½*
C225 AP83 £1 multicolored   1.25 1.25
   Sarabas (180-211), mumified Egyptian.

World
Book and
Copyright
Day
AP84

1997, Oct. 24 Litho. *Perf. 12½x13*
C226 AP84 £1 multicolored   1.25 1.25

African Ministries of Transport and Communications, 11th Conference — AP85

1997, Nov. 22   Litho.   Perf. 13x12½
C227 AP85 75p multicolored   .90 .90

Arab Scout Movement, 85th Anniv. — AP86

1997, Nov. 24   Perf. 12½x13
C228 AP86 75p multicolored   .90 .90

8th G-15 Summit Meeting — AP87

Lighthouse of Alexandria AP88

1998, May 11   Litho.   Perf. 13
C229 AP87 £1 multicolored   1.00 1.00

1998, May 20   Litho.   Perf. 13
C230 AP88 £1 multicolored   1.25 1.25

King Tut Type of 1997
1998, July 25   Litho.   Perf. 11x11¼
C231 AP66a 125p Tutankhamen   1.50 1.50
  a.   Wmk. 342 ('99)   1.50 1.50

AP90

AP91

1998, Aug. 3   Perf. 13
C232 AP90 £1 multicolored   1.10 1.10
        Arab Post Day.

1998, Oct. 9   Litho.   Perf. 13
C233 AP91 125p multicolored   1.25 1.25
        World Post Day.

AP92

AP93

1998, Oct. 22
C234 AP92 125p multicolored   1.25 1.25
        67th Interpol Meeting, Cairo.

1998, Oct. 24
C235 AP93 125p multicolored   1.25 1.25
        Universal Declaration of Human Rights, 50th anniv.

Statue of Akhnaton Type of 1985
1998   Litho.   Perf. 13
C236 AP55 25p lt bl, brn & tan   1.00 1.00

AP94

AP95

1999, Oct. 12   Litho.   Perf. 13x12¾
C237 AP94 125p multicolored   1.75 1.75
Performance of opera "Aida" at the Pyramids.

1999, Oct. 16
C238 AP95 125p multicolored   1.75 1.75
        Discovery of the Rosetta Stone, bicent.

World Tourism Day — AP96

Perf. 13¼x12¾
2000, Sept. 27   Litho.
C239 AP96 125p multi   1.50 1.50

Awarding of Nobel Prize for Chemistry to Dr. Ahmed Zewail — AP97

Illustration reduced.

1999, Dec. 10   Imperf.
C240 AP97 125p multi   1.50 1.50

UN High Commissioner for Refugees, 50th Anniv. — AP98

2000, Dec. 13
C241 AP98 125p multi   1.75 1.75

AIR POST SEMI-POSTAL STAMPS

Catalogue values for unused stamps in this section are for Never Hinged items.

United Arab Republic

Pharaonic Mail Carriers and Papyrus Plants SPAP1

Design: 115m+55m, Jet plane, world map and stamp of Egypt, 1926 (No. C1).

Wmk. 342
1966, Jan. 2   Photo.   Perf. 11½
CB1 SPAP1 80m + 40m multi   2.50 2.00
CB2 SPAP1 115m + 55m multi   3.00 2.25
  a.   Pair, #CB1-CB2   7.50 7.00
        Post Day, Jan. 2.

SPECIAL DELIVERY STAMPS

Motorcycle Postman — SD1

Perf. 13x13½
1926, Nov. 28   Photo.   Wmk. 195
E1 SD1 20m dark green   30.00 8.50

1929, Sept.
E2 SD1 20m brown red & black   4.50 1.50

Inscribed "Postes Expres"
1943-44   Litho.
E3 SD1 26m brn red & gray blk   4.00 *6.00*
E4 SD1 40m dl brn & pale gray
        ('44)   2.50 1.00
    For overprints see Nos. E5, NE1.

Catalogue values for unused stamps in this section, from this point to the end of the section, are for Never Hinged items.

No. E4 Overprinted in Black

Overprint 27mm Wide

1952, Jan.
E5 SD1 40m dl brn & pale gray   2.75 2.00
        See notes after No. 316.

POSTAGE DUE STAMPS

D1

D2

Wmk. Crescent and Star (119)
1884, Jan. 1   Litho.   Perf. 10½
J1 D1 10pa red   40.00   9.00
  a.   Horiz. pair, imperf. vert.   150.00
J2 D1 20pa red   175.00 50.00
J3 D1 1pi red   125.00 40.00
J4 D1 2pi red   225.00 11.00
J5 D1 5pi red   20.00 *60.00*
        Nos. J1-J5 (5)   585.00 170.00

1886, Aug. 1 — Unwmk.
J6	D1	10pa red	52.50	7.00
a.	Horiz. pair, imperf. vert.		135.00	
J7	D1	20pa red	225.00	30.00
J8	D1	1pi red	26.00	5.00
a.	Pair, imperf. between		200.00	
J9	D1	2pi red	26.00	5.00
a.	Pair, imperf. between		175.00	
	Nos. J6-J9 (4)		329.50	47.00

1888, Jan. 1 — Perf. 11½
J10	D2	2m green	10.00	15.00
a.	Horiz. pair, imperf. between		225.00	
J11	D2	5m rose red	35.00	14.00
J12	D2	1pi blue	140.00	40.00
a.	Pair, imperf. between		300.00	
J13	D2	2pi yellow	150.00	20.00
J14	D2	5pi gray	210.00	190.00
a.	Period after "PIASTRES"		275.00	250.00
	Nos. J10-J14 (5)		545.00	279.00

Excellent counterfeits of #J1-J14 are plentiful.

There are 4 types of each of Nos. J1-J14, so placed that any block of 4 contains all types.

D3

Perf. 14x13½
1889 — Wmk. 119 — Typo.
J15	D3	2m green	7.00	.55
a.	Half used as 1m on cover			275.00
J16	D3	4m maroon	2.50	.55
J17	D3	1pi ultra	6.25	.55
J18	D3	2pi orange	6.00	.80
a.	Half used as 1p on cover			—
	Nos. J15-J18 (4)		21.75	2.45

Nos. J15-J18 exist on both ordinary and chalky paper. Imperf. examples of Nos. J15-J17 are proofs.

Black Surcharge

Type I — D4

1898
J19	D4	3m on 2pi orange	1.50	*4.50*
a.	Inverted surcharge		65.00	82.50
b.	Pair, one without surcharge			—
f.	Double surcharge		225.00	—

There are two types of this surcharge. In type I, the spacing between the last two Arabic characters at the right is 2mm. In type II, this spacing is 3mm, and there is an added sign on top of the second character from the right. See *Scott Classic Specialized Catalogue of Stamps & Covers* for detailed listing.

D5   D6

1921 — Wmk. 120 — Perf. 14x13½
J20	D5	2m green	.25	.25
J21	D5	4m vermilion	1.10	.90
J22	D6	10m deep blue	1.25	1.00
	Nos. J20-J22 (3)		2.60	2.15

1921-22
J23	D5	2m vermilion	.25	.20
J24	D5	4m green	.25	.20
J25	D6	10m lake ('22)	.50	.40
	Nos. J23-J25 (3)		1.00	.80

Nos. J18, J23-J25 Overprinted

1922, Oct. 10 — Wmk. 119
J26	D3	2pi orange	5.00	*5.00*
a.	Overprint right side up		25.00	25.00

Wmk. 120
J27	D5	2m vermilion	.60	.90
J28	D5	4m green	.90	.90
J29	D6	10m lake	1.25	.90
	Nos. J26-J29 (4)		7.75	7.70

Overprint on Nos. J26-J29 is inverted.

Arabic Numeral — D7

Perf. 13x13½
1927-56 — Litho. — Wmk. 195
Size: 18x22½mm
J30	D7	2m slate	.60	.40
J31	D7	2m orange ('38)	.80	.50
J32	D7	4m green	.60	.45
J33	D7	4m ol brn ('32)	6.25	4.25
J34	D7	5m brown	3.50	.80
J35	D7	6m gray grn ('41)	1.50	1.50
J36	D7	8m brn vio	1.00	.40
J37	D7	10m brick red ('29)	1.00	.30
a.	10m deep red		1.10	.35
J38	D7	12m rose lake ('41)	1.50	1.50
J38A	D7	20m dk red ('56)	2.00	2.00

Perf. 13½x14
Size: 22x28mm
J39	D7	30m purple	4.25	2.25
	Nos. J30-J39 (11)		23.00	14.35

See Nos. J47-J59. For overprints see Nos. J40-J46, NJ1-NJ7.

> **Catalogue values for unused stamps in this section, from this point to the end of the section, are for Never Hinged items.**

Postage Due Stamps and Type of 1927 Overprinted in Various Colors

1952, Jan. 16 — Perf. 13x13½
J40	D7	2m orange (Bl)	1.25	1.00
J41	D7	4m green	1.25	1.00
J42	D7	6m gray grn (RV)	1.50	1.25
J43	D7	8m brn vio (Bl)	2.00	1.75
J44	D7	10m dl rose (Bl)	3.50	2.75
a.	10m brown red (Bk)		3.00	3.00
J45	D7	12m rose lake (Bl)	1.75	1.75

Perf. 14
J46	D7	30m purple (C)	2.75	2.75
	Nos. J40-J46 (7)		14.00	12.25

See notes after No. 316.

United Arab Republic
1960 — Wmk. 318 — Perf. 13x13½
Size: 18x22½mm
J47	D7	2m orange	.50	.25
J48	D7	4m light green	1.00	.25
J49	D7	6m green	1.50	.50
J50	D7	8m brown vio	3.00	1.25
J51	D7	12m rose brown	5.00	1.65
J52	D7	20m dull rose brn	1.00	.25

Perf. 14
Size: 22x28mm
J53	D7	30m violet	5.00	1.50
	Nos. J47-J53 (7)		17.00	5.65

1962 — Wmk. 328 — Perf. 13x13½
Size: 18x22½mm
J54	D7	2m salmon	.50	.50
J55	D7	4m light green	.75	.75
J56	D7	10m red brown	1.50	1.50
J57	D7	12m rose brown	3.50	3.50
J58	D7	20m dull rose brn	7.50	7.50

Perf. 14
Size: 22x28mm
J59	D7	30m light violet	10.00	10.00
	Nos. J54-J59 (6)		23.75	23.75

D8

1965 — Unwmk. — Photo. — Perf. 11
J60	D8	2m org & vio blk	.60	.50
J61	D8	8m lt bl & dk bl	1.00	.60
J62	D8	10m yel & emer	1.50	.75

J63	D8	20m lt bl & vio blk	2.00	1.25
J64	D8	40m org & emer	3.75	2.00
	Nos. J60-J64 (5)		8.85	5.10

MILITARY STAMPS

The "British Forces" and "Army post" stamps were special issues provided at a reduced rate for the purchase and use by the British military forces in Egypt and their families for ordinary letters sent to Great Britain and Ireland by a concessionary arrangement made with the Egyptian government. From Nov. 1, 1932 to Feb. 29, 1936, in order to take advantage of the concessionary rate, it was mandatory to use #M1-M11 by affixing them to the backs of envelopes. An "Egypt Postage Prepaid" handstamp was applied to the face of the envelopes. Envelopes bearing these stamps were to be posted only at British military post boxes. Envelopes bearing the 1936-39 "Army Post" stamps (#M12-M15, issued by the Egyptian Postal Administration), also were sold at the concessionary rate and also were to be posted only at British military post boxes. The "Army Post" stamps were withdrawn in 1941, but the concession continued without the use of special stamps. The concession was finally canceled in 1951.

Imperf examples of Nos. M1-M4, M6, M9 (without overprint) and M10 are proofs.

M1

Unwmk.
1932, Nov. 1 — Perf. 11
M1	M1	1pi red & deep blue	100.00	4.25

For similar design see #M3.

M2

1932, Nov. 26 — Typo. — Perf. 11½
M2	M2	3m blk, *sage grn*	57.50	*80.00*

See #M4, M6, M10.

M3

1933, Aug. — Typo. — Perf. 11
M3	M3	1pi red & deep blue	40.00	1.10

Camel Type of 1932
1933, Nov. 13 — Typo. — Perf. 11½
M4	M2	3m brown lake	8.75	*57.50*

M4

1934, June 1 — Photo. — Perf. 14½x14
M5	M4	1pi bright carmine	50.00	1.25

See #M7-M8. For overprint and surcharge see #M9, M11.

Camel Type of 1932
1934, Nov. 17 — Typo. — Perf. 11½
M6	M2	3m deep blue	8.25	30.00

Type of 1934
1934, Dec. 5 — Photo. — Perf. 14½x14
M7	M4	1pi green	6.00	6.00

Type of 1934
1935, Apr. 24 — Perf. 13½x14
M8	M4	1pi bright carmine	2.90	*3.75*

Type of 1934 Overprinted in Red

1935, May 6 — Perf. 14
M9	M4	1pi ultramarine	325.00	240.00

Camel Type of 1932
1935, Nov. 23 — Typo. — Perf. 11½
M10	M2	3m vermilion	2.25	*45.00*

No. M8 Surcharged

1935, Dec. 16 — Photo. — Perf. 13½x14
M11	M4	3m on 1pi brt car	25.00	*100.00*

Fuad Type of 1927
Inscribed "Army Post"

M5

1936, Mar. 1 — Wmk. 195
M12	M5	3m green	2.50	2.50
M13	M5	10m carmine	5.50	.20

King Farouk — M6

1939, Dec. 16 — Perf. 13x13½
M14	M6	3m green	4.50	*12.00*
M15	M6	10m carmine rose	7.00	.20

> **Catalogue values for unused stamps in this section, from this point to the end of the section, are for Never Hinged items.**

United Arab Republic

Arms of UAR and Military Emblems — M7

Perf. 11x11½
1971, Apr. 15 — Photo. — Wmk. 342
M16	M7	10m purple	.30	.30

OFFICIAL STAMPS

O1

Wmk. Crescent and Star (119)
1893, Jan. 1   Typo.   *Perf. 14x13½*
O1   O1   orange brown   3.00   .20

No. O1 exists on ordinary and chalky paper. Imperf. examples of No. O1 are proofs.

Regular Issues of 1884-93 Overprinted

1907
O2   A18   1m brown   2.40   .35
O3   A19   2m green   2.40   .20
O4   A20   3m orange   2.40   .20
O5   A22   5m car rose   6.00   .20
O6   A14   1pi ultra   4.75   .20
O7   A16   5pi gray   17.00   4.75
   Nos. O2-O7 (6)   34.95   5.90

Nos. O2-O3, O5-O7 imperf. are proofs.

Overprinted

1913
O8   A22   5m carmine rose   7.50   .60
   a.   Inverted overprint   90.00
   b.   No period after "S"   65.00   19.00

Regular Issues Overprinted

1914-15
On Issues of 1888-1906
O9   A19   2m green   2.00   1.50
   a.   Inverted overprint   42.50   42.50
   b.   Double overprint   450.00
   c.   No period after "S"   16.00   16.00
O10   A21   4m brown red   2.00   1.50
   a.   Inverted overprint   225.00   160.00
On Issue of 1914
O11   A24   1m olive brown   1.75   1.50
   a.   No period after "S"   14.00   30.00
O12   A26   3m orange   1.75   1.50
   a.   No period after "S"   16.00   30.00
O13   A28   5m lake   4.75   1.50
   a.   No period after "S"   17.50   26.00
   b.   Two periods after "S"   17.50   26.00
   Nos. O9-O13 (5)   12.25   7.50

Regular Issues Overprinted

1915, Oct.
On Issues of 1888-1906
O14   A19   2m green   3.00   5.00
   a.   Inverted overprint   24.00   24.00
   b.   Double overprint   30.00
O15   A21   4m brown red   7.50   9.00
On Issue of 1914
O16   A28   5m lake   10.00   1.50
   a.   Pair, one without overprint   325.00
   Nos. O14-O16 (3)   20.50   15.50

1922   Wmk. 120
On Issue of 1921-22
O17   A24   1m olive brown   4.25   13.00
O18   A25   2m red   9.50   20.00
O19   A26   3m orange   77.50   150.00
O20   A28   5m pink   21.00   5.00
   Nos. O17-O20 (4)   112.25   188.00

Regular Issues of 1921-22 Overprinted

1922
O21   A24   1m olive brn   .65   2.25
O22   A25   2m red   1.00   3.25
O23   A26   3m orange   2.25   3.50
O24   A27   4m green   6.00   6.00
   a.   Two periods after "H" none after "S"   175.00   175.00
O25   A28   5m pink   3.00   .75
   a.   Two periods after "H" none after "S"   75.00   75.00
O26   A29   10m deep blue   5.00   2.50
O27   A29   10m lake ('23)   7.00   2.25
   a.   Two periods after "H" none after "S"   100.00   100.00
O28   A34   15m indigo   6.00   5.00
O29   A35   15m indigo   100.00   100.00
   a.   Two periods after "H" none after "S"   250.00   250.00
O30   A31   50m maroon   20.00   15.00

Regular Issue of 1923 Overprinted in Black or Red

1924   *Perf. 13½x14*
O31   A36   1m orange   1.50   1.50
O32   A36   2m gray (R)   2.00   2.00
O33   A36   3m brown   5.00   5.00
O34   A36   4m yellow green   6.00   6.00
O35   A36   5m orange brown   1.50   .75
O36   A36   10m rose   4.00   3.00
O37   A36   15m ultra   7.00   7.00
Perf. 14
O38   A36   50m myrtle green   18.00   7.00
   Nos. O31-O38 (8)   45.00   30.25

O2

O3

1926-35   Litho.   Wmk. 195
Size: 18½x22mm
O39   O2   1m lt orange   .75   .40
O40   O2   2m black   .50   .30
O41   O2   3m olive brn   1.40   1.00
O42   O2   4m lt green   1.25   1.10
O43   O2   5m brown   1.50   .40
O44   O2   10m dull red   3.75   .40
O45   O2   10m brt vio ('34)   2.25   .45
O46   O2   15m dp blue   3.75   .90
O47   O2   15m brown vio ('34)   3.75   .80
O48   O2   20m dp blue ('35)   3.75   1.10
Perf. 13½
Size: 22½x27½mm
O49   O2   20m olive green   6.00   2.25
O50   O2   50m myrtle green   8.00   1.60
   Nos. O39-O50 (12)   36.65   10.70

1938, Dec.
Size: 22½x19mm
O51   O3   1m orange   .30   .30
O52   O3   2m red   .30   .30
O53   O3   3m olive brown   1.25   1.25
O54   O3   4m yel green   .80   .80
O55   O3   5m brown   .40   .40
O56   O3   10m brt violet   .50   .50
O57   O3   15m rose violet   1.25   1.25
O58   O3   20m blue   1.25   1.25
Perf. 14x13½
Size: 26½x22mm
O59   O3   50m myrtle green   3.00   2.50
   Nos. O51-O59 (9)   9.05   8.55

Catalogue values for unused stamps in this section, from this point to the end of the section, are for Never Hinged items.

Nos. O51 to O59 Overprinted in Various Colors

Overprint 19mm Wide
1952, Jan.   *Perf. 13x13½*
O60   O3   1m orange (Br)   1.75   1.75
O61   O3   2m red (Br)   1.75   1.75
O62   O3   3m olive brn (Bl)   2.00   2.00
O63   O3   4m yel green (Bl)   2.00   2.00
O64   O3   5m brown (Bl)   2.00   2.00
O65   O3   10m brt violet (Bl)   2.00   2.00
O66   O3   15m rose violet (Bl)   2.50   2.50
O67   O3   20m blue   3.00   3.00

Overprint 24½mm Wide
Perf. 14x13½
O68   O3   50m myrtle grn (RV)   6.50   6.50
   Nos. O60-O68 (9)   23.50   23.50

See notes after No. 316.

United Arab Republic

O4 — — Arms of UAR — O5

Perf. 13x13½
1959   Litho.   Wmk. 318
O69   O4   10m brown violet   .65   .25
O70   O4   35m chalky blue   1.75   .30

1962-63   Wmk. 328
O71   O4   1m orange ('63)   .30   .30
O72   O4   4m yel grn ('63)   .60   .60
O73   O4   5m brown   .60   .25
O74   O4   10m dk brown   .75   .30
O75   O4   35m dark blue   2.25   .50
O76   O4   50m green   3.50   .60
O77   O4   100m violet ('63)   7.00   1.75
O78   O4   200m rose red ('63)   15.00   8.00
O79   O4   200m gray ('63)   22.50   15.00
   Nos. O71-O79 (9)   52.50   27.30

Perf. 11½x11
1966-68   Unwmk.   Photo.
O80   O5   1m ultra   .20   .20
O81   O5   4m brown   .25   .20
O82   O5   5m olive   .30   .20
O83   O5   10m brown blk   1.00   .35
O84   O5   20m magenta   .60   .30
O85   O5   35m dk purple   1.00   .35
O86   O5   50m orange   1.10   .45
O87   O5   55m dk purple   1.10   .45
Wmk. 342
O88   O5   100m brt grn & brick red   2.25   1.00
O89   O5   200m blue & brick red   4.50   2.00
O90   O5   500m olive & brick red   10.00   6.25
   Nos. O80-O90 (11)   22.30   11.75

1969   Wmk. 342
O91   O5   10m magenta   1.10   .65

Arab Republic of Egypt

Arms of Egypt
O6 — — O7

Wmk. 342
1972, June 30   Photo.   Perf. 11
O92   O6   1m black & vio blue   .30   .25
   a.   1m black & light blue ('75)   .20   .20
O93   O6   10m black & car   .65   .30
   a.   10m black & rose red ('76)   .20   .20
O94   O6   20m black & olive   .90   .40
O95   O6   50m black & orange   .50   .50
O96   O6   55m black & purple   3.00   1.00

1973
O97   O6   20m lilac & sepia   .90   .40
   a.   20m purple & light brown ('76)   2.50   .75
O98   O6   70m black & grn ('79)   .75   .45

1982   Photo.   Unwmk.   Perf. 11
O99   O6   30m purple & brown   .30   .30
O100   O6   60m black & orange   .60   .30
O101   O6   80m black & green   .65   .35
   Nos. O92-O101 (10)   8.55   4.25

Issued: 30m, 2/12; 60m, 2/24; 80m, 2/18.

1985-89   Photo.   Perf. 11½
Size: 21x25mm
O102   O7   1p vermilion   .20   .20
O103   O7   2p brown   .20   .20
O104   O7   3p sepia   .20   .20
O105   O7   5p orange yel   .35   .30
O106   O7   8p green   .50   .35
O107   O7   10p brown olive   .20   .20
O108   O7   15p dull violet   1.00   .65
O109   O7   20p blue   .75   .75
O110   O7   25p red   .80   .80
O111   O7   30p dull violet   .60   .60
O112   O7   50p green   2.25   2.25
O113   O7   60p myrtle green   1.10   1.10
   Nos. O102-O113 (12)   8.15   7.60

Issued: 1p, 3p, 5p, 8p, 15p, 5/1/85; 20p, 50p, 4/88; 10p, 30p, 60p, 12/1/89; 2p, 25p, 1989.

1991-99   Wmk. 342   Perf. 11½x11
Size: 18x22mm
O114   O7   5p orange yellow   .20   .20
O115   O7   10p brown violet   .20   .20
O116   O7   15p brown   .20   .20
O117   O7   20p blue   .20   .20
O118   O7   20p violet   .20   .20
O119   O7   25p purple   .25   .25
O120   O7   30p dk violet   .45   .25
O121   O7   50p green   .75   .50
O122   O7   55p red   .60   .30
O123   O7   75p brown   .75   .50
O124   O7   £1 green blue   1.25   .75
O125   O7   £2 green   2.50   1.50
   Nos. O114-O125 (12)   7.55   5.05

Issued: 10p, 30p, 7/1/91; 50p, 12/1/91; 55p, 4/1/93; £1, £2, 3/22/94; No. O123, 75p, 2/1/97; No. O118, 4/11/99.

Arms Type of 1985-89
Perf. 11½x11
2001, Mar. 25   Photo.   Unwmk.
Size: 18x22mm
O127   O7   10p brown   2.00   .50

Issued: 10p, 3/25.

Arms Type of 1985-89
Perf. 11½x11
2002 ?   Photo.   Unwmk.
O131   O7   30p violet   3.00   .60

OCCUPATION STAMPS

Catalogue values for unused stamps in this section are for Never Hinged items.

For Use in Palestine

Stamps of 1939-46 Overprinted in Red, Green or Black — a

Perf. 13x13½, 13½x13
1948, May 15   Wmk. 195
N1   A77   1m yellow brn (G)   .20   .20
N2   A77   2m red org (G)   .20   .20
N3   A66   3m brown (G)   .20   .20
N4   A77   4m dp green   .20   .20
N5   A77   5m red brown (Bk)   .20   .20
N6   A66   6m lt yel grn (Bk)   .20   .20
N7   A77   10m dp violet   .20   .20
N8   A66   13m rose car (G)   .25   .25
N9   A77   15m dk violet   .25   .25
N10   A77   17m olive green   .25   .25
N11   A77   20m dk gray   .30   .30
N12   A77   22m deep blue   .40   .40
N13   A74   50pi green & sep   25.00   25.00
N14   A75   £1 dp bl & dk brn   40.00   40.00

The two lines of the overprint are more widely separated on Nos. N13 and N14.

Nos. 267-269, 237 and 238 Overprinted in Red — b

Perf. 14x13½

N15	A73	30m olive green	1.00	1.00
N16	A73	40m dark brown	1.25	1.25
N17	A73	50m Prus green	1.50	1.50
N18	A73	100m brown violet	4.00	4.00
N19	A73	200m dark violet	10.00	10.00
		Nos. N1-N19 (19)	85.60	85.60

Overprint arranged to fit size of stamps.

Nos. N1-N19 Overprinted in Black with Three Bars to Obliterate Portrait

Perf. 13x13½, 13½x13, 14x13½

1953 **Wmk. 195**

N20	A77	1m yellow brown	.20	.20
N21	A77	2m red orange	.20	.20
N22	A66	3m brown	.20	.20
N23	A77	4m deep green	.20	.20
N24	A77	5m red brown	.20	.20
N25	A66	6m lt yel grn	.20	.20
N26	A77	10m deep violet	.30	.30
N27	A66	13m rose carmine	.40	.40
N28	A77	15m dark violet	.40	.40
N29	A77	17m olive green	.45	.45
N30	A77	20m dark gray	.60	.60
N31	A77	22m deep blue	.75	.75
N32	A73	30m olive green	.75	.75
N33	A73	40m dark brown	1.25	1.25
N34	A73	50m Prus green	5.00	5.00
N35	A73	100m brown violet	9.50	9.50
N36	A73	200m dark violet	24.00	24.00
N37	A74	50pi green & sepia	50.00	50.00
N38	A75	£1 dp bl & dk brn	135.00	135.00
		Nos. N20-N38 (19)	229.60	229.60

Regular Issue of 1953-55 Overprinted Type "a" in Blue or Red

1954-56 **Perf. 13x13½**

N39	A115	1m red brown	.20	.20
N40	A115	2m dark lilac	.20	.20
N41	A115	3m brt blue (R)	.20	.20
N42	A115	4m dark green (R)	.20	.20
N43	A115	5m deep carmine	.20	.20
N44	A110	10m dark brown	.20	.20
N45	A110	15m gray (R)	.20	.20
N46	A110	17m dk grnsh bl (R)	.20	.20
N47	A110	20m purple (R) ('54)	.30	.30

Nos. 331-333 and 335-340 Overprinted in Blue or Red — c

Perf. 13½

N48	A111	30m dull green (R)	.65	.65
N49	A111	32m brt blue (R)	.75	.75
N50	A111	35m violet (R)	1.00	1.00
N51	A111	40m red brown	1.50	1.50
N52	A111	50m violet brown	1.75	1.75
N53	A112	100m henna brown	4.50	4.50
N54	A112	200m dk grnsh bl (R)	12.50	12.50
N55	A112	500m purple (R)	55.00	55.00
N56	A112	£1 dk grn, blk & red (R) ('56)	90.00	90.00
		Nos. N39-N56 (18)	169.55	169.55

Type of 1957 Overprinted in Red — d

1957 **Wmk. 195** **Perf. 13½x13**

N57	A127	10m blue green	2.00	2.00

Nos. 414-417 Overprinted Type "d" in Red

1957-58 **Wmk. 315** **Perf. 13½**

N58	A137	10m violet	.30	.30

Wmk. 318

N59	A136	1m lt bl grn ('58)	.30	.30
N60	A138	5m brown ('58)	.30	.30
N61	A137	10m violet ('58)	.80	.80
		Nos. N58-N61 (4)	1.70	1.70

United Arab Republic

Nos. 438-444 Overprinted Type "d" in Red or Green

Perf. 13½x14

1958 **Wmk. 318** **Photo.**

N62	A136	1m crimson	.30	.30
N63	A138	2m blue	.30	.30
N64	A143	3m dk red brn (G)	.30	.30
N65	A217	4m green	.30	.30
N66	A138	5m brown	.30	.30
N67	A137	10m violet	.30	.30
N68	A138	35m lt ultra	2.75	2.75
		Nos. N62-N68 (7)	4.55	4.55

Same Overprint in Red on Freedom Struggle Type of 1958

1958 **Perf. 13½x13**

N69	A145	10m dark brown	1.25	1.25

Same Overprint in Green on Declaration of Human Rights Type

1958 **Perf. 13½x13½**

N70	A151	10m rose violet	1.50	1.50
N71	A151	35m red brown	2.50	2.50

No. 460 Overprinted Type "d" in Green

1959 **Wmk. 195** **Perf. 13½**

N72	A112	55m on 100m henna brn	2.25	2.25

World Refugee Year Type
"PALESTINE" Added in English and Arabic to Stamps of Egypt

OS1

1960 **Wmk. 328** **Perf. 13x13½**

N73	OS1	10m orange brown	.75	.75
N74	OS1	35m dk blue gray	1.25	1.25

Type of Regular Issue 1959-60

1960 **Perf. 13½x14**

N75	A136	1m brown orange	.30	.30
N76	A217	4m olive gray	.30	.30
N77	A138	5m dk dull pur	.30	.30
N78	A137	10m dk olive grn	.30	.30
		Nos. N75-N78 (4)	1.20	1.20

Palestine Day Type

1961, May 15 **Perf. 13½x13**

N79	A184	10m purple	1.00	1.00

WHO Day Type

1961 **Wmk. 328** **Perf. 13½x13**

N80	A182	10m blue	.30	.30

U.N.T.A.P. Type

1961, Oct. 24

N81	A191	10m dk blue & org	.50	.50
N82	A191	35m vermilion & blk	.50	.50

Education Day Type

1961, Dec. 18 **Photo.** **Perf. 13½**

N83	A194	10m red brown	.50	.50

Victory Day Type

1961, Dec. 23 **Photo.** **Perf. 11½**

N84	A195	10m brn org & brn	.40	.40

Gaza Strip Type

Perf. 13½x13

1962, Mar. 7 **Wmk. 328**

N85	A200	10m red brown	.40	.40

Arab Publicity Week Type

1962, Mar. 22 **Perf. 13½x13**

N86	SP16	10m dark purple	.30	.30

Anti-Malaria Type

1962, June 20 **Photo.**

N87	A204	10m brn & dk car rose	.45	.45
N88	A204	35m black & yellow	.55	.55

Hammarskjold Type

Perf. 11½x11

1962, Oct. 24 **Wmk. 342**
Portrait in Slate Blue

N89	A214	5m bright rose	.35	.35
N90	A214	10m brown	.45	.45
N91	A214	35m blue	.60	.60
		Nos. N89-N91 (3)	1.40	1.40

Lamp Type of Regular Issue

Perf. 11x11½

1963, Feb. 20 **Unwmk.**

N92	A217	4m dk brn, org & ultra	.30	.30

"Freedom from Hunger" Type

Perf. 11½x11, 11x11½

1963, Mar. 21 **Wmk. 342**

N93	A220	5m lt grn & dp org	.35	.35
N94	A220	10m olive & yellow	.45	.45
N95	A220	35m dull pur, yel & blk	.60	.60
		Nos. N93-N95 (3)	1.40	1.40

Red Cross Centenary Type

Designs: 10m, Centenary emblem, bottom panel added. 35m, Globe and emblem, top and bottom panels added.

1963, May 8 **Unwmk.** **Perf. 11x11½**

N96	A221	10m dk blue & crim	.35	.35
N97	A221	35m crim & dk blue	.60	.60

"Save Abu Simbel" Type, 1963

1963, Oct. 15 **Wmk. 342** **Perf. 11**

N98	A224	5m black & yellow	.40	.40
N99	A224	10m gray, blk & yellow	.50	.50
N100	A224	35m org yel & violet	.75	.75
		Nos. N98-N100 (3)	1.65	1.65

Human Rights Type

1963, Dec. 10 **Photo.** **Perf. 11½x11**

N101	A228	5m dk brown & yellow	.35	.35
N102	A228	10m dp claret, gray & blk	.40	.40
N103	A228	35m lt grn, pale grn & blk	.60	.60
		Nos. N101-N103 (3)	1.35	1.35

Types of Regular Issue

1964 **Unwmk.** **Perf. 11**

N104	A231	1m citron & lt vio	.30	.30
N105	A230	2m orange & slate	.30	.30
N106	A230	3m blue & ocher	.30	.30
N107	A235	4m ol gray, ol, brn & rose	.30	.30
N108	A230	5m rose & brt blue	.30	.30
a.		5m rose & dark blue	1.25	1.25
N109	A231	10m ol, rose & brn	.30	.30
N110	A230	15m lilac & yellow	.40	.40
N111	A230	20m brown blk & ol	.60	.60
N112	A231	30m dp org & ind	1.25	1.25
N113	A231	35m buff, ocher & emer	1.00	1.00
N114	A231	40m ultra & emer	1.25	1.25
N115	A231	60m grnsh bl & brn org	2.00	2.00

Wmk. 342

N116	A232	100m bluish blk & yel brn	3.00	3.00
		Nos. N104-N116 (13)	11.30	11.30

Arab League Council Type

1964, Jan. 13 **Photo.**

N117	A234	10m olive & black	.30	.30

Minaret Type

1964 **Unwmk.** **Perf. 11**

N118	A235	4m ol, red brn & red	.30	.30

Arab Postal Union Type

1964, Apr. 1 **Wmk. 342** **Perf. 11**

N119	A239	10m emer & ultra, lt grn	.30	.30

WHO Type

1964, Apr. 7

N120	A240	10m violet blk & red	.30	.30

Minaret Type

1965, Jan. 20 **Unwmk.** **Perf. 11**

N121	A255	4m green & dk brn	.30	.30

Arab League Type

1965, Mar. 22 **Wmk. 342** **Perf. 11**

N122	A258	10m green, red & blk	.30	.30
N123	A258	20m green & brown	.30	.30

World Health Day Type

1965, Apr. 7 **Wmk. 342** **Perf. 11**

N124	A259	10m brt green & crim	.30	.30

Massacre Type

1965, Apr. 9 **Photo.**

N125	A260	10m slate blue & red	.60	.60

ITU Type

1965, May 17 **Wmk. 342** **Perf. 11**

N126	A261	5m sl grn, sl bl & yel	.40	.40
N127	A261	10m car, rose red & gray	.50	.50
N128	A261	35m vio bl, ultra & yel	.75	.75
		Nos. N126-N128 (3)	1.65	1.65

United Nations Type

5m, WHO Headquarters Building, Geneva. 10m, UN Refugee emblem. 35m, UNICEF emblem.

1966, Oct. 24 **Wmk. 342** **Perf. 11**

N129	A288	5m rose & brt pur	.35	.35
N130	A288	10m yel brn & brt pur	.40	.40
N131	A288	35m brt green & brt pur	.60	.60
		Nos. N129-N131 (3)	1.35	1.35

Victory Day Type

Wmk. 342

1966, Dec. 23 **Photo.** **Perf. 11½**

N132	A290	10m olive & car rose	.40	.40

Arab Publicity Week Type

Perf. 11x11½

1967, Mar. 22 **Photo.** **Wmk. 342**

N133	A294	10m vio blue & brn	.30	.30

Labor Day Type

Perf. 11½x11

1967, May 1 **Photo.** **Wmk. 342**

N134	A296	10m olive & sepia	.30	.30

OCCUPATION AIR POST STAMPS

Catalogue values for unused stamps in this section are for Never Hinged items.

Nos. C39-C50 Overprinted Type "b" in Black, Carmine or Red

Perf. 13x13½

1948, May 15 **Wmk. 195**

NC1	AP3	2m red org (Bk)	.50	.50
NC2	AP3	3m dk brn (C)	.50	.50
NC3	AP3	5m red brn (Bk)	.50	.50
NC4	AP3	7m dp yel org (Bk)	.60	.60
NC5	AP3	8m green (C)	.60	.60
NC6	AP3	10m violet	.70	.70
NC7	AP3	20m brt bl	1.25	1.25
NC8	AP3	30m brn vio (Bk)	3.00	3.00
NC9	AP3	40m car rose (Bk)	2.00	2.00
NC10	AP3	50m Prus grn	2.75	2.75
NC11	AP3	100m olive grn	4.50	4.50
NC12	AP3	200m dark gray	22.50	22.50
		Nos. NC1-NC12 (12)	39.40	39.40

Nos. NC1-NC12 Overprinted in Black with Three Bars to Obliterate Portrait

1953

NC13	AP3	2m red org	2.75	2.75
NC14	AP3	3m dk brn	.70	.70
NC15	AP3	5m red brn	15.00	12.00
NC16	AP3	7m dp yel org	1.00	1.00
NC17	AP3	8m green	2.50	2.00
NC18	AP3	10m violet	2.50	2.00
NC19	AP3	20m brt bl	2.75	2.00
NC20	AP3	30m brn vio	2.75	2.00
NC21	AP3	40m car rose	4.50	4.50
NC22	AP3	50m Prus grn	22.50	22.50
NC23	AP3	100m olive grn	85.00	85.00
NC24	AP3	200m dk gray	20.00	20.00
		Nos. NC13-NC24 (12)	161.95	156.45

Nos. NC1-NC3, NC6, NC10, NC11 with Additional Overprint in Various Colors

1953

NC25	AP3	2m red org (Bk + Bl)	.50	.50
NC26	AP3	3m dk brn (Bk + RV)	12.00	12.00
NC27	AP3	5m red brn (Bk)	2.00	2.00
NC28	AP3	10m vio (R + G)	22.50	22.50
NC29	AP3	50m Prus grn (R + RV)	5.50	5.50
NC30	AP3	100m ol grn (R + Bk)	40.00	40.00
		Nos. NC25-NC30 (6)	82.50	82.50

Nos. C65-C66 Overprinted Type "b" in Black or Red

1955   Wmk. 195   Perf. 13x13½

NC31	AP4	5m red brn	4.50	4.50
NC32	AP4	15m ol grn (R)	5.25	5.25

United Arab Republic

OAP1

Designs: 80m, Al Azhar University. 115m, Temple of Queen Nefertari, Abu Simbel. 140m, Ramses II, Abu Simbel.

Perf. 11½x11

1963, Oct. 24   Photo.   Wmk. 342

NC33	OAP1	80m blk & brt bl	2.25	2.25
NC34	OAP1	115m blk & yel	3.25	3.25
NC35	OAP1	140m bl, ultra & org red	4.00	4.00
		Nos. NC33-NC35 (3)	9.50	9.50

Cairo Tower Type, 1964

1964, Nov. 2 Unwmk. Perf. 11x11½

NC36	AP11	50m dl vio & lt bl	1.00	1.00

World Meteorological Day Type

1965, Mar. 23   Wmk. 342   Perf. 11

NC37	AP12	80m dk bl & org	2.50	2.50

Tutankhamen Type of 1965

1965, July 1   Photo.   Perf. 11

NC38	AP13	10m brn org & brt grn	1.25	1.25

OCCUPATION SPECIAL DELIVERY STAMP

Catalogue values for unused stamps in this section are for Never Hinged items.

No. E4 Overprinted Type "b" in Carmine

1948   Wmk. 195   Perf. 13x13½

NE1	SD1	40m dl brn & pale gray	8.00	8.00

OCCUPATION POSTAGE DUE STAMPS

Catalogue values for unused stamps in this section are for Never Hinged items.

Postage Due Stamps of Egypt, 1927-41, Overprinted Type "a" in Black or Rose

1948   Wmk. 195   Perf. 13x13½

NJ1	D7	2m orange	1.50	*2.00*
NJ2	D7	4m green (R)	1.00	*1.25*
NJ3	D7	6m gray green	1.00	*1.25*
NJ4	D7	8m brown violet	1.10	*1.25*
NJ5	D7	10m brick red	1.10	*1.25*
NJ6	D7	12m rose lake	1.10	*1.25*

Overprinted Type "b" in Red
Perf. 14
Size: 22x28mm

NJ7	D7	30m purple	3.25	*6.00*
		Nos. NJ1-NJ7 (7)	10.05	*14.25*

ELOBEY, ANNOBON & CORISCO

ˌel-ə-ˈbä, ˌan-ə-ˈbän and kə-ˈris-ˌkō

LOCATION — A group of islands near the Guinea Coast of western Africa
GOVT. — Spanish colonial possessions administered as part of the Continental Guinea District. A second district under the same governor-general included Fernando Po.
AREA — 13¾ sq. mi.
POP. — 2,950 (estimated 1910)
CAPITAL — Santa Isabel

100 Centimos = 1 Peseta

King Alfonso XIII — A1

1903   Unwmk.   Typo.   Perf. 14
Control Numbers on Back

1	A1	¼c carmine	.80	.55
2	A1	½c dk violet	.80	.55
3	A1	1c black	.80	.55
4	A1	2c red	.80	.55
5	A1	3c dk green	.80	.55
6	A1	4c dk blue grn	.80	.55
7	A1	5c violet	.80	.55
8	A1	10c rose lake	1.60	1.60
9	A1	15c orange buff	4.75	1.75
10	A1	25c dark blue	8.25	6.00
11	A1	50c red brown	10.00	10.50
12	A1	75c black brn	10.00	*14.50*
13	A1	1p orange red	16.00	*20.00*
14	A1	2p chocolate	44.00	*60.00*
15	A1	3p dp olive grn	65.00	*75.00*
16	A1	4p claret	150.00	*150.00*
17	A1	5p blue green	175.00	*110.00*
18	A1	10p dull blue	325.00	*165.00*
		Nos. 1-18 (18)	815.20	*568.20*
		Set, never hinged	1,250.	

Dated "1905"

1905
Control Numbers on Back

19	A1	1c carmine	1.40	.70
20	A1	2c dp violet	5.25	.70
21	A1	3c black	1.40	.70
22	A1	4c dull red	1.40	.70
23	A1	5c dp green	1.40	.70
24	A1	10c blue grn	4.75	.90
25	A1	15c violet	5.25	4.75
26	A1	25c rose lake	5.25	4.75
27	A1	50c orange buff	9.50	7.25
28	A1	75c dark blue	9.50	7.25
29	A1	1p red brown	19.50	16.00
30	A1	2p black brn	21.00	22.50
31	A1	3p orange red	21.00	23.00
32	A1	4p dk brown	160.00	72.50
33	A1	5p bronze grn	170.00	80.00
34	A1	10p claret	375.00	225.00
		Nos. 19-34 (16)	811.60	*467.40*
		Set, never hinged	1,300.	

Nos. 19-22 Surcharged in Black or Red

1906

35	A1	10c on 1c rose (Bk)	11.50	6.50
a.		Inverted surcharge	11.50	6.50
b.		Value omitted	30.00	16.00
c.		Frame omitted	16.00	7.50
d.		Double surcharge	11.50	6.50
e.		Surcharged "15 cents"	30.00	16.00
f.		Surcharged "25 cents"	52.50	22.50
g.		Surcharged "50 cents"	37.50	22.50
h.		"1906" omitted	17.50	7.50
36	A1	15c on 2c dp vio (R)	11.50	6.50
a.		Frame omitted	12.50	6.50
b.		Surcharged "25 cents"	16.00	9.00
c.		Inverted surcharge	11.50	6.50
d.		Double surcharge	11.50	6.50
37	A1	25c on 3c blk (R)	11.50	6.50
a.		Inverted surcharge	11.50	6.50
b.		Double surcharge	11.50	6.50
c.		Surcharged "15 cents"	16.00	6.50
d.		Surcharged "50 cents"	25.00	11.00
38	A1	50c on 4c red (Bk)	11.50	6.50
a.		Inverted surcharge	11.50	6.50
b.		Value omitted	35.00	17.50
c.		Frame omitted	17.50	8.00
e.		Double surcharge	11.50	6.50
f.		"1906" omitted	17.50	8.00
g.		Surcharged "10 cents"	32.50	16.00
h.		Surcharged "25 cents"	32.50	16.00
		Nos. 35-38 (4)	46.00	26.00

Eight other surcharges were prepared but not issued: 10c on 50c, 75c, 1p, 2p and 3p; 15c on 50c and 5p; 50c on 5c.
Exist with surcharges in different colors; #35 in blue, red or violet; #36 in black or violet; #37 in black or violet; #38 in blue, violet or red. Value, set of 10, $135.

King Alfonso XIII — A2

1907
Control Numbers on Back

39	A2	1c dk violet	.60	.45
40	A2	2c black	.60	.45
41	A2	3c red orange	.60	.45
42	A2	4c dk green	.60	.45
43	A2	5c blue green	.60	.45
44	A2	10c violet	6.00	5.50
45	A2	15c carmine	2.00	1.75
46	A2	25c orange	2.00	1.75
47	A2	50c blue	2.00	1.75
48	A2	75c brown	6.25	2.75
49	A2	1p black brn	10.50	4.75
50	A2	2p orange red	14.50	7.50
51	A2	3p dk brown	14.00	8.25
52	A2	4p bronze grn	14.50	7.75
53	A2	5p claret	21.00	8.25
54	A2	10p rose	52.50	25.00
		Nos. 39-54 (16)	148.25	77.25
		Set, never hinged	210.00	

Stamps of 1907 Surcharged

1908-09
Black Surcharge

55	A2	5c on 3c red org ('09)	2.25	1.25
56	A2	5c on 4c dk grn ('09)	2.25	1.25
57	A2	5c on 10c violet	4.50	5.00
58	A2	25c on 10c violet	22.50	15.00
		Nos. 55-58 (4)	31.50	22.50

1910
Red Surcharge

59	A2	5c on 1c dark violet	1.75	.90
60	A2	5c on 2c black	1.75	.90

Nos. 55-60 exist with surcharge inverted (value set, $125 unused or used); with double surcharge, one black, one red (value set, $300 unused or used); with "PARA" omitted (value set, $150.00 unused or used)
The same 5c surcharge was also applied to Nos. 45-54, but these were not issued (value set, $250).
In 1909, stamps of Spanish Guinea replaced those of Elobey, Annobon and Corisco.

CORREOS
1909
10 cen de peseta

Revenue stamps surcharged as above were unauthorized although some were postally used.

EPIRUS

i-'pī-rəs

LOCATION — A region of southeastern Europe, now divided between Greece and Albania.

During the First Balkan War (1912-13), this territory was occupied by the Greek army, and the local Greek majority wished to be united with Greece. Italy and Austria-Hungary favored its inclusion in the newly created Albania, however, which both powers expected to dominate. Greek forces were withdrawn subsequently in early 1914. The local population resisted inclusion in Albania and established the Autonomous Republic of Northern Epirus on Feb. 28, 1914. Resistance to Albanian control continued until October, when Greece reoccupied the country. Northern Epirus was administered as an integral part of Greece, and it was expected that Greece's annexation of the territory would become official following World War I. Instead, in 1916, Italian pressure and its own military reverses in Anatolia caused Greece to withdraw from Epirus and to formally cede the territory to Albania.

100 Lepta = 1 Drachma

Chimarra Issue

Double-headed Eagle, Skull and Crossbones — A1

Handstamped
1914, Feb. 10   Unwmk.   *Imperf.*
Control Mark in Blue
Without Gum

1	A1	1 l black & blue	475.00	240.00
a.		Tête-bêche pair		3,000.
2	A1	5 l red	475.00	240.00
3	A1	10 l red & blk	475.00	240.00
4	A1	25 l blue & red	475.00	240.00
		Nos. 1-4 (4)	1,900.	960.00

All values exist without control mark. This mark is a solid blue oval, about 12x8mm, containing the colorless Greek letters "SP," the first two letters of Spiromilios, the Chimarra commander.

All four exist with denomination inverted and the 1 l, 5 l and 10 l with denomination double. The values above are for the first printing on somewhat transparent shiny, white, thin, wove paper, which is sometimes known as "rice paper."

A second printing was made from original handstamps, on similar thin wove paper, but not transluscent, known as "Spetsiotis Reprints." Value, unused or canceled to order, each $55. Later printings were made from original handstamps on other papers, generally thicker and whiter, sometimes surfaced. Value, unused or canceled to order, each $45.

Values above are for genuine stamps expertized by knowledgeable authorities. Most of the stamps offered as Nos. 1-4 in the marketplace are forgeries. Most resemble the stamps from the second reprinting, but the designs differ in details of the lettering, monogram and skull. Such forgeries have only nominal commercial value.

Some experts question the official character of this issue.

Argyrokastro Issues
Stamps of Turkey surcharged "AUTONOMOUS EPIRUS" and new denominations in several formats in Greek currency.
On Turkish stamps of 1908

No. 4A   No. 4B

1914, Mar. 2

4A	A19	1d on 2½pi (#137)	9.50	10.00
4B	A19	2d on 2½pi (#137)	9.50	10.00

No. 4C   No. 4D

4C	A19	5d on 25pi (#140)	75.00	80.00
4D	A19	5d on 50pi (#141)	115.00	120.00

On Turkish stamps of 1909-10

4E	A21	5 l on 5pa (#151)	75.00	

No. 4F   No. 4G

4F	A21	5 l on 10pa (#152)	3.00	3.00
4G	A21	10 l (oval "O") on 20pa (#153)	2.00	2.00
a.		Double surcharge	75.00	

No. 4H   No. 4I

4H	A21	10 l (round "O") on 20pa (#153)	2.00	2.00
a.		Double surcharge	75.00	
4I	A21	20 l on 1pi (#154)	2.00	2.00
a.		Double surcharge	75.00	

No. 4J   No. 4K

4J	A21	25 l on 1pi (#154)	2.00	2.00
a.		Double surcharge	75.00	
4K	A21	40 l on 2pi (#155)	3.00	3.00

No. 4L   No. 4M

4L	A21	80 l on 2pi (#155)	3.00	3.00
4M	A21	1d on 5pi (#157)	12.00	12.00

No. 4N   No. 4O

4N	A21	2d on 5pi (#157)	12.00	12.00
4O	A21	5d on 10pi (#158)	75.00	80.00
a.		Double surcharge		

4P	A21	5d on 10pa (#152)	125.00	*150.00*
4Q	A21	5d on 20pa (#153)	125.00	*150.00*
4R	A21	5d on 1pi (#154)	125.00	*150.00*
4S	A21	5d on 50pi (#160)	125.00	*150.00*

On Turkish stamps of 1909-11 (with "Béhié")

4T	A21	5 l on 10pa (#161)	75.00	
4U	A21	10 l (oval "O") on 20pa (#162)	75.00	
4V	A21	10 l (round "O") on 20pa (#162)	75.00	
4W	A21	20 l on 1pi (#163)	75.00	
4X	A21	25 l on 1pi (#163)	75.00	
4Y	A21	40 l on 2pi (#164)	75.00	
4Z	A21	80 l on 2pi (#164)	75.00	
4AA	A21	5d on 10pa (#161)	125.00	
4BB	A21	5d on 20pa (#162)	125.00	
4CC	A21	5d on 1pi (#163)	125.00	

On Turkish Printed Matter stamps of 1910-11

No. 4DD   No. 4EE

4DD	A21	30 l on 2pa on 5pa (#P67)	80.00	
4EE	A21	50 l on 2pa on 5pa (#P67)	80.00	

No. 4FF

4FF	A21	30 l on 2pa (#P68)	2.00	2.00
4GG	A21	50 l on 2pa (#P68)	2.00	2.00

Provisional Government Issues

Infantryman with Rifle
A2   A3

Serrate Roulette 13½

1914, Mar.   *Litho.*

5	A2	1 l orange	.50	.95
6	A2	5 l green	.50	.95
7	A3	10 l carmine	.50	.95
8	A3	25 l deep blue	.50	.95
9	A2	50 l brown	1.50	1.40
10	A2	1d violet	2.40	2.40
11	A2	2d blue	13.25	13.00
12	A2	5d gray green	17.00	17.00
		Nos. 5-12 (8)	36.15	37.60

Issue dates: 10 l, 25 l, Mar. 5; balance of set, Mar. 26.

Flag of Epirus — A5

1914, Aug. 28

15	A5	1 l brown & blue	.55	*.65*
16	A5	5 l green & blue	.55	*.65*
17	A5	10 l rose red & blue	.60	*.70*
18	A5	25 l dk blue & blue	1.10	1.10
19	A5	50 l violet & blue	1.10	1.10
20	A5	1d carmine & blue	5.75	*7.00*
21	A5	2d orange & blue	1.50	2.00
22	A5	5d dk green & blue	9.50	9.50
		Nos. 15-22 (8)	20.65	*22.70*

Koritsa Issue

A7

1914, Sept. 25

26	A7	25 l dk blue & blue	5.00	4.75
27	A7	50 l violet & blue	11.00	11.00

Nos. 26 and 27 were issued at Koritsa (Korce) to commemorate that city's occupation by Epirot forces.

Chimarra Issues

King Constantine I — A8

1914, Oct.

28	A8	1 l yellow green	125.00	75.00
29	A8	2 l red	110.00	40.00
30	A8	5 l dark blue	110.00	75.00
31	A8	10 l orange brown	75.00	25.00
32	A8	20 l carmine	160.00	80.00
33	A8	25 l gray blue	110.00	75.00
33A	A8	50 l yellow green	160.00	80.00
33B	A8	1d carmine	160.00	80.00
33C	A8	2d pale yellow green	225.00	110.00
33D	A8	5d orange brown	400.00	275.00
		Nos. 28-33D (10)	1,635.	915.00

Nos. 28-33D were printed by Papachrysanthou, Athens. The papermaker's watermark "PARCHIMINE JOHANNOT" appears on some stamps in the set.

1911-23 Issues of Greece Overprinted

1914, Aug. 24   *Perf. Perf. 11 ½*

34	A24	1 l green	60.00	60.00
35	A25	2 l carmine	50.00	50.00
36	A24	3 l vermilion	50.00	50.00
37	A26	5 l green	60.00	60.00
38	A24	10 l carmine	60.00	60.00
39	A25	20 l slate	85.00	85.00
40	A25	25 l blue	170.00	170.00
41	A26	50 l violet brn	100.00	100.00
		Nos. 34-41 (8)	635.00	635.00

The 2 l and 3 l are engraved stamps of the 1911-21 issue; the others are lithographed stamps of the 1912-23 issue.

Overprint reads: "Greek Chimarra 1914."

Stamps of this issue are with or without a black monogram (S.S., for S. Spiromilios) in manuscript. Counterfeits are plentiful.

Moschopolis Issue

A9   A10

Arms   Ancient Epirot Coins/Medals

1914, Sept.   Engr.   *Perf. 14 ½*

42	A9	1 l yellow brown	1.00	3.00
43	A9	2 l black	1.00	3.00
44	A9	3 l yellow	1.00	3.00
45	A9	5 l green	1.00	3.00
46	A9	10 l red	1.00	3.00
47	A9	25 l deep blue	1.00	3.00
48	A9	30 l violet	1.00	3.00
49	A9	40 l olive gray	1.00	3.00
50	A9	50 l violet black	1.00	3.00
51	A10	1d yellow brown & olive	5.00	10.00
52	A10	2d carmine & gray	4.00	10.00
53	A10	3d gray green & red brown	4.50	10.00
54	A10	5d olive & yellow brown	4.00	10.00
55	A10	10d orange & blue	4.50	12.50
56	A10	25d violet & blue	4.50	17.50
		Nos. 42-56 (15)	35.50	97.00

Nos. 42-56 were privately printed in early 1914. In June 1914, the Epirots occupied Moschopolis (Voskopoj), and these stamps were authorized for use by the local military commander in Sept. After the occupation of Moschopolis by Greek forces in Nov., remaining stocks of this issue were sent to Athens, where they were destroyed in 1931.

All values exist imperf., and all but the 5 l and 10 l stamps exist in different colors. For

details, see the *Scott Classic Specialized Catalogue of Stamps and Covers.*

The 1d exists with center omitted. Value $100. The 1d, 2d, 10d and 25d exist with center inverted. Values, each $65.

Stamps of the following designs were locals, privately produced. Issued primarily for propaganda and for philatelic purposes, their postal use is in dispute. The 1920 design is a fantasy item, created long after Epirus was annexed by Albania.

From 1914: 1st design, 3 varieties. 2nd design, 6 varieties. 3rd design, 7 varieties.

From 1920: 4th design, 4 varieties.

OCCUPATION STAMPS

Issued under Greek Occupation
Greek Occupation Stamps of 1913
Overprinted Horizontally

Serrate Roulette 13½
1914-15   Black Overprint   Unwmk.

N1	O1	1 brown		
	l		.80	.80
b.	Inverted overprint		24.00	19.00
c.	Double overprint		24.00	19.00
d.	Double overprint, one inverted		25.00	20.00
N2	O2	2 red		
	l		.80	.80
b.	2 l rose		1.25	1.25
c.	As #N2, inverted overprint		24.00	19.00
d.	As "b," inverted overprint		28.00	22.50
e.	As #N2, double overprint		24.00	19.00
f.	As "b," double overprint		28.00	22.50
g.	As #N2, double overprint, one inverted		25.00	25.00
N4	O2	3 orange		
	l		.80	.80
b.	Inverted overprint		19.00	15.00
c.	Double overprint		19.00	15.00

d.	Double overprint, one inverted		25.00	20.00
N5	O1	5 green		
	l		2.00	2.00
b.	Inverted overprint		33.00	26.50
N6	O1	10 rose red		
	l		2.75	2.75
a.	Inverted overprint		47.50	37.50
b.	Double overprint		47.50	37.50
N7	O1	20 violet		
	l		7.50	7.50
a.	Inverted overprint		47.50	37.50
b.	Double overprint		80.00	65.00
N8	O2	25 pale blue		
	l		2.75	2.75
N9	O1	30 gray green		
	l		14.00	14.00
N10	O2	40 indigo		
	l		19.00	19.00
N11	O1	50 dark blue		
	l		21.00	21.00
N12	O2	1d violet brown		135.00	135.00
a.	souv. sheets		300.00	225.00
b.	Double overprint		360.00	300.00
	Nos. N1-N12 (11)		206.40	206.40

Red Overprint

N1a	O1	1 l brown		5.75
N2a	O2	2 l red		5.75
N4a	O2	3 l orange		5.75
N5a	O1	5 l green		5.75

Nos. N1a-N5a were not issued. Exist canceled.

Regular Issues of Greece, 1911-23, Overprinted Reading Up

On Issue of 1911-21

1916				Engr.
N17	A24	3 l vermilion	11.50	11.50
a.	Overprint reading down		14.50	
N18	A26	30 l carmine rose	40.00	40.00
a.	Overprint reading down		225.00	
N19	A27	1d ultra	85.00	85.00
N20	A27	2d vermilion	95.00	95.00
N21	A27	3d carmine rose	122.50	122.50
N22	A27	5d ultra		
a.	Double overprint		950.00	950.00
b.	Overprint reading down		675.00	
	Nos. N17-N22 (6)		354.00	354.00

On Issue of 1912-23

1916				Litho.
N23	A24	1 l green	2.75	2.75
a.	Overprint reading down		9.50	
N24	A25	2 l carmine	2.75	2.75
a.	Overprint reading down		9.50	
N25	A24	3 l vermilion	2.75	2.75
a.	Overprint reading down		14.00	
N26	A26	5 l green	2.75	2.75
a.	Overprint reading down		14.00	
N27	A24	10 l carmine	2.75	2.75
a.	Overprint reading down		27.50	
N28	A25	20 l slate	2.75	2.75
N29	A25	25 l blue	3.75	3.75
N30	A26	30 l rose	21.00	21.00
a.	Overprint reading down		225.00	
N31	A25	40 l indigo	14.00	14.00
a.	Overprint reading down		225.00	
N32	A26	50 l violet brown	24.00	24.00
	Nos. N23-N32 (10)		79.25	64.75

In each sheet, there are two varieties in the overprint. For listings, see the *Scott Classic Catalogue.*

Counterfeits exist of Nos. N1-N32.

Postage stamps issued in 1940-41, during Greek occupation, are listed under Greece.

EQUATORIAL GUINEA

ē-kwə-ˈtō-ē-əl ˈgi-nē

LOCATION — Gulf of Guinea, West Africa
GOVT. — Republic
AREA — 10,832 sq. mi.
POP. — 465,746 (1999 est.)
CAPITAL — Malabo

The Spanish provinces Fernando Po and Rio Muni united and became independent as the Republic of Equatorial Guinea, Oct. 12, 1968.

100 Centimos = 1 Peseta
100 centimos = 1 ekuele, bipkwele is plural (1973)
100 centimes = 1 CFA franc (1985)

> **Catalogue values for all unused stamps in this country are for Never Hinged items.**

Clasped Hands and Laurel — A1   Pres. Francisco Macias Nguema — A2

Unwmk.

1968, Oct. 12		Photo.	Perf. 13	
1	A1	1p dp bl, gold & sep	.30	.30
2	A1	1.50p dk grn, gold & brn	.30	.30
3	A1	6p cop red, gold & brn	.30	.30
		Nos. 1-3 (3)	.90	.90

Attainment of independence, Oct. 12, 1968.

1970, Jan. 27			Perf. 13x12½	
4	A2	50c dl org, brn & crim	.20	.20
5	A2	1p pink, grn & lil	.20	.20
6	A2	1.50p pale ol, brn & bl grn	.25	.20
7	A2	2p buff, grn & ol	.25	.20
8	A2	2.50p pale grn, dk grn & dk bl	.30	.20
9	A2	10p bis, Prus bl & vio brn	1.00	.20
10	A2	25p gray, blk & brn	2.10	.20
		Nos. 4-10 (7)	4.30	1.40

Pres. Macias Nguema and Cock — A3

1971, Apr.		Photo.	Perf. 13	
11	A3	3p lt bl & multi	.25	.20
12	A3	5p buff & multi	.30	.20
13	A3	10p pale lilac & multi	.70	.20
14	A3	25p pale grn & multi	1.25	.20
		Nos. 11-14 (4)	2.50	.80

2nd anniv. of independence, Oct. 12, 1970.

Torch, Bow and Arrows — A4

1972		Photo.	Perf. 11½	
15	A4	50p ocher & multi	1.50	.50

"3rd Triumphal Year."

Apollo 15, set of seven, 1p, 3p, 5p, 8p, 10p, airmail 15p, 25p, plus two airmail semi-postal gold foil perf. 200p+25p, imperf. 250p+50p, and two souv. sheets, perf. 25p+200p, imperf. 50p+250p, issued Jan. 28. Nos. 7201-7211.

1972 Winter Olympics, Sapporo, set of seven, 1p, 2p, 3p, 5p, 8p, airmail 15p, 50p, plus two airmail semi-postal gold foil perf., imperf., 200p+25p, 250p+50p, and two souv. sheets, perf. 200p+25p, imperf. 250p+50p, issued Feb. 3, 1972. Nos. 7212-7222.

Christmas, paintings, set of seven, 1p, 3p, 5p, 8p, 10p, airmail 15p, 25p, plus two airmail semi-postal gold foil

perf. 200p+25p, imperf. 250p+50p, and two souv. sheets, perf. 25p+200p, imperf. 50p+250p (Virgin and Child by da Vinci, Murillo, Raphael, Mabuse, van der Weyden, Durer), issued Feb. 20. Nos. 7223-7233.

Easter, set of seven, 1p, 3p, 5p, 8p, 10p, airmail 15p, 25p, plus two airmail semi-postal gold foil perf., imperf., 200p+25p, 250p+50p (designs by Velazquez and El Greco), two souv. sheets, perf. (25p, 200p), and imperf. 250p+50p, issued Apr. 28. Nos. 7234-7244.

1972 Summer Olympics, Munich, set of seven, 1p, 2p, 3p, 5p, 8p, airmail 15p, 50p, plus two airmail semi-postal souv. sheets, perf. 200p+25p, imperf. 250p+50p, and presentation folder with two gold foil, perf. 200p+25p, imperf. 250p+50p, issued May 5, 1972. Nos. 7245-7255.

Gold Medal Winners, Sapporo, set of seven, 1p, 2p, 3p, 5p, 8p, airmail 15p, 50p, plus 12 airmail semi-postal gold foil perf. 200p+25p (6), imperf. 250p+50p (6), imperf. souv. sheet 250p+50p, and perf. souv. sheet of two (25p, 200p), issued May 25. Nos. 7256-7276.

Black Gold Medal Winners, Munich, set of seven, 1p, 2p, 3p, 5p, 8p, airmail 15p, 50p, plus 18 gold foil airmail semi-postal perf. 200p+25p (9), imperf. 250p+50p (9), and two souv. sheets, perf. 200p+25p, imperf. 250p+50p, issued June 26. Nos. 7277-72103.

Olympic Games, Regatta in Kiel and Oberschleissheim, set of seven, 1p, 2p, 3p, 5p, 8p, airmail 15p, 50p, plus four airmail semi-postal gold foil, perf. 200p+25p (2), imperf. 250p+50p (2), and two souv. sheets, perf. 200p+25p, imperf. 250p+50p, issued July 25. Nos. 72104-72116.

1972 Summer Olympics, Munich, set of seven, 1p, 2p, 3p, 5p, 8p, airmail 15p, 50p, plus two airmail semi-postal souv. sheets, perf. 200p+25p, imperf, 250p+50p, issued Aug. 10, 1972; and 20 gold foil, perf. 200p+25p (10), imperf. 250+50p (10), issued Aug. 17. Nos. 72117-72145.

Olympic Equestrian Events, set of seven, 1p, 2p, 3p, 5p, 8p, airmail 15p, 50p, plus two airmail semi-postal souv. sheets, perf. 200p+25p, imperf. 250p+50p, two gold foil, perf. 200p+25p, imperf. 250p+50p, four gold foil souv. sheets of two, 200p+25p (2 perf., 2 imperf.), and 16 souv. sheets, perf. 200p+25p (8), imperf. 250p+50p (8), issued Aug. 24. Nos. 72146-72176.

Japanese Railroad Cent. (locomotives), set of seven, 1p, 3p, 5p, 8p, 10p, airmail 15p, 25p, plus 2 airmail semi-postal souv. sheets, perf. 200p+25p, imperf. 250p+50p, 11 gold foil souv. sheets of 1, perf. 200p+25p (9), imperf. 200p+25p (2), and 2 souv. sheets of 2, perf., imperf., 200p+25p, issued Sept. 21. Nos. 72177-72198.

Gold Medal Winners, Munich, set of seven, 1p, 2p, 3p, 5p, 8p, airmail 15p, 50p, plus two airmail semi-postal souv. sheets, perf. 200p+25p, imperf. 250p+50p, and four gold foil souv. sheets, perf. 200p+25p (2), imperf. 250p+50p (2), issued Oct. 30. Nos. 72199-72211.

Christmas and 500th Birth Anniv. of Lucas Cranach, Madonnas and Christmas seals, set of seven, 1p, 3p, 5p, 8p, 10p, airmail 15p, 25p (Giotto, Schongauer, Fouquet, de Morales, Fini, David, Sassetta), plus two airmail semi-postal souv. sheets, perf. 200p+25p, imperf. 250p+50p, 12 gold foil souv. sheets, perf. 200p+25p (6), imperf. 250p+50p (6), two souv. sheets of two, perf., imperf., 200p+25p, and ovptd. 200p+25p stamp, issued Nov. 22. Nos. 72212-72234.

American and Russian Astronaut Memorial, set of seven, 1p, 3p, 5p, 8p, 10p, airmail 15p, 25p, plus two airmail semi-postal souv. sheets, perf. 200p+25p, imperf. 250p+50p, and four gold foil ovptd. "Apollo 16 and 17" perf. 200p+25p (2), imperf. 250p+50p (2), issued Dec. 14. Nos. 72235-72247.

United Natl. Workers' Party Emblem — A5

1973		Litho.	Perf. 13½x13	
16	A5	1p multi	.25	.25
17	A5	1.50p multi	.25	.25
18	A5	3p multi	.25	.25
19	A5	4p multi	.25	.25
20	A5	5p multi	.25	.25
		Nos. 16-20 (5)	1.25	1.25

Natl. Independence, 4th Anniv. — A6

Pres. Macias Nguema and: 1.50p, Agriculture. 2p, 4p, Education. 3p, 5p, Natl. defense.

1973			Perf. 13½	
21	A6	1.50p multi	.25	.25
22	A6	2p multi	.25	.25
23	A6	3p multi	.25	.25
24	A6	4p multi	.25	.25
25	A6	5p multi	.25	.25
		Nos. 21-25 (5)	1.25	1.25

1973

Transatlantic Yacht Race, set of seven, 1p, 2p, 3p, 5p, 8p, airmail 15p, 50p, and two airmail semi-postal souv. sheets, perf. 200p+25p, imperf. 250p+50p, issued Jan. 22. Nos. 7301-7309.

Renoir paintings, set of seven, 1p, 2p, 3p, 5p, 8p, airmail 15p, 50p, plus two airmail semi-postal gold foil, perf. 200p+25p, imperf. 250p+50p, and two souv. sheets, perf. 200p+25p, imperf. 250p+50p, issued Feb. 22. Nos. 7310-7320.

Conquest of Venus (spacecraft), set of seven, 1p, 3p, 5p, 8p, 10p, airmail 5p, 25p, and two airmail semi-postal souv. sheets, perf. 200p+25p, imperf. 250p+50p, issued Mar. 22. Nos. 7321-7329.

Apollo 11-17 Flights, gold foil airmail semi-postal souv. sheets, perf. 200p+25p (7), 250p+50p (7), and four souv. sheets of two, perf. 200p+25p (2), imperf. 250p+50p (2), issued Mar. 22. Nos. 7330-7347.

Easter, paintings, set of seven, 1p, 3p, 5p, 8p, 10p, airmail 15p, 25p (Verrocchio, Perugino, Tintoretto, Witz, Pontormo), plus two airmail semi-postal souv. sheets, perf. 200p+25p, imperf. 250p+50p, and four gold foil issue of 1972 souv. sheets ovptd., perf. 200p+25p (2), imperf. 250p+50p (2), issued Apr. 25. Nos. 7348-7360.

Copernicus, 500th birth anniv. (US and USSR space explorations), four gold foil airmail semi-postal souv. sheets, perf. 200p+25p (2), imperf. 250p+50p (2), issued May 15. Nos. 7361-7364.

Tour de France bicycle race, set of seven, 1p, 2p, 3p, 5p, 8p, airmail 15p, 50p, and two airmail semi-postal souv. sheets, perf. 200p+25p, imperf.

250p+50p, issued May 22. Nos. 7365-7373.

Paintings, set of seven, 1p, 2p, 3p, 5p, 8p, airmail 15p, 50p, and two airmail semi-postal souv. sheets, perf. 200p+25p, imperf. 250p+50p, issued June 29. Nos. 7374-7382.

1974 World Cup Soccer Championships, Munich, set of nine, 5c, 10c, 15c, 20c, 25c, 55c, 60c, airmail 5p, 70p, and two airmail souv. sheets, perf. 130p, imperf. 200p, issued Aug. 30. Nos. 7383-7393.

Rubens paintings, set of seven, 1p, 2p, 3p, 5p, 8p, airmail 15p, 50p, and two airmail semi-postal souv. sheets, perf. (25p, 200p), imperf. (50p, 250p), issued Sept. 23. Nos. 7394-73102.

1974 World Cup Soccer Championships, Munich, four gold foil airmail souv. sheets, perf. 130e (2), imperf. 200e (2), and two souv. sheets of two, perf. 130e, imperf. 200e, issued Oct. 24. Nos. 73103-73108.

Christmas, paintings, set of seven, 1p, 3p, 5p, 8p, 10p, airmail 15p, 25p, and two airmail semi-postal souv. sheets, perf. 200p+25p, imperf. 250p+50p (Nativity, by van der Weyden, Bosco, de Carvajal, Mabuse, Lucas Jordan, P. Goecke, Maino, Fabriano, Lochner), issued Oct. 30. Nos. 73109-73117.

Apollo Program and J.F. Kennedy, two gold foil airmail semi-postals, perf. 200p+25p, imperf. 250p+50p, and two souv. sheets, perf. 200p+25p, imperf. 250p+50p, issued Nov. 10. Nos. 73118-73121.

World Cup Soccer (famous players), set of nine, 30c, 35c, 40c, 45c, 50c, 65c, 70c, airmail 8p, 60p, and two airmail souv. sheets, perf. 130p, imperf. 200p, issued Nov. 20. Nos. 73122-73132.

Princess Anne's Wedding, six gold foil airmail souv. sheets, perf., imperf., two sheets of one, each 250e, one sheet of two 250e, issued Dec. 17. Nos. 73133-73141.

Pablo Picasso Memorial (Blue Period paintings), set of seven, 30c, 35c, 40c, 45c, 50c, airmail 8e, 60e, and two airmail souv. sheets, perf. 130e, imperf. 200e, issued Dec. 20. Nos. 73142-73150.

1974

Copernicus, 500th birth anniv., set of seven, 5c, 10c, 15c, 20c, 4e, airmail 10e, 70e, two airmail souv. sheets, perf. 130e, imperf. 200e, issued Feb. 8, 1974; eight gold foil airmail souv. sheets, perf. 130e (3), 250e, imperf. 200e (3), 300e, and four souv. sheets of two, perf. 250e (2), imperf. 250e (2), issued Apr. 10. Nos. 7401-7421.

World Cup Soccer Championships (final games), set of nine, 75c, 80c, 85c, 90c, 95c, 1e, 1.25e, airmail 10e, 50e, and two airmail souv. sheets, perf. 130e, imperf. 200e, issued Feb. 28. Nos. 7422-7432.

Easter, paintings, set of seven, 1p, 3p, 5p, 8p, 10p, airmail 15p, 25p (Fra Angelico, Castagno, Allori, Multscher, della Francesca, Pleydenwurff, Correggio), and two airmail semi-postal souv. sheets, perf. 200p+25p, imperf. 250p+50p, issued Mar. 27. Nos. 7433-7441.

Holy Year 1975 (famous churches), set of seven, 5c, 10c, 15c, 20c, 3.50e, airmail 10e, 70e, and two airmail souv. sheets, perf. 130e, imperf. 200e, issued Apr. 11. Nos. 7442-7450.

World Cup Soccer (contemporary players), set of nine, 1.50, 1.75, 2, 2.25, 2.50, 3, 3.50e, airmail 10, 60e, and 2 airmail souv. sheets of 2, perf. (2x65e), imperf. (2x100e), issued Apr. 30. Nos. 7451-7461.

UPU Cent. (transportation from messenger to rocket), set of seven, 60c, 70c, 80c, 1e, 1.50e, airmail 30e, 50e, and two airmail souv. sheets, perf. 225e, imperf. (150e, 150e), issued May 30; three airmail deluxe souv. sheets, 130e, and 2x130e, issued June 8. Nos. 7462-7472A.

Picasso Memorial (Pink Period paintings), set of seven, 55c, 60c, 65c, 70c, 75c, airmail 10e, 50e, and two airmail souv. sheets, perf. 130e, imperf. 200e, issued June 28. Nos. 7473-7481.

World Cup Soccer Championships, gold foil airmail souv. sheets, four sheets of one, 130e (2), 250e (2), two sheets of two (2x130e; 2x250e), issued July 8. Nos. 7482-7487.

Aleksander Solzhenitsyn, two gold foil airmail souv. sheets, perf. 250e, imperf. 300e, issued July 25. Nos. 7488-7489.

Opening of American West, set of seven, 30c, 35c, 40c, 45c, 50c, airmail 8p, 60p, and two souv. sheets, perf. 130p, imperf. 200p, issued July 30. Nos. 7490-7498.

Flowers, set of 14, 5c, 10c, 15c, 20c, 25c, 1p, 3p, 5p, 8p, 10p, airmail 5p, 15p, 25p, 70p, and 4 airmail souv. sheets, perf. 130p, imperf. 200p, 50p+250p, issued Aug. 20. Nos. 7499-74116.

Christmas, set of seven, 60c, 70c, 80c, 1e, 1.50e, airmail 30e, 50e, and two souv. sheets, perf. 225e, imperf. 300e, issued Sept. 16. Nos. 74117-74125.

Barcelona Soccer Team, 75th anniv., set of seven, 1e, 3e, 5e, 8e, 10e, airmail 15e, 60e, miniature sheet of seven plus label, two airmail souv. sheets, perf. 200e, imperf. 300e, and two gold foil airmail souv. sheets, perf., imperf., 200e each, issued Sept. 25. Nos. 74126-74137.

UPU Cent. and ESPANA 75, set of seven, 1.25e, 1.50e, 1.75e, 2e, 2.25e, airmail 35e, 60e, and 2 airmail souv. sheets, perf. 225e, imperf. 300e, issued Oct. 9; 6 gold foil sheets, perf. 250e, 250e, 2x250e, imperf. 300e, 300e, 2x300e, issued Oct. 14. Nos. 74138-74152.

Nature Protection

Australian Animals, set of seven, 80c, 85c, 90c, 95c, 1e, airmail 15e, 40e, and two airmail souv. sheets, perf. 130e, imperf. 200e, issued Oct. 25. Nos. 74153-74161.

African Animals, set of seven, 55c, 60c, 65c, 70c, 75c, airmail 10e, 70e, and two airmail souv. sheets, perf. 130e, imperf. 200e, issued Nov. 6. Nos. 74162-74170.

Australian and South American Birds, set of 14, 1.25p, 1.50p, 1.75p, 2p, 2.25p, 2.50p, 2.75p, 3p, 3.50p, 4p, airmail 20p, 25p, 30p, 35p, and four souv. sheets, perf. 130p (2), imperf. 200p (2), issued Nov. 26. Nos. 74171-74188.

Endangered Species, set of 15, 10c, 15c, 20c, 25c, 30c, 35c, 40c, 45c, 50c, 55c, 60c, 1e, 2e, airmail 10e, 70e, se-tenant in sheet of 15, issued Dec. 17. Nos. 74189-74203.

Monkeys, various species, set of 16, 5c, 10c, 15c, 20c, 25c, 30c, 35c, 40c, 45c, 50c, 55c, 60c, 1e, 2e, airmail 10e, 70e, se-tenant in sheet of 16, issued Dec. 27. Nos. 74204-74219.

Cats, various species, set of 16, 5c, 10c, 15c, 20c, 25c, 30c, 35c, 40c, 45c, 50c, 55c, 60c, 1e, 2e, airmail 10e, 70e, se-tenant in sheet of 16, issued Dec. 27. Nos. 74220-74235.

Fish, various species, set of 16, 5c, 10c, 15c, 20c, 25c, 30c, 35c, 40c, 45c, 50c, 55c, 60c, 1e, 2e, airmail 10e, 70e, se-tenant in sheet of 16, issued Dec. 27. Nos. 74236-74251.

Butterflies, various species, set of 16, 5c, 10c, 15c, 20c, 25c, 30c, 35c, 40c, 45c, 50c, 55c, 60c, 1e, 2e, airmail 10e, 70e, se-tenant in sheet of 16, issued Dec. 27. Nos. 74252-74267.

1975

Picasso Memorial (paintings from last period), set of seven, 5c, 10c, 15c, 20c, 25c, airmail 10e, 70e, and two souv. sheets, perf. 130e, imperf. 200e, issued Jan. 27. Nos. 7501-7509.

ARPHILA 75 Phil. Exhib., Paris, 8 gold foil airmail souv. sheets: perf. 3 sheets of 1 250e, 1 sheet of 2 250e, imperf. 3 sheets of 1 300e, 1 sheet of 2 300e, issued Jan. 27. Nos. 7510-7517.

Easter and Holy Year 1975, set of seven, 60c, 70c, 80c, 1e, 1.50e, airmail 30e, 50e, and two airmail souv. sheets, perf. 225e, imperf. 300e, issued Feb. 15. Nos. 7518-7526.

1976 Winter Olympics, Innsbruck, set of 11, 5c, 10c, 15c, 20c, 25c, 30c, 35c, 40c, 45c, 25c, 70c, two airmail souv. sheets, perf. 130e, imperf. 200e, and two gold foil airmail souv. sheets, 1 sheet of 1 250e, 1 sheet of 2 250e, issued Mar. 10. Nos. 7527-7541.

Don Quixote, set of seven, 30c, 35c, 40c, 45c, 50c, airmail 25e, 60e, and two airmail souv. sheets, perf. 130e, imperf. 200e, issued Apr. 4. Nos. 7542-7550.

American Bicent. (1st issue), set of nine, 5c, 20c, 40c, 75c, 2e, 5e, 8e, airmail 25e, 30e, and two airmail souv. sheets, perf. 130e, imperf. 200e, issued Apr. 30. Nos. 7551-7561.

American Bicent. (2nd issue), set of nine, 10c, 30c, 50c, 1e, 3e, 6e, 10e, airmail 12e, 40e, and two airmail souv. sheets, perf. 130e, imperf. 200e, issued Apr. 30. Nos. 7562-7572.

American Bicent. (Presidents), set of 18, 5c, 10c, 20c, 30c, 40c, 50c, 75c, 1e, 2e, 3e, 5e, 6e, 8e, 10e, airmail 12e, 25e, 30e, 40e, four airmail souv. sheets, perf. 225e (2), imperf. 300e (2), and six embossed gold foil airmail souv. sheets, perf. 200e, 200e, 2x200e, imperf. 300e, 300e, 2x300e, issued July 4. Nos. 7573-75100.

Bull Fight, set of seven, 80c, 85c, 90c, 95c, 8e, airmail 35e, 40e, and two airmail souv. sheets, perf. 130e, imperf. 200e, issued May 26. Nos. 75101-75109.

Apollo-Soyuz Space Project, set of 11, 1e, 2e, 3e, 5e, 5.50e, 7e, 7.50e, 9e, 15e, airmail 20e, 30e, and two airmail souv. sheets, perf. 225e, imperf. 300e, issued June 20, 1975; airmail souv. sheet, perf. 250e, issued July 17. Nos. 75110-75123.

Famous Painters, Nudes, set of 16, 5c, 10c, 15c, 20c, 25c, 30c, 35c, 40c, 45c, 50c, 55c, 60c, 1e, 2e, airmail 10e, 70e (Egyptian Greek, Roman, Indian art, Goes, Durer, Liss, Beniort, Renoir, Gauguin, Stenlen, Picasso, Modigliani, Matisse, Padua), se-tenant in sheet of 16, and 20 airmail embossed gold foil souv. sheetlets, perf. 200p+25p (10), imperf. 250p+50p (10), issued Aug. 10. Nos. 75124-75159.

Conquerors of the Sea, set of 14, 30c, 35c, 40c, 45c, 50c, 55c, 60c, 65c, 70c, 75c, airmail 8p, 10p, 50p, 60p, and four airmail souv. sheets, perf. 130p (2), imperf. 200p (2), issued Sept. 5. Nos. 75160-75177.

Christmas and Holy Year, 1975, set of seven, 60c, 70c, 80c, 1e, 1.50e, airmail 30e, 50e (Jordan, Barocci, Vereycke, Rubens, Mengs, Del Castillo, Cavedone), two airmail souv. sheets, perf. 225e, imperf. 300e, plus four embossed gold foil souv. sheets, perf. 200e (2), imperf. 300e (2), and two gold foil miniature sheets of two, perf. 200e+200e, imperf. 300e+300e, issued Oct. Nos. 75178-75192.

President Macias, IWY, set of eight, 1.50e, 3e, 3.50e, 5e, 7e, 10e, airmail 100e, 300e, and two imperf. airmail souv. sheets (world events), 100e (US 2c Yorktown), 300e, issued Dec. 25. Nos. 75193-75202.

1976

Cavalry Uniforms, set of seven, 5c, 10c, 15c, 20c, 25c, airmail 5p, 70p, and two airmail souv. sheets, perf. 130p, imperf. 200p, issued Feb. 2. Nos. 7601-7609.

1976 Winter Olympics, Innsbruck, set of 11, 50c, 55c, 60c, 65c, 70c, 75c, 80c, 85c, 90c, airmail 35e, 60e, and two airmail souv. sheets, perf. 130e, imperf. 200e, issued Feb. Nos. 7610-7622.

1976 Summer Olympics, Montreal, Ancient to Modern Games, set of seven, 50c, 60c, 70c, 80c, 90c, airmail 35e, 60e, and two airmail souv. sheets, perf. 225e, imperf. 300e, issued Feb. Nos. 7623-7631.

1976 Summer Olympics, Montreal, set of seven, 50c, 60c, 70c, 80c, 90c, airmail 30e, 60e, plus two airmail souv. sheets, perf. 225e, imperf. 300e, four embossed gold foil airmail souv. sheets, per. 250e (2), imperf. 300e (2), and two imperf. miniature sheets of two, perf. 2x250e, imperf. 2x300e, issued Mar. 5. Nos. 7632-7646.

El Greco, paintings, set of seven, 1e, 3e, 5e, 8e, 10e, airmail 15e, 25e, and two airmail semi-postal souv. sheets, perf. 200e+25e, imperf. 250e+50e, issued Apr. 5. Nos. 7647-7655.

1976 Summer Olympics, modern games, set of 11, 50c, 55c, 60c, 65c, 70c, 75c, 80c, 85c, 90c, airmail 35e, 60e, plus two airmail souv. sheets, perf. 225e, imperf. 300e, four embossed gold foil airmail souv. sheets, perf. 250e (2), imperf. 300e (2), and two miniature sheets of two, perf. 2x250e, imperf. 2x300e, issued May 7. Nos. 7656-7674.

UN 30th Anniv., airmail souv. sheet, 250e, issued June. No. 7675.

Contemporary Automobiles, set of seven, 1p, 3p, 5p, 8p, 10p, airmail 15p, 25p, and two airmail semi-postal souv. sheets, perf. 200p+24p, imperf. 250p+50p, issued June 10. Nos. 7675-7684.

Nature Protection

European Animals, set of seven, 5c, 10c, 15c, 20c, 25c, airmail 5p, 70p, and two airmail souv. sheets, perf. 130p, imperf. 200p, issued July 1. Nos. 7685-7693.

Asian Animals, set of seven, 30c, 35c, 40c, 45c, 8p, airmail 50c, 60p, and two airmail souv. sheets, perf. 130p, imperf. 200p, issued Sept. 20. Nos. 7694-74102.

Asian Birds, set of seven, 55c, 60c, 65c, 70c, 75c, airmail 10p, 50p, and two airmail souv. sheets, perf. 130p, imperf. 200p, issued Sept. 20. Nos. 76103-76111.

European Birds, set of seven, 5c, 10c, 15c, 20c, 25c, airmail 5p, 70p, and two airmail souv. sheets, perf. 130p, imperf. 200p, issued Sept. 20. Nos. 76112-76120.

North American Birds, set of seven, 80c, 85c, 90c, 95c, 1p, airmail 15p, 40p, and two airmail souv. sheets, perf. 130p, imperf. 200p, issued Sept. 20. Nos. 76121-76129.

Motorcycle Aces, set of 16, two each 1e, 2e, 3e, 4e, 5e, 10e, 30e, 40e, in se-tenant blocks of eight diff. values, issued July 22. Nos. 76130-76145.

1976 Summer Olympics, Montreal, set of five, 10e, 25e se-tenant strip of 3, airmail 200e, and imperf. airmail souv. sheet, 300e, issued Aug. 7. Nos. 76146-76151.

South American Flowers, set of seven, 30c, 35c, 40c, 45c, 50c, airmail 8p, 60p, and two airmail souv. sheets, perf. 130p, imperf. 200p, issued Aug. 16. Nos. 76152-76160.

Oceania, set of seven, 80c, 85c, 90c, 95c, 1p, airmail 15p, 40p, and two air-mail souv. sheets, perf. 130p, imperf. 200p, issued 1976. Nos. 76161-76169.

1977

Butterflies, set of seven, 80c, 85c, 90c, 95c, 8e, airmail 35e, 40e, and two airmail souv. sheets, perf. 130e, imperf. 200e, issued Jan. Nos. 7701-7709.

Madrid Real, 75th Anniv., set of nine, 2e, 4e, 5e, 8e, 10e, 15e, airmail 20e, 35e, 150e, issued Jan. Nos. 7710-7718.

Ancient Carriages, set of 16, 5c, 10c, 15c, 20c, 25c, 30c, 35c, 40c, 45c, 50c, 55c, 60c, 1e, 2e, airmail 10e, 70e, issued Feb. Nos. 7719-7734.

Chinese Art, set of seven, 60c, 70c, 80c, 1e, 1.50e, airmail 30e, 50e, and two airmail souv. sheets, perf. 130e, imperf. 200e, issued Feb. Nos. 7735-7743.

African Masks, set of seven, 5c, 10c, 15c, 20c, 25c, airmail 5e, 70e, and two airmail souv. sheets, perf. 130e, imperf. 200e, issued Mar. Nos. 7744-7752.

North American Animals, set of seven, 1.25e, 1.50e, 1.75e, 2e, 2.25e, airmail 20e, 50e, and two airmail souv. sheets, perf. 130e, imperf. 200e, issued 1977. Nos. 7753-7761.

World Cup Soccer Championships, Argentina '78 (famous players), set of eight, 2e, 4e, 5e, 8e, 10e, 15e, airmail 20e, 35e, and two airmail souv. sheets, perf. 150e, imperf. 250e, issued July 25. Nos. 7762-7771.

World Cup Soccer (famous teams), se-tenant set of eight, 2e, 4e, 5e, 8e, 10e, 15e, airmail 20e, 35e, and two gold foil embossed souv. sheets, 500e (AMPHILEX '77, Cutty Sark, Concorde), airmail 500e (World Cup), issued Aug. 25.Nos. 7772-7781.

Napoleon, Life and Battle Scenes, se-tenant sheet of 16, 5c, 10c, 15c, 20c, 25c, 30c, 35c, 40c, 45c, 50c, 55c, 60c, 1e, 2e, airmail 10e, 70e, issued Aug. 20. Nos. 7782-7797.

Napoleon, Military Uniforms, se-tenant sheet of 16, 5c, 10c, 15c, 20c, 25c, 30c, 35c, 40c, 45c, 50c, 55c, 60c, 1e, 2e, airmail 10e, 70e, issued Aug. 20. Nos. 7798-77113.

South American Animals, set of seven, 2.50e, 2.75e, 3e, 3.50e, 4e, airmail 25e, 35e, and two airmail souv. sheets, perf. 130e, imperf. 200e, issued Aug. Nos. 77114-77122.

USSR Space Program, 20th Anniv., set of eight, 2e, 4e, 5e, 8e, 10e, 15e, airmail 20e, 35e, and two airmail souv. sheets, imperf. 150e, perf. 250e, issued Dec. 15. Nos. 77123-77132.

1978

Ancient Sailing Ships, set of 12, 5c, 10c, 15c, 20c, 25c, airmail 5e, 70e, also 5e, 10e, 20e, 25e, 70e, plus four airmail souv. sheets, perf. 150e, 225e, imperf. 250e, 300e, and two embossed gold foil airmail souv. sheets, perf., imperf., 500e, issued Jan. 6. Nos. 7801-7818.

1980 Winter Olympics, Lake Placid, set of five, 5e, 10e, 20e, 25e, airmail 70e, two airmail souv. sheets, perf. 150e, imperf. 250e, and two embossed gold foil airmail souv. sheets, perf., imperf., 500e, issued Jan. 17. Nos. 7819-7827.

1980 Summer Olympics, Moscow, set of eight, 2e, 3e, 5e, 8e, 10e, 15e, airmail 30e, 50e, two airmail souv. sheets, perf. 150e, imperf. 250e, and two embossed gold foil airmail souv. sheets, perf., imperf., 500e, issued Jan. 17. Nos. 7828-7839.

1980 Summer Olympic Water Games, Tallinn, set of five, 5e, 10e, 20e, 25e, airmail 70e, two airmail souv. sheets, perf. 150e, imperf. 250e, and two embossed gold foil airmail souv. sheets, perf., imperf., 500e, issued Jan. 17. Nos. 7840-7848.

Eliz. II Coronation, 25th Anniv., set of eight, 2e, 5e, 8e, 10e, 12e, 15e, airmail 30e, 50e, and two airmail souv. sheets, perf. 150e, imperf. 250e, issued Apr. 25. Nos. 7849-7858.

English Knights of 1200-1350 A.D., set of seven, 5e, 10e, 15e, 20e, 25e, airmail 15e, 70e, and two airmail souv. sheets, perf. 130e, imperf. 250e, issued Apr. 25. Nos. 7859-7867.

Old Locomotives, set of seven, 1e, 2e, 3e, 5e, 10e, airmail 25e, 70e, and two airmail souv. sheets, perf. 150e, imperf. 250e, issued Aug. Nos. 7868-7876.

Prehistoric Animals, set of seven, 30e, 35e, 40e, 45e, 50e, airmail 25e, 60e, and airmail souv. sheet, 130e, issued Aug. Nos. 7877-7884.

Francisco Goya, "Maja Vestida," airmail souv. sheet, 150e, issued Aug. No. 7885.

Peter Paul Rubens — UNICEF, airmail souv. sheet, 250e, issued Aug. No. 7886.

Europa — CEPT — Europhila '78, airmail souv. sheet, 250e, issued Aug. No. 7887.

30th Intl. Stamp Fair, Riccione, airmail souv. sheet, 150e, issued Aug. Nos. 7888.

Eliz. II Coronation, 25th anniv., airmail souv. sheet of three, 150e, issued CEPT, airmail souv. sheet, 250e, issued Aug. Nos. 7890.

World Cup Soccer Championships, Argentina '78 and Spain '82, airmail souv. sheet, 150e, issued Aug. Nos. 7891.

Christmas, Titian painting, "The Virgin," airmail souv. sheet, 150e, issued Aug. Nos. 7892.

Natl. Independence, 5th Anniv. (in 1973) — A7

1979 *Perf. 13x13½*
26　A7　1e Ekuele coin　　　　1.10　.25

Natl. Independence, 5th Anniv. (in 1973) — A8

1979
27　A8　　1e Port Bata　　　　.20　.20
28　A8　1.50e State Palace　　.25　.25
29　A8　　2b Central Bank, Bata　.30　.30
30　A8　2.50b Nguema Biyogo
　　　　　　 Bridge　　　　　.35　.35
31　A8　　3b Port, palace, bank,
　　　　　　 bridge　　　　　.60　.60
　　　Nos. 27-31 (5)　　　　1.70　1.70

Pres. Nguema — A9

Independence Martyrs — A10

1979 *Perf. 13½x13*
32　A9　1.50e multi　　　　.50　.35
United Natl. Workers's Party (PUNT), 3rd Congress.

1979
33　A10　　1e Enrique Nvo　　.20　.20
34　A10　1.50e Salvador Ndongo
　　　　　　　 Ekang　　　　.30　.30
35　A10　　2b Acacio Mane　　.40　.40
　　　Nos. 33-35 (3)　　　　.90　.90

Agricultural Experiment Year A11

1979 *Perf. 13x13½*
36　A11　　1e multi　　　　.65　.25
37　A11　1.50e multi, diff.　　.95　.35

Independence Martyrs — A12　　Natl. Coat of Arms — A13

1981, Mar.　Photo.　*Perf. 13½x12½*
38　A12　　5b Obiang Esono
　　　　　　　 Nguema　　　.55　.20
39　A12　 15b Fermando Nvara
　　　　　　　 Engonga　　　.55　.20
40　A12　 25b Ela Edjodjomo
　　　　　　　 Mangue　　　.55　.20
41　A12　 35b Obiang Nguema
　　　　　　　 Moasogo, presi-
　　　　　　　 dent　　　　　.75　.20
42　A12　 50b Hipolito Micha
　　　　　　　 Eworo　　　1.10　.20
43　A13　100b multi　　　2.25　.35
　　　Nos. 38-43 (6)　　　5.75　1.35
　　　Dated 1980.

Christmas 1980 A14

1981, Mar. 30 *Perf. 13½*
44　A14　　8b Cathedral, infant　.25　.20
45　A14　 25b Bells, youth　　　.30　.20
　　　Dated 1980.

Souvenir Sheet

Pres. Obiang Nguema
Mbasogo — A15

1981, Aug. 30   Litho.   Imperf.
46 A15 400b multi   7.75 2.25

State Visit of King Juan Carlos of
Spain — A16

Perf. 13x13½, 13½x13
1981, Nov. 30
47 A16 50b Government recep-
           tion   .95   .20
48 A16 100b Arrival at airport   1.75 .35
49 A16 150b King, Pres.
           Mbasogo, vert.   2.75 .60
       Nos. 47-49 (3)   5.45 1.15

State Visit of Pope John Paul II — A17

1982, Feb. 18
50 A17 100b Papal and natl.
           arms   1.90 .70
51 A17 200b Pres. Mbasogo
           greeting Pope   3.50 1.40
52 A17 300b Pope, vert.   5.25 2.10
       Nos. 50-52 (3)   10.65 4.20

Christmas
1981
A18

1982, Feb. 25   Photo.
53 A18 100b Carolers, vert.   1.25 .35
54 A18 150b Magi, African youth   1.90 .60
       Dated 1981.

1982 World Cup Soccer
Championships, Spain — A19

1982, June 13   Perf. 13½
55 A19 40b Emblem   .55   .25
56 A19 60b Naranjito character
           trademark   .80   .35
57 A19 100b World Cup trophy   1.40   .60
58 A19 200b Players, palm tree,
           emblem   2.75 1.10
       Nos. 55-58 (4)   5.50 2.30

Fauna
A20

1983, Feb. 4   Litho.
59 A20 40b Gorilla   .65   .20
60 A20 60b Hippopotamus   1.10   .25
61 A20 80b Atherurus africanus   1.50   .35
62 A20 120b Felis pardus   2.25   .50
       Nos. 59-62 (4)   5.50 1.30
       Dated 1982.

Christmas
1982
A21

1983, Feb. 25   Photo.
63 A21 100b Stars   .95   .35
64 A21 200b King offering frank-
           incense   2.25 .75
       Dated 1982.

World Communications Year — A22

1983, July 18   Litho.
65 A22 150b Postal runner   1.00   .45
66 A22 200b Microwave station,
           drummer   2.40 1.00

Banana
Trees
A23

1983, Oct. 8
67 A23 300b shown   3.25 1.00
68 A23 400b Forest, vert.   4.50 1.40

Christmas
1983
A24

1984
69 A24 80b Folk dancer, musical
           instruments   .90   .30
70 A24 100b Holy Family   1.10   .50
       Dated 1983.

Constitution of State Powers — A25

Scales of justice, fundamental lawbook and
various maps.

1984, Feb. 15
71 A25 50b Annobon and Bioko   .60   .25
72 A25 100b Mainland regions   1.10   .50

Turtle Hunting, Rio
Muni — A26

World Food
Day — A27

1984, May 1
73 A26 125b Hunting Whales,
           horiz.   1.25 .50
74 A26 150b shown   1.50   .60

1984, Sept.
75 A27 60b Papaya   1.00 .40
76 A27 80b Malanga   1.25   .50

Abstract Wood-Carved Figurines and
Art — A28

Designs: 25b, *Black Gazelle* and *Anxiety*.
30b, *Black Gazelle*, diff., and *Woman*. 60b,
Man and woman, vert. 75b, *Poster*, vert. 100b,
Mother and Child, vert. 150b, *Man and
Woman*, diff., and *Bust of a Woman*.

1984, Nov. 15
77 A28 25b multi   .25   .20
78 A28 30b multi   .35   .20
79 A28 60b multi   .65   .25
80 A28 75b multi   .85   .30
81 A28 100b multi   1.10   .40
82 A28 150b multi   1.60   .60
       Nos. 77-82 (6)   4.80 1.95

Christmas
A29

1984, Dec. 24
83 A29 60b Mother and child,
           vert.   .70   .25
84 A29 100b Musical instruments   1.00   .40

Immaculate Conception Missions,
Cent. — A30

50fr, Emblem, vert. 60fr, Map, nun and
youths, vert. 80fr, First Guinean nuns. 125fr,
Missionaries landing at Bata Beach, 1885.

1985, Apr.   Perf. 14
85 A30 50fr multi   .45   .20
86 A30 60fr multi   .50   .20
87 A30 80fr multi   .60   .20
88 A30 125fr multi   1.10   .40
       Nos. 85-88 (4)   2.65 1.00

Jose
Mavule
Ndjong,
First
Postmaster
A31

1985, July   Perf. 13½
89 A31 50fr Postal emblem, vert.   .85   .20
90 A31 80fr shown   1.50   .35

Equatorial Guinea Postal Service.

Christmas
A32

1985, Dec.
91 A32 40fr Nativity   .55   .20
92 A32 70fr Folk band, dancers,
           mother and child   .90   .35

Nature Conservation — A33

1985
93 A33 15fr Crab, snail   .75   .20
94 A33 35fr Butterflies, bees,
           birds   1.40 .25
95 A33 45fr Flowering plants   2.10   .35
96 A33 65fr Spraying and har-
           vesting cacao   3.25 .50
       Nos. 93-96 (4)   7.50 1.30

Folklore — A34

A35

1986, Apr. 15
97 A34 10fr Ndowe dance,
           Mekuyo, horiz.   .25   .20
98 A34 50fr Fang dance,
           Mokom   .50   .20
99 A34 65fr Cacha Bubi, Bisila   .65   .25
100 A34 80fr Fang dance,
           Ndong-Mba   .80   .35
       Nos. 97-100 (4)   2.20 1.00

1986, June 25

1986 World Cup Soccer Championships,
Mexico: Various soccer plays.

101 A35 50fr multi, horiz.   .25   .20
102 A35 100fr multi, horiz.   .75   .25
103 A35 150fr multi   1.10   .40
104 A35 200fr multi   1.40   .55
       Nos. 101-104 (4)   3.50 1.40

Christmas — A36

Conf. of the Union of Central African States — A37

1986, Dec. 12
105 A36 100fr Musical instruments, horiz. .85 .35
106 A36 150fr Holy Family, lamb 1.40 .50

1986, Dec. 29
107 A37 80fr Flags, map .80 .35
108 A37 100fr Emblem, map, horiz. 1.00 .40

Campaign Against Hunger A38

1987, June 5
109 A38 60fr Chicken .65 .25
110 A38 80fr Fish .95 .35
111 A38 100fr Wheat 1.10 .40
Nos. 109-111 (3) 2.70 1.00

Intl. Peace Year A39

1987, July 15 Litho. Perf. 13½
112 A39 100fr shown .75 .40
113 A39 200fr Hands holding dove 1.60 .80

Stamp Day 1987 A40

1987, Oct. 5 Litho. Perf. 13½
114 A40 150fr shown 1.25 .50
115 A40 300fr Posting envelope 2.75 .85

Christmas 1987 — A41

Mother and child (wood carvings).

1987, Dec. 22 Litho. Perf. 13½
116 A41 80fr multi .95 .35
117 A41 100fr multi, diff. 1.40 .50

Climbing Palm Tree — A42

Democratic Party — A43

1988, May 4 Litho. Perf. 13½
118 A42 50fr shown .50 .20
119 A42 75fr Woman carrying fish .60 .30
120 A42 150fr Chopping down trees 1.25 .60
Nos. 118-120 (3) 2.35 1.10

1988, Nov. 16
121 A43 40fr Crest .35 .20
122 A43 75fr Torch, motto, horiz. .60 .30
123 A43 100fr Torch, flag, weaving, horiz. .85 .40
Nos. 121-123 (3) 1.80 .90

Cultural Revolution Day — A44

Geometric shapes.

1988, June 4
124 A44 35fr shown .25 .20
125 A44 50fr Squares, sphere .35 .20
126 A44 100fr Bird .75 .50
Nos. 124-126 (3) 1.35 .90

Christmas — A45

1988, Dec. 22
127 A45 50fr shown .40 .20
128 A45 100fr Mother and child .95 .40

Natl. Independence, 20th Anniv. — A46

Designs: 10fr, Lumber on truck. 35fr, Folk dancers. 45fr, Officials on dais.

1989, Apr. 14 Perf. 14
129 A46 10fr multicolored .25 .20
130 A46 35fr multicolored .30 .20
131 A46 45fr multicolored .35 .20
Nos. 129-131 (3) .90 .60

Youths Bathing, Ilachi Falls — A47

25fr, Waterfall in the jungle. 60fr, Boy drinking from fruit, boys swimming at Luba Beach.

1989, July 7 Perf. 13½
132 A47 15fr shown .20 .20
133 A47 25fr multicolored .25 .20
134 A47 60fr multicolored .45 .25
Nos. 132-134 (3) .90 .65

1st Congress of the Democratic Party of Equatorial Guinea A48

1989, Oct. 23 Litho. Perf. 13½
135 A48 25fr shown .30 .20
136 A48 35fr Torch, vert. .50 .20
137 A48 40fr Pres. Nguema, vert. .60 .20
Nos. 135-137 (3) 1.40 .60

Christmas — A49

1989, Dec. 18 Litho. Perf. 13½
138 A49 150fr shown 1.60 .75
139 A49 300fr Nativity, horiz. 2.00 1.00

Boy Scouts A50

1990, Mar. 23 Litho. Perf. 13
140 A50 100fr Lord Baden-Powell 1.75 .50
141 A50 250fr Salute 4.00 1.10
142 A50 350fr Bugler 5.25 1.50
Nos. 140-142 (3) 11.00 3.10

World Cup Soccer Championships, Italy — A51

1990, June 8 Litho. Perf. 13
143 A51 100fr Soccer player, map .75 .35
144 A51 250fr Goalkeeper 1.50 .65
145 A51 350fr Trophy 2.25 1.00
Nos. 143-145 (3) 4.50 2.00

Musical Instruments of the Ndowe People — A52

Instruments of the: 250fr, Fang. 350fr, Bubi.

1990, June 19
146 A52 100fr multicolored .60 .20
147 A52 250fr multicolored 1.25 .55
148 A52 350fr multicolored 1.60 .85
Nos. 146-148 (3) 3.45 1.60

Discovery of America, 500th Anniv. (in 1992) A53

1990, Oct. 10
149 A53 170fr Arrival in New World 1.00 .35
150 A53 300fr Columbus' fleet 1.75 .55

Christmas — A54

1990, Dec. 23 Litho. Perf. 13½
151 A54 170fr shown 1.00 .45
152 A54 300fr Bubi tribesman 1.75 .75

1992 Summer Olympics, Barcelona A55

1991, Apr. 22 Litho. Perf. 13½x14
153 A55 150fr Tennis 2.10 .75
154 A55 250fr Cycling 3.25 1.10
Souvenir Sheet
155 A55 500fr Equestrian 14.50 6.00

La Maja Desnuda by Goya A56

Designs: 250fr, Eve by Durer, vert. 350fr, The Three Graces by Rubens, vert.

1991, May 6 Litho. Perf. 14
156 A56 100fr shown 1.75 .50
157 A56 250fr multicolored 3.75 1.10
158 A56 350fr multicolored 5.00 1.50
Nos. 156-158 (3) 10.50 3.10

Madrillus Sphinx — A57

1991, July 1 Litho. Perf. 13½x14
159 A57 25fr shown 3.50 1.50
160 A57 25fr Face 3.50 1.50
161 A57 25fr Seated 3.50 1.50
162 A57 25fr Walking, horiz. 3.50 1.50
Nos. 159-162 (4) 14.00 6.00

World Wildlife Fund.

Discovery of America, 500th Anniv. A58

Captains, ships: 150fr, Vicente Yanez Pinzon, Nina. 260fr, Martin Alonso Pinzon, Pinta. 350fr, Christopher Columbus, Santa Maria.

1991 Litho. Perf. 13½x14
163 A58 150fr multicolored 1.10 .40
164 A58 250fr multicolored 2.00 .75
165 A58 350fr multicolored 2.75 1.25
   Nos. 163-165 (3) 5.85 2.40

Locomotives — A59

150fr, Electric, Japan, 1932. 250fr, Steam, US, 1873. 500fr, Steam, Germany, 1841.

1991, Sept. 10
166 A59 150fr multicolored 1.25 .50
167 A59 250fr multicolored 2.00 .75
   Souvenir Sheet
168 A59 500fr multicolored 12.50 6.00

1992 Summer Olympics, Barcelona A60

1992, Feb. 12 Litho. Perf. 13½x14
169 A60 200fr Basketball 1.75 .75
170 A60 300fr Swimming 2.50 1.10
   Souvenir Sheet
171 A60 400fr Baseball 22.50 12.50

   Souvenir Sheet

Discovery of America, 500th Anniv. — A61

Columbus: a, 300fr, Departing from Palos, Spain. b, 500fr, Landing in New World.

1992, Apr. 8
172 A61 Sheet of 2, #a.-b. 22.50 12.50

Motion Pictures, Cent. A61a

Scenes from movies: 100fr, Humphrey Bogart, Ingrid Bergman, Dooley Wilson in "Casablanca," 1942. 250fr, "Viridiana," 1961. 350fr, Laurel and Hardy in "Sons of the Desert," 1933.

1992, Sept. Litho. Perf. 14
172C A61a 100fr multicolored .90 .20
172D A61a 250fr multicolored 1.75 .45
172E A61a 350fr multicolored 2.75 .60
   Nos. 172C-172E (3) 5.40 1.25

A62

A62a

Mushrooms: 75fr, Termitomyces globulus. 125fr, Termitomyces le testui. 150fr, Termitomyces robustus.

1992, Nov. Litho. Perf. 14x13½
173 A62 75fr multicolored 1.00 .20
174 A62 125fr multicolored 1.25 .35
175 A62 150fr multicolored 1.75 .45
   Nos. 173-175 (3) 4.00 1.00

1992 Litho. Perf. 14x13½
Wildlife Protection: 150fr, Halcyon malimbicus. 250fr, Corythaeola cristata. 500fr, Mariposa nymphalidae, horiz.
175A A62a 150fr multicolored 2.00 .50
175B A62a 250fr multicolored 3.50 1.00
   Souvenir Sheet
   Perf. 13½x14
175C A62a 500fr multicolored 17.50 8.00

Virgin and Child with Virtuous Saints, by Claudio Coello (c. 1635-1693) — A63

Paintings, by Jacob Jordaens (1593-1678): 300fr, Apollo Conquering Marsias. 400fr, Meleager and Atalanta.

1993, Mar. Litho. Perf. 13½x14
176 A63 200fr multicolored 2.50 .75
177 A63 300fr multicolored 3.50 1.25
   Souvenir Sheet
178 A63 400fr multicolored 17.00 8.00

1992 Olympic Gold Medalists A64

Designs: 100fr, Quincy Watts, 400-meter dash, US. 250fr, Martin Lopez Zubero, swimming, Spain. 350fr, Petra Kronberger, women's slalom, Austria. 400fr, Flying Dutchman class yachting, Spain.

1993 Litho. Perf. 13½x14
179 A64 100fr multicolored .90 .35
180 A64 250fr multicolored 1.90 .75
181 A64 350fr multicolored 2.50 1.00
182 A64 400fr multicolored 3.00 1.25
   Nos. 179-182 (4) 8.30 3.35

Scene from Romeo and Juliet, by Tchaikovsky — A65

Design: 200fr, Scene from Faust, by Charles-Francois Gounod (1818-93).

1993, June Litho. Perf. 13½x14
183 A65 100fr multicolored .85 .40
184 A65 200fr multicolored 1.50 .75

First Ford Gasoline Engine, Cent. A66

1993 Perf. 13½x14, 14x13½
185 A66 200fr First Ford vehicle 3.50 1.00
186 A66 300fr Ford Model T 5.50 1.50
187 A66 400fr Henry Ford, vert. 7.75 2.10
   Nos. 185-187 (3) 16.75 4.60

25th Anniv. of Independence — A67

Designs: 150fr, Pres. Obiang Nguema Mbasogo, vert. 250fr, Cargo ship, map, communications . 300fr, Hydroelectric plant, Riaba. 350fr, Bridge.

Perf. 14x13½, 13½x14
1993, Oct. 12 Litho.
188 A67 150fr multicolored 1.25 .50
189 A67 250fr multicolored 2.00 .75
190 A67 300fr multicolored 2.50 1.00
191 A67 350fr multicolored 2.75 1.10
   Nos. 188-191 (4) 8.50 3.35

1994 World Cup Soccer Championships, US — A68

Designs: 200fr, German team, 1990 champions. 300fr, Rose Bowl Stadium, Pasadena, Calif. 500fr, Player kicking ball, vert.

1994 Litho. Perf. 13½x14, 14x13½
192 A68 200fr multicolored 1.25 .45
193 A68 300fr multicolored 1.75 .65
194 A68 500fr multicolored 3.25 1.10
   Nos. 192-194 (3) 6.25 2.20

First Manned Moon Landing, 25th Anniv. A69

Designs: 500fr, Lunar module, Eagle. 700fr, "Buzz" Aldrin, Michael Collins, Neil Armstrong. 900fr, Footprint on moon, astronaut.

1994 Perf. 13½x14
195 A69 500fr multicolored 2.75 .70
196 A69 700fr multicolored 4.25 1.00
197 A69 900fr multicolored 6.50 1.75
   Nos. 195-197 (3) 13.50 3.45

Dinosaurs A70

Designs: 300fr, Chasmosaurus. 500fr, Tyrannosaurus rex. 700fr, Triceratops. 800fr, Styracosaurus, deinonychus.

1994
198 A70 300fr multicolored 2.00 .65
199 A70 500fr multicolored 3.25 1.10
200 A70 700fr multicolored 4.50 1.60
   Nos. 198-200 (3) 9.75 3.35
   Souvenir Sheet
201 A70 800fr multicolored 18.50 17.50

Famous Men A71

Designs: 300fr, Jean Renoir (1894-1979), French film director. 500fr, Ferdinand de Lesseps (1805-94), French diplomat, promoter of Suez Canal. 600fr, Antoine de Saint Exupery (1900-44), French aviator, writer. 700fr, Walter Gropius (1883-1969), architect.

1994 Litho. Perf. 13½x14
202 A71 300fr multicolored 2.25 .75
203 A71 500fr multicolored 3.50 1.25
204 A71 600fr multicolored 4.25 1.50
205 A71 700fr multicolored 5.00 1.75
   Nos. 202-205 (4) 15.00 5.25

Establishment of The Bauhaus, 75th anniv. (#205).

Minerals A72

1994 Litho. Perf. 13½x14
206 A72 300fr Aurichalcite 2.50 1.00
207 A72 400fr Pyromorphite 3.00 1.40
208 A72 600fr Fluorite 4.00 1.90
209 A72 700fr Halite 5.50 2.25
   Nos. 206-209 (4) 15.00 6.55

Domestic Animals A73

Designs: a, Cat. b, Dog. c, Pig.

1995 Litho. Perf. 13½x14
210 Strip of 3, #a.-c. 8.50 8.50
a.-c. A73 500fr Any single 1.50 1.50

Butterflies & Orchids A74

a, Hypolimnas salmacis. b, Myrina silenus. c, Palla ussheri. d, Pseudacraea boisduvali.

1995
211 Strip of 4, #a.-d. 12.00 12.00
a.-d. A74 400fr Any single 2.25 1.50

Anniversaries — A75

Designs: a, 350fr, End of World War II, 50th Anniv. b, 450fr, UN, 50th anniv. c, 600fr, Sir Rowland Hill, birth bicent.

1995 Perf. 13½x14
212 Strip of 3, #a.-c. 8.50 8.50
a. A75 350fr multi 1.25 1.25
b. A75 450fr multi 1.50 1.50
c. A75 600fr multi 2.25 2.25

Trains
A76

Designs: No. 213a, English steam engine. b, German diesel engine. c, Japanese Shinkansen train.
800fr, Swiss electric locomotive.

1995
213 Strip of 3, #a.-c. 12.50 12.50
a.-c. A76 500fr Any single 2.00 2.00
Souvenir Sheet
214 A76 800fr multicolored 9.00 9.00

Formula 1
Driving
Champions
A77

Designs: a, Juan Manuel Fangio. b, Ayrton Senna. c, Jim Clark. d, Jochen Rindt.

1995 Litho. Perf. 14
215 Strip of 4, #a.-d. 10.00 10.00
a.-d. A77 400fr Any single 1.50 1.50

Motion
Pictures,
Cent.
A78

Designs: a, Marilyn Monroe. b, Elvis Presley. c, James Dean. d, Vittorio de Sica.

1996 Litho. Perf. 14
216 Strip of 4, #a.-d. 9.00 9.00
a.-d. A78 350fr Any single 1.50 1.50

Famous
People
A79

Designs: a, Alfred Nobel (1833-96), inventor, philanthropist. b, Anton Bruckner (1824-96), composer. c, Abraham and Three Angels, by Giovanni B. Tiepolo (1696-1770).
800fr, Family of Charles IV, by Francisco de Goya, (1746-1828).

1996
217 Strip of 3, #a.-c. 12.50 12.50
a.-c. A79 500fr Any single 2.00 2.00
Souvenir Sheet
218 A79 800fr multicolored 7.75 7.75

Chess
A80

Designs: a, World Chess Festival for youth and children, Minorca, Spain. b, Women's World Chess Championship, Jaén, Spain. c, Men's World Chess Championship, Karpov versus Kamsky, Elista, Kalmyk. d, Chess Olympiad, Yerevan, Armenia.

1996 Litho. Perf. 14
219 Strip of 4, #a.-d. 10.00 10.00
a.-d. A80 400fr Any single 1.50 1.50

1996
Summer
Olympic
Games,
Atlanta
A81

Designs: a, Olympic Stadium, Athens, 1896. b, Cycling. c, Tennis. d, Equestrian show jumping.

1996 Litho. Perf. 14
220 Strip of 4, #a.-d. 10.00 10.00
a.-d. A81 400fr Any single 1.50 1.50

Ships
A82

Designs: a, Paddle steamer with sails, 19th cent. b, Bark "Galatea," 1896. c, Modern ferry.

1996
221 Strip of 3, #a.-c. 11.00 11.00
a.-c. A82 500fr Any single 2.00 2.00

Franz Schubert
(1797-1828),
Composer — A83

Miguel de Cervantes (1547-1616),
Novelist — A84

Designs: a, shown. b, Chinese Lunar New Year, 1997, (Year of the Ox). c, Johannes Brahms (1833-97), composer.
Illustration A84 reduced.

1997, Apr. 23 Litho. Perf. 14
222 Strip of 3, #a.-c. 9.00 9.00
a.-c. A83 500fr Any single 2.00 2.00
Souvenir Sheet
223 A84 800fr multicolored 5.50 5.50

Mushrooms — A85

a, Sparassis laminosa. b, Amanita pantherina. c, Morchella esculenta. d, Aleuria aurantia.

1997
224 Strip of 4, #a.-d. 13.50 13.50
a.-d. A85 400fr Any single 2.00 1.75

1998 World Cup
Soccer
Championships,
France — A86

Designs: a, Players with ball on field. b, Stadium. c, Kicking ball.

1997 Litho. Perf. 14
225 Strip of 3, #a.-c. 6.00 6.00
a.-c. A86 300fr Any single 1.10 1.10

Fauna
A88

a, Snake. b, Snail. c, Turtle. d, Monitor lizard.

1998 Litho. Perf. 14
230 Strip of 4, #a.-d. 14.00 14.00
a.-d. A88 400fr Any single 2.25 1.50

A89   A90

Military Uniforms: a, Alsace Regiment, French Infantry, 18th cent. b, English Marine, 18th cent. c, Georgian Hussars Regiment, Russian Calvary, 18th cent. d, Prussian Artillery, 19th cent.

1998
231 Strip of 4, #a.-d. 10.00 10.00
a.-d. A89 400fr Any single 1.50 1.50

1999 Litho. Perf. 14
Easter (Museum paintings): a, Crucifixion of Christ, by Velázquez. b, Adoration of the Magi, by Rubens. c, Holy Family, by Michelangelo.
232 Strip of 3, #a.-c.
a.-c. A90 500fr Any single 2.00 2.00

Orchids — A91

Designs: a, Angraecum eburneum. b, Paphiopedilum insigne. c, Ansellia africana. d, Cattleya leopoldii.

1999
233 Strip of 4, #a.-d. 15.00 15.00
a.-d. A91 400fr Any single 2.75 1.50

Birth and Death
Anniversaries
A92

No. 234: a, 750fr, Portrait of Frederic Chopin (1810-49), by Eugene Delacroix. b, 100fr, Christ Crowned With Thorns, by Anthony Van Dyck (1599-1641). c, 250fr, Portrait of Johann Wolfgang von Goethe (1749-1832), by Joseph Carl Stieler. d, 500fr, Jacques-Etienne Montgolfiere (1745-1799) and balloon.

1999 Litho. Perf. 14x13¾
234 Horiz. strip of 4, #a-d 10.00 10.00
a. A92 750fr multi 3.00 3.00
b. A92 100fr multi .35 .35
c. A92 250fr multi 1.10 1.10
d. A92 500fr multi 2.00 2.00

Parrots — A93

No. 235: a, Aratinga guarouba. b, Ara ambigua. c, Anodorhynchus hyacinthinus. 800fr, Alisterus amboinensis.

1999
235 Vert. strip of 3, #a-c 10.00 10.00
a.-c. A93 500fr Any single 2.25 2.00
Souvenir Sheet
236 A93 800fr multi 7.50 7.50

Economic and
Monetary
Community of
Central Africa
Week — A93a

Designs: 100fr, Map of Africa, flags of member nations.

1999 Litho. Perf. 14½
236A A93a 100fr multi —

An additional stamp was issued in this set. The editors would like to examine any example.

Locomotives — A94

No. 237: a, Swiss. b, German. c, Japanese.

2000 Litho. Perf. 13¾x14
237 Horiz. strip of 3 7.00 7.00
a.-c. A94 500fr Any single 2.25 2.25
Souvenir Sheet
238 A94 800fr AVE Train 3.50 3.50

Butterflies
A95

a, Fabriciana niobe. b, Palaeochrysophanus hippothoe. c, Inachis io. d, Apatura iris.

2000
239 Horiz. strip of 4 7.50 7.50
a.-d. A95 400fr Any single 1.75 1.75

UPU, 125th Anniv. (in 1999) — A96

2000 Litho. **Perf. 13¾**
240 A96 400fr multi 1.75 1.75

Mushrooms A97

No. 241: a, Gyroporus cyanescens. b, Terfezia arenaria. c, Battarrea stevenii. d, Amanita muscaria.

2001 Litho. **Perf. 13¾**
241 Horiz. strip of 4 6.75 6.75
a.-d. A97 400fr Any single 1.60 1.60

Fire Trucks A98

No. 242: a, Truck, 1915. b, Tanker, 1943. c, Ladder truck, 1966. d, Merryweather pumper, 1888.

2001
242 Horiz. strip of 4 10.00 10.00
a.-d. A98 400fr Any single 1.75 1.60

Soldiers — A99

No. 243: a, Infantry officer, 1700. b, Harquebusier, 1534. c, Musketeer, 17th cent. d, Fusilier, 1815.

2001 Litho. **Perf. 14x13¾**
243 Horiz. strip of 4 6.75 6.75
a.-d. A99 400fr Any single 1.60 1.60

Prehistoric Animals A100

No. 244: a, Carnotaurus sastrei. b, Iberomesornis romerali. c, Troodon.
800fr, Diplodocus carnegiei.

2001 **Perf. 13¾x14**
244 Horiz. strip of 3 6.25 6.25
a.-c. A100 500fr Any single 2.00 2.00

Souvenir Sheet
245 A100 800fr multi 3.50 3.50

Millennium A101

Designs: No. 246, 200fr, Intl. Conference Center. No. 247, 200fr, Offshore petroleum exploration. No. 248, 200fr, Women's Plaza, Malabo.
400fr, Statue at Intl. Conference Center, vert.

2001 Litho. **Perf. 13¾x14**
246-248 A101 Set of 3 3.50 3.50
Souvenir Sheet
Perf. 14x13¾
249 A101 400fr multi 1.75 1.75

Flora — A102

No. 250: a, Alstonia congensis. b, Harongana madagascariensis. c, Caloncoba glauca. d, Cassia occidentalis.

2002 **Perf. 14x13¾**
250 Horiz. strip of 4 6.75 6.75
a.-d. A102 400fr Any single 1.60 1.60

Automobiles — A103

No. 251: a, 1924 Rochet Schneider 20,000. b, 1930 Bugatti T49. c, 1931 Ford Model A. d, 1925 Alfa Romeo RLSS.

2002 **Perf. 13¾x14**
251 Vert. strip of 4 6.75 6.75
a.-d. A103 400fr Any single 1.60 1.60

Butterflies A104

No. 252: a, Papilio menestheus canui. b, Papilio policenes. c, Papilio tynderaeus. d, Papilio zalmoxis.

2002
252 Strip of 4 6.75 6.75
a.-d. A104 400fr Any single 1.60 1.60

Famous Men A105

No. 253: a, Victor Hugo (1802-85), writer. b, Santiago Ramón y Cajal (1852-1934), histologist. c, Emile Zola (1840-1902), writer.

2002
253 Horiz. strip of 3 5.25 5.25
a.-c. A105 400fr Any single 1.60 1.60

2002 World Cup Soccer Championships, Japan and Korea — A106

No. 254: a, Player with yellow shirt with knee on ground. b, Stadium. c, Player with yellow shirt on ground.

2002
254 Horiz. strip of 3 6.75 6.75
a.-c. A106 500fr Any single 2.10 2.10

Souvenir Sheet

2002 Chess Olympiad, Bled, Slovenia — A107

2002
255 A107 800fr multi 3.50 3.50

Anniversaries and Events — A108

No. 256: a, Painting by Henri de Toulouse-Lautrec (1864-1901). b, Year of Dialogue Among Civilizations. c, Giuseppe Verdi (1813-1901), composer.

2004 ? Litho. **Perf. 14x13¾**
256 Vert. strip of 3 5.50 5.50
a.-c. A108 400fr Any single 1.75 1.75

Dated 2001. Stamps did not appear in philatelic market until 2004.

Anniversaries and Events — A109

No. 257: a, Tour de France bicycle race, cent. b, Painting by Vincent van Gogh (1853-90). c, Wright Brothers and Wright Flyer.

2004 ? **Perf. 13¾x14**
257 Horiz. strip of 3 8.50 8.50
a. A109 400fr multi 2.25 2.25
b. A109 500fr multi 2.75 2.75
c. A109 600fr multi 3.50 3.50

Dated 2003. Stamps did not appear in philatelic market until 2004.

Minerals A110

2004 ?
258 Vert. strip of 4 8.50 8.50
a. A110 400fr Realgar 1.75 1.75
b. A110 450fr Gypsum 2.00 2.00
c. A110 550fr Red quartz 2.25 2.25
d. A110 600fr Chrysoberyl 2.50 2.50

Dated 2003. Stamps did not appear in philatelic market until 2004.

Lighthouses A111

Designs: a, Marina Lighthouse, Luba, Equatorial Guinea. b, La Plata Lighthouse, Spain. c, Prodecao Lighthouse, Luba. d, Torre de Hércules, Spain.

2004 ? **Perf. 14x13¾**
259 Horiz. strip of 4 11.00 11.00
a. A111 400fr multi 2.25 2.25
b. A111 450fr multi 2.50 2.50
c. A111 550fr multi 2.75 2.75
d. A111 600fr multi 3.50 3.50

Dated 2003. Stamps did not appear in philatelic market until 2004.

Space Shuttle Columbia Accident — A112

No. 260: a, Rocket lift-off. b, Rocket on launch pad. c, Flight crew patch.
1000fr, View of earth from outer space.

2004 ?
260 Vert. strip of 3 8.00 8.00
a. A112 500fr multi 2.25 2.25
b. A112 600fr multi 2.50 2.50
c. A112 700fr multi 3.00 3.00

Souvenir Sheet
261 A112 1000fr multi 4.50 4.50

Dated 2003. Stamps did not appear in philatelic market until 2004.

Motorcycles — A113

No. 262: a, 1944-47 Soriano Tigre. b, 1970 Derbi 50 Grand Prix. c, 1938 DKW 250 with sidecar.
1000fr, Harley-Davidson VRSCA V-Rod.

2004 ? **Perf. 13¾x14**
262 Horiz. strip of 3 7.00 7.00
a. A113 450fr multi 1.90 1.90
b. A113 500fr multi 2.25 2.25
c. A113 550fr multi 2.75 2.75

Souvenir Sheet
263 A113 1000fr multi 5.50 5.50

Dated 2003. Stamps did not appear in philatelic market until 2004.

Souvenir Sheet

Wedding of Spanish Prince Felipe and Letizia Ortiz Rocasolano — A114

2004 Litho. **Perf. 13¾x14**
264 A114 1400fr multi 5.75 5.75

2004 Summer Olympics, Athens A115

2004
265 Horiz. strip of 4 8.25 8.25
a. A115 400fr Basketball 1.60 1.60
b. A115 450fr Track 1.90 1.90
c. A115 550fr Tennis 2.25 2.25
d. A115 600fr Cycling 2.50 2.50

2004
Anniversaries
A116

No. 266: a, FIFA (Fédération Internationale de Football Association), cent. b, Pablo Neruda (1904-73), poet. c, Anton Dvorak (1841-1904), composer.

2005 ?	**Litho.**	**Perf. 14x13¾**	
266	Vert. strip of 3	6.75	6.75
a.	A116 450fr multi	1.90	1.90
b.	A116 500fr multi	2.10	2.10
c.	A116 550fr multi	2.40	2.40

Dated 2004. Stamps did not appear in philatelic marketplace until 2005.

Airplanes
A117

No. 267: a, Concorde. b, Airbus A340-600. c, Boeing 747-400. d, Eurofighter C-16 Typhoon.

2005 ?		**Perf. 13¾x14**	
267	Vert. strip of 4	8.50	8.50
a.	A117 400fr multi	1.60	1.60
b.	A117 450fr multi	1.90	1.90
c.	A117 500fr multi	2.10	2.10
d.	A117 600fr multi	2.25	2.25

Dated 2004. Stamps did not appear in philatelic marketplace until 2005.

Churches — A118

No. 268: a, Cathedral, Pisa, Italy. b, Notre-Dame-la-Grande Church, Poitiers, France. c, Speyer Cathedral, Germany. d, Cathedral, Santiago de Compostela, Spain.

2005		**Perf. 14x13¾**	
268	Horiz. strip of 4	9.00	9.00
a.	A118 400fr multi	1.60	1.60
b.	A118 450fr multi	1.90	1.90
c.	A118 550fr multi	2.40	2.40
d.	A118 600fr multi	2.50	2.50

Paintings by
Salvador Dali
(1904-89) — A119

Various unnamed paintings.

2005		**Perf. 14x13¾**	
269	Vert. strip of 3	8.00	8.00
a.	A119 500fr multi	2.00	2.00
b.	A119 600fr multi	2.50	2.50
c.	A119 700fr multi	2.75	2.75
	Souvenir Sheet		
270	A119 1000fr multi	4.50	4.50

Art and Architecture — A120

No. 271: a, Statue of African Woman, Malabo. b, Building, Bioko Sur. c, Eyi Muan Ndong, troubador.

2005	**Litho.**	**Perf. 13¾x14**	
271	Horiz. strip of 3	7.25	7.25
a.	A120 450fr multi	2.00	2.00
b.	A120 550fr multi	2.40	2.40
c.	A120 600fr multi	2.75	2.75

Trains
A121

No. 272: a, Tren Basculante. b, Tren Talgo Pendular. c, Tren Electrotrén. d, Tren T. A. F.

2005			
272	Strip of 4	9.00	9.00
a.	A121 400fr multi	1.75	1.75
b.	A121 450fr multi	1.90	1.90
c.	A121 550fr multi	2.40	2.40
d.	A121 600fr multi	2.50	2.50

Publication of
Don Quixote,
400th
Anniv. — A122

No. 273: a, Emblem. b, Don Quixote and Sancho Panza riding. c, Quixote catching falling Panza. d, Quixote on horse, windmill.

2005		**Perf. 14x13¾**	
273	Horiz. strip of 4	9.00	9.00
a.	A122 400fr multi	1.75	1.75
b.	A122 450fr multi	1.90	1.90
c.	A122 550fr multi	2.40	2.40
d.	A122 600fr multi	2.50	2.50

Famous
People
A123

No. 274: a, Christopher Columbus (1451-1506), explorer. b, Federico García Lorca (1898-1936), poet. c, Wolfgang Amadeus Mozart (1756-91), composer.

2006		**Perf. 13¾x14**	
274	Horiz. strip of 3	7.25	7.25
a.	A123 450fr multi	2.00	2.00
b.	A123 550fr multi	2.25	2.25
c.	A123 600fr multi	2.75	2.75

Pope
Benedict
XVI
A124

No. 275: a, Coat of Arms. b, St. Peter's Basilica.
1000fr, Pope Benedict XVI.

2006			
275	Vert. pair	4.50	4.50
a.	A124 450fr multi	2.00	2.00
b.	A124 550fr multi	2.40	2.40
	Souvenir Sheet		
276	A124 1000fr multi	4.50	4.50

Tourism
A125

No. 277: a, Road from Boloko to Luba. b, Malabo Intl. Airport Terminal. c, Sculpture, Avenida de Juan Pablo II. d, National Parliament.

2006	**Litho.**	**Perf. 13¾x14**	
277	Strip of 4	8.00	8.00
a.	A125 400fr multi	1.60	1.60
b.	A125 450fr multi	1.75	1.75
c.	A125 550fr multi	2.25	2.25
d.	A125 600fr multi	2.40	2.40

Spain, 2006
World Basketball
Champions
A126

No. 278: a, Emblem of Spanish Basketball Federation. b, Basketball and hoop. c, Players.

2006		**Perf. 14x13¾**	
278	Vert. strip of 3	6.50	6.50
a.	A126 450fr multi	1.75	1.75
b.	A126 550fr multi	2.25	2.25
c.	A126 600fr multi	2.40	2.40

Christmas
A127

No. 279 — Baby and: a, People and drummer. b, People. c, People and airplane.

2006		**Perf. 13¾x14**	
279	Horiz. strip of 3	6.50	6.50
a.	A127 450fr multi	1.75	1.75
b.	A127 550fr multi	2.25	2.25
c.	A127 600fr multi	2.40	2.40

European Economic Community, 50th
Anniv. — A128

No. 280: a, Orchard, Spain. b, Mountain, France. c, Farm fields, Italy. d, Village, Germany.

2007	**Litho.**	**Perf. 13¾x14**	
280	Horiz. strip of 4	9.25	9.25
a.	A128 400fr multi	1.75	1.75
b.	A128 500fr multi	2.25	2.25
c.	A128 550fr multi	2.50	2.50
d.	A128 600fr multi	2.75	2.75

Locomotives in Madrid Train
Museum — A129

No. 281: a, Steam locomotive 242F-2009. b, Diesel locomotive 1615. c, Electric locomotive 6101. d, Talgo II train.
1000fr, Steam locomotive, diff.

2007			
281	Strip of 4	10.50	10.50
a.	A129 450fr multi	2.00	2.00
b.	A129 550fr multi	2.50	2.50
c.	A129 600fr multi	2.75	2.75
d.	A129 650fr multi	3.00	3.00
	Souvenir Sheet		
282	A129 1000fr multi	4.50	4.50

Native
Toys
A130

No. 283: a, Airplane. b, Car. c, Scooter. d, Songo game.

2007	**Litho.**	**Perf. 13¾x14**	
283	Horiz. strip of 4	8.50	8.50
a.	A130 400fr Airplane	1.75	1.75
b.	A130 450fr Car	2.00	2.00
c.	A130 500fr Scooter	2.25	2.25
d.	A130 500fr Songo game	2.50	2.50

Flora
A131

No. 284: a, Artocarpus communis. b, Hibiscus sabdariffa. c, Spathodea campanulata. d, Theobroma cacao.

2007	**Litho.**	**Perf. 13¾x14**	
284	Horiz. strip of 4	9.00	9.00
a.	A131 400fr multi	1.75	1.75
b.	A131 450fr multi	2.00	2.00
c.	A131 550fr multi	2.50	2.50
d.	A131 600fr multi	2.75	2.75

African
Children
A132

No. 285: a, Child and basket. b, Five children and toy cars. c, Six children and net.

2008	**Litho.**	**Perf. 13¾**	
285	Horiz. strip of 3	6.50	6.50
a.	A132 400fr multi	1.90	1.90
b.	A132 450fr multi	2.10	2.10
c.	A132 500fr multi	2.40	2.40

2008 African Cup of Nations Soccer
Championships, Ghana — A133

No. 286 — Emblem and: a, Soccer ball and player's foot. b, Soccer ball being caught. c, Goalie. d, Goalie, diff.

2008			
286	Horiz. strip of 4	9.25	9.25
a.	A133 400fr multi	1.90	1.90
b.	A133 450fr multi	2.10	2.10
c.	A133 500fr multi	2.40	2.40
d.	A133 600fr multi	2.75	2.75

Flora and
Fauna
A134

No. 287: a, Sitatunga. b, Passiflora quadrangularis. c, Pachylobus edulis.

2008			
287	Horiz. strip of 3	6.25	6.25
a.	A134 450fr multi	1.75	1.75
b.	A134 500fr multi	2.00	2.00
c.	A134 600fr multi	2.40	2.40

Intl. Year of Planet Earth A135

No. 288: a, Seedlings. b, Parched earth. c, Waterfall.

2008

288		Horiz. strip of 3	5.50	5.50
a.	A135	400fr multi	1.60	1.60
b.	A135	450fr multi	1.75	1.75
c.	A135	550fr multi	2.10	2.10

Declaration of the Rights of Children, 50th Anniv. — A136

No. 289: a, Child drinking glass of milk. b, Children playing with ball. c, Children reading. d, Child coloring.

2009, Mar. 27   Litho.   Perf. 14x13¾

289		Horiz. strip of 4	8.50	8.50
a.	A136	400fr multi	1.60	1.60
b.	A136	500fr multi	2.10	2.10
c.	A136	550fr multi	2.25	2.25
d.	A136	600fr multi	2.50	2.50

Women's Soccer A137

No. 290: a, Cheering crowd. b, Soccer ball hitting net. c, Players battling for ball. d, Corner of field.

2009, May 14   Litho.   Perf. 13¾

290		Vert. strip of 4	9.75	9.75
a.	A137	450fr multi	1.90	1.90
b.	A137	550fr multi	2.40	2.40
c.	A137	600fr multi	2.60	2.60
d.	A137	650fr multi	2.75	2.75

Medicinal Plants — A138

No. 291: a, Asystasia gangetica. b, Bryophyllum pinnatum. c, Solanum torvum. 1000fr, Cassia alata.

2009, Aug. 14

291		Vert. strip of 3	6.25	6.25
a.	A138	400fr multi	1.75	1.75
b.	A138	450fr multi	2.00	2.00
c.	A138	550fr multi	2.40	2.40

Souvenir Sheet

292	A138	1000fr multi	4.50	4.50

Christmas — A139

No. 293 — Paintings: a, Birth of Christ, by Federico Barocci. b, Adoration of the Kings, by J. B. Maíno. c, Adoration of the Shepherds, by Maíno. d, Nativity, by Master of Sopetrán.

2009, Sept. 25

293		Horiz. strip of 4	8.50	8.50
a.	A139	400fr multi	1.75	1.75
b.	A139	450fr multi	2.00	2.00
c.	A139	500fr multi	2.25	2.25
d.	A139	550fr multi	2.50	2.50

Paintings by Joaquin Sorolla y Bastida A140

No. 294: a, Paseo a Orillas del Mar. b, El Balandrito. c, La Hora del Baño. d, Self-portrait.

Perf. 13¾x13¼

2010, Mar. 15   Litho.

294		Horiz. strip of 4	9.75	9.75
a.	A140	475fr multi	2.00	2.00
b.	A140	575fr multi	2.40	2.40
c.	A140	625fr multi	2.60	2.60
d.	A140	675fr multi	2.75	2.75

Architecture — A141

No. 295: a, La Paz Medical Center, Bata. b, Gepetrol Building, Malabo. c, Gecotel Building, Bata. d, Central African Economic and Monetary Community Parliament Building, Malabo.

2010, June 15

295		Horiz. strip of 4	9.25	9.25
a.	A141	475fr multi	1.90	1.90
b.	A141	575fr multi	2.25	2.25
c.	A141	625fr multi	2.40	2.40
d.	A141	675fr multi	2.60	2.60

SPECIAL DELIVERY STAMPS

Archer with Crossbow — SD1

1971, Oct. 12   Photo.   Perf. 12½x13

E1	SD1	4p blue & multi	.75	.20
E2	SD1	8p rose & multi	1.25	.20

3rd anniversary of independence.

ERITREA

ˌer-ə-ˈtrē-ə

LOCATION — In northeast Africa, bordering on the Red Sea, Sudan, Ethiopia and Djibouti.
GOVT. — Independent state
AREA — 45,300 (?) sq. mi.
POP. — 3,984,723 (1999 est.)
CAPITAL — Asmara

Formerly an Italian colony, Eritrea was incorporated as a State of Italian East Africa in 1936.

Under British occupation (1941-52) until it became part of Ethiopia as its northernmost region. Eritrea became independent May 24, 1993.

100 Centesimi = 1 Lira
100 cents = 1 birr (1991)
100 cents = 1 nakfa (1997)

> **Catalogue values for unused stamps in this country are for Never Hinged items, beginning with Scott 200 in the regular postage section.**

All used values to about 1916 are for postally used stamps. From 1916-1934, used values in italics are for postally used stamps. CTO's, for stamps valued postally used, sell for about the same as unused, hinged stamps.

Watermark

Wmk. 140 — Crown

Stamps of Italy Overprinted

a   b

1892   Wmk. 140   Perf. 14
Overprinted Type "a" in Black

1	A6	1c bronze grn	10.00	10.00
a.		Inverted overprint	600.00	600.00
b.		Double overprint	1,800.	
		Never hinged	2,200.	
c.		Vert. pair, one without overprint	3,600.	
		Never hinged	4,500.	
2	A7	2c org brn	5.00	5.00
a.		Inverted overprint	550.00	500.00
b.		Double overprint	1,800.	
		Never hinged	2,200.	
3	A33	5c green	150.00	15.00
a.		Inverted overprint	6,750.	3,750.
		Never hinged	8,250.	

Overprinted Type "b" in Black

4	A17	10c claret	200.00	15.00
5	A17	20c orange	375.00	10.00
6	A17	25c blue	1,350.	50.00
7	A25	40c brown	13.50	30.00
8	A26	45c slate grn	13.50	32.50
9	A27	60c violet	13.50	67.50
10	A28	1 l brn & yel	50.00	67.50
11	A38	5 l bl & rose	650.00	550.00
		Nos. 1-11 (11)	2,830.	852.50
		Set, never hinged	6,500.	

1895-99
Overprinted type "a" in Black

12	A39	1c brown ('99)	20.00	10.00
13	A40	2c org brn ('99)	3.25	1.75
14	A41	5c green	3.25	1.75
a.		Inverted overprint	450.00	3,750.

Overprinted type "b" in Black

15	A34	10c claret ('98)	3.25	1.75
16	A35	20c orange	3.25	2.10
17	A36	25c blue	3.25	4.25
18	A37	45c olive grn	32.50	25.00
		Nos. 12-18 (7)	68.75	46.60
		Set, never hinged	160.00	

1903-28
Overprinted type "a" in Black

19	A42	1c brown	.85	*1.25*
a.		Inverted overprint	135.00	135.00
20	A43	2c orange brn	.85	.60
21	A44	5c blue green	42.50	.60
22	A45	10c claret	50.00	.60
23	A45	20c orange	3.25	1.25
24	A45	25c blue	425.00	18.00
a.		Double overprint	1,050.	—
25	A45	40c brown	450.00	30.00
26	A45	45c olive grn	4.25	*10.00*
27	A45	50c violet	175.00	32.50
28	A46	75c dk red & rose ('28)	90.00	10.00

29	A46	1 l brown & grn	4.25	.85
30	A46	1.25 l bl & ultra ('28)	40.00	5.00
31	A46	2 l dk grn & org ('25)	72.50	*90.00*
32	A46	2.50 l dk grn & org ('28)	225.00	60.00
33	A46	5 l blue & rose	27.50	*45.00*
		Nos. 19-33 (15)	1,610.	305.65
		Set, never hinged	3,325.	

Surcharged in Black

1905

34	A45	15c on 20c orange	72.50	17.50
		Never hinged	175.00	

1908-28
Overprinted type "a" in Black

35	A48	5c green	1.20	1.00
36	A48	10c claret ('09)	1.20	1.00
37	A48	15c slate ('20)	22.50	12.50
38	A49	20c green ('25)	16.00	12.00
39	A49	20c lilac brn ('28)	8.00	3.25
40	A49	25c blue ('09)	5.50	2.25
41	A49	30c gray ('25)	16.00	16.00
42	A49	40c brown ('16)	55.00	37.50
43	A49	50c violet ('16)	16.00	2.10
44	A49	60c brown car ('18)	27.50	*25.00*
a.		Printed on both sides		*1,500.*
45	A49	60c brown org ('28)	95.00	*190.00*
46	A51	10 l gray grn & red ('16)	400.00	*725.00*
		Nos. 35-46 (12)	663.90	*1,027.*
		Set, never hinged	1,650.	

See No. 53.

A1

Government Building at Massaua — A2

1910-29   Unwmk.   Engr.   Perf. 13½

47	A1	15c slate	350.00	25.00
a.		Perf. 11 ('29)	40.00	*55.00*
		Never hinged	82.50	
48	A2	25c dark blue	7.25	*17.00*
a.		Perf. 12	800.00	800.00

For surcharges see Nos. 51-52.

A3

Farmer Plowing — A4

1914-28

49	A3	5c green	1.20	*2.50*
a.		Perf. 11 ('28)	190.00	65.00
		Never hinged	475.00	
50	A4	10c carmine	4.75	*4.25*
a.		Perf. 11 ('28)	12.00	*45.00*
		Never hinged	25.00	
b.		Perf. 13½x14	62.50	62.50

No. 47 Surcharged in Red or Black

1916

51	A1	5c on 15c slate (R)	8.75	15.00
52	A1	20c on 15c slate	4.00	4.25
a.		"CEN" for "CENT"	32.50	32.50
b.		"CENT" omitted	200.00	200.00
c.		"ENT"	50.00	50.00
		Set, never hinged	30.00	

Italy No. 113
Overprinted in Black —
f

1921   Wmk. 140   Perf. 14

53	A50	20c brown orange	4.75	15.00
		Never hinged	12.00	

Victory Issue
Italian Victory Stamps of 1921
Overprinted type "f" 13mm long

1922

54	A64	5c olive green	2.00	7.25
55	A64	10c red	2.00	7.50
56	A64	15c slate green	2.00	11.00
57	A64	25c ultra	2.00	11.00
		Nos. 54-57 (4)	8.00	36.75
		Set, never hinged	20.00	

Somalia Nos. 10-16 Overprinted In
Black and Bars over Original Values

g

1922   Wmk. 140

58	A1	2c on 1b brn	5.00	18.00
a.		Pair, one missing "ERITREA"	2,000.	
59	A1	5c on 2b bl grn	5.00	13.50
60	A2	10c on 1a claret	5.00	2.50
61	A2	15c on 2a brn org	5.00	2.50
62	A2	25c on 2½a blue	5.00	2.50
63	A2	50c on 5a yellow	22.50	13.50
a.		"ERITREA" double		1,250.
64	A2	1 l on 10a lilac	22.50	24.00
a.		"ERITREA" double	1,250.	1,250.
b.		Pair, one missing "ERITREA"	2,600.	
		Nos. 58-64 (7)	70.00	76.50
		Set, never hinged	160.00	

See Nos. 81-87.

Propagation of the Faith Issue

Italy Nos. 143-146 Overprinted

1923

65	A68	20c ol grn & brn org	11.50	47.50
66	A68	30c claret & brn org	11.50	47.50
67	A68	50c vio & brn org	6.00	55.00
68	A68	1 l bl & brn org	6.00	75.00
		Nos. 65-68 (4)	35.00	225.00
		Set, never hinged	80.00	

Fascisti Issue

Italy Nos. 159-164
Overprinted in Red
or Black — j

1923   Unwmk.   Perf. 14

69	A69	10c dk green (R)	10.00	17.00
70	A69	30c dk violet (R)	10.00	17.00
71	A69	50c brown carmine	10.00	21.00

Wmk. 140

72	A70	1 l blue	10.00	45.00
73	A70	2 l brown	10.00	55.00
74	A71	5 l black & blue (R)	10.00	80.00
		Nos. 69-74 (6)	60.00	235.00
		Set, never hinged	135.00	

Manzoni Issue

Italy Nos. 165-170 Overprinted in Red

1924   Perf. 14

75	A72	10c brown red & blk	12.00	67.50
76	A72	15c blue grn & blk	12.00	67.50
77	A72	30c black & slate	12.00	67.50
78	A72	50c org brn & blk	12.00	67.50
79	A72	1 l blue & blk	72.50	375.00
80	A72	5 l violet & blk	475.00	2,800.
		Nos. 75-80 (6)	595.50	3,445.
		Set, never hinged	1,500.	

On Nos. 79 and 80 the overprint is placed
vertically at the left side.

Somalia Nos. 10-16 Overprinted type
"g" in Blue or Red

1924
Bars over Original Values

81	A1	2c on 1b brn	17.50	30.00
a.		Pair, one without "ERITREA"	2,000.	
82	A1	5c on 2b bl grn (R)	17.50	19.00
83	A2	10c on 1a rose red	9.50	17.00
84	A2	15c on 2a brn org	9.50	17.00
a.		Pair, one without "ERITREA"	2,000.	
b.		"ERITREA" inverted	1,450.	1,450.
85	A2	25c on 2½a bl (R)	9.50	12.00
a.		Double surcharge	1,050.	
86	A2	50c on 5a yellow	9.50	21.00
87	A2	1 l on 10a lil (R)	9.50	30.00
		Nos. 81-87 (7)	82.50	146.00
		Set, never hinged	200.00	

Stamps of Italy, 1901-08 Overprinted
type "j" in Black

1924

88	A42	1c brown	9.50	10.00
a.		Inverted overprint	300.00	
b.		Vertical pair, one without ovpt.	1,450.	
89	A43	2c orange brown	6.50	8.50
b.		Vertical pair, one without ovpt.	1,450.	
90	A48	5c green	9.50	9.25
		Nos. 88-90 (3)	25.50	27.75
		Set, never hinged	60.00	

Victor Emmanuel Issue

Italy Nos. 175-177
Overprinted — k

1925-26   Unwmk.   Perf. 11

91	A78	60c brown car	1.60	9.25
a.		Perf. 13½	12.00	32.00
92	A78	1 l dark blue	1.60	12.50
a.		Perf. 13½	24,000.	8,750.

		Never hinged	36,000.	

Perf. 13½

93	A78	1.25 l dk blue ('26)	3.25	25.00
a.		Perf. 11	11.00	36.00
		Nos. 91-93 (3)	6.45	46.75
		Set, never hinged	16.00	

Saint Francis of Assisi Issue

Italian Stamps of 1926 Overprinted

1926   Wmk. 140   Perf. 14

94	A79	20c gray green	2.50	13.50
95	A80	40c dark violet	2.50	13.50
96	A81	60c red violet	2.50	24.00

Overprinted in Red

Unwmk.   Perf. 11

97	A82	1.25 l dark blue	2.50	32.50

Perf. 14

98	A83	5 l + 2.50 l ol grn	6.75	67.50
		Nos. 94-98 (5)	16.75	151.00
		Set, never hinged	42.50	

Italian Stamps of 1926 Overprinted
type "f" in Black

1926   Wmk. 140   Perf. 14

99	A46	75c dk red & rose	72.50	18.00
a.		Double overprint	375.00	
100	A46	1.25 l blue & ultra	36.00	18.00
101	A46	2.50 l dk green & org	145.00	55.00
		Nos. 99-101 (3)	253.50	91.00
		Set, never hinged	600.00	

Volta Issue

Type of Italy, 1927, Overprinted — o

1927

102	A84	20c purple	6.75	36.00
103	A84	50c deep orange	8.50	24.00
a.		Double overprint	190.00	
104	A84	1.25 l brt blue	13.50	60.00
		Nos. 102-104 (3)	28.75	120.00
		Set, never hinged	70.00	

Italian Stamps of 1925-28 Overprinted
type "a" in Black

1928-29

105	A86	7½c lt brown ('29)	24.00	72.50
106	A86	50c brt violet	80.00	62.50
		Set, never hinged	240.00	

Italian Stamps of 1927-28 Overprinted
type "f"

1928-29

107	A86	50c brt violet	65.00	55.00
		Never hinged	160.00	

Unwmk.   Perf. 11

107A	A85	1.75 l deep brown	87.50	47.50
		Never hinged	220.00	

Italy No. 192 Overprinted type "o"

1928   Wmk. 140   Perf. 14

108	A85	50c brown & slate	19.00	10.00
		Never hinged	47.50	

Monte Cassino Issue

Types of
1929 Issue
of Italy
Overprinted
in Red or
Blue

1929   Perf. 14

109	A96	20c dk green (R)	6.00	21.00
110	A96	25c red orange (Bl)	6.00	21.00
111	A98	50c + 10c crim (Bl)	6.00	24.00
112	A98	75c + 15c ol brn (R)	6.00	24.00
113	A96	1.25 l + 25c dl vio (R)	13.50	42.50
114	A98	5 l + 1 l saph (R)	13.50	47.50

Overprinted in Red

Unwmk.

115	A100	10 l + 2 l gray brn	13.50	67.50
		Nos. 109-115 (7)	64.50	247.50
		Set, never hinged	160.00	

Royal Wedding Issue

Type of
Italian
Stamps of
1930
Overprinted

1930   Wmk. 140

116	A101	20c yellow green	1.60	5.00
117	A101	50c + 10c dp orange	1.25	8.50
118	A101	1.25 l + 25c rose red	1.25	17.00
		Nos. 116-118 (3)	4.10	30.50
		Set, never hinged	10.00	

Lancer — A5

Scene in
Massaua
A6

2c, 35c, Lancer. 5c, 10c, Postman. 15c,
Lineman. 25c, Askari (infantryman). 2 l, Rail-
road viaduct. 5 l, Asmara Deghe Selam. 10 l,
Camels.

1930   Wmk. 140   Litho.   Perf. 14

119	A5	2c brt bl & blk	4.25	17.00
120	A5	5c dk vio & blk	6.75	2.50
121	A5	10c yel brn & blk	6.75	1.25
122	A5	15c dk grn & blk	6.75	1.70
123	A5	25c gray grn & blk	6.75	1.25
124	A5	35c red brn & blk	13.50	30.00
125	A6	1 l dk bl & blk	6.75	1.25
126	A6	2 l choc & blk	13.50	32.50
127	A6	5 l ol grn & blk	21.00	45.00
128	A6	10 l dl bl & blk	30.00	85.00
		Nos. 119-128 (10)	116.00	217.45
		Set, never hinged	275.00	

Ferrucci Issue
Types of Italian Stamps of 1930
Overprinted type "f" in Red or Blue

1930

129	A102	20c violet (R)	6.00	6.00
130	A103	25c dk green (R)	6.00	6.00
131	A103	50c black (R)	6.00	12.00
132	A103	1.25 l dp blue (R)	6.00	21.00
133	A104	5 l + 2 l dp car (Bl)	12.00	37.50
		Nos. 129-133 (5)	36.00	82.50
		Set, never hinged	90.00	

Virgil Issue
Types of Italian Stamps of 1930
Overprinted in Red or Blue

1930   Photo.

134	A106	15c violet black	1.25	10.00
135	A106	20c orange brown	1.25	4.25
136	A106	25c dark green	1.25	4.25
137	A106	30c lt brown	1.25	4.25
138	A106	50c dull violet	1.25	4.25
139	A106	75c rose red	1.25	8.50
140	A106	1.25 l gray blue	1.25	10.00

Unwmk.   **Engr.**

141	A106	5 l + 1.50 l dk vio	3.75	4.25
142	A106	10 l + 2.50 l ol brn	3.75	72.50
		Nos. 134-142 (9)	16.25	163.00
		Set, never hinged	40.00	

Saint Anthony of Padua Issue
Types of Italian Stamps of 1931
Overprinted type "f" in Blue, Red or Black

1931   Photo.   Wmk. 140

143	A116	20c brown (Bl)	1.60	21.00
144	A116	25c green (R)	1.60	6.75
145	A118	30c gray brn (Bl)	1.60	6.75
146	A118	50c dl violet (Bl)	1.60	6.75
147	A120	1.25 l slate bl (R)	1.60	4.25

Unwmk.   **Engr.**

148	A121	75c black (R)	1.60	37.50
149	A122	5 l + 2.50 l dk brn (Bk)	6.50	75.00
		Nos. 143-149 (7)	16.10	174.75
		Set, never hinged	45.00	

Victor Emmanuel III — A13

1931   Photo.   Wmk. 140

150	A13	7 ½c olive brown	1.25	4.25
151	A13	20c slate bl & car	1.25	.20
152	A13	30c ol grn & brn vio	1.25	.20
153	A13	40c bl & yel grn	1.60	.20
154	A13	50c bis brn & ol	.85	.20
155	A13	75c carmine rose	3.25	.20
156	A13	1.25 l violet & indigo	4.25	4.25
157	A13	2.50 l dull green	4.25	10.00
		Nos. 150-157 (8)	17.95	19.50
		Set, never hinged	45.00	

Camel A14

Temple Ruins — A18

Designs: 2c, 10c, Camel. 5c, 15c, Shark fishery. 25c, Baobab tree. 35c, Pastoral scene. 2 l, African elephant. 5 l, Eritrean man. 10 l, Eritrean woman.

1934   Photo.   Wmk. 140

158	A14	2c deep blue	2.50	5.00
159	A14	5c black	4.25	.40
160	A14	10c brown	4.25	.35
161	A14	15c orange brn	5.00	1.60
162	A14	25c gray green	4.25	.35
163	A14	35c purple	8.50	10.00
164	A18	1 l dk blue gray	.85	.35
165	A14	2 l olive black	28.00	3.25
166	A18	5 l carmine rose	16.00	6.75
167	A18	10 l red orange	22.50	24.00
		Nos. 158-167 (10)	96.10	52.05
		Set, never hinged	230.00	

Abruzzi Issue
Types of 1934 Issue Overprinted in Black or Red

1934

168	A14	10c dull blue (R)	17.50	22.50
169	A14	15c blue	12.00	22.50
170	A14	35c green (R)	6.75	22.50
171	A18	1 l copper red	6.75	22.50
172	A14	2 l rose red	22.50	22.50
173	A18	5 l purple (R)	14.50	36.00
174	A18	10 l olive grn (R)	14.50	47.50
		Nos. 168-174 (7)	94.50	196.00
		Set, never hinged	220.00	

Grant's Gazelle A22

1934   Photo.

175	A22	5c ol grn & brn	4.25	21.00
176	A22	10c yel brn & blk	4.25	21.00
177	A22	20c scar & indigo	4.25	17.00
178	A22	50c dk vio & brn	4.25	17.00
179	A22	60c org brn & ind	4.25	25.00
180	A22	1.25 l dk bl & grn	4.25	42.50
		Nos. 175-180 (6)	25.50	143.50
		Set, never hinged	62.50	

Second Colonial Arts Exhibition, Naples. See Nos. C1-C6.

Between 1981 and 1986 unofficial labels appeared showing such non-Eritrean subjects as the British royal weddings, Queen Mother, Queen's birthday, and the Duke & Duchess of York. These labels are not listed.

In 1978, two sets of stamps were issued for use within liberated areas of Eritrea and to publicize the liberation effort. A May 26 set of 5c, 10c, 80c and 1b commemorated the 8th anniv. of the Eritrean People's Liberation Front (EPLF). An August 1 set of 80c, 1b, 1.50b featured the Future of Eritrea theme. A September 1, 1991 set of 5c, 15c and 20c was issued with a Freedom Fighter design in orange and black almost identical to design A24. Although the 80c from the 1st 1978 issue was available at the Asmara post office in late 1992 and early 1993, there is no evidence that any of these stamps were available at the time of independence. Thus these stamps are more properly considered locals and provisionals.

A23

A24

Freedom Fighter with EPLF Flags
1991, Jan. 16   Typo.   *Perf. 11 rough*

192	A23	5c lt bl, blk & org	30.00	40.00
193	A23	15c pale green, blk & org	30.00	40.00
194	A23	20c pale yel, blk & org	30.00	40.00
195	A23	3b silver, blk & org	25.00	25.00
196	A23	5b gold, blk & org	25.00	25.00

See footnotes following #199.

1993, Feb. 1   Litho.   *Perf. 10*

197	A24	5c lt bl, blk & org	25.00	25.00
198	A24	15c pale grn, blk & org	25.00	25.00
199	A24	20c pale yel, blk & org	25.00	25.00

Nos. 192-199 commemorate 30 years of the war for national liberation.

Nos. 192-199 were issued for local use, and became valid for international mail on Sept. 13, 1993.

Catalogue values for unused stamps in this section, from this point to the end of the section, are for Never Hinged items.

Referendum for Independence A25

Designs: 15c, Placing ballot in box. 60c, Group of arrows pointing right, one pointing left. 75c, Signs indicating "yes" & "no." 1b, Candle burning. 2b, Peace dove, horn over country map.

1993, Apr. 22   Litho.   **Wmk. 373**

Perf. 14x15

200	A25	15c multicolored	1.50	1.50
201	A25	60c multicolored	2.75	2.75
202	A25	75c multicolored	4.00	4.00
203	A25	1b multicolored	7.00	7.00
204	A25	2b multicolored	9.75	9.75
		Nos. 200-204 (5)	25.00	25.00

Natl. Flag — A26

1993   Litho.   *Perf. 11 rough*
Blue Border

205	A26	5c multicolored	3.50	.50
206	A26	20c multicolored	—	—
207	A26	35c multicolored	6.00	2.00
208	A26	50c multicolored	9.00	2.50
209	A26	70c multicolored	5.00	3.50
210	A26	80c multicolored	5.00	4.00

The border of the 40c, No. 215, is similar to that of this issue but it was issued with next set. And the type face of the "0.40" matches that set.

1994   Litho.   *Perf. 11 rough*
Color of Border

211	A26	5c brown	1.50	1.50
212	A26	15c red	1.50	1.50
213	A26	20c gold	15.00	—
214	A26	25c lt blue	1.50	1.50
215	A26	40c blue	15.00	15.00
216	A26	60c yellow	2.00	2.00
217	A26	70c purple	2.25	2.25
218	A26	3b light green	6.00	6.00
219	A26	5b silver	6.00	6.00

Flag & Map — A27

1994, Sept. 2   Litho.   *Perf. 13½x14*
Color of Border

220	A27	5c deep yellow	.45	.40
221	A27	10c yellow green	.50	.45
222	A27	20c salmon	.70	.65
223	A27	25c red	1.25	1.25
224	A27	40c lilac rose	1.40	1.25
225	A27	60c blue green	1.50	1.25
226	A27	70c dark green	1.60	1.50
227	A27	1b yellow	1.60	1.50
228	A27	2b orange	1.75	1.50
229	A27	3b blue violet	1.90	1.75
230	A27	5b red lilac	2.25	2.00
231	A27	10b pale violet	3.75	3.50
		Nos. 220-231 (12)	18.65	17.00

See Nos. 277A-277D.

World Tourism Organization, 20th Anniv. — A29

Perf. 14x13½, 13½x14

1995, Jan. 2   Litho.

232	A29	10c Fishing from boat	1.50	1.50
233	A29	35c Monument, vert.	1.50	1.50
234	A29	85c Winding road	3.00	3.00
235	A29	2b Stone dwelling, vert.	5.00	5.00
		Nos. 232-235 (4)	11.00	11.00

Fish — A30

Designs: 30c, Horned butterflyfish. 55c, Gonochaetodon larvatus. 70c, Shrimp lobster. 1b, Bluestripe snapper.

1995, Apr. 1   *Perf. 14x13½*

236	A30	30c multicolored	.60	.60
237	A30	55c multicolored	.85	.85
238	A30	70c multicolored	1.25	1.25
239	A30	1b multicolored	1.50	1.50
		Nos. 236-239 (4)	4.20	4.20

Independence Day — A31

Designs: 25c, Breaking chains, mountain, buildings, animals. 40c, Raising natl. flag, vert. 70c, Three men, holding natl. flag, sword, vert. 3b, Natl. flag, fireworks, vert.

Perf. 14x13½, 13½x14

1995, May 23   Litho.

240	A31	25c multicolored	.40	.40
241	A31	40c multicolored	.45	.45
242	A31	70c multicolored	.70	.70
243	A31	3b multicolored	1.40	1.40
		Nos. 240-243 (4)	2.95	2.95

Future Development Plan — A32

1995, Aug. 28   Litho.   *Perf. 13*

244	A32	60c Building bridge	.60	.60
245	A32	80c Trees	.75	.75
246	A32	90c Rural village	.90	.90
247	A32	1b Camels	1.00	1.00
		Nos. 244-247 (4)	3.25	3.25

A33

A34

1995, Oct. 23 *Perf. 13½x14*
248 A33 40c shown .30 .30
249 A33 60c Tree, emblem .40 .40
250 A33 70c Dove, "50," emblem .50 .50
251 A33 2b like No. 248 2.25 2.25
Nos. 248-251 (4) 3.45 3.45

UN, 50th anniv.

1995, Oct. 2 *Perf. 13½x14, 14x13½*
COMESA, Committee for Economic Growth and Development in Southern Africa: 40c, Map of African member countries. 50c, Tree with country names on branches. 60c, Emblem. 3b, Emblem surrounded by country flags, horiz.
252 A34 40c multicolored .30 .30
253 A34 50c multicolored .50 .50
254 A34 60c multicolored .60 .60
255 A34 3b multicolored 2.25 2.25
Nos. 252-255 (4) 3.65 3.65

FAO, 50th
Anniv. — A35

5c, Food bowl with world map on it, spoon. 25c, Men with tractor. 80c, Mother bird feeding chicks. 3b, Vegetables in horn of plenty.

1995, Dec. 18 *Litho.* *Perf. 13x14*
256 A35 5c multicolored .40 .40
257 A35 25c multicolored .40 .40
258 A35 80c multicolored .80 .80
259 A35 3b multicolored 2.50 2.50
Nos. 256-259 (4) 4.10 4.10

Endangered Fauna — A36

No. 260: a, Green monkey. b, Aardwolf. c, Dugong. d, Maned rat.
Beisa oryx: No. 261: a, With young. b, One facing left. c, Two with heads together. d, One facing right.
White-eyed gull: No. 262: a, Preening. b, In flight. c, Two standing. d, One facing right.

1996, July 15 *Litho.* *Perf. 14*
260-262 A36 3b Set of 3 strips 26.00 26.00

Nos. 260-262 were each issued in sheets of 12 stamps, containing three strips of four stamps, #a.-d. No. 261 for World Wildlife Fund.

Martyrs
Day — A37

1996, June 17 *Litho.* *Perf. 13½x14*
263 A37 40c People, flag .40 .40
264 A37 60c At grave .40 .40
265 A37 70c Mother, child .80 .80
266 A37 80c Planting crops 1.00 1.00
Nos. 263-266 (4) 2.60 2.60

1996
Summer
Olympic
Games,
Atlanta
A38

No. 267, Cycling. No. 268, Basketball, vert. No. 269, Volleyball, vert. No. 270, Soccer.
No. 271, vert: a, Volleyball. b, Laurel wreath. c, Basketball. d, Torch. e, Cycling, yellow shirt. f, Torch, diff. g, Cycling, green shirt. h, Gold medal. i, Soccer.
Each 10b: #272, Soccer, vert. #273, Cycling, vert.

1996, Nov. 20 *Litho.* *Perf. 14*
267-270 A38 3b Set of 4 7.50 7.50
271 A38 2b Sheet of 9, #a.-i. 11.00 11.00
Souvenir Sheets
272-273 A38 Set of 2 11.00 11.00

UNICEF,
50th Anniv.
A39

UNICEF emblem and: 40c, Mother with child. 55c, Nurse helping child. 60c, Weighing baby. 95c, Boy with one leg walking with crutch.

1996, Dec. 9 *Litho.* *Perf. 14x13½*
274 A39 40c multicolored .45 .45
275 A39 55c multicolored .45 .45
276 A39 60c multicolored 1.00 1.00
277 A39 95c multicolored 1.00 1.00
Nos. 274-277 (4) 2.90 2.90

Flag and Map Type of 1994 Redrawn With Islands Added on Map at Lower Right

1996, Dec. 25 *Litho.* *Perf. 13½x14*
Color of Border
277A A27 20c salmon — —
277B A27 40c lilac rose — —
277C A27 60c blue green — —
277D A27 3b blue violet — —

Revival of
Eritrea
Railway
A40

Designs: 40c, Repairing track. 55c, Steam train arriving at station. 60c, Train shuttle transporting people. 95c, Train tunnel.

1997, Jan. 10
278 A40 40c multicolored .50 .50
279 A40 55c multicolored .50 .50
280 A40 60c multicolored .50 .50
281 A40 95c multicolored 1.50 1.50
Nos. 278-281 (4) 3.00 3.00

National
Service
A41

40c, Service members, speaker's platform, flags, vert. 55c, People looking over mountainside, vert. 60c, People digging ditches. 95c, Man standing on mountain top, overlooking valley, lake.

1996, Dec. 28 *Perf. 13½x14, 14x13½*
282 A41 40c multicolored .75 .75
283 A41 55c multicolored .75 .75
284 A41 60c multicolored 1.25 1.25
285 A41 95c multicolored 2.00 2.00
Nos. 282-285 (4) 4.75 4.75

Butterflies
and
Moths
A42

1b, Pieris napi. 2b, Heliconius melpomerie. 4b, Ornithoptera goliath. 8b, Heliconius astraea.
No. 290, vert, each 3b: a, Psaphis eusehemoides. b, Papilio brookiana. c, Parnassius charitonius. d, Morpho cypris. e, Dariaus plexippus. f, Precis octavia. g, Teinopalpus imperialis. h, Samia gloreri. i, Automeris nyctimene.
No. 291, each 3b: a, Papilio polymnestar. b, Ornithoptera paradiseo. c, Graphium marcellus. d, Panaxia quadripunctaria. e, Cardui japonica. f, Papilio childrence. g, Philosamea cynthis. h, Actias luna. i, Heticopis acit.
Each 10b: No. 292, Papilio glaucus. No. 293, Parnassius phoebus.

1997, June 16 *Litho.* *Perf. 14*
286-289 A42 Set of 4 12.00 12.00
Sheets of 9
290-291 A42 3b Set of 2
Sheets, #a.-i. 30.00 30.00
Souvenir Sheets
292-293 A42 10b Set of 2
Sheets 15.00 15.00

Environmental Protection — A43

1997, Aug. 15 *Litho.* *Perf. 14x13½*
294 A43 60c Irrigation .90 .90
295 A43 90c Reforestation .90 .90
296 A43 95c Preventing erosion 2.00 2.00
Nos. 294-296 (3) 3.80 3.80

Marine
Life
A44

No. 297, each 3n: a, Sergeant major, white tipped reef shark. b, Hawksbill turtle, devil ray (e). c, Surgeonfish. d, Red sea houndfish, humpback whale (a, g). e, Devil ray (b, f, h). f, Devil ray (e, c), two-banded clownfish. g, Long-nosed butterflyfish. h, Red sea houndfish (g), yellow sweetlips (i). i, White moray eel.
No. 298, each 3n: a, Masked butterflyfish. b, Suckerfish (a), whale shark (a). c, Sunrise dottyback, bluefin trevally. d, Moon wrasse (a), purple moon angel (a), two-banded anemonefish. e, Lionfish (b, f). f, White tipped shark, sand diver fish. g, Golden jacks (d), lunar tailed grouper. h, Batfish (e, i). i, Black triggerfish.
Each 10n: No. 299, Powder-blue surgeonfish. No. 300, Twin-spot wrasse.

1997, Dec. 29 *Litho.* *Perf. 14*
Sheets of 9
297-298 A44 Set of 2 Sheets,
#a.-i. 20.00 20.00
Souvenir Sheets
299-300 A44 Set of 2 Sheets 12.50 12.50

A45

A46

Natl. Constitution: 10c, Speaker, crowd seated beneath tree. 40c, Dove, scales of justice. 85c, Hands holding constitution.

1997, Oct. 24 *Litho.* *Perf. 13½x14*
301-303 A45 Set of 3 3.50 3.50

1998, Mar. 16 *Litho.* *Perf. 14*
Birds — No. 304, each 3n: a, African darter (b, d, e). b, White-headed vulture (e). c, Egyptian vulture (f). d, Yellow-billed hornbill (g). e, Helmeted guineafowl (d, f). f, Secretary bird (d, e, i). g, Martial eagle (h). h, Bateleur eagle (i). i, Red-billed queleas.
No. 305, each 3n: a, Black-headed weaver. b, Abyssinian roller (c, f). c, Abyssinian ground hornbill (b, e, f). d, Lichtenstein's sandgrouse. e, Erckel's francolin (d, g, h). f, Arabian bustard (e, i). g, Chestnut-backed finch-lark. h, Desert lark. i, Bifasciated lark.
Each 10n: #306, Peregrine falcon. #307, Hoopoe.

Sheets of 9
304-305 A46 Set of 2 Sheets,
#a.-i. 25.00 25.00
Souvenir Sheets
306-307 A46 Set of 2 Sheets 12.00 12.00

Dwellings — A47

Traditional Hair
Styles — A48

1998, July 1 *Litho.* *Perf. 13½x14*
308 A47 50c Highlanders 1.50 1.50
309 A47 60c Lowlanders 1.50 1.50
310 A47 85c Danakils (Afars) 1.50 1.50
Nos. 308-310 (3) 4.50 4.50

1998, Nov. 23 *Litho.* *Perf. 13½x14*
311 A48 10c Cunama .30 .30
312 A48 50c Tignnys .60 .60
313 A48 85c Bllen 1.00 1.00
314 A48 95c Tigre 1.25 1.25
Nos. 311-314 (4) 3.15 3.15

Dated 1997.

A49

A50

Traditional Musical Instruments: 15c, Chirawata. 60c, Imbilta, malaket, shambeko. 75c, Kobero. 85c, K'rar.

1998, Dec. 28   Litho.   Perf. 13½x14

315	A49	15c multicolored	.35	.35
316	A49	60c multicolored	.60	.60
317	A49	75c multicolored	.80	.80
318	A49	1n multicolored	1.00	1.00
		Nos. 315-318 (4)	2.75	2.75

1999, May 25   Litho.   Perf. 13¼x14

319	A50	60c green & multi	.60	.60
320	A50	1n red & multi	1.00	1.00
321	A50	3n blue & multi	4.00	4.00
		Nos. 319-321 (3)	5.60	5.60

Independence, 8th Anniv.

1997 Introduction of Nakfa Currency — A51

Bank notes: 10c, 1 Nakfa. 60c, 5 Nakfa. 80c, 10 Nakfa. 1n, 20 Nakfa. 2n, 50 Nakfa. 3n, 100 Nakfa.

1999, Nov. 8   Litho.   Perf. 13¼

322	A51	10c multicolored	.45	.45
323	A51	60c multicolored	.60	.60
324	A51	80c multicolored	.75	.75
325	A51	1n multicolored	1.00	1.00
326	A51	2n multicolored	2.00	2.00
327	A51	3n multicolored	3.50	3.50
		Nos. 322-327 (6)	8.30	8.30

Natl. Union of Eritrean Women, 20th Anniv. A52

Designs: 5c, Woman and child, vert. 10c, Three women. 25c, Women and flag. 1n, Woman with binoculars.

Perf. 13¼x14, 14x13¼

1999, Nov. 26

328	A52	5c multicolored	.35	.35
329	A52	10c multicolored	.35	.35
330	A52	25c multicolored	.50	.50
331	A52	1n multicolored	.75	.75
		Nos. 328-331 (4)	1.95	1.95

A53

Marine Life A54

No. 332, each 3n: a, Coachwhip ray. b, Sulfur damselfish. c, "Gray moray." d, Sabre squirrelfish. e, Rusty parrotfish. f, "Striped eel catfish."

No. 333, each 3n: a, Spangled emperor. b, Devil scorpionfish. c, Crown squirrelfish. d, Vanikoro sweeper. e, Sergeant major. f, Giant manta.

No. 334, each 3n: a, Chilomycterus spilostylus. b, Dascyllus marginatus. c, Balistapus undulatus. d, Pomacanthus semicirculatus. e, Rhinecanthus assasi. f, Millepora.

No. 335, each 3n: a, Epinephalus fasciata. b, Pygoplites diacanthus. c, Cephalopholis miniata. d, Centropyge eibli. e, Ostracion cubicus. f, Heniochus acuminatus.

Each 10n: No. 336, Centropyge flavissimus. No. 337, Larabicus quadrilineatus. No. 338, Anthias squamipinnis. 15n, Pomacanthus maculosus.

2000, Apr. 17   Litho.   Perf. 14

Sheets of 6, #a.-f.

| 332-333 | A53 | Set of 2 | 13.50 | 13.50 |
| 334-335 | A54 | Set of 2 | 13.50 | 13.50 |

Souvenir Sheets

| 336-338 | A54 | Set of 3 | 15.00 | 15.00 |
| 339 | A54 | 15n multi | 6.00 | 6.00 |

Illustrations on Nos. 332c and 332f were switched.

A55

Flag and: 5c, Man with sword. 10c, Ship Denden Assab. 25c, Independence Day festivities. 60c, Soldiers and barracks. 1n, Finger, heart and map. 2n, People under tree. 3n, Ballot box. 5n, Eritrean seal, military plane, tank, ship. 7n, Seal. 10n, Ten-nakfa note.

Perf. 13¾x13¼

2000, Mar. 17   Litho.

Denominations in Sans-Serif Type

| 340-349 | A55 | Set of 10 | 16.00 | 16.00 |

See Nos. 363A-363F.

Worldwide Fund for Nature (WWF) — A56

Proteles cristatus: a, Laying down. b, Pair in den. c, Walking. d, Close-up.
Illustration reduced.

2001, Oct. 1   Litho.   Perf. 14

| 350 | A56 | 3n Block or strip of 4, #a-d | 4.50 | 4.50 |

Wild Animals — A57

No. 351, 3n: a, Salt's dik-dik. b, Klipspringer. c, Greater kudu. d, Soemmering's gazelle. e, Dorcas gazelle. f, Somali wild ass.

No. 352, 3n: a, Aardvark. b, Black-backed jackal. c, Striped hyena. d, Spotted hyena. e, East African leopard. f, African elephant.

2001, Oct. 29

Sheets of 6, #a-f

| 351-352 | A57 | Set of 2 | 10.00 | 10.00 |

Struggle for Independence, 10th Anniv. — A58

Designs: 20c, Women, flag, jewelry. 60c, Doves, stylized flag, vert. 1n, Bees, honeycomb, flag, vert. 3n, Men with sticks, vert.

Perf. 13x13¼, 13¼x13

2001, May 23   Litho.

| 353-356 | A58 | Set of 4 | 3.00 | 3.00 |

Liberation of Nakfa, 25th Anniv. A59

Designs: 50c, Denden. 1n, Town of Nakfa, 1977 (77x27mm). 3n, First Organizational Congress of the Eritrean People's Liberation Front (77x27mm).

2002, Mar. 23   Litho.   Perf. 14x13¼

| 357-359 | A59 | Set of 3 | 1.75 | 1.75 |

Martyr's Day — A60

Designs: 1n, People and map. 2n, Hand, map of Badma area, and flag. 3n, Map and ship. 5n, Dove, map and dead man (49x29mm, triangular).

Perf. 14x13¼, 13½ (5n)

2002, June 20

| 360-363 | A60 | Set of 4 | 4.50 | 4.50 |

Type of 2000 Redrawn

Flag and: 30c, People under tree. 45c, Man with sword. 50c, Independence Day festivities. 60c, Soldiers and barracks. 75c, Ship Denden Assab. 3n, Ballot box.

2002, Oct. 21   Litho.   Perf. 13¼x14¼

Denominations in Serifed Type

363A	A55	30c multi	—	—
363B	A55	45c multi	—	—
363C	A55	50c multi	—	—
363D	A55	60c multi	—	—
363E	A55	75c multi	—	—
363F	A55	3n multi	—	—

Denominations on Nos. 340-349 are in sans-serif type.

Dr. Fred C. Hollows (1929-93), Ophthalmologist A61

Designs: 50c, Portrait. 1n, Hollows wearing ophthalmological equipment. 2n, Hollows with man.

2003, Feb. 10   Perf. 13¼x14

| 364-366 | A61 | Set of 3 | 2.00 | 2.00 |

Eritrea — People's Republic of China Diplomatic Relations, 10th Anniv. A62

2003, May 24   Perf. 12

| 367 | A62 | 4.50n multi | 2.50 | 2.50 |

Eritrean postal authorities have declared "illegal" the following items:

Sheetlet of nine 5n stamps depicting Trains;

Sheetlets of nine 3n stamps depicting Marilyn Monroe (two different), Dogs, The Beatles "Yellow Submarine," September 11 firefighters, Brigitte Bardot, Grace Kelly, Sophia Loren, Golf etiquette, Sexy actresses, Sexy models, Boris Vallejo nudes, Dorian Cleavenger, Michael Möbius, Olivia, Ricky Carralero, Concorde;

Sheetlets of six stamps with various denominations depicting Lighthouses (with Rotary emblem) (two different), Hopper paintings (two different), Vettriano paintings (two different), Marilyn Monroe (two different), Elvgren pin-ups (two different), Teddy bears (two different);

Sheetlets of six 3n stamps depicting Van Gogh paintings, Paintings of nudes;

Sheetlets of five 3n stamps depicting Corot paintings, Pisarro paintings, Renoir paintings, Elvis Presley, Marilyn Monroe;

Sheetlets of four stamps with various denominations depicting Pandas (with Scouting emblem), Crocodiles (with Scouting emblem), Buffalos (with Rotary emblem), Elephants (with Rotary emblem), Monkeys (with Scouting emblem), Lizards (with Scouting emblem), Snakes (with Scouting Emblem), Turtles (with Rotary emblem), Wild cats (with Scouting emblem), Birds of prey (with Rotary emblem), Fowl (with Rotary emblem), Parrots (with Scouting emblem), Penguins (with Rotary emblem), Fish (with Rotary emblem), Marine life (with Scouting emblem), Mushrooms (with Rotary emblem), Butterflies (with Scouting emblem), Bees (with Scouting emblem), Spiders (with Scouting emblem);

Sheetlets of four 3n stamps depicting Dinosaurs (with Scouting emblem), Dinosaurs (with Rotary emblem) Elephants (with Scouting emblem), Elephants (with Rotary emblem), Horses (with Scouting emblem), Horses (with Rotary emblem), Birds (with Scouting emblem), Birds (with Rotary emblem), Penguins (with Scouting emblem), Penguins (with Rotary emblem), Orchids (with Scouting emblem), Orchids (with Rotary emblem), Butterflies (with Scouting emblem), Butterflies (with Rotary emblem), Cars (with Scouting emblem), Cars (with Rotary emblem), Motorcycles (with Scouting emblem), Motorcycles (with Rotary emblem), Trains (with Scouting emblem), Trains (with Rotary emblem);

Sheetlets of three 5n stamps depicting Dinosaurs (with Rotary emblem) (two different), Pandas;

Strips of three 5n stamps depicting Steam trains (four different);

Souvenir sheet with one 8n stamp depicting Steam Trains (with Rotary emblem) (two different), Dinosaurs (with Rotary emblem), Pandas (with Scouting emblem), Elephants (with Scouting emblem), Tigers (with Scouting emblem), Birds of prey (with Scouting emblem);

Souvenir sheets with one 5n stamp depicting Marilyn Monroe (six different), Lighthouses (with Rotary emblem) (four different), Teddy bears (four different), Hopper paintings (two different), Vettriano paintings (two different).

Eritrean Railway — A63

Independence Celebrations A63a

Massawa A63b

2003 **Litho.** **Perf. 14x13¼**
Denomination Color

368	A63	5c Prussian blue	.20	.20
369	A63	10c greenish blk	.20	.20
370	A63	15c lilac	.20	.20
371	A63	35c violet	.20	.20
372	A63	50c orange	.20	.20
373	A63	90c olive green	.25	.25
374	A63	1n red	.25	.25
375	A63	2n blue violet	.55	.55
376	A63	10n red	2.75	2.75
376A	A63a	50n white	12.00	12.00
376B	A63b	75n white	18.00	18.00
376C	A63	100n white	24.00	24.00
		Nos. 368-376C (12)	58.80	58.80

Issued: 50n, 75n, 100n, 8/29.

Liberation of Massawa, 14th Anniv. A64

Designs: 40c, Tanks as fountains. 50c, Boat with soldiers.
No. 379: a, 3n, Crashed airplane, people, soldiers in shallow water. b, 3n, Tank, soldier, flag, boat. c, 4n, People, buildings at shore.

2004

377-378	A64	Set of 2	1.00	1.00

Miniature Sheet

379	A64	Sheet of 3, #a-c	4.00	4.00

Man and Camels — A65

Man and Cattle A66

Highland Woman, Child and Camel — A67

2004, July 12 **Litho.** **Perf. 12**
Frame Color

380	A65	20c violet blue	.20	.20
381	A65	25c red violet	.20	.20
382	A65	40c brown	.25	.25
383	A66	50c red	.25	.25
384	A66	55c green	.25	.25
385	A66	60c light blue	.25	.25
386	A67	80c olive green	.50	.50
387	A67	1n orange	.50	.50
388	A67	4.50n blue	1.25	1.25
		Nos. 380-388 (9)	3.65	3.65

A68

A69

Monuments and Statues — A70

Perf. 13¼x14, 14x13¼
2006, Jan. 5 **Litho.**

389	A68	1.50n multi	.20	.20
390	A69	6n multi	.80	.80
391	A70	25n multi	3.50	3.50
		Nos. 389-391 (3)	4.50	4.50

China - Africa Cooperation Forum, Beijing — A71

2006, Nov. 3 **Litho.** **Perf. 12**

392	A71	7n multi	.95	.95

African Soccer Confederation, 50th Anniv. — A72

Anniversary emblem and: 3n, Eritrean soccer players and flags. 5n, Soccer field. 10n, Soccer players in action.

2007, May 29 **Litho.** **Perf. 13x13¼**

393-395	A72	Set of 3	2.40	2.40

Soldiers Carrying Flag — A73

2008, Dec. 31 **Litho.** **Perf. 14x13¼**
Denomination Color

396	A73	15c dark blue	.20	.20
397	A73	35c green	.20	.20
398	A73	50c orange	.20	.20
399	A73	70c red	.20	.20
400	A73	75c blue	.20	.20
401	A73	90c brown	.20	.20
402	A73	1.50n red violet	.20	.20
403	A73	2n indigo	.25	.25
404	A73	3n org yellow	.40	.40
405	A73	5n gray	.65	.65
406	A73	10n yel green	1.25	1.25
		Nos. 396-406 (11)	3.95	3.95

SEMI-POSTAL STAMPS

Many issues of Italy and Italian Colonies include one or more semipostal denominations. To avoid splitting sets, these issues are generally listed as regular postage, airmail, etc., unless all values carry a surtax.

Italy Nos. B1-B3 Overprinted type "f"

1915-16 **Wmk. 140** **Perf. 14**

B1	SP1	10c + 5c rose	4.25	17.00
a.		"EPITREA"	32.50	45.00
b.		Inverted overprint	675.00	675.00
B2	SP2	15c + 5c slate	24.00	30.00
B3	SP2	20c + 5c orange	5.00	37.50
a.		"EPITREA"	37.50	60.00
b.		Inverted overprint	675.00	675.00
c.		Pair, one without opvt.		3,600.
		Nos. B1-B3 (3)	33.25	84.50
		Set, never hinged	80.00	

No. B2 Surcharged

1916

B4	SP2	20c on 15c+5c slate	24.00	37.50
		Never hinged	57.50	
a.		"EPITREA"	67.50	110.00
b.		Pair, one without overprint		1,750.
		Never hinged		2,200.

Counterfeits exist of the minor varieties of Nos. B1, B3-B4.

Holy Year Issue
Italy Nos. B20-B25 Overprinted in Black or Red

1925 **Perf. 12**

B5	SP4	20c + 10c dk grn & brn	3.25	22.50
B6	SP4	30c + 15c dk brn & brn	3.25	25.00
a.		Double overprint		
B7	SP4	50c + 25c vio & brn	3.25	22.50
B8	SP4	60c + 30c dp rose & brn	3.25	29.00
a.		Inverted overprint		
B9	SP8	1 l + 50c dp bl & vio (R)	3.25	37.50
B10	SP8	5 l + 2.50 l org brn & vio (R)	3.25	55.00
		Nos. B5-B10 (6)	19.50	191.50
		Set, never hinged	47.50	

Colonial Institute Issue

"Peace" Substituting Spade for Sword — SP1

1926 **Typo.** **Perf. 14**

B11	SP1	5c + 5c brown	1.00	10.00
B12	SP1	10c + 5c olive grn	1.00	10.00
B13	SP1	20c + 5c blue grn	1.00	10.00
B14	SP1	40c + 5c brown red	1.00	10.00
B15	SP1	60c + 5c orange	1.00	10.00
B16	SP1	1 l + 5c blue	1.00	21.00
		Nos. B11-B16 (6)	6.00	71.00
		Set, never hinged	15.00	

The surtax of 5c on each stamp was for the Italian Colonial Institute.

Types of Italian Semi-Postal Stamps of 1926 Overprinted type "k"

1927 **Unwmk.** **Perf. 11½**

B17	SP10	40c + 20c dk brn & blk	2.50	37.50
B18	SP10	60c + 30c brn red & ol brn	2.50	37.50
B19	SP10	1.25 l + 60c dp bl & blk	2.50	60.00
B20	SP10	5 l + 2.50 l dk grn & blk	4.25	85.00
		Nos. B17-B20 (4)	11.75	220.00
		Set, never hinged	29.00	

The surtax on these stamps was for the charitable work of the Voluntary Militia for Italian National Defense.

Fascism and Victory SP2

Agriculture SP3

1928 **Wmk. 140** **Typo.** **Perf. 14**

B21	SP2	20c + 5c blue grn	3.25	13.50
B22	SP2	30c + 5c red	3.25	13.50
B23	SP2	50c + 10c purple	3.25	22.50
B24	SP2	1.25 l + 20c dk blue	4.25	30.00
		Nos. B21-B24 (4)	14.00	79.50
		Set, never hinged	35.00	

The surtax was for the Society Africana d'Italia, whose 46th anniv. was commemorated by the issue.

Types of Italian Semi-Postal Stamps of 1928 Overprinted type "f"

1929 **Unwmk.** **Perf. 11**

B25	SP10	30c + 10c red & blk	4.25	22.50
B26	SP10	50c + 20c vio & blk	4.25	27.50
B27	SP10	1.25 l + 50c brn & bl	5.00	45.00
B28	SP10	5 l + 2 l olive grn & blk	5.00	85.00
		Nos. B25-B28 (4)	18.50	180.00
		Set, never hinged	45.00	

Surtax for the charitable work of the Voluntary Militia for Italian Natl. Defense.

Types of Italian Semi-Postal Stamps of 1929 Overprinted type "f" in Black or Red

1930 **Perf. 14**

B29	SP10	30c + 10c dk grn & bl (Bk)	25.00	45.00
B30	SP10	50c + 10c dk grn & vio	25.00	62.50
B31	SP10	1.25 l + 30c ol brn & red brn	25.00	75.00

B32	SP10	5 l + 1.50 l ind & grn	85.00	200.00
		Nos. B29-B32 (4)	160.00	382.50
		Set, never hinged	400.00	

Surtax for the charitable work of the Voluntary Militia for Italian Natl. Defense.

1930 Photo. Wmk. 140

B33	SP3	50c + 20c ol brn	4.25	22.50
B34	SP3	1.25 l + 20c dp bl	4.25	22.50
B35	SP3	1.75 l + 20c green	4.25	27.50
B36	SP3	2.55 l + 50c purple	8.00	42.50
B37	SP3	5 l + 1 l dp car	8.50	75.00
		Nos. B33-B37 (5)	29.25	190.00
		Set, never hinged	70.00	

Italian Colonial Agricultural Institute, 25th anniv. The surtax aided that institution.

AIR POST STAMPS

Desert Scene AP1

Design: 80c, 1 l, 2 l, Plane and globe.

Wmk. Crowns (140)

1934 Photo. Perf. 14

C1	AP1	25c sl bl & org red	4.25	21.00
C2	AP1	50c grn & indigo	4.25	17.00
C3	AP1	75c brn & org red	4.25	17.00
C4	AP1	80c org brn & ol grn	4.25	21.00
C5	AP1	1 l scar & ol grn	4.25	25.00
C6	AP1	2 l dk bl & brn	4.25	42.50
		Nos. C1-C6 (6)	25.50	143.50
		Set, never hinged	62.50	

Second Colonial Arts Exhibition, Naples.

Plowing AP3

Plane and Cacti AP6

Designs: 25c, 1.50 l, Plowing. 50c, 2 l, Plane over mountain pass. 60c, 5 l, Plane and trees. 75c, 10 l, Plane and cacti. 1 l, 3 l, Bridge.

1936 Photo.

C7	AP3	25c deep green	3.25	4.25
C8	AP3	50c dark brown	2.50	.35
C9	AP3	60c brown orange	4.25	15.00
C10	AP6	75c orange brown	3.25	1.60
C11	AP3	1 l deep blue	1.60	.35
C12	AP3	1.50 l purple	4.25	.85
C13	AP3	2 l gray blue	4.25	3.25
C14	AP3	3 l copper red	25.00	27.50
C15	AP3	5 l green	18.50	6.75
C16	AP6	10 l rose red	42.50	27.50
		Nos. C7-C16 (10)	109.35	87.40
		Set, never hinged	275.00	

AIR POST SEMI-POSTAL STAMPS

King Victor Emmanuel III — SPAP1

1934 Wmk. 140 Photo. Perf. 14

CB1	SPAP1	25c + 10c	6.75	25.00
CB2	SPAP1	50c + 10c	6.75	25.00
CB3	SPAP1	75c + 15c	6.75	25.00
CB4	SPAP1	80c + 15c	6.75	25.00
CB5	SPAP1	1 l + 20c	6.75	25.00
CB6	SPAP1	2 l + 20c	6.75	25.00
CB7	SPAP1	3 l + 25c	22.50	125.00
CB8	SPAP1	5 l + 25c	22.50	125.00
CB9	SPAP1	10 l + 30c	22.50	125.00
CB10	SPAP1	25 l + 2 l	22.50	125.00
		Nos. CB1-CB10 (10)	130.50	650.00
		Set, never hinged	300.00	

65th birthday of King Victor Emmanuel III and the nonstop flight from Rome to Mogadiscio. Used values are for stamps canceled to order.

AIR POST SEMI-POSTAL OFFICIAL STAMP

Type of Air Post Semi-Postal Stamps, 1934, Overprinted Crown and "SERVIZIO DI STATO" in Black

1934 Wmk. 140 Perf. 14

CBO1	SPAP1	25 l + 2 l cop red	2,800.	
		Never hinged	5,500.	

SPECIAL DELIVERY STAMPS

Special Delivery Stamps of Italy, Overprinted type "a"

1907 Wmk. 140 Perf. 14

E1	SD1	25c rose red	24.00	20.00
		Never hinged	60.00	
a.		Double overprint		

1909

E2	SD2	30c blue & rose	145.00	240.00
		Never hinged	375.00	

1920

E3	SD1	50c dull red	4.00	24.00
		Never hinged	10.00	

"Italia" SD1

1924 Engr. Unwmk.

E4	SD1	60c dk red & brn	6.50	25.00
a.		Perf. 13½	15.00	42.50
E5	SD1	2 l dk blue & red	17.50	30.00
		Set, never hinged	60.00	

For surcharges see Nos. E6-E8.

Nos. E4 and E5 Surcharged in Dark Blue or Red:

v

w

1926

E6	SD1	70c on 60c (Bl)	6.50	17.00
E7	SD1	2.50 l on 2 l (R)	17.50	30.00
		Set, never hinged	60.00	

Type of 1924 Surcharged in Blue or Black:

1927-35 Perf. 11

E8	SD1	1.25 l on 60c dk red & brn (Bl)	14.50	3.25
		Never hinged	36.00	
a.		Perf. 14 (Bl) ('35)	100.00	21.00
		Never hinged	240.00	
b.		Perf. 11 (Bk) ('35)	10,000.	1,050.
		Never hinged	15,000.	
c.		Perf. 14 (Bk) ('35)	325.00	55.00
		Never hinged	800.00	

AUTHORIZED DELIVERY STAMP

Authorized Delivery Stamp of Italy, No. EY2, Overprinted Type "f" in Black

1939-41 Wmk. 140 Perf. 14

EY1	AD2	10c dk brown ('41)	.80	
		Never hinged	1.90	
a.		10c reddish brown	19.00	45.00
		Never hinged	47.50	

On No. EY1a, which was used in Italian East Africa, the overprint hits the figures "10." On No. EY1, which was sold in Rome, the overprint falls above the 10's.

POSTAGE DUE STAMPS

Postage Due Stamps of Italy Overprinted type "a" at Top

1903 Wmk. 140 Perf. 14

J1	D3	5c buff & mag	24.00	42.50
a.		Double overprint	600.00	
J2	D3	10c buff & mag	17.50	42.50
J3	D3	20c buff & mag	17.50	30.00
J4	D3	30c buff & mag	25.00	32.50
J5	D3	40c buff & mag	80.00	67.50
J6	D3	50c buff & mag	87.50	67.50
J7	D3	60c buff & mag	25.00	67.50
J8	D3	1 l blue & mag	17.50	37.50
J9	D3	2 l blue & mag	200.00	170.00
J10	D3	5 l blue & mag	325.00	300.00
J11	D3	10 l blue & mag	3,600.	800.00
		Never hinged	7,200.	
		Set, #J1-J10, never hinged	1,600.	

Same with Overprint at Bottom

1920-22

J1b	D3	5c buff & magenta	4.75	15.00
c.		Numeral and ovpt. inverted	600.00	600.00
J2a	D3	10c buff & magenta	8.00	15.00
J3a	D3	20c buff & magenta	950.00	450.00
J4a	D3	30c buff & magenta	65.00	45.00
J5a	D3	40c buff & magenta	52.50	50.00
J6a	D3	50c buff & magenta	28.00	45.00
J7a	D3	60c buff & magenta	28.00	45.00
J8a	D3	1 l blue & magenta	47.50	45.00
J9a	D3	2 l blue & magenta	1,900.	1,300.
J10a	D3	5 l blue & magenta	475.00	375.00
J11a	D3	10 l blue & magenta	57.50	100.00
		Set, never hinged	7,200.	

1903 Wmk. 140

J12	D4	50 l yellow	775.00	300.00
J13	D4	100 l blue	475.00	170.00
		Set, never hinged	2,600.	

1927

J14	D3	60c buff & brown	150.00	220.00
		Never hinged	300.00	

Postage Due Stamps of Italy, 1934, Overprinted type "j" in Black

1934

J15	D6	5c brown	.85	12.50
J16	D6	10c blue	.85	2.50
J17	D6	20c rose red	4.00	4.25
a.		Inverted overprint		
J18	D6	25c green	4.00	5.00
J19	D6	30c red orange	4.00	12.50
J20	D6	40c black brown	4.00	12.50
J21	D6	50c violet	4.00	1.70
J22	D6	60c black	8.00	21.00
J23	D7	1 l red orange	4.00	2.50
a.		Inverted overprint	550.00	
J24	D7	2 l green	16.00	45.00
J25	D7	5 l violet	28.00	55.00
J26	D7	10 l blue	32.50	60.00
J27	D7	20 l carmine rose	40.00	67.50
a.		Inverted overprint	550.00	
		Nos. J15-J27 (13)	150.20	301.95
		Set, never hinged	360.00	

PARCEL POST STAMPS

These stamps were used by affixing them to the way bill so that one half remained on it following the parcel, the other half staying on the receipt given the sender. Most used halves are right halves. Complete stamps were obtainable canceled, probably to order. Both unused and used values are for complete stamps.

Parcel Post Stamps of Italy, 1914-17, Overprinted type "j" in Black on Each Half

1916 Wmk. 140 Perf. 13½

Q1	PP2	5c brown	145.00	225.00
Q2	PP2	10c deep blue	2,600.	4,250.
		Never hinged	5,250.	
Q3	PP2	25c red	300.00	350.00
Q4	PP2	50c orange	75.00	225.00
Q5	PP2	1 l violet	145.00	225.00
Q6	PP2	2 l green	110.00	225.00
Q7	PP2	3 l bister	875.00	625.00
Q8	PP2	4 l slate	875.00	625.00
		Set #Q1, Q3-Q8, never hinged	4,800.	

Halves Used, Each

Q1	4.25
Q2	85.00
Q3	5.50
Q4	3.00
Q5	3.00
Q6	8.50
Q7	19.00
Q8	19.00

Overprinted type "f" on Each Half

1917-24

Q9	PP2	5c brown	3.25	8.50
Q10	PP2	10c deep blue	3.25	8.50
Q11	PP2	20c black	3.25	8.50
Q12	PP2	25c red	3.25	8.50
Q13	PP2	50c orange	6.75	12.50
Q14	PP2	1 l violet	6.75	12.50
Q15	PP2	2 l green	6.75	12.50
Q16	PP2	3 l bister	6.75	12.50
Q17	PP2	4 l slate	6.75	21.00
Q18	PP2	10 l rose lil ('24)	105.00	200.00
Q19	PP2	12 l red brn ('24)	240.00	375.00
Q20	PP2	15 l olive grn ('24)	240.00	375.00
Q21	PP2	20 l brn vio ('24)	325.00	525.00
		Nos. Q9-Q21 (13)	956.75	1,580.
		Set, never hinged	1,850.	

Halves Used, Each

Q9	1.20
Q10	1.20
Q11	1.20
Q12	1.20
Q13	1.20
Q14	1.60
Q15	4.25
Q16	4.25
Q17	8.50
Q18	12.50
Q19	12.50
Q20	12.50
Q21	17.00

Parcel Post Stamps of Italy, 1927-39, Overprinted type "f" on Each Half

1927-37

Q21A	PP3	10c dp blue ('37)	9,250.	1,100.
		Never hinged	14,000.	
Q22	PP3	25c red ('37)	550.00	67.50
Q23	PP3	30c ultra ('29)	4.25	21.00
Q24	PP3	50c orange ('36)	725.00	42.50
Q25	PP3	60c red ('29)	4.25	21.00
Q26	PP3	1 l brown vio ('36)	325.00	42.50
a.		1 l lilac	400.00	42.50
Q27	PP3	2 l green ('36)	300.00	42.50
Q28	PP3	3 l bister ('36)	10.00	37.50
Q29	PP3	4 l gray ('36)	10.00	37.50
Q30	PP3	10 l rose lilac ('36)	550.00	750.00
Q31	PP3	20 l lilac brn ('36)	550.00	750.00
		Nos. Q22-Q31 (10)	3,028.	
		Set, never hinged	5,600.	
		Nos. Q21A-Q31 (11)	2,912.	

Halves Used, Each

Q21A	27.50
Q22	1.20
Q23	.65
Q24	1.70

Q25		.85
Q26		1.25
Q26a		1.25
Q27		1.25
Q28		1.25
Q29		1.25
Q30		37.50
Q31		37.50

ESTONIA

e-ˈstō-nē-ə

LOCATION — Northern Europe, bordering on the Baltic Sea and the Gulf of Finland
GOVT. — Independent republic
AREA — 17,462 sq. mi.
POP. — 1,408,523 (1999 est.)
CAPITAL — Tallinn

Formerly a part of the Russia empire, Estonia declared its independence in 1918. In 1940 it was incorporated in the Union of Soviet Socialist Republics. Estonia declared the restoration of its independence from the USSR on Aug. 20, 1991. Estonian independence was recognized by the Soviet Union on Sept. 6, 1991.

100 Kopecks = 1 Ruble (1918, 1991)
100 Penni = 1 Mark (1919)
100 Sents = 1 Kroon (1928, 1992)

Catalogue values for unused stamps in this country are for Never Hinged items, beginning with Scott 200 in the regular postage section, Scott B60 in the semipostal section, and Scott F1 in the registration section.

Watermark

Wmk. 207 — Arms of Finland in the Sheet

Illustration reduced. Watermark covers a large part of sheet.

A1   A2

1918-19   Unwmk. Litho.   *Imperf.*

1	A1	5k pale red	1.00	.85
2	A1	15k bright blue	1.00	.85
3	A2	35p brown ('19)	1.00	.90
a.		Printed on both sides	175.00	
b.		35p olive	62.50	62.50
4	A2	70p olive grn ('19)	1.60	2.10
		Nos. 1-4 (4)	4.60	4.70

Nos. 1-4 exist privately perforated.

Russian Stamps of 1909-17 Handstamped in Violet or Black

1919, May 7   *Perf. 14, 14½x15, 13½*

8	A14	1k orange	5,000.	5,000.
9	A14	2k green	45.00	45.00
10	A14	3k red	52.50	52.50
11	A14	5k claret	45.00	45.00
12	A15	10k dk bl (Bk)	85.00	85.00
13	A15	10k dk bl	500.00	500.00
14	A14	10k on 7k lt bl	1,500.	1,500.
15	A11	15k red brn & bl	67.50	67.50
16	A11	25k grn & vio	77.50	77.50
17	A11	35k red brn & grn	5,000.	5,000.
18	A8	50k vio & grn	190.00	190.00
19	A9	1r pale brn, brn & org	325.00	325.00
20	A13	10r scar, yel & gray	8,500.	8,500.

Imperf.

21	A14	1k orange	62.50	62.50
22	A14	2k green	850.00	850.00
23	A14	3k red	85.00	85.00
24	A9	1r pale brn, brn & red org	425.00	425.00
25	A12	3½r maroon & grn	1,100.	1,100.
26	A13	5r dk bl, grn & pale bl	1,250.	1,250.

Provisionally issued at Tallinn. This overprint has been extensively counterfeited. Values are for genuine examples competently expertized. No. 20 is always creased.

Gulls — A3

1919, May 13   *Imperf.*

27	A3	5p yellow	2.50	5.50

A4   A5   A6

A7   Viking Ship — A8

1919-20   *Perf. 11½*

28	A4	10p green	.45	.80

Imperf

29	A4	5p orange	.20	.25
30	A4	10p green	.25	.25
31	A5	15p rose	.20	.30
32	A6	35p blue	.25	.30
33	A7	70p dl vio ('20)	.25	.30
34	A8	1m bl & blk brn	4.25	1.60
a.		Gray granite paper ('20)	1.60	.80
35	A8	5m yel & blk	6.25	4.75
a.		Gray granite paper ('20)	3.25	1.25
36	A8	15m yel grn & vio ('20)	3.50	2.40
37	A8	25m ultra & blk brn ('20)	6.50	5.50
		Nos. 28-37 (10)	22.10	16.45
		Set, never hinged	32.50	

The 5m exists with inverted center. Not a postal item.
See #76-77. For surcharges see #55, 57.

Skyline of Tallinn — A9

1920-24   *Imperf.*

Pelure Paper

39	A9	25p green	.35	.40
40	A9	25p yellow ('24)	.35	.30
41	A9	35p rose	.40	.40
42	A9	50p green ('21)	.40	.25
43	A9	1m vermilion	1.25	.80
44	A9	2m blue	.80	.40

45	A9	2m ultramarine	1.00	1.25
46	A9	2.50m blue	1.25	.80
		Nos. 39-46 (8)	5.80	4.60
		Set, never hinged	16.50	

Nos. 39-46 with sewing machine perforation are unofficial.
For surcharge see No. 56.

Stamps of 1919-20 Surcharged

1920   *Imperf.*

55	A5	1m on 15p rose	.50	.50
56	A9	1m on 35p rose	.70	.50
57	A7	2m on 70p dl vio	.85	.60
		Nos. 55-57 (3)	2.05	1.60
		Set, never hinged	4.25	

 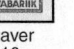

Weaver   Blacksmith
A10   A11

1922-23   Typo.   *Imperf.*

58	A10	½m orange ('23)	2.75	8.00
59	A10	1m brown ('23)	4.75	11.00
60	A10	2m yellow green	4.75	8.00
61	A10	2½m claret	5.50	8.00
62	A11	5m rose	8.00	8.00
63	A11	9m red ('23)	12.00	24.00
64	A11	10m deep blue	6.00	16.00
		Nos. 58-64 (7)	43.75	83.00
		Set, never hinged	105.00	

1922-25   *Perf. 14*

65	A10	½m orange ('23)	1.25	.80
66	A10	1m brown ('23)	2.40	.80
67	A10	2m yellow green	2.40	.40
68	A10	2½m claret	4.75	.80
69	A10	3m blue green ('24)	2.00	.40
70	A11	5m rose	2.75	.40
71	A11	9m red ('23)	4.75	1.60
72	A11	10m deep blue	6.00	.40
73	A11	12m red ('25)	6.00	1.75
74	A11	15m plum ('25)	8.00	1.40
75	A11	20m ultra ('25)	20.00	.80
		Nos. 65-75 (11)	60.30	9.55
		Set, never hinged	130.00	

See No. 89. For surcharges see Nos. 84-88.

Viking Ship Type of 1920

1922, June 8   *Perf. 14x13½*

76	A8	15m yel grn & vio	8.00	.80
77	A8	25m ultra & blk brn	10.00	3.25
		Set, never hinged	35.00	

Map of Estonia — A13

1923-24

Paper with Lilac Network

78	A13	100m ol grn & bl	20.00	3.50

Paper with Buff Network

79	A13	300m brn & bl ('24)	72.50	17.50
		Set, never hinged	210.00	

For surcharges see Nos. 106-107.

National Theater, Tallinn — A14

1924, Dec. 9   *Perf. 14x13½*

Paper with Blue Network

81	A14	30m violet & blk	10.00	4.00

Paper with Rose Network

82	A14	70m car rose & blk	15.00	8.00
		Set, never hinged	50.00	

For surcharge see No. 105.

Vanemuine Theater, Tartu — A15

1927, Oct. 25

Paper with Lilac Network

83	A15	40m dp bl & ol brn	10.00	3.50
		Never hinged	18.00	

Stamps of 1922-25 Surcharged in New Currency in Red or Black

1928   *Perf. 14*

84	A10	2s yellow green	1.50	1.25
85	A11	5s rose red (B)	1.50	1.25
86	A11	10s deep blue	2.40	1.25
a.		Imperf., pair	1,000.	—
87	A11	15s plum (B)	6.50	1.25
88	A11	20s ultra	4.50	1.25
		Nos. 84-88 (5)	16.40	6.25
		Set, never hinged	35.00	

10th anniversary of independence.

3rd Philatelic Exhibition Issue
Blacksmith Type of 1922-23

1928, July 6

89	A11	10m gray	5.00	7.50
		Never hinged	10.00	

Sold only at Tallinn Philatelic Exhibition. Exists imperf. Value $1,000.

Arms — A16

Paper with Network in Parenthesis

1928-40   *Perf. 14, 14½x14*

90	A16	1s dk gray (bl)	.50	.25
a.		Thick gray-toned laid paper ('40)	10.00	27.50
91	A16	2s yel grn (org)	.60	.25
92	A16	4s grn (brn) ('29)	1.25	.25
93	A16	5s red (grn)	.35	.25
a.		5 feet on lowest lion	45.00	32.50
94	A16	8s vio (buff) ('29)	3.00	.25
95	A16	10s lt bl (lilac)	3.00	.25
96	A16	12s crimson (grn)	2.25	.25
97	A16	15s yel (blue)	3.00	.25
98	A16	15s car (gray) ('35)	14.50	1.75
99	A16	20s slate bl (red)	4.25	.25
100	A16	25s red vio (grn) ('29)	10.50	.25
101	A16	25s bl (brn) ('35)	12.00	1.75
102	A16	40s red org (bl) ('29)	11.00	.60
103	A16	60s gray (brn) ('29)	15.00	.60
104	A16	80s brn (bl) ('29)	15.00	.60
		Nos. 90-104 (15)	96.20	7.80
		Set, never hinged	175.00	

Types of 1924 Issues Surcharged:

KROON 1 KROON

2 KROONI 2

3 KROONI 3

1930, Sept. 1   **Perf. 14x13½**
Paper with Green Network
105 A14 1k on 70m car & blk   12.00   5.50
Paper with Rose Network
106 A13 2k on 300m brn & bl   30.00 16.00
Paper with Blue Network
107 A13 3k on 300m brn & bl   60.00 27.50
     Nos. 105-107 (3)   102.00 49.00
     Set, never hinged   210.00

University
Observatory
A17

University of
Tartu
A18

Paper with Network as in Parenthesis
1932, June 1   **Perf. 14**
108 A17 5s red (yellow)   6.50   .80
109 A18 10s light bl (lilac)   3.00   .80
110 A17 12s car (blue)   10.00   4.00
111 A18 20s dk bl (green)   7.25   1.60
     Nos. 108-111 (4)   26.75   7.20
     Set, never hinged   67.50

University of Tartu tercentenary.

Narva Falls — A19

Ancient Bard
Playing
Harp — A20

1933, Apr. 1   Photo.   Perf. 14x13½
112 A19 1k gray black   7.00   3.00
     Never hinged   15.00

See No. 149.

Paper with Network as in Parenthesis
1933, May 29   Typo.   Perf. 14
113 A20 2s green (orange)   1.60   .30
114 A20 5s red (green)   2.75   .30
115 A20 10s blue (lilac)   3.50   .30
     Nos. 113-115 (3)   7.85   .90
     Set, never hinged   17.00

Tenth National Song Festival.
Nos. 113-115 exist imperf. Value $125.

Woman
Harvester
A21

Pres.
Konstantin
Päts
A22

1935, Mar. 1   Engr.   Perf. 13½
116 A21 3k black brown   .80   6.50
     Never hinged   1.60

1936-40   Typo.   Perf. 14
117 A22 1s chocolate   .80   .25
118 A22 2s olive green   .80   .25
119 A22 3s dp org ('40)   8.00   6.00
120 A22 4s rose vio   1.25   .80
121 A22 5s lt blue grn   1.50   .30
122 A22 6s rose lake   1.25   .25
123 A22 6s dp green ('40)   27.50 42.00
124 A22 10s greenish blue   1.50   .25
125 A22 15s crim rose ('37)   1.90   .40
126 A22 15s dp bl ('40)   3.25   2.50
127 A22 18s dp car ('39)   20.00   7.00
128 A22 20s brt vio   3.00   .35
129 A22 25s dk bl ('38)   8.00   1.25
130 A22 30s bister ('38)   14.00   1.25
131 A22 30s ultra ('39)   16.00   5.00
132 A22 50s org brn   7.00   1.00
133 A22 60s brt pink   16.00   4.50
     Nos. 117-133 (17)   131.75 73.35
     Set, never hinged   255.00

St. Brigitta
Convent
Entrance
A23

Ruins of
Convent, Pirita
River
A24

Front View of
Convent — A25

Seal of
Convent — A26

Paper with Network as in Parenthesis
1936, June 10   **Perf. 13½**
134 A23 5s green (buff)   .40   .40
135 A24 10s blue (lil)   .40   .40
136 A25 15s red (org)   1.25   4.00
137 A26 25s ultra (brn)   1.60   5.50
     Nos. 134-137 (4)   3.65 10.30
     Set, never hinged   8.00

St. Brigitta Convent, 500th anniversary.

Harbor at
Tallinn — A27

1938, Apr. 11   Engr.   Perf. 14
138 A27 2k blue   1.00   8.00
     Never hinged   1.75

Friedrich R.
Faehlmann
A28

Friedrich R.
Kreutzwald
A29

1938, June 15   Typo.   Perf. 13½
139 A28 5s dark green   .70   .50
140 A29 10s deep brown   .70   .50
141 A29 15s dark carmine   1.00   .90
142 A28 25s ultra   1.60   1.40
  a. Sheet of 4, #139-142   10.00 80.00
     Nos. 139-142 (4)   4.00   3.30
     Set, never hinged   10.00

Society of Estonian Scholars centenary.

Hospital at
Pärnu — A30

Beach
Hotel — A31

1939, June 20   Typo.   Perf. 14x13½
144 A30 5s dark green   1.60   1.60
145 A31 10s deep red violet   .80   1.60
146 A30 18s dark carmine   1.50   5.50
147 A31 30s deep blue   1.75   7.25
  a. Sheet of 4, #144-147   15.00 87.50
     Nos. 144-147 (4)   5.65 15.95
     Set, never hinged   11.00

Cent. of health resort and baths at Pärnu.

Narva Falls Type of 1933
1940, Apr. 15   **Engr.**
149 A19 1k slate green   1.40 12.00
     Never hinged   2.50

The sky consists of heavy horizontal lines
and the background consists of horizontal and
vertical lines.

Carrier Pigeon
and Plane — A32

1940, July 30   **Typo.**
150 A32 3s red orange   .25   .25
151 A32 10s purple   .25   .25
152 A32 15s rose brown   .25   .25
153 A32 30s dark blue   1.60   1.25
     Nos. 150-153 (4)   2.35   2.00
     Set, never hinged   5.00

Centenary of the first postage stamp.
The 15s exists imperf. Value $6.25.

> Centenary of the first postage
> stamp. Catalogue values for
> unused stamps in this section,
> from this point to the end of the
> section, are for Never Hinged
> items.

Natl.
Arms — A40

A41

1991, Oct. 1   Litho.   Perf. 13x12½
200 A40 5k salmon & red   .30   .30
201 A40 10k lt grn & dk bl grn   .30   .30
202 A40 15k lt bl & dk bl   .30   .30
203 A40 30k vio & gray   .45   .45
204 A40 50k org & brn   .60   .60
205 A40 70k pink & purple   .75   .75
206 A40 90k pur & rose lilac   .90   .90

Size: 20½x27mm
Engr.
Perf. 12½ Horiz.
207 A40 1r dark brown   1.10   1.10
208 A40 2r lt bl & dk bl   2.25   2.25
     Nos. 200-208 (9)   6.95   6.95

See Nos. 211-213, 215, 216, 230, 299-301,
314-314A, 317, 333-334, 339-340. For
surcharge, see No. 217.

Perf. 13½x14, 14x13½
1991, Nov. 1   **Litho.**
209 A41 1.50r Flag, vert.   1.75   1.75
210 A41 2.50r shown   2.75   2.75

National Arms — A42

1992, Mar. 16   Litho.   Perf. 13x12½
211 A42 E (1r) lemon   .20   .20
212 A42 I (20r) deep green   1.25   1.25
213 A42 A (40r) blue   2.75   2.75
     Nos. 211-213 (3)   4.20   4.20

No. 211 was valid for postage within Esto-
nia. No. 212 was valid for postage within
Europe. No. 213 was valid for overseas mail.
See Nos. 214, 219, 220, 224-229.

**No. 202 Surcharged and Arms Types
of 1991-1992**

And

Natl. Arms —
A42a

**Perf. 14, 13x12½ (#214, 217, 219-
220)**
1992-96
214 A42 E (10s) orange   .25   .25
215 A40 10s blue & gray   .25   .25
216 A40 50s gray & brt bl   .25   .25
217 A40 60s on 15k #202   .25   .25
218 A40 60s lilac & olive   .25   .25
219 A42 I (1k) emerald   .75   .75
220 A42 A (2k) violet blue   1.50   1.50
221 A42a 5k bis & red vio   1.25   1.25
  a. 5k yel orange & red violet   2.75   2.75
222 A42a 10k blue & olive   2.50   2.50
223 A42a 20k pale lilac & slate grn   4.25   4.25
     Nos. 214-223 (10)   11.50 11.50

Coil Stamps
Engr.
Size: 20½x27mm
Perf. 12½ Horiz.
224 A42 X (10s) brown   .30   .30
225 A42 X (10s) olive   .30   .30
226 A42 X (10s) black   .30   .30
227 A42 Z (30s) red lilac   .30   .30
228 A42 Z (30s) red   .30   .30
229 A42 Z (30s) dark blue   .30   .30

Litho.
230 A40 60s lilac brown   .30   .30
     Nos. 224-230 (7)   2.10   2.10

Issued: #214, 219-220, 6/22; #224, 8/29;
#225, 9/25; #226, 10/31; #227, 11/16; #228,
12/1; #229, 12/22; #230, 1/8/93; #217, 3/5/93;
10s, 5/23 1993; 10s, 5/25/93; 5k, 7/7/93;
#218, 8/5/93; 20k, 9/8/93; #221a, 9/19/96.
See note after No. 213. Nos. 224-229 were
valid for postage within Estonia.
See No. F1.

A44

A45

Birds of the Baltic shores.

1992, Oct. 3   Litho. & Engr.   Perf. 13
Booklet Stamps
231 A44 1k Pandion haliaetus   .25   .25
232 A44 1k Limosa limosa   .25   .25
233 A44 1k Mergus merganser   .25   .25
234 A44 1k Tadorna todorna   .25   .25
  a. Booklet pane of 4, #231-234   1.50

See Latvia Nos. 332-335a, Lithuania Nos.
427-430a and Sweden Nos. 1975-1978a.

1992, Dec. 15   Litho.   Perf. 14
235 A45 30s gray & multi   .30   .30
236 A45 2k light brown & multi   .70   .70

Christmas.
Exist on ordinary and fluorescent paper.
Values are for former. Value for set on fluores-
cent paper, $27.50.

Friendship
A46

1993, Feb. 8   Litho.   Perf. 14
237 A46 1k multicolored   .30 .30
  a. Booklet pane of 6   1.60
    See Finland No. 906.

A47   A48

1993, Feb. 16   Perf. 13x13½
238 A47 60s black & multi   .25 .25
239 A47 1k violet & multi   .30 .30
240 A47 2k blue & multi   .60 .60
    Nos. 238-240 (3)   1.15 1.15
    First Republic, 75th anniv.

1993, June 9   Litho.   Perf. 13½x14
241 A48 60s Wrestling   .25 .25
242 A48 1k +25s Viking ship,
    map   .30 .30
243 A48 2k Shot put with rock   .45 .45
    Nos. 241-243 (3)   1.00 1.00
    First Baltic sea games.

Tallinn
Castle — A49

    Designs: 1k, Toolse Castle. #245, Paide
Castle, vert. #246, Purtse Castle. #247, Haapsalu Castle and Cathedral. 2.70k, Narva Fortress. 2.90k, Haapsalu Cathedral. 3k, Monks'
Tower, Kiiu. 3.20k, Rakvere Castle. 4k, Kuressaare Castle. 4.80k, Viljandi Castle.

1993-97   Litho.   Perf. 14
244 A49 1k gray & black   .40 .40
245 A49 2k tan & brown   .40 .40
246 A49 2.50k lt vio & dk vio   .55 .55
247 A49 2.50k gray   .55 .55
248 A49 2.70k lt blue & dk blue   .55 .55
249 A49 2.90k lt grn & dk grn   .60 .60
250 A49 3k rose & brown   .60 .60
251 A49 3.20k lt grn & dk grn   .85 .85
252 A49 4k lt gray vio & gray
    vio   .90 .90
253 A49 4.80k dull org & brn   .95 .95
    Nos. 244-253 (10)   6.35 6.35

    Issued: 1k, 2/22/94; 2k, 10/12/93; 2.70k,
12/10/93; 2.90k, 12/23/93; 3k, 3/31/94; 3.20,
12/28/94; 4k, 9/20/94; #246, 1/25/96; 247,
7/25/96; 4.80k, 1/21/97.

First Estonian
Postage Stamp,
75th
Anniv. — A50

1993, Nov. 13   Litho.   Perf. 14
259 A50 1k multicolored   .40 .40
Souvenir Sheet
Imperf
260 A50 4k multicolored   3.25 3.25
  a. Ovptd. in sheet margin   12.50 12.50

    No. 260 sold for 5k. Overprint on No. 260a
reads "FILATEELIANAITUS / MARE BAL-
TICUM '93 / 24.-28. NOVEMBER 1993".

Christmas
A51

    80s, Haapsalu Cathedral. 2k, Tallinn
Church.

1993, Nov.   Litho.   Perf. 14
261 A51 80s red   .25 .25
262 A51 2k blue, vert.   .40 .40
    See Nos. 279-280.

Lydia
Koidula — A52

1993, Dec. 14   Litho.   Perf. 14
263 A52 1k multicolored   .25 .25

A53   A54

1994, Jan. 26
264 A53 1k +25s Ski jumping   .45 .45
265 A53 2k Speed skating   .55 .55
    1994 Winter Olympics, Lillehammer.

1994, May 31   Litho.   Perf. 13½x14
    Festival badges: 1k+25s, Tartu, 1869. 2k,
Tallinn, 1923. 3k, Tallinn, 1969. 15k, Anniversary badge.
266 A54 1k +25s olive & multi   .25 .25
267 A54 2k blue & brown   .45 .45
268 A54 3k brown, buff & bister   .60 .60
    Nos. 266-268 (3)   1.30 1.30
Souvenir Sheet
269 A54 15k multicolored   3.50 3.50
    All Estonian Song Festival, 125th anniv.

Flying
Squirrel — A55

A56

1994, June 27   Litho.   Perf. 13½x14
270 A55 1k shown   .40 .40
271 A55 2k On leafy branch   .50 .50
272 A55 3k In fir tree   .85 .85
273 A55 4k With young   1.10 1.10
    Nos. 270-273 (4)   2.85 2.85
    World Wildlife Fund.

1994, July 19
    Europa (Estonian Inventions): 1k, Rotating
horizontal millstones, by Aleksander Mikiver.
2.70k, First mini-camera, by Walter Zapp.
274 A56 1k multicolored   .25 .25
275 A56 2.70k multicolored   .50 .50

A57   A58

    Folk Costumes.

1994, Aug. 23   Litho.   Perf. 14
276 A57 1k Jamaja   .25 .25
277 A57 1k Mustjala   .25 .25
    See Nos. 286-287, 303-304, 325-326, 347-
348, 369-370, 476-477, 497-498, 524-525.

1994, Sept. 27   Litho.   Perf. 13½
278 A58 1.70k multicolored   .35 .35
    Estonian Art Museum, 75th anniv.

Christmas Type of 1993
    Designs: 1.20k, Ruhnu Church, vert. 2.50k,
Urvaste Church.

1994, Nov. 15   Litho.   Perf. 14
279 A51 1.20k brown   .30 .30
280 A51 2.50k green   .55 .55
    For surcharge see No. B63.

A59   A60

1994, Oct. 18
281 A59 1.70k multicolored   .40 .40
    Intl. Year of the Family.

1994, Dec. 9
    Gustavus II Adolphus (1594-1632), King of
Sweden.
282 A60 2.50k lilac   1.00 1.00

A61   A62

1995, Jan. 26   Litho.   Perf. 14
283 A61 1.70k Branta leucopsis   .35 .35
284 A61 3.20k Anser anser   .60 .60
    Matsalu Nature Reserve.

1995, Feb. 28   Litho.   Perf. 14
    Farm Laborer's Family at Table, by Efraim
Allsalu.
285 A62 2.70k multicolored   .60 .60
    FAO, 50th anniv.

Folk Costumes Type of 1994
1995, Mar. 30   Litho.   Perf. 14
286 A57 1.70k Muhu couple   .50 .50
287 A57 1.70k Three Muhu girls   .50 .50

A63

A64

    Via Baltica Highway Project: #288, 289a,
Beach Hotel, Parnu. #289b, Castle, Bauska,
Latvia. #289c, Kaunas, Lithuania.

1995, Apr. 20   Litho.   Perf. 14
288 A63 1.70k multicolored   .45 .45
Souvenir Sheet
289 A63 3.20k Sheet of 3, #a.-c.   2.00 2.00
    See Latvia Nos. 394-395, Lithuania Nos.
508-509.

1995, Apr. 20   Litho.   Perf. 14
290 A64 2.70k multicolored   .85 .85
    Europa. Liberation of Nazi Concentration
Camps, 50th anniv.

UN, 50th
Anniv. — A65

1995, June 1   Litho.   Perf. 14
291 A65 4k multicolored   .85 .85

Pakri
Lighthouse
A66

1995, July 5   Litho.   Perf. 14
292 A66 1.70k multicolored   .45 .45
    See Nos. 309, 318, 338, 356, 388-389, 408,
434, 452, 501-502.

Vanemuine
Theater, 125th
Anniv. — A67

1995, Aug. 14   Litho.   Perf. 14
293 A67 1.70k multicolored   .45 .45

Louis Pasteur
(1822-95)
A68

1995, Sept. 20   Litho.   Perf. 14
294 A68 2.70k multicolored   .75 .75

Finno-Ugric
Peoples
A69

Aleksander
Kunileid (1845-
75), Composer
A70

    Ethnographic object, languages: a, 2.50k,
Drawing on shaman's drum, Saami. b, 3.50k,
Duck-shaped brooch, Mordva, Mari. c, 4.50k,
Duck-feet necklace pendant, Udmurdi, Komi.
d, 2.50k, Khanty band ornament, Ungari,
Mansi, Handi. e, 3.50k, Bronze amulet,
Neenetsi, Eenetsi, Nganassaani, Solkupi,
Kamassi. f, 4.50k, Karelian writing on
birchbark, Eesti, Vadia, Soome, Liivi, Isuri,
Karjala, Vespa.

1995, Oct. 17   Litho.   Perf. 14
Miniature Sheet
295 A69 Sheet of 6, #a.-f.   4.50 4.50

1995, Nov. 1   Engr.   Perf. 12½ Horiz.
296 A70 2k dark blue black   .50 .50

Christmas — A71

Churches: 2k, St. Martin's, Türi. 3.50k, Charles' Church of the Toompea Congregation, Tallinn.

1995, Nov. 15   Litho.   *Perf. 14*
297 A71   2k yellow orange   .60 .60
298 A71   3.50k dull carmine   1.00 1.00
     See Nos. 315-316, 331.

Natl. Arms Type of 1991
1995, Oct. 26   Litho.   *Perf. 14*
299 A40   20s blue green & black   .20 .20
300 A40   30s gray & magenta   .20 .20
301 A40   80s lilac & blue black   .25 .25
   a.   Perf. 13   .25 .25
    Nos. 299-301 (3)   .65 .65
    No. 301a issued in 1996.

Submarine
Lembit — A72

1996, Feb. 29   Litho.   *Perf. 14*
302 A72   2.50k multicolored   .65 .65
     See No. 308, 328.

Folk Costume Type of 1994
1996, Mar. 26   Litho.   *Perf. 14*
303 A57   2.50k Emmaste   .70 .70
304 A57   2.50k Reigi   .70 .70

A73

A74

Designs: a, 2.50k, First gold medal, 1896. b, 3.50k, Alfred Neuland, weight lifter, first to win gold medal for Estonia, 1920. c, 4k, Cyclist.

1996, Apr. 25   Litho.   *Perf. 14*
305 A73   Sheet of 3, #a.-c.   2.25 2.25
   Modern Olympic Games, Cent. & 1996 Summer Olympics, Atlanta.

1996, May 10
   Europa: Marie Under (1883-1980), poet.
306 A74   2.50k multicolored   *1.00 1.00*

Radio,
Cent. — A75

1996, June 27   Litho.   *Perf. 14*
307 A75   3.50k Guglielmo Marconi   .95 .95

Ship Type of 1996
   Design: Icebreaker, Suur Toll.

1996, Aug. 30   Litho.   *Perf. 14*
308 A72   2.50k multicolored   .60 .60

Lighthouse Type of 1995
1996, Sept. 25   Litho.   *Perf. 14*
309 A66   2.50k Vaindloo   .70 .70

Estonian
Narrow Gauge
Railway,
Cent. — A76

Designs: 3.20k, Class Gk steam locomotive. 3.50k, DeM 1 diesel motor wagon. 4.50k, Class Sk steam locomotive.

1996, Oct. 17   Litho.   *Perf. 14*
310 A76   3.20k multicolored   .75 .75
311 A76   3.50k multicolored   .80 .80
312 A76   4.50k multicolored   1.00 1.00
    Nos. 310-312 (3)   2.55 2.55
     See No. 397.

Christmas
A77

1996, Nov. 27   Litho.   *Perf. 14*
313 A77   2.50k multicolored   .65 .65

Natl. Arms Type of 1991
1996-97   *Perf. 14*
314 A40   3.30k lilac and claret   .80 .80
     Perf. 13x13¼
314A A40   3.30k blue & lt claret   .80 .80
    Issued: #314, 12/2; #314A, 12/10/97.

Church Type of 1995
   Christmas: 3.30k, Harju-Madise Church. 4.50k, Holy Spirit Church, Tallinn.

1996, Dec. 12
315 A71   3.30k blue   .80 .80
316 A71   4.50k pink   1.00 1.00

Natl. Arms Type of 1991
1996, Oct. 24   Litho.   *Perf. 13½*
317 A40   2.50k grn & dark grn   1.00 1.00

Lighthouse Type of 1995
1997, Feb. 11   Litho.   *Perf. 14*
318 A66   3.30k Ruhnu   .75 .75

Tallinn Zoo — A78

a, Haliaeetus pelagicus. b, Mustela lutreola. c, Aegypius monachus. d, Panthera pardus orientalis. e, Diceros bicornis. f, Capra cylindricornis.

1997, Mar. 26   Litho.   *Perf. 14*
319 A78   3.30k Sheet of 6, #a.-f.   3.75 3.75

Heinrich von
Stephan (1831-
97), Founder of
UPU — A79

1997, Apr. 8   Litho.   *Perf. 14*
320 A79   7k black & bister   1.40 1.40

A80

A81

1997, May 5   Litho.   *Perf. 14*
321 A80   4.80k Goldspinners
       Fairy Tale   1.25 1.25
     Europa.

1997, May 10
   No. 323: a, like #322. b, Linijkugis, 17th cent. c, Kurenas, 16th cent.
322 A81   3.30k multicolored   .80 .80
     Perf. 14x14½
323 A81   4.50k Sheet of 3, #a.-c.   6.00 6.00
    Maasilinn ship, 16th cent.
   See Latvia Nos. 443-444, Lithuania Nos. 571-572.

Folk Costume Type of 1994
1997, June 10   Litho.   *Perf. 14*
325 A57   3.30k Ruhnu   .70 .70
326 A57   3.30k Vormsi   .70 .70

One Kroon
Coin — A82

1997, June 12   Litho.   *Perf. 14*
327 A82   50k bl grn, blk & gray   9.75 9.75
     See Nos. 345, 363, 391.

Ship Type of 1996
   Design: Four-masted barkentine, Tormilind.

1997, July 2
328 A72   5.50k multicolored   1.25 1.25

Stone Bridge,
Tartu — A83

1997, Sept. 16   Litho.   *Perf. 14*
329 A83   3.30k multicolored   .75 .75

Wastne
Testament,
Estonian Bible
Translation,
1686 — A84

1997, Oct. 14   Litho.   *Perf. 14*
330 A84   3.50k multicolored   .75 .75

Church Type of 1995
   Christmas: St. Anne's, Halliste.

1997, Nov. 27   Litho.   *Perf. 14*
331 A71   3.30k brown   .75 .75

Christmas
A85

1997, Dec. 3
332 A85   2.90k Elves   .70 .70

Natl. Arms Type of 1991
1998, Jan. 19   Litho.   *Perf. 13x13½*
333 A40   3.10k lt violet & rose   .65 .65
334 A40   3.60k lt blue & ultra   .75 .75
   a.   3.60k gray & vio bl   .75 .75
     Issued: #334a, 8/4/98.

1998 Winter
Olympic Games,
Nagano — A86

1998, Jan. 28   Litho.   *Perf. 14*
335 A86   3.60k multicolored   .75 .75

Republic of Estonia, 80th
Anniv. — A87

1998, Feb. 6   Litho.   *Imperf.*
336 A87   7k Proclamation, arms   1.60 1.60

Eduard Wiiralt
(1898-1954), Print
Artist — A88

Various sections of print, "Hell," showing faces: a, 3.60k, shown. b, 3.60k, Explosion coming from center figure. c, 5.50k, Cat on top of one figure's head. d, 5.50k, Faces within faces.

1998, Feb. 18   *Perf. 14*
337 A88   Sheet of 4, #a.-d.   3.50 3.50

Lighthouse Type of 1995
1998, Mar. 12   Litho.   *Perf. 14*
338 A66   3.60k Kunda   .80 .80

Natl. Arms Type of 1991
1998, Mar. 16   *Perf. 13*
339 A40   10s grn bl & brn blk   .25 .25
340 A40   4.50k pale orange &
       brick red   .80 .80
    Issued: 10s, 3/25/97; 4.50k, 3/16/98.

A88a   A89

1998, Apr. 16   Litho.   Perf. 14
341 A88a 7k multicolored   1.50 1.50
    1998 World Cup Soccer Championship, France.

1998, May 5   Litho.   Perf. 14
342 A89 5.20k St. John's Day   *1.50 1.50*
    Europa.

Use of Lübeck Charter in Tallinn, 750th Anniv. — A90

1998, June 1
343 A90 4.80k multicolored   1.00 1.00

Beautiful Homes Year — A91

1998, June 16   Litho.   Perf. 14
344 A91 3.60k multicolored   .85 .85

One Kroon Coin Type of 1997
1998, June 18
345 A82 25k green, gray & black   5.50 5.50

A92   A93

1998, Aug. 4   Litho.   Perf. 14
346 A92 5.50k multicolored   1.25 1.25
    470 Class World Yachting Championships.

Folk Costume Type of 1994
1998, Aug. 21   Litho.   Perf. 14
347 A57 3.60k Kihnu couple   .80 .80
348 A57 3.60k Kihnu family   .80 .80

1998, Sept. 3
349 A93 3.60k yel, blue & blk   .80 .80
    Juhan Jaik (1899-1948), author.

Tallinn Zoo — A94

    Design: Panthera tigris altaica.

1998, Sept. 17
350 A94 3.60k multicolored   .80 .80
    See No. 357.

Estonian Post, 80th Anniv. — A95

1998, Oct. 22   Litho.   Perf. 14
351 A95 3.60k multicolored   .90 .90

Military Aid from Finland, 90th Anniv. — A96

1998, Nov. 5   Litho.   Perf. 14
352 A96 4.50k Freedom Cross   1.00 1.00

Christmas A97

1998, Nov. 26   Litho.   Perf. 14
353 A97 3.10k Santa, child, vert.   .75 .75
354 A97 5k shown   1.10 1.10

Friedrich Robert Faehlmann, Founder of Learned Estonian Society, Birth Bicent. — A98

1998, Dec. 2
355 A98 3.60k multicolored   .85 .85

Lighthouse Type of 1995
1999, Jan. 20   Litho.   Perf. 14
356 A66 3.60k Vilsandi   .85 .85

Tallinn Zoo Type of 1998
1999, Feb. 18   Litho.   Perf. 14
357 A94 3.60k Uncia uncia   .70 .70

Council of Europe, 50th Anniv. — A99

1999, Mar. 24   Litho.   Perf. 14
358 A99 5.50k multicolored   1.10 1.10

Estonian Pres. Lennart Meri, 70th Birthday A100

1999, Mar. 29
359 A100 3.60k multicolored   .85 .85

Tolkuse Bog — A101

1999, Apr. 27   Litho.   Perf. 14
360 A101 5.50k multicolored   *1.40 1.40*
    Europa.

Bank of Estonia, 80th Anniv. — A102

1999, May 3   Litho.   Perf. 14
361 A102 5k multicolored   1.10 1.10

Olustvere Manor — A103

1999, June 1
362 A103 3.60k multicolored   .70 .70
    See Nos. 395, 414, 433, 456, 490, 520, 551, 562, 603, 627, 648.

One Kroon Coin Type of 1997
1999, June 18   Litho.   Perf. 14
363 A82 100k bl, bister & blk   18.50 18.50

Estonian Natl. Anthem — A104

1999, June 30   Litho.   Perf. 14
364 A104 3.60k multicolored   .80 .80
    No. 364 is printed se-tenant with label.

Tower on Suur Munamägi, Highest Point in Baltic Countries A105

1999, July 17
365 A105 5.20k multicolored   1.10 1.10

A106

A107

    Families holding hands and: 3.60k, Estonian flag.
    No. 367: a, like #366. b, Latvian flag. c, Lithuanian flag.

1999, Aug. 23   Litho.   Perf. 14
366 A106 3.60k multicolored   .85 .85
Souvenir Sheet
367 A106 5.50k Sheet of 3, #a.-c. 3.50 3.50
    Baltic Chain, 10th Anniv.

See Latvia #493-494, Lithuania #639-640.

1999, Sept. 23   Litho.   Perf. 14x13¾
368 A107 7k multicolored   1.60 1.60
    UPU, 125th Anniv.

Folk Costumes Type of 1994
1999, Oct. 12   Litho.   Perf. 13¾x14
369 A57 3.60k Setu couple   .80 .80
370 A57 5k Setu man, boy   1.10 1.10

Three Lions — A108

Perf. 13x13¼, 13¾x14 (#371, 373, 374, 378-382)

1999-2002			Litho.	
371	A108	10s brn & dk brn	.25	.20
372	A108	30s lt bl & dk bl	.25	.20
a.		Perf. 13¾x14	.25	.20
373	A108	30s blue & slate blue, dated 2003	.25	.20
374	A108	50s olive & dk grn	.25	.20
375	A108	1k brown & fawn	.25	.20
376	A108	2k gray	.40	.40
377	A108	3.60k sky bl & dk bl	.65	.65
a.		Bright blue green ('00)	.65	.65
378	A108	4.40k grn & bl grn	.85	.70
a.		Inscribed "2001"	.85	.70
b.		Inscribed "2002"	.85	.70
379	A108	4.40k bl grn & brt bl grn, wide 2001 date	.85	.25
380	A108	4.40k Prus bl & lt bl, narrow 2001 date	.85	.25
381	A108	4.40k green & lt grn, dated 2002	.85	.25
382	A108	4.40k grn & apple grn, dated 2002	.85	.25
382A	A108	4.40k ol grn & apple grn, dated 2003	.85	.30
382B	A108	5k grn & lt grn	1.10	1.10
a.		Inscribed "2003"	1.00	1.00
b.		Inscribed "2004"	.65	.65
382C	A108	6k bis & yel	1.25	1.25
382D	A108	6.50k bis & org	1.25	1.25
382E	A108	8k lake & pink	1.50	1.50
		Nos. 371-382E (17)	12.50	9.15

    Issued: 30s, 2k, 11/4; 3.60k (377), 10/22; #377a, 3/31/00; No. 378, 8/21/00; 6k, 10/12/00; 6.50k, 10/5/00; 8k, 10/19/00; No. 372a: 4/17/01; 1k, 5k, 8/28/01; 10s, 2/2/02. 50s, 1/7/03; No. 373, 3/11/03; No. 379, 4/17/01; No. 380, 9/24/01; No. 381, 2/2/02; No. 382, 11/14/02; No. 382A, 3/11/03.
    The background color of No. 379 is bolder than that on No. 380.
    See Nos. 467, 472-474.

Christmas A109

1999, Nov. 25   Litho.   Perf. 14x13¾
383 A109 3.10k multicolored   .70 .70

A110   A111

1999, Nov. 25   Perf. 13¾x14
384 A110 7k multicolored   1.50 1.50
    1st public Christmas tree in Tallinn, 1441.

Christmas Lottery A110a

1999, Dec. 1   Litho.   Perf. 14x13¾
384A A110a 3.10k + 1.90k multi   1.50 1.50

1999, Dec. 14   Litho.   Perf. 13¾x14
385 A111 5.50k Millennium   1.25 1.25

2000 Census — A112

2000, Jan. 5
386 A112 3.60k multicolored   .80 .80

Tartu Peace Treaty, 80th Anniv. — A113

2000, Feb. 2   Litho.   Perf. 14x13¾
387 A113 3.60k multi   .80 .80

Lighthouse Type of 1995
2000, Feb. 25
388 A66 3.60k Ristna   .90 .90
389 A66 3.60k Kopu   .90 .90
a.   Pair, #388-389   1.50 1.50

Congress, 10th Anniv. — A114

2000, Mar. 9   Perf. 13¾x14
390 A114 3.60k multi   .75 .75

One Kroon Coin Type of 1997
2000, Mar. 14   Perf. 14x13¾
391 A82 10k red, sil & blk   2.00 2.00

Cornflower (Natl. Flower) — A115

2000, Apr. 7
392 A115 4.80k multi   1.00 1.00

Natl. Book Year — A116

2000, Apr. 22   Perf. 13¾x14
393 A116 3.60k multi   .70 .70
   First book printed in Estonian language, 475th anniv.

Europa, 2000
Common Design Type
2000, May 9
394 CD17 4.80k multi   1.25 1.25

Manor Type of 1999
2000, May 23   Litho.   Perf. 14x13¾
395 A103 3.60k Palmse Hall   .75 .75

Tallinn Zoo — A117

2000, June 13   Litho.   Perf. 14x13¾
396 A117 3.60k Naemorhedus caudatus   .75 .75

Railway Type of 1996
4.50k, Viljandi-Tallinn Railway, cent.

2000, June 30
397 A76 4.50k multi   .90 .90

9th Intl. Finno-Ugric Congress A118

2000, Aug. 1
398 A118 5k multi   1.00 1.00

2000 Summer Olympics, Sydney — A119

2000, Sept. 5   Litho.   Perf. 13¾x14
399 A119 8k multi   1.50 1.50

Folk Costume Type of 1994
Designs: 4.40k, Hargla. 8k, Polva.

2000, Sept. 12
400-401 A57   Set of 2   2.50 2.50

August Mälk (1900-87), Writer — A120

2000, Sept. 20   Perf. 14x13¾
402 A120 4.40k multi   .90 .90

Lake Peipus Fish — A121

No. 403: a, Osmerus eperlanus spirinchus. b, Stizostedion lucioperka.

2000, Oct. 25
403   Horiz. pair + central label   2.50 2.50
a.-b.   A121 6.50k Any single   1.10 1.10
   See Russia No. 6607.

Souvenir Sheet

Estonian Bookplates, Cent. — A122

Various bookplates. Denominiations in: a, LR. b, UR.

2000, Nov. 11   Perf. 13¾x14
404 A122 6k Sheet of 2, #a-b   2.25 2.25

Christmas A123

3.60k, Horn and bow. 6k, Ornament.

2000, Nov. 29   Perf. 14x13¾
405-406 A123   Set of 2   2.00 2.00

Erki Nool, Olympic Decathlon Champion A124

2001, Jan. 10   Litho.   Perf. 14x13¾
407 A124 4.40k multi   1.00 1.00

Lighthouse Type of 1995
2001, Jan. 24
408 A66 4.40k Mohni   1.00 1.00

Valentine's Day — A125

2001, Feb. 6   Litho.   Perf. 13¾x14
409 A125 4.40k multi   1.00 1.00

Stenbock House, Seat of Government A126

2001, Feb. 20   Perf. 14x13¾
410 A126 6.50k multi   1.25 1.25

Souvenir Sheet

Paintings of Johann Köler (1826-99) — A127

No. 411: a, Girl on the Spring, 1858-62. b, Eve of the Pomegranate, 1879-80.

2001, Feb. 27
411 A127 4.40k Sheet of 2, #a-b   1.90 1.90

European Year of Languages A128

2001, Mar. 6
412 A128 4.40k multi   1.00 1.00

Vanellus Vanellus A129

2001, Apr. 4   Perf. 12¾x13
413 A129 4.40k multi   .90 .90
   See No. 435.

Manor Type of 1999
2001, Apr. 17   Perf. 14x13¾
414 A103 4.40k Laupa Hall   .90 .90

Europa — A130

2001, May 9   Perf. 13¾x14
415 A130 6.50k multi   1.30 1.30

Kalev Sports Association, Cent. — A131

2001, May 24
416 A131 6.50k multi   1.25 1.25

Pärnu, 750th Anniv. — A132

2001, June 5 Litho. Perf. 14x13¾
417 A132 4.40k multi .90 .90

Illustrations from Pokuland, by Edgar Valter — A133

Characters and — No. 418: a, Lake. b, Owl. c, Crane. d, Bird in nest.
No. 419: a, Fence. b, Flowers. c, Dog. d, Moon.

2001, June 19
418 Booklet pane of 4 2.75
a.-d. A133 3.60k Any single .75 .75
419 Booklet pane of 4 3.75
a.-d. A133 4.40k Any single .90 .90
Booklet, #418-419 7.25

Entire booklet sold for 35k, 3k of which went to the Pokuland Project of the Estonian Nature Fund.

Restoration of Independence, 10th Anniv. — A134

2001, Aug. 7 Perf. 13¾x14
420 A134 4.40k multi .90 .90

Establishment of St. Mary's Land, 800th Anniv. — A135

2001, Aug. 15 Perf. 14x13¾
421 A135 6.50k multi 1.25 1.25

Resumption of Issuing Stamps, 10th Anniv. — A136

2001, Sept. 4 Perf. 13¾x14
422 A136 4.40k #200 .90 .90

Baltic Coast Landscapes A137

Designs: 4.40k, No. 424a, Lahemaa. No. 424b, Vidzeme. No. 424c, Palanga.

2001, Sept. 15 Perf. 14x13¾
423 A137 4.40k multi .90 .90

Souvenir Sheet
Perf. 13¼x13½
424 Sheet of 3 3.50 3.50
a.-c. A137 6k Any single 1.10 1.10

No. 424 contains three 35x29mm stamps. See Lithuania Nos.
See Latvia Nos. 534-535, Lithuania Nos. 698-699.

Tallinn Zoo — A138

2001, Oct. 4 Perf. 14x13¾
425 A138 4.40k Alligator sinensis .90 .90

Estonia 26/9 Racing Car — A139

2001, Oct. 23
426 A139 6k multi 1.25 1.25

Folk Costume Type of 1994
Designs: 4.40k, Paistu woman. 7.50k, Tarvastu man.

2001, Nov. 7 Litho. Perf. 13¾x14
427-428 A57 Set of 2 2.50 2.50

A140

Christmas A141

Perf. 13¾x14, 14x13¾
2001, Nov. 22
429 A140 3.60k multi .70 .70
430 A141 6.50k multi 1.40 1.40

Radio Broadcasting in Estonia, 75th Anniv. — A142

2001, Dec. 4 Perf. 14x13¾
431 A142 4.40k multi .90 .90

2002 Winter Olympics, Salt Lake City — A143

2002, Jan. 10 Litho. Perf. 14x13¾
432 A143 8k multi 1.60 1.60

Manor Type of 1999
2002, Jan. 22
433 A103 4.40k Sangaste Hall .90 .90

Lighthouse Type of 1995
2002, Feb. 20
434 A66 4.40k Laidunina .90 .90

Bird Type of 2001
Design: Passer domesticus and Passer montanus.

2002, Mar. 7 Perf. 12¾x13
435 A129 4.40k multi .90 .90

Spring Flowers — A144

2002, Mar. 20 Perf. 14x13¾
436 A144 4.40k multi .90 .90

Estonian Puppet Theater, 50th Anniv. — A145

2002, Mar. 27 Perf. 13¾x14
437 A145 4.40k multi + label .90 .90

PTO-4 Training Airplane — A146

2002, Apr. 10 Perf. 14x13¾
438 A146 6k multi 1.25 1.25

Andrus Veerpalu, Gold Medalist at 2002 Winter Olympics A147

2002, Apr. 12
439 A147 4.40k multi .90 .90

Tartu University Anniversaries — A148

No. 440: a, Main building, 1806-09, founding act of 1632. b, University Library, 1982, text from Biblia Latina.

2002, Apr. 24
440 A148 4.40k Horiz. pair, #a-b,
+ central label 3.50 3.50

Europa A149

2002, May 9 Perf. 12¾x13
441 A149 6.50k multi 1.60 1.60

Re-adoption of Constitution, 10th Anniv. — A150

2002, May 23 Perf. 13¾x14
442 A150 4.40k multi .90 .90

Adoption of Lübeck Charter by Town of Rakvere, 700th Anniv. — A151

2002, June 5
443 A151 4.40k multi .90 .90

Souvenir Sheet

Re-introduction of the Kroon, 10th Anniv. — A152

No. 444 — Portraits from bank notes: a, Lydia Koidula, poet. b, Carl Rober Jakobson, journalist.

2002, June 10 Perf. 14x13¾
444 A152 4.40k Sheet of 2, #a-b 2.75 2.75

Souvenir Sheet

Adamson-Eric (1902-68), Painter — A153

Denomination at: a, LL. b, LR. c, UL. d, UR.

2002, Aug. 8 Litho. Perf. 14x13¾
445 A153 4.40k Sheet of 4, #a-d 3.50 3.50

Sus Scrofa A154

2002, Aug. 21 Perf. 12¾x13
446 A154 4.40k multi .90 .90

Limestone, Estonia's National Stone A155

2002, Sept. 18
447 A155 4.40k multi .90 .90

Folk Costume Type of 1994

Designs: 4.40k, Kolga-Jaani women. 5.50k, Suure-Jaani boy and girl.

2002, Oct. 1 *Perf. 13¾x14*
448-449 A57 Set of 2 2.00 2.00

A156

Christmas — A157

Perf. 14x13¾, 13¾x14
2002, Nov. 20 **Litho.**
450 A156 3.60k Reindeer .70 .70
451 A157 6.50k Christmas tree 1.40 1.40

Lighthouse Type of 1995
2003, Jan. 15 *Perf. 14x13¾*
452 A66 4.40k Keri .90 .90

Anton Hansen Tammsaare (1878-1940), Novelist — A158

2003, Jan. 30 **Litho.** *Perf. 14x13¾*
453 A158 4.40k multi .90 .90

Pica Pica A159

2003, Feb. 13 *Perf. 12¾x13*
454 A159 4.40k multi .90 .90
See Nos. 485, 509, 540, 566, 595, 625.

Spring Flowers — A160

No. 455: a, Tulips. b, Helleborus purpurascens. c, Narcissus poeticus. d, Crocus vernus.

2003, Mar. 20 *Perf. 13¾x14*
455 A160 4.40k Sheet of 4, #a-d 8.50 8.50
  e. Booklet pane, like #455, without
    date in margin 3.75 —
    Complete booklet, #455e 3.75
  See No. 484.

Manor Type of 1999
2003, Apr. 9 *Perf. 14x13¾*
456 A103 4.40k Alatskivi Hall .90 .90

Pres. Arnold Rüütel, 75th Birthday — A161

2003, Apr. 24
457 A161 4.40k multi + label .90 .90

Europa — A162

2003, May 8 *Perf. 13¾x14*
458 A162 6.50k multi 1.75 1.75

Tartu University Botanical Gardens, Bicent. — A163

2003, June 11 **Litho.** *Perf. 14x13¾*
459 A163 4.40k multi .90 .90

14th Junior World Orienteering Championships A164

2003, June 27
460 A164 7.50k multi 1.50 1.50

Circumnavigation of Adam Johann von Krusenstern (1770-1846) — A165

2003, Aug. 6 *Perf. 12½*
461 A165 8k multi 1.60 1.60

Phoca Hispida A166

2003, Aug. 27 *Perf. 12¾x13*
462 A166 4.40k multi .90 .90

Adm. Fabian Gottlieb von Bellingshausen (1778-1852) — A167

2003, Sept. 10
463 A167 8k multi 2.00 2.00

Ancient Trade Routes — A168

Map and: No. 464, 6.50k, Silver coin of Prince Volodymyr Sviatoslavovych, Slavic warship with sail. No. 465, 6.50k, Arrival of Scandinavian Seamen, coin of Danish King Svend Estridsen.

2003, Sept. 10 *Perf. 11½*
464-465 A168 Set of 2 2.50 2.50
  See Ukraine No. 524.

Three Lions Type of 1999-2002
2003-04 **Litho.** *Perf. 13¾x14*
467 A108 20s blk & gray .20 .20
472 A108 4.40k ol grn & apple
    grn .75 .75
473 A108 5k dk grn & apple
    grn, dated 2004 1.00 1.00
474 A108 5.50k dk grn & yel grn 1.10 1.10
  Issued: 20s, 4.40k, 8/22; 5k, 1/20/04; 5.50k, 3/25/04.

Folk Costume Type of 1994

Designs: 4.40k, Aksi woman and girl. 6.50k, Otepää man, woman and girl.

2003, Oct. 9 **Litho.** *Perf. 13¾x14*
476-477 A57 Set of 2 2.10 2.10

A169

Christmas A170

2003, Nov. 26 *Perf. 14x13¾*
478 A169 3.60k multi .75 .75
479 A170 6k multi 1.25 1.25

Souvenir Sheet

Friedrich Reinhold Kreutzwald (1803-82), Writer — A171

No. 480: a, 4.40k, Illustration by Kristjan Raud of "Voyage to the End of the World," from "Kalevipoeg," by Kreutzwald. b, 6.50k, Portrait of Kreutzwald.

2003, Dec. 4 *Perf. 13x12¾*
480 A171 Sheet of 2, #a-b 2.10 2.10

Lighthouse Type of 1995
2004, Jan. 7 **Litho.** *Perf. 14x13¾*
481 A66 4.40k Sorgu .90 .90

Canis Lupus A172

2004, Feb. 3 *Perf. 12¾x13*
482 A172 4.40k multi .90 .90

Voyage Around Cape Horn of the Hioma, 150th Anniv. — A173

2004, Feb. 18 *Perf. 13¾x14*
483 A173 8k multi 1.90 1.90

Spring Flowers Type of 2003

No. 484: a, Viola riviniana. b, Anemone nemorosa. c, Hepatica nobilis. d, Trollius europaeus.

2004, Mar. 17
484 A160 4.40k Sheet of 4, #a-d 4.50 4.50
  e. Booklet pane, like #484 without
    date in margin 4.50
    Complete booklet, #484e 4.50

Bird Type of 2003
2004, Apr. 6 *Perf. 12¾x13*
485 A159 4.40k Ciconia ciconia .90 .90

Admission to European Union A174

2004, May 1 *Perf. 13¼x13*
486 A174 6.50k multi 1.40 1.40

Europa — A175

2004, May 4 *Perf. 13*
487 A175 6.50k multi 1.25 1.25

Tallinn Town Hall, 600th Anniv. A176

2004, May 13 **Litho.** *Perf. 12¾x13*
488 A176 4.40k multi .90 .90

Consecration of Estonian Flag, 120th Anniv. — A177

2004, June 4 *Perf. 13¾x14*
489 A177 4.40k multi .90 .90

Manor Type of 1999
2004, June 15   *Perf. 14x13¾*
490 A103 4.40k Vasalemma Hall .90 .90

Admission to NATO — A178

2004, June 28   *Perf. 13¾x14*
491 A178 6k multi 1.25 1.25

2004 Summer Olympics, Athens — A179

2004, July 15   Litho.   *Perf. 13¾x14*
492 A179 8k multi 1.50 1.50

Dragon Class Yachting European Championships — A180

2004, Aug. 17   *Perf. 14x13¾*
493 A180 6k multi 1.10 1.10

Taraxacum Officinale — A181

Serpentine Die Cut 12½
2004, Sept. 14
  Self-Adhesive
494 A181 30s multi .25 .25
See Nos. 547, 560, 572.

County Arms — A182

2004, Sept. 28   **Self-Adhesive**
495 A182 4.40k Harjumaa .80 .80
496 A182 4.40k Hiiumaa .80 .80
See Nos. 506-507, 518-519, 532-533, 536, 552, 561, 573, 588, 594, 608.

Folk Costumes Type of 1994
Designs: 4.40k, Viru-Jaagupi boy and girl. 7.50k, Jõhvi woman and girl.

2004, Oct. 5   Litho.   *Perf. 13¾x14*
497-498 A57   Set of 2 2.40 2.40

A183

Christmas A184

2004, Nov. 23   *Perf. 13¾x14*
499 A183 4.40k multi .90 .90
    Perf. 14x13¾
500 A184 6.50k multi 1.25 1.25

Lighthouse Type of 1995
Norrby Lighthouse with: 4.40k, White top, vert. 6.50k, Red top, vert.

2005, Jan. 11   Litho.   *Perf. 14*
501-502 A66   Set of 2 2.00 2.00

Castor Fiber A185

2005, Jan. 25   *Perf. 12¾x13*
503 A185 4.40k multi .90 .90

Rotary International, Cent. — A186

2005, Feb. 11   *Perf. 13¾x14*
504 A186 8k multi 1.50 1.50

Flag Over Pikk Hermann Tower, Tallinn — A187

Serpentine Die Cut 12½
2005, Feb. 22
  Self-Adhesive
505 A187 5k multi 1.00 1.00
See Nos. 530, 559, 574.

County Arms Type of 2004
2005   **Litho.**
  Self-Adhesive
506 A182 4.40k Ida-Virumaa .90 .90
507 A182 4.40k Järvamaa .90 .90
Issued: No. 506, 3/8; No. 507, 3/15.

Souvenir Sheet

Spring — A188

No. 508: a, Two swans, denomination at UL. b, One swan, denomination at UL. c, One swan, denomination at LL. d, Two swans, denomination at LR.

2005, Mar. 22   Litho.   *Perf. 14x13¾*
508 A188 4.40k Sheet of 4, #a-d 3.25 3.25

Bird Type of 2003
2005, Apr. 5   *Perf. 12¾x13*
509 A159 4.40k Accipiter gentilis .90 .90

Mother's Day — A189

2005, Apr. 20   *Perf. 14x13¾*
510 A189 4.40k multi .90 .90

Europa — A190

Designs: 6k, Vegetable wrap. 6.50k, Tomato, carrots, egg yolk, parsley, fish, onion, beet.

2005, May 3
511-512 A190   Set of 2 2.50 2.50

Eduard Tubin (1905-82), Composer A191

2005, May 18
513 A191 6k multi 1.10 1.10

Intl. Children's Day — A192

No. 514: a, Birds. b, Butterflies.

2005, June 1   *Perf. 13¼x13¾*
514 A192 4.40k Horiz. pair, #a-b, + central label 1.75 1.75

Orchids — A193

Designs: 4.40k, Epipactis palustris. 8k, Epipogium aphyllum.

2005, June 16   Litho.   *Perf. 13¾x14*
515-516 A193   Set of 2 2.40 2.40

Restoration of St. John's Cathedral, Tartu — A194

2005, June 29
517 A194 4.40k multi .90 .90
Tartu, 975th anniv.

County Arms Type of 2004
Serpentine Die Cut 12½
2005   **Litho.**
  Self-Adhesive
518 A182 4.40k Jõgevamaa .90 .90
519 A182 4.40k Läänemaa .90 .90
Issued: No. 518, 7/5; No. 519, 7/8.

Manor Type of 1999
2005, July 12   *Perf. 14x13¾*
520 A103 4.40k Kiltsi Hall .90 .90

St. Catherine's Church, Karja — A195

2005, Sept. 20
521 A195 4.40k multi .90 .90

Souvenir Sheet

Sculptures by Amandus Adamson (1855-1929) — A196

No. 522: a, Igavesti Voidutsev Armastus, 1889. b, Lüüriline Muusika, 1891. c, Memento Mori, 1907. d, Koit ja Hämarik, 1895.

2005, Oct. 12   *Perf. 13½*
522 A196 650s Sheet of 4, #a-d 4.75 4.75

Dogs — A197

No. 523: a, Kazakh hound (Kasaahi hurt). b, Estonian hound (Eesti hagijas).

2005, Oct. 19   *Perf. 14x13¾*
523 A197 6.50k Horiz. pair, #a-b 2.40 2.40
See Kazakhstan No. 495.

Folk Costumes Type of 1994
Designs: 4.40k, Ambla man, woman and girl. 8k, Türi women.

2005, Oct. 28   *Perf. 13¾x14*
524-525 A57   Set of 2 2.40 2.40

New Year's Goat — A198   Adoration of the Magi — A199

2005, Nov. 22
526 A198 4.40k multi .85 .85
527 A199 8k sil & red lil 1.50 1.50
Christmas and New Year's Day.

Due to the postponed conversion to the euro, originally scheduled for Jan. 1, 2007, Estonian stamps of 2006 until conversion will show denominations in kroons and the as-yet-uncirculating euros.

Europa Stamps, 50th Anniv. — A200

CEPT emblem and: 6k, Superimposed letters. 6.50k, Map of Europe.

2006, Jan. 4 Litho. Perf. 14x13¾
528 A200 6k multi 1.00 1.00

Souvenir Sheet
529 A200 6.50k multi 1.10 1.10

Flag Over Pikk Hermann Tower Type of 2005 With Euro Denominations Added
2006, Jan. 11 Die Cut Perf. 12½
Self-Adhesive
530 A187 11k multi 2.00 2.00

2006 Winter Olympics, Turin, Italy — A201

2006, Jan. 18 Perf. 14x13¾
531 A201 8k multi 1.50 1.50

County Arms Type of 2004 With Euro Denominations Added
2006 Die Cut Perf. 12½
Self-Adhesive
532 A182 4.40k Lääne-Virumaa .85 .85
533 A182 4.40k Polvamaa .85 .85

Issued: No. 532, 1/25; No. 533, 2/8.

Alces Alces A202

2006, Feb. 1 Perf. 12¾x13
534 A202 4.40k multi .85 .85

Opening of KUMU Art Museum — A203

2006, Feb. 17 Litho. Perf. 13¾x14
535 A203 4.40k multi .85 .85

County Arms Type of 2004 With Euro Denominations Added
2006, Mar. 8 Die Cut Perf. 12½
Self-Adhesive
536 A182 4.40k Pärnumaa .85 .85

Souvenir Sheet

National Opera, Cent. — A204

No. 537: a, Characters from Vikerlased, first opera staged in 1928. b, Ballerina.

2006, Mar. 27 Perf. 13¾x14
537 A204 6.50k Sheet of 2, #a-b, + central label 2.50 2.50

A205

Gold Medalists at 2006 Winter Olympics — A206

No. 539: a, Andrus Veerpalu. b, Kristina Smigun.
Illustrations reduced.

2006, Mar. 30 Perf. 14x13¾
538 A205 4.40k multi .85 .85

Souvenir Sheet
539 A206 8k Sheet of 2, #a-b 3.00 3.00

Bird Type of 2003 With Euro Denominations Added
2006, Apr. 5 Perf. 12¾x13
540 A159 4.40k multi .85 .85

Lighthouses A207

Designs: 4.40k, Tallinn Bay lower lighthouse. 6.50k, Tallinn Bay upper lighthouse.

2006, Apr. 12 Perf. 13¾x14
541-542 A207 Set of 2 2.00 2.00

See Nos. 564, 587, 624.

Estonian Shooting Sport Federation, 75th Anniv. — A208

2006, Apr. 26
543 A208 4.40k car & sil .85 .85

Europa — A209

2006, May 3
544 A209 6.50k multi 1.25 1.25

Confectionery Industry in Estonia, Bicent. A210

2006, May 18 Perf. 14x13¾
545 A210 4.40k multi .85 .85

Posthorns — A211

2006, May 22 Die Cut Perf. 10
Self-Adhesive
546 A211 4.40k gray brn + label .85 .85
Labels could be personalized.
See No. 563.

Flower Type of 2004 with Euro Denominations Added
2006, May 24 Die Cut Perf. 12½
Self-Adhesive
547 A181 30s Hepatica nobilis .25 .25

Souvenir Sheet

Tori Stud Farm, 150th Anniv. — A212

No. 548: a, Three horses, denomination at UL. b, Pony and three horses, denomination at UR.

2006, June 7 Perf. 14x13¾
548 A212 4.40k Sheet of 2, #a-b 1.75 1.75

Victory Day — A213

2006, June 23
549 A213 4.40k multi .85 .85

20th Intl. Organ Music Festival, Tallinn — A214

2006, July 28 Litho. Perf. 14x13¾
550 A214 4.40k multi .85 .85

Manor Type of 1999 With Added Euro Denomination
2006, Aug. 16
551 A103 4.40k Taagepera Hall .85 .85

County Arms Type of 2004 With Added Euro Denomination
2006, Sept. 6 Die Cut Perf. 12½
Self-Adhesive
552 A182 4.40k Raplamaa .85 .85

St. Lawrence's Church, Noo — A215

2006, Sept. 20 Perf. 13¾x14
553 A215 4.40k multi .85 .85

Betti Alver (1906-89), Writer — A216

2006, Oct. 11 Perf. 13
554 A216 4.40k multi .85 .85

Antarctic Wildlife — A217

No. 555 — Estonian and Chilean flags and: a, Aptenodytes forsteri. b, Balaenoptera acutorostrata.

2006, Oct. 25 Perf. 13½
555 A217 8k Pair, #a-b 3.00 3.00

See Chile No. 1468.

A218

Christmas — A219

2006, Nov. 22 Litho. Perf. 13¾x14
556 A218 4.40k multi .75 .75
557 A219 6k multi 1.10 1.10

Estonia's conversion to euro currency was postponed until certain mandated economic requirements are met. Until the conversion, stamps will continue to show denominations in kroons and the as-yet-uncirculating euros.

Lotte From Gadgetville A220

2007, Jan. 4 Perf. 14x13¾
558 A220 4.40k multi .85 .85

Flag Over Pikk Hermann Tower Type of 2005 With Euro Denomination Added
2007, Jan. 11 Die Cut Perf. 12½
Self-Adhesive
559 A187 5k tan & multi 1.00 1.00

Flower Type of 2004 With Euro Denomination Added
2007, Jan. 17 Die Cut Perf. 12½
Self-Adhesive
560 A181 30s Leucanthemum vulgare .25 .25

County Arms Type of 2004 With Euro Denomination Added
2007, Jan. 25 Die Cut Perf. 12½
Self-Adhesive
561 A182 4.40k Saaremaa .85 .85

Manor Type of 1999 With Euro Denomination Added

2007, Feb. 14   *Perf. 14x13¾*
562 A103 5.50k Sagadi Hall   1.10 1.10

Posthorns Type of 2006

2007, Feb. 22   *Die Cut Perf. 10*
Self-Adhesive
563 A211 5.50k bl grn + label   1.25 1.25
Labels could be personalized.

Lighthouse Type of 2006

2007, Mar. 8   *Perf. 14x13¾*
564 A207 6k Juminda, horiz.   1.25 1.25

Meles Meles
A221

2007, Mar. 22   *Perf. 12¾x13*
565 A221 4.40k multi   .90 .90

Bird Type of 2003 With Euro Denomination Added

2007, Apr. 5   *Perf. 12¾x13*
566 A159 4.40k Cygnus bewickii   .90 .90

Miniature Sheet

Summer Flowers — A222

No. 567: a, Paeonia officinalis. b, Lilium lancifolium. c, Rosa ecae Golden Chersonese. d, Iris latifolia.

2007, Apr. 19   *Perf. 13¾x14*
567 A222 4.40k Sheet of 4, #a-d   3.50 3.50

Europa — A223

2007, May 3   *Perf. 12½*
568 A223 20.50k multi   4.00 4.00
Scouting, cent.

Intl. Children's Day — A224

2007, June 1   Litho.   *Perf. 13½*
569 A224 10k multi   2.00 2.00

Souvenir Sheet

1941-51 Deportation of Estonians — A225

2007, June 14   *Perf. 13*
570 A225 8k multi   1.60 1.60

Pirita Convent, 600th Anniv. — A226

2007, June 15   Litho.   *Perf. 12½*
571 A226 5.50k multi   1.00 1.00

Flower Type of 2004 With Euro Denominations Added

2007, July 2   *Die Cut Perf. 12½*
Self-Adhesive
572 A181 1.10k Centaurea phrygia   .25 .25

County Arms Type of 2004 With Euro Denominations Added

2007, July 2
Self-Adhesive
573 A182 5.50k Tartumaa   1.00 1.00

Flag Over Pikk Hermann Tower Type of 2005 With Euro Denominations Added

2007, Aug. 1
Self-Adhesive
574 A187 10k multi   1.90 1.90

Hellenurme Mill — A227

2007, Aug. 9   *Perf. 14x13¾*
575 A227 5.50k multi   1.10 1.10

Hirvepark Demonstration, 20th Anniv. — A228

2007, Aug. 23   *Perf. 14x14¼*
576 A228 5.50k multi   1.10 1.10

Souvenir Sheet

Matthias Johann Eisen (1857-1934), Folklorist — A229

2007, Sept. 14   *Imperf.*
577 A229 10k multi   2.10 2.10
No. 577 has simulated perforations.

Ragnar Nurkse (1907-59), Economist — A230

2007, Oct. 5   *Perf. 13*
578 A230 10k multi   2.10 2.10

St. John's Church, Kanepi — A231

2007, Oct. 11   *Perf. 13¾x14*
579 A231 5.50k multi   1.10 1.10

Arms of Viljandi — A232

2007, Oct. 25   Litho.   *Perf. 13¾x14*
580 A232 5.50k multi   1.10 1.10

A233

Christmas A234

Die Cut Perf. 11¼ Syncopated
2007, Nov. 22
Self-Adhesive
581 A233 5.50k multi   1.10 1.10
582 A234 8k multi   1.60 1.60

Post Horn — A235

2008   Litho.   *Die Cut Perf. 12½*
Self-Adhesive
583 A235 5.50k brt orange   1.10 1.10
584 A235 6.50k brt yel green   1.25 1.25
585 A235 9k blue   1.90 1.90
    Nos. 583-585 (3)   4.25 4.25
Issued: 5.50k, 1/10; 6.50k, 3/6; 9k, 4/1. See Nos. 600, 638, 649.

Gustav Ernesaks (1908-93), Composer A236

2008, Jan. 17   Litho.   *Perf. 13*
586 A236 5.50k multi   1.10 1.10

Lighthouse Type of 2006

2008, Jan. 24   *Perf. 14x13¾*
587 A207 5.50k Mehikoorma, horiz.   1.10 1.10

County Arms Type of 2004 With Euro Denominations Added

2008, Feb. 7   *Die Cut Perf. 12½*
Self-Adhesive
588 A182 5.50k Valgamaa   1.10 1.10

Plecotus Auritus A237

2008, Feb. 14   *Perf. 12¾x13*
589 A237 5.50k multi   1.10 1.10

Oak Tree — A238

2008, Feb. 23   *Perf. 13*
590 A238 5.50k multi   1.10 1.10
Republic of Estonia, 90th anniv.

Kristjan Palusalu (1908-87), Olympic Wrestling Gold Medalist — A239

2008, Mar. 10   *Perf. 12½*
591 A239 10k multi   2.00 2.00

State Awards of the Baltic Countries — A240

Designs: Nos. 592, 593a, Order of the National Coat of Arms, Estonia. No. 593b, Order of Three Stars, Latvia. No. 593c, Order of Vytautas the Great, Lithuania.

2008, Mar. 15   Litho.   Perf. 13¾
592 A240 5.50k multi   1.10 1.10

Souvenir Sheet
593 A240 10k Sheet of 3, #a-c,
            + label   6.00 6.00

See Latvia Nos. 701-702, Lithuania Nos. 862-863.

County Arms Type of 2004 With Euro Denominations Added
2008, Mar. 27   Die Cut Perf. 12½
Self-Adhesive
594 A182 5.50k Viljandimaa   1.10 1.10

Bird Type of 2003 With Euro Denomination Added
2008, Apr. 3   Perf. 12¾x13
595 A159 5.50k Tetrao tetrix   1.10 1.10

Europa A241

2008, Apr. 30   Perf. 14x14¼
596 A241 9k multi   1.75 1.75

Otto Strandman (1875-1941), Statesman — A242

2008, May 9   Litho.   Perf. 13¾x14
597 A242 5.50k brown   1.10 1.10

Wavy Lines A243

2008, May 22   Serpentine Die Cut 10
Self-Adhesive
598 A243 9k multi + label   1.90 1.90

The label shown is generic. Labels could be personalized for a fee.

Peasant War at Mahtra, 150th Anniv. — A244

2008, May 31   Perf. 14x13¾
599 A244 5.50k multi   1.10 1.10

Posthorn Type of 2008
Die Cut Perf. 12½
2008, May 31   Litho.
Self-Adhesive
600 A235 50s gray   .30 .30

2008 Summer Olympics, Beijing — A245

2008, Aug. 8   Litho.   Perf. 13¾x14
601 A245 9k multi   1.75 1.75

Polma Windmill A246

2008, Aug. 28   Perf. 14x13¾
602 A246 5.50k multi   1.10 1.10

Manor Type of 1999 With Euro Denomination Added
2008, Sept. 18   Litho.   Perf. 14x13¾
603 A103 5.50k Kalvi Hall   1.10 1.10

Gerd Kanter, Olympic Discus Champion A247

2008. Sept. 25   Perf. 13½
604 A247 5.50k multi   1.10 1.10

Church of the Holy Cross, Audru — A248

2008, Oct. 16   Litho.   Perf. 13¾x14
605 A248 5.50k multi   1.10 1.10

County Arms Type of 2004 With Euro Denominations Added
2008, Oct. 30   Die Cut Perf. 12½
Self-Adhesive
606 A182 5.50k Vorumaa   1.10 1.10

Estonia Post, 90th Anniv. — A249

2008, Nov. 13   Perf. 13¾x14
607 A249 5.50k multi   1.10 1.10

Christmas A250

Designs: 5.50k, Gift on skis. 9k, Snowman on gift.

Die Cut Perf. 11¼ Syncopated
2008, Nov. 20   Litho.
Booklet Stamps
Self-Adhesive
608 A250 5.50k multi   1.00 1.00
  a.   Booklet pane of 10   9.00
609 A250 9k multi   1.75 1.75
  a.   Booklet pane of 10   15.00

Souvenir Sheet

International Polar Year — A251

No. 610 — Antarctic glacier with snowflake emblem in: a, White. b, Blue.

2009, Jan. 15   Litho.   Perf. 13x12¾
610 A251 15k Sheet of 2, #a-b   6.25 6.25

Battle of Paju, 90th Anniv. A252

2009, Jan. 29   Perf. 12¾x13
611 A252 5.50k multi   1.10 1.10

Gen. Johan Laidoner (1884-1953) — A253

2009, Feb. 12   Litho.   Perf. 13
612 A253 5.50k multi   1.10 1.10

Ants Piip (1884-1942), Prime Minister — A254

2009, Feb. 26   Perf. 14
613 A254 5.50k maroon   1.10 1.10

Pres. Lennart Meri (1929-2006) A255

2009, Mar. 26   Litho.   Perf. 14
614 A255 5.50k blue   1.10 1.10

Estonian National Museum, Cent. A256

2009, Apr. 14   Perf. 13
615 A256 5.50k multi   1.10 1.10

Estonian Parliament, 90th Anniv. — A257

2009, Apr. 23   Perf. 14
616 A257 5.50k multi   1.10 1.10

Europa — A258

No. 617: a, Galaxies and hexagonal cells. b, Galaxy and hexagonal cells at left.

2009, May 5   Litho.   Perf. 13¾x14
617 A258 9k Horiz. pair, #a-b   3.50 3.50

Intl. Year of Astronomy.

Räpina Paper Mill, 275th Anniv. — A259

2009, May 14
618 A259 5.50k multi   1.10 1.10

Estonian Flag, 125th Anniv. — A260

Die Cut Perf. 11¼ Syncopated
2009, June 5
Self-Adhesive
619 A260 9k multi   1.75 1.75

25th Song Festival — A261

2009, June 18   Perf. 14x13¾
620 A261 5.50k multi   1.10 1.10

Alexander Church, Narva, 125th Anniv. — A262

2009, July 10   Litho.   Perf. 13¾x14
621 A262 5.50k multi   1.00 1.00

Ursus Arctos
A263

2009, Sept. 10   *Perf. 12¾x13*
622 A263 5.50k multi   1.10 1.10

First Track and Field Competition in Estonia, Cent. — A264

2009, Sept. 22   *Perf. 14x13¾*
623 A264 5.50k multi   1.10 1.10

Lighthouse Type of 2006
2009, Sept. 24   *Perf. 14x13¾*
624 A207 5.50k Hara Tuletorn,
       horiz.   1.10 1.10

Bird Type of 2003 With Euro Denomination Added
2009, Oct. 8   Litho.   *Perf. 12¾x13*
625 A159 5.50k Strix aluco   1.10 1.10

Windmill, Angla — A265

2009, Oct. 22   *Perf. 13¾x14*
626 A265 5.50k multi   1.10 1.10

Manor Type of 1999 With Euro Denomination Added
2009, Nov. 5   *Perf. 14x13¾*
627 A103 5.50k Saku Hall   1.10 1.10

A266

Christmas
A267

Die Cut Perf. 11¼ Syncopated
2009, Nov. 19
Self-Adhesive

628 A266 5.50k multi   1.10 1.10
629 A267 9k multi   1.75 1.75

Fabric Design — A268

Die Cut Perf. 11¼ Syncopated
2010, Jan. 7   Litho.
Self-Adhesive

630 A268 50k orange & multi   9.50 9.50
     See Nos. 646, 650.

Jüri Jaakson (1870-1942), Politician — A269

2010, Jan. 15   *Perf. 14*
631 A269 5.50k multi   1.10 1.10

2010 Winter Olympics, Vancouver — A270

2010, Jan. 19   *Perf. 12¾x13*
632 A270 9k multi   1.75 1.75

Tartu Peace Treaty, 90th Anniv. A271

2010, Feb. 2   *Perf. 13*
633 A271 5.50k multi   1.10 1.10

Post Horn Type of 2008
2010, Feb. 4   *Die Cut Perf. 12½*
Self-Adhesive
634 A235 9k deep blue   1.75 1.75
     Dated 2010. Compare with No. 585.

2010 Winter Olympics, Vancouver — A272

2010, Feb. 4   *Perf. 14*
635 A272 9k multi   1.75 1.75

Platanthera Bifolia — A273

2010, Feb. 19
636 A273 5.50k multi   1.10 1.10

Estonia Pavilion, Expo 2010, Shanghai A274

2010, Mar. 11
637 A274 9k multi   1.75 1.75

Posthorn Type of 2008
Die Cut Perf. 12½
2010, Mar. 23   Litho.
Self-Adhesive
638 A235 5.50k bright pink   1.10 1.10

St. Catherine's Church, Pärnu — A275

2010, Mar. 23   *Perf. 13¾x14*
639 A275 6.50k multi   1.25 1.25

Juhan Kukk (1885-1942), State Elder — A276

2010, Apr. 13
640 A276 5.50k olive brown   1.10 1.10

Lighthouses Type of 2006
   Designs: 6.50k, Suurupi front lighthouse. 8k, Suurupi rear lighthouse.

2010, Apr. 22
641-642 A207   Set of 2   2.75 2.75

Europa — A277

   Children's book illustrations: No. 643, 9k, Family of mice, by Jüri Mildeberg. No. 644, 9k, Skaters in snow, by Viive Noor.

2010, May 6   *Perf. 14x13¾*
643-644 A277   Set of 2   2.75 2.75

Bird Type of 2003 With Euro Denominations Added
2010, May 13   *Perf. 12¾x13*
645 A159 5.50k Lanius collurio   1.10 1.10

Fabric Design Type of 2010
Die Cut Perf. 11¼ Syncopated
2010, June 1
Self-Adhesive
646 A268 26k brt yel grn & multi   5.00 5.00

Intl. Children's Day — A278

2010, June 1   Litho.
Self-Adhesive
647 A278 5.50k multi   1.10 1.10

Manor Type of 1999 With Euro Denominations Added
2010, Aug. 5   Litho.   *Perf. 14x13¾*
648 A103 5.50k Suuremõisa Hall   .95 .95

Posthorn Type of 2008
2010, Aug. 18   *Die Cut Perf. 12*
Self-Adhesive
649 A235 9k bright yellow   1.50 1.50

Fabric Design Type of 2010
Die Cut Perf. 11¼ Syncopated
2010, Aug. 18
Self-Adhesive
650 A268 26k lilac & multi   4.25 4.25

Tallinn, 2011 European Capital of Culture — A279

2010, Sept. 9   Litho.
Self-Adhesive
651 A279 5.50k multi   .90 .90

Eliomys Quercinus A280

2010, Sept. 23   *Perf. 12¾x13*
652 A280 5.50k multi   1.00 1.00

A281

A282

A283

Worldwide Fund for Nature (WWF) — A284

   Various views of Triturus cristatus.

2010, Oct. 14   *Perf. 14x13¾*
653   Horiz. strip of 4   6.50 6.50
   a.   A281 9k multi   1.60 1.60
   b.   A282 9k multi   1.60 1.60
   c.   A283 9k multi   1.60 1.60
   d.   A284 9k multi   1.60 1.60

SEMI-POSTAL STAMPS

Assisting Wounded Soldier — SP1

Offering Aid to Wounded Hero — SP2

1920, June   Unwmk.   Litho.   *Imperf.*
B1   SP1 35p + 10p red & ol grn   .40 2.00
B2   SP2 70p + 15p dp bl & brn   .40 2.00

Surcharged

1920
B3	SP1	1m on No. B1	.30	.30
B4	SP2	2m on No. B2	.30	.30

Nurse and Wounded
Soldier — SP3

1921, Aug. 1   Imperf.
B5	SP3	2½ (3½)m org, brn & car	2.00	7.25
B6	SP3	5 (7)m ultra, brn & car	2.00	7.25

1922, Apr. 26   Perf. 13½x14
B7	SP3	2½ (3½)m org, brn & car	2.00	7.25
a.		Vert. pair, imperf. horiz.	30.00	80.00
B8	SP3	5 (7)m ultra, brn & car	2.00	7.25
a.		Vert. pair, imperf. horiz.	30.00	80.00

Nos. B5-B8
Overprinted

1923, Oct. 8   Imperf.
B9	SP3	2½ (3½)m	60.00	160.00
B10	SP3	5 (7)m	60.00	160.00

Perf. 13½x14
B11	SP3	2½ (3½)m	60.00	160.00
a.		Vert. pair, imperf. horiz.	200.00	800.00
B12	SP3	5 (7)m	60.00	160.00
a.		Vert. pair, imperf. horiz.	200.00	800.00
		Nos. B9-B12 (4)	240.00	640.00

Excellent forgeries are plentiful.

Nos. B7 and B8
Surcharged

1926, June 15
B13	SP3	5 (6)m on #B7	3.75	8.00
a.		Vert. pair, imperf. horiz.	24.00	120.00
B14	SP3	10 (12)m on #B8	4.50	8.00
a.		Vert. pair, imperf. horiz.	24.00	120.00

Nos. B5-B14 had the franking value of the lower figure. They were sold for the higher figure, the excess going to the Red Cross Society.

Kuressaare
Castle
SP4

Tartu
Cathedral
SP5

Tallinn
Castle
SP6

Narva Fortress
SP7

View of
Tallinn — SP8

Laid Paper
Perf. 14½x14
1927, Nov. 19   Typo.   Wmk. 207
B15	SP4	5m + 5m bl grn & ol, grysh	.90	8.00
B16	SP5	10m + 10m dp bl & brn, cream	.90	8.00
B17	SP6	12m + 12m rose red & ol grn, bluish	.90	8.00

Perf. 14x13½
B18	SP7	20m + 20m bl & choc, gray	1.75	8.00
B19	SP8	40m + 40m org brn & slate, buff	1.75	8.00
		Nos. B15-B19 (5)	6.20	40.00

The money derived from the surtax was donated to the Committee for the commemoration of War for Liberation.

Red Cross Issue

Symbolical of
Succor to
Injured — SP9

Symbolical of
"Light of
Hope" — SP10

1931, Aug. 1   Unwmk.   Perf. 13½
B20	SP9	2s + 3s grn & car	8.00	8.00
B21	SP10	5s + 3s red & car	8.00	8.00
B22	SP10	10s + 3s lt bl & car	8.00	8.00
B23	SP9	20s + 3s dk bl & car	12.00	20.00
		Nos. B20-B23 (4)	36.00	44.00
		Set, never hinged	72.50	

Nurse and
Child
SP11

Taagepera
Sanatorium
SP12

Lorraine Cross and
Flower — SP13

Paper with Network as in Parenthesis
1933, Oct. 1   Perf. 14, 14½
B24	SP11	5s + 3s ver (grn)	6.00	8.00
B25	SP12	10s + 3s lt bl & red (vio)	6.00	8.00
B26	SP13	12s + 3s rose & red (grn)	8.00	12.00
B27	SP12	20s + 3s dk bl & red (org)	10.00	16.00
		Nos. B24-B27 (4)	30.00	44.00
		Set, never hinged	60.00	

The surtax was for a fund to combat tuberculosis.

Coats of Arms

Narva — SP14

Pärnu — SP15

Tartu — SP16

Tallinn — SP17

Paper with Network as in Parenthesis
1936, Feb. 1   Perf. 13½
B28	SP14	10s + 10s grn & ultra (gray)	3.50	8.00
B29	SP15	15s + 15s car & bl (gray)	3.50	12.00
B30	SP16	25s + 25s gray bl & red (brn)	4.50	16.00
B31	SP17	50s + 50s blk & dl org (ol)	17.00	52.50
		Nos. B28-B31 (4)	28.50	88.50
		Set, never hinged	52.50	

Paide
SP18

Valga
SP20

Rakvere
SP19

Viljandi
SP21

Paper with Network as in Parenthesis
1937, Jan. 2   Perf. 13½x14
B32	SP18	10s + 10s grn (gray)	3.00	6.50
B33	SP19	15s + 15s red brn (gray)	3.00	6.50
B34	SP20	25s + 25s dk bl (lil)	5.00	9.50
B35	SP21	50s + 50s dk vio (gray)	9.00	24.00
		Nos. B32-B35 (4)	20.00	46.50
		Set, never hinged	40.00	

Baltiski — SP22

Haapsalu
SP24

Võru — SP23

Kuressaare
SP25

Designs are the armorial bearings of various cities

1938, Jan. 21
Paper with Gray Network
B36	SP22	10s + 10s dk brn	3.00	8.00
B37	SP23	15s + 15s car & grn	3.50	12.00
B38	SP24	25s + 25s dk bl & car	5.00	20.00

B39	SP25	50s + 50s blk & org yel	8.00	40.00
a.		Sheet of 4, #B36-B39	35.00	80.00
		Nos. B36-B39 (4)	19.50	80.00
		Set, never hinged	40.00	

Annual charity ball, Tallinn, Jan. 2, 1938.

Viljandimaa
SP27

Pärnumaa
SP28

Tartumaa
SP29

Harjumaa
SP30

Designs are the armorial bearings of various districts

1939, Jan. 10   Perf. 13½
Paper with Gray Network
B41	SP27	10s + 10s dk bl grn	3.50	8.00
B42	SP28	15s + 15s carmine	4.00	8.00
B43	SP29	25s + 25s dk blue	5.50	20.00
B44	SP30	50s + 50s brn lake	14.00	47.50
a.		Sheet of 4, #B41-B44	45.00	175.00
		Nos. B41-B44 (4)	27.00	83.50
		Set, never hinged	47.50	

Võrumaa
SP32

Läänemaa
SP34

Järvamaa
SP33

Saaremaa
SP35

Designs are the armorial bearings of various districts

1940, Jan. 2   Typo.   Perf. 13½
Paper with Gray Network
B46	SP32	10s + 10s dp grn & ultra	2.50	12.00
B47	SP33	15s + 15s dk car & ultra	2.50	16.00
B48	SP34	25s + 25s dk bl & scar	3.00	24.00
B49	SP35	50s + 50s ocher & ultra	8.00	32.50
		Nos. B46-B49 (4)	16.00	84.50
		Set, never hinged	30.00	

Catalogue values for unused stamps in this section, from this point to the end of the section, are for Never Hinged items.

1992 Summer
Olympics,
Barcelona — SP40

1992, June 22   Litho.   Perf. 14

B60	SP40	1r +50k red	.55	.55
B61	SP40	3r +1.50r green	2.40	2.40
B62	SP40	5r +2.50r blue & blk	1.10	1.10
		Nos. B60-B62 (3)	4.05	4.05

While face values are shown in kopecks and rubles, the stamps were sold in the new currency at the rate of 1 ruble = 10 sents.

No. 280
Surcharged

1994, Nov. 18   Litho.   Perf. 14

B63	A51	2.50k +20k green	7.50	7.50

Surtax for benefit of survivors of sinking of ferry "Estonia."

Haliaeetus
Albicilla — SP41

1995, Aug. 29   Litho.   Perf. 14

B64	SP41	2k +25k black & blue	.55	.55

Surtax for Keep the Estonian Sea Clean Assoc.

UNICEF,
60th Anniv.
SP42

2006, June 1   Litho.   Perf. 13½

B65	SP42	4.40k +1k multi	1.10	1.10

AIR POST STAMPS

Airplane
AP1

Unwmk.

1920, Mar. 13   Typo.   Imperf.

C1	AP1	5m yel, blk & lt grn	3.00	5.50
		Never hinged	7.00	

No. C1 Overprinted "1923" in Red

1923, Oct. 1

C2	AP1	5m multicolored	8.00	32.50
		Never hinged	15.00	

No. C1 Surcharged in Red

1923, Oct. 1

C3	AP1	15m on 5m multi	16.00	47.50
		Never hinged	30.00	

Pairs of No. C1
Surcharged in
Black or Red

1923, Oct.

C4	AP1	10m on 5m+5m		
C5	AP1	20m on 5m+5m	10.00	35.00
C6	AP1	45m on 5m+5m	20.00	55.00
			80.00	200.00

Rough Perf. 11½

C7	AP1	10m on 5m+5m		
		(B)	550.00	1,200.
C8	AP1	20m on 5m+5m	200.00	525.00
		Nos. C4-C8 (5)	860.00	2,015.
		Set, never hinged	1,400.	

The pairs comprising Nos. C7 and C8 are imperforate between. Forged surcharges and perforations abound. Authentication is required.

Monoplane in Flight — AP2

Designs: Various views of planes in flight.

1924, Feb. 12   Imperf.

C9	AP2	5m yellow & blk	2.00	8.00
C10	AP2	10m blue & blk	2.00	8.00
C11	AP2	15m red & blk	2.00	8.00
C12	AP2	20m green & blk	2.00	8.00
C13	AP2	45m violet & blk	2.00	16.00
		Nos. C9-C13 (5)	10.00	48.00
		Set, never hinged	15.00	

The paper is covered with a faint network in pale shades of the frame colors. There are four varieties of the frames and five of the pictures.

1925, July 15   Perf. 13½

C14	AP2	5m yellow & blk	1.50	8.00
C15	AP2	10m blue & blk	1.50	8.00
C16	AP2	15m red & blk	1.50	8.00
C17	AP2	20m green & blk	1.50	8.00
C18	AP2	45m violet & blk	1.50	16.00
		Nos. C14-C18 (5)	7.50	48.00
		Set, never hinged	11.00	

Counterfeits of Nos. C1-C18 are plentiful.

REGISTRATION STAMP

> Catalogue values for unused stamps in this section are for Never Hinged items.

Arms Type of 1992

1992, Mar. 16   Litho.   Perf. 13x12½

F1	A42	R (10r) pink & red	.70	.70

OCCUPATION STAMPS

Issued under German Occupation
For Use in Tartu (Dorpat)

Russian Stamps of 1909-
12 Surcharged

1918   Unwmk.   Perf. 14x14½

N1	A15	20pf on 10k dk bl	35.00	80.00
N2	A8	40pf on 20k bl & car	35.00	80.00
		Set, Never Hinged	130.00	

Forged overprints exist.

Estonian Arms and
Swastika — OS1

Perf. 11½

1941, Aug.   Typo.   Unwmk.

N3	OS1	15k brown	10.00	10.00
N4	OS1	20k green	10.00	10.00
N5	OS1	30k dark blue	10.00	10.00
		Nos. N3-N5 (3)	30.00	30.00
		Set, never hinged	50.00	

Exist imperf. Value, set, $200.
Nos. N3-N5 were issued on both ordinary paper with colorless gum and thick chalky paper with yellow gum. Same values.

OCCUPATION SEMI-POSTAL STAMPS

Castle Tower,
Tallinn — OSP1

Designs: 20k+20k, Stone Bridge, Tartu, horiz. 30k+30k, Narva Castle, horiz. 50k+50k, Tallinn view, horiz. 60k+60k, Tartu University. 100k+100k, Narva Castle, close view.

Paper with Gray Network

Perf. 11½

1941, Sept. 29   Photo.   Unwmk.

NB1	OSP1	15k + 15k dk brn	.60	4.75
NB2	OSP1	20k + 20k red lil	.60	4.75
NB3	OSP1	30k + 30k dk bl	.60	4.75
NB4	OSP1	50k + 50k bluish grn	.70	9.50
NB5	OSP1	60k + 60k car	1.00	8.00
NB6	OSP1	100k + 100k gray	1.50	9.50
		Nos. NB1-NB6 (6)	5.00	41.25
		Set, never hinged	12.00	

Nos. NB1-NB6 exist imperf. Value, set unused $70, used $200.
A miniature sheet containing one each of Nos. NB1-NB6, imperf., exists in various colors. Value, mint $40, used $60. It was not postally valid. Reproductions are common.

ETHIOPIA

ē-thē-'ō-pē-ə

(Abyssinia)

LOCATION — Northeastern Africa
GOVT. — Republic (1988)
AREA — 426,260 sq. mi.
POP. — 59,680,383 (1999 est.)
CAPITAL — Addis Ababa

During the Italian occupation (1936-1941) Nos. N1-N7 were used, also stamps of Italian East Africa, Eritrea and Somalia.
During the British administration (1941-42) stamps of Great Britain and Kenya were used when available.

16 Guerche = 1 Menelik Dollar or 1 Maria Theresa Dollar
100 Centimes = 1 Franc (1905)
40 Paras = 1 Piaster (1908)
16 Mehalek = 1 Thaler or Talari (1928)
100 Centimes = 1 Thaler (1936)
100 Cents = 1 Ethiopian Dollar (1946)
100 Cents = 1 Birr (1978)

> Catalogue values for unused stamps in this country are for Never Hinged items, beginning with Scott 247 in the regular postage section, Scott B6 in the semipostal section, Scott C18 in the airpost section, Scott E1 in the special delivery section, and Scott J57 in the postage due section.

Watermarks

Wmk. 140 —
Crown

Wmk. 282 — Ethiopian Star and
Amharic Characters, Multiple

Excellent forgeries of Nos. 1-86 exist.

> Very Fine examples of Nos. 1-86 and J1-J42 will have perforations touching the design on one or more sides due to the narrow spacing of the stamps on the plates and imperfect perforating methods. Stamps with margins clear on all sides are scarce and command high premiums.

On March 9, 1894 Menelik II awarded Alfred Ilg a concession to develop a railway, including postal service. Ilg's stamps, Nos. 1-79, were valid locally and to Djibouti. Mail to other countries had to bear stamps of Obock, Somali Coast, etc.
Ethiopia joined the UPU Nov. 1, 1908.

Menelik II
A1

Lion of
Judah
A2

Anharic numeral "8"

Perf. 14x13½

1895, Jan.   Unwmk.   Typo.

1	A1	¼g green	3.00	2.00
2	A1	½g red	3.00	2.00
3	A1	1g blue	3.00	2.00
4	A1	2g dark brown	3.00	2.00
5	A2	4g lilac brown	3.00	2.00
6	A2	8g violet	3.00	2.00
7	A2	16g black	3.00	2.00
		Nos. 1-7 (7)	21.00	14.00

For 4g, 8g and 16g stamps of type A1, see Nos. J3a, J4a and J7a.
Earliest reported use is Jan. 29, 1895.
Forged cancellations are plentiful.
For overprints see #8-86, J8-J28, J36-J42.
For surcharges see #94-100, J29-J35.

Nos. 1-7 Handstamped
in Violet or Blue

Overprint 9¼x2½mm, Serifs on "E"

1901, July 18

8	A1	¼g green	24.00	24.00
9	A1	½g red	24.00	24.00
10	A1	1g blue	24.00	24.00
11	A1	2g dark brown	24.00	24.00
12	A2	4g lilac brown	27.50	27.50

13	A2	8g violet	42.50	42.50
14	A2	16g black	52.50	52.50
		Nos. 8-14 (7)	297.50	297.50

Violet overprints were issued July 18, 1901, for postal use, while the blue overprints were issued in Jan. 1902 for philatelic purposes. The blue overprints were not used in the mails. Values for unused stamps are for examples with violet overprints. Unused stamps with violet overprints are worth much more.

Overprints 8¼mm wide are unofficial reproductions.

Nos. 1-7 Handstamped in Violet, Blue or Black

Overprint 11x3mm, Low Colons

1902, Apr. 1

15	A1	¼g green	6.00	6.00
16	A1	½g red	9.00	7.00
17	A1	1g blue	10.00	10.00
18	A1	2g dark brown	14.00	14.00
19	A2	4g lilac brown	27.50	27.50
20	A2	8g violet	40.00	40.00
21	A2	16g black	65.00	65.00
		Nos. 15-21 (7)	171.50	169.50

The handstamp reads "Bosta" (Post). Overprints 10¾mm and 11mm wide with raised colons are unofficial reproductions.

Nos. 1-7 Handstamped in Black

Overprint 16x3¾mm

1903, Apr. 15

22	A1	¼g green	7.00	7.00
23	A1	½g red	11.00	11.00
24	A1	1g blue	14.00	14.00
25	A1	2g dark brown	17.50	17.50
26	A2	4g lilac brown	25.00	25.00
27	A2	8g violet	35.00	35.00
28	A2	16g black	52.50	52.50
		Nos. 22-28 (7)	162.00	162.00

The handstamp reads "Malekt." (Also "Melekt," message.)

Original stamps have blurred colons. Unofficial reproductions have clean colons.

Nos. 22-28 have black overprints only. All other colors are fakes.

Nos. 1-7 Handstamped in Violet or Blue

Overprint 18¼mm Wide

1904, Dec.

36	A1	¼g green	15.00	15.00
37	A1	½g red	20.00	
38	A1	1g blue	25.00	
39	A1	2g dark brown	27.50	
40	A2	4g lilac brown	35.00	
41	A2	8g violet	57.50	
42	A2	16g black	75.00	
		Nos. 36-42 (7)	255.00	

The handstamp reads "Malekathe" (message). This set was never issued.

Preceding Issues Surcharged with New Values in French Currency in Blue, Violet, Rose or Black:

a			b	

Overprint 3mm High

1905, Jan. 1

On Nos. 1-7

43	A1 (a)	5c on ¼g	10.00	10.00
44	A1 (a)	10c on ½g	10.00	10.00
45	A1 (a)	20c on 1g	10.00	10.00
46	A1 (a)	40c on 2g	11.00	11.00
47	A1 (a)	80c on 4g	18.50	18.50

48	A2 (b)	1.60fr on 8g	22.50	22.50
49	A2 (b)	3.20fr on 16g	32.50	32.50
		Nos. 43-49 (7)	114.50	114.50

Nos. 48-49 exist with period or comma.

On No. 8, "Ethiopie" in Blue

50	A1 (a)	5c on ¼g	120.00	100.00

On No. 15, "Bosta" in Black

51	A1 (a)	5c on ¼g	40.00	40.00

On No. 22, "Malekt" in Black

52	A1 (a)	5c on ¼g	100.00	75.00

Unofficial reproductions exist of Nos. 50, 51, 52. The 5c on #36, 10c, 20c, 40c, 80c, and 1.60fr surcharges exist as unofficial reproductions only.

c			d	

1905

On No. 2

54	A1 (c)	5c on half of ½g	10.00	10.00

On No. 21, "Bosta" in Black

55	A2 (d)	5c on 16g blk	200.00	100.00

On #55, "Bosta" is in black.

On No. 28, "Malekt" in Black

56	A2 (d)	5c on 16g blk	250.00	250.00
		Nos. 54-56 (3)	460.00	360.00

Nos. 55-56 issued Mar. 30.

The overprints and surcharges on Nos. 8 to 56 inclusive were handstamped, the work being very roughly done.

As is usual with handstamped overprints and surcharges there are many inverted and double, but most of them are fakes or unofficial reproductions.

Surcharged with New Values in Various Colors

and in Violet:

Overprint 14¾x3½mm

1906, Jan. 1

57	A1	5c on ¼g green	10.00	10.00
58	A1	10c on ½g red	12.00	12.00
59	A1	20c on 1g blue	12.00	12.00
60	A1	40c on 2g dk brn	12.00	12.00
61	A2	80c on 4g lilac brn	18.00	18.00
62	A2	1.60fr on 8g violet	27.50	27.50
63	A2	3.20fr on 16g black	45.00	45.00
		Nos. 57-63 (7)	136.50	136.50

Two types of the 4-character overprint ("Menelik"): 14x¾x3½mm and 16x4mm.

Surcharged with New Values

and in Violet Brown:

Overprint 16x4¼mm

1906, July 1

64	A1	5c on ¼g grn	8.50	8.50
a.		Surcharged "20"	75.00	75.00
65	A1	10c on ½g red	10.00	10.00
66	A1	20c on 1g blue	16.00	16.00
67	A1	40c on 2g dk brn	16.00	16.00
68	A2	80c on 4g lil brn	22.50	22.50
69	A2	1.60fr on 8g vio	22.50	22.50
70	A2	3.20fr on 16g blk	55.00	55.00
		Nos. 64-70 (7)	150.50	150.50

The control overprint reads "Menelik."

Surcharged in Violet:

e		f

1907, June 21

71	A1 (e)	¼ on ¼g grn	8.00	8.00
72	A1 (e)	½ on ½g red	8.00	8.00
73	A1 (f)	1 on 1g blue	9.50	9.50
74	A1 (f)	2 on 2g dk brn	11.00	11.00
a.		Surcharged "40"	65.00	
75	A2 (f)	4 on 4g lil brn	12.00	12.00
a.		Surcharged "80"	57.50	
76	A2 (f)	8 on 8g vio	27.50	27.50
77	A2 (f)	16 on 16g blk	35.00	35.00
		Nos. 71-77 (7)	111.00	111.00

Nos. 71-72 are also found with stars farther away from figures.

The control overprint reads "Dagmawi" ("Second"), meaning Emperor Menelik II.

On stamps with "1" in surcharge, genuine examples have straight serifs, forgeries have curved serifs.

Nos. 2, 23 Surcharged in Bluish Green

1908, Aug. 14

78	A1	1pi on ½g red (#2)	10.00	10.00
79	A1	1pi on ½g red (#23)	850.00	—

Official reproductions exist. Value, set $25. Forgeries exist.

The surcharges on Nos. 57-78 are handstamped and are found double, inverted, etc.

Surcharged in Black

1908, Nov. 1

80	A1	¼p on ¼g grn	1.25	1.25
81	A1	½p on ½g red	1.25	1.25
82	A1	1p on 1g blue	1.75	1.75
83	A1	2p on 2g dk brn	3.00	3.00
84	A2	4p on 4g lil brn	4.25	4.25
85	A2	8p on 8g vio	10.00	10.00
86	A2	16p on 16g blk	15.00	15.00
		Nos. 80-86 (7)	36.50	36.50

Surcharges on Nos. 80-85 are found double, inverted, etc. Forgeries exist.

These are the 1st stamps valid for international mail.

King Solomon's Throne — A3	Menelik in Native Costume — A4

Menelik in Royal Dress — A5

1909, Jan. 29   *Perf. 11½*

87	A3	¼g blue green	.80	.60
88	A3	½g rose	.90	.60
89	A3	1g green & org	4.50	1.75
90	A4	2g blue	3.50	2.25
91	A4	4g green & car	5.00	4.00

92	A5	8g ver & dp grn	11.00	7.50
93	A5	16g ver & car	16.50	12.00
		Nos. 87-93 (7)	42.20	28.70

For overprints see Nos. 101-115, J43-J49, J55-J56. For surcharges see Nos. 116-119.

Nos. 1-7 Handstamped and Surcharged in ms.

1911, Oct. 1   *Perf. 14x13½*

94	A1	¼g on ¼g grn	50.00	
95	A1	½g on ½g red	50.00	
96	A1	1g on 1g blue	50.00	
97	A1	2g on 2g dk brn	50.00	
98	A2	4g on 4g lil brn	50.00	
99	A2	8g on 8g violet	50.00	
100	A2	16g on 16g black	50.00	
		Nos. 94-100 (7)	350.00	

Nos. 94-100 are provisionals used at Dire-Dawa for 5 days. The overprint is abbreviated from "Affranchissement Exceptionnel Faute Timbres" (Special Franking Lacking Stamps). The overprints and surcharges were applied to stamps on cover and then canceled.

Nos. 94-100 without surcharge are forgeries.

Stamps of 1909 Handstamped in Violet or Black:

Nos. 101-102	Nos. 104-107

1917, Mar. 30   *Perf. 11½*

101	A3	¼g blue grn (V)	4.75	4.25
102	A3	½g rose (V)	4.75	4.25
104	A4	2g blue (Bk)	6.00	5.25
105	A4	4g grn & car (Bk)	14.00	11.00
106	A5	8g ver & dp grn (Bk)	17.50	16.00
107	A5	16g ver & car (Bk)	35.00	32.50
		Nos. 101-107 (6)	82.00	73.25

Coronation of Empress Zauditu and appointment of Prince Tafari as Regent and Heir to the throne.
Exist with overprint inverted and double.

Stamps of 1909 Overprinted in Blue, Black or Red:

Nos. 108-111   Nos. 112-115

1917, Apr. 5-Oct. 1

108	A3	¼g blue grn (Bl)	1.25	1.25
109	A3	½g rose (Bl)	1.25	1.25
110	A3	1g grn & org (Bl)	2.25	2.25
111	A4	2g blue (R)	82.50	87.25
112	A4	2g blue (Bk)	1.25	1.25
113	A4	4g grn & car (Bl)	1.25	1.25
a.		Black overprint	11.00	11.00
114	A5	8g ver & dp grn (Bl)	1.25	1.25
115	A5	16g ver & car (Bl)	2.25	2.25
		Nos. 108-115 (8)	93.25	98.00

Coronation of Empress Zauditu.
Nos. 108-115 all exist with double overprint, inverted overprint, double overprint, one inverted, and various combinations.

Nos. 114-115 with Additional Surcharge

k   l

m   n

1917, May 28

116	A5 (k)	¼g on 8g	3.00	2.50
117	A5 (l)	½g on 8g	3.00	2.50
118	A5 (m)	1g on 16g	9.00	6.50
119	A5 (n)	2g on 16g	10.00	7.00
		Nos. 116-119 (4)	25.00	18.50

Nos. 116-119 all exist with the numerals double and inverted and No. 116 with the Amharic surcharge missing.

Sommering's Gazelle — A6   Prince Tafari — A9

Cathedral of St. George A12

Empress Waizeri Zauditu — A18

¼g, Giraffes. ½g, Leopard. 2g, Prince Tafari, diff. 4g, Prince Tafari, diff. 8g, White rhinoceros. 12g, Somali ostriches. 1t, African elephant. 2t, Water buffalo. 3t, Lions. 5t, 10t, Empress Zauditu.

1919, June 16   *Typo.*   *Perf. 11½*

120	A6	⅛g violet & brn	.20	.20
121	A6	¼g bl grn & drab	.20	.20
122	A9	½g scar & ol grn	.20	.20
123	A9	1g rose lil & gray grn	.20	.20
124	A9	2g dp ultra & fawn	.20	.20
125	A9	4g turq bl & org	.20	*2.50*
126	A12	6g lt blue & org	.25	.20
127	A12	8g ol grn & blk brn	.35	.20
128	A12	12g red vio & gray	.90	.30
129	A12	1t rose & gray blk	.90	.40
130	A12	2t black & brown	2.50	
131	A12	3t grn & dp org	2.50	1.90
132	A18	4t brn & lil rose	3.00	2.50
133	A18	5t carmine & gray	4.00	4.00
134	A18	10t gray grn & bis	8.00	5.25
		Nos. 120-134 (15)	23.20	
		Nos. 120-129,131-134 (14)		18.25

No. 130 was not issued.
For overprints see Nos. J50-J54. For surcharges see Nos. 135-154.
Reprints have brownish gum that is cracked diagonally. Originals have smooth, white gum. Reprints exist imperf. and some values with inverted centers. Value for set, unused or canceled, $5.

No. 132 Surcharged in Blue

1919, Oct.

135	A18	4g on 4t brn & lil rose	3.00	3.00

Nos. 135-154
The Amharic surcharge indicates the new value and, therefore, varies on Nos. 135-154. There are numerous defective letters and figures, several types of the "2" of "½," the errors "guerhce," "gnerche," etc.
Many varieties of surcharge, such as double, inverted, lines transposed or omitted, and inverted "2" in "½," exist.
There are many irregularly produced settings in imitation of Nos. 136-154 which differ slightly from the originals. These may be essays or proofs.

Stamps of 1919 Surcharged

1921-22

136	A6	½g on ⅛g vio & brn ('22)	1.00	1.00
137	A6	1g on ¼g grn & db	2.50	1.00
138	A9	2g on 1g lil brn & gray grn ('22)	1.00	1.50
139	A18	2g on 4t brn & lil rose ('22)	35.00	15.00
140	A6	2½g on ½g scar & ol grn	1.00	*1.50*
141	A9	4g on 2g ultra & fawn ('22)	1.00	1.25
		Nos. 136-141 (6)	41.50	21.25

No. 139 has been forged.

Stamps and Type of 1919 Surcharged

1925-28

142	A12	½g on 1t rose & gray blk ('26)	1.00	1.00
a.		Without colon ('28)	12.50	12.50
143	A18	½g on 5t car & gray ('26)	2.00	1.00
144	A12	1g on 6g bl & org ('26)	1.00	1.00
145	A12	1g on 12g lil & gray	400.00	400.00
146	A12	1g on 3t grn & org ('26)	22.50	16.00
147	A18	1g on 10t gray grn & bis ('26)	1.00	*1.00*
		Nos. 142-147 (6)	427.50	420.00

On #142 the surcharge is at the left side of the stamp, reading upward. On #142a it is at the right, reading downward. The two surcharges are from different, though similar, settings. On #146 the surcharge is at the right, reading upward. See note following #154.

Type of 1919 Surcharged

1926

147A	A12	1g on 12g lil & gray	400.00

Forgeries exist.

Nos. 126-128 Surcharged

1926

148	A12	½g on 8g	3.00	1.25
149	A12	1g on 6g	80.00	50.00
150	A12	1g on 12g	350.00	
		Nos. 148-150 (3)	433.00	51.25

The Amharic line has 7 (½g) or 6 characters (1g).

Nos. 126-128, 131 Surcharged

1927

151	A12	½g on 8g	1.50	1.50
152	A12	1g on 6g	60.00	40.00
153	A12	1g on 12g	5.00	1.50
154	A12	1g on 3t	400.00	
		Nos. 151-154 (4)	466.50	43.00

The Amharic line has 7 (½g) or 4 characters (1g). No. 152 has the lines closer together than do the others.
Forgeries of No. 154 exist.

Prince Tafari — A22   Empress Zauditu — A23

1928, Sept. 5   *Typo.*   *Perf. 13½x14*

155	A22	⅛m org & lt bl	.50	.45
156	A23	¼m ind & red org	.30	.45
157	A22	½m gray grn & blk	.50	.45
158	A23	1m dk car & blk	.30	.45
159	A22	2m dk bl & blk	.30	.45
160	A23	4m yel & olive	.30	.45
161	A22	8m vio & olive	.80	.45
162	A23	1t org brn & vio	.95	.65
163	A22	2t grn & bister	1.40	1.10
164	A23	3t choc & grn	2.25	1.25
		Nos. 155-164 (10)	7.60	6.15

For overprints and surcharges see Nos. 165-209, 217-230, C1-C10.

Preceding Issue Overprinted in Black, Violet or Red

1928, Sept. 1

165	A22	⅛m (Bk)	1.25	1.25
166	A23	¼m (V)	1.25	1.25
167	A22	½m (V)	1.25	1.25
168	A23	1m (V)	1.25	1.25
169	A22	2m (R)	1.25	1.25
170	A23	4m (R)	1.25	1.25
171	A22	8m (R)	1.25	1.25
172	A23	1t (Bk)	1.25	1.25
173	A22	2t (R)	1.90	1.90
174	A23	3t (R)	2.75	2.75
		Nos. 165-174 (10)	14.65	14.65

Opening of General Post Office, Addis Ababa.
Exist with overprint inverted, double, double, one inverted, etc.

Nos. 155, 157, 159, 161, 163
Handstamped in Violet, Red or Black

1928, Oct. 7

175	A22	⅛m (V)	1.40	1.40
176	A22	½m (R)	1.40	1.40
177	A22	2m (R)	1.40	1.40
178	A22	8m (Bk)	1.40	1.40
179	A22	2t (V)	1.40	1.40
		Nos. 175-179 (5)	7.00	7.00

Crowning of Prince Tafari as king (Negus) on Oct. 7, 1928.
Nos. 175-177 exist with overprint vertical, inverted, double, etc.
Forgeries exist.

Nos. 155-164
Overprinted in Red
or Green

1930, Apr. 3
180	A22	⅛m org & lt bl (R)	.25	.35
181	A23	¼m ind & red org (G)	.35	.35
182	A22	½m gray grn & blk (R)	.25	.35
183	A23	1m dk car & blk (G)	.35	.35
184	A22	2m dk bl & blk (R)	.35	.35
185	A23	4m yel & ol (R)	.50	.50
186	A22	8m vio & ol (R)	1.00	1.00
187	A23	1t org brn & vio (R)	2.25	2.25
188	A22	2t grn & bis (R)	3.00	3.00
189	A23	3t choc & grn (R)	4.00	4.00
		Nos. 180-189 (10)	12.30	12.50

Proclamation of King Tafari as King of Kings of Abyssinia under the name "Haile Selassie."
A similar overprint, set in four vertical lines, was printed on all denominations of the 1928 issue. It was not considered satisfactory and was rejected. The trial impressions were not placed on sale to the public, but some stamps reached private hands and have been passed through the post.

Nos. 155-164
Overprinted in Red
or Olive Brown

1930, Apr. 3
190	A22	⅛m orange & lt bl	.35	.35
191	A23	¼m ind & red org (OB)	.35	.35
192	A22	½m gray grn & blk (OB)	.75	.75
193	A23	1m dk car & blk	.35	.35
194	A22	2m dk blue & blk	.35	.35
195	A23	4m yellow & ol	.60	.60
196	A22	8m violet & ol	1.00	1.00
197	A23	1t org brn & vio	2.25	2.25
198	A22	2t green & bister	3.00	3.00
199	A23	3t chocolate & grn	3.75	3.75
		Nos. 190-199 (10)	12.75	12.75

Proclamation of King Tafari as Emperor Haile Selassie.
All stamps of this series exist with "H" of "HAILE" omitted and with many other varieties.

Nos. 155-164
Handstamped in
Violet or Red

1930, Nov. 2
200	A22	⅛m (V)	.50	.50
201	A23	¼m (V)	.50	.50
202	A23	½m (R)	.50	.50
203	A23	1m (V)	.50	.50
204	A22	2m (R)	.50	.50
205	A23	4m (V)	.50	.50
206	A22	8m (V or R)	1.00	1.00
207	A23	1t (V)	1.50	1.50
208	A22	2t (V or R)	2.50	2.50
209	A23	3t (V or R)	3.50	3.50
		Nos. 200-209 (10)	11.50	11.50

Coronation of Emperor Haile Selassie, Nov. 2, 1930.

Haile Selassie
Coronation
Monument, Symbols
of Empire — A24

1930, Nov.   Engr.   Perf. 12½
210	A24	1g orange	.40	.40
211	A24	2g ultra	.40	.40
212	A24	4g violet	.40	.40
213	A24	8g dull green	.70	.65
214	A24	1t brown	1.00	1.00
215	A24	3t green	1.50	1.50
216	A24	5t red brown	1.50	1.50
		Nos. 210-216 (7)	5.90	5.85

Coronation of Emperor Haile Selassie.
Issued: 4g, 11/2; others, 11/23.
Reprints of Nos. 210 to 216 exist. Colors are more yellow and the ink is thicker and slightly glossy. Ink on the originals is dull and granular. Value 35c each.

Nos. 158-160, 164 Surcharged in
Green, Red or Blue

1/8 Mehalek

1/2 Mehalek   1/2 Mehalek

Type I   Type II

1931   Perf. 13½x14
217	A23	⅛m on 1m	.45	.45
218	A22	⅛m on 2m (R)	.45	.45
219	A23	⅛m on 4m	.45	.45
220	A23	¼m on 1m (Bl)	.45	.45
221	A22	¼m on 2m (R)	1.50	1.50
222	A23	¼m on 4m	1.50	1.50
225	A23	½m on 1m (Bl)	1.50	1.50
226	A22	½m on 2m (R)	1.50	1.50
227	A23	½m on 4m, type II	1.50	1.50
a.		½m on 4m, type I	10.00	10.00
228	A23	½m on 3t (R)	11.00	11.00
230	A23	1m on 2m (R)	1.75	1.75
		Nos. 217-230 (11)	22.05	22.05

The ½m on ⅛m orange & light blue and ½m on ¼m indigo & red orange were clandestinely printed and never sold at the post office.
No. 230 with double surcharge in red and blue is a color trial.
Many varieties exist.
Issued: 1m, Apr.; others, 3/20.

Prince
Makonnen
A25

Empress Menen
A27

View of
Hawash
River and
Railroad
Bridge
A26

Designs: 2g, 8g, Haile Selassie (profile). 4g, 1t, Statue of Menelik II. 3t, Empress Menen (full face). 5t, Haile Selassie (full face).

Perf. 12½, 12x12½, 12½x12
1931, June 27   Engr.
232	A25	⅛g red	.40	.20
233	A25	¼g olive green	.40	.20
234	A25	½g dark violet	.40	.20
235	A27	1g red orange	.50	.25
236	A25	2g ultra	.50	.25
237	A25	4g violet	.90	.40
238	A27	8g blue green	2.00	1.00
239	A25	1t chocolate	24.00	10.00
240	A27	3t yellow green	7.00	3.00
241	A27	5t red brown	12.00	5.50
		Nos. 232-241 (10)	48.10	22.00

For overprints see Nos. B1-B5. For surcharges see Nos. 242-246.
Reprints of Nos. 232-236, 238-240 are on thinner and whiter paper than the originals. On originals the ink is dull and granular. On reprints, heavy, caked and shiny. Value 20c each.

Nos. 232-236 Surcharged in
Blue or Carmine similar to cut

1936, Jan. 29   Perf. 12x12½, 12½x12
242	A25	1c on ⅛g red	2.00	1.00
243	A26	2c on ¼g ol grn (C)	2.00	1.00
244	A25	3c on ½g dk vio	2.00	1.10
245	A27	5c on 1g red org	2.50	1.50
246	A27	10c on 2g ultra (C)	3.25	1.90
		Nos. 242-246 (5)	11.75	6.50

> **Catalogue values for unused stamps in this section, from this point to the end of the section, are for Never Hinged items.**

Haile Selassie I
A32   A33

1942, Mar. 23   Litho.   Perf. 14x13½
247	A32	4c lt bl grn, ind & blk	.50	.25
248	A32	10c rose, indigo & blk	1.50	.45
249	A32	20c dp ultra, ind & blk	3.00	.80
		Nos. 247-249 (3)	5.00	1.50

1942-43   Unwmk.
250	A33	4c lt bl grn & indigo	.90	.20
251	A33	8c yel org & indigo	1.00	.20
252	A33	10c rose & indigo	1.25	.20
253	A33	12c dull vio & indigo	1.25	.30
254	A33	20c dp ultra & indigo	2.00	.50
255	A33	25c dull grn & indigo	2.50	.70
256	A33	50c dull brn & indigo	4.75	1.25
257	A33	60c lilac & indigo	7.25	1.50
		Nos. 250-257 (8)	20.90	4.85

Issued: 25c, 50c, 60c, 4/1/43; others, 6/22/42.
For surcharges see #258-262, 284, C18-C20.

Nos. 250-254
Surcharged in Black
or Brown

1943, Nov. 3
258	A33	5c on 4c	85.00	85.00
259	A33	10c on 8c	85.00	85.00
260	A33	15c on 10c	85.00	85.00
261	A33	20c on 12c (Br)	85.00	85.00
262	A33	30c on 20c (Br)	85.00	85.00
		Nos. 258-262 (5)	425.00	425.00

Restoration of the Obelisk in Myazzia Place, Addis Ababa, and the 13th anniv. of the coronation of Emperor Haile Selassie.
No. 258 exists with inverted "5" in surcharge. Value $150. On No. 262, "3" is surcharged on "2" of "20" to make "30."
Approximately 40 sets exist with a somewhat different handstamped surcharge. Value, set *$2,000.*

Palace of
Menelik II
A34

Menelik   Statue — A36
II — A35

50c, Mausoleum. 65c, Menelik II (with scepter).

1944, Dec. 31   Litho.   Perf. 10½
263	A34	5c green	1.25	.65
264	A35	10c red lilac	2.25	1.10
265	A36	20c deep blue	4.00	2.25
266	A34	50c dull purple	4.50	2.25
267	A35	65c bister brown	8.50	3.50
		Nos. 263-267 (5)	20.50	9.75

Cent. of the birth of Menelik II, 8/18/44.
Printed on gum-impregnated paper.

Unissued Semi-Postal Stamps
Overprinted in Carmine:

Nurse &
Baby — A39

Various Designs
Inscribed "Croix Rouge"

1945, Aug. 7   Photo.   Perf. 11½
268	A39	5c brt green	.95	.45
269	A39	10c brt red	.95	.45
270	A39	25c brt blue	.95	.45
271	A39	50c dk yellow brn	5.00	2.00
272	A39	1t brt violet	7.75	2.75
		Nos. 268-272 (5)	15.60	6.10

Nos. 268-272 without overprint were ordered printed in Switzerland before Ethiopia fell to the invading Italians, so were not delivered to Addis Ababa. After that country's liberation, the set was overprinted "V" and issued for ordinary postage. These stamps exist without overprint, but were not so issued. Value $1.25.
Some values exist inverted or double.
Forged overprints exist.
For surcharges see #B11-B15, B36-B40.

Lion of   Menelik II — A45
Judah — A44

Mail Transport, Old and New A46

Designs: 50c, Old Post Office, Addis Ababa. 70c, Menelik II and Haile Selassie.

1947, Apr. 18   Engr.   Perf. 13
273	A44	10c yellow org	3.00	.75
274	A45	20c deep blue	5.00	1.10
275	A46	30c orange brn	8.00	1.75
276	A46	50c dk slate grn	19.00	3.75
277	A46	70c red violet	37.50	7.50
		Nos. 273-277 (5)	72.50	14.85

50th anniv. of Ethiopia's postal system.

Haile Selassie and Franklin D. Roosevelt — A49

Design: 65c, Roosevelt and US Flags.

Engraved and Photogravure
1947, May 23   Unwmk.   Perf. 12½
278	A49	12c car lake & bl grn	2.75	3.00
279	A49	25c dk blue & rose	2.75	3.00
280	A49	65c blk, red & dp bl	6.00	6.50
		Nos. 278-280,C21-C22 (5)	50.00	47.50

King Sahle Selassie Reclining A50

King Sahle Selassie — A52

Design: 30c, View of Ankober.

1947, May 1   Engr.   Perf. 13
281	A50	20c deep blue	2.25	.90
282	A50	30c dark purple	3.25	1.25
283	A52	$1 deep green	8.00	3.50
		Nos. 281-283 (3)	13.50	5.65

150th anniversary of Selassie dynasty.

No. 255 Surcharged in Orange

1947, July 14   Perf. 14x13½
284	A33	12c on 25c	95.00	95.00

Amba Alaguie A53

Designs: 2c, Trinity Church. 4c, Debra Sina. 5c, Mecan, near Achanguie. 8c, Lake Tana. 12c, 15c, Parliament Building, Addis Ababa. 20c, Aiba, near Mai Cheo. 30c, Bahr Bridge over Blue Nile. 60c, 70c, Canoe on Lake Tana. $1, Omo Falls. $3, Mt. Alamata. $5, Ras Dashan Mountains.

Perf. 13x13½
1947-53   Engr.   Wmk. 282
285	A53	1c rose violet	.20	.20
286	A53	2c blue violet	.20	.20
a.		Unwatermarked ('51)	37.50	15.00
287	A53	4c green	.35	.20
288	A53	5c dark green	.35	.20
289	A53	8c deep orange	.65	.20
290	A53	12c red	.80	.20
290A	A53	15c dk ol brn ('53)	.75	.20
291	A53	20c blue	1.10	.40
292	A53	30c orange brown	1.90	.55
292A	A53	60c red ('51)	2.25	.95
293	A53	70c rose lilac	3.25	.70
294	A53	$1 dk carmine rose	5.25	.70
295	A53	$3 bright blue	14.00	2.75
296	A53	$5 olive	22.50	5.50
		Nos. 285-296 (14)	53.55	12.95

Issue dates: 15c, May 25, 1953; 60c, Feb. 10, 1951; others, Aug. 23, 1947. Shades exist.
For overprints see Nos. 355-356. For surcharges see Nos. B6-B10, B16-B20.

Empress Waizero Menen and Emperor Haile Selassie A54

1949, May 5   Wmk. 282   Perf. 13
297	A54	20c blue	1.75	.85
298	A54	30c yellow org	1.75	1.10
299	A54	50c purple	3.50	2.10
300	A54	80c green	4.25	2.50
301	A54	$1 red	7.75	3.50
		Nos. 297-301 (5)	19.00	10.05

Central ornaments differ on each denomination.
8th anniv. of Ethiopia's liberation from Italian occupation.

Dejach Balcha Hospital A55

Abuna Petros — A56

Designs: 20c, Haile Selassie raising flag. 30c, Lion of Judah statue. 50c, Empress Waizero Menen, Haile Selassie and building.

Perf. 13x13½, 13½x13
1950, Nov. 2   Engr.   Wmk. 282
302	A55	5c purple	1.25	.35
303	A56	10c deep plum	3.00	.70
304	A56	20c deep carmine	4.25	.90
305	A56	30c green	7.00	2.00
306	A55	50c deep blue	12.00	3.50
		Nos. 302-306 (5)	27.50	7.45

20th anniv. of the coronation of Emperor Haile Selassie and Empress Menen.

Abbaye Bridge — A57

1951, Jan. 1   Unwmk.   Perf. 14
308	A57	5c dk green & dk brn	4.25	.50
309	A57	10c dp orange & blk	5.75	.50
310	A57	15c dp blue & org brn	8.25	.50
311	A57	30c olive & lil rose	15.00	.80
312	A57	60c brown & dp bl	20.00	2.00
313	A57	80c purple & green	30.00	3.00
		Nos. 308-313 (6)	83.25	7.30

Opening of the Abbaye Bridge over the Blue Nile.

Tomb of Prince Makonnen A58

1951, Mar. 2
Center in Black
314	A58	5c dark green	3.25	.65
315	A58	10c deep ultra	3.25	.40
316	A58	15c blue	5.50	.40
317	A58	30c claret	11.00	1.50
318	A58	80c rose carmine	17.00	2.25
319	A58	$1 orange brown	22.50	2.25
		Nos. 314-319 (6)	62.50	7.45

55th anniversary of the Battle of Adwa.

Emperor Haile Selassie — A59

1952, July 23   Perf. 13½
320	A59	5c dark green	.60	.20
321	A59	10c red orange	.85	.25
322	A59	15c black	1.40	.40
323	A59	25c ultra	1.75	.40
324	A59	30c violet	2.25	.45
325	A59	50c rose red	3.50	.90
326	A59	65c chocolate	6.75	1.60
		Nos. 320-326 (7)	17.10	4.40

60th birthday of Haile Selassie.

Open Road to Sea A60

Designs: 25c, 50c, Road and broken chain. 65c, Map. 80c, Allegory: Reunion. $1, Haile Selassie raising flag. $2, Ethiopian flag and seascape. $3, Haile Selassie addressing League of Nations.

Wmk. 282
1952, Sept. 11   Engr.   Perf. 13
327	A60	15c brown carmine	.85	.20
328	A60	25c red brown	1.10	.40
329	A60	30c yellow brown	2.00	.60
330	A60	50c purple	3.00	1.25
331	A60	65c gray	5.75	1.40
332	A60	80c blue green	6.50	.95
333	A60	$1 rose carmine	13.00	2.00
334	A60	$2 deep blue	22.50	3.25
335	A60	$3 magenta	47.50	5.50
		Nos. 327-335 (9)	102.20	15.55

Issued to celebrate Ethiopia's federation with Eritrea, effected Sept. 11, 1952.

Haile Selassie and New Ethiopian Port A61

15c, 30c, Haile Selassie on deck of ship.

1953, Oct. 4
337	A61	10c red & dk brn	4.75	1.75
338	A61	15c blue & dk grn	5.00	1.75
339	A61	25c orange & dk brn	9.00	3.50
340	A61	30c red brn & dk grn	16.00	5.00
341	A61	50c purple & dk brn	29.00	6.75
		Nos. 337-341 (5)	63.75	18.75

Federation of Ethiopia and Eritrea, 1st anniv.

Princess Tsahai at a Sickbed A62

Perf. 13x13½
1955, July 8   Engr.   Wmk. 282
Cross Typo. in Red
342	A62	15c choc & ultra	2.50	1.25
343	A62	20c green & orange	3.75	1.50
344	A62	30c ultra & green	6.25	1.90
		Nos. 342-344 (3)	12.50	4.65

Ethiopian Red Cross, 20th anniv.
For surcharges see Nos. B33-B35.

Promulgating the Constitution — A63

Bishops' Consecration by Archbishop — A64

25c, Kagnew Battalion. 35c, Reunion with the Motherland. 50c, "Progress." 65c, Empress Waizero Menen & Emperor Haile Selassie.

Perf. 12½
1955, Nov. 3   Unwmk.   Engr.
345	A63	5c green & choc	1.25	.55
346	A64	20c carmine & brn	2.50	.90
347	A64	25c magenta & gray	3.50	1.40
348	A63	35c brown & red org	4.75	1.75
349	A64	50c dk brn & ultra	7.00	2.50
350	A64	65c violet & car	9.75	4.00
		Nos. 345-350 (6)	28.75	11.10

Silver jubilee of the coronation of Emperor Haile Selassie and Empress Waizero Menen.

Emperor Haile Selassie and Fair Emblem — A65

1955, Nov. 5   Wmk. 282
351	A65	5c green & ol grn	1.00	.20
352	A65	10c car & dp ultra	1.50	.40
353	A65	15c vio blk & grn	2.00	.60
354	A65	50c mag & red brn	3.00	1.50
		Nos. 351-354 (4)	7.50	2.70

Silver Jubilee Fair, Addis Ababa.

Nos. 291 and 292A Overprinted

1960, Apr. 7   Perf. 13x13½
355	A53	20c blue	1.75	1.25
356	A53	60c red	3.00	2.40

WRY, July 1, 1959-June 30, 1960.
The 60c without serifs is a trial printing.

Map of Africa, "Liberty" and Haile Selassie — A66

Emperor Haile Selassie — A67

Perf. 13½
1960, June 14   Engr.   Unwmk.
357 A66 20c orange & green   .85   .85
358 A66 80c orange & violet   2.40   .85
359 A66 $1 orange & maroon   2.75   1.10
    Nos. 357-359 (3)   6.00   2.80

2nd Conf. of Independent African States at Addis Ababa. Issued in sheets of 10.

1960, Nov. 2   Wmk. 282   Perf. 14
360 A67 10c brown & blue   .75   .20
361 A67 25c violet & emerald   1.50   .55
362 A67 50c dk bl & org yel   2.75   1.75
363 A67 65c slate grn & sal
           pink   3.50   1.75
364 A67 $1 indigo & rose vio   6.00   2.75
    Nos. 360-364 (5)   14.50   7.00

30th anniv. of the coronation of Emperor Haile Selassie.

Africa Hall, UN Economic Commission for Africa — A68

1961, Apr. 15   Wmk. 282   Perf. 14
365 A68 80c ultra   2.75   1.40

Africa Freedom Day, Apr. 15. Sheets of 10.

Map of Ethiopia, Olive Branch A69

1961, May 5   Perf. 13x13½
366 A69 20c green   .40   .20
367 A69 30c violet blue   .60   .20
368 A69 $1 brown   2.75   1.10
    Nos. 366-368 (3)   3.75   1.50

20th anniv. of Ethiopia's liberation from Italian occupation.

African Wild Ass — A70

1961, June 16   Wmk. 282   Perf. 14
369 A70 5c shown   .75   .20
370 A70 15c Eland   .75   .20
371 A70 25c Elephant   .90   .40
372 A70 35c Giraffe   2.00   .50
373 A70 50c Beisa   2.00   .50
374 A70 $1 Lion   4.00   1.50
    Nos. 369-374 (6)   10.40   3.30

Issued in sheets of 10. Used values are for CTO's.

Emperor Haile Selassie and Empress Waizero Menen — A71

1961, July 27   Unwmk.   Perf. 11
375 A71 10c green   .90   .45
376 A71 50c violet blue   1.60   .80
377 A71 $1 carmine rose   3.00   1.60
    Nos. 375-377 (3)   5.50   2.85

Golden wedding anniv. of the Emperor and Empress.

Warlike Horsemanship (Guks) — A72

15c, Hockey. 20c, Bicycling. 30c, Soccer. 50c, 1960 Olympic marathon winner, Abebe Bikila.

Photogravure and Engraved
1962, Jan. 14   Perf. 12x11½
378 A72 10c yel grn & car   .20   .20
379 A72 15c pink & dk brn   .20   .20
380 A72 20c red & black   .85   .20
381 A72 30c ultra & dl pur   1.50   .20
382 A72 50c yellow & green   2.75   .20
    Nos. 378-382 (5)   5.50   1.00

Third Africa Football (soccer) Cup, Addis Ababa, Jan. 14-22.

Malaria Eradication Emblem, World Map and Mosquito — A73

Wmk. 282
1962, Apr. 7   Engr.   Perf. 13½
383 A73 15c black   .20   .20
384 A73 30c purple   .40   .25
385 A73 60c red brown   1.25   .65
    Nos. 383-385 (3)   1.85   1.10

WHO drive to eradicate malaria.

Abyssinian Ground Hornbill A74

Birds: 15c, Abyssinian roller. 30c, Bateleur, vert. 50c, Double-toothed barbet, vert. $1, Didric cuckoo.

Perf. 11½
1962, May 5   Unwmk.   Photo.
Granite Paper
386 A74 5c multicolored   1.00   .20
387 A74 15c emer, brn & ultra   1.75   .50
388 A74 30c lt brn, blk & red   2.00   1.75
389 A74 50c multicolored   3.75   1.50
390 A74 $1 multicolored   8.50   2.50
    Nos. 386-390 (5)   17.00   6.45

See Nos. C77-C81, C97-C101, C107-C111.

Assab Hospital A75

15c, School at Assab. 20c, Church at Massawa. 50c, Mosque at Massawa. 60c, Assab port.

Wmk. 282
1962, Sept. 11   Engr.   Perf. 13½
391 A75 3c purple   .20   .20
392 A75 15c dark blue   .20   .20
393 A75 20c green   .40   .20
394 A75 50c brown   .70   .40
395 A75 60c carmine rose   1.00   .50
    Nos. 391-395 (5)   2.50   1.50

Federation of Ethiopia and Eritrea, 10th anniv.

King Bazen, Madonna and Stars over Bethlehem — A76

15c, Ezana, obelisks & temple. 20c, Kaleb & sailing fleet. 50c, Lalibela, rock-church and frescoes, vert. 60c, King Yekuno Amlak & Abuna Tekle Haimanot preaching in Ankober. 75c, King Zara Yacob & Maskal celebration. $1, King Lebna Dengel & battle against Mohammed Gragn.

Perf. 14½
1962, Nov. 2   Unwmk.   Photo.
396 A76 10c multicolored   .20   .20
397 A76 15c multicolored   .40   .20
398 A76 20c multicolored   .50   .20
399 A76 50c multicolored   .85   .20
400 A76 60c multicolored   .95   .50
401 A76 75c multicolored   1.50   .85
402 A76 $1 multicolored   2.10   1.25
    Nos. 396-402 (7)   6.50   3.40

32nd anniv. of the coronation of Emperor Haile Selassie and to commemorate ancient kings and saints.

Map of Ethiopian Telephone Network — A77

Wheat Emblem — A78

Designs: 50c, Radio mast and waves. 60c, Telegraph pole and rising sun.

Perf. 13½x14
1963, Jan. 1   Engr.   Wmk. 282
403 A77 10c dark red   .50   .20
404 A77 50c ultra   1.25   .50
405 A77 60c brown   1.50   .60
    Nos. 403-405 (3)   3.25   1.30

10th anniv. of the Imperial Board of Telecommunications.

1963, Mar. 21   Unwmk.   Perf. 13½
406 A78 5c deep rose   .20   .20
407 A78 10c rose carmine   .20   .20
408 A78 15c violet blue   .20   .20
409 A78 30c emerald   1.10   .20
    Nos. 406-409 (4)   1.70   .80

FAO "Freedom from Hunger" campaign.

Abuna Salama — A79

Queen of Sheba — A80

Spiritual Leaders: 15c, Abuna Aregawi. 30c, Abuna Tekle Haimanot. 40c, Yared. 60c, Zara Yacob.

1964, Jan. 3   Unwmk.   Perf. 13½
410 A79 10c blue   .45   .20
411 A79 15c dark green   .75   .20
412 A79 30c brown red   1.10   .45
413 A79 40c dark blue   2.00   .75
414 A79 60c brown   2.75   1.40
    Nos. 410-414 (5)   7.05   3.00

1964, Mar. 2   Photo.   Perf. 11½
Ethiopian Empresses: 15c, Helen. 50c, Seble Wongel. 60c, Mentiwab. 80c, Taitu, consort of Menelik II.

Granite Paper
415 A80 10c multicolored   .75   .30
416 A80 15c multicolored   1.00   .50
417 A80 50c multicolored   1.75   1.00
418 A80 60c multicolored   3.50   1.75
419 A80 80c multicolored   4.50   2.50
    Nos. 415-419 (5)   11.50   6.05

Priest Teaching Alphabet to Children — A81

Eleanor Roosevelt (1884-1962) — A82

10c, Classroom. 15c, Woman learning to read. 40c, Students in chemistry laboratory. 60c, Graduation procession.

1964, June 1   Unwmk.   Perf. 11½
Granite Paper
420 A81 5c brown   .20   .20
421 A81 10c emerald   .20   .20
422 A81 15c rose vio, vert.   .20   .20
423 A81 40c vio blue, vert.   .65   .30
424 A81 60c dark pur, vert.   1.25   .55
    Nos. 420-424 (5)   2.50   1.45

Issued to publicize education.

1964, Oct. 11   Photo.
Granite Paper
Portrait in Slate Blue
425 A82 10c yellow bister   .20   .20
426 A82 60c orange brown   1.25   .75
427 A82 80c green & gold   1.50   1.00
    Nos. 425-427 (3)   2.95   1.95

King Serse Dengel and View of Gondar, 1563 A83

Ethiopian Leaders: 10c, King Fasiladas and Gondar in 1632. 20c, King Yassu the Great and Gondar in 1682. 25c, Emperor Theodore II and map of Ethiopia. 60c, Emperor John IV and Battle of Gura, 1876. 80c, Emperor Menelik II and Battle of Adwa, 1896.

1964, Dec. 12   Photo.   Perf. 14½x14
428 A83 5c multicolored   .20   .20
429 A83 10c multicolored   .20   .20
430 A83 20c multicolored   .60   .20
431 A83 25c multicolored   .95   .20
432 A83 60c multicolored   1.75   .95
433 A83 80c multicolored   2.25   1.25
    Nos. 428-433 (6)   5.95   3.00

Ethiopian Rose — A84

Flowers: 10c, Kosso tree. 25c, St.-John's-wort. 35c, Parrot's-beak. 60c, Maskal daisy.

1965, Mar. 30   Perf. 12x13½
434	A84	5c multicolored	.20	.20
435	A84	10c multicolored	.20	.20
436	A84	25c multicolored	.90	.20
437	A84	35c multicolored	1.75	.50
438	A84	60c green, yel & org	2.25	.80
		Nos. 434-438 (5)	5.30	1.90

ITU Emblem, Old and New
Communication Symbols — A85

Perf. 13½x14½
1965, May 17   Litho.   Unwmk.
439	A85	5c blue, indigo & yel	.20	.20
440	A85	10c blue, indigo & org	.55	.20
441	A85	60c blue, indigo & lil rose	1.75	.95
		Nos. 439-441 (3)	2.50	1.35

Cent. of the ITU.

Laboratory
A86

Designs: 5c, Textile spinning mill. 10c,
Sugar factory. 20c, Mountain road. 25c, Autobus. 30c, Diesel locomotive and bridge. 35c,
Railroad station, Addis Ababa.

1965, July 19   Photo.   Perf. 11½
Granite Paper
Portrait in Black
442	A86	3c sepia	.20	.20
443	A86	5c dull pur & buff	.20	.20
444	A86	10c black & gray	.20	.20
445	A86	20c green & pale yel	.35	.20
446	A86	25c dk brown & yel	.50	.20
447	A86	30c maroon & gray	.80	.35
448	A86	35c dk blue & gray	.95	.50
		Nos. 442-448 (7)	3.20	1.85

For overprints see Nos. 609-612.

ICY Emblem
A87

1965, Oct. 24   Unwmk.   Perf. 11½
Granite Paper
449	A87	10c blue & red brn	.50	.20
450	A87	50c dp blue & red brn	1.40	.75
451	A87	80c vio blue & red brn	1.90	1.10
		Nos. 449-451 (3)	3.80	2.05

International Cooperation Year, 1965.

National
Bank
Emblem
A88

Designs: 10c, Commercial Bank emblem.
60c, Natl. and Commercial Bank buildings.

1965, Nov. 2   Photo.   Perf. 13
452	A88	10c dp car, blk & indigo	.40	.20
453	A88	30c ultra, blk & indigo	.85	.40
454	A88	60c black, yel & indigo	1.25	.65
		Nos. 452-454 (3)	2.50	1.25

Natl. and Commercial Banks of Ethiopia.

"Light and
Peace"
Press
Building
A89

1966, Apr. 5   Engr.   Perf. 13
455	A89	5c pink & black	.20	.20
456	A89	15c lt yel grn & blk	.60	.20
457	A89	30c orange yel & blk	.95	.55
		Nos. 455-457 (3)	1.75	.95

Opening of the "Light and Peace" Printing
Press building.

Kabaro
Drum — A90

Musical Instruments: 10c, Bagana harp.
35c, Messenko guitar. 50c, Krar lyre. 60c,
Wachent flutes.

1966, Sept. 9   Photo.   Perf. 13½
458	A90	5c brt green & blk	.20	.20
459	A90	10c dull blue & blk	.20	.20
460	A90	35c orange & blk	1.25	.50
461	A90	50c yellow & blk	1.90	.70
462	A90	60c rose car & blk	2.40	1.25
		Nos. 458-462 (5)	5.95	2.85

Emperor Haile Selassie — A91

1966, Nov. 1   Unwmk.   Perf. 12
463	A91	10c black, gold & grn	.25	.20
464	A91	15c black, gold & dp car	.45	.20
465	A91	40c black & gold	1.40	.65
		Nos. 463-465 (3)	2.10	1.05

50 years of leadership of Emperor Haile
Selassie.

UNESCO
Emblem
and Map
of Africa
A92

Wmk. 282
1966, Nov. 30   Litho.   Perf. 13½
466	A92	15c blue car & blk	.50	.20
467	A92	60c olive, brn & dk bl	1.40	.60

20th anniv. of UNESCO.

WHO Headquarters, Geneva — A93

1966, Nov. 30
468	A93	5c olive, ultra & brn	.80	.20
469	A93	40c brown, pur & emer	2.50	.35

Opening of WHO Headquarters, Geneva.

Expo '67 Ethiopian
Pavilion and
Columns of Axum
(Replica) — A94

Perf. 12x13½
1967, May 2   Photo.   Unwmk.
470	A94	30c brt blue & multi	.65	.30
471	A94	45c multicolored	.85	.40
472	A94	80c gray & multi	1.50	.60
		Nos. 470-472 (3)	3.00	1.30

EXPO '67, Intl. Exhibition, Montreal, Apr.
28-Oct. 27, 1967.

Diesel Train and Map — A95

1967, June 7   Photo.   Perf. 12
473	A95	15c multicolored	1.10	.55
474	A95	30c multicolored	2.75	1.40
475	A95	50c multicolored	3.75	1.75
		Nos. 473-475 (3)	7.60	3.70

Djibouti-Addis Ababa railroad, 50th anniv.

Papilionidae Aethiops — A96

Various Butterflies.

Perf. 13½x13
1967, June 30   Photo.   Unwmk.
476	A96	5c buff & multi	.50	.20
477	A96	10c lilac & multi	1.75	.40
478	A96	20c multicolored	2.25	.75
479	A96	35c blue & multi	4.00	1.50
480	A96	40c multicolored	6.50	2.00
		Nos. 476-480 (5)	15.00	4.85

Emperor
Haile
Selassie
and Lion
of Judah
A97

1967, July 21   Perf. 11½
Granite Paper
481	A97	10c dk brn, emer & gold	.45	.20
482	A97	15c dk brn, yel & gold	.80	.20
483	A97	$1 dk brn, red & gold	3.50	1.50
		Nos. 481-483 (3)	4.75	1.90

Souvenir Sheet
484	A97	$1 dk brn, pur & gold	15.00	15.00

75th birthday of Emperor Haile Selassie.

Microscope and Ethiopian Flag — A98

1967, Nov. 6   Litho.   Perf. 13
Flag in Grn, Yel, Red & Blk
485	A98	5c blue	.20	.20
486	A98	30c ocher	.65	.30
487	A98	$1 violet	2.10	.95
		Nos. 485-487 (3)	2.95	1.45

2nd Intl. Conf. on the Global Impact of
Applied Microbiology, Addis Ababa, 11/6-12.

Wall Painting from Debre Berhan
Selassie Church, Gondar, 17th
Century — A99

ITY Emblem and: 25c, Votive throne from
Atsbe Dera, 4th Cent. B.C., vert. 35c, Prehistoric cave painting, Harar Province. 50c, Prehistoric stone tools, Melke Kontoure, vert.

1967, Nov. 20   Photo.   Perf. 14½
488	A99	15c multicolored	2.75	1.40
489	A99	25c yel grn, buff & blk	3.00	1.40
490	A99	35c green, brn & blk	2.75	1.75
491	A99	50c yellow & blk	5.00	2.75
		Nos. 488-491 (4)	13.50	7.30

International Tourist Year, 1967.

A100   A101

Crosses of Lalibela: 5c, Processional
Bronze Cross, Biet-Maryam Church. 10c, Processional copper cross. 15c, Copper cross,
Biet-Maryam church. 20c, Lalibela-style cross.
50c, Chiseled copper cross, Madhani Alem
church.

1967, Dec. 7   Photo.   Perf. 14½
Crosses in Silver
492	A100	5c yellow & blk	.20	.20
493	A100	10c red orange & blk	.20	.20
494	A100	15c violet & blk	.30	.20
495	A100	20c brt rose & blk	.55	.20
496	A100	50c orange yel & blk	1.75	.60
		Nos. 492-496 (5)	3.00	1.40

Perf. 14x13½
1968, Apr. 18   Litho.   Unwmk.

Designs: 10c, Emperor Theodore (1818?-
1868). 20c, Emperor Theodore and lions,
horiz. 50c, Imperial crown.
497	A101	10c lt vio, ocher & brn	.55	.20
498	A101	20c lilac, brn & dk vio	.95	.20
499	A101	50c dk grn, org & rose cl	1.90	.75
		Nos. 497-499 (3)	3.40	1.15

Human
Rights
Flame
A102

1968, May 31   Unwmk.   Perf. 14½
500	A102	15c pink, red & blk	.40	.40
501	A102	$1 lt bl, brt bl & blk	2.10	2.10

International Human Rights Year, 1968.

Shah Riza
Pahlavi,
Emperor
and Flags
A103

1968, June 3   Litho.   Perf. 13½
502	A103	5c multicolored	.20	.20
503	A103	15c multicolored	.30	.30
504	A103	30c multicolored	1.25	1.25
		Nos. 502-504 (3)	1.75	1.75

Visit of Shah Mohammed Riza Pahlavi of
Iran.

Emperor Haile Selassie Appealing to League of Nations, 1935 — A104

35c, African Unity Building and map of Africa. $1, World map, symbolizing intl. relations.

1968, July 22 Photo. Perf. 14x13½
505 A104 15c bl, red, blk & gold   .40 .20
506 A104 35c blk, emer, red & gold   .75 .75
507 A104 $1 dk bl, lil, blk & gold 2.10 2.75
  Nos. 505-507 (3)   3.25 3.70

Ethiopia's struggle for peace. Issued with tabs on bottom row. Value, set $10.

WHO Emblem A105

Perf. 14x13½
1968, Aug. 30 Litho. Unwmk.
508 A105 15c brt green & blk   .35 .35
509 A105 60c red lilac & blk   1.90 1.90

20th anniv. of the WHO.

Abebe Bikila, Marathon Runner A106

1968, Oct. 12 Perf. 11½
510 A106 10c shown   .20 .20
511 A106 15c Soccer   .40 .40
512 A106 20c Boxing   .50 .50
513 A106 40c Basketball   1.25 1.25
514 A106 50c Bicycling   1.90 1.90
  Nos. 510-514 (5)   4.25 4.25

19th Olympic Games, Mexico City, 10/12-27.

Arrussi Woman — A107

Regional Costumes: 15c, Man from Gemu Gefa. 20c, Gojam man. 30c, Kefa man. 35c, Harar woman. 40c, Ilubabor grass coat. 60c, Woman from Eritrea.

Perf. 13½x13
1968, Dec. 10 Photo. Unwmk.
515 A107 5c silver & multi   .50 .20
516 A107 15c silver & multi   .50 .20
517 A107 20c silver & multi   .50 .20
518 A107 30c silver & multi   .65 .55
519 A107 35c silver & multi   .75 .65
520 A107 50c silver & multi   1.50 1.10
521 A107 60c silver & multi   2.10 1.60
  Nos. 515-521 (7)   6.50 4.50

See Nos. 575-581.

Message Stick and Amharic Postal Emblem A108

1969, Mar. 10 Litho. Perf. 14
522 A108 10c emerald, blk & brn   .70 .70
523 A108 15c yellow, blk & brn   .70 .70
524 A108 35c multicolored   1.10 1.10
  Nos. 522-524 (3)   2.50 2.50

Ethiopian postal service, 75th anniv.

ILO Emblem A109

1969, Apr. 11 Litho. Perf. 14½
525 A109 15c orange & blk   .50 .50
526 A109 60c emerald & blk   2.00 2.00

50th anniv. of the ILO.

Dove, Red Cross, Crescent, Lion and Sun Emblems A110

1969, May 8 Wmk. 282 Perf. 13
527 A110 5c lt ultra, blk & red   .20 .20
528 A110 15c lt ultra, grn & red   .65 .65
529 A110 30c lt ultra, vio bl & red   1.40 1.40
  Nos. 527-529 (3)   2.25 2.25

League of Red Cross Societies, 50th anniv.

Endybis Silver Coin, 3rd Century — A111

Ancient Ethiopian Coins: 10c, Gold of Ezana, 4th cent. 15c, Gold of Kaleb, 6th cent. 30c, Bronze of Armah, 7th cent. 40c, Bronze of Wazena, 7th cent. 50c, Silver of Gersem, 8th cent.

1969, June 19 Photo. Perf. 14½
530 A111 5c ultra, blk & sil   .20 .20
531 A111 10c brt red, blk & gold   .45 .45
532 A111 15c brown, blk & gold   .70 .70
533 A111 30c dp car, blk & brnz   1.25 1.25
534 A111 40c dk green, blk & brnz   1.50 1.50
535 A111 50c dp violet, blk & sil   2.40 2.40
  Nos. 530-535 (6)   6.50 6.50

Zebras and Tourist Year Emblem A112

Designs: 10c, Camping. 15c, Fishing. 20c, Water skiing. 25c, Mountaineering, vert.

Perf. 13x13½, 13½x13
1969, Aug. 29 Litho. Unwmk.
536 A112 5c multicolored   .20 .20
537 A112 10c multicolored   .20 .20
538 A112 15c multicolored   .65 .75

539 A112 20c multicolored   1.25 1.50
540 A112 25c multicolored   1.50 2.00
  Nos. 536-540 (5)   3.80 4.65

International Year of African Tourism.

Stylized Bird and UN Emblem A113

UN 25th anniv.: 30c, Stylized flowers, UN and peace emblems, vert. 60c, Stylized bird, UN emblem and plane.

1969, Oct. 24 Unwmk. Perf. 11½
541 A113 10c lt blue & multi   .20 .20
542 A113 30c lt blue & multi   .80 .80
543 A113 60c lt blue & multi   2.00 2.00
  Nos. 541-543 (3)   3.00 3.00

Ancient Cross and Holy Family A114

Designs: Various ancient crosses.

Perf. 14½x13½
1969, Dec. 10 Photo.
544 A114 5c black, yel & dk bl   .20 .20
545 A114 10c black & yellow   .20 .30
546 A114 25c black, yel & grn   1.10 1.40
547 A114 60c black & ocher   2.75 3.00
  Nos. 544-547 (4)   4.25 4.90

Ancient Figurines — A115

Ancient Ethiopian Pottery: 20c, Vases, Yeha period, 4th-3rd centuries B.C. 25c, Vases and jugs, Axum, 4th-6th centuries A.D. 35c, Bird-shaped jug and jugs, Matara, 4th-6th centuries A.D. 60c, Decorated pottery, Adulis, 6th-7th centuries A.D.

1970, Feb. 6 Photo. Perf. 14½
548 A115 10c black & multi   .55 .55
549 A115 20c black & multi   .55 .55
550 A115 25c black & multi   .55 .55
551 A115 35c black & multi   1.25 1.25
552 A115 60c black & multi   2.25 2.25
  Nos. 548-552 (5)   5.15 5.15

Medhane Alem Church — A116

Rock Churches of Lalibela, 12th-13th Centuries: 10c, Bieta Emmanuel. 15c, The four Rock Churches of Lalibela. 20c, Bieta Mariam. 50c, Bieta Giorgis.

1970, Apr. 15 Unwmk. Perf. 13
553 A116 5c brown & multi   .20 .20
554 A116 10c brown & multi   .20 .20
555 A116 15c brown & multi   .40 .40
556 A116 20c brown & multi   .65 .65
557 A116 50c brown & multi   1.50 1.50
  Nos. 553-557 (5)   2.95 2.95

Sailfish Tang A117

Tropical Fish: 10c, Undulate triggerfish. 15c, Orange butterflyfish. 25c, Butterflyfish. 50c, Imperial Angelfish.

1970, June 19 Photo. Perf. 12½
558 A117 5c multicolored   .20 .20
559 A117 10c multicolored   .20 .20
560 A117 15c multicolored   .60 .60
561 A117 25c multicolored   1.50 1.50
562 A117 50c multicolored   3.00 3.00
  Nos. 558-562 (5)   5.50 5.50

Education Year Emblem — A118

1970, Aug. 14 Unwmk. Perf. 13½
563 A118 10c multicolored   .20 .20
564 A118 20c gold, ultra & emer   .45 .45
565 A118 50c gold, emer & org   1.10 1.10
  Nos. 563-565 (3)   1.75 1.75

Issued for International Education Year.

Map of Africa — A119

30c, Flag of Organization of African Unity. 40c, OAU Headquarters, Addis Ababa.

1970, Sept. 21 Photo. Perf. 13½
566 A119 20c multicolored   .35 .35
567 A119 30c multicolored   .55 .55
568 A119 40c green & multi   1.00 1.00
  Nos. 566-568 (3)   1.90 1.90

Africa Unity Day and Organization of African Unity.

Emperor Haile Selassie — A120

1970, Oct. 30 Unwmk. Perf. 14½
569 A120 15c Prus bl & multi   .20 .20
570 A120 50c multicolored   .85 .85
571 A120 60c multicolored   2.00 2.00
  Nos. 569-571 (3)   3.05 3.05

Coronation, 40th anniv.

Buildings — A121

1970, Dec. 30　Litho.　Perf. 13½
572 A121 10c ver & multi .20 .20
573 A121 50c brown & multi 1.25 1.25
574 A121 80c multicolored 1.50 1.50
　　Nos. 572-574 (3) 2.95 2.95

Opening of new Posts, Telecommunications and General Post Office buildings.

Costume Type of 1968

Regional Costumes: 5c, Warrior from Begemdir and Semien. 10c, Woman from Bale. 15c, Warrior from Welega. 20c, Woman from Shoa. 25c, Man from Sidamo. 40c, Woman from Tigre. 50c, Man from Welo.

1971, Feb. 17　Photo.　Perf. 11½
Granite Paper
575 A107 5c gold & multi .20 .20
576 A107 10c gold & multi .20 .20
577 A107 15c gold & multi .50 .50
578 A107 20c gold & multi .60 .60
579 A107 25c gold & multi .80 .80
580 A107 40c gold & multi 1.10 1.10
581 A107 50c gold & multi 2.10 2.10
　　Nos. 575-581 (7) 5.50 5.50

Plane's Tail with Emblem — A122

Designs: 10c, Ethiopian scenes. 20c, Nose of Boeing 707. 60c, Pilots in cockpit, and engine. 80c, Globe with routes shown.

1971, Apr. 8　　Perf. 14½x14
582 A122 5c multicolored .40 .40
583 A122 10c multicolored .40 .40
584 A122 20c multicolored .50 .50
585 A122 60c multicolored 1.50 1.50
586 A122 80c multicolored 2.25 2.25
　　Nos. 582-586 (5) 5.05 5.05

Ethiopian Airlines, 25th anniversary. Issued with tabs on bottom row. Value, set $11.

Fountain of Life, 15th Century Gospel Book — A123

Ethiopian Paintings: 10c, King David, 15th cent. manuscript. 25c, St. George, 17th cent. painting on canvas. 50c, King Lalibela, 18th cent. painting on wood. 60c, Yared singing before King Kaleb. Mural in Axum Cathedral.

1971, June 15　Photo.　Perf. 11½
Granite Paper
587 A123 5c tan & multi .20 .20
588 A123 10c pale sal & multi .20 .20
589 A123 25c lemon & multi .60 .60
590 A123 50c yellow & multi 1.60 1.60
591 A123 60c gray & multi 2.50 2.50
　　Nos. 587-591 (5) 5.10 5.10

Black and White Heads, Globes A124

Designs: 60c, Black and white hand holding globe. 80c, Four races, globes.

1971, Aug. 31　　　Unwmk.
592 A124 10c org, red brn & blk .45 .45
593 A124 60c green, bl & blk 1.40 1.40
594 A124 80c bl, org, yel & blk 2.25 2.25
　　Nos. 592-594 (3) 4.10 4.10

Intl. Year Against Racial Discrimination.

Emperor Menelik II and Reading of Treaty of Ucciali A125

Contemporary Paintings: 30c, Menelik II on horseback gathering the tribes. 50c, Ethiopians and Italians in Battle of Adwa. 60c, Menelik II and Taitu at head of their armies.

1971, Oct. 20　Litho.　Perf. 13½
595 A125 10c multicolored .35 .35
596 A125 30c multicolored .95 .95
597 A125 50c multicolored 1.40 1.40
598 A125 60c multicolored 2.40 2.40
　　Nos. 595-598 (4) 5.10 5.10

75th anniversary of victory of Adwa over the Italians, March 1, 1896.

Two telephones, 1897, Menelik II and Prince Makonnen — A126

Designs: 10c, Haile Selassie Broadcasting and Map of Ethiopia. 30c, Ethiopians around television set. 40c, Telephone microwave circuits. 60c, Map of Africa on globe and telephone dial.

1971, Nov. 2
599 A126 5c brown & multi .35 .35
600 A126 10c yellow & multi .35 .35
601 A126 30c vio bl & multi .45 .45
602 A126 40c black & multi 1.00 1.00
603 A126 60c vio bl & multi 2.00 2.00
　　Nos. 599-603 (5) 4.15 4.15

Telecommunications in Ethiopia, 75th anniv.

UNICEF Emblem, Mother and Child — A127

UNICEF Emblem and: 10c, Children drinking milk. 15c, Man holding sick child. 30c, Kindergarten class. 50c, Father and son.

1971, Dec. 15　　　Unwmk.
604 A127 5c yellow & multi .35 .35
605 A127 10c pale brn & multi .35 .35
606 A127 15c rose & multi .35 .35
607 A127 30c violet & multi .80 .80
608 A127 50c green & multi 1.40 1.40
　　Nos. 604-608 (5) 3.25 3.25

25th anniv. of UNICEF.

Nos. 445-448 Overprinted

1972, Jan. 28　Photo.　Perf. 11
Portrait in Black
609 A86 20c grn & pale yel .45 .45
610 A86 25c dk brn & yel .80 .80
611 A86 30c maroon & gray 3.00 3.00
612 A86 35c dk blue & gray 3.00 3.00
　　Nos. 609-612 (4) 7.25 7.25

1st meeting of UN Security Council in Africa.

River Boat on Lake Haik — A128

1972, Feb. 7　Litho.　Perf. 11½
Granite Paper
613 A128 10c shown .30 .30
614 A128 20c Boats on Lake Abaya .55 .55
615 A128 30c on Lake Tana 1.00 1.00
616 A128 60c on Baro River 1.75 1.75
　　Nos. 613-616 (4) 3.60 3.60

Proclamation of Cyrus the Great — A129

1972, Mar. 28　Photo.　Perf. 14x14½
617 A129 10c red & multi .40 .40
618 A129 60c emerald & multi 1.60 1.60
619 A129 80c gray & multi 2.25 2.25
　　Nos. 617-619 (3) 4.25 4.25

2500th anniversary of the founding of the Persian empire by Cyrus the Great.

Houses, Sidamo Province A130

Ethiopian Architecture: 10c, Tigre Province. 20c, Eritrea Province. 40c, Addis Ababa. 80c, Shoa Province.

1972, Apr. 11　Litho.　Perf. 13½
620 A130 5c black & multi .30 .30
621 A130 10c black, gray & brn .30 .30
622 A130 20c black & multi .65 .65
623 A130 40c black, bl grn & brn 1.10 1.10
624 A130 80c black, brn & red brn 2.75 2.75
　　Nos. 620-624 (5) 5.10 5.10

Hands Holding Map of Ethiopia — A131

10c, Hands shielding Ethiopians. 25c, Map of Africa, hands reaching for African Unity emblem. 50c, Brown & white hands clasped, UN emblem. 60c, Hands protecting dove. Each denomination shows different portrait of the Emperor.

**　　　Perf. 14½x14**
1972, July 21　Litho.　　Unwmk.
625 A131 5c scarlet & multi .35 .35
626 A131 10c ultra & multi .35 .35
627 A131 25c vio bl & multi .60 .60
628 A131 50c lt blue & multi 1.25 1.25
629 A131 60c brown & multi 1.50 1.50
　　Nos. 625-629 (5) 4.05 4.05

80th birthday of Emperor Haile Selassie.

Running, Flags of Mexico, Japan, Italy — A132

1972, Aug. 25　　Perf. 13½x13
630 A132 10c shown .35 .35
631 A132 30c Soccer .80 .80
632 A132 50c Bicycling 1.50 1.50
633 A132 60c Boxing 2.10 2.10
　　Nos. 630-633 (4) 4.75 4.75

20th Olympic Games, Munich, Germany, Aug. 26-Sept. 11.

Open Bible, Cross and Orbit A133

Designs: 50c, First and 1972 headquarters of the British and Foreign Bible Society, vert. 80c, First Amharic Bible.

1972, Sept. 25　Photo.　Perf. 13½
634 A133 20c deep red & multi .60 .60
635 A133 50c deep red & multi 1.25 1.25
636 A133 80c deep red & multi 2.25 2.25
　　Nos. 634-636 (3) 4.10 4.10

United Bible Societies World Assembly, Addis Ababa, Sept. 1972.

Security Council Meeting A134

Designs: 60c, Building where Security Council met. 80c, Map of Africa with flags of participating members.

1972, Nov. 1　Litho.　Perf. 13½
637 A134 10c lt bl & vio bl .25 .25
638 A134 60c multicolored 1.25 1.25
639 A134 80c multicolored 2.00 2.00
　　Nos. 637-639 (3) 3.50 3.50

First United Nations Security Council meeting, Addis Ababa, Jan. 28-Feb. 4, 1972.

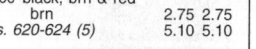

Fish in Polluted Sea A135

Designs: 30c, Fisherman, beacon, family. 80c, Polluted seashore.

1973, Feb. 23　Photo.　Perf. 13½
640 A135 20c gold & multi .50 .50
641 A135 30c gold & multi .85 .85
642 A135 80c gold & multi 2.50 2.50
　　Nos. 640-642 (3) 3.85 3.85

World message from the sea, Ethiopian anti-pollution campaign.

INTERPOL and Ethiopian Police Emblems — A136

50c, INTERPOL emblem & General Secretariat, Paris. 60c, INTERPOL emblem.

1973, Mar. 20　Photo.　Perf. 13½
643 A136 40c dull orange & blk 1.00 1.00
644 A136 50c blue, blk & yel 1.75 1.75
645 A136 60c dk carmine & blk 2.00 2.00
　　Nos. 643-645 (3) 4.75 4.75

50th anniversary of International Criminal Police Organization (INTERPOL).

Virgin of Emperor Zara Yaqob — A137

Ethiopian Art: 15c, Crucifixion, Zara Yaqob period. 30c, Virgin and Child, from Entoto Mariam Church. 40c, Christ, contemporary mosaic. 80c, The Evangelists, contemporary bas-relief.

1973, May 15   Photo.   Perf. 11½
Granite Paper

646	A137	5c brown & multi	.30	.30
647	A137	15c dp blue & multi	.45	.45
648	A137	30c gray grn & multi	.90	.90
649	A137	40c multicolored	1.10	1.10
650	A137	80c slate & multi	2.75	2.75
		Nos. 646-650 (5)	5.50	5.50

Free African States in 1963 and 1973 A138

Designs (Map of Africa and): 10c, Flags of OAU members. 20c, Symbols of progress. 40c, Dove and people. 80c, Emblems of various UN agencies.

1973 May 25   Perf. 14½x14

651	A138	5c red & multi	.25	.25
652	A138	10c ol gray & multi	.30	.30
653	A138	20c green & multi	.45	.45
654	A138	40c sepia & multi	1.25	1.25
655	A138	80c lt blue & multi	2.50	2.50
		Nos. 651-655 (5)	4.75	4.75

OAU, 10th anniv.

Scouts Saluting Ethiopian and Scout Flags — A139

Designs: 15c, Road and road sign. 30c, Girl Scout reading to old man. 40c, Scout and disabled people. 60c, Ethiopian Boy Scout.

1973, July 10   Photo.   Perf. 11½
Granite Paper

656	A139	5c blue & multi	.30	.30
657	A139	15c lt green & multi	.45	.45
658	A139	30c yellow & multi	.85	.85
659	A139	40c crimson & multi	1.10	1.10
660	A139	60c violet & multi	2.40	2.40
		Nos. 656-660 (5)	5.10	5.10

24th Boy Scout World Conference, Nairobi, Kenya, July 16-21.

WMO Emblem A140

50c, WMO emblem, anemometer. 60c, Weather satellite over earth, WMO emblem.

1973, Sept. 4   Photo.   Perf. 13½

661	A140	40c black, bl & dl bl	.95	.95
662	A140	50c dull blue & blk	1.25	1.25
663	A140	60c dull blue & multi	1.90	1.90
		Nos. 661-663 (3)	4.10	4.10

Cent. of intl. meteorological cooperation. Printed with tabs at top of sheet inscribed in Amharic and tabs at bottom with "ETHIOPIA."

Prince Makonnen, Duke of Harar — A141

Human Rights Flame — A142

5c, Old wall of Harar. 20c, Operating room. 40c, Boy Scouts learning 1st aid & hospital. 80c, Prince Makonnen & hospital.

1973, Nov. 1   Unwmk.   Perf. 14½

664	A141	5c gray & multi	.30	.30
665	A141	10c red brn & multi	.30	.30
666	A141	20c green & multi	.65	.65
667	A141	40c brown red & multi	1.50	1.50
668	A141	80c ultra & multi	2.75	2.75
		Nos. 664-668 (5)	5.50	5.50

Opening of Prince Makonnen Memorial Hospital.

Perf. 11½
1973, Nov. 16   Photo.   Unwmk.
Granite Paper

669	A142	40c yel, gold & dk grn	.70	.70
670	A142	50c lt grn, gold & dk grn	1.00	1.00
671	A142	60c org, gold & dk grn	1.25	1.25
		Nos. 669-671 (3)	2.95	2.95

25th anniversary of the Universal Declaration of Human Rights.

Emperor Haile Selassie — A143

1973, Nov. 5   Photo.   Perf. 11½

672	A143	5c yellow & multi	.35	.30
673	A143	10c brt blue & multi	.35	.30
674	A143	15c green & multi	.45	.40
675	A143	20c dull yel & multi	.55	.40
676	A143	25c multicolored	.65	.40
677	A143	30c multicolored	.80	.40
678	A143	35c multicolored	.85	.40
679	A143	40c ultra & multi	.95	.40
680	A143	45c multicolored	1.10	.50
681	A143	50c orange & multi	1.25	.50
682	A143	55c magenta & multi	1.60	.85
683	A143	60c multicolored	1.75	1.10
684	A143	70c red org & multi	2.10	1.25
685	A143	90c brt vio & multi	2.75	1.40
686	A143	$1 multicolored	3.25	1.90
687	A143	$2 orange & multi	6.25	3.25
688	A143	$3 multicolored	10.50	5.00
689	A143	$5 multicolored	17.00	8.25
		Nos. 672-689 (18)	52.50	27.00

Wicker Furniture A144

Designs: Various wicker baskets, wall hangings, dinnerware.

1974, Jan. 31   Photo.   Perf. 11½
Granite Paper

690	A144	5c violet bl & multi	.25	.25
691	A144	10c violet bl & multi	.30	.30
692	A144	30c violet bl & multi	.55	.55
693	A144	50c violet bl & multi	1.00	1.00
694	A144	60c violet bl & multi	1.10	1.10
		Nos. 690-694 (5)	3.20	3.20

Cow, Calf, Syringe — A145

Designs: 15c, Inoculation of cattle. 20c, Bullock and syringe. 50c, Laboratory technician, cow's head, syringe. 60c, Map of Ethiopia, cattle, syringe.

1974, Feb. 20   Litho.   Perf. 13½x13

695	A145	5c sepia & multi	.20	.20
696	A145	15c ultra & multi	.40	.40
697	A145	20c ultra & multi	.50	.50
698	A145	50c orange & multi	1.25	1.25
699	A145	60c gold & multi	1.75	1.75
		Nos. 695-699 (5)	4.10	4.10

Campaign against cattle plague.

Umbrella Makers A146

Designs: 30c, Weaving. 50c, Child care. 60c, Foundation headquarters.

1974, Apr. 17   Photo.   Perf. 14½

700	A146	10c lt lilac & multi	.30	.30
701	A146	30c multicolored	.45	.45
702	A146	50c multicolored	.85	.85
703	A146	60c blue & multi	1.00	1.00
		Nos. 700-703 (4)	2.60	2.60

20th anniv. of Haile Selassie Foundation.

Ceremonial Robe — A147

Designs: Ceremonial robes.

1974, June 26   Litho.   Perf. 13

704	A147	15c multicolored	.40	.40
705	A147	25c ocher & multi	.60	.60
706	A147	35c green & multi	1.10	1.10
707	A147	40c lt brown & multi	1.25	1.25
708	A147	60c gray & multi	2.50	2.50
		Nos. 704-708 (5)	5.85	5.85

World Population Statistics — A148

Designs: 50c, "Larger families-lower living standard." 60c, Rising population graph.

1974, Aug. 19   Photo.   Perf. 14½

709	A148	40c yellow & multi	1.10	1.10
710	A148	50c violet & multi	1.40	1.40
711	A148	60c green & multi	1.75	1.75
		Nos. 709-711 (3)	4.25	4.25

World Population Year 1974.

UPU Emblem, Letter Carrier's Staff — A149

Celebration Around "Damara" Pillar — A150

UPU Emblem and: 50c, Letters and flags. 60c, Globe. 70c, Headquarters, Bern.

1974, Oct. 9   Photo.   Perf. 11½
Granite Paper

712	A149	10c yellow & multi	.40	.30
713	A149	50c multicolored	1.10	.85
714	A149	60c ultra & multi	1.40	1.10
715	A149	70c multicolored	1.60	1.25
		Nos. 712-715 (4)	4.50	3.50

Centenary of Universal Postal Union.

1974, Dec. 17   Photo.   Perf. 14x14½

5c, Site of Gishen Mariam Monastery. 20c, Cross and festivities. 80c, Torch (Chibos) Parade.

716	A150	5c yellow & multi	.40	.40
717	A150	10c yellow & multi	.45	.45
718	A150	20c yellow & multi	.55	.55
719	A150	80c yellow & multi	2.25	2.25
		Nos. 716-719 (4)	3.65	3.65

Meskel Festival, Sept. 26-27, commemorating the finding in the 4th century of the True Cross, of which a fragment is kept at Gishen Mariam Monastery in Welo Province.

Precis Clelia — A151

Adoration of the Kings — A152

Butterflies: 25c, Charaxes achaemenes. 45c, Papilio dardanus. 50c, Charaxes druceanus. 60c, Papilio demodocus.

1975, Feb. 18   Photo.   Perf. 12x12½

720	A151	10c silver & multi	1.00	.35
721	A151	25c gold & multi	1.50	.75
722	A151	45c purple & multi	3.00	1.75
723	A151	50c green & multi	3.50	2.50
724	A151	60c brt blue & multi	5.00	3.00
		Nos. 720-724 (5)	14.00	8.35

1975, Apr. 23   Photo.   Perf. 11½

10c, Baptism of Jesus. 15c, Jesus teaching in the Temple. 30c, Jesus giving sight to the blind. 40c, Crucifixion. 80c, Resurrection.

Granite Paper

725	A152	5c brown & multi	.35	.35
726	A152	10c black & multi	.40	.40
727	A152	15c dk brown & multi	.45	.45
728	A152	30c dk brown & multi	.70	.70
729	A152	40c black & multi	1.50	1.50
730	A152	80c slate & multi	2.60	2.60
		Nos. 725-730 (6)	6.00	6.00

Murals from Ethiopian churches.

Wild Animals A153

1975, May 27   Photo.   Perf. 11½
Granite Paper

731	A153	5c Warthog	1.00	.90
732	A153	10c Aardvark	1.00	.90
733	A153	20c Semien wolf	1.50	1.25
734	A153	40c Gelada baboon	2.75	2.50
735	A153	80c Civet	5.50	5.00
		Nos. 731-735 (5)	11.75	10.55

"Peace," Dove, Globe, IWY Emblem — A154

50c, Symbols of development. 90c, Equality between men and women.

1975, June 30   Litho.   Perf. 14x14½
736	A154	40c blue & black	.70	.70
737	A154	50c salmon & multi	.90	.90
738	A154	90c multicolored	1.75	1.75
		Nos. 736-738 (3)	3.35	3.35

International Women's Year 1975.

Postal Museum A155

Various interior views of Postal Museum.

1975, Aug. 19   Photo.   Perf. 13x12½
739	A155	10c ocher & multi	.35	.30
740	A155	30c pink & multi	.65	.50
741	A155	60c multicolored	1.50	1.10
742	A155	70c lt green & multi	1.75	1.25
		Nos. 739-742 (4)	4.25	3.15

Ethiopian Natl. Postal Museum, opening.

Map of Ethiopia and Sun — A156

1975, Sept. 11   Photo.   Perf. 11½
Granite Paper
743	A156	5c lilac & multi	.20	.20
744	A156	10c ultra & multi	.20	.20
745	A156	25c brown & multi	.35	.35
746	A156	50c yellow & multi	.90	.90
747	A156	90c brt green & multi	1.75	1.75
		Nos. 743-747 (5)	3.40	3.40

1st anniv. of Ethiopian revolution.

UN Emblem A157

1975, Oct. 24   Photo.   Perf. 11½
748	A157	40c lilac & multi	.90	.90
749	A157	50c multicolored	1.00	1.00
750	A157	90c blue & multi	2.00	2.00
		Nos. 748-750 (3)	3.90	3.90

United Nations, 30th anniversary.

Regional Hair Styles — A158   Delphinium Wellbyi — A159

1975, Dec. 15   Photo.   Perf. 11½
751	A158	5c Ilubabor	.30	.30
752	A158	15c Arusi	.40	.40
753	A158	20c Eritrea	.60	.60
754	A158	30c Bale	.85	.85
755	A158	35c Kefa	1.10	1.10

756	A158	50c Begemir	1.50	1.50
757	A158	60c Shoa	2.00	2.00
		Nos. 751-757 (7)	6.75	6.75

See Nos. 832-838.

1976, Jan. 15   Photo.   Perf. 11½
Flowers: 10c, Plectocephalus varians. 20c, Brachystelma asmarensis, horiz. 40c, Ceropegia inflata. 80c, Erythrina brucei.
758	A159	5c multicolored	.35	.35
759	A159	10c multicolored	.40	.40
760	A159	20c multicolored	.60	.60
761	A159	40c multicolored	1.50	1.50
762	A159	60c multicolored	2.50	2.50
		Nos. 758-762 (5)	5.35	5.35

Goalkeeper, Map of Africa, Games' Emblem A160

Designs: Various scenes from soccer, map of Africa and ball.

1976, Feb. 27   Photo.   Perf. 14½
763	A160	5c orange & multi	.20	.20
764	A160	10c yellow & multi	.35	.35
765	A160	25c lilac & multi	.70	.70
766	A160	50c green & multi	1.40	1.40
767	A160	90c brt grn & multi	2.40	2.40
		Nos. 763-767 (5)	5.05	5.05

10th African Cup of Nations, Addis Ababa and Dire Dawa, Feb. 29-Mar. 14.

Telephones, 1876 and 1976 — A161   Ethiopian Jewelry — A162

Designs: 60c, Alexander Graham Bell. 90c, Transmission tower.

1976, Mar. 10   Litho.   Perf. 12x13½
768	A161	30c lt ocher & multi	.85	.75
769	A161	60c emerald & multi	1.60	1.25
770	A161	90c ver, blk & buff	2.50	2.00
		Nos. 768-770 (3)	4.95	4.00

Centenary of first telephone call by Alexander Graham Bell, Mar. 10, 1876.

1976, May 14   Photo.   Perf. 11½
Designs: Women wearing various kinds of Ethiopian jewelry.
Granite Paper
771	A162	5c blue & multi	.25	.20
772	A162	10c plum & multi	.35	.25
773	A162	20c gray & multi	.75	.50
774	A162	40c green & multi	1.25	.90
775	A162	80c orange & multi	2.50	1.75
		Nos. 771-775 (5)	5.10	3.60

Boxing — A163   Hands Holding Map of Ethiopia — A164

Designs (Montreal Olympic Emblem and): 80c, Runner and maple leaf. 90c, Bicycling.

1976, July 15   Litho.   Perf. 12½x12
776	A163	10c multicolored	.50	.40
777	A163	80c brt red, blk & grn	2.25	1.75
778	A163	90c brt red & multi	2.75	2.00
		Nos. 776-778 (3)	5.50	4.15

21st Olympic Games, Montreal, Canada, July 17-Aug. 1.

1976, Aug. 5   Photo.   Perf. 14½
779	A164	5c rose & multi	.25	.20
780	A164	10c olive & multi	.30	.25
781	A164	25c orange & multi	.40	.30
782	A164	50c multicolored	.95	.70
783	A164	90c dk blue & multi	1.75	1.40
		Nos. 779-783 (5)	3.65	2.85

Development through cooperation.

Revolution Emblem: Eye and Map A165

1976, Sept. 9   Photo.   Perf. 13½
784	A165	5c multicolored	.20	.20
785	A165	10c multicolored	.30	.25
786	A165	25c multicolored	.40	.30
787	A165	50c yellow & multi	.95	.70
788	A165	90c green & multi	1.60	1.25
		Nos. 784-788 (5)	3.45	2.70

2nd anniversary of the revolution.

Sunburst Around Crest — A166   Plane Over Man with Donkey — A167

1976, Sept. 13   Photo.   Perf. 11½
789	A166	5c green, gold & blk	.20	.20
790	A166	10c org, gold & blk	.25	.20
791	A166	15c grnsh bl, gold & blk	.40	.20
792	A166	20c lilac, gold & blk	.50	.25
793	A166	25c brt grn, gold & blk	.60	.25
794	A166	30c car, gold & blk	.75	.25
795	A166	35c yel, gold & blk	.90	.25
796	A166	40c ol, gold & blk	1.00	.40
797	A166	45c brt grn, gold & blk	1.10	.50
798	A166	50c car rose, gold & blk	1.25	.70
799	A166	55c ultra, gold & blk	1.50	.90
800	A166	60c fawn, gold & blk	1.75	.90
801	A166	70c rose, gold & blk	2.00	.90
802	A166	90c blue, gold & blk	2.25	.90
803	A166	$1 dull grn, gold & blk	2.75	1.00
804	A166	$2 gray, gold & blk	6.00	2.00
805	A166	$3 brn vio, gold & blk	8.00	3.25
806	A166	$5 slate bl, gold & blk	15.00	5.00
		Nos. 789-806 (18)	46.20	18.05

Denomination Expressed as "BIRR"

1983, June 16
806A	A166	1b dull grn, gold & blk	15.00	2.25
806B	A166	2b gray, gold & blk	37.50	4.50
806C	A166	3b brn vio, gold & blk	45.00	6.25

1976, Oct. 28   Litho.   Perf. 12x12½
10c, Globe showing routes. 25c, Crew and passengers forming star. 50c, Propeller and jet engine. 90c, Airplanes surrounding map of Ethiopia.
807	A167	5c dull bl & multi	.40	.30
808	A167	10c lilac & multi	.50	.35
809	A167	25c multicolored	.70	.50
810	A167	50c orange & multi	1.40	1.25
811	A167	90c olive & multi	2.75	2.25
		Nos. 807-811 (5)	5.75	4.65

Ethiopian Airlines, 30th anniversary.

Tortoises A168   Hand Holding Makeshift Hammer A169

Reptiles: 20c, Chameleon. 30c, Python. 40c, Monitor lizard. 80c, Nile crocodiles.

1976, Dec. 15   Photo.   Perf. 14½
812	A168	10c multicolored	.50	.40
813	A168	20c multicolored	.75	.50
814	A168	30c multicolored	1.00	.80
815	A168	40c multicolored	1.50	1.10
816	A168	80c multicolored	3.00	2.25
		Nos. 812-816 (5)	6.75	5.05

1977, Jan. 20   Litho.   Perf. 12½
Designs: 5c, Hands holding bowl and plane dropping food. 45c, Infant with empty bowl, and bank note. 60c, Map of affected area, footprints and tire tracks. 80c, Film strip, camera and Ethiopian sitting between eggshells.
817	A169	5c multicolored	.30	.25
818	A169	10c multicolored	.45	.40
819	A169	45c multicolored	1.00	.85
820	A169	60c multicolored	1.25	1.00
821	A169	80c multicolored	1.75	1.60
		Nos. 817-821 (5)	4.75	4.10

Ethiopian Relief and Rehabilitation Commission for drought and disaster areas.

Elephant and Ruins, Axum, 7th Century A170

Designs: 10c, Ibex and temple, 5th century, B.C., Yeha. 25c, Megalithic dolmen and pottery, Sourre Kabanawa. 50c, Awash Valley, stone axe, Acheulean period. 80c, Omo Valley, hominid jawbone.

1977, Mar. 15   Photo.   Perf. 13½
822	A170	5c gold & multi	.50	.35
823	A170	10c gold & multi	.60	.45
824	A170	25c gold & multi	.75	.65
825	A170	50c gold & multi	1.25	1.10
826	A170	80c gold & multi	2.25	1.50
		Nos. 822-826 (5)	5.35	4.05

Archaeological sites and finds in Ethiopia.

Map of Africa with Trans-East Highway — A171

1977, Mar. 30   Perf. 14
827	A171	10c gold & multi	.40	.35
828	A171	20c gold & multi	.50	.40
829	A171	40c gold & multi	.90	.80
830	A171	50c gold & multi	1.25	1.00
831	A171	60c gold & multi	1.75	1.25
		Nos. 827-831 (5)	4.80	3.80

Addis Ababa to Nairobi Highway and projected highways to Cairo, Egypt, and Gaborone, Botswana.

Hairstyle Type of 1975

1977, Apr. 28   Photo.   Perf. 11½
832	A158	5c Welega	.20	.20
833	A158	10c Gojam	.30	.25
834	A158	15c Tigre	.40	.35
835	A158	20c Harar	.70	.65
836	A158	25c Gemu Gefa	.85	.70
837	A158	40c Sidamo	1.40	1.25
838	A158	50c Welo	1.75	1.50
		Nos. 832-838 (7)	5.60	4.90

Addis Ababa
A172

Towns of Ethiopia: 10c, Asmara. 25c, Harar. 50c, Jima. 90c, Dese.

1977, June 20   Photo.   Perf. 14½
839 A172 5c silver & multi   .30   .25
840 A172 10c silver & multi   .40   .35
841 A172 25c silver & multi   .60   .55
842 A172 50c silver & multi   1.25 1.00
843 A172 90c silver & multi   2.25 1.50
   Nos. 839-843 (5)   4.80 3.65

Terebratula Abyssinica — A173   Fractured Imperial Crown — A174

Fossil Shells: 10c, Terebratula subalata. 25c, Cuculloea lefeburiaua. 50c, Ostrea plicatissima. 90c, Trigonia cousobrina.

1977, Aug. 15   Photo.   Perf. 14x13½
844 A173 5c multicolored   .75   .25
845 A173 10c multicolored   1.25 .50
846 A173 25c multicolored   1.50 .85
847 A173 50c multicolored   2.50 1.50
848 A173 90c multicolored   4.00 2.50
   Nos. 844-848 (5)   10.00 5.60

1977, Sept. 9   Litho.   Perf. 15

Designs: 10c, Symbol of the Revolution (spade, axe, torch). 25c, Warriors, hammer and sickle, map of Ethiopia. 60c, Soldier, farmer and map. 80c, Map and emblem of revolutionary government.

849 A174 5c multicolored   .25   .20
850 A174 10c multicolored   .40   .35
851 A174 25c multicolored   .50   .45
852 A174 60c multicolored   1.25 1.00
853 A174 80c multicolored   1.50 1.25
   Nos. 849-853 (5)   3.90 3.25

Third anniversary of the revolution.

Cicindela Petitii — A175   Lenin, Globe, Map of Ethiopia and Emblem — A176

Insects: 10c, Heliocopris dillonii. 25c, Poekilocerus vignaudii. 50c, Pepsis heros. 90c, Pepsis dedjaz.

1977, Sept. 30   Photo.   Perf. 14x13½
854 A175 5c multicolored   .55   .50
855 A175 10c multicolored   .75   .75
856 A175 25c multicolored   1.50 1.50
857 A175 50c multicolored   3.50 3.50
858 A175 90c multicolored   5.50 5.50
   Nos. 854-858 (5)   11.80 11.75

1977, Nov. 15   Litho.   Perf. 12
859 A176 5c orange & multi   .40   .25
860 A176 10c multicolored   .45   .35
861 A176 25c salmon & multi   .50   .40
862 A176 50c lt blue & multi   1.00 .85
863 A176 90c yellow & multi   1.75 1.25
   Nos. 859-863 (5)   4.10 3.10

60th anniv. of Russian October Revolution.

Chondrostoma Dilloni — A177

Salt-water Fish: 10c, Ostracion cubicus. 25c, Serranus summana. 50c, Serranus luti. 90c, Tetraodon maculatus.

1978, Jan. 20   Litho.   Perf. 15½
864 A177 5c multicolored   .65   .65
865 A177 10c multicolored   .75   .75
866 A177 25c multicolored   1.25 1.25
867 A177 50c multicolored   2.25 2.25
868 A177 90c multicolored   4.00 4.00
   Nos. 864-868 (5)   8.90 8.90

Domestic Animals — A178

1978, Mar. 27   Litho.   Perf. 13½x14
869 A178 5c Cattle   .25   .20
870 A178 10c Mules   .40   .25
871 A178 25c Goats   .75   .55
872 A178 50c Dromedaries   1.50 1.25
873 A178 90c Horses   2.75 2.25
   Nos. 869-873 (5)   5.65 4.50

Weapons and Shield, Map of Ethiopia — A179   Bronze Ibex, 5th Century B.C. — A180

"Call of the Motherland." (Map of Ethiopia and): 10c, Civilian fighters. 25c, Map of Africa. 60c, Soldiers. 80c, Red Cross nurse and wounded man.

1978, May 13   Litho.   Perf. 15½
874 A179 5c multicolored   .30   .25
875 A179 10c multicolored   .40   .35
876 A179 25c multicolored   .70   .60
877 A179 60c multicolored   1.25 1.00
878 A179 80c multicolored   2.25 1.50
   Nos. 874-878 (5)   4.90 3.70

1978, June 21   Litho.   Perf. 15½

Ancient Bronzes: 10c, Lion, Yeha, 5th cent. B.C., horiz. 25c, Lamp with ibex attacked by dog, Matara, 1st cent. B.C. 50c, Goat, Axum, 3rd cent. A.D., horiz. 90c, Ax, chisel and sickle, Yeha, 5th-4th centuries B.C.

879 A180 5c multicolored   .25   .20
880 A180 10c multicolored   .35   .30
881 A180 25c multicolored   .60   .50
882 A180 50c multicolored   1.50 1.25
883 A180 90c multicolored   2.50 1.75
   Nos. 879-883 (5)   5.20 4.00

See Nos. 1024-1027.

Globe and Argentina '78 Emblem A181

20c, Soccer player kicking ball. 30c, Two players embracing, net and ball. 55c, World map and ball. 70c, Soccer field, vert.

Perf. 14x13½, 13½x14
1978, July 19   Litho.
884 A181 5c multicolored   .45   .40
885 A181 20c multicolored   .70   .50
886 A181 30c multicolored   1.00 .65

887 A181 55c multicolored   1.75 1.25
888 A181 70c multicolored   2.25 1.75
   Nos. 884-888 (5)   6.15 4.55

11th World Cup Soccer Championship, Argentina, June 1-25.

Map of Africa, Oppressed African — A182

Namibia Day: 10c, Policeman pointing gun. 25c, Sniper with gun. 60c, African caught in net. 80c, Head of free man.

1978, Aug. 25   Perf. 12½x13½
889 A182 5c multicolored   .30   .25
890 A182 10c multicolored   .50   .45
891 A182 25c multicolored   .60   .50
892 A182 60c multicolored   1.50 1.00
893 A182 80c multicolored   2.25 1.50
   Nos. 889-893 (5)   5.15 3.70

Soldiers, Guerrilla and Jets A183

Design: 1b, People looking toward sun, crushing snake, flags.

1978, Sept. 8   Photo.   Perf. 14
894 A183 80c multicolored   1.75 1.25
895 A183 1b multicolored   2.50 1.75

4th anniversary of revolution.

Hand and Globe with Tools — A184

Designs: 15c, Symbols of energy, communications, education, medicine, agriculture and industry. 25c, Cogwheels and world map. 60c, Globe and hands passing wrench. 70c, Flying geese and turtle over globe.

1978, Nov. 14   Litho.   Perf. 12x12½
896 A184 10c multicolored   .30   .25
897 A184 15c multicolored   .35   .30
898 A184 25c multicolored   .55   .50
899 A184 60c multicolored   1.40 1.00
900 A184 70c multicolored   1.75 1.25
   Nos. 896-900 (5)   4.35 3.30

Technical Cooperation Among Developing Countries Conference, Buenos Aires, Argentina, Sept. 1978.

Human Rights Emblem — A185

1978, Dec. 7   Photo.   Perf. 12½x13½
901 A185 5c multicolored   .30   .25
902 A185 15c multicolored   .30   .25
903 A185 25c multicolored   .45   .40
904 A185 35c multicolored   .75   .70
905 A185 1b multicolored   2.25 1.75
   Nos. 901-905 (5)   4.05 3.35

Declaration of Human Rights, 30th anniv.

Broken Chain, Anti-Apartheid Emblem — A186

Stele from Osole — A187

1978, Dec. 28   Litho.   Perf. 12½x12
906 A186 5c multicolored   .30   .25
907 A186 20c multicolored   .45   .40
908 A186 30c multicolored   .75   .65
909 A186 55c multicolored   1.25 1.00
910 A186 70c multicolored   1.50 1.25
   Nos. 906-910 (5)   4.25 3.55

Anti-Apartheid Year.

1979, Jan. 25   Perf. 14

Ancient Carved Stones, Soddo Region: 10c, Anthropomorphous stele, Gorashino. 25c, Leaning stone, Wado. 60c, Round stones, Ambeut. 80c, Bas-relief, Tiya.

911 A187 5c multicolored   .30   .25
912 A187 10c multicolored   .40   .30
913 A187 25c multicolored   .65   .50
914 A187 60c multicolored   1.75 1.25
915 A187 80c multicolored   2.25 1.75
   Nos. 911-915 (5)   5.35 4.05

Cotton Plantation A188

Shemma Industry: 10c, Women spinning cotton yarn. 20c, Man reeling cotton. 65c, Weaver. 80c, Shemma (Natl. dress).

1979, Mar. 15   Litho.   Perf. 15½
916 A188 5c multicolored   .40   .25
917 A188 10c multicolored   .45   .35
918 A188 20c multicolored   .60   .40
919 A188 65c multicolored   1.75 1.25
920 A188 80c multicolored   2.25 1.50
   Nos. 916-920 (5)   5.45 3.75

Ethiopian Trees — A189

1979, Apr. 26   Photo.   Perf. 13½x14
921 A189 5c Grar   .35   .25
922 A189 10c Weira   .45   .30
923 A189 25c Tidh   .65   .40
924 A189 50c Shola   1.25 1.00
925 A189 90c Zigba   2.00 1.50
   Nos. 921-925 (5)   4.70 3.45

Agricultural Development A190

Revolutionary Development Campaign: 15c, Industry. 25c, Transportation and communication. 60c, Education and health. 70c, Commerce.

1979, July 3   Litho.   Perf. 12x12½
926	A190	10c multicolored	.30	.25
927	A190	15c multicolored	.45	.30
928	A190	25c multicolored	.60	.50
929	A190	60c multicolored	1.25	1.00
930	A190	70c multicolored	1.75	1.50
	Nos. 926-930 (5)		4.35	3.55

IYC Emblem — A191

Intl. Year of the Child: 15c, Adults leading children. 25c, Adult helping child. 60c, IYC emblem surrounded by children. 70c, Adult and children embracing.

1979, Aug. 16   Litho.   Perf. 12x12½
931	A191	10c multicolored	.40	.35
932	A191	15c multicolored	.50	.40
933	A191	25c multicolored	.75	.65
934	A191	60c multicolored	1.75	1.40
935	A191	70c multicolored	2.00	1.75
	Nos. 931-935 (5)		5.40	4.55

Guerrilla Fighters — A192

15c, Soldiers. 25c, Map of Africa within cogwheel, star. 60c, Students with book, torch. 70c, Family, hammer & sickle emblem.

1979, Sept. 11   Photo.   Perf. 14
936	A192	10c multicolored	.40	.35
937	A192	15c multicolored	.50	.45
938	A192	25c multicolored	.75	.65
939	A192	60c multicolored	1.75	1.25
940	A192	70c multicolored	2.25	1.75
	Nos. 936-940 (5)		5.65	4.45

Fifth anniversary of revolution.

Telephone Receiver A193   Incense Container A194

Telecom Emblem and: 5c, Symbolic waves. 35c, Satellite beaming to earth. 45c, Dish antenna. 65c, Television cameraman.

1979, Sept. 20   Photo.   Perf. 11½
941	A193	5c multicolored	.35	.30
942	A193	30c multicolored	.75	.60
943	A193	35c multicolored	.95	.75
944	A193	45c multicolored	1.50	1.00
945	A193	65c multicolored	2.25	1.50
	Nos. 941-945 (5)		5.80	4.15

3rd World Telecommunications Exhibition, Geneva, Sept. 20-26.

1979, Nov. 15   Litho.   Perf. 15
946	A194	5c shown	.45	.30
947	A194	10c Vase	.85	.45
948	A194	25c Earthenware cover	1.00	.75
949	A194	60c Milk container	1.75	1.25
950	A194	80c Storage container	2.50	1.75
	Nos. 946-950 (5)		6.55	4.50

Wooden Grain Bowl — A195   Lappet-faced Vulture — A196

1980, Jan. 3   Litho.   Perf. 13½x13
951	A195	5c shown	.50	.35
952	A195	30c Chair, stool	.90	.50
953	A195	35c Mortar, pestle	1.00	.75
954	A195	45c Buckets	1.75	1.25
955	A195	65c Storage jars	2.75	2.00
	Nos. 951-955 (5)		6.90	4.85

1980, Feb. 12   Perf. 13½x14

Birds of Prey: 15c, Long-crested hawk eagle. 25c, Secretary bird. 60c, Abyssinian long-eared owl. 70c, Lanner falcon.
956	A196	10c multicolored	1.25	1.25
957	A196	15c multicolored	1.50	1.50
958	A196	25c multicolored	2.25	2.25
959	A196	60c multicolored	4.00	4.00
960	A196	70c multicolored	6.00	6.00
	Nos. 956-960 (5)		15.00	15.00

Fight Against Cigarette Smoking — A197

1980, Apr. 7   Photo.   Perf. 13x13½
961	A197	20c shown	1.25	1.00
962	A197	60c Cigarette	1.75	1.25
963	A197	1b Respiratory system	3.00	2.50
	Nos. 961-963 (3)		6.00	4.75

"110" and Lenin House Museum A198

Lenin, 110th "Birthday" (Paintings): 15c, In hiding. 20c, As a young man. 40c, Returning to Russia. 1b, Speaking on the Goelro Plan.

1980, Apr. 22   Litho.   Perf. 12x12½
964	A198	5c multicolored	.35	.30
965	A198	15c multicolored	.40	.35
966	A198	20c multicolored	.50	.45
967	A198	40c multicolored	.95	.80
968	A198	1b multicolored	2.25	2.00
	Nos. 964-968 (5)		4.45	3.90

Grévy's Zebras A199

1980, June 10   Litho.   Perf. 12½x12
969	A199	10c shown	.75	.75
970	A199	15c Gazelles	1.00	1.00
971	A199	25c Wild hunting dogs	1.50	1.50
972	A199	60c Swayne's hartebeests	2.75	2.75
973	A199	70c Cheetahs	3.50	3.50
	Nos. 969-973 (5)		9.50	9.50

Runner, Moscow '80 Emblem — A200

1980, July 19   Photo.   Perf. 11½x12
974	A200	30c shown	1.00	1.00
975	A200	70c Cycling	2.25	2.25
976	A200	80c Boxing	3.00	3.00
	Nos. 974-976 (3)		6.25	6.25

22nd Summer Olympic Games, Moscow, July 19-Aug. 3.

Removing Blindfold — A201   Bamboo Folk Craft — A202

1980, Sept. 10   Photo.   Perf. 14x13½
977	A201	30c shown	.75	.50
978	A201	40c Revolutionary	1.00	.65
979	A201	50c Woman breaking chain	1.50	1.00
980	A201	70c Russian & Ethiopian flags	2.25	1.25
	Nos. 977-980 (4)		5.50	3.40

6th anniversary of revolution.

1980, Oct. 23   Litho.   Perf. 14
981	A202	5c Bamboo food basket	.30	.25
982	A202	15c Lamp shade	.40	.35
983	A202	25c Stool	.75	.60
984	A202	35c Fruit basket	1.25	1.00
985	A202	1b Lamp shade	2.75	1.75
	Nos. 981-985 (5)		5.45	3.95

Mekotkocha (Used in Weeding) A203

Traditional Harvesting Tools: 15c, Layda (grain separator). 40c, Mensh (fork). 45c, Mededekia (soil turner). 70c, Mofer & Kenber (plow and yoke).

1980, Dec. 18   Litho.   Perf. 12½x12
986	A203	10c multicolored	.30	.25
987	A203	15c multicolored	.35	.30
988	A203	40c multicolored	.90	.75
989	A203	45c multicolored	1.25	1.00
990	A203	70c multicolored	2.50	1.75
	Nos. 986-990 (5)		5.30	4.05

Baro River Bridge Opening A204

1981, Feb. 28   Photo.   Perf. 13½x13
991	A204	15c Canoes and ferry	.50	.40
992	A204	65c Bridge construction	1.75	1.25
993	A204	1b shown	3.00	2.25
	Nos. 991-993 (3)		5.25	3.90

Semien National Park — A205

World Heritage Year: 5c, Wawel Castle, Poland. 15c, Quito Cathedral, Ecuador. 20c, Old Slave Quarters, Goree Island, Senegal. 30c, Mesa Verde Indian Village, US. 1b, L'Anse aux Meadows excavation, Canada.

Perf. 11x11½, 11½x11

1981, Mar. 10   Photo.
994	A205	5c multicolored	.40	.30
995	A205	15c multicolored	.55	.45
996	A205	20c multicolored	.70	.55
997	A205	30c multicolored	1.00	.75
998	A205	80c multicolored	2.25	1.50
999	A205	1b multicolored	3.00	2.25
	Nos. 994-999 (6)		7.90	5.80

1981, June 16   Photo.

10c, Biet Medhanialem Church, Ethiopia. 15c, Nahanni Natl. Park, Canada. 20c, Yellowstone River Lower Falls, U.S. 30c, Aachen Cathedral, Germany. 80c, Kicker Rock, San Cristobal Island, Ecuador. 1b, The Lizak corridor, Holy Cross Chapel, Cracow, Poland.
1000	A205	10c multi	.45	.30
1001	A205	15c multi	.55	.45
1002	A205	20c multi	.75	.60
1003	A205	30c multi	.95	.80
1004	A205	80c multi	3.25	2.25
1005	A205	1b multi, vert.	4.50	2.75
	Nos. 1000-1005 (6)		10.45	7.15

Ancient Drinking Vessel A206

1981, May 5   Litho.   Perf. 12½x12
1006	A206	20c shown	.40	.30
1007	A206	25c Spice container	.50	.40
1008	A206	35c Jug	1.00	.75
1009	A206	40c Cooking pot holder	1.50	1.10
1010	A206	60c Animal figurine	2.25	1.60
	Nos. 1006-1010 (5)		5.65	4.15

Intl. Year of the Disabled — A207

7th Anniv. of Revolution A208

1981, July 16   Photo.   Perf. 11½x12
1011	A207	5c Prostheses	.30	.20
1012	A207	15c Boys writing	.35	.25
1013	A207	20c Activities	.65	.50
1014	A207	40c Knitting	1.25	1.00
1015	A207	1b Weaving	3.00	2.25
	Nos. 1011-1015 (5)		5.55	4.20

1981, Sept. 10   Perf. 14
1016	A208	20c Children's Center	.65	.35
1017	A208	60c Heroes' Center	1.25	1.00
1018	A208	1b Serto Ader (state newspaper)	2.25	1.75
	Nos. 1016-1018 (3)		4.15	3.10

World Food Day — A209

1981, Oct. 15   Litho.   Perf. 13½x12½
1019	A209	5c Wheat airlift	.20	.20
1020	A209	15c Plowing	.30	.25
1021	A209	20c Malnutrition	.40	.30
1022	A209	40c Agriculture education	.85	.70
1023	A209	1b Cattle, corn	2.25	1.75
	Nos. 1019-1023 (5)		4.00	3.20

Ancient Bronze Type of 1978

1981, Dec. 15   Litho.   Perf. 14x13½
1024	A180	15c Pitcher	.35	.35
1025	A180	45c Tsenatsil (musical instrument)	1.00	1.00
1026	A180	50c Pitcher, diff.	1.25	1.25
1027	A180	70c Pot	1.50	1.50
	Nos. 1024-1027 (4)		4.10	4.10

Horn Artifacts — A210

1982, Feb. 18   Photo.   Perf. 12x12½
1028	A210	10c	Tobacco containers	.25	.20
1029	A210	15c	Cup	.35	.30
1030	A210	40c	Container, diff.	.90	.70
1031	A210	45c	Goblet	1.25	.95
1032	A210	70c	Spoons	1.75	1.25
		Nos. 1028-1032 (5)		4.50	3.40

Coffee Cultivation A211

1982, May, 6   Photo.   Perf. 13½
1033	A211	5c	Plants	.20	.20
1034	A211	15c	Bushes	.35	.30
1035	A211	25c	Mature bushes	.60	.50
1036	A211	35c	Picking beans	1.00	.75
1037	A211	1b	Drinking coffee	2.25	1.75
		Nos. 1033-1037 (5)		4.40	3.50

1982 World Cup — A212

Various soccer plays.

Perf. 13½x12½
1982, June 10   Litho.
1038	A212	5c	multicolored	.25	.20
1039	A212	15c	multicolored	.40	.40
1040	A212	20c	multicolored	.55	.50
1041	A212	40c	multicolored	1.25	1.10
1042	A212	1b	multicolored	2.50	2.25
		Nos. 1038-1042 (5)		4.95	4.35

TB Bacillus Centenary A213

1982, July 12   Litho.   Perf. 13½x12½
1043	A213	15c	Cow	.50	.40
1044	A213	20c	Magnifying glass	.60	.50
1045	A213	30c	Koch, microscope	.80	.70
1046	A213	35c	Koch	1.00	.85
1047	A213	80c	Man coughing	2.00	1.75
		Nos. 1043-1047 (5)		4.90	4.20

8th Anniv. of Revolution — A214

Designs: Symbols of justice.

1982, Sept. 10   Perf. 12½x13½
1048	A214	80c	multicolored	2.00	1.50
1049	A214	1b	multicolored	2.25	1.75

World Standards Day — A215

1982, Oct. 14   Litho.   Perf. 13½x12½
1050	A215	5c	Hand, foot, square	.20	.20
1051	A215	15c	Scales	.40	.30
1052	A215	20c	Rulers	.50	.40
1053	A215	40c	Weights	1.00	.80
1054	A215	1b	Emblem	2.50	1.75
		Nos. 1050-1054 (5)		4.60	3.45

10th Anniv. of UN Conference on Human Environment A216

1982, Dec. 13   Litho.   Perf. 12
1055	A216	5c	Wildlife conservation	.20	.20
1056	A216	15c	Environmental health and settlement	.40	.35
1057	A216	20c	Forest protection	.60	.45
1058	A216	40c	Natl. literacy campaign	1.00	.90
1059	A216	1b	Soil and water conservation	2.50	2.00
		Nos. 1055-1059 (5)		4.70	3.90

Cave of Sof Omar A217

Various views.

1983, Feb. 10   Photo.   Perf. 13½
1060	A217	5c	multicolored	.20	.20
1061	A217	10c	multicolored	.30	.25
1062	A217	15c	multicolored	.40	.35
1063	A217	70c	multicolored	1.50	1.10
1064	A217	80c	multicolored	1.75	1.50
		Nos. 1060-1064 (5)		4.15	3.40

A218   A219

1983, Apr. 29   Photo.   Perf. 14
1065	A218	80c	multicolored	2.00	1.50
1066	A218	1b	multicolored	2.25	1.75

25th Anniv. of Economic Commission for Africa.

Perf. 12½x11½
1983, June 3   Photo.
1067	A219	85c	Emblem	1.60	1.25
1068	A219	1b	Lighthouse, ship	3.25	2.25

25th Anniv. of Intl. Maritime Org.

WCY   9th Anniv. of
A220   Revolution
                   A221

1983, July 22   Litho.
1069	A220	25c	UPU emblem	.70	.60
1070	A220	55c	Dish antenna, emblems	1.40	1.25
1071	A220	1b	Bridge, tunnel	3.25	2.50
		Nos. 1069-1071 (3)		5.35	4.35

1983, Sept. 10   Litho.   Perf. 14½
1072	A221	25c	Dove	.50	.40
1073	A221	55c	Star	1.40	1.00
1074	A221	1b	Emblems	2.00	1.60
		Nos. 1072-1074 (3)		3.90	3.00

Musical Instruments — A222

Charaxes Galawadiwosi A223

1983, Oct. 17   Litho.   Perf. 12½x13½
1075	A222	5c	Hura	.25	.20
1076	A222	15c	Dinke	.45	.40
1077	A222	20c	Meleket	.75	.65
1078	A222	40c	Embilta	1.25	1.00
1079	A222	1b	Tom	2.25	2.00
		Nos. 1075-1079 (5)		4.95	4.25

1983, Dec. 13   Photo.   Perf. 14
1080	A223	10c	shown	1.25	1.00
1081	A223	15c	Epiphora elianae	1.75	1.50
1082	A223	55c	Batuana rouge-oti	4.75	3.00
1083	A223	1b	Achaea saboeareginae	9.00	7.50
		Nos. 1080-1083 (4)		16.75	13.00

Intl. Anti-Apartheid Year (1983) — A224

Perf. 13½x12½
1984, Feb. 10   Litho.
1084	A224	5c	multicolored	.35	.30
1085	A224	15c	multicolored	.55	.50
1086	A224	20c	multicolored	.75	.65
1087	A224	40c	multicolored	1.25	1.00
1088	A224	1b	multicolored	2.50	2.00
		Nos. 1084-1088 (5)		5.40	4.45

Local   Traditional
Flowers — A225   Houses — A226

1984, Apr. 13   Litho.   Perf. 13½
1089	A225	5c	Protea gaguedi	.30	.25
1090	A225	25c	Sedum epidendrum	1.25	.90
1091	A225	50c	Echinops amplexicaulis	2.25	1.75
1092	A225	1b	Canarina eminii	4.25	3.25
		Nos. 1089-1092 (4)		8.05	6.15

1984, June 13   Photo.
1093	A226	15c	Konso	.55	.40
1094	A226	65c	Dorze	1.75	1.40
1095	A226	1b	Harer	3.00	2.50
		Nos. 1093-1095 (3)		5.30	4.30

10th Anniv. of the Revolution A227

1984, Sept. 10   Photo.   Perf. 11½
1096	A227	5c	Sept. 12, 1974	.25	.20
1097	A227	10c	Mar. 4, 1975	.35	.30
1098	A227	15c	Apr. 20, 1976	.45	.35

1099	A227	20c	Feb. 11, 1977	.60	.50
1100	A227	25c	Mar. 1978	.75	.60
1101	A227	40c	July 8, 1980	1.10	.80
1102	A227	45c	Dec. 17, 1980	1.40	1.00
1103	A227	50c	Sept. 15, 1980	1.75	1.25
1104	A227	70c	Sept. 18, 1981	2.00	1.50
1105	A227	1b	June 6, 1983	2.75	2.00
		Nos. 1096-1105 (10)		11.40	8.45

Traditional Sports A228

1984, Dec. 7   Photo.   Perf. 14
1106	A228	5c	Gugs	.25	.20
1107	A228	25c	Tigil	.55	.50
1108	A228	50c	Genna	1.25	1.00
1109	A228	1b	Gebeta	2.25	1.75
		Nos. 1106-1109 (4)		4.30	3.45

Birds — A229

1985, Jan. 4   Photo.   Perf. 14½
1110	A229	5c	Francolinus harwoodi	.50	.40
1111	A229	15c	Rallus rougetti	1.00	.75
1112	A229	80c	Merops pusillus	3.50	3.00
1113	A229	85c	Malimbus rubriceps	4.00	3.50
		Nos. 1110-1113 (4)		9.00	7.65

Indigenous Fauna A230

1985, Feb. 4   Litho.   Perf. 12½x12
1114	A230	20c	Hippopotamus amphibius	.90	.75
1115	A230	25c	Litocranius walleri	1.25	1.00
1116	A230	40c	Sylvicapra grimmia	2.00	1.50
1117	A230	1b	Rhynchotragus guentheri	4.50	3.25
		Nos. 1114-1117 (4)		8.65	6.50

Freshwater Fish — A231

1985, Apr. 3   Perf. 13½
1118	A231	10c	Barbus degeni	.45	.40
1119	A231	20c	Labeo cylindricus	.75	.60
1120	A231	55c	Protopterus annectens	1.75	1.50
1121	A231	1b	Alestes dentex	3.75	3.25
		Nos. 1118-1121 (4)		6.70	5.75

Medicinal Plants A232

1985, May 23   Perf. 11½x12½
1122	A232	10c	Securidaca longepedunculata	.40	.30
1123	A232	20c	Plumbago zeylanicum	.65	.45
1124	A232	55c	Brucea antidysenteric	1.50	1.25
1125	A232	1b	Dorstenia barminiana	3.50	2.75
		Nos. 1122-1125 (4)		6.05	4.75

Ethiopian Red
Cross Soc., 50th
Anniv. — A233

1985, Aug. 6   Litho.   Perf. 13½x13
1126 A233 35c multicolored .90 .75
1127 A233 55c multicolored 1.50 1.25
1128 A233 1b multicolored 3.00 2.50
Nos. 1126-1128 (3) 5.40 4.50

Ethiopian
Revolution,
11th Anniv.
A234

10c, Kombolcha Mills, Welo Region. 80c,
Muger Cement Factory, Mokoda, Shoa. 1b,
Relocating famine and drought victims.

1985, Sept. 10   Litho.   Perf. 13½
1129 A234 10c multicolored .30 .25
1130 A234 80c multicolored 2.25 2.00
1131 A234 1b multicolored 3.00 2.50
Nos. 1129-1131 (3) 5.55 4.75

UN 40th
Anniv. — A235

1985, Nov. 22   Litho.   Perf. 13½x14
1132 A235 25c multicolored .90 .75
1133 A235 55c multicolored 1.75 1.50
1134 A235 1b multicolored 3.25 2.50
Nos. 1132-1134 (3) 5.90 4.75

Anti-Polio
Campaign
A236

1986, Jan. 10   Litho.   Perf. 11½x12½
1135 A236 5c Boy, prosthesis .25 .20
1136 A236 10c Boy on crutches .35 .30
1137 A236 20c Nurse, boy .65 .50
1138 A236 55c Man, sewing ma-
        chine 1.75 1.25
1139 A236 1b Nurse, mother,
        child 3.00 2.50
Nos. 1135-1139 (5) 6.00 4.75

Indigenous
Trees
A237

1986, Feb. 10   Perf. 13½x14½
1140 A237 10c Millettia fer-
        ruginea .40 .35
1141 A237 30c Syzygium
        guineense 1.00 .75
1142 A237 50c Cordia africana 1.50 1.25
1143 A237 1b Hagenia abyssini-
        ca 3.25 2.75
Nos. 1140-1143 (4) 6.15 5.10

Spices — A238

1986, Mar. 10   Perf. 13½
1144 A238 10c Zingiber officinale
        rosc .50 .40
1145 A238 15c Ocimum
        bacilicum .75 .50
1146 A238 55c Sinapsis alba 1.75 1.50
1147 A238 1b Cuminum
        cyminum 3.50 3.00
Nos. 1144-1147 (4) 6.50 5.40

Current
Coins,
Obverse
and
Reverse
A239

1986, May 9   Litho.   Perf. 13½x14
1148 A239 5c 1-cent .25 .20
1149 A239 10c 25-cent .40 .35
1150 A239 35c 5-cent 1.25 1.00
1151 A239 50c 50-cent 1.50 1.25
1152 A239 1b 10-cent 3.00 2.50
Nos. 1148-1152 (5) 6.40 5.30

Discovery of 3.5
Million Year-old
Hominid
Skeleton,
"Lucy" — A240

1986, July 4   Perf. 13½
1153 A240 2b multicolored 7.00 7.00

Ethiopian Revolution, 12th
Anniv. — A241

Designs: 20c, Military service. 30c,
Tiglachin monument. 55c, Delachin Exhibition
emblem. 85c, Food processing plant, Merti.

1986, Sept. 10   Litho.   Perf. 14
1154 A241 20c multicolored .50 .40
1155 A241 30c multicolored .75 .60
1156 A241 55c multicolored 1.50 1.00
1157 A241 85c multicolored 2.00 1.75
Nos. 1154-1157 (4) 4.75 3.75

Ethiopian Airlines,
40th
Anniv. — A242

Intl. Peace
Year — A243

1986, Oct. 14
1158 A242 10c DC-7 .40 .30
1159 A242 20c DC-3 .60 .50
1160 A242 30c Personnel, jet tail 1.00 .75
1161 A242 40c Engine 1.25 1.00
1162 A242 1b DC-7, map 2.75 2.25
Nos. 1158-1162 (5) 6.00 4.80

1986, Nov. 13   Perf. 13½
1163 A243 10c multicolored .40 .30
1164 A243 80c multicolored 2.25 2.00
1165 A243 1b multicolored 3.00 2.50
Nos. 1163-1165 (3) 5.65 4.80

UN Child Survival Campaign — A244

1986, Dec. 11   Perf. 12½
1166 A244 10c Breast feeding .35 .30
1167 A244 35c Immunization 1.00 .75
1168 A244 50c Hygiene 1.25 1.00
1169 A244 1b Growth monitor-
        ing 2.50 2.00
Nos. 1166-1169 (4) 5.10 4.05

Umbrellas
A245

1987, Feb. 10   Perf. 13½
1170 A245 35c Axum 1.00 .85
1171 A245 55c Negele-Borena 1.50 1.25
1172 A245 1b Jimma 3.00 2.50
Nos. 1170-1172 (3) 5.50 4.60

Artwork by
Afewerk
Tekle
(b. 1932)
A246

Designs: 50c, Defender of His Country —
Afar, stained glass window. 2b, Defender of
His Country — Adwa, painting.

1987, Mar. 19   Litho.   Perf. 13½
1173 A246 50c multicolored 1.50 1.00
1174 A246 2b multicolored 5.25 4.50

Stained Glass Windows by Afewerk
Tekle — A247

1987, June 16   Photo.   Perf. 11½x12
Granite Paper
1175 A247 50c multicolored 8.00 4.00

Size: 26x38mm
1176 A247 80c multicolored 10.00 5.50
1177 A247 1b multicolored 15.00 8.00
Nos. 1175-1177 (3) 33.00 17.50
Struggle of the African People.
Sold out in Addis Ababa on date of issue.

Simien Fox
A248

1987, June 29   Litho.   Perf. 13½
1178 A248 5c multicolored .25 .20
1179 A248 10c multicolored .40 .30
1180 A248 15c multicolored .60 .40
1181 A248 20c multicolored .75 .50
1182 A248 25c multicolored 1.00 .75
1183 A248 45c multicolored 1.50 1.00
1184 A248 55c multicolored 1.75 1.50
Nos. 1178-1184 (7) 6.25 4.60

For overprints see Nos. 1234-1237. For similar design see A294a.

Ethiopian
Revolution,
13th Anniv.
A249

1987, Sept. 10   Perf. 12½
1185 A249 5c Constitution, free-
        dom of press .35 .30
1186 A249 10c Popular elections .45 .40
1187 A249 80c Referendum 1.75 1.50
1188 A249 1b Bahir Dar Airport,
        map 2.50 2.00
Nos. 1185-1188 (4) 5.05 4.20

Addis
Ababa,
Cent.
A251

"100" and views: 5c, Emperor Menelik II,
Empress Taitu and city. 10c, Traditional buildings. 80c, Central Addis Ababa. 1b, Aerial
view of city.

1987, Sept. 7   Perf. 13½
1193 A251 5c multicolored .50 .30
1194 A251 10c multicolored .65 .40
1195 A251 80c multicolored 2.00 1.50
1196 A251 1b multicolored 2.50 2.00
Nos. 1193-1196 (4) 5.65 4.20

Wooden
Spoons
A252

1987, Nov. 30
1197 A252 85c Hurso, Harerge 1.75 1.75
1198 A252 1b Borena, Sidamo 2.25 2.25

Intl. Year
of Shelter
for the
Homeless
A253

1987, Dec. 12   Litho.   Perf. 13
1199 A253 10c Village revitaliza-
        tion program .50 .40
1200 A253 35c Resettlement pro-
        gram 1.00 .90
1201 A253 50c Urban improve-
        ment 1.25 1.00

1202	A253	1b Cooperative and government housing	2.00	1.50
		Nos. 1199-1202 (4)	4.75	3.80

October Revolution, Russia, 70th Anniv. (in 1987) — A254

Painting: 1b, Lenin receiving Workers' Council delegates in the Smolny Institute.

1988, Feb. 17   Perf. 12½x12
1203	A254	1b multicolored	2.50	1.75

Traditional Hunting Methods and Prey — A255

1988, Mar. 30   Litho.   Perf. 13½
1204	A255	85c Bow and arrow	2.50	2.25
1205	A255	1b Double-pronged spear	3.75	3.50

A256

A257

1988, May 6
1206	A256	85c multicolored	1.75	1.50
1207	A256	1b multicolored	2.25	1.75

Intl. Red Cross and Red Crescent Organizations, 125th annivs.

1988, June 7   Photo.   Perf. 11½x12
1208	A257	2b multicolored	3.50	2.25

Organizaton of African Unity, 25th anniv.

Ethiopian Revolution, 14th Anniv. A258

Design: Various details of *The Victory of Ethiopia*, six-panel mural by Afewerk Tekle (b. 1932) in the museum of the Heroes Center, Debre Zeit.

1988, June 28   Litho.   Perf. 13½x13
1209	A258	10c Jet over farm, vert.	.35	.30
1210	A258	20c Farm workers on road, vert.	.45	.35
1211	A258	35c Allegory of unity, vert.	.75	.50
1212	A258	55c Jet over industry	1.25	1.00

1213	A258	80c Steel works	1.75	1.25
1214	A258	1b Weaving	2.25	2.00
		Nos. 1209-1214 (6)	6.80	5.40

Nos. 1209-1211 vert.

Women, Bracelets and Maps A259

1988, July 27   Litho.   Perf. 13x13½
1215	A259	15c Sidamo	.40	.30
1216	A259	85c Arsi	1.75	1.25
1217	A259	1b Harerge	2.50	2.00
		Nos. 1215-1217 (3)	4.65	3.55

Immunize Every Child A260

1988, June 14   Litho.   Perf. 13x13½
1218	A260	10c Measles	.35	.25
1219	A260	35c Tetanus	.75	.60
1220	A260	50c Whooping cough	1.25	1.00
1221	A260	1b Diphtheria	2.25	1.75
		Nos. 1218-1221 (4)	4.60	3.60

Intl. Fund for Agricultural Development (IFAD), 10th Anniv. — A261

1988, Aug. 16   Perf. 13½
1222	A261	15c Monetary aid	.30	.25
1223	A261	85c Farming activities	1.50	1.10
1224	A261	1b Harvest	2.25	1.25
		Nos. 1222-1224 (3)	4.05	2.60

People's Democratic Republic of Ethiopia, 1st Anniv. — A262

5c, 1st Session of the natl. Shengo (congress). 10c, Mengistu Haile-Mariam, 1st president of the republic. 80c, Natl. crest, flag & crowd. 1b, State assembly building.

1988, Sept. 9   Perf. 14
1225	A262	5c multicolored	.20	.20
1226	A262	10c multicolored	.30	.25
1227	A262	80c multicolored	1.75	1.50
1228	A262	1b multicolored	2.25	2.00
		Nos. 1225-1228 (4)	4.50	3.95

Bank Notes A263

1988, Nov. 10   Photo.   Perf. 13
1229	A263	5c 1-Birr	.20	.20
1230	A263	10c 5-Birr	.35	.30
1231	A263	20c 10-Birr	.75	.50
1232	A263	75c 50-Birr	1.75	1.50
1233	A263	85c 100-Birr	2.25	2.00
		Nos. 1229-1233 (5)	5.30	4.50

Nos. 1181-1184 Overprinted "WORLD AIDS DAY" in Two Languages

1988, Dec. 1   Litho.   Perf. 13½
1234	A248	20c multicolored	4.75	4.50
1235	A248	25c multicolored	6.25	5.50
1236	A248	45c multicolored	12.50	10.50
1237	A248	85c multicolored	13.00	11.00
		Nos. 1234-1237 (4)	36.50	31.50

Intl. Day for the Fight Against AIDS.

WHO, 40th Anniv. A264

1988, Dec. 30   Litho.   Perf. 14
1238	A264	50c multicolored	1.00	.80
1239	A264	65c multicolored	1.40	1.00
1240	A264	85c multicolored	1.75	1.50
		Nos. 1238-1240 (3)	4.15	3.30

Traditional Musical Instruments A265

1989, Feb. 9   Perf. 13x13½
1241	A265	30c Gere	.75	.45
1242	A265	40c Fanfa	1.00	.65
1243	A265	50c Chancha	1.25	.90
1244	A265	85c Negareet	1.75	1.25
		Nos. 1241-1244 (4)	4.75	3.25

Ethiopian Shipping Lines, 25th Anniv. A266

1989, Mar. 27   Litho.   Perf. 14
1245	A266	15c Abyot	.40	.30
1246	A266	30c Wolwol	.75	.60
1247	A266	55c Queen of Sheba	1.40	1.25
1248	A266	1b Abbay Wonz	2.75	2.25
		Nos. 1245-1248 (4)	5.30	4.40

Birds — A267

1989, May 18   Litho.   Perf. 13½x13
1249	A267	10c Yellow-fronted parrot	.40	.30
1250	A267	35c White-winged cliff chat	1.25	1.00
1251	A267	50c Yellow-throated seed eater	1.75	1.25
1252	A267	1b Black-headed forest oriole	2.75	2.25
		Nos. 1249-1252 (4)	6.15	4.80

Production of Early Manuscripts — A268

1989, June 16   Litho.   Perf. 13½
1253	A268	5c Preparing vellum	.20	.20
1254	A268	10c Ink horns, pens	.30	.25
1255	A268	20c Scribe	.50	.40
1256	A268	75c Book binding	1.50	1.25

1257	A268	85c Illuminated manuscript	2.00	1.75
		Nos. 1253-1257 (5)	4.50	3.85

Indigenous Wildlife — A269

1989, July 18
1258	A269	30c Greater kudu	1.00	.75
1259	A269	40c Lesser kudu	1.25	1.00
1260	A269	50c Roan antelope	1.50	1.25
1261	A269	85c Nile lechwe	2.50	2.00
		Nos. 1258-1261 (4)	6.25	5.00

People's Democratic Republic of Ethiopia, 2nd Anniv. A270

Designs: 15c, Melka Wakana Hydroelectric Power Station. 75c, Adea Berga Dairy Farm. 1b, Pawe Hospital.

1989, Sept. 8
1262	A270	15c multicolored	.35	.25
1263	A270	75c multicolored	1.50	1.25
1264	A270	1b multicolored	2.50	2.00
		Nos. 1262-1264 (3)	4.35	3.50

African Development Bank, 25th Anniv. — A271

1989, Nov. 10   Litho.   Perf. 13½x13
1265	A271	20c multicolored	.35	.30
1266	A271	80c multicolored	1.50	1.25
1267	A271	1b multicolored	2.75	2.00
		Nos. 1265-1267 (3)	4.60	3.55

Pan-African Postal Union, 10th Anniv. — A272

1990, Jan. 18   Litho.   Perf. 13½
1268	A272	50c multicolored	1.00	.75
1269	A272	70c multicolored	1.50	1.25
1270	A272	80c multicolored	2.00	1.75
		Nos. 1268-1270 (3)	4.50	3.75

UNESCO World Literacy Year — A273

15c, Illiterate man holding newspaper upside down. 85c, Adults learning alphabet in school. 1b, Literate man holding newspaper upright.

1990, Mar. 13
1271	A273	15c multicolored	.50	.40
1272	A273	85c multicolored	1.75	1.50
1273	A273	1b multicolored	2.50	2.25
		Nos. 1271-1273 (3)	4.75	4.15

Abebe Bikila, Marathon Runner
A274

1990, Apr. 17
1274	A274	5c Race	.20	.20
1275	A274	10c Flag bearer, Olympic team	.30	.25
1276	A274	20c Race, Rome Olympics	.60	.50
1277	A274	75c Race, Tokyo Olympics	1.75	1.50
1278	A274	85c Bikila, trophies, vert.	2.25	2.00
		Nos. 1274-1278 (5)	5.10	4.45

Flag — A275

1990, Apr. 30   Litho.   Perf. 13½x13
1279	A275	5c multicolored	.20	.20
1280	A275	10c multicolored	.20	.20
1281	A275	15c multicolored	.30	.20
1282	A275	20c multicolored	.40	.30
1283	A275	25c multicolored	.45	.35
1284	A275	30c multicolored	.55	.40
1285	A275	35c multicolored	.65	.45
1286	A275	40c multicolored	.80	.50
1287	A275	45c multicolored	.90	.65
1288	A275	50c multicolored	1.00	.65
1289	A275	55c multicolored	1.10	.70
1290	A275	60c multicolored	1.20	.80
1291	A275	70c multicolored	1.25	.90
1292	A275	80c multicolored	1.40	1.00
1293	A275	85c multicolored	1.50	1.10
1294	A275	90c multicolored	1.60	1.25
1295	A275	1b multicolored	1.75	1.25
1296	A275	2b multicolored	3.75	2.75
1297	A275	3b multicolored	5.50	4.00
		Nos. 1279-1297 (19)	24.50	17.65

Dated 1989.

Sowing of Teff
A276

1990, May 18   Litho.   Perf. 13½
1298	A276	5c shown	.20	.20
1299	A276	10c Harvesting	.25	.20
1300	A276	20c Threshing	.50	.40
1301	A276	75c Storage, preparation	1.75	1.50
1302	A276	85c Consumption	2.25	2.00
		Nos. 1298-1302 (5)	4.95	4.30

Walia Ibex — A277

1990, June 18   Perf. 14x13½
1303	A277	5c multi	.75	.50
1304	A277	15c multi	1.75	1.00
1305	A277	20c multi	2.50	1.50
1306	A277	1b multi, horiz.	10.00	5.75
		Nos. 1303-1306 (4)	15.00	8.75

World AIDS Day
A278

1991, Jan. 31   Litho.   Perf. 14
1307	A278	15c Stages of disease	.40	.30
1308	A278	85c Education	1.75	1.50
1309	A278	1b Causes, preventatives	2.25	2.00
		Nos. 1307-1309 (3)	4.40	3.80

Intl. Decade for Natural Disaster Reduction
A279

Map of disaster-prone African areas and: 5c, Volcano. 10c, Earthquake. 15c, Drought. 30c, Flood. 50c, Red Cross health education. 1b, Red Cross assisting fire victims.

1991, Apr. 9   Litho.   Perf. 14
1310	A279	5c multicolored	.20	.20
1311	A279	10c multicolored	.25	.20
1312	A279	15c multicolored	.30	.25
1313	A279	30c multicolored	.60	.50
1314	A279	50c multicolored	1.25	1.00
1315	A279	1b multicolored	2.25	2.00
		Nos. 1310-1315 (6)	4.85	4.15

The Cannon of Tewodros
A280

Designs: 15c, Villagers receiving cannon. 85c, Warriors leaving with cannon. 1b, Hauling cannon up mountainside.

1991, June 18   Litho.   Perf. 13½
1316	A280	15c multicolored	.50	.40
1317	A280	85c multicolored	1.75	1.50
1318	A280	1b multicolored	2.25	2.00
		Nos. 1316-1318 (3)	4.50	3.90

Fish
A281

1991, Sept. 6   Litho.   Perf. 13½
1319	A281	5c Lacepede	.50	.30
1320	A281	15c Black-finned butterflyfish	.60	.40
1321	A281	80c Regal angelfish	2.25	1.75
1322	A281	1b Bleeker	3.00	2.50
		Nos. 1319-1322 (4)	6.35	4.95

A282   A283

Traditional Ceremonial Robes: Various robes.

1992, Jan. 1   Litho.   Perf. 13½x14
1323	A282	5c yellow & multi	.35	.20
1324	A282	15c orange & multi	.40	.25
1325	A282	80c yel green & multi	1.75	1.50
1326	A282	1b blue & multi	2.00	1.75
		Nos. 1323-1326 (4)	4.50	3.70

1992, Mar. 5   Litho.   Perf. 13½x14

Flowers: 5c, Cissus quadrangularis. 15c, Delphinium dasycaulon. 80c, Epilobium hirsutum. 1b, Kniphofia foliosa.

1327	A283	5c multicolored	.40	.30
1328	A283	15c multicolored	.50	.40
1329	A283	80c multicolored	2.25	1.75
1330	A283	1b multicolored	2.75	2.00
		Nos. 1327-1330 (4)	5.90	4.45

Traditional Homes
A284

1992, May 14   Litho.   Perf. 12½x12
1331	A284	15c Afar	.40	.30
1332	A284	35c Anuak	.80	.60
1333	A284	50c Gimira	1.00	.90
1334	A284	1b Oromo	2.25	1.75
		Nos. 1331-1334 (4)	4.45	3.55

A285

A286

Pottery.

1992, July 7   Litho.   Perf. 13x13½
1335	A285	15c Cover	.40	.30
1336	A285	85c Jug	1.50	1.25
1337	A285	1b Tall jar	2.25	1.75
		Nos. 1335-1337 (3)	4.15	3.30

1992, Sept. 29   Perf. 14x13½
1338	A286	20c multicolored	.40	.30
1339	A286	80c multicolored	1.50	1.25
1340	A286	1b multicolored	2.00	1.75
		Nos. 1338-1340 (3)	3.90	3.30

Pan-African Rinderpest campaign.

A287

Birds — A288

Musical instruments.

1993, Feb. 16   Litho.   Perf. 14x13½
1341	A287	15c Catchel	.40	.30
1342	A287	35c Huludwa	.75	.55
1343	A287	50c Dita	1.00	.75
1344	A287	1b Atamo	2.50	2.00
		Nos. 1341-1344 (4)	4.65	3.60

1993, Apr. 22   Litho.   Perf. 14x13½
1345	A288	15c Banded barbet	.45	.45
1346	A288	35c Ruppell's chat	.80	.75
1347	A288	50c Abyssinian catbird	1.25	1.00
1348	A288	1b White-billed starling	3.00	2.25
		Nos. 1345-1348 (4)	5.50	4.45

Animals
A289

1993, May 14   Perf. 13½x14
1349	A289	15c Honey badger	.30	.25
1350	A289	35c Spotted necked otter	.50	.40
1351	A289	50c Rock hyrax	.80	.60
1352	A289	1b White-tailed mongoose	1.50	1.25
		Nos. 1349-1352 (4)	3.10	2.50

Herbs — A290

1993, June 10   Perf. 14x13½
1353	A290	5c Caraway seed	.65	.50
1354	A290	15c Garlic	.75	.60
1355	A290	80c Turmeric	1.50	1.00
1356	A290	1b Capsicum peppers	2.50	2.25
		Nos. 1353-1356 (4)	5.40	4.35

Butterflies
A291

Insects — A292

1993, July 9   Litho.   Perf. 14x13½
1357	A291	20c Papilio echeriodes	.75	.60
1358	A291	30c Papilio rex	.90	.75
1359	A291	50c Graphium policenes	1.25	1.00
1360	A291	1b Graphium leonidas	2.50	1.75
		Nos. 1357-1360 (4)	5.40	4.10

1993, Aug. 10
1361	A292	15c C. Variabilis	.40	.30
1362	A292	35c Lycus trabeatus	.60	.50
1363	A292	50c Malachius bifasciatus	.80	.70
1364	A292	1b Homoeogryllus xanthographus	1.60	1.25
		Nos. 1361-1364 (4)	3.40	2.75

Trees
A293

1993, Oct. 12   Litho.   Perf. 13½x14

1365	A293	15c Euphorbia am-		
		pliphylla	.25	.20
1366	A293	35c Erythrina brucei	.35	.30
1367	A293	50c Dracaena		
		steudneri	.65	.50
1368	A293	1b Allophylus abys-		
		sinicus	1.25	1.00
		Nos. 1365-1368 (4)	2.50	2.00

Lakes
A294

1993, Dec. 14

1369	A294	15c Wonchi	.25	.20
1370	A294	35c Zuquala	.35	.30
1371	A294	50c Ashengi	.60	.50
1372	A294	1b Tana	1.10	.90
		Nos. 1369-1372 (4)	2.30	1.90

Simien Fox
A294a

Rough Perf. 13½

1994, Jan. 18   Litho.

Color of Border

1372A	A294a	5c violet
1372B	A294a	10c brown
1372C	A294a	15c lemon
1372D	A294a	20c salmon
1372E	A294a	40c pale rose
1372F	A294a	55c dull green
1372G	A294a	60c dark blue
1372H	A294a	80c bright blue
1372I	A294a	85c gray green
1372J	A294a	1b bright green
		Nos. 1372A-1372J (10)	—	—

Nos. 1372A-1372J have rough perforations and a poor quality printing impression. Dated "1991."
See Nos. 1393A-1393T. For overprints see Nos. 1393U-1393X, 1396A-1396D.

A295

A296

Transitional government: 15c, First anniversary of EPRDF's control of Addis Ababa. 35c, Transition Conference. 50c, National, regional elections. 1b, Coat of arms of Transitional Government.

1994, Mar. 31   Litho.   Perf. 14

1373	A295	15c multicolored	.35	.25
1374	A295	35c multicolored	.40	.30
1375	A295	50c multicolored	.45	.35
1376	A295	1b multicolored	.90	.55
		Nos. 1373-1376 (4)	2.10	1.45

1994, May 17   Perf. 13½

1377	A296	15c blue & multi	.35	.25
1378	A296	85c green & multi	.55	.40
1379	A296	1b violet & multi	.75	.50
		Nos. 1377-1379 (3)	1.65	1.15

Intl. Year of the Family.

Ethiopian Postal Service, Cent. A297

Designs: 60c, Early, modern postal workers, Scott Type A1. 75c, Early letter carriers. 80c, Older building, methods of transportation. 85c, People, mail buses. 1b, Modern methods of transportation, modern high-rise building.

1994, July 4   Perf. 13½

1380	A297	60c multicolored	.50	.35
1381	A297	75c multicolored	.60	.40
1382	A297	80c multicolored	.75	.45
1383	A297	85c multicolored	.80	.50
1384	A297	1b multicolored	.95	.70
a.		Souvenir sheet, #1380-1384 + label	10.00	8.00
		Nos. 1380-1384 (5)	3.60	2.40

Enset Plant — A298

Hair Ornaments A299

1994, Aug. 3

1385	A298	10c shown	.25	.20
1386	A298	15c Young plants, hut	.35	.30
1387	A298	25c Root, women processing leaves	.40	.35
1388	A298	50c Mature plants	.60	.40
1389	A298	1b Uses as food	.90	.65
		Nos. 1385-1389 (5)	2.50	1.90

1994, Sept. 2

1390	A299	5c Gamo gofa	.40	.30
1391	A299	15c Sidamo	.50	.35
1392	A299	80c Gamo gofa, diff.	.70	.50
1393	A299	1b Wello	.90	.65
		Nos. 1390-1393 (4)	2.50	1.80

Simien Fox Type of 1994

1994, Oct. 18   Litho.   Perf. 14
Size: 39x25mm
Color of Border

1393A	A294a	5c dull lilac
1393B	A294a	10c brown
1393C	A294a	15c lemon
1393D	A294a	20c salmon
1393E	A294a	25c lemon
1393F	A294a	30c yellow brown
1393G	A294a	35c orange
1393H	A294a	40c pale rose
1393I	A294a	45c pale red org
1393J	A294a	50c rose lilac
1393K	A294a	55c pale green
1393L	A294a	60c dark blue
1393M	A294a	65c pale lilac
1393N	A294a	70c bright green
1393O	A294a	75c pale bl grn
1393P	A294a	80c bright blue
1393Q	A294a	85c dark greenish blue
1393R	A294a	90c pale brown
1393S	A294a	1b greenish blue
1393T	A294a	2b yellow brown
		Nos. 1393A-1393T (20)	—	40.00

Nos. 1393A-1393T have sharp impressions, Questa imprint, clean perforations. Dated "1993."

Nos. 1393L, 1393P-1393Q, 1393S
Ovptd. in Blue

1994, Oct. 20   Litho.   Perf. 14

1393U	A294a	60c on #1393L	27.50	4.25
1393V	A294a	80c on #1393P	35.00	5.50
1393W	A294a	85c on #1393Q	72.50	10.50
1393X	A294a	1b on #1393S	80.00	9.50
		Nos. 1393U-1393X (4)	215.00	29.75

UNFPA, 50th anniv.

ICAO, 50th Anniv. A300

1994, Dec. 7   Litho.   Perf. 13½

1394	A300	20c mag, lt bl & yel	.40	.35
1395	A300	80c yel & lt bl	.60	.45
1396	A300	1b dk bl, lt bl & yel	.80	.70
		Nos. 1394-1396 (3)	1.80	1.50

Nos. 1393M-1393O, 1393R Ovptd.

1994, Dec. 20   Litho.   Perf. 14

1396A	A294a	65c on #1393M	27.50	4.25
1396B	A294a	70c on #1393N	35.00	5.50
1396C	A294a	75c on #1393O	72.50	10.50
1396D	A294a	90c on #1393R	80.00	9.50
		Nos. 1396A-1396D (4)	215.00	29.75

African Development Bank, 30th anniv.

Baskets for Serving Food A301

1995, June 7   Litho.   Perf. 13½

1397	A301	30c Erbo	.30	.25
1398	A301	70c Sedieka	.70	.55
1399	A301	1b Tirar	1.00	.80
		Nos. 1397-1399 (3)	2.00	1.60

Traditional Hair Styles — A302

1995, July 5   Litho.   Perf. 13½

1400	A302	25c Kuncho	.25	.20
1401	A302	75c Gamme	.75	.55
1402	A302	1b Sadulla	1.00	.80
		Nos. 1400-1402 (3)	2.00	1.55

FAO, 50th Anniv. A303

1995, Aug. 29   Litho.   Perf. 13½

1403	A303	20c green & multi	.20	.20
1404	A303	80c blue & multi	.80	.65
1405	A303	1b brown & multi	1.50	.90
		Nos. 1403-1405 (3)	2.50	1.75

Cultivating Tools A304

1995, Sept. 7

1406	A304	15c Dangora	.30	.20
1407	A304	35c Gheso	.45	.40
1408	A304	50c Akafa	.75	.55
1409	A304	1b Ankasse	1.00	.85
		Nos. 1406-1409 (4)	2.50	2.00

UN, 50th Anniv. — A305

1995, Oct. 18   Litho.   Perf. 13½
Color of UN Emblem

1410	A305	20c black	.50	.40
1411	A305	80c bister	.60	.50
1412	A305	1b blue	.85	.75
		Nos. 1410-1412 (3)	1.95	1.65

Intergovernmental Authority on Drought and Development (IGADD), 10th Anniv. — A306

Flags of member nations and: 15c, Seedling being planted in arid region. 35c, People carrying supplies through desert. 50c, Person picking fruit. 1b, Map of member nations.

1995, Dec. 27   Litho.   Perf. 13½

1413	A306	15c multicolored	.35	.25
1414	A306	35c multicolored	.45	.35
1415	A306	50c multicolored	.55	.45
1416	A306	1b multicolored	.85	.75
		Nos. 1413-1416 (4)	2.20	1.80

Victory at Battle of Adwa, Cent. — A307

Designs: 40c, Battle sites. 50c, Map of Africa focused at Ethiopia. 60c, Troops, ship. 70c, Warriors, soldiers in two battle scenes. 80c, Italians surrendering, Ethiopian troops, cannons. 1b, Emperor Menelik II, constitution, Empress Taitu.

1996, Mar. 2   Litho.   Perf. 13½x14½

1417	A307	40c multicolored	.25	.20
1418	A307	50c multicolored	.30	.25
1419	A307	60c multicolored	.45	.35
1420	A307	70c multicolored	.55	.40
1421	A307	80c multicolored	.75	.60

1422	A307	1b multicolored	1.00	.80
a.		Souvenir sheet, #1417-1422	4.50	4.50
		Nos. 1417-1422 (6)	3.30	2.60

UN Volunteers, 25th Anniv. A308

Designs: 20c, People, temporary housing huts. 30c, Planting seedlings. 50c, Instructing students. 1b, Caring for infant.

1996, June 6   Litho.   Perf. 13½

1423	A308	20c multicolored	.25	.20
1424	A308	30c multicolored	.35	.25
1425	A308	50c multicolored	.50	.40
1426	A308	1b multicolored	.95	.80
		Nos. 1423-1426 (4)	2.05	1.65

1996 Summer Olympic Games, Atlanta A310

1996, Aug. 1   Litho.   Perf. 12½x12
Overprint in Black

1427	A310	15c Boxing	.35	.25
1428	A310	20c Swimming	.40	.30
1429	A310	40c Cycling	.45	.35
1430	A310	85c Athletics	.60	.50
1431	A310	1b Soccer	.75	.65
		Nos. 1427-1431 (5)	2.55	2.05

Nos. 1427-1431 were originally prepared for the 1984 Summer Olympic Games in Los Angeles, but were not released due to the Soviet-led boycott. Nos. 1427-1431 exist without overprint. Value, set $100.

A311

A312

UNICEF, 50th Anniv.: 10c, Emblems. 15c, Mother, child receiving vaccination. 25c, Woman carrying water, boy drinking from faucet. 50c, Children studying. 1b, Mother breastfeeding infant.

1996, Sept. 10   Litho.   Perf. 13½

1432	A311	10c multicolored	.25	.20
1433	A311	15c multicolored	.30	.25
1434	A311	25c multicolored	.35	.30
1435	A311	50c multicolored	.60	.45
1436	A311	1b multicolored	.95	.75
		Nos. 1432-1436 (5)	2.45	1.95

1996, Dec. 26   Litho.   Perf. 13½

Creation of Federal Democratic Republic of Ethiopia: 10c, People discussing new Constitution, approved Dec. 8, 1994. 20c, Ballot boxes, hand placing ballot in box. 30c, Marking ballot, placing into box, tower building, items from country's environment. 40c, Building, ballot, assembly hall. 1b, Natl. flag, transition of power.

1437	A312	10c multicolored	.20	.20
1438	A312	20c multicolored	.20	.20
1439	A312	30c multicolored	.30	.25
1440	A312	40c multicolored	.45	.35
1441	A312	1b multicolored	.90	.70
		Nos. 1437-1441 (5)	2.05	1.70

Traditional Baskets — A313

1997, Feb. 20   Litho.   Perf. 13½

1442	A313	5c Jimma	.50	.35
1443	A313	15c Wello	.50	.35
1444	A313	80c Welega	.85	.40
1445	A313	1b Shewa	1.00	.60
		Nos. 1442-1445 (4)	2.85	1.70

Traditional Baskets A314

1997, May 22   Litho.   Perf. 13½

1446	A314	35c Arssi	.30	.25
1447	A314	65c Gojam	.55	.45
1448	A314	1b Harer	.85	.75
		Nos. 1446-1448 (3)	1.70	1.45

See Nos. 1464-1466.

UN Decade Against Drug Abuse & Illicit Trafficking A315

1997, Sept. 9   Litho.   Perf. 14

1449	A315	20c green & multi	.50	.35
1450	A315	80c brown & multi	.70	.55
1451	A315	1b blue & multi	1.00	.80
		Nos. 1449-1451 (3)	2.20	1.70

Historic Buildings, Addis Ababa A316

45c, Bitwoded Haile Giorgis' house. 55c, Alfred Ilg's house, vert. 3b, Menelik's Elfign.

Perf. 14½x14, 14x14½
1997, Dec. 23   Litho.

1452	A316	45c multicolored	.35	.30
1453	A316	55c multicolored	.45	.40
1454	A316	3b multicolored	1.60	1.25
		Nos. 1452-1454 (3)	2.40	1.95

Addis Ababa's Oldest Historical Buildings A317

Designs: 60c, Ras Biru W/Gabriel's house. 75c, Sheh Hojele Alhassen's house. 80c, Fitawrari H/Giorgis Dinegde's house. 85c, Etege Taitu Hotel. 1b, Dejazmach Wube Atnafseged's house.

1997, Dec. 30   Litho.   Perf. 14½x14

1455	A317	60c multicolored	.35	.30
1456	A317	75c multicolored	.40	.35
1457	A317	80c multicolored	.45	.40
1458	A317	85c multicolored	.50	.45
1459	A317	1b multicolored	.75	.60
		Nos. 1455-1459 (5)	2.45	2.10

Pan African Postal Union, 18th Anniv. A318

Union's emblem and wildlife: 45c, Deculla bushback. 55c, Soemmering's gazelle. 1b, Defassa waterbuck. 2b, Black buffalo.

1998, Mar. 25   Litho.   Perf. 14½x14

1460	A318	45c multicolored	.50	.35
1461	A318	55c multicolored	.55	.45
1462	A318	1b multicolored	.90	.65
1463	A318	2b multicolored	1.75	1.25
		Nos. 1460-1463 (4)	3.70	2.70

Traditional Basket Type of 1997

1998, May 21   Litho.   Perf. 13½

1464	A314	45c Gonder	.25	.20
1465	A314	55c Harere	.35	.30
1466	A314	3b Tigray	1.50	1.25
		Nos. 1464-1466 (3)	2.10	1.75

Golden-Backed Woodpecker A319

1998, Jan. 12   Photo.   Perf. 11½
Granite Paper
Panel Color

1467	A319	5c green blue	.45	.30
1468	A319	10c yellow	.45	.30
1469	A319	15c blue	.45	.30
1470	A319	20c light brown	20.00	.30
1471	A319	25c violet	.45	.30
1472	A319	30c light blue	.45	.30
1473	A319	35c salmon rose	.45	.30
1474	A319	40c lilac	.45	.30
1475	A319	45c green	.45	.30
1476	A319	50c salmon	.50	.35
1477	A319	55c blue	.50	.35
1478	A319	60c brick red	.55	.40
1479	A319	65c light gray	.60	.45
1480	A319	70c bright yellow	.65	.50
1481	A319	75c pale violet	.75	.65
1482	A319	80c apple green	.80	.70
1483	A319	85c gray	.85	.75
1484	A319	90c orange	.95	.75
1485	A319	1b yellow green	1.25	.95
1486	A319	2b pale rose	1.50	1.25
1487	A319	3b lilac rose	2.50	2.00
1488	A319	5b bister	3.50	3.00
1489	A319	10b orange yellow	7.00	6.00
		Nos. 1467-1489 (23)	45.50	20.85

Agreement for Return of Axum Obelisk from Italy — A320

45c, Map of Italy, pieces of obelisk. 55c, Obelisk in Rome. 3b, Map of E. Africa, obelisk, ruins of Axum.

1998, Sept. 3   Litho.   Perf. 13½

1490	A320	45c multicolored	.40	.25
1491	A320	55c multicolored	.50	.45
1492	A320	3b multicolored	1.60	1.25
		Nos. 1490-1492 (3)	2.50	1.95

Ethiopia-Djibouti Railway, Cent. — A321

Designs: 45c, Men carrying rails during construction. 55c, Early steam train, CFE 404. 1b, Terminal building. 2b, Modern train, BB 1212.

1998, Nov. 24   Litho.   Perf. 11½
Granite Paper

1493	A321	45c multicolored	.40	.35
1494	A321	55c multicolored	.50	.45
1495	A321	1b multicolored	.85	.75
1496	A321	2b multicolored	1.75	1.25
		Nos. 1493-1496 (4)	3.50	2.80

Universal Declaration of Human Rights, 50th Anniv. A322

1998, Dec. 23   Litho.   Perf. 13x13½

1497	A322	45c red & multi	.35	.25
1498	A322	55c yellow & multi	.35	.30
1499	A322	1b green & multi	.60	.50
1500	A322	2b blue & multi	.90	.75
		Nos. 1497-1500 (4)	2.20	1.80

Mother Teresa (1910-97) — A323

Various portraits.

1999, Mar. 9   Litho.   Perf. 13½x13

1501	A323	45c brown & multi	.55	.35
1502	A323	55c green & multi	.60	.45
1503	A323	1b yel org & multi	.75	.60
1504	A323	2b blue & multi	1.75	1.25
		Nos. 1501-1504 (4)	3.65	2.65

Intl. Year of the Ocean A324

1999, May 6   Litho.   Perf. 13½x13¼

1505	A324	45c black & multi	.35	.25
1506	A324	55c red & multi	.45	.30
1507	A324	1b blue & multi	.60	.50
1508	A324	2b green & multi	1.25	1.00
		Nos. 1505-1508 (4)	2.65	2.05

World Environment Day — A325

1999, June 17   Litho.   Perf. 13½

1509	A325	45c pink & multi	.45	.30
1510	A325	55c vio & multi	.55	.40
1511	A325	1b yel org & multi	.90	.70
1512	A325	2b grn & multi	1.50	1.00
		Nos. 1509-1512 (4)	3.40	2.40

National Parks — A326

45c, Abijata, Shalla Lakes. 70c, Nechisar. 85c, Bale Mountains. 2b, Awash.

Perf. 13¾x13¼, 13¼x13¾
1999, Sept. 8   **Litho.**
1513	A326	45c multi, vert.	.60	.50
1514	A326	70c multi, vert.	.80	.70
1515	A326	85c multi, vert.	1.00	.90
1516	A326	2b multi	2.50	1.50
	Nos. 1513-1516 (4)		4.90	3.60

See Nos. 1521-1524.

UPU, 125th Anniv. — A327

1999, Oct. 28   **Perf. 13¼x13**
1517	A327	20c multicolored	.30	.25
1518	A327	80c multicolored	.40	.35
1519	A327	1b multicolored	.70	.60
1520	A327	2b multicolored	1.00	.80
	Nos. 1517-1520 (4)		2.40	2.00

National Parks Type of 1999

Designs: 50c, Omo, vert. 70c, Mago, vert. 80c, Yangudi-Rassa, vert. 2b, Gambella.

1999, Nov. 30   **Litho.**   **Perf. 13¼**
1521-1524	A326	Set of 4	3.25 2.50

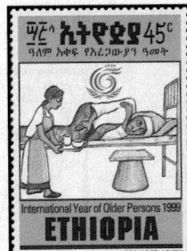

Intl. Year of Older Persons A328

45c, Woman attending to sick man. 70c, Older people gardening. 85c, Four men, bench. 2b, Older man, two young people.

1999, Dec. 30   **Perf. 13¾x13¼**
1525-1528	A328	Set of 4	3.25 2.50

Alexander Pushkin, Writer, Birth Bicent. (in 1999) — A329

Various portraits: 45c, 70c, 85c, 2b.

2000, Mar. 9   **Litho.**   **Perf. 13¾x13¼**
1529-1532	A329	Set of 4	3.25 2.50

Worldwide Fund for Nature (WWF) — A330

Grevy's zebra: a, Grazing. b, Running. c, Resting. d, Head.

2001, Jan. 30 Litho. Perf. 13¼x13¾
1533		Strip of 4	7.50 5.00
	a.	A330 45c multi	.60 .45
	b.	A330 55c multi	.75 .55
	c.	A330 1b multi	1.40 1.00
	d.	A330 3b multi	4.25 3.00

Operation Sunset — A331

Designs: 45c, President Meles Zenawi, Parliament. 55c, Soldiers, flag ceremony. 1b, People, house. 2b, Agriculture, construction.

2000, June 27   **Perf. 13¾**
1534-1537	A331	Set of 4	3.25 2.50

Flags A332

Designs: 25c, Harar Region. 30c, Oromia Region. 50c, Amhara Region. 60c, Tigre Region. 70c, Benishangi Region. 80c, Somalia Region. 90c, Peoples of the South Region. 95c, Gambella Region. 1b, Afar Region. 2b, Ethiopia.

2000, Oct. 26   **Perf. 13¼x13¾**
1538-1547	A332	Set of 10	4.75 4.00

Afro Ayigeba, Cross of St. Lalibela A333

2000, Apr. 27   **Perf. 13¾x13¼**
1548	A333	4b multi	2.75 2.25

Menelik's Bushbuck A334

Perf. 13¾x13¼
2000, June 19   **Litho.**
Frame Color
1548A	A334	5c	dk Prus blue
1549	A334	10c	lilac
1549A	A334	15c	blue
1549B	A334	20c	yellow bister
1549C	A334	25c	purple
1549D	A334	30c	lt Prus blue
1549E	A334	35c	brt red
1549F	A334	40c	lilac
1549G	A334	45c	emerald
1549H	A334	50c	red
1549I	A334	55c	blue
1549J	A334	60c	yellow orange
1549K	A334	65c	deep blue
1549L	A334	70c	dull blue
1549M	A334	75c	orange yellow
1549N	A334	80c	carmine
1549O	A334	85c	light blue
1550	A334	90c	ocher
1551	A334	1b	green
1552	A334	2b	red violet
1553	A334	3b	purple
1554	A334	5b	dark carmine
1555	A334	10b	light carmine
	Nos. 1548A-1555 (23)		— 40.00

Haile Gebreselassie, Runner — A335

Design: #1557, 50c, Gebreselassie running. #1557A, 60c, Gebreselassie running, diff. #1557B, 90c, Gebreselassie running, diff. #1558, 2b, Gebreselassie with arms raised.

2000, Nov. 9   **Litho.**   **Perf. 13½**
1557-1558	A335	Set of 4	2.75 2.00

World Meteorological Organization, 50th Anniv. — A336

Color of inscriptions: 40c, Gray. 75c, Green. 85c, Brown. 2b, Blue.

2000, Oct. 10   **Litho.**   **Perf. 13½**
1559-1562	A336	Set of 4	3.25 2.50

Addis Ababa University, 50th Anniv. — A337

2000, Nov. 30   **Perf. 13½x14¼**
1563	A337	4b multi	3.25 2.50

UN High Commissioner for Refugees, 50th Anniv. — A338

Frame color: 40c, Brown. 75c, Green. 85c, Blue. 2b, Gold.

2000 Dec. 14   **Perf. 13½x14**
1564-1567	A338	Set of 4	3.25 2.50

Freshwater Fish — A340

Designs: 45c, Catfish. 55c, Tilapia. 3b, Nile perch.

2001, July 26   **Litho.**   **Perf. 14¼**
1572-1574	A340	Set of 3	3.50 2.75

Traditional Means of Transportation — A341

Designs: 40c, Man on horseback, horse-drawn cart. 60c, Camel caravan. 1b, Man on horseback, horse carrying load. 2b, Man on donkey, donkeys carrying goods.

2001, Aug. 30   **Perf. 13¼x13½**
1575-1578	A341	Set of 4	3.50 2.75

Year of Dialogue Among Civilizations A342

Color of country name: 25c, Light blue. 75c, White. 1b, Light yellow. 2b, Pink.

2001, Oct. 9   **Perf. 14**
1579-1582	A342	Set of 4	3.00 2.25

Birds — A343

Designs: 50c, White-tailed swallow. 60c, Spot-breasted plover. 90c, Abyssinian long-claw. 2b, Prince Ruspoli's turaco.

2001, Nov. 29   **Perf. 14¼**
1583-1586	A343	Set of 4	3.75 3.00

Traditional Beehives A344

Various beehives: 40c, 70c, 90c, 2b.

2002, Jan. 24   **Litho.**   **Perf. 14**
1587-1590	A344	Set of 4 3.50 2.75

Traditional Grain Storage — A345

Designs: 30c, Gota. 70c, Bekollo Gotera. 1b, Gotera. 2b, Gotera, diff.

2002, Mar. 28   **Perf. 13½x14**
1591-1594 A345   Set of 4   3.00 2.40

Lions Club Intl. — A346

Lions Club Intl. emblem and: 45c, Quality emblem. 55c, Woman at pump. 1b, Eye doctor treating patient. 2b, Man in wheelchair.

2002, Apr. 26   **Litho.**   **Perf. 13x13¼**
1595-1598 A346   Set of 4   4.00 3.25

Trees A347

Designs: 50c, Acacia abyssinica. 60c, Boswellia papyrifera, vert. 90c, Aningeria adolfi-freiderici, vert. 2b, Prunus africana, vert.

Perf. 13½x13¼, 13¼x13½
2002, June 27
1599-1602 A347   Set of 4   3.75 3.00

Traditional Beehives A348

Various beehives with panel colors of: 45c, Pink. 55c, Yellow. 1b, Light blue. 2b, Light green.

2002, Sept. 19   **Litho.**   **Perf. 13¼x13**
1603-1606 A348   Set of 4   3.25 2.50

Granite — A349

Designs: 45c, Sidamo. 55c, Harrar. 1b, Tigray. 2b, Wollega.

2002, Oct. 24   **Perf. 13x13¼**
1607-1610 A349   Set of 4   4.00 3.50

Konso Waka A350

Various wooden sculptures with background colors of: 40c, Green. 60c, Blue. 1b, Yellow. 2b, Red.

2002, Nov. 28   **Perf. 14**
1611-1614 A350   Set of 4   3.50 2.50

Menelik's Bushbuck — A351

2002, Dec. 12   **Perf. 13½x13¾**
Frame Color

1615	A351	5c	brt grn blue	.20 .20
1616	A351	10c	lilac	.20 .20
1617	A351	15c	bright blue	.20 .20
1618	A351	20c	brn orange	.25 .20
1619	A351	25c	purple	.25 .20
1620	A351	30c	bright blue	.25 .20
1621	A351	35c	carmine	.25 .20
1622	A351	40c	purple	.25 .20
1623	A351	45c	emerald	.25 .20
1624	A351	50c	red	.25 .20
1625	A351	55c	blue	.25 .20
1626	A351	60c	bright yel	.35 .25
1627	A351	65c	red	.35 .25
1628	A351	70c	light blue	.35 .25
1629	A351	75c	bright yel	.40 .35
1630	A351	80c	carmine	.40 .35
1631	A351	85c	bright blue	.50 .40
1632	A351	90c	orange brn	.50 .40
1633	A351	95c	green	.50 .40
1634	A351	1b	red violet	.60 .50
1635	A351	2b	purple	.85 .75
1636	A351	3b	blue	1.00 .90
1637	A351	5b	dull red	2.00 1.50
1638	A351	10b	light green	4.00 3.00
1639	A351	20b	rose pink	8.00 6.00
		Nos. 1615-1639 (25)		22.40 17.50

Oil Crops A352

Designs: 40c, Abyssinian mustard. 60c, Linseed. 3b, Niger seed.

2002, Dec. 31   **Litho.**   **Perf. 13¼x13**
1640-1642 A352   Set of 3   2.00 2.00

Pan-African Postal Union, 23rd Anniv. — A353

Background color: 20c, Green. 80c, Blue green. 1b, Orange brown. 2b, Purple.

2003, Feb. 18   **Perf. 13x13¼**
1643-1646 A353   Set of 4   2.00 2.00

Opals — A354

Designs: 45c, Milk opal. 60c, Brown precious opal. 95c, Fire opal. 2b, Yellow precious opal.

2003, May 8   **Perf. 14**
1647-1650 A354   Set of 4   2.50 2.50

Emperor Tewodros's Amulet — A355

Various views with frame color of: 40c, Green. 60c, Yellow orange. 3b, Red.

2003, Sept. 4   **Litho.**   **Perf. 13x13¼**
1651-1653 A355   Set of 3   2.00 2.00

Flowers — A356

Designs: 45c, Kniphofia isoetfolia. 55c, Kniphofia insignis. 1b, Crinum bambusetum. 2b, Crinum abyssinicum, horiz.

2003, Nov. 27   **Litho.**   **Perf. 13x13¼**
1654-1657 A356   Set of 4   2.50 2.50

Konso Terracing System A357

Designs: 40c, Village, crops. 60c, Man and woman, ears of grains. 1b, Terraces, tool. 2b, Farmers working on terraces, crops.

2003, Dec. 30   **Perf. 13¼x13¾**
1658-1661 A357   Set of 4   2.00 2.00

Amaranths A358

Designs: 20c, Seeds. 80c, White amaranth. 1b, Red amaranth. 2b, Amaranth bread.

2004, Mar. 11   **Litho.**   **Perf. 13¼x14**
1662-1665 A358   Set of 4   2.25 2.25

Marble A359

Designs: 25c, Sabian multicolored marble. 75c, Eshet blue marble. 1b, Sabian rose green marble. 2b, Sabian purple marble.

2004, July 27   **Perf. 14**
1666-1669 A359   Set of 4   1.50 1.50

FIFA (Fédération Internationale de Football Association), Cent. — A360

Soccer field, "100" and: 5c, FIFA emblem. 95c, Old soccer ball. 1b, Cleats. 2b, Modern soccer ball.

2004, Sept. 7   **Litho.**   **Perf. 14**
1670-1673 A360   Set of 4   1.75 1.75

2004 Summer Olympics, Athens A361

Designs: 20c, Track. 35c, Hammer throw. 45c, Boxing. 3b, Cycling.

2004, Dec. 7
1674-1677 A361   Set of 4   1.75 1.75

Gesho — A362

Designs: 40c, Chopped plant. 60c, Plants, horiz. 1b, Cut logs. 2b, Branch with berries.

2004, Dec. 28
1678-1681 A362   Set of 4   1.75 1.75

Black Rhinoceros A363

2005, June 20   **Litho.**   **Perf. 14**
Background Color

1682	A363	5c	bright blue	.20 .20
1683	A363	10c	lilac	.20 .20
1684	A363	15c	dark blue	.20 .20
1685	A363	20c	bister	.40 .40
1686	A363	25c	dark purple	.40 .40
1687	A363	30c	blue	.40 .40
1688	A363	35c	red	.40 .40
1689	A363	40c	purple	.40 .40
1690	A363	45c	green	.40 .40
1691	A363	4b	bright red	1.75 1.75
		Nos. 1682-1691 (10)		4.75 4.75

Sabean Inscriptions — A364

Various inscriptions with background colors of: 15c, Green. 40c, Red, vert. 45c, Orange, vert. 3b, Blue, vert.

Perf. 13¾x14, 14x13¾
2005, Aug. 20   **Litho.**
1692-1695 A364   Set of 4   1.60 1.60

B4 A27 8g brown .65 .65
B5 A25 1t purple .65 .65
Nos. B1-B5 (5) 2.65 2.65

Nos. B1-B5 were sold at twice face value, the surtax going to the Red Cross.

Catalogue values for unused stamps in this section, from this point to the end of the section, are for Never Hinged items.

Surma Hairstyles
A365

Various hairstyles with background colors of: 15c, Red. 40c, Green. 45c, Blue. 3b, Lilac.

2005, Dec. 20 **Perf. 14x13¾**
1696-1699 A365 Set of 4 1.50 1.50

Flowers
A366

Designs: 45c, Chlorophytum neghellense. 55c, Aloe bertemariae, vert. 3b, Aloe schelpei, vert.

Perf. 13¾x14, 14x13¾
2006, June 6 Litho.
1700-1702 A366 Set of 3 1.75 1.75

Ethiopian Airlines, 60th Anniv.
A367

Designs: 15c, Douglas C-47A Dakota III. 40c, Douglas DC-6B Super Cloudmaster. 45c, Boeing 720-060B. 1b, Boeing 767-300ER. 2b, Boeing 787 Dreamliner.

2006, Sept. 28 **Perf. 13x13¼**
1703-1707 A367 Set of 5 1.75 1.75

Intl. Year of Deserts and Desertification — A368

Emblem and: 15c, United Nations emblem. 40c, Map of Ethiopia showing desertification vulnerability. 45c, Map of Africa showing climate types. 3b, Map of world showing climate types.

2006, Oct. 31 **Perf. 14x13½**
1708-1711 A368 Set of 4 1.75 1.75

Ethiopian Millennium
A369

Panel color: 40c, Pink. 60c, Buff. 3b, Green.

2007, Nov. 15 Litho. **Perf. 13¾**
1712-1714 A369 Set of 3 1.75 1.75

Minerals
A370

Designs: 40c, Gypsum. 60c, Quartz. 1b, Ambo sandstone. 2b, Feldspar.

2007, Dec. 25 **Perf. 14**
1715-1718 A370 Set of 4 1.75 1.75

Onslaught Martyrs Memorial
A371

Designs: 40c, Martyrs Memorial Center. 60c, Emblem of Association for the Erection of the Martyrs Memorial Monument, vert. 3b, Woman, jail cell, gun, vert.

2008, Aug. 26 Litho. **Perf. 14**
1719-1721 A371 Set of 3 .85 .85

Catha Edulis — A372

Designs: 45c, Red leaves. 55c, Harvesting of plant. 3b, Plant.

2008, Sept. 8 **Perf. 13¾**
1722-1724 A372 Set of 3 .85 .85

Diplomatic Relations Between Ethiopia and India, 60th Anniv.
A373

"60" and: 30c, Ethiopian and Indian flowers. 70c, Rock church, Lalibela, and Taj Mahal, India. 3b, Symbols of India and Ethiopia.

2008, Dec. 30 Litho. **Perf. 14x13¼**
1725-1727 A373 Set of 3 .80 .80

Pan-African Tsetse and Trypanosomiasis Eradication Campaign
A374

Designs: 15c, Campaign emblem. 40c, Tsetse fly. 45c, Tsetse fly and blood drop, horiz. 3b, Tsetse fly, cow, silhouette of human, map of Africa, horiz.

Perf. 13½x14, 14x13½
2009, July 21 Litho.
1728-1731 A374 Set of 4 .70 .70

Addis Ababa Monuments — A375

Designs: 45c, Arat Kilo, Miazia 27 Square Monument. 55c, Sidist Kilo, Yekatit 12 Square Monument. 3b, Abune Petros Monument, vert.

2009, Sept. 17 Litho. **Perf. 13¾**
1732-1734 A375 Set of 3 .65 .65

Eradication of Rinderpest in Ethiopia
A376

Designs: 15c, First laboratory in Addis Ababa where rinderpest vaccine was produced. 40c, Certificate from World Organization for Animal Health. 45c, Dead cattle. 3b, Dr. Alemework Beyene, monument to Dr. Engueda Johannes, veterinarians.

2009, Dec. 31 **Perf. 14**
1735-1738 A376 Set of 4 .65 .65

Pan-African Postal Union, 30th Anniv. — A377

Background color: 45c, Green. 55c, Yellow. 3b, Rose.

2010, Apr. 6 Litho. **Perf. 13¼x14**
1739-1741 A377 Set of 3 .60 .60

Writers — A378

Designs: No. 1742, 1b, Tsegaye Gebremedhin (1936-2006). No. 1743, 1b, Dr. Sindehu Gebru (1915-2009). No. 1744, 1b, Dr. Haddis Alemayehu (1910-2003). No. 1745, 1b, Dr. Kebede Michael (1915-98).

2010, Aug. 6 **Perf. 14**
1742-1745 A378 Set of 4 .60 .60

SEMI-POSTAL STAMPS

Types of 1931, Overprinted in Red at Upper Left

Perf. 12x12½, 12½x12
1936, Feb. 24 Unwmk.
B1 A27 1g light green .45 .45
B2 A27 2g rose .45 .45
B3 A25 4g blue .45 .45

Nos. 289, 290, 292-294 Surcharged in Blue

Perf. 13x13½
1949, June 13 Wmk. 282
B6 A53 8c + 8c deep org 2.40 2.40
B7 A53 12c + 5c red 2.40 2.40
B8 A53 30c + 15c org brn 3.75 3.75
B9 A53 70c + 70c rose lilac 22.50 22.50
B10 A53 $1 + 80c dk car rose 29.00 29.00
Nos. B6-B10 (5) 60.05 60.05

No. B10 exists with "80+" error.
See Nos. B16-B20.

Type A39 Surcharged in Red or Carmine

Perf. 11½
1950, May 8 Unwmk. Photo.
Various Designs
Inscribed "Croix Rouge"

B11 A39 5c + 10c brt grn 1.00 1.50
B12 A39 10c + 10c brt red 1.50 1.75
B13 A39 25c + 10c brt bl 2.40 3.25
B14 A39 50c + 10c dk yel brn 6.75 5.25
B15 A39 1t + 10c brt vio 10.50 12.00
Nos. B11-B15 (5) 22.15 23.75

The surtax was for the Red Cross.
The surcharge includes two dots which invalidate the original surtax. The original surcharge with uneven cross was red, a 1951 printing with even cross was carmine. Forgeries exist.

Nos. B6-B10 Overprinted in Black

Perf. 13x13½
1951, Nov. 17 Wmk. 282
B16 A53 8c + 8c dp org .70 .70
B17 A53 12c + 5c red .70 .70
B18 A53 30c + 15c org brn 1.10 1.10
B19 A53 70c + 70c rose lilac 11.50 11.50
B20 A53 $1 + 80c dk car rose 17.00 17.00
Nos. B16-B20 (5) 31.00 31.00

No. B20 exists with "80 +" error.

Tree, Staff and Snake — SP1

Wmk. 282

1951, Nov. 25 Engr. *Perf. 13*

Lower Panel in Red

B21	SP1	5c + 2c dp bl grn	.45	.20
B22	SP1	10c + 3c orange	.65	.30
B23	SP1	15c + 3c dp bl	.85	.50
B24	SP1	30c + 5c red	2.00	1.25
B25	SP1	50c + 7c red brn	4.25	2.50
B26	SP1	$1 + 10c purple	7.50	4.00
		Nos. B21-B26 (6)	15.70	8.75

The surtax was for anti-tuberculosis work.

1958, Dec. 1

Lower Panel in Red

B27	SP1	20c + 3c dl pur	.40	.30
B28	SP1	25c + 4c emerald	.50	.35
B29	SP1	35c + 5c rose vio	.75	.40
B30	SP1	60c + 7c vio bl	1.50	.80
B31	SP1	65c + 7c violet	3.00	1.75
B32	SP1	80c + 9c car rose	5.00	3.00
		Nos. B27-B32 (6)	11.15	6.60
		Nos. B21-B32 (12)	26.85	15.35

The surtax was for anti-tuberculosis work. Nos. B21-B32 were the only stamps on sale from Dec. 1-25, 1958.

Type of Regular Issue, 1955, Overprinted and Surcharged

Engr.; Cross Typo. in Red

1959, May 30 Wmk. 282

B33	A62	15c + 2c olive bister & rose red	.70	.70
B34	A62	20c + 3c vio & emer	.95	.95
B35	A62	30c + 5c rose car & grnsh bl	1.60	1.60
		Nos. B33-B35 (3)	3.25	3.25

Cent. of the Intl. Red Cross idea. Surtax for the Red Cross.

The overprint includes the cross, "RED CROSS CENTENARY" and date in two languages. The surcharge includes the date in Amharic and the new surtax. The surcharge was applied locally.

Design A39 Surcharged

Perf. 11½

1960, May 7 Photo. Unwmk.

B36	A39	5c + 1c brt green	.85	.85
B37	A39	10c + 2c brt red	1.25	1.00
B38	A39	25c + 3c brt blue	1.90	1.25
B39	A39	50c + 4c dk yel brn	3.00	2.50
B40	A39	1t + 5c brt vio	5.00	4.50
		Nos. B36-B40 (5)	12.00	10.10

25th anniversary of Ethiopian Red Cross. Forgeries exist.

Crippled Boy on Crutches — SP2

Wmk. 282

1963, July 23 Engr. *Perf. 13½*

B41	SP2	10c + 2c ultra	.30	.30
B42	SP2	15c + 3c red	.45	.35
B43	SP2	50c + 5c brt green	1.40	1.25
B44	SP2	60c + 5c red lilac	2.10	1.50
		Nos. B41-B44 (4)	4.25	3.40

The surtax was to aid the disabled.

───────────

AIR POST STAMPS

Regular Issue of 1928 Handstamped in Violet, Red, Black or Green

Perf. 13½x14

1929, Aug. 17 Unwmk.

C1	A22	⅛m orange & lt bl	.90	1.00
C2	A23	¼m ind & red org	.90	1.00
C3	A22	½m gray grn & blk	.90	1.00
C4	A23	1m dk car & blk	.90	1.00
C5	A22	2m dk blue & blk	1.00	1.25
C6	A23	4m yellow & olive	1.00	1.25
C7	A23	8m violet & olive	1.00	1.25
C8	A23	1t org brn & vio	1.25	1.25
C9	A22	2t green & bister	1.60	2.00
C10	A23	3t choc & grn	1.75	2.00
		Nos. C1-C10 (10)	11.20	13.00

The overprint signifies "17 August 1929-Airplane of the Ethiopian Government." The stamps commemorate the arrival at Addis Ababa of the 1st airplane of the Ethiopian Government.

There are 3 types of the overprint: (I) 19½mm high; "colon" at right of bottom word. (II) 20mm high; same "colon." (III) 19½mm high; no "colon." Many errors exist.

Symbols of Empire, Airplane and Map — AP1

1931, June 17 Engr. *Perf. 12½*

C11	AP1	1g orange red	.20	.25
C12	AP1	2g ultra	.20	.30
C13	AP1	4g violet	.20	.40
C14	AP1	8g blue green	.50	.80
C15	AP1	1t olive brown	1.25	1.00
C16	AP1	2t carmine	2.25	3.75
C17	AP1	3t yellow green	3.25	5.00
		Nos. C11-C17 (7)	7.85	11.50

Nos. C11 to C17 exist imperforate. *Reprints of C11 to C17 exist. Paper is thinner and gum whiter than the originals and the ink is heavy and shiny. Originals have ink that is dull and granular. Reprints usually sell at about one-tenth of above values.*

Catalogue values for unused stamps in this section, from this point to the end of the section, are for Never Hinged items.

Nos. 250, 255 and 257 Surcharged in Black

a   b

Perf. 14x13½

1947, Mar. 20 Unwmk.

C18	A33 (a)	12c on 4c	77.50	77.50
C19	A33 (b)	50c on 25c	72.50	72.50
a.		"26-12-46"	275.00	
C20	A33 (b)	$2 on 60c	125.00	125.00
a.		"26-12-46"	340.00	
		Nos. C18-C20 (3)	275.00	275.00
	Set, hinged		175.00	

Resumption of airmail service, 12/29/46.

Franklin D. Roosevelt AP2

Design: $2, Haile Selassie.

Engraved and Photogravure

1947, May 23 *Perf. 12½*

C21	AP2	$1 dk purple & sepia	16.00	12.50
C22	AP2	$2 carmine & dp blue	22.50	22.50

Farmer Plowing AP3

Designs: 10c, 25c, Zoquala, extinct volcano. 30c, 35c, Tesissat Falls, Abai River. 65c, 70c, Amba Alaguie. $1, Sacala, source of Nile. $3, Gorgora and Dembia, Lake Tana. $5, Magdala, former capital. $10, Ras Dashan, mountain peak.

Perf. 13x13½

1947-55 Wmk. 282 Engr.

C23	AP3	8c purple brown	.20	.20
C24	AP3	10c bright green	.20	.20
C25	AP3	25c dull pur ('52)	.35	.20
C26	AP3	30c orange yellow	.75	.20
C27	AP3	35c blue ('55)	.75	.35
C28	AP3	65c purple ('55)	.85	.60
C29	AP3	70c red	1.40	.60
C30	AP3	$1 deep blue	1.50	.75
C31	AP3	$3 rose lilac	6.00	3.75
C32	AP3	$5 red brown	11.50	5.25
C33	AP3	$10 rose violet	22.50	13.50
		Nos. C23-C33 (11)	46.00	25.60

For overprints see Nos. C64-C70.

UPU Monument, Bern — AP4

1950, Apr. 3 Unwmk. *Perf. 12½*

C34	AP4	5c green & red	.20	.20
C35	AP4	15c dk sl grn & car	1.75	1.75
C36	AP4	25c org yel & grn	2.25	1.75
C37	AP4	50c carmine & ultra	5.25	4.00
		Nos. C34-C37 (4)	9.45	7.70

75th anniv. of the UPU.

No. C34 exists in the colors of Nos. C35-C37. These are considered to be trial color proofs.

Convair Plane over Mountains AP5

Engraved and Lithographed

1955, Dec. 30 Unwmk. *Perf. 12½*

Center Multicolored

C38	AP5	10c gray green	1.00	.20
C39	AP5	15c carmine	1.25	.65
C40	AP5	20c violet	2.00	1.00
		Nos. C38-C40 (3)	4.25	1.85

10th anniversary of Ethiopian Airlines.

Promulgating the Constitution — AP6

Perf. 14x13½

1956, July 16 Engr. Wmk. 282

C41	AP6	10c redsh brn & ultra	.60	.70
C42	AP6	15c dk car rose & ol grn	.95	1.00
C43	AP6	20c blue & org red	1.25	1.00
C44	AP6	25c purple & green	1.40	1.60
C45	AP6	30c dk grn & red brn	2.40	2.50
		Nos. C41-C45 (5)	6.60	6.80

25th anniversary of the constitution.

Aksum AP7

Ancient Capitals: 10c, Lalibela. 15c, Gondar. 20c, Mekele. 25c, Ankober.

1957, Feb. 7 *Perf. 14*

Centers in Green

C46	AP7	5c red brown	.55	.30
C47	AP7	10c rose carmine	.55	.30
C48	AP7	15c red orange	.65	.35
C49	AP7	20c ultramarine	1.00	.50
C50	AP7	25c claret	1.50	.70
		Nos. C46-C50 (5)	4.25	2.15

Amharic "A" — AP8

Designs: Various Amharic characters and views of Addis Ababa. The characters, arranged by values, spell Addis Ababa.

1957, Feb. 14 Engr.

Amharic Letters in Scarlet

C51	AP8	5c ultra, *sal pink*	.20	.20
C52	AP8	10c ol grn, *pink*	.25	.20
C53	AP8	15c dl pur, *yel*	.40	.20
C54	AP8	20c grn, *buff*	.65	.30
C55	AP8	25c plum, *pale bl*	1.90	.40
C56	AP8	30c red, *pale grn*	1.25	.45
		Nos. C51-C56 (6)	4.65	1.75

70th anniversary of Addis Ababa.

Map, Rock Church at Lalibela and Obelisk AP9

1958, Apr. 15 Wmk. 282 *Perf. 13½*

C57	AP9	10c green	.20	.20
C58	AP9	20c rose red	1.25	.20
C59	AP9	30c bright blue	2.00	.90
		Nos. C57-C59 (3)	3.45	1.30

Conf. of Independent African States, Accra, Apr. 15-22.

Map of Africa and UN Emblem AP10

1958, Dec. 29   *Perf. 13*
C60	AP10	5c emerald	.20	.20
C61	AP10	20c carmine rose	.55	.20
C62	AP10	25c ultramarine	.75	.55
C63	AP10	50c pale purple	1.50	.75
		Nos. C60-C63 (4)	3.00	1.70

1st session of the UN Economic Conf. for Africa, opened in Addis Ababa Dec. 29.

Nos. C23-C29 Overprinted

Perf. 13x13½
1959, Aug. 16   Engr.   **Wmk. 282**
C64	AP3	8c purple brown	.35	.30
C65	AP3	10c brt green	.50	.35
C66	AP3	25c dull purple	.75	.40
C67	AP3	30c orange yellow	.80	.60
C68	AP3	35c blue	1.00	.65
C69	AP3	65c purple	1.60	1.00
C70	AP3	70c red	2.00	1.25
		Nos. C64-C70 (7)	7.00	4.55

30th anniv. of Ethiopian airmail service.

Ethiopian Soldier and Map of Congo — AP11

Globe with Map of Africa — AP12

Perf. 11½
1962, July 23   Unwmk.   Photo.
Granite Paper
C71	AP11	15c org, bl, brn & grn	.20	.20
C72	AP11	50c pur, bl, brn & grn	.95	.65
C73	AP11	60c red, bl, brn & grn	1.60	.80
		Nos. C71-C73 (3)	2.75	1.65

2nd anniv. of the Ethiopian contingent of the UN forces in the Congo and in honor of the 70th birthday of Emperor Haile Selassie.

1963, May 22
Granite Paper
C74	AP12	10c magenta & blk	.20	.20
C75	AP12	40c emerald & blk	1.25	.70
C76	AP12	60c blue & blk	2.00	.95
		Nos. C74-C76 (3)	3.45	1.85

Conf. of African heads of state for African Unity, Addis Ababa.

Bird Type of Regular Issue

Birds: 10c, Black-headed forest oriole. 15c, Broad-tailed paradise whydah, vert. 40c, Lammergeier, vert. 50c, White-checked touraco. 80c, Purple indigo bird.

1963, Sept. 12   *Perf. 11½*
Granite Paper
C77	A74	10c multicolored	.60	.20
C78	A74	15c multicolored	.75	.20
C79	A74	20c blue, blk & ocher	1.50	.60
C80	A74	50c lemon & multi	2.40	1.10
C81	A74	80c ultra, blk & brn	4.75	1.90
		Nos. C77-C81 (5)	10.00	4.00

Swimming AP13

Sport: 10c, Basketball, vert. 15c, Javelin. 80c, Soccer game in stadium.

Perf. 14x13½
1964, Sept. 15   Litho.   Unwmk.
C82	AP13	5c multicolored	.20	.20
C83	AP13	10c multicolored	.20	.20
C84	AP13	15c multicolored	.65	.55
C85	AP13	80c multicolored	2.25	1.10
		Nos. C82-C85 (4)	3.30	2.05

18th Olympic Games, Tokyo, Oct. 10-25.

Queen Elizabeth II and Emperor Haile Selassie — AP14

1965, Feb. 1   Photo.   *Perf. 11½*
Granite Paper
C86	AP14	5c multicolored	.20	.20
C87	AP14	35c multicolored	.70	.40
C88	AP14	60c multicolored	1.10	.70
		Nos. C86-C88 (3)	2.00	1.30

Visit of Queen Elizabeth II, Feb. 1-8.

Koka Dam and Power Plant — AP15

Designs: 15c, Sugar cane field. 50c, Blue Nile bridge. 60c, Gondar castles. 80c, Coffee tree. $1, Cattle at water hole. $3, Camels at well. $5, Ethiopian Air Lines jet plane.

1965, July 19   Unwmk.   *Perf. 11½*
Granite Paper
Portrait in Black
C89	AP15	15c vio brn & buff	.20	.20
C90	AP15	40c vio bl & lt bl	.45	.30
C91	AP15	50c grn & lt bl	.60	.35
C92	AP15	60c claret & yel	1.00	.60
C93	AP15	80c grn, yel & red	1.25	.70
C94	AP15	$1 brn & lt bl	1.50	.85
C95	AP15	$3 claret & pink	5.00	2.25
C96	AP15	$5 ultra & lt bl	10.50	4.25
		Nos. C89-C96 (8)	20.50	9.50

Bird Type of Regular Issue

Birds: 10c, White-collared kingfisher. 15c, Blue-breasted bee-eater. 25c, African paradise flycatcher. 40c, Village weaver. 60c, White-collared pigeon.

1966, Feb. 15   Photo.   *Perf. 11½*
Granite Paper
C97	A74	10c dull yel & multi	.60	.20
C98	A74	15c lt blue & multi	.80	.20
C99	A74	25c gray & multi	1.60	.80
C100	A74	40c pink & multi	3.25	1.10
C101	A74	60c multicolored	3.75	1.75
		Nos. C97-C101 (5)	10.00	4.05

Black Rhinoceros — AP16

Animals: 10c, Leopard. 20c, Black-and-white colobus (monkey). 30c, Mountain nyala. 60c, Nubian ibex.

1966, June 20   Litho.   *Perf. 13*
C102	AP16	5c dp grn, blk & gray	.20	.20
C103	AP16	10c grn, blk & ocher	.55	.20
C104	AP16	20c cit, blk & grn	1.10	.20
C105	AP16	30c yel grn, blk & ocher	1.75	.20
C106	AP16	60c yel grn, blk & dk brn	3.25	.65
		Nos. C102-C106 (5)	6.85	1.45

Bird Type of Regular Issue

Birds: 10c, Blue-winged goose, vert. 15c, Yellow-billed duck. 20c, Wattled ibis. 25c, Striped swallow. 40c, Black-winged lovebird, vert.

1967, Sept. 29   Photo.   *Perf. 11½*
Granite Paper
C107	A74	10c lt ultra & multi	.20	.20
C108	A74	15c green & multi	1.10	.20
C109	A74	20c yellow & multi	1.25	.20
C110	A74	25c salmon & multi	2.10	.20
C111	A74	40c pink & multi	4.50	1.60
		Nos. C107-C111 (5)	9.15	2.40

SPECIAL DELIVERY STAMPS

> Catalogue values for unused stamps in this section are for Never Hinged items.

Motorcycle Messenger — SD1

Addis Ababa Post Office SD2

Unwmk.
1947, Apr. 24   Engr.   *Perf. 13*
E1	SD1	30c orange brown	5.00	1.25
E2	SD2	50c blue	9.00	3.50

1954-62   **Wmk. 282**
E3	SD1	30c org brown ('62)	5.75	3.75
E4	SD2	50c blue	3.75	1.40

POSTAGE DUE STAMPS

> Very Fine examples of Nos. J1-J42 will have perforations touching the design on one or more sides.

Nos. 1-4 and unissued values Overprinted

Perf. 14x13½
1896, June 10   **Unwmk.**
Black Overprint
J1	A1	¼g green	1.25
J2	A1	½g red	1.25
J3	A1	4g lilac brown	.90
a.		*Without overprint*	.90
J4	A1	8g violet	.90
a.		*Without overprint*	

Red Overprint
J5	A1	1g blue	1.25
J6	A1	2g dark brown	1.25
J7	A1	16g black	.90
a.		*Without overprint*	
		Nos. J1-J7 (7)	7.70

Nos. J1-J7 were not issued.

Nos. 1-7 Handstamped in Various Colors:

a   b

1905, Jan. 1
J8	A1 (a)	¼g green	42.50	42.50
J9	A1 (a)	½g red	42.50	42.50
J10	A1 (a)	1g blue	42.50	42.50
J11	A1 (a)	2g dk brown	42.50	42.50
J12	A2 (a)	4g lilac brown	42.50	42.50
J13	A2 (a)	8g violet	42.50	42.50
J14	A2 (a)	16g black	42.50	42.50
		Nos. J8-J14 (7)	297.50	297.50

1905, June 1
J15	A1 (b)	¼g green	42.50	42.50
J16	A1 (b)	½g red	42.50	42.50
J17	A1 (b)	1g blue	42.50	42.50
J18	A1 (b)	2g dark brown	42.50	42.50
J19	A2 (b)	4g lilac brown	42.50	42.50
J20	A2 (b)	8g violet	42.50	42.50
J21	A2 (b)	16g black	42.50	42.50
		Nos. J15-J21 (7)	297.50	297.50

Excellent forgeries of Nos. J8-J42 exist.

Nos. 1-7 Handstamped in Blue or Violet

1906, July 1
J22	A1	¼g green	10.00	10.00
J23	A1	½g red	10.00	10.00
J24	A1	1g blue	10.00	10.00
J25	A1	2g dark brown	10.00	10.00
J26	A2	4g lilac brown	10.00	10.00
J27	A2	8g violet	15.00	15.00
J28	A2	16g black	21.00	21.00
		Nos. J22-J28 (7)	86.00	86.00

Nos. J22-J27 exist with inverted overprint, also No. J22 with double overprint.
Forgeries exist.

With Additional Surcharge of Value Handstamped as on Nos. 71-77

1907, July 1
J29	A1 (e)	¼ on ¼g grn	14.00	14.00
J30	A1 (e)	½ on ½g red	14.00	14.00
J31	A1 (f)	1 on 1g blue	14.00	14.00
J32	A1 (f)	2 on 2g dk brown	14.00	14.00
J33	A2 (f)	4 on 4g lilac brn	14.00	14.00
J34	A2 (f)	8 on 8g violet	14.00	14.00
J35	A2 (f)	16 on 16g blk	22.50	22.50
		Nos. J29-J35 (7)	106.50	106.50

Nos. J30-J35 exist with inverted surcharge. Nos. J30, J33-J35 exist with double surcharge.

Nos. 1-7 Handstamped in Black

1908, Dec. 1
J36	A1	¼g green	1.00	.90
J37	A1	½g red	1.00	.90
J38	A1	1g blue	1.00	.90
J39	A1	2g dark brown	1.25	1.10
J40	A2	4g lilac brown	1.75	1.75
J41	A2	8g violet	4.00	4.50
J42	A2	16g black	12.50	14.00
		Nos. J36-J42 (7)	22.50	24.05

Nos. J36 to J42 exist with inverted overprint and Nos. J36, J37, J38 and J40 with double overprint.
Forgeries of Nos. J36-J56 exist.

Same Handstamp on Nos. 87-93

1912, Dec. 1   *Perf. 11½*
J43	A3	¼g blue green	1.25	.85
J44	A3	½g rose	1.25	1.10

1913, July 1
J45	A3	1g green & org	4.25	3.00
J46	A4	2g blue	5.00	4.25
J47	A4	4g green & car	7.50	5.00

J48 A5 8g ver & dp grn 10.00 8.00
J49 A5 16g ver & car 25.00 19.00
Nos. J43-J49 (7) 54.25 41.20

Nos. J43-J49, all exist with inverted, double and double, one inverted overprint.

Same Handstamp on Nos. 120-124 in Blue Black

1925-27 **Perf. 11½**
J50 A6 ⅛g violet & brn 18.00 18.00
J51 A6 ¼g bl grn & db 18.00 18.00
J52 A6 ½g scar & ol grn 20.00 20.00
J53 A9 1g rose lil & gray grn 20.00 20.00
J54 A9 2g dp ultra & fawn 20.00 20.00
Nos. J50-J54 (5) 96.00 96.00

Same Handstamp on Nos. 110, 112

1930 (?)
J55 A3 (i) 1g green & org 30.00 30.00
J56 A4 (j) 2g blue 30.00 30.00
The status of Nos. J55-J56 is questioned.

> **Catalogue values for unused stamps in this section, from this point to the end of the section, are for Never Hinged items.**

 D2

Perf. 11½
1951, Apr. 2 Unwmk. Litho.
J57 D2 1c emerald .35 .20
J58 D2 5c rose red .75 .20
J59 D2 10c violet 1.40 .55
J60 D2 20c ocher 2.00 1.25
J61 D2 50c bright ultra 3.75 2.75
J62 D2 $1 rose lilac 7.75 3.75
Nos. J57-J62 (6) 16.00 8.70

OCCUPATION STAMPS

Issued under Italian Occupation
100 Centesimi = 1 Lira

 OS1

 Emperor Victor Emmanuel III — OS2

1936 Wmk. 140 Perf. 14
N1 OS1 10c org brn 14.50 9.50
N2 OS1 20c purple 12.50 4.00
N3 OS2 25c dark green 8.00 .80
N4 OS2 30c dark brown 8.00 1.60
N5 OS2 50c rose car 3.25 .40
N6 OS1 75c deep orange 27.50 8.00
N7 OS1 1.25 l deep blue 27.50 12.00
Nos. N1-N7 (7) 101.25 36.30
Set, never hinged 250.00

Issued: Nos. N3-N5, May 22; others Dec. 5.
For later issues see Italian East Africa.

FALKLAND ISLANDS
'fol-klənd 'i-lənds

LOCATION — A group of islands about 300 miles east of the Straits of Magellan at the southern limit of South America
GOVT. — British Crown Colony
AREA — 4,700 sq. mi.
POP. — 2,607 (1996)
CAPITAL — Stanley

Dependencies of the Falklands are South Georgia and South Sandwich. In March 1962, three other dependencies — South Shetland Islands, South Orkneys and Graham Land—became the new separate colony of British Antarctic Territory. In 1985 South Georgia and the South Sandwich Islands became a separate colony.

12 Pence = 1 Shilling
20 Shillings = 1 Pound
100 Pence = 1 Pound (1971)

> **Catalogue values for unused stamps in this country are for Never Hinged items, beginning with Scott 97 in the regular postage section, Scott B1 in the semipostal section, Scott J1 in the postage due section, Scott 1L1 in Falkland Island Dependencies regular issues, Scott 1LB1 in Falkland Island Dependencies semi-postals, and Scott 2L1, 3L1, 4L1, 5L1 in the Issues for Separate Islands.**

Values for unused stamps are for examples with original gum as defined in the catalogue introduction.
Nos. 1-4, 7-8, and some printings of Nos. 5-6, exist with straight edges on one or two sides, being the imperforate margins of the sheets. This occurs in 24 out of 60 stamps. Catalogue values are for stamps with perforations on all sides.

 Queen Victoria — A1

1878-79 Unwmk. Engr. Perf. 14
1 A1 1p claret 850.00 500.00
2 A1 4p dark gray ('79) 1,400. 200.00
3 A1 6p green 100.00 85.00
4 A1 1sh bister brown 80.00 80.00

1883-95 Wmk. 2
5 A1 1p brt claret ('94) 130.00 95.00
a. 1p claret 425.00 190.00
b. Horiz. pair, imperf. vert. 75,000.
c. 1p red brown ('91) 250.00 95.00
d. Diag. half of #5c used as ½p on cover 3,750.
6 A1 4p olive gray ('95) 14.00 27.50
a. 4p gray black 500.00 100.00
b. 4p olive gray black ('89) 180.00 65.00
c. 4p brownish black ('94) 900.00 400.00

No. 6c has watermark reversed.
For surcharge see No. 19E.

1886 Wmk. 2 Sideways
7 A1 1p claret 95.00 65.00
a. 1p brownish claret 125.00 60.00
b. Diagonal half of #7a used as ½p on cover 3,500.
8 A1 4p olive gray 525.00 60.00
a. 4p pale gray black 825.00 90.00

For surcharge see No. 19.

1891-1902 Wmk. 2
9 A1 ½p green ('92) 19.00 18.00
a. ½p blue green 27.50 32.50
10 A1 ½p yel green ('99) 2.25 3.50
11 A1 1p orange brown 100.00 80.00
a. Diagonal half used as ½p on cover 2,750.
11B A1 1p pale red ('99) 9.00 5.00
12 A1 1p org red ('02) 16.00 4.75
a. 1p Venetian red ('95) 32.50 30.00
13 A1 2p magenta ('96) 7.00 14.00
14 A1 2½p deep blue ('94) 275.00 160.00
15 A1 2½p ultra ('94) 45.00 14.00
a. 2½p pale ultra ('98) 45.00 20.00
b. 2½p dull blue 225.00 30.00
c. 2½p deep ultra ('01) 45.00 40.00
d. 2½p pale chalky ultra 200.00 60.00
16 A1 6p yellow ('96) 50.00 55.00
a. 6p orange ('92) 250.00 175.00
17 A1 9p ver ('96) 50.00 65.00
a. 9p salmon 57.50 70.00
18 A1 1sh gray brn ('95) 70.00 65.00
a. 1sh bis brn ('96) 70.00 55.00
Nos. 9-18 (11) 643.25 484.25

Nos. 7 and 5a Surcharged in Black

1891 Wmk. 2 Sideways
19 A1 ½p on half of 1p, #7 725.00 360.00
d. Unsevered pair 3,500. 1,350.

Wmk. 2
19E A1 ½p on half of 1p, #5a 825.00 325.00
f. Unsevered pair 4,500. 1,800.

Genuine used bisects should be canceled with a segmented circular cork cancel. Any other cancel must be linked by date to known mail ship departures. This surcharge exists on "souvenir" bisects, including examples of No. 11, and can be found inverted, double and sideways.

 A3 A4

1898 Wmk. 1
20 A3 2sh6p dark blue 300.00 300.00
21 A4 5sh brown red 240.00 275.00

 A5

 King Edward VII — A6

1904-07 Wmk. 3 Perf. 14
22 A5 ½p yellow green 5.25 1.80
23 A5 1p red, wmk. sideways ('07) 1.25 3.50
a. Wmk. upright ('04) 15.00 1.80
24 A5 2p dull vio ('05) 21.00 32.50
25 A5 2½p ultramarine 35.00 10.00
a. 2½p deep blue 300.00 200.00
26 A5 6p orange ('05) 50.00 57.50
27 A5 1sh bis brn ('05) 50.00 40.00
28 A6 3sh gray green 175.00 160.00
29 A6 5sh dull red ('05) 240.00 180.00
Nos. 22-29 (8) 577.50 485.30

 A7 A8

King George V

1912-14
30 A7 ½p yel grn 3.00 3.75
31 A7 1p red 5.50 2.75
32 A7 2p brn vio 9.50 19.00
33 A7 2½p deep ultra 9.50 19.00
34 A7 6p orange 17.50 22.50
35 A7 1sh bis brn 40.00 37.50
36 A8 3sh dark green 100.00 95.00
37 A8 5sh brown red 110.00 120.00
38 A8 5sh plum ('14) 250.00 200.00
39 A8 10sh red, green 200.00 300.00
40 A8 £1 black, red 525.00 600.00
Nos. 30-40 (11) 1,270. 1,469.
For overprints see Nos. MR1-MR3.

1921-29 Wmk. 4
41 A7 ½p yellow green 3.50 4.50
42 A7 1p red ('24) 6.00 1.50
43 A7 2p brown vio ('23) 20.00 8.50
44 A7 2½p dark blue 9.00 20.00
a. 2½p Prussian blue ('29) 375.00 550.00
45 A7 2½p vio, yel ('23) 6.00 42.50
46 A7 6p orange ('25) 9.50 45.00
47 A7 1sh bister brown 20.00 57.50
48 A8 3sh dk green ('23) 100.00 190.00
Nos. 41-48 (8) 174.00 369.50

No. 43 Surcharged

1928
52 A7 2½p on 2p brn vio 1,200. 1,200.
a. Double surcharge 45,000.
Beware of forged surcharges.

 King George V — A9

1929-31 Perf. 14
54 A9 ½p green 1.40 3.25
55 A9 1p scarlet 4.00 .90
56 A9 2p gray 3.50 3.00
57 A9 2½p blue 3.75 2.50
58 A9 4p deep orange 20.00 15.00
59 A9 6p brown violet 20.00 15.00
60 A9 1sh black, green 25.00 37.50
a. 1sh black, emerald 26.00 30.00
61 A9 2sh6p red, blue 60.00 60.00
62 A9 5sh green, yel 100.00 120.00
63 A9 10sh red, green 200.00 250.00
Wmk. 3
64 A9 £1 black, red 350.00 425.00
Nos. 54-64 (11) 787.65 932.15
Issue dates: 4p, 1931, others, Sept. 2.

 Romney Marsh Ram — A10

 Iceberg A11

 Whaling Ship — A12

 Port Louis A13

 Map of the Islands A14

 South Georgia A15

Blue Whale
A16

Government
House
A17

Battle
Memorial — A18

King
Penguin — A19

Coat of
Arms — A20

King George
V — A21

1933, Jan. 2		**Wmk. 4**		**Perf. 12**
65	A10	½p green & blk	3.25	8.50
66	A11	1p dl red & blk	4.00	2.50
67	A12	1½p lt bl & blk	19.00	20.00
68	A13	2p ol brn & blk	12.50	25.00
69	A14	3p dl vio & blk	21.00	26.00
70	A15	4p orange & blk	21.00	22.50
71	A16	6p gray & black	57.50	75.00
72	A17	1sh ol grn & blk	50.00	85.00
73	A18	2sh6p dp vio & blk	200.00	300.00
74	A19	5sh yellow & blk	750.00	1,100.
a.		5sh yellow orange & black	2,000.	2,500.
75	A20	10sh lt brn & blk	725.00	1,200.
76	A21	£1 rose & black	2,000.	2,750.
		Nos. 65-76 (12)	3,863.	5,614.

Cent. of the permanent occupation of the islands as a British colony.

Common Design Types
pictured following the introduction.

Silver Jubilee Issue
Common Design Type

1935, May 7				**Perf. 11x12**
77	CD301	1p carmine & blue	2.10	.50
78	CD301	2½p ultra & brown	4.50	2.10
79	CD301	4p indigo & grn	9.25	6.00
80	CD301	1sh brn vio & ind	21.00	4.75
		Nos. 77-80 (4)	36.85	13.35
		Set, never hinged	55.00	

Coronation Issue
Common Design Type

1937, May 12				**Perf. 11x11½**
81	CD302	½p deep green	.20	.20
82	CD302	1p dark carmine	.35	.50
83	CD302	2½p deep ultra	.60	1.25
		Nos. 81-83 (3)	1.15	1.95
		Set, never hinged	3.50	

Whale Jawbones (Centennial
Monument) — A22

#85, 86A, Black-necked swan. #85B, 86, Battle memorial. 2½p, 3p, Flock of sheep. 4p, Upland goose. 6p, R.R.S. "Discovery II." 9p, R.R.S. "William Scoresby." 1sh, Mt. Sugar Top. 1sh3p, Turkey vultures. 2sh6p, Gentoo penguins. 5sh, Sea lions. 10sh, Deception Island. £1, Arms of Colony.

1938-46				**Perf. 12**
84	A22	½p green & blk	.20	.20
85	A22	1p red & black	2.50	2.75
a.		1p rose carmine & black	16.00	1.75
85B	A22	1p dk vio & blk	.20	.30
86	A22	2p dk vio & blk	1.75	1.90
86A	A22	2p rose car & black	.25	.30
87	A22	2½p ultra & blk	1.50	1.40
87A	A22	3p deep bl & black	.75	.80
88	A22	4p rose vio & blk	1.75	1.90
89	A22	6p brown & blk	5.00	4.75
90	A22	9p sl bl & blk	1.75	1.60
91	A22	1sh dull blue	7.75	3.25
92	A22	1sh3p carmine & blk	1.75	3.25
93	A22	2sh6p gray black	37.50	22.50
94	A22	5sh org brown & ultra	55.00	47.50
a.		5sh yel brown & indigo	625.00	300.00
95	A22	10sh org & blk	60.00	47.50
96	A22	£1 dk vio & blk	125.00	92.50
		Nos. 84-96 (16)	302.65	232.30
		Set, never hinged	550.00	

Issued: Nos. 85B, 86A, 3p, 7/14/41; 1sh3p, 12/10/46; No. 94a, 1942; others, 1/3/38.
See Nos. 101-102. For overprints see Nos. 2L1-2L8, 3L1-3L8, 4L1-4L8.

> **Catalogue values for unused stamps in this section, from this point to the end of the section, are for Never Hinged items.**

Peace Issue
Common Design Type

				Perf. 13½x14
1946, Oct. 7		**Engr.**		**Wmk. 4**
97	CD303	1p purple	.35	.75
98	CD303	3p deep blue	.55	.50

Silver Wedding Issue
Common Design Types

1948, Nov. 1		**Photo.**		**Perf. 14x14½**
99	CD304	2½p bright ultra	2.00	1.00
		Engr.; Name Typo.		
				Perf. 11½x11
100	CD305	£1 purple	110.00	82.50

Types of 1938-46
2½p, Upland goose. 6p, R.R.S. "Discovery II."

				Perf. 12
1949, June 15		**Engr.**		**Wmk. 4**
101	A22	2½p dp blue & black	6.50	8.00
102	A22	6p gray black	6.50	4.25

UPU Issue
Common Design Types
Engr.; Name Typo. on 3p, 1sh3p

1949, Oct. 10		**Perf. 13½, 11x11½**		
103	CD306	1p violet	.60	.60
104	CD307	3p indigo	1.50	1.50
105	CD308	1sh3p green	5.00	4.50
106	CD309	2sh blue	11.00	9.50
		Nos. 103-106 (4)	18.10	16.10

Sheep
A35

Arms of the
Colony — A36

Designs: 1p, R.M.S. Fitzroy. 2p Upland goose. 2½p, Map. 4p, Auster plane. 6p, M.S.S. John Biscoe. 9p, "Two Sisters" peaks. 1sh, Gentoo penguins. 1sh 3p, Kelp goose and gander. 2sh 6p, Sheep shearing. 5sh, Battle memorial. 10sh, Sea lion and clapmatch. £1, Hulk of "Great Britain."

		Perf. 13½x13, 13x13½		
1952, Jan. 2		**Engr.**		**Wmk. 4**
107	A35	½p green	1.00	1.40
108	A35	1p red	2.10	.70
109	A35	2p violet	4.75	4.50
110	A35	2½p ultra & blk	1.25	.95
111	A36	3p deep ultra	1.40	1.75
112	A35	4p claret	10.00	2.75
113	A35	6p yellow brn	16.00	1.75
114	A35	9p orange yel	12.50	3.50
115	A36	1sh black	29.00	1.50
116	A35	1sh3p red orange	18.00	9.25
117	A36	2sh6p olive	22.50	20.00
118	A36	5sh red violet	14.00	15.00
119	A35	10sh gray	30.00	25.00
120	A35	£1 black	37.50	32.50
		Nos. 107-120 (14)	200.00	120.55

Coronation Issue
Common Design Type

1953, June 4				**Perf. 13½x13**
121	CD312	1p car & black	1.10	1.40

Types of 1952 with Portrait of Queen
Elizabeth II

1955-57		**Perf. 13½x13, 13x13½**		
122	A35	½p green ('57)	.75	1.50
123	A35	1p red ('57)	1.25	1.25
124	A35	2p violet ('56)	3.50	6.25
125	A35	6p light brown	8.75	.70
126	A35	9p ocher ('57)	13.00	21.00
127	A36	1sh black	7.75	1.40
		Nos. 122-127 (6)	35.00	32.10

Marsh
Starling
A37

Birds: ½p, Falkland Islands Thrush. 1p, Dominican gull. 2p, Gentoo penguins. 3p, Upland geese. 4p, Steamer ducks. 5½p, Rock-hopper penguin. 6p, black-browed albatross. 9p, Silver grebe. 1sh, Pied oystercatchers. 1sh3p, Yellow-billed teal. 2sh, Kelp geese. 5sh, King shag. 10sh, Guadelupe caracara. £1, Black-necked swan.

		Perf. 13½x13		
1960, Feb. 10		**Engr.**		**Wmk. 314**
		Center in Black		
128	A37	½p green	3.75	.50
a.		Wmk. sideways ('66)	.45	.30
129	A37	1p rose red	1.40	.80
130	A37	2p blue	3.75	1.00
131	A37	2½p bister brn	1.25	.30
132	A37	3p olive	.70	.30
133	A37	4p rose car	1.00	1.00
134	A37	5½p violet	1.75	2.25
135	A37	6p sepia	2.00	.30
136	A37	9p orange	1.75	.30
137	A37	1sh dull purple	.65	.30
138	A37	1sh3p ultra	9.50	13.00
139	A37	2sh brown car	27.50	2.50
140	A37	5sh grnsh blue	27.50	11.00
141	A37	10sh rose lilac	47.50	13.00
142	A37	£1 yellow org	50.00	32.50
		Nos. 128-142 (15)	180.00	80.00

Morse Key — A38

1962, Oct. 5   Photo.   Perf. 11½x11
143	A38	6p dp org & dk red	1.00	.60
144	A38	1sh brt ol grn & dp green	1.10	1.00
145	A38	2sh brt ultra & violet	1.90	1.90
		Nos. 143-145 (3)	4.00	3.50

Falkland Islands radio station, 50th anniv.

Freedom from Hunger Issue
Common Design Type

1963, June 4   Perf. 14x14½
146	CD314	1sh ultramarine	13.50	5.00

Red Cross Centenary Issue
Common Design Type
Wmk. 314

1963, Sept.2   Litho.   Perf. 13
147	CD315	1p black & red	3.00	1.00
148	CD315	1sh ultra & red	6.00	6.00

Shakespeare Issue
Common Design Type

1964, Apr. 23   Photo.   Perf. 14x14½
149	CD316	6p black	1.75	.50

H.M.S. Glasgow A39

6p, H.M.S. Kent. 1sh, H.M.S. Invincible. 2sh, Falkland Islands Battle Memorial, vert.

1964, Dec. 8   Engr.   Perf. 13
150	A39	2½p ver & black	10.50	3.75
151	A39	6p blue & black	.45	.30
a.		"Glasgow" vignette	32,500.	
152	A39	1sh carmine & blk	.45	1.10

Perf. 13x14
153	A39	2sh dk blue & blk	.35	.85
		Nos. 150-153 (4)	11.75	6.00

Battle of the Falkland Islands between the British and German navies, 50th anniv.

ITU Issue
Common Design Type
Perf. 11x11½

1965, May 26   Litho.   Wmk. 314
154	CD317	1p blue & dl dk bl	.65	.40
155	CD317	2sh lilac & dl yel	9.50	3.25

Intl. Cooperation Year Issue
Common Design Type

1965, Oct. 25   Perf. 14½
156	CD318	1p blue grn & claret	1.00	.25
157	CD318	1sh lt violet & grn	7.50	1.75

Churchill Memorial Issue
Common Design Type

1966, Jan. 24   Photo.   Perf. 14
Design in Black, Gold and Carmine Rose
158	CD319	½p bright blue	.40	.20
159	CD319	1p green	1.60	.30
160	CD319	1sh brown	4.00	1.75
161	CD319	2sh violet	8.50	4.25
		Nos. 158-161 (4)	14.50	6.50

Human Rights Flame and Globe A40

Perf. 14x14½
1968, July 4   Photo.   Wmk. 314
162	A40	2p brt rose & multi	.20	.20
163	A40	6p brt green & multi	.40	.40
164	A40	1sh orange & multi	.65	.65
165	A40	2sh ultra & multi	1.25	1.25
		Nos. 162-165 (4)	2.50	2.50

International Human Rights Year.

Dusty Miller — A41

Falkland Islands flora: 1½p, Pig vine, horiz. 2p, Pale maiden. 3p, Dog orchid. 3½p, Sea cabbage, horiz. 4½p, Vanilla daisy. 5½p, Arrowleaf marigold, horiz. 6p, Diddle-dee, horiz. 1sh, Scurvy grass, horiz. 1sh6p, Prickly burr. 2sh, Fachine. 3sh, Lavender. 5sh, Felton's flower, horiz. £1, Yellow orchid.

1968, Oct. 9   Photo.   Perf. 14
166	A41	½p multicolored	.20	.20
167	A41	1½p multicolored	.45	.20
168	A41	2p multicolored	.60	.20
169	A41	3p multicolored	6.00	.40
170	A41	3½p multicolored	.35	.55
171	A41	4½p multicolored	1.75	.75
172	A41	5½p multicolored	1.75	1.00
173	A41	6p multicolored	.85	1.25
174	A41	1sh multicolored	.85	2.40
175	A41	1sh6p multicolored	4.75	11.00
176	A41	2sh multicolored	6.00	5.50
177	A41	3sh multicolored	8.50	8.00
178	A41	5sh multicolored	30.00	15.00
179	A41	£1 multicolored	13.25	8.75
		See #166-179 (14)	75.30	55.20

See #210-222. For surcharges see #197-209.

Beaver DHC 2 Seaplane A42

Designs: 6p, Norseman seaplane. 1sh, Auster plane. 2sh, Falkland Islands arms.

1969, Apr. 8   Litho.   Perf. 14
180	A42	2p multicolored	.20	.20
181	A42	6p multicolored	.35	.35
182	A42	1sh multicolored	.70	.70
183	A42	2sh multicolored	1.75	1.25
		Nos. 180-183 (4)	3.00	2.50

21st anniv. of Government Air Service.

Bishop Stirling A43

2p, Holy Trinity Church, 1869. 6p, Christ Church Cathedral, 1969. 2sh, Bishop's miter.

1969, Oct. 30   Perf. 14
184	A43	2p emerald & black	.60	.60
185	A43	6p red orange & black	.60	.60
186	A43	1sh lilac & black	.60	.60
187	A43	2sh yellow & multi	.70	.70
		Nos. 184-187 (4)	2.50	2.50

Consecration of Waite Hocking Stirling (1829-1923), as first Bishop of the Bishopric of the Falkland Islands, cent.

Gun Emplacement — A44

2p, Volunteer on horseback, vert. 1sh, Volunteer in dress uniform, vert. 2sh, Defense Force badge.

Perf. 13½x13, 13x13½
1970, Apr. 30   Litho.   Wmk. 314
188	A44	2p ultra & multi	.65	.30
189	A44	6p multicolored	1.25	.75
190	A44	1sh buff & multi	2.50	1.25
191	A44	2sh yellow & multi	5.25	2.50
		Nos. 188-191 (4)	9.65	4.80

Falkland Islands Defense Force, 50th anniv.

The Great Britain, 1843 A45

The Great Britain in: 4p, 1845. 9p, 1876. 1sh, 1886. 2sh, 1970.

1970, Oct. 30   Litho.   Perf. 14½
192	A45	2p lemon & multi	.35	.20
193	A45	4p lilac & multi	.70	.50
194	A45	9p bister & multi	1.40	1.10
195	A45	1sh org brn & multi	2.25	1.75
196	A45	2sh multicolored	4.75	3.75
		Nos. 192-196 (5)	9.45	7.30

Nos. 166-178 Surcharged

1971, Feb. 15   Photo.   Perf. 14
197	A41	½p on ½p multi	1.00	1.00
198	A41	1p on 1½p multi	.20	.20
199	A41	1½p on 2p multi	.35	.35
200	A41	2p on 3p multi	.40	.40
201	A41	2½p on 3½p multi	.60	.60
202	A41	3p on 4½p multi	.65	.65
203	A41	4p on 5½p multi	.90	.90
204	A41	5p on 6p multi	1.25	1.25
205	A41	6p on 1sh multi	1.90	1.60
206	A41	7½p on 1sh6p multi	2.25	2.10
207	A41	10p on 2sh multi	3.50	3.00
208	A41	15p on 3sh multi	6.50	5.25
209	A41	25p on 5sh multi	13.50	11.00
		Nos. 197-209 (13)	33.00	28.30

Flower Type of 1968
"p" instead of "d"

Designs as before. 1p, 2½p, 4p, 5p, 6p, 25p, horizontal.

Wmk. 314, Sideways on Vert. Stamps
1972, June 1   Perf. 14
210	A41	½p Dusty miller	1.25	1.00
a.		Wmk. upright ('74)	12.50	30.00
b.		Wmk. 373 ('75)	3.25	3.50
211	A41	1p Pig vine	.40	.30
212	A41	1½p Pale maiden	.55	.40
213	A41	2p Dog orchid	3.50	3.00
a.		Wmk. upright ('74)	27.50	30.00
214	A41	2½p Sea cabbage	.95	.70
215	A41	3p Vanilla daisy	.95	.85
216	A41	4p Arrowleaf marigold	1.25	.85
217	A41	5p Diddle-dee	1.50	1.00
218	A41	6p Scurvy grass	17.00	12.50
a.		Wmk. sideways ('74)	1.90	2.25
219	A41	7½p Prickly burr	3.50	3.00
220	A41	10p Fachine	7.25	6.50
221	A41	15p Lavender	6.25	5.50
222	A41	25p Felton's flower	11.50	11.50
		Nos. 210-222 (13)	55.85	47.10

No. 213 has watermark sideways.

Silver Wedding Issue, 1972
Common Design Type

Design: Queen Elizabeth II, Prince Philip, Romney Marsh sheep and giant sea lions.

1972, Nov 20   Photo.   Perf. 14x14½
223	CD324	1p sl grn & multi	.30	.30
224	CD324	10p multicolored	1.00	1.00

Princess Anne's Wedding Issue
Common Design Type

1973, Nov. 14   Litho.   Perf. 14
225	CD325	5p lilac & multi	.20	.20
226	CD325	15p citron & multi	.70	.70

Fur Seals A46

Tourist Publicity: 4p, Trout fishing. 5p, Rockhopper penguins. 15p, Military starling.

1974, Mar. 6   Litho.   Wmk. 314
227	A46	2p lt ultra & multi	2.50	.95
228	A46	4p brt blue & multi	3.50	1.40
229	A46	5p yellow & multi	11.50	1.40
230	A46	15p lt ultra & multi	13.50	3.00
		Nos. 227-230 (4)	31.00	6.75

Early 19th Cent. Mail Coach, UPU Emblem — A47

UPU Cent.: 5p, Packet, 1841. 8p, First British mail planes, 1911. 16p, Catapult mail, 1920's.

1974, July 31   Perf. 14
231	A47	2p multicolored	.25	.25
232	A47	5p multicolored	.40	.40
233	A47	8p multicolored	.45	.45
234	A47	16p multicolored	.65	.65
		Nos. 231-234 (4)	1.75	1.75

Churchill, Parliament and Big Ben A48

Design: 20p, Churchill and warships.

1974, Nov. 30   Perf. 13x13½
235	A48	16p multicolored	1.50	1.50
236	A48	20p multicolored	2.00	2.00
a.		Souvenir sheet of 2, #235-236	8.50	8.50

Sir Winston Churchill (1874-1965).

HMS Exeter A49

Battleships: 6p, HMNZS Achilles. 8p, Admiral Graf Spee. 16p, HMS Ajax.

1974, Dec. 13   Perf. 14
237	A49	2p multicolored	2.40	.85
238	A49	6p multicolored	4.00	2.00
239	A49	8p multicolored	5.00	3.00
240	A49	16p multicolored	12.50	8.00
		Nos. 237-240 (4)	23.90	13.85

35th anniv. of the Battle of the River Plate between British ships and the German battleship Graf Spee.

Seal and Flag Badge — A50

7½p, Coat of arms, 1925. 10p, Arms, 1948. 16p, Arms (Falkland Islands Dependencies), 1952.

1975, Oct. 28 Litho. Wmk. 373

241	A50	2p multicolored	1.00	1.00
242	A50	7½p multicolored	1.90	1.90
243	A50	10p multicolored	2.10	2.10
244	A50	16p multicolored	3.00	3.00
		Nos. 241-244 (4)	8.00	8.00

Falkland Islands heraldic arms, 50th anniv.

½p-Coin and Trout
A51

New Coinage: 5½p, 1p-coin and gentoo penguins, 8p, 2p-coin and upland geese. 10p, 5p-coin and black-browed albatross. 16p, 10p-coin and sea lions.

1975, Dec. 31 Litho. Wmk. 373

245	A51	2p copper & multi	.25	.25
246	A51	5½p copper & multi	.70	.70
247	A51	8p copper & multi	1.40	1.40
248	A51	10p silver & multi	2.10	2.10
249	A51	16p silver & multi	5.75	5.75
		Nos. 245-249 (5)	10.20	10.20

Gathering Sheep — A52

Sheep Farming: 7½p, Shearing. 10p, Dipping sheep. 20p, Motor Vessel Monsunen collecting wool.

1976, Apr. 28 Litho. Perf. 13½

250	A52	2p multicolored	.55	.25
251	A52	7½p multicolored	1.10	.50
252	A52	10p multicolored	1.60	.75
253	A52	20p multicolored	3.75	1.90
		Nos. 250-253 (4)	7.00	3.40

Prince Philip, 1957 Visit A53

11p, Queen, ampulla and spoon. 33p, Queen awaiting anointment, and Knights of the Garter.

1977, Feb. 7 Perf. 13½x14

254	A53	6p multicolored	.35	.35
a.		Booklet pane of 4, wmk. 314	9.00	
b.		Single stamp from #254a	2.25	
255	A53	11p multicolored	.60	.60
a.		Booklet pane of 4	3.50	
256	A53	33p multicolored	1.50	1.50
a.		Booklet pane of 4	8.00	
		Nos. 254-256 (3)	2.45	2.45

25th anniv. of the reign of Elizabeth II.

Map of West and East Falkland with Communications Centers — A54

Telecommunications: 11p, Ship to shore communications at Fox Bay. 40p, Globe with Telex tape and telephone.

1977, Oct. 24 Litho. Perf. 14½x14

257	A54	3p yel brown & multi	.40	.25
258	A54	11p lt ultra & multi	1.00	.60
259	A54	40p rose & multi	4.25	3.00
		Nos. 257-259 (3)	5.65	3.85

A.E.S., 1957-1974 — A55

Designs: Mail ships.

1978, Jan. 25 Wmk. 373 Perf. 14
No Date Inscription

260	A55	1p shown	.25	.25
261	A55	2p Darwin, 1957-75	.25	.25
262	A55	3p Merak-N 1951-53	.25	.25
263	A55	4p Fitzroy, 1936-57	.25	.25
264	A55	5p Lafonia 1936-41	.30	.40
265	A55	6p Fleurus, 1924-33	.35	.50
266	A55	7p S.S. Falkland, 1914-34	.50	.70
267	A55	8p Oravia, 1900-12	.55	.75
268	A55	9p Memphis, 1890-97	.60	.85
269	A55	10p Black Hawk, 1873-80	.75	1.00
270	A55	20p Foam, 1963-72	.95	1.40
271	A55	25p Fairy, 1857-61	1.25	1.75
272	A55	50p Amelia, 1852-54	2.00	2.75
273	A55	£1 Nautilus, 1846-48	4.25	6.00
274	A55	£3 Hebe, 1842-46	12.00	14.00
		Nos. 260-274 (15)	24.50	31.10

The 1p, 3p, 5p, 6p and 10p were also issued in booklet panes of 4.
For overprints see Nos. 352-353.

1982, Dec. 1
Inscribed "1982"

260a	A55	1p shown	.25	.25
261a	A55	2p Darwin, 1957-75	.25	.25
262a	A55	3p Merak-N 1951-53	.25	.25
263a	A55	4p Fitzroy, 1936-57	.25	.25
264a	A55	5p Lafonia 1936-41	.30	.40
265a	A55	6p Fleurus, 1924-33	.35	.50
266a	A55	7p S.S. Falkland, 1914-34	.50	.70
267a	A55	8p Oravia, 1900-12	.55	.75
268a	A55	9p Memphis, 1890-97	.60	.85
269a	A55	10p Black Hawk, 1873-80	.75	1.00
270a	A55	20p Foam, 1963-72	.95	1.40
271a	A55	25p Fairy, 1857-61	1.25	1.75
272a	A55	50p Amelia, 1852-54	2.00	2.75
273a	A55	£1 Nautilus, 1846-48	4.25	6.00
274a	A55	£3 Hebe, 1842-46	12.00	14.00
		Nos. 260a-274a (15)	24.50	31.10

Elizabeth II Coronation Anniversary Issue
Souvenir Sheet
Common Design Type

1978, June 2 Unwmk. Perf. 15

275		Sheet of 6	4.00	4.00
a.	CD326	25p Red Dragon of Wales	.60	.60
b.	CD327	25p Elizabeth II	.60	.60
c.	CD328	25p Hornless ram	.60	.60

No. 275 contains 2 se-tenant strips of Nos. 275a-275c, separated by horizontal gutter with commemorative and descriptive inscriptions.

Short Sunderland Mark III — A56

Design: 33p, Pane in flight and route Southampton to Stanley.

1978, Apr. 28 Wmk. 373 Perf. 14

276	A56	11p multicolored	2.40	1.90
277	A56	33p multicolored	5.00	3.25

First direct flight Southampton, England to Stanley, Falkland Islands, 26th anniv.

First Fox Bay PO and No. 1 — A57

Macrocystis Pyrifera — A58

Designs: 11p, Second Stanley Post Office and #2. 15p, New Island Post Office and #3. 22p, 1st Stanley Post Office and #4.

1978, Aug. 8 Litho. Perf. 13½x13

278	A57	3p multicolored	.20	.20
279	A57	11p multicolored	.40	.40
280	A57	15p multicolored	.55	.55
281	A57	22p multicolored	.85	.85
		Nos. 278-281 (4)	2.00	2.00

Falkland Islands postage stamps, cent.

1979, Feb. 19 Litho. Perf. 14

Kelp: 7p, Durvillea. 11p, Lessoniae, horiz. 15p, Callophyllis, horiz. 25p, Iridea.

282	A58	3p multicolored	.20	.20
283	A58	7p multicolored	.40	.40
284	A58	11p multicolored	.60	.60
285	A58	15p multicolored	.75	.75
286	A58	25p multicolored	1.25	1.25
		Nos. 282-286 (5)	3.20	3.20

Britten-Norman Islander over Map — A59

Opening of Stanley Airport: 11p, Fokker F27 over map. 15p, Fokker F28 over Stanley. 25p, Cessna 172 Skyhawk, Islander and Fokkers F27, F28 over runway.

1979, May 1 Litho. Perf. 13½

287	A59	3p multicolored	.20	.20
288	A59	11p multicolored	.80	.80
289	A59	15p multicolored	1.10	1.10
290	A59	25p multicolored	1.90	1.90
		Nos. 287-290 (4)	4.00	4.00

Rowland Hill and No. 121 A60

Sir Rowland Hill (1795-1879), originator of penny postage, and: 11p, Falkland Islands No. 1, vert. 25p, Penny Black. 33p, Falkland Islands No. 37, vert.

1979, Aug. 27 Perf. 14

291	A60	3p multicolored	.20	.20
292	A60	11p multicolored	.45	.45
293	A60	25p multicolored	.90	.90
		Nos. 291-293 (3)	1.55	1.55

Souvenir Sheet

294	A60	33p multicolored	1.50	1.50

Mail Delivery by Air, UPU Emblem A61

UPU Membership Cent. (Modes of Mail Delivery): 11p, Horseback. 25p, Schooner Gwendolin.

1979, Nov. 26

295	A61	3p multicolored	.20	.20
296	A61	11p multicolored	.45	.45
297	A61	25p multicolored	.95	.95
		Nos. 295-297 (3)	1.60	1.60

Commerson's Dolphin — A62

1980, Feb. 25 Wmk. 373 Perf. 14

298	A62	3p Peale's porpoise, vert.	.20	.20
299	A62	6p shown	.30	.30
300	A62	7p Hour-glass dolphin	.35	.35
301	A62	11p Spectacled porpose, vert.	.55	.55
302	A62	15p Dusky dolphin	.90	.90
303	A62	15p Killer whale	1.60	1.60
		Nos. 298-303 (6)	3.90	3.90

Miniature Sheet

Falkland Islands Cancel, 1878 A63

Designs: b, New Islds., 1915. c, Falklands Islds., 1901. d, Port Stanley, 1935. e, Port Stanley airmail, 1952. f, Fox Bay, 1934.

1980, May 6 Litho. Perf. 14

304		Sheet of 6	2.25	2.25
a.-f.		A63 11p any single	.35	.35

London 1980 Intl. Stamp Exhib., May 6-14.

Queen Mother Elizabeth Birthday
Common Design Type

1980, Aug. 4 Litho. Perf. 14

305	CD330	11p multicolored	.50	.50

Striated Caracara A64

1980, Aug. 11 Wmk. 373 Perf. 13½

306	A64	3p shown	.35	.20
307	A64	11p Red-backed buzzard	.70	.60
308	A64	15p Crested caracara	.85	.70
309	A64	25p Cassin's falcon	1.60	1.40
		Nos. 306-309 (4)	3.50	2.90

Port Egmont, Early Settlement — A65

1980, Dec. 22 Litho. Perf. 14

310	A65	3p Stanley	.20	.20
311	A65	11p shown	.45	.45
312	A65	25p Port Louis	.95	.50
313	A65	33p Mission House, Keppel Island	1.10	.95
		Nos. 310-313 (4)	2.70	2.10

Polwarth Sheep A66

1981, Jan. 19 Litho. Perf. 14

314	A66	3p shown	.20	.20
315	A66	11p Frisian cow and calf	.40	.40
316	A66	25p Horse	.85	.85
317	A66	33p Welsh collies	1.10	1.10
		Nos. 314-317 (4)	2.55	2.55

Map of Falkland Islands, Bowles and Carver, 1779 A67

1981, May 22 Litho. Perf. 14

318	A67	3p shown	.20	.20
319	A67	10p Hawkin's Mainland, 1773	.30	.25
320	A67	13p New Isles, 1747	.40	.35
321	A67	15p French & British Islands	.50	.40
322	A67	25p Falklands, 1771	.75	.60
323	A67	26p Falklands, 1764	.85	.65
		Nos. 318-323 (6)	3.00	2.45

Royal Wedding Issue
Common Design Type

1981, July 22   Litho.   Perf. 13½x13

324	CD331	10p Bouquet	.30	.30
325	CD331	13p Charles	.45	.45
326	CD331	52p Couple	1.25	1.25
		Nos. 324-326 (3)	2.00	2.00

Duke of Edinburgh's Awards, 25th Anniv. — A68

1981, Sept. 28   Litho.   Perf. 14

327	A68	10p Spinning	.30	.30
328	A68	13p Camping	.35	.35
329	A68	15p Kayaking	.45	.45
330	A68	26p Duke of Edinburgh	.80	.80
		Nos. 327-330 (4)	1.90	1.90

The Holy Virgin, by Guido Reni (1575-1642) A69

Christmas: 3p, Adoration of the Holy Child, 16th cent. Dutch. 13p, Holy Family in an Italian Landscape, 17th cent. Italian.

1981, Nov. 9   Litho.   Perf. 14

331	A69	3p multicolored	.20	.20
332	A69	13p multicolored	.45	.45
333	A69	26p multicolored	.80	.80
		Nos. 331-333 (3)	1.45	1.45

This set was issued Nov. 2 in London by the Crown Agents.

Designs: Shelf fish. 5p, 15p, 25p horiz.

Rock Cod — A70

1981, Dec. 7

334	A70	5p Falkland herring	.20	.20
335	A70	13p shown	.40	.40
336	A70	15p Patagonian hake	.50	.50
337	A70	25p Southern blue whiting	.80	.80
338	A70	26p Gray-tailed skate	.80	.80
		Nos. 334-338 (5)	2.70	2.70

Shipwrecks — A71

1982, Feb. 15   Wmk. 373   Perf. 14½

339	A71	5p Lady Elizabeth, 1913	.25	.25
340	A71	13p Capricorn, 1882	.50	.50
341	A71	15p Jhelum, 1870	.60	.60
342	A71	25p Snowsquall, 1864	.80	.80
343	A71	26p St. Mary, 1890	.80	.80
		Nos. 339-343 (5)	2.95	2.95

Sesquicentennial of Charles Darwin's Visit — A72

1982, Apr. 19   Litho.   Perf. 14

344	A72	5p Darwin	.20	.20
345	A72	17p Microscope	.65	.65
346	A72	25p Warrah	1.00	1.00
347	A72	34p Beagle	1.25	1.25
		Nos. 344-347 (4)	3.10	3.10

Princess Diana Issue
Common Design Type

1982, July 5   Wmk. 373   Perf. 13

348	CD333	5p Arms	.30	.20
349	CD333	17p Diana	.75	.50
350	CD333	37p Wedding	1.90	1.00
351	CD333	50p Portrait	2.50	1.40
		Nos. 348-351 (4)	5.45	3.10

Nos. 264, 271 Overprinted: "1st PARTICIPATION / COMMONWEALTH GAMES 1982"

1982, Oct. 7   Litho.   Perf. 14

352	A55	5p multicolored	.20	.20
353	A55	25p multicolored	.65	.65

12th Commonwealth Games, Brisbane, Australia, Sept. 30-Oct. 9.

Tussock Bird — A73

1982, Dec. 6   Perf. 15x14½

354	A73	5p shown	.20	.20
355	A73	10p Black-chinned siskin	.25	.25
356	A73	13p Grass wren	.45	.45
357	A73	17p Black-throated finch	.60	.60
358	A73	25p Falkland-correndera pipit	1.00	1.00
359	A73	34p Dark-faced ground-tyrant	1.10	1.10
		Nos. 354-359 (6)	3.60	3.60

British Occupation Sesquicentennial — A74

1p, Raising the Standard, Port Louis, 1833. 2p, Chelsea pensioners & barracks, 1849. 5p, Wool trade, 1874. 10p, Ship repairing trade, 1850-90. 15p, Government House, early 20th cent. 20p, Battle of the Falkland Islands, 1914. 25p, Whalebone Arch centenary, 1933. 40p, Contribution to World War II effort, 1939-45. 50p, Visit of Duke of Edinburgh, 1957. £1, Royal Marines, 1933, 1983, vert. £2, Queen Elizabeth II.

1983, Jan. 1   Litho.   Perf. 14

360	A74	1p multi, vert.	.25	.30
361	A74	2p multi	.25	.30
362	A74	5p multi, vert.	.25	.30
363	A74	10p multi	.25	.30
364	A74	15p multi	.30	.40
365	A74	20p multi, vert.	.45	.60
366	A74	25p multi	.60	.70
367	A74	40p multi, vert.	.90	1.10
368	A74	50p multi	1.10	1.40
369	A74	£1 multi	1.75	3.00
370	A74	£2 multi, vert.	6.40	6.50
		Nos. 360-370 (11)	10.10	14.90

For surcharges see Nos. 402-403.

A75

1983, Mar. 14

371	A75	5p No. 69	.25	.25
372	A75	17p No. 65	.50	.50
373	A75	34p No. 75, vert.	.75	1.00
374	A75	50p No. 370, vert.	.90	1.00
		Nos. 371-374 (4)	2.40	2.75

Commonwealth Day.

First Anniv. of Liberation A76

1983, June 14   Wmk. 373   Perf. 14

375	A76	5p Army	.25	.25
376	A76	13p Merchant Navy	.35	.35
377	A76	17p Royal Air Force	.50	.50
378	A76	50p Royal Navy	1.40	1.40
a.		Souvenir sheet of 4, #375-378	3.25	3.25
		Nos. 375-378 (4)	2.50	2.50

Local Fruit A77

1983, Oct. 10   Litho.   Perf. 14

379	A77	5p Diddle dee	.20	.20
380	A77	17p Tea berries	.40	.40
381	A77	25p Mountain berries	.60	.60
382	A77	34p Native strawberries	.80	.80
		Nos. 379-382 (4)	2.00	2.00

Britten-Norman Islander — A78

1983, Nov. 14   Litho.   Perf. 14

383	A78	5p shown	.25	.20
384	A78	13p DHC-2 Beaver	.40	.25
385	A78	17p Noorduyn Norseman	.50	.30
386	A78	50p Auster	1.25	.85
		Nos. 383-386 (4)	2.40	1.60

Green Spider A79

Insects and Spiders.

1984, Jan. 1   Litho.   Perf. 14

387	A79	1p shown	.20	.20
388	A79	2p Ichneumon-Fly	.20	.20
a.		Inscribed "1986"	4.00	3.50
389	A79	3p Brocade Moth	.20	.20
390	A79	4p Black Beetle	.20	.20
391	A79	5p Fritillary	.20	.20
392	A79	6p Green Spider, diff.	.30	.30
393	A79	7p Ichneumon-Fly, diff.	.30	.30
394	A79	8p Ochre Shoulder	.30	.30
395	A79	9p Clocker Weevil	.30	.45
396	A79	10p Hover Fly	.30	.45
397	A79	20p Weevil	.60	1.00
398	A79	25p Metallic Beetle	.80	1.25
399	A79	50p Camel Cricket	1.50	2.50
400	A79	£1 Beauchene Spider	3.25	5.50
401	A79	£3 Southern Painted Lady	9.75	15.00
		Nos. 387-401 (15)	18.40	28.05

Nos. 364, 366 Surcharged

1984, Jan. 3   Litho.   Perf. 14

402	A74	17p on 15p multi	.45	.45
403	A74	22p on 25p multi	.55	.55

Lloyd's List Issue
Common Design Type

1984, May 7   Wmk. 373   Perf. 14½

404	CD335	6p Wavertree	.25	.25
405	CD335	17p Port Stanley, 1910	.65	.65
406	CD335	22p Oravia	.80	.80
407	CD335	52p Cunard Countess	2.00	2.00
		Nos. 404-407 (4)	3.70	3.70

Great Grebe — A80

1984, Aug. 6   Perf. 14½x14

408	A80	17p shown	1.10	1.10
409	A80	22p Silver grebe	1.40	1.40
410	A80	52p Rolland's grebe	4.00	4.00
		Nos. 408-410 (3)	6.50	6.50

See Nos. 450-453.

1984 UPU Congress A81

1984, June 25   Litho.   Perf. 14

411	A81	22p Emblem, jet, ship	.60	.60

Wildlife Conservation A82

1984, Nov. 5   Litho.   Perf. 14½

412	A82	6p Birds	.60	.90
413	A82	17p Plants	1.25	.90
414	A82	22p Mammals	1.40	1.00
415	A82	52p Marine Life	3.00	2.25
a.		Souvenir sheet of 4, #412-415	8.50	6.00
		Nos. 412-415 (4)	6.25	4.55

Camber Railway, 1915-1927 A83

1985, Feb. 18   Litho.   Perf. 14

416	A83	7p multicolored	.35	.30
417	A83	22p multicolored	.85	.75
418	A83	27p multicolored	.90	1.00

Size: 77x26mm

419	A83	54p multicolored	1.90	1.90
		Nos. 416-419 (4)	4.00	3.95

Queen Mother 85th Birthday
Common Design Type

Designs: 7p, Commonwealth Visitor's Reception. 22p, With Prince Charles, Mark Phillips, Princess Anne. 27p, 80th birthday celebration. 54p, Holding Prince Henry. £1, In coach with Princess Diana.

Perf. 14½x14

1985, June 7	**Litho.**	**Wmk. 384**	
420	CD336	7p multicolored	.20 .20
421	CD336	22p multicolored	.85 .85
422	CD336	27p multicolored	1.10 1.10
423	CD336	54p multicolored	2.10 2.10
		Nos. 420-423 (4)	4.25 4.25

Souvenir Sheet

424	CD336	£1 multicolored	4.50 4.50

Mount Pleasant Airport Opening A84

1985, May 12	**Litho.**	**Perf. 14½**	
425	A84	7p Pioneer camp, docked ship	.40 .40
426	A84	22p Construction site	1.25 1.25
427	A84	27p Runway layout	1.60 1.60
428	A84	54p Aircraft landing	3.00 3.00
		Nos. 425-428 (4)	6.25 6.25

Captain J. McBride, HMS Jason, 1765 — A85

18th-19th century naval explorers: 22p, Commodore J. Byron, HMS Dolphin and Tamar, 1765. 27p, Vice-Adm. R. Fitzroy, HMS Beagle, 1831. 54p, Adm. Sir B.J. Sulivan, HMS Philomel, 1842.

1985, Sept. 23			
429	A85	7p multicolored	.50 .50
430	A85	22p multicolored	1.40 1.40
431	A85	27p multicolored	1.50 1.50
432	A85	54p multicolored	3.25 3.25
		Nos. 429-432 (4)	6.65 6.65

Philibert Commerson (1727-1773), Commerson's Dolphin — A86

Naturalists, endangered species: 22p, Rene Primevere Lesson (1794-1849), kelp. 27p, Joseph Paul Gaimard (1796-1858), diving petrel. 54p, Charles Darwin (1803-1882), Calceolaria darwinii.

1985, Nov. 4		**Perf. 14½**	
433	A86	7p multicolored	.50 .35
434	A86	22p multicolored	1.50 1.10
435	A86	27p multicolored	1.75 1.25
436	A86	54p multicolored	3.50 2.50
		Nos. 433-436 (4)	7.25 5.20

Seashells A87

1986, Feb. 10	**Wmk. 384**	**Perf. 14½**	
437	A87	7p Painted keyhole limpet	.45 .45
438	A87	22p Magellanic volute	1.60 1.60
439	A87	27p Falkland scallop	2.25 2.25
440	A87	54p Rough thorn drupe	4.25 4.25
		Nos. 437-440 (4)	8.55 8.55

Queen Elizabeth II 60th Birthday
Common Design Type

Designs: 10p, With Princess Margaret at St. Paul's, Waldenbury, 1943. 24p, Christmas broadcast from Sandringham, 1958. 29p, Order of the Thistle, St. Giles Cathedral, Edinburgh, 1962. 45p, Royal reception on the Britannia, US visit, 1976. 58p, Visiting Crown Agents' offices, 1983.

1986, Apr. 21	**Litho.**	**Perf. 14x14½**	
441	CD337	10p scar, blk & sil	.30 .30
442	CD337	24p ultra, blk & sil	.65 .65
443	CD337	29p green & multi	.85 .85
444	CD337	45p violet & multi	1.40 1.40
445	CD337	58p rose vio & multi	1.75 1.75
		Nos. 441-445 (5)	4.95 4.95

AMERIPEX '86 — A88

SS Great Britain's arrival in the Falkland Isls., Cent.: 10p, Maiden voyage, crossing the Atlantic, 1845. 24p, Wreck in Sparrow Cove, 1937. 29p, Refloating wreck, 1970. 58p, Restored vessel, Bristol, 1986.

1986, May 22			
446	A88	10p multicolored	.25 .25
447	A88	24p multicolored	.75 .75
448	A88	29p multicolored	1.00 1.00
449	A88	58p multicolored	2.00 2.00
a.		Souvenir sheet of 4, #446-449	5.00 5.00
		Nos. 446-449 (4)	4.00 4.00

Bird Type of 1984

Rockhopper Penguins.

1986, Aug. 25	**Wmk. 373**	**Perf. 14½**	
450	A80	10p Adult	.70 .50
451	A80	24p Adults swimming	1.60 1.50
452	A80	29p Adults, diff.	2.25 1.75
453	A80	58p Adult and young	4.25 3.50
		Nos. 450-453 (4)	8.80 7.00

Wedding of Prince Andrew and Sarah Ferguson — A90

Various photographs: 17p, Presenting Queen's Polo Cup, Windsor, 1986. 22p, Open carriage, wedding. 29p, Andrew wearing military fatigues.

1986, Nov. 10	**Wmk. 384**	**Perf. 14½**	
454	A90	17p multicolored	.80 .80
455	A90	22p multicolored	1.00 1.00
456	A90	29p multicolored	1.40 1.40
		Nos. 454-456 (3)	3.20 3.20

Royal Engineers, 200th Anniv. A91

1987, Feb. 9	**Litho.**	**Perf. 14½**	
457	A91	10p Surveying Sapper Hill	.55 .55
458	A91	24p Explosives disposal	1.90 1.90
459	A91	29p Boxer Bridge, Pt. Stanley	2.25 2.25
460	A91	58p Postal services, Stanley Airport	5.00 5.00
		Nos. 457-460 (4)	9.70 9.70

Seals A92

1987, Apr. 27			
461	A92	10p Southern sea lion	.80 .80
462	A92	24p Falkland fur seal	2.25 2.25
463	A92	29p Southern elephant seal	2.40 2.40
464	A92	58p Leopard seal	4.25 4.25
		Nos. 461-464 (4)	9.70 9.70

Hospitals A93

Designs: 10p, Victorian Cottage Home, c. 1912. 24p, King Edward VII Memorial Hospital, c. 1914. 29p, Churchill Wing, 1953. 58p, Prince Andrew Wing, 1987.

1987, Dec. 8		**Perf. 14**	
465	A93	10p multicolored	.50 .50
466	A93	24p multicolored	1.10 1.10
467	A93	29p multicolored	1.40 1.40
468	A93	58p multicolored	2.50 2.50
		Nos. 465-468 (4)	5.50 5.50

Fungi — A94

1987, Sept. 14	**Litho.**	**Perf. 14½**	
469	A94	10p Suillus luteus	1.50 1.50
470	A94	24p Mycena	2.75 2.75
471	A94	29p Camarophyllus adonis	3.75 3.75
472	A94	58p Gerronema schusteri	8.00 8.00
		Nos. 469-472 (4)	16.00 16.00

1940 Morris Truck, Fitzroy A95

Classic automobiles: 24p, 1929 Citroen Kegresse, San Carlos. 29p, 1933 Ford 1-Ton Truck, Port Stanley. 58p, 1935 Ford Model T Saloon, Darwin.

1988, Apr. 11	**Litho.**	**Perf. 14**	
473	A95	10p multicolored	.45 .45
474	A95	24p multicolored	1.10 1.10
475	A95	29p multicolored	1.40 1.40
476	A95	58p multicolored	2.50 2.50
		Nos. 473-476 (4)	5.45 5.45

Geese A96

1988, July 25			
477	A96	10p Kelp	1.50 .35
478	A96	24p Upland	3.00 .85
479	A96	29p Ruddy-headed	3.75 1.00
480	A96	58p Ashy-headed	7.75 2.25
		Nos. 477-480 (4)	16.00 4.45

Lloyds of London, 300th Anniv.
Common Design Type

Designs: 10p, Lloyd's Nelson Collection silver service. 24p, Hydroponic Gardens, horiz. 29p, Supply ship A.E.S., horiz. 58p, Wreck of the Charles Cooper near the Falklands, 1866.

1988, Nov. 14	**Litho.**	**Wmk. 373**	
481	CD341	10p multicolored	.50 .50
482	CD341	24p multicolored	1.00 1.00
483	CD341	29p multicolored	1.25 1.25
484	CD341	58p multicolored	2.50 2.50
		Nos. 481-484 (4)	5.25 5.25

Ships of Cape Horn A97

1989, Feb. 28			
485	A97	1p Padua	.45 .25
486	A97	2p Priwall, vert.	.45 .25
a.		Wmk. 384	.60 .45
487	A97	3p Passat	.45 .25
			.60 .45
488	A97	4p Archibald Russell, vert.	.45 .25
489	A97	5p Pamir, vert.	.45 .25
490	A97	6p Mozart	.45 .25
a.		Wmk. 384	.60 .45
491	A97	7p Pommern	.45 .25
492	A97	8p Preussen	.60 .45
493	A97	9p Fennia	.65 .50
a.		Wmk. 384	1.00 .75
494	A97	10p Cassard	.75 .60
495	A97	20p Lawhill	1.60 1.25
496	A97	25p Garthpool	1.90 1.40
497	A97	50p Grace Harwar	3.75 2.75
498	A97	£1 Criccieth Castle	8.50 5.50
a.		Wmk. 384	7.75 6.00
499	A97	£3 Cutty Sark, vert.	29.00 18.00
500	A97	£5 Flying Cloud	40.00 22.50
		Nos. 485-500 (16)	89.90 54.70

Nos. 486a, 487a, 490a, 493a, 498a are dated "1991."

Whales — A98

1989, May 15	**Wmk. 384**	**Perf. 14**	
501	A98	10p Southern right	1.00 1.00
502	A98	24p Minke	2.25 2.25
503	A98	29p Humpback	3.00 3.00
504	A98	58p Blue	6.00 6.00
		Nos. 501-504 (4)	12.25 12.25

Sports Assoc. Activities A99

Children's drawings.

1989, Sept. 16			
505	A99	5p Gymkhana	.20 .20
506	A99	10p Steer Riding	.25 .25
507	A99	17p Sheep shearing	.55 .55
508	A99	24p Dog trial	.70 .70
509	A99	29p Horse racing	.95 .95
510	A99	45p Sack race	1.50 1.50
		Nos. 505-510 (6)	4.15 4.15

Battles — A100

Commanders, ships and ship crests: 10p, Vice-Adm. Sturdee, HMS Invincible. 24p, Vice-Adm. Von Spee, SMS Scharnhorst. 29p, Commodore Harwood, HMS Ajax. 58p, Capt. Langsdorff, Admiral Graff Spee.

1989, Dec. 8		**Perf. 14x13½**	
511	A100	10p multicolored	.65 .65
512	A100	24p multicolored	1.75 1.75
513	A100	29p multicolored	2.40 2.40
514	A100	58p multicolored	4.25 4.25
		Nos. 511-514 (4)	9.05 9.05

Battle of the Falklands, 75th anniv. (10p, 24p); Battle of the River Plate, 50th anniv. (29p, 58p).

Emblems and Presentation Spitfires, 1940 — A101

1990, May 3 Wmk. 373 *Perf. 14*

515	A101	12p No. 92 Squadron	.60	.60
516	A101	26p No. 611 Squadron	1.40	1.40
517	A101	31p No. 92 Squadron, diff.	1.75	1.75
518	A101	62p Spitfires scramble	3.25	3.25
		Nos. 515-518 (4)	7.00	7.00

Souvenir Sheet

519	A101	£1 Battle of Britain	7.50	7.50

Stamp World London '90.
For souvenir sheet similar to #519, see #530.

A102

A103

1990, Apr. 1 Wmk. 384 *Perf. 14½*

520	A102	12p Kidney Is.	.50	.50
521	A102	26p Beauchene Is.	1.25	1.25
522	A102	31p Bird Is.	1.50	1.50
523	A102	62p Elephant Jason Is.	3.00	3.00
		Nos. 520-523 (4)	6.25	6.25

Nature reserves and bird sanctuaries.

Queen Mother, 90th Birthday
Common Design Types

1990, Aug. 4 Wmk. 384 *Perf. 14x15*

524	CD343	26p Queen Mother in Dover	1.00	1.00

Perf. 14½

525	CD344	£1 Steering the "Queen Elizabeth," 1946	4.25	4.25

Wmk. 384

1990, Oct. 3 Litho. *Perf. 14*

526	A103	12p Black browed albatross	.75	.75
527	A103	26p Adult bird	1.75	1.75
528	A103	31p Adult, chick	2.25	2.25
529	A103	62p Bird in flight	4.50	4.50
		Nos. 526-529 (4)	9.25	9.25

Battle of Britain Type of 1990 inscribed "SECOND VISIT OF / HRH THE DUKE OF EDINBURGH"
Souvenir Sheet

1991, Mar. 7

530	A101	£1 multicolored	11.00	11.00

Orchids — A104

King Penguin — A105

1991, Mar. 18 Wmk. 373

531	A104	12p Gavilea australis	.70	.70
532	A104	26p Codonorchis lessonii	1.60	1.60
533	A104	31p Chlorea gaudichaudii	2.00	2.00
534	A104	62p Gavilea littoralis	4.00	4.00
		Nos. 531-534 (4)	8.30	8.30

1991, Aug. 26 Wmk. 384

535	A105	2p Two adults crossing bills	1.00	1.00
536	A105	6p Two adults, one brooding	2.00	1.50
537	A105	12p Adult with two young	3.00	1.75
538	A105	20p Adult swimming	4.00	2.00
539	A105	31p Adult feeding young	2.00	2.00
540	A105	62p Two adults, diff.	3.00	3.00
		Nos. 535-540 (6)	15.00	11.25

World Wildlife Fund.

Falkland Islands Bisects, Cent. A106

1991, Sept. 10 Wmk. 384 *Perf. 14½*

541	A106	12p #9, #15	.70	.70
542	A106	26p On cover	1.60	1.60
543	A106	31p Unsevered pair	1.75	1.75
544	A106	62p S.S. Isis	3.50	3.50
		Nos. 541-544 (4)	7.55	7.55

Discovery of America, 500th Anniv. (in 1992) — A107

Sailing ships: 14p, STV Eye of the Wind. 29p, STV Soren Larsen. 34p, Nina, Santa Maria, Pinta. 68p, Columbus and Santa Maria.

1991, Dec. 12 Wmk. 373 *Perf. 14*

545	A107	14p multicolored	.85	.85
546	A107	29p multicolored	1.75	1.75
547	A107	34p multicolored	2.25	2.25
548	A107	68p multicolored	4.25	4.25
		Nos. 545-548 (4)	9.10	9.10

World Columbian Stamp Expo '92, Chicago and Genoa '92 Intl. Philatelic Exhibitions.

Queen Elizabeth II's Accession to the Throne, 40th Anniv.
Common Design Type

1992, Feb. 6

549	CD349	7p multicolored	.45	.45
550	CD349	14p multicolored	.70	.70
551	CD349	29p multicolored	1.40	1.40
552	CD349	34p multicolored	1.60	1.60
553	CD349	68p multicolored	3.25	3.25
		Nos. 549-553 (5)	7.40	7.40

Christ Church Cathedral, Cent. — A108

1992, Feb. 21 Wmk. 384 *Perf. 14½*

554	A108	14p Laying foundation stone	.70	.70
555	A108	29p Interior, 1920	1.60	1.60
556	A108	34p Bishop's chair	2.10	2.10
557	A108	68p Without tower c. 1900, horiz.	4.00	4.00
		Nos. 554-557 (4)	8.40	8.40

First Sighting of Falkland Islands by Capt. John Davis, 400th Anniv.
A109

Designs: 22p, Capt. John Davis using backstaff. 29p, Capt. Davis working on chart. 34p, Queen Elizabeth I, Queen Elizabeth II. 68p, The Desire sights Falkland Islands.

1992, Aug. 14 Wmk. 373

558	A109	22p multicolored	1.40	1.40
559	A109	29p multicolored	1.60	1.60
560	A109	34p multicolored	2.00	2.00
561	A109	68p multicolored	3.75	3.75
		Nos. 558-561 (4)	8.75	8.75

Falkland Islands Defense Force and West Yorkshire Regiment — A110

7p, Private, Falkland Islands Volunteers, 1892. 14p, Officer, Falkland Islands Defense Corps, 1914. 22p, Officer, Falkland Islands Defense Force, 1920. 29p, Private, Falkland Islands Defense Force, 1939-45. 34p, Officer, West Yorkshire Regiment, 1942. 68p, Private, West Yorkshire Regiment, 1942.

1992, Oct. 1 *Perf. 14*

562	A110	7p multicolored	.40	.40
563	A110	14p multicolored	.75	.75
564	A110	22p multicolored	1.25	1.25
565	A110	29p multicolored	1.60	1.60
566	A110	34p multicolored	1.75	1.75
567	A110	68p multicolored	3.50	3.50
		Nos. 562-567 (6)	9.25	9.25

Gulls and Terns A111

Perf. 14x14½

1993, Jan. 2 Litho. Wmk. 384

568	A111	15p South American tern	.90	.90
569	A111	31p Pink breasted gull	1.90	1.90
570	A111	36p Dolphin gull	2.25	2.25
571	A111	72p Dominican gull	4.25	4.25
		Nos. 568-571 (4)	9.30	9.30

Souvenir Sheet

Visit of Liner QE II to Falkland Islands — A112

Wmk. 373

1993, Jan. 22 Litho. *Perf. 14*

572	A112	£2 multicolored	10.00	10.00

Royal Air Force, 75th Anniv.
Common Designs Type

Designs: No. 573, Lockheed Tristar. No. 574, Lockheed Hercules. No. 575, Boeing Vertol Chinook. No. 576, Avro Vulcan.
No. 577a, Hawker Siddeley Andover. b, Westland Wessex. c, Panavia Tornado F3. d, McDonnell Douglas Phantom.

1993, Apr. 3 Wmk. 373 Litho. *Perf. 14*

573	CD350	15p multicolored	1.25	1.25
574	CD350	15p multicolored	1.25	1.25
575	CD350	15p multicolored	1.25	1.25
576	CD350	15p multicolored	1.25	1.25
		Nos. 573-576 (4)	5.00	5.00

Souvenir Sheet of 4

577	CD350	36p #a.-d.	6.50	6.50

Fisheries A113

Designs: 15p, Short-finned squid. 31p, Stern haul of whiptailed hake. 36p, Fishery Patrol Vessel Falkalnds Protector. 72p, Aerial surveillance by Britten-Norman Islander.

Wmk. 384

1993, July 1 Litho. *Perf. 14*

578	A113	15p multicolored	.85	.85
579	A113	31p multicolored	1.60	1.60
580	A113	36p multicolored	2.10	2.10
581	A113	72p multicolored	3.75	3.75
		Nos. 578-581 (4)	8.30	8.30

Launch of SS Great Britain, 150th Anniv. — A114

Perf. 14x13½

1993, July 19 Litho. Wmk. 384

582	A114	8p In drydock, Bristol	.40	.40
583	A114	£1 At sea	5.00	5.00

Cruise Ships and Penguins A115

Wmk. 373

1993, Oct. 1 Litho. *Perf. 14*

584	A115	16p Explorer	1.00	1.00
585	A115	34p Rockhopper penguins	2.25	2.25
586	A115	39p World Discoverer	2.50	2.50
587	A115	78p Columbus Caravelle	5.25	5.25
		Nos. 584-587 (4)	11.00	11.00

Pets — A116

Perf. 14x14½

1993, Dec. 1 Litho. Wmk. 384

588	A116	8p Pony	.50	.35
589	A116	16p Lamb	.90	.65
590	A116	34p Puppy, kitten	2.10	1.50

Perf. 14½x14

591	A116	39p Kitten, vert.	2.50	1.75
592	A116	78p Collie, vert.	5.00	3.50
		Nos. 588-592 (5)	11.00	7.75

Ovptd. with Hong Kong '94 Emblem

1994, Feb. 18

593	A116	8p on #588	.65	.65
594	A116	16p on #589	1.10	1.10
595	A116	34p on #590	2.25	2.25
596	A116	39p on #591	2.50	2.50
597	A116	78p on #592	5.00	5.00
		Nos. 593-597 (5)	11.50	11.50

Inshore Marine Life A117

Wmk. 384

1994, Apr. 4   Litho.   Perf. 14

598	A117	1p Goose barnacles, vert.	.30	.30
599	A117	2p Painted shrimp	.30	.30
600	A117	8p Common limpet	.30	.30
601	A117	9p Mullet	.35	.35
602	A117	10p Sea anemones	.40	.40
603	A117	20p Rock eel	.85	.85
604	A117	25p Spider crab	1.10	1.10
605	A117	50p Lobster krill, vert.	2.50	2.50
606	A117	80p Falkland skate	3.75	3.75
607	A117	£1 Centollon crab	5.00	5.00
a.		Souv. sheet of 1, wmk. 373	8.00	8.00
608	A117	£3 Rock cod	13.00	13.00
609	A117	£5 Octopus, vert.	22.50	22.50
		Nos. 598-609 (12)	50.35	50.35

No. 607a for return of Hong Kong to China. Issued 7/1/97.
See No. 671.

Founding of Stanley, 150th Anniv. A118

9p, Blacksmith's shop, dockyard, Sir James Clark Ross, explorer. 17p, James Leith Mody, 1st colonial chaplain, home at 21 Fitzroy Road. 30p, Stanley cottage, Dr. Henry J. Hamblin, 1st colonial surgeon. 35p, Pioneer row, Sergeant Major Henry Felton. 40p, Government House, Governor R. C. Moody R.E. 65p, View of Stanley, Edward Stanley, 14th Earl of Derby, Secretary of State for Colonies.

Wmk. 373

1994, July 1   Litho.   Perf. 14

610	A118	9p multicolored	.60	.60
611	A118	17p multicolored	1.10	1.10
612	A118	30p multicolored	1.90	1.90
613	A118	35p multicolored	2.10	2.10
614	A118	40p multicolored	2.75	2.75
615	A118	65p multicolored	4.00	4.00
		Nos. 610-615 (6)	12.45	12.45

Methods of Transportation — A119

17p, Tristar over Gypsy Cove. 35p, Cruise ship, Sea Lion Island. 40p, FIGAS Islander, Pebble Island Beach. 65p, Land Rover, Volunteer Beach.

Wmk. 384

1994, Oct. 24   Litho.   Perf. 14

616	A119	17p multicolored	.95	.55
617	A119	35p multicolored	2.00	1.10
618	A119	40p multicolored	2.40	1.25
619	A119	65p multicolored	3.25	2.00
		Nos. 616-619 (4)	8.60	4.90

South American Missionary Society, 150th Anniv. — A120

Designs: 5p, Mission House, Keppel Island. 17p, Thomas Bridges, compiler of Yahgan dictionary. 40p, Fuegian Indians. 65p, Schooner Allen Gardiner, Capt. Allen Gardiner.

1994, Dec. 1

620	A120	5p multicolored	.30	.30
621	A120	17p multicolored	.85	.85
622	A120	40p multicolored	1.90	1.90
623	A120	65p multicolored	3.00	3.00
		Nos. 620-623 (4)	6.05	6.05

Flowering Shrubs — A121

Designs: 9p, Lupinus arboreus. 17p, Boxwood. 30p, Fuchsia magellanica. 35p, Berberis ilicifolia. 40p, Gorse. 65p, Veronica.

Perf. 14½x14

1995, Jan. 3   Litho.   Wmk. 384

624	A121	9p multicolored	.35	.35
625	A121	17p multicolored	.70	.70
626	A121	30p multicolored	1.60	1.60
627	A121	35p multicolored	2.10	2.10
628	A121	40p multicolored	2.25	2.25
629	A121	65p multicolored	4.00	4.00
		Nos. 624-629 (6)	11.00	11.00

Shore Birds A122

Designs: 17p, Magellanic oystercatcher. 35p, Rufous chested dotterel. 40p, Black oystercatcher. 65p, Two banded plover.

Wmk. 373

1995, Mar. 1   Litho.   Perf. 13½

630	A122	17p multicolored	1.10	1.10
631	A122	35p multicolored	2.50	2.50
632	A122	40p multicolored	3.00	3.00
633	A122	65p multicolored	4.75	4.75
		Nos. 630-633 (4)	11.35	11.35

End of World War II, 50th Anniv.
Common Design Types

17p, Falkland Islands Victory Parade contingent. 35p, Governor Sir Alan Wolsey Cardinall on Bren gun carrier. 40p, HMAS Esperance Bay, 1942. 65p, HMS Exeter, 1939.
£1, Reverse of War Medal 1939-45.

Wmk. 373

1995, May 8   Litho.   Perf. 14

634	CD351	17p multicolored	1.10	1.10
635	CD351	35p multicolored	2.25	2.25
636	CD351	40p multicolored	2.75	2.75
637	CD351	65p multicolored	4.25	4.25
		Nos. 634-637 (4)	10.35	10.35

Souvenir Sheet

638	CD352	£1 multicolored	6.00	6.00

Transporting Peat — A123

Wmk. 384

1995, Aug. 1   Litho.   Perf. 14

639	A123	17p Ox, cart	.70	.70
640	A123	35p Horse, cart	2.10	2.10
641	A123	40p Tractor, sledge	2.10	2.10
642	A123	65p Truck, peat bank	3.50	3.50
		Nos. 639-642 (4)	8.40	8.40

Miniature Sheet of 6

Wildlife — A124

Designs: a, Kelp geese. b, Albatross. c, Cormorants. d, Magellanic penguins. e, Fur seals. f, Rockhopper penguins.

1995, Sept. 11

643	A124	35p #a.-f.	17.50	17.50

No. 643 is a continuous design.

Wild Animals A125

1995, Nov. 6   Wmk. 373

644	A125	9p Rabbit	.65	.65
645	A125	17p Hare	1.10	1.10
646	A125	35p Guanaco	2.50	2.50
647	A125	40p Fox	3.00	3.00
648	A125	65p Otter	4.75	4.75
		Nos. 644-648 (5)	12.00	12.00

Visit by Princess Anne A126

Princess Anne and: 9p, Government House. 19p, San Carlos Cemetery. 30p, Christ Church Cathedral. 73p, Goose Green.

1996, Jan. 30   Perf. 14½

649	A126	9p multicolored	.50	.50
650	A126	19p multicolored	1.50	1.50
651	A126	30p multicolored	2.50	2.50
652	A126	73p multicolored	5.50	5.50
		Nos. 649-652 (4)	10.00	10.00

Queen Elizabeth II, 70th Birthday
Common Design Type

Various portraits of Queen, scenes from Falkland Islands: 17p, Steeple Jason. 40p, Ship, KV Tamar. 45p, New Island with shipwreck on beach. 65p, Community School.
£1, Queen in formal dress at Sandringham Ball.

1996, Apr. 21   Perf. 13½

653	CD354	17p multicolored	.75	.75
654	CD354	40p multicolored	2.00	2.00
655	CD354	45p multicolored	2.50	2.50
656	CD354	65p multicolored	3.50	3.50
		Nos. 653-656 (4)	8.75	8.75

Souvenir Sheet

657	CD354	£1 multicolored	5.00	5.00

CAPEX '96 A127

Mail delivery: 9p, Horseback, 1890. 40p, Norseman floatplane. 45p, Inter-island ship. 76p, Beaver floatplane.
£1, LMS Jubilee Class 4-6-0 locomotive.

1996, June 8   Wmk. 384   Perf. 14

658	A127	9p multicolored	.50	.50
659	A127	40p multicolored	1.75	1.75
660	A127	45p multicolored	2.00	2.00
661	A127	76p multicolored	4.00	4.00
		Nos. 658-661 (4)	8.25	8.25

Souvenir Sheet

662	A127	£1 multicolored	4.25	4.25

No. 662 contains one 48x32mm stamp.

Beaked Whales — A128

Designs: 9p, Southern bottlenose whale. 30p, Cuvier's beaked whale. 35p,

Straptoothed beaked whale. 75p, Gray's beaked whale.

Wmk. 373

1996, Sept. 2   Litho.   Perf. 14

663	A128	9p multicolored	.50	.50
664	A128	30p multicolored	1.75	1.75
665	A128	35p multicolored	1.75	1.75
666	A128	75p multicolored	4.25	4.25
		Nos. 663-666 (4)	8.25	8.25

Magellanic Penguins — A129

Designs: 17p, Two adults. 35p, Young in nest. 40p, Chick, adult. 65p, Swimming.

Wmk. 373

1997, Jan. 2   Litho.   Perf. 14

667	A129	17p multicolored	1.25	1.25
668	A129	35p multicolored	3.00	3.00
669	A129	40p multicolored	3.50	3.50
670	A129	65p multicolored	5.25	5.25
		Nos. 667-670 (4)	13.00	13.00

Fish Type of 1994
Souvenir Sheet
Wmk. 373

1997, Feb. 3   Litho.   Perf. 14

671	A117	£1 Smelt	5.50	5.50

Hong Kong '97.

Ferns — A130

Perf. 14½x14

1997, Mar. 3   Litho.   Wmk. 373

672	A130	17p Coral	1.10	1.10
673	A130	35p Adder's tongue	2.50	2.50
674	A130	40p Fuegian tall	2.75	2.75
675	A130	65p Small fern	5.00	5.00
		Nos. 672-675 (4)	11.35	11.35

Lighthouses — A131

Wmk. 373

1997, July 1   Litho.   Perf. 14

676	A131	9p Bull Point	1.50	1.50
677	A131	30p Cape Pembroke	3.00	3.00
678	A131	£1 Cape Meredith	10.00	10.00
		Nos. 676-678 (3)	14.50	14.50

Queen Elizabeth II and Prince Philip, 50th Wedding Anniv. — A132

#679, Queen holding flowers. #680, Prince with horse. #681, Queen riding in open carriage. #682, Prince in uniform. #683, Queen in red coat & hat, Prince. #684, Princes William and Harry on horseback.
£1.50, Queen, Prince riding in open carriage.

1997   Wmk. 384   Perf. 14½x14

679	9p multicolored		.75	.75
680	9p multicolored		.75	.75
a.	A132 Pair, #679-680		1.75	1.75
681	17p multicolored		1.50	1.50
682	17p multicolored		1.50	1.50
a.	A132 Pair, #681-682		3.50	3.50
683	40p multicolored		3.25	3.25
684	40p multicolored		3.25	3.25
a.	A132 Pair, #683-684		7.25	7.25
	Nos. 679-684 (6)		11.00	11.00

Souvenir Sheet

685	A132	£1.50 multicolored	10.00	10.00

Endangered Species — A133

Designs: 17p, Phalcoboenus australis. 19p, Otaria flavescens. 40p, Calandrinia feltonii. 73p, Aplochiton zebra.

Wmk. 373

1997, Oct. 16   Litho.   Perf. 14½

686	A133	17p multicolored	2.00	2.00
687	A133	19p multicolored	2.50	2.50
688	A133	40p multicolored	4.75	4.75
689	A133	73p multicolored	8.50	8.50
		Nos. 686-689 (4)	17.75	17.75

Fire Service in Falkland Islands, Cent. — A134

Equipment, manufacturer: 9p, Greenwich Gem, Merryweather & Son. 17p, Hatfield trailer pump, Merryweather & Son. 40p, Godiva trailer pump, Coventry Climax. 65p, Water tender type B, Carmichael Bedford.

Wmk. 384

1998, Feb. 26   Litho.   Perf. 14½

690	A134	9p multicolored	1.00	1.00
691	A134	17p multicolored	2.25	2.25
692	A134	40p multicolored	6.00	6.00
693	A134	65p multicolored	9.75	9.75
		Nos. 690-693 (4)	19.00	19.00

Diana, Princess of Wales (1961-97)
Common Design Type

Portraits: a, Looking left. b, In red dress. c, Hand on cheek. d, Investigating land mines.

Perf. 14½x14

1998, Mar. 31   Wmk. 373

694	CD355 30p Sheet of 4, #a-d	6.25	6.25

No. 694 sold for £1.20 + 20p, with surtax from international sales being donated to the Princess Diana Memorial Fund and surtax from national sales being donated to designated local charity.

Birds A135

1p, Tawny-throated dotterel. 2p, Hudsonian godwit. 5p, Eared dove. #698, Great grebe. #699, Roseate spoonbill. 10p, Southern lapwing. 16p, Buff-necked ibis. 17p, Astral parakeet. 30p, Ashy-headed goose. 35p, American kestrel. 65p, Red-legged shag. 88p, Red shoveler. £1, Red-fronted coot. £3, Chilean flamingo. £5, Fork-tailed flycatcher.

Wmk. 373

1998, July 14   Litho.   Perf. 14

695	A135	1p multicolored	.30	.30
696	A135	2p multicolored	.30	.30
697	A135	5p multicolored	.30	.30
698	A135	9p multicolored	.45	.45
699	A135	9p multicolored	.45	.45
700	A135	10p multicolored	.50	.50
701	A135	16p multicolored	.70	.70

702	A135	17p multicolored	.80	.80
a.	Booklet pane, 2 #699, 8 #702 + 2 labels		7.25	
	Complete booklet, #702a		7.25	
703	A135	30p multicolored	1.40	1.40
704	A135	35p multicolored	1.60	1.60
	Complete booklet, 6 #704		9.75	
705	A135	65p multicolored	3.00	3.00
706	A135	88p multicolored	4.00	4.00
707	A135	£1 multicolored	4.50	4.50
708	A135	£3 multicolored	15.00	15.00
709	A135	£5 multicolored	24.00	22.50
	Nos. 695-709 (15)		57.30	55.80

Boats — A136

Boat, country flag, year: 17p, Penelope, Germany, 1926. 35p, Ilen, Italy, 1926. 40p, Weddell, Chile, 1940. 65p, Lively, Scotland, 1940.

Wmk. 373

1998, Sept. 30   Litho.   Perf. 14

710	A136	17p multicolored	1.50	1.50
711	A136	35p multicolored	3.00	3.00
712	A136	40p multicolored	3.25	3.25

Size: 29x18mm

713	A136	65p multicolored	5.25	5.25
		Nos. 710-713 (4)	13.00	13.00

FIGAS (First Medivac Air Ambulance Service), 50th Anniv. — A137

17p, Man carrying patient, airplane. £1, Airplane, map of Islands, float plane.

Wmk. 373

1998, Dec. 1   Litho.   Perf. 14

714	A137	17p multicolored	1.75	1.75
715	A137	£1 multicolored	12.00	12.00

Military Uniforms — A138

Uniform, background location: 17p, Marine Private, 1776, The Block House at Port Egmont, Saunders Island. 30p, Marine Officer, 1833, Port Louis, East Falkland. 35p, Royal Marine Corporal, 1914, HMS Kent. 65p, Royal Marine Bugler, 1976, Government House.

Wmk. 373

1998, Dec. 8   Litho.   Perf. 14½

716	A138	17p multicolored	2.00	2.00
717	A138	30p multicolored	4.00	4.00
718	A138	35p multicolored	4.25	4.25
719	A138	65p multicolored	8.75	8.75
		Nos. 716-719 (4)	19.00	19.00

St. Mary's Church, Cent. A139

Wmk. 373

1999, Feb. 12   Litho.   Perf. 14

720	A139	17p Inside view	1.25	1.25
721	A139	40p Outside view	4.00	4.00
722	A139	75p Laying cornerstone, 1899	7.75	7.75
		Nos. 720-722 (3)	13.00	13.00

Australia '99, World Stamp Expo A140

25p, HMS Beagle. 35p, HMAS Australia. 40p, SS Canberra. #726, SS Great Britain. #727, All-England Eleven visit Australia, 1861-62.

1999, Mar. 5   Wmk. 384

723	A140	25p multicolored	2.50	2.50
724	A140	35p multicolored	3.50	3.50
725	A140	40p multicolored	4.00	4.00
726	A140	50p multicolored	4.75	4.75
727	A140	50p multicolored	4.75	4.75
a.	Pair, #726-727		9.50	9.50
	Nos. 723-727 (5)		19.50	19.50

1999 Visit of HRH Prince of Wales — A141

1999, Mar. 13   Litho.   Perf. 14x13½   Wmk. 384

728	A141 £2 multicolored	15.00	15.00

Wedding of Prince Edward and Sophie Rhys-Jones
Common Design Type

Perf. 13¾x14

1999, June 15   Litho.   Wmk. 384

729	CD356	80p Separate portraits	5.25	5.25
730	CD356	£1.20 Couple	8.25	8.25

PhilexFrance '99, World Philatelic Exhibition — A142

Designs: 35p, French cruiser, Jeanne d'Arc, Port Stanley, 1931. 40p, CAMS 37/11 Flying Boat's first flight.
£1, CAMS 37 Flying Boat over Port Stanley, 1931.

1999, June 21   Wmk. 373   Perf. 14

731	A142	35p multicolored	4.25	4.25
732	A142	40p multicolored	5.00	5.00

Souvenir Sheet

733	A142	£1 multicolored	12.00	12.00

No. 733 contains one 48x31mm stamp.

Queen Mother's Century
Common Design Type

Queen Mother: 9p, With King George VI at Port of London. 20p, With Queen Elizabeth at Women's Institute, Sandringham. 30p, With Princes Charles, William and Harry at Clarence House, 95th birthday. 67p, As Colonel-in-Chief of the Queen's Royal Hussars.
£1.40, With Ernest Shackleton, Robert F. Scott and Edward A. Wilson.

Wmk. 384

1999, Aug. 18   Litho.   Perf. 13½

734	CD358	9p multi	1.00	1.00
735	CD358	20p multi	2.10	2.10
736	CD358	30p multi	3.25	3.25
737	CD358	67p multi	7.50	7.50
		Nos. 734-737 (4)	13.85	13.85

Souvenir Sheet

738	CD358	£1.40 multi	16.00	16.00

For overprint see No. 767.

Waterfowl A143

Perf. 14¼x14½

1999, Sept. 9   Litho.   Wmk. 384

739	A143	9p Chiloe wigeon	.85	.85
740	A143	17p Crested duck	1.90	1.90
741	A143	30p Brown pintail	3.50	3.50
742	A143	35p Silver teal	4.00	4.00
743	A143	40p Yellow billed teal	5.25	5.25
744	A143	65p Flightless steamer duck	7.50	7.50
		Nos. 739-744 (6)	23.00	23.00

California Gold Rush A144

Designs: 9p, Vicar of Bray, 1999. 35p, Gold panning, 1849. 40p, Gold rocking cradle, 1849. 80p, Vicar of Bray, 1849.
£1, Vicar of Bray in San Francisco Harbor, 1849.

Wmk. 373

1999, Nov. 3   Litho.   Perf. 14

745	A144	9p multicolored	1.10	1.10
746	A144	35p multicolored	4.25	4.25
747	A144	40p multicolored	4.75	4.75
748	A144	80p multicolored	10.00	10.00
		Nos. 745-748 (4)	20.10	20.10

Souvenir Sheet

Perf. 13¾

749	A144	£1 multicolored	13.00	13.00

No. 749 contains one 48x31mm stamp.

Millennium A145

Designs: No. 750, Kelp gull. No. 751, Upland goose. No. 752, Christchurch Cathedral. No. 753, Night heron. No. 754, King penguin. No. 755, Christmas at home.

1999, Dec. 6   Perf. 14x14½

750	A145	9p multicolored	1.50	1.50
751	A145	9p multicolored	1.50	1.50
752	A145	9p multicolored	1.50	1.50
753	A145	30p multicolored	5.25	5.25
754	A145	30p multicolored	5.25	5.25
755	A145	30p multicolored	5.25	5.25
		Nos. 750-755 (6)	20.25	20.25

Visit of Princess Alexandra A146

Designs: 9p, Princess in blue dress, trees. £1, Princess in patterned dress, trees.

Perf. 13¼x13¾

2000, Feb. 1   Litho.   Wmk. 373

756	A146	9p multi	1.00	1.00
757	A146	£1 multi	10.00	10.00

Sir Ernest Shackleton (1874-1922), Polar Explorer — A147

17p, Ship Endurance, discovery of the Caird Coast. 45p, Endurance trapped in pack ice. 75p, Shackleton, Chilean tugboat Yelcho.

2000, Feb. 10   **Wmk. 373**   **Perf. 14**

758	A147	17p multi	2.50	2.50
759	A147	45p multi	8.00	8.00
760	A147	75p multi	13.50	13.50
		Nos. 758-760 (3)	24.00	24.00

See British Antarctic Territory Nos. 285-287, South Georgia and South Sandwich Islands Nos. 254-256.

British Monarchs — A148

a, Elizabeth I. b, James II. c, George I. d, William IV. e, Edward VIII. f, Elizabeth II.

2000, Feb. 29   **Wmk. 373**   **Perf. 14**

761	A148	40p Sheet of 6, #a.-		
	f.		17.00	17.00

The Stamp Show 2000, London.

Prince William, 18th Birthday
Common Design Type

William: 10p, As toddler with fireman's helmet, vert. 20p, In checked suit and in navy suit, vert. 37p, With blue shirt. 43p, In gray suit and in navy suit holding flowers. 50p, As child with dog.

Perf. 13¾x14¼, 14¼x13¾

2000, June 21   **Litho.**   **Wmk. 373**
Stamps with White Border

762	CD359	10p multi	.65	.65
763	CD359	20p multi	1.60	1.60
764	CD359	37p multi	3.00	3.00
765	CD359	43p multi	3.25	3.25
		Nos. 762-765 (4)	8.50	8.50

Souvenir Sheet
Stamps Without White Border
Perf. 14¼

766		Sheet of 5	12.00	12.00
a.	CD359	10p multi	.60	.60
b.	CD359	20p multi	1.25	1.25
c.	CD359	37p multi	2.25	2.25
d.	CD359	43p multi	2.50	2.50
e.	CD359	50p multi	3.00	3.00

No. 738 Ovptd. in Gold

Wmk. 384
2000, Aug. 4   **Litho.**   **Perf. 13½**

767	CD358	£1.40 multi	15.00	15.00

Gold overprint in sheet margin reads "100TH BIRTHDAY OF HM QUEEN / ELIZABETH THE QUEEN MOTHER."

Bridges A149

Bridges over: 20p, Malo River. 37p, Bodie Creek. 43p, Fitzroy River.

2000, Oct. 16   **Perf. 14¼x14½**

768-770	A149	Set of 3	14.00	14.00

Christmas — A150

Designs: 10p, Shepherd, sheep. 20p, Shepherds, sheep, angel. 33p, Holy family, shepherds, Magus, donkey, sheep. 43p, Angel, two Magi. 78p, Camel.

2000, Nov. 1   **Wmk. 373**

771-775	A150	Set of 5	14.00	14.00
775a		Souvenir sheet, #771-775	17.00	17.00

Sunrises and Sunsets A151

Various photos: 10p, 20p, 37p, 43p.

2001, Jan. 10   **Perf. 14½x14¼**

776-779	A151	Set of 4	13.00	13.00

Souvenir Sheet

New Year 2001 (Year of the Snake) — A152

Birds: a, Striated caracara. b, Mountain hawk eagle.

Perf. 14½x14¼

2001, Feb. 1   **Litho.**   **Wmk. 373**

780	A152	37p Sheet of 2, #a-b	9.50	9.50

Hong Kong 2001 Stamp Exhibition.

Age of Victoria — A153

Designs: 3p, Falkland Islands #1. 10p, S.S. Great Britain, horiz. 20p, Stanley Harbor, 1888, horiz. 43p, Cape Pembroke Lighthouse, telephones, 1897. 93p, Royal Marines, 1900. £1.50, Queen Victoria, by Franz Xavier Winterhalter, 1859.
£1, Funeral procession for Queen Victoria.

2001, May 24   **Perf. 14**

781-786	A153	Set of 6	25.00	25.00

Souvenir Sheet

787	A153	£1 multi	9.00	9.00

Royal Navy Connections to Falkland Islands — A154

Designs: 10p, Welfare, ship that made first recorded landing, 1690. 17p, HMS Invincible, ship in Battle of the Falklands, 1914. 20p,

HMS Exeter, ship in Battle of the River Plate, 1939. 37p, SN.R6 Hovercraft, 1967. 43p, Antarctic patrol ship HMS Protector and Wasp helicopter, 1955. 68p, Desire, ship that made first sighting, 1592.

2001, July 24

788-793	A154	Set of 6	22.50	22.50

Carcass Island and its Flora and Fauna — A155

No. 794, 37p: a, Yellow violet. b, Tussac bird.
No. 795, 43p: a, Carcass Island settlement. b, Black-crowned night heron.

Wmk. 373
2001, Sept. 28   **Litho.**   **Perf. 13¾**
Pairs, #a-b

794-795	A155	Set of 2	14.50	14.50

Gentoo Penguins — A156

Designs: 10p, Birds flapping wings. 33p, Feeding young. 37p, Bird with beak open. 43p, Four birds walking.

2001, Oct. 26   **Perf. 14½x14¼**

796-799	A156	Set of 4	9.00	9.00

Falkland Islands Company, 150th Anniv. A157

Designs: 10p, Company coat of arms, and gathering of cattle. 20p, Company flag, and ship Amelia. 43p, Manager F. E. Cobb, and company buildings. £1, Sheep farmer William Wickham Bertrand, sheep dip.

Wmk. 373
2002, Jan. 10   **Litho.**   **Perf. 14**

800-803	A157	Set of 4	15.00	15.00

Reign Of Queen Elizabeth II, 50th Anniv. Issue
Common Design Type

Designs: Nos. 804, 808a, 20p, Princess Elizabeth reading, 1945. Nos. 805, 808b, 37p, In 1977. Nos. 806, 808c, 43p, Holding Prince Charles, 1949. Nos. 807, 808d, 50p, At Garter ceremony, 1994. No. 808e, 50p, 1955 portrait by Annigoni (38x50mm).

Perf. 14¼x14½, 13¾ (#808e)

2002, Feb. 6   **Litho.**   **Wmk. 373**
With Gold Frames

804-807	CD360	Set of 4	10.50	10.50

Souvenir Sheet
Without Gold Frames

808	CD360	Sheet of 5, #a-e	12.00	12.00

Falkland Islands War, 20th Anniv. — A158

No. 809, 22p: a, HMS Hermes, 1982. b, Fishery patrol vessel, 2002.
No. 810, 40p: a, Troops landing, 1982. b, Mine clearing, 2002.

No. 811, 45p: a, RAF Harrier on HMS Hermes, 1982. b, RAF Tristar, 2002.

Wmk. 373
2002, June 14   **Litho.**   **Perf. 14**
Horiz. pairs, #a-b

809-811	A158	Set of 3	16.00	16.00

Queen Mother Elizabeth (1900-2002)
Common Design Type

Designs: 22p, Wearing hat and scarf (black and white photograph). 25p, Wearing blue hat with polka dots. Nos. 814, 816a, 95p, Wearing feathered hat (black and white photograph). Nos. 815, 816b, £1.20, Wearing blue hat.

Wmk. 373
2002, Aug. 5   **Litho.**   **Perf. 14¼**
With Purple Frames

812-815	CD361	Set of 4	16.00	16.00

Souvenir Sheet
Without Purple Frames
Perf. 14½x14¼

816	CD361	Sheet of 2, #a-b	16.00	16.00

Worldwide Fund for Nature (WWF) — A159

Penguins: 36p, Rockhopper. 40p, Magellanic. 45p, Gentoo. 70p, Macaroni.

Wmk. 373

817-820	A159	Set of 4	11.00	11.00
a.		Horiz. strip of 4, #817-820	11.00	11.00

2002, Aug. 30   **Perf. 14¼**

West Point Island and its Flora and Fauna — A160

No. 821, 40p: a, Felton's flower. b, Black-browed albatross.
No. 822, 45p: a, Rockhopper penguin. b, Island settlement.

Perf. 14¼x14½

2002, Oct. 31   **Litho.**   **Wmk. 373**
Horiz. Pairs, #a-b

821-822	A160	Set of 2	12.00	12.00

Visit of Prince Andrew — A161

No. 823: a, 22p, In uniform. b, £1.52, In suit and tie.

2002, Nov. 11   **Perf. 13¼x13½**

823	A161	Horiz. pair, #a-b	12.00	12.00

Shepherds' Houses — A162

Designs: 10p, Gun Hill shanty, Little Chartres. 22p, Paragon House, Lafonia. 45p, Dos Lomas, Lafonia. £1, Old House, Shallow Bay Farm.

Wmk. 373
2003, Mar. 31   **Litho.**   **Perf. 14**

824-827	A162	Set of 4	12.00	12.00

Head of Queen Elizabeth II
Common Design Type
Wmk. 373

2003, June 2   Litho.   *Perf. 13¾*
828   CD362   £2 multi   10.00   10.00

Prince William, 21st Birthday
Common Design Type
Color photographs: a, In suit at right. b, With Prince Harry at left.

Wmk. 373

2003, June 21   Litho.   *Perf. 14¼*
829   Horiz. pair   12.00   12.00
   a.-b.   CD364 95p Either single   5.50   5.50

Birds — A163

Designs: 1p, Chiloe widgeon. 2p, Dolphin gull, vert. 5p, Falkland flightless steamer duck. 10p, Black-throated finch, vert. 22p, White-tufted grebe. 25p, Rufous-chested dotterel, vert. 45p, Upland goose. 50p, Dark-faced ground-tyrant, vert. 95p, Black-crowned night heron. £1, Red-backed hawk, vert. £3, Black-necked swan. £5, Short-eared owl, vert.

Perf. 13x13¼, 13¼x13

2003, July 21   Litho.   **Wmk. 373**
830   A163   1p multi   .20   .20
831   A163   2p multi   .20   .20
832   A163   5p multi   .20   .20
833   A163   10p multi   .35   .35
834   A163   22p multi   .80   .80
835   A163   25p multi   .90   .90
836   A163   45p multi   1.60   1.60
837   A163   50p multi   1.90   1.90
838   A163   95p multi   3.75   3.75
839   A163   £1 multi   4.00   4.00
840   A163   £3 multi   12.00   12.00
841   A163   £5 multi   21.00   21.00
   Nos. 830-841,C1 (13)   48.65   48.65

See Nos. 917-919.

Bird Life International A164

Black-browed albatross: No. 842, Adult on nest, facing right. No. 843, Chick. 40p, Heads of two adults, vert. £1, Adult on nest, facing left, vert.
16p, In flight.

Perf. 14¼x13¾, 13¾x14¼

2003, Sept. 26
842   A164   22p multi   1.40   1.40
   a.   Perf. 14¼x14½   1.40   1.40
843   A164   22p multi   1.40   1.40
   a.   Perf. 14¼x14½   1.40   1.40
844   A164   40p multi   2.50   2.50
   a.   Perf. 14½x14¼   2.40   2.40
845   A164   £1 multi   6.75   6.75
   a.   Perf. 14½x14¼   6.25   6.25
   Nos. 842-845 (4)   12.05   12.05

Souvenir Sheet
846   Sheet, #842a-846a   14.50   14.50
   a.   A164 16p multi, perf. 14¼x14½   .75   .75

New Island and its Flora and Fauna A165

No. 847, 40p: a, Striated caracara. b, Lady's slipper.
No. 848, 45p: a, Stone Cottage. b, King penguin.

Wmk. 373

2003, Oct. 24   Litho.   *Perf. 13¾*
Pairs, #a-b
847-848   A165   Set of 2   16.00   16.00

Christmas — A166

Various depictions of Pale maiden flower: 16p, 30p, 40p, 95p.

2003, Nov. 3   *Perf. 14x14¼*
849-852   A166   Set of 4   16.00   16.00

Sheep Farming A167

Designs: 19p, Traditional hand shearing. 22p, Driving the sheep. 45p, Big House, Hill Cove. 70p, The early years. £1, Wool collection, SS Fitzroy.

Unwmk.
2004, Apr. 30   Litho.   *Perf. 14*
853-857   A167   Set of 5   21.00   21.00

Wildlife Conservation in Falkland Islands, 25th Anniv. — A168

Designs: 20p, Man planting tussac grass. 24p, People cleaning beach. 50p, Satellite tracking of rockhopper penguins. £1, Weighing of albatross chick.

2004, June 17   Litho.   *Perf. 14*
858-861   A168   Set of 4   16.00   16.00

Sir Rowland Hill (1795-1879) and Falkland Islands Postage Stamps — A169

Hill and: 24p, #20. 50p, #74. 75p, #94. £1, #151a.

2004, Aug. 31   Litho.   *Perf. 13¼*
862-865   A169   Set of 4   16.00   16.00

Sea Lion Island and its Flora and Fauna — A170

No. 866, 42p: a, King cormorant. b, Dog orchid.
No. 867, 50p: a, Magellanic penguin. b, Sea Lion Lodge.

2004, Sept. 15   *Perf. 13¾*
Pairs, #a-b
866-867   A170   Set of 2   16.00   16.00

Owls — A171

Designs: 18p, Head of short-eared owl. 45p, Short-eared owl. 50p, Barn owl in flight. £1.50, Barn owl.
£2, Barn owl in flight, horiz.

2004, Oct. 25
868-871   A171   Set of 4   16.00   16.00
Souvenir Sheet
872   A171   £2 multi   11.00   11.00

Battle of the Falkland Islands, 90th Anniv. A172

No. 873: a, HMS Kent, HMS Inflexible, half of HMS Carnarvon, half of HMS Cornwall. b, British Navy flag, HMS Glasgow, half of HMS Carnarvon, half of HMS Cornwall, half of HMS Invincible. c, Medals, half of HMS Invincible.
No. 874: a, Medals, half of SMS Scharnhorst. b, German imperial war ensign, SMS Dresden, half of SMS Scharnhorst, half of SMS Leipzig. c, SMS Nürnberg, SMS Gneisenau, half of SMS Leipzig.

2004, Dec. 8   *Perf. 14*
873   Horiz. strip of 3   6.00   6.00
   a.-c.   A172 24p Any single   1.75   1.75
874   Horiz. strip of 3   10.00   10.00
   a.-c.   A172 50p Any single   3.00   3.00

Camber Railway, 90th Anniv. — A173

Designs: 3p, Old track bed. 24p, Kerr Stuart Wren Class locomotive at Camber Depot, horiz. 50p, Kerr Stuart Wren Class locomotive Falkland Islands Express, horiz. £2, Camber sailing wagon.

2005, Feb. 28   *Perf. 13¾*
875-878   A173   Set of 4   15.00   15.00

Wedding of Prince Charles and Camilla Parker Bowles A174

Designs: 24p, Couple. 50p, Couple in formal wear, vert. £2, Couple, Windsor Castle.

2005, Apr. 29   *Perf. 14*
879-880   A174   Set of 2   5.00   5.00
Souvenir Sheet
881   A174   £2 multi   10.50   10.50

End of World War II, 60th Anniv. — A175

No. 882, 24p: a, Walrus reconnaissance seaplane. b, Presentation Spitfire X4616.
No. 883, 80p: a, HMS Exeter at Port Stanley. b, Governor, King Edward Memorial Hospital staff, Rear Admiral Harwood and Capt. Bell.

No. 884, £1: a, Fitzroy. b, HMS William Scoresby.

Perf. 13¼x13½

2005, June 29   Litho.
Horiz. Pairs, #a-b
882-884   A175   Set of 3   22.50   22.50

Maritime Heritage A176

Designs: 24p, Snow Squall escaping CSS Tuscaloosa, 1863. No. 886, 1870. No. 887, 55p, Charles Cooper, 1866. £1.20, SS Imo colliding with the Mont Blanc, Halifax Harbor, 1917.

2005, Aug. 29   Litho.   *Perf. 14*
885-888   A176   Set of 4   12.00   12.00

Pebble Island and its Flora and Fauna — A177

No. 889, 45p: a, Gentoo penguin. b, Falkland lavender.
No. 890, 55p: a, Pebble Island Lodge. b, Black-necked swan.

2005, Sept. 12   *Perf. 13¾*
Pairs, #a-b
889-890   A177   Set of 2   10.50   10.50

Souvenir Sheet

The Fall of Nelson, Battle of Trafalgar, 21 October 1805, by Denis Dighton — A178

2005, Oct. 21
891   A178   £2 multi   10.50   10.50
Battle of Trafalgar, bicent.

Hans Christian Andersen (1805-75), Author — A179

Stories: 18p, The Little Mermaid. 30p, The Snowman. 45p, The Ugly Duckling. £1, Thumbelina.

2005, Oct. 28   *Perf. 14*
892-895   A179   Set of 4   11.00   11.00
Stanley Infant and Junior School, 50th anniv.

Black-crowned Night Heron — A180

Designs: 24p, Head. 55p, Bird on one leg. 80p, Juvenile standing. £1, Head of juvenile.

2006, Feb. 10   Litho.   Perf. 13¾
896-899 A180   Set of 4   13.00 13.00

Queen Elizabeth II, 80th Birthday — A181

Queen wearing: 24p, Yellow hat. 55p, Green hat. 80p, Blue hat. £1, Red hat. £2, Tiara and white hat, horiz.

2006, Apr. 21   Perf. 14
900-903 A181   Set of 4   13.00 13.00
Souvenir Sheet
904 A181   £2 multi   11.00 11.00

SS Great Britain — A182

View of: 24p, Bow. 55p, Stern. £1.50, Deck and masts.

2006, May 19   Perf. 13¾x13¼
905-907 A182   Set of 3   12.00 12.00

Birds A183

Designs: No. 908, 25p, Gentoo penguin chicks. No. 909, 25p, King cormorants. No. 910, 60p, King penguin. No. 911, 60p, Wandering albatross.

2006, Aug. 30   Litho.   Perf. 14¼x14
908-911 A183   Set of 4   10.00 10.00

Bleaker Island and its Flora and Fauna — A184

No. 912, 50p: a, Woolly Falkland ragwort. b, Macaroni penguin.
No. 913, 60p: a, The Outlook and sheep. b, Long-tailed meadowlark.

2006, Sept. 18   Perf. 13¼x13
Pairs, #a-b
912-913 A184   Set of 2   13.00 13.00

Victoria Cross, 150th Anniv. — A185

Designs: Nos. 914, 916a, 60p, Lt. Col. H. Jones. Nos. 915, 916b, 60p, Sgt. Ian McKay. No. 916c, £1, Victoria Cross.

2006, Nov. 11   Perf. 13¼
Stamps With White Frames
914-915 A185   Set of 2   6.25 6.25
Souvenir Sheet
Stamps Without White Frames
916 A185   Sheet of 3, #a-c   10.00 10.00

Bird Type of 2003

Designs: 20p, Black-browed albatross, vert. 25p, Rufous-chested dotterel, vert. £5, Short-eared owl, vert.

Perf. 13¼x13
2006, Nov. 15   Litho.   Unwmk.
917 A163   20p multi   1.00 1.00
918 A163   25p multi   1.25 1.25
919 A163   £5 multi   21.00 21.00
  Nos. 917-919 (3)   23.25 23.25

Nos. 918-919 differ from Nos. 835 and 841 by having less color around the Queen's head. Nos. 917-919 are dated "2006."

Worldwide Fund for Nature (WWF) A186

Striated caracara: 25p, Heads of two birds. 50p, Bird in flight. 60p, Bird standing. 85p, Bird eating shellfish.

2006, Dec. 20   Litho.   Perf. 13¾
920-923 A186   Set of 4   10.50 10.50
923a   Miniature sheet, 4 each
        #920-923   45.00 45.00

Fisheries, 20th Anniv. A187

Designs: 3p, Fishermen at sea. 11p, Fishing boat at night. 25p, Fishermen leaving boat. 30p, Japanese jigger. 60p, Fishery protection boat Dorada. £1.05, Trawler transferring fish to a freezer container ship.

2007, Feb. 24   Perf. 14¼
924-929 A187   Set of 6   12.00 12.00

HMS Plymouth A188

HMS Plymouth: 25p, Joining Falkland Islands Task Force. 40p, Supporting SBS. 60p, Under attack by Argentine fighters. £1.05, Docked at Port Stanley.

2007, Mar. 27
930-933 A188   Set of 4   12.00 12.00

Souvenir Sheet

Falkland Islands War, 25th Anniv. — A189

No. 934: a, Avro Vulcan prototype VX770. b, Avro Vulcan XM597. c, Avro Vulcan XM607. d, Vulcan in the Sky Project.

2007, May 25   Litho.   Perf. 13¼
934 A189 60p Sheet of 4, #a-d 12.00 12.00

Miniature Sheets

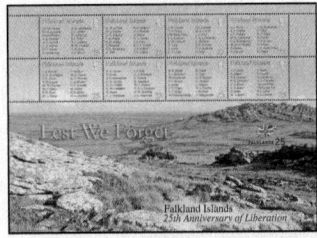

British and Falkland Islander Casualties of the Falkland Islands War — A190

No. 935, 25p — Casualties beginning with: a, Doreen Bonner. b, G. W. J. Batt. c, J. R. Carlyle. d, S. J. Dixon. e, I. R. Farrell. f, G. C. Grace. g, R. R. Heath. h, A. S. James.
No. 936, 60p: a, D. Lee. b, P. B. McKay. c, G. T. Nelson. d, J. B. Pashley. e, M. Sambles. f, D. A. Strickland. g, R. G. Thomas. h, P. A. West.

2007, June 14   Litho.   Perf. 14¼
Sheets of 8, #a-h
935-936 A190   Set of 2   29.00 29.00

Scouting, Cent. — A191

Designs: 10p, Scouts on ladder of RRS Discovery. 20p, Dignitaries on ship's deck. 25p, Dignitaries, diff. £2, RRS Discovery.

2007, July 23 Litho. Perf. 13½x13¼
937-940 A191   Set of 4   11.00 11.00

Voyage of RRS Discovery from Falkland Islands for presentation to British Scout Association, 70th anniv.

Princess Diana (1961-97) — A192

2007, Aug. 31   Perf. 14
941 A192 60p multi   3.00 3.00
Printed in sheets of 8 stamps + 21 labels.

Saunders Island and its Flora and Fauna — A193

No. 942, 50p: a, Rockhopper penguin. b, Dusty miller.
No. 943, 55p: a, Crested caracara. b, Earliest British settlement at Port Egmont.

2007, Sept. 28   Litho.   Perf. 13¾
Pairs, #a-b
942-943 A193   Set of 2   9.25 9.25

Wedding of Queen Elizabeth II and Prince Philip, 60th Anniv. A194

2007, Nov. 20   Litho.   Perf. 14
944 A194   £1 multi   4.25 4.25

Polar Explorers and Their Ships A195

Explorers and ships: 4p, James Weddell (1787-1834), and Jane. 25p, James Clark Ross (1800-62), and HMS Erebus. 85p, William Spiers Bruce (1867-1921), and Scotia. £1.61, James Marr (1902-65), and Discovery II.

2008, Apr. 7
945-948 A195   Set of 4   11.00 11.00

Southern Elephant Seals A196

Designs: 27p, Seal pup. 55p, Male and female. 65p, Seals play fighting. £1.10, Seal and tussock bird.

2008, July 15   Litho.   Perf. 14
949-952 A196   Set of 4   10.50 10.50

Aircraft A197

Designs: 1p, Taylorcraft Auster Mk 5. 2p, Boeing 747-300. 5p, De Havilland Canada DHC-6 Twin Otter. 10p, Lockheed C-130 Hercules. 27p, De Havilland Canada DHC-2 Beaver. 55p, Airbus A320. 65p, Lockheed L-1011-385-3 Tristar C2. 90p, Avro Vulcan B2. £1, Britten-Norman BN-2 Islander. £2, Panavia Tornado F3. £3, De Havilland Canada DHC-7-110 Dash 7. £5, BAE Sea Harrier.

2008, Aug. 1   Litho.   Perf. 14
953 A197   1p multi   .20 .20
954 A197   2p multi   .20 .20
955 A197   5p multi   .20 .20
956 A197   10p multi   .40 .40
957 A197   27p multi   1.10 1.10
958 A197   55p multi   2.25 2.25
959 A197   65p multi   2.60 2.60
960 A197   90p multi   3.50 3.50
961 A197   £1 multi   4.00 4.00
962 A197   £2 multi   8.00 8.00
963 A197   £3 multi   12.00 12.00
964 A197   £5 multi   20.00 20.00
  Nos. 953-964 (12)   54.45 54.45
Souvenir Sheet
Stamps With Royal Air Force 90th Anniv. Emblem Added
965   Sheet of 4   14.50 14.50
  a. A197 10p Like #956   .40 .40
  b. A197 65p Like #959   2.60 2.60
  c. A197 90p Like #960   3.50 3.50
  d. A197 £2 Like #962   8.00 8.00

Port Louis, 175th
Anniv. — A198

Designs: 27p, Sailor raising British flag. 65p,
Royal Marines, British flag.
£2, Capt. Onslow of HMS Clio, British flag.

2008, Sept. 22   Litho.   *Perf. 14*
966-967   A198   Set of 2   3.25   3.25

Souvenir Sheet

968   A198   £2 multi   7.25   7.25

Islands and
Rocks
A199

Designs: 22p, The Slipper. 40p, Kidney
Island. 60p, Stephens Bluff and Castle Rock.
£1, The Colliers.

2008, Oct. 1   Litho.   *Perf. 13¾*
969-972   A199   Set of 4   8.00   8.00

See Nos. 986-989.

Retirement of
Queen
Elizabeth 2 as
Ocean
Liner — A200

Designs: 23p, Launch of Queen Elizabeth 2.
27p, Service of Queen Elizabeth 2 as troop
ship in Falkland Islands War. 65p, Queen Elizabeth 2, Palm Jumeirah, Dubai. £2, Queen
Elizabeth 2 (70x34mm).

2008, Nov. 21   Litho.   *Perf. 13¼*
973-976   A200   Set of 4   9.50   9.50

Charles Darwin (1809-82),
Naturalist — A201

Designs: 4p, Darwin seated. 27p, Warrah.
65p, HMS Beagle in Berkeley Sound, 1834.
£1.10, Darwin encountering a Magellanic
penguin.

2009, Apr. 23   Litho.   *Perf. 14*
977-980   A201   Set of 4   6.00   6.00

Naval
Aviation,
Cent.
A202

Royal Navy aircraft and ships: 30p, West-
land/Aerospatiale Gazelle AH1 helicopter.
50p, Westland Lynx HAS2 helicopter. 65p,
Westland Wessex HU5 helicopter. £1.10,
Westland Sea King HAS5 helicopter. £2, BAe
Sea Harrier, HMS Hermes.

2009, May 7   Litho.   *Perf. 14*
981-984   A202   Set of 4   7.75   7.75

Souvenir Sheet

985   A202   £2 multi   6.00   6.00

Islands and Rocks Type of 2008

Designs: 27p, Seal Rocks. 40p, Beauchene
Island. 65p, Jason East Cay, Steeple Jason.
£1.50, Horse Block.

2009, Aug. 14   Litho.   *Perf. 13¾*
986-989   A199   Set of 4   9.50   9.50

Albatrosses
A203

Designs: 22p, Black-browed albatross. 27p,
Gray-headed albatross. 60p, Light-mantled
sooty albatross. 90p, Wandering albatross.

2009, Oct. 19   Litho.   *Perf. 13¾*
990-993   A203   Set of 4   6.75   6.75

Cobb's
Wren
A204

Designs: Nos. 994, 998a, 27p, Wren on
seaweed. Nos. 995, 998b, 65p, Wrens at nest.
Nos. 996, 998c, 90p, Wren on rock. Nos. 997,
998d, £1.10, Two wrens.

2009, Nov. 10   *Perf. 13¾*
Stamps With WWF Emblem
994-997   A204   Set of 4   9.75   9.75
997a   Sheet of 16, 4 each
       #994-997   39.00   39.00

Souvenir Sheet
**Stamps With Falklands
Conservation Emblem**

998   A204   Sheet of 4, #a-d   9.75   9.75

Ships
Named
HMS
Exeter
A205

Ship used from: 4p, 1931-42. 20p, 1931-42,
with helicopter. 30p, 1980-2009, with helicopter. £1.66, 1980-2009, with helicopter, diff.

2009, Dec. 8   Litho.   *Perf. 14*
999-1002   A205   Set of 4   7.25   7.25

Skies in
Four
Seasons
A206

Designs: 27p, Carcass Island in spring. 55p,
Beach on New Island in summer. 65p, Rainbow over Stanley in autumn. £1.10, Islands in
winter.

2010, Jan. 25   Litho.   *Perf. 13*
1003-1006   A206   Set of 4   8.25   8.25

Restoration of
the SS Great
Britain
A207

SS Great Britain: 27p, On pontoon near jetty
in Stanley. 50p, Beached at Sparrow Cove.
65p, Bow. £1.10, Mast and rigging.

2010, Apr. 12   *Perf. 13¼*
1007-1010   A207   Set of 4   7.75   7.75

Miniature Sheet

Battle of Britain, 70th Anniv. — A208

No. 1011 — Airplanes: a, Hawker Hurricane
P2961. b, Supermarine Spitfire P9398. c,
Hawker Hurricane P3854. d, Supermarine
Spitfire P7350. e, Hawker Hurricane V6665. f,
Supermarine Spitfire L1035. g, Hawker Hurri-
cane P3576. h, Supermarine Spitfire X4620.

2010, May 7   Litho.   *Perf. 14x14¼*
1011   A208   65p Sheet of 8, #a-
     h   15.50   15.50

London 2010 Festival of Stamps.

Birds
A209

Designs: Nos. 1012, 1016a, 27p, Sooty
shearwater. Nos. 1013, 1016b, 70p, White-
chinned petrel. Nos. 1014, 1016c, 95p, Southern giant petrel. Nos. 1015, 1016d, £1.15,
Greater shearwater.

2010, July 8   Litho.   *Perf. 13¾*
Stamps With White Frames
1012-1015   A209   Set of 4   9.25   9.25

Souvenir Sheet
Stamps Without White Frames
1016   A209   Sheet of 4, #a-d   9.25   9.25

Flowering
Shrubs
A210

Designs: 27p, Fuchsia. 70p, Boxwood. 95p,
Gorse. £1.15, Honeysuckle.

2010, Oct. 27   Litho.   *Perf. 13¼x13*
1017-1020   A210   Set of 4   10.00   10.00

SEMI-POSTAL STAMPS

Catalogue values for unused
stamps in this section are for
Never Hinged items.

Rebuilding after Conflict with
Argentina — SP1

Wmk. 373
1982, Sept. 13   Litho.   *Perf. 11*
B1   SP1   £1 + £1 Battle sites   3.00   3.00

Liberation of
Falkland Islands,
10th
Anniv. — SP2

Designs: 14p+6p, San Carlos Cemetery.
29p+11p, 1982 War Memorial, Port Stanley.
34p+16p, South Atlantic Medal. 68p+32p,
Government House, Port Stanley.

Wmk. 373
1992, June 14   Litho.   *Perf. 14*
B2   SP2   14p + 6p multicolored   .75   .75
B3   SP2   29p + 11p multicolored   1.50   1.50
B4   SP2   34p + 16p multicolored   2.00   2.00
B5   SP2   68p + 32p multicolored   3.75   3.75
a.   Souvenir sheet of 4, #B2-B5   9.50   9.50
     Nos. B2-B5 (4)   8.00   8.00

Surtax for Soldiers', Sailors' and Airmen's
Families Association.

AIR POST STAMPS

Bird Type of 2003

Design: Rockhopper penguins, vert.

*Serpentine Die Cut 6x6½
Syncopated*

2003, Sept. 19   Litho.

Booklet Stamp
Self-Adhesive

C1   A163   (40p) multi   1.75   1.75
a.   Booklet pane of 8   14.00

Penguins — AP1

Designs: No. C2, (55p), King penguin. No.
C3, (55p), Macaroni penguin. No. C4, (55p),
Magellanic penguin. No. C5, (55p), Rockhop-
per penguin. No. C6, (55p), Gentoo penguin.
No. C7, (55p), Albino rockhopper penguin.

2008, Dec. 1   Litho.   *Perf. 13¼*
C2-C7   AP1   Set of 6   9.75   9.75
C7a   Souvenir sheet, #C2-C7   9.75   9.75

Penguins — AP2

Designs: Nos. C8, C14a, (70p), King penguin. Nos. C9, C14b, (70p), Macaroni penguin. Nos. C10, C14c, (70p), Rockhopper penguins. Nos. C11, C14d, (70p), Albino and
normal rockhopper penguins. Nos. C12, C14e,
(70p), Magellanic penguin. Nos. C13, C14f,
(70p), Gentoo penguins.

2010, Sept. 29   Litho.   *Perf. 13¾*

Stamps With White Frames

C8-C13	AP2	Set of 6	13.50	13.50

Stamps Without White Frames

C14	AP2	(70p) Sheet of 6, #a-f	13.50	13.50

POSTAGE DUE STAMPS

> Catalogue values for unused stamps in this section are for never hinged items.

Penguin — D1

Perf. 14½x14

1991, Jan. 7   Litho.   Wmk. 373

J1	D1	1p lilac rose & lake	.20	.50
J2	D1	2p buff & brown org	.20	.50
J3	D1	3p yel & orange yel	.20	.50
J4	D1	4p lt bl grn & dk bl grn	.25	.50
J5	D1	5p sky blue & Prus bl	.25	.50
J6	D1	10p lt blue & dk blue	.35	.70
J7	D1	20p lt violet & dk vio	.90	1.50
J8	D1	50p brt yel grn & dk yel green	2.00	3.25
		Nos. J1-J8 (8)	4.35	7.95

Penguins D2

Various penguins.

2005, Dec. 2   Litho.   *Perf. 13¾*

J9	D2	1p multi	.20	.20
J10	D2	3p multi	.20	.20
J11	D2	5p multi	.20	.20
J12	D2	10p multi	.50	.50
J13	D2	20p multi	.90	.90
J14	D2	50p multi	2.00	2.00
J15	D2	£1 multi	4.00	4.00
J16	D2	£2 multi	8.00	8.00
J17	D2	£3 multi	12.00	12.00
J18	D2	£5 multi	20.00	20.00
		Nos. J9-J18 (10)	48.00	48.00

WAR TAX STAMPS

Regular Issue of 1912-14 Overprinted

1918, Oct. 7   Wmk. 3   Perf. 14

MR1	A7	½p yellow green	.55	7.25
MR2	A7	1p red	.55	4.00
a.		Double overprint	3,000.	
MR3	A7	1sh bister brown	6.50	52.50
a.		Pair, one without overprint	13,000.	
		Nos. MR1-MR3 (3)	7.60	63.75

No. MR3a probably is caused by a foldover and is not constant.

FALKLAND ISLANDS DEPENDENCIES

> Catalogue values for unused stamps in this section are for Never Hinged items.

Map of Falkland Islands — A1

Engr., Center Litho. in Black

1946, Feb. 1   Wmk. 4   *Perf. 12*

1L1	A1	½p yellow green	.95	1.90
1L2	A1	1p blue violet	.95	1.90
1L3	A1	2p deep carmine	.95	1.90
1L4	A1	3p ultramarine	1.90	1.90
1L5	A1	4p deep plum	1.90	3.00
1L6	A1	6p orange yellow	3.00	3.50
1L7	A1	9p brown	3.00	3.50
1L8	A1	1sh rose violet	5.75	7.50
		Nos. 1L1-1L8 (8)	18.40	24.70

Nos. 1L1-1L8 were reissued in 1948, printed on more opaque paper with the lines of the map finer and clearer. Value for set, unused or used $120.
See No. 1L13.

Common Design Types pictured following the introduction.

Peace Issue
Common Design Type

1946, Oct. 4   *Perf. 13½x14*

1L9	CD303	1p purple	.60	.20
1L10	CD303	3p deep blue	1.10	.20

Silver Wedding Issue
Common Design Types

1948, Dec. 6   Photo.   *Perf. 14x14½*

1L11	CD304	2½p brt ultra	1.25	1.25

Perf. 11½x11
Engr.

1L12	CD305	1sh blue violet	5.75	5.75

Type of 1946

1949, Mar. 6   *Perf. 12*
Center Litho. in Black

1L13	A1	2½p deep blue	13.00	12.00

UPU Issue
Common Design Types
Engr.; Name Typo. on 2p, 3p

1949, Oct. 10   *Perf. 13½, 11x11½*

1L14	CD306	1p violet	1.60	1.90
1L15	CD307	2p deep carmine	4.25	1.90
1L16	CD308	3p indigo	6.50	4.25
1L17	CD309	6p red orange	11.00	8.50
		Nos. 1L14-1L17 (4)	23.35	16.55

Coronation Issue
Common Design Type

1953, June 4   *Perf. 13½x13*

1L18	CD312	1p purple & black	1.50	1.50

John Biscoe — A2

Trepassey — A3

Ships: 1½p, Wyatt Earp. 2p, Eagle. 2½p, Penola. 3p, Discovery II. 4p, William Scoresby. 6p, Discovery. 9p, Endurance. 1sh, Deutschland. 2sh, Pourquoi-pas? 2sh6p, Français. 5sh, Scotia. 10sh, Antarctic. £1, Belgica.

1954, Feb. 1   Engr.   *Perf. 12½*
Center in Black

1L19	A2	½p blue green	.20	2.00
1L20	A3	1p sepia	1.75	1.50
1L21	A3	1½p olive	2.00	1.75
1L22	A3	2p rose red	1.25	.20
1L23	A3	2½p yellow	1.25	.20
1L24	A3	3p ultra	1.25	.20
1L25	A3	4p red violet	3.00	.45
1L26	A2	6p rose violet	3.50	.45
1L27	A2	9p black	3.50	1.25
1L28	A3	1sh org brown	3.50	1.00
1L29	A3	2sh lilac rose	18.00	10.00
1L30	A2	2sh6p blue gray	19.00	6.25
1L31	A3	5sh violet	40.00	6.75
1L32	A3	10sh brt blue	55.00	18.00
1L33	A2	£1 black	87.50	50.00
		Nos. 1L19-1L33 (15)	240.70	100.00

Nos. 20, 23-24, 26 Overprinted in Black

1956, Jan 30   Center in Black

1L34	A3	1p sepia	.20	.20
1L35	A3	2½p yellow	.50	.50
1L36	A3	3p ultramarine	.60	.60
1L37	A2	6p rose violet	.70	.70
		Nos. 1L34-1L37 (4)	2.00	2.00

Trans-Antarctic Expedition, 1955-1958.

A4

Wmk. 373

1980, May 5   Litho.   *Perf. 13½*

1L38	A4	1p Map of Dependencies	.20	.25
1L39	A4	2p Shag Rocks	.20	.25
1L40	A4	3p Bird and Willis Islds.	.20	.25
1L41	A4	4p Gulbrandsen Lake	.20	.25
1L42	A4	5p King Edward Point	.20	.25
1L43	A4	6p Shackleton's Memorial Cross	.20	.25
1L44	A4	7p Shackleton's grave	.20	.25
1L45	A4	8p Grytviken Church	.20	.25
1L46	A4	9p Coaling Hulk "Louise"	.25	.30
1L47	A4	10p Clerke Rocks	.25	.30
1L48	A4	20p Candlemas Island	.45	.55
1L49	A4	25p Twitcher Rock, Cook Island	.60	.70
1L50	A4	50p "John Biscoe"	1.10	1.25
1L51	A4	£1 "Bransfield"	2.25	2.75
1L52	A4	£3 "Endurance"	7.50	9.00
		Nos. 1L38-1L52 (15)	14.00	16.85

Nos. 38-50 exist dated 1984; issued May 3, 1984. Value, set $16.

1985, Nov. 18   Wmk. 384

1L48a	A4	20p	.75	1.10
1L49a	A4	25p	1.00	1.25
1L50a	A4	50p	2.75	3.50
1L51a	A4	£1	4.00	5.00
1L52a	A4	£3	12.50	16.00
		Nos. 1L48a-1L52a (5)	21.00	26.85

Magellanic Clubmoss — A5

1981, Feb. 5   Litho.   *Perf. 14*

1L53	A5	3p shown	.25	.25
1L54	A5	6p Alpine cat's-tail	.25	.25
1L55	A5	7p Greater burnet	.25	.25
1L56	A5	11p Antarctic bedstraw	.35	.35
1L57	A5	15p Brown rush	.50	.50
a.		Brown missing	3,000.	
1L58	A5	25p Antarctic hair grass	.75	.75
		Nos. 1L53-1L58 (6)	2.35	2.35

Royal Wedding Issue
Common Design Type

1981, July 22   Litho.   *Perf. 14*

1L59	CD331	10p Bouquet	.25	.25
1L60	CD331	13p Charles	.35	.35
1L61	CD331	52p Couple	.85	.85
		Nos. 1L59-1L61 (3)	1.45	1.45

Reindeer in Spring — A6

1982, Jan. 29   Litho.   *Perf. 14*

1L62	A6	5p shown	.20	.20
1L63	A6	13p Autumn	.45	.45
1L64	A6	25p Winter	.80	.80
1L65	A6	26p Late winter	.85	.85
		Nos. 1L62-1L65 (4)	2.30	2.30

Gamasellus Racovitzai — A7

1982, Mar. 16   Litho.   *Perf. 14*

1L66	A7	5p shown	.20	.20
1L67	A7	10p Alaskozetes antarcticus	.25	.25
1L68	A7	13p Cryptopygus antarcticus	.30	.30
1L69	A7	15p Notiomaso australis	.40	.40
1L70	A7	25p Hydromedion sparsutum	.60	.60
1L71	A7	26p Parochlus steinenii	.65	.65
		Nos. 1L66-1L71 (6)	2.40	2.40

Princess Diana Issue
Common Design Type

1982, July 1   Litho.   *Perf. 14x14½*

1L72	CD333	5p Arms	.45	.20
1L73	CD333	17p Diana	1.40	.60
a.		Perf. 14	9.00	9.00
1L74	CD333	37p Wedding	3.25	1.40
1L75	CD333	50p Portrait	4.25	1.75
		Nos. 1L72-1L75 (4)	9.35	3.95

Crustacea — A8

Perf. 14½x14

1984, Mar. 23   Wmk. 373

1L76	A8	5p Euphausia superba	.20	.20
1L77	A8	17p Glyptonotus antarcticus	.65	.65
1L78	A8	25p Epimeria monodon	1.00	1.00
1L79	A8	34p Serolis pagenstecheri	1.40	1.40
		Nos. 1L76-1L79 (4)	3.25	3.25

Manned Flight Bicentenary — A9

1983, Dec. 23   Litho.   *Perf. 14*

1L80	A9	5p Westland Whirlwind	.20	.20
1L81	A9	13p Westland Wasp	.45	.45
1L82	A9	17p Saunders-Roe Walrus	.65	.65
1L83	A9	50p Auster	2.00	2.00
		Nos. 1L80-1L83 (4)	3.30	3.30

South Sandwich Islds. Volcanoes — A10

1984, Nov. 8   Wmk. 373   Perf. 14½

1L84	A10	6p Zavodovski Isld.	.60	.60
1L85	A10	17p Mt. Michael, Saunders Isld.	1.40	1.40
1L86	A10	22p Bellingshausen Isld.	2.00	2.00
1L87	A10	52p Bristol Isld.	4.75	4.75
		Nos. 1L84-1L87 (4)	8.75	8.75

Albatrosses — A11

1985, May 5   Wmk. 384   Perf. 14½

1L88	A11	7p Diomedea chrysostoma	.80	.80
1L89	A11	22p Diomedea melanophris	2.50	2.50
1L90	A11	27p Diomedea exulans	2.75	2.75
1L91	A11	54p Phoebetria palpebrata	5.75	5.75
		Nos. 1L88-1L91 (4)	11.80	11.80

Queen Mother 85th Birthday
Common Design Type

Designs: 7p, 14th birthday celebration. 22p, With Princess Anne, Lady Sarah Armstrong-Jones, Prince Edward. 27p, Queen Mother. 54p, Holding Prince Henry. £1, On the Britannia.

1985, June 23   Perf. 14½x14

1L92	CD336	7p multicolored	.25	.25
1L93	CD336	22p multicolored	.75	.75
1L94	CD336	27p multicolored	1.00	1.00
1L95	CD336	54p multicolored	2.00	2.00
		Nos. 1L92-1L95 (4)	4.00	4.00

Souvenir Sheet

1L96	CD336	£1 multicolored	4.25	4.25

Falkland Islands Naturalists Type of 1985

Naturalists, endangered species: 7p, Dumont d'Urville (1790-1842), kelp. 22p, Johann Reinhold Forster (1729-1798), king penguin. 27p, Johann Georg Adam Forster (1754-1794), tussock grass. 54p, Sir Joseph Banks (1743-1820), dove prion.

1985, Nov. 4   Perf. 13½x14

1L97	A86	7p multicolored	.65	.65
1L98	A86	22p multicolored	1.60	1.60
1L99	A86	27p multicolored	2.40	2.40
1L100	A86	54p multicolored	4.75	4.75
		Nos. 1L97-1L100 (4)	9.40	9.40

SEMI-POSTAL STAMP

Rebuilding Type of Falkland Islands
Wmk. 373

1982, Sept. 13   Litho.   Perf. 11

1LB1	SP1	£1 Map of So. Georgia	3.00	3.00

ISSUES FOR THE SEPARATE ISLANDS

Graham Land

Nos. 84, 85B, 86A, 87A, 88-91
Overprinted in Red

1944, Feb. 12   Wmk. 4   Perf. 12

2L1	A22	½p green & black	.55	.50
2L2	A22	1p dk vio & black	.60	.60
2L3	A22	2p rose car & blk	.90	.85
2L4	A22	3p deep bl & blk	1.25	1.10
2L5	A22	4p rose vio & blk	2.00	1.50
2L6	A22	6p brown & black	10.00	3.50
2L7	A22	9p slate bl & blk	3.00	3.00
2L8	A22	1sh dull blue	3.00	2.75
		Nos. 2L1-2L8 (8)	21.30	13.80

South Georgia

1944, Apr. 3   Wmk. 4   Perf. 12

3L1	A22	½p green & black	.60	.50
3L2	A22	1p dark vio & blk	.65	.60
3L3	A22	2p rose car & blk	1.00	.85
3L4	A22	3p deep bl & blk	1.40	1.10
3L5	A22	4p rose vio & blk	2.00	1.50
3L6	A22	6p brown & black	10.00	4.00
3L7	A22	9p slate bl & blk	3.25	3.00
3L8	A22	1sh dull blue	3.25	3.00
		Nos. 3L1-3L8 (8)	22.15	14.55

South Orkneys

1944, Feb. 21   Wmk. 4   Perf. 12

4L1	A22	½p green & black	.55	.50
4L2	A22	1p dark vio & blk	.60	.60
4L3	A22	2p rose car & blk	.90	.85
4L4	A22	3p deep bl & blk	1.25	1.10
4L5	A22	4p rose vio & blk	2.00	1.50
4L6	A22	6p brown & black	10.00	3.50
4L7	A22	9p slate bl & blk	3.00	3.00
4L8	A22	1sh dull blue	3.00	2.75
		Nos. 4L1-4L8 (8)	21.30	13.80

South Shetlands

1944   Wmk. 4   Perf. 12

5L1	A22	½p green & black	.50	.50
5L2	A22	1p dark vio & blk	.60	.60
5L3	A22	2p rose car & blk	.90	.85
5L4	A22	3p deep bl & blk	1.25	1.10
5L5	A22	4p rose vio & blk	2.00	1.50
5L6	A22	6p brown & black	10.00	3.50
5L7	A22	9p slate bl & blk	3.00	3.00
5L8	A22	1sh dull blue	3.00	2.75
		Nos. 5L1-5L8 (8)	21.25	13.80

FAR EASTERN REPUBLIC

'fär 'ē-stərn ri-'pə-blik

LOCATION — In Siberia east of Lake Baikal
GOVT. — Republic
AREA — 900,745 sq. mi.
POP. — 1,560,000 (approx. 1920)
CAPITAL — Chita

A short-lived independent government was established here in 1920.

100 Kopecks = 1 Ruble

Watermark

Wmk. 171 — Diamonds

Vladivostok Issue
Russian Stamps Surcharged or Overprinted:

a   b

c

On Stamps of 1909-17
Perf. 14, 14½x15, 13½

1920   Unwmk.

2	A14(a)	2k green	10.00	10.00
3	A14(a)	3k red	10.00	10.00
4	A11(b)	3k on 35k red brn & grn	30.00	50.00
5	A15(a)	4k carmine	10.00	12.00
6	A11(b)	4k on 70k brn & org	10.00	8.00
8	A11(b)	7k on 15k red brn & bl	2.00	2.00
a.		Inverted surcharge	100.00	
b.		Pair, one ovptd. "DBP" only		100.00
9	A15(a)	10k dark blue	50.00	55.00
a.		Overprint on back	80.00	
10	A12(c)	10k on 3½r mar & lt grn	25.00	25.00
11	A11(a)	14k blue & rose	35.00	35.00
12	A11(a)	15k red brn & bl	25.00	25.00
13	A8(a)	20k blue & car	75.00	100.00
14	A11(b)	20k on 14k bl & rose	10.00	8.00
a.		Surcharge on back	30.00	
15	A11(a)	25k green & vio	25.00	15.00
16	A11(a)	35k red brn & grn	35.00	35.00
17	A8(a)	50k brn vio & grn	10.00	12.00
18	A9(a)	1r pale brn, dk brn & org	750.00	750.00

On Stamps of 1917
Imperf

21	A14(a)	1k orange	10.00	10.00
22	A14(a)	2k gray grn	10.00	5.00
23	A14(a)	3k red	10.00	10.00
25	A11(b)	7k on 15k red brn & dp bl	2.00	5.00
a.		Pair, one without surcharge	100.00	
b.		Pair, one ovptd. "DBP" only	100.00	
26	A12(c)	10k on 3½r mar & lt grn	15.00	15.00
27	A9(a)	1r pale brn, brn & red org	20.00	20.00

On Stamps of Siberia 1919
Perf. 14, 14½x15

30	A14(a)	35k on 2k green	5.00	8.00
a.		"DBP" on back	25.00	50.00

Imperf

31	A14(a)	35k on 2k green	25.00	25.00
32	A14(a)	70k on 1k orange	10.00	10.00

Counterfeit surcharges and overprints abound, including digital forgeries.

On Russia Nos. AR2, AR3

A1

Perf. 14½x15
Wmk. 171

35	A1(b)	1k on 5k green, buff	20.00	15.00
36	A1(b)	2k on 10k brown, buff	30.00	30.00

The letters on these stamps resembling "DBP," are the Russian initials of "Dalne Vostochnaya Respublika" (Far Eastern Republic).

Chita Issue

A2   A2a

1921   Unwmk.   Typo.   Imperf.

38	A2	2k gray green	1.50	1.50
39	A2a	4k rose	3.00	3.00
40	A2	5k claret	3.00	3.00
41	A2a	10k rose	2.50	2.50
		Nos. 38-41 (4)	10.00	10.00

For overprints see Nos. 62-65.

Blagoveshchensk Issue

A3

1921   Litho.   Imperf.

42	A3	2r red	2.75	2.00
43	A3	3r dark green	2.75	2.00
44	A3	5r dark blue	2.75	2.00
a.		Tête bêche pair	25.00	30.00
45	A3	15r dark brown	2.75	2.00
46	A3	30r dark violet	2.75	2.00
a.		Tête bêche pair	35.00	30.00
		Nos. 42-46 (5)	13.75	10.00

Remainders of Nos. 42-46 were canceled in colored crayon or by typographed bars. These sell for half of foregoing values.

Chita Issue

A4   A5

1922   Litho.   Imperf.

49	A4	1k orange	.75	.85
50	A4	3k dull red	.40	.45
51	A4	4k dp rose & buff	.40	.45
52	A4	5k orange brown	.80	.45
53	A4	7k light blue	1.00	1.25
a.		Perf. 11½	2.00	2.50
b.		Rouletted 9	3.00	3.00
c.		Perf. 11½x rouletted	5.00	3.00
54	A5	10k dk blue & red	.60	.65
55	A5	15k dull rose	.75	.85
56	A5	20k blue & red	.75	.85
57	A5	30k green & red org	1.00	1.10
58	A5	50k black & red org	1.60	1.75
		Nos. 49-58 (10)	8.05	8.65

The 4k exists with "4" omitted. Value $100.

Vladivostok Issue

Stamps of 1921
Overprinted in Red

1922   Imperf.

62	A2	2k gray green	35.00	25.00
a.		Inverted overprint	250.00	
63	A2a	4k rose	35.00	25.00
a.		Inverted overprint	250.00	
b.		Double overprint	250.00	
64	A2	5k claret	35.00	35.00
a.		Inverted overprint	100.00	
b.		Double overprint	350.00	
65	A2a	10k blue	35.00	35.00
a.		Inverted overprint	100.00	
		Nos. 62-65 (4)	140.00	120.00

Russian revolution of Nov. 1917, 5th anniv.
Once in the setting the figures "22" of 1922 have the bottom stroke curved instead of straight. Value, each $75.

Vladivostok Issue

Russian Stamps of
1922-23 Surcharged in
Black or Red

1923 — *Imperf.*

66	A50	1k on 100r red	.40 1.00
a.		Inverted surcharge	60.00
67	A50	2k on 70r violet	.40 .75
68	A49	5k on 10r blue (R)	.40 .75
69	A50	10k on 50r brown	.90 1.25
a.		Inverted surcharge	250.00

Perf. 14½x15

70	A50	1k on 100r red	.90 1.25
		Nos. 66-70 (5)	3.00 5.00

OCCUPATION STAMPS

**Issued under Occupation of General
Semenov
Chita Issue**
Russian Stamps of 1909-12
Surcharged:

p. 1 p.   2p.50к.

a   b

c

P. 5 P.

1920   Unwmk.   Perf. 14, 14x15½

N1	A15 (a)	1r on 4k car	150.00 100.00
N2	A8 (b)	2r50k on 20k bl	
		& car	40.00 40.00
N3	A14 (c)	5r on 5k clar-	
		et	20.00 40.00
a.		Double surcharge	65.00
N4	A11 (a)	10r on 70k brn	
		& org	20.00 30.00
		Nos. N1-N4 (4)	230.00 210.00

FAROE ISLANDS

'far-͵ü 'i-lənds

(The Faroes)

LOCATION — North Atlantic Ocean
GOVT. — Self-governing part of Kingdom of Denmark
AREA — 540 sq. mi.
POP. — 41,059 (1999 est.)
CAPITAL — Thorshavn

100 Ore = 1 Krone

> **Catalogue values for unused stamps in this country are for Never Hinged items, beginning with Scott 7.**

Denmark No. 97
Handstamp Surcharged

1919, Jan.   Typo.   Perf. 14x14½
1	A16	2o on 5o green	1,400.	475.00

Counterfeits of surcharge exist.
Denmark No. 88a, the bisect, was used with Denmark No. 97 in Faroe Islands Jan. 3-23, 1919.

Denmark Nos. 220, 224, 238A, 224C
Surcharged in Blue or Black

Nos. 2, 5-6   No. 3

No. 4

1940-41   Engr.   Perf. 13
2	A32	20o on 1o ('41)	45.00	110.00
3	A32	20o on 5o ('41)	45.00	35.00
4	A30	20o on 15o (Bk)	60.00	22.50
5	A32	50o on 5o (Bk)	300.00	90.00
6	A32	60o on 6o (Bk)	125.00	250.00
		Nos. 2-6 (5)	575.00	507.50
		Set, never hinged	1,150.	

Issued during British administration.

> **Catalogue values for unused stamps in this section, from this point to the end of the section, are for Never Hinged items.**

Map of Islands, 1673 — A1   Map of North Atlantic, 1573 — A2

West Coast, Sandoy — A3

Vidoy and Svinoy, by Eyvindur Mohr — A4

Designs: 200o, like 70o. 250o, 300o, View of Streymoy and Vagar. 450o, Houses, Nes, by Ruth Smith. 500o, View of Hvitanes and Skalafjordur, by S. Joensen-Mikines.

1975, Jan. 30   Engr.   Perf. 13
7	A1	5o sepia	.25	.25
8	A2	10o emer & dark blue	.25	.25
9	A1	50o graysh green	.25	.25
10	A2	60o brown & dark blue	1.00	1.00
11	A3	70o vio bl & slate grn	1.00	1.00
12	A2	80o ocher & dark blue	.50	.50
13	A1	90o red brown	1.00	1.00
14	A2	120o brt bl & dark bl	.75	.50
15	A3	200o vio bl & slate grn	.75	.75
16	A3	250o multicolored	.75	.75
17	A3	300o multicolored	6.50	2.25

Photo.   Perf. 12½x13
18	A4	350o multicolored	1.00	1.00
19	A4	450o multicolored	1.10	1.00
20	A4	500o multicolored	1.25	1.10
		Nos. 7-20 (14)	16.35	11.60

Faroe Boat — A5   Faroe Flag — A6

Faroe Mailman — A7

Perf. 12½x13, 12 (A6)
1976, Apr. 1   Engr.; Litho. (A6)
21	A5	125o copper red	2.00	1.50
22	A6	160o multicolored	.50	.50
23	A7	800o olive	2.25	1.50
		Nos. 21-23 (3)	4.75	3.50

Faroe Islands independent postal service, Apr. 1, 1976.

Motor Fishing Boat — A8

Faroese Fishing Vessels and Map of Islands: 125o, Inland fishing cutter. 160o, Modern seine fishing vessel. 600o, Deep-sea fishing trawler.

1977, Apr. 28   Photo.   Perf. 14½x14
24	A8	100o green & black	5.50	4.75
25	A8	125o carmine & black	1.00	1.00
26	A8	160o blue & black	1.00	.75
27	A8	600o brown & black	2.00	1.25
		Nos. 24-27 (4)	9.50	7.75

Common Snipe A9

Photogravure & Engraved
1977, Sept. 29   Perf. 14½x14
28	A9	70o shown	.25	.25
29	A9	180o Oystercatcher	.65	.65
30	A9	250o Whimbrel	.90	.75
		Nos. 28-30 (3)	1.80	1.65

North Coast, Puffins — A10   Mykines Village — A11

Mykines Island: 140o, Coast. 150o, Aerial view. 180o, Map.

Perf. 13x13½, 13½x13
1978, Jan. 26   Photo.
Size: 21x28mm, 28x21mm
31	A10	100o multicolored	.25	.25
32	A11	130o multicolored	.50	.50
33	A11	140o multicolored	.65	.65
34	A10	150o multicolored	.65	.65

Size: 37x26mm
Perf. 14½x14
35	A11	180o multicolored	.65	.65
		Nos. 31-35 (5)	2.70	2.70

Sea Birds — A12

Old Library — A13

Lithographed and Engraved
1978, Apr. 13   Perf. 12x12½
36	A12	140o Gannets	.50	.50
37	A12	180o Puffins	.65	.65
38	A12	400o Guillemots	1.60	1.25
		Nos. 36-38 (3)	2.75	2.40

1978, Dec. 7   Perf. 13
39	A13	140o shown	.50	.50
40	A13	180o New library	.60	.60

Completion of New Library Building.

Girl Guide, Tent and Fire — A14   Ram — A15

1978, Dec. 7   Photo.   Perf. 13½
41	A14	140o multicolored	.50	.50

Faroese Girl Guides, 50th anniversary.

Lithographed and Engraved
1979, Mar. 19   Perf. 12
42	A15	25k multicolored	6.50	6.50

Denmark No. 88a — A16

Europa: 180o, Faroe Islands No. 1.

1979, May 7   Perf. 12½
43	A16	140o yellow & blue	.50	.50
44	A16	180o rose, grn & blk	.60	.60

Girl Wearing Festive Costume — A17

Children's Drawings and IYC Emblem: 150o, Fisherman. 200o, Two friends.

1979, Oct. 1   Perf. 12
45	A17	110o multicolored	.40	.40
46	A17	150o multicolored	.50	.50
47	A17	200o multicolored	.60	.60
		Nos. 45-47 (3)	1.50	1.50

International Year of the Child.

Sea Plantain — A18

1980, Mar. 17   Photo.   Perf. 12x11½
48	A18	90o shown	.30	.30
49	A18	110o Glacier buttercup	.40	.40
50	A18	150o Purple saxifrage	.55	.55
51	A18	200o Starry saxifrage	.65	.65
52	A18	400o Lady's mantle	1.00	1.00
		Nos. 48-52 (5)	2.90	2.90

Jakob Jakobsen (1864-1918), Linguist — A19   Coat of Arms, Virgin and Child, Gothic Pew Gable — A20

Europa: 200o, Vensel Ulrich Hammershaimb (1819-1909), theologian, linguist and folklorist.

1980, Oct. 6   Engr.   Perf. 11½
53	A19	150o dull green	.40	.40
54	A19	200o dull red brown	.60	.60

Photo. & Engr.
1980, Oct. 6   Perf. 13½

Kirkjubour Pew Gables, 15th Century: 140o, Norwegian coat of arms, John the Baptist. 150o, Christ's head, St. Peter. 200o, Hand in halo, Apostle Paul.

55	A20	110o multicolored	.30	.30
56	A20	140o multicolored	.50	.50
57	A20	150o multicolored	.50	.50
58	A20	200o multicolored	.65	.65
		Nos. 55-58 (4)	1.95	1.95

See Nos. 102-105, 389-392.

A21

Sketches of Old Torshavn by Ingalzur Reyni.

1981, Mar. 2   **Engr.**
59	A21	110o dark green	.30	.30
60	A21	140o black	.50	.50
61	A21	150o dark brown	.50	.50
62	A21	200o dark blue	.60	.60
		Nos. 59-62 (4)	1.90	1.90

The Ring Dance A22

Europa: 200o, The garter dance.

1981, June 1   **Engr.**   **Perf. 13x14**
63	A22	150o pale rose & grn	.35	.35
64	A22	200o pale yel grn & dk brn	.55	.55

Rune Stones, 800-1000 AD — A23

Historic Writings: 1k, Folksong, 1846. 3k, Sheep Letter excerpt, 1298. 6k, Seal and text, 1533. 10k, Titlepage from Faeroae et Faeroa, by Lucas Jacobson Debes, library.

Photo. & Engr.

1981, Oct. 19   **Perf. 11½**
65	A23	10o multicolored	.25	.25
66	A23	1k multicolored	.30	.30
67	A23	3k multicolored	.85	.75
68	A23	6k multicolored	1.75	1.40
69	A23	10k multicolored	3.00	3.00
		Nos. 65-69 (5)	6.15	5.70

Nos. 70-80 not assigned.

Europa 1982 — A24

1982, Mar. 15   **Engr.**   **Perf. 13½**
81	A24	1.50k Viking North Atlantic routes	.45	.45
82	A24	2k Viking house foundation	.65	.65

View of Gjogv, by Ingalvur av Reyni A25

1982, June 7   **Litho.**   **Perf. 12½x13**
83	A25	180o shown	.40	.40
84	A25	220o Hvalvik	1.10	.90
85	A25	250o Kvivik	.65	.65
		Nos. 83-85 (3)	2.15	1.95

Ballad of Harra Paetur and Elinborg — A26

Scenes from the medieval ballad of chivalry.

1982, Sept. 27   **Litho.**
86	A26	220o multicolored	.65	.65
87	A26	250o multicolored	.75	.75
88	A26	350o multicolored	1.00	1.00
89	A26	450o multicolored	1.40	1.40
		Nos. 86-89 (4)	3.80	3.80

Cargo Ships A27

1983, Feb. 21   **Litho.**   **Perf. 14x14½**
90	A27	220o Arcturus, 1856	.75	.75
91	A27	250o Laura, 1882	.90	.90
92	A27	700o Thyra, 1866	2.40	2.40
		Nos. 90-92 (3)	4.05	4.05

Chessmen, by Pol i Buo (1791-1857) — A28

1983, May 2   **Engr.**   **Perf. 13 Vert.**
Booklet Stamps
93		250o King	3.00	3.00
94		250o Queen	3.00	3.00
a.		Bklt. pane of 6, 3 each #93-94	17.50	
b.		A28 Pair, #93-94	6.00	6.00

Europa 1983 — A29

Nobel Prizewinners in Medicine: 250o, Niels R. Finsen (1860-1903), ultraviolet radiation pioneer. 400o, Alexander Fleming (1881-1955), discoverer of penicillin.

1983, June 6   **Engr.**   **Perf. 12x11½**
95	A29	250o dark blue	.65	.65
96	A29	400o red brown	1.10	1.10

A30

1983, Sept. 19   **Litho.**   **Perf. 12½x13**
97	A30	250o Tusk	.80	.80
98	A30	280o Haddock	1.10	1.10
99	A30	500o Halibut	1.60	1.60
100	A30	900o Catfish	3.00	3.00
		Nos. 97-100 (4)	6.50	6.50

Souvenir Sheet

Traditional Costumes — A31

Various national costumes.

1983, Nov. 4   **Litho.**   **Perf. 12**
101	A31	Sheet of 3	10.00	11.00
a.-c.		250o multicolored	2.25	2.25

Nordic House Cultural Center opening. Margin shows Scandinavian flags.

Pew Gables Type of 1980

Designs: 250o, John, shield with three crowns. 300o, St. Jacob, shield with crossed keys. 350o, Thomas, shield with crossbeam. 400o, Judas Taddeus, Toulouse cross halo.

Photo. & Engr.

1984, Jan. 30   **Perf. 14x13½**
102	A20	250o lil, pur & dk brn	.80	.80
103	A20	300o red brn, dk buff & dk brn	1.00	1.00
104	A20	350o blk, lt gray & dk brn	1.10	1.10
105	A20	400o ol grn, pale yel & dk brn	1.25	1.25
		Nos. 102-105 (4)	4.15	4.15

Europa (1959-84) A33

1984, Apr. 2   **Engr.**   **Perf. 13½**
106	A33	250o red	.60	.60
107	A33	500o dark blue	1.40	1.40

Sverri Patursson (1871-1960), Writer — A34

Poets: 2.50k, Joannes Patursson (1866-1946). 3k, J. H. O. Djurhuus (1881-1948). 4.50k, H.A. Djurhuus (1883-1951).

1984, May 28   **Engr.**   **Perf. 13½**
108	A34	2k olive green	.65	.65
109	A34	2.50k red	.75	.75
110	A34	3k dark blue	1.00	1.00
111	A34	4.50k violet	1.50	1.50
		Nos. 108-111 (4)	3.90	3.90

Faroese Smack (Fishing Boat) — A35

Perf. 12½x13, 13x12½

1984, Sept. 10   **Engr.**
112	A35	280o shown	.95	.95
113	A35	300o Fishermen, vert.	1.10	1.10
114	A35	12k Helmsman, vert.	4.50	4.50
		Nos. 112-114 (3)	6.55	6.55

Fairytale Illustrations by Elinborg Lutzen — A36

1984, Oct. 29   **Litho.**   **Perf. 13 Vert.**
Booklet Stamps
115	A36	140o Beauty of the Veils	6.00	6.00
116	A36	280o Veils, diff.	6.00	6.00
117	A36	280o Girl Shy Prince	6.00	6.00
118	A36	280o The Glass Sword	6.00	6.00
119	A36	280o Little Elin	6.00	6.00
120	A36	280o The Boy and the Ox	6.00	6.00
a.		Booklet pane of 6, #115-120	37.50	

View of Torshavn and the Forts, by Edward Dayes A37

Dayes' Landscapes, 1789: 280o, Skaeling. 550o, View Towards the North Seen from the Hills Near Torshavn in Stremoy, Faroes. 800o, The Moving Stones in Eysturoy, Faroes.

Litho. & Engr.

1985, Feb. 4   **Perf. 13**
121	A37	250o multicolored	.75	.75
122	A37	280o multicolored	1.00	1.00
123	A37	550o multicolored	2.25	2.25
124	A37	800o multicolored	3.00	3.00
		Nos. 121-124 (4)	7.00	7.00

Europa 1985 — A38

Children taking music lessons.

1985, Apr. 1   **Litho.**   **Perf. 13½x14½**
125	A38	280o multicolored	.85	.85
126	A38	550o multicolored	1.90	1.90

Paintings, Faroese Museum of Art A39

Designs: 550o, Winter's Day in Nolsoy, 1959, by Steffan Danielsen (1922-76). 450o, Self-Portrait, 1952, by Ruth Smith (1913-58), vert. 280o, The Garden, Hoyvik, 1973, by Thomas Arge (1942-78).

Litho. & Engr.

1985, June 3   **Perf. 12½**
127	A39	280o multicolored	1.25	1.25
128	A39	450o multicolored	1.75	1.75
129	A39	550o multicolored	2.50	2.50
		Nos. 127-129 (3)	5.50	5.50

Lighthouses — A40

1985, Sept. 23   **Litho.**   **Perf. 13½x14**
130	A40	270o Nolsoy, 1893	1.25	1.25
131	A40	320o Thorshavn, 1909	1.75	1.75
132	A40	350o Mykines, 1909	1.90	1.90
133	A40	470o Map of locations	2.40	2.40
		Nos. 130-133 (4)	7.30	7.30

Passenger Aviation in the Faroes, 22nd Anniv. A41

Perf. 13½ Horiz.

1985, Oct. 28   **Photo.**
Booklet Stamps
134	A41	300o Douglas DC-3	3.00	3.00
135	A41	300o Fokker Friendship	3.00	3.00
136	A41	300o Boeing 737	3.00	3.00
137	A41	300o Interisland LM-IKB	3.00	3.00
138	A41	300o Helicopter Snipan	3.00	3.00
a.		Booklet pane of 5, #134-138	16.00	16.00

Skrimsla, Ancient Folk Ballad — A42

1986, Feb. 3   **Litho.**   **Perf. 12½x13**
139	A42	300o Peasant in woods	1.10	1.10
140	A42	420o Meets Giant	1.75	1.75
141	A42	550o Giant loses game	2.00	2.00

142 A42 650o Giant grants Peas-
　　　　　ant's wish　　　　2.25 2.25
　　　Nos. 139-142 (4)　　　7.10 7.10

Europa
1986 — A43

Amnesty Intl.,
25th
Anniv. — A44

1986, Apr. 7　Litho.　Perf. 13½
143 A43　3k shown　　　　*1.00 1.00*
144 A43　5.50k Sea pollution　*1.75 1.75*

1986, June 2　　　Perf. 14x13½
Winning design competition artwork.
145 A44　3k Olivur vid Neyst　1.25 1.25
146 A44　4.70k Eli Smith　　1.90 1.90
147 A44　5.50k Ranna Kunoy　2.40 2.40
　　　Nos. 145-147 (3)　　　5.55 5.55

Nos. 145-146 horiz.

Souvenir Sheet

HAFNIA '87, Copenhagen — A45

Design: East Bay of Torshavn, watercolor,
1782, by Christian Rosenmeyer (1728-1802).

1986, Aug. 29　Litho.　Perf. 13x13½
148 A45　Sheet of 3　　　10.00 10.00
　a.　3k multicolored　　　3.25 3.25
　b.　4.70k multicolored　　3.25 3.25
　c.　6.50k multicolored　　3.25 3.25

Sold for 20k.

Old Stone
Bridges
A46

2.70k, Glyvrar on Eysturoy. 3k,
Leypanagjogv on Vagar, vert. 13k, Skaelinger
on Streymoy.

Perf. 13½x14½, 14½x13½
1986, Oct. 13　　　　　　Engr.
149 A46　2.70k dp brown vio　2.25 2.25
150 A46　3k bluish blk　　1.90 1.90
151 A46　13k gray green　　4.00 4.00
　　　Nos. 149-151 (3)　　　8.15 8.15

Farmhouses — A47

Traditional architecture: 300o, Depil on
Borooy, 1814. 420o, Depil, diff. 470o, Frammi
vio Gjonna on Streymoy, c. 1814. 650o,
Frammi, diff.

1987, Feb. 9　Engr.　Perf. 13x14½
152 A47　300o pale blue & blue　1.10 1.10
153 A47　420o buff & brown　1.75 1.75
154 A47　470o pale grn & dp grn　2.10 2.10
155 A47　650o pale gray & black　2.75 2.75
　　　Nos. 152-155 (4)　　　7.70 7.70

Europa 1987 — A48

Nordic House.

1987, Apr. 6　　　　Perf. 13x14
156 A48　300o Exterior　　*.85　.85*
157 A48　550o Interior　　*1.90 1.60*

Fishing
Trawlers
A49

1987, June 1　Litho.　Perf. 14x13½
158 A49　3k Joannes Patur-
　　　　　sson　　　　　.90　.90
159 A49　5.50k Magnus Heinason　1.90 1.90
160 A49　8k Sjurdarberg　　4.00 4.00
　　　Nos. 158-160 (3)　　　6.80 6.80

Hestur
(Horse)
Island
A50

Litho. & Engr.
1987, Sept. 7　　　　　　Perf. 13
161 A50　270o Map　　　1.00 1.00
162 A50　300o Seaport　　.90　.90
163 A50　420o Bird cliff　　1.90 1.90
164 A50　470o Pasture, sheep　2.25 2.25
165 A50　550o Seashore　　2.25 2.25
　　　Nos. 161-165 (5)　　　8.30 8.30

Nos. 161, 163 and 165 vert.

Collages
by
Zacharias
Heinesen
A51

West Bay of Torshavn, Watercolor by
Rosenmeyer — A52

1987, Oct. 16　Litho.　Perf. 13½x14
166 A51　4.70k Eystaravag　1.75 1.75
167 A51　6.50k Vestarvag　　2.25 2.25

Souvenir Sheet
Perf. 13½x13
168 A52　3k multicolored　　3.50 3.50

HAFNIA '87. Sold for 4k.

Flowers — A53　　Europa — A54

1988, Feb. 8　Litho.　Perf. 11½
Granite Paper
169 A53　2.70k Bellis perennis　1.40 1.40
170 A53　3k Dactylorchis
　　　　　maculata　　　.75　.75
171 A53　4.70k Potentilla erecta　2.10 2.10
172 A53　9k Pinguicula vul-
　　　　　garis　　　　3.00 3.00
　　　Nos. 169-172 (4)　　　7.25 7.25

1988, Apr. 11　Photo.　Perf. 11½
Communication and transport.
173 A54　3k Satellite dish, sat-
　　　　　ellite　　　*1.10 1.10*
174 A54　5.50k Fork lift, crane,
　　　　　ship　　　*1.90 1.90*

A55　　　　　　A56

Writers: 270o, Jorgen-Frantz Jacobsen
(1900-38). 300o, Christian Matras (b. 1900).
470o, William Heinesen (b. 1900). 650o,
Hedin Bru (1901-87).

1988, June 6　Engr.　Perf. 13½
175 A55　270o myrtle green　1.60 1.60
176 A55　300o rose lake　　1.40 1.40
177 A55　470o dark blue　　2.10 2.10
178 A55　650o brown black　2.40 2.40
　　　Nos. 175-178 (4)　　　7.50 7.50

1988, Sept. 5　Photo.　Perf. 12
Text, illustrations and cameo portraits of
organizers: 3k, Announcement and Djoni Geil,
Enok Baerentsen and H.H. Jacobsen. 3.20k,
Meeting, Rasmus Effersoe, C.L. Johannesen
and Samal Krakusteini. 12k, Oystercatcher
and lyrics of *Now the Hour Has Come,* by poet
Sverri Patursson (1871-1960), Just A. Husum,
Joannes Patursson and Jens Olsen.

Granite Paper
179 A56　3k multicolored　　1.25 1.25
180 A56　3.20k multicolored　1.50 1.50
181 A56　12k multicolored　　5.00 5.00
　　　Nos. 179-181 (3)　　　7.75 7.75

1888 Christmas meeting to preserve cultural
traditions and the natl. language, cent.

Kirkjubour
Cathedral
Ruins
A57

270o, Exterior. 300o, Arch. 470o, Crucifixion, bas-relief. 550o, Interior.

1988, Oct. 17　Engr.　Perf. 13
182 A57　270o dark green　1.90 1.90
183 A57　300o dark bl, vert.　1.50 1.50
184 A57　470o dark brn, vert.　2.10 2.10
185 A57　550o dark violet　　2.25 2.25
　　　Nos. 182-185 (4)　　　7.75 7.75

Havnar
Church,
Torshavn,
200th
Anniv.
A58

Designs: 350o, Church exterior. 500o,
Crypt, vert. 15k, Bell, vert.

1989, Feb. 6　Engr.　Perf. 13
186 A58　350o dark green　1.25 1.25
187 A58　500o dark brown　2.40 2.40
188 A58　15k deep blue　　4.50 4.50
　　　Nos. 186-188 (3)　　　8.15 8.15

Folk
Costumes — A59

Photo. & Engr.
1989, Apr. 10　　　　Perf. 13½
189 A59　350o Man　　　1.25 1.25
190 A59　600o Woman　　2.50 2.50

Europa
1989 — A60

Wooden children's toys.

1989, Apr. 10　Photo.　Perf. 12x11½
Granite Paper
191 A60　3.50k Boat　　*1.25 1.25*
192 A60　6k Horse　　*2.00 2.00*

Island Games,
July 5-
13 — A61

1989, June 5　Photo.　Perf. 12½
Granite Paper
193 A61　200o Rowing　　.90　.90
194 A61　350o Handball　　1.50 1.50
195 A61　600o Soccer　　2.40 2.40
196 A61　700o Swimming　2.75 2.75
　　　Nos. 193-196 (4)　　　7.55 7.55

A62　　　　　　A63

Bird cliffs of Suduroy.

1989, Oct. 2　Engr.　Perf. 14x13½
197 A62　320o Tvoran　　1.25 1.25
198 A62　350o Skuvanes　　1.60 1.60
199 A62　500o Beinisvord　2.10 2.10
200 A62　600o Asmundarstakkur　2.40 2.40
　　　Nos. 197-200 (4)　　　7.35 7.35

1990, Feb. 5　Litho.　Perf. 14x13½
Modern fish factory (filleting station).
201 A63　3.50k Unloading fish　1.25 1.25
202 A63　3.70k Cleaning and sort-
　　　　　ing　　　　1.75 1.75
203 A63　5k Filleting　　2.00 2.00
204 A63　7k Packaged frozen
　　　　　fish　　　　2.50 2.50
　　　Nos. 201-204 (4)　　　7.50 7.50

Europa
1990 — A64

Post offices.

1990, Apr. 9　Litho.　Perf. 13½x14
205 A64　3.50k Gjogv　　*1.10 1.10*
206 A64　6k Klaksvik　　*2.00 2.00*

Souvenir Sheet

Recognition of the Merkid, Flag of the Faroes, by the British, 50th Anniv. — A65

Designs: a, Flag. b, Fishing trawler *Nyggjaberg,* disappeared, 1942. c, Sloop *Saana,* sunk by the Germans, 1942.

1990, Apr. 9 Photo. *Perf. 12*
Granite Paper
207 A65 Sheet of 3   5.00 5.00
a.-c.   3.50k any single   1.60 1.60

Whales A66

1990, June 6 Photo. *Perf. 11½*
Granite Paper
208 A66 320o *Mesoplodon bidens*   1.75 1.75
209 A66 350o *Balaena mysticetus*   2.25 2.25
210 A66 600o *Eubalaena glacialis*   3.50 3.50
211 A66 700o *Hyperoodon ampullatus*   5.50 5.50
   Nos. 208-211 (4)   13.00 13.00

Nolsoy Island by Steffan Danielsen A67

1990, Oct. 8 Photo. *Perf. 11½*
Granite Paper
212 A67 50o shown   .25 .25
213 A67 350o Coastline   1.60 1.60
214 A67 500o Town   1.90 1.90
215 A67 1000o Coastline, cliffs   3.75 3.75
   Nos. 212-215 (4)   7.50 7.50

Flora and Fauna — A68   Europa — A69

1991, Feb. 4 Litho. *Perf. 13*
216 A68 3.70k Plantago lanceolata   1.40 1.40
217 A68 4k Rumex longifolius   1.40 1.40
218 A68 4.50k Amara aulica   1.75 1.75
219 A68 6.50k Lumbricus terrestris   3.00 3.00
   Nos. 216-219 (4)   7.55 7.55

1991, Apr. 4 Litho. *Perf. 13*
Designs: 3.70k, Weather satellite. 6.50k, Celestial navigation.
220 A69 3.70k multicolored   *1.00 1.00*
221 A69 6.50k multicolored   *2.25 2.25*

Town of Torshavn, 125th Anniv. — A70

1991, Apr. 4 *Perf. 14x13½*
222 A70 3.70k Town Hall   1.25 1.25
223 A70 3.70k View of town   1.50 1.50

Birds — A71

1991, June 3 Litho. *Perf. 13½*
224 A71 3.70k Rissa tridactyla   1.50 1.50
225 A71 3.70k Sterna paradisaea   1.50 1.50
a.   Bklt. pane, 3 each #224-225   9.00

Village of Saksun A72

1991, June 3
226 A72 370o shown   1.50 1.50
227 A72 650o Cliffs of Vestmanna   2.50 2.50

Samal Joensen-Mikines (1906-1979), Painter — A73

1991, Oct. 7 Litho. *Perf. 13½*
228 A73 340o Funeral Procession   1.25 1.25
229 A73 370o The Farewell   1.40 1.40
230 A73 550o Handanagarthur   2.00 2.00
231 A73 1300o Winter morning   4.50 4.50
   Nos. 228-231 (4)   9.15 9.15

Mail Boats A74

1992, Feb. 10 Litho. *Perf. 13½x14*
232 A74 200o Ruth   .90 .90
233 A74 370o Ritan   1.50 1.50
234 A74 550o Sigmundur   2.25 2.25
235 A74 800o Masin   3.25 3.25
   Nos. 232-235 (4)   7.90 7.90

Europa A75

Designs: 3.70k, Map of North Atlantic, Viking ship. 6.50k, Map of Central Atlantic region, one of Columbus' ships.

1992, Apr. 6 Litho. *Perf. 13½x14*
236 A75 3.70k multicolored   *1.10 1.10*

237 A75 6.50k multicolored   *2.40 2.40*
Souvenir Sheet
238 A75 Sheet of 2, #236-237   *11.00 11.00*

First landing in the Americas by Leif Erikson (#236). Discovery of America by Christopher Columbus, 500th anniv. (#237).

Seals A76

1992, June 9 Litho. *Perf. 14x13½*
239 A76 3.70k Halichoerus grypus   1.60 1.60
240 A76 3.70k Phoca vitulina   1.60 1.60
a.   Bklt. pane, 3 #239, 3 #240   20.00

Minerals — A77

1992, June 9 Photo. *Perf. 12*
Granite Paper
241 A77 370o Stilbite   1.75 1.75
242 A77 650o Mesolite   2.25 2.25

Traditional Houses A78

1992, Oct. 5 Litho. *Perf. 13½*
243 A78 3.40k Hja Glyvra Hanusi   1.25 1.25
244 A78 3.70k I Nordragotu   1.90 1.90
245 A78 6.50k Blasastova   2.40 2.40
246 A78 8k Jakupsstova   2.75 2.75
   Nos. 243-246 (4)   8.30 8.30

Nordic House Entertainers — A79

1993, Feb. 8 Litho. *Perf. 13½*
247 A79 400o Dancers   1.50 1.50
248 A79 400o Pianist   1.50 1.50
249 A79 400o Trio   1.50 1.50
a.   Souv. sheet, #247-249, perf 12½   4.75 4.75
   Nos. 247-249 (3)   4.50 4.50

Village of Gjogv A80

1993, Apr. 5
250 A80 4k View toward sea   1.75 1.75
251 A80 4k Ravine, village   1.75 1.75
a.   Booklet pane, 3 each #250-251   10.50

Europa — A81   Horses — A82

Sculptures by Hans Pauli Olsen: 4k, Movement. 7k, Reflection.

1993, Apr. 5
252 A81 4k multicolored   *1.50 1.50*
253 A81 7k multicolored   *2.50 2.50*

Perf. 13½x13, 13x13½
1993, June 7 Engr.
254 A82 400o shown   1.50 1.50
255 A82 20k Mare, foal, horiz.   7.50 7.50

Butterflies A83

1993, Oct. 4 Litho. *Perf. 14½*
256 A83 350o Apamea zeta   1.50 1.50
257 A83 400o Hepialus humuli   1.75 1.75
258 A83 700o Vanessa atalanta   2.50 2.50
259 A83 900o Perizoma albulata   3.25 3.25
   Nos. 256-259 (4)   9.00 9.00

Fish — A84

1994, Feb. 7 Litho. *Perf. 14½*
260 A84 10o Gasterosteus aculeatus   .50 .50
261 A84 4k Neocyttus helgae   1.75 1.75
262 A84 7k Salmo trutta fario   2.50 2.50
263 A84 10k Hoplostethus atlanticus   3.50 3.50
   Nos. 260-263 (4)   8.25 8.25

Voyages of St. Brendan (484-577) A85

Europa: 4k, St. Brendan on island with sheep, Irish monks in boat. 7k, St. Brendan, monks sailing past volcano.

1994, Apr. 18 *Perf. 14½x14*
264 A85 4k multicolored   *1.25 1.25*
265 A85 7k multicolored   *2.40 2.00*
a.   Miniature sheet of 2, #264-265   4.75 4.75

Nos. 264-265 have designers name below the design. Stamps in No. 265a do not.
See Iceland Nos. 780-781; Ireland Nos. 923-924.

Sheepdogs — A86

School of Navigation A87

Design: No. 267, Dog watching over sheep.

1994, June 6　Litho.　Perf. 13½
266　A86　4k multicolored　1.50 1.50

Size: 39x25mm
267　A86　4k multicolored　1.50 1.50
　a.　Booklet pane, 3 each #266-267　9.00
　　　Complete booklet, #267a　10.00

1994, June 6

Designs: 3.50k, Man using sextant, schooner. 7k, Ship, man at computer.

268　A87　3.50k multicolored　1.25 1.25
269　A87　7k multicolored　2.75 2.75

Brusajokil's Lay — A88

Scenes, verses of the ballad: 1k, Ship at sea. 4k, Asbjorn entering Brusajokil's cave. 6k, Ormar with cat, trolls. 7k, Ormar pulling Brusajokil's beard.

1994, Sept. 19　Litho.　Perf. 14
270　A88　1k multicolored　.40 .40
271　A88　4k multicolored　1.75 1.75
272　A88　6k multicolored　2.25 2.25
273　A88　7k multicolored　2.75 2.75
　　Nos. 270-273 (4)　7.15 7.15

Twelve Days of Christmas A89

#274, Goats, men, deer, hides. #275, Ducks, cattle, sheep, horses, banners, barrels.

1994, Oct. 31　Litho.　Perf. 14x13
274　A89　4k multicolored　1.50 1.50
275　A89　4k multicolored　1.50 1.50
　a.　Bklt. pane, 3 each #274-275　9.00
　　　Complete booklet, #275a　9.00

Leafhoppers — A90

Designs: 50o, Ulopa reticulata. 4k, Streptanus sordidus. 5k, Anoscopus flavostriatus. 13k, Macrosteles alpinus.

1995, Feb. 6　Litho.　Perf. 14
276　A90　50o multicolored　.30 .30
277　A90　4k multicolored　1.75 1.75
278　A90　5k multicolored　1.75 1.75
279　A90　13k multicolored　5.25 5.25
　　Nos. 276-279 (4)　9.05 9.05

Tourism A91

1995, Apr. 10　Litho.　Perf. 13½x14
280　A91　4k Village of Famjin　1.50 1.50
281　A91　4k Vatnsdalur valley　1.50 1.50

Peace & Freedom A92

Europa: 4k, Island couple, "Vidar, vali og baldur." 7k, Couple looking toward sun, "Liv og livtrasir."

1995, Apr. 10　Perf. 13x14
282　A92　4k multicolored　1.50 1.50
283　A92　7k multicolored　2.50 2.50

Nordic Art — A93

Designs: 2k, Museum of Art, Torshavn. 4k, Woman, by Frimod Joensen, vert. 5.50k, Self-portrait, by Joensen, vert.

Perf. 13½x14, 14x13½
1995, June 12　Litho.
284　A93　2k multicolored　.75 .75
285　A93　4k multicolored　1.50 1.50
286　A93　5.50k multicolored　2.00 2.00
　　Nos. 284-286 (3)　4.25 4.25

Corvus Corax A94

1995, June 12　Perf. 13½x14
287　A94　4k Black raven　1.50 1.50
288　A94　4k White-speckled raven　1.50 1.50
　a.　Booklet pane, 5 each #287-288　15.00
　　　Complete booklet, #288a　15.00

Saint Olaf (955?-1030), Patron Saint of Faroe Islands — A95

Litho. & Engr.
1995, Sept. 12　Perf. 13½x13
289　A95　4k multicolored　1.75 1.75

See Aland Islands No. 119.

Early Folk Life — A95a

4k, Dairy maids carrying buckets. 6k, Peasants fleecing sheep. 15k, Schooners, saltfish being brought ashore, vert.

1995, Sept. 12　Engr.　Perf. 12½
290　A95a　4k dark green　1.50 1.50
291　A95a　6k dark brn, vert.　2.25 2.25
292　A95a　15k dark blue　5.50 5.50
　　Nos. 290-292 (3)　9.25 9.25

Church of Mary Catholic Church — A96

Designs: No. 293, Stained glass window. No. 294, Exterior view of church.

1995, Nov. 9　Litho.　Perf. 13½
293　A96　4k multicolored　1.50 1.50
294　A96　4k multicolored　1.50 1.50
　a.　Booklet pane, 5 ea #293-294　15.00
　　　Complete booklet, #294a　15.00

Rocky Coastline — A97　　Seaweed — A98

1996, Jan. 1　Litho.　Perf. 14
295　A97　4.50k multicolored　1.60 1.60

1996, Feb. 12　Perf. 15

4k, Ptilota plumosa. 5.50k, Fucus spiralis. 6k, Ascophyllum nodosum. 9k, Laminaria hyperborea.

296　A98　4k multicolored　1.40 1.40
297　A98　5.50k multicolored　2.00 2.00
298　A98　6k multicolored　2.00 2.00
299　A98　9k multicolored　3.25 3.25
　　Nos. 296-299 (4)　8.65 8.65

Birds — A99

A100

1996, Apr. 15　Litho.　Perf. 14x15
300　A99　4.50k Laxia curvirostra　1.50 1.50
301　A99　4.50k Bombycilla garrulus　1.50 1.50
　a.　Booklet pane, 5 each #300-301　15.00
　　　Complete booklet, #301a　15.00

See Nos. 313-314.

1996, Apr. 15　Perf. 15x14½, 14½x15

Europa (Wives of Faroese Seamen): 4.50k, Woman standing beside sea coast. 7.50k, Portrait of a woman, vert.

302　A100　4.50k multicolored　1.50 1.50
303　A100　7.50k multicolored　2.50 2.50

A101

Nordatlantex '96 (Children's drawings): a, Boy playing with hoop, stick, by Bugvi. b, Two girls on steet, road sign, by Gudrid. c, Girl on bicycle, car on street, by Herborg.

1996, June 7　Litho.　Perf. 14½
Souvenir Sheet of 3
304　A101　4.50k #a.-c.　5.00 5.00

A102

Sea bed off the Faroes.

Litho. & Engr.
1996, June 7　Perf. 13
305　A102　10k violet & multi　3.50 3.50
306　A102　16k green & multi　5.50 5.50

See Nos. 319-320, 343, 377-378.

Janus Kamban (b. 1913), Sculptor, Graphic Artist A103

Works of art: 4.50k, Flock of Sheep. 6.50k, Fisherman on the Way Home. 7.50k, View from Tórshavn's Old Quarter.

1996, Sept. 16　Litho.　Perf. 14
307　A103　4.50k multicolored　1.50 1.50
308　A103　6.50k multicolored　2.25 2.25
309　A103　7.50k multicolored　2.50 2.50
　　Nos. 307-309 (3)　6.25 6.25

A104

Christianschurch, Klaksvík — A105

1996, Nov. 4　Litho.　Perf. 14x15
310　A104　4.50k Exterior　1.50 1.50
311　A105　4.50k Interior, altar fresco　1.50 1.50
　a.　Booklet pane, 6 #310, 4 #311　15.00
　　　Complete booklet, #311a　15.00

Christmas.

Souvenir Sheet

Reign of Queen Margaret II, 25th Anniv. — A106

1997, Jan. 14　Litho.　Perf. 14½
312　A106　4.50k multicolored　1.50 1.50

Bird Type of 1996

1997, Feb. 27　Litho.　Perf. 14x15
313　A99　4.50k Pyrrhula pyrrhula　1.50 1.50
314　A99　4.50k Carduelis flammea　1.50 1.50
　a.　Booklet pane, 5 each #313-314　15.00
　　　Complete booklet, #314a　15.00

Mushrooms — A107

Designs: 4.50k, Hygrocybe helobia. 6k, Hygrocybe chlorophana. 6.50k, Hygrocybe virginea. 7.50k, Hygrocybe psittacina.

1997, Feb. 17　Perf. 14½
315　A107　4.50k multicolored　1.40 1.40
316　A107　6k multicolored　2.00 2.00
317　A107　6.50k multicolored　2.25 2.25
318　A107　7.50k multicolored　2.50 2.50
　　Nos. 315-318 (4)　8.15 8.15

Map Type of 1996
Litho. & Engr.

1997, May 20		Perf. 13	
319	A102 11k red & multi	3.50	3.50
320	A102 18k claret & multi	5.50	5.50

Europa — A108

Kalmar Union, 600th Anniv. — A109

Legends illustrated by William Heinesen: 4.50k, The Temptations of Saint Anthony. 7.50k, The Merman sitting at bottom of sea eating fish bait.

1997, May 20	Litho.	Perf. 14½	
321	A108 4.50k multicolored	1.50	1.50
322	A108 7.50k multicolored	2.50	2.50

1997, May 20	Engr.	Perf. 12½	
323	A109 4.50k deep blue violet	1.50	1.50

A110

A111

Barbara, Film Shot in Faroe Islands (Scenes from film): 4.50k, Danish theologian Poul Aggerso arriving at Faroe Islands. 6.50k, Barbara and Poul. 7.50k, Barbara with men on boat. 9k, Barbara in row boat, sailing ship.

1997, Sept. 15	Litho.	Perf. 14	
324	A110 4.50k multicolored	1.50	1.50
325	A110 6.50k multicolored	2.10	2.10
326	A110 7.50k multicolored	2.40	2.40
327	A110 9k multicolored	2.75	2.75
	Nos. 324-327 (4)	8.75	8.75

1997, Sept. 15

Hvalvik church.

328	A111 4.50k Interior	1.50	1.50
329	A111 4.50k Exterior	1.50	1.50
a.	Booklet pane, 5 each #328-329	15.00	—
	Complete booklet, #329a	15.00	

Birds — A112

A113

1998, Feb. 23	Litho.	Perf. 14x14½	
330	A112 4.50k Sturnus vulgaris	1.40	1.40
331	A112 4.50k Turdus merula	1.40	1.40
a.	Bklt. pane, 5 each #330-331	14.00	
	Complete booklet, #331a	14.00	

1998, Feb. 23   **Perf. 14**

Scenes from the Sigurd poem "Brynhild's Ballad": 4.50k, King Buole, daughter Brynhild. 6.50k, Sigurd riding through wall of fire on

horseback. 7.50k, Sigurd, Brynhild together. 10k, Guthrun alone leading horse.

332	A113 4.50k multicolored	1.40	1.40
333	A113 6.50k multicolored	2.00	2.00
334	A113 7.50k multicolored	2.25	2.25
335	A113 10k multicolored	3.00	3.00
	Nos. 332-335 (4)	8.65	8.65

Europa — A114

A115

1998, May 18	Litho.	Perf. 14	
336	A114 4.50k Parade	1.50	1.50
337	A114 7.50k Processional	2.50	2.50

Olavsoka, Natl. Festival of Faroe Islands.

1998, May 18		Perf. 14½	
338	A115 7.50k multicolored	2.25	2.25

UN Declaration of Human Rights, 50th anniv.

Intl. Year of the Ocean A116

Toothed whales: 4k, Lagenorhynchus acutus. 4.50k, Orcinus orca. 7k, Tursiops truncatus. 9k, Delphinapterus leucas.

1998, May 18		Perf. 14½x14	
339	A116 4k multicolored	1.25	1.25
340	A116 4.50k multicolored	1.40	1.40
341	A116 7k multicolored	2.25	2.25
342	A116 9k multicolored	2.75	2.75
	Nos. 339-342 (4)	7.65	7.65

Map Type of 1996
Litho. & Engr.

1998, Sept. 14		Perf. 13	
343	A102 14k multicolored	4.50	4.50

Frederickschurch A117

1998, Sept. 14	Litho.	Perf. 14	
344	A117 4.50k Exterior, coast-line	1.40	1.40
345	A117 4.50k Interior	1.40	1.40
a.	Bklt. pane, 5 each #344-345	14.00	
	Complete booklet, #345a	14.00	

A118

A119

Paintings by Hans Hansen (1920-70): 4.50k, Fell-field, 1966. 5.50k, Village Interior, 1965. 6.50k, Portrait of Farmer Ólavur í Utistovu from Mikladalur, 1968. 8k, Self-portrait, 1968.

Perf. 13½x14, 14x13½
1998, Sept. 14

346	A118 4.50k multi	1.40	1.40
347	A118 5.50k multi	1.75	1.75
348	A118 6.50k multi, vert.	2.10	2.10
349	A118 8k multi, vert.	2.50	2.50
	Nos. 346-349 (4)	7.75	7.75

1999, Feb. 22	Litho.	Perf. 13½	
Birds.			
350	A119 4.50k Passer domesticus	1.40	1.40
351	A119 4.50k Troglodytes troglodytes	1.40	1.40
a.	Bklt. pane, 5 each #350-351	14.00	
	Complete booklet, #351a	14.00	

Ships Named "Smyril" A120

1999, Feb. 22		Perf. 14½x14	
352	A120 4.50k 1895	1.40	1.40
353	A120 5k 1932	1.60	1.60
354	A120 8k 1967	2.50	2.50
355	A120 13k 1975	4.25	4.25
	Nos. 352-355 (4)	9.75	9.75

Northern Islands A121

1999, May 25	Litho.	Perf. 13½	
356	A121 50o Kalsoy	.20	.20
357	A121 100o Vithoy	.35	.35
358	A121 400o Svinoy	1.25	1.25
359	A121 450o Fugloy	1.40	1.40
360	A121 600o Kunoy	1.90	1.90
361	A121 800o Borthoy	2.75	2.75
	Nos. 356-361 (6)	7.85	7.85

See Nos. 383-386.

Waterfalls — A122

Europa: 6k, Svartifossur. 8k, Foldarafossur.

1999, May 25		Perf. 14x14½	
362	A122 6k multicolored	2.00	2.00
363	A122 8k multicolored	2.75	2.75

Abstract Paintings of Ingálvur av Reyni — A123

1999, Sept. 27	Litho.	Perf. 12½	
364	A123 4.50k Bygd	1.40	1.40
365	A123 6k Húsavik	1.75	1.75
366	A123 8k Reytt regn	2.40	2.40
367	A123 20k Genta	6.25	6.25
	Nos. 364-367 (4)	11.80	11.80

Bible Stories — A124

1999, Sept. 27		Perf. 14½x14	
368	A124 450o John 1:1-5	1.50	1.50
a.	Booklet pane of 6	9.00	
	Complete booklet, #368a	9.00	
369	A124 600o Luke 1:26-28	2.00	2.00
a.	Booklet pane of 6	12.00	
	Complete booklet, #369a	12.00	

See Nos. 387-388, 407-408.

A125

A126

Christianity in the Faroes, 1000th Anniv.: 4.50k, Man on rocks in ocean. 5.50k, Monk with cross, man with sword. 8k, People, flags. 16k, Cross in sky.

Perf. 13½x13¼

2000, Feb. 21		Litho.	
370	A125 4.50k multi	1.40	1.40
371	A125 5.50k multi	1.75	1.75
372	A125 8k multi	2.50	2.50
373	A125 16k multi	5.00	5.00
	Nos. 370-373 (4)	10.65	10.65

2000, Feb. 21

School and: No. 374, Sanna av Skarthi, Anna Suffia Rasmussen, wives of founders. No. 375, Rasmus Rasmussen (1871-1962), Símun av Skarthi (1872-1942), school founders.

374	A126 4.50k multi	1.40	1.40
375	A126 4.50k multi	1.40	1.40
a.	Bklt. pane, 4 ea #374-375	11.50	
	Complete booklet, #375a	11.50	

Faroese Folk High School, cent.

Europa, 2000
Common Design Type

2000, May 9	Litho.	Perf. 13¼x13	
376	CD17 8k multi	3.00	3.00

Map Type of 1996
Litho. & Engr.

2000, May 22		Perf. 13¼x13	
377	A102 15k multi	4.50	4.50
378	A102 22k multi	7.00	7.00

Stampin' The Future Children's Stamp Design Contest Winners A127

Art by: 4k, Katrin Mortensen. 4.50k, Sigga Andreassen. 6k, Steingrímur Joensen. 8k, Dion Dam Frandsen.

2000, May 22	Litho.	Perf. 13x13¼	
379	A127 4k multi	1.25	1.25
380	A127 4.50k multi	1.40	1.40
381	A127 6k multi	2.00	2.00
382	A127 8k multi	2.50	2.50
	Nos. 379-382 (4)	7.15	7.15

Island Type of 1999

2000, Sept. 18	Litho.	Perf. 13½	
383	A121 200o Skúvoy	.75	.75
384	A121 650o Hestoy	2.00	2.00
385	A121 750o Koltur	2.25	2.25
386	A121 1000o Nólsoy	3.25	3.25
	Nos. 383-386 (4)	8.25	8.25

Bible Story Type of 1999

2000, Sept. 18	Litho.	Perf. 13x13¼	
387	A124 4.50k Micah 5:1	1.50	1.50
a.	Booklet pane of 6	9.00	
	Booklet, #387a	9.00	
388	A124 6k John 1:14	2.00	2.00
a.	Booklet pane of 6	12.00	
	Booklet, #388a	12.00	

Pew Gables Type of 1980

Kirkjubour pew gables: 430o, St. Andrew with cross. 650o, St. Bartholomew. 800o, Unknown apostle. 18k, Unknown apostle, diff.

Photo. & Engr.

2001, Feb. 12		Perf. 12¾x12½	
389	A20 450o multi	1.40	1.40
390	A20 650o multi	2.10	2.10
391	A20 800o multi	2.50	2.50
392	A20 18k multi	5.50	5.50
	Nos. 389-392 (4)	11.50	11.50

Faroese Red Cross, 75th Anniv. A128

Designs: 4.50k, Old person. 6k, Relief worker.

2001, Feb. 12   Litho.   Perf. 14½x14

393	A128	4.50k multi	1.50	1.50
a.		Booklet pane of 6	9.00	
		Booklet, #393a	9.00	
394	A128	6k multi	2.00	2.00
a.		Booklet pane of 6	12.00	
		Booklet, #394a	12.00	

Souvenir Sheet

Faroe Islands Postal Service, 25th Anniv. — A129

No. 395: a, Boat for interisland mail transport, 19th cent. b, Tórshavn post office, 1906. c, Simon Pauli Poulsen (Morkabóndin), mail carrier.

Photo. & Engr.

2001, Apr. 1   Perf. 13x13¼

395	A129	4.50k Sheet of 3, #a-c	5.00	5.00

Nordic Myths and Legends About Light and Darkness — A130

No. 396: a, The Death of Hogni. b, The Tree of the Year. c, The Harp. d, Gram and Grane. e, The Ballad of Nornagest. f, Gudrun's Evil Magic.

Litho. with Foil Application

2001, Apr. 1   Perf. 13½x13¼

396	A130	6k Sheet of 6, #a-f	12.00	12.00

Hafnia 2001 Philatelic Exhibition, Copenhagen.

Paintings by Zacharias Heinesen A131

Designs: 4k, The Artist's Mother, 1992. 4.50k, Úti á Reyni, 1974. 10k, Ur Vágunum, 2000. 15k, Sunrise, 1975.

2001, June 11   Litho.   Perf. 13¼x13

397	A131	4k multi	1.25	1.25
398	A131	4.50k multi	1.40	1.40
399	A131	10k multi	3.25	3.25
400	A131	15k multi	4.75	4.75
		Nos. 397-400 (4)	10.65	10.65

Europa A132

Hydroelectric power stations: 6k, Fossáverkith. 8k, Eithisverkith.

2001, June 11   Perf. 13x13½

401	A132	6k multi	2.00	2.00
402	A132	8k multi	2.75	2.75

Whales — A133

Designs: 4.50k, Physeter macrocephalus. 6.50k, Balaenoptera physalus. 9k, Balaenoptera musculus. 20k, Balaenoptera borealis.

Perf. 13¾x13¼

2001, Sept. 17   Litho.

403	A133	4.50k multi	1.40	1.40
404	A133	6.50k multi	2.10	2.10
405	A133	9k multi	2.75	2.75
406	A133	20k multi	6.50	6.50
		Nos. 403-406 (4)	12.75	12.75

Bible Stories Type of 1999

2001, Sept. 17   Perf. 13

407	A124	5k Luke 2:34-35	1.75	1.75
a.		Booklet pane of 6	10.50	
		Booklet, #407a	10.50	
408	A124	6.50k Matthew 2:18	2.00	2.00
a.		Booklet pane of 6	12.00	
		Booklet, #408a	12.00	

Mollusks — A134

Designs: 5k, Sepiola atlantica. 7k, Modiolus modiolus. 7.50k, Polycera faeroensis. 18k, Buccinum undatum.

2002, Feb. 11   Litho.   Perf. 13

409	A134	5k multi	1.75	1.75
410	A134	7k multi	2.40	2.40
411	A134	7.50k multi	2.50	2.50
412	A134	18k multi	6.00	6.00
		Nos. 409-412 (4)	12.65	12.65

Portions of the designs were applied by a thermographic process producing a shiny, raised effect.

Souvenir Sheet

Viking Voyages — A135

No. 413: a, Navigation tool. b, Viking sailor on boat. c, Viking boat.

Litho. & Engr.

2002, Feb. 11   Perf. 13

413	A135	6.50k Sheet of 3, #a-c	6.75	6.75

Europa A136

Designs: 6.50k, Clowns. 8k, Various circus performers.

2002, Apr. 8   Litho.   Perf. 13¼x13½

414	A136	6.50k multi	2.25	2.25
415	A136	8k multi	2.75	2.75

Art by Tróndur Patursson A137

Designs: 5k, Bládypi. 6.50k, Kosmiska Rúmith.

2002, Apr. 8

416	A137	5k multi	1.75	1.75
417	A137	6.50k multi	2.25	2.25
a.		Booklet pane of 8, 4 each #416-417	16.00	—
		Booklet, #417a	16.00	

Eggs and Chicks — A138

Designs: 5k, Numenius phaeopus. 7.50k, Gallinago gallinago. 12k, Haematopus ostralegus. 20k, Pluvialis apricaria.

2002, June 17   Perf. 14x14½

418	A138	5k multi	1.75	1.75
419	A138	7.50k multi	2.50	2.50
420	A138	12k multi	4.00	4.00
421	A138	20k multi	6.75	6.75
		Nos. 418-421 (4)	15.00	15.00

Souvenir Sheet

Faroese Representative Council, 150th Anniv. — A139

Designs: 5k, Royal book and seal. 6.50k, Royal book, Protocol of 1852.

2002, June 17   Perf. 14

422	A139	Sheet of 2, #a-b	4.50	4.50

Falco Columbarius Subaesalon — A140

Litho. & Embossed

2002, Sept. 23   Perf. 13¼

423	A140	30k multi	9.75	9.75

Gota Church — A141

2002, Sept. 23   Litho.   Perf. 12½

424	A141	5k Exterior	1.75	1.75
425	A141	6.50k Interior	2.25	2.25
a.		Booklet pane, 5 each #424-425	20.00	
		Booklet, #425a	20.00	

Souvenir Sheet

Intl. Council for the Exploration of the Sea, Cent. — A142

No. 426: a, Micromesistius poutassou and island. b, Exploration ship Magnus Heinason and fish.

Litho. & Engr.

2002, Sept. 23   Perf. 13

426	A142	8k Sheet of 2, #a-b	5.50	5.50

See Denmark Nos. 1237-1238, Greenland Nos. 401-402.

Opening of Vagár-Streymoy Tunnel, Nov. 2002 — A143

Designs: No. 427, Wheeled tunneling machine at right. No. 428, Workers in red uniforms at left.

2003, Feb. 24   Litho.   Perf. 13¼x13

427	A143	5k multi	1.50	1.50
428	A143	5k multi	1.50	1.50
a.		Booklet pane, 5 each #427-428	15.00	
		Complete booklet, #428a	15.00	

Voluspá, Ancient Norse Poem — A144

No. 429: a, Seeress Heid holding staff. b, Heid sees animal and man in vision. c, Nude man and woman. d, Scribe and horseman. e, Battle between group with swords and man with hammer. f, Horseman and warriors. g, Men, large sword. h, Longboat. i, Attack on man holding spear, fire. j, Two figures with staffs, winged serpent.

2003, Feb. 24   Perf. 14

429	A144	Sheet of 10	22.50	22.50
a.-j.		6.50k Any single	2.25	2.25

Europa — A145

Poster art for Nordic House: 6.50k, Fish Tree, by Astrid Andreasen, 1991. 8k, Ceramics by Guthrith Poulsen, 1997.

2003, Apr. 14   *Perf. 13½x13¼*
430 A145 6.50k multi   2.00 2.00
431 A145   8k multi   2.50 2.50

Children's Songs — A146

No. 432: a, Woman playing hopscotch (26x44mm). b, Boy on rocks, moon (26x44mm). c, Girl with missing teeth (26x26mm). d, Boy with toy sailboat (26x26mm). e, Cat, horse and girl (26x26mm). f, Butterfly and fly (26x26mm). g, Girl in bed, boy with stars (44x26mm). h, Cat on stairs, mouse (26x36mm). i, Man playing drums (26x26mm). j, King and queen in longboat (44x26mm).

Perf. 13¼, 13¼x13¼x13¼x14 (#432g, 432j), 13¼x14 (#432h)
2003, Apr. 14
432 A146   Sheet of 10   16.00 16.00
  a.-j.   5k Any single   1.60 1.60

Small
Towns
A147

2003, June 10   Litho.   *Perf. 13x13¼*
433 A147 5k Bour   1.60 1.60
434 A147 5k Gásadalur   1.60 1.60

Communities With Post Offices 100
Years Old — A148

No. 435: a, Fuglafjorthur. b, Strendur. c, Sandur. d, Eithi. e, Vestmanna. f, Vágur. g, Mithvágur. h, Hvalba.

2003, June 10   *Perf. 13¼x13*
435   A148   Sheet of 8   13.00 13.00
  a.-h.   5k Any single   1.60 1.60

FØROYAR 5.00   Theologians — A149

Designs: 5k, Jesper Rasmussen Brochmand (1585-1652). 6.50k, Thomas Kingo (1634-1703).

2003, Sept. 22   *Perf. 13x13¼*
436 A149   5k multi   1.50 1.50
437 A149 6.50k multi   2.00 2.00
  a.   Booklet pane, 5 each #436-437 17.50 —
     Complete booklet, #437a   17.50

Souvenir Sheet

Dancing in the Inn's Smoking Room,
by Emil Krause — A150

Litho. & Engr.
2003, Sept. 22   *Perf. 12¼*
438 A150 25k multi   11.00 11.00
100th Faroese stamp engraved by Czeslaw Slania.

Islands Type of 1999
2004, Jan. 26   Litho.   *Perf. 13½*
439 A121 550o Stóra Dímun   1.90 1.90
440 A121 700o Lítla Dímun   2.40 2.40

Suthuroy Island — A151

No. 441: a, Sigmundargjogv, Sandvik. b, Fiskieithi, Hvalba. c, A Hamri, Frothba. d, Tjaldavíkshólmur, Oravík. e, Fossurin Stóri, Fámjin. f, Hovsfjorthur, Hov. g, I Eystrum, Porkeri. h, A Okrum. i, I Horg, Sumba. j, I Akrabergi.

2004, Jan. 26   *Perf. 13x13¼*
441 A151 5k Sheet of 10, #a-j   17.00 17.00

1854 Cruise of Yacht "Maria" — A152

No. 442: a, Gáshólmur and Tindhólmur. b, Framvith "Diamantunum." c, Hús av tí betra slagnum. d, Mylingur sunnanífrá. e, Mylingur northanífrá. f, Kalsoyggin northanífrá. g, Raetha teir infoddu. h, Sunnari endi av Kunoynni.

2004, Mar. 26   Litho.   *Perf. 13*
442 A152 6.50k Sheet of 8,
     #a.-h.   17.00 17.00

Souvenir Sheet

Norse Gods — A153

No. 443: a, Thor, in boat, fighting Midgard serpent. b, Ran in fishing net.

2004, Mar. 26
443 A153 6.50k Sheet of 2, #a.-
     b.   4.75 4.75

Souvenir Sheet

Wedding of Crown Prince Frederik and
Mary Donaldson — A154

Litho. & Photo.
2004, May 14   *Perf. 13¼*
444 A154   Sheet of 2 + central   4.25 4.25
     label
  a.   5k Couple facing right   1.60 1.60
  b.   6.50k Couple facing left   2.25 2.25

Soccer
Organization
Centenaries
A155

Soccer players and emblems of: 5k, Klaksvík and Tórshavn teams. 6.50k, FIFA (Fédération Internationale de Football Association).

2004, May 24   Litho.   *Perf. 13¼x13*
445 A155   5k multi   1.75 1.75
446 A155 6.50k multi   2.25 2.25
  a.   Booklet pane, 4 each #445-446 16.00 —
     Complete booklet, #446a   16.00

Europa
A156

Designs: 6.50k, Tourists in gorge, Hestur. 8k, Tourists at shore, Stóra Dímun.

2004, May 24   *Perf. 13x13¼*
447 A156 6.50k multi   2.10 2.10
448 A156   8k multi   2.60 2.60

Churches
A157

2004, Sept. 20   Litho.   *Perf. 13¼x13*
449 A157 5.50k Vágur   1.90 1.90
450 A157 7.50k Tvoroyri   2.50 2.50
  a.   Booklet pane, 4 each #449-450 18.00 —
     Complete booklet, #450a   18.00

Poems by Janus Djurhuus (1881-
1948) — A158

No. 451: a, Atlantis. b, Grímur Kamban. c, Gandkvaethi Tróndar. d, Til Foroya I-III. e, Mín sorg. f, Loki. g, I búri og Slatur. h, Heimferth Nólsoyar Páls. i, Móses á Sinai fjalli. j, Cello.

2004, Sept. 20   *Perf. 13*
451   A158   Sheet of 10   24.00 24.00
  a.-j.   7.50k Any single   2.40 2.40

Souvenir Sheet

Life of the Vikings — A159

No. 452: a, Men tending sheep. b, Men with farm implements. c, Women weaving and woman milking cow.

Litho. & Engr.
2005, Feb. 7   *Perf. 13*
452   A159   Sheet of 3   7.50 7.50
  a.-c.   7.50k Any single   2.40 2.40

Miniature Sheet

Vágar Island — A160

No. 453: a, Víkar. b, Gásadalur. c, Bour. d, Slaettanes. e, Kvígandalsá. f, Sorvágur. g, Sandavágur. h, Vatnsoyrar. i, Fjallavatn. j, Mithvágur.

2005, Feb. 7   Litho.   *Perf. 13x13¼*
453   A160   Sheet of 10   19.00 19.00
  a.-j.   5.50k Any single   1.90 1.90

Lepus
Timidus — A161

2005, Apr. 18   **Perf. 13¼x13½**
454 A161 5.50k shown   1.90 1.90
455 A161 5.50k Brown fur   1.90 1.90
  a.   Booklet pane, 4 each #454-455   15.50 —
      Complete booklet, #455a   15.50

Europa — A162

Various traditional foods with: 7.50k, Brown panel. 10k, Green panel.

2005, Apr. 18   **Perf. 13¼x13**
456 A162 7.50k multi   2.60 2.60
457 A162   10k multi   3.50 3.50

Worldwide
Fund for
Nature
(WWF)
A163

Petrels: 8.50k, Oceanodroma leucorhoa. 9k, Hydrobates pelagicus. 12k, Oceanodroma leucorhoa on ground. 20k, Hydrobates pelagicus on ground.

2005, June 6   **Perf. 13**
458 A163 8.50k multi   2.25 2.25
459 A163   9k multi   3.00 3.00
460 A163 12k multi   4.00 4.00
461 A163 20k multi   6.25 6.25
    Nos. 458-461 (4)   15.50 15.50

Miniature Sheet

Landscapes by Jógvan Waagstein
(1879-1949) — A164

No. 462: a, Path and wall at LL, denomination in red, year date in black in grass. b, Path and wall at LL, denomination in white, year date in black on wall. c, Stone hut at left, denomination in red, year date in black. d, Path at right, denomination in red, year date in black. e, Two large rocks at right, denomination in red, year date in black. f, Rocks at LL, denomination in red, year date in white. g, Path at center, denomination in white, year date in black on path. h, Buildings at LL, denomination in red, year date in black in path. i, Churches, denomination in white, year date in black in water.

2005, Sept. 19   Litho.   **Perf. 14x14¼**
462   A164   Sheet of 9   20.00 20.00
  a.-i.   7.50k Any single   2.25 2.25

End of
British
Occupation
In World
War II, 60th
Anniv.
A165

Soldiers with: 5.50k, Arms. 9k, Children.

2005, Sept. 19   **Perf. 14**
463 A165 5.50k blue & blk   1.75 1.75
464 A165   9k yel & blk   3.00 3.00

Christmas — A166

Ballads: 5.50k, Jólavísan. 7.50k, Rudisar Vísa.

2005, Nov. 7   **Perf. 13½x13¼**
465 A166 5.50k multi   1.75 1.75
466 A166 7.50k multi   2.40 2.40
  a.   Booklet pane, 5 each #465-466   16.00
      Complete booklet, #466a   16.00

Villages
A167

2006, Feb. 13   Litho.   **Perf. 13¾**
467 A167   7k Sythrugota   2.25 2.25
468 A167 12k Fuglafjorthur   4.25 4.25
469 A167 20k Leirvík   6.75 6.75
    Nos. 467-469 (3)   13.25 13.25

Miniature Sheet

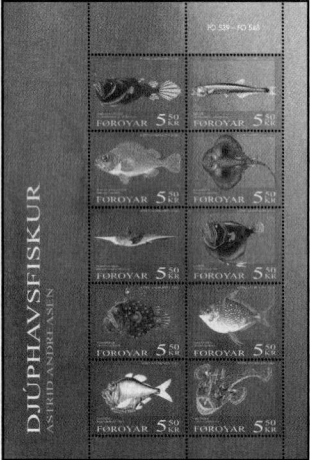

Fish — A168

No. 470: a, Himantolophus groenlandicus. b, Gonostoma elongatum. c, Sebastes mentella. d, Neoraja caerulea. e, Rhinochimaera atlantica. f, Linophryne lucifer. g, Ceratias holboelli. h, Lampris guttatus. i, Argyropelecus olfersi. j, Lophius piscatorius.

2006, Feb. 13   **Perf. 14**
470   A168   Sheet of 10   19.00 19.00
  a.-j.   5.50k Any single   1.90 1.90

Souvenir Sheet

Norse Folklore — A169

No. 471: a, Norns surrounding sleeping child. b, Sea ghost.

2006, Mar. 29   **Perf. 13**
471 A169 7.50k Sheet of 2, #a-b   5.00 5.00

Miniature Sheet

Ballad of the Long Serpent, by Jens
Christian Djurhuus — A170

No. 472: a, Building of ship. b, Launch of ship. c, King on throne. d, King's fleet at sea (brown ship at LL, blue ship at LR). e, King and sailors on shore. f, King pointing. g, Ship with red sail at R. h, Battle scene (injured men falling into water). i, Battle scene (men with shields jumping from ship to ship). j, Dead men on ship's deck.

2006, Mar. 29   **Perf. 13¼x13**
472   A170   Sheet of 10   18.00 18.00
  a.-j.   5.50k Any single   1.75 1.75

Opening of
Northoy
Tunnel — A171

Tunnel and: No. 473, Fish. No. 474, Canoe.

2006, June 12   **Perf. 13¼**
473 A171 5.50k multi   1.90 1.90
474 A171 5.50k multi   1.90 1.90
  a.   Booklet pane, 4 each #473-474   15.50 —
      Complete booklet, #474a   15.50

Europa
A172

2006, June 12   **Perf. 13¾**
475 A172 7.50k shown   2.60 2.60
476 A172   10k Hands, diff.   3.50 3.50

Miniature Sheet

Sandoy Island — A173

No. 477: a, Sunnan fyri Skopun. b, Dalur. c, Soltuvík. d, Skálavík. e, Skopun. f, Sandur. g, Skarvanes. h, Húsavík.

2006, Sept. 18   Litho.   **Perf. 13x13¼**
477   A173   Sheet of 8   20.00 20.00
  a.-h.   7.50k Any single   2.50 2.50

Sandur
Church
A174

Designs: 5.50k, Building exterior, steeple cross. 7.50k, Interior.

2006, Sept. 18   **Perf. 14**
478 A174 5.50k multi   1.90 1.90
479 A174 7.50k multi   2.60 2.60
  a.   Booklet pane, 4 each #478-479   18.00
      Complete booklet, #479a   18.00

Wave
Energy
A175

2007, Feb. 12   Litho.   **Perf. 12½x13**
480 A175 7.50k multi   2.60 2.60

Art From
1838 La
Recherche
Expedition
A176

Art by Barthélemy Lauvergne: 5.50k, La Recherche off Nólsoy. 7.50k, Skaelingsfjall.

2007, Feb. 12
481 A176 5.50k multi   1.90 1.90
482 A176 7.50k multi   2.60 2.60
  a.   Booklet pane, 4 each #481-482   18.00
      Complete booklet, #482a   18.00

Miniature Sheet

Legend of the Seal Woman — A177

No. 483: a, Man, head of white seal. b, Woman and seals in ring. c, Man, nude woman, seals. d, Man and nude woman seated on chest. e, Ship and two seals. f, Children, seal woman nursing child. g, Seal woman and man. h, Sleeping man and seal woman with hands open. i, Man and dead seals. j, Seal woman.

2007, Feb. 12   **Perf. 14**
483   A177   Sheet of 10   19.00 19.00
  a.-j.   5.50k Any single   1.90 1.90

Miniature Sheet

The Old Man and His Sons, Novel by
Hethin Brú — A178

No. 484: a, Ketil cutting whale's throat. b, Men carrying injured Klávus on log. c, Kálvur and fiancee, Klávusardóttir with pot and kettle.

d, Ketil and Kálvur in fishing boat. e, Ketil's wife arguing with daughter-in-law. f, Ketil catching flying northern fulmars. g, Kálvur and stone fence. h, Ketil, Kálvur and cow.

2007, Apr. 10   Litho.   Perf. 13x12½
484   A178   Sheet of 8   20.00 20.00
a.-h.   7.50k Any single   2.50   2.50

Europa — A179

Design: 5.50k, Scout holding bird. 10k, Tent.

2007, Apr. 10
485   A179   5.50k multi   2.00   2.00
486   A179   10k multi   3.75   3.75

Scouting, cent.

Souvenir Sheet

Bible Translators — A180

No. 487: a, Jákup Dahl (1878-1944). b, Kristian O. Videro (1906-91). c, Victor Danielsen (1894-1961).

2007, June 11   Litho.   Perf. 13x12½
487   A180   Sheet of 3   6.00   6.00
a.-c.   5.50k Any single   2.00   2.00

Domesticated Birds — A181

Designs: 9k, Chickens and rooster. 20k, Ducks. 25k, Geese.

2007, June 11   Perf. 12½x13
488   A181   9k multi   3.25   3.25
489   A181   20k multi   7.25   7.25
490   A181   25k multi   9.25   9.25
Nos. 488-490 (3)   19.75   19.75

Hoyvík — A182

2007, Oct. 1   Perf. 13½
491   A182   7.50k multi   2.75   2.75

Wooden Religious Statues of Kirkjubour Cathedral — A183

2007, Oct. 1   Perf. 13x12½
492   A183   5.50k Jesus   2.10   2.10
493   A183   7.50k Mary   2.75   2.75
a.   Booklet pane, 4 each #492-493   19.50
    Complete booklet, #493a   19.50

Miniature Sheet

Stone Fence and Wildlife — A184

No. 494: a, Bird, worm. b, Two red beetles, fern. c, Mouse, purple flowers. d, Mosquito, pink flowers. e, Large black and white bird, dandelions. f, Bird with black wings, buttercups. g, Earwigs, grass. h, Bird and eggs.

2007, Oct. 1   Perf. 13½x14¼
494   A184   Sheet of 8   17.00   17.00
a.-h.   5.50k Any single   2.10   2.10

Klaksvík, Cent. — A185

Litho. & Embossed
2008, Feb. 11   Perf. 14
495   A185   5.50k multi   2.25   2.25

Tinganes A186

2008, Feb. 11   Litho.   Perf. 13¼
496   A186   14k multi   5.25   5.25

Hoydalar Tuberculosis Sanatorium, Cent. — A187

Lungs and: 5.50k, Patients, buildings. 9k, Dr. Vilhelm Magnussen examining patient, child.

2007, Feb. 11   Perf. 12½x13
497   A187   5.50k multi   2.25   2.25
498   A187   9k multi   3.75   3.75
a.   Booklet pane, 4 each #497-498   24.00
    Complete booklet, #498a   24.00

Miniature Sheet

Prints by Elinborg Lützens — A188

No. 499: a, Houses below mountain. b, Milk maids (30x30mm). c, Houses. d, Underwater scene. e, Chicken (30x30mm). f, Person and bird near wooden bucket.

2008, Feb. 11   Perf. 13¼
499   A188   Sheet of 6   22.50   22.50
a.-f.   10k Any single   3.75   3.75

Souvenir Sheet

Mythical Places — A189

No. 500: a, Alvheyggur. b, Klovningasteinur.

2008, Mar. 27   Litho.   Perf. 12½x13
500   A189   Sheet of 2   6.50   6.50
a.-b.   7.50k Either single   3.25   3.25

Caltha Palustris A190

2008, May 19   Perf. 13¼
501   A190   30k multi   13.00   13.00

Europa A191

Designs: 550o, Heart and "Teg." 750o, Posthorn with "@" symbol and "Hey."

2008, May 19   Perf. 13¼x13
502   A191   550o multi   2.25   2.25
503   A191   750o multi   3.25   3.25

Miniature Sheet

Famous People — A192

No. 504: a, Niels Winther (1822-92), politician and newspaper publisher. b, Súsanna Helena Patursson (1864-1916), writer and newspaper publisher. c, Rasmus C. Effersoe (1857-1916), writer and newspaper editor. d, Jógvan Poulsen (1854-1941), religious and school book writer. e, Frithrikur Petersen (1853-1917), poet. f, Andreas Christian Evensen (1874-1917), magazine publisher and school book writer.

2008, May 19   Perf. 13½x13¼
504   A192   Sheet of 6   14.00   14.00
a.-f.   5.50k Any single   2.25   2.25

Miniature Sheet

Ferns — A193

No. 505: a, Gymnocarpium dryopteris. b, Polypodium vulgare. c, Dryopteris dilatata. d, Asplenium adiantum-nigrum. e, Athyrium filix-femina. f, Dryopteris filix-mas. g, Cystopteris fragilis. h, Phegopteris connectilis. i, Polystichum lonchitis. j, Asplenium trichomanes.

2008, Sept. 22   Litho.   Perf. 13x13½
505   A193   Sheet of 10   30.00   30.00
a.-j.   800o Any single   3.00   3.00

Christmas — A194

2008, Sept. 22   Perf. 13x12½
506   A194   6k shown   2.25   2.25
507   A194   10k Wooden cross   3.75   3.75
a.   Booklet pane of 8, 4 each #506-507   24.00
    Complete booklet, #507a   24.00

Global Warming — A195

Designs: 6k, Earth and "No entry" sign. 8k, Earth in shape of water droplet.

2009, Feb. 23   Litho.   Perf. 13¾x14
508   A195   6k multi   2.10   2.10
509   A195   8k multi   2.75   2.75
a.   Souvenir sheet, #508-509

Portions of the designs were applied by a thermographic process producing a shiny raised effect.

Miniature Sheet

Scenes From *The Lost Musicians,* by William Heinesen — A196

No. 510: a, People, stylized harp. b, Ring of silhouetted dancers. c, Woman on roof of house, kneeling people and standing woman near house. d, Silhouetted man approaching woman on park bench. e, Women and seated cellist. f, Violinist and two silhoutted men. g, Man in bed. h, People in rowboat.

2009, Feb. 23   Perf. 13½
510   A196   Sheet of 8   22.00   22.00
a.-h.   8k Any single   2.75   2.75

Europa — A197

Designs: 10k, Trollhovdi Island and Saturn. 12k, Heygadrangur Island, Jupiter and one of its moons, Europa.

2009, May 25   Litho.   Perf. 13x12½
511 A197 10k multi   3.75 3.75
512 A197 12k multi   4.50 4.50

Intl. Year of Astronomy.

Miniature Sheet

Geological Formation of the Faroe Islands — A198

No. 513: a, Large volcano spewing lava, trees. b, Smaller volcano spewing ash, dead tree, lava on landscape. c, Map of area 60 million years ago. d, Map of area 15 million years ago. e, Map of Faroe Isands, map of Faroe Islands and area nearby. f, Glacier, rock pinnacles.

2009, May 25   Perf. 12½x13
513 A198 Sheet of 6   22.50 22.50
a.-f. 10k Any single   3.75 3.75

Thorshavn Gymnastics Club, Cent. — A199

Gymnasts: 6k, Male lifting female. 10k, Female doing handstand. 26k, Male on rings.

2009, May 25   Perf. 14
514 A199 6k multi   2.25 2.25
515 A199 10k multi   3.75 3.75
516 A199 26k multi   9.75 9.75
     Nos. 514-516 (3)   15.75 15.75

Serpentine Die Cut 14
Booklet Stamps
Self-Adhesive
517 A199 6k multi   2.25 2.25
518 A199 10k multi   3.75 3.75
a.   Booklet pane of 8, 4 each
     #517-518   24.00

Leynar — A200

2009, Sept. 16   Perf. 12¾
519 A200 10k multi   4.00 4.00

Rock Pigeons A201

Designs: 14k, Two pigeons on rocks. 36k, Head of pigeon, two pigeons in flight.

2009, Sept. 16   Perf. 13
520 A201 14k multi   5.50 5.50
521 A201 36k multi   14.50 14.50

Altarpiece at Vestmanna Church — A202

Altarpiece at Hattarvik Church A203

2009, Sept. 16   Perf. 13¾x13¼
522 A202 6k multi   2.40 2.40
a.   Perf. 13¾ vert.   2.40 2.40
523 A203 10k multi   4.00 4.00
a.   Perf. 14¼x13¾ on 3 sides 4.00 4.00
b.   Booklet pane of 8, 4 each
     #522a, 523a   26.00   —
     Complete booklet, #523b 26.00

Christmas.

Globicephala Melas — A204

2010, Feb. 22   Litho.   Perf. 14¾
524 A204 50k multi   18.50 18.50

Marine Flora and Fauna — A205

Various photographs.

2010, Feb. 22   Perf. 13¼x13½
525 A205 1k multi   .35   .35
526 A205 6k multi   2.25 2.25
527 A205 8k multi   3.00 3.00
528 A205 12k multi   4.50 4.50
     Nos. 525-528 (4)   10.10 10.10

Butterflies and Moths A206

Designs: 6k, Inachis io. 8k, Vanessa cardui. 14k, Ägrius convolvuli. 16k, Acherontia atropos.

2010, Feb. 22   Perf. 13x12¾
529 A206 6k multi   2.25 2.25
530 A206 8k multi   3.00 3.00
531 A206 14k multi   5.25 5.25
532 A206 16k multi   6.00 6.00
     Nos. 529-532 (4)   16.50 16.50

Souvenir Sheet

Aquaculture — A207

No. 533: a, Fish, net. b, Fisherman holding net.

Perf. 14¼x14½
2010, Mar. 24   Litho.
533   A207 Sheet of 2   7.25 7.25
a.-b.   10k Either single   3.50 3.50

Paintings by Eli Smith — A208

Various paintings.

2010, Apr. 26   Perf. 14½
534 A208 18k multi   6.50 6.50
535 A208 24k multi   8.75 8.75

Europa A209

Scenes from children's books: 10k, A Dog, A Cat and A Mouse, by Bárthur Oskarsson. 12k, Moss Mollis's Journey, by Janus á Húsagarthi.

2010, Apr. 26   Perf. 13¾
536 A209 10k multi   3.75 3.75
537 A209 12k multi   4.25 4.25

Booklet Stamps
Self-Adhesive
Serpentine Die Cut 14
538 A209 10k multi   3.75 3.75
539 A209 12k multi   4.25 4.25
a.   Booklet pane of 8, 4 each
     #538-539   32.00

Jens Christian Svabo (1746-1824), Writer and Lexicographer — A210

Writings of Svabo and Svabo: 6k, Holding walking stick. 12k, At desk. 14k, Holding book. 22k, With sheaf of papers, pen and inkwell.

Perf. 13¼x13¾
2010, Sept. 20   Litho. & Engr.
540 A210 6k multi   2.25 2.25
541 A210 12k multi   4.50 4.50
542 A210 14k multi   5.25 5.25
543 A210 22k multi   8.25 8.25
     Nos. 540-543 (4)   20.25 20.25

Vegetables A211

Christmas A212

2010, Sept. 20 Litho. Perf. 13x13¼
544 A211 6k Potatoes   2.25 2.25
545 A211 8k Turnips   3.00 3.00

2010, Sept. 20   Perf. 13x12½
Carols: 6k, My Little Sweet Brownie (Lítla Fitta Nissa Mín). 10k, In My Early Childhood (A Barnaárum Ungu).
546 A212 6k multi   2.25 2.25
547 A212 10k multi   3.75 3.75

FERNANDO PO

fər-'nan-ˌdō 'pō

LOCATION — An island in the Gulf of Guinea off west Africa.
GOVT. — Former province of Spain
AREA — 800 sq. mi.
POP. — 62,612 (1960)
CAPITAL — Sånta Isabel

Together with the islands of Elobey, Annobon and Corisco, Fernando Po came under the administration of Spanish Guinea. Postage stamps of Spanish Guinea were used until 1960.

The provinces of Fernando Po and Rio Muni united Oct. 12, 1968, to form the Republic of Equatorial Guinea.

100 Centimos = 1 Escudo = 2.50 Pesetas

100 Centimos = 1 Peseta

1000 Milesimas = 100 Centavos = 1 Peso (1882)

> Catalogue values for unused stamps in this country are for Never Hinged items, beginning with Scott 181 in the regular postage section and Scott B1 in the semi-postal section.

Isabella II — A1	Alfonso XII — A2

1868   Unwmk.   Typo.   Perf. 14

1	A1	20c brown	500.00	140.00
a.		20c red brown	525.00	140.00

No. 1 is valued in the grade of fine, as illustrated. Examples with very fine centering are uncommon and sell for more.
Forgeries exist.

1879

Centimos de Peseta

2	A2	5c green	60.00	15.00
3	A2	10c rose	60.00	15.00
4	A2	50c blue	105.00	15.00
		Nos. 2-4 (3)	225.00	45.00

1882-89

Centavos de Peso

5	A2	1c green	9.50	5.50
6	A2	2c rose	18.00	8.75
7	A2	5c gray blue	60.00	12.00
8	A2	10c dk brown ('89)	82.50	6.75
		Nos. 5-8 (4)	170.00	33.00

Nos. 5-7 Handstamp Surcharged Type "a" in Blue, Black or Violet

a

1884-95

9	A2	50c on 1c green ('95)	105.00	19.00
11	A2	50c on 2c rose	32.00	6.00
12	A2	50c on 5c blue ('87)	115.00	25.00
		Nos. 9-12 (3)	252.00	50.00

Values above are for examples surcharged in black. Stamps surcharged in violet or blue are worth about 25% more.
Inverted and double surcharges exist. No. 12 exists overprinted in carmine. Value $100.

King Alfonso XIII — A4

1894-97   Perf. 14

13	A4	½c slate ('96)	22.00	3.00
14	A4	2c rose ('96)	15.50	2.50
15	A4	5c blue grn ('97)	16.00	2.50
16	A4	6c dk violet ('96)	13.00	3.00
17	A4	10c blk vio ('94)	450.00	115.00
18	A4	10c lake ('95)	50.00	8.75
19	A4	10c org brn ('96)	10.50	2.50
20	A4	12½c dk brown ('96)	11.50	3.00
21	A4	20c slate bl ('96)	11.50	3.00
22	A4	25c claret ('96)	23.00	3.00
		Nos. 13-22 (10)	623.00	146.25

Stamps of 1894-97 Handstamped in Blue, Black or Red

b	c

Type "b" Surcharge

1896-98

23	A4	5c on 2c rose (Bl)	45.00	6.25
24	A4	5c on 10c brn vio (Bl)	130.00	17.50
25	A4	5c on 12½c brn (Bl)	30.00	5.25
a.		Black surcharge	30.00	5.25
		Nos. 23-25 (3)	205.00	29.00

Type "c" Surcharge

26	A4	5c on ½c slate (Bk)	29.00	6.75
27	A4	5c on 2c rose (Bl)	29.00	6.75
a.		Black surcharge	29.00	6.75
28	A4	5c on 5c green (R)	125.00	22.00
29	A4	5c on 6c dk vio (R)	22.00	14.00
a.		Violet surcharge	23.00	15.50
30	A4	5c on 10c org brn (Bk)	160.00	27.50
31	A4	5c on 12½c brn (R)	62.50	11.00
32	A4	5c on 20c sl bl (R)	34.00	10.50
33	A4	5c on 25c claret (Bk)	34.00	11.00
a.		Blue surcharge	34.00	13.50
		Nos. 26-33 (8)	495.50	109.50

Exist surcharged in other colors.

Type "a" Surch. in Blue or Black

1898-99

34	A4	50c on 2c rose	92.50	11.50
35	A4	50c on 10c brn vio	220.00	33.00
36	A4	50c on 10c lake	230.00	33.00
37	A4	50c on 10c org brn	220.00	33.00
38	A4	50c on 12½c brn (Bk)	190.00	22.00

The "a" surch. also exists on ½c, 5c & 25c. Values, $325, $225 and $210, respectively.

A5	A6

Arms
Revenue Stamps Handstamped in Blue

1897-98   Imperf.

39	A5	5c on 10c rose	28.00	12.50
40	A6	10c rose	24.00	11.00

A7

A8

A9

Arms — A9a

Revenue Stamps Handstamped in Black or Red

1899   Imperf.

41	A7	15c on 10c green	45.00	23.00
a.		Blue surcharge, vertical	39.00	21.00
42	A8	10c on 25c green	120.00	65.00
43	A9	15c on 25c green	190.00	120.00
43A	A9a	15c on 25c green (R)	1,800.	1,100.
b.		Black surcharge	1,800.	1,100.

Surcharge on No. 41 is either horizontal, inverted or vertical.
On No. 42 "CORREOS" is ovptd. in red.

King Alfonso XIII — A10

Double-lined shaded letters at sides.

1899   Perf. 14

44	A10	1m orange brn	2.40	.45
45	A10	2m orange brn	2.40	.45
46	A10	3m orange brn	2.40	.45
47	A10	4m orange brn	2.40	.45
48	A10	5m orange brn	2.40	.45
49	A10	1c black vio	2.40	.45
50	A10	2c dk blue grn	2.40	.45
51	A10	3c dk brown	2.40	.45
52	A10	4c orange	14.00	1.10
53	A10	5c carmine rose	2.40	.45
54	A10	6c dark blue	2.40	.45
55	A10	8c gray brn	8.75	.45
56	A10	10c vermilion	5.50	.45
57	A10	15c slate grn	5.50	.45
58	A10	20c maroon	15.00	1.10
59	A10	40c violet	100.00	19.00
60	A10	60c black	100.00	19.00
61	A10	80c red brown	100.00	19.00
62	A10	1p yellow grn	375.00	92.50
63	A10	2p slate blue	375.00	95.00
		Nos. 44-63 (20)	1,122.	252.55

Nos. 44-63 exist imperf. Value for set, $1,650.
See Nos. 66-85. For surcharges see Nos. 64-65, 88-88B.

1900

Surcharged type "a"

64	A10	50c on 20c maroon	16.00	2.50
a.		Blue surcharge	32.00	4.75

Surcharged type "b"

64B	A10	5c on 20c maroon	210.00	10.50

Surcharged type "c"

65	A10	5c on 20c maroon	9.50	2.40
		Nos. 64-65 (3)	235.50	15.40

Dated "1900"

Solid letters at sides.

1900

66	A10	1m black	3.00	.50
67	A10	2m black	3.00	.50
68	A10	3m black	3.00	.50
69	A10	4m black	3.00	.50
70	A10	5m black	3.00	.50
71	A10	1c green	3.00	.50
72	A10	2c violet	3.00	.50
73	A10	3c rose	3.00	.50
74	A10	4c black brn	3.00	.50
75	A10	5c blue	3.00	.50
76	A10	6c orange	3.00	.50
77	A10	8c bronze grn	3.00	.50
78	A10	10c claret	3.00	.50
79	A10	15c dk violet	3.00	.50
80	A10	20c olive brn	3.00	.50
81	A10	40c brown	7.75	2.25
82	A10	60c green	16.50	2.50
83	A10	80c dark blue	17.50	3.75
84	A10	1p red brown	110.00	30.00
85	A10	2p orange	190.00	62.50
		Nos. 66-85 (20)	386.75	108.50
		Set, never hinged	625.00	

Nos. 66-85 exist imperf. Value, set $1,750.

A11

A12

Revenue Stamps Overprinted or Surcharged with Handstamp in Red or Black

1900   Imperf.

86	A11	10c blue (R)	37.50	17.50
87	A12	5c on 10c blue	100.00	40.00
		Set, never hinged	175.00	

Nos. 52 and 80 Surcharged type "a" in Violet or Black

1900

88	A10	50c on 4c orange (V)	14.00	4.00
a.		Green surcharge	22.50	12.00
88B	A10	50c on 20c ol brn	14.00	3.50
		Set, never hinged	37.50	

A13	A14

1901   Perf. 14

89	A13	1c black	2.75	.90
90	A13	2c orange brn	2.75	.90
91	A13	3c dk violet	2.75	.90
92	A13	4c lt violet	2.75	.90
93	A13	5c orange red	1.75	.90
94	A13	10c violet brn	1.75	.90
95	A13	25c dp blue	1.75	.90
96	A13	50c claret	2.75	.90
97	A13	75c dk brown	2.00	.90
98	A13	1p blue grn	62.50	6.00
99	A13	2p red brown	39.00	9.00
100	A13	3p olive grn	39.00	12.00
101	A13	4p dull red	38.00	12.00
102	A13	5p dk green	47.50	12.00
103	A13	10p buff	105.00	35.00
		Nos. 89-103 (15)	352.00	94.10
		Set, never hinged	650.00	

Dated "1902"

1902

Control Numbers on Back

104	A13	5c dk green	2.60	.45
105	A13	10c slate	2.90	.50
106	A13	25c claret	6.25	1.00
107	A13	50c violet brn	15.00	3.25
108	A13	75c lt violet	15.00	3.25
109	A13	1p car rose	18.50	4.00
110	A13	2p olive grn	40.00	9.50
111	A13	5p orange red	57.50	20.00
		Nos. 104-111 (8)	157.75	41.95
		Set, never hinged	230.00	

Exist imperf. Value for set, $850.

Dated "1903"

1903   *Perf. 14*

Control Numbers on Back

112	A14	¼c dk violet	.45	.25
113	A14	½c black	.45	.25
114	A14	1c scarlet	.45	.25
115	A14	2c dk green	.45	.30
116	A14	3c blue grn	.45	.30
117	A14	4c violet	.45	.30
118	A14	5c rose lake	.50	.30
119	A14	10c orange buff	.60	.45
120	A14	15c blue green	2.50	1.00
121	A14	25c red brown	2.75	1.25
122	A14	50c black brn	4.50	2.00
123	A14	75c carmine	16.50	3.50
124	A14	1p dk brown	25.00	6.00
125	A14	2p dk olive grn	32.50	7.50
126	A14	3p claret	32.50	7.50
127	A14	4p dark blue	40.00	12.50
128	A14	5p dp dull blue	60.00	16.00
129	A14	10p dull red	130.00	27.50
		Nos. 112-129 (18)	350.05	87.15
		Set, never hinged	500.00	

Dated "1905"

1905

Control Numbers on Back

136	A14	1c dp violet	.40	.30
137	A14	2c black	.40	.30
138	A14	3c vermilion	.40	.30
139	A14	4c dp green	.40	.30
140	A14	5c blue grn	.45	.35
141	A14	10c violet	1.60	.75
142	A14	15c car lake	1.60	.75
143	A14	25c orange buff	12.50	2.25
144	A14	50c green	8.00	2.75
145	A14	75c red brown	11.00	7.50
146	A14	1p dp gray brn	12.50	7.50
147	A14	2p carmine	20.00	12.50
148	A14	3p deep brown	32.50	14.00
149	A14	4p bronze grn	40.00	18.00
150	A14	5p claret	62.50	25.00
151	A14	10p deep blue	90.00	36.00
		Nos. 136-151 (16)	294.25	127.55
		Set, never hinged	525.00	

King Alfonso XIII — A15

1907

Control Numbers on Back

152	A15	1c blue black	.30	.20
153	A15	2c car rose	.30	.20
154	A15	3c dp violet	.30	.20
155	A15	4c black	.30	.20
156	A15	5c orange buff	.35	.20
157	A15	10c maroon	2.00	.80
158	A15	15c bronze grn	.55	.35
159	A15	25c dk brown	30.00	10.50
160	A15	50c blue green	.35	.30
161	A15	75c vermilion	.45	.30
162	A15	1p dull blue	3.00	.60
163	A15	2p brown	11.00	3.50
164	A15	3p lake	11.00	3.50
165	A15	4p violet	11.00	3.50
166	A15	5p black brn	11.00	3.50
167	A15	10p orange brn	11.00	3.50
		Nos. 152-167 (16)	92.90	31.35
		Set, never hinged	165.00	

No. 157 Handstamp Surcharged in Black or Blue

1908

168	A15	5c on 10c mar (Bk)	2.75	2.00
169	A15	5c on 10c mar (Bl)	10.00	5.50
		Set, never hinged	16.00	

The surcharge on Nos. 168-169 exist inverted, double, etc. The surcharge also exists on other stamps. A 25c on 10c also exists.

Seville-Barcelona Issue of Spain, 1929, Overprinted in Blue or Red

1929   *Perf. 11*

170	A52	5c rose lake	.20	.20
171	A53	10c green (R)	.20	.20
a.		*Perf. 14*	.65	.65
172	A50	15c Prus bl (R)	.25	.20
173	A51	20c purple (R)	.25	.20
174	A50	25c brt rose	.25	.20
175	A52	30c black brn	.25	.20
176	A53	40c dk blue (R)	.70	.70
177	A51	50c dp orange	1.50	1.50
178	A52	1p blue blk (R)	5.75	5.75
179	A53	4p deep rose	27.50	27.50
180	A53	10p brown	35.00	35.00
		Nos. 170-180 (11)	71.85	71.65
		Set, never hinged	135.00	

> Catalogue values for unused stamps in this section, from this point to the end of the section, are for Never Hinged items.

Virgin Mary — A16

1960 Unwmk. Photo. *Perf. 13x12½*

181	A16	25c dull gray vio	.35	.20
182	A16	50c brown olive	.35	.20
183	A16	75c violet brn	.35	.20
184	A16	1p orange ver	.35	.25
185	A16	1.50p lt blue grn	.35	.25
186	A16	2p red lilac	.35	.25
187	A16	3p dark blue	3.50	.80
188	A16	5p lt red brn	.35	.25
189	A16	10p lt olive grn	.55	.30
		Nos. 181-189 (9)	6.50	2.70

Tricorn and Windmill from "The Three-Cornered Hat" by Falla — A17

Manuel de Falla A18

1960   *Perf. 13x12½, 12½x13*

190	A17	35c slate green	.60	.60
191	A18	80c Prus green	.70	.70

Issued to honor Manuel de Falla (1876-1946), Spanish composer. See Nos. B1-B2.

Map of Fernando Po — A19

General Franco A20

Designs: 70c, Santa Isabel Cathedral.

Ocean Liner A21

Design: 50c, S.S. San Francisco.

1961, Oct. 1   Photo.   Unwmk.

192	A19	25c gray violet	.35	.35
193	A20	50c olive brown	.35	.35
194	A19	70c brt green	.40	.40
195	A20	1p red orange	.45	.45
		Nos. 192-195 (4)	1.55	1.55

25th anniv. of the nomination of Gen. Francisco Franco as Chief of State.

1962, July 10   *Perf. 12½x13*

196	A21	25c dull violet	.30	.30
197	A21	50c gray olive	.35	.35
198	A21	1p orange brn	.35	.35
		Nos. 196-198 (3)	1.00	1.00

Mailman — A22

Mail Transport Symbols A23

Perf. 13x12½, 12½x13

1962, Nov. 23   Unwmk.

199	A22	15c dark green	.30	.30
200	A23	35c lilac rose	.35	.35
201	A22	1p brown	.35	.35
		Nos. 199-201 (3)	1.00	1.00

Issued for Stamp Day.

Fetish — A24

1963, Jan. 29   *Perf. 13x12½*

202	A24	50c olive gray	.30	.30
203	A24	1p deep magenta	.35	.35

Issued to help victims of the Seville flood.

Nuns A25

Design: 50c, Nun and child, vert.

Perf. 12½x13, 13x12½

1963, July 6   Photo.   Unwmk.

204	A25	25c bright lilac	.30	.30
205	A25	50c dull green	.35	.35
206	A25	1p red orange	.35	.35
		Nos. 204-206 (3)	1.00	1.00

Issued for child welfare.

Child and Arms A26

1963, July 12   *Perf. 12½x13*

207	A26	50c brown olive	.30	.30
208	A26	1p carmine rose	.35	.35

Issued for Barcelona flood relief.

Governor Chacon A27

Orange Blossoms A28

Men in Dugout Canoe A29

1964, Mar. 6   *Perf. 12½x13, 13x12½*

209	A27	25c violet black	.30	.30
210	A28	50c dark olive	.35	.35
211	A27	1p brown red	.35	.35
		Nos. 209-211 (3)	1.00	1.00

Issued for Stamp Day 1963.

1964, June 1   Photo.   *Perf. 13x12½*

Design: 50c, Pineapple.

212	A29	25c purple	.30	.30
213	A28	50c dull olive	.35	.35
214	A29	1p deep claret	.35	.35
		Nos. 212-214 (3)	1.00	1.00

Issued for child welfare.

Ring-necked Francolin — A30

Designs: 15c, 70c, 3p, Ring-necked francolin. 25c, 1p, 5p, Two mallards. 50c, 1.50p, 10p, Head of great plate touraco.

1964, July 1

215	A30	15c chestnut	.35	.30
216	A30	25c dull violet	.35	.30
217	A30	50c dk olive grn	.35	.30
218	A30	70c green	.35	.30
219	A30	1p brown orange	.40	.30
220	A30	1.50p grnsh blue	.45	.35
221	A30	3p violet blue	.75	.35
222	A30	5p dull purple	1.75	.40
223	A30	10p bright green	2.75	1.00
		Nos. 215-223 (9)	7.50	3.60

The Three Kings A31

Designs: 50c, 1.50p, Caspar, vert.

Perf. 13x12½, 12½x13

1964, Nov. 23   Unwmk.

224	A31	50c green	.35	.35
225	A31	1p orange ver	.40	.35
226	A31	1.50p deep green	.45	.35
227	A31	3p ultra	1.75	1.40
		Nos. 224-227 (4)	2.95	2.45

Issued for Stamp Day, 1964.

Boy — A32

Woman Fruit Picker — A33

1.50p, Girl learning to write, and church.

1964, Mar. 1   Photo.   Perf. 13x12½
228 A32 50c indigo   .30 .30
229 A33 1p dark red   .35 .30
230 A33 1.50p grnsh blue   .40 .35
    Nos. 228-230 (3)   1.05 .95
Issued to commemorate 25 years of peace.

Plectrocnemia Cruciata — A34

Design: 1p, Metopodontus savagei, horiz.

Perf. 13x12½, 12½x13
1965, June 1   Photo.   Unwmk.
231 A34 50c slate green   .45 .35
232 A34 1p rose red   .45 .35
233 A34 1.50p Prus blue   .45 .35
    Nos. 231-233 (3)   1.35 1.05
Issued for child welfare.

Pole Vault A35

Arms of Fernando Po — A36

Perf. 12½x13, 13x12½
1965, Nov. 23   Photo.   Unwmk.
234 A35 50c yellow green   .30 .30
235 A36 1p brt org brn   .35 .30
236 A35 1.50p brt blue   .40 .35
    Nos. 234-236 (3)   1.05 .95
Issued for Stamp Day, 1965.

Children Reading A37

1.50p, St. Elizabeth of Hungary, vert.

Perf. 12½x13, 13x12½
1966, June 1   Photo.   Unwmk.
237 A37 50c dark green   .30 .30
238 A37 1p brown red   .35 .30
239 A37 1.50p dark blue   .35 .35
    Nos. 237-239 (3)   1.00 .95
Issued for child welfare.

White-nosed Monkey — A38

Stamp Day: 40c, 4p, Head of moustached monkey, vert.

1966, Nov. 23   Photo.   Perf. 13
240 A38 10c dk blue & yel   .35 .30
241 A38 40c lt brn, bl & blk .40 .30
242 A38 1.50p ol bis, brn org & blk .45 .40
243 A38 4p sl grn, brn org & blk .55 .45
    Nos. 240-243 (4)   1.75 1.45

Flowers — A39

Designs: 40c, 4p, Six flowers.

1967, June 1   Photo.   Perf. 13
244 A39 10c brt car & pale grn .30 .30
245 A39 40c red brn & org   .35 .30
246 A39 1.50p red lil & lt red brn .40 .35
247 A39 4p dk blue & lt grn .45 .40
    Nos. 244-247 (4)   1.50 1.35
Issued for child welfare.

Linsang — A40

Stamp Day: 1.50p, Needle-clawed galago, vert. 3.50p, Fraser's scaly-tailed flying squirrel.

1967, Nov. 23   Photo.   Perf. 13
248 A40 1p black & bister   .35 .30
249 A40 1.50p brown & olive .40 .35
250 A40 3.50p rose lake & dl grn .50 .45
    Nos. 248-250 (3)   1.25 1.05

Stamp of 1868, No. 1, and Arms of San Carlos A41

Fernando Po No. 1 and: 1.50p, Arms of Santa Isabel. 2.50p, Arms of Fernando Po.

1968, Feb. 4   Photo.   Perf. 13
251 A41 1p brt plum & brn org .30 .30
252 A41 1.50p dp blue & brn org .40 .35
253 A41 2.50p brn & brn org .50 .40
    Nos. 251-253 (3)   1.20 1.00
Centenary of the first postage stamp.

Signs of the Zodiac — A42

1968, Apr. 25   Photo.   Perf. 13
254 A42 1p Libra   .30 .30
255 A42 1.50p Leo   .40 .35
256 A42 2.50p Aquarius   .50 .40
    Nos. 254-256 (3)   1.20 1.05
Issued for child welfare.

SEMI-POSTAL STAMPS

Catalogue values for unused stamps in this section are for Never Hinged items.

Types of Regular Issue, 1960

Designs: 10c+5c, Manuel de Falla. 15c+5c, Dancers from "Love, the Magician."

Perf. 12½x13, 13x12½
1960   Photo.   Unwmk.
B1 A18 10c + 5c maroon   .35 .30
B2 A17 15c + 5c dk brn & bister .35 .35
The surtax was for child welfare.

Whale SP1

Design: Nos. B4, B6, Harpooning whale.

1961   Perf. 12½x13
B3 SP1 10c + 5c rose brown .35 .30
B4 SP1 20c + 5c dk slate grn .35 .30
B5 SP1 30c + 10c olive brn .40 .30
B6 SP1 50c + 20c dark brn   .45 .30
    Nos. B3-B6 (4)   1.55 1.20
Issued for Stamp Day, 1960.

Hand Blessing Woman — SP2

Design: 25c+10c, Boy making sign of the cross, and crucifix.

1961, June 21   Perf. 13x12½
B7 SP2 10c + 5c rose brn   .40 .30
B8 SP2 25c + 10c gray vio   .40 .30
B9 SP2 80c + 20c dk grn   .50 .35
    Nos. B7-B9 (3)   1.30 .95
The surtax was for child welfare.

Ethiopian Tortoise SP3

Stamp Day: 25c+10c, 1p+10c, Native carriers, palms and shore.

1961, Nov. 23   Perf. 12½x13
B10 SP3 10c + 5c rose red   .35 .30
B11 SP3 25c + 10c dk pur   .40 .30
B12 SP3 30c + 10c vio brn   .40 .30
B13 SP3 1p + 10c red org   .50 .40
    Nos. B10-B13 (4)   1.65 1.30

FIJI

'fē-ˌjē

LOCATION — Group of 332 islands (106 inhabited) in the South Pacific Ocean east of Vanuatu
GOVT. — Independent nation in British Commonwealth
AREA — 7,078 sq. mi.
POP. — 812,918 (1999 est.)
CAPITAL — Suva

A British colony since 1874, Fiji became fully independent in 1970.

12 Pence = 1 Shilling
20 Shillings = 1 Pound
100 Cents = 1 Dollar (1872-74, 1969)

Syncopated Perforations

Type A (1st stamp #873): On shorter sides, the seventh hole from the larger side is an oval hole equal in width to three holes.

Catalogue values for unused stamps in this country are for Never Hinged items, beginning with Scott 137 in the regular postage section and Scott B1 in the semi-postal section.

Values for unused stamps are for examples with original gum as defined in the catalogue introduction except for Nos. 1-10 which are valued without gum. Additionally, Nos. 1-10 are valued with roulettes showing on two or more sides, but expect small faults which do not detract from the appearance of the stamps. Very few examples of Nos. 1-10 will be found free of faults and these will command substantial premiums.

Watermark

Wmk. 17 — FIJI POSTAGE Across Center Row of Sheet

A1

1870   Unwmk.   Typeset   Rouletted   Quadrille Paper
1 A1 1p black, pink   3,750. 4,000.
2 A1 3p black, pink   4,000. 4,000.
3 A1 6p black, pink   2,350. 2,750.
5 A1 1sh black, pink   1,750. 2,250.

1871   Laid Batonne Paper
6 A1 1p black, pink   1,200. 2,000.
7 A1 3p black, pink   1,750. 3,250.
8 A1 6p black, pink   1,400. 2,000.
9 A1 9p black, pink   3,450. 3,500.
10 A1 1sh black, pink   1,600. 1,700.

This service was established by the *Fiji Times*, a weekly newspaper, for the delivery of the newspaper. Since there was no postal service to the other islands, delivery of letters to agents of the newspaper on the islands was offered to the public.

Nos. 1-5 were printed in the same sheet, one horizontal row of 6 of each (6p, 1sh, 1p, 3p). Nos. 6-10 were printed from the same plate with three 9p replacing three 3p.

Most used examples have pen cancels.
Up to three sets of imitations exist. One on pink laid paper, pin-perforated, measuring 22½x16mm. Originals measure 22½x18½mm. A later printing was made on pink wove paper. Forgeries also exist plus fake cancellations.

Crown and "CR" (Cakobau Rex)
A2   A3

A4

1871   Typo.   Wmk. 17   Perf. 12½
Wove Paper
15 A2 1p blue   62.50 140.00
16 A3 3p green   125.00 400.00
17 A4 6p rose   150.00 325.00
    Nos. 15-17 (3) 337.50 865.00
Sheets of 50 (10x5).

For overprints and surcharges see Nos. 18-39.

Stamps of 1871 Surcharged in Black

1872, Jan. 13

18	A2	2c on 1p blue	47.50	57.50
19	A3	6c on 3p green	80.00	80.00
20	A4	12c on 6p rose	110.00	85.00
		Nos. 18-20 (3)	237.50	222.50

Nos. 18-20 with Additional Overprint in Black:

b   c

1874, Oct. 10

21	A2(b)	2c on 1p blue	1,150.	325.00
22	A2(c)	2c on 1p blue	1,000.	300.00
a.		Invtd. "A" instead of "V"	2,600.	1,500.
b.		Period after "R" is a Maltese Cross	2,600.	1,500.
23	A3(b)	6c on 3p green	2,250.	1,000.
24	A3(c)	6c on 3p green	1,800.	775.00
a.		Inverted "A"	4,500.	1,850.
b.		Period after "R" is a Maltese Cross	4,500.	1,850.
25	A4(b)	12c on 6p rose	900.00	250.00
a.		"V.R." inverted	6,000.	
26	A4(c)	12c on 6p rose	750.00	225.00
a.		Inverted "A"	2,250.	1,350.
b.		Period after "R" is a Maltese Cross	2,250.	1,350.
c.		"V.R." inverted	—	5,000.

Types "b" and "c" were in the same sheet.

Nos. 23-26 with Additional Surcharge in Black or Red

1875

27	A3(b)	2p on 6c on 3p	2,250.	750.00
a.		Period btwn. "2" and "d"	3,750.	1,400.
b.		"V.R." double	4,250.	3,750.
28	A3(b)	2p on 6c on 3p (R)	800.00	325.00
a.		Period btwn. "2" and "d"	1,750.	750.00
29	A3(c)	2p on 6c on 3p	1,700.	550.00
a.		Inverted "A"	3,750.	1,400.
b.		Period after "R" is a Maltese Cross	3,750.	1,400.
c.		No period after "2d"	3,750.	1,400.
30	A3(c)	2p on 6c on 3p (R)	650.00	225.00
a.		Inverted "A"	1,750.	750.00
b.		Period after "R" is a Maltese Cross	1,750.	750.00
c.		No period after "2d"	2,200.	925.00
31	A4(b)	2p on 12c on 6p	2,750.	950.00
a.		Period btwn. "2" and "d"		
b.		No period after "2d"		
c.		"2d, VR" double		4,500.
32	A4(c)	2p on 12c on 6p	2,500.	900.00
a.		Inverted "A"	3,250.	1,250.
b.		No period after "2d"		
c.		"2d, VR" double		4,250.

Types of 1871 Overprinted or Surcharged in Black:

e   f

1876, Jan. 31   **Wove Paper**   **Unwmk.**

33	A2(e)	1p ultramarine	57.50	57.50
a.		Inverted surcharge		
b.		Dbl. impression of stamp	1,000.	
c.		Horiz. pair, imperf vert.	1,000.	
34	A3(e+f)	2p on 3p dk grn	60.00	60.00
a.		Dbl. surch. "Two Pence"		
c.		Dbl. impression of stamp	2,850.	
35	A4(e)	6p rose	70.00	70.00
b.		Surcharge inverted		
c.		Dbl. impression of stamp	2,850.	
		Nos. 33-35 (3)	187.50	187.50

1877   **Laid Paper**

36	A2(e)	1p ultramarine	24.00	40.00
a.		Horiz. pair, imperf. vert.	1,100.	
37	A3(e+f)	2p on 3p dk grn	70.00	80.00
38	A3(e+f)	4p on 3p lilac	95.00	30.00
a.		Horiz. pair, imperf. vert.	1,000.	
39	A4(e)	6p rose	55.00	35.00
a.		Horiz. pair, imperf. vert.	800.00	
		Nos. 36-39 (4)	244.00	185.00

Many of the preceding stamps are known imperforate. They are printer's waste and were never issued.

A12   A13

Queen Victoria
A14   A15

Perf. 10-13½ & Compound

1878-90   **Wove Paper**   **Typo.**

40	A12	1p ultra ('79)	13.00	13.00
a.		1p blue	60.00	3.75
41	A12	2p green	15.00	1.10
b.		2p ultramarine (error)	28,500.	
42	A12	4p brt vio ('90)	8.50	7.00
a.		4p mauve	11.50	8.50
43	A13	6p brt rose ('80)	7.50	4.25
a.		Printed on both sides	1,150.	975.00
44	A14	1sh yel brn ('81)	40.00	10.00
a.		1sh deep brown	95.00	22.50

Litho. & Typo.

45	A15	5sh blk & red brn ('82)	62.50	37.50
		Nos. 40-45 (6)	146.50	72.85

Official facsimiles of the 5sh were officially made in 1900, differing in shades and detail of design from No. 45. They exist imperf., perf. 10 and 12; are all canceled "SUVA" and usually dated "15 Dec., 00."

No. 41b was not put on sale. All examples were supposed to be destroyed.

For surcharges see Nos. 46-52.

Surcharged type "f" in Black

1878-90   **Typo.**

46	A12	2p on 3p green	9.00	27.50
47	A12	4p on 1p vio ('90)	60.00	50.00
48	A12	4p on 2p lilac ('83)	85.00	14.00
		Nos. 46-48 (3)	154.00	91.50

Nos. 40-43 Surcharged in Black:

g   h

j   k

1891-92   **Perf. 10**

49	A12(g)	½p on 1p ('92)	55.00	80.00
50	A12(h)	2½p on 2p	50.00	57.50
a.		Wider space (2mm) between "2" and "½"	150.00	160.00
51	A12(j)	5p on 4p ('92)	57.50	75.00
52	A13(k)	5p on 6p ('92)	62.50	80.00
a.		"FIVE" and "PENCE" 3mm apart	75.00	85.00
		Nos. 49-52 (4)	225.00	292.50

A18

Fijian Canoe — A19

A20

1891-96   **Perf. 10-12 & Compound**

53	A18	½p grnsh blk ('92)	4.50	6.00
a.		½p gray	3.50	10.00
54	A19	1p black ('93)	22.50	6.00
55	A19	1p lilac rose ('96)	7.50	1.00
56	A19	2p green ('93)	22.50	7.50
a.		Perf. 10x12 ('94)	700.00	425.00
57	A20	2½ red brown	12.00	12.00
58	A19	5p ultra ('93)	17.00	8.50
		Nos. 53-58 (6)	86.00	41.00

Edward VII   George V
A22   A23

1903, Feb. 1   **Wmk. 2**   **Perf. 14**

59	A22	½p gray grn & pale grn	2.60	2.25
60	A22	1p vio & blk, red	15.00	.65
61	A22	2p vio & orange	4.50	1.40
62	A22	2½p vio & ultra, bl	16.00	4.00
63	A22	3p vio & red vio	1.75	4.50
64	A22	4p violet & blk	1.75	2.75
65	A22	5p vio & green	1.75	3.00
66	A22	6p vio & car rose	1.75	2.00
67	A22	1sh grn & car rose	12.50	75.00
68	A22	5sh green & blk	75.00	160.00
69	A22	£1 gray & ultra	400.00	550.00
		Revenue cancel		70.00
		Nos. 59-68 (10)	132.60	255.55

Numerals of 2p, 4p, 6p and 5sh of type A22 are in color on plain tablet.

1904-12   **Wmk. 3**

Ordinary Paper

70	A22	½p grn & pale grn ('04)	15.00	3.50
70A	A22	½p green ('08)	12.50	3.50
71	A22	1p vio & black, red ('04)	30.00	.20
72	A22	1p carmine ('06)	14.00	.20
73	A22	2½p ultra ('10)	7.50	8.50

Chalky Paper

74	A22	6p violet ('10)	19.00	32.50
75	A22	1sh grn & car rose ('09)	32.50	45.00
76	A22	1sh black, green ('11)	7.00	11.00
77	A22	5sh grn & scarlet, yel ('11)	67.50	90.00
78	A22	£1 vio & black, red ('12)	400.00	325.00
		Nos. 70-77 (9)	205.00	194.40

Die I

For description of Dies I and II see "Dies of British Colonial Stamps" in Table of Contents.

1912-23

Ordinary Paper

79	A23	¼p brown ('16)	2.50	.30
80	A23	½p green	1.50	1.00
81	A23	1p scarlet	2.25	.75
a.		1p carmine ('16)	2.25	.25
82	A23	2p gray ('14)	2.00	.20
83	A23	2½p ultra ('14)	3.50	4.00

84	A23	3p violet, yel	4.25	7.50
a.		Die II ('21)	2.75	25.00
85	A23	4p black & red, yel ('14)	3.75	15.00
a.		Die II ('23)	3.75	27.50

Chalky Paper

86	A23	5p dl vio & ol grn ('14)	5.50	12.50
87	A23	6p dl vio & red vio ('14)	2.40	6.00
88	A23	1sh black, green	1.10	14.00
a.		1sh black, blue green, ol back	4.50	11.00
b.		1sh black, emerald ('21)	6.25	55.00
c.		Die II ('22)	3.25	30.00
89	A23	2sh 6p black & red, blue	37.50	35.00
90	A23	5sh grn & scar, yellow	37.50	45.00
91	A23	£1 vio & black, red	300.00	325.00
a.		Die II ('21)	300.00	325.00
		Revenue cancel		52.50

Surface-colored Paper

92	A23	1sh black, green	1.25	12.50
		Nos. 79-90,92 (13)	105.00	153.75

Numerals of ¼p, 1½p, 2p, 4p, 6p, 2sh, 2sh6p and 5sh of type A23 are in color on plain tablet.

For overprints see Nos. MR1-MR2.

Die II

1922-27   **Wmk. 4**

Ordinary Paper

93	A23	¼p dark brown	3.00	27.50
94	A23	½p green	.85	2.40
95	A23	1p rose red	3.00	1.25
96	A23	1p violet ('27)	1.40	.20
97	A23	1½p rose red ('27)	4.50	2.00
98	A23	2p gray	1.40	.20
99	A23	3p ultra ('23)	3.00	1.20
100	A23	4p blk & red, yel	9.00	7.50
101	A23	5p dl vio & ol green	1.75	2.25
102	A23	6p dl vio & red violet	2.40	1.50

Chalky Paper

103	A23	1sh blk, emerald	7.00	6.75
104	A23	2sh vio & ultra, bl ('27)	30.00	67.50
105	A23	2sh6p blk & red, bl	12.50	35.00
106	A23	5sh grn & scar, yellow	37.50	75.00
		Nos. 93-106 (14)	117.30	230.25

Common Design Types pictured following the introduction.

Silver Jubilee Issue
Common Design Type

1935, May 6   **Perf. 13½x14**

110	CD301	1½p carmine & blue	1.10	8.50
111	CD301	2p gray blk & ultra	1.75	.50
112	CD301	3p blue & brown	3.00	4.00
113	CD301	1sh brt vio & indigo	7.50	10.00
		Nos. 110-113 (4)	13.35	23.00
		Set, never hinged	22.50	

Coronation Issue
Common Design Type

1937, May 12   **Perf. 11x11½**

114	CD302	1p dark violet	.45	1.25
115	CD302	2p gray black	.45	2.25
116	CD302	3p indigo	.45	2.25
		Nos. 114-116 (3)	1.35	5.75
		Set, never hinged	2.00	

Outrigger   Fijian
Canoe — A24   Village — A25

Outrigger
Canoe
A26

Map of Fiji Islands A27

Canoe and Arms of Fiji — A28

Sugar Cane — A29

Spear Fishing at Night — A30

Arms of Fiji — A31

Suva Harbor — A32

River Scene — A33

Fijian House — A34

Papaya Tree — A35

Bugler — A36

Designs: No. 121, Government buildings. 8p, 1sh5p, 1sh6p, Arms of Fiji.

Perf. 13½, 12½ (1p)

			Engr.	Wmk. 4
1938-55				
117	A24	½p green	.25	1.00
c.		Perf. 14 ('41)	16.00	4.50
d.		Perf. 12 ('48)	.80	4.00
118	A25	1p blue & brn	.40	.25
119	A26	1½p rose car (empty canoe)	12.00	2.00
120	A27	2p grn & org brn (no "180 degree")	30.00	.50
121	A27	2p mag & grn	.45	.80
a.		Perf. 12 ('46)	.45	.90

Perf. 12½, 13x12 (6p), 14 (8p)

122	A28	3p dp ultra	.80	.40
123	A29	5p rose red & blue	32.50	13.00
124	A29	5p rose red & yel grn	.25	.40
125	A27	6p blk (no "180 degree")	50.00	16.00

126	A31	8p rose car	.80	3.00
a.		Perf. 13 ('50)	.55	3.50
127	A30	1sh black & yel	.60	.90

Perf. 14

128	A31	1sh5p car & black	.20	.20
128A	A31	1sh6p ultra	2.75	3.50
b.		Perf. 13 ('55)	1.10	20.00

Perf. 12½

129	A32	2sh vio & org	2.00	.55
130	A33	2sh6p brn & grn	2.25	2.00
131	A34	5sh dk vio & grn	2.25	2.25
131A	A35	10sh emer & brn org	27.50	52.50
131B	A36	£1 car & ultra	37.50	65.00
		Nos. 117-131B (18)	202.50	164.25

Issued: 1sh5p, 6/13/40; 5p, 10/1/40; #121, 5/19/42; 8p, 11/15/48; 10sh, £1, 3/13/50; 1sh6p, 8/1/50; others, 4/5/38.

Types of 1938-40 Redrawn

Perf. 13½ (1½p, 2p, 6p), 14 (2½p)

1940-49				Wmk. 4
132	A26	1½p rose car (man in canoe)	1.00	1.00
a.		Perf. 12 ('49)	.80	1.60
b.		Perf. 14 ('42)	14.50	25.00
133	A27	2p grn & org brn ("180 degree")	12.50	21.00
134	A27	2½p grn & org brn	.50	1.25
a.		Perf. 12 ('48)	.80	.60
b.		Perf. 13½ ('42)	.55	1.00
135	A27	6p blk ("180 degree")	2.50	3.00
a.		Perf. 12 ('47)	1.40	2.00
		Nos. 132-135 (4)	16.50	26.25

No. 132, type A26, has a man sitting in the canoe.

Nos. 133-135, type A27, have 180 degree added to the lower right hand corner of the design.

Issued: 2½p, Jan. 6, 1942; others Oct. 1, 1940.

No. 133 Surcharged in Black

2½d.

1941, Feb. 10				**Perf. 13½**
136	A27	2½p on 2p grn & org brn	1.50	.40
		Never hinged	2.50	

> **Catalogue values for unused stamps in this section, from this point to the end of the section, are for Never Hinged items.**

Peace Issue
Common Design Type

1946, Aug. 17				**Perf. 13½**
137	CD303	2½p bright green	.25	1.50
138	CD303	3p deep blue	.25	.20

Silver Wedding Issue
Common Design Types

1948, Dec. 17		Photo.	**Perf. 14x14½**	
139	CD304	2½p dark green	.70	1.75

Engr.; Name Typo.
Perf. 11½x11

140	CD305	5sh blue violet	22.50	16.00

UPU Issue
Common Design Types
Engr.; Name Typo. on 3p, 8p
Perf. 13½, 11x11½

1949, Oct. 10				Wmk. 4
141	CD306	2p red violet	.65	.75
142	CD307	3p indigo	4.00	3.75
143	CD308	8p dp carmine	.65	3.75
144	CD309	1sh6p blue	.70	1.60
		Nos. 141-144 (4)	6.00	9.85

Coronation Issue
Common Design Type

1953, June 2				**Perf. 13½x13**
145	CD312	2½p dk green & blk	1.75	.60

Type of 1938-40 with Portrait of Queen Elizabeth II Inscribed: "Royal Visit 1953"

1953, Dec. 16			**Perf. 13**	
146	A31	8p carmine lake	.65	.35

Visit of Queen Elizabeth II and the Duke of Edinburgh, 1953.

Types of 1938-50 with Portrait of Queen Elizabeth II, and:

A39

Loading Copra A40

Designs: 1sh6p, Sugar cane train. 2sh, Bananas for export. 5sh, Gold industry.

Perf. 11½, 11½x11, 12, 12½, 13

1954-56				Engr.
147	A24	½p green	.20	1.25
148	A39	1p grnsh blue	2.00	.20
149	A39	1½p brown	1.10	.65
150	A27	2p mag & green	1.40	.40
151	A39	2½p blue vio	2.75	.20
152	A40	3p purple & brn	3.00	.20
154	A27	6p black	3.00	.85
155	A31	8p carmine lake	4.25	1.25
156	A30	1sh black & yel	2.75	1.25
157	A40	1sh6p grn & dp ultra	21.00	1.00
158	A40	2sh brt car & black	6.25	.50
159	A33	2sh6p brn & bl grn	1.40	.20
160	A40	5sh dp ultra & yel	17.00	1.25
161	A35	10sh emer & brn org	8.00	20.00
162	A36	£1 car & ultra	42.50	19.00
		Nos. 147-162 (15)	116.60	47.15

Issued: 2p, 1sh, 2sh6p, 2/1/54; ½p, 6p, 8p, 10sh, £1, 7/1/54; 1p, 6/1/56; 1½p, 2½p, 3p, 1sh6p, 2sh, 5sh, 10/1/56.

Types of 1954-56 and:

Nautilus Shells — A41

Hibiscus — A42

Kandavu Parrot A43

½p, 2p, 2½p, Queen Elizabeth II (A39). 1p, Queen, turtles in bottom panels. 6p, Fijian beating drum (lali). 10p, Yaqona ceremony. 1sh, South Pacific map. 2sh6p, Nadi Airport. 10sh, Cutting sugar cane. £1, Arms of Fiji.

Perf. 11½ (A39, A41); 11½x11 (A40); 14½x14 (A42); 14x14½ (A43)
Engr. (A39, A40, A41); others Photo.

1959-63				Wmk. 4
163	A39	½p green ('61)	.25	2.75
164	A41	1p dk blue ('62)	4.00	2.75
165	A41	1½p dk brown ('62)	3.25	2.00
166	A39	2p crim rose ('61)	.90	.20
167	A39	2½p brown org ('62)	2.75	4.25
168	A40	6p blk & car rose ('61)	2.25	.20
169	A42	8p gray, red, yel & grn ('61)	.90	.40
170	A40	10p car & brn ('63)	1.10	.80
171	A40	1sh dk bl & bl ('61)	2.75	.25
172	A40	2sh6p pur & blk ('61)	4.50	1.40
173	A43	4sh dk grn, red, bl & emer	3.25	2.40

174	A40	10sh sep & emer ('61)	8.00	8.00
175	A40	£1 org & blk ('61)	24.00	10.00
		Nos. 163-175 (13)	57.90	35.90

Issued: 4sh, 7/13; 8p, 8/1; ½p, 2p, 6p, 1sh, 2sh6p, 10sh, £1, 11/14; 1p, 1½p, 2½p, 12/3; 10p, 4/1.

For type overprinted see No. 205.

Types of 1954-63 and:

Elizabeth II — A44

1sh6p, 180th meridian and Intl. Date Line. 2sh, White orchids. 5sh, Orange dove.

Perf. 11½ (A41); 12½ (A44); 11½x11 (A40); 14x14½ (A43)
Engr. (A40, A41); others Photo.

1962-67				Wmk. 314
176	A41	1p dark blue ('64)	.75	4.25
177	A39	2p crim rose ('65)	.95	.20
178	A44	3p rose cl & multi	.20	.20
179	A40	6p blk & car rose ('64)	1.10	.20
180	A42	9p ultra, red, yel & grn ('63)	1.10	1.00
181	A40	10p car & brn ('64)	1.10	.85
182	A40	1sh dk bl & bl ('66)	1.90	.75
183	A43	1sh6p dk bl & multi	2.25	1.60
184	A42	2sh gold, yel grn & grn	11.00	5.75
185	A40	2sh6p pur & blk ('65)	2.25	1.25
186	A43	4sh grn & multi, wmk. sideways ('67)	4.75	3.25
a.		As #186, wmk. upright ('64)	3.50	6.50
b.		4sh dark green & multi ('66)	4.00	5.25
187	A43	5sh dk gray, yel & red	8.00	1.00
188	A40	10sh sep & emer ('64)	5.50	5.75
189	A40	£1 org & blk ('64)	21.00	15.00
		Nos. 176-189 (14)	61.85	41.05

Issued: 3p, 1sh6p, 2sh, 5sh, 12/3; 9p, #186a, 4/1; 1p, 10p, 10sh, 1/14; 6p, £1, 6/9; 2p, 2sh6p, 8/3; #186b, 3/1; #186, 2/16.

Nos. 178 and 171 Overprinted: "ROYAL VISIT 1963"

1963, Feb. 1				
196	A44	3p multicolored	.50	.35
197	A40	1sh dark blue & blue	.50	.35

Visit of Elizabeth II & Prince Philip, Feb. 3.

Freedom from Hunger Issue
Common Design Type

1963, June 4	Photo.		**Perf. 14x14½**	
198	CD314	2sh ultramarine	6.00	3.25

Running A45

9p, Throwing the discus, vert. 1sh, Field hockey, vert. 2sh6p, Women's high jump.

Perf. 14½x14, 14x14½

1963, Aug. 6				Wmk. 314
199	A45	3p yel, blk & brn	.60	.20
200	A45	9p violet, blk & brn	.60	1.10
201	A45	1sh green, blk & brn	.60	.25
202	A45	2sh6p blue, blk & brn	1.25	1.25
		Nos. 199-202 (4)	3.05	2.80

1st So. Pacific Games, Suva, 8/29-9/7.

Red Cross Centenary Issue
Common Design Type

1963, Sept. 2	Litho.		**Perf. 13**	
203	CD315	2p black & red	1.00	.30
204	CD315	2sh ultra & red	4.00	4.00

Type of 1959-63 Overprinted

1963, Dec. 2   Engr.   Perf. 11½x11
205 A40 1sh dark blue & blue   1.00 .35

Opening of the Commonwealth Pacific (telephone) Cable service, COMPAC.

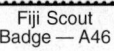

Fiji Scout Badge — A46

Scouts of India, Fiji and Europe Tying Knot — A47

1964, Aug. 3   Photo.   Perf. 12½
206 A46 3p multicolored   .65 .50
207 A47 1sh ocher & purple   1.00 .75

50th anniv. of the founding of the Fiji Boy Scouts.

Amphibian "Aotearoa," 1939 — A48

Map of Fiji and Tonga Islands and Plane A49

Design: 6p, Heron plane.

1964, Oct. 24   Perf. 12½, 14½
208 A48 3p brt red & black   .65 .35
209 A48 6p ultra & red   1.10 1.10
210 A49 1sh grnsh blue & black   1.10 1.10
    Nos. 208-210 (3)   2.85 2.55

Fiji-Tonga airmail service, 25th anniv.

ITU Issue
Common Design Type
Perf. 11x11½
1965, May 17   Litho.   Wmk. 314
211 CD317 3p blue & rose red   .40 .30
212 CD317 2sh yel & bister   2.75 2.75

Intl. Cooperation Year Issue
Common Design Type
1965, Oct. 25   Perf. 14½
213 CD318 2p blue grn & claret   .40 .40
214 CD318 2sh6p lt vio & grn   2.60 2.10

Churchill Memorial Issue
Common Design Type
1966, Jan. 24   Photo.   Perf. 14
Design in Black, Gold and Carmine Rose
215 CD319 3p brt blue   1.25 .35
216 CD319 9p green   1.75 1.75
217 CD319 1sh brown   1.75 .35
218 CD319 2sh6p violet   2.00 2.00
    Nos. 215-218 (4)   6.75 4.45

World Cup Soccer Issue
Common Design Type
1966, July 1   Litho.   Perf. 14
219 CD321 2p multicolored   .60 .30
220 CD321 2sh multicolored   1.75 .90

H.M.S. Pandora and Split Island, Rotuma A50

Designs: 10p, Rotuma chiefs, Pandora, and Rotuma's position in Pacific. 1sh6p, Rotuma islanders welcoming Pandora.

1966, Aug. 29   Photo.   Perf. 14x13
221 A50 3p multicolored   .60 .25
222 A50 10p multicolored   .75 .40
223 A50 1sh6p multicolored   1.00 1.00
    Nos. 221-223 (3)   2.35 1.65

175th anniv. of the discovery of Rotuma, a group of eight islands forming part of the colony of Fiji.

WHO Headquarters Issue
Common Design Type
1966, Sept. 20   Litho.   Perf. 14
224 CD322 6p multicolored   2.10 .50
225 CD322 2sh6p multicolored   4.50 4.00

Woman Runner A51

Designs: 9p, Shot put, vert. 1sh, Diver.

1966, Dec. 8   Photo.   Perf. 14x14½
226 A51 3p ol, black & lt brn   .40 .40
227 A51 9p brt blue, blk & brn   .65 .65
228 A51 1sh blue green & multi   .65 .65
    Nos. 226-228 (3)   1.70 1.70

2nd South Pacific Games, Noumea, New Caledonia, Dec. 8-18.

Military Band A52

Intl. Tourist Year: 9p, Reef diving. 1sh, Beqa fire walkers. 2sh, Liner Oriana and Mt. Rama volcano.

1967, Oct. 20   Perf. 14x13
229 A52 3p multi & gold   .90 .20
230 A52 9p multi & silver   .35 .25
231 A52 1sh multi & gold   .35 .35
232 A52 2sh multi & silver   .90 .60
    Nos. 229-232 (4)   2.50 1.40

Admiral Bligh, H.M.S. Providence and Old Map of "Feejee" A53

Designs: 1sh, Bligh's longboat being chased by double canoe and map of Fiji Islands. 2sh6p, Bligh's tomb, St. Mary's Cemetery, Lambeth, London.

Perf. 15x14, 12½x13 (1sh)
1967, Dec. 7   Photo.   Wmk. 314
Size: 35x21mm
233 A53 4p emer, blk & yel   .30 .30
Size: 54x20mm
234 A53 1sh brt bl, brn org & blk   .45 .45
Size: 35x21mm
235 A53 2sh6p sepia & multi   1.25 1.25
    Nos. 233-235 (3)   2.00 2.00

150th anniv. of the death of Adm. William Bligh (1754-1817), captain of the Bounty and principal discoverer of the Fiji Islands.

Simmonds "Spartan" Seaplane — A54

Designs: 6p, Fiji Airways Hawker-Siddeley H748 and emblems of various airlines. 1sh, Fokker "Southern Cross," Capt. Charles Kingsford-Smith, his crew and Southern Cross constellation. 2sh, Lockheed Altair "Lady Southern Cross."

Perf. 14x14½
1968, June 5   Wmk. 314
236 A54 2p green & black   .30 .30
237 A54 6p brt blue, car & blk   .30 .30
238 A54 1sh dp violet & green   .50 .50
239 A54 2sh orange brn & dk blue   .90 .90
    Nos. 236-239 (4)   2.00 2.00

40th anniv. of the first Trans-Pacific Flight through Fiji under Capt. Charles Kingsford-Smith.

Fijian Bures — A55

Eastern Reef Heron — A56

1p, Passion fruit flowers. 2p, Nautilus pompilius shell. 4p, Hawk moth. 6p, Reef butterflyfish. 9p, Bamboo raft (bilibili). 10p, Tiger moth. 1sh, Black marlin. 1sh6p, Orange-breasted honey eaters. 2sh, Ringed sea snake, horiz. 2sh6p, Outrigger canoes (takia), horiz. 3sh, Golden cowrie shell. 4sh, Emperor gold mine and gold ore. 5sh, Bamboo orchids, horiz. 10sh, Tabua (ceremonial whale's tooth). £1, Coat of Arms and Queen Elizabeth II, horiz.

Perf. 13½ (A55), 14 (A56)
1968, July 15   Photo.   Wmk. 314
240 A55 ½p multicolored   .20 .20
241 A55 1p multicolored   .20 .20
242 A55 2p multicolored   .20 .20
243 A56 3p multicolored   .30 .20
244 A56 4p multicolored   .65 .20
245 A55 6p multicolored   .25 .30
246 A55 9p multicolored   .20 .45
247 A55 10p multicolored   1.00 .60
248 A56 1sh multicolored   1.25 .65
249 A56 1sh6p multicolored   2.75 .75
250 A56 2sh multicolored   1.50 1.50
251 A56 2sh6p multicolored   1.50 1.50
252 A56 3sh multicolored   3.00 2.00
253 A56 4sh multicolored   5.25 1.75
254 A56 5sh multicolored   2.60 2.25
255 A56 10sh multicolored   4.00 3.50
256 A56 £1 red & multi   5.00 4.00
    Nos. 240-256 (17)   29.85 20.25

See Nos. 260-276.

WHO Emblem, Map of Fiji and Nurses — A57

WHO Emblem and: 9p, Medical team loading patient on stretcher on dinghy and medical ship "Vuniwai." 3sh, People playing on beach.

1968, Dec. 9   Litho.   Perf. 14
257 A57 3p blue green & multi   .20 .20
258 A57 9p brt blue & multi   .30 .30
259 A57 3sh dk blue & multi   .90 .90
    Nos. 257-259 (3)   1.40 1.40

WHO, 20th anniv.

Types of 1968
Values in Cents and Dollars

Designs: 1c, Passion fruit flowers. 2c, Nautilus pompilius shell. 3c, Reef heron. 4c, Hawk moth. 5c, Reef butterflyfish. 6c, Fijian bures. 8c, Bamboo raft. 9c, Tiger moth. 10c, Black marlin. 15c, Orange-breasted honey-eater. 20c, Ringed sea snake, horiz. 25c, Outrigger canoes (takia), horiz. 30c, Golden cowrie shell. 40c Emperor gold mine and gold ore. 50c, Bamboo orchids, horiz. $1, Tabua (ceremonial whale's tooth). $2, Coat of Arms and Queen Elizabeth II, horiz.

Perf. 13½ (A55), 14 (A56)
1969, Jan. 13   Photo.   Wmk. 314
260 A55 1c multicolored   .20 .20
261 A55 2c multicolored   .20 .20
262 A56 3c multicolored   .50 .35
263 A56 4c multicolored   1.25 .35
264 A55 5c multicolored   .20 .20
265 A55 6c multicolored   .20 .20
266 A56 8c multicolored   .20 .20
267 A55 9c multicolored   1.25 1.60
268 A56 10c multicolored   .20 .20
269 A56 15c multicolored   7.25 3.50
270 A56 20c multicolored   .90 .65
271 A56 25c multicolored   .90 .25
272 A55 30c multicolored   5.25 1.40
273 A56 40c multicolored   6.00 3.25
274 A56 50c multicolored   3.50 .25
275 A56 $1 multicolored   5.00 2.00
276 A56 $2 red & multi   6.00 5.00
    Nos. 260-276 (17)   39.00 19.80

For overprints & surcharges see #286-288, B5-B6.

Fiji Soldiers and Map of Solomon Islands A58

Designs: 10c, Flags of Fiji Military Force, soldiers in full and battle dress. 25c, Cpl. Sefanaia Sukanaivalu and Victoria Cross.

1969, June 23   Wmk. 314   Perf. 14
277 A58 3c emerald & multi   .80 .80
278 A58 10c red & multi   .95 .95
279 A58 25c black & multi   1.25 1.25
    Nos. 277-279 (3)   3.00 3.00

25th anniv. of the Fiji Military Forces campaign in the Solomon Islands and of the posthumous award of the Victoria Cross to Cpl. Sefanaia Sukanaivalu.

Yachting — A59

Designs: 4c, Javelin. 20c, Winners and South Pacific Games medal.

1969, Aug. 18   Photo.   Perf. 14½x14
280 A59 4c red, brown & blk   .45 .45
281 A59 8c blue & black   .60 .60
282 A59 20c olive grn, blk & ocher   1.25 1.25
    Nos. 280-282 (3)   2.30 2.30

3rd South Pacific Games, Port Moresby, Papua New Guinea, Aug. 13-23.

Students in Laboratory — A60

2c, Map of South Pacific and mortarboard. 8c, Site of University at Royal New Zealand Air Force Seaplane Station, Laucala Bay, RNZAF badge and Sunderland flying boat.

1969, Nov. 10 *Perf. 14x14½*
283 A60 2c multicolored .30 .30
284 A60 8c red & multi .50 .50
285 A60 25c dk green & multi 1.40 1.40
Nos. 283-285 (3) 2.20 2.20

Inauguration of the University of the South Pacific, Laucala Bay, Suva.

Nos. 261, 268 and 271 Overprinted: "ROYAL VISIT / 1970"

1970, Mar. 4 *Perf. 13½, 14*
286 A55 2c multicolored .30 .30
287 A56 10c multicolored .40 .40
288 A55 25c multicolored 1.75 1.75
Nos. 286-288 (3) 2.45 2.45

Visit of Queen Elizabeth II, Prince Philip and Princess Anne, Mar. 4-5.

Nuns Sitting under Chaulmoogra Tree, and Chaulmoogra Fruit — A61

Designs: 10c, Paintings by Semisi Maya (former patient). No. 290, Cascade, vert. No. 291, Sea urchins, vert. 30c, Aerial view of Makogai Hospital.

Perf. 14x14½, 14½x14
1970, May 25 Photo. **Wmk. 314**
289 A61 2c brt pink & multi .40 .40
290 A61 10c gray green & blk .60 .60
291 A61 10c blue, car & blk .60 .60
a. Pair, #290-291 1.25 1.25
292 A61 30c orange & multi 1.75 1.75
Nos. 289-292 (4) 3.35 3.35

Closing of the Leprosy Hospital on Makogai Island in 1969.

Abel Tasman and Ship's Log, 1643 — A62

3c, Capt. James Cook & "Endeavour." 8c, Capt. William Bligh & longboat, 1789. 25c, Man of Fiji & Fijian ocean-going canoe.

1970, Aug. 18 Litho. *Perf. 13x12½*
293 A62 2c blue green & multi 1.00 1.00
294 A62 3c gray green & multi 1.25 1.25
295 A62 8c multicolored 1.50 1.50
296 A62 25c dull lilac & multi 2.25 2.25
Nos. 293-296 (4) 6.00 6.00

Discoverers and explorers of Fiji Islands.

King Cakobau and Cession Stone at Lavuka A63

Designs: 3c, Chinese, Fijian, Indian and European children. 10c, Prime Minister Ratu Sir Kamisese Mara and flag of Fiji. 25c, Fijian male dancer and Indian female dancer.

1970, Oct. 10 Wmk. 314 *Perf. 14*
297 A63 2c multicolored .25 .25
298 A63 3c multicolored .35 .35
299 A63 10c multicolored .55 .55
300 A63 25c multicolored 1.60 1.60
Nos. 297-300 (4) 2.75 2.75

Fijian independence.

Fiji Nos. 1 and 3 — A64

15c, Fiji #15, 44, 59, 81, 127, 166. 20c, Fiji Times Office, Levuka, & G. P. O., Suva.

1970, Nov. 2 Photo. *Perf. 14½x14*
Size: 35x21mm
301 A64 4c multicolored .40 .40
Size: 60x21½mm
302 A64 15c multicolored 1.10 1.10
Size: 35x21mm
303 A64 20c multicolored 1.50 1.50
Nos. 301-303 (3) 3.00 3.00

Centenary of first postage stamps of Fiji.

Gray-backed White Eyes — A65

Yellow-breasted Musk Parrots — A66

Designs: 1c, Cirrhopetalum umbellatum. 2c, Cardinal honey eaters. 3c, Calanthe furcata. 4c, Bulbophyllum. 6c, Phaius tancarvilliae. 8c, Blue-crested broadbills. 10c, Acanthephippiumvitiense. 15c, Dendrobium tokai. 20c, Slaty flycatchers. 25c, Kandavu honey eaters. 30c, Dendrobium gordonii. 50c, White-throated pigeon. $1, Collared lories (kula). $2, Dendrobium platygastrium. (Orchids shown on 1c, 3c, 4c, 6c, 10c, 15c, 30c, $2.)

Wmk. 314 Upright
1971-72 Litho. *Perf. 13½x14*
305 A65 1c blk & multi ('72) .20 .20
306 A65 2c carmine & multi .20 .20
307 A65 3c multi ('72) .85 .20
308 A65 4c blk & multi ('72) .75 1.50
309 A65 5c brown & multi 2.75 .25
310 A65 6c lt bl & multi ('72) .45 .30
311 A65 8c black & multi .50 .35
312 A65 10c multi ('72) .55 .40
313 A65 15c multi ('72) 2.50 .55
314 A65 20c gray & multi 1.50 .60
Perf. 14
315 A66 25c sepia & multi 1.50 .95
316 A66 30c grn & multi ('72) 3.00 1.10
317 A66 40c blue & multi 3.50 .55
318 A66 50c gray & multi 4.00 1.90
319 A66 $1 red & multi 6.25 3.75
320 A66 $2 multi ('72) 12.50 7.25
Nos. 305-320 (16) 41.00 21.00

Issued: 5c, 20c, 40c, 50c, 8/6; 2c, 8c, 25c, $1, 11/22; 1c, 10c, 30c, $2, 1/4; 3c, 4c, 6c, 15c, 6/23.

1972-74 Wmk. 314 Sideways
306c A65 2c ('73) .70 11.00
307a A65 3c ('73) 2.00 .60
308a A65 4c ('73) 6.50 .90
309a A65 5c ('73) 6.50 4.25
310a A65 6c ('73) 8.75 1.60
311a A65 8c ('73) 4.25 1.00
313a A65 15c ('73) 3.75 2.75
314a A65 20c 14.00 2.50
315a A66 25c ('73) 2.00 1.10
317a A66 40c ('74) 3.25 8.75
318a A66 50c ('74) 3.25 4.25
319a A66 $1 3.25 6.50
320a A66 $2 4.25 7.00
Nos. 306c-320a (13) 62.45 52.20

Issued: 20c, $1, $2, 11/17; 3c, 5c, 3/8; 4c, 6c, 8c, 15c, 25c, 4/11; 2c, 12/12; 40c, 50c, 3/15.

1975-77 Wmk. 373
305b A65 1c 1.00 4.75
306d A65 2c 1.00 4.75
307b A65 3c .50 4.75
308b A65 4c ('76) 4.50 .20
309b A65 5c 1.60 4.75
310b A65 6c ('76) 3.75 .20
311b A65 8c ('76) .45 .20
312b A65 10c .50 2.25
313b A65 15c ('76) 3.25 .50
314b A66 20c ('77) 4.75 .65
316b A66 30c ('76) 6.75 1.10
317b A66 40c ('76) 3.75 .70
318b A66 50c ('76) 3.75 .80
319b A66 $1 ('76) 3.75 1.75
320b A66 $2 ('76) 1.90 1.75
Nos. 305b-320b (15) 41.20 29.10

Issued: 1c, 2c, 3c, 5c, 10c, 4/9; 20c, 7/15; others, 9/3.

Women's Basketball — A67

Community Education — A68

1971, Sept. 6 Wmk. 314 *Perf. 14*
321 A67 8c shown .50 .50
322 A67 10c Running .75 .75
323 A67 25c Weight lifting 1.50 1.50
Nos. 321-323 (3) 2.75 2.75

4th South Pacific Games, Papeete, French Polynesia, Sept. 8-19.

1972, Feb. 7
Designs: 4c, Public health. 50c, Economic growth (farm scenes).
324 A68 2c bright rose & multi .20 .20
325 A68 4c gray & multi .30 .30
326 A68 50c bright blue & multi 2.00 2.00
Nos. 324-326 (3) 2.50 2.50

South Pacific Commission, 25th anniv.

Arts Festival Emblem — A69

Rugby — A70

1972, Apr. 10
327 A69 10c blue, org & black .50 .50
South Pacific Festival of Arts, May 6-20.

Silver Wedding Issue, 1972
Common Design Type

Queen Elizabeth II, Prince Philip, flowers, shells.

1972, Nov. 20 Photo. *Perf. 14x14½*
328 CD324 10c slate grn & multi .40 .40
329 CD324 25c red lilac & multi .60 .60

1973, Mar. 9 Litho. *Perf. 14*
330 A70 2c shown .40 .40
331 A70 8c Tackle .80 .80
332 A70 25c Kicking ball 1.25 1.25
Nos. 330-332 (3) 2.45 2.45

60th anniversary of Fiji Rugby Union.

Forestry Development — A71

Development projects: 8c, Irrigation of rice field. 10c, Low income housing. 25c, Highway construction.

1973, July 23 *Perf. 14*
333 A71 5c multicolored .30 .30
334 A71 8c multicolored .40 .40
335 A71 10c multicolored .45 .45
336 A71 25c multicolored 1.25 1.25
Nos. 333-336 (4) 2.40 2.40

Holy Family — A72

Runners — A73

Festivals: 10c, Diwali (Candles; Indian New Year). 20c, Id-Ul-Fitar (Friendly greeting and mosque; Moslem, Ramadan). 25c, Chinese New Year (dragon dance).

1973, Oct. 26 *Perf. 14x14½*
337 A72 3c blue & multi .45 .45
338 A72 10c purple & multi .45 .45
339 A72 20c emerald & multi .75 .75
340 A72 25c red & multi .75 .75
Nos. 337-340 (4) 2.40 2.40

Festivals celebrated by various groups in Fiji.

1974, Jan. 7
341 A73 3c shown .60 .35
342 A73 8c Boxing .60 .35
343 A73 50c Lawn bowling 2.25 2.25
Nos. 341-343 (3) 3.45 2.95

10th British Commonwealth Games, Christchurch, N.Z., Jan. 24-Feb. 2.

Centenary of Cricket in Fiji — A74

Designs: 3c, Bowler. 25c, Batsman and wicketkeeper. 40c, Fielder, horiz.

Perf. 14x14½, 14½x14
1974, Feb. 21 Litho.
344 A74 3c multicolored 1.10 1.10
345 A74 25c multicolored 1.50 1.50
346 A74 40c multicolored 1.75 1.75
Nos. 344-346 (3) 4.35 4.35

Mailman and UPU Emblem A75

UPU Emblem and: 8c, Loading mail on ship. 30c, Post office and truck. 50c, Jet.

1974, May 22 Wmk. 314 *Perf. 14*
347 A75 3c orange & multi .40 .40
348 A75 8c multicolored .45 .45
349 A75 30c lt blue & multi .75 .75
350 A75 40c multicolored 1.40 1.40
Nos. 347-350 (4) 3.00 3.00

Centenary of the Universal Postal Union.

Cub Scouts A76

Designs: 10c, Boy Scouts reading map. 40c, Scouts and Fiji flag, vert.

1974, Aug. 30
351 A76 3c multicolored .25 .25
352 A76 10c multicolored .75 .75
353 A76 40c multicolored 2.00 2.00
Nos. 351-353 (3) 3.00 3.00

First National Boy Scout Jamboree, Lautoka, Viti Levu Island.

Cakobau Club and Flag — A77

King Cakobau, Queen Victoria A78

Design: 50c, Signing ceremony at Levuka.

1974, Oct. 9   Litho.   Perf. 13½x13
354 A77 3c multicolored   .20 .20
355 A78 8c multicolored   .40 .40
356 A78 50c multicolored   1.10 1.10
    Nos. 354-356 (3)   1.70 1.70

Deed of Cession, cent. and 4th anniv. of independence.

Diwali, Hindu Festival of Lights — A79

Designs: 15c, Id-Ul-Fitar (women exchanging greetings under moon). 25c, Chinese New Year (girl twirling streamer, and fireworks). 30c, Christmas (man and woman singing hymns, and star).

1975, Oct. 31   Wmk. 373   Perf. 14
357 A79 3c black & multi   .20 .20
358 A79 15c black & multi   .45 .45
359 A79 25c black & multi   .90 .90
360 A79 30c black & multi   1.10 1.10
    a. Souvenir sheet of 4, #357-360 5.50 5.50
    Nos. 357-360 (4)   2.65 2.65

Festivals celebrated by various groups in Fiji.

Steam Locomotive No. 21 — A80

Sugar mill trains: 15c, Diesel locomotive No. 8. 20c, Diesel locomotive No. 1. 30c, Free passenger train.

1976, Jan. 26   Litho.   Perf. 14½
361 A80 4c yellow & multi   .45 .45
362 A80 15c salmon & multi   1.10 1.10
363 A80 20c multicolored   1.50 1.50
364 A80 30c blue & multi   2.25 2.25
    Nos. 361-364 (4)   5.30 5.30

Fiji Blind Society and Rotary Emblems A81

Rotary Intl. of Fiji, 40th Anniv.: 25c, Ambulance and Rotary emblems.

Perf. 13x13½
1976, Mar. 26   Wmk. 373
365 A81 10c lt green, brn, ultra   .40 .40
366 A81 25c multicolored   1.00 1.00

De Havilland Drover — A82

Planes: 15c, BAC One-Eleven. 25c, Hawker-Siddeley 748. 30c, Britten Norman Trislander.

1976, Sept. 1   Litho.   Perf. 14
367 A82 4c multicolored   .20 .20
368 A82 15c multicolored   .80 .80
369 A82 25c multicolored   2.00 2.00
370 A82 30c multicolored   2.25 2.25
    Nos. 367-370 (4)   5.25 5.25

Fiji air service, 25th anniversary.

Queen's Visit, 1970 — A83

Designs: 25c, King Edward's Chair. 30c, Queen wearing cloth-of-gold supertunica.

1977, Feb. 7   Litho.   Perf. 14x13½
371 A83 10c silver & multi   .25 .25
372 A83 25c silver & multi   .75 .75
373 A83 30c silver & multi   .90 .90
    Nos. 371-373 (3)   1.90 1.90

25th anniv. of reign of Elizabeth II.

World Map, Sinusoidal Projection — A84

Design: 30c, Map showing Fiji Islands.

Wmk. 373
1977, Apr. 12   Litho.   Perf. 14½
374 A84 4c multicolored   .20 .20
375 A84 30c multicolored   1.10 1.10

First Joint Council of Ministers Conference of the European Economic Community (EEC) and of African, Caribbean and Pacific States (ACP).

Hibiscus A85

1977, Aug. 27   Wmk. 373   Perf. 14
376 A85 4c red   .20 .20
377 A85 15c orange   .40 .35
378 A85 30c pink   .90 .70
379 A85 35c yellow   1.10 .90
    Nos. 376-379 (4)   2.60 2.15

Fiji Hibiscus Festival, 21st anniversary.

Drua, Double Canoe A86

Canoes: 15c, Tabilai. 25c, Takia, dugout outrigger canoe. 40c, Camakau.

1977, Nov. 7   Litho.   Perf. 14½
380 A86 4c multicolored   .20 .20
381 A86 15c multicolored   .40 .30
382 A86 25c multicolored   .70 .60
383 A86 40c multicolored   .90 .90
    Nos. 380-383 (4)   2.20 2.00

Elizabeth II Coronation Anniversary Issue
Common Design Types
Souvenir Sheet
Unwmk.
1978, Apr. 21   Litho.   Perf. 15
384 Sheet of 6   3.25 3.25
    a. CD326 25c White hart of Richard II .60 .60
    b. CD327 25c Elizabeth II   .60 .60
    c. CD328 25c Banded iguana   .60 .60

No. 384 contains 2 se-tenant strips of Nos. 348a-348c, separated by horizontal gutter.

Southern Cross on Naselai Beach — A87

4c, Fiji Defence Force surrounding Southern Cross. 25c, Wright Flyer. 30c, Bristol F2B.

1978, June 26   Wmk. 373   Perf. 14½
385 A87 4c multicolored   .20 .20
386 A87 15c multicolored   .40 .30
387 A87 25c multicolored   .75 .60
388 A87 30c multicolored   1.10 .75
    Nos. 385-388 (4)   2.45 1.85

50th anniv. of Kingsford-Smith's Trans-Pacific flight, May 31-June 10, 1928 (4c, 15c); 75th anniv. of Wright brothers' first powered flight, Dec. 17, 1903 (25c); 60th anniv. of Royal Air Force, Apr. 1, 1918 (30c).

Necklace of Sperm Whale Teeth A88

Fiji artifacts: 4c, Wooden oil dish in shape of man, vert. 25c, Twin water bottles. 30c, Carved throwing club (Ula), vert.

1978, Aug. 14   Litho.   Perf. 14
389 A88 4c multicolored   .30 .30
390 A88 15c multicolored   .35 .35
391 A88 25c multicolored   .60 .60
392 A88 30c multicolored   .75 .75
    Nos. 389-392 (4)   2.00 2.00

Christmas Wreath and Candles A89

Festivals: 15c, Diwali (oil lamps). 25c, Id-Ul-Fitr (fruit, coffeepot and cups). 40c, Chinese New Year (paper dragon).

1978, Oct. 30   Perf. 14
393 A89 4c multicolored   .25 .25
394 A89 15c multicolored   .35 .35
395 A89 25c multicolored   .55 .55
396 A89 40c multicolored   .85 .85
    Nos. 393-396 (4)   2.00 2.00

Banded Iguana A90

Endangered species and Wildlife Fund emblem: 15c, Tree frog. 25c, Long-legged warbler. 30c, Pink-billed parrot finch.

1979, Mar. 19   Litho.   Wmk. 373
397 A90 4c multicolored   2.00 2.00
398 A90 15c multicolored   5.00 5.00
399 A90 25c multicolored   8.00 8.00
400 A90 30c multicolored   10.00 10.00
    Nos. 397-400 (4)   25.00 25.00

Indian Women Making Music A91

15c, Indian men sitting around kava bowl. 30c, Indian sugar cane, houses. 40c, Sailing ship Leonidas, map of South Pacific.

1979, May 11   Wmk. 373   Perf. 14
401 A91 4c multicolored   .20 .20
402 A91 15c multicolored   .25 .25
403 A91 30c multicolored   .45 .45
404 A91 40c multicolored   .65 .65
    Nos. 401-404 (4)   1.55 1.55

Arrival of Indians as indentured laborers, cent.

Soccer A92

Games Emblem and: 15c, Rugby. 30c, Tennis. 40c, Weight lifting.

1979, July 2   Litho.   Perf. 14
405 A92 4c multicolored   .30 .30
406 A92 15c multicolored   .45 .45
407 A92 30c multicolored   .90 .90
408 A92 40c multicolored   1.25 1.25
    Nos. 405-408 (4)   2.90 2.90

6th South Pacific Games.

Old Town Hall, Suva A93

2c, Dudley Church, Suva. 3c, Telecommunications building, Suva. 4c, 5c, Lautoka Mosque. 6c, GPO, Suva. 8c, 12c, Levuka Public School. 10c, Visitors' Bureau, Suva. 15c, Colonial War Memorial Hospital Suva. 18c, Labasa Sugar Mill. 20c, Rewa Bridge, Nausori. 30c Sacred Heart Cathedral, Suva. 35c Grand Pacific Hotel, Suva. 45c, Shiva Temple, Suva. 50c Serua Island Village. $1, Solo Lighthouse. $2, Baker memorial Hall, Nausori. $5, Government House.

1979-94   Wmk. 373   Perf. 14
Without Inscribed Date, except #411B (1991)
Chalky Paper (#409-411, 414, 416, 418-419, 425)
Ordinary Paper (#412-413, 415, 417, 420-424)
409 A93 1c multicolored   .20 .20
    a. Ordinary paper   3.00 3.00
    b. Inscribed "1994"   2.00 2.00
410 A93 2c multicolored   .20 .20
    a. Ordinary paper   3.00 3.00
    b. Inscribed "1983"   1.00 3.00
    c. Inscribed "1986"   1.25 1.25
    d. Inscribed "1991"   .75 .75
    e. Inscribed "1993"   3.50 3.50
    f. Inscribed "1994"   1.00 1.50
411 A93 3c multicolored   .20 .20
    a. Ordinary paper   3.00 3.00
    b. Inscribed "1993"   4.50 4.50
411B A93 4c multicolored   1.50 1.50
    a. Inscribed "1993"   6.00 6.00
    b. Inscribed "1994"   3.50 5.50
412 A93 5c multicolored   .20 .20
    a. Inscribed "1983"   1.00 .50
413 A93 6c multicolored   .20 .20
    a. Inscribed "1983"   1.00 .50
414 A93 10c multicolored   .20 .20
    a. Ordinary paper   3.00 3.00
    b. Inscribed "1991"   .75 .75
415 A93 12c multicolored   .50 .50
    a. Inscribed "1993"   5.50 5.50
    b. Inscribed "1994"   2.00 3.50
416 A93 15c multicolored   .25 .25
    a. Ordinary paper   3.50 3.50
    b. Inscribed "1991"   .75 .75

417	A93 18c multicolored	.25	.25
418	A93 20c multicolored	.30	.30
a.	Ordinary paper	7.50	7.50
b.	Inscribed "1993"	3.75	6.50
c.	Inscribed "1994"	3.50	3.50
419	A93 30c multi, vert.	.35	.35
a.	Ordinary paper	4.50	4.50
420	A93 35c multicolored	.40	.40
421	A93 45c multicolored	.45	.45
422	A93 50c multicolored	.60	.60
a.	Inscribed "1994"	3.50	3.50

Perf. 14x13½, 13½x14
Size: 45x29mm, 29x45mm (#423)

423	A93 $1 multi, vert.	4.00	3.00
424	A93 $2 multicolored	2.25	3.00
425	A93 $5 multicolored	5.50	5.50
	Nos. 409-425 (18)	17.55	17.30

Issued: 5c, 6c, 12c, 18c, 35c-$2, 12/22/80; No. 411B, 11/1991; others, 11/11/79.

1986-92   **Wmk. 384**
With Date Inscription

1986
410g	A93 2c multicolored	1.25	1.25
413B	A93 8c multicolored	4.50	4.50

1988
410h	A93 2c multicolored	1.00	1.00
411h	A93 3c multicolored	1.00	1.00
411Bh	A93 4c multicolored	1.00	1.00
418h	A93 20c multicolored	2.00	2.00

1990
414i	A93 10c multicolored	1.50	1.50
418i	A93 20c multicolored	2.00	2.00

1991
409j	A93 1c multicolored	1.75	3.50
410j	A93 2c multicolored	1.00	1.00
411j	A93 3c multicolored	1.75	1.75
411Bj	A93 4c multicolored	1.00	1.00
414j	A93 10c multicolored	2.00	2.00
416j	A93 15c multicolored	1.00	1.00
420j	A93 35c multicolored	2.75	2.75
422j	A93 50c multicolored	3.75	3.75
423j	A93 $1 multi, vert.	9.00	9.00

1992
409k	A93 1c multicolored	2.00	2.00
411k	A93 3c multicolored	3.75	3.75
411Bk	A93 4c multicolored	3.75	3.75
416k	A93 15c multicolored	2.75	2.75
418k	A93 20c multicolored	5.50	5.50
420k	A93 35c multicolored	5.50	5.50
422k	A93 50c multicolored	5.50	5.50
423k	A93 $1 multi, vert.	11.00	11.00

Southern Cross, 1873, London 1980 Emblem A94

1980, Apr. 28   **Wmk. 373**   **Perf. 13½**
426	A94 6c shown	.25	.25
427	A94 20c Levuka, 1910	.30	.30
428	A94 45c Matua, 1936	.70	.70
429	A94 50c Oronsay, 1951	.75	.75
	Nos. 426-429 (4)	2.00	2.00

London 80 Intl. Stamp Exhib., May 6-14.

Sovi Bay A95

1980, Aug. 18   **Perf. 13½x14**
430	A95 6c shown	.20	.20
431	A95 20c Yanuca Island, evening scene	.25	.25
432	A95 45c Dravuni Beach	.55	.55
433	A95 50c Wakaya Island	.65	.65
	Nos. 430-433 (4)	1.65	1.65

Opening of Parliament, 1979 — A96

1980, Oct. 6   **Litho.**   **Perf. 13**
434	A96 6c shown	.25	.25
435	A96 20c Coat of arms, vert.	.30	.30
436	A96 45c Fiji flag	.55	.55
437	A96 50c Elizabeth II, vert.	.65	.65
	Nos. 434-437 (4)	1.75	1.75

Independence, 10th anniversary.

Coastal Scene, by Semisi Maya A97

Intl. Year of the Disabled: Paintings and portrait of disabled artist Semisi Maya.

1981, Apr. 21   **Wmk. 373**   **Perf. 14**
438	A97 6c shown	.20	.20
439	A97 35c Underwater Scene	.45	.45
440	A97 50c Maya Painting, vert.	.60	.60
441	A97 60c Peacock, vert.	.75	.75
	Nos. 438-441 (4)	2.00	2.00

Royal Wedding Issue
Common Design Type

1981, July 22   **Wmk. 373**   **Perf. 14**
442	CD331 6c Bouquet	.20	.20
443	CD331 45c Charles	.50	.50
444	CD331 $1 Couple	1.10	1.10
	Nos. 442-444 (3)	1.80	1.80

Operator Assistance Center — A98

1981, Aug. 7   **Litho.**   **Perf. 14**
445	A98 6c shown	.25	.20
446	A98 35c Microwave station, map	.60	.55
447	A98 50c Satellite earth station	1.00	.75
448	A98 60c Cableship Retriever	1.10	.90
	Nos. 445-448 (4)	2.95	2.40

World Food Day — A99

1981, Sept. 21   **Litho.**   **Perf. 14½x14**
449	A99 20c multicolored	.50	.50

Ratu Sir Lala Sukuna, First Legislative Council Speaker — A100

1981, Oct. 19   **Litho.**   **Perf. 14**
450	A100 6c shown	.20	.20
451	A100 35c Mace, flag	.55	.55
452	A100 50c Suva Civic Center	.75	.75
	Nos. 450-452 (3)	1.50	1.50

Souvenir Sheet
453	A100 60c Emblem, participants' flags	.90	.90

27th Commonwealth Parliamentary Assoc. Conf., Suva.

World War II Aircraft A101

1981, Dec. 7   **Litho.**   **Perf. 14**
454	A101 6c Bell P-39 Aircobra	1.10	.20
455	A101 18c Consolidated PBY-5 Catalina	2.40	.30
456	A101 35c Curtiss P-40 Warhawk	4.00	.65
457	A101 60c Short Singapore	4.50	1.00
	Nos. 454-457 (4)	12.00	2.15

Scouting Year A102

1982, Feb. 22   **Litho.**   **Perf. 14½**
458	A102 6c Building	.25	.25
459	A102 20c Sailing, vert.	.50	.50
460	A102 45c Campfire	1.10	1.10
461	A102 60c Baden-Powell, vert.	1.25	1.25
	Nos. 458-461 (4)	3.10	3.10

Disciplined Forces — A103

1982, May 10   **Wmk. 373**   **Perf. 14**
462	A103 12c UN checkpoint	.50	.20
463	A103 30c Construction project	1.25	.50
464	A103 40c Police, car	2.00	.65
465	A103 70c Navy ship	2.25	1.25
	Nos. 462-465 (4)	6.00	2.60

1982 World Cup A104

1982, June 15   **Litho.**   **Perf. 14**
466	A104 6c Fiji Soccer Assoc. emblem	.20	.20
467	A104 18c Flag, ball	.35	.35
468	A104 50c Stadium	.90	.90
469	A104 90c Emblem	1.75	1.75
	Nos. 466-469 (4)	3.20	3.20

Princess Diana Issue
Common Design Type

1982, July 1   **Perf. 14½x14**
470	CD333 20c Arms	.50	.50
471	CD333 35c Diana	.80	.80
472	CD333 45c Wedding	1.10	1.10
473	CD333 $1 Portrait	2.50	2.50
	Nos. 470-473 (4)	4.90	4.90

October Royal Visit — A105

1982, Nov. 1   **Litho.**   **Perf. 14**
474	A105 6c Duke of Edinburgh	.25	.25
475	A105 45c Elizabeth II	.90	.90

Souvenir Sheet
476	Sheet of 3	4.00	4.00
c.	A105 $1 Britannia	1.60	1.60

No. 476 contains Nos. 474-475 and 476c.

Christmas A106

1982, Nov. 22   **Perf. 14x14½**
477	A106 6c Holy Family	.20	.20
478	A106 20c Adoration of the Kings	.40	.40
479	A106 35c Carolers	.75	.75
	Nos. 477-479 (3)	1.35	1.35

Souvenir Sheet
480	A106 $1 Faith, from The Three Virtues, by Raphael	2.00	2.00

Red-throated Lory — A107

Parrots.

1983, Feb. 14   **Litho.**   **Perf. 14**
481	A107 20c shown	1.50	1.50
482	A107 40c Blue-crowned lory	2.25	2.25
483	A107 55c Sulphur-breasted musk parrot	3.50	3.50
484	A107 70c Red-breasted musk parrot	4.25	4.25
	Nos. 481-484 (4)	11.50	11.50

A108

1983, Mar. 14
485	A108 8c Traditional house	.20	.20
486	A108 25c Barefoot firewalkers	.35	.35
487	A108 50c Sugar cane crop	.70	.70
488	A108 80c Kava Yagona ceremony	1.10	1.10
	Nos. 485-488 (4)	2.35	2.35

Commonwealth Day.

Manned Flight Bicentenary — A109

1983, July 18   **Wmk. 373**   **Perf. 14**
489	A109 8c Montgolfier, 1783	.45	.20
490	A109 20c Wright Flyer	.55	.35
491	A109 25c DC-3	.65	.40
492	A109 40c DeHavilland Comet	1.00	.70
493	A109 50c Boeing 747	1.25	.85
494	A109 58c Columbia space shuttle	1.60	1.00
	Nos. 489-494 (6)	5.50	3.50

Cordia Subcordata A110

Earth Satellite Station, Fijian Playing Lali A111

Flowers.

1983, Sept. 26   **Litho.**   **Perf. 14**
495	A110 8c shown	.20	.20
496	A110 25c Gmelina vitiensis	.35	.35
497	A110 40c Carruthersia scandens	.60	.60
498	A110 $1 Amylotheca insularum	1.50	1.50
	Nos. 495-498 (4)	2.65	2.65

See Nos. 505-508.

Perf. 14x13½

1983, Nov. 7   **Wmk. 373**
499 A111 50c multicolored .85 .85

Dacryopinax
Spathularia
A112

Various fungi.

1984, Jan. 9   **Perf. 14x13½, 13½x14**
500 A112 8c shown .65 .20
501 A112 15c Podoscypha in-
     voluta 1.10 .45
502 A112 40c Lentinus squar-
     rosulus 2.25 1.10
503 A112 50c Scleroderma
     flavidum 3.50 1.50
504 A112 $1 Phillipsia dom-
     ingensia 6.50 2.75
     Nos. 500-504 (5) 14.00 6.00

Flower Type of 1983

1984   **Litho.**   **Perf. 14x14½**
505 A110 15c Pseuderanthemum
     laxiflorum .25 .25
506 A110 20c Storkiella vitiensis .30 .30
507 A110 50c Paphia vitiensis .80 .80
508 A110 70c Elaeocarpus storkii 1.10 1.10
     Nos. 505-508 (4) 2.45 2.45

Lloyd's List Issue
Common Design Type
Perf. 14½x14

1984, May 7   **Wmk. 373**
509 CD335 8c Tui Lau on reef .40 .40
510 CD335 40c Tofua 1.50 1.50
511 CD335 55c Canberra 2.00 2.00
512 CD335 60c Suva Wharf 2.25 2.25
     Nos. 509-512 (4) 6.15 6.15

Souvenir Sheet

1984 UPU Congress — A113

1984, June 14   **Litho.**   **Perf. 14½**
513 A113 25c Map 2.25 2.25

Ausipex
'84 — A114

1984, Sept. 17   **Wmk. 373**   **Perf. 14**
514 A114 8c Yalavou cattle .20 .20
515 A114 25c Wailoa Power Sta-
     tion, vert. .55 .55
516 A114 40c Boeing 737 .95 .95
517 A114 $1 Cargo ship Fua
     Kavenga 2.50 2.50
     Nos. 514-517 (4) 4.20 4.20

Christmas
A115

1984, Nov. 5   **Litho.**   **Perf. 14**
518 A115 8c Church on hill .20 .20
519 A115 20c Sailing .35 .35
520 A115 25c Santa, children,
     tree .40 .40
521 A115 40c Going to church .65 .65
522 A115 $1 Family, tree, vert. 1.75 1.75
     Nos. 518-522 (5) 3.35 3.35

Butterflies
A116

1985, Feb. 4   **Perf. 14**
523 A116 8c Monarch 1.00 .25
524 A116 25c Common eggfly 2.50 .80
525 A116 40c Long-tailed blue,
     vert. 4.00 1.40
526 A116 $1 Meadow argus,
     vert. 10.50 3.50
     Nos. 523-526 (4) 18.00 5.95

EXPO '85,
Tsukuba,
Japan — A117

1985, Mar. 18   **Litho.**   **Perf. 14**
527 A117 20c Outrigger canoe,
     Toberua Isl. .55 .50
528 A117 25c Wainivalu Falls .60 .55
529 A117 50c Mana Island 1.60 1.40
530 A117 $1 Sawa-I-Lau Caves 2.75 2.50
     Nos. 527-530 (4) 5.50 4.95

Queen Mother 85th Birthday Issue
Common Design Type
Perf. 14½x14

1985, June 7   **Wmk. 384**
531 CD336 8c Holding Prince
     Andrew .20 .20
532 CD336 25c With Prince
     Charles .60 .60
533 CD336 40c On Oaks Day,
     Epsom Races .95 .95
534 CD336 50c Holding Prince
     Henry 1.25 1.25
     Nos. 531-534 (4) 3.00 3.00

Souvenir Sheet
535 CD336 $1 In Royal Wed-
     ding Cavalcade,
     1981 4.00 4.00

Shallow
Water
Fish
A118

1985, Sept. 23   **Perf. 14½**
536 A118 40c Horned squirrel
     fish 1.50 1.10
537 A118 50c Yellow-banded
     goatfish 2.25 1.40
538 A118 55c Fairy cod 2.25 1.50
539 A118 $1 Peacock rock cod 4.00 2.75
     Nos. 536-539 (4) 10.00 6.75

Sea Birds — A119

1985, Nov. 4   **Perf. 14**
540 A119 15c Collared petrel 1.25 .45
541 A119 20c Lesser frigate
     bird 2.25 .70

542 A119 50c Brown booby 6.00 1.75
543 A119 $1 Crested tern 11.50 4.25
     Nos. 540-543 (4) 21.00 7.15

Queen Elizabeth II 60th Birthday
Issue
Common Design Type

     20c, With the Duke of York at the Royal
Tournament, 1936. 25c, On Buckingham Palace balcony, wedding of Princess Margaret
and Anthony Armstrong-Jones, 1960. 40c,
Inspecting the Guard of Honor, Suva, 1982.
50c, State visit to Luxembourg, 1976. $1, Visit-
ing Crown Agents' offices, 1983.

Perf. 14x14½

1986, Apr. 21   **Wmk. 384**
544 CD337 20c scar, blk & sil .40 .40
545 CD337 25c ultra & multi .45 .45
546 CD337 40c green & multi .75 .75
547 CD337 50c violet & multi .95 .95
548 CD337 $1 rose vio & multi 1.90 1.90
     Nos. 544-548 (5) 4.45 4.45

Intl. Peace   Halley's
Year — A120   Comet — A121

1986, June 23   **Wmk. 373**   **Perf. 14½**
549 A120 8c shown .20 .20
550 A120 40c Dove 1.10 1.10

1986, July 7   **Perf. 13½**
551 A121 25c Newton's reflector
     telescope .90 .60
552 A121 40c Comet over
     Lomaiviti 1.10 .95
553 A121 $1 Comet nucleus,
     Giotto probe 6.00 2.50
     Nos. 551-553 (3) 8.00 4.05

Reptiles and Amphibians — A122

1986, Aug. 1   **Perf. 14½**
554 A122 8c Ground frog .40 .20
555 A122 20c Burrowing snake .65 .70
556 A122 25c Spotted gecko .70 .90
557 A122 40c Crested iguana 1.10 1.25
558 A122 50c Blotched skink 3.00 1.60
559 A122 $1 Speckled skink 6.00 3.50
     Nos. 554-559 (6) 11.85 8.15

Ancient War   Cone
Clubs — A123   Shells — A124

1986, Nov. 10   **Wmk. 384**   **Perf. 14**
560 A123 25c Gatawaka .90 .80
561 A123 40c Siriti 1.25 1.00
562 A123 50c Bulibuli 1.60 1.40
563 A123 $1 Culacula 3.25 2.75
     Nos. 560-563 (4) 7.00 5.95

1987, Feb. 26   **Litho.**   **Perf. 14x14½**
564 A124 15c Weasel .60 .35
565 A124 20c Pertusus .65 .45
566 A124 25c Admiral 1.10 .95
567 A124 40c Leaden 1.40 .95
568 A124 50c Imperial 2.75 1.45
569 A124 $1 Geography 5.50 2.50
     Nos. 564-569 (6) 12.00 6.10

Souvenir Sheet

Tagimoucia Flower — A125

1987, Apr. 23   **Wmk. 373**   **Perf. 14½**
570 A125 $1 multicolored 5.50 3.75

No. 570 Overprinted with CAPEX '87
Emblem

1987, June 13
571 A125 $1 multicolored 40.00 40.00

Intl. Year
of Shelter
for the
Homeless
A126

1987, July 20   **Perf. 14**
572 A126 55c Hut .70 .70
573 A126 70c Government hous-
     ing .95 .95

Beetles — A127

1987, Sept. 7   **Wmk. 384**
574 A127 20c Bulbogaster cte-
     nostomoides 1.00 .45
575 A127 25c Paracupta
     flaviventris 1.75 .65
576 A127 40c Cerambyrhynchus
     schoenherri 2.25 1.00
577 A127 50c Rhinoscapha
     lagopyga 3.75 1.25
578 A127 $1 Xixuthrus heros 8.25 2.50
     Nos. 574-578 (5) 17.00 5.85

Christmas — A128

1987, Nov. 19
579 A128 8c Holy Family, vert. .25 .20
580 A128 40c Shepherds see
     star 1.00 .65
581 A128 50c Three Kings follow
     star 2.75 .75
582 A128 $1 Adoration of the
     Magi 5.75 1.50
     Nos. 579-582 (4) 9.75 3.10

World
Expo '88,
Apr. 30-
Oct. 30,
Brisbane,
Australia
A129

1988, Apr. 27   **Litho.**   **Perf. 14**
583 A129 30c Windsurfing 1.75 1.75

Intl. Council of Women, Cent. A130

1988, June 14
584 A130 45c Fiji Nouna — 1.25 1.25

Pottery A131

Wmk. 384, 373 (69c)
1988, Aug. 29   Litho.   Perf. 13½
585 A131 9c Lapita (bowl) — .25 .20
586 A131 23c Kuro (cooking pot) — .50 .40
587 A131 58c Saqa (ritual drinking vessel) — 1.00 .90
588 A131 63c Saqa, diff. — 1.50 1.25
589 A131 69c Ramarama (oil lamp) — 1.75 1.50
590 A131 75c Kuro, diff., vert. — 2.50 2.00
Nos. 585-590 (6) — 7.50 6.25

Fiji Tree Frog — A132

Indigenous Flowering Plants — A133

1988, Oct. 3   Wmk. 384   Perf. 14
591 A132 18c multi — 5.00 5.00
592 A132 23c multi, diff. — 5.75 5.75
593 A132 30c multi, diff. — 7.25 7.25
594 A132 45c multi, diff. — 12.00 12.00
Nos. 591-594 (4) — 30.00 30.00

World Wildlife Fund.

1988, Nov. 21   Wmk. 373
595 A133 9c Dendrobium mohlianum — .35 .25
596 A133 30c Dendrobium cattilare — 1.25 1.00
597 A133 45c Degeneria vitiensis — 2.00 1.50
598 A133 $1 Degeneria roseiflora — 4.00 3.00
Nos. 595-598 (4) — 7.60 5.75

Intl. Red Cross and Red Crescent Orgs., 125th Anniv. — A134

1989, Feb. 6   Wmk. 384
599 A134 58c Battle of Solferino, 1859 — 1.75 1.10
600 A134 63c Jean-Henri Dunant, vert. — 2.00 1.10
601 A134 69c Medicine — 2.25 1.25
602 A134 $1 Anniv. emblem, vert. — 5.00 1.90
Nos. 599-602 (4) — 11.00 5.35

Epic Voyage of William Bligh A135

Designs: 45c, Plans (line drawing) of the Bounty's launch. 58c, Diary and inscription on artifacts "The cup I eat my miserable allowance out of." 80c, Silhouette, lightning, quote "O Almighty God, relieve us. . ." $1, Map of Bligh's Islands, launch and compass rose.

1989, Apr. 28   Perf. 14½
603 A135 45c multicolored — 2.10 .70
604 A135 58c multicolored — 2.50 .95
605 A135 80c multicolored — 4.50 1.25
606 A135 $1 multicolored — 6.00 1.50
Nos. 603-606 (4) — 15.10 4.40

Coral A136

1989, Aug. 21   Wmk. 373   Perf. 14
607 A136 46c Platygyra daedalea — 2.50 2.50
608 A136 60c Caulastrea furcata — 3.25 3.25
609 A136 75c Acropora echinata — 4.00 4.00
610 A136 90c Acropora humilis — 5.25 5.25
Nos. 607-610 (4) — 15.00 15.00

Nos. 609-610 vert.

1990 World Cup Soccer Championships, Italy — A137

Various Fijian soccer players.

1989, Sept. 25   Wmk. 384   Perf. 14½
611 A137 35c shown — 1.60 1.60
612 A137 63c multi, diff. — 2.50 2.50
613 A137 70c multi, diff. — 3.00 3.00
614 A137 85c multi, diff. — 3.50 3.50
Nos. 611-614 (4) — 10.60 10.60

Christmas A138

1989, Nov. 1   Wmk. 373
615 A138 9c Church service — .35 .35
616 A138 45c Delonix regia tree — 1.10 1.10
617 A138 $1 Holy family — 2.10 2.10
618 A138 $1.40 Tree, Fijian children — 3.00 3.00
Nos. 615-618 (4) — 6.55 6.55

Fish A139

1990, Apr. 23   Litho.   Wmk. 384
619 A139 50c Mangrove jack — 3.00 3.00
620 A139 70c Orange-spotted therapon perch — 4.50 4.50
621 A139 85c Spotted scat — 5.00 5.00
622 A139 $1 Flagtail — 6.00 6.00
Nos. 619-622 (4) — 18.50 18.50

Souvenir Sheet

Stamp World London '90 — A140

1990, May 1
623 A140 Sheet of 2 — 13.50 6.00
a. $1 No. 243 — 4.25 1.75
b. $2 No. 249 — 8.50 4.25

Soil Conservation — A141

50c, Vertiver grass contours. 70c, Mulching. 90c, Contour cultivation. $1, Proper land use.

1990, July 23   Litho.   Wmk. 373
625 A141 50c multi — 1.10 1.10
626 A141 70c multi — 1.60 1.60
627 A141 90c multi — 2.10 2.10
628 A141 $1 multi, vert. — 2.25 2.25
Nos. 625-628 (4) — 7.05 7.05

Trees — A142

1990, Oct. 2
629 A142 25c Dacrydium nidulum — .90 .90
630 A142 35c Decussocarpus vitiensis — 1.10 1.10
631 A142 $1 Agathis vitiensis — 3.50 3.50
632 A142 $1.55 Santalum yasi — 5.00 5.00
Nos. 629-632 (4) — 10.50 10.50

Christmas — A143

Christmas carols: 10c, Hark! The Herald Angels Sing. 35c, Silent Night. 65c, Joy to the World! $1, The Race that Long in Darkness Pined.

1990, Nov. 26   Wmk. 373   Perf. 14
633 A143 10c multicolored — .40 .40
634 A143 35c multicolored — 1.10 1.10
635 A143 65c multicolored — 2.00 2.00
636 A143 $1 multicolored — 3.00 3.00
Nos. 633-636 (4) — 6.50 6.50

Scenic Views — A144

1991, Feb. 25   Wmk. 384
637 A144 35c Sigatoka sand dunes — 1.50 1.50
638 A144 50c Monu, Monuriki Islands — 2.75 2.75
639 A144 65c Ravilevu Nature Reserve — 3.25 3.25
640 A144 $1 Colo-I-Suva Forest Park — 5.50 5.50
Nos. 637-640 (4) — 13.00 13.00

Discovery of Rotuma Island, Bicent. A145

1991, Aug. 8   Wmk. 373   Perf. 14
641 A145 54c HMS Pandora — 2.75 2.75
642 A145 70c Map of Rotuma Island — 3.50 3.50
643 A145 75c Natives — 3.75 3.75
644 A145 $1 Mt. Solroroa, Uea Island — 5.00 5.00
Nos. 641-644 (4) — 15.00 15.00

Crabs A146

Designs: 38c, Scylla serrata. 54c, Metopograpsus messor. 96c, Parasesarma erythrodactyla. $1.65, Cardisoma carnifex.

1991, Sept. 26   Perf. 14½x14
645 A146 38c multicolored — 1.10 1.10
646 A146 54c multicolored — 1.75 1.75
647 A146 96c multicolored — 2.75 2.75
648 A146 $1.65 multicolored — 5.50 5.50
Nos. 645-648 (4) — 11.10 11.10

Christmas A147

Designs: 11c, Mary, Joseph travelling to Bethlehem. 75c, Manger scene. 96c, Jesus being blessed at temple in Jerusalem. $1, Baby Jesus.

1991, Oct. 31   Wmk. 384   Perf. 14
649 A147 11c multicolored — .45 .45
650 A147 75c multicoloed — 2.10 2.10
651 A147 96c multicolored — 2.50 2.50
652 A147 $1 multicolored — 2.50 2.50
Nos. 649-652 (4) — 7.55 7.55

Air Pacific, 40th Anniv. A148

Airplanes: 54c, Dragon Rapide, Harold Gatty, founder. 75c, Douglas DC3. 96c, ATR 42. $1.40, Boeing 767.

1991, Nov. 18   Perf. 14½
653 A148 54c multicolored — 3.00 3.00
654 A148 75c multicolored — 3.25 3.25
655 A148 96c multicolored — 4.25 4.25
656 A148 $1.40 multicolored — 6.50 6.50
Nos. 653-656 (4) — 17.00 17.00

Expo '92, Seville A149

Designs: 27c, Traditional dance and costumes. 75c, Faces of people. 96c, Train and gold bars. $1.40, Cruise ship in port.

Perf. 14½x14
1992, Mar. 23   Litho.   Wmk. 373
657 A149 27c multicolored — 1.50 1.50
658 A149 75c multicolored — 4.00 4.00
659 A149 96c multicolored — 5.75 5.75
660 A149 $1.40 multicolored — 7.75 7.75
Nos. 657-660 (4) — 19.00 19.00

Inter-Islands Shipping — A150

1992, June 22			Perf. 14	
661	A150	38c Tabusoro	2.00	2.00
662	A150	54c Degei II	2.75	2.75
663	A150	$1.40 Dausoko	6.25	6.25
664	A150	$1.65 Nivanga	7.00	7.00
		Nos. 661-664 (4)	18.00	18.00

1992 Summer Olympics, Barcelona — A151

1992, July 30			Perf. 13½	
665	A151	20c Running	.65	.65
666	A151	86c Yachting	2.75	2.75
667	A151	$1.34 Swimming	4.00	4.00
668	A151	$1.50 Judo	5.00	5.00
		Nos. 665-668 (4)	12.40	12.40

Levuka A152

30c, European War Memorial. 42c, Map. 59c, Beach Street. 77c, Sacred Heart Church, vert. $2, Deed of Cession Site, vert.

1992, Sept. 21			Perf. 14½	
669	A152	30c multicolored	.55	.55
670	A152	42c multicolored	.75	.75
671	A152	59c multicolored	1.10	1.10
672	A152	77c multicolored	1.50	1.50
673	A152	$2 multicolored	3.50	3.50
		Nos. 669-673 (5)	7.40	7.40

Intl. Planned Parenthood Federation, 40th Anniv. — A153

1992, Nov. 2			Perf. 15x14½	
674	A153	77c Globe	1.50	1.50
675	A153	$2 Family	3.75	3.75

Christmas — A154

Bible interpretations: 12c, "God so loved the world..." 77c, "We love because God first loved us." 83c, "It is more blessed to give..." $2, "Every good gift..."

1992, Nov. 17				
676	A154	12c multicolored	.35	.35
677	A154	77c multicolored	1.90	1.90
678	A154	83c multicolored	2.25	2.25
679	A154	$2 multicolored	5.50	5.50
		Nos. 676-679 (4)	10.00	10.00

Peace Corps in Fiji, 25th Anniv. A155

Designs: 59c, Voluntary service. 77c, Fiji/US friendship. $1, Education. $2, Income generating business through volunteer help.

1993, Feb. 22	Litho.		Perf. 14½	
	Wmk. 373			
680	A155	59c multicolored	1.25	1.25
681	A155	77c multicolored	1.60	1.60
682	A155	$1 multicolored	2.00	2.00
683	A155	$2 multicolored	4.25	4.25
		Nos. 680-683 (4)	9.10	9.10

Hong Kong Rugby Sevens — A156

Designs: 77c, Players performing traditional Cibi Dance. $1.06, Two players, map of Fiji, Hong Kong, and Australia. $2, Stadium, players in scrum.

1993, Mar. 26		Perf. 14x15	Wmk. 384	
684	A156	77c multicolored	1.75	1.75
685	A156	$1.06 multicolored	2.50	2.50
686	A156	$2 multicolored	4.50	4.50
		Nos. 684-686 (3)	8.75	8.75

Royal Air Force, 75th Anniv.
Common Design Type

Designs: 59c, Gloster Gauntlet. 77c, Armstrong Whitworth Whitley. 83c, Bristol F2b. $2, Hawker Tempest.
No. 691: a, Vickers Vildebeest. b, Handley Page Hampden. c, Vickers Vimy. d, British Aerospace Hawk.

1993, Apr. 1			Perf. 14	
687	CD350	59c multicolored	1.25	1.25
688	CD350	77c multicolored	1.60	1.60
689	CD350	83c multicolored	1.60	1.60
690	CD350	$2 multicolored	4.50	4.50
		Nos. 687-690 (4)	8.95	8.95

Souvenir Sheet of 4

691	CD350	$1 #a.-d.	10.00	10.00
a.		Overprinted in sheet margin	11.00	11.00

Overprint on No. 691a is exhibition emblem for Hong Kong '94.

Nudibranchs A157

1993, July 27	Litho.		Perf. 14	
	Wmk. 373			
692	A157	12c Chromodoris fidelis	.50	.50
693	A157	42c Halgerda carlsoni	1.25	1.25
694	A157	53c Chromodoris lochi	1.75	1.75
695	A157	83c Glaucus atlanticus	2.75	2.75
696	A157	$1 Phyllidia bourguini	3.25	3.25
697	A157	$2 Hexabranchus sanguineus	6.50	6.50
		Nos. 692-697 (6)	16.00	16.00

Tropical Fruit — A158

1993, Oct. 25	Litho.		Perf. 13½	
	Wmk. 373			
698	A158	30c Mango	1.25	1.25
699	A158	42c Guava	2.25	2.25
700	A158	$1 Lemon	4.50	4.50
701	A158	$2 Soursop	9.00	9.00
		Nos. 698-701 (4)	17.00	17.00

Souvenir Sheet

Hong Kong '94 — A159

Butterflies: a, Caper white. b, Blue branded king crow. c, Vagrant. d, Glasswing.

1994, Feb. 18	Litho.	Perf. 14½x13	Wmk. 373	
702	A159	$1 Sheet of 4, #a.-d.	11.00	11.00

Easter A160

59c, The Last Supper. 77c, The Crucifixion. $1, The Resurrection. $2, Jesus showing his wounds to his disciples.

1994, Mar. 31	Litho.	Perf. 14x15, 15x14	Wmk. 373	
703	A160	59c multi	1.25	1.25
704	A160	77c multi, vert.	1.75	1.75
705	A160	$1 multi	2.00	2.00
706	A160	$2 multi, vert.	4.25	4.25
		Nos. 703-706 (4)	9.25	9.25

Edible Seaweeds A161

42c, Codium bulbopilum. 83c, Coulerpa racemosa. $1, Hypnea pannosa. $2, Gracilaria.

1994, June 6	Litho.		Perf. 14	
	Wmk. 384			
707	A161	42c multicolored	1.25	.95
708	A161	83c multicolored	2.25	1.90
709	A161	$1 multicolored	2.75	2.40
710	A161	$2 multicolored	5.75	4.75
		Nos. 707-710 (4)	12.00	10.00

Souvenir Sheet

White-Collared Kingfisher — A162

Designs: a, On branch. b, In flight.

1994, Aug.	Litho.	Perf. 13½	Wmk. 373	
711	A162	$1.50 Sheet of 2, #a.-b.	12.50	12.50
c.		Overprinted in sheet margin	13.00	13.00

Overprint on No. 711c consists of exhibition emblem and "JAKARTA '95."
Issued: #711, 8/16; #711c, 8/19.

Souvenir Sheet

Singpex '94 — A163

Neoveitchia storckii: a, Complete tree. b, Fruits, inflorescence.

1994, Aug. 31	Wmk. 384	Perf. 14		
712	A163	$1.50 Sheet of 2, #a.-b.	11.00	11.00

First Catholic Missionaries in Fiji, 150th Anniv. — A164

1994, Dec. 16	Litho.		Perf. 14	
	Wmk. 373			
713	A164	23c Father Ioane Batita	.60	.60
714	A164	31c Local catechist	.70	.70
715	A164	44c Sacred Heart Cathedral	.95	.95
716	A164	63c Lomary Church	1.25	1.25
717	A164	81c Pope Gregory XVI	1.75	1.75
718	A164	$2 Pope John Paul II	4.00	4.00
		Nos. 713-718 (6)	9.25	9.25

Souvenir Sheet

Ecotourism in Fiji — A165

Designs: a, Waterfalls, banded iguana. b, Mountain trekking, Fiji tree frog. c, Bilibili River trip, kingfisher. d, Historic sites, flying fox.

1995, Mar. 27	Litho.		Perf. 14	
	Wmk. 373			
719	A165	81c Sheet of 4, #a.-d.	9.00	9.00

End of World War II, 50th Anniv.
Common Design Types

Designs: 13c, Fijian regiment guarding crashed Japanese Zero Fighter. 63c, Kameli

Airstrip, Solomon Islands, built by Fijian regiment. 87c, Corp. Sukanaivalu VC, Victoria Cross. $1.12, HMS Fiji.
$2, Reverse side of War Medal 1939-45.

Wmk. 373

1995, May 8		**Litho.**	**Perf. 13½**	
720	CD351	13c multicolored	.50	.50
721	CD351	63c multicolored	2.75	2.75
722	CD351	87c multicolored	3.75	3.75
723	CD351	$1.12 multicolored	5.00	5.00
	Nos. 720-723 (4)		12.00	12.00

Souvenir Sheet
Perf. 14

724	CD352	$2 multicolored	5.25	5.25

Birds — A166

1995		**Litho. Wmk. 373**	**Perf. 13**	
725	A166	1c Red-headed parrotfinch	.20	.20
726	A166	2c Golden whistler	.20	.20
727	A166	3c Ogea flycatcher	.20	.20
728	A166	4c Peale's pigeon	.20	.20
729	A166	6c Blue-crested broadbill	.20	.20
730	A166	13c Island thrush	.20	.20
731	A166	23c Many-colored fruit dove	.40	.40
732	A166	31c Mangrove heron	.55	.55
733	A166	44c Purple swamphen	1.00	1.00
734	A166	63c Fiji goshawk	1.25	1.25
735	A166	81c Kadavu fantail	1.60	1.60
736	A166	87c Collared lory	1.75	1.75
737	A166	$1 Scarlet robin	2.00	2.00
738	A166	$2 Peregrine falcon	4.00	4.00
739	A166	$3 Barn owl	5.75	5.75
739A	A166	$5 Yellow-breasted musk parrot	10.50	10.50
	Nos. 725-739A (16)		30.00	30.00

Issued: 13c, 23c, 31c, 44c, 63c, 81c, $2, $3, 7/25; 1c, 2c, 3c, 4c, 6c, 87c, $1, $5, 11/7.
See No. 1011.
For surcharges, see Nos. 1149-1160, 1191-1197C, 1214-1223A.

Souvenir Sheet

Singapore '95 — A167

Orchids: a, Arundina graminifolia. b, Phaius tankervilliae.

Wmk. 373

1995, Sept. 1		**Litho.**	**Perf. 14**	
740	A167	$1 Sheet of 2, #a.-b.	9.00	9.00

Independence, 25th Anniv. — A168

Designs: 81c, Pres. Kamisese Mara, Parliament Building. 87c, Fijian youth. $1.06, Playing rugby. $2, Air Pacific Boeing 747.

Wmk. 373

1995, Oct. 4		**Litho.**	**Perf. 14**	
741	A168	81c multicolored	1.60	1.60
742	A168	87c multicolored	1.90	1.90
743	A168	$1.06 multicolored	2.25	2.25
744	A168	$2 multicolored	4.25	4.25
	Nos. 741-744 (4)		10.00	10.00

Christmas — A169

Paintings: 10c, Praying Madonna with the Crown of Stars, from Correggio Workshop. 63c, Madonna and Child with Crowns on porcelain. 87c, The Holy Virgin with the Holy Child and St. John, after Titian. $2, The Holy Family and St. John, from Rubens Workshop.

Wmk. 373

1995, Nov. 22		**Litho.**	**Perf. 13**	
745	A169	10c multicolored	.25	.25
746	A169	63c multicolored	1.25	1.25
747	A169	87c multicolored	1.75	1.75
748	A169	$2 multicolored	4.00	4.00
	Nos. 745-748 (4)		7.25	7.25

Arrival of Banabans in Fiji, 50th Anniv. A170

Perf. 14x14½, 14½x14

1996, Jan. 24		**Litho.**	**Wmk. 373**	
749	A170	81c Trolling lure	2.25	2.25
750	A170	87c Canoes	2.50	2.50
751	A170	$1.12 Warrior, vert.	2.75	2.75
752	A170	$2 Frigate bird, vert.	5.25	5.25
	Nos. 749-752 (4)		12.75	12.75

A171

A172

Radio, Cent.: 44c, L2B portable tape recorder. 63c, Fiji Broadcasting Center. 81c, Communications satellite in orbit. $3, Marconi.

Wmk. 373

1996, Mar. 11		**Litho.**	**Perf. 14½**	
753	A171	44c multicolored	.90	.90
754	A171	63c multicolored	1.25	1.25
755	A171	81c multicolored	1.60	1.60
756	A171	$3 multicolored	6.25	6.25
	Nos. 753-756 (4)		10.00	10.00

Wmk. 384

1996, Apr. 25		**Litho.**	**Perf. 13½**	

Ancient Chinese artifacts: 63c, Bronze monster mask and ring, c. 450 BC. 81c, Archer, 210 BC. $1, Plate, Hsuan Te Period, 1426-35. $2, Central Asian horseman, dated 706. 30c, Yan Deng Mountain.

757	A172	63c multicolored	1.25	1.25
758	A172	81c multicolored	1.50	1.50
759	A172	$1 multicolored	2.00	2.00
760	A172	$2 multicolored	4.25	4.25
	Nos. 757-760 (4)		9.00	9.00

Souvenir Sheet
Perf. 13½x13

761	A172	30c multicolored	2.50	2.50

No. 761 contains one 48x76mm stamp.
CHINA '96, 9th Asian Intl. Philatelic Exhibition.

A173

A174

Wmk. 373

1996, June 18		**Litho.**	**Perf. 14**	
762	A173	31c Hurdling	.65	.65
763	A173	63c Judo	1.50	1.50
764	A173	87c Sailboarding	2.10	2.10
765	A173	$1.12 Swimming	2.50	2.50
	Nos. 762-765 (4)		6.75	6.75

Souvenir Sheet

766	A173	$2 Athlete, 1896	4.00	4.00

Modern Olympic Games, cent.

1996, July 1

31c, Computerized telephone exchange, horiz. 44c, Mail being unloaded, horiz. 81c, Manual switchboard operator. $1, Mail delivery.
No. 771: a, #117. b, #527.

767	A174	31c multicolored	.60	.60
768	A174	44c multicolored	.80	.80
769	A174	81c multicolored	1.40	1.40
770	A174	$1 multicolored	1.90	1.90
	Nos. 767-770 (4)		4.70	4.70

Souvenir Sheet of 2

771	A174	$1.50 #a.-b.	6.00	6.00

Creation of independent Postal, Telecommunications Companies.

UNICEF, 50th Anniv. A175

Designs: 81c, "Our children, our future." 87c, Village scene. $1, "Living in harmony the world over." $2, "Their future."

Wmk. 384

1996, Aug. 13		**Litho.**	**Perf. 14**	
772	A175	81c multicolored	2.00	2.00
773	A175	87c multicolored	2.00	2.00
774	A175	$1 multicolored	2.25	2.25
775	A175	$2 multicolored	4.50	4.50
	Nos. 772-775 (4)		10.75	10.75

Nadi Intl. Airport, 50th Anniv. A176

Designs: 31c, First airplane in Fiji, 1921. 44c, Nadi Airport commences Commercial Operations, 1946. 63c, First jet in Fiji, 1959. 87c, Airport entrance. $1, Control tower, 1996. $2, Global positioning system, first commercial use, 1994.

Wmk. 373

1996, Oct. 1		**Litho.**	**Perf. 14**	
776	A176	31c multicolored	.75	.75
777	A176	44c multicolored	1.00	1.00
778	A176	63c multicolored	1.50	1.50
779	A176	87c multicolored	2.00	2.00
780	A176	$1 multicolored	2.25	2.25
781	A176	$2 multicolored	4.50	4.50
	Nos. 776-781 (6)		12.00	12.00

Christmas — A177

Scene from the Christmas story and native story or scene: 13c, Angel Gabriel & Mary, beating of Lali. 81c, Shepherds with sheep, Fijian canoe. $1, Wise men on camels, multiracial Fiji. $3, Mary, Christ Child in stable, blowing of conch shell.

1996, Nov. 20			**Wmk. 373**	
782	A177	13c multicolored	.30	.30
783	A177	81c multicolored	2.00	2.00
784	A177	$1 multicolored	2.40	2.40
785	A177	$3 multicolored	7.25	7.25
	Nos. 782-785 (4)		11.95	11.95

Hong Kong '97 A178

Cattle: a, Brahman. b, Freisian (Holstein). c, Hereford. d, Fiji draught bullock.

1997, Feb. 12

786	A178	$1 Sheet of 4, #a.-d.	9.25	9.25

Souvenir Sheet

Black-Faced Shrikebill — A179

1997, Feb. 21 **Perf. 14x15**

787	A179	$2 multicolored	4.50	4.50

Singpex '97.

Orchids — A180

Designs: 81c, Dendrobium biflorum. 87c, Dendrobium dactylodes. $1.06, Spathoglottis pacifica. $2, Dendrobium macropus.

Wmk. 384

1997, Apr. 22		**Litho.**	**Perf. 14**	
788	A180	81c multicolored	2.25	2.25
789	A180	87c multicolored	2.25	2.25

Wmk. 373

790	A180	$1.06 multicolored	3.00	3.00
791	A180	$2 multicolored	5.25	5.25
	Nos. 788-791 (4)		12.75	12.75

Souvenir Sheet

Hawksbill Turtle — A181

Designs: a, 63c, Female laying eggs. b, 81c, Baby turtles emerging from nest. c, $1.06 Young turtles in water. d, $2, One adult in water, coral.

1997, May 26   **Wmk. 373**
792 A181 Sheet of 4, #a.-d.   11.00 11.00

Coral
A182

Designs: 63c, Branching hard coral 87c, Massive hard coral. $1, Soft coral, sinularia. $3, Soft coral, dendronephthya.

Wmk. 373

			1997, July 16	**Litho.**	**Perf. 14**
793	A182	63c multicolored		1.40	1.40
794	A182	87c multicolored		1.90	1.90
795	A182	$1 multicolored		2.25	2.25
796	A182	$3 multicolored		6.75	6.75
		Nos. 793-796 (4)		12.30	12.30

Fijian Monkey-faced Bat — A183

63c, With nose pointed downward. 81c, Hanging below flower. $2, Between leaves on tree branch.

				Perf. 13½	
1997, Oct. 15		**Litho.**		**Unwmk.**	
797	A183	44c multicolored		1.25	1.00
798	A183	63c multicolored		1.75	1.50
799	A183	81c multicolored		2.25	1.75
800	A183	$2 multicolored		4.75	4.25
a.		Sheet, 2 each #797-800		21.00	21.00
		Nos. 797-800 (4)		10.00	8.50

World Wildlife Fund.

Christmas
A184

Designs: 13c, Angel, shepherd. 31c, Birth of Jesus. 87c, Magi. $3, Madonna and Child.

				Perf. 14x14½	
1997, Nov. 18				**Wmk. 373**	
801	A184	13c multicolored		.20	.20
802	A184	31c multicolored		.60	.60
803	A184	87c multicolored		1.60	1.60
804	A184	$3 multicolored		5.50	5.50
		Nos. 801-804 (4)		7.90	7.90

A185   A186

1997 Rugby World Cup Sevens Champions: a, 50c, Waisale Serevi, captain, highest point scorer. b, 50c, Taniela Qauqau. c, 50c, Jope Tuikabe. d, 50c, Leveni Duvuduvukula. e, 50c, Inoke Maraiwai. f, 50c, Aminiasi Naituyaga. g, 50c, Lemeki Koroi. h, 50c, Marika Vunibaka, highest try scorer. i, 50c, Luke Erenavula. j, 50c, Manasa Bari. k, $1, Entire team.

Wmk. 373
1997, Oct. 30   **Litho.**   **Perf. 14**
805 A185 Sheet of 11, #a.-k.   15.00 15.00
    No. 805k is 53x39mm.

Wmk. 373
1998, Jan. 20   **Litho.**   **Perf. 14**
Chief's Traditional Costumes: 81c, War dress. 87c, Formal dress. $1.12, Presentation dress. $2, Highland war dress.

806	A186	81c multicolored	1.25	1.25
807	A186	87c multicolored	1.25	1.25
808	A186	$1.12 multicolored	1.75	1.75
809	A186	$2 multicolored	3.00	3.00
		Nos. 806-809 (4)	7.25	7.25

Asian and Pacific Decade of Disabled Persons, 1993-2000
A187

63c, Mastering modern technology. 87c, Assisting the will to overcome. $1, Using natural born skills. $2, Competing to win.

Wmk. 373
1998, Mar. 18   **Litho.**   **Perf. 13**

810	A187	63c multicolored	1.00	1.00
811	A187	87c multicolored	1.40	1.40
812	A187	$1 multicolored	1.50	1.50
813	A187	$2 multicolored	3.00	3.00
		Nos. 810-813 (4)	6.90	6.90

Royal Air Force, 80th Anniv.
Common Design Type of 1993 Re-Inscribed

Designs: 44c, R34 Airship. 63c, Handley Page Heyford. 87c, Supermarine Swift FR.5. $2, Westland Whirlwind.
No. 818: a, Sopwith Dolphin. b, Avro 504K. c, Vickers Warwick V. d, Shorts Belfast.

1998, Apr. 1   **Perf. 13½x14**

814	CD350	44c multicolored	1.00	1.00
815	CD350	63c multicolored	1.25	1.25
816	CD350	87c multicolored	1.75	1.75
817	CD350	$2 multicolored	4.00	4.00
		Nos. 814-817 (4)	8.00	8.00

Souvenir Sheet of 4
818 CD350 $1 #a.-d.   7.50 7.50

Diana, Princess of Wales (1961-97)
Common Design Type

Design: No. 819, Wearing plaid jacket.
No. 820: a, Wearing blue jacket. b, In high-collared blouse. c, Holding flowers.

1998, Mar. 31   **Litho.**   **Perf. 14x14½**
819 CD355 81c multicolored   .75 .75
820 CD355 81c Sheet of 4, #819,
     a.-c.   5.25 5.25

No. 820 sold for $3.24 + 50c, with surtax from international sales being donated to the Princess Diana Memorial Fund and surtax from national sales being donated to designated local charity.

Sperm Whale
A188

Wmk. 373
1998, June 22   **Litho.**   **Perf. 14**

821	A188	63c shown	1.40	1.40
822	A188	81c Adult, calf	1.90	1.90
823	A188	87c Breaching	1.90	1.90
824	A188	$2 Sperm whale tooth	4.50	4.50
a.		Souvenir sheet	7.50	7.50
		Nos. 821-824 (4)	9.70	9.70

16th Commonwealth Games, Kuala Lumpur, Malaysia — A189

Wmk. 384
1998, Sept. 11   **Litho.**   **Perf. 14**

825	A189	44c Athletics	.70	.70
826	A189	63c Lawn bowls	1.00	1.00
827	A189	81c Javelin	1.40	1.40
828	A189	$1.12 Weight lifting	1.90	1.90
		Nos. 825-828 (4)	5.00	5.00

Souvenir Sheet
829 A189 $2 Waisale Serevi, rugby sevens   5.00 5.00

Maritime Heritage
A190

Designs: 13c, Takia, hollowed-out log with outrigger. 44c, Camakau, sailing canoe. 87c, Drua, twin-hulled sailing canoe. $3, MV Pioneer motor yacht.
$1.50, Camakau, map of Fiji.

Wmk. 384
1998, Oct. 26   **Litho.**   **Perf. 13½**

830	A190	13c multicolored	.30	.30
831	A190	44c multicolored	.85	.85
832	A190	87c multicolored	1.60	1.60
833	A190	$3 multicolored	5.25	5.25
		Nos. 830-833 (4)	8.00	8.00

Souvenir Sheet
834 A190 $1.50 multicolored   4.75 4.75

Australia '99, World Stamp Expo (#834). See Nos. 843-847.

Christmas
A191

Children's drawings: 13c, "Jesus in a Manger." 50c, "A Time for Family and Friends." $1, "What Christmas Means to Me," vert. $2, "The Joy of Christmas," vert.

1998, Nov. 23   **Wmk. 373**

835	A191	13c multicolored	.30	.30
836	A191	50c multicolored	.95	.95
837	A191	$1 multicolored	1.90	1.90
838	A191	$2 multicolored	4.00	4.00
		Nos. 835-838 (4)	7.15	7.15

Traditional Dances — A192

Designs: 13c, Vakamalolo (women's sitting dance). 81c, Mekeiwau (club dance). 87c, Seasea (women's fan dance). $3, Meke ni yaqona (Kava serving dance).

Wmk. 373
1999, Jan. 20   **Litho.**   **Perf. 14½**

839	A192	13c multicolored	.25	.25
840	A192	81c multicolored	1.60	1.60
841	A192	87c multicolored	1.90	1.90
842	A192	$3 multicolored	5.75	5.75
		Nos. 839-842 (4)	9.50	9.50

Maritime Heritage Type of 1998
Designs: 63c, SS Toufua, 1920-30's. 81c, MF Adi Beti, 1920-30's. $1, SS Niagara, 1920-30's. $2, MV Royal Viking Sun, 1990's.
$1.50, SS. Makatea, 1920's.

1999, Mar. 19   **Wmk. 384**   **Perf. 13½**

843	A190	63c multicolored	1.10	1.10
844	A190	81c multicolored	1.90	1.90
845	A190	$1 multicolored	2.25	2.25
846	A190	$2 multicolored	4.50	4.50
		Nos. 843-846 (4)	9.75	9.75

Souvenir Sheet
847 A190 $1.50 multicolored   4.50 4.50

Australia '99, World Stamp Exhibition (#847).

Souvenir Sheet

Ducks — A193

a, Wandering whistling. b, Pacific black.

1999, Apr. 27   **Wmk. 373**
848 A193 $2 Sheet of 2, #a.-b.   8.00 8.00

IBRA '99, Intl. Philatelic Exhibition, Nuremberg.

Orchids — A194

Designs: 44c, Calanthe ventilabrum. 63c, Dendrobium prasinum. 81c, Dendrobium macrophyllum. $3, Dendrobium tokai.

1999, June 28

849	A194	44c multicolored	.75	.75
850	A194	63c multicolored	1.00	1.00
851	A194	81c multicolored	1.25	1.25
852	A194	$3 multicolored	5.00	5.00
		Nos. 849-852 (4)	8.00	8.00

1st Manned Moon Landing, 30th Anniv.
Common Design Type

13c, Astronaut waves goodbye. 87c, Stage 3 fires towards moon. $1, Aldrin walks on lunar surface. $2, Command module fires towards earth.
$2, Looking at earth from moon.

Perf. 14x13¾
1999, July 20   **Wmk. 384**

853	CD357	13c multicolored	.25	.25
854	CD357	87c multicolored	1.50	1.50
855	CD357	$1 multicolored	1.75	1.75
856	CD357	$2 multicolored	3.50	3.50
		Nos. 853-856 (4)	7.00	7.00

Souvenir Sheet
Perf. 14
857 CD357 $2 multicolored   4.00 4.00

No. 857 contains one circular stamp 40mm in diameter.

Queen Mother's Century
Common Design Type

Queen Mother: 13c, Visiting Hull to see bomb damage. 63c, With Prince Charles. 81c, As Colonel-in-Chief of Light Infantry. $3, With Prince Charles at Clarence House.
$2, With crowd on Armistice Day.

Wmk. 384
1999, Aug. 18   **Litho.**   **Perf. 13½**

858	CD358	13c multicolored	.50	.50
859	CD358	63c multicolored	1.25	1.25
860	CD358	81c multicolored	1.75	1.75
861	CD358	$3 multicolored	5.50	5.50
		Nos. 858-861 (4)	9.00	9.00

Souvenir Sheet
862 CD358 $2 multicolored   6.00 6.00

Sugar Mills rolling stock: 50c, Diesel loco-motive. 87c, Steam locomotive. $1, Diesel locomotive, diff. $2, Free passenger train.

UPU, 125th Anniv. A195

Wmk. 373

1999, Oct. 26		**Litho.**		**Perf. 13¾**
863	A195	50c multicolored	.60	.60
864	A195	87c multicolored	1.25	1.25
865	A195	$1 multicolored	1.40	1.40
866	A195	$2 multicolored	2.75	2.75
		Nos. 863-866 (4)	6.00	6.00

Christmas — A196

Designs: 13c, Giving gifts. 31c, Angels and star. 63c, Bible, Magi, Holy family. 87c, Joseph, mary, donkey, vert. $1, Mary, Jesus, animals, vert. $2, Children, Santa, vert.

Perf. 13¼x13

1999, Nov. 29		**Litho.**	**Wmk. 373**	
867	A196	13c multicolored	.20	.20
868	A196	31c multicolored	.45	.45
869	A196	63c multicolored	.90	.90
870	A196	87c multicolored	1.25	1.25
871	A196	$1 multicolored	1.40	1.40
872	A196	$2 multicolored	2.75	2.75
		Nos. 867-872 (6)	6.95	6.95

Millennium A197

Designs: No. 873, Outstretched hands, islands (arch at top). No. 874, Map, flag (arch at right). No. 875, Globe, warrior beating lali, temple (arch at bottom). No. 876, Globe, drua, red line (arch at left).

No. 877: a, Fiji petrel (arch at top). b, Crested iguana, islands (arch at top). c, Red prawns (arch at bottom). d, Tagimaucia (arch at bottom).

Perf. 13¼ Syncopated Type A
Litho. with Foil Application

2000, Jan. 1			**Unwmk.**	
873	A197	$5 gold & multi	8.00	8.00
874	A197	$5 gold & multi	8.00	8.00
875	A197	$5 gold & multi	8.00	8.00
876	A197	$5 gold & multi	8.00	8.00
		Nos. 873-876 (4)	32.00	32.00

Souvenir Sheet

877	A197	$10 Sheet of 4, #a-d	65.00	65.00

Beetles — A198

Designs: 15c, Paracupta sulcata. 87c, Agrilus sp. $1.06, Cyphogastra abdominalis. $2, Paracupta sp.

Perf. 13¾x14

2000, Mar. 14		**Litho.**	**Wmk. 373**	
878	A198	15c multi	.25	.25
879	A198	87c multi	1.50	1.50
880	A198	$1.06 multi	1.75	1.75
881	A198	$2 multi	3.00	3.00
		Nos. 878-881 (4)	6.50	6.50

Sesame Street — A199

No. 882: a, Big Bird. b, Oscar the Grouch. c, Cookie Monster. d, Grover. e, Elmo. f, Ernie. g, Zoe. h, The Count. i, Bert.
No. 883, Big Bird, Elmo and Ernie, horiz. No. 884, Cookie Monster, Bert and Ernie, horiz.

Perf. 14½x14¾

2000, Apr. 20		**Litho.**	**Wmk. 373**	
882	A199	50c Sheet of 9, #a-i	8.00	8.00

Souvenir Sheets
Perf. 14¾x14½

883	A199	$2 multi	3.50	3.50
884	A199	$2 multi	3.50	3.50

The Stamp Show 2000, London (#882).

Pres. Ratu Sir Kamisese Mara, 80th Birthday — A200

President with: 15c, Lumberjack, timber truck. 81c, Women. $1, Workers in cane field. $3, Ships.

2000, May 13			**Perf. 14x13¾**	
885	A200	15c multi	.25	.25
886	A200	81c multi	1.25	1.25
887	A200	$1 multi	1.50	1.50
888	A200	$3 multi	5.50	5.50
		Nos. 885-888 (4)	8.50	8.50

Prince William, 18th Birthday
Common Design Type

William: Nos. 889, 893a, As child, wearing fireman's helmet, vert. Nos. 890, 893b, Wearing navy suit, vert. Nos. 891, 893c, Wearing scarf. Nos. 892, 893d, Wearing suit and wearing blue shirt. No. 893e, As child, wearing camouflage and beret.

Perf. 13¾x14¼, 14¼x13¾

2000, June 21			**Wmk. 373**	
Stamps With White Border				
889	CD359	$1 multi	1.50	1.50
890	CD359	$1 multi	1.50	1.50
891	CD359	$1 multi	1.50	1.50
892	CD359	$1 multi	1.50	1.50
		Nos. 889-892 (4)	6.00	6.00

Souvenir Sheet
Stamps Without White Border
Perf. 14¼

893	CD359	$1 Sheet of 5, #a-e	9.00	9.00

2000 Summer Olympics, Sydney — A201

Wmk. 373

2000, Aug. 8		**Litho.**	**Perf. 13¾**	
894	A201	44c Swimming, vert.	.50	.50
895	A201	87c Judo, vert.	1.25	1.25
896	A201	$1 Running	1.50	1.50
897	A201	$2 Windsurfing	2.75	2.75
		Nos. 894-897 (4)	6.00	6.00

Souvenir Sheet

Alsmithia Longipes — A202

No. 898: a, Red frond at R. b, Red frond at L. c, Yellow frond. d, Fruit.

Wmk. 373

2000, Sept. 12		**Litho.**	**Perf. 13½**	
898	A202	$1 Sheet of 4, #a-d	7.50	7.50

Lapita Pottery Shards and Discovery Sites — A203

44c, Yanuca Island. 63c, Mago Island. $1, Ugaga Island. $2, Sigatoka sand dunes.

2000, Oct. 24			**Perf. 13¾**	
899-902	A203	Set of 4	7.00	7.00

Christmas A204

Designs: 15c, Jungle. 81c, Cliffside trail. 87c, Coastal village. $3, Outrigger canoe.

2000, Nov. 21				
903-906	A204	Set of 4	8.00	8.00

Souvenir Sheet

Taveuni Rain Forest — A205

Designs: a, Orange dove. b, Xixuthrus heyrovskyi.

Perf. 13¾x13½

2001, Feb. 1		**Litho.**	**Unwmk.**	
907	A205	$2 Sheet of 2, #a-b	6.25	6.25

Moths A206

Designs: 17c, Macroglossum hirundo vitiensis. 48c, Hippotion celerio. 69c, Gnathothlibus erotus eras. 89c, Theretra pinastrina intersecta. $1.17, Deilephila placida torenia. $2, Psilogramma jordana.

2001, Mar. 20			**Perf. 13¼x13**	
908-913	A206	Set of 6	8.00	8.00

Souvenir Sheet

Gallus Gallus — A207

Designs: a, Hen. b, Rooster.

2001, May 22			**Perf. 13¾x14**	
914	A207	$2 Sheet of 2, #a-b	7.00	7.00

Society for Prevention of Cruelty — A208

Designs: 34c, Girl, cat. 96c, Boy, dogs. $1.23, Girl, cat, diff. $2, Boy, dog.

Perf. 14x13¾

2001, June 26		**Litho.**	**Unwmk.**	
915-918	A208	Set of 4	6.50	6.50

Pigeons — A209

Designs: 69c, White-throated. 89c, Pacific, vert. $1.23, Peal's, vert. $2, Rock.

2001, July 20		**Perf. 14x14¾, 14¾x14**		
919-922	A209	Set of 4	7.25	7.25

Westpac Pacific Bank, 100th Anniv. in Fiji — A210

Bank office in: 48c, 1901. 96c, 1916. $1, 1934. $2, 2001.

2001, Aug. 10   Perf. 13¼x13¾
923-926 A210   Set of 4   6.00 6.00

Fish
A211

Designs: 50c, Yellowfin tuna. 96c, Wahoo. $1.17, Dolphin fish. $2, Pacific blue marlin.

2001, Aug. 23
927-930 A211   Set of 4   6.50 6.50

Christmas
A212

Designs: 17c, Angel appears to Mary. 34c, Nativity. 48c, Adoration of the shepherds. 69c, Adoration of the Magi. 89c, Flight to Egypt. $2, Fijian Chirst child.

2001, Oct. 29 Litho.   Perf. 13¾x13¼
931-936 A212   Set of 6   7.00 7.00

Colonial Financial Services Group, 125th Anniv. in Fiji — A213

Designs: 17c, Bank office. 48c, Women using automatic teller machine. $1, Suva Private Hospital. $3, Hoisting of British flag.

2001, Nov. 16 Litho.   Perf. 13¼
937-940 A213   Set of 4   7.00 7.00

Air Pacific, 50th Anniv. — A214

No. 941: a, De Havilland Drover. b, Hawker Siddley HS-748. c, Douglas DC-10-30. d, Boeing 747-200.

2001, Nov. 30 Litho.   Perf. 13
941   Horiz. strip of 4   7.25 7.25
  a.   A214 89c multi   1.25 1.00
  b.   A214 96c multi   1.40 1.10
  c.   A214 $1 multi   1.50 1.25
  d.   A214 $2 multi   3.00 1.50

Spices — A215

Designs: 69c, Pepper. 89c, Nutmeg. $1, Vanilla. $2, Cinnamon.

2002, Mar. 12 Litho.   Perf. 13¼
942-945 A215   Set of 4   6.25 6.25

Souvenir Sheet

Balaka Palm — A216

Palm and: a, Bird, butterfly, beetle. b, Lizard, butterfly

2002, Apr. 29
946 A216 $2 Sheet of 2, #a-b   7.00 7.00

Freshwater Fish — A217

Designs: 48c, Redigobius sp. 96c, Spotted flagtail. $1.23, Silverstripe mudskipper. $2, Snakehead gudgeon.

2002, May 13
947-950 A217   Set of 4   7.00 7.00

Fruit — A218

Designs: 25c, Breadfruit. 34c, Wi. $1, Jakfruit. $3, Avocado.

2002, July 25 Litho.   Perf. 13¾x13¼
951-954 A218   Set of 4   6.25 6.25

Murex Shells — A219

Designs: 69c, Saul's murex. 96c, Caltrop murex. $1, Purple Pacific drupe. $2, Ramose murex.

2002, Aug. 20   Perf. 13¾
955-958 A219   Set of 4   7.00 7.00

Fiji Goshawk
A220

Designs: 48c, Goshawk and eggs. 89c, Chicks in nest. $1, Juvenile on branch. $3, Adult.

2002, Sept. 10
959-962 A220   Set of 4   8.00 8.00

2002 Operation Open Heart Visit to Fiji — A221

Designs: 34c, Doctors performing operation, vert. 69c, Doctor listening to patient's heart with stethoscope. $1.17, Technician administering echocardiogram. $2, Administration of anesthesia to patient, vert.

2002, Oct. 30   Perf. 13¼
963-966 A221   Set of 4   7.25 7.25

Fiji Natural Artesian Water — A222

Designs: 25c, Bottle of water, flowers, vert. 48c, Bottling plant. $1, Delivery truck. $3, Children with bottled water, vert.

2002, Nov. 5
967-970 A222   Set of 4   7.50 7.50

Christmas — A223

Designs: 17c, Christian church. 89c, Mosque. $1, Hindu temple. $3, Christian church, diff.

2002, Nov. 20
971-974 A223   Set of 4   7.50 7.50

Post Fiji, Ltd. Improvements — A224

Designs: 48c, General Post Office. 96c, Post Fiji Mail Center. $1, Post Fiji Logistics Center. $2, Smart Mail.

2003, Mar. 19 Litho.   Perf. 13¼
975-978 A224   Set of 4   6.75 6.75

Souvenir Sheet

Intl. Year of Fresh Water — A225

No. 979: a, Top of waterfall, flowers. b, Base of waterfall, butterfly.

2003, Apr. 22
979 A225 $2 Sheet of 2, #a-b   7.25 7.25

2003 South Pacific Games, Suva — A226

Designs: 10c, Track athlete with arms raised. 14c, Baseball. 20c, Netball. No. 983, $5, Shot put.
No. 984, $5, Flags of participating nations, venues, volleyball players.

2003   Perf. 13¼
980-983 A226   Set of 4   7.25 7.25
Size: 120x85mm
Imperf
984 A226 $5 multi   7.50 7.50

Issued: Nos. 980-983, 5/26; No. 984, 6/28.

Fish
A227

Siganus uspi: 58c, Fish, crab and coral. 83c, Two fish and coral. $1.15, Two fish, coral, and other fish species. $3, Fish and coral.

2003, Aug. 12   Perf. 13¼
985-988 A227   Set of 4   8.00 8.00

Bird Life International A228

Designs: 41c, Long-legged warbler. 60c, Silktail. $1.07, Red-throated lorikeet. $3, Pink-billed parrot finch.

2003, Sept. 16
989-992 A228   Set of 4   13.00 13.00

Geckos
A229

Designs: 83c, Pacific slender-toed gecko. $1.07, Indopacific tree gecko. $1.15, Mann's gecko. $2, Voracious gecko.

2003, Oct. 21   Litho.   Perf. 13¼
993-996 A229 Set of 4   10.00 10.00

Christmas — A230

Children's art: 18c, Children, Christmas tree. 41c, Children, flag of Fiji. 58c, Children, Santa Claus, reindeer pulling sleighs, vert. 83c, Santa Claus on chimney, gifts, children, Christmas tree, vert. $1.07, Children with candles, Christmas tree, vert. $1.15, Santa Claus, children, bell, rainbow, vert. $1.41, Handshake.

2003, Nov. 26   Litho.   Perf. 13¼
997-1002 A230 Set of 6   7.50 7.50
Souvenir Sheet
1003 A230 $1.41 multi   3.50 3.50

Tagimoucia — A231

2003, Dec. 1   Litho.   Perf. 14½x14
1004 A231 50c multi + label   1.75 1.75
Sold in sheets of 10 stamps + 10 labels that could be personalized for $15 per sheet.

Xixuthrus Heyrovskyi, Longest Beetle in the World — A232

2003, Feb. 27   Imperf.
1005 A232 $5 multi   8.50 8.50

Miniature Sheet

Worldwide Fund for Nature (WWF) — A233

No. 1006: a, 58c, Skipjack tuna. b, 83c, Albacore tuna. c, $1.07, Yellowfin tuna. d, $3, Bigeye tuna.

2004, Apr. 7   Perf. 13¼
1006 A233 Sheet of 4, #a-d   8.50 8.50
e.   Like #1006, with artist's name
      at LL of each stamp   8.50 8.50

Land Snails A234

Designs: 18c, Malleated placostyle. 41c, Kandavu placostyle. $1.15, Fragile orpiella. $3, Thin Fijian placostyle.

2004, May 28
1007-1010 A234 Set of 4   8.50 8.50

Bird Type of 1995
Perf. 13¼x13
2004, June 26   Unwmk.
1011 A166 18c Island thrush   1.00 1.00

Coral Reef Shrimp — A235

Designs: 58c, Boxer shrimp. 83c, Bumblebee shrimp. $1.07, Mantis shrimp. $3, Anemone shrimp.

2004, June 30   Perf. 13¼
1012-1015 A235 Set of 4   8.00 8.00

Birds A236

Designs: 41c, Wandering tattler. 58c, Whimbrel. $1.15, Pacific golden plover. $3, Bristlethighed curlew.

2004, July 28
1016-1019 A236 Set of 4   12.00 12.00

2004 Summer Olympics, Athens A237

Designs: 41c, Swimming. 58c, Judo, vert. $1.40, Weight lifting, vert. $2, Makelesi Bulikiobo, runner.

2004, Aug. 12
1020-1023 A237 Set of 4   8.75 8.75

Musket Cove to Port Vila Yacht Race, 25th Anniv. — A238

Various yachts: 83c, $1.07, $1.15, $2. $1.07 and $2 are vert.

2004, Sept. 18   Perf. 14¼
1024-1027 A238 Set of 4   10.00 10.00
1027a   Souvenir sheet of 1   5.00 5.00
See Vanuatu Nos. 858-861.

Souvenir Sheet

Coconut Crab — A239

2004, Oct. 20   Litho.   Perf. 14
1028 A239 $5 multi   9.00 9.00

Papilio Schmeltzii — A240

Designs: 58c, Newly-emerged adult, vert. 83c, Larva. $1.41, Adult. $3, Pupa, vert.

Perf. 14x14½, 14½x14
2004, Nov. 10
1029-1032 A240 Set of 4   11.00 11.00

Christmas A241

Designs: 18c, Annunciation. 58c, Infant in manger. $1.07, Madonna and child. $3, Adoration of the Shepherds.

2004, Dec. 1   Litho.   Perf. 13¼
1033-1036 A241 Set of 4   11.00 11.00

Birds — A242

No. 1037: a, Little heron. b, Great white egret. c, White-faced heron. d, Pacific reef heron.

2005, Jan. 26
1037   Horiz. strip of 4   9.00 9.00
a.-d. A242 $1 Any single   2.25 2.25

Flowers For Perfume — A243

Designs: 58c, Cananga odorata. $1.15, Euodia hortensis. $1.41, Pandanus tecorius. $2, Santalum yasi.

2005, Feb. 20   Perf. 14x14½
1038-1041 A243 Set of 4   8.50 8.50

Peregrine Falcons — A244

Designs: 41c, Head of falcon. 83c, Adult at nest. $1.07, Chicks. $3, Adult on rock.

2005, Mar. 14   Litho.   Perf. 14½x14
1042-1045 A244 Set of 4   10.00 10.00

Triggerfish — A245

Designs: 58c, Whitebanded triggerfish. 83c, Yellow-spotted triggerfish. $1.15, Orange-lined triggerfish. $2, Clown triggerfish.

2005, Apr. 27
1046-1049 A245 Set of 4   8.50 8.50

European Philatelic Cooperation, 50th Anniv. (in 2006) — A246

Color of arches: 58c, Red. 83c, Blue green. $1.41, Purple. $4, Yellow bister.

2005, June 1   Perf. 13¾
1050-1053 A246 Set of 4   11.00 11.00
1053a   Souvenir sheet, #1050-
         1053   11.00 11.00
Europa stamps, 50th anniv. (in 2006).

Miniature Sheet

End of World War II, 60th Anniv. — A247

No. 1054: a, HMNZS Achilles. b, Japanese Yokosuka E14Y "Glen" over Suva Harbor. c, Fijian South Pacific Scouts in Solomon Islands. d, USS Chicago. e, Patrol vessel HMS Viti. f, British Prime Minister Winston Churchill. g, HMS Hood. h, Dambusters Raid. i, German King Tiger tank in Ardennes. j, Gen. Dwight D. Eisenhower.

2005, June 27   Litho.   Perf. 13¾
1054 A247 83c Sheet of 10,
            #a-j   13.00 13.00

Game Fish
A248

Designs: 41c, Great barracuda. 58c, Narrow-barred Spanish mackerel. $1.07, Giant trevally. $3, Indo-Pacific sailfish.

2005, July 27   Litho.   Perf. 14½x14
1055-1058 A248   Set of 4   9.00 9.00

Pope John Paul II
(1920-2005)
A249

2005, Aug. 18   Perf. 14
1059 A249 $1 multi   2.25 2.25

Dragonflies — A250

Designs: 83c, Yellow-striped flutterer. $1.07, Agrionoptera insignis. $1.15, Green skimmer. $2, Common percher.

2005, Aug. 30   Litho.   Perf. 13¼
1060-1063 A250   Set of 4   8.75 8.75

Albert Einstein
(1879-1955),
Physicist — A251

Einstein: 83c, As a child. $1.07, In 1905. $1.15, And blackboard. $2, And galaxies.

2005, Sept. 27   Litho.   Perf. 14¼x14
1064-1067 A251   Set of 4   6.75 6.75
Intl. Year of Physics.

Root Crops — A252

Designs: 41c, Manihot utilissima. 83c, Ipomoea satatas. $1.41, Colocasia esculenta. $2, Dioscorea sativa.

2005, Oct. 13   Perf. 13¼
1068-1071 A252   Set of 4   6.50 6.50

Tall Ships
A253

Designs: 83c, Eliza of Province. $1.15, Elbe. $1.41, HMS Rosario. $2, L'Astrolabe.

2005, Nov. 21   Litho.   Perf. 14x14¼
1072-1075 A253   Set of 4   7.50 7.50

Barn
Owls — A254

Owl: 18c, And eggs. $1.15, Juvenile. $1.41, With prey. $2, Perched.

2006, Jan. 10   Litho.   Perf. 14¼x14
1076-1079 A254   Set of 4   8.00 8.00

Platymantis Vitianus — A255

Various depictions: 50c, 83c, $1.15, $2.

2006, Feb. 8   Litho.   Perf. 14x14¼
1080-1083 A255   Set of 4   7.00 7.00

Skinks
A256

Designs: 18c, Pygmy snake-eyed skink. 58c, Brown-tailed copper striped skink. $1.15, Pacific black skink. $3, Pacific blue-tailed skink.

2006, Mar. 22
1084-1087 A256   Set of 4   7.25 7.25

Queen
Elizabeth
II, 80th
Birthday
A257

Designs: 50c, As child. 65c, Wearing tiara. 90c, Wearing blue hat. $3, Wearing blue hat, diff.
No. 1092: a, Like 65c. b, Like 90c.

2006, Apr. 21   Litho.   Perf. 14
With White Frames
1088-1091 A257   Set of 4   6.00 6.00
Souvenir Sheet
Without White Frames
1092 A257 $2 Sheet of 2, #a-b   5.50 5.50

Miniature Sheet

Vijay Singh, Golfer — A258

No. 1097 — Singh: a, Head. b, With arm raised. c, Leaning on golf club. d, Hitting ball from sand trap. e, Holding trophy (60x87mm).

Perf. 14x14¼
2006, May 26   Litho.   Unwmk.
1097 A258 $1 Sheet of 5, #a-e   8.00 8.00

2006 World Cup
Soccer
Championships,
Germany — A259

Various players: 65c, 90c, $1.20, $2.

2006, June 9   Perf. 14¼x14
1098-1101 A259   Set of 4   7.00 7.00

Souvenir Sheet

Purple Swamphen — A260

No. 1102: a, Swamphen and flowers. b, Swamphen on nest.

2006, July 20   Perf. 14½x14
1102 A260 $2 Sheet of 2, #a-b   6.00 6.00

Extinct
Species
A261

Designs: 50c, Brachylophus vitiensis. $1.10, Natunaornis gigoura, vert. $1.20, Vitirallus watlingi, vert. $1.50, Platymantis megabotoniviti.

Perf. 14x14¼, 14¼x14
2006, Aug. 15   Litho.
1103-1106 A261   Set of 4   6.50 6.50

Phasmids — A262

Designs: 10c, Hermarchus apollonius. $1.10, Cotylosoma dipneusticum. $1.20, Chitoniscus feejeeanus. $2, Graeffea crouanii.

2006, Sept. 7   Perf. 14½x14
1107-1110 A262   Set of 4   6.50 6.50

Honey
Production
A263

Designs: 18c, Bees and honeycomb. 40c, Apiarist examining honeycomb, horiz. $1, Woman and beehives, horiz. $3, Man and bottle of honey.

2006, Oct. 16   Perf. 14x14½, 14½x14
1111-1114 A263   Set of 4   6.00 6.00

Christmas
A264

Flowering plants: 18c, Decaspermum vitiense. 65c, Quisqualis indica. 90c, Mussaendra raiateensis. $3, Delonix regia.

2006, Dec. 5   Perf. 14x14½
1115-1118 A264   Set of 4   6.50 6.50

Anemonefish — A265

Designs: 18c, Spine-cheek anemonefish. 60c, Pink anemonefish. 90c, Orange-fin anemonefish. $3, Dusky anemonefish.

Perf. 14½x14, 14x14½
2006, Nov. 7   Litho.
1119-1122 A265   Set of 4   6.50 6.50

Souvenir Sheet

Thalassina Anomala — A266

2007, Jan. 24   *Perf. 13½*
1123 A266 $4 multi   5.00 5.00

Traditional Architecture — A267

Designs: 20c, Coastal dwelling. 65c, Inland dwelling. $1.10, Temple, Bau. $3, Lauan-style house.

2007, Mar. 20   *Litho.*   *Perf. 13¼*
1124-1127 A267   Set of 4   6.25 6.25

Freshwater Gobies — A268

Designs: 20c, Sicyopterus lagocephalus. $1.10, Stiphodon rutilaureus. $1.20, Sicyopus zosterophorum. $2, Stiphodon sp.

2007, Apr. 5   *Litho.*   *Perf. 13¼*
1128-1131 A268   Set of 4   5.50 5.50

Birds Introduced to Fiji — A269

Designs: 50c, Red-vented bulbul. 65c, Spotted dove, horiz. $1.50, Australian magpie, horiz. $2, Java sparrow.

2007, May 22
1132-1135 A269   Set of 4   6.00 6.00

Scouting, Cent. A270

Designs: 50c, Scout in kayak, hand holding compass. 90c, Three Scouts wearing helmets, hands tying knot. No. 1138, $1.50, Scout in harness climbing, Scout saluting. $2, Scout writing observation notes, hands tying neckerchief.
No. 1140, $1.50, vert.: a, Scout emblem. b, Lord Robert Baden-Powell.

2007, July 9   *Perf. 13¾*
1136-1139 A270   Set of 4   6.25 6.25

Souvenir Sheet

1140 A270 $1.50 Sheet of 2, #a-b   4.00 4.00

Snails A271

Designs: 40c, Clithon diadema. 90c, Neritina variegata. $1.20, Fijidoma maculata. $2, Neritina squamaepicta.

2007, Aug. 18   *Perf. 14x14¼*
1141-1144 A271   Set of 4   5.50 5.50

Orchids — A272

Designs: 20c, Liparis layardii. 65c, Dendrobium catillare, horiz. $1.10, Dendrobium mohlianum, horiz. $3, Glomera montana.

Perf. 14¼x14, 14x14¼
2007, Aug. 21   Set of 4   6.25 6.25
1145-1148 A272

Nos. 725 and 729 Surcharged

No. 1149

No. 1150

Methods, Types and Watermarks As Before

2006-08
1149 A166   1c on 6c #729   1.00 1.00
No. 1149 exists with inverted surcharge. Value, $90.
1150 A166   1c on 6c #729   7.00 7.00

No. 1151

No. 1152

1151 A166   2c on 1c #725   4.00 4.00
1152 A166   2c on 1c #725, larger font   2.00 2.00

No. 1152A

No. 1152Ab

1152A A166   2c on 1c #725, 4mm between "c" and obliterator   200.00 200.00
   b.   5mm between "c" and obliterator   200.00 200.00

No. 1153

No. 1153a

1153 A166   2c on 6c #729, 4mm between "c" and obliterator   1.25 1.25
   a.   5mm between "c" and obliterator   1.25 1.25
No. 1153a exists with inverted surcharge. Value, $90.

No. 1153B

No. 1154

1153B A166   2c on 6c #729   200.00 200.00
1154 A166   3c on 1c #725   1.25 1.25

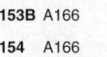
No. 1155

No. 1155a

1155 A166   4c on 1c #725   1.50 1.50
   a.   1½mm gap between "4" and "c" (position 67)   30.00 30.00

No. 1156

No. 1156a

1156 A166   4c on 6c #729, 4mm between "c" and obliterator   1.25 1.25
   a.   5mm between "c" and obliterator   1.25 1.25
No. 1156a exists with inverted surcharge. Value, $90.

No. 1156B

No. 1157

1156B A166   6c on 6c #729   200.00 200.00
1157 A166   18c on 6c #729, 4mm between "c" and obliterator   6.50 6.50
No. 1157 exists with double surcharge, one with normal 4mm between "c" and obliterator and the other with 2½mm between "c" and obliterator. One surcharge is shifted 75% upward. Half of the errors have the normal separation between "c" and obliterator at top and half have it at bottom. Each error variety is equally scarce. Value, each $110.
No. 1157 also exists with normal surcharge shifted 75% upward but with no second surcharge. Value, $50.

No. 1158

No. 1158a

1158 A166   18c on 6c #729, 2½mm between "c" and obliterator   11.00 11.00
   a.   4mm between "c" and obliterator   22.00 22.00

No. 1159

No. 1159a

1159 A166   20c on 6c #729, 2½mm between "c" and obliterator   6.50 6.50
   a.   4mm between "c" and obliterator   14.50 14.50
No. 1159 exists with inverted surcharge. Value, $90.

No. 1160

No. 1160a

1160 A166   20c on 6c #729, 4mm between "c" and obliterator   14.50 14.50
   a.   1½mm between "c" and obliterator   35.00 35.00
Nos. 1149-1160 (15)   657.75 657.75

Issued: No. 1149, 5/30/07; No. 1150, 9/19/07; No. 1151, 4/3; No. 1152, 11/13; No. 1152A, July 2007, No. 1152Ab, 8/20/08; Nos. 1153, 1153B 2/19/07; No. 1153a, 2/27/07; No. 1154, 3/13; No. 1155, 6/27; No. 1156, 6/6/07; No. 1156a, 2/19/08; No. 1156B, Feb. 2007; No. 1157, 6/8; No. 1158, 9/8; No. 1158a, Aug. 2007; No. 1159, 1/19/07; No. 1159a, Jan. 2007; No. 1160, 3/8/07; No. 1160a, 4/12/08.

Fish A273

Designs: 50c, Coronation trout. 90c, Roving coral trout. $1.50, Squaretail coral trout. $2, Chinese footballer.

2007, Oct. 15   *Litho.*   *Perf. 13¼*
1161-1164 A273   Set of 4   6.75 6.75

Butterflies — A274

Designs: 20c, Polyura caphontis. $1.10, Hypolimnas bolina, horiz. $1.20, Doleschallia bisaltide, horiz. $2, Danaus hamata.

2007, Nov. 20　　Litho.　　Perf. 13¼
1165-1168　A274　Set of 4　　6.00　6.00

Souvenir Sheet

Barred-winged Rail — A275

No. 1169: a, Head of adult. b, Chick.

2007, Dec. 3
1169　A275　$2 Sheet of 2, #a-b　　5.25　5.25

National Medals — A276

Designs: 50c, Medal of the Order of Fiji. 65c, Member of the Order of Fiji. $1.20, Officer of the Order of Fiji. $2, Companion of the Order of Fiji.

2008, Feb. 20　　Litho.　　Perf. 13¼
1170-1173　A276　Set of 4　　6.00　6.00

Souvenir Sheet

Spiny Lobster — A277

2008, Apr. 22　　Litho.　　Perf. 14x14½
1174　A277　$4 multi　　5.50　5.50

First Trans-Pacific Flight of the Southern Cross, 80th Anniv. — A278

Southern Cross: 20c, Over Fiji. 90c, In Albert Park, Suva. $1.50, Surrounded by police guard. $2, With crew.

2008, June 13　　　　　　Perf. 13½
1175-1178　A278　Set of 4　　6.25　6.25

2008 Summer Olympics, Beijing A279

Designs: 20c, Bamboo, Running. 65c, Dragon, Judo. 90c, Lanterns, Shooting. $1.50, Carp, Swimming.

2008, May 5　　Litho.　　Perf. 13¼
1179-1182　A279　Set of 4　　4.50　4.50

Red-breasted Musk Parrot Varieties — A280

Prosopeia tabuensis: 65c, Koroensis. 90c, Atrogularis, horiz. $1.50, Taviunensis, horiz. $2, Splendens.

2008, Mar. 25　　Litho.　　Perf. 13½
1183-1186　A280　Set of 4　　6.75　6.75

Humpback Whales — A281

Humpback whale: 20c, Pair underwater. 50c, Breaching water's surface. $1.10, Reentering water. $3, Flukes.

2008, July 17　　Litho.　　Perf. 14½x14
1187-1190　A281　Set of 4　　6.50　6.50

Nos. 729-731 Surcharged Like Nos. 1149-1160

No. 1191　　　　　No. 1191A

No. 1191Ab

Methods, Perfs and Watermarks As Before

2007-09
1191	A166	1c on 13c #730	1.50	1.50
1191A	A166	1c on 23c #731, 4mm between "c" and obliterator	1.00	1.00
b.		5mm between "c" and obliterator	1.00	1.00

No. 1191C　　　　No. 1192

1191C	A166	2c on 6c #729	175.00	175.00
1192	A166	2c on 6c #729	175.00	175.00

No. 1192A　　　　No. 1193

1192A	A166	2c on 6c #729	175.00	175.00
1193	A166	2c on 6c #730	1.25	1.25

No. 1193 exists with double surcharge, one inverted. Value, $130.

No. 1194　　　　　No. 1195

1194	A166	4c on 13c #730	1.25	1.25
1195	A166	20c on 6c #729	100.00	100.00

No. 1195A

1195A	A166	20c on 23c #731	200.00	200.00

No. 1196　　　　　No. 1196a

1196	A166	20c on 23c #731	2.00	2.00
a.		No gap between "c" and obliterator (position 70)	35.00	35.00

No. 1196 exists with inverted surcharge. Value, $90. No. 1196 also exists surcharged on gum side only. Value, $150. No. 1196 also exists with surcharge shifted 50% upward. Value, $70.

No. 1197　　　　　No. 1197a

No. 1197d　　　　No. 1197e

No. 1197f

1197	A166	20c on 23c #731, 1½mm between "c" and obliterator	72.50	72.50
a.		2½mm between "c" and obliterator	50.00	50.00
d.		3mm between "c" and obliterator	72.50	72.50
e.		4mm between "c" and obliterator	50.00	50.00
f.		5mm between "c" and obliterator	72.50	72.50

No. 1197B　　　　No. 1197C

1197B	A166	20c on 23c #731	35.00	35.00

1197C A166   20c on 23c
          #731   175.00 175.00
Nos. 1191-1197C (13)   1,114.   1,114.

Issued: No. 1191, 8/22/08; No. 1191A,
12/18/08; No. 1191Ab, 1/23/09; No. 1191C,
1192, 1192A, 2/19/07; Nos. 1193, 1194,
8/20/08; No. 1195, 4/28/08; No. 1195A, Apr.
2008; Nos. 1196, 4/12/08; No. 1197, 1197a,
1197d, 1197e, 1197f. Apr. 2008; 1197B,
4/12/08; 1197C, Apr. 2008.

Bananas — A282

Various banana varieties: 65c, $1.10, $1.20,
$2.

2008, Sept. 23   Litho.   Perf. 14x14½
1198-1201 A282   Set of 4   6.00 6.00

Eels
A283

Designs: 50c, Anguilla obscura. 90c,
Anguilla marmorata. $1.50, Anguilla obscura,
diff. $2, Gymnothorax potyuranodon.

2008, Oct. 15   Perf. 14½x14
1202-1205 A283   Set of 4   5.50 5.50

Christmas — A284

Various choirs: 20c, 50c, 65c, $3.

2008, Dec. 10   Litho.   Perf. 14½x14
1206-1209 A284   Set of 4   5.00 5.00

Fruit
Doves — A285

Designs: 50c, Many-colored fruit dove. 65c,
Crimson-crowned fruit dove. 90c, Whistling
dove. $3, Orange dove.

2009, Feb. 17   Litho.   Perf. 14x14½
1210-1213 A285   Set of 4   5.50 5.50

**Nos. 729-731 Surcharged Like Nos.
1149-1160**

No. 1214   No. 1215

No. 1215A

**Methods, Perfs and Watermarks As
Before**

2009-10
1214 A166   1c on 13c
                 #730   22.50 22.50
1215 A166   1c on 23c
                 #731   1.25 1.25
1215A A166   1c on 23c
                 #731,
                 small
                 font   1.00 1.00

No. 1216   No. 1216A

1216 A166   2c on 13c
                 #730   22.50 22.50
1216A A166   2c on 23c
                 #731   175.00 175.00

No. 1217   No. 1217A

1217 A166   2c on 23c
                 #731   70.00 70.00
1217A A166   2c on 23c
                 #731,
                 small
                 font   1.00 1.00

No. 1218   No. 1218A

1218 A166   3c on 23c
                 #731   22.50 22.50
1218A A166   3c on 23c
                 #731,
                 small
                 font   1.00 1.00

No. 1218 exists with "3" of surcharge omitted. Most of the known singles have irregular
perforations from being roughly removed from
sheets. Value thus, $100. Errors with intact
perforations are extremely scarce. Value,
$300. Value of single error in pair with normal
stamp, $350.

No. 1219   No. 1220

1219 A166   4c on 6c
                 #729   70.00 70.00
1220 A166   4c on 13c
                 #730   22.50 22.50

No. 1221   No. 1222

No. 1222A

1221 A166   4c on 23c
                 #731   90.00 90.00
1222 A166   4c on 23c
                 #731   1.50 1.50
1222A A166   4c on 23c
                 #731,
                 small
                 font   1.00 1.00

No. 1223   No. 1223b

No. 1223A

1223 A166   5c on 23c
                 #731,
                 4mm be-
                 tween
                 "c" and
                 oblitera-
                 tor   1.50 1.50
   b.   2½mm between "c"
                 and obliterator (po-
                 sitions 3 and 89) 30.00 30.00
1223A A166   5c on 23c
                 #731,
                 small
                 font   1.00 1.00

No. 1223 exists with surcharge shifted 50%
upward. Value, $60.

Nos. 1214-1223A (16)   504.25 504.25

Issued: Nos. 1214, 1215, 1219-1222, 3/10;
Nos. 1216, 1217, 3/30; No. 1218, 8/27; No.
1223, 7/8.
On Nos. 1215, 1217, 1218, 1222 and 1223,
the "c" and obliterator are 4mm apart.
Issued: Nos. 1214, 1215, Mar. 10; Nos.
1215A, 1217A, 1218A, 8/5/10; No. 1216, Mar.
30; No. 1216A, Mar.; No. 1217, Mar. 30; No.
1218, Aug. 27; No. 1219, 1220, 1221, 1222,
Mar. 10; No. 1222A, 8/3/10; No. 1223, July 8;
No. 1223A, 8/6/10.

Weddings in Fiji — A286

Designs: 20c, Chinese wedding. 40c, Muslim wedding. $1.50, Indian wedding. $3, Fijian
wedding, vert.

Perf. 14½x14, 14x14½
2009, Aug. 17   Litho.   Unwmk.
1224-1227 A286   Set of 4   5.25 5.25

Passion
Fruit — A287

Designs: 20c, Passiflora foetida. 65c, Passiflora edulis (yellow green). $1.20, Passiflora
maliformis. $2, Passiflora edulis (purple).

2009, Sept. 29   Perf. 14x14¼
1228-1231 A287   Set of 4   4.25 4.25

Souvenir Sheet

People's Republic of China, 60th
Anniv. — A288

2009, Oct. 1   Perf. 13¼
1232 A288 $5 multi   5.25 5.25

Ferns — A289

Designs: 20c, Cyathea lunulata. 40c,
Asplenium australasicum. $1.50, Diplazium
proliferum. $3, Nephrolepsis biserrata.

2009, Dec. 15   Perf. 14x14½
1233-1236 A289   Set of 4   5.25 5.25

Snakes — A290

Designs: 20c, Yellow-bellied sea snake. 90c,
Fiji burrowing snake. $1.10, Banded sea krait.
$2, Pacific boa.

2010, Mar. 30   Litho.   Perf. 14½x14
1237-1240 A290   Set of 4   4.50 4.50

Peonies — A291

No. 1241: a, 20c, Pink peony. b, 40c, Red
peony.

2010, Apr. 8   Litho.   Perf. 13¼
1241 A291   Horiz. pair, #a-b   .65 .65

SEMI-POSTAL STAMPS

Catalogue values for unused
stamps in this section are for
Never Hinged items.

Children at
Play — SP1

Rugby Player — SP2

Perf. 13x13½

1951, Sept. 17   Engr.   Wmk. 4

B1	SP1	1p + 1p brown	.30	.30
B2	SP2	2p + 1p deep green	.35	.35

Bamboo River Raft — SP3

Design: 2½p+ ½p, Cross of Lorraine.

1954, Apr. 1   *Perf. 11x11½*

B3	SP3	1½p + ½p green & brn	.25	.25
B4	SP3	2½p + ½p black & org	.30	.30

Nos. 269 and 272 Surcharged

1972, Dec. 4   Photo.   Perf. 14, 13½

B5	A56	15c + 5c multi	.50	.50
B6	A55	30c + 10c multi	1.10	1.10

Indian Boy, Map of Fiji SP4

Map of Fiji and: 15c+2c, European girl. 30c+3c, Chinese girl. 40c+4c, Fijian boy.

Wmk. 373

1979, Sept. 17   Litho.   *Perf. 14½*

B7	SP4	4c + 1c multicolored	.20	.20
B8	SP4	15c + 2c multicolored	.25	.25
B9	SP4	30c + 3c multicolored	.50	.50
B10	SP4	40c + 4c multicolored	.70	.70
		Nos. B7-B10 (4)	1.65	1.65

The surtax was for IYC fund.

POSTAGE DUE STAMPS

D1   D2

D3

1917   Unwmk.   Typeset   *Perf. 11*
Laid Papers; Without Gum

J1	D1	½p black	1,300.	475.00
J2	D2	½p black	550.00	300.00
J3	D3	1p black	425.00	140.00
J4	D3	2p black	325.00	80.00
J5	D3	3p black	425.00	120.00

J6	D3	4p black	1,000.	550.00
a.		Strip of 8, 3 #J3, 1 ea. #J1 and #J6, and 3 #J5	16,000.	
		Nos. J1-J6 (6)	4,025.	1,665.

There were two printings of this issue. In the first printing, the 2d was printed in sheets of 84 (7x12), and the other four values were printed together in sheets of 96 (8x12), with each row consisting of three 1p, one ½p, one 4p and three 3p values. Setenant multiples exist. Sheets were not perforated on the margins, so that marginal stamps were not perforated on the outer edge. Examples from the first printing are 25mm wide (including margins).

In the second printing, the ½p, 1p and 2p were printed in separate sheets of 84 (7x12). The clichés were set a little closer, and so that examples of this printing are 23mm wide.

D4   D5

Perf. 14

1918, June 1   Typo.   Wmk. 3

J7	D4	½p black	4.25	26.00
J8	D4	1p black	4.25	15.00
J9	D4	2p black	5.50	22.50
J10	D4	3p black	7.00	27.50
J11	D4	4p black	8.25	40.00
		Nos. J7-J11 (5)	29.25	131.00

1940   Wmk. 4   *Perf. 12½*

J12	D5	1p bright green	4.75	70.00
J13	D5	2p bright green	8.50	70.00
J14	D5	3p bright green	11.00	77.50
J15	D5	4p bright green	12.00	82.50
J16	D5	5p bright green	15.00	85.00
J17	D5	6p bright green	8.00	87.50
J18	D5	1sh dk carmine	20.00	140.00
J19	D5	1sh6p dk carmine	20.00	200.00
		Nos. J12-J19 (8)	99.25	812.50
		Set, never hinged	140.00	

WAR TAX STAMPS

Regular Issue of 1912-16 Overprinted

Die I

1916   Wmk. 3   *Perf. 14*

MR1	A23	½p green	1.25	*3.25*
a.		Inverted overprint	700.00	
b.		Double overprint		
MR2	A23	1p scarlet	2.75	.75
a.		1p carmine	30.00	26.00
b.		Pair, one without ovpt.	9,000.	
c.		Inverted overprint	800.00	

Most examples of #MR2b are within horiz. strips of 12.

FINLAND

ˈfin-lənd

(Suomi)

LOCATION — Northern Europe bordering on the Gulfs of Bothnia and Finland
GOVT. — Republic
AREA — 130,119 sq. mi.
POP. — 5,147,349 (1997)
CAPITAL — Helsinki

Finland was a Grand Duchy of the Russian Empire from 1809 until December 1917, when it declared its independence.

100 Kopecks = 1 Ruble
100 Pennia = 1 Markka (1866)
100 Cents = 1 Euro (2002)

> **Catalogue values for unused stamps in this country are for Never Hinged items, beginning with Scott 220 in the regular postage section, Scott B39 in the semipostal section, Scott C2 in the airpost section, Scott M1 in the military stamp section, and Scott Q6 in the parcel post section.**

Unused stamps are valued with original gum as defined in the catalogue introduction except for Nos. 1-3B which are valued without gum. Used values for Nos. 1-3B are for pen-canceled examples. Very fine examples of the serpentine rouletted issues, Nos. 4-13c, will have roulettes cutting the design slightly on one or more sides and will have all "teeth" complete and intact. Stamps with roulettes clear of the design on all four sides are extremely scarce and sell for substantial premiums. Stamps with teeth entirely missing or with several short roulettes are worth much less. See *Scott Classic Specialized Catalogue* for values for used stamps with one or two short roulettes.

Watermarks

Wmk. 121 — Multiple Swastika   Wmk. 208 — Post Horn

Wmk. 168 — Wavy Lines and Letters

Wmk. 273 — Roses   Wmk. 363 — Tree Stump

Syncopated Perforations

Type A (1st stamp #1065): On one longer side, groups of five holes are separated by an oval hole equal in width to eight holes.

Type B (1st stamp, #1142): On the top groups of 3 holes at left and right and a middle group of 4 holes separated by rectangular perforations equal in width to 4 holes.

Issues under Russian Empire

Coat of Arms — A1

1856-58   Unwmk.   Typo.   *Imperf.*
Small Pearls in Post Horns
Wove Paper

1	A1	5k blue	6,750.	1,500.
		Pen and town cancellation		1,900.
		Town cancellation		3,250.
a.		Tête bêche pair	80,000.	65,000.
		Pen and town cancellation		90,000.
2	A1	10k rose	8,750.	400.
		Pen and town cancellation		575.
		On cover		1,800.
		Town cancellation		925.
		On cover		2,800.
a.		Tête bêche pair	80,000.	60,000.
		Pen and town cancellation		75,000.

Cut to shape

1	A1	5k blue		150.
		Pen and town cancellation		200.
		Town cancellation		250.
2	A1	10k rose		65.00
		Pen and town cancellation		90.00
		Town cancellation		100.00

Wide Vertically Laid Paper

2C	A1	10k rose ('58)	—	1,400.
		Pen and town cancellation		1,800.
		Town cancellation		2,500.
d.		Tête bêche pair		

Cut to shape

2C	A1	10k rose		225.
		Pen and town cancellation		275.
		Town cancellation		350.

The wide vertically laid paper has 13-14 distinct lines per 2 centimeters. The 10k rose also exists on a narrow laid paper with lines sometimes indistinct. Value, 45 per cent of that for a wide laid paper example.

A 5k blue with small pearls exists on narrow vertically laid paper. It is rare.

Stamps on diagonally laid paper are envelope cut squares.

Large Pearls in Post Horns

1858   Wove Paper

3	A1	5k blue	8,500.	1,400.
		Pen and town cancellation		1,550.
		Town cancellation		2,500.
a.		Tête bêche pair		60,000.
		Pen and town cancellation		65,000.

Cut to shape

3	A1	5k blue		125.00
		Pen and town cancellation		175.00
		Town cancellation		225.00

1859   Wide Vertically Laid Paper

3B	A1	5k blue	—	18,000.
		Pen and town cancellation		25,000.

Cut to shape

3B	A1	5k blue		2,400.
		Pen and town cancellation		3,500.

Reprints of Nos. 2 and 3, made in 1862, are on brownish paper, on vertically laid paper, and in tête bêche pairs on normal and vertically laid paper. Reprints of 1871, 1881 and 1893 are on yellowish or white paper. Value for least costly of each, $85.

In 1956, Nos. 2 and 3 were reprinted for the Centenary with post horn watermark and gum. Value, $85 each.

> Values for rouletted stamps with one or two short teeth are considerably less than the values shown, which are for stamps with all teeth full and intact. See the *Scott Classic Specialized Catalogue* for greater detail. Stamps with several short teeth or teeth entirely missing sell for very small percentages of the values shown.

Coat of Arms — A2

1860 — Serpentine Roulette 7½, 8

Four types of indentation are noted:

I — Depth 1-1¼mm II — Depth 1½-1¾mm

III — Depth 2-2¼mm IV — Shovel-shaped teeth. Depth 1¼-1½mm

Wove Paper

4	A2	5k blue, *bluish,* I		725.00	200.00
a.		Roulette II		875.00	275.00
b.		Perf. vert.			
5	A2	10k rose, *pale rose,* I		625.00	65.00
a.		Roulette II		1,300.	190.00

A3 A4

1866-74 — Serpentine Roulette

6	A3	5p pur brn, *lil,* I ('73)		450.00	200.00
a.		Roulette II			4,500.
b.		5p red brn, *lil,* III ('71)		400.00	200.00
7	A3	8p blk, *grn,* III ('67)		325.00	200.00
a.		Ribbed paper, III ('72)		1,300.	1,000.
b.		Roulette II ('74)		400.00	300.00
c.		As "b," ribbed paper ('74)		400.00	275.00
d.		Roulette I ('73)		575.00	375.00
e.		As "d," ribbed paper		1,100.	475.00
f.		Serpentine roulette 10½ ('67)			15,000.
8	A3	10p blk, *yel,* III ('70)		750.00	400.00
a.		10p blk, *buff,* II		850.00	450.00
b.		10p blk, *buff,* I ('73)		800.00	425.00
9	A3	20p bl, *bl,* III		650.00	67.50
a.		Roulette II		650.00	97.50
b.		Roulette I ('73)		750.00	150.00
c.		Roulette IV ('74)		—	1,300.
d.		Perf. horiz.			
e.		Printed on both sides (40p blue on back)			
10	A3	40p rose, *lil rose,* III		575.00	77.50
a.		Ribbed paper, III ('73)		750.00	250.00
b.		Roulette II		575.00	92.50
c.		As "b," ribbed paper ('73)		750.00	200.00
d.		Roulette I		800.00	200.00
e.		As "d," ribbed paper		750.00	150.00
f.		Roulette IV		—	2,500.
g.		As "f," ribbed paper			
h.		Serpentine roulette 10½			
11	A4	1m yel brn, III ('67)		2,500.	900.00
a.		Roulette II		3,100.	1,900.

Nos. 7f and 10h are private roulettes and are also known in compound serpentine roulette 10½ and 7½.

Nos. 4-11 were reprinted in 1893 on thick wove paper. Colors differ from originals. Roulette type IV. Value for Nos. 4-5, each $40, Nos. 6-10, each $50. Value for No. 11, $55.

Thin or Thick Laid Paper

12	A3	5p red brn, *lil,* III		300.00	160.00
a.		Roulette II		325.00	325.00
b.		Roulette I		300.00	325.00
d.		5p blk, *buff,* roul. III (error)			22,500.
e.		Tête bêche pair			

13	A3	10p black, *buff,* III		750.00	300.00
a.		10p black, *yel,* II		900.00	300.00
b.		10p black, *yel,* I		1,300.	800.00
c.		10p red brn, *lil,* III (error)		8,500.	7,750.

Forgeries of No. 13c exist.

A5

1875 — Perf. 14x13½

16	A5	32p lake		2,400.	500.00

1875-81 — Perf. 11

17	A5	2p gray		55.00	65.00
18	A5	5p orange		140.00	15.00
a.		5p yellow		140.00	15.00
19	A5	8p blue green		275.00	75.00
a.		8p yellow green		275.00	85.00
20	A5	10p brown ('81)		625.00	67.50
21	A5	20p ultra		160.00	3.75
a.		20p blue		175.00	6.00
b.		20p Prussian blue		350.00	40.00
c.		Tête bêche pair			3,500.
22	A5	25p carmine ('79)		300.00	16.00
a.		25p rose		425.00	65.00
23	A5	32p carmine		410.00	57.50
a.		32p rose		500.00	160.00
24	A5	1m violet ('77)		875.00	175.00
		Nos. 17-24 (8)		2,840.	474.75

A souvenir card issued in 1974 for NORDIA 1975 reproduced a block of four of the unissued "1 MARKKAA" design.
Nos. 19, 23 were reprinted in 1893, perf. 12½. Value $17.50 each.

1881-83 — Perf. 12½

25	A5	2p gray		15.00	17.00
a.		Imperf., pair		575.00	
26	A5	5p orange		57.50	7.00
a.		Tête bêche pair		7,500.	4,500.
b.		Imperf. vert., pair			—
c.		Imperf. horiz., pair			—
27	A5	10p brown		100.00	20.00
28	A5	20p ultra		60.00	2.00
a.		20p blue		60.00	2.00
b.		Tête bêche pair		3,000.	2,400.
c.		Imperf., pair		65.00	
29	A5	25p rose		50.00	10.00
a.		25p carmine		67.50	20.00
b.		Tête bêche pair		15,000.	
30	A5	1m violet ('82)		400.00	50.00
		Nos. 25-30 (6)		682.50	106.00

Nos. 27-29 were reprinted in 1893 in deeper shades, perf. 12½. Value $35 each.
Most examples of No. 28c are from printer's waste.

1881 — Perf. 11x12½

26d	A5	5p orange		500.00	100.00
27a	A5	10p brown		1,000.	275.00
28d	A5	20p ultra		650.00	50.00
28e	A5	20p blue		650.00	50.00
29c	A5	25p rose		750.00	200.00
29d	A5	25p carmine		650.00	125.00
30a	A5	1m violet			1,600.

1881 — Perf. 12½x11

26e	A5	5p orange		500.00	100.00
27b	A5	10p brown			350.00
28f	A5	20p ultra		650.00	50.00
28g	A5	20p blue		650.00	50.00
29e	A5	25p rose			300.00
29f	A5	25p carmine		650.00	125.00

1885 — Perf. 12½

31	A5	5p emerald		19.00	.65
a.		5p yellow green		21.00	1.25
b.		Tête bêche pair		—	10,000.
32	A5	10p carmine		29.00	3.00
a.		10p rose		29.00	3.00
33	A5	20p orange		32.50	.50
a.		20p yellow		37.50	1.75
b.		Tête bêche pair		—	3,500.
34	A5	25p ultra		62.50	3.50
a.		25p blue		57.50	3.00
35	A5	1m gray & rose		35.00	20.00
36	A5	5m green & rose		500.00	375.00
37	A5	10m brown & rose		625.00	625.00

A6

1889-92 — Perf. 12½

38	A6	2p slate ('90)		.65	1.00
39	A6	5p green ('90)		32.50	.40
40	A6	10p carmine ('90)		62.50	.55
a.		10p rose ('90)		77.50	.60
b.		Imperf.		100.00	100.00
41	A6	20p orange ('92)		72.50	.35
a.		20p yellow ('90)		77.50	1.25
42	A6	25p ultra ('91)		72.50	1.00
a.		25p blue		77.50	1.25
43	A6	1m slate & rose ('92)		4.75	3.75
a.		1m brnsh gray & rose ('90)		27.50	4.00
44	A6	5m green & rose ('90)		27.50	72.50
45	A6	10m brown & rose ('90)		40.00	100.00
		Nos. 38-45 (8)		312.90	179.55

The 2p slate, perf. 14x13, is believed to be an essay.
See Nos. 60-63.

See Russia for types similar to A7-A18.

Finnish stamps have "dot in circle" devices or are inscribed "Markka," "Markkaa," "Pen." or "Pennia."

Imperial Arms of Russia
A7   A8   A9

A10   A11

Laid Paper

1891-92 — Wmk. 168 — Perf. 14½x15

46	A7	1k orange yel		5.25	11.00
47	A7	2k green		6.25	9.50
48	A7	3k carmine		12.50	17.50
49	A8	4k rose		15.00	15.00
50	A7	7k dark blue		6.25	2.50
51	A8	10k dark blue		15.00	16.00
52	A9	14k blue & rose		21.00	27.50
53	A8	20k blue & car		19.00	18.00
54	A9	35k violet & grn		26.00	57.50
55	A8	50k violet & grn		35.00	40.00

Perf. 13½

56	A10	1r brown & org		90.00	90.00
57	A11	3½r black & gray		325.00	475.00
a.		3½r black & yellow (error)		14,000.	17,000.

58	A11	7r black & yellow		225.00	300.00
		Nos. 46-58 (13)		801.25	1,079.

Forgeries of Nos. 57, 57a, 58 exist.

Type of 1889-90 — Wove Paper

1895-96 — Unwmk. — Perf. 14x13

60	A6	5p green		.60	.40
61	A6	10p rose		.70	.50
62	A6	20p orange		.60	.25
a.		Imperf.		150.00	—
63	A6	25p ultra		1.00	.70
a.		25p blue		1.75	.75
b.		Imperf.		100.00	—
		Nos. 60-63 (4)		2.90	1.85

A12   A13

A14   A15

1901 — Litho. — Perf. 14½x15 — Chalky Paper

64	A12	2p yellow		5.25	5.25
65	A12	5p green		10.00	1.00
66	A13	10p carmine		27.50	1.25
67	A13	20p dark blue		62.50	.85
68	A14	1m violet & grn		325.00	9.25

Perf. 13½

69	A15	10m black & gray		300.00	300.00
		Nos. 64-69 (6)		730.25	317.60

Imperf sheets of 10p and 20p, stolen during production, were privately perforated 11½ to defraud the P.O. Uncanceled imperfs. of Nos. 65-68 are believed to be proofs.
See Nos. 70-75, 82.

Types of 1901 Redrawn

No. 64   No. 70

2p. On No. 64, the "2" below "II" is shifted slightly leftward. On No. 70, the "2" is centered below "II."

No. 65   No. 71

5p. On No. 65, the frame lines are very close. On No. 71, a clear white space separates them.

Nos. 66, 67   Nos. 72, 73

10p, 20p. On Nos. 66-67, the horizontal central background lines are faint and broken. On Nos. 72-73, they are clear and solid, though still thin.

20p. On No. 67, "H" close to "2" with period midway. On No. 73 they are slightly separated with period close to "H."

No. 68   Nos. 74, 74a

1m. On No. 68, the "1" following "MARKKA" lacks serif at base. On Nos. 74-74a, this "1" has serif.

No. 69   No. 75

10m. On No. 69, the serifs of "M" and "A" in top and bottom panels do not touch. On No. 75, the serifs join.

Perf. 14¼x14¾, 14¼x14

1901-14   **Typo.**

Ordinary Paper

70	A12	2p orange	.60	1.10
71	A12	5p green	1.75	.50
a.		Perf 14¼x14 ('06)	1.75	.50
72	A13	10p carmine	10.00	.50
a.		Perf 14¼x14 ('07)	55.00	.50
b.		Background inverted, perf 14¼x14¾	16.00	2.50
c.		Background inverted, perf 14¼x14	62.50	2.50
73	A12	20p dark blue	5.25	.50
a.		Perf 14¼x14 ('06)	70.00	.65
74	A14	1m lil & grn, perf. 14¼x14 ('14)	1.40	.65
a.		1m violet & blue green, perf. 14¼x14¾ ('02)	10.00	1.00
		Nos. 70-74 (5)	19.00	3.25

Perf. 13½

75	A15	10m blk & drab ('03)	150.00	52.50

Imperf Pairs

70a	A12	2p	290.00	410.00
71b	A12	5p	77.50	160.00
72d	A13	10p	90.00	160.00
73b	A12	20p	160.00	160.00
74b	A14	1m	150.00	160.00
		Nos. 70a-74b (5)	767.50	1,050.

A16   A17   A18

1911-16   **Perf. 14, 14¼x14¾**

77	A16	2p orange	.30	1.00
78	A16	5p green	.35	.35
a.		Imperf.	410.00	
b.		Perf 14¼x14¾	425.00	75.00
79	A17	10p rose ('15)	.30	.25
a.		Imperf.	77.50	160.00
b.		Perf. 14¼x14¾ ('16)	1.75	2.75
80	A16	20p deep blue	.30	.25
a.		Imperf.	200.00	150.00
b.		Perf. 14¼x14¾	8.00	1.60
81	A18	40p violet & blue	.30	.25
a.		Imperf.	4,000.	4,000.
		Nos. 77-81 (5)	1.55	2.10

There are three minor types of No. 79. Values are for the least expensive type.

Perf. 14½

82	A15	10m blk & grnsh gray ('16)	150.00	200.00
a.		Horiz. pair, imperf. vert.	3,750.	

Republic
Helsinki Issue

Arms of the Republic
A19   A20

Two types of the 40p.
Type I — Thin figures of value.
Type II — Thick figures of value.

Perf. 14, 14¼x14¾

1917-29   **Unwmk.**

83	A19	5p green	.25	.20
84	A19	5p gray ('19)	.25	.20
85	A19	10p rose	.30	.50
a.		Imperf., pair	240.00	400.00
86	A19	10p green ('19)	1.75	.75
a.		Perf. 14¼x14¾		2,750.
87	A19	10p lt blue ('21)	.30	.50
88	A19	20p buff	.30	.50
89	A19	20p rose ('20)	.60	.50
90	A19	20p brown ('24)	.60	.90
a.		Perf. 14¼x14¾	.75	30.00
91	A19	25p blue	.25	.50
92	A19	25p lt brown ('19)	.25	.20
93	A19	30p green ('23)	.30	.65
94	A19	40p violet (I)	.25	.20
a.		Perf. 14¼x14¾	400.00	26.00
95	A19	40p bl grn (II) ('29)	.50	3.25
a.		Type I ('24)	13.00	5.75
b.		Perf. 14¼x14¾	1.25	24.00
96	A19	50p orange brn	.25	.50
a.		Perf. 14¼x14¾		2,000.
97	A19	50p dp blue ('19)	4.00	.20
a.		Perf. 14¼x14¾		2,000.
98	A19	50p green ('21)	4.50	.50
a.		Perf. 14¼x14¾	.30	2.50
99	A19	60p red vio ('21)	.50	.50
a.		Imperf., pair	75.00	100.00
100	A19	75p yellow ('21)	.25	.80
101	A19	1m dull rose & blk	13.00	.20
102	A19	1m red org ('25)	8.50	26.00
103	A19	1½m bl grn & red vio ('29)	.25	2.50
a.		Perf. 14¼x14¾	.25	1.60
104	A19	2m green & blk ('21)	2.75	.80
105	A19	2m dk blue & ind ('22)	2.50	.50
a.		Perf. 14¼x14¾	.65	4.00
106	A19	3m blue & blk ('21)	70.00	.65
107	A19	5m red vio & blk ('21)	17.00	.50
108	A19	10m brn & gray blk, perf. 14	1.00	1.25
a.		10m light brown & black, perf. 14¼x14¾ ('29)	4.00	500.00
110	A19	25m dull red & yel ('21)	.90	29.00
		Nos. 83-108,110 (27)	131.30	72.75

Examples of a 2½p gray of this type exist. They are proofs from the original die which were distributed through the UPU. No plate was made for this denomination.

See Nos. 127-140, 143-152. For surcharge and overprints see Nos. 119-126, 153-154.

Vasa Issue

1918   **Litho.**   **Perf. 11½**

111	A20	5p green	.50	1.25
112	A20	10p red	.50	1.25
113	A20	30p slate	.90	3.25
114	A20	40p brown vio	.30	1.25
115	A20	50p orange brn	.50	5.25
116	A20	70p gray brown	3.00	25.00
117	A20	1m red & gray	.50	1.75
118	A20	5m red violet & gray	45.00	110.00
		Nos. 111-118 (8)	51.20	149.00

Nos. 111-118 exist imperforate but were not regularly issued in that condition.

Sheet margin examples, perf. on 3 sides, imperf. on margin side, were sold by post office.

Stamps and Type of
1917-29 Surcharged

1919   **Perf. 14**

119	A19	10p on 5p green	.50	.65
120	A19	20p on 10p rose	.50	.65
121	A19	50p on 25p blue	1.00	.65
122	A19	75p on 20p orange	.50	1.00
		Nos. 119-122 (4)	2.50	2.95

Stamps and Type of 1917-29
Surcharged:

Nos. 123-   No. 126
125

1921

123	A19	30p on 10p green	.65	1.00
124	A19	60p on 40p red violet	4.00	1.25
125	A19	90p on 20p rose	.40	.50
126	A19	1½m on 50p blue	1.40	.50
a.		Thin "2" in 1½	12.00	8.00
b.		Imperf., pair	260.00	450.00
		Nos. 123-126 (4)	6.45	3.25

Arms Type of 1917-29
Perf. 14, 14¼x14¾

1925-29   **Wmk. 121**

127	A19	10p ultra ('27)	.50	2.50
128	A19	20p brown	.50	2.00
129	A19	25p brn org ('29)	.90	100.00
130	A19	30p yel green	.25	.90
a.		Perf. 14¼x14¾	.25	
131	A19	40p blue grn (I) ('26)	3.50	.90
a.		Perf. 14¼x14¾ ('26)	5.00	1.25
b.		Type II ('28)	130.00	77.50
c.		As "b," perf. 14¼x14¾ ('28)	4.50	1.25
132	A19	50p gray grn ('26)	1.25	.80
a.		Perf. 14¼x14¾ ('26)	.40	.50
133	A19	60p red violet	.25	.90
134	A19	1m dp orange	5.25	.50
a.		Perf. 14¼x14¾	100.00	.80

Perf. 14¼x14¾

135	A19	1½m blue green & red violet ('26)	5.25	.50
a.		Perf. 14 ('26)	52.50	.50
136	A19	2m dk blue & indigo ('27)	.65	.50
a.		Perf. 14	1.00	.50
137	A19	3m chlky blue & blk ('26)	1.00	.50
138	A19	5m red violet & blk ('27)	.50	.50
a.		Perf. 14	1.25	.50
139	A19	10m lt brn & blk ('27)	4.00	35.00
140	A19	25m dp org & yel ('27)	20.00	350.00
		Nos. 127-140 (14)	43.80	495.50

No. 130a is not known cancelled during the period in which it was valid for postal use.

A21

1927, Dec. 6   **Typo.**   **Perf. 14**

141	A21	1½m deep violet	.20	.50
142	A21	2m deep blue	.25	2.00

10th anniv. of Finnish independence.

Arms Type of 1917-29
Perf. 14, 14¼x14¾

1927-29   **Wmk. 208**

143	A19	20p lt brown ('29)	1.75	25.00
144	A19	40p bl grn (II) ('28)	.20	.65
145	A19	50p gray grn ('28)	.20	.50
146	A19	1m dp orange	.20	1.00
a.		Imperf., pair	130.00	250.00
		Perf. 14	1.10	1.10
147	A19	1½m bl grn & red vio ('28)	2.50	.80
a.		Perf. 14	1,000.	26.00
148	A19	2m dk bl & ind ('28)	.40	.80
149	A19	3m chlky bl & blk ('28)	.40	.90
a.		Perf. 14	1.75	5.25
150	A19	5m red vio & blk ('28)	.60	.60
151	A19	10m lt brown & blk ('28)	1.40	45.00
152	A19	25m brown org & yel	1.75	225.00
		Nos. 143-152 (10)	9.40	300.25

Nos. 146-147
Overprinted

1928, Nov. 10   **Litho.**   **Wmk. 208**

153	A19	1m deep orange	7.75	21.00
154	A19	1½m bl grn & red vio	7.75	21.00
		Set, never hinged	35.00	

Nos. 153 and 154 were sold exclusively at the Helsinki Philatelic Exhibition, Nov. 10-18, 1928, and were valid only during that period.

S. S. "Bore"
Leaving
Turku — A23

Turku
Cathedral — A24

Turku
Castle — A25

Wmk. 208

1929, May 22   **Typo.**   **Perf. 14**

155	A23	1m olive green	1.50	5.75
156	A24	1½m bl grn & red vio	2.40	4.50
157	A25	2m dark gray	.85	5.25
		Nos. 155-157 (3)	4.75	15.50
		Set, never hinged	15.00	

Founding of the city of Turku (Abo), 700th anniv.

A26

1930-46   **Unwmk.**   **Perf. 14**

158	A26	5p chocolate	.20	.50
159	A26	10p dull violet	.20	.20
160	A26	20p yel grn	.30	.50
161	A26	25p yel brn	.20	.20
162	A26	40p blue grn	2.00	.35
163	A26	50p yellow	.50	.35
164	A26	50p blue grn ('32)	.20	.20
b.		Imperf., pair	140.00	200.00
165	A26	60p dark gray	.50	.80
165A	A26	75p dp org ('42)	.20	.50
166	A26	1m red org	.20	.20
166B	A26	1m yel org ('42)	.20	.20
167	A26	1.20m crimson	.35	1.25
168	A26	1.25m yel ('32)	.20	.20
169	A26	1½m red vio	2.10	.20
170	A26	1½m car ('32)	.20	.20
170A	A26	1½m sl ('40)	.20	.20
170B	A26	1.75m org yel ('40)	.65	.65
171	A26	2m indigo	.30	.20
172	A26	2m dp vio ('32)	6.25	.50
173	A26	2m car ('36)	.20	.20
		Complete booklet, panes of 4 #161, 164, 166, 168, 173	7.00	
173B	A26	2m yel org ('42)	.30	.20
173C	A26	2m blue grn ('45)	.20	.20
174	A26	2½m brt blue ('32)	3.25	.50
174A	A26	2½m car ('42)	.20	.20
174B	A26	2.75m rose vio ('40)	.20	.20
175	A26	3m olive blk ('32)	26.00	.50
175B	A26	3m car ('45)	.20	.20
175C	A26	3m yel ('45)	.35	.80
176	A26	3½m brt bl ('36)	9.00	.35
176A	A26	3½m olive ('42)	.20	.20

176B	A26	4m olive ('45)	.50	.20
176C	A26	4½m saph	.20	.20
		('42)		
176D	A26	5m saph	.50	.20
176E	A26	5m pur ('45)	.50	.50
j.		Imperf., pair	150.00	200.00
176F	A26	5m yel ('46)	.70	.20
k.		Imperf., pair	150.00	190.00
176G	A26	6m car ('45)	.50	.50
m.		Imperf., pair	190.00	275.00
176H	A26	8m pur ('46)	.20	.20
176I	A26	10m saph		
			1.00	.20
	Nos. 158-176I (38)		59.45	13.15

See Nos. 257-262, 270-274, 291-296, 302-304. For surcharges and overprints see Nos. 195-196, 212, 221-222, 243, 250, 275, M2-M3.

Stamps of types A26-A29 overprinted "ITA KARJALA" are listed under Karelia, Nos. N1-N15.

Castle in Savonlinna A27

Lake Saima — A28

Woodchopper A29

1930   **Engr.**

177	A27	5m blue	.20	.50
178	A28	10m gray lilac	60.00	5.25
179	A29	25m black brown	.95	.50
	Nos. 177-179 (3)		61.15	6.25
	Set, never hinged		170.00	

See #205, 305. For overprint see #C1.

Elias Lönnrot — A30

Seal of Finnish Literary Society — A31

1931, Jan. 1   **Typo.**

180	A30	1m olive brown	2.75	6.50
181	A31	1½m dull blue	14.00	6.50

Centenary of Finnish Literary Society.

A32

1931, Feb. 28

182	A32	1½m red	3.00	10.50
183	A32	2m blue	3.00	13.00

1st use of postage stamps in Finland, 75th anniv.

Nos. 162-163 Surcharged

1931, Dec.

195	A26	50p on 40p blue grn	1.40	.80
196	A26	1.25m on 50p yellow	4.25	2.40

Svinhufvud A33   Alexis Kivi A34

1931, Dec. 15

197	A33	2m gray blue & blk	1.50	4.50

Pres. Pehr Eyvind Svinhufvud, 70th birthday.

Lake Saima Type of 1930

1932-43   **Re-engraved**

205	A28	10m red violet ('43)	.50	.50
a.		10m dark violet	21.00	.80

On Nos. 205 and 205a the lines of the islands, the clouds and the foliage are much deeper and stronger than on No. 178.

1934, Oct. 10   **Typo.**

206	A34	2m red violet	2.25	5.00
	Never hinged		5.25	

Alexis Kivi, Finnish poet (1834-1872).

Bards Reciting the "Kalevala" A35

Goddess Louhi, As Eagle Seizing Magic Mill — A36

Kullervo — A37

1935, Feb. 28   **Engr.**

207	A35	1¼m brown lake	1.25	2.00
208	A36	2m black	3.25	3.00
209	A37	2½m blue	3.00	2.40
	Nos. 207-209 (3)		7.50	7.40
	Set, never hinged		21.00	

Cent. of the publication of the "Kalevala" (Finnish National Epic).

No. 170 Surcharged in Black

1937, Feb.

212	A26	2m on 1½m car	5.25	1.00
	Never hinged		14.00	

Gustaf Mannerheim — A38

Swede-Finn Co-operation in Colonization A39

1937, June 4   **Photo.**   *Perf. 14*

213	A38	2m ultra	.65	*1.60*
	Never hinged		2.00	

70th birthday of Field Marshal Baron Carl Gustaf Mannerheim, June 4th, 1937.

1938, June 1

214	A39	3½m dark brown	1.25	*3.25*
	Never hinged		3.50	

Tercentenary of the colonization of Delaware by Swedes and Finns.

Early Post Office — A40

Designs: 1¼m, Mail delivery in 1700. 2m, Modern mail plane. 3½m, Helsinki post office.

1938, Sept. 6   **Photo.**   *Perf. 14*

215	A40	50p green	.35	.75
216	A40	1¼m dk blue	1.25	4.00
217	A40	2m scarlet	1.50	1.25
218	A40	3½m slate black	4.00	10.50
	Nos. 215-218 (4)		7.10	16.50
	Set, never hinged		20.00	

300th anniv. of the Finnish Postal System. Margin strips of each denomination (3 of #215, 2 each of #216, 217, 218) were pasted on to advertising sheets and stapled into a booklet. Value, $120.

Post Office, Helsinki — A44

1939-42   **Photo.**

219	A44	4m brown black	.20	*.50*

         Engr.

219A	A44	7m black brn ('42)	.35	*.50*
219B	A44	9m rose lake ('42)	.50	.50
	Nos. 219-219B (3)		1.05	1.50
	Set, never hinged		3.00	

See No. 248.

> Catalogue values for unused stamps in this section, from this point to the end of the section, are for **Never Hinged** items.

University of Helsinki — A45

1940, May 1   **Photo.**

220	A45	2m dp blue & blue	.80	*1.00*

300th anniv. of the founding of the University of Helsinki.

Nos. 168 and 173 Surcharged in Black

1940, June 16   **Typo.**

221	A26	1.75m on 1.25m yel	3.00	*4.00*
222	A26	2.75m on 2m carmine	7.25	.70

President Kallio Reviewing Military Band — A46

1941, May 24   **Engr.**

223	A46	2.75m black	.80	*1.10*

Pres. Kyösti Kallio (1873-1940).

Castle at Viborg — A47

1941, Aug. 30   **Typo.**

224	A47	1.75m yellow orange	.60	.90
225	A47	2.75m rose violet	.60	.90
226	A47	3.50m blue	.90	2.00

Field Marshal Mannerheim A48   Pres. Risto Ryti A49

1941, Dec. 31   **Engr.**   **Wmk. 273**

227	A48	50p dull green	1.25	2.50
228	A48	1.75m deep brown	1.25	2.50
229	A48	2m dark red	2.50	2.50
230	A48	2.75m dull vio brn	2.50	2.50
231	A48	3.50m deep blue	1.25	2.00
232	A48	5m slate blue	1.25	2.00
	Nos. 227-232 (6)		10.00	14.00
233	A49	50p dull green	1.10	2.00
234	A49	1.75m deep brown	1.10	2.00
235	A49	2m dark red	1.10	2.00
236	A49	2.75m dull vio brn	1.10	2.50
237	A49	3.50m deep blue	1.10	2.00
238	A49	5m slate blue	1.60	2.00
	Nos. 233-238 (6)		7.10	12.50

Types A48-A49 overprinted "ITA KARJALA" are listed under Karelia, Nos. N16-N27.

Häme Bridge, Tampere
A50

South Harbor, Helsinki — A51

1942 **Unwmk.**
239 A50 50m dull brown vio 3.25 .50
240 A51 100m indigo 4.00 .50
See No. 350.

Altar and Open Bible — A52 17th Century Printer — A53

1942, Oct. 10
241 A52 2.75m dk brown .65 1.25
242 A53 3.50m violet blue 1.00 3.25
300th anniv. of the printing of the 1st Bible in Finnish.

No. 174B Surcharged in Black

1943, Feb. 1
243 A26 3.50m on 2.75m rose vio .50 .50

Minna Canth (1844-96), Author and Playwright — A54

1944, Mar. 20
244 A54 3.50m dk olive grn .60 1.00

Pres. P. E. Svinhufvud A55 K. J. Stahlberg A56

1944, Aug. 1
245 A55 3.50m black .50 1.25
Death of President Svinhufvud (1861-1944).

1945, May 16 Engr. Perf. 14
246 A56 3.50m brown vio .50 .65
80th birthday of Dr. K. J. Stahlberg.

Castle in Savonlinna A57

Jean Sibelius — A58

1945, Sept. 4
247 A57 15m lilac rose 2.25 .50
248 A44 20m sepia 1.75 .50
For a 35m of type A57, see No. 280.

1945, Dec. 8
249 A58 5m dk slate green .65 .65
Jean Sibelius (1865-1957), composer.

No. 176E Surcharged in Black

1946, Mar. 16
250 A26 8(m) on 5m purple .50 .50

Victorious Athletes — A59 Lighthouse at Uto — A60

1946, June 1 Engr. Perf. 13½
251 A59 8m brown violet .50 .65
3rd Sports Festival, Helsinki, June 27-30, 1946.

1946, Sept. 19
252 A60 8m deep violet .50 .65
250th anniv. of the Finnish Department of Pilots and Lighthouses.

Post Bus — A61

1946-47 Unwmk. Perf. 14
253 A61 16m gray black .80 1.00
253A A61 30m gray black ('47) 2.50 .50
Issue dates: 16m, Oct. 16, 30m, Feb. 10.

Old Town Hall, Porvoo — A62

Cathedral, Porvoo — A63

1946, Dec. 3
254 A62 5m gray black .50 .65
255 A63 8m deep claret .50 .65
600th anniv. of the founding of the city of Porvoo (Borga).

Waterfront, Tammisaari A64

1946, Dec. 14
256 A64 8m grnsh black .50 .65
400th anniv. of the founding of the town of Tammisaari (Ekenas).

Lion Type of 1930

1947		**Typo.**	**Perf. 14**
257	A26	2½m dark green	.65 .50
258	A26	3m slate gray	.50 .20
259	A26	6m deep orange	2.00 .50
260	A26	7m carmine	1.00 .20
261	A26	10m purple	3.25 .20
262	A26	12m deep blue	3.00 .20
		Nos. 257-262 (6)	10.40 1.80

Issued: 3m, 6/9; 7m, 12m, 2/10; others, 1/20.

Pres. Juho K. Paasikivi — A65 Postal Savings Emblem — A66

1947, Mar. 15 Engr.
263 A65 10m gray black .65 .50

1947, Apr. 1
264 A66 10m brown violet .50 .50
60th anniv. of the foundation of the Finnish Postal Savings Bank.

Ilmarinen, the Plowman A67 Girl and Boy Athletes A68

1947, June 2
265 A67 10m gray black .50 .50
2nd year of peace following WW II.

1947, June 2
266 A68 10m bright blue .50 .65
Finnish Athletic Festival, Helsinki, June 29-July 3, 1947.

Wheat and Savings Bank Assoc. Emblem — A69 Sower — A70

1947, Aug. 21
267 A69 10m red brown .50 .80
Finnish Savings Bank Assoc., 125th anniv.

1947, Nov. 1
268 A70 10m gray black .65 .65
150th anniv. of Finnish Agricultural Societies.

Koli Mountain and Lake Pielisjärvi A71

1947, Nov. 1
269 A71 10m indigo .65 .80
60th anniv. of the Finnish Touring Assoc.

Lion Type of 1930

1948		**Typo.**	**Perf. 14**
270	A26	3m dark green	3.25 .20
271	A26	6m yellow green	1.25 .65
272	A26	9m carmine	1.25 .20
273	A26	15m dark blue	5.25 .20
274	A26	24m brown lake	2.00 .20
		Nos. 270-274 (5)	13.00 1.75

Issued: 3m, 2/9; 24m, 4/26; others, 9/13.

No. 261 Surcharged in Black

1948, Feb. 9
275 A26 12(m) on 10m purple 1.25 .50

Statue of Michael Agricola — A72

1948, Oct. 2 Engr. Perf. 14
12m, Agricola translating New Testament.
276 A72 7m rose violet 1.25 2.25
277 A72 12m gray blue 1.25 2.25
400th anniv. of publication of the Finnish translation of the New Testament, by Michael Agricola.

Sveaborg Fortress A73

Post Rider — A74

1948, Oct. 15
278 A73 12m deep green 1.60 2.25
200th anniv. of the construction of Sveaborg Fortress on the Gulf of Finland.

1948, Oct. 27
279 A74 12m green 9.00 20.00
Helsinki Philatelic Exhibition. Sold only at exhibition for 62m, of which 50m was entrance fee.

Castle Type of 1945

1949
280 A57 35m violet 9.00 .50

Sawmill and Cellulose Plant — A75

Pine Tree and Globe — A76

Woman with Torch — A77

1949, June 15
281 A75 9m brown   2.75 *4.00*
282 A76 15m dull green   2.75 *4.00*

Issued to publicize the Third World Forestry Congress, Helsinki, July 10-20, 1949.

1949, July 16   Engr.   Perf. 14
283 A77 5m dull green   5.50 *12.00*
284 A77 15m red *(Worker)*   5.50 *12.00*

50th anniv. of the Finnish labor movement.

Harbor of Lappeenranta (Willmanstrand) — A78

Raahe (Brahestad) — A79

1949
285 A78 5m dk blue grn   1.25 1.25
286 A79 9m brown carmine   1.60 *2.00*
287 A78 15m brt blue *(Kristi-
              inan-kaupunki)* 2.00 *4.00*
      Nos. 285-287 (3)   4.85 7.25

300th anniv. of the founding of Willmanstrand, Brahestad and Kristinestad (Kristiinankaupunki). Issued: 5m, 8/6; 9m, 8/13; 15m, 7/30.

Technical High School Badge — A80

Hannes Gebhard — A81

1949, Sept. 13
288 A80 15m ultra   1.25 *1.60*

Founding of the technical school, cent.

1949, Oct. 2
289 A81 15m dull green   1.25 *1.60*

Establishment of Finnish cooperatives, 50th anniv.

Finnish Lake Country — A82

1949, Oct. 8
290 A82 15m blue   1.60 *2.00*

75th anniv. of the UPU.

Lion Type of 1930
1950, Jan. 9   Typo.   Perf. 14
291 A26 8m brt green   2.25 1.25
292 A26 9m red orange   2.40 .50
293 A26 10m violet brown   7.25 .20
294 A26 12m scarlet   1.40 .50
295 A26 15m plum   17.00 .20
296 A26 20m deep blue   8.50 .20
      Nos. 291-296 (6)   38.80 2.85

Forsell's Map of Old Helsinki — A83

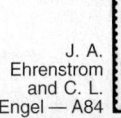

J. A. Ehrenstrom and C. L. Engel — A84

City Hall — A85

1950, June 11   Engr.
297 A83 5m emerald   .65   *1.00*
298 A84 9m brown   1.00   *1.60*
299 A85 15m deep blue   .80   *1.00*
      Nos. 297-299 (3)   2.45   3.60

400th anniv. of the founding of Helsinki.

J. K. Paasikivi — A86

View of Kajaani — A87

1950, Nov. 27
300 A86 20m deep ultra   .65   .50

80th birthday of Pres. J. K. Paasikivi.

1951, July 7   Unwmk.   Perf. 14
301 A87 20m red brown   .80   *1.00*

Tercentenary of Kajaani.

Lion and Chopper Types of 1930
1952, Jan. 18   Typo.
302 A26 10m emerald   4.00   .20
303 A26 15m red   4.25   .20
304 A26 25m blue   5.50   .20
      Engr.
305 A29 40m black brown   4.25   .50
      Nos. 302-305 (4)   18.00 1.10

Arms of Pietarsaari A88

Rooftops of Vaasa A89

1952, June 19   Unwmk.   Perf. 14
306 A88 25m blue   1.25   1.25

300th anniv. of the founding of Pietarsaari (Jacobstad).

1952, Aug. 3
307 A89 25m brown   1.25   1.25

Centenary of the burning of Vaasa.

Chess Symbols — A90

Torch Bearers — A91

1952, Aug. 10
308 A90 25m gray   2.50   *3.25*

10th Chess Olympics, Helsinki, 8/10-31/52.

1953, Jan. 27
309 A91 25m blue   1.25   1.25

Temperance movement in Finland, cent.

Air View of Hamina (Fredrikshamn) A92

1953, June 20
310 A92 25m dk gray green 1.10   1.10

Tercentenary of Hamina.

Ivar Wilskman — A93

1954, Feb. 26
311 A93 25m blue   1.00   1.00

Centenary of the birth of Prof. Ivar Wilskman, "father of gymnastics in Finland."

Arms of Finland A94

"In the Outer Archipelago" A95

1954-59   Perf. 11½
312 A94 1m red brown ('55)   .40   .20
313 A94 2m green ('55)   .40   .20
314 A94 3m deep orange   .40   .20
314A A94 4m gray ('58)   .80   .50
315 A94 5m violet blue   .90   .20
316 A94 10m blue green   1.25   .20
  a. Bkt. pane of 5 (vert. strip) 22.50 22.50
        Complete booklet, #316a   25.00
317 A94 15m rose red   4.00   .20
318 A94 15m yellow org ('57) 10.00   .20
319 A94 20m rose lilac   14.00   .20
320 A94 20m rose red ('56)   2.75   .20

321 A94 25m deep blue   4.50   .20
322 A94 25m rose lilac ('59) 13.00   .20
323 A94 30m lt ultra ('56)   2.75   .20
      Nos. 312-323 (13)   55.15   2.90

See Nos. 398, 400-405A, 457-459, 461A-462, 464-464B.

1954, July 21   Perf. 14
324 A95 25m black   .90   .80

Cent. of the birth of Albert Edelfelt, painter.

J. J. Nervander A96

1955, Feb. 23
325 A96 25m blue   1.25   1.25

150th anniv. of the birth of J. J. Nervander, astronomer and poet.

Composite of Finnish Public Buildings A97

Bishop Henrik with Foot on Lalli, his Murderer A98

1955, Mar. 30   Engr.   Perf. 14
326 A97 25m gray   12.50 20.00

Sold for 125m, which included the price of admission to the Natl. Postage Stamp Exhibition, Helsinki, Mar. 30-Apr. 3, 1955.

1955, May 19

25m, Arrival of Bishop Henrik and monks.
327 A98 15m rose brown   1.25   1.00
328 A98 25m green   1.25   1.00

Adoption of Christianity in Finland, 800th anniv.

Conference Hall, Helsinki — A99

1955, Aug. 25
329 A99 25m bluish green   1.25   *2.00*

44th conf. of the Interparliamentarian Union, Helsinki, Aug. 25-31, 1955.

Sailing Vessel and Merchant A100

1955, Sept. 2
330 A100 25m sepia   2.00   2.50

350th anniv. of founding of Oulu.

Town Hall, Lahti — A101

Radio Sender, Map of Finland — A102

1955, Nov. 1   **Perf. 14x13½**
331 A101 25m violet blue   1.25 *2.50*

50th anniversary of founding of Lahti.

1955, Dec. 10   **Perf. 14**

Designs: 15m, Otto Nyberg. 25m, Telegraph wires and pines under snow.

Inscribed: Lennatin 1855-1955 Telegrafen

332 A102 10m green   1.60 *2.00*
333 A102 15m dull violet   1.60 1.25
334 A102 25m lt ultra   2.40 1.60
    Nos. 332-334 (3)   5.60 4.85

Cent. of the telegraph in Finland.

A103

1956, Jan. 26   **Unwmk.**   **Perf. 14**
335 A103 25m Lighthouse, Porkkala Peninsula   .90 *1.25*

Return of the Porkkala Region to Finland by Russia, Jan. 1956.

A104

30m, 50m, Church at Lammi. 40m, House of Parliament. 60m, Fortress of Olavinlinna (Olofsborg).

1956-57   **Perf. 11½**
336 A104 30m gray olive   1.60 .50
337 A104 40m dull purple   3.25 .20
338 A104 50m gray ol ('57)   8.50 .20
338A A104 60m pale pur ('57)   13.00 .20
    Nos. 336-338A (4)   26.35 1.10

Issued: 30m, 3/4; 40m, 3/11; 50m, 3/3; 60m, 4/7. See Nos. 406-408A.

Johan V. Snellman A105

Gymnast and Athletes A106

1956, May 12   **Engr.**   **Perf. 14**
339 A105 25m dk violet brn   .90 *1.10*

Johan V. Snellman (1806-81), statesman.

1956, June 28
340 A106 30m violet blue   1.60 1.25

Finnish Gymnastic and Sports Games, Helsinki, June 28-July 1, 1956.

A107

Wmk. 208
1956, July 7   **Typo.**   **Rouletted**
341 A107 30m deep ultra   4.00 *6.50*
   a.   Tête bêche pair   10.00 *15.00*
   b.   Pane of 10   50.00 *75.00*

Issued to publicize the FINLANDIA Philatelic Exhibition, Helsinki, July 7-15, 1956.
Printed in sheets containing four 2x5 panes, with white margins around each group. The stamps in each double row are printed tetebeche, making the position of the watermark differ in the vertical row of each pane of ten. Sold for 155m, price including entrance ticket to exhibition.

Town Hall at Vasa — A108

Unwmk.
1956, Oct. 2   **Engr.**   **Perf. 14**
342 A108 30m bright blue   1.60 1.25

350th anniversary of Vasa.

Northern Countries Issue

Whooper Swans — A108a

1956, Oct. 30   **Perf. 12½**
343 A108a 20m rose red   2.25 2.25
344 A108a 30m ultra   8.00 2.25

See footnote after Denmark No. 362.

University Clinic, Helsinki A109

Scout Sign, Emblem and Globe — A110

1956, Dec. 17   **Perf. 11½**
345 A109 30m dull green   2.00 1.25

Public health service in Finland, bicent.

1957, Feb. 22   **Perf. 14**
346 A110 30m ultra   2.50 1.60

50th anniversary of Boy Scouts.

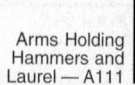

Arms Holding Hammers and Laurel — A111

"Lex" from Seal of Parliament — A112

Design: 20m, Factories and cogwheel.

1957   **Engr.**   **Perf. 13½**
347 A111 20m dark blue   1.00 1.00
348 A111 30m carmine   1.25 1.25

50th anniv.: Central Fed. of Finnish Employers (20m, issued 9/27); Finnish Trade Union Movement (30m, issued 4/15).

1957, May 23   **Perf. 14**
349 A112 30m olive gray   1.60 1.60

50th anniv. of the Finnish parliament.

Harbor Type of 1942
1957   **Unwmk.**   **Perf. 14**
350 A51 100m grnsh blue   15.00 .50

Ida Aalberg — A114

Arms of Finland A115

1957, Dec. 4   **Perf. 14**
351 A114 30m vio gray & mar   1.10 *1.25*

Birth cent. of Ida Aalberg, Finnish actress.

1957, Dec. 6   **Perf. 11½**
352 A115 30m blue   1.25 *1.60*

40th anniv. of Finland's independence.

Jean Sibelius — A116

Ski Jump — A117

1957, Dec. 8   **Perf. 14**
353 A116 30m black   2.40 1.25

Jean Sibelius (1865-1957), composer.

1958, Feb. 1   **Engr.**   **Perf. 11½**

Design: 30m, Skier, vert.

354 A117 20m slate green   1.10 *1.60*
355 A117 30m blue   1.10 .80

Nordic championships of the Intl. Ski Federation, Lahti.

"March of the Bjorneborgienses," by Edelfelt — A118

1958, Mar. 8
356 A118 30m violet gray   1.75 1.10

400th anniv. of the founding of Pori (Bjorneborg).

South Harbor, Helsinki A119

1958, June 2   **Unwmk.**   **Perf. 11½**
357 A119 100m bluish green   22.00 .20

See No. 410.

Seal of Jyväskylä Lyceum A120

1958, Oct. 1   **Perf. 11½**
358 A120 30m rose carmine   2.00 1.50

Cent. of the founding of the 1st Finnish secondary school.

Chrismon and Globe — A121

Diet at Porvoo, 1809 — A122

1959, Jan. 19
359 A121 30m dull violet   .90 .80

Finnish Missionary Society, cent.

1959, Mar. 22   **Perf. 11½**
360 A122 30m dk blue gray   .90 .80

150th anniv. of the inauguration of the Diet at Porvoo.

Saw Cutting Log — A123

Pyhakoski Power Station — A124

1959, May 13   **Engr.**
361 A123 10m shown   .65 .65
362 A123 30m Forest   .90 .90

No. 361 for the cent. of the establishment of the 1st steam saw-mill in Finland; No. 362, cent. of the Dept. of Forestry.

1959, May 24
363 A124 75m gray   5.75 .50

See No. 409.

Oil Lamp — A125

Woman Gymnast A126

1959, Dec. 19
364 A125 30m blue   1.00 .90
Cent. of the liberation of the country trade.

1959, Nov. 14   **Unwmk.**
365 A126 30m rose lilac   1.25 1.00
Finnish women's gymnastics and the cent. of the birth of Elin Oihonna Kallio, pioneer of Finnish women's physical education.

Arms of Six New Towns — A127

1960, Jan. 2   **Perf. 14**
366 A127 30m light violet   1.10 1.10
Issued to commemorate the founding of new towns in Finland: Hyvinkaa, Kouvola, Riihimaki, Rovaniemi, Salo and Seinajoki.

Type of 1860 Issue A128

1960, Mar. 25 **Typo.** **Rouletted 4½**
367 A128 30m blue & gray   7.50 9.00
Cent. of Finland's serpentine roulette stamps, and in connection with HELSINKI 1960, 40th anniv. exhib. of the Federation of Philatelic Societies of Finland, Mar. 25-31. Sold only at the exhibition for 150m including entrance ticket.

Mother and Child, Waiting Crowd and Uprooted Oak Emblem A129

1960, Apr. 7   **Engr.**   **Perf. 11½**
368 A129 30m rose claret   .80 .80
369 A129 40m dark blue   .80 .80
World Refugee Year, 7/1/59-6/30/60.

Johan Gadolin A130   Hj. Nortamo A131

1960, June 4   **Perf. 11½**
370 A130 30m dark brown   1.00 .90
Bicent. of the birth of Gadolin, chemist.

1960, June 13   **Unwmk.**
371 A131 30m gray green   1.00 .90
Cent. of the birth of Hj. Nortamo (Hjalmar Nordberg), writer.

Symbolic Tree and Cuckoo A132

1960, June 18
372 A132 30m vermilion   1.00 .90
Karelian Natl. Festival, Helsinki, June 18-19.

Geodetic Instrument A133

Urho Kekkonen — A134

Design: 30m, Aurora borealis and globe.

1960, July 26 **Unwmk.** **Perf. 13½**
373 A133 10m blue & pale brn   .50 .65
374 A133 30m ver & rose car   .85 .65
12th General Assembly of the Intl. Union of Geodesy and Geophysics, Helsinki.

1960, Sept. 3   **Engr.**   **Perf. 11½**
375 A134 30m violet blue   1.10 .50
Issued to honor President Urho Kekkonen on his 60th birthday.

Common Design Types pictured following the introduction.

Europa Issue, 1960
Common Design Type
1960, Sept. 19   **Perf. 13½**
Size: 30½x21mm.
376 CD3 30m dk bl & Prus bl   *.90* .90
377 CD3 40m dk brn & plum   *.80* .90
A 30m gray similar to No. 376 was printed with simulated perforations in a non-valid souvenir sheet privately released in London for STAMPEX 1961.

Uno Cygnaeus A135   "Pommern" and Arms of Mariehamn A136

1960, Oct. 13   **Perf. 11½**
378 A135 30m dull violet   1.00 1.00
150th anniv. of the birth of Pastor Uno Cygnaeus, founder of elementary schools.

1961, Feb. 21   **Perf. 11½**
379 A136 30m grnsh blue   3.25 2.40
Centenary of the founding of Mariehamn.

Lake and Rowboat A137

Turku Castle — A138

1961   **Engr.**   **Unwmk.**
380 A137 5m green   .40 .20
381 A138 125m slate green   24.50 .50
See Nos. 399, 411.

Postal Savings Bank Emblem — A139

Symbol of Standardization — A140

1961, May 24
382 A139 30m Prus green   .90 .50
75th anniv. of Finland's Postal Savings Bank.

1961, June 5 **Litho.** **Perf. 14x13½**
383 A140 30m dk sl grn & org   .90 .65
Meeting of the Intl. Organization for Standardization (ISO), Helsinki, June 5.

Juhani Aho A141   Various Buildings A142

Perf. 11½
1961, Sept. 11 **Unwmk.** **Engr.**
384 A141 30m red brown   .90 .90
Juhani Aho (1861-1921), writer.

1961, Oct. 16   **Perf. 11½**
385 A142 30m slate   .90 .90
150 years of the Central Board of Buildings.

Arvid Jarnefelt A143

1961, Nov. 16
386 A143 30m deep claret   .90 .80
Cent. of the birth of Arvid Jarnefelt, writer.

Bank of Finland — A144   First Finnish Locomotive — A145

1961, Dec. 12   **Engr.**   **Perf. 11½**
387 A144 30m brown violet   .90 .90
150th anniversary of Bank of Finland.

1962, Jan. 31 **Unwmk.** **Perf. 11½**
30m, Steam locomotive & timber car. 40m, Diesel locomotive & passenger train.
388 A145 10m gray green   2.00 .80
389 A145 30m violet blue   3.00 .80
390 A145 40m dull red brown   7.00 .80
Nos. 388-390 (3)   12.00 2.40
Centenary of the Finnish State Railways.

Mora Stone — A146

1962, Feb. 15
391 A146 30m gray brown   .90 1.00
Issued to commemorate 600 years of political rights of the Finnish people.

Senate Place, Helsinki A147

1962, Apr. 8 **Unwmk.** **Perf. 11½**
392 A147 30m violet brown   .90 1.00
Sesquicentennial of the proclamation of Helsinki as capital of Finland.

Customs Emblem A148

Staff of Mercury — A149

1962, Apr. 11
393 A148 30m red   .90 1.00
Finnish Board of Customs, sesquicentennial.

1962, May 21   **Engr.**
394 A149 30m bluish green   .90 .90
Cent. of the 1st commercial bank in Finland.

Santeri Alkio — A150   Finnish Labor Emblem and Conveyor Belt — A151

1962, June 17 **Unwmk.** **Perf. 11½**
395 A150 30m brown carmine   1.00 1.00
Cent. of the birth of Santeri Alkio, writer and pioneer of the young people's societies in Finland.

1962, Oct. 19
396 A151 30m chocolate   .90 .50
National production progress.

Survey Plane and Compass — A152

1962, Nov. 14
397 A152 30m yellow green   1.10   .90
Finnish Land Survey Board, 150th anniv.

Types of 1954-61 and

House of Parliament — A152a

Church at Lammi — A152b

Fortress of Olavinlinna — A152c

Log Floating A153

Parainen Bridge — A154

Farm on Lake Shore — A155

Aerial View of Punkaharju — A155a

A155b

Ristikallio in Kuusamo A156

1963-67   **Engr.**   **Perf. 11½**
398 A94   5p violet blue   .50   .20
  a.   Booklet pane of 2 (vert. pair)   22.50   20.00
  b.   Bklt. pane of 2 (horiz. pair)   12.00   10.00
399 A137   5p green   .30   .20
400 A94   10p blue green   .90   .20
  a.   Booklet pane of 2 (vert. pair)   22.50   20.00
401 A94   15p yellow org   1.10   .20

---

402 A94   20p rose red   2.00   .20
  a.   Booklet pane of 2 (vert. pair)   24.00
   Complete booklet, #398a, 400a, 402a   85.00
  b.   Bklt. pane, 2 #400, 1 #402 + label; horiz. strip   45.00   35.00
   Complete booklet, #398b, 402b   100.00
  c.   Bklt. pane, 2 #398, 2 #400, 1 #402; horiz. strip   3.50   3.50
   Complete booklet, #402c   5.00
403 A94   25p rose lilac   1.75   .20
404 A94   30p lt ultra   6.00   .20
404A A94   30p blue gray ('65)   7.75   .20
405 A94   35p blue   1.50   .20
405A A94   40p ultra ('67)   1.75   .35
406 A152a   40p dull purple   3.50   .35
407 A152b   50p gray olive   5.75   .50
408 A152c   60p pale purple   10.00   .50
408A A152c   65p pale pur ('67)   1.10   .20
409 A124   75p gray   2.25   .50
410 A119   1m bluish grn   .50   .20
411 A138   1.25m slate grn   2.00   .50
412 A153   1.50m dk grnsh gray   1.60   .20
413 A154   1.75m blue   1.60   .50
414 A155   2m green ('64)   14.00   .20
414A A155a   2.50m ultra & yel grn ('67)   11.00   .65
414B A155b   2.50m ultra, dk grn & yel grn ('69)   8.00   .40
415 A156   5m dk slate grn ('64)   20.00   .50
  Nos. 398-415 (23)   104.85   7.35

Pennia denominations expressed: "0.05," "0.10," etc.
Four stamps of type A94 (5p, 10p, 20p, 25p) come in two types: I. Four vertical lines in "O" of SUOMI. II. Three lines in "O."
For similar designs see #457-470A.

Mother and Child — A157

1963, Mar. 21   **Unwmk.**   **Perf. 11½**
416 A157 40p red brown   .70   .50
FAO "Freedom from Hunger" campaign.

"Christ Today" — A158

Design: 10p, Crown of thorns and medieval cross of consecration.

1963, July 30   **Engr.**   **Perf. 11½**
417 A158 10p maroon   .50   .45
418 A158 30p dark green   .80   .65
4th assembly of the Lutheran World Federation, Helsinki, July 30-Aug. 8.

Europa Issue, 1963
Common Design Type
1963, Sept. 16
Size: 30x20mm
419 CD6 40p red lilac   1.60   .80

Assembly Building, Helsinki A159

1963, Sept. 18
420 A159 30p violet blue   .90   .50
Representative Assembly of Finland, cent.

Convair Metropolitan A160

M. A. Castrén A161

Design: 40p, Caravelle jetliner.

1963, Nov. 1
421 A160 35p slate green   1.00   .80
422 A160 40p brt ultra   1.00   .50
40th anniversary of Finnish air traffic.

1963, Dec. 2   **Unwmk.**
423 A161 35p violet blue   .90   .65
Matthias Alexander Castrén (1813-52), ethnologist and philologist.

Stone Elk's Head, 2000 B.C. — A162

Emil Nestor Setälä — A163

1964, Feb. 5   **Litho.**   **Perf. 11½**
424 A162 35p ocher & slate grn   .90   .65
Cent. of the Finnish Artists' Association. The soapstone sculpture was found at Huittinen.

1964, Feb. 27   **Engr.**
425 A163 35p dk red brown   .90   .65
Emil Nestor Setälä (1864-1946), philologist, minister of education and foreign affairs and chancellor of Abo University.

Staff of Aesculapius A164

1964, June 13   **Unwmk.**   **Perf. 11½**
426 A164 40p slate green   1.25   .65
18th General Assembly of the World Medical Association, Helsinki, June 13-19, 1964.

Ice Hockey — A165

1965, Jan. 4   **Engr.**
427 A165 35p dark blue   1.25   .80
World Ice Hockey Championships, Finland, March 3-14, 1965.

Design from Centenary Medal — A166

1965, Feb. 6   **Unwmk.**   **Perf. 11½**
428 A166 35p olive gray   .90   .50
Centenary of communal self-government in Finland.

K. J. Stahlberg and "Lex" by W. Runeberg A167

1965, Mar. 22   **Engr.**
429 A167 35p brown   .90   .50
Kaarlo Juho Stahlberg (1865-1952), 1st Pres. of Finland.

International Cooperation Year Emblem A168

1965, Apr. 2   **Litho.**   **Perf. 14**
430 A168 40p bis, dull red, blk & grn   .90   .50
UN International Cooperation Year.

"Fratricide" by Gallen-Kallela A169

Sibelius, Piano and Score — A170

35p, Girl's Head by Akseli Gallen-Kallela.

1965, Apr. 26   **Perf. 13½x14**
431 A169 25p multicolored   1.60   .80
432 A169 35p multicolored   1.60   .80
Centenary of the birth of the painter Aksell Gallen-Kallela.

1965, May 15   **Engr.**   **Perf. 11½**
Design: 35p, Musical score and bird.
433 A170 25p violet   1.60   .80
434 A170 35p dull green   1.60   .50
Jean Sibelius (1865-1957), composer.

Antenna for Satellite Telecommunication — A171

"Winter Day" by Pekka Halonen — A172

1965, May 17
435 A171 35p blue   1.00   .65
Cent. of the ITU.

Perf. 14x13½
1965, Sept. 23   **Litho.**   **Unwmk.**
436 A172 35p gold & multi   .90   .50
Centenary of the birth of the painter Pekka Halonen.

Europa Issue, 1965
Common Design Type
Engraved and Lithographed
1965, Sept. 27 **Perf. 13½x14**
437 CD8 40p bister, red brn, dk
bl & grn 1.50 .65

"Growth" — A173

Old Post Office — A174

1966, May 11 **Litho.** **Perf. 14**
438 A173 35p vio blue & blue .90 .50
Centenary of the promulgation of the Elementary School Decree.

1966, June 11 **Litho.** **Perf. 14**
439 A174 35p ocher, yel, dk bl
& blk 7.00 8.00
Cent. of the 1st postage stamps in Finnish currency, and in connection with the NORDIA Stamp Exhibition, Helsinki, June 11-15. The stamp was sold only to buyers of a 1.25m exhibition entrance ticket.

UNESCO Emblem and World Map — A175

Finnish Police Emblem — A176

Lithographed and Engraved
1966, Oct. 9 **Perf. 14**
440 A175 40p grn, yel, blk & brn
org .90 .50
20th anniv. of UNESCO.

1966, Oct. 15
441 A176 35p dp ultra, blk & sil .90 .50
Issued to honor the Finnish police.

Insurance Sesquicentennial Medal — A177

1966, Oct. 28 **Engr. & Photo.**
442 A177 35p maroon, olive &
blk .90 .50
150th anniv. of the Finnish insurance system.

UNICEF Emblem A178

1966, Nov. 14
443 A178 15p lt ultra, pur & grn .40 .30
Activities of UNICEF.

"FINEFTA," Finnish Flag and Circle — A179

1967, Feb. 15 **Engr.** **Perf. 14**
444 A179 40p ultra 1.00 .50
European Free Trade Association, EFTA. See note after Denmark No. 431.

Windmill and Arms of Uusikaupunki A180

Mannerheim Monument by Aimo Tukiainen A181

Lithographed and Engraved
1967, Apr. 19 **Perf. 14**
445 A180 40p multicolored .90 .50
350th anniv. of Uusikaupunki (Nystad).

1967, June 4 **Perf. 14**
446 A181 40p violet & multi .90 .50
Cent. of the birth of Field Marshal Carl Gustav Emil Mannerheim.

Double Mortise Corner — A182

Watermark of Thomasböle Paper Mill — A183

1967, June 16 **Litho. & Photo.**
447 A182 40p multicolored .90 .50
Issued to honor Finnish settlers in Sweden.

1967, Sept. 6 **Perf. 14**
448 A183 40p olive & black .90 .50
300th anniv. of the Finnish paper industry.

Martin Luther, by Lucas Cranach A184

Photogravure and Engraved
1967, Nov. 4 **Perf. 14**
449 A184 40p bister & brown .90 .50
450th anniversary of the Reformation.

"Wood and Water" Globe and Flag — A185

Designs (Globe, Flag and): 25p, Flying swan. 40p, Ear of wheat.

1967, Dec. 5 **Perf. 11½**
450 A185 20p green & blue .90 .40
451 A185 25p ultra & blue .90 .40
452 A185 40p magenta & bl .90 .40
 Nos. 450-452 (3) 2.70 1.20
50th anniv. of Finland's independence.

Zachris Topelius and Blue Bird — A186

1968, Jan. 14 **Litho.** **Perf. 14**
453 A186 25p blue & multi 1.25 .65
Topelius (1818-98), writer and educator.

Skiers and Ski Lift — A187

1968, Feb. 19 **Photo.** **Perf. 14**
454 A187 25p multicolored 1.00 .90
Winter Tourism in Finland.

Paper Making, by Hannes Autere — A188

1968, Mar. 12 **Litho.** **Wmk. 363**
455 A188 45p dk red, brn & org .90 .65
Finnish paper industry and 150th anniv. of the oldest Finnish paper mill, Tervakoski, whose own watermark was used for this stamp.

World Health Organization Emblem A189

Lithographed and Photogravure
1968, Apr. 6 **Unwmk.** **Perf. 14**
456 A189 40p red org, dk blue &
gold .90 .50
To honor World Health Organization.

Lion Type of 1954-58 and

Market Place and Mermaid Fountain, Helsinki A190

Keuru Wooden Church, 1758 — A191

Häme Bridge, Tampere A192

Finnish Arms from Grave of King Gustav Vasa, 1581 — A194

25p, Post bus. 30p, Aquarium-Planetarium, Tampere. No. 463, P.O., Tampere. #465, National Museum, Helsinki, vert. #467A, like 70p. 1.30m, Helsinki railroad station.

Engr. (type A94, except #459A); Litho. (#459A, 465 & type A190); Engr. & Litho. (others)
Perf. 11½; 12½ (type A190); 13 (#465); 13½ (#470); 14 (#470A)
1968-78
457 A94 1p lt red brn .40 .50
458 A94 2p gray green .40 .50
459 A94 4p gray .50 .65
459A A94 5p violet blue 2.00 3.00
460 A192 25p multi ('71) .40 .20
461 A191 30p multi ('71) 1.25 .20
461A A94 35p dull org
('74) .40 .50
 b. Bklt. pane of 4, #459A,
 461A, 400, 464A + label 2.50 2.50
 Complete booklet, #461b 3.50
462 A94 40p orange
('73) .90 .65
 a. Bklt. pane of 3, #462, 2
 #404A + 2 labels 6.00 8.00
 Complete booklet, #462a 8.00
463 A192 40p multi ('73) 1.00 .20
464 A94 50p lt ultra ('70) 3.00 .20
 c. Bklt. pane of 5, #401, 403,
 464, 2 #459A + 5 labels 13.00 14.50
 Complete booklet, #464c 14.00
464A A94 50p rose lake
('74) .80 .20
 d. Bklt. pane of 4, #400,
 464A, 2 #402 + label 1.75 1.75
 Complete booklet, #464Ad 2.00
464B A94 60p blue ('73) .70 .20
465 A191 60p multi ('73) .90 .50
466 A190 70p multi ('73) .90 .50
467 A191 80p multi ('70) 5.25 .50
467A A190 80p multi ('76) .90 .50
468 A192 90p multicolored 2.00 .50
469 A191 1.30m multi ('71) 1.25 .50
470 A194 10m multi ('74) 5.00 .50
470A A194 20m multi ('78) 10.00 1.25
 Nos. 457-470A (20) 37.55 11.75

Issued: 5p, 6/72.

Infantry Monument, Vaasa — A195

Camping Ground A196

Designs: 25p, War Memorial (cross), Hietaniemi Cemetery. 40p, Soldier, 1968.

1968, June 4 **Photo.** **Perf. 14**
471 A195 20p lt violet & multi 1.25 .40
472 A195 25p lt blue & multi 1.25 .40
473 A195 40p orange & multi 1.25 .40
 Nos. 471-473 (3) 3.75 1.20
To honor Finnish national defense.

1968, June 10 **Litho.**
474 A196 25p multicolored 1.00 .90
Issued to publicize Finland for summer vacations.

Paper, Pulp and Pine — A197

Mustola Lock, Saima Canal — A198

Lithographed and Embossed
1968, July 2   **Unwmk.**   **Perf. 14**
475 A197 40p multicolored   .90   .50

Finnish wood industry.

1968, Aug. 5   **Litho.**   **Perf. 14**
476 A198 40p multicolored   .90   .50

Opening of the Saima Canal.

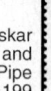

Oskar Merikanto and Pipe Organ — A199

1968, Aug. 5   **Unwmk.**
477 A199 40p vio, silver & lt brn   1.25   .50

Centenary of the birth of Oskar Merikanto, composer.

Ships in Harbor and Emblem of Central Chamber of Commerce A200

Welder — A201

1968, Sept. 13   **Litho.**   **Perf. 14**
478 A200 40p lt bl, brt bl & blk   .90   .50

Publicizing economic development and for the 50th anniv. of the Central Chamber of Commerce of Finland.

1968, Oct. 11   **Litho.**   **Perf. 14**
479 A201 40p blue & multi   .90   .50

Finnish metal industry.

Lyre, Students' Emblem — A202

Five Ancient Ships — A203

Lithographed and Engraved
1968, Nov. 24   **Perf. 14**
480 A202 40p ultra, vio bl & gold   .90   .50

Issued to publicize the work of the student unions in Finnish social life.

Nordic Cooperation Issue
1969, Feb. 28   **Engr.**   **Perf. 11½**
481 A203 40p lt ultra   2.50   .50

50th anniv. of the Nordic Society and centenary of postal cooperation among the northern countries. The design is taken from a coin found at the site of Birka, an ancient Swedish town. See also Denmark Nos. 454-455, Iceland Nos. 404-405, Norway Nos. 523-524 and Sweden Nos. 808-810.

Town Hall and Arms of Kemi — A203a

1969, Mar. 5   **Photo.**   **Perf. 14**
482 A203a 40p multicolored   .90   .50

Centenary of the town of Kemi.

Europa Issue, 1969
Common Design Type
1969, Apr. 28   **Photo.**   **Perf. 14**
Size: 30x20mm
483 CD12 40p dl rose, vio bl & dk bl   4.50   1.00

ILO Emblem A204

Armas Järnefelt — A205

Lithographed and Engraved
1969, June 2   **Perf. 11½**
484 A204 40p dp rose & vio blue   .90   .50

50th anniv. of the ILO.

1969, Aug. 14   **Photo.**   **Perf. 14**
485 A205 40p multicolored   1.25   .50

Järnefelt (1869-1958), composer and conductor. Portrait on stamp by Vilho Sjöström.

Emblems and Flag — A206

Johannes Linnankoski — A207

1969, Sept. 19   **Photo.**   **Perf. 14**
486 A206 40p lt bl, blk, grn & lil   .90   .50

Publicizinge the importance of National and International Fairs in Finnish economy.

1969, Oct. 18   **Litho.**
487 A207 40p dk brn red & multi   .90   .50

Linnankoski (1869-1913), writer.

Educational Symbols A208

Lithographed and Engraved
1969, Nov. 24   **Perf. 11½**
488 A208 40p gray, vio & grn   .90   .50

Centenary of the Central School Board.

DC-8-62 CF Plane and Helsinki Airport — A209

1969, Dec. 22   **Photo.**   **Perf. 14**
489 A209 25p sky blue & multi   1.25   .90

Golden Eagle — A210

1970, Feb. 10   **Litho.**   **Perf. 14**
490 A210 30p multicolored   4.00   1.25

Year of Nature Conservation, 1970.

Swatches in Shape of Factories A211

1970, Mar. 9   **Litho.**   **Perf. 14**
491 A211 50p multicolored   1.00   .50

Finnish textile industry.

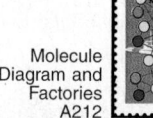

Molecule Diagram and Factories A212

UNESCO Emblem and Lenin — A213

Atom Diagram and Laurel — A214

UN Emblem and Globe — A215

1970, Mar. 26   **Photo.**   **Perf. 14**
492 A212 50p multicolored   1.00   .50

Finnish chemical industry.

1970   **Litho. and Engr.**
493 A213 30p gold & multi   .90   .50
494 A214 30p red & multi   .90   .50

Photogravure and Gold Embossed
495 A215 50p bl, vio bl & gold   .90   .50
     Nos. 493-495 (3)   2.70   1.50

25th anniv. of the UN. No. 493 also publicizes the UNESCO-sponsored Lenin Symposium, Tampere, Apr. 6-10. No. 494 also publicizes the Nuclear Data Conf. of the Atomic Energy Commission, Otaniemi (Helsinki), June 15-19.
Issued: #493, 4/6; #494, 6/15; #495, 10/24.

Handicapped Volleyball Player — A216

Meeting of Auroraseura Society — A217

1970, June 27   **Litho.**   **Perf. 14**
496 A216 50p orange, red & blk   1.10   .50

Issued to publicize the position of handicapped civilians and war veterans in society and their potential contributions to it.

1970, Aug. 15   **Photo.**   **Perf. 14**
497 A217 50p multicolored   .90   .50

200th anniv. of the Auroraseura Soc., dedicated to the study of Finnish history, geography, economy and language. The design of the stamp is after a painting by Eero Jarnefelt.

Uusikaarlepyy Arms, Church and 17th Cent. Building A218

Design: No. 499, Arms of Kokkola, harbor, Sports Palace and 17th century building.

1970   **Perf. 14**
498 A218 50p multicolored   .90   .50
499 A218 50p multicolored   .90   .50

Towns of Uusikaarlepyy and Kokkola, 350th anniv.
Issued: #498, Aug. 21; #499, Sept. 17.

Urho Kekkonen, Medal by Aimo Tukiainen — A219

1970, Sept. 3   **Litho. & Engr.**
500 A219 50p ultra, sil & blk   .90   .50

70th birthday of Pres. Urho Kekkonen.

Globe, Maps of US, Finland, USSR A220

Pres. Paasikivi by Essi Renavall A221

Lithographed and Gold Embossed
1970, Nov. 2
501 A220 50p blk, bl, pink & gold   .90   .50

Strategic Arms Limitation Talks (SALT) between the US & USSR, Helsinki, 11/2-12/18.

1970, Nov. 27   **Photo.**   **Perf. 14**
502 A221 50p gold, brt bl & slate   .90   .50

Centenary of the birth of Juho Kusti Paasikivi (1870-1956), President of Finland.

Cogwheels
A222

1971, Jan. 28   Litho.   *Perf. 14*
503 A222 50p multicolored   .90   .50
Finnish industry.

Europa Issue, 1971
Common Design Type
1971, May 3   Litho.   *Perf. 14*
Size: 30x20mm
504 CD14 50p dp rose, yel & blk   *5.00*   .75

Tornio
Church — A223

Front Page,
January 15,
1771 — A224

1971, May 12   Litho.   *Perf. 14*
505 A223 50p multicolored   1.10   .50
350th anniversary of the town of Tornio.

1971, June 1   Litho.   *Perf. 14*
506 A224 50p multicolored   .90   .50
Bicentenary of the Finnish press.

Athletes in
Helsinki
Stadium
A225

50p, Running & javelin in Helsinki Stadium.
1971, July 5   Litho.   *Perf. 14*
507 A225 30p multicolored   1.75   .50
508 A225 50p multicolored   3.00   .90
European Athletic Championships.

Sailboats
A226

1971, July 14
509 A226 50p multicolored   1.50   .80
International Lightning Class Championships, Helsinki, July 14-Aug. 1.

Silver Tea Pot,
Guild's
Emblem,
Tools — A227

1971, Aug. 6
510 A227 50p lilac & multi   1.00   .50
600th anniv. of Finnish goldsmiths' art.

"Plastic
Buttons and
Houses"
A228

Photogravure and Embossed
1971, Oct. 20   *Perf. 14*
511 A228 50p multicolored   1.00   .50
Finnish plastics industry.

Europa Issue 1972
Common Design Type
1972, May 2   Litho.   *Perf. 14*
Size: 20x30mm
512 CD15 30p dk red & multi   4.00   .70
513 CD15 50p lt brn & multi   4.50   .70

Finnish
National
Theater
A229

1972, May 22.   Litho.   *Perf. 14*
514 A229 50p lt violet & multi   .90   .50
Centenary of the Finnish National Theater, founded by Kaarlo and Emilie Bergbom.

Globe, US and
USSR
Flags — A230

1972, June 2
515 A230 50p multicolored   1.50   .50
Strategic Arms Limitation Talks (SALT), final meeting, Helsinki, Mar. 28-May 26; treaty signed, Moscow, May 26.

Map and Arms
of
Aland — A231

Training Ship
Suomen
Joutsen — A232

1972, June 9
516 A231 50p multicolored   4.00   .80
1st Provincial Meeting of Aland, 50th anniv.

1972, June 19
517 A232 50p orange & multi   1.50   .50
Tall Ships' Race 1972, Helsinki, Aug. 20.

Costume from
Perni, 12th
Cent. — A233

Circle
Surrounding
Map of
Europe — A234

1972, Nov. 19   Litho.   *Perf. 13*
518 A233 50p shown   2.50   .65
519 A233 50p Couple, Tenho-
    la, 18th cent.   2.50   .65
520 A233 50p Girl, Nastola,
    19th cent.   2.50   .65
521 A233 50p Man, Voyni,
    19th cent.   2.50   .65

522 A233 50p Lapps, Inari,
    19th cent.   2.50   .65
a.   Strip of 5, #518-522   12.50   14.50
    Complete booklet, 2 each
    #518-522   30.00
    Regional costumes.
See Nos. 533-537.

1972, Dec. 11   *Perf. 14x13½*
523 A234 50p multicolored   2.50   .65
Preparatory Conference on European Security and Cooperation.

Book, Finnish
and Soviet
Colors — A235

Litho.; Gold Embossed
1973, Apr. 6   *Perf. 14*
524 A235 60p gold & multi   .65   .50
Soviet-Finnish Treaty of Friendship, 25th anniv.

Kyösti Kallio
(1873-1940), Pres.
of Finland — A236

1973, Apr. 10   Litho.   *Perf. 13*
525 A236 60p multicolored   .65   .50

Europa Issue 1973
Common Design Type
1973, Apr. 30   Photo.   *Perf. 14*
Size: 31x21mm
526 CD16 60p bl, brt bl & emer   1.40   1.25

Nordic Cooperation Issue

Nordic
House,
Reykjavik
A236a

1973, June 26   Engr.   *Perf. 12½*
527 A236a 60p multicolored   1.10   .50
528 A236a 70p multicolored   1.10   .50
A century of postal cooperation among Denmark, Finland, Iceland, Norway and Sweden, and in connection with the Nordic Postal Conference, Reykjavik.

Map of Europe,
"EUROPA" as a
Maze — A237

Litho. & Embossed
1973, July 3   *Perf. 13*
529 A237 70p multicolored   .90   .50
Conference for European Security and Cooperation, Helsinki, July 1973.

Paddling
A238

Radiosonde, WMO
Emblem — A239

1973, July 18   Litho.   *Perf. 14*
530 A238 60p multicolored   .90   .50
Canoeing World Championships, Tampere, July 26-29.

1973, Aug. 6   Litho.   *Perf. 14*
531 A239 60p multicolored   .65   .50
Cent. of intl. meteorological cooperation.

Eliel
Saarinen
and
Design for
Parliament,
Helsinki
A240

1973, Aug. 20   *Perf. 12½x13*
532 A240 60p multicolored   .65   .50
Eliel Saarinen (1873-1950), architect.

Costume Type of 1972
1973, Oct. 10   Litho.   *Perf. 13*
533 A233 60p Woman, Kauko-
    la   5.25   .65
534 A233 60p Woman, Jaaski   5.25   .65
535 A233 60p Married couple,
    Koivisto   5.25   .65
536 A233 60p Mother and son,
    Sakyla   5.25   .65
537 A233 60p Girl, Hainavesi   5.25   .65
a.   Strip of 5, #533-537   27.50   14.00
    Regional costumes.

DC10-30
Jet — A241

1973, Nov. 1   Litho.   *Perf. 14*
538 A241 60p multicolored   1.00   .50
50th anniv. of regular air service, Finnair.

Santa Claus in
Reindeer
Sleigh — A242

1973, Nov. 15   Litho.   *Perf. 14*
539 A242 30p multicolored   1.10   .50
Christmas 1973.

"The Barber of
Seville"
A243

1973, Nov. 21
540 A243 60p multicolored   .75   .50
Centenary of opera in Finland.

Production of
Porcelain
Jug — A244

Nurmi, by Waino
Aaltonen — A245

1973, Nov. 23
541 A244 60p blue & multi   .75 .50
Finnish porcelain.

1973, Dec. 11
542 A245 60p multicolored   1.00 .50
Paavo Nurmi (1897-1973), runner, Olympic
winner, 1920-1924-1928.

Arms, Map
and Harbor of
Hanko — A246

1974, Jan. 10   Litho.   Perf. 14
543 A246 60p blue & multi   .90 .50
Centenary of the town of Hanko.

Ice Hockey
A247

1974, Mar. 5   Litho.   Perf. 14
544 A247 60p multicolored   .90 .50
European and World Ice Hockey Championships, held in Finland.

Seagulls (7
Baltic
States)
A248

1974, Mar. 18   Perf. 12½
545 A248 60p multicolored   1.10 .50
Protection of marine environment of the Baltic Sea.

Goddess of
Freedom, by
Waino
Aaltonen — A249

Ilmari Kianto and
Old Pine — A250

1974, Apr. 29   Litho.   Perf. 13x12½
546 A249 70p multicolored   5.00 .50
Europa.

1974, May 7   Perf. 13
547 A250 60p multicolored   .70 .50
Ilmari Kianto (1874-1970), writer.

Society
Emblem,
Symbol
A251

Lithographed and Embossed
1974, June 12   Perf. 13½x14
548 A251 60p gold & multi   .70 .50
Centenary of Adult Education.

Grid
A252

UPU Emblem
A253

1974, June 14   Litho.   Perf. 14x13½
549 A252 60p multicolored   .70 .50
Rationalization Year in Finland, dedicated to
economic and business improvements.

1974, Oct. 10   Litho.   Perf. 13½x14
550 A253 60p multicolored   .70 .50
551 A253 70p multicolored   .70 .50
Centenary of Universal Postal Union.

Elves
Distributing
Gifts — A254

1974, Nov. 16   Litho.   Perf. 14x13½
552 A254 35p multicolored   1.25 .40
Christmas 1974.

Concrete Bridge and
Granite Bridge,
Aunessilta — A255

Litho. & Engr.
1974, Dec. 17   Perf. 14
553 A255 60p multicolored   .90 .65
Royal Finnish Directorate of Roads and
Waterways, 175th anniversary.

Coat of Arms,
1581 — A256

Chimneyless Log
Sauna — A256a

Carved
Wooden
Distaffs
A258

Kirvu Weather
Vane
A258a

Cheese
Frames
A257

1.50m, Wood-carved high drinking bowl,
1542.

1975-90   Engr.   Perf. 11½; 14 (2m)
555   A256   10p red lilac
                    ('78)   .25   .50
  a.   Bklt. pane of 4 (#555, 2
                    #556, #559) + label   2.25 2.25
                    Complete booklet, #555a   2.50
  b.   Bklt. pane of 5 (2 #555,
                    #557, #563, #564)   2.50 2.25
                    Complete booklet, #555b   3.00
  c.   As "a," no label   2.50 2.50
                    Complete booklet, #555c   3.00
  d.   Perf. 13x12½   .35   .20
556   A256   20p olive ('77)   .25   .50
  a.   20p yellow bister ('85) .25   .50
  b.   As "a," perf. 13x12½   .65   .65
557   A256   30p carmine
                    ('77)   .25   .20
557A   A256   30p car, litho.   1.50 1.00
558   A256   40p orange   .25   .20
  a.   Perf. 13x12½   1.25   .90
559   A256   50p green ('76)   .25   .20
  a.   Perf. 13x12½   1.00 1.00
560   A256   60p blue   .50   .20
  a.   Perf. 13x12½   .80   .80
561   A256   70p sepia   .50   .20
562   A256   80p dl red & bl
                    grn ('76)   .50   .50
  a.   Perf. 13x12½   1.25 1.25
563   A256   90p vio bl ('77)   .50   .50
564   A256   1.10m yellow ('79) .60   .50
565   A256   1.20m dk blue ('79) .60   .60
566   A258   1.50m multi ('76)   .80   .20

Litho.
567   A256a   2m multi ('77)   .90   .20

Lithographed and Engraved
568   A257   2.50m multi ('76) 1.25   .50
  a.   Perf. 14   2.25 1.00
569   A258   4.50m multi ('76) 2.25   .50
  a.   Perf. 14   3.25 2.50
570   A258a   5m multi ('77)   2.50   .20
                    Nos. 555-570 (17) 13.65 6.70

Some denominations of design A256 exist
in up to three engraving types.
Nos. 560a and 562a was only issued within
the booklet panes Nos. 713a and 715a.
Issued: #557A, 6/3/80; #560a, 7/25/88;
#555d, 7/25/89; #562a, 3/1/90; #558a,
8/18/94; #568a, 12/28/88; #569a, 9/26/88; No.
556b, 4/3/98.
See Nos. 629, 631-633, 711-715, 861.

Finland
No. 16 — A259

Girl Combing Hair,
by Magnus
Enckell — A260

Lithographed and Typographed
1975, Apr. 26   Perf. 13
571 A259 70p multicolored   3.25 3.50
Nordia 75 Philatelic Exhibition, Helsinki,
Apr. 26-May 1. Sold only at exhibition for 3m
including entrance ticket.

1975, Apr. 28   Litho.   Perf. 13x12½
Europa: 90p, Washerwoman, by Tyko Sallinen (1879-1955).

572 A260 70p gray & multi   3.00 .50
573 A260 90p tan & multi   3.00 .50

Balance of Justice,
Sword of
Legality — A261

Rescue Boat
and Sinking
Ship — A262

1975, May 7   Perf. 14
574 A261 70p vio blue & multi   .65 .50
Sesquicentennial of State Economy Comptroller's Office.

1975, June 2   Litho.   Perf. 14
575 A262 70p multicolored   1.00 .50
12th Intl. Salvage Conf., Finland, stressing
importance of coordinating sea, air and communications resources in salvage operations.

Safe and
Unsafe Levels
of
Drugs — A263

1975, July 21   Litho.   Perf. 14
576 A263 70p multicolored   .65 .50
Importance of pharmacological studies and
for the 6th Intl. Pharmacology Cong., Helsinki.

Olavinlinna
Castle
A264

1975, July 29   Perf. 13
577 A264 70p multicolored   .65 .50
500th anniversary of Olavinlinna Castle.

Swallows over
Finlandia
Hall — A265

"Men and Women
Working for
Peace" — A266

1975, July 30
578 A265 90p multicolored   .90 .50
European Security and Cooperation Conference, Helsinki, July 30-Aug. 1. (The swallows
of the design represent freedom, mobility and
continuity.) See No. 709.

1975, Oct. 24   Litho.   Perf. 13x12½
579 A266 70p multicolored   .65 .50
International Women's Year 1975.

"Continuity and Growth" — A267

Boys as Three Kings and Herod — A268

1975, Oct. 29   *Perf. 13*
580 A267 70p brown & multi   .65   .50
Industrial Art and for the centenary of the Finnish Society of Industrial Art.

1975, Nov. 8   *Perf. 14*
581 A268 40p blue & multi   1.25   .50
Christmas 1975.

Top Border of State Debenture A269

Lithographed and Engraved
1976, Jan. 9   *Perf. 11½*
582 A269 80p multicolored   .65   .50
Centenary of State Treasury.

Glider over Lake Region A270

1976, Jan. 13   Litho.   *Perf. 14*
583 A270 80p multicolored   .90   .50
15th World Glider Championships, Rayskala, June 13-27.

Prof. Heikki Klemetti (1876-1953), Musician & Writer — A271

1976, Feb. 14   Litho.   *Perf. 13*
584 A271 80p green & multi   .65   .50

Map with Areas of Different Dialects — A272

Aino Ackté, by Albert Edelfelt — A273

1976, Mar. 10   Litho.   *Perf. 13*
585 A272 80p multicolored   .65   .50
Finnish Language Society, centenary.

1976, Apr. 23
586 A273 70p yellow & multi   .90   .50
Aino Ackté (1876-1944), opera singer.

Europa Issue 1976

Knife from Voyri, Sheath and Belt — A274

1976, May 3   Litho.   *Perf. 13*
587 A274 80p violet bl & multi   3.75   .65

Radio and Television A275

1976, Sept. 9   Litho.   *Perf. 13*
588 A275 80p multicolored   .65   .50
Radio broadcasting in Finland, 50th anniv.

Christmas Morning Ride to Church A276

1976, Oct. 23   Litho.   *Perf. 14*
589 A276 50p multicolored   1.10   .50
Christmas 1976.

Turku Chapter Seal (Virgin and Child) A277

1976, Nov. 1   Litho.   *Perf. 12½*
590 A277 80p buff, brn & red   .65   .50
Cathedral Chapter of Turku, 700th anniv.

Alvar Aalto, Finlandia Hall, Helsinki A278

1976, Nov. 4
591 A278 80p multicolored   .65   .50
Hugo Alvar Henrik Aalto (1898-1976), architect.

Ice Dancers — A280

Five Water Lilies — A281

1977, Jan. 25   Litho.   *Perf. 13*
592 A280 90p multicolored   .80   .50
European Figure Skating Championships, Finland, Jan. 25-29.

Photogravure and Engraved
1977, Feb. 2   *Perf. 12½*
593 A281 90p brt green & multi   .90   .50
594 A281 1m ultra & multi   .90   .50
Nordic countries cooperation for protection of the environment and 25th Session of Nordic Council, Helsinki, Feb. 19.

Icebreaker Rescuing Merchantman A282

1977, Mar. 2   Litho.   *Perf. 13*
595 A282 90p multicolored   1.00   .50
Winter navigation between Finland and Sweden, centenary.

Nuclear Reactor A283

1977, Mar. 3   *Perf. 12½x13*
596 A283 90p multicolored   .65   .50
Opening of nuclear power station on Hästholmen Island.

Europa Issue 1977

Autumn Landscape, Northern Finland — A284

1977, May 2   Litho.   *Perf. 12½x13*
597 A284 90p multicolored   3.25   .65

Tree, Birds and Nest — A285

Orthodox Church, Valamo Cloister — A286

1977, May 4   *Perf. 13x12½*
598 A285 90p multicolored   .65   .50
75th anniversary of cooperative banks.

1977, May 31   Litho.   *Perf. 14*
599 A286 90p multicolored   .65   .50
Consecration festival of new Orthodox Church at Valamo Cloister, Heinävesi; 800th anniversary of introduction of orthodoxy in Karelia and of founding of Valamo Cloister.

Paavo Ruotsalainen (1777-1852), Lay Leader of Pietists in Finland — A287

1977, July 8   Litho.   *Perf. 13*
600 A287 90p multicolored   .65   .50

People Fleeing Fire and Water — A288

Volleyball — A289

1977, Sept. 14   Litho.   *Perf. 14*
601 A288 90p multicolored   .65   .50
Civil defense for security.

1977, Sept. 15
602 A289 90p multicolored   .80   .50
European Women's Volleyball Championships, Finland, Sept. 29-Oct. 2.

Children Bringing Water for Sauna — A290

1977, Oct. 25
603 A290 50p multicolored   1.25   .50
Christmas 1977.

Finnish Flag — A291

Wall Telephone, 1880, New Telephone — A292

1977, Dec. 5   Litho.   *Perf. 14*
     Size: 31x21mm
604 A291 80p multicolored   .80   .50
     Size: 37x25mm
       Perf. 13
605 A291 1m multicolored   1.10   .50
Finland's declaration of independence, 60th anniv.

1977, Dec. 9   *Perf. 14*
606 A292 1m multicolored   .80   .50
Centenary of first telephone in Finland.

Harbor, Sunila Factory, Kotka Arms — A293

1978, Jan. 2   Litho.   *Perf. 14*
607 A293 1m multicolored   .80   .50
Centenary of founding of Kotka.

Paimio Sanitarium by Alvar Aalto — A294

Europa: 1.20m, Hvittrask studio house, 1902, horiz.

1978, May 2   **Litho.**   **Perf. 13**
608 A294 1m multicolored   7.00 1.25
609 A294 1.20m multicolored   9.00 11.00

Rural Bus Service A295

1978, June 8   **Litho.**   **Perf. 14**
610 A295 1m multicolored   .80 .50

Eino Leino and Eagle — A296

1978, July 6   **Litho.**   **Perf. 13**
611 A296 1m multicolored   .80 .50
Eino Leino (1878-1926), poet.

Function Theory and Rhythmical Lines — A297

1978, Aug. 15   **Litho.**   **Perf. 14**
612 A297 1m multicolored   .80 .50
ICM 78, International Congress of Mathematicians, Helsinki, Aug. 15-23.

Child Feeding Birds — A298

1978, Oct. 23   **Litho.**   **Perf. 14**
613 A298 50p multicolored   1.10 .50
Christmas 1978.

A299

A300

1979, Jan. 2   **Litho.**   **Perf. 13**
614 A299 1.10m multicolored   1.50 .50
International Year of the Child.

1979, Feb. 7   **Litho.**   **Perf. 14**
615 A300 1.10m Runner   .70 .50
8th Orienteering World Championships, Finland, Sept. 1-4.

Old School, Hamina, Academy Flag — A301

1979, Mar. 20   **Litho.**   **Perf. 14**
616 A301 1.10m multicolored   .60 .50
200th anniv. of Finnish Military Academy.

A302   A303

Design: Turku Cathedral and Castle, Prinkkala house, Brahe statue.

1979, Mar. 31
617 A302 1.10m multicolored   .60 .50

1979, May 2   **Litho.**   **Perf. 14**
618 A303 1.10m Streetcar, Helsinki   .65 .50
Non-polluting urban transportation.

View of Tampere, 1779 — A304

View of Tampere, 1979 — A305

1979, May 2
619 A304 90p multicolored   .60 .50

1979, Oct. 1   **Perf. 13**
620 A305 1.10m multicolored   .65 .50
Bicentenary of founding of Tampere.

Optical Telegraph, 1796, Map of Islands A306

Europa: 1.10m, Letter of Queen Christina to Per Brahe, 1638, establishing postal service.

1979, May 2   **Perf. 13**
621 A306 1.10m multi   2.00 .35
622 A306 1.30m multi, vert   4.50 .85

Shops and Merchants' Signs — A307

1979, Sept. 26   **Perf. 14**
623 A307 1.10m multicolored   .60 .50
Business and industry regulation centenary.

Old and New Cars, Street Crossing A308

1979, Oct. 1
624 A308 1.10m multicolored   .65 .50
Road safety.

Elves Feeding Horse — A309

1979, Oct. 24
625 A309 60p multicolored   1.10 .50
Christmas 1979.

Korppi House, Lapinjarvi A310

Farm houses, First Row: Syrjala House, Tammela, 2 stamps in continuous design; Murtovaara House, Valtimo; Antila House, Lapua. Second row: Lofts, Pohjanmaa; Courtyard gate, Kanajarvi House, Kalvola; Main door, Havuselka House, Kauhajoki; Maki-Rasinpera House and dinner bell tower; Gable and eaves, Rasula Kuortane granary.

1979, Oct. 27   **Litho.**   **Perf. 13**
626   Booklet pane of 10   6.00 6.00
a.-j. A310 1.10m single stamp   .60 .35
Complete booklet, #626   6.00
See design A349a.

Type of 1975 and

Kauhaneva Swamp A315

Hame Castle, Hameenlinna A316   Windmill, Harrstrom A318

Multiharju Forest, Seitseminen Natl. Park — A319

Shuttle, Raanu Designs A322

Kaspaikka Towel Design — A323   Bridal Rug, Teisko, 1815 — A324

Iron-forged Door, Hollola Church — A325

Iron Fish Spear c. 1100 — A326

Design: 1.80m, Eastern Gulf natl. park.

Litho. & Engr., Litho., Engr.
1979-98   **Perf. 14, 11½ (A256, A318)**
627 A315 70p multicolored   .50 .50
628 A316 90p brown red   .50 .50
629 A256 1m red brown   .70 .50
   a.   Perf. 13x12½ ('98)   1.25 1.25
630 A318 1m bl & red brn   .50 .50
631 A256 1.30m dk green   .65 .80
631A A256 1.30m dk green, litho.   1.00 1.10
   b.   Booklet pane, #555-556, 557A, 560, 631A   3.00 3.00
     Complete booklet, #631Ab   3.25
632 A256 1.40m purple   .65 .80
633 A256 1.50m grnsh blue   .80 .80
634 A256 1.60m multicolored   .80 .50
635 A315 1.80m multicolored   2.00 .80
636 A322 3m multicolored   1.40 .50
637 A323 6m multicolored   2.75 .25
638 A324 7m multicolored   3.25 .80
639 A325 8m multicolored   3.75 .65
640 A326 9m blk & dk bl   4.25 .90
Nos. 627-640 (15)   23.50 9.90

Coil Stamps
Perf. 11½ Vert.
641 A316 90p brown red   .50 .50

Perf. 12½ Horiz.
642 A318 1m blue & red brn   .55 .80

Issued: 3m, 10/27/79; 6m, 4/9/80; #629, 1/2/81; 70p, 1/12/81; 90p, 9/1/82; 1.60m, 2/8/82; 7m, 2/15/82; #631, 1/3/83; #630, 642, 1/12/83; 1.80m, 8m, 2/10/83; 1.40m, 9m, 1/2/84; 1.50m, 1/2/85; #631A, 11/1/85.

Maria Jotuni (1880-1943), Writer — A327

1980, Apr. 9   **Litho.**
643 A327 1.10m multicolored   .60 .50

Frans Eemil Sillanpaa (1888-1964), Writer — A328

Europa: 1.30m, Artturi Ilmari Virtanen (1895-1973), chemist, vert.

1980, Apr. 28   *Perf. 13*
644 A328 1.10m multicolored   *2.25*   *.40*
645 A328 1.30m multicolored   *2.50*   *1.25*

Pres. Urho Kekkonen, 80th Birthday — A329

1980, Sept. 3   Litho.   *Perf. 13*
646 A329 1.10m multicolored   .65   .50

Nordic Cooperation Issue

Back-piece Harness, 19th century A330

1980, Sept. 9   *Perf. 14*
647 A330 1.10m shown   .65   .50
648 A330 1.30m Collar harness, vert.   .65   .50

Biathlon A331

1980, Oct. 17   Litho.   *Perf. 14*
649 A331 1.10m multicolored   .65   .50

World Biathlon Championship, Lahti, Feb. 10-15, 1981.

Pull the Roller, Weighing out the Salt — A332

Christmas 1980 (Traditional Games): 1.10m, Putting out the shoemaker's eye.

1980, Oct. 27
650 A332 60p multicolored   1.25   .50
651 A332 1.10m multicolored   1.25   .50

Boxing Match — A333

Glass Blowing A334

1981, Feb. 28   Litho.   *Perf. 14*
652 A333 1.10m multicolored   .60   .50

European Boxing Championships, Tampere, May 2-10.

1981, Mar. 12
653 A334 1.10m multicolored   .60   .50

Glass industry, 300th anniversary.

Mail Boat Furst Menschikoff, 1836 — A335

Litho. & Engr.

1981, May 6   *Perf. 13*
654 A335 1.10m brown & tan   3.50   3.25

Nordia '81 Stamp Exhibition, Helsinki, May 6-10. Sold only at exhibition for 3m including entrance ticket.

Europa Issue 1981

Rowing to Church A336

1981, May 18   Litho.   *Perf. 13*
655 A336 1.10m shown   *.75*   *.30*
656 A336 1.50m Midsummer's Eve dance   *1.50*   *.50*

Traffic Conference Emblem — A337

Boy and Girl Riding Pegasus A338

1981, May 26   Litho.   *Perf. 14*
657 A337 1.10m multicolored   .50   .50

European Conference of Ministers of Transport, May 25-28.

1981, June 11
658 A338 1m multicolored   .50   .50

Youth associations centenary.

Intl. Year of the Disabled — A339

1981, Sept. 2   Litho.   *Perf. 13*
659 A339 1.10m multicolored   .60   .50

Christmas 1981 — A340

1981, Oct. 27   Litho.   *Perf. 14*
660 A340 70p Children, Christmas tree   1.00   .50
661 A340 1.10m Decorating tree, vert.   1.00   .50

"Om Konsten att Ratt Behaga" First Issue (Periodicals Bicentenary) A341

1982, Jan. 15
662 A341 1.20m multicolored   .60   .50

Kuopio Bicentenary A343

Score, String Instrument Neck A344

1982, Mar. 4   Litho.   *Perf. 14*
664 A343 1.20m multicolored   .60   .50

1982, Mar. 11   *Perf. 13*
665 A344 1.20m multicolored   1.00   .50

Centenaries of Sibelius Academy of Music and Helsinki Orchestra.

Electric Power Plant Centenary A345

1982, Mar. 15   *Perf. 14*
666 A345 1.20m multicolored   .60   .50

Gardening A346

1982, Apr. 16   Litho.   *Perf. 14*
667 A346 1.10m multicolored   .55   .50

Europa — A347

1.20m, Publication of Abckiria (1st Finnish book), 1543 (Sculpture of Mikael Agricola, translator, by Oskari Jauhiainen, 1951). 1.50m, Turku Academy, 1st Finnish university (Turku Academy Inaugural Procession, 1640, after Albert Edelfelt).

1982, Apr. 29   Litho.   *Perf. 13x12½*
668 A347 1.20m multicolored   *1.50*   *.45*

Size: 47x31mm

Perf. 12½
669 A347 1.50m multicolored   *1.90*   *.60*

Intl. Monetary Fund and World Bank Emblems A348

1982, May 12   *Perf. 14*
670 A348 1.60m multicolored   .75   .65

IMF Interim Committee and IMF-WB Joint Development Committee Meeting, Helsinki, May 12-14.

75th Anniv. of Unicameral Parliament A349

1982, May 25
671 A349 2.40m Future, by Waino Aaltonen, Parliament   1.10   1.00

Manor Houses A349a

1st Row: a, Kuitia, Parainen, 1490. b, Louhisaari, Askainen, 1655. c, Frugard, Joroinen, 1780. d, Jokioinen, 1798. e, Moisio, Elimaki, 1820.
2nd Row: f, Sjundby, Siuntio, 1560. g, Fagervik, Inkoo, 1773. h, Mustio, Karjaa, 1792. i, Fiskars, Pohja, 1818. j, Kotkaniemi, Vihti, 1836.

1982, June 14   Litho.   *Perf. 13x13½*
672   Booklet pane of 10   11.00   11.00
   a.-j. A349a 1.20m single stamp   1.00   .50
   Complete booklet, #672   12.00   12.00

See design A310.

Christmas 1982 — A350

1982, Oct. 25
673 A350 90p Feeding forest animals   1.00   .50
674 A350 1.20m Children eating porridge   1.00   .50

Nordic Cooperation A351

1983, Mar. 24   Litho.   *Perf. 14*
675 A351 1.20m Panning for gold   .65   .50
676 A351 1.30m Kitkajoki River rapids   .65   .50

World Communications Year — A352

1983, Apr. 9   Litho.   *Perf. 13*
677 A352 1.30m Postal services   .65   .50
678 A352 1.70m Sound waves, optical cables   .80   .65

Europa 1983 A353

1983, May 2   Litho.   *Perf. 12½x13*
679 A353 1.30m Flash smelting method   5.00   .45
680 A353 1.70m Temppeliaukio Church   6.00   .90

Pres. Lauri
Kristian
Relander
(1883-1942)
A354

Running
A355

1983, May 31   Litho.   Perf. 14
681 A354 1.30m multicolored   .65 .50

1983, June 6
682 A355 1.20m Javelin, horiz.   .65 .50
683 A355 1.30m shown   .70 .50

First World Athletic Championships, Helsinki, Aug. 7-14.

Toivo Kuula (1883-
1918),
Composer — A356

1983, July 7   Perf. 14
684 A356 1.30m multicolored   .65 .50

Christmas
1983 — A357

Childrens drawings: 1m, Santa, reindeer, sled and gifts by Eija Myllyviita. 1.30m, Two candles by Camilla Lindberg.

Engr., Litho.
1983, Nov. 4   Perf. 12, 14
685 A357 1m dark blue   1.00 .50
686 A357 1.30m multi, vert.   1.00 .50

A358

A360

1983, Nov. 25   Litho.   Perf. 14
687 A358 1.30m brt blue & blk   .65 .50

President Mauno Henrik Koivisto, 60th birthday.

1984, Mar. 1   Engr.   Perf. 12
689 A360 1.10m Letters (2nd
    class rate)   .50 .50

Photo. & Engr.
690 A360 1.40m Automated sort-
    ing (1st class
    rate), vert.   .65 .50

Inauguration of Nordic postal rates.

Museum
Pieces — A361

Work and
Skill — A362

Designs: No. 691, Pottery, 3200 B.C.; Silver chalice, 1416; Crossbow, 16th cent. No. 692, Kaplan hydraulic turbine.

1984, Apr. 30   Litho.   Perf. 13½
691 A361 1.40m multicolored   .65 .50
692 A362 1.40m multicolored   .65 .50

Europa
(1959-84)
A363

1984, May 7   Perf. 12½x13
693 A363 1.40m multicolored   4.00 .25
694 A363 2m multicolored   4.00 .80

Dentistry — A364

1984, Aug. 27   Litho.   Perf. 14
695 A364 1.40m Dentist, teeth   .90 .65

Astronomy
A365

1984, Sept. 12
696 A365 1.10m Observatory,
    planets, sun   .50 .50

Aleksis Kivi
(1934-72),
Writer — A366

1984, Oct. 10   Litho.   Perf. 14
697 A366 1.40m Song of my
    Heart   .65 .50

Christmas
1984 — A367

Litho. & Engr.
1984, Nov. 30   Perf. 12
698 A367 1.10m Father Christ-
    mas, brownie   1.00 .50

Common Law of
1734 — A368

1984, Dec. 6   Perf. 14
699 A368 2m Statute Book   .95 .95

25th Anniv. of
EFTA — A369

1985, Feb. 2   Litho.
700 A369 1.20m multicolored   .65 .50

100th Anniv. of
Society of
Swedish
Literature in
Finland
A370

1985, Feb. 5   Litho.
701 A370 1.50m Johan Ludvig
    Runeberg   .70 .50

A371

A372

1985, Feb. 18   Litho.   Perf. 11½x12
702 A371 1.50m Icon   .70 .50

Order of St. Sergei and St. Herman, 100th anniv.

Litho. & Engr.
1985, Feb. 28   Perf. 13x12½
703 A372 1.50m Pedri Shemeik-
    ka   .70 .50
704 A372 2.10m Larin Paraske   1.00 .75

150th anniv. of Kalevala.

A373

A374

Litho. & Engr.
1985, May 15   Perf. 13
705 A373 1.50m Mermaid and
    sea lions   5.00 6.25

NORDIA 1985 philatelic exhibition, May 15-19. Sold for 10m, which included admission ticket.

Photo. & Engr.
1985, May 18   Perf. 11½

Finnish Banknote Cent.: banknotes of 1886, 1909, 1922, 1945 and 1955.

706   Booklet pane of 8   8.50 9.50
a.-h. A374 1.50m any single   1.00 .80
    Complete booklet, #706   9.00

A375

A376

Europa: 1.50m, Children playing the recorder. 2.10m, Excerpt "Ramus Virens Olivarum" from the "Piae Cantiones," 1582.

1985, June 17   Litho.   Perf. 13
707 A375 1.50m multicolored   5.50   .50
708 A375 2.10m multicolored   6.50 1.10

Security Conference Type of 1975
1985, June 19   Litho.
709 A265 2.10m multicolored   1.00   .75

European Security and Cooperation Conference, 10th Anniv.

1985, Sept. 5   Litho.   Perf. 14
710 A376 1.50m Provincial arms, Count's seal   1.00   .50

Provincial Administration Established by Count Per Brahe, 350th Anniv.

Arms Type of 1975 and

Kerimaki Church A376a

Urho Kekkonen Natl. Park — A376b

Tulip Damask Table Cloth, 18th Cent. A377

Postal Service A377a

Brown Bear — A377b

Perf. 11½, 13x12½ (2m)

1985-90				**Engr.**	
711	A256	1.60m vermilion		.80	.80
712	A256	1.70m black		.80	.80
a.		Bklt. pane, #558, 560, 2 each #555, 556a, 712 + 2 labels		8.00	10.00
		Complete booklet, #712a		10.00	
713	A256	1.80m olive green		.90	.80
a.		Bklt. pane, 2 ea #555d, 560a, 713b		3.00	2.75
		Complete booklet, #713a		3.50	
b.		Perf. 13x12½		1.25	1.00
714	A256	1.90m brt orange		.90	.25
715	A256	2m blue grn, bklt. stamp		2.00	.90
a.		Bklt. pane, #562a, 2 ea #715, 555d		6.50	6.50
		Complete booklet, #715a		7.00	

		Litho.		**Perf. 14**	
716	A376a	2.20m multi		1.00	.25
717	A376b	2.40m multi		1.10	.50
718	A377	12m multi		5.75	1.00

Litho. & Engr.
Perf. 13x12½
719 A377b 50m blk, grn & lt red brn   24.00 12.50
Nos. 711-719 (9)   37.25 17.80

No. 712a contains two labels inscribed to publicize FINLANDIA '88.

Issued: 12m, 9/13/85; 1.60m, 1/2/86; 1.70m, 1/2/87; #712a, 8/10/87; 1.80m, 1/4/88; 2.20m, 2.40m, 1/20/88; #713b, 7/25/88; 1.90m, 1/2/89; 2m, 1/19/90; 50m, 8/30/89.

Booklet Stamps

#720, Telephone, mailbox. #721, Postal truck, transport plane. #722, Transport plane, fork lift. #723, Postman delivering letter. #724, Woman accepting letter.

Perf. 12½ on 3 Sides

1988, Feb. 1				**Litho.**	
720	A377a 1.80m	multi-ticolored		1.00	.50
721	A377a 1.80m	mul-ticolored		1.00	.50
722	A377a 1.80m	mul-ticolored		1.00	.50
723	A377a 1.80m	mul-ticolored		1.00	.50
724	A377a 1.80m	mul-ticolored		1.00	.50
a.	Bklt. pane, 2 each #720-724			10.50	10.50
	Complete booklet, #724a			11.00	
	Nos. 720-724 (5)			5.00	2.50

Nos. 721-722 and 723-724 printed se-tenant in continuous designs. No. 724c sold for 14m to households on mainland Finland. Each household entitled to buy 2 booklets at discount price from Feb. 1 to May 31, with coupon.

Miniature Sheet

Postal Map, 1698 A378

Designs: a, Postman on foot. c, Sailing vessel, diff. d, Postrider, vert.

Litho. & Engr.
1985, Oct. 16   Perf. 14
728 A378   Sheet of 4   15.00 13.50
a.-d. A378 1.50m any single   3.50 2.50

FINLANDIA '88, 350th anniv. of Finnish Postal Service, founded in 1638 by Gov.-Gen. Per Brahe. Sheet sold for 8m.

Intl. Youth Year — A379

Christmas 1985 — A380

1985, Nov. 1   Litho.   Perf. 13
729 A379 1.50m multicolored   .70   .50

1985, Nov. 29   Perf. 14
730 A380 1.20m Bird, tulips   1.25   .50
731 A380 1.20m Cross of St. Thomas, hyacinths   1.25   .50

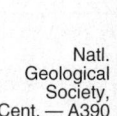

Natl. Geological Society, Cent. — A390

1986, Feb. 8   Litho.   Perf. 14
732 A390 1.30m Orbicular granite   .80   .50
733 A390 1.60m Rapaviki   .90   .55
734 A390 2.10m Veined gneiss   1.10   .75
Nos. 732-734 (3)   2.80 1.80

Europa 1986 A391

1986, Apr. 10   Perf. 12½x13
735 A391 1.60m Saimaa ringed seal   5.00   .25
736 A391 2.20m Environmental conservation   5.50   .80

Conference Palace, Baghdad, 1982 — A392

Natl. Construction Year. b, Lahti Theater, 1983. c, Kuusamo Municipal Offices, 1978. d, Hamina Court Building, 1983. e, Finnish Embassy, New Delhi, 1986. f, Western Sakyla Daycare Center, 1980.

1986, Apr. 19   Perf. 14
737   Booklet pane of 6   5.75 5.75
a.-f. A392 1.60m, any single   .90   .80
Complete booklet, #737   5.75

Nordic Cooperation Issue 1986 — A393

Sister towns.

1986, May 27   Litho.   Perf. 14
738 A393 1.60m Joensuu   .75   .50
739 A393 2.20m Jyvaskyla   1.00   .80

Souvenir Sheet

FINLANDIA '88 — A394

Postal ships: a, Iron paddle steamer Aura, Stockholm-St. Petersburg, 1858. b, Screw vessel Alexander, Helsinki-Tallinn-Lubeck, 1859. c, Steamship Nicolai, Helsinki-Tallinn-St. Petersburg, 1858. d, 1st Ice steamship Express II, Helsinki-Stockholm, 1877-98, vert.

Litho. & Engr.
1986, Aug. 29   Perf. 13
740 A394   Sheet of 4   15.00 15.00
a.-b. 1.60m, any single   3.50 3.25
c.-d. 2.20m, any single   3.50 3.25
Sold for 10k.

Pierre-Louis Moreau de Maupertuis (1698-1759) — A395

1986, Sept. 5   Litho.   Perf. 12½x13
741 A395 1.60m multicolored   .90   .50

Lapland Expedition, 250th anniv., proved Earth's poles are flattened.
See France No. 2016.

Urho Kaleva Kekkonen (1900-86), Pres. — A396

Intl. Peace Year — A397

1986, Sept. 30   Engr.   Perf. 14
742 A396 5m black   2.50 2.25

1986, Oct. 13   Litho.   Perf. 13
743 A397 1.60m multicolored   .75   .50

A398

Christmas A399

Photo. & Engr.
1986, Oct. 31   Perf. 12
744   1.30m Denomination at L   .90   .50
745   1.30m Denomination at R   1.50   .50
a. A398 Pair, #744-745   3.00 2.40
746 A399 1.60m Elves   1.10   .50
Nos. 744-746 (3)   3.50 1.50

No. 745a has a continuous design.

Postal Savings Bank, Cent. — A400

1987, Jan. 2   Litho.   Perf. 14
747 A400 1.70m multicolored   .80   .50

Natl. Tourism, Cent. — A401

1987, Feb. 4   Litho.   Perf. 14
748 A401 1.70m Winter   .80   .50
749 A401 2.30m Summer   1.10   .80

A402

A403

1987, Feb. 4   Perf. 14
750 A402 1.40m multicolored   .65   .50

Metric system in Finland, cent.

1987, Feb. 17   Litho.   Perf. 14
751 A403 2.10m multicolored   1.25   .50

Leevi Madetoja (1887-1947), composer.

European Wrestling Championships A404

1987 World Bowling Championships A405

1987, Feb. 17
752 A404 1.70m multicolored   .80   .50

1987, Apr. 13
753 A405 1.70m multicolored   .80   .50

Mental Health — A406

1987, Apr. 13
754   A406   1.70m multicolored   .80   .50

Souvenir Sheet

FINLANDIA '88 — A407

Locomotives and mail cars: a, Steam locomotive, 6-wheeled tender. b, 4-window mail car. c, 7-window mail car.

Litho. & Engr.
1987, May 8   **Perf. 12½x13**
755   A407   Sheet of 4   15.00   15.00
a.-c.   1.70m any single   4.00   4.00
d.   2.30m multicolored   4.00   4.00

Sold for 10m.

Europa 1987 A408

Modern architecture: 1.70m, Tampere Main Library, 1986, designed by Raili and Reima Pietila. 2.30m, Stoa Monument, Helsinki, c. 1981, by sculptor Hannu Siren.

1987, May 15   Litho.   **Perf. 13**
756   A408   1.70m multicolored   5.25   .25
757   A408   2.30m multicolored   5.25   .90

Natl. Art Museum, Ateneum, Cent. — A409

Paintings: a, Strawberry Girl, by Nils Schillmark (1745-1804). b, Still-life on a Lady's Work Table, by Ferdinand von Wright (1822-1906). c, Old Woman with Basket, by Albert Edelfelt (1854-1906). d, Boy and Crow, by Akseli Gallen-Kallela (1865-1931). e, Late Winter, by Tyko Sallinen (1879-1955).

1987, May 15
758   Booklet pane of 5   8.50   8.50
a.-e.   A409 1.70m any single   1.60   .90
      Complete booklet, #758   9.00

A410   A411

1987, Aug. 12   **Perf. 14**
759   A410   1.70m multicolored   .80   .50
European Physics Soc. 7th gen. conf., Helsinki, Aug. 10-14.

1987, Oct. 12
760   A411   1.70m ultra, sil & pale lt gray   .80   .50

Size: 30x41mm
761   A411   10m dark ultra, lt blue & sil   5.00   2.25
Natl. independence, 70th anniv.

Ylppo, Child and Lastenlinna Children's Hospital A412

1987, Oct. 27
762   A412   1.70m multicolored   .80   .50
Arvo Ylppo (b. 1887), pediatrics pioneer.

Christmas   Finnish News
A413   Agency (STT), Cent. A414

1987, Oct. 30
763   A413   1.40m Santa Claus, youths, horiz.   1.25   .50
764   A413   1.70m shown   1.25   .50

1987, Nov. 1
765   A414   2.30m multicolored   1.10   .85

Lauri "Tahko" Pihkala (1888-1981), Promulgator of Sports and Physical Education A415

1988, Jan. 5   Litho.   **Perf. 14**
766   A415   1.80m blk, chalky blue & brt blue   .90   .50

A416

1988, Mar. 14   **Litho.**
767   A416   1.40m multicolored   .65   .50
Meteorological Institute, 150th anniv.

Settlement of New Sweden in America, 350th Anniv. — A417

Design: 17th Century European settlers negotiating with 3 American Indians, map of New Sweden, the Swedish ships Kalmar Nyckel and Fogel Grip, based on an 18th cent. illustration from a Swedish book about the American Colonies.

Litho. & Engr.
1988, Mar. 29   **Perf. 13**
768   A417   3m multicolored   1.60   1.00
See US No. C117 and Sweden No. 1672.

FINLANDIA '88, June 1-12, Helsinki Fair Center — A418

Agathon Faberge (1876-1951), famed philatelist, & rarities from his collection.

Booklet Stamp
1988, May 2   Litho.   **Perf. 13**
769   A418   5m Pane of 1+2 labels   14.00   17.50
     Complete booklet, #769   15.00

350th Anniv. of the Finnish Postal Service. No. 769 sold for 30m to include the price of adult admission to the exhibition.

Achievements of Finnish Athletes at the 1988 Winter Olympics, Calgary — A419

Design: Matti Nykanen, gold medalist in all 3 ski jumping events at the '88 Games.

1988, Apr. 6   **Perf. 14**
770   A419   1.80m multicolored   .85   .50

Europa 1988 A420

Communication and transport.

1988, May 23   Litho.   **Perf. 13**
771   A420   1.80m shown   5.00   .25
772   A420   2.40m Horse-drawn tram, 1890   5.00   .90

Souvenir Sheet

FINLANDIA '88 — A421

1st airmail flights: a, Finnish air force Breguet 14 biplane transporting mail from Helsinki to Tallinn, Feb. 12, 1920. b, AERO Junkers F-13 making 1st airmail night flight from Helsinki to Copenhagen, May 15, 1930. c, AERO Douglas DC-3, 1st intl. route, Helsinki-Norrkoping-Copenhagen-Amsterdam, 1947. d, Douglas DC 10-30, 1975-88, inauguration of Helsinki-Beijing route, June 2, 1988.

Litho. & Engr.
1988, June 2   **Perf. 13½**
773   Sheet of 4   15.00   15.00
a.-c.   A421 1.80m any single   3.75   3.75
d.   2.40m multicolored   3.75   3.75

Sold for 11m.

Turku Fire Brigade, 150th Anniv. — A422

Design: 1902 Horse-drawn, steam-driven fire pump, preserved at the brigade.

1988, Aug. 15   Litho.   **Perf. 14**
774   A422   2.20m multicolored   1.10   .65

A423   A424

Missale Aboense, the 1st printed book in Finland, 500th anniv.

1988, Aug. 17
775   A423   1.80m multicolored   .85   .50

Booklet Stamps
1988, Sept. 6   Litho.   **Perf. 13**

Finnish Postal Service, 350th Anniv.: #776, Postal tariff issued by Queen Christina of Sweden, Sept. 6, 1638. #777, Postal cart, c. 1880. #778, Leyland Sherpa 185 mail van, 1976. #779, Malmi P.O. interior. #780, Skier using mobile telephone, c. 1970. #781, Telecommunications satellite in orbit.

776   A424   1.80m multicolored   1.00   .80
777   A424   1.80m multicolored   1.00   .80
778   A424   1.80m multicolored   1.00   .80
779   A424   1.80m multicolored   1.00   .80
780   A424   1.80m multicolored   1.00   .80
781   A424   1.80m multicolored   1.00   .80
a.   Booklet pane of 6, #776-781   6.25   6.25
     Complete booklet, #781a   6.50

Children's Playgroups (Preschool) A425

1988, Oct. 10   **Perf. 14**
782   A425   1.80m multicolored   .85   .50

Christmas A426

1988, Nov. 4   **Litho.**
783   A426   1.40m multicolored   1.00   .50
784   A426   1.80m multicolored   1.25   .50

Hameenlinna Township, 350th Anniv. — A427

Design: Market square, coat of arms and 17th century plan of the town.

1989, Jan. 19   **Litho.**
785   A427   1.90m multicolored   .90   .50

1989 Nordic Ski Championships, Lahti, Feb. 17-26 — A428

1989, Jan. 25
786   A428   1.90m multicolored   .90   .50

Salvation Army in Finland, Cent. — A429

Photography, 150th Anniv. — A430

1989, Feb. 6   Litho.
787 A429 1.90m multicolored   .90 .50

1989, Feb. 6
788 A430 1.50m Photographer, box camera, c.1900   .80 .80

31st Intl. Physiology Congress, Basel, July 9-14 — A431

Design: Congress emblem, silhouettes of Robert Tigerstedt and Ragnar Granit, eye, flowmeter measuring flow of blood through heart, color-sensitive retinal cells and microelectrode.

1989, Mar. 2
789 A431 1.90m multicolored   .90 .50

Sports — A432

1989, Mar. 10   **Booklet Stamps**
790 A432 1.90m Skiing   1.00 .50
791 A432 1.90m Jogging   1.00 .50
792 A432 1.90m Cycling   1.00 .50
793 A432 1.90m Canoeing   1.00 .50
a.   Booklet pane of 4, #790-793   4.25 4.25
   Complete booklet, #793a   4.50

Souvenir Sheet

Finnish Kennel Club, Cent. — A433

Dogs: a, Lapponian herder. b, Finnish spitz. c, Karelian bear dog. d, Finnish hound.

1989, Mar. 17   Litho.   Perf. 14
794 A433 Sheet of 4   5.00 5.00
a.-d.   1.90m any single   1.25 .70

Europa — A434   A435

1989, Mar. 31   Perf. 13
795 A434 1.90m Hopscotch   2.50 .25
796 A434 2.50m Sledding   2.50 .65

1989, Apr. 20   Perf. 14
Nordic Cooperation Year: Folk Costumes.
797 A435 1.90m Sakyla (man)   1.25 .50
798 A435 2.50m Veteli (woman)   1.25 .75

Finnish Pharmacies, 300th Anniv. — A436

Foxglove, distilling apparatus, mortar, flask.

1989, June 2   Litho.
799 A436 1.90m multicolored   .90 .50

A437

A438

1989, June 2
800 A437 1.90m multicolored   .90 .50
Savonlinna Municipal Charter, 350th anniv.

1989, June 12
801 A438 1.90m Panthera uncia   .90 .50
802 A438 2.50m Capra falconeri   1.25 .90
Helsinki Zoo, cent.

Vocational Training, 150th Anniv. — A439

Interparliamentary Union, Cent. — A440

Council of Europe, 40th Anniv. — A441

1989, Sept. 4   Litho.   Perf. 14
803 A439 1.50m multicolored   .75 .90
804 A440 1.90m multicolored   .90 .50
805 A441 2.50m multicolored   1.25 .90
   Nos. 803-805 (3)   2.90 2.30
Admission of Finland to the Council of Europe (2.50m).

A442

A443

1989, Oct. 9   Litho.
806 A442 1.90m multicolored   .90 .50
Hannes Kolehmainen (1889-1966) winning the 5000-meter race at the Stockholm Olympics, 1912.

1989, Oct. 20
807 A443 1.90m multicolored   .90 .50
Continuing Education in Finland, cent.

A444   A445

Christmas: 1.90m, Sodankyla Church, Siberian jays in snow.

1989, Nov. 3
808 A444 1.50m shown   1.25 .50
809 A444 1.90m multicolored   1.25 .50

1990, Jan. 19   Litho.   Perf. 13x13½
810 A445 1.90m multicolored   1.00 1.00
811 A445 2.50m multicolored   1.25 1.10
Incorporation of the State Posts and Telecommunications Services.
Emblem of the corporation was produced by holography. Soaking may affect the design.

Musical Soc. of Turku and Finnish Orchestras, 200th Annivs. A446

1990, Jan. 26   Perf. 14
812 A446 1.90m multicolored   1.25 .50

Disabled Veteran's Assoc., 50th Anniv. — A447

1990, Mar. 13   Litho.
813 A447 2m multicolored   .95 .50

End of the Winter (Russo-Finnish) War, 50th Anniv. — A448

1990, Mar. 13
814 A448 2m blue   .95 .50

University of Helsinki, 350th Anniv. — A449

University crest and: 2m, Queen Christina on horseback. 3.20m, Degree ceremony procession in front of the main university building.

1990, Mar. 26   Litho.   Perf. 13
815 A449 2m multicolored   .95 .50
816 A449 3.20m multicolored   1.50 .90

Europa 1990 A450

Post Offices: 2m, Lapp man, P.O. at Nuvvus, Mt. Nuvvus Ailigas. 2.70m, Turku main P.O.

1990, Mar. 26   Perf. 12½x13
817 A450 2m multicolored   6.00 .25
818 A450 2.70m multicolored   6.00 .65

Rural Postal Service and Address Reform, Cent. — A451

1990, Apr. 19   Litho.   Perf. 13
819 A451 2m multicolored   .95 .50

"Ali Baba and the Forty Thieves" A452   "Story of the Great Musician" A453

"Story of the Giants, the Witches and the Daughter of the Sun" A454   "The Golden Bird, the Golden Horse and the Princess" A455

"Lamb Brother" A456   "The Snow Queen" A457

Fairy tale illustrations by Rudolf Koivu.

Booklet Stamps
Perf. 14 on 3 sides
1990, Aug. 29   Litho.
820 A452 2m multicolored   2.00 .75
821 A453 2m multicolored   2.00 .75
822 A454 2m multicolored   2.00 .75
823 A455 2m multicolored   2.00 .75
824 A456 2m multicolored   2.00 .75
825 A457 2m multicolored   2.00 .75
a.   Booklet pane of 6, #820-825   12.50 12.50
   Complete booklet, #825a   13.50

Souvenir Sheet

Horse Care — A458

a, Feeding. b, Riding. c, Watering. d, Currying.

1990, Oct. 10   Litho.   Perf. 14
826   A458   Sheet of 4   5.00 5.00
a.-d.   2m any single   1.10   .75

Christmas
A459

1990, Nov. 2
827   A459   1.70m Santa's elves   1.25 .50
828   A459   2m Santa, reindeer   1.25 .50

Provincial Flowers

A460

A460a

A460b

A460c

A460d

A460e

A460f

A460g

A460h

A460i

A460j

A460k

1990-99   Perf. 13x12½
829   A460   2m Wood anem-
             one   1.00 .20
830   A460   2.10m Rowan   1.00 .20
831   A460   2.70m Heather   1.25 .50
832   A460   2.90m Sea buck-
             thorn   1.40 .50
833   A460   3.50m Oak   1.75 .50
834   A460   2 Globeflower   1.40 .30
835   A460b   1 Hepatica   1.60 .20
      Nos. 829-835 (7)   9.40 2.40

Self-Adhesive
Die Cut

836   A460c   2 Iris   1.60 .65
a.   Booklet pane of 20   36.00 20.00
837   A460   2.10m like #830   1.00 .50
838   A460d   1 Rosebay
             willowherb   1.60 .50
839   A460e   1 Labrador
             tea   1.60 .50
a.   Booklet pane of 10   18.00 12.50
840   A460f   1 Karelian
             rose   1.60 .50
841   A460g   1 Daisy   1.60 .50
842   A460h   1 Water lily   1.60 .50
843   A460i   1 Bird cherry   1.60 .20

---

844   A460j   1 Harebell   1.60 .20
845   A460k   1 Cowslip   1.75 .50
      Nos. 836-845 (10)   15.55 4.25

Issued: 2m, 2.70m, 1/19/90; #830, 2.90m, 3.50m, 2/5/90; 2.10m, 1991; #834-835, 3/2/92; #838, 10/9/92; #836, 3/1/93; #839, 6/14/93; #840, 5/5/94; #841, 3/15/95; #842, 6/3/96; #843, 3/18/97; #844, 3/12/98; #845, 4/28/99.
#834 sold for 1.60m, #836 sold for 1.90m, #835, 838 for 2.10m, #839-840 for 2.30m, #841-844 sold for 2.80m, #845 sold for 3m at time of release.
#837-838, 840-845 issued in sheets of 10. Nos. 836a and 839a were issued as complete booklets. The peelable backing serves as a booklet cover.
The numbers on the stamps represent the class of mail for which each was intended at time of release.

A461

1991, Mar. 1   Perf. 14
846   A461   2.10m multicolored   1.00 .50
World Hockey Championships, Turku.

A462

1991, Mar. 1
847   A462   2.10m Cooking class   1.00 .50
Home economics teacher education, cent.

Sauna Type of 1977 and:

Birds — A463

Perf. 13x12½, 14 (#861)

1991-99   Litho.
Booklet Stamps (#848-859)
848   A463   10p Great tit   .50 .20
849   A463   10p Wagtail   .25 .20
850   A463   10p Aegolius
             funereus   1.00 .60
850A   A463   20p Phoenicurus
             phoenicurus   4.00 2.50
851   A463   60p Chaffinches   4.00 .65
852   A463   60p Robin   3.25 1.25
856   A463   2.10m Bullfinch   1.25 .20
a.   Bklt. pane, #851, 2 each
          #848, 856   7.50 7.50
      Complete booklet, #856a   8.00
857   A463   2.10m Waxwing   1.25 .25
a.   Bklt. pane, #852, 2 each
          #849, 857   6.25 6.25
      Complete booklet, #857a   6.75
859   A463   2.30m Dendroco-
             pos
             leucotos   1.40 .50
a.   Booklet pane of #850A, 2
          each #850, #859 + 1 label   7.50 7.50
      Complete booklet, #859a   8.00

Sheet Stamp
861   A256a   4.80m multicolored   2.50 1.25
      Nos. 848-861 (10)   19.40 7.60

Issued: Nos. 848, 851, 856, 3/20/91; Nos. 849, 852, 857, 4/22/92; Nos. 850, 850A, 859, 6/4/93. 861, 7/1/99.
"SUOMI" is in upper left on Nos. 849, 852, 857.

Fishing
A464

Tourism
A465

Designs: a, Fly fisherman, trout. b, Perch, bobber. c, Crayfish, trap. d, Trawling for herring. e, Stocking powan.

1991, Mar. 20   Perf. 14
863   Booklet pane of 5   6.50 6.50
a.-e.   A464 2.10m any single   1.25 .50
      Complete booklet, #863   6.75

1991, June 4   Litho.   Perf. 14
864   A465   2.10m Seurasaari Is-
             land   1.00 .25
865   A465   2.90m Steamship, Lake
             Saimaa   1.40 .80

Europa
A466

European map and: 2.10m, Human figures. 2.90m, Satellites, dish antennae.

1991, June 7   Litho.   Perf. 12½x13
866   A466   2.10m multicolored   5.50 .25
867   A466   2.90m multicolored   5.50 .70

Alfred W. Finch
(1854-1930)
A467

Designs: 2.10m, Iris, ceramic vase. 2.90m, Painting, The English Coast at Dover.

1991, Sept. 7   Litho.   Perf. 13
868   A467   2.10m multicolored   2.00 .50
869   A467   2.90m multicolored   2.00 .65
      See Belgium No. 1410.

Finnish Candy
Industry,
Cent. — A468

1991, Sept. 17   Photo.   Perf. 11½
870   A468   2.10m multicolored   1.00 .50

Souvenir Sheets

Children's Stamp Designs — A469

a, Sun. b, Rainbow. c, Cows grazing.

1991, Sept. 17   Litho.   Perf. 13½
871   A469   Sheet of 3   3.00 3.00
a.-c.   2.10m any single   1.00 .75

Skiing — A470

1991, Oct. 4   Perf. 14
Color of skisuit: a, red. b, green. c, yellow. d, blue.
872   A470   Sheet of 4   4.00 4.00
a.-d.   2.10m any single   1.00 .65

Town Status
for Iisalmi,
Cent. — A471

1991, Oct. 18   Litho.   Perf. 14
873   A471   2.10m multicolored   1.00 .65

Christmas
A472

1.80m, Santa, animals carrying candles. 2.10m, Reindeer pulling Santa's sleigh.

1991, Nov. 1   Litho.   Perf. 14
874   A472   1.80m multi   1.25 .50
875   A472   2.10m multi, vert.   1.25 .50

Chemists'
Club, Finnish
Chemists'
Society,
Cent. — A473

1991, Nov. 1
876   A473   2.10m multi   1.00 .50
877   A473   2.10m multi, diff.   1.00 .50
a.   Pair, #876-877 + label   2.50 2.50

Second and third vertical branches merge while second and third branches below almost touch in the upper left part of camphor molecular structure on No. 877. Nos. 876-877 are designed to produce a three dimensional effect when viewed together.

1992 Olympic
Games
A474

Designs: No. 878, Skier, Albertville. No. 879, Swimmer, Barcelona.

1992, Feb. 4   Litho.   Perf. 14
878   A474   2.10m multicolored   1.10 .50
879   A474   2.90m multicolored   1.60 .65

Expo '92,
Seville — A475

1992, Mar. 20   Litho.   Perf. 14
880   A475   3.40m multicolored   1.60 .90

Conference
on Security
and
Cooperation
in Europe,
Helsinki
A476

1992, Mar. 20   Perf. 14½x15
881   A476   16m multicolored   7.75 3.75

Town of
Rauma, 550th
Anniv. — A477

1992, Mar. 27   Perf. 14
882   A477   2.10m multicolored   1.50 .50

Healthy
Brains — A478

1992, Mar. 27
883 A478 3.50m multicolored   1.75 1.00

Discovery
of
America,
500th
Anniv.
A479

1992, May 8   Litho.   Perf. 12½x13
884 A479 2.10m Santa Maria,
                    map   2.25   .30
885 A479 2.10m Map, Columbus   2.25   .30
  a.   Pair, #884-885   5.00 4.00

Europa.

Finnish
Technology
A480

Hologram of trees and: 2.10m, Drawing of
blowing machine. 2.90m, Schematic of electronic circuits. 3.40m, Triangles and grid.

1992, May 8   Perf. 13x12½
886 A480 2.10m multicolored   1.25 .65
887 A480 2.90m multicolored   1.60 1.00
888 A480 3.40m multicolored   2.00 1.25
          Nos. 886-888 (3)   4.85 2.90

First Finnish patent granted, sesqui. (#886),
Finnish chairmanship of Eureka (#887), Gov-
ernment Technology Research Center, 50th
anniv. (#888).
  Nos. 886-888 have holographic images.
Soaking in water may affect the hologram.

Natl. Board of
Agriculture,
Cent. — A481

1992, June 4   Litho.   Perf. 14
889 A481 2.10m Currant harvest-
                    ing   1.00 .50

Finnish
Women
A482

#890, Aurora Karamzin (1808-1902),
founder of Deaconesses' Institution of Helsinki. #891, Baroness Sophie Mannerheim
(1863-1928), reformer of nursing education.
#892, Laimi Leidenius (1877-1938), physician
and educator. #893, Miina Sillanpaa (1866-
1952), Minister for social affairs. #894, Edith
Sodergran (1892-1923), poet. #895, Kreeta
Haapasalo (1813-1893), folk singer.

Litho. & Engr.
1992, June 8   Perf. 14
Booklet Stamps
890 A482 2.10m multicolored   1.00 .65
891 A482 2.10m multicolored   1.00 .65
892 A482 2.10m multicolored   1.00 .65
893 A482 2.10m multicolored   1.00 .65
894 A482 2.10m multicolored   1.00 .65
895 A482 2.10m multicolored   1.00 .65
  a.   Booklet pane of 6, #890-895   6.00 5.50
       Complete booklet, #895a   6.00 5.50

Child's
Painting
A483

Independence, 75th Anniv. — A484

1992, Oct. 5   Litho.   Perf. 13
896 A483 2.10m multicolored   1.00 .50

Souvenir Sheet
Perf. 13½
897 A484 2.10m multicolored   1.00 1.00

Nordia
'93 — A485

A486

Illustrations depicting "Moomin" characters,
by Tove Jansson: No. 898, Winter scene, ice
covered bridges. No. 899, Winter scene in forest. No. 900, Boats in water. No. 901, Characters on beach.

Perf. 13 on 3 Sides
1992, Oct. 9   Litho.
Booklet Stamps
898 A485 2.10m multicolored   2.50 .65
899 A485 2.10m multicolored   2.50 .65
900 A485 2.10m multicolored   2.50 .65
901 A485 2.10m multicolored   2.50 .65
  a.   Booklet pane of 4, #898-901   10.50 10.50
       Complete booklet, #901a   11.00

1992, Oct. 20   Litho.   Perf. 13
902 A486 2.10m multicolored   1.00 .50

Printing in Finland, 350th anniv.

Christmas
A487

Designs: 1.80m, Church of St. Lawrence,
Vantaa. 2.10m, Stained glass window of nativity scene, Karkkila Church, vert.

1992, Oct. 30   Litho.   Perf. 14
903 A487 1.80m multicolored   1.25 .50
904 A487 2.10m multicolored   1.25 .50

Central
Chamber of
Commerce,
75th
Anniv. — A488

1993, Feb. 8   Litho.   Perf. 14
905 A488 1.60m multicolored   .75 .50

Friendship
A489

1993, Feb. 8   Litho.   Perf. 14
906 A489 1 multicolored   2.00 .50
  a.   Booklet pane of 5 + label   12.00 12.00
       Complete booklet, 2 #906a   24.00

No. 906 sold for 2m at time of release. See
note following No. 845.
  See Estonia No. 237.

Alopex Lagopus — A490

a, Adult with winter white coat. b, Face, full
view, winter white coat. c, Mother, kits, summer coat. d, Two on rock, summer coat.

1993, Mar. 19   Litho.   Perf. 12½x13
907 A490   Block of 4   6.00 6.00
  a.-d. 2.30m Any single   1.50 .50

World Wildlife Fund.

Sculptures
A491

Europa: 2m, Rumba, by Martti Aiha. 2.90m,
Complete Works, by Kari Caven.

1993, Apr. 26   Perf. 13
908 A491   2m multicolored   1.90 .25
909 A491   2.90m multicolored   1.40 .60

Organized
Philately in
Finland,
Cent. — A492

1993, May 6   Perf. 13x12½
910 A492 2.30m Rosa pimpinel-
                    lifolia   1.25 .90

Vyborg
Castle, 700th
Anniv.
A493

1993, May 6   Perf. 13½
911 A493 2.30m multicolored   1.10 .25

Tourism
A494

1993, May 7   Perf. 13x12½
912 A494 2.30m Naantali   1.10 .25
913 A494 2.90m Imatra   1.40 .65

550th anniv. of Naantali (#912).

A495

A496

Independent Finland Defense Forces, 75th
Anniv.: 2.30m, Finnish landscape in form of
soldier's silhouette. 3.40m, UN checkpoint of
Finnish battalion, Middle East.

1993, June 4   Litho.   Perf. 14
914 A495 2.30m multicolored   1.10 .25
915 A495 3.40m multicolored   1.60 1.00

1993, June 14   Litho.   Perf. 12½x13
Art by Martta Wendelin (1893-1986): #916,
Boy on skis, 1936. #917, Mother, daughter
knitting, 1931. #918, Children building snowman, 1931. #919, Mother, children at fence,
1935. #920, Girl with lamb, 1936.

Booklet Stamps
916 A496 2.30m multicolored   1.75 .50
917 A496 2.30m multicolored   1.75 .50
918 A496 2.30m multicolored   1.75 .50
919 A496 2.30m multicolored   1.75 .50
920 A496 2.30m multicolored   1.75 .50
  a.   Booklet pane of 5, #916-920   8.75 8.75
       Complete booklet, #920a   9.50

Water Birds — A497

#921, Flock of gavia arctica. #922, Pair of
gavia arctica. #923, Mergus merganser. #924,
Anas platyrhynchos. #925, Mergus serrator.

Perf. 12½x13 on 3 or 4 Sides
1993, Sept. 20   Litho.
Booklet Stamps
921 A497 2.30m multicolored   1.25 .85
922 A497 2.30m multicolored   1.25 .85

Size: 26x40mm
923 A497 2.30m multicolored   1.25 .85
924 A497 2.30m multicolored   1.25 .85
925 A497 2.30m multicolored   1.25 .85
  a.   Booklet pane of 5, #921-925   7.00 7.50
       Complete booklet, #925a   7.50

Physical Education in
Finnish Schools,
150th Anniv. — A498

1993, Oct. 8   Perf. 14
926 A498 2.30m multicolored   1.10 .25

Souvenir Sheet

New Opera
House,
Helsinki
A499

Operas and ballet: a, 2.30m, Ostrobothni-
ans, by Leevi Madetoja. b, 2.30m, The Faun
(four dancers), by Claude Debussy. c, 2.90m,
Giselle, by Adolphe Adam. d, 3.40m, The
Magic Flute, by Wolfgang Amadeus Mozart.

1993, Oct. 8   Perf. 13
927   Sheet of 4   7.00 7.00
  a.-b. A499 2.30m Either single   1.25 1.00
  c.   A499 2.90m multi   2.00 2.00
  d.   A499 3.40m multi   2.00 2.50

Christmas
A500

Pres. Mauno
Koivisto, 70th
Birthday
A501

1993, Nov. 5   **Litho.**   *Perf. 14*
928 A500 1.80m Christmas
    tree, elves   1.25   .50
   a.   Booklet pane of 10   16.00   16.00
      Complete booklet, #928a   16.00
929 A500 2.30m Three angels   1.25   .50

1993, Nov. 25
930 A501 2.30m multicolored   1.10   .25

Friendship — A502

Moomin characters: No. 931, Two standing.
No. 932, Seven running.

1994, Jan. 27   **Litho.**   *Perf. 12½x13*
Booklet Stamps
931 A502 1 multicolored   2.00   .25
932 A502 1 multicolored   2.00   .25
   a.   Bklt. pane, 4 each #931-932   17.00   17.00
      Complete booklet, #932a   17.50

Nos. 931-932 each sold for 2.30m at time of
release. See note following No. 845.

Souvenir Sheet

Intl. Olympic Committee,
Cent. — A503

Winter Olympics medalists from Finland: a,
Marja-Liisa Kirvesniemi, Marjo Matikainen,
cross-country skiing. b, Clas Thunberg, speed
skating. c, Veikko Kankkonen, ski jumping. d,
Veikko Hakulinen, cross-country skiing.

1994, Jan. 27   *Perf. 13*
933 A503 4.20m Sheet of 4, #a-d 8.00 8.00
     See No. 939.

A504

Waino Aaltonen
(1894-1966),
Sculptor — A505

1994, Mar. 8
934 A504 2m "Peace"   1.00   .50
935 A505 2m "Muse"   .95   .25
   a.   Pair, #934-935   2.10   2.10

Postal Service
Civil Servants'
Federation,
Cent. — A506

1994, Mar. 11
936 A506 2.30m multicolored   1.10   .50

Finnish
Technology
A507

Europa: 2.30m, Paper roll, nitrogen fixation,
safety lock, ice breaker MS Fennica. 4.20m,
Radiosonde, fishing lure, mobile phone, wind
power plant.

1994, Mar. 18
937 A507 2.30m multicolored   *1.40 .25*
938 A507 4.20m multicolored   *1.90 1.10*

Olympic Athlete Type of 1994
Souvenir Sheet

Finnish athletes: a, Riitta Salin, Pirjo
Haggman, runners. b, Lasse Viren, runner. c,
Tiina Lillak, javelin thrower. d, Pentti Nikula,
pole vaulter.

1994, May 5   **Litho.**   *Perf. 13*
939 A503 4.20m Sheet of 4, #a-d 8.00 8.00

European Track & Field Championships,
Finlandia '95.

Finlandia '95, Helsinki — A508

1994, May 10   *Perf. 13½x13*
940 A508 16m Coccinella
     septempunctata12.00 12.00
     See Nos. 962, 1009.

Miniature Sheet

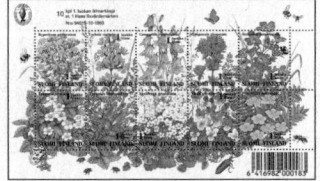

Wildflowers — A509

Designs: a, Hypericum perforatum (b). b,
Lychnis viscaria. c, Campanula rotundifolia. d,
Campanula glomerata. e, Geranium
sanguineum (d). f, Fragaria vesca. g, Veronica
chamaedrys (f, h). h, Saxifraga granulata (c, i).
i, Viola tricolor (j). j, Potentilla anserina.

1994, June 1   *Perf. 12*
941 A509 1 Sheet of 10   20.00 20.00
   a.-j.   Any single   2.00   .50

No. 941 sold for 23m at time of release. See
note following No. 845.

Finland-Sweden
Track and Field
Meet — A510

No. 942, Seppo Raty, Finland, javelin. No.
943, Patrick Sjoberg, Sweden, high jump.

1994, Aug. 26   **Litho.**   *Perf. 12½*
Booklet Stamps
942 A510 2.40m multicolored   1.25   .65
943 A510 2.40m multicolored   1.25   .65
   a.   Booklet pane, 2 each #942-943   5.25   5.25
      Complete booklet, #943a   5.25

See Sweden Nos. 2091-2092.

Population
Registers,
450th
Anniv. — A511

1994, Sept. 1
944 A511 2.40m multicolored   1.25   .40

Intl. Year of the
Family — A512

1994, Sept. 1
945 A512 3.40m multicolored   1.60 1.00

Souvenir Sheet

Letter Writing Day — A513

Dog Hill Kids in the Post Office: a, At Post
Office window. b, Standing in doorway, mail
cart. c, Blowing horn, pig. d, Putting letters in
mailbox.

1994, Oct. 7   **Litho.**   *Perf. 14*
946 A513 2.80m Sheet of 10, #a-d 5.50 5.50

Christmas
A514

2.10m, Reindeer, bullfinches on antlers.
2.80m, Elves among snow-covered trees.

1994, Nov. 4
947 A514 2.10m multi   1.25   .25
   a.   Booklet pane of 10   16.00   16.00
      Complete booklet, #947a   18.00
948 A514 2.80m multi, vert.   1.40   .50

Greetings — A515

"Dog Hill Kids," sending/receiving greetings:
No. 949, Delivering mail to Moon, spaceman.
No. 950, Cat writing letter, clown. No. 951,
Receiving mail from postman, baby. No. 952,
Writing in bed, friend. No. 953, Winter scene
at mailbox, characters at beach. No. 954, On
bus, girl friend. No. 955, Standing at
microphone with guitar, fan. No. 956, Baby in
play pen, teddy bear.

Perf. 13 on 3 Sides
1995, Jan. 30   **Litho.**
Booklet Stamps
949 A515 2.80m multicolored   2.00   .75
950 A515 2.80m multicolored   2.00   .75
951 A515 2.80m multicolored   2.00   .75
952 A515 2.80m multicolored   2.00   .75
953 A515 2.80m multicolored   2.00   .75
954 A515 2.80m multicolored   2.00   .75
955 A515 2.80m multicolored   2.00   .75
956 A515 2.80m multicolored   2.00   .75
   a.   Booklet pane, #949-956   16.00   16.00
      Complete booklet, 956a   17.00

Nos. 949-952 are printed tete beche with
Nos. 953-956. Soaking in water may affect the
holographic images on Nos. 949-956.

Souvenir Sheet

Team Sports — A516

a, Paivi Ikola, pesapallo. b, Jari Kurri, ice
hockey. c, Jari Litmanen, soccer. d, Lea
Hakala, basketball.

1995, Jan. 30   *Perf. 13*
957 A516 3.40m Sheet of 4, #a-d 8.00 8.00
     See No. 961.

Membership in
European
Union — A517

1995, Jan. 30   *Perf. 14*
958 A517 3.50m multicolored   1.75   .90

Peace &
Liberty — A518

Europa: 2.90m, Stylized parachutists.

1995, Mar. 1   **Litho.**   *Perf. 14*
959 A518 2.90m multicolored   *1.40 .45*

Endangered Species — A519

Designs: a, Felis lynx. b, Lake, forest. c,
Rocks, lake. d, Pusa hispida.

1995, Mar. 1   *Perf. 13*
960   Block of 4   7.00 7.00
   a.-d.   A519 2.90m Any single   1.50 1.00

Nos. 960a-960b, 960c-960d are continuous
designs. See Russia No. 6249.

Athlete Type of 1995
Souvenir Sheet

Motor sports drivers in cars, on motorcycles:
a, Timo Makinen. b, Juha Kankkunen. c,
Tommi Ahvala. d, Heikki Mikkola.

1995, May 10   **Litho.**   *Perf. 13*
961 A516 3.50m Sheet of 4, #a-
     d.   6.75 6.75

Insect Type of 1994

1995, May 11
962 A508 19m Geotrupes
      stercorarius   12.50 12.50

Tourism — A520

Designs: 2.80m, Linnanmaki amusement park, Helsinki. 2.90m, Town of Mantyharju.

1995, May 12
963 A520 2.80m multicolored   1.25 .65
964 A520 2.90m multicolored   1.25 .90

Town of
Loviisa, 250th
Anniv. — A521

1995, June 30   **Litho.**   **Perf. 14**
965 A521 3.20m multicolored   1.60 1.25

Intl. Union of Forestry
Research
Organizations, 20th
World Congress,
Tampere — A522

Designs: No. 966, Betula pendula. No. 967, Pinus sylvestris. No. 968, Picea abies. No. 969, Research, tree grown from needle.

Perf. 14 on 2 or 3 Sides
1995, Aug. 8   **Litho.**
Booklet Stamps
966 A522 2.80m multicolored   1.25 .65
967 A522 2.80m multicolored   1.25 .65
968 A522 2.80m multicolored   1.25 .65
969 A522 2.80m multicolored   1.25 .65
   a. Booklet pane of 4, #966-969 5.00 5.00
      Complete booklet, #969a 5.00 5.00

Wilhelm
Roentgen
(1845-1923),
Discovery of
the X-Ray,
Cent. — A523

1995, Aug. 8   **Perf. 14**
970 A523 4.30m multicolored   2.10 1.60

Cats — A525

1995, Oct. 9   **Litho.**   **Perf. 13½**
972 A525 2.80m Somali   2.00 .75
973 A525 2.80m Siamese   2.00 .75
974 A525 2.80m Norwegian for-
            est   2.00 .75
975 A525 2.80m Persian   2.00 .75
Size: 59x35mm
976 A525 2.80m European do-
            mestic female   2.00 .75
977 A525 2.80m Three kittens,
            frog   2.00 .75
   a. Booklet pane of 6, #972-977 12.00
      Complete booklet, #977a 12.00

UN, 50th
Anniv. — A526

1995, Oct. 20   **Perf. 14**
978 A526 3.40m multicolored   1.60 1.25

A527

Christmas
A528

1995, Nov. 3   **Litho.**   **Perf. 14**
979 A527 2m Santa on skates 1.25 .20
980 A528 2.80m Poinsettias   1.25 .70

Letter
Stamps
A529

UNICEF, 50th Anniv.
A530

1996, Feb 2   **Litho.**   **Perf. 13½x14**
Booklet Stamps
981 A529 1m "M"   .65 .65
982 A529 1m "O"   .65 .65
983 A529 1m "I"   .65 .65
984 A529 1m "H"   .65 .65
985 A529 1m "E"   .65 .65
986 A529 1m "J"   .65 .65
987 A529 1m "A"   .65 .65
988 A529 1m "N"   .65 .65
989 A529 1m "T"   .65 .65
990 A529 1m "P"   .65 .65
991 A529 1m "U"   .65 .65
992 A529 1m "S"   .65 .65
   a. Booklet pane of 12, #981-992 7.75 7.75
      Complete booklet, No. 992a 7.75

1996, Feb. 2   **Perf. 14**
993 A530 2.80m multicolored   1.40 .65

Women's
Gymnastics in
Finland,
Cent. — A531

1996, Feb. 26   **Litho.**   **Perf. 13**
994 A531 2.80m multicolored   1.40 .65

Woman
Suffrage,
90th Anniv.
A532

Litho. & Engr.
1996, Mar. 8   **Perf. 13**
995 A532 3.20m multicolored   1.25 .75

Europa.

Cinema,
Cent. — A533

Finnish films: No. 996, "Juha," 1937. No. 997, "Laveata Tieta," 1931. No. 998, "Tuntematon Sotilas," 1935. No. 999, Oldest known photo of a motion picture show, 1896. No. 1000, "Jäniksen Vuosi," 1977. No. 1001, "Valkoinen Peura," 1952. No. 1002, "Kaikki Rakastavat," 1935. No. 1003, "Varjoja Paratiisissa," 1986.

1996, Apr. 1   **Litho.**   **Perf. 14x13½**
Booklet Stamps
996 A533 2.80m multicolored 1.40 .75
997 A533 2.80m multicolored 1.40 .75
998 A533 2.80m multicolored 1.40 .75
999 A533 2.80m multicolored 1.40 .75
1000 A533 2.80m multicolored 1.40 .75
1001 A533 2.80m multicolored 1.40 .75
1002 A533 2.80m multicolored 1.40 .75
1003 A533 2.80m multicolored 1.40 .75
   a. Bklt. pane of 8, #996-1003 11.50 11.50
      Complete booklet, #1003a 11.50

Radio,
Cent. — A534

1996, Apr. 25   **Perf. 14**
1004 A534 4.30m multicolored 2.10 1.25

1996 Summer
Olympic Games,
Atlanta — A535

1996, June 3   **Litho.**   **Perf. 12 Vert.**
Booklet Stamps
1005 A535 3.40m Kayaking   2.00 2.00
1006 A535 3.40m Sailing   2.00 2.00
1007 A535 3.40m Rowing   2.00 2.00
1008 A535 3.40m Swimming   2.00 2.00
   a. Booklet pane of 4, #1005-1008 8.00 8.00
      Complete booklet, #1008a 8.00

Insect Type of 1994

1996, July 1   **Litho.**   **Perf. 13**
1009 A508 19m Dytiscus
           marginalis   11.00 11.00

Shore
Birds — A536

#1010, Gallinago gallinago. #1011, Haematopus ostralegus. #1012, Scolopax rusticola. #1013, Vanellus vanellus. #1014, Numenius arquata.

Perf. 13½ on 3 Sides
1996, Sept. 6   **Litho. & Engr.**
1010 A536 2.80m multicolored 1.60 .75
1011 A536 2.80m multicolored 1.60 .75
1012 A536 2.80m multicolored 1.60 .75
1013 A536 2.80m multicolored 1.60 .75
Size: 30x52mm
1014 A536 2.80m multicolored 1.60 .75
   a. Sheet of 5, #1010-1014 8.00 8.00

Finnish Comic
Strips — A537

#1015, "Professor Itikainen" examining plant with magnifying glass, by Ilmari Vainio. #1016, "Pekka Puupää (Peter Blockhead)" taking letter from mailbox, by Ola Fogelberg. #1017, "Joonas" holding drawing pencil, by Veikko Savolainen. #1018, "Mämmilä" wearing helmet, by Tarmo Koivisto. #1019, "Rymy-Eetu" smoking pipe, by Erkki Tanttu. #1020, "Kieku" writing letter, by Asmo Alho. # 1021, "Pikku Risunen" with animal, by Riitta Uusitalo. # 1022, "Kiti" holding up pencil, by Kati Kovács.

1996, Oct. 9   **Litho.**   **Perf. 13½**
Booklet Stamps
1015 A537 2.80m black & red 1.60 .75
1016 A537 2.80m black & red 1.60 .75
1017 A537 2.80m red & black 1.60 .75
1018 A537 2.80m black & red 1.60 .75
1019 A537 2.80m black & red 1.60 .75
1020 A537 2.80m red & black 1.60 .75
1021 A537 2.80m red & black 1.60 .75
1022 A537 2.80m red & black 1.60 .75
   a. Bklt. pane of 8, #1015-1022 13.00 13.00
      Complete booklet, #1022a 13.50

Christmas
A538

2m, Snowman, Santa, gnome playing musical instruments. 2.80m, Rabbit, reindeer watching northern lights. 3.20m, Santa reading letters.

1996, Nov. 1   **Litho.**   **Perf. 14**
1023 A538 2m multi   1.25 .50
1024 A538 2.80m multi   1.40 .55
1025 A538 3.20m multi, vert. 1.50 .85
   Nos. 1023-1025 (3) 4.15 1.90

Greetings
Stamps — A539

End of 19th cent.: #1026, Two angels. #1027, Flowers in basket. #1028, Hand reaching through garland, bluebird. #1029, Boy, girl dancing. #1030, Boy, envelope, shamrocks. #1031, Clasping hands through heart-shaped garlands. #1032, Roses. #1033, Angel.

Perf. 13x12½ on 3 Sides
1997, Jan. 30   **Litho.**
Booklet Stamps
1026 A539 1 multicolored 2.00 .75
1027 A539 1 multicolored 2.00 .75
1028 A539 1 multicolored 2.00 .75
1029 A539 1 multicolored 2.00 .75
1030 A539 1 multicolored 2.00 .75
1031 A539 1 multicolored 2.00 .75
1032 A539 1 multicolored 2.00 .75
1033 A539 1 multicolored 2.00 .75
   a. Bklt. pane of 8, #1026-1033 16.00 16.00
      Complete booklet, #1033a 17.50

Nos. 1026-1033 sold for 2.80m on day of issue.
Number on stamp represents class of mail.

Mail Order
Sales in
Finland,
Cent. — A540

1997, Jan. 30   **Perf. 13½x14**
1034 A540 2.80m multicolored 1.40 .50

1997 Ice Hockey
World
Championships,
Helsinki — A541

1997, Jan. 30
1035 A541 2.80m multicolored   1.40   .50

On each stamp from the right vertical row of
the sheet, No. 1035 exists without the thin,
curved black line at the center right edge of
the stamp. Value, single stamp $2.50

Lepus Timidus
A542

1997, Mar. 4   Litho.   Perf. 14
1036 A542 2.80m multicolored   1.40   .50

Saami Folktale, "Girl Who Turned into
a Golden Merganser" — A543

Europa: 3.20m, Duck, girl, prince. 3.40m,
Girl falling into crevice.

1997, Mar. 4   Perf. 13
1037 A543 3.20m multicolored   1.50   .50
1038 A543 3.40m multicolored   1.60   .60

Paavo Nurmi
(1897-1973),
Winner of 9
Olympic Gold
Medals — A544

1997, Mar. 18   Perf. 14
1039 A544 3.40m multicolored   1.60 1.60

Southwest
Archipelago
Natl.
Park — A545

Litho. & Engr.
1997, Apr. 25   Perf. 14
1040 A545 4.30m multicolored   2.10 1.25

Tango — A546

A547

1997, May 19   Litho.
1041 A546 1 multicolored   1.60   .50
        Complete booklet of 5   8.25

No. 1041 sold for 2.80m on day of release.
Number on stamp represents class of mail.

1997, May 19   Perf. 13½
Sailing Ships: #1042, Astrid. #1043, Jacob-
stads Wapen. #1044, Tradewind. #1045, Mer-
ikokko. #1046, Suomen Joutsen. #1047,
Sigyn.

Booklet Stamps
1042 A547 2.80m multicolored   1.40   .65
1043 A547 2.80m multicolored   1.40   .65
1044 A547 2.80m multicolored   1.40   .65
1045 A547 2.80m multicolored   1.40   .65

Size: 48x25½mm
1046 A547 2.80m multicolored   1.40   .65
1047 A547 2.80m multicolored   1.40   .65
   a.   Booklet pane of 6, #1042-1047   8.50
        Complete booklet, #1047a   8.50

Pres. Martti
Ahtisaari, 60th
Birthday
A548

1997, June 23   Litho.   Perf. 14
1048 A548 2.80m multicolored   1.40   .50

Independence,
80th
Anniv. — A549

Four seasons: No. 1049, Spring, lily-of-the-
valley (natl. flower). No. 1050, Summer, white
clouds. No. 1051, Fall, colorful leaves. No.
1052, Winter, snow crystals.

Perf. 13x12½ on 2 or 3 Sides
1997, June 23
Booklet Stamps
1049 A549 2.80m multicolored   1.40   .75
1050 A549 2.80m multicolored   1.40   .75
1051 A549 2.80m multicolored   1.40   .75
1052 A549 2.80m multicolored   1.40   .75
   a.   Booklet pane, #1049-1052   6.00 6.00
        Complete booklet, #1052a   6.25

Souvenir Sheet

A550

Grus Grus (Cranes): a, With young. b, With
frog. c, Performing mating dance. d, In flight.

1997, Aug. 19   Litho.   Perf. 14
1053 A550 2.80m Sheet of 4,
              #a.-d.   8.00 8.00

A551

1997, Oct. 9   Litho.   Perf. 14¼, 14½
Finnish Writers Assoc. (Covers from books):
No. 1054, "Seven Brothers," by Aleksis Kivi.
No. 1055, "Sinuhe the Egyptian," by Mika
Waltari. No. 1056, "Täällä Pohjantähden alla
I," by Väinö Linna. No. 1057, "Hyvästi Iijoki,"
by Kalle Päätalo. No. 1058, "Haukka, minum
rakkaani," by Kaari Utrio. No. 1059, "Juhan-
nustanssit," by Hannu Salama. No. 1060,
"Manillaköysi," by Veijo Meri. No. 1061, "Uppo-
Nalle ja Kumma," by Elina Karjalainen.

Booklet Stamps
1054 A551 2.80m multicolored   1.40   .75
1055 A551 2.80m multicolored   1.40   .75
1056 A551 2.80m multicolored   1.40   .75
1057 A551 2.80m multicolored   1.40   .75
1058 A551 2.80m multicolored   1.40   .75
1059 A551 2.80m multicolored   1.40   .75

1060 A551 2.80m multicolored   1.40   .75
1061 A551 2.80m multicolored   1.40   .75
   a.   Booklet pane, #1054-1061   11.50 11.50
        Complete booklet, #1061a   11.50

No. 1056 exists perf 14½x14¼. The other
values also should exist thus. The editors
would like to examine such stamps.

Christmas
A552

1997, Oct. 31
1062 A552 2m Village   1.25   .50
1063 A552 2.80m Candelabra,
              vert.   1.40   .55
1064 A552 3.20m Church, vert.   1.60   .85
        Nos. 1062-1064 (3)   4.25 1.90

Wildlife
A553

2nd, Stizostedion lucioperca. 1st, Turdus
merula.

**Die Cut 10 Horiz., Syncopated Type
A**
1998, Jan. 15   Litho.
**Self-Adhesive
Coil Stamps**
1065 A553 2 multicolored   1.50 1.00
1066 A553 1 multicolored   1.50 1.00

Nos. 1065-1066 were valued at 2.40m and
2.80m, respectively, on date of issue. Number
on stamp represents class of mail.
See Nos. 1099-1100.

A554   A555

Moomin Cartoon Characters, by Tove Jansson: No. 1067, Boy Moomin drawing with pad
and pencil. No. 1068, Girl Moomin in sunshine. No. 1069, Organ grinder. No. 1070, Boy
Moomin giving flower to girl Moomin.

1998, Jan. 15   Perf. 13 (on 3 Sides)
Booklet Stamps
1067 A554 1 multicolored   2.50   .90
1068 A554 1 multicolored   2.50   .90
1069 A554 1 multicolored   2.50   .90
1070 A554 1 multicolored   2.50   .90
   a.   Booklet pane, #1067-1070   11.00 11.00
        Complete booklet, #1070a   12.00

Nos. 1067-1070 each sold for 2.80m on day
of issue. Number on stamp represents class of
mail.
See No. 1127.

1998, Feb. 3   Perf. 14
1071 A555 2.80m multicolored   1.40   .50

Finnish Federation of Nurses, cent.

A556   A557

Valentine's Day Surprise Stamps. (Designs
beneath scratch-off heart): a, Musical notes,
two dogs. b, Elephant, mouse and flowers. c,
Puppy, sealed envelope. d, Kittens, kittens
hugging. e, Dog with nose in air, bouquet of
flowers. f, Flowers, two rodents.

1998, Feb. 3   Perf. 12
1072   1 Sheet of 6   12.50 12.50
  a.-f. A556 Any single, un-
             scratched   2.00   .90

Nos. 1072a-1072f were each valued at
2.80m on day of issue. Number on stamp represents class of mail. Unused values are for
singles with attached selvage. Inscriptions are
shown in selvage above or below each stamp.
Each stamp bears a heart-shaped, golden
scratch-off overlay. Values are for unscratched
examples. Scratched stamps, with hearts partially or fully removed, sell for about 20 percent
less.

1998, Mar. 27   Litho.   Perf. 14
1073 A557 2.80m Tussilago
              farfara   1.40   .50

National
Festivals
A558

Europa: 3.20m, Boy and girl, balloons,
"Vappu" (May Day). 3.40m, Boy and girl in a
dream floating over water, Midsummer
Festival.

1998, Mar. 27   Perf. 14x14½
1074 A558 3.20m multicolored   1.50   .50
1075 A558 3.40m multicolored   1.60   .60

Finnish Marine
Research
Institute, 80th
Anniv. — A559

Designs: 2.80m, Research vessel, "Aranda."
3.20m, "Vega," chart showing route of Nils
Adolf Erik Nordenskjold's expedition.

Litho. & Engr.
1998, May 7   Perf. 14x13
1076 A559 2.80m multicolored   1.40   .90
1077 A559 3.20m multicolored   1.50   .90

First Performance of National Anthem,
150th Anniv. — A560

1998, May 7   Perf. 13
1078 A560 5m multicolored   2.40 1.25

Puppies
A561

#1079, Bernese Mountain dog. #1080, Puli.
#1081, Boxer. #1082, Bichon Frisé. #1083,
Finnish lapphound. #1084, Wire-haired dachs-
hund. #1085, Scottish cairn terrier. #1086,
Labrador retriever.

Perf. 13½x13 on 2 or 3 Sides
1998, June 4   Litho.
Booklet Stamps
1079 A561 1 multicolored   2.00   .65
1080 A561 1 multicolored   2.00   .65
1081 A561 1 multicolored   2.00   .65
1082 A561 1 multicolored   2.00   .65
1083 A561 1 multicolored   2.00   .65
1084 A561 1 multicolored   2.00   .65
1085 A561 1 multicolored   2.00   .65
1086 A561 1 multicolored   2.00   .65
   a.   Booklet pane, #1079-1086   16.00 16.00
        Complete booklet, #1086a   18.00

Nos. 1079-1086 each sold for 2.80m on day
of issue. Number on stamp represents class of
mail.

Owls — A562   Cycling — A563

Designs: a, Bubo bubo. b, Wing of bubo bubo. c, Bubo bubo, aegolius funereus. d, Strix nebulosa. e, Nyctea scandiaca.

1998, Sept. 4   Litho.   Perf. 13½
1087   Sheet of 5 + label   10.50 10.50
a.-e. A562 3m any single   2.00   1.00

#1087b is 52x27mm; #1087c-1087d, 26x44mm; #1087e, 30x44mm.
See No. 1113.

1998, Sept. 4   Perf. 14
1088 A563 3m multicolored   1.25   .50

Finnish Design — A564

#1089, Savoy vases, by Alvar Aalto. #1090, Karuselli chair, by Yrjö Kukkapuro. #1091, Tasaraita knitwear, designed by Annika Rimala for Marimekko. #1092, Kilta tableware set, by Kaj Franck. #1093, Cast iron pot, by Timo Sarpaneva. #1094, Carelia cutlery set, by Bertel Gardberg.

Perf. 13½ on 3 Sides
1998, Oct. 9   Litho.
Booklet Stamps
1089 A564 3m multicolored   2.00   1.00
1090 A564 3m multicolored   2.00   1.00
1091 A564 3m multicolored   2.00   1.00
1092 A564 3m multicolored   2.00   1.00
1093 A564 3m multicolored   2.00   1.00
1094 A564 3m multicolored   2.00   1.00
a. Booklet pane, #1089-1094   12.00 12.00
   Complete booklet, #1094a   12.50

Nos. 1090-1091, 1093-1094 are 29x34mm.

Christmas A565

Designs: 2m, Christmas tree, children, vert. 3m, Children, dog riding sled. 3.20m, Winter scene of cottage in center of island.

1998, Oct. 30   Perf. 14
1095 A565 2m multicolored   1.25   .50
1096 A565 3m multicolored   1.40   .65
1097 A565 3.20m multicolored 1.50   .90
   Nos. 1095-1097 (3)   4.15 2.05

Souvenir Sheet

Mika Häkkinen, Formula 1 Driving Champion — A566

1999, Jan. 15   Perf. 13½
1098 A566 3m multicolored   1.60 1.60

Native Wildlife Type of 1998
2nd, Salmo salar. 1st, Luscinia svecica.

1999, Jan. 27   Litho.   Die Cut
Coil Stamps
Self-Adhesive
1099 A553 2 multi   1.60   .75
Die Cut
1100 A553 1 multi, vert.   1.60   .50

Nos. 1099-1100 were valued at 2.40m and 3m, respectively, on day of issue. Number on stamp represents class of mail.

Friendship A567

Animals' tails: No. 1101, Zebra, lion. No. 1102, Dog, cat.

Serpentine Die Cut Perf. 13xDie Cut
1999, Jan. 27
Booklet Stamps
Self-Adhesive
1101 A567 3m multicolored   1.40   .65
1102 A567 3m multicolored   1.40   .65
a.   Bklt. pane, 3 each #1101-1102   8.50   8.00

No. 1102a is a complete booklet.

Finnish Labor Movement, Cent. — A568

1999, Jan. 27   Perf. 13½
1103 A568 4.50m multicolored   2.50 2.50

Finland's Roads — A569

#1104, Snow-covered landscape, Arctic Ocean Road. #1105, Freeway interchanges, Jyväsjtkä Lakeshore Road. #1106, Raippaluoto Bridge. #1107, Wooded drive, Kitee.

1999, Feb. 15   Litho.   Perf. 14 Horiz.
Booklet Stamps
1104 A569 3m multicolored   1.60 1.25
a.   Perf. 12¾ horiz.   75.00 13.00
1105 A569 3m multicolored   1.60 1.25
a.   Perf. 12¾ horiz.   75.00 13.00
1106 A569 3m multicolored   1.60 1.25
a.   Perf. 12¾ horiz.   75.00 13.00
1107 A569 3m multicolored   1.60 1.25
a.   Booklet pane, #1104-1107   6.50
   Complete booklet, #1107a   7.50
b.   Perf. 12¾ horiz.   75.00 13.00
c.   Booklet pane, #1104a, 1105a, 1106a, 1107b   300.00 300.00
   Complete booklet, #1107c   325.00

A570   A571

Women's Kalevala-style brooches: a, Horse clasp. b, Bird clasp. c, Virusmäki clasp.

1999, Feb. 15   Perf. 13½x14
1108   Sheet of 3   4.25 4.25
a.-c. A570 3m any single   1.40 1.00

1st Publication of Legend of the Kalevala, 150th Anniv.

1999, Mar. 15   Perf. 13x13½
1109 A571 3m Crocus vernus   1.40   .65

Martha Organization, Cent. — A572

1999, Mar. 15   Perf. 13½x13
1110 A572 3m multicolored   1.40   .65

Europa A573

1999, Mar. 15   Perf. 13½x14
1111 A573 2.70m Esplanade Park   1.25   .50
1112 A573 3.20m Ruissalo Park   1.50   .60

Bird Type of 1998
Designs: a, Luscinia luscinia. b, Cuculus canorus. c, Botaurus stellaris. d, Caprimulgus europaeus. e, Crex crex.

1999, May 18   Perf. 13½
1113   Sheet of 5 + label   8.00 8.00
a.-e. A562 3m any single   1.60 1.25

No. 1113b is 25x43mm. No. 1113c is 45x30mm. No. 1113d-1113e are 26x37mm.

Finland's Presidency of European Union — A574

1999, July 1   Litho.   Perf. 13¾x13½
1114 A574 3.50m multicolored   1.60   .75

Finnish Entertainers A575

a, Harmony Sisters, Vera (1914-97), Maire (1916-95) & Raija (1918-97) Valtonen. b, Olavi Virta (1915-72), singer. c, Georg Malmstén (1902-81), composer, conductor. d, Topi Kärki (1915-22), composer, and Reino (Repe) Helismaa (1913-65), lyricist. e, Tapio Rautavaara (1915-79), singer. f, Esa Parkarinen (1911-89), musician, actor.

Perf. 13¼ on 3 Sides
1999, Sept. 6   Litho.
1115   Booklet pane of 6   9.75
a.-f. A575 3.50m any single   1.60   .85
   Complete booklet, #1115   9.75

Nos. 1115a, 1115d are each 60x34mm.

Finnish Commercial Product Design — A576

---

a, Fiskars cutting tools. b, Zoel/Versoul guitars. c, Ergo II/Silenta hearing protectors. d, Ponsse Cobra HS 10 tree harvester. e, Suunto compass. f, Exel Avanti QLS ski pole.
Illustration reduced.

Perf. 13¼ on 3 sides
1999, Oct 8   Litho.
1116   Booklet pane of 6   10.00
a.-f. A576 3.50m any single   1.60   .85
   Complete booklet, #1116   10.50

Size of b, c, e, f: 30x35mm.

"The Nativity," by Giorgio di Chirico (1888-1978) A577

Rabbits, Birds — A578

1999, Nov. 5   Perf. 14
1117 A578 2.50m Santa Claus, vert.   1.25   .50
1118 A577 3m multicolored   1.50 1.50
1119 A578 3.50m multicolored   2.00   .75
   Nos. 1117-1119 (3)   4.75 2.75

Christmas. See Italy Nos. 2314-2315.

Sveaborg Fortress — A579

2000, Jan. 12 Litho. Perf. 13¾x13½
1120 A579 7.20m multi   3.50 2.00

Helsinki, 450th Anniv. A580

Designs: No. 1121, Baltic herring market (designer's name at UL).
No. 1122: a, Museum of Contemporary Art (blue building), vert. b, Cathedral, Senate Square (green building). c, Finlandia Hall (orange building). d, Glass Palace Film and Media Center (red building), vert.
No. 1123: a, Quest for the Lost Crown, Sveaborg Fortress (children and arch), vert. b, Like No. 1121, no designer's name. c, Forces of Light City Festival. d, Cellist at outdoor concert, Kaivopuisto Park.

2000, Jan. 12   Perf. 14
1121 A580 3.50m multi   2.00 2.00
Perf. 14½x14¾ (vert. stamps),
14¾x14½
1122   Booklet pane of 4   8.00 8.00
a.-d. A580 3.50m Any single   2.00 2.00
1123   Booklet pane of 4   8.00 8.00
a.-d. A580 3.50m Any single   2.00 2.00
   Complete booklet, #1122-1123   17.00

Valentine's Day — A581

Designs: a, Earth as backpack. b, Painters on ladder. c, Birds in balloon. d, Alien with magnet. e, Boy with heart-shaped balloon. f, Polar bear and igloo.

Perf. 13x12¾ on 3 sides
2000, Jan. 12
1124   Bklt. pane of 6 + 4 labels   10.00
a.-f. A581 3.50m Any single   1.60   .90
   Complete booklet, #1124   10.50

Souvenir Sheet of 2

Tommi Mäkinen, 1999 Rally World
Champion — A582

a, Mäkinen behind wheel. b, Race car.

2000, Mar. 3		**Perf. 13x13¼**
1125 A582 3.50m #a.-b.		3.25 3.25

Easter — A583

2000, Mar. 15		**Perf. 13¾x13¼**
1126 A583 3.50m Caltha palus-		
tris		1.60 .75

Moomin Type of 1998

a, Rat with broom looking at Moomins. b,
Moomin with uniform, figures sprouting from
ground. c, Moomin with hat in forest. d,
Moomin with hat, children, in front of stove.

Perf. 13x12¾ on 3 sides		
2000, Mar. 15		
1127 Booklet pane of 4		30.00 30.00
a.-d. A554 1 Any single		7.50 1.25
Complete booklet, #1127		30.00 12.00
e. As #1127, perf. 13¼ on 3		
sides		12.00
f.-i. As #a-d, perf. 13¼ on 3 sides		2.75 .65
Booklet, #1127e		12.50

Nos. 1127a-1127d sold for 3.50m on day of
issue. Number on stamp represents class of
mail.
Issued: No. 1127e, 7/10/00.

Jubilee
Year — A584

Turku Cathedral: a, Nave. b, Woman, votive
candles. c, Christ on the Mount of Transfiguration, alterpiece. d, Infant baptism.

2000, Mar. 15 Litho.		**Perf. 14 Vert.**
1128 Booklet pane of 4		8.00
a.-d. A584 3.50m Any single		2.00 1.00
Complete booklet, #1128		8.00

Europa, 2000
Common Design Type

2000, May 9		**Perf. 13¼x13**
1129 CD17 3.50m multi		2.00 .90

Provincial Flowers

Spring   Blue
Anemone   Cornflower
A585   A586

Pulsatilla
Patens — A587

Die Cut Perf. 13x12½		
2000-2001		**Litho.**
Self-Adhesive		
1130 A585 1 multi		1.60 .50
1131 A586 1 multi		1.60 .50
1132 A587 1 multi		1.60 .50
a. Pane, 5 each #1131-1132		17.00

Number on stamp represents class of mail.
No. 1130 sold for 3.50m at time of release and
was issued in sheets of 10. Nos. 1131-1132
each sold for 3.60m on day of issue.
Issued: No. 1130, 5/9. Nos. 1131-1132,
5/16/01.

Souvenir Sheet

Science — A595

Designs: a, Children, molecuar model (triangular stamp). b, Man's face, DNA strand
(rhomboid stamp). c, Man's face, Sierpinski
triangles (square stamp).

2000, May 30		**Perf. 14¼**
1140 A595 3.50m Sheet of 3,		
#a.-c.		5.00 5.00

No. 1140 has holographic image. Soaking in
water may affect the hologram.

Finnish Design — A596

No. 1141: a, Rug, by Akseli Gallen-Kallela
(1865-1931). b, Pearl Bird, by Birger
Kaipiainen (1915-88). c, Pot, by Kyllikki
Salmenhaara (1915-81). d, Leaf, by Tapio
Wirkkala (1915-85). e, Detail from damask, by
Dora Jung (1906-80). f, Glass vase, by Valter
Jung (1879-1946).

Perf. 13¼ on 3 sides		
2000, Sept. 5		**Litho.**
1141 Booklet pane of 6		12.00 12.00
a.-f. A596 3.50m Any single		2.00 1.25
Booklet, #1141		12.50

Size of b, c, e, f: 30x35mm.

Coregonus
Lavaretus
A597

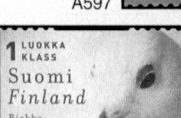

Lagopus
Lagopus
A598

Die Cut 10 Horiz. Sync. Type B		
2000, Sept. 5		
Self-Adhesive		
Coil Stamps		
1142 A597 2 multi		1.60 1.00
Die Cut 10 Horiz. Sync. Type A		
1143 A598 1 multi		1.60 .50

Nos. 1142-1143 sold for 3m and 3.50m
respectively on day of sale.

> On modern stamps bearing the
> "denominations" "1" or "2," the num-
> ber represents the class of mail.

Christmas
A599

2.50m, Costumed Tiernapojat carol singers.
3.50m, Bullfinch on door ornament, vert.

Serpentine Die Cut 14¼		
2000, Nov. 3		**Photo.**
Self-Adhesive		
1144-1145 A599 Set of 2		3.00 1.25

Christmas Type of 2000

Design: No. 1146, Like #1145.

Serpentine Die Cut 13¾		
2000, Nov. 3		**Litho.**
Self-Adhesive		
1146 A599 3.50m multi + label		5.25 5.25

No. 1146 issued in sheets of 20 that sold for
120m, together with a separate sheet of stickers that could be affixed on the label. The
labels attached to the stamps are separated
by a row of interrupted serpentine die cutting.
Labels could be personalized with photographs taken at some sale sites.

European
Year of
Languages
A600

2001, Jan. 17 Litho.		**Perf. 13¼**
1147 A600 1 multi		2.00 .80

No. 1147 sold for 3.50m on day of sale.

World Ski Championships,
Lahti — A601

No. 1148: a, Ski jumper Janne Ahonen (yellow helmet). b, Skier Mika Myllylä.

2001, Jan. 17		
1148 A601 3.50m Horiz. pair,		
#a-b		4.00 4.00

Valentine's
Day — A602

No. 1149: a, Oval wreath. b, Basket of flowers, letter. c, Heart-shaped wreath. d, Bouquet
of flowers, letter. e, Flowers, tea set. f, Flowers, heart-shaped pastry.

Serpentine Die Cut 11½x11¾ on 3 Sides		
2001, Jan. 17		**Photo.**
Self-Adhesive		
1149 Booklet pane of 6		12.50 12.50
a.-f. A602 1 Any single		2.00 .90
Booklet, #1149		13.00

Nos. 1149a-1149f each sold for 3.50m on
day of issue.

Souvenir Sheet

Donald Duck Comics in Finland, 50th
Anniv. — A603

No. 1150: a, Mickey Mouse, Donald Duck,
Santa Claus, Goofy. b, First comics, silhouette
of boy. c, Tin soldier with Finnish flag, Chip
and Dale (25x30mm). d, Finnish epic hero
Väinämöinien, silhouette of Donald Duck. e,
Helsinki Cathedral, Donald Duck.

Perf. 7¾ on 3 or 4 Sides		
2001, Mar. 13		**Litho.**
1150 A603 1 Sheet of 5, #a-e		10.00 10.00

Nos. 1150a-1150e sold for 3.50m each on
day of issue.

Santa Claus and
Sleigh — A604

2001-04 Serpentine Die Cut 14½x14		
Self-Adhesive		
1151 A604		2.00 .75
a. Serpentine die cut 13¾x13¼ ('04)		2.00 1.75

No. 1151 sold for 3.60m on day of issue. No.
1151a sold for 65c on day of issue.
No. 1151, 4/2/01. No. 1151a, 12/04.

Europa
A605

2001, Apr. 2		**Perf. 13x13½**
1152 A605 5.40m multi		3.50 3.50

Easter — A606

No. 1153: a, Chick. b, Decorated egg.

2001, Apr. 2		**Perf. 13¼**
1153 A606 3.60m Horiz. pair,		
#a-b		4.00 4.00

Souvenir Sheet

Verla Mill, UNESCO World Heritage Site — A607

Denominations in: a, UL. b, UR. c, LL. d, LR.

2001, Apr. 2
1154 A607 3.60m Sheet of 4, #a-d   8.00 7.75

Orienteering World Championships, Tampere — A608

2001, May 16
1155 A608 3.60m multi   1.75 .75

Values are for stamps with surrounding selvage.

Souvenir Sheet

Woodpeckers — A609

No. 1156: a, Dendrocopos minor (32x36mm). b, Picoides tridactylus (29x36mm). c, Dendrocopos leucotos (32x42mm). d, Dendrocopos major (29x42mm). e, Picus canus (32x41mm). f, Dryocopus martius (29x41mm).

Perf. 14½x14¼ on 2, 3 or 4 Sides
2001, May 16
1156 A609 3.60m Sheet of 6, #a-f   12.00 12.00

Marine Life — A610

No. 1157: a, Lampetra fluviatilis. b, Aspius aspius. c, Coregonus albula.
Type C Syncopation (1st stamp, #1157): On the top, groups of 3 holes at left and right and a central group of four holes, separated by 2 oval holes equal in width to 4 holes.

Perf. 10 Horiz. Sync. Type C
2001, Sept. 6   **Photo.**
Self-Adhesive
Coil Stamps
1157   Horiz. strip of 3   6.25 6.00
a.-c.   A610 2 Any single   2.00 2.00

Nos. 1157a-1157c were sold in boxes of 100 stamps that sold at a discount price of 270m on day of sale. The franking value on the day of sale for each stamp was 3m.

Birds A611

No. 1158: a, Parus caeruleus. b, Motacilla alba. c, Oriolus oriolus.

Perf. 10 Horiz. Sync. Type B
2001, Sept. 6   **Photo.**
Self-Adhesive
Coil Stamps
1158   Horiz. strip of 3   6.25 4.75
a.-c.   A611 1 Any single   2.00 .65

Nos. 1158a-1158c were sold in boxes of 100 stamps that sold at a discount price of 330m on day of sale. The franking value on the day of sale for each stamp was 3.60m.

History of Gulf of Finland A612

No. 1159: a, Utö Lighthouse. b, Wreck of the St. Mikael. c, Diver exploring St. Mikael. d, Opossum shrimp, isopod. e, Ship's cabin and nautical chart (32x55mm).

Perf. 13¼x13¾ on 2 or 3 Sides
2001, Sept. 6   **Litho.**
1159   Booklet pane of 5   10.00 10.00
a.-e.   A612 1 Any single   2.00 1.25
    Booklet, #1159   10.50

Nos. 1159a-1159e each sold for 3.60m on day of sale.
See No. 1177.

Christmas A613

Designs: 2.50m, Elf reading Santa's book, candle. 3.60m, Elf delivering package on sled, horiz.

Serpentine Die Cut 14¼
2001, Oct. 26   **Photo.**
Self-Adhesive
1160 A613 2.50m multi   1.25 .50
1161 A613 3.60m multi   1.75 .90

Slightly larger examples of Nos. 1160-1161 serpentine die cut 14 are known on first day and other covers produced by the postal service. They were not sold unused to the public.

100 Cents = 1 Euro (€)

Flowers — A614

National Symbols A615

Heraldic Lion — A616

Type A614 — No. 1162, Myosotis scorpioides: a, Forty-one flowers. b, Four flowers, five buds. c, One flower, four buds. d, Entire plant. e, Five flowers.
No. 1163, Convallaria majallis: a, Leaf, stem with five flowers. b, Two leaves, stem with eight flowers. c, Two flowers. d, Two leaves, stem with five flowers. e, Entire plants.
Type A615: 50c, Swan, vert. 60c, Birch. 1, Flag and bird. 90c, Kymintehtaalta, by Victor Westerholm. €1.30, Granite cliff. €2.50, Spruce. €3.50, Pine.

Die Cut Perf. 15
2002, Jan. 1   **Photo.**
Self-Adhesive
1162   Vert. strip of 5   .75 .75
a.-e.   A614 5c Any single   .20 .20
f.   As #1162, die cut perf 14   .75
g.-k.   A614 5c Any single, die cut perf 14   .20 .20
1163   Vert. strip of 5   1.50 1.50
a.-e.   A614 10c Any single   .30 .20

Die Cut Perf. 14
1164 A615   50c multi   1.40 .50
1165 A615   60c multi   2.25 .50

Die Cut Perf. 13¾
1166 A615   1 multi   1.75 .50
a.   Booklet pane of 8   17.00
    Booklet, #1166a   17.50

Die Cut Perf. 14¾x15
1167 A615   90c multi   2.50 1.50

Die Cut Perf. 12 Syncopated
1168 A616   €1 blue & multi   3.00 1.75

Die Cut Perf. 14¾x15
1169 A615   €1.30 multi   3.75 2.75
a.   Die cut perf 14 ('04)   3.75 2.75

Die Cut Perf. 14
1170 A615   €2.50 multi   7.25 4.00
1171 A615   €3.50 multi   10.00 5.50

Die Cut Perf. 12 Syncopated
1172 A616   €5 red & multi   14.50 10.50
    Nos. 1162-1172 (11)   48.65 29.75

No. 1166 sold for 60c on day of issue.
Die cut perf 14 examples of No. 1167 exist on first day and other covers produced by the postal service. They were not sold unused to the public.
No. 1169a issued 7/04. No. 1169a has a duller blue panel and a duller black denomination than that found on No. 1169, and a die cut perf. 14 version of No. 1169 that was available only on first day covers with 1/1/02 cancels, and which was not made available to the public unused. Nos. 1169 and 1169a were produced by different printers.
Nos. 1162f-1162k were printed and put on first day and other covers in 2002 but were not sold to the public until 2006.
See Nos. 1179-1180.

Easter — A617

Die Cut Perf. 14
2002, Mar. 6   **Photo.**
Self-Adhesive
1173 A617 60c multi   1.75 1.75

Souvenir Sheet

Elias Lönnrot (1802-84), Botanist, Linguist — A618

No. 1174: a, Plantain. b, Opening lines of "Kalevala" (denomination at UL). c, Closing lines of "Kalevala" (denomination at UR). d, Portrait.

Perf. 13¼ on 3 or 4 Sides
2002, Mar. 6   **Litho.**
1174 A618 60c Sheet of 4, #a-d   7.00 7.00

Souvenir Sheet

Old Rauma, UNESCO World Heritage Site — A619

Denominations at: a, UL. b, UR. c, LL. d, LR.

2002, Mar. 6   **Perf. 13½**
1175 A619 60c Sheet of 4, #a-d   7.00 7.00

Europa — A620

2002, Apr. 15   **Perf. 13**
1176 A620 60c multi   1.75 1.75

Gulf of Finland Type of 2001

No. 1177: a, Birds, fish. b, Sailboat, plankton. c, Flounder on sea bed. d, Shrimp, herring. e, Tvärminne Zoological Station, ship, isopod, oceanographic equipment, mussels (32x55mm).

Perf. 13¼x13¾ on 2 or 3 Sides
2002, Apr. 15
1177   Booklet pane of 5   10.00 10.00
a.-e.   A612 1 Any single   2.00 1.25
    Booklet, #1177   11.00

Nos. 1177a-1177e each sold for 60c on day of issue.

Sibelius Monument, Helsinki, by Eila Hiltunen A621

2002, May 3   **Perf. 13**
1178 A621 60c multi   1.75 .50

National Symbols Type of 2002
Without Finland Post Emblem

Designs: 60c, Juniperus communis. 1, Reindeer in Lapland.

Die Cut Perf. 14

2002, Oct. 9   **Photo.**

Self-Adhesive

1179	A615	60c multi	1.75	.50
1180	A615	1 multi	1.75	.50

No. 1180 sold for 60c on day of issue.

Christmas
A622

Designs: 45c, Horse-drawn sleigh. 60c, Angel with trumpet, vert.

Serpentine Die Cut 14¼

2002, Nov. 1

Self-Adhesive

1181-1182 A622   Set of 2   3.50 1.50

Fish — A623

No. 1183: a, Abramis brama. b, Salmo trutta lacustris. c, Esox lucius.

Syncopated Die Cut Perf. 10 Horiz.
2003, Jan. 15

Self-Adhesive
Coil Stamps

1183   Horiz. strip of 3   6.25 4.50
a.-c.   A623 2 Any single   2.00 2.00

Nos. 1183a-1183c were sold in boxes of 100 that sold at a discount price of €47 on day of issue. The franking value on the day of issue for each stamp was 50c.

Birds — A624

No. 1184: a, Cuculus canorus. b, Alauda arvensis. c, Perisoreus infaustus.

Syncopated Die Cut Perf. 10 Horiz.
2003, Jan. 15

Self-Adhesive
Coil Stamps

1184   Horiz. strip of 3   6.25 3.75
a.-c.   A624 1 Any single   2.00 1.25

Nos. 1184a-1184c were sold in boxes of 100 that sold at a discount price of €57 on day of issue. The franking value on the day of issue for each stamp was 60c.

Viivi and Wagner, by Jussi Tuomola — A625

No. 1185: a, Viivi and Wagner running. b, Viivi and Wagner dancing. c, Viivi writing love letter. d, Wagner and Viivi in bed. e, Viivi and Wagner kissing. f, Wagner reading love letter.

Serpentine Die Cut 11½x11¾ on 3 Sides

2003, Jan. 15

Self-Adhesive

1185   Booklet pane of 6   12.00
a.-f.   A625 1 Any single   2.00 1.25
    Booklet, #1185   12.00

Nos. 1185a-1185f each sold for 60c on day of issue.

Ice Hockey World Championships — A626

2003, Mar. 3   **Litho.**   **Perf. 13¼x13¾**
1186 A626 65c multi   1.90 1.00

St. Bridget (1303-73)   Viola Wittrockiana
A627   A628

2003, Mar. 3   **Perf. 13**
1187 A627 65c multi   1.90 .75

Die Cut Perf. 13¾x14
2003, Mar. 3   **Photo.**

Self-Adhesive
1188 A628 65c multi   1.90 .65

Fighting Wood Grouses, by Ferdinand von Wright — A629

2003, Mar. 3   **Die Cut Perf. 13¾**

Self-Adhesive
1189 A629 90c multi   2.50 1.25

Airplanes A630

No. 1190: a, Super Caravelle. b, Airbus 320. c, Junkers Ju 52/3m. d, Douglas DC-3.

Perf. 14x14½ on 3 Sides
2003, Mar. 3
1190   Booklet pane of 4 + 4 etiquettes   7.75 —
a.-d.   A630 65c Any single   1.90 1.00
    Complete booklet, #1190   7.75

Finnair, 80th anniv.; Powered flight, cent.

Europa A631

No. 1191 — Posters by Lasse Hietala: a, Woman with newspaper. b, Hearts.

2003, May 7   **Litho.**   **Perf. 13¾x13¼**
1191 A631   Pair   4.25 4.25
a.-b.   65c Either single   1.90 1.50

Souvenir Sheet

Flora and Fauna Seen in Summer — A632

No. 1192: a, Moth, flowers (35x29mm). b, Dragonfly, grasshopper (44x35mm). c, Grasshopper, caterpillar, thistle (35x25mm). d, Frog, flowers, butterfly, insects (44x36mm). e, Magpie, snail, flowers (35x46mm). f, Hedgehog, bee, ant, spider, flowers (44x29mm).

Perf. 14½ on 2 or 3 Sides
2003, May 7
1192 A632   Sheet of 6   11.50 11.50
a.-f.   65c Any single   1.50 1.25

Moomins A633

No. 1193: a, Moomin ancestors. b, Moomins around stove. c, Moomin standing on hands in water. d, Moomin and fox. e, Moomin looking at film negative. f, Moomin with hat, flowers.

Serpentine Die Cut 11½x11¾ on 3 Sides

2003, May 7   **Photo.**

Self-Adhesive
1193   Booklet pane of 6   12.50 —
a.-f.   A633 1 Any single   2.00 .75
    Complete booklet, #1193   13.00

Nos. 1193a-1193f each sold for 65c on day of issue.

Cupid A634

Serpentine Die Cut 11½ Syncopated
2003, May 14   **Litho.**

Self-Adhesive
1194 A634 1 multi   1.90 1.90

No. 1194 could be personalized. It sold for 65c on day of issue.

Lingonberries — A635

Serpentine Die Cut 14
2003, Sept. 10   **Photo.**

Self-Adhesive
1195 A635 65c multi   1.90 .75

Philanthropists A636

No. 1196: a, Juho (1852-1913) and Maria (1858-1923) Lallukka. b, Emil Aaltonen (1869-1949), vert. c, Heikki Huhtamäki (1900-70), vert. d, Antti (1883-1962) and Jenny Wihuri. e, Alfred Kordelin (1868-1917), vert. f, Amos Anderson (1878-1961), vert.

Perf. 13¼x13¾, 13¾x13¼ on 3 Sides
2003, Sept. 10   **Litho.**
1196   Booklet pane of 6   11.50 —
a.-f.   A636 65c Any single   1.90 1.90
    Complete booklet, #1196   11.50

Lighthouses — A637

No. 1197: a, Bengtskär. b, Russarö. c, Rönnskär. d, Harmaja Grahara. e, Söderskär.

2003, Sept. 10   **Perf. 13¼x13¾**
1197 A637   Sheet of 5   10.50 10.50
a.-e.   1 Any single   2.00 .85

Nos. 1197a-1197e sold for 65c on day of issue. Size of No. 1197a, 28x45mm; Nos. 1197b-1197e, 21x36mm.

Christmas A638

Designs: 45c, Elf mailing letter. 65c, Elf with ginger biscuit on baking pan, vert.

Serpentine Die Cut 14x14¼, 14¼x14
2003, Oct. 31   **Photo.**

Self-Adhesive
1198-1199 A638   Set of 2   3.25 1.50

Slightly larger versions of No. 1198 with a serpentine die cutting of 13¼x13¾ and of No. 1199 with a serpentine die cutting of 13¾x13¼ exist only on first day and other covers produced by the postal service. They were not sold unused to the public.

Apples A639

Serpentine Die Cut 11½ Syncopated
2003, Oct. 31   **Litho.**

Self-Adhesive
1200 A639 1 multi   1.90 1.90

No. 1200 could be personalized. It sold for 65c on day of issue.

Pres. Tarja Halonen, 60th Birthday — A640

2003, Dec. 1   **Litho.**   **Perf. 13**
1201 A640 65c multi   1.90 .75

Linnaea
Borealis — A641

Die Cut Perf. 14
2004, Jan. 14   **Photo.**
Self-Adhesive
1202 A641 30c multi   .90 .90

Souvenir Sheet

Johan Ludvig Runeberg (1804-77),
Poet — A642

No. 1203: a, Title page of *Tales of Ensign
Stahl.* b, Sven Dufva with gun. c, Illustration for
"Our Country." d, Sculpture of Runeberg.

Perf. 13½x13¼ on 3 or 4 Sides
2004, Jan. 14   **Litho.**
1203 A642 65c Sheet of 4, #a-d   7.50 7.50

Jean Sibelius
(1865-1957),
Composer
A643

No. 1204: a, Satu, and Sibelius, paintings by
Akseli Gallen-Kallela. b, Hands of Sibelius on
piano keyboard. c, Swans, musical score by
Sibelius.
No. 1205: a, Sibelius' house, Ainola. b,
Sibelius and wife, Aino. c, Score of "Voces
Intimae."

**Die Cut Perf. 10 Horiz., Syncopated
at Top**
2004, Jan. 14   **Photo.**
Coil Stamps
Self-Adhesive
1204   Horiz. strip of 3   6.00   —
a.-c. A643 2 Any single   2.00 2.00
1205   Horiz. strip of 3   6.00   —
a.-c. A643 1 Any single   2.00   .65

Nos. 1204a-1204c each sold for 55c on day
of issue and have two short syncopations;
Nos. 1205a-1205c each sold for 65c on day of
issue, and have one large syncopation.

Love — A644

Text and: a, Rose. b, Man kissing. c,
Woman's eye. d, Man and woman embracing.
e, Elderly woman. f, Hand pulling petal from
daisy.

**Serpentine Die Cut 11½x11¾ on 3
Sides**
2004, Jan. 14
Self-Adhesive
1206   Booklet pane of 6   12.50   —
a.-f. A644 1 Any single   2.00   .75

Nos. 1206a-1206f each sold for 65c on day
of issue.

Ursus Arctos — A645

2004, Mar. 1   Die Cut Perf. 14
Self-Adhesive
1207 A645 2 multi   1.60 1.00

No. 1207 sold for 55c on day of issue.

Rose — A646

2004, Mar. 1   Booklet Stamp
Self-Adhesive
1208 A646 1 multi   1.90   .35
a.   Booklet pane of 10   19.00

No. 1208 sold for 65c on day of issue. Booklet pane was sold folded.

Easter
Flowers — A647

Die Cut Perf. 14
2004, Mar. 1   **Litho.**
Self-Adhesive
1209 A647 65c multi   1.90   .60

Heraldic Lion Type of 2002
Die Cut Perf. 12 Syncopated
2004, Mar. 1
Self-Adhesive
1210 A616 €3 multi   8.75 8.75

Swallows
A648

Orchid
A649

Serpentine Die Cut 11½ Syncopated
2004, Mar. 26
Self-Adhesive
1211 A648 1 multi   2.00 2.00
1212 A649 1 multi   2.00 2.00

Nos. 1211-1212 each sold for 65c on day of
issue, and they could be personalized.

Souvenir Sheet

Norse Gods — A650

No. 1213: a, Head of Luonnotar (33x30mm).
b, Luonnotar with arms extended (22x42mm).

**Perf. 14¼x14½ (#1213a), 14½x14
(#1213b)**
2004, Mar. 26
1213 A650 65c Sheet of 2, #a-b   4.25 4.25

Forest Animals — A651

No. 1214: a, Red squirrel (40x40mm). b,
Raven (40x31mm). c, Variable hare
(40x34mm). d, Stoat (40x37mm). e, Lizard
(40x34mm). f, Red fox (40x40mm).

Perf. 13¼x14 on 2 or 3 Sides
2004, Apr. 28
1214 A651   Sheet of 6   11.50 11.50
a.-f.   65c Any single   1.75   1.25

Fragaria
Vesca — A652

Die Cut Perf. 14
2004, Apr. 28   **Photo.**
Self-Adhesive
1215 A652 65c multi   1.90   .75

Luxembourg
Gardens, by
Albert
Edelfelt
(1854-1905)
A653

2004, Apr. 28   Self-Adhesive
1216 A653 1 multi   1.90   .75

No. 1216 sold for 65c on day of issue.

Europa — A654

No. 1217: a, People around campfire. b,
Family in rowboat.

2004, Apr. 28   Litho.   Perf. 13
1217 A654 65c Horiz. pair, #a-b   3.75 3.75

Snufkin and
Moomintroll
A655

Litho. & Embossed
2004, Sept. 8   **Perf. 13**
Flocked Paper
1218 A655 1 multi   2.25 2.25

No. 1218 sold for 65c on day of issue.

Shipwreck
Treasures
A656

No. 1219: a, Tankard. b, Fabric seal. c, Gold
watch. d, Powder keg. e, Figurehead
(23x40mm).

Perf. 14¼x13 on 3 or 4 Sides
2004, Sept. 8
1219   Booklet pane of 5   10.00   —
a.-e. A656 1 Any single   2.00   2.00
          Complete booklet, #1219   10.00

Stamps sold for 65c each on day of issue.

Souvenir Sheet

Sammallahdenmäki, UNESCO World
Heritage Site — A657

No. 1220: a, Stone wall and trees. b, Lichen-
covered rocks.

2004, Sept. 8 Litho.   Perf. 14¾x14¼
1220 A657 65c Sheet of 2, #a-b   4.00 4.00

Rights of the Child — A658

No. 1221: a, Two girls. b, Boy painting.

2004, Oct. 29   **Perf. 13**
1221 A658 65c Horiz. pair, #a-b   4.00 3.00

Christmas
A659

Designs: 45c, Boy writing Santa Claus. 65c,
Christmas tree branch, candle, ornaments,
vert.

**Serpentine Die Cut 13¼x13¾,
13¾x13¼**
2004, Oct. 29   **Photo.**
Self-Adhesive
1222-1223 A659 Set of 2   3.25 2.00

Rotary International, Cent. — A660

2005, Jan. 14   Litho.   Perf. 13
1224 A660 65c blue & gold   1.90 1.25

Lahti, Cent. — A661

No. 1225: a, Sibelius Concert Hall. b, Illuminated radio towers.

2005, Jan. 14
1225 A661 65c Pair, #a-b   4.00 4.00

Oulo, 400th Anniv. — A662

No. 1226: a, Child with pail and shovel. b, Woman riding bicycle.

2005, Jan. 14
1226 A662 65c Horiz. pair, #a-b   4.00 4.00

Publishing of First Finnish Almanac, 300th Anniv. — A663

Die Cut Perf. 14
2005, Jan. 14   Photo.
Self-Adhesive
1227 A663 65c multi   1.90 .75

Children's Toys — A664

No. 1228: a, Stuffed lion and tiger. b, Stuffed elephant and dog. c, Airplane, train and car. d, Stuffed bear and rabbit.

Serpentine Die Cut 9¼x8½ on 3 Sides
2005, Jan. 14
Self-Adhesive
1228   Booklet pane of 4   7.75   —
a.-d. A664 1 Any single   1.90 1.25
Stamps sold for 65c each on day of issue.

End of Winter War, 65th Anniv. — A665

2005, Mar. 2   Litho.   Perf. 13
1229 A665 65c multi   1.90 1.25

Easter — A666

2005, Mar. 2   Serpentine Die Cut 14
Self-Adhesive
1230 A666 65c multi   1.90 1.00

Apple Blossom — A667

Die Cut Perf. 14
2005, Mar. 2   Photo.
Self-Adhesive
Booklet Stamp
1231 A667 1 multi   1.90 1.90
a.   Booklet pane of 10   19.00
No. 1231 sold for 65c on day of issue.

Door Decoration, by Eliel Saarinen A668

Copper Stove Door — A669

Chair Back — A670

Stained Glass Window, by Olga Gummerus-Ehrström — A671

Dining Room — A672

Exterior of Hvitträsk A673

Die Cut Perf. 10 Horiz., Syncopated at Top
2005, Mar. 2   Litho.
Self-Adhesive
Coil Stamps
1232   Horiz. strip of 3   5.75
a.   A668 2 multi   1.90 1.90
b.   A669 2 multi   1.90 1.90
c.   A670 2 multi   1.90 1.90

1233   Horiz. strip of 3   5.75
a.   A671 1 multi   1.90 1.90
b.   A672 1 multi   1.90 1.90
c.   A673 1 multi   1.90 1.90

Hvitträsk, home and studio of architects Eliel Saarinen, Armas Lindgren and Herman Gesellius. Nos. 1232a-1232c each sold for 55c on day of issue and have two short syncopations. Nos. 1233a-1233c each sold for 65c on day of issue and have one large syncopation.

Miniature Schnauzer A674

Serpentine Die Cut 11½ Syncopated
2005, Apr. 6
1234 A674 1 multi   1.90 1.90
Sold for 65c on day of issue. Sheets could be personalized.

Europa — A675

No. 1235 — Plates with: a, Whitefish and beetroot tartare on lettuce. b, Sauteed reindeer and grouse breast.

2005, May 11   Perf. 13
1235 A675 65c Pair, #a-b   4.00 4.00

Souvenir Sheet

Golf — A676

No. 1236: a, Man driving ball (44x31mm). b, Boy holding flag, vert. (30x44mm). c, Boy putting, vert. (33x44mm). d, Putter and golf ball (44x32mm).

Perf. 13¼ on 3 or 4 Sides
2005, May 11
1236 A676 65c Sheet of 4, #a-d   7.50 7.50

World Track Championships, Helsinki — A677

Serpentine Die Cut 12½
2005, May 11
Self-Adhesive
1237 A677 65c multi   1.90 1.90

Buses in Finland, Cent. A678

Die Cut Perf. 14
2005, May 11   Photo.
Self-Adhesive
1238 A678 65c brown & black   1.90 1.90

Horses — A679

No. 1239: a, Icelandic horse with saddle. b, White Welsh Mountain pony. c, New Forest pony with blanket. d, Shetland Pony.

Serpentine Die Cut 9¼x8½ on 3 Sides
2005, May 11
Self-Adhesive
1239   Booklet pane of 4   7.50
a.-d. A679 1 Any single   1.90 1.90
Stamps sold for 65c each on day of issue.

Cloudberries — A680

Die Cut Perf. 14
2005, Sept. 7   Photo.
Self-Adhesive
1240 A680 1 multi   1.90 1.90
Sold for 65c on day of issue.

Fruits I, by Kari Huhtamo A681

Die Cut Perf. 11½ Syncopated
2005, Sept. 7   Litho.
Self-Adhesive
1241 A681 90c multi   2.50 2.50
Sheets could be personalized.

Souvenir Sheet

Petäjävesi Church, UNESCO World Heritage Site — A682

No. 1242: a, Bell tower (26x47mm). b, Church (34x39mm). c, Angel (26x39mm). d, Chandelier (27x39mm).

2005, Sept. 7   **Litho.**   *Perf. 13*
1242 A682 65c Sheet of 4, #a-d   7.50 7.50

Icebreakers — A683

No. 1243: a, Urho, 1975. b, Otso, 1986. c, Fennica, 1993. d, Botnica, 1998.

2005, Sept. 7   *Perf. 13¼ Horiz.*
1243   Booklet pane of 4   7.50 —
a.-d. A683 1 Any single   1.90 1.90

Each stamp sold for 65c on day of issue.

Souvenir Sheet

Imperial Winter Egg, by Carl Fabergé — A684

No. 684: a, Flowers in egg. b, Frost detail of egg.

Litho. & Embossed with Foil Application
2005, Oct. 28   *Perf. 13*
1244 A684 €3.50 Sheet of 2,   #a-b   22.50 22.50

A limited quantity of 2,500 numbered sheets, which sold for €30, exist. Value, $100.

Christmas — A685

Designs: 50c, Santa Claus reading letters. 1, Santa Claus and wife dancing, horiz.

Serpentine Die Cut 13¾x13¼, 13¼x13¾
2005, Oct. 28   **Photo.**
Self-Adhesive
1245-1246 A685   Set of 2   3.75 2.00

No. 1246 sold for 65c on day of issue.

Postal Employees Union, Cent. — A686

2006, Jan. 11   **Litho.**   *Perf. 13*
1247 A686 65c multi   2.25 1.90

Heart — A687

2006, Jan. 11   *Die Cut*
Self-Adhesive
1248 A687 65c bright pink   2.25 1.90

Renaming of Helsinki University Library as National Library of Finland — A688

2006, Jan. 11 *Die Cut Perf. 14x13¾*
Self-Adhesive
1249 A688 1 multi   2.25 1.90

Sold for 65c on day of issue.

Forest in Winter — A689

2006, Jan. 11   **Photo.**
Self-Adhesive
1250 A689 1 multi   2.25 1.90

Sold for 65c on day of issue.

Taxis, Cent. — A690

No. 1251: a, Women passengers in taxi, 1906. b, Driver standing in front of 1929 Chevrolet taxi. c, Driver leaning on 1957 Pobeda taxi. d, Driver on phone at taxi stand next to Mercedes-Benz taxi.

Serpentine Die Cut 11¼ Vert.
2006, Jan. 11   **Litho.**
Self-Adhesive
1251   Booklet pane of 4   9.00 —
a.-d. A690 65c Any single   2.25 1.00

Souvenir Sheet

Johan Vilhelm Snellman (1806-81), Philosopher — A691

No. 1252: a, Caricature of Snellman, masthead of his newspaper "Saima." b, Snellman's portrait on 1940 five thousand mark note. c, Snellman and European railway map. d, Ilmarinen, first Finnish locomotive, and European railway map.

2006, Jan. 11   *Perf. 13¼x13¾*
1252 A691 65c Sheet of 4, #a-d   7.50 7.50

Parliament, Cent. — A692

Serpentine Die Cut 14
2006, Feb. 3   **Litho.**
Self-Adhesive
1253 A692 1 multi   2.25 1.90

Sold for 65c on day of sale.

Flag — A693

2006, Mar. 1
Self-Adhesive
1254 A693 1 multi   2.25 1.90

Sold for 65c on day of sale.

Lilacs — A694

Die Cut Perf. 13¾x14
2006, Mar. 1   **Photo.**
Self-Adhesive
1255 A694 1 multi   2.25 1.90

Sold for 65c on day of sale.

Easter — A695

2006, Mar. 1   **Litho.**   *Die Cut*
Self-Adhesive
1256 A695 65c multi   2.25 1.90

Fortune Teller, by Helene Schjerfbeck — A696

Die Cut Perf. 13¾x14
2006, Mar. 1   **Photo.**
Self-Adhesive
1257 A696 95c multi   2.75 2.75

Bil-Bol Poster A697

Errotaja 2 Poster A698

Concert Finnois Poster A699

Madonna A700

Self-Portrait A701

Home of Artist Akseli Gallen-Kallela, Tarvaspää — A702

Die Cut Perf. 10 Horiz., Syncopated at Top
2006, Mar. 1
Coil Stamps
Self-Adhesive
1258   Horiz. strip of 3   6.75 —
  a. A697 2 multi   2.00 2.00
  b. A698 2 multi   2.00 2.00
  c. A699 2 multi   2.00 2.00

Die Cut Perf. 10, Syncopated at Right
1259   Vert. strip of 3   6.75 —
  a. A700 1 multi   2.25 .75
  b. A701 1 multi   2.25 .75
  c. A702 1 multi   2.25 .75

Akseli Gallen-Kallela (1865-1931), artist. Nos. 1258a-1258c each sold for 55c and Nos. 1259a-1259c each sold for 65c on day of issue.

Souvenir Sheet

Norse Mythology — A703

No. 1260 — Fairy tale book cover illustrations by Rudolf Koivu: a, Fairy. b, Fairy dancing with Santa Claus, vert.

Perf. 13½x13¼, 13¼x13½ (#1260b)
2006, Mar. 29   **Litho.**
1260 A703 65c Sheet of 2, #a-b   4.00 4.00

Europa A704

2006, May 4   *Perf. 13*
1261 A704 65c multi   1.90 1.90

Vaasa, 400th Anniv. — A705

2006, May 4
1262 A705 1 multi   1.90 1.90

Sold for 65c on day of issue.

A706

Serpentine Die Cut 10 Syncopated
2006, May 4

Booklet Stamp
Self-Adhesive

1263 A706 1 multi   1.90 1.90
   a. Booklet pane of 8   15.00

No. 1263 sold for 65c on day of issue. Design portion of stamp could be personalized.

Summer Activities
A707

No. 1264: a, Woman fishing. b, Children making flower garlands. c, Man making sauna whisk. d, Woman weeding flower garden.

Serpentine Die Cut 11¼ Vert.
2006, May 4

Self-Adhesive

1264 Booklet pane of 4   7.50
   a.-d. A707 1 Any single   1.90 1.90

Nos. 1264a-1264d each sold for 65c on day of issue.

 Cats — A708

No. 1265: a, Striped house cat. b, British shorthair (gray cat). c, Ragdoll cat (brown and white). d, Chocolate Persian cat.

2006, May 4

Self-Adhesive

1265 Booklet pane of 4   7.50
   a.-d. A708 1 Any single   1.90 1.90

Nos. 1265a-1265d each sold for 65c on day of issue.

Suomenlinna (Sveaborg) Fortress, Helsinki — A709

No. 1266: a, Ship without oars. b, Ship with oars facing fortress. c, Ship with oars, windmill.

Litho. & Engr.
2006, May 4   **Perf. 13x12¾**

1266 A709 Booklet pane of 3   5.75   —
   a.-c. 1 Any single   1.90 1.90
    Complete booklet, #1266   5.75

Nos. 1266a-1266c each sold for 65c on day of issue. See Sweden No. 2530.

Blueberries and Blueberry Pie — A710

Die Cut Perf. 14
2006, Aug. 24   **Photo.**

Self-Adhesive

1267 A710 1 multi   2.00 2.00

Sold for 70c on day of issue.

Miniature Sheet

Family Life — A711

No. 1268: a, Family watching television. b, Woman writing letter to husband.

2006, Aug. 24   **Die Cut**

Self-Adhesive

1268 A711 1 Sheet of 2, #a-b   4.00 4.00

Nos. 1268a-1268b each sold for 70c on day of issue.

Newspaper Journalism — A712

Die Cut Perf. 14
2006, Sept. 22   **Litho.**

Self-Adhesive

1269 A712 70c multi   2.00 2.00

Points, Textile Art by Ritva Puotila — A713

Serpentine Die Cut 11½ Syncopated
2006, Sept. 22

Self-Adhesive

1270 A713 1 multi   2.00 2.00

Sold for 70c on day of issue.

Dryas Octopetala
A714

Serpentine Die Cut 14
2006, Sept. 22   **Photo.**

Self-Adhesive

1271 A714 1 multi   2.00 2.00

Sold for 70c on day of issue.

Art of Snow and Ice — A715

No. 1272: a, Horse. b, Kemi Snow Castle. c, Wall of ice tiles. d, Snowball lantern.

Serpentine Die Cut 11¾ Vert.
2006, Sept. 22

Self-Adhesive

1272 Booklet pane of 4   8.00
   a.-d. 1 Any single   2.00 2.00

Nos. 1272a-1272d each sold for 70c on day of issue. Denominations are printed in thermographic ink that changes color when warmed.

Miniature Sheet

Finnish Postage Stamps, 150th Anniv. — A716

No. 1273: a, 70c, Heraldic lion and fleurons in white. b, 95c, Part of vignette of type A1. c, €1.40, Heraldic lion in gold, fleurons in red.

Litho. & Embossed With Foil Application
2006, Oct. 27   **Perf. 13½x13**

1273 A716 Sheet of 3, #a-c   8.75 8.75

A717

Christmas — A718

Serpentine Die Cut 13¼x13¾
2006, Oct. 27   **Photo.**

Self-Adhesive

1274 A717 50c multi   1.40 1.40

Serpentine Die Cut 13¾x13¼

1275 A718 1 multi   2.00 2.00

No. 1275 sold for 70c on day of issue.

Television Broadcasting in Finland, 50th Anniv. — A719

Die Cut Perf. 14
2007, Jan. 24   **Litho.**

Self-Adhesive

1276 A719 70c multi   1.90 1.90

Faces — A720

2007, Jan. 24

Self-Adhesive

1277 A720 70c multi   1.90 1.90

Winter Landscape, Haminalahti, by Ferdinand von Wright
A721

2007, Jan. 24   **Photo.**

Self-Adhesive Booklet Stamp

1278 A721 1 multi   1.90 1.90
   a. Booklet pane of 10   19.00

Sold for 70c on day of issue.

Sun Setting Over Flower Field — A722

2007, Jan. 24   **Litho.**

Self-Adhesive

1279 A722 €1.40 multi   3.75 3.75

Souvenir Sheet

Intl. Polar Year — A723

No. 1280: a, Snowflake. b, Aurora borealis.

Perf. 13 Syncopated (#1280a), 13 (#1280b)
Litho. With Hologram Affixed
2007, Jan. 24

1280 A723 70c Sheet of 2, #a-b
    + label   4.00 4.00

Truck Transport — A724

No. 1281: a, Log truck. b, Milk truck. c, Dump truck. d, Tractor trailer.

Serpentine Die Cut 12¼ Horiz.
2007, Jan. 24   **Litho.**

Self-Adhesive

1281 Booklet pane of 4   7.75
   a.-d. A724 70c Any single   1.90 1.90

Central Organization of Finnish Trade Unions — A725

2007, Mar. 7   *Perf. 13*
1282 A725 70c multi   1.90 1.90

Soccer Association of Finland, Cent. — A726

2007, Mar. 7   *Die Cut*
Self-Adhesive
1283 A726 70c multi   1.90 1.90

Easter — A727

2007, Mar. 7   *Die Cut Perf. 14*
Self-Adhesive
1284 A727 1 multi   1.90 1.90

Sold for 70c on day of issue. Portions of design were applied by a thermographic process producing a shiny, raised effect.

Lilium Enchantment A728

2007, Mar. 7   *Litho.*
Booklet Stamp
Self-Adhesive
1285 A728 1 multi   1.90 1.90
  a.   Booklet pane of 10   19.00

No. 1285 sold for 70c on day of issue.

Souvenir Sheet

Bishop Michael Agricola (1509-57) — A729

No. 1286: a, Text and open book. b, Agricola preaching.

2007, Mar. 7   *Perf. 13½*
1286 A729 70c Sheet of 2, #a-b   4.00 4.00

Tampere Cathedral, Cent. — A730

2007, May 9   *Perf. 13¼*
1287 A730 70c multi   1.90 1.90

Europa — A731

No. 1288: a, Scouts on sailboat. b, Scouts around campfire.

2007, May 9   *Perf. 12½x13*
1288 A731   Horiz. pair   3.25 3.25
  a.-b.   70c Either single   1.60 1.60
            Scouting, cent.

Helsinki Public Transportation — A732

No. 1289: a, Commuter train in station. b, Tram on street. c, Subway train on bridge. d, People in Kamppi Bus Station.

Serpentine Die Cut 12¼ Horiz.
2007, May 9
Self-Adhesive
1289   Booklet pane of 4   7.75
  a.-d.   A732 1 Any single   1.90 1.90

Nos. 1289a-1289d each sold for 70c on day of issue.

Moomins A733

No. 1290: a, Little My in water. b, Moomintroll running across rocks. c, Moominpappa at typewriter. d, Snork Maiden picking flowers. e, Moominmamma making pancakes. f, Snufkin amid flowers.

Serpentine Die Cut 11¾ Vert.
2007, May 9   *Photo.*
Self-Adhesive
1290   Booklet pane of 6   11.50
  a.-f.   A733 1 Any single   1.90 1.90

Nos. 1290a-1290f each sold for 70c on day of issue.

Souvenir Sheet

2007 Eurovision Song Contest, Helsinki — A734

No. 1291: a, Eurovision Song Contest emblem. b, Finnish singers Laila Kinnunen, Marion Rung, Kirka Babitzin and Katri Helena. c, 2006 Finnish contest-winning band, Lordi. d, Lead singer of Lordi.

Litho. With Foil Application
2007, May 9   *Die Cut*
Self-Adhesive
1291 A734 70c Sheet of 4, #a-d   7.75 7.75

A735

Serpentine Die Cut 11½ Syncopated
2007, Aug. 24   *Litho.*
Self-Adhesive
1292 A735 1 multi   1.90 1.90

No. 1292 sold for 70c on day of issue. Design portion of stamp could be personalized.

Home Furnishings — A736

No. 1293 — Picture frame and: a, Empire-style chair, "Porvoo Garland" wallpaper, 19th cent. (country name at LR). b, Paimio chair, "2+3" wallpaper, 20th cent. (country name at LL).

Die Cut Perf. 14
2007, Aug. 24   *Litho.*
Self-Adhesive
1293   Pair   3.80
  a.-b.   A736 1 Either single   1.90 1.90

Nos. 1293a-1293b each sold for 70c on day of issue.

Raspberries and Raspberry Cake — A737

Die Cut Perf. 14
2007, Aug. 24   *Photo.*
Self-Adhesive
Booklet Stamp
1294 A737 1 multi   1.90 1.90

No. 1294 sold for 70c on day of issue.

Finnish Olympic Committee, Cent. — A738

2007, Aug. 24   *Litho.*
Self-Adhesive
Booklet Stamp
1295 A738 1 multi   1.90 1.90

No. 1295 sold for 70c on day of issue.

Butterflies — A739

No. 1296: a, Apatura iris. b, Scolitantides orion. c, Colias palaeno.

Die Cut Perf. 10 Vert., Syncopated at Right
2007, Aug. 24
Self-Adhesive
Coil Stamps
1296   Vert. strip of 3   5.75
  a.-c.   A739 1 Any single   1.90 1.90

Nos. 1296a-1296c had a franking value of 70c on day of issue. A roll of 100 stamps sold for €68.

Miniature Sheet

Independence, 90th Anniv. — A740

No. 1297 — Photographs of people at work and play: a, Man and horse hauling wood. b, Girl blowing horn. c, Four boys with skis. d, People at coffee break. e, People near bonfire. f, Boy ski jumping. g, Boy diving. h, Ice fisherman. Nos. 1297a-1297d are black and white photos.

2007, Nov. 2   *Perf. 13¼*
1297 A740   Sheet of 8   16.50 16.50
  a.-h.   70c Any single   2.00 2.00

Souvenir Sheet

Woodwork — A741

No. 1298: a, Zitan armchair with dragon design, China (denomination at left). b, Modern Finnish bowls (denomination at right).

2007, Nov. 2   **Perf. 13¼x14¼**
1298 A741 Sheet of 2   4.25 4.25
a.-b.   70c Either single   2.00 2.00

   See Hong Kong Nos. 1298-1299.

A742

Christmas — A743

Serpentine Die Cut 13¼x13¾
2007, Nov. 2   **Photo.**
Self-Adhesive
1299 A742 55c multi   1.60 1.60

Serpentine Die Cut 13¾x13¼
1300 A743 1 multi   2.00 2.00

   No. 1300 sold for 70c on day of issue.

A744   A745

Water — A746

A747   A748

Islands — A749

2008, Jan. 24   **Photo.**   **Die Cut**
Self-Adhesive
1301   Horiz. strip of 3   .45
  a.   A744 5c multi   .20   .20
  b.   A745 5c multi   .20   .20
  c.   A746 5c multi   .20   .20
1302   Horiz. strip of 3   .90
  a.   A747 10c multi   .30   .30
  b.   A748 10c multi   .30   .30
  c.   A749 10c multi   .30   .30

Souvenir Sheet

Helsinki University of Technology, Cent. — A750

No. 1303: a, Robot. b, University building.

2008, Jan. 24   **Litho.**   **Perf. 13½x13¼**
1303 A750 Sheet of 2   4.25 4.25
a.-b.   1 Any single   2.10 2.10
   Nos. 1303a-1303b each sold for 70c on day of issue.

Miniature Sheet

Love — A751

No. 1304: a, Airplane pulling heart banner. b, Carrier pigeon with envelope. c, Heart-shaped smoke signals. d, Heart and cell phone. e, Bottle with hearts.

2008, Jan. 24   **Die Cut**
Self-Adhesive
1304 A751 Sheet of 5   10.50
a.-e.   1 Any single   2.10   2.10
   Nos. 1304a-1304e each sold for 70c on day of issue.

Miniature Sheet

Snow Sports — A752

No. 1305: a, Matti Räty in yellow ski suit. b, Antti Autti (snowboarder) in air in red ski suit. c, Tapio Saarimaki in red ski suit. d, Tanja Poutiainen in white and green ski suit.

Litho. With Three-Dimensional Plastic Affixed
Serpentine Die Cut 9 Syncopated
2008, Jan. 24
Self-Adhesive
1305 A752 Sheet of 4   8.50
a.-d.   1 Any single   2.10 2.10
   Nos. 1305a-1305d each sold for 70c on day of issue.

Clock and Lamp on Desk — A753

Die Cut Perf. 13¾
2008, Feb. 27   **Litho.**
Self-Adhesive
1306 A753 €1.05 multi   3.25 3.25
  a.   Booklet pane of 10   32.50

Finnish Book Publishers Association, 150th Anniv. — A754

Serpentine Die Cut 13¼
2008, Feb. 27
Self-Adhesive
1307 A754 1 multi   2.10 2.10
   No. 1307 sold for 70c on day of issue.

Lathyrus Odoratus — A755

Die Cut Perf. 13¾
2008, Feb. 27   **Photo.**
Self-Adhesive
1308 A755 1 multi   2.10 2.10
   No. 1308 sold for 70c on the day of issue and has Braille dots applied by a thermographic process.

Easter — A756

Litho. With Foil Application
Serpentine Die Cut 13¾
2008, Feb. 27
Self-Adhesive
1309 A756 1 multi   2.10 2.10
   No. 1309 sold for 70c on day of issue.

Fauna Associated With Weather Forecasting Folk Beliefs — A757

No. 1310: a, Perch. b, Lambs. c, Frogs. d, Swallows. e, Snail.

Serpentine Die Cut 12¼ Horiz.
2008, Feb. 27   **Litho.**
Self-Adhesive
1310   Booklet pane of 5   10.50
a.-e.   A757 1 Any single   2.10 2.10
   Nos. 1310a-1310e each sold for 70c on day of issue.

Souvenir Sheet

Mythical Places — A758

No. 1311: a, Cliff resembling human face, Astuvansalmi. b, Amber carving of head found at Astuvansalmi.

2008, Mar. 27   **Perf. 13½**
1311 A758 Sheet of 2   4.50 4.50
a.-b.   70c Either single   2.25 2.25

Europa — A759

No. 1312 — Handwritten letters and portraits by Pekka Halonen of: a, Himself. b, His wife, Maija.

2008, May 9   **Perf. 13**
1312 A759 Horiz. pair   4.50 4.50
a.-b.   70c Either single   2.25 2.25

Kvarken Archipelago UNESCO World Heritage Site — A760

Serpentine Die Cut 13¾
2008, May 9
Self-Adhesive
1313 A760 €1.50 blk & red   4.75 4.75

Moths — A761

No. 1314: a, Arctia caja. b, Aglia tau. c, Deilephila elpenor.

Die Cut Perf. 10 Syncopated
2008, May 9   **Photo.**
Coil Stamps
Self-Adhesive
1314   Vert. strip of 3   6.75
a.-c.   A761 1 Any single   2.25 2.25
   Nos. 1314a-1314c each sold for 70c on day of issue.

Psychedelic Art — A762

No. 1315: a, Melting mushrooms and tear-drops. b, Guitars. c, Flying fish. d, Flowers and woman's legs in high heels. e, Six balloons.

Serpentine Die Cut 12½ Horiz.
2008, May 9   **Litho.**
Self-Adhesive
1315   Booklet pane of 5   11.50
a.-e.   A762 1 Any single   2.25 2.25
   Nos. 1315a-1315e each sold for 70c on day of issue.

Modern
Art — A763

No. 1316: a, Sinistä ja Punaista, by Sam Vanni. b, Merirosvolaiva, by Kimmo Kaivanto. c, Hiljaisuuden Kuuntelija, by Juhani Linnovaara. d, Odotan Kevään Tuloa, by Göran Augustson. e, Minä, by Carolus Enckell. f, Pöytä, by Reino Hietanen.

Serpentine Die Cut 11¾ Vert.
2008, May 9
Self-Adhesive
1316   Booklet pane of 6   13.50
a.-f.   A763 1 Any single   2.25 2.25
Nos. 1316a-1316f each sold for 70c on day of issue.

Personalized
Stamp — A764

Serpentine Die Cut 10
2008, Sept. 5   Litho.
Self-Adhesive
1317 A764 1 multi   2.40 2.40
No. 1317 sold for 80c on day of issue. The generic design portion of the stamp shown could be personalized.

Dogs — A765

No. 1318: a, Spitz with open mouth, facing forward. b, Rough collie, with open mouth, facing right. c, Boxer, facing left. d, Finnish hound, facing left. e, Cavalier King Charles spaniel, facing right. f, Jack Russell terrier, looking over shoulder.

Serpentine Die Cut 11¾ Vert.
2008, Sept. 5
Self-Adhesive
1318   Booklet pane of 6   14.50
a.-f.   A765 1 Any single   2.40 2.40
Nos. 1318a-1318f each sold for 80c on day of issue.

Souvenir Sheet

Mika Waltari (1908-79), Writer — A766

No. 1319: a, Waltari. b, Cover of Waltari's book, Komisario Palmun Erehyds.

2008, Sept. 5   **Perf. 14x13½**
1319 A766   Sheet of 2   5.00 5.00
a.-b.   80c Either single   2.40 2.40

Souvenir Sheet

Kimi Räikkönen, 2007 Formula 1
Racing Champion — A767

No. 1320: a, Räikkönen (24x30mm). b, Räikkönen's Ferrari Formula 1 race car (74x30mm).

Die Cut Perf. 11x11½ on 2 Sides (#1320a), 11½ Vert. (#1320b)
2008, Sept. 5
Self-Adhesive
1320 A767   Sheet of 2   5.00 5.00
a.-b.   1 Either single   2.40 2.40
Nos. 1320a-1320b each sold for 80c on day of issue.

Souvenir Sheet

Adolf Erik Nordenskiöld (1832-1901),
Arctic Explorer — A768

No. 1321: a, Nordenskiöld (29x34mm). b, Ship Sofia (58x34mm).

Litho. & Engr.
2008, Oct. 20   **Perf. 13x13¼**
1321 A768   Sheet of 2   4.50 4.50
a.-b.   1 Either single   2.25 2.25
Nos. 1321a-1321b each sold for 80c on day of issue. See Greenland Nos. 527-528.

A769

A770

Christmas
A771

Die Cut Perf. 14
2008, Nov. 6   Litho.
Self-Adhesive
1322 A769 60c multi   1.60 1.60
Serpentine Die Cut 13¼x13¾
Photo.
1323 A770   1 multi   2.10 2.10
Booklet Stamp
Printed On Plastic
Die Cut Perf. 13¾
1324 A771   1 multi   2.10 2.10
Nos. 1322-1324 (3)   5.80 5.80
On day of issue, Nos. 1323 and 1324 each sold for 80c.

Pres.
Martti
Ahtisaari,
2008
Nobel
Peace
Laureate
A772

2008, Dec. 10   Litho.   **Perf. 13**
1325 A772 80c light blue   2.10 2.10

Hospital
Work — A773

2009, Jan. 22   Litho.   **Perf. 13**
1326 A773 80c multi   2.25 2.25

Pallas-Yllästunturi
National
Park — A774

2009, Jan. 22   **Die Cut Perf. 14**
Self-Adhesive
1327 A774 1 multi   2.25 2.25
No. 1327 sold for 80c on day of issue and has Braille dots applied in varnish.

Peony — A775

Die Cut Perf. 14
2009, Jan. 22   **Photo.**
Self-Adhesive
1328 A775 €1.10 multi   3.25 3.25

Children's Dream
Occupations
A776

No. 1329 — Child dressed as: a, Policeman. b, Doctor. c, Firefighter. d, Skier. e, Construction worker.

Serpentine Die Cut 12¼ Vert.
2009, Jan. 22   Litho.
Self-Adhesive
1329   Booklet pane of 5   11.50
a.-e. A776 1 Any single   2.25 2.25
Nos. 1329a-1329e each sold for 80c on day of issue.

Miniature Sheet

Finland as Grand Duchy of Russia,
200th Anniv. — A777

No. 1330: a, Tsar Alexander I (1777-1825), facing left with blue sash. b, Count Georg Magnus Sprengtporten (1740-1819), with red sash and gold epaulets. c, Count Carl Erik Mannerheim (1759-1837), without epaulets. d, Count Gustaf Mauritz Armfelt (1757-1814), facing right, with blue sash. Names are on sheet margin.

Litho. & Embossed With Foil
Application
2009, Jan. 22   **Perf. 13¾**
1330 A777 80c Sheet of 4, #a-d   9.00 9.00

Miniature Sheet

St. Valentine's Day — A778

No. 1331: a, Birthday cake and candle. b, Cupid. c, Three people, flower. d, Swans. e, Teddy bear hugging heart.

2009, Jan. 22   Litho.   **Die Cut**
Self-Adhesive
1331 A778 1 Sheet of 5, #a-e   11.50 11.50
Nos. 1331a-1331e each sold for 80c on day of issue.

Rose — A779

Die Cut Perf. 14
2009, Mar. 18   Litho.
Self-Adhesive
1332 A779 1 multi   2.25 2.25
No. 1332 sold for 80c on day of issue.

Easter — A780

2009, Mar. 18
Self-Adhesive
1333 A780 1 multi   2.25 2.25
No. 1333 sold for 80c on day of issue.

Souvenir Sheet

Preservation of Polar Regions and Glaciers — A781

No. 1334: a, Sky, blue emblem. b, Sea and ice, silver emblem.

Litho. With Foil Application
2009, Mar. 18 **Perf.**
1334 A781 Sheet of 2 4.50 4.50
a.-b. 1 Either single 2.25 2.25
Nos. 1334a-1334b each sold for 80c on day of issue.

Greetings A782

No. 1335: a, Gift and tulips. b, Chocolate-covered strawberries, cake. c, Flowers. d, Coffee cup, letter and rose. e, Dove and apples.

Serpentine Die Cut 10¼ Horiz.
2009, Mar. 18 **Litho.**
Self-Adhesive
1335 Booklet pane of 5 + 5 labels 11.50
a.-e. A782 1 Any single 2.25 2.25
Nos. 1335a-1335e each sold for 80c on day of issue.

Europa — A783

No. 1336: a, Lake, birds, Moon, stars and other heavenly bodies. b, Lake, comet, Saturn, stars and other heavenly bodies.

2009, May 6 **Perf. 13**
1336 A783 Horiz. pair 4.50 4.50
a.-b. 80c Either single 2.25 2.25
Intl. Year of Astronomy.

Sauna — A784

No. 1337: a, Towels, scrubber, bucket of birch branches (55x23mm). b, People in sauna (55x23mm). c, Waterside sauna (55x23mm). d, Birch whisk (27x45mm). e, Water tubs and window (27x45mm).

Serpentine Die Cut 11¾ Horiz.
2009, May 6
Self-Adhesive
1337 Booklet pane of 5 11.50
a.-e. A784 1 Any single 2.25 2.25
Nos. 1337a-1337e each sold for 80c on day of issue. No. 1337d is impregnated with a birch scent.

Moomins — A785

No. 1338: a, Moomin carrying purse. b, Moominpappa with hat holding paper. c, Little My holding large pair of glasses. d, Moomin at mirror. e, Moomin and Snufkin fishing. f, Moominpappa slipping down hill.

Serpentine Die Cut 11¾ Horiz.
2009, May 6
Self-Adhesive
1338 Booklet pane of 6 13.50
a.-f. A785 1 Any single 2.25 2.25
Nos. 1338a-1338f each sold for 80c on day of issue.

Miniature Sheet

Women's Fashion — A786

No. 1339: a, Dress by Anna and Tuomas Laitinen (30x45mm). b, Dress by Jasmin Santanen (30x45mm). c, Handbag by Lumi (30x35mm). d, Red shoes by Minna Parikka (30x25mm). e, Shoes by Julia Lundsten (30x30mm).

Serpentine Die Cut 14¼x13¾
2009, May 6
Self-Adhesive
1339 A786 Sheet of 5 11.50 11.50
a.-e. 1 Any single 2.25 2.25
Nos. 1339a-1339e each sold for 80c on day of issue.

Gustavian Style Clock, Table and Candle Holder — A787

Die Cut Perf. 13¾
2009, Sept. 9 **Litho.**
Self-Adhesive
1340 A787 1 multi 2.40 2.40
a. Booklet pane of 10 24.00
No. 1340 sold for 80c on day of issue.

Aurora Borealis — A788

No. 1341 — Various pictures of Aurora Borealis taken at: a, 65 degrees, 1 minute, 17.03 seconds north; 25 degrees, 39 minutes, 31.26 seconds east. b, 65 degrees, 57.16 seconds north; 25 degrees, 39 minutes, 41.01

seconds east. c, 67 degrees, 45 minutes, 2.44 seconds north; 23 degrees, 36 minutes, 41.53 seconds east.

Die Cut Perf. 10 Vert., Syncopated at Right
2009, Sept. 9
Coil Stamps
Self-Adhesive
1341 Vert. strip of 3 7.25
a.-c. A788 1 Any single 2.40 2.40
Nos. 1341a-1341c each sold for 80c on day of issue.

Paintings of Flowers — A789

No. 1342: a, Snapdragons, by Helene Schjerfbeck. b, Blooming Irises, by Wäinö Aaltonen. c, Burnet Roses, by Eero Järnefelt. d, Lone Calla, by Ester Helenius. e, Amaryllis, by Birger Carlstedt. f, Still Life with Carnations, by Tuomas von Boehm.

Serpentine Die Cut 11¾ Horiz.
2009, Sept. 9
Self-Adhesive
1342 Booklet pane of 6 14.50
a.-f. A789 1 Any single 2.40 2.40
Nos. 1342a-1342f each sold for 80c on day of issue.

Wreath — A790

Girl and Basket of Apples — A791

Amaryllis A792

Personalized Stamp — A793

Die Cut Perf. 14
2009, Nov. 6 **Litho.**
Self-Adhesive
1343 Horiz. pair 3.50
a. A790 60c multi 1.75 1.75
b. A791 60c multi 1.75 1.75
1344 A792 1 multi 2.40 2.40

Serpentine Die Cut 11½x11¾ Syncopated
1345 A793 1 multi 2.40 2.40
Nos. 1344 and 1345 each sold for 80c on day of issue. The generic design portion of No. 1345, shown, could be personalized.

Antennaria Dioica — A794

Die Cut Perf. 11 Syncopated
2010, Jan. 25 **Litho.**
Self-Adhesive
1346 A794 1 multi 2.25 2.25
No. 1346 sold for 80c on day of issue.

Miniature Sheet

Fairies — A795

No. 1347 - Fairy: a, Holding flowers. b, Holding heart. c, On swing. d, Holding violin. e, With stars.

Serpentine Die Cut 14½x14
Litho. & Silk-screened
2010, Jan. 25
Self-Adhesive
1347 A795 Sheet of 5 11.50
a.-e. 1 Any single 2.25 2.25
Nos. 1347a-1347e each sold for 80c on day of issue.

Rock Stars A796

No. 1348: a, Eppu Normaali (45x33mm). b, Yö (41x31mm). c, Popeda (40x28mm). d, Dingo (44x33mm). e, Maarit (34x41mm). f, Mamba (38x36mm).

Die Cut Perf. 8½
2010, Jan. 25 **Litho.**
Self-Adhesive
1348 Booklet pane of 6 13.50
a.-f. A796 1 Any single 2.25 2.25
Nos. 1348a-1348f each sold for 80c on day of issue.

A797

Easter — A798

Serpentine Die Cut 12½
2010, Mar. 8   Litho. & Embossed
Self-Adhesive
1349 A797 1 multi   2.25 2.25
Litho.
Die Cut Perf. 14
1350 A798 1 multi   2.25 2.25
Nos. 1349 and 1350 each sold for 80c on day of issue.

Rural Life — A799

No. 1351: a, Mussels, children lifting caught fish. b, Children on swing, strawberries, flowers, horse in meadow. c, Farmer on tractor, farmhouses. d, Milk cans, girl milking cow. e, Musicians and dancers.

Serpentine Die Cut 10¼ Horiz.
2010, Mar. 8   Litho.
Self-Adhesive
1351   Booklet pane of 5   11.50
a.-e. A799 1 Any single   2.25 2.25
Nos. 1351a-1351e each sold for 80c on day of issue.

Famous Women — A800

No. 1352: a, Ritva-Liisa Pohjalainen, jewelry and clothing designer. b, Elina Haavio-Mannila, sociologist. c, Aira Samulin, dance instructor. d, Maria-Liisa Nevala, director of National Theater. e, Laila Hirvisaari, writer. f, Leena Palotie (1952-2010), geneticist.

Serpentine Die Cut 11 Horiz.
Syncopated
Litho. & Silk-screened
2010, Mar. 8
Self-Adhesive
1352   Booklet pane of 6   13.50
a.-f. A800 1 Any single   2.25 2.25
Nos. 1352a-1352f each sold for 80c on day of issue.

Vegetables
A801

No. 1353: a, Tomato (38x33mm). b, Onions (47x34mm). c, Pumpkin (34x36mm). d, Cucumber (27x43mm). e, Eggplant (42x41mm). f, Carrot (29x44mm). g, Broccoli (43x35mm). h, Potato (40x30mm).

2010, Mar. 8   Litho.   Die Cut
Self-Adhesive
1353   Booklet pane of 8   18.00
a.-h. A801 1 Any single   2.25 2.25
Nos. 1353a-1353h each sold for 80c on day of issue.

Souvenir Sheet

Kotka Harbor — A802

No. 1354: a, Vellamo Maritime Center, museum ship Tarmo, crane. b, Sailboat, Wooden Boat Center, vert.

2010, Mar. 24   Perf. 13¾
1354 A802 Sheet of 2   4.50 4.50
a.-b.   1 Either single   2.25 2.25
Nos. 1354a-1354b each sold for 80c on day of issue.

Europa — A803

No. 1355 — Children, books, characters and background in: a, Orange. b, Blue green.

2010, May 4   Perf. 14x13¼
1355 A803 Horiz. pair   4.25 4.25
a.-b.   80c Either single   2.10 2.10

Personalized Stamp — A804

Serpentine Die Cut 11¾ Syncopated
2010, May 4
Self-Adhesive
1356 A804 1 multi   2.10 2.10
No. 1356 sold for 80c on day of issue. The generic design part of the stamp shown could be personalized.

Sculpture — A805

No. 1357: a, Hymy, by Kain Tapper (28x33mm). b, Hefaistos, by Laila Pullinen (28x33mm). c, Cyclist, by Pekka Aarnio (28x33mm). d, Construction, by Kari Huhtamo (28x33mm). e, Salvos, by Mauno Hartman, horiz. (56x29mm). f, Joy, by Miina Akkijyrkka, horiz. (56x29mm).

Serpentine Die Cut 11¾ Horiz.
2010, May 4
Self-Adhesive
1357   Booklet pane of 6   13.00
a.-f. A805 1 Any single   2.10 2.10
Nos. 1357a-1357f each sold for 80c on day of issue.

Souvenir Sheet

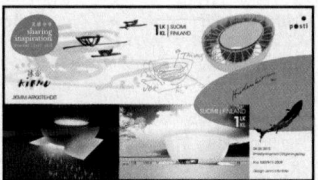

Finnish Pavilion, Expo 2010,
Shanghai — A806

No. 1358: a, Aerial view of model and drawing. b, Side view of model.

Serpentine Die Cut 4½ At Bottom
2010, May 4
Self-Adhesive
1358 A806 Sheet of 2   4.25
a.-b.   1 Either single   2.10 2.10
Nos. 1358a-1358b each sold for 80c on day of issue.

Miniature Sheet

People Jumping — A807

No. 1359 — Jumpers in: a, Purple. b, Red. c, Yellow. d, Blue. e, Green.

2010, May 4   Serpentine Die Cut 5
Self-Adhesive
1359 A807 Sheet of 5   10.50
a.-e.   1 Any single   2.10 2.10
Nos. 1359a-1359e each sold for 80c on day of issue.

Torronsuo National
Park — A808

Die Cut Perf. 14
2010, Sept. 13   Litho.
Self-Adhesive
1360 A808 1 multi   2.10 2.10
No. 1360 sold for 75c on day of issue.

1960s-1970s
Era Room
Furnishings
A809

2010, Sept. 13
Self-Adhesive
1361 A809 1 multi   2.10 2.10
No. 1361 sold fo 75c on day of issue.

Souvenir Sheet

Autumn — A810

No. 1362 — Forest and: a, Crayfish. b, Ducks. c, Elk.

Serpentine Die Cut 12¾x13¼
Syncopated
Litho. & Silk-screened
2010, Sept. 13
Self-Adhesive
1362 A810 Sheet of 3   6.50
a.-c.   1 Any single   2.10 2.10
On day of issue, Nos. 1362a-1362c each sold for 75c.

Santa   Reindeer and
Claus — A811   Moon — A812

Sleigh of
Santa Claus
Over Lapland
A813

No. 1365: a, Star and Santa Claus with sack. b, Poinsettias, ribbon and bell. c, Sleigh of Santa Claus over church. d, Heart-shaped wreath. e, Reindeer and Aurora Borealis.

Die Cut Perf. 14
2010, Nov. 5   Litho.
Self-Adhesive
1363   Horiz. pair   3.25
a.   A811 55c multi   1.60 1.60
b.   A812 55c multi   1.60 1.60
1364 A813 1 multi   2.10 2.10
Souvenir Sheet
1365   Sheet of 5   8.00
a.   A811 55c multi   1.60 1.60
b.   A811 55c multi   1.60 1.60
c.   A813 55c multi   1.60 1.60
d.   A811 55c multi   1.60 1.60
e.   A811 55c multi   1.60 1.60
Christmas. No. 1364 sold for 75c on day of issue. See Japan No. 3269.

SEMI-POSTAL STAMPS

Arms — SP1

Unwmk.
1922, May 15   Typo.   Perf. 14
B1 SP1 1m + 50p gray & red 1.25 12.00
      Never hinged   2.50
a.   Perf. 13x13½   12.00
      Never hinged   25.00

Red Cross   Symbolic
Standard   SP3
SP2

Ship of Mercy — SP4

1930, Feb. 6
B2 SP2 1m + 10p red org &
           red   2.00 13.00
B3 SP3 1½m + 15p grysh grn
           & red   1.50 13.00

B4 SP4 2m + 20p dk bl & red — 3.75 *57.50*

Nos. B2-B4 (3) — 7.25 *83.50*
Set, never hinged — 15.00

The surtax on this and subsequent similar issues was for the benefit of the Red Cross Society of Finland.

Church in Hattula — SP5

SP8

Designs: 1½m+15p, Castle of Hameenlinna. 2m+20p, Fortress of Viipuri.

1931, Jan. 1 — Engr.
Cross in Red

B5 SP5 1m + 10p gray grn — 2.00 *15.00*
B6 SP5 1½m + 15p lil brn — 12.00 *18.00*
B7 SP5 2m + 20p dull bl — 2.00 *36.00*

Nos. B5-B7 (3) — 16.00 *69.00*
Set, never hinged — 40.00

1931, Oct. 15 Typo. *Rouletted 4, 5*
B8 SP8 1m + 4m black — 15.00 *57.50*
Never hinged — 25.00

The surtax was to assist the Postal Museum of Finland in purchasing the Richard Granberg collection of entire envelopes.

Helsinki University Library SP9

Nikolai Church at Helsinki SP10

2½m+25p, Parliament Building, Helsinki.

1932, Jan. 1 — Perf. 14

B9 SP9 1¼m + 10p ol bis & red — 1.60 *16.00*
B10 SP10 2m + 20p dp vio & red — .75 *8.50*
B11 SP9 2½m + 25p lt blue & red — 1.25 *32.50*

Nos. B9-B11 (3) — 3.60 *57.00*
Set, never hinged — 9.00

Bishop Magnus Tawast SP12

Michael Agricola SP13

Design: 2½m+25p, Isacus Rothovius.

1933, Jan. 20 — Engr.
B12 SP12 1¼m + 10p blk brn & red — 3.50 *12.50*
B13 SP13 2m + 20p brn vio & red — 1.00 *3.50*
B14 SP13 2½m + 25p indigo & red — 1.00 *6.50*

Nos. B12-B14 (3) — 5.50 *22.50*
Set, never hinged — 13.50

Evert Horn — SP15

Designs: 2m+20p, Torsten Stalhandske. 2½m+25p, Jakob (Lazy Jake) de la Gardie.

1934, Jan.
Cross in Red

B15 SP15 1¼m + 10p brown — .80 *3.25*
B16 SP15 2m + 20p gray lil — 1.60 *5.75*
B17 SP15 2½m + 25p gray — .80 *3.50*

Nos. B15-B17 (3) — 3.20 *12.50*
Set, never hinged — 11.50

Mathias Calonius SP18

Robert Henrik Rehbinder SP21

Designs: 2m+20p, Henrik C. Porthan. 2½m+25p, Anders Chydenius.

1935, Jan. 1
Cross in Red

B18 SP18 1¼m + 15p brown — 1.00 *3.50*
B19 SP18 2m + 20p gray lil — 2.00 *5.75*
B20 SP18 2½m + 25p gray bl — .80 *3.25*

Nos. B18-B20 (3) — 3.80 *12.50*
Set, never hinged — 8.75

1936, Jan. 1

2m+20p, Count Gustaf Mauritz Armfelt. 2½m+25p, Count Arvid Bernard Horn.

Cross in Red

B21 SP21 1¼m + 15p dk brn — .85 *2.75*
B22 SP21 2m + 20p vio brn — 3.50 *9.00*
B23 SP21 2½m + 25p blue — .80 *4.00*

Nos. B21-B23 (3) — 5.15 *15.75*
Set, never hinged — 12.00

Type "Uusimaa" SP24

Type "Turunmaa" SP25

Design: 3½m+35p, Type "Hameenmaa."

1937, Jan. 1
Cross in Red

B24 SP24 1¼m + 15p brown — .80 *3.25*
B25 SP25 2m + 20p brn lake — 14.00 *9.75*
B26 SP24 3½m + 35p indigo — 1.00 *4.00*

Nos. B24-B26 (3) — 15.80 *17.00*
Set, never hinged — 52.50

Aukuste Makipeska SP27

Skiing SP31

Designs: 1¼m+15p, Robert Isidor Orn. 2m+20p, Edward Bergenheim. 3½m+35p, Johan Mauritz Nordenstam.

1938, Jan. 5 — Engr.
Cross in Red

B27 SP27 50p + 5p dk grn — .50 *1.50*
B28 SP27 1¼m + 15p dk brn — .90 *2.50*
B29 SP27 2m + 20p rose lake — 7.75 *8.50*
B30 SP27 3½m + 35p dk blue — .65 *4.00*

Nos. B27-B30 (4) — 9.80 *16.50*
Set, never hinged — 20.00

1938, Jan. 18

Designs: #B32, Skijumper. #B33, Skier.

B31 SP31 1.25m + 75p sl grn — 3.25 *15.00*
B32 SP31 2m + 1m dk car — 3.25 *15.00*
B33 SP31 3.50m + 1.50m dk blue — 3.25 *15.00*

Nos. B31-B33 (3) — 9.75 *45.00*
Set, never hinged — 24.00

Ski championships held at Lahti.

Soldier SP34

Battlefield at Solferino SP35

1938, May 16

B34 SP34 2m + ½m blue — 1.50 *5.25*
Never hinged — 4.00

Victory of the White Army over the Red Guards. The surtax was for the benefit of the members of the Union of the Finnish Front.

1939, Jan. 2
Cross in Scarlet

B35 SP35 50p + 5p dk grn — .80 *2.00*
B36 SP35 1¼m + 15p dk brn — .90 *2.50*
B37 SP35 2m + 20p lake — 13.00 *16.00*
B38 SP35 3½m + 35p dk bl — .80 *3.25*

Nos. B35-B38 (4) — 15.50 *23.75*
Set, never hinged — 37.50

Intl. Red Cross Soc., 75th anniv.

> **Catalogue values for unused stamps in this section, from this point to the end of the section, are for Never Hinged items.**

Soldiers with Crossbows SP36

Arms of Finland SP40

1¼m+15p, Cavalryman. 2m+20p, Soldier of Charles XII of Sweden. 3½m+35p, Officer and soldier of War with Russia, 1808-1809.

1940, Jan. 3
Cross in Red

B39 SP36 50p + 5p dk grn — 1.25 *2.00*
B40 SP36 1¼m + 15p dk brn — 3.25 *3.25*
B41 SP36 2m + 20p lake — 5.25 *4.00*
B42 SP36 3½m + 35p dp ultra — 3.25 *4.50*

Nos. B39-B42 (4) — 13.00 *13.75*

The surtax aided the Finnish Red Cross.

1940, Feb. 15 — Litho.
B43 SP40 2m + 2m indigo — .50 *2.00*

The surtax was given to a fund for the preservation of neutrality.

Mason SP41

Soldier's Emblem SP45

1.75m+15p, Farmer plowing. 2.75m+25p, Mother and child. 3.50m+35p, Finnish flag.

1941, Jan. 2 — Engr.
Cross in Red

B44 SP41 50p + 5p green — .55 *.55*
B45 SP41 1.75m + 15p brown — 1.50 *2.25*
B46 SP41 2.75m + 25p brn car — 7.75 *10.00*
B47 SP41 3.50m + 35p dp ultra — 2.00 *3.25*

Nos. B44-B47 (4) — 11.80 *16.05*

See Nos. B65-B68.

1941, May 24 — Unwmk.
B48 SP45 2.75m + 25p brt ultra — 1.25 *1.25*

The surtax was for the aid of the soldiers who fought in the Russo-Finnish War.

Aland Arms — SP46

Lapland Arms — SP51

Coats of Arms: 1.75m+15p, Nyland. 2.75m+25p, Finland's first arms. 3.50m+35p, Karelia. 4.75m+45p, Satakunta.

1942, Jan. 2 — Perf. 14
Cross in Red

B49 SP46 50p + 5p green — 1.25 *1.25*
B50 SP46 1.75m + 15p brown — 2.00 *3.25*
B51 SP46 2.75m + 25p dark red — 2.50 *3.25*
B52 SP46 3.50m + 35p deep ultra — 2.00 *5.25*
B53 SP46 4.75m + 45p dk sl grn — 1.25 *4.00*

Nos. B49-B53 (5) — 9.00 *17.00*

The surtax aided the Finnish Red Cross.

1943, Jan. 6 — Inscribed "1943"

Coats of Arms: 2m+20p, Hame. 3.50m+35p, Eastern Bothnia. 4.50m+45p, Savo.

Cross in Red

B54 SP51 50p + 5p green — .65 *1.50*
B55 SP51 2m + 20p brown — 1.50 *2.40*
B56 SP51 3.50m + 35p dark red — 1.50 *2.40*
B57 SP51 4.50m + 45p brt ultra — 4.00 *10.50*

Nos. B54-B57 (4) — 7.65 *16.80*

The surtax aided the Finnish Red Cross.

Soldier's Helmet and Sword — SP55

Mother and Children — SP56

1943, Feb. 1 — Perf. 13
B58 SP55 2m + 50p dk brown — .65 *1.00*
B59 SP56 3.50m + 1m brown red — .65 *1.00*

The surtax was for national welfare.

Red Cross Train — SP57

2m+50p, Ambulance. 3.50m+75p, Red Cross Hospital, Helsinki. 4.50m+1m, Hospital plane.

1944, Jan. 2   **Perf. 14**

Cross in Red

B60	SP57	50p + 25p green	.30	.50
B61	SP57	2m + 50p sepia	.65	1.50
B62	SP57	3.50m + 75p ver	.65	1.25
B63	SP57	4.50m + 1m brt ultra	1.10	5.25
		Nos. B60-B63 (4)	2.70	8.50

The surtax aided the Finnish Red Cross.

Symbols of
Peace
SP61

Wrestling
SP62

1944, Dec. 1

B64	SP61	3.50m + 1.50m dk red brn	.50	1.00

The surtax was for national welfare.

Type of 1941 Inscribed "1945"

1945, May 2   **Photo. & Engr.**

Cross in Red

B65	SP41	1m + 25p green	.20	.50
B66	SP41	2m + 50p brown	.20	1.00
B67	SP41	3.50m + 75p brn car	.20	.80
B68	SP41	4.50m + 1m dp ultra	.80	2.50
		Nos. B65-B68 (4)	1.40	4.80

The surtax was for the Finnish Red Cross.

1945, Apr. 16   **Engr.**   **Perf. 13½**

2m+1m, Gymnast. 3.50m+1.75m, Runner. 4.50m+2.25m, Skier. 7m+3.50m, Javelin thrower.

B69	SP62	1m + 50p bluish grn	.20	1.10
B70	SP62	2m + 1m dp red	.20	1.10
B71	SP62	3.50m + 1.75m dull vio	.20	1.10
B72	SP62	4.50m + 2.25m ultra	.50	1.50
B73	SP62	7m + 3.50m dull brn	1.00	2.50
		Nos. B69-B73 (5)	2.10	7.30

Fishing
SP67

Nurse and
Children
SP71

Designs: 3m+75p, Churning. 5m+1.25m, Reaping. 10m+2.50m, Logging.

Engraved; Cross Typo. in Red

1946, Jan. 7

B74	SP67	1m + 25p dull grn	.50	.65
B75	SP67	3m + 75p lilac brn	.30	.50
B76	SP67	5m + 1.25m rose red	.50	.65
a.		Red cross omitted	850.00	850.00
B77	SP67	10m + 2.50m ultra	.65	1.25
		Nos. B74-B77 (4)	1.95	3.05

The surtax was for the Finnish Red Cross.

1946, Sept. 2   **Engr.**

Design: 8m+2m, Doctor examining infant.

B78	SP71	5m + 1m green	.30	.65
B79	SP71	8m + 2m brown vio	.30	.65

The surtax was for the prevention of tuberculosis.

Nos. B78 and B79 Surcharged with New Values in Black

1947, Apr. 1

B80	SP71	6m + 1m on 5m + 1m	.50	.90
B81	SP71	10m + 2m on 8m + 2m	.50	.90

The surtax was for the prevention of tuberculosis.

SP73

Medical Examination
of Infants — SP74

Designs: 10m+2.50m, Infant held by the feet. 12m+3m, Mme. Alli Paasikivi and a child. 20m+5m, Infant standing.

1947, Sept. 15   **Engr.**

B82	SP73	2.50m + 1m green	.50	1.25
B83	SP74	6m + 1.50m dk red	.65	2.00
B84	SP74	10m + 2.50m red brn	1.00	2.00
B85	SP73	12m + 3m dp blue	1.25	2.50
B86	SP74	20m + 5m dk red vio	2.00	3.25
		Nos. B82-B86 (5)	5.40	11.00

The surtax was for the prevention of tuberculosis.
For surcharges see Nos. B91-B93.

Zachris
Topelius — SP78

7m+2m, Fredrik Pacius. 12m+3m, Johan L. Runeberg. 20m+5m, Fredrik Cygnaeus.

Engraved; Cross Typo. in Red

1948, May 10   **Unwmk.**   **Perf. 14**

B87	SP78	3m + 1m green	.50	.80
B88	SP78	7m + 2m rose red	.65	1.50
B89	SP78	12m + 3m brt blue	.80	1.50
B90	SP78	20m + 5m dk vio	.90	2.10
		Nos. B87-B90 (4)	2.85	5.90

The surtax was for the Finnish Red Cross.

Nos. B83, B84 and B86 Surcharged with New Values and Bars in Black

1948, Sept. 13   **Engr.**   **Perf. 13½**

B91	SP74	7m + 2m on #B83	2.10	3.25
B92	SP74	15m + 3m on #B84	2.10	3.25
B93	SP74	24m + 6m on #B86	2.50	5.25
		Nos. B91-B93 (3)	6.70	11.75

The surtax was for the prevention of tuberculosis.

Tying Birch
Boughs
SP79

Wood Anemone
SP83

9m+3m, Bathers in Sauna house. 15m+5m, Rural bath house. 30m+10m, Cold plunge in lake.

Engraved; Cross Typo. in Red

1949, May 5   **Perf. 13½x14**

B94	SP79	5m + 2m dull grn	.50	.80
B95	SP79	9m + 3m dk car	.90	1.40
B96	SP79	15m + 5m dp blue	.90	1.40
B97	SP79	30m + 10m dk vio brn	2.00	3.25
		Nos. B94-B97 (4)	4.30	6.85

The surtax was for the Finnish Red Cross.

1949, June 2   **Engr.**

Inscribed: "1949"

B98	SP83	5m + 2m shown	.80	1.10
B99	SP83	9m + 3m Wild rose	1.00	1.25
B100	SP83	15m + 5m Coltsfoot	1.00	1.50
		Nos. B98-B100 (3)	2.80	3.85

The surtax was for the prevention of tuberculosis.

Similar to Type of 1949

Designs: 5m+2m, Water lily. 9m+3m, Pasqueflower. 15m+5m, Bell flower cluster.

1950, Apr. 1

Inscribed: "1950"

B101	SP83	5m + 2m emer	3.25	2.75
B102	SP83	9m + 3m rose car	2.40	2.40
B103	SP83	15m + 5m blue	2.40	2.00
		Nos. B101-B103 (3)	8.05	6.75

The surtax was for the prevention of tuberculosis.

Hospital
Entrance,
Helsinki
SP84

Blood Donor's
Medal
SP86

Design: 12m+3m, Giving blood.

Engraved; Cross Typo. in Red

1951, Mar. 17   **Unwmk.**   **Perf. 14**

B104	SP84	7m + 2m chocolate	1.10	2.00
B105	SP84	12m + 3m bl vio	1.50	2.50
B106	SP86	20m + 5m car	2.00	3.25
		Nos. B104-B106 (3)	4.60	7.75

The surtax was for the Finnish Red Cross.

Capercaillie — SP87

Designs: 12m+3m, European cranes. 20m+5m, Caspian terns.

1951, Oct. 26   **Engr.**

B107	SP87	7m + 2m dk grn	3.50	3.75
B108	SP87	12m + 3m rose brn	3.50	3.75
B109	SP87	20m + 5m blue	3.50	3.75
		Nos. B107-B109 (3)	10.50	11.25

The surtax was for the prevention of tuberculosis.

Diver — SP88

Soccer Players
SP89

#B112, Stadium, Helsinki. #B113, Runners.

1951-52

B110	SP88	12m + 2m rose car	2.00	1.50
B111	SP89	15m + 2m grn ('52)	2.00	1.75
B112	SP88	20m + 3m deep blue	2.40	2.00
B113	SP89	25m + 4m brn ('52)	2.50	2.75
		Nos. B110-B113 (4)	8.90	8.00

XV Olympic Games, Helsinki, 1952. The surtax was to help finance the games.
Issued: B110, B112, 11/16; B111, B113, 2/15/52.

Margin blocks of four of each denomination were cut from regular or perf-through-margin sheets and pasted by the selvage, overlapping, in a printed folder to create a kind of souvenir booklet. Value $60.

Field Marshal
Mannerheim
SP90

Great Titmouse
SP91

Engraved; Cross Typo. in Red

1952, Mar. 4

B114	SP90	10m + 2m gray	2.00	2.50
B115	SP90	15m + 3m rose vio	2.00	2.50
B116	SP90	25m + 5m blue	2.00	2.50
		Nos. B114-B116 (3)	6.00	7.50

The surtax was for the Red Cross.

1952, Dec. 4   **Engr.**

Designs: 15m+3m, Spotted flycatchers and nest. 25m+5m, Swift.

B117	SP91	10m + 2m green	2.75	3.25
B118	SP91	15m + 3m plum	2.75	3.25
B119	SP91	25m + 5m deep blue	2.75	3.25
		Nos. B117-B119 (3)	8.25	9.75

The surtax was for the prevention of tuberculosis.

European Red
Squirrel
SP92

No. B121, Brown bear. No. B122, European elk.

Unwmk.

1953, Nov. 16   **Engr.**   **Perf. 14**

B120	SP92	10m + 2m red brown	3.50	4.00
B121	SP92	15m + 3m violet	3.50	4.00
B122	SP92	25m + 5m dark grn	3.50	4.00
		Nos. B120-B122 (3)	10.50	12.00

Surtax for the prevention of tuberculosis.

Children Receiving
Parcel from Welfare
Worker — SP93

Designs: 15m+3m, Aged woman knitting. 25m+5m, Blind basket-maker and dog.

Engraved; Cross Typo. in Red

1954, Mar. 8   **Perf. 11½**

B123	SP93	10m + 2m dk ol grn	1.50	2.00
B124	SP93	15m + 3m dk blue	1.50	2.00
B125	SP93	25m + 5m dk brown	1.50	2.00
		Nos. B123-B125 (3)	4.50	6.00

The surtax was for the Finnish Red Cross.

Bumblebees,
Dandelions — SP94

European Perch — SP95

15m+3m, Butterfly. 25m+5m, Dragonfly.

Engraved; Cross Typo. in Red

1954, Dec. 7   *Perf. 14*

B126 SP94 10m + 2m brown   2.50 2.00
B127 SP94 15m + 3m carmine   3.00 2.50
B128 SP94 25m + 5m blue   3.00 2.50
    Nos. B126-B128 (3)   8.50 7.00

The surtax was for the prevention of tuberculosis.

Engraved; Cross Typo. in Red

1955, Sept. 26   *Perf. 14*

Designs: 15m+3m, Northern pike. 25m+5m, Atlantic salmon.

B129 SP95 10m + 2m dl grn   2.00 2.00
B130 SP95 15m + 3m vio brn   2.50 2.00
B131 SP95 25m + 5m dk bl   3.25 2.00
    Nos. B129-B131 (3)   7.75 6.00

Surtax for the Anti-Tuberculosis Society.

Gen. von Dobeln in Battle of Juthas, 1808 SP96

Waxwing SP97

Illustrations by Albert Edelfelter from J. L. Runeberg's "Tales of Ensign Stal": 15m+3m, Col. J. Z. Duncker holding flag. 25m+5m, Son of fallen Soldier.

Engraved; Cross Typo. in Red

1955, Nov. 24

B132 SP96 10m + 2m dp ultra   1.50 *2.00*
B133 SP96 15m + 3m dk red brn   1.50 *2.00*
B134 SP96 25m + 5m green   1.50 *2.00*
    Nos. B132-B134 (3)   4.50 6.00

The surtax was for the Red Cross.

Engraved; Cross Typo. in Red

1956, Sept. 25   *Perf. 11½*

Birds: 20m+3m, Eagle owl. 30m+5m, Mute swan.

B135 SP97 10m + 2m dl red brn   2.10 1.25
B136 SP97 20m + 3m bl grn   2.75 2.10
B137 SP97 30m + 5m blue   3.75 2.10
    Nos. B135-B137 (3)   8.60 5.45

Surtax for the Anti-Tuberculosis Society.

Pekka Aulin SP98

Wolverine (Glutton) SP99

Portraits: 10m+2m, Leonard von Pfaler. 20m+3m, Gustaf Johansson. 30m+5m, Viktor Magnus von Born.

Engraved; Cross Typo. in Red

1956, Nov. 26   *Unwmk.*

B138 SP98   5m + 1m grysh
             grn   1.00 1.25
B139 SP98 10m + 2m brown   1.50 1.50
B140 SP98 20m + 3m magen-
             ta   2.40 2.40
B141 SP98 30m + 5m lt ultra   2.40 2.40
    Nos. B138-B141 (4)   7.30 7.55

The surtax was for the Red Cross.

Engraved; Cross Typo. in Red

1957, Sept. 5   *Perf. 11½*

20m+3m, Lynx. 30m+5m, Reindeer.

B142 SP99 10m + 2m dull purple   2.00 1.50
B143 SP99 20m + 3m sepia   3.00 2.40
B144 SP99 30m + 5m dark blue   3.00 2.40
    Nos. B142-B144 (3)   8.00 6.30

The surtax was for the Anti-Tuberculosis Society. See Nos. B160-B165.

Red Cross Flag SP100

Raspberry SP101

1957, Nov. 25   **Engr.**   *Perf. 14*
Cross in Red

B145 SP100 10m + 2m ol grn   1.75 2.40
B146 SP100 20m + 3m maroon   2.00 3.25
B147 SP100 30m + 5m dull blue   2.00 3.25
    Nos. B145-B147 (3)   5.75 8.90

80th anniv. of the Finnish Red Cross.

Type of 1952

Flowers: 10m+2m, Lily of the Valley. 20m+3m, Red clover. 30m+5m, Hepatica.

Engraved; Cross Typo. in Red

1958, May 5   **Unwmk.**   *Perf. 14*

B148 SP91 10m + 2m green   2.40 1.50
B149 SP91 20m + 3m lilac rose   2.50 2.50
B150 SP91 30m + 5m ultra   2.75 2.50
    Nos. B148-B150 (3)   7.65 6.50

Surtax for the Anti-Tuberculosis Society.

Engraved; Cross Typo. in Red

1958, Nov. 20   *Perf. 11½*

20m+3m, Cowberry. 30m+5m, Blueberry.

B151 SP101 10m + 2m orange   2.40 1.75
B152 SP101 20m + 3m red   2.75 2.25
B153 SP101 30m + 5m dk blue   2.75 2.25
    Nos. B151-B153 (3)   7.90 6.25

The surtax was for the Red Cross.

Daisy — SP102

Reindeer SP103

20m+5m, Primrose. 30m+5m, Cornflower.

Engraved; Cross Typo. in Red

1959, Sept. 7   *Unwmk.*

B154 SP102 10m + 2m green   4.00 2.00
B155 SP102 20m + 3m lt brown   4.75 3.00
B156 SP102 30m + 5m blue   4.75 3.00
    Nos. B154-B156 (3)   13.50 8.00

Surtax for the Anti-Tuberculosis Society.

Engraved; Cross Typo. in Red

1960, Nov. 24   *Perf. 11½*

#B158, Lapp & lasso. #B159, Mountains.

B157 SP103 10m + 2m dk gray   1.50 1.50
B158 SP103 20m + 3m gray vio   2.40 2.40
B159 SP103 30m + 5m rose vio   2.40 2.40
    Nos. B157-B159 (3)   6.30 6.30

The surtax was for the Red Cross.

Animal Type of 1957

Designs: 10m+2m, Muskrat. 20m+3m, Otter. 30m+5m, Seal.

Engr.; Cross at right, Typo. in Red

1961, Sept. 4

B160 SP99 10m + 2m brn car   1.75 1.50
B161 SP99 20m + 3m slate bl   2.50 2.10
B162 SP99 30m + 5m bl grn   2.50 2.10
    Nos. B160-B162 (3)   6.75 5.70

Surtax for the Anti-Tuberculosis Society.

Animal Type of 1957

Designs: 10m+2m, Hare. 20m+3m, Pine marten. 30m+5m, Ermine.

Engraved; Cross Typo. in Red

1962, Oct. 1

B163 SP99 10m + 2m gray   2.00 2.00
B164 SP99 20m + 3m dl red brn   2.50 2.25
B165 SP99 30m + 5m vio bl   2.50 2.25
    Nos. B163-B165 (3)   7.00 6.50

The surtax was for the Anti-Tuberculosis Society.

Cross and Outstretched Hands SP104

Engraved; Cross Typo. in Red

1963, May 8   **Unwmk.**   *Perf. 11½*

B166 SP104 10p + 2p red brn   .90 1.00
B167 SP104 20p + 3p violet   1.25 1.50
B168 SP104 30p + 5p green   1.25 1.50
    Nos. B166-B168 (3)   3.40 4.00

The surtax was for the Red Cross.

Attending the Wounded SP105

Red Cross Activities: 25p+4p, Hospital ship. 35p+5p, Prisoner-of-war health examination. 40p+7p, Gift parcel distribution.

Engraved; Cross Typo. in Red

1964, May 26   *Perf. 11½*

B169 SP105 15p + 3p vio bl   1.25 .90
B170 SP105 25p + 4p green   1.50 1.10
B171 SP105 35p + 5p vio brn   1.50 1.10
B172 SP105 40p + 7p dk ol grn   1.50 1.10
    Nos. B169-B172 (4)   5.75 4.20

The surtax was for the Red Cross.

Finnish Spitz — SP106

Artificial Respiration — SP107

Designs: 25p+4p, Karelian bear dog. 35p+5p, Finnish hunting dog.

Engraved; Cross Typo. in Red

1965, May 10   *Perf. 11½*

B173 SP106 15p + 3p org brn   2.00 1.50
B174 SP106 25p + 4p black   3.00 2.40
B175 SP106 35p + 5p gray brn   3.00 2.40
    Nos. B173-B175 (3)   8.00 6.30

Surtax for Anti-Tuberculosis Society.

1966, May 7   **Litho.**   *Perf. 14*

First Aid: 25p+4p, Skin diver rescuing occupants of submerged car. 35p+5p, Helicopter rescue in winter.

B176 SP107 15p + 3p multi   1.10 1.25
B177 SP107 25p + 4p multi   1.25 1.50
B178 SP107 35p + 5p multi   1.25 1.50
    Nos. B176-B178 (3)   3.60 4.25

The surtax was for the Red Cross.

Birch — SP108

Horse-drawn Ambulance SP109

Trees: 25p+4p, Pine. 40p+7p, Spruce.

1967, May 12   **Litho.**   *Perf. 14*

B179 SP108 20p + 3p multi   1.00 1.00
B180 SP108 25p + 4p multi   1.00 1.00
B181 SP108 40p + 7p multi   1.00 1.00
    Nos. B179-B181 (3)   3.00 3.00

Surtax for Anti-Tuberculosis Society. See Nos. B185-B187.

Cross in Red

25p+4p, Ambulance, 1967. 40p+7p, Red Cross.

1967, Nov. 24   **Litho.**   *Perf. 14*

B182 SP109 20p + 3p dl yel, grn
             & blk   1.10 1.10
B183 SP109 25p + 4p vio & blk   1.10 1.10
B184 SP109 40p + 7p dk grn, blk
            & dk ol   1.10 1.10
    Nos. B182-B184 (3)   3.30 3.30

The surtax was for the Red Cross.

Tree Type of 1967

Trees: 20p+3p, Juniper. 25+4p, Aspen. 40p+7p, Chokecherry.

1969, May 12   **Litho.**   *Perf. 14*

B185 SP108 20p + 3p multi   .90 1.10
B186 SP108 25p + 4p multi   .90 1.10
B187 SP108 40p + 7p multi   .90 1.10
    Nos. B185-B187 (3)   2.70 3.30

Surtax for Anti-Tuberculosis Society.

"On the Lapp's Magic Rock" SP110

Designs: 30p+6p, Juhani blowing horn on Impivaara Rock, vert. 50p+10p, The Pale Maiden. The designs are from illustrations by Askeli Gallen-Kallelas for "The Seven Brothers" by Aleksis Kivi.

1970, May 8   **Litho.**   *Perf. 14*

B188 SP110 25p + 5p multi   .80 .80
B189 SP110 30p + 6p multi   .90 1.00
B190 SP110 50p + 10p multi   .90 1.00
    Nos. B188-B190 (3)   2.60 2.80

The surtax was for the Red Cross.

Cutting and Loading Timber SP111

Designs: 30p+6p, Floating logs downstream. 50p+10p, Sorting logs at sawmill.

1971, Apr. 25   **Litho.**   *Perf. 14*

B191 SP111 25p + 5p multi   .90 1.00
B192 SP111 30p + 6p multi   .90 1.00
B193 SP111 50p + 10p multi   1.00 1.00
    Nos. B191-B193 (3)   2.80 3.00

Surtax for Anti-Tuberculosis Society.

Blood Donor and Nurse SP112

30p+6p, Blood research (microscope, slides), vert. 50p+10p, Blood transfusion.

1972, Oct. 23
B194 SP112 25p + 5p multi .80 .90
B195 SP112 30p + 6p multi 1.10 1.10
B196 SP112 50p + 10p multi 1.10 1.10
Nos. B194-B196 (3) 3.00 3.10

Surtax was for the Red Cross.

Girl with Lamb, by Hugo Simberg — SP113

Paintings: 40p+10p, Summer Evening, by Vilho Sjöström. 60p+15p, Woman at Mountain Fountain, by Juho Rissanen.

1973, Sept. 12   Litho.   Perf. 13x12½
B197 SP113 30p + 5p multi 1.25 1.25
B198 SP113 40p + 10p multi 1.75 1.75
B199 SP113 60p + 15p multi 1.75 1.75
Nos. B197-B199 (3) 4.75 4.75

Surtax for the Finnish Anti-Tuberculosis Assoc. Birth centenaries of featured artists.

Morel SP114

Mushrooms: 50p+10p, Chanterelle. 60p+15p, Boletus edulis.

1974, Sept. 24   Litho.   Perf. 12½x13
B200 SP114 35p + 5p multi 2.50 1.50
B201 SP114 50p + 10p multi 2.25 1.50
B202 SP114 60p + 15p multi 2.25 1.50
Nos. B200-B202 (3) 7.00 4.50

Finnish Red Cross.

Echo, by Ellen Thesleff (1869-1954) SP115

Paintings: 60p+15p, Hilda Wiik, by Maria Wiik (1853-1928). 70p+20p, At Home (old woman in chair), by Helene Schjerfbeck (1862-1946).

1975, Sept. 30   Litho.   Perf. 13x12½
B203 SP115 40p + 10p multi 1.10 1.10
B204 SP115 60p + 15p multi 1.25 .125
B205 SP115 70p + 20p multi 1.25 1.25
Nos. B203-B205 (3) 3.60 2.48

Finnish Red Cross. In honor of International Women's Year paintings by women artists were chosen.

Disabled Veterans' Emblem SP116

Lithographed and Photogravure
1976, Jan. 15   Perf. 14
B206 SP116 70p + 30p multi 1.00 .95

The surtax was for hospitals for disabled war veterans.

Wedding Procession SP117

Designs: 70p+15p, Wedding dance, vert. 80p+20p, Bride, groom, matron and pastor at wedding dinner.

1976, Sept. 15   Litho.   Perf. 13
B207 SP117 50p + 10p multi .80 .80
B208 SP117 70p + 15p multi 1.00 1.00
B209 SP117 80p + 20p multi 1.00 1.00
Nos. B207-B209 (3) 2.80 2.80

Surtax for Anti-Tuberculosis Society.

Disaster Relief SP118

Designs: 80p+15p, Community work. 90p+20p, Blood transfusion service.

1977, Jan. 19   Litho.   Perf. 14
B210 SP118 50p + 10p multi .65 .65
B211 SP118 70p + 15p multi .80 .80
B212 SP118 90p + 20p multi .80 .80
Nos. B210-B212 (3) 2.25 2.25

Finnish Red Cross centenary.

Long-distance Skiing SP119

Design: 1m+50p, Ski jump.

1977, Oct. 5   Litho.   Perf. 13
B213 SP119 80p + 40p multi 2.50 3.75
B214 SP119 1m + 50p multi 2.00 2.00

Surtax was for World Ski Championships, Lahti, Feb. 17-26, 1978.

Saffron Milkcap SP120

Edible Mushrooms: 80p+15p, Parasol, vert. 1m+20p, Gypsy.

1978, Sept. 13   Litho.   Perf. 13
B215 SP120 50p + 10p multi 1.75 1.10
B216 SP120 80p + 15p multi 2.00 2.00
B217 SP120 1m + 20p multi 2.00 2.00
Nos. B215-B217 (3) 5.75 5.10

Surtax was for Red Cross. See Nos. B221-B223.

Pehr Kalm, 1716-1779 SP121

Finnish Scientists: 90p+15p, Title page of Pehr Adrian Gadd's (1727-97) book, vert. 1.10m+20p, Petter Forsskal (1732-63).

Perf. 12½x13, 13x12½
1979, Sept. 26   Litho.
B218 SP121 60p + 10p multi .65 .80
B219 SP121 90p + 15p multi .85 .85
B220 SP121 1.10m + 20p multi .85 .85
Nos. B218-B220 (3) 2.35 2.50

Surtax for Finnish Anti-Tuberculosis Assoc.

Mushroom Type of 1978
Edible Mushrooms: 60p+10p, Woolly milkcap. 90p+15p, Orange-cap boletus, vert. 1.10m+20p, Russula paludosa.

1980, Apr. 19   Litho.   Perf. 13
B221 SP120 60p + 10p multi 1.50 1.10
B222 SP120 90p + 15p multi 2.00 2.00
B223 SP120 1.10m + 20p multi 2.00 2.00
Nos. B221-B223 (3) 5.50 5.10

Surtax was for Red Cross.

Fuchsia — SP122

1981, Aug. 24   Litho.   Perf. 13
B224 SP122 70p + 15p shown 1.10 1.10
B225 SP122 1m + 15p African violet 1.10 1.10
B226 SP122 1.10m + 20p Geranium 1.10 1.10
Nos. B224-B226 (3) 3.30 3.30

Surtax for Finnish Anti-Tuberculosis Assoc.

Garden Dormouse SP123

1982, Aug. 16   Litho.   Perf. 13
B227 SP123 90p + 10p shown 1.10 1.00
B228 SP123 1.10m + 15p Flying squirrels 1.10 1.10
B229 SP123 1.20m + 20p European minks 1.25 1.10
Nos. B227-B229 (3) 3.45 3.20

Surtax was for Red Cross. No. B228 vert.

Forest and Wetland Plants SP124

1m+20p, Chickweed wintergreen. 1.20m+25p, Marsh violet. 1.30m+30p, Marsh marigold.

1983, July 7   Litho.   Perf. 13
B230 SP124 1m + 20p multi 1.00 1.00
B231 SP124 1.20m + 25p multi 1.00 1.00
B232 SP124 1.30m + 30p multi 1.00 1.00
Nos. B230-B232 (3) 3.00 3.00

Surtax for Finnish Anti-Tuberculosis Assoc.

Globe Puzzle — SP125

2m+40p, Symbolic world communication.

1984, May 28   Litho.   Perf. 13
B233 SP125 1.40m + 35p multi .85 .85
B234 SP125 2m + 40p multi 1.25 1.25

Surtax for Red Cross.

Butterflies SP126

1986, May 22   Litho.   Perf. 13
#B235, Anthocharis cardamines. #B236, Nymphalis antiopa. #B237, Parnassius apollo.

B235 SP126 1.60m + 40p multi 1.25 .80
B236 SP126 2.10m + 45p multi 2.00 1.50
B237 SP126 5m + 50p multi 4.00 4.00
Nos. B235-B237 (3) 7.25 6.30

Surtax for Red Cross.

Festivals SP127

1988, Mar. 14   Litho.   Perf. 13
B238 SP127 1.40m +40p Christmas 1.10 .85
B239 SP127 1.80m +45p Easter 1.25 1.25
B240 SP127 2.40m +50p Midsummer 1.50 1.50
Nos. B238-B240 (3) 3.85 3.60

Surtax for the Red Cross.

Heodes virgaureae on Goldrod Plant SP128

Butterflies and plants: No. B242, Agrodiaetus amandus on meadow vetchling. No. B243, Inachis io on tufted vetch.

1990, Apr. 6   Photo.   Perf. 12x11½
B241 SP128 1.50m +40p multi 1.00 1.00
B242 SP128 2m +50p multi 1.25 1.25
B243 SP128 2.70m +60p multi 1.50 1.50
Nos. B241-B243 (3) 3.75 3.75

Surtax for the natl. Red Cross Soc.

Paintings by Helene Schjerfbeck — SP129

Designs: No. B244a, The Little Convalescent, No. B244b, Green Still-Life.

1991, Mar. 8   Litho.   Perf. 13
B244 SP129 Pair 3.00 3.00
a.-b.   2.10m +50p any single 1.50 1.50

Surtax for philately.

Butterflies SP130

#B245, Xestia brunneopicta. #B246, Acerbia alpina. #B247, Baptria tibiale.

Litho. & Embossed
1992, Apr. 22   Perf. 13
B245 SP130 1.60m +40p multi 1.00 1.00
B246 SP130 2.10m +50p multi 1.25 1.25
B247 SP130 5m +60p multi 2.75 2.75
Nos. B245-B247 (3) 5.00 5.00

Surtax for Finnish Red Cross. Embossed "Arla 100" in braille for Arla Institute, training center for the blind, cent.

Autumn Landscape of Lake Pielisjarvi, by Eero Jarnefelt SP131

a, Tree-covered hill. b, Lake shoreline.

1993, Mar. 19   Litho.   Perf. 13
B248 SP131 2.30m + 70p Pair,
             #a.-b.   3.00 3.00

Surtax for philately.

Finnhorses SP132

1994, Mar. 11   Litho.   Perf. 13
B249 SP132 2m +40p Draft
             horses   1.25 1.25
B250 SP132 2.30m +50p Trotter 1.50 1.50
B251 SP132 4.20m +60p War
             horses, vert.   2.40 2.40
      Nos. B249-B251 (3)   5.15 5.15

Surtax for Finnish Red Cross.

Paintings, by Albert Edelfelt (1854-1905) — SP133

No. B252, Playing Boys on the Shore. No. B253, Queen Blanche.

1995, Mar. 1   Litho.   Perf. 13½
B252 2.40m +60p multi   1.50 1.50
      Size: 22x31mm
B253 2.40m +60p multi   1.50 1.50
  a. SP133 Pair, #B252-B253   3.00 3.00

Surtax for philately.

Chickens SP134

1996, Mar. 18   Litho.   Perf. 13
B254 SP134 2.80m +60p Chicks   1.75 1.75
B255 SP134 3.20m +70p Hens   1.90 1.90
B256 SP134 3.40m +70p Roost-
             er, vert.   2.00 2.50
      Nos. B254-B256 (3)   5.65 6.15

Surtax for Finnish Red Cross.

The Aino Myth, by Akseli Gallen-Kallela (1865-1931) SP135

Designs: No. B257, Väinämöinen proposing marriage to Aino in forest. No. B258, Aino jumping into water to escape Väinämöinen. No. B259, Aino at shore for bath.

1997, Sept. 5   Litho.   Perf. 13½x13
Booklet Stamps
B257 SP135 2.80m +60p multi   1.90 1.90
B258 SP135 2.80m +60p multi   1.90 1.90
B259 SP135 2.80m +60p multi   1.90 1.90
  a. Booklet pane, #B257-B259   6.00 6.00
      Complete booklet, #B259a   6.00

No. B258 is 33x46mm.
Surtax for philately.

Pigs — SP136

2.80m+60p, Sow, piglets. 3.20m+70p, Three piglets. 3.40m+70p, Pig's head.

1998, Mar. 12   Litho.   Perf. 13
B260 SP136 2.80m +60p multi   1.60 1.60
B261 SP136 3.20m +70p multi   1.90 1.90
B262 SP136 3.40m +70p multi   2.00 2.00
      Nos. B260-B262 (3)   5.50 5.50

Surtax for Finnish Red Cross.

Paintings by Hugo Simberg (1873-1917) SP137

a, Garden of Death. b, Wounded Angel.

Perf. 13¼x13¾
1999, Sept. 24   Litho.
B263   Booklet pane of 2   4.25 4.25
  a.-b. SP137 3.50m +50p any single 2.00
         Complete booklet, #B263 4.25

Surtax for philately.

Cow and Calf — SP138

Perf. 13¾x13¼
2000, Mar. 15   Litho.
B264 SP138 3.50m +70p Bull,
             vert.   2.00 2.00
      Perf. 13¼x13¾
B265 SP138 4.80m +80p shown   2.75 2.75

Surtax for Finnish Red Cross.

Post Horn SP139

2010, May 4   Litho.   Perf. 14½x14¼
B266 SP139 1 +5c multi   2.25 2.25

No. B266 had a franking value of 80c on day of issue. Surtax for construction of Finland's first solar energy plant.

AIR POST STAMPS

No. 178 Overprinted in Red

1930, Sept. 24   Unwmk.   Perf. 14
C1 A28 10m gray lilac   140.00 300.00
  a.   1830 for 1930   2,500. 11,000.

Overprinted expressly for use on mail carried in "Graf Zeppelin" on return flight from Finland to Germany on Sept. 24, 1930, after which trip the stamps ceased to be valid for postage. Forgeries are almost always on No. 205, rather than No. 178.

> **Catalogue values for unused stamps in this section, from this point to the end of the section, are for Never Hinged items.**

Douglas DC-2 — AP1

1944   Engr.
C2 AP1 3.50m dark brown   .65   1.25
Air Transport Service anniv., 1923-43.

Douglas DC-6 Over Winter Landscape — AP2

1950, Feb. 13
C3 AP2 300m blue   20.00 10.00
Available also for ordinary postage.

Redrawn
1958, Jan. 20   Perf. 11½
C4 AP2 300(m) blue   35.00 1.25
On No. C4 "mk" is omitted.
See Nos. C9-C9a.

Convair 440 over Lakes — AP3

1958, Oct. 31   Unwmk.   Perf. 11½
C5 AP3 34m blue   1.25 1.25

No. C5 Surcharged with New Value and Bars

1959, Apr. 5
C6 AP3 45m on 34m blue   2.50 3.00

1959, Nov. 2
C7 AP3 45m blue   3.00 2.00

1963, Feb. 15
C8 AP3 45p blue   1.60 .55

On No. C7 the denomination is "45." On No. C8 it is "0.45."

DC-6 Type, Comma After "3"
Type I — 16 lines in "O"
Type II — 13 lines in "O"

1963, Oct. 10
C9 AP2 3m blue, Type II ('73) 3.25 .65
  a.   Type I   30.00 1.00

Convair Type of 1958
1970, July 15
C10 AP3 57p ultra   2.00 1.25

MILITARY STAMPS

> **Catalogue values for unused stamps in this section are for Never Hinged items.**

M1

Unwmk.
1941, Nov. 1   Typo.   Imperf.
M1 M1 (4m) blk, dk org   .50   .90
#M1 has simulated roulette printed in black.

Type of 1930-46 Overprinted in Black

1943, Oct. 16   Perf. 14
M2 A26 2m deep orange   .40   .90
M3 A26 3½m greenish blue   .40   .90

Post Horn and Sword — M2

1943, July 1   Size: 29½x19½mm
M4 M2 (2m) green   .65   .65
M5 M2 (3m) rose violet   .90   .65

1944, Feb. 16   Size: 20x16mm
M6 M2 (2m) green   .50   .50
M7 M2 (3m) rose violet   .65   .50

Post Horns and Arms of Finland — M3

1963, Sept. 26   Litho.   Perf. 14
M8 M3 violet blue   160.00 175.00

Used during maneuvers Sept. 30-Oct. 5, 1963. Valid from Sept. 26.

No. M8 Overprinted "1983"

1983, Apr. 20
M9 M3 violet blue   250.00 175.00

Used during maneuvers Apr. 24-30.

PARCEL POST STAMPS

PP1

Wmk. Rose & Triangles Multiple
Rouletted 6 on 2 or 3 Sides
1949-50   Typo.
Q1 PP1 1m brt grn & blk   1.25   4.50
Q2 PP1 5m red & blk   11.00 22.50
Q3 PP1 20m org & blk   21.00 40.00
Q4 PP1 50m bl & blk ('50)   7.50 16.00
Q5 PP1 100m brn & blk ('50)   8.50 11.00
    Nos. Q1-Q5 (5)   49.25 94.00
    Set, never hinged   90.00

> **Catalogue values for unused stamps in this section, from this point to the end of the section, are for Never Hinged items.**

Mail Bus — PP2

1952-58 Unwmk. Engr. Perf. 14

Q6	PP2	5m car rose	5.00	5.00
Q7	PP2	20m orange	15.00	8.50
Q8	PP2	50m blue ('54)	30.00	13.00
Q9	PP2	100m brn ('58)	40.00	25.00
	Nos. Q6-Q9 (4)		90.00	51.50

Mail Bus — PP3

1963 Perf. 12

Q10	PP3	5p red & blk	5.00	5.00
Q11	PP3	20p org & blk	5.00	4.50
Q12	PP3	50p blue & blk	6.50	5.00
Q13	PP3	1m brn & blk	3.25	4.50
	Nos. Q10-Q13 (4)		19.75	19.00

Nos. Q1-Q13 were issued only in booklets: panes of 6 for Nos. Q1-Q5, 10 for Nos. Q6-Q9 and 5 for Nos. Q10-Q13.

Used values are for regular postal or mail-bus cancels. Pen strokes, cutting or other cancels sell for half as much.

1981 SISU Bus — PP4

Photo. & Engr.

1981, Dec. 7 Perf. 12 Horiz.

Q14	PP4	50p dk bl & blk	1.25	5.75
Q15	PP4	1m dk brn & blk	2.00	5.75
Q16	PP4	5m grn & blk	3.50	16.00
Q17	PP4	7m brn & blk	7.25	32.50
	Nos. Q14-Q17 (4)		14.00	60.00

Parcel post stamps invalid after Jan. 9, 1985.

ALAND ISLANDS

LOCATION — A group of 6,554 islands at the mouth of the Gulf of Bothnia, between Finland and Sweden.

GOVT. — Province of Finland

AREA — 590 sq. mi.

POP. — 23,761

CAPITAL — Mariehamn

The province of Aland was awarded to Finland in 1921 by the League of Nations. The Swedish language is spoken and the province has a considerable amount of self-determination.

> Catalogue values for unused stamps in this country are for Never Hinged items.

Gaff-rigged Sloop — A1

Aland Flag — A2

Midsummer Pole — A3

Landscapes — A4

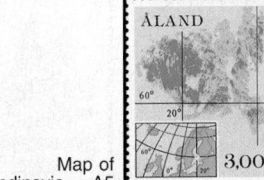

Map of Scandinavia — A5

Seal of St. Olaf and Aland Province, 1326 — A6

Artifacts — A7

Sea Birds — A8

Gothic Tower, Jomala Church, 12th Cent. — A9

Mariehamn Town Hall, Designed by Architect Lars Sonck — A9a

Designs: 1.50m, Statue of Frans Petter von Knorring, vicar from 1834 to 1875, and St. Michael's Church, Finstrom, 12th cent. 1.60m, Burial site, clay hands. 1.70m, Somateria mollissima. 2.20m, Bronze Staff of Finby, apostolic decoration. 2.30m, Aythya fuligula. 5m, Outer Aland Archipelago. 8m, Farm and windmill. 12m, Melantha fusca. 20m, Ancient court site, contemporary monument.

1984-90 Engr. Unwmk. Perf. 12

1	A1	10p magenta	.20	.20
2	A1	20p brown olive	.20	.20
3	A1	50p bright green	.20	.20
4	A1	1.10m deep blue	.50	.50
5	A1	1.20m black	.55	.50
6	A1	1.30m dark green	.60	.60

Litho.

Perf. 14, 13x14 (#8)

7	A2	1.40m multi	.75	.45
8	A9	1.40m multi	1.50	1.50
9	A3	1.50m multi, I	1.50	.65
9A	A3	1.50m multi, II	.90	1.10
10	A9	1.50m multi	1.50	1.25

Perf. 13, 14 (#13)

11	A7	1.60m multi, vert.	2.00	.90
12	A8	1.70m multi	7.75	7.75
13	A9a	1.90m multi	1.00	.80
14	A4	2m multi	2.00	.65
15	A7	2.20m multi, vert.	1.00	1.00
16	A8	2.30m multi	4.00	4.00
17	A5	3m multi	2.00	2.00
18	A4	5m multi, horiz.	2.50	1.75
19	A4	8m multi, horiz.	4.00	3.25

Litho. & Engr.

20	A6	10m multi	4.75	4.75

Litho.

21	A8	12m multi	6.00	6.00
22	A7	20m multi	9.75	9.75
	Nos. 1-22 (23)		55.15	49.75

On No. 9A (type II) "Aland" is 10½mm long, figure support is 2mm wide, pole supports are thinner, diagonal black highlighting lines in pole greenery and horizontal black line on support under the man removed.

Issued: Nos. 2-4, 7, 17, 20, 3/1/84; Nos. 1, 5, 6, 9, 1/2/85; Nos. 14, 18-19, 9/16/85; Nos. 11, 15, 22, 4/4/86; Nos. 12, 16, 21, 1/2/87; No. 8, 8/26/88; No. 13, 1/2/89; No. 10, 9/4/89; No. 9A, 5/21/90.

See Nos. 39-42, 87-92.

A10

A11

Bark Pommern and car ferries, Mariehamn West Harbor

1984, Mar. 1 Litho. Perf. 14

23	A10	2m multicolored	3.00	3.00

1986, Jan. 2 Litho. Perf. 14

24	A11	1.60m multicolored	1.90	1.90

1986 Nordic Orienteering Championships, Aug. 30-31.

Onningeby Artists' Colony, Cent. — A12

Design: Pallette, pen and ink drawing of Onningeby landscape, 1891, by Victor Westerholm (1860-1919), founder.

1986, Sept. 1 Litho.

25	A12	3.70m multicolored	1.75	2.00

Mariehamn Volunteer Fire Brigade, Cent. — A13

1987, Apr. 27 Litho. Perf. 14

26	A13	7m multicolored	7.00	7.00

Farjsund Bridge, 50th Anniv., Rebuilt in 1980 — A14

1987, Apr. 27 Engr. Perf. 13x13½

27	A14	1m greenish black	.50	.50

Municipal Meeting, Finstrom, 1917 — A15

1987, Aug. 20 Litho. Perf. 14

28	A15	1.70m multicolored	1.25	1.25

Movement for reunification with Sweden, 70th anniv.

Loading of Mail Barrels on Sailboat, Post Office, Eckero — A16

1988, Jan. 4 Litho. Perf. 14

29	A16	1.80m multicolored	2.25	2.00

Postal Service, 350th anniv. From Feb. I to May 31, Alanders were entitled to buy 20 stamps for 28m with a discount coupon.

New Aland Farm School, Horse-Drawn Plow — A17

1988, Mar. 29 Litho. Perf. 14

30	A17	2.20m multicolored	1.75	2.25

Haga Farm School, cent.; Aland Farm School, 75th anniv.; 50th anniv. of experimental farming on Aland.

Sailing Ships — A18

1988, June 4 Litho. Perf. 13

31	A18	1.80m Albanus, 1904, vert.	2.50	1.50
32	A18	2.40m Ingrid, c. 1900	4.00	4.00
33	A18	11m Pamir, c. 1900	10.00	10.00
	Nos. 31-33 (3)		16.50	15.50

Type of 1988 and

Orchids — A19

Fish
A20

Handicrafts
A21

Fresco, St.
Anna's Church
of Kumlinge
A22

Mammals
A23

Geological Formations
A24   A25

Designs: 10p, Boulder field, Geta. No. 35,
Dactylorhiza sambucina. No. 36, *Clupea
harengus membras.* No. 37, *Erinaceus
europauus.* No. 38, Drumlin, Finstrom. 1.70m,
St. Andrew Church, Lumparland. No. 40,
Vardo Church. No. 41, Hammarland Church.
No. 42, Sottunga Church. No. 43, *Esox lucius.*
No. 45, Diabase dike, Sottunga, Basskar.
2.10m, *Sciurus vulgaris.* 2.50m,
Cephalanthera longifolia. No. 48, *Platichthys
flesus.* No. 49, Pillow lava, Kumlinge, western
Varpskar. No. 50, *Capreolus capreolus.* No.
51, Rouche Moutonne, Roda Kon, Lumparn.
6m, Folded gneiss, Sottunga, Gloskar. 13m,
Tapestry, 1793. 14m, *Cypripedium calceolus.*

*Perf. 13, 14 (Nos. 39-42, 44, 53),
15x14½ (10p, Nos. 38, 45, 49, 51-52)*

1989-94			Litho.	
34	A25	10p multicolored	.20	.20
35	A19	1.50m multicolored	2.75	2.25
36	A20	1.50m multicolored	1.25	1.00
37	A23	1.60m multicolored	1.25	1.00
38	A25	1.60m multicolored	.90	.90
39	A9	1.70m multicolored	1.50	1.10
40	A9	1.80m multicolored	1.50	1.00
41	A9	1.80m multicolored	1.50	1.25
42	A9	1.80m multicolored	1.25	1.25
43	A20	2m multicolored	1.25	1.00
44	A22	2m multicolored	1.00	1.00
45	A24	2m multicolored	.90	.80
46	A23	2.10m multicolored	1.50	1.25
47	A19	2.50m multicolored	3.25	2.50
48	A20	2.70m multicolored	1.50	1.50
49	A24	2.70m multicolored	1.25	1.00
50	A23	2.90m multicolored	1.50	1.75
51	A25	2.90m multicolored	1.25	1.25
52	A24	6m multicolored	2.50	2.50
53	A21	13m multicolored	6.00	5.25
54	A19	14m multicolored	10.50	10.50
	Nos. 34-54 (21)		44.50	40.25

Issued: 2.50m, 14m, No. 35, 4/10/89;
2.70m, No. 36, 43, 3/1/90; 13m, 4/19/90;
1.70m, No. 44, 9/10/90; 1.60m, 2.10m, No. 50,
3/3/91; No. 40, 10/9/91; No. 41 10/5/92; Nos.
45, 49, 52, 9/3/93; No. 42, 10/8/93; 10p, Nos.
38, 51, 2/1/94.
See Nos. 96, 102, 105.

Educational
System of the
Province,
350th
Anniv. — A33

1989, May 31	Litho.	*Perf. 14*
57	A33 1.90m multicolored	1.50 1.25

Souvenir Sheet

1991 Aland Island Games — A34

a, Volleyball. b, Shooting. c, Soccer. d,
Running.

1991, Apr. 5	Litho.	*Perf. 13x12½*
58	A34 2.10m Sheet of 4, #a.-d.	5.50 5.50

Autonomy of
Aland, 70th
Anniv. — A35

1991, June 4		*Perf. 13*
59	A35 16m multicolored	8.75 8.00

Kayaking
A36

1991, June 4		*Perf. 14*
60	A36 2.10m shown	1.25 .75
61	A36 2.90m Cycling	1.75 1.25

Rev. Frans Peter
Von Knorring
(1792-1875),
Educator — A37

1992, Mar. 2	Litho.	*Perf. 13*
62	A37 2 multicolored	1.50 1.25

Litho. & Engr.
Perf. 13½x14

63	A38 1 multicolored	1.75 1.75

No. 62 sold for 1.60m, No. 63 for 2.10m.

Cape Horn Congress, Mariehamn,
June 8-11 — A38

On stamps bearing the "denominations" "1" or "2," the number represents the class of mail.

Lighthouses
A39

1992, May 8	Litho.	*Perf. 13*
Booklet Stamps		
64	A39 2.10m Ranno	5.25 5.25
65	A39 2.10m Salskar	5.25 5.25
66	A39 2.10m Lagskar	5.25 5.25
67	A39 2.10m Market	5.25 5.25
a.	Booklet pane of 4, #64-67	22.50 22.50

First Aland
Provincial
Parliament,
70th
Anniv. — A40

1992, June 8	Litho.	*Perf. 13*
68	A40 3.40m multicolored	1.75 1.75

Joel
Pettersson
(1892-1937),
Painter — A41

1992, June 8

69	A41	2.90m Landscape from		
		Lemland	1.50	1.50
70	A41	16m Self-Portrait	8.50	8.25

Arms of
Aland — A42

1993, Mar. 1	Litho.	*Perf. 14*
71	A42 1.60m gray, sepia & blue	1.00 1.00

Autonomy Act, Jan. 1.

Souvenir Sheet

Autonomous Postal
Administration — A43

Designs: a, Inscriptions from old letter canceled in Kastelholm, vert. b, Mariehamn post
office. c, Ferry, mail truck. d, New post office
emblem, vert.

Perf. 12½x13, 14 (#b.-c.)

1993, Mar. 1	Litho., Engr. (#b.-c.)
72	A43 1.90m Sheet of 4, #a.-d.	4.00 4.00

Fiddler, Jan
Karlsgarden
Museum — A44

Folk
Dresses — A45

2.30m, Boat Shed, Jan Karlsgarden
Museum.

Perf. 13x12½, 12½x13

1993, May 7			Litho.	
73	A44	2m multicolored	1.10	1.00
74	A44	2.30m multi, horiz.	1.40	1.25

1993, June 1		*Perf. 12½*

Clothing from: 1.90m, Saltvik. 3.50m,
Brando, Eckero, Mariehamn. 17m, Finstrom.

75	A45	1.90m multicolored	1.25	1.50
76	A45	3.50m multicolored	2.00	2.25
77	A45	17m multicolored	9.00	9.00
	Nos. 75-77 (3)		12.25	12.75

Butterflies
A46

A47

Perf. 14 on 3 Sides

1994, Mar. 1		Litho.	
Booklet Stamps			
78	A46 2.30m Melitaea cinxia	1.25	1.25
79	A46 2.30m Quercusia		
	quercus	1.25	1.25
80	A46 2.30m Parnassius		
	mnemosyne	1.25	1.25
81	A46 2.30m Hesperia com-		
	ma	1.25	1.25
a.	Booklet pane, 2 each #78-81	10.00	11.00
	Nos. 78-81 (4)	5.00	5.00

1994, May 5	Litho.	*Perf. 13*

Europa, Inventions and Discoveries: 2.30m,
Diagram showing transmission of von Wil-
lebrand's Disease, discovered by E. A. von
Willebrand. 2.90m, Purification of heparin, by
Erik Jorpes.

82	A47 2.30m multicolored	*2.75 2.50*
83	A47 2.90m multicolored	*1.90 1.60*

Types of 1989-93 and:

Ice Age
Survivors — A48

Fossils — A49

Sea
Birds — A50

Bronze
Age — A51

Stone
Age — A52

Ships — A53

Lichens — A54

Primula Veris — A55

30p, Saduria entomon, mysis relicta. 40p, Trilobita asaphus. 1.80m, Sterna paradisaea. No. 87, Church of Mariehamn. No. 88, Church of Eckerö. No. 89, St. Bridget's Church, Lemland. No. 90, Church of St. John the Baptist, Sund. No. 91, St. George Church, Geta. No. 92, Church of Brando. No. 93, Bronze sword, bronze dagger. No. 94, Ship tumulus grave. No. 95, Larus canus. 2.30m, Pitcher of Kallskar. No. 97, Pottery. No. 98, Myoxocephalus quadricornis. 2.60m, Larus marinus. No. 100, Stone tools. No. 101, SS Thornbury. 3.40m, Erratic boulders. 3.50m, SS Osmo. 4.30m, Phoca hispida. 7m, Potholes. 9m, Gastropoda euomophalus. 18m, Settlement. 2, Hypogmnia physodes. 1, Xanthoria parietina.

Perf. 13 (A48, A50, A52, A54), 15x14½ (No. 89), 14½x15 (Nos. 101-103, 105), 14½ (40p, Nos. 88, 93-94, 96), 14 (Nos. 87, 90-92), 15 (No. 106)

1994-2000				Engr.	
84	A48	30p	multi	.20	.20
85	A49	40p	multi	.20	.50
86	A50	1.80m	multi	.85	.85
87	A9	1.90m	multi	1.25	1.25
88	A9	1.90m	multi	1.25	1.50
89	A9	1.90m	multi	1.25	1.50
90	A9	2m	multi	1.25	1.25
91	A9	2m	multi	1.25	1.25
92	A9	2m	multi	1.25	1.00
93	A51	2m	multi	1.25	1.10
94	A51	2.20m	multi, vert.	1.10	1.25
95	A50	2.20m	multi, vert.	1.10	1.10
96	A24	2.30m	multi	1.10	1.00
97	A52	2.40m	multi, vert.	1.50	2.00
98	A48	2.40m	multi	1.25	1.10
99	A50	2.60m	multi	1.25	1.10
100	A52	2.80m	multi, vert.	1.50	1.50
101	A53	2.80m	multi	1.50	2.00
102	A24	3.40m	multi, horiz.	1.75	1.50
103	A53	3.50m	multi	1.75	2.25
104	A48	4.30m	multi	2.25	1.90
105	A24	7m	multi, horiz.	4.00	3.00
106	A49	9m	multi	5.00	4.00
107	A52	18m	multi	8.75	8.25

Perf. 13

107A	A54	2	multi	1.50	1.50
107B	A54	1	multi	1.75	1.75

Self-Adhesive
Serpentine Die Cut Perf. 10

108	A55	2.40m	multi	1.25	1.25
	Nos. 84-108 (27)			48.30	46.85

No. 108 was issued in sheets of 10.
Nos. 107A-107B sold for 2m and 2.40m, respectively, on day of issue.
Issued: Nos. 97, 100, 18m, 8/16/94; No. 90, 10/7/94; 2.30m, 3.40m, 7m, 1/2/95; No. 91, 9/15/95; 40p, No. 92, 9m, 10/9/96; 30p, No. 98, 4.30m, 2/3/97; Nos. 101, 103, 9/8/97; No. 87, 10/9/97; No. 88, 10/9/98; Nos. 93-94, 2/1/99; No. 108, 4/28/99; Nos. 107A-107B, 9/25/99; No. 89, 10/8/99; 1.80m, No. 95, 2.60m, 1/3/00.

Cargo Vessels — A58

Perf. 14 on 3 Sides
1995, Mar. 1   Litho.
Booklet Stamps

109	A58	2.30m	Skuta	1.10	1.00
110	A58	2.30m	Sump	1.10	1.00
111	A58	2.30m	Storbat	1.10	1.00
112	A58	2.30m	Jakt	1.10	1.00
a.	Booklet pane, 2 each #109-112			9.00	10.00
	Complete booklet, #112a			9.50	
	Nos. 109-112 (4)			4.40	4.00

Entry into European Union — A59

1995, Mar. 1   Litho.   *Perf. 13x14*
113	A59	2.90m	multicolored	1.50	1.75

Europa — A60

Tourism — A61

1995, May 5   Litho.   *Perf. 13x14*
114	A60	2.80m	shown	1.40	1.25
115	A60	2.90m	Dove, island in sea	1.40	1.25

1995, May 12
116	A61	2	Golf	1.25	1.00
117	A61	1	Fishing	1.50	1.00

Nos. 116-117 sold for value 2m and 2.30m, respectively.

Optimist Dinghy World Championships — A62

1995, June 2   Litho.   *Perf. 13½x14*
118	A62	3.40m	multicolored	1.75	2.00

St. Olaf (995?-1030), Patron Saint of Aland — A63

Litho. & Engr.
1995, Sept. 15   *Perf. 13½x13*
119	A63	4.30m	multicolored	2.25	2.25

See Faroe Islands No. 289

A64

A65

Greeting Stamps (stylized designs): No. 120, Fish with natl. flag, "Hälsningar fran Aland." No. 121, Yellow bird with flower, "Grattis."

1996, Feb. 14   Litho.   *Perf. 13x14*
120	A64	1	multicolored	1.75	.90
121	A64	1	multicolored	1.75	1.50

Nos. 120-121 had a face value of 2.30m on day of issue.

1996, Mar. 1   *Perf. 14 on 3 Sides*
Eagle owl (bubo bubo): No. 122, Landing on tree branch over lake. No. 123, Perched on branch over lake. No. 124, Male, darker feathers. No. 125, Female, lighter feathers.

Booklet Stamps
122	A65	2.40m	multicolored	1.40	1.25
123	A65	2.40m	multicolored	1.40	1.25
124	A65	2.40m	multicolored	1.40	1.25
125	A65	2.40m	multicolored	1.40	1.25
a.	Booklet pane, 2 ea #122-125			11.50	11.50
	Complete booklet, No. 125a			12.50	
	Nos. 122-125 (4)			5.60	5.00

World Wildlife Fund.

Famous Women A66

Europa: 2.80m, Sally Salminen (1906-76), writer. 2.90m, Fanny Sundström (1883-1944), politician.

1996, May 6   Litho.   *Perf. 14x13*
126	A66	2.80m	multicolored	1.40	2.00
127	A66	2.90m	multicolored	1.75	2.25

A67

A68

1996, June 7   Litho.   *Perf. 13½x14*
128	A67	2.40m	multicolored	1.25	1.25

Aland '96 Song and Music Festival.

1996, June 7   *Perf. 13*
"Haircut," by Karl Emanuel Jansson (1846-74).

129	A68	18m	multicolored	9.00	9.00

Spring Flowers — A69

Designs: No. 130, Tussilago farfara. No. 131, Hepatica nobilis. No. 132, Anemone nemorosa. No. 133, Anemone ranunculoides.

1997, Feb. 3   Litho.   *Perf. 14*
Booklet Stamps
130	A69	2.40m	multicolored	1.10	1.10
131	A69	2.40m	multicolored	1.10	1.10
132	A69	2.40m	multicolored	1.10	1.10
133	A69	2.40m	multicolored	1.10	1.10
a.	Booklet pane, 2 each #130-133			9.00	10.00
	Complete booklet, #133a			9.50	

A70

A71

1997, May 3   Litho.   *Perf. 14x13½*
134	A70	3.40m	multicolored	1.60	1.60

1st Floorball World Championships, Aland.

1997, May 9   *Perf. 13x14*
Devil's Dance with Clergyman's Wife.

135	A71	2.90m	multicolored	1.75	1.25

Europa.

Kalmar Union, 600th Anniv. — A72

Design: Kastelholm Castle, arms of Lord High Chancellor Bo Jonsson Grip.

1997, May 30   Litho.   *Perf. 14x13*
136	A72	2.40m	multicolored	1.25	1.10

Souvenir Sheet

Autonomy, 75th Anniv. — A73

1997, June 9   *Perf. 13*
137	A73	20m	multicolored	10.00	15.00

No. 137 contains a holographic image. Soaking in water may affect the hologram.

Horticulture A74

1998, Feb. 2   Litho.   *Perf. 14½x15*
138	A74	2m	Apples	.95	1.10
139	A74	2.40m	Cucumbers	1.25	1.25

Youth Activities A75

No. 140, Riding moped. No. 141, Computer. No. 142, Listening to music. No. 143, Aerobics.

1998, Mar. 28   *Perf. 14 on 3 Sides*
Booklet Stamps
140	A75	2.40m	multicolored	1.10	1.10
141	A75	2.40m	multicolored	1.10	1.10
142	A75	2.40m	multicolored	1.10	1.10
143	A75	2.40m	multicolored	1.10	1.10
a.	Booklet pane, 2 each #140-143			9.00	10.00
	Complete booklet, #143a			9.50	

Midsummer Celebration in Aland — A76

1998, Apr. 27   Litho.   *Perf. 14*
144	A76	4.20m	multicolored	2.50	2.50

Europa.

Passenger Ferry — A77

1998, May 8   *Perf. 14½*
145	A77	2.40m	multicolored	1.10	1.10

Intl. Year of the Ocean — A78

1998, May 8
146 A78 6.30m multicolored 2.50 2.50

ATP Senior Tour of Champions Tennis Tournament, Mariehamn A79

Serpentine Die Cut
1998, June 25 **Litho.**
Self-Adhesive
147 A79 2.40m multicolored 1.10 1.10
Issued in sheets of 10.

Scouting — A80

1998, Aug. 1 **Perf. 14**
148 A80 2.80m multicolored 1.25 1.25

Foyers — A81

Homesteads: 1.60m, Seffers. 2m, Labbas. 2.90m, Abras.

1998, Sept. 11 **Litho.** **Perf. 14½**
149 A81 1.60m multicolored .75 .75
150 A81 2m multicolored .90 .90
151 A81 2.90m multicolored 1.25 1.25
Nos. 149-151 (3) 2.90 2.90

18th Century Furniture Ornamentation A82

Perf. 14 on 3 Sides
1999, Feb. 1 **Litho.**
Booklet Stamps
152 A82 2.40m Wardrobe 1.00 1.25
153 A82 2.40m Distaff 1.00 1.25
154 A82 2.40m Chest 1.00 1.25
155 A82 2.40m Spinning wheel 1.00 1.25
a. Booklet pane, 2 each #152-155 8.00 10.00
Complete booklet, #155a 8.50

Passage of Cape Horn by Grain Ships Pamir & Passat, 50th Anniv. A83

1999, Mar. 19 **Litho.** **Perf. 14½**
156 A83 3.40m multicolored 1.50 1.50

Beginning with No. 157, denominations are indicated on many stamps in both Markkas and Euros. The value shown is in Markkas.

Nature Reserve, Kökar — A84

1999, Apr. 28 **Litho.** **Perf. 13**
157 A84 2.90m multicolored 1.50 1.75
Europa.

Match Sailboat Racing — A85

1999, Aug. 5 **Litho.** **Perf. 14½x15**
158 A85 2.70m multicolored 1.25 1.25

UPU, 125th Anniv. A86

1999, Sept. 25
159 A86 2.90m multicolored 1.40 1.40

Finnish Cross-Country Championships, Mariehamn — A87

1999, Oct. 9 **Litho.** **Perf. 14¾x14½**
160 A87 3.50m multicolored 1.60 1.60

Souvenir Sheet

Peace Symbol, Aland Flag — A88

Background colors: a, Yellow. b, Red. c, Blue. d, White.

Litho. & Embossed
2000, Jan. 3 **Perf. 13**
161 A88 3.40m Sheet of 4, #a.-d. 6.50 6.50

Elk — A89

Elk in: No. 162, Spring. No. 163, Summer. No. 164, Autumn. No. 165, Winter.

Perf. 11¾on 3 sides
2000, Mar. 1 **Litho.**
Booklet Stamps
162 A89 2.60m multicolored 1.25 1.25
163 A89 2.60m multicolored 1.25 1.25
164 A89 2.60m multicolored 1.25 1.25
165 A89 2.60m multicolored 1.25 1.25
a. Block of 4, #162-165 5.00 5.00
b. Booklet pane, 2 #165a 10.00 11.00
Complete booklet, #165b 10.50

Europa, 2000
Common Design Type
2000, May 9 **Perf. 13**
166 CD17 3m multicolored 1.75 1.50

A90 A91

2000, June 9 ***Die Cut Perf. 13x13¼***
Self-Adhesive
Coil Stamp
167 A90 2.60m multicolored 1.25 1.25
Gymnastics Festival, Mariehamn.

2000, July 21 **Litho.** **Perf. 13½x13¼**
168 A91 3.40m multicolored 1.60 1.60
Cutty Sark Tall Ships race to Mariehamn.

Vikings From Aland — A92

2000, July 28
169 A92 4.50m multicolored 2.10 2.10
Recreation of Viking market, Saltvik.

Architecture by Hilda Hongell (1867-1952) A93

2000, Aug. 25 **Perf. 13¼x13¾**
170 A93 3.80m shown 1.75 1.75
171 A93 10m House, diff. 4.75 4.75

Christianity, 2000th Anniv. — A94

2000, Oct. 9 **Perf. 13**
172 A94 3m multicolored 1.40 1.25

Church Type of 1984-90 and:

Swamp Plants — A95

Swamp plants: 1.90m, Equisetum fluviatile. 2.80m, Lycopodium annotinum. 3.50m, Polypodium vulgare.
Churches: No. 179, Föglö Church, Föglö. 2m, Kökar Church, Kökar.

Perf. 13x13¼, 13 (#178)
2000-01 **Litho.**
177 A95 1.90m multicolored .90 .85
178 A9 2m multicolored .95 .90
179 A9 2m multi .95 .90

180 A95 2.80m multicolored 1.40 1.40
182 A95 3.50m multicolored 1.75 1.75
Nos. 177-182 (5) 5.95 5.80
These stamps are part of an ongoing definitive set. Numbers have been reserved for additional stamps.
Issued: 2m, 10/9; 1.90m, 2.80m, 3.50m, 1/2/01; No. 179, 10/9/01.

Worldwide Fund for Nature (WWF) — A100

Polysticta stelleri: a, Pair in flight. b, Pair on rock. c, Pair in water. d, Male in water.

Perf. 13¼ on 3 sides
2001, Jan. 2 **Litho.**
Booklet Stamps
185 A100 Block of 4 5.00 5.00
a.-d. 2.70m any single 1.25 1.10
e. Booklet pane, 2 #185 10.00 11.00
Booklet, #185e 11.00

Valentine's Day — A101

2001, Feb. 14 **Perf. 14½x14¾**
186 A101 3.20m multicolored 1.75 1.75

Europa A102

2001, May 9 **Litho.** **Perf. 14½x14¾**
187 A102 3.20m multi 1.60 1.25

Windmills A103

Windmill types: 3m, Archipelago. 7m, Timbered, horiz. 20m, Nest, horiz.

Perf. 13¾x14¼, 14¼x13¾
2001, June 8
188-190 A103 Set of 3 14.00 14.00

Puppies — A104

Designs: 2, Golden retriever. 1, Wire-haired dachshund.

2001, Sept. 3 **Perf. 13¼**
191-192 A104 Set of 2 2.75 2.75
Nos. 191-192 sold for 2.30m and 2.70m respectively on day of issue.

100 Cents = 1 Euro (€)
Church Type of 1998 with Euro Denominations and

Fauna — A105

Post Terminal — A106

Mushrooms A107

Designs: 5c, Coronella austriaca. 10c, Chanterelle mushroom. 35c, Saltviks Church. 40c, Kumlinge Church. 50c, King Bolete mushroom. 70c, Triturus cristatus. €1, Post Terminal. €2.50, Parasol mushroom.

Perf. 12½, 13 (#193, 196), 13¼ (#198), 14¾x14 (#195)

2002-03			Litho.	
193	A105	5c multi	.20	.20
194	A107	10c multi	.30	.30
195	A9	35c multi	1.00	1.00
196	A9	40c multi	1.10	1.10
197	A107	50c multi	1.40	1.40
198	A105	70c multi	2.00	2.00
199	A106	€1 multi	3.00	2.75
200	A107	€2.50 multi	7.25	7.25
		Nos. 193-200 (8)	16.25	16.00

Issue dates: 5c, 70c, 1/2/02; €1, 2/28/02; 35c, 10/9/02; 10c, 50c, €2.50, 1/2/03. No. 196, 10/9/03.
This is an expanding set. Numbers may change.

Introduction of the Euro — A108

2002, Jan. 2   Litho.   Perf. 12½
201   A108 60c multi   2.00 2.00

St. Canute's Day — A109

2002, Jan. 2
202   A109 €2 multi   5.75 5.75

Cuisine — A110

Flowers and: a, Gravlax, boiled potatoes. b, Fried herring, beets, mashed potatoes. c, Black bread, cheese, butter. d, Pancake with prune sauce and whipped cream, coffee.

Perf. 13½x13¼ on 3 Sides
2002, Feb. 28   Litho.
203   A110   Block of 4   6.00 5.00
a.-d.   1 Any single   1.50 1.25
e.   Booklet pane, 2 #203 12.00 9.00
           Booklet, #203e   13.00

Nos. 203a-203d each sold for 55c on day of issue.

Europa — A111

2002, May 3   Perf. 13¼
204   A111 40c multi   1.25 1.00

Radar II, Sculpture by Stefan Lindfors A112

2002, May 3   Perf. 13
205   A112 €3 multi   8.50 8.50

"My Aland," by Lill Lindfors A113

2002, Aug. 12   Litho.   Perf. 13¼
206   A113 90c multi   2.50 2.50

Iron Age Artifacts — A114

Designs: No. 207, 2, Buckle found in Persby. No. 208, 1, Ornamental pin found in Syllöda.

2002, Sept. 2   Perf. 13x13¼
207-208 A114   Set of 2   2.75 2.25

Nos. 207-208 sold for 45c and 55c respectively on day of issue.

Janne Holmén, Marathon Gold Medalist in European Track and Field Championships A115

2002, Nov. 1   Perf. 12½
209   A115 1 multi   1.50 1.50

Sold for 55c on day of issue.

House Cats — A116

2003, Mar. 14   Litho.   Perf. 13¼
210   A116 2 Tovis   2.00 1.75
211   A116 1 Randi, horiz.   2.50 2.25

Nos. 210-211 sold for 45c and 55c respectively on day of issue.

Landscape in Summer, by Elin Danielson-Gambogi (1861-1919) — A117

No. 212: a, Woman at fence. b, Tree without leaves. c, Sun. d, Boat.

2003, Mar. 28   Perf. 14 Vert.
Booklet Stamps
212   A117   Horiz. strip of 4   7.00 7.00
a.-d.   1 single   1.50 1.25
e.   Booklet pane, 2 #212 14.00 14.00
           Complete booklet, #212e 14.50

Nos. 212a-212d each sold for 55c on day of issue.

Europa — A118

2003, May 9   Perf. 13¼
213   A118 45c multi   1.25 1.00

Museum Ship "Pommern," Cent. A119

2003, June 6   Die Cut Perf. 9¼x9½
Booklet Stamp
Self-Adhesive
214   A119 55c multi   3.00 1.50
a.   Booklet pane of 4   12.00 6.00
           Complete booklet, 2 #214a 25.00

Mark and Stephen Levengood on Beach — A120

2003, June 18   Perf. 12½
215   A120 55c multi   1.60 1.60

Aland Folk Music Association, 50th Anniv. — A121

2003, Aug. 1   Perf. 14¼
216   A121 €1.10 buff & black   3.00 3.00

St. Lucia's Day Celebrations A122

2003, Oct. 9   Litho.   Perf. 12½
217   A122 60c multi   1.75 1.75

Mammals — A123

Designs: 20c, Mustela erminea. 60c, Vulpes vulpes. €3, Martes martes.

2004, Feb. 2   Litho.   Perf. 14½x14¼
218   A123 20c multi   .90   .60
219   A123 60c multi   2.00 1.75
220   A123 €3 multi   10.00 9.00
      Nos. 218-220 (3)   12.90 11.35

Souvenir Sheet

Norse Gods Fenja and Menja — A124

2004, Mar. 26   Perf. 14¼x14¾
221   A124 55c multi   1.60 1.60

Aland Flag, 50th Anniv. — A125

Serpentine Die Cut 12½
2004, Apr. 23
Booklet Stamp
Self-Adhesive
222   A125 1 multi   1.50 1.50
a.   Booklet pane of 4   6.00 5.75
           Complete booklet, 2 #222a 13.00

No. 222a was reprinted in 2007 with a hole for a pegboard hook.

Finnish Pres. Mauno Koivisto and Guests on Boat — A126

2004, Apr. 23   Perf. 12½
223   A126 90c multi   2.50 2.50

Europa — A127

2004, May 10   Perf. 13¾x14¼
224   A127 75c multi   2.00 1.75

Destruction of
Bomarsund
Fortress, 150th
Anniv. — A128

No. 225: a, Fortress, six ships in harbor. b, Fortress, three ships in harbor. c, Three soldiers in foreground. d, Six soldiers in foreground.

2004, June 9   **Perf. 13**
225   Booklet pane of 4   8.50 8.25
a.-d.   A128 75c Any single   2.10 2.10
    Complete booklet, 2 #225   18.00

2004
Summer
Olympics,
Athens
A183

2004, Aug. 13   **Litho.**   **Perf. 14¼**
226 A183 80c multi   2.25 2.25

Landscapes
A184

Designs: 2, Storklynkan, Brändö. 1, Prästgardsnäset Nature Reserve, Finström.

2004, Aug. 13   **Perf. 12½**
227-228 A184   Set of 2   3.00 3.00

Nos. 227-228 sold for 50c and 60c respectively on day of issue.
See Nos. 252-253, 260.

Christmas
A185

2004, Oct. 8   **Perf. 14½x14¾**
229 A185 45c multi   1.25 1.25

Birds — A186

Designs: 15c, Phalacrocorax carbo sinensis. 65c, Cygnus cygnus. €4, Ardea cinerea, vert.

2005, Jan. 14   **Litho.**   **Perf. 13¼**
230 A186 15c multi   .45 .45
231 A186 65c multi   1.75 1.75
232 A186 €4 multi   12.00 12.00
   Nos. 230-232 (3)   14.20 14.20

Automobiles — A187

No. 233: a, 1928 Oakland Sport Cabriolet. b, 1939 Ford V8. c, 1957 Buick Super 4D HT. d, 1964 Volkswagen 1200.

2005, Mar. 4   **Perf. 13¼ Horiz.**
    Booklet Stamps
233   Vert. strip of 4   7.00 7.00
a.-d.   A187 1 Any single   1.75 1.75
e.   Booklet pane, 2 #233   14.00 —
    Complete booklet, #233e   14.00

Stamps sold for 60c each on day of issue.

Europa
A188

2005, Apr. 29   **Perf. 13¼**
234 A188 90c multi   2.50 2.10

Walpurgis
Night Bonfire
A189

Serpentine Die Cut 12½
2005, Apr. 29
    Self-Adhesive
    Booklet Stamp
235 A189 2 multi   1.40 1.40
a.   Booklet pane of 4   5.75
    Complete booklet, 2 #235a   11.50

Stamp sold for 50c on day of issue.

Tennis Player
Bjorn
Borg — A190

2005, May 26   **Perf. 12½**
236 A190 55c multi   1.50 1.50

Mr. Black
and Mr.
Smith at
Bomarsund,
by Fritz von
Dardel
A191

2005, Aug. 12   **Litho.**   **Perf. 13¾**
237 A191 €1.30 multi   3.50 3.50

Schooner
Linden — A192

2005, Aug. 26   **Perf. 13¼**
238 A192 60c multi   1.75 1.75

    Landscapes Type of 2004
Designs: 70c, Pine tree on Sandö Island. 80c, Cliffs, Gröndal.

2005, Aug. 26   **Perf. 12½**
239-240 A184   Set of 2   4.25 4.25

Christmas — A193

    Litho. with Hologram Applied
2005, Oct. 10   **Perf. 13**
241 A193 45c multi   1.25 1.25

Stars in hologram differ on each stamp.

Beetles
A194

Designs: 40c, Potosia cuprea. 65c, Coccinella septempunctata. €2, Oryctes nasicornis.

    Litho. & Embossed
2006, Jan. 2   **Perf. 13½**
242 A194 40c multi   1.10 1.10
243 A194 65c multi   1.90 1.90
244 A194 €2 multi   5.75 5.75
   Nos. 242-244 (3)   8.75 8.75

Woman
Suffrage in
Finland,
Cent. — A195

2006, Mar. 8   **Litho.**   **Perf. 12½**
245 A195 85c multi   2.40 2.40

Demilitarization of Aland, 150th
Anniv. — A196

2006, Mar. 29   **Perf. 13¾**
246 A196 €1.50 multi   4.25 4.25

    Souvenir Sheet

Lettesgubbe, Mythological
Being — A197

2006, Mar. 29   **Perf. 12½x13**
247 A197 85c multi   2.50 2.50

Europa — A198

2006, May 4
248 A198 €1.30 multi   3.75 3.75

A199

Serpentine Die Cut 10 Syncopated
2006, May 26
249 A199 1 multi   2.00 2.00
a.   Booklet pane of 8   16.50

No. 249 sold for 65c on day of issue. Design portion of stamp could be personalized at €10.40 per booklet with a minimum purchase of three booklets. The label design shown is a generic vignette. Other generic vignettes were created for sale at stamp shows beginning in 2008.

Tattoos — A200

No. 250: a, Tribal tattoo on man's biceps. b, Sailor's tattoo on man's forearm. c, Flower tattoo, on woman's torso.

2006, Sept. 7   **Perf. 14 Vert.**
    Booklet Stamps
250   Horiz. strip of 3   5.75 5.75
a.-c.   A200 65c Any single   1.90 1.90
d.   Booklet pane, 3 #250   17.50
    Complete booklet, #250d   17.50

Fishing Boat
From
Television
Film Directed
by Ake
Lindman
A201

2006, Aug. 4   **Litho.**   **Perf. 12½**
251 A201 75c multi   2.25 2.25

    Landscapes Type of 2004
Designs: 55c, Foggy grove, windmill and houses, Söderby, Lemland. €1.20, Rocks, Norra Essvik, Sottunga.

2006, Aug. 4
252-253 A184   Set of 2   5.00 5.00

Christmas
A202

Litho. With Holograms Affixed
2006, Oct. 9   **Perf. 13**
254 A202 (50c) multi   1.40 1.40

Flowers
A203

Designs: 80c, Tripolium vulgare. 90c, Lythrum salicaria. €5, Angelica archangelica.

2007, Feb. 1   **Litho.**   **Perf. 12½x13**
255 A203 80c multi   2.25   2.25
256 A203 90c multi   2.50   2.50
257 A203 €5 multi   14.00 14.00
    Nos. 255-257 (3)   18.75 18.75

Mail Planes
A204

Designs: 2, Junkers F13. 1, Saab 340.

2007, Mar. 1   **Perf. 12½**
258-259 A204   Set of 2   3.25 3.25

    No. 258 sold for 55c, and No. 259 sold for 70c on day of issue.

Landscapes Type of 2004
2007, Mar. 13
260 A184 2 Skaftö, Kumlinge   1.50 1.50
    Sold for 55c on day of issue.

Untitled Painting by Tove Jansson A205

2007, Apr. 18   **Perf. 13¼x13¾**
261 A205 85c multi   2.40 2.40

Europa — A206

2007, May 9   **Perf. 12½x13¼**
262 A206 70c multi   1.90 1.90
    Scouting, cent.

Contemporary Crafts — A207

Designs: No. 263, Bridal crown, by Titti Sundblom. No. 264, Floral textile design, by Maria Korpi-Gordon and Adam Gordon. No. 265, Cups, bowl and plate, by Judy Kuyitunen.

2007, May 18   **Perf. 13 Horiz.**
Booklet Stamps
263 A207 1 multi   1.90 1.90
264 A207 1 multi   1.90 1.90
265 A207 1 multi   1.90 1.90
   a. Booklet pane, 3 each #263-265   17.50 —
    Complete booklet, #265a   17.50

    Nos. 263-265 each sold for 70c on day of issue.

A208

Serpentine Die Cut 10 Syncopated
2007, June 7
Booklet Stamp
Self-Adhesive
266 A208 1 multi   3.00 3.00
   a. Booklet pane of 8   24.00
    Complete booklet, #266a   24.00

    No. 266 sold for 70c on day of issue. Design portion of stamp could be personalized at €10.40 per booklet with a minimum purchase of three booklets.

Emigration to America A209

2007, Aug. 9   **Litho.**   **Perf. 13¼x12½**
267 A209 75c multi   2.10 2.10

Kjusan, Hammarland A210

2007, Oct. 1   **Perf. 12½**
268 A210 1 multi   2.00 2.00
    No. 268 sold for 70c on day of issue.

Christmas — A211

2007, Oct. 9   **Perf. 14**
269 A211 (50c) multi   1.50 1.50

Fish A212

Designs: 45c, Perca fluviatilis. €4.50, Sander lucioperca.

2008, Feb. 1   **Litho.**   **Perf. 13¼x13**
270 A212 45c multi   1.40   1.00
271 A212 €4.50 multi   13.50 10.00

Souvenir Sheet

Mythical Princess Signhild at Drottningkleven — A213

Perf. 12½x13¼
2008, Mar. 27   **Litho.**
272 A213 (85c) multi   2.75 2.75

Badhusberget, Mariehamn — A214

Langvikshagen, Lumparland — A215

2008, Apr. 15   **Perf. 13x12½**
273 A214 (70c) multi   2.25 2.25
274 A215 (70c) multi   2.25 2.25

2008 Summer Olympics, Beijing A216

2008, May 9   **Perf. 13¾**
275 A216 (90c) multi   2.75 2.75

Europa A217

2008, May 9   **Perf. 13¼x13**
276 A217 €1 multi   3.25 3.25

Lighthouses A218

    No. 277: a, Marhällan Lighthouse. b, Gustaf Dalén Lighthouse. c, Kökarsören Lighthouse. d, Bogskär Lighthouse.

Litho., Litho & Engr (#277c-277d)
2008, June 6   **Perf. 12¾ on 3 Sides**
Booklet Stamps
277   Block or strip of 4   9.75 9.75
   a.-d. A218 (75c) Any single   2.40 2.40
   e. Booklet pane, 2 #277   19.50
    Complete booklet, #277e   19.50

    Within the booklet pane, stamps in one row are tete-beche in relation to stamps in the adjacent row.

Gravel Road and Profiles of Marcus Grönholm, Rally Driver, and Christoph Treier, Trainer A219

2008, July 26   **Litho.**   **Perf. 13½**
278 A219 (90c) multi   3.00 3.00

    Particles of granite were applied to portions of the design using a thermographic process.

Aland Peasant Bride, by Karl Emanuel Jansson — A220

2008, Aug. 15   **Perf. 13x13¼**
279 A220 €1.50 multi   4.50 4.50

Christmas A221

Litho. With Hologram Applied
2008, Oct. 9   **Perf. 13¾x13¼**
280 A221 (55c) multi   1.50 1.50

Personalized Stamp — A222

Serpentine Die Cut 10 Syncopated
2008, Oct. 9   **Litho.**
Booklet Stamp
Self-Adhesive
281 A222 (75c) multi   3.00 3.00
   a. Booklet pane of 8   24.00
    Complete booklet, #281a   24.00

    The generic design portion of the stamp shown could be personalized. Other generic vignettes were created for sale at stamp shows in 2009.

1810 Boundary Post — A223

Litho. & Embossed With Foil Application

2009, Jan. 22			**Perf. 14¼**
282	A223	(80c) multi	3.00 2.25

Souvenir Sheet

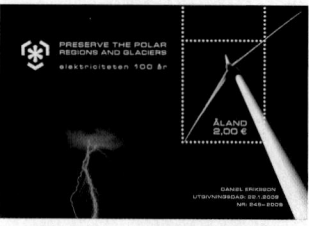

Electricity on Aland Islands, Cent. — A224

Litho. & Embossed

2009, Jan. 22			**Perf. 12½x13¼**
283	A224	€2 black	6.00 5.50

Writers — A225

No. 284: a, Ulla-Lena Lundberg and ship. b, Anni Blomqvist (1909-90), sailboat and dockside shack. c, Valdemar Nyman (1904-98), flowers, cattle.

2009, Mar. 21	**Litho.**	**Perf. 13 Horiz.**	
Booklet Stamps			
284		Vert. strip of 3	9.00 9.00
a.-c.	A225	(80c) Any single	2.75 2.75
d.		Booklet pane, 3 #284	27.00
		Complete booklet, #284d	28.00

Movie Theaters in Aland, Cent. — A226

2009, Apr. 6			**Perf. 12½x13¼**
285	A226	€1.60 multi	4.25 4.25

Divers at Plus Shipwreck A227

2009, May 8			
286	A227	(75c) multi	2.10 2.10

Europa A228

2009, May 8			**Perf. 13**
287	A228	(80c) multi	3.00 2.25

Intl. Year of Astronomy. Star-shaped holes are die cut in stamp.

Passenger Ferries A229

Designs: (75c), SS Viking. (80c), New Viking Line ferry, 2009.

2009, June 1	**Litho.**	**Perf. 13**	
288-289	A229	Set of 2	4.50 4.50

See Nos. 301-302.

Personalized Stamp — A230

Serpentine Die Cut 10 Syncopated
2009, June 27
Booklet Stamp
Self-Adhesive

290	A230	(90c) multi	3.75 3.50
a.		Booklet pane of 8	30.00
		Complete booklet, #290a	30.00

The generic design portion of the stamp shown could be personalized.

Cliffs, Föglö A231

Islets, Saltvik A232

2009, Sept. 16			**Perf. 12½**
291	A231	(75c) multi	2.00 1.00
292	A232	(80c) multi	3.00 2.40

Honeymoon Cabin of Finland President Martti Ahtisaari A233

2009, Sept. 29			**Perf. 13x12½**
293	A233	(90c) multi	3.00 3.00

Christmas A234

Poinsettia and: (60c), Man and woman. (90c), Woman with scroll.

2009, Oct. 9			**Perf. 13¾**
294-295	A234	Set of 2	4.50 4.50

Flag Type of 2004 Inscribed "Inrikes"
Serpentine Die Cut 12½
2009, July 1   **Litho.**
Booklet Stamp
Self-Adhesive

296	A125	(75c) multi	2.10 2.10
a.		Booklet pane of 4	8.50
		Complete booklet, 2 #296a	17.00

Mail Jetty at Eckerö, Painting by Victor Westerholm — A235

2010, Jan. 4			**Perf. 13**
297	A235	(80c) multi	2.25 2.25

Jesus Christ, Painting by Warner Sallman — A236

Litho. With Foil Application

2010, Mar. 24			**Perf. 14x14¼**
298	A236	(90c) multi	2.50 2.50

Souvenir Sheet

Kobba Klintar Pilot Station — A237

2010, Mar. 24	**Litho.**	**Perf. 12½**	
299	A237	(90c) multi	2.50 2.50

Europa — A238

2010, Apr. 19			**Perf. 12½x13**
300	A238	(85c) multi	2.25 2.25

Ferries Type of 2009

Designs: 75c, MS Skandia. €3.50, MS Prinsessan.

2010, May 3	**Litho.**	**Perf. 13**	
301-302	A229	Set of 2	11.00 11.00

Plastic Toys Made By Plasto — A239

No. 303: a, Scooter. b, Dump truck. c, Ducks.

2010, May 10			**Perf. 13¾ Horiz.**
Booklet Stamps			
303		Vert. strip of 3	6.50 6.50
a.-c.	A239	(85c) Any single	2.10 2.10
d.		Booklet pane, 3 #303	19.50
		Complete booklet, #303d	19.50

Farmhand Delivering Mail — A240

2010, June 12			**Perf. 12½x13¼**
304	A240	(75c) multi	1.90 1.90

Personalized Stamp — A241

2010, June 12			**Perf. 12½**
305	A241	(85c) black	2.25 2.25

No. 305 was printed in sheets of 8. The generic design portion of the stamp shown could be personalized for an extra fee.

Stained-Glass Windows — A242

Stained-glass window from church in Jomala: 80c, St. Olaf. €1.60, St. Olaf and other figures, horiz.

2010, Aug. 30	**Litho.**	**Perf. 13**	
306	A242	80c multi	2.10 2.10
Souvenir Sheet			
307	A242	€1.60 multi	4.25 4.25

See Macao Nos. 1317-1318.

Shoreline, Eckerö A243

Cliffs, Sund A244

2010, Sept. 16			**Perf. 12½**
308	A243	80c multi	2.25 2.25
309	A244	(85c) multi	2.40 2.40

Christmas
A245

2010, Oct. 8 **Perf. 13**
310 A245 (65c) multi 1.90 1.90

FIUME

ˈfyü-ˌmā

LOCATION — A city and surrounding territory on the Adriatic Sea
GOVT. — Formerly a part of Italy
AREA — 8 sq. mi.
POP. — 44,956 (estimated 1924)

Fiume was under Hapsburg rule after 1466 and was transferred to Hungarian control after 1870. Of mixed Italian and Croatian population and strategically important - it was Hungary's only international seaport - Fiume was disputed between Italy and the newly-created Kingdom of the Serbs, Croats and Slovenes (later Yugoslavia), following World War I. A force of Allied troops occupied the city in Nov. 1918, while its future status was negotiated at the Paris Peace Conference.

In Sept., 1919, the Italian nationalist poet Gabriele d'Annunzio organized his legionnaires and seized Fiume, together with the islands of Arbe, Carnaro and Veglia, in the name of Italy. D'Annunzio established an autonomous administration, which soon came into conflict with the Italian government. There followed several years of instability, with three Italian interventions after 1920. In Jan. 1924, the Treaty of Rome between Italy anf Yugoslavia established formal Italian sovereignty over Fiume, and Fiume stamps were replaced by those of Italy after March 31, 1924.

100 Filler = 1 Korona

100 Centesimi = 1 Corona (1919)

100 Centesimi = 1 Lira

See note on FIUME-KUPA Zone, Italian Occupation, after Yugoslavia No. NJ22.

The overprints on Nos. 1-23a have been extensively forged. Even the inexpensive values are difficult to find with genuine overprints. Forgeries of many later issues also exist, most created for the packet trade in the 1920s. Values are for genuine stamps. Collectors should be aware that stamps sold "as is" are likely to be forgeries, and unexpertized collections should be assumed to consist of mostly forged stamps. Education plus working with knowledgeable dealers is mandatory in this collecting area. More valuable stamps should be expertized.

Hungarian Stamps of 1916-18 Typograph Overprinted

1918, Dec. 2   Wmk. 137   Perf. 15
On Stamps of 1916
White Numerals
1a A8 10f rose 100.00 47.50
2 A8 15f violet 42.50 34.00

Value for No. 1a is for handstamped overprint. Value for No. 2 is for typographed overprint.

On Stamps of 1916-18
Colored Numerals
3 A9 2f brown orange 3.50 1.75
4 A9 3f red violet 3.50 1.75
5 A9 5f green 3.50 1.75
6 A9 6f grnsh blue 3.50 1.75
8 A9 15f violet 3.50 1.75
7a A9 10f rose red *67.50* *25.00*
9 A9 20f gray brown 3.50 1.75
10 A9 25f deep blue 13.00 2.10
11 A9 35f brown 6.75 3.50
12a A9 40f olive green 42.50 21.00

White Numerals
13 A10 50f red vio & lil 4.25 2.50
14 A10 75f brt bl & pale bl 10.00 3.50
15 A10 80f grn & pale grn 10.00 2.50
16 A10 1k red brn & claret 34.00 6.75
17 A10 2k ol brn & bis 4.25 2.50
18 A10 3k dk vio & ind 47.50 22.50
19 A10 5k dk brn & lt brn 110.00 40.00
20a A10 10k vio brn & vio 450.00 200.00

Inverted or double overprints exist on most of Nos. 4-15.

On Stamps of 1918
21 A11 10f scarlet 3.50 3.50
22 A11 20f dark brown 2.50 1.75
23a A12 40f olive green 30.00 20.00

The overprint on Nos. 3-23a was applied by 2 printing plates and 6 handstamps. Values are for the less costly. Values of Nos. 7a, 12a, 20a and 23a are for handstamps. See the *Scott Specialized Catalogue of Stamps and Covers* for detailed listings.

Postage Due Stamps of Hungary, 1915-20 Ovptd. & Surcharged in Black

1919, Jan.
24 D1 45f on 6f green & red 17.00 15.00
25 D1 45f on 20f green & red 47.50 15.00
Set, never hinged 150.00

Hungarian Savings Bank Stamp Surcharged in Black — A2

1919, Jan. 29
26 A2 15f on 10f dk violet 22.50 17.00
Never hinged 55.00

Overprints on Nos. 24-26 are typographed.

"Italy" — A3

Italian Flag on Clock-Tower in Fiume — A4

"Revolution" A5

Sailor Raising Italian Flag at Fiume (1918) A6

Nos. 30-43 exist on three types of paper: (A) grayish, porous paper, printed in sheets of 70 stamps (Jan, Feb. printings); (B) translucent or semi-translucent good quality white paper, printed in sheets of 70 stamps (March printing); and (C) good quality medium white paper, plain and opaque, sometimes grayish or yellowish, printed in sheets of 100 (April printing). Values are for the least expensive variety. See the *Scott Specialized Catalogue of Stamps and Covers* for detailed listings.

Perf. 11½

			Unwmk.	Litho.
1919, April				
27	A3	2c dull blue	1.75	1.75
28	A3	3c gray brown	1.75	1.75
29	A3	5c yellow green	1.75	1.75
30a	A4	10c rose	25.00	13.00
31	A4	15c violet	1.75	1.75
32a	A4	20c emerald green	3.50	*3.50*
33	A4	25c dark blue	2.50	1.75
34	A6	30c deep violet	2.50	1.75
35	A6	40c brown	2.50	1.75
36	A5	45c orange	2.50	2.50
37	A6	50c yellow green	2.50	2.50
38	A6	60c claret	2.50	1.75
39	A6	1cor brown orange	4.25	2.50
40	A6	2cor brt blue	4.25	2.50
41	A6	3cor orange red	5.00	2.50
42	A6	5cor deep brown	34.00	34.00
43a	A6	10cor olive green	42.50	*67.50*
		Nos. 27-43 (17)	140.50	144.50

The earlier printings of Jan. and Feb. are on thin grayish paper, the Mar. printing is on semi-transparent white paper, all in sheets of 70. An Apr. printing is on white paper of medium thickness in sheets of 100. Part-perf. examples of most of this series are known.

For surcharges see Nos. 58, 60, 64, 66-69.

A7

A8

A9

A10

1919, July 28   Perf. 11½
46 A7 5c yellow green 1.75 .85
47 A8 10c rose 1.75 .85
48 A9 30c violet 10.00 2.50
49 A10 40c yellow brown 1.75 *1.75*
50 A9 45c orange 10.00 6.75
51 A9 50c yellow green 10.00 6.75
52 A9 60c claret 10.00 6.75
a. Perf. 13x12½ 190.00
 Never hinged 475.00
b. Perf. 10½ 350.00
 Never hinged 875.00
53 A9 10cor olive green 10.00 *20.00*
a. Perf. 13x12½ 60.00 100.00
 Never hinged 150.00
b. Perf. 10½ 350.00 *375.00*
 Never hinged 875.00
 Nos. 46-53 (8) 55.25 46.20
 Set, never hinged 127.50

Five other denominations (25c, 1cor, 2cor, 3cor and 5cor) were not officially issued. Some examples of the 25c are known canceled.

For surcharges see Nos. 59, 61-63, 65, 70.

Stamps of 1919 Handstamp Surcharged

1919-20
58 A4 5c on 20c grn ('20) 1.75 1.75
59 A10 5c on 25c blue 1.75 1.75
60 A5 10c on 45c orange 1.75 1.75
61 A9 15c on 30c vio ('20) 1.75 1.75
62 A10 15c on 45c orange 1.75 1.75
63 A9 15c on 60c cl ('20) 1.75 1.75
64 A6 25c on 50c yel grn ('20) 17.00 *34.00*
65 A9 25c on 50c yel grn ('20) 1.75 1.75
66 A6 55c on 1cor brn org 37.50 37.50
67 A6 55c on 2cor brt bl 4.50 *8.50*
68 A6 55c on 3cor org red 4.50 7.00
69 A6 55c on 5cor dp brn 4.50 7.00
70 A9 55c on 10cor ol grn 30.00 34.00
 Nos. 58-70 (13) 110.25 *140.25*
 Set, never hinged 260.00

Semi-Postal Stamps of 1919 Surcharged:

a

b

1919-20

73	SP6(a)	5c on 5c green	1.75	1.75
74	SP6(a)	10c on 10c rose	1.75	1.75
75	SP6(a)	15c on 15c gray	1.75	1.75
76	SP6(a)	20c on 20c org	1.75	1.75
77	SP9(a)	25c on 25c bl ('20)	1.75	1.75
78	SP7(b)	45c on 45c ol grn	2.50	2.50
79	SP7(b)	60c on 60c rose	2.50	2.50
80	SP7(b)	80c on 80c violet	1.75	1.75
81	SP7(b)	1cor on 1cor sl	2.50	2.50
82	SP8(a)	2cor on 2cor red brn	4.25	4.25
83	SP8(a)	3cor on 3cor blk brn	6.75	6.75
84	SP8(a)	5cor on 5cor yel	8.50	8.50
85	SP8(a)	10cor on 10cor dk vio ('20)	2.50	2.50
		Nos. 73-85 (13)	40.00	40.00
		Set, never hinged	87.50	

Double or inverted surcharges, or imperf. varieties, exist on most of Nos. 73-85.

There were three settings of the surcharges on Nos. 73-85 except No. 77 which is known only with one setting.

Gabriele d'Annunzio — A11

Severing the Gordian Knot — A12

1920, Sept. 12   Typo.   Perf. 11½
Pale Buff Background

86	A11	5c green	1.75	1.75
87	A11	10c carmine	1.75	1.75
88	A11	15c dark gray	1.75	1.75
89	A11	20c orange	1.75	1.75
90	A11	25c dark blue	2.50	2.50
91	A11	30c red brown	2.50	2.50
92	A11	45c olive gray	3.50	3.50
93	A11	50c lilac	3.50	3.50
94	A11	55c bister	3.50	3.50
95	A11	1 l black	17.00	24.00
96	A11	2 l red violet	17.00	24.00
97	A11	3 l dark green	17.00	24.00
98	A11	5 l brown	77.50	50.00
99	A11	10 l gray violet	17.50	27.50
		Nos. 86-99 (14)	168.50	172.00
		Set, never hinged	400.00	

Counterfeits of Nos. 86 to 99 are plentiful.
For overprints see Nos. 134-148.

1920, Sept. 12

Designs: 10c, Ancient emblem of Fiume. 20c, Head of "Fiume." 25c, Hands holding daggers.

100	A12	5c green	57.50	34.00
101	A12	10c deep rose	34.00	25.00
102	A12	20c brown orange	57.50	25.00
103	A12	25c indigo	34.00	60.00
a.		25c blue	130.00	130.00
		Nos. 100-103 (4)	183.00	144.00
		Set, never hinged	425.00	

Anniv. of the occupation of Fiume by d'Annunzio. They were available for franking the correspondence of the legionnaires on the day of issue only, Sept. 12, 1920.

Counterfeits of Nos. 100-103 are plentiful.
For overprints and surcharges see Nos. 104-133, E4-E9.

Nos. 100-103
Overprinted or
Surcharged in
Black or Red and
New Values

1920, Nov. 20

104	A12	1c on 5c green	1.75	1.75
a.		Inverted overprint	50.00	50.00
b.		Double overprint	190.00	
105	A12	2c on 25c indigo (R)	1.75	1.75
a.		Inverted overprint	50.00	50.00
b.		Double overprint	67.50	67.50
c.		2c on 25c blue (R)	80.00	80.00
106	A12	5c green	20.00	1.75
a.		Inverted overprint	42.50	42.50
b.		Double overprint	67.50	67.50
107	A12	10c rose	20.00	1.75
a.		Inverted overprint	50.00	50.00
b.		Double overprint	67.50	67.50
108	A12	15c on 10c rose	1.75	1.75
a.		Inverted overprint	60.00	60.00
b.		Double overprint	67.50	67.50
109	A12	15c on 20c brn org	1.75	1.75
a.		Inverted overprint	60.00	60.00
b.		Double overprint	67.50	67.50
110	A12	15c on 25c indigo (R)	1.75	1.75
a.		Inverted overprint	60.00	60.00
b.		Double overprint	67.50	67.50
c.		15c on 25c blue (R)	210.00	210.00
111	A12	20c brown orange	1.75	1.75
a.		Inverted overprint	25.00	25.00
b.		Double overprint	120.00	120.00
112	A12	25c indigo (R)	1.75	1.75
a.		Inverted overprint	21.00	21.00
b.		25c blue (R)	7.50	7.50
113	A12	25c indigo (Bk)	175.00	175.00
a.		Inverted overprint	425.00	350.00
b.		25c blue (Bk)	225.00	225.00
c.		As "b," inverted overprint	625.00	
114	A12	25c on 10c rose	2.00	3.75
a.		Double overprint	67.50	67.50
115	A12	50c on 20c brn org	5.00	2.00
a.		Double overprint	67.50	67.50
116	A12	55c on 5c green	21.00	3.75
a.		Inverted overprint	92.50	92.50
b.		Double overprint	67.50	67.50
117	A12	1 l on 10c rose	42.50	30.00
a.		Inverted overprint	240.00	240.00
b.		Double overprint	275.00	
118	A12	1 l on 25c indigo (R)	100.00	100.00
a.		1 l on 25c blue (R)	600.00	600.00
b.		As "a," inverted overprint	850.00	675.00
119	A12	2 l on 5c green	42.50	34.00
a.		Inverted overprint	300.00	
b.		Double overprint	190.00	
120	A12	5 l on 10c rose	210.00	240.00
a.		Inverted overprint	675.00	675.00
b.		Double overprint	675.00	
121	A12	10 l on 20c brn org	700.00	550.00
a.		Double overprint	1,500.	750.00
b.		Inverted overprint	1,500.	750.00
		Nos. 104-121 (18)	1,350.	1,154.
		Set, never hinged	3,350.	

The Fiume Legionnaires of d'Annunzio occupied the islands of Arbe and Veglia in the Gulf of Carnaro Nov. 13, 1920-Jan. 5, 1921.

Varieties of overprint or surcharge exist for most of Nos. 104-121.

Nos. 113, 117-121, 125, 131 have a backprint.

Nos. 106-107, 111,
113, 115-116
Overprinted or
Surcharged at top

1920, Nov. 28

122	A12	5c green	32.00	22.50
123	A12	10c rose	40.00	45.00
124	A12	20c brown org	80.00	47.50
125	A12	25c deep blue	47.50	47.50
126	A12	50c on 20c brn org	90.00	47.50
127	A12	55c on 5c green	90.00	47.50
		Nos. 122-127 (6)	379.50	257.50
		Set, never hinged		

The overprint on Nos. 122-125 comes in two widths: 11mm and 14mm. Values are for the 11mm width.

Nos. 106-107, 111,
113, 115-116
Overprinted or
Surcharged at top

1920, Nov. 28

128	A12	5c green	32.50	22.50
129	A12	10c rose	40.00	45.00
130	A12	20c brown orange	80.00	47.50
131	A12	25c deep blue	47.50	47.50

132	A12	50c on 20c brn org	90.00	47.50
133	A12	55c on 5c green	90.00	47.50
		Nos. 128-133 (6)	380.00	257.50
		Set, never hinged	900.00	

The overprint on Nos. 128-131 comes in two widths: 17mm and 19mm. Values are for the 17mm width.

Nos. 122-133 exist with double and inverted overprints.

Counterfeits of these overprints exist.

Nos. 86-99
Overprinted

1921, Feb. 2
Pale Buff Background

134	A11	5c green	1.75	1.75
a.		Inverted overprint	25.00	25.00
b.		Double overprint	50.00	50.00
135	A11	10c carmine	1.75	1.75
a.		Inverted overprint	25.00	25.00
b.		Double overprint	50.00	50.00
136	A11	15c dark gray	1.75	1.75
a.		Inverted overprint	25.00	25.00
b.		Double overprint	50.00	50.00
137	A11	20c orange	2.50	2.50
a.		Inverted overprint	25.00	25.00
b.		Double overprint	25.00	25.00
138	A11	25c dark blue	2.50	2.50
a.		Inverted overprint	25.00	25.00
b.		Double overprint	50.00	50.00
139	A11	30c red brown	2.50	2.50
a.		Inverted overprint	25.00	25.00
b.		Double overprint	25.00	25.00
140	A11	45c olive gray	1.75	1.75
a.		Inverted overprint	50.00	50.00
b.		Double overprint	34.00	34.00
141	A11	50c lilac	2.75	2.50
a.		Inverted overprint	25.00	25.00
142	A11	55c bister	2.50	2.50
a.		Inverted overprint	13.00	13.00
143	A11	1 l black	140.00	170.00
a.		Inverted overprint	325.00	325.00
144	A11	2 l red violet	92.50	92.50
145	A11	3 l dark green	92.50	92.50
146	A11	5 l brown	92.50	92.50
147	A11	10 l gray violet	92.50	92.50

With Additional
Surcharge

148	A11	1 l on 30c red brown	1.75	1.75
a.		Inverted overprint	275.00	275.00
b.		Double overprint	50.00	50.00
		Nos. 134-148 (15)	531.50	561.25
		Set, never hinged	1,300.	

Most of Nos. 134-143, 148 and E10-E11 exist with inverted or double overprint.
See Nos. E10-E11.

First Constituent Assembly

Nos. B4-B15
Overprinted

1921, Apr. 24

149	SP6	5c blue green	5.00	4.25
150	SP6	10c rose	5.00	4.25
a.		Inverted overprint	65.00	65.00
151	SP6	15c gray	5.00	4.25
152	SP6	20c orange	5.00	4.25
153	SP7	45c olive green	15.00	10.00
154	SP7	60c car rose	15.00	10.00
a.		Inverted overprint	47.50	47.50
155	SP7	80c brt violet	25.00	21.00

With Additional Overprint "L"

156	SP7	1 l on 1cor dk slate	30.00	34.00
a.		Inverted overprint	77.50	77.50
157	SP8	2 l on 2cor red brn	120.00	3.50
a.		Inverted overprint	325.00	150.00
158	SP8	3 l on 3cor black brn	120.00	130.00

159	SP8	5 l on 5cor yel brn	120.00	4.25
160	SP8	10 l on 10cor dk vio	170.00	170.00
a.		Inverted overprint	475.00	375.00
		Nos. 149-160 (12)	635.00	399.75
		Set, never hinged	1,590.	

The overprint exists inverted on several denominations.

Second Constituent Assembly
"Constitution" Issue of 1921 With
Additional Overprint "1922"

1922

161	SP6	5c blue green	4.25	2.75
a.		Inverted overprint	21.00	21.00
162	SP6	10c rose	1.75	1.75
a.		Inverted overprint	21.00	21.00
b.		Double overprint, one inverted	34.00	34.00
163	SP6	15c gray	19.00	10.00
164	SP6	20c orange	1.75	1.75
a.		Double overprint	34.00	34.00
c.		Double overprint, one inverted	—	—
165	SP7	45c olive grn	12.00	10.00
a.		Double overprint	34.00	34.00
166	SP7	60c car rose	1.75	2.75
167	SP7	80c brt violet	1.75	2.75
168	SP7	1 l on 1cor dk slate	1.75	2.25
a.		Inverted overprint	50.00	50.00
b.		Double overprint	34.00	34.00
169	SP8	2 l on 2cor red brn	19.00	10.00
170	SP8	3 l on 3cor blk brn	1.75	2.75
171	SP8	5 l on 5cor yel brn	1.75	2.75
		Nos. 161-171 (11)	66.50	49.50
		Set, never hinged	165.00	

Nos. 161-171 have the overprint in heavier type than Nos. 149-160 and "IV" in Roman instead of sans-serif numerals.

The overprint exists inverted or double on almost all values.

Venetian
Ship — A16

Roman
Arch — A17

St. Vitus — A18

Rostral
Column — A19

1923, Mar. 23   Perf. 11½
Pale Buff Background

172	A16	5c blue green	1.75	1.75
173	A16	10c violet	1.75	1.75
174	A16	15c brown	1.75	1.75
175	A17	20c orange red	1.75	1.75
176	A17	25c dark gray	1.75	1.75
177	A17	30c dark green	1.75	1.75
178	A18	50c dull blue	1.75	1.75
179	A18	60c rose	2.50	2.50
180	A18	1 l dark blue	2.50	2.50
181	A19	2 l violet brown	65.00	17.00
182	A19	3 l olive bister	50.00	42.50
183	A19	5 l yellow brown	50.00	50.00
		Nos. 172-183 (12)	182.25	126.75
		Set, never hinged	450.00	

Nos. 172-183
Overprinted

1924, Feb. 22
Pale Buff Background

184	A16	5c blue green	1.75	4.25
a.		Inverted overprint	17.00	17.00
b.		Double overprint	130.00	
185	A16	10c violet	1.75	4.25
a.		Inverted overprint	13.00	13.00
186	A16	15c brown	1.75	4.25
a.		Inverted overprint	17.00	17.00

187	A17	20c orange red	1.75	4.25
a.		Inverted overprint	21.00	21.00
b.		Double overprint	250.00	
188	A17	25c dk gray	1.75	4.25
189	A17	30c dk green	1.75	4.25
a.		Inverted overprint	42.50	
190	A18	50c dull blue	1.75	4.25
a.		Inverted overprint	42.50	42.50
191	A18	60c red	1.75	4.25
a.		Inverted overprint	85.00	
192	A18	1 l dark blue	1.75	4.25
a.		Inverted overprint	21.00	21.00
193	A19	2 l violet brown	3.50	15.00
194	A19	3 l olive	6.00	19.00
195	A19	5 l yellow brown	6.00	19.00
		Nos. 184-195 (12)	31.25	91.25
		Set, never hinged	77.00	

The overprint exists inverted on almost all values.

Nos. 172-183
Overprinted

1924, Mar. 1
Pale Buff Background

196	A16	5c blue green	1.75	16.00
197	A16	10c violet	1.75	16.00
198	A16	15c brown	1.75	16.00
199	A17	20c orange red	1.75	16.00
200	A17	25c dark gray	1.75	16.00
201	A17	30c dark green	1.75	16.00
202	A18	50c dull blue	1.75	16.00
203	A18	60c red	1.75	16.00
204	A18	1 l dark blue	1.75	16.00
205	A19	2 l violet brown	2.50	24.00
206	A19	3 l olive	2.75	24.00
207	A19	5 l yellow brown	2.75	24.00
		Nos. 196-207 (12)	23.75	216.00
		Set, never hinged	58.50	

Postage stamps of Fiume were superseded by stamps of Italy.

SEMI-POSTAL STAMPS

Semi-Postal Stamps of Hungary, 1916-17 Overprinted

1918, Dec. 2   Wmk. 137   Perf. 15

B1	SP3	10f + 2f rose	6.75	6.00
a.		Inverted overprint	67.50	40.00
b.		Double overprint	225.00	110.00
B2	SP4	15f + 2f dl vio	6.75	6.00
a.		Inverted overprint	130.00	40.00
b.		Double overprint	40.00	40.00
B3	SP5	40f + 2f brn car	12.00	6.00
a.		Inverted overprint	80.00	37.50
		Nos. B1-B3 (3)	25.50	18.00
		Set, never hinged	65.00	

Examples of Nos. B1-B3 with overprint handstamped sell for higher prices.

Statue of Romulus and Remus Being Suckled by Wolf — SP6

Venetian Galley — SP7

Church of St. Mark's, Venice — SP8

Perf. 11½
1919, May 18   Unwmk.   Typo.

B4	SP6	5c +5 l bl grn	40.00	28.00
B5	SP6	10c +5 l rose	40.00	28.00
B6	SP6	15c +5 l dk gray	40.00	28.00
B7	SP6	20c +5 l orange	40.00	28.00
B8	SP7	45c +5 l ol grn	40.00	28.00
B9	SP7	60c +5 l car rose	40.00	28.00
B10	SP7	80c +5 l lilac	40.00	28.00
B11	SP7	1cor +5 l dk slate	40.00	28.00
B12	SP8	2cor +5 l red brn	40.00	28.00
B13	SP8	3cor +5 l blk brn	40.00	28.00
B14	SP8	5cor +5 l yel brn	40.00	28.00
B15	SP8	10cor +5 l dk vio	40.00	28.00
		Nos. B4-B15 (12)	480.00	336.00
		Set, never hinged	1,125.	

200th day of peace. The surtax aided Fiume students in Italy. "Posta di Fiume" is printed on the back of Nos. B4-B16.

The surtax is shown on the stamps as "LIRE 5" but actually was 5cor.

For surcharges and overprints see Nos. 73-85, 149-171, J15-J26.

Dr. Antonio Grossich — SP9

1919, Sept. 20

B16	SP9	25c + 2 l blue	3.00	3.00
		Never hinged	7.50	

Surtax for the Dr. Grossich Foundation.

SPECIAL DELIVERY STAMPS

Special Delivery Stamp of Hungary, 1916, Overprinted like Nos. 1-23

1918, Dec. 2   Wmk. 137   Perf. 15
Typographed Overprint

E1	SD1	2f gray green & red	4.00	4.00
		Never hinged	10.00	
a.		Double overprint	160.00	140.00

Handstamped overprints sell for more.

SD3

Perf. 11½
1920, Sept. 12   Unwmk.   Typo.

E2	SD3	30c slate blue	25.00	25.00
E3	SD3	50c rose	25.00	25.00
		Set, never hinged	125.00	

For overprints see Nos. E10-E11.

Nos. 102 and 100 Surcharged

1920, Nov.

E4	A12	30c on 20c brn org	150.00	135.00
a.		Inverted overprint	500.00	
b.		Double overprint	500.00	

E5	A12	50c on 5c green	225.00	100.00
a.		Inverted overprint	850.00	
b.		Double overprint	850.00	
c.		Double overprint, one inverted	925.00	

Nos. E4-E5 have a backprint.

Same Surcharge as on Nos. 124, 122

E6	A12	30c on 20c brn org	225.00	145.00
E7	A12	50c on 5c green	175.00	145.00
a.		Double overprint		800.00

Overprint on Nos. E6-E7 is 11mm wide.

Same Surcharge as on Nos. 130, 128

E8	A12	30c on 20c brn org	225.00	145.00
E9	A12	50c on 5c green	175.00	145.00
a.		Double overprint	800.00	800.00
		Nos. E4-E9 (6)	1,175.	815.00
		Set, never hinged	2,900.	

Overprint on Nos. E8-E9 is 17mm wide.

Nos. E2 and E3 Overprinted

1921, Feb. 2

E10	SD3	30c slate blue	10.00	12.00
a.		Inverted overprint	120.00	120.00
b.		Double overprint	34.00	34.00
E11	SD3	50c rose	15.00	12.00
a.		Inverted overprint	25.00	25.00
b.		Double overprint	100.00	100.00
		Set, never hinged	62.50	

Fiume in 16th Century SD4

1923, Mar. 23   Perf. 11, 11½

E12	SD4	60c rose & buff	20.00	13.50
E13	SD4	2 l dk bl & buff	20.00	15.00
		Set, never hinged	100.00	

Nos. E12-E13 Overprinted

1924, Feb. 22

E14	SD4	60c car & buff	2.25	7.00
E15	SD4	2 l dk bl & buff	2.25	7.00
a.		Inverted overprint	130.00	130.00
		Set, never hinged	11.00	

Nos. E12-E13 Overprinted

1924, Mar. 1

E16	SD4	60c car & buff	2.75	60.00
E17	SD4	2 l dk bl & buff	2.75	60.00
		Set, never hinged	14.00	

POSTAGE DUE STAMPS

Postage Due Stamps of Hungary, 1915-1916, Overprinted

1918, Dec.   Wmk. 137   Perf. 15

J1c	D1	6f green & black	450.00	125.00
a.		Inverted overprint	1,000.	
J2c	D1	12f green & black	300.00	65.00
a.		Double overprint		925.00
J3	D1	50f green & black	210.00	125.00
a.		Double overprint		925.00
J4c	D1	1f green & red	36.00	20.00
J5	D1	2f green & red	5.00	5.00
a.		Inverted overprint	50.00	42.50
b.		Double overprint	170.00	
J6c	D1	5f green & red	32.50	45.00
J7	D1	6f green & red	5.00	5.00
a.		Inverted overprint	25.00	25.00
b.		Double overprint	160.00	
J8	D1	10f green & red	30.00	24.00
a.		Double overprint	425.00	
J9	D1	12f green & red	5.00	5.00
J10	D1	15f green & red	30.00	30.00
J11	D1	20f green & red	5.00	5.00
a.		Double overprint	42.50	30.00
J12	D1	30f green & red	30.00	30.00
		Nos. J1c-J12 (12)	1,138.	484.00
		Set, never hinged	755.00	

Eagle — D2

Perf. 11½
1919, July 28   Unwmk.   Typo.

J13	D2	2c brown	2.10	2.10
J14	D2	5c brown	2.10	2.10
		Set, never hinged	10.50	

Semi-Postal Stamps of 1919 with Overprint "Valore Globale" Surcharged:

1921, Mar. 21

J15	SP6	2c on 15c gray	5.00	5.00
J16	SP6	4c on 10c rose	4.25	4.25
J17	SP9	5c on 25c blue	4.25	4.25
J18	SP6	6c on 20c orange	4.25	4.25
J19	SP6	10c on 20c orange	5.00	5.00

Surcharged:

J20	SP7	20c on 45c olive grn	2.00	3.50
J21	SP7	30c on 1cor dk slate	8.50	10.00
J22	SP7	40c on 80c violet	4.25	5.00
J23	SP7	50c on 60c carmine	4.25	5.00
J24	SP7	60c on 45c olive grn	2.00	3.50
J25	SP7	80c on 45c olive grn	2.00	3.50

Surcharged like Nos. J15-J19

J26	SP8	1 l on 2cor red brown	21.00	21.00
		Nos. J15-J26 (12)	66.75	74.25
		Set, never hinged	166.00	

See note below No. 85 regarding settings of "Valore Globale" overprint.

NEWSPAPER STAMPS

Newspaper Stamp of Hungary, 1914, Overprinted like Nos. 1-23

1918, Dec. 2   Wmk. 137   Imperf.

P1	N5	(2f) orange	4.25	2.50
		Never hinged	10.50	
a.		Inverted overprint	55.00	52.50
b.		Double overprint	200.00	190.00

Handstamped overprints sell for more.

Eagle
N1

1919   **Unwmk.**   **Perf. 11½**
P2   N1   2c deep buff   8.50   *13.00*

Re-engraved
P3   N1   2c deep buff   8.50   *13.00*
   Set, never hinged   35.00

In the re-engraved stamp the top of the "2" is rounder and broader, the feet of the eagle show clearly and the diamond at bottom has six lines instead of five.

Steamer — N2

1920, Sept. 12
P4   N2   1c gray green   3.50   2.50
   Never hinged   8.75
  a.   Imperf   21.00   21.00

FRANCE

ˈfran̝t͜s

LOCATION — Western Europe
GOVT. — Republic
AREA — 210,033 sq. mi.
POP. — 58,978,172 (1999 est.)
CAPITAL — Paris

100 Centimes = 1 Franc
100 Cents = 1 Euro (2002)

Catalogue values for unused stamps in this country are for Never Hinged items, beginning with Scott 299 in the regular postage section, Scott B42 in the semipostal section, Scott C18 in the airpost section, Scott CB1 in the airpost semi-postal section, Scott J69 in the postage due section, Scott M10 in the military stamps section, Scott 1O1 in the section for official stamps for the Council of Europe, Scott 2O1 for the section for UNESCO, Scott S1 for franchise stamps, Scott N27 for occupation stamps, and Scott 2N1 for AMG stamps.

Ceres — A1

FORTY CENTIMES

4

Type I

4

Type II

			Unwmk.	**Imperf.**
1849-50		**Typo.**		
1	A1	10c bis, *yelsh* ('50)	2,000.	275.00
a.		10c dark bister, *yelsh*	2,300.	350.00
b.		10c greenish bister	2,750.	425.00
d.		As #1, tête bêche pair	115,000.	25,000.
2	A1	15c green, *grnsh*	23,000.	900.00
a.		15c yellow green, *grnsh*	22,500.	900.00
c.		Tête bêche pair	—	
3	A1	20c blk, *yelsh*	400.00	45.00
a.		20c black	475.00	55.00
b.		20c black, *buff*	1,400.	225.00
c.		Tête bêche pair	10,000.	6,600.
4	A1	20c dark blue	2,850.	
a.		20c blue, *bluish*	2,200.	
b.		20c blue, *bluish*	3,500.	
c.		Tête bêche pair	70,000.	
6	A1	25c lt bl, *blu-ish*	6,750.	40.00
a.		25c blue, *bluish* ('50)	6,750.	40.00
b.		25c blue, *bluish*	6,400.	50.00
c.		Tête bêche pair	185,000.	13,500.
7	A1	40c org, *yelsh* (I)		
		('50)	3,750.	475.00
a.		40c org ver, *yelsh* (I)	4,250.	525.00
b.		40c orange, *yelsh* (II)	25,000.	6,750.
c.		Pair, types I and II	40,000.	13,250.
g.		Vertical half used as 20c on cover		215,000.
8	A1	1fr vermilion, *yelsh*	90,000.	15,500.
a.		1fr dull orange red	90,000.	19,500.
b.		Tête bêche pair, no gum	95,000.	172,500.
c.		1fr pale ver ("Vervelle")	26,500.	
d.		As "c," tête bêche pair	480,000.	
9	A1	1fr light carmine	11,000.	800.00
a.		Tête bêche pair	235,000.	23,500.
b.		1fr brown carmine	13,250.	1,100.
c.		1fr dark carmine, *yelsh*	11,500.	825.00

No. 4 was printed but not yet gummed when the rate change to 25c made them unnecessary. An essay with a red "25" surcharge on No. 4 was rejected.

An ungummed sheet of No. 8c was found in 1895 among the effects of Anatole A. Hulot, the printer. It was sold to Ernest Vervelle, a Parisian dealer, by whose name the stamps are known.

See Nos. 329-329e, 612-613, 624.

Nos. 1, 4a, 6a, 7 and 13 are of similar designs and colors to French Colonies Nos. 9, 11, 12, 14, and 8. There are numerous shades of each. Identification by those who are not experts can be difficult, though cancellations can be used as a guide for used stamps.

Because of the date of issue the Colonies stamps are similar in shades and papers to the perforated French stamps, Nos. 23a, 54, 57-59, and are not as clearly printed. Except for No. 13, unused, the French Colonies stamps sell for much less than the values shown here for properly identified French versions.

Expertization of these stamps is recommended.

				Re-issue
1862				
1g	A1	10c bister		550.
2d	A1	15c yellow green		700.
3d	A1	20c black, *yellowish*		450.
4d	A1	20c blue		450.
6d	A1	25c blue		500.

7d	A1	40c orange (I)		700.
7e	A1	40c orange (II)		11,500.
h.		Pair, types I and II		16,500.
9d	A1	1fr pale lake		750.

The re-issues are fine impressions in lighter colors and on whiter paper than the originals. An official imitation of the essay, 25c on 20c blue, also in a lighter shade and on whiter paper, was made at the same time as the re-issues.

President Louis
Napoleon — A2

Emperor Napoleon
III — A3

1852				
10	A2	10c pale bister, *yelsh*	34,500.	575.00
a.		10c dark bister, *yelsh*	37,000.	650.00
11	A2	25c blue, *bluish*	2,900.	40.00
b.		25c dark blue, *bluish*	3,500.	70.00

Full margins = ¾mm.

				Re-issue
1862				
10b	A2	10c bister		700.00
11a	A2	25c blue		450.00

The re-issues are in lighter colors and on whiter paper than the originals.

1853-60   **Imperf.**

Die I. The curl above the forehead directly below "R" of "EMPIRE" is made up of two lines very close together, often appearing to form a single thick line. There is no shading across the neck.

Die II. The curl is made of two distinct, more widely separated lines. There are lines of shading across the upper neck.

12	A3	1c ol grn, *pale bl* ('60)	190.00	80.00
a.		1c bronze grn, *pale bluish*	200.00	95.00
13	A3	5c grn, *grnsh* (I) ('54)	800.00	85.00
14	A3	10c bis, *yelsh* (I)	425.00	9.00
a.		10c yellow, *yelsh* (I)	1,500.	37.50
b.		10c bister brn, *yelsh* (I)	550.00	25.00
c.		10c bister, *yelsh* (II) ('60)	550.00	22.50
15	A3	20c bl, *bluish* (I) ('54)	190.00	1.50
a.		20c dark bl, *bluish* (I)	250.00	2.00
b.		20c milky blue (I)	275.00	12.50
c.		20c blue, *lilac* (I)	4,500.	82.50
d.		20c blue, *bluish* (II) ('60)	325.00	4.75
e.		Half used as 10c on cover		18,500.
f.		Tête bêche pair	190,000.	
16	A3	20c bl, *grnsh* (II)	5,000.	190.00
a.		20c blue, *greenish* (II)	4,250.	125.00
17	A3	25c bl, *bluish* (I)	2,300.	250.00
18	A3	40c org, *yelsh* (I)	2,250.	12.50
a.		40c org ver, *yellowish*	2,750.	20.00
b.		Half used as 20c on cover		135,000.
19	A3	80c lake, *yelsh* (I) ('54)	3,400.	82.50
a.		Tête bêche pair	325,000.	17,500.
b.		Half used as 40c on cover		40,000.
20	A3	80c rose, *pnksh* ('60)	2,400.	47.50
a.		Tête-bêche pair	57,500.	13,000.
21	A3	1fr lake, *yelsh* (I)	8,000.	3,250.
a.		Tête bêche pair	310,000.	130,000.

Most values of the 1853-60 issue are known privately rouletted, pin-perf., perf. 7 and percé en scie.

				Re-issue
1862				
17c	A3	25c blue (I)		425.
19c	A3	80c lake (I)		1,350.
21c	A3	1fr lake (I)		1,800.
		Tête bêche pair (II)		30,000.

The re-issues are in lighter colors and on whiter paper than the originals.

				Perf. 14x13½
1862-71				
22	A3	1c ol grn, *pale bl* (II)	160.00	40.00
a.		1c bronze grn, *pale bl* (II)	160.00	40.00
23	A3	5c yel grn, *grnsh* (I)	375.00	20.00
a.		5c deep green, *grnsh* (I)	250.00	16.00
24	A3	5c grn, *pale bl* ('71) (I)	1,950.	100.00
25	A3	10c bis, *yelsh* (II)	1,450.	4.25
a.		10c yel brn, *yelsh* (II)	2,000.	10.50
26	A3	20c bl, *bluish* (II)	225.00	1.25
a.		Tête bêche pair (II)	4,750.	1,000.
27	A3	40c org, *yelsh* (I)	1,300.	7.50
28	A3	80c rose, *pnksh* (I)	1,200.	37.50
a.		80c bright rose, *pinkish* (I)	1,500.	57.50
c.		Tête bêche pair (I)	20,500.	8,250.

No. 26a imperf is from a trial printing.

A4   A5

Napoleon
III — A6

				Perf. 14x13½
1863-70				
29	A4	1c brnz grn, *pale bl* ('70)	45.00	20.00
a.		1c olive green, *pale blue*	45.00	20.00
30	A4	2c red brn, *yelsh*	82.50	25.00
b.		Half used as 1c on cover		42,500.
31	A4	4c gray	200.00	52.50
c.		Tete beche pair	20,000.	13,250.
d.		Half used as 2c on cover		60,000.
32	A5	10c bis, *yelsh* ('67)	325.00	6.00
c.		Half used as 5c on cover with other stamps		3,750.
33	A5	20c bl, *bluish* ('67)	225.00	1.60
c.		Half used as 10c on cover		52,500.
34	A5	30c brn, *yelsh* ('67)	750.00	17.00
a.		30c dk brn, *yellowish*	1,225.	37.50
35	A5	40c pale org, *yellow-ish*	750.00	10.00
a.		40c org, *yelsh* ('68)	750.00	10.00
c.		Half used as 20c on cover		42,500.
36	A5	80c rose, *pnksh* ('68)	1,000.	24.00
a.		80c carmine, *yellowish*	1,400.	40.00
d.		Half used as 40c on cover		50,000.
e.		Quarter used as 20c on cover		57,500.
37	A6	5fr gray lil, *lav* ('69)	6,000.	825.00
a.		"5" and "F" omitted		112,500.
c.		5fr bluish gray, *lavender*	6,500.	1,000.
d.		As #37, "5" and "F" in light blue	8,000.	1,100.

No. 33 exists in two types, differing in the size of the dots at either side of POSTES.

On No. 37, the "5" and "F" vary in height from 3¾mm to 4½mm. These figures normally appear in gray but exist in blue or black. All known examples of No. 37a are more or less damaged.

No. 29 was reprinted in 1887 by authority of Granet, Minister of Posts. The reprints show a yellowish shade under the ultraviolet lamp. Value $850.
For surcharge see No. 49.

Original Issue Imperfs

31b	A4	4c gray	400.	175.
32b	A5	10c bis, *yelsh*	450.	175.
33b	A5	20c bl, *bluish*	375.	160.
36c	A5	80c rose, *pnksh*	—	8,500.
37b	A6	5fr gray lil, *lav*	8,500.	

Imperfs, "Rothschild" Re-issue
Paper Colors are the Same

29b	A4	1c olive green	1,200.
30a	A4	2c pale red brown	190.
31b	A4	4c pale gray	140.
32a	A5	10c pale bister	140.
33a	A5	20c pale blue	250.
34c	A5	30c pale brown	150.
35b	A5	40c pale orange	225.
36b	A5	80c rose	425.

The re-issues constitute the "Rothschild Issue." These stamps were authorized exclusively for the banker to use on his correspondence. Used copies exist.

Ceres
A7   A8

A9   A10

A11

Bordeaux Issue

On the lithographed stamps, except for type I of the 20c, the shading on the cheek and neck is in lines or dashes, not in dots. On the typographed stamps the shading is in dots. The 2c, 5c, 10c and 20c (types II and III) occur in two or more types. The most easily distinguishable are:

2c — Type A. To the left of and within the top of the left "2" are lines of shading composed of dots.

2c — Type B. These lines of dots are replaced by solid lines.

5c — Type A. The head and hairline merge with the background of the medallion, without a distinct separation.

5c — Type B. A white line separates the contour of the head and hairline from the background of the medallion.

10c — Type A. The inner frame lines are of the same thickness as all other frame lines.

10c — Type B. The inner frame lines are much thicker than the others.

Three Types of the 20c.

A9 — The inscriptions in the upper and lower labels are small and there is quite a space between the upper label and the circle containing the head. There is also very little shading under the eye and in the neck.

A10 — The inscriptions in the labels are similar to those of the first type, the shading under the eye and in the neck is heavier and the upper label and circle almost touch.

A11 — The inscriptions in the labels are much larger than those of the two preceding types, and are similar to those of the other values of the same type in the set.

1870-71   Litho.   *Imperf.*

38	A7	1c ol grn, *pale bl*	160.00	115.00
a.		1c bronze green, *pale blue*	200.00	150.00
39	A7	2c red brn, *yelsh (B)*	275.00	250.00
a.		2c brick red, *yelsh (B)*	825.00	625.00
b.		2c chestnut, *yelsh (B)*	1,500.	850.00
c.		2c chocolate, *yelsh (A)*	825.00	725.00
40	A7	4c gray	275.00	225.00
41	A8	5c yel green, *greenish (B)*	275.00	175.00
a.		5c grn, *grn (B)*	350.00	175.00
b.		5c emerald, *greenish (B)*	5,000.	1,250.
c.		5c yellowish green, *greenish (A)*	2,250.	3,000.
42	A8	10c bis, *yelsh (A)*	1,000.	60.00
a.		10c bister, *yellowish (B)*	1,000.	90.00

43	A9	20c bl, *bluish*	22,000.	575.00
a.		20c dark blue, *bluish*	24,500.	825.00
44	A10	20c bl, *bluish*	950.00	45.00
a.		20c dark blue, *bluish*	1,250.	100.00
b.		20c ultra, *bluish*	22,000.	3,300.
45	A11	20c bl, *bluish* ('71)	950.00	18.00
a.		20c ultra, *bluish*	2,750.	1,250.
46	A8	30c brn, *yelsh*	375.00	225.00
a.		30c blk brn, *yelsh*	2,000.	825.00
47	A8	40c orange, *yelsh*	475.00	115.00
a.		40c yel orange, *yelsh*	1,450.	250.00
b.		40c red orange, *yelsh*	725.00	190.00
c.		40c scarlet, *yelsh*	3,200.	775.00
48	A8	80c rose, *pinkish*	750.00	250.00
a.		80c dull rose, *pinkish*	1,000.	275.00

All values of the 1870 issue are known privately rouletted, pin-perf and perf. 14. See Nos. 50-53.

A12

Dark Blue Surcharge
1871   Typo.   *Perf. 14x13½*

49	A12	10c on 10c bister	1,900.	
a.		Pale blue surcharge	1,900.	

#49 was never placed in use. Counterfeits exist.

A13   A14

Two types of the 40c as in the 1849-50 issue.

1870-73   Typo.   *Perf. 14x13½*

50	A7	1c ol grn, *pale bl*	45.00	13.00
a.		1c bronze grn, *pale bl* ('72)	52.50	15.00
51	A7	2c red brn, *yelsh* ('70)	90.00	15.00
52	A7	4c gray ('70)	275.00	45.00
53	A7	5c yel grn, *pale bl* ('72)	175.00	8.25
a.		5c green	175.00	8.25
54	A13	10c bis, *yelsh*	600.00	65.00
a.		Tête beche pair	6,250.	2,600.
b.		Half used as 5c on cover		5,000.
55	A13	10c bis, *rose* ('73)	300.00	10.50
a.		Tête bêche pair	4,250.	2,000.
56	A13	15c bis, *yelsh* ('71)	350.00	5.00
a.		Tête bêche pair	42,500.	13,500.
57	A13	20c dl bl, *bluish*	250.00	7.50
a.		20c bright blue, *bluish*	400.00	9.00
b.		Tête bêche pair	4,250.	1,650.
c.		Half used as 10c on cover		62,500.
d.		Quarter used as 5c on cover		57,500.
58	A13	25c bl, *bluish* ('71)	125.00	1.25
a.		25c dk bl, *bluish*	150.00	1.25
b.		Tête bêche pair	7,500.	3,500.
59	A13	40c org, *yelsh* (I)	525.00	7.00
a.		40c orange yel, *yelsh* (I)	650.00	10.00
b.		40c orange, *yelsh* (II)	3,500.	150.00
c.		40c orange red, *yelsh* (II)	3,500.	150.00
d.		Pair, types I and II	7,250.	575.00
f.		Half used as 20c on circular		25,000.
g.		Half used as 20c on cover		50,000.

No. 58 exists in three main plate varieties, differing in one or another of the flower-like corner ornaments.
Margins on this issue are extremely small.
Nos. 54, 57 and 58 were reprinted imperf. in 1887. See note after No. 37.

Imperf.

50b	A7	1c	300.00	
51a	A7	2c	400.00	
52a	A7	4c	500.00	
53b	A7	5c yel grn, *pale bl*	325.00	
55b	A13	10c	400.00	
56b	A13	15c	425.00	

1872-75   *Perf. 14x13½*
Larger Numerals

60	A14	10c bis, *rose* ('75)	375.00	12.00
a.		Cliché of 15c in plate of 10c	4,250.	4,750.
b.		Pair, #60, 60a	7,500.	9,500.
61	A14	15c bister ('73)	375.00	4.00
62	A14	30c brn, *yelsh*	650.00	6.50
63	A14	80c rose, *pnksh*	725.00	13.50

Imperf.

62a	A14	30c	575.00
63a	A14	80c	825.00

Peace and Commerce ("Type Sage") — A15

Type I. The "N" of "INV" is under the "B" of "REPUBLIQUE."
Type II. The "N" of "INV" is under the "U" of "REPUBLIQUE."

1876-78   *Perf. 14x13½*
Type I

64	A15	1c grn, *grnsh*	140.00	70.00
65	A15	2c grn, *grnsh*	1,450.	250.00
66	A15	4c grn, *grnsh*	160.00	55.00
67	A15	5c grn, *grnsh*	700.00	45.00
68	A15	10c grn, *grnsh*	825.00	22.50
69	A15	15c gray lil, *grysh*	825.00	18.00
70	A15	20c red brn, *straw*	600.00	18.00
71	A15	20c bl, *bluish*	32,500.	
72	A15	25c ultra, *bluish*	7,750.	57.50
73	A15	30c brn, *yelsh*	425.00	8.25
74	A15	40c red, *straw* ('78)	600.00	35.00
75	A15	75c car, *rose*	950.00	13.50
76	A15	1fr brnz grn, *straw*	925.00	11.00

No. 71 was never put into use.
The reprints of No. 71 are type II. They are imperforate or with forged perforation.
For overprints and surcharges see Offices in China Nos. 1-17, J7-J10, J20-J22, Offices in Egypt, Alexandria 1-15, Port Said 1-17, Offices in Turkish Empire 1-7, Cavalle 1-8, Dedeagh 1-8, Port Lagos 1-5, Vathy 1-9, Offices in Zanzibar 1-33, 50-54, Offices in Morocco 1-8, and Madagascar 14-27.

Imperf.

64a	A15	1c	175.00
65a	A15	2c	1,100.
66a	A15	4c	190.00
67a	A15	5c	575.00
68a	A15	10c	650.00
69a	A15	15c	650.00
70a	A15	20c	425.00
73a	A15	30c	300.00
74a	A15	40c	275.00
75a	A15	75c	600.00
76a	A15	1fr	450.00

Beware of French Colonies #24-29.

1876-77   *Perf. 14x13½*
Type II

77	A15	2c grn, *grnsh*	115.00	19.00
78	A15	5c grn, *grnsh*	25.00	.60
a.		Imperf.	175.00	
79	A15	10c grn, *grnsh*	1,100.	240.00
80	A15	15c gray lil, *grysh*	675.00	1.90
81	A15	25c ultra, *bluish*	425.00	1.00
a.		25c blue, *bluish*	475.00	1.50
b.		Pair, types I & II	65,000.	17,500.
c.		Imperf.	325.00	
82	A15	30c yel brn, *yelsh*	82.50	1.40
a.		30c brown, *yellowish*	90.00	1.40
b.		Imperf.	525.00	
83	A15	75c car, *rose* ('77)	1,775.	110.00
84	A15	1fr brnz grn, *straw* ('77)	150.00	7.50
a.		Imperf.	1,100.	

Beware of French Colonies #31, 35.

1877-80

86	A15	1c blk, *lil bl*	3.75	1.75
a.		1c black, *gray blue*	3.75	1.75
b.		Imperf.	75.00	
87	A15	1c blk, *Prus bl* ('80)	11,000.	4,350.

Values for No. 87 are for examples with the perfs touching the design on at least one side.

88	A15	2c brn, *straw*	4.50	1.90
a.		2c brown, *yellow*	4.50	1.90
b.		Imperf.	200.00	
89	A15	3c yel, *straw* ('78)	200.00	42.50
a.		Imperf.	150.00	
90	A15	4c claret, *lav*	5.00	1.90
a.		4c vio brown, *lavender*	8.25	4.50
b.		Imperf.	60.00	
91	A15	10c blk, *lavender*	35.00	1.00
a.		10c black, *rose lilac*	37.50	1.00
b.		10c black, *lilac*	37.50	1.00
c.		Imperf.	70.00	
92	A15	15c blue ('78)	22.50	.60
a.		Imperf.	95.00	
b.		15c blue, *bluish*	450.00	15.00
93	A15	25c blk, *red* ('78)	1,075.	25.00
a.		Imperf.	675.00	
94	A15	35c blk, *yel* ('78)	525.00	35.00
a.		35c blk, *yel org*	525.00	35.00
b.		Imperf.	250.00	
95	A15	40c red, *straw* ('80)	90.00	2.10
a.		Imperf.	250.00	
96	A15	5fr vio, *lav*	450.00	70.00
a.		Imperf.	750.00	
b.		5fr red lilac, *lavender*	650.00	90.00

Beware of French Colonies #38-40, 42, 44.

1879-90

97	A15	3c gray, *grysh* ('80)	4.00	1.75
a.		Imperf.	65.00	

98	A15	20c red, *yel grn*	37.50	4.25
a.		20c red, *deep green* ('84)	70.00	5.75
b.		Imperf.	100.00	
99	A15	25c yel, *straw*	325.00	5.00
a.		Imperf.	250.00	
100	A15	25c blk, *pale rose* ('86)	70.00	1.00
a.		Imperf.	150.00	
101	A15	50c rose, *rose* ('90)	200.00	2.75
a.		50c carmine, *rose*	225.00	3.25
102	A15	75c dp vio, *org* ('90)	200.00	32.50
a.		75c deep violet, *yellow*	275.00	45.00
		Nos. 97-102 (6)	836.50	47.25

Beware of French Colonies #43.

1892
Quadrille Paper

103	A15	15c blue	17.00	.80
a.		Imperf.	175.00	

1898-1900
Ordinary Paper

104	A15	5c yel grn	16.00	1.25
a.		Imperf.	82.50	

Type I

105	A15	5c yel grn	14.00	1.25
a.		Imperf.	550.00	
106	A15	10c blk, *lavender*	25.00	3.00
a.		Imperf.	250.00	
107	A15	50c car, *rose*	250.00	40.00
108	A15	2fr brn, *azure* ('00)	140.00	50.00
b.		Imperf.	2,400.	
		Nos. 104-108 (5)	445.00	95.50

See No. 226.
Reprints of A15, type II, were made in 1887 and left imperf. See note after No. 37. Value for set of 27, $4,000.

Liberty, Equality, Fraternity
A16

"The Rights of Man"
A17

Liberty and Peace
A18

1900-29   Perf. 14x13½

109	A16	1c gray	.55	.40
110	A16	2c violet brn	.70	.25
111	A16	3c orange	.45	.45
a.		3c red	19.00	7.50
112	A16	4c yellow brn	3.25	1.60
113	A16	5c green	2.00	.35
b.		Booklet pane of 10	350.00	
114	A16	7½c lilac ('26)	.60	.40
115	A16	10c lilac ('29)	4.00	.60
116	A17	10c carmine	25.00	1.50
a.		Numerals printed separately	24.00	10.00
117	A17	15c orange	8.00	.60
118	A17	20c brown vio	55.00	9.00
119	A17	25c blue	125.00	1.75
a.		Numerals printed separately	115.00	9.00
120	A17	30c violet	70.00	5.75
121	A18	40c red & pale bl	15.00	.85
122	A18	45c green & bl ('06)	29.00	2.10
123	A18	50c bis brn & gray	100.00	1.65
124	A18	60c vio & ultra ('20)	1.00	1.25
125	A18	1fr claret & ol grn	26.50	.85
126	A18	2fr gray vio & yel	600.00	75.00
127	A18	2fr org & pale bl ('20)	42.50	.60
128	A18	3fr vio & bl ('25)	26.50	7.50
129	A18	3fr brt vio & rose ('27)	55.00	2.75
130	A18	5fr dk bl & buff	82.50	5.00
131	A18	10fr grn & red ('26)	125.00	16.50
132	A18	20fr mag & grn ('26)	200.00	37.50
		Nos. 109-132 (24)	1,597.	174.20

In the 10c and 25c values, the first printings show the numerals to have been impressed by a second operation, whereas, in later printings, the numerals were inserted in the plates. Two operations were used for all 20c and 30c, and one operation for the 15c.

No. 114 was issued precanceled only. Values for precanceled stamps in first column are for those which have not been through the post and have original gum. Values in the second column are for postally used, gumless stamps.

See Offices in China Nos. 34, 40-44, Offices in Crete 1-5, 10-15, Offices in Egypt, Alexandria 16-20, 26-30, 77, 84-86, Port Said 18-22, 28-32, 83, 90-92, Offices in Turkish Empire 21-26, 31-33, Cavalle 9, Dedeagh 9.

For overprints and surcharge see Nos. 197, 246, C1-C2, M1, P7. Offices in China 57, 62-65, 71, 73, 75, 83-85, J14, J27, Offices in Crete 17-20, Offices in Egypt, Alexandria 31-32, 34-35, 40-48, 57-64, 66, 71-73, Port Said

33, 35-40, 43, 46-57, 59, 65-71, 73, 78-80, Offices in Turkish Empire 35-38, 47-49, Cavalle 13-15, Dedeagh 16-18, Offices in Zanzibar 39, 45-49, 55, Offices in Morocco 11-15, 20-22, 26-29, 35-41, 49-54, 72-76, 84-85, 87-89, B6.

Imperf.

109a	A16	1c	62.50	
110a	A16	2c	75.00	60.00
111b	A16	3c	62.50	
112a	A16	4c	160.00	
113a	A16	5c	82.50	
116b	A17	10c #116 or 116a	275.00	140.00
117a	A17	15c	200.00	175.00
119b	A17	25c #119 or 119a	550.00	
121a	A18	40c	225.00	160.00
122a	A18	45c	300.00	
123a	A18	50c	425.00	375.00
124a	A18	60c	575.00	
125a	A18	1fr	275.00	225.00
126a	A18	2fr Without gum	1,450.	
127a	A18	2fr	525.00	
128a	A18	3fr	800.00	500.00
129a	A18	3fr	475.00	
130a	A18	5fr	1,050.	

Flat Plate & Rotary Press
The following stamps were printed by both flat plate and rotary press: Nos. 109-113, 144-146, 163, 166, 168, 170, 177-178, 185, 192 and P7.

"Rights of Man"
A19

Sower
A20

1902

133	A19	10c rose red	26.50	.90
134	A19	15c pale red	11.00	.60
135	A19	20c brown violet	82.50	14.00
136	A19	25c blue	100.00	2.25
137	A19	30c lilac	250.00	14.50
		Nos. 133-137 (5)	470.00	32.25

Imperf.

133a	A19	10c rose red	450.00	275.00
134a	A19	15c pale red	450.00	325.00
135a	A19	20c brown violet	800.00	475.00
136a	A19	25c blue	950.00	625.00
137a	A19	30c lilac	1,100.	675.00

See Offices in China Nos. 35-39, Offices in Crete 6-10, Offices in Egypt, Alexandria 21-25, 81-82, Port Said 23-27, 87-88, Offices in Turkish Empire 26-30, Cavalle 10-11, Dedeagh 10-11.

For overprints and surcharges see Nos. M2, Offices in China 45, 58-61, 66-70, 76-82, J15-J16, J28-J30, Offices in Crete 16, Offices in Egypt, Alexandria 33, 36-39, 49-50, 52-56, 65, 67-70, B1-B4, Port Said 34, 41-42, 44-45, 57, 60-64, 77, 74-77, B1-B4, Offices in Turkish Empire 34, 39, Cavalle 12, Dedeagh 15, Offices in Zanzibar 40-44, 56-59, Offices in Morocco 16-19, 30-34, 42-48, 77-83, 86, B1-B5, B7, B9.

1903-38

138	A20	10c rose	8.00	.40
139	A20	15c slate grn	4.00	.25
b.		Booklet pane of 10	450.00	
140	A20	20c violet brn	67.50	1.90
141	A20	25c dull blue	75.00	1.40

142	A20	30c violet	175.00	5.25
143	A20	45c lt violet ('26)	6.00	1.90
144	A20	50c dull blue ('21)	27.50	1.40
145	A20	50c gray grn ('26)	6.25	1.25
146	A20	50c vermilion ('26)	1.25	.25
a.		Booklet pane of 10	40.00	
147	A20	50c grnsh bl ('38)	1.00	.35
148	A20	60c lt vio ('24)	6.25	2.10
149	A20	65c rose ('24)	3.00	1.75
150	A20	65c gray grn ('27)	6.50	2.10
151	A20	75c rose lil ('26)	5.25	.60
152	A20	80c ver ('25)	26.50	9.50
153	A20	85c ver ('24)	13.50	3.25
154	A20	1fr dull blue ('26)	6.00	.75
		Nos. 138-154 (17)	438.50	34.40
		Set, never hinged	940.00	

See Nos. 941, 942A. For surcharges and overprints see Nos. 229-230, 232-233, 236, 256, B25, B29, B32, B36, B40, M3-M4, M6, Offices in Turkish Empire 46, 54.

Imperf.

138a	A20	10c	175.00	
139a	A20	15c	140.00	55.00
140a	A20	20c	300.00	160.00
141a	A20	25c	350.00	
142a	A20	30c	625.00	
144a	A20	50c	140.00	
145a	A20	50c	125.00	
146b	A20	50c Without gum	70.00	
147a	A20	50c	67.50	
149a	A20	65c	300.00	
151a	A20	75c	450.00	
154a	A20	1fr	1,000.	

Ground A21

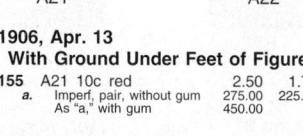
No Ground A22

1906, Apr. 13
With Ground Under Feet of Figure

155	A21	10c red	2.50	1.75
a.		Imperf., pair, without gum	275.00	225.00
		As "a," with gum	450.00	

1906-37

TEN AND THIRTY-FIVE CENTIMES
Type I — Numerals and letters of the inscriptions thin.
Type II — Numerals and letters thicker.

No Ground Under the Feet

156	A22	1c olive bis ('33)	.20	.30
157	A22	2c dk green ('33)	.20	.30
158	A22	3c ver ('33)	.20	.30
159	A22	5c green ('07)	1.50	.25
a.		Imperf., pair	40.00	30.00
b.		Booklet pane of 10	100.00	
160	A22	5c orange ('21)	1.25	.30
a.		Booklet pane of 10	72.50	
161	A22	5c cerise ('34)	.20	.25
162	A22	10c red (II) ('07)	1.50	.25
a.		Imperf., pair	37.50	115.00
b.		10c red (I) ('06)	8.25	1.00
c.		As #162b, imperf., pair	37.50	115.00
d.		Booklet pane of 10 (I)	125.00	
e.		Booklet pane of 10 (II)	75.00	
f.		Booklet pane of 6 (II)	240.00	
163	A22	10c grn (II) ('21)	1.00	.55
a.		10c green (I) ('27)	32.50	37.50
b.		Booklet pane of 10 (II, "Phena")	350.00	
c.		Booklet pane of 10 (I, "Mineraline")	3,200.	
164	A22	10c ultra ('32)	1.40	.25
165	A22	15c red brn ('26)	.25	.20
a.		Booklet pane of 10	27.50	
166	A22	20c brown	3.00	.65
a.		Imperf., pair	82.50	100.00
b.		20c black brown	6.00	2.00
167	A22	20c red vio ('26)	.25	.25
a.		Booklet pane of 10	7.50	
168	A22	25c blue	2.40	.25
a.		Booklet pane of 10	37.50	
b.		Imperf, pair (dark blue)	45.00	60.00
169	A22	25c yel brown ('27)	.20	.20
a.		25c red brown	.30	.20
170	A22	30c orange	13.50	1.40
a.		Imperf, pair	200.00	175.00
171	A22	30c red ('21)	6.50	2.25
172	A22	30c cerise ('25)	1.25	.80
a.		Booklet pane of 10	13.50	
b.		Imperf, pair	575.00	
173	A22	30c lt blue ('25)	3.75	.60
a.		Booklet pane of 10	35.00	
b.		Imperf, pair	2,200.	
174	A22	30c cop red ('37)	.25	.30
a.		Booklet pane of 10	9.00	
175	A22	35c vio (II) ('26)	8.25	.90
a.		Imperf, pair	150.00	120.00
b.		35c violet (I) ('06)	150.00	7.50
c.		As "b," Imperf, pair, without gum	575.00	
176	A22	35c grn ('37)	.50	.55
a.		Imperf, pair	750.00	
177	A22	40c violet ('25)	1.40	.55
a.		Booklet pane of 10	30.00	
178	A22	40c ver ('26)	2.50	.80
a.		Booklet pane of 10	25.00	
179	A22	40c violet ('27)	2.00	.90
180	A22	40c lt ultra ('28)	1.25	.50
181	A22	1.05fr ver ('25)	9.50	5.25
182	A22	1.10fr cerise ('27)	11.50	2.50

183	A22	1.40fr cerise ('26)	20.00	22.50
184	A22	2fr Prus grn ('31)	14.00	1.75
		Nos. 156-184 (29)	109.70	45.85
		Set, never hinged	225.00	

The 10c and 35c, type I, were slightly retouched by adding thin white outlines to the sack of grain, the underside of the right arm and the back of the skirt. It is difficult to distinguish the retouches except on clearly-printed copies. The white outlines were made stronger on the stamps of type II.

Stamps of types A16, A18, A20 and A22 were printed in 1916-20 on paper of poor quality, usually grayish and containing bits of fiber. This is called G. C. (Grande Consommation) paper.

Nos. 160, 162b, 163, 175b and 176 also exist imperf.

See Nos. 241-241b. For surcharges and overprint see Nos. 227-228, 234, 238, 240, 400, B1, B24, B28, B31, B35, B37, B39, B41, M5, P8, Offices in Turkish Empire 40-45, 52, 55.

Louis Pasteur — A23

1923-26

185	A23	10c green	.55	.30
a.		Booklet pane of 10	15.00	
186	A23	15c green ('24)	1.40	.30
187	A23	20c green ('26)	2.75	.90
188	A23	30c red	.90	1.50
189	A23	30c green ('26)	.55	.50
190	A23	45c red ('24)	1.90	2.10
191	A23	50c blue	4.50	.50
192	A23	75c blue ('24)	3.75	1.00
a.		Imperf., pair	250.00	
193	A23	90c red ('26)	11.00	3.50
194	A23	1fr blue ('25)	21.00	.50
195	A23	1.25fr blue ('26)	25.00	8.00
196	A23	1.50fr blue ('26)	5.25	.50
		Nos. 185-196 (12)	78.55	19.60
		Set, never hinged	150.00	

Nos. 185, 188 and 191 were issued to commemorate the cent. of the birth of Pasteur.

For surcharges and overprint see Nos. 231, 235, 257, B26, B30, B33, C4.

No. 125 Overprinted in Blue

1923, June 15

197	A18	1fr claret & ol grn	400.00	440.00
		Never hinged	825.00	

Allegory of Olympic Games at Paris
A24

The Trophy
A25

Milo of Crotona — A26

Victorious Athlete — A27

1924, Apr. 1   Perf. 14x13½, 13½x14

198	A24	10c gray grn & yel grn	2.25	1.25
199	A25	25c rose & dk rose	3.00	.90

200	A26	30c brn red & blk	9.50	11.00
201	A27	50c ultra & dk bl	26.00	5.75
		Nos. 198-201 (4)	40.75	18.80
		Set, never hinged	125.00	

Imperf Singles

198a	A24	10c	1,000.	
199a	A25	25c	1,000.	725.
200a	A26	30c	1,000.	1,000.
201a	A27	50c	1,000.	

8th Olympic Games, Paris.

Pierre de Ronsard
(1524-85), Poet — A28

1924, Oct. 6   *Perf. 14x13½*

| 219 | A28 | 75c blue, *bluish* | 1.90 | 1.40 |
| | | Never hinged | 2.75 | |

"Light and
Liberty"
Allegory
A29

Majolica Vase — A30

Potter
Decorating
Vase — A31

Terrace of
Château
A32

1924-25   *Perf. 14x13½, 13½x14*

220	A29	10c dk grn & yel ('25)	.55	.75
221	A30	15c ind & grn ('25)	.55	.85
a.		Imperf.	375.00	
		Never hinged	600.00	
222	A31	25c vio brn & garnet	.80	.50
223	A32	25c gray bl & vio ('25)	1.60	.65
a.		Imperf.	425.00	150.00
		Never hinged	700.00	
224	A31	75c indigo & ultra	3.50	2.25
225	A29	75c dk bl & lt bl ('25)	18.00	6.50
a.		Imperf.	375.00	
		Never hinged	600.00	
		Nos. 220-225 (6)	25.00	11.50
		Set, never hinged	52.50	

Intl. Exhibition of Decorative Modern Arts at Paris, 1925.

Philatelic Exhibition Issue
Souvenir Sheet

A32a

1925, May 2   *Perf. 14x13½*

226	A32a	Sheet of 4, A15 II	1,100.	1,100.
		Never hinged	3,750.	
a.		Imperf. sheet	5,000.	1,750.
		Never hinged	7,750.	
b.		5fr carmine, perf.	125.00	140.00
		Never hinged	225.00	
c.		5fr carmine, imperf.	900.00	
		Never hinged	1,325.	

These were on sale only at the Intl. Phil. Exhib., Paris, May, 1925. Size: 140x220mm.

Nos. 148-149, 152-153,
173, 175, 181, 183,
192, 195 Surcharged

1926-27

227	A22	25c on 30c lt bl	.20	.50
a.		Pair, one without surcharge	1,050.	925.00
228	A22	25c on 35c violet	.20	.50
a.		Double surcharge	525.00	350.00
b.		Pair, one without surcharge	550.00	925.00
229	A20	50c on 60c lt vio ('27)	1.40	1.10
a.		Pair, one without surcharge	525.00	925.00
230	A20	50c on 65c rose ('27)	.75	.55
a.		Inverted surcharge	1,225.	1,400.
b.		Pair, one without surcharge	675.00	925.00
231	A23	50c on 75c blue	3.25	1.50
232	A20	50c on 80c ver ('27)	1.25	1.10
a.		Pair, one without surcharge	475.00	925.00
233	A20	50c on 85c ver ('27)	2.25	1.00
234	A22	50c on 1.05fr ver	1.25	.75
a.		Pair, one without surcharge	475.00	925.00
235	A23	50c on 1.25fr blue	2.75	2.25
a.		Pair, one without surcharge	525.00	925.00
236	A20	55c on 60c lt vio	125.00	52.50
238	A22	90c on 1.05fr ver ('27)	2.25	2.75
a.		Pair, one without surcharge	1,000.	925.00
240	A22	1.10fr on 1.40fr cer	1.00	1.10
a.		Pair, one without surcharge	575.00	925.00
		Nos. 227-240 (12)	141.55	65.60
		Set, never hinged	275.00	

Issue dates: Nos. 229-230, 232-234, 1927. No. 236 is known only precanceled. See second note after No. 132.

Nos. 229, 230, 234, 238 and 240 have three bars instead of two. The 55c surcharge has thinner, larger numerals and a rounded "c." Width, including bars, is 17mm, instead of 13mm.

The 55c was used only precanceled at the Magasins du Louvre department store in Paris, August 1926.

Strasbourg Exhibition Issue
Souvenir Sheet

A32b

1927, June 4

241	A32b	Sheet of 2	1,000.	1,000.
		Never hinged	2,300.	
a.		5fr light ultra (A22)	200.00	225.00
		Never hinged	300.00	
b.		10fr carmine rose (A22)	200.00	225.00
		Never hinged	300.00	

Sold at the Strasbourg Philatelic Exhibition as souvenirs. Size: 111x140mm.

Marcelin Berthelot
(1827-1907), Chemist
and Statesman — A33

1927, Sept. 7

| 242 | A33 | 90c dull rose | 1.90 | .60 |
| | | Never hinged | 3.00 | |

For surcharge see No. C3.

Lafayette, Washington, S. S. Paris and
Airplane "Spirit of St. Louis" — A34

1927, Sept. 15

243	A34	90c dull red	1.25	1.75
a.		Value omitted	2,000.	1,725.
244	A34	1.50fr deep blue	4.00	2.50
a.		Value omitted	1,450.	
		Set, never hinged	10.00	

Visit of American Legionnaires to France, September, 1927. Exist imperf.

Joan of Arc — A35

1929, Mar.

245	A35	50c dull blue	1.90	.20
		Never hinged	2.75	
a.		Booklet pane of 10	50.00	
b.		Imperf.	140.00	

500th anniv. of the relief of Orleans by the French forces led by Joan of Arc.

No. 127 Overprinted in Blue

1929, May 18
246 A18 2fr org & pale bl   600.00   600.00
      Never hinged   1,325.

Sold exclusively at the Intl. Phil. Exhib., Le Havre, May, 1929, for 7fr, which included a 5fr admission ticket.

Excellent counterfeits of No. 246 exist.

Reims Cathedral — A37

Die I, II, III   Die IV

Die I   Die II   Die III

Die I — The window of the 1st turret on the left is made of 2 lines. The horizontal line of the frame surrounding 3F is not continuous.
Die II — Same as Die I but the line under 3F is continuous.
Die III — Same as Die II but there is a deeply cut line separating 3 and F.
Die IV — Same as Die III but the window of the first turret on the left is made of three lines.

Mont-Saint-Michel — A38

Die I   Die II

Die I — The line at the top of the spire is broken.
Die II — The line is unbroken.

Port of La Rochelle A39

Dies I & II   Die III

Die I — The top of the "E" of "POSTES" has a serif. The oval of shading inside the "0" of "10 fr" and the outer oval are broken at their bases.
Die II — The same top has no serif. Interior and exterior of "0" broken as in Die I.
Die III — Top of "E" has no serif. Interior and exterior of "0" complete.

Pont du Gard, Nimes A40

Dies I & II

Die III

Die I — Shading of the first complete arch in the left middle tier is made of horizontal lines. Size 36x20¾mm. Perf. 13½.
Die II — Same, size 35½x21mm. Perf. 11.
Die III — Shading of same arch is made of three diagonal lines. Thin paper. Perf. 13.

1929-33   Engr.   Perf. 11, 13, 13½
247 A37 3fr dk gray
              ('30) (I)   62.50   2.40
      Never hinged   115.00
247A A37 3fr dk gray
              ('30) (II)   125.00   3.50
      Never hinged   200.00
247B A37 3fr dk gray
              ('30) (III)   375.00   24.00
      Never hinged   600.00
248 A37 3fr bluish sl
              ('31) (IV)   60.00   2.40
      Never hinged   115.00
249 A38 5fr brn ('30) (I)   24.00   4.25
      Never hinged   40.00
250 A38 5fr brn ('31)
              (II)   21.00   .75
      Never hinged   32.50
251 A39 10fr lt ultra (I)   95.00   15.00
      Never hinged   160.00
251A A39 10fr ultra (II)   140.00   26.00
      Never hinged   225.00
252 A39 10fr dk ultra
              ('33) (III)   70.00   6.50
      Never hinged   140.00
253 A40 20fr red brown
              (I)   275.00   40.00
      Never hinged   500.00
254 A40 20fr brt red brn
              ('30) (II)   1,000.   350.00
      Never hinged   1,650.
254A A40 20fr org brn
              ('31) (III)   250.00   35.00
      Never hinged   450.00
      Nos. 247-254A (12)   2,497. 509.40

View of Algiers A41

1929, Jan. 1   Typo.
255 A41 50c blue & rose red   2.40   .50
      Never hinged   5.00

Cent. of the 1st French settlement in Algeria.

Nos. 146 and 196 Overprinted

1930, Apr. 23   Perf. 14x13½
256 A20 50c vermilion   3.00   3.25
257 A23 1.50fr blue   20.00   14.50
      Set, never hinged   47.50

Intl. Labor Bureau, 48th Congress, Paris.

Colonial Exposition Issue

Fachi Woman — A42

French Colonials A43

1930-31   Typo.   Perf. 14x13½
258 A42 15c gray black   1.10   .30
259 A42 40c dark brown   2.40   .30
260 A42 50c dark red   .65   .20
a.   Booklet pane of 10   12.50
261 A42 1.50fr deep blue   9.00   .65

Perf. 13½
Photo.
262 A43 1.50fr dp blue ('31) 45.00   2.75
      Nos. 258-262 (5)   58.15   4.20
      Set, never hinged   90.00

No. 260 has two types: type 1 shows four short downward hairlines near top of head, type 2 has no lines. Booklet stamps are type 2.

Arc de Triomphe A44

1931   Engr.   Perf. 13
263 A44 2fr red brown   40.00   1.25
      Never hinged   80.00

Peace with Olive Branch — A45

1932-39   Typo.   Perf. 14x13½
264 A45 30c dp green   1.00   .55
265 A45 40c brt violet   .30   .30
266 A45 45c yellow brown   1.75   1.00
267 A45 50c rose red   .20   .25
a.   Imperf., pair   140.00
b.   Booklet pane of 10   5.50
268 A45 55c dull vio   .60   .25
269 A45 60c ocher ('37)   .30   .25
270 A45 65c violet brown   .50   .50
271 A45 65c brt ultra ('37) .25   .20
a.   Booklet pane of 10   7.00
272 A45 75c olive green   .20   .30
273 A45 80c orange ('38)   .20   .25
274 A45 90c dk red   32.50   2.00
275 A45 90c brt green ('38) .20   .20
276 A45 90c ultra ('38)   .90   .20
a.   Booklet pane of 10   8.50
277 A45 1fr orange   3.25   .25
278 A45 1fr rose pink ('38) 3.25   .25
279 A45 1.25fr brown ol   75.00   4.75
280 A45 1.25fr rose car ('39) 1.90 2.25
281 A45 1.40fr brt red vio
              ('39)   5.75   5.25
282 A45 1.50fr deep blue   .30   .30
283 A45 1.75fr magenta   4.00   .50
      Nos. 264-283 (20)   132.35   20.00
      Set, never hinged   275.00

The 50c is found in 4 types, differing in the lines below belt and size of "c."

For surcharges and overprints see Nos. 298, 333, 401-403, 405-409, M7-M9, S1.

Le Puy-en-Velay — A46

1933   Engr.   Perf. 13
290 A46 90c rose   3.00   1.10
      Never hinged   5.75

Aristide Briand A47

Paul Doumer A48

Victor Hugo — A49

1933, Dec. 11   Typo.   Perf. 14x13½
291 A47 30c blue green   17.00   8.00
292 A48 75c red violet   27.50   1.90
293 A49 1.25fr claret   6.00   2.25
      Nos. 291-293 (3)   50.50   12.15
      Set, never hinged   110.00

Dove and Olive Branch A50

Joseph Marie Jacquard A51

1934, Feb. 20
294 A50 1.50fr ultra   50.00   15.00
      Never hinged   95.00

1934, Mar. 14   Engr.   Perf. 14x13
295 A51 40c blue   3.00   1.10
      Never hinged   4.50

Jacquard (1752-1834), inventor of an improved loom for figured weaving.

Jacques Cartier A52

1934, July 18   Perf. 13
296 A52 75c rose lilac   30.00   2.25
297 A52 1.50fr blue   50.00   4.25
      Set, never hinged   210.00

Cartier's discovery of Canada, 400th anniv.

No. 279 Surcharged

1934, Nov.   Perf. 14x13½
298 A45 50c on 1.25fr brn ol 3.75   .65
      Never hinged   7.00

Catalogue values for unused stamps in this section, from this point to the end of the section, are for Never Hinged items.

Breton River Scene A53

1935, Feb.   Engr.   Perf. 13
299 A53 2fr blue green   70.00   1.00
      Hinged   32.50

S. S. Normandie A54

1935, Apr.
300 A54 1.50fr dark
              blue   29.00   2.00
      Hinged   14.00
a.   1.50fr pale blue ('36) 145.00 19.00
      Hinged   55.00
b.   1.50fr blue green
              ('36)   30,000. 12,500.

c.   Hinged   *19,000.*
    1.50fr turquoise ('36)   400.00   40.00
    Hinged   275.00

Maiden voyage of the transatlantic steamship, the "Normandie."

Benjamin Delessert A55

1935, May 20
301 A55 75c blue green   42.50   1.75
    Hinged   15.00

Opening of the International Savings Bank Congress, May 20, 1935.

View of St. Trophime at Arles A56   Victor Hugo (1802-85) A57

1935, May 3
302 A56 3.50fr dark brown   70.00   4.25
    Hinged   27.50

1935, May 30   *Perf. 14x13*
303 A57 1.25fr magenta   8.25   2.00
    Hinged   4.00

Cardinal Richelieu — A58   Jacques Callot — A59

1935, June 12   *Perf. 13*
304 A58 1.50fr deep rose   70.00   1.75
    Hinged   20.00

Tercentenary of the founding of the French Academy by Cardinal Richelieu.

1935, Nov.   *Perf. 14x13*
305 A59 75c red   19.00   .75
    Hinged   10.00

300th anniv. of the death of Jacques Callot, engraver.

André Marie Ampère (1775-1836), Scientist, by Louis Boilly — A60

1936, Feb. 27   *Perf. 13*
306 A60 75c brown   37.50   2.00
    Hinged   17.50

Windmill at Fontvielle, Immortalized by Daudet — A61

1936, Apr. 27
307 A61 2fr ultra   5.75   .40
    Hinged   3.00

Publication, in 1866, of Alphonse Daudet's "Lettres de mon Moulin," 75th anniv.

Pilâtre de Rozier and his Balloon A62

1936, June 4
308 A62 75c Prus blue   37.50   2.75
    Hinged   19.00

150th anniversary of the death of Jean Francois Pilâtre de Rozier, balloonist.

Rouget de Lisle — A63

"La Marseillaise" — A64

1936, June 27
309 A63 20c Prus green   5.75   2.00
    Hinged   3.25
310 A64 40c dark brown   11.50   3.25
    Hinged   5.50

Cent. of the death of Claude Joseph Rouget de Lisle, composer of "La Marseillaise."

Canadian War Memorial at Vimy Ridge A65

1936, July 26
311 A65   75c henna brown   25.00   2.00
    Hinged   9.50
312 A65 1.50fr dull blue   32.50   9.50
    Hinged   16.00

Unveiling of the Canadian War Memorial at Vimy Ridge, July 26, 1936.

A66

Jean Léon Jaurès A67

1936, July 30
313 A66   40c red brown   5.75   1.40
    Hinged   4.00
314 A67 1.50fr ultra   29.00   3.75
    Hinged   13.00

Assassination of Jean Léon Jaurès (1859-1914), socialist and politician.

Herald — A68

Allegory of Exposition A69

1936, Sept. 15   *Typo.*   *Perf. 14x13½*
315 A68   20c brt violet   1.00   .50
    Hinged   .30
316 A68   30c Prus green   4.00   1.75
    Hinged   2.40
317 A68   40c ultra   2.50   .50
    Hinged   1.00
318 A68   50c red orange   2.25   .25
    Hinged   1.00
319 A69   90c carmine   25.00   7.50
    Hinged   11.00
320 A69 1.50fr ultra   67.50   4.00
    Hinged   30.00
    Nos. 315-320 (6)   102.25   14.50

Publicity for the 1937 Paris Exposition.

"Peace" A70

1936, Oct. 1   *Engr.*   *Perf. 13*
321 A70 1.50fr blue   27.50   4.00
    Hinged   12.50

Skiing A71

1937, Jan. 18
322 A71 1.50fr dark blue   14.00   1.75
    Hinged   7.00

Intl. Ski Meet at Chamonix-Mont Blanc.

Pierre Corneille, Portrait by Charles Le Brun — A72

1937, Feb. 15
323 A72 75c brown carmine   3.75   1.40
    Hinged   1.90

300th anniv. of the publication of "Le Cid."

Paris Exposition Issue

Exposition Allegory A73

1937, Mar. 15
324 A73 1.50fr turq blue   4.00   1.25
    Hinged   2.25

Jean Mermoz (1901-36), Aviator A74

Memorial to Mermoz — A75

1937, Apr. 22
325 A74 30c dk slate green   1.00   .55
    Hinged   .50
326 A75   3fr dark violet   13.50   3.75
    Hinged   6.25
a.   3fr violet   15.00   4.50
    Hinged   6.75

Electric Train A76

Streamlined Locomotive A77

1937, May 31
327 A76 30c dk green   1.40   1.75
    Hinged   1.00
328 A77 1.50fr dk ultra   15.00   8.25
    Hinged   7.25

13th International Railroad Congress.

Intl. Philatelic Exhibition Issue
Souvenir Sheet

Ceres Type A1 of 1849-50 — A77a

1937, June 18   *Typo.*   *Perf. 14x13½*
329 A77a   Sheet of 4   700.00   300.00
    Lightly hinged in margins   360.00
a.   5c ultra & dark brown   90.00   47.50
b.   15c red & rose red   90.00   47.50
c.   30c ultra & rose red   90.00   47.50
d.   50c red & dark brown   90.00   47.50
e.   Sheet of 4, imperf   3,000.
    Lightly hinged in margins   2,350.

Issued in sheets measuring 150x220mm. The sheets were sold only at the exhibition in Paris, a ticket of admission being required for each sheet purchased.

René Descartes, by Frans Hals — A78

1937, June   **Engr.**   *Perf. 13*
Inscribed "Discours sur la Méthode"
330 A78 90c copper red   3.25   1.40
   Hinged   1.90

Inscribed "Discours de la Méthode"
331 A78 90c copper red   11.00   1.75
   Hinged   5.50

3rd centenary of the publication of "Discours de la Méthode" by René Descartes.

France Congratulating USA — A79

1937, Sept. 17
332 A79 1.75fr ultra   4.50   2.00
   Hinged   2.50

150th anniv. of the US Constitution.

No. 277 Surcharged in Red

1937, Oct.   *Perf. 14x13½*
333 A45 80c on 1fr orange   1.90   .85
   Hinged   .80
a.   Inverted surcharge   1,225.
   Hinged   825.00

Mountain Road at Iseran A80

1937, Oct. 4   **Engr.**   *Perf. 13*
334 A80 90c dark green   3.75   .30
   Hinged   1.90

Issued in commemoration of the opening of the mountain road at Iseran, Savoy.

Ceres — A81

1938-40   **Typo.**   *Perf. 14x13½*
335 A81 1.75fr dk ultra   1.40   .55
   Hinged   .55
336 A81 2fr car rose ('39)   .30   .30
   Hinged   .20
337 A81 2.25fr ultra ('39)   15.00   1.10
   Hinged   8.00
338 A81 2.50fr green ('39)   3.00   .50
   Hinged   1.25
339 A81 2.50fr vio blue ('40)   1.25   .75
   Hinged   .65
340 A81 3fr rose lilac ('39)   1.25   .50
   Hinged   .55
   Nos. 335-340 (6)   22.20   3.70

For surcharges see Nos. 397-399.

Léon Gambetta (1838-82), Lawyer and Statesman — A82

1938, Apr. 2   **Engr.**   *Perf. 13*
341 A82 55c dark violet   .55   .40
   Hinged   .35

Arc de Triomphe of Orange A82a

Miners A83   Keep and Gate of Vincennes A86

Palace of the Popes, Avignon A84

Medieval Walls of Carcassonne — A85

Port of St. Malo — A87

1938
342 A82a 2fr brown black   1.75   1.25
      .55
343 A83 2.15fr violet brn   9.50   1.00
   Hinged   4.75
344 A84 3fr car brown   26.50   5.00
   Hinged   12.50
345 A85 5fr deep ultra   1.50   .40
   Hinged   .75
346 A86 10fr brown, *blue*   3.25   1.90
   Hinged   1.50
347 A87 20fr dk blue green   80.00   19.00
   Hinged   37.50
   Nos. 342-347 (6)   122.50   28.55

For surcharges see Nos. 410-413.

Clément Ader, Air Pioneer A88

1938, June 16
348 A88 50fr ultra (thin paper)   150.00   65.00
   Hinged   95.00
a.   50fr dark ultra (thick paper)   175.00   77.50
   Hinged   100.00

For surcharge, see No. 414.

Soccer Players A89

1938, June 1
349 A89 1.75fr dark ultra   29.00   13.50
   Hinged   13.50

World Cup Soccer Championship.

Costume of Champagne Region — A90   Jean de La Fontaine — A91

1938, June 13
350 A90 1.75fr dark ultra   7.50   4.50
      3.75

Tercentenary of the birth of Dom Pierre Pérignon, discoverer of the champagne process.

1938, July 8
351 A91 55c dk blue green   1.00   .80
      .65

Jean de La Fontaine (1621-1695) the fabulist.

Seal of Friendship and Peace, Victoria Tower and Arc de Triomphe A92

1938, July 19
352 A92 1.75fr ultra   1.25   .80
      .65

Visit of King George VI and Queen Elizabeth of Great Britain to France.

Mercury A93   Self-portrait A95

1938-42   **Typo.**   *Perf. 14x13½*
353 A93 1c dark brown ('39)   .20   .20
   Hinged   .20
354 A93 2c slate grn ('39)   .20   .20
   Hinged   .20
355 A93 5c rose   .20   .20
   Hinged   .20
356 A93 10c ultra   .20   .20
   Hinged   .20
357 A93 15c red orange   .20   .20
   Hinged   .20
358 A93 15c orange brn ('39)   1.00   .50
   Hinged   .55
359 A93 20c red violet   .20   .20
   Hinged   .20
360 A93 25c blue green   .20   .20
   Hinged   .20
361 A93 30c rose red ('39)   .20   .20
   Hinged   .20
362 A93 40c dk violet ('39)   .20   .20
   Hinged   .20
363 A93 45c lt green ('39)   .80   .50
   Hinged   .50
364 A93 50c deep blue ('39)   4.00   .40
   Hinged   2.25
365 A93 50c dk green ('41)   .55   .35
   Hinged   .30
366 A93 50c grnsh blue ('42)   .20   .20
   Hinged   .20
367 A93 60c red orange ('39)   .25   .25
   Hinged   .20
368 A93 70c magenta ('39)   .25   .20
   Hinged   .20
369 A93 75c dk org brn ('39)   7.50   2.50
   Hinged   3.75
   Nos. 353-369 (17)   16.35   6.70

No. 366 exists imperforate. See Nos. 455-458. For overprints and surcharge see #404, 499-502.

1939, Mar. 15   **Engr.**   *Perf. 13*
370 A95 2.25fr Prussian blue   8.25   3.50
   Hinged   3.50

Paul Cézanne (1839-1906), painter.

Georges Clemenceau and Battleship Clemenceau — A96

1939, Apr. 18
371 A96 90c ultra   1.00   .75
   Hinged   .50

Laying of the keel of the warship "Clemenceau," Jan. 17, 1939.

Statue of Liberty, French Pavilion, Trylon and Perisphere A97

1939-40
372 A97 2.25fr ultra   17.00   6.50
   Hinged   8.00
373 A97 2.50fr ultra ('40)   22.50   9.50
   Hinged   8.50

New York World's Fair.

Joseph Nicéphore Niepce and Louis Jacques Mandé Daguerre A98

1939, Apr. 24
374 A98 2.25fr dark blue   16.00   7.00
   Hinged   7.00

Centenary of photography.

Iris — A99

Pumping Station at Marly A100

1939-44   **Typo.**   *Perf. 14x13½*
375 A99 80c red brown ('40)   .25   .20
      .20
376 A99 80c yellow grn ('44)   .20   .20
      .20
377 A99 1fr green   1.00   .20
   Hinged   .55
378 A99 1fr crimson ('40)   .40   .35
   Hinged   .20
a.   Booklet pane of 10   7.50
379 A99 1fr grnsh blue ('44)   .20   .20
      .20
380 A99 1.20fr violet ('44)   .20   .20
      .20
381 A99 1.30fr ultra ('40)   .25   .25
      .20
382 A99 1.50fr red org ('41)   .20   .20
      .20
383 A99 1.50fr henna brn ('44)   .20   .20
      .20
384 A99 2fr violet brn ('44)   .20   .20
      .20
385 A99 2.40fr car rose ('44)   .20   .20
      .20
386 A99 3fr orange ('44)   .20   .20
      .20
387 A99 4fr ultra ('44)   .20   .20
      .20
   Nos. 375-387 (13)   3.70   2.80

1939	**Engr.**	**Perf. 13**	
388 A100	2.25fr brt ultra	25.00	5.00
	Hinged	11.00	

France's participation in the International Water Exposition at Liège.

St. Gregory of Tours — A101

1939, June 10

389 A101	90c red	.90	.55
	Hinged	.50	

14th centenary of the birth of St. Gregory of Tours, historian and bishop.

"The Oath of the Tennis Court" by Jacques David A102

1939, June 20

390 A102	90c deep slate green	3.50	1.90
	Hinged	1.90	

150th anniversary of French Revolution.

Cathedral of Strasbourg — A103

1939, June 23

391 A103	70c brown carmine	1.50	1.00
	Hinged	.75	

500th anniv. of the completion of Strasbourg Cathedral.

Porte Chaussée, Verdun A104

1939, June 23

392 A104	90c black brown	1.00	.80
	Hinged	.80	

23rd anniv. of the Battle of Verdun.

View of Pau A105

1939, Aug. 25

393 A105	90c brt rose, *gray bl*	1.25	1.25
	Hinged	.80	

Maid of Languedoc A106

Bridge at Lyons A107

1939

394 A106	70c black, *blue*	.50	.40
	Hinged	.40	
395 A107	90c dull brown vio	1.00	*1.25*
	Hinged	.90	

Imperforates

Nearly all French stamps issued from 1940 onward exist imperforate. Officially 20 sheets, ranging from 25 to 100 subjects, were left imperforate.

Georges Guynemer (1894-1917), World War I Ace — A108

1940, Nov. 7

396 A108	50fr ultra	16.00	9.00
	Hinged	8.00	

Stamps of 1938-39 Surcharged in Carmine

1940-41 **Perf. 14x13½**

397 A81	1fr on 1.75fr dk ultra	.25	.25
		.20	
398 A81	1fr on 2.25fr ultra ('41)	.25	.25
		.20	
399 A81	1fr on 2.50fr grn ('41)	1.40	1.40
	Hinged	.65	
	Nos. 397-399 (3)	1.90	1.90

Stamps of 1932-39 Surcharged in Carmine, Red (#408) or Black (#407)

1940-41 **Perf. 13, 14x13½**

400 A22	30c on 35c grn ('41)	.25	.25
	Hinged	.20	
401 A45	50c on 55c dl vio ('41)	.25	.25
	Hinged	.20	
a.	Inverted surcharge	1,000.	
402 A45	50c on 65c brt ultra ('41)	.20	.20
	Hinged	.20	
403 A45	50c on 75c ol grn ('41)	.25	.25
	Hinged	.20	
404 A93	50c on 75c dk org brn ('41)	.25	.25
	Hinged	.20	
405 A45	50c on 80c org ('41)	.25	.25
	Hinged	.20	
406 A45	50c on 90c ultra ('41)	.20	.20
	Hinged	.20	
a.	Inverted surcharge	550.00	
b.	"05" instead of "50"	9,000.	6,400.
407 A45	1fr on 1.25fr rose car (Bk) ('41)	.25	.25
	Hinged	.20	
408 A45	1fr on 1.40fr brt red vio (R) ('41)	.40	.40
	Hinged	.20	
a.	Double surcharge	1,600.	
409 A45	1fr on 1.50fr dk bl ('41)	1.40	1.40
	Hinged	.20	
410 A83	1fr on 2.15fr vio brn	.40	.40
	Hinged	.25	
411 A85	2.50fon 5fr dp ultra ('41)	.40	.40
	Hinged	.25	
a.	Double surcharge	350.00	190.00
412 A86	5fr on 10fr brn, *bl* ('41)	1.90	1.90
	Hinged	1.00	

---

413 A87	10fr on 20fr dk bl grn ('41)	1.60	1.60
	Hinged	1.00	
414 A88	20fr on 50fr dk ultra (#348a) ('41)	70.00	37.50
	Hinged	29.00	
a.	20fr on 50fr ultra, thin paper (#348)	75.00	50.00
	Nos. 400-414 (15)	78.00	45.50

Issued: #410, 1940; others, 1941

Marshal Pétain A109

Frédéric Mistral A110

1941 **Perf. 13**

415 A109	40c red brown	.40	.40
416 A109	80c turq blue	.55	.55
417 A109	1fr red	.25	.25
418 A109	2.50fr deep ultra	1.50	1.10
	Nos. 415-418 (4)	2.70	2.30

For No. 417 with surcharge, see No. B111.

1941, Feb. 20 **Perf. 14x13**

419 A110	1fr brown lake	.25	.25

Issued in honor of Frédéric Mistral, poet and Nobel prize winner for literature in 1904.

Beaune Hospital A111

View of Angers A112

Ramparts of St. Louis, Aiguesmortes — A113

1941

420 A111	5fr brown black	.40	.25
421 A112	10fr dark violet	.90	.55
422 A113	20fr brown black	1.40	1.00
	Nos. 420-422 (3)	2.70	1.80

Inscribed "Postes Francaises"

1942

Imprint: "FELTESSE" at right

423 A111	15fr brown lake	.65	.55

A114

A115

Marshal Pétain — A116

A117

A118

1941-42 **Typo.** **Perf. 14x13½**

427 A114	20c lilac ('42)	.20	.20
428 A114	30c rose red	.20	.20
429 A114	40c ultra	.20	.20
431 A115	50c dp green	.20	.20
432 A115	60c violet ('42)	.20	.20
433 A115	70c saph ('42)	.20	.20
434 A115	70c orange ('42)	.20	.20
435 A115	80c brown	.25	.25
436 A115	80c emerald ('42)	.20	.20
437 A115	1fr rose red	.20	.20
438 A115	1.20fr red brn ('42)	.20	.20
439 A115	1.50fr rose	.20	.20
440 A116	1.50fr dl red brn ('42)	.20	.20
a.	Booklet pane of 10	2.75	
441 A116	2fr blue grn ('42)	.20	.20
443 A116	2.40fr rose red ('42)	.25	.25
444 A116	2.50fr ultra	.85	.85
445 A116	3fr orange	.20	.20
446 A115	4fr ultra ('42)	.20	.20
447 A115	4.50fr dk green ('42)	1.00	.65
	Nos. 427-447 (19)	5.40	5.05

Nos. 431 to 438 measure 16½x20½mm.

No. 440 was forged by the French Underground ("Defense de la France") and used to frank clandestine journals, etc., from Feb. to June, 1944. The forgeries were ungummed, both perf. 11½ and imperf., with a back handstamp covering six stamps and including the words: "Atelier des Faux."

For surcharge see No. B134.

1942 **Engr.** **Perf. 14x13**

448 A115	4fr brt ultra	.25	.25
449 A115	4.50fr dark green	.25	.25
450 A117	5fr Prus green	.25	.25

Perf. 13
451 A118 50fr black   4.50 4.00
    Nos. 448-451 (4)   5.25 4.75

Nos. 448 and 449 measure 18x21½mm.

Jules Massenet — A119

Stendhal (Marie Henri Beyle) — A120

1942, June 22   Perf. 14x13
452 A119 4fr Prus green   .25 .25

Jules Massenet (1842-1912), composer.

1942, Sept. 14   Perf. 13
453 A120 4fr blk brn & org red   .55 .55

Stendhal (1783-1842), writer.

André Blondel — A121

Town-Hall Belfry, Arras — A122

1942, Sept. 14
454 A121 4fr dull blue   .55 .55

André Eugène Blondel (1863-1938), physicist.

Mercury Type of 1938-42
Inscribed "Postes Françaises"

1942   Perf. 14x13½
455 A93 10c ultra   .20 .20
456 A93 30c rose red   .20 .20
457 A93 40c dark violet   .25 .25
458 A93 50c turq blue   .20 .20
    Nos. 455-458 (4)   .85 .85

1942, Dec. 8   Engr.   Perf. 13
459 A122 10fr green   .25 .25

Coats of Arms

Lyon — A123

1943   Typo.   Perf. 14x13½
460 A123 5fr shown   .40 .40
461 A123 10fr Brittany   .65 .55
462 A123 15fr Provence   1.90 1.40
463 A123 20fr Ile de France   1.60 1.60
    Nos. 460-463 (4)   4.55 3.95

Antoine Lavoisier (1743-94), French Scientist — A127

1943, July 5   Engr.   Perf. 14x13
464 A127 4fr ultra   .25 .25

Lake Lerie and Meije Dauphiné Alps A128

1943, July 5   Perf. 13
465 A128 20fr dull gray grn   .90 .90

Nicolas Rolin, Guigone de Salins and Hospital of Beaune A129

1943, July 21
466 A129 4fr blue   .25 .25

500th anniv. of the founding of the Hospital of Beaune.

Arms of Flanders — A130

1944, Mar. 27   Typo.   Perf. 14x13½
467 A130 5fr shown   .25 .25
468 A130 10fr Languedoc   .25 .25
469 A130 15fr Orleans   .85 .85
470 A130 20fr Normandy   1.25 1.00
    Nos. 467-470 (4)   2.60 2.35

Edouard Branly — A134

Early Postal Car A135

1944, Feb. 21   Engr.   Perf. 14x13
471 A134 4fr ultra   .25 .25

Cent. of the birth of Edouard Branly, electrical inventor.

1944, June 10   Perf. 13
472 A135 1.50fr dark blue green   .85 .65

Cent. of France's traveling postal service.

Chateau de Chenonceaux — A136

Claude Chappe — A137

1944, June 10
473 A136 15fr lilac brown   .65 .55
    a. 15fr black brown   11.50 3.25
    b. 15fr black   100.00 55.00

See No. 496.

1944, Aug. 14   Perf. 14x13
474 A137 4fr dark ultra   .20 .20

150th anniv. of the invention of an optical telegraph by Claude Chappe (1763-1805).

Arc de Triomphe — OS2

Unwmk.
1944, Oct. 9   Litho.   Perf. 11
475 OS2 5c brt red violet   .35 .35
476 OS2 10c lt gray   .35 .35
476A OS2 25c brown   .35 .35
476B OS2 50c olive bis   .50 .50
476C OS2 1fr pck green   .90 .90
476D OS2 1.50fr rose pink   1.90 1.90
476E OS2 2.50fr purple   .90 .90
476F OS2 4fr ultra   1.90 1.90
476G OS2 5fr black   1.90 1.90
476H OS2 10fr yellow org   37.50 35.00
    Nos. 475-476H (10)   46.55 43.05

Nos 475-476H were printed by the U.S. Bureau of Engraving and Printing and were intended to be used by an Allied Military government, which was expected to administer the liberated areas of France. Instead, the Allies recognized the authority of Gen. de Gaulle's Provisional Government over these territories, and these stamps were transferred to the Free French in July, 1944. They were put on sale in liberated areas as the Allied armies advanced, and on Oct. 9, they were officially issued in Paris.

See Nos. 523A-523J.

Gallic Cock A138

Marianne A139

1944   Litho.   Perf. 12
477 A138 10c yellow grn   .20 .20
478 A138 30c dk rose vio   .40 .40
479 A138 40c blue   .20 .20
480 A138 50c dark red   .20 .20
481 A139 60c olive brown   .20 .20
482 A139 70c rose lilac   .20 .20
483 A139 80c yellow grn   1.10 1.10
484 A139 1fr violet   .25 .25
485 A139 1.20fr dp carmine   .25 .25
486 A139 1.50fr deep blue   .20 .20
487 A138 2fr indigo   .20 .20
488 A139 2.40fr red orange   1.50 1.50
489 A139 3fr dp blue grn   .25 .25
490 A139 4fr grnsh blue   .25 .25
491 A139 4.50fr black   .20 .20
492 A139 5fr violet blue   4.50 4.50
493 A138 10fr violet   5.00 5.00
494 A138 15fr olive brown   5.00 5.00
495 A138 20fr dk slate grn   4.50 4.50
    Nos. 477-495 (19)   24.60 24.60

Nos. 477-495 were issued first in Corsica after the Allied landing, and released in Paris Nov. 15, 1944.

Chateau Type Inscribed "RF"
1944, Oct. 30   Engr.   Perf. 13
496 A136 25fr black   .85 .65

Thomas Robert Bugeaud — A141

1944, Nov. 20
497 A141 4fr myrtle green   .25 .25

Battle of Isly, Aug. 14th, 1844.

Church of St. Denis A142

1944, Nov. 20
498 A142 2.40fr brown carmine   .40 .40

800th anniv. of the Church of St. Denis.

Type of 1938-42, Overprinted in Black

Inscribed "Postes Francaises"
1944   Perf. 14x13½
499 A93 10c ultra   .20 .20
500 A93 30c rose red   .20 .20
501 A93 40c dark violet   .20 .20
502 A93 50c grnsh blue   .20 .20
    Nos. 499-502 (4)   .80 .80

The overprint "RF" in various forms, with or without Lorraine Cross, was also applied to stamps of the French State at Lyon and fourteen other cities.

French Forces of the Interior and Symbol of Liberation — A143

1945, Jan.
503 A143 4fr dark ultra   .40 .40

Issued to commemorate the Liberation.

Stamps of the above design, and of one incorporating "FRANCE" in the top panel, were printed by photo. in England during WW II upon order of the Free French Government. They were not issued. There are 3 values in each design; 25c green, 1fr red, 2.50fr blue. Value: set, above design, $100; set inscribed "FRANCE," $500.

Marianne — A144

Perf. 11½x12½
1944-45   Engr.   Unwmk.
504 A144 10c ultra   .20 .20
505 A144 30c bister   .20 .20
506 A144 40c indigo   .20 .20
507 A144 50c red orange   .20 .20
508 A144 60c chalky blue   .20 .20
509 A144 70c sepia   .20 .20
510 A144 80c deep green   .20 .20
511 A144 1fr lilac   .20 .20
512 A144 1.20fr dk ol grn   .20 .20
513 A144 1.50fr rose ('44)   .20 .20
514 A144 2fr dk brown   .20 .20
515 A144 2.40fr red   .20 .20
516 A144 3fr brt ol grn   .20 .20
517 A144 4fr brt ultra   .25 .25
518 A144 4.50fr slate gray   .25 .25
519 A144 5fr brt orange   .25 .25
520 A144 10fr yellow grn   .30 .30
521 A144 15fr lake   .40 .40

522	A144	20fr brown org	1.75	1.50
523	A144	50fr deep purple	3.50	2.50
		Nos. 504-523 (20)	9.30	8.05

The 2.40fr exists imperf. in a miniature sheet of 4 which was not issued. Value: never hinged $3,750; unused $2,750.

Arc de Triomphe Type of 1944

1945, Feb. 12   Litho.   Perf. 11
Denominations in Black

523A	OS2	30c orange	.40	.40
523B	OS2	40c pale gray	.40	.40
523C	OS2	50c olive bis	.40	.40
523D	OS2	60c violet	.40	.40
523E	OS2	80c emerald	.40	.40
523F	OS2	1.20fr brown	.40	.40
523G	OS2	1.50fr vermilion	.40	.40
523H	OS2	2fr yellow	.40	.40
523I	OS2	2.40fr dark rose	.40	.40
523J	OS2	3fr brt red violet	.40	.40
		Nos. 523A-523J (10)	4.00	4.00

Coat of Arms
A145

Ceres
A146

Marianne — A147

1945-47   Typo.   Perf. 14x13½

524	A145	10c brown black	.20	.20
525	A145	30c dk blue green	.20	.20
526	A145	40c lilac rose	.30	.30
527	A145	50c violet blue	.20	.20
528	A146	60c brt ultra	.20	.20
530	A146	80c brt green	.20	.20
531	A146	90c dull grn ('46)	.65	.55
532	A146	1fr rose red	.20	.20
533	A146	1.20fr brown black	.20	.20
534	A146	1.50fr rose lilac	.20	.20
535	A147	1.50fr rose pink	.20	.20
536	A147	2fr myrtle green	.20	.20
536A	A146	2fr lt bl grn ('46)	.85	.65
537	A147	2.40fr scarlet	.40	.40
538	A146	2.50fr brown ('46)	.40	.40
539	A147	3fr sepia	.20	.20
540	A147	3fr deep rose ('46)	.20	.20
541	A147	4fr ultra	.20	.20
541A	A147	4fr violet ('46)	.20	.20
541B	A147	4.50fr ultra ('47)	.20	.20
542	A147	5fr lt green	.25	.20
542A	A147	5fr rose pink ('47)	.20	.20
543	A147	6fr brt ultra	.35	.25
544	A147	6fr crim rose ('46)	1.60	1.10
545	A147	10fr red orange	.65	.55
546	A147	10fr ultra ('46)	1.60	.85
547	A147	15fr brt red vio	3.25	1.90
		Nos. 524-547 (27)	13.50	10.35

No. 531 is known only precanceled. See second note after No. 132.

Due to a reduction of the domestic postage rate, No. 542A was sold for 4.50fr.

See Nos. 576-580, 594-602, 614, 615, 650-654. For surcharges see Nos. 589, 610, 706, Reunion 270-276, 278, 285, 290-291, 293, 295.

1945-46   Engr.   Perf. 14x13

548	A147	4fr dark blue	.25	.25
549	A147	10fr dp blue ('46)	1.25	.55
550	A147	15fr brt red vio ('46)	9.00	2.00
551	A147	20fr blue grn ('46)	1.25	.55
552	A147	25fr red ('46)	9.00	1.50
		Nos. 548-552 (5)	20.75	4.85

Marianne — A148

1945   Engr.   Perf. 13

553	A148	20fr dark green	1.25	1.10
554	A148	25fr violet	1.65	1.25
555	A148	50fr red brown	2.00	2.00
556	A148	100fr brt rose car	12.50	6.25
		Nos. 553-556 (4)	17.40	10.60

CFA

French stamps inscribed or surcharged "CFA" and new value are listed under Réunion at the end of the French listings.

Arms of Metz
A149

Arms of Strasbourg
A150

1945, Mar. 3   Perf. 14x13

557	A149	2.40fr dull blue	.25	.25
558	A150	4fr black brown	.25	.25

Liberation of Metz and Strasbourg.

Costumes of Alsace and Lorraine and Cathedrals of Strasbourg and Metz
A151

1945, May 16   Perf. 13

559	A151	4fr henna brown	.25	.25

Liberation of Alsace and Lorraine.

World Map Showing French Possessions — A152

1945, Sept. 17

560	A152	2fr Prussian blue	.25	.25

No. B193 Surcharged in Black

1946   Perf. 14x13½

561	SP147	3fr on 2fr+1fr red org	.25	.25

Arms of Corsica — A153

1946   Unwmk.   Typo.   Perf. 14x13½

562	A153	10c shown	.20	.20
563	A153	30c Alsace	.20	.20
564	A153	50c Lorraine	.20	.20
565	A153	60c County of Nice	.20	.20
		Nos. 562-565 (4)	.80	.80

For surcharges see Reunion Nos. 268-269.

Reaching for "Peace" — A157

Holding the Dove of Peace — A158

1946, July 29   Engr.   Perf. 13

566	A157	3fr Prussian green	.25	.25
567	A158	10fr dark blue	.25	.25

Peace Conference of Paris, 1946.

Vézelay
A159

Luxembourg Palace — A160

Rocamadour
A161

Pointe du Raz, Finistère
A162

1946   Unwmk.   Perf. 13

568	A159	5fr rose violet	.25	.25
569	A160	10fr dark blue	.25	.25
570	A161	15fr dk violet brn	4.25	.55
571	A162	20fr slate gray	1.25	.25
		Nos. 568-571 (4)	6.00	1.30

See Nos. 591-592. For surcharges see Reunion Nos. 277, 279.

Globe and Wreath — A163

1946, Nov.

572	A163	10fr dark blue	.25	.25

Gen. conf. of UNESCO, Paris, 1946.

Cannes
A164

Stanislas Square, Nancy
A165

1946-48   Engr.   Perf. 13

573	A164	6fr rose red	1.50	.65
574	A165	25fr black brown	4.25	1.25
575	A165	25fr dark blue ('48)	11.50	1.25
		Nos. 573-575 (3)	17.25	2.30

For surcharges see Reunion Nos. 280-281.

Ceres & Marianne Types of 1945

1947   Unwmk.   Typo.   Perf. 14x13½

576	A146	1.30fr dull blue	.20	.20
577	A147	3fr green	1.90	.40
578	A147	3.50fr brown red	.85	.55
579	A147	5fr blue	.25	.25
580	A147	6fr carmine	.25	.20
		Nos. 576-580 (5)	3.45	1.60

Colonnade of the Louvre
A166

La Conciergerie, Paris Prison — A167

La Cité, Oldest Section of Paris
A168

Place de la Concorde
A169

1947, May 7   Engr.   Perf. 13

581	A166	3.50fr chocolate	.40	.40
582	A167	4.50fr dk slate gray	.60	.40
583	A168	6fr red	1.10	1.00
584	A169	10fr bright ultra	1.10	1.00
		Nos. 581-584 (4)	3.20	2.80

12th UPU Cong., Paris, May 7-July 7.

Auguste Pavie — A170

Francois Fénelon — A171

1947, May 30

585	A170	4.50fr sepia	.40	.40

Cent. of the birth of Auguste Pavie, French pioneer in Laos.

1947, July 12

586	A171	4.50fr chocolate	.40	.40

Issued to honor Francois de Salignac de la Mothe-Fénelon, prelate and writer.

Fleur-de-Lis and Double Carrick Bend — A172

1947, Aug. 2   **Unwmk.**
587 A172 5fr brown   .40 .40
6th World Boy Scout Jamboree held at Moisson, Aug. 9th-18th, 1947.

Captured Patriot A173   View of Conques A174

1947, Nov. 10   Engr.   Perf. 13
588 A173 5fr sepia   .40 .35

No. 576 Surcharged in Carmine

1947, Nov.   Typo.   Perf. 14x13½
589 A146 1fr on 1.30fr dull blue   .20 .20

1947, Dec. 18   Engr.   Perf. 13
590 A174 15fr henna brown   4.50 1.00
For surcharge see Reunion No. 282.

Types of 1946-47
1948   **Re-engraved**
591 A160 12fr rose carmine   3.25 .65
592 A160 15fr bright red   .85 .85
593 A174 18fr dark blue   4.50 .40
    Nos. 591-593 (3)   8.60 1.90
"FRANCE" substituted for inscriptions "RF" and "REPUBLIQUE FRANCAISE."

Marianne Type of 1945
1948-49   Typo.   Perf. 14x13½
594 A147 2.50fr brown   2.75 1.25
595 A147 3fr lilac rose   .25 .25
596 A147 4fr lt blue grn   .25 .25
597 A147 4fr brown org   3.00 .90
598 A147 5fr lt blue grn   .85 .25
599 A147 8fr blue   .40 .25
600 A147 10fr brt violet   .25 .20
601 A147 12fr ultra ('49)   3.00 .40
602 A147 15fr crim rose ('49) 1.00 .20
  a. Booklet pane of 10   150.00
    Nos. 594-602 (9)   11.75 3.95
No. 594 known only precanceled. See second note after No. 132.

François René de Chateaubriand — A175

1948, July 3   Engr.   Perf. 13
603 A175 18fr dark blue   .40 .40
Vicomte de Chateaubriand (1768-1848).

Philippe François M. de Hautecloque (Gen. Jacques Leclerc) — A176

1948, July 3   **Unwmk.**
604 A176 6fr gray black   .40 .40
See Nos. 692-692A.

Chaillot Palace A177

A178

1948, Sept. 21
605 A177 12fr carmine rose   .55 .55
606 A178 18fr indigo   .55 .55
Meeting of the UN General Assembly, Paris, 1948.

Genissiat Dam A179

Paul Langevin — A180

1948, Sept. 21
607 A179 12fr carmine rose   .85 .85

1948, Nov. 17   Perf. 14x13
608 A180 5fr shown   .40 .25
609 A180 8fr Jean Perrin   .40 .25
Placing of the ashes of physicists Langevin (1872-1946) and Perrin (1870-1942) in the Pantheon.

No. 580 Surcharged with New Value and Bars in Black
1949, Jan.   Perf. 14x13½
610 A147 5fr on 6fr carmine   .25 .25

Arctic Scene — A181

1949, May 2   Perf. 13
611 A181 15fr indigo   .40 .40
French polar explorations.

Types of 1849 and 1945
1949, May 9   Engr.   Imperf.
612 A1 15fr red   3.25 3.25
613 A1 25fr deep blue   3.25 3.25
        Perf. 14x13
614 A147 15fr red   3.25 3.25
615 A147 25fr deep blue   3.25 3.25
  a. Strip of 4, #612-615 + label 16.50 16.50
    Nos. 612-615 (4)   13.00 13.00
Cent. of the 1st French postage stamps.

Arms of Burgundy — A182

Arms: 50c, Guyenne (Aquitania). 1fr, Savoy. 2fr, Auvergne. 4fr, Anjou.

1949, May 11   Typo.   Perf. 14x13½
616 A182 10c blue, red & yel .20 .20
617 A182 50c blue, red & yel .20 .20
618 A182 1fr brown & red   .55 .40
619 A182 2fr green, yel & red .55 .25
620 A182 4fr blue, red & yel .40 .40
    Nos. 616-620 (5)   1.90 1.45
See Nos. 659-663, 694-699, 733-739, 782-785. For surcharges see Reunion Nos. 283-284, 288-289, 297, 301, 305, 311.

Collegiate Church of St. Barnard and Dauphiné Arms A183

1949, May 14   Engr.   Perf. 13
621 A183 12fr red brown   .40 .40
600th anniv. of France's acquisition of the Dauphiné region.

US and French Flags, Plane and Steamship A184

1949, May 14
622 A184 25fr blue & carmine .65 .65
Franco-American friendship.

Cloister of St. Wandrille Abbey A185

1949, May 18
623 A185 25fr deep ultra   .40 .25
See No. 649. For surcharge see Reunion No. 287.

Type of 1849 Inscribed "1849-1949" in Lower Margin
1949, June 1
624 A1 10fr brown orange   55.00 45.00
  a. Sheet of 10   700.00 500.00
Cent. of the 1st French postage stamp. No. 624 has wide margins, 40x52mm from perforation to perforation. Sold for 110fr, which included cost of admission to the Centenary Intl. Exhib., Paris, June 1949.

Claude Chappe — A186

Jean Racine — A187

15fr, François Arago & André M. Ampère. 25fr, Emile Baudot. 50fr, Gen. Gustave A. Ferrié.

Inscribed: "C.I.T.T. PARIS 1949"
1949, June 13   Unwmk.   Perf. 13
625 A186 10fr vermilion   .90 .85
626 A186 15fr sepia   1.00 .90
627 A186 25fr deep claret   2.50 2.25
628 A186 50fr deep blue   4.50 4.00
    Nos. 625-628 (4)   8.90 8.00
International Telegraph and Telephone Conference, Paris, May-July 1949.

1949
629 A187 12fr sepia   .40 .40
Death of Jean Racine, dramatist, 250th anniv.

Abbey of St. Bertrand de Comminges A188

Meuse Valley, Ardennes A189

Mt. Gerbier de Jonc, Vivarais A190

1949   **Engr.**
630 A188 20fr dark red   .25 .20
631 A189 40fr Prus green   15.00 .30
632 A190 50fr sepia   2.50 .20
    Nos. 630-632 (3)   17.75 .70
For surcharge see Reunion No. 286.

A191

1949, Oct. 18
633 A191 15fr deep carmine   .25 .25
50th anniv. of the Assembly of Presidents of Chambers of Commerce of the French Union.

UPU Allegory A192

1949, Nov. 7
634 A192 5fr dark green   .25 .25
635 A192 15fr deep carmine   .40 .25
636 A192 25fr deep blue   1.25 .90
    Nos. 634-636 (3)   1.90 1.40
UPU, 75th anniversary.

Raymond Poincaré — A193

1950, May 27   Unwmk.   Perf. 13
637 A193 15fr indigo   .35 .25

Charles Péguy and Cathedral at Chartres A194

François Rabelais — A195

1950, June
638 A194 12fr dk brown .40 .25
639 A195 12fr red brown .85 .75

Chateau of Chateaudun — A196

1950, Nov. 25
640 A196 8fr choc & bis brn .70 .45

Madame Récamier A197

Marie de Sévigné A198

1950
641 A197 12fr dark green .65 .40
642 A198 15fr ultra .65 .40

Palace of Fontainbleau — A199

1951, Jan. 20
643 A199 12fr dark brown .90 .75

Jules Ferry — A200

Jean-Baptiste de la Salle — A202

Hands Holding Shuttle A201

1951, Mar. 17
644 A200 15fr bright red .55 .55

1951, Apr. 9
645 A201 25fr deep ultra 1.00 .65
Intl. Textile Exposition, Lille, April-May, 1951.

1951, Apr. 28
646 A202 15fr chocolate .65 .55
300th anniv. of the birth of Jean-Baptiste de la Salle, educator and saint.

Map and Anchor A203

1951, May 12
647 A203 15fr deep ultra .60 .40
50th anniv. of the creation of the French colonial troops.

Vincent d'Indy A204

1951, May 15
648 A204 25fr deep green 2.00 2.00
Vincent d'Indy, composer, birth cent.

Abbey Type of 1949

1951
649 A185 30fr bright blue 5.00 4.25

Marianne Type of 1945-47

1951 Typo. Perf. 14x13½
650 A147 5fr dull violet .50 .20
651 A147 6fr green 6.50 .60
652 A147 12fr red orange .85 .25
653 A147 15fr ultra .35 .20
a. Booklet pane of 10 30.00
654 A147 18fr cerise 16.00 1.40
Nos. 650-654 (5) 24.20 2.65

Professors Nocard, Bouley and Chauveau; Gate at Lyons School A205

1951, June 8 Engr. Perf. 13
655 A205 12fr red violet .60 .55
Issued to honor Veterinary Medicine.

Gen. Picqué, Cols. Roussin and Villemin; Val de Grace Dome A206

1951, June 17 Unwmk.
656 A206 15fr red brown .75 .55
Issued to honor Military Medicine.

St. Nicholas, by Jean Didier — A207

1951, June 23
657 A207 15fr ind, dp claret & org 1.40 1.00

Chateau Bontemps, Arbois A208

1951, June 23
658 A208 30fr indigo 1.00 .25
For surcharge see Reunion No. 296.

Arms Type of 1949

Arms of: 10c, Artois. 50c, Limousin. 1fr, Béarn. 2fr, Touraine. 3fr, Franche-Comté.

1951, June Typo. Perf. 14x13½
659 A182 10c red, vio bl & yel .20 .20
660 A182 50c green, red & blk .20 .20
661 A182 1fr blue, red & yel .25 .25
662 A182 2fr vio bl, red & yel .90 .40
663 A182 3fr red, vio bl & yel .85 .40
Nos. 659-663 (5) 2.40 1.45

Seal of Paris — A209

Maurice Noguès and Globe — A210

Unwmk.

1951, July 7 Engr. Perf. 13
664 A209 15fr dp bl, dk brn & red .65 .40
2,000th anniv. of the founding of Paris.

1951, Oct. 13
665 A210 12fr indigo & blue .90 .85
Maurice Nogues, aviation pioneer.

Charles Baudelaire A211

Poets: 12fr, Paul Verlaine. 15fr, Arthur Rimbaud.

1951, Oct. 27
666 A211 8fr purple .85 .75
667 A211 12fr gray .85 .75
668 A211 15fr dp green .85 .75
Nos. 666-668 (3) 2.55 2.25

Georges Clemenceau, Birth Cent. — A212

1951, Nov. 11
669 A212 15fr black brown .55 .45

Chateau du Clos, Vougeot A213

1951, Nov. 17
670 A213 30fr blk brn & brn 6.25 2.50

Chaillot Palace and Eiffel Tower A214

1951, Nov. 6
671 A214 18fr red 1.10 .60
672 A214 30fr deep ultra 2.00 1.10
Opening of the Geneva Assembly of the United Nations, Paris, Nov. 6, 1951.

Observatory, Pic du Midi — A215

Abbaye aux Hommes, Caen — A216

1951, Dec. 22
673 A215 40fr violet 5.50 .20
674 A216 50fr black brown 5.00 .20
For surcharge see Reunion No. 294.

Marshal Jean de Lattre de Tassigny, 1890-1952 A217

1952, May 8 Unwmk. Perf. 13
675 A217 15fr violet brown 1.00 .45
See No. 717.

Gate of France, Vaucouleurs — A218

1952, May 11
676 A218 12fr brown black 1.25 .90

Flags and Monument at Narvik, Norway A219

1952, May 28
677 A219 30fr violet blue 2.75 2.00
Battle of Narvik, May 27, 1940.

Chateau de Chambord A220

1952, May 30
678 A220 20fr dark purple .45 .20
For surcharge see Reunion No. 292.

Assembly Hall, Strasbourg A221

1952, May 31
679 A221 30fr dark green 7.25 5.25
Issued to honor the Council of Europe.

Monument, Bir-Hacheim Cemetery — A222

1952, June 14
680 A222 30fr rose lake 3.25 2.00
10th anniv. of the defense of Bir-Hacheim.

Abbey of the Holy Cross, Poitiers — A223

1952, June 21
681 A223 15fr bright red .40 .40
14th cent. of the foundation of the Abbey of the Holy Cross at Poitiers.

Leonardo da Vinci, Amboise Chateau and La Signoria, Florence A224

1952, July 9
682 A224 30fr deep ultra 8.00 6.50
Leonardo da Vinci, 500th birth anniv.

Garabit Viaduct A225

1952, July 5
683 A225 15fr dark blue .55 .45

Sword and Military Medals, 1852-1952 A226

Dr. René Laennec A227

1952, July 5
684 A226 15fr choc, grn & yel .50 .40
Cent. of the creation of the Military Medal.

1952, Nov. 7
685 A227 12fr dark green .50 .50

Versailles Gate, Painted by Utrillo A228

1952, Dec. 20
686 A228 18fr violet brown 2.75 1.75
Publicity for the restoration of Versailles Palace. See No. 728.

Mannequin — A229

1953, Apr. 24 Unwmk. Perf. 13
687 A229 30fr blue blk & rose vio .90 .35
Dressmaking industry of France.

Gargantua of François Rabelais A230

Célimène from The Misanthrope A231

Figaro, from the Barber of Seville — A232

Hernani of Victor Hugo — A233

1953
688 A230 6fr dp plum & car .25 .20
689 A231 8fr indigo & ultra .25 .20
690 A232 12fr vio brn & dk grn .25 .20
691 A233 18fr vio brn & blk brn .50 .30
Nos. 688-691 (4) 1.25 .90
For surcharge see Reunion No. 298.

Type of 1948
Inscribed "Général Leclerc Maréchal de France"

1953-54
692 A176 8fr red brown .80 .75
692A A176 12fr dk grn & gray grn ('54) 2.50 1.60
Issued to honor the memory of General Jacques Leclerc.

Map and Cyclists, 1903-1953 A234

1953, July 26
693 A234 12fr red brn, ultra & blk 2.00 1.25
50th anniv. of the Bicycle Tour de France.

Arms Type of 1949
50c, Picardy. 70c, Gascony. 80c, Berri. 1fr, Poitou. 2fr, Champagne. 3fr, Dauphiné.

1953 Typo. Perf. 14x13½
694 A182 50c blue, yel & red .25 .20
695 A182 70c red, blue & yel .25 .20
696 A182 80c blue, red & yel .25 .20
697 A182 1fr black, red & yel .25 .20
698 A182 2fr brown, bl & yel .30 .25
699 A182 3fr red, blue & yel .50 .25
Nos. 694-699 (6) 1.80 1.30

Swimming A235

1953, Nov. 28 Engr. Perf. 13
700 A235 20fr shown 2.00 .25
701 A235 25fr Track 13.00 .55
702 A235 30fr Fencing 2.00 .25
703 A235 40fr Canoe racing 13.00 .55
704 A235 50fr Rowing 7.25 .25
705 A235 75fr Equestrian 32.50 12.00
Nos. 700-705 (6) 69.75 13.85
For surcharges see Reunion Nos. 299-300.

No. 654 Surcharged with New Value and Bars in Black
1954 Perf. 14x13½
706 A147 15fr on 18fr cerise .55 .20

Farm Woman A236

Gallic Cock A237

1954 Typo.
707 A236 4fr blue .25 .20
708 A236 8fr brown red 4.75 1.00
709 A237 12fr cerise 3.00 .65
710 A237 24fr blue green 16.00 4.00
Nos. 707-710 (4) 24.00 5.85
Nos. 707-710 are known only precanceled. See second note after No. 132.
See #833-834, 840-844, 910-913, 939, 952-955. For surcharges see Reunion #324, 326-327.

Tapestry and Gobelin Workshop A238

Entrance to Exhibition Park A239

Designs: 30fr, Book manufacture. 40fr, Porcelain and glassware. 50fr, Jewelry and metalsmith's work. 75fr, Flowers and perfumes.

1954, May 6 Engr. Perf. 13
711 A238 25fr red brn car & blk brn 12.00 .50
712 A238 30fr dk grn & lil gray 2.25 .20
713 A238 40fr dk brn, vio brn & org brn 3.50 .20
714 A238 50fr brt ultra, dl grn & org brn 2.25 .20
715 A238 75fr dp car & magenta 12.00 .95
Nos. 711-715 (5) 32.00 2.05
For surcharges see Reunion Nos. 303-304.

1954, May 22
716 A239 15fr blue & dk car .30 .25
Founding of the Fair of Paris, 50th anniv.

De Lattre Type of 1952
1954, June 5
717 A217 12fr vio bl & indigo 2.00 1.75

Allied Landings A240

1954, June 5
718 A240 15fr scarlet & ultra 1.75 1.00
The 10th anniversary of the liberation.

View of Lourdes A241

Street Corner, Quimper — A242

Views: 8fr, Seine valley, Les Andelys. 10fr, Beach at Royan. 18fr, Cheverny Chateau. 20fr, Beach, Gulf of Ajaccio.

1954
719 A241 6fr ultra, ind & dk grn .40 .30
720 A241 8fr brt blue & dk grn .30 .20
721 A241 10fr aqua & org brn .30 .20
722 A242 12fr rose vio & dk vio .50 .20
723 A241 18fr bl, dk grn & ind 3.25 .90
724 A241 20fr blk brn, bl grn & red brn 2.75 2.00
Nos. 719-724 (6) 7.50 2.00
See No. 873. For surcharges see Reunion Nos. 302, 306-310.

Abbey Ruins, Jumièges A243

St. Philibert Abbey, Tournus A244

1954, June 13
725 A243 12fr vio bl, ind & dk grn 1.50 .90
13th centenary of Abbey of Jumièges.

1954, June 18
726 A244 30fr indigo & blue 6.00 4.00
1st conf. of the Intl. Center of Romance Studies.

View of Stenay
A245

1954, June 26
727 A245 15fr dk brn & org brn .85 .50
Acquisition of Stenay by France, 300th anniv.

Versailles Type of 1952
1954, July 10
728 A228 18fr dp bl, ind & vio brn 9.00 5.50

Villandry Chateau
A246

1954, July 17
729 A246 18fr dk bl & dk bl grn 5.00 3.25

Napoleon Awarding Legion of Honor Decoration
A247

1954, Aug. 14
730 A247 12fr scarlet 1.50 .80
150th anniv. of the 1st Legion of Honor awards at Camp de Boulogne.

Cadets Marching Through Gateway
A248

1954, Aug. 1
731 A248 15fr vio gray, dk bl & car 1.10 1.10
150th anniversary of the founding of the Military School of Saint-Cyr.

Allegory
A249

Duke de Saint-Simon
A250

1954, Oct. 4
732 A249 30fr indigo & choc 6.00 3.50
Issued to publicize the fact that the metric system was first introduced in France.

Arms Type of 1949
Arms: 50c, Maine. 70c, Navarre. 80c, Nivernais. 1fr, Bourbonnais. 2fr, Angoumois. 3fr, Aunis. 5fr, Saintonge.

1954		**Typo.**	**Perf. 14x13½**	
733	A182	50c multicolored	.20	.20
734	A182	70c green, red & yel	.25	.20
735	A182	80c blue, red & yel	.25	.20
736	A182	1fr red, blue & yel	.20	.20
737	A182	2fr black, red & yel	.20	.20
738	A182	3fr brown, red & yel	.20	.20
739	A182	5fr blue & yellow	.20	.20
		Nos. 733-739 (7)	1.50	1.40

1955, Feb. 5 Engr. Perf. 13
740 A250 12fr dk brn & vio brn .70 .60
Louis de Rouvroy, Duke de Saint-Simon (1675-1755).

Allegory and Rotary Emblem
A251

Marianne — A252

1955, Feb. 23
741 A251 30fr vio bl, bl & org 2.25 1.25
50th anniv. of Rotary International.

1955-59		**Typo.**	**Perf. 14x13½**	
751	A252	6fr fawn	2.75	1.75
752	A252	12fr green	3.25	1.25
a.		Bklt. pane of 10 + 2 labels	45.00	
753	A252	15fr carmine	.20	.20
a.		Booklet pane of 10	10.00	
754	A252	18fr green ('58)	.25	.20
755	A252	20fr ultra ('57)	.45	.20
756	A252	25fr rose red ('59)	1.40	.20
a.		Booklet pane of 8	15.00	
b.		Booklet pane of 10	16.00	
		Nos. 751-756 (6)	8.30	3.80

No. 751 was issued in coils of 1,000.
No. 752 was issued in panes of 10 stamps and two labels with marginal instructions for folding to form a booklet.
Nos. 754-755 are found in two types, distinguished by the numerals. On the 18fr there is no serif at left of base of the "1" on the 1st type. The 2nd type has a shorter "1" with no serifs at base. On the 20fr the 2nd type has a well formed "2" and the horiz. lines of the "F" of the denomination are longer and of equal length.
No. 756 also in two types, distinguished by border width. On the 1st type, the border is thicker than the width of the letters. On the 2nd type, the border is thinner than the width of the letters.
For surcharges see Reunion Nos. 330-331.

Philippe Lebon, Inventor of Illuminating Gas
A253

Inventors: 10fr, Barthélemy Thimonnier, sewing machine. 12fr, Nicolas Appert, canned foods. 18fr, Dr. E. H. St. Claire Deville, aluminum. 25fr, Pierre Martin, steel making. 30fr, Bernigaud de Chardonnet, rayon.

1955, Mar. 5			**Engr.**	
757	A253	5fr dk vio bl & bl	.75	.75
758	A253	10fr dk brn & org brn	.90	.90
759	A253	12fr dk green	1.25	1.25
760	A253	18fr dk vio bl & ind	2.90	1.40
761	A253	25fr dk brnsh pur & vio	3.25	1.60
762	A253	30fr rose car & scar	3.25	1.60
		Nos. 757-762 (6)	12.30	7.50

St. Stephen Bridge, Limoges
A254

1955, Mar. 26 Unwmk. Perf. 13
763 A254 12fr yel brn & dk vio brn 1.40 1.10

Gloved Model in Place de la Concorde — A255

1955, Mar. 26
764 A255 25fr blk brn, vio bl & blk .80 .20
French glove manufacturing.

Jean Pierre Claris de Florian
A256

1955, Apr. 2
765 A256 12fr blue green .65 .40
200th anniv. of the birth of Jean Pierre Claris de Florian, fabulist.

Eiffel Tower and Television Antennas
A257

1955, Apr. 16
766 A257 15fr indigo & ultra 1.00 .90
French advancement in television.

Wire Fence and Guard Tower
A258

1955, Apr. 23
767 A258 12fr dk gray bl & brn blk .90 .60
10th anniv. of the liberation of concentration camps.

Electric Train
A259

1955, May 11
768 A259 12fr blk brn & slate bl 2.75 1.25
Issued to publicize the electrification of the Valenciennes-Thionville railroad line.

Jacquemart of Moulins — A260

1955, May 28
769 A260 12fr black brown 1.50 1.25

Jules Verne and Nautilus
A261

1955, June 3
770 A261 30fr indigo 8.00 4.50
50th anniv. of the death of Jules Verne.

Auguste and Louis Lumière and Motion Picture Projector
A262

1955, June 12
771 A262 30fr rose brown 6.00 4.00
Invention of motion pictures, 60th anniv.

Jacques Coeur and His Mansion at Bourges
A263

1955, June 18
772 A263 12fr violet 2.25 1.25
5th centenary of the death of Jacques Coeur (1395?-1456), French merchant.

Corvette "La Capricieuse" — A264

1955, July 9
773 A264 30fr aqua & dk blue 5.50 3.50
Centenary of the voyage of La Capricieuse to Canada.

Bordeaux
A265

Designs: 8fr, Marseille. 10fr, Nice. 12fr, Valentre bridge, Cahors. 18fr, Uzerche. 25fr, Fortifications, Brouage.

1955, Oct. 15				
774	A265	6fr carmine lake	.20	.20
775	A265	8fr indigo	.45	.20
776	A265	10fr dp ultra	.20	.20
777	A265	12fr violet & brn	.20	.20
778	A265	18fr bluish grn & ind	.85	.20
779	A265	25fr org brn & red brn	1.25	.20
		Nos. 774-779 (6)	3.15	1.20

See Nos. 838-839. For surcharges see Reunion Nos. 312-317, 323.

Mount Pelée, Martinique
A266

1955, Nov. 1
780 A266 20fr dk & lt purple 3.50 2.00

Gérard de Nerval — A267

1955, Nov. 11
781 A267 12fr lake & sepia .45 .30
Centenary of the death of Gérard de Nerval (Labrunie), author.

Arms Type of 1949
Arms of: 50c, County of Foix. 70c, Marche. 80c, Roussillon. 1fr, Comtat Venaissin.

Perf. 14x13½
1955, Nov. 19   Typo.   Unwmk.
782 A182 50c multicolored   .20 .20
783 A182 70c red, blue & yel   .20 .20
784 A182 80c brown, yel & red   .20 .20
785 A182 1fr blue, red & yel   .20 .20
   Nos. 782-785 (4)   .80 .80

Concentration Camp Victim and Monument A268

Belfry at Douai A269

1956, Jan. 14   Engr.   Perf. 13
786 A268 15fr brn blk & red brn   .65 .50

Natl. memorial for Nazi deportation victims erected at the Natzwiller Struthof concentration camp in Alsace.

1956, Feb. 11
787 A269 15fr ultra & indigo   .55 .55

Col. Emil Driant A270

1956, Feb. 21
788 A270 15fr dark blue   .30 .25

40th anniv. of the death of Col. Emil Driant during the battle of Verdun.

Trench Fighting — A271

1956, Mar. 3
789 A271 30fr indigo & dk olive   2.00 1.40
40th anniversary of Battle of Verdun.

Jean Henri Fabre, Entomology A272

Scientists: 15fr, Charles Tellier, Refrigeration. 18fr, Camille Flammarion, Popular Astronomy. 30fr, Paul Sabatier, Catalytic Chemistry.

1956, Apr. 7
790 A272 12fr vio brn & org brn   .90 .60
791 A272 15fr vio bl & int blk   .90 .60
792 A272 18fr brt ultra   1.75 1.50
793 A272 30fr Prus grn & dk grn   4.25 2.75
   Nos. 790-793 (4)   7.80 5.45

Grand Trianon, Versailles A273

1956, Apr. 14
794 A273 12fr vio brn & gray grn   1.50 .80

Symbols of Latin American and French Culture A274

1956, Apr. 21
795 A274 30fr brown & red brn   2.25 1.60
Issued in recognition of the friendship between France and Latin America.

"The Smile of Reims" and Botticelli's "Spring" A275

1956, May 5
796 A275 12fr black & green   .75 .40
Issued to emphasize the cultural and artistic kinship of Reims and Florence.

Leprosarium and Maltese Cross — A276

1956, May 12
797 A276 12fr sepia, red brn & red   .40 .35
Issued in honor of the Knights of Malta.

St. Yves de Treguier A277

1956, May 19
798 A277 15fr bluish gray & blk   .35 .25
St. Yves, patron saint of lawyers.

Marshal Franchet d'Esperey A278

Miners Monument A279

1956, May 26
799 A278 30fr deep claret   2.75 1.50
Centenary of the birth of Marshal Louis Franchet d'Esperey.

1956, June 2
800 A279 12fr violet brown   .45 .40
Town Montceau-les-Mines, 100th anniv.

Basketball A280

"Rebuilding Europe" A281

Sports: 40fr, Pelota (Jai alai). 50fr, Rugby. 75fr, Mountain climbing.

1956, July 7
801 A280 30fr gray vio & blk   1.25 .20
802 A280 40fr brown & vio brn   5.25 .30
803 A280 50fr rose vio & vio   1.75 .20
804 A280 75fr indigo, grn & bl   10.50 2.00
   Nos. 801-804 (4)   18.75 2.70
For surcharges see Reunion Nos. 318-321.

Europa Issue
Perf. 13½x14
1956, Sept. 15   Typo.   Unwmk.
805 A281 15fr rose & rose lake   .80 .25
Perf. 13
Engr.
806 A281 30fr lt blue & vio bl   6.00 .85

Issued to symbolize the cooperation among the six countries comprising the Coal and Steel Community.
No. 805 measures 21x35½mm, No. 806 measures 22x35½mm.

Dam at Donzère-Mondragon — A282

Cable Railway to Pic du Midi — A283

Rhine Port of Strasbourg A284

1956, Oct. 6   Engr.   Perf. 13
807 A282 12fr gray vio & vio brn   1.60 1.10
808 A283 18fr indigo   3.25 2.25
809 A284 30fr indigo & dk blue   14.00 6.25
   Nos. 807-809 (3)   18.85 9.60
French technical achievements.

Antoine-Augustin Parmentier — A285

1956, Oct. 27
810 A285 12fr brown red & brown   .75 .65
Parmentier, nutrition chemist, who popularized the potato in France.

Petrarch — A286

Portraits: 12fr, J. B. Lully. 15fr, J. J. Rousseau. 18fr, Benjamin Franklin. 20fr, Frederic Chopin. 30fr, Vincent van Gogh.

1956, Nov. 10
811 A286 8fr green   .75 .55
812 A286 12fr claret   .75 .55
813 A286 15fr dark red   1.10 .55
814 A286 18fr ultra   2.40 1.90
815 A286 20fr brt violet   3.25 1.50
816 A286 30fr brt grnsh blue   5.00 2.50
   Nos. 811-816 (6)   13.25 7.55
Famous men who lived in France.

Pierre de Coubertin and Olympic Stadium A287

1956, Nov. 24
817 A287 30fr dk blue gray & pur   1.60 1.00
Issued in honor of Baron Pierre de Coubertin, founder of the modern Olympic Games.

Homing Pigeon A288

1957, Jan. 12
818 A288 15fr dp ultra, ind & red brn   .45 .25

Victor Schoelcher — A289

1957, Feb. 16   Engr.
819 A289 18fr lilac rose   .60 .40
Issued in honor of Victor Schoelcher, who freed the slaves in the French Colonies.

Sèvres Porcelain A290

1957, Mar. 23   Unwmk.   Perf. 13
820 A290 30fr ultra & vio blue   .75 .40
Bicentenary of the porcelain works at Sèvres (in 1956).

Gaston Planté and Storage Battery A291

Designs: 12fr, Antoine Béclère and X-ray apparatus. 18fr, Octave Terrillon, autoclave, microscope and surgical instruments. 30fr, Etienne Oemichen and early helicopter.

1957, Apr. 13

821	A291	8fr gray blk & dp cl	.45	.45
822	A291	12fr dk bl, blk & emer	.50	.50
823	A291	18fr rose red & mag	1.25	1.25
824	A291	30fr green & slate grn	2.25	2.25
		Nos. 821-824 (4)	4.45	4.45

Uzès Chateau A292

1957, Apr. 27

825	A292	12fr slate bl & bis brn	.40	.40

Jean Moulin A293

Le Quesnoy A294

Portraits: 10fr, Honoré d'Estienne d'Orves. 12fr, Robert Keller. 18fr, Pierre Brossolette. 20fr, Jean-Baptiste Lebas.

1957, May 18

826	A293	8fr violet brown	1.00	.45
827	A293	10fr black & vio bl	1.00	.45
828	A293	12fr brown & sl grn	1.00	.80
829	A293	18fr purple & blk	1.50	1.25
830	A293	20fr Prus bl & dk bl	1.40	.90
		Nos. 826-830 (5)	5.90	3.85

Issued in honor of the heroes of the French Underground of World War II.
See #879-882, 915-919, 959-963, 990-993.

1957, June 1

831	A294	8fr dk slate green	.25	.20

See No. 837. For surcharge see Reunion No. 322.

Symbols of Justice A295

1957, June 1

832	A295	12fr sepia & ultra	.25	.20

French Cour des Comptes, 150th anniv.

Farm Woman Type of 1954

			Perf. 14x13½	
1957-59				
833	A236	6fr orange	.20	.20
833A	A236	10fr brt green ('59)	.75	.20
834	A236	12fr red lilac	.25	.20
		Nos. 833-834 (3)	1.20	.60

Nos. 833-834 issued without precancellation.

Symbols of Public Works A296

1957, June 20   Engr.   Perf. 13

835	A296	30fr sl grn, brn & ocher	1.90	1.10

Brest A297

1957, July 6

836	A297	12fr gray grn & brn ol	.90	.80

Scenic Types of 1955, 1957

Designs: 15fr, Le Quesnoy. 35fr, Bordeaux. 70fr, Valentre bridge, Cahors.

1957, July 19   Unwmk.

837	A294	15fr dk bl grn & sep	.40	.20
838	A265	35fr dk bl grn & sl grn	3.25	1.10
839	A265	70fr black & dull grn	22.50	2.00
		Nos. 837-839 (3)	26.15	3.30

Gallic Cock Type of 1954

1957		**Typo.**	**Perf. 14x13½**	
840	A237	5fr olive bister	.40	.20
841	A237	10fr bright blue	1.75	.35
842	A237	15fr plum	2.25	.75
843	A237	30fr bright red	10.00	3.00
844	A237	45fr green	21.00	12.50
		Nos. 840-844 (5)	35.40	16.80

Nos. 840-844 are known only precanceled.
See second note after No. 132.

Leo Lagrange and Stadium A298

1957, Aug. 31   Engr.   Perf. 13

845	A298	18fr lilac gray & blk	.55	.55

Intl. University Games, Paris, 8/31-9/8.

"United Europe" — A299

Auguste Comte — A300

1957, Sept. 16

846	A299	20fr red brown & green	.40	.30
847	A299	35fr dk brown & blue	.90	.80

A united Europe for peace and prosperity.

1957, Sept. 14

848	A300	35fr brown red & sepia	.45	.30

Centenary of the death of Auguste Comte, mathematician and philosopher.

Roman Amphitheater, Lyon — A301

1957, Oct. 5   Perf. 13

849	A301	20fr brn org & brn vio	.45	.30

2,000th anniv. of the founding of Lyon.

Sens River, Guadeloupe A302

Beynac-Cazenac, Dordogne A303

Nicolaus Copernicus A304

Designs: 10fr, Elysee Palace. 25fr, Chateau de Valencay, Indre. 35fr, Rouen Cathedral. 50fr, Roman Ruins, Saint-Remy. 65fr, Evians-les-Bains.

1957, Oct. 19

850	A302	8fr green & lt brn	.20	.20
851	A302	10fr dk ol bis & vio brn	.20	.20
852	A303	18fr indigo & dk brn	.20	.20
853	A303	25fr bl gray & vio brn	.55	.20
854	A303	35fr car rose & lake	.20	.20
855	A302	50fr ol grn & ol bister	.45	.20
856	A302	65fr dk blue & indigo	.60	.30
		Nos. 850-856 (7)	2.40	1.50

See #907-909. For overprint and surcharges see #1O1, Reunion 325, 328-329, 332-334.

1957, Nov. 9   Engr.   Perf. 13

Portraits: 10fr, Michelangelo. 12fr, Miguel de Cervantes. 15fr, Rembrandt. 18fr, Isaac Newton. 25fr, Mozart. 35fr, Johann Wolfgang von Goethe.

857	A304	8fr dark brown	.80	.60
858	A304	10fr dark green	.80	.60
859	A304	12fr dark purple	.80	.70
860	A304	15fr brown & org brn	1.00	.80
861	A304	18fr deep blue	1.40	.90
862	A304	25fr lilac & claret	1.40	.90
863	A304	35fr blue	1.75	1.00
		Nos. 857-863 (7)	7.95	5.50

Louis Jacques Thénard A305

1957, Nov. 30   Unwmk.

864	A305	15fr ol bis & grnsh blk	.40	.30

Centenary of the death of L. J. Thenard, chemist, and the founding of the Charitable Society of the Friends of Science.

Dr. Philippe Pinel A306

Joseph Louis Lagrange A307

French Physicians: 12fr, Fernand Widal. 15fr, Charles Nicolle. 35fr, René Leriche.

1958, Jan. 25

865	A306	8fr brown olive	.90	.60
866	A306	12fr brt vio blue	.90	.60
867	A306	15fr deep blue	1.40	.80
868	A306	35fr black	1.75	1.10
		Nos. 865-868 (4)	4.95	3.10

1958, Feb. 15   Perf. 13

French Scientists: 12fr, Urbain Jean Joseph Leverrier. 15fr, Jean Bernard Leon Foucault. 35fr, Claude Louis Berthollet.

869	A307	8fr blue grn & vio bl	.90	.55
870	A307	12fr sepia & gray	1.00	.70
871	A307	15fr slate grn & grn	1.90	.95
872	A307	35fr maroon & cop red	2.40	1.25
		Nos. 869-872 (4)	6.20	3.45

Lourdes Type of 1954

1958				
873	A241	20fr grnsh bl & ol	.30	.20

Le Havre A308

Maubeuge — A309

Designs: 18fr, Saint-Die. 25fr, Sete.

1958, Mar. 29   Engr.   Perf. 13

874	A308	12fr ol grn & car rose	.65	.35
875	A309	15fr brt purple & brn	.65	.35
876	A309	18fr ultra & indigo	1.00	.75
877	A308	25fr dk bl, bl grn & brn	1.25	.75
		Nos. 874-877 (4)	3.55	2.20

Reconstruction of war-damaged cities.

French Pavilion, Brussels A310

1958, Apr. 12

878	A310	35fr brn, dk grn & bl	.30	.25

Issued for the Universal and International Exposition at Brussels.

Heroes Type of 1957

8fr, Jean Cavaillès. 12fr, Fred Scamaroni. 15fr, Simone Michel-Levy. 20fr, Jacques Bingen.

1958, Apr. 19

879	A293	8fr violet & black	.60	.60
880	A293	12fr ultra & green	.60	.60
881	A293	15fr brown & gray	1.50	.85
882	A293	20fr olive & ultra	1.25	.95
		Nos. 879-882 (4)	3.95	3.00

Issued in honor of the heroes of the French Underground in World War II.

Bowling A311

Sports: 15fr, Naval joust. 18fr, Archery, vert. 25fr, Breton wrestling, vert.

1958, Apr. 26

883	A311	12fr rose & brown	.85	.75
884	A311	15fr bl, ol gray & grn	1.10	.85
885	A311	18fr green & brown	2.00	1.10
886	A311	25fr brown & indigo	2.90	1.75
		Nos. 883-886 (4)	6.85	4.45

Senlis Cathedral — A312

1958, May 17

887	A312	15fr ultra & indigo	.40	.25

Bayeux Tapestry Horsemen A313

1958, June 21

888	A313	15fr blue & carmine	.35	.25

Common Design Types pictured following the introduction.

Europa Issue, 1958
Common Design Type
1958, Sept. 13   **Engr.**   **Perf. 13**
Size: 22x36mm

| 889 | CD1 | 20fr rose red | .40 | .20 |
| 890 | CD1 | 35fr ultra | 1.25 | .30 |

Foix
Chateau
A314

1958, Oct. 11

891 A314 15fr ultra, grn & ol brn   .40 .25

City Halls,
Paris and
Rome
A315

1958, Oct. 11

892 A315 35fr gray, grnsh bl & rose
red   .40 .25

Issued to publicize the cultural ties between Rome and Paris and the need for European unity.

UNESCO
Building,
Paris
A316

Design: 35fr, Different view of building.

1958, Nov. 1   **Perf. 13**

| 893 | A316 | 20fr grnsh blue & ol bis | .20 | .20 |
| 894 | A316 | 35fr dk sl grn & red org | .20 | .20 |

UNESCO Headquarters in Paris opening, Nov. 3.

Soldier's Grave   Arms of
in Wheat Field   Marseille
A317   A318

1958, Nov. 11

895 A317 15fr dk green & ultra   .30 .25

40th anniv. of the World War I armistice.

1958-59   **Typo.**   **Perf. 14x13½**

Cities: 70c, Lyon. 80c, Toulouse. 1fr, Bordeaux. 2fr, Nice. 3fr, Nantes. 5fr, Lille. 15fr, Algiers.

896	A318	50c dk blue & ultra	.20	.20
897	A318	70c multicolored	.20	.20
898	A318	80c red, blue & yel	.20	.20
899	A318	1fr dk bl, yel & red	.20	.20
900	A318	2fr dk bl, red & grn	.20	.20
901	A318	3fr multicolored	.20	.20
902	A318	5fr dk brown & red	.20	.20
903	A318	15fr multi ('59)	.20	.20
		Nos. 896-903 (8)	1.60	1.60

See Nos. 938, 940, 973, 1040-1042, 1091-1095, 1142-1144. For surcharges see Reunion Nos. 336, 345-346, 350-351, 353.

Arc de Triomphe
and Flowers — A319

1959, Jan. 17   **Engr.**   **Perf. 13**

904 A319 15fr brn, bl, grn, cl & red .45 .30

Paris Flower Festival.

Symbols of
Learning
and Medal
A320

1959, Jan. 24   **Perf. 13**

905 A320 20fr lake, blk & vio   .25 .20

Sesquicentennial of the Palm Leaf Medal of the French Academy.

Charles de
Foucauld
A321

1959, Jan. 31

906 A321 50fr dp brn, bl & mar   .50 .35

Issued to honor Father Charles de Foucauld, explorer and missionary of the Sahara.

Type of 1957

Designs: 30fr, Elysee Palace. 85fr, Evian-les Bains. 100fr, Sens River, Guadeloupe.

1959, Feb. 10

907	A302	30fr dk slate green	2.25	.25
908	A302	85fr deep claret	3.25	.30
909	A302	100fr deep violet	27.50	.45
		Nos. 907-909 (3)	33.00	1.00

Gallic Cock Type of 1954

1959   **Typo.**   **Perf. 14x13½**

910	A237	8fr violet	.55	.25
911	A237	20fr yellow grn	1.75	.65
912	A237	40fr henna brn	4.00	2.25
913	A237	55fr emerald	17.00	10.00
		Nos. 910-913 (4)	23.30	13.15

Nos. 910-913 were issued with precancellation. See second note after No. 132. See Nos. 952-955.

Miners'
Tools and
School
A322

1959, Apr. 11   **Engr.**   **Perf. 13**

914 A322 20fr red, blk & blue   .25 .20

175th anniv. of the National Mining School.

Heroes Type of 1957

Portraits: No. 915, The five martyrs of the Buffon school. No. 916, Yvonne Le Roux. No. 917, Médéric-Védy. No. 918, Louis Martin-Bret. 30fr, Gaston Moutardier.

1959, Apr. 25   **Engr.**   **Perf. 13**

915	A293	15fr black & vio	.40	.20
916	A293	15fr mag & rose vio	.40	.30
917	A293	20fr green & grnsh bl	.40	.30
918	A293	20fr org brn & brn	.50	.40
919	A293	30fr magenta & vio	.65	.40
		Nos. 915-919 (5)	2.35	1.60

Dam at
Foum el
Gherza
A323

Marcoule Atomic
Center — A324

Designs: 30fr, Oil field at Hassi Messaoud, Sahara. 50fr, C. N. I. T. Building (Centre National des Industries et des Techniques).

1959, May 23

920	A323	15fr olive & grnsh bl	.35	.20
921	A324	20fr brt car & red brn	.50	.40
922	A324	30fr dk blue, brn & grn	.50	.40
923	A324	50fr ol grn & sl blue	.75	.45
		Nos. 920-923 (4)	2.10	1.45

French technical achievements.

Marceline Desbordes-Valmore — A325

1959, June 20

924 A325 30fr blue, brn & grn   .25 .20

Centenary of the death of Marceline Desbordes-Valmore, poet.

Pilots
Goujon and
Rozanoff
A326

1959, June 13

925 A326 20fr lt blue & org brn   .50 .40

Issued in honor of Charles Goujon and Col. Constantin Rozanoff, test pilots.

Tancarville
Bridge
A327

1959, Aug. 1   **Engr.**   **Perf. 13**

926 A327 30fr dk blue, brn & ol   .50 .20

Marianne
and Ship of
State
A328

Jean Jaures
A329

1959, July   **Typo.**   **Perf. 14x13½**

927 A328 25fr black & red   .30 .20

See Nos. 942, 3521. For surcharge see No. B336.

1959, Sept. 12   **Engr.**   **Perf. 13**

928 A329 50fr chocolate   .40 .25

Jean Jaures, socialist leader, birth cent.

Europa Issue, 1959
Common Design Type
1959, Sept. 19
Size: 22x36mm

| 929 | CD2 | 25fr bright green | .75 | .35 |
| 930 | CD2 | 50fr bright violet | 1.10 | .55 |

Blood
Donors
A330

1959, Oct. 17   **Engr.**

931 A330 20fr magenta & gray   .25 .20

French-Spanish Handshake — A331

1959, Oct. 24   **Perf. 13**

932 A331 50fr blue, rose car & org .55 .35

300th anniv. of the signing of the Treaty of the Pyrenees.

Polio Victim   Henri Bergson
Holding   A333
Crutches
A332

1959, Oct. 31

933 A332 20fr dark blue   .25 .20

Vaccination against poliomyelitis.

1959, Nov. 7

934 A333 50fr lt red brown   .35 .25

Henri Bergson, philosopher, birth cent.

Avesnes-sur-Helpe — A334

Design: 30fr, Perpignan.

1959, Nov. 14
935 A334 20fr sepia & blue .40 .20
936 A334 30fr brn, dp claret & bl .40 .20

New NATO Headquarters,
Paris — A335

1959, Dec. 12
937 A335 50fr green, brn & ultra .60 .40

10th anniv. of the NATO.

Types of 1958-59 and

Farm Woman
A336

Sower
A337

Designs: 5c, Arms of Lille. 15c, Arms of Algiers. 25c, Marianne and Ship of State.

Perf. 14x13½

		Unwmk.	**Typo.**
1960-61			
938	A318	5c dk brown & red	7.25 .20
939	A336	10c brt green	.25 .20
940	A318	15c red, ultra, yel & grn	.60 .20
941	A337	20c grnsh bl & car rose	.20 .20
942	A328	25c ver & ultra	2.25 .20
b.		Booklet pane of 8	27.50
c.		Booklet pane of 10	32.50
942A	A337	30c gray & ultra ('61)	2.00 .30
		Nos. 938-942A (6)	12.55 1.30

See Nos. 707-708, 833-834 for the Farm Woman type (A336), but with no decimals in denominations.

For surcharges see Reunion Nos. 337-338, 341. For overprint see Algeria No. 286.

Laon
Cathedral
A338

Kerrata
Gorge — A339

Designs: 30c, Fougères Chateau. 50c, Mosque, Tlemcen. 65c, Sioule Valley. 85c, Chaumont Viaduct. 1fr, Cilaos Church, Reunion.

1960, Jan. 16   Engr.   Perf. 13
943 A338 15c blue & indigo .40 .20
944 A338 30c blue, sepia & grn 3.75 .20
945 A339 45c brt vio & ol gray .85 .20
946 A339 50c sl grn & lt cl 2.50 .20
947 A338 65c sl grn, bl & blk brn 1.25 .20
948 A338 85c blue, sep & grn 3.00 .20
949 A339 1fr vio bl, bl & grn 3.00 .20
    Nos. 943-949 (7) 14.75 1.40

For surcharges see Reunion Nos. 335, 340, 342. For overprint see Algeria Nos. 288-289.

Pierre de
Nolhac
A340

1960, Feb. 13
950 A340 20c black & gray .50 .35

Centenary of the birth of Pierre de Nolhac, curator of Versailles and historian.

Museum of Art and Industry, Saint-
Etienne — A341

1960, Feb. 20
951 A341 30c brn, car & slate .60 .30

Gallic Cock Type of 1954

1960   Typo.   Perf. 14x13½
952 A237 8c violet .95 .20
953 A237 20c yellow grn 3.25 .30
954 A237 40c henna brn 9.00 2.00
955 A237 55c emerald 29.00 16.00
    Nos. 952-955 (4) 42.20 18.50

Nos. 952-955 were issued only precanceled. See second note after No. 132. See Nos. 910-913.

View of
Cannes
A342

1960, Mar. 5   Engr.   Perf. 13
956 A342 50c red brn & lt grn .70 .45

Meeting of European municipal administrators, Cannes, Mar., 1960.

Woman of
Savoy and
Alps
A343

Woman of
Nice and
Shore
A344

1960   Unwmk.   Perf. 13
957 A343 30c slate green .65 .40
958 A344 50c brn, yel & rose .65 .30

Cent. of the annexation of Nice and Savoy.

Heroes Type of 1957

Portraits: No. 959, Edmund Debeaumarché. No. 960, Pierre Massé. No. 961, Maurice Ripoche. No. 962, Leonce Vieljeux. 50c, Abbé René Bonpain.

1960, Mar. 26
959 A293 20c bister & blk 2.40 1.40
960 A293 20c pink & rose cl 1.75 1.40
961 A293 30c vio & brt vio 1.75 1.40
962 A293 30c sl bl & brt bl 3.25 2.40
963 A293 50c sl grn & red brn 3.25 3.00
    Nos. 959-963 (5) 12.40 9.60

Issued in honor of the heroes of the French Underground of World War II.

"Education"
and
Children
A345

1960, May 21   Engr.   Perf. 13
964 A345 20c rose lilac, pur & blk .25 .20

1st secondary school in Strasbourg, 150th anniv.

Blois
Chateau
A346

View of La
Bourboule
A347

1960, May
965 A346 30c dk bl, sep & grn .85 .65
966 A347 50c ol brown, car & grn .65 .50

Lorraine Cross
A348

Marianne
A349

1960, June 18
967 A348 20c red brn, dk brn & yel grn .65 .25

20th anniv. of the French Resistance Movement in World War II.

1960, June 18   Typo.   Perf. 14x13½
968 A349 25c lake & gray .20 .20
a. Booklet pane of 8 4.50
b. Booklet pane of 10 3.50

See No. 3522. For surcharge see Reunion No. 339. For overprint see Algeria No. 287.

Jean Bouin
and
Stadium
A350

1960, July 9   Engr.   Perf. 13
969 A350 20c blue, mag & ol gray .35 .25

17th Olympic Games, Rome, 8/25-9/11.

Europa Issue, 1960
Common Design Type

1960, Sept. 17   Perf. 13
Size: 36x22mm
970 CD3 25c green & bluish grn .20 .20
971 CD3 50c maroon & red lilac .30 .20

Lisieux
Basilica
A351

1960, Sept. 24   Perf. 13
972 A351 15c blue, gray & blk .25 .20

Arms Type of 1958-59

Design: Arms of Oran.

1960, Oct. 15   Typo.   Perf. 14x13½
973 A318 5c red, bl, yel & emer .20 .20

Madame de Stael
by François
Gerard — A352

1960, Oct. 22   Engr.   Perf. 13
974 A352 30c dull claret & brn .35 .25

Madame de Stael (1766-1817), writer.

Gen. J. B.
E. Estienne
A353

1960, Nov. 5
975 A353 15c lt lilac & black .25 .20

Centenary of the birth of Gen. Jean Baptiste Eugene Estienne.

Marc
Sangnier
and Youth
Hostel at
Bierville
A354

1960, Nov. 5
976 A354 20c blue, blk & lilac .25 .20

Issued to honor Marc Sangnier, founder of the French League for Youth Hostels.

Badge of Order of
Liberation — A355

1960, Nov. 14   Engr.   Perf. 13
977 A355 20c black & brt green .40 .25

Order of Liberation, 20th anniversary.

Lapwings
A356

Birds: 30c, Puffin. 45c, European teal. 50c, European bee-eaters.

1960, Nov. 12
978 A356 20c multicolored .30 .20
979 A356 30c multicolored .30 .20
980 A356 45c multicolored .95 .50
981 A356 50c multicolored .85 .25
    Nos. 978-981 (4) 2.40 1.20

Issued to publicize wildlife protection.

André Honnorat
A357

1960, Nov. 19
982 A357 30c blue, blk & green .30 .25
Honnorat, statesman, fighter against tuberculosis and founder of the University City of Paris, an intl. students' community.

St. Barbara and Medieval View of School
A358

1960, Dec. 3 Engr.
983 A358 30c red, bl & ol brn .35 .30
St. Barbara School, Paris, 500th anniv.

"Mediterranean" by Aristide Maillol — A359

1961, Feb. 18 Unwmk. Perf. 13
984 A359 20c carmine & indigo .25 .25
Aristide Maillol, sculptor, birth cent.

Marianne by Cocteau — A360

1961, Feb. 23
985 A360 20c blue & carmine .25 .20
A second type has an extra inverted V-shaped mark (a blue flag top) at right of hair tip. Value unused $3.25, used 60 cents.
See No. 3523.
For surcharge see Reunion No. 357.

Paris Airport, Orly
A361

1961, Feb. 25
986 A361 50c blk, dk bl, & bluish grn .45 .35
Inauguration of new facilities at Orly airport.

George Méliès and Motion Picture Screen
A362

1961, Mar. 11
987 A362 50c pur, indigo & ol bis .50 .35
Cent. of the birth of George Méliès, motion picture pioneer.

Jean Baptiste Henri Lacordaire — A363

1961, Mar. 25 Perf. 13
988 A363 30c lt brown & black .30 .30
Cent. of the death of the Dominican monk Lacordaire, orator and liberal Catholic leader.

A364

1961, Mar. 25
989 A364 30c grn, red brn & red .30 .25
Introduction of tobacco use into France, fourth centenary. By error stamp portrays Jan Nicquet instead of Jean Nicot.

Heroes Type of 1957
Portraits: No. 990, Jacques Renouvin. No. 991, Lionel Dubray. No. 992, Paul Gateaud. No. 993, Mère Elisabeth.

1961, Apr. 22
990 A293 20c blue & lilac 1.00 .50
991 A293 20c gray grn & blue 1.00 .50
992 A293 30c brown org & blk 1.60 .90
993 A293 30c violet & blk 1.25 1.00
   Nos. 990-993 (4) 4.85 2.90

Bagnoles-de-l'Orne — A365

1961, May 6
994 A365 20c olive, ocher, bl & grn .20 .20

Dove, Olive Branch and Federation Emblem — A366

1961, May 6
995 A366 50c brt bl, grn & mar .30 .20
World Federation of Ex-Service Men.

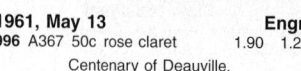

Deauville in 19th Century
A367

1961, May 13 Engr.
996 A367 50c rose claret 1.90 1.20
Centenary of Deauville.

La Champmeslé
A368

Mont-Dore, Snowflake and Cable Car
A369

French actors: #998, Talma. #999, Rachel. #1000, Gérard Philipe. #1001, Raimu.

1961, June 10 Unwmk. Perf. 13
Dark Carmine Frame
997 A368 20c choc & yel grn .90 .35
998 A368 30c brown & crimson .90 .35
999 A368 30c yel grn & sl grn .90 .35
1000 A368 50c olive & choc 1.25 .55
1001 A368 50c bl grn & red brn 1.25 .55
   Nos. 997-1001 (5) 5.20 2.15
Issued to honor great French actors and in connection with the Fifth World Congress of the International Federation of Actors.

1961, July 1 Unwmk.
1002 A369 20c orange & rose lilac .20 .20

Pierre Fauchard
A370

St. Theobald's Church, Thann
A371

1961, July 1
1003 A370 50c dk green & blk .55 .30
Bicentenary of the death of Pierre Fauchard, 1st surgeon dentist.

1961, July 1
1004 A371 20c sl grn, vio & brn .55 .30
800th anniversary of Thann.

Europa Issue, 1961
Common Design Type

1961, Sept. 16 Perf. 13
Size: 35x22mm
1005 CD4 25c vermilion .20 .20
1006 CD4 50c ultramarine .25 .25

Beach and Sailboats, Arcachon
A372

Designs: 15c, Saint-Paul, Maritime Alps. 45c, Sully-sur-Loire Chateau. 50c, View of Cognac. 65c, Rance Valley and Dinan. 85c, City hall and Rodin's Burghers, Calais. 1fr, Roman gates of Lodi, Medea, Algeria.

1961, Oct. 9 Engr. Perf. 13
1007 A372 15c blue & purple .20 .20
1008 A372 30c ultra, sl grn & lt brn .25 .20
1009 A372 45c vio bl, red brn & grn .25 .20
1010 A372 50c grn, Prus bl & sl 1.25 .20
1011 A372 65c red brn, sl grn & bl .50 .20
1012 A372 85c sl grn, sl & red brn .60 .25
1013 A372 1fr dk bl, sl & bis 5.00 .25
   Nos. 1007-1013 (7) 8.05 1.50

For surcharges see Reunion Nos. 347-348.
For overprint see Algeria No. 290.

Blue Nudes, by Matisse — A373

Paintings: 50c, "The Messenger," by Braque. 85c, "The Cardplayers," by Cézanne. 1fr, "The 14th July," by Roger de La Fresnaye.

1961, Nov. 10 Perf. 13x12
1014 A373 50c dk brn, bl, blk & gray 2.90 1.60
1015 A373 65c grn, vio, & ultra 5.00 2.50
1016 A373 85c blk, brn, red & ol 2.50 1.25
1017 A373 1fr multicolored 4.00 2.50
   Nos. 1014-1017 (4) 14.40 7.85

Liner France
A374

1962, Jan. 11 Engr. Perf. 13
1018 A374 30c dk blue, blk & car .60 .45
New French liner France.

Skier Going Downhill — A375

Maurice Bourdet — A376

1962, Jan. 27 Perf. 13
1019 A375 30c shown .20 .20
1020 A375 50c Slalom .40 .30
Issued to publicize the World Ski Championships, Chamonix, Feb. 1962.

1962, Feb. 17
1021 A376 30c slate .30 .20
60th anniv. of the birth of Maurice Bourdet, radio commentator and resistance hero.

Pierre-Fidele Bretonneau — A377

1962, Feb. 17
1022 A377 50c brt lilac & blue .35 .25
Centenary of the death of Pierre-Fidele Bretonneau, physician.

Chateau and Bridge, Laval, Mayenne A378

Gallic Cock A379

1962, Feb. 24
1023 A378 20c bis brn & slate grn .25 .20

1962-65   **Perf. 13**
1024 A379 25c ultra, car & brn   .25 .20
  a.   Bklt. pane of 4 (horiz. strip) 2.50
1024B A379 30c gray grn, red &
              brn ('65)   .85 .20
  c.   Booklet pane of 5   5.00
  d.   Booklet pane of 10   10.00

No. 1024 was also issued on experimental luminescent paper in 1963. Value $750. See No. 3524.

Ramparts of Vannes A380

Dunkirk — A381

Paris Beach, Le Touquet A381a

1962   **Engr.**   **Perf. 13**
1025 A380 30c dark blue   .80 .50
1026 A381 95c grn, bis & red lil 1.25 .75
1027 A381a 1fr grn, red brn & bl .45 .20
  Nos. 1025-1027 (3)   2.50 1.45

No. 1026 for the 300th anniv. of Dunkirk.

Stage Setting and Globe A382

1962, Mar. 24   **Unwmk.**
1028 A382 50c sl grn, ocher & mag .40 .25

International Day of the Theater, Mar. 27.

Memorial to Fighting France, Mont Valerien A383

Resistance Heroes' Monument, Vercors — A384

Design: 50c, Ile de Sein monument.

1962, Apr. 7
1029 A383 20c olive & slate grn .70 .50
1030 A384 30c bluish black   .70 .50
1031 A384 50c blue & indigo   .90 .80
  Nos. 1029-1031 (3)   2.30 1.80

Issued to publicize memorials for the French Underground in World War II.

Malaria Eradication Emblem and Swamp — A385

Nurses with Child and Hospital — A386

1962, Apr. 14   **Engr.**
1032 A385 50c dk blue & dk red   .35 .30

WHO drive to eradicate malaria.

1962, May 5   **Unwmk.**   **Perf. 13**
1033 A386 30c bl grn, gray & red
              brn   .35 .30

National Hospital Week, May 5-12.

Glider A387

20c, Planes showing development of aviation.

1962, May 12
1034 A387 15c orange red & brn   .30 .20
1035 A387 20c lil rose & rose cl .35 .25

Issued to publicize sports aviation.

School Emblem — A388

1962, May 19   **Engr.**
1036 A388 50c mar, ocher & dk vio .40 .30

Watchmaker's School at Besançon, cent.

Louis XIV and Workers Showing Modern Gobelin A389

1962, May 26   **Unwmk.**   **Perf. 13**
1037 A389 50c ol, sl grn & car   .40 .30

Gobelin tapestry works, Paris, 300th anniv.

Blaise Pascal A390

1962, May 26
1038 A390 50c slate grn & dp org .40 .30

Blaise Pascal (1623-1662), mathematician, scientist and philosopher.

Palace of Justice, Rennes A391

1962, June 12
1039 A391 30c blk, grysh bl & grn 1.40 .60

Arms Type of 1958-59

5c, Amiens. 10c, Troyes. 15c, Nevers.

1962-63   **Typo.**   **Perf. 14x13½**
1040 A318 5c ver, ultra & yel   .20 .20
1041 A318 10c red, ultra & yel
              ('63)   .20 .20
1042 A318 15c ver, ultra & yel   .20 .20
  Nos. 1040-1042 (3)   .60 .60

Phosphor Tagging
In 1970 France began to experiment with luminescence. Phosphor bands have been added to Nos. 1041, 1143, 1231, 1231C, 1292A-1294B, 1494-1498, 1560-1579B, etc.

Rose — A392

Design: 30c, Old-fashioned rose.

1962, Sept. 8   **Engr.**   **Perf. 13**
1043 A392 20c ol, grn & brt car .65 .40
1044 A392 30c dk sl grn, ol & car .65 .40

Europa Issue, 1962
Common Design Type
1962, Sept. 15
Size: 36x22mm
1045 CD5 25c violet   .20 .20
1046 CD5 50c henna brown   .35 .20

Space Communications Center, Pleumeur-Bodou, France — A394

Telstar, Earth and Television Set — A395

1962, Sept. 29   **Engr.**   **Perf. 13**
1047 A394 25c gray, yel & grn   .25 .20
1048 A395 50c dk bl, grn & ultra .40 .30

1st television connection of the US and Europe through Telstar satellite, July 11-12. For surcharges see Reunion Nos. 343-344.

"Bonjour Monsieur Courbet" by Gustave Courbet — A396

Paintings: 65c, "Madame Manet on Blue Sofa," by Edouard Manet. 1fr, "Guards officer on horseback," by Theodore Géricault, vert.

1962, Nov. 9   **Perf. 13x12, 12x13**
1049 A396 50c multicolored   3.00 2.25
1050 A396 65c multicolored   2.25 1.40
1051 A396 1fr multicolored   5.00 3.00
  Nos. 1049-1051 (3)   10.25 6.65

Bathyscaph "Archimede" — A397

1963, Jan. 26   **Unwmk.**   **Perf. 13**
1052 A397 30c dk blue & blk   .25 .20

French deep-sea explorations.

Flowers and Nantes Chateau A398

1963, Feb. 11
1053 A398 30c vio bl, car & sl grn .25 .20

Nantes flower festival.

St. Peter, Window at St. Foy de Conches A399

50c, Jacob Wrestling with the Angel, by Delacroix.

1963, Mar. 2   **Perf. 12x13**
1054 A399 50c multicolored   3.25 2.25
1055 A399 1fr multicolored   4.00 3.25

See Nos. 1076-1077.

Hungry Woman and Wheat Emblem A400

1963, Mar. 21   **Engr.**   **Perf. 13**
1056 A400 50c slate grn & brn   .30 .20

FAO "Freedom from Hunger" campaign.

Cemetery and Memorial, Glières — A401

Design: 50c, Memorial, Ile de la Cité, Paris.

1963, Mar. 23   Unwmk.   Perf. 13
1057 A401 30c dk brown & olive   .55 .55
1058 A401 50c indigo   .55 .55
Heroes of the resistance against the Nazis.

Beethoven, Birthplace at Bonn and Rhine A402

#1060, Emile Verhaeren, memorial at Roisin & residence. #1061, Giuseppe Mazzini, Marcus Aurelius statue & Via Appia, Rome. #1062, Emile Mayrisch, Colpach Chateau & blast furnace, Esch. #1063, Hugo de Groot, Palace of Peace, The Hague & St. Agatha Church, Delft.

1963, Apr. 27   Unwmk.   Perf. 13
1059 A402 20c ocher, sl & brt grn   .35 .25
1060 A402 20c purple, blk & mar   .35 .25
1061 A402 20c maroon, sl & ol   .35 .25
1062 A402 20c mar, dk brn & ocher   .35 .25
1063 A402 30c dk brn, vio & ocher   .35 .25
     Nos. 1059-1063 (5)   1.75 1.25
Issued to honor famous men of the European Common Market countries.

Hotel des Postes and Stagecoach, 1863 — A403

1963, May 4
1064 A403 50c grayish black   .35 .25
1st Intl. Postal Conference, Paris, 1863.

Lycée Louis-le-Grand, Belvédère, Panthéon and St. Etienne du Mont Church — A404

1963, May 18
1065 A404 30c slate green   .30 .25
400th anniversary of the Jesuit Clermont secondary school, named after Louis XIV.

St. Peter's Church and Ramparts, Caen A405

1963, June 1   Unwmk.   Perf. 13
1066 A405 30c gray blue & brn   .25 .25

Radio Telescope, Nançay — A406

1963, June 8   Engr.
1067 A406 50c dk bl & dk brn   .45 .35

Amboise Chateau A407

Saint-Flour — A408

Designs: 50c, Côte d'Azur Varoise. 85c, Vittel. 95c, Moissac.

1963, June 15
1068 A407 30c slate, grn & bis   .25 .20
1069 A407 50c dk grn, dk bl & hn brn   .40 .20
1070 A408 60c ultra, dk grn & hn brn   .45 .20
1071 A407 85c dk grn, yel grn & brn   1.50 .30
1072 A408 95c dk brown & black   .90 .25
     Nos. 1068-1072 (5)   3.50 1.15
For surcharge see Reunion No. 355.

Water Skiing Slalom A409

1963, Aug. 31   Unwmk.   Perf. 13
1073 A409 30c sl grn, blk & car   .30 .20
World Water Skiing Championships, Vichy.

Europa Issue, 1963
Common Design Type
1963, Sept. 14
     Size: 36x22mm
1074 CD6 25c red brown   .25 .25
1075 CD6 50c green   .35 .25

Art Type of 1963
Designs: 85c, "The Married Couple of the Eiffel Tower," by Marc Chagall. 95c, "The Fur Merchants," window, Chartres Cathedral.

1963, Nov. 9   Engr.   Perf. 12x13
1076 A399 85c multicolored   1.75 1.25
1077 A399 95c multicolored   .65 .65

Philatec Issue
Common Design Type
1963, Dec. 14   Unwmk.   Perf. 13
1078 CD118 25c dk gray, sl grn & dk car   .20 .20
For surcharge see Reunion No. 349.

Radio and Television Center, Paris A411

1963, Dec. 15   Engr.
1079 A411 20c org brn, slate & ol   .20 .20

Fire Brigade Insignia, Symbols of Fire, Water and Civilian Defense A412

1964, Feb. 8   Engr.   Perf. 13
1082 A412 30c blue, org & red   .50 .25
Issued to honor the fire brigades and civilian defense corps.

Handicapped Laboratory Technician — A413

1964, Feb. 22   Unwmk.   Perf. 13
1083 A413 30c grn, red brn & brn   .25 .20
Rehabilitation of the handicapped.

John II the Good (1319-64) by Girard d'Orleans A414

1964, Apr. 25   Perf. 12x13
1084 A414 1fr multicolored   1.60 1.10

Stamp of 1900 A415

Mechanized Mail Handling A416

Designs: No. 1086, Stamp of 1900, Type A17. No. 1088, Telecommunications.

1964, May 9   Perf. 13
1085 A415 25c bister & dk car   .30 .30
1086 A415 25c bister & blue   .30 .30
1087 A416 30c blk, bl & org brn   .30 .30
1088 A416 30c blk, car rose & bluish grn   .30 .30
   a.   Strip of 4, #1085-1088 + label   1.25 1.25
Printed in sheets of 20 stamps, containing five No. 1088a. The label shows the Philatec emblem in green.

Type of Semi-Postal Issue
with "25e ANNIVERSAIRE" added
1964, May 9
1089 SP208 25c multicolored   .25 .20
25th anniversary, night airmail service.

Madonna and Child from Rose Window of Notre Dame A417

1964, May 23   Perf. 12x13
1090 A417 60c multicolored   .55 .55
Notre Dame Cathedral, Paris, 800th anniv.

Arms Type of 1958-59
Arms: 1c, Niort. 2c, Guéret. 12c, Agen. 18c, Saint-Denis, Réunion. 30c, Paris.

1964-65   Typo.   Perf. 14x13½
1091 A318 1c vio blue & yel   .20 .20
1092 A318 2c emer, vio bl & yel   .20 .20
1093 A318 12c black, red & yel   .20 .20
1094 A318 18c multicolored   .40 .25
1095 A318 30c vio bl & red ('65)   .50 .20
   a.   Booklet pane of 10   15.00
     Nos. 1091-1095 (5)   1.50 1.05

Gallic Coin — A418

Perf. 13½x14
1964-66   Typo.   Unwmk.
1096 A418 10c emer & bister   .75 .20
1097 A418 15c org & bister ('66)   .30 .20
1098 A418 25c lilac & brn   .45 .20
1099 A418 50c brt blue & brn   .85 .75
     Nos. 1096-1099 (4)   2.35 1.35

Nos. 1096-1099 are known only precanceled. See second note after No. 132. See Nos. 1240-1242, 1315-1318, 1421-1424.

Postrider, Rocket and Radar Equipment — A419

1964, June 5   Engr.   Perf. 13
1100 A419 1fr brn, dk red & dk bl   25.00 20.00
Sold for 4fr, including 3fr admission to PHILATEC. Issued in sheets of 8 stamps and 8 labels (2x8 subjects with labels in horizontal rows 1, 4, 5, 8; stamps in rows 2, 3, 6, 7). Commemorative inscriptions on side margins. Value $200.

Caesar's Tower, Provins — A420

Chapel of Notre Dame du Haut, Ronchamp A421

1964-65
1101 A421 40c sl grn, dk brn & brn ('65) .25 .20
1102 A420 70c slate, grn & car .35 .20
1103 A421 1.25fr brt bl, sl grn & ol .75 .30
Nos. 1101-1103 (3) 1.35 .70

The 40c was issued in vertical coils in 1971. Every 10th coil stamp has a red control number printed twice on the back.
For surcharges see Reunion Nos. 352, 361.

Mandel — A422   Judo — A423

1964, July 4   Unwmk.   Perf. 13
1104 A422 30c violet brown .25 .20

Georges Mandel (1885-1944), Cabinet minister, executed by the Nazis.

1964, July 4
1105 A423 50c dk blue & vio brn .25 .20

18th Olympic Games, Tokyo, 10/10-25/64.

Champlevé Enamel from Limoges, 12th Century A424

Design: No. 1107, The Lady (Claude Le Viste?) with the Unicorn, 15th cent. tapestry.

1964   Perf. 12x13
1106 A424 1fr multicolored 1.25 .80
1107 A424 1fr multicolored .65 .45

No. 1106 shows part of an enamel sepulchral plate portraying Geoffrey IV, Count of Anjou and Le Maine (1113-1151), who was called Geoffrey Plantagenet.
Issue dates: #1106, July 4. #1107, Oct. 31.

Paris Taxis Carrying Soldiers to Front, 1914 A425

1964, Sept. 5   Unwmk.   Perf. 13
1108 A425 30c black, blue & red .25 .20

50th anniversary of Battle of the Marne.

Europa Issue, 1964
Common Design Type

1964, Sept. 12   Engr.
Size: 22x36mm
1109 CD7 25c dk car, dp ocher & grn .20 .20
1110 CD7 50c vio, yel grn & dk car .25 .20

Cooperation Issue
Common Design Type

1964, Nov. 6   Unwmk.   Perf. 13
1111 CD119 25c red brn, dk brn & dk bl .25 .20

Joux Chateau — A427

1965, Feb. 6   Engr.
1112 A427 1.30fr redsh brn, brn red & dk brn 1.50 .35

"The English Girl from the Star" by Toulouse-Lautrec — A428

St. Paul on the Damascus Road, Window, Cathedral of Sens — A429

Leaving for the Hunt — A430

Apocalypse Tapestry, 14th Century A431

"The Red Violin" by Raoul Dufy — A432

Designs: No. 1115, "August" miniature of Book of Hours of Jean de France, Duc de Berry ("Les Très Riches Heures du Duc de Berry"), painted by Flemish brothers, Pol, Hermant and Jannequin Limbourg, 1411-16. No. 1116, Scene from oldest existing set of French tapestries, showing the Winepress of the Wrath of God (Revelations 14: 19-20).

1965   Perf. 12x13, 13x12
1113 A428 1fr multicolored .50 .40
1114 A429 1fr multicolored .50 .40
1115 A430 1fr multicolored .30 .30
1116 A431 1fr multicolored .30 .30
1117 A432 1fr blk, pink & car .30 .30
Nos. 1113-1117 (5) 1.90 1.70

No. 1114 issued to commemorate the 800th anniversary of the Cathedral of Sens.
Issued: #1113, 3/12; #1114, 6/5; #1115, 9/25; #1116, 10/30; #1117, 11/6.

Returning Deportees, 1945 — A433

1965, Apr. 1   Unwmk.   Perf. 13
1118 A433 40c Prussian green .50 .30

20th anniv. of the return of people deported during World War II.

House of Youth and Culture, Troyes A434

1965, Apr. 10   Engr.
1119 A434 25c ind, brn & dk grn .25 .20

20th anniv. of the establishment of recreational cultural centers for young people.

Woman Carrying Flowers A435   Flags of France, US, USSR and Great Britain Crushing Swastika A436

1965, Apr. 24   Unwmk.   Perf. 13
1120 A435 60c dk grn, dp org & ver .25 .20

Tourist Campaign of Welcome & Amiability.

1965, May 8
1121 A436 40c black, car & ultra .40 .20

20th anniv. of victory in World War II.

Telegraph Key, Syncom Satellite and Pleumeur-Bodou Station — A437

1965, May 17
1122 A437 60c dk blue, brn & blk .50 .30

Centenary of the ITU.

Croix de Guerre — A438

1965, May 22   Engr.
1123 A438 40c red, brn & brt grn .55 .35

50th anniv. of the Croix de Guerre medal.

Cathedral of Bourges — A439

Moustiers-Sainte-Marie — A440

Views: 30c, Road and tunnel, Mont Blanc. 60c, Aix-les-Bains, sailboat. 75c, Tarn Gorge, Lozère mountains. 95c, Vendée River, man poling boat, and windmill. 1fr, Prehistoric stone monuments, Carnac.

1965
1124 A439 30c bl, vio bl & brn vio .25 .20
1125 A439 40c gray bl & redsh brn .40 .20
1126 A440 50c grn, bl gray & bis .40 .20
1127 A439 60c blue & red brn .85 .25
1128 A439 75c brown, bl & grn 1.25 .90
1129 A440 95c brown, grn & bl 5.75 .90
1130 A440 1fr gray, grn & brn 1.40 .25
Nos. 1124-1130 (7) 10.30 2.90

No. 1124 for the opening of the Mont Blanc Tunnel. No. 1125 (Bourges Cathedral) was issued in connection with the French Philatelic Societies Federation Congress, held at Bourges.
Issued: 40c, June 5; 50c, June 19; 30c, 60c, July 17; others, July 10.
For surcharges see Reunion #354, 362, 365.

Europa Issue, 1965
Common Design Type

1965, Sept. 25   Perf. 13
Size: 36x22mm
1131 CD8 30c red .25 .30
1132 CD8 60c gray .50 .50

Planting Seedling A441   Etienne Régnault, "Le Taureau" and Coast of Reunion A442

1965, Oct. 2
1133 A441 25c slate grn, yel grn & red brn .20 .20

National reforestation campaign.

1965, Oct. 2
1134 A442 30c indigo & dk car .20 .20

Tercentenary of settlement of Reunion.

Atomic Reactor and Diagram, Symbols of Industry, Agriculture and Medicine — A443

1965, Oct. 9
1135 A443 60c brt blue & blk   .50   .30
Atomic Energy Commission, 20th anniv.

Air Academy and Emblem A444

1965, Nov. 6   *Perf. 13*
1136 A444 25c dk blue & green   .35   .30
Air Academy, Salon-de-Provence, 50th anniv.

French Satellite A-1 Issue
Common Design Type
Design: 60c, A-1 satellite.

1965, Nov. 30   **Engr.**   *Perf. 13*
1137 CD121 30c Prus bl, brt bl &
      blk   .25   .20
1138 CD121 60c blk, Prus bl & brt
      bl   .40   .25
   a.   Strip of 2, #1137-1138 + label   .65   .65
Launching of France's 1st satellite, 11/26/65.
For surcharges see Reunion Nos. 358-359.

Arms of Auch — A446

Cities: 20c, Saint-Lô. 25c, Mont-de-Marsan.

Typographed, Photogravure (20c)
1966   *Perf. 14x13; 14 (20c)*
1142 A446 5c blue & red   .20   .20
1143 A446 20c vio bl, sil, gold &
      red   .20   .20
1144 A446 25c red brown & ultra   .60   .20
   Nos. 1142-1144 (3)   1.00   .60

The 5c and 20c were issued in sheets and in vertical coils. In the coils, every 10th stamp has a red control number on the back.
For surcharges see Reunion Nos. 360-360A.

French Satellite D-1 Issue
Common Design Type
1966, Feb. 18   **Engr.**   *Perf. 13*
1148 CD122 60c blue blk, grn & cl   .25   .20

Horses from Bronze Vessel of Vix — A448

"The Newborn" by Georges de La Tour — A449

The Baptism of Judas (4th Century Bishop of Jerusalem) — A450

"The Moon and the Bull" Tapestry by Jean Lurçat A451

"Crispin and Scapin" by Honoré Daumier — A452

1966   *Perf. 13x12, 12x13*
1149 A448 1fr multicolored   .40   .35
1150 A449 1fr multicolored   .40   .35
1151 A450 1fr multicolored   .40   .35
1152 A451 1fr multicolored   .40   .30
1153 A452 1fr multicolored   .40   .30
   Nos. 1149-1153 (5)   2.00   1.65

The design of No. 1149 is a detail from a 6th century B.C. vessel, found in 1953 in a grave near Vix, Cote d'Or.
The design of No. 1151 is from a stained glass window in the 13th century Sainte-Chapelle, Paris.
No. 1150 exists in an imperf, ungummed souv. sheet with 2 progressive die proofs, issued for benefit of the Postal Museum, and not postally valid. Value $2.
Issued: #1149, 3/26; #1150, 6/25; #1151, 10/22; #1152, 11/19; #1153, 12/10.

Chessboard, Knight, Emblems for King and Queen — A453

St. Michael Slaying the Dragon — A455

Rhone Bridge, Pont-Saint-Esprit — A454

1966, Apr. 2   **Engr.**   *Perf. 13*
1154 A453 60c sepia, gray & dk vio
      bl   .60   .45
Issued to publicize the Chess Festival.

1966, Apr. 23   **Unwmk.**   *Perf. 13*
1155 A454 25c black & dull blue   .20   .20

1966, Apr. 30   **Litho. & Engr.**
1156 A455 25c multicolored   .20   .20
Millenium of Mont-Saint-Michel.

Stanislas Leszczynski, Lunéville Chateau — A456

1966, May 6   **Engr.**
1157 A456 25c slate, grn & brn   .20   .20
200th anniv. of the reunion of Lorraine and Bar (Barrois) with France.

St. Andrew's and Sèvre River, Niort — A457

1966, May 28   **Engr.**   *Perf. 13*
1158 A457 40c brt bl, indigo & grn   .30   .20

Bernard Le Bovier de Fontenelle and 1666 Meeting Room A458

1966, June 4
1159 A458 60c dk car rose & brn   .30   .25
300th anniversary, Académie des Sciences.

William the Conqueror, Castle and Norman Ships — A459

1966, June 4
1160 A459 60c brown red & dp bl   .40   .30
900th anniversary of Battle of Hastings.

Tracks, Globe and Eiffel Tower A460

1966, June 11
1161 A460 60c dk brn, car & dull bl   .85   .45
19th International Railroad Congress.

Oléron Bridge A461

1966, June 20
1162 A461 25c Prus bl, brn & bl   .20   .20
Issued to commemorate the opening of Oléron Bridge, connecting Oléron Island in the Bay of Biscay with the French mainland.

Europa Issue, 1966
Common Design Type
1966, Sept. 24   **Engr.**   *Perf. 13*
      Size: 22x36mm
1163 CD9 30c Prussian blue   .25   .25
1164 CD9 60c red   .35   .25

Vercingetorix at Gergovie, 52 B.C. — A462

Bishop Remi Baptizing King Clovis, 496 A.D. — A463

Design: 60c, Charlemagne attending school (page holding book for crowned king).

1966, Nov. 5   *Perf. 13*
1165 A462 40c choc, grn & gray
      bl   .35   .30
1166 A463 40c dk red brn & blk   .35   .30
1167 A463 60c pur, rose car &
      brn   .35   .30
   Nos. 1165-1167 (3)   1.05   .90

Map of Pneumatic Post and Tube A464

1966, Nov. 11
1168 A464 1.60fr maroon & indigo   .65   .30
Centenary of Paris pneumatic post system.

Val Chateau — A465

1966, Nov. 19   **Engr.**   *Perf. 13*
1169 A465 2.30fr dk bl, sl grn &
      brn   2.00   .30

Rance Power Station A466

1966, Dec. 3
1170 A466 60c dk bl, sl grn & brn .45 .45

Tidal power station in the estuary of the Rance River on the English Channel.

European Broadcasting Union Emblem — A467

1967, Mar. 4   Engr.   Perf. 13
1171 A467 40c dk blue & rose brn .25 .20

3rd Intl. Congress of the European Broadcasting Union, Paris, Mar. 8-22.

Father Juniet's Gig by Henri Rousseau — A468

Francois I by Jean Clouet A469

The Bather by Jean-Dominique Ingres — A470

St. Eloi, the Goldsmith, at Work — A471

1967   Engr.   Perf. 13x12, 12x13
1172 A468 1fr multicolored .40 .40
1173 A469 1fr multicolored .40 .40
1174 A470 1fr multicolored .40 .35
1175 A471 1fr multicolored .40 .35
Nos. 1172-1175 (4) 1.60 1.50

The design of No. 1175 is from a 16th century stained glass window in the Church of Sainte Madeleine, Troyes.
Issued: #1172, 4/15; #1173, 7/1; #1174, 9/9; #1175, 10/7.

Snow Crystal and Olympic Rings — A472

1967, Apr. 22   Photo.   Perf. 13
1176 A472 60c brt & lt blue & red .40 .25

Issued to publicize the 10th Winter Olympic Games, Grenoble, Feb. 6-18, 1968.

French Pavilion, EXPO '67 — A473

1967, Apr. 22   Engr.
1177 A473 60c dull bl & bl grn .35 .30

Intl. Exhibition EXPO '67, Montreal, Apr. 28-Oct. 27, 1967.
For surcharge see Reunion No. 363.

Europa Issue, 1967
Common Design Type
1967, Apr. 29   Size: 22x36mm
1178 CD10 30c blue & gray .25 .25
1179 CD10 60c brown & lt blue .55 .45

Great Bridge, Bordeaux A474

1967, May 8
1180 A474 25c olive, blk & brn .25 .20

Nungesser, Coli and "L'Oiseau Blanc" A475

1967, May 8
1181 A475 40c slate, dk & lt brn .50 .35

40th anniv. of the attempted transatlantic flight of Charles Nungesser and François Coil, French aviators.

Goüin House, Tours — A476

1967, May 13   Engr.   Perf. 13
1182 A476 40c vio bl, red brn & red .55 .25

Congress of the Federation of French Philatelic Societies in Tours.

Ramon and Alfort Veterinary School A477

1967, May 27
1183 A477 25c brn, dp bl & yel grn .25 .20

200th anniv. of the Alfort Veterinary School and to honor Professor Gaston Ramon (1886-1963).

Robert Esnault-Pelterie, Diamant Rocket and A-1 Satellite — A478

1967, May 27
1184 A478 60c slate & vio blue .50 .30

Issued to honor Robert Esnault-Pelterie (1881-1957), aviation and space expert.

City Hall, Saint-Quentin A479

Saint-Germain-en-Laye — A480

Views: 60c, Clock Tower, Vire. 75c, Beach, La Baule, Brittany. 95c, Harbor, Boulogne-sur-Mer. 1fr, Rodez Cathedral. 1.50fr, Morlaix; old houses, grotesque carving, viaduct.

1967
1185 A479 50c bl, sl bl & brn .40 .20
1186 A479 60c dp bl, sl bl & dk red brn .60 .50
1187 A479 70c rose car, red brn & bl .40 .20
1188 A480 75c multicolored 1.60 1.25
1189 A480 95c sky bl, lil & sl grn 1.25 1.10
1190 A479 1fr indigo & bl gray .65 .20
1191 A479 1.50fr brt bl, brt grn & red brn 1.25 .30
Nos. 1185-1191 (7) 6.15 3.75

Issued: 1fr, 1.50fr, June 10; 70c, June 17; 50c, 60c, 95c, July 8; 75c, July 24.

Orchids — A481

1967, July 29   Engr.   Perf. 13
1192 A481 40c dp car, brt pink & pur .90 .50

Orleans flower festival.

Scales of Justice, City and Harbor A482

1967, Sept. 4
1193 A483 60c dk plum, dl bl & ocher .50 .30

9th Intl. Accountancy Cong., Paris, 9/6-12.

Cross of Lorraine, Soldiers and Sailors — A483

1967, Oct. 7   Engr.   Perf. 13
1194 A482 25c brn, dp ultra & bl .20 .20

25th anniv. of the Battle of Bir Hacheim.

Marie Curie, Bowl Glowing with Radium A484

1967, Oct. 23   Engr.   Perf. 13
1195 A484 60c dk blue & ultra .40 .30

Marie Curie (1867-1934), scientist who discovered radium and polonium, Nobel prize winner for physics and chemistry.

Lions Emblem A485

Marianne (by Cheffer) — A486

1967, Oct. 28
1196 A485 40c dk car & vio bl 1.00 .50

50th anniversary of Lions International. For surcharge see Reunion No. 364.

1967, Nov. 4   Engr.
1197 A486 25c dark blue .40 .20
1198 A486 30c bright lilac .45 .20
a. Booklet pane of 5 6.00
b. Booklet pane of 10 12.00

Coils (vertical) of Nos. 1197 and 1231 show a red number on the back of every 10th stamp. See Nos. 1230-1231C, 3525. For surcharges see Reunion Nos. 367-368, 389.

King Philip II (Philip Augustus) at Battle of Bouvines A487

Designs: No. 1200, Election of Hugh Capet as King, horiz. 60c, King Louis IX (St. Louis) holding audience for the poor.

1967, Nov. 13   **Engr.**   *Perf. 13*
1199 A487 40c gray & black   .40   .30
1200 A487 40c steel bl & ultra   .40   .30
1201 A487 60c grn & dk red brn   .50   .30
   Nos. 1199-1201 (3)   1.30   .90

Commemorative Medal — A488

1968, Jan. 6   **Engr.**   *Perf. 13*
1202 A488 40c dk slate grn & bis   .25   .20

50th anniversary of postal checking service.

Various Road Signs — A489

1968, Feb. 24
1203 A489 25c lil, red & dk bl grn   .25   .20

Issued to publicize road safety.

Prehistoric Paintings, Lascaux Cave — A490

Arearea (Merriment) by Paul Gauguin — A491

The Dance by Emile Antoine Bourdelle A492

Portrait of the Model by Auguste Renoir A493

1968   **Engr.**   *Perf. 13x12, 12x13*
1204 A490 1fr multicolored   .55   .40
1205 A491 1fr multicolored   .65   .40
1206 A492 1fr car & gray olive   .65   .40
1207 A493 1fr multicolored   .65   .40
   Nos. 1204-1207 (4)   2.50   1.60

Issue dates: #1204, Apr. 13; #1205, Sept. 21; #1206, Oct. 26; #1207, Nov. 9.

Audio-visual Institute, Royan — A494

1968, Apr. 13   *Perf. 13*
1208 A494 40c slate grn, brn & Prus bl   .25   .20

5th Conference for World Cooperation with the theme of teaching living languages by audio-visual means.

Europa Issue, 1968
Common Design Type
1968, Apr. 27
Size: 36x22mm
1209 CD11 30c brt red lil & ocher   .30   .20
1210 CD11 60c brown & lake   .60   .30

Alain René Le Sage — A495

1968, May 4
1211 A495 40c blue & rose vio   .25   .20

Alain René Le Sage (1668-1747), novelist and playwright.

Chateau de Langeais A496

1968, May 4
1212 A496 60c slate bl, grn & red brn   .50   .40

Pierre Larousse A497

1968, May 11   **Engr.**   *Perf. 13*
1213 A497 40c rose vio & brown   .25   .20

Pierre Larousse (1817-75), grammarian, lexicographer and encyclopedist.

Gnarled Trunk and Fir Tree — A498

1968, May 18   **Engr.**   *Perf. 13*
1214 A498 25c grnsh bl, brn & grn   .25   .20

Twinning of Rambouillet Forest in France and the Black Forest in Germany.

Map of Papal Enclave, Valréas, and John XXII Receiving Homage A499

1968, May 25
1215 A499 60c brn, bis brn & pur   .55   .40

Papal enclave at Valréas, 650th anniv.

Louis XIV, Arms of France and Flanders A500

1968, June 29
1216 A500 40c rose car, gray & lemon   .25   .20

300th anniv. of the Treaty of Aachen which reunited Flanders with France.

Martrou Bridge, Rochefort A501

1968, July 20
1217 A501 25c sky bl, blk & dk red brn   .25   .20

Letord Lorraine Bimotor Plane over Map of France A502

1968, Aug. 17   **Engr.**   *Perf. 13*
1218 A502 25c brt blue, indigo & red   .50   .30

1st regularly scheduled air mail route in France from Paris to St. Nazaire, 50th anniv.

Tower de Constance, Aigues-Mortes A503

1968, Aug. 31
1219 A503 25c red brn, sky bl & olive bister   .25   .20

Bicentenary of the release of Huguenot prisoners from the Tower de Constance, Aigues-Mortes.

Cathedral and Pont Vieux, Beziers A504

1968, Sept. 7   **Engr.**   *Perf. 13*
1220 A504 40c ind, bis & grn   .85   .50

"Victory" over White Tower of Salonika — A505

1968, Sept. 28
1221 A505 40c red lilac & plum   .25   .20

50th anniv. of the armistice on the eastern front in World War I, Sept. 29, 1918.

Louis XV, Arms of France and Corsica A506

1968, Oct. 5   *Perf. 13*
1222 A506 25c ultra, grn & blk   .25   .20

Return of Corsica to France, 200th anniv.

Relay Race A507

1968, Oct. 12
1223 A507 40c ultra, brt grn & ol brn   .50   .30

19th Olympic Games, Mexico City, 10/12-27.

Polar Camp with Helicopter, Plane and Snocat Tractor — A508

1968, Oct. 19
1224 A508 40c Prus bl, lt grnsh bl & brn bl   .35   .20

20 years of French Polar expeditions. For surcharge see Reunion No. 366.

Leon Bailby, Paris Opera Staircase and Hospital Beds — A509   "Victory" over Arc de Triomphe and Eternal Flame — A510

1968, Oct. 26
1225 A509 40c ocher & maroon   .25   .20

50th anniv. of the "Little White Beds" children's hospital fund.

1968, Nov. 9   **Engr.**   *Perf. 13*
1226 A510 25c dk car rose & dp blue   .25   .20

50th anniv. of the armistice which ended World War I.

Death of Bertrand Du Guesclin at Chateauneuf-de-Randon, 1380 — A511

#1228, King Philip IV (the Fair) and first States-General assembly, 1302, horiz. 60c, Joan of Arc leaving Vaucouleurs, 1429.

1968, Nov. 16
1227 A511 40c green, ultra & brn .40 .30
1228 A511 40c cop red, grn & gray .40 .30
1229 A511 60c vio bl, sl bl & bis .40 .30
Nos. 1227-1229 (3) 1.20 .90

See No. 1260.

Marianne Type of 1967
1969-70 Engr. Perf. 13
1230 A486 30c green .35 .20
a. Booklet pane of 10 8.50
1231 A486 40c deep carmine .45 .20
a. Booklet pane of 5 (horiz. strip) 7.50
b. Booklet pane of 10 8.50
d. With label ('70) .50 .25

Typo. Perf. 14x13
1231C A486 30c blue green .20 .20
Nos. 1230-1231C (3) 1.00 .60

No. 1231d was issued in sheets of 50 with alternating labels showing coat of arms of Perigueux, arranged checkerwise, to commemorate the inauguration of the Perigueux stamp printing plant.
The 40c coil is noted after No. 1198.

Church of Brou, Bourg-en-Bresse — A512

Views: 80c, Vouglans Dam, Jura. 85c, Chateau de Chantilly. 1.15fr, Sailboats in La Trinité-sur-Mer harbor.

1969 Engr. Perf. 13
1232 A512 45c olive, bl & red brn .25 .20
1233 A512 80c ol bis, brn red & dk brn .45 .20
1234 A512 85c sl grn, dl bl & gray .90 .45
1235 A512 1.15fr brt bl, gray grn & brn .90 .40
Nos. 1232-1235 (4) 2.50 1.25

"February" Bas-relief from Amiens Cathedral A513

Philip the Good, by Roger van der Weyden A514

Sts. Savin and Cyprian before Ladicius, Mural, St. Savin, Vienne — A515

The Circus, by Georges Seurat A515a

1969 Perf. 12x13
1236 A513 1fr dk green & brn .50 .35
1237 A514 1fr multicolored .50 .35
1238 A515 1fr multicolored .50 .35
1239 A515a 1fr multicolored .50 .35
Nos. 1236-1239 (4) 2.00 1.40

Issue dates: No. 1236, Feb. 22; No. 1237, May 3; No. 1238, June 28; No. 1239, Nov. 8.

Gallic Coin Type of 1964-66
1969 Typo. Perf. 13½x14
1240 A418 22c brt green & vio .80 .20
1241 A418 35c red & ultra 1.65 .40
1242 A418 70c ultra & red brn 6.00 2.00
Nos. 1240-1242 (3) 8.45 2.60

Nos. 1240-1242 are known only precanceled. See note after No. 132.

Hautefort Chateau A516

1969, Apr. 5 Engr. Perf. 13
1243 A516 70c blue, slate & bister .40 .30

Irises A517

1969, Apr. 12 Photo.
1244 A517 45c multicolored .40 .30

3rd Intl. Flower Show, Paris, 4/23-10/5.

Europa Issue, 1969
Common Design Type
1969, Apr. 26 Engr. Perf. 13
Size: 36x22mm
1245 CD12 40c carmine rose .20 .20
1246 CD12 70c Prussian blue .30 .25

Albert Thomas and Thomas Memorial, Geneva A518

1969, May 10 Engr. Perf. 13
1247 A518 70c brn, ol bis & ind .40 .30

ILO, 50th anniv., and honoring Thomas (1878-1932), director of the ILO (1920-32).

Garigliano Battle Scene, 1944 — A519

1969, May 10
1248 A519 45c black & violet .40 .40

25th anniv. of the Battle of the Garigliano against the Germans.

Chateau du Marché, Chalons-sur-Marne A520

Parachutists over Normandy Beach A521

1969, May 24
1249 A520 45c bis, dull bl & grn .50 .40

Federation of French Philatelic Societies, 42nd congress.

1969, May 31
1250 A521 45c dk blue & vio bl .95 .40

Landing of Special Air Service and Free French commandos in Normandy, June 6, 1944, 25th anniv.

Monument of the French Resistance, Mt. Mouchet — A522

1969, June 7
1251 A522 45c dk grn, slate & ind .90 .65

25th anniv. of the battle of Mt. Mouchet between French resistance fighters and the Germans, June 2 and 10, 1944.

French Troops Landing in Provence — A523

1969, Aug. 23 Engr. Perf. 13
1252 A523 45c slate & blk brn 1.00 .65

25th anniv. of the landing of French and American forces in Provence, Aug. 15, 1944.

Russian and French Aviators — A524

1969, Oct. 18 Engr. Perf. 13
1253 A524 45c slate, dp bl & car 1.00 .80

Issued to honor the French aviators of the Normandy-Neman Squadron who fought on the Russian Front, 1942-45.

Kayak on Isère River A525

1969, Aug. 2 Engr. Perf. 13
1254 A525 70c org brn, ol & dk bl .45 .30

Intl. Canoe and Kayak Championships, Bourg-Saint-Maurice, Savoy, July 31-Aug. 6.

Napoleon as Young Officer and his Birthplace, Ajaccio — A526

1969, Aug. 16
1255 A526 70c brt grnsh bl, ol & rose vio .45 .30

Napoleon Bonaparte (1769-1821).
For surcharge see Reunion No. 370.

Drops of Water and Diamond A527

Mediterranean Mouflon A528

1969, Sept. 27
1256 A527 70c blk, dp bl & brt grn .50 .30
European Water Charter.

1969, Oct. 11
1257 A528 45c ol, blk & org brn 3.25 1.25
Issued to publicize wildlife protection.

Central School of Arts and Crafts A529

1969, Oct. 18
1258 A529 70c dk grn, yel grn & org .40 .30

Inauguration of the Central School of Arts and Crafts at Chatenay-Malabry.

Nuclear Submarine "Le Redoutable" — A530

1969, Oct. 25
1259 A530 70c dp bl, grn & sl grn .40 .30

Type of 1968 and

Henri IV and Edict of Nantes — A531

Designs: No. 1260, Pierre Terrail de Bayard wounded at Battle of Brescia (after a painting in Versailles). No. 1262, Louis XI, Charles the Bold and map of France.

1969, Nov. 8   Engr.   Perf. 13
1260 A511 80c brn, bister & blk .50 .30
1261 A531 80c blk & vio bl .50 .30
1262 A531 80c ol, dp grn & dk red brn .50 .30
    Nos. 1260-1262 (3) 1.50 .90

"Firecrest" and Alain Gerbault — A532

1970, Jan. 10   Engr.   Perf. 13
1263 A532 70c ind, brt bl & gray .75 .50

Completion of Alain Gerbault's trip around the world aboard the "Firecrest," 1923-29, 40th anniv.

Gendarmery Emblem, Mountain Climber, Helicopter, Motorcyclists and Motorboat — A533

1970, Jan. 31
1264 A533 45c sl grn, dk bl & brn 1.25 .50

National Gendarmery, founded 1791.

Field Ball Player — A534

1970, Feb. 21   Engr.   Perf. 13
1265 A534 80c slate green .50 .50

7th Intl. Field Ball Games, Feb. 26-Mar. 8.

Alphonse Juin and Church of the Invalides — A535

1970, Feb. 28
1266 A535 45c gray bl & dk brn .35 .20

Issued to honor Marshal Alphonse Pierre Juin (1888-1967), military leader.

Aerotrain A536

1970, Mar. 7
1267 A536 80c purple & gray .65 .50

Introduction of the aerotrain, which reaches a speed of 320 miles per hour.

Pierre Joseph Pelletier, Joseph Bienaimé Caventou, Quinine Formula and Cell — A537

1970, Mar. 21   Engr.   Perf. 13
1268 A537 50c slate grn, sky bl & dp car .35 .30

Discovery of quinine, 150th anniversary.

Pink Flamingos A538

Diamant B Rocket and Radar A539

1970, Mar. 21
1269 A538 45c olive, gray & pink .35 .25

European Nature Conservation Year, 1970.

1970, Mar. 28
1270 A539 45c bright green .65 .40

Space center in Guyana and the launching of the Diamant B rocket, Mar. 10, 1970.

Europa Issue, 1970
Common Design Type

1970, May 2   Engr.   Perf. 13
    Size: 36x22mm
1271 CD13 40c deep carmine .25 .20
1272 CD13 80c sky blue .40 .20

Annunication, by Primitive Painter of Savoy, 1480 — A540

The Triumph of Flora, by Jean Baptiste Carpeaux — A541

Diana Returning from the Hunt, by François Boucher — A542

Dancer with Bouquet, by Edgar Degas A543

1970   Perf. 12x13, 13x12
1273 A540 1fr multicolored .85 .45
1274 A541 1fr red brown .85 .45
1275 A542 1fr multicolored .85 .45
1276 A543 1fr multicolored .85 .45
    Nos. 1273-1276 (4) 3.40 1.80

Issue dates: #1273, May 9; #1274, July 4; #1275, Oct. 10; #1276, Nov. 14.

Arms of Lens, Miner's Lamp and Pit Head A544

1970, May 16   Engr.   Perf. 13
1277 A544 40c scarlet .25 .20

43rd Natl. Congress of the Federation of French Philatelic Societies, Lens, May 14-21.

Diamond Rock, Martinique A545

Haute Provence Observatory and Spiral Nebula — A546

Designs: 95c, Chancelade Abbey, Dordogne. 1fr, Gosier Islet, Guadeloupe.

1970, June 20   Engr.   Perf. 13
1278 A545 50c sl grn, brt bl & plum .45 .20
1279 A545 95c lt ol, car & brn 1.25 1.00
1280 A545 1fr sl grn, brt bl & dk car rose .55 .20
1281 A546 1.30fr dk bl, vio bl & dk grn 1.90 1.00
    Nos. 1278-1281 (4) 4.15 2.40

Hand Reaching for Freedom A547

Handicapped Javelin Thrower A548

1970, June 27
1282 A547 45c vio bl, bl & bister .40 .25

Liberation of concentration camps, 25th anniv.

1970, June 27
1283 A548 45c rose car, ultra & emer .40 .25

Issued to publicize the International Games of the Handicapped, St. Etienne, June 1970.

Pole Vault — A549

1970, Sept. 11   Engr.   Perf. 13
1284 A549 45c car, bl & indigo .45 .25

First European Junior Athletic Championships, Colombes, Sept. 11-13.

Royal Salt Works, Arc-et-Senans — A550

1970, Sept. 26
1285 A550 80c bl, brn & dk grn 1.50 .65

Restoration of the 18th cent. Royal Salt Works buildings, by Claude Nicolas Ledoux (1736-1806) at Arc-et-Senans, for use as a center for studies of all aspects of future human life.

Armand Jean du Plessis, Duc de Richelieu — A551

Designs: No. 1287, Battle of Fontenoy, 1745. No. 1288, Louis XIV and Versailles.

1970, Oct. 17   **Engr.**   **Perf. 13**
1286 A551 45c blk, sl & car rose   .65   .35
1287 A551 45c org, brn & indigo   .65   .35
1288 A551 45c sl grn, lem & org brn   .65   .35
    Nos. 1286-1288 (3)   1.95   1.05

UN Headquarters in New York and Geneva — A552

1970, Oct. 24   **Engr.**   **Perf. 13**
1289 A552 80c ol, dp ultra & dk pur   .40   .25
25th anniversary of the United Nations.

View of Bordeaux and France No. 43 — A553

1970, Nov. 7
1290 A553 80c vio bl & gray bl   .40   .25
Centenary of the Bordeaux issue.

Col. Denfert-Rochereau and Lion of Belfort, by Frederic A. Bartholdi — A554

1970, Nov. 14
1291 A554 45c dk bl, ol & red brn   .40   .25
Centenary of the siege of Belfort during Franco-Prussian War.

Marianne (by Bequet) — A555

1971-74   **Typo.**   **Perf. 14x13**
1292 A555 45c sky blue   .30   .20
1292A A555 60c green ('74)   .90   .20
For surcharges see Reunion #371, 397-398.

        Engr.   **Perf. 13**
1293 A555 50c rose carmine   .30   .20
   a.   Bklt. pane of 5 (horiz. strip)   5.00
   b.   Booklet pane of 10   10.00
1294 A555 60c green ('74)   5.00   .35
   a.   Booklet pane of 10   65.00
1294B A555 80c car rose ('74)   .50   .20
   c.   Booklet pane of 5   9.00
   d.   Booklet pane of 10   12.00
    Nos. 1293-1294B (3)   5.80   .75

Nos. 1294 and 1294B issued also in vertical coils with control number on back of every 10th stamp.

No. 1293 issued only in booklets and in vertical coils with red control number on back of every 10th stamp.
    See Nos. 1494-1498, 3526.

St. Matthew, Sculpture from Strasbourg Cathedral A556

Winnower, by François Millet A557

The Dreamer, by Georges Rouault A558

1971   **Engr.**   **Perf. 12x13**
1295 A556 1fr dark red brown   .85   .50
1296 A557 1fr multicolored   .75   .40
1297 A558 1fr multicolored   .75   .40
    Nos. 1295-1297 (3)   2.35   1.30

Issued: #1295, 1/23; #1296, 4/3; #1297, 6/5.

Figure Skating Pair A560

1971, Feb. 20   **Engr.**   **Perf. 13**
1299 A560 80c vio bl, sl & aqua   .55   .30
World Figure Skating Championships, Lyons, Feb. 23-28.

Underwater Exploration — A561

1971, Mar. 6
1300 A561 80c blue blk & bl grn   .40   .25
International Exhibition of Ocean Exploration, Bordeaux, Mar. 9-14.

Cape Horn Clipper "Antoinette" and Solidor Castle, Saint-Malo — A562

1971, Apr. 10   **Engr.**   **Perf. 13**
1301 A562 80c blue, pur & slate   1.25   .90
For surcharge see Reunion No. 372.

Pyrenean Chamois — A563

1971, Apr. 24   **Engr.**   **Perf. 13**
1302 A563 65c bl, dk brn & brn ol   .65   .30
National Park of Western Pyrenees.

Europa Issue, 1971
Common Design Type and

Santa Maria della Salute, Venice A564

1971, May 8   **Engr.**   **Perf. 13**
1303 A564 50c blue gray & ol bis   .30   .25
      Size: 36x22mm
1304 CD14 80c rose lilac   .45   .40

Cardinal, Nobleman and Lawyer — A565

Storming of the Bastille — A566

Design: No. 1306, Battle of Valmy.

1971
1305 A565 45c bl, rose red & pur   .55   .40
1306 A565 45c bl, ol bis & brn red   .65   .40
1307 A566 65c dk brn, gray bl & mag   1.00   .40
    Nos. 1305-1307 (3)   2.20   1.20

No. 1305 commemorates the opening of the Estates General, May 5, 1789; No. 1306, Battle of Valmy (Sept. 20, 1792) between French and Prussian armies; 65c, Storming of the Bastille, Paris, July 14, 1789.
    Issued: #1305, 5/8; #1306, 9/18; 65c, 7/10.

Grenoble A568

1971, May 29   **Engr.**   **Perf. 13**
1308 A568 50c ocher, lil & rose red   .35   .20
44th Natl. Cong. of the Federation of French Philatelic Societies, Grenoble, May 30-31.

"Rural Family Aid" Shedding Light on Village — A569

1971, June 5
1309 A569 40c vio, bl & grn   .25   .20
Aid for rural families.
For surcharge see Reunion No. 373.

Chateau and Fort de Sedan A570

Pont d'Arc, Ardèche Gorge — A571

Views: 60c, Sainte Chapelle, Riom. 65c, Fountain and tower, Dole. 90c, Tower and street, Riquewihr.

1971   **Engr.**   **Perf. 13**
1310 A571 60c black, grn & bl   .25   .20
1311 A571 65c lil, ocher & blk   .35   .20
1312 A571 90c grn, vio brn & red brn   .50   .20
1313 A570 1.10fr sl grn, Prus bl & brn   .60   .30
1314 A571 1.40fr sl grn, bl & dk brn   .75   .20
    Nos. 1310-1314 (5)   2.45   1.10

Issued: 60c, 6/19; 65c, 90c, 7/3; 1.10fr, 1.40fr, 6/12.
For surcharges see Reunion Nos. 374, 381.

Gallic Coin Type of 1964-66
1971, July 1   **Typo.**   **Perf. 13½x14**
1315 A418 26c lilac & brn   .40   .20
1316 A418 30c lt brown & brn   .75   .20
1317 A418 45c dull green & brn   1.40   .25
1318 A418 90c red & brown   1.90   .40
    Nos. 1315-1318 (4)   4.45   1.05

Nos. 1315-1318 are known only precanceled. See second paragraph after No. 132.

Bourbon Palace A572

1971, Aug. 28   **Engr.**   **Perf. 13**
1319 A572 90c violet blue   .75   .25
59th Conf. of the Interparliamentary Union.

Embroidery and Tool Making A573

1971, Oct. 16
1320 A573 90c brn red, brt lil & cl .50 .30
40th anniv. of the first assembly of presidents of artisans' guilds.
For surcharge see Reunion No. 375.

Reunion Chameleon A574

1971, Nov. 6 Photo. Perf. 13
1321 A574 60c brn, yel, grn & blk 1.10 .65
Nature protection.

De Gaulle Issue
Common Design Type and

De Gaulle in Brazzaville, 1944 — A576

Designs: No. 1324, De Gaulle entering Paris, 1944. No. 1325, Pres. de Gaulle, 1970.

1971, Nov. 9 Engr.
1322 CD134 50c black 1.10 .65
1323 A576 50c ultra 1.10 .65
1324 A576 50c rose red 1.10 .65
1325 CD134 50c black 1.10 .65
  a. Strip of 4, #1322-1325 + label 4.50 4.00
1st anniv. of the death of Charles de Gaulle.
See Reunion Nos. 377, 380.

Antoine Portal and first Session of Academy — A577

1971, Nov. 13
1326 A577 45c dk purple & mag .30 .25
Sesquicentennial of the founding of the National Academy of Medicine; Baron Antoine Portal was first president.

L'Etude, by Jean Honoré Fragonard A578

Women in Garden, by Claude Monet A579

St. Peter Presenting Pierre de Bourbon, by Maitre de Moulins A580

Boats, by André Derain — A581

1972 Engr. Perf. 12x13, 13x12
1327 A578 1fr black & multi .90 .75
1328 A579 1fr slate grn & multi 1.75 .75
1329 A580 2fr dk brown & multi 2.50 1.25
1330 A581 2fr yellow & multi 3.50 1.50
  Nos. 1327-1330 (4) 8.65 4.25
Issue dates: #1327, Jan. 22; #1328, June 17; #1329, Oct. 14; #1330, Dec. 16.

Map of South Indian Ocean, Penguin and Ships — A582

1972, Jan. 29 Perf. 13
1331 A582 90c black, bl & ocher .65 .40
Bicentenary of discovery of the Crozet and Kerguelen Islands.

Slalom and Olympic Emblems A583

1972, Feb. 7
1332 A583 90c dk olive & dp car .55 .35
11th Winter Olympic Games, Sapporo, Japan, Feb. 3-13.

Hearts, UN Emblem, Caduceus and Pacemaker A584

1972, Apr. 8 Engr. Perf. 13
1333 A584 45c dk car, org & gray .35 .25
"Your heart is your health," world health month.

Red Deer, Sologne Plateau — A585

Charlieu Abbey A585a

Bazoches-du-Morvand Chateau — A586

Saint-Just Cathedral, Narbonne A587

1972 Perf. 13
1334 A585 1fr ocher & red brn .65 .20
1335 A585a 1.20fr sl & dull brn .65 .20
1336 A586 2fr sl grn, blk & red brn 1.00 .20
1337 A587 3.50fr bl, gray ol & car rose 1.90 .55
  Nos. 1334-1337 (4) 4.20 1.15
Issued: 1fr, 9/10; 1.20fr, 4/29; 2fr, 9/9; 3.50fr, 4/8.
For surcharge see Reunion No. 388.

Eagle Owl — A588

Nature protection: 60c, Salmon, horiz.

1972
1338 A588 60c grn, ind & brt bl 2.25 .60
1339 A588 65c sl, ol brn & sep 1.40 .30
Issue dates: 60c, May 27; 65c, Apr. 15.

Europa Issue 1972
Common Design Type and

Aix-la-Chapelle Cathedral — A589

1972, Apr. 22 Engr. Perf. 13
1340 A589 50c yel, vio brn & dk ol .25 .25
Photo.
Size: 22x36mm
1341 CD15 90c red org & multi .50 .35

Bouquet Made of Hearts and Blood Donors' Emblem A590

Newfoundlander "Côte d'Emeraude" A591

1972, May 5 Engr.
1342 A590 40c red .30 .20
20th anniv. of the Blood Donors Association of Post and Telecommunications Employees.
For surcharge see Reunion No. 383.

1972, May 6
1343 A591 90c org, vio bl & sl grn 1.00 .80

Cathedral, Saint-Brieuc A592

1972, May 20
1344 A592 50c lilac rose .30 .20
45th Congress of the Federation of French Philatelic Societies, Saint-Brieuc, May 21-22.

Hand Holding Symbol of Postal Code A593

1972, June 3 Typo. Perf. 14x13
1345 A593 30c green, blk & car .20 .20
1346 A593 50c car, blk & yel .30 .20
Introduction of postal code system.
For surcharges see Reunion Nos. 384-385.

Old and New Communications A594

1972, July 1 Engr. Perf. 13
1347 A594 45c slate & vio blue .40 .20
21st Intl. Congress of P.T.T. (Post, Telegraph & Telephone) Employees, Paris, 7/1-7.

Hurdler and Olympic Rings
A595

1972, July 8
1348 A595 1fr deep olive   .50 .20
20th Olympic Games, Munich, 8/26-9/11.

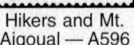

Hikers and Mt. Aigoual — A596   Bicyclist — A597

1972, July 15   Photo.   Perf. 13
1349 A596 40c brt rose & multi 1.50 .60
Intl. Year of Tourism and 25th anniv. of the Natl. Hikers Association.

1972, July 22   Engr.
1350 A597 1fr gray, brn & lil 1.90 .60
World Bicycling Championships, Marseille, July 29-Aug. 2.

"Incroyables and Merveilleuses," 1794 — A598

French History: 60c, Bonaparte at the Arcole Bridge. 65c, Egyptian expedition (soldiers and scientists finding antiquities; pyramids in background).

1972   Engr.   Perf. 13
1351 A598 45c ol, dk grn & car rose   .40 .30
1352 A598 60c red, blk & ind   .85 .40
1353 A598 65c ocher, ultra & choc   .85 .40
  Nos. 1351-1353 (3)   2.10 1.10
. Issued: 45c, Oct. 7; 60c, 65c, Nov. 11.

Champollion, Rosetta Stone with Key Inscription — A599

1972, Oct. 14
1354 A599 90c vio bl, brn red & blk .60 .30
Sesquicentennial of the deciphering of hieroglyphs by Jean-François Champollion.

St. Teresa, Portal of Notre Dame of Alençon
A600

1973, Jan. 6   Engr.   Perf. 13
1355 A600 1fr Prus blue & indigo .60 .45
Centenary of the birth of St. Teresa of Lisieux, the Little Flower (Thérèse Martin, 1873-1897), Carmelite nun.

Anthurium (Martinique) — A601

1973, Jan. 20   Photo.
1356 A601 50c gray & multi   .40 .20

Colors of France and Germany Interlaced — A602

1973, Jan. 22
1357 A602 50c multicolored   .40 .20
10th anniv. of the Franco-German Cooperation Treaty. See Germany No. 1101.

Polish Immigrants — A603

1973, Feb. 3   Engr.   Perf. 13
1358 A603 40c slate grn, dp car & brn   .25 .25
50th anniversary of Polish immigration into France, 1921-1923.

Last Supper, St. Austremoine Church, Issoire — A604

Kneeling Woman, by Charles Le Brun
A605

Angel, Wood, Moutier-D'Ahun — A606

Lady Playing Archlute, by Antoine Watteau
A607

1973   Engr.   Perf. 12x13
1359 A604 2fr brown & multi 1.75 1.25
1360 A605 2fr dk red & yel 1.75 1.40
1361 A606 2fr ol brn & vio brn 1.75 1.25
1362 A607 2fr black & multi 1.75 1.25
  Nos. 1359-1362 (4)   7.00 5.15
Issue dates: #1359, Feb. 10; #1360, Apr. 28; #1361, May 26; #1362, Sept. 22.

Tuileries Palace, Telephone Relays
A608

Oil Tanker, Francis I Lock
A609

Airbus A300-B
A610

1973
1363 A608 45c ultra, sl grn & bis .30 .20
1364 A609 90c plum, blk & bl .55 .20
1365 A610 3fr dk brn, bl & blk 1.90 .80
  Nos. 1363-1365 (3)   2.75 1.20
French technical achievements.
Issued: 45c, 5/15; 90c, 10/27; 3fr, 4/7.

Europa Issue 1973
Common Design Type and

City Hall, Brussels, CEPT Emblem — A611

1973, Apr. 14   Engr.   Perf. 13
1366 A611 50c brt pink & choc .45 .25

Photo.
Size: 36x22mm
1367 CD16 90c slate grn & multi 1.60 .75

Masonic Lodge Emblem
A612

1973, May 12   Engr.   Perf. 13
1368 A612 90c magenta & vio bl .55 .30
Bicentenary of the Free Masons of France.

Guadeloupe Raccoon
A613

White Storks
A614

1973
1369 A613 40c lilac, sepia & olive .35 .20
1370 A614 60c blk, aqua & org red .50 .25
Nature protection.
Issue dates: 40c, June 23; 60c, May 12.

Tourist Issue

Doubs Waterfall
A615

Clos-Lucé, Amboise
A617

Palace of Dukes of Burgundy, Dijon
A616

Design: 90c, Gien Chateau.

1973   Engr.   Perf. 13
1371 A615 60c multicolored   .30 .20
1372 A616 65c red & purple   .30 .20
1373 A616 90c Prus bl, ind & brn .35 .20
1374 A617 1fr ocher, bl & sl grn .35 .20
  Nos. 1371-1374 (4)   1.30 .80
Issued: 60c, 9/8; 65c, 5/19; 90c, 8/18; 1fr, 6/23.
For surcharge see Reunion No. 387.

Academy Emblem — A618

1973, May 26
1375 A618 1fr lil, slate grn & red .50 .30
Academy of Overseas Sciences, 50th anniv.

Racing Car and Clocks
A619

1973, June 2
1376 A619 60c dk brown & blue   .65 .50
24-hour automobile race at Le Mans, 50th anniv.

Five-master France II — A620

1973, June 9
1377 A620 90c ultra, Prus bl & ind   1.10 .55
For surcharge see Reunion No. 386.

Tower and Square, Toulouse — A621

1973, June 9
1378 A621 50c purple & red brn   .30 .20
46th Congress of the Federation of French Philatelic Societies, Toulouse, June 9-12.

Dr. Armauer G. Hansen — A622   Ducretet and his Transmission Diagram — A623

1973, Sept. 29   Engr.   Perf. 13
1379 A622 45c grn, dk ol & ocher   .30 .20
Centenary of the discovery of the Hansen bacillus, the cause of leprosy.

1973, Oct. 6
1380 A623 1fr yel grn & magenta   .40 .30
75th anniversary of the first transmission of radio signals from the Eiffel Tower to the Pantheon by Eugene Ducretet (1844-1915).

Molière as Sganarelle — A624

1973, Oct. 20
1381 A624 1fr dk red & olive brn   .55 .35
Moliere (Jean-Baptiste Poquelin; 1622-1673), playwright and actor.

Pierre Bourgoin and Philippe Kieffer
A625

1973, Oct. 27
1382 A625 1fr red, rose cl & vio bl   .50 .30
Pierre Bourgoin (1907-70), and Philippe Kieffer (1899-1963), heroes of the Free French forces in World War II.

Napoleon, Jean Portalis and Palace of Justice, Paris — A626

Exhibition Halls — A627

The Coronation of Napoleon, by Jean Louis David — A628

1973   Engr.   Perf. 13
1383 A626 45c blue, choc & gray   .55 .30
1384 A627 60c ol, sl grn & brn   .55 .50
1385 A628 1fr sl grn, ol & claret   .65 .55
    Nos. 1383-1385 (3)   1.75 1.35
History of France. 45c, for the preparation of the Code Napoleon; 60c, Napoleon's encouragement of industry; 1fr, his coronation.
Issued: 45c, 11/3; 60c, 11/24; 1fr, 11/12.

Eternal Flame, Arc de Triomphe A629   Weather Vane A630

1973, Nov. 10
1386 A629 40c pur, vio bl & red   .40 .30
50th anniv. of the Eternal Flame at the Arc de Triomphe, Paris.

1973, Dec. 1
1387 A630 65c ultra, blk & grn   .40 .30
50th anniv. of the Dept. of Agriculture.

Human Rights Flame and Man — A631   Postal Museum — A632

1973, Dec. 8   Engr.   Perf. 13
1388 A631 45c car, org & blk   .30 .25
25th anniversary of the Universal Declaration of Human Rights.

1973, Dec. 19
1389 A632 50c maroon & bister   .30 .25
Opening of new post and philately museum, Paris.

ARPHILA 75 Emblem A633

1974, Jan. 19   Engr.   Perf. 13
1390 A633 50c brn, bl & brt lil   .25 .20
ARPHILA 75 Philatelic Exhibition, Paris, June 1975.
For surcharge see Reunion No. 390.

Concorde over Charles de Gaulle Airport A634

Turbotrain T.G.V. 001 A635

Phenix Nuclear Power Station A636

1974   Engr.   Perf. 13
1391 A634 60c pur & ol gray   .40 .30
1392 A635 60c multicolored   1.10 .55
1393 A636 65c multicolored   .40 .30
    Nos. 1391-1393 (3)   1.90 1.15
French technical achievements.
Issued: #1391, 3/18; #1392, 8/31; 65c, 9/21.

Cardinal Richelieu, by Philippe de Champaigne — A637

Painting by Joan Miró A638

Canal du Loing, by Alfred Sisley — A639

"In Honor of Nicolas Fouquet," Tapestry by Georges Mathieu A640

Engr., Photo. (#1395, 1397)
1974   Perf. 12x13, 13x12
1394 A637 2fr multicolored   1.25 1.00
1395 A638 2fr multicolored   1.25 1.25
1396 A639 2fr multicolored   1.75 1.25
1397 A640 2fr multicolored   1.75 1.25
    Nos. 1394-1397 (4)   6.00 4.75
Nos. 1394-1397 are printed in sheets of 25 with alternating labels publicizing "ARPHILA 75," Paris, June 6-16, 1975.
Issue dates: #1394, Mar. 23; #1395, Sept. 14; #1396, Nov. 9; #1397, Nov. 16.
For surcharges see Reunion Nos. 391-394.

French Alps and Gentian A641

1974, Mar. 30   Engr.   Perf. 13
1398 A641 65c vio blue & gray   .40 .25
Centenary of the French Alpine Club.

Europa Issue 1974

"Age of Bronze," by Auguste Rodin — A642

"Air," by Aristide Maillol A643

1974, Apr. 20   Perf. 13
1399 A642 50c brt rose lil & blk   .30 .25
1400 A643 90c olive & brown   .55 .40

Sea Rescue — A644

1974, Apr. 27
1401 A644 90c multicolored   .40 .30
  Reorganized sea rescue organization.
For surcharge see Reunion No. 395.

Council Building, View of Strasbourg
and Emblem — A645

1974, May 4   Engr.   Perf. 13
1402 A645 45c indigo, bister & bl .30 .25
  25th anniversary of the Council of Europe.

Tourist Issue

View of
Salers
A646

Basilica of St.   Seashell over
Nicolas de   Corsica — A648
Porte — A647

Design: 1.10fr, View of Lot Valley.

1974   Engr.   Perf. 13
1403 A646 65c yel grn & choc   .25 .20
1404 A646 1.10fr choc & sl grn .45 .30
1405 A647 2fr gray & lilac   .80 .30
1406 A648 3fr multicolored   1.00 .40
  Nos. 1403-1406 (4)   2.50 1.20

  Issued: 65c, 6/22; 1.10fr, 9/7; 2fr, 10/12; 3fr, 5/11.

Bison
A649

Giant
Armadillo
of Guyana
A650

1974
1407 A649 40c bis, choc & bl   .35 .20
1408 A650 65c slate, olive & grn .35 .20
  Nature protection.
Issued: #1407, May 25; #1408, Oct. 19.

Americans Landing in Normandy and
Arms of Normandy — A651

General Marie-
Pierre
Koenig — A652

Order of the French
Resistance — A653

1974
1409 A651 45c grn, rose & ind   .80 .50
1410 A652 1fr multicolored   .50 .35
1411 A653 1fr multicolored   .65 .50
  Nos. 1409-1411 (3)   1.95 1.35

  30th anniversary of the liberation of France
from the Nazis. Design of No. 1410 includes
diagram of battle of Bir-Hakeim and Free
French and Bir-Hakeim memorials.
  Issued: 45c, 6/8; #1410, 5/25; #1411, 11/23.
See No. B478.

Pfister House, 16th
Century,
Colmar — A654

1974, June 1
1412 A654 50c multicolored   .25 .20
  47th Congress of the Federation of French
Philatelic Societies, Colmar, May 30-June 4.

Chess
A655

1974, June 8
1413 A655 1fr dk brown & multi .60 .35
  21st Chess Olympiad, Nice, June 6-30.

Facade with
Statue of Louis
XIV, and 1675
Medal — A656

1974, June 15
1414 A656 40c indigo, bl & brn   .30 .20
  300th anniversary of the founding of the
Hotel des Invalides (Home for poor and sick
officers and soldiers).

Peacocks Holding Letter, and
Globe — A657

1974, Oct. 5   Engr.   Perf. 13
1415 A657 1.20fr ultra, dp grn &
            dk car   .40 .30
  Centenary of Universal Postal Union.
For surcharge see Reunion No. 396.

Copernicus and Heliocentric
System — A658

1974, Oct. 12
1416 A658 1.20fr multicolored   .35 .25
  500th anniversary of the birth of Nicolaus
Copernicus (1473-1543), Polish astronomer.

Tourist Issue

Palace of
Justice,
Rouen
A659

Saint-Pol-de-Leon
A660

Chateau de Rochechouart — A661

1975   Engr.   Perf. 13
1417 A659 85c multicolored   .35 .30
1418 A660 1.20fr bl, bis & choc .40 .30
1419 A661 1.40fr brn, ind & grn .50 .30
  Nos. 1417-1419 (3)   1.25 .90

Issued: 85c, 1/25; 1.20fr, 1/18; 1.40fr, 1/11.

Snowy
Egret — A662

Gallic
Coin — A663

1975, Feb. 15   Engr.   Perf. 13
1420 A662 70c brt blue & bister .40 .30
  Nature protection.

1975, Feb. 16   Typo.   Perf. 13½x14
1421 A663 42c orange & mag   1.10 .45
1422 A663 48c lt bl & red brn 1.25 .70
1423 A663 70c brt pink & red   2.25 1.10
1424 A663 1.35fr lt green & brn 2.40 1.25
  Nos. 1421-1424 (4)   7.00 3.50

  Nos. 1421-1424 are known only precanceled. See second note after No. 132. See
Nos. 1460-1463, 1487-1490.

The Eye — A664

Ionic Capital — A665

Graphic Art — A666

Ceres — A667

1975   Engr.   Perf. 13
1425 A664 1fr red, pur & org   .45 .30
1426 A665 2fr grn, sl grn & mag .80 .55
1427 A666 3fr dk car & ol grn 1.25 .90
1428 A667 4fr red, sl grn & bis 1.60 1.25
  Nos. 1425-1428 (4)   4.10 3.00

Souvenir Sheet
1429   Sheet of 4   7.50 7.50
  a. A664 2fr dp car & slate blue 1.00 1.00
  b. A665 3fr brt bl, sl bl & dp car 1.40 1.40
  c. A666 4fr slate blue, brt bl & plum 2.00 2.00
  d. A667 6fr brt bl, sl bl & plum 2.50 2.50

  ARPHILA 75, Intl. Philatelic Exhibition,
Paris, 6/6-16. Issued: 1fr, 3/1; 2fr, 3/22; 3fr,
4/19; 4fr, 5/17; #1429, 4/2.

Pres. Georges
Pompidou
A668

Paul as Harlequin,
by Picasso
A669

1975, Apr. 3 **Engr.** *Perf. 13*
1430 A668 80c black & gray .30 .20
Georges Pompidou (1911-74), President of
France, 1969-74.

1975, Apr. 26 **Photo.** *Perf. 13*
Europa; 1.20fr, Woman on Balcony, by Kees
van Dongen
1431 A669 80c multi .45 .35
1432 A669 1.20fr multi, horiz. .90 .70

Machines,
Globe,
Emblem
A670

1975, May 3 **Engr.**
1433 A670 1.20fr blue, blk & red .40 .30
World Machine Tool Exhib., Paris, 6/7-26.

Senate
Assembly
Hall
A671

1975, May 24 **Engr.** *Perf. 13*
1434 A671 1.20fr olive & dk car .40 .30
Centenary of the Senate of the Republic.

Meter Convention Document, Atom
Diagram and Waves — A672

1975, May 31
1435 A672 1fr multicolored .40 .30
Cent. of Intl. Meter Convention, Paris, 1875.

Metro
Regional
Train
A673

"Gazelle"
Helicopter
A674

1975
1436 A673 1fr indigo & brt bl .90 .30
1437 A674 1.30fr vio bl & grn .65 .40

French technical achievements.
Issue dates: 1fr, June 21; 1.30fr, May 31.

Youth and Flasks,
Symbols of Study
and Growth — A675

1975, June 21
1438 A675 70c red pur & blk .30 .20
Student Health Foundation.

People's
Theater,
Bussang,
and
Maurice
Pottecher
A676

1975, Aug. 9 **Engr.** *Perf. 13*
1439 A676 85c multicolored .30 .20
80th anniversary of the People's Theater at
Bussang, founded by Maurice Pottecher.

Regions of France

Central
France
A677

Aquitaine
A678

Limousin
A679

Picardy
A680

Burgundy
A681

Loire
A682

Guyana
A683

Auvergne
A684

Poitou-Charentes
A685

Southern
Pyrenees
A686

Pas-de-Calais — A687

1975-76 **Engr.** *Perf. 13*
1440 A677 25c blue & yel grn .25 .20
1441 A678 60c multicolored .25 .20
1442 A679 70c multicolored .50 .35
1443 A680 85c bl, grn & org .70 .35
1444 A681 1fr red, yel & mar .70 .35
1445 A682 1.15fr bl, bis & grn .70 .35
1446 A683 1.25fr multicolored .65 .50
1447 A684 1.30fr dk bl & red .85 .50
1448 A685 1.90fr sl, ol & Prus
bl 1.00 .50
1449 A686 2.20fr multicolored 1.10 1.00
1450 A687 2.80fr car, bl & blk 1.40 1.00
Nos. 1440-1450 (11) 8.10 5.30

Issued: 85c, 11/15; 1fr, 10/25; 1.15fr, 9/6;
1.30fr, 10/4/75; 1.90fr, 12/6; 2.80fr, 12/13;
25c, 1/31/76; 2.20fr, 1/10/76; 60c, 5/22/76;
70c, 5/29/76; 1.25fr, 10/16/76.

A690

A691

French Flag, F.-H. Manhes, Jean Verneau,
Pierre Kaan

1975, Sept. 27
1453 A690 1fr multicolored .40 .30
Liberation of concentration camps, 30th
anniversary. F.-H. Manhes (1889-1959), Jean
Verneau (1890-1944) and Pierre Kaan (1903-
1945) were French resistance leaders, imprisoned in concentration camps.

1975, Oct. 11
Monument, by Joseph Riviere.
1454 A691 70c multicolored .40 .30
Land Mine Demolition Service, 30th anniversary. Monument was erected in Alsace to
honor land mine victims.

Symbols of
Suburban
Living
A692

1975, Oct. 18
1455 A692 1.70fr brown, bl & grn .75 .50
Creation of new towns.

Women and
Rainbow — A693

1975, Nov. 8 **Photo.**
1456 A693 1.20fr silver & multi .45 .40
International Women's Year 1975.

Saint-Nazaire Bridge — A694

1975, Nov. 8 **Engr.**
1457 A694 1.40fr bl, ind & grn .60 .30

French and
Russian
Flags — A695

Frigate
Melpomene
A696

1975, Nov. 22
1458 A695 1.20fr bl, red & ocher .50 .30
Franco-Soviet diplomatic relations, 50th
anniv.

1975, Dec. 6
1459 A696 90c multicolored 1.10 .50

Gallic Coin Type of 1975

1976, Jan. 1 **Typo.** *Perf. 13½x14*
1460 A663 50c lt green & brn 1.00 .65
1461 A663 60c lilac & brn 1.60 .95
1462 A663 90c orange & brn 2.00 1.25
1463 A663 1.60fr violet & brn 3.75 1.90
Nos. 1460-1463 (4) 8.35 4.75

Nos. 1460-1463 are known only precanceled. See second note after No. 132.

Lintel, St.
Genis des
Fontaines
Church
A697

Venus of Brassempouy
(Paleolithic) — A698

"The Joy
of Life," by
Robert
Delaunay
A699

Ramses II, from Abu Simbel Temple,
Egypt — A700

Still Life, by Maurice de
Vlaminck — A701

1976		Engr.		Perf. 13
1464	A697	2fr blue & slate bl	1.10	.60
1465	A698	2fr dk brn & yel	1.10	.60
		Photo.	Perf. 12½x13	
1466	A699	2fr multicolored	1.10	.60
		Engr.	Perf. 13x12½	
1467	A700	2fr multicolored	.80	.50
		Perf. 13		
1468	A701	2fr multicolored	.80	.50
		Nos. 1464-1468 (5)	4.90	2.80

Issued: #1464, 1/24; #1465, 3/6; #1466,
7/24; #1467, 9/4; #1468, 12/18.

Tourist Issue

Chateau
Fort de
Bonaguil
A702

Lodève
Cathedral — A703

Biarritz
A704

Thiers — A705

Ussel — A706

Chateau de
Malmaison
A707

1976		Engr.		Perf. 13
1469	A702	1fr multicolored	.35	.20
1470	A703	1.10fr violet blue	.40	.25
1471	A704	1.40fr multicolored	.60	.25
1472	A705	1.70fr multicolored	.60	.25
1473	A706	2fr multicolored	.90	.25
1474	A707	3fr multicolored	1.10	.25
		Nos. 1469-1474 (6)	3.95	1.45

Issue dates: 1fr, 2fr, July 10; 1.10fr, Nov. 13;
1.40fr, Sept. 25; 1.70fr, Oct. 9; 3fr, Apr. 10.

Destroyers,
Association
Emblem
A708

1976, Apr. 24
1475 A708 1fr vio bl, mag & lem .50 .30
Naval Reserve Officers Assoc., 50th anniv.

Gate,
Rouen — A709

Young
Person — A710

1976, Apr. 24
1476 A709 80c olive gray & sal .35 .20
49th Congress of the Federation of French
Philatelic Societies, Rouen, Apr. 23-May 2.

1976, Apr. 27
1477 A710 60c bl grn, ind & car .35 .25
JUVAROUEN 76, International Youth Philatelic Exhibition, Rouen, Apr. 25-May 2.

Europa Issue 1976

Ceramic
Pitcher,
Strasbourg,
18th
Century
A711

1.20fr, Sevres porcelain plate & CEPT
emblem.

1976, May 8		Photo.		Perf. 13
1478	A711	80c multicolored	.30	.30
1479	A711	1.20fr multicolored	.65	.55

Count de Vergennes and Benjamin
Franklin — A712

1976, May 15   Engr.   Perf. 13
1480 A712 1.20fr multicolored .50 .30
American Bicentennial.

A713

A714

Battle of Verdun Memorial

1976, June 12   Engr.
1481 A713 1fr multicolored .45 .20
Battle of Verdun, 60th anniversary.

1976, June 12   Photo.
1482 A714 1.20fr Communication .50 .40

Troncais
Forest — A715

Cross of
Lorraine — A716

1976, June 19   Engr.
1483 A715 70c green & multi .35 .20
Protection of the environment.

1976, June 19
1484 A716 1fr multicolored .60 .25
Association of Free French, 30th anniv.

Symphonie Communications
Satellite — A717

1976, June 26   Photo.
1485 A717 1.40fr multicolored .65 .50
French technical achievements.

Gallic Coin Type of 1975

1976, July 1		Typo.	Perf. 13½x14	
1487	A663	52c ver & dk brn	.60	.35
1488	A663	62c vio & dk brn	1.10	.70
1489	A663	95c tan & dk brn	1.50	.90
1490	A663	1.70fr dk bl & dk brn	2.75	1.40
		Nos. 1487-1490 (4)	5.95	3.35

Nos. 1487-1490 are known only precanceled. See second note after No. 132.

Paris Summer
Festival — A719

1976, July 10   Engr.
1491 A719 1fr multicolored .65 .30
Summer festival in Tuileries Gardens, Paris.

Emblem
and
Soldiers
A720

1976, July 8
1492 A720 1fr blk, dp bl & mag .50 .25
Officers Reserve Corps, centenary.

Sailing
A721

1976, July 17
1493 A721 1.20fr blue, blk & vio .50 .25
21st Olympic Games, Montreal, Canada,
July 17-Aug. 1.

Marianne Type of 1971-74

1976		Typo.	Perf. 14x13	
1494	A555	80c green	.40	.20
		Engr.	Perf. 13	
1495	A555	80c green	1.25	.50
a.		Booklet pane of 10	15.00	
1496	A555	1fr carmine rose	.55	.20
a.		Booklet pane of 5	4.00	
b.		Booklet pane of 10	8.00	
		Nos. 1495-1496 (2)	1.80	.70

No. 1495 issued in booklets only.
"POSTES" 6mm long on Nos. 1292A and
1494; 4mm on others.
#1494, 1496 were issued untagged in 1977.

Coil Stamps

1976, Aug. 1	Engr.	Perf. 13 Horiz.		
1497	A555	80c green	.80	.55
1498	A555	1fr carmine rose	.80	.55

Red control number on back of every 10th
stamp.

Woman's Head, by Jean
Carzou — A722

1976, Sept. 18   Engr.   Perf. 13x12½
1499 A722 2fr multicolored .90 .65

Old and
New
Telephones
A723

1976, Sept. 25   Engr.   Perf. 13
1500 A723 1fr multicolored .40 .25
Centenary of first telephone call by Alexander Graham Bell, Mar. 10, 1876.

Festival Emblem and Trophy, Pyrenees, Hercules and Pyrène — A724

Police Emblem — A725

1976, Oct. 2
1501 A724 1.40fr multicolored .65 .45
10th Intl. Tourist Film Festival, Tarbes, 10/4-10.

1976, Oct. 9   **Engr.**   **Perf. 13**
1502 A725 1.10fr ultra, red & ol .50 .30
National Police, help and protection.

Atomic Particle Accelerator, Diagram A726

1976, Oct. 22   **Photo.**
1503 A726 1.40fr multicolored .75 .45
European Center for Nuclear Research (CERN).

"Exhibitions" — A727

1976, Nov. 20   **Engr.**   **Perf. 13**
1504 A727 1.50fr multicolored .75 .50
Trade Fairs and Exhibitions.

Abstract Design A728

1976, Nov. 27   **Photo.**
1505 A728 1.10fr multicolored .50 .40
Customs Service.

Atlantic Museum, Port Louis — A729

1976, Dec. 4   **Engr.**
1506 A729 1.45fr grnsh bl & olive .65 .50

Regions of France

Réunion A730

Martinique A731

Franche-Comté A732

Brittany A733

Languedoc-Roussillon — A734

Rhône-Alps A735

Champagne-Ardennes A736

Alsace A737

Photo. (1.45fr, 1.50fr, 2.50fr); Engr.
1977   **Perf. 13**
1507 A730 1.45fr grn & lil rose .65 .40
1508 A731 1.50fr multicolored .65 .60
1509 A732 2.10fr multicolored .90 .65
1510 A733 2.40fr multicolored 1.10 .35
1511 A734 2.50fr multicolored 1.10 .85
1512 A735 2.75fr Prus blue 1.40 .80
1513 A736 3.20fr multicolored 1.40 .80
1514 A737 3.90fr multicolored 2.50 1.50
   Nos. 1507-1514 (8) 9.70 5.95

   Issued: 1.45fr, 2/5; 1.50fr, 1/29; 2.10fr, 1/8; 2.40fr, 2/19; 2.50fr, 1/15; 2.75fr, 1/22; 3.20fr, 4/16; 3.90fr, 2/26.

Pompidou Cultural Center — A738

1977, Feb. 5   **Engr.**   **Perf. 13**
1515 A738 1fr multicolored .35 .20
Inauguration of the Georges Pompidou National Center for Art and Culture, Paris.

Dunkirk Harbor A739

1977, Feb. 12
1516 A739 50c multicolored .25 .20
Expansion of Dunkirk harbor facilities.

Bridge at Mantes, by Corot — A740

Virgin and Child, by Rubens A741

Tridimensional Design, by Victor Vasarely — A742

Head and Eagle, by Pierre-Yves Tremois A743

1977   **Engr.**   **Perf. 13x12½**
1517 A740 2fr multicolored .95 .75
   Perf. 12x13
1518 A741 2fr multicolored 1.10 .75
   Perf. 12½x13
1519 A742 3fr ultra & sl grn 1.25 .75
   Photo.
1520 A743 3fr dark red & blk 1.60 1.25
   Nos. 1517-1520 (4) 4.90 3.50

   Issue dates: No. 1517, Feb. 12; No. 1518, Nov. 5; No. 1519, Apr. 7; No. 1520, Sept. 17.

Hand Holding Torch and Sword — A744

Pisces — A745

1977, Mar. 5   **Engr.**   **Perf. 13**
1521 A744 80c ultra & multi .50 .30
"France remembers its dead."

1977-78   **Engr.**   **Perf. 13**
Zodiac Signs: 58c, Cancer. 61c, Sagittarius. 68c, Taurus. 73c, Aries. 78c, Libra. 1.05fr, Scorpio. 1.15fr, Capricorn. 1.25fr, Leo. 1.85fr, Aquarius. 2fr, Virgo. 2.10fr, Gemini.

1522 A745 54c violet blue .65 .30
1523 A745 58c emerald 1.00 .40
1524 A745 61c brt blue .55 .30
1525 A745 68c deep brown .85 .35
1526 A745 73c rose carmine 1.50 .80
1527 A745 78c vermilion .65 .35
1528 A745 1.05fr brt lilac 1.50 .75
1529 A745 1.15fr orange 2.25 1.40
1530 A745 1.25fr lt olive grn 1.25 .60
1531 A745 1.85fr slate grn 2.75 1.25
1532 A745 2fr blue green 3.00 1.75
1533 A745 2.10fr lilac rose 1.65 1.00
   Nos. 1522-1533 (12) 17.60 9.25

   Issued: 54c, 68c, 1.05fr, 1.85fr, 4/1/77; others, 1978.
   Nos. 1522-1533 are known only precanceled. See second note after No. 132.

Village in Provence A746

Europa: 1.40fr, Brittany port.

1977, Apr. 23
1534 A746 1fr multicolored .45 .25
1535 A746 1.40fr multicolored 1.00 .35

Flowers and Gardening A747

1977, Apr. 23   **Engr.**   **Perf. 13**
1536 A747 1.70fr multicolored .80 .50
National Horticulture Society, centenary.

Symbolic Flower A748

1977, May 7
1537 A748 1.40fr multicolored .65 .45
Intl. Flower Show, Nantes, May 12-23.

Battle of Cambray
A749

1977, May 14
1538 A749 80c multicolored .40 .30
Capture of Cambray and the incorporation of Cambresis District into France, 300th anniv.

Carmes Church, School, Map of France
A750

Modern Constructions
A751

1977, May 14
1539 A750 1.10fr multicolored .50 .30
Catholic Institutes in France.

1977, May 21
1540 A751 1.10fr multicolored .55 .30
European Federation of the Construction Industry.

Annecy Castle
A752

1977, May 28
1541 A752 1fr multicolored .60 .30
Congress of the Federation of French Philatelic Societies, Annecy, May 28-30.

Tourist Issue

Abbey, Pont-à-Mousson — A753

Abbey Tower, Saint-Amand-les-Eaux
A754

Collegiate Church of Dorat
A755

Fontenay Abbey
A756

Bayeux Cathedral — A757

Chateau de Vitré
A758

1977 Engr. Perf. 13
1542 A753 1.25fr multicolored .50 .30
1543 A754 1.40fr multicolored .50 .30
1544 A755 1.45fr multicolored .55 .35
1545 A756 1.50fr multicolored .55 .25
1546 A757 1.90fr black & yel .75 .30
1547 A758 2.40fr black & yel .80 .30
Nos. 1542-1547 (6) 3.65 1.80

Issued: 1.25fr, 10/1; 1.40fr, 9/17; 1.45fr, 7/16; 1.50fr, 6/4; 1.90fr, 7/9; 2.40fr, 9/24.

Polytechnic School and "X" — A759

1977, June 4 Engr. Perf. 13
1548 A759 1.70fr multicolored .70 .30
Relocation at Palaiseau of Polytechnic School, founded 1794.

Soccer and Cup — A760

1977, June 11
1549 A760 80c multicolored .90 .50
Soccer Cup of France, 60th anniversary.

De Gaulle Memorial — A761

Stylized Map of France — A762

Photo. & Embossed
1977, June 18
1550 A761 1fr gold & multi 1.00 .50
5th anniversary of dedication of De Gaulle memorial at Colombey-les-Deux-Eglises.

1977, June 18 Engr. Perf. 13
1551 A762 1.10fr ultra & red .55 .30
French Junior Chamber of Commerce.

Battle of Nancy
A763

Arms of Burgundy
A764

1977, June 25
1552 A763 1.10fr blue & slate 1.10 .40
Battle of Nancy between the Dukes of Burgundy and Lorraine, 500th anniversary.

1977, July 2
1553 A764 1.25fr ol brn & slate grn .55 .25
Annexation of Burgundy by the French Crown, 500th anniversary.

Association Emblem
A765

1977, July 8
1554 A765 1.40fr ultra, olive & red .55 .25
French-speaking Parliamentary Association.

Red Cicada — A766

1977, Sept. 10 Photo. Perf. 13
1555 A766 80c multicolored .55 .30
Nature protection.

French Handicrafts
A767

1977, Oct. 1 Engr. Perf. 13
1556 A767 1.40fr multicolored .65 .45
French craftsmen.

Industry and Agriculture — A768

1977, Oct. 22
1557 A768 80c brown & olive .30 .25
Economic & Social Council, 30th anniv.

Table Tennis
A769

1977, Dec. 17 Engr. Perf. 13
1558 A769 1.10fr multicolored 3.25 1.00
French Table Tennis Federation, 50th anniv., and French team, gold medal winner, Birmingham.

Abstract, by Roger Excoffon — A770

1977, Dec. 17 Perf. 13x12½
1559 A770 3fr multicolored 2.00 1.00

Sabine, after David — A771

1977-78 Engr. Perf. 13
1560 A771 1c slate .20 .20
1561 A771 2c brt violet .20 .20
1562 A771 5c slate green .20 .20
1563 A771 10c red brown .20 .20
1564 A771 15c Prus blue .20 .20
1565 A771 20c brt green .20 .20
1566 A771 30c orange .20 .20
1567 A771 50c red lilac .20 .20
1568 A771 80c green 1.10 .20
a. Booklet pane of 10 11.00
1569 A771 80c olive .30 .20
1570 A771 1fr red 1.25 .20
a. Booklet pane of 5 8.50
b. Booklet pane of 10 15.00
1571 A771 1fr green .55 .20
a. Booklet pane of 10 5.50
1572 A771 1.20fr red .55 .20
a. Booklet pane of 5 4.25
b. Booklet pane of 10 7.75
1573 A771 1.40fr brt blue 2.00 .20
1574 A771 1.70fr grnsh blue .70 .20
1575 A771 2fr emerald .70 .20
1576 A771 2.10fr lilac rose .75 .20
1577 A771 3fr dark brown 1.00 .30
Nos. 1560-1577 (18) 10.50 3.70

Issued: #1560-1567, 1573, 1575, 1577, 4/3/78; #1568, 1570, 12/19/77; #1569, 1571, 1572, 1574, 1576, 6/5/78.

Coil Stamps
1978 Perf. 13 Horiz.
1578 A771 80c bright green 1.40 1.00
1579 A771 1fr bright green 1.10 1.00
1579A A771 1fr bright red 1.40 1.00
1579B A771 1.20fr bright red 1.10 1.00
Nos. 1578-1579B (4) 5.00 4.00

See Nos. 1658-1677, 3527.
For similar design inscribed "REPUBLIQUE FRANCAISE" see type A900.

Percheron, by Jacques Birr
A772

Osprey — A773

1978   **Photo.**   **Perf. 13**
1580 A772 1.70fr multicolored   1.00 .80
Engr.
1581 A773 1.80fr multicolored   .90 .50
Nature protection.
Issue dates: 1.70fr, Jan. 7; 1.80fr, Oct. 14.

Tournament, 1662, Etching — A774

Institut de France and Pont des Arts,
Paris, by Bernard Buffet — A776

Horses, by Yves Brayer — A777

1978   **Engr.**   **Perf. 12x13**
1582 A774 2fr black   3.00 1.25
Perf. 13x12
1584 A776 3fr multicolored   2.75 1.40
1585 A777 3fr multicolored   2.00 1.20
Nos. 1582-1585 (3)   7.75 3.85
Issued: 2fr, 1/14; #1584, 2/4; #1585, 12/9.

Communications
School and
Tower — A778

1978, Jan. 19   **Engr.**   **Perf. 13**
1586 A778 80c Prussian blue   .30 .25
Natl. Telecommunications School, cent.

Swedish
and French
Flags, Map
of Saint
Barthelemy
A779

1978, Jan. 19
1587 A779 1.10fr multicolored   .45 .25
Centenary of the reunion with France of
Saint Barthelemy Island, West Indies.

Regions of France

Ile de
France — A780

Tanker,
Refinery,
Flower,
Upper
Normandy
A781

Lower
Normandy
A782

1978   **Photo.**   **Perf. 13**
1588 A780 1fr red, blue & blk   .40 .20
Engr.
1589 A781 1.40fr multicolored   .70 .30
Photo.
1590 A782 1.70fr multicolored   1.00 .50
Nos. 1588-1590 (3)   2.10 1.00
Issued: 1fr, 3/4; 1.40fr, 1/21; 1.70fr, 3/31.

Stylized Map of
France
A788

Young Stamp
Collector
A789

1978, Feb. 11   **Engr.**   **Perf. 13**
1596 A788 1.10fr violet & green   .45 .25
Program of administrative changes, 15th
anniv.

1978, Feb. 25
1597 A789 80c multicolored   .30 .25
JUVEXNIORT, Youth Philatelic Exhibition,
Niort, Feb. 25-March 5.

Tourist Issue

Verdon
Gorge — A790

Saint-Saturnin
Church — A792

Pont Neuf,
Paris
A791

Our Lady of Bec-Hellouin
Abbey — A793

Chateau D'Esquelbecq — A794

Aubazine
Abbey
A795

Fontevraud
Abbey
A796

1978   **Engr.**   **Perf. 13**
1598 A790 50c multicolored   .20 .20
1599 A791 80c multicolored   .35 .25
1600 A792 1fr black   .35 .25
1601 A793 1.10fr multicolored   .50 .25
1602 A794 1.10fr multicolored   .50 .20
1603 A795 1.25fr carmine & brn   .85 .30
1604 A796 1.70fr multicolored   .90 .40
Nos. 1598-1604 (7)   3.65 1.85
Issued: 1.25fr, 2/18; 50c, 3/6; #1601, 3/26;
80c, 5/27; 1fr, 6/10; 1.70fr, 6/3; #1602, 6/17.

Fish and Corals — A797

1978, Apr. 15   **Photo.**   **Perf. 13**
1605 A797 1.25fr multicolored   1.00 .85
Port Cros National Park, 15th anniversary.

Flowers, Butterflies
and Houses — A798

1978, Apr. 22   **Engr.**   **Perf. 13**
1606 A798 1.70fr multicolored   2.75 .35
Beautification of France campaign, 50th
anniv.

Hands
Shielding
Source of
Heat and
Light
A799

1978, Apr. 22
1607 A799 1fr multicolored   .60 .25
Energy conservation.

World War I
Memorial near
Lens — A800

Fountain of the
Innocents,
Paris — A801

1978, May 6
1608 A800 2fr lemon & magenta 1.00 .30
Colline Notre Dame de Lorette memorial of
World War I.

1978, May 6
Europa: 1.40fr, Flower Park Fountain, Paris.
1609 A801 1fr multicolored   .40 .25
1610 A801 1.40fr multicolored   .90 .50

Maurois Palace,
Troyes — A802

1978, May 13
1611 A802 1fr multicolored   .45 .25
51st Congress of the Federation of French
Philatelic Societies, Troyes, May 13-15.

Roland Garros Tennis Court and
Player — A803

1978, May 27
1612 A803 1fr multicolored   2.50 .40
Roland Garros Tennis Court, 50th anniv.

Hand and
Plant — A804

Printing Office
Emblem — A805

1978, Sept. 9   **Engr.**   **Perf. 13**
1613 A804 1.30fr brown, red & grn .50 .25
Encouragement of handicrafts.

1978, Sept. 23
1614 A805 1fr multicolored   .50 .20
National Printing Office, established 1538.

Fortress, Besançon, and Collegiate Church, Dole — A806

Valenciennes and Maubeuge — A807

1978
1615 A806 1.20fr multicolored .55 .20
1616 A807 1.20fr multicolored .55 .20
Reunion of Franche-Comté and Valenciennes and Maubeuge with France, 300th anniversary.
Issued: #1615, Sept. 23; #1616, Sept. 30.

Sower Type of 1906-1937 and Academy Emblem — A808

Gymnasts, Strasbourg Cathedral, Storks — A809

1978, Oct. 7
1617 A808 1fr multicolored .45 .30
Academy of Philately, 50th anniversary.

1978, Oct. 21
1618 A809 1fr multicolored .70 .30
19th World Gymnastics Championships, Strasbourg, Oct. 23-26.

Various Sports A810

Polish Veterans' Monument A811

1978, Oct. 21
1619 A810 1fr multicolored 1.10 .40
Sports for all.

1978, Nov. 11
1620 A811 1.70fr multicolored .60 .40
Polish veterans of World War II.

Railroad Car and Monument, Compiègne Forest, Rethondes A812

1978, Nov. 11 Engr. Perf. 13
1621 A812 1.20fr indigo .75 .30
60th anniversary of World War I armistice.

Handicapped People — A813

1978, Nov. 18
1622 A813 1fr multicolored .45 .25
Rehabilitation of the handicapped.

Human Rights Emblem A814

1978, Dec. 9 Engr. Perf. 13
1623 A814 1.70fr dk brown & blue .80 .40
30th anniversary of Universal Declaration of Human Rights.

Child and IYC Emblem A815

1979, Jan. 6 Engr. Perf. 13
1624 A815 1.70fr multicolored 3.50 2.00
International Year of the Child.

"Music," 15th Century Miniature — A816

1979, Jan. 13 Perf. 13x12½
1625 A816 2fr multicolored 1.50 .90

Diana Taking a Bath, d'Ecouen Castle A817

Church at Auvers-on-Oise, by Vincent Van Gogh — A818

Head of Marianne, by Salvador Dali A819

Fire Dancer from The Magic Flute, by Chaplain Midy A820

1979 Photo. Perf. 12½x13
1626 A817 2fr multicolored 1.40 1.00
1627 A818 2fr multicolored 5.50 1.25
1628 A819 3fr multicolored 1.50 1.00
1629 A820 3fr multicolored 1.50 1.00
Nos. 1626-1629 (4) 9.90 4.25
Issue dates: #1626, Sept. 22; #1627, Oct. 27; #1628, Nov. 19; #1629, Nov. 26.

Orange Agaric — A821

Mushrooms: 83c, Death trumpet. 1.30fr, Olive wood pleurotus. 2.25fr, Cauliflower claveria.

1979, Jan. 15 Engr. Perf. 13
1630 A821 64c orange .40 .20
1631 A821 83c brown .40 .25
1632 A821 1.30fr yellow bister .85 .40
1633 A821 2.25fr brown purple 1.25 .85
Nos. 1630-1633 (4) 2.90 1.70
Nos. 1630-1633 are known only precanceled. See second note after No. 132.

Victor Segalen A822

1979, Jan. 20
1634 A822 1.50fr multicolored .50 .30
Physician, explorer and writer (1878-1919).

Hibiscus and Palms — A823

1979, Feb. 3
1635 A823 35c multicolored .20 .20
International Flower Festival, Martinique.

Buddha, Stupas, Temple of Borobudur A824

1979, Feb. 24
1636 A824 1.80fr ol & slate grn .85 .40
Save the Temple of Borobudur, Java, campaign.

Boy, by Francisque Poulbot (1879-1946) A825

1979, Mar. 24 Photo.
1637 A825 1.30fr multicolored .60 .25

Tourist Issue

Chateau de Maisons, Laffitte A826

Bernay and St. Pierre sur Dives Abbeys — A827

View of Auray — A827a

Steenvorde Windmill — A828

Wall Painting, Niaux Cave A829

Royal Palace, Perpignan A830

1979 Engr. Perf. 13
1638 A826 45c multicolored .30 .20
1639 A827 1fr multicolored .45 .25
1640 A827a 1fr multicolored .45 .25
1641 A828 1.20fr multicolored .55 .25
1642 A829 1.50fr multicolored .70 .40
1643 A830 1.70fr multicolored .75 .60
Nos. 1638-1643 (6) 3.20 1.95
Issued: 45c, 10/6; #1639, 6/16; #1640, 6/30; 1.20fr, 6/12; 1.50fr, 7/9; 1.70fr, 4/21.

Honey Bee
A831

1979, Mar. 31   Engr.   Perf. 13
1644 A831 1fr multicolored   .70 .30
Nature protection.

St. Germain
des Prés
Abbey
A832

1979, Apr. 21
1645 A832 1.40fr multicolored   .50 .30

Simoun Mail Monoplanes, 1935, and
Map of Mail Routes — A833

Europa: 1.70fr, Floating spheres used on
Seine during siege of Paris, 1870.

1979, Apr. 28
1646 A833 1.20fr multicolored   .75 .35
1647 A833 1.70fr multicolored   1.00 .50

Ship and
View of
Nantes
A834

1979, May 5   Engr.   Perf. 13
1648 A834 1.20fr multicolored   .55 .30
52nd National Congress of French Philatelic
Societies, Nantes, May 5-7.

Royal Palace,
1789 — A835

1979, May 19
1649 A835 1fr car rose & pur   .40 .25

European
Elections
A836

1979, May 19   Photo.   Perf. 13
1650 A836 1.20fr multicolored   .50 .25
European Parliament, 1st direct elections,
June 10.

Joan of Arc
Monument
A837

1979, May 24   Engr.
1651 A837 1.70fr brt lilac rose   .70 .40
Joan of Arc, the Maid of Orleans (1412-
1431).

Felix Guyon
and
Catheters
A840

1979, June 23
1652 A840 1.80fr sepia & blue   .60 .20
Felix Guyon (1831-1920), urologist.

Lantern Tower,
La Rochelle
A841

Telecom '79
A842

Towers: 88c, Chartres Cathedral. 1.40fr,
Bourges Cathedral. 2.35fr, Amiens Cathedral.

1979, Aug. 13   Engr.   Perf. 13
1653 A841 68c vio brn & blk   .30 .30
1654 A841 88c ultra & blk   .40 .30
1655 A841 1.40fr gray grn & blk   .65 .50
1656 A841 2.35fr dull brn & blk   1.10 .60
　　Nos. 1653-1656 (4)   2.45 1.70
Nos. 1653-1656 are known only precanceled. See second note after No. 132. See
Nos. 1684-1687, 1719-1722, 1814-1817.

1979, Sept. 22
1657 A842 1.10fr multicolored   .40 .20
3rd World Telecommunications Exhibition.

Sabine Type of 1977-78

1979-81   Engr.   Perf. 13
1658 A771 40c brown ('81)   .20 .20
1659 A771 60c red brn ('81)   .25 .20
1660 A771 70c violet blue   .30 .25
1661 A771 90c brt lilac ('81)   .40 .30
1662 A771 1fr gray olive   .45 .20
1663 A771 1.10fr green   .70 .25
1664 A771 1.20fr green ('80)   .55 .20
1665 A771 1.30fr rose red   .70 .20
1666 A771 1.40fr rose red ('80)   .65 .20
1667 A771 1.60fr purple   1.00 .30
1668 A771 1.80fr ocher   .85 .40
1669 A771 3.50fr lt ol grn ('81)   1.60 .60
1670 A771 4fr brt car ('81)   1.80 .40
1671 A771 5fr brt grnsh bl
　　　　　　　('81)   2.25 .30
　　Nos. 1658-1671 (14)   11.70 4.20

Coil Stamps

1979-80   Perf. 13 Horiz.
1674 A771 1.10fr green   1.75 .60
1675 A771 1.20fr green ('80)   .65 .50
1676 A771 1.30fr rose red   1.75 .60
1677 A771 1.40fr rose red ('80)   .90 .40
　　Nos. 1674-1677 (4)   5.05 2.10

Lorraine
Region — A845

1979, Nov. 10
1678 A845 2.30fr multicolored   1.00 .30

Gears
A847

1979, Nov. 17   Perf. 13
1680 A847 1.80fr multicolored   .70 .30
Central Technical School of Paris, 150th
anniv.

Judo Throw
A848

1979, Nov. 24   Engr.
1681 A848 1.60fr multicolored   .60 .40
World Judo Championships, Paris, Dec.

Violins — A849

1979, Dec. 10
1682 A849 1.30fr multicolored   .60 .35

Eurovision
A850

1980, Jan. 12   Engr.   Perf. 13x13½
1683 A850 1.80fr multicolored   1.00 .70

Tower Type of 1979

Designs: 76c, Chateau d'Angers. 99c, Chateau de Kerjean. 1.60fr, Chateau de Pier-
refonds. 2.65fr, Chateau de Tarascon.

1980, Jan. 21   Engr.
1684 A841 76c grnsh bl & blk   .35 .30
1685 A841 99c slate grn & blk   .45 .30
1686 A841 1.60fr red & blk   .75 .55
1687 A841 2.65fr brn org & blk   1.25 .65
　　Nos. 1684-1687 (4)   2.80 1.80
Nos. 1684-1687 are known only precanceled. See second note after No. 132.

Self-portrait, by Albrecht Dürer,
Philexfrance '82 Emblem — A851

Woman
Holding
Fan, by
Ossip
Zadkine
A852

Abstract, by Raoul Ubak — A853

Hommage to J.S. Bach, by Jean
Picart Le Doux — A854

Peasant,
by Louis
Le Nain
A855

Woman
with Blue
Eyes, by
Modigliani
A856

Abstract,
by Hans
Hartung
A857

Engraved, Photogravure (#1691, 1694)

1980   Perf. 12½x13, 13x12½
1688 A851 2fr multicolored   1.00 .90
1689 A852 3fr multicolored   1.50 1.00
1690 A853 3fr multicolored   1.50 1.00
1691 A854 3fr multicolored   1.50 1.00
1692 A855 3fr multicolored   1.50 1.00

1693 A856 4fr multicolored 3.00 1.25
1694 A857 4fr ultra & black 2.00 1.25
Nos. 1688-1694 (7) 12.00 7.40

Issued: #1688, 6/7; #1689, 1/19; #1690, 2/2; #1691, 9/20; #1693, 10/26; #1692, 11/10; #1694, 12/20.

Giants of the North Festival — A858

French Cuisine — A859

1980, Feb. 16 *Perf. 13*
1695 A858 1.60fr multicolored .75 .35

1980, Feb. 23
1696 A859 90c red & lt brown .80 .40

Woman Embroidering A860

Fight Against Cigarette Smoking A861

Photogravure and Engraved
1980, Mar. 29 *Perf. 13*
1697 A860 1.10fr multicolored .50 .30

1980, Apr. 5 *Photo.* *Perf. 13*
1698 A861 1.30fr multicolored .50 .20

Aristide Briand — A862

Europa: 1.80fr, St. Benedict.

1980, Apr. 26 *Engr.* *Perf. 13*
1699 A862 1.30fr multicolored .60 .30
1700 A862 1.80fr red & red brown .85 .50

Aristide Briand (1862-1932), prime minister, 1909-1911, 1921-1922; St. Benedict, patron saint of Europe.

Liancourt, College, Map of Northwestern France — A863

1980, May 19 *Engr.* *Perf. 13*
1701 A863 2fr dk green & pur .80 .35

National College of Arts and Handicrafts (founded by Larochefoucauld Liancourt) bicentenary.

Cranes, Town Hall Tower, Dunkirk — A864

1980, May 24
1702 A864 1.30fr multicolored .60 .20

53rd Natl. Congress of French Federation of Philatelic Societies, Dunkirk, May 24-26.

Tourist Issue

Chateau de Maintenon A866

Cordes A865

Montauban A867

St. Peter's Abbey, Solesmes A868

Puy Cathedral A869

1980 *Engr.* *Perf. 13*
1703 A865 1.50fr multicolored .65 .30
1704 A866 2fr multicolored .80 .30
1705 A867 2.30fr multicolored .90 .30
1706 A868 2.50fr multicolored 1.00 .30
1707 A869 3.20fr multicolored 1.40 .50
Nos. 1703-1707 (5) 4.75 1.70

Issued: #1703, 4/5; #1704, 6/7; #1705, 5/7; #1706, 9/20; #1707, 5/12.

Graellsia Isabellae A870

1980, May 31 *Photo.*
1708 A870 1.10fr multicolored .75 .35

Association Emblem — A871

1980, June 10 *Photo.*
1709 A871 1.30fr red & blue .50 .25

Intl. Public Relations Assoc., 25th anniv.

Marianne, French Architecture A872

1980, June 21 *Engr.*
1710 A872 1.50fr bluish & gray blk .70 .30

Heritage Year.

Earth Sciences A873

1980, July 5
1711 A873 1.60fr dk brown & red .75 .50

International Geological Congress.

Rochambeau's Landing — A874

1980, July 15
1712 A874 2.50fr multicolored 1.10 .50

Rochambeau's landing at Newport, R.I. (American Revolution), bicentenary.

Message of Peace, by Yaacov Agam — A875

1980, Oct. 4 *Photo.* *Perf. 11½x13*
1713 A875 4fr multicolored 3.50 1.00

French Golf Federation A876

1980, Oct. 18 *Engr.*
1714 A876 1.40fr multicolored .65 .30

Comedie Francaise, 300th Anniversary A877

1980, Oct. 18
1715 A877 2fr multicolored .70 .40

Charles de Gaulle — A878

1980, Nov. 10 *Photo.* *Perf. 13*
1716 A878 1.40fr multicolored 1.00 .50

40th anniversary of De Gaulle's appeal of June 18, and 10th anniversary of his death.

Guardsman — A879

1980, Nov. 24 *Engr.* *Perf. 13*
1717 A879 1.70fr multicolored .80 .45

Rambouillet Chateau A880

1980, Dec. 6 *Engr.* *Perf. 13*
1718 A880 2.20fr multicolored 1.00 .35

Tower Type of 1979

Designs: 88c, Imperial Chapel, Ajaccio. 1.14fr, Astronomical Clock, Besancon. 1.84fr, Coucy Castle ruins. 3.05fr, Font-de-Gaume cave drawing, Les Eyzies de Tayac.

1981, Jan. 11 *Engr.* *Perf. 13*
1719 A841 88c dp mag & blk .40 .20
1720 A841 1.14fr ultra & blk .55 .30
1721 A841 1.84fr dk green & blk .85 .50
1722 A841 3.05fr brn red & blk 1.40 .80
Nos. 1719-1722 (4) 3.20 1.80

Nos. 1719-1722 are known only precanceled. See second note after No. 132.

Microelectronics — A881

1981 *Photo.*
1723 A881 1.20fr shown .75 .30
1724 A881 1.20fr Biology .55 .30
1725 A881 1.40fr Energy .65 .30
1726 A881 1.80fr Marine explora- tion .85 .50
1727 A881 2fr Telemetry .90 .65
Nos. 1723-1727 (5) 3.70 2.05

Issue dates: #1723, Feb. 5; others, Mar. 28.

Abstract, by Albert Gleizes A882

1981, Feb. 28 *Perf. 12½x13*
1728 A882 4fr multicolored 2.00 .90

The Footpath by Camille
Pissaro — A883

1981, Apr. 18   Engr.   Perf. 13x12½
1729 A883 2fr multicolored   1.25 .90

Child Watering
Smiling Map of
France — A884

1981, Mar. 14   Engr.   Perf. 13
1730 A884 1.40fr multicolored   .65 .25

Sully Chateau, Rosny-sur-
Seine — A885

1981, Mar. 21
1731 A885 2.50fr multicolored   .90 .40

Tourist Issue

Roman Temple,
Nimes — A886

Church of St.   St. Anne d'Auray
Jean,   Basilica — A888
Lyon — A887

Vaucelles
Abbey
A889

Notre Dame
of Louviers
A890

1981, Apr. 11   Engr.   Perf. 13
1732 A886 1.70fr multicolored   .85 .30

1981
1733 A887 1.40fr dk red & dk brn   .65 .30
1734 A888 2.20fr blue & black   .90 .40
  Issue dates: 1.40fr, May 30; 2.20fr, July 4.

1981
1735 A889   2fr red & black   .90 .40
1736 A890 2.20fr red brn & dk
             brn   1.00 .50
  Nos. 1732-1736 (5)   4.30 1.90
  Issue dates: 2fr, Sept. 19; 2.20fr, Sept. 26.

Europa Issue 1981

Folkdances
A891

1981, May 4   Perf. 13
1737 A891 1.40fr Bouree   .65 .25
1738 A891   2fr Sardane   1.25 .40

Bookbinding   Cadets
A892   A893

1981, Apr. 4   Perf. 13
1739 A892 1.50fr olive & car rose   .70 .40

1981, May 16
1740 A893 2.50fr multicolored   .90 .30
  Military College at St. Maixent centenary.

Man Drawing Geometric
Diagram — A894

1981, May 23   Photo.
1741 A894 2fr shown   1.40 .90
1742 A894 2fr Faces   1.40 .90
  a.   Pair, #1741-1742 + label   3.50 3.00
  PHILEXFRANCE '82 Stamp Exhibition,
Paris, June 11-21, 1982.

Theophraste   Public Gardens,
Renaudot and   Vichy — A896
Emile de
Girardin — A895

1981, May 30   Engr.
1743 A895 2.20fr black & red   .80 .30
  350th anniversary of La Gazette (founded
by Renaudot), and death centenary of founder
of Le Journal (de Girardin).

1981, June 6
1744 A896 1.40fr multicolored   .65 .30
  54th National Congress of French Federation of Philatelic Societies, Vichy.

Higher
National
College for
Commercial
Studies
A897

1981, June 20   Perf. 13
1745 A897 1.40fr multicolored   .55 .30

Sea Shore Conservation — A898

1981, June 20
1746 A898 1.60fr multicolored   .75 .55

World Fencing Championship,
Clermont-Ferrand, July 2-13 — A899

1981, June 27
1747 A899 1.80fr multicolored   .85 .45

Sabine, after
David — A900

1981, Sept. 1   Engr.
1755 A900 1.40fr green   .85 .20
1756 A900 1.60fr red   1.00 .25
1757 A900 2.30fr blue   1.40 .85
  Nos. 1755-1757 (3)   3.25 1.30

Coil Stamps
1981   Engr.   Perf. 13 Horiz.
1758 A900 1.40fr green   .75 .50
1759 A900 1.60fr red   .75 .40

Highway
Safety
("Drink or
Drive")
A901

1981, Sept. 5   Perf. 13
1768 A901 1.60fr multicolored   .75 .35

45th Intl. PEN   Jules Ferry,
Club Congress   Statesman
A902   A903

1981, Sept. 19   Perf. 13
1769 A902 2fr multicolored   .75 .35

1981, Sept. 26   Perf. 12½x13
1770 A903 1.60fr multicolored   .75 .35
  Free compulsory public school centenary.

Natl.
Savings
Bank
Centenary
A904

1981, Sept. 21   Photo.   Perf. 13
1771 A904 1.40fr multicolored   .65 .20
1772 A904 1.60fr multicolored   .75 .20

The Divers, by Edouard
Pignon — A905

1981, Oct. 3   Perf. 13x12½
1773 A905 4fr multicolored   1.90 .90

Alleluia, by
Alfred
Manessier
A906

1981, Dec. 19   Photo.   Perf. 12x13
1774 A906 4fr multicolored   1.90 .90

Tourist Issue

Saint-Emilion — A907

Crest — A908

1981   Engr.   Perf. 13x12½
1775 A907 2.60fr dk red & lt ol grn   1.10 .35
    Perf. 13
1776 A908 2.90fr dk green   1.20 .25
  Issued: #1775, Oct. 10; #1776, Nov. 28.

150th
Anniv. of
Naval
Academy
A909

1981, Oct. 17   Perf. 13
1777 A909 1.40fr multicolored   .65 .35

A910

A911

St. Hubert Kneeling before the Stag, 15th cent. sculpture.

1981, Oct. 24
1778 A910 1.60fr multicolored   .75 .35
Museum of hunting and nature.

1981, Nov. 2
V. Schoelcher, J. Jaures, J. Moulin, the Pantheon.
1779 A911 1.60fr blue & dull pur   .75 .30

Intl. Year of the Disabled A912

1981, Nov. 7
1780 A912 1.60fr multicolored   .75 .25

Men Leading Cattle, 2nd Cent. Roman Mosaic — A913

1981, Nov. 14   **Perf. 13x12**
1781 A913 2fr multicolored   1.10 .90
Virgil's birth bimillennium.

Martyrs of Chateaubriant A914

1981, Dec. 12   **Engr.**   **Perf. 13**
1782 A914 1.40fr multicolored   .55 .25

Liberty, after Delacroix — A915

1982   **Engr.**   **Perf. 13**
1783 A915 5c dk green   .20 .20
1784 A915 10c dull red   .20 .20
1785 A915 15c brt rose lilac .35 .35
1786 A915 20c brt green   .20 .20
1787 A915 30c orange   .20 .20
1788 A915 40c brown   .20 .20
  a.   Bklt. pane of 5, 4 No.
        1784, No. 1788 ('87)   1.00
1789 A915 50c lilac   .25 .20
1790 A915 60c lt red brn   .30 .20
1791 A915 70c ultra   .30 .20
1792 A915 80c lt olive grn   .35 .20
1793 A915 90c brt lilac   .40 .20
1794 A915 1fr olive green   .45 .20
1795 A915 1.40fr green   .65 .20
1796 A915 1.60fr green   .75 .20
1797 A915 1.60fr red   .75 .20
1798 A915 1.80fr red   .85 .20

1799 A915 2fr brt yel grn   .90 .20
1800 A915 2.30fr blue   2.00 1.25
1801 A915 2.60fr blue   2.00 1.00
1802 A915 3fr chocolate   1.40 .30
1803 A915 4fr brt carmine   1.90 .30
1804 A915 5fr gray blue   2.25 .20
  Nos. 1783-1804 (22)   16.85 6.60

Coil Stamps
Perf. 13 Horiz.
1805 A915 1.40fr green   1.25 .90
1806 A915 1.60fr red   1.25 .90
1807 A915 1.60fr green   .85 .50
1807A A915 1.80fr red   .90 .50
  Nos. 1805-1807A (4)   4.25 2.80

Issued: 5c-50c, 1fr-1.40fr, 2fr, 2.30fr, 5fr, #1797, 1/2; 1.80fr, 2.60fr, #1796, 6/1; 60c-90c, 3fr, 4fr, 11/3.
See Nos. 1878-1897A, 2077-2080, 3528.
For surcharge see No. 2115.

Tourist Issue

St. Pierre and Miquelon A916

Corsica A917

Renaissance Fountain, Aix-en Provence — A918

Collonges-la-Rouge — A919

Castle of Henry IV, Pau A920

Lille — A921

Chateau Ripaille, Haute-Savoie — A921a

1982   **Engr.**   **Perf. 12½**
1808 A916 1.60fr dk blue & blk   .75 .25
1809 A917 1.90fr blue & red   .90 .25
Perf. 13
1810 A918 2fr multicolored   .90 .40
1811 A919 3fr multicolored   1.40 .30
1812 A920 3fr ultra & dk bl   1.40 .40
Issued: 1.60fr, 1.90fr, Jan. 9; 2fr, June 21, No. 1811, July 5, No. 1812, May 15.

1982   **Perf. 13x12½**
1813 A921   1.80fr dull red & ol .85 .25
1813A A921a 2.90fr multicolored 1.40 .80
  Nos. 1808-1813A (7)   7.60 2.65
Issue dates: 1.80fr, Oct. 16; 2.90fr, Sept. 4.

Tower Type of 1979
97c, Tanlay Castle, Yonne. 1.25fr, Salses Fort, Pyrenees-Orientales. 2.03fr, Montlhery Tower, Essonne. 3.36fr, Chateau d'If Bouches-du-Rhone.

1982, Jan. 11   **Engr.**   **Perf. 13**
1814 A841 97c olive grn & blk   .45 .20
1815 A841 1.25fr red & blk   .55 .25
1816 A841 2.03fr sepia & blk   .95 .50
1817 A841 3.36fr ultra & blk   1.50 .80
  Nos. 1814-1817 (4)   3.45 1.75

Nos. 1814-1817 are known only precanceled. See second note after No. 132.

800th Birth Anniv. of St. Francis of Assisi A922

1982, Feb. 6   **Photo. & Engr.**
1818 A922 2fr black & blue   .90 .50

Posts and Mankind — A923

Posts and Technology — A924

1982, Feb. 13   **Photo.**
1819 A923 2fr multicolored   3.50 2.00
1820 A924 2fr multicolored   3.50 2.00
  a.   Pair, #1819-1820 + label 9.00 6.50
PHILEXFRANCE '82 Stamp Exhibition, Paris, June 11-21.

Souvenir Sheet

Marianne, by Jean Cocteau — A925

1982, June 11
1821 A925 Sheet of 2   14.00 14.00
  a.   4fr red & blue   6.00 6.00
  b.   6fr blue & red   6.00 6.00
Sold only with 20fr show admission ticket.

Scouting Year A926

1982, Feb. 20   **Engr.**
1822 A926 2.30fr yel grn & blk .90 .30

31st Natl. Census — A927

1982, Feb. 27   **Photo.**
1823 A927 1.60fr multicolored   .75 .20

Bale-Mulhouse Airport Opening — A928

1982, Mar. 15   **Engr.**   **Perf. 13**
1824 A928 1.90fr multicolored   .90 .50

Fight Against Racism A929

1982, Mar. 20
1825 A929 2.30fr brn & red org 1.00 .50

Blacksmith — A930

1982, Apr. 17
1826 A930 1.40fr multicolored   .65 .40

Europa 1982 A931

1982, Apr. 24
1827 A931 1.60fr Treaty of
            Rome, 1957   .75 .30
1828 A931 2.30fr Treaty of Ver-
            dun, 843   1.30 .40

1982 World Cup A932

1982, Apr. 28
1829 A932 1.80fr multicolored 1.60 .35

Young Greek Soldier, Hellenic Sculpture, Agde
A933

1982, May 15   **Perf. 12½x13**
1830 A933 4fr multicolored   1.90 1.00

Embarkation for Ostia, by Claude Gellee — A934

The Lacemaker, by Vermeer
A935

Turkish Chamber, by Balthus — A936

1982   **Photo.**   **Perf. 13x12½, 12½x13**
1831 A934 4fr multicolored   1.90 1.00
1832 A935 4fr multicolored   1.90 1.00
1833 A936 4fr multicolored   1.90 1.00
   Nos. 1831-1833 (3)   5.70 3.00

   Issued: #1831, 6/19; #1832, 9/4; #1833, 11/6.

35th Intl. Film Festival, Cannes — A937   Natl. Space Studies Center, 20th Anniv. — A938

1982, May 15   **Photo.**   **Perf. 13**
1834 A937 2.30fr multicolored   1.00 .80

1982, May 15   **Engr.**
1835 A938 2.60fr multicolored   1.20 .50

A939   A940

1982, June 4   **Photo.**
1836 A939 2.60fr multicolored   1.20 .50
   Industrialized Countries' Summit Meeting, Versailles, June 4-6.

1982, June 4   **Engr.**   **Perf. 13**
1837 A940 1.60fr ol grn & dk grn   .75 .20
   Jules Valles (1832-1885), writer.

Frederic and Irene Curie, Radiation Diagrams
A941

1982, June 26
1838 A941 1.80fr multicolored   .75 .25

Electric Street Lighting Centenary
A942

1982, July 10
1839 A942 1.80fr dk blue & vio   .75 .25

The Family, by Marc Boyan
A943

Photogravure and Engraved
1982, Sept. 18   **Perf. 12½x13**
1840 A943 4fr multicolored   2.00 1.00

Natl. Fed. of Firemen, Cent.
A944   Marionettes
A945

1982, Sept. 18   **Engr.**   **Perf. 13**
1841 A944 3.30fr red & sepia   1.75 .40

1982, Sept. 25
1842 A945 1.80fr multicolored   .85 .35

Rugby
A946

1982, Oct. 9
1843 A946 1.60fr multicolored   2.00 .35

Higher Education
A947

1982, Oct. 16
1844 A947 1.80fr red & black   .75 .35

TB Bacillus Centenary
A948

1982, Nov. 13
1845 A948 2.60fr red & black   1.10 .40

St. Teresa of Avila (1515-82)
A949   Leon Blum (1872-1950), Politician
A950

1982, Nov. 20
1846 A949 2.10fr multicolored   .95 .45

1982, Dec. 18   **Engr.**   **Perf. 13**
1847 A950 1.80fr dk brn & brn   .85 .25

Cavelier de la Salle (1643-1687), Explorer — A951

1982, Dec. 18   **Perf. 13x12½**
1848 A951 3.25fr multicolored   1.25 .50

Spring — A952

1983, Jan. 17   **Engr.**   **Perf. 13**
1849 A952 1.05fr shown   .45 .35
1850 A952 1.35fr Summer   .50 .45
1851 A952 2.19fr Autumn   .85 .65
1852 A952 3.63fr Winter   1.40 1.10
   Nos. 1849-1852 (4)   3.20 2.55

   Nos. 1849-1852 known only precanceled. See second note after No. 132.

Provence-Alpes-Cote d'Azur — A953

Brantome (Perigord)
A954

Concarneau — A955

Noirlac Abbey
A956

Jarnac
A957

Charleville-Mezieres — A958

   Illustration A958 reduced.

1983   **Photo.**   **Perf. 13**
1853 A953 1fr multicolored   .45 .25
           Engr.
        Perf. 13x12½
1854 A954 1.80fr multicolored   .85 .20
        Perf. 13
1855 A955 3fr multicolored   1.40 .60
        Perf. 13x12½
1856 A956 3.60fr multicolored   1.60 .35
   Issued: 1fr, 1/8; 1.80fr, 2/5; 3fr, 6/11; 3.60fr, 7/2.

1983   **Perf. 13x12½**
1857 A957 2fr multicolored   .90 .35
1858 A958 3.10fr multicolored   1.40 .85
   Nos. 1853-1858 (6)   6.60 2.60

   Issued: 2fr, Oct. 8; 3.10fr, Sept. 17.

Martin Luther (1483-1546) — A959

1983, Feb. 12   **Engr.**   **Perf. 13**
1859 A959 3.30fr dk brn & tan   1.40 .55

Alliance Francaise Centenary
A960

1983, Feb. 19
1860 A960 1.80fr multicolored   .65 .35

Danielle Casanova (d. 1942), Resistance Leader A961

1983, Mar. 8
1861 A961 3fr blk & red brn   1.25 .35

World Communications Year — A962

1983, Mar. 12   Photo.
1862 A962 2.60fr multicolored   1.10 .65

Manned Flight Bicentenary — A963

1983, Mar. 19   Photo.   Perf. 13
1863   2fr Hot air balloon   .80 .55
1864   3fr Hydrogen balloon   1.25 .70
a.   A963 Pair, #1863-1864 + label   2.25 2.25

Female Nude, by Raphael A964

Aurora-Set, by Dewasne — A965

1983   Engr.   Perf. 13
1865 A964 4fr multicolored   1.60 1.00
Photo.
1866 A965 4fr multicolored   1.60 1.00
Issue dates: #1866, Mar. 19; #1865, Apr. 9.

Illustration from Perrault's Folk Tales, by Gustave Doré A966

1983, June 18   Engr.   Perf. 13
1867 A966 4fr red & black   1.60 1.00

Homage to Jean Effel A967

1983, Oct. 15
1868 A967 4fr multicolored   1.60 1.00

Le Lapin Agile, by Utrillo — A968

1983, Dec. 3   Perf. 13x12½
1869 A968 4fr multicolored   1.60 1.00

Thistle — A969   Europa 1983 — A970

1983, Apr. 23   Engr.   Perf. 12½x12
1870 A969 1fr shown   .30 .30
1871 A969 2fr Martagon lily   .90 .30
1872 A969 3fr Aster   1.25 .60
1873 A969 4fr Aconite   1.75 .60
Nos. 1870-1873 (4)   4.20 1.80

1983, Apr. 29   Perf. 13
1874 A970 1.80fr Symbolic shutter   2.00 .50
1875 A970 2.60fr Lens-to-screen diagram   2.10 .75

Centenary of Paris Convention for the Protection of Industrial Property — A971

1983, May 14   Photo.   Perf. 13
1876 A971 2fr multicolored   .90 .30

French Philatelic Societies Congress, Marseille A972

1983, May 21   Engr.   Perf. 13
1877 A972 1.80fr multicolored   .85 .35

Liberty Type of 1982
1983-87   Engr.   Perf. 13
1878 A915 1.70fr green   .75 .20
1879 A915 1.80fr green   .80 .20
1880 A915 1.90fr green   .85 .20
1881 A915 2fr red   .90 .20
1882 A915 2fr green   .90 .20
1883 A915 2.10fr red   .95 .20

1884 A915 2.20fr red   1.00 .20
a.   Booklet pane of 10   10.00
b.   Bklt. pane, #1788, 4 #1884   5.00
c.   With label ('87)   1.00 .20
1885 A915 2.80fr blue   1.25 .90
1886 A915 3fr blue   1.40 .50
1887 A915 3.20fr blue   1.50 .90
1888 A915 3.40fr blue   1.60 .75
1889 A915 3.60fr blue   1.60 .65
1890 A915 10fr purple   4.50 .20
1891 A915 (1.90fr) green   .90 .20
1892 A915 (2fr) green   .90 .20
Nos. 1878-1892 (15)   19.80 5.70

Coil Stamps
Engr.   Perf. 13 Horiz.
1893 A915 1.70fr green   1.00 .80
1894 A915 1.80fr green   1.00 .50
1895 A915 1.90fr green   1.25 .30
1896 A915 2fr red   1.00 .30
1897 A915 2.10fr red   1.00 .60
1897A A915 2.20fr red   1.00 .50
Nos. 1893-1897A (6)   6.35 3.00

#1891 is inscribed "A," #1892 "B."
No. 1884c was issued in sheets of 50 plus 50 alternating labels picturing the PHILEXFRANCE '89 emblem to publicize the international philatelic exhibition.
Issued: 2.80fr, 10fr, #1881, 6/1; 1.70fr, 2.10fr, 3fr, 7/1/84; 1.80fr, 2.20fr, 3.20fr, 8/1/85; 3.40fr, #1891, 8/1/86; 1.90fr, 9/13/86; #1882, 10/15/87; 3.60fr, #1892, 8/1/87.
For surcharge see No. 2115.

50th Anniv. of Air France A973

1983, June 18
1898 A973 3.45fr multicolored   1.50 .85

Treaties of Versailles and Paris Bicentenary — A974

1983, Sept. 2   Perf. 13x12½
1899 A974 2.80fr multicolored   1.25 .60

Jewelry Making A975

1983, Sept. 10   Photo.   Perf. 13
1900 A975 2.20fr multicolored   .90 .35

30th Anniv. of Customs Cooperation Council — A976

1983, Sept. 22   Engr.   Perf. 13x12½
1901 A976 2.30fr multicolored   .90 .45

Michaux's Bicycle A977

1983, Oct. 1   Engr.   Perf. 13
1902 A977 1.60fr multicolored   1.00 .40

Natl. Weather Forecasting — A978

1983, Oct. 22   Engr.   Perf. 12½x13
1903 A978 1.50fr multicolored   .70 .20

Berthie Albrecht (1893-1943) — A979

1983, Nov. 5
1904 A979 1.60fr dk brown & olive   .75 .35
1905 A979 1.60fr Rene Levy (1906-1943)   .75 .35
Resistance heroines.

A980   A981

1983, Dec. 16
1906 A980 2fr dk gray & red   .90 .25
Pierre Mendes France (1907-1982), Premier.

1984, Mar. 22   Perf. 13
1907 A981 3.60fr Union leader Waldeck-Rousseau   1.40 .35
Trade Union centenary.

Homage to the Cinema, by Cesar A982

1984, Feb. 4   Engr.   Perf. 12½x13
1908 A982 4fr multicolored   2.00 1.00

Four Corners of the Sky, by Jean Messagier — A983

1984, Mar. 31   Photo.   Perf. 13x12½
1909 A983 4fr multicolored   2.00 1.00

Dining Room Corner, at Cannet, by Pierre Bonnard — A984

Photogravure and Engraved
1984, Apr. 14   *Perf. 12½x12*
1910 A984 4fr multicolored   2.00 1.00

Pythia, by Andre Masson A985

Painter at the Feet of His Model, by Helion A986

1984   **Photo.**   *Perf. 12x13*
1911 A985 5fr multicolored   2.25 1.00
1912 A986 5fr multicolored   2.25 1.00
Issue dates: #1911, Oct. 13; #1912, Dec. 1.

Guadeloupe — A987

1984, Feb. 25   *Perf. 13*
1913 A987 2.30fr Map, West Indian dancers   .90 .35

Vauban Citadel, Belle Ile-en-Mer A988

Cordouan Lighthouse — A989

La Grande Chartreuse Monastery, 900th Anniv. A990

Palais Ideal, Hauterives-Drome — A991

Montsegur Chateau A992

1984   **Engr.**   *Perf. 13*
1914 A988 2.50fr multicolored   1.10 .35
1915 A989 3.50fr multicolored   1.60 .40
Issued: #1914, 5/26; #1915, 6/23.

1984
1916 A990 1.70fr multicolored   .80 .40
1917 A991 2.10fr multicolored   .95 .30
1917A A992 3.70fr multicolored   1.75 .40
   Nos. 1914-1917A (5)   6.20 1.85
Issued: 1.70fr, 7/7; 2.10fr, 6/30; 3.70fr, 9/15.

Flora Tristan (1803-44), Feminist A992a

1984, Mar. 8
1918 A992a 2.80fr multicolored   1.00 .50

Playing Card Suits — A993

1984, Apr. 11   **Engr.**
1919 A993 1.14fr Hearts   .50 .45
1920 A993 1.47fr Spades   .65 .55
1921 A993 2.38fr Diamonds   1.00 .75
1922 A993 3.95fr Clubs   1.60 1.25
   Nos. 1919-1922 (4)   3.75 3.00
Nos. 1919-1922 known only precanceled. See second note after No. 132.

450th Anniv. of Cartier's Landing in Quebec A994

1984, Apr. 20   **Photo. & Engr.**
1923 A994 2fr multicolored   .90 .25
See Canada No. 1011.

Philex '84, Dunkirk A995

1984, Apr. 21   *Perf. 13x12½*
1924 A995 1.60fr multicolored   .75 .35

Europa (1959-84) A996

1984, Apr. 28   **Engr.**   *Perf. 13*
1925 A996 2fr red brown   .80 .35
1926 A996 2.80fr blue   1.75 .60

2nd European Parliament Election A997

1984, Mar. 24   **Photo.**   *Perf. 13*
1927 A997 2fr multicolored   .90 .25

Foreign Legion A998

1984, Apr. 30   **Engr.**   *Perf. 13x12½*
1928 A998 3.10fr multicolored   1.25 .50

40th Anniv. of Liberation A999

Photogravure and Engraved
1984, May 8   *Perf. 12½x13*
1929 A999 2fr Resistance   .90 .50
1930 A999 3fr Landing   1.40 .60
  a.   Pair, #1929-1930 + label   2.50 2.50

Olympic Events — A1000

1984, June 1   *Perf. 13*
1931 A1000 4fr multicolored   1.50 .60
Intl. Olympic Committee, 90th anniv. and 1984 Summer Olympics.

Engraving — A1001

1984, June 8   **Engr.**
1932 A1001 2fr multicolored   .90 .25

Bordeaux A1002

1984, June 9   *Perf. 13x12½*
1933 A1002 2fr red   .75 .25
French Philatelic Societies Congress, Bordeaux.

Natl. Telecommunications College, 40th Anniv. — A1003

1984, June 16   **Photo.**   *Perf. 13*
1934 A1003 3fr Satellite, phone, keyboard   1.25 .35

25th Intl. Geography Congress, Paris — A1004

1984, Aug. 25   **Engr.**   *Perf. 13x12½*
1935 A1004 3fr Alps   1.25 .35

Telecom I Satellite A1005

1984, Sept. 1   **Photo.**   *Perf. 13*
1936 A1005 3.20fr multicolored   1.50 .50

High-speed Train Mail Transport A1006

1984, Sept. 8
1937 A1006 2.10fr Electric train, Paris-Lyon   1.00 .25

Local Birds A1007

Marx Dormoy (1888-1941) A1008

Photogravure and Engraved
1984, Sept. 22   *Perf. 12½x12*
1938 A1007 1fr Gypaetus barbatus   .45 .25
1939 A1007 2fr Circaetus gallicus   .90 .25
1940 A1007 3fr Accipiter nisus   1.40 .75
1941 A1007 5fr Peregrine falcon   2.25 .55
   Nos. 1938-1941 (4)   5.00 1.80

1984, Sept. 22   **Engr.**   *Perf. 13*
1942 A1008 2.40fr multicolored   1.00 .35

A1009   — A1010

1984, Oct. 6   **Engr.**   *Perf. 12½x13*
1943 A1009 3fr Automobile plans 1.40 .35
100th anniv. of the automobile.

1984, Nov. 3
1944 A1010 2.10fr multicolored   .95 .25
Pres. Vincent Auriol (1884-1966).

9th 5-Year Plan A1011

1984, Dec. 8   **Photo.**   *Perf. 13*
1945 A1011 2.10fr dk blue & scar   .95 .25

French Language Promotion — A1012

1985, Jan. 15 Engr. Perf. 12½x13
1946 A1012 3fr multicolored 1.25 .35

Tourism Issue

View of Vienne A1013

Cathedral at Montpelier A1014

St. Michel de Cuxa (Codalet) Abbey — A1015

Talmont Church, Saintonge Romane A1016

Solutre A1017

1985 Perf. 13x12½
1947	A1013	1.70fr ol blk & dk grn	.75 .25
1948	A1014	2.10fr sepia & org	.90 .25
1949	A1015	2.20fr multicolored	.90 .35
1950	A1016	3fr multicolored	1.25 .55
1951	A1017	3.90fr multicolored	1.50 .40
	Nos. 1947-1951 (5)		5.30 1.80

Issue dates: 1.70fr, Jan. 19; 2.10fr, Mar. 30; 2.20fr, July 6; 3fr, June 15; 3.90fr, Sept. 28.

French TV, 50th Anniv. A1018

1985, Jan. 26 Photo. Perf. 13
1952 A1018 2.50fr multicolored 1.10 .50

Months of the Year — A1019

1985, Feb. 11 Engr.
1953	A1019	1.22fr January	.65 .35
1954	A1019	1.57fr February	.75 .50
1955	A1019	2.55fr March	1.25 1.00
1956	A1019	4.23fr April	2.25 1.50

1986, Feb. 10 Engr. Perf. 13
1957	A1019	1.28fr May	.65 .35
1958	A1019	1.65fr June	.75 .50
1959	A1019	2.67fr July	1.25 1.10
1960	A1019	4.44fr August	2.25 1.60

1987, Feb. 16 Engr.
1961	A1019	1.31fr September	.70 .35
1962	A1019	1.69fr October	.90 .50
1963	A1019	2.74fr November	1.40 1.10
1964	A1019	4.56fr December	2.50 1.90
	Nos. 1953-1964 (12)		15.30 10.75

Nos. 1953-1964 are known only precanceled. See second note after No. 132.

St. Valentine, by Raymond Peynet A1020

1985, Feb. 14 Photo. Perf. 13x12½
1965 A1020 2.10fr multicolored .95 .25

Pauline Kergomard (1838-1925) A1021

1985, Mar. 8 Engr. Perf. 13x12½
1966 A1021 1.70fr int bl & cop red .75 .25

Stained Glass Window, Strasbourg Cathedral A1022

Still-life with Candle, Nicolas de Stael — A1023

1985 Engraved Perf. 12x13
1967 A1022 5fr multicolored 4.00 1.25
Photo.
Perf. 13x12
1968 A1023 5fr multicolored 3.00 1.00
Issue dates: #1967, Apr. 13; #1968, June 1.

Untitled Abstract by Jean Dubuffet — A1024

Octopus Overlaid on Manuscript, by Pierre Alechinsky — A1025

Photogravure; Engraved (#1970)
1985 Perf. 13x12½
1969 A1024 5fr multicolored 2.50 1.25
1970 A1025 5fr multicolored 2.50 1.00
Issued: #1969, Sept. 14; #1970, Oct. 12.

The Dog, Abstract by Alberto Giacometti (1901-1966) — A1026

1985, Dec. 7 Engr. Perf. 13x12½
1971 A1026 5fr grnsh blk & lt lem 2.50 1.00

Housing in Givors A1027

Contemporary architecture by Jean Renaude.

1985, Apr. 20 Engr. Perf. 13
1972 A1027 2.40fr blk, yel org & ol grn .90 .50

Landevennec Abbey, 1500th Anniv. — A1028

1985, Apr. 20 Perf. 13x12½
1973 A1028 1.70fr green & brn vio .60 .20

A1029   A1030

Europa: 2.10fr, Adam de la Halle (1240-1285), composer. 3fr, Darius Milhaud (1892-1974), composer.

1985, Apr. 27 Perf. 12½x13
1974	A1029	2.10fr dr bl, blk, & brt bl	.65 .40
1975	A1029	3fr dk bl, brt bl & blk	1.00 .50

1985, May 8 Perf. 13x12½
1976 A1030 2fr Return of peace .70 .50
1977 A1030 3fr Return of liberty 1.25 .50
 a. Pair, #1976-1977 + label 2.00 2.00
Liberation of France from German occupation forces, 40th anniv.

Natl. Philatelic Congress, Tours — A1031

1985, May 25 Perf. 12½x13
1978 A1031 2.10fr Tours Cathedral .95 .35

Rabies Vaccine Cent. A1032

1985, June 1 Perf. 13x12½
1979 A1032 1.50fr Pasteur inoculating patient .55 .25

Mystere Falcon-900 A1033

1985, June 1 Perf. 13
1980 A1033 10fr blue 4.50 2.00

Lake Geneva Life-Saving Society Cent. A1034

1985, June 15
1981 A1034 2.50fr blk, red & brt ultra 1.00 .40

UN, 40th Anniv. — A1035   Huguenot Cross — A1036

1985, June 26 Perf. 13x12½
1982 A1035 3fr multicolored 1.10 .35

1985, Aug. 31 Engr. Perf. 12½x13
1983 A1036 2.50fr dp vio, dk red brn & dk red 1.00 .35

King Louis XIV revoked the Edict of Nantes on Oct. 18, 1685, dispossessing French Protestants of religious and civil liberty.

A1037   A1038

Trees, leaves and fruit of the beech, elm, oak and spruce varieties.

1985, Sept. 21   **Engr.**   **Perf. 12½**
1984 A1037 1fr shown   .45   .25
1985 A1037 2fr Ulmus montana   .90   .25
1986 A1037 3fr Quercus
          pedunculata   1.40   .60
1987 A1037 5fr Picea abies   2.25   .35
     Nos. 1984-1987 (4)   5.00 1.45

1985, Nov. 2   **Engr.**   **Perf. 12½x13**

La France Mourning the Dead, Eternal Flame.

1988 A1038 1.80fr brn, org & lake   .85   .25
     Memorial Day.

A1039   A1040

1985, Nov. 9   **Engr.**
1989 A1039 3.20fr black & blue   1.25   .40

Charles Dullin, 1885-1949, impresario, theater.

1985, Nov. 16   **Engr.**   **Perf. 13x12½**
1990 A1040 2.20fr red & black   1.00   .20
     National information system.

Thai Ambassadors at the Court of King Louis XIV, Painting A1041

1986, Jan. 25   **Engr.**   **Perf. 13**
1991 A1041 3.20fr rose lake & blk   1.25   .65

Normalization of diplomatic relations with Thailand, 300th anniv.

Leisure, by Fernand Leger A1042

1986, Feb. 1   **Photo.**   **Perf. 13**
1992 A1042 2.20fr multicolored   1.00   .20
     1936 Popular Front, 50th anniv.

Venice Carnival, Paris — A1043

1986, Feb. 12   **Perf. 12½x13**
1993 A1043 2.20fr multicolored   1.00   .20

La Marianne, Typograph by Raymond Gid A1044

Photogravure & Engraved
1986, Mar. 3   **Perf. 12½x13½**
1994 A1044 5fr black & dk red   2.25 1.00

Tourism Issue

Filitosa, South Corsica A1045

Loches Chateau A1046

Norman Manor, St. Germain de Livet A1047

Notre-Dame-en-Vaux Monastery, Marne — A1048

Market Square, Bastide de Monpazier, Dordogne — A1049

Illustration A1049 reduced.

1986   **Engr.**   **Perf. 13**
1995 A1045 1.80fr multicolored   .85   .25
1996 A1046   2fr int blue & blk   .90   .50
1997 A1047 2.20fr grnsh bl, brn
           & grn   1.00   .35
1998 A1048 2.50fr henna brn &
           sepia   1.10   .40
     Perf. 13x12½
1999 A1049 3.90fr blk & yel org   1.75   .90
     Nos. 1995-1999 (5)   5.60 2.40
     Issued: 2.20fr, 3/3; 2fr, 6/14; 2.50fr, 6/9; 1.80fr, 3.90fr, 7/5.

Louise Michel (1830-1905), Anarchist — A1050

1986, Mar. 10   **Engr.**
2000 A1050 1.80fr dk red & gray
           blk   .80   .20

City of Science and Industry, La Villette — A1051

1986, Mar. 17
2001 A1051 3.90fr multicolored   1.40   .50

Center for Modern Asia-Africa Studies A1052

1986, Apr. 12   **Photo.**   **Perf. 13**
2002 A1052 3.20fr Map   1.25   .30

Skibet, Abstract by Maurice Esteve — A1053

Virginia, Abstract by Alberto Magnelli — A1054

Abstract, by Pierre Soulages — A1055

The Dancer, by Jean Arp A1056

Isabelle d'Este, by Leonardo da Vinci A1057

Perf. 12½x13, 13x12½ (#2005, 2006)
1986   **Photo., Engr. (#2005, 2007)**
2003 A1053 5fr multicolored   2.25 1.00
2004 A1054 5fr multicolored   2.25 1.00
2005 A1055 5fr brt vio, blk &
           brn gray   2.25 1.00
2006 A1056 5fr multicolored   2.25 1.00
2007 A1057 5fr blk, red brn &
           grnsh yel   2.25 1.00
     Nos. 2003-2007 (5)   11.25 5.00
     Issued: #2003, Apr. 14; #2004, June 25; #2005, Dec. 22; #2006, 2007, Nov. 10.

Victor Basch (1863-1944), IPY Emblem — A1058

1986, Apr. 28   **Engr.**   **Perf. 13**
2008 A1058 2.50fr black & yel grn   1.10   .30
     International Peace Year.

Europa 1986 A1059

1986, Apr. 28   **Perf. 13x12½**
2009 A1059 2.20fr Civet cat   1.00   .35
2010 A1059 3.20fr Bat   1.50   .65

St. Jean-Marie Vianney, Curé of Ars A1060

1986, May 3   **Engr.**   **Perf. 13x12½**
2011 A1060 1.80fr sepia, brn org
           & brn   .80   .25

Philatelic Societies Federation Congress, Nancy — A1061

1986, May 17   **Perf. 13**
2012 A1061 2.20fr Exposition
           Center   1.00   .25

Mens World Volleyball Championship A1062

Statue of Liberty, Cent. A1063

1986, May 24   **Engr.**   **Perf. 13**
2013 A1062 2.20fr dk vio, brn vio & scar   1.00 .35

1986, July 4   **Perf. 13**
2014 A1063 2.20fr scar & dk blue   1.00 .25
See US No. 2224.

1st Ascent of Mt. Blanc, 1786 A1064

1986, Aug. 8   **Engr.**   **Perf. 13x12½**
2015 A1064 2fr J. Balmat, M.G. Paccard   .90 .50

Pierre-Louis Moreau de Maupertuis (1698-1759), La Condamine and Sextant — A1065

1986, Sept. 5
2016 A1065 3fr multicolored   1.25 .55
Lapland Expedition, 250th anniv., proved Earth's poles are flattened.
See Finland No. 741.

Marcassite A1066

1986, Sept. 13   **Perf. 12½**
2017 A1066 2fr shown   .90 .25
2018 A1066 3fr Quartz   1.40 .45
2019 A1066 4fr Calcite   1.75 .70
2020 A1066 5fr Fluorite   2.25 .70
     Nos. 2017-2020 (4)   6.30 1.90

Souvenir Sheet

Natl. Film Industry, 50th Anniv. A1067

Personalities and film scenes: a, Louis Feuillade, The Vampires. b, Max Linder. c, Sacha Guitry, Romance of the Trickster. d, Jean Renoir, The Grand Illusion. e, Marcel Pagnol, The Baker's Woman. f, Jean Epstein, The Three-Sided Mirror. g, Rene Clair, Women of the Night. h, Jean Gremillon, Talk of Love. i, Jacques Becker, Helmet of Gold. j, Francois Truffaut, The Young Savage.

1986, Sept. 20   **Photo.**   **Perf. 13x12½**
2021   Sheet of 10   10.00 10.00
   a.-j. A1067 2.20fr any single   1.00 1.00

Scene from Le Grand Meaulnes, by Henry Alain-Fournier (b. 1886), Novelist A1068

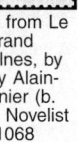

Professional Education, Cent. A1069

1986, Oct. 4   **Engr.**   **Perf. 12½x13**
2022 A1068 2.20fr black & dk red   1.00 .25

1986, Oct. 4
2023 A1069 1.90fr brt vio & dp lil rose   .85 .25

World Energy Conf., Cannes A1070

Mulhouse Technical Museum A1071

1986, Oct. 5   **Photo.**   **Perf. 13**
2024 A1070 3.40fr multicolored   1.50 .50

1986, Dec. 1   **Engr.**
2025 A1071 2.20fr int blue, dk red & blk   1.00 .45

Museum at Orsay, Opening — A1072

1986, Dec. 10   **Photo.**
2026 A1072 3.70fr bluish blk & pck bl   1.75 .60

Fulgence Bienvenue (1852-1934), and the Metro — A1073

1987, Jan. 17   **Engr.**   **Perf. 13**
2027 A1073 2.50fr vio brn, brn & dk grn   1.10 .35

A1074   A1075

1987, Jan. 24
2028 A1074 1.90fr grn & grnsh blk   .85 .20
Raoul Follereau (1903-1977), care for lepers.

1987, Mar. 7   **Engr.**   **Perf. 12½x13**
2029 A1075 1.90fr black & red   .85 .20
Cutlery industry, Thiers.

Tourist Issue

Redon, Ille et Vilaine A1076

Azay-le-Rideau Chateau — A1077

Meuse District — A1078

Etretat A1079

Les Baux-de-Provence — A1080

Illustration A1078 reduced.

1987   **Engr.**   **Perf. 13**
2030 A1076 2.20fr dp rose lil, blk & brn ol   1.10 .25
2031 A1077 2.50fr Prus blue & olive grn   1.25 .25
     Perf. 12½
2032 A1078 3.70fr multicolored   1.75 .25
     Photo.   **Perf. 13**
2033 A1079 2.20fr multicolored   1.00 .25
     Engr.
2034 A1080   3fr dk ol bis & dp vio   1.40 .90
     Nos. 2030-2034 (5)   6.50 1.90
Issued: #2030, 3/7; #2033, 6/12; 2.50fr, 5/9; 3fr, 6/27; 3.70fr, 5/30.

Charles Edouard Jenneret (Le Corbusier) (1887-1965), Architect — A1081

1987, Apr. 11   **Photo.**   **Perf. 13x12½**
2035 A1081 3.70fr Abstract   1.75 .50

Europa 1987 A1082

Modern architecture: 2.20fr, Metal factory at Boulogne-Billancourt, by architect Claude Vasconi. 3.40fr, Rue Mallet-Stevens housing, by Robert Mallet-Stevens.

1987, Apr. 25   **Engr.**   **Perf. 13x12½**
2036 A1082 2.20fr dk blue & grn   *1.25 .50*
2037 A1082 3.40fr brn & dk grn   *1.75 .65*

Abstract Painting, by Bram van Velde — A1083

Woman under Parasol, by Eugene Boudin (1824-1898) — A1084

Precambrien, by Camille Bryen — A1085

World, Bronze Sculpture by Antoine Pevsner — A1086

Perf. 12½x13, 13x12½ (Nos. 2039, 2041)

Photo., Engr. (Nos. 2039, 2041)

1987

2038	A1083	5fr multicolored	2.25	1.00
2039	A1084	5fr multicolored	2.25	1.00
2040	A1085	5fr multicolored	2.25	1.00
2041	A1086	5fr bister & blk	2.25	1.00
		Nos. 2038-2041 (4)	9.00	4.00

Issue dates: #2038, Apr. 25; #2039, May 23; #2040, Sept. 12; #2041, Nov. 14.

Gaspard de Montagnes, from a Manuscript Illustration — A1087

1987, May 9   **Engr.**   *Perf. 13*

2042 A1087 1.90fr dp grn & sepia   .85   .20

Henri Pourrat (1887-1959), novelist.

Natl. Philatelic Societies Congress, Lens A1088

1987, June 6   *Perf. 13x13½*

2043 A1088 2.20fr choc & red   1.00   .30

Involvement of U.S. Forces in WW I, 70th Anniv. A1089

Design: Stars and Stripes, troops, Gen. John J. Pershing (1860-1948), American army commander.

1987, June 13   *Perf. 13*

2044 A1089 3.40fr olive grn, saph & ver   1.50   .70

A1090   A1091

1987, June 17   **Photo.**

2045 A1090 2fr multicolored   .90   .60

6th Intl. Cable Car Transport Congress, Grenoble.

1987, June 20   **Litho.**

2046 A1091 1.90fr pale chalky blue & blk   .90   .55

Accession of Hugh Capet (c.938-996), 1st king of France, millenary.

A1092   A1093

1987, June 20   **Engr.**   *Perf. 12½x13*

2047 A1092 2.20fr multicolored   1.00   .30

La Fleche Natl. Military School.

1987, June 27   **Photo.**   *Perf. 13*

2048 A1093 1.90fr multicolored   .90   .55

World Assembly of Expatriate Algerians, Nice.

World Wrestling Championships — A1094

1987, Aug. 21   **Engr.**

2049 A1094 3fr brt pur, vio gray & brt olive grn   1.40   .60

Mushrooms   William the
A1095   Conqueror (c.
              1027-1087)
               A1096

1987, Sept. 5   *Perf. 12½*

2050	A1095	2fr Gyroporus cy-anescens	.90	.25
2051	A1095	3fr Gomphus clavatus	1.40	.35
2052	A1095	4fr Morchella conica	1.75	.60
2053	A1095	5fr Russula virescens	2.25	.60
		Nos. 2050-2053 (4)	6.30	1.80

1987, Sept. 5   *Perf. 13*

2054 A1096 2fr Bayeux Tapestry detail   .90   .35

Montbenoit Le Saugeais A1097

Design: Abbey of Medieval Knights, cloisters, winter scene.

1987, Sept. 19

2055 A1097 2.50fr saph, blk & scar   1.10   .55

Pasteur Institute, Cent. — A1098

1987, Oct. 3

2056 A1098 2.20fr dp blue & dk red   1.00   .20

Blaise Cendrars (1887-1961), Poet and Novelist — A1099   Treaty of Andelot, 1400th Anniv. — A1100

Pen and ink portrait by Modigliani.

1987, Nov. 6   *Perf. 12½*

2057 A1099 2fr brt grn, buff & blk   .90   .35

1987, Nov. 28   *Perf. 12½x13*

2058 A1100 3.70fr multicolored   1.75   .55

Gen. Leclerc (1902-1947), Marshal of France — A1101

1987, Nov. 28   *Perf. 13x12½*

2059 A1101 2.20fr multicolored   1.00   .25

Liberty Type of 1982

1987-90   *Perf. 13*

2077	A915	3.70fr brt lilac rose	1.75	.35
2078	A915	(2.10fr) green ('90)	.95	.20
2079	A915	(2.30fr) red ('90)	1.00	.20
		Nos. 2077-2079 (3)	3.70	.75

Coil Stamp
Engr.
Perf. 13 Horiz.

2080 A915 2fr emerald green   .90   .30

Issued: 2fr, 8/1; 3.70fr, 11/16; #2078-2079, 1/2.

Nos. 2078-2079 are inscribed "C."

Franco-German Cooperation Treaty, 25th Anniv. — A1102

1988, Jan. 15   *Perf. 13*

2086 A1102 2.20fr Adenauer, De Gaulle   1.00   .35

See Fed. Rep. of Germany No. 1546.

Marcel Dassault (1892-1986), Aircraft Designer — A1103

1988, Jan. 23   **Photo.**

2087 A1103 3.60fr brt ultra, gray blk & dk red   1.60   .70

Communications A1104   Great Synagogue, Rue Victoire, Paris A1105

Angouleme Festival prize-winning cartoons.

1988, Jan. 29   **Photo.**   *Perf. 13½x13*
Booklet Stamps

2088	A1104	2.20fr Pellos	1.00	.50
2089	A1104	2.20fr Reiser	1.00	.50
2090	A1104	2.20fr Marijac	1.00	.50
2091	A1104	2.20fr Fred	1.00	.50
2092	A1104	2.20fr Moebius	1.00	.50
2093	A1104	2.20fr Gillon	1.00	.50
2094	A1104	2.20fr Bretecher	1.00	.50
2095	A1104	2.20fr Forest	1.00	.50
2096	A1104	2.20fr Mezieres	1.00	.50
2097	A1104	2.20fr Tardi	1.00	.50
2098	A1104	2.20fr Lob	1.00	.50
2099	A1104	2.20fr Bilal	1.00	.50
a.		Bklt. pane of 12, #2088-2099	12.00	

1988, Feb. 7   **Litho.**   *Perf. 13*

2100 A1105 2fr black & gold   .90   .25

The Four Elements — A1106

1988, Feb. 1   **Engr.**   *Perf. 13*

2101	A1106	1.36fr Air	.65	.40
2102	A1106	1.75fr Water	.80	.40
2103	A1106	2.83fr Fire	1.25	1.00
2104	A1106	4.75fr Earth	2.25	1.75
		Nos. 2101-2104 (4)	4.95	3.55

Nos. 2101-2104 known only precanceled. See second note after No. 132.

PHILEXFRANCE '89 — A1107

1988, Mar. 4

2105 A1107 2.20fr #1885, emblem   1.00   .20

Postal Training College, Cent. A1108

1988, Mar. 29

2106 A1108 3.60fr multicolored   1.60   .40

Philex-Jeunes '88, Youth Stamp Show — A1109

1988, Apr. 8   *Perf. 13x12½*

2107 A1109 2fr multicolored   .90   .25

Blood
Donation — A1110

1988, Apr. 9 Photo. Perf. 13½x13
2108 A1110 2.50fr multicolored 1.10 .40

Europa
1988
A1111

Communication and transportation.

1988, Apr. 30 Engr. Perf. 13
2109 A1111 2.20fr Cables, satellites 1.75 .35
2110 A1111 3.60fr Rail cars 2.50 .60

Jean Monnet (1888-
1979),
Economist — A1112

1988, May 10 Perf. 12½x13
2111 A1112 2.20fr black & brn ol 1.00 .25

Philatelic
Congress,
Valence
A1113

1988, May 21 Perf. 13x12½
2112 A1113 2.20fr multicolored 1.00 .35

Intl.
Medical
Assistance
A1114

1988, May 28 Photo. Perf. 13
2113 A1114 3.60fr multicolored 1.60 .50

Aid to the Handicapped — A1115

1988, May 28
2114 A1115 3.70fr multicolored 1.60 .50

No. 1884 Surcharged in
European Currency
Units

1988, Apr. 16 Engr.
2115 A915 2.20fr red 1.00 .25

Tourist Issue

Hermes Dicephalus (Roman Empire),
Frejus — A1116

Ship Museum, Douarnenez — A1117

Chateau Sedieres,
Correze — A1118

Cirque de
Gavarnie
A1119

View of
Perouges,
Ain
A1120

1988, June 12 Engr. Perf. 13x12½
2116 A1116 3.70fr multicolored 1.75 .80

1988 Perf. 13, 12½x13 (#2118)
2117 A1117 2fr multicolored .90 .25
2118 A1118 2.20fr multicolored 1.00 .35
2119 A1119 3fr multicolored 1.40 .40

Issued: 2.20fr, 7/2; 2fr, 7/4; 3fr, 7/23.

1988, Sept. 10 Perf. 13x12½
2120 A1120 2.20fr multicolored 1.00 .25
Nos. 2116-2120 (5) 6.05 2.05

French Revolution, Bicent. — A1121

Designs: 3fr, Assembly of the Three
Estates, Vizille. 4fr, Day of the Tiles (Barricades), Grenoble.

1988, June 18 Engr.
2121 A1121 3fr multicolored 1.40 1.00
2122 A1121 4fr multicolored 1.90 1.00
a. Pair, #2121-2122 + label 3.50 3.00
PHILEXFRANCE '89.

Buffon's Natural
History — A1122

Alpine Troops,
Cent. — A1123

1988, June 18 Perf. 12½
2123 A1122 2fr Otters .90 .20
2124 A1122 3fr Stag 1.40 .30
2125 A1122 4fr Fox 1.90 .70
2126 A1122 5fr Badger 2.25 .60
Nos. 2123-2126 (4) 6.45 1.80

1988, June 25 Perf. 13
2127 A1123 2.50fr multicolored 1.10 .65

Roland Garros (1888-1918), 1st Pilot
to Fly Across the Mediterranean, Sept.
23, 1913 — A1124

1988, July 2 Engr. Perf. 13x12½
2128 A1124 2fr brt grn bl & olive .90 .25

Nov. 11, 1918 Armistice Ending World
War I, 70th Anniv.
A1125

1988, Sept. 10 Engr. Perf. 13
2129 A1125 2.20fr brt blue, gray &
blk 1.00 .25

Homage to
Leon
Degand,
Sculpture
by Robert
Jacobsen
A1126

1988, Sept. 22 Perf. 12½x13
2130 A1126 5fr blk & dp claret 2.25 1.00
French-Danish cultural exchange program,
10th anniv. See Denmark No. 860.

Strasbourg, 2000th
Anniv. — A1127

1988, Sept. 24 Perf. 13
2131 A1127 2.20fr Municipal arms 1.00 .25

St. Mihiel Sepulcher, by Ligier Richier
(c. 1500-1567), Sculptor — A1128

Composition, 1954, by Serge Poliakoff
(1906-1969) — A1129

La Pieta de Villeneuve-les-Avignon, by
Enguerrand Quarton (1444-
1466) — A1130

Anthropometry of the Blue Period, by
Yves Klein — A1131

1988-89 Engr. Perf. 13x12½
2132 A1128 5fr black brown 2.25 1.00
Photo.
2133 A1129 5fr multicolored 2.25 1.00
2134 A1130 5fr multicolored 2.25 1.00
2135 A1131 5fr multi ('89) 2.25 1.00
Nos. 2132-2135 (4) 9.00 4.00

Issue dates: #2132, Oct. 15; #2133, Oct. 22;
#2134, Dec. 10; #2135, Jan. 21.

Thermal
Springs
A1132

1988, Nov. 21 Engr. Perf. 13x12½
2136 A1132 2.20fr multicolored 1.00 .25

Metamecanique, by Jean
Tinguely — A1133

1988, Nov. 25 Photo.
2137 A1133 5fr multicolored 3.00 1.00
See Switzerland No. 828.

UN Declaration of Human Rights, 40th Anniv. A1134

1988, Dec. 12   **Litho.**   **Perf. 13**
2138 A1134 2.20fr dk bl & grnsh bl 1.00 .25

French Revolution, Bicent. — A1135

1989, Jan. 1   **Photo.**   **Perf. 13x12½**
2139 A1135 2.20fr red & vio blue 1.00 .20

Valentin Hauy (1745-1822), Founder of the School for the Blind, Paris, 1791 — A1136

Photo. & Embossed
1989, Jan. 28
2140 A1136 2.20fr multicolored 1.00 .40

Estienne School, Cent. — A1137

1989, Feb. 4   **Engr.**   **Perf. 12½**
2141 A1137 2.20fr gray, black & red 1.00 .25

European Parliament Elections A1138

1989, Mar. 4   **Litho.**   **Perf. 13**
2142 A1138 2.20fr multicolored 1.00 .20

A1139

1989   **Engr.**   **Perf. 12½x13**
2143 A1139 2.20fr Liberty 1.00 .25
2144 A1139 2.20fr Equality 1.00 .25
2145 A1139 2.20fr Fraternity 1.00 .25
a. Strip of 3, #2143-2145 + label 3.00 2.50

Bicent. of the French revolution and the Declaration of Rights of Man and the Citizen. No. 2145a contains inscribed label picturing PHILEXFRANCE '89 emblem.
Issue dates: #2143, Mar. 18; #2144, Apr. 22; #2145, May 27; #2145a, July 14.

French-Soviet Joint Space Flight — A1140

1989, Mar. 4   **Litho.**   **Perf. 13**
2146 A1140 3.60fr multicolored 1.60 .60

Historic Sights, Paris — A1141

Designs: No. 2147, Arche de la Defense. No. 2148, Eiffel Tower. No. 2149, Grand Louvre. No. 2150, Notre Dame Cathedral. No. 2151, Bastille Monument and Opera de la Bastille. #2151a has a continuous design.

1989, Apr. 21   **Engr.**   **Perf. 13x12½**
2147 A1141 2.20fr multicolored 1.00 .85
2148 A1141 2.20fr multicolored 1.00 .85
2149 A1141 2.20fr multicolored 1.00 .85
2150 A1141 2.20fr multicolored 1.00 .85
2151 A1141 2.20fr multicolored 1.00 .85
a. Strip of 5, #2147-2151 5.00 5.00

Europa 1989 A1142

Children's games.

1989, Apr. 29   **Perf. 13**
2152 A1142 2.20fr Hopscotch 1.00 .30
2153 A1142 3.60fr Catch (ball) 2.50 .70

ITU Plenipotentiaries Conference, Nice — A1143

1989, May 23   **Litho.**
2154 A1143 3.70fr dk bl, dl org & red 1.75 .40

Tourist Issue

Fontainebleau Forest — A1144

Vaux le Vicomte — A1145

La Brenne — A1146

Illustrations A1145-A1146 reduced.

1989, May 20   **Engr.**   **Perf. 13**
2155 A1144 2.20fr multicolored 1.00 .30

Perf. 13x12½
2156 A1145 3.70fr ol bis & blk 1.75 .75
2157 A1146 4fr violet blue 1.75 .75
Nos. 2155-2157 (3) 4.50 1.80

Issued: 2.20fr, 5/20; 3.70fr, 7/14; 4fr, 8/25.

World Cycling Championships, Chambery — A1147

1989, June 3   **Litho.**   **Perf. 13**
2158 A1147 2.20fr multi 1.00 .25

Jehan de Malestroit, Dept. of Morbihan — A1148

1989, June 10   **Engr.**   **Perf. 12½x13**
2159 A1148 3.70fr multicolored 1.75 .55

Preliminary Sketch (Detail) for *Oath of the Tennis Court,* by David — A1149

Regatta with Wind Astern, by Charles Lapicque A1150

1989, June 19   **Photo.**   **Perf. 13x12½**
2160 A1149 5fr multicolored 2.25 1.00
Perf. 12½
2161 A1150 5fr multicolored 2.25 1.00

No. 2160 for French revolution bicent.
Issued: #2160, 6/19; #2161, 9/23.

Souvenir Sheet

Revolution Bicentennial — A1151

Revolutionaries: a, Madame Roland (1754-1793). b, Camille Desmoulins (1760-1794). c, Condorcet (1743-1794). d, Kellermann (1735-1820).

1989, June 26   **Engr.**   **Perf. 13**
2162 A1151 Sheet of 4 4.00 3.50
a.-d. 2.20fr any single 1.00 .75

15th Summit of the Arch Meeting of Leaders from Industrial Nations, July 14-16 A1152

1989, July 14   **Photo.**
2163 A1152 2.20fr multicolored 1.00 .35

Declaration of the Rights of Man and the Citizen, Versailles, Aug. 26, 1789 — A1153

Details of an anonymous 18th-19th cent. painting in Carnavalet Museum: No. 2168a, Preamble, Article I. No. 2168b, Articles VII-XI. No. 2168c, Articles II-VI. No. 2168d, Articles XII-XVII.

Litho. & Engr.
1989, Aug. 26   **Perf. 13x11½**
2164 A1153 2.50fr Preamble, Article I 1.00 .90
2165 A1153 2.50fr Art. II-VI 1.00 .90
2166 A1153 2.50fr Art. VII-XI 1.00 .90
2167 A1153 2.50fr Art. XII-XVII 1.00 .90
a. Strip, #2164-2167 + label 4.00 3.50

Souvenir Sheet
Perf. 13x12½
2168 Sheet of 4 20.00 20.00
a.-d. A1153 5fr any single 5.00 5.00

No. 2168 contains 4 52x41mm stamps. Sold for 50fr, including admission fee to PHILEX-FRANCE '89.
Value of No. 2168 is for examples on plain paper. Examples on fluorescent paper seem to have been distributed in North America, and may not have been distributed widely or made available in Europe. Value $250.

Musical Instruments — A1154

1989 Litho. **Perf. 12x12½**
2169 A1154 1.39fr Harp .65 .50
2170 A1154 1.79fr Piano .80 .50
2171 A1154 2.90fr Trumpet 1.25 1.00
2172 A1154 4.84fr Violin 2.25 1.75
Nos. 2169-2172 (4) 4.95 3.75
Nos. 2169-2172 are known only precanceled. See second note after No. 132.
See #2233-2239, 2273-2283, 2368-2371.

TGV Atlantic A1155

1989, Sept. 23 Photo. **Perf. 13**
2173 A1155 2.50fr dk bl, sil & red 1.10 .50

Clermont-Ferrand Tramway, Cent. — A1156

1989, Oct. 28 Engr.
2174 A1156 3.70fr blk & dk ol bis 1.75 .40

Villers-Cotterets Ordinance, 450th Anniv. — A1157

1989, Oct. 28 Engr.
2175 A1157 2.20fr blk, dp cl & red 1.00 .25

Baron Augustin-Louis Cauchy (1789-1857), Mathematician — A1158

1989, Nov. 10 **Perf. 13x12½**
2176 A1158 3.60fr red, blk & bl grn 1.60 .50

Marshal Jean de Lattre de Tassigny (1889-1952) — A1159

1989, Nov. 18 **Perf. 13**
2177 A1159 2.20fr bl, blk & red 1.00 .35

Harki Soldiers of France A1160

1989, Dec. 9 Photo.
2178 A1160 2.20fr multicolored 1.00 .35

Marianne — A1161

1990-92 Engr. **Perf. 13**
2179 A1161 10c brn blk .20 .20
 a. Bklt. pane, #2180, 4 #2179 1.00
2180 A1161 20c lt green .20 .20
2181 A1161 50c brt violet .20 .20
2182 A1161 1fr orange .45 .20
2183 A1161 2fr apple grn .90 .20
2184 A1161 2.10fr dark grn .95 .20
2185 A1161 2.20fr dark grn 1.00 .20
2186 A1161 2.20fr emerald 1.00 .20
2187 A1161 2.30fr red 1.00 .20
 a. Bklt. pane, #2180, 4 #2187 5.00
2188 A1161 2.50fr red 1.10 .20
2189 A1161 3.20fr blue 1.50 .75
2190 A1161 3.40fr blue 1.60 .40
2191 A1161 3.80fr lilac rose 1.75 .30
2192 A1161 4fr lilac rose 1.90 .20
2193 A1161 4.20fr lilac rose 1.90 .20
2194 A1161 5fr greenish blue 2.25 .20
2195 A1161 10fr violet 4.50 .25
2196 A1161 (2.20fr) dk grn 1.00 .20
2197 A1161 (2.50fr) red 1.10 .20
Nos. 2179-2197 (19) 24.50 4.70

Coil Stamps
Perf. 13 Horiz.
2198 A1161 2.10fr dk grn 1.00 .20
2199 A1161 2.20fr dk grn 1.00 .60
2200 A1161 2.30fr red 1.00 .20
2201 A1161 2.50fr red 1.10 .20
Nos. 2198-2201 (4) 4.10 1.20

Die Cut
Self-Adhesive
2202 A1161 2.30fr red 1.00 .20
 a. Booklet pane of 10 10.00
2203 A1161 2.50fr red 1.10 .20
 a. Booklet pane of 10 11.00
 b. Booklet pane of 5 5.50
2204 A1161 (2.50fr) red 1.10 .20
 a. Booklet pane of 10 11.00
Nos. 2202-2204 (3) 3.20 .60

Issued: #2187, 1/2; #2198, 1/1; 10c, 20c, 50c, 3.20fr, 3.80fr, 3/26; #2202, 1/29; #2182-2183, 2194-2195, 5/21; #2196-2197, 8/19/91; 2.20fr, 2.50fr, 3.40fr, 4fr, 9/30/91; #2179a, 2187a, 2199, 2201, 1991; 4.20fr, 9/24/92; #2203-2204, 1992; 2.10fr, 1993.
Peelable paper backing serves as booklet cover for Nos. 2202, 2203. No. 2203b has separate backing with no printing.
Nos. 2196-2197, 2204 inscribed "D."
See Nos. 2333-2348, 3529.

Lace Work A1162

1990, Feb. 3 Engr. **Perf. 13x12½**
2205 A1162 2.50fr red 1.10 .40

1992 Winter Olympics, Albertville — A1163

1990, Feb. 9 Photo. **Perf. 13**
2206 A1163 2.50fr multicolored 1.10 .20

Charles de Gaulle (1890-1970) A1164

Max Hymans (1900-1961), Planes and ACC Emblem A1165

1990, Feb. 24 Engr. **Perf. 12½x13**
2207 A1164 2.30fr brt vio, vio bl & blk 1.00 .25

1990, Mar. 3 **Perf. 13**
2208 A1165 2.30fr brt vio, brt bl & dk ol grn 1.00 .25

Profile of a Woman, by Odilon Redon A1166

Head of Christ, Wissembourg — A1167

Cambodian Dancer by Auguste Rodin — A1168

Jaune et Gris by Roger Bissiere A1169

1990 Litho. **Perf. 13½x14**
2209 A1166 5fr multicolored 2.25 1.00
Perf. 12½x13
Engr.
2210 A1167 5fr multicolored 2.25 1.00
2211 A1168 5fr multicolored 2.25 1.00

Photo.
2212 A1169 5fr multicolored 2.25 1.00
Nos. 2209-2212 (4) 9.00 4.00
Issue dates: No. 2209, Mar. 3; No. 2210, June 16; No. 2211, June 9; No. 2212, Dec. 8.

Jean Guehenno (1890-1978) A1170

Litho. & Engr.
1990, Mar. 24 **Perf. 13**
2213 A1170 3.20fr buff & red brn 1.50 .40

Tourism Series

Flaran Abbey, Gers A1171

Cluny A1172

Pont Canal de Briare A1173

Cap Canaille, Cassis A1174

1990, Apr. 21 Engr. **Perf. 13**
2214 A1171 3.80fr sepia & blk 1.75 .50

1990
2215 A1172 2.30fr multicolored 1.00 .25
2216 A1173 2.30fr multicolored 1.00 .25
2217 A1174 3.80fr multicolored 1.75 .50
Nos. 2215-2217 (3) 3.75 1.00

Issued: #2215, 6/23; #2216, 7/7; 3.80fr, 7/14.

Europa 1990 A1175

Post offices.

1990, Apr. 28 Engr. **Perf. 13**
2218 A1175 2.30fr Macon *1.50* *.50*
2219 A1175 3.20fr Cerizay *2.25* *.80*

Arab World Institute — A1176

1990, May 5 **Perf. 12½x13**
2220 A1176 3.80fr brt bl, dk red & dp bl 1.75 .45

Labor Day, Cent. A1177

1990, May 1 **Photo.** *Perf. 13*
2221 A1177 2.30fr multicolored 1.00 .25

Villefranche-sur-Saone — A1178

1990, June 2 **Engr.** *Perf. 13x12½*
2222 A1178 2.30fr multicolored 1.00 .25
National philatelic congress.

A1179 A1181

1990, June 6 *Perf. 13x12½*
2223 A1179 2.30fr La Poste 1.00 .25
Whitbread trans-global yacht race.

1990, June 17 *Perf. 12½x13*
2225 A1181 2.30fr multicolored 1.00 .25
De Gaulle's Call for French Resistance, 50th anniv.

Franco-Brazilian House, Rio de Janeiro — A1182

1990, July 14 *Perf. 13*
2226 A1182 3.20fr multicolored 1.50 .75
See Brazil No. 2255.

A1183

A1184

1990, Oct. 6 **Engr.** *Perf. 12½*
2227 A1183 2fr Rutilus rutilus .90 .20
2228 A1183 3fr Perca fluviatilis 1.40 .25
2229 A1183 4fr Salmo salar 1.90 .50
2230 A1183 5fr Esox lucius 2.25 .50
Nos. 2227-2230 (4) 6.45 1.45

1990, Sept. 29 **Photo.** *Perf. 12½x13*
2231 A1184 2.30fr multicolored 1.00 .50
Natl. Institute of Geography, 50th anniv.

Souvenir Sheet

French Revolution, Bicentennial — A1185

Designs: a, Gaspard Monge. b, Abbe Gregoire. c, Creation of the Tricolor. d, Creation of the French departments.

1990, Oct. 15 **Engr.** *Perf. 13*
2232 A1185 Sheet of 4 4.50 4.50
a.-d. 2.50fr any single 1.10 1.10

Musical Instrument Type of 1989

1990, Sept. 1 **Litho.** *Perf. 13*
2233 A1154 1.46fr Accordion .65 .40
2234 A1154 1.89fr Breton bagpipe .85 .60
2235 A1154 3.06fr Tambourin 1.75 1.50
2236 A1154 5.10fr Hurdy-gurdy 3.00 2.40
Nos. 2233-2236 (4) 6.25 4.90

1990, Nov. **Litho.** *Perf. 13*
2237 A1154 1.93fr like #2169 1.10 .75
2238 A1154 2.39fr like #2170 1.25 .90
2239 A1154 2.74fr like #2172 2.00 1.25
Nos. 2237-2239 (3) 4.35 2.90

Nos. 2233-2239 are known only precanceled. See second note after No. 132.

Maurice Genevoix (1890-1980), Novelist — A1186

1990, Nov. 12 **Engr.** *Perf. 13*
2240 A1186 2.30fr lt green & blk 1.00 .20

Organization for Economic Cooperation and Development, 30th Anniv. — A1187

1990, Dec. 15 **Litho.**
2241 A1187 3.20fr dk & lt blue 1.50 .75

"The Swing" by Auguste Renoir (1841-1919) — A1188

1991, Feb. 23 **Engr.** *Perf. 12½x13*
2242 A1188 5fr multicolored 2.25 1.00

Youth Philatelic Exhibition, Cholet A1189

1991, Mar. 30 **Litho.** *Perf. 13*
2243 A1189 2.50fr multicolored 1.10 .40

Art Series

Le Noeud Noir by Georges Seurat (1859-1891) — A1190

Apres Nous La Maternite, by Max Ernst (1891-1976) — A1191

Volte Faccia by Francois Rouan A1192

O Tableau Noir by Roberto Matta (b. 1911) — A1193

1991 **Engr.** *Perf. 12½x13*
2244 A1190 5fr pale yellow & blk 2.25 1.00

Photo. *Perf. 13*
2245 A1191 2.50fr multicolored 1.10 .80

Engr. *Perf. 12½x13*
2246 A1192 5fr black 2.25 1.00

Photo. *Perf. 13x12½*
2247 A1193 5fr multicolored 2.25 1.00
Nos. 2244-2247 (4) 7.85 3.80

Issued: #2244, 4/13: #2245, 10/10; #2246, 11/9; #2247, 11/30.

Wolfgang Amadeus Mozart (1756-1791), Composer — A1194

1991, Apr. 9 **Photo.** *Perf. 13*
2248 A1194 2.50fr bl, blk & red 1.10 .60

National Printing Office, 350th Anniv. — A1195

1991, Apr. 13
2249 A1195 4fr multicolored 1.90 .60

Tourism Series

Chevire Bridge, Nantes — A1196

Carennac Castle A1197

Pipe Organ, Wasquehal A1198

Valley of Munster
A1199

1991   **Engr.**   **Perf. 13**
2250 A1196 2.50fr multicolored   1.10   .25
       Perf. 12x13
2251 A1197 2.50fr multicolored   1.10   .30
       Perf. 12
2252 A1198 4fr black & buff   1.90   .55
       Perf. 13x12½
2253 A1199 4fr violet   1.90   .55
    Nos. 2250-2253 (4)   6.00 1.65

Issue dates: No. 2250, Apr. 27; Nos. 2251, 2253, July 6; No. 2252, June 22.

Europa
A1200

Concours Lepine, 90th Anniv.
A1201

1991, Apr. 27   **Perf. 12½x13**
2254 A1200 2.50fr Ariane launch
       site, French
       Guiana   1.10   .20
2255 A1200 3.50fr Television sat-
       ellite   1.60   .55

Compare with No. 2483.

1991, Apr. 27   **Perf. 13**
2256 A1201 4fr multicolored   1.90   .80

French Assoc. of Small Manufacturers and Inventors.

Philatelic Society Congress, Perpignan
A1202

1991, May 18
2257 A1202 2.50fr multicolored   1.10   .25

French Open Tennis Championships, Cent. — A1203

1991, May 24   **Engr.**   **Perf. 13**
2258 A1203 3.50fr multicolored   1.60   .50

Souvenir Sheet

French Revolution, Bicent. — A1204

Designs: a, Theophile Malo Corret, La Tour d'Auvergne (1743-1800). b, Liberty Tree. c,

---

National police, bicent. d, Louis Antoine-Leon de St. Just (1767-1794).

1991, June 1   **Engr.**   **Perf. 13**
2259 A1204 Sheet of 4   4.50 3.00
  a.-d.   2.50fr any single   1.10   .75

A1205   A1206

1991, June 13   **Photo.**   **Perf. 13**
2260 A1205 2.50fr multicolored   1.10   .45

Gaston III de Foix (Febus) (1331-1391), general.

1991, Sept. 14   **Engr.**   **Perf. 12½**

Designs: Wildlife.

2261 A1206 2fr Ursus arctos   .90   .30
2262 A1206 3fr Testudo herman-
       ni   1.40   .30
2263 A1206 4fr Castor fiber   1.90   .75
2264 A1206 5fr Alcedo atthis   2.25   .75
    Nos. 2261-2264 (4)   6.45 2.10

10th World Forestry Congress
A1207

1991, Sept. 22   **Engr.**   **Perf. 13x12½**
2265 A1207 2.50fr multicolored   1.10   .25

School of Public Works, Cent.
A1208

1991, Oct. 5   **Litho. & Engr.**   **Perf. 13**
2266 A1208 2.50fr multicolored   1.10   .35

Marcel Cerdan (1916-1949), Middleweight Boxing Champion — A1209

1991, Oct. 19   **Photo.**   **Perf. 13**
2267 A1209 2.50fr black & red   1.10   .35

Amnesty International, 30th Anniv. — A1210

1991, Oct. 19
2268 A1210 3.40fr multicolored   1.60   .60

A1211   A1212

1991, Nov. 14   **Engr.**   **Perf. 13**
2269 A1211 2.50fr Olympic flame   1.10   .25

1992 Winter Olympics, Albertville.

1991, Dec. 7   **Perf. 13**
2270 A1212 2.50fr dk & lt blue   1.10   .30

Fifth Handicapped Olympics.

Voluntary Attachment of Mayotte to France, Sesquicentennial — A1213

1991, Dec. 21   **Engr.**
2271 A1213 2.50fr multicolored   1.10   .25

French Pavilion, Expo '92, Seville
A1214

       Litho. & Engr.
1992, Jan. 18   **Perf. 13**
2272 A1214 2.50fr multicolored   1.10   .25

Musical Instruments Type of 1989

1992, Jan. 31   **Litho.**   **Perf. 13**
2273 A1154 1.60fr Guitar   45.00 25.00
2274 A1154 1.98fr like
       #2233   4.00   3.00
2275 A1154 2.08fr Saxo-
       phone   2.00   1.50
2276 A1154 2.46fr like
       #2234   2.00   1.50
2277 A1154 2.98fr Banjo   2.00   1.50
2278 A1154 3.08fr like
       #2235   6.00   4.00
2279 A1154 3.14fr like
       #2236   2.75   2.00
2280 A1154 3.19fr like
       #2169   7.00   4.00
2281 A1154 5.28fr Xylo-
       phone   5.50   3.50
2282 A1154 5.30fr like
       #2170   3.50   2.00
2283 A1154 5.32fr like
       #2172   3.50   2.50
    Nos. 2273-2283 (11)   83.25 50.50

       Perf. 12
2273a A1154   1.60fr   Guitar   7.50   4.50
2274a A1154   1.98fr   like #2233   150.00 140.00
2275a A1154   2.08fr   Saxophone   40.00 30.00
2276a A1154   2.46fr   like #2234   12.00   7.50
2278a A1154   3.08fr   like #2235   12.00   7.50
2279a A1154   3.14fr   like #2236   60.00 50.00
2280a A1154   3.19fr   like #2169   8.00   5.00
2281a A1154   5.28fr   Xylophone   30.00 20.00
2282a A1154   5.30fr   like #2170   75.00 60.00
2283a A1154   5.32fr   like #2172   25.00 20.00
    Nos. 2273a-2283a (10)   419.50 344.50

Nos. 2273-2283 are known only precanceled. See 2nd note after No. 132. See Nos. 2303-2306.

1992 Summer Olympics, Barcelona
A1215

1992, Apr. 3   **Photo.**   **Perf. 13**
2284 A1215 2.50fr multicolored   1.10   .25

See Greece No. 1730.

Marguerite d'Angouleme (1492-1549)
A1216

1992, Apr. 11   **Litho.**   **Perf. 13**
2285 A1216 3.40fr multicolored   1.60   .90

Founding of Ajaccio, 500th Anniv.
A1217

Virgin and Child Beneath a Garland by Botticelli.

1992, Apr. 30   **Photo.**   **Perf. 13**
2286 A1217 4fr multicolored   1.90   .60

A1218   A1219

Discovery of America, 500th Anniv.: 2.50fr, Map, navigation instruments. 3.40fr, Sailing ship, map.

1992, May 9   **Engr.**   **Perf. 13x12½**
2287 A1218 2.50fr multicolored   1.25   .30
2288 A1218 3.40fr multicolored   2.00   .65

Europa.

1992, May 30   **Litho.**   **Perf. 13**
2289 A1219 3.40fr multicolored   1.60   .80

Intl. Bread and Cereal Congress.

Tourism Series

Ourcq Canal
A1220

Mt. Aiguille
A1221

Biron Castle
A1223

Lorient
A1222

1992, May 30   **Engr.**   **Perf. 13**
2290 A1220 4fr black, blue & grn   1.90   .50

1992, June 27   **Engr.**   **Perf. 13**
2291 A1221 3.40fr multicolored   1.60   .75

First ascension of Mt. Aiguille, 500th anniv.

1992, July 4   **Engr.**   **Perf. 13**
2292 A1222 4fr multicolored   1.90   .25

1992, July 4   **Perf. 12½x13**
2293 A1223 2.50fr multicolored   1.10   .50

Natl.
Philatelic
Societies
Congress,
Niort
A1224

1992, June 6   **Photo.**   **Perf. 13**
2294 A1224 2.50fr multicolored   1.10   .25

Natl. Art Festival.

1992
Olympic
Games,
Albertville
and
Barcelona
A1225

1992, June 19   **Perf. 12½x13½**
2295 A1225 2.50fr multicolored   1.10   .35

Tautavel
Man
A1226

1992, June 20   **Photo.**   **Perf. 13**
2296 A1226 3.40fr multicolored   1.60   .60

Portrait of Jacques Callot (1592-1635),
by Claude Deruet — A1227

1992, June 27   **Engr.**   **Perf. 12x13**
2297 A1227 5fr buff & brown   2.25   .75

Flowers — A1228

2fr, Pancratium maritimum. 3fr, Drosera rotundifolia. 4fr, Orchis palustris. 5fr, Nuphar luteum.

1992, Sept. 12   **Engr.**   **Perf. 12½**
2298 A1228 2fr multicolored   .90   .30
2299 A1228 3fr multicolored   1.40   .30
2300 A1228 4fr multicolored   1.90   .70
2301 A1228 5fr multicolored   2.25   .70
   Nos. 2298-2301 (4)   6.45   2.00

First French
Republic,
Bicent.
A1229

1992, Sept. 26   **Perf. 13**
2302 A1229 2.50fr multicolored   1.10   .20

Musical Instruments Type of 1989

1992, Oct.   **Litho.**   **Perf. 13**
2303 A1154 1.73fr like #2273   .80   .20
2304 A1154 2.25fr like #2275   1.00   .50
2305 A1154 3.51fr like #2277   1.60   1.00
2306 A1154 5.40fr like #2281   2.50   1.75
   Nos. 2303-2306 (4)   5.90   3.45

Nos. 2303-2306 are known only precancelled. See second note after No. 132.

Proclamation of First
French Republic,
Bicent. — A1230

Paintings or drawings by contemporary artists: No. 2307, Tree of Freedom, by Pierre Alechinsky. No. 2308, Portrait of a Young Man, by Martial Raysse. No. 2309, Marianne with Body and Head of Rooster, by Gerard Garouste. No. 2310, "Republique Francaise," by Jean-Charles Blais.

1992, Sept. 26   **Engr.**   **Perf. 13**
2307 A1230 2.50fr red   1.10   .20
2308 A1230 2.50fr red   1.10   .20
2309 A1230 2.50fr red   1.10   .20
2310 A1230 2.50fr red   1.10   .20
   Nos. 2307-2310 (4)   4.40   .80

Single
European
Market
A1231

1992, Nov. 6   **Photo.**   **Perf. 12½x13½**
2311 A1231 2.50fr multicolored   1.10   .35

First Mail
Flight from
Nancy to
Luneville,
80th Anniv.
A1232

1992, Nov. 12   **Perf. 13**
2312 A1232 2.50fr multicolored   1.10   .45

Marcel Paul (1900-1982), Minister of Industrial Production — A1233

1992, Nov. 13   **Engr.**
2313 A1233 4.20fr claret & blue   1.90   .55

Contemporary Art — A1234

#2314, Le Rendezvous d'Ephese, by Paul Delvaux, Belgium. #2315, Abstract painting, by Alberto Burri, Italy. #2316, Abstract painting, by Antoni Tapies, Spain. #2317, Portrait of John Edwards, by Francis Bacon, Great Britain.

1992   **Photo.**   **Perf. 13x12½**
2314 A1234 5fr multicolored   2.25   1.00
2315 A1234 5fr multicolored   2.25   1.00
2316 A1234 5fr multicolored   2.25   1.00
2317 A1234 5fr multicolored   2.25   1.00
   Nos. 2314-2317 (4)   9.00   4.00

Issued: #2314, 11/20; #2315-2317, 11/21.
See Nos. 2379-2390.

Gypsy
Culture — A1235

1992, Dec. 5   **Photo.**   **Perf. 13**
2318 A1235 2.50fr multicolored   1.10   .30

Yacht "La Poste," Entrant in Whitbread
Trans-Global Race — A1236

1993, Feb. 6   **Engr.**   **Perf. 12**
2319 A1236 2.50fr multicolored   1.10   .40

See No. 2375.

Water
Birds — A1237

1993, Feb. 6   **Perf. 12½x12**
2320 A1237 2fr Harle piette   .90   .30
2321 A1237 3fr Fuligule nyroca   1.40   .30
2322 A1237 4fr Tadorne de belon   1.90   .75
2323 A1237 5fr Harle huppe   2.25   .70
   Nos. 2320-2323 (4)   6.45   2.05

Memorial to
Indochina
War, Frejus
A1238

Litho. & Engr.
1993, Feb. 16   **Perf. 13x13½**
2324 A1238 4fr multicolored   1.90   .60

Stamp
Day — A1239

1993, Mar. 6   **Photo.**   **Perf. 13**
2325 A1239 2.50fr red & multi   1.75   1.00
2326 A1239 2.50fr +60c red & multi   1.40   .80
   a.   Bklt. pane of 4 #2325, 3 #2326 + label   13.00

Mediterranean Youth Games,
Agde — A1240

1993, Mar. 13   **Photo.**   **Perf. 13**
2327 A1240 2.50fr multicolored   1.10   .20

Human Rights, Intl.
Mixed Masonic
Order,
Cent. — A1241

1993, Apr. 3   **Engr.**   **Perf. 13**
2328 A1241 3.40fr blue & black   1.60   .50

Contemporary Art — A1242

Europa: 2.50fr, Painting, Rouge Rythme Bleu, by Olivier Debre. 3.40fr, Sculpture, Le Griffu, by Germaine Richier, vert.

Perf. 13x12½, 12½x13
1993, Apr. 17   **Litho.**
2329 A1242 2.50fr multicolored   1.10   .35
2330 A1242 3.40fr multicolored   1.60   .80

Marianne Type of 1990

1993-96   **Engr.**   **Perf. 13**
2333 A1161 2fr blue   1.75   .20
2334 A1161 2.40fr emerald   1.40   .20
2335 A1161 2.70fr emerald   1.60   .25
2336 A1161 3.50fr apple green   1.75   .30
2337 A1161 3.80fr blue   1.90   .50
2338 A1161 4.40fr blue   2.25   .40
2339 A1161 4.50fr mag   2.25   .40
2340 A1161 (2.50fr) red   1.25   .20
   Nos. 2333-2340 (8)   14.15   2.45

Perf. 13 Horiz.
Coil Stamps
2341 A1161 2.40fr emerald   1.40   .60
2342 A1161 2.70fr emerald   3.00   .20
2343 A1161 (2.80fr) red   1.75   .20

Self-Adhesive
Die Cut
2344 A1161 70c brown   13.00   12.00

Serpentine Die Cut Vert.
2345 A1161 70c brown   13.00   10.00
2346 A1161 1fr orange   7.00   2.50
   a.   Booklet pane, 3 #2348, 1 #2346   9.00

Complete bklt., 2 #2346a   20.00

Die Cut

2347	A1161 (2.50fr) red	1.50	.20
a.	Booklet pane of 10 (see footnote)	16.00	
b.	Bklt. pane of 4 + label	6.00	
c.	Booklet pane, #2344, 3 #2347 + label	30.00	
d.	Booklet pane of 10 (see footnote)	15.00	

Serpentine Die Cut Vert.

2348	A1161 (2.80fr) red	1.25	.20
a.	Bklt. pane of 4 + label	5.00	
b.	Booklet pane of 10 (see footnote)	13.00	
c.	Booklet pane, #2345, 3 #2348 + label	18.00	
d.	Booklet pane of 10 (see footnote)	13.00	
e.	Booklet pane of 10 (see footnote)	13.00	
f.	Booklet pane of 10 (see footnote)	13.00	

Nos. 2340, 2347 pay postage for the first class letter rate and sold for 2.50fr when first released. They have no denomination or letter inscription. Nos. 2343 and 2348 had a face value of 2.80fr when released.

No. 2347a has all stamps adjoining and has selvage covering backing paper (booklet cover). No. 2347d is comprised of two strips of 5 stamps each with yellow backing paper showing.

No. 2348b has the same format as No. 2347a. No. 2348d has a format similar to No. 2347d except there is a narrow selvage strip between the left six stamps and the right four stamps. No. 2348e is like No. 2348f but lacks the selvage strip. No. 2348f has a format similar to No. 2347a except it has a wide selvage strip between the left four stamps and the right six stamps.

Backing paper of Nos. 2347b and 2347c may have cuts along fold and were sold in a booklet for 20fr.

Issued: #2340, 2347, 4/19/93; 70c, July; 2fr, 7/31/94; #2341-2343, 4/1/94; #2345, 2348, 2/14/94; 1fr, 2.70fr, 3.80fr, 4.50fr, 3/18/96.

Tourism Series

Chinon — A1243

Village of Minerve — A1244

Chaise-Dieu Abbey — A1245

Montbeliard — A1246

1993, Apr. 24   **Engr.**   **Perf. 13x12½**
2355   A1243   4.20fr dk grn, ol grn & brn   2.00   .80

1993, July 17   **Perf. 13**
2356   A1244   4.20fr red brown & yel grn   2.00   .50

1993
2357   A1245   2.80fr multicolored   1.25   .35
2358   A1246   4.40fr multicolored   2.00   .60
   Nos. 2355-2358 (4)   7.25   2.25

Issued: #2357, Sept. 4; #2358, Sept. 11.

Ninth European Conference on Protection of Human Rights — A1247

1993, May 8   **Engr.**   **Perf. 12½x13**
2359   A1247   2.50fr multicolored   1.10   .30

Django Reinhardt (1910-1953), Musician — A1248

1993, May 14   **Litho.**   **Perf. 13**
2360   A1248   4.20fr multicolored   1.90   .60

Louise Weiss (1893-1983), Suffragist — A1249

1993, May 15   **Engr.**   **Perf. 13x12½**
2361   A1249   2.50fr blk, buff & red   1.10   .35

Philatelic Society Congress, Lille A1250

1993, May 29   **Engr.**   **Perf. 13x12½**
2362   A1250   2.50fr bl, dk bl & lil   1.10   .45

Natural History Museum, Bicent. A1251

Litho. & Engr.

1993, June 5   **Perf. 13**
2363   A1251   2.50fr multicolored   1.10   .30

Martyrs and Heroes of the Resistance — A1252

1993, June 18   **Photo.**   **Perf. 13**
2364   2.50fr red, black & gray   1.10   .60
2365   4.20fr red, black & gray   1.90   1.00
  a.   A1252 Pair, #2364-2365   3.00   2.50

A1254   A1255

1993, July 10   **Engr.**   **Perf. 13x12½**
2366   A1254   2.50fr multicolored   1.10   .30

Claude Chappe's Semaphore Telegraph, bicent.

1993, July 10   **Engr.**   **Perf. 12½x13**
2367   A1255   3.40fr bl, grn & red   1.60   .75

Train to Lake Artouste, Laruns, highest train ride in Europe.

Musical Instruments Type of 1989

1993, July 1   **Litho.**   **Perf. 13**
2368   A1154   1.82fr like #2171   .85   .40
2369   A1154   2.34fr like #2235   1.10   .75
2370   A1154   3.86fr like #2236   1.75   1.00
2371   A1154   5.93fr like #2281   2.75   2.00
   Nos. 2368-2371 (4)   6.45   4.15

Nos. 2368-2371 are known only precanceled. See note after No. 132.

Liberation of Corsica, 50th Anniv. — A1256

1993, Sept. 9   **Engr.**   **Perf. 13**
2372   A1256   2.80fr lake, bl & blk   1.25   .30

Saint Thomas, by Georges de la Tour (1593-1652) — A1257

1993, Sept. 9   **Photo.**   **Perf. 12½x13**
2373   A1257   5fr multicolored   2.25   1.00

Service as Military Hospital of Val de Grace Monastery, Bicent. — A1258

1993, Sept. 25   **Engr.**   **Perf. 13**
2374   A1258   3.70fr multicolored   1.75   .35

Whitbread Trans-Global Race Type

1993, Sept. 27   **Engr.**   **Perf. 12**
2375   A1236   2.80fr multicolored   1.25   .40

The Muses, by Maurice Denis (1870-1943) — A1259

1993, Oct. 2   **Photo.**   **Perf. 12½x13**
2376   A1259   5fr multicolored   2.25   1.00

The Clowns, by Albert Gleizes (1881-1953) A1260

1993, Oct. 2   **Photo.**   **Perf. 13½x12½**
2377   A1260   2.80fr multicolored   1.25   .30

Natl. Circus Center, Chalons-sur-Marne.

Clock Tower Bellringer Statues of Lambesc — A1261

1993, Oct. 9   **Engr.**   **Perf. 13x12½**
2378   A1261   4.40fr multicolored   2.00   .70

European Contemporary Art Type

Designs: No. 2379, Abstract, by Takis. No. 2380, Abstract, by Maria Helena Vieira da Silva. No. 2381, Abstract Squares, by Sean Scully. No. 2382, Abstract, by Georg Baselitz, Germany.

1993-94   **Photo.**   **Perf. 13x12½**
2379   A1234   5fr blk & ver   2.25   1.00
2380   A1234   5fr multicolored   2.25   1.00
2381   A1234   6.70fr multicolored   3.00   1.00
        Perf. 13
2382   A1234   6.70fr multicolored   3.00   1.00
   Nos. 2379-2382 (4)   10.50   4.00

Issued: #2379, 10/9/93; #2380, 12/11/93; #2381, 1/29/94; #2382, 11/19/94.

Greetings A1266

Greeting, artist: #2383, Happy Birthday, Claire Wendling. #2384, Happy Birthday, Bernard Olivie. #2385, Happy Anniversary, Stephane Colman. #2386, Happy Anniversary, Guillaune Sorel. #2387, With Love, Jean-Michel Thiriet. #2388, Please Write, Etienne Davodeau. #2389, Congratulations, Johan de Moor. #2390, Good luck, "Mezzo." #2391, Best Wishes, Nicolas de Crecy. #2392, Best Wishes, Florence Magnin. #2393, Merry Christmas, Thierry Robin. #2394, Merry Christmas, Patrick Prugne.

1993, Oct. 21   **Photo.**   **Perf. 13½x13**
Booklet Stamps

2383   A1266   2.80fr multicolored   1.25   .30
2384   A1266   2.80fr multicolored   1.25   .30
2385   A1266   2.80fr multicolored   1.25   .30

2386	A1266	2.80fr multicolored	1.25	.30
2387	A1266	2.80fr multicolored	1.25	.30
2388	A1266	2.80fr multicolored	1.25	.30
2389	A1266	2.80fr multicolored	1.25	.30
2390	A1266	2.80fr multicolored	1.25	.30
2391	A1266	2.80fr multicolored	1.25	.30
2392	A1266	2.80fr multicolored	1.25	.30
2393	A1266	2.80fr multicolored	1.25	.30
2394	A1266	2.80fr multicolored	1.25	.30
a.		Bklt. pane, #2383-2394	12.50	

Perf. 12½

2383a	A1266	2.80fr	1.25	.30
2384a	A1266	2.80fr	1.25	.30
2385a	A1266	2.80fr	1.25	.30
2386a	A1266	2.80fr	1.25	.30
2387a	A1266	2.80fr	1.25	.30
2388a	A1266	2.80fr	1.25	.30
2389a	A1266	2.80fr	1.25	.30
2390a	A1266	2.80fr	1.25	.30
2391a	A1266	2.80fr	1.25	.30
2392a	A1266	2.80fr	1.25	.30
2393a	A1266	2.80fr	1.25	.30
2394b	A1266	2.80fr	1.25	.30
c.		Booklet pane of 12, #2383a-2393a, 2394b	14.00	

Souvenir Sheet

European Stamp Exhibition, Salon du Timbre A1267

a, Rhododendrons. b, Flowers in park, Paris.

1993, Nov. 10   Perf. 13
2395 A1267 2.40fr #a.-b.+ 2 labels   16.00 16.00
Sold for 15fr.

Louvre Museum, Bicent. A1268

1993, Nov. 20
2396 A1268 2.80fr Louvre, 1793   1.25 1.00
2397 A1268 4.40fr Louvre, 1993   2.00 1.25
a.   Pair, #2396-2397   3.50 2.50

Glassware, 1901 — A1269

Cast Iron, c. 1900 — A1270

Furniture, c. 1902 — A1271

Stoneware, c. 1898 — A1272

Decorative arts by: No. 2398, Emile Galle (1846-1904). No. 2399, Hector Guimard (1867-1942). No. 2400, Louis Majorelle (1859-1926). No. 2401, Pierre-Adrien Dalpayrat (1844-1910).

Perf. 13½x12½

1994. Jan. 22   Photo.
2398 A1269 2.80fr multicolored   1.25 .35
2399 A1270 2.80fr multicolored   1.25 .35
2400 A1271 4.40fr multicolored   2.00 .65
2401 A1272 4.40fr multicolored   2.00 .65
     Nos. 2398-2401 (4)   6.50 2.00

Stained Glass Window, St. Julian's Cathedral, Le Mans A1273

1994, Feb. 12   Engr.   Perf. 12½x13
2402 A1273 6.70fr multicolored   3.00 1.00

City of Bastia — A1274

1994, Feb. 19   Perf. 13x12½
2403 A1274 4.40fr blue & brown   2.00 .30

Tourism Series

Argentat A1275

1994, June 18   Engr.   Perf. 12x12½
2404 A1275 4.40fr red brown & rose carmine   2.00 .60

European Parliamentary Elections — A1276

1994, Feb. 26   Litho.   Perf. 13
2405 A1276 2.80fr multicolored   1.25 .25

Laurent Mourguet (1769-1844), Creator of Puppet, Guignol — A1277

1994, Mar. 4   Photo.   Perf. 13
2406 A1277 2.80fr multicolored   1.25 .35

French Polytechnic Institute, Bicent. A1277a

1994, Mar. 11
2407 A1277a 2.80fr multicolored   1.25 .35

Stamp Day A1278

1994, Mar. 12   Engr.   Perf. 13
2408 A1278 2.80fr blue & red   5.00 2.25
2409 A1278 2.80fr +60c blue & red   1.40 1.25
a.   Booklet pane of 4 #2408, 3 #2409 + 1 label   25.00
No. 2408 issued only in booklets.

Swedish Ballet Costume — A1279

Banquet for Gustavus III at the Trianon, 1784, by Lafrensen — A1280

French-Swedish cultural relations: No. 2411, Tuxedo costume for Swedish ballet. No. 2412, Viking ships. No. 2413, Viking ship. No. 2415, Swedish, French flags.

1994, Mar. 18   Engr.   Perf. 13
2410 A1279 2.80fr multicolored   3.50 1.25
2411 A1279 2.80fr multicolored   3.50 1.25
2412 A1279 2.80fr multicolored   3.50 1.25
2413 A1279 2.80fr multicolored   3.50 1.25
2414 A1280 3.70fr multicolored   4.00 2.00
2415 A1280 3.70fr multicolored   4.00 2.00
a.   Booklet pane of #2410-2415   25.00

See Sweden Nos. 2065-2070.

Pres. Georges Pompidou (1911-1974) A1281

1994, Apr. 9   Engr.   Perf. 13
2416 A1281 2.80fr olive brown   1.25 .30

Resistance of the Maquis, 50th Anniv. A1282

1994, Apr. 9
2417 A1282 2.80fr multicolored   1.25 .30

Philexjeunes '94, Grenoble — A1283

1994, Apr. 22   Photo.
2418 A1283 2.80fr multicolored   1.25 .30

Europa A1284

Discoveries: 2.80fr, AIDS virus, by scientists of Pasteur Institute. 3.70fr, Formula for wave properties of matter, developed by Louis de Brogile.

1994, Apr. 30   Photo. & Engr.
2419 A1284 2.80fr multicolored   1.25 .30
a.   With label   1.25 .75
2420 A1284 3.70fr multicolored   1.75 .85
No. 2419a issued Dec. 1, 1994.

Opening of Channel Tunnel — A1285

Designs: Nos. 2421, 2423, British lion, French rooster, meeting over Channel. Nos. 2422, 2424, Joined hands above speeding train.

1994, May 3   Photo.   Perf. 13
2421 A1285 2.80fr dk blue & multi   1.25 .30
2422 A1285 2.80fr dk blue & multi   1.25 .30
a.   Pair, #2421-2422   2.75 1.50
2423 A1285 4.30fr lt blue & multi   2.00 .90
2424 A1285 4.30fr multicolored   2.00 .90
a.   Pair, #2423-2424   4.50 2.25
     Nos. 2421-2424 (4)   6.50 2.40

See Great Britain Nos. 1558-1561.

Asian Development Bank, Board of Governors Meeting, Nice — A1286

1994, May 3   **Photo.**   *Perf. 13*
2425 A1286 2.80fr multicolored   1.25   .30

Federation of French Philatelic Societies, 67th Congress, Martigues A1287

1994, May 20   **Engr.**   *Perf. 12x12½*
2426 A1287 2.80fr multicolored   1.25   .30

Court of Cassation A1288

Litho. & Engr.
1994, June 3   *Perf. 13*
2427 A1288 2.80fr multicolored   1.25   .30

D-Day, 50th Anniv. A1289

No. 2429, Tank, crowd waving Allied flags.

1994, June 4   **Engr.**
2428 A1289 4.30fr multicolored   2.00   .50
2429 A1289 4.30fr multicolored   2.00   .50
Liberation of Paris, 50th anniv. (#2429).

Mount St. Victoire, by Paul Cezanne (1839-1906) — A1290

1994, June 18   **Photo.**   *Perf. 13*
2430 A1290 2.80fr multicolored   1.25   .30

Intl. Olympic Committee, Cent. A1291

1994, June 23   **Litho.**   *Perf. 13*
2431 A1291 2.80fr multicolored   1.25   .25

Saulx River Bridge, Rupt aux Nonains A1292

1994, July 2   **Engr.**
2432 A1292 2.80fr blackish blue   1.25   .25

Organ, Poitiers Cathedral — A1293

1994, July 2   *Perf. 13x12½*
2433 A1293 4.40fr multicolored   2.00   .55

Allied Landings in Provence, 50th Anniv. A1294

1994, Aug. 13   **Engr.**   *Perf. 13*
2434 A1294 2.80fr multicolored   1.25   .30

Moses and the Daughters of Jethro, by Nicolas Poussin (1594-1665) — A1295

1994, Sept. 10
2435 A1295 4.40fr yel brn & blk   1.90   .90

Natl. Conservatory of Arts and Crafts, Bicent. — A1296

1994, Sept. 24   *Perf. 13x12½*
2436 A1296 2.80fr Foucault's pendulum   1.25   .30

The Great Cascade, St. Cloud Park — A1297

1994, Sept. 24   *Perf. 12½x13*
2437 A1297 3.70fr multicolored   1.75   .50

Leaves — A1298

1994   **Litho.**   *Perf. 13*
2438 A1298 1.91fr Oak   .85   .40
2439 A1298 2.46fr Sycamore   1.10   .70
2440 A1298 4.24fr Chestnut   2.00   1.00
2441 A1298 6.51fr Holly   3.00   2.00
   Nos. 2438-2441 (4)   6.95   4.10
Nos. 2438-2441 are known only precanceled. See second note after No. 132. See Nos. 2517-2520.

Ecole Normale Superieure (Teachers' School), Bicent. — A1299

1994, Oct. 8   **Engr.**   *Perf. 13*
2442 A1299 2.80fr red & dk bl   1.25   .45

Georges Simenon (1903-89), Writer A1300

Litho. & Engr.
1994, Oct. 15   *Perf. 13*
2443 A1300 2.80fr multicolored   1.25   .25
See Belgium No. 1567, Switzerland No. 948.

Souvenir Sheet

European Stamp Exhibition — A1301

a, Flowers in park, Paris. b, Dalhias, vert.

1994, Oct. 15   **Photo.**   *Perf. 13*
2444 A1301 2.80fr Sheet of 2, #a.-b.   15.00   15.00
   No. 2444 sold for 16fr.

Natl. Drug Addiction Prevention Day — A1302

1994, Oct. 15
2445 A1302 2.80fr multicolored   1.25   .25

Grand Lodge of France, Cent. A1303

1994, Nov. 5   **Engr.**
2446 A1303 2.80fr multicolored   1.25   .25

Alain Colas (1943-78), Sailor A1304

1994, Nov. 19
2447 A1304 3.70fr green & black   1.75   .60

French Natl. Press Federation, 50th Anniv. A1305

1994, Dec. 9   **Photo.**   *Perf. 13*
2448 A1305 2.80fr multicolored   1.25   .30

Champs Elysees — A1306

1994, Dec. 31
2449 A1306 4.40fr multicolored   2.00   .75
No. 2449 printed with se-tenant label.

Souvenir Sheet

Motion Pictures, Cent. — A1307

Faces on screen and: a, Projector at right. b, Projector facing away from screen. c, Projector facing screen. d, Reels of film.

1995, Jan. 14   **Photo.**   *Perf. 13*
2450 A1307 Sheet of 4   5.00   5.00
a.-d.   2.80fr any single   1.00   1.00

Normandy Bridge — A1308

1995, Jan. 20   **Engr.**   *Perf. 13*
2451 A1308 4.40fr multicolored   2.00   .75

A1309   A1310

1995, Jan. 21   *Perf. 13x12*
2452 A1309 2.80fr multicolored   1.25   .30
European Notaries Public.

1995, Feb. 18   **Photo.**   *Perf. 13*
2453 A1310 3.70fr multicolored   1.75   1.00
Louis Pasteur (1822-95).

Art Series

St. Taurin's Reliquary, Evreaux A1311

Study for the Dream of Happiness, by
Pierre Prud'hon (1758-1823) — A1312

Abstract, by Zao Wou-ki — A1313

Abstract, by Per Kirkeby,
Denmark — A1314

1995 Photo. & Engr. Perf. 12x13
2454 A1311 6.70fr multicolored 3.00 1.10
Engr.
Perf. 13x12
2455 A1312 6.70fr slate & blue 3.00 1.10
Litho.
Perf. 14
2456 A1313 6.70fr multicolored 3.00 1.10
Photo.
Perf. 13
2457 A1314 6.70fr multicolored 3.00 1.10
Nos. 2454-2457 (4) 12.00 4.40

Issued: #2454, 2/25/95; #2455, 5/12/95;
#2456, 6/10/95; #2457, 9/23/95.

Tourism Series

Stenay Malt
Works
A1315

Remiremont, Vosges — A1316

Nyons
Bridge,
Drome
A1317

Barbizon,
Home of
Landscape
Artists
A1318

1995, Feb. 25 Engr. Perf. 13x12½
2458 A1315 2.80fr ol & dk grn 1.25 .30

2459 A1316 2.80fr brn, grn & bl 1.25 .30
Perf. 12½x13
2460 A1317 4.40fr multicolored 2.00 .75
Photo.
Perf. 13½
2461 A1318 4.40fr multicolored 2.00 .75
Nos. 2458-2461 (4) 6.50 2.10
Issued: #2458, 2/25/95; #2459, 5/13/95;
#2460, 5/20/95; #2461, 9/30/95.

A1319

John J. Audubon
(1785-1851)
A1320

Designs: No. 2462, Snowy egret. No. 2463,
Band-tailed pigeon. 4.30fr, Common tern.
4.40fr, Brown-colored rough-legged buzzard.

1995, Feb. 25 Photo. Perf. 12½x12
2462 A1319 2.80fr multicolored 1.25 .40
2463 A1320 2.80fr multicolored 1.25 .40
2464 A1319 4.30fr multicolored 2.00 .75
2465 A1320 4.40fr multicolored 2.00 .75
a. Souvenir sheet of 4, #2462-
2465, perf. 13 7.00 7.00
Nos. 2462-2465 (4) 6.50 2.30

Stamp Day
A1321

1995, Mar. 4 Engr. Perf. 13
2466 A1321 2.80fr multicolored 6.00 3.00
2467 A1321 2.80fr +60c multi 1.60 1.40
a. Booklet pane, 4 #2466, 3
#2467+label 29.00
Complete booklet, #2467 30.00

No. 2466 issued only in booklets.

Work Councils, 50th
Anniv. — A1322

1995, Mar. 7 Engr. Perf. 13
2468 A1322 2.80fr dk bl, brn &
sky bl 1.25 .30

Advanced
Institute of
Electricity,
Cent.
A1323

1995, Mar. 11 Photo.
2469 A1323 3.70fr multicolored 1.75 .40

Institute of
Oriental
Languages,
Bicent.
A1324

1995, Mar. 25 Photo. Perf. 13
2470 A1324 2.80fr multicolored 1.25 .30

Jean Giono (1895-1970),
Writer — A1325

1995, Mar. 25 Engr.
2471 A1325 3.70fr multicolored 1.75 1.00

Iron and Steel
Industry in
Lorraine — A1326

1995, Apr. 1 Perf. 13x12
2472 A1326 2.80fr multicolored 1.25 .30

End of
World War
II, 50th
Anniv.
A1327

Europa: 2.80fr, Barbed wire, laurel wreath.
3.70fr, Broken sword, emblem of European
Union.

1995, Apr. 29 Photo. Perf. 13
2473 A1327 2.80fr multicolored 1.25 .30
2474 A1327 3.70fr multicolored 1.75 .75

Forestry Profession,
Ardennes — A1328

1995, May 2 Engr. Perf. 12½x13
2475 A1328 4.40fr multicolored 2.00 .80

End of
World War
II, 50th
Anniv.
A1329

1995, May 8 Photo. Perf. 13
2476 A1329 2.80fr multicolored 1.25 .35

Natl. Assembly — A1330

1995, May 13 Photo. Perf. 13x12½
2477 A1330 2.80fr multicolored 1.25 .60

French's
People's
Relief
Assoc.,
50th Anniv.
A1331

1995, May 20 Engr. Perf. 12½x13
2478 A1331 2.80fr multicolored 1.25 .30

Scenes of
France — A1332

#2479, Forest, Vosges. #2480, Massif, Brit-
tany. #2481, Wetlands, cattle, Camargue.
#2482, Volcanoes, Auvergne.

1995, May 27 Perf. 13
2479 A1332 2.40fr green 1.10 .25
2480 A1332 2.40fr green 1.10 .25
2481 A1332 2.80fr red 1.25 .30
2482 A1332 2.80fr red 1.25 .30
Nos. 2479-2482 (4) 4.70 1.10

Ariane Rocket on
Launch Pad, French
Guiana — A1333

1995, June 1 Engr. Perf. 12½x13
2483 A1333 2.80fr bl, grn & red 1.25 .30
Compare with No. 2254.

A1334   A1335

1995, June 2 Engr. Perf. 13
2484 A1334 2.80fr multicolored 1.25 .30

68th Congress of French Federation of Philatelic Organizations, Orleans.

1995, June 3
2485 A1335 4.40fr Town of Correze 2.00 .75

A1336   A1337

Fables of Jean de la Fontaine (1621-95):
No. 2486, The Grasshopper and The Ant. No.
2487, The Frog Who Could Make Himself
Larger than an Ox. No. 2488, The Wolf and
the Lamb. No. 2489, The Crow and the Fox.
No. 2490, The Cat, the Weasel, and the Small
Rabbit. No. 2491, The Tortoise and the Hare.

1995, June 24 Photo. Perf. 13
2486 A1336 2.80fr multicolored 1.40 .75
2487 A1336 2.80fr multicolored 1.40 .75
2488 A1336 2.80fr multicolored 1.40 .75
2489 A1336 2.80fr multicolored 1.40 .75

2490 A1336 2.80fr multicolored 1.40 .75
2491 A1336 2.80fr multicolored 1.40 .75
  a.   Strip, #2486-2491 + 2 labels 9.00 8.00

1995, July 9   Photo.   *Perf. 13*
2492 A1337 2.80fr multicolored 1.25 .30

Velodrome d'Hiver raid.

André Maginot (1877-1932), Creator of Maginot Line — A1338

1995, Sept. 9   Engr.   *Perf. 13*
2493 A1338 2.80fr multicolored 1.25 .30

Women's Grand Masonic Lodge of France, 50th Anniv. — A1339

1995, Sept. 16   *Perf. 13x12½*
2494 A1339 2.80fr multicolored 1.25 .30

Hospital Pharmacies, 500th Anniv. — A1340

1995, Sept. 23   *Perf. 12½x13*
2495 A1340 2.80fr multicolored 1.25 .30

Natl. School of Administration, 50th Anniv. — A1341

1995, Oct. 5   Photo.   *Perf. 13*
2496 A1341 2.80fr multicolored 1.25 .30

The Cradle, by Berthe Morisot (1841-95) — A1342

1995, Oct. 7   Litho.   *Perf. 13½x14*
2497 A1342 6.70fr multicolored 3.00 1.00

The French Institute, Bicent. — A1343

1995, Oct. 14   Engr.   *Perf. 12½x13*
2498 A1343 2.80fr blk, grn & red 1.25 .30

Automobile Club of France, Cent. — A1344

1995, Nov. 4   Engr.   *Perf. 13x12½*
2499 A1344 4.40fr blk, bl & red 2.00 .60

UN, 50th Anniv. — A1345

1995, Nov. 16   Photo.   *Perf. 13*
2500 A1345 4.30fr multicolored 2.00 1.00

Francis Jammes (1868-1938), Poet — A1346

1995, Dec. 2   Engr.   *Perf. 13*
2501 A1346 3.70fr black & blue 1.75 1.00

A1347

A1348

1995, Dec. 9   Litho. & Engr.
2502 A1347 2.80fr Evry Cathedral 1.25 .30

1995, Dec. 12   Photo.   *Perf. 13*
2503 A1348 2.80fr multicolored 1.25 .30

1998 World Cup Soccer Championships, France.

Art Series

Abstract, by Lucien Wercollier — A1349

Design: No. 2505, The Netherlands (Horizon), abstract photograph, by Jan Dibbets.

1996   *Perf. 13x12½*
2504 A1349 6.70fr multicolored 3.00 1.00
2505 A1349 6.70fr multicolored 3.00 1.00

Issued: #2504, 1/20; #2505, 2/10.

Arawak Civilization, Saint Martin — A1350

Design: 2.80fr, Dog figurine, 550 B.C.

1996, Feb. 10   Engr.   *Perf. 13*
2506 A1350 2.80fr multicolored 1.25 .40

The Augustus Bridge over the Nera River, by Camille Corot (1796-1875) — A1351

1996, Mar. 2   Litho.   *Perf. 13*
2507 A1351 6.70fr multicolored 3.00 1.00

St. Patrick A1352

1996, Mar. 16   Photo.   *Perf. 13*
2508 A1352 2.80fr multicolored 1.25 .50

The Sower, 1903 — A1353

1996, Mar. 16   Litho. & Engr.
2509 A1353 2.80fr multicolored 6.00 5.00
2510 A1353 2.80fr +60c multi 1.75 1.25
  a.   Booklet pane, 4 #2509, 3
        #2510 + label 30.00
        Complete booklet, #2510a 32.50

Stamp Day.

Jacques Rueff (1896-1978), Economist — A1354

1996, Mar. 23   Engr.   *Perf. 13x12½*
2511 A1354 2.80fr multicolored 1.25 .50

René Descartes (1596-1650) A1355

1996, Mar. 30   Engr.   *Perf. 12½x13*
2512 A1355 4.40fr red 2.00 1.00

Gas & Electric Industries, 50th Anniv. A1356

1996, Apr. 6   Photo.   *Perf. 13*
2513 A1356 3fr multicolored 1.40 .35

Natl. Parks A1357

1996, Apr. 20
2514 A1357 3fr Cévennes 1.40 .60
2515 A1357 4.40fr Vanoise 2.00 1.00
2516 A1357 4.40fr Mercantour 2.00 1.25
    Nos. 2514-2516 (3) 5.40 2.85

See Nos. 2569-2572.

Leaf Type of 1994
1996, Mar.   Litho.   *Perf. 13*
2517 A1298 1.87fr Ash .85 .30
2518 A1298 2.18fr Beech 1.00 .65
2519 A1298 4.66fr Walnut 2.10 1.25
2520 A1298 7.11fr Elm 3.25 2.00
    Nos. 2517-2520 (4) 7.20 4.20

Nos. 2517-2520 are known only precanceled. Values for precanceled stamps in first column are for those which have not been through the post and have original gum. Values in second column are for postally used, gumless stamps.

Madame Marie de Sévigné (1626-96), Writer — A1358

1996, Apr. 27   Photo.   *Perf. 13*
2521 A1358 3fr multicolored 1.40 .65

Europa.

Natl. Institute of Agronomy Research, 50th Anniv. A1359

1996, May 4   Photo.   *Perf. 13*
2522 A1359 3.80fr multicolored 1.75 1.00

Joan of Arc's House, Domremy-La-Pucelle — A1360

1996, May 11
2523 A1360 4.50fr multicolored 2.10 .70

RAMOGE Agreement Between France, Italy, Monaco, 20th Anniv. A1361

1996, May 14 Photo. & Engr.
2524 A1361 3fr multicolored 1.40 .35
See Monaco No. 1998, Italy No. 2077.

69th Congress of Federation of Philatelic Assoc., Clermont-Ferrand — A1362

1996, May 24 Engr. Perf. 13
2525 A1362 3fr brn, red & grn 1.40 .35

Tourism Series

Bitche, Moselle A1363

Iles Sanguinaires, Ajaccio, Southern Corsica — A1364

Thoronet Abbey, Var A1365

Chambéry Cathedral, Savoie A1366

1996 Engr. Perf. 12½x13
2526 A1363 3fr multicolored 1.40 .35
2527 A1364 3fr multicolored 1.40 .35

Perf. 13x12½
2528 A1365 3.80fr brn & claret 1.75 .70

Photo.
Perf. 13
2529 A1366 4.50fr multicolored 2.10 .75
Issued: #2526, 5/25/96; #2527, 6/1/96; 3.80fr, 7/6/96; 4.50fr, 6/8/96.

1998 World Cup Soccer Championships, France — A1367

Various stylized soccer plays, name of host city in France.

1996, June 1 Photo. Perf. 13
2530 A1367 3fr Lens 1.40 .35
2531 A1367 3fr Toulouse 1.40 .35
2532 A1367 3fr Saint-Etienne 1.40 .35
2533 A1367 3fr Montpellier 1.40 .35
Nos. 2530-2533 (4) 5.60 1.40
See Nos. 2584-2587, 2623-2624, sheet of 10, #2624a.

Art Series

Gallo-Roman Bronze Statue of Horse, Neuvy-en-Sullias, Loiret — A1368

Imprints of Cello Fragments, by Arman — A1369

1996 Engr. Perf. 13
2534 A1368 6.70fr multicolored 3.00 1.00
Photo.
2535 A1369 6.70fr multicolored 3.00 1.00
Issued: #2534, 6/8/96; #2535, 9/21/96.

A1371 A1372

1996, June 15 Photo. Perf. 13
2537 A1371 3fr multicolored 1.40 .50
Modern Olympic Games, cent.

1996, June 15 Engr. Perf. 12½x13
2538 A1372 4.40fr deep purple 2.00 1.00
Jacques Marette (1922-84), Member of Parliament.

A1373 A1374

1996, June 29 Photo. Perf. 13
2539 A1373 3fr multicolored 1.40 .35
Train between Ajaccio and Vizzavona, cent.

1996, Sept. 6 Engr. Perf. 13x12½
2540 A1374 3fr dark blue & yel 1.40 .30
Notre Dame de Fourvière Basilica, Lyon, cent.

Baptism of Clovis, 1500th Anniv. A1375

1996, Sept. 14 Perf. 13
2541 A1375 3fr multicolored 1.40 .30

Henri IV High School, Bicent. — A1376

1996, Oct. 12 Engr. Perf. 12½x13
2542 A1376 4.50fr brown & blue 2.10 .80

UNICEF, 50th Anniv. A1377

1996, Oct. 19 Photo. Perf. 13
2543 A1377 4.50fr multicolored 2.10 .80

Economic and Social Council, 50th Anniv. — A1378

1996, Oct. 26 Engr. Perf. 13
2544 A1378 3fr red, black & blue 1.40 .30

UNESCO, 50th Anniv. A1379

1996, Nov. 2 Litho. Perf. 13
2545 A1379 3.80fr multicolored 1.75 .75

A1380 A1381

1996, Nov. 7 Photo. Perf. 13
2546 A1380 3fr multicolored 1.40 .30
Autumn Stamp Show, 50th anniv.

1996, Nov. 16
2547 A1381 3fr multicolored 1.40 .30
Creation of French Overseas Departments, 50th anniv.

André Malraux (1901-76), Writer A1382

1996, Nov. 23 Engr. Perf. 13
2548 A1382 3fr deep green black 1.40 .30

French School in Athens, 150th Anniv. A1383

1996, Nov. 23 Photo.
2549 A1383 3fr multicolored 1.40 .30

Cannes Film Festival, 50th Anniv. A1384

1996, Nov. 30
2550 A1384 3fr multicolored 1.40 .30

New National Library of France A1385

1996, Dec. 14
2551 A1385 3fr multicolored 1.40 .30

A1386 A1387

1997, Jan. 4
2552 A1386 3fr multicolored 1.40 .30
Francois Mitterrand (1916-96).

1997, Jan. 24 Photo. Perf. 13
2553 A1387 3fr multicolored 1.40 .30
Participatory innovation.

Georges Pompidou Natl. Center of Art and Culture, 20th Anniv. A1388

1997, Jan. 31   Engr.   Perf. 12½x13
2554 A1388 3fr multicolored   1.40   .30

Happy Holiday A1389

1997, Feb. 8   Photo.   Perf. 13
2555 A1389 3fr shown   1.40   .30
2556 A1389 3fr Happy birthday   1.40   .30

Natl. School of Bridges and Highways, 250th Anniv. A1390

Photo. & Engr.
1997, Feb. 14   Perf. 12½x13
2557 A1390 3fr multicolored   1.40   .30

Saint-Laurent-du-Maroni, French Guiana — A1391

Photo. & Engr.
1997, Feb. 22   Perf. 12½x13
2558 A1391 3fr multicolored   1.40   .30

Art Series

Church Fresco, Tavant A1392

Painting by Bernard Moninot — A1393

The Thumb, Polished Bronze, by César A1394

Grapes and Pomegranates, by Jean Baptiste Chardin — A1395

1997   Engr.   Perf. 13
2559 A1392 6.70fr multicolored   3.00   1.00
Photo.
2560 A1393 6.70fr multicolored   3.00   1.00
2561 A1394 6.70fr multicolored   3.00   1.00
2562 A1395 6.70fr multicolored   3.00   1.00
    Nos. 2559-2562 (4)   12.00   4.00

Issued: #2559, 3/1; #2560, 3/29; #2561, 9/13; #2562, 9/27.

Tourism Series

Millau — A1396   Guimiliau Church Close — A1398

Fresco, Saint Eutrope des Salles-Lavauguyon — A1397

Sablé-Sur-Sarthe — A1399

1997   Engr.   Perf. 12½x13
2563 A1396 3fr grn & dk bl grn   1.40   .30
Perf. 13
2564 A1397 4.50fr multicolored   2.10   .75
2565 A1398 3fr multicolored   1.40   .30
Perf. 12½x13
2566 A1399 3fr multicolored   1.40   .20
    Nos. 2563-2566 (4)   6.30   1.55

Issued: #2563, 3/15; #2564, 6/14; #2565, 7/12; #2566, 9/20.

Vignette of Type A17 — A1400

Litho. & Engr.
1997, Mar. 15   Perf. 13½x13
2567 A1400 3fr multicolored   6.00   5.00
2568 A1400 3fr +60c multi   2.50   2.00
a.   Booklet pane, 4 #2567, 3
     #2568 + label   32.50
     Complete booklet, #2568a   35.00

Stamp Day.
No. 2567 issued only in booklets.

National Parks Type of 1996
1997, Apr. 12   Photo.   Perf. 13
2569 A1357 3fr Parc des Ecrins   1.40   .40
2570 A1357 3fr Guadeloupe Park   1.40   .40
2571 A1357 4.50fr Parc des Pyrénées 2.10   .90
2572 A1357 4.50fr Port-Cros Park   2.10   .90
    Nos. 2569-2572 (4)   7.00   2.60

Puss-in-Boots A1401

1997, Apr. 26   Engr.   Perf. 13
2573 A1401 3fr blue   1.40   .30

Europa.

Philexjeunes '97, Nantes — A1402

1997, May 2   Litho.   Perf. 13
2574 A1402 3fr multicolored   1.40   .30

Cartoon Journey of a Letter A1403

"Envelope": No. 2575, Writing letter. No. 2576, Climbing ladder to go into letter box. No. 2577, On wheels. No. 2578, Following postman carrying another "Envelope." No. 2579, Held by girl. No. 2580, At feet of girl reading long letter.

1997, May 8   Photo.   Perf. 13
2575   A1403 3fr multicolored   2.50   1.00
2576   A1403 3fr multicolored   2.50   1.00
2577   A1403 3fr multicolored   2.50   1.00
2578   A1403 3fr multicolored   2.50   1.00
2579   A1403 3fr multicolored   2.50   1.00
2580   A1403 3fr multicolored   2.50   1.00
a.   Strip of 6, #2575-2580
     + label   18.00 12.00

Self-Adhesive
Serpentine Die Cut 11

2580B A1403 3fr like #2575   2.00   1.25
2580C A1403 3fr like #2576   2.00   1.25
2580D A1403 3fr like #2577   2.00   1.25
2580E A1403 3fr like #2578   2.00   1.25
2580F A1403 3fr like #2579   2.00   1.25
2580G A1403 3fr like #2580   2.00   1.25
h.   Booklet pane, 2 each
     #2580B-2580G   27.50 27.50

By its nature No. 2580h is a complete booklet. The peelable paper backing serves as a booklet cover.

See Nos. 2648-2659.

Honoring French Soldiers in North Africa (1952-62) A1404

1997, May 10   Litho.   Perf. 13
2581 A1404 3fr multicolored   1.40   .30

French Federation of Philatelic Associations, 70th Congress, Versailles — A1405

1997, May 17   Photo.   Perf. 13
2582 A1405 3fr multicolored   1.40   .30

Printed with se-tenant label.

Château de Plessis-Bourré, Maine and Loire Rivers — A1406

1997, May 24   Litho. & Engr.
2583 A1406 4.40fr multicolored   2.00   1.00

1998 World Cup Soccer Championships Type

Stylized action scenes, name of host city in France.

1997, May 31   Photo.   Perf. 13½
2584 A1367 3fr Lyon   1.40   .35
2585 A1367 3fr Marseilles   1.40   .35
2586 A1367 3fr Nantes   1.40   .35
2587 A1367 3fr Paris   1.40   .35
    Nos. 2584-2587 (4)   5.60   1.40

Saint Martin of Tours (316-97) Apostle of the Gauls A1408

1997, July 5   Engr.   Perf. 13
2588 A1408 4.50fr multicolored   2.00   .65

Marianne — A1409

1997, July 14   Engr.   Perf. 13
2589   A1409 10c brown   .20   .20
2590   A1409 20c brt blue grn   .20   .20
2591   A1409 50c purple   .25   .20
2592   A1409 1fr bright org   .45   .20
2593   A1409 2fr bright blue   .90   .30
2594   A1409 2.70fr bright grn   1.25   .20
2595   A1409 (3fr) red   1.40   .25
2596   A1409 3.50fr apple grn   1.60   .25
2597   A1409 3.80fr blue   1.75   .25
2598   A1409 4.20fr dark org   1.90   .30
2599   A1409 4.40fr blue   2.00   .30
2600   A1409 4.50fr bright pink   2.10   .30
2601   A1409 5fr brt grn blue   5.25   .30
2602   A1409 6.70fr dark green   3.00   .30
a.   Souvenir sheet, #2594-
     2600, 2602   14.00 14.00
2603   A1409 10fr violet   4.50   .35
a.   Souvenir sheet, #2589-
     2593, 2601, 2603   12.00 12.00
    Nos. 2589-2603 (15)   26.75   3.90

Self-Adhesive
Booklet Stamps
Die Cut x Serpentine Die Cut 7

2603B	A1409	1fr brt org	2.25	.50
c.	Booklet pane, #2603B, 3			
	#2604		7.75	
	Booklet, 2 #2603Bc		16.00	
2604	A1409	(3fr) red	1.40	.25
a.	Booklet pane of 10		14.00	

Coil Stamps
Perf. 13 Horiz.

2604B	A1409	2.70fr bright grn	1.25	.50
2605	A1409	(3fr) red	1.40	.30

Nos. 2595, 2604-2605 were valued at 3fr on day of issue.
Issued: Nos. 2602a, 2603a, 11/12/01. No. 2603B, 9/1/97.
See Nos. 2835-2835C, 2921-2922, 3530.

1997 World Rowing Championships, Savoie — A1410

1997, Aug. 30   **Engr.**   **Perf. 13x12½**
2606   A1410   3fr blue & magenta   1.40   .30

Basque Corsairs A1411

1997, Sept. 13   **Perf. 13**
2607   A1411   3fr multicolored   1.40   .30

Saint-Maurice Basilica, Epinal — A1412

1997, Sept. 20   **Perf. 13x12½**
2608   A1412   3fr multicolored   1.40   .30

Fresh Fish Merchants, Port of Boulogne A1413

1997, Sept. 26   **Perf. 13**
2609   A1413   3fr multicolored   1.40   .30

Japan Year — A1414

1997, Oct. 4   **Engr.**   **Perf. 13**
2610   A1414   4.90fr multicolored   2.25   1.25

1997 World Judo Championships — A1415

1997, Oct. 9   **Photo.**   **Perf. 13**
2611   A1415   3fr multicolored   1.40   .35

Sceaux Estate, Hauts-de-Seine — A1416

1997, Oct. 11
2612   A1416   3fr multicolored   1.40   .30

Saar-Lorraine-Luxembourg Summit — A1417

1997, Oct. 16   **Photo.**   **Perf. 13**
2613   A1417   3fr multicolored   1.40   .30

See Germany #1982, Luxembourg #972.

College of France A1418

1997, Oct. 18   **Engr.**
2614   A1418   4.40fr multicolored   2.00   .90

Quality — A1419

1997, Oct. 18   **Photo.**
2615   A1419   4.50fr multicolored   2.10   .60

A1420

Season's Greetings A1421

1997   **Photo.**   **Perf. 13**
2616   A1420   3fr Cat & mouse   1.40   .30

Photo. & Embossed
2617   A1421   3fr Mailman   1.40   .30

Issued: No. 2616, 11/8; No. 2617, 11/22.

Protection of Abused Children — A1422

1997, Nov. 20   **Photo.**
2618   A1422   3fr multicolored   1.40   .30

Marshal Jacques Leclerc (Philippe de Haute Cloque) (1902-47) A1423

1997, Nov. 28   **Photo.**   **Perf. 13**
2619   A1423   3fr multicolored   1.40   .30

Philexfrance '99, World Stamp Exposition — A1424

1997, Dec. 6   **Engr.**
2620   A1424   3fr red & blue   1.40   .30

Abbey of Moutier D'Ahun, Creuse A1425

1997, Dec. 13
2621   A1425   4.40fr multicolored   2.00   1.00

Michel Debré (1912-96), Politician A1426

1998, Jan. 15   **Photo.**
2622   A1426   3fr multicolored   1.40   .30

1998 World Cup Soccer Championships Type

Stylized action scenes, name of host city in France.

1998, Jan. 24   **Perf. 13½**

2623	A1367	3fr Saint-Denis	1.40	.30
2624	A1367	3fr Bordeaux	1.40	.30
a.	Sheet of 10, #2530-2533,			
	#2584-2587, #2623-2624			
	+ label		14.00	14.00

National Assembly, Bicent. — A1427

1998, Jan. 24   **Perf. 13**
2625   A1427   3fr multicolored   1.40   .30

Valentine's Day A1428

1998, Jan. 31
2626   A1428   3fr multicolored   1.40   .30

Office of Mediator of the Republic, 25th Anniv. A1429

1998, Feb. 5
2627   A1429   3fr multicolored   1.40   .30

A1430

1998, Feb. 28   **Photo.**   **Perf. 12½**
2628   A1430   3fr multicolored   1.40   .30

Self-Adhesive
Serpentine Die Cut

2629	A1430	3fr like #2628	1.40	.30
a.	Booklet pane of 10		14.00	14.00
b.	Sheet of 1 + 7 labels		14.00	14.00

1998 World Cup Soccer Championships, France.
The peelable paper backing of No. 2629a serves as a booklet cover.
See No. 2665.

A1431

1998, Feb. 21   **Engr.**   **Perf. 13½x13**

2630	A1431	3fr Detail of design		
		A16	5.00	3.50
2631	A1431	3fr +60c like #2630	1.90	1.90
a.	Booklet pane, 4 #2630, 3			
	#2631 + label		26.00	
	Complete booklet, #2631a		27.00	

Stamp Day. No. 2630 issued only in booklets.

A1432

1998, Feb. 28   **Engr.**   **Perf. 13**
2632   A1432   4.50fr blue   2.10   .75

Father Franz Stock (1904-48), prison chaplain.

Happy Birthday A1433

1998, Mar. 13   **Photo.**   **Perf. 13x13½**
2633   A1433   3fr multicolored   1.40   .30

Union of Mulhouse with France, Bicent. A1434

1998, Mar. 14
2634 A1434 3fr multicolored 1.40 .30

Citeaux Abbey, 900th Anniv. A1435

1998, Mar. 14 **Engr.** *Perf. 13*
2635 A1435 3fr multicolored 1.40 .30

Sous-Préfecture Hotel, Saint-Pierre, Réunion — A1436

1998, Apr. 4 **Engr.** *Perf. 13*
2636 A1436 3fr multicolored 1.40 .30
Réunion's architectural heritage.

"The Return," by René Magritte — A1437

1998, Apr. 18 **Photo.**
2637 A1437 3fr multicolored 1.40 .50
See Belgium No. 1691.

Edict of Nantes, 400th Anniv. A1438

1998, Apr. 18 **Litho.**
2638 A1438 4.50fr Henry IV 2.10 .75

Art Series

Detail from "Entry of the Crusaders into Constantinople," by Delacroix (1798-1863) — A1439

Le Printemps, by Pablo Picasso (1881-1973) — A1440

Neuf Moules Malic, by Marcel Duchamp (1887-1968) — A1441

Vision After the Sermon, by Paul Gauguin (1848-1903) — A1442

1998 **Engr.** *Perf. 12x13*
2639 A1439 6.70fr multicolored 3.00 1.00
Litho.
Perf. 13
2640 A1440 6.70fr multicolored 3.00 1.00
Photo.
2641 A1441 6.70fr multicolored 3.00 1.00
2642 A1442 6.70fr multicolored 3.00 1.00
Issued: #2639, 4/25; #2640, 5/15; #2641, 10/17; #2642, 12/5.

Abolition of Slavery, 150th Anniv. A1443

1998, Apr. 25 **Litho.** *Perf. 13*
2643 A1443 3fr multicolored 1.40 .30

Tourism Series

Le Gois Causeway, Island of Noirmoutier, Vendée — A1444

Bay of Somme, Picardy — A1445

Château de Crussol, Ardèche A1446

Collegiate Church of Mantes — A1447

1998, May 2 **Photo.**
2644 A1444 3fr multicolored 1.40 .30
2645 A1445 3fr multicolored 1.40 .30
Engr.
2646 A1446 3fr multicolored 1.40 .30
2647 A1447 4.40fr multicolored 2.00 1.00
Nos. 2644-2647 (4) 6.20 1.90
Issued: #2644, 5/2; #2645, 6/27; #2646, 7/4; #2647, 9/19.

Journey of a Letter Type

Historic "letters:" No. 2648, Dove carrying letter, Noah's Ark. No. 2649, Egyptian writing letter on papyrus. No. 2650, Soldier running to Athens with letter to victory at Marathon. No. 2651, Knight carrying letter on horseback. No. 2652, Writing letters with quill and ink. No. 2653, Astronaut carrrying letter in space from earth to the moon.

1998, May 9 **Photo.** *Perf. 13x13½*
2648 A1403 3fr multicolored 2.50 1.00
2649 A1403 3fr multicolored 2.50 1.00
2650 A1403 3fr multicolored 2.50 1.00
2651 A1403 3fr multicolored 2.50 1.00
2652 A1403 3fr multicolored 2.50 1.00
2653 A1403 3fr multicolored 2.50 1.00
a. Strip, #2648-2653 + label 16.00 10.00

Booklet Stamps
Self-Adhesive
Serpentine Die Cut 11
2654 A1403 3fr like #2648 2.25 1.25
2655 A1403 3fr like #2649 2.25 1.25
2656 A1403 3fr like #2650 2.25 1.25
2657 A1403 3fr like #2651 2.25 1.25
2658 A1403 3fr like #2652 2.25 1.25
2659 A1403 3fr like #2653 2.25 1.25
a. Bklt. pane, 2 ea #2654-2659 27.50 27.50

By its nature No. 2659a is a complete booklet. The peelable paper backing serves as a booklet cover.

League of Human Rights, Cent. — A1448

1998, May 9 *Perf. 13*
2660 A1448 4.40fr multicolored 2.00 1.00

Henri Collet (1885-1951), Composer — A1449

1998, May 15 **Engr.** *Perf. 12x13*
2661 A1449 4.50fr black, gray & buff 2.10 .90

French Federation of Philatelic Assoc., 71st Congress, Dunkirk — A1450

Photo. & Engr.
1998, May 29 *Perf. 13*
2662 A1450 3fr multicolored 1.40 .30

Mont-Saint-Michel — A1451

1998, June 6 **Photo.** *Perf. 13*
2663 A1451 3fr multicolored 1.40 .30

Natl. Music Festival — A1452

1998, June 13
2664 A1452 3fr multicolored 1.40 .50
Europa.

1998 World Cup Soccer Championships Type with Added
Inscription, "Champion du Monde"
1998, July 12 **Photo.** *Perf. 12½*
2665 A1430 3fr multicolored 1.40 .30

Stéphane Mallarmé (1842-98), Poet A1453

Photo. & Engr.
1998, Sept. 5 *Perf. 13*
2666 A1453 4.40fr multicolored 2.00 .90

Flowers — A1453a

1998, Sept. 9 **Litho.** *Perf. 13*
2666A A1453a 1.87fr Liseron .85 .30
2666B A1453a 2.18fr Coqueli-cot 1.00 .55
2666C A1453a 4.66fr Violette 2.10 1.25
2666D A1453a 7.11fr Bouton d'or 3.25 2.00
Nos. 2666A-2666D (4) 7.20 4.10
Nos. 2666A-2666D are known only precanceled. See second note after #132.

A1454   A1455

1998, Sept. 12   **Photo.**
2667 A1454 3fr multicolored   1.40   .30
     Aéro Club of France, cent.

1998, Oct. 23   **Photo.**   *Perf. 13*
   "The Little Prince," by Antoine de Saint-Exupéry (1900-44): a, Standing in uniform with sword, horiz. b, Seated on wall. c, "The Little Prince on Asteroid B-612." d, Pouring water from sprinkling can. e, Walking along cliff, fox, horiz.
2668   Strip of 5 + 2 labels   7.00   6.00
   a.-e.   A1455 3fr any single   1.40   .60
   f.   Souv. sheet, #2668a-2668e   9.00   9.00
   Philexfrance '99. No. 2668f was released 9/12 and sold for 25fr.

Hall of Heavenly Peace, Imperial Palace, Beijing, China
A1456

1998, Sept. 12   **Photo.**   *Perf. 13x13½*
2669 A1456   3fr shown   1.40   .40
2670 A1456   4.90fr The Louvre, France   2.25   1.00
   See China People's Republic #2895-2896.

Garnier Palace, Home of the Paris Opera — A1457

1998, Sept. 19   **Photo.**   *Perf. 13*
2671 A1457 4.50fr multicolored   2.10   .75

Horses
A1458

1998, Sept. 27
2672 A1458 2.70fr Camargue   1.25   .30
2673 A1458   3fr Pottok   1.40   .50
2674 A1458   3fr French trotter   1.40   .50
2675 A1458 4.50fr Ardennais   2.10   .80
   Nos. 2672-2675 (4)   6.15   2.10

Paris Auto Show, Cent.
A1459

1998, Oct. 1   *Perf. 12*
2676 A1459 3fr multicolored   1.40   .30

5th Republic, 40th Anniv.
A1460

1998, Oct. 3   **Photo.**   *Perf. 13*
2677 A1460 3fr blue, gray & red   1.40   .30

Saint-Dié, Capital of Vosges Mountain Region — A1461

1998, Oct. 3   **Engr.**   *Perf. 13*
2678 A1461 3fr Tower of Liberty   1.40   .30

End of World War I, 80th Anniv.
A1462

1998, Oct. 17   **Photo.**   *Perf. 13x13½*
2679 A1462 3fr multicolored   1.40   .40

Intl. Union for the Conservation of Nature and Natural Resources, 50th Anniv. — A1463

1998, Nov. 3   **Litho.**
2680 A1463 3fr multicolored   1.40   .40

New Year   Christmas
A1464   A1465

1998, Nov. 7   **Photo.**   *Perf. 13*
Background Colors
2681 A1464 3fr deep blue   1.40   .75
2682 A1465 3fr green   1.40   .75
2683 A1464 3fr yellow   1.40   .75
2684 A1465 3fr red   1.40   .75
2685 A1464 3fr green   1.40   .75
   a.   Strip of 5, #2681-2685   7.00   6.00
   Issued in sheets of 10 stamps. Location of "Bonne Annee" and "Meilleurs Voeux" varies.

Doctors Without Borders
A1466

1998, Nov. 21   *Perf. 13x13½*
2686 A1466 3fr multicolored   1.40   .30

European Parliament, Strasbourg
A1467

1998, Dec. 5   **Photo.**   *Perf. 13*
2687 A1467 3fr multicolored   1.40   .30

Universal Declaration of Human Rights, 50th Anniv.
A1468

   #2688, Faces of people of various races, globe. #2689, René Cassin (1887-1976), principal author of Declaration, Eleanor Roosevelt (1884-1962), Chaillot Palace, Paris.

1998, Dec. 10   **Litho.**   *Perf. 13*
2688 A1468 3fr multicolored   1.40   .30
2689 A1468 3fr multicolored   1.40   .30

Discovery of Radium, Cent., ZOE Reactor, 50th Anniv.
A1469

1998, Dec. 15   **Photo.**   *Perf. 13*
2690 A1469 3fr multicolored   1.40   .40

Introduction of the Euro — A1470

1999   **Engr.**   *Perf. 13*
2691   A1470 3fr red & blue   1.40   .25
Booklet Stamps
Self-Adhesive
Die Cut x Serpentine Die Cut 7
2691A A1470 3fr red & blue   1.40   .25
   b.   Booklet pane of 10   14.00
   Issued: No. 2691, 1/1/99. No. 2691A, 2/15/99. Values are shown in both Francs and Euros on Nos. 2691-2691A. No. 2691Ab is a complete booklet.
   Euro currency did not circulate until 2002.

French Postage Stamps, 150th Anniv.
A1471

1999, Jan. 1   **Photo.**   *Perf. 13*
Booklet Stamps
2692 A1471 3fr black & red   6.50   4.50
2693 A1471 3fr red & black   1.25   .75
   a.   Booklet pane, #2692, 4 #2693 + label   11.50
     Complete booklet, #2693a   12.00
   No. 2692 has black denomination; No. 2693 has red denomination.
   Stamp Day.

Public Assistance Hospital, Paris, 150th Anniv.
A1472

1999, Jan. 9
2694 A1472 3fr multicolored   1.40   .30

Diplomatic Relations with Israel, 50th Anniv. — A1473

1999, Jan. 24
2695 A1473 4.40fr multicolored   2.00   .75

Festival Stamps
A1474

1999, Feb. 6   **Photo.**   *Perf. 13*
2696 A1474 3fr Stars, "Je t'aime"   1.40   .30
2697 A1474 3fr Rose   1.40   .30
Booklet Stamps
Self-Adhesive
Die Cut Perf. 10
2698 A1474 3fr like #2696   1.40   .30
2699 A1474 3fr like #2697   1.40   .30
   a.   Bklt. pane, 5 ea #2698-2699   14.00
   No. 2699a is a complete booklet.

Art Series

St. Luke the Evangelist, Sculpture by Jean Goujon (1510-66)
A1475

Painting, "Waterlillies in Moonlight," by Claude Monet (1840-1926) — A1476

Stained Glass, Cathedral of Auch, by Arnauld de Moles, 16th Cent.
A1477

Charles I, King of England, by Sir Anthony Van Dyck — A1478

1999 **Engr.** **Perf. 13**
2700 A1475 6.70fr multicolored 3.00 1.00
Litho.
2701 A1476 6.70fr multicolored 3.00 1.00
Engr.
2702 A1477 6.70fr multicolored 3.00 1.00
Photo.
Perf. 13¼x13
2703 A1478 6.70fr multicolored 3.00 1.00
Nos. 2700-2703 (4) 12.00 4.00
Issued: #2700, 2/13; #2701, 5/29; #2702, 6/19; #2703, 11/11.

National Census — A1479

1999, Feb. 20 **Photo.** **Perf. 13½**
2704 A1479 3fr multicolored 1.40 .30

Cultural Heritage of Lebanon — A1480

Mosaic illustrating transformation of Zeus into bull, Natl. Museum of Beirut.

1999, Feb. 27 **Perf. 12½**
2705 A1480 4.40fr multicolored 2.00 .90

Asterix, by Albert Uderzo and Rene Goscinny — A1481

1999, Mar. 6 **Photo.** **Perf. 13¼**
2706 A1481 3fr multicolored 1.75 .50
a. Perf. 13¼x12¾ 1.75 .90
Booklet Stamp
Perf. 13¼x12¾
2707 A1481 3fr +60c like
#2706 3.50 2.00
b. Booklet pane, 4 #2706a, 3
#2707 + label 15.00
Complete booklet, #2707b 16.00
Souvenir Sheet
2707A A1481 3fr +60c like
#2706 3.00 2.50
Stamp Day. Stamp design in #2707A continues into the margins.

Council of Europe, 50th Anniv. A1482

1999, Mar. 19
2708 A1482 3fr multicolored 1.40 .30

A1483

Announcements — A1483a

1999, Mar. 20 **Perf. 13**
2709 A1483 3fr Marriage (Oui) 1.40 .30
2710 A1483 3fr It's a boy (C'est
un garcon) 1.40 .30
2711 A1483 3fr It's a girl(C'est
une fille) 1.40 .30
2712 A1483a 3fr Thank you 1.40 .30
Nos. 2709-2712 (4) 5.60 1.20
See Nos. 2721-2722.

Souvenir Sheet

PhilexFrance '99 — A1484

Works of art: a, Venus de Milo. b, Mona Lisa, by Da Vinci. c, Liberty Guiding the People, by Delacroix.

Litho. & Engr.
1999, Mar. 26 **Perf. 13¼**
2713 A1484 Sheet of 3 50.00 50.00
a.-b. 5fr each 10.00 10.00
c. 10fr multicolored 20.00 20.00
No. 2713 sold for 50fr, with 30fr serving as a donation to the Assoc. for the Development of Philately.

Elections to the European Parliament A1485

1999, Mar. 27 **Photo.** **Perf. 13**
2714 A1485 3fr multicolored 1.40 .30

Richard I, the Lion-Hearted (1157-1199), King of England — A1486

1999, Apr. 10 **Engr.** **Perf. 13x12½**
2715 A1486 3fr multicolored 1.40 .35

Tourism Series

Dieppe A1487

Haut-Koenigsbourg Castle, Bas-Rhin — A1488

Birthpalce of Champollion, Figeac — A1489

Chateau, Arnac-Pompadour — A1490

1999 **Engr.** **Perf. 13½**
2716 A1487 3fr multicolored 1.40 .30
Litho. & Engr.
Perf. 13
2717 A1488 3fr multicolored 1.40 .50
2718 A1489 3fr multicolored 1.40 .30
Engr.
2719 A1490 3fr multicolored 1.40 .30
Nos. 2716-2719 (4) 5.60 1.40
Issued: #2716, 4/17; #2717, 5/15; #2718, 6/26; #2719, 7/10.

The Camargue Nature Preserve A1491

1999, Apr. 24 **Photo.** **Perf. 13x13½**
2720 A1491 3fr multicolored 1.40 .50
Europa.

Announcements Type of 1999 and

A1492

1999, May 13 **Photo.** **Perf. 13**
2721 A1483 3fr Nice Holiday
(bonnes va-
cances) 1.40 .30
2722 A1483 3fr Happy Birthday
(joyeux anniver-
saire) 1.40 .30
2723 A1492 3fr Long Live Vacations (Vive les
vacances) 1.40 .30
Nos. 2721-2723 (3) 4.20 .90

Saint Pierre, Martinique A1493

1999, May 15
2724 A1493 3fr multicolored 1.10 .25

Detail of "Noctuelles" Dish, by Émile Gallé, School of Nancy Museum A1494

1999, May 22
2725 A1494 3fr multicolored 1.40 .30

Souvenir Sheet

World Old Roses Competition, Lyon — A1495

a, 4.50fr, Mme. Caroline Testout. b, 3fr, Mme. Alfred Carrière. c, 4.50fr, La France.

1999, May 28 **Perf. 13½x13**
2726 A1495 Sheet of 3, #a.-c. 6.00 6.00

Court of Saint-Emilion, 800th Anniv. — A1496

1999, May 29 **Engr.** **Perf. 13¼x13**
2727 A1496 3.80fr multicolored 1.75 .90

Hotel de la Monnaie, French Mint Headquarters — A1497

1999, June 5 **Engr.** **Perf. 13**
2728 A1497 4.50fr brn org & bl 2.10 .75

A1498

A1499

1999, June 12 **Photo.** **Perf. 13¼**
2729 A1498 3fr multicolored 1.40 .40
Countess of Segur (1799-1874), children's storyteller.

1999, June 19 **Perf. 13**
2730 A1499 3fr Welcome 1.40 .30

René Caillié (1799-1838), Explorer of Africa — A1500

1999, June 26 Engr. Perf. 13¼
2731 A1500 4.50fr multicolored 2.10 .75

1st French Postage Stamps, 150th Anniv. A1501

1999, July 2 Photo. Perf. 11¾x13
2732 A1501 6.70fr multicolored 3.00 1.75

PhilexFrance '99, World Philatelic Exhibition. No. 2732 was printed with a se-tenant label and contains a holographic image. Soaking in water may affect the hologram.

Celebrating the Year 2000 A1502

1999, July 5 Photo. Perf. 13
2733 A1502 3fr multicolored 1.40 .30

Year 2000 Stamp Design Contest Winner — A1503

1999, July 6
2734 A1503 3fr multicolored 1.40 .30

Total Solar Eclipse, Aug. 11, 1999 A1504

1999, July 8 Perf. 12x12¼
2735 A1504 3fr multicolored 1.40 .40

Gathering of Tall Ships, Rouen, July 9-18 A1505

Sailing ships: a, Simón Bolivar. b, Iskra. c, Statsraad Lehmkuhl. d, Asgard II. e, Belle Poule. f, Belem. g, Amerigo Vespucci. h, Sagres. i, Europa. j, Cuauhtemoc.

1999, July 10 Photo. Perf. 13
2736 1fr Sheet of 10 6.00 6.00
a.-j. A1505 any single .50 .50

1999 Rugby World Cup, Cardiff, Wales A1506

1999, Sept. 11 Photo. Perf. 13¼
2737 A1506 3fr multicolored 1.40 .40
a. Miniature sheet of 10 11.00

Value is for copy with surrounding selvage. One stamp in No. 2737a has a missing "F" in the printer's mark.

Frédéric Ozanam (1813-53), Historian — A1507

1999, Sept. 11 Engr. Perf. 13
2738 A1507 4.50fr multicolored 2.10 .75

Emmaus Movement, 50th Anniv. A1508

1999, Sept. 26 Photo. Perf. 13
2739 A1508 3fr multicolored 1.40 .40

Cats and Dogs — A1509

1999, Oct. 2 Photo. Perf. 13¼
2740 A1509 2.70fr Chartreux cat 1.25 .30
2741 A1509 3fr European cat 1.40 .30
2742 A1509 3fr Pyrenean Mountain dog 1.40 .30
2743 A1509 4.50fr Brittany spaniel 2.10 .75
Nos. 2740-2743 (4) 6.15 1.65

Frédéric Chopin (1810-49), Composer A1510

1999, Oct. 17 Engr. Perf. 13¼
2744 A1510 3.80fr multicolored 1.75 .75
See Poland No. 3484.

A1511

Best Wishes for Year 2000 A1512

1999, Nov. 20 Photo. Perf. 13x13¼
2745 A1511 3fr multi 1.40 .30
2746 A1512 3fr multi 1.40 .30

No. 2746 was printed with se-tenant label.

Paris Metro, Cent. A1513

1999, Dec. 4 Photo. Perf. 13
2747 A1513 3fr multi 1.40 .30

Council of State, Bicent. — A1514

1999, Dec. 11
2748 A1514 3fr multi 1.40 .30

Reconstruction of Lighthouses — A1515

2000, Jan. 1 Photo. Perf. 13x12¾
2749 A1515 3fr multi 1.40 .30

Reconstruction of San Juan de Salvamento Lighthouse, Argentina and replication of its design at La Rochelle, France.

Hearts A1516

2000, Jan. 8 Photo. Perf. 13
2750 A1516 3fr Snakes 1.40 .30
2751 A1516 3fr Face 1.40 .30
a. Souvenir sheet, 3 #2750, 2 #2751 9.00 9.00

Self-Adhesive Booklet Stamps
Serpentine Die-Cut
2752 A1516 3fr Like #2750 1.40 .30
2753 A1516 3fr Like #2751 1.40 .30
a. Bklt. pane, 5 ea #2752-2753 14.00

Values for Nos. 2750-2751 are for copies with surrounding selvage. No. 2753a is a complete booklet.

Bank of France, Bicent. — A1517 Prefectorial Corps, Bicent. — A1518

2000, Jan. 15 Litho. Perf. 13
2754 A1517 3fr multi 1.40 .30

2000, Feb. 17 Photo. Perf. 13x12¼
2755 A1518 3fr multi 1.40 .30

Art Series

Venus and the Graces Offering Gifts to a Young Girl, by Sandro Botticelli (1445-1510) — A1519

The Waltz, by Camille Claudel A1520

Visage Rouge, by Gaston Chaissac A1521

Carolingian Mosaic, Germigny-des-Prés — A1522

2000 Photo. Perf. 13¼x13
2756 A1519 6.70fr multi 3.00 1.00
2757 A1520 6.70fr multi 3.00 1.00
2758 A1521 6.70fr multi 3.00 1.00
2759 A1522 6.70fr multi 3.00 1.00
Issued: #2756, 2/25; #2757, 4/8; #2758, 9/23; 10/21.

Tourism Series

Carcassonne — A1523

Saint-Guilhem-Le-Désert — A1524

Gérardmer A1525

Abbey Church of Ottmarsheim — A1526

Illustration A1523 reduced.

2000		Photo.	Perf. 13	
2760	A1523	3fr multi	1.40	.30
		Engr.		
		Perf. 13¼		
2761	A1524	3fr multi	1.40	.30
2762	A1525	3fr multi	1.40	.30
		Perf. 12¼x13		
2763	A1526	3fr multi	1.40	.30
		Nos. 2760-2763 (4)	5.60	1.20

Issued: #2760, 3/3; #2761, 4/8; #2762, 4/17; #2763, 6/17.

Tintin — A1527

2000, Mar. 11		Photo.	Perf. 13¼	
2764	A1527	3fr multi	1.40	.50
a.		Perf. 13½x13	2.00	.75
		Perf. 13½x13		
2765	A1527	3fr + 60c multi	4.00	2.00
a.		Booklet pane, 4 #2764a, 3 #2765 + label	20.00	
		Complete booklet, #2765a	21.00	
b.		Souvenir sheet of 1	3.00	2.50

Stamp Day.

Bretagne Parliament Building Restoration — A1528

2000, Mar. 25		Photo.	Perf. 13¼	
2766	A1528	3fr multi	1.40	.30

Madagascar Periwinkles — A1529

2000, Mar. 25		Litho.	Perf. 13x13¼	
2767	A1529	4.50fr multi	2.10	.60

Felicitations A1530

2000, Apr. 7		Photo.	Perf. 13x13¼	
2768	A1530	3fr multi	1.40	.30

The 20th Century — A1531

No. 2769: a, France as World Cup soccer champions, 1998, vert. b, Marcel Cerdan wins middleweight boxing title, 1948. c, Charles Lindbergh flies solo across Atlantic, 1927. d, Jean-Claude Killy wins three Winter Olympics gold medals, 1968, vert. e, Carl Lewis wins four Olympic gold medals, 1984, vert.

Perf. 13¼x13 (vert. stamps), 13x13¼

2000, Apr. 15				
2769	A1531	Sheet, 2 ea #a-e	14.00	14.00
a.-e.		3fr any single	1.40	.75

Top part of No. 2769 contains Nos. 2769a-2769e and is separated from bottom part of sheet by a row of rouletting.

See No. 2787, 2804, 2837, 2881, 2915.

Automobiles — A1532

No. 2770: a, Bugatti 35. b, Citroen Traction. c, Renault 4CV. d, Simca Chambord. e, Hispano-Suiza K6. f, Volkswagen Beetle. g, 1962

Cadillac. h, Peugeot 203. i, Citroen DS19. j, Ferrari 250 GTO.

2000, May 5		Perf. 13¼x13		
2770	A1532	Sheet of 10, #a.-j.	7.50	7.50
a.-e.		1fr any single	.45	.35
f.-j.		2fr any single	.90	.60

Europa, 2000
Common Design Type

2000, May 9		Photo.	Perf. 13¼	
2771	CD17	3fr multi	1.40	.40

Henry-Louis Duhamel du Monceau (1700-82), Agronomist — A1533

2000, May 13		Engr.	Perf. 13	
2772	A1533	4.50fr multi	2.10	.65

French Federation of Philatelic Associations, 73rd Congress, Nevers — A1534

2000, May 19		Engr.	Perf. 13¼	
2773	A1534	3fr multi	1.40	.30

A1535   A1536

2000, June 1		Photo.	Perf. 13¼x13	
2774	A1535	3fr Happy Vacation	1.40	.30

2000, June 3		Engr.	Perf. 13x12¼	
2775	A1536	3fr multi	1.40	.30

First Ascent of Annapurna, 50th anniv.

Nature A1537

2.70fr, Agrias sardanapalus butterfly. #2777, Giraffe. #2778, Allosaurus. 4.50fr, Tulipa lutea.

2000, June 17		Photo.	Perf. 13¼	
2776	A1537	2.70fr multi	1.00	.40
2777	A1537	3fr multi, vert.	1.10	.40
2778	A1537	3fr multi	1.10	.40
2779	A1537	4.50fr multi, vert	1.75	.75
a.		Souvenir sheet, #2776-2779	5.75	5.75
		Nos. 2776-2779 (4)	4.95	1.95

Antoine de Saint-Exupéry (1900-44), Aviator, Writer — A1538

2000, June 24		Photo.	Perf. 13¼x13	
2780	A1538	3fr multi	1.40	.30

Yellow Train of Cerdagne, Cent. A1539

2000, July 14			Perf. 13x13¼	
2781	A1539	3fr multi	1.40	.30

Folklore A1540

2000, Aug. 12		Photo.	Perf. 13	
2782	A1540	4.50fr multi	2.10	.65

2000 Summer Olympics, Sydney A1541

Designs: No. 2783, Cycling, fencing, relay racer. No. 2784, Relay racer, judo, diving.

2000, Sept. 9				
2783	A1541	3fr multi	1.40	.50
2784	A1541	3fr multi	1.40	.50
a.		Pair, #2783-2784	3.00	2.00
b.		Sheet, 5 #2784a + label	15.00	15.00

Olymphilex 2000, Sydney (#2784b).

Brother Alfred Stanke (1904-75) A1542

2000, Sept. 23			Engr.	
2785	A1542	4.40fr multi	2.00	.90

S.O.S. Amitié, 40th Anniv. A1543

2000, Sept. 30		Litho.	Perf. 13	
2786	A1543	3fr multi	1.40	.30

20th Century Type

No. 2787: a, Man on the Moon, 1969, vert. b, Paid vacations, 1936. c, Invention of washing machine, 1901, vert. d, Woman suffrage, 1944, vert. e, Universal Declaration of Human Rights, 1948.

Perf. 13¼x13 (vert. stamps), 13x13¼

2000, Sept. 30		Photo.		
2787	A1531	Sheet, 2 each #a-e	14.00	14.00
a.-e.		3fr Any single	1.40	.50

The top and bottom parts of No. 2787 contains Nos. 2787a-2787e and are separated by a row of rouletting.

2001,
Start of
New
Millennium
A1544

2000, Oct. 14 **Litho.** *Perf. 13*
2788 A1544 3fr multi 1.40 .30

The
Lovers'
Kiosk, by
Peynet
A1545

2000, Nov. 4 **Engr.** *Perf. 13¼x13*
2789 A1545 3fr multi 1.40 .50

Endangered Birds — A1546

2000, Nov. 4 **Photo.** *Perf. 13¼*
2790 A1546 3fr Kiwi 1.40 .40
2791 A1546 5.20fr Falcon 2.50 1.50
See New Zealand Nos. 1688, 1694.

Start of the 3rd Millennium — A1547

2000, Nov. 9 **Photo.** *Perf. 13x13¼*
2792 A1547 3fr multi + label 1.40 .30
Issued in sheets of 10 stamps + 10 labels,
which could be personalized for an extra fee.

Holiday
Greetings
A1548

2000, Nov. 11 *Perf. 12¼x13*
2793 A1548 3fr Meilleurs voeux 1.40 .30
Perf. 13¼
2794 A1548 3fr Bonne année 1.40 .30

Union of
Metallurgical &
Mining Industries,
Cent. — A1549

Engr. with Foil Application
2000, Dec. 9 *Perf. 13x13¼*
2795 A1549 4.50fr multi 2.10 .90

World Handball
Championships — A1550

2001, Jan. 20 **Photo.** *Perf. 13¼*
2796 A1550 3fr multi 1.40 .30

Heart
A1551

2001, Jan. 27
2797 A1551 3fr multi 1.40 .30
a. Souvenir sheet of 5 10.00 10.00
Value of No. 2797 is for copy with surrounding selvage.

Art Series

The Peasant Dance, by Pieter
Breughel, the Elder — A1552

Hotel des Chevaliers de Saint-Jean-
de-Jérusalem — A1553

Yvette Guilbert Singing "Linger,
Longer, Loo," by Henri de Toulouse-
Lautrec (1864-1901) — A1554

Honfleur at Low Tide, by Johan
Barthold Jongkind — A1555

Engr., Photo (#2800), Litho (#2801)
2001 *Perf. 13x13¼, 13¼x13 (#2800)*
2798 A1552 6.70fr multi 3.00 1.00
2799 A1553 6.70fr multi 3.00 1.00
2800 A1554 6.70fr multi 3.00 1.00
2801 A1555 6.70fr multi 3.00 1.00
Nos. 2798-2801 (4) 12.00 4.00
Issued: No. 2798, 2/3; No. 2799, 4/21; No.
2800, 9/8; No. 2801, 10/27.

Gaston Lagaffe,
by André
Franquin
A1556

2001, Feb. 24 **Photo.** *Perf. 13¼*
2802 A1556 3fr multi 1.40 .50
a. Perf. 13¼x13 1.40 .65
Perf. 13¼x13
2803 A1556 3fr +60c multi 5.00 3.50
a. Souvenir sheet of 1 3.50 2.50
b. Booklet pane, 5 #2802a, 3
#2803 22.00
Booklet, #2803b 22.50
Stamp Day.

20th Century Type of 2000
No. 2804 — Communications: a, Television.
b, Compact disc. c, Advertisements, vert. d,
Radio, vert. e, Portable telephone, vert.

Perf. 13¼x13 (vert. stamps), 13x13¼
2001, Mar. 17 **Photo.**
2804 A1531 Sheet, 2 each
#a-e 14.00 14.00
a.-e. 3fr Any single 1.40 .75
Top part of No. 2804 contains Nos. 2804a-
2804e and is separated from bottom part by a
row of rouletting.

Announcements — A1557

Designs: No. 2805, It's a girl. No. 2806, It's
a boy. No. 2807, Thank you. 4.50fr, Yes
(marriage).

2001 *Perf. 13*
Frame Color
2805 A1557 3fr brt pink 1.40 .30
a. Litho., stamp + label 6.50 6.50
2806 A1557 3fr brt blue 1.40 .30
a. Litho., stamp + label 6.50 6.50
2807 A1557 3fr brt yel grn 1.40 .30
a. Litho., stamp + label 6.50 6.50
2808 A1557 4.50fr orange 2.10 .75
Nos. 2805-2808 (4) 6.30 1.65
Issued: Nos. 2805-2808, 3/23; Nos. 2805a-
2807a, 11/8.
Nos. 2805a-2807a were issued in sheets of
10 stamps and 10 labels that sold for 60fr on
day of issue. The labels could be personalized. Frames on Nos. 2805 and 2806 look
splotchy, while those on Nos. 2805a and
2806a have a distinct dot structure. The frame
on No. 2807 has tightly spaced small dots,
while on No. 2807a, the dots are more widely
spaced.

Wildlife — A1558

2001, Apr. 21 **Photo.** *Perf. 13¼*
2809 A1558 2.70fr Squirrel 1.25 .40
2810 A1558 3fr Roe deer 1.40 .40
2811 A1558 3fr Hedgehog,
horiz. 1.40 .40
2812 A1558 4.50fr Ermine 2.10 .75
a. Souvenir sheet, #2809-2812 7.00 6.50

Tourism Issue

Nogent-le-Rotrou
A1559

Besançon
A1560

Calais
A1561

Château
de
Grignan
A1562

Engr., Litho & Engr. (#2813)
2001 *Perf. 13¼x13 (#2813), 13*
2813 A1559 3fr multi 1.40 .40
2814 A1560 3fr multi 1.40 .30
2815 A1561 3fr multi 1.40 .30
2816 A1562 3fr multi 1.40 .30
Nos. 2813-2816 (4) 5.60 1.30
Issued: No. 2813, 4/28; No. 2814, 5/5; No.
2815, 6/16; No. 2816, 7/7.

Europa — A1563

2001, May 8 **Photo.** *Perf. 13*
2817 A1563 3fr multi 1.40 .35

Gardens of Versailles — A1564

2001, May 12
2818 A1564 4.40fr multi 2.00 1.00

Singers — A1565

Designs: No. 2819, Claude François (1939-78). No. 2820, Léo Ferré (1916-93). No. 2821, Serge Gainsbourg (1928-91). No. 2822, Dalida (1933-87). No. 2823, Michel Berger (1947-92). No. 2824, Barbara (1930-97).

2001, May 19	Photo.	Perf. 13	
2819	A1565	3fr multi	1.40	.75
2820	A1565	3fr multi	1.40	.75
2821	A1565	3fr multi	1.40	.75
2822	A1565	3fr multi	1.40	.75
2823	A1565	3fr multi	1.40	.75
2824	A1565	3fr multi	1.40	.75
a.	Souvenir sheet, #2819-2824		11.00	11.00
	Nos. 2819-2824 (6)		8.40	4.50

No. 2824a sold for 28fr with the Red Cross receiving 10fr of that.

Old Lyon — A1566

2001, May 19	Engr.	Perf. 13¼	
2825	A1566	3fr multi	1.40	.30

French Federation of Philatelic Associations 74th Congress, Tours — A1567

2001, June 1			
2826	A1567	3fr multi	1.40	.30

Jean Vilar (1912-71), Actor A1568

Litho. & Engr.		Perf. 13	
2001, June 7			
2827	A1568	3fr multi	1.40	.40

Vacation A1569

2001, June 10	Litho.	Perf. 13	
2828	A1569	3fr multi	1.40	.30

Booklet Stamp
Self-Adhesive

2829	A1569	3fr multi	1.40	.30
a.	Booklet of 10		14.00	

1 Euro Coin A1570

2001, June 23	Photo.	Perf. 12½	
2830	A1570	3fr multi	1.40	.30

Value is for copy with surrounding selvage.

Albert Caquot (1881-1976), Engineer — A1571

2001, June 30	Engr.	Perf. 13¼	
2831	A1571	4.50fr multi	2.00	.75

Law Guaranteeing Freedom of Association, Cent. — A1572

2001, July 1	Photo.	Perf. 13	
2832	A1572	3fr multi	1.40	.30

Trains — A1573

No. 2833: a, Eurostar. b, American 220. c, Crocodile. d, Crampton. e, Garratt 59. f, Pacific Chapelon. g, Mallard. h, Capitole. i, Autorail Panoramique. j, 230 Class P8.

2001, July 6	Photo.	Perf. 13¼	
2833	A1573	Sheet of 10	7.50	7.50
a.-j.	1.50fr Any single		.75	.65

Geneva Convention on Refugees, UN High Commisioner for Refugees, 50th Anniv. — A1574

2001, July 28		Perf. 13	
2834	A1574	4.50fr multi	2.00	.75

Marianne Type of 1997 Inscribed "RF" at Lower Left

2001	Engr.	Perf. 13	
2835	A1409	(3fr) red	1.40	.25
d.	Sheet of 15 + 15 labels		60.00	

Serpentine Die Cut 6¾ Vert.
Self-Adhesive

2835A	A1409	(3fr) red	1.40	.25
b.	Booklet of 10		15.00	
e.	No. 2835 with attached label		6.00	

No. 2835Ae is from a sheet having eiter small or large-sized labels that could be personalized.

2001, Aug. 1	Engr.	Perf. 13 Horiz.	

Coil Stamp
Water-Activated Gum

2835C	A1409	(3fr) red	1.40	.25

Issued: Nos. 2835, 2835C, 8/1; No. 2835A, 9/24. No. 2835Ae, 2004.

No. 2835d sold for €10.03. Labels could be personalized for an additional price. "La Poste" and engraver are at right.

Pierre de Fermat (1601-65), Mathematician — A1575

2001, Aug. 19	Engr.	Perf. 13¼x13	
2836	A1575	4.50fr multi	2.00	.75

20th Century Type of 2000

No. 2837 — Science: a, First man in space. b, DNA. c, Chip cards. d, Laser. e, Penicillin.

Perf. 13¼x13 (vert. stamps), 13

2001, Sept. 22		Photo.	
2837	A1531	Sheet, 2 each		
		#a-e	14.00	14.00
a.-e.	3fr Any single		1.40	.70

Top part of No. 2837 contains Nos. 2837a-2837e and is separated from bottom part of sheet by a row of rouletting.

Astrolabe Sculpture, Val-de-Reuil A1576

2001, Sept. 29		Perf. 13	
2838	A1576	3fr multi	1.40	.30

Halloween A1577

2001, Oct. 20			
2839	A1577	3fr multi	1.40	.30
a.	Souvenir sheet of 5 + 4 labels		8.00	8.00

Jean Pierre-Bloch (1905-99), Human Rights Advocate — A1578

2001, Nov. 8	Engr.	Perf. 13	
2840	A1578	4.50fr multi	2.00	.75

Albert Decaris (1901-88), Artist A1579

2001, Nov. 9	Engr.	Perf. 13¼x13	
2841	A1579	3fr multi	1.40	.40

Jacques Chaban-Delmas (1915-2000), Politician — A1580

2001, Nov. 10	Engr.	Perf. 13x13¼	
2842	A1580	3fr multi	1.40	.40

Holiday Greetings A1581

Designs: Nos. 2843, 2845 Bonne Année (Happy New Year). Nos. 2844, 2846 Meilleurs Voeux (Best wishes).

2001, Nov. 9	Litho.	Perf. 13	
2843	A1581	3fr multi	1.40	.30
2844	A1581	3fr multi	1.40	.30

Serpentine Die Cut 11
Self-Adhesive
Booklet Stamps

2845	A1581	3fr multi	1.40	.30
2846	A1581	3fr multi	1.40	.30
a.	Booklet, 5 each # 2845-2846		14.00	

Fountains A1582

Designs: 3fr, Nejjarine Fountain, Fez, Morocco. 3.80fr, Wallace Fountain, Paris.

2001, Dec. 14	Photo.	Perf. 13¼	
2847	A1582	3fr multi	1.40	.40
2848	A1582	3.80fr multi	1.75	1.00

See Morocco Nos. 914-915.

100 Cents = 1 Euro (€)

Marianne (With Euro Denominations) A1583   Orchids A1584

2002, Jan. 1	Engr.	Perf. 13	
2849	A1583	1c yellow	.20	.20
2850	A1583	2c brown	.20	.20
2851	A1583	5c brt bl grn	.20	.20
2852	A1583	10c purple	.25	.20
2853	A1583	20c brt org	.60	.30
2854	A1583	41c brt green	1.20	.20
2855	A1583	50c brt blue	1.50	.25
2856	A1583	53c apple grn	1.60	.40
2857	A1583	58c blue	1.75	.50
2858	A1583	64c dark org	1.90	.50
2859	A1583	67c brt blue	2.00	.50
a.	deep blue		2.00	.50
2860	A1583	69c brt pink	2.10	.60
2861	A1583	€1 Prus blue	3.00	.80
2862	A1583	€1.02 dk green	3.00	.90
a.	Souvenir sheet #2835, 2854, 2856-2858, 2859a, 2860, 2862		15.00	15.00
2863	A1583	€2 violet	6.00	1.50
a.	Souvenir sheet #2849-2853, 2855, 2861, 2863		12.00	12.00
	Nos. 2849-2863 (15)		25.50	7.25

Coil Stamp
Perf. 13 Horiz.

2864	A1583	41c brt green	1.25	.30

See Nos. 2952-2957, 3043, 3043P-3043Q.

2002, Jan. 2   **Litho.**   *Perf. 13*

Designs: 29c, Orchis insularis. 33c, Ophrys fuciflora.

2865	A1584	29c multi	.80	.30
2866	A1584	33c multi	1.00	.40

Nos. 2865-2866 are known only precanceled. See second note after #132.
See Nos. 2958-2959, 3046.

Heart of Voh, Photograph by Yann Arthurs-Bertrand — A1585

2002, Jan. 18   **Photo.**   *Perf. 13¼*

2867	A1585	46c multi	1.40	.40
a.		Souvenir sheet of 5	7.00	7.00

Value of No. 2867 is for copy with surrounding selvage.

2002 Winter Olympics, Salt Lake City — A1586

2002, Jan. 26   *Perf. 13*

2868	A1586	46c multi	1.40	.30

Art Series

Sphere Concorde, by Jesús Rafael Soto A1587

The Kiss, by Gustav Klimt A1588

The Dancers, by Fernando Botero A1589

Self-Portrait, by Elisabeth Vigée-Lebrun — A1590

2002   **Photo.**   *Perf. 13¼x13*

2869	A1587	75c multi	2.25	1.00
2870	A1588	€1.02 multi	3.00	1.00
2871	A1589	€1.02 multi	3.00	1.00

Engr.

2872	A1590	€1.02 multi	3.00	1.00
		Nos. 2869-2872 (4)	11.25	4.00

Issued: No. 2869, 11/11. No. 2870, 2/8; No. 2871, 4/27. No. 2872, 10/12.

Alain Bosquet (1919-98), Poet — A1591

2002, Feb. 16   **Engr.**   *Perf. 13*

2873	A1591	58c multi	1.75	1.00

It's A Girl A1592

It's A Boy A1593

Yes A1594

2002, Feb. 23   **Photo.**

2874	A1592	46c multi	1.40	.30
2875	A1593	46c multi	1.40	.30
2876	A1594	69c multi	2.00	.30
		Nos. 2874-2876 (3)	4.80	.90

Europa — A1595

2002, Mar. 2   *Perf. 13¼*

2877	A1595	46c multi	1.40	.30

Boule and Bill, by Jean Roba — A1596

Designs: 46c, Boule, Bill, bird. 46c+9c, Boule, Bill, ball.

2002, Mar. 16   *Perf. 13¼*

2878	A1596	46c multi	1.40	.50
a.		Perf. 13¼x13	2.00	.60

Perf. 13¼x13

2879	A1596	46c +9c multi	4.00	3.00
a.		Souvenir sheet of 1	3.00	2.50
b.		Booklet pane, 5 #2878a, 3 #2879	22.00	—
		Booklet, #2879b	22.50	

Stamp Day. Stamp on No. 2879a has continuous design.

Nimes Amphitheater — A1597

Litho. & Engr.

2002, Mar. 22   *Perf. 13*

2880	A1597	46c multi	1.40	.30

20th Century Type of 2000

No. 2881 — Transportation: a, Concorde supersonic airplane. b, TGV train. c, Ocean liner France, vert. d, Mobylette motor scooter, vert. e, Citroen 2 CV automobile, vert.

Perf. 13, 13¼x13 (vert. stamps)

2002, Mar. 23   **Photo.**

2881	A1531	Sheet, 2 each #a-e	14.00	14.00
a.-e.		46c Any single	1.40	.75

Top part of No. 2881 contains Nos. 2881a-2881e and is separated from bottom part of sheet by a row of rouletting.

Encounter of Matthew Flinders and Nicolas Boudin, Bicent. A1598

Map of Australia, portrait and ship of: 46c, Flinders. 79c, Boudin.

2002, Apr. 4   *Perf. 13¼*

2882	A1598	46c multi	1.40	.40
2883	A1598	79c multi	2.25	1.25

See Australia Nos. 2053-2054.

Tourism Series

La Charité-sur-Loire — A1599

Collioure A1600

Locronan A1601

Neufchateau — A1602

Engraved (#2884, 2886), Photo. (#2885)

2002   *Perf. 13¼*

2884	A1599	46c multi	1.40	.30
2885	A1600	46c multi	1.40	.30
2886	A1601	46c multi	1.40	.30
2887	A1602	46c multi	1.40	.30
		Nos. 2884-2887 (4)	5.60	1.20

Issue dates: No. 2884, 4/6; No. 2885, 6/22; No. 2886, 7/13; No. 2887, 10/12/02.
Numbers have been reserved for additional stamps in this set.

Birthday Greetings A1603

Invitation A1604

2002, Apr. 6   **Photo.**   *Perf. 13*

2888	A1603	46c multi	1.40	.30
a.		Litho., stamp + label	6.00	6.00
2889	A1604	46c multi	1.40	.30
a.		Litho., stamp + label	6.00	6.00

Issued: Nos. 2888a, 2889a, 11/7. Nos. 2888a and 2889a were issued in sheets of 10 stamps and 10 labels that sold for €6.19 on day of issue. The labels could be personalized.
No. 2888a has a duller blue in "Anniversaire" than No. 2888, but is otherwise quite similar in appearance. The gold ink on No. 2889a has a more coppery look than that on No. 2889.

100th Paris-Roubaix Bicycle Race — A1605

2002, Mar. 13

2890	A1605	46c multi	1.40	.30

2002 World Cup Soccer Championships, Japan and Korea — A1606

No. 2891: a, Flags, soccer ball and field (32mm diameter). b, Soccer player, year of French championship.

2002, Apr. 27   **Perf. 12¾**
2891   A1606   Horiz. pair   2.75   2.50
a.-b.   46c Any single   1.40   .30
c.   Sheet, 5 #2891   15.00   15.00

Issued: No. 2891c, 5/18.
See Argentina No. 2184, Brazil No. 2840, Germany No. 2163, Italy No. 2526 and Uruguay No. 1946.

Marine Life
A1607

Designs: 41c, Sea turtle (tortue luth), vert. No. 2893, Killer whale (orque). No. 2894, Dolphin (grand dauphin). 69c, Seal (phoque veau marin).

2002, May 4   **Perf. 13¼**
2892   A1607   41c multi   1.25   .30
2893   A1607   46c multi   1.25   .30
2894   A1607   46c multi   1.25   .30
2895   A1607   69c multi   2.00   .75
a.   Souvenir sheet, #2892-2895   6.50   6.50
    Nos. 2892-2895 (4)   5.75   1.65

Worldwide Fund for Nature (#2895a).

French Federation of Philatelic Associations 75th Congress, Marseilles — A1608

2002, May 17   **Engr.**   **Perf. 13**
2896   A1608   46c multi   1.40   .30

Legion of Honor, Bicent.   Rocamadour
A1609   A1610

2002, May 18   **Photo.**
2897   A1609   46c multi   1.40   .30

2002, May 25   **Perf. 13¼**
2898   A1610   46c multi   1.40   .30

Louis Delgrés (1766-1802), Soldier — A1611

2002, May 25
2899   A1611   46c multi   1.40   .30

Vacation
A1612

2002, June 8   **Litho.**   **Perf. 13**
2900   A1612   46c multi   1.40   .30

Self-Adhesive
Serpentine Die Cut 11
2901   A1612   46c multi   1.40   .30
a.   Booklet pane of 10   14.00

World Disabled Athletics Championships — A1613

2002, June 15   **Photo.**   **Perf. 13¼**
2902   A1613   46c multi   1.40   .30

Saint-Ser Chapel — A1614

2002, June 22   **Engr.**   **Perf. 13x13¼**
2903   A1614   46c multi   1.40   .30

Metz Cathedral Stained Glass A1615

2002, July 6   **Engr.**   **Perf. 13¼x13**
2904   A1615   46c multi   1.40   .40

Jazz Musicians — A1616

Designs: No. 2905, Louis Armstrong (1901-71). No. 2906, Ella Fitzgerald (1918-96). No. 2907, Duke Ellington (1899-1974). No. 2908, Stéphane Grappelli (1908-97). No. 2909, Michel Petrucciani (1962-99), horiz. No. 2910, Sidney Bechet (1897-1959), horiz.

2002, July 13   **Photo.**   **Perf. 13**
2905   A1616   46c multi   1.40   .75
2906   A1616   46c multi   1.40   .75
2907   A1616   46c multi   1.40   .75
2908   A1616   46c multi   1.40   .75
2909   A1616   46c multi   1.40   .75
2910   A1616   46c multi   1.40   .75
a.   Souvenir sheet, #2905-2910   12.00   12.00
    Nos. 2905-2910 (6)   8.40   4.50

No. 2910a sold for €4.36, with the Red Cross receiving €1.60 of that.

Pilgrimages to Notre Dame de la Salette, 150th Anniv. A1617

2002, Aug. 15   **Engr.**   **Perf. 13¼x13**
2911   A1617   46c multi   1.40   .30

Choreography — A1618

2002, Sept. 13 Photo.   **Perf. 13x13¼**
2912   A1618   53c multi   1.50   .60

Motorcycles — A1619

No. 2913: a, Honda 750 four. b, Terrot 500 RGST. c, Majestic. d, Norton Commando 750. e, Voxan 1000 Café Racer. f, BMW R90S. g, Harley Davidson Hydra Glide. h, Triumph Bonneville 650. i, Ducati 916. j, Yamaha 500 XT.

2002, Sept. 14   **Perf. 13¼x13**
2913   A1619   Sheet of 10   12.00   12.00
a.-e.   16c any single   .75   .60
f.-j.   30c any single   .90   .75

Georges Perec (1936-82), Writer — A1620

2002, Sept. 21   **Engr.**   **Perf. 13¼**
2914   A1620   46c multi   1.40   .30

20th Century Type of 2000

No. 2915 — Photographs of everyday life: a, Family on motor scooter, 1955, vert. b, Man, horse and wagon, 1947. c, Woman ironing, 1950. d, Boy at fountain, 1950, vert. e, Girl in classroom, 1965, vert.

Perf. 13¼x13 (vert. stamps), 13
2002, Sept. 28   **Photo.**
2915   A1531   Sheet, 2 each
    #a-e   14.00   14.00
a.-e.   46c Any single   1.40   .75

Top part of No. 2915 contains Nos. 2915a-2915e and is separated from bottom part of sheet by a row of rouletting.

Emile Zola (1840-1902), Novelist — A1621

2002, Oct. 5   **Perf. 13**
2916   A1621   46c multi   1.40   .30

Souvenir Sheet

European Capitals — A1622

Attractions in Rome: a, Trevi Fountain. b, Coliseum, horiz. c, Trinità de Monti Church and Spanish Steps. d, St. Peter's Basilica, horiz.

2002, Nov. 7   **Perf. 13¼x13, 13x13¼**
2917   A1622   Sheet of 4   6.00   6.00
a.-d.   46c Any single   1.40   .75

See Nos. 2985, 3052, 3138, 3223, 3340, 3535, 3728.

Globe and Microcircuits A1623

2002, Nov. 8   **Photo.**   **Perf. 13**
2918   A1623   46c multi   1.40   .30
a.   Litho., stamp + label   6.00   6.00

Issued: No. 2918a, 11/7. No. 2918a was issued in sheets of 10 stamps and 10 labels that sold for €6.19 on day of issue. The labels could be personalized.
No. 2918a has a hairline at top, above "RF" that No. 2918 does not have, but is otherwise quite similar in appearance.

Holiday Greetings A1624

2002, Nov. 8   **Photo.**   **Perf. 13**
2919   A1624   46c multi   1.40   .30
a.   Litho., stamp + label   6.00   6.00

Booklet Stamp
Self-Adhesive
Serpentine Die Cut 11
2920   A1624   46c multi   1.40   .30
a.   Booklet pane of 10   14.00

Issued: No. 2919a, 11/7. No. 2919a was issued in sheets of 10 stamps and 10 labels that sold for €6.19 on day of issue. The labels could be personalized.
No. 2919a has a finer dot structure, which is most noticeable in the chimney smoke, than No. 2919.

Marianne Type of 1997 Inscribed "RF" at Lower Left
2002, Nov. 9   **Engr.**   **Perf. 13**
2921   A1409   (41c) bright green   1.20   .25
Coil Stamp
Perf. 13 Horiz.
2922   A1409   (41c) bright green   1.20   .25

Alexandre Dumas (Father) (1802-70), Writer A1625

2002, Nov. 30   **Photo.**   **Perf. 13**
2924   A1625   46c multi   1.40   .30

Léopold Sédar Senghor (1906-2001),
President of Senegal, Poet — A1626

2002, Dec. 20
2925 A1626 46c multi .... 1.40 .30

Hearts
A1627

2003, Jan. 11   **Perf. 13¼**
2926 A1627 46c Four hearts ..... 1.40 .30
  a.   Souvenir sheet of 5 .... 7.00 7.00
2927 A1627 69c Roses .... 2.00 .60

Values for Nos. 2926-2927 are for copies
with surrounding selvage.

Thank You
A1628

Birth
A1629

2003, Jan. 11   **Perf. 13**
2928 A1628 46c multi .... 1.40 .30
2929 A1629 46c brt org & brt bl .. 1.40 .30

Franco-German Cooperation Treaty,
40th Anniv. — A1630

2003, Jan. 16   **Perf. 13¼**
2930 A1630 46c multi .... 1.40 .40

Delegation for Land-use Planning and
Regional Action, 40th Anniv.
A1631

2003, Feb. 8   **Photo.**   **Perf. 13**
2931 A1631 46c multi .... 1.40 .30

Geneviève de Gaulle
Anthonioz (1920-
2002), World War II
Resistance
Fighter — A1632

2003, Feb. 11
2932 A1632 46c blk & ol brn ..... 1.40 .30

Paris Chamber of
Commerce and
Industry,
Bicent. — A1633

2003, Feb. 22   **Perf. 13¼**
2933 A1633 46c multi .... 1.40 .30

Lucky Luke, by
Morris (Maurice
De
Bevere) — A1634

Lucky Luke and Jolly Jumper: 46c, Skipping
rope on ball on high wire. 46c+9c, Following
dog, Rantanplan.

2003, Mar. 15   **Photo.**   **Perf. 13¼**
2934 A1634 46c multi .... 1.40 .65
  a.   Perf. 13¼x13 .... 1.40 .65

        Perf. 13¼x13
2935 A1634 46c +9c multi 3.50 2.00
  a.   Souvenir sheet of 1 .... 3.00 2.50
  b.   Booklet pane, 5 #2934a, 3
        #2935 .... 17.50 —
        Complete booklet, #2935b . 18.00

      Stamp Day.

Birds
A1635

Designs: 41c, Colibri à tete bleue (Cya-
nophaia bicolor). No. 2937, Toucan ariel
(Ramphastos vitellinus). No. 2938, Colibri
grenat (Eulampis jugularis), vert. 69c, Terpsiphone de Bourbon (Terpsiphone
bourbonnensis).

2003, Mar. 22   **Photo.**   **Perf. 13¼**
2936 A1635 41c multi .... 1.20 .30
2937 A1635 46c multi .... 1.40 .30
2938 A1635 46c multi .... 1.40 .30
2939 A1635 69c multi .... 2.00 .75
  a.   Souvenir sheet, #2936-2939 7.00 7.00
      Nos. 2936-2939 (4) 6.00 1.65

Nantes
A1636

2003, Apr. 4   **Engr.**
2940 A1636 46c multi .... 1.40 .30

Pierre Bérégovoy
(1925-93), Prime
Minister — A1637

2003, Apr. 30   **Engr.**   **Perf. 13x13¼**
2941 A1637 46c multi .... 1.40 .30

Milan Stefanik (1880-1919),
Czechoslovakian General — A1638

2003, May 3   **Perf. 13¼**
2942 A1638 50c multi .... 1.50 .40

    See Slovakia No. 428.

Europa — A1639

2003, May 8   **Photo.**
2943 A1639 50c multi .... 1.50 .40

Charter of
Fundamental
Rights of the
European
Union — A1640

2003, May 8
2944 A1640 50c multi .... 1.50 .30

Aircraft
Carrier
"Charles de
Gaulle"
A1641

2003, May 8   **Engr.**
2945 A1641 50c multi .... 1.50 .30

Aspects of
Life in the
French
Regions
A1642

No. 2946: a, Beach cabins. b, Fishing net. c,
Vineyards of Champagne. d, Camembert
cheese, vert. e, Foie gras, vert. f, Petanque. g,
Puppet show (Guignol), vert. h, Crepe, vert. i,
Cassoulet. j, Limoges porcelain.

2003, May 24   **Photo.**   **Perf. 13**
2946   Sheet of 10 .... 16.00 16.00
  a.-j.   A1642 50c Any single 1.50 1.30

No. 2946 has three vertical rows of rouletting, separating sheet into quarters.
Nos. 2946a-2946j were also issued in large
booklets containing panes of 1 of each stamp.
The booklet sold for €19.
See Nos. 2978, 3007, 3047, 3106, 3139,
3192, 3234, 3299, 3300, 3357, 3427, 3505.

Art Series

"The Dying Slave" and "The Rebel
Slave," by Michelangelo — A1643

The Red
Buoy, by
Paul Signac
A1644

Untitled
Abstract by
Vassily
Kandinsky
A1645

Marilyn, by
Andy
Warhol
A1646

2003   **Engr.**   **Perf. 13¼x13**
2947 A1643 75c multi 2.25 1.00
         Photo.
2948 A1644 75c multi 2.25 1.00
         Litho.
2949 A1645 €1.11 multi 3.25 1.25
2950 A1646 €1.11 multi 3.25 1.40
      Nos. 2947-2950 (4) 11.00 4.65

Issued: No. 2947, 5/24. Nos. 2948, 2949,
7/5. No. 2950, 11/8.
A sheet containing 3 No. 2949 and 12
imperforate color progressive proofs was
bound in a book that sold for €60.

Happy
Birthday
A1647

2003, May 31   **Photo.**   **Perf. 13¼**
2951 A1647 50c multi .... 1.50 .35
  a.   Souvenir sheet of 5 .... 7.50 7.50
  b.   Litho., stamp + label 1.75 1.75

Issued: No. 2951b, 2004. No. 2951b was
issued in sheets of 10 stamps + 10 labels that
sold for €6.67 on day of issue. The labels
could be personalized. The background on,

No. 2951 looks splotchy while that of No. 2951b has a dot structure.

Marianne With Euro Denominations
Type of 2002

2003, June 1		**Engr.**		**Perf. 13**	
2952	A1583	58c apple grn		1.60	.40
2953	A1583	70c yellow grn		2.00	.50
2954	A1583	75c bright blue		2.25	.50
2955	A1583	90c dark blue		2.60	1.00
2956	A1583	€1.11 red lilac		3.25	1.00
2957	A1583	€1.90 violet brown		5.50	1.25
a.	Souvenir sheet, #2835, 2921, 2952-2957			22.00	22.00
	Nos. 2952-2957 (6)			17.20	4.65

No. 2957a issued 2/28/04.

Orchids Type of 2002

Designs: 30c, Platanthera chlorantha. 35c, Dactylorhiza savogiensis.

2003, June 1		**Litho.**		**Perf. 13**	
2958	A1584	30c multi		.85	.30
2959	A1584	35c multi		1.00	.40

Nos. 2958-2959 are known only precanceled. See second note after #132.

French Federation of Philatelic Associations 76th Congress, Mulhouse A1648

2003, June 6		**Engr.**		**Perf. 13¼**	
2960	A1648	50c multi		1.50	.40

Vacation — A1649

		Perf. 12¾x13¼			
2003, June 14				**Litho.**	
2961	A1649	50c multi		1.50	.30

Self-Adhesive
Booklet Stamp
Serpentine Die Cut 11

2962	A1649	50c multi		1.50	.30
a.	Booklet pane of 10			15.00	

Tourism Issue

Notre Dame de l'Epine Basilica — A1650

Tulle A1651

Arras — A1652

Pontarlier A1653

		Perf. 13x13¼, 13 (#2965)			
2003, June 21				**Engr.**	
2963	A1650	50c multi		1.50	.30
2964	A1651	50c multi		1.50	.30
2965	A1652	50c multi		1.50	.40
2966	A1653	50c multi		1.50	.40
		Nos. 2963-2966 (4)		6.00	1.40

Issued: Nos. 2963, 2964, 6/21. No. 2965, 9/20. No. 2966, 10/11.

French Freemasonry, 275th Anniv. — A1654

2003, June 28		**Engr.**		**Perf. 13¼x13**	
2967	A1654	50c multi		1.50	.30

Tour de France Bicycle Race, Cent. A1655

No. 2968: a, Maurice Garin, winner of 1903 race. b, Cyclist with arms raised.

2003, June 28		**Photo.**		**Perf. 13**	
2968	A1655	Vert. pair		3.00	2.00
a.-b.	50c Either single			1.50	.30

Values are for stamps with surrounding selvage.

Saint-Père Church, Yonne — A1656

2003, July 12		**Engr.**		**Perf. 13¼**	
2969	A1656	50c multi		1.50	.30

World Track and Field Championships, Paris — A1657

2003, July 19		**Photo.**		**Perf. 13**	
2970	A1657	50c multi		1.50	.30

Characters From French Literature — A1658

Designs: No. 2971, Eugène-François Vidocq (1775-1857), convict and police official. No. 2972, Esmeralda, from *Notre-Dame de Paris*, by Victor Hugo. No. 2973, Claudine, from *Claudine* novels, by Colette. No. 2974, Nana, from *Rougon-Macquart*, by Emile Zola. No. 2975, La Comte de Monte-Cristo, from *La Comte de Monte-Cristo*, by Alexandre Dumas (pere). No. 2976, Gavroche, from *Les Miserables*, by Hugo.

2003, Aug. 30		**Photo.**		**Perf. 13**	
2971	A1658	50c multi		1.50	.75
2972	A1658	50c multi		1.50	.75
2973	A1658	50c multi		1.50	.75
2974	A1658	50c multi		1.50	.75
2975	A1658	50c multi		1.50	.75
2976	A1658	50c multi		1.50	.75
a.	Souvenir sheet, #2971-2976			14.00	14.00
	Nos. 2971-2976 (6)			9.00	4.50

No. 2976a sold for €4.60, with the Red Cross receiving €1.60 of that.

Ahmad Shah Massoud (1953-2001), Afghan Northern Alliance Leader — A1659

2003, Sept. 9					
2977	A1659	50c multi		1.50	.30

Aspects of Life in French Regions
Type of 2003

No. 2978: a, Chateau de Chenonceau. b, House, Alsace. c, Roof, Bourgogne. d, Genoese Tower, Corsica, vert. e, Arc de Triomphe, vert. f, Farm house, Provence. g, Pointe du Raz, vert. h, Mont Blanc, vert. i, Basque house. j, Pont du Gard.

2003, Sept. 20		**Photo.**		**Perf. 13**	
2978		Sheet of 10		15.00	15.00
a.-j.	A1642 50c Any single			1.50	1.25

No. 2978 has three vertical rows of rouletting, separating sheet into quarters.

Nos. 2978a-2978j were also issued in large booklets containing panes of 1 of each stamp. The booklet sold for €19.

Gardens and Parks — A1660

No. 2979: a, Buttes-Chaumont Park. b, Jardin du Luxembourg.

2003, Sept. 27				**Perf. 13¼x13**	
2979		Sheet of 2		11.00	11.00
a.-b.	A1660 €1.90 Either single			5.50	5.50

Salon du Timbre 2004. No. 2979 has four vertical rows of rouletting, separating sheet into fifths, with the two stamps in the central fifth.

See Nos. 3029, 3118, 3201, 3316, 3429.

Motor Vehicles — A1661

No. 2980: a, 1954 Isobloc 648 DP 102 bus (Autocar). b, 1950 SFV 302 Tractor. c, 1938 Delahaye fire truck with mechanical aerial ladder. d, Renault Kangaroo Express postal van. e, 1932 Renault TN6 Paris city bus. f, 1910 Berliet 22hp Type M delivery truck. g, 1957 Berliet T100 heavy-duty truck. h, Citroen police van. i, Citroen DS ambulance. j, 1964 Hotchkiss fire truck.

2003, Oct. 24		**Photo.**		**Perf. 13¼**	
2980	A1661	Sheet of 10		9.00	9.00
a.-e.	20c Any single			.55	.55
f.-j.	30c Any single			.85	.65

Philexjeunes 2003 Philatelic Exhibition, Dunkerque.

A1662

Holiday Greetings A1663

2003, Nov. 6		**Photo.**		**Perf. 13**	
2981	A1662	50c multi		1.50	.35
a.	Litho., stamp + label			6.00	6.00
		Litho.			
2982	A1663	50c multi		1.50	.35
a.	Sheet of 10 + 10 labels			60.00	60.00

Booklet Stamp
Self-Adhesive
Serpentine Die Cut 11¼

2983	A1663	50c multi		1.50	.35
a.	Booklet pane of 10			15.00	

Nos. 2981a, 2982a, 2004. Nos. 2981a and 2982 were issued in sheets of 10 stamps + 10 labels that sold for €6.67 each on day of issue. The labels could be personalized. The background on No. 2981 looks splotchy while that of No. 2981a has a dot structure.

A souvenir sheet containing No. 2982 was sold for €6 by mail order only. It was not available through standing order subscriptions and was not offered in the philatelic bureau's sales catalog. 50,000 copies of this sheet were printed. Value $250.

Sower Type of 1903, Cent. — A1664

Serpentine Die Cut 6¾ Vert.
2003, Nov. 6   **Engr.**
Booklet Stamp
2984   A1664   50c red   3.50   3.00
  a.   Booklet pane, 5 each #   2984, 2835A   25.00

European Capitals Type of 2002
No. 2985 — Attractions in Luxembourg: a, Citadelle Saint-Esprit. b, Notre Dame Cathedral, horiz. c, Adolphe Bridge, horiz. d, Grand Duke's Palace.

Perf. 13¼x13, 13x13¼
2003, Nov. 7   **Photo.**
2985   A1622   Sheet of 4   7.50   7.50
  a.-d.   50c Any single   1.50   1.00

Indian and French Artisan's Work — A1665

Designs: 50c, Illumination depicting rooster, France, 15th cent. 90c, Jewelry design, India, 19th cent.

2003, Nov. 29   **Engr.**   **Perf. 13¼x13**
2986   A1665   50c multi   1.50   .40
2987   A1665   90c multi   2.60   1.50
See India No. 2040.

Launch of the Queen Mary 2 — A1666

2003, Dec. 12   **Photo.**   **Perf. 13¼**
2988   A1666   50c multi   1.50   .30

Greetings — A1667

Holes punched through dots in "i's."
2004, Jan. 9   **Photo.**   **Perf. 13**
2989   A1667   50c shown   1.50   .30
2990   A1667   50c Un grand merci   1.50   .30
No Holes Punched Through Dots of "i's"
Stamp + Label
2991   A1667   50c Like No. 2989   6.00   6.00
2992   A1667   50c Like No. 2990   6.00   6.00

Nos. 2991-2992 were issued in sheets of 10 stamps + 10 labels that sold for €6.67 on day of issue. The labels could be personalized. See Nos. 3096-3097D, 3569A-3569B.

It's a Boy A1668

It's a Girl A1669

2004   **Litho.**   **Perf. 13**
Stamp + Label
2993   A1668   50c multi   6.00   6.00
2994   A1669   50c multi   6.00   6.00
Booklet Stamps
Self-Adhesive
Serpentine Die Cut 11
2995   A1668   50c multi   1.50   .35
  a.   Booklet pane of 10   15.00
2996   A1669   50c multi   1.50   .35
  a.   Booklet pane of 10   15.00

Nos. 2993-2994 were issued in sheets of 10 stamps + 10 labels that sold for €6.67 on day of issue. The labels could be personalized. Nos. 2995-2996 issued 1/9/04.

Hearts A1670

Designs: 50c, Chanel No. 5 perfume bottle. 75c, Woman, Eiffel Tower.

2004, Jan. 9   **Photo.**   **Perf. 13**
2997   A1670   50c multi   1.50   .35
  a.   Souvenir sheet of 5   7.50   7.50
  b.   Litho., stamp + label, perf. 13¼   6.00   6.00
2998   A1670   75c multi   2.25   .75
  a.   Litho., stamp + label, perf. 13¼   6.00   6.00

Nos. 2997b and 2998a were each printed in sheets of 10 stamps + 10 labels that could be personalized and sold for €6.69 and €10 respectively. On No. 2997b, there are large brown dots arranged in circles in the shading on the green rectangles, while on No. 2997 the brown dots are small and arranged in rows. On No. 2998a, the dots in the sky are larger and father apart than the tiny dots found on No. 2998.
Values are for stamps with surrounding selvage.
See Nos. 3133, 3135.

Tourism Issue

Lille, 2004 European Cultural Capital A1671

2004, Jan. 10   **Photo.**   **Perf. 13**
2999   A1671   50c multi   1.50   .35

Art Series

Statue of Liberty, Sculpted by Frederic Auguste Bartholdi (1834-1904) — A1672

2004, Feb. 21   **Engr.**   **Perf. 13¼x13**
3000   A1672   90c multi   2.60   1.50

Queen Eleanor of Aquitaine (c. 1122-1204) A1673

2004, Feb. 28   **Perf. 13x13¼**
3001   A1673   50c multi   1.50   .35

Stamp Day — A1674

Characters of Walt Disney: 45c, Donald Duck. 50c, Mickey Mouse. 75c, Minnie Mouse.

2004, Mar. 6   **Photo.**   **Perf. 13¼**
3002   A1674   50c multi   1.50   .35
  a.   Perf. 13¼x13 (from booklet pane)   1.50   .35
Booklet Stamps
Perf. 13¼x13
3003   A1674   45c multi   2.00   .30
3004   A1674   75c multi   2.25   .60
  a.   Booklet pane, 2 #3003, 4 each #3002a, 3004   19.50   —
     Complete booklet, #3004a   20.00

Civil Code, Bicent. A1675

2004, Mar. 12   **Engr.**   **Perf. 13¼x13**
3005   A1675   50c multi   1.50   .35

George Sand (1804-76), Writer A1676

2004, Mar. 20   **Engr.**   **Perf. 13¼x13**
3006   A1676   50c multi   1.50   .35

Aspects of Life in French Regions Type of 2003
No. 3007: a, Cutlery. b, Produce of Provence, vert. c, Beaujolais grapes, vert. d, Bread. e, Woman wearing coif, vert. f, Oysters, vert. g, Quiche Lorraine. h, Bullfighting. i, Clafoutis. j, Bagpipers.

2004, Mar. 26   **Photo.**   **Perf. 13**
3007   Sheet of 10   15.00   15.00
  a.-j.   A1642 50c Any single   1.50   1.00

No. 3007 has three vertical rows of rouletting, separating sheet into quarters.

Clermont-Ferrand — A1677

2004, Mar. 26   **Engr.**   **Perf. 13¼**
3008   A1677   50c multi   1.50   .35

Entente Cordiale, Cent. — A1678

Designs: 50c, Coccinelle, by Sonia Delaunay. 75c, Lace 1 (trial proof) 1968, by Sir Terry Frost.

2004, Apr. 6   **Photo.**   **Perf. 13¼**
3009   A1678   50c multi   1.50   .35
3010   A1678   75c multi   2.25   .75
See Great Britain Nos. 2200-2201.

Road Safety — A1679

2004, Apr. 7
3011   A1679   50c multi   1.50   .35
See United Nations Offices in Geneva No. 424.

Art Series

La Méridienne d'Après Millet, by Vincent van Gogh — A1680

2004, July 2   **Photo.**   **Perf. 13x13¼**
3012   A1680   75c multi   2.25   .95

Art Series

Un Combat de Coqs, by Jean-Léon Gérôme — A1681

Galatée aux Sphères, by Salvador Dalí A1682

2004   **Photo.**   **Perf. 13x13¼**
3013   A1681   €1.11 multi   3.25   1.40
3014   A1682   €1.11 multi   3.25   1.40
Issued: No. 3013, 4/17; No. 3014, 6/19.

Tourism Issue

Bordeaux — A1683

Vaux-sur-Mer — A1684

Notre Dame de l'Assomption Cathedral, Luçon — A1685

2004   **Litho. & Engr.**   **Perf. 13**
3015   A1683   50c multi   1.50   .35

Engr.
Perf. 13¼
3016   A1684   50c multi   1.50   .35
3017   A1685   50c multi   1.50   .35

Issued: No. 3015, 4/26; No. 3016, 7/17; No. 3017, 10/2.

Farm Animals A1686

2004, Apr. 26   **Photo.**   **Perf. 13¼**
3018   A1686   45c Rabbit   1.25   .30
3019   A1686   50c Cow, vert.   1.50   .35
3020   A1686   50c Chicken   1.50   .35
3021   A1686   75c Burro, vert.   2.25   .60
   a.   Souvenir sheet, #3018-3021   7.00   6.50

Expansion of the European Union A1687

2004, May 1   **Photo.**   **Perf. 13¼**
3022   A1687   50c multi   1.50   .40

Battle of Dien Bien Phu, 50th Anniv. — A1688

2004, May 7   **Perf. 13¼x13**
3023   A1688   50c multi   1.50   .40

Europa A1689

2004   **Photo.**   **Perf. 13x13¼**
3024   A1689   50c multi   1.50   .35

Litho.
Booklet Stamp
Self-Adhesive
Serpentine Die Cut 11
3025   A1689   50c multi   2.00   .35
   a.   Booklet pane of 10   15.00

Issued: No. 3024, 5/9; No. 3025, 6/4.

Blake and Mortimer, Comic Book Characters by Edgar P. Jacobs A1690

Blake and Mortimer and: 50c, Brick wall, vert. €1, Blue background.

2004, May 15   **Photo.**   **Perf. 13¼**
3026   A1690   50c multi   1.50   .35
3027   A1690   €1 multi   3.00   1.25

See Belgium No. 2020.

FIFA (Fédération Internationale de Football Association), Cent. — A1691

2004, May 20   **Perf. 13¼x13**
3028   A1691   50c multi   1.50   .35

Gardens and Parks Type of 2003

No. 3029: a, Jardin des Tuileries. b, Parc Floral de Paris.

2004, June 4   **Perf. 13¼x13**
3029   Sheet of 2   11.50   11.50
   a.-b.   A1660 €1.90 Either single   5.75   5.75
   c.   Souvenir sheet, #2979a-2979b, 3029a-3029b   25.00   25.00

Salon du Timbre 2004. No. 3029 has four vertical rows of rouletting, separating sheet into fifths, with the two stamps in the central fifth.

D-Day Invasion of France, 60th Anniv. — A1692

2004, June 5   **Perf. 13**
3030   A1692   50c multi   1.50   .35

Organ Donation A1693

2004, June 22   **Perf. 13¼**
3031   A1693   50c multi   1.50   .35

Pierre Dugua de Mons, Leader of First French Settlement in Acadia, and Ship A1694

Litho. & Engr.
2004, June 26   **Perf. 13**
3032   A1694   90c multi   2.75   1.50

See Canada No. 2044.

Napoleon I and the Imperial Guard — A1695

Designs: No. 3033, Light cavalry (Chasseur à cheval). No. 3034, Artilleryman and cannon (Artilleur à pied), horiz. No. 3035, Dragoon. No. 3036, Mameluke. No. 3037, Napoleon I. No. 3038, Grenadier (Grenadier à pied).

2004, June 26   **Photo.**
3033   A1695   50c multi   1.75   .75
3034   A1695   50c multi   1.75   .75
3035   A1695   50c multi   1.75   .75
3036   A1695   50c multi   1.75   .75
3037   A1695   50c multi   1.75   .75
3038   A1695   50c multi   1.75   .75
   a.   Souvenir sheet, #3033-3038   12.50   12.50
    Nos. 3033-3038 (6)   10.50   4.50

No. 3038a sold for €4.60, with the Red Cross receiving €1.60 of that.

French Federation of Philatelic Associations 77th Congress, Paris — A1696

Litho. & Engr.
2004, June 27   **Perf. 13¼x13**
3039   A1696   50c multi   1.50   .35

2004 Summer Olympics, Athens — A1697

2004, June 28   **Photo.**   **Perf. 13¼**
3040   50c Modern athletes   1.50   .60
3041   50c Ancient athletes   1.50   .60
   a.   A1697 Pair, #3040-3041   3.25   2.25

Printed in sheets containing five of each stamp.
A souvenir sheet containing No. 3041 was issued Aug. 2 and sold for €2.51. Value $20.

Happy Birthday A1698

2004, June 30   **Photo.**   **Perf. 13¼**
3042   A1698   50c multi   1.50   .35
   a.   Souvenir sheet of 5   7.50   7.50
   b.   Litho. stamp + label   6.00   6.00

No. 3042b printed in sheets of 10 stamps + 10 labels that could be personalized that sold for €8. No. 3042b has a dark green inscription at left with a distinct dot pattern. No. 3042 has a lighter green inscription.

Marianne Type of 1997 Inscribed "RF" at Lower Left and Type of 2002 With Euro Denominations

2004   **Litho.**   **Perf. 13**
3043   Sheet of 15 + 15 labels   50.00   50.00
   a.   A1583 1c orange yellow   .20   .20
   b.   A1583 2c brown   .20   .20
   c.   A1583 5c brt bl green   .20   .20
   d.   A1583 10c purple   .30   .30
   e.   A1583 20c orange   .60   .60
   f.   A1583 58c apple green   1.75   1.75
   g.   A1583 70c olive   2.10   2.10
   h.   A1583 75c sky blue   2.25   2.25
   i.   A1583 90c dark blue   2.75   2.75
   j.   A1583 €1 Prussian blue   3.00   3.00
   k.   A1583 €1.11 red lilac   3.25   3.25
   l.   A1583 €1.90 violet brown   5.75   5.75
   m.   A1583 €2 violet   6.00   6.00
   n.   A1409 (45c) green   1.40   1.40
   o.   A1409 (50c) red   1.50   1.50

Engr.
Serpentine Die Cut 6¾ Vert
Self-Adhesive
3043P   A1583   75c bright blue + label   8.75   8.75
3043Q   A1583   €1.11 red lilac + label   10.50   10.50

No. 3043 sold for €10.03. Stamps have a glossy varnish.
Labels on Nos. 3043P-3043Q could be personalized.

Marianne and Emblem of World Fund to Combat AIDS, Tuberculosis and Smoking — A1699

2004, July 1   **Engr.**   **Perf. 13**
3044   A1699   (50c) red   1.50   .35

Extreme Sports — A1700

No. 3045: a, Skateboarding. b, Parachuting. c, Sailboarding. d, Surfing. e, Luge. f, BMX bicycling. g, Paragliding. h, Jetskiing. i, Snowboarding. j, Rollerblading.

2004, July 3　Photo.　Perf. 13¼x13
3045	A1700	Sheet of 10	7.50	7.50
a.-e.		20c Any single	.60	.50
f.-j.		30c Any single	.90	.75

Orchid Type of 2002

Design: 39c, Orchis insularis.

2004, Sept. 1　Litho.　Perf. 13
3046	A1584	39c multi	1.20	.75

No. 3046 known only precanceled. See second note after No. 132.

Aspects of Life in the French Regions Type of 2003

No. 3047: a, House, Normandy. b, Chambord Chateau. c, Gorges, Tarn, vert. d, Notre Dame Cathedral, Paris, vert. e, Windmill, vert. f, Cave dwellings. g, Creek, Cassis, vert. h, Cap-Ferret Lighthouse, vert. i, Castle ruins. j, Alpine chalet.

2004, Sept. 18　Photo.　Perf. 13
3047		Sheet of 10	15.00	15.00
a.-j.	A1642	50c Any single	1.50	1.25

No. 3047 has three vertical rows of rouletting separating sheet into quarters.
Each stamp exists in booklet pane of 1 from booklet that sold for €19.

Halloween
A1701

2004, Oct. 9　Litho.　Perf. 13
3048	A1701	50c multi	1.50	.35

Félix Eboué (1884-1944), Colonial Governor — A1702

2004, Oct. 16　　　　Photo.
3049	A1702	50c multi	1.50	.40

Ouistreham Lighthouse
A1703

2004, Oct. 30　　　Perf. 13¼
3050	A1703	50c multi	1.50	.40

Marianne — A1704

Serpentine Die Cut 6¾ Vert.
2004, Nov. 10　　　　Engr.
Booklet Stamp
Self-Adhesive
3051	A1704	50c multi	3.50	3.00
a.		Booklet pane, 5 each #2835A, 3051	25.00	

European Capitals Type of 2002

No. 3052 — Attractions in Athens: a, Greek Academy. b, Parthenon. c, Odeon of Herodes Atticus. d, Church of the Holy Apostles, vert.

Perf. 13x13¼, 13¼x13
2004, Nov. 11　　　　Photo.
3052	A1622	Sheet of 4	7.50	7.50
a.-d.		50c Any single	1.50	.90

A1705

A1706

A1707

A1708

A1709

Holiday Greetings
A1710

2004, Nov. 12　Photo.　Perf. 13
3053	A1705	50c multi	1.50	.40

Litho.
3054	A1706	50c multi + label	6.00	6.00
3055	A1707	50c multi + label	6.00	6.00
3056	A1708	50c multi + label	6.00	6.00
3057	A1709	50c multi + label	6.00	6.00
3058	A1710	50c multi + label	6.00	6.00
a.		Vert. strip of 5, #3054-3059 + 5 labels	30.00	30.00
		Miniature sheet, 2 #3058a + 10 labels	60.00	60.00

Booklet Stamps
Self-Adhesive
Serpentine Die Cut 11¼x11
3059	A1706	50c multi	1.50	.40
3060	A1707	50c multi	1.50	.40
3061	A1708	50c multi	1.50	.40
3062	A1709	50c multi	1.50	.40
3063	A1710	50c multi	1.50	.40
a.		Booklet pane, 2 each #3059-3063	15.00	
		Nos. 3053-3063 (11)	39.00	32.40

Miniature sheet containing Nos. 3054-3058 sold for €6.69. Labels could be personalized. No. 3055 exists in a souvenir sheet of 1 stamp without label that sold for €3. Value $35.

Henri Wallon (1812-1904), Historian and Politician — A1711

2004, Nov. 13　Photo.　Perf. 13
3064	A1711	50c multi	1.50	.40

Opening of Millau Viaduct — A1712

2004, Dec. 14　Photo.　Perf. 13
3065	A1712	50c multi	1.50	.40

Marianne — A1713

Inscribed "ITVF" at Bottom

2005-07　　Engr.　Perf. 13
3066	A1713	1c yellow	.20	.20
a.		Inscribed "Phil@poste" at bottom	.20	.20
3067	A1713	5c brown black	.20	.20
a.		Inscribed "Phil@poste" at bottom	.20	.20
3068	A1713	10c violet	.25	.20
3069	A1713	(45c) green	1.25	.25
a.		Inscribed "Phil@poste" at bottom	1.25	.25
3070	A1713	(50c) red	1.50	.25
a.		Sheet of 15 + 15 labels	60.00	60.00
b.		Inscribed "Phil@poste" at bottom	1.40	.25
3071	A1713	55c dark blue	1.60	.50
3072	A1713	58c olive green	1.75	.40
3073	A1713	64c dark green	1.90	.40
3074	A1713	70c dark green	2.10	.50
3075	A1713	75c light blue	2.25	.40
3076	A1713	82c fawn	2.40	.45
3077	A1713	90c dark blue	2.75	.90
3078	A1713	€1 orange	3.00	1.00
a.		Inscribed "Phil@poste" at bottom	2.60	.55
3079	A1713	€1.11 red violet	3.25	.80
3080	A1713	€1.22 red violet	3.50	.75
3081	A1713	€1.90 chocolate	5.75	1.20
3082	A1713	€1.98 chocolate	6.00	2.00
		Nos. 3066-3082 (17)	39.65	10.40

Self-Adhesive (#3083-3085)
Serpentine Die Cut 6¾ Vert.
3083	A1713	(50c) red	1.50	.20
a.		Booklet pane of 10 (see footnote)	15.00	
b.		Booklet pane of 10 (see footnote)	15.00	
c.		Booklet pane of 20	30.00	
d.		As #3083, with "Phil@poste" inscription	1.50	.20
e.		Booklet pane, 10 #3083d	15.00	
f.		Booklet pane of 12 #3083d	17.00	
g.		No. 3083 with attached label	7.50	
3084	A1713	82c fawn + label	12.00	12.00
3085	A1713	€1.22 red violet	15.00	15.00

Coil Stamps
Perf. 13 Horiz.
3086	A1713	(45c) green	1.25	.30
a.		Inscribed "Phil@poste" at bottom	1.40	.25
3087	A1713	(50c) red	1.50	.25
3087A	A1713	55c dark blue	1.60	.60
b.		Inscribed "Phil@poste" at bottom	1.60	.25
		Nos. 3083-3087A (6)	32.85	28.35

Issued: Nos. 1c, 10c, (45c), (50c), 58c, 70c, 75c, 90c, €1, €1.11, €1.90, 1/8. 5c, No. 3071, 64c, 82c, €1.22, €1.98, 3/1. No. 3087A, 7/15. Nos. 3083d, 3083e, 10/1/06. Nos. 3066a, 3067a, 3069a, 3070b, 2006. No. 3083f, Jan. 2007. Nos. 3083g, 3084-3085, Apr. 2007. No. 3086a was issued in 2008 and sold for 50c. No. 3087b was issued in 2008 and sold for 55c.

Face values shown for Nos. 3069, 3070, 3083, 3086 and 3087 are those the stamps sold for on the day of issue. On day of issue, No. 3069a sold for 49c; No. 3070b sold for 54c.

No. 3070a sold for €10.03 and the labels could be personalized for an additional fee.

No. 3083a has a narrow strip of selvage separating the four stamps at left, from the six

stamps, at right, and is on a white backing paper. No. 3083b is comprised of two horizontal strips of five stamps on a yellow backing paper. No. 3083d sold for 54c on day of issue.

No. 3083g was printed in sheets containing 15 stamps + 15 small or large-sized labels that could be personalized. Nos. 3084 and 3085 were each printed in sheets of 30 stamps + 30 large-sized labels that could be personalized.

A sheet of 10 litho. stamps similar to No. 3068 + 10 labels exists, but was not sold.

See Nos. 3211, 3211N, 3212, 3247-3255E, 3302, 3383-3388A, 3389, 3531.

Rabbi Shlomo Yitshaqi (Rashi) (1040-1105) — A1714

2005, Jan. 16　Engr.　Perf. 13¼
3088	A1714	50c multi	1.75	.40

Hearts
A1715

Designs: 53c, Polka dots. 82c, Bird and flowers.

2005, Jan. 29　Photo.　Perf. 13¼
3089	A1715	53c multi	1.50	.40
a.		Souvenir sheet of 5	7.50	7.50
b.		Litho, stamp + label	5.00	5.00
3090	A1715	82c multi	2.50	1.00
a.		Litho, stamp + label	6.00	6.00

Values are for stamps with surrounding selvage.

Sheets of 10 of No. 3089b sold for €6.86, and sheets of 10 of No. 3090a sold for €8.78. Labels could be personalized for an additional fee.

See Nos. 3134, 3136.

New Year 2005 (Year of the Rooster)
A1716

Photo. & Embossed
2005, Jan. 29　　　Perf. 13½x13
3091	A1716	(50c) multi	1.75	.40

Printed in sheets of 10.

Rotary International, Cent. — A1717

2005, Feb. 19　Photo.　Perf. 13¼
3092	A1717	53c multi	1.50	.40

Titeuf — A1718

Nadia — A1719

Manu — A1720

2005, Feb. 28   Photo.   Perf. 13¼
3093 A1718 (50c) red & multi   1.50   .40
  a. Perf. 13¼x13 (booklet
     stamp)   1.50   .40

Booklet Stamps
3094 A1719 (45c) green & multi   1.40   .35
3095 A1720 (90c) blue & multi   2.75   .70
  a. Booklet pane, 2 #3094, 4
     each #3093a, 3095   20.00   —
     Complete booklet, #3095a   21.00

Characters from Titeuf, comic strip by Zep.
Stamp Day.

Greetings Type of 2004 Inscribed
"Lettre 20g"

Designs: Nos. 3096, 3097A, "Ceci est une
invitation." Nos. 3097, 3097B, "Un grand
merci."
No. 3097C, "Ceci est une invitation." No.
3097D, "Un grand merci."

2005-06   Photo.   Perf. 13
Holes Punched Through Dots of
"i's"
3096   A1667 (53c) brt lil rose &
       yel   1.50   .40
3097   A1667 (53c) brt yel grn &
       red lil   1.50   .40

Litho.
No Holes Punched Through Dots of
"i's"

Stamp + Label
3097A A1667 (53c) brt lil rose &
       yel   4.50   4.50
3097B A1667 (53c) brt yel grn &
       red lil   4.50   4.50

Self-Adhesive
No Holes Punched Through Dots of
"i's"

Serpentine Die Cut 11¼x11

Stamp + Label
3097C A1667 (53c) brt lil rose &
       yel   2.40   2.40
3097D A1667 (53c) brt yel grn &
       rrd lil   2.40   2.40

Nos. 3097A-3097B were issued in sheets of
10 stamps + 10 labels that sold for €8 on day
of issue. The labels could be personalized.
Nos. 3097C-3097D were each issued in
sheets of 10 stamps + 10 labels that sold for
€8.61. Labels could be personalized.
Issued: Nos. 2096-3097B, 3/1/05. Nos.
3097C-3097D, 2006.

Art Series

The Guitarist, by Jean-Baptiste Greuze
(1725-1805) — A1721

White Bear, Sculpture by François
Pompon — A1722

Sicile, by Nicolas de Stael — A1723

2005   Photo.   Perf. 13x13¼
3098 A1721   82c multi   2.50   1.00
3099 A1722   90c multi   3.00   1.50
3100 A1723 €1.22 multi   3.75   1.60

Issued: €1.22, 3/5. 90c, 7/2. 82c, 9/24.

Orchids — A1725

Designs: No. 3102, Cypripedium calceolus.
No. 3103, Paphiopedilum Mabel Sanders. 55c,
Oncidium papilio. 82c, Paphinia cristata, horiz.

2005, Mar. 11   Photo.   Perf. 13¼
3102 A1725   53c multi   1.60   .40
3103 A1725   53c multi   1.60   .40
3104 A1725   55c multi   1.60   .45
3105 A1725   82c multi   2.40   1.00
  a. Souvenir sheet, #3102-3105   7.50   7.50
  Nos. 3102-3105 (4)   7.20   2.25

Aspects of Life in French Regions
Type of 2003

No. 3106: a, Nautical jousting. b, Clocks of
Franche-Comte, vert. c, Cantal cheese and
bread, vert. d, Dancers and accordion player.
e, Bouillabaisse. f, P'tit Quinquin statue, vert.
g, Rillettes (chopped pork). h, Sauerkraut and
sausage, beer stein. i, Pelota, vert. j, Sugar
cane, vert.

2005, Mar. 19   Photo.   Perf. 13
3106   Sheet of 10   16.00   16.00
  a.-j. A1642 53c Any single   1.50   1.25

No. 3106 has three vertical rows of rouletting, separating sheet into quarters.
Each stamp exists in a booklet pane of 1
from a booklet that sold for €19. Value $50.

Tourism Issue

Aix-en-Provence — A1726

Gulf of Morbihan — A1727

Villefranche-sur-Mer — A1728

La Roque-Gageac — A1729

Illustration A1727 is reduced.

2005   Engr.   Perf. 13¼, 13 (#3108)
3107 A1726   53c multi   1.60   .40
Photo.
3108 A1727   53c multi   1.60   .40
3109 A1728   53c multi   1.60   .40
Engr.
3110 A1729   53c multi   1.60   .40

Issued: No. 3107, 4/1; No. 3108, 5/5; No.
3109, 6/4; No. 3110, 7/23.

Happy
Birthday
A1730

2005, Apr. 2   Photo.   Perf. 13
3111 A1730 (53c) multi   1.60   .40
  a. Souvenir sheet of 5   8.00   8.00
  b. Litho., stamp + label   6.00   6.00

Sheets of 10 and 10 labels of No. 3111b
sold for €6.86. Labels could be personalized
for an additional fee.

Albert Einstein (1879-1955),
Physicist — A1731

2005, Apr. 16   Perf. 13¼
3112 A1731   53c multi   1.60   .40

Alexis de
Tocqueville (1805-
59),
Writer — A1732

2005, Apr. 23   Engr.   Perf. 13x13¼
3113 A1732   90c multi   2.75   1.00

Liberation of Concentration Camp
Internees, 60th Anniv. — A1733

2005, Apr. 24   Photo.   Perf. 13¼
3114 A1733   53c multi   1.60   .40

Battle of
Austerlitz,
Bicent.
A1734

Litho. & Engr.
2005, May 4   Perf. 13¼
3115 A1734   55c multi   1.60   .45

See Czech Republic No. 3273.

French Federation of Philatelic
Associations, 78th Congress,
Nancy — A1735

2005, May 5   Engr.   Perf. 13
3116 A1735   53c multi + label   1.60   .40

A souvenir sheet of one stamp without label
exists. Value $12.

Europa — A1736

2005, May 8   Photo.   Perf. 13¼
3117 A1736   53c multi   1.60   .50

Gardens and Parks Type of 2003
Souvenir Sheet

No. 3118 — Sculptures in Jardin de la Fontaine, Nimes: a, Denomination in green. b,
Denomination in white.

2005, May 15   Perf. 13¼x13
3118   Sheet of 2   12.00   12.00
  a.-b. A1660 €1.98 Either single 6.00   6.00

Salon du Timbre 2005. No. 3118 has four
vertical rows of rouletting, separating sheet
into fifths, with the two stamps in the central
fifth.

Vacation
A1737

Serpentine Die Cut 11
2005, May 23   **Litho.**
Booklet Stamp
Self-Adhesive
3119 A1737 (53c) multi   1.75   .40
a.   Booklet pane of 10   17.50

Stories by Jules
Verne (1828-1905)
A1738

Designs: No. 3120, Five Weeks in a Balloon
(Cinq Semaines en Ballon). No. 3121, From
the Earth to the Moon (De la Terre à la Lune).
No. 3122, Journey to the Center of the Earth
(Voyage au Centre de la Terre), horiz. No.
3123, Michael Strogoff, horiz. No. 3124,
Around the World in Eighty Days (Le Tour du
Monde en Quatre-vingts Jours). No. 3125,
20,000 Leagues Under the Sea (Vingt Mille
Lieues Sous les Mers).

2005, May 28   **Photo.**   **Perf. 13**
3120 A1738 53c multi   1.60   .75
3121 A1738 53c multi   1.60   .75
3122 A1738 53c multi   1.60   .75
3123 A1738 53c multi   1.60   .75
3124 A1738 53c multi   1.60   .75
3125 A1738 53c multi   1.60   .75
a.   Souvenir sheet, #3120-
        3125   12.00 12.00
        Nos. 3120-3125 (6)   9.60   4.50

No. 3125a sold for €4.80 with the Red
Cross receiving €1.62 of that.

Miniature Sheet

Gordon Bennett Cup, Cent. — A1739

No. 3126 — Inscriptions: a, La Coupe
Gordon Bennett (Car No. 1 facing right). b, La
Coupe Gordon Bennett (Car No. 1 facing left).
c, La Formule 1, vert. d, Le Rallye-Raid, vert.
e, Les Rallyes. f, La Course d'endurance.

2005, June 2   **Photo.**   **Perf.**
3126 A1739 Sheet of 10,
              #a-b, 2 each
              #c-f   19.00 19.00
a.-f.   53c Any single   1.75   .85

A souvenir sheet containing No. 3126a sold
for €3. Value $100.

Environmental Charter — A1740

2005, June 5   **Litho.**   **Perf. 13**
3127 A1740 53c multi, lt green   1.60   .40

Enactment of
Handicapped
Persons Rights
Law — A1741

2005, June 18   **Photo.**   **Perf. 13¼**
3128 A1741 53c multi   1.60   .35

It's a Boy
A1742

It's a Girl
A1743

2005   **Litho.**   **Perf. 13x13¼**
3129 A1742 (53c) multi + label   4.00   4.00
3130 A1743 (53c) multi + label   4.00   4.00

Booklet Stamps
Self-Adhesive
Serpentine Die Cut 11¼x11
3131 A1742 (53c) multi   1.60   .35
a.   Booklet pane of 10   16.00
b.   Sheet of 10 + 10 labels   23.00
3132 A1743 (53c) multi   1.60   .35
a.   Booklet pane of 10   16.00
b.   Sheet of 10 + 10 labels   23.00

Sheets of 10 stamps and 10 labels of Nos.
3129 and 3130 each sold for €6.86. Nos.
3131b and 3132b each sold for €8.61. Labels
could be personalized for an additional fee.

Hearts Types of 2004-05
Serpentine Die Cut
2005, July 15   **Photo.**
Self-Adhesive
3133 A1670 50c Like #2997   5.00   3.50
3134 A1715 53c Like #3089   6.00   4.50
3135 A1670 75c Like #2998   6.00   4.50
3136 A1715 82c Like #3090   7.00   5.50
        Nos. 3133-3136 (4)   24.00 18.00

Haras du
Pin Natl.
Stud Farm
A1744

2005, July 16   **Perf. 13**
3137 A1744 53c multi   1.60   .40

European Capitals Type of 2002
No. 3138 — Attractions in Berlin: a, Bran-
denburg Gate. b, Kaiser Wilhelm Memorial
Church, vert. c, Philharmonic Hall. d,
Reichstag.

Perf. 13x13¼, 13¼x13
2005, Aug. 27   **Photo.**
3138 A1622 Sheet of 4   6.50   6.50
a.-d.   53c Any single   1.60   1.00

Aspects of Life in the French
Regions Type of 2003
No. 3139 — a, Lake Annecy. b, Etretat Cliffs,
vert. c, Pigeon house, vert. d, Wash house
(lavoir). e, Banks of the Seine. f, Carnac
megaliths. g, House, Sologne. h, Pilat Sand
Dune. i, Stiff Lighthouse, vert. j, Stone hut
(borie), vert.

2005, Sept. 17   **Perf. 13**
3139   Sheet of 10   16.00 16.00
a.-j.   A1642 53c Any single   1.60   1.25

No. 3139 has three vertical rows of rouletting, separating sheet into quarters.
Nos. 3139a-3139j were also issued in large
booklets containing panes of 1 of each stamp.
The booklet sold for €19. Value $60.

Art Series

Les Halles Centrales, Designed by
Victor Baltard (1805-74) — A1745

2005, Sept. 17   **Engr.**   **Perf. 13x13¼**
3140 A1745 €1.22 multi   3.75 1.25

Breast Cancer
Awareness
A1746

2005, Oct. 1   **Photo.**   **Perf. 13¼**
3141 A1746 53c multi   1.60   .35

A1747

A1748

A1749

A1750

A1751

A1752

A1753

A1754

A1755

Cat, Comics
by Philippe
Geluck
A1756

Serpentine Die Cut 11¼x11
2005, Oct. 1   **Litho.**
Booklet Stamps
Self-Adhesive
3142 A1747 (53c) multi   1.60   .35
3143 A1748 (53c) multi   1.60   .35
3144 A1749 (53c) multi   1.60   .35
3145 A1750 (53c) multi   1.60   .35
3146 A1751 (53c) multi   1.60   .35
3147 A1752 (53c) multi   1.60   .35
3148 A1753 (53c) multi   1.60   .35
3149 A1754 (53c) multi   1.60   .35
3150 A1755 (53c) multi   1.60   .35
3151 A1756 (53c) multi   1.60   .35
a.   Booklet pane of 10, #3142-
        3151   16.00

Raymond Aron
(1905-83),
Philosopher
A1757

2005, Oct. 7   **Engr.**   **Perf. 13¼x13**
3152 A1757 53c multi   1.60   .35

Souvenir Sheet

The Annunciation, by
Raphael — A1758

No. 3153: a, Drawing of Angel, painting of
Virgin Mary. b, Painting of Angel, drawing of
Virgin Mary.

Litho. & Engr.
2005, Nov. 10   **Perf. 13x13¼**
3153 A1758 Sheet of 2   4.00   4.00
a.   53c multi   1.60   1.60
b.   55c multi   1.60   1.60

See Vatican City Nos. 1312-1314.

Marianne — A1759

Serpentine Die Cut 6¾ Vert.
2005, Nov. 11   **Engr.**
Booklet Stamp
Self-Adhesive
3154 A1759 53c red   3.50   3.00
a.   Booklet pane, 5 each #3083,
        3154   25.00

Video Game Characters — A1760

No. 3155: a, Link. b, Pac-Man. c, Prince of Persia. d, Spyro. e, Donkey Kong. f, Mario. g, Adibou. h, Rayman. i, Lara Croft. j, The Sims.

2005, Nov. 11   Photo.   Perf. 13¼x13
3155	A1760	Sheet of 10		9.00	9.00
a.-e.		20c Any single		.60	.50
f.-j.		33c Any single		1.00	.75

Avicenna (980-1037),
Scientist — A1761

2005, Nov. 12   Engr.   Perf. 13x13¼
3156	A1761	53c multi	1.60	.35

Holiday Greetings
A1762

Designs: Nos. 3157, 3162, Bear, three penguins and sled. Nos. 3158, 3163, Two penguins, reindeer and sled. Nos. 3159, 3164, Two penguins, bear and sled. Nos. 3160, 3165, Three penguins. Nos. 3161, 3166, Two penguins, reindeer and snowman.

2005, Nov. 12   Litho.   Perf. 13
3157	A1762	(53c) multi + label	6.00	4.00
3158	A1762	(53c) multi + label	6.00	4.00
3159	A1762	(53c) multi + label	6.00	4.00
3160	A1762	(53c) multi + label	6.00	4.00
3161	A1762	(53c) multi + label	6.00	4.00
a.		Vert. strip of 5, #3157-3161, + 5 labels	30.00	30.00
		Miniature sheet, 2 #3161a	60.00	60.00

Booklet Stamps
Self-Adhesive
Serpentine Die Cut 11¼x11
3162	A1762	(53c) multi	1.60	.35
3163	A1762	(53c) multi	1.60	.35
3164	A1762	(53c) multi	1.60	.35
3165	A1762	(53c) multi	1.60	.35
3166	A1762	(53c) multi	1.60	.35
a.		Booklet pane, 2 each #3162-3166	16.00	
		Nos. 3157-3166 (10)	38.00	21.75

Miniature sheet containing Nos. 3157-3161 sold for €6.86. Labels could be personalized.
No. 3161 exists in a souvenir sheet of one stamp without label, that sold for €3. Value $35.

Jacob Kaplan (1895-1994), Grand Rabbi of France — A1763

2005, Nov. 14   Engr.   Perf. 13
3167	A1763	53c multi	1.60	.35

Orchid Type of 2002

Design: Orchis insularis.

2005   Litho.   Perf. 13
3168	A1584	42c multi	1.40	.75

No. 3168 is known only precanceled. See second note after #132.

Law Separating Church and State, Cent. — A1764

2005, Dec. 3   Photo.   Perf. 13¼x13
3169	A1764	53c multi	1.60	.35

Hearts
A1765

Designs: (53c), Hearts, octagons and diamonds. (82c), Heart and stripes.

2006, Jan. 7   Photo.   Perf. 13¼
3170	A1765	(53c) multi	1.60	.40
a.		Souvenir sheet of 5	8.00	8.00
b.		Litho., stamp + label	4.00	4.00
3171	A1765	(82c) multi	2.40	.70
a.		Litho., stamp + label	4.00	4.00

Self-Adhesive
Serpentine Die Cut
3172	A1765	(53c) Like #3170	3.00	1.50
a.		Sheet of 10 + 10 labels	23.00	
3173	A1765	(82c) Like #3171	4.00	3.00
a.		Sheet of 10 + 10 labels	30.00	

Values are for stamps with surrounding selvage. Sheets of 10 of No. 3170b sold for €6.86, and sheets of No. 3172a. No. 3172a sold for €8.61; No. 3173a for €11.54. Labels could be personalized for an additional fee.

New Year 2006 (Year of the Dog) — A1766

2006, Jan. 21   Photo.   Perf. 13¼x13
3174	A1766	(53c) multi	1.60	.40

A souvenir sheet containing No. 3174 sold for €3. Value $14.

Impressionist Paintings — A1767

Designs: Nos. 3175a, 3176, Portraits from the Country, by Gustave Caillebotte. Nos. 3175b, 3183, Dancers, by Edgar Degas. Nos. 3175c, 3181, Marguerite Gachet in the Garden, by Vincent van Gogh. Nos. 3175d, 3179, Two Young Girls at the Piano, by Auguste Renoir. Nos. 3175e, 3177, The Butterfly Hunt, by Berthe Morisot. Nos. 3175f, 3184, Luncheon on the Grass, by Edouard Manet. Nos. 3175g, 3182, Evening Air, by Henri-Edmond Cross. Nos. 3175h, 3180, The Shepherdess (Young Peasant Girl with a Stick), by Camille Pissarro. Nos. 3175i, 3178, Mother and Child, by Mary Cassatt. Nos. 3175j, 3185, Women of Tahiti on the Beach, by Paul Gauguin.

2006   Litho.   Perf. 13¼
3175		Sheet of 10 +10 labels	35.00	35.00
a.-j.		A1767 (53c) Any single + label	3.50	3.50

Booklet Stamps
Self-Adhesive
Serpentine Die Cut 11¼x11
3176	A1767	(53c) multi	1.60	.40
3177	A1767	(53c) multi	1.60	.40
3178	A1767	(53c) multi	1.60	.40
3179	A1767	(53c) multi	1.60	.40
3180	A1767	(53c) multi	1.60	.40
3181	A1767	(53c) multi	1.60	.40
3182	A1767	(53c) multi	1.60	.40
3183	A1767	(53c) multi	1.60	.40
3184	A1767	(53c) multi	1.60	.40
3185	A1767	(53c) multi	1.60	.40
a.		Booklet pane of 10, #3176-3185	16.00	
b.		Sheet of 10 #3176-3185, + 10 labels	65.00	

Issued: No. 3175, 6/1; Nos. 3176-3185, 1/21. No. 3175 sold for €6.86. No. 3185b sold for €8.61. Labels could be personalized.

2006 Winter Olympics, Turin — A1768

2006, Feb. 4   Photo.   Perf. 13
3186	A1768	53c multi	1.60	.35

Spirou — A1769

Fantasio, Spip and Spirou — A1770

Fantasio A1771

2006, Feb. 25   Perf. 13¼
3187	A1769	(53c) multi	1.60	.40
a.		Perf. 13¼x13 (booklet stamp)	1.60	.40

Booklet Stamps
Perf. 13¼x13
3188	A1770	(48c) multi	1.40	.35
3189	A1771	(90c) multi	2.75	.65
a.		Booklet pane, 4 each #3187a, 3188, 2 #3189	17.50	—
		Complete booklet, #3189a	18.00	

Characters from Spirou, by Robert Velter. Stamp Day.

Courrières Coal Mine Disaster, Cent. — A1772

2006, Feb. 25   Perf. 13¼
3190	A1772	53c multi	1.60	.40

Douaumont Ossuary — A1773

2006, Mar. 4   Engr.
3191	A1773	53c multi	1.60	.40

Aspects of Life in the French Regions Type of 2003

No. 3192: a, Yellow plums (mirabelle). b, Salt marsh (marais salants). c, Butter (beurre). d, Roquefort cheese, vert. e, Olive oil, vert. f, Carnival, vert. g, Grape harvests (vendanges), vert. h, Waiter at café, vert. i, Transhumance of livestock. j, Marshland gardens (hortillonages).

2006, Mar. 25   Photo.   Perf. 13
3192		Sheet of 10	16.00	16.00
a.-j.		A1642 53c Any single	1.60	1.25

No. 3192 has three vertical rows of rouletting, separating sheet into quarters.
Nos. 3192a-3192j were also issued in large booklets containing panes of 1 of each stamp. The booklet sold for €19. Value $42.50.

Tourism Issue

Yvoire A1774

Dijon A1775

Antibes Juan-les-Pins — A1776

Thionville A1777

2006   Photo.   Perf. 13
3193	A1774	53c multi	1.60	.40

Engr.
Perf. 13¼
3194	A1775	53c multi	1.60	.40

Litho. & Engr.
Perf. 13x13¼
3195	A1776	53c multi	1.60	.40

Engraved
3196	A1777	54c multi	1.60	.40
	Nos. 3193-3196 (4)		6.40	1.60

Issued: No. 3193, 3/25; No. 3194, 4/7. No. 3195, 7/15. No. 3196, 9/16.

Art Series

Prehistoric Drawings in Rouffignac Cave — A1778

Bathers, by Paul Cézanne — A1779

Untitled Painting by Claude Viallat A1780

Beggars Receiving Alms at the Door of a House, by Rembrandt A1781

Engr., Photo (#3198, 3199)
2006			Perf. 13x13¼	
3197	A1778	55c multi	1.60	.75
3198	A1779	82c multi	2.40	.75

Perf. 13¼x13
3199	A1780	€1.22 brt pink & bl grn	3.50	1.00
3200	A1781	€1.30 multi	3.75	1.00
	Nos. 3197-3200 (4)		11.25	3.50

Issued: 82c, 4/8; 55c, 5/27; No. 3199, 6/3. No. 3200, 11/10.

Gardens and Parks Type of 2003
Souvenir Sheet

No. 3201 — a, Vallée-aux-Loups Park. b, Albert Kahn Gardens.

2006, Apr. 22		Photo.	Perf. 13¼x13	
3201		Sheet of 2	16.50	16.50
a.-b.	A1660	€1.98 Either single	6.50	6.50 •
c.		Souvenir sheet #3118a, 3118b, 3201a, 3201b	34.00	34.00

Salon du Timbre 2006. No. 3201 has four vertical rows of rouletting, separating sheet

---

into fifths, with the two stamps in the central fifth. No. 3201c issued 6/16.

Young Animals A1782

Designs: No. 3202, Puppy. No. 3203, Kitten. 55c, Foal, horiz. 82c, Lamb, horiz..

2006, Apr. 22			Perf. 13¼	
3202	A1782	53c multi	1.60	.40
3203	A1782	53c multi	1.60	.40
3204	A1782	55c multi	1.60	.40
3205	A1782	82c multi	2.40	.65
a.		Souvenir sheet, #3202-3205	7.50	7.50
	Nos. 3202-3205 (4)		7.20	1.85

Europa A1783

2006, Apr. 30				
3206	A1783	53c multi	1.60	.40

Pierre Bayle (1647-1706), Philiosopher A1784

2006, May 2		Engr.	Perf. 13x13¼	
3207	A1784	53c blk & brn	1.60	.40

Remembrance of Slavery Day, 5th Anniv. — A1785

2006, May 10		Photo.	Perf. 13¼	
3208	A1785	53c multi	1.60	.40

Vacation A1786

Serpentine Die Cut 11¼x11
2006, May 27			Litho.	

Booklet Stamp
Self-Adhesive
3209	A1786	(53c) multi	1.60	.40
a.		Booklet pane of 10	16.00	

Miniature Sheet

2006 World Cup Soccer Championships, Germany — A1787

No. 3210: a, Replacement players (39x25mm). b, Fans (39x25mm). c, Player with ball near chest (32mm diameter). d, Player kicking ball (32mm diameter). e, Goalie throwing ball (32mm diameter). f, Player making scissor kick (32mm diameter). g, Two players (32mm diameter). h, Referee (25x39mm). i, Coach (39x25mm). j, Cameramen (39x25mm).

2006, May 27		Photo.	Perf. 12¾	
3210	A1787	Sheet of 10	16.00	16.00
a.-j.		53c Any single	1.60	1.25

Marianne Type of 2005
2006		Litho.	Perf. 13	
3211		Sheet of 15, #a-k, 2 each #l-m, + 15 labels	50.00	50.00
a.	A1713	1c yellow orange	.20	.20
b.	A1713	5c dark brown	.20	.20
c.	A1713	10c violet	.40	.40
d.	A1713	55c blue	2.00	2.00
e.	A1713	64c olive green	2.25	2.25
f.	A1713	75c light blue	2.50	2.50
g.	A1713	82c fawn	3.00	3.00
h.	A1713	90c dark blue	3.25	3.25
i.	A1713	€1 dull orange	3.50	3.50
j.	A1713	€1.22 red violet	4.25	4.25
k.	A1713	€1.98 brown	6.75	6.75
l.	A1713	(48c) green	1.75	1.75
m.	A1713	(53c) red	1.90	1.90

Serpentine Die Cut 11¼
Self-Adhesive
3211N		Sheet of 15, #3211No-3211Ny, 2 each #3211Nz, 3211Naa, + 15 labels	100.00	
o.	A1713	1c yellow orange	.30	.30
p.	A1713	5c dark brown	.30	.30
q.	A1713	10c violet	.50	.50
r.	A1713	55c blue	2.75	2.75
s.	A1713	64c olive green	3.00	3.00
t.	A1713	75c light blue	3.50	3.50
u.	A1713	82c fawn	3.75	3.75
v.	A1713	90c dark blue	4.50	4.50
w.	A1713	€1 dull orange	4.75	4.75
x.	A1713	€1.22 red violet	6.00	6.00
y.	A1713	€1.98 brown	8.00	8.00
z.	A1713	(48c) green	2.25	2.25
aa.	A1713	(53c) red	2.50	2.50

Etched on Foil
Die Cut Perf. 13
3212	A1713	€5 silver	18.50	18.50

Nos. 3211a-3211m, 3211No-3211Naa and 3212 have "Phil@poste" inscription at bottom. Nos. 3211 and 3211N have stamps with a glossy varnish. No. 3211 sold for €12.04 and labels could be personalized. No. 3211N sold for €15.05 and labels could be personalized. No. 3212 was sold in a protective package.

Costumes From Operas by Wolfgang Amadeus Mozart — A1788

Designs: No. 3213, The Magic Flute. No. 3214, Don Giovanni. No. 3215, The Marriage of Figaro. No. 3216, The Clemency of Titus. No. 3217, The Abduction from the Seraglio (L'enlèvement au Sérail). No. 3218, Cosi Fan Tutte.

2006, June 17		Photo.	Perf. 13	
3213	A1788	53c multi	1.60	.75
3214	A1788	53c multi	1.60	.75
3215	A1788	53c multi	1.60	.75
3216	A1788	53c multi	1.60	.75
3217	A1788	53c multi	1.60	.75
3218	A1788	53c multi	1.60	.75
a.		Souvenir sheet, #3213-3218	12.00	12.00
	Nos. 3213-3218 (6)		9.60	4.50

Nos. 3213-3218 were each printed in souvenir sheets containing one stamp that sold as a

---

set for €15, and in booklet panes containing one stamp in a large book that sold for €19. Value: set of 6 sheets $40; set of 6 panes in book $50. No. 3218a sold for €4.80, with the Red Cross receiving €1.62 of that.

UNESCO World Heritage Sites A1789

Designs: 53c, Provins. 90c, Mont Saint-Michel.

2006, June 17		Photo.	Perf. 13¼	
3219	A1789	53c multi	1.60	.40
3220	A1789	90c multi	2.60	.70

See United Nations Offices in Geneva Nos. 459-461.

Garnier Opera House, Paris — A1790

2006, June 18		Engr.	Perf. 13x13¼	
3221	A1790	53c multi + label	1.60	.40

French Federation of Philatelic Associations 79th Congress, Paris. No. 3221 exists in a souvenir sheet of 1 (without label), issued in 2007 that sold for €3.

Happy Birthday A1791

2006, June 19		Photo.	Perf. 13	
3222	A1791	(53c) multi	1.60	.40
a.		Souvenir sheet of 5	8.00	8.00
b.		Litho. stamp + label	4.00	4.00

Serpentine Die Cut 11
Self-Adhesive
3222C	A1791	(53c) multi + label	2.40	2.40

Sheets of 10 of No. 3222b sold for €6.86. No. 3222C was printed in sheets of 10 stamps + 10 labels that sold for €8.61. Labels could be personalized for an additional fee.

European Capitals Type of 2002
Souvenir Sheet

No. 3223 — Attractions in Nicosia, Cyprus: a, Chrysaliniotissa Church. b, Archaeological Museum. c, Famagusta Gate. d, Archbishop's residence (Archeveché).

2006, June 20		Photo.	Perf. 13x13¼	
3223	A1622	Sheet of 4	7.00	7.00
a.-d.		53c Any single	1.60	1.60

Tango Dancing A1792

2006, June 21		Photo.	Perf. 12¼	
3224	A1792	53c Dancers	1.60	.40
3225	A1792	90c Musician	2.60	.70

See Argentina Nos. 2395-2396.

La Poste's Business Foundation, 10th Anniv. — A1793

2006, June 22 **Litho.** **Perf. 13**
3226 A1793 (53c) multi, *tan* 1.60 .40

French Open Golf Championship, Cent. — A1794

Photo. & Embossed
2006, June 24 **Perf. 13**
3227 A1794 53c multi 1.60 .40
A souvenir sheet containing No. 3227 sold for €3. Value $12.

Rotary International Type of 2005
Serpentine Die Cut 11
2006, July 1 **Photo.**
Self-Adhesive
3227A A1717 53c multi 1.60 .40

French Soccer Team's Second-Place Showing in 2006 World Cup — A1795

2006, July 5 **Photo.** **Perf. 13¼**
Size: 35x26mm
3228 A1795 53c multi 1.60 .40
Litho.
Size: 35x22mm
Perf. 13
3229 A1795 53c multi + label 5.00 4.00
Serpentine Die Cut 11¼x11
Self-Adhesive
3229A A1795 53c multi + label 10.00 5.00
No. 3229 was printed in sheets of 10 stamps and 10 labels that sold for €6.94. Value $55. No. 3229A was printed in sheets of 10 stamps + 10 labels that sold for €8.61. Value $140. Labels could be personalized.

Quai Branly Museum — A1796

2006, July 8 **Photo.** **Perf. 13x13¼**
3230 A1796 53c multi 1.60 .40

Reinstatement of Capt. Alfred Dreyfus, Cent. — A1797

2006, July 12 **Engr.**
3231 A1797 53c multi 1.60 .40

Claude-Joseph Rouget de Lisle (1760-1836), Composer of "La Marseillaise" — A1798

2006, July 13 **Photo.** **Perf. 13¼**
3232 A1798 53c multi 1.60 .40

Pablo Casals (1876-1973), Cellist — A1799

2006, July 29
3233 A1799 53c multi 1.60 .40

Aspects of Life in French Regions Type of 2003
No. 3234: a, Catalan Towers. b, La Croisette, Cannes. c, Brocéliande Forest. d, Volcanic craters, Auvergne, vert. e, Les Invalides, Paris, vert. f, Chateau de Chaumont, Chaumont-sur-Loire. g, Ardèche Gorges, vert. h, Flour mill, Valmy, vert. i, Grotto of Messabielle, Lourdes. j, Calanches de Piana, Corsica.

2006, Sept. 2 **Photo.** **Perf. 13**
3234 Sheet of 10 16.00 16.00
  a.-j. A1642 54c Any single 1.60 1.25
No. 3234 has three vertical rows of rouletting, separating sheet into quarters.
Nos. 3234a-3234j were also issued in large booklets containing panes of 1 of each stamp. The booklet sold for €19. Value $42.50.

A1800

A1801

A1802

A1803

A1804

A1805

A1806

A1807

A1808

Cubitus, Comics by Michel Rodrigue and Pierre Aucaigne A1809

Serpentine Die Cut 11¼x11
2006, Sept. 20 **Litho.**
Self-Adhesive
Booklet Stamps
3235 A1800 (54c) multi 1.60 .40
3236 A1801 (54c) multi 1.60 .40
3237 A1802 (54c) multi 1.60 .40
3238 A1803 (54c) multi 1.60 .40
3239 A1804 (54c) multi 1.60 .40
3240 A1805 (54c) multi 1.60 .40
3241 A1806 (54c) multi 1.60 .40
3242 A1807 (54c) multi 1.60 .40
3243 A1808 (54c) multi 1.60 .40
3244 A1809 (54c) multi 1.60 .40
  a. Booklet pane of 10, #3235-3244 16.00

Sculptures by Constantin Brancusi (1876-1957) — A1810

Designs: 54c, Sleeping Muse. 85c, Sleep.

2006, Sept. 25 **Photo.** **Perf. 13¼**
3245 A1810 54c multi 1.60 .40
3246 A1810 85c multi 2.50 .75
See Romania Nos. 4878-4879.

Marianne Type of 2005
2006 **Engr.** **Perf. 13**
Inscribed "Phil@poste" at Bottom
3247 A1713 10c gray .50 .20
3248 A1713 60c dark blue 2.50 .40
3249 A1713 70c yel green 2.75 .40
3250 A1713 85c purple 4.00 .60
3251 A1713 86c fawn 4.00 .60
3252 A1713 €1.15 blue 5.00 1.00
3253 A1713 €1.30 red violet 5.50 1.00
3254 A1713 €2.11 chocolate 9.00 1.50
  Nos. 3247-3254 (8) 33.25 5.70

Coil Stamp
Perf. 13 Horiz.
3255 A1713 60c dark blue 2.00 .50
Serpentine Die Cut 11¼
Self-Adhesive
3255A A1713 (54c) red + label 2.40 2.40
3255C A1713 60c dark blue + label 2.50 2.50
3255D A1713 82c fawn + label 13.50 13.50
3255E A1713 86c fawn + label 3.00 3.00
  Nos. 3255A-3255E (4) 21.40 21.40
Issued: Nos. 3247-3255, 10/1, others, 2006. A number has been reserved for an additional stamp. Nos. 3255A, 3255C and 3255E were printed in sheets of 15 stamps + 15 labels that could be personalized. No. 3255D was printed in sheets containing 10 stamps + 10 large labels or 15 stamps and 15 small labels. Labels could be personalized. Sheets of No. 3255A sold for €13.29; No. 3255C, €14.04; No. 3255E, €17.31. For Nos. 3255A, 3255C,

3255D and 3255E, adjacent labels came in large and small sizes.

Aviation Without Borders — A1811

2006, Oct. 7 **Photo.** **Perf. 13**
3256 A1811 54c multi 1.60 .40

Henri Moissan (1852-1907), 1906 Nobel Chemistry Laureate — A1812

2006, Oct. 14 **Engr.** **Perf. 13¼x13**
3257 A1812 54c multi 1.60 .40

"Shared Memories," Intl. Conference on Veterans, Paris — A1813

2006, Oct. 26 **Photo.** **Perf. 13¼**
3258 A1813 54c multi 1.60 .40

Marianne — A1814

Serpentine Die Cut 6¾ Vert.
2006, Nov. 8 **Engr.**
Self-Adhesive
Booklet Stamp
3259 A1814 54c red 3.00 2.50
  a. Booklet pane, 5 each #3083d, 3259 22.50

Miniature Sheet

Flying Machines — A1815

No. 3260: a, Gustave Ponton d'Amécourt's helicopter. b, Alberto Santos-Dumont's monoplane, "Demoiselle," horiz. c, Jean Marie Le Bris's bird-shaped glider, horiz. d, Clément Ader's "Avion III," horiz. e, Henri Fabré's seaplane, horiz. f, Jean-Pierre Blanchard's balloon.

Litho. & Engr.
2006, Nov. 9 **Perf. 13**
3260 A1815 Sheet of 6 10.00 10.00
  a.-f. 54c Any single 1.60 1.25

Inauguration of Aulnay-sous-Bois to
Bondy Tram-Train Line — A1816

2006, Nov. 18   Photo.   Perf. 13x13¼
3261   A1816   54c multi   1.60   .50

Holiday
Greetings
A1817

Designs: No. 3262, Reindeer, sleigh, four
penguins. No. 3263, Reindeer with fishing
pole, three penguins. No. 3264, Reindeer,
Christmas tree, two penguins. No. 3265, Reindeer skating, three penguins. No. 3266, Reindeer with gift boxes, three penguins.

2006, Nov. 25   Litho.   Perf. 13¼
3261A	A1817	(54c) multi + la-bel	1.90	1.90
3261B	A1817	(54c) multi + la-bel	1.90	1.90
3261C	A1817	(54c) multi + la-bel	1.90	1.90
3261D	A1817	(54c) multi + la-bel	1.90	1.90
3261E	A1817	(54c) multi + la-bel	1.90	1.90
f.		Vert. strip of 5, #3261A-3261E, + 5 labels	12.00	12.00
		Miniature sheet, 2 #3261Ef	30.00	30.00

Self-Adhesive
Booklet Stamps
Serpentine Die Cut 11¼x11
3262	A1817	(54c) multi	1.60	.50
3263	A1817	(54c) multi	1.60	.50
3264	A1817	(54c) multi	1.60	.50
3265	A1817	(54c) multi	1.60	.50
3266	A1817	(54c) multi	1.60	.50
a.		Booklet pane, 2 each #3262-3266	16.00	
		Nos. 3262-3266 (5)	8.00	2.50

Miniature sheet containing Nos. 3261A-
3261E sold for €6.94. Value $60. Labels could
be personalized. Value $60.
A souvenir sheet containing a perf. 13
example of No. 3266 sold for €3. Value
$17.50. A sheet containing 5 No. 3261A + 5
labels exists, but was not sold.

Grand
Masonic
Lodge of
France
A1818

2006, Dec. 1   Photo.   Perf. 13x13¼
3267   A1818   54c multi   1.60   .50

Alain
Poher
(1909-96),
Politician,
and
Senate
Building
A1819

2006, Dec. 2   Engr.   Perf. 13¼
3268   A1819   54c multi   1.60   .50

Opening
of New
Paris
Tramway
A1820

2006, Dec. 16   Photo.   Perf. 13¼
3269   A1820   54c multi   1.75   .75

Orchids Type of 2002

Designs: 31c, Platanthera chlorantha. 36c,
Dactylorhiza savogiensis. 43c, Orchis
insularis.

2007, Jan. 2   Litho.   Perf. 13
3270	A1584	31c multi	.80	.20
3271	A1584	36c multi	.95	.20
3272	A1584	43c multi	1.10	.20
		Nos. 3270-3272 (3)	2.85	.60

Nos. 3270-3272 are known only precanceled. See second note after #132.

Hearts
A1821

"Givenchy" in: (54c), Black and white. (86c),
Red.

2007, Jan. 6   Photo.   Perf. 13¼
Inscribed "Lettre 20 g"
3273	A1821	(54c) red & black	1.60	.45
a.		Souvenir sheet of 5	8.00	8.00

Inscribed "Lettre 50 g"
3274   A1821   (86c) black & red   2.50   .75
Values are for stamps with surrounding
selvage.

Serpentine Die Cut
Self-Adhesive
3275   A1821   (54c) Like #3273   1.60   .45
Inscribed "Lettre 50 g"
3276   A1821   (86c) Like #3274   2.25   .75

New Year 2007
(Year of the
Pig) — A1822

2007, Jan. 27   Photo.   Perf. 13¼x13
3277	A1822	(54c) multi	1.60	.45
a.		Litho., stamp + label	2.75	2.50

Serpentine Die Cut 11
Self-Adhesive
3277B   A1822   (54c) multi + label   12.00   12.00

No. 3277 has a somewhat blurrier image
than No. 3277a. Sheets of 5 #3277a + 5 labels
sold for €3.51. Value $15. Labels could be
personalized. No. 3277 exists in a souvenir
sheet of 1 that sold for €3. Value $10.
No. 3277B was printed in sheets of 10 + 10
labels that sold for €8.86. Value $125. Labels
could be personalized.

Egyptian Hippopotamus
Figurine — A1823

Head of
Aphrodite
A1824

Winged
Victory of
Samothrace
A1825

Fresco,
Pompeii
A1826

King
Amenemhet
III of Egypt
A1827

Statue of
Juno
A1828

Egyptian
Harpist
A1829

Etruscan Sarcophagus of Husband
and Wife — A1830

Egyptian
Statue of
Seated
Scribe
A1831

Head of
Pericles
A1832

Serpentine Die Cut 11¼x11
2007, Jan. 27   Litho.
Booklet Stamps
Self-Adhesive
3279	A1823	(54c) multi	1.60	.45
3280	A1824	(54c) multi	1.60	.45
3281	A1825	(54c) multi	1.60	.45
3282	A1826	(54c) multi	1.60	.45
3283	A1827	(54c) multi	1.60	.45
3284	A1828	(54c) multi	1.60	.45
3285	A1829	(54c) multi	1.60	.45
3286	A1830	(54c) multi	1.60	.45
3287	A1831	(54c) multi	1.60	.45
3288	A1832	(54c) multi	1.60	.45
a.		Booklet pane of 10, #3279-3288	17.00	

Tourism Issue

Valenciennes
A1833

2007   Engr.   Perf. 13¼
3289   A1833   54c red & blue   1.50   .50
Issued: No. 3289, 2/3.

Tourism Issue

Limoges
A1834

2007   Engr.   Perf. 13¼
3290   A1834   54c multi   1.50   .50
Issued: No. 3290, 3/23.

Tourism Issue

Arcachon
A1835

2007, May 19   Photo.   Perf. 13¼
3291   A1835   54c multi   1.50   .50

Tourism Issue

Castres
A1836

2007, July 20   Engr.   Perf. 13¼
3292   A1836   54c multi   1.50   .50

Tourism Issue

Firminy — A1837

2007, Sept. 15   Engr.   Perf. 13¼
3293   A1837   54c multi   1.60   .55

Rights of
France
A1838

2007, Feb. 5   Photo.   Perf. 13¼
3294   A1838   54c multi   1.60   .50

Art Issue

Book Illumination from Sélestat
Library — A1839

Galerie des Glaces, Versailles Palace — A1840

La Barrière Fleurie, by Paul Sérusier A1841

Gallic Boar Ensign — A1842

Perf. 12¼x13, 13¼x13 (#3297), 13x13¼ (#3296, 3298)
Engraved, Photo. (#3296, 3297, 3298A)

2007-08
3295	A1839	60c multi	1.60	.80
3296	A1840	85c multi	2.50	1.25
3297	A1841	86c multi	2.50	1.25
3298	A1842	€1.30 multi	3.50	1.75
	Nos. 3295-3298 (4)		10.10	5.05

Self-Adhesive
Serpentine Die Cut 11
3298A	A1840	85c multi	2.40	2.40

Issued: No. 3295, 2/10. No. 3297, 10/13. No. 3298, 6/2. No. 3296, 11/10. No. 3298A, 2008.

Aspects of Life in the French Regions Type of 2003

No. 3299: a, Baux-de-Provence. b, Banks of the Loire. c, Grande-Chartreuse Massif. d, Saint-Tropez. e, Doubs Waterfall, vert. f, Fontainebleau Forest, vert. g, Chantilly Castle. h, Saint-Malo. i, Ballon d'Alsace, vert. j, Midi Canal, vert.

2007, Feb. 24   Photo.   Perf. 13
3299		Sheet of 10	15.00	15.00
a.-j.	A1642	54c Any single	1.50	.50

No. 3299 has three vertical rows of rouletting, separating sheet into quarters.
Nos. 3299a-3299j were also issued in large booklets containing panes of 1 of each stamp. The booklet sold for €19.

Aspects of Life in French Regions Type of 2003 Inscribed "Lettre Prioritaire 20g"

Designs: Nos. 3300-3301, Arc de Triomphe, vert.

2007, Feb.   Photo.   Perf. 13
3300	A1642	(54c) multi + label	4.00	4.00

Serpentine Die Cut 11x11¼
3301	A1642	(54c) multi + label	30.00	30.00

Nos. 3300-3301 each were printed in sheets of 10 stamps + 10 different labels that sold for €6.85. Value of sheet of No. 3300, $45.

Marianne Type of 2005
2007   Litho.   Perf. 13
Stamps Inscribed "Phil@poste"
Without Varnish
3302		Sheet of 15, #a-k, 2 each #l-m, + 15 labels	60.00	60.00
a.	A1713	1c yellow orange	.30	.30
b.	A1713	5c brown	.40	.40
c.	A1713	10c gray	.75	.75
d.	A1713	60c blue	2.75	2.75
e.	A1713	70c lt yellow green	3.25	3.25
f.	A1713	85c purple	3.75	3.75
g.	A1713	86c pink	4.00	4.00
h.	A1713	€1 orange	5.00	5.00
i.	A1713	€1.15 light blue	5.50	5.50
j.	A1713	€1.30 red violet	6.00	6.00
k.	A1713	€2.11 maroon	9.00	9.00
l.	A1713	(49c) blue green	2.50	2.50
m.	A1713	(54c) red	2.75	2.75

No. 3302 sold for €14.40 and has personalizable labels.

Harry Potter — A1843

Designs: (49c), Hermione Granger. (85c), Ron Weasley.

2007, Mar. 12   Photo.   Perf. 13¼
3303	A1843	(54c) red & multi	1.50	.50
a.		Souvenir sheet of 1	1.50	1.50
b.		Perf. 13¼x13 (booklet stamp)	1.75	.50

Booklet Stamps
Perf. 13¼x13
3304	A1843	(49c) blue & multi	1.50	.45
3305	A1843	(85c) grn & multi	2.50	.75
a.		Booklet pane of 10, 4 #3303b, 3 each #3304-3305	17.00	—
		Complete booklet, #3305a	17.00	

Stamp Day. Sheets of five serpentine die cut 11 self-adhesive stamps of each denomination and five labels that could be personalized exist. Each sheet sold for €6.50. Value, set $70.

Albert Londres (1884-1932), Journalist — A1844

2007, Mar. 16   Engr.   Perf. 13x13¼
3306	A1844	54c multi	1.60	.50

Six different souvenir sheets containing one No. 3306 exist. The set sold for €15. Value, set $45.

Audit Office, Bicent. A1845

2007   Perf. 13¼x13
3307	A1845	54c multi	1.60	.50

Serpentine Die Cut 11
Self-Adhesive
3307A	A1845	54c multi		4.00	4.00

Issued: No. 3307, 3/17; No. 3307A, 7/20.

Treaty of Rome, 50th Anniv. A1846

2007, Mar. 23   Photo.   Perf. 13¼
3308	A1846	54c multi	1.50	.50

Sébastaen Le Prestre de Vauban (1633-1707), Military Engineer — A1847

2007, Mar. 30   Engr.
3309	A1847	54c multi	1.50	.50

2007 Rugby World Cup A1848

2007, Apr. 14   Photo.   Perf. 13¼
3310	A1848	54c multi	1.50	.50
a.		Perf. 13x13¼ + label	4.00	4.00

Serpentine Die Cut 11¼
Self-Adhesive
3311	A1848	54c multi + label		

No. 3310a was printed in sheets of 5 stamps and 5 labels that could be personalized that sold for €4.20. Value $45.
No. 3311 was printed in sheets of 10 + 10 labels that could be personalized. Sheets sold for €10.60.

Endangered Animals in Overseas Departments A1849

Designs: No. 3312, Antillean iguana. No. 3313, Raccoon, horiz. 60c, Jaguar, horiz. 86c, Barau's petrel, horiz..

2007, Apr. 28   Photo.   Perf. 13¼
3312	A1849	54c multi	1.50	.50
3313	A1849	54c multi	1.50	.50
3314	A1849	60c multi	1.75	.60
3315	A1849	86c multi	2.40	.80
a.		Souvenir sheet, #3312-3315	7.25	7.25
	Nos. 3312-3315 (4)		7.15	2.40

Gardens and Parks Type of 2003
Souvenir Sheet

No. 3316 — Parc de la Tete d'Or, Lyon: a, Red flowers. b, White flowers.

2007, Apr. 28   Perf. 13¼x13
3316		Sheet of 2	11.50	11.50
a.-b.	A1660	€2.11 Either single	5.75	3.00

Salon du Timbre. No. 3316 has four vertical rows of rouletting, separating sheet into fifths, with the two stamps in the central fifth.

Vacations A1850

Designs: No. 3317, Wooden fence and red hollyhocks. No. 3318, Angelfish. No. 3319,

---

Blue flowers. No. 3320, Blueberries. No. 3321, Canoes. No. 3322, Dyed wool hanging on rods. No. 3323, Glacier. No. 3324, Palm tree. No. 3325, Beach umbrellas and woman. No. 3326, Boxes of color pigments.

Serpentine Die Cut 11¼x11
2007, Apr. 28   Litho.
Booklet Stamps
Self-Adhesive
3317	A1850	(54c) multi	1.50	.50
3318	A1850	(54c) multi	1.50	.50
3319	A1850	(54c) multi	1.50	.50
3320	A1850	(54c) multi	1.50	.50
3321	A1850	(54c) multi	1.50	.50
3322	A1850	(54c) multi	1.50	.50
3323	A1850	(54c) multi	1.50	.50
3324	A1850	(54c) multi	1.50	.50
3325	A1850	(54c) multi	1.50	.50
3326	A1850	(54c) multi	1.50	.50
a.		Booklet pane of 10, #3317-3326	15.00	

Europa A1851

2007, May 1   Photo.   Perf. 13¼
3327	A1851	60c multi	1.50	.40

Scouting, cent.

Intl. Sailing Federation, Cent. — A1852

2007, May 4   Perf. 13
3328	A1852	85c multi	2.00	.80

A souvenir sheet containing No. 3328 sold for €3.

Tintin and Snowy — A1853

Characters from Tintin comic strips and books, by Hergé: No. 3330, Professor Calculus (Tournesol). No. 3331, Captain Haddock. No. 3332, Thomson and Thompson (Dupondt). No. 3333, Bianca Castafiore. No. 3334, Chang (Tchang).

2007, May 12
3329	A1853	54c multi	1.50	.50
3330	A1853	54c multi	1.50	.50
3331	A1853	54c multi	1.50	.50
3332	A1853	54c multi	1.50	.50
3333	A1853	54c multi	1.50	.50
3334	A1853	54c multi	1.50	.50
a.		Souvenir sheet, #3329-3334	13.50	13.50

No. 3334a sold for €5, with the Red Cross receiving €1.76 of that.

Religious Art — A1854

Designs: 54c, Nativity, 15th cent. miniature, from Armenia. 85c, The Smile of Reims.

2007, May 22   Perf. 13¼
3335	A1854	54c multi	1.60	.50
3336	A1854	85c multi	2.40	.80

See Armenia Nos. 749-750.

Inauguration of Eastern France TGV
Train Service — A1855

2007, June 9   *Perf. 13*
3337 A1855 54c multi   1.50   .50

French Federation of Philatelic
Associations 80th Congress,
Poitiers — A1856

2007, June 15   Engr.   Perf. 13x13¼
3338 A1856 54c multi + label   1.50   .50

Miniature Sheet

2007 Rugby World Cup,
France — A1857

No. 3339 — Inscriptions: a, Touche (Throw-in, 30x39mm elliptical). b, Melée (scrum). c, Attaque (player running with ball). d, Essai (try). e, Transformation (kick, 30x39mm elliptical). f, Passe (pass). g, Raffut (stiff-arm). h, Haka (dance). i, Plaquage (tackle). j, Supporteurs (fans).

2007, June 23   *Perf. 13x13¼*
3339 A1857   Sheet of 10   15.00 15.00
a.-j.   54c Any single   1.50   .50

European Capitals Type of 2002
Souvenir Sheet

No. 3340 — Attractions in Brussels: a, Maison du Roi (Royal Palace). b, Hotel du Ville (City Hall), vert. c, Mannekin Pis, vert. d, Atomium.

Perf. 13x13¼, 13¼x13 (vert. stamps)
2007, June 30
3340 A1622   Sheet of 4   6.00 6.00
a.-d.   54c Any single   1.50   .50

Association of French Mayors,
Cent. — A1858

2007, July 5   Photo.   Perf. 13¼
3341 A1858 54c multi   1.50   .50

Pierre Pfimlin
(1907-2000),
Mayor of
Strasbourg
A1859

2007, July 7   Photo.   Perf. 13¼
3342 A1859 60c multi   1.75   .60

2007
Rugby
World
Cup,
France
A1860

**Litho. With Three-Dimensional
Plastic Affixed**
2007, Sept. 5   Serpentine Die Cut 11
Self-Adhesive
3343 A1860 €3 multi   8.25 4.25

Happy
Birthday
A1861

2007, Sept. 8   Photo.   Perf. 13x13¼
3344 A1861 (54c) multi   1.60   .55
a.   Litho., with attached label   2.40 2.40

No. 3344 was printed in a sheet of 5; No. 3344a was printed in a sheet of 5 + 5 labels that sold for €4.20.

Gift Boxes — A1862

Boxes and: Nos. 3345a, 3346, Butterflies. Nos. 3345b, 3348, Flowers. Nos. 3345c, 3347, Hearts. Nos. 3345d, 3350, Musical notes. Nos. 3345e, 3349, Bubbles.

2007, Sept. 8   Litho.   Perf. 13¼
3345   Sheet of 5 + 5 labels 12.00 12.00
a.-e. A1862 (54c) Any single + label   2.40 2.40

Self-Adhesive
Booklet Stamps
Serpentine Die Cut 11
3346 A1862 (54c) multi   1.60   .55
3347 A1862 (54c) multi   1.60   .55
3348 A1862 (54c) multi   1.60   .55
3349 A1862 (54c) multi   1.60   .55
3350 A1862 (54c) multi   1.60   .55
a.   Booklet pane of 5 #3346-3350   8.00

No. 3345 sold for €4.20.

Sully
Prudhomme
(1839-1907),
Poet — A1863

2007, Sept. 15   Engr.   Perf. 13¼
3351 A1863 €1.30 multi   3.75 1.25

A1864

A1865

A1866

A1867

Cows
A1868

Serpentine Die Cut 11
2007, Sept. 20   Litho.
Self-Adhesive
Booklet Stamps
3352 A1864 (54c) multi   1.60   .55
3353 A1865 (54c) multi   1.60   .55
3354 A1866 (54c) multi   1.60   .55
3355 A1867 (54c) multi   1.60   .55
3356 A1868 (54c) multi   1.60   .55
a.   Booklet pane, 2 each #3352-3356   16.00
   Nos. 3352-3356 (5)   8.00 2.75

Aspects of Life in French Regions
Type of 2003

No. 3357: a, Sèvres porcelain. b, Grasse perfume. c, Christmas market. d, Marseille soap. e, Giants, vert. f, Basque beret, vert. g, Aubusson tapestries. h, Lyonnaise tavern. i, Slipper, vert. j, Canteloupe, vert.

2007, Sept. 29   Photo.   Perf. 13
3357   Sheet of 10   16.00 16.00
a.-j. A1642 54c Any single   1.60   .55

No. 3357 has three vertical rows of rouletting separating sheet into quarters.

Nos. 3357a-3357j were also issued in large booklets containing panes of 1 of each stamp. The booklet sold for €19. Value $55.

Space Age, 50th Anniv. — A1869

2007, Oct. 4   *Perf. 13x12½*
3358 A1869 85c multi   2.40   .80

Medical Research Foundation, 60th
Anniv. — A1870

2007, Oct. 20   *Perf. 13¼*
3359 A1870 54c multi   1.60   .55

Guy Moquet
(1924-41), World
War II
Resistance
Fighter — A1871

2007, Oct. 22   Engr.
3360 A1871 54c multi   1.60   .55

Dole
A1872

2007, Nov. 2
3361 A1872 54c multi   1.60   .55

Personalized Stamp With Country
Name on Short Side — A1873

Personalized
Stamp With
Country
Name on
Long Side
A1874

Serpentine Die Cut 11¼ Syncopated
2007, Nov.   Litho.
Self-Adhesive
Inscribed: "Lettre Prioritaire 20 g"
3362 A1873 (54c) multi   3.00 3.00
3363 A1874 (54c) multi   3.00 3.00
Inscribed: "Monde 20 g"
3364 A1873 (85c) multi   4.00 4.00
3365 A1874 (85c) multi   4.00 4.00
Inscribed: "Lettre Prioritaire 50 g"
3366 A1873 (86c) multi   4.00 4.00
3367 A1874 (86c) multi   4.00 4.00
   Nos. 3362-3367 (6)   22.00 22.00

Nos. 3362-3367 were each printed in sheets of ten, having vignettes that could be personalized or chosen from a library of stock designs, two of which are shown on the illustrated stamps. Sheets of Nos. 3362 and 3363 each sold for €10.03, and sheets of Nos. 3364-3367 each sold for €13.38. Sheets were made available with different frame colors. Starting in 2008, numerous sheets containing stamps with these frames having various preselected vignettes were produced and sold by La Poste for various prices per sheet, each well above the franking value of the stamps at the time of issue. Any stamp with a vignette and/or frame color differing from the items shown is an equivalent item to those shown.

Jean-Baptiste
Charcot (1867-
1936), Polar
Explorer
A1875

Ship Pourquoi-Pas? — A1876

2007, Nov. 8   Engr.   Perf. 13x12¾
3368 A1875 54c multi   1.60   .55
3369 A1876 60c multi   1.75   .60
  a. Horiz. pair, #3368-3369   3.50   1.25

See Greenland No. 505. A sheet containing Nos. 3368-3369 sold for €4 in 2008.

Marianne — A1877

Serpentine Die Cut 6¾ Vert.
2007, Nov. 8   Engr.
Self-Adhesive
Booklet Stamp
3370 A1877 54c red   2.75   2.00
  a. Booklet pane, 6 each
      #3083d, 3370   25.50

Miniature Sheet

Lighthouses — A1878

No. 3371: a, Cap Fréhel Lighthouse. b, Espiguette Lighthouse. c, D'ar-Men Lighthouse. d, Grand-Léjon Lighthouse. e, Porquerolles Lighthouse, horiz. f, Chassiron Lighthouse, horiz.

Litho. & Engr.
2007, Nov. 9   Perf. 13
3371 A1878 Sheet of 6   9.75   9.75
  a.-f. 54c Any single   1.60   .55

2007 Women's World Handball
Championships, France — A1879

2007, Nov. 10   Photo.   Perf. 13¼
3372 A1879 54c multi   1.60   .55

Holiday
Greetings
A1880

No. 3377: a, Squirrel with stocking cap. b, Bird with party hat. c, Hedgehog with party cap. d, Dog with stocking cap. e, Deer with stocking cap.

No. 3378, Squirrel with stocking cap. No. 3379, Bird with party hat. No. 3380, Deer with stocking cap. No. 3381, Hedgehog with party hat. No. 3382, Dog with stocking cap.

2007, Nov. 24   Litho.   Perf. 13¼
3377   Sheet of 5 + 5 labels 12.50 12.50
  a.-e. A1880 (54c) Any single + la-
         bel   2.50   2.50

Booklet Stamps
Self-Adhesive
Serpentine Die Cut 11
3378 A1880 (54c) multi   1.60   .55
3379 A1880 (54c) multi   1.60   .55
3380 A1880 (54c) multi   1.60   .55
3381 A1880 (54c) multi   1.60   .55
3382 A1880 (54c) multi   1.60   .55
  a. Booklet pane, 2 each #3378-
      3382   16.00

No. 3377 sold for €4.20 and had labels that could not be personalized.
A souvenir sheet of 1 of No. 3381 sold for €3.

Marianne Type of 2005
2008   Engr.   Perf. 13
3383 A1713 (65c) dark
                    blue   2.00   .40
3384 A1713 72c yel
                   green   2.25   .45
3385 A1713 88c fawn   2.75   .55
3386 A1713 €1.25 blue   4.00   .80
3387 A1713 €1.33 red vio-
                   let   4.25   .85
3388 A1713 €2.18 choco-
                   late   6.75   1.40
  Nos. 3383-3388 (6)   22.00   4.45

Coil Stamp
Perf. 13 Horiz.
3388A A1713 (65c) dark
                     blue   2.00   .40

Issued: Nos. 3383-3388A, 3/1.

Marianne Type of 2005
Serpentine Die Cut 6¾ Vert.
2008   Engr.
Booklet Stamp
Self-Adhesive
3389 A1713 (60c) blue   1.90   .50
  a. Booklet pane of 12   23.00

Issued: No. 3389, 1/2.

Hearts
A1881

Designs: (54c), Face. (86c), (88c), Plant with heart-shaped leaves.

2008, Jan. 5   Photo.   Perf. 13¼
3390 A1881 (54c) multi   1.60   .55
  a. Souvenir sheet of 5   8.00   8.00
  b. Sheet of 10 + 10 labels   20.00
3391 A1881 (86c) multi   2.60   .90

Self-Adhesive
Serpentine Die Cut
3392   A1881 (54c) multi   1.60   .55
3392A A1881 (88c) multi   2.50   2.50

Values are for stamps with surrounding selvage.
Nos. 3390, 3390a, 3390b, 3391-3392 issued 1/5/08. No. 3390b was sold for €6.86. Labels could not be personalized.

New Year 2008
(Year of the
Rat) — A1882

2008, Jan. 26   Photo.   Perf. 13¼x13
3393 A1882 (54c) multi   1.60   .55

Printed in sheets of 5. A souvenir sheet of one #3393 sold for €3.

Paintings
A1883

Designs: No. 3394, Legend of St. Francis: Sermon to the Birds, by Giotto di Bondone. No. 3395, Seaport at Sunset, by Claude Lorrain. No. 3396, The Birth of Venus, by Sandro Botticelli. No. 3397, Napoleon Bonaparte Crossing the Alps, by Jacques-Louis David. No. 3398, La Belle Jardinière (Madonna and Child with St. John the Baptist), by Raphael, vert. No. 3399, Head of a Girl in a Turban, by Jan Vermeer, vert. No. 3400, Summer, by Giuseppe Arcimboldo, vert. No. 3401, Mona Lisa, by Leonardo da Vinci, vert. No. 3402, Infant Maria Marguerita, by Diego Velásquez, vert. No. 3403, Money Changer with Wife, by Quentin Massys (Metsys), vert.

Serpentine Die Cut 11
2008, Jan. 26   Litho.
Booklet Stamps
Self-Adhesive
3394 A1883 (54c) multi   1.60   .55
3395 A1883 (54c) multi   1.60   .55
3396 A1883 (54c) multi   1.60   .55
3397 A1883 (54c) multi   1.60   .55
3398 A1883 (54c) multi   1.60   .55
3399 A1883 (54c) multi   1.60   .55
3400 A1883 (54c) multi   1.60   .55
3401 A1883 (54c) multi   1.60   .55
3402 A1883 (54c) multi   1.60   .55
3403 A1883 (54c) multi   1.60   .55
  a. Booklet pane of 10, #3394-
      3403   16.00

France
Stadium,
10th Anniv.
A1884

2008, Jan. 28   Photo.   Perf. 13¼
3404 A1884 54c multi   1.60   .55

Tourism Issue

Vendôme
A1885

2008   Engr.   Perf. 13¼
3405 A1885 54c multi   1.60   .40

Issued: No. 3405, 2/2.

Tourism Issue

La Rochelle — A1886

Toulon
A1887

Richelieu
A1888

Le
Havre — A1889

Illustration A1886 reduced.

2008   Engr.   Perf. 13
3406 A1886 55c multi   1.50   .60
3407 A1887 55c multi   1.50   .60
3408 A1888 55c multi   1.50   .60
3409 A1889 55c multi   1.50   .50
  Nos. 3406-3409 (4)   6.00   2.30

Issued: No. 3406, 4/5; Nos. 3407-3408, 7/5; No. 3409, 9/13. A souvenir sheet of one of No. 3406 sold for €3.

Art Issue

Globes of
Vincenzo
Coronelli
A1890

Young Girl Warming Her Hands at a
Large Stove, by Jean-Jacues
Henner — A1891

Untitled
Work by
Gérard
Garouste
A1892

A Theater
Box
Office, by
Honoré
Daumier
A1893

Litho. & Engr., Photo (A1891-
A1892), Engr. (A1893)
2008   Perf. 13¼x13
3410 A1890 85c   multi   2.60   1.25
3411 A1891 88c   multi   2.25   1.10
3412 A1892 €1.33 multi   4.25   2.10
3413 A1893 €1.33 choc &
                   bl gray   3.50   1.75
  Nos. 3410-3413 (4)   12.60   6.20

Self-Adhesive
Serpentine Die Cut 11
3413A A1891 88c   multi   2.50   2.50
3413B A1892 €1.33 multi   3.75   3.75
3413C A1893 €1.33 choc &
                    bl gray   3.75   3.75
  Nos. 3413A-3413C (3)   10.00 10.00

Issued: No. 3410, 2/11; No. 3412, 6/19; No. 3411, 10/18; No. 3413, 11/7.
A souvenir sheet containing No. 3410 sold for €3.

Emir Abdelkader
(1808-83),
Algerian
Leader — A1894

2008, Feb. 20   Engr.   Perf. 13¼
3414   A1894   54c multi   1.75   .60

Droopy Dog
A1895

Red-haired
Woman
A1896

The Wolf
A1897

Design: €2.18, Droopy Dog, diff.

2008, Mar. 1   Photo.   Perf. 13¼
3415   A1895   (55c) multi   1.75   .60
3416   A1896   (55c) multi   1.75   .60
3417   A1897   (55c) multi   1.75   .60
   a.   Strip of 3, #3415-3417   5.25   1.90

Souvenir Sheet
Perf. 13x13¼
3418   A1895   €2.18 multi   6.75   6.75

Booklet Stamps
Self-Adhesive
3419   A1895   (55c) multi   1.75   .60
3420   A1896   (55c) multi   1.75   .60
3421   A1897   (55c) multi   1.75   .60
   a.   Booklet pane of 10, 4 #3419,   17.50
       3 each #3420-3421

Cartoon characters created by Tex Avery;
Stamp Day. No. 3418 contains one 35x27mm
stamp that has thermographic ink (on cartoon
balloon) that when warmed, changes color
allowing a message below the ink to appear.
Nos. 3419-3421 exist in three sheets, each
containing 5 of each stamp + 5 non-personal-
izable labels. Each sheet sold for €6.50.

Sound
Recording
Libraries
A1898

2008, Mar. 15   Photo.   Perf. 13¼
3422   A1898   55c multi   1.75   .60

Flowers — A1899

Designs: 37c, Aquilegia. 38c, Tulipa sp. 44c,
Bellis perennis. 45c, Primula veris.

2008, Mar. 1   Litho.   Perf. 13
3423   A1899   37c multi   1.10   .25
3424   A1899   38c multi   1.25   .25
3425   A1899   44c multi   1.40   .30
3426   A1899   45c multi   1.40   .30
     Nos. 3423-3426 (4)   5.15   1.10

Nos. 3423-3426 are known only precanceled. See second note after #132.

Aspects of Life in French Regions
Type of 2003

No. 3427: a, Chateau d'Ussé, Rigny-Ussé.
b, Vézelay. c, Place des Vosges, Le Marais
district, Paris. d, Le Marais Poitevin (Poitevin
Marsh). e, Cugarel Windmill, Castelnaudary,
vert. f, Red granite coastal rocks, vert. g, Honfleur. h, La Petite France district, Strasbourg. i,
La Boétie House, Sarlat-la-Canéda, vert. j,
Marfate Cirque, Reunion, vert.

2008, Mar. 29   Photo.   Perf. 13
3427   Sheet of 10   17.50   17.50
   a.-j.   A1642 55c Any single   1.75   1.25

No. 3427 has three vertical rows of rouletting, separating sheet into quarters. Nos.
3427a-3427j were also issued in a large booklet containing panes of 1 of each stamp. The
booklet sold for €19.

Lyon — A1900

Litho. & Engr.
2008, Apr. 4   Perf. 13
3428   A1900   55c multi   1.75   .60

Gardens and Parks Type of 2003

No. 3429: a, Parc Longchamp, Marseille. b,
Parc Borely, Marseille.

2008   Photo.   Perf. 13¼x13
3429   Sheet of 2   13.50   13.50
   a.-b.   A1660 €2.18 Either single   6.75   3.50
   c.   Miniature sheet of 4, #3316a,   27.50   27.50
       3316b, 3429a, 3429b

Salon du Timbre. No. 3429 has four vertical
rows of rouletting, separating sheet into fifths,
with the two stamps in the central fifth.
Issued: No. 3429, 4/12; No. 3429c, 6/14.

Prehistoric
Animals
A1901

Designs: No. 3430, Phorusrhacos. No.
3431, Smilodon. 65c, Megaloceros, horiz. 88c,
Mammoth, horiz.

2008, Apr. 19   Perf. 13¼
3430   A1901   55c multi   1.75   .60
3431   A1901   55c multi   1.75   .60
3432   A1901   65c multi   2.00   .65
3433   A1901   88c multi   2.75   .90
   a.   Miniature sheet, #3430-3433   8.25   8.25
      Nos. 3430-3433 (4)   8.25   2.75

First Heart
Transplant in
Europe, 40th
Anniv. — A1902

2008, Apr. 24   Perf. 13¼x13
3434   A1902   55c red & black   1.60   .40

Valentré
Bridge,
Cahors
A1903

2008, Apr. 26   Engr.   Perf. 13x13¼
3435   A1903   55c multi   1.60   .40

Europa
A1904

2008, May 4   Photo.   Perf. 13x13¼
3436   A1904   55c multi   1.75   .60

Self-Adhesive
Serpentine Die Cut 11
3436A   A1904   55c multi   2.40   2.40

Quebec
City,
Canada,
400th
Anniv.
A1905

2008, May 16   Engr.   Perf. 13
3437   A1905   85c multi   2.50   .75

See Canada No. 2269.
A souvenir sheet containing No. 3437 and
Canada No. 2269 sold for $4.99 in Canada
and was sold in France for €15 as part of a set
additionally containing six different souvenir
sheets containing only No. 3437.

Happy
Birthday
A1906

2008, May 28   Photo.
3438   A1906   (55c) multi   1.75   .60

Printed in sheets of 5.

It's a Boy
A1907

It's a Girl
A1908

2008, May 28   Serpentine Die Cut 11
Booklet Stamps
Self-Adhesive
3439   A1907   (55c) multi, un-
               scratched
               panel   1.75   .60
   a.   Scratched panel   .60
   b.   Booklet pane of 10 #3439   17.50
3440   A1908   (55c) multi, un-
               scratched
               panel   1.75   .60
   a.   Scratched panel   .60
   b.   Booklet pane of 10 #3440   17.50

Scratch-off panels on Nos. 3439-3440 cover
pictures and text for baby boy and girl,
respectively.

Vacations
A1909

Designs: No. 3441, Ferns. No. 3442, Butterfly on leaf. No. 3443, Hands holding plant's

---

leaves. No. 3444, Coconut palm tree. No.
3445, Path beside forest lake. No. 3446, Golf
ball, putter and hole. No. 3447, Water lily and
lily pads. No. 3448, Watering cans and foliage.
No. 3449, Sliced kiwi fruit. No. 3450, Shelled
and unshelled peas.

Serpentine Die Cut 11
2008, May 28   Litho.
Booklet Stamps
Self-Adhesive
3441   A1909   (55c) multi   1.75   .60
3442   A1909   (55c) multi   1.75   .60
3443   A1909   (55c) multi   1.75   .60
3444   A1909   (55c) multi   1.75   .60
3445   A1909   (55c) multi   1.75   .60
3446   A1909   (55c) multi   1.75   .60
3447   A1909   (55c) multi   1.75   .60
3448   A1909   (55c) multi   1.75   .60
3449   A1909   (55c) multi   1.75   .60
3450   A1909   (55c) multi   1.75   .60
   a.   Booklet pane of 10, #3441-   17.50
       3450

Evreux
Belfry — A1910

2008, May 31   Engr.   Perf. 13
3451   A1910   55c multi   1.75   .60

French Federation of Philatelic
Associations 81st Congress,
Paris — A1911

2008, June 14   Perf. 13x13¼
3452   A1911   55c multi + label   1.75   .60

Marianne and
Stars
A1912

Hand
Depositing
Ballot
A1913

Tree in Hand
A1914

Dove
A1915

2008   Engr.   Perf. 13
3453   A1912   1c yellow   .20   .20
3454   A1912   5c gray brown   .20   .20
3455   A1912   10c gray   .30   .20
3456   A1912   (50c) green   1.60   .25
3457   A1912   (55c) red   1.75   .40
3458   A1912   (65c) dark blue   2.10   .50
3459   A1912   72c olive green   2.25   .60
3460   A1912   85c purple   2.75   .70
3461   A1912   88c fawn   2.75   .70
3462   A1912   €1 orange   3.25   .80
3463   A1912   €1.25 blue   4.00   1.00
3464   A1912   €1.33 red violet   4.25   1.10
3465   A1912   €2.18 chocolate   7.00   2.40

Self-Adhesive (#3466)
Etched on Foil
Die Cut Perf. 13
3466   A1912   €5 silver   16.00   16.00
      Nos. 3453-3466 (14)   48.40   25.05

Litho.
Perf. 13

3467 Sheet of 15, #3467a-3467k, 2 each #3467l-3467m, + 15 labels — 40.00 40.00

a.	A1912 1c yellow	.20	.20
b.	A1912 5c brown	.20	.20
c.	A1912 10c gray	.35	.35
d.	A1912 (65c) dark blue	2.40	2.40
e.	A1912 72c olive green	2.60	2.60
f.	A1912 85c purple	3.00	3.00
g.	A1912 88c fawn	3.25	3.25
h.	A1912 €1 orange	3.50	3.50
i.	A1912 €1.25 blue	4.50	4.50
j.	A1912 €1.33 red violet	4.75	4.75
k.	A1912 €2.18 brn violet	7.75	7.75
l.	A1912 (50c) green	1.75	1.75
m.	A1912 55c red	2.00	2.00

Coil Stamps
Perf. 13 Horiz.
Engr.

3468	A1912 (50c) green	1.60	.25
3469	A1912 (55c) red	1.75	.40
3470	A1912 (65c) dark blue	2.10	.50

Booklet Stamps (Types A1913-A1915)
Self-Adhesive
Serpentine Die Cut 6¾ Vert.

3471	A1912 (55c) red	1.75	.40
a.	Booklet pane of 20	35.00	
b.	Booklet pane of 10	17.50	
c.	Booklet pane of 12	21.00	
3472	A1913 55c red	1.75	.40
3473	A1914 55c red	1.75	.40
3474	A1915 55c red	1.75	.40
a.	Booklet pane of 12, 6 #3471, 2 each #3472-3474	21.00	
3475	A1912 (65c) dark blue	2.10	.50
a.	Booklet pane of 12	26.00	
3476	A1913 65c dark blue	2.10	.50
3477	A1914 65c dark blue	2.10	.50
3478	A1915 65c dark blue	2.10	.50
a.	Booklet pane of 12, 6 #3475, 2 each #3476-3478	26.00	
	Nos. 3471-3478 (8)	15.40	3.60

Issued: No. 3457, 6/17; No. 3741c, 9/8; No. 3466, 7/1; No. 3475a, 2009; others, 6/14. On day of issue, No. 3467 sold for €12.54. Labels on No. 3467 could not be personalized.

No. 3471b is comprised of two horizontal strips of five stamps on a yellow backing paper. Nos. 3471 and 3475 were also printed in sheets of 100 later in 2008.

See Nos. 3532, 3551-3566, 3612-3616E, 3730.

Ecology A1916

Designs: No. 3479, Tree. No. 3480, Bicycle. No. 3481, World map. No. 3482, Computer. No. 3483, Water droplets. No. 3484, Sun. No. 3485, Two plastic bottles. No. 3486, Three plastic bottles. No. 3487, Apple core. No. 3488, Strawberry.

Serpentine Die Cut 11
2008, June 14   Photo.
Booklet Stamps
Self-Adhesive

3479	A1916 (55c) multi	1.75	.60
3480	A1916 (55c) multi	1.75	.60
3481	A1916 (55c) multi	1.75	.60
3482	A1916 (55c) multi	1.75	.60
3483	A1916 (55c) multi	1.75	.60
3484	A1916 (55c) multi	1.75	.60
3485	A1916 (55c) multi	1.75	.60
3486	A1916 (55c) multi	1.75	.60
3487	A1916 (55c) multi	1.75	.60
3488	A1916 (55c) multi	1.75	.60
a.	Booklet pane of 10, #3479-3488	17.50	

Trapeze Artist — A1917

Bareback Rider — A1918

Clown — A1919

Lion Tamer — A1920

Clown — A1921

Juggler — A1922

2008, June 15   Photo.   **Perf. 13**

3489	A1917 55c multi	1.75	.60
3490	A1918 55c multi	1.75	.60
3491	A1919 55c multi	1.75	.60
3492	A1920 55c multi	1.75	.60
3493	A1921 55c multi	1.75	.60
3494	A1922 55c multi	1.75	.60
a.	Souvenir sheet, #3489-3494	16.50	16.50
	Nos. 3489-3494 (6)	10.50	3.60

No. 3494a sold for €5.10, with the Red Cross receiving €1.80 of that.

2008 Summer Olympics, Beijing — A1923

Designs: No. 3495, Equestrian, cycling. No. 3496, Swimming, rowing, horiz. No. 3497, Judo, fencing, horiz. No. 3498, Tennis, running.

Perf. 13¼x13, 13x13¼
2008, June 16

3495	A1923 55c multi	1.75	.60
3496	A1923 55c multi	1.75	.60
3497	A1923 55c multi	1.75	.60
a.	Pair, #3496-3497	3.50	1.75
3498	A1923 55c multi	1.75	.60
a.	Vert. pair, #3495, 3498	3.50	1.75
	Nos. 3495-3498 (4)	7.00	2.40

Nos. 3495-3498 were printed in a sheet of 10 containing 2 each #3495 and #3498 and 3 each #3496-3497.

Charles de Gaulle Memorial, Paris A1924

2008, June 18   Engr.   **Perf. 13¼**
3499 A1924 55c multi   1.75   .60

European Projects — A1925

No. 3500: a, Map of Europe, 1-euro coin. b, Flags of France and European Union, horiz (French Presidency of European Union). c, Earth and Galileo probe, horiz. d, Students and flags (Erasmus higher education program).

2008, June 19   Photo.   **Perf. 13**

3500	A1925 Sheet of 4	7.00	7.00
a.-d.	55c Any single	1.75	.60

Miniature Sheet

Famous Ships — A1926

No. 3501: a, Confiance. b, Grande Hermine, horiz. c, Boudeuse, horiz. d, Astrolabe, horiz. e, Hermione, horiz. f, Boussole.

2008, June 20

3501	A1926 Sheet of 6	10.50	10.50
a.-f.	55c Any single	1.75	.60

French and Brazilian Landscapes — A1927

Designs: 55c, Amazonian forest, Brazil. 85c, Glacier, France.

2008, July 13

3502	A1927 55c multi	1.75	.60
3503	A1927 85c multi	2.75	.90
a.	Horiz. pair, #3502-3503	4.50	2.25

See Brazil No. 3052.

Mediterranean Summit, Paris — A1928

2008, July 13   **Perf. 13¼**
3504 A1928 55c multi   1.75   .60

Aspects of Life in French Regions Type of 2003

No. 3505: a, Espadrilles. b, Stew (pot au feu). c, Chestnuts (chataigne). d, Fireworks (feu d'artifice). e, Epinal prints (l'image d'Epinal), vert. f, Lentils (lentille), vert. g, Reblochon cheese. h, Calissons (candy). i, Stilt walker (les échasses), vert. j, Mustard (moutarde), vert.

2008, Sept. 6   Photo.   **Perf. 13**

3505	Sheet of 10	15.00	15.00
a.-j.	A1642 55c Any single	1.50	.50

No. 3505 has three vertical rows of rouletting, separating sheet into quarters.

Nos. 3505a-3505j also were issued in large booklets containing panes of 1 of each stamp. The booklet sold for €19.

Josselin A1929

2008, Sept. 20   Engr.   **Perf. 13¼**
3506 A1929 55c multi   1.50   .50

A1930

A1931

A1932

A1933

A1934

A1935

A1936

A1937

A1938

Garfield, Comic Strip by Jim Davis A1939

Serpentine Die Cut 11¼x11
2008, Sept. 18   **Photo.**
Booklet Stamps
Self-Adhesive

3507	A1930	(55c)	multi	1.50	.50
3508	A1931	(55c)	multi	1.50	.50
3509	A1932	(55c)	multi	1.50	.50
3510	A1933	(55c)	multi	1.50	.50
3511	A1934	(55c)	multi	1.50	.50
3512	A1935	(55c)	multi	1.50	.50
3513	A1936	(55c)	multi	1.50	.50
3514	A1937	(55c)	multi	1.50	.50
3515	A1938	(55c)	multi	1.50	.50
3516	A1939	(55c)	multi	1.50	.50
a.		Booklet pane of 10, #3507-3516		15.00	

Nos. 3507-3516 (10)   15.00   5.00

"I Am Sport"
A1940

2008, Oct. 2   **Photo.**   *Perf. 12½*
3517   A1940   55c multi   1.50   .50

Values are for stamps with surrounding selvage.

Fifth Republic, 50th Anniv. A1941

2008, Oct. 4   *Perf. 13¼*
3518   A1941   55c multi   1.50   .50

Seascapes of Viet Nam and France — A1942

Designs: 55c, Along Bay, Viet Nam. 85c, Strait of Bonifacio, France.

2008, Oct. 15   **Photo.**   *Perf. 13x12¾*
3519   A1942   55c multi   1.40   .45
3520   A1942   85c multi   2.25   .75

See Viet Nam Nos. 3340-3341.

Types of 1959-2008
Serpentine Die Cut 6¾ Vert.
2008, Nov. 6   **Photo.**
Booklet Stamps
Self-Adhesive

3521	A328	55c	multi	1.40	.45
3522	A349	55c	multi	1.40	.45
3523	A360	55c	multi	1.40	.45
3524	A379	55c	multi	1.40	.45
3525	A486	55c	dark red	1.40	.45
3526	A555	55c	rose carmine	1.40	.45
3527	A771	55c	bright red	1.40	.45
3528	A915	55c	red	1.40	.45
3529	A1161	55c	red	1.40	.45
3530	A1409	55c	red	1.40	.45
3531	A1713	55c	red	1.40	.45
3532	A1912	55c	red	1.40	.45
a.		Booklet pane of 12, #3521-3532		17.00	

Nos. 3521-3532 (12)   16.80   5.40

Landmarks of France and Israel — A1943

Airplane, stamped first flight cover and: 55c, Haifa waterfront, Israel. 85c, Eiffel Tower, Paris.

2008, Nov. 6   **Photo.**   *Perf. 13*
3533   A1943   55c multi   1.40   .45
3534   A1943   85c multi   2.25   .75

First flight between France and Israel, 60th anniv. See Israel Nos. 1750-1751.

European Capitals Type of 2002

No. 3535 — Attractions in Prague: a, Tour du Petit Coté (Charles Bridge and Tower), vert. b, Hotel de ville horloge astronomique et calandrier (City Hall astronomical clock), vert. c, Eglise Notre-Dame-de-Tyn (Tyn Cathedral), vert. d, Le Chateau (Hradcany Castle).

Perf. 13¼x13, 13x13¼ (#3535d)
2008, Nov. 7   **Photo.**
3535   A1622   Sheet of 4   5.75   5.75
a.-d.   55c Any single   1.40   .45

A1944   A1945

A1946   A1947

A1948   A1949

A1950

A1951

A1952

A1953

A1954

A1955

A1956

Happy Holidays — A1957

Serpentine Die Cut 11¼x11
2008, Nov. 8   **Photo.**
Booklet Stamps
Self-Adhesive

3536	A1944	(55c)	multi	1.40	.45
3537	A1945	(55c)	multi	1.40	.45
3538	A1946	(55c)	multi	1.40	.45
3539	A1947	(55c)	multi	1.40	.45
3540	A1948	(55c)	multi	1.40	.45
3541	A1949	(55c)	multi	1.40	.45

Serpentine Die Cut 11x11¼

3542	A1950	(55c)	multi	1.40	.45
3543	A1951	(55c)	multi	1.40	.45
3544	A1952	(55c)	multi	1.40	.45
3545	A1953	(55c)	multi	1.40	.45
3546	A1954	(55c)	multi	1.40	.45
3547	A1955	(55c)	multi	1.40	.45
3548	A1956	(55c)	multi	1.40	.45
3549	A1957	(55c)	multi	1.40	.45
a.		Booklet pane of 14, #3536-3549		20.00	

Nos. 3536-3549 (14)   19.60   6.30

A souvenir sheet containing one perf. 13x13¼ stamp like No. 3543 with water-activated gum sold for €3.

End of World War I, 90th Anniv. A1958

2008, Nov. 11   **Engr.**   *Perf. 13¼*
3550   A1958   55c multi   1.40   .45

Marianne and Stars Type of 2008
Serpentine Die Cut 6¾ Vert.
2008   **Engr.**
Self-Adhesive

3551	A1912	1c	yellow	.20	.20
3552	A1912	5c	gray brown	.20	.20
3553	A1912	10c	gray	.30	.30
3554	A1912	(50c)	green	1.40	1.40
3555	A1912	72c	olive green	2.00	2.00
3556	A1912	85c	purple	2.40	2.40
3557	A1912	88c	fawn	2.50	2.50
3558	A1912	€1	orange	2.75	2.75
3559	A1912	€1.25	blue	3.50	3.50
3560	A1912	€1.33	red violet	3.75	3.75
3561	A1912	€2.18	chocolate	6.00	6.00

Nos. 3551-3561 (11)   25.00   25.00

Serpentine Die Cut 6¾ Horiz.
Coil Stamps

3564	A1912	(50c)	green	1.40	1.40
3565	A1912	(55c)	red	1.50	1.50
3566	A1912	(65c)	dark blue	1.90	1.90

Nos. 3564-3566 (3)   4.80   4.80

Nos. 3551-3561 each were printed in sheets of 100.

Flowers — A1959

Designs: 31c, Helianthus annuus. 33c, Magnolia.

2008, Nov. 12   **Litho.**   *Perf. 13*
3567   A1959   31c multi   .80   .25
3568   A1959   33c multi   .85   .25

Nos. 3567-3568 are known only precanceled. See note under #132.

Trees and Map of Mediterranean Area — A1960

2008, Nov. 20   **Photo.**   *Perf. 13x12¾*
3569   A1960   85c multi   2.25   .75

See Lebanon No. 645.

Greetings Type of 2004 Inscribed "Lettre Prioritaire 20g"

Designs: No. 3569A, "Ceci est une invitation." No. 3569B, "Un grand merci."

2008   **Photo.**   *Serpentine Die Cut 11*
Self-Adhesive

3569A	A1667	(55c)	brt lil rose & yel	1.60	1.60
3569B	A1667	(55c)	brt yel grn & red lil	1.60	1.60

Louis Braille (1809-52), Educator of the Blind — A1961

Engr. & Embossed
2009, Jan. 4   *Perf. 13x12¾*
3570   A1961   55c blk & violet   1.50   .50

New Year 2009 (Year of the Ox) — A1962

2009, Jan. 10   **Photo.**   *Perf. 13¼x13*
3571   A1962   (55c) multi   1.50   .50

No. 3571 was printed in sheets of 5. A souvenir sheet of 1 sold for €3. Value, $8.

Decorated Glasses, Nancy Museum A1963

Decorated Clock, Louvre Museum A1964

Marquetry, Valençay Chateau A1965

Quimper Faience, Sèvres Museum A1966

Enamelwork, Apt Cathedral — A1967

Tapestry, Malmaison Chateau A1968

Stained Glass, St. Joan of Arc Church, Rouen A1969

Cabinetwork, Louvre Museum — A1970

Wrought Iron, Army Museum, Paris A1971

Mosaic, Palace of Versailles A1972

Jewelry, Malmaison Chateau A1973

Crystal, Clichy Glassworks — A1974

Serpentine Die Cut 11
2009, Jan. 10
Booklet Stamps
Self-Adhesive

3572	A1963	(55c) multi	1.50	.50
3573	A1964	(55c) multi	1.50	.50
3574	A1965	(55c) multi	1.50	.50
3575	A1966	(55c) multi	1.50	.50
3576	A1967	(55c) multi	1.50	.50
3577	A1968	(55c) multi	1.50	.50
3578	A1969	(55c) multi	1.50	.50
3579	A1970	(55c) multi	1.50	.50
3580	A1971	(55c) multi	1.50	.50
3581	A1972	(55c) multi	1.50	.50
3582	A1973	(55c) multi	1.50	.50
3583	A1974	(55c) multi	1.50	.50

a. Booklet pane of 12, #3572-3583 .... 18.00
Nos. 3572-3583 (12) ... 18.00 6.00

René I, Duke of Anjou (1409-80) A1975

2009, Jan. 16   Engr.   Perf. 13¼
3584 A1975 55c multi   1.50 .50

Hearts A1976

Flowers and: (55c) One parrot. (88c), Two parrots.

2009, Jan. 17   Photo.   Perf. 13¼
3585 A1976 (55c) multi   1.50 .50
a. Souvenir sheet of 5 ... 7.50 7.50
3586 A1976 (88c) multi   2.40 1.25
Self-Adhesive
Serpentine Die Cut
3587 A1976 (55c) multi   1.50 .50
3588 A1976 (88c) multi   2.40 1.25
a. Booklet pane of 12 ... 29.00
Nos. 3585-3588 (4) ... 7.80 3.50

Tourism Issue

Les Sables D'Olonne A1977

Menton — A1978

Chaumont A1979

Château de la Bâtie d'Urfé A1980

Bordeaux — A1981

Abbey of Royaumont A1982

Illustration A1981 reduced.

Photo., Engr. (#3590, 3592-3594)
2009   Perf. 13¼, 13 (#3593)
3589 A1977 55c multi   1.40 .45
3590 A1978 56c multi   1.40 .45
3591 A1979 56c multi   1.60 .55
3592 A1980 56c multi   1.60 .55
Perf. 13
3593 A1981 56c multi   1.60 .55
3594 A1982 56c multi   1.75 .60
Nos. 3589-3594 (6) ... 9.35 3.15
Serpentine Die Cut 11
3594A A1981 56c multi   1.60 1.60

Issued: No. 3589, 1/31; No. 3590, 2/21; No. 3591, 5/16. No. 3592, 6/6; Nos. 3593, 3594A, 6/20. No. 3594, 9/26.

Miniature Sheet

World Alpine Skiing Championships, Val d'Isère — A1983

No. 3595: a, Super combined skier. b, Slalom skier. c, Downhill (Descente) skier. d, Giant slalom skier. e, Skiers at Val d'Isère.

2009, Jan. 31   Photo.   Perf. 13x13¼
3595 A1983 Sheet of 5   7.00 7.00
a.-e. 55c Any single   1.40 .45

France Foundation, 40th Anniv. — A1984

2009, Feb. 5   Photo.   Perf. 13¼
3596 A1984 55c multi   1.40 .45

Art Series

Angel, St. Cecilia Cathedral, Albi A1985

La Promenade, by Hansi (Jean-Jacques Waltz) — A1986

Wrapping of Pont-Neuf, by Christo and Jeanne-Claude — A1987

Paintings by Pierre-Auguste Renoir — A1988

No. 3600: a, Monsieur et Madame Bernheim de Villers. b, Gabrielle à la Rose.

Perf. 13, 13x13¼ (#3598), 13¼x13 (#3599)
2009   Litho. (#3597), Photo.
3597 A1985 85c multi   2.25 1.10
3598 A1986 90c multi   2.75 1.40
3599 A1987 €1.35 multi   3.75 1.90
Nos. 3597-3599 (3) ... 8.75 4.40
Souvenir Sheet
Perf. 13¼
3600 A1988 Sheet of 2   6.50 6.50
a. 85c multi   2.50 1.25
b. €1.35 multi   4.00 2.00
Self-Adhesive
Serpentine Die Cut 11
3601 A1985 85c multi   2.50 2.50
3602 A1986 90c multi   2.75 2.75
3603 A1987 €1.35 multi   3.75 3.75

Issued: No. 3597, 2/7; No. 3598, 10/24; Nos. 3599, 3603, 6/13 No. 3600, 11/5. A souvenir sheet of 1 of No. 3597 sold for €3.

Road Runner and Wile E. Coyote A1989

Sylvester and Tweety Bird A1990

Daffy Duck and Bugs Bunny A1991

Design: €1, Yosemite Sam, Wile E. Coyote, Sylvester, Tasmanian Devil, Bugs Bunny, Daffy Duck, Road Runner, Marvin the Martian and Tweety Bird.

2009, Feb. 28   Photo.   Perf. 13x13¼
3605 A1989 56c multi   1.40 .45
3606 A1990 56c multi   1.40 .45
3607 A1991 56c multi   1.40 .45
a. Strip of 3, #3605-3607 ... 4.25 1.40
Nos. 3605-3607 (3) ... 4.20 1.35
Souvenir Sheet
3608 A1989 €1 multi   2.60 1.25

Booklet Stamps
Self-Adhesive
Litho.
Serpentine Die Cut 11

3609	A1989	(56c)	multi	1.40	.45
3610	A1991	(56c)	multi	1.40	.45
3611	A1990	(56c)	multi	1.40	.45
a.	Booklet pane of 12, 4 each #3609-3611			17.00	
	Nos. 3609-3611 (3)			4.20	1.35

Stamp Day. No. 3608 contains one 80x26mm stamp. Sheets of five serpentine die cut 11 self-adhesive stamps like Nos. 3605-3607 and 5 labels each sold for €6.50.

Marianne and Stars Type of 2008
2009, Feb. 28   Engr.   Perf. 13

3612	A1912	73c olive green		1.90	.50
3613	A1912	90c fawn		2.25	.55
3614	A1912	€1.30 blue		3.25	.85
3615	A1912	€1.35 red violet		3.50	.90
3616	A1912	€2.22 chocolate		5.75	1.40
	Nos. 3612-3616 (5)			16.65	4.20

Serpentine Die Cut 6¾ Vert.
Self-Adhesive

3616A	A1912	73c olive green		1.90	1.90
3616B	A1912	90c fawn		2.25	2.25
3616C	A1912	€1.30 blue		3.25	3.25
3616D	A1912	€1.35 red violet		3.50	3.50
3616E	A1912	€2.22 chocolate		5.75	5.75
	Nos. 3616A-3616E (5)			16.65	16.65

Constitutional Council — A1992

2009, Mar. 5   Photo.   Perf. 13¼

3617	A1992	56c multi		1.40	.45

Self-Adhesive
Serpentine Die Cut 11

3617A	A1992	56c multi		1.60	1.60

Papal Palace, Avignon — A1993

2009, Mar. 7   Engr.   Perf. 13x12¾

3618	A1993	70c multi		1.90	.65

Portraits of Women by Titouan Lamazou A1994

Designs: No. 3619, Helena, United States. No. 3620, Dayu, Indonesia. No. 3621, Deborah, France. No. 3622, Kabari, Bangladesh. No. 3623, Mei Mei, China. No. 3624, Malika, Morocco. No. 3625, Dayan, Colombia. No. 3626, Francine, Rwanda. No. 3627, Blessing, Nigeria. No. 3628, Nandita, India. No. 3629, Elmas, Turkey. No. 3630, Nadia, Brazil.

Serpentine Die Cut 11
2009, Mar. 9   Litho.
Booklet Stamps
Self-Adhesive

3619	A1994	(56c)	multi	1.50	.50
3620	A1994	(56c)	multi	1.50	.50
3621	A1994	(56c)	multi	1.50	.50
3622	A1994	(56c)	multi	1.50	.50
3623	A1994	(56c)	multi	1.50	.50
3624	A1994	(56c)	multi	1.50	.50
3625	A1994	(56c)	multi	1.50	.50
3626	A1994	(56c)	multi	1.50	.50
3627	A1994	(56c)	multi	1.50	.50
3628	A1994	(56c)	multi	1.50	.50
3629	A1994	(56c)	multi	1.50	.50

3630	A1994	(56c)	multi	1.50	.50
a.	Booklet pane of 12, #3619-3630			18.00	
	Nos. 3619-3630 (12)			18.00	6.00

Mâcon — A1995

2009, Mar. 27   Engr.   Perf. 13x12¾

3631	A1995	56c multi		1.50	.50

Souvenir Sheet

Protection of Polar Regions — A1996

No. 3632: a, Iceberg and bird. b, Emperor penguins, vert.

Perf. 13x13¼, 13¼x13 (85c)
2009, Mar. 28   Litho. & Engr.

3632	A1996	Sheet of 2		4.00	4.00
a.		56c multi		1.50	.50
b.		85c multi		2.50	.85

Aimé Césaire (1913-2008), Martinique Politician A1997

2009, Apr. 17   Photo.   Perf. 13¼x13

3633	A1997	56c multi		1.50	.50

Flora of the French Regions A1998

Designs: No. 3634, Plum (quetsche), Alsace. No. 3635, Plum (mirabelle), Lorraine. No. 3636, Birch tree, Centre. No. 3637, Bee orchid, Champagne-Ardenne. No. 3638, Lily, Paris. No. 3639, Bluebells, Ile de France. No. 3640, Gorse, Bretagne. No. 3641, Lily-of-the-valley, Pays de la Loire. No. 3642, Apples, Basse-Normandie. No. 3643, Beech leaves, Haute-Normandie. No. 3644, Rose, Picardie. No. 3645, Potatoes, Nord-Pas de Calais. No. 3646, Olives, Provence-Alpes-Côte d'Azur. No. 3647, Chestnut, Corse. No. 3648, Wild thyme, Languedoc-Roussillon. No. 3649, Yellow gentian, Auvergne. No. 3650, Boletus mushroom, Limousin. No. 3651, Saltwort, Poitou-Charentes. No. 3652, Maritime pine, Aquitaine. No. 3653, Norway spruce, Franche-Comté. No. 3654, Awara palm, French Guiana. No. 3655, Toulouse violet, Midi-Pyrénées. No. 3656, Blueberries, Rhône-Alpes. No. 3657, Black currants, Bourgogne.

Serpentine Die Cut 11
2009, Apr. 25   Photo.
Booklet Stamps
Self-Adhesive

3634	A1998	(56c)	multi	1.50	.50
3635	A1998	(56c)	multi	1.50	.50
a.	Booklet pane of 2, #3634-3635			3.00	
3636	A1998	(56c)	multi	1.50	.50
3637	A1998	(56c)	multi	1.50	.50
a.	Booklet pane of 2, #3636-3637			3.00	

3638	A1998	(56c)	multi	1.50	.50
3639	A1998	(56c)	multi	1.50	.50
a.	Booklet pane of 2, #3638-3639			3.00	
3640	A1998	(56c)	multi	1.50	.50
3641	A1998	(56c)	multi	1.50	.50
a.	Booklet pane of 2, #3640-3641			3.00	
3642	A1998	(56c)	multi	1.50	.50
3643	A1998	(56c)	multi	1.50	.50
a.	Booklet pane of 2, #3642-3643			3.00	
3644	A1998	(56c)	multi	1.50	.50
3645	A1998	(56c)	multi	1.50	.50
a.	Booklet pane of 2, #3644-3645			3.00	
	Complete booklet, #3635a, 3637a, 3639a, 3641a, 3643a, 3645a			18.00	
3646	A1998	(56c)	multi	1.50	.50
3647	A1998	(56c)	multi	1.50	.50
a.	Booklet pane of 2, #3646-3647			3.00	
3648	A1998	(56c)	multi	1.50	.50
3649	A1998	(56c)	multi	1.50	.50
a.	Booklet pane of 2, #3648-3649			3.00	
3650	A1998	(56c)	multi	1.50	.50
3651	A1998	(56c)	multi	1.50	.50
a.	Booklet pane of 2, #3650-3651			3.00	
3652	A1998	(56c)	multi	1.50	.50
3653	A1998	(56c)	multi	1.50	.50
a.	Booklet pane of 2, #3652-3653			3.00	
3654	A1998	(56c)	multi	1.50	.50
3655	A1998	(56c)	multi	1.50	.50
a.	Booklet pane of 2, #3654-3655			3.00	
3656	A1998	(56c)	multi	1.50	.50
3657	A1998	(56c)	multi	1.50	.50
a.	Booklet pane of 2, #3656-3657			3.00	
	Complete booklet, #3647a, 3649a, 3651a, 3653a, 3655a, 3657a			18.00	
	Nos. 3634-3657 (24)			36.00	12.00

Souvenir Sheet

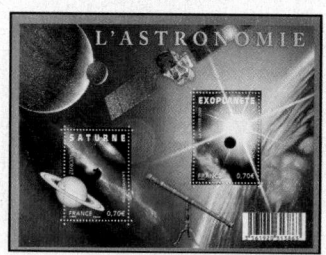

Europa — A1999

No. 3658: a, Saturn. b, Exoplanet.

2009, May 3   Litho.   Perf. 13¼x13

3658	A1999	Sheet of 2		4.00	4.00
a.-b.	70c Either single			2.00	.65

Intl. Year of Astronomy.

A2000

Vacations — A2001

Designs: No. 3659, Tennis ball on red clay court. No. 3660, Red-striped director's chair. No. 3661, Red turban. No. 3662, Ladybug. No. 3663, Red air mattress. No. 3664, Cherry tomatoes. No. 3665, Rooster. No. 3666, Poppy. No. 3667, License plate of Bonaire, Netherlands Antilles. No. 3668, Monarch butterfly. No. 3669, Raspberries. No. 3670, Doorknocker on red door. No. 3671, Flowers near house number. No. 3672, Red boat, rope and cleat.

Serpentine Die Cut 11
2009, May 13   Litho.
Booklet Stamps
Self-Adhesive

3659	A2000	(56c)	multi	1.60	.55
3660	A2000	(56c)	multi	1.60	.55
3661	A2000	(56c)	multi	1.60	.55
3662	A2000	(56c)	multi	1.60	.55
3663	A2000	(56c)	multi	1.60	.55
3664	A2000	(56c)	multi	1.60	.55

3665	A2001	(56c)	multi	1.60	.55
3666	A2001	(56c)	multi	1.60	.55
3667	A2001	(56c)	multi	1.60	.55
3668	A2001	(56c)	multi	1.60	.55
3669	A2001	(56c)	multi	1.60	.55
3670	A2001	(56c)	multi	1.60	.55
3671	A2001	(56c)	multi	1.60	.55
3672	A2001	(56c)	multi	1.60	.55
a.	Booklet pane of 14, #3659-3672			22.50	
	Nos. 3659-3672 (14)			22.40	7.70

Timber-frame Houses, Alsace — A2002

Azay-le-Rideau Chateau — A2003

Notre Dame Cathedral, Paris A2004

Vineyards, Bordeaux A2005

Nice A2006

Mont-Saint-Michel — A2007

Eiffel Tower A2008

Provence A2009

Serpentine Die Cut 11
2009, May 13   Litho.
Booklet Stamps
Self-Adhesive

3673	A2002	(85c)	multi	2.40	.80
3674	A2003	(85c)	multi	2.40	.80
3675	A2004	(85c)	multi	2.40	.80
3676	A2005	(85c)	multi	2.40	.80
3677	A2006	(85c)	multi	2.40	.80
3678	A2007	(85c)	multi	2.40	.80
3679	A2008	(85c)	multi	2.40	.80
3680	A2009	(85c)	multi	2.40	.80
a.	Booklet pane of 8, #3673-3680			19.50	
	Nos. 3673-3680 (8)			19.20	6.40

John Calvin (1509-64), Theologian and Religious Reformer A2010

2009, May 22   Engr.   Perf. 13¼
3681 A2010 56c multi   1.60   .55

Miniature Sheet

Chocolate — A2011

No. 3682: a, Cacao leaves, pods and beans. b, Aztec Indian. c, Spanish soldier. d, Castle. e, Map of French Atlantic coast. f, European man and woman of 16th cent. g, Production of chocolate. h, Chocolate bar. i, Cocoa service. j, Person eating chocolate bar.

2009, May 23   Photo.   Perf. 13
3682 A2011 Sheet of 10   16.00 16.00
a.-j.   56c Any single   1.60   .55

No. 3682 is impregnated with a chocolate scent.

French Federation Of Philatelic Associations 82nd Congress, Tarbes — A2012

2009, June 12   Engr.   Perf. 13x13¼
3683 A2012 56c multi + label   1.60   .55

Jean Moulin Memorial, Rhône A2013

2009, June 20   Engr.   Perf. 13¼
3684 A2013 56c multi   1.60   .55

Serpentine Die Cut 11
Self-Adhesive
3685 A2013 56c multi   1.60 1.60

Endangered Animals A2014

Designs: No. 3686, Giant panda. No. 3687, Rhinoceros. 70c, Aurochs, horiz. 90c, California condor, horiz.

2009, June 20   Photo.   Perf. 13¼
3686 A2014 56c multi   1.60   .55
3687 A2014 56c multi   1.60   .55
3688 A2014 70c multi   2.00   .65
3689 A2014 90c multi   2.50   .85
a.   Souvenir sheet of 4, #3686-
          3689   7.75   7.75
        Nos. 3686-3689 (4)   7.70 2.60

Gordon Bennett Aviation Cup, Cent. A2015

2009, June 27   Engr.   Perf. 13¼
3690 A2015 56c blk & brn   1.60   .55

Etienne Dolet (1509-46), Printer and Translator — A2016

2009, July 4   Engr.   Perf. 13x13¼
3691 A2016 56c multi   1.60   .55

Miniature Sheet

Fair Attractions — A2017

Designs: a, Parachute jump. b, Ferris wheel. c, Roller coaster. d, Carousel. e, Candy apple. f, Fishing arcade game.

2009, Sept. 5   Photo.   Perf. 13
3692 A2017 Sheet of 6   10.50 10.50
a.-f.   56c Any single   1.75   .60

A2018

Invitation — A2019

Designs: No. 3693, Yellow background, man with red violet pants and shoes. No. 3694, Red background, woman wearing dress. No. 3695, Red violet background, woman scattering papers. No. 3696, Light blue background, cow with flowers. No. 3697, Blue background, man with red violet pants and blue shoes. No. 3698, Brown black background, birthday cake with slice on cake server. No. 3699, Yellow green background, woman with brown pants and green shoes. No. 3700, Green background, man with blue pants and shoes. No. 3701, Brown background, cut birthday cake. No. 3702, Red violet background, woman with red violet pants and shoes. No. 3703, Pink background, woman with balloons. No. 3704, Red background, bird. No. 3705, Yellow green background, woman with green skirt and shoes. No. 3706, Orange background, woman scattering papers.

Serpentine Die Cut 11
2009, Sept. 5   Litho.
Booklet Stamps
Self-Adhesive
3693 A2018 (56c) multi   1.75   .60
3694 A2018 (56c) multi   1.75   .60
3695 A2018 (56c) multi   1.75   .60
3696 A2018 (56c) multi   1.75   .60
3697 A2018 (56c) multi   1.75   .60

3698 A2018 (56c) multi   1.75   .60
3699 A2018 (56c) multi   1.75   .60
3700 A2019 (56c) multi   1.75   .60
3701 A2019 (56c) multi   1.75   .60
3702 A2019 (56c) multi   1.75   .60
3703 A2019 (56c) multi   1.75   .60
3704 A2019 (56c) multi   1.75   .60
3705 A2019 (56c) multi   1.75   .60
3706 A2019 (56c) multi   1.75   .60
a.   Booklet pane of 14, #3693-
          3706   24.50
        Nos. 3693-3706 (14)   24.50 8.40

Eugène Vaillé (1875-1959), First Conservator of the Postal Museum — A2020

2009, Sept. 19   Engr.   Perf. 13¼
3707 A2020 56c multi   1.75   .60

Self-Adhesive
Serpentine Die Cut 11
3708 A2020 56c multi   1.75 1.75

Souvenir Sheet

Jardin des Plantes, Paris — A2021

No. 3709: a, Gazebo. b, Mexican Hothouse.

2009, Sept. 19 Photo.   Perf. 13¼x13
3709 A2021 Sheet of 2   13.00 13.00
a.-b.   €2.22 Either single   6.50   3.25

Salon du Timbre.

A2022

Le Petit Nicolas, by René Goscinny A2023

Designs: No. 3710, Nicolas, wearing striped shirt, holding envelope and book bag. No. 3711, Geoffroy. No. 3712, Eudes. No. 3713, Nicolas, wearing scarf, holding envelope and book bag. No. 3714, Nicolas writing. No. 3715, Joachim. No. 3716, "Chouette, des nouvelles!" No. 3717, Character at typewriter. No. 3718, "Vous me ferez cent lignes!" No. 3719, "Chère Maman. . . No. 3720, "C'est toi la plus jolie!", vert. No. 3721, "J'ai fait le bonheur de tout le monde.", vert. No. 3722, "Moi, je veux pas grand chose réellement. . .", vert. No. 3723, "C'est pout toi, Maman!", vert.

Serpentine Die Cut 11
2009, Sept. 19   Litho.
Booklet Stamps
Self-Adhesive
3710 A2022 (56c) multi   1.75   .60
3711 A2022 (56c) multi   1.75   .60
3712 A2022 (56c) multi   1.75   .60
3713 A2022 (56c) multi   1.75   .60
3714 A2022 (56c) multi   1.75   .60

3715 A2022 (56c) multi   1.75   .60
3716 A2023 (56c) multi   1.75   .60
3717 A2023 (56c) multi   1.75   .60
3718 A2023 (56c) multi   1.75   .60
3719 A2023 (56c) multi   1.75   .60
3720 A2023 (56c) multi   1.75   .60
3721 A2023 (56c) multi   1.75   .60
3722 A2023 (56c) multi   1.75   .60
3723 A2023 (56c) multi   1.75   .60
a.   Booklet pane of 14, #3710-
          3723   24.50
        Nos. 3710-3723 (14)   24.50 8.40

René de Saint-Marceaux (1845-1915), Sculptor of UPU Monument — A2024

Litho. & Engr.
2009, Oct. 9   Perf. 13x13¼
3724 A2024 70c multi   2.10   .70

See Switzerland No. 9O22.

Miniature Sheet

Dolls — A2025

No. 3725: a, Porcelain doll. b, GéGé doll, horiz. c, Rag doll, horiz. d, Bella doll, horiz. e, Baigneur Petitcollin, horiz. f, Unglazed porcelain doll (poupée en biscuit).

2009, Oct. 17   Perf. 13
3725 A2025 Sheet of 6   10.50 10.50
a.-f.   56c Any single   1.75   .60

Juliette Dodu (1848-1909), Spy — A2026

2009, Oct. 28   Engr.   Perf. 13¼
3726 A2026 56c multi   1.75   .60

Self-Adhesive
Serpentine Die Cut 11
3727 A2026 56c multi   1.75 1.75

European Capitals Type of 2002
Miniature Sheet

No. 3728 — Attractions in Lisbon: a, Hieronymites Monastery. b, Bairro Alto Quarter, vert. c, Belém Tower. d, Monument to the Discoveries.

Perf. 13x13¼, 13¼x13 (#3728b)
2009, Nov. 5   Photo.
3728 A1622 Sheet of 4   7.00   7.00
a.-d.   56c Any single   1.75   .60

Francisco de Miranda (1750-1816), Revolutionist in France and Venezuela — A2027

2009, Nov. 6   Photo.   *Perf. 13¼*
3729 A2027 85c multi   2.60   .90

See Venezuela No. 1693.

Marianne and Stars Type of 2008
Miniature Sheet
Photo., Engr. (#3456-3458)
2009, Nov. 6   *Perf. 13*
3730   Sheet of 13, #3456-
     3458, 3730a-3730j
     + label   31.00 31.00
a. A1912 1c yellow   .20   .20
b. A1912 5c gray brown   .20   .20
c. A1912 10c gray   .30   .30
d. A1912 73c olive green   2.25 2.25
e. A1912 85c purple   2.60 2.60
f. A1912 90c fawn   2.75 2.75
g. A1912 €1 orange   3.00 3.00
h. A1912 €1.30 blue   4.00 4.00
i. A1912 €1.35 red violet   4.00 4.00
j. A1912 €2.22 chocolate   6.50 6.50

Euromed Postal Conference — A2028

2009, Nov. 7   Engr.   *Perf. 13¼*
3731 A2028 56c multi   1.75   .60

A2029   A2030

A2031   A2032

A2033   A2034

A2035   A2036

A2037   A2038

A2039   A2040

A2041   A2042

Serpentine Die Cut 11
2009, Nov. 7   Photo.
Booklet Stamps
Self-Adhesive

3732 A2029 (56c) multi   1.75   .60
3733 A2030 (56c) multi   1.75   .60
3734 A2031 (56c) multi   1.75   .60
3735 A2032 (56c) multi   1.75   .60
3736 A2033 (56c) multi   1.75   .60
3737 A2034 (56c) multi   1.75   .60
3738 A2035 (56c) multi   1.75   .60
3739 A2036 (56c) multi   1.75   .60
3740 A2037 (56c) multi   1.75   .60
3741 A2038 (56c) multi   1.75   .60
3742 A2039 (56c) multi   1.75   .60
3743 A2040 (56c) multi   1.75   .60
3744 A2041 (56c) multi   1.75   .60
3745 A2042 (56c) multi   1.75   .60
a.   Booklet pane of 14, #3732-
    3745   24.50
Nos. 3732-3745 (14)   24.50 8.40

A souvenir sheet containing one No. 3743 sold for €3.

Helicopter Carrier Jeanne d'Arc — A2043

Sailors of the Jeanne d'Arc — A2044

2009, Nov. 21   Engr.   *Perf. 13x12¾*
3746 A2043 56c multi   1.75   .60
3747 A2044 56c multi   1.75   .60
a.   Horiz. pair, #3746-3747   3.50 1.20

A souvenir sheet containing Nos. 3746-3747 sold for €3.

Asterix, Comic Strip by René Goscinny and Albert Uderzo — A2045

No. 3749: a, Assurancetourix on rope (40x30mm). b, Eight characters, horiz. (80x26mm). c, Falbala with basket (30x40mm). d, Idefix and bone, horiz. (22x19mm). e, Obelix carrying rock (50x100mm).

2009, Dec. 2   Photo.   *Perf. 13*
3748 A2045 56c multi   1.75   .60
3749   Sheet of 6, #3748,
     3749a-3749e   15.50 15.50
a. A2045 56c multi, perf. 13x13¼   2.50 2.50
b. A2045 56c multi, perf. 13   2.50 2.50
c. A2045 56c multi, perf. 13¼x13   2.50 2.50

d. A2045 56c multi, perf.
   13¼x12½   2.50 2.50
e. A2045 56c multi, perf. 13x12¼   2.50 2.50

No. 3749 sold for €5.20, with the Red Cross receiving €1.84 of that. No. 3749e has a gritty substance affixed to the rock.

A2046

Hearts A2047

Type I — Bow ties extend to perforations.
Type II — Bow ties do not touch perforations (red frame all around).

2010, Jan. 8   Photo.   *Perf. 13¼*
3750 A2046 56c multi, type I   1.60   .55
          Perf.
3751 A2046 56c multi, type II   1.60   .55
          Perf. 13¼
3752 A2047 90c multi   2.50 1.25
Nos. 3750-3752 (3)   5.70 2.35
     Self-Adhesive
   Serpentine Die Cut
3753 A2046 56c multi, type I   1.60 1.60
3754 A2047 90c multi   2.50 2.50

Values for Nos. 3750, 3752 are for stamps with surrounding selvage. No. 3751 was printed in sheets of 5.

New Year 2010 (Year of the Tiger) — A2048

2010, Jan. 15   Photo.   *Perf. 13¼x13*
3755 A2048 56c multi   1.60   .55

No. 3755 was printed in sheets of 5. A souvenir sheet of 1 sold for €3.

Abbé Pierre (1912-2007), Founder of Emmaus Movement A2049

2010, Jan. 22   Engr.   *Perf. 13¼*
3756 A2049 56c multi   1.60   .55
     Self-Adhesive
   Serpentine Die Cut 11
3757 A2049 56c multi   1.60 1.60

Musical Instruments in Art — A2050

Designs: No. 3758, Lyre, by Gustave Moreau. No. 3759, Harp (Harpe), by François André Vincent. No. 3760, Violincello (Violincelle), by Karl Gustav Klingstedt. No. 3761, Guitar (Guitare), by Camille Roqueplan. No. 3762, Horn (Cor), by Daniel Rabel. No. 3763, Saxophone, by Marthe and Juliette Vesque. No. 3764, Organ (Orgue), by François Garas. No. 3765, Bugle (Clairon), by Auguste Mayer. No. 3766, Clavecin, by Louis Carrogis Carmontelle. No. 3767, Piano, by Pierre-Désiré Lamy. No. 3768, Tambourine (Tambourin), by Théodore Chassériau. No. 3769, Drums (Tambour), by Jacques-Antoine Delaistre.

Serpentine Die Cut 11
2010, Jan. 30   Photo.
Booklet Stamps
Self-Adhesive

3758 A2050 (56c) multi   1.60   .55
3759 A2050 (56c) multi   1.60   .55
3760 A2050 (56c) multi   1.60   .55
3761 A2050 (56c) multi   1.60   .55
3762 A2050 (56c) multi   1.60   .55
3763 A2050 (56c) multi   1.60   .55
3764 A2050 (56c) multi   1.60   .55
3765 A2050 (56c) multi   1.60   .55
3766 A2050 (56c) multi   1.60   .55
3767 A2050 (56c) multi   1.60   .55
3768 A2050 (56c) multi   1.60   .55
3769 A2050 (56c) multi   1.60   .55
a.   Booklet pane of 12, #3758-
    3769   19.50
Nos. 3758-3769 (12)   19.20 6.60

See Nos. 3882A-3882B.

2010 Winter Olympics, Vancouver A2051

2010, Feb. 6   *Perf. 13x13¼*
3770 A2051 85c Figure skaters   2.40 1.25
3771 A2051 85c Skier   2.40 1.25
a.   Horiz. pair, #3770-3771   4.80 2.50
b.   Tete-beche block of 4, 2
    #3771a   9.60 5.00

Art Issue

Museum of Art and Industry (La Piscine), Roubaix — A2052

The Beach at Calais at Ebb Tide, by Joseph Mallord William Turner — A2053

Maman, by Louise Bourgeois — A2054

Allegory of Spring, by Sandro Botticelli — A2055

No. 3775: a, Flora, Zephyrus and Chloris. b, The Three Graces.

2009-10 **Photo.** **Perf. 13x13¼**

3772	A2052	85c multi		2.10	1.10
3773	A2053	€1.35 multi		3.75	1.90
3774	A2054	€1.35 multi		3.50	1.75
		Nos. 3772-3774 (3)		9.35	4.75

Perf. 13¼x13

3775	A2055	Sheet of 2		6.25	6.25
a.		87c multi		2.40	1.25
b.		€1.40 multi		3.75	1.90

Self-Adhesive
Serpentine Die Cut 11
Photo.

3776	A2052	85c multi		2.10	2.10
3777	A2053	€1.35 multi		3.75	3.75
3778	A2054	€1.35 multi		3.50	3.50
		Nos. 3776-3778 (3)		9.35	9.35

Issued: Nos. 3772, 3776, 5/15; Nos. 3773, 3777, 2/19; Nos. 3774, 3778, 6/17; No. 3775, 11/8/10.

A2056

Stamp Day — A2057

2010, Feb. 27 **Engr.** **Perf. 13**

3780	A2056	56c blue & red		1.60	.55

Souvenir Sheet
Litho. & Embossed
Perf. 13¼x13

3781	A2057	€2 multi		5.50	2.75

Protection of Water A2058

Inscriptions: No. 3782, Grands mammifères marins (large marine mammals). No. 3783, Marée noire (black tide). No. 3784, Irrigation. No. 3785, Plaisir de l'eau (pleasure of water). No. 3786, Inondation (flood). No. 3787, Source. No. 3788, Aigues vertes (green water). No. 3789, Secheresse (drought). No. 3790, Hydro-électricité (hydroelectricity). No. 3791, Géothermie (geothermal energy). No.

3792, Pluies acides (acid rain). No. 3793, Fonte des glaciers (melting of glaciers).

Serpentine Die Cut 11
2010, Feb. 27 **Litho.**
Booklet Stamps
Self-Adhesive

3782	A2058	(56c) multi		1.60	.55
3783	A2058	(56c) multi		1.60	.55
3784	A2058	(56c) multi		1.60	.55
3785	A2058	(56c) multi		1.60	.55
3786	A2058	(56c) multi		1.60	.55
3787	A2058	(56c) multi		1.60	.55
3788	A2058	(56c) multi		1.60	.55
3789	A2058	(56c) multi		1.60	.55
3790	A2058	(56c) multi		1.60	.55
3791	A2058	(56c) multi		1.60	.55
3792	A2058	(56c) multi		1.60	.55
3793	A2058	(56c) multi		1.60	.55
a.		Booklet pane of 12, #3782-3793		19.50	
		Nos. 3782-3793 (12)		19.20	6.60

Savoy as Part of France, 150th Anniv. A2059

2010, Mar. 27 **Engr.** **Perf. 13¼x13**

3794	A2059	56c multi		1.60	.55

Self-Adhesive
Serpentine Die Cut 11

3795	A2059	56c multi		1.60	1.60

Tourism Issue

Villeneuve lez Avignon A2060

Orcival Basilica — A2061

Pornic — A2062

Arcueil-Cachan Aqueduct Bridge — A2063

2010 **Engr.** **Perf. 13¼**

3796	A2060	56c multi		1.50	.50
3797	A2061	56c multi		1.40	.45

Perf. 13

3798	A2062	56c multi		1.40	.45

Perf. 13¼

3799	A2063	58c multi		1.60	.55
		Nos. 3796-3799 (4)		5.90	1.95

Self-Adhesive
Engr.
Serpentine Die Cut 11

3800	A2060	56c multi		1.50	1.50

Issued: Nos. 3796, 3800, 4/17; No. 3797, 5/13; No. 3798, 5/25; No. 3799, 9/24.

A2064

A2065

A2066

A2067

A2068   A2069

A2070   A2071

A2072   A2073

A2074

Campaign Against Violence Toward Women — A2075

Serpentine Die Cut 11
2010, Apr. 20 **Litho.**
Booklet Stamps
Self-Adhesive

3801	A2064	(56c) multi		1.50	.50
3802	A2065	(56c) multi		1.50	.50
3803	A2066	(56c) multi		1.50	.50
3804	A2067	(56c) multi		1.50	.50
3805	A2068	(56c) multi		1.50	.50
3806	A2069	(56c) multi		1.50	.50
3807	A2070	(56c) multi		1.50	.50
3808	A2071	(56c) multi		1.50	.50
3809	A2072	(56c) multi		1.50	.50
3810	A2073	(56c) multi		1.50	.50
3811	A2074	(56c) multi		1.50	.50
3812	A2075	(56c) multi		1.50	.50
a.		Booklet pane of 12, #3801-3812		18.00	
		Nos. 3801-3812 (12)		18.00	6.00

Colmar A2076

2010, Apr. 23 **Engr.** **Perf. 13¼**

3813	A2076	56c multi		1.50	.50

Self-Adhesive
Serpentine Die Cut 11

3814	A2076	56c multi		1.50	1.50

National Sheepcote, Rambouillet — A2077

2010, May 1 **Perf. 13¼**

3815	A2077	90c multi		2.40	1.25

Europa A2078

2010, May 9 **Photo.**

3816	A2078	70c multi		1.75	.60

Miniature Sheet

Stamp Bourse in Paris, 150th Anniv. — A2079

No. 3817 — Famous philatelists: a, Pres. Franklin Delano Roosevelt (1882-1945). b, Lucien Berthelot (1903-85), President of International Philatelic Federation. c, Louis Yvert (1866-1950), stamp catalogue publisher, horiz. d, Arthur Maury (1844-1907), stamp catalogue publisher, horiz. e, Alberto Bolaffi (1874-1944), stamp catalogue publisher.

2010, May 13   Engr.   Perf. 13
3817   A2079   Sheet of 5   7.00   7.00
a.-e.   56c Any single   1.40   .45

Deauville, 150th Anniv. A2080

2010, May 14   Photo.   Perf. 13¼
3818   A2080   85c multi   2.10   1.10

Mother Teresa (1910-97), Humanitarian A2081

2010, May 27   Engr.   Perf. 13¼x13
3819   A2081   85c multi   2.10   1.10
Self-Adhesive
Serpentine Die Cut 11
3820   A2081   85c multi   2.10   2.10

Institute of Human Paleontology, Paris, Cent. — A2082

2010, June 1   Perf. 13x12¾
3821   A2082   56c multi   1.40   .45
See Monaco No. 2597.

Nice as Part of France, 150th Anniv. A2083

2010, June 11   Photo.   Perf. 13¼
3822   A2083   56c multi   1.40   .45
Self-Adhesive
Serpentine Die Cut 11
3823   A2083   56c multi   1.40   1.40

Front Side of No. 3824

Rear Side of No. 3824 — A2084

A2085

2010 World Cup Soccer Championships, South Africa — A2086

No. 3825: a, Soccer player and ball. b, Soccer players, vert. c, South African building, vert. d, Aerial view of Cape Town.

2010   Photo.   Perf. 13x12¾
3824   A2084   56c multi   2.75   .50
Perf. 13x13¼, 13¼x13
3825   A2085   Sheet of 4   8.50   8.50
a.-d.   85c Any single   2.10   1.10
Embossed and Etched on Silver
Die Cut Perf. 12¾
Self-Adhesive
3826   A2086   €5 silver   12.50   12.50

Issued: Nos. 3824, 3825, 6/13; No. 3826, 6/11. No. 3824 is gummed on both sides and sold for €1.12. Both sides of the stamp could be used. Values for used examples of No. 3824 are for stamps canceled on either or both sides.

Launch of Soyuz Space Flights From French Guiana A2087

2010, June 12   Photo.   Perf. 13¼
3827   A2087   85c multi   2.25   1.10
Self-Adhesive
Serpentine Die Cut 11
3828   A2087   85c multi   2.25   2.25

Souvenir Sheet

Jardins de Giverny, by Claude Monet — A2088

No. 3829: a, Bridge. b, Pond.

2010, June 12   Perf. 13¼x13
3829   A2088   Sheet of 2   11.50   11.50
a.-b.   €2.22 Either single   5.75   3.00
c.   Souvenir sheet, #3709a,   3709b, 3829a, 3829b   22.50   22.50

2010 Salon du Timbre (#3829c).

Regional Cuisine A2089

Designs: No. 3830, Eclade (grilled mussels), Poitou-Charentes. No. 3831, Baeckaoffe (stew), Alsace. No. 3832, Tomme des Pyrénées cheese, Midi-Pyrénées. No. 3833, Tarte aux mirabelles (plum tart), Lorraine. No. 3834, Potage aux cresson (watercress soup), Ile-de-France. No. 3835, Flamiche (leek pie), Picardy. No. 3836, Pont l'Evêque cheese, Basse-Normandie. No. 3837, Blanc-manger (blancmange), Antilles. No. 3838, Caviar, Aquitaine. No. 3839, Chapon (capon), Franche-Comté. No. 3840, Fourme d'Ambert cheese, Auvergne. No. 3841, Tarte tatin (upside-down apple tart), Centre.

No. 3842, Quenelles (dumplings), Rhône-Alpes. No. 3843, Escalope normande (veal cutlet), Haute-Normandie. No. 3844, Maroilles cheese, Nord-Pas-de-Calais. No. 3845, Clafoutis (baked fruit and batter), Limousin. No. 3846, Gougères (cheese pastry), Bourgogne. No. 3847, Tian (baked vegetables), Provence-Alpes-Côte d'Azur. No. 3848, Brocciu cheese, Corsica. No. 3849, Abricots rouges au miel (apricots in honey), Languedoc-Roussillon. No. 3850, Homard breton (lobster), Bretagne. No. 3851, Brochet au beurre blanc (pike with white butter), Pays de la Loire. No. 3852, Chaource cheese, Champagne-Ardennes. No. 3853, Paris-Brest (butter cream-filled pastry), Paris.

Serpentine Die Cut 11
2010, June 12   Photo.
Booklet Stamps
Self-Adhesive
3830   A2089   (56c) multi   1.40   .45
3831   A2089   (56c) multi   1.40   .45
3832   A2089   (56c) multi   1.40   .45
3833   A2089   (56c) multi   1.40   .45
a.   Booklet pane of 4, #3830-3833   5.60
3834   A2089   (56c) multi   1.40   .45
3835   A2089   (56c) multi   1.40   .45
3836   A2089   (56c) multi   1.40   .45
3837   A2089   (56c) multi   1.40   .45
a.   Booklet pane of 4, #3834-3837   5.60
3838   A2089   (56c) multi   1.40   .45
3839   A2089   (56c) multi   1.40   .45
3840   A2089   (56c) multi   1.40   .45
3841   A2089   (56c) multi   1.40   .45
a.   Booklet pane of 4, #3838-3841   5.60
     Complete booklet, #3833a, 3837a, 3841a   17.00
3842   A2089   (56c) multi   1.40   .45
3843   A2089   (56c) multi   1.40   .45
3844   A2089   (56c) multi   1.40   .45
3845   A2089   (56c) multi   1.40   .45
a.   Booklet pane of 4, #3842-3845   5.60
3846   A2089   (56c) multi   1.40   .45
3847   A2089   (56c) multi   1.40   .45
3848   A2089   (56c) multi   1.40   .45
3849   A2089   (56c) multi   1.40   .45
a.   Booklet pane of 4, #3846-3849   5.60
3850   A2089   (56c) multi   1.40   .45
3851   A2089   (56c) multi   1.40   .45
3852   A2089   (56c) multi   1.40   .45
3853   A2089   (56c) multi   1.40   .45
a.   Booklet pane of 4, #3850-3853   5.60

     Complete booklet, #3845a,   3849a, 3853a   17.00
Nos. 3830-3853 (24)   33.60   10.80

Romanesque Art — A2090

Designs: No. 3854, Bas-relief, Tournus. No. 3855, Interior of Cistercian Abbey, Léoncel. No. 3856, Painting, St. Sever. No. 3857, Serrabone Priory, Boule d'Amont. No. 3858, Sculpture, L'Ile-Bouchard. No. 3859, Painting, Citeaux Abbey. No. 3860, Fresco from St. Martin's Church, Nohant-Vic. No. 3861, Bas-relief, Clermont-Ferrand. No. 3862, Fresco, St. Jacques-des-Guérets. No. 3863, Bas-relief, Angouleme. No. 3864, Painting of the Consecration of the third Abbey Church, Cluny. No. 3865, Bas-reliefs, tympanum of Saint-Foy Abbey Church, Conques.

Serpentine Die Cut 11
2010, June 14   Photo.
Booklet Stamps
Self-Adhesive
3854   A2090   (56c) multi   1.40   .45
3855   A2090   (56c) multi   1.40   .45
3856   A2090   (56c) multi   1.40   .45
3857   A2090   (56c) multi   1.40   .45
3858   A2090   (56c) multi   1.40   .45
3859   A2090   (56c) multi   1.40   .45
3860   A2090   (56c) multi   1.40   .45
3861   A2090   (56c) multi   1.40   .45
3862   A2090   (56c) multi   1.40   .45
3863   A2090   (56c) multi   1.40   .45
3864   A2090   (56c) multi   1.40   .45
3865   A2090   (56c) multi   1.40   .45
a.   Booklet pane of 12, #3854-3865   17.00
Nos. 3854-3865 (12)   16.80   5.40
See Nos. 3870A-3870B.

Miniature Sheet

Mills — A2091

No. 3866: a, Windmill, Montbrun-Lauragais. b, Windmill, Cassel. c, Aigremonts Windmill, Bléré, horiz. d, Daudet Windmill, Fontvieille, horiz. e, Flour mill, Villeneuve-d'Ascq. f, Birlot Watermill, Ile-de-Bréhat, horiz.

2010, June 15   Litho. & Engr.   Perf. 13
3866   A2091   Sheet of 6   8.50   8.50
a.-f.   56c Any single   1.40   .45

2010 Youth Olympics, Singapore A2092

2010, June 16   Photo.   Perf. 13¼
3867   A2092   85c multi   2.25   1.10

Souvenir Sheet

Charles de Gaulle's Appeal of June 18 Speech, 70th Anniv. — A2093

2010, June 18 Engr. Perf. 13x13¼
3868 A2093 56c multi 1.40 .45

Conciergerie, Paris — A2094

2010, June 19
3869 A2094 56c multi + label 1.40 .45

French Federation of Philatelic Associations, 83rd Congress, Paris.

French Pavilion, Expo 2010, Shanghai A2095

2010, June 20 Photo. Perf. 13¼
3870 A2095 85c multi 2.25 1.10

Romanesque Art Type of 2010

Designs: No. 3870A, Like #3855. No. 3870B, Like #3858.

Serpentine Die Cut 11
2010, June 21 Litho.
Self-Adhesive
3870A A2090 (56c) multi 1.40 1.40
3870B A2090 (56c) multi 1.40 1.40

Nos. 3870A-3870B each were printed in sheets of 50. The red panels of Nos. 3855 and 3858 are splotchy, typical of photogravure printings. Under magnification black dots can be seen in the red panels on Nos. 3870A-3870B.

Marianne and Stars Type of 2008

2010, July 1		**Engr.**	**Perf. 13**	
3871	A1912	75c olive green	1.90	.50
3872	A1912	87c purple	2.25	.55
3873	A1912	95c fawn	2.40	.60
3874	A1912	€1.35 blue	3.50	.90
3875	A1912	€1.40 red violet	3.50	.90
3876	A1912	€2.30 chocolate	5.75	1.50
	Nos. 3871-3876 (6)		19.30	4.95

Self-Adhesive
Serpentine Die Cut 6¾ Vert.

3877	A1912	75c olive green	1.90	1.90
3878	A1912	87c purple	2.25	2.25
3879	A1912	95c fawn	2.40	2.40
3880	A1912	€1.35 blue	3.50	3.50
3881	A1912	€1.40 red violet	3.50	3.50
3882	A1912	€2.30 chocolate	5.75	5.75
	Nos. 3877-3882 (6)		19.30	19.30

Musical Instruments Type of 2010

Designs: No. 3882A, Like #3761. No. 3882B, Like #3767.

Serpentine Die Cut 11
2010, July 1 Litho.
Self-Adhesive
3882A A2050 (58c) multi 1.50 1.50
3882B A2050 (58c) multi 1.50 1.50

Nos. 3882A-3882B were each printed in sheets of 50. The gray blue portions of Nos. 3761 and 3767 are splotchy, typical of photogravure printings, and not splotchy on Nos. 3882A and 3882B.

Independence of French Colonies in Africa, 50th Anniv. — A2096

2010, July 15 Photo. Perf. 13¼
3883 A2096 87c multi 2.25 1.10

Self-Adhesive
Serpentine Die Cut 11
3884 A2096 87c multi 2.25 2.25

Butterflies A2097

Designs: Nos. 3885, 3886b, Morpho menelaus. No. 3886a, Cerura vinula caterpillar. 75c, Thersamolycaena dispar, vert. 95c, Callophrys rubi.

Litho. (#3885, 3886a), Litho. & Embossed
2010, Sept. 3 Perf. 13¼
3885	A2097 58c multi	1.50	.50
3886	Sheet of 4	7.50	7.50
a.	A2097 58c multi	1.50	.50
b.	A2097 58c multi	1.50	.50
c.	A2097 75c multi	2.00	.65
d.	A2097 95c multi	2.50	.85

Universal Israelite Alliance, 150th Anniv. A2098

Litho. & Engr.
2010, Sept. 7 Perf. 13¼
3887 A2098 58c multi 1.50 .50

A2099

A2100

A2101

A2102

A2103

A2104

A2105

A2106

A2107

A2108

A2109

Cartoons With Letters A2110

Serpentine Die Cut 11
2010, Oct. 11 Photo.
Booklet Stamps
Self-Adhesive
3888	A2099	(58c) multi	1.75	.60
3889	A2100	(58c) multi	1.75	.60
3890	A2101	(58c) multi	1.75	.60
3891	A2102	(58c) multi	1.75	.60
3892	A2103	(58c) multi	1.75	.60
3893	A2104	(58c) multi	1.75	.60
3894	A2105	(58c) multi	1.75	.60
3895	A2106	(58c) multi	1.75	.60
3896	A2107	(58c) multi	1.75	.60
3897	A2108	(58c) multi	1.75	.60
3898	A2109	(58c) multi	1.75	.60
3899	A2110	(58c) multi	1.75	.60
a.	Booklet pane of 12, #3888-3899		21.00	
	Nos. 3888-3899 (12)		21.00	7.20

Aviation Pioneers — A2111

Designs: Nos. 3900, 3902, Elise Deroche (1882-1919).
No. 3901: a, Hubert Latham (1883-1912). b, Orville (1871-1948) and Wilbur Wright (1867-1912). c, Henry Farman (1874-1958). d, Jules Védrines (1881-1919). e, Léon Delagrange (1872-1910).

2010, Oc. 15 Photo. Perf. 13
3900	A2111 58c multi	1.75	.60
3901	Sheet of 6, #3900, 3901a-3901e	15.00	15.00
a.-e.	A2111 58c Any single	2.50	2.50

Self-Adhesive
Serpentine Die Cut 11
3902 A2111 58c multi 1.75 1.75

No. 3901 sold for € 5.40, with the Red Cross receiving €1.92 of that.

World Fencing Championships, Paris — A2112

Designs: 58c, Wheelchair fencing. 87c, Fencing.

2010, Oct. 22 Engr. Perf. 13x13¼
3903	A2112 58c multi	1.75	.60
3904	A2112 87c multi	2.50	.85
a.	Horiz. pair, #3903-3904 + central label	4.25	1.50

Paris Bar Association,
Bicent. — A2113

2010, Oct. 28   Photo.   Perf. 13¼
3905 A2113 58c black & lt blue   1.75   .60

Self-Adhesive
Serpentine Die Cut 11
3906 A2113 58c black & lt blue   1.75   1.75

Villeneuve-sur-Lot — A2114

2010, Oct. 30   Engr.   Perf. 13¼
3907 A2114 58c multi   1.75   .60

European Capitals Type of 2002
Miniature Sheet

No. 3908 — Attractions in Paris: a, Arc de Triomphe de l'Etoile. b, Notre Dame Cathedral. c, Garnier Opera House. d, Eiffel Tower, vert.

Perf. 13x13¼, 13¼x13 (#3908d)
2010, Nov. 4   Photo.
3908 A1622   Sheet of 4   7.00   7.00
a.-d.   58c Any single   1.75   .60

A2115   A2116

A2117   A2118

A2119   A2120

A2121   A2122

A2123   A2124

A2125   A2126

A2127   "Best
Wishes" — A2128

Serpentine Die Cut 11
2010, Nov. 5   Photo.
Booklet Stamps
Self-Adhesive
3909 A2115 (58c) multi   1.75   .60
3910 A2116 (58c) multi   1.75   .60
3911 A2117 (58c) multi   1.75   .60
3912 A2118 (58c) multi   1.75   .60
3913 A2119 (58c) multi   1.75   .60
3914 A2120 (58c) multi   1.75   .60
3915 A2121 (58c) multi   1.75   .60
3916 A2122 (58c) multi   1.75   .60
3917 A2123 (58c) multi   1.75   .60
3918 A2124 (58c) multi   1.75   .60
3919 A2125 (58c) multi   1.75   .60
3920 A2126 (58c) multi   1.75   .60
3921 A2127 (58c) multi   1.75   .60
3922 A2128 (58c) multi   1.75   .60
a.   Booklet pane of 14, #3909-
3922, + 14 stickers   24.50
Nos. 3909-3922 (14)   24.50   8.40

Souvenir Sheet

Primitive Flemish Paintings — A2130

No. 3924: a, Madonna and Child, by Roger de la Pasture. b, Portrait of Laurent Froimont, by Rogier van der Weyden.

2010, Nov. 6   Photo.   Perf. 13
3924 A2130   Sheet of 2   10.00   10.00
a.-b.   €1.80 Either single   5.00   2.50
See Belgium No.

Independence
Movements of
Latin America
and the
Caribbean,
Bicent. — A2131

2010, Nov. 27   Perf. 13¼
3925 A2131 87c multi   2.40   .80

Subject Index of French Commemorative Issues

FRANCE

SEMI-POSTAL STAMPS

No. 162 Surcharged in Red and:

No. B1 — SP2

1914 Unwmk. Typo. Perf. 14x13½
B1	A22	10c + 5c red	5.00	4.25
		Never hinged	7.00	
B2	SP2	10c + 5c red	32.50	3.25
		Never hinged	90.00	
a.		Booklet pane of 10	600.00	
		Never hinged	800.00	

Issue dates: #B1, Aug. 11; #B2, Sept. 10.
For overprint see Offices in Morocco #B8.

Widow at Grave SP3 — War Orphans SP4

Woman Plowing — SP5

"Trench of Bayonets" SP6

Lion of Belfort SP7

"La Marseillaise" — SP8

1917-19
B3	SP3	2c + 3c vio brn	4.50	5.00
		Never hinged	10.00	
B4	SP4	5c + 5c grn ('19)	21.00	9.50
		Never hinged	60.00	
B5	SP5	15c + 10c gray green	30.00	27.50
		Never hinged	85.00	
B6	SP5	25c + 15c dp bl	80.00	57.50
		Never hinged	175.00	
B7	SP6	35c + 25c slate & vio	135.00	125.00
		Never hinged	350.00	
B8	SP7	50c + 50c pale brn & dk brn	225.00	180.00
		Never hinged	650.00	
B9	SP8	1fr + 1fr cl & mar	425.00	400.00
		Never hinged	1,100.	
B10	SP8	5fr + 5fr dp bl & blk	1,600.	1,550.
		Never hinged	4,000.	
		Nos. B3-B10 (8)	2,520.	2,354.

See #B20-B23. For surcharges see #B12-B19.

Hospital Ship and Field Hospital SP9

1918, Aug.
B11	SP9	15c + 5c sl & red	125.00	60.00
		Never hinged	250.00	

Semi-Postal Stamps of 1917-19 Surcharged

1922, Sept. 1
B12	SP3	2c + 1c violet brn	.50	.80
		Never hinged	1.00	
B13	SP4	5c + 2½c green	.80	1.25
		Never hinged	1.50	
B14	SP5	15c + 5c gray grn	1.25	1.60
		Never hinged	2.60	
B15	SP5	25c + 5c deep bl	2.30	2.50
		Never hinged	4.75	
B16	SP6	35c + 5c slate & vio	13.00	15.00
		Never hinged	30.00	
B17	SP7	50c + 10c pale brn & dk brn	19.00	24.00
		Never hinged	39.00	
a.		Pair, one without surcharge		
B18	SP8	1fr + 25c cl & mar	32.50	37.50
		Never hinged	60.00	
B19	SP8	5fr + 1fr bl & blk	150.00	155.00
		Never hinged	275.00	
		Nos. B12-B19 (8)	219.35	237.65
		Set, never hinged	415.00	

Style and arrangement of surcharge differs for each denomination.

Types of 1917-19

1926-27
B20	SP3	2c + 1c violet brn	1.50	1.40
		Never hinged	4.00	
B21	SP7	50c + 10c ol brn & dk brn	20.00	12.50
		Never hinged	72.50	
B22	SP8	1fr + 25c dp rose & red brn	55.00	42.50
		Never hinged	150.00	
B23	SP8	5fr + 1fr sl bl & blk	105.00	100.00
		Never hinged	240.00	
		Nos. B20-B23 (4)	181.50	156.40

Sinking Fund Issues

Types of Regular Issues of 1903-07 Surcharged in Red or Blue

1927, Sept. 26
B24	A22	40c + 10c lt blue (R)	5.75	5.75
		Never hinged	10.50	
B25	A20	50c + 25c green (Bl)	8.25	9.00
		Never hinged	14.00	

Surcharge on #B25 differs from illustration.

Type of Regular Issue of 1923 Surcharged in Black

B26	A23	1.50fr + 50c orange	14.50	14.00
		Never hinged	37.50	
a.		Pair, one without surcharge	2,000.	
		Nos. B24-B26 (3)	28.50	28.75

See Nos. B28-B33, B35-B37, B39-B41.

Industry and Agriculture SP10

1928, May Engr. Perf. 13½
B27	SP10	1.50fr + 8.50fr dull blue	130.00	150.00
		Never hinged	200.00	
a.		Blue green	500.00	550.00
		Never hinged	725.00	

Types of 1903-23 Issues Surcharged like Nos. B24-B26

1928, Oct. 1 Perf. 14x13½
B28	A22	40c + 10c gray lilac (R)	13.00	14.00
		Never hinged	32.50	

B29	A20	50c + 25c orange brn (Bl)	32.50	29.00
		Never hinged	60.00	
B30	A23	1.50fr + 50c rose lilac (Bk)	52.50	42.50
		Never hinged	100.00	
		Nos. B28-B30 (3)	98.00	85.50

Types of 1903-23 Issues Surcharged like Nos. B24-B26

1929, Oct. 1
B31	A22	40c + 10c green	18.00	19.00
		Never hinged	37.50	
B32	A20	50c + 25c lilac rose	30.00	30.00
		Never hinged	60.00	
B33	A23	1.50fr + 50c chestnut	60.00	65.00
		Never hinged	130.00	
		Nos. B31-B33 (3)	108.00	114.00

"The Smile of Reims" SP11

1930, Mar. 15 Engr. Perf. 13
B34	SP11	1.50fr + 3.50fr red vio	80.00	82.50
		Never hinged	130.00	
a.		Booklet pane of 4	300.00	
		Never hinged	525.00	
b.		Booklet pane of 8	600.00	
		Never hinged	1,050.	
		Complete booklet, #B34b	1,100.	

Booklets containing No. B34 have two panes of 4 (#B34a) connected by a gutter, the complete piece constituting #B34b, which is stapled into the booklet through the gutter.

Types of 1903-07 Issues Surcharged like Nos. B24-B25

1930 Oct. 1 Perf. 14x13½
B35	A22	40c + 10c cerise	20.00	21.00
		Never hinged	70.00	
B36	A20	50c + 25c gray brown	37.50	42.50
		Never hinged	120.00	
B37	A22	1.50fr + 50c violet	65.00	70.00
		Never hinged	190.00	
		Nos. B35-B37 (3)	122.50	133.50

Allegory, French Provinces SP12

1931, Mar. 1 Perf. 13
B38	SP12	1.50fr + 3.50fr green	125.00	140.00
		Never hinged	300.00	

Types of 1903-07 Issues Surcharged like Nos. B24-B25

1931, Oct. 1 Perf. 14x13½
B39	A22	40c + 10c ol grn	40.00	45.00
		Never hinged	100.00	
B40	A20	50c + 25c gray vio	100.00	110.00
		Never hinged	235.00	
B41	A22	1.50fr + 50c deep red	100.00	110.00
		Never hinged	200.00	
		Nos. B39-B41 (3)	240.00	265.00

Catalogue values for unused stamps in this section, from this point to the end of the section, are for Never Hinged items.

"France" Giving Aid to an Intellectual SP13

Symbolic of Music SP14

1935, Dec. 9 Engr. Perf. 13
B42	SP13	50c + 10c ultra	4.00	2.50
		Never hinged	2.50	
B43	SP14	50c + 2fr dull red	125.00	45.00
		Hinged	55.00	

The surtax was for the aid of distressed and exiled intellectuals.
For surcharge see No. B47.

Statue of Liberty SP15 — Children of the Unemployed SP16

1936-37
B44	SP15	50c + 25c dk blue ('37)	7.50	5.00
		Hinged	4.00	
B45	SP15	75c + 50c violet	20.00	10.00
		Hinged	9.50	

Surtax for the aid of political refugees.
For surcharge see No. B47.

1936, May
B46	SP16	50c + 10c copper red	7.50	5.00
		Hinged	4.50	

The surtax was for the aid of children of the unemployed.

No. B43 Surcharged in Black

1936, Nov.
B47	SP14	20c on 50c + 2fr dull red	4.00	3.00
		Hinged	2.75	

Jacques Callot SP17

Anatole France (Jacques Anatole Thibault) — SP18

Hector Berlioz SP19

Victor Hugo SP20

Auguste Rodin SP21

Louis
Pasteur
SP22

1936-37   Engr.

B48 SP17   20c + 10c brown
                              car   4.50   2.50
  Hinged   2.25
B49 SP18   30c + 10c emer
                              ('37)   5.00   2.75
  Hinged   2.25
B50 SP19   40c + 10c emer   4.50   2.75
  Hinged   2.25
B51 SP20   50c + 10c copper
                              red   8.75   3.75
  Hinged   3.75
B52 SP21   90c + 10c rose
                              red ('37)   13.00   6.50
  Hinged   6.00
B53 SP22   1.50fr + 50c deep
                              ultra   40.00   20.00
  Hinged   20.00
  Nos. B48-B53 (6)   75.75   38.25

The surtax was used for relief of unemployed intellectuals.

1938

B54 SP18   30c + 10c brown
                              car   3.00   1.75
  Hinged   1.75
B55 SP17   35c + 10c dull
                              green   3.50   2.40
  Hinged   2.40
B56 SP19   55c + 10c dull vio   10.00   4.00
  Hinged   6.00
B57 SP20   65c + 10c ultra   11.50   4.00
  Hinged   6.00
B58 SP21   1fr + 10c car
                              lake   8.50   4.50
  Hinged   4.75
B59 SP22   1.75fr + 25c dp blue   35.00   17.00
  Hinged   17.00
  Nos. B54-B59 (6)   71.50   33.65

Tug of War
SP23

Foot Race
SP24

Hiking — SP25

1937, June 16

B60 SP23   20c + 10c brown   3.00   2.25
  Hinged   1.60
B61 SP24   40c + 10c red
                              brown   3.00   2.25
  Hinged   1.60
B62 SP25   50c + 10c black brn   3.00   2.25
  Hinged   1.60
  Nos. B60-B62 (3)   9.00   6.75

The surtax was for the Recreation Fund of the employees of the Post, Telephone and Telegraph.

Pierre Loti
(Louis
Marie Julien
Viaud)
SP26

1937, Aug.

B63 SP26   50c + 20c rose car   7.50   5.00
  Hinged   3.75

The surtax was for the Pierre Loti Monument Fund.

"France"
and Infant
SP27

1937-39

B64 SP27   65c + 25c brown vio   5.25   2.75
  Hinged   3.25
B65 SP27   90c + 30c pck bl ('39)   3.50   2.75
  Hinged   2.10

The surtax was used for public health work.

Winged Victory   Jean Baptiste
of Samothrace   Charcot
SP28   SP29

1937, Aug.

B66 SP28   30c blue green   175.00   40.00
  Hinged   65.00
B67 SP28   55c red   175.00   40.00
  Hinged   65.00

On sale at the Louvre for 2.50fr. The surtax of 1.65fr was for the benefit of the Louvre Museum.

1938-39

B68 SP29   65c + 35c dk bl grn   3.25   3.25
  Hinged   1.60
B69 SP29   90c + 35c brt red
                              vio ('39)   37.50   19.00
  Hinged   11.00

Surtax for the benefit of French seamen.

Palace of
Versailles
SP30

1938, May 9

B70 SP30   1.75fr + 75c dp bl   37.50   19.00
  Hinged   19.00

Natl. Exposition of Painting and Sculpture at Versailles.
The surtax was for the benefit of the Versailles Concert Society.

French Soldier   Monument
SP31   SP32

1938, May 16

B71 SP31   55c + 70c brown vio   8.50   5.25
  Hinged   4.75
B72 SP31   65c + 1.10fr pck bl   8.50   5.25
  Hinged   4.75

The surtax was for a fund to erect a monument to the glory of the French Infantrymen.

1938, May 25

B73 SP32   55c + 45c vermilion   22.50   12.50
  Hinged   10.00

The surtax was for a fund to erect a monument in honor of the Army Medical Corps.

Reims Cathedral   "France"
SP33   Welcoming Her
                              Sons
                              SP34

1938, July 10

B74 SP33   65c + 35c ultra   17.50   10.50
  Hinged   8.50

Completion of the reconstruction of Reims Cathedral, July 10, 1938.

1938, Aug. 8

B75 SP34   65c + 60c rose car   8.50   5.75
  Hinged   4.00

The surtax was for the benefit of French volunteers repatriated from Spain.

Curie Issue
Common Design Type
1938, Sept. 1

B76 CD80   1.75fr + 50c dp ul-
                              tra   21.00   12.50
  Hinged   8.75

Victory
Parade
Passing Arc
de
Triomphe
SP36

1938, Oct. 8

B77 SP36   65c + 35c brown car   5.75   4.50
  Hinged   3.25

20th anniversary of the Armistice.

Student and
Nurse — SP37

1938, Dec. 1

B78 SP37   65c + 60c pck blue   15.00   8.25
  Hinged   8.00

The surtax was for Student Relief.

Blind Man
and Radio
SP38

1938, Dec.

B79 SP38   90c + 25c brown vio   15.00   9.00
  Hinged   8.00

The surtax was used to help provide radios for the blind.

Civilian Facing   Red Cross
Firing   Nurse — SP40
Squad — SP39

1939, Feb. 1

B80 SP39   90c + 35c black brn   17.00   10.50
  Hinged   8.75

The surtax was used to erect a monument to civilian victims of World War I.

1939, Mar. 24

B81 SP40   90c + 35c dk sl grn,
                              turq bl & red 13.00   8.25
  Hinged   6.75

75th anniv. of the Intl. Red Cross Soc.

Army
Engineer
SP41

1939, Apr. 3

B82 SP41   70c + 50c vermilion   12.50   8.25
  Hinged   6.00

Army Engineering Corps. The surtax was used to erect a monument to those members who died in World War I.

Ministry of
Post,
Telegraph
and
Telephone
SP42

1939, Apr. 8

B83 SP42   90c + 35c turq blue   37.50   20.00
  Hinged   19.00

The surtax was used to aid orphans of employees of the postal system. Opening of the new building for the Ministry of Post, Telegraph and Telephones.

Mother and   Eiffel
Child — SP43   Tower — SP44

1939, Apr. 24

B84 SP43   90c + 35c red   3.75   2.50
  Hinged   2.40

The surtax was used to aid children of the unemployed.

1939, May 5

B85 SP44   90c + 50c red violet   15.00   9.00
  Hinged   8.75

50th anniv. of the Eiffel Tower. The surtax was used for celebration festivities.

Puvis de
Chavannes — SP45

Claude
Debussy
SP46

Honoré de
Balzac
SP47

Claude
Bernard
SP48

1939-40
B86	SP45	40c + 10c ver	1.75	1.00
	Hinged			.80
B87	SP46	70c + 10c brn vio	8.25	2.50
	Hinged			3.50
B87A	SP46	80c + 10c brn vio ('40)	9.00	7.50
	Hinged			4.25
B88	SP47	90c + 10c brt red vio	7.25	2.50
	Hinged			3.25
B88A	SP47	1fr + 10c brt red vio ('40)	9.00	7.50
	Hinged			4.25
B89	SP48	2.25fr + 25c brt ultra	28.00	11.50
	Hinged			14.50
B89A	SP48	2.50fr + 25c brt ultra ('40)	9.00	7.50
	Hinged			4.25
	Nos. B86-B89A (7)		72.25	40.00

The surtax was used to aid unemployed intellectuals.

Mothers and Children
SP49   SP50

1939, June 15
B90	SP49	70c + 80c bl, grn & vio	5.25	4.50
	Hinged			3.25
B91	SP50	90c + 60c dk brn, dl vio & brn	8.50	5.25
	Hinged			4.75

The surtax was used to aid France's repopulation campaign.

"The Letter" by
Jean Honoré
Fragonard
SP51

Statue of Widow
and Children
SP52

1939, July 6
B92	SP51	40c + 60c multi	4.25	2.75
	Hinged			2.40

The surtax was used for the Postal Museum.

1939, July 20
B93	SP52	70c + 30c brown vio	25.00	12.00
				12.00

Surtax for the benefit of French seamen.

French
Soldier
SP53

Colonial
Trooper
SP54

1940, Feb. 15
B94	SP53	40c + 60c sepia	3.75	2.75
	Hinged			2.00
B95	SP54	1fr + 50c turq blue	3.75	2.75
	Hinged			2.00

The surtax was used to assist the families of mobilized men.

World Map Showing French
Possessions — SP55

1940, Apr. 15
B96	SP55	1fr + 25c scarlet	2.75	2.75
	Hinged			2.00

Marshal
Joseph J.
C. Joffre
SP56

Marshal Ferdinand
Foch — SP57

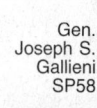

Gen.
Joseph S.
Gallieni
SP58

Woman
Plowing
SP59

1940, May 1
B97	SP56	80c + 45c choc	8.25	6.00
	Hinged			3.50
B98	SP57	1fr + 50c dk vio	7.50	6.00
	Hinged			3.25
B99	SP58	1.50fr + 50c brown red	7.50	4.00
	Hinged			3.25
B100	SP59	2.50fr + 50c indigo & dl bl	15.00	11.50
	Hinged			7.50
	Nos. B97-B100 (4)		38.25	27.50

The surtax was used for war charities.

Doctor,
Nurse,
Soldier and
Family
SP60

Nurse and
Wounded
Soldier
SP61

1940, May 12
B101	SP60	80c + 1fr dk grn & red	8.25	6.00
	Hinged			4.00
B102	SP61	1fr + 2fr sep & red	11.50	6.50
	Hinged			5.25

The surtax was used for the Red Cross.

Nurse with Injured
Children — SP62

1940, Nov. 12
B103	SP62	1fr + 2fr sepia	1.25	.80
	Hinged			.80

The surtax was used for victims of the war.

Wheat
Harvest
SP63

Sowing
SP64

Picking
Grapes
SP65

Grazing
Cattle
SP66

1940, Dec. 2
B104	SP63	80c + 2fr brn blk	3.25	2.10
	Hinged			1.60
B105	SP64	1fr + 2fr chestnut	3.25	2.10
	Hinged			1.60
B106	SP65	1.50fr + 2fr brt vio	3.25	2.10
	Hinged			1.60
B107	SP66	2.50fr + 2fr dp grn	4.00	2.25
	Hinged			2.00
	Nos. B104-B107 (4)		13.75	8.55

The surtax was for national relief.

Prisoners of War
SP67   SP68

1941, Jan. 1
B108	SP67	80c + 5fr dark grn	1.60	1.50
B109	SP68	1fr + 5fr rose brn	1.75	1.60

The surtax was for prisoners of war.

Science
Fighting
Cancer
SP69

1941, Feb. 20
B110	SP69	2.50fr+ 50c slate blk & brn	1.60	1.40

Surtax used for the control of cancer.

No. 417 Surcharged +10c in Blue
1941, Mar. 4
B111	A109	1fr + 10c crimson	.25	.20

Men
Hauling
Coal
SP70

"France"
Aiding
Needy Man
SP71

1941
B112	SP70	1fr + 2fr sepia	2.75	1.40
B113	SP71	2.50fr + 7.50fr dk bl	9.00	3.00

The surtax was for Marshal Pétain's National Relief Fund.

Liner
Pasteur
SP72

Red Surcharge
1941, July 17
B114	SP72	1fr + 1fr on 70c dk bl grn	.40	.40

World Map,
Mercator
Projection
SP73

1941
B115	SP73	1fr + 1fr multi	.80	.50

Fisherman — SP74

1941, Oct. 23
B116	SP74	1fr + 9fr dk blue grn	1.00	.90

Surtax for benefit of French seamen.

Arms of Various Cities

Nancy
SP75

Lille
SP76

Rouen
SP77

Bordeaux
SP78

Toulouse
SP79

Clermont-
Ferrand
SP80

Marseille
SP81

Lyon
SP82

Rennes
SP83

Reims
SP84

Montpellier
SP85

Paris
SP86

1941   *Perf. 14x13*

B117	SP75	20c + 30c brn blk	2.75	2.75
B118	SP76	40c + 60c org brn	2.75	2.75
B119	SP77	50c + 70c grnsh blue	2.75	2.75
B120	SP78	70c + 80c rose vio	2.75	2.75
B121	SP79	80c + 1fr dp rose	2.75	2.75
B122	SP80	1fr + 1fr black	2.75	2.75
B123	SP81	1.50fr + 2fr dk bl	2.75	2.75
B124	SP82	2fr + 2fr dk vio	2.75	2.75
B125	SP83	2.50fr + 3fr brt grn	2.75	2.75
B126	SP84	3fr + 5fr org brn	2.75	2.75
B127	SP85	5fr + 6fr brt ultra	2.75	2.75
B128	SP86	10fr + 10fr dk red	2.75	2.75
	Nos. B117-B128 (12)		33.00	33.00

Count de
La Pérouse
SP87

1942, Mar. 23   *Perf. 13*
B129 SP87 2.50fr + 7.50fr ultra   1.25 1.40

Jean Francois de Galaup de La Pérouse, (1741-88), French navigator and explorer. The surtax was for National Relief.

Planes over
Fields
SP88

1942, Apr. 4
B130 SP88 1.50fr + 3.50fr lt vio   2.40 2.40

The surtax was for the benefit of French airmen and their familes.

Alexis
Chabrier
SP89

1942, May 18
B131 SP89 2fr + 3fr sepia   1.25 1.25

Emmanuel Chabrier (1841-1894), composer, birth centenary. The surtax was for works of charity among musicians.

Symbolical
of French
Colonial
Empire
SP90

1942, May 18
B132 SP90 1.50fr + 8.50fr black   1.10 1.10

The surtax was for National Relief.

Jean de
Vienne
SP91

1942, June 16
B133 SP91 1.50fr + 8.50fr sepia   1.10 1.10

600th anniv. of the birth of Jean de Vienne, 1st admiral of France. The surtax was for the benefit of French seamen.

Type of Regular Issue,
1941 Surcharged in
Carmine

1942, Sept. 10   *Perf. 14x13½*
B134 A116 1.50fr + 50c brt ultra   .20 .20

The surtax was for national relief ("Secours National").

Arms of Various Cities

Chambéry
SP92

La Rochelle
SP93

Poitiers
SP94

Orléans
SP95

Grenoble
SP96

Dijon
SP98

Le Havre
SP100

Nice
SP102

Angers
SP97

Limoges
SP99

Nantes
SP101

St. Etienne
SP103

      Perf. 14x13

1942, Oct.		Unwmk.	Engr.
B135	SP92	50c + 60c blk	3.50 3.50
B136	SP93	60c + 70c grnsh blue	3.50 3.50
B137	SP94	80c + 1fr rose	3.50 3.50
B138	SP95	1fr + 1.30fr dk green	3.50 3.50
B139	SP96	1.20fr + 1.50fr rose vio	3.50 3.50
B140	SP97	1.50fr + 1.80fr slate bl	3.50 3.50
B141	SP98	2fr + 2.30fr deep rose	3.50 3.50
B142	SP99	2.40fr + 2.80fr slate grn	3.50 3.50
B143	SP100	3fr + 3.50fr dp violet	3.50 3.50
B144	SP101	4fr + 5fr lt ultra	3.50 3.50
B145	SP102	4.50fr + 6fr red	3.50 3.50
B146	SP103	5fr + 7fr brt red vio	3.50 3.50
	Nos. B135-B146 (12)		42.00 42.00

The surtax was for national relief.

Tricolor
Legion
SP104

1942, Oct. 12   *Perf. 13*
B147	SP104	1.20 + 8.80fr dk blue	10.00	10.00
a.		Vert. pair, #B147, B148 + albino impression	22.50	25.00
B148	SP104	1.20 + 8.80fr crim	10.00	10.00

These stamps were printed in sheets of 20 stamps and 5 albino impressions arranged: 2 horizontal rows of 5 dark blue stamps, 1 row of 5 albino impressions, and 2 rows of 5 crimson stamps.

Marshal Henri Philippe Pétain
SP105   SP106

1943, Feb. 8
B149	SP105	1fr + 10fr rose red	2.75	2.75
B150	SP105	1fr + 10fr blue	2.75	2.75
B151	SP106	2fr + 12fr rose red	2.75	2.75
B152	SP106	2fr + 12fr blue	2.75	2.75
a.		Strip, #B149-B152 + label	12.50	12.50

The surtax was for national relief. Printed in sheets of 20, the 10 blue stamps at left, the 10 rose red at right, separated by a vert. row of 5 white labels bearing a tri-colored battle-ax.

Marshal
Pétain — SP107

"Work" — SP108

"Family"
SP109

"State"
SP110

Marshal
Pétain — SP111

1943, June 7
B153	SP107	1.20fr + 1.40fr dull vio	15.00	15.00
B154	SP108	1.50fr + 2.50fr red	15.00	15.00
B155	SP109	2.40fr + 7fr brown	15.00	15.00
B156	SP110	4fr + 10fr dk violet	15.00	15.00
B157	SP111	5fr + 15fr red brown	15.00	15.00
a.		Strip of 5, #B153-B157	110.00	110.00

Pétain's 87th birthday.
The surtax was for national relief.

Civilians Under
Air
Attack — SP112

Civilians Doing
Farm
Work — SP113

Prisoner's
Family
Doing Farm
Work
SP114

1943, Aug. 23
B158 SP112 1.50fr + 3.50fr black   .50 .50

Surtax was for bomb victims at Billancourt, Dunkirk, Lorient, Saint-Nazaire.

1943, Sept. 27

B159 SP113 1.50fr + 8.50fr sepia .90 .90
B160 SP114 2.40fr + 7.60fr dk grn 1.00 1.00

The surtax was for families of war prisoners.

Michel de Montaigne SP115

Picardy Costume SP121

1.20fr+1.50fr, Francois Clouet. 1.50fr+3fr, Ambrose Paré. 2.40fr+4fr, Chevalier Pierre de Bayard. 4fr+6fr, Duke of Sully. 5fr+10fr, Henri IV.

1943, Oct. 2

B161 SP115 60c + 80c Prus green 2.00 2.00
B162 SP115 1.20fr + 1.50fr black 2.00 2.00
B163 SP115 1.50fr + 3fr deep ultra 2.00 2.00
B164 SP115 2.40fr + 4fr red 2.00 2.00
B165 SP115 4fr + 6fr dull brn red 2.00 2.00
B166 SP115 5fr + 10fr dull green 2.00 2.00
Nos. B161-B166 (6) 12.00 12.00

The surtax was for national relief. Issued to honor famous 16th century Frenchmen.

1943, Dec. 27

Designs: 18th Century Costumes: 1.20fr+2fr, Brittany. 1.50fr+4fr, Ile de France. 2.40+5fr, Burgundy. 4fr+6fr, Auvergne. 5fr+7fr, Provence.

B167 SP121 60c + 1.30fr sepia 2.00 2.00
B168 SP121 1.20fr + 2fr lt vio 2.00 2.00
B169 SP121 1.50fr + 4fr turq blue 2.00 2.00
B170 SP121 2.40fr + 5fr rose car 2.00 2.00
B171 SP121 4fr + 6fr chlky blue 3.00 3.00
B172 SP121 5fr + 7fr red 3.00 3.00
Nos. B167-B172 (6) 14.00 14.00

The surtax was for national relief.

Admiral Tourville SP127

Charles Gounod SP128

1944, Feb. 21

B173 SP127 4fr + 6fr dull red brn .75 .75

300th anniv. of the birth of Admiral Anne-Hilarion de Cotentin Tourville (1642-1701).

1944, Mar. 27   Perf. 14x13

B174 SP128 1.50fr + 3.50fr sepia 1.00 .80

50th anniv. of the death of Charles Gounod, composer (1818-1893).

Marshal Pétain SP129

Farming SP130

Industry SP131

1944, Apr. 24   Perf. 13

B175 SP129 1.50fr + 3.50fr sepia 3.50 3.50
B176 SP130 2fr + 3fr dp ultra .60 .60
B177 SP131 4fr + 6fr rose red .60 .60
Nos. B175-B177 (3) 4.70 4.70

Marshal Henri Pétain's 88th birthday.

Modern Streamliner, 19th Cent. Train SP132

Molière (Jean-Baptiste Poquelin) SP133

1944, Aug. 14

B178 SP132 4fr + 6fr black 2.10 1.90

Centenary of the Paris-Rouen, Paris-Orléans railroad.

1944, July 31

Designs: 80c+2.20fr, Jules Hardouin Mansart. 1.20fr+2.80fr, Blaise Pascal. 1.50fr+3.50fr, Louis II of Bourbon. 2fr+4fr, Jean-Baptiste Colbert. 4fr+6fr, Louis XIV.

B179 SP133 50c + 1.50fr rose car 1.50 1.50
B180 SP133 80c + 2.20fr dk green 1.50 1.50
B181 SP133 1.20fr + 2.80fr black 1.50 1.50
B182 SP133 1.50fr + 3.50fr brt ultra 1.50 1.50
B183 SP133 2fr + 4fr dull brn red 1.50 1.50
B184 SP133 4fr + 6fr red 1.50 1.50
Nos. B179-B184 (6) 9.00 9.00

Noted 17th century Frenchmen.

Angoulême SP139

Chartres SP140

Amiens SP141

Beauvais SP142

Albi — SP143

1944, Nov. 20

B185 SP139 50c + 1.50fr black .60 .60
B186 SP140 80c + 2.20fr rose vio .60 .60
B187 SP141 1.20fr + 2.80fr brn car .60 .60
B188 SP142 1.50fr + 3.50fr dp blue .60 .60
B189 SP143 4fr + 6fr orange red .60 .60
Nos. B185-B189 (5) 3.00 3.00

French Cathedrals.

Coat of Arms of Renouard de Villayer SP144

Sarah Bernhardt SP145

1944, Dec. 9   Engr.

B190 SP144 1.50fr + 3.50fr dp brn .25 .25

Stamp Day.

1945, May 16   Unwmk.   Perf. 13

B191 SP145 4fr + 1fr dk violet brn .30 .30

100th anniv. of the birth of Sarah Bernhardt, actress.

War Victims SP146

1945, May 16

B192 SP146 4fr + 6fr dk violet brn .20 .20

The surtax was for war victims of the P.T.T.

Tuberculosis Patient — SP147

1945, May 16   Typo.   Perf. 14x13½

B193 SP147 2fr + 1fr red orange .20 .20

Surtax for the aid of tuberculosis victims. For surcharge see No. 561.

Boy and Girl SP148

Burning of Oradour Church SP149

1945, July 9   Engr.   Perf. 13

B194 SP148 4fr + 2fr Prus green .20 .20

The surtax was used for child welfare.

1945, Oct. 13

B195 SP149 4fr + 2fr sepia .20 .20

Destruction of Oradour, June, 1944.

Louis XI and Post Rider SP150

1945, Oct. 13

B196 SP150 2fr + 3fr deep ultra .40 .40

Stamp Day.
For overprint see French West Africa #B2.

Ruins of Dunkirk SP151

Ruins of Rouen SP152

Ruins of Caen SP153

Ruins of Saint-Malo SP154

1945, Nov. 5

B197 SP151 1.50fr + 1.50fr red brown .40 .40
B198 SP152 2fr + 2fr violet .50 .50
B199 SP153 2.40fr + 2.60fr blue .50 .50
B200 SP154 4fr + 4fr black .60 .60
Nos. B197-B200 (4) 2.00 2.00

The surtax was to aid the suffering residents of Dunkirk, Rouen, Caen and Saint Malo.

Alfred Fournier SP155

Henri Becquerel SP156

1946, Feb. 4   **Engr.**   *Perf. 13*
B201 SP155 2fr + 3fr red brown   .30   .30
B202 SP156 2fr + 3fr violet   .30   .30

Issued to raise funds for the fight against venereal disease (#B201) and for the struggle against cancer (#B202).

No. B202 for the 50th anniv. of the discovery of radioactivity by Henri Becquerel.

See No. B221.

Church of the Invalides, Paris — SP157

1946, Mar. 11
B203 SP157 4fr + 6fr red brown   .40   .40

The surtax was to aid disabled war veterans.

French Warships SP158

1946, Apr. 8
B204 SP158 2fr + 3fr gray black   .80   .75

The surtax was for naval charities.

"The Letter" by Jean Siméon Chardin SP159

Fouquet de la Varane SP160

1946, May 25
B205 SP159 2fr + 3fr brown red   .50   .50

The surtax was used for the Postal Museum.

1946, June 29
B206 SP160 3fr + 2fr sepia   .50   .50

Stamp Day.

François Villon — SP161

Designs: 3fr+1fr, Jean Fouquet. 4fr+3fr, Philippe de Commynes. 5fr+4fr, Joan of Arc. 6fr+5fr, Jean de Gerson. 10fr+6fr, Charles VII.

1946, Oct. 28
B207 SP161 2fr + 1fr dk Prus grn   1.50   1.50
B208 SP161 3fr + 1fr dk blue vio   1.50   1.50
B209 SP161 4fr + 3fr henna brn   1.50   1.50
B210 SP161 5fr + 4fr ultra   1.50   1.50
B211 SP161 6fr + 5fr sepia   1.50   1.50
B212 SP161 10fr + 6fr red   1.50   1.50
Nos. B207-B212 (6)   9.00   9.00

Church of St. Sernin, Toulouse SP167

Notre Dame du Port, Clermont-Ferrand SP168

Cathedral of St. Front, Perigueux SP169

Cathedral of St. Julien, Le Mans SP170

Cathedral of Notre Dame, Paris SP171

François Michel le Tellier de Louvois SP172

1947   **Engr.**
B213 SP167 1fr + 1fr car rose   1.10   1.10
B214 SP168 3fr + 2fr dk bl vio   3.00   3.00
B215 SP169 4fr + 3fr henna brn   1.10   1.10
B216 SP170 6fr + 4fr dp bl   1.10   1.10
B217 SP171 10fr + 6fr dk gray grn   3.00   3.00
Nos. B213-B217 (5)   9.30   9.30

1947, Mar. 15
B218 SP172 4.50fr + 5.50fr car rose   1.50   1.50

Stamp Day, Mar. 15, 1947.

Submarine Pens, Shipyard and Monument SP173

1947, Aug. 2
B219 SP173 6fr + 4fr bluish black   .60   .60

British commando raid on the Nazi U-boat base at St. Nazaire, 1942.

Liberty Highway Marker — SP174

Louis Braille — SP175

1947, Sept. 5
B220 SP174 6fr + 4fr dk green   1.00   1.00

The surtax was to help defray maintenance costs of the Liberty Highway.

Fournier Type of 1946

1947, Oct. 20
B221 SP155 2fr + 3fr indigo   .40   .40

1948, Jan. 19
B222 SP175 6fr + 4fr purple   .40   .40

Etienne Arago SP176

Alphonse de Lamartine SP177

1948, Mar. 6
B223 SP176 6fr + 4fr black brn   .50   .50

Stamp Day, March 6-7, 1948.

1948, Apr. 5   **Engr.**   *Perf. 13*

Designs: 3fr+2fr, Alexandre A. Ledru-Rollin. 4fr+3fr, Louis Blanc. 5fr+4fr, Albert (Alexandre Martin). 6fr+5fr, Pierre J. Proudhon. 10fr+6fr, Louis Auguste Blanqui. 15fr+7fr, Armand Barbés. 20fr+8fr, Dennis A. Affre.

B224 SP177 1fr + 1fr dk grn   1.25   1.25
B225 SP177 3fr + 2fr henna brn   1.25   1.25
B226 SP177 4fr + 3fr vio brn   1.25   1.25
B227 SP177 5fr + 4fr lt bl grn   3.25   3.25
B228 SP177 6fr + 5fr indigo   2.50   2.50
B229 SP177 10fr + 6fr car rose   2.50   2.50
B230 SP177 15fr + 7fr sl blk   3.25   3.25
B231 SP177 20fr + 8fr purple   3.25   3.25
Nos. B224-B231 (8)   18.50   18.50

Centenary of the Revolution of 1848.

Dr. Léon Charles Albert Calmette SP178

1948, June 18
B232 SP178 6fr + 4fr dk grnsh bl   .80   .50

1st Intl. Congress on the Calmette-Guerin bacillus vaccine.

Farmer — SP179

Designs: 5fr+3fr, Fisherman. 8fr+4fr, Miner. 10fr+6fr, Metal worker.

1949, Feb. 14
B233 SP179 3fr + 1fr claret   .90   .75
B234 SP179 5fr + 3fr dk blue   .90   .75
B235 SP179 8fr + 4fr indigo   .90   .75
B236 SP179 10fr + 6fr dk red   1.00   .75
Nos. B233-B236 (4)   3.70   3.00

Étienne François de Choiseul and Post Cart SP180

Baron de la Brède et de Montesquieu SP181

1949, Mar. 26
B237 SP180 15fr + 5fr dk green   1.20   1.20

Stamp Day, Mar. 26-27, 1949.

1949, Nov. 14

Designs: 8fr+2fr, Voltaire. 10fr+3fr, Antoine Watteau. 12fr+4fr, Georges de Buffon. 15fr+5fr, Joseph F. Dupleix. 25fr+10fr, A. R. J. Turgot.

B238 SP181 5fr + 1fr dk grn   3.50   3.50
B239 SP181 8fr + 2fr indigo   3.50   3.50
B240 SP181 10fr + 3fr brn red   3.50   3.50
B241 SP181 12fr + 4fr purple   3.50   3.50
B242 SP181 15fr + 5fr rose car   5.00   5.00
B243 SP181 25fr + 10fr ultra   6.00   6.00
Nos. B238-B243 (6)   25.00   25.00

"Spring" SP182

Designs: 8fr+2fr, Summer. 12fr+3fr, Autumn. 15fr+4fr, Winter.

1949, Dec. 19
B244 SP182 5fr + 1fr green   1.90   1.75
B245 SP182 8fr + 2fr yel org   2.50   2.00
B246 SP182 12fr + 3fr purple   2.50   2.00
B247 SP182 15fr + 4fr dp blue   4.00   3.75
Nos. B244-B247 (4)   10.90   9.50

Postman — SP183

1950, Mar. 11
B248 SP183 12fr + 3fr dp bl   3.75   3.00

Stamp Day, Mar. 11-12, 1950.

André de Chénier SP184

Alexandre Brongniart, Bust by Houdon SP185

8fr+3fr, J. L. David. 10fr+4fr, Lazare Carnot. 12fr+5fr, G. J. Danton. 15fr+6fr, Maximilian Robespierre. 20fr+10fr, Louis Hoche.

1950, July 10   **Engr.**   *Perf. 13*
Frames in Indigo
B249 SP184 5fr + 2fr brn vio   10.00   10.00
B250 SP184 8fr + 3fr blk brn   10.00   10.00
B251 SP184 10fr + 4fr lake   11.00   11.00
B252 SP184 12fr + 5fr red brn   13.00   13.00
B253 SP184 15fr + 6fr dk grn   14.00   14.00
B254 SP184 20fr + 10fr dk vio bl   14.00   14.00
Nos. B249-B254 (6)   72.00   72.00

1950, Dec. 22

15fr+3fr, "L'Amour" by Etienne M. Falconet.

B255	SP185	8fr + 2fr ind & car	2.50 2.50
B256	SP185	15fr + 3fr red brn & car	2.50 2.50

The surtax was for the Red Cross.

Mail Car Interior SP186 — Alfred de Musset SP187

1951, Mar. 10   Unwmk.   Perf. 13

B257	SP186	12fr + 3fr lilac gray	3.75 3.75

Stamp Day, Mar. 10-11, 1951.

1951, June 2

8fr+2fr, Eugène Delacroix. 10fr+3fr, J.-L. Gay-Lussac. 12fr+4fr, Robert Surcouf. 15fr+5fr, C. M. Talleyrand. 30fr+10fr, Napoleon I.

Frames in Dark Brown

B258	SP187	5fr + 1fr dk grn	7.50 5.75
B259	SP187	8fr + 2fr vio brn	7.50 5.75
B260	SP187	10fr + 3fr grnsh black	8.00 5.75
B261	SP187	12fr + 4fr dk vio	8.00 5.75
B262	SP187	15fr + 5fr brn car	9.00 5.75
B263	SP187	30fr + 10fr indigo	14.00 11.00
	Nos. B258-B263 (6)		54.00 39.75

Child at Prayer by Le Maître de Moulins SP188 — 18th Century Child by Quentin de la Tour SP189

1951, Dec. 15

Cross in Red

B264	SP188	12fr + 3fr dk brown	3.25 3.25
B265	SP189	15fr + 5fr dp ultra	3.75 3.75

The surtax was for the Red Cross.

Stagecoach of 1844 SP190

1952, Mar. 8   Perf. 13

B266	SP190	12fr + 3fr dp green	5.00 5.00

Stamp Day, Mar. 8, 1952.

Gustave Flaubert — SP191

Portraits: 12fr+3fr, Edouard Manet. 15fr+4fr, Camille Saint-Saens. 18fr+5fr, Henri Poincaré. 20fr+6fr, Georges-Eugene Haussmann. 30fr+7fr, Adolphe Thiers.

1952, Oct. 18

Frames in Dark Brown

B267	SP191	8fr + 2fr indigo	7.00 7.00
B268	SP191	12fr + 3fr vio blue	7.00 7.00
B269	SP191	15fr + 4fr dk grn	7.00 7.00
B270	SP191	18fr + 5fr dk brn	9.00 9.00
B271	SP191	20fr + 6fr car	9.00 9.00
B272	SP191	30fr + 7fr purple	9.00 9.00
	Nos. B267-B272 (6)		48.00 48.00

Cupid from Diana Fountain Versailles SP192

15fr+5fr, Similar detail, cupid facing left.

1952, Dec. 13

Cross in Red

B273	SP192	12fr + 3fr dk grn	5.00 5.00
B274	SP192	15fr + 5fr indigo	5.00 5.00
a.	Booklet pane of 10		225.00
	Complete booklet		375.00

The surtax was for the Red Cross.

Count d'Argenson SP193 — St. Bernard SP194

1953, Mar. 14

B275	SP193	12fr + 3fr dp blue	3.00 3.00

Day of the Stamp. Surtax for the Red Cross.

1953, July 9

12fr+3fr, Olivier de Serres. 15fr+4fr, Jean Philippe Rameau. 18fr+5fr, Gaspard Monge. 20fr+6fr, Jules Michelet. 30fr+7fr, Marshal Hubert Lyautey.

B276	SP194	8fr + 2fr ultra	6.50 6.50
B277	SP194	12fr + 3fr dk grn	6.50 6.50
B278	SP194	15fr + 4fr brn car	10.00 10.00
B279	SP194	18fr + 5fr dk blue	11.00 11.00
B280	SP194	20fr + 6fr dk pur	11.00 11.00
B281	SP194	30fr + 7fr brown	11.50 11.50
	Nos. B276-B281 (6)		56.50 56.50

The surtax was for the Red Cross.

Madame Vigée-Lebrun and her Daughter SP195 — Count Antoine de La Vallette SP196

Design: 15fr+5fr, "The Return from Baptism," by Louis Le Nain.

1953, Dec. 12

Cross in Red

B282	SP195	12fr + 3fr red brn	7.50 7.00
a.	Bklt. pane, 4 each, gutter btwn.		85.00
B283	SP195	15fr + 5fr indigo	10.00 9.50

The surtax was for the Red Cross.

1954, Mar. 20   Engr.   Perf. 13

B284	SP196	12fr + 3fr dp grn & choc	4.50 3.25

Stamp Day, Mar. 20, 1954.

Louis IX SP197 — "The Sick Child," by Eugene Carrière SP198

Portraits: 15fr+5fr, Jacques Benigne Bossuet. 18fr+6fr, Sadi Carnot. 20fr+7fr, Antoine Bourdelle. 25fr+8fr, Dr. Emile Roux. 30fr+10fr, Paul Valéry.

1954, July 10

B285	SP197	12fr + 4fr dp bl	21.00 21.00
B286	SP197	15fr + 5fr pur	21.00 21.00
B287	SP197	18fr + 6fr dk brn	21.00 21.00
B288	SP197	20fr + 7fr crim	29.00 29.00
B289	SP197	25fr + 8fr ind	29.00 29.00
B290	SP197	30fr + 10fr dp claret	29.00 29.00
	Nos. B285-B290 (6)		150.00 150.00

See Nos. B303-B308, B312-B317.

1954, Dec. 18

Design: 15fr+5fr, "Young Girl with Doves," by Jean Baptiste Greuze.

Cross in Red

B291	SP198	12fr + 3fr vio gray & indigo	11.00 11.00
a.	Bklt. pane, 4 each, gutter btwn.		110.00
B292	SP198	15fr + 5fr dk brn & org brn	11.00 11.00

No. B291a for 90th anniv. of the Red Cross.
The surtax was for the Red Cross.

Balloon Post, 1870 SP199

1955, Mar. 19   Unwmk.   Perf. 13

B293	SP199	12fr + 3fr multi	5.00 4.00

Stamp Day, Mar. 19-20, 1955.

King Philip II — SP200 — Child with Cage by Pigalle — SP201

Portraits: 15fr+6fr, Francois de Malherbé. 18fr+7fr, Sebastien de Vauban. 25fr+8fr, Charles G. de Vergennes. 30fr+9fr, Pierre S. de Laplace. 50fr+15fr, Pierre Auguste Renoir.

1955, June 11

B294	SP200	12fr + 5fr brt pur	16.00 16.00
B295	SP200	15fr + 6fr dp bl	16.00 16.00
B296	SP200	18fr + 7fr dp green	16.00 16.00
B297	SP200	25fr + 8fr gray	25.00 25.00
B298	SP200	30fr + 9fr rose brn	26.00 26.00
B299	SP200	50fr + 15fr blue grn	30.00 30.00
	Nos. B294-B299 (6)		129.00 129.00

See Nos. B321-B326.

1955, Dec. 17

Design: 15fr+5fr, Child with Goose, by Boethus of Chalcedon.

Cross in Red

B300	SP201	12fr + 3fr claret	7.50 7.50
B301	SP201	15fr + 5fr dk bl	5.25 5.25
a.	Booklet pane of 10		150.00
	Complete booklet		300.00

The surtax was for the Red Cross.

Francois of Taxis SP202

1956, Mar. 17   Engr.   Perf. 13

B302	SP202	12fr + 3fr ultra, grn & dk brn	2.75 2.75

Stamp Day, Mar. 17-18, 1956.

Portrait Type of 1954

Portraits: No. 303, Guillaume Budé. No. B304, Jean Goujon. No. B305, Samuel de Champlain. No. B306, Jean Simeon Chardin. No. B307, Maurice Barrès. No. B308, Maurice Ravel.

1956, June 9   Perf. 13

B303	SP197	12fr + 3fr saph	5.25 5.25
B304	SP197	12fr + 3fr lil gray	5.25 5.25
B305	SP197	12fr + 3fr brt red	5.25 5.25
B306	SP197	15fr + 5fr green	7.75 7.75
B307	SP197	15fr + 5fr vio brn	7.75 7.75
B308	SP197	15fr + 5fr dp vio	7.75 7.75
	Nos. B303-B308 (6)		39.00 39.00

Peasant Boy by Le Nain — SP203

Design: 15fr+5fr, Gilles by Watteau.

1956, Dec. 8   Unwmk.

Cross in Red

B309	SP203	12fr + 3fr ol gray	3.00 3.00
a.	Bklt. pane, 4 ea, gutter btwn.		40.00
B310	SP203	15fr + 5fr rose lake	3.00 3.00

The surtax was for the Red Cross.

Genoese Felucca, 1750 SP204

1957, Mar. 16   Perf. 13

B311	SP204	12fr + 3fr bluish gray & brn blk	1.90 1.60

Day of the Stamp, Mar. 16, 1957, and honoring the Maritime Postal Service.

Portrait Type of 1954

1957, June 15

Portraits: No. B312, Jean de Joinville. No. B313, Bernard Palissy. No. B314, Quentin de la Tour. No. B315, Hugues Félicité Robert de Lamennais. No. B316, George Sand. No. B317, Jules Guesde.

B312	SP197	12fr + 3fr ol gray & ol grn	2.75 2.75
B313	SP197	12fr + 3fr grnsh blk & grnsh bl	2.75 2.75
B314	SP197	15fr + 5fr cl & brt red	3.25 3.25
B315	SP197	15fr + 5fr ultra & ind	3.25 3.25
B316	SP197	18fr + 7fr grnsh blk & dk grn	4.50 4.50
B317	SP197	18fr + 7fr dk vio brn & red brn	4.50 4.50
	Nos. B312-B317 (6)		21.00 21.00

Blind Man and Beggar, Engraving by Jacques Callot — SP205

Design: 20fr+8fr, Women beggars.

1957, Dec. 7   **Engr.**   *Perf. 13*
B318 SP205 15fr + 7fr ultra &
     red   4.50   4.50
    a.   Bklt. pane, 4 ea, gutter
      btwn.   45.00   45.00
B319 SP205 20fr + 8fr dk vio
     brn & red   4.50   4.50

The surtax was for the Red Cross.

Motorized Mail Distribution SP206

1958, Mar. 15
B320 SP206 15fr + 5fr multi   1.90   1.50

Stamp Day, Mar. 15.

Portrait Type of 1955

Portraits: No. B321, Joachim du Bellay. No. B322, Jean Bart. No. B323, Denis Diderot. No. B324, Gustave Courbet. 20fr+8fr, J. B. Carpeaux. 35fr+15fr, Toulouse-Lautrec.

1958, June 7   **Engr.**   *Perf. 13*
B321 SP200 12fr + 4fr yel grn   1.75   1.75
B322 SP200 12fr + 4fr dk blue   1.75   1.75
B323 SP200 15fr + 5fr dull cl   2.00   2.00
B324 SP200 15fr + 5fr ultra   2.25   2.25
B325 SP200 20fr + 8fr brt red   2.25   2.25
B326 SP200 35fr + 15fr green   2.25   2.25
    Nos. B321-B326 (6)   12.25   12.25

St. Vincent de Paul — SP207

Portrait: 20fr+8fr, J. H. Dunant.

1958, Dec. 6   **Unwmk.**
     Cross in Carmine
B327 SP207 15fr + 7fr grayish
     grn   1.25   1.25
    a.   Bklt. pane, 4 each, gutter
      btwn.   20.00
B328 SP207 20fr + 8fr violet   1.25   1.25

The surtax was for the Red Cross.

Plane Landing at Night SP208

1959, Mar. 21
B329 SP208 20fr + 5fr sl grn, blk
     & rose   .50   .50

Issued for Stamp Day, Mar. 21, and to publicize night air mail service.
The surtax was for the Red Cross.
See No. 1089.

Geoffroi de Villehardouin and Ships — SP209

Designs: No. B331, André Le Nôtre and formal garden. No. B332, Jean Le Rond d'Alembert, books and wheel. No. B333, David d'Angers, statue and building. No. B334, M. F. X. Bichat and torch. No. B335, Frédéric Auguste Bartholdi, Statue of Liberty and Lion of Belfort.

1959, June 13   **Engr.**   *Perf. 13*
B330 SP209 15fr + 5fr vio blue   1.25   1.25
B331 SP209 15fr + 5fr dk sl grn   1.25   1.25
B332 SP209 20fr + 10fr olive bis   1.25   1.25
B333 SP209 20fr + 10fr dk gray   1.25   1.25
B334 SP209 30fr + 10fr dk car
     rose   1.75   1.75
B335 SP209 30fr + 10fr org brn   1.75   1.75
    Nos. B330-B335 (6)   8.50   8.50

The surtax was for the Red Cross.

No. 927 Surcharged

1959, Dec.   **Typo.**   *Perf. 14x13½*
B336 A328 25fr + 5fr black & red   .30   .30

Surtax for the flood victims at Frejus.

Charles Michel de l'Épée — SP210

Design: 25fr+10fr, Valentin Hauy.

1959, Dec. 5   **Engr.**   *Perf. 13*
     Cross in Carmine
B337 SP210 20fr + 10fr blk & cl   2.00   2.00
    a.   Bklt. pane, 4 each, gutter
      btwn.   30.00
B338 SP210 25fr + 10fr dk blue
     & blk   2.50   2.50

The surtax was for the Red Cross.

Ship Laying Underwater Cable SP211

1960, Mar. 12
B339 SP211 20c + 5c grnsh bl
     & dk bl   1.50   1.50

Issued for the Day of the Stamp. The surtax went to the Red Cross.

Refugee Girl Amid Ruins — SP212

1960, Apr. 7
B340 SP212 25c + 10c grn, brn &
     ind   .30   .25

World Refugee Year, July 1, 1959-June 30, 1960. The surtax was for aid to refugees.

Michel de L'Hospital SP213

#B342, Henri de la Tour D'Auvergne, Viscount of Turenne. #B343, Nicolas Boileau (Despreaux). #B344, Jean-Martin Charcot, M.D. #B345, Georges Bizet. 50c+15c, Edgar Degás.

1960, June 11   **Engr.**   *Perf. 13*
B341 SP213 10c + 5c pur &
     rose car   2.50   2.50
B342 SP213 20c + 10c ol &
     vio brn   3.25   3.25
B343 SP213 20c + 10c Prus
     grn & dp yel
     grn   3.25   3.25
B344 SP213 30c + 10c rose
     car & rose
     red   5.00   5.00
B345 SP213 30c + 10c dk bl &
     vio bl   5.00   5.00
B346 SP213 50c + 15c sl bl &
     gray   5.50   5.50
    Nos. B341-B346 (6)   24.50   24.50

The surtax was for the Red Cross.
See Nos. B350-B355.

Staff of the Brotherhood of St. Martin — SP214

Letter Carrier, Paris 1760 — SP215

25c+10c, St. Martin, 16th cent. wood sculpture.

1960, Dec. 3   **Unwmk.**   *Perf. 13*
B347 SP214 20c + 10c rose cl
     & red   3.25   3.25
    a.   Bklt. pane, 4 each, gutter
      btwn.   32.50
B348 SP214 25c + 10c lt ultra
     & red   3.25   3.25

The surtax was for the Red Cross.

1961, Mar. 18   *Perf. 13*
B349 SP215 20c + 5c sl grn, brn
     & red   .75   .75

Stamp Day. Surtax for Red Cross.

Famous Men Type of 1960

Designs: 15c+5c, Bertrand Du Guesclin. B351, Pierre Puget. #B352, Charles Coulomb. 30c+10c, Antoine Drouot. 45c+10c, Honoré Daumier. 50c+15c, Guillaume Apollinaire.

1961, May 20   **Engr.**
B350 SP213 15c + 5c red brn
     & blk   2.50   2.50
B351 SP213 20c + 10c dk grn
     & lt bl   2.50   2.50
B352 SP213 20c + 10c ver &
     rose car   2.50   2.50
B353 SP213 30c + 10c blk &
     brn org   3.50   3.50
B354 SP213 45c + 10c choc &
     dk grn   3.50   3.50
B355 SP213 50c + 15c dk car
     rose & vio   4.00   4.00
    Nos. B350-B355 (6)   18.50   18.50

"Love" by Rouault SP216

Medieval Royal Messenger SP217

Designs from "Miserere" by Georges Rouault: 25c+10c, "The Blind Consoles the Seeing."

1961, Dec. 2   *Perf. 13*
B356 SP216 20c + 10c brn,
     blk & red   2.50   2.50
    a.   Bklt. pane, 4 each, gutter   30.00
B357 SP216 25c + 10c brn,
     blk & red   2.50   2.50

The surtax was for the Red Cross.

1962, Mar. 17
B358 SP217 20c + 5c rose red, bl
     & sepia   .80   .80

Stamp Day. Surtax for Red Cross.

Denis Papin, Scientist SP218

Rosalie Fragonard by Fragonard SP219

Portraits: No. B360, Edme Bouchardon, sculptor. No. B361, Joseph Lakanal, educator. 30c+10c, Gustave Charpentier, composer. 45c+15c, Edouard Estaunié, writer. 50c+20c, Hyacinthe Vincent, physician and bacteriologist.

1962, June 2   **Engr.**
B359 SP218 15c + 5c bluish
     grn & dk
     gray   2.25   2.25
B360 SP218 20c + 10c cl brn   2.25   2.25
B361 SP218 20c + 10c gray &
     sl   2.50   2.50
B362 SP218 30c + 10c brt bl
     & ind   3.00   3.00
B363 SP218 45c + 15c org brn
     & choc   3.00   3.00
B364 SP218 50c + 20c grnsh
     bl & blk   3.50   3.50
    Nos. B359-B364 (6)   16.50   16.50

The surtax was for the Red Cross.

1962, Dec. 8

Design: 25c+10c, Child dressed as Pierrot.

     Cross in Red
B365 SP219 20c + 10c redsh
     brown   1.75   1.75
    a.   Bklt. pane, 4 ea, gutter
      btwn.   32.00
B366 SP219 25c + 10c dull grn   2.25   2.25

The surtax was for the Red Cross.
For surcharges see Reunion Nos. B16-B17.

Jacques Amyot, Classical Scholar SP220

30c+10c, Pierre de Marivaux, playwright. 50c+20c, Jacques Daviel, surgeon.

1963, Feb. 23   **Unwmk.**   *Perf. 13*
B367 SP220 20c + 10c mar, gray
     & pur   1.25   1.25
B368 SP220 30c + 10c Prus grn
     & mar   1.25   1.25
B369 SP220 50c + 20c ultra,
     ocher & ol   1.50   1.50
    Nos. B367-B369 (3)   4.00   4.00

The surtax was for the Red Cross.

Roman Chariot SP221

1963, Mar. 16   **Engr.**
B370 SP221 20c + 5c brn org &
     vio brn   .25   .25
Stamp Day. Surtax for Red Cross.

Étienne Méhul, Composer SP222

Designs: 30c+10c, Nicolas-Louis Vauquelin, chemist. 50c+20c, Alfred de Vigny, poet.

1963, May 25   **Unwmk.**   **Perf. 13**
B371 SP222 20c + 10c dp bl,
     dk brn & dp
     org   1.25   1.25
B372 SP222 30c + 10c mag,
     gray ol & blk   1.25   1.25
B373 SP222 50c + 20c sl, blk &
     brn   1.50   1.50
    Nos. B371-B373 (3)   4.00   4.00
The surtax was for the Red Cross.

"Child with Grapes" by David d'Angers and Centenary Emblem — SP223

25c+10c, "The Fifer," by Edouard Manet.

1963, Dec. 9   **Unwmk.**   **Perf. 13**
B374 SP223 20c + 10c black &
     red   .75   .75
  a.   Bklt. pane, 4 each, gutter
     btwn.   9.00   9.00
B375 SP223 25c + 10c sl grn &
     red   .75   .75
Cent. of the Intl. and French Red Cross. Surtax for the Red Cross.
For surcharges see Reunion Nos. B18-B19.

Post Rider, 18th Century SP224

1964, Mar. 14   **Engr.**
B376 SP224 20c + 5c Prus green   .30   .30
Issued for Stamp Day.

Resistance Memorial by Watkin, Luxembourg Gardens — SP225

De Gaulle's 1940 Poster "A Tous les Francais" SP226

Street Fighting in Paris and Strasbourg. SP227

Designs: 20c+5c, "Deportation," concentration camp with watchtower and barbed wire. No. B379, Allied troops landing in Normandy and Provence.

1964   **Engr.**   **Perf. 13**
B377 SP225 20c + 5c slate blk   .50   .50
        Perf. 12x13
B378 SP226 25c + 5c dk red,
     bl, red & blk   .65   .65
        Perf. 13
B379 SP227 30c + 5c blk, bl &
     org brn   .75   .75
B380 SP227 30c + 5c org brn,
     cl & blk   .75   .75
B381 SP225 50c + 5c dk grn   .90   .90
    Nos. B377-B381 (5)   3.55   3.55
20th anniv. of liberation from the Nazis. Issue dates: #B377, B381, Mar. 21; #B378, June 18; #B379, June 6; #B380, Aug. 22.

President René Coty SP229   Jean Nicolas Corvisart SP230

Portraits: No. B383, John Calvin. No. B384, Pope Sylvester II (Gerbert).

1964   **Unwmk.**   **Perf. 13**
B382 SP229 30c + 10c dp cl & blk   .25   .25
B383 SP229 30c + 10c dk grn, blk
     & brn   .25   .25
B384 SP229 30c + 10c slate & cl   .25   .25
    Nos. B382-B384 (3)   .75   .75
The surtax was for the Red Cross.
Issued: #B382, 4/25; #B383, 5/25; #B384, 6/1.

1964, Dec. 12   **Engr.**
Portrait: 25c+10c, Dominique Larrey.
     Cross in Carmine
B385 SP230 20c + 10c black   .35   .35
  a.   Bklt. pane, 4 ea, gutter btwn.   3.50
B386 SP230 25c + 10c black   .35   .35
Jean Nicolas Corvisart (1755-1821), physician of Napoleon I, and Dominique Larrey (1766-1842), Chief Surgeon of the Imperial Armies. The surtax was for the Red Cross.
For surcharges see Reunion Nos. B20-B21.

Paul Dukas, Composer — SP231

#B387, Duke François de La Rochefoucauld, writer. #B388, Nicolas Poussin, painter. #B389, Duke Charles of Orléans, poet.

1965, Feb.   **Engr.**   **Perf. 13**
B387 SP231 30c + 10c org brn &
     dk bl   .40   .40
B388 SP231 30c + 10c car & dk
     red brn   .40   .40
B389 SP231 40c + 10c dk red
     brn, dk red &
     Prus bl   .50   .50
B390 SP231 40c + 10c dk brn &
     sl bl   .50   .50
    Nos. B387-B390 (4)   1.80   1.80
The surtax was for the Red Cross.
Issued: #B387, B390 2/13; #B388-B389 2/20.

Packet "La Guienne" SP232

1965, Mar. 29   **Unwmk.**   **Perf. 13**
B391 SP232 25c + 10c multi   .75   .50
Issued for Stamp Day, 1965. "La Guienne" was used for transatlantic mail service. Surtax was for the Red Cross.

Infant with Spoon by Auguste Renoir — SP233

Design: 30c+10c, Coco Writing (Renoir's daughter Claude).

1965, Dec. 11   **Engr.**   **Perf. 13**
     Cross in Carmine
B392 SP233 25c + 10c slate   .30   .30
  a.   Bklt. pane, 4 ea, gutter btwn.   2.75
B393 SP233 30c + 10c dull red
     brn   .30   .30
The surtax was for the Red Cross.
For surcharges see Reunion Nos. B22-B23.

Francois Mansart and Carnavalet Palace, Paris SP234

#B395, St. Pierre Fourier and Basilica of St. Pierre Fourier, Mirecourt. #B396, Marcel Proust and St. Hilaire Bridge, Illiers. #B397, Gabriel Fauré, monument and score of "Penelope." #B398, Elie Metchnikoff, microscope and Pasteur Institute. #B399, Hippolyte Taine and birthplace.

1966   **Engr.**   **Perf. 13**
B394 SP234 30c + 10c dk red
     brn & grn   .35   .35
B395 SP234 30c + 10c blk &
     gray grn   .35   .35
B396 SP234 30c + 10c ind, sep
     & grn   .35   .35
B397 SP234 30c + 10c bis brn &
     ind   .35   .35
B398 SP234 30c + 10c blk & dl
     bl   .35   .35
B399 SP234 30c + 10c grn & ol
     brn   .35   .35
    Nos. B394-B399 (6)   2.10   2.10
The surtax was for the Red Cross.
Issued: #B394-B396, 2/12; others, 6/25.

Engraver Cutting Die and Tools SP235

1966, Mar. 19   **Engr.**   **Perf. 13**
B400 SP235 25c + 10c slate, dk
     brn & dp org   .30   .30
Stamp Day. Surtax for Red Cross.

Angel of Victory, Verdun Fortress, Marching Troops — SP236   First Aid on Battlefield, 1859 — SP237

1966, May 28   **Perf. 13**
B401 SP236 30c + 5c Prus bl, ul-
     tra & dk bl   .20   .20
Victory of Verdun, 50th anniversary.

1966, Dec. 10   **Engr.**   **Perf. 13**
#B403, Nurse giving first aid to child, 1966.
     Cross in Carmine
B402 SP237 25c + 10c green   .35   .35
  a.   Bklt. pane, 4 ea, gutter btwn.   3.50
B403 SP237 30c + 10c slate   .40   .40
The surtax was for the Red Cross.
For surcharges see Reunion Nos. B24-B25.

Emile Zola — SP238   Letter Carrier, 1865 — SP239

No. B405, Beaumarchais (pen name of Pierre Augustin Caron). No. B406, St. François de Sales (1567-1622). No. B407, Albert Camus (1913-1960).

1967   **Engr.**   **Perf. 13**
B404 SP238 30c + 10c sl bl & bl   .35   .35
B405 SP238 30c + 10c rose brn
     & lil   .35   .35
B406 SP238 30c + 10c dl vio &
     pur   .35   .35
B407 SP238 30c + 10c brn & dl
     cl   .35   .35
    Nos. B404-B407 (4)   1.40   1.40
The surtax was for the Red Cross.
Issued: #B404-B405, 2/4; others, 6/24.

1967, Apr. 8
B408 SP239 25c + 10c indigo, grn
     & red   .30   .25
Issued for Stamp Day.

Ivory Flute Player — SP240   Ski Jump and Long Distance Skiing — SP241

30c+10c, Violin player, ivory carving.

1967, Dec. 16   **Engr.**   **Perf. 13**
     Cross in Carmine
B409 SP240 25c + 10c dl vio & lt
     brn   .40   .40
  a.   Bklt. pane, 4 ea, gutter btwn.   3.50
B410 SP240 30c + 10c grn & lt
     brn   .40   .40
The surtax was for the Red Cross.
For surcharges see Reunion Nos. B26-B27.

1968, Jan. 27

Designs: 40c+10c, Ice hockey. 60c+20c, Olympic flame and snowflakes. 75c+25c, Woman figure skater. 95c+35c, Slalom.

B411	SP241	30c + 10c ver, gray & blk	.35	.35
B412	SP241	40c + 10c lil, lem & brt mag	.35	.35
B413	SP241	60c + 20c dk grn, org & brt vio	.50	.50
B414	SP241	75c + 25c brt pink, yel grn & blk	.60	.60
B415	SP241	95c + 35c bl, brt pink & red brn	.60	.60
Nos. B411-B415 (5)			2.40	2.40

Issued for the 10th Winter Olympic Games, Grenoble, Feb. 6-18.

Rural Mailman, 1830 — SP242

1968, Mar. 16   Engr.   Perf. 13

B416	SP242	25c + 10c multi	.25	.25

Issued for Stamp Day.

François Couperin, Composer, and Instruments SP243

Portraits: No. B418, Gen. Louis Desaix de Veygoux (1768-1800) and scene showing his death at the Battle of Marengo, Italy. No. B419, Saint-Pol-Roux (pen name of Paul-Pierre Roux, 1861-1940), Christ on the Cross and ruins of Camaret-sur-Mer. No. B420, Paul Claudel (poet and diplomat, 1868-1955) and Joan of Arc at the stake.

1968   Engr.   Perf. 13

B417	SP243	30c + 10c pur & rose lil	.25	.25
B418	SP243	30c + 10c dk grn & brn	.25	.25
B419	SP243	30c + 10c cop red & ol bis	.25	.25
B420	SP243	30c + 10c dk brn & lil	.25	.25
Nos. B417-B420 (4)			1.00	1.00

Issue dates: Nos. B417-B418, Mar. 23; Nos. B419-B420, July 6.

Spring, by Nicolas Mignard — SP244

Paintings by Nicolas Mignard; 30c+10c, Fall. No. B423, Summer. No. B424, Winter.

1968-69   Engr.   Perf. 13
Cross in Carmine

B421	SP244	25c + 10c pur & sl bl	.30	.30
a.		Bklt. pane, 4 ea #B421-B422 with gutter btwn.)	3.00	
B422	SP244	30c + 10c brn & rose car	.30	.30
B423	SP244	40c + 15c dk brn & brn ('69)	.50	.50
a.		Bklt. pane, 4 ea #B423, B424 with gutter btwn.)	3.50	
B424	SP244	40c + 10c car & Prus bl ('69)	.50	.50
Nos. B421-B424 (4)			1.60	1.60

The surtax was for the Red Cross.
For surcharges see Reunion Nos. B28-B31.

Mailmen's Omnibus, 1881 SP245

1969, Mar. 15   Engr.   Perf. 13

B425	SP245	30c + 10c brn, grn & blk	.25	.25

Issued for Stamp Day.
For surcharge see Reunion No. B32.

Gen. Francois Marceau — SP246

Portraits: No. B427, Charles Augustin Sainte-Beuve (1804-1869), writer. No. B428, Albert Roussel (1869-1937), musician. No. B429, Marshal Jean Lannes (1769-1809). No. B430, Georges Cuvier (1769-1832), naturalist. No. B431, André Gide, (1869-1951), writer.

1969

B426	SP246	50c + 10c brn red	.50	.50
B427	SP246	50c + 10c slate bl	.50	.50
B428	SP246	50c + 10c dp vio bl	.50	.50
B429	SP246	50c + 10c choc	.50	.50
B430	SP246	50c + 10c dp plum	.50	.50
B431	SP246	50c + 10c blue grn	.50	.50
Nos. B426-B431 (6)			3.00	3.00

The surtax was for the Red Cross.
Issued: Nos. B426-B428, Mar. 24; No. B429, May 10; Nos. B430-B431, May 17.

Gen. Jacques Leclerc, La Madeleine and Battle — SP247

1969, Aug. 23   Engr.   Perf. 13

B432	SP247	45c + 10c slate & ol	1.00	1.00

Liberation of Paris, 8/25/44, 25th anniv.

Same Inscribed Liberation de Strasbourg

1969, Nov. 22   Engr.   Perf. 13

B433	SP247	70c + 10c brn, choc & olive	3.50	3.50

25th anniv. of the liberation of Strasbourg.

Philibert Delorme, Architect, and Chateau d'Anet SP248

Designs: No. B435, Louis Le Vau (1612-1670), architect, and Vaux-le-Vicomte Chateau, Paris. No. B436, Prosper Merimée (1803-1870), writer, and Carmen. No. B437, Alexandre Dumas (1802-1870), writer, and Three Musketeers. No. B438, Edouard Branly (1844-1940), physicist, electric circuit and convent of the Carmes, Paris. No. B439, Maurice de Broglie (1875-1960), physicist, and X-ray spectrograph.

1970   Engr.   Perf. 13

B434	SP248	40c + 10c slate grn	.50	.50
B435	SP248	40c + 10c dk car	.50	.50
B436	SP248	40c + 10c Prus blue	.50	.50
B437	SP248	40c + 10c violet bl	.50	.50
B438	SP248	40c + 10c dp brown	.50	.50
B439	SP248	40c + 10c dk gray	.50	.50
Nos. B434-B439 (6)			3.00	3.00

The surtax was for the Red Cross.
Issued: #B434-B436, 2/14; others, 4/11.

City Mailman, 1830 — SP249

"Life and Death" — SP250

1970, Mar. 14

B440	SP249	40c + 10c blk, ultra & dk car rose	.40	.40

Issued for Stamp Day.
For surcharge see Reunion No. B33.

1970, Apr. 4

B441	SP250	40c + 10c brt bl, ol & car rose	.25	.25

Issued to publicize the fight against cancer in connection with Health Day, Apr. 7.

Marshal de Lattre de Tassigny — SP251

1970, May 8   Engr.   Perf. 13

B442	SP251	40c + 10c slate & vio bl	.50	.50

25th anniv. of the entry into Berlin of French troops under Marshal Jean de Lattre de Tassigny, May 8, 1945.

Lord and Lady, Dissay Chapel Fresco — SP252

#B444, Angel holding whips, from fresco in Dissay Castle Chapel, Vienne, c. 1500.

1970, Dec. 12   Engr.   Perf. 13
Cross in Carmine

B443	SP252	40c + 15c green	.55	.55
a.		Bklt. pane, 4 ea, gutter btwn.	12.50	
B444	SP252	40c + 15c cop red	.55	.55

The surtax was for the Red Cross.
For surcharges see Reunion Nos. B34-B35.

Daniel-Francois Auber and "Fra Diavolo" Music — SP253

#B446, Gen. Charles Diego Brosset (1898-1944), Basilica of Fourvière. #B447, Victor Grignard (1871-1935), chemist, Nobel Prize medal. #B448, Henri Farman (1874-1958), plane. #B449, Gen. Charles Georges Delestraint (1879-1945), scroll. #B450, Jean Eugène Robert-Houdin (1805-71), magician's act.

1971   Engr.   Perf. 13

B445	SP253	50c + 10c brn vio & brn	.75	.75
B446	SP253	50c + 10c dk sl grn & ol gray	.75	.75
B447	SP253	50c + 10c brn red & olive	.75	.75
B448	SP253	50c + 10c vio bl & vio	.75	.75
B449	SP253	50c + 10c pur & cl	.85	.85
B450	SP253	50c + 10c sl grn & bl grn	.85	.85
Nos. B445-B450 (6)			4.70	4.70

The surtax was for the Red Cross.
Issued: #B445-B446, 3/6; #B447, 5/8; #B448, 5/29; #B449-B450, 10/16.

Army Post Office, 1914-1918 SP254

1971, Mar. 27   Engr.   Perf. 13

B451	SP254	50c + 10c ol, brn & bl	.45	.45

Stamp Day, 1971.
For surcharge see Reunion No. B36.

Girl with Dog, by Greuze SP255

Aristide Bergès (1833-1904) SP256

Design: 50c+10c, "The Dead Bird," by Jean-Baptiste Greuze (1725-1805).

1971, Dec. 11
Cross in Carmine

B452	SP255	30c + 10c violet bl	.70	.70
a.		Bklt. pane, 4 each, gutter btwn.	6.00	
B453	SP255	50c + 10c dp car	.70	.70

The surtax was for the Red Cross.
For surcharges see Reunion Nos. B37-B38.

1972   Engr.   Perf. 13

#B455, Paul de Chomedey (1612-76), founder of Montreal, and arms of Neuville-sur-Vanne. #B456, Edouard Belin (1876-1963), inventor. #B457, Louis Blériot (1872-1936), aviation pioneer. #B458, Adm. François Joseph, Count de Grasse (1722-88), hero of the American Revolution. #B459, Théophile Gautier (1811-72), writer.

B454	SP256	50c + 10c blk & grn	.75	.75
B455	SP256	50c + 10c blk & bl	.75	.75
B456	SP256	50c + 10c blk & lil rose	.75	.75
B457	SP256	50c + 10c red & blk	.75	.75
B458	SP256	50c + 10c org & blk	1.00	1.00
B459	SP256	50c + 10c blk & brn	1.00	1.00
Nos. B454-B459 (6)			5.00	5.00

The surtax was for the Red Cross.
Issued: #B454-B455, Feb. 19; #B456, June 24; #B457, July 1; #B458-B459, Sept. 9.

Rural Mailman, 1894 SP257

Nicolas Desgenettes SP258

1972, Mar. 18   Engr.   Perf. 13

B460	SP257	50c + 10c bl, yel & ol gray	1.00	.75

Stamp Day 1972.
For surcharge see Reunion No. B39.

1972, Dec. 16   Engr.   Perf. 13

Designs: 30c+10c, René Nicolas Dufriche, Baron Desgenettes, M.D. (1762-1837).

50c+10c, François Joseph Broussais, M.D. (1772-1838).

B461 SP258 30c + 10c sl grn & red .65 .50
a. Bklt. pane, 4 ea, gutter btwn. 7.00
B462 SP258 50c + 10c red .65 .50

The surtax was for the Red Cross.
For surcharges see Reunion Nos. B40-B41.

Tony Garnier (1869-1948), architect — SP259

#B463, Gaspard de Coligny (1519-1572), admiral and Huguenot leader. #B464, Ernest Renan (1823-1892), philologist and historian. #B465, Alberto Santos Dumont (1873-1932), Brazilian aviator. #B466, Gabrielle-Sidonie Colette (1873-1954), writer. #B467, René Duguay-Trouin (1673-1736), naval commander. #B468, Louis Pasteur (1822-1895), chemist, bacteriologist. #B469, Tony Garnier (1869-1948), architect.

1973 **Engr.** **Perf. 13**
B463 SP259 50c + 10c multi .85 .85
B464 SP259 50c + 10c multi .85 .85
B465 SP259 50c + 10c multi .85 .85
B466 SP259 50c + 10c multi .85 .85
B467 SP259 50c + 10c multi .85 .85
B468 SP259 50c + 10c multi .85 .85
B469 SP259 50c + 10c multi .85 .85
Nos. B463-B469 (7) 5.95 5.95

Issued: #B463, 2/17; #B464, 4/28; #B465, 5/26; #B466, 6/2; #B467, 6/9; #B468, 10/6; #B469, 11/17.

Mail Coach, 1835 SP260

1973, Mar. 24 **Engr.** **Perf. 13**
B470 SP260 50c + 10c grnsh blue .35 .35

Stamp Day, 1973.
For surcharge see Reunion No. B42.

Mary Magdalene SP261 | St. Louis-Marie de Montfort SP262

50c+10c, Mourning woman. Designs are from 15th cent. Tomb of Tonnerre.

1973, Dec. 1
B471 SP261 30c + 10c sl grn & red .55 .55
a. Bklt. pane, 4 each, gutter btwn. 6.00
B472 SP261 50c + 10c dk gray & red .55 .55

Surtax was for the Red Cross.
For surcharges see Reunion Nos. B43-B44.

1974, Feb. 23 **Engr.** **Perf. 13**

Portraits: No. B474, Francis Poulenc (1899-1963), composer. No. B475, Jules Barbey d'Aurevilly (1808-1889), writer. No. B476, Jean Giraudoux (1882-1944), writer.

B473 SP262 50c + 10c multi 1.10 1.10
B474 SP262 50c + 10c multi .70 .70
B475 SP262 80c + 15c multi .80 .80
B476 SP262 80c + 15c multi .80 .80
Nos. B473-B476 (4) 3.40 3.40

Issue dates: No. B473, Mar. 9; No. B474, July 20; Nos. B475-B476, Nov. 16.

Automatically Sorted Letters — SP263

1974, Mar. 9 **Engr.** **Perf. 13**
B477 SP263 50c + 10c multi .30 .25

Stamp Day 1974. Automatic letter sorting center, Orleans-la-Source, opened 1/30/73.
For surcharge see Reunion No. B45.

Order of Liberation and 5 Honored Cities — SP264

1974, June 15 **Engr.** **Perf. 13**
B478 SP264 1fr + 10c multi .75 .40

30th anniv. of liberation from the Nazis.

"Summer" — SP265 | "Winter" — SP266

Designs: B481, "Spring" (girl on swing). B482, "Fall" (umbrella and rabbits).

1974, Nov. 30 **Engr.** **Perf. 13**
B479 SP265 60c + 15c multi .60 .60
a. Bklt. pane, 4 ea, gutter btwn. 6.00
B480 SP266 80c + 15c multi .60 .60

For surcharges see Reunion Nos. B46-B47.

1975, Nov. 29
B481 SP265 60c + 15c multi .50 .50
a. Bklt. pane, 4 ea, gutter btwn. 4.75
B482 SP266 80c + 20c multi .50 .50

Surtax was for the Red Cross.

Dr. Albert Schweitzer SP267 | Edmond Michelet SP268

André Siegfried and Map SP269

#B483, Albert Schweitzer (1875-1965), medical missionary. #B484, Edmond Michelet (1899-1970), Resistance hero, statesman. #B485, Robert Schuman (1886-1963), promoter of United Europe. #B486, Eugene Thomas (1903-69), minister of PTT. #B487, André Siegfried (1875-1959), political science professor, writer.

1975 **Engr.** **Perf. 13**
B483 SP267 80c + 20c multi .50 .50
B484 SP268 80c + 20c bl & ind .50 .50
B485 SP268 80c + 20c blk & ind .50 .50
B486 SP268 80c + 20c blk & sl .50 .50
B487 SP269 80c + 20c blk & bl .50 .50
Nos. B483-B487 (5) 2.50 2.50

Issued: #B483, 1/11; #B484, 2/22; #B485, 5/10; #B486, 6/28; #B487, 11/15.

Second Republic Mailman's Badge — SP270

1975, Mar. 8 **Photo.**
B488 SP270 80c + 20c multi .50 .40

Stamp Day.

"Sage" Type of 1876 SP271 | Marshal A. J. de Moncey SP272

1976, Mar. 13 **Engr.** **Perf. 13**
B489 SP271 80c + 20c blk & lil .45 .45

Stamp Day 1976.

1976 **Engr.** **Perf. 13**

#B491, Max Jacob (1876-1944), Dadaist writer, by Picasso. #B492, Jean Mounet-Sully (1841-1916), actor. #B493, Gen. Pierre Daumesnil (1776-1832). #B494, Eugène Fromentin (1820-1876), painter.

B490 SP272 80c + 20c multi .50 .50
B491 SP272 80c + 20c red brn & ol .50 .50
B492 SP272 80c + 20c multi .50 .50
B493 SP272 1fr + 20c multi .50 .50
B494 SP272 1fr + 20c multi .50 .50
Nos. B490-B494 (5) 2.50 2.50

Issued: #B490, 5/22; #B491, 7/22; #B492, 8/28; #B493, 9/4; #B494, 9/25.

Anna de Noailles SP273 | St. Barbara SP274

1976, Nov. 6 **Engr.** **Perf. 13**
B495 SP273 1fr + 20c multi .60 .60

Anna de Noailles (1876-1933), writer & poet.

1976, Nov. 20

Design: 1fr+25c, Cimmerian Sibyl. Sculptures from Brou Cathedral.

Cross in Carmine

B496 SP274 80c + 20c violet .60 .60
a. Bklt. pane, 4 ea, gutter btwn. 6.00
B497 SP274 1fr + 25c dk brown .80 .80

Surtax was for the Red Cross.

Marckolsheim Relay Station Sign — SP275

1977, Mar. 26 **Engr.** **Perf. 13**
B498 SP275 1fr + 20c multi .40 .40

Stamp Day.

Edouard Herriot, Statesman and Writer SP276 | Christmas Figurine, Provence SP277

Designs: No. B500, Abbé Breuil (1877-1961), archaeologist. No. B501, Guillaume de Machault (1305-1377), poet and composer. No. B502, Charles Cross (1842-1888).

1977 **Engr.** **Perf. 13**
B499 SP276 1fr + 20c multi .60 .60
B500 SP276 1fr + 20c multi .60 .60
B501 SP276 1fr + 20c multi .60 .60
B502 SP276 1fr + 20c multi .60 .60
Nos. B499-B502 (4) 2.40 2.40

Issued: #B499, Oct. 8; #B500, Oct. 15; #B501, Nov. 12; #B502, Dec. 3.

1977, Nov. 26

1fr+25c, Christmas figurine (woman), Provence.

B503 SP277 80c + 20c red & ind .45 .45
a. Bklt. pane, 4 ea, gutter btwn. 4.50
B504 SP277 1fr + 25c red & sl grn .55 .55

Surtax was for the Red Cross.

Marie Noel, Writer — SP278 | Mail Collection, 1900 — SP279

#B506, Georges Bernanos (1888-1948), writer. #B507, Leo Tolstoi (1828-1910), Russian writer. #B508, Charles Marie Leconte de Lisle (1818-1894), poet. #B509, Voltaire (1694-1778) and Jean Jacques Rousseau (1712-1778). #B510, Claude Bernard (1813-1878), physiologist.

1978 **Engr.** **Perf. 13**
B505 SP278 1fr + 20c multi .55 .55
B506 SP278 1fr + 20c multi .55 .55
B507 SP278 1fr + 20c multi .55 .55
B508 SP278 1fr + 20c multi .55 .55
B509 SP278 1fr + 20c multi .55 .55
B510 SP278 1fr + 20c multi .55 .55
Nos. B505-B510 (6) 3.30 3.30

Issued: #B505, 2/11; #B506, 2/18; #B507, 4/15; #B508, 3/26; #B509, 7/1; #B510, 9/16.

1978, Apr. 8 **Engr.** **Perf. 13**
B511 SP279 1fr + 20c multi .50 .40

Stamp Day 1978.

SP280

SP281

1fr+25c, The Hare & the Tortoise. 1.20fr+30c, The City Mouse & the Country Mouse.

1978, Dec. 2   Engr.   Perf. 13
B512 SP280   1fr + 25c multi   .75 .65
 a.   Bklt. pane, 4 ea, gutter btwn.   6.00
B513 SP280   1.20fr + 30c multi   .75 .65
Surtax was for the Red Cross.

1979   Engr.   Perf. 13
#B514, Ladislas Marshal de Berchény (1689-1778). #B515, Leon Jouhaux (1879-1954), labor leader. #B516, Peter Abelard (1079-1142), theologian and writer. #B517, Georges Courteline (1860-1929), humorist. #B518, Simone Weil (1909-1943), social philosopher. #B519, André Malraux (1901-1976), novelist.

B514 SP281   1.20fr + 30c multi   .60 .60
B515 SP281   1.20fr + 30c multi   .60 .60
B516 SP281   1.20fr + 30c multi   .60 .60
B517 SP281   1.20fr + 30c multi   .60 .60
B518 SP281   1.30fr + 30c multi   .60 .60
B519 SP281   1.30fr + 30c multi   .60 .60
    Nos. B514-B519 (6)   3.60 3.60
Issued: #B514, 1/13; #B515, 5/12; #B516, 6/9; #B517, 6/25; #B518, 11/12; #B519, 11/26.

General Post Office, from 1908 Post Card SP282

1979, Mar. 10   Engr.   Perf. 13
B520 SP282   1.20fr + 30c multi   .60 .40
Stamp Day 1979.

Woman, Stained-Glass Window — SP283

Stained-glass windows, Church of St. Joan of Arc, Rouen: 1.30fr+30c, Simon the Magician.

1979, Dec. 1   Perf. 13
B521 SP283   1.10fr + 30c multi   .50 .40
B522 SP283   1.30fr + 30c multi   .60 .45
 a.   Bklt. pane, 4 each #521-522, with gutter btwn., perf. 12½x13   6.00
Surtax was for the Red Cross.

Eugene Viollet le Duc (1814-1879), Architect — SP284

Jean-Marie de Le Mennais (1780-1860), Priest and Educator — SP285

#B524, Jean Monnet (1888-1979), economist and diplomat. #B525, Viollet le Duc (1814-1879), architect and writer. #B526, Frederic Mistral (1830-1914), poet. #B527, Saint-John Perse (Alexis Leger, 1887-1975), poet and diplomat. #B528, Pierre Paul de Riquet (1604-1680), canal builder.

1980   Engr.   Perf. 13
B523 SP284   1.30fr + 30c multi   .70 .70
B524 SP285   1.30fr + 30c multi   .70 .70
B525 SP285   1.40fr + 30c blue   .70 .70
B526 SP285   1.40fr + 30c black   .70 .70
B527 SP285   1.40fr + 30c multi   .70 .70
B528 SP285   1.40fr + 30c multi   .70 .70
    Nos. B523-B528 (6)   4.20 4.20
Issued: #B523, Feb. 16; #B524-B526, Sept. 6; #B527-B528, Oct. 11.

The Letter to Melie, by Avati, Stamp Day, 1980 — SP286

1980, Mar. 8   Photo.
B529 SP286   1.30fr + 30c multi   .60 .45

Filling the Granaries, Choir Stall Detail, Amiens Cathedral — SP287

#B531, Grapes from the Promised Land.

1980, Dec. 6   Engr.   Perf. 13
B530 SP287   1.20fr + 30c red & dk red brn   .70 .70
B531 SP287   1.40fr + 30c red & dk red brn   .80 .80
 a.   Bklt. pane, 4 #B530-B531, with gutter btwn., perf. 12½x13   6.50

Sister Anne-Marie Javouhey (1779-1851), Founded Congregation of St. Joseph of Cluny — SP288

#B532, Louis Armand (1905-71), railway engineer. #B533, Louis Jouvet (1887-1951), theater director. #B534, Marc Boegner (1881-1970), peace worker. #B536, Jacques Offenbach (1819-80), composer. #B537, Pierre Teilhard de Chardin (1881-1955), philosopher. Nos. B532-B533, B537 vert.

1981   Engr.   Perf. 13
B532 SP288   1.20 + 30c multi   .65 .65
B533 SP288   1.20 + 30c multi   .65 .65
B534 SP288   1.40 + 30c multi   .65 .65
B535 SP288   1.40 + 30c multi   .65 .65
B536 SP288   1.40 + 30c multi   .65 .65
B537 SP288   1.40 + 30c multi   .65 .65
    Nos. B532-B537 (6)   3.90 3.90
Issued: #B532, 5/23; #B533, 6/13; #B534, 11/14; #B535, 2/7; #B536, 2/14; #B537, 5/23.

The Love Letter, by Goya — SP289

1981, Mar. 7   Perf. 13x12½
B538 SP289   1.40 + 30c multi   1.00 .90
Stamp Day 1981.

Scourges of the Passion SP290

Guillaume Postel (1510-1581), Theologian — SP291

Stained-glass Windows, Church of the Sacred Heart, Audincourt: 1.60fr+30c, "Peace."

1981, Dec. 5   Photo.   Perf. 13
B539 SP290   1.40 + 30c multi   .75 .75
B540 SP290   1.60 + 30c multi   .80 .80
 a.   Bklt. pane, 4 ea, gutter btwn.   6.00

1982   Engr.   Perf. 13
#B542, Henri Mondor (1885-1962), physician. #B543, Andre Chantemesse (1851-1919), Scientist. #B544, Louis Pergaud (1882-1915), writer. #B545, Robert Debre (1882-1978), writer. #B546, Gustave Eiffel (1832-1923), engineer.

B541 SP291   1.40 + 30c multi   .65 .45
B542 SP291   1.40 + 30c dk brn & dk bl   .65 .40
B543 SP291   1.60 + 30c multi   .70 .70
B544 SP291   1.60 + 40c multi   .70 .70
B545 SP291   1.60 + 40c dk blue   .90 .70
B546 SP291   1.80 + 40c sepia   .90 .70
    Nos. B541-B546 (6)   4.50 3.65

Woman Reading, by Picasso — SP292

1982, Mar. 27   Perf. 13x12½
B547 SP292   1.60 + 40c multi   1.00 .75
Stamp Day.

SP293

SP294

Jules Verne books: 1.60fr+30c, Five Weeks in a Balloon. 1.80fr+40c, 20,000 Leagues under the Sea.

1982, Nov. 20   Perf. 13
B548 SP293   1.60 + 30c multi   .75 .65
B549 SP293   1.80 + 40c multi   .75 .65
 a.   Bklt. pane, 4 each #B548-B549, with gutter btwn., perf. 12½x13   8.00
Surtax was for Red Cross.

1983   Engr.   Perf. 12½x13
#B550, Andre Messager (1853-1929). #B551, J.A. Gabriel (1698-1782), architect. #B552, Hector Berlioz (1803-69), composer. #B553, Max Fouchet (1913-80). #B554, Rene Cassin (1887-1976). #B555, Stendhal (Marie Henri Beyle, 1783-1842).

B550 SP294   1.60 + 30c multi   .65 .65
B551 SP294   1.60 + 30c multi   .65 .65
B552 SP294   1.80 + 40c dp lil & blk   .75 .75
B553 SP294   1.80 + 40c multi   .75 .75
B554 SP294   2fr + 40c multi   .80 .80
B555 SP294   2fr + 40c multi   .80 .80
    Nos. B550-B555 (6)   4.40 4.40
Issued: #B550, 1/15; #B551, 4/16; #B552, 1/22; #B553, 4/30; #B554, 6/25; #B555, 11/12.

Man Dictating a Letter, by Rembrandt — SP295

Photo. & Engr.
1983, Feb. 26   Perf. 13X12½
B556 SP295   1.80 + 40c multi   1.20 .75
Stamp Day.

Virgin with Child, Baillon, 14th Cent. — SP296

Design: No. B558, Virgin with Child, Genainville, 16th Cent.

1983, Nov. 26   Engr.   Perf. 13
B557 SP296   1.60 + 40c shown   .65 .45
B558 SP296   2fr + 40c multi   .85 .55
 a.   Bklt. pane, 4 #B557-B558, with gutter btwn., perf. 12½x13   6.50

Emile Littre (1801-1881), Physician — SP297

#B560, Jean Zay (1904-44). #B561, Pierre Corneille (1606-1684). #B562, Gaston Bachelard (1884-1962). #B563, Jean Paulhan (1884-1968). #B564, Evariste Galois (1811-1832).

1984   Engr.   Perf. 13
B559 SP297   1.60fr + 40c plum & blk   .85 .85
B560 SP297   1.60fr + 40c dk grn & blk   .85 .85
B561 SP297   1.70fr + 40c dp vio & blk   .85 .85
B562 SP297   2fr + 40c gray & blk   .85 .85
B563 SP297   2.10fr + 40c dk brn & blk   .90 .80
B564 SP297   2.10fr + 40c ultra & blk   .90 .80
    Nos. B559-B564 (6)   5.20 5.00

SP298

SP299

Diderot Holding a Letter, by L.M. Van Loo.

1984, Mar. 17   Engr.   Perf. 12½x13
B565 SP298 2fr + 40c multi   1.25 .90

1984, Nov. 24   Photo.   Perf. 12½x13
The Rose Basket, by Caly.
B566 SP299 2.10fr + 50c pnksh
           (basket) &
           multi   1.10 .90
a.   Salmon (basket) & multi,
      perf. 13½x13   1.10 .90
b.   As "a," bklt. pane of 10 + 2
      labels   11.00

Surtax was for the Red Cross.

Jules Romains (1885-1972) — SP300

Authors: No. B568, Jean-Paul Sartre (1905-1980). No. B569, Romain Rolland (1866-1944). No. B570, Roland Dorgeles (1885-1973). No. B571, Victor Hugo (1802-1885). No. B572, Francois Mauriac (1885-1970).

1985, Feb. 23   Engr.   Perf. 13
B567 SP300 1.70fr + 40c   2.50 2.50
B568 SP300 1.70fr + 40c   2.50 2.50
B569 SP300 1.70fr + 40c   2.50 2.50
B570 SP300 2.10fr + 50c   2.50 2.50
B571 SP300 2.10fr + 50c   2.50 2.50
B572 SP300 2.10fr + 50c   2.50 2.50
a.   Bklt. pane, 1 each + 2 la-
      bels, perf. 15x14½   25.00
      Nos. B567-B572 (6)   15.00 15.00

SP301

SP302

Stamp Day: Canceling apparatus invented by Eugene Daguin (1849-1888).

1985, Mar. 16   Engr.   Perf. 12½x13
B573 SP301 2.10fr + 50c brn blk
           & bluish gray   1.00 .85

1985, Nov. 23   Photo.
Issenheim Altarpiece retable.
B574 SP302 2.20fr + 50c multi   1.00 .85
a.   As "b," bklt. pane of 10   10.00
b.   Perf. 13½x13   1.00 .85

Surtax for the Red Cross.

SP303

SP304

Famous men: No. B575, Francois Arago (1786-1853), physician, politician. No. B576, Henri Moissan (1852-1907), chemist. No. B577, Henri Fabre (1882-1984), engineer. No. B578, Marc Seguin (1786-1875), engineer. No. B579, Paul Heroult (1863-1914), chemist.

1986, Feb. 22   Engr.   Perf. 13
B575 SP303 1.80fr + 40c multi   .95 .95
B576 SP303 1.80fr + 40c multi   .95 .95
B577 SP303 1.80fr + 40c multi   .95 .95
B578 SP303 2.20fr + 50c multi   1.10 1.10
B579 SP303 2.20fr + 50c multi   1.10 1.10
a.   Bklt. pane of 5, #B575-B579,
      + 3 labels   8.00
      Nos. B575-B579 (5)   5.05 5.05

1986, Mar. 1   Engr.   Perf. 13x12½
B580 SP304 2.20fr + 50c brn blk 6.00 6.00
Pierre Cot (1895-1977).

Mail Britzska SP305

1986, Apr. 5   Perf. 13
B581 SP305 2.20fr + 60c pale
           tan & dk vio
           brn   1.10 1.00

Booklet Stamp
B582 SP305 2.20fr + 60c buff &
           blk   1.20 1.00
a.   Bklt. pane of 6 + 2 labels 7.50
Stamp Day. See Nos. B590-B591, B599-B600, B608-B609.

Stained Glass Window (detail), by Vieira da Silva, St. Jacques of Reims Church, Marne — SP306

1986, Nov. 24   Photo.   Perf. 12½x13
B583 SP306 2.20fr + 60c multi   1.20 .95
a.   As "b," bklt. pane of 10   12.00
b.   Perf. 13½x13   1.20 .95
Surtaxed to benefit the natl. Red Cross.

Physicians and Biologists SP307

#B584, Charles Richet (1850-1935). #B585, Eugene Jamot (1879-1937). #B586, Bernard Halpern (1904-1978). #B587, Alexandre Yersin (1863-1943). #B588, Jean Rostand (1894-1977). #B589, Jacques Monod (1910-1976).

1987, Feb. 21   Engr.   Perf. 13
B584 SP307 1.90fr + 50c deep
           ultra   .95 .95
B585 SP307 1.90fr + 50c dull lil .95 .95
B586 SP307 1.90fr + 50c grnish
           gray   .95 .95
B587 SP307 2.20fr + 50c grnish
           gray   1.10 1.10
B588 SP307 2.20fr + 50c deep
           ultra   1.10 1.10
B589 SP307 2.20fr + 50c dull lil 1.10 1.10
a.   Bklt. pane of 6, #B584-B589 6.50
      Nos. B584-B589 (6)   6.15 6.15

Stamp Day Type of 1986
Stamp Day 1987: Berline carriage.

1987, Mar. 14   Engr.
B590 SP305 2.20fr + 60c buff &
           sepia   1.10 .95
Booklet Stamp
B591 SP305 2.20fr + 60c pale &
           dk bl   1.25 .95
a.   Bklt. pane of 6 + 2 labels 8.00

Flight Into Egypt, Retable by Melchior Broederlam SP308

1987, Nov. 21   Photo.   Perf. 12½x13
B592 SP308 2.20fr + 60c multi   1.10 .95
a.   As "b," bklt. pane of 10 + 2
      labels   11.00
b.   Perf. 13½x13   1.10 .95
Surtaxed to benefit the Red Cross.

Explorers SP309

Profiles & maps: #B593, Marquis Abraham Duquesne (1610-1688), naval commander. #B594, Pierre Andre de Suffren (1729-1788). #B595, Jean-Francois de La Perouse (1741-1788). #B596, Mahe de La Bourdonnais (1699-1753). #B597, Louis-Antoine de Bougainville (1729-1811). #B598, Jules Dumont d'Urville (1790-1842).

1988, Feb. 20   Engr.   Perf. 13
B593 SP309 2fr + 50c multi   .90 .80
B594 SP309 2fr + 50c multi   .90 .80
B595 SP309 2fr + 50c multi   .90 .80
B596 SP309 2.20fr + 50c multi   1.00 .85
B597 SP309 2.20fr + 50c multi   1.00 .85
B598 SP309 2.20fr + 50c multi   1.00 .85
a.   Bklt. pane of 6, #B593-B598 6.00

Stamp Day Type of 1986
Stamp Day 1988: Postal coach.

1988, Mar. 29   Engr.
B599 SP305 2.20fr +60c dk lilac 1.10 1.00
Booklet Stamp
B600 SP305 2.20fr +60c sepia   1.10 1.00
a.   Bklt. pane of 6 + 2 labels 6.50

Intl. Red Cross, 125th Anniv. — SP310

1988, Nov. 19   Engr.   Perf. 12½x13
B601 SP310 2.20fr +60c multi   1.10 1.00
a.   As "b," bklt. pane of 10+2
      labels   11.00
b.   Perf. 13½x13   1.10 1.00

Revolution Leaders and Heroes SP311

#B602, Emmanuel Joseph Sieyes (1748-1836). #B603, Honore Gabriel Riqueti, Comte de Mirabeau (1749-91). #B604, Louis Marie de Noailles (1756-1804). #B605, Lafayette. #B606, Antoine Pierre Joseph Marie Barnave (1761-92). #B607, Jean Baptiste Drouet (1763-1824).

1989, Feb. 25   Engr.   Perf. 13
B602 SP311 2.20fr +50c multi   1.10 .90
B603 SP311 2.20fr +50c multi   1.10 .90
B604 SP311 2.20fr +50c multi   1.10 .90
B605 SP311 2.20fr +50c multi   1.10 .90

B606 SP311 2.20fr +50c multi   1.10 .90
B607 SP311 2.20fr +50c multi   1.10 .90
a.   Bklt. pane, 1 each + 2 labels 6.60
French Revolution, bicent.

Stamp Day Type of 1986
Design: Paris-Lyon stagecoach.

1989, Apr. 15   Engr.   Perf. 13
B608 SP305 2.20fr +60c pale bl
           & dk bl   1.10 .95
Booklet Stamp
B609 SP305 2.20fr +60c pale lil
           & pur   1.00 .95
a.   Bklt. pane of 6 + 2 labels 8.00
Stamp Day 1989.

Bird From a Silk Tapestry, Lyon, 18th Cent. — SP312

1989, Nov. 18   Photo.   Perf. 12½x13
B610 SP312 2.20fr +60c multi   1.10 .90
a.   As "b," bklt. pane of 10   12.00
b.   Perf. 13½x13   1.10 .90
Surtax for the natl. Red Cross.

1992 Winter Olympics, Albertville SP313

1990, Feb. 9   Engr.   Perf. 13
B611 SP313 2.30fr +20c red, bl
           & blk   1.10 .85
See Nos. B621-B627, B636-B637, B639.

Stamp Day SP314

1990, Mar. 17   Photo.
B612 SP314 2.30fr +60c ultra, bl
           & brt yel   1.20 1.00
Booklet Stamp
B613 SP314 2.30fr +60c ultra,
           grn, yel &
           brt grn   1.20 1.00
a.   Bklt. pane of 6 + 2 labels 8.00

SP315

SP316

Quimper or Brittany Ware Faience plate.

1990, May 5   Photo.   Perf. 12½x13
B614 SP315 2.30fr +60c multi   1.10 1.00
a.   As "b," bklt. pane of 10+2 la-
      bels   12.00
b.   Perf. 13½x13   1.20 1.00
Surcharge benefited the Red Cross.

1990, June 16   Photo.   Perf. 13
#B615, Aristide Bruant. #B616, Maurice Chevalier. #B617, Tino Rossi. #B618, Edith Piaf. #B619, Jacques Brel. #B620, Georges Brassens.

B615 SP316 2.30fr +50c multi   1.00 1.00
B616 SP316 2.30fr +50c multi   1.00 1.00
B617 SP316 2.30fr +50c multi   1.00 1.00
B618 SP316 2.30fr +50c multi   1.00 1.00

B619	SP316	2.30fr +50c multi	1.00 1.00
B620	SP316	2.30fr +50c multi	1.00 1.00
a.		Bklt. pane, 1 each +2 labels	6.00

Albertville Olympic Type

Designs: No. B621, Ski jumping. No. B622, Speed skiing. No. B623, Slalom skiing. No. B624, Cross-country skiing. No. B625, Ice hockey. No. B626, Luge. No. B627, Curling.

1990-91 Engr. Perf. 13

B621	SP313	2.30fr +20c multi	1.00 .95
B622	SP313	2.30fr +20c multi	1.00 .95
B623	SP313	2.30fr +20c multi	1.00 .95
B624	SP313	2.30fr +20c multi	1.00 .95
B625	SP313	2.30fr +20c multi	1.00 .95
B626	SP313	2.50fr +20c multi	1.10 1.10
B627	SP313	2.50fr +20c multi	1.10 1.10
		Nos. B621-B627 (7)	7.20 6.95

Issued: #B621, 12/22/90; #B622, 12/29/90; #B623, 1/19/91; #B624, 2/2/91; #B625, 2/9/91; #B626, 3/2/91; #B627, 4/20/91.
No. B624 inscribed "

Paul Eluard (1895-1952) — SP317

Poets: No. B629, Andre Breton (1896-1966). No. B630, Louis Aragon (1897-1982). No. B631, Francis Ponge (1899-1988). No. B632, Jacques Prevert (1900-1977). No. B633, Rene Char (1907-1988).

1991, Feb. 23 Engr. Perf. 12½x13

B628	SP317	2.50fr +50c multi	1.10 1.10
B629	SP317	2.50fr +50c multi	1.10 1.10
B630	SP317	2.50fr +50c multi	1.10 1.10
B631	SP317	2.50fr +50c multi	1.10 1.10
B632	SP317	2.50fr +50c multi	1.10 1.10
B633	SP317	2.50fr +50c multi	1.10 1.10
a.		Bklt. pane, 1 each +2 labels, perf. 13	7.50

Stamp Day
SP318

1991, Mar. 16 Photo. Perf. 13

B634	SP318	2.50fr +60c blue machine	1.25 1.25
B635	SP318	2.50fr +60c purple machine	1.25 1.25
a.		Bklt. pane of 6 + 2 labels	8.50

Winter Olympics Type of 1990

#B636, Acrobatic skiing. #B637, Alpine skiing.

1991 Engr. Perf. 13

B636	SP313	2.50fr +20c multi	1.10 .95
B637	SP313	2.50fr +20c multi	1.10 .95

Issued: #B636, Aug. 3; #B637, Aug. 17.
Nos. B636-B637 inscribed "La Poste 1992."

The Harbor of Toulon by Francois Nardi
SP319

1991, Dec. 2 Photo. Perf. 13x12½

B638	SP319	2.50fr +60c multi	1.20 1.10
a.		Perf. 13x13½	1.20 1.10
b.		As "a," bklt. pane of 10 + 2 labels	12.00

Surtax for the Red Cross.

Winter Olympics Type of 1990
Miniature Sheet

a, like #B611. b, like #B621. c, like #B622. d, like #B623. e, like #B624. f, like #B625.

1992, Feb. 8 Engr. Perf. 13

B639		Sheet of 10 + label	18.00 18.00
a.-f.		SP313 2.50fr +20c multi	1.75 1.75

No. B639 contains one each B626-B627, B636-B637, B639a-B639f. Central label is litho.

Stamp Day
SP320

1992, Mar. 7 Litho. Perf. 13

B640	SP320	2.50fr +60c gray people	1.10 1.10

Booklet Stamp
Photo.

B641	SP320	2.50fr +60c red people	1.25 1.10
a.		Bklt. pane of 6 + 2 labels	8.00

SP321

SP322

Composers: No. B642, Cesar Franck (1822-1890). No. B643, Erik Satie (1866-1925). No. B644, Florent Schmitt (1870-1958). No. B645, Arthur Honegger (1892-1955). No. B646, Georges Auric (1899-1983). No. B647, Germaine Tailleferre (1892-1983).

1992, Apr. 11 Photo. Perf. 13

B642	SP321	2.50fr +50c multi	1.10 1.10
B643	SP321	2.50fr +50c multi	1.10 1.10
B644	SP321	2.50fr +50c multi	1.10 1.10
B645	SP321	2.50fr +50c multi	1.10 1.10
B646	SP321	2.50fr +50c multi	1.10 1.10
B647	SP321	2.50fr +50c multi	1.10 1.10
a.		Bklt. pane of 6, #B642-B647	8.00

1992, Nov. 28 Photo. Perf. 13½x13

B648	SP322	2.50fr +60c multi	1.20 1.10
a.		Bklt. pane of 10 + 2 labels	12.00

Mutual Aid, Strasbourg. Surtax for the Red Cross.

Writers
SP323

#B649, Guy de Maupassant (1850-93). #B650, Alain (Emile Chartier) (1868-1951). #B651, Jean Cocteau (1889-1963). #B652, Marcel Pagnol (1895-1974). #B653, Andre Chamson (1900-83). #B654, Marguerite Yourcenar (1903-87).

1993, Apr. 24 Engr. Perf. 13

B649	SP323	2.50fr +50c multi	1.10 1.10
B650	SP323	2.50fr +50c multi	1.10 1.10
B651	SP323	2.50fr +50c multi	1.10 1.10
B652	SP323	2.50fr +50c multi	1.10 1.10
B653	SP323	2.50fr +50c multi	1.10 1.10
B654	SP323	2.50fr +50c multi	1.10 1.10
a.		Bklt. pane of 6, #B649-B654 + 2 labels	8.00

When Nos. B650-B654 are normally centered, inscriptions at base of the lower panel are not parallel to the perforations at bottom. On all six stamps the lower panel is not centered between the side perforations.

SP324

SP325

St. Nicolas, Image of Metz.

1993, Nov. 27 Engr. Perf. 12½x13

B655	SP324	2.80fr +60c multi	1.25 1.10
a.		Perf. 13½x13	1.25 1.10
b.		As "a," Bklt. pane of 10 +2 labels	15.00

Surtax for Red Cross.

1994, Sept. 17 Photo. Perf. 13

Stage and Screen Personalities: No. B656, Yvonne Printemps (1894-1977). No. B657, Fernandel (1903-71). No. B658, Josephine Baker (1906-75). No. B659, Bourvil (1917-70). No. B660, Yves Montand (1921-91). No. B661, Coluche (1944-86).

B656	SP325	2.80fr +60c multi	1.25 1.25
B657	SP325	2.80fr +60c multi	1.25 1.25
B658	SP325	2.80fr +60c multi	1.25 1.25
B659	SP325	2.80fr +60c multi	1.25 1.25
B660	SP325	2.80fr +60c multi	1.25 1.25
B661	SP325	2.80fr +60c multi	1.25 1.25
a.		Bklt. pane, #B656-B661 + 2 labels	8.00

SP326

SP327

Designs: #B662, St. Vaast, Arras Tapestry. #B663, Brussels tapestry from Reydams workshop, Horse Museum, Saumur.

1994-95 Photo. Perf. 12½x13

B662	SP326	2.80fr +60c multi	1.50 1.40
a.		Perf. 13½x13	1.50 1.40
b.		Bklt. pane, 10 #B662a + 2 labels	15.00
		Complete booklet, #B662b	16.00
B663	SP326	2.80fr +60c multi	1.50 1.50
a.		Perf. 13½x13	1.50 1.50
b.		Bklt. pane, 10 #B663a + 2 labels	15.00
		Complete booklet, #B663b	15.00

Surtax for Red Cross.
Issued: #B662, 11/26/94; #B663, 5/13/95.

1995, Nov. 25 Engr. Perf. 13

Provencal Nativity Figures: No. B664, The Shepherd. No. B665, The Miller. No. B666, The Simpleton and the Tambour Player. No. B667, The Fishmonger. No. B668, The Scissor Grinder. No. B669, The Elders.

B664	SP327	2.80fr +60c multi	1.40 1.40
B665	SP327	2.80fr +60c multi	1.40 1.40
B666	SP327	2.80fr +60c multi	1.40 1.40
B667	SP327	2.80fr +60c multi	1.40 1.40
B668	SP327	2.80fr +60c multi	1.40 1.40
B669	SP327	2.80fr +60c multi	1.40 1.40
a.		Booklet pane, Nos. B664-B669 + 2 labels	10.00
		Complete booklet, No. B669a	11.00

SP328

Famous Fictional Detectives and Criminals: #B670, Rocambole. #B671, Arsène Lupin. #B672, Joseph Rouletabille. #B673, Fantômas. #B674, Commissioner Maigret. #B675, Nestor Burma.

1996, Oct. 5 Photo. Perf. 13

B670	SP328	3fr +60c multi	1.40 1.40
B671	SP328	3fr +60c multi	1.40 1.40
B672	SP328	3fr +60c multi	1.40 1.40
B673	SP328	3fr +60c multi	1.40 1.40
B674	SP328	3fr +60c multi	1.40 1.40
B675	SP328	3fr +60c multi	1.40 1.40
a.		Booklet pane, #B670-B675 + 2 labels	9.00
		Complete booklet, #B675a	11.00

Christmas
SP329

1996, Nov. 16 Photo. Perf. 12¾x13

B676	SP329	3fr +60c multi	1.45 1.45
a.		Perf. 13¼x13	1.50 1.50
b.		Booklet pane, 10 #B676a + 2 labels	15.00
		Complete booklet, #B676b	15.00

Surtax for Red Cross.

Adventure Heroes
SP330

1997, Oct. 25 Photo. Perf. 13

B677	SP330	3fr +60c Sir Lancelot	1.40 1.40
B678	SP330	3fr +60c Pardaillan	1.40 1.40
B679	SP330	3fr +60c D'Artagnan	1.40 1.40
B680	SP330	3fr +60c Cyrano de Bergerac	1.40 1.40
B681	SP330	3fr +60c Captain Fracasse	1.40 1.40
B682	SP330	3fr +60c Le Bossu	1.40 1.40
a.		Booklet pane, #B677-B682 + 2 labels	9.00
		Complete booklet, #682a	9.00

Christmas, New Year — SP331

1997, Nov. 6 Photo. Perf. 12¾x13

B683	SP331	3fr +60c multi	1.40 1.25
a.		Perf. 13¼x13	1.40 1.25
b.		Booklet pane, 10 #B683a + 2 labels	14.00
		Complete booklet, #B683b	15.00

Surtax for the Red Cross.

SP332

Actors of the French Cinema: #B684, Romy Schneider (1938-82). #B685, Simone Signoret (1921-85). #B686, Jean Gabin (1904-76). #B687, Louis de Funés (1914-83). #B688, Bernard Blier (1916-89). #B689, Lino Ventura (1919-87).

1998, Oct. 3 Photo. Perf. 13

B684	SP332	3fr +60c multi	1.40 1.40
B685	SP332	3fr +60c multi	1.40 1.40
B686	SP332	3fr +60c multi	1.40 1.40
B687	SP332	3fr +60c multi	1.40 1.40
B688	SP332	3fr +60c multi	1.40 1.40
B689	SP332	3fr +60c multi	1.40 1.40
a.		Booklet pane, #B684-B689 + label	9.50
		Complete booklet, #B689a	10.00

Christmas
SP333

1998, Nov. 5 Photo. Perf. 12½x13
B690 SP333 3fr +60c multi 1.40 1.40
  a.   Perf. 13½x13 .... 1.40 1.40
  b.   Booklet pane, 10 #B690a +
      2 labels 15.00
      Complete booklet, #B690b .. 15.00
      Surtax for Red Cross.

Famous Photographers — SP334

  Photographs by: #B691, Robert Doisneau (1912-94). #B692, Brassai (Gyula Halasz) (1899-1984). #B693, Jacques Lartigue (1894-1986). #B694, Henri Cartier-Bresson (b. 1908). #B695, Eugene Atget (1857-1927). #B696, Felix Nadar (1820-1910).

1999, July 10 Photo. Perf. 13
B691 SP334 3fr +60c multi 1.40 1.40
B692 SP334 3fr +60c multi 1.40 1.40
B693 SP334 3fr +60c multi 1.40 1.40
B694 SP334 3fr +60c multi 1.40 1.40
B695 SP334 3fr +60c multi 1.40 1.40
B696 SP334 3fr +60c multi 1.40 1.40
  a.   Booklet pane, #B691-B696 .. 8.50
      Complete booklet, #B696a .. 9.00

New Year 2000 — SP335

1999, Nov. 10 Photo. Perf. 12¾x13
B697 SP335 3fr +60c multi 1.40 1.40
  a.   Perf. 13½x13 .... 1.40 1.40
  b.   Booklet pane, 10 #B697a +
      2 labels 14.00
      Complete booklet, #B697b .. 14.00
      Surtax for Red Cross.

Adventurers SP336

  #B698, Eric Tabarly (1931-98), sailor. #B699, Alexandra David-Néel (1868-1969), opera singer, Asian traveler. #B700, Haroun Tazieff (1914-98), vulcanologist. #B701, Paul-Emile Victor (1907-55), ethnologist, polar explorer. #B702, Jacques-Yves Cousteau (1910-97), oceanographer. #B703, Norbert Casteret (1897-1987), speleologist.

2000, Sept. 16 Photo. Perf. 13¼x13
B698 SP336 3fr +60c multi 1.40 1.40
B699 SP336 3fr +60c multi 1.40 1.40
B700 SP336 3fr +60c multi 1.40 1.40
B701 SP336 3fr +60c multi 1.40 1.40
B702 SP336 3fr +60c multi 1.40 1.40
B703 SP336 3fr +60c multi 1.40 1.40
  a.   Booklet pane, #B698-B703 .. 8.50
      Booklet, #B703a 8.50

Toy Airplane — SP337

2000, Nov. 9 Photo. Perf. 13¼x13
B704 SP337 3fr +60c multi 1.40 1.40
  a.   Booklet pane of 10 + 2 la-
      bels 14.00
      Booklet, #B704a 15.00
      Surtax for Red Cross.

Santa Claus and Tree Ornaments SP338

2001, Nov. 8 Photo. Perf. 12¾x13
B705 SP338 3fr +60c multi 1.40 1.40
  a.   Perf. 13½x13 .... 1.40 1.40
  b.   Booklet pane of 10 .... 14.00
      Booklet, #B705a 14.00
      Surtax for Red Cross.

Infant Jesus Asleep, by Giovanni Battista Salvi — SP339

2002, Nov. 7 Photo. Perf. 12¾x13
B706 SP339 46c +9c multi 1.40 1.40
  a.   Perf. 13½x13 .... 1.40 1.40
  b.   As "a," booklet pane of 10 .. 14.00
      Booklet, #B706b 14.00
      Surtax for Red Cross.

Virgin with Grapes, by Pierre Mignard — SP340

2003, Nov. 6 Photo. Perf. 13¼x13
Booklet Stamp
B707 SP340 50c +(16c) multi 1.50 1.50
  a.   Booklet pane of 10 .... 15.00
      Complete booklet, #B707a .. 15.00
      Surtax for Red Cross.

Virgin With Child, Attributed to Cretan School — SP341

2004, Nov. 10 Photo. Perf. 13¼x13
Booklet Stamp
B708 SP341 50c +(16c) multi 1.75 1.75
  a.   Booklet pane of 10 + 2 la-
      bels 17.50
      Complete booklet, #B708a .. 17.50
      Surtax for Red Cross.

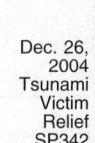

Dec. 26, 2004 Tsunami Victim Relief SP342

2005, Jan. 13 Engr. Perf. 13
B709 SP342 (50c) +20c red 1.90 1.90

Virgin and Child, by Hans Memling SP343

2005, Nov. 10 Photo. Perf. 13½x13
Booklet Stamp
B710 SP343 53c +(17c) multi 1.75 1.75
  a.   Booklet pane of 10 + 2 la-
      bels 17.50
      Complete booklet, #B710a .. 17.50
      Surtax for Red Cross.

SP344

Children's Art — SP345

2006, Nov. 25 Photo. Perf. 13½x13
Booklet Stamps
B711 SP344 (54c) +(17c) multi ... 1.90 1.90
B712 SP345 (54c) +(17c) multi ... 1.90 1.90
  a.   Booklet pane, 5 each
      #B711-B712, + 2 labels 19.00
      Complete booklet, #B712a .. 19.00
      Surtax for Red Cross.

Red Cross
SP346   SP347

Serpentine Die Cut 11
2007, Nov. 24
Self-Adhesive
Booklet Stamps   **Photo.**
B713 SP346 (54c) +(17c) multi ... 2.10 2.10
B714 SP347 (54c) +(17c) multi ... 2.10 2.10
  a.   Booklet pane, 5 each
      #B713-B714 .... 21.00
      Surtax for Red Cross.

Red Cross
SP348   SP349

Serpentine Die Cut 11x11¼
2008, Nov. 8   **Photo.**
Booklet Stamps
Self-Adhesive
B715 SP348 (55c) +(18c) multi ... 1.90 1.90
B716 SP349 (55c) +(18c) multi ... 1.90 1.90
  a.   Booklet pane of 10, 2 each
      #B715-B716 .... 19.00
      Surtax for Red Cross.

Miniature Sheet

Red Cross — SP350

  No. B717: a, Henri Dunant. b, Battle of Solferino. c, Pélias et Nélée, by Georges Braque, horiz. d, Geneva Conventions. e, Globe and symbols of the International Red Cross and Red Crescent Societies.

2009, Sept. 19 Photo. Perf. 13
B717 SP350 Sheet of 5 .... 14.00 14.00
  a.-e. 56c +(40c) Any single 2.75 2.75
      Surtax for Red Cross.

Haiti Earthquake Relief — SP351

2010, Jan. 19 Engr. Perf. 13
B718 SP351 (56c) +44c red 2.75 2.75
Self-Adhesive
Serpentine Die Cut 11
B719 SP351 (56c) +44c red 2.75 2.75
  Surtax was for French Red Cross relief efforts in Haiti.

Miniature Sheet

Red Cross — SP352

  No. B720: a, Woman on telephone. b, Man assisting unconscious woman. c, Red Cross emblem, horiz. d, Woman performing Heimlich maneuver on choking man. e, Cardio-pulmonary resuscitation.

Photo., Photo. & Embossed (#B720c)
2010, Nov. 5   **Perf. 13**
B720 SP352 Sheet of 5 .... 14.00 14.00
  a.-e. 58c +(40c) Any single 2.75 2.75
      Surtax for Red Cross.

AIR POST STAMPS

Nos. 127, 130 Overprinted in Dark Blue or Black

Perf. 14x13½
1927, June 25   **Unwmk.**
C1 A18 2fr org & bl (DB) 200.00 225.00
      Never hinged 400.00
C2 A18 5fr dk bl & buff 200.00 225.00
      Never hinged 400.00

  On sale only at the Intl. Aviation Exhib. at Marseilles, June, 1927. One set could be purchased by each holder of an admission ticket. Excellent counterfeits exist.

Nos. 242, 196
Surcharged

1928, Aug. 23
C3 A33 10fr on 90c   2,400.   1,800.
  Never hinged   3,500.
  a. Inverted surcharge   16,500. 16,500.
  Never hinged   25,000.
  b. Space between "10" and
    bars 6½mm   3,100.   3,100.
  Never hinged   5,100.
C4 A23 10fr on 1.50fr   10,000.   8,250.
  Never hinged   14,000.
  a. Space between "10" and
    bars 6½mm   13,000. 13,000.
  Never hinged   20,000.

Nos. C3-C4 received their surcharge in New York by order of the French consul general. They were for use in paying the 10fr fee for letters leaving the liner Ile de France on a catapulted hydroplane when the ship was one day off the coast of France on its eastward voyage.

The normal space between "10" and bars is 4½mm, but on 10 stamps in each pane of 50 the space is 6½mm. Counterfeits exist.

View of
Marseille,
Church of
Notre
Dame at
Left — AP1

1930-31   Engr.   Perf. 13
C5 AP1 1.50fr dp car-
  mine   21.00   4.00
  Never hinged   40.00
C6 AP1 1.50fr dk bl ('31)   19.00   2.25
  Never hinged   35.00
  a. 1.50fr ultramarine   50.00   21.00
  Never hinged   90.00
  b. As "a," with perf. initials
    "E.I.P.A.30"   450.00 350.00
  Never hinged   700.00

Nos. C5a, C6a were sold at the Intl. Air Post Exhib., Paris, Nov. 6-20, 1930, at face value plus 5fr, the price of admission.

Forgeries abound of Nos. C5a and C6b. Certificates from recognized authorities are recommended.

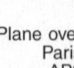

Blériot's
Monoplane
AP2

1934, Sept. 1   Perf. 13
C7 AP2 2.25fr violet   24.00   6.00
  Never hinged   32.50

1st flight across the English Channel, by Louis Blériot.

Plane over
Paris
AP3

1936
C8 AP3 85c deep green   2.25   2.25
  Never hinged   6.50
C9 AP3 1.50fr blue   10.50   5.50
  Never hinged   18.00
C10 AP3 2.25fr violet   18.00   7.00
  Never hinged   35.00
C11 AP3 2.50fr rose   32.50   8.25
  Never hinged   45.00
C12 AP3 3fr ultra   26.00   2.50
  Never hinged   37.50
C13 AP3 3.50fr orange brn   62.50   24.00
  Never hinged   105.00
C14 AP3 50fr emerald   825.00 325.00
  Never hinged   1,450.
  b. 50fr green   850.00 350.00
  Never hinged   1,500.
  Nos. C8-C14 (7)   976.75 374.50

Monoplane over Paris — AP4

Paper with Red Network Overprint
1936, July 10   Perf. 12½
C15 AP4 50fr ultra   575.00 310.00
  Never hinged   1,700.

Airplane and
Galleon — AP5

Airplane
and Globe
AP6

1936, Aug. 17   Perf. 13
C16 AP5 1.50fr dk ultra   17.50   5.25
  Never hinged   35.00
C17 AP6 10fr Prus green   290.00 130.00
  Never hinged   700.00

100th air mail flight across the South Atlantic.

Catalogue values for unused stamps in this section, from this point to the end of the section, are for Never Hinged items.

Centaur and
Plane — AP7

Iris — AP8

Zeus
Carrying
Hebe
AP9

Chariot of
the Sun
AP10

1946-47   Engr.   Unwmk.
C18 AP7 40fr dk green   .65   .20
C19 AP8 50fr rose pink   .65   .20
C20 AP9 100fr dk blue ('47) 7.00   4.00
C21 AP10 200fr red   6.00   1.50
  Nos. C18-C21 (4)   14.30   5.90

Issued: 50fr, 200fr, 5/27; 40fr, 7/1; 100fr, Jan.
For surcharges see Reunion Nos. C35-C38.

Ile de la Cité, Paris, and Gull — AP11

1947, May 7
C22 AP11 500fr dk Prus grn   50.00   45.00
UPU 12th Cong., Paris, May 7-July 7.

View of Lille
AP12

Air View of Paris — AP13

200fr, Bordeaux. 300fr, Lyon. 500fr, Marseille.

1949-50   Unwmk.   Perf. 13
C23 AP12 100fr sepia   1.40   .40
C24 AP12 200fr dk bl grn   12.50   .75
C25 AP12 300fr purple   15.00   10.00
C26 AP12 500fr brt red   57.50   5.75
C27 AP13 1000fr sep & blk,
  bl ('50)   150.00   27.50
  Nos. C23-C27 (5)   236.40   44.40

For surcharges see Reunion Nos. C39-C41.

Alexander III Bridge and Petit Palais,
Paris — AP14

1949, June 13
C28 AP14 100fr brown car   7.50   5.75
International Telegraph and Telephone Conference, Paris, May-July 1949.

Jet Plane,
Mystère
IV — AP15

Planes: 200fr, Noratlas. 500fr, Miles Magister. 1000fr, Provence.

1954, Jan. 16
C29 AP15 100fr red brn & bl   3.00   .20
C30 AP15 200fr blk brn &
  vio bl   11.00   .25
C31 AP15 500fr car & org   200.00   12.50
C32 AP15 1000fr vio brn, bl
  grn & ind   110.00   16.00
  Nos. C29-C32 (4)   324.00   28.95

See No. C37. For surcharges see Reunion Nos. C42-C45, C48.

Maryse
Bastié and
Plane
AP16

1955, June 4   Unwmk.   Perf. 13
C33 AP16 50fr dp plum & rose
  pink   6.50   4.00

Issued to honor Maryse Bastié, 1898-1952.

Morane
Saulnier
760 Paris
AP17

Designs: 300fr, Morane Saulnier 760 "Paris." 1000fr, Alouette helicopter.

1957-59   Engr.   Perf. 13
C34 AP17 300fr sl grn,
  grnsh bl &
  sep ('59)   5.00   3.00
C35 AP17 500fr dp ultra &
  blk   30.00   3.75
C36 AP17 1000fr lil, ol blk &
  blk ('58)   52.50   19.00
  Nos. C34-C36 (3)   87.50   25.75

See Nos. C38-C41. For surcharges see Reunion Nos. C46-C47, C49-C51.

Types of 1954-59

Planes: 2fr, Noratlas. 3fr, MS760, Paris. 5fr, Caravelle. 10fr, Alouette helicopter.

1960, Jan. 11
C37 AP15 2fr vio bl & ultra   1.60   .20
  a. 2fr ultramarine   3.25   .40
C38 AP17 3fr sl grn, grnsh bl
  & sep   1.60   .20
C39 AP17 5fr dp ultra & blk   3.25   .75
C40 AP17 10fr lil, ol blk & blk 13.00   2.00
  Nos. C37-C40 (4)   19.45   3.15

Type of 1957-59

Design: 2fr, Jet plane, Mystère 20.

1965, June 12   Engr.   Perf. 13
C41 AP17 2fr slate bl & indigo .85   .20

Concorde Issue
Common Design Type
1969, Mar. 2   Engr.   Perf. 13
C42 CD129 1fr indigo & brt bl 1.00   .35

The 0.95fr stamp in this design was prepared but not issued. Value $30,000.

Jean Mermoz, Antoine de Saint-
Exupéry and Concorde — AP19

1970, Sept. 19   Engr.   Perf. 13
C43 AP19 20fr blue & indigo   9.00   .60

Jean Mermoz (1901-36) and writer Antoine de Saint-Exupéry (1900-44), aviators and air mail pioneers.

Balloon, Gare
d'Austerlitz,
Paris — AP20

1971, Jan. 16   Engr.   Perf. 13
C44 AP20 95c bl, vio bl, org & sl
  grn   .90   .55

Centenary of the balloon post from besieged Paris, 1870-71.

Didier Daurat, Raymond Vanier and Plane Landing at Night — AP21

1971, Apr. 17   Engr.   *Perf. 13*
C45 AP21 5fr Prus bl, blk & lt grn 2.00 .20

Didier Daurat (1891-1969) and Raymond Vanier (1895-1965), aviation pioneers. For surcharge see Reunion No. C52.

Hélène Boucher, Maryse Hilsz and Caudron-Renault and Moth-Morane Planes — AP22

Design: 15fr, Henri Guillaumet, Paul Codos, Latécoère 521, Guillaumet's crashed plane in Andes, skyscrapers.

1972-73   Engr.   *Perf. 13*
C46 AP22 10fr plum, red & sl 4.50 .40
C47 AP22 15fr dp car, gray & brn ('73) 6.50 .65

Hélène Boucher (1908-34), Maryse Hilsz (1901-46), Henri Guillaumet (1902-40) and Paul Codos (1896-1960), aviation pioneers. Issue dates: 10fr, June 10; 15fr, Feb. 24.

Concorde AP23

1976, Jan. 10   Engr.   *Perf. 13*
C48 AP23 1.70fr brt bl, red & blk 1.00 .50

First flight of supersonic jet Concorde from Paris to Rio de Janeiro, Jan. 21.

Planes over the Atlantic, New York-Paris — AP24

1977, June 4   Engr.   *Perf. 13*
C49 AP24 1.90fr multicolored .90 .50

1st transatlantic flight by Lindbergh from NY to Paris, 50th anniv., and 1st attempted westbound flight by French aviators Charles Nungesser and Francois Coli.

Plane over Flight Route AP25

1978, Oct. 14   Engr.   *Perf. 13*
C50 AP25 1.50fr multicolored .90 .35

75th anniversary of first airmail route from Villacoublay to Pauillac, Gironde.

Rocket, Concorde, Exhibition Hall — AP26

1979, June 9   Engr.   *Perf. 13*
C51 AP26 1.70fr ultra, org & brn 1.25 .80

33rd International Aerospace and Space Show, Le Bourget, June 11-15.

First Nonstop Transatlantic Flight, Paris-New York — AP27

1980, Aug. 30   Engr.   *Perf. 13*
C52 AP27 2.50fr vio brn & ultra 1.00 .40

34th Intl. Space and Aeronautics Exhibition, June 5-14 AP28

1981, June 6   Engr.   *Perf. 13*
C53 AP28 2fr multicolored 2.00 .50

Dieudonné Costes and Joseph Le Brix and their Breguet Bi-plane — AP29

1981, Sept. 12   Engr.
C54 AP29 10fr dk brown & red 4.50 .40

1st So. Atlantic crossing, Oct. 14-15, 1927.

Seaplane Late-300 — AP30

1982, Dec. 4   Engr.
C55 AP30 1.60fr multicolored .80 .60

Farman F-60 Goliath — AP31

Planes: 20fr, CAMS-53 seaplane. 30fr, Wibault 283 Monoplane. 50fr, Dewoitine 338.

1984-87   Engr.
C56 AP31 15fr dark blue 5.00 .60
C57 AP31 20fr dp org ('85) 7.50 .60
C58 AP31 30fr brt vio ('86) 10.00 1.50
C59 AP31 50fr green ('87) 15.00 4.50
   Nos. C55-C59 (5) 38.30 7.80

Issued: 15fr, 3/3; 20fr, 3/2; 30fr, 10/11; 50fr, 4/11.

Breguet XIV — AP32

1997, Nov. 15   Photo.   *Perf. 13x13¼*
C60 AP32 20fr shown 10.00 4.00
   a.   Perf. 13x12½ 9.00 1.75
C61 AP32 30fr Potez 25 15.00 4.00
   a.   Perf. 13x12½ 14.00 2.50

Issued: No. C60 11/15/97; No. C60a, 7/13/98; 30fr, 7/13/98.
Nos. C60 and C61 were issued in panes of 40 (5x8), Nos. C60a and C61a in panes of 10 (2x5).

Airbus A300-B4 — AP33

1999, Apr. 10   Photo.   *Perf. 13x13¼*
C62 AP33 15fr multicolored 16.00 4.00
   a.   Perf. 13x12½ 7.00 1.25

No. C62 was issued in panes of 40 (5x8), No. C62a in panes of 10 (2x5).

Couzinet 70 — AP34

2000, Feb. 12   *Perf. 13¼x13¼*
C63 AP34 50fr multi 22.50 9.00
   a.   Perf. 13x12½ 22.50 6.00

No. C63 was issued in panes of 40 (5x8), No. C63a in panes of 10 (2x5).

First Flight of Airbus A300, 30th Anniv. — AP35

2002, Oct. 26   Photo.   *Perf. 13x13¼*
C64 AP35 €3 multi 9.00 1.75

No. C64 was issued both in panes of 40 and 10, same perforation.

Jacqueline Auriol (1917-2000), Pilot, and Jet — AP36

Marie Marvingt (1875-1963), Pilot — AP37

Litho. & Engr.

2003, June 21   *Perf. 13*
C65 AP36 €4 multi 12.00 2.50
   a.   Miniature sheet of 10 120.00

Litho. & Engr.

2004, June 29   *Perf. 13¼x13*
C66 AP37 €5 multi 15.00 3.00
   a.   Sheet of 10 150.00

Adrienne Bolland (1895-1975), Pilot — AP38

Litho. & Engr.

2005, Oct. 22   *Perf. 13*
C67 AP38 €2 multi 6.00 1.50
   a.   Miniature sheet of 10 60.00

Airbus A380 — AP39

2006, June 23   Photo.   *Perf. 13x13¼*
C68 AP39 €3 multi 9.00 1.75
   a.   Miniature sheet of 10 90.00

Helicopters, Cent. — AP40

2007, Feb. 19   Photo.   *Perf. 13x12½*
C69 AP40 €3 multi 8.00 1.60
   a.   Perf. 13x13¼ 8.00 1.60

No. C69 was issued in panes of 40; No. C69a in panes of 10.

French Acrobatic Patrol — AP41

Litho. & Engr.

2008, Sept. 13   *Perf. 13*
C70 AP41 €3 multi 8.25 1.75

Louis Blériot (1872-1936) and Blériot XI Airplane — AP42

Litho. & Engr.

2009, July 25   **Perf. 13x12¾**
C71 AP42 €2 multi   5.75 1.25
First flight across English Channel, cent.

Henri Fabre (1882-1984) and Le Canard Seaplane — AP43

Litho. & Engr.

2010, Mar. 27   **Perf. 13**
C72 AP43 €3 multi   8.25 1.75
First seaplane flight, cent.

AIR POST SEMI-POSTAL STAMPS

Catalogue values for unused stamps in this section are for Never Hinged items.

Antoine de Saint-Exupéry — SPAP1

Col. Jean Dagnaux SPAP2

1948   Unwmk.   Engr.   Perf. 13
CB1 SPAP1 50fr + 30fr vio brn   2.75 1.60
CB2 SPAP2 100fr + 70fr dk blue   3.75 2.25

Modern Plane and Ader's "Eole" SPAP3

1948, Feb.
CB3 SPAP3 40fr + 10fr dk blue   1.60 1.50
50th anniv. of the flight of Clément Ader's plane, the Eole, in 1897.

POSTAGE DUE STAMPS

D1

D2

1859-70   Unwmk.   Litho.   Imperf.

J1	D1	10c black	26,000.	240.00
J2	D1	15c black ('70)	130.00	250.00

In the lithographed stamps the central bar of the "E" of "CENTIMES" is very short, and the accent on "a" slants at an angle of 30 degree, for the 10c and 17 degree for the 15c, while on the typographed the central bar of the "E" is almost as wide as the top and bottom bars and the accent on the "a" slants at an angle of 47 degree.

No. J2 is known rouletted unofficially.

1859-78   Typo.

J3	D1	10c black	30.00	17.50
J4	D1	15c black ('63)	35.00	15.00
J5	D1	20c black ('77)	4,100.	
J6	D1	25c black ('71)	150.00	50.00
J7	D1	30c black ('78)	225.00	125.00
J8	D1	40c blue ('71)	325.00	425.00
a.		40c ultramarine	6,500.	5,700.
b.		40c Prussian blue	2,600.	
J9	D1	60c bister ('71)	475.00	1,050.
J10	D1	60c blue ('78)	60.00	110.00
a.		60c dark blue	600.00	725.00
J10B	D1	60c black	2,700.	

The 20c & 60c black were not put into use.
Nos. J3, J4, J6, J8 and J9 are known rouletted unofficially and Nos. J4, J6, J7 and J10 pin-perf. unofficially.

1882-92   Perf. 14x13½

J11	D2	1c black	2.50	2.50
J12	D2	2c black	30.00	26.00
J13	D2	3c black	30.00	25.00
J14	D2	4c black	60.00	40.00
J15	D2	5c black	130.00	32.50
J16	D2	10c black	110.00	2.50
J17	D2	15c black	77.50	10.50
J18	D2	20c black	350.00	140.00
J19	D2	30c black	210.00	2.50
J20	D2	40c black	140.00	60.00
J21	D2	50c blk ('92)	600.00	175.00
J22	D2	60c blk ('84)	600.00	57.50
J23	D2	1fr black	750.00	350.00
J24	D2	2fr blk ('84)	1,400.	825.00
J25	D2	5fr blk ('84)	3,000.	1,600.

Excellent counterfeits exist of Nos. J23-J25.
See Nos. J26-J45A. For overprints and surcharges see Offices in China Nos. J1-J6, J33-J40, Offices in Egypt, Alexandria J1-J5, Port Said J1-J8, Offices in Zanzibar 60-62, J1-J5, Offices in Morocco 9-10, 24-25, J1-J5, J10-J12, J17-J22, J35-J41.

1884

J26	D2	1fr brown	400.00	90.00
J27	D2	2fr brown	190.00	130.00
J28	D2	5fr brown	450.00	325.00

1893-1941

J29	D2	5c blue ('94)	.25	.30
J30	D2	10c brown	.25	.30
J31	D2	15c lt grn ('94)	28.00	1.40
J32	D2	20c ol grn ('06)	6.50	.65
J33	D2	25c rose ('23)	6.50	3.75
J34	D2	30c red ('94)	.25	.20
J35	D2	30c org red ('94)	475.00	85.00
J36	D2	40c rose ('25)	11.50	4.50
J37	D2	45c grn ('24)	9.00	5.25
J38	D2	50c brn vio ('95)	.50	.30
a.		50c lilac	.50	.30
J39	D2	60c bl grn ('25)	1.00	.55
J40	D2	1fr rose, straw ('96)	475.00	375.00
J41	D2	1fr red brn, straw ('20)	9.50	.30
J42	D2	1fr red brn ('35)	1.25	.40
J43	D2	2fr red org ('10)	225.00	65.00
J44	D2	2fr brt vio ('26)	.65	.75
J45	D2	3fr magenta ('26)	.65	.75
J45A	D2	5fr red org ('41)	1.40	2.25

D3

D4

1908-25

J46	D3	1c olive grn	1.00	1.25
J47	D3	10c violet	1.10	.30
a.		Imperf., pair	175.00	
J48	D3	20c bister ('19)	40.00	1.25
J49	D3	30c bister ('09)	14.00	.40
J50	D3	50c red ('09)	275.00	60.00
J51	D3	60c red ('25)	2.75	3.75
		Nos. J46-J51 (6)	333.85	66.95

"Recouvrements" stamps were used to recover charges due on undelivered or refused mail which was returned to the sender.
For surcharges see Offices in Morocco Nos. J6-J9, J13-J16, J23-J26, J42-J45.

Nos. J49-J50 Surcharged

1917

J52	D3	20c on 30c bister	20.00	4.00
J53	D3	40c on 50c red	10.50	4.00
a.		Double surcharge	475.00	

In Jan. 1917 several values of the current issue of postage stamps were handstamped "T" in a triangle and used as postage due stamps.

Recouvrements Stamps of 1908-25 Surcharged

1926

J54	D3	50c on 10c lilac	3.50	3.25
J55	D3	60c on 1c ol grn	7.00	5.00
J56	D3	1fr on 60c red	18.00	10.00
J57	D3	2fr on 60c red	18.00	10.50
		Nos. J54-J57 (4)	46.50	28.75

1927-31

J58	D4	1c olive grn ('28)	1.00	1.00
J59	D4	10c rose ('31)	1.90	1.40
J60	D4	30c bister	4.50	.50
J61	D4	60c red	4.50	.50
J62	D4	1fr violet	14.00	3.25
J63	D4	1fr Prus grn ('31)	17.00	.55
J64	D4	2fr blue	80.00	42.50
J65	D4	2fr olive brn ('31)	150.00	26.00
		Nos. J58-J65 (8)	272.90	75.70

Nos. J62 to J65 have the numerals of value double-lined.

Nos. J64, J62 Surcharged in Red or Black

1929

J66	D4	1.20fr on 2fr blue	42.50	11.00
J67	D4	5fr on 1fr vio (Bk)	65.00	15.00

No. J61 Surcharged

1931

J68	D4	1fr on 60c red	30.00	2.75

Catalogue values for unused stamps in this section, from this point to the end of the section, are for Never Hinged items.

Sheaves of Wheat
D5   D6

Perf. 14x13½

1943-46   Unwmk.   Typo.

J69	D5	10c sepia	.20	.20
J70	D5	30c brt red vio	.20	.20
J71	D5	50c blue grn	.20	.20
J72	D5	1fr brt ultra	.20	.20
J73	D5	1.50fr rose red	.45	.40
J74	D5	2fr turq blue	.45	.40
J75	D5	3fr brn org	.45	.40
J76	D5	4fr dp vio ('45)	5.50	3.00
J77	D5	5fr brt pink	.60	.40
J78	D5	10fr red org ('45)	3.50	.40
J79	D5	20fr ol bis ('46)	10.00	2.75
		Nos. J69-J79 (11)	21.75	8.55

Type of 1943
Inscribed "Timbre Taxe"

1946-53

J80	D5	10c sepia ('47)	1.25	1.25
J81	D5	30c brt red vio ('47)	1.25	1.25
J82	D5	50c blue grn ('47)	25.00	9.50
J83	D5	1fr brt ultra ('47)	.25	.25
J85	D5	2fr turq blue	.25	.25
J86	D5	3fr brown org	.25	.25
J87	D5	4fr deep violet	.25	.25
J88	D5	5fr brt pink ('47)	.25	.25
J89	D5	10fr red org ('47)	.25	.25
J90	D5	20fr olive bis ('47)	2.00	.45
J91	D5	50fr dk green ('50)	25.00	1.40
J92	D5	100fr dp green ('53)	77.50	6.75
		Nos. J80-J92 (12)	133.50	22.10

For surcharges see Reunion Nos. J36-J44.

1960   Typo.   Perf. 14x13½

J93	D6	5c bright pink	3.25	.40
J94	D6	10c red orange	5.00	.30
J95	D6	20c olive bister	4.00	.30
J96	D6	50c dark green	12.50	1.25
J97	D6	1fr deep green	50.00	2.00
		Nos. J93-J97 (5)	74.75	4.25

For surcharges see Reunion Nos. J46-J48.
For overprints see Algeria Nos. J49-J53.

D7

D8

Flowers: 5c, Centaury. 10c, Gentian. 15c, Corn poppy. 20c, Violets. 30c, Forget-me-not. 40c, Columbine. 50c, Clover. 1fr, Soldanel.

1964-71   Typo.   Perf. 14x13½

J98	D7	5c car rose, red & grn ('65)	.20	.20
J99	D7	10c car rose, brt bl & grn ('65)	.20	.20
J100	D7	15c brn, grn & red ('71)	.20	.20
J101	D7	20c dk grn, grn & vio ('71)	.20	.20
J102	D7	30c brn, ultra & grn ('65)	.20	.20
J103	D7	40c dk grn, scar & yel ('71)	.25	.20
J104	D7	50c vio bl, car & grn ('65)	.25	.20
J105	D7	1fr vio bl, lil & grn ('65)	.40	.20
		Nos. J98-J105 (8)	1.90	1.60

For surcharges see Reunion Nos. J49-J55.

1982-83   Engr.   Perf. 13

J106	D8	10c Ampedus Cinnabarinus	.20	.20
J107	D8	20c Dorcadion fuliginator	.20	.20
J108	D8	30c Leptura cordigera	.20	.20
J109	D8	40c Paederus littoralis	.20	.20
J110	D8	50c Pyrochroa coccinea	.20	.20
J111	D8	1fr Scarites laevigatus	.30	.20
J112	D8	2fr Trichius gallicus	.55	.20
J113	D8	3fr Adalia alpina	.90	.20
J114	D8	4fr Apoderus coryli	1.20	.20
J115	D8	5fr Trichodes alvearius	1.90	.20
		Nos. J106-J115 (10)	5.85	2.00

Issued: 30c, 40c, 3fr, 5fr, 1/3/83; others, 1/4/82.

MILITARY STAMPS

Regular Issue Overprinted in Black or Red

1901-39   Unwmk.   Perf. 14x13½

M1	A17	15c orange ('01)	65.00	6.00
a.		Inverted overprint	300.00	150.00
b.		Imperf., pair	425.00	
M2	A19	15c pale red ('03)	65.00	6.00
M3	A20	15c dark grn ('04)	52.50	6.00
a.		No period after "M"	110.00	57.50
b.		Imperf., pair	290.00	
M4	A20	10c rose ('06)	30.00	8.25
a.		No period after "M"	82.50	45.00
b.		Imperf., pair	350.00	
M5	A22	10c red ('07)	1.75	1.00
a.		Inverted overprint	105.00	65.00
b.		Imperf., pair	190.00	
M6	A20	50c vermilion ('29)	4.75	1.00
a.		No period after "M"	32.50	18.00
b.		Period in front of F	32.50	18.00
M7	A45	50c rose red ('34)	2.75	.55
a.		No period after "M"	29.00	16.00
b.		Inverted overprint	150.00	110.00

M8 A45 65c brt ultra (R)
('38)   .30 .30
a. No period after "M"   29.00 16.00
M9 A45 90c ultra (R) ('39)   .40 .35
Nos. M1-M9 (9)   222.45 29.45

"F. M." are initials of Franchise Militaire (Military Frank). See No. S1.

> Catalogue values for unused stamps in this section, from this point to the end of the section, are for Never Hinged items.

M1

Flag — M2

1946-47   **Typo.**
M10 M1 dark green   1.75 .65
M11 M1 rose red ('47)   .30 .20

Nos. M10-M11 were valid also in the French colonies.

1964, July 20   **Perf. 13x14**
M12 M2 multicolored   .30 .35

OFFICIAL STAMPS

FOR THE COUNCIL OF EUROPE

For use only on mail posted in the post office in the Council of Europe Building, Strasbourg.

> Catalogue values for unused stamps in this section are for Never Hinged items.

For French stamp inscribed "Conseil de l'Europe" see No. 679.

France No. 854 Overprinted:
"CONSEIL DE L'EUROPE"
Unwmk.
1958, Jan. 14 **Engr.** **Perf. 13**
1O1 A303 35fr car rose & lake 1.25 *2.25*

Council of Europe Flag — O1

1958-59
Flag in Ultramarine
1O2 O1 8fr red org & brn vio .25 .25
1O3 O1 20fr yel & brn .35 .35
1O4 O1 25fr lil rose & sl grn ('59) .60 .60
1O5 O1 35fr red .55 .55
1O6 O1 50fr lilac rose ('59) 1.00 1.00
Nos. 1O2-1O6 (5) 2.75 2.75

1963, Jan. 3
Flag in Ultramarine
1O7 O1 20c yel & lt brn 1.25 1.25
1O8 O1 25c lil rose & sl grn 2.00 2.00
1O9 O1 50c lilac rose 2.50 2.50
Nos. 1O7-1O9 (3) 5.75 5.75

Centime value stamps shown the denomination as "0,20," etc.

1965-71
Flag in Ultramarine & Yellow
1O10 O1 25c ver, yel & sl grn .90 .90
1O11 O1 30c ver & yel .50 .50
1O12 O1 40c ver, yel & gray 1.00 1.00
1O13 O1 50c red, yel & grn 2.00 2.00
1O14 O1 60c ver, yel & vio 1.10 1.10
1O15 O1 70c ver, yel & dk brn 4.00 4.00
Nos. 1O10-1O15 (6) 9.50 9.50

Issue dates: 25c, 30c, 60c, Jan. 16, 1965; 50c, Feb. 20, 1971; others, Mar. 24, 1969.

Type of 1958 Inscribed "FRANCE"
1975-76 **Engr.** **Perf. 13**
Flag in Ultramarine & Yellow
1O16 O1 60c org, yel & ember .85 .85
1O17 O1 80c yel & mag 1.25 1.25
1O18 O1 1fr car, yel & gray ol ('76) 2.00 2.00
1O19 O1 1.20fr org, yel & bl 5.50 5.50
Nos. 1O16-1O19 (4) 9.60 9.60

Issue dates: 1fr, Oct. 16; others, Nov. 22.

New Council Headquarters, Strasbourg — O2

1977, Jan. 22 **Engr.** **Perf. 13**
1O20 O2 80c car & multi 1.00 .50
1O21 O2 1fr brown & multi 1.00 .50
1O22 O2 1.40fr gray & multi 2.00 1.00
Nos. 1O20-1O22 (3) 4.00 2.00

Human Rights Emblem in Upper Left Corner

1978, Oct. 14
1O23 O2 1.20fr red lilac & multi .45 .40
1O24 O2 1.70fr blue & multi .75 .55

30th anniversary of the Universal Declaration of Human Rights.

Council Headquarters Type of 1977
1980, Nov. 24 **Engr.** **Perf. 13**
1O25 O2 1.40fr olive .50 .50
1O26 O2 2fr blue gray .90 .90

New Council Headquarters, Strasbourg — O3

1981-84   **Engr.**
1O27 O3 1.40fr multicolored .50 .50
1O28 O3 1.60fr multicolored .50 .40
1O29 O3 1.70fr emerald .75 .75
1O30 O3 1.80fr multicolored .70 .70
1O31 O3 2fr multicolored .90 .90
1O32 O3 2.10fr red 1.00 1.00
1O33 O3 2.30fr multicolored 1.00 1.00
1O34 O3 2.60fr multicolored 1.00 1.00
1O35 O3 2.80fr multicolored 1.00 1.00
1O36 O3 3fr brt blue 1.25 1.25
Nos. 1O27-1O36 (10) 8.60 8.50

Issued: 1.40, 1.60, 2.30fr, 11/21; 1.80, 2.60fr, 11/13/82; 2, 2.80fr, 11/21/83; 1.70, 2.10, 3fr, 11/5/84.

Youth's Leg, Sneaker, Shattered Eggshell O4

1985, Aug. 31 **Engr.** **Perf. 13**
1O37 O4 1.80fr brt green .90 .90
1O38 O4 2.20fr vermilion .90 .90
1O39 O4 3.20fr brt blue 1.40 1.40
Nos. 1O37-1O39 (3) 3.20 3.20

New Council Headquarters, Strasbourg — O5

1986-87 **Engr.** **Perf. 13**
1O40 O5 1.90fr green .90 .90
1O41 O5 2fr brt yel grn 1.10 1.10
1O42 O5 2.20fr red .90 .90

1O43 O5 3.40fr blue 1.75 1.75
1O44 O5 3.60fr brt blue 2.00 2.00
Nos. 1O40-1O44 (5) 6.65 6.65

Issued: 1.90, 2.20, 3.40fr, 12/13; 2, 3.60fr, 10/10/87.

Council of Europe, 40th Anniv. O6

1989, Feb. 4 **Litho. & Engr.**
1O45 O6 2.20fr multicolored 1.40 1.40
1O46 O6 3.60fr multicolored 2.25 2.25

Denominations also inscribed in European Currency Units (ECUs).

Map of Europe O7

1990-91 **Litho.** **Perf. 13**
1O47 O7 2.30fr multicolored 1.00 1.00
1O48 O7 2.50fr multicolored 1.00 1.00
1O49 O7 3.20fr multicolored 1.60 1.60
1O50 O7 3.40fr multicolored 1.60 1.60
Nos. 1O47-1O50 (4) 5.20 5.20

Issued: 2.30fr, 3.20fr, 5/26/90; 2.50fr, 3.40fr, 11/23/91.

36 Heads, by Hundertwasser O8

1994, Jan. 15 **Litho.** **Perf. 13**
1O51 O8 2.80fr multicolored 1.40 1.40
1O52 O8 3.70fr multicolored 1.75 1.75

Palace of Human Rights, Strasbourg O9

1996, June 1 **Litho.** **Perf. 13**
1O53 O9 3fr multicolored .90 .90
1O54 O9 3.80fr multicolored 1.60 1.60

Charioteer of Delphi — O10

1999, Sept. 18 **Photo.** **Perf. 13**
1O55 O10 3fr shown 1.40 1.40
1O56 O10 3.80fr Nike 1.75 1.75

Girl, Penguin and Boy — O11

2001, Dec. 1 **Litho.** **Perf. 13**
1O57 O11 3fr red & multi 1.25 1.25
1O58 O11 3.80fr grn & multi 2.00 2.00

Hiker on Stars — O12

2003, Oct. 18 **Litho.** **Perf. 13**
1O59 O12 50c Hiker facing left 1.25 1.25
1O60 O12 75c Hiker facing right 2.00 2.00

O13

O14

2005, Sept. 18 **Litho.** **Perf. 13**
1O61 O13 55c multi 1.40 1.40
1O62 O14 75c multi 1.90 1.90

Map of Europe O15

Sculpture by Mariano González Beltrán O16

2007, June 23 **Litho.** **Perf. 13**
1O63 O15 60c multi 1.75 1.75
1O64 O16 85c multi 2.40 2.40

Council of Europe, 60th Anniv. O17

European Court of Human Rights, 50th Anniv. O18

2009, May 16 **Litho.** **Perf. 13**
1O65 O17 56c multi 1.60 1.60
1O66 O18 80c multi 2.00 2.00

Tree — O19

Chain — O20

2010, Sept. 17   Litho.   *Perf. 13*

1067	O19	75c multi	2.10	2.10
1068	O20	87c multi	2.40	2.40

European Human Rights Convention, 60th anniv. (No. 1068).

FOR THE UNITED NATIONS EDUCATIONAL, SCIENTIFIC AND CULTURAL ORGANIZATION

For use only on mail posted in the post office in the UNESCO Building, Paris.

> Catalogue values for unused stamps in this section are for Never Hinged items.

> For French stamps inscribed "UNESCO" see Nos. 572, 893-894, 2545.

Khmer Buddha and Hermes by Praxiteles O1

1961-65   Unwmk.   Engr.   *Perf. 13*

2O1	O1	20c dk gray, ol bis & bl	.25	*.55*
2O2	O1	25c blk, lake & grn	.40	*.90*
2O3	O1	30c choc & bis brn ('65)	.60	*.60*
2O4	O1	50c blk, red & vio bl	1.50	*1.75*
2O5	O1	60c grnsh bl, red brn & rose lil ('65)	1.40	1.40
		Nos. 2O1-2O5 (5)	4.15	5.20

Book and Globe — O2

1966, Dec. 17

2O6	O2	25c gray	.50	.50
2O7	O2	30c dark red	.65	.65
2O8	O2	60c green	1.10	1.10
		Nos. 2O6-2O8 (3)	2.25	2.25

20th anniversary of UNESCO.

Human Rights Flame — O3

1969-71   Engr.   *Perf. 13*

2O9	O3	30c sl grn, red & dp brn	.60	.60
2O10	O3	40c dk car rose, red & dp brn	.95	.95
2O11	O3	50c ultra, car & brn ('71)	2.00	2.00
2O12	O3	70c pur, red & sl	2.25	2.25
		Nos. 2O9-2O12 (4)	5.80	5.80

Universal Declaration of Human Rights.

Type of 1969 Inscribed "FRANCE"

1975, Nov. 15   Engr.   *Perf. 13*

2O13	O3	60c grn, red & dk brn	1.10	1.10
2O14	O3	80c ocher, red & red brn	1.65	1.65
2O15	O3	1.20fr ind, red & brn	3.75	3.75
		Nos. 2O13-2O15 (3)	6.50	6.50

O4

1976-78   Engr.   *Perf. 13*

2016	O4	80c multi	.85	.85
2017	O4	1fr multi	.85	.85
2018	O4	1.20fr multi	.50	.50
2019	O4	1.40fr multi	2.25	1.25
2020	O4	1.70fr multi	.75	.75
		Nos. 2016-2020 (5)	5.20	4.20

Issued: 1.20, 1.70fr, 10/14/78; others, 10/23/76.

Slave Quarters, Senegal O5

Designs: 1.40fr, Mohenjo-Daro excavations, Pakistan. 2fr, Sans-Souci Palace, Haiti.

1980, Nov. 17   Engr.   *Perf. 13*

2021	O5	1.20fr multi	.50	.50
2022	O5	1.40fr multi	.60	.60
2023	O5	2fr multi	1.00	1.00
		Nos. 2021-2023 (3)	2.10	2.10

Hue, Vietnam — O7

Designs: 1.40fr, Building, Fez, Morocco. 1.60fr, Seated deity, Sukhotai, Thailand. 2.30fr, Fort St. Elmo, Malta, horiz. 2.60fr, St. Michael Church ruins, Brazil.

1981-82

2024	O7	1.40fr multi	.60	.60
2025	O7	1.60fr multi	.60	.60
2026	O7	1.80fr shown	.70	.70
2027	O7	2.30fr multi	.80	.80
2028	O7	2.60fr multi	.90	.90
		Nos. 2024-2028 (5)	3.60	3.60

Issued: 1.80fr, 2.60fr, 10/23/82; others, 12/12/81.

Mosque, Chinguetti, Mauritania O8

Roman Theater and Female Standing Sculpture, Carthage, Tunisia — O8a

Architecture: 1.70fr, Church, Lalibela, Ethiopia. 2.10fr, San'a, Yemen. 2.20fr, Old Town Square and wrought iron latticework, Havana. 2.80fr, Enclosure wall interior, Istanbul. 3fr, Church, Kotor, Yugoslavia. 3.20fr, Temple of Anuradhapura and bas-relief of two women, Sri Lanka.

1983-85   Engr.

2029	O8	1.70fr multi	.70	.70
2030	O8a	1.80fr multi	.80	.80
2031	O8	2fr multi	.75	.75
2032	O8	2.10fr multi	.80	.80
2033	O8a	2.20fr multi	.90	.90
2034	O8	2.80fr multi	1.00	1.00

2035	O8	3fr multi	1.10	1.10
2036	O8a	3.20fr multi	1.50	1.50
		Nos. 2029-2036 (8)	7.55	7.55

Issued: 2fr, 2.80fr, 10/10; 1.70fr, 2.10fr, 3fr, 10/22/84; 1.80fr, 2.20fr, 3.20fr, 10/26/85.

Tikal Temple, Guatemala — O9

1986, Dec. 6   Engr.   *Perf. 13*

2037	O9	1.90fr shown	1.00	1.00
2038	O9	3.40fr Bagerhat Mosque, Bangladesh	1.75	1.75

The Parthenon, Athens O10

1987, Dec. 5   Engr.   *Perf. 13x12½*

2039	O10	2fr shown	.90	.90
2040	O10	3.60fr Temple of Philae, Egypt	1.60	1.60

Shibam, Yemen People's Democratic Republic O11

Perf. 13x12½, 12½x13

1990, Apr. 7   Engr.

2041	O11	2.30fr San Francisco de Lima, Peru, vert.	1.10	1.10
2042	O11	3.20fr shown	1.50	1.50

Bagdaon Temple, Nepal — O12

3.40fr, Citadel of Harat, Afghanistan, horiz.

1991, Nov. 23

2043	O12	2.50fr choc & dk red	1.25	1.25
2044	O12	3.40fr grn, brn & ol	1.50	1.50

Tassili N'Ajjer Natl. Park, Algeria O13

Design: 2.80fr, Angkor Wat Archaeological Park, Cambodia, vert.

1993, Oct. 23   Litho.   *Perf. 13*

2045	O13	2.80fr multicolored	1.25	1.25
2046	O13	3.70fr multicolored	2.00	2.00

UNESCO, 50th Anniv. O14

Designs: 3fr, Uluru Natl. Park, Australia. 3.80fr, Los Glaciares Natl. Park, Argentina.

1996, June 1   Litho.   *Perf. 13*

2047	O14	3fr multicolored	1.50	1.50
2048	O14	3.80fr multicolored	2.00	2.00

Detail of Dionysus Fresco, Pompeii — O15

Moai Statues, Easter Island O16

1998, Oct. 24   Litho.   *Perf. 13*

2049	O15	3fr multicolored	1.50	1.50
2050	O16	3.80fr multicolored	1.90	1.90

Sphinx and Pyramids, Egypt O17

Komodo Dragon, Komodo Natl. Park, Indonesia O18

2001, Dec. 1   Litho.   *Perf. 13*

2051	O17	3fr multi	1.60	1.60
2052	O18	3.80fr multi	2.00	2.00

Reindeer, Lapland O19

Church of the Resurrection, St. Petersburg, Russia — O20

2003, Dec. 6   Litho.   *Perf. 13*

2053	O19	50c multi	1.40	1.40
2054	O20	75c multi	2.00	2.00

Bison in Bialowieza Forest, Poland — O21

Petra, Jordan O22

2005, Nov. 26   Litho.   *Perf. 13*

2055	O21	55c multi	1.50	1.50
2056	O22	90c multi	2.25	2.25

Siberian Tiger — O23

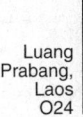

Luang Prabang, Laos O24

2006, Dec. 7   Litho.   Perf. 13
2O57	O23	60c multi	2.00	.75
2O58	O24	85c multi	2.50	1.25

Ksar d'Ait-Ben-Haddou, Morocco — O25

Koala, Australia — O26

2007, Dec. 13   Litho.   Perf. 13
2O59	O25	60c multi	2.00	2.00
2O60	O26	85c multi	2.50	2.50

Gorilla — O27

Machu Picchu, Peru O28

2008, Dec. 3   Litho.   Perf. 13
2O61	O27	65c multi	1.75	1.75
2O62	O28	85c multi	2.25	2.25

Polar Bear O29

Suzhou, China O30

2009, Dec. 9   Litho.   Perf. 13
2O63	O29	70c multi	2.10	2.10
2O64	O30	85c multi	2.50	2.50

Alhambra, Spain O31

Alpaca O32

2010, Dec. 1   Litho.   Perf. 13
2O65	O31	75c multi	2.00	2.00
2O66	O32	87c multi	2.40	2.40

NEWSPAPER STAMPS

Coat of Arms — N1

1868   Unwmk.   Typo.   Imperf.
P1	N1	2c lilac	300.00	65.00
P2	N1	2c (+ 2c) blue	600.00	275.00

Perf. 12½
P3	N1	2c lilac	52.50	25.00
P4	N1	2c (+ 4c) rose	250.00	100.00
P5	N1	2c (+ 2c) blue	75.00	35.00
P6	N1	5c lilac	1,250.	550.00

Nos. P2, P4, and P5 were sold for face plus an added fiscal charge indicated in parenthesis. Nos. P1, P3 and P6 were used simply as fiscals.

The 2c rose and 5c lilac imperforate and the 5c rose and 5c blue, both imperforate and perforated, were never put into use.

Nos. P1-P6 were reprinted for the 1913 Ghent Exhibition and the 1937 Paris Exhibition (PEXIP).

No. 109 Surcharged in Red

1919   Perf. 14x13½
P7	A16	½c on 1c gray	.30	.30
a.		Inverted surcharge	1,200.	1,150.

No. 156 Surcharged

1933
P8	A22	½c on 1c olive bister	.30	.30

PARCEL POST STAMPS

Inscribed "I APPORT A LA GARE" — PP1

Perfs As Noted

1892   Unwmk.   Typo.
Q1	PP1	25c brown, *yel,* perf 13½	825.00	290.00
		Never hinged	1,500.	

Q2	PP1	25c brown, *yel,* perf 11	30.00	24.00
		Never hinged	45.00	
a.		Printed on both sides	400.00	
		Never hinged	650.00	

Inscribed "II VALEUR DECLAREE" — PP2

Q3	PP2	10c red, perf 13½	1,000.	275.00
		Never hinged	1,750.	
Q4	PP2	10c red, perf 10x13½	875.00	325.00
		Never hinged	1,600.	
Q5	PP2	10c org red, perf 11	30.00	14.00
		Never hinged	42.50	
Q6	PP2	10c red, imperf	22.50	16.50
		Never hinged	32.50	

Inscribed "III LIVRAISON PAR EXPRESS" — PP3

Q7	PP3	25c green, perf 13½	57.50	32.50
		Never hinged	115.00	
Q8	PP3	25c green, perf 11	45.00	24.00
		Never hinged	70.00	

See Nos. Q22-Q26.

Locomotive — PP4

A set of six stamps, in the design above, was prepared in 1901 as postal tax stamps for expedited parcels but were not issued. All are perf 14x13½. Values: 5c gray, $3, never hinged $4; 10c gray, $3, never hinged $5; 20c rose, $20, never hinged $29; 50c blue, $7, never hinged $11.50; 1fr brown, $8, never hinged $12; 2fr brown red, $37.50, never hinged $57.50.

PP5

1918   Perf. 11

Type I: Large Trefoil Under "N" of "MAJORATION"
Q9	PP5	5c black	1.25	.85
		Never hinged	2.00	
Q10	PP5	15c brn lilac	1.25	.85
		Never hinged	2.00	

Imperforate
Q11	PP5	5c black	3.25	2.50
		Never hinged	6.25	
Q12	PP5	15c brn lilac	9.00	4.25
		Never hinged	14.00	
		Nos. Q9-Q12 (4)	14.75	8.45

40c values, perforated 11 and imperf, in orange, were prepared but not issued. Value, perf or imperf, $375.

Type II: Small Trefoil Under "O" of "MAJORATION"

Perf. 11
Q13	PP5	5c black	140.00	45.00
		Never hinged	275.00	
Q14	PP5	35c red	3.75	2.50
		Never hinged	5.00	
Q15	PP5	50c vio blue	4.50	1.60
		Never hinged	7.00	
Q16	PP5	1fr yellow	4.25	1.60
		Never hinged	7.00	

Imperforate
Q17	PP5	5c black	130.00	45.00
		Never hinged	260.00	
Q18	PP5	15c brn lilac	30.00	16.50
		Never hinged	50.00	
Q19	PP5	35c red	3.25	2.50
		Never hinged	6.75	
Q20	PP5	50c vio blue	24.00	14.00
		Never hinged	40.00	
Q21	PP5	1fr yellow	18.50	12.50
		Never hinged	30.00	
		Nos. Q13-Q21 (9)	358.25	141.20

See Nos. Q41-Q44, Q143-Q145.
For surcharges, see Nos. Q28-Q40.

Type of 1892

1918-23   Perf. 10½x11
Q22	PP1	30c brn, *yel*	37.50	16.50
		Never hinged	55.00	
a.		Imperf	200.00	
		Never hinged	290.00	
Q23	PP1	60c brn, *straw* ('23)	47.50	30.00
		Never hinged	70.00	
a.		Imperf	190.00	
		Never hinged	275.00	
Q24	PP2	15c vermilion ('22)	16.00	11.00
		Never hinged	23.00	
Q25	PP3	30c green	40.00	21.00
		Never hinged	57.50	
a.		Imperf	240.00	
		Never hinged	325.00	
Q26	PP3	60c green ('23)	75.00	50.00
		Never hinged	110.00	
		Nos. Q22-Q26 (5)	216.00	128.50

PP6

1924, Oct.   Perf. 14
Q27	PP6	15c rose & blue	4.00	3.75
		Never hinged	5.00	
a.		Imperf	550.00	
		Never hinged	750.00	

No. Q27 is a postal tax stamp, issued to show the collection of a new 15c excise fee on rail parcels. On July 3, 1925, its use was extended to all fiscal categories.

Surcharged in Black or Red (R) on Nos. Q9//Q16 and Types of 1918

1926   Perf. 13
Q28	PP5	20c on 2fr rose	1.90	1.10
		Never hinged	2.75	
Q29	PP5	30c on 2fr yellow	1.90	1.10
		Never hinged	2.75	
a.		"0f30" omitted	190.00	
		Never hinged	250.00	
Q30	PP5	40c on 3fr gray	1.90	1.40
		Never hinged	2.75	
Q31	PP5	45c on 3fr orange	1.90	1.40
		Never hinged	2.75	
a.		Period after "f" omitted	19.00	19.00
		Never hinged	30.00	
Q32	PP5	95c on 1fr yel	8.00	2.75
		Never hinged	12.50	
a.		Imperf	90.00	
		Never hinged	150.00	
Q33	PP5	1.35fr on 3fr vio	10.50	4.50
		Never hinged	14.00	
		On postal document		70.00
a.		Imperf	150.00	
		Never hinged	225.00	
Q34	PP5	1.45fr on 5fr black (R)	1.90	1.00
		Never hinged	2.75	
Q35	PP5	1.75fr on 2fr blue	10.50	4.50
		Never hinged	14.00	
Q36	PP5	1.85fr on 10c orange	1.90	1.20
		Never hinged	2.75	
Q37	PP5	1.95fr on 15c lilac ben	2.50	1.75
		Never hinged	3.50	
a.		Imperf	110.00	
		Never hinged	175.00	

Q38 PP5 2.35fr on 25c

		green	1.90	1.00
	Never hinged		2.75	
a.	Imperf		110.00	
	Never hinged		175.00	

Q39 PP5 2.90fr on 35c red

			2.50	1.00
	Never hinged		3.50	
a.	Dots before and after "f"		140.00	
	Never hinged		200.00	
b.	Imperf		125.00	
	Never hinged		190.00	

Q40 PP5 3.30fr on 50c blue

		violet (R)	2.50	1.25
	Never hinged		3.50	
a.	Double surcharge		250.00	
	Never hinged		375.00	
b.	Imperf		90.00	
	Never hinged		140.00	

Nos. Q28-Q40 (13) 49.80 23.95

Type of 1918

1926   *Perf. 11*

Q41 PP5 10c orange

			2.00	1.25
	Never hinged		3.75	
a.	Imperf		4.00	
	Never hinged		6.50	

Q42 PP5 25c pale green

			2.00	1.25
	Never hinged		3.75	
a.	Imperf		4.00	
	Never hinged		6.50	

Q43 PP5 2fr pale blue

			25.00	14.50
	Never hinged		42.50	
a.	Imperf		50.00	
	Never hinged		80.00	

Q44 PP5 3fr violet

			110.00	67.50
	Never hinged		190.00	
a.	Imperf		225.00	
	Never hinged		360.00	

Nos. Q41-Q44 (4) 139.00 84.50

Inscribed "APPORT A LA GARE" — PP7

1926

Q45 PP7 1fr on 60c brn,

		yel	13.50	10.50
	Never hinged		24.00	
a.	Imperf		190.00	
	Never hinged		300.00	

Q46 PP7 1fr brn, *yel*

			17.50	13.00
	Never hinged		30.00	

Q47 PP7 1.30fr on 1fr brn,

		yel	17.50	12.50
	Never hinged		30.00	

Q48 PP7 1.50fr brn, *yel*

			20.00	11.50
	Never hinged		32.50	

Q49 PP7 1.65fr brn, *yel*

			15.00	12.50
	Never hinged		24.00	

Q50 PP7 1.90fr on 1fr brn,

		yel	17.50	12.50
	Never hinged		30.00	

Q51 PP7 2.10fr on 1.65fr

		brn, yel	17.50	12.50
	Never hinged		30.00	

Nos. Q45-Q51 (7) 118.50 85.00

See Nos. Q91-Q95, footnote following No. Q102, Q143-Q145.

For overprints and surcharges, see Nos. Q76-Q78, Q83-Q86, Q91-Q92, boxed note following Q95, Q96-Q99, Q107-QQ109, boxed note following Q159.

PP8

Type I   Type II   Type III

1926-38

Q52 PP8 15c brown, *yel,*

		type I	7.50	3.00
	Never hinged		11.00	
a.	Imperf		180.00	
	Never hinged		275.00	

Q53 PP8 15c brown, *yel,*

		type II ('32)	8.00	4.25
	Never hinged		11.50	
a.	Type III ('38)		210.00	
	Never hinged		275.00	
b.	As "a," imperf		240.00	
	Never hinged		300.00	

Nos. Q52-Q53a were issued for use in Paris only. No. Q53a was prepared but not issued.

Inscribed "VALEUR DECLAREE" — PP9

The additional numerals overprinted on Nos. Q56-Q63 and on Nos. Q72-Q75 indicate the weight category of the parcels being sent.

1926

Q54 PP9 50c on 15c red

			3.00	1.60
	Never hinged		5.00	
a.	Imperf		180.00	
	Never hinged		275.00	

Q55 PP9 50c red

			750.00	750.00
	Never hinged		1,200.	
a.	Imperf		1,200.	
	Never hinged		1,650.	

Q56 PP9 50c red, ovptd.

		"1"	4.50	2.00
	Never hinged		7.00	
a.	Imperf		200.00	
	Never hinged		300.00	
b.	Double overprint "1"		300.00	
	Never hinged		400.00	

Q57 PP9 55c on 15c red,

		ovptd. "1"	6.75	5.00
	Never hinged		11.50	
a.	Imperf		190.00	—

Q58 PP9 55c on 50c red,

		ovptd. "1"	6.75	5.00
	Never hinged		11.50	

Q59 PP9 65c on 50c red

			2.50	2.50
	Never hinged		4.25	

Q60 PP9 65c on 50c red,

		ovptd. "1"	15.00	8.25
	Never hinged		27.50	

Q61 PP9 1.50fr on 50c red,

		ovptd. "3"	7.00	5.00
	Never hinged		12.00	
a.	Imperf		275.00	
	Never hinged		375.00	

Q62 PP9 2.00fr on 50c red,

		ovptd. "4"	8.25	3.75
	Never hinged		14.00	

Q63 PP9 2.50fr on 50c red,

		ovptd. "5"	15.00	8.25
	Never hinged		27.50	

Nos. Q54-Q63 (10) 818.75 791.35

See Nos. Q79, Q93, Q150-Q152.
For overprints and surcharges, see No. Q87, boxed note following No. Q95, Q100, Q110, Q123-Q124, Q138.

Inscribed "LIVRAISON PAR EXPRESS" — PP10

Q64 PP10 1.00fr on 60c

		grn	13.50	10.50
	Never hinged		24.00	
a.	Imperf		225.00	
	Never hinged		325.00	

Q65 PP10 1.00fr green

			125.00	75.00
	Never hinged		250.00	

Q66 PP10 1.30fr on 1fr

		grn	16.50	12.50
	Never hinged		29.00	

Q67 PP10 1.50fr green

			16.50	15.00
	Never hinged		32.50	

Q68 PP10 1.65fr green

			16.50	15.00
	Never hinged		32.50	

Q69 PP10 1.90fr on 1.50fr

		grn	16.50	12.50
	Never hinged		30.00	

Q70 PP10 2.10fr on 1.65fr

		grn	30.00	14.00
	Never hinged		50.00	

Nos. Q64-Q70 (7) 234.50 154.50

For overprints and surcharges, see Nos. Q80-Q82, Q88-Q90, Q94, boxed note following Q95, Q101-Q105, Q111-Q113, Q125-Q132, Q139-Q141, Q146-Q149.

Inscribed "INTERETS A LA LIVRAISON" — PP11

Q71 PP11 50c lilac

			3.00	1.60
	Never hinged		5.00	
a.	Imperf		225.00	190.00
	Never hinged		325.00	

Q72 PP11 50c lil, ovptd. "1"

			6.75	4.25
	Never hinged		10.00	
a.	Imperf		200.00	
	Never hinged		300.00	

Q73 PP11 1.50fr on 50c lil,

		ovptd. "3"	7.50	5.00
	Never hinged		11.50	
a.	Imperf		200.00	
	Never hinged		300.00	

Q74 PP11 2.00fr on 50c lil

		ovptd. "4"	10.00	7.00
	Never hinged		16.00	

Q75 PP11 2.50fr on 50c lil

		ovptd. "5"	10.00	7.00
	Never hinged		16.50	
a.	Imperf		210.00	
	Never hinged		310.00	

Nos. Q71-Q75 (5) 37.25 24.85

1926 Issues Overprinted

1928

Inscribed "APPORT A LA GARE"

Q76 PP7 1.00fr brn, *yel*

			16.50	14.00
	Never hinged		25.00	
a.	Imperf		190.00	190.00
	Never hinged		300.00	

Q77 PP7 1.50fr brn, *yel*

			16.50	13.00
	Never hinged		25.00	

Q78 PP7 1.65fr brn, *yel*

			16.50	13.00
	Never hinged		25.00	

Inscribed "VALEUR DECLAREE"

Q79 PP9 50c red

			5.75	4.25
	Never hinged		8.25	
a.	Imperf		190.00	190.00
	Never hinged		300.00	
b.	Inverted overprint		210.00	
	Never hinged		310.00	

Inscribed "LIVRAISON PAR EXPRESS"

Q80 PP10 1.00fr green

			17.00	13.50
	Never hinged		26.00	

Q81 PP10 1.50fr green

			17.00	13.50
	Never hinged		26.00	

Q82 PP10 1.65fr green

			17.00	13.50
	Never hinged		26.00	

Nos. Q76-Q82 (7) 106.25 84.75

1926 Issues Surcharged

1928

Inscribed "APPORT A LA GARE"

Q83 PP7 1.45fr on 60c

		brn, yel	7.00	6.75
	Never hinged		10.00	

Q84 PP7 1.45fr on 1fr brn,

		yel	40.00	32.50
	Never hinged		70.00	

Q85 PP7 2.15fr on 1.50fr

		brn, yel	62.50	42.50
	Never hinged		105.00	

Q86 PP7 2.35fr on 1.65fr

		brn, yel	62.50	42.50
	Never hinged		105.00	

Inscribed "VALEUR DECLAREE"

Q87 PP9 75c on 50c red

			2.10	1.60
	Never hinged		3.25	
a.	Imperf		210.00	
	Never hinged		400.00	

Inscribed "LIVRAISON PAR EXPRESS"

Q88 PP10 1.45fr on 1fr

		green	62.50	42.50
	Never hinged		105.00	

Q89 PP10 2.15fr on 1.50fr

		green	62.50	42.50
	Never hinged		105.00	

Q90 PP10 2.35fr on 1.65fr

		green	62.50	42.50
	Never hinged		105.00	

Nos. Q83-Q90 (8) 361.60 253.35

Types of 1926 and

PP12

1933-34

Inscribed "APPORT A LA GARE"

Q91 PP7 1.45fr brn, *yel*

			55.00	25.00
	Never hinged		82.50	

Q92 PP7 2.35fr brn, *yel*

			1,400.	
	Never hinged		1,900.	

A 2.15fr value, brown on yellow paper, was prepared but not issued without overprint or surcharge.
For overprints and surcharges, see Nos. Q96, Q98, Q99, Q107-Q109, Q115, Q116, Q118, Q120-Q122, Q135-Q137.

Inscribed "VALEUR DECLAREE"

Q93 PP9 75c red

			18.00	3.25
	Never hinged		22.50	
a.	Imperf			180.00

For overprints and surcharges on No. Q93, see Nos. Q110, Q123, Q124, Q138.
A 1.15fr black in this design, imperf, was prepared but not issued. Value, $400.

Inscribed "LIVRAISON PAR EXPRESS"

Q94 PP10 1.45fr yel grn

			450.00	300.00
	Never hinged		675.00	

Two other values, 2.15fr and 2.35fr were prepared but not issued without overprint or surcharge.
For overprints and surcharges, see Nos. Q101, Q103, Q105, Q111-Q113, Q125, Q126, Q128, Q130-Q132, Q139-Q141.

Inscribed "COLIS ENCOMBRANT"

Q95 PP12 2fr blue ('34)

			45.00	21.00
	Never hinged		70.00	

For overprints and surcharges, see Nos. Q106, Q114, Q133, Q134, Q142.

Nos. Q46, Q48, Q49, Q55, Q65, Q67 and Q68 overprinted "B" were not issued. Values: 1fr (#Q46), $95; never hinged $130; 1.50fr (#Q48), $130, never hinged $130; 1.65fr (#Q49), $95, never hinged $130; 50c (#Q55), $95, never hinged $130; 1fr (#Q65), $92.50, never hinged $140; 1.50fr (#Q67), $92.50, never hinged $140; 1.65fr (#Q68), $92.50, never hinged $140.

Stamps and Types of 1926-34 Overprinted

1937

Inscribed "APPORT A LA GARE"

Q96 PP7 1.45fr brn, *yel*

			6.75	6.75
	Never hinged		10.00	

Q97 PP7 2.15fr on 1.50fr

		brn, yel	37.50	31.00
	Never hinged		57.50	

Q98 PP7 2.15fr brn, *yel*

			25.00	19.00
	Never hinged		37.50	

Q99 PP7 2.35fr brn, *yel*

			25.00	19.00
	Never hinged		37.50	

Inscribed "VALEUR DECLAREE"

Q100 PP9 75c red

			17.50	16.50
	Never hinged		25.00	
a.	Imperf		225.00	
	Never hinged		325.00	

Inscribed "LIVRAISON PAR EXPRESS"

Q101 PP10 1.45fr green

			17.50	16.50
	Never hinged		25.00	

Q102 PP10 2.15fr on 1.50fr

		grn	17.50	16.50
	Never hinged		25.00	

Q103 PP10 2.15fr green

			42.50	30.00
	Never hinged		67.50	
a.	Imperf		210.00	
	Never hinged		315.00	

Q104 PP10 2.35fr on 1.65fr

		grn	250.00	110.00
	Never hinged		350.00	

Q105	PP10 2.35fr green		17.50	12.50
	Never hinged		26.00	

Inscribed "COLIS ENCOMBRANT"

Q106	PP12 2fr blue		37.50	35.00
	Never hinged		57.50	
	Nos. Q96-Q106 (11)		494.25	312.75

For overprints and surcharges, see Nos. Q146-Q149.

Types of 1933-34 Surcharged

1937

Inscribed "APPORT A LA GARE"

Q107	PP7 1.85fr on 1.45fr			
		brn, yel	15.00	12.50
	Never hinged		26.00	
Q108	PP7 2.75fr on 2.15fr			
		brn, yel	26.00	17.50
	Never hinged		45.00	
Q109	PP7 3.05fr on 2.55fr			
		brn, yel	50.00	26.00
	Never hinged		90.00	

Inscribed VALEUR DECLAREE

Q110	PP9 .95fr on 75c			
		red	42.50	25.00
	Never hinged		67.50	

Inscribed LIVRAISON PAR EXPRESS

Q111	PP10 1.85fr on 1.45fr			
		grn	70.00	45.00
	Never hinged		120.00	
Q112	PP10 2.75fr on 2.15fr			
		grn	70.00	45.00
	Never hinged		120.00	
Q113	PP10 3.05fr on 2.35fr			
		grn	70.00	45.00
	Never hinged		120.00	

Inscribed COLIS ENCOMBRANT

Q114	PP12 2.60fr on 2fr bl		17.50	17.50
	Never hinged		26.00	
	Nos. Q107-Q114 (8)		361.00	233.50

Stamps and Types of 1926-34 Overprinted

1937

Inscribed "APPORT A LA GARE"

Q115	PP7 1.45fr brn, yel		3.00	2.50
	Never hinged		4.50	
Q116	PP7 1.85fr on 1.45fr			
		brn, yel	3.00	2.50
	Never hinged		4.50	
Q117	PP7 2.15fr on 1.50fr			
		brn, yel	2.50	2.50
	Never hinged		4.25	
Q118	PP7 2.15fr brn, yel		42.50	35.00
	Never hinged		62.50	
Q119	PP7 2.35fr on 1.65fr			
		brn, yel	575.00	475.00
	Never hinged		800.00	
Q120	PP7 2.35fr brn, yel		3.00	2.50
	Never hinged		4.50	
Q121	PP7 2.75fr on 2.15fr			
		brn, yel	3.25	2.50
	Never hinged		5.75	
Q122	PP7 3.05fr on 2.35fr			
		brn, yel	6.50	6.25
	Never hinged		10.00	

Inscribed VALEUR DECLAREE

Q123	PP9 75c red		3.75	3.50
	Never hinged		5.50	
a.	Pair, one without over-print		225.00	
	Never hinged		350.00	
Q124	PP9 95c on 75c red		3.00	3.00
	Never hinged		3.75	

Inscribed LIVRAISON PAR EXPRESS

Q125	PP10 1.45fr green		4.25	3.25
	Never hinged		6.25	
Q126	PP10 1.85fr on 1.45fr			
		brn, yel	5.75	4.25
	Never hinged		8.25	
Q127	PP10 2.15fr on 1.50fr			
		grn	375.00	325.00
	Never hinged		500.00	
Q128	PP10 2.15fr green		18.50	16.50
	Never hinged		27.50	
Q129	PP10 2.35fr on 1.65fr			
		grn	675.00	725.00
	Never hinged		775.00	
Q130	PP10 2.35fr green		11.00	10.50
	Never hinged		15.00	
Q131	PP10 2.75fr on 2.15fr			
		grn	35.00	45.00
	Never hinged		55.00	

Q132	PP10 3.05fr on 2.35fr			
		grn	35.00	45.00
	Never hinged		55.00	

Inscribed COLIS ENCOMBRANT

Q133	PP12 2fr blue		3.00	2.10
a.	Pair, imperf between		130.00	
	Never hinged		210.00	
Q134	PP12 2.60fr on 2fr bl		3.25	2.50
	Never hinged		5.50	
	Nos. Q115-Q134 (20)		1,811.	1,714.

For additional surcharges, see Nos. Q146-Q149.

Stamps and Types of 1933-34 Surcharged

1938

Inscribed "APPORT A LA GARE"

Q135	PP7 2.30fr on 1.45fr			
		brn, yel	3.75	3.00
	Never hinged		5.50	
Q136	PP7 3.45fr on 2.15fr			
		brn, yel	3.75	3.00
	Never hinged		5.50	
Q137	PP7 3.85fr on 1.45fr			
		brn, yel	3.75	3.00
	Never hinged		5.50	

Inscribed VALEUR DECLAREE

Q138	PP9 1.15fr on 75c			
		red	1.60	1.60
	Never hinged		2.50	

Inscribed LIVRAISON PAR EXPRESS

Q139	PP10 2.30fr on 1.45fr			
		grn	3.75	3.00
	Never hinged		5.50	
Q140	PP10 3.45fr on 2.15fr			
		grn	3.75	3.00
	Never hinged		5.50	
Q141	PP10 3.85fr on 2.35fr			
		grn	3.75	3.00
	Never hinged		5.50	

Inscribed COLIS ENCOMBRANT

Q142	PP12 3.25fr on 2fr bl		1.60	1.60
	Never hinged		2.50	
	Nos. Q135-Q142 (8)		25.70	21.20

For Nos. Q135-Q138, Q140-Q142 overprinted "E," see editor's note following No. Q159.

Type of 1918

1938   11, Imperf (#Q161)

Q143	PP5 10c gray black		17.50	16.00
	Never hinged		26.00	
a.	Imperf		26.00	
	Never hinged		42.50	
Q144	PP5 20c brown lilac		17.50	16.00
	Never hinged		26.00	
a.	Imperf		42.50	
	Never hinged		62.50	
Q145	PP5 25c green, imperf		50.00	20.00
	Never hinged		80.00	
	Nos. Q143-Q145 (3)		85.00	52.00

Two additional values, a 10c rose lilac and a 15c ultramarine, were prepared with this set but not issued. Values, each stamp: $90, never hinged $150. Both stamps also exist imperf. Values, each: $82.50; never hinged $150.

Nos. Q103, Q105, Q112, Q113 Overprinted

1938   Perf. 11

Q146	PP10 2.30fr on 2.15fr			
		green	62.50	62.50
	Never hinged		80.00	
Q147	PP10 2.30fr on 2.35fr			
		green	62.50	62.50
	Never hinged		80.00	
Q148	PP10 2.30fr on 2.75fr on 2.15fr			
		green	140.00	100.00
	Never hinged		200.00	
Q149	PP10 2.30fr on 3.05fr on 2.35fr			
		green	140.00	100.00
	Never hinged		200.00	
	Nos. Q146-Q149 (4)		405.00	325.00

Types of 1926 and

"PP13"

"PP14"

PP15

PP16

1938-39

Inscribed VALEUR DECLAREE

Q150	PP9 1fr red ('39)		2.50	2.50
	Never hinged		4.00	
Q151	PP9 1.15fr red		1.25	1.25
	Never hinged		2.10	
	Imperf		140.00	
	Never hinged		225.00	
Q152	PP9 5fr red ('39)		2.50	2.75
	Never hinged		4.00	

Inscribed AU DESSUS DE 10

Q153	PP13 2.40fr brown, yellow		2.50	2.75
	Never hinged		4.00	
Q154	PP13 3.50fr brown, yellow		2.50	2.75
	Never hinged		4.00	
Q155	PP13 3.80fr brown, yelloe		2.50	2.75
	Never hinged		4.00	
	Imperf		125.00	
	Never hinged		190.00	

Inscribed REMBOURSEMENT

Q156	PP14 2.50fr yel grn ('39)		2.50	2.25
	Never hinged		4.00	
Q157	PP14 7.50fr yel grn ('39)		2.75	2.50
	Never hinged		4.25	

Inscribed INTERET A LA LIVRAISON

Q158	PP15 1fr lilac ('39)		9.50	6.75
	Never hinged		14.00	

Inscribed ENCOMBRANT

Q159	PP16 3.20fr blue		11.00	7.50
	Never hinged		16.00	
	Nos. Q150-Q159 (10)		39.50	33.75

Two additional values, 3.45fr and 3.85fr, type PP7, brown on yellow paper, imperforate, were prepared but not issued. Values, each: $140; never hinged, $225.

Nos. Nos. Q135-Q138, Q140-Q142 were overprinted "E" in 1939, in anticipation of new rates to take effect April 1, but were not issued. Values: 2.30fr on 1.45fr, $675, never hinged $1,000; 3.45fr on 2.15fr, $875, never hinged $1,300; 3.85fr on 2.35fr, $875, never hinged $1,300; 1.15fr on 75c, $300, never hinged $450; 3.45fr on 2.15fr, $2,800, never hinged $4,000; 3.85fr on 2.35fr, $2,800, never hinged $4,000; 3.25fr on 2fr, $675, never hinged $1,000.

In 1941, two sets were prepared in anticipation of new rate increases on April 1. They were not issued.

Six stamps in a new design, consisting of a 10c greenish gray, 30c blue, 50c brown, 1fr blue violet, 2fr orange and 5fr red. Values: 10c $185, never hinged $275; 30c $240, never hinged $350; 50c $240, never hinged $350; 1fr $185, never hinged $275; 2fr $185, never hinged $275; 5fr $185, never hinged $275.

Nos. Q93, Q153-Q155 and Q159 overprinted "E." Values: 75c; other values $575, never hinged.

PP17

PP18

1941   Perf. 12½

Without Denominations

Q160	PP17 (2.70fr) brown		5.50	4.50
	Never hinged		9.00	
Q161	PP17 (3.90fr) blue		5.50	4.50
	Never hinged		9.00	
Q162	PP17 (4.20fr) green		5.50	4.50
	Never hinged		9.00	
Q163	PP18 (3.50fr) blue		10.50	9.50
	Never hinged		14.00	
	Nos. Q160-Q163 (4)		27.00	23.00

Five stamps in the designs of PP20-PP22 below, but with blank value tablets, were prepared with Nos. Q160-Q163 but were not issued. Values: (1fr) brown, (5fr) red and (2.50fr) blue, each $67.50, never hinged $90; (7.50fr) green, $290, never hinged $400; (1fr) violet, $120, never hinged $180.

See Nos. Q178-Q181, Q200-Q206.

"Domicile" PP19

"Valeur Declaree" PP20

"Remboursement" PP21

"Interet A La Livraison" PP22

"Encombrant" — PP23

1941   Perf. 12½, 13 (#Q167-171)

Q164	PP19	2.70fr brown	6.75	5.50
		Never hinged	11.00	
Q165	PP19	3.90fr blue	6.75	5.50
		Never hinged	11.00	
Q166	PP19	4.20fr green	6.75	5.50
		Never hinged	11.00	
Q167	PP20	1fr brown	2.75	1.25
		Never hinged	4.25	
Q168	PP20	5fr red	1.50	*1.75*
		Never hinged	2.25	
Q169	PP21	2.50fr blue	1.50	*1.75*
		Never hinged	2.25	
Q170	PP21	7.50fr green	3.75	3.50
		Never hinged	6.00	
Q171	PP22	1fr violet	1.00	1.00
		Never hinged	1.75	
Q172	PP23	3.50fr blue	37.50	16.50
		Never hinged	52.50	
	Nos. Q164-Q172 (9)		68.25	42.25

See Nos. Q173-Q177, Q186-Q194, Q200-Q206.

For surcharges, see footnote following No. Q177, Nos. Q182-Q185, Q207-Q210.

Types of 1941 with Bold Numerals

1942, Feb.			Perf. 13	
Q173	PP20	1fr brown	2.75	1.25
		Never hinged	4.25	
Q174	PP20	5fr red	1.50	*1.75*
		Never hinged	2.25	
Q175	PP21	2.50fr blue	1.50	1.25
		Never hinged	2.25	
Q176	PP21	7.50fr green	6.75	*7.00*
		Never hinged	11.00	
Q177	PP22	1fr violet	67.50	1.00
		Never hinged	100.00	
	Nos. Q173-Q177 (5)		80.00	12.25

See Nos. Q173-Q177, Q186-Q194, Q200-Q206. See No. Q194.

Nine stamps from the 1941-42 issues were surcharged "+3F / C.N.S. / Chemi-nots" to raise funds for a philatelic exhibition organized by railroad employees, which took place in Paris on Dec. 26 and 27, 1942. They were not valid for postage. Value, set: $110; never hinged $160.

Type of 1941 Inscribed "F" in Value Tablets

1943			Perf. 12½	
Q178	PP17	(3fr) brown	3.00	3.00
		Never hinged	4.25	
Q179	PP17	(4.30fr) blue	3.00	3.00
		Never hinged	4.25	
Q180	PP17	(4.70fr) green	3.00	3.00
		Never hinged	4.25	
Q181	PP18	(3.50fr) blue	7.00	7.00
		Never hinged	14.00	
	Nos. Q178-Q181 (4)		16.00	16.00

Stamps of 1941 Surcharged in Deep Blue or Red

1943				
Q182	PP19	3fr on 2.70fr brn	13.50	13.50
		Never hinged	20.00	
Q183	PP19	4.3fr on 3.90fr blue (R)	2.50	*3.00*
		Never hinged	4.50	
Q184	PP19	4.7fr on 4.20fr green (R)	3.50	3.50
		Never hinged	5.00	
Q185	PP23	3.9fr on 3.50fr blue (R)	3.50	3.50
		Never hinged	5.00	
	Nos. Q182-Q185 (4)		23.00	23.50

Denominations in Black or Red

1943			Unwmk.	
Q186	PP19	3fr brn	3.75	*4.25*
		Never hinged	5.50	
Q187	PP19	4.3fr blue (R)	10.00	5.75
		Never hinged	12.50	
Q188	PP19	4.7fr green (R)	11.50	2.50
		Never hinged	15.00	
Q189	PP23	3.9fr blue (R)	70.00	60.00
		Never hinged	110.00	
	Nos. Q186-Q189 (4)		95.25	72.50

1943			Wmk. 407	
Q190	PP19	3fr brn	12.50	11.00
		Never hinged	21.00	
Q191	PP19	4.3fr blue	20.00	13.00
		Never hinged	32.50	
Q192	PP19	4.7fr green	21.00	13.50
		Never hinged	32.50	
Q193	PP23	3.9fr blue	12.50	12.50
		Never hinged	110.00	
	Nos. Q190-Q193 (4)		66.00	50.00

1944				
Q194	PP21	20fr orange	5.00	*6.75*
		Never hinged	6.75	

Hydroelectric Dam — PP24

Electric Train — PP25

Power Line — PP26

1944   Perf. 12½, 13 (#Q167-171)

Q195	PP24	1fr violet	6.75	6.75
		Never hinged	9.00	
Q196	PP24	5fr red brn	6.75	6.75
		Never hinged	9.00	
Q197	PP25	2.5fr blue	6.75	6.75
		Never hinged	9.00	
Q198	PP25	7.5fr green	6.75	6.75
		Never hinged	9.00	
Q199	PP26	1fr vio blue	6.75	6.75
		Never hinged	9.00	
	Nos. Q195-Q199 (5)		33.75	33.75

A 20fr orange, design PP25, was prepared but not issued. Values: $1,150; never hinged, $1,650.

Nos. Q195-Q199 exist unwatermarked, but were not issued in this form Values, each: $275; never hinged $425.

Types of 1941 Inscribed "G" in Value Tablets

1945			Unwmk.	
Q200	PP17	(5fr) brown	5.50	*6.00*
		Never hinged	7.00	
Q201	PP17	(7.20fr) blue	5.50	*6.00*
		Never hinged	7.00	
Q202	PP17	(7.60fr) green	5.50	*6.00*
		Never hinged	7.00	
Q203	PP18	(6.60fr) blue	6.25	*6.75*
		Never hinged	8.75	
	Nos. Q200-Q203 (4)		22.75	24.75

			Wmk. 407	
Q204	PP17	(5fr) brown	16.50	16.50
		Never hinged	24.00	
Q205	PP17	(7.20fr) blue	12.50	*12.50*
		Never hinged	18.00	
Q206	PP17	(7.60fr) green	12.50	*12.50*
		Never hinged	18.00	
	Nos. Q204-Q206 (3)		41.50	41.50

Nos. Q190-Q193 Surcharged

1945			Wmk. 407	
Q207	PP19	5fr on 3fr brown	6.25	6.25
		Never hinged	8.75	
Q208	PP19	7.2fr on 4fr blue	6.25	6.25
		Never hinged	8.75	
Q209	PP19	7.8fr on 4.70fr green	6.25	6.25
		Never hinged	8.75	
Q210	PP23	6.6fr on 3.90fr blue	7.50	7.50
		Never hinged	11.50	
	Nos. Q207-Q210 (4)		26.25	26.25

Nos. Q186-Q189 were also surcharged but were not issued. Values, each: $45; never hinged $72.50.

Electric Train — PP27

Transformer PP28

Denominations in Black

1945				
Q211	PP27	5fr brown	16.00	16.00
		Never hinged	22.50	
Q212	PP27	7.2fr blue	15.00	15.00
		Never hinged	22.50	
Q213	PP27	7.8fr green	15.00	15.00
		Never hinged	22.50	
Q214	PP28	3.95fr blue	6.75	6.75
		Never hinged	9.00	
	Nos. Q211-Q214 (4)		52.75	52.75

Nos. Q211-Q213 without watermark were not issued. Value, set: $50; never hinged, $80.

A set of ten stamps in the design above were prepared in 1945 but were not issued. Value, each: $300; never hinged $450.

Four stamps of types PP27-PP28, inscribed "H" in the value tablet, were prepared but not issued. Value, set: $2,500; never hinged $4,000.

Locomotive — PP29

1944			Wmk. 407	Perf. 13	
Q215	PP29	1fr deep green	4.25	1.25	
		Never hinged	8.25		
Q216	PP29	2fr gray brown	5.75	1.60	
		Never hinged	12.50		
Q217	PP29	5fr ultramarine	27.50	1.60	
		Never hinged	35.00		
Q218	PP29	10fr red	13.50	1.60	
		Never hinged	22.50		
Q219	PP29	20fr olive green	11.50	1.60	
		Never hinged	17.50		
Q220	PP29	50fr red orange	21.00	1.60	
		Never hinged	30.00		
Q221	PP29	100fr gray black	37.50	1.60	
		Never hinged	57.50		
	Nos. Q215-Q221 (7)		121.00	10.85	

			Unwmk.	
Q222	PP29	1fr deep green	11.00	5.50
		Never hinged	16.50	
Q223	PP29	2fr gray brown	14.00	5.50
		Never hinged	21.00	
Q224	PP29	5fr ultramarine	45.00	5.50
		Never hinged	70.00	
Q225	PP29	10fr red	29.00	5.50
		Never hinged	42.50	
Q226	PP29	20fr olive green	21.00	5.50
		Never hinged	32.50	
Q227	PP29	50fr red orange	42.50	5.50
		Never hinged	62.50	

Q228	PP29	100fr gray black	75.00	6.00
		Never hinged	110.00	
	Nos. Q222-Q228 (7)		237.50	39.00

Nos. Q215-Q234 were issued for use on small packets. Effective January 1, 1946, the parcel and small packet services were unified, and all issued thereafter were valid for both services.

See Nos. Q229-Q254.

1944-45			Wmk. 407	
Q229	PP29	3fr gray	6.75	1.60
		Never hinged	12.50	
Q230	PP29	4fr black	11.00	2.50
		Never hinged	16.50	
Q231	PP29	7fr violet	70.00	3.00
		Never hinged	110.00	
Q232	PP29	8fr yel grn	20.00	2.50
		Never hinged	32.50	
Q233	PP29	9fr dk blue	32.50	5.00
		Never hinged	55.00	
Q234	PP29	30fr red brn	90.00	1.60
		Never hinged	140.00	
	Nos. Q229-Q234 (6)		230.25	16.20

1946				
Q235	PP29	6fr claret	17.50	1.60
		Never hinged	26.00	
Q236	PP29	40fr yel brn	27.50	1.60
		Never hinged	40.00	
Q237	PP29	60fr lake red	29.00	1.60
		Never hinged	42.50	
Q238	PP29	70fr violet	200.00	30.00
		Never hinged	275.00	
Q239	PP29	80fr yel grn	27.50	2.50
		Never hinged	40.00	
Q240	PP29	90fr dk blue	150.00	27.50
		Never hinged	240.00	
Q241	PP29	200fr emer grn	32.50	2.50
		Never hinged	55.00	
	Nos. Q235-Q241 (7)		484.00	67.30

1947				
Q242	PP29	5fr pale blue	21.00	2.25
		Never hinged	32.50	
Q243	PP29	7fr pale vio	275.00	18.50
		Never hinged	425.00	
Q244	PP29	9fr pale grn	200.00	16.50
		Never hinged	300.00	
Q245	PP29	30fr pale gray brn	75.00	2.25
		Never hinged	110.00	
Q246	PP29	70fr pale viol	200.00	7.50
		Never hinged	300.00	
Q247	PP29	90fr pale ultra	140.00	2.50
		Never hinged	225.00	
Q248	PP29	100fr pale yellow	400.00	3.00
		Never hinged	550.00	
	Nos. Q242-Q248 (7)		1,311.	52.50

1948				
Q249	PP29	500fr yel	87.50	2.50
		Never hinged	140.00	
Q250	PP29	1000fr yel	325.00	17.50
		Never hinged	500.00	

1951-52				
Q251	PP29	10fr grn	57.50	8.25
		Never hinged	90.00	
Q252	PP29	20fr vio	57.50	15.00
		Never hinged	90.00	
Q253	PP29	50fr blue	70.00	10.00
		Never hinged	110.00	
Q254	PP29	100fr rose ver	21.00	1.75
		Never hinged	30.00	
	Nos. Q251-Q254 (4)		206.00	35.00

Electric Train — PP30

1960				
Q255	PP30	5c orange	11.50	2.10
		Never hinged	17.50	
Q256	PP30	10c red	10.50	8.25
		Never hinged	16.00	
Q257	PP30	20c dp red	8.75	3.75
		Never hinged	13.50	
Q258	PP30	30c dp red	8.75	3.75
		Never hinged	13.50	
Q259	PP30	40c dp red	8.75	7.50
		Never hinged	13.50	
Q260	PP30	50c dp red	8.75	4.25
		Never hinged	13.50	
Q261	PP30	60c dp red	7.50	4.25
		Never hinged	11.00	
Q262	PP30	70c dp red	7.50	4.25
		Never hinged	11.00	
Q263	PP30	80c dp red	11.50	4.25
		Never hinged	17.50	
Q264	PP30	90c dp red	11.50	4.25
		Never hinged	17.50	
Q265	PP30	1fr blue	13.00	2.25
		Never hinged	20.00	
Q266	PP30	2fr blue	13.00	2.25
		Never hinged	20.00	
Q267	PP30	3fr blue	13.00	2.25
		Never hinged	20.00	
Q268	PP30	4fr blue	13.00	2.25
		Never hinged	20.00	

Q269	PP30	5fr blue	13.00	2.25
		Never hinged	20.00	
Q270	PP30	10fr yellow	15.00	2.50
		Never hinged	22.50	
Q271	PP30	20fr dp grn	20.00	16.00
		Never hinged	30.00	
		Nos. Q255-Q271 (17)	195.00	76.35

1960   **Unwmk.**

Q272	PP30	5c orange	14.00	6.25
		Never hinged	32.50	
Q273	PP30	20c dp red	210.00	55.00
		Never hinged	325.00	
Q274	PP30	30c dp red	150.00	55.00
		Never hinged	325.00	
Q275	PP30	40c dp red	110.00	30.00
		Never hinged	160.00	
Q276	PP30	70c dp red	22.50	7.50
		Never hinged	32.50	
Q277	PP30	80c dp red	22.50	6.50
		Never hinged	32.50	
Q278	PP30	90c dp red	22.50	6.50
		Never hinged	32.50	
Q279	PP30	1fr blue	20.00	3.75
		Never hinged	30.00	
Q280	PP30	2fr blue	20.00	3.75
		Never hinged	30.00	
Q281	PP30	3fr blue	20.00	3.75
		Never hinged	30.00	
Q282	PP30	4fr blue	20.00	3.75
		Never hinged	30.00	
Q283	PP30	5fr blue	20.00	3.75
		Never hinged	30.00	
Q284	PP30	10fr yellow	25.00	6.25
		Never hinged	37.50	
Q285	PP30	20fr dp grn	30.00	21.00
		Never hinged	45.00	
		Nos. Q272-Q285 (14)	706.50	212.75

FRANCHISE STAMPS

No. 276 Overprinted "F"

1939   **Unwmk.**   **Perf. 14x13½**

S1	A45	90c ultramarine	1.90	2.50
		Never hinged	2.75	
a.		Period following "F"	30.00	30.00
		Never hinged	50.00	

No. S1 was for the use of Spanish refugees in France. "F" stands for "Franchise."

OCCUPATION STAMPS

FRANCO-PRUSSIAN WAR
Issued under German Occupation
(Alsace and Lorraine)

OS1

1870   **Typo.**   **Unwmk.**   **Perf. 13½x14**
Network with Points Up

N1	OS1	1c bronze green	100.00	110.00
a.		1c olive grn	110.00	110.00
N2	OS1	2c dark brown	190.00	190.00
a.		2c red brown	190.00	190.00
N3	OS1	4c gray	200.00	115.00
N4	OS1	5c yel grn	200.00	15.00
N5	OS1	10c bistre brn	155.00	6.50
a.		10c yellow brown	170.00	7.00
b.		Network lemon yellow	200.00	10.00
N6	OS1	20c ultra	190.00	17.50
N7	OS1	25c brown	210.00	110.00
a.		25c black brown	210.00	110.00

There are three varieties of the 4c and two of the 10c, differing in the position of the figures of value, and several other setting varieties.

Network with Points Down

N8	OS1	1c olive grn	525.00	725.00
N9	OS1	2c red brn	265.00	625.00
N10	OS1	4c gray	265.00	225.00
N11	OS1	5c yel grn	6,500.	650.00
N12	OS1	10c bister	265.00	21.50
a.		Network lemon yellow	325.00	57.50
N13	OS1	20c ultra	340.00	100.00
N14	OS1	25c brown	725.00	325.00

Official imitations have the network with points downward. The "P" of "Postes" is 2½mm from the border in the imitations and 3mm in the originals.

The word "Postes" measures 12¾ to 13mm on the imitations, and from 11 to 12½mm on the originals.

The imitations are perf. 13½x14½; originals, perf. 13½x14¼.

The stamps for Alsace and Lorraine were replaced by stamps of the German Empire on Jan. 1, 1872.

WORLD WAR I
German Stamps of 1905-16
Surcharged:

1916   **Wmk. 125**   **Perf. 14, 14½**

N15	A16	3c on 3pf brown	1.25	1.25
N16	A16	5c on 5pf green	1.25	1.25
N17	A22	8c on 7½pf org	2.00	2.00
N18	A16	10c on 10pf car	2.00	2.00
N19	A22	15c on 15pf yel brn	1.25	1.25
N20	A16	25c on 20pf blue	1.25	1.25
a.		25c on 20pf ultramarine	2.00	2.00
N21	A16	40c on 30pf org & blk, *buff*	2.90	2.75
N22	A16	50c on 40pf lake & blk	2.90	2.75
N23	A16	75c on 60pf mag	12.50	12.50
N24	A16	1fr on 80pf lake & blk, *rose*	12.50	12.50

N25	A17	1fr25c on 1m car	47.50	47.50
a.		Double surcharge	—	
N26	A21	2fr50c on 2m gray bl	47.50	47.50
a.		Double surcharge	—	
		Nos. N15-N26 (12)	134.80	134.50

These stamps were also used in parts of Belgium occupied by the German forces.

> Catalogue values for unused stamps in this section, from this point to the end of the section, are for Never Hinged items.

WORLD WAR II
Alsace
Issued under German Occupation

Stamps of Germany
1933-36 Overprinted in Black

1940   **Wmk. 237**   **Perf. 14**

N27	A64	3pf olive bister	.80	.55
N28	A64	4pf dull blue	.80	.55
N29	A64	5pf brt green	.80	.55
N30	A64	6pf dark green	.80	.55
N31	A64	8pf vermilion	.80	.55
N32	A64	10pf chocolate	.80	.55
N33	A64	12pf dp carmine	1.00	.55
N34	A64	15pf maroon	1.00	.55
N35	A64	20pf brt blue	1.65	.75
N36	A64	25pf ultra	1.65	.75
N37	A64	30pf olive grn	1.65	.75
N38	A64	40pf red violet	2.90	1.00
N39	A64	50pf dk grn & blk	7.00	3.25
N40	A64	60pf claret & blk	7.00	3.25
N41	A64	80pf dk blue & blk	17.50	7.00
N42	A64	100pf orange & blk	17.50	7.00
		Nos. N27-N42 (16)	63.65	28.15

Lorraine
Issued under German Occupation

Stamps of Germany
1933-36 Overprinted in Black

1940   **Wmk. 237**   **Perf. 14**

N43	A64	3pf olive bister	1.00	.75
N44	A64	4pf dull blue	1.00	.75
N45	A64	5pf brt green	1.00	4.00
N46	A64	6pf dark green	1.00	.75
N47	A64	8pf vermilion	1.00	.75
N48	A64	10pf chocolate	1.50	.85
N49	A64	12pf deep carmine	1.50	.85

N50	A64	15pf maroon	1.50	.75
a.		Inverted surcharge	—	
N51	A64	20pf brt blue	1.65	1.00
N52	A64	25pf ultra	1.40	1.00
N53	A64	30pf olive grn	2.10	1.00
N54	A64	40pf red violet	2.50	1.25
N55	A64	50pf dk grn & blk	6.00	3.00
N56	A64	60pf claret & blk	6.00	3.00
N57	A64	80pf dk blue & blk	18.00	7.50
N58	A64	100pf orange & blk	18.00	7.50
		Nos. N43-N58 (16)	65.15	34.70

Besetztes Gebiet Nordfrankreich

These three words, in a rectangular frame covering two stamps, were hand-stamped in black on Nos. 267, 367 and 369 and used in the Dunkerque region in July-August, 1940. The German political officer of Dunkerque authorized the overprint. The prevalence of forgeries and later favor overprints makes expertization mandatory.

ALLIED MILITARY GOVERNMENT

> Stamps formerly listed in this section as Nos. 2N1-2N20 are now listed with regular stamps of France as Nos. 475-476H and 523A-523J.

FRENCH OFFICES ABROAD

OFFICES IN CHINA

Prior to 1923 several of the world powers maintained their own post offices in China for the purpose of sending and receiving overseas mail. French offices were maintained in Canton, Hoi Hao (Hoihow), Kwangchowan (Kouang-tchéou-wan), Mongtseu (Mong-tseu), Packhoi (Paknoi), Tong King (Tchongking), Yunnan Fou (Yunnanfu).

100 Centimes = 1 Franc
100 Cents = 1 Piaster
100 Cents = 1 Dollar

Peace and Commerce Stamps of France Overprinted in Red, Carmine or Black

1894-1900   **Unwmk.**   **Perf. 14x13½**

1	A15	5c green, *greenish* (R)	3.25	3.00
2	A15	5c yel grn, I (R) ('00)	4.25	3.00
a.		Type II	47.50	32.50
3	A15	10c blk, *lav*, I (R)	9.25	3.00
a.		Type II	27.50	17.50
4	A15	15c bl (R)	12.50	4.25
5	A15	20c red, *grn*	7.50	5.00
6	A15	25c blk, *rose* (C)	9.25	2.50
a.		Double overprint	225.00	
b.		Pair, one without overprint	550.00	
d.		Imperf	110.00	40.00
7	A15	30c brn, *bis*	9.25	6.25
8	A15	40c red, *straw*	9.25	7.50
9	A15	50c car, *rose*, I	26.00	17.50
a.		Carmine overprint	62.50	
b.		Type II (Bk)	18.00	9.25
10	A15	75c dp vio, *org* (R)	80.00	60.00
11	A15	1fr brnz grn, *straw*	17.00	8.50
a.		Double overprint	425.00	450.00
12	A15	2fr brn, *az* ('00)	30.00	29.00
12A	A15	5fr red lil, *lav*	75.00	60.00
b.		Red overprint	525.00	
		Nos. 1-12A (13)	292.50	209.50

For surcharges and overprints see Nos. 13-17, J7-J10, J20-J23.

No. 11 Surcharged in Black

13	A15	25c on 1fr brnz grn, *straw*	125.00	75.00

No. 6 Surcharged in Red

1901

14	A15	2c on 25c blk, *rose*	1,100.	340.00
15	A15	4c on 25c blk, *rose*	1,350.	450.00
16	A15	6c on 25c blk, *rose*	1,100.	375.00
17	A15	16c on 25c blk, *rose*	325.00	200.00
a.		Black surcharge		7,250.
		Nos. 14-17 (4)	3,875.	1,365.

18a	A3	1c blk, *lil bl*	2.50	2.50
19	A3	2c brn, *buff*	4.25	4.25
20a	A3	4c claret, *lav*	4.25	3.40
21a	A3	5c yellow grn	5.00	3.40
22	A3	10c red	6.75	6.00
23	A3	15c gray	7.50	6.75
24a	A3	20c red, *grn*	9.25	8.50
25a	A3	25c blk, *rose*	12.50	12.50
26	A3	25c blue	10.00	8.50
27a	A3	30c brn, *bis*	9.25	8.50
28a	A3	40c red, *straw*	25.00	21.00
29	A3	50c car, *rose*	67.50	67.50
30	A3	50c brn, *azure*	10.00	9.25
31a	A3	75c vio, *org*	40.00	37.50
32a	A3	1fr brnz grn, *straw*	45.00	42.50
33a	A3	5fr red lil, *lavender*	97.50	90.00
		Nos. 18a-33a (16)	356.25	332.05

The Chinese characters surcharged on Nos. 18-33 are the Chinese equivalents of the French values and therefore differ on each denomination. Two printings exist, differing slightly in the size of "CHINE." Values above are for the less expensive variety. See the *Scott Classic Specialized Cataloue of Stamps and Covers* for detailed listings. Many varieties of surcharge exist.

Liberty, Equality and Fraternity		"Rights of Man"
A3		A4

A5

1902-03   **Typo.**

34	A3	5c green	6.00	3.75
35	A4	10c rose red ('03)	3.00	2.10
36	A4	15c pale red	3.00	2.10
37	A4	20c brn vio ('03)	8.50	7.25
38	A4	25c blue ('03)	6.75	3.40
39	A4	30c lilac ('03)	9.25	7.50
40	A5	40c red & pale bl	19.00	16.00
41	A5	50c bis brn & lav	23.00	19.00
42	A5	1fr claret & ol grn	30.00	19.00
43	A5	2fr gray vio & yel	62.50	45.00
44	A5	5fr dk bl & buff	92.50	72.50
		Nos. 34-44 (11)	263.50	197.60

For surcharges and overprints see Nos. 45, 57-85, J14-J16, J27-J30.

Surcharged in Black

1903

45	A4	5c on 15c pale red	17.50	12.00
a.		Inverted surcharge	135.00	75.00

Stamps of Indo-China, 1904-06, Surcharged as Nos. 18-33 in Black

1904-05

46	A4	1c olive grn	2.10	2.10
47	A4	2c vio brn, *buff*	2.10	2.10
47A	A4	4c cl, *bluish*	975.00	800.00
48	A4	5c deep grn	2.10	2.10
49	A4	10c carmine	3.00	3.00
50	A4	15c org brn, *bl* (I)	3.00	3.00
51	A4	20c red, *grn*	11.50	11.00
52	A4	25c deep blue	10.00	6.00
53	A4	40c blk, *bluish*	8.50	6.00
54	A4	1fr pale grn	360.00	300.00
55	A4	2fr brn, *org*	42.50	37.50
56	A4	10fr org brn, *grn*	165.00	155.00
		Nos. 46-56 (12)	1,584.	1,327.

Many varieties of the surcharge exist.

Stamps of 1902-03 Surcharged in Black

1907

57	A3	2c on 5c green	2.50	1.15
58	A4	4c on 10c rose red	2.50	1.75
a.		Pair, one without surcharge	—	
59	A4	6c on 15c pale red	3.40	2.50
60	A4	8c on 20c brn vio	6.00	6.00
a.		"8" inverted	75.00	75.00
61	A4	10c on 25c blue	2.10	1.25
62	A5	20c on 50c bis brn & lav	6.25	3.75
a.		Double surcharge	—	
b.		Triple surcharge	440.00	440.00
63	A5	40c on 1fr claret & ol grn	22.00	13.50
64	A5	2pi on 5fr dk bl & buff	23.00	13.50
a.		Double surcharge	2,300.	1,900.
		Nos. 57-64 (8)	67.75	43.40

Stamps of 1902-03 Surcharged in Black

1911-22

65	A3	2c on 5c green	2.10	1.50
66	A4	4c on 10c rose red	2.50	1.75
67	A4	6c on 15c org	5.00	2.10
68	A4	8c on 20c brn vio	2.10	1.80
69	A4	10c on 25c bl ('21)	4.25	2.10
70	A4	20c on 50c bl ('22)	55.00	55.00
71	A5	40c on 1fr cl & ol grn	7.50	6.00

No. 44 Surcharged

73	A5	$2 on 5fr bl & buff ('22)	175.00	200.00
		Nos. 65-73 (8)	253.45	270.25

Types of 1902-03 Surcharged like Nos. 65-71

1922

75	A3	1c on 5c org	6.00	6.75
76	A4	2c on 10c grn	6.75	7.50
77	A4	3c on 15c org	9.25	11.00
78	A4	4c on 20c red brn	11.00	13.50
79	A4	5c on 25c dk vio	6.00	6.00
80	A4	6c on 30c red	12.00	11.00
82	A4	10c on 50c blue	14.50	12.00
83	A5	20c on 1fr claret & ol grn	55.00	55.00
84	A5	40c on 2fr org & pale bl	45.00	55.00
85	A5	$1 on 5fr dk bl & buff	150.00	160.00
		Nos. 75-85 (10)	315.50	337.75

POSTAGE DUE STAMPS

Postage Due Stamps of France Handstamped in Red or Black

1901-07			**Unwmk.**	**Perf. 14x13½**
J1	D2	5c lt bl (R)	7.50	4.25
a.		Double overprint	145.00	
J2	D2	10c choc (R)	11.00	6.00
a.		Double overprint	145.00	
J3	D2	15c lt grn (R)	11.00	7.50
a.		Pair, one stamp without ovpt.	225.00	
b.		Imperf, single	145.00	90.00
J4	D2	20c ol grn (R) ('07)	12.50	11.00
J5	D2	30c carmine	17.00	12.00
a.		Double overprint	145.00	
J6	D2	50c lilac	17.00	12.50
a.		Triple overprint	145.00	
b.		Pair, one stamp without overprint	225.00	
		Nos. J1-J6 (6)	76.00	53.25

Stamps of 1894-1900 Handstamped in Carmine

A PERCEVOIR

1903

J7	A15	5c yel grn	—	2,250.
a.		Purple handstamp	—	
b.		5c green, *greenish*	—	
J8	A15	10c blk, *lavender*	—	—
a.		Purple handstamp	—	
J9	A15	15c blue	2,750.	1,250.
a.		Purple handstamp	—	
J10	A15	30c brn, *bister*	1,500.	350.00
a.		Purple handstamp	—	

Same Handstamp on Stamps of 1902-03 in Carmine

1903

J14	A3	5c green	—	2,000.
a.		Purple handstamp	—	
J15	A4	10c rose red	750.	425.00
a.		Purple handstamp	—	
J16	A4	15c pale red	750.	325.00
a.		Purple handstamp	—	

Stamps of 1894-1900 Handstamped in Carmine

1903

J20	A1	5c yellow green	—	1,100.
a.		Purple handstamp	—	
b.		5c green, *greenish*	—	
J21	A1	10c blk, *lavender*	—	—
a.		Purple handstamp	—	
J22	A1	15c blue	1,250.	350.
a.		Purple handstamp	—	
J23	A1	30c brn, *bister*	600.	325.
a.		Purple handstamp	—	

Same Handstamp on Stamps of 1902-03 in Carmine or Purple

1903

J27	A3	5c green (C)	—	1,750.
a.		Purple handstamp	—	
J28	A4	10c rose red (C)	340.	225.
a.		Purple handstamp	—	
J29	A4	15c pale red (C)	675.	225.
a.		Purple handstamp	—	
J30	A4	30c lilac (P)	—	—

The handstamps on Nos. J7-J30 are found inverted, double, etc.

The cancellations on these stamps should have dates between Sept. 1, and Nov. 30, 1903, to be genuine.

Postage Due Stamps of France, 1893-1910 Surcharged like Nos. 65-71

1911

J33	D2	2c on 5c blue	3.00	2.50
a.		Double surcharge	140.00	
J34	D2	4c on 10c choc	3.00	2.50
a.		Double surcharge	140.00	
J35	D2	8c on 20c ol grn	3.40	3.00
a.		Double surcharge	140.00	
J36	D2	20c on 50c lilac	3.40	3.00
		Nos. J33-J36 (4)	12.80	11.00

1922

J37	D2	1c on 5c blue	82.50	95.00
J38	D2	2c on 10c brn	145.00	165.00
J39	D2	4c on 20c ol grn	145.00	165.00
J40	D2	10c on 50c brn vio	125.00	185.00
		Nos. J37-J40 (4)	497.50	610.00

CANTON

Stamps of Indo-China, 1892-1900, Overprinted in Red

1901			**Unwmk.**	**Perf. 14x13½**
1	A3	1c blk, *lil bl*	2.10	2.10
1A	A3	2c brn, *buff*	2.50	2.50
2	A3	4c claret, *lav*	4.25	4.25
2A	A3	5c grn, *grnsh*	600.00	600.00
3	A3	5c yel grn	3.40	3.40
4	A3	10c blk, *lavender*	7.25	7.25
5	A3	15c blue, quadrille paper	6.75	6.75
6	A3	15c gray	7.50	7.50
a.		Double overprint	19.00	
7	A3	20c red, *grn*	22.50	22.50
8	A3	25c blk, *rose*	13.50	13.50
9	A3	30c brn, *bister*	32.50	32.50
10	A3	40c red, *straw*	32.50	32.50
11	A3	50c car, *rose*	35.00	35.00
12	A3	75c dp vio, *org*	35.00	35.00
13	A3	1fr brnz grn, *straw*	45.00	45.00
14	A3	5fr red lil, *lav*	250.00	250.00
		Nos. 1-14 (16)	1,099.	1,099.

The Chinese characters in the overprint on Nos. 1-14 read "Canton." On Nos. 15-64, they restate the denomination of the basic stamp.

Surcharged in Black

1903-04

15	A3	1c blk, *lil bl*	4.25	4.25
16	A3	2c brn, *buff*	4.50	4.25
17	A3	4c claret, *lav*	4.25	4.25
18	A3	5c yellow green	4.25	4.25
19	A3	10c rose red	4.50	4.25
20	A3	15c gray	4.50	4.25
21	A3	20c red, *grn*	21.00	17.50
22	A3	25c blue	7.50	7.50
23	A3	25c blk, *rose* ('04)	10.00	8.50
24	A3	30c brn, *bister*	27.50	21.00
25	A3	40c red, *straw*	67.50	55.00
26	A3	50c car, *rose*	340.00	310.00
27	A3	75c brn, *az* ('04)	85.00	72.50
28	A3	75c dp vio, *org*	67.50	67.50
a.		"INDO-CHINE" inverted	55,000.	
29	A3	1fr brnz grn, *straw*	67.50	67.50
30	A3	5fr red lil, *lav*	67.50	67.50
		Nos. 15-30 (16)	787.50	720.00

Many varieties of the surcharge exist on #15-30.

Stamps of Indo-China, 1892-1906, Surcharged in Red or Black

A second printing of the 1906 surcharges of Canton, Hoi Hao, Kwangchowan, Mongtseu, Packhoi, Tong King and Yunnan Fou was made in 1908. The inks are grayish instead of full black and vermilion instead of carmine. Values are for the cheaper variety which usually is the second printing.

The 4c and 50c of the 1892 issue of Indo-China are known with this surcharge and similarly surcharged for other cities in China. The surcharges on these two stamps are always inverted. It is stated that they were irregularly produced and never issued.

1906

31	A4	1c ol grn (R)	2.50	2.50
32	A4	2c vio brn, *buff*	2.50	2.50
33	A4	4c cl, *bluish* (R)	2.50	2.50
34	A4	5c dp grn (R)	2.10	2.10
35	A4	10c carmine	3.00	3.00
36	A4	15c org brn, *bl*	22.50	22.50
37	A4	20c red, *grn*	12.50	12.50
38	A4	25c deep blue	5.00	5.00
39	A4	30c pale brn	17.00	17.00
40	A4	35c blk, *yel*	12.50	12.50
41	A4	40c blk, *bluish* (R)	21.00	21.00
42	A4	50c bister brn	14.50	14.50
43	A4	75c dp vio, *org* (R)	67.50	67.50
44	A4	1fr pale grn	30.00	30.00
45	A4	2fr brn, *org* (R)	42.50	42.50

46	A3	5fr red lil, *lav*	92.50	92.50
47	A4	10fr org brn, *grn*	85.00	85.00
		Nos. 31-47 (17)	435.10	435.10

Surcharge exists inverted on 1c, 25c & 1fr.

Stamps of Indo-China, 1907, Surcharged "CANTON", and Chinese Characters, in Red or Blue

1908

48	A5	1c ol brn & blk	1.25	1.25
49	A5	2c brn & blk	1.25	1.25
50	A5	4c bl & blk	2.50	1.25
51	A5	5c grn & blk	2.50	2.10
52	A5	10c red & blk (Bl)	3.40	2.50
53	A5	15c vio & blk	4.25	3.40
54	A6	20c vio & blk	5.00	5.00
55	A6	25c bl & blk	5.00	4.25
56	A6	30c brn & blk	8.50	8.50
57	A6	35c ol grn & blk	8.50	8.50
58	A6	40c brn & blk	11.00	8.50
59	A6	50c car & blk (Bl)	11.00	8.50
60	A7	75c ver & blk (Bl)	11.00	10.00
61	A8	1fr car & blk (Bl)	18.00	15.00
62	A9	2fr grn & blk	45.00	37.50
63	A10	5fr bl & blk	62.50	55.00
64	A11	10fr org & blk	92.50	92.50
		Nos. 48-64 (17)	293.15	265.00

Nos. 48-64 Surcharged with New Values in Cents or Piasters in Black, Red or Blue

1919

65	A5	⅖c on 1c	1.25	1.25
66	A5	⅘c on 2c	1.25	1.25
67	A5	1⅗c on 4c (R)	1.25	1.25
68	A5	2c on 5c	1.60	1.60
69	A6	4c on 10c (Bl)	2.10	1.60
a.		Chinese "2" instead of "4"	42.50	42.50
70	A5	6c on 15c	2.50	2.10
71	A6	8c on 20c	4.25	2.10
72	A6	10c on 25c	5.00	1.60
73	A6	12c on 30c	2.10	2.10
a.		Double surcharge	140.00	140.00
74	A6	14c on 35c	2.10	1.60
a.		Closed "4"	10.00	10.00
75	A6	16c on 40c	2.50	1.60
76	A6	20c on 50c (Bl)	2.50	2.10
77	A7	30c on 75c (Bl)	2.50	2.10
78	A8	40c on 1fr (Bl)	12.50	7.50
79	A9	80c on 2fr (R)	19.00	12.00
80	A10	2pi on 5fr (R)	32.50	32.50
81	A11	4pi on 10fr (R)	32.50	32.50
		Nos. 65-81 (17)	127.40	106.75

HOI HAO

Stamps of Indo-China Overprinted in Red

1901			**Unwmk.**	**Perf. 14x13½**
1	A3	1c blk, *lil bl*	3.40	3.40
2	A3	2c brn, *buff*	4.25	4.25
3	A3	4c claret, *lav*	4.25	4.25
4	A3	5c yel grn	5.00	5.00
5	A3	10c blk, *lavender*	13.50	12.00
6	A3	15c blue	1,850.	800.00
7	A3	15c gray	7.50	5.00
8	A3	20c red, *grn*	32.50	25.00
9	A3	25c blk, *rose*	17.00	12.50
10	A3	30c brn, *bister*	67.50	67.50
11	A3	40c red, *straw*	67.50	67.50
12	A3	50c car, *rose*	67.50	67.50
13	A3	75c dp vio, *org*	250.00	225.00
14	A3	1fr brnz grn, *straw*	800.00	740.00
15	A3	5fr red lil, *lav*	800.00	675.00
		Nos. 1-15 (15)	3,989.	2,713.

The Chinese characters in the overprint on Nos. 1-15 read "Hoi Hao." On Nos. 16-66, they restate the denomination of the basic stamp.

Surcharged in Black

1903-04

16	A3	1c blk, *lil bl*	2.50	2.50
17	A3	2c brn, *buff*	2.50	2.50
18	A3	4c claret, *lav*	4.25	4.25
19	A3	5c yel grn	4.25	4.25
20	A3	10c red	4.25	4.25
21	A3	15c gray	5.00	5.00
22	A3	20c red, *grn*	7.50	5.00
23	A3	25c blue	5.00	5.00
24	A3	25c blk, *rose* ('04)	8.50	8.50
25	A3	30c brn, *bister*	6.75	6.75
26	A3	40c red, *straw*	32.50	32.50

27	A3	50c car, *rose*	30.00	30.00
28	A3	50c brn, *az* ('04)	170.00	170.00
29	A3	75c dp vio, *org*	50.00	50.00
a.		"INDO-CHINE" inverted	45,000.	
30	A3	1fr brnz grn, *straw*	67.50	67.50
31	A3	5fr red lil, *lav*	225.00	225.00
		Nos. 16-31 (16)	625.50	625.50

Many varieties of the surcharge exist on #1-31.

Stamps of Indo-China, 1892-1906, Surcharged in Red or Black

1906

32	A4	1c ol grn (R)	8.50	8.50
33	A4	2c vio brn, *buff*	8.50	8.50
34	A4	4c cl, *bluish* (R)	8.50	8.50
35	A4	5c dp grn (R)	8.50	8.50
36	A4	10c carmine	8.50	8.50
37	A4	15c org brn, *bl*	32.50	32.50
38	A4	20c red, *grn*	13.50	13.50
39	A4	25c deep blue	11.00	11.00
40	A4	30c pale brn	13.50	13.50
41	A4	35c blk, *yel* (R)	21.00	21.00
42	A4	40c blk, *bluish* (R)	21.00	21.00
43	A4	50c gray brn	21.00	21.00
44	A3	75c dp vio, *org* (R)	62.50	62.50
45	A4	1fr pale grn	62.50	62.50
46	A4	2fr brn, *org* (R)	62.50	62.50
47	A3	5fr red lil, *lav*	135.00	135.00
48	A4	10fr org brn, *grn*	150.00	150.00
		Nos. 32-48 (17)	648.50	648.50

Stamps of Indo-China, 1907, Surcharged "HOI HAO" and Chinese Characters, in Red or Blue

1908

49	A5	1c ol brn & blk	1.70	1.70
50	A5	2c brn & blk	1.70	1.70
51	A5	4c bl & blk	1.70	1.70
52	A5	5c grn & blk	3.00	3.00
53	A5	10c red & blk (Bl)	3.00	3.00
54	A5	15c vio & blk	6.75	6.75
55	A6	20c vio & blk	7.50	7.50
56	A6	25c bl & blk	7.50	7.50
57	A6	30c brn & blk	7.50	7.50
58	A6	35c ol grn & blk	7.50	7.50
59	A6	40c brn & blk	8.50	8.50
61	A6	50c car & blk (Bl)	10.00	10.00
62	A7	75c ver & blk (Bl)	10.00	10.00
63	A8	1fr car & blk (Bl)	29.00	29.00
64	A9	2fr grn & blk	42.50	42.50
65	A10	5fr bl & blk	75.00	75.00
66	A11	10fr pur & blk	110.00	110.00
		Nos. 49-66 (17)	332.85	332.85

Nos. 49-66 Surcharged with New Values in Cents or Piasters in Black, Red or Blue

1919

67	A5	⅖c on 1c	1.25	1.25
68	A5	⅗c on 2c	1.25	1.25
69	A5	1⅗c on 4c (R)	2.10	2.10
70	A5	2c on 5c	2.50	2.50
71	A5	4c on 10c (Bl)	3.00	3.00
a.		Chinese "2" instead of "4"	14.50	14.50
72	A5	6c on 15c	2.50	2.50
73	A6	8c on 20c	4.25	4.25
a.		"S" of "CENTS" omitted	170.00	170.00
74	A6	10c on 25c	6.75	6.75
75	A6	12c on 30c	4.25	4.25
76	A6	14c on 35c	3.40	3.40
a.		Closed "4"	42.50	42.50
77	A6	16c on 40c	4.25	4.25
79	A6	20c on 50c (Bl)	3.40	3.40
80	A7	30c on 75c (Bl)	11.00	11.00
81	A8	40c on 1fr (R)	22.00	22.00
82	A9	80c on 2fr (R)	62.50	62.50
83	A10	2pi on 5fr (R)	92.50	92.50
a.		Triple surch. of new value	750.00	750.00
84	A11	4pi on 10fr (R)	225.00	225.00
		Nos. 67-84 (17)	451.90	451.90

KWANGCHOWAN

A Chinese Territory leased to France, 1898 to 1945.

Stamps of Indo-China, 1892-1906, Surcharged in Red or Black

1906   Unwmk.   Perf. 14x13½

1	A4	1c ol grn (R)	8.50	8.50
2	A4	2c vio brn, *buff*	8.50	8.50
3	A4	4c cl, *bluish* (R)	8.50	8.50
4	A4	5c dp grn (R)	8.50	8.50

5	A4	10c carmine	8.50	8.50
6	A4	15c org brn, *bl*	32.50	32.50
7	A4	20c red, *grn*	13.50	13.50
8	A4	25c deep blue	11.00	11.00
9	A4	30c pale brn	13.50	13.50
10	A4	35c blk, *yel* (R)	21.00	21.00
11	A4	40c blk, *bluish* (R)	21.00	21.00
12	A4	50c bister brn	25.00	25.00
13	A3	75c dp vio, *org* (R)	67.50	67.50
14	A4	1fr pale grn	42.50	42.50
15	A4	2fr brn, *org* (R)	55.00	55.00
16	A3	5fr red lil, *lav*	225.00	225.00
17	A4	10fr org brn, *grn*	275.00	275.00
		Nos. 1-17 (17)	845.00	845.00

Various varieties of the surcharge exist on Nos. 2-10.

Stamps of Indo-China, 1907, Surcharged "KOUANG-TCHEOU" and Value in Chinese in Red or Blue

1908

18	A5	1c ol brn & blk	1.70	1.70
19	A5	2c brn & blk	1.70	1.70
20	A5	4c bl & blk	1.70	1.70
21	A5	5c grn & blk	1.70	1.70
22	A5	10c red & blk (Bl)	1.70	1.70
23	A5	15c vio & blk	4.25	4.25
24	A6	20c vio & blk	6.75	6.75
25	A6	25c bl & blk	6.75	6.75
26	A6	30c brn & blk	10.00	10.00
27	A6	35c ol grn & blk	14.50	14.50
28	A6	40c brn & blk	14.50	14.50
30	A6	50c car & blk (Bl)	17.00	17.00
31	A7	75c ver & blk (Bl)	17.00	17.00
32	A8	1fr car & blk (Bl)	24.00	24.00
33	A9	2fr grn & blk	32.50	32.50
34	A10	5fr bl & blk	75.00	75.00
35	A11	10fr pur & blk	105.00	105.00
a.		Double surcharge	1,050.	
b.		Triple surcharge	1,050.	
		Nos. 18-35 (17)	335.75	335.75

The Chinese characters overprinted on Nos. 1 to 35 repeat the denomination of the basic stamp.

Nos. 18-35 Surcharged with New Values in Cents or Piasters in Black, Red or Blue

1919

36	A5	⅖c on 1c	1.25	.85
37	A5	⅗c on 2c	1.25	.85
38	A5	1⅗c on 4c (R)	1.25	.85
39	A5	2c on 5c	2.10	1.25
a.		"2 CENTS" inverted	97.50	
40	A5	4c on 10c (Bl)	3.75	3.40
41	A5	6c on 15c	2.10	2.10
42	A6	8c on 20c	4.25	4.25
43	A6	10c on 25c	14.50	13.50
44	A6	12c on 30c	3.40	3.40
45	A6	14c on 35c	3.40	3.40
a.		Closed "4"	45.00	37.50
46	A6	16c on 40c	2.10	2.10
48	A6	20c on 50c (Bl)	2.10	2.10
49	A7	30c on 75c (Bl)	11.00	11.00
50	A8	40c on 1fr (R)	12.00	12.00
a.		"40 CENTS" inverted		
51	A9	80c on 2fr (R)	20.00	20.00
52	A10	2pi on 5fr (R)	175.00	175.00
53	A11	4pi on 10fr (R)	32.50	32.50
		Nos. 36-53 (17)	291.95	288.55

Stamps of Indo-China, 1922-23, Overprinted in Black, Red or Blue

1923

54	A12	¹⁄₁₀c blk & sal (Bl)	.35	.35
55	A12	⅕c dp bl & blk (R)	.35	.35
a.		Black overprint	135.00	
56	A12	⅖c ol brn & blk (R)	.40	.40
57	A12	⅗c brt rose & blk	.60	.60
58	A12	1c yel brn & blk (Bl)	.60	.60
59	A12	2c gray grn & blk	.95	.95
60	A12	3c vio & blk (R)	1.00	1.00
61	A12	4c org & blk	1.25	1.25
62	A12	5c car & blk	1.25	1.25
63	A13	6c dl red & blk	1.25	1.25
64	A13	7c ol grn & blk	1.70	1.70
65	A13	8c black (R)	2.50	2.50
66	A13	9c yel & blk	2.50	2.50
67	A13	10c bl & blk	2.10	2.10
68	A13	11c vio & blk	2.10	2.10
69	A13	12c brn & blk	2.10	2.10
70	A13	15c org & blk	3.00	3.00
71	A13	20c bl & blk, *straw* (R)	3.00	3.00
72	A13	40c ver & blk, *bluish* (Bl)	3.40	3.40
73	A13	1pi bl grn & blk, *grnsh*	7.50	7.50
74	A13	2pi vio brn & blk, *pnksh* (Bl)	17.00	17.00
		Nos. 54-74 (21)	54.90	54.90

Indo-China Stamps of 1927 Overprinted in Black or Red

1927

75	A14	¹⁄₁₀c lt ol grn (R)	.35	.35
76	A14	⅕c yellow	.35	.35
77	A14	⅖c lt blue (R)	.50	.50
78	A14	⅗c dp brown	.50	.50
79	A14	1c orange	.85	.85
80	A14	2c blue grn (R)	1.25	1.25
81	A14	3c indigo (R)	1.25	1.25
82	A14	4c lilac rose	1.25	1.25
83	A14	5c deep violet	1.25	1.25
84	A15	6c deep red	1.25	1.25
85	A15	7c lt brown	1.25	1.25
86	A15	8c gray grn (R)	1.25	1.25
87	A15	9c red violet	1.70	1.70
88	A15	10c lt bl (R)	1.70	1.70
89	A15	11c orange	1.70	1.70
90	A15	12c myr grn (R)	1.70	1.70
91	A16	15c dl rose & ol brn	3.00	3.00
92	A16	20c vio & sl (R)	2.50	2.50
93	A17	25c org brn & lil rose	2.50	2.50
94	A17	30c dp bl & ol gray (R)	1.70	1.70
95	A18	40c ver & lt bl	1.70	1.70
96	A18	50c lt grn & sl (R)	2.50	2.50
97	A19	1pi dk bl, blk & yel (R)	4.25	4.25
98	A19	2pi red, dp bl & org (R)	6.00	6.00
a.		Double overprint	160.00	
		Nos. 75-98 (24)	42.25	42.25

Stamps of Indo-China, 1931-41, Overprinted in Black or Red

1937-41   Perf. 13, 13½

99	A20	¹⁄₁₀c Prus blue	.25	.25
100	A20	⅕c lake	.25	.25
101	A20	⅖c orange red	.40	.40
102	A20	½c red brown	.35	.35
103	A20	⅗c dk violet	.35	.35
104	A20	1c black brown	.35	.35
105	A20	2c dk green	.35	.35
a.		Inverted overprint	140.00	
106	A21	3c dk green	.75	.75
107	A21	3c yel brn ('41)	.35	.35
108	A21	4c dk blue (R)	1.00	1.00
109	A21	4c dk green ('41)	.35	.35
110	A21	4c yel org ('41)	2.75	2.75
111	A21	5c dp blue	.95	.95
112	A21	5c dp green ('41)	.50	.50
113	A21	6c orange red	.65	.65
114	A21	7c black ('41)	.65	.65
115	A21	8c rose lake ('41)	.75	.75
116	A21	9c blk, *yel* ('41)	1.00	1.00
d.		Black overprint	9.25	9.25
117	A22	10c dk blue (R)	1.10	1.10
118	A22	10c ultra, *pink* (R) ('41)	.85	.85
119	A22	15c dk bl (R)	.75	.75
120	A22	15c dk bl (R) ('41)	.65	.65
121	A22	20c rose	.75	.75
122	A22	21c olive grn	.75	.75
123	A22	25c green ('41)	.60	.60
124	A22	25c dp violet	3.00	3.00
125	A22	25c dk bl (R) ('41)	.85	.85
126	A22	30c orange brn	.85	.85
127	A23	50c dk brown	1.10	1.10
128	A23	60c dl violet	1.10	1.10
129	A23	70c lt bl (R) ('41)	.85	.85
130	A23	1pi yel green	2.10	2.10
131	A23	2pi red	2.25	2.25
		Nos. 99-131 (33)	29.55	29.55

Common Design Types pictured following the introduction.

Colonial Arts Exhibition Issue
Common Design Type
Souvenir Sheet

1937   Engr.   Imperf.

| 132 | CD79 | 30c grn & sepia | 9.25 | 11.00 |

New York World's Fair Issue
Common Design Type

1939   Unwmk.   Perf. 12½x12

| 133 | CD82 | 13c car lake | 1.25 | 1.25 |
| 134 | CD82 | 23c ultra | 1.25 | 1.25 |

Petain Issue
Indo-China Nos. 209-209A Overprinted "KOUANG TCHEOU" in Blue or Red

1941   Engr.   Perf. 12½x12

| 135 | A27a | 10c car lake (B) | .85 | |
| 136 | A27a | 25c blue (R) | .85 | |

Nos. 135-136 were issued by the Vichy government in France, but were not placed on sale in Kwangchowan.
For surcharges, see Nos. B9-B10.

Indo-China Types of 1937-41 without "RF" Overprinted "KOUANG TCHEOU" in Blue or Red

1942-44

137	A20	⅖c orange red	.25	
138	A20	½c red brown	.25	
139	A20	1c black brown	.35	
140	A20	2c dark green	.65	
141	A21	3c yellow brown	.65	
142	A21	4c yellow orange	.35	
143	A21	5c deep green	.50	
144	A21	9c black, *yellow*	.35	
145	A22	10c ultramarine, *pink* (R)	.60	
146	A22	18c blue (R)	190.00	
147	A22	22c green	.60	
148	A22	30c orange brown	.60	
149	A23	50c dark brown	.60	
150	A23	60c dull violet	.65	
151	A23	70c light blue (R)	.85	
152	A23	1pi yellow green	1.30	
153	A23	2pi red	1.40	
		Nos. 137-153 (17)	200.00	

Nos. 137-153 were issued by the Vichy government in France, but were not placed on sale in Kwangchowan.

SEMI-POSTAL STAMPS

French Revolution Issue
Common Design Type

**1939   Unwmk.   Photo.   Perf. 13
Name and Value typo. in Black**

B1	CD83	6c + 2c green	9.25	9.25
B2	CD83	7c + 3c brown	9.25	9.25
B3	CD83	9c + 4c red org	9.25	9.25
B4	CD83	13c + 10c rose pink	9.25	9.25
B5	CD83	23c + 20c blue	9.25	9.25
		Nos. B1-B5 (5)	46.25	46.25

Indo-China Nos. B19A and B19C Overprinted "KOUANG-TCHEOU" in Blue or Red, and Common Design Type

1941   Photo.   Perf. 13½

B6	SP1	10c + 10c red (B)	.85	
B7	CD86	15c + 30c mar & car	.85	
B8	SP2	25c + 10c blue (R)	.85	
		Nos. B6-B8 (3)	2.55	

Nos. B6-B8 were issued by the Vichy government in France, but were not placed on sale in Kwangchowan.

Indo-China Nos. B21A-B21B Overprinted "KOUANG-TCHEOU" in Blue or Red

1944   Engr.   Perf. 12½x12

| B9 | A27a | 5c + 15c on 25c deep blue (R) | 1.00 | |
| B10 | A27a | +25c on 10c car lake | 1.10 | |

Colonial Development Fund.
Nos. B9-B10 were issued by the Vichy government in France, but were not placed on sale in Kwangchowan.

AIR POST SEMI-POSTAL STAMPS

Indo-China Nos. CB2-CB4 Overprinted "KOUANG-TCHEOU" in Blue or Red

Methods and Perfs as Before

1942, June 22

CB1	SPAP1	15c + 35c green	.95	
CB2	SPAP2	20c + 60c brown	.95	
CB3	SPAP3	30c +90c car red	.95	
		Nos. CB1-CB3 (3)	2.85	

Native children's welfare fund.
Nos. CB1-CB3 were issued by the Vichy government in France, but were not placed on sale in Kwangchowan.

Colonial Education Fund

Indo-China No. CB5 Overprinted
"KOUANG-TCHEOU" in Blue or Red

Perf. 12½x13½

1942, June 22			Engr.
CB4	CD86a	12c + 18c blue & red	1.00

No. CB4 was issued by the Vichy government in France, but was not placed on sale in Kwangchowan.

MONGTSEU (MENGTSZ)

Stamps of Indo-China
Surcharged in Black

1903-04		**Unwmk.**	**Perf. 14x13½**	
1	A3	1c blk, *lil bl*	7.50	7.50
2	A3	2c brn, *buff*	6.75	6.75
3	A3	4c claret, *lav*	8.50	8.50
4	A3	5c yel grn	6.00	6.00
5	A3	10c red	9.25	9.25
6	A3	15c gray	10.00	10.00
7	A3	20c red, *grn*	12.50	12.50
7C	A3	25c blk, *rose*	725.00	725.00
8	A3	25c blue	12.50	12.50
9	A3	30c brn, *bister*	11.00	11.00
10	A3	40c red, *straw*	75.00	75.00
11	A3	50c car, *rose*	440.00	440.00
12	A3	50c brn, *az* ('04)	150.00	150.00
13	A3	75c dp vio, *org*	120.00	120.00
a.		"INDO-CHINE" inverted	67,500.	
14	A3	1fr brnz grn, *straw*	110.00	110.00
15	A3	5fr red lil, *lav*	110.00	110.00
		Nos. 1-15 (16)	1,814.	1,814.

Many Surcharge varieties exist on #1-15.

Stamps of Indo-China,
1892-1906, Surcharged
in Red or Black

1906				
16	A4	1c ol grn (R)	5.00	5.00
17	A4	2c vio brn, *buff*	5.00	5.00
18	A4	4c cl, *bluish* (R)	5.00	5.00
19	A4	5c dp grn (R)	6.00	6.00
20	A4	10c carmine	5.00	5.00
21	A4	15c org brn, *bl*	35.00	35.00
22	A4	20c red, *grn*	13.50	13.50
23	A4	25c deep blue	10.00	10.00
24	A4	30c pale brn	13.50	13.50
25	A4	35c blk, *yel*	12.50	12.50
26	A4	40c blk, *bluish* (R)	20.00	20.00
27	A4	50c bister brn	21.00	21.00
28	A3	75c dp vio, *org* (R)	67.50	67.50
a.		"INDO-CHINE" inverted	67,500.	
29	A4	1fr pale grn	42.50	42.50
30	A4	2fr brn, *org* (R)	55.00	55.00
31	A3	5fr red lil, *lav*	140.00	140.00
32	A4	10fr org brn, *grn*	150.00	150.00
a.		Chinese characters inverted	1,750.	2,100.
		Nos. 16-32 (17)	606.50	606.50

Inverted varieties of the surcharge exist on Nos. 19, 22 and 32.

Stamps of Indo-China, 1907,
Surcharged "MONGTSEU" and Value
in Chinese in Red or Blue

1908				
33	A5	1c ol brn & blk	1.25	1.25
34	A5	2c brn & blk	1.25	1.25
35	A5	4c bl & blk	1.25	1.25
36	A5	5c grn & blk	1.25	1.25
37	A5	10c red & blk (Bl)	3.00	3.00
38	A5	15c vio & blk	3.00	3.00
39	A6	20c vio & blk	6.00	6.00
40	A6	25c bl & blk	15.00	15.00
41	A6	30c brn & blk	6.75	6.75
42	A6	35c ol grn & blk	7.50	7.50
43	A6	40c brn & blk	5.00	5.00
44	A6	50c car & blk (Bl)	6.75	6.75
45	A7	75c ver & blk (Bl)	14.50	14.50
46	A8	1fr car & blk (Bl)	13.50	13.50
47	A9	2fr grn & blk	19.00	19.00
48	A10	5fr bl & blk	105.00	105.00
49	A11	10fr pur & blk	125.00	125.00
		Nos. 33-50 (17)	335.00	335.00

The Chinese characters overprinted on Nos. 1 to 50 repeat the denomination of the basic stamp.

Nos. 33-50 Surcharged with New
Values in Cents or Piasters in Black,
Red or Blue

1919				
51	A5	⅖c on 1c	1.70	1.70
52	A5	⅖c on 2c	1.70	1.70
53	A5	1⅗c on 4c	1.70	1.70
54	A5	2c on 5c	1.70	1.70
55	A5	4c on 10c (Bl)	3.00	3.00
56	A5	6c on 15c	3.00	3.00
57	A6	8c on 20c	6.75	6.75
58	A6	10c on 25c	5.00	5.00
59	A6	12c on 30c	5.00	5.00
60	A6	14c on 35c	3.40	3.40
a.		Closed "4"	21.00	21.00
61	A6	16c on 40c	4.25	4.25
63	A6	20c on 50c (Bl)	5.00	5.00
64	A7	30c on 75c (Bl)	9.25	9.25
65	A8	40c on 1fr (Bl)	10.00	10.00
66	A9	80c on 2fr (R)	10.00	10.00
a.		Triple surch., one inverted	550.00	550.00
67	A10	2pi on 5fr (R)	200.00	200.00
a.		Triple surch., one inverted	625.00	625.00
b.		Double surcharge	925.00	925.00
68	A11	4pi on 10fr (R)	30.00	30.00
		Nos. 51-68 (17)	301.45	301.45

PAKHOI

Stamps of Indo-China
Surcharged in Black

1903-04		**Unwmk.**	**Perf. 14x13½**	
1	A3	1c blk, *lil bl*	6.75	6.75
2	A3	2c brn, *buff*	6.75	6.75
3	A3	4c claret, *lav*	6.75	6.75
4	A3	5c yel grn	5.00	5.00
5	A3	10c red	5.00	5.00
6	A3	15c gray	5.00	5.00
7	A3	20c red, *grn*	11.00	11.00
8	A3	25c blue	9.25	9.25
9	A3	25c blk, *rose* ('04)	6.75	6.75
10	A3	30c brn, *bister*	8.50	8.50
11	A3	40c red, *straw*	57.50	57.50
12	A3	50c car, *rose*	340.00	340.00
13	A3	50c brn, *az* ('04)	47.50	47.50
14	A3	75c dp vio, *org*	67.50	67.50
a.		"INDO-CHINE" inverted	47,500.	
15	A3	1fr brnz grn, *straw*	67.50	67.50
16	A3	5fr red lil, *lav*	135.00	135.00
		Nos. 1-16 (16)	785.75	785.75

Many varieties of the surcharge exist.

Stamps of Indo-China
1892-1906, Surcharged
in Red or Black

1906				
17	A4	1c ol grn (R)	8.50	8.50
18	A4	2c vio brn, *buff*	8.50	8.50
19	A4	4c cl, *bluish* (R)	8.50	8.50
20	A4	5c dp grn (R)	8.50	8.50
21	A4	10c carmine	8.50	8.50
22	A4	15c org brn, *bl*	32.50	32.50
23	A4	20c red, *grn*	13.50	13.50
24	A4	25c deep blue	11.00	11.00
25	A4	30c pale brn	13.50	13.50
26	A4	35c blk, *yel* (R)	21.00	21.00
27	A4	40c blk, *bluish*(R)	21.00	21.00
28	A4	50c bister brn	21.00	21.00
29	A3	75c dp vio, *org* (R)	67.50	67.50
30	A4	1fr pale grn	42.50	42.50
31	A4	2fr brn, *org*(R)	55.00	55.00
32	A3	5fr red lil, *lav*	140.00	140.00
33	A4	10fr org brn, *grn*	150.00	150.00
		Nos. 17-33 (17)	631.00	631.00

Various surcharge varieties exist on #17-24.

Stamps of Indo-China, 1907,
Surcharged "PAKHOI" and Value in
Chinese in Red or Blue

1908				
34	A5	1c ol brn & blk	1.25	1.25
35	A5	2c brn & blk	1.25	1.25
36	A5	4c bl & blk	1.25	1.25
37	A5	5c grn & blk	1.70	1.70
38	A5	10c red & blk (Bl)	1.70	1.70
39	A5	15c vio & blk	2.10	2.10
40	A6	20c vio & blk	2.50	2.50
41	A6	25c bl & blk	3.00	3.00
42	A6	30c brn & blk	3.40	3.40
43	A6	35c ol grn & blk	3.40	3.40
44	A6	40c brn & blk	3.40	3.40
45	A6	50c car & blk (Bl)	3.40	3.40
46	A7	75c ver & blk (Bl)	7.25	7.25
47	A8	1fr car & blk (Bl)	7.50	7.50
48	A9	2fr grn & blk	16.00	16.00

50	A10	5fr bl & blk	85.00	85.00
51	A11	10fr pur & blk	150.00	150.00
		Nos. 34-51 (17)	294.10	294.10

The Chinese characters overprinted on Nos. 1 to 51 repeat the denomination of the basic stamps.

Nos. 34-51 Surcharged with New
Values in Cents or Piasters in Black,
Red or Blue

1919				
52	A5	⅖c on 1c	1.25	1.25
a.		"PAK-HOI" and Chinese double	170.00	
53	A5	⅖c on 2c	1.25	1.25
54	A5	1⅗c on 4c (R)	1.25	1.25
55	A5	2c on 5c	2.50	2.50
56	A5	4c on 10c (Bl)	3.40	3.40
57	A6	6c on 15c	1.70	1.70
58	A6	8c on 20c	3.40	3.40
59	A6	10c on 25c	5.00	5.00
60	A6	12c on 30c	1.70	1.70
61	A6	14c on 35c	1.25	1.25
a.		Closed "4"	14.50	14.50
62	A6	16c on 40c	3.00	3.00
64	A6	20c on 50c (Bl)	2.10	2.10
65	A7	30c on 75c (Bl)	9.25	9.25
66	A8	40c on 1fr (Bl)	12.50	12.50
67	A9	80c on 2fr (R)	10.00	10.00
68	A10	2pi on 5fr (R)	16.00	16.00
69	A11	4pi on 10fr (R)	35.00	35.00
		Nos. 52-69 (17)	110.55	110.55

TCHONGKING (CHUNGKING)

Stamps of Indo-China
Surcharged in Black

1903-04		**Unwmk.**	**Perf. 14x13½**	
1	A3	1c blk, *lil bl*	5.00	5.00
2	A3	2c brn, *buff*	5.00	5.00
3	A3	4c claret, *lav*	6.00	6.00
4	A3	5c yel grn	6.00	6.00
5	A3	10c red	6.00	6.00
6	A3	15c gray	6.00	6.00
7	A3	20c red, *grn*	8.50	8.50
8	A3	25c blue	55.00	55.00
9	A3	25c blk, *rose* ('04)	10.00	10.00
10	A3	30c brn, *bister*	15.00	15.00
11	A3	40c red, *straw*	62.50	62.50
12	A3	50c car, *rose*	225.00	225.00
13	A3	50c brn, *az* ('04)	140.00	140.00
14	A3	75c vio, *org*	45.00	45.00
15	A3	1fr brnz grn, *straw*	60.00	60.00
16	A3	5fr red lil, *lav*	105.00	105.00
		Nos. 1-16 (16)	760.00	760.00

Many surcharge varieties exist on #1-14.
Stamps of Indo-China and French China, issued in 1902 with similar overprint, but without Chinese characters, were not officially authorized.

Stamps of Indo-China,
1892-1906, Surcharged
in Red or Black

1906				
17	A4	1c ol grn (R)	8.50	8.50
18	A4	2c vio brn (R)	8.50	8.50
19	A4	4c cl, *bluish* (R)	8.50	8.50
20	A4	5c dp grn (R)	8.50	8.50
21	A4	10c carmine	8.50	8.50
22	A4	15c org brn, *bl*	32.50	32.50
23	A4	20c red, *grn*	13.50	13.50
24	A4	25c deep blue	11.00	11.00
25	A4	30c pale brn	13.50	13.50
26	A4	35c blk, *yellow* (R)	21.00	21.00
27	A4	40c blk, *bluish* (R)	21.00	21.00
28	A4	50c bis brn	25.00	25.00
29	A3	75c dp vio, *org* (R)	67.50	67.50
30	A4	1fr pale grn	42.50	42.50
31	A4	2fr brn, *org* (R)	55.00	55.00
32	A3	5fr red lil, *lav*	140.00	140.00
33	A4	10fr org brn, *grn*	150.00	150.00
		Nos. 17-33 (17)	635.00	635.00

Variety "T" omitted in surcharge occurs once in each sheet of Nos. 17-33. Other surcharge varieties exist, such as inverted surcharge on 1c and 2c.

Stamps of Indo-China, 1907,
Surcharged "TCHONGKING" and
Value in Chinese in Red or Blue

1908				
34	A5	1c ol brn & blk	.85	.85
35	A5	2c brn & blk	.85	.85
36	A5	4c bl & blk	1.25	1.25
37	A5	5c grn & blk	2.10	2.10
38	A5	10c red & blk (Bl)	2.10	2.10
39	A5	15c vio & blk	3.00	3.00
40	A6	20c vio & blk	3.00	3.00
41	A6	25c bl & blk	5.50	5.50
42	A6	30c brn & blk	3.40	3.40
43	A6	35c ol grn & blk	7.50	7.50
44	A6	40c brn & blk	15.00	15.00
45	A6	50c car & blk (Bl)	12.00	12.00
46	A7	75c ver & blk (Bl)	10.00	10.00
47	A8	1fr car & blk (Bl)	13.50	13.50
48	A9	2fr grn & blk	85.00	85.00
49	A10	5fr bl & blk	37.50	37.50
50	A11	10fr pur & blk	225.00	225.00
		Nos. 34-50 (17)	427.55	427.55

The Chinese characters overprinted on Nos. 1 to 50 repeat the denomination of the basic stamp.

Nos. 34-50 Surcharged with New
Values in Cents or Piasters in Black,
Red or Blue

1919				
51	A5	⅖c on 1c	1.25	1.25
52	A5	⅖c on 2c	1.25	1.25
53	A5	1⅗c on 4c (R)	1.25	1.25
54	A5	2c on 5c	1.70	1.70
55	A5	4c on 10c (Bl)	1.25	1.25
56	A5	6c on 15c	1.70	1.70
57	A6	8c on 20c	3.00	1.25
58	A6	10c on 25c	8.50	8.50
59	A6	12c on 30c	3.00	1.25
60	A6	14c on 35c	2.10	1.70
a.		Closed "4"	35.00	35.00
61	A6	16c on 40c	2.10	1.70
a.		"16 CENTS" double	125.00	125.00
62	A6	20c on 50c (Bl)	11.00	10.00
63	A7	30c on 75c (Bl)	9.25	6.75
64	A8	40c on 1fr (Bl)	9.25	6.75
65	A9	80c on 2fr (R)	9.25	6.75
66	A10	2pi on 5fr (R)	9.25	9.25
67	A11	4pi on 10fr (R)	17.50	17.50
		Nos. 51-67 (17)	92.60	79.80

YUNNAN FOU

(Formerly Yunnan Sen, later known as Kunming)

Stamps of Indo-China
Surcharged in Black

1903-04		**Unwmk.**	**Perf. 14x13½**	
1	A3	1c blk, *lil bl*	6.75	6.75
2	A3	2c brn, *buff*	6.75	6.75
3	A3	4c claret, *lav*	7.50	7.50
4	A3	5c yel green	6.75	6.75
5	A3	10c red	7.50	7.50
6	A3	15c gray	7.50	7.50
7	A3	20c red, *grn*	12.50	12.50
8	A3	25c blue	7.50	7.50
9	A3	30c brn, *bister*	12.50	12.50
10	A3	40c red, *straw*	75.00	60.00
11	A3	50c car, *rose*	350.00	350.00
12	A3	50c brn, *az* ('04)	180.00	180.00
13	A3	75c dp vio, *org*	67.50	62.50
a.		"INDO-CHINE" inverted	47,500.	
14	A3	1fr brnz grn, *straw*	67.50	62.50
15	A3	5fr red lil, *lav*	125.00	125.00
		Nos. 1-15 (15)	940.25	915.25

The Chinese characters overprinted on Nos. 1 to 15 repeat the denomination of the basic stamp.

Many varieties of the surcharge exist.

Stamps of Indo-China,
1892-1906, Surcharged
in Red or Black

1906		**Unwmk.**	**Perf. 14x13½**	
17	A4	1c ol grn (R)	5.00	5.00
18	A4	2c vio brn, *buff*	5.00	5.00
19	A4	4c cl, *bluish* (R)	5.00	5.00
20	A4	5c dp grn (R)	5.00	5.00
21	A4	10c carmine	5.00	5.00
22	A4	15c org brn, *bl*	35.00	35.00
23	A4	20c red, *grn*	13.50	13.50
24	A4	25c deep blue	11.00	11.00
25	A4	30c pale brn	13.50	13.50
26	A4	35c blk, *yel* (R)	17.00	17.00
27	A4	40c blk, *bluish* (R)	17.00	17.00

28	A4	50c bister brn	21.00	21.00
29	A3	75c dp vio, *org* (R)	67.50	67.50
30	A4	1fr pale grn	42.50	42.50
31	A4	2fr brn, *org* (R)	55.00	55.00
32	A3	5fr red lil, *lav*	140.00	140.00
33	A4	10fr org brn, *grn*	150.00	150.00
		Nos. 17-33 (17)	608.00	608.00

Various varieties of the surcharge exist on Nos. 18, 20, 21 and 27.

Stamps of Indo-China, 1907, Surcharged "YUNNANFOU," and Value in Chinese in Red or Blue

1908

34	A5	1c ol brn & blk	1.25	1.25
35	A5	2c brn & blk	1.25	1.25
36	A5	4c bl & blk	2.10	2.10
37	A5	5c grn & blk	3.00	3.00
38	A5	10c red & blk (Bl)	3.00	3.00
39	A5	15c vio & blk	6.75	6.75
40	A6	20c vio & blk	6.25	6.25
41	A6	25c bl & blk	9.25	9.25
42	A6	30c brn & blk	7.50	7.50
43	A6	35c ol grn & blk	7.50	7.50
44	A6	40c brn & blk	8.50	8.50
45	A6	50c car & blk (Bl)	9.25	9.25
46	A7	75c ver & blk (Bl)	11.00	11.00
47	A8	1fr car & blk (Bl)	17.00	17.00
48	A9	2fr car & blk	29.00	29.00
a.		"YUNNANFOU"	2,500.	2,500.
49	A10	5fr bl & blk	60.00	60.00
a.		"YUNNANFOU"	2,500.	2,500.
50	A11	10fr pur & blk	120.00	120.00
a.		"YUNNANFOU"	2,500.	2,500.
		Nos. 34-50 (17)	302.60	302.60

The Chinese characters overprinted on Nos. 17-50 repeat the denomination of the basic stamp.

Nos. 34-50 Surcharged with New Values in Cents or Piasters in Black, Red or Blue

1919

51	A5	⅖c on 1c	1.25	1.25
a.		New value double	140.00	
52	A5	⅘c on 2c	1.25	1.25
53	A5	1⅗c on 4c (R)	1.25	1.25
54	A5	2c on 5c	2.10	2.10
a.		Triple surcharge	210.00	
55	A5	4c on 10c (Bl)	1.70	1.70
56	A5	6c on 15c	3.00	3.00
57	A6	8c on 20c	2.10	2.10
58	A6	10c on 25c	3.75	3.75
59	A6	12c on 30c	9.25	9.25
60	A6	14c on 35c	14.50	14.50
a.		Closed "4"	140.00	140.00
61	A6	16c on 40c	9.25	9.25
62	A6	20c on 50c (Bl)	3.00	3.00
63	A7	30c on 75c (Bl)	9.25	9.25
64	A8	40c on 1fr (Bl)	35.00	35.00
65	A9	80c on 2fr (R)	14.50	14.50
a.		Triple surch., one inverted	250.00	
66	A10	2pi on 5fr (R)	67.50	67.50
67	A11	4pi on 10fr (R)	35.00	35.00
		Nos. 51-67 (17)	213.65	213.65

OFFICES IN CRETE

Austria, France, Italy and Great Britain maintained their own post offices in Crete during the period when that country was an autonomous state.

100 Centimes = 1 Franc

Liberty, Equality and Fraternity
A1

"Rights of Man"
A2

Liberty and Peace (Symbolized by Olive Branch) — A3

Perf. 14x13½

1902-03   Unwmk.   Typo.

1	A1	1c gray	2.50	2.50
2	A1	2c violet brown	2.50	2.50
3	A1	3c red orange	2.50	2.50
4	A1	4c yellow brown	2.50	2.50
5	A1	5c green	2.50	2.50
6	A2	10c rose red	3.00	2.50
7	A2	15c pale red ('03)	4.25	3.00
8	A2	20c brown vio ('03)	6.75	3.75
9	A2	25c blue ('03)	6.75	4.25
10	A2	30c lilac ('03)	6.25	4.25
11	A3	40c red & pale bl	12.50	11.00

12	A3	50c bis brn & lav	17.00	12.50
13	A3	1fr claret & ol grn	24.00	22.00
14	A3	2fr gray vio & yel	37.50	35.00
15	A3	5fr dk blue & buff	62.50	55.00
		Nos. 1-15 (15)	191.25	165.75

A4

A5

Black Surcharge

1903

16	A4	1pi on 25c blue	55.00	45.00
17	A5	2pi on 50c bis brn & lav	72.50	55.00
18	A5	4pi on 1fr claret & ol grn	110.00	97.50
19	A5	8pi on 2fr gray vio & yel	135.00	135.00
20	A5	20pi on 5fr dk bl & buff	225.00	215.00
		Nos. 16-20 (5)	597.50	547.50

OFFICES IN EGYPT

French post offices formerly maintained in Alexandria and Port Said.

100 Centimes = 1 Franc

ALEXANDRIA

Stamps of France Overprinted in Red, Blue or Black

1899-1900   Unwmk.   Perf. 14x13½

1	A15	1c blk, *lil bl* (R)	2.10	2.10
a.		Double overprint	150.00	
b.		Triple overprint	180.00	
2	A15	2c brn, *buff* (Bl)	3.25	2.50
3	A15	3c gray, *grysh* (Bl)	3.25	2.50
4	A15	4c cl, *lav* (Bl)	4.25	3.25
5	A15	5c yel grn, (I) (R)	6.00	3.25
a.		Type II (R)	160.00	97.50
6	A15	10c blk, *lav*, (I) (R)	9.25	7.50
a.		Type II (R)	62.50	37.50
7	A15	15c blue (R)	9.25	4.25
8	A15	20c red, *grn*	14.50	7.50
a.		Double overprint		
9	A15	25c blk, *rose* (R)	7.50	4.25
a.		Inverted overprint	97.50	
b.		Double ovpt., one invtd.	160.00	
10	A15	30c brn, *bis*	15.00	12.00
11	A15	40c red, *straw*	13.50	13.50
12	A15	50c car, *rose* (II)	35.00	17.50
		Type I	100.00	27.50
13	A15	1fr brnz grn, *straw*	32.50	22.50
14	A15	2fr brn, *az* ('00)	82.50	80.00
15	A15	5fr red lil, *lav*	120.00	110.00
		Nos. 1-15 (15)	357.85	292.60

A2

A3

A4

1902-13

16	A2	1c gray	.75	.60
17	A2	2c violet brn	.75	.75
18	A2	3c red orange	.75	.75
19	A2	4c yellow brn	1.00	.85
20	A2	5c green	5.00	4.25
21	A3	10c rose red	1.50	.75
22	A3	15c orange ('13)	1.75	1.25
a.		15c pale red ('03)	4.75	1.60
23	A3	20c brn vio ('03)	3.00	1.50
24	A3	25c blue ('03)	1.75	.75
25	A3	30c violet ('03)	7.50	4.25
26	A4	40c red & pale bl	5.00	2.50
27	A4	50c bis brn & lav	11.00	3.00
28	A4	1fr cl & ol grn	10.00	4.25

29	A4	2fr gray vio & yel	24.00	12.00
30	A4	5fr dk bl & buff	29.00	17.00
		Nos. 16-30 (15)	102.75	54.45

The 2c, 5c, 10c, 20c and 25c exist imperf. Value, each $55.

See #77-86. For surcharges see #31-73, B1-B4.

Stamps of 1902-03 Surcharged Locally in Black

1921

31	A2	2m on 5c green	7.50	5.00
32	A2	3m on 3c red org	14.50	12.00
a.		Larger numeral	140.00	125.00
33	A3	4m on 10c rose	6.75	6.00
34	A2	4m on 1c dk gray	14.50	12.00
35	A2	5m on 4c yel brn	19.00	13.50
36	A3	6m on 15c orange	6.75	6.00
a.		Larger numeral	110.00	110.00
37	A3	8m on 20c brn vio	7.50	6.00
a.		Larger numeral	80.00	60.00
38	A3	10m on 25c blue	4.25	4.25
a.		Inverted surcharge	45.00	45.00
b.		Double surcharge	45.00	45.00
39	A3	12m on 30c vio	17.50	17.50
40	A2	15m on 2c vio brn	14.50	14.50

Nos. 26-30 Surcharged

41	A4	15m on 40c	25.00	19.00
42	A4	15m on 50c	12.00	12.00
43	A4	30m on 1fr	175.00	175.00
44	A4	60m on 2fr	250.00	250.00
a.		Larger numeral	1,050.	1,050.
45	A4	15m on 5fr	350.00	350.00

Port Said Nos. 20 and 19 Surcharged like Nos. 32 and 40

45A	A2	3m on 3c red org	150.00	150.00
46	A2	15m on 2c vio brn	150.00	150.00
		Nos. 31-46 (17)	1,224.	1,202.

Alexandria No. 28 Surcharged

1921

46A	A4	30m on 15m on 1fr	1,200.	1,350.

The surcharge "15 Mill." was made in error and is canceled by a bar.

The surcharges were lithographed on Nos. 31, 33, 38, 39 and 42 and typographed on the other stamps of the 1921 issue. Nos. 34, 36 and 37 were surcharged by both methods.

Alexandria Stamps of 1902-03 Surcharged in Paris

1921-23

47	A2	1m on 1c gray	3.25	2.50
48	A2	2m on 5c green	2.25	1.90
49	A3	4m on 10c rose	2.75	2.50
50	A3	4m on 10c green ('23)	2.50	2.50
51	A2	5m on 3c red org ('23)	6.75	5.00
52	A3	6m on 15c orange	2.25	1.90
53	A3	8m on 20c brn vio	2.25	1.25
54	A3	10m on 25c blue	1.40	1.25
55	A3	10m on 30c vio	4.25	3.25
56	A3	15m on 50c bl ('23)	3.25	3.00

Nos. 27-30 and Type of 1902 Surcharged

57	A4	15m on 50c	5.00	3.25
58	A4	30m on 1fr	4.25	3.00
59	A4	60m on 2fr	2,250.	2,400.

60	A4	60m on 2fr org & pale bl ('23)	13.50	13.00
61	A4	150m on 5fr	13.50	13.00
		Nos. 47-58,60-61 (14)	67.15	52.80

Stamps and Types of 1902-03 Surcharged with New Values and Bars in Black

1925

62	A2	1m on 1c gray	1.25	1.25
63	A2	2m on 5c orange	1.25	1.25
64	A2	2m on 5c green	1.75	1.75
65	A3	4m on 10c green	1.10	.85
66	A3	5m on 3c red org	1.50	1.25
67	A3	6m on 15c orange	1.40	1.25
68	A3	8m on 20c brn vio	1.75	1.40
69	A3	10m on 25c blue	1.10	1.00
70	A3	15m on 50c blue	2.40	1.40
71	A4	30m on 1fr cl & ol grn	3.50	2.90
72	A4	60m on 2fr org & pale bl	4.25	3.50
73	A4	150m on 5fr dk bl & buff	6.00	6.00
		Nos. 62-73 (12)	27.25	22.80

Types of 1902-03 Issue

1927-28

77	A2	3m orange ('28)	2.50	2.10
81	A3	15m slate blue	2.50	2.10
82	A3	20m rose lil ('28)	6.75	5.00
84	A4	50m blue	11.00	9.35
85	A4	100m sl bl & buff	15.00	12.00
86	A4	250m gray grn & red	25.00	16.00
		Nos. 77-86 (6)	62.75	46.55

SEMI-POSTAL STAMPS

Stamps and Types of 1902-03 Surcharged in Black Regular Issue of 1902-03 Surcharged in Carmine

1915   Unwmk.   Perf. 14x13½

B1	A3	10c + 5c rose	1.25	1.25

Sinking Fund Issue

Type of 1902-03 Issue Surcharged in Blue or Black

1927-30

B2	A3	15m + 5m deep org	6.00	6.00
B3	A3	15m + 5m red vio ('28)	9.25	9.25
a.		15m + 5m violet ('30)	15.00	15.00

Type of 1902-03 Issue Surcharged as in 1927-28

1929

B4	A3	15m + 5m fawn	12.00	12.00

POSTAGE DUE STAMPS

Postage Due Stamps of France, 1893-1920, Surcharged in Paris in Black

1922   Unwmk.   Perf. 14x13½

J1	D2	2m on 5c blue	2.50	2.50
J2	D2	4m on 10c brown	2.50	2.50
J3	D2	10m on 30c rose red	3.00	3.00
J4	D2	15m on 50c brn vio	3.25	3.25
J5	D2	30m on 1fr red brn, *straw*	4.50	4.50
		Nos. J1-J5 (5)	15.75	15.75

D3

1928   **Typo.**

J6	D3	1m slate	1.60	1.60
J7	D3	2m light blue	1.25	1.25
J8	D3	4m lilac rose	1.75	1.75
J9	D3	5m gray green	2.00	2.00
J10	D3	10m light red	2.50	2.50
J11	D3	20m violet brn	2.25	2.25
J12	D3	30m green	5.00	5.00
J13	D3	40m lt violet	6.25	6.25
		Nos. J6-J13 (8)	22.60	22.60

#J6-J13 were also available for use in Port Said.

PORT SAID

Stamps of France Overprinted in Red, Blue or Black

1899-1900   Unwmk.   Perf. 14x13½

1	A15	1c blk, *lil bl* (R)	2.10	1.70
2	A15	2c brn, *buff* (bl)	2.10	1.70
3	A15	3c gray, *grysh* (Bl)	2.10	2.10
4	A15	4c claret, *lav* (Bl)	1.75	2.10
5	A15	5c yel grn (I) (R)	11.00	5.00
a.		Type II (R)	55.00	25.00
6	A15	10c blk, *lav* (I) (R)	14.00	12.50
a.		Type II (R)	72.50	55.00
7	A15	15c blue (R)	14.00	8.50
8	A15	20c red, *grn*	17.00	11.00
9	A15	25c blk, *rose* (R)	14.00	5.00
a.		Double overprint	300.00	
b.		Inverted overprint	300.00	
10	A15	30c brn, *bister*	17.00	14.00
a.		Inverted overprint	325.00	
11	A15	40c red, *straw*	14.00	14.00
12	A15	50c car, *rose* (II)	20.00	14.00
a.		Type I	300.00	100.00
b.		Double overprint (II)	425.00	
13	A15	1fr brnz grn, *straw*	30.00	17.50
14	A15	2fr brn, *az* ('00)	75.00	65.00
15	A15	5fr red lil, *lav*	120.00	92.50
		Nos. 1-15 (15)	354.05	266.60

Regular Issue Surcharged in Red

1899

16	A15	25c on 10c blk, *lav*	130.00	32.50
a.		Inverted surcharge		250.00

With Additional Surcharge "25" in Red

17	A15	25c on 10c blk, *lav*	475.00	160.00
a.		"25" inverted	1,500.	1,400.
b.		"25" in black		2,600.
c.		As "b," "VINGT CINQ" inverted		3,400.
d.		As "b," "25" vertical		3,400.
e.		As "c" and "d"		3,400.

A2   A3

A4

1902-03   **Typo.**

18	A2	1c gray	.65	.65
19	A2	2c violet brn	.75	.75
20	A2	3c red orange	.85	.75
21	A2	4c yellow brown	1.10	.90
22	A2	5c blue green	1.20	.85
a.		5c yellow green	5.00	3.00
23	A3	10c rose red	1.60	1.10
24	A3	15c pale red ('03)	3.25	2.25
a.		15c orange	5.00	3.00
25	A3	20c brn vio ('03)	3.25	2.25
26	A3	25c blue ('03)	2.50	1.60
27	A3	30c violet ('03)	6.75	5.00
28	A4	40c red & pale bl	6.00	4.25
29	A4	50c bis brn & lav	9.25	6.75

30	A4	1fr claret & ol grn	12.00	9.25
31	A4	2fr gray vio & yel	15.00	15.00
32	A4	5fr dk bl & buff	35.00	32.50
		Nos. 18-32 (15)	99.15	83.85

See #83-92. For surcharges see #33-80, B1-B4.

Stamps of 1902-03 Surcharged Locally

2 Millièmes

1921

33	A2	2m on 5c green	10.00	10.00
a.		Inverted surcharge	50.00	50.00
34	A3	4m on 10c rose	9.25	9.25
a.		Inverted surcharge	50.00	50.00
35	A2	5m on 1c	14.00	14.00
a.		Inverted surcharge	92.50	92.50
c.		Surcharged "2 Millièmes"	67.50	67.50
36	A2	5m on 2c	24.00	24.00
a.		Surcharged "2 Millièmes"	75.00	75.00
b.		As "a," inverted	160.00	160.00
37	A2	5m on 3c	15.00	15.00
a.		Inverted surcharge	62.50	62.50
b.		On Alexandria #18	400.00	400.00
38	A2	5m on 4c	11.00	11.00
a.		Inverted surcharge	80.00	80.00
39	A2	10m on 2c	25.00	25.00
40	A2	10m on 4c	35.00	35.00
a.		Inverted surcharge	85.00	85.00
41	A3	10m on 25c	9.25	9.25
a.		Inverted surcharge	85.00	85.00
42	A3	12m on 30c	42.50	42.50
43	A2	15m on 4c	10.00	10.00
a.		Inverted surcharge	85.00	85.00
44	A3	15m on 15c pale red	67.50	67.50
a.		Inverted surcharge	160.00	160.00
45	A3	15m on 20c	67.50	67.50
a.		Inverted surcharge	160.00	160.00
46	A4	30m on 50c	300.00	300.00
47	A4	60m on 50c	350.00	350.00
48	A4	150m on 50c	400.00	400.00

Nos. 46, 47 and 48 have a bar between the numerals and "Millièmes," which is in capital letters.

Same Surcharge on Stamps of French Offices in Turkey, 1902-03

49	A2	2m on 2c vio brn	160.00	160.00
50	A2	5m on 1c gray	150.00	150.00
a.		"5" inverted		7,250.
		Nos. 33-50 (18)	1,700.	1,700.

Nos. 28-32 Surcharged

15 MILLIÈMES

51	A4	15m on 40c	60.00	60.00
52	A4	15m on 50c	85.00	85.00
b.		Bar below 15	50.00	50.00
53	A4	30m on 1fr	300.00	300.00
54	A4	60m on 2fr	85.00	92.50
55	A4	150m on 5fr	250.00	275.00
		Nos. 51-55 (5)	780.00	812.50

Overprinted "MILLtEMES"

51a	A4	15m on 40c	425.00	425.00
52a	A4	15m on 50c	500.00	500.00
53a	A4	30m on 1fr	1,400.	1,400.
54a	A4	60m on 2fr	400.00	400.00
55a	A4	150m on 5fr	1,050.	1,050.
		Nos. 51a-55a (5)	3,775.	3,775.

Stamps of 1902-03 Surcharged in Paris

2 MILLIÈMES

1921-23

56	A2	1m on 1c gray	1.60	1.60
57	A2	2m on 5c green	1.60	1.60
58	A3	4m on 10c rose	2.50	2.50
59	A2	5m on 3c red org	9.25	9.25
60	A3	6m on 15c orange	3.25	3.25
a.		6m on 15c pale red	14.00	14.00
61	A3	8m on 20c brn vio	5.00	5.00
62	A3	10m on 25c blue	2.50	2.50
63	A3	10m on 30c violet	7.50	7.50
64	A3	15m on 50c blue	6.75	6.75

Nos. 29-32 and Type of 1902 Surcharged

15 MILLIÈMES

65	A4	15m on 50c	6.00	6.00
66	A4	30m on 1fr	9.25	9.25
67	A4	60m on 2fr	130.00	130.00
68	A4	60m on 2fr org & pale blue	12.50	12.50
69	A4	150m on 5fr	20.00	20.00
		Nos. 56-69 (14)	217.70	217.70

1 MILLIEME

Stamps and Types of 1902-03 Surcharged

1925

70	A2	1m on 1c gray	.75	.75
71	A2	2m on 5c green	1.10	1.10
72	A3	4m on 10c rose red	.90	.90
73	A2	5m on 3c red org	1.10	1.10
74	A3	6m on 15c orange	1.10	1.10
75	A3	8m on 20c brn vio	1.00	1.00
76	A3	10m on 25c blue	1.40	1.40
77	A3	15m on 50c blue	1.40	1.40
78	A4	30m on 1fr cl & ol grn	2.75	2.75
79	A4	60m on 2fr org & pale blue	2.50	2.50
80	A4	150m on 5fr dk bl & buff	4.25	4.25
		Nos. 70-80 (11)	18.45	18.45

Types of 1902-03 Issue

1927-28

83	A2	3m orange ('28)	2.10	2.10
87	A3	15m slate bl	2.50	2.50
88	A3	20m rose lil ('28)	2.50	2.50
90	A4	50m org & blue	4.50	4.50
91	A4	100m slate bl & buff	6.00	6.00
92	A4	250m gray grn & red	9.25	9.25
		Nos. 83-92 (6)	26.85	26.85

SEMI-POSTAL STAMPS

Regular Issue of 1902-03 Surcharged in Carmine

1915   Unwmk.   Perf. 14x13½

B1	A3	10c + 5c rose	1.60	1.60

Sinking Fund Issue

Type of 1902-03 Issue Surcharged like Alexandria Nos. B2-B3 in Blue or Black

1927-30

B2	A3	15m + 5m dp org (Bl)	5.00	5.00
B3	A3	15m + 5m red vio ('28)	8.50	8.50
a.		15m + 5m violet ('30)	14.00	14.00
B4	A3	15m + 5m fawn ('29)	10.00	10.00
		Nos. B2-B4 (3)	23.50	23.50

POSTAGE DUE STAMPS

Postage Due Stamps of France, 1893-1906, Surcharged Locally in Black

15 Millièmes

1921   Unwmk.   Perf. 14x13½

J1	D2	12m on 10c brown	62.50	67.50
J2	D2	15m on 5c blue	92.50	105.00
J3	D2	30m on 20c ol grn	92.50	105.00
a.		Inverted surcharge	1,100.	1,100.
J4	D2	30m on 50c red vio	3,000.	3,400.

Same Surcharged in Red or Blue

4 MILLIÈMES

1921

J5	D2	2m on 5c bl (R)	55.00	60.00
a.		Blue surcharge	300.00	300.00
J6	D2	4m on 10c brn (Bl)	62.50	62.50
a.		Surcharged "15 Millièmes"	725.00	725.00
J7	D2	10m on 30c red (Bl)	55.00	60.00
a.		Inverted surcharge	160.00	160.00
J8	D2	15m on 50c brn vio (Bl)	67.50	72.50
a.		Inverted surcharge	160.00	160.00
		Nos. J5-J8 (4)	232.50	255.00

Nos. J5-J8 exist with second "M" in "Millemes" inverted, also with final "S" omitted. Value, each $190-$225.

Alexandria Nos. J6-J13 were also available for use in Port Said.

OFFICES IN TURKEY (LEVANT)

Various powers maintained post offices in the Turkish Empire before World War I by authority of treaties which ended with the signing of the Treaty of Lausanne in 1923. The foreign post offices were closed Oct. 27, 1923.

100 Centimes = 1 Franc

25 Centimes = 40 Paras = 1 Piaster

Stamps of France Surcharged in Black or Red

1885-1901   Unwmk.   Perf. 14x13½

1	A15	1pi on 25c yel, *straw*	550.00	16.00
a.		Inverted surcharge	2,500.	2,400.
2	A15	1pi on 25c blk, *rose* (R) ('86)	4.25	1.25
a.		Inverted surcharge	400.00	325.00
3	A15	2pi on 50c car, *rose* (II) ('90)	18.00	3.00
a.		Type I ('01)	375.00	50.00
4	A15	3pi on 75c car, *rose*	30.00	15.00
5	A15	4pi on 1fr brnz grn, *straw*	30.00	15.00
6	A15	8pi on 2fr brn, *az* ('00)	37.50	25.00
7	A15	20pi on 5fr red lil, *lav* ('90)	110.00	60.00
		Nos. 1-7 (7)	779.75	135.25

A2   A3

A4

A5

A6

1902-07   Typo.   Perf. 14x13½

21	A2	1c gray	.65	.65
22	A2	2c vio brn	.65	.65
23	A2	3c red org	.65	.65
24	A2	4c yel brn	3.00	1.10
a.		Imperf., pair	90.00	
25	A2	5c grn ('06)	1.00	.65
26	A3	10c rose red	1.00	.65
27	A3	15c pale red ('03)	3.00	1.45

28	A3	20c brn vio ('03)	3.25	2.00
29	A3	25c blue ('07)	45.00	60.00
a.		Imperf., pair	425.00	
30	A3	30c lilac ('03)	6.00	3.00
31	A4	40c red & pale bl	6.00	3.25
32	A4	50c bis brn & lav ('07)	190.00	225.00
a.		Imperf., pair	925.00	
33	A4	1fr claret & ol grn ('07)	425.00	450.00
a.		Imperf., pair	1,100.	

Black Surcharge

34	A5	1pi on 25c bl ('03)	1.20	.65
a.		Second "I" omitted	32.50	25.00
b.		Double surcharge	72.50	60.00
35	A6	2pi on 50c bis brn & lavender	4.25	1.60
36	A6	4pi on 1fr cl & ol grn	5.00	2.10
a.		Imperf., pair	750.00	
37	A6	8pi on 2fr gray vio & yel	20.00	15.00
38	A6	20pi on 5fr dk bl & buff	10.00	6.00
		Nos. 21-38 (18)	725.65	774.20

Nos. 29, 32-33 were used during the early part of 1907 in the French Offices at Harar and Diredawa, Ethiopia. Djibouti and Port Said stamps were also used.

No. 27 Surcharged in Green

1905

| 39 | A3 | 1pi on 15c pale red | 2,100. | 325. |
| a. | | "Piastte" | 6,500. | 1,450. |

Stamps of France 1900-21 Surcharged:

On A22

On A20

On A18

1921-22

40	A22	30pa on 5c grn	1.00	1.00
41	A22	30pa on 5c org	1.00	.85
42	A22	1pi20pa on 10c red	1.10	1.10
43	A22	1pi20pa on 10c grn	1.10	.85
44	A22	3pi30pa on 25c bl	1.60	1.00
45	A22	4pi20pa on 30c org	1.60	1.10
a.		"4" omitted	1,050.	
46	A22	7pi20pa on 50c bl	1.60	1.25
47	A18	15pi on 1fr car & ol grn	3.00	2.10
48	A18	30pi on 2fr org & pale bl	12.50	10.00
49	A18	75pi on 5fr dk bl & buff	11.00	7.50
		Nos. 40-49 (10)	35.50	26.75

Stamps of France, 1903-07, Handstamped

1923

52	A22	1pi20pa on 10c red	62.50	60.00
54	A20	3pi30pa on 15c gray grn	25.00	25.00
55	A22	7pi20pa on 35c vio	30.00	30.00
a.		1pi20pa on 35c violet	1,400.	1,400.
		Nos. 52-55 (3)	117.50	115.00

CAVALLE (CAVALLA)

Stamps of France Overprinted or Surcharged in Red, Blue or Black

1893-1900   Unwmk.   Perf. 14x13½

1	A15	5c grn, grnsh (R)	25.00	21.00
2	A15	5c yel grn (I) ('00) (R)	21.00	20.00
3	A15	10c blk, lav (II)	40.00	24.00
a.		10c black, lavender (I)	160.00	130.00
4	A15	15c blue (R)	45.00	27.50
5	A15	1pi on 25c blk, rose	27.50	19.00
6	A15	2pi on 50c car, rose	87.50	60.00
7	A15	4pi on 1fr brnz grn, straw (R)	87.50	80.00
8	A15	8pi on 2fr brn, az ('00) (Bk)	110.00	110.00
		Nos. 1-8 (8)	443.50	361.50

A3   A4

A5

A6

1902-03

9	A3	5c green	2.00	1.60
10	A4	10c rose red ('03)	2.00	1.60
11	A4	15c orange	2.40	1.60
a.		15c pale red ('03)	11.00	11.00

Surcharged in Black

12	A5	1pi on 25c bl	4.25	2.40
13	A6	2pi on 50c bis brn & lav	12.00	6.75
14	A6	4pi on 1fr cl & ol grn	15.00	12.00
15	A6	8pi on 2fr gray vio & yel	20.00	18.00
		Nos. 9-15 (7)	57.65	43.95

DEDEAGH (DEDEAGATCH)

Stamps of France Overprinted or Surcharged in Red, Blue or Black

1893-1900   Unwmk.   Perf. 14x13½

1	A15	5c grn, grnsh (II) (R)	16.00	14.00
2	A15	5c yel grn (I) ('00) (R)	14.00	14.00
3	A15	10c blk, lav (II)	25.00	19.00
a.		Type I	42.50	29.00
4	A15	15c blue (R)	32.50	29.00
5	A15	1pi on 25c blk, rose	37.50	32.50
6	A15	2pi on 50c car, rose	62.50	45.00
7	A15	4pi on 1fr brnz grn, straw (R)	75.00	67.50
8	A15	8pi on 2fr brn, az ('00) (Bk)	110.00	92.50
		Nos. 1-8 (8)	372.50	313.50

A3   A4

A5

A6

1902-03

9	A3	5c green	3.00	2.50
10	A4	10c rose red ('03)	3.00	2.50
11	A4	15c orange	6.00	5.00

Black Surcharge

15	A5	1pi on 25c bl ('03)	3.25	2.50
16	A6	2pi on 50c bis brn & lav	11.00	9.25
a.		Double surcharge	275.00	
17	A6	4pi on 1fr cl & ol grn	20.00	16.00
18	A6	8pi on 2fr gray vio & yel	30.00	25.00
		Nos. 9-18 (7)	76.25	62.75

PORT LAGOS

Stamps of France Overprinted or Surcharged in Red or Blue

1893   Unwmk.   Perf. 14x13½

1	A15	5c grn, grnsh (R)	30.00	30.00
2	A15	10c blk, lav	60.00	45.00
3	A15	15c blue (R)	85.00	67.50
4	A15	1pi on 25c blk, rose	70.00	55.00
5	A15	2pi on 50c car, rose	175.00	92.50
6	A15	4pi on 1fr brnz grn, straw (R)	110.00	92.50
		Nos. 1-6 (6)	530.00	382.50

VATHY (SAMOS)

Stamps of France Overprinted or Surcharged in Red, Blue or Black

1894-1900   Unwmk.   Perf. 14x13½

1	A15	5c grn, grnsh (R)	8.50	7.50
2	A15	5c yel grn (I) ('00) (R)	8.50	7.50
a.		Type II	80.00	80.00
3	A15	10c blk, lav (I)	16.00	13.00
a.		Type II	50.00	42.50
4	A15	15c blue (R)	16.00	15.00
5	A15	1pi on 25c blk, rose	16.00	11.00
6	A15	2pi on 50c car, rose	29.00	25.00
7	A15	4pi on 1fr brnz grn, straw (R)	37.50	32.50
8	A15	8pi on 2fr brn, az ('00) (Bk)	70.00	70.00
9	A15	20pi on 5fr lil, lav ('00) (Bk)	100.00	100.00
		Nos. 1-9 (9)	301.50	281.50

OFFICES IN ZANZIBAR

Until 1906 France maintained post offices in the Sultanate of Zanzibar, but in that year Great Britain assumed direct control over this protectorate and the French withdrew their postal system.

16 Annas = 1 Rupee

Stamps of France Surcharged in Red, Carmine, Blue or Black

1894-96   Unwmk.   Perf. 14x13½

1	A15	½a on 5c grn, grnsh	10.00	7.50
2	A15	1a on 10c blk, lav (Bl)	15.00	12.50
3	A15	1½a on 15c bl ('96)	22.50	21.00
a.		"ANNAS"	100.00	92.50
4	A15	2a on 20c red, grn ('96) (Bk)	19.00	15.00
a.		"ANNA"	2,300.	2,300.
5	A15	2½a on 25c blk, rose (Bl)	12.50	9.25
a.		Double surcharge	250.00	250.00
6	A15	3a on 30c brn, bis ('96) (Bk)	21.00	18.00
7	A15	4a on 40c red, straw ('96) (Bk)	29.00	25.00
8	A15	5a on 50c car, rose (Bl)	37.50	32.50
9	A15	7½a on 75c vio, org ('96)	500.00	400.00
10	A15	10a on 1fr brnz grn, straw	67.50	55.00
11	A15	50a on 5fr red lil, lav ('96) (Bk)	325.00	260.00
		Nos. 1-11 (11)	1,059.	855.75

1894

12	A15	½a & 5c on 1c blk, lil bl (R)	200.00	220.00
13	A15	1a & 10c on 3c gray, grysh (R)	180.00	200.00
14	A15	2½a & 25c on 4c cl, lav (Bk)	230.00	275.00
15	A15	5a & 50c on 20c red, grn (Bk)	250.00	275.00
16	A15	10a & 1fr on 40c red, straw (Bk)	475.00	525.00
		Nos. 12-16 (5)	1,335.	1,495.

There are two distinct types of the figures 5c, four of the 25c and three of each of the others of this series.

Stamps of France Surcharged in Red, Carmine, Blue or Black

1896-1900

17	A15	½a on 5c grn, grnsh (R)	11.00	8.50
18	A15	½a on 5c yel grn (I) (R)	7.50	6.75
a.		Type II	9.25	7.50
19	A15	1a on 10c blk, lav (II) (Bl)	9.25	7.50
a.		Type I	22.50	19.00
20	A15	1½a on 15c bl (R)	11.00	9.25
21	A15	2a on 20c red, grn	9.25	9.25
a.		"ZANZIBAR" double	210.00	210.00
b.		"ZANZIBAR" triple	210.00	210.00
22	A15	2½a on 25c blk, rose (Bl)	11.00	9.25
a.		Inverted surcharge	275.00	210.00
23	A15	3a on 30c brn, bis	11.00	9.00
24	A15	4a on 40c red, straw	13.50	10.00
25	A15	5a on 50c rose, rose (II) (Bl)	45.00	32.50
a.		Type I	125.00	100.00

26	A15	10a on 1fr brnz grn, *straw* (R)	29.00	25.00
27	A15	20a on 2fr brn, *az*	35.00	29.00
a.		"ZANZIBAS"	675.00	750.00
b.		"ZANZIBAS" triple	1,600.	
28	A15	50a on 5fr lil, *lav*	67.50	62.50
a.		"ZANZIBAS"	9,250.	
		Nos. 17-28 (12)	260.00	218.75

For surcharges see Nos. 50-54.

A4   A5

1897

29	A4	2½a & 25c on ½a on 5c grn, *grnsh*	1,300.	240.
30	A4	2½a & 25c on 1a on 10c *lav*	4,500.	1,100.
31	A4	2½a & 25c on 1½a on 15c blue	4,400.	950.
32	A5	5a & 50c on 3a on 30c brn, *bis*	4,400.	950.
33	A5	5a & 50c on 4a on 40c red, *straw*	4,500.	1,300.

A6   A7

Printed on the Margins of Sheets of French Stamps
Perf. 14x13½ on one or more sides
1897

34	A6	2½a & 25c grn, *grnsh*	1,300.
35	A6	2½a & 25c blk, *lav*	4,000.
36	A6	2½a & 25c blue	3,000.
37	A7	5a & 50c brn, *bis*	2,900.
38	A7	5a & 50c red, *straw*	4,000.

There are 5 varieties of figures in the above surcharges.

A8   A9

A10

Surcharged in Red or Black

1902-03			*Perf. 14x13½*	
39	A8	½a on 5c grn (R)	6.75	6.00
40	A9	1a on 10c rose red ('03)	7.50	7.50
41	A9	1½a on 15c pale red ('03)	15.00	14.00
42	A9	2a on 20c brn vio ('03)	18.00	15.00
43	A9	2½a on 25c bl ('03)	18.00	15.00
44	A9	3a on 30c lil ('03)	13.00	13.00
a.		5a on 30c (error)	325.00	375.00
45	A10	4a on 40c red & pale bl	30.00	25.00
46	A10	5a on 50c bis brn & lav	25.00	21.00
47	A10	10a on 1fr cl & ol grn	32.50	29.00
48	A10	20a on 2fr gray vio & yel	85.00	75.00
49	A10	50a on 5fr dk bl & buff	100.00	92.50
		Nos. 39-49 (11)	350.75	313.00

For see Reunion Nos. 55-59.

Nos. 23-24 Surcharged in Black:

a   b

c

1904

50	A15	25c & 2½a on 4a on 40c		1,000.
51	A15	50c & 5a on 3a on 30c		1,200.
52	A15	50c & 5a on 4a on 40c	6,500.	1,200.
53	A15	1fr & 10a on 3a on 30c		2,000.
54	A15	1fr & 10a on 4a on 40c		2,000.

Nos. 39-40, 44 Surcharged in Red or Black:

d   e

f   g

55	A8	25c & 2a on ½a on 5c (R)	3,100.	140.00
56	A9	25c & 2½a on 1a on 10c	6,500.	150.00
a.		Inverted surcharge		1,500.
57	A9	25c & 2½a on 3a on 30c		2,400.
a.		Inverted surcharge		4,100.
b.		Double surch., both invtd.		2,600.
58	A9	50c & 5a on 3a on 30c		1,250.
59	A9	1fr & 10a on 3a on 30c		2,000.

No. J1-J3 With Various Surcharges Overprinted:
"Timbre" in Red

60	D1	½a on 5c blue	450.00

Overprinted "Affrancht" in Black

61	D1	1a on 10c brown	450.00

With Red Bars Across "CHIFFRE" and "TAXE"

62	D1	1½a on 15c green	1,000.

The illustrations are not exact reproductions of the new surcharges but are merely intended to show their relative positions and general styles.

POSTAGE DUE STAMPS

Postage Due Stamps of France Surcharged in Red, Blue or Black Like Nos. 17-28

1897		Unwmk.	*Perf. 14x13½*	
J1	D2	½a on 5c blue (R)	21.00	12.50
J2	D2	1a on 10c brn (Bl)	21.00	12.50
a.		Inverted surcharge	160.00	190.00
J3	D2	1½a on 15c grn (R)	32.50	12.50
J4	D2	3a on 30c car (Bk)	29.00	21.00
J5	D2	5a on 50c lil (Bl)	32.50	25.00
a.		2½a on 50c lilac (Bl)	1,400.	1,300.
		Nos. J1-J5 (5)	136.00	83.50

For overprints see Nos. 60-62.

REUNION

LOCATION — An island in the Indian Ocean about 400 miles east of Madagascar
GOVT. — Department of France
AREA — 970 sq. mi.
POP. — 490,000 (est. 1974)
CAPITAL — St. Denis

The colony of Réunion became an integral part of the Republic, acquiring the same status as the departments in metropolitan France, under a law effective Jan. 1, 1947.

On Jan. 1, 1975, stamps of France replaced those inscribed or overprinted "CFA."

100 Centimes = 1 Franc

Catalogue values for unused stamps in this country are for Never Hinged items, beginning with Scott 224 in the regular postage section, Scott B15 in the semipostal section, Scott C18 in the airpost section, and Scott J26 in the postage due section.

For French stamps inscribed "Reunion" see Nos. 949, 1507.

A1   A2

1852		Unwmk.	Typo.	*Imperf.*	
1	A1	15c black, *blue*		37,500.	23,500.
2	A2	30c black, *blue*		37,500.	23,000.

Four varieties of each value.
The reprints are printed on a more bluish paper than the originals. They have a frame of a thick and a thin line, instead of one thick and two thin lines. Value, $55 each.

Stamps of French Colonies Surcharged or Overprinted in Black:

a   b

1885

3	A1(a)	5c on 40c org, *yelsh*	400.00	350.00
a.		Inverted surcharge	1,750.	1,750.
4	A1(a)	25c on 40c org, *yelsh*	65.00	52.50
a.		Inverted surcharge	900.00	800.00
b.		Double surcharge	900.00	800.00
5	A5(a)	5c on 30c brn, *yelsh*	65.00	52.50
a.		"5" inverted	3,250.	3,000.
b.		Double surcharge	900.00	875.00
6	A4(a)	5c on 40c org, *yelsh*	57.50	45.00
a.		5c on 40c org, *yelsh* (II)	2,500.	2,500.
b.		Inverted surcharge (I)	900.00	875.00
c.		Double surcharge (I)	900.00	875.00
7	A8(a)	5c on 30c brn, *yelsh*	20.00	16.00
8	A8(a)	5c on 40c ver, *straw*	130.00	105.00
a.		Inverted surcharge	900.00	800.00
b.		Double surcharge	875.00	800.00
9	A8(a)	10c on 40c ver, *straw*	25.00	20.00
a.		Inverted surcharge	900.00	800.00
b.		Double surcharge	900.00	800.00
10	A8(a)	20c on 30c brn, *yelsh*	80.00	72.50

Overprint Type "b"
With or Without Accent on "E"

1891				
11	A4	40c org, *yelsh* (I)	575.00	550.00
a.		40c orange, *yelsh* (II)	6,750.	6,750.
b.		Double overprint	350.00	350.00
12	A7	80c car, *pnksh*	72.50	60.00
13	A8	30c brn, *yelsh*	50.00	50.00
14	A8	40c ver, *straw*	37.50	37.50
15	A8	75c car, *rose*	440.00	440.00

16	A8	1fr brnz grn, *straw*	52.50	45.00

Perf. 14x13½

17	A9	1c blk, *lil bl*	4.75	4.00
a.		Inverted overprint	60.00	60.00
b.		Double overprint	52.50	52.50
18	A9	2c brn, *buff*	6.50	5.00
a.		Inverted overprint	40.00	40.00
19	A9	4c claret, *lav*	9.75	8.00
a.		Inverted overprint	72.50	72.50
20	A9	5c grn, *grnsh*	11.50	9.00
a.		Inverted overprint	60.00	60.00
b.		Double overprint	60.00	57.50
21	A9	10c blk, *lav*	37.50	8.00
a.		Inverted overprint	90.00	80.00
b.		Double overprint	100.00	80.00
22	A9	15c blue	52.50	9.00
a.		Inverted overprint	120.00	110.00
23	A9	20c red, *grn*	40.00	30.00
a.		Inverted overprint	150.00	130.00
b.		Double overprint	150.00	135.00
24	A9	25c blk, *rose*	45.00	7.25
a.		Inverted overprint	125.00	120.00
25	A9	35c dp vio, *yel*	40.00	32.50
b.		Inverted overprint	180.00	175.00
26	A9	40c red, *straw*	70.00	60.00
a.		Inverted overprint	240.00	225.00
27	A9	75c car, *rose*	600.00	525.00
a.		Inverted overprint	1,600.	1,400.
28	A9	1fr brnz grn, *straw*	525.00	475.00
a.		Inverted overprint	1,600.	1,500.
b.		Double overprint	1,500.	1,400.

The varieties "RUNION," "RUENION," "REUNIONR," "ERUNION," "EUNION," "REUNIN," "REUNIOU" and "REUNOIN" are found on most stamps of this group. See *Scott Classic Specialized Catalogue of Stamps and Covers* for detailed listings. There are also many broken letters.

For surcharges see Nos. 29-33, 53-55.

No. 23 with Additional Surcharge in Black:

c   d

e   f

1891

29	A9(c)	02c on 20c red, *grn*	14.50	14.50
a.		Inverted surcharge	70.00	70.00
b.		No "c" after "02"	52.50	52.50
30	A9(c)	15c on 20c red, *grn*	18.00	18.00
a.		Inverted surcharge	70.00	70.00
31	A9(d)	2c on 20c red, *grn*	5.00	5.00
32	A9(e)	2c on 20c red, *grn*	6.00	5.75
33	A9(f)	2c on 20c red, *grn*	9.00	9.00
		Nos. 29-33 (5)	52.50	52.25

The varieties "RUNION" and "RUENION" appear on several stamps from this set. See *Scott Classic Specialized Catalogue of Stamps and Covers* for listings.

Navigation and Commerce — A14

1892-1905		Typo.	*Perf. 14x13½*	

Name of Colony in Blue or Carmine

34	A14	1c blk, *lil bl*	2.00	1.20
35	A14	2c brn, *buff*	2.00	1.20
36	A14	4c claret, *lav*	2.75	2.00
37	A14	5c grn, *grnsh*	6.75	2.00
38	A14	5c yel grn ('00)	1.40	1.40
39	A14	10c blk, *lav*	8.75	2.75
40	A14	10c red ('00)	3.25	2.00
41	A14	15c bl, quadrille paper	30.00	3.25
42	A14	15c gray ('00)	8.75	3.25
43	A14	20c red, *grn*	20.00	8.75
44	A14	25c blk, *rose*	21.00	3.50
a.		"Reunion" double	400.00	425.00
45	A14	25c blue ('00)	26.00	25.00
46	A14	30c brn, *bis*	23.00	12.00
47	A14	40c red, *straw*	30.00	19.00
48	A14	50c car, *rose*	72.50	40.00
a.		"Reunion" in red and blue	500.00	500.00

49	A14	50c brn, *az* ("Reunion" in car) ('00)	52.50	47.50
50	A14	50c brn, *az* ("Reunion" in bl) ('05)	52.50	47.50
51	A14	75c dp vio, *org*	60.00	45.00
a.		"Reunion" double	350.00	350.00
52	A14	1fr brnz grn, *straw*	47.50	35.00
a.		"Reunion" double	350.00	360.00
		Nos. 34-52 (19)	470.65	302.80

Perf. 13½x14 stamps are counterfeits.
For surcharges and overprint see Nos. 56-59, 99-106, Q1.

French Colonies No. 52 Surcharged in Black:

g

h

j

1893

53	A9(g)	2c on 20c red, *grn*	3.25	3.25
54	A9(h)	2c on 20c red, *grn*	5.50	5.50
55	A9(j)	2c on 20c red, *grn*	21.00	21.00
		Nos. 53-55 (3)	29.75	29.75

Reunion Nos. 47-48, 51-52 Surcharged in Black

1901

56	A14	5c on 40c red, *straw*	6.50	6.50
a.		Inverted surcharge	45.00	45.00
b.		No bar	240.00	240.00
c.		Thin "5"	—	—
d.		"5" inverted	1,400.	1,200.
57	A14	5c on 50c car, *rose*	7.25	7.25
a.		Inverted surcharge	45.00	45.00
b.		No bar	240.00	240.00
c.		Thin "5"	—	—
58	A14	15c on 75c vio, *org*	20.00	20.00
a.		Inverted surcharge	55.00	55.00
b.		No bar	240.00	240.00
c.		Thin "5" and small "1"	45.00	45.00
d.		As "c," inverted	800.00	800.00
59	A14	15c on 1fr brnz grn, *straw*	18.00	18.00
a.		Inverted surcharge	55.00	55.00
b.		No bar	240.00	240.00
c.		Thin "5" and small "1"	40.00	40.00
d.		As "c," inverted	—	—
		Nos. 56-59 (4)	51.75	51.75

Map of Réunion
A19

Coat of Arms and View of St. Denis
A20

View of St. Pierre
A21

1907-30 Typo.

60	A19	1c vio & lt rose	.30	.30
61	A19	2c brn & ultra	.30	.30
62	A19	4c ol grn & red	.40	.40
a.		Center double	225.00	

63	A19	5c grn & red	1.25	.40
64	A19	5c org & vio ('22)	.30	.30
65	A19	10c car & grn	2.50	.40
66	A19	10c grn ('22)	.30	.30
67	A19	10c brn red & org red, bluish ('26)	.70	.70
68	A19	15c blk & ultra ('17)	.55	.40
a.		Center double	250.00	250.00
69	A19	15c gray grn & bl grn ('26)	.40	.40
70	A19	15c bl & lt red ('28)	.55	.45
71	A20	20c gray grn & bl grn	.45	.45
a.		Center omitted	1,100.	1,100.
72	A20	25c dp bl & vio brn	6.50	3.25
73	A20	25c lt brn & bl ('22)	.55	.55
74	A20	30c yel brn & grn	1.40	.85
75	A20	30c rose & pale rose ('22)	1.40	1.40
76	A20	30c gray & car rose ('26)	.55	.55
77	A20	30c dp grn & yel grn ('28)	1.20	1.10
78	A20	35c ol grn & bl	1.60	1.00
79	A20	40c gray grn & brn ('25)	.70	.70
80	A20	45c vio & car rose	1.75	1.00
81	A20	45c red brn & ver ('25)	.85	.85
82	A20	45c vio & red org ('28)	2.75	2.50
83	A20	50c red brn & ultra	4.50	1.50
84	A20	50c bl & ultra ('22)	1.40	1.40
85	A20	50c yel & vio ('26)	1.10	1.10
86	A20	60c bl & yel brn ('25)	1.00	1.00
87	A20	65c vio & lt bl ('28)	1.50	1.40
88	A20	75c red & car rose	.80	.70
89	A20	75c ol brn & red vio ('28)	2.25	2.10
90	A20	90c brn red & brt red ('30)	8.00	7.25
91	A21	1fr ol grn & bl	1.40	1.25
92	A21	1fr blue ('25)	.95	.95
93	A21	1fr yel brn & lav ('28)	1.50	.70
94	A21	1.10fr org brn & rose lil ('28)	1.40	1.25
95	A21	1.50fr dk bl & ul- tra ('30)	12.50	12.50
96	A21	2fr red & grn	4.75	3.25
97	A21	3fr red vio ('30)	12.00	8.75
98	A21	5fr car & vio brn	9.50	5.50
		Nos. 60-98 (39)	91.80	69.15

For surcharges see Nos. 107-121, 178-180, B1-B3.

Stamps of 1892-1900 Surcharged in Black or Carmine

1912

Spacing between figures of surcharge 1.5mm (5c), 2mm (10c)

99	A14	5c on 2c brn, *buff*	1.40	1.40
100	A14	5c on 15c gray (C)	1.40	1.40
a.		Inverted surcharge	210.00	210.00
101	A14	5c on 20c red, *grn*	2.40	2.40
102	A14	5c on 25c blk, *rose* (C)	1.60	1.60
103	A14	5c on 30c brn, *bis* (C)	1.40	1.40
104	A14	10c on 40c red, *straw*	1.40	1.40
105	A14	10c on 50c brn, *az* (C)	5.50	5.50
106	A14	10c on 75c dp vio, *org*	8.75	8.75
		Nos. 99-106 (8)	23.85	23.85

Two spacings between the surcharged numerals are found on Nos. 99 to 106. For

detailed listings, see the *Scott Classic Specialized Catalogue of Stamps and Covers.*

No. 62 Surcharged

1917

107	A19	1c on 4c ol grn & red	1.75	1.75
a.		Inverted surcharge	80.00	80.00
b.		Double surcharge	60.00	60.00
c.		In pair with unsurcharged #62	625.00	625.00

Stamps and Types of 1907-30 Surcharged in Black or Red

1922-33

108	A20	40c on 20c grn & yel	.80	.80
a.		Double surcharge, one inverted	175.00	175.00
b.		Center double	175.00	175.00
c.		Surcharge omitted	1,200.	1,200.
109	A20	50c on 45c red brn & ver ('33)	1.20	1.20
109A	A20	50c on 45c vio & red org ('33)	325.00	275.00
b.		Double surcharge	1,750.	
110	A20	50c on 65c vio & lt bl ('33)	1.20	1.20
111	A20	60c on 75c red & rose	.85	.85
a.		Double surcharge	225.00	225.00
112	A19	65c on 15c blk & ultra (R) ('25)	1.90	1.90
113	A19	85c on 15c blk & ultra (R) ('25)	1.90	1.90
114	A20	85c on 75c red & cer ('25)	2.10	2.10
115	A20	90c on 75 brn red & rose red ('27)	2.10	2.10
		Nos. 108-109,110-115 (8)	12.05	12.05

Stamps and Type of 1907-30 Surcharged in Black or Red

1924-27

116	A21	25c on 5fr car & brn	1.00	1.00
a.		Double surcharge	110.00	
117	A21	1.25fr on 1fr bl (R) ('26)	1.00	.95
a.		Double surcharge	125.00	
118	A21	1.50fr on 1fr ind & ultra, *bluish* ('27)	1.40	1.40
a.		Double surcharge	140.00	
b.		Surcharge omitted	200.00	
119	A21	3fr on 5fr dl red & lt bl ('27)	3.50	3.00
120	A21	10fr on 5fr bl grn & brn red ('27)	16.00	14.00
121	A21	20fr on 5fr blk brn & rose ('27)	20.00	16.00
		Nos. 116-121 (6)	42.90	36.35

Common Design Types pictured following the introduction.

Colonial Exposition Issue
Common Design Types

1931 Engr. Perf. 12½
Name of Country Typo. in Black

122	CD70	40c dp green	5.25	5.25
123	CD71	50c violet	5.25	5.25
124	CD72	90c red orange	5.25	5.25
125	CD73	1.50fr dull blue	5.25	5.25
		Nos. 122-125 (4)	21.00	21.00

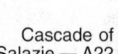

Cascade of Salazie — A22

Waterfowl Lake and Anchain Peak — A23

Léon Dierx Museum, St. Denis — A24

Perf. 12, 12½ and Compound

1933-40 Engr.

126	A22	1c violet	.25	.25
127	A22	2c dark brown	.25	.25
128	A22	3c rose vio ('40)	.25	.25
129	A22	4c olive green	.25	.25
130	A22	5c red orange	.25	.25
131	A22	10c ultramarine	.25	.25
132	A22	15c black	.25	.25
133	A22	20c indigo	.30	.25
134	A22	25c red brown	.40	.30
135	A22	30c dark green	.40	.40
136	A23	35c green ('38)	.55	.55
137	A23	40c ultramarine	.55	.55
138	A23	40c brn blk ('40)	.40	.40
139	A23	45c red violet	.85	.85
140	A23	45c green ('40)	.45	.45
141	A23	50c red	.30	.25
142	A23	55c brn org ('38)	1.25	1.00
143	A23	60c dull bl ('40)	.45	.45
144	A23	65c olive green	.95	.80
145	A23	70c ol grn ('40)	.65	.65
146	A23	75c dark brown	4.50	3.75
147	A23	80c black ('38)	.85	.80
148	A23	90c carmine	2.25	2.00
149	A23	90c dl rose vio ('39)	.85	.85
150	A23	1fr green	1.75	.70
151	A23	1fr dk car ('38)	2.25	.70
152	A23	1fr black ('40)	.70	.70
153	A24	1.25fr orange brown	.70	.55
154	A24	1.25fr brt car rose ('39)	.85	.85
155	A22	1.40fr pck bl ('40)	.85	.85
156	A24	1.50fr ultramarine	.40	.40
157	A22	1.60fr dk car rose ('40)	1.25	1.25
158	A24	1.75fr olive green	.85	.65
159	A22	1.75fr dk bl ('38)	1.40	.85
160	A24	2fr vermilion	.55	.55
161	A22	2.25fr brt ultra ('39)	1.75	1.75
162	A22	2.50fr chnt ('40)	1.25	1.25
163	A24	3fr purple	.55	.55
164	A24	5fr magenta	.55	.55
165	A24	10fr dark blue	.95	.95
166	A24	20fr red brown	1.50	1.50
		Nos. 126-166 (41)	35.80	30.65

For overprints and surcharges see Nos. 177A, 181-220, 223, C1.
60c, 1fr without "RF," see Nos. 237A-238B.

Paris International Exposition Issue
Common Design Types

1937 Perf. 13

167	CD74	20c dp vio	2.25	2.25
168	CD75	30c dk grn	2.25	2.25
169	CD76	40c car rose	2.25	2.25
170	CD77	50c dk brn & blk	2.10	2.10
171	CD78	90c red	2.10	2.10
172	CD79	1.50fr ultra	2.25	2.25
		Nos. 167-172 (6)	13.20	13.20
		Set, never hinged	20.00	

Colonial Arts Exhibition Issue
Souvenir Sheet
Common Design Type

1937 Imperf.

173	CD74	3fr ultra	8.50	10.00
		Never hinged	16.00	

New York World's Fair Issue
Common Design Type

1939 Engr. Perf. 12½x12

174	CD82	1.25fr car lake	1.40	1.40
175	CD82	2.25fr ultra	1.40	1.40
		Set, never hinged	4.50	

For overprints, see Nos. 221-222.

St. Denis Roadstead and Marshal Pétain
A25

1941	Unwmk.	Perf. 11½x12	
176	A25	1fr brown	.80
177	A25	2.50fr blue	.80
	Set, never hinged		2.00

Nos. 176-177 were issued by the Vichy government in France, but were not placed on sale in Réunion.

For surcharges, see Nos. B13-B14.

No. 144 Surcharged in Carmine

1943			
177A	1fr on 65c olive grn	1.10	.65
	Never hinged	1.60	

De Pronis Landing on Reunion — A25a

1943		Perf. 12½x12	
177B	A25a	60c blk brn & red	.55
177C	A25a	80c green & blue	.40
177D	A25a	1.50fr dk brn red	.35
177E	A25a	4fr ultra & red	.35
177F	A25a	5fr red brn & black	.55
177G	A25a	10fr violet & green	.65
	Nos. 177B-177G,C13A-C13F (12)	5.70	
	Set, never hinged	8.00	

300th Ann. of French settlement on Réunion. Nos. 177B-177G were issued by the Vichy government in France, but were not placed on sale in Réunion.

Stamps of 1907 Overprinted in Blue Violet

q

1943	Unwmk.	Perf. 14x13½	
178	A19(q)	4c ol gray & pale red	5.00	5.00
179	A20(q)	75c red & lil rose	1.60	1.60
180	A21(q)	5fr car & vio brn	60.00	60.00

Stamps of 1933-40 Overprinted in Carmine, Black or Blue Violet

181	A22(r)	1c rose vio (C)	.90	.90
182	A22(r)	2c blk brn (C)	.90	.90
183	A22(r)	3c rose vio (C)	.90	.90
184	A22(r)	4c ol yel (C)	.90	.90
185	A22(r)	5c red org	.90	.90
186	A22(r)	10c ultra (C)	.90	.90
187	A22(r)	15c blk (C)	.90	.90
188	A22(r)	20c ind (C)	.90	.90
189	A22(r)	25c red brn (BIV)	1.10	1.10
190	A22(r)	30c dk grn (C)	1.25	1.25
191	A23(q)	35c green	.75	.75

192	A23(q)	40c dl ultra (C)	.75	.75
193	A23(q)	40c brn blk (C)	.75	.75
194	A23(q)	45c red vio	.75	.75
195	A23(q)	45c green	.75	.75
196	A23(q)	50c org red	.75	.75
197	A23(q)	55c brn org	.75	.75
198	A23(q)	60c dl bl (C)	3.00	3.00
199	A23(q)	65c ol grn	.75	.75
200	A23(q)	70c ol grn (C)	2.10	2.10
201	A23(q)	75c dk brn (C)	4.75	4.75
202	A23(q)	80c blk (C)	.90	.90
203	A23(q)	90c dl rose vio	.90	.90
204	A23(q)	1fr green	.90	.90
205	A23(q)	1fr dk car	.90	.90
206	A23(q)	1fr blk (C)	2.50	2.50
207	A24(q)	1.25fr org brn (BIV)	.90	.90
208	A24(q)	1.25fr brt car rose	2.75	2.75
209	A22(r)	1.40fr pck bl (C)	1.90	1.90
210	A24(r)	1.50fr ultra (C)	.90	.90
211	A22(r)	1.60fr dk car rose	2.10	2.10
212	A24(q)	1.75fr org (C)	2.40	2.40
213	A24(q)	1.75fr dk bl (C)	4.25	4.25
214	A24(q)	2fr vermilion	.90	.90
215	A22(r)	2.25fr brt ultra (C)	4.25	4.25
216	A22(r)	2.50fr chnt (BIV)	6.50	6.50
217	A24(q)	3fr pur (C)	.90	.90
218	A24(q)	5fr brn lake (BIV)	2.00	2.00
219	A24(q)	10fr dk bl (C)	7.75	7.75
220	A24(q)	20fr red brn (BIV)	11.00	11.00

New York World's Fair Issue Overprinted in Black or Carmine

221	CD82(q)	1.25fr car lake (C)	3.50	3.50
222	CD82(q)	2.25fr ultra (C)	3.50	3.50
	Nos. 178-222 (45)	153.60	153.60
	Set, never hinged	235.00	

No. 177A Overprinted Type "q"

1943	Unwmk.	Perf. 12½	
223	A23	1fr on 65c ol grn	.65	.65

Catalogue values for unused stamps in this section, from this point to the end of the section, are for Never Hinged items.

Produce of Réunion
A26

1943	Photo.	Perf. 14½x14	
224	A26	5c dull brown	.20	.20
225	A26	10c dk blue	.20	.20
226	A26	25c emerald	.20	.20
227	A26	30c dp orange	.20	.20
228	A26	40c dk slate grn	.20	.20
229	A26	80c rose violet	.65	.50
230	A26	1fr red brown	.20	.20
231	A26	1.50fr crimson	.65	.50
232	A26	2fr black	.65	.50
233	A26	2.50fr ultra	.95	.70
234	A26	4fr dk violet	1.25	.90
235	A26	5fr bister	1.25	.90
236	A26	10fr dark brown	1.75	1.40
237	A26	20fr dark green	2.50	1.75
	Nos. 224-237 (14)	10.85	8.35

For surcharges see Nos. 240-247.

Type of 1933-40 without "RF"

1944	Engr.	Perf. 12½	
237A	A23	60c dull blue	1.40	1.00
237B	A23	1fr black & blue	1.40	1.00

Nos. 237A-237B were issued by the Vichy government in France, but were not placed on sale in Réunion.

Eboue Issue
Common Design Type

1945	Engr.	Perf. 13	
238	CD91	2fr black	1.00	1.00
239	CD91	25fr Prussian green	1.40	1.00

Nos. 224, 226 and 233 Surcharged with New Values and Bars in Carmine or Black

1945		Perf. 14½x14	
240	A26	50c on 5c dl brn (C)	.20	.20
241	A26	60c on 5c dl brn (C)	.20	.20
242	A26	70c on 5c dl brn (C)	.20	.20
243	A26	1.20fr on 5c dl brn (C)	.70	.50
244	A26	2.40fr on 25c emer	.70	.50
245	A26	3fr on 25c emer	1.25	.90
246	A26	4.50fr on 25c emer	1.25	.90
247	A26	15fr on 2.50fr ultra (C)	1.50	1.10
	Nos. 240-247 (8)	6.00	4.50

Cliff — A27

Cutting Sugar Cane — A28

Cascade
A29

Banana Tree
A30

Mountain Scene
A31

15f

Ship Approaching Réunion — A32

1947	Unwmk.	Photo.	Perf. 13½	
249	A27	10c org & grnsh blk	.20	.20
250	A27	30c org & brt bl	.20	.20
251	A27	40c org & brn	.20	.20
252	A28	50c bl grn & brn	.20	.20
253	A28	60c dk bl & brn	.20	.20
254	A28	80c brn & ol brn	.55	.45
255	A29	1fr dl bl & vio brn	.55	.45
256	A29	1.20fr bl grn & gray	.80	.65
257	A29	1.50fr org & vio brn	.80	.65
258	A30	2fr gray bl & bl grn	.80	.65
259	A30	3fr vio brn & bl grn	.80	.65
260	A30	3.60fr dl red & rose red	.90	.70
261	A30	4fr gray bl & buff	.80	.65
262	A31	5fr rose lil & brn	1.10	.65
263	A31	6fr bl & brn	1.25	.70
264	A31	10fr org & ultra	3.00	1.40
265	A32	15fr gray bl & vio brn	4.25	2.50
266	A32	20fr brn & org	6.00	3.75
267	A32	25fr rose lil & brn	7.00	4.00
	Nos. 249-267 (19)	29.60	18.85

Stamps of France, 1945-49, Surcharged type "a" or "b" in Black or Carmine

On A147   Others

1949	Unwmk.	Perf. 14x13½, 13	
268	A153	10c on 10c	.20	.20
269	A153	30c on 50c	.55	.20
270	A146	50c on 1fr	1.25	.90
271	A146	60c on 2fr	7.25	1.40
272	A147	1fr on 3fr	1.75	.70
273	A147	2fr on 4fr	6.75	1.60
274	A147	2.50fr on 5fr	18.00	10.50
275	A147	3fr on 6fr	2.10	1.40
276	A147	4fr on 10fr	1.90	1.60
277	A162	5fr on 20fr (C)	9.25	1.40
278	A147	6fr on 12fr	27.50	2.25
279	A160	7fr on 12fr	8.50	3.00
280	A165	8fr on 25fr (C)	35.00	3.25
281	A165	10fr on 25fr (C)	2.50	1.40
282	A174	11fr on 18fr (C)	16.00	2.10
	Nos. 268-282 (15)	138.50	31.90

The letters "C. F. A." are the initials of "Colonies Francaises d'Afrique," referring to the currency which is expressed in French Africa francs.

The surcharge on Nos. 277, 279, 282 includes two bars.

1950		Perf. 14x13½	
283	A182	10c on 50c bl, red & yel	.55	.55
284	A182	1fr on 2fr grn, yel & red (#619)	9.50	3.50
285	A147	2fr on 5fr lt grn	16.00	4.25
	Nos. 283-285 (3)	26.05	8.30

Surcharged Type "a" and Bars

1950-51		Perf. 13	
286	A188	5fr on 20fr dk red	9.25	1.75
287	A185	8fr on 25fr dp ultra ('51)	9.25	1.75

Stamps of France, 1951-52, Surcharged in Black or Red

1951-52		Perf. 14x13½, 13	
288	A182	50c on 1fr bl, red & yel	.65	.70
289	A182	1fr on 2fr vio bl, red & yel (#662)	.65	.70
290	A147	2fr on 5fr dl vio	4.00	1.90
291	A147	3fr on 6fr grn	7.75	1.60
292	A220	5fr on 20fr dk pur (R; '52)	2.75	1.60
293	A147	6fr on 12fr red org ('52)	8.50	2.00
294	A215	8fr on 40fr vio (R) ('52)	6.00	.70
295	A147	9fr on 18fr cerise	19.00	4.25
296	A208	15fr on 30fr ind (R)	10.00	2.25
	Nos. 288-296 (9)	59.30	15.70

The surcharge on Nos. 292, 294 and 296 include two bars.

France No. 697 Surcharged Type "a" in Black

1953		Perf. 14x13½	
297	A182	50c on 1fr blk, red & yel	.35	.20

France No. 688 Surcharged type "c" in Black

		Perf. 13	
298	A230	3fr on 6fr dp plum & car	1.10	.80

France Nos. 703 and 705 Surcharged Type "a" in Red or Blue

1954			
299	A235	8fr on 40fr (R)	32.50	7.50
300	A235	20fr on 75fr	72.50	32.50

France Nos. 698, 721, 713, and 715 Surcharged Type "a" in Black

		Perf. 14x13½, 13	
301	A182	1fr on 2fr	4.25	2.00
302	A241	4fr on 10fr	4.00	1.25
303	A238	8fr on 40fr	9.25	1.60
304	A238	20fr on 75fr	12.00	1.60

The surcharge on Nos. 303 and 304 includes two bars.

France Nos. 737, 719 and 722-724 Surcharged in Black or Red

305	A182(b)	1fr on 2fr	.50	.50
306	A241(a)	2fr on 6fr (R)	.80	.50
307	A242(a)	6fr on 12fr	8.50	1.60
308	A241(b)	9fr on 18fr	9.50	4.50
309	A241(a)	10fr on 20fr	6.75	1.40
	Nos. 299-309 (11)	160.55	54.95

The surcharge on Nos. 306-308 includes two bars; on No. 309 three bars.

France No. 720 Surcharged Type "c" in Red, Bars at Lower Left

1955		Perf. 13	
310	A241	3fr on 8fr brt bl & dk grn	1.25	1.10

France Nos. 785, 774-779 Surcharged Type "a" in Black or Red

		Perf. 14x13½, 13	
1955-56		Typo., Engr.	
311	A182	50c on 1fr	.30	.30
312	A265	2fr on 6fr ('56)	1.10	.70
313	A265	3fr on 8fr	.95	.50
314	A265	4fr on 10fr	1.10	.50
315	A265	5fr on 12fr (R)	1.10	.50

316	A265	6fr on 18fr (R)	.95	.50
317	A265	10fr on 25fr	1.40	.50
		Nos. 311-317 (7)	6.90	3.50

The surcharge on Nos. 312-317 includes two bars.

France Nos. 801-804 Surcharged Type "a" or "b" in Black or Red

1956		**Engr.**	**Perf. 13**
318	A280(a)	8fr on 30fr (R)	4.75	1.10
319	A302(b)	9fr on 40fr	7.00	2.75
320	A280(a)	15fr on 50fr	8.75	1.60
321	A280(a)	20fr on 75fr (R)	8.50	2.10
		Nos. 318-321 (4)	29.00	7.55

The surcharge on Nos. 318, 319 and 321 includes two bars.

France Nos. 837 and 839 Surcharged Type "a" in Red

1957			**Perf. 13**
322	A294	7fr on 15fr	1.10	.50
323	A265	17fr on 70fr	5.75	2.10

The surcharge on Nos. 322-323 includes two bars.

No. 322 has three types of "7" in the sheet of 50. There are 34 of the "normal" 7; 10 of a slightly thinner 7, and 6 of a slightly thicker 7.

France Nos. 755-756, 833-834, 851-855, 908, 949 Surcharged in Black or Red Type "a", "b" or

d

Typographed, Engraved

1957-60		**Perf. 14x13½, 13**
324	A236(b)	2fr on 6fr	.30	.30
325	A302(b)	3fr on 10fr ('58)	.50	.50
326	A236(b)	4fr on 12fr	3.25	.75
327	A236(b)	5fr on 10fr	2.00	1.00
328	A303(a)	6fr on 18fr	1.10	.50
329	A302(a)	9fr on 25fr (R) ('58)	1.10	.65
330	A252(a)	10fr on 20fr (R)	1.60	.30
331	A252(a)	12fr on 25fr	5.75	.50
332	A303(a)	17fr on 35fr	2.50	1.60
333	A302(a)	20fr on 50fr	1.60	.80
334	A302(a)	25fr on 85fr	3.50	1.60
335	A339(d)	50fr on 1fr ('60)	2.75	.80
		Nos. 324-335 (12)	25.95	9.30

The surcharge includes two bars on Nos. 324, 326-327, 329-331, 333 and 335.

France Nos. 973, 939 and 968 Surcharged

e

f

1961-63		**Typo.**	**Perf. 14x13½**
336	A318(e)	2fr on 5c multi	.30	.20
337	A336(e)	5fr on 10c brt grn	1.25	.50
338	A336(b)	5fr on 10c brt grn ('63)	1.40	.75
339	A349(f)	12fr on 25c lake & gray	.30	.30
		Nos. 336-339 (4)	3.25	1.75

The surcharge on No. 337 includes three bars. No. 338 has "b" surcharge and two bars.

France Nos. 943, 941 and 946 Surcharged "CFA" and New Value in Two Lines in Black or Red

Engraved, Typographed

1961		**Unwmk.**	**Perf. 13, 14x13½**
340	A338	7fr on 15c	1.00	.80
341	A337	10fr on 20c	.30	.30
342	A339	20fr on 50c (R)	16.00	4.50
		Nos. 340-342 (3)	17.30	5.60

Surcharge on No. 342 includes 3 bars.

France Nos. 1047-1048 Surcharged with New Value, "CFA" and Two Bars

1963, Jan. 2		**Engr.**	**Perf. 13**
343	A394	12fr on 25c	.90	.90
344	A395	25fr on 50c	.90	.90

1st television connection of the US and Europe through the Telstar satellite, July 11-12, 1962.

France Nos. 1040-1041, 1007 and 1009 Surcharged Similarly to Type "e"

Typographed, Engraved

1963			**Perf. 14x13½, 13**
345	A318	2fr on 5c	.30	.30
346	A318	5fr on 10c	.25	.20
347	A372	7fr on 15c	.60	.50
348	A372	20fr on 45c	1.25	.75
		Nos. 345-348 (4)	2.40	1.75

Two-line surcharge on No. 345; No. 347 has currency expressed in capital "F" and two heavy bars through old value; two thin bars on No. 348.

France No. 1078 Surcharged Type "e" in Two Lines in Dark Blue

1964, Feb. 8			**Perf. 13**
349	CD118	12fr on 25c	1.25	1.25

"PHILATEC," Intl. Philatelic and Postal Techniques Exhib., Paris, June 5-21, 1964.

France Nos. 1092, 1094 and 1102 Surcharged with New Value and "CFA"

Typographed, Engraved

1964			**Perf. 14x13½, 13**
350	A318	1fr on 2c	.25	.20
351	A318	6fr on 18c	.30	.30
352	A420	35fr on 70c	1.40	.90
		Nos. 350-352 (3)	1.95	1.40

Surcharge on No. 352 includes two bars.

France Nos. 1095, 1126, 1070 Surcharged with New Value and "CFA"

1965			
353	A318	15fr on 30c	.50	.30
354	A440	25fr on 50c	.95	.90
355	A408	30fr on 60c	1.40	.95
		Nos. 353-355 (3)	2.85	2.15

Two bars obliterate old denomination on Nos. 354-355.

Etienne Regnault, "Le Taureau" and Coast of Reunion — A33

1965, Oct. 3		**Engr.**	**Perf. 13**
356	A33	15fr bluish blk & dk car	.90	.65

Tercentenary of settlement of Reunion.

France No. 985 Surcharged with New Value, Two Bars and "CFA"

1966, Feb. 13		**Engr.**	**Perf. 13**
357	A360	10fr on 20c bl & car	1.25	.70

French Satellite A-1 Issue
France Nos. 1137-1138 Surcharged with New Value, Two Bars and "CFA" and Red

1966, Mar. 27		**Engr.**	**Perf. 13**
358	CD121	15fr on 30c	1.10	1.00
359	CD121	30fr on 60c	1.25	1.10
a.		Strip of 2 + label	3.25	3.00

France Nos. 1142, 1143, 1101 and 1127 Surcharged with New Value, "CFA" and Two Bars

1967-69		**Typo.**	**Perf. 14x13**
360	A446	2fr on 5c bl & red	.30	.30

		Photo.	**Perf. 13**
360A	A446	10fr on 20c multi ('69)	.30	.30

		Engr.	
361	A421	20fr on 40c multi	.90	.70
362	A439	30fr on 60c bl & red brn	1.90	1.25

EXPO '67 Issue
France No. 1177 Surcharged with New Value, "CFA" and Two Bars

1967, June 12		**Engr.**	**Perf. 13**
363	A473	30fr on 60c dl bl & bl grn	2.25	1.60

EXPO '67, Montreal, Apr. 28-Oct. 27.

Lions Issue
France No. 1196 Surcharged in Violet Blue with New Value, "CFA" and Two Bars

1967, Oct. 29		**Engr.**	**Perf. 13**
364	A485	20fr on 40c	2.50	1.10

50th anniversary of Lions International.

France No. 1130 Surcharged in Violet Blue with New Value, "CFA" and Two Bars

1968, Feb. 26		**Engr.**	**Perf. 13**
365	A440	50fr on 1fr	2.40	1.50

France No. 1224 Surcharged with New Value, "CFA" and Two Bars

1968, Oct. 21		**Engr.**	**Perf. 13**
366	A508	20fr on 40c multi	1.25	.90

20 years of French Polar expeditions.

France Nos. 1230-1231 Surcharged with New Value, "CFA" and Two Bars

1969, Apr. 13		**Engr.**	**Perf. 13**
367	A486	15fr on 30c green	.65	.50
368	A486	20fr on 40c dp car	.70	.30

France No. 1255 Surcharged with New Value, "CFA" and Two Bars

1969, Aug. 18		**Engr.**	**Perf. 13**
370	A526	35fr on 70c multi	1.40	1.25

Napoleon Bonaparte (1769-1821).

France No. 1293 Surcharged with New Value and "CFA"

1971, Jan. 16		**Engr.**	**Perf. 13**
371	A555	25fr on 50c rose car	.70	.30

France No. 1301 Surcharged with New Value and "CFA"

1971, Apr. 13		**Engr.**	**Perf. 13**
372	A562	40fr on 80c multi	1.75	1.25

France No. 1309 Surcharged with New Value, "CFA" and 2 Bars

1971, June 5		**Engr.**	**Perf. 13**
373	A569	40fr on 40c multi	.90	.70

Aid for rural families.

France No. 1312 Surcharged with New Value and "CFA"

1971, Aug. 30		**Engr.**	**Perf. 13**
374	A571	45fr on 90c multi	1.10	.90

France No. 1320 Surcharged with New Value and "CFA"

1971, Oct. 18			
375	A573	45fr on 90c multi	1.25	.95

40th anniversary of the first assembly of presidents of artisans' guilds.

Réunion Chameleon A34

1971, Nov. 8		**Photo.**	**Perf. 13**
376	A34	25fr multi	1.40	.90

Nature protection.

Common Design Type and

De Gaulle in Brazzaville, 1944 — A35

Designs: No. 377, Gen. de Gaulle, 1940. No. 379, de Gaulle entering Paris, 1944. No. 380, Pres. de Gaulle, 1970.

1971, Nov. 9			**Engr.**
377	CD134	25fr black	1.60	1.60
378	A35	25fr ultra	1.60	1.60
379	A35	25fr rose red	1.60	1.60
380	CD134	25fr black	1.60	1.60
a.		Strip of 4 + label	8.75	8.00

Charles de Gaulle (1890-1970), president of France. Nos. 377-380 printed se-tenant in sheets of 20 containing 5 strips of 4 plus labels with Cross of Lorraine and inscription.

France No. 1313 Surcharged with New Value and "CFA"

1972, Jan. 17		**Engr.**	**Perf. 13**
381	A570	50fr on 1.10fr multi	1.25	1.10

Map of South Indian Ocean, Penguin and Ships — A36

1972, Jan. 31		**Engr.**	**Perf. 13**
382	A36	45fr blk, bl & ocher	2.10	2.10

Bicentenary of the discovery of the Crozet and Kerguelen Islands.

France No. 1342 Surcharged with New New Value, "CFA" and 2 Bars in Red

1972, May 8		**Engr.**	**Perf. 13**
383	A590	15fr on 40c red	.90	.90

20th anniv. of Blood Donors' Assoc. of Post and Telecommunications Employees.

France Nos. 1345-1346 Surcharged with New Value, "CFA" and 2 Bars

1972, June 5		**Typo.**	**Perf. 14x13**
384	A593	15fr on 30c multi	.45	.45
385	A593	25fr on 50c multi	.75	.65

Introduction of postal code system.

France No. 1377 Surcharged with New Value, "CFA" and 2 Bars in Ultramarine

1973, June 12		**Engr.**	**Perf. 13**
386	A620	45fr on 90c multi	1.75	1.25

France Nos. 1374, 1336 Surcharged with New Value and "CFA" in Ultramarine or Red

1973			**Perf. 13**
387	A617	50fr on 1fr multi (U)	1.10	.95
388	A586	100fr on 2fr multi (R)	1.75	1.10

On No. 388, two bars cover "2.00". Issue dates: 50fr, June 24; 100fr, Oct. 13.

France No. 1231C Surcharged with New Value, "CFA" and 2 Bars

1973, Nov.		**Typo.**	**Perf. 14x13**
389	A486	15fr on 30c bl grn	4.50	.70

France No. 1390 Surcharged with New Value, "CFA" and 2 Bars in Red

1974, Jan. 20		**Engr.**	**Perf. 13**
390	A633	25fr on 50c multi	.70	.70

ARPHILA 75 Phil. Exhib., Paris, June 1975.

France Nos. 1394-1397 Surcharged "100 FCFA" in Black, Ultramarine or Brown

Engr. (#391, 393), Photo. (#392, 394)

1974		Perf. 12x13, 13x12		
391	A637	100fr on 2fr (Bk)	2.40	2.40
392	A638	100fr on 2fr (U)	2.75	2.25
393	A639	100fr on 2fr (Br)	2.75	2.25
394	A640	100fr on 2fr (U)	2.75	2.25
		Nos. 391-394 (4)	10.65	9.15

Nos. 391-394 printed in sheets of 25 with alternating labels publicizing "ARPHILA 75," Paris June 6-16, 1975.

Two bars obliterate original denomination on Nos. 391-393.

France No. 1401 Surcharged "45 FCFA" and 2 Bars in Red

1974, Apr. 29		Engr.	Perf. 13	
395	A644	45fr on 90c multi	1.75	1.25

Reorganized sea rescue organization.

France No. 1415 Surcharged with New Value, 2 Bars and "FCFA" in Ultramarine

1974, Oct. 6		Engr.	Perf. 13	
396	A657	60fr on 1.20fr multi	1.40	1.25

Centenary of Universal Postal Union.

France Nos. 1292A and 1294B Surcharged with New Value and "FCFA" in Ultramarine

1974, Oct. 19		Typo.	Perf. 14x13	
397	A555	30fr on 60c grn	1.75	1.60

Engr.

Perf. 13

398	A555	40fr on 80c car rose	2.10	1.75

SEMI-POSTAL STAMPS

No. 65 Surcharged in Black or Red

1915		Unwmk.	Perf. 14x13½	
B1	A19	10c + 5c (Bk)	160.00	120.00
a.		Inverted surcharge	400.00	350.00
B2	A19	10c + 5c (R)	1.60	1.60
a.		Inverted surcharge	72.50	72.50
b.		Double surcharge, both inverted	675.00	675.00

No. 65 Surcharged in Red

1916				
B3	A19	10c + 5c	1.90	1.90

Curie Issue
Common Design Type

1938			Perf. 13	
B4	CD80	1.75fr + 50c brt ultra	13.50	13.50
		Never hinged	22.50	

French Revolution Issue
Common Design Type

1939		Photo.	Unwmk.	

Name and Value Typo. in Black

B5	CD83	45c + 25c grn	12.50	12.50
B6	CD83	70c + 30c brn	12.50	12.50
B7	CD83	90c + 35c red org	12.50	12.50
B8	CD83	1.25fr + 1fr rose pink	12.50	12.50
B9	CD83	2.25fr + 2fr blue	12.50	12.50
		Nos. B5-B9 (5)	62.50	62.50
		Set, never hinged	105.00	

See CB1.

Common Design Type and

Artillery Colonel — SP1

Colonial Infantry SP2

1941		Unwmk.	Perf. 13½	
B10	SP1	1fr + 1fr red	1.60	
B11	CD86	1.50fr + 3fr claret	1.60	
B12	SP2	2.50fr + 1fr blue	1.60	
		Nos. B10-B12 (3)	4.80	
		Set, never hinged	6.00	

Nos. B10-B12 were issued by the Vichy government in France, but were not placed on sale in Reunion.

Nos. 176-177 Surcharged in Black or Red

1944		Engr.	Perf. 12½x12	
B13		50c + 1.50fr on 2.50fr deep blue (R)	.80	
B14		+ 2.50fr on 1fr yel brn	.80	
		Set, never hinged	2.00	

Colonial Development Fund.

Nos. B13-B14 were issued by the Vichy government in France, but were not placed on sale in Réunion.

> **Catalogue values for unused stamps in this section, from this point to the end of the section, are for Never Hinged items.**

Red Cross Issue
Common Design Type

1944			Perf. 14½x14	
B15	CD90	5fr + 20fr black	1.60	1.10

The surtax was for the French Red Cross and national relief.

France Nos. B365-B366 Surcharged with New Value, "CFA" and Two Bars

1962, Dec. 10		Engr.	Perf. 13	
B16	SP219	10 + 5fr on 20 + 10c	2.10	2.10
B17	SP219	12 + 5fr on 25 + 10c	2.40	2.40

The surtax was for the Red Cross.

France Nos. B374-B375 Surcharged with New Value, "CFA" and Two Bars in Red

1963, Dec. 9				
B18	SP223	10 + 5fr on 20 + 10c	2.75	2.75
B19	SP223	12 + 5fr on 25 + 10c	2.75	2.75

Centenary of the Intl. Red Cross. The surtax was for the Red Cross.

France Nos. B385-B386 Surcharged with New Value, "CFA" and Two Bars in Dark Blue

1964, Dec. 13		Unwmk.	Perf. 13	
B20	SP230	10 + 5fr on 20 + 10c	1.60	1.60
B21	SP230	12 + 5fr on 25 + 10c	1.90	1.90

Jean Nicolas Corvisart (1755-1821) and Dominique Larrey (1766-1842), physicians. The surtax was for the Red Cross.

France Nos. B392-B393 Surcharged with New Value, "CFA" and Two Bars

1965, Dec. 12		Engr.	Perf. 13	
B22	SP233	12 + 5fr on 25 + 10c	1.40	1.40
B23	SP233	15 + 5fr on 30 + 10c	1.50	1.50

The surtax was for the Red Cross.

France Nos. B402-B403 Surcharged with New Value, "CFA" and Two Bars

1966, Dec. 11		Engr.	Perf. 13	
B24	SP237	12 + 5fr on 25 + 10c	1.40	1.40
B25	SP237	15 + 5fr on 30 + 10c	1.40	1.40

The surtax was for the Red Cross.

France Nos. B409-B410 Surcharged with New Value, "CFA" and Two Bars

1967, Dec. 17		Engr.	Perf. 13	
B26	SP240	12 + 5fr on 25 + 10c	2.75	2.75
B27	SP240	15 + 5fr on 30 + 10c	3.50	3.50

Surtax for the Red Cross.

France Nos. B421-B424 Surcharged with New Value, "CFA" and Two Bars

1968-69		Engr.	Perf. 13	
B28	SP244	12 + 5fr on 25 + 10c	1.60	1.40
B29	SP244	15 + 5fr on 30 + 10c	1.75	1.40
B30	SP244	20 + 7fr on 40 + 15c ('69)	1.40	1.40
B31	SP244	20 + 7fr on 40 + 15c ('69)	1.40	1.40
		Nos. B28-B31 (4)	6.15	5.60

The surtax was for the Red Cross.

France No. B425 Surcharged with New Value, "CFA" and Two Bars

1969, Mar. 17		Engr.	Perf. 13	
B32	SP245	15fr + 5fr on 30c + 10c	1.40	1.40

Stamp Day.

France No. B440 Surcharged with New Value, "CFA" and Two Bars

1970, Mar. 16		Engr.	Perf. 13	
B33	SP249	20fr + 5fr on 40c + 10c	1.10	.95

Stamp day.

France Nos. B443-B444 Surcharged with New Value "CFA" and Two Bars

1970, Dec. 14		Engr.	Perf. 13	
B34	SP252	20 + 7fr on 40 + 15c	2.40	2.00
B35	SP252	20 + 7fr on 40 + 15c	2.40	2.40

The surtax was for the Red Cross.

France No. B451 Surcharged with New Value, "CFA" and Two Bars

1971, Mar. 29		Engr.	Perf. 13	
B36	SP254	25fr + 5fr on 50c + 10c	1.10	.90

Stamp Day.

France Nos. B452-B453 Surcharged with New Value, "CFA" and Two Bars

1971, Dec. 13				
B37	SP255	15fr + 5fr on 30c + 10c	1.25	1.25
B38	SP255	25fr + 5fr on 50c + 10c	1.25	1.25

The surtax was for the Red Cross.

France No. B460 Surcharged with New Value and "CFA"

1972, Mar. 20		Engr.	Perf. 13	
B39	SP257	25fr + 5fr on 50c + 10c	1.10	1.10

Stamp Day.

France Nos. B461-B462 Surcharged with New Value, "CFA" and Two Bars in Red or Green

1972, Dec. 16		Engr.	Perf. 13	
B40	SP258	15 + 5fr on 30 + 10c	1.10	1.10
B41	SP258	25 + 5fr on 50 + 10c (G)	1.25	1.25

Surtax was for the Red Cross.

France No. B470 Surcharged with New Value, "CFA" and Two Bars in Red

1973, Mar. 26		Engr.	Perf. 13	
B42	SP260	25fr + 5fr on 50c + 10c	1.25	1.25

Stamp Day.

France Nos. B471-B472 Surcharged with New Value, "CFA" and Two Bars in Red

1973, Dec. 3		Engr.	Perf. 13	
B43	SP261	15 +5fr on 30c +10c	1.25	1.25
B44	SP261	25 +5fr on 50c +10c	1.25	1.25

Surtax was for the Red Cross.

France No. B477 Surcharged "25 + 5 FCFA"

1974, Mar. 11		Engr.	Perf. 13	
B45	SP263	25fr + 5fr on 50c + 10c	.95	.95

Stamp Day.

France Nos. B479-B480 Surcharged with New Value, "FCFA" and Two Bars in Green or Red

1974, Nov. 30		Engr.	Perf. 13	
B46	SP265	30 + 7fr on 60 + 15c (G)	1.25	1.25
B47	SP266	40 + 7fr on 80 + 15c (R)	1.25	1.25

Surtax was for the Red Cross.

AIR POST STAMPS

No. 141 Overprinted in Blue

1937, Jan. 23		Unwmk.	Perf. 12½	
C1	A23	50c red	290.00	250.00
a.		Vert. pair, one without overprint	1,800.	1,800.
b.		Inverted overprint	6,000.	
c.		As "b," in pair with unoverprinted stamp	26,000.	

Flight of the "Roland Garros" from Reunion to France by aviators Laurent, Lenier and Touge in Jan.-Feb., 1937.

Airplane and Landscape — AP2

1938, Mar. 1		Engr.	Perf. 12½	
C2	AP2	3.65fr slate blue & car	.95	.85
C3	AP2	6.65fr brown & org red	.95	.85
C4	AP2	9.65fr car & ultra	.95	.85
C5	AP2	12.65fr brown & green	1.90	1.40
		Nos. C2-C5 (4)	4.75	3.95
		Set, never hinged	7.00	

For overprints see Nos. C14-C17.

Plane and Bridge over East River AP3

Plane and Landscape AP4

1942, Oct. 19			Perf. 12x12½	
C6	AP3	50c olive & pur	.35	
C7	AP3	1fr dk bl & scar	.35	
C8	AP3	2fr brn & blk	.60	
C9	AP3	3fr rose lil & grn	1.10	
C10	AP3	5fr red org & red brn	1.10	

Frame Engr., Center Photo.

C11 AP4 10fr dk grn, red org & vio 1.10
C12 AP4 20fr dk bl, brn vio & red 1.10
C13 AP4 50fr brn car, Prus grn & bl 1.50
Nos. C6-C13 (8) 7.20
Set, never hinged 9.50

Nos. C6-C13 were issued by the Vichy government in France, but were not placed on sale in Réunion.

De Poivre
AP4a

1943 Perf. 12½x12
C13A AP4a 1fr sepia & red .25
C13B AP4a 2fr green & blue .35
C13C AP4a 3fr dk brown red .40
C13D AP4a 5fr ultramarine & red .55
C13E AP4a 10fr red brown & black .55
C13F AP4a 20fr violet & green .75
Nos. C13A-C13F (6) 2.85
Set, never hinged 4.00

300th Ann. of French settlement on Réunion.
Nos. C13A-C13F were issued by the Vichy government in France, but were not placed on sale in Réunion.

Nos. C2-C5 Overprinted in Black or Carmine

1943 Unwmk. Perf. 12½
C14 AP2 3.65fr sl bl & car 5.25 5.25
C15 AP2 6.65fr brn & org red 5.25 5.25
C16 AP2 9.65fr car & ultra (C) 5.25 5.25
C17 AP2 12.65fr brn & grn 5.25 5.25
Nos. C14-C17 (4) 21.00 21.00
Set, never hinged 30.00

> Catalogue values for unused stamps in this section, from this point to the end of the section, are for Never Hinged items.

Common Design Type

1944 Photo. Perf. 14½x14
C18 CD87 1fr dk org .45 .30
C19 CD87 1.50fr brt red .45 .30
C20 CD87 5fr brn red .60 .45
C21 CD87 10fr black 1.10 .80
C22 CD87 25fr ultra 1.25 .95
C23 CD87 50fr dk grn 1.25 .95
C24 CD87 100fr plum 1.75 1.25
Nos. C18-C24 (7) 6.85 5.00

Victory Issue
Common Design Type

1946, May 8 Engr. Perf. 12½
C25 CD92 8fr olive gray 1.10 .90

European victory of the Allied Nations in WWII.

Chad to Rhine Issue
Common Design Types

1946, June 6
C26 CD93 5fr orange 1.25 .85
C27 CD94 10fr sepia 1.25 .85
C28 CD95 15fr grnsh blk 1.25 .85
C29 CD96 20fr lilac rose 1.75 1.25
C30 CD97 25fr greenish blue 1.75 1.25
C31 CD98 50fr green 2.00 1.50
Nos. C26-C31 (6) 9.25 6.55

Shadow of Plane — AP5

Plane over Réunion — AP6

Air View of Réunion and Shadow of Plane — AP7

Perf. 13x12½
1947, Mar. 24 Photo. Unwmk.
C32 AP5 50fr ol grn & bl gray 10.50 8.00
C33 AP6 100fr dk brn & org 16.00 16.00
C34 AP7 200fr dk bl & org 20.00 13.00
Nos. C32-C34 (3) 46.50 37.00

France, Nos. C18-C21 Surcharged and Bars, in Carmine or Black

c

1949 Unwmk. Perf. 13
C35 AP7 20fr on 40fr (C) 3.50 1.25
C36 AP8 25fr on 50fr 4.25 1.40
C37 AP9 50fr on 100fr (C) 10.00 4.25
C38 AP10 100fr on 200fr 52.50 21.00
Nos. C35-C38 (4) 70.25 27.90

France Nos. C24, C26 and C27 Surcharged Type "c" and Bars in Black

1949-51
C39 AP12 100fr on 200fr ('51) 125.00 26.50
C40 AP12 200fr on 500fr 52.50 21.00
C41 AP13 500fr on 1000fr ('51) 315.00 210.00
Nos. C39-C41 (3) 492.50 257.50

France Nos. C29-C32 Surcharged "CFA," New Value and Bars in Blue or Red

1954, Feb. 10
C42 AP15(c) 50fr on 100fr 2.50 1.25
C43 AP15 100fr on 200fr (R) 5.00 1.40
C44 AP15(c) 200fr on 500fr 40.00 12.50
C45 AP15 500fr on 1000fr 35.00 12.50
Nos. C42-C45 (4) 82.50 27.65

France Nos. C35-C36 Surcharged "CFA," New Values and Bars in Red or Black

1957-58 Engr. Perf. 13
C46 AP17 200fr on 500fr (R) 24.00 6.75
C47 AP17 500fr on 1000fr ('58) 24.00 13.00

France Nos. C37, C39-C40 Surcharged "CFA," New Value and Bars in Red or Black

1961-64
C48 AP15 100fr on 2fr 6.25 1.25
C49 AP17 200fr on 5fr 6.25 3.00
C50 AP17 500fr on 10fr (B;'64) 14.00 6.25
Nos. C48-C50 (3) 26.50 10.50

France No. C41 Surcharged "CFA," New Value and Two Bars in Red

1967, Jan. 27 Engr. Perf. 13
C51 AP17 100fr on 2fr sl bl & ind 2.00 .80

France No. C45 Surcharged in Red with "CFA," New Value and Two Bars in Red

1972, May 14 Engr. Perf. 13
C52 AP21 200fr on 5fr multi 4.50 1.75

AIR POST SEMI-POSTAL STAMP

French Revolution Issue
Common Design Type

1939 Unwmk. Perf. 13
Name and Value Typo. in Orange
CB1 CD83 3.65fr + 4fr brn blk 24.00 24.00
Never hinged 35.00

Felix Guyon Hospital, St. Denis — SPAP1

Perf. 13½x12½
1942, June 22 Engr.
CB2 SPAP1 1.50fr + 3.50fr lt green 1.00
CB3 SPAP1 2fr + 6fr yellow brown 1.00
Set, never hinged 2.50

Native children's welfare fund.
Nos. CB2-CB3 were issued by the Vichy government in France, but were not placed on sale in Réunion.

Colonial Education Fund
Common Design Type

1942, June 22
CB4 CD86a 1.20fr + 1.80fr blue & red .90
Never hinged 1.25

No. CB4 was issued by the Vichy government in France, but was not placed on sale in Réunion.

POSTAGE DUE STAMPS

D1   D2

1889-92 Unwmk. Type-set Imperf.
Without Gum
J1 D1 5c black 27.50 13.50
J2 D1 10c black 32.50 13.50
J3 D1 15c black ('92) 65.00 40.00
J4 D1 20c black 47.50 26.00
J5 D1 30c black 45.00 26.00
Nos. J1-J5 (5) 217.50 119.00

Ten varieties of each value.
Nos. J1-J2, J4-J5 issued on yellowish paper in 1889; Nos. J1-J3, J5 on bluish white paper in 1892.
Nos. J1-J5 exist with double impression. Values, each $125-$190.

1907 Typo. Perf. 14x13½
J6 D2 5c carmine, *yel* .85 .85
J7 D2 10c blue, *bl* .85 .85
J8 D2 15c black, *bluish* 1.40 1.40
J9 D2 20c carmine 1.40 1.40
J10 D2 30c green, *grnsh* 2.10 2.10

J11 D2 50c red, *green* 2.50 2.50
J12 D2 60c carmine, *bl* 2.50 2.50
J13 D2 1fr violet 2.75 2.75
Nos. J6-J13 (8) 14.35 14.35
Set, never hinged 25.00

Type of 1907 Issue Surcharged

1927
J14 D2 2fr on 1fr org red 12.00 12.00
J15 D2 3fr on 1fr org brn 12.00 12.00
Set, never hinged 38.00

Arms of Réunion D3   Numeral D4

1933 Engr. Perf. 13x13½
J16 D3 5c deep violet .20 .20
J17 D3 10c dark green .20 .20
J18 D3 15c orange brown .20 .20
J19 D3 20c light red .35 .35
J20 D3 30c olive green .35 .35
J21 D3 50c ultramarine .80 .80
J22 D3 60c black brown .80 .80
J23 D3 1fr light violet .80 .80
J24 D3 2fr deep blue .80 .80
J25 D3 3fr carmine 1.00 1.00
Nos. J16-J25 (10) 5.50 5.50
Set, never hinged 8.75

> Catalogue values for unused stamps in this section, from this point to the end of the section, are for Never Hinged items.

1947 Unwmk. Photo. Perf. 13
J26 D4 10c dark violet .20 .20
J27 D4 30c brown .20 .20
J28 D4 50c blue green .20 .20
J29 D4 1fr orange .55 .45
J30 D4 2fr red violet .55 .45
J31 D4 3fr red brown .80 .65
J32 D4 4fr blue 1.40 1.10
J33 D4 5fr henna brown 1.75 1.40
J34 D4 10fr slate green 1.75 1.40
J35 D4 20fr violet blue 1.75 .90
Nos. J26-J35 (10) 9.15 6.95

France, Nos. J83-J92 Surcharged in Black

1949-53
J36 D5 10c on 1fr brt ultra .20 .20
J37 D5 50c on 2fr turq bl .40 .35
J38 D5 1fr on 3fr brn org .55 .35
J39 D5 2fr on 4fr dp vio .55 .35
J40 D5 3fr on 5fr brt pink 6.00 2.50
J41 D5 5fr on 10fr red org .95 .70
J42 D5 10fr on 20fr ol bis 1.90 1.90
J43 D5 20fr on 50fr dk grn ('50) 12.00 5.25
J44 D5 50fr on 100fr dp grn ('53) 29.00 13.00
Nos. J36-J44 (9) 51.55 24.60

Same Surcharge on France Nos. J93, J95-J96

1962-63 Typo. Perf. 14x13½
J46 D6 1fr on 5c brt pink ('63) 2.75 1.10
J47 D6 10fr on 20c ol bis ('63) 5.25 2.50
J48 D6 20fr on 50c dk grn 20.00 12.00
Nos. J46-J48 (3) 28.00 15.60

France Nos. J98-J102, J104-J105 Surcharged with New Value and "CFA"

1964-71 Unwmk. Perf. 14x13½
J49 D7 1fr on 5c .20 .20
J50 D7 5fr on 10c .30 .20
J51 D7 7fr on 15c .50 .45
J52 D7 10fr on 20c ('71) 1.40 .55
J53 D7 15fr on 30c .65 .45
J54 D7 20fr on 50c .80 .55
J55 D7 50fr on 1fr 1.40 1.25
Nos. J49-J55 (7) 5.25 3.65

PARCEL POST STAMP

No. 40 Overprinted

1906   Unwmk.   Perf. 14x13½
Q1 A14 10c red   21.00 21.00

FRENCH COLONIES

ˈfrench ˈkä-lə-nēz

From 1859 to 1906 and from 1943 to 1945 special stamps were issued for use in all French Colonies which did not have stamps of their own.

100 Centimes = 1 Franc

Catalogue values for unused stamps in this country are for Never Hinged items, beginning with Scott B1 in the semi-postal section and Scott J23 in the postage due section.

Perforations: Nos. 1-45 are known variously perforated privately.
Gum: Many of Nos. 1-45 were issued without gum. Some were gummed locally.
Reprints: Nos. 1-7, 9-12, 24, 26-42, 44 and 45 were reprinted officially in 1887. These reprints are ungummed and the colors of both design and paper are deeper or brighter than the originals. Value for Nos. 1-6, $20 each.

Eagle and Crown — A1

1859-65   Unwmk.   Typo.   Imperf.
1 A1 1c ol grn, *pale bl* ('62)   24.00 27.50
2 A1 5c yel grn, *grnsh* ('62)   24.00 16.00
3 A1 10c bister, *yel*   32.50 8.00
   a. Pair, one sideways   1,000. 525.00
4 A1 20c bl, *bluish* ('65)   35.00 13.50
5 A1 40c org, *yelsh* ('65)   27.50 13.50
6 A1 80c car rose, *pnksh* ('65)   110.00 60.00
   Nos. 1-6 (6)   253.00 138.50

For surcharges, see Reunion Nos. 1-4.

Napoleon III
A2   A3

Ceres   Napoleon III
A4   A5

1871-72   Imperf.
7 A2 1c ol grn, *pale bl* ('72)   80.00 80.00
8 A3 5c yel grn, *grnsh* ('72)   1,000. 400.00
9 A4 10c bis, *yelsh*   375.00 130.00
   a. Tête bêche pair   55,000. 22,500.
10 A4 15c bis, *yelsh* ('72)   325.00 13.00
11 A4 20c blue, *bluish*   525.00 125.00
   a. Tête bêche pair   18,000.
12 A4 25c bl, *bluish* ('72)   175.00 13.00
13 A5 30c brn, *yelsh*   175.00 60.00

14 A4 40c org, *yelsh* (I)   250.00 13.00
   a. Type II   3,500. 650.00
   b. Pair, types I & II   7,250. 1,750.
15 A5 80c rose, *pnksh*   1,100. 115.00
   Nos. 7-15 (9)   4,005. 949.00

For 40c types I-II see illustrations over France #1.
For surcharges, see Reunion Nos. 5-6.
See note after France No. 9 for additional information on Nos. 8-9, 11-12, 14.

Ceres
A6   A7

1872-77   Imperf.
16 A6 1c ol grn, *pale bl* ('73)   13.00 14.50
17 A6 2c red brn, *yelsh* ('76)   475.00 750.00
18 A6 4c gray ('76)   11,000. 475.00
19 A6 5c grn, *pale bl*   17.50 9.50
20 A7 10c bis, *rose* ('76)   240.00 13.00
21 A7 15c bister ('77)   525.00 100.00
22 A7 30c brn, *yelsh*   130.00 21.00
23 A7 80c brn, *pnksh* ('73)   625.00 140.00

No. 17 was used only in Cochin China, 1876-77. Excellent forgeries of Nos. 17 and 18 exist.
With reference to the stamps of France and French Colonies in the same designs and colors see the note after France No. 9.

Peace and Commerce   Commerce
A8   A9

1877-78   Type I   Imperf.
24 A8 1c grn, *grnsh*   35.00 45.00
25 A8 4c grn, *grnsh*   24.00 14.50
26 A8 30c brn, *yelsh* ('78)   52.50 52.50
27 A8 40c ver, *straw*   35.00 21.00
28 A8 75c rose, *rose* ('78)   75.00 100.00
29 A8 1fr brnz grn, *straw*   60.00 67.50
   Nos. 24-29 (6)   281.50 300.50

Type II
30 A8 2c grn, *grnsh*   17.50 11.00
31 A8 5c grn, *grnsh*   24.00 5.50
32 A8 10c grn, *grnsh*   125.00 24.00
33 A8 15c gray, *grnsh*   250.00 72.50
34 A8 20c red brn, *straw*   52.50 9.50
35 A8 25c ultra *bluish*   52.50 8.75
   a. 25c blue, *bluish* ('78)   4,250. 175.00
36 A8 35c vio blk, *org* ('78)   67.50 32.50
   Nos. 30-36 (7)   589.00 163.75
   Nos. 24-36 (13)   870.50 464.25

1878-80
Type II
38 A8 1c blk, *lil bl*   21.00 21.00
39 A8 2c brn, *buff*   21.00 24.00
40 A8 4c claret, *lav*   32.50 45.00
41 A8 10c blk, *lav* ('79)   120.00 27.50
42 A8 15c blue ('79)   35.00 17.50
43 A8 20c red, *grn* ('79)   87.50 17.50
44 A8 25c blk, *red* ('79)   600.00 275.00
45 A8 25c yel, *straw* ('80)   725.00 32.50
   Nos. 38-45 (8)   1,642. 460.00

No. 44 was used only in Mayotte, Nossi-Be and New Caledonia. Forgeries exist.
The 3c yellow, 3c gray, 15c yellow, 20c blue, 25c rose and 5fr lilac were printed together with the reprints, and were never issued.

1881-86   Perf. 14x13½
46 A9 1c blk, *lil bl*   5.50 4.75
47 A9 2c brn, *buff*   5.50 4.75
48 A9 4c claret, *lav*   5.50 5.50
49 A9 5c grn, *grnsh*   6.50 3.25
50 A9 10c blk, *lavender*   11.00 4.75
51 A9 15c blue   16.00 3.25
52 A9 20c red, *yel grn*   52.50 18.00
53 A9 25c yel, *straw*   17.50 5.50
54 A9 25c blk, *rose* ('86)   24.00 3.25
55 A9 30c brn, *bis*   45.00 21.00
56 A9 35c vio blk, *yel org*   40.00 30.00
   a. 35c violet black, *yellow*   100.00 52.50

57 A9 40c ver, *straw*   45.00 27.50
58 A9 75c car, *rose*   120.00 60.00
59 A9 1fr brnz grn, *straw*   80.00 45.00
   Nos. 46-59 (14)   474.00 236.50

Nos. 46-59 exist imperforate. They are proofs and were not used for postage, except the 10c.
For stamps of type A9 surcharged with numerals see: Cochin China, Diego Suarez, Gabon, Malagasy (Madagascar), Nossi-Be, New Caledonia, Reunion, Senegal, Tahiti.

SEMI-POSTAL STAMPS

Catalogue values for unused stamps in this section are for Never Hinged items.

Resistance Fighters — SP1

1943   Unwmk.   Litho.   Rouletted
B1 SP1 1.50fr + 98.50fr ind & gray   47.50 65.00
   Without label   21.00 35.00

The surtax was for the benefit of patriots and the French Committee of Liberation.
No. B1 was printed in sheets of 10 (5x2) with adjoining labels showing the Lorraine cross.

Colonies Offering Aid to France
SP2

1943   Perf. 12
B2 SP2 9fr + 41fr red violet   3.50 10.50

Surtax for the benefit of French patriots.

Patriots and Map of France
SP3

1943
B3 SP3 50c + 4.50fr yel grn   1.25 10.50
B4 SP3 1.50fr + 8.50fr cerise   1.25 10.50
B5 SP3 3fr + 12fr grnsh bl   1.25 10.50
B6 SP3 5fr + 15fr olive gray   1.25 1.50
   Nos. B3-B6 (4)   5.00 33.00

Surtax for the aid of combatants and patriots.

Refugee Family
SP4

1943
B7 SP4 10fr + 40fr dull blue   5.25 12.50

The surtax was for refugee relief work.

Woman and Child with Wing — SP5

1944
B8 SP5 10fr + 40fr grnsh blk   6.75 21.00

Surtax for the benefit of aviation.
Nos. B1-B8 were prepared for use in the French Colonies, but after the landing of Free French troops in Corsica they were used there and later also in Southern France. They became valid throughout France in Nov. 1944.

POSTAGE DUE STAMPS

D1

1884-85   Unwmk.   Typo.   Imperf.
J1 D1 1c black   4.00 4.00
J2 D1 2c black   4.00 4.00
J3 D1 3c black   4.00 4.00
J4 D1 4c black   4.75 4.00
J5 D1 5c black   6.50 3.25
J6 D1 10c black   8.75 6.50
J7 D1 15c black   13.00 10.50
J8 D1 20c black   16.00 10.50
J9 D1 30c black   17.50 8.75
J10 D1 40c black   21.00 8.75
J11 D1 60c black   27.50 16.00
J12 D1 1fr brown   35.00 27.50
   a. 1fr black   300.00
J13 D1 2fr brown   35.00 27.50
   a. 2fr black   300.00 325.00
J14 D1 5fr brown   110.00 67.50
   a. 5fr black   425.00 450.00

Nos. J12a, J13a and J14a were not regularly issued.

1894-1906
J15 D1 5c pale blue   1.60 1.60
J16 D1 10c gray brown   1.60 1.60
J17 D1 15c pale green   1.60 1.60
J18 D1 20c olive grn ('06)   1.60 1.60
J19 D1 30c carmine   2.75 1.60
J20 D1 50c lilac   2.75 1.60
J21 D1 60c brown, *buff*   4.50 2.75
   a. 60c dark violet, *buff*   4.75 2.75
J22 D1 1fr red, *buff*   7.50 4.50
   a. 1fr rose, *buff*   27.50 19.00
   Nos. J15-J22 (8)   23.90 16.85

For overprints see New Caledonia Nos. J1-J8.

Catalogue values for unused stamps in this section, from this point to the end of the section, are for Never Hinged items.

D2

1945   Litho.   Perf. 12
J23 D2 10c slate blue   .45 16.00
J24 D2 15c yel green   .45 16.00
J25 D2 25c deep orange   .45 16.00
J26 D2 50c greenish blk   1.00 16.00
J27 D2 60c copper brn   1.00 16.00
J28 D2 1fr deep red lil   1.00 16.00
J29 D2 2fr red   1.00 16.00
J30 D2 4fr slate gray   4.50 20.00
J31 D2 5fr brt ultra   4.50 20.00
J32 D2 10fr purple   22.50 52.50
J33 D2 20fr dull brown   4.00 20.00
J34 D2 50fr deep green   7.25 27.50
   Nos. J23-J34 (12)   48.10 252.00

FRENCH CONGO

'french 'käŋˌgō

LOCATION — Central Africa
GOVT. — French possession

French Congo was originally a separate colony, but was joined in 1888 to Gabon and placed under one commissioner-general with a lieutenant-governor presiding in Gabon and another in French Congo. In 1894 the military holdings in Ubangi were attached to French Congo, and in 1900 the Chad military protectorate was added. Postal service was not established in Ubangi or Chad, however, at that time. In 1906 Gabon and Middle Congo were separated and French Congo ceased to exist as such. Chad and Ubangi remained attached to Middle Congo as the joint dependency of "Ubangi-Chari-Chad," and Middle Congo stamps were used there.

Issues of the Republic of the Congo are listed under Congo People's Republic (ex-French).

100 Centimes = 1 Franc

Watermarks

Wmk. 122
Thistle
Branch

Wmk. 123 —
Rose Branch

Wmk. 124
Olive Branch

Stamps of French
Colonies Surcharged
Horizontally in Red or
Black

1891		Unwmk.	Perf. 14x13½
1	A9 5c on 1c blk, lil bl (R)	6,250.	4,500.
2	A9 5c on 1c blk, lil bl	185.00	100.00
a.	Double surcharge	625.00	425.00
3	A9 5c on 15c blue	325.00	165.00
a.	Double surcharge	675.00	350.00
5	A9 5c on 25c blk, rose	120.00	50.00
a.	Inverted surcharge		

First "O" of "Congo" is a Capital,
"Francais" with Capital "F"

1891-92			
6	A9 5c on 20c red, grn	1,250.	425.00
7	A9 5c on 25c blk, rose	185.00	95.00
a.	Surcharge vertical	250.00	105.00
8	A9 10c on 25c blk, rose	225.00	65.00
a.	Inverted surcharge	400.00	150.00
b.	Surcharge vertical	275.00	100.00
d.	Double surcharge	400.00	210.00

9	A9 10c on 40c red, straw	2,500.	375.00
10	A9 15c on 25c blk, rose	210.00	50.00
a.	Surcharge vertical	250.00	85.00
c.	Double surcharge	375.00	185.00

First "O" of Congo small
Surcharge Vert., Down or Up
No period

11	A9 5c on 25c blk, rose	250.00	120.00
12	A9 10c on 25c blk, rose	—	—
13	A9 15c on 25c blk, rose	400.00	165.00

Postage Due Stamps of
French Colonies
Surcharged in Red or
Black Reading Down or
Up

1892			Imperf.
14	D1 5c on 5c blk (R)	175.00	135.00
a.	Double surcharge	1,450.	
15	D1 5c on 20c blk (R)	175.00	135.00
16	D1 5c on 30c blk (R)	225.00	165.00
17	D1 10c on 1fr brown	175.00	130.00
a.	Double surcharge	4,100.	
b.	Surcharge horiz.		2,350.
c.	"Congo" omitted		475.00
	Nos. 14-17 (4)	750.00	565.00

Excellent counterfeits of Nos. 1-17 exist.

Navigation and
Commerce — A3

1892-1900	Typo.	Perf. 14x13½
Colony Name in Blue or Carmine		
18	A3 1c blk, lil bl	1.60	1.60
a.	Name double	200.00	165.00
19	A3 2c brn, buff	3.00	3.00
a.	Name double	200.00	175.00
20	A3 4c claret, lav	3.00	3.00
a.	Name in blk and in blue	200.00	175.00
21	A3 5c grn, grnsh	6.00	6.00
22	A3 10c blk, lavender	20.00	19.00
a.	Name double	825.00	550.00
23	A3 10c red ('00)	3.00	2.25
24	A3 15c blue, quadrille paper	52.50	18.50
25	A3 15c gray ('00)	9.25	6.75
26	A3 20c red, grn	22.00	18.50
27	A3 25c blk, rose	24.00	16.00
28	A3 25c blue ('00)	10.50	10.50
29	A3 30c brn, bis	30.00	20.00
30	A3 40c red, straw	52.50	32.50
31	A3 50c car, rose	47.50	32.50
32	A3 50c brn, az ('00)	15.00	14.00
a.	Name double	750.00	750.00
33	A3 75c dp vio, org	40.00	32.50
34	A3 1fr brnz grn, straw	55.00	32.50
	Nos. 18-34 (17)	394.85	269.10

Perf. 13½x14 stamps are counterfeits.
For surcharges see Nos. 50-51.

Leopard — A4

Bakalois
Woman — A5

Coconut
Grove — A6

Design A4 exists in two types. Type 1: end of left tusk extends behind and above right tusk. Type 2: end of left tusk does not appear behind right tusk. Type 2 of design A4 appears in position 91 of each pane of 100. For detailed listings, see the Scott Catalogue Classic Spcialized of Stamps & Covers.

1900-04		Wmk. 122	Perf. 11
35	A4 1c brn vio & gray lilac (1)	.80	.80
a.	Background inverted	72.50	72.50
36	A4 2c brn & org (1)	.80	.80
a.	Imperf., pair	75.00	75.00
b.	Pair, imperf between	92.50	105.00
37	A4 4c scar & gray bl	1.60	1.20
a.	Background inverted	90.00	75.00
b.	Type 2	52.50	52.50
38	A4 5c grn & gray grn (1)	2.75	1.50
a.	Imperf., pair	140.00	140.00
39	A4 10c dk red & red (1)	7.50	3.00
a.	Imperf., pair	140.00	140.00
40	A4 15c dl vio & ol grn	2.40	1.20
a.	Imperf. pair	120.00	

		Wmk. 123	
41	A5 20c yel grn & org (1)	2.40	2.00
42	A5 25c bl & pale bl	3.50	2.25
43	A5 30c car rose & org	4.50	2.40
44	A5 40c org brn & brt grn	5.25	2.75
a.	Imperf., pair	105.00	105.00
b.	Center and value inverted	190.00	160.00
45	A5 50c gray vio & lil	6.75	6.00
46	A5 75c red vio & org	15.00	10.50
a.	Imperf., pair	105.00	105.00

		Wmk. 124	
47	A6 1fr gray lil & ol	24.00	18.50
a.	Center and value inverted	280.00	275.00
b.	Imperf., pair	140.00	140.00
48	A6 2fr car & brn	45.00	30.00
a.	Imperf., pair	275.00	275.00
49	A6 5fr brn org & gray	85.00	72.50
a.	5fr ocher & gray	750.00	950.00
b.	Center and value inverted	425.00	425.00
c.	Wmk. 123	500.00	500.00
d.	Imperf., pair	750.00	750.00
	Nos. 35-49 (15)	207.25	155.40

For surcharges see Nos. 52-53.

Nos. 26 and 29 Surcharged
in Black

Valeur
15

1900		Unwmk.	Perf. 14x13½
50	A3 5c on 20c red, grn 26,000.		6,000.
a.	Double surcharge		18,500.
51	A3 15c on 30c brn, bis 20,000.		2,600.
a.	Double surcharge		6,000.

Nos. 43 and 48 Surcharged in Black:

a

b

1903		Wmk. 123	Perf. 11
52	A5 5c on 30c	300.00	150.00
a.	Inverted surcharge	2,750.	

		Wmk. 124	
53	A6 10c on 2fr	350.00	145.00
a.	Inverted surcharge	2,750.	
b.	Double surcharge	3,250.	

Counterfeits of the preceding surcharges are known.

FRENCH EQUATORIAL AFRICA

ˈfrench ˌē-kwə-ˈtōr-ē-əl ˈa-fri-kə

LOCATION — North of Belgian Congo and south of Libya
GOVT. — French Colony
AREA — 959,256 square miles
POP. — 4,491,785
CAPITAL — Brazzaville

In 1910 Gabon and Middle Congo, with its military dependencies, were politically united as French Equatorial Africa. The component colonies were granted administrative autonomy. In 1915 Ubangi-Chari-Chad was made an autonomous civilian colony and in 1920 Chad was made a civil colony. In 1934 the four colonies were administratively united as one colony, but this federation was not completed until 1936. Each colony had its own postal administration until 1936. The postal issues of the former colonial subdivisions are listed under the names of those colonies.

In 1958, French Equatorial Africa was divided into four republics: Chad, Congo, Gabon and Central African Republic (formerly Ubangi-Chari).

Stamps other than Nos. 189-192 are inscribed with "Afrique Equatoriale Francaise" or "AEF" and the name of one of the component colonies are listed under those colonies.

100 Centimes = 1 Franc

Catalogue values for unused stamps in this country are for Never Hinged items, beginning with Scott 142 in the regular postage section, Scott B8A in the semi-postal section, Scott C17 in the airpost section, and Scott J12 in the postage due section.

Stamps of Gabon, 1932, Overprinted "Afrique Equatoriale Francaise" and Bars Similar to "a" and "b" in Black
Perf. 13x13½, 13½x13

1936 Unwmk.

1	A16	1c brown violet	.30	.50
2	A16	2c black, *rose*	.70	.80
3	A16	4c green	1.25	1.60
4	A16	5c grnsh blue	1.25	1.60
5	A16	10c red, *yel*	1.25	1.50
6	A17	40c brown violet	3.50	2.75
7	A17	50c red brown	2.75	2.00
8	A17	1fr yel grn, *bl*	30.00	13.50
9	A18	1.50fr dull blue	8.75	2.75
10	A18	2fr brown red	17.50	13.00
		Nos. 1-10 (10)	67.25	40.00

Stamps of Middle Congo, 1933 Overprinted in Black:

a

b

c

1936

11	A4 (b)	1c lt brown	.30	.50
12	A4 (b)	2c dull blue	.30	.50
13	A4 (b)	4c olive green	1.40	1.60
14	A4 (b)	5c red violet	.80	1.00
15	A4 (b)	10c slate	1.60	1.25
16	A4 (b)	15c dk violet	2.00	1.60
17	A4 (b)	20c red, *pink*	2.00	1.60

18	A4 (b)	25c orange	3.25	2.40
19	A5 (a)	40c orange brn	4.00	2.75
20	A5 (c)	50c black violet	4.00	2.40
21	A5 (c)	75c black, *pink*	5.50	4.75
22	A5 (a)	90c carmine	5.50	4.00
23	A5 (c)	1.50fr dark blue	3.50	2.00
24	A6 (a)	5fr slate blue	55.00	35.00
25	A6 (a)	10fr black	35.00	30.00
26	A6 (a)	20fr dark brown	35.00	32.50
		Nos. 11-26 (16)	159.15	123.85

Other overprints inscribed "Afrique Equitoriale Française" in a different type font on earlier Middle Congo stamps are listed under Middle Congo.

Common Design Types pictured following the introduction.

Paris International Exposition Issue
Common Design Types

1937, Apr. 15   Engr.   Perf. 13

27	CD74	20c dark violet	2.40	2.40
28	CD75	30c dark green	2.40	2.40
29	CD76	40c carmine rose	2.40	2.40
30	CD77	50c dk brn & bl	2.40	2.40
31	CD78	90c red	2.50	2.50
32	CD79	1.50fr ultra	2.50	2.50
		Nos. 27-32 (6)	14.60	14.60

Logging on Loéme River — A1

People of Chad — A2

Pierre Savorgnan de Brazza A3

Emile Gentil — A4

Paul Crampel A5

Governor Victor Liotard A6

Two types of 25c:
Type I — Wide numerals (4mm).
Type II — Narrow numerals (3½mm).

1937-40   Photo.   Perf. 13½x13

33	A1	1c brown & yel	.25	.25
34	A1	2c violet & grn	.25	.25
35	A1	3c blue & yel ('40)	.25	.30
36	A1	4c magenta & bl	.30	.30
37	A1	5c dk & lt green	.50	.30
38	A2	10c magenta & blue	.30	.30
39	A2	15c blue & buff	.30	.30
40	A2	20c brown & yellow	.30	*.30*
41	A2	25c cop red & bl (I)	.75	.30
a.		Type II	2.75	2.00
42	A3	30c gray grn & grn	.80	.55
43	A3	30c chlky bl, ind & buff ('40)	.40	.50
44	A2	35c dp grn & yel ('38)	.95	.90
45	A3	40c cop red & bl	.40	.30
46	A3	45c dk bl & lt grn	4.50	3.50
47	A3	45c dp grn & yel grn ('40)	.55	.65
48	A3	50c brown & yellow	.40	.25
49	A3	55c pur & bl ('38)	.80	.75

50	A3	60c mar & gray bl ('40)	.65	.75
51	A4	65c dk bl & lt grn	.80	.40
52	A4	70c dp vio & buff ('40)	.75	.80
53	A4	75c ol blk & dl yel	5.25	4.50
54	A4	80c brn & yel ('38)	.55	.55
55	A4	90c copper red & buff	.55	.40
56	A4	1fr dk vio & lt grn	2.10	1.10
57	A3	1fr cer & dl org ('38)	3.00	1.25
58	A4	1fr bl grn & sl grn ('40)	.55	.55
59	A5	1.25fr cop red & buff	1.25	.90
60	A5	1.40fr dk brn & pale grn ('40)	1.00	1.25
61	A5	1.50fr dk & lt blue	1.50	.75
62	A5	1.60fr dp vio & buff ('40)	1.00	1.25
63	A5	1.75fr brn & yel	1.75	.90
64	A5	1.75fr bl & lt bl ('38)	.75	.65
65	A5	2fr dk & lt green	.95	.75
66	A6	2.15fr brn, vio & yel ('38)	1.00	.80
67	A6	2.25fr bl & lt bl ('39)	1.60	1.60
68	A6	2.50fr rose lake & buff ('40)	1.25	1.25
69	A6	3fr dk blue & buff	.75	.40
70	A6	5fr dk & lt green	1.40	.95
71	A6	10fr dk violet & bl	3.25	2.50
72	A6	20fr ol blk & bl ('40)	2.50	2.50
		Nos. 33-72 (40)	47.15	37.65

For overprints and surcharges see Nos. 80-127, 129-141, B2-B3, B10-B13, B22-B23.

Colonial Arts Exhibition Issue
Souvenir Sheet
Common Design Type

1937   Imperf.

73	CD79	3fr red brown	11.00	*12.00*
		Never hinged	15.00	

Count Louis Edouard Bouet-Willaumez and His Ship "La Malouine" — A7

1938, Dec. 5   Perf. 13½

74	A7	65c gray brown	1.25	1.25
75	A7	1fr deep rose	1.25	1.25
76	A7	1.75fr blue	1.60	1.60
77	A7	2fr dull violet	2.40	2.40
		Nos. 74-77 (4)	6.50	6.50
		Set, never hinged	9.00	

Centenary of Gabon.

New York World's Fair Issue
Common Design Type

1939, May 10   Engr.   Perf. 12½x12

78	CD82	1.25fr carmine lake	1.75	1.75
79	CD82	2.25fr ultra	1.90	1.90
		Set, never hinged	4.75	

Libreville View and Marshal Petain A7a

1941   Engr.   Perf. 12½x12

79A	A7a	1fr bluish green	1.20	
79B	A7a	2.50fr blue	1.20	
		Set, never hinged	3.25	

Nos. 79A-79B were issued by the Vichy government in France, but were not placed on sale in French Equatorial Africa.
For surcharges, see Nos. B36-B37.

Stamps of 1936-40, Overprinted in Carmine or Black:

Nos. 80-82, 84-88, 93

Nos. 83, 89-92, 94-125

1940-41   Perf. 13½x13

80	A1	1c brn & yel (C)	2.40	2.40
81	A1	2c vio & grn (C)	2.40	2.40
82	A1	3c blue & yel (C)	2.40	2.40
83	A1	4c ol grn (No. 13)	16.00	13.00
b.		Inverted overprint	120.00	150.00
84	A1	5c dk grn & lt grn (C)	2.40	2.40
85	A2	10c magenta & bl	2.40	2.40
86	A2	15c blue & buff (C)	2.40	2.40
87	A2	20c brn & yel (C)	2.40	2.40
88	A2	25c cop red & bl	9.50	9.50
89	A3	30c gray grn & grn (C)	20.00	13.50
90	A3	30c gray grn & grn ('41)	3.25	3.25
91	A3	30c chlky bl, ind & buff (C) ('41)	10.50	8.75
92	A3	30c chlky bl, ind & buff ('41)	14.50	13.00
93	A2	35c dp grn & yel (C)	2.40	2.40
94	A3	40c cop red & bl	1.60	1.60
b.		Inverted overprint		100.00
95	A3	45c dp grn & yel (C)	1.60	1.20
96	A3	45c dp grn & yel grn ('41)	2.00	2.00
97	A3	50c brn & yel (C)	8.00	6.50
98	A3	50c brn & yel ('41)	7.25	7.25
99	A3	55c pur & bl (C)	1.60	1.20
100	A3	55c pur & bl ('41)	2.00	2.00
101	A3	60c mar & gray bl	1.60	1.60
102	A4	65c dk bl & lt grn	1.60	1.60
103	A4	70c dp vio & buff	1.60	1.60
104	A4	75c ol blk & dl yel	67.50	67.50
105	A4	80c brown & yellow	1.60	1.60
106	A4	90c cop red & buff	1.60	1.60
107	A4	1fr bl grn & lt grn	10.50	9.50
108	A4	1fr bl grn & sl grn (C) ('41)	9.50	8.00
109	A3	1fr cer & dl org	2.40	2.40
110	A5	1.40fr dk brn & pale grn	1.60	1.60
111	A5	1.50fr dk bl & lt bl	1.60	1.60
112	A5	1.60fr dp vio & buff	1.60	1.60
113	A5	1.75fr brown & yel	2.00	2.00
114	A6	2.15fr brn, vio & yel	2.00	2.00
115	A6	2.25fr bl & lt bl (C)	1.60	1.60
116	A6	2.25fr bl & lt bl ('41)	4.00	4.00
117	A6	2.50fr rose lake & buff	1.60	1.60
118	A6	3fr dk bl & buff (C)	1.60	1.60
119	A6	3fr dk bl & buff ('41)	4.00	4.00
120	A6	5fr dk grn & lt grn (C)	4.00	4.00
121	A6	5fr dk grn & lt grn ('41)	120.00	67.50
122	A6	10fr dk vio & bl (C)	3.25	3.25
123	A6	10fr dk vio & bl ('41)	110.00	67.50
124	A6	20fr ol blk & dl yel (C)	2.40	2.40
125	A6	20fr ol blk & dl yel ('41)	18.00	16.00
		Nos. 80-125 (46)	494.15	379.60

For overprints and surcharges see Nos. 129-132, B12-B13, B22-B23.
For types of Nos. 38//61 without "RF," see Nos. 155A-155B.

Double Overprint

80a	A1	1c	325.00	225.00
81a	A1	2c	32.50	
82a	A1	3c	32.50	
83a	A4	4c	75.00	
84a	A1	5c	32.50	
85a	A2	10c	32.50	40.00
86a	A2	15c	32.50	
87a	A2	20c	55.00	
88a	A2	25c	55.00	
89a	A3	30c	110.00	120.00
90a	A3	30c		55.00
91a	A3	30c	47.50	47.50
93a	A2	35c	250.00	
94a	A3	40c	45.00	
96a	A3	45c	45.00	65.00
98a	A3	50c	45.00	
100a	A3	55c	45.00	
102a	A4	65c	47.50	
103a	A4	70c	47.50	
105a	A4	80c	47.50	
106a	A4	90c	45.00	
b.		one inverted	120.00	
109a	A4	1fr One inverted	120.00	
110a	A5	1.40fr	47.50	
111a	A5	1.50fr	47.50	
114a	A6	2.15fr	40.00	
115a	A6	2.25fr	60.00	
116a	A6	2.25fr	45.00	
117a	A6	2.50fr	47.50	
119a	A6	3fr	45.00	
123a	A6	10fr	60.00	67.50
124a	A6	20fr	60.00	
		Nos. 96a-124a (17)	895.00	

Nos. 48, 51
Surcharged
in Black or
Carmine

1940
126	A3	75c on 50c	.75	.75
a.		Double surcharge	40.00	
127	A4	1fr on 65c (C)	.90	.90
a.		Double surcharge	32.50	
		Set, never hinged	2.35	

Middle Congo No. 67 Overprinted in
Carmine like No. 80
Perf. 13½

128	A4	4c olive green	65.00	60.00

Stamps of
1940 With
Additional
Overprint in
Black

1940   *Perf. 13½x13*
129	A4	80c brown & yel	17.50	13.50
a.		Overprint without "2"	150.00	
130	A4	1fr bl grn & sl grn	22.50	18.00
131	A3	1fr cer & dull org	19.00	14.50
132	A5	1.50fr dk bl & lt bl	17.00	13.50
		Nos. 129-132 (4)	76.00	59.50
		Set, never hinged	85.00	

Arrival of General de Gaulle in Brazzaville,
capital of Free France, Oct. 24, 1940.

These stamps were sold affixed to post
cards and at a slight increase over face value
to cover the cost of the cards. Values for
unused stamps are for examples without gum.
For surcharges see Nos. B12-B13, B22-
B23.

Stamps of
1937-40
Overprinted
in Black

1941
133	A1	1c brown & yel	2.40	2.40
134	A1	2c violet & grn	2.40	2.40
135	A1	3c blue & yel	2.40	2.40
136	A1	5c dk & lt green	2.40	2.40
137	A2	10c magenta & bl	2.40	2.40
138	A2	15c blue & buff	2.40	2.40
139	A2	20c brown & grn	2.40	2.40
140	A2	25c copper red & bl	6.50	6.50
141	A2	35c dp grn & yel	6.50	6.50
a.		Double overprint	120.00	
		Nos. 133-141 (9)	29.80	29.80
		Set, never hinged	47.50	

There are 2 settings of the overprint on Nos.
133-141 & C10. The 1st has 1mm between
lines of the overprint (Nos. 133-141), the 2nd
has 2mm. Value, set with 2mm spacing $95.

**Catalogue values for unused
stamps in this section, from this
point to the end of the section, are
for Never Hinged items.**

Phoenix — A8

1941   **Photo.**   *Perf. 14x14½*
142	A8	5c brown	.30	.25
143	A8	10c dark blue	.30	.25
144	A8	25c emerald	.30	.25
145	A8	30c deep orange	.30	.25
146	A8	40c dk slate grn	.55	.30
147	A8	80c red brown	.55	.30
148	A8	1fr deep red lilac	.55	.30
149	A8	1.50fr brt red	.75	.40
150	A8	2fr gray	.75	.40
151	A8	2.50fr brt ultra	.95	.70
152	A8	4fr dull violet	.95	.70
153	A8	5fr yellow bister	.95	.70

154	A8	10fr deep brown	1.40	1.00
155	A8	20fr deep green	1.75	1.25
		Nos. 142-155 (14)	10.35	7.05

For surcharges see #158-165, B14-B21,
B24-B35.

Types of 1937-40 without "RF"
1944   *Perf. 13½*
155A	A2	10c magenta & blue	1.20
155B	A2	15c blue & buff	1.60
155C	A3	60c maroon & gray blue	1.60
155D	A5	1.50fr dk & lt blue	2.00
		Nos. 155A-155D (4)	6.40

Nos. 155A-155D were issued by the Vichy
government in France, but were not sold in
French Equatorial Africa.

Eboue Issue
Common Design Type
1945   **Unwmk.**   **Engr.**   *Perf. 13*
156	CD91	2fr black	.65	.50
157	CD91	25fr Prussian green	1.90	1.50

Nos. 156-157 exist imperforate. Value, set
$65.

Nos. 142, 144 and 151 Surcharged
with New Values and Bars in Red,
Carmine or Black
1946   *Perf. 14x14½*
158	A8	50c on 5c (R)	.80	.65
159	A8	60c on 5c (R)	.80	.65
160	A8	70c on 5c (R)	.80	.65
161	A8	1.20fr on 5c (C)	.80	.65
162	A8	2.40fr on 25c	1.40	1.00
163	A8	3fr on 25c	1.40	1.00
164	A8	4.50fr on 25c	1.75	1.20
165	A8	15fr on 2.50fr (C)	1.90	1.40
		Nos. 158-165 (8)	9.65	7.20

Black
Rhinoceros
and Rock
Python
A9

Jungle
Scene — A10

Mountainous
Shore
Line — A11

Gabon
Forest — A12

Niger
Boatman — A13

Young Bacongo
Woman — A14

1946   **Unwmk.**   **Engr.**   *Perf. 12½*
166	A9	10c deep blue	.30	.25
167	A9	30c violet blk	.30	.25
168	A9	40c dp orange	.30	.25
169	A10	50c violet bl	.65	.50
170	A10	60c dk carmine	.65	.50
171	A10	80c dk ol grn	.65	.50
172	A11	1fr dp orange	.95	.30
173	A11	1.20fr dp claret	.95	.65
174	A11	1.50fr dk green	1.40	.95
175	A12	2fr dk vio brn	.55	.25

176	A12	3fr rose carmine	.80	.50
177	A12	3.60fr red brown	3.50	2.50
178	A12	4fr deep blue	.80	.30
179	A13	5fr dk brown	1.00	.25
180	A13	6fr deep blue	1.25	.30
181	A13	10fr black	2.25	.75
182	A14	15fr brown	2.25	.75
183	A14	20fr dp claret	2.25	.80
184	A14	25fr black	2.75	.80
		Nos. 166-184 (19)	23.55	11.35

Imperforates
Most French Equatorial Africa stamps
from 1951 onward exist imperforate in
issued and trial colors, and also in small
presentation sheets in issued colors.

Pierre Savorgnan de
Brazza — A15

1951, Nov. 5   *Perf. 13*
185	A15	10fr indigo & dk grn	1.60	.40

Cent. of the birth of Pierre Savorgnan de
Brazza, explorer.

Military Medal Issue
Common Design Type
Engraved and Typographed
1952, Dec. 1   *Perf. 13*
186	CD101	15fr multicolored	7.25	5.50

Lt. Gov.
Adolphe L.
Cureau
A16

1954, Sept. 20   **Engr.**
187	A16	15fr ol grn & red brn	2.00	.80

Savannah
Monitor
A17

1955, May 2   **Unwmk.**
188	A17	8fr dk grn & claret	2.40	1.25

International Exhibition for Wildlife Protection, Paris, May 1955.

FIDES Issue
Common Design Type
Designs: 5fr, Boali Waterfall and Power
Plant, Ubangi-Chari. 10fr, Cotton, Chad. 15fr,
Brazzaville Hospital, Middle Congo. 20fr,
Libreville Harbor, Gabon.
1956, Apr. 25   *Perf. 13x12½*
189	CD103	5fr dk brn & claret	.65	.30
190	CD103	10fr blk & bluish grn	.80	.40
191	CD103	15fr ind & gray vio	.80	.40
192	CD103	20fr dk red & red org	1.10	.65
		Nos. 189-192 (4)	3.35	1.75

Coffee Issue

Coffee
A19

1956, Oct.   **Engr.**   *Perf. 13*
193	A19	10fr brn vio & vio bl	1.60	.40

Leprosarium at Mayumba and Maltese
Cross — A20

1957, Mar. 11
194	A20	15fr grn, bl grn & red	2.00	.80

Issued in honor of the Knights of Malta.

Giant Eland
A21

1957, Nov. 4
195	A21	1fr shown	.75	.40
196	A21	2fr Lions	.75	.40
197	A21	3fr Elephant, vert.	.90	.40
198	A21	4fr Greater kudu, vert.	.90	.40
		Nos. 195-198 (4)	3.30	1.60

WHO
Building,
Brazzaville
A22

1958, May 19   **Engr.**   *Perf. 13*
199	A22	20fr dk green & org brn	1.60	.80

10th anniv. of WHO.

Flower Issue
Common Design Type
1958, July 7   **Photo.**   *Perf. 12x12½*
200	CD104	10fr Euadania	1.40	.65
201	CD104	25fr Spathodea	1.90	.95

Human Rights Issue
Common Design Type
1958, Dec. 10   **Engr.**   *Perf. 13*
202	CD105	20fr Prus grn & dk bl	2.40	1.25

SEMI-POSTAL STAMPS

Common Design Type
1938, Oct. 24   **Engr.**
B1	CD80	1.75fr + 50c brt ultra	22.50	22.50
		Never hinged	35.00	

Nos. 51,
64
Surcharged
in Black or
Red

1938, Nov. 7   *Perf. 13x13½*
B2	A4	65c + 35c dk bl & lt grn (R)	2.40	2.40
B3	A4	1.75fr + 50c bl & lt bl	2.40	2.40
		Set, never hinged	7.00	

The surtax was for welfare.

French Revolution Issue
Common Design Type
Name and Value Typo. in Black
1939, July 5   **Photo.**
B4	CD83	45c + 25c green	14.50	14.50
B5	CD83	70c + 30c brown	14.50	14.50
B6	CD83	90c + 35c red org	14.50	14.50

B7	CD83	1.25fr + 1fr rose pink	14.50 14.50
B8	CD83	2.25fr + 2fr blue	14.50 14.50
		Nos. B4-B8 (5)	72.50 72.50
		Set, never hinged	110.00

Surtax used for the defense of the colonies.

> **Catalogue values for unused stamps in this section, from this point to the end of the section, are for Never Hinged items.**

Common Design Type and

Native Artilleryman SP1

Gabon Infantryman SP2

1941 Photo. Perf. 13½

B8A	SP1	1fr + 1fr red	3.50
B8B	CD86	1.50fr + 3fr maroon	3.50
B8C	SP2	2.50fr + 1fr blue	3.50
		Nos. B8A-B8C (3)	10.50

Nos. B8A-B8C were issued by the Vichy government in France, but were not placed on sale in French Equatorial Africa.

Brazza and Stanley Pool SP3

1941 Photo. Perf. 14½x14

B9	SP3	1fr + 2fr dk brn & red	2.00 1.60

The surtax was for a monument to Pierre Savorgnan de Brazza.

Nos. 67, 71 Surcharged in Red

1943, June 28 Perf. 13½x13

B10	A6	2.25fr + 50fr	27.50 16.00
B11	A6	10fr + 100fr	95.00 55.00

Nos. 129 and 132 with additional Surcharge in Carmine

1944

B12	A4	80c + 10fr	45.00 27.50
B13	A5	1.50fr + 15fr	45.00 27.50

Same surcharge printed Vertically on Nos. 142-146, 148, 150-151
Perf. 14x14½

B14	A8	5c + 10fr brown	13.50 8.75
B15	A8	10c + 10fr dk bl	13.50 8.75
B16	A8	25c + 10fr emer	13.50 8.75
B17	A8	30c + 10fr dp org	13.50 8.75
B18	A8	40c + 10fr dk sl grn	13.50 8.75
B19	A8	1fr + 10fr dp red lil	13.50 8.75
B20	A8	2fr + 20fr gray	13.50 8.75
B21	A8	2.50fr + 25fr brt ultra	13.50 8.75
		Nos. B12-B21 (10)	198.00 125.00

Nos. 129 and 132 with additional Surcharge in Carmine

1944 Perf. 13½x13

B22	A4	80c + 10fr	45.00 27.50
B23	A5	1.50fr + 15fr	45.00 27.50

Same Surcharge printed Vertically on Nos. 142-146, 148, 150-155
Perf. 14x14½

B24	A8	5c + 10fr brn	13.50 8.75
B25	A8	10c + 10fr dk bl	13.50 8.75
B26	A8	25c + 10fr emer	13.50 8.75
B27	A8	30c + 10fr dp org	13.50 8.75
B28	A8	40c + 10fr dk sl grn	13.50 8.75
B29	A8	1fr + 10fr dp red lil	13.50 8.75
B30	A8	2fr + 20fr gray	13.50 8.75
B31	A8	2.50fr + 25fr brt ultra	13.50 8.75
B32	A8	4fr + 40fr dl vio	13.50 8.75
B33	A8	5fr + 50fr yel bis	13.50 8.75
B34	A8	10fr + 100fr dp brn	13.50 8.75
B35	A8	20fr + 200fr dp grn	13.50 8.75
		Nos. B22-B35 (14)	252.00 160.00

Nos. B12 to B35 were issued to raise funds for the Committee to Aid the Fighting Men and Patriots of France.

Nos. 79A-79B Surcharged in Black or Red

1944 Engr. Perf. 12½x12

B36		50c + 1.50fr on 2.50fr deep blue (R)	1.60
B37		+ 2.50fr on 1fr green	1.60

Colonial Development Fund.
Nos. B36-B37 were issued by the Vichy government in France, but were not placed on sale in French Equatorial Africa.

Red Cross Issue
Common Design Type

1944 Photo. Perf. 14½x14

B38	CD90	5fr + 20fr royal blue	1.60 1.20

The surtax was for the French Red Cross and national relief.

Tropical Medicine Issue
Common Design Type

1950, May 15 Engr. Perf. 13

B39	CD100	10fr + 2fr dk bl grn & vio brn	7.25 5.50

The surtax was for charitable work.

AIR POST STAMPS

Hydroplane over Pointe-Noire — AP1

Trimotor over Stanley Pool — AP2

1937 Unwmk. Photo. Perf. 13½

C1	AP1	1.50fr ol blk & yel	.40 .40
C2	AP1	2fr mag & blue	.55 .55
C3	AP1	2.50fr grn & buff	.55 .55
C4	AP1	3.75fr brn & lt grn	.80 .80
C5	AP2	4.50fr cop red & bl	.80 .80

C6	AP2	6.50fr bl & lt grn	1.60 1.60
C7	AP2	8.50fr red brn & yel	1.60 1.60
C8	AP2	10.75frvio & lt grn	1.60 1.60
		Nos. C1-C8 (8)	7.90 7.90

For overprints and surcharges see #C9-C16, CB2.

Nos. C1, C3-C7 Overprinted in Black like Nos. 133-141

1940-41

C9	AP1	1.50fr ('41)	240.00 240.00
C10	AP1	2.50fr	2.40 2.40
a.		Double overprint	275.00 275.00
b.		Inverted overprint	275.00 275.00
C11	AP1	3.75fr ('41)	240.00 240.00
C12	AP2	4.50fr	3.25 3.25
a.		Double overprint	275.00 275.00
C13	AP2	6.50fr	4.00 4.00
a.		Double overprint	130.00 130.00
C14	AP2	8.50fr	3.25 3.25

No. C8 Surcharged in Carmine

C15	AP2	50fr on 10.75fr	11.00 11.00

No. C3 Surcharged in Black

C16	AP1	10fr on 2.50fr ('41)	95.00 95.00
		Nos. C9-C16 (8)	598.90 598.90

Counterfeits of Nos. C9 and C11 exist. See note following No. 141.

> **Catalogue values for unused stamps in this section, from this point to the end of the section, are for Never Hinged items.**

Common Design Type

1941 Photo. Perf. 14½x14

C17	CD87	1fr dark orange	.65 .30
C18	CD87	1.50fr brt red	.95 .50
C19	CD87	5fr brown red	1.60 .90
C20	CD87	10fr black	1.75 1.00
C21	CD87	25fr ultra	1.60 1.20
C22	CD87	50fr dark green	1.60 1.20
C23	CD87	100fr plum	2.25 1.25
		Nos. C17-C23 (7)	10.40 6.35

Types of 1937 without "RF" and

Sikorsky 5.43 Seaplane and Canoe — AP2a

Perf. 13½, 13 (#C23M)

1943, Oct. 18-1944 Unwmk.

C23A	AP1	1.50fr ol blk & yel	.40
C23B	AP1	2fr mag & blue	.40
C23C	AP1	2.50fr grn & buff	.40
C23D	AP1	3.75fr brn & lt grn	.65
C23E	AP2	4.50fr cop red & bl	.65
C23F	AP2	5fr green	1.00
C23G	AP2	6.50fr bl & lt grn	.95
C23H	AP2	8.50fr red brn & yel	.90
C23I	AP2	10fr gray & brn ('44)	1.00
C23J	AP2	10.75fr vio & lt grn	1.10
C23K	AP2	20fr yel & brn red ('44)	1.10
C23L	AP2	50fr gray grn & blk ('44)	1.75
C23M	AP2a	100fr red brown ('44)	1.60
		Nos. C23A-C23M (13)	11.90

Issue dates: Nos. C23I, C23K-L, 4/3/44; C23M, 6/26/44.
Nos. C23A-C23M were issued by the Vichy government in France, but were not sold in French Equatorial Africa.

Victory Issue
Common Design Type
Perf. 12½

1946, May 8 Unwmk. Engr.

C24	CD92	8fr lilac rose	1.60 1.25

Chad to Rhine Issue
Common Design Types

1946, June 6

C25	CD93	5fr dk violet	1.40 1.10
C26	CD94	10fr slate green	1.50 1.20
C27	CD95	15fr deep blue	2.50 1.90
C28	CD96	20fr red orange	2.50 1.90
C29	CD97	25fr sepia	2.50 1.90
C30	CD98	50fr brown carmine	3.00 2.25
		Nos. C25-C30 (6)	13.40 10.25

Palms and Village — AP3

Village and Waterfront — AP4

Bearers in Jungle — AP5

1946 Engr. Perf. 13

C31	AP3	50fr red brn	3.50 .80
C32	AP4	100fr grnsh blk	5.25 1.25
C33	AP5	200fr deep blue	11.00 2.00
		Nos. C31-C33 (3)	19.75 4.05

UPU Issue
Common Design Type

1949, July 4

C34	CD99	25fr green	14.50 11.00

Brazza Holding Map — AP6

1951, Nov. 5

C35	AP6	15fr brn, indigo & red	2.40 1.60

Cent. of the birth of Pierre Savorgnan de Brazza, explorer.

Archbishop Augouard and St. Anne Cathedral, Brazzaville — AP7

1952, Dec. 1

C36	AP7	15fr ol grn, dk brn & vio brn	6.50 2.40

Cent. of the birth of Archbishop Philippe-Prosper Augouard.

Anhingas — AP8

1953, Feb. 16
C37 AP8 500fr grnsh blk, blk &
slate   47.50 8.00

Liberation Issue
Common Design Type
1954, June 6
C38 CD102 15fr vio & vio brn   9.50 7.25

Log Rafts — AP9

Designs: 100fr, Fishing boats and nets,
Lake Chad. 200fr, Age of mechanization.

1955, Jan. 24   **Engr.**
C39 AP9 50fr ind, brn & dk grn   2.40   .80
C40 AP9 100fr aqua, dk grn &
blk brn   8.00   1.60
C41 AP9 200fr red & deep plum   12.00   2.40
Nos. C39-C41 (3)   22.40   4.80

Gov. Gen. Félix Eboué, View of
Brazzaville and the Pantheon — AP10

1955, Apr. 30   Unwmk.   Perf. 13
C42 AP10 15fr sep, brn & slate
bl   6.50   2.40

Gen. Louis
Faidherbé and
African
Sharpshooter
AP11

1957, July 20
C43 AP11 15fr sepia & org ver   3.50   2.00
Centenary of French African Troops.

AIR POST SEMI-POSTAL STAMPS

French Revolution Issue
Common Design Type
1939   Unwmk.   Photo.   Perf. 13
Name and Value Typo. in Orange
CB1 CD83 4.50fr + 4fr brn blk   35.00 35.00

SPAP1

SPAP2

SPAP3

Unwmk.
1942, June 22   Engr.   Perf. 13
CB2 SPAP1 1.50fr + 3.50fr green   1.50
CB3 SPAP2 2fr + 6fr brown   1.50
CB4 SPAP3 3fr + 9fr carmine   1.50
Nos. CB2-CB4 (3)   4.50

Native children's welfare fund.
Nos. CB2-CB4 were issued by the Vichy
government in France, but were not placed on
sale in French Equatorial Africa.

Colonial Education Fund
Common Design Type
1942, June 22
CB5 CD86a 1.20fr + 1.80fr bl &
red   1.50

No. CB5 was issued by the Vichy government in France, but was not placed on sale in
French Equatorial Africa.

#C8 Surcharged in Red like #B10-B11
1943, June 28   Perf. 13½
CB6 AP2 10.75fr + 200fr   210.00 210.00

Counterfeits exist.

POSTAGE DUE STAMPS

Numeral of Value on
Equatorial
Butterfly — D1

1937   Unwmk.   Photo.   Perf. 13
J1 D1 5c redsh pur & lt bl   .25   .40
J2 D1 10c cop red & buff   .25   .40
J3 D1 20c dk grn & grn   .30   .50
J4 D1 25c red brn & buff   .30   .50
J5 D1 30c cop red & lt bl   .50   .55
J6 D1 45c mag & yel grn   .75   .80
J7 D1 50c dk ol grn & buff   .80   .95
J8 D1 60c redsh pur & yel   .95   1.10
J9 D1 1fr brown & yel   1.00   1.20
J10 D1 2fr dk bl & buff   1.40   1.50
J11 D1 3fr red brn & lt grn   1.50   1.60
Nos. J1-J11 (11)   8.00   9.50
Set, never hinged   11.00

**Catalogue values for unused
stamps in this section, from this
point to the end of the section, are
for Never Hinged items.**

D2

1947   Engr.
J12 D2 10c red   .40   .25
J13 D2 30c dp org   .40   .25
J14 D2 50c greenish bl   .50   .30
J15 D2 1fr carmine   .55   .40
J16 D2 2fr emerald   .65   .50
J17 D2 3fr dp red lil   .65   .50
J18 D2 4fr dp ultra   1.60   1.20

J19 D2 5fr red brown   1.60   1.20
J20 D2 10fr peacock blue   2.00   1.60
J21 D2 20fr sepia   2.10   1.75
Nos. J12-J21 (10)   10.45   7.95

FRENCH GUIANA

'french gē-'a-nə

LOCATION — On the northeast coast
of South America bordering on the
Atlantic Ocean.
GOVT. — French colony
AREA — 34,740 sq. mi.
POP. — 28,537 (1946)
CAPITAL — Cayenne

French Guiana became an overseas
department of France in 1946.

100 Centimes = 1 Franc

**Catalogue values for unused
stamps in this country are for
Never Hinged items, beginning
with Scott 171 in the regular postage section, Scott B12 in the semi-
postal section, Scott C9 in the airpost section, and Scott J22 in the
postage due section.**

See France No. 1446 for French
stamp inscribed "Guyane."

Stamps of French
Colonies Surcharged in
Black

1886, Dec.   Unwmk.   Imperf.
1 A8 5c on 2c grn,
grnsh, srchg
12mm high   725.00 650.00
a. Double surcharge   1,800. 1,800.
b. Surcharge 10½mm high   875.00 825.00
c. No "f" after "O"   725.00 675.00
Perf. 14x13½
2 A9 5c on 2c brn, buff,
srchg 12mm
high   560.00 525.00
a. No "f" after "O"   490.00 425.00
b. As "a," double surcharge 1,600. 1,600.

Nos. 1-2 unused are valued without gum.

"Av" of Date Line Inverted-Reversed
1887, Apr.   Imperf.
4 A8 20c on 35c blk, org   65.00 52.50
a. Double surcharge   210.00 210.00
b. No "f" after "O"   140.00 140.00
Date Line Reads "Avril 1887"
5 A8 5c on 2c grn,
grnsh   160.00 125.00
a. Double surcharge   800.00 800.00
b. No "f" after "O"   360.00 360.00
c. Pair, one stamp without
surcharge   1,450.
6 A8 20c on 35c blk, org   340.00 300.00
a. Double surcharge   1,100. 1,100.
b. No "f" after "O"   750.00 750.00
c. Vertical pair, #6 + #4 2,000.
7 A7 25c on 30c brn,
yelsh   52.50 45.00
a. Double surcharge   800.00 800.00
b. No "f" after "O"   225.00 225.00

Nos. 4-7 unused are valued without gum.

French Colonies Nos.
22 and 26 Surcharged

8 A7 5c on 30c brn,
yelsh   150.00 130.00
a. Double surcharge   750.00 750.00
b. Inverted surcharge   1,100. 1,100.
c. Pair, one without
surcharge   1,600.
9 A8 5c on 30c brn,
yelsh   1,500. 1,500.

Nos. 8-9 unused are valued without gum.

French Colonies Nos. 22 and 28
Surcharged:

1888
10 A7 5c on 30c brn,
yelsh   150.00 125.00
b. Double surcharge   475.00 475.00
c. Inverted surcharge   575.00 525.00
11 A8 10c on 75c car,
rose   400.00 290.00
No gum   290.00
a. Double surcharge   1,050. 1,050.
b. Pair, one stamp without
surcharge   2,400.

No. 10 unused is valued without gum.

Stamps of French
Colonies Overprinted in
Black

1892, Feb. 20   Imperf.
12 A8 2c grn, grnsh   800.00 875.00
a. Inverted overprint   3,000.
13 A7 30c brn, yelsh   150.00 150.00
a. Inverted overprint   550.00 550.00
14 A8 35c blk, orange   2,700. 2,900.
15 A8 40c red, straw   175.00 130.00
16 A8 75c car, rose   180.00 130.00
a. Inverted overprint   625.00 525.00
17 A8 1fr brnz grn, straw 210.00 160.00
a. Inverted overprint   725.00 725.00
b. Double overprint   725.00 725.00
c. Triple overprint   1,700. 1,700.

Nos. 12-14 unused are valued without gum.

1892   Perf. 14x13½
18 A9 1c blk, lil bl   45.00 32.50
19 A9 2c brn, buff   45.00 35.00
20 A9 4c claret, lav   40.00 35.00
21 A9 5c grn, grnsh   45.00 35.00
a. Inverted overprint   130.00 130.00
b. Double overprint   130.00 130.00
22 A9 10c blk, lavender 65.00 40.00
a. Inverted overprint   190.00 190.00
b. Double overprint   260.00 260.00
23 A9 15c blue   65.00 45.00
a. Double overprint   260.00 260.00
24 A9 20c red, grn   52.50 40.00
a. Inverted overprint   210.00 210.00
25 A9 25c blk, rose   72.50 35.00
a. Double overprint   240.00 260.00
b. Triple overprint   240.00 260.00
26 A9 30c brn, bis   45.00 40.00
27 A9 35c blk, orange   225.00 225.00
a. Inverted overprint   560.00 560.00
28 A9 40c red, straw   130.00 120.00
a. Inverted overprint   260.00 260.00
29 A9 75c car, rose   140.00 110.00
30 A9 1fr brnz grn, straw 250.00 210.00
a. Double overprint   350.00
Nos. 18-30 (13)   1,220. 1,002.

French Colonies No. 51
Surcharged

1892, Dec.
31 A9 5c on 15c blue   60.00 45.00
a. Double surcharge   300.00 275.00
b. No "f" after "O"   150.00 130.00
c. Pair, one stamp without
surcharge   1,600. 1,600.

Navigation and Commerce — A12

1892-1904   Typo.   Perf. 14x13½
Name of Colony in Blue or Carmine

32	A12	1c blk, *lil bl*	1.75	1.75
33	A12	2c brn, *buff*	1.25	1.25
34	A12	4c claret, *lav*	1.75	1.75
a.		"GUYANE" double	260.00	
35	A12	5c grn, *grnsh*	11.00	10.00
36	A12	5c yel grn ('04)	1.90	1.60
37	A12	10c blk, *lavender*	12.00	7.25
38	A12	10c red ('00)	4.50	1.60
39	A12	15c blue, quadrille paper	40.00	4.00
40	A12	15c gray, *lt gray* ('00)	120.00	100.00
41	A12	20c red, *grn*	24.00	17.50
42	A12	25c blk, *rose*	20.00	5.50
43	A12	25c blue ('00)	19.00	22.50
44	A12	30c brn, *bis*	21.00	16.00
45	A12	40c red, *straw*	22.50	16.00
46	A12	50c car, *rose*	32.50	18.00
47	A12	50c brn, *az* ('00)	26.00	26.00
48	A12	75c dp vio, *org*	32.50	26.00
49	A12	1fr brn grn, *straw*	16.00	14.00
50	A12	2fr vio, *rose* ('02)	160.00	16.00
		Nos. 32-50 (19)	567.65	306.70

Perf. 13½x14 stamps are counterfeits.
For surcharges see Nos. 87-93.

Great Anteater — A13

Washing Gold — A14

Palm Grove at Cayenne A15

1905-28

51	A13	1c black	.40	.40
52	A13	2c blue	.40	.40
a.		Imperf	55.00	
53	A13	4c red brn	.40	.40
54	A13	5c green	1.20	1.00
55	A13	5c org ('22)	.40	.45
56	A13	10c rose	1.25	1.10
57	A13	10c grn ('22)	.65	.40
58	A13	10c red, *bluish* ('25)	.45	.45
59	A13	15c violet	1.50	1.25
60	A14	20c red brn	.65	.65
61	A14	25c blue	2.50	1.60
62	A14	25c vio ('22)	.60	.50
63	A14	30c black	1.50	1.00
64	A14	30c rose ('22)	.50	.60
65	A14	30c red org ('25)	.45	.45
66	A14	30c dk grn, *grnsh* ('28)	1.10	1.10
67	A14	35c blk, *yel* ('06)	.65	.65
68	A14	40c rose	.85	.85
69	A14	40c black ('22)	.40	.45
70	A14	45c olive ('07)	.95	.95
71	A14	50c violet	3.50	3.00
72	A14	50c blue ('22)	.55	.65
73	A14	50c gray ('25)	.80	.80
74	A14	60c lil, *rose* ('25)	.65	.65
75	A14	65c myr grn ('26)	.80	.80
76	A14	75c green	1.40	1.40
77	A14	85c magenta ('26)	.80	.80
78	A14	1fr rose	.85	.85
a.		Imperf	80.00	
79	A15	1fr bl, *bluish* ('25)	.80	.80
80	A15	1fr bl, *yel grn* ('28)	2.25	2.25
81	A15	1.10fr lt red ('28)	1.40	1.40
82	A15	2fr blue	1.00	1.00
83	A15	2fr org red, *yel* ('26)	2.40	2.40
84	A15	5fr black	6.75	6.00
a.		Imperf	80.00	
85	A15	10fr grn, *yel* ('24)	12.00	13.50
a.		Printed on both sides	130.00	
86	A15	20fr brn lake ('24)	14.50	16.00
		Nos. 51-86 (36)	67.25	66.95

For surcharges see Nos. 94-108, B1-B2.

Issue of 1892 Surcharged in Black or Carmine

1912
Spacing between figures of surcharge 1.5mm (5c), 2mm (10c)

87	A12	5c on 2c brn, *buff*	1.60	2.00
88	A12	5c on 4c cl, *lav* (C)	1.20	1.60
89	A12	5c on 20c red, *grn*	1.40	1.90
90	A12	5c on 25c blk, *rose* (C)	4.00	4.75
91	A12	5c on 30c brn, *bis* (C)	1.40	1.90
92	A12	10c on 40c red, *straw*	1.40	1.90
a.		Pair, one stamp without surcharge	1,250.	
93	A12	10c on 50c car, *rose*	4.00	5.25
a.		Double surcharge	525.00	
		Nos. 87-93 (7)	15.00	19.30

Two spacings between the surcharged numerals are found on Nos. 87 to 93. For detailed listings, see the *Scott Classic Specialized Catalogue of Stamps and Covers.*

No. 59 Surcharged in Various Colors

1922

94	A13	1c on 15c vio (Bk)	.65	.75
a.		Double surcharge	87.50	
95	A13	2c on 15c vio (Bl)	.65	.75
a.		Inverted surcharge	95.00	
b.		In pair with unovptd. stamp	240.00	
c.		No. 95a, in pair with unovptd. stamp	800.00	
96	A13	4c on 15c vio (G)	.65	.75
a.		Double surcharge	87.50	
b.		In pair with unovptd. stamp	275.00	
97	A13	5c on 15c vio (R)	.65	.75
		Nos. 94-97 (4)	2.60	3.00

Type of 1905-28 Surcharged in Blue

1923

98	A15	10fr on 1fr grn, *yel*	21.00	24.00
99	A15	20fr on 5fr lilac, *rose*	21.00	24.00

Stamps and Types of 1905-28 Surcharged in Black or Red

1924-27

100	A13	25c on 15c vio ('25)	.70	.80
a.		Triple surcharge	120.00	110.00
b.		In pair with unovptd. stamp	240.00	
101	A15	25c on 2fr bl ('24)	.80	.90
a.		Double surcharge	140.00	
b.		Triple surcharge	150.00	
102	A14	65c on 45c ol (R) ('25)	1.60	1.75
103	A14	85c on 45c ol (R) ('25)	1.60	1.75
104	A14	90c on 75c red ('27)	1.25	1.40
105	A15	1.05fr on 2fr lt yel brn ('27)	1.25	1.40
106	A15	1.25fr on 1fr ultra (R) ('26)	1.40	1.60
107	A15	1.50fr on 1fr lt bl ('27)	1.40	1.60
108	A15	3fr on 5fr vio ('27)	1.60	1.80
a.		No period after "F"	12.00	12.00
		Nos. 100-108 (9)	11.60	13.00

Carib Archer — A16

Shooting Rapids, Maroni River A17

Government Building, Cayenne — A18

1929-40   Perf. 13½x14

109	A16	1c gray lil & grnsh bl	.25	.25
a.		Imperf	32.50	
110	A16	2c dk red & bl grn	.25	.25
a.		Imperf	32.50	
111	A16	3c gray lil & grnsh bl ('40)	.30	.30
112	A16	4c ol brn & red vio	.30	.30
113	A16	5c Prus bl & red org	.30	.30
114	A16	10c mag & brn	.30	.30
115	A16	15c yel brn & red org	.30	.30
a.		Imperf	32.50	
116	A16	20c dk bl & ol grn	.30	.30
117	A16	25c dk red & dk brn	.45	.45
		Perf. 14x13½		
118	A17	30c dl & lt grn	.65	.65
119	A17	30c grn & brn ('40)	.45	.45
120	A17	35c Prus grn & ol grn ('38)	.95	.95
121	A17	40c org brn & ol gray	.30	.30
122	A17	45c grn & dk brn	.90	.90
123	A17	45c ol grn & lt grn ('40)	.70	.70
124	A17	50c dk bl & ol gray	.40	.40
a.		Imperf	32.50	
125	A17	55c vio bl & car ('38)	1.40	1.40
126	A17	60c sal & grn ('40)	.70	.70
a.		Imperf	47.50	
127	A17	65c sal & grn	.90	.90
128	A17	70c ind & sl bl ('40)	1.20	1.20
129	A17	75c ind & sl bl	.95	.95
130	A17	80c blk & vio bl ('38)	.80	.80
131	A17	90c dk red & ver	.90	.90
132	A17	90c red vio & brn ('39)	1.10	1.10
133	A17	1fr lt vio & brn	.65	.65
134	A17	1fr car & lt red ('38)	1.90	1.90
135	A17	1fr blk & vio bl ('40)	.80	.80
136	A18	1.05fr ver & olivine	4.75	4.75
137	A18	1.10fr ol brn & red vio	6.50	5.50
138	A18	1.25fr blk brn & bl grn ('33)	.80	.80
139	A18	1.25fr rose & lt red ('39)	.95	.95
140	A18	1.40fr ol brn & red vio ('40)	1.10	1.10
141	A18	1.50fr dk bl & lt bl ('40)	.40	.40
142	A18	1.60fr ol brn & bl grn ('40)	1.10	1.10
143	A18	1.75fr brn red & blk brn ('33)	2.00	2.00
144	A18	1.75fr vio bl ('38)	1.40	1.40
145	A18	2fr dk grn & rose red	.65	.65
146	A18	2.25fr vio bl ('39)	1.10	1.10
147	A18	2.50fr cop red & brn ('40)	1.10	1.10
148	A18	3fr brn red & red vio	.70	.70
149	A18	5fr dl vio & yel grn	1.00	1.00
150	A18	10fr ol gray & dp ultra	1.25	1.25
151	A18	20fr indigo & ver	2.25	2.25
		Nos. 109-151 (43)	45.45	44.45

For types A16-A18 without "RF," see Nos. 170C-170E.

Common Design Types pictured following the introduction.

Colonial Exposition Issue
Common Design Types

1931   Engr.   Perf. 12½
Name of Country in Black

152	CD70	40c dp green	5.25	5.25
153	CD71	50c violet	5.25	5.25
154	CD72	90c red orange	5.25	5.25
155	CD73	1.50fr dull blue	5.25	5.25
		Nos. 152-155 (4)	21.00	21.00

Recapture of Cayenne by d'Estrées, 1676 — A19

Products of French Guiana A20

1935, Oct. 21   Perf. 13

156	A19	40c gray brn	5.25	5.25
157	A19	50c dull red	9.50	8.00
158	A19	1.50fr ultra	5.25	5.25
159	A20	1.75fr lilac rose	12.00	11.00
160	A20	5fr brown	9.50	8.75
161	A20	10fr blue green	10.50	9.50
		Nos. 156-161 (6)	52.00	47.75

Tercentenary of the founding of French possessions in the West Indies.

Paris International Exposition Issue
Common Design Types

1937, Apr. 15

162	CD74	20c deep violet	1.60	1.60
163	CD75	30c dark green	1.60	1.60
164	CD76	40c carmine rose	1.60	1.60
165	CD77	50c dark brown	1.40	1.40
166	CD78	90c red	1.60	1.60
167	CD79	1.50fr ultra	1.90	1.90
		Nos. 162-167 (6)	9.70	9.70

Colonial Arts Exhibition Issue
Souvenir Sheet
Common Design Type

1937   Imperf.

168	CD75	3fr violet	10.50	13.50

New York World's Fair Issue
Common Design Type

1939, May 10   Engr.   Perf. 12½x12

169	CD82	1.25fr car lake	1.20	1.20
170	CD82	2.25fr ultra	1.20	1.20

View of Cayenne and Marshal Petain A21a

1941   Engr.   Perf. 12½x12

170A	A21a	1fr deep lilac	.80	.80
170B	A21a	2.50fr blue	.80	.80

For surcharges, see Nos. B11A-B11B.

Types of 1929-40 without "RF"

1944   Methods and Perfs as Before

170C	A16	15c yel brn & red org	1.10	
170D	A17	1fr black & vio blue	1.10	
170E	A18	1.50fr dk blue & lt blue	1.40	
		Nos. 170C-170E (3)	3.60	

Nos. 170C-170E were issued by the Vichy government in France, but were not issued in French Guiana.

> **Catalogue values for unused stamps in this section, from this point to the end of the section, are for Never Hinged items.**

Eboue Issue
Common Design Type

1945   Engr.   Perf. 13

171	CD91	2fr black	.95	.80
172	CD91	25fr Prussian green	1.40	1.20

This issue exists imperforate.

Arms of Cayenne A22

1945   Litho.   *Perf. 12*

173	A22	10c dp gray violet	.30	.25
174	A22	30c brown org	.30	.25
175	A22	40c lt blue	.30	.25
176	A22	50c violet brn	.70	.55
177	A22	60c orange yel	.70	.55
178	A22	70c pale brown	.70	.55
179	A22	80c lt green	.70	.55
180	A22	1fr blue	.30	.25
181	A22	1.20fr brt violet	.70	.55
182	A22	1.50fr dp orange	.95	.70
183	A22	2fr black	1.00	.80
184	A22	2.40fr red	1.00	.80
185	A22	3fr pink	1.00	.80
186	A22	4fr dp ultra	1.25	.95
187	A22	4.50fr dp yel grn	1.25	.95
188	A22	5fr orange brn	1.25	.95
189	A22	10fr dk violet	1.25	.95
190	A22	15fr rose carmine	1.25	.95
191	A22	20fr olive green	1.40	1.10
		Nos. 173-191 (19)	16.30	12.70

Hammock
A23

Guiana Girl
A26

Maroni
River Bank
A24

Inini Scene
A25

Toucans
A27

Parrots
A28

Perf. 13.
1947, June 2   Unwmk.   Engr.

192	A23	10c dk blue grn	.30	.25
193	A23	30c brt red	.30	.25
194	A23	50c dk vio brn	.30	.25
195	A24	60c grnsh blk	.55	.40
196	A24	1fr red brn	.80	.55
197	A24	1.50fr black brn	.80	.55
198	A25	2fr dp yel grn	1.00	.70
199	A25	2.50fr dp ultra	1.00	.70
200	A25	3fr red brn	.80	.65
201	A26	4fr black brn	2.00	1.20
202	A26	5fr deep blue	1.60	1.00
203	A26	6fr red brown	1.60	1.00
204	A27	10fr deep ultra	6.75	4.50
205	A27	15fr black brn	6.75	4.75
206	A27	20fr red brn	8.75	4.75
207	A28	25fr brt bl grn	12.00	7.25
208	A28	40fr black brn	10.50	7.25
		Nos. 192-208 (17)	55.80	36.00

SEMI-POSTAL STAMPS

Regular Issue of
1905-28 Surcharged
in Red

1915   Unwmk.   *Perf. 13½x14*

B1	A13	10c + 5c rose	15.00	18.00
a.		Inverted surcharge	240.00	240.00
b.		Double surcharge	240.00	240.00

Regular Issue of
1905-28 Surcharged
in Rose

B2	A13	10c + 5c rose	1.60	1.60

Curie Issue
Common Design Type

1938   *Perf. 13*

B3	CD80	1.75fr + 50c brt ultra	12.50	12.50

French Revolution Issue
Common Design Type

1939   Photo.
Name and Value in Black

B4	CD83	45c + 25c green	11.00	11.00
B5	CD83	70c + 30c brown	11.00	11.00
B6	CD83	90c + 35c red org	11.00	11.00
B7	CD83	1.25fr + 1fr rose pink	11.00	11.00
B8	CD83	2.25fr + 2fr blue	11.00	11.00
		Nos. B4-B8 (5)	55.00	55.00

Common Design Type and

Colonial
Infantryman — SP1

Colonial
Policeman
SP2

1941   Photo.   *Perf. 13½*

B9	SP1	1fr + 1fr red		1.25
B10	CD86	1.50fr + 3fr maroon		1.40
B11	SP2	2.50fr + 1fr blue		1.25
		Nos. B9-B11 (3)		3.90

Nos. B9-B11 were issued by the Vichy government in France, but were not placed on sale in French Guiana.

Nos. 170A-170B
Surcharged in Black or Red

1944   Engr.   *Perf. 12½x12*

B11A		50c + 1.50fr on 2.50fr deep blue (R)		.80
B11B		+ 2.50fr on 1fr dp lilac		.80

Colonial Development Fund.
Nos. B11A-B11B were issued by the Vichy government in France, but were not placed on sale in French Guiana.

Catalogue values for unused stamps in this section, from this point to the end of the section, are for Never Hinged items.

Red Cross Issue
Common Design Type

1944   *Perf. 14½x14*

B12	CD90	5fr + 20fr dk copper brn		1.60	1.20

The surtax was for the French Red Cross and national relief.

AIR POST STAMPS

Cayenne
AP1

Perf. 13½
1933, Nov. 20   Unwmk.   Photo.

C1	AP1	50c orange brn	.30	.30
C2	AP1	1fr yellow grn	.45	.45
C3	AP1	1.50fr dk blue	.65	.65
C4	AP1	2fr orange	.65	.65
C5	AP1	3fr black	.80	.80
C6	AP1	5fr violet	.80	.80
C7	AP1	10fr olive grn	.80	.80
C8	AP1	20fr scarlet	1.10	1.10
		Nos. C1-C8 (8)	5.55	5.55

For No. C1 without "RF," see No. C8A.

Catalogue values for unused stamps in this section, from this point to the end of the section, are for Never Hinged items.

Type of 1933 without "RF" and

AP1a

AP1b

Perf. 13½, 13 (#C8C)
1941-44   Photo, Engr. (#C8C)

C8A	AP1	50c orange brn	1.00
C8B	AP1a	50f bl grn & red brown ('42)	1.40
C8C	AP1b	100f dk blue ('44)	1.60
		Nos. C8A-C8C (3)	4.00

Nos. C8A-C8C were issued by the Vichy government in France, but were not placed on sale in French Guiana.

Common Design Type

1945   Photo.   *Perf. 14½x14*

C9	CD87	50f dark green	1.25	.95
C10	CD87	100fr plum	2.25	1.80

Victory Issue
Common Design Type

1946, May 8   Engr.   *Perf. 12½*

C11	CD92	8fr black		1.60	1.20

Chad to Rhine Issue
Common Design Types

1946, June 6

C12	CD93	5fr dk slate bl	1.60	1.40
C13	CD94	10fr lilac rose	1.60	1.40
C14	CD95	15fr dk vio brn	1.60	1.40
C15	CD96	20fr dk slate grn	1.90	1.50
C16	CD97	25fr vio brown	2.25	1.80
C17	CD98	50fr bright lilac	2.75	2.10
		Nos. C12-C17 (6)	11.70	9.60

Eagles — AP2

Tapir — AP3

Toucans — AP4

1947, June 2   Engr.   *Perf. 13*

C18	AP2	50fr deep green	21.00	17.00
C19	AP3	100fr red brown	14.50	12.00
C20	AP4	200fr dk gray bl	29.00	22.50
		Nos. C18-C20 (3)	64.50	51.50

AIR POST SEMI-POSTAL STAMP

French Revolution Issue
Common Design Type
Unwmk.
1939, July 5   Photo.   *Perf. 13*
Name & Value Typo. in Orange

CB1	CD83	5fr + 4fr brn blk	20.00 20.00

Nurse with Mother & Child — SPAP1

Unwmk.
1942, June 22   Engr.   *Perf. 13*

CB2	SPAP1	1.50fr + 50c green		1.00
CB3	SPAP1	2fr + 6fr brn & red		1.00

Native children's welfare fund.
Nos. CB2-CB3 were issued by the Vichy government in France, but were not placed on sale in French Guiana.

Colonial Education Fund
Common Design Type
1942, June 22

CB4	CD86a	1.20fr + 1.80fr blue & red		1.10

No. CB4 was issued by the Vichy government in France, but was not placed on sale in French Guiana.

POSTAGE DUE STAMPS

Postage Due Stamps of
France, 1893-1926,
Overprinted

1925-27   Unwmk.   *Perf. 14x13½*

J1	D2	5c light blue	.65	.70
a.		In pair with unovptd. stamp	350.00	
J2	D2	10c brown	.85	1.00
J3	D2	20c olive green	1.00	1.20
J4	D2	50c violet brown	1.40	1.60
J5	D2	3fr magenta ('27)	10.50	12.50

Surcharged in Black

J6	D2	15c on 20c ol grn	.95	1.10
a.		Blue surcharge	65.00	
J7	D2	25c on 5c lt bl	1.25	1.40
a.		In pair with unovptd. stamp	350.00	
J8	D2	30c on 20c ol grn	1.40	1.60
J9	D2	45c on 10c brn	1.40	1.60
J10	D2	60c on 5c lt bl	1.40	1.60
J11	D2	1fr on 20c ol grn	1.90	2.10
J12	D2	2fr on 50c vio brn	1.90	2.25
		Nos. J1-J12 (12)	24.60	28.65

Royal Palms — D3

Guiana Girl — D4

1929, Oct. 14   Typo.   Perf. 13½x14

J13	D3	5c indigo & Prus bl	.40	.50
J14	D3	10c bis brn & Prus grn	.40	.50
J15	D3	20c grn & rose red	.40	.50
J16	D3	30c ol brn & rose red	.40	.50
J17	D3	50c vio & ol brn	.90	1.00
J18	D3	60c brn red & ol brn	1.25	1.40
J19	D4	1fr dp bl & org brn	1.60	1.90
J20	D4	2fr brn red & bluish grn	1.90	2.10
J21	D4	3fr violet & blk	4.00	4.50
		Nos. J13-J21 (9)	11.25	12.90

> **Catalogue values for unused stamps in this section, from this point to the end of the section, are for Never Hinged items.**

D5

1947, June 2   Engr.   Perf. 14x13

J22	D5	10c dk car rose	.30	.30
J23	D5	30c dull green	.40	.40
J24	D5	50c black	.40	.40
J25	D5	1fr brt ultra	.50	.50
J26	D5	2fr dk brown red	.50	.50
J27	D5	3fr deep violet	.90	.70
J28	D5	4fr red	1.25	1.00
J29	D5	5fr brown violet	1.40	1.10
J30	D5	10fr blue green	2.10	1.75
J31	D5	20fr lilac rose	2.75	2.10
		Nos. J22-J31 (10)	10.50	8.75

FRENCH GUINEA

'french 'gi-nē

LOCATION — On the coast of West Africa, between Portuguese Guinea and Sierra Leone.
GOVT. — French colony
AREA — 89,436 sq. mi.
POP. — 2,058,442 (est. 1941)
CAPITAL — Conakry

French Guinea stamps were replaced by those of French West Africa around 1944-45. French Guinea became the Republic of Guinea Oct. 2, 1958. See "Guinea" for issues of the republic.

100 Centimes = 1 Franc

> **See French West Africa No. 66 for additional stamp inscribed "Guinee" and "Afrique Occidentale Francaise."**

Navigation and Commerce A1

Fulah Shepherd A2

Perf. 14x13½

1892-1900   Typo.   Unwmk.
Name of Colony in Blue or Carmine

1	A1	1c black, *lilac bl*	1.60	1.60
2	A1	2c brown, *buff*	2.00	2.00
3	A1	4c claret, *lav*	2.75	2.00
4	A1	5c green, *grnsh*	8.75	4.75
5	A1	10c blk, *lavender*	8.00	4.75
6	A1	10c red ('00)	45.00	40.00
7	A1	15c blue, quadrille paper	14.50	7.25
8	A1	15c gray, *lt gray* ('00)	100.00	87.50
9	A1	20c red, *grn*	21.00	13.50
10	A1	25c black, *rose*	14.50	8.00
11	A1	25c blue ('00)	24.00	24.00
12	A1	30c brown, *bis*	37.50	32.50
13	A1	40c red, *straw*	37.50	32.50
a.		"GUINEE FRANCAISE" double	475.00	475.00
14	A1	50c car, *rose*	40.00	35.00
15	A1	50c brown, *az* ('00)	40.00	40.00
16	A1	75c dp vio, *org*	55.00	47.50
17	A1	1fr brnz grn, *straw*	47.50	40.00
		Nos. 1-17 (17)	499.60	422.85

Perf. 13½x14 stamps are counterfeits.
For surcharges see Nos. 48-54.

1904

18	A2	1c black, *yel grn*	1.20	1.20
19	A2	2c vio brn, *buff*	1.20	1.20
20	A2	4c carmine, *bl*	1.60	1.60
21	A2	5c green, *grnsh*	1.60	1.60
22	A2	10c carmine	3.25	2.00
23	A2	15c violet, *rose*	9.50	5.25
24	A2	20c carmine, *grn*	13.00	13.00
25	A2	25c blue	16.00	10.50
26	A2	30c brown	21.00	21.00
27	A2	40c red, *straw*	32.50	22.50
28	A2	50c brown, *az*	32.50	24.00
29	A2	75c green, *org*	32.50	27.50
30	A2	1fr brnz grn, *straw*	45.00	45.00
31	A2	2fr red, *org*	85.00	85.00
32	A2	5fr green, *yel grn*	100.00	100.00
		Nos. 18-32 (15)	395.85	361.35

For surcharges see Nos. 55-62.

Gen. Louis Faidherbé A3

Oil Palm — A4

Dr. Noel Eugène Ballay A5

1906-07
Name of Colony in Red or Blue

33	A3	1c gray	.80	.80
34	A3	2c brown	1.20	1.20
35	A3	4c brown, *bl*	1.60	1.60
36	A3	5c green	3.25	2.00
37	A3	10c carmine (B)	24.00	1.60
38	A4	20c black, *blue*	6.00	4.00
39	A4	25c blue, *pnksh*	6.50	6.50
40	A4	30c brown, *pnksh*	8.00	4.00
41	A4	35c black, *yellow*	4.75	2.40
42	A4	45c choc, *grnsh gray*	6.50	4.00
43	A4	50c dp violet	13.00	10.50
44	A4	75c blue, *org*	8.75	4.00
45	A5	1fr black, *az*	20.00	20.00
46	A5	2fr blue, *pink*	40.00	45.00
47	A5	5fr car, *straw* (B)	60.00	65.00
		Nos. 33-47 (15)	204.35	172.60

Regular Issues Surcharged in Black or Carmine

1912
On Issue of 1892-1900

48	A1	5c on 2c brown, *buff*	1.60	2.00
49	A1	5c on 4c cl, *lav* (C)	1.20	1.60
50	A1	5c on 15c blue (C)	1.20	1.60
51	A1	5c on 20c red, *grn*	4.00	5.25
52	A1	5c on 30c brn, *bis* (C)	5.50	6.50
53	A1	10c on 40c red, *straw*	2.40	3.25
54	A1	10c on 75c dp vio, *org*	8.00	9.50
a.		Double surcharge, inverted	300.00	

On Issue of 1904

55	A2	5c on 2c vio brn, *buff*	1.00	1.20
a.		Pair, one without surcharge	650.00	
b.		Inverted surcharge	210.00	
56	A2	5c on 4c car, *blue*	1.10	1.20
57	A2	5c on 15c violet, *rose*	1.10	1.20
58	A2	5c on 20c car, *grn*	1.60	1.60
59	A2	5c on 25c blue (C)	1.60	2.00
60	A2	5c on 30c brown (C)	2.00	2.40
61	A2	5c on 40c red, *straw*	2.00	2.40
62	A2	10c on 50c brn, *az* (C)	4.75	5.50
		Nos. 48-62 (15)	39.05	47.20

Two spacings between the surcharged numerals are found on Nos. 48 to 62. For detailed listings, see the *Scott Classic Specialized Catalogue of Stamps and Covers.*

Ford at Kitim — A6

1913-33   Perf. 13½x14

63	A6	1c violet & bl	.25	.25
64	A6	2c brn & vio brn	.25	.25
65	A6	4c gray & black	.25	.25
66	A6	5c yel grn & bl grn	1.20	.40
a.		Booklet pane of 4		
		Complete booklet, 10 #66a	200.00	
67	A6	5c brn vio & grn	.25	.25
68	A6	10c red org & rose	1.00	.40
a.		Booklet pane of 4		
		Complete booklet, 10 #68a	400.00	
69	A6	10c yel grn & bl grn ('22)	.50	.25
70	A6	10c vio & ver ('25)	.70	.30
71	A6	15c vio brn & rose, chalky paper ('16)	.80	.40
a.		Booklet pane of 4		
		Complete booklet, 10 #71a	1,000.	
72	A6	15c gray grn & yel grn ('25)	.40	.25
73	A6	15c red brn & rose lil ('27)	.40	.30
74	A6	20c brown & violet	.40	.40
75	A6	20c grn & bl grn ('26)	.80	.80
76	A6	20c brn red & brn ('27)	.80	.50
77	A6	25c ultra & blue	2.75	1.60
78	A6	25c black & vio ('22)	.80	.80
79	A6	30c vio brn & grn	1.60	1.20
80	A6	30c red org & rose ('22)	1.20	1.00
81	A6	30c rose red & grn ('25)	.30	.30
82	A6	30c dl grn & bl grn ('28)	1.60	1.20
83	A6	35c blue & rose	.55	.55
84	A6	40c green & gray	1.00	.90
85	A6	45c brown & red	1.00	1.00
86	A6	50c ultra & black	6.50	4.50
87	A6	50c ultra & bl ('22)	1.25	.80
88	A6	50c yel brn & ol ('25)	.80	.65
89	A6	60c vio, *pnksh* ('25)	.65	.65
90	A6	65c yel brn & sl bl ('26)	2.00	1.20
91	A6	75c red & ultra	1.25	1.25
92	A6	75c indigo & dl bl ('25)	1.25	1.00
93	A6	75c mag & yel grn ('27)	1.60	1.20
94	A6	85c ol grn & red brn ('26)	1.20	1.20
95	A6	90c brn red & rose ('30)	5.50	4.75
96	A6	1fr violet & black	1.60	1.60

97	A6	1.10fr vio & ol brn ('28)	6.50	7.50
98	A6	1.25fr vio & yel brn ('33)	2.40	1.60
99	A6	1.50fr dk bl & lt bl ('30)	5.50	2.40
100	A6	1.75fr ol brn & vio ('33)	1.60	1.60
101	A6	2fr orange & vio brn	3.50	2.40
102	A6	3fr red violet ('30)	8.00	5.50
103	A6	5fr black & vio	13.00	13.00
104	A6	5fr dl bl & blk ('22)	2.40	2.40
		Nos. 63-104 (42)	85.30	68.75

For surcharges see Nos. 105-115, B1.
Nos. 66, 68 and 77 pasted on colored cardboard and overprinted "VALEUR D'ECHANGE" were used as emergency currency in 1920.

Type of 1913-33 Surcharged

1922

105	A6	60c on 75c violet, *pnksh*	.65	.65

Stamps and Type of 1913-33 Surcharged with New Value and Bars

1924-27

106	A6	25c on 2fr org & brn (R)	.50	.50
107	A6	25c on 5fr dull bl & blk	.50	.50
108	A6	65c on 75c rose & ultra ('25)	1.25	1.25
109	A6	85c on 75c rose & ultra ('25)	2.00	2.00
110	A6	90c on 75c brn red & cer ('27)	2.40	2.40
111	A6	1.25fr on 1fr dk bl & ultra ('26)	1.25	1.25
112	A6	1.50fr on 1fr dp bl & lt bl ('27)	2.00	2.00
113	A6	3fr on 5fr mag & sl ('27)	4.00	4.00
114	A6	10fr on 5fr bl & bl grn, *bluish* ('27)	8.00	8.00
115	A6	20fr on 5fr rose lil & brn ol, *pnksh* ('27)	20.00	20.00
		Nos. 106-115 (10)	41.90	41.90

Common Design Types pictured following the introduction.

Colonial Exposition Issue
Common Design Types

1931   Engr.   Perf. 12½
Name of Country in Black

116	CD70	40c deep green	4.75	4.75
a.		"GUINEE FRANCAISE" omitted	55.00	67.50
117	CD71	50c violet	4.75	4.75
118	CD72	90c red orange	4.75	4.75
a.		"GUINEE FRANCAISE" omitted	55.00	67.50
119	CD73	1.50fr dull blue	4.75	4.75
a.		"GUINEE FRANCAISE" omitted	55.00	67.50
		Nos. 116-119 (4)	19.00	19.00
		Set, never hinged	32.00	

Paris International Exposition Issue
Common Design Types

1937   Perf. 13

120	CD74	20c deep violet	2.00	2.00
121	CD75	30c dark green	2.00	2.00
122	CD76	40c carmine rose	2.00	2.00
123	CD77	50c dark brown	1.60	1.60
124	CD78	90c red	1.75	1.75
125	CD79	1.50fr ultra	2.00	2.00
		Nos. 120-125 (6)	11.35	11.35
		Set, never hinged	18.50	

Colonial Arts Exhibition Issue
Souvenir Sheet
Common Design Type

1937   Imperf.

126	CD76	3fr Prussian green	8.75	10.50
		Never hinged	13.00	

Guinea
Village
A7

Hausa
Basket
Workers
A8

Forest
Waterfall
A9

Guinea
Women — A10

1938-40 — Perf. 13

128	A7	2c vermilion	.25	.25
129	A7	3c ultra	.25	.25
130	A7	4c green	.25	.25
131	A7	5c rose car	.25	.25
132	A7	10c peacock blue	.25	.25
133	A7	15c violet brown	.25	.25
134	A8	20c dk carmine	.30	.25
135	A8	25c pck blue	.40	.25
136	A8	30c ultra	.40	.25
137	A8	35c green	.55	.50
138	A8	40c blk brn ('40)	.30	.30
139	A8	45c dk green ('40)	.30	.30
140	A8	50c red brown	.55	.50
141	A9	55c dk ultra	1.10	.80
142	A9	60c dk ultra ('40)	.80	.80
143	A9	65c green	1.25	.80
144	A9	70c green ('40)	1.25	1.25
145	A9	80c rose violet	.75	.55
146	A9	90c rose vio ('39)	1.25	1.25
147	A9	1fr orange red	2.50	2.00
148	A9	1fr brn blk ('40)	.50	.50
149	A10	1.25fr org red ('39)	1.40	1.40
150	A10	1.40fr brown ('40)	1.25	1.25
151	A10	1.50fr violet	2.40	2.00
152	A10	1fr org red ('40)	1.40	1.40
153	A10	1.75fr ultra	.90	.80
154	A10	2fr magenta	1.00	.70
155	A10	2.25fr brt ultra ('39)	1.40	1.40
156	A10	2.50fr brn blk ('40)	1.40	1.40
157	A10	3fr peacock blue	.95	.40
158	A10	5fr rose violet	.95	.80
159	A10	10fr slate green	1.40	1.25
160	A10	20fr chocolate	2.50	2.00
		Nos. 128-160 (33)	30.65	26.60

For surcharges see Nos. B8-B11.

Caillié Issue
Common Design Type

1939 — Engr. — Perf. 12½x12

161	CD81	90c org brn & org	.90	.90
162	CD81	2fr brt violet	1.10	1.10
163	CD81	2.25fr ultra & dk bl	1.20	1.20
		Nos. 161-163 (3)	3.20	3.20

René Caillié, French explorer, death cent.

New York World's Fair Issue
Common Design Type

1939

164	CD82	1.25fr carmine lake	1.40	1.40
165	CD82	2.25fr ultra	1.40	1.40

Ford at Kitim and
Marshal
Petain — A11

1941 — Perf. 12x12½

166	A11	1fr green	.80	—
167	A11	2.50fr deep blue	.80	—

For surcharges, see Nos. B15-B16.

Types of 1933-40 without "RF"

1943-44 — Perf. 13

168	A7	10c peacock blue	.50	
169	A8	20c dk carmine	.75	
170	A8	30c ultramarine	.75	
171	A8	40c black brown	1.10	
172	A9	60c dk ultramarine	1.25	
173	A9	1.50fr violet	1.40	
174	A10	2fr magenta	1.50	
		Nos. 168-174 (7)	7.25	

Nos. 168-174 were issued by the Vichy government in France, but were not placed on sale in French Guinea.

SEMI-POSTAL STAMPS

Regular Issue of
1913 Surcharged in
Red

1915 — Unwmk. — Perf. 13½x14

B1	A6	10c + 5c org & rose	1.60	1.60

Exists on both ordinary and chalky paper.

Curie Issue
Common Design Type

1938 — Engr. — Perf. 13

B2	CD80	1.75fr + 50c brt ultra	9.00	9.00

French Revolution Issue
Common Design Type

1939 — Photo.
Name and Value Typo. in Black

B3	CD83	45c + 25c green	9.50	9.50
B4	CD83	70c + 30c brown	9.50	9.50
B5	CD83	90c + 35c red org	9.50	9.50
B6	CD83	1.25fr + 1fr rose pink	9.50	9.50
B7	CD83	2.25fr + 2fr blue	9.50	9.50
		Nos. B3-B7 (5)	47.50	47.50
		Set, never hinged	75.00	

Stamps of
1938,
Surcharged
in Black

1941 — Unwmk. — Perf. 13

B8	A8	50c + 1fr red brn	2.40	2.40
B9	A9	80c + 2fr rose vio	7.25	7.25
B10	A9	1.50fr + 2fr brn	7.25	7.25
B11	A10	2fr + 3fr magenta	7.25	7.25
		Nos. B8-B11 (4)	24.15	24.15

Common Design Type and

Senegalese
Soldier
SP1

Colonial
Infantryman
SP2

1941 — Unwmk. — Perf. 13

B12	SP1	1fr + 1fr red	1.25	
B13	CD86	1.50fr + 3fr maroon	1.40	
B14	SP2	2.50fr + 1fr blue	1.40	
		Nos. B12-B14 (3)	4.05	

Nos. B12-B14 were issued by the Vichy government in France, but were not placed on sale in the French Guinea.

Nos. 166-167
Surcharged in Black or Red

1944 — Engr. — Perf. 12½x12

B15	50c + 1.50fr on 2.50fr deep blue (R)	.80	
B16	+ 2.50fr on 1fr green	.80	

Colonial Development Fund.
Nos. B15-B16 were issued by the Vichy government in France, but were not placed on sale in French Guinea.

AIR POST STAMPS

Common Design Type

1940 — Unwmk. Engr. — Perf. 12½x12

C1	CD85	1.90fr ultra	.70	.70
C2	CD85	2.90fr dark red	.80	.80
C3	CD85	4.50fr dk gray grn	.95	.95
C4	CD85	4.90fr yellow bis	.95	.95
C5	CD85	6.90fr dp orange	1.40	1.40
		Nos. C1-C5 (5)	4.80	4.80

Common Design Types

1942 — Engr.

C6	CD88	50c car & blue	.25
C7	CD88	1fr brown & blk	.30
C8	CD88	2fr dk grn & red brn	.30
C9	CD88	3fr dk bl & scar	.50
C10	CD88	5fr vio & brn red	.90

Frame Engraved, Center Typographed

C11	CD89	10fr multicolored	.90	
C12	CD89	20fr multicolored	1.00	
C13	CD89	50fr multicolored	1.40	—
		Nos. C6-C13 (8)	5.55	

There is doubt whether Nos. C6-C12 were officially placed in use.

AIR POST SEMI-POSTAL STAMPS

Dahomey types SPAP1-SPAP3
inscribed "Guinée Frcaise" or "Guinée"
Perf. 13½x12½, 13 (#CB3)
Photo, Engr. (#CB3)

1942, June 22

CB1	SPAP1	1.50fr + 3.50fr green	.80	5.50
CB2	SPAP2	2fr + 6fr brown	.80	5.50
CB3	SPAP3	3fr + 9fr car red	.80	5.50
		Nos. CB1-CB3 (3)	2.40	16.50

Native children's welfare fund.

Colonial Education Fund
Common Design Type
Perf. 12½x13½

1942, June 22 — Engr.

CB4	CD86a	1.20fr + 1.80fr blue & red	.80	5.50

POSTAGE DUE STAMPS

Fulah
Woman
D1

Heads and
Coast
D2

1905 — Unwmk. Typo. — Perf. 14x13½

J1	D1	5c blue	2.40	3.25
J2	D1	10c brown	2.40	3.25
J3	D1	15c brown	6.50	6.50
J4	D1	30c rose	6.50	6.50
J5	D1	50c black	9.50	13.00

J6	D1	60c dull orange	13.00	16.00
J7	D1	1fr violet	40.00	47.50
		Nos. J1-J7 (7)	80.30	96.00

1906-08

J8	D2	5c grn, grnsh ('08)	20.00	13.00
J9	D2	10c violet brn ('08)	5.50	5.50
J10	D2	15c dk blue ('08)	5.50	5.50
J11	D2	20c blk, yellow	5.50	5.50
J12	D2	30c red, straw ('08)	27.50	26.00
J13	D2	50c violet ('08)	24.00	26.00
J14	D2	60c blk, buff ('08)	22.50	22.50
J15	D2	1fr blk, pnksh ('08)	13.50	13.50
		Nos. J8-J15 (8)	124.00	117.50

D3

D4

1914

J16	D3	5c green	.40	.55
J17	D3	10c rose	.40	.65
J18	D3	15c gray	.55	.90
J19	D3	20c brown	.80	.80
J20	D3	30c blue	.80	.80
J21	D3	50c black	1.00	1.25
J22	D3	60c orange	2.00	2.40
J23	D3	1fr violet	2.00	2.40
		Nos. J16-J23 (8)	7.95	9.75

Type of 1914 Issue
Surcharged

1927

J24	D3	2fr on 1fr lil rose	7.25	8.00
a.		No period after "F"	27.50	32.50
J25	D3	3fr on 1fr org brn	7.25	8.00

1938 — Engr.

J26	D4	5c dk violet	.25	.30
J27	D4	10c carmine	.25	.30
J28	D4	15c green	.25	.30
J29	D4	20c red brown	.30	.40
J30	D4	30c rose violet	.30	.40
J31	D4	50c chocolate	.65	.70
J32	D4	60c peacock blue	1.00	1.00
J33	D4	1fr vermilion	1.00	1.00
J34	D4	2fr violet	1.00	1.00
J35	D4	3fr black	1.60	1.60
		Nos. J26-J35 (10)	6.60	7.00

For No. J27 without "RF," see No. J36.

Type of 1938 without "RF"

1944

J36	D4	10c carmine	.80

No. J36 was issued by the Vichy government in France, but was not placed on sale in French Guinea.

FRENCH INDIA

'french 'in-dē-ə

LOCATION — East coast of India bordering on Bay of Bengal.
GOVT. — French Territory
AREA — 196 sq. mi.
POP. — 323,295 (1941)
CAPITAL — Pondichéry

French India was an administrative unit comprising the five settlements of Chandernagor, Karikal, Mahé, Pondichéry and Yanaon. These united with India in 1949 and 1954.

100 Centimes = 1 Franc
24 Caches = 1 Fanon (1923)
8 Fanons = 1 Rupie

Catalogue values for unused stamps in this country are for Never Hinged items, beginning with Scott 210 in the regular postage section, Scott B14 in the semipostal section, and Scott C7 in the airpost section.

Navigation and Commerce — A1

A2

Perf. 14x13½
1892-1907   **Typo.**   **Unwmk.**
Colony Name in Blue or Carmine

1	A1	1c blk, *lil blk*	1.40	1.00
2	A1	2c brn, *buff*	2.25	1.50
3	A1	4c claret, *lav*	2.75	2.25
4	A1	5c grn, *grnsh*	5.50	3.50
5	A1	10c blk, *lavender*	12.00	2.75
6	A1	10c red ('00)	4.75	2.40
7	A1	15c blue, quadrille paper	16.00	5.25
8	A1	15c gray, *lt gray* ('00)	30.00	27.50
9	A1	20c red, *grn*	7.25	5.25
10	A1	25c blk, *rose*	4.75	2.40
11	A1	25c blue ('00)	18.00	12.00
12	A1	30c brn, *bis*	52.50	47.50
13	A1	35c blk, *yel* ('06)	19.00	8.00
14	A1	40c red, *straw*	7.25	6.50
15	A1	45c blk, *gray grn* ('07)	4.75	5.50
16	A1	50c car, *rose*	6.50	6.50
17	A1	50c blk, *az* ('00)	15.00	17.50
18	A1	75c dp vio, *org*	8.75	9.50
19	A1	1fr brnz grn, *straw*	14.00	14.00
		Nos. 1-19 (19)	232.40	180.80

Perf. 13½x14 stamps are counterfeits.

Nos. 10 and 16
Surcharged in Carmine
or Black

1903

20	A1	5c on 25c blk, *rose*	375.00	225.00
21	A1	10c on 25c blk, *rose*	375.00	225.00
22	A1	15c on 25c blk, *rose*	125.00	110.00
23	A1	40c on 50c car, *rose* (Bk)	475.00	400.00
		Nos. 20-23 (4)	1,350.00	960.00

Counterfeits of Nos. 20-23 abound.

1903

Revenue Stamp Surcharged in Black

24	A2	5c gray blue	27.50	27.50

The bottom of the revenue stamps were cut off.

Brahma — A5

Kali Temple near Pondichéry A6

1914-22   **Perf. 13½x14, 14x13½**

25	A5	1c gray & blk	.30	.30
a.		1c light gray & black	.55	.55
26	A5	2c brn vio & blk	.30	.30
27	A5	2c grn & brn vio ('22)	.40	.40
28	A5	3c brown & blk	.40	.40
29	A5	4c orange & blk	.40	.40
30	A5	5c bl grn & blk	.65	.65
31	A5	5c vio brn & blk ('22)	.40	.40
32	A5	10c dp rose & blk	1.25	1.25
33	A5	10c grn & blk ('22)	.80	.80
34	A5	15c vio & blk	1.00	1.00
35	A5	20c org red & blk	1.60	1.60
36	A5	25c blue & blk	1.60	1.60
37	A5	25c ultra & fawn ('22)	1.25	1.25
38	A5	30c ultra & blk	3.00	3.00
39	A5	30c rose & blk ('22)	1.25	1.25
40	A5	35c choc & blk	1.75	1.75
41	A6	40c org red & blk	1.75	1.75
42	A6	45c bl grn & blk	1.75	1.75
43	A6	50c dp rose & blk	1.75	1.75
44	A6	50c ultra & bl ('22)	1.90	1.90
45	A6	75c blue & blk	3.50	3.50
46	A6	1fr yellow & blk	3.50	3.50
47	A6	2fr violet & blk	5.25	5.25
48	A6	5fr ultra & blk	2.75	2.75
49	A6	5fr rose & blk ('22)	4.00	4.00
		Nos. 25-49 (25)	42.50	42.50

For surcharges see Nos. 50-79, 113-116, 156A, B1-B5.

No. 34 Surcharged in Various Colors

1922

50	A5	1c on 15c (Bk)	.80	.80
51	A5	2c on 15c (Bl)	.80	.80
53	A5	5c on 15c (Bk)	.80	.80
		Nos. 50-53 (3)	2.40	2.40

Stamps and Types of 1914-22
Surcharged with New Values in
Caches, Fanons and Rupies in Black,
Red or Blue:

1923-28

54	A5	1ca on 1c gray & blk (R)	.30	.30
55	A5	2ca on 5c vio brn & blk	.50	.50
a.		Horizontal pair, imperf. between	—	
56	A5	3ca on 3c brn & blk	.55	.55
57	A5	4ca on 4c org & blk	.80	.80
58	A5	6ca on 10c grn & blk	.95	.95
a.		Double surcharge	150.00	
59	A6	6ca on 45c bl grn & blk (R)	.95	.95
60	A5	10ca on 20c dp red & bl grn ('28)	2.50	2.50
61	A5	12ca on 15c vio & blk	.95	.95
62	A5	15ca on 20c org & blk	1.40	1.40
63	A6	16ca on 35c lt bl & yel brn ('28)	2.50	2.50
64	A5	18ca on 30c rose & blk	2.10	2.10
65	A6	20ca on 45c grn & dl red ('28)	1.75	1.40
66	A5	1fa on 25c dp grn & rose red ('28)	3.25	3.25
67	A6	1fa3ca on 35c choc & blk (Bl)	1.10	1.10
68	A6	1fa6ca on 40c org & blk (R)	1.40	1.10
69	A6	1fa12ca on 50c ultra & bl (Bl)	1.60	1.50
70	A6	1fa12ca on 75c bl & blk (Bl)	1.25	1.25
a.		Double surcharge	140.00	
71	A6	1fa16ca on 75c brn red & grn ('28)	3.00	2.50
72	A5	2fa9ca on 25c ultra & fawn (Bl)	1.40	1.10
73	A6	2fa12ca on 1fr vio & dk brn ('28)	2.75	2.75
74	A6	3fa3ca on 1fr yel & blk (R)	1.60	1.40
a.		Double surcharge	140.00	
75	A6	6fa6ca on 2fr vio & blk (R)	4.75	4.00
76	A6	1r on 1fr grn & dp bl (R)	8.75	7.25
77	A6	2r on 5fr rose & blk (R)	7.25	6.50
a.		Double surcharge	140.00	
78	A6	3r on 2fr gray & bl vio (R) ('26)	19.00	17.50
79	A6	5r on 5fr rose & blk, *grnsh* ('26)	24.00	21.00
		Nos. 54-79 (26)	96.35	87.10

Nos. 60, 63, 66 and 73 have the original value obliterated by bars.

A7

A8

1929

80	A7	1ca dk gray & blk	.25	.25
81	A7	2ca vio brn & blk	.25	.25
82	A7	3ca brn & blk	.25	.25
83	A7	4ca org & blk	.30	.30
84	A7	6ca gray grn & blk	.30	.30
85	A7	10ca brn, red & grn	.30	.30
86	A8	12ca grn & lt grn	.70	.65
87	A7	16ca brt bl & blk	.90	.90
88	A7	18ca brn red & ver	.90	.90
89	A7	20ca dk bl & grn, *bluish*	.70	.70

90	A8	1fa gray grn & rose red	.70	.65
91	A8	1fa6ca red org & blk	.70	.65
92	A8	1fa12ca dp bl & ultra	.70	.65
93	A8	1fa16ca rose red & grn	.90	.90
94	A8	2fa12ca brt vio & brn	1.10	.95
95	A8	6fa6ca dl vio & blk	1.25	.95
96	A8	1r gray grn & dp bl	1.10	.95
97	A8	2r rose & blk	1.50	1.10
98	A8	3r lt gray & gray lil	2.75	2.10
99	A8	5r rose & blk, *grnsh*	2.75	2.25
		Nos. 80-99 (20)	18.30	15.95

For overprints and surcharges see Nos. 117-134, 157-176, 184-209G.

Common Design Types pictured following the introduction.

Colonial Exposition Issue
Common Design Types

1931   **Engr.**   **Perf. 12½**

100	CD70	10ca deep green	4.00	4.00
101	CD71	12ca violet	4.00	4.00
102	CD72	18ca red orange	4.00	4.00
103	CD73	1fa12ca dull blue	4.00	4.00
		Nos. 100-103 (4)	16.00	16.00

Paris International Exposition Issue
Common Design Types

1937   **Perf. 13**

104	CD74	8ca dp violet	2.00	2.00
105	CD75	12ca dk green	2.25	2.25
106	CD76	16ca car rose	2.25	2.25
107	CD77	20ca dk brown	1.40	1.40
108	CD78	1fa12ca red	1.75	1.75
109	CD79	2fa12ca ultra	2.25	2.25
		Nos. 104-109 (6)	11.90	11.90

For overprints see Nos. 135-139, 177-181.

Colonial Arts Exhibition Issue
Souvenir Sheet
Common Design Type

1937   **Imperf.**

110	CD79	5fa red violet	8.75	12.00

For overprint see No. 140.

New York World's Fair Issue
Common Design Type

1939   **Engr.**   **Perf. 12½x12**

111	CD82	1fa12ca car lake	1.25	1.25
112	CD82	2fa12ca ultra	1.60	1.60

For overprints see Nos. 141-142, 182-183.

Temple near Pondichéry and Marshal Petain A9

1941   **Engr.**   **Perf. 12½x12**

112A	A9	1fa16ca car & red		.80
112B	A9	4fa4ca blue		.80

Nos. 112A-112B were issued by the Vichy government in France, but were not placed on sale in French India.
For surcharges, see Nos. B13B-B13C.

Nos. 62, 64, 67, 72 Overprinted in Carmine or Blue (#116):

a   b

FRANCE LIBRE

1941   **Unwmk.**   **Perf. 13½x14**

113	A5 (a)	15ca on 20c	80.00	80.00
114	A5 (a)	18ca on 30c	15.00	15.00
115	A6 (a)	1fa3ca on 35c	125.00	125.00
a.		Horiz. overprint	125.00	125.00
116	A5 (b)	2fa9ca on 25c	1,400.	1,000.
a.		Overprint "a" (Bl)	1,300.	1,000.
b.		Overprint "b" (C)	2,000.	2,000.

Nos. 81-99 Overprinted Type "a" in Carmine or Blue

1941

117	A7	2ca	(C)	12.00	12.00
118	A7	3ca	(C)	4.75	4.75
119	A7	4ca	(C)	13.50	13.50
120	A7	6ca	(C)	4.75	4.75
121	A7	10ca	(Bl)	6.50	6.50
122	A8	12ca	(C)	4.75	4.75
123	A7	16ca	(C)	4.75	4.75
123A	A7	18ca	(Bl)	600.00	600.00
124	A7	20ca	(C)	4.75	4.75
125	A8	1fa	(Bl)	4.75	4.75
126	A8	1fa6ca	(C)	4.75	4.75
127	A8	1fa12ca	(C)	6.50	6.50
128	A8	1fa16ca	(C)	4.75	4.75
129	A8	2fa12ca	(C)	4.75	4.75
130	A8	6fa6ca	(C)	4.75	4.75
131	A8	1r	(C)	4.75	4.75
132	A8	2r	(C)	4.75	4.75
133	A8	3r	(C)	6.50	6.50
134	A8	5r	(C)	10.50	10.50
	Nos. 117-123,124-134 (18)			112.50	112.50

Same Overprints on Paris Exposition Issue of 1937

1941   **Perf. 13**

135	CD74	(b)	8ca	(C)	8.75	8.75
135A	CD74	(b)	8ca	(Bl)	240.00	240.00
135B	CD74	(a)	8ca	(C)	175.00	175.00
135C	CD74	(a)	8ca	(Bl)	225.00	225.00
136	CD75	(a)	12ca	(C)	6.00	6.00
137	CD76	(a)	16ca	(Bl)	6.00	6.00
138	CD78	(a)	1fa12ca	(C)	6.00	6.00
139	CD79	(a)	2fa12ca	(C)	6.00	6.00
	Nos. 135-139 (8)				672.75	672.75

Inverted overprints exist.

Souvenir Sheet
No. 110 Overprinted "FRANCE LIBRE" Diagonally in Blue Violet

Two types of overprint:
I — Overprint 37mm. With serifs.
II — Overprint 24mm, as type "a" shown above No. 113. No serifs.

1941   **Unwmk.**   **Imperf.**

140	CD79	5fa red vio (I)	725.00	650.00
a.		Type II	875.00	875.00

Overprinted on New York World's Fair Issue, 1939
Perf. 12½x12

141	CD82	(a)	1fa12ca	(Bl)	4.75 4.75
142	CD82	(a)	2fa12ca	(C)	4.75 4.75

Lotus Flowers — A10

1942 **Unwmk.** **Photo.** **Perf. 14x14½**

143	A10	2ca brown	.30	.30
144	A10	3ca dk blue	.30	.30
145	A10	4ca emerald	.30	.30
146	A10	6ca dk orange	.30	.30
147	A10	12ca grnsh blk	.30	.30
148	A10	16ca rose violet	.30	.30
149	A10	20ca dk red brn	.65	.65
150	A10	1fa brt red	.70	.65
151	A10	1fa18ca slate blk	.90	.80
152	A10	6fa6ca brt ultra	1.50	1.40
153	A10	1r dull violet	1.25	1.25
154	A10	2r bister	1.50	1.25
155	A10	3r chocolate	1.50	1.40
156	A10	5r dk green	2.00	1.90
	Nos. 143-156 (14)		11.80	11.10

Stamps of 1923-39 Overprinted in Blue or Carmine

c

---

d

1942-43   **Perf. 13½x14, 14x13½**
Overprinted on No. 64

156A	A5	(c)	18ca on 30c (B)	275.00	225.00

Overprinted on #81-82, 84, 86-99

157	A7	(c)	2ca	(C)	3.25	3.25
a.		"FRANCE LIBRE" in black			225.00	175.00
158	A7	(c)	3ca	(C)	2.40	2.40
159	A7	(d)	6ca	(Bl)	3.25	3.25
160	A8	(d)	12ca	(Bl)	3.25	3.25
161	A7	(d)	16ca	(C)	3.25	3.25
162	A7	(c)	18ca	(Bl)	2.40	2.40
163	A7	(c)	20ca	(C)	7.25	5.50
				('43)		
164	A7	(c)	20ca	(Bl)	2.40	2.40
165	A8	(d)	1fa	(Bl)	2.40	2.40
166	A8	(d)	1fa6ca	(C)	3.25	3.25
167	A8	(d)	1fa12ca	(C)	3.25	3.25
168	A8	(d)	1fa16ca	(Bl)	3.25	3.25
169	A8	(d)	2fa12ca	(Bl)	80.00	80.00
170	A8	(d)	2fa12ca	(C)	3.25	3.25
171	A8	(d)	6fa6ca	(C)	4.00	4.00
172	A8	(d)	1r	(C)	7.25	7.25
173	A8	(d)	2r	(C)	7.25	7.25
174	A8	(d)	3r	(C)	7.25	7.25
175	A8	(d)	3r	(Bl)		
				('43)	175.00	175.00
176	A8	(d)	5r	(C)	7.25	7.25
	Nos. 156A-176 (21)				605.85	554.10

Same Overprints on Paris International Exposition Issue of 1937
Perf. 13

177	CD74	(c)	8ca	(Bl)	7.25	7.25
178	CD75	(d)	12ca	(Bl)	7.25	7.25
179	CD76	(d)	16ca	(Bl)	1,300.	1,300.
180	CD78	(d)	1fa12ca	(Bl)	7.25	7.25
181	CD79	(d)	2fa12ca	(C)	7.25	7.25

Same Overprint on New York World's Fair Issue, 1939
Perf. 12½x12

182	CD82	(d)	1fa12ca	(Bl)	7.25	7.25
183	CD82	(d)	2fa12ca	(C)	7.25	7.25

No. 87 Surcharged in Carmine

1942-43   **Perf. 13½x14**

184	A7	1ca on 16ca	72.50	45.00
185	A7	4ca on 16ca ('43)	72.50	45.00
186	A7	10ca on 16ca	55.00	35.00
187	A7	15ca on 16ca	55.00	35.00
188	A7	1fa3ca on 16ca ('43)	72.50	45.00
189	A7	2fa9ca on 16ca ('43)	72.50	45.00
190	A7	3fa3ca on 16ca ('43)	55.00	35.00
	Nos. 184-190 (7)		455.00	285.00

Nos. 95-99 Surcharged in Carmine

1943   **Perf. 14x13½**

191	A8	1ca on 6fa6ca	11.00	11.00
192	A8	4ca on 6fa6ca	11.00	11.00
193	A8	10ca on 6fa6ca	11.00	11.00
194	A8	15ca on 6fa6ca	11.00	11.00
195	A8	1fa3ca on 6fa6ca	11.00	11.00
196	A8	2fa9ca on 6fa6ca	12.00	12.00
197	A8	3fa3ca on 6fa6ca	12.00	12.00
198	A8	1ca on 1r	4.50	4.50
199	A8	2ca on 1r	1.60	1.60
200	A8	4ca on 1r	1.60	1.60
201	A8	6ca on 2r	1.60	1.60
202	A8	10ca on 2r	1.60	1.60
203	A8	12ca on 3r	1.60	1.60
204	A8	15ca on 3r	1.60	1.60
205	A8	16ca on 3r	1.60	1.60
206	A8	1fa3ca on 3r	1.60	1.60
207	A8	1fa6ca on 5r	2.00	2.00
208	A8	1fa12ca on 5r	2.40	2.40
209	A8	1fa16ca on 5r	2.40	2.40
	Nos. 191-209 (19)		103.10	103.10

In 1943, 200 each of 27 stamps were overprinted in red or dark blue, "FRANCE TOUJOURS" and a Lorraine Cross within a circle measuring 17½mm in diameter. Overprinted were Nos. 81-99, 104-109, 111-112.

No. 95 Surcharged in Carmine with New Value and Bars

1943   **Unwmk.**   **Perf. 14x13½**

209A	A8	1ca on 6fa6ca	35.00	27.50
209B	A8	4ca on 6fa6ca	35.00	27.50
209C	A8	10ca on 6fa6ca	24.00	16.00
209D	A8	15ca on 6fa6ca	24.00	16.00
209E	A8	1fa3ca on 6fa6ca	32.50	27.50
209F	A8	2fa9ca on 6fa6ca	32.50	27.50
209G	A8	3fa3ca on 6fa6ca	35.00	27.50
	Nos. 209A-209G (7)		218.00	169.50

Catalogue values for unused stamps in this section, from this point to the end of the section, are for Never Hinged items.

Eboue Issue
Common Design Type

1945   **Engr.**   **Perf. 13**

210	CD91	3fa8ca black	.70	.70
211	CD91	5r1fa16ca Prus grn	1.25	1.25

Nos. 210 and 211 exist imperforate.

 Apsaras — A11   Brahman Ascetic — A12

Designs: 6ca, 8ca, 10ca, Dvarabalagar. 12ca, 15ca, 1fa, Vishnu. 1fa6ca, 2fa, 2fa2ca, Dvarabalagar (foot raised). 2fa12ca, 3fa, 5fa, Temple Guardian. 7fa12ca, 1r2fa, 1r4fa12ca, Tigoupalagar.

1948   **Photo.**   **Perf. 13x13½**

212	A11	1ca dk ol grn	.25	.25
213	A11	2ca orange brn	.25	.25
214	A11	4ca vio, cr	.30	.30
215	A11	6ca yellow org	1.00	.65
216	A11	8ca gray blk	1.00	1.00
217	A11	10ca dl yel grn,		
		pale grn	1.00	1.00
218	A11	12ca violet brn	.70	.65
219	A11	15ca Prus grn	.70	.65
220	A11	1fa vio, pale		
		rose	1.00	.80
221	A11	1fa6ca brown red	1.00	.80
222	A11	2fa dk green	1.00	.80
223	A11	2fa2ca blue, cr	1.25	1.00
224	A11	2fa12ca brown	1.25	1.00
225	A11	3fa dp orange	2.40	1.00
226	A11	5fa red vio,		
		rose	2.10	1.25
227	A11	7fa12ca dk brown	2.40	1.25
228	A11	1r2fa brown blk	4.25	4.25
229	A11	1r4fa12ca olive grn	4.25	4.25
	Nos. 212-229 (18)		26.10	21.15

1952

230	A12	18ca rose red	1.75	1.75
231	A12	1fa15ca vio blue	2.40	2.40
232	A12	4fa olive grn	3.00	3.00
	Nos. 230-232 (3)		7.15	7.15

Military Medal Issue
Common Design Type

1952   **Engr. and Typo.**   **Perf. 13**

233	CD101	1fa multi	4.75	4.75

SEMI-POSTAL STAMPS

Regular Issue of 1914 Surcharged in Red

Two printings: 1st, surcharge at bottom of stamp; 2nd, surcharge centered toward top.

1915   **Unwmk.**   **Perf. 14x13½**

B1	A5	10c + 5c rose & blk		
		(1st)	2.10	2.10
b.		Inverted surcharge	200.00	200.00

There were two printings of this surcharge. In the first, it was placed at the bottom of the stamp; in the second, it was centered toward the top.

Regular Issue of 1914 Surcharged in Red

1916

B2	A5	10c + 5c rose & blk	21.00	21.00
a.		Inverted surcharge	200.00	200.00
b.		Double surcharge	200.00	200.00

Surcharged

B3	A5	10c + 5c rose & blk	3.25	3.25

Surcharged

B4	A5	10c + 5c rose & blk	1.60	1.60

Surcharged

B5	A5	10c + 5c rose & blk	2.25	2.25

Curie Issue
Common Design Type

1938   **Engr.**   **Perf. 13**

B6	CD80	2fa12ca + 20ca brt ultra	8.75	8.75

French Revolution Issue
Common Design Type
1939   **Photo.**
Name and Value Typo. in Black

B7	CD83	18ca + 10ca grn	8.75	8.75
B8	CD83	1fa6ca + 12ca brn	8.75	8.75
B9	CD83	1fa12ca + 16ca red org	8.75	8.75
B10	CD83	1fa16ca + 1fa16ca rose pink	8.75	8.75
B11	CD83	2fa12ca + 3fa blue	8.75	8.75
		Nos. B7-B11 (5)	43.75	43.75

Common Design Type and

Non-Commissioned Officer, Native Guard — SP1

Sepoy SP2

1941   **Photo.**   **Perf. 13½**

B12	SP1	1fa16ca + 1fa16ca red	1.25
B13	CD86	2fa12ca + 5fa mar	1.25
B13A	SP2	4fa4ca + 1fa16ca bl	1.25
		Nos. B12-B13A (3)	3.75

Nos. B12-B13A were issued by the Vichy government in France, but were not placed on sale in French India.

Nos. 112A-112B
Surcharged in Black or Red

1944   **Engr.**   **Perf. 12½x12**

B13B		20ca + 2fa12ca on 4fa4ca deep blue (R)	1.00
B13C		+ 4fa4ca on 1fa16ca car & red	1.00

Colonial Development Fund.
Nos. B13B-B13C were issued by the Vichy government in France, but were not placed on sale in French India.

> **Catalogue values for unused stamps in this section, from this point to the end of the section, are for Never Hinged items.**

Red Cross Issue
Common Design Type
1944   **Photo.**   **Perf. 14½x14**

B14	CD90	3fa + 1r4fa dk ol brn	1.25	1.25

The surtax was for the French Red Cross and national relief.

Tropical Medicine Issue
Common Design Type
1950   **Engr.**   **Perf. 13**

B15	CD100	1fa + 10ca ind & dp bl	4.00	4.00

The surtax was for charitable work.

AIR POST STAMPS

Common Design Type
1942   **Unwmk.**   **Photo.**   **Perf. 14½x14**

C1	CD87	4fa dark orange	.90	.90
C2	CD87	1r bright red	.90	.90
C3	CD87	2r brown red	1.40	1.40
C4	CD87	5r black	1.40	1.40

C5	CD87	8r ultra	2.10	2.10
C6	CD87	10r dark green	2.10	2.10
		Nos. C1-C6 (6)	8.80	8.80

> **Catalogue values for unused stamps in this section, from this point to the end of the section, are for Never Hinged items.**

Victory Issue
Common Design Type
1946   **Engr.**   **Perf. 12½**

C7	CD92	4fa dk blue green	.95	.95

Chad to Rhine Issue
Common Design Types
1946, June 6

C8	CD93	2fa12ca olive bis	.95	.95
C9	CD94	5fa dark blue	.95	.95
C10	CD95	7fa12ca dk purple	1.50	1.50
C11	CD96	1r2fa green	1.50	1.50
C12	CD97	1r4fa12ca dk car	1.90	1.90
C13	CD98	3r1fa violet brn	2.40	2.40
		Nos. C8-C13 (6)	9.20	9.20

A 3r ultramarine and red, picturing the Temple of Chindambaram, was sold at Paris June 7 to July 8, 1948, but not placed on sale in the colony. Value $5.75.

Bas-relief Figure of Goddess — AP1

Wing and Temple — AP2

Bird over Palms — AP3

Perf. 12x13, 13x12

			Unwmk.	
C14	AP1	1r yellow & plum	4.75	3.50
C15	AP2	2r green & dk grn	4.75	4.50
C16	AP3	5r lt bl & vio brn	21.00	16.00
		Nos. C14-C16 (3)	30.50	24.00

UPU Issue
Common Design Type
1949   **Engr.**   **Perf. 13**

C17	CD99	6fa lilac rose	8.75	8.75

Universal Postal Union, 75th anniv.

Liberation Issue
Common Design Type
1954, June 6

C18	CD102	1fa sepia & vio brn	8.00	8.00

AIR POST SEMI-POSTAL STAMPS

Girl's School SPAP1

1942, June 22   **Unwmk.**   **Photo.**

CB1	SPAP1	2fa12ca + 5fa20ca green		.95
CB2	SPAP1	3fa8ca + 1r2fa yel brn		.95

Native children's welfare fund.
Nos. CB1-CB2 were issued by the Vichy government in France, but were not placed on sale in French India.

Colonial Education Fund
Common Design Type
1942, June 22

CB3	CD86a	2fa + 3fa blue & red		.90

No. CB3 was issued by the Vichy government in France, but was not placed on sale in French India.

POSTAGE DUE STAMPS

Postage Due Stamps of France Surcharged like Nos. 54-75 in Black, Blue or Red
1923   **Unwmk.**   **Perf. 14x13½**

J1	D2	6ca on 10c brn	1.25	1.25
J2	D2	12ca on 25c rose (Bk)	1.25	1.25
J3	D2	15ca on 20c ol grn (R)	1.60	1.60
J4	D2	1fa6ca on 30c red	1.60	1.60
J5	D2	1fa12a on 50c brn vio	2.75	2.75
J6	D2	1fa15ca on 5c bl (Bk)	2.75	2.75
J7	D2	3fa3ca on 1fr red brn, straw	3.25	3.25
		Nos. J1-J7 (7)	14.45	14.45

Types of Postage Due Stamps of French Colonies, 1884-85, Surcharged with New Values as in 1923 in Red or Black Bars over Original Values
1928

J8	D1	4ca on 20c gray lil	1.60	1.60
J9	D1	1fa on 30c orange	3.00	3.00
J10	D1	1fa16ca on 5c bl blk		
			3.00	3.00
J11	D1	3fa on 1fr lt grn	3.50	3.50
		Nos. J8-J11 (4)	11.10	11.10

D3

1929   **Typo.**

J12	D3	4ca deep red	.50	.50
J13	D3	6ca blue	.65	.65
J14	D3	12ca green	.65	.65
J15	D3	1fa brown	1.25	1.25
J16	D3	1fa12ca lilac gray	1.25	1.25
J17	D3	1fa16ca buff	1.75	1.75
J18	D3	3fa lilac	2.10	2.10
		Nos. J12-J18 (7)	8.15	8.15

D4

1948   **Unwmk.**   **Photo.**   **Perf. 13x13½**

J19	D4	1ca dk violet	.30	.30
J20	D4	2ca dk brown	.50	.50
J21	D4	6ca blue green	.50	.50
J22	D4	12ca dp orange	.70	.70

J23	D4	1fa dk car rose	.80	.80
J24	D4	1fa12ca brown	.80	.80
J25	D4	2fa dk slate bl	1.25	1.25
J26	D4	2fa12ca henna brn	1.60	1.60
J27	D4	5fa dk olive grn	2.10	2.10
J28	D4	1r dk blue vio	2.75	2.75
		Nos. J19-J28 (10)	11.30	11.30

FRENCH MOROCCO

ˈfrench mə-ˈrä-ˌkō

LOCATION — Northwest coast of Africa
GOVT. — French Protectorate
AREA — 153,870 sq. mi.
POP. — 8,340,000 (estimated 1954)
CAPITAL — Rabat

French Morocco was a French Protectorate from 1912 until 1956 when it, along with the Spanish and Tangier zones of Morocco, became the independent country, Morocco.

Stamps inscribed "Tanger" were for use in the international zone of Tangier in northern Morocco.

100 Centimos = 1 Peseta
100 Centimes = 1 franc (1917)

> **Catalogue values for unused stamps in this country are for Never Hinged items, beginning with Scott 177 in the regular postage section, Scott B26 in the semipostal section, Scott C27 in the airpost section, Scott CB23A in the airpost semi-postal section, and Scott J46 in the postage due section.**

French Offices in Morocco

A1   A2

Stamps of France Surcharged in Red or Black
1891-1900   **Unwmk.**   **Perf. 14x13½**

1	A1	5c on 5c grn, grnsh (R)	13.00	4.00
a.		Imperf., pair	175.00	
2	A1	5c on 5c yel grn (II) (R) ('99)	32.50	27.50
a.		Type I	32.50	27.50
3	A1	10c on 10c blk, lav (II) (R)	32.50	3.25
a.		Type I	45.00	20.00
b.		10c on 25c black, rose	1,100.	1,200.
4	A1	20c on 20c red, grn	35.00	27.50
5	A1	25c on 25c blk, rose (R)	32.50	4.00
a.		Double surcharge	225.00	
b.		Imperf., pair	175.00	
6	A1	50c on 50c car, rose (II)	100.00	45.00
a.		Type I	375.00	260.00
7	A1	1p on 1fr brnz grn, straw	110.00	75.00
8	A1	2p on 2fr brn, az (Bk) ('00)	240.00	240.00
		Nos. 1-8 (8)	595.50	426.25

No. 3b was never sent to Morocco.

France Nos. J15-J16 Overprinted in Carmine
1893

9	A2	5c black	3,000.	1,200.
10	A2	10c black	2,600.	800.

Counterfeits exist.

A3   A4

A5

Surcharged in Red or Black

1902-10

11	A3	1c on 1c gray (R) ('08)	2.40	1.20
12	A3	2c on 2c vio brn ('08)	2.40	1.20
13	A3	3c on 3c red org ('08)	3.25	1.60
14	A3	4c on 4c yel brn ('08)	13.00	8.00
15	A3	5c on 5c grn (R)	8.75	4.00
a.		Double surcharge		340.00
16	A4	10c on 10c rose red	7.25	3.25
a.		Surcharge omitted		225.00
17	A4	20c on 20c brn vio ('03)	32.50	22.50
18	A4	25c on 25c bl ('03)	32.50	3.25
19	A4	35c on 35c vio ('10)	40.00	24.00
20	A5	50c on 50c bis brn & lav ('03)	60.00	14.50
21	A5	1p on 1fr cl & ol grn ('03)	110.00	72.50
22	A5	2p on 2fr gray vio & yel ('03)	140.00	100.00
		Nos. 11-22 (12)	452.05	256.00

Nos. 11-14 exist spelled CFNTIMOS or GENTIMOS.
The 25c on 25c with surcharge omitted is listed as No. 81a.
For overprints and surcharges see Nos. 26-37, 72-79, B1, B3.

Postage Due Stamps
Nos. J1-J2
Handstamped

1903

24	D2	5c on 5c light blue	1,500.	1,400.
25	D2	10c on 10c chocolate	2,800.	2,600.

Nos. 24 and 25 were used only on Oct. 10, 1903. Used stamps were not canceled, the overprint serving as a cancellation.
Counterfeits exist.

Types of 1902-10 Issue Surcharged in Red or Blue

1911-17

26	A3	1c on 1c gray (R)	.90	.90
27	A3	2c on 2c vio brn	.95	.95
28	A3	3c on 3c orange	.95	.95
29	A3	5c on 5c green (R)	.95	.55
30	A4	10c on 10c rose	1.00	.65
a.		Imperf., pair	275.00	
31	A4	15c on 15c org ('17)	3.25	2.40
32	A4	20c on 20c brn vio	4.75	3.25
33	A4	25c on 25c blue (R)	2.40	1.60
34	A4	35c on 35c violet (R)	9.50	4.75
35	A5	40c on 40c red & pale bl ('17)	8.00	5.50
36	A5	50c on 50c bis brn & lav (R)	24.00	14.50
37	A5	1p on 1fr cl & ol grn	21.00	8.00
		Nos. 26-37 (12)	77.65	44.00

For surcharges see Nos. B1, B3.

Stamps of this design were issued by the Cherifien posts in 1912-13. The Administration Cherifinne des Postes, Telegraphes et Telephones was formed in 1911 under French guidance. See Morocco in Vol. 4 for listings.

French Protectorate

A6

A7

A8

Issue of 1911-17 Overprinted "Protectorat Francais"

1914-21

38	A6	1c on 1c lt gray	.65	.50
a.		1c dk gray ('22)	.65	.50
39	A6	2c on 2c vio brn	.65	.50
40	A6	3c on 3c orange	.95	.65
41	A6	5c on 5c green	.95	.50
a.		Imperf., pair	87.50	
42	A7	10c on 10c rose	.80	.30
a.		New value omitted	275.00	275.00
43	A7	15c on 15c org ('17)	.80	.60
a.		New value omitted	550.00	550.00
44	A7	20c on 20c brn vio	4.75	3.50
a.		"Protectorat Francais" double	300.00	300.00
45	A7	25c on 25c blue	2.40	.80
a.		New value omitted	350.00	350.00
46	A7	25c on 25c violet ('21)	1.20	.40
a.		"Protectorat Francais" omitted	80.00	80.00
b.		"Protectorat Francais" double	175.00	175.00
c.		"Protectorat Francais" dbl. (R + Bk)	175.00	175.00
47	A7	30c on 30c vio ('21)	17.50	8.75
48	A7	35c on 35c violet	4.75	1.60
49	A8	40c on 40c red & pale bl	20.00	8.75
a.		New value omitted	375.00	375.00
50	A8	45c on 45c grn & bl ('21)	47.50	40.00
51	A8	50c on 50c bis brn & lav	1.60	.80
a.		"Protectorat Francais" invtd.	200.00	200.00
b.		"Protectorat Francais" double	450.00	450.00
52	A8	1p on 1fr cl & ol grn	3.25	.80
a.		"Protectorat Francais" invtd.	350.00	350.00
b.		New value double	200.00	200.00
c.		New value dbl., one invtd.	210.00	210.00
53	A8	2p on 2fr gray vio & yel	5.50	1.60
a.		New value omitted	175.00	175.00
b.		"Protectorat Francais" omitted	110.00	110.00
c.		New value double		225.00
d.		New value dbl., one invtd.		
54	A8	5p on 5fr dk bl & buff	15.00	4.75
		Nos. 38-54 (17)	128.25	75.00

For surcharges see Nos. B2, B4-B5.

Tower of Hassan, Rabat — A9

Mosque of the Andalusians, Fez — A10

City Gate Chella A11

Koutoubiah, Marrakesh A12

Bab Mansour, Meknes A13

Roman Ruins, Volubilis A14

1917 Engr. Perf. 13½x14, 14x13½

55	A9	1c grnsh gray	.50	.50
56	A9	2c brown vio	.65	.50
57	A9	3c orange brn	.70	.55
a.		Imperf., pair	87.50	
58	A10	5c yellow grn	.70	.40
59	A10	10c rose red	.70	.40
60	A10	15c dark gray	.70	.50
a.		Imperf., pair	65.00	
61	A11	20c red brown	3.25	2.40
62	A11	25c dull blue	3.50	1.25
63	A11	30c gray violet	4.50	2.75
64	A12	35c orange	4.50	2.75
65	A12	40c ultra	1.60	1.25
66	A12	45c gray green	29.00	13.00
67	A13	50c dk brown	5.25	2.75
a.		Imperf., pair	65.00	
68	A13	1fr slate	13.00	4.00
a.		Imperf., pair	65.00	
69	A14	2fr black brown	160.00	92.50
70	A14	5fr dk gray grn	45.00	37.50
71	A14	10fr black	45.00	37.50
		Nos. 55-71 (17)	318.55	200.50

See note following #115. See #93-105. For surcharges see #120-121.

Types of the 1902-10 Issue Overprinted

1918-24 Perf. 14x13½

72	A3	1c dk gray	.55	.55
73	A3	2c violet brn	.65	.65
74	A3	3c red orange	.95	.95
75	A3	5c green	1.00	1.00
76	A3	5c orange ('23)	2.00	2.00
77	A4	10c rose	2.00	1.60
78	A4	10c green ('24)	2.00	1.60
79	A4	15c orange	1.60	1.20
80	A4	20c violet brn	2.40	2.00
81	A4	25c blue	2.40	2.00
a.		"TANGER" omitted	400.00	400.00
82	A4	30c red org ('24)	3.25	2.75
83	A4	35c violet	3.25	2.40
84	A5	40c red & pale bl	3.25	2.40
85	A5	50c bis brn & lav	27.50	16.00
86	A5	50c blue ('24)	21.00	13.50
87	A5	1fr claret & ol grn	15.00	6.75
88	A5	2fr org & pale bl ('24)	80.00	72.50
89	A5	5fr dk bl & buff ('24)	67.50	65.00
		Nos. 72-89 (18)	236.30	194.85

Types of 1917 and

Tower of Hassan, Rabat — A15

Bab Mansour, Meknes A16

Roman Ruins, Volubilis A17

1923-27 Photo. Perf. 13½

90	A15	1c olive green	.25	.25
91	A15	2c brown vio	.25	.25
92	A15	3c yellow brn	.25	.25
93	A10	5c orange	.25	.25
94	A10	10c yellow grn	.25	.25
95	A10	15c dk gray	.25	.25
96	A11	20c red brown	.25	.25
97	A11	20c red vio ('27)	.50	.50
98	A11	25c ultra	.30	.30
99	A11	30c deep red	.30	.30
100	A11	30c turq bl ('27)	1.00	.75
101	A12	35c violet	.95	.80
102	A12	40c orange red	.25	.25
103	A12	45c deep green	.30	.30
104	A16	50c dull turq	.50	.50
105	A12	50c olive grn ('27)	.65	.30
106	A16	60c lilac	.95	.50
107	A16	75c red vio ('27)	.70	.50
108	A16	1fr deep brown	.70	.55
109	A16	1.05fr red brn ('27)	1.50	.80
110	A16	1.40fr dull rose ('27)	.90	.75
111	A16	1.50fr turq bl ('27)	1.25	.30
112	A17	2fr olive brn	1.25	.95
113	A17	3fr dp red ('27)	1.50	.95
114	A17	5fr dk gray grn	3.25	2.40
115	A17	10fr black	8.75	4.50
		Nos. 90-115 (26)	27.25	17.75

Nos. 90-110, 112-115 exist imperf. The stamps of 1917 were line engraved. Those of 1923-27 were printed by photogravure and have in the margin at lower right the imprint "Helio Vaugirard."
See #B36. For surcharges see #122-123.

No. 102 Surcharged in Black

1930

120	A12	15c on 40c orange red	1.60	1.60

Nos. 100, 106 and 110 Surcharged in Blue Similarly to No. 176

1931

121	A11	25c on 30c turq blue	2.40	2.00
a.		Inverted surcharge	140.00	140.00
122	A16	50c on 60c lilac	.95	.40
a.		Inverted surcharge	150.00	150.00
b.		Double surcharge	150.00	150.00
123	A16	1fr on 1.40fr rose	3.00	1.60
a.		Inverted surcharge	150.00	150.00
		Nos. 121-123 (3)	6.35	4.00

Old Treasure House and Tribunal, Tangier A18

Roadstead at Agadir A19

Post Office at Casablanca A20

Moulay Idriss of the Zehroun A21

Kasbah of the Oudayas, Rabat A22

Court of the Medersa el Attarine at Fez A23

Saadiens' Tombs at Marrakesh A25

Kasbah of Si Madani el Glaoui at Ouarzazat A24

1933-34		Engr.	Perf. 13	
124	A18	1c olive blk	.25	.25
125	A18	2c red violet	.25	.25
126	A19	3c dark brown	.25	.25
127	A19	5c brown red	.25	.25
128	A20	10c blue green	.30	.30
129	A20	15c black	.30	.30
130	A20	20c red brown	.30	.30
131	A21	25c dark blue	.30	.30
132	A21	30c emerald	.50	.30
133	A21	40c black brn	.50	.30
134	A22	45c brown vio	.75	.65
135	A22	50c dk blue grn	.75	.30
a.		Booklet pane of 10	—	
b.		Booklet pane of 20	—	
		Complete booklet, #135b	1,500.	
136	A22	65c brown red	.30	.30
a.		Booklet pane of 10	—	
b.		Booklet pane of 20	—	
		Complete booklet, #136b	60.00	
137	A23	75c brown vio	.75	.30
138	A23	90c orange red	.50	.30
139	A23	1fr deep brown	1.00	.50
140	A23	1.25fr black ('34)	1.40	.95
141	A24	1.50fr ultra	.50	.30
142	A24	1.75fr myr grn ('34)	.75	.30
143	A24	2fr yellow brn	4.25	.80
144	A24	3fr car rose	55.00	6.50
145	A25	5fr red brown	11.00	2.40
146	A25	10fr black	8.75	6.50
147	A25	20fr bluish gray	8.00	6.50
		Nos. 124-147 (24)	96.90	29.40

Booklets containing Nos. 135 and 136 each have two panes of 10 (#135a, 136a) connected by a gutter, the complete piece constituting No. 135b or 136b, which is stapled into the booklet through the gutter.

For surcharges see Nos. 148, 176, B13-B20.

No. 135 Surcharged in Red

1939
148	A22	40c on 50c dk bl grn	.95	.50

Mosque of Salé — A26

Sefrou — A27

Cedars — A28

Goatherd A29

Ramparts of Salé — A30

Scimitar-horned Oryxes — A31

Fez — A33

Valley of Draa A32

1939-42				
149	A26	1c rose violet	.25	.25
150	A27	2c emerald	.25	.25
151	A27	3c ultra	.25	.25
152	A26	5c dk bl grn	.25	.25
153	A27	10c brt red vio	.25	.25
154	A28	15c dk green	.25	.25
155	A28	20c black grn	.25	.25
156	A29	30c deep blue	.25	.25
157	A29	40c chocolate	.25	.25
158	A29	45c Prus green	.55	.55
159	A30	50c rose red	1.50	.90
159A	A30	50c Prus grn ('40)	.30	.25
160	A30	60c turq blue	1.25	.75
160A	A30	60c choc ('40)	.30	.25
161	A31	70c dk violet	.25	.25
162	A32	75c grnsh blk	.50	.25
163	A32	80c pck bl ('40)	.30	.25
163A	A32	80c dk grn ('42)	.30	.25
164	A30	90c ultra	.30	.25
165	A28	1fr chocolate	.30	.25
165A	A32	1.20fr rose vio ('42)	.70	.30
166	A32	1.25fr henna brn	1.10	.65
167	A32	1.40fr rose violet	.65	.30
168	A30	1.50fr cop red ('40)	.30	.25
168A	A30	1.50fr rose ('42)	.25	.25
169	A33	2fr Prus green	.25	.25
170	A33	2.25fr dark blue	.65	.50
170A	A26	2.40fr red ('42)	.30	.30
171	A26	2.50fr scarlet	1.00	.65
171A	A26	2.50fr dp blue ('40)	.95	.65
172	A33	3fr black brown	.50	.30
172A	A26	4fr dp ultra ('42)	.30	.30
172B	A32	4.50fr grnsh blk ('42)	.65	.55
173	A31	5fr dark blue	.65	.50
174	A31	10fr red	1.20	.90
174A	A31	15fr Prus grn ('42)	4.25	3.50
175	A31	20fr dk vio brn	2.00	1.75
		Nos. 149-175 (37)	23.80	18.60
		Set, never hinged	30.00	

See Nos. 197-219. For surcharges see Nos. 244, 261-262, B21-B24, B26, B28, B32.

No. 136 Surcharged in Black

1940
176	A22	35c on 65c brown red	1.75	.95
a.		Pair, one without surcharge	3.25	2.40

The surcharge was applied on alternate rows in the sheet, making No. 176a. This was done to make a pair equal 1fr, the new rate.

Catalogue values for unused stamps in this section, from this point to the end of the section, are for Never Hinged items.

One Aim Alone-Victory A34

Tower of Hassan, Rabat A35

1943		Litho.	Perf. 12	
177	A34	1.50fr deep blue	.30	.25

1943				
178	A35	10c rose lilac	.40	.25
179	A35	30c blue	.40	.25
180	A35	40c lake	.40	.25
181	A35	50c blue green	.40	.25
182	A35	60c dk vio brn	.40	.25
183	A35	70c rose violet	.40	.25
184	A35	80c gray green	.40	.25
185	A35	1fr car lake	.40	.25
186	A35	1.20fr violet	.40	.25
187	A35	1.50fr red	.40	.25
188	A35	2fr lt bl grn	.40	.25
189	A35	2.40fr car rose	.40	.25
190	A35	3fr olive brn	.40	.25
191	A35	4fr dk ultra	.40	.25
192	A35	4.50fr slate blk	.40	.25
193	A35	5fr dull blue	.55	.25
194	A35	10fr orange brn	.55	.40
195	A35	15fr slate grn	1.50	.55
196	A35	20fr deep plum	2.50	.80
		Nos. 178-196 (19)	11.10	5.75

Types of 1939-42
Perf. 13½x14, 14x13½
1945-47		Typo.	Unwmk.	
197	A27	10c red violet	.30	.25
199	A29	40c chocolate	.30	.25
200	A30	50c Prus grn	.30	.25
203	A28	1fr choc ('46)	.30	.25
204	A32	1.20fr vio brn ('46)	.40	.25
205	A27	1.30fr blue ('47)	.65	.30
206	A30	1.50fr deep red	.30	.25
207	A33	2fr Prus grn	.30	.25
209	A33	3fr black brn	.30	.25
210	A29	3.50fr dk red ('47)	.90	.55
212	A31	4.50fr magenta ('47)	.65	.30
214	A31	5fr indigo	1.00	.55
215	A32	6fr chlky bl ('46)	.55	.30
216	A31	10fr red	2.00	.80
217	A31	15fr Prus grn	2.25	.80
218	A31	20fr dk vio brn	3.25	1.40
219	A31	25fr black brn	3.00	2.10
		Nos. 197-219 (17)	16.75	9.10

For surcharges see #261-263, B26, B28, B32.

The Terraces — A37

Mountain District — A39

Fortress A38

Marrakesh A40

Gardens of Fez — A41

Ouarzazat District — A42

1947		Engr.	Unwmk.	Perf. 13	
221	A37	10c black brn		.30	.25
222	A37	30c brt red		.40	.25
223	A37	50c brt grnsh bl		.30	.25
224	A37	60c brt red vio		.30	.25
225	A38	1fr black		.30	.25
226	A38	1.50fr blue		.40	.25
227	A39	2fr brt green		.65	.30
228	A39	3fr brown red		.30	.25
229	A40	4fr dk bl vio		.40	.25
230	A41	5fr dk green		.90	.55
231	A40	6fr crimson		.40	.25
232	A41	10fr dp blue		.90	.40
233	A42	15fr dk grn		1.60	1.10
234	A42	20fr henna brn		1.25	.65
235	A42	25fr purple		2.00	1.25
		Nos. 221-235 (15)		10.40	6.50

1948-49				
236	A37	30c purple	.30	.25
237	A38	2fr vio brn ('49)	.55	.30
238	A40	4fr green	.65	.30
239	A41	8fr org ('49)	1.40	.90
240	A41	10fr blue	.90	.30
241	A42	10fr car rose	.75	.55
242	A38	12fr red	1.00	.65
243	A42	18fr deep blue	2.00	1.10
		Nos. 236-243 (8)	7.55	4.35

For surcharges see Nos. 263, 293-294.

No. 175 Surcharged with New Value and Wavy Lines in Carmine
1948
244	A31	8fr on 20fr dk vio brn	1.25	.75

Fortified Oasis A43

Walled City — A44

1949				
245	A43	5fr blue green	.90	.40
246	A44	15fr red	1.25	.55
247	A44	25fr ultra	1.50	.65
		Nos. 245-247 (3)	3.65	1.60

See No. 300.

Detail, Gate of Oudayas, Rabat — A45

Nejjarine Fountain, Fez — A46

Garden, Meknes — A47

1949			Perf. 14x13	
248	A45	10c black	.30	.25
249	A45	50c rose brn	.30	.25
250	A45	1fr blue vio	.30	.25
251	A46	2fr dk car rose	.30	.25
252	A46	3fr dark brn	.50	.25
253	A46	5fr brt green	.95	.25
254	A47	8fr dk bl grn	1.25	.50
255	A47	10fr brt red	1.25	.50
		Nos. 248-255 (8)	5.15	2.50

Postal Administration Building, Meknes — A48

1949, Oct. **Perf. 13**
256 A48 5fr dark green 2.40 2.00
257 A48 15fr deep carmine 2.40 2.00
258 A48 25fr deep blue 2.75 2.40
 Nos. 256-258 (3) 7.55 6.40

75th anniv. of the UPU.

Todra Valley
A49

1950
259 A49 35fr red brown 1.40 .40
260 A49 50fr indigo 1.40 .40

See No. 270.

Nos. 204 and 205 Surcharged in Black or Blue

1950 **Perf. 14x13½, 13½x14**
261 A32 1fr on 1.20fr vio brn (Bk) .40 .30
262 A27 1fr on 1.30fr blue (Bl) .30 .25

The surcharge is transposed and spaced to fit the design on No. 262.

No. 231 Surcharged with New Value and Wavy Lines in Black

1951 **Perf. 13**
263 A40 5fr on 6fr crimson .40 .25

Statue of Gen. Jacques Leclerc — A50

1951, Apr. 28 **Engr.**
264 A50 10fr blue green 2.00 1.60
265 A50 15fr deep carmine 2.50 2.00
266 A50 25fr indigo 2.50 2.00
 Nos. 264-266 (3) 7.00 5.60

Unveiling of a monument to Gen. Leclerc at Casablanca, Apr. 28, 1951. See No. C39.

Loustau Hospital, Oujda
A51

Designs: 15fr, New Hospital, Meknes. 25fr, New Hospital, Rabat.

1951
267 A51 10fr indigo & pur 2.10 1.60
268 A51 15fr Prus grn & red brn 2.10 1.60
269 A51 25fr dk brn & ind 2.40 2.00
 Nos. 267-269 (3) 6.60 5.20

Todra Valley Type of 1950
1951
270 A49 30fr ultramarine 1.60 .40

Pigeons at Fountain
A52

Patio, Oudayas
A54

Karaouine Mosque, Fez
A53

Oudayas Point, Rabat
A55

Patio of Old House — A56

Type I (No. 275)   Type II (No. 276)

 Perf. 14x13, 13
1951-53 **Engr.** **Unwmk.**
271 A52 5fr magenta ('52) .30 .25
272 A53 6fr bl grn ('52) .45 .30
273 A52 8fr brown ('52) .45 .30
273A A53 10fr rose red ('53) .45 .30
274 A53 12fr dp ultra ('52) .75 .30
275 A54 15fr red brn (I) 3.50 .25
276 A54 15fr red brn (II) 1.25 .25
277 A55 15fr pur ('52) 1.25 .25
278 A55 18fr red ('52) 2.00 .75
279 A56 20fr dp grnsh bl ('52) 2.00 .50
 Nos. 271-279 (10) 12.40 3.45

See Nos. 297-299.

8th-10th Cent. Capital
A57

Casablanca Monument
A58

Capitals: 20fr, 12th Cent. 25fr, 13th-14th Cent. 50fr, 17th Cent.

1952, Apr. 5 **Perf. 13**
280 A57 15fr deep blue 3.25 2.40
281 A57 20fr red 3.25 2.40
282 A57 25fr purple 3.25 2.40
283 A57 50fr deep green 3.25 2.40
 Nos. 280-283 (4) 13.00 9.60

1952 Sept. 22 **Engr. & Typo.**
284 A58 15fr multicolored 3.50 2.50

Creation of the French Military Medal, cent.

Daggers of South Morocco
A59

Post Rider and Public Letter-writer
A60

Designs: 20fr and 25fr, Antique brooches.

1953, Mar. 27 **Engr.**
285 A59 15fr dk car rose 4.00 3.25
286 A59 20fr violet brn 4.00 3.25
287 A59 25fr dark blue 4.00 3.25
 Nos. 285-287 (3) 12.00 9.75

See No. C46.

1953, May 16
288 A60 15fr violet brown 2.00 1.60

Stamp Day, May 16, 1953.

Bine el Ouidane Dam — A61

1953, Nov. 3 **Perf. 13**
290 A61 15fr indigo 2.00 1.60

See No. 295.

Mogador Fortress — A62

Design: 30fr, Moorish knights.

1953, Dec. 4
291 A62 15fr green 2.40 1.60
292 A62 30fr red brown 2.40 1.60

Issued to aid Army Welfare Work.

Nos. 226 and 243 Surcharged with New Value and Wavy Lines in Black

1954
293 A38 1fr on 1.50fr blue .30 .25
294 A42 15fr on 18fr dp bl .90 .75

Dam Type of 1953
1954, Mar. 8
295 A61 15fr red brn & indigo 1.40 1.00

Station of Rural Automobile Post — A63

1954, Apr. 10
296 A63 15fr dk blue grn 1.40 .80

Stamp Day, April 10, 1954.

Types of 1951-53
1954 **Engr.** **Perf. 14x13**
297 A52 15fr dk blue green 1.10 .30
 Typo.
298 A52 5fr magenta 1.10 .30
299 A55 15fr rose violet 1.60 .40
 Nos. 297-299 (3) 3.80 1.00

Walled City Type of 1949
1954 **Engr.** **Perf. 13**
300 A44 25fr purple 1.75 .55

Marshal Lyautey at Rabat
A64

Lyautey, Builder of Cities — A65

Designs: 15fr, Marshal Lyautey at Khenifra. 50fr, Hubert Lyautey, Marshal of France.

1954, Nov. 17
301 A64 5fr indigo 2.40 2.00
302 A64 15fr dark green 2.75 2.40
303 A65 30fr rose brown 4.00 3.25
304 A65 50fr dk red brn 4.00 3.25
 Nos. 301-304 (4) 13.15 10.90

Marshal Hubert Lyautey, birth cent.

Franco-Moslem Education — A66

Moslem Student at Blackboard — A67

Designs: 30fr, Moslem school at Camp Boulhaut. 50fr, Moulay Idriss College at Fez.

1955, Apr. 16 **Unwmk.** **Perf. 13**
305 A66 5fr indigo 2.00 1.60
306 A67 15fr rose lake 2.40 2.00
307 A66 30fr chocolate 2.40 2.00
308 A67 50fr dk blue grn 2.75 2.10
 Nos. 305-308 (4) 9.55 7.70

Franco-Moslem solidarity.

Map and Rotary Emblem
A68

1955, June 11
309 A68 15fr bl & org brn 1.75 1.00

Rotary Intl., 59th anniv.

Post Office, Mazagan
A69

1955, May 24
310 A69 15fr red 1.10 .65

Stamp Day.

Bab el Chorfa, Fez
A70

Mahakma (Courthouse), Casablanca
A71

Fortress,
Safi — A72

Designs: 50c, 1fr, 2fr, 3fr, Mrissa Gate, Salé. 10fr, 12fr, 15fr, Minaret at Rabat. 30fr, Menara Garden Marrakesh. 40fr, Tafraout Village. 50fr, Portuguese cistern, Mazagan. 75fr, Garden of Oudaya, Rabat.

1955   *Perf. 13½x13, 13x13½, 13*
311	A70	50c brn vio	.30	.25
312	A70	1fr blue	.30	.25
313	A70	2fr red lilac	.30	.25
314	A70	3fr bluish blk	.40	.25
315	A70	5fr vermilion	1.25	.30
316	A70	6fr green	.75	.30
317	A70	8fr orange brn	1.20	.50
318	A70	10fr violet brn	1.60	.30
319	A70	12fr greenish bl	.80	.25
320	A70	15fr magenta	1.10	.25
321	A71	18fr dk green	2.00	.80
322	A71	20fr brown lake	1.10	.40
323	A72	25fr brt ultra	2.75	.40
324	A72	30fr green	2.40	.50
325	A72	40fr orange red	2.40	.30
326	A72	50fr black brn	6.75	.65
327	A71	75fr greenish bl	2.50	1.00
	Nos. 311-327 (17)		27.90	7.20

Succeeding issues, released under the Kingdom, are listed under Morocco in Vol. 4.

SEMI-POSTAL STAMPS

French Protectorate

No. 30 Surcharged in Red   ÷ 5ᶜ

1914   **Unwmk.**   *Perf. 14x13½*
B1	A4 10c + 5c on 10c	23,000.	27,000.

Known only with inverted red surcharge.

Same Surcharge on No. 42 with "Protectorat Francais"
B2	A7 10c + 5c on 10c		
	rose	6.50	6.50
a.	Double surcharge	175.00	175.00
b.	Inverted surcharge	225.00	225.00
c.	"c" omitted	110.00	110.00

On Nos. B1 and B2 the cross is set up from pieces of metal (quads), the horizontal bar being made from two long pieces, the vertical bar from two short pieces. Each cross in the setting of twenty-five differs from the others.

No. 30 Handstamp
Surcharged in Red   ✚ 5ᶜ

B3	A4 10c + 5c on 10c		
	rose	1,600.	1,300.

No. B3 was issued at Oujda. The surcharge ink is water-soluble.

No. 42 Surcharged in Vermilion or Carmine

B4	A7 10c + 5c on 10c		
	(V)	24.00	24.00
a.	Double surcharge	240.00	240.00
b.	Inverted surcharge	240.00	240.00
c.	Double surch., one invtd.	200.00	200.00
B5	A7 10c +5c on 10c		
	(C)	475.00	525.00
a.	Inverted surcharge	1,600.	1,600.

On Nos. B4-B5 the horizontal bar of the cross is single and not as thick as on Nos. B1-B2.

No. B5 was sold largely at Casablanca.

SP1   SP2

Carmine Surcharge

1915
B6	SP1	5c + 5c green	3.25	2.40
a.		Inverted surcharge	300.00	300.00
B7	SP2	10c + 5c rose	4.75	4.75

No. B6 was not issued without the Red Cross surcharge. No. B7 was used in Tangier.

SP3   SP4

France No. B2 Overprinted in Black
B8	SP3 10c + 5c red	7.25	7.25

No. 30 Surcharged in Carmine

1917
B9	SP4 10c + 5c on 10c rose	3.25	3.25

On No. B9 the horizontal bar of the cross is made from a single, thick piece of metal.

Marshal Hubert
Lyautey — SP5

1935, May 15   **Photo.**   *Perf. 13x13½*
B10	SP5	50c + 50c red	9.50	9.50
B11	SP5	1fr + 1fr dk grn	11.00	11.00
B12	SP5	5fr + 5fr blk brn	45.00	45.00
	Nos. B10-B12 (3)		65.50	65.50
	Set, never hinged		98.50	

Stamps of 1933-34 Surcharged in Blue or Red

1938   *Perf. 13*
B13	A18	2c + 2c red vio	4.75	4.75
B14	A19	3c + 3c dk brn	4.75	4.75
B15	A20	20c + 20c red brn	4.75	4.75
B16	A21	40c + 40c blk brn (R)	4.75	4.75
B17	A22	65c + 65c brn red	5.25	5.25
B18	A23	1.25fr + 1.25fr blk (R)	5.25	5.25
B19	A24	2fr + 2fr yel brn	5.25	5.25
B20	A25	5fr + 5fr red brn	5.25	5.25
	Nos. B13-B20 (8)		40.00	40.00
	Set, never hinged		60.00	

Stamps of 1939 Surcharged in Black

1942
B21	A29	45c + 2fr Prus grn	4.75	4.75
B22	A30	90c + 4fr ultra	4.75	4.75
B23	A32	1.25fr + 6fr henna brn	4.75	4.75
B24	A26	2.50fr + 8fr scarlet	4.75	4.75
	Nos. B21-B24 (4)		19.00	19.00
	Set, never hinged		27.00	

The arrangement of the surcharge differs slightly on each denomination.

> **Catalogue values for unused stamps in this section, from this point to the end of the section, are for Never Hinged items.**

No. 207 Surcharged in Black

1945   **Unwmk.**   *Perf. 13½x14*
B26	A33 2fr + 1fr Prus green	.65	.50

For surcharge see No. B28.

Mausoleum of Marshal Lyautey — SP7   Statue of Marshal Lyautey — SP8

1945   **Litho.**   *Perf. 11½*
B27	SP7 2fr + 3fr dark blue	.65	.30

The surtax was for French works of solidarity.

No. B26 Surcharged in Red

1946   *Perf. 13½x14*
B28	A33 3fr (+ 1fr) on 2fr + 1fr	.40	.25

Perf. 13½x14, 13
1946, Dec. 16   **Engr.**
B29	SP8	2fr + 10fr black	2.00	1.60
B30	SP8	3fr + 15fr cop red	2.00	1.60
B31	SP8	10fr + 20fr brt bl	2.75	2.00
	Nos. B29-B31 (3)		6.75	5.20

The surtax was for works of solidarity.

No. 212 Surcharged in Rose Violet

1947, Mar. 15   *Perf. 13½x14*
B32	A31 4.50fr + 5.50fr magenta	2.50	1.50

Stamp Day, 1947.

Map and Symbols of Prosperity from Phosphates SP9

1947   *Perf. 13*
B33	SP9 4.50fr + 5.50fr green	1.60	.95

25th anniv. of the exploitations of the Cherifien Office of Phosphates.

Power — SP10   Health — SP11

1948, Feb. 9
B34	SP10	6fr + 9fr red brn	3.25	2.40
B35	SP11	10fr + 20fr dp ultra	3.25	2.40

The surtax was for combined works of Franco-Moroccan solidarity.

Type of Regular Issue of 1923, Inscribed: "Journee du Timbre 1948"

1948, Mar. 6
B36	A16 6fr + 4fr red brown	1.20	.90

Stamp Day, Mar. 6, 1948.

Battleship off Moroccan Coast SP12

1948, Aug.
B37	SP12 6fr + 9fr purple	2.00	1.60

The surtax was for naval charities.

Wheat Field near Meknes SP13

Designs: 2fr+5fr, Olive grove, Taroudant. 3fr+7fr, Net and coastal view. 5fr+10fr, Aguedal Gardens, Marrakesh.

1949, Apr. 12   **Engr.**   **Unwmk.**
Inscribed: "SOLIDARITÉ 1948"
B38	SP13	1fr + 2fr orange	2.00	1.60
B39	SP13	2fr + 5fr car	2.00	1.60
B40	SP13	3fr + 7fr pck bl	2.00	1.60
B41	SP13	5fr + 10fr dk brn vio	2.00	1.60
a.		Sheet of 4, #B38-B41	25.00	20.00
	Nos. B38-B41,CB31-CB34 (8)		17.60	14.40

Gazelle Hunter, from 1899 Local Stamp SP14

1949, May 1
B42	SP14 10fr + 5fr choc & car		
	rose	2.00	1.60

Stamp Day and 50th anniversary of Mazagan-Marrakesh local postage stamp.

Moroccan Soldiers, Flag SP15   Rug Weaving SP16

1949
B43	SP15 10fr + 10fr bright red	2.00	1.60

The surtax was for Army Welfare Work.

1950, Apr. 11

Designs: 2fr+5fr, Pottery making, 3fr+7fr, Bookbinding. 5fr+10fr, Copper work.

Inscribed: "SOLIDARITE 1949"

B44	SP16	1fr + 2fr dp car	2.75	2.40
B45	SP16	2fr + 5fr dk brnsh bl	2.75	2.40
B46	SP16	3fr + 7fr dk pur	2.75	2.40
B47	SP16	5fr + 10fr red brn	2.75	2.40
a.		Sheet of 4, #B44-B47	32.50	24.00
		Nos. B44-B47,CB36-CB39 (8)	21.70	18.30

Ruins of Sala Colonia at Chella SP17

1950, Sept. 25   Engr.   Perf. 13

B48	SP17	10fr + 10fr dp magenta	2.00	1.75
B49	SP17	15fr + 15fr indigo	2.00	1.75

The surtax was for Army Welfare Work.

AIR POST STAMPS

French Protectorate

Biplane over Casablanca AP1

1922-27   Photo.   Unwmk.   Perf. 13½

C1	AP1	5c dp orange ('27)	.50	.50
C2	AP1	25c dp ultra	1.10	.95
C3	AP1	50c grnsh blue	1.25	.90
C4	AP1	75c dp blue	80.00	12.50
C5	AP1	75c dp green	1.00	.50
C6	AP1	80c vio brn ('27)	1.75	.55
C7	AP1	1fr vermilion	1.00	.50
C8	AP1	1.40fr brn lake ('27)	2.40	1.25
C9	AP1	1.90fr dp blue ('27)	2.50	1.60
C10	AP1	2fr black vio	2.25	1.10
a.		2fr deep violet	2.25	1.40
C11	AP1	3fr gray blk	2.50	1.60
		Nos. C1-C11 (11)	96.25	21.95

The 25c, 50c, 75c deep green and 1fr each were printed in two of three types, differing in frameline thickness, or hyphen in "Helio-Vaugirard" imprint.

Imperf., Pairs

C1a	AP1	5c	65.00	65.00
C2a	AP1	25c	72.50	72.50
C3a	AP1	50c	72.50	72.50
C4a	AP1	75c	550.00	550.00
C5a	AP1	75c	72.50	72.50
C6a	AP1	80c	72.50	72.50
C7a	AP1	1fr	87.50	87.50
C10b	AP1	2fr	225.00	225.00

Nos. C8-C9 Surcharged in Blue or Black

1931, Apr. 10

C12	AP1	1fr on 1.40fr (B)	1.75	1.75
a.		Inverted surcharge	300.00	300.00
C13	AP1	1.50fr on 1.90fr (Bk)	1.90	1.90

Rabat and Tower of Hassan AP2

Casablanca AP3

1933, Jan.   Engr.

C14	AP2	50c dark blue	.80	.80
C15	AP2	80c orange brn	.80	.65
C16	AP2	1.50fr brown red	.80	.80
C17	AP3	2.50fr carmine rose	6.00	1.25
C18	AP3	5fr violet	3.25	1.75
C19	AP3	10fr blue green	1.25	1.25
		Nos. C14-C19 (6)	12.90	6.50

For surcharges see Nos. CB22-CB23.

Storks and Minaret, Chella — AP4

Plane and Map of Morocco AP5

1939-40   Perf. 13

C20	AP4	80c Prus green	.25	.25
C21	AP4	1fr dk red	.25	.25
C22	AP5	1.90fr ultra	.40	.30
C23	AP5	2fr red vio ('40)	.40	.30
C24	AP5	3fr chocolate	.50	.25
C25	AP5	5fr violet	1.40	.80
C26	AP5	10fr turq blue	1.25	.55
		Nos. C20-C26 (7)	4.45	2.70

> **Catalogue values for unused stamps in this section, from this point to the end of the section, are for Never Hinged items.**

Plane over Oasis — AP6

1944   Litho.   Perf. 11½

C27	AP6	50c Prus grn	.50	.30
C28	AP6	2fr ultra	.50	.30
C29	AP6	5fr scarlet	.50	.30
C30	AP6	10fr violet	1.40	1.00
C31	AP6	50fr black	2.00	1.60
C32	AP6	100fr dp bl & red	4.00	3.25
		Nos. C27-C32 (6)	8.90	6.75

For surcharge see No. CB24.

Plane AP7

1945   Engr.   Perf. 13

C33	AP7	50fr sepia	1.20	.95

Moulay Idriss — AP8

La Medina AP9

1947-48

C34	AP8	9fr dk rose car	.40	.30
C35	AP8	40fr dark blue	.95	.55
C36	AP8	50fr dp claret ('47)	1.40	.40
C37	AP9	100fr dp grnsh bl	3.25	1.10
C38	AP9	200fr henna brn	6.75	1.60
		Nos. C34-C38 (5)	12.75	3.95

Leclerc Type of Regular Issue

1951, Apr. 28

C39	A50	50fr purple	3.25	2.75

Unveiling of a monument to Gen. Leclerc at Casablanca, Apr. 28, 1951.

Kasbah of the Oudayas, Rabat AP11

1951, May 22

C40	AP11	300fr purple	24.00	11.00

Ben Smine Sanatorium AP12

1951, June 4

C41	AP12	50fr pur & Prus grn	3.50	2.75

Fortifications, Chella — AP13

Plane Near Marrakesh AP14

Fort, Anti-Atlas Mountains AP15

View of Fez AP16

1952, Apr. 19   Unwmk.   Perf. 13

C42	AP13	10fr blue green	1.25	.55
C43	AP14	40fr red	2.00	.65
C44	AP15	100fr brown	4.50	1.25
C45	AP16	200fr purple	10.00	4.25
		Nos. C42-C45 (4)	17.75	6.70

Antique Brooches — AP17

1953, Mar. 27

C46	AP17	50fr dark green	4.00	3.25

"City" of the Agdal, Meknes AP18

20fr, Yakoub el Mansour, Rabat. 40fr, Ainchock, Casablanca. 50fr, El Aliya, Fedala.

1954, Mar. 8

C47	AP18	10fr olive brown	3.50	2.75
C48	AP18	20fr purple	3.50	2.75
C49	AP18	40fr red brown	3.50	2.75
C50	AP18	50fr deep green	3.50	2.75
		Nos. C47-C50 (4)	14.00	11.00

Franco-Moroccan solidarity.

Naval Vessel and Sailboat AP19

Village in the Anti-Atlas AP20

"Ksar es Souk," Rabat and Plane AP21

1954, Oct. 18

C51	AP19	15fr dk blue green	2.10	1.60
C52	AP19	30fr violet blue	2.40	2.00

1955, July 25   Engr.   Perf. 13

200fr, Estuary of Bou Regreg, Rabat and Plane.

C53	AP20	100fr brt violet	2.75	.50
C54	AP20	200fr brt carmine	6.50	.95
C55	AP21	500fr grnsh blue	14.50	3.25
		Nos. C53-C55 (3)	23.75	4.70

AIR POST SEMI-POSTAL STAMPS

French Protectorate

Moorish Tribesmen SPAP1

Designs: 25c, Moor plowing with camel and burro. 50c, Caravan nearing Saffi. 75c, Walls, Marrakesh. 80c, Sheep grazing at Azrou. 1fr, Gate at Fez. 1.50fr, Aerial view of Tangier. 2fr, Aerial view of Casablanca. 3fr, Storks on old wall, Rabat. 5fr, Moorish fete.

Perf. 13½

1928, July 26		**Photo.**	**Unwmk.**	
CB1	SPAP1	5c dp blue	5.25	5.25
CB2	SPAP1	25c brn org	5.25	5.25
CB3	SPAP1	50c red	5.25	5.25
CB4	SPAP1	75c org brn	5.25	5.25
CB5	SPAP1	80c olive grn	5.25	5.25
CB6	SPAP1	1fr orange	5.25	5.25
CB7	SPAP1	1.50fr Prus bl	5.25	5.25
CB8	SPAP1	2fr dp brown	5.25	5.25

CB9	SPAP1	3fr dp violet	5.25	5.25
CB10	SPAP1	5fr brown blk	5.25	5.25
	Nos. CB1-CB10 (10)		52.50	52.50

These stamps were sold in sets only and at double their face value. The money received for the surtax was divided among charitable and social organizations. The stamps were not sold at post offices but solely by subscription to the Moroccan Postal Administration.

Overprinted in Red or Blue (25c, 50c, 75c, 1fr)

Tanger

1929, Feb. 1

CB11	SPAP1	5c dp blue	5.25	5.25
CB12	SPAP1	25c brown org	5.25	5.25
CB13	SPAP1	50c red	5.25	5.25
CB14	SPAP1	75c org brn	5.25	5.25
CB15	SPAP1	80c olive grn	5.25	5.25
CB16	SPAP1	1fr orange	5.25	5.25
CB17	SPAP1	1.50fr Prus bl	5.25	5.25
CB18	SPAP1	2fr dp brown	5.25	5.25
CB19	SPAP1	3fr dp violet	5.25	5.25
CB20	SPAP1	5fr brown blk	5.25	5.25
	Nos. CB11-CB20 (10)		52.50	52.50

These stamps were sold at double their face values and only in Tangier. The surtax benefited various charities.

Marshal Hubert Lyautey SPAP10

1935, May 15   *Perf. 13½*

CB21	SPAP10	1.50fr + 1.50fr blue	20.00	20.00

Nos. C14, C19 Surcharged in Red

O.S.E. +50c

1938   *Perf. 13*

CB22	AP2	50c + 50c dk bl	6.50	6.50
CB23	AP3	10fr + 10fr bl grn	6.50	6.50

Catalogue values for unused stamps in this section, from this point to the end of the section, are for Never Hinged items.

Plane over Oasis SPAP11

Statue of Marshal Lyautey SPAP12

1944   **Litho.**   *Perf. 11½*

CB23A	SPAP11	1.50fr + 98.50fr	3.25	1.60

The surtax was for charity among the liberated French.

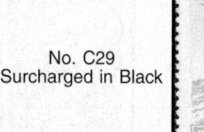

No. C29 Surcharged in Black

+5F
18 Juin 1940
18 Juin 1946

1946, June 18   *Perf. 11*

CB24	AP6	5fr + 5fr scarlet	2.75	2.00

6th anniv. of the appeal made by Gen. Charles de Gaulle, June 18, 1940. The surtax was for the Free French Association of Morocco.

1946, Dec.   **Engr.**   *Perf. 13*

CB25	SPAP12	10fr +30fr dk grn	2.75	2.00

The surtax was for works of solidarity.

Replenishing Stocks of Food — SPAP13

Agriculture SPAP14

1948, Feb. 9   **Unwmk.**

CB26	SPAP13	9fr +26fr dp grn	2.00	1.60
CB27	SPAP14	20fr +35fr brown	2.00	1.60

The surtax was for combined works of Franco-Moroccan solidarity.

Tomb of Marshal Hubert Lyautey — SPAP15

1948, May 18   *Perf. 13*

CB28	SPAP15	10fr +25fr dk grn	1.60	1.25

Lyautey Exposition, Paris, June, 1948.

P.T.T. Clubhouse SPAP16

1948, June 7   **Engr.**

CB29	SPAP16	6fr + 34fr dk grn	2.40	2.00
CB30	SPAP16	9fr + 51fr red brn	2.40	2.00

The surtax was used for the Moroccan P.T.T. employees vacation colony at Ifrane.

View of Agadir SPAP17

Plane over Globe SPAP18

Designs: 6fr+9fr, Fez. 9fr+16fr, Atlas Mountains. 15fr+25fr, Valley of Draa.

1949, Apr. 12   *Perf. 13*
Inscribed: "SOLIDARITÉ 1948"

CB31	SPAP17	5fr +5fr dk grn	2.40	2.00
CB32	SPAP17	6fr +9fr org red	2.40	2.00
CB33	SPAP17	9fr +16fr blk brn	2.40	2.00
CB34	SPAP17	15fr +25fr ind	2.40	2.00
a.	Sheet of 4, #CB31-CB34		27.50	22.50
	Nos. CB31-CB34 (4)		8.70	7.30

1950, Mar. 11   **Engr. & Typo.**

CB35	SPAP18	15fr + 10fr bl grn & car	1.60	1.25

Day of the Stamp, Mar. 11-12, 1950, and 25th anniv. of the 1st post link between Casablanca and Dakar.

Scenes and Map: Northwest Corner SPAP19

Designs (quarters of map): 6fr+9fr, NE, 9fr+16fr, SW. 15fr+25fr, SE.

1950, Apr. 11   **Engr.**
Inscribed: "SOLIDARITE 1949"

CB36	SPAP19	5fr +5fr dp ultra	2.60	2.10
CB37	SPAP19	6fr +9fr Prus grn	2.60	2.10
CB38	SPAP19	9fr +16fr dk brn	2.75	2.25
CB39	SPAP19	15fr +25fr brn red	2.75	2.25
a.	Sheet of 4, #CB36-CB39		32.50	24.00
	Nos. CB36-CB39 (4)		10.70	8.70

Arch of Triumph of Caracalla at Volubilis SPAP20

1950, Sept. 25   **Unwmk.**

CB40	SPAP20	9fr + 10fr sepia	2.00	1.60
CB41	SPAP20	15fr + 15fr bl grn	2.00	1.60

The surtax was for Army Welfare Work.

Casablanca Post Office and First Air Post Stamp SPAP21

1952, Mar. 8   *Perf. 13*

CB42	SPAP21	15fr + 5fr red brn & dp grn	4.75	4.00

Day of the Stamp, Mar. 8, 1952, and 30th anniv. of French Morocco's 1st air post stamp.

POSTAGE DUE STAMPS

French Offices in Morocco

Postage Due Stamps and Types of France Surcharged in Red or Black

5 CENTIMOS

1896   **Unwmk.**   *Perf. 14x13½*
On Stamps of 1891-93

J1	D2	5c on 5c lt bl (R)	8.75	5.50
J2	D2	10c on 10c choc (R)	13.00	5.50
J3	D2	30c on 30c car	30.00	24.00
a.	Pair, one without surcharge			
J4	D2	50c on 50c lilac	30.00	24.00
a.	"S" of "CENTIMOS" omitted		340.00	250.00
J5	D2	1p on 1fr lil brn	340.00	325.00

1909-10   **On Stamps of 1908-10**

J6	D3	1c on 1c ol grn (R)	3.25	3.25
J7	D3	10c on 10c violet	37.50	32.50
J8	D3	30c on 30c bister	47.50	40.00
J9	D3	50c on 50c red	72.50	72.50
	Nos. J6-J9 (4)		160.75	148.25

Postage Due Stamps of France Surcharged in Red or Blue

5 CENTIMES

1911   **On Stamps of 1893-96**

J10	D2	5c on 5c blue (R)	4.75	4.75
J11	D2	10c on 10c choc (R)	16.00	16.00
a.	Double surcharge		225.00	260.00
J12	D2	50c on 50c lil (Bl)	17.50	17.50

On Stamps of 1908-10

J13	D3	1c on 1c ol grn (R)	3.25	3.25
J14	D3	10c on 10c vio (R)	8.00	8.00
J15	D3	30c on 30c bis (R)	9.50	9.50
J16	D3	50c on 50c red (Bl)	15.00	15.00
	Nos. J10-J16 (7)		74.00	74.00

For surcharges see Nos. JN23-J26.

French Protectorate

D4   D5

Type of 1911 Issue Overprinted "Protectorat Francais"

1915-17

J17	D4	1c on 1c black	.55	.55
a.	New value double		175.00	
J18	D4	5c on 5c blue	2.50	1.90
J19	D4	10c on 10c choc	3.25	2.00
J20	D4	20c on 20c ol grn	3.25	2.00
J21	D4	30c on 30c rose red, grayish	7.25	5.50
J22	D4	50c on 50c vio brn	11.00	6.50
	Nos. J17-J22 (6)		27.80	18.45

Nos. J13 to J16 With Additional Overprint "Protectorat Francais"

1915

J23	D3	1c on 1c ol grn	1.60	1.60
J24	D3	10c on 10c violet	3.25	2.75
J25	D3	30c on 30c bister	3.25	2.75
J26	D3	50c on 50c red	3.25	3.25
	Nos. J23-J26 (4)		11.35	10.35

1917-26   **Typo.**

J27	D5	1c black	.25	.25
J28	D5	5c deep blue	.30	.25
J29	D5	10c brown	.55	.30
J30	D5	20c olive green	2.25	1.40
J31	D5	30c rose	.30	.30
J32	D5	50c lilac brown	.55	.25
J33	D5	1fr red brn, *straw* ('26)	1.00	.70
J34	D5	2fr violet ('26)	1.90	1.25
	Nos. J27-J34 (8)		7.10	4.70

See #J49-J56, Morocco #J1-J4. For surcharges see #J46-J48.

Postage Due Stamps of France, 1882-1906 Overprinted

TANGER

1918

J35	D2	1c black	1.25	1.25
J36	D2	5c blue	2.00	2.00
J37	D2	10c chocolate	2.00	2.00
J38	D2	15c green	4.50	4.50
J39	D2	20c olive green	6.50	6.50
J40	D2	30c rose red, *grayish*	14.50	14.50
J41	D2	50c violet brown	21.00	21.00
	Nos. J35-J41 (7)		51.75	51.75

Postage Due Stamps of France, 1908-19 Overprinted

TANGER

1918

J42	D3	1c olive green	1.25	1.25
J43	D3	10c violet	2.75	2.75
J44	D3	20c bister, *grayish*	8.00	8.00
J45	D3	40c red	20.00	20.00
		Nos. J42-J45 (4)	32.00	32.00

> Catalogue values for unused stamps in this section, from this point to the end of the section, are for Never Hinged items.

Nos. J31 and J29
Surcharged

1944 Unwmk. Perf. 14x13½

J46	D5	50c on 30c rose	3.00	2.50
J47	D5	1fr on 10c brown	5.25	3.75
J48	D5	3fr on 10c brown	12.50	9.50
		Nos. J46-J48 (3)	20.75	15.75

1945-52 Type of 1917-1926 Typo.

J49	D5	1fr brn lake ('47)	.95	.75
J50	D5	2fr rose lake ('47)	1.20	.80
J51	D5	3fr ultra	.65	.40
J52	D5	4fr red orange	.75	.30
J53	D5	5fr green	1.40	.50
J54	D5	10fr yellow brn	1.60	.50
J55	D5	20fr carmine ('50)	1.60	1.00
J56	D5	30fr dull brn ('52)	2.50	1.60
		Nos. J49-J56 (8)	10.65	5.85

PARCEL POST STAMPS

French Protectorate

PP1

1917 Unwmk. Perf. 13½x14

Q1	PP1	5c green	1.00	.65
Q2	PP1	10c carmine	1.00	.65
Q3	PP1	20c lilac brown	1.10	.80
Q4	PP1	25c blue	1.60	.80
Q5	PP1	40c dark brown	2.40	1.20
Q6	PP1	50c red orange	3.25	.80
Q7	PP1	75c pale slate	4.00	2.40
Q8	PP1	1fr ultra	5.50	.80
Q9	PP1	2fr gray	8.00	1.50
Q10	PP1	5fr violet	11.00	1.60
Q11	PP1	10fr black	17.00	1.60
		Nos. Q1-Q11 (11)	55.85	12.80

FRENCH POLYNESIA

'french ˌpä-lə-'nē-zhə

(French Oceania)

LOCATION — South Pacific Ocean
GOVT. — French Overseas Territory
AREA — 1,522 sq. mi.
POP. — 242,073 (1999 est.)
CAPITAL — Papeete

In 1903 various French Establishments in the South Pacific were united to form a single colony. Most important of the island groups are the Society Islands, Marquesas Islands, the Tuamotu group and the Gambier, Austral, and Rapa Islands. Tahiti, largest of

the Society group, ranks first in importance.

100 Centimes = 1 Franc

> Catalogue values for unused stamps in this country are for Never Hinged items, beginning with Scott 136 in the regular postage section, Scott B11 in the semipostal section, Scott C2 in the airpost section, Scott J18 in the postage due section, and Scott O1 in the officials section.

Navigation and
Commerce — A1

Perf. 14x13½

1892-1907 Typo. Unwmk.
Name of Colony in Blue or Carmine

1	A1	1c black, *lil bl*	1.60	1.60
2	A1	2c brown, *buff*	2.40	2.40
3	A1	4c claret, *lav*	4.00	3.75
4	A1	5c green, *grnsh*	12.00	9.25
5	A1	5c yellow grn ('06)	4.00	2.40
6	A1	10c blk, *lavender*	27.50	12.50
7	A1	10c red ('00)	4.00	2.40
8	A1	15c blue, quadrille paper	32.50	12.00
9	A1	15c gray, *lt gray* ('00)	8.00	7.25
10	A1	20c red, *grn*	17.50	14.50
11	A1	25c black, *rose*	55.00	27.50
12	A1	25c blue ('00)	27.50	16.00
13	A1	30c brown, *bis*	16.00	13.50
14	A1	35c black, *yel* ('06)	9.50	9.50
15	A1	40c red, *straw*	132.50	80.00
16	A1	45c blk, *gray grn* ('07)	6.50	*6.50*
17	A1	50c car, *pale rose*	9.00	9.00
a.		50c rose, *pale rose*	9.00	9.00
18	A1	50c brown, *az* ('00)	250.00	200.00
19	A1	75c dp vio, *org*	12.00	12.00
20	A1	1fr brnz grn, *straw*	13.50	13.50
		Nos. 1-20 (20)	645.00	455.55

Perf. 13½x14 stamps are counterfeits.
For overprint and surcharge see #55, B1.

Tahitian
Girl — A2

Kanakas — A3

Fautaua
Valley — A4

1913-30

21	A2	1c violet & brn	.25	.25
22	A2	2c brown & blk	.25	.25
23	A2	4c orange & bl	.35	.35
24	A2	5c grn & yel grn	1.25	.80
25	A2	5c bl & blk ('22)	.50	.50
26	A2	10c rose & org	1.90	1.25
27	A2	10c bl grn & yel grn ('22)	1.25	1.25
28	A2	10c org red & brn red, *bluish* ('26)	1.40	1.40
29	A2	15c org & blk ('15)	.80	.65
a.		Imperf., pair	175.00	
30	A2	20c black & vio	1.10	1.00
a.		Imperf., pair	175.00	
31	A2	20c grn & bl grn ('26)	1.00	1.00
32	A2	20c brn red & dk brn ('27)	1.60	1.60
33	A3	25c ultra & blue	1.50	1.00
34	A3	25c vio & rose ('22)	.75	.75
35	A3	30c gray & brown	4.00	3.25
a.		Imperf., pair	325.00	
36	A3	30c rose & red org ('22)	2.75	2.75
37	A3	30c blk & red org ('26)	.75	.75
38	A3	30c slate bl & bl grn ('27)	1.75	1.75
39	A3	35c green & rose	1.25	1.25

40	A3	40c black & green	1.10	1.10
41	A3	45c orange & red	1.10	1.10
42	A3	50c dk brown & blk	15.00	13.00
43	A3	50c ultra & bl ('22)	1.25	1.25
44	A3	50c gray & bl vio ('26)	.90	.90
45	A3	60c green & blk ('25)	1.25	1.25
46	A3	65c ol brn & red vio ('27)	3.00	3.00
47	A3	75c vio brn & vio	2.25	2.25
48	A3	90c brn red & rose ('30)	14.50	14.50
49	A4	1fr rose & black	5.25	3.50
50	A4	1.10fr vio & dk brn ('28)	1.60	1.60
51	A4	1.40fr bis brn & vio ('29)	4.00	4.00
52	A4	1.50fr ind & bl ('30)	15.00	15.00
53	A4	2fr dk brown & grn	5.25	3.50
54	A4	5fr violet & bl	10.50	10.50
		Nos. 21-54 (34)	106.35	98.25

For surcharges see Nos. 56-71, B2-B4.

No. 7 Overprinted

1915

55	A1	10c red	5.50	5.50
a.		Inverted overprint	200.00	200.00

For surcharge see No. B1.

No. 29 Surcharged

1916

56	A2	10c on 15c org & blk	3.00	3.00

Nos. 22, 41 and 29
Surcharged

1921

57	A2	5c on 2c brn & blk	36.00	36.00
58	A3	10c on 45c org & red	36.00	36.00
59	A2	25c on 15c org & blk	7.25	7.25
		Nos. 57-59 (3)	79.25	79.25

On No. 58 the new value and date are set wide apart and without bar.

Types of 1913-30
Issue Surcharged in
Black or Red

1923-27

60	A3	60c on 75c bl & brn	.75	.75
61	A4	65c on 1fr dk bl & ol (R) ('25)	2.00	2.00
62	A4	85c on 1fr dk bl & ol (R) ('25)	2.25	2.25
63	A3	90c on 75c brn red & cer ('27)	2.75	2.75
		Nos. 60-63 (4)	7.75	7.75

No. 26 Surcharged

1924

64	A2	45c on 10c rose & org	2.75	2.75
a.		Inverted surcharge	2,400.	2,400.

Stamps and Type of 1913-30
Surcharged with New Value and Bars
in Black or Red

1924-27

65	A4	25c on 2fr dk brn & grn	1.10	1.10
66	A4	25c on 5fr vio & bl	1.10	1.10
67	A4	1.25fr on 1fr dk bl & ultra (R) ('26)	1.10	1.10
68	A4	1.50fr on 1fr dk bl & lt bl ('27)	3.50	3.50
69	A4	20fr on 5fr org & brt vio ('27)	32.50	26.00
		Nos. 65-69 (5)	39.30	32.80

Surcharged in Black or Red

1926

70	A4	3fr on 5fr gray & blue	3.25	2.50
71	A4	10fr on 5fr grn & blk (R)	6.75	6.75

Papetoai Bay, Moorea A5

1929, Mar. 25

72	A5	3fr green & dk brn	8.00	8.00
73	A5	5fr lt blue & dk brn	14.50	14.50
74	A5	10fr lt red & dk brn	42.50	42.50
75	A5	20fr lilac & dk brn	47.50	47.50
		Nos. 72-75 (4)	112.50	112.50

For overprints see Nos. 128, 130, 132, 134.

Common Design Types pictured following the introduction.

Colonial Exposition Issue
Common Design Types

1931, Apr. 13   Engr.   Perf. 12½
Name of Country Printed in Black

76	CD70	40c deep green	7.25	7.25
77	CD71	50c violet	7.25	7.25
78	CD72	90c red orange	7.25	7.25
79	CD73	1.50fr dull blue	7.25	7.25
		Nos. 76-79 (4)	29.00	29.00

Spear Fishing A12

Tahitian Girl — A13

Idols A14

1934-40   Photo.   Perf. 13½, 13½x13

80	A12	1c gray black	.25	.25
81	A12	2c claret	.35	.35
82	A12	3c lt blue ('40)	.35	.35
83	A12	4c orange	.60	.60
84	A12	5c violet	.90	.90
85	A12	10c dark brown	.40	.40
86	A12	15c green	.60	.60
87	A12	20c red	.60	.60
88	A13	25c gray blue	.90	.90
89	A13	30c yellow green	1.20	1.20
90	A13	30c orange brn ('40)	.80	.80
91	A14	35c dp green ('38)	3.50	3.50
92	A13	40c red violet	.60	.60
93	A13	45c brown orange	8.75	8.75
94	A13	45c dk green ('39)	1.50	1.50
95	A13	50c violet	.60	.60
96	A13	55c blue ('38)	6.50	6.50
97	A13	60c black ('39)	.75	.75
98	A13	65c brown	3.25	3.25
99	A13	70c brt pink ('39)	1.40	1.40
100	A13	75c olive green	8.00	8.00
101	A13	80c violet brn ('38)	2.00	2.00
102	A13	90c rose red	.90	.90
103	A14	1fr red brown	.90	.90
104	A14	1.25fr brown violet	6.75	6.75
105	A14	1.25fr rose red ('39)	1.25	1.25
106	A14	1.40fr orange yel ('39)	1.10	1.10
107	A14	1.50fr blue	.90	.90
108	A14	1.60fr dull vio ('39)	1.25	1.25
109	A14	1.75fr olive	6.50	6.50
110	A14	2fr red	1.10	1.10
111	A14	2.25fr deep blue ('39)	1.25	1.25
112	A14	2.50fr black ('39)	1.25	1.25
113	A14	3fr brown org ('39)	1.50	1.50
114	A14	5fr red violet ('39)	1.25	1.25

115	A14	10fr dark green ('39)	3.00	3.00
116	A14	20fr dark brown ('39)	3.50	3.50
		Nos. 80-116 (37)	75.95	75.95

For overprints see #126-127, 129, 131, 133, 135.

Paris International Exposition Issue
Common Design Types

1937   Engr.   Perf. 13

117	CD74	20c deep violet	3.25	3.25
118	CD75	30c dark green	3.25	3.25
119	CD76	40c carmine rose	3.25	3.25
120	CD77	50c dk brown & blue	4.00	4.00
121	CD78	90c red	4.00	4.00
122	CD79	1.50fr ultra	4.75	4.75
		Nos. 117-122 (6)	22.50	22.50

Colonial Arts Exhibition Issue
Souvenir Sheet
Common Design Type

1937   Imperf.

123	CD78	3fr emerald	36.00	52.50
		Never hinged	55.00	

New York World's Fair Issue
Common Design Type

1939, May 10   Engr.   Perf. 12½x12

124	CD82	1.25fr carmine lake	2.40	2.40
125	CD82	2.25fr ultra	2.40	2.40
		Set, never hinged	8.00	

Fautaua Valley and Marshal Plan — A15

1941   Engr.   Perf. 12½x12

125A	A15	1fr bluish green	1.10
125B	A15	2.50fr deep blue	1.25
		Set, never hinged	3.25

Nos. 125A-125B were issued by the Vichy government in France, but were not placed on sale in the French Polynesia.
For surcharges, see Nos. B12B-B12C.

Stamps of 1929-39 Overprinted in Black or Red

1941   Perf. 14x13½, 13½x13

126	A14	1fr red brown (BK)	4.75	6.50
127	A14	2.50fr black	7.25	9.50
128	A5	3fr grn & dk brn	7.25	7.25
129	A14	3fr brn org (Bk)	8.00	10.50
130	A5	5fr lt bl & dk brn	7.25	7.25
131	A14	5fr red vio (Bk)	8.00	10.50
132	A5	10fr lt red & dk brn	21.50	25.00
133	A14	10fr dark green	80.00	100.00
134	A5	20fr lil & dk brn	120.00	120.00
135	A14	20fr dark brown	72.50	92.50
		Nos. 126-135 (10)	336.50	
		Set, never hinged	480.00	

Types of 1934-39 without "RF"

1942-44   Photo.   Perf. 13½

135A	A12	10c dark brown	.65
135B	A13	30c orange brown	.85
135C	A14	1.50fr blue	1.00
135D	A14	10fr dark green	1.75
135E	A14	20fr dark brown	2.50
		Nos. 135A-135E (5)	6.75

Nos. 135A-135E were issued by the Vichy government in France, but were not placed on sale in French Polynesia.

Catalogue values for unused stamps in this section, from this point to the end of the section, are for Never Hinged items.

Ancient Double Canoe A16

1942   Photo.   Perf. 14½x14

136	A16	5c dark brown	.40	.25
137	A16	10c dk gray bl	.40	.25
138	A16	25c emerald	.40	.25
139	A16	30c red orange	.40	.25
140	A16	40c dk slate grn	.40	.25
141	A16	80c red brown	.40	.25
142	A16	1fr rose violet	.50	.35
143	A16	1.50fr brt red	.65	.50
144	A16	2fr gray black	1.00	.75
145	A16	2.50fr brt ultra	2.50	1.75
146	A16	4fr dull violet	1.75	1.25
147	A16	5fr bister	1.75	1.25
148	A16	10fr deep brown	2.50	1.90
149	A16	20fr deep green	3.00	2.10
		Nos. 136-149 (14)	16.05	11.35

For surcharges see Nos. 152-159.

Eboue Issue
Common Design Type

1945   Engr.   Perf. 13

150	CD91	2fr black	1.00	.75
151	CD91	25fr Prus green	2.60	2.10

Nos. 150 and 151 exist imperforate.

Nos. 136, 138 and 145 Surcharged with New Values and Bars in Carmine or Black

1946   Perf. 14½x14

152	A16	50c on 5c (C)	.65	.50
153	A16	60c on 5c (C)	.65	.50
154	A16	70c on 5c (C)	.65	.50
155	A16	1.20fr on 5c (C)	.80	.65
156	A16	2.40fr on 25c (Bk)	1.60	1.25
157	A16	3fr on 25c (Bk)	1.00	.75
158	A16	4.50fr on 25c (Bk)	2.00	1.50
159	A16	15fr on 2.50fr (C)	2.40	1.75
		Nos. 152-159 (8)	9.75	7.40

Coast of Moorea A17

Fisherman and Catch — A18   Tahitian Girl — A20

House at Faa — A19

Island of Borabora A21

Island Women A22

1948   Unwmk.   Engr.   Perf. 13

160	A17	10c brown	.50	.35
161	A17	30c blue green	.50	.35
162	A17	40c deep blue	.50	.35
163	A18	50c red brown	.50	.35

164	A18	60c dk brown ol	.65	.50
165	A18	80c brt blue	.65	.50
166	A19	1fr red brown	.65	.35
167	A19	1.20fr slate	.65	.50
168	A19	1.50fr deep ultra	.65	.50
169	A20	2fr sepia	1.10	.75
170	A20	2.40fr red brown	1.25	1.00
171	A20	3fr purple	11.50	2.50
172	A20	4fr blue black	2.40	1.40
173	A21	5fr sepia	3.75	1.60
174	A21	6fr steel blue	3.75	2.10
175	A21	10fr dk brown ol	4.75	1.75
176	A22	15fr vermilion	7.25	2.75
177	A22	20fr slate	7.25	3.25
178	A22	25fr sepia	9.00	5.00
		Nos. 160-178 (19)	57.25	25.85

Imperforates
Most French Polynesia stamps from 1948 onward exist imperforate in issued and trial colors, and also in small presentation sheets in issued colors.

Military Medal Issue
Common Design Type

1952, Dec. 1   Engr. & Typo.

179	CD101	3fr multicolored	13.50	10.00

Girl of Bora Bora — A23   Girl Playing Guitar — A24

1955, Sept. 26   Engr.

180	A23	9fr dk brn, blk & red	11.00	7.25

FIDES Issue
Common Design Type

Design: 3fr, Dry dock at Papeete.

1956, Oct. 22   Engr.   Perf. 13x12½

181	CD103	3fr grnsh blue	4.00	2.00

1958, Nov. 3   Unwmk.   Perf. 13

Designs: 4fr, 7fr, 9fr, Man with headdress. 10fr, 20fr, Girl with shells on beach.

182	A24	10c grn & redsh brn	.70	.60
183	A24	25c slate grn, cl & car	.85	.65
184	A24	1fr brt bl, brn & red org	1.10	.70
185	A24	2fr brn, vio brn & vio	1.25	.70
186	A24	4fr sl grn & org yel	1.60	1.10
187	A24	7fr red brn, brn & org	3.25	1.75
188	A24	9fr vio brn, grn & org	5.75	2.50
189	A24	10fr dk bl, brn & car	5.25	2.50
190	A24	20fr pur, rose red & brn	9.50	5.50
		Nos. 182-190 (9)	29.25	16.00

See Nos. 304-306.

Human Rights Issue
Common Design Type

1958, Dec. 10

191	CD105	7fr dk gray & dk bl	13.00	8.75

Flower Issue
Common Design Type

1959, Jan. 3   Photo.   Perf. 12½x12

192	CD104	4fr Breadfruit	6.50	4.00

Spear Fishing — A25

Tahitian Dancers A26

1960, May 16   Engr.   Perf. 13
193 A25 5fr green, brn & lil   1.40 1.10
194 A26 17fr ultra, brt grn & red
brn   6.25 2.75

Post Office, Papeete A27

1960, Nov. 19   Unwmk.   Perf. 13
195 A27 16fr green, bl & claret   6.00 3.50

Saraca Indica — A28

1962, July 12   Photo.   Perf. 13
196 A28 15fr shown   16.00 14.00
197 A28 25fr Hibiscus   24.00 16.00

Map of Australia and South Pacific — A29

1962, July 18   Perf. 13x12
198 A29 20fr multicolored   18.00 8.00

5th South Pacific Conf., Pago Pago, July 1962.

Spined Squirrelfish A30

Fish: 10fr, One-spot butterflyfish. 30fr, Radiate lionfish. 40fr, Horned boxfish.

1962, Dec. 15   Engr.   Perf. 13
199 A30 5fr black, mag & bis   4.50 2.00
200 A30 10fr multicolored   6.50 3.00
201 A30 30fr multicolored   13.00 8.00
202 A30 40fr multicolored   16.00 12.00
Nos. 199-202 (4)   40.00 25.00

Soccer — A30a

Design: 50fr, Throwing the javelin.

1963, Aug. 29   Photo.   Perf. 12½
203 A30a 20fr brt yellow & brn   9.50 6.50
204 A30a 50fr brt car rose & ultra   17.00 9.50

South Pacific Games, Suva, 8/29-9/7.

Red Cross Centenary Issue
Common Design Type
1963, Sept. 2   Engr.   Perf. 13
205 CD113 15fr vio brn, gray & car   14.50 11.50

Human Rights Issue
Common Design Type
1963, Dec. 10   Unwmk.   Perf. 13
206 CD117 7fr green & vio bl   14.50 9.50

Philatec Issue
Common Design Type
1964, Apr. 9   Unwmk.   Perf. 13
207 CD118 25fr grn, dk sl grn & red   17.00 12.00

Tahitian Dancer A31

1964, May 14   Engr.   Perf. 13
208 A31 1fr multicolored   .45 .45
209 A31 3fr dp claret, blk & org   1.00 1.00

Soldiers, Truck and Battle Flag — A32

1964, July 10   Photo.   Perf. 12½
210 A32 5fr multicolored   12.00 4.50

Issued to honor the Tahitian Volunteers of the Pacific Battalion. See No. C31.

Tuamotu Scene A33

Views: 4fr, Borabora. 7fr, Papeete Harbor. 8fr, Paul Gauguin's tomb, Marquesas. 20fr, Mangareva, Gambier Islands.

1964, Dec. 1   Litho.   Perf. 12½x13
211 A33 2fr multicolored   .95 .55
212 A33 4fr multicolored   1.60 .55
213 A33 7fr multicolored   3.25 1.40
214 A33 8fr multicolored   4.25 2.00
215 A33 20fr multicolored   10.00 3.25
Nos. 211-215,C32 (6)   29.55 11.75

Painting from a School Dining Room — A34

1965, Nov. 29   Engr.   Perf. 13
216 A34 20fr dk brn, sl grn & dk car   21.00 12.50

Publicizing the School Canteen Program. See #C38.

Outrigger Canoe on Lagoon A35

Ships: 11fr, Large cruising yacht, vert. 12fr, Motorboat for sport fishing. 14fr, Outrigger

canoes with sails. 19fr, Schooner, vert. 22fr, Modern coaster "Oiseau des Isles II."

1966, Aug. 30   Engr.   Perf. 13
217 A35 10fr brt ultra, emer & mar   3.00 .95
218 A35 11fr mar, dk bl & sl grn   3.00 1.75
219 A35 12fr emer, dk bl & red lil   4.00 1.90
220 A35 14fr brn, bl & slate grn   6.00 2.10
221 A35 19fr scar, sl grn & dp bl   7.00 2.25
222 A35 22fr multicolored   10.00 4.25
Nos. 217-222 (6)   33.00 13.20

High Jump A36

Designs: 20fr, Pole vault, vert. 40fr, Women's basketball, vert. 60fr, Hurdling.

1966, Dec. 15   Engr.   Perf. 13
223 A36 10fr dk red, lem & blk   2.40 1.60
224 A36 20fr blue, emer & blk   5.50 2.10
225 A36 40fr emer, brt pink & blk   10.50 5.25
226 A36 60fr dull yel, bl & blk   17.50 9.00
Nos. 223-226 (4)   35.90 17.95

2nd South Pacific Games, Nouméa, New Caledonia, Dec. 8-18.

Poi Pounder — A37   Javelin Throwing — A38

1967, June 15   Engr.   Perf. 13
227 A37 50fr orange & blk   17.50 10.50

Society for Oceanic Studies, 50th anniv.

1967, July 11

5fr, Spring dance. 15fr, Horse race. 16fr, Fruit carriers' race. 21fr, Canoe race.

228 A38 5fr multi, horiz.   1.25 .95
229 A38 13fr multi   4.75 1.60
230 A38 15fr multi, horiz.   4.75 1.75
231 A38 16fr multi   4.75 3.00
232 A38 21fr multi, horiz.   10.00 5.25
Nos. 228-232 (5)   25.50 12.55

Issued to publicize the July Festival.

Earring — A39

Art of the Marquesas Islands: 10fr, Carved mother-of-pearl. 15fr, Decorated canoe paddle. 23fr, Oil vessel. 25fr, Carved stilt stirrups. 30fr, Fan handles. 35fr, Tattooed man. 50fr, Tikis.

1967-68   Engr.   Perf. 13
233 A39 10fr dp cl, dl red & ultra   2.50 .70
234 A39 15fr black & emerald   3.25 1.50
235 A39 20fr ol gray, dk car & lt bl   5.50 2.25
236 A39 23fr dk brn, ocher & bl   7.00 4.25
237 A39 25fr brn, dk bl & lil   7.00 4.00
238 A39 30fr brown & red lilac   8.75 4.25
239 A39 35fr ultra & dk brn   14.50 6.50
240 A39 50fr brn, sl grn & lt bl   15.50 7.50
Nos. 233-240 (8)   64.00 30.95

Issued: 20fr, 25fr, 30fr, 50fr, 12/19/67; others 2/28/68.

WHO Anniversary Issue
Common Design Type
1968, May 4   Engr.   Perf. 13
241 CD126 15fr bl grn, mar & dp vio   10.50 4.50
242 CD126 16fr org, lil & bl grn   10.50 7.50

Human Rights Year Issue
Common Design Type
1968, Aug. 10   Engr.   Perf. 13
243 CD127 15fr blue, red & brn   11.50 5.75
244 CD127 16fr brn, brt pink & ultra   11.50 7.50

Tiare Apetahi A40

Flower: 17fr, Tiare Tahiti.

1969, Mar. 27   Photo.   Perf. 12½x13
245 A40 9fr multicolored   2.25 1.25
246 A40 17fr multicolored   4.50 2.25

3rd South Pacific Games, Port Moresby, Papua and New Guinea, Aug. 13-23 — A41

1969, Aug. 13   Engr.   Perf. 13
247 A41 9fr Boxer, horiz   3.50 1.40
248 A41 17fr High jump   7.50 2.25
249 A41 18fr Runner   9.50 3.75
250 A41 22fr Long jump   12.50 7.50
Nos. 247-250 (4)   33.00 14.90

ILO Issue
Common Design Type
1969, Nov. 24   Engr.   Perf. 13
251 CD131 17fr org, emer & ol   11.00 5.50
252 CD131 18fr org, dk brn & vio bl   11.00 6.50

Territorial Assembly A42

Buildings: 14fr, Governor's Residence. 17fr, House of Tourism. 18fr, Maeva Hotel. 24fr, Taharaa Hotel.

1969, Dec. 22   Photo.   Perf. 12½x12
253 A42 13fr black & multi   3.00 1.40
254 A42 14fr black & multi   4.50 1.75
255 A42 17fr black & multi   7.25 3.75
256 A42 18fr black & multi   8.00 4.25
257 A42 24fr black & multi   13.75 7.50
Nos. 253-257 (5)   36.50 18.65

Stone Figure with Globe — A43

Designs: 40fr, Globe, plane, map of Polynesia and men holding "PATA" sign, horiz. 60fr, Polynesian carrying globe.

1970, Apr. 7   Engr.   Perf. 13
258 A43 20fr deep plum, gray & bl   7.00 3.50
259 A43 40fr emer, rose lil & ultra   11.50 5.50
260 A43 60fr red brn, bl & dk brn   19.50 10.50
Nos. 258-260 (3)   38.00 19.50

Issued to publicize the 1970 Pacific Area Travel Association Congress (PATA).

UPU Headquarters Issue
Common Design Type

1970, May 20   Engr.   Perf. 13
261 CD133 18fr maroon, pur &
                brn   10.50 5.00
262 CD133 20fr lilac rose, ol &
                ind   10.50 5.50

Night Fishing — A44

1971, May 11   Photo.   Perf. 13
263 A44 10fr multicolored   12.50 5.25
        Nos. 263,C71-C73 (4)   37.50 19.75

Flowers — A45

Designs: Various flowers. 12fr is horiz.

Perf. 12½x13, 13x12½
1971, Aug. 27
264 A45 8fr multicolored   2.25 1.10
265 A45 12fr multicolored   3.75 1.90
266 A45 22fr multicolored   6.00 3.00
        Nos. 264-266 (3)   12.00 6.00
Day of a Thousand Flowers.

Water-skiing Slalom — A46

Designs: 20fr, Water-skiing, jump, vert. 40fr,
Figure water-skiing.

1971, Oct. 11   Engr.   Perf. 13
267 A46 10fr grnsh bl, dk red
                & brn   6.50 2.25
268 A46 20fr car, emer & brn   9.50 4.25
269 A46 40fr brn, grn & lil   21.00 13.00
        Nos. 267-269 (3)   37.00 19.50
World water-skiing championships, Oct.
1971.

De Gaulle Issue
Common Design Type

30fr, As general, 1940. 50fr, As president,
1970.

1971, Nov. 9   Engr.   Perf. 13
270 CD134 30fr red lilac & blk 20.00 10.50
271 CD134 50fr red lilac & blk 27.50 17.50

Map of
Tahiti and
Jerusalem
Cross
A47

1971, Dec. 18   Photo.   Perf. 13x12½
272 A47 28fr lt blue & multi   14.50 9.00
2nd rally of French Boy Scouts and Guides,
Taravao, French Polynesia.

"Alcoholism"   Mother and Child
A48   A49

1972, Mar. 24   Photo.   Perf. 13
273 A48 20fr brown & multi   12.00 6.00
Fight against alcoholism.

1973, Sept. 26   Photo.   Perf. 12½x13
274 A49 28fr pale yellow & multi 10.00 5.25
Day nursery.

Polynesian
Golfer — A50

Design: 24fr, Atimaono Golf Course.

1974, Feb. 27   Photo.   Perf. 13
275 A50 16fr multicolored   8.75 3.50
276 A50 24fr multicolored   11.00 5.50
Atimaono Golf Course.

Hand Throwing Life Preserver to
Puppy — A51

1974, May 9   Photo.   Perf. 13
277 A51 21fr brt blue & multi 12.50 5.25
Society for the Protection of Animals.

Around a
Fire, on the
Beach
A52

Polynesian Views: 2fr, Lagoons and mountains. 6fr, Pebble divers. 10fr, Lonely Mountain and flowers, vert. 15fr, Sailing ship at sunset. 20fr, Lagoon and mountain.

1974, May 22
278 A52 2fr multicolored   .90 .60
279 A52 5fr multicolored   1.10 .90
280 A52 6fr multicolored   1.90 1.10
281 A52 10fr multicolored   2.10 1.25
282 A52 15fr multicolored   4.25 1.75
283 A52 20fr multicolored   7.00 2.10
        Nos. 278-283 (6)   17.25 7.70

Polynesian
Woman and UPU
Emblem — A53

Lion, Sun and
Emblem — A54

1974, Oct. 9   Engr.   Perf. 13
284 A53 65fr multicolored   12.50 8.00
Centenary of Universal Postal Union.

1975, June 17   Photo.
285 A54 26fr multicolored   12.50 5.25
15th anniv. of Lions Intl. in Tahiti.

Fish
and
Leaf
A55

1975, July 9   Litho.   Perf. 12
286 A55 19fr dp ultra & green 11.00 4.50
Polynesian Association for the Protection of
Nature.

Georges Pompidou,
Pres. of
France — A55a

1976, Feb. 16   Engr.   Perf. 13
287 A55a 49fr dk violet & black 12.00 7.25
See France No. 1430.

Alain
Gerbault
and
Sailboat
A56

1976, May 25   Photo.   Perf. 13
288 A56 90fr multicolored   14.50 9.50
Alain Gerbault's arrival in Bora Bora, 50th
anniv.

Turtle — A57

Design: 42fr, Hand protecting bird.

1976, June 24   Litho.   Perf. 12½
289 A57 18fr multicolored   15.00 4.50
290 A57 42fr multicolored   21.00 11.50
World Ecology Day.

A. G. Bell, Telephone, Radar and
Satellite — A58

1976, Sept. 15   Engr.   Perf. 13
291 A58 37fr multicolored   11.00 5.25
Centenary of first telephone call by Alexander Graham Bell, Mar. 10, 1876.

Dugout Canoes — A59

1976, Dec. 16 Litho.   Perf. 13x12½
292 A59 25fr Marquesas   4.00 3.00
293 A59 30fr Raiatea   5.00 4.00
294 A59 75fr Tahiti   10.00 6.00
295 A59 100fr Tuamotu   12.50 7.50
        Nos. 292-295 (4)   31.50 20.50

Sailing Ship — A60

Designs: Various sailing vessels.

1977, Dec. 22   Litho.   Perf. 13
296 A60 20fr multicolored   6.50 2.10
297 A60 50fr multicolored   7.50 2.40
298 A60 85fr multicolored   9.50 4.00
299 A60 120fr multicolored   16.00 6.00
        Nos. 296-299 (4)   39.50 14.50

Hibiscus — A61   Girl with Shells
                      on Beach — A62

Designs: 10fr, Vanda orchids. 16fr, Pua (fagraea berteriana). 22fr, Gardenia.

1978-79   Photo.   Perf. 12½x13
300 A61 10fr multicolored   1.25   .50
301 A61 13fr multicolored   2.75   1.25
302 A61 16fr multicolored   3.00   2.00
303 A61 22fr multicolored   2.00   1.25
    Nos. 300-303 (4)   9.00   5.00

Issued: 13fr, 16fr, 8/23; 10fr, 22fr, 1/25/79.

1978, Nov. 3   Engr.   Perf. 13
Design A24 with "1958 1978" added: 28fr, Man with headdress. 36fr, Girl playing guitar.
304 A62 20fr multicolored   3.25   .80
305 A62 28fr multicolored   4.00   1.75
306 A62 36fr multicolored   6.00   2.75
    a. Souvenir sheet of 3   30.00 30.00
    Nos. 304-306 (3)   13.25   5.30

20th anniv. of stamps inscribed: Polynesie Francaise. #306a contains #304-306 in changed colors.

Ships — A63

1978, Dec. 29   Litho.   Perf. 13x12½
307 A63 15fr Tahiti   1.75   .85
308 A63 30fr Monowai   3.00   1.40
309 A63 75fr Tahitien   4.75   3.50
310 A63 100fr Mariposa   9.00   3.50
    Nos. 307-310 (4)   18.50   9.25

Porites Coral A64

Design: 37fr, Montipora coral.

1979, Feb. 15   Perf. 13x12½
311 A64 32fr multicolored   2.75   1.40
312 A64 37fr multicolored   4.00   2.25

Raiatea A65

Landscapes: 1fr, Moon over Bora Bora. 2fr, Mountain peaks, Ua Pou. 3fr, Sunset over Motu Tapu. 5fr, Motu. 6fr, Palm and hut, Tuamotu.

1979, Mar. 8   Photo.   Perf. 13x13½
313 A65 1fr multicolored   .20   .20
314 A65 2fr multicolored   .20   .20
315 A65 3fr multicolored   .35   .20
316 A65 4fr multicolored   .50   .20
317 A65 5fr multicolored   .85   .40
318 A65 6fr multicolored   1.00   .65
    Nos. 313-318 (6)   3.10   1.85

See Nos. 438-443 for redrawn designs.

Dance Costumes A66

1979, July 14   Litho.   Perf. 12½
319 A66 45fr Fetia   2.00   1.10
320 A66 51fr Teanuanua   3.00   1.40
321 A66 74fr Temaeva   4.00   2.50
    Nos. 319-321 (3)   9.00   5.00

Hill, Great Britain No. 53, Tahiti No. 28 A67

1979, Aug. 1   Engr.   Perf. 13
322 A67 100fr multicolored   5.25   3.25
    Sir Rowland Hill (1795-1879), originator of penny postage.

Hastula Strigilata — A68

Statue Holding Rotary Emblem — A69

Shells: 28fr, Scabricola variegata. 35fr, Fusinus undatus.

1979, Aug. 22   Litho.   Perf. 12½
323 A68 20fr multicolored   1.60   .50
324 A68 28fr multicolored   2.10   1.10
325 A68 35fr multicolored   3.00   2.10
    Nos. 323-325 (3)   6.70   3.70

1979, Nov. 30   Litho.   Perf. 13
326 A69 47fr multicolored   3.00   2.10

Rotary International, 75th anniversary; Papeete Rotary Club, 20th anniversary. For overprint see No. 330.

Myripristis Murdjan A70

Fish: 8fr, Napoleon. 12fr, Emperor.

1980, Jan. 21   Litho.   Perf. 12½
327 A70 7fr multicolored   1.10   .55
328 A70 8fr multicolored   1.10   .70
329 A70 12fr multicolored   1.75   1.00
    Nos. 327-329 (3)   3.95   2.25

No. 326 Overprinted and Surcharged in Gold: "75eme / ANNIVERSAIRE / 1905-1980"

1980, Feb. 23   Litho.   Perf. 13
330 A69 77fr on 47fr multi   6.00   3.50
    Rotary International, 75th anniversary.

CNEXO Fish Hatchery A71

1980, Mar. 17   Photo.   Perf. 13x13½
331 A71 15fr shown   1.50   1.00
332 A71 22fr Crayfish   1.50   1.00

Papeete Post Office Building Opening A72

1980, Apr. 30   Photo.   Perf. 13x12½
333 A72 50fr multicolored   2.75   1.75

Tiki and Festival Emblem — A73

1980, June 30   Photo.   Perf. 13½
334 A73 34fr shown   1.50   1.00
335 A73 39fr Drum (pahu)   2.25   1.40
336 A73 49fr Ax (to'i)   3.00   2.00
    a. Souv. sheet of 3, #334-336   13.50 13.00
    Nos. 334-336 (3)   6.75   4.40

South Pacific Arts Festival, Port Moresby, Papua New Guinea.

Titmouse Henparrot — A74

Charles de Gaulle — A75

Perf. 13x12½, 12½x13
1980, Oct. 20   Photo.
337 A74 25fr White sea-swallow,
          horiz.   1.75   .75
338 A74 35fr shown   2.00   1.00
339 A74 45fr Minor frigate bird,
          horiz.   3.00   1.25
    Nos. 337-339 (3)   6.75   3.00

1980, Nov. 9   Engr.   Perf. 12½x13
340 A75 100fr multicolored   5.00   3.25

Naso Vlamingi (Karaua) A76

1981, Feb. 5   Litho.   Perf. 12½
341 A76 13fr shown   1.00   .50
342 A76 16fr Lutjanus vaigensis
          (toau)   1.25   .60
343 A76 24fr Plectropomus le-
          opardus (tonu)   2.50   .75
    Nos. 341-343 (3)   4.75   1.85

Indoor Fish Breeding Tanks, Cnexo Hatchery A77

1981, May 14   Photo.   Perf. 13x13½
344 A77 23fr shown   1.25   .80
345 A77 41fr Mussels   2.00   1.10

Folk Dancers A78

Perf. 13x13½, 13½x13
1981, July 10   Litho.
346 A78 26fr shown   1.25   .65
347 A78 28fr Dancer   1.25   1.10
348 A78 44fr Dancers, vert.   2.10   1.50
    Nos. 346-348 (3)   4.60   3.25

Sterna Bergii — A79

1981, Sept. 24   Litho.   Perf. 13
349 A79 47fr shown   1.50   .90
350 A79 53fr Ptilinopus
          purpuratus, vert.   1.50   1.10
351 A79 65fr Estrilda astrild,
          vert.   2.00   1.50
    Nos. 349-351 (3)   5.00   3.50

    See Nos. 370-372.

Huahine Island A80

1981, Oct. 22   Litho.   Perf. 12½
352 A80 34fr shown   1.50   .80
353 A80 134fr Maupiti   3.50   2.10
354 A80 136fr Bora-Bora   3.50   2.10
    Nos. 352-354 (3)   8.50   5.00

A81

1982, Feb. 4   Photo.   Perf. 13x13½
355 A81 30fr Parrotfish   1.10   .80
356 A81 31fr Regal angel   1.50   .80
357 A81 45fr Spotted bass   1.60   1.25
    Nos. 355-357 (3)   4.20   2.85

Pearl Industry A82

1982, Apr. 22   Photo.   Perf. 13x13½
358 A82 7fr Pearl beds   .90   .50
359 A82 8fr Extracting pearls   .90   .50
360 A82 10fr Pearls   1.25   .90
    Nos. 358-360 (3)   3.05   1.90

Tahiti "No. 1A," Emblem — A83

1982, May 12 Engr. Perf. 13
361 A83 150fr multicolored 4.75 3.50
    a. Souvenir sheet 16.00 16.00
    PHILEXFRANCE Stamp Exhibition, Paris,
June 11-21. No. 361a contains No. 361 in
changed colors.

King Holding
Carved
Scepter — A84

Designs: Coronation ceremony.

1982, July 12 Photo. Perf. 13½x13
362 A84 12fr shown .50 .20
363 A84 13fr King, priest .50 .20
364 A84 17fr Procession 1.00 .50
    Nos. 362-364 (3) 2.00 .90

Championship Emblem — A85

1982, Aug. 13 Perf. 13
365 A85 90fr multicolored 3.00 2.10
    4th Hobie-Cat 16 World Catamaran Sailing
Championship, Tahiti, Aug. 15-21.

First Colloquium
on New Energy
Sources — A86

1982, Sept. 29 Litho.
366 A86 46fr multicolored 2.00 1.00

Motu,
Tuamotu
Islet — A87

1982, Oct. 12 Litho. Perf. 13
367 A87 20fr shown .75 .35
368 A87 33fr Tupai Atoll 1.00 .50
369 A87 35fr Gambier Islds. 1.50 .60
    Nos. 367-369 (3) 3.25 1.45

Bird Type of 1981
1982, Nov. 17 Litho. Perf. 13
370 A79 37fr Sacred egret 1.50 .60
371 A79 39fr Pluvialis dominica,
    vert. 1.50 .70

372 A79 42fr Lonchura castane-
    othorax 2.00 .95
    Nos. 370-372 (3) 5.00 2.25

Fish — A88

1983, Feb. 9 Litho. Perf. 13x13½
373 A88 8fr Acanthurus lineatus .75 .35
374 A88 10fr Caranx me-
    lampygus 1.00 .35
375 A88 12fr Carcharhinus mela-
    nopterus 1.50 .50
    Nos. 373-375 (3) 3.25 1.20

The Way of the
Cross, Sculpture
by Damien
Haturau — A89

1983, Mar. 9 Litho. Perf. 13
376 A89 7fr shown .30 .30
377 A89 21fr Virgin and Child .75 .65
378 A89 23fr Christ 1.00 .65
    Nos. 376-378 (3) 2.05 1.60

Traditional
Hats — A90

1983, May 24 Litho. Perf. 13x12½
379 A90 11fr Acacia .50 .35
380 A90 13fr Niau .65 .35
381 A90 25fr Ofe .85 .55
382 A90 35fr Ofe, diff. 1.25 .70
    Nos. 379-382 (4) 3.25 1.95
    See Nos. 393-396.

Chieftain in
Traditional
Costume, Sainte-
Christine
Isld. — A91

Traditional Costumes, Marquesas Islds.

1983, July 12 Photo. Perf. 13
383 A91 15fr shown .75 .50
384 A91 17fr Man 1.00 .50
385 A91 28fr Woman 1.25 .50
    Nos. 383-385 (3) 3.00 1.50
    See Nos. 397-399, 419-421.

Polynesian Crowns — A92

Various flower garlands.

1983, Oct. 19 Litho. Perf. 13
386 A92 41fr multicolored 1.25 .90
387 A92 44fr multicolored 1.40 .95
388 A92 45fr multicolored 1.50 1.00
    Nos. 386-388 (3) 4.15 2.85
    See Nos. 400-402.

Martin Luther
(1483-1546)
A93

1983, Nov. 10 Engr. Perf. 13
389 A93 90fr black, brn & lil gray 2.50 1.25

Tiki
Carvings — A94

1984, Feb. 8 Litho. Perf. 12½x13

Various carvings.

390 A94 14fr multicolored .55 .30
391 A94 16fr multicolored .65 .50
392 A94 19fr multicolored .80 .50
    Nos. 390-392 (3) 2.00 1.30

Hat Type of 1983
1984, June 20 Litho. Perf. 13x12½
393 A90 20fr Aeho ope .50 .35
394 A90 24fr Paeore .60 .35
395 A90 26fr Ofe fei .75 .50
396 A90 33fr Hua .80 .50
    Nos. 393-396 (4) 2.65 1.70

Costume Type of 1983
1984, July 11 Litho. Perf. 13
397 A91 34fr Tahitian playing
    nose flute .75 .50
398 A91 35fr Priest, Oei-eitia .90 .50
399 A91 39fr Tahitian adult and
    child .90 .50
    Nos. 397-399 (3) 2.55 1.50

Garland Type of 1983
1984, Oct. 24 Litho. Perf. 13x12½
400 A92 46fr Moto'i Lei .90 .60
401 A92 47fr Pitate Lei 1.00 .60
402 A92 53fr Bougainvillea Lei 1.25 .80
    Nos. 400-402 (3) 3.15 1.90

4th Pacific Arts Festival, Noumea, New
Caledonia, Dec. 8-22 — A95

1984, Nov. 20 Litho. Perf. 13
403 A95 150fr Statue, head-
    dress 3.50 2.25
    See No. C213.

Paysage D'Anaa, by Jean
Masson — A96

Paintings: 50fr, Sortie Du Culte, by Jacques
Boulaire. 75fr, La Fete, by Robert Tatin. 85fr,
Tahitiennes Sur La Plage, by Pierre Heyman.

Perf. 12½x13, 13x12½
1984, Dec. 12 Litho.
404 A96 50fr multi, vert. 1.25 .70
405 A96 65fr multicolored 1.40 .90
406 A96 75fr multicolored 1.90 1.00
407 A96 85fr multicolored 2.25 1.75
    Nos. 404-407 (4) 6.80 4.35

Tiki
Carvings — A97

Polynesian
Faces — A98

1985, Jan. 23 Litho. Perf. 13½
408 A97 30fr multicolored .60 .35
409 A97 36fr multicolored .80 .45
410 A97 40fr multicolored .90 .75
    Nos. 408-410 (3) 2.30 1.55

1985, Feb. 20 Photo. Perf. 12½x13
411 A98 22fr multicolored .45 .35
412 A98 39fr multicolored .80 .45
413 A98 44fr multicolored 1.00 .75
    Nos. 411-413 (3) 2.25 1.55

Early Tahiti — A99

Perf. 13x12½, 12½x13
1985, Apr. 24 Litho.
414 A99 42fr Entrance to Papee-
    te 1.00 .60
415 A99 45fr Girls, vert. 1.40 .80
416 A99 48fr Papeete market 1.50 .90
    Nos. 414-416 (3) 3.90 2.30

5th Intl.
Congress
on Coral
Reefs,
Tahiti
A100

1985, May 28 Litho. Perf. 13½
417 A100 140fr Local reef for-
    mation 3.00 2.00
    Printed se-tenant with label picturing con-
gress emblem.

National
Flag
A101

1985, June 28
418 A101 9fr Flag, natl. arms .65 .30

Costume Type of 1983

18th-19th Cent. Prints, Beslu Collection.

1985, July 17 Perf. 13
419 A91 38fr Tahitian dancer .95 .65
420 A91 55fr Man and woman
from Otahiti, 1806 1.25 .90
421 A91 70fr Traditional chief 1.75 1.25
Nos. 419-421 (3) 3.95 2.80

Local Foods — A103

1985-86 Litho. Perf. 13
422 A103 25fr Roasted pig .90 .65
423 A103 35fr Pit fire 1.10 .70
423A A103 80fr Fish in coconut milk 2.00 1.60
423B A103 110fr Fafaru 2.50 2.00
Nos. 422-423B (4) 6.50 4.95

Issued: 25fr, 35fr, 11/14; 80fr, 110fr, 5/20/86.
See Nos. 458-459, 474-475.

Catholic Churches — A104

1985, Dec. 11 Litho. Perf. 13
424 A104 90fr St. Anne's,
Otepipi 1.90 1.10
425 A104 100fr St. Michael's
Cathedral, Rik-
itea 2.00 1.10
426 A104 120fr Cathedral, exterior 2.40 1.60
Nos. 424-426 (3) 6.30 3.80

Nos. 424-426 printed se-tenant with labels
picturing local religious art.

Crabs
A105

1986, Jan. 22 Perf. 13½
427 A105 18fr Fiddler .90 .50
428 A105 29fr Hermit 1.40 .65
429 A105 31fr Coconut 2.40 .65
Nos. 427-429 (3) 4.70 1.80

Faces of
Polynesia
A106

1986, Feb. 19 Perf. 12½x13, 13x12½
430 A106 43fr Boy, fish 1.00 .50
431 A106 49fr Boy, coral 1.25 .50
432 A106 51fr Boy, turtle, vert. 1.40 .60
Nos. 430-432 (3) 3.65 1.60

Old Tahiti — A107

1986, Mar. 18 Perf. 13x12½
433 A107 52fr Papeete 1.10 .60
434 A107 56fr Harpoon fishing 1.25 .60
435 A107 57fr Royal Palace, Papeete 1.40 .75
Nos. 433-435 (3) 3.75 1.95

Tiki Rock
Carvings — A108

1986, Apr. 16
436 A108 58fr Atuona, Hiva Oa 1.40 .70
437 A108 59fr Ua Huka Hill,
Hane Valley 1.40 .70

Landscapes Type Redrawn

1986-88 Litho. Perf. 13½
438 A65 1fr multi, type 2 ('88) 2.00 .35
a. Type 1 ('86) 4.25 1.00
b. Type 3 ('91) 15.00 4.00
439 A65 2fr multicolored .40 .20
440 A65 3fr multicolored .45 .20
441 A65 4fr multicolored ('87) .75 .30
442 A65 5fr multicolored .75 .30
443 A65 6fr multicolored .65 .30
Nos. 438-443 (6) 5.00 1.65

Nos. 438-443 printed in sharper detail, and
box containing island name is taller. Nos. 439-
443 margin is inscribed "CARTOR" instead of
"DELRIEU."

No. 438 has three types of inscription below
design: type 1, photographer's name at left, no
inscription at right; type 2, photographer's
name at left 9.5mm long, printer's name
(Cartor) at right; type 3, photographer's name
at left 12.5mm long, Cartor at right.

Traditional
Crafts
A109

Perf. 13x12½, 12½x13
1986, July 17 Litho.
444 A109 8fr Quilting, vert. .25 .20
445 A109 10fr Baskets, hats .25 .25
446 A109 12fr Grass skirts .85 .30
Nos. 444-446 (3) 1.35 .75

Building a
Pirogue
(Canoe)
A110

1986, Oct. 21 Litho. Perf. 13½
447 A110 46fr Boat-builders 1.10 .70
448 A110 50fr Close-up 1.25 .90

Medicinal
Plants — A111

Polynesians
A112

1986, Nov. 19 Perf. 13
449 A111 40fr Phymatosorus .90 .50
450 A111 41fr Barringtonia asiati-
ca 1.00 .50
451 A111 60fr Ocimum bacilicum 1.60 .90
Nos. 449-451 (3) 3.50 1.90

See Nos. 495-497.

1987, Jan. 21 Litho. Perf. 13½
452 A112 28fr Old man .60 .35
453 A112 30fr Mother and child .75 .50
454 A112 37fr Old woman 1.00 .60
Nos. 452-454 (3) 2.35 1.45

Crustaceans — A113

1987, Feb. 18 Perf. 12½x13
455 A113 34fr Carpilius maculatus 1.75 .60
456 A113 35fr Parribacus antar-
ticus 1.75 .60
457 A113 39fr Justitia longimana 2.25 .60
Nos. 455-457 (3) 5.75 1.80

Local Foods Type of 1985
1987, Mar. 19 Litho. Perf. 13
458 A103 33fr Papaya poe 1.10 .70
459 A103 65fr Chicken fafa 2.00 1.00

Polynesian
Petroglyphs
A114

1987, May 13 Perf. 12½
460 A114 13fr Tipaerui, Tahiti .35 .20
461 A114 21fr Turtle, Raiatea Is. .60 .35

Calling Devices and Musical
Instruments, Museum of Tahiti and the
Isles — A115

1987, July 1 Perf. 13½
462 A115 20fr Wood horn .65 .30
463 A115 26fr Triton's conch .80 .65
464 A115 33fr Nose flutes 1.00 .70
Nos. 462-464 (3) 2.45 1.65

Medicinal
Plants — A116

1987, Sept. 16 Perf. 12½x13
465 A116 46fr Thespesia
populnea 1.10 .60
466 A116 53fr Ophioglossum
reticulatum 1.50 .60
467 A116 54fr Dicrocephala latifolia 1.60 .60
Nos. 465-467 (3) 4.20 1.80

Ancient Weapons and Tools — A117

Designs: 25fr, Adze, war club, chisel, flute.
27fr, War clubs, tatooing comb, mallet. 32fr,
Headdress, necklaces, nose flute.

1987, Oct. 14 Engr. Perf. 13
468 A117 25fr lt olive grn & blk .60 .40
469 A117 27fr Prus grn & int blue .75 .45
470 A117 32fr brt olive bis & brn
blk .80 .55
Nos. 468-470 (3) 2.15 1.40

Catholic Missionaries — A118

Monsignors: 95fr, Rene Ildefonse Dordillon
(1808-1888), bishop of the Marquesas Isls.
105fr, Tepano Jaussen (1815-1891), first
bishop of Polynesia. 115fr, Paul Laurent Maze
(1885-1976), archbishop of Papeete.

1987, Dec. 9 Litho.
471 A118 95fr multicolored 2.00 1.50
472 A118 105fr multicolored 2.25 1.75
473 A118 115fr multicolored 2.50 1.90
Nos. 471-473 (3) 6.75 5.15

Local Foods Type of 1985
1988, Jan. 12 Litho. Perf. 13
474 A103 40fr Crayfish (varo) 2.00 .60
475 A103 75fr Bananas in coconut milk 3.00 1.25

Nos. 474-475 are vert.

Authors — A119

62fr, James Norman Hall (1887-1951). 85fr,
Charles Bernard Nordhoff (1887-1947).

1988, Feb. 10
476 A119 62fr multicolored 1.50 .80
477 A119 85fr multicolored 2.00 .90

Traditional Housing — A120

11fr, Taranpoo Opoa Is., Raiatea. 15fr,
Tahaa Village. 17fr, Community meeting
house, Tahiti.

1988, Mar. 16 Litho. Perf. 13x12½
478 A120 11fr multicolored .55 .30
479 A120 15fr multicolored .65 .30
480 A120 17fr multicolored .65 .30
Nos. 478-480 (3) 1.85 .90

Point Venus Lighthouse, 120th Anniv. — A121

1988, Apr. 21 Litho. Perf. 13
481 A121 400fr multicolored 9.00 6.00

Tapa-cloth Paintings by Paul Engdahl A122

1988, May 20
482 A122 52fr multicolored 1.40 .80
483 A122 54fr multicolored 1.50 .90
484 A122 64fr multicolored 1.60 1.25
Nos. 482-484 (3) 4.50 2.95

POLYSAT (Domestic Communications Network) — A123

1988, June 15 Litho. Perf. 12½x12
485 A123 300fr multicolored 6.00 4.75

Tahitian Dolls — A124

Designs: 42fr, Wearing grass skirt and headdress. 45fr, Wearing print dress and straw hat, holding guitar. 48fr, Wearing print dress and straw hat, holding straw bag.

1988, June 27 Perf. 13x12½
486 A124 42fr multicolored 1.00 .60
487 A124 45fr multicolored 1.25 .60
488 A124 48fr multicolored 1.50 .75
Nos. 486-488 (3) 3.75 1.95

Visiting a Marae at Nuku Hiva, Engraving by J. & E. Verreaux A125

1988, Aug. 1 Engr. Perf. 13
489 A125 68fr black brown 2.00 1.25
Size: 143x101mm
490 A125 145fr violet brn & grn 5.25 4.00
SYDPEX '88, July 30-Aug. 7, Australia. No. 490 pictures a Russian navy officer (probably Krusenstern) visiting the Marquesas Islanders; denomination LR.

Map Linking South America and South Pacific Islands — A126

1988, Aug. 30 Engr.
491 A126 350fr multicolored 7.50 4.50
Eric de Bisschop (1890-1958), explorer who tried to prove that there was an exchange of peoples between the South Pacific islands and So. America, rather than that the island populations originated from So. America.

Seashells A127

1988, Sept. 21 Litho. Perf. 13½
492 A127 24fr Kermia barnardi .60 .35
493 A127 35fr Vexillum suavis 1.00 .50
494 A127 44fr Berthelinia 1.40 .75
Nos. 492-494 (3) 3.00 1.60

Medicinal Plants Type of 1986

1988, Oct. 18 Engr. Perf. 13
495 A111 23fr Davallia solida .80 .35
496 A111 36fr Rorippa sarmentosa 1.25 .50
497 A111 49fr Lindernia crustacea 1.50 .75
Nos. 495-497 (3) 3.55 1.60

Protestant Missionaries — A128

1988, Dec. 7 Litho.
498 A128 80fr Henry Nott (1774-1844) 1.50 .90
499 A128 90fr Papeiha (1800-40) 2.00 1.25
500 A128 100fr Samuel Raapoto (1921-76) 2.25 1.40
Nos. 498-500 (3) 5.75 3.55

Tahiti Post Office A129

1989, Jan. 12 Engr.
501 A129 30fr P.O., 1875 .75 .40
502 A129 40fr P.O., 1915 1.00 .55

Center for Arts and Crafts A130

1989, Feb. 15 Litho. Perf. 12½
503 A130 29fr Marquesas Is. lidded bowl .85 .40
504 A130 31fr Mother-of-pearl pendant .95 .45

Copra Industry

Extracting Coconut Meat From Shell — A131a

Drying Coconut Meat in Sun — A131

1989, Mar. 16 Litho. Perf. 13
505 A131a 55fr multicolored 55.00 40.00
506 A131 70fr multicolored 2.50 2.00

Tapa Art — A132

43fr, Wood statue (pole), Marquesas Islands, vert. 51fr, Hand-painted bark tapestry, Society Is. 56fr, Concentric circles, Tubuai, Austral Islands.

1989, Apr. 18 Litho. Perf. 13½
507 A132 43fr multicolored .90 .60
508 A132 51fr shown 1.25 .75
509 A132 56fr multicolored 1.50 .90
Nos. 507-509 (3) 3.65 2.25

Polynesian Environment A133

1989, May 17 Litho. Perf. 13x12½
510 A133 120fr multicolored 2.40 1.60
511 A133 140fr Diving for seashells 3.00 1.90

Polynesian Folklore A134

Perf. 13x12½, 12½x13
1989, June 28 Litho.
512 A134 47fr Stone-lifting contest, vert. 1.25 .60
513 A134 61fr Dancer, vert. 1.50 .75
514 A134 67fr Folk singers 1.90 .80
Nos. 512-514 (3) 4.65 2.15

Bounty Castaways, from an Etching by Robert Dodd — A135

1989, July 7 Engr. Perf. 13
515 A135 100fr dp blue & bl grn 2.50 1.60
Souvenir Sheet
Imperf
516 A135 200fr dk ol grn & dk brn 12.50 12.50
PHILEXFRANCE '89 and 200th annivs. of the mutiny on the Bounty and the French revolution.
No. 515 printed se-tenant with label picturing exhibition emblem.

Reverend-Father Patrick O'Reilly (1900-1988) A136

1989, Aug. 7 Engr. Perf. 13x13½
517 A136 52fr yel brn & myrtle grn 1.40 .75

Miniature Sheet

Messages A137

a, Get well soon. b, Good luck. c, Happy birthday. d, Keep in touch. e, Congratulations.

1989, Sept. 27 Litho. Perf. 12½
518 A137 42fr Sheet of 5, #a.-e. 11.00 11.00

Sea Shells A138

1989, Oct. 12 Litho. Perf. 13½
523 A138 60fr Triphoridae 1.60 .80
524 A138 69fr Muricidae favartia 1.75 .90
525 A138 73fr Muricidae morula 2.00 1.00
Nos. 523-525 (3) 5.35 2.70

Te Faaturama, c. 1892, by Gauguin
A139

1989, Nov. 19 Litho. Perf. 12½x13
526 A139 1000fr multicolored 22.50 13.00

Legends — A140

Designs: 66fr, Maui, birth of the islands, vert. 82fr, Mt. Rotui, the pierced mountain. 88fr, Princess Hina and the eel King of Lake Vaihiria.

1989, Dec. 6 Litho. Perf. 13
527 A140 66fr olive brn & blk 1.40 .90
528 A140 82fr buff & blk 1.90 1.10
529 A140 88fr cream & blk 2.00 1.15
  Nos. 527-529 (3) 5.30 3.15

Vanilla Orchid — A141

1990, Jan. 11 Litho.
530 A141 34fr Flower 1.40 .60
531 A141 35fr Bean pods 1.75 .60

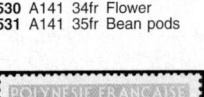

Marine Life A142

1990, Feb. 9 Litho. Perf. 13½
532 A142 40fr *Kuhlia marginata* 1.40 .60
533 A142 50fr *Macrobrachium* 1.60 .75

Tahiti, Center of Polynesian Triangle — A143

Maohi settlers and maps of island settlements: 58fr, Hawaiian Islands. 59fr, Easter Island. 63fr, New Zealand.

1990, Mar. 14 Engr. Perf. 13
534 A143 58fr black 1.75 .85
535 A143 59fr bluish gray 42.50 22.50
536 A143 63fr olive green 2.25 .95
537 A143 71fr Prussian blue 2.50 1.10
  Nos. 534-537 (4) 49.00 25.40

See Nos. 544-545.

Papeete Village, Cent. — A144

1990, May 16 Litho.
538 A144 150fr New City Hall 3.50 2.00
539 A144 250fr Old Town Hall 5.00 3.25

A145

A146

Designs: Endangered birds.

1990, June 5 Perf. 13½
540 A145 13fr Porzana tabuensis .75 .20
541 A145 20fr Vini ultramarina 1.75 .35

1990, July 10 Perf. 13
542 A146 39fr multicolored 1.00 .60

Lions Club in Papeete, 30th anniv.

Gen. Charles de Gaulle, Birth Cent. — A147

1990, Sept. 2 Litho.
543 A147 200fr multi 4.00 3.00

No. 536 with Different Colors and Inscriptions

1990, Aug. 24 Engr. Perf. 13
544 A143 125fr Man, map 3.00 2.00

Souvenir Sheet
Imperf
545 A143 230fr like No. 544 6.00 6.00

New Zealand 1990.

Intl. Tourism Day — A148

1990, Sept. 27 Litho. Perf. 12½
546 A148 8fr red & yellow pareo 1.00 .35
547 A148 10fr yellow pareo 1.00 .35
548 A148 12fr blue pareo 1.00 .75
  Nos. 546-548 (3) 3.00 1.45

Polynesian Legends — A149

170fr, Legend of the Uru. 290fr, Pipiri-ma, vert. 375fr, Hiro, God of Thieves, vert.

1990, Nov. 7 Litho. Perf. 13
549 A149 170fr multicolored 4.00 2.50
550 A149 290fr multicolored 7.50 4.50
551 A149 375fr multicolored 11.00 5.75
  Nos. 549-551 (3) 22.50 12.75

Tiare Flower — A150

1990, Dec. 5 Perf. 12½
552 A150 28fr multicolored .75 .45
553 A150 30fr multicolored 1.00 .50
554 A150 37fr multicolored 1.25 .60
  Nos. 552-554 (3) 3.00 1.55

Pineapple A151

Designs: 28fr, Flower crown, lei. 30fr, Flowers in bloom. 37fr, Lei.

1991, Jan. 9 Die Cut
Self-adhesive
555 A151 42fr shown 1.25 .90
556 A151 44fr Pineapple field 1.75 1.10

#555-556 are on paper backing perf. 12½.

Marine Life A152

1991, Feb. 7 Perf. 12½
557 A152 7fr Nudibranch .50 .20
558 A152 9fr Galaxaura tenera .75 .20
559 A152 11fr Adusta cumingii .75 .20
  Nos. 557-559 (3) 2.00 .60

Maohi Islands A153

18th Century scenes of: 68fr, Woman of Easter Island, vert. 84fr, Twin-hulled canoe, Hawaii. 94fr, Maori village, New Zealand.

1991, Mar. 13 Engr. Perf. 13
560 A153 68fr olive 47.50 32.50
561 A153 84fr black 2.50 1.75
562 A153 94fr brown 3.00 1.75
  Nos. 560-562 (3) 53.00 36.00

Basketball, Cent. — A154

1991, May 15 Litho. Perf. 13
563 A154 80fr multicolored 1.75 1.25

Birds — A155

1991, June 5 Perf. 13½
564 A155 17fr Halcyon gambieri .60 .25
565 A155 21fr Vini kuhlii .90 .35

Still Life with Oranges in Tahiti by Paul Gauguin — A156

1991, June 9 Litho. Perf. 13
566 A156 700fr multicolored 17.50 9.50

Sculptures of the Marquesas Islands — A157

56fr, White Tiki with Club, vert. 102fr, Warriors Carrying Tired Man, vert. 110fr, Native Canoe.

1991, July 17 Litho. Perf. 13
567 A157 56fr multicolored 1.25 .85
568 A157 102fr multicolored 2.25 1.50
569 A157 110fr multicolored 2.50 1.75
  Nos. 567-569 (3) 6.00 4.10

Wolfgang Amadeus Mozart, Death
Bicent. — A158

1991, Aug. 28   Engr.   Perf. 13x12½
570 A158 100fr multicolored   3.00 1.75

Stone Fishing — A159

1991, Oct. 9   Litho.   Perf. 13
571 A159 25fr Fishing boats,
             vert.   .60   .40
572 A159 57fr Man hurling stone,
             vert.   1.25   .90
573 A159 62fr Trapped fish   1.50 1.25
         Nos. 571-573 (3)   3.35 2.55

Phila
Nippon '91
A160

Designs: 50fr, Drawings of marine life by
Jules-Louis Lejeune, vert. 70fr, Sailing ship,
La Coquille. 250fr, Contains designs from
Nos. 574-575.

Perf. 12½x13, 13x12½
1991, Nov. 16   Engr.
574 A160 50fr multicolored   1.40   .60
575 A160 70fr multicolored   1.90 1.00
         Size: 100x75mm
         Imperf
576 A160 250fr multicolored   6.00 6.00
         Nos. 574-576 (3)   9.30 7.60

Central Bank for Economic Cooperation, 50th Anniv. — A161

1991, Dec. 2   Litho.   Perf. 13x12½
577 A161 307fr multicolored   7.00 4.50

Christmas
A162

Perf. 12½x13, 13x12½
1991, Dec. 11   Litho.
578 A162 55fr Scuba divers   1.25   .75
579 A162 83fr Underwater scene   1.75 1.35
580 A162 86fr Nativity, vert.   1.75 1.35
         Nos. 578-580 (3)   4.75 3.45

Tourism — A163

1992, Feb. 12   Perf. 13
581 A163 1fr shown   .20   .20
582 A163 2fr Horses, beach   .35   .25
583 A163 3fr Girl holding fish   .50   .30
584 A163 4fr Waterfalls, vert.   .60   .35
585 A163 5fr Sailing   .75   .40
586 A163 6fr Waterfalls, helicop-
             ter, vert.   1.00   .45
         Nos. 581-586 (6)   3.40 1.95

Views from Space — A164

1992, Mar. 18   Litho.   Perf. 13x12½
587 A164 46fr Tahiti   1.40   .90
588 A164 72fr Mataiva   1.90 1.40
589 A164 76fr Bora Bora   2.00 1.50
         Size: 130x100mm
         Imperf
590 A164 230fr Satellite imaging
             system   6.00 5.75
         Nos. 587-590 (4)   11.30 9.55

International Space Year.

World
Health Day
A165

1992, Apr. 7   Perf. 13½
591 A165 136fr multicolored   3.00 2.25

Discovery of America, 500th
Anniv. — A166

1992, May 22   Perf. 13
592 A166 130fr multicolored   3.00 2.25
         Size: 140x100mm
         Imperf
593 A166 250fr multicolored   6.00 6.00

World Columbian Stamp Expo '92, Chicago.

Traditional Dances — A167

Dance from: 95fr, Tahiti. 105fr, Hawaii.
115fr, Tonga.

1992, June 17   Engr.   Perf. 13
594 A167 95fr brown black   2.00 1.75
595 A167 105fr olive brown   2.25 1.75
596 A167 115fr red brn & olive
             grn   2.75 1.75
         Nos. 594-596 (3)   7.00 5.25

Tattoos
A168

1992, July 8   Litho.   Perf. 12½
597 A168 61fr Hand   1.75 1.00
598 A168 64fr Man, vert.   1.75 1.00

Children's
Games
A169

1992, Aug. 5   Perf. 13½
599 A169 22fr Outrigger canoe
             models   .50   .35
600 A169 31fr String game   .75   .45
601 A169 45fr Stilt game, vert.   1.25   .70
         Nos. 599-601 (3)   2.50 1.50

Herman Melville,
150th Anniv. of
Arrival in French
Polynesia — A170

1992, Sept. 16   Perf. 12½
602 A170 78fr multicolored   4.50 1.25

6th Festival of Pacific Arts,
Rarotonga — A171

40fr, Men on raft. 65fr, Pirogues, Tahiti.

1992, Oct. 16   Engr.   Perf. 13
603 A171 40fr lake   1.50   .60
604 A171 65fr blue   2.00 1.00

First French Polynesian Postage
Stamps, Cent. — A172

1992, Nov. 18   Photo.   Perf. 13
605 A172 200fr multicolored   4.75 3.25

Paintings
A173

55fr, Two Women Talking, by Erhard Lux.
60fr, Bouquet of Flowers, by Uschi. 75fr,
Spearfisherman, by Pierre Kienlen. 85fr,
Mother Nursing Child, by Octave Morillot.

1992, Dec. 9   Perf. 12½x13
606 A173 55fr multicolored   1.50   .75
607 A173 60fr multicolored   1.75 1.40
608 A173 75fr multicolored   1.90 1.50
609 A173 85fr multicolored   2.50 1.60
         Nos. 606-609 (4)   7.65 5.25

Net Thrower
A174

Bonito Fishing
A175

1993, Feb. 10   Litho.   Die Cut
         Self-Adhesive
         Size: 26x36mm
610 A174 46fr blue & multi   1.50 1.00
         Size: 17x23mm
611 A174 46fr green & multi   1.50 1.00
  a.   Booklet pane of 10   15.00

1993, Mar. 10   Perf. 13½
612 A175 68fr Line & hook   1.60 1.25
613 A175 84fr Boat, horiz.   1.90 1.50
614 A175 86fr Drying catch   2.10 1.50
         Nos. 612-614 (3)   5.60 4.25

Allied Airfield on Bora Bora, 50th
Anniv. — A176

1993, Apr. 5   Perf. 13
615 A176 120fr multicolored   3.00 2.25

Jacques Boullaire, Artist, Birth Cent. — A177

Various scenes depicting life on: 32fr, Moorea. 36fr, Tuamotu. 39fr, Rururtu. 51fr, Nuku Hiva.

1993, May 6   **Engr.**
616 A177 32fr brown black   .90   .50
617 A177 36fr brick red   .90   .65
618 A177 39fr violet   1.25   .90
619 A177 51fr light brown   1.50   1.00
    Nos. 616-619 (4)   4.55   3.05

Sports Festival — A178

1993, May 15   **Litho.**   **Perf. 12½**
620 A178 30fr multicolored   .85   .50

Australian Mathematics Competition, 15th Anniv. — A179

1993, July 1   **Litho.**   **Perf. 13½**
621 A179 70fr multicolored   1.75   1.10

Intl. Symposium on Inter-Plate Volcanism, French University of the Pacific, Punaauia
A180

1993, Aug. 2   **Litho.**   **Perf. 13**
622 A180 140fr tan, blk & brn   3.50   2.50

Taipei '93 — A181

Tourism — A182

1993, Aug. 14   **Litho.**   **Perf. 13½**
623 A181 46fr multicolored   1.75   .85
    Exists without the Cartor imprint. Value, unused $17.50.

1993, Sept. 27
    14fr, Boat tour. 20fr, Groom preparing for traditional wedding. 29fr, Beachside brunch.
624 A182 14fr multi, horiz.   .60   .35
625 A182 20fr multi   .65   .35
626 A182 29fr multi, horiz.   .75   .45
    Nos. 624-626 (3)   2.00   1.15
    Exist without the Cartor imprint. Value, set unused $30.

Arrival of First French Gendarme in Tahiti, 150th Anniv. — A183

1993, Oct. 14   **Perf. 13**
627 A183 100fr multicolored   2.50   1.60
    Exists without the Cartor imprint. Value, unused $17.50.

Alain Gerbault (1893-1941), Sailor — A184

1993, Nov. 17   **Engr.**   **Perf. 13**
628 A184 150fr red, green & blue   4.00   2.75

Paintings — A185

Artists: 40fr, Vaea Sylvain. 70fr, A. Marere, vert. 80fr, J. Shelsher. 90fr, P.E. Victor, vert.

1993, Dec. 3   **Photo.**   **Perf. 13**
629 A185 40fr multicolored   1.75   .70
630 A185 70fr multicolored   2.50   1.25
631 A185 80fr multicolored   3.00   1.25
632 A185 90fr multicolored   3.50   1.50
    Nos. 629-632 (4)   10.75   4.70

French School of the Pacific, 30th Anniv.
A186

1993, Dec. 7   **Litho.**   **Perf. 12½**
633 A186 200fr multicolored   5.00   3.50

Whales and Dolphins
A187

1994, Jan. 12   **Litho.**   **Perf. 13½**
634 A187 25fr Whale breeching   .75   .45
635 A187 68fr Dolphins   1.75   1.10
636 A187 72fr Humpback whales, vert.   2.00   1.25
    Nos. 634-636 (3)   4.50   2.80

A188

A189

1994, Feb. 18   **Litho.**   **Perf. 13½**
637 A188 51fr multicolored   2.25   .95
    Hong Kong '94. New Year 1994 (Year of the Dog).

1994, Mar. 16
638 A189 180fr Sister Germaine Bruel   4.00   3.00
    Arrival of Nuns from St. Joseph of Cluny, 150th anniv.

Church of Jesus Christ of Latter-day Saints in French Polynesia, 150th Anniv.
A190

1994, Apr. 30   **Litho.**   **Perf. 13½**
639 A190 154fr Tahiti temple   3.50   2.75

Conservatory of Arts and Crafts, Bicent. — A191

1994, May 25   **Photo.**   **Perf. 13**
640 A191 316fr multicolored   7.50   5.50
    Regional Associated Center of Papeete, 15th anniv.

Internal Self-Government, 10th Anniv. — A192

1994, June 29   **Litho.**   **Perf. 13**
641 A192 500fr multicolored   12.00   7.50

Tahitian Academy, 20th Anniv. — A193

1994, July 2   **Engr.**   **Perf. 13**
642 A193 136fr multicolored   3.00   2.00

Scenes of Old Tahiti — A194

1994, Aug. 10   **Litho.**   **Perf. 13**
643 A194 22fr Papara   .90   .50
644 A194 26fr Mataiea   1.10   .65
645 A194 51fr Taravao, vert.   1.90   .95
    Nos. 643-645 (3)   3.90   2.10
    See Nos. 673-675.

Faaturuma, by Paul Gauguin (1848-1903)
A195

1994, Sept. 14   **Litho.**   **Perf. 13**
646 A195 1000fr multicolored   24.00   16.00

Epiphyllum Oxypetalum
A196

1994, Oct. 15   **Litho.**   **Perf. 13½**
647 A196 51fr multicolored   1.75   .95

Hawaiki Nui Va'a '94 (Canoe Race)
A197

Designs: a, 52fr, Yellow canoe, bow paddler. b, 76fr, Paddlers. c, 80fr, Paddlers, blue canoe. d, 94fr, Stern paddler, yellow canoe.

1994, Nov. 10   **Litho.**   *Perf. 13½x13*
648 A197 Strip of 4, #a.-d.   8.00   4.75

No. 648 is a continuous design.

Paintings of French Polynesia — A198

62fr, Young girl, by Michelle Villemin. 78fr, Ocean tide, fish, by Michele Dallet. 102fr, Native carrying bundles of fruit, by Johel Blanchard. 110fr, View of coastline, by Pierre Lacouture.

1994, Dec. 19   **Litho.**   *Perf. 13*
649	A198	62fr multi, vert.	1.75	.95
650	A198	78fr multi, vert.	2.00	1.25
651	A198	102fr multi, vert.	2.25	1.60
652	A198	110fr multi	2.75	1.75
		Nos. 649-652 (4)	8.75	5.55

Don Domingo de Boenechea's Tautira Expedition, 220th Anniv. — A199

1995, Jan. 1
653 A199 92fr multicolored   2.25   1.25

South Pacific Tourism Year — A200

1995, Jan. 11   **Litho.**   *Perf. 13½*
654 A200 92fr multicolored   2.25   1.40

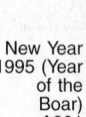

New Year 1995 (Year of the Boar) A201

1995, Feb. 1   **Litho.**
655 A201 51fr multicolored   1.75   .80

Portions of the design on No. 655 were applied by a thermographic process producing a shiny, raised effect.
Exists without the Cartor imprint. Value, unused $9.

University Teacher's Training Institute of the Pacific — A202

1995, Mar. 8   **Litho.**   *Perf. 13½*
656 A202 59fr multicolored   1.50   .95

Nature Protection A203

1995, May 4   **Litho.**   *Perf. 13*
657		Strip of 3 + 2 labels	4.25	4.25
a.	A203	22fr Head of turtle	.75	.35
b.	A203	29fr Turtle swimming	1.00	.50
c.	A203	91fr Black coral	2.50	1.50

Louis Pasteur (1822-95) — A204

1995, May 8
658 A204 290fr dk blue & blue   6.75   4.00

Loti's Marriage, Novel by Julien Viaud (1850-1923) — A205

1995, May 19   **Photo.**   *Perf. 13*
659 A205 66fr multicolored   2.00   1.10

A206

1995, May 24   **Litho.**   *Perf. 13½*
660 A206 150fr multicolored   3.50   2.25

Tahitian Monoi beauty aid.

Birds — A207

1995, June 7
661	A207	22fr Ptilinopus huttoni	.65	.50
662	A207	44fr Ducula galeata	1.40	.75

Tahitian Pearls A208

1995, June 14
663	A208	66fr shown	1.60	1.10
664	A208	84fr Eight pearls	2.10	1.40

On Nos. 663-664 portions of the design were applied by a thermographic process producing a shiny, raised effect.

Discovery of Marquesas Islands, 400th Anniv. — A209

a, Alvaro de Mendana de Neira, sailing ships. b, Pedro Fernandez de Quiros, map of islands.

1995, July 21   **Litho.**   *Perf. 13*
665		Pair + label	8.00	6.00
a.	A209	161fr multicolored	3.50	2.75
b.	A209	195fr multicolored	4.50	3.25

A210

A211

1995, Aug. 12   **Litho.**   *Perf. 13*
666 A210 83fr multicolored   2.00   1.40

10th South Pacific Games, Tahiti.

1995, Sept. 1   *Perf. 13½x13*
Pandanus plant: No. 667a, Entire plant. b, Flower. c, Fruit. d, Using dry leaves for weaving.
667		Strip of 4	8.50	6.00
a.-d.	A211	91fr any single	2.00	1.50

Singapore '95.

UN, 50th Anniv. — A212

1995, Oct. 24   **Litho.**   *Perf. 13*
668 A212 420fr multicolored   9.50   6.00

Paintings — A213

Designs: 57fr, The Paddler with the Yellow Dog, by Philippe Dubois, vert. 76fr, An Afternoon in Vaitape, by Maui Seaman, vert. 79fr, The Mama with the White Hat, by Simone Testeguide. 100fr, In Front of the Kellum House in Moorea, by Christian Deloffre.

1995, Dec. 6   **Photo.**   *Perf. 13*
669	A213	57fr multicolored	1.50	.90
670	A213	76fr multicolored	1.75	1.25
671	A213	79fr multicolored	1.90	1.25
672	A213	100fr multicolored	2.50	1.60
		Nos. 669-672 (4)	7.65	5.00

Scenes of Old Tahiti Type

1996, Jan. 17   **Litho.**   *Perf. 13*
673	A194	18fr Fautaua	.65	.45
674	A194	30fr District of Punaauia	.80	.50
675	A194	35fr Tautira	.90	.60
		Nos. 673-675 (3)	2.35	1.55

New Year 1996 (Year of the Rat) — A214

1996, Feb. 19   **Photo.**   *Perf. 13*
676 A214 51fr multicolored   1.75   .80

Portions of the design on No. 676 were applied by a thermographic process producing a shiny, raised effect.

Paul-Emile Victor (1907-95), Explorer, Writer — A215

1996, Mar. 7   **Litho.**
677 A215 500fr multicolored   12.00   8.00

Queen Pomare IV — A216

1996, Mar. 1   **Litho.**   *Perf. 13*
678 A216 (51fr) multicolored   1.50   .80

Serpentine Die Cut 7 Vert.
Self-Adhesive
Size: 17x24mm

678A	A216	(51fr) multicolored	2.00	1.15
b.		Booklet pane of 5	10.00	
		Complete booklet, 2 #678b	20.00	

Sea Shells A217

10fr, Conus pertusus. 15fr, Cypraea alisonae. 25fr, Vexillum roseotinctum.

1996, Apr. 10 Photo. Perf. 13½x13
679 A217 10fr multicolored .45 .20
680 A217 15fr multicolored .50 .25
681 A217 25fr multicolored .95 .40
  Nos. 679-681 (3) 1.90 .85

Portions of the designs on Nos. 679-681 were applied by a thermographic process producing a shiny, raised effect.

Return of the Pacific Battalion, 50th Anniv. — A218

1996, May 5 Litho. Perf. 13
682 A218 100fr multicolored 3.00 1.60

CHINA '96, 9th Asian Intl. Philatelic Exhibition A219

Design: 200fr, Chinese School, Tahiti, 1940. Illustration reduced.

1996, May 18 Perf. 13x13½
683 A219 50fr multicolored 1.25 .80
Souvenir Sheet
Imperf
684 A219 200fr multicolored 4.50 3.40

Birds A220

1996, June 12 Litho. Perf. 13x13½
685 A220 66fr Sula sula 1.50 1.10
686 A220 79fr Fregata minor 2.00 1.25
687 A220 84fr Anous stolidus 2.00 1.40
  Nos. 685-687 (3) 5.50 3.75

Musical Instruments A221

1996, July 10 Perf. 13x13½
688 A221 5fr Pahu, ukulele, toere .30 .20
689 A221 9fr Toere .40 .20
690 A221 14fr Pu, vivo .50 .20
  Nos. 688-690 (3) 1.20 .60

Raiateana Oulietea A222

1996, Aug. 7 Litho. Perf. 13x13½
691 A222 66fr multicolored 1.75 1.10

A223

A224

1996, Sept. 9 Litho. Perf. 13
692 A223 70fr Ruahatu, God of the Ocean 1.75 1.10

7th Pacific Arts Festival.

1996, Oct. 16 Engr. Perf. 13
Stamp Day: Young Tahitian girl (Type A2), Noho Mercier, taken from photo by Henry Lemasson (1870-1956), postal administrator.

693 A224 92fr black, red & blue 2.50 1.50

First Representative Assembly, 50th Anniv. — A225

1996, Nov. 7 Litho. Perf. 13
694 A225 85fr multicolored 2.00 1.10

Paintings of Tahitian Women — A226

Designs: 70fr, Woman lounging on Bora Bora Beach, by Titi Bécaud. 85fr, "Woman with Crown of Auti leaves," by Maryse Noguier, vert. 92fr, "Dreamy Woman," by Christine de Dinechin, vert. 96fr, Two working women, by Andrée Lang, vert.

1996, Dec. 4 Litho. Perf. 13
695 A226 70fr multicolored 2.00 .75
696 A226 85fr multicolored 2.25 .90
697 A226 92fr multicolored 2.50 1.00
698 A226 96fr multicolored 3.00 1.00
  Nos. 695-698 (4) 9.75 3.65

A227

A228

1997, Jan. 2 Litho. Perf. 13
699 A227 55fr brown 1.25 .55

Society of South Sea Studies, 80th anniv.

1997, Feb. 7 Photo. Perf. 13½x13
700 A228 13fr multicolored 1.00 .30

New Year 1997 (Year of the Ox). Portions of the design were applied by a thermographic process producing a shiny, raised effect.

Arrival of Evangelists in Tahiti, Bicent. — A229

Designs: a, Sailing ship, "Duff." b, Painting, "Transfer of the Matavai District to the L.M.S. Missionaries," by Robert Smirke.

1997, Mar. 5 Litho. Perf. 13
701 A229 43fr Pair, #a.-b. + label 2.00 1.25

Tifaifai (Tahitian Bedspread) A230

Various leaf and floral patterns.

1997, Apr. 16
702 A230 1fr multicolored .20 .20
703 A230 5fr multicolored .20 .20
704 A230 70fr multicolored 1.60 .70
  Nos. 702-704 (3) 2.00 1.10

PACIFIC 97 — A231

Sailing ships carrying mail, passengers between Tahiti and San Francisco: No. 705, Tropic Bird, 1897. No. 706, Papeete/Zélee, 1892.

1997, May 29 Litho. Perf. 13
705 A231 92fr multicolored 3.25 1.60
706 A231 92fr multicolored 3.25 1.60
  a. Pair, #705-706 6.50 6.50
  b. Souvenir sheet, #705-706 65.00 65.00

No. 706b sold for 400fr.

Island Scenes A232

#707, Flower. #708, Rowing canoe, sun behind mountain. #709, Throwing spears. #710. Aerial view of island. #711, Fish. #712, Women walking on beach. #713, Holding oyster shell with pearls. #714, Boat with sail down, sunset across water. #715, Snorkeling, sting ray. #716, Bananas, pineapples. #717,

Palm tree, beach. #718, Women dancers in costume.

1997, June 25 Litho. Perf. 13
Booklet Stamps
707 A232 85fr multicolored 14.00 14.00
708 A232 85fr multicolored 14.00 14.00
709 A232 85fr multicolored 14.00 14.00
710 A232 85fr multicolored 14.00 14.00
711 A232 85fr multicolored 14.00 14.00
712 A232 85fr multicolored 14.00 14.00
  a. Bklt. pane of 6, #707-712 90.00
713 A232 85fr multicolored 14.00 14.00
714 A232 85fr multicolored 14.00 14.00
715 A232 85fr multicolored 14.00 14.00
716 A232 85fr multicolored 14.00 14.00
717 A232 85fr multicolored 14.00 14.00
718 A232 85fr multicolored 14.00 14.00
  a. Bklt. pane of 6, #713-718 90.00
  Complete booklet, 2 each #712a, #718a 350.00

Traditional Dance Costumes A233

Designs: 4fr, Warrior's costume. 9fr, Women's costume. 11fr, Couple.

1997, July 10 Litho. Perf. 13½x13
719 A233 4fr multicolored 1.00 .30
720 A233 9fr multicolored 1.25 .30
721 A233 11fr multicolored 2.00 .30
  Nos. 719-721 (3) 4.25 .90

Kon-Tiki Expedition, 50th Anniv. — A234

1997, Aug. 7 Litho. Perf. 13
722 A234 88fr multicolored 2.25 .80

Artists in Tahiti — A235

Designs: 85fr, Painting, "The Fruit Carrier," by Monique "Mono" Garnier-Bissol. 96fr, "Revival of Our Resources," mother of pearl painting, by Camélia Maraea. 110fr, "Tahitian Spirit," pottery, by Peter Owen, vert. 126fr, "Monoi," surrealist painting, by Elisabeth Stefanovitch.

1997, Oct. 15 Litho. Perf. 13
723 A235 85fr multicolored 1.90 .80
724 A235 96fr multicolored 2.00 .90
725 A235 110fr multicolored 2.50 1.00
726 A235 126fr multicolored 3.00 1.10
  Nos. 723-726 (4) 9.40 3.80

Te Arii Vahine, by Paul Gauguin (1848-1903) — A236

1997, Nov. 6 Litho. Perf. 13
727 A236 600fr multicolored 13.00 8.00

Christmas
A237

1997, Dec. 3   **Litho.**   *Perf. 13*
728 A237 118fr multicolored   3.00 1.10

New Year
1998 (Year
of the
Tiger)
A238

1998, Jan. 28   **Photo.**   *Perf. 13*
729 A238 96fr multicolored   2.50 .90

Portions of the design on No. 729 were applied by a thermographic process producing a shiny, raised effect.

Domestic Airline
Network — A239

Designs: a, 70fr, Grumman Widgeon, 1950. b, 85fr, DHC 6 Twin-Otter, 1968. c, 70fr, Fairchild FH 227, 1980. d, 85fr, ATR 42-500, 1998.

1998, Apr. 16   **Photo.**   *Perf. 13*
730 A239   Strip of 4, #a.-d. + label   6.50 2.90

Orchids
A240

5fr, Dendrobium "Royal King." 20fr, Oncidium "Ramsey." 50fr, Ascondena "Laksi." 100fr, Cattleya "hybride."

1998, May 14   **Photo.**   *Perf. 13*
731 A240   5fr multi   .25 .20
732 A240   20fr multi, vert.   .50 .20
733 A240   50fr multi, vert.   1.25 .45
734 A240   100fr multi   2.25 .95
    Nos. 731-734 (4)   4.25 1.80

On Nos. 731-734 portions of the design were applied by a thermographic process producing a shiny, raised effect.

The Lovers, by Paul Gauguin (1848-1903) — A241

1998, June 7   **Photo.**   *Perf. 13x12½*
735 A241 1000fr multicolored   22.50 9.00

Printed se-tenant with label.

1998 World Cup
Soccer
Championships,
France — A242

1998, June 10
736 A242 85fr multicolored   2.00 .75

For overprint see No. 742.

Tahiti Festival of
Flower and Shell
Garlands — A243

Women wearing various garlands of flowers or shells.

1998, July 16   **Photo.**   *Perf. 13½*
737 A243 55fr multicolored   1.50 .50
738 A243 65fr multicolored   1.75 .60
739 A243 70fr multicolored   2.00 .65
740 A243 80fr multicolored   2.25 .75
    Nos. 737-740 (4)   7.50 2.50

Painting,
"Underwater
World of
Polynesia," by
Stanley Haumani
A244

1998, Sept. 10   **Photo.**   *Perf. 12½x13*
741 A244 200fr multicolored   4.00 2.00

No. 736 Ovptd. in Blue & Black
"France / Championne / du Munde"

1998, Oct. 28   **Photo.**   *Perf. 13½*
742 A242 85fr multicolored   3.00 1.00

Autumn Philatelic Fair, Paris — A246

Watercolor paintings of Papeete Bay, by René Gillotin (1814-61), 250fr each: a, Beach at left, people. b, Beach at right, people.

1998, Nov. 5   *Perf. 13*
743 A246   Pair, #a.-b. + label   12.00 5.00
   c.   Souvenir sheet, #a.-b., imperf.   12.00 5.00

Life in
Tahiti and
the Islands
A247

Paintings by André Deymonaz: 70fr, Return to the Market, vert. 100fr, Bonito Fish Stalls, vert. 102fr, Going Fishing. 110fr, Discussion after Church Services.

1998, Dec. 10   **Photo.**   *Perf. 13*
744 A247 70fr multicolored   1.50 .80
745 A247 100fr multicolored   2.00 1.00
746 A247 102fr multicolored   2.25 1.00
747 A247 110fr multicolored   2.50 1.10
    Nos. 744-747 (4)   8.25 3.90

St. Valentine's
Day — A248

1999, Feb. 11   **Litho.**   *Perf. 13*
748 A248 96fr multicolored   2.50 .90

New Year
1999 (Year
of the
Rabbit)
A249

1999, Feb. 16
749 A249 118fr Rabbits, flowers   2.50 1.10

Portions of the design of No. 749 were applied by a thermographic process producing a shiny, raised effect.

Marine Life
A250

Designs: 70fr, Ptérois volitans. 85fr, Hippocampus histrix. 90fr, Antennarius pictus. 120fr, Taenianotus triacanthus.

1999, Mar. 18   **Photo.**   *Perf. 13*
750 A250 70fr multicolored   1.50 .65
751 A250 85fr multicolored   1.90 .80
752 A250 90fr multicolored   2.00 .80
753 A250 120fr multicolored   2.75 1.10
    Nos. 750-753 (4)   8.15 3.35

Portions of the designs on Nos. 750-753 were applied by a thermographic process producing a shiny, raised effect.

IBRA '99, World
Philatelic
Exhibition,
Nuremberg
A251

Tatooed men of Marquesas Islands, 1804: 90fr, Holding staff, fan. 120fr, Wearing blue cape.

Photo. & Engr.

1999, Apr. 27   *Perf. 13¼*
754 A251 90fr multicolored   2.00 .80
755 A251 120fr multicolored   2.75 1.25

Mother's
Day
A252

1999, May 27   **Litho.**   *Perf. 13¼*
756 A252 85fr Children, vert.   1.90 .75
757 A252 120fr shown   2.75 1.00

A253

Island Fruits
A254

#758, Breadfruit, vert. 120fr, Coconut.
#760: a, Papaya. b, Guava (goyave). c, Mombin. d, Rambutan. e, Star apple (pomme-etoile). f, Otaheite gooseberry (seurette). g, Rose apple. h, Star fruit (carambole). i, Spanish lime (quenette). j, Sweetsop (pomme-cannelle). k, Cashew (pomme de cajou). l, Passion fruit.

1999   **Litho.**   *Perf. 13½x13, 13x13½*
758 A253 85fr multicolored   1.90 .75
759 A253 120fr multicolored   2.75 1.10
     Souvenir Booklet
760   Complete bklt.   32.50
  a.-l.   A254 85fr Any single   2.00 1.40

Issued: #758, 120fr, 7/21; #760, 7/21.
No. 760 sold for 1200fr, and contains two booklet panes, containing Nos. 760a-760f, and Nos. 760g-760l. A second variety of No. 760 exists with selling price on cover as 1020fr. Value, complete booklet, $100.

No. 720, 1856 Letter, 1864
Postmark — A255

1999, July 2   **Litho.**   *Perf. 13*
761 A255 180fr multicolored   4.00 2.25
  a.   Souvenir sheet of 1   12.00 12.00

150th anniv. of French postage stamps, PhilexFrance 99.
No. 761 issued se-tenant with label. No. 761a sold for 500fr.

Frédéric Chopin (1810-49),
Composer — A256

1999, July 2   **Litho.**   *Perf. 13*
762 A256 250fr multicolored   5.50 2.50

Malardé Medical Research Institute,
50th Anniv. — A257

1999, Sept. 27
763 A257 400fr multicolored   8.75 3.75

Nudes
A258

Paintings by: 85fr, J. Sorgniard. 120fr, J. Dubrusk. 180fr, C. Deloffre. 250fr, J. Gandouin.

1999, Oct. 14   Litho.   Perf. 13
764 A258 85fr multi   2.10   .75
765 A258 120fr multi   3.25 1.10
766 A258 180fr multi   4.50 1.60
767 A258 250fr multi   6.00 2.25
　　　Nos. 764-767 (4)   15.85 5.70

Tahiti on the Eve of the Year 2000
A259

1999, Nov. 10   Litho.   Perf. 13
768 A259 85fr multi   2.50   .75

5th Marquesas Islands Arts Festival
A260

1999, Dec. 10
769 A260 90fr multi   2.00   .80

Year 2000 — A261

85fr, Hands of adult and infant. 120fr, Eye.

2000, Jan. 3   Perf. 13¼x13, 13x13¼
770 A261 85fr multi, vert.   2.50   .75
771 A261 120fr multi   3.25 1.10

New Year 2000 (Year of the Dragon)
A262

2000, Feb. 5   Litho.   Perf. 13x13¼
772 A262 180fr multi   5.50 1.50

Portions of the design were applied by a thermographic process producing a shiny, raised effect.

Postal Service Emblem and Stamps
A263

2000, Mar. 15   Litho.   Perf. 13x13¼
773 A263 90fr multi   2.00   .75

First Intl. Tattoo Festival, Raiatea — A264

Various tattoos.

2000, Apr. 28   Perf. 13
774 A264 85fr multi   1.90   .70
775 A264 120fr multi   2.75   .95
776 A264 130fr multi   2.90 1.00
777 A264 160fr multi   3.50 1.25
　　　Nos. 774-777 (4)   11.05 3.90

Beautiful Women of French Polynesia — A265

2000, May 30
778 A265 300fr multi   7.50 3.00
　a.　Souvenir sheet of 1   12.00 12.00

No. 778a sold for 500fr.

Traditional Dresses — A266

Denominations: 85fr, 120fr, 160fr, 250fr.

2000, June 21   Litho.   Perf. 13¼x13
779-782 A266   Set of 4   13.50 6.00

Mountains A267

Designs: 90fr, Mts. Aorai and Orohena. 180fr, Mts. Orohena and Aorai.

2000, July 10   Perf. 13x13¼
783-784 A267   Set of 2   6.00 2.60

Traditional Sports
A268

120fr, Fruit carrying. 250fr, Stone lifting, vert.

Perf. 13x13¼, 13¼x13
2000, Sept. 15
785-786 A268   Set of 2   8.25 3.50

Native Woven Crafts
A269

No. 787, Fans. No. 788, Hat.

2000, Oct. 3   Litho.   Perf. 13x13¼
787-788 A269 85fr set of 2   3.75 1.75

Year of Ancient Tahitian Language Reo Ma'ohi
A270

2000, Nov. 9   Litho.   Perf. 13x13¼
789 A270 120fr multi   2.75 1.20

Portions of the design were applied by a thermographic process producing a shiny, raised effect.

Advent of New Millennium — A271

2000, Dec. 28
790 A271 85fr multi   2.50   .90

Central School, Cent. — A272

Designs: No. 791, 85fr, Central School. No. 792, 85fr, Paul Gauguin High School.

2001, Jan. 16
791-792 A272   Set of 2   3.75 1.75

New Year 2001 (Year of the Snake) — A273

2001, Jan. 24   Perf. 13¼x13
793 A273 120fr multi   2.75 1.20

Portions of the design were applied by a thermographic process producing a shiny, raised effect.

Landscapes
A274

Designs: 35fr, Vaiharuru Waterfall. 50fr, Vahiria Lake, horiz. 90fr, Hakaui Valley.

Perf. 13¼x13, 13x13¼
2001, Feb. 26   Litho.
794-796 A274   Set of 3   6.00 1.75

Year of the Polynesian Child — A275

2001, Mar. 28   Litho.   Perf. 13x13¼
797 A275 55fr multi   1.25   .55

Polynesian Singers — A276

Designs: 85fr, Eddie Lund. 120fr, Charley Mauu. 130fr, Bimbo. 180fr, Marie Mariteragi and Emma Terangi, horiz.

2001, Apr. 12   Perf. 13¼x13, 13x13¼
798-801 A276   Set of 4   11.50 5.00

Volunteers of the Pacific Batallion, 60th Anniv.
A277

2001, Apr. 21   Perf. 13x13¼
802 A277 85fr multi   2.25   .90

Surfing Waves of Teahupoo
A278

2001, May 4
803 A278 120fr multi   2.75 1.20

Internal Autonomy, 17th Anniv.
A279

2001, June 29   Litho.   Perf. 13
804 A279 250fr multi   5.50 2.50
　a.　Souvenir sheet of 1   12.00 12.00

No. 804a sold for 500fr.

Pirogue Racing — A280

Designs: 85fr, Male racers. 120fr, Female racers.

2001, July 12   **Perf. 13¼x13**
805-806 A280   Set of 2   4.50 2.00
   a.   Souvenir sheet, #805-806, imperf.   5.50 5.50
       No. 806a sold for 250fr.

Hardwood Trees A281

Designs: 90fr, Tou. 130fr, Ati. 180fr, Miro.

2001, Oct. 23   **Litho.**   **Perf. 13x13½**
807-809 A281   Set of 3   11.00 8.00

AIDS Prevention A282

2001, Sept. 20   **Litho.**   **Perf. 13x13¼**
810 A282 55fr multi   2.75 1.10

Year of Dialogue Among Civilizations A283

2001, Oct. 9   **Perf. 13**
811 A283 500fr multi   11.50 10.00

Perfume Flowers — A284

Designs: 35fr, Gardenia tahitensis. 50fr, Fagraea berteriana. 85fr, Gardenia jasminoides.

2001, Nov. 8   **Perf. 13¼x13**
812-814 A284   Set of 3   6.00 3.50
   Portions of the designs were applied by a thermographic process producing a shiny, raised effect.

Christmas A285

2001, Dec. 6   **Perf. 13x13¼**
815 A285 120fr multi   2.75 2.40

New Year 2002 (Year of the Horse) A286

2002, Feb. 12   **Litho.**   **Perf. 13x13¼**
816 A286 130fr multi   3.25 2.60
   Portions of the design were applied by a thermographic process producing a shiny, raised effect.

Happy Holidays A287

Greetings A288

2002, Feb. 28   **Background Colors**
817 A287 55fr red   1.25 1.10
818 A288 55fr blue   1.25 1.10
819 A287 85fr blue   1.90 1.75
820 A288 85fr green   1.90 1.75
      Nos. 817-820 (4)   6.30 5.70

10th World Outrigger Canoe Championships — A289

Canoe rowers and emblems: 120fr, 180fr.

2002, Mar. 9   **Photo.**   **Perf. 13¼**
821-822 A289   Set of 2   6.75 6.25

Sea Urchins A290

Designs: 35fr, Echinometra sp. 50fr, Heterocentrotus trigonarius. 90fr, Echinothrix calamaris. 120fr, Toxopneustes sp.

2002, Apr. 18   **Litho.**   **Perf. 13x13¼**
823-826 A290   Set of 4   6.50 6.25

Blood Donation — A291

2002, May 3   **Litho.**   **Perf. 13¼x13**
827 A291 130fr multi   4.00 3.25

2002 World Cup Soccer Championships, Japan and Korea — A292

2002, May 30
828 A292 85fr multi   2.10 1.75

Traditional Sports — A293

Designs: 85fr, Coconut husking. 120fr, Fruit carrying. 250fr, Javelin throwing.

2002, June 27
829-831 A293   Set of 3   10.00 9.00

House of James Norman Hall — A294

2002, July 4   **Perf. 13x13¼**
832 A294 90fr multi   2.00 1.90

Papeete Market — A295

2002, Aug. 30   **Litho.**   **Perf. 13**
833 A295 400fr multi   8.75 8.00
   a.   Souvenir sheet of 1   11.00 11.00
   Amphilex 2002 Stamp Exhibition, Amsterdam (#833a). No. 833a sold for 500fr.

Pacific Oceanology Center, Vairoa A296

Designs: 55fr, Research pond, fish, shrimp, oyster, and flasks. 90fr, Aeriel view of center, fish, shrimp and oyster.

2002, Sept. 26   **Photo.**   **Perf. 13¼**
834-835 A296   Set of 2   3.50 2.40

Taapuna Master 2002 Surfing Competition A297

2002, Oct. 21   **Litho.**   **Perf. 13x13¼**
836 A297 120fr multi   2.75 2.00

Halophilic Flowers A298

Designs: 85fr, Hibiscus tiliaceus. 130fr, Scaveola sericea. 180fr, Guettarda speciosa.

2002, Nov. 7   Set of 3   8.75 6.75
837-839 A298

Polynesians at Festivals A299

Designs: 55fr, Dancers and bus. 120fr, Musicians, vert.

2002, Dec. 5   **Perf. 13x13¼, 13¼x13**
840-841 A299   Set of 2   3.75 3.00

New Year 2003 (Year of the Ram) — A300

2003, Feb. 1   **Litho.**   **Perf. 13¼x13**
842 A300 120fr multi   3.00 2.25
   Portions of the design was applied by a thermographic process producing a shiny, raised effect.

Polynesian Women — A301

2003, Mar. 8   **Litho.**   **Perf. 13¼x13**
843 A301 55fr multi   1.25 1.00

Waterfalls — A302

2003, Apr. 10   **Perf. 13**
844 A302 330fr multi   7.25 6.00

Old Papeete
A303

Designs: 55fr, Automobiles and buildings, vert. 85fr, Ship in harbor. 90fr, People with bicycles in front of buildings (50x28mm). 120fr, Tree-lined street (50x28mm).

Perf. 13¼x13, 13x13¼, 13
2003, May 15
845-848 A303   Set of 4   7.75   7.00
848a   Souvenir sheet, #845-848   12.00 12.00
   No. 848a sold for 550fr.

Fish — A304

2003, June 12   Litho.   Perf. 13
849 A304 460fr multi   9.50   9.50
   Portions of the design were applied by a thermographic process producing a shiny, raised effect.

Outrigger
Canoes
A305

Designs: No. 850, 85fr, shown. No. 851, 85fr, Three sailors on canoe at sea. No. 852, 85fr, Three sailors on canoe, vert. No. 853, 85fr, Sailor sitting on outrigger, vert.

Perf. 13x13¼, 13¼x13
2003, July 11   Litho.
850-853 A305   Set of 4   7.50   6.50

Firewalkers
A306

Orange-banded Cowrie — A307

2003, Aug. 14   Photo.   Perf. 13¼
854 A306 130fr multi   2.50   2.50
Perf. 13x13¼
855 A307 420fr multi   8.50   8.50

Are You Jealous? by Paul Gauguin
(1848-1903) — A308

2003, Sept. 11   Perf. 13x12¼
856 A308 250fr multi   6.50   3.50

Office of Posts and
Telecommunications
Emblem — A308a

Type I: "Postes 2003" at right.
Type II: "Postes" only at right.

Serpentine Die Cut 6½ Vert.
2003, Oct. 1   Engr.
Booklet Stamp
Self-Adhesive
856A A308a (60fr) blue (type
       II), 2006   10.00   1.00
  b.   Booklet pane of 10   100.00
  c.   Type I   40.00 24.00
  d.   As "c," booklet pane of 10 400.00
  e.   As #856A, inscribed
       "Phil@poste"   8.00   1.00
  f.   Booklet pane of 10
       #856Ae   80.00
   Issued: No. 856Ac, 10/1/03. No. 856A, 2006. No. 856Ae, 2007.
   See No. 869.

French
Polynesian
Flag
A309

2003, Oct. 1   Litho.   Perf. 13x13¼
857 A309 (60fr) multi   1.50   1.25

Tiki — A310

2003, Oct. 1   Perf. 13¼x13
858 A310 100fr multi   3.00   2.00
   Reissued in 2006 on shiny paper with much deeper colors. Values the same.

Flowers
A311

Designs: 90fr, Orchid. 130fr, Rose de porcelain (torch ginger).

2003, Oct. 4   Litho.   Perf. 13x13¼
859-860 A311   Set of 2   6.50   4.50
   Portions of the designs were applied by a thermographic process producing a shiny, raised effect.

Bora Bora
A312

Designs: No. 861, 60fr, Painting of Bora Bora by A. Van Der Heyde. No. 862, 60fr, Aerial photograph of Bora Bora.

2003, Nov. 6   Litho.   Perf. 13x13¼
861-862 A312   Set of 2   5.00   2.75

Tiki — A313

2003, Dec. 6   Perf. 13
863 A313 190fr multi   4.00   4.00

Buildings
and Palm
Trees
A314

2003, Dec. 19   Perf. 13x13¼
864 A314 90fr multi   3.00   1.90

New Year 2004
(Year of the
Monkey) — A315

2004, Jan. 22   Litho.   Perf. 13¼x13
865 A315 130fr multi   3.50   3.50
   A portion of the design was applied by a thermographic process producing a shiny, raised effect.

Scenes
From
Everyday
Life
A316

Designs: 60fr, Women working with cloth. 90fr, Street scene, vert.

Perf. 13x13¼, 13¼x13
2004, Feb. 13   Litho.
866-867 A316   Set of 2   3.25   3.25

Polynesian
Woman — A317

2004, Mar. 8   Perf. 13¼x13
868 A317 90fr multi   4.00   1.90

Post Emblem Type of 2003
Serpentine Die Cut 6½ Vert.
2004, Apr. 22   Engr.
Booklet Stamp
Self-Adhesive
869 A308a (90fr) red   6.00   2.00
  a.   Booklet pane of 10   60.00
   Serpentine Die Cut 6¾ Vert.
  b.   As #869, inscribed
       "Phil@poste"   —   —
  c.   Booklet pane of 10 #869b —
   No. 869 lacks year date.

Polynesian Economic
Development — A318

2004, Apr. 23   Litho.   Perf. 13x12¾
870 A318 500fr multi   11.00 10.00

Araharahu Marae, Paea — A319

2004, Apr. 23
871 A319 500fr multi   11.00 10.00

Vanilla — A320

2004, May 14   Perf. 13¼x13
872 A320 90fr multi   2.10   1.90
   No. 872 is impregnated with a vanilla scent.

Mobile Snack Bars — A321

2004, May 28   Perf. 13x12¾
873 A321 300fr multi   6.50   6.25

Handicrafts
A322

Designs: No. 874, 60fr, Artisan braiding fibers. No. 875, 60fr, Mother-of-pearl carving. No. 876, 90fr, Artisan carving statue. No. 877, 90fr, Hat.

2004, June 26   Perf. 13x13¼
874-877 A322   Set of 4   10.00   6.25
   Portion of the designs were applied by a thermographic process producing a shiny, raised effect.

Involvement in South Pacific Area of
Office of Posts and
Telecommunications — A323

Designs: 100fr, Earth, Sun on horizon. 130fr, Satellite dish, building.

2004, July 23 **Photo.** **Perf. 13¼**
878-879 A323 Set of 2   5.50 4.75

Information Technology and Communications A324

Designs: No. 880, 190fr, Computer keyboard, "@." No. 881, 190fr, Satellite, satellite dish.

2004, Sept. 23 **Litho.** **Perf. 13¼x13**
880-881 A324 Set of 2   8.00 8.00

Omai, Polynesian Capt. James Cook Brought to England — A325

2004, Oct. 14 **Perf. 13**
882 A325 250fr multi   5.25 5.25

Shell Collectors A326

2004, Nov. 10 **Photo.** **Perf. 13¼**
883 A326 60fr multi   1.60 1.40
A souvenir sheet of one sold for 250fr. Value $7.

Adenium Obesum A327

Alpinia Purpurata A328

Ixora Chinensis A329

Gardenia Taitensis A330

Heliconia Psittacorum — A331

Allamanda Blanchetii A332

Otacanthus Caeruleus — A333

Hibiscus Rosa-sinensis — A334

Euphorba Milii A335

Asocenda Hybrid of Vanda x Ascocentrum — A336

Mussaenda Erythrophylia — A337

Bougainvillea Glabra — A338

2004, Nov. 10 **Litho.** **Perf. 13x13¼**
884	Booklet pane of 6	17.50	—
a.	A327 90fr multi	2.50	2.50
b.	A328 90fr multi	2.50	2.50
c.	A329 90fr multi	2.50	2.50
d.	A330 90fr multi	2.50	2.50
e.	A331 90fr multi	2.50	2.50
f.	A332 90fr multi	2.50	2.50
885	Booklet pane of 6	17.50	—
a.	A333 90fr multi	2.50	2.50
b.	A334 90fr multi	2.50	2.50
c.	A335 90fr multi	2.50	2.50
d.	A336 90fr multi	2.50	2.50
e.	A337 90fr multi	2.50	2.50
f.	A338 90fr multi	2.50	2.50
	Complete booklet, #884-885	30.00	

Complete booklet sold for 1200fr.

Christmas A339

2004, Dec. 17
886 A339 60fr multi   1.60 1.40
A portion of the design was applied by a thermographic process producing a shiny, raised effect.

Bamboo — A340

2005, Feb. 9 **Perf. 13¼x13**
887 A340 130fr multi   3.00 3.00
New Year 2005. A portion of the design was applied by a thermographic process producing a shiny, raised effect.

People and Hut A341

2005, Feb. 25 **Perf. 13x13¼**
888 A341 90fr multi   2.00 2.00

Polynesian Women — A342

Designs: 60fr, Woman wearing lei. 90fr, Woman wearing flower garland on head and robe.

2005, Mar. 8 **Perf. 13¼x13**
889-890 A342 Set of 2   4.00 3.50

Woman Making Tapa Cloth — A343

2005, Apr. 22 **Perf. 13**
891 A343 250fr multi   5.50 5.50

Tifaifai A344

2005, Mar. 23 **Litho.** **Perf. 13x13¼**
892 A344 5fr multi   .25 .20

Angelfish A345

Designs: No. 893, 90fr, Centropyge bispinosa. No. 894, 90fr, Centropyge loricula. No. 895, 130fr, Centropyge heraldi. No. 896, 130fr, Centropyge flavissima.

2005, May 27 **Litho.** **Perf. 13x13¼**
893-896 A345 Set of 4   9.50 9.50
896a Souvenir sheet, #893-896   9.50 9.50
Portions of the designs were applied by a thermographic process producing a shiny, raised effect.

Historic Airplanes A346

Designs: No. 897, 60fr, TAI DC-8, first jet in Tahiti, 1961. No. 898, 60fr, Pan American Boeing 707, first foreign flight, 1963. No. 899, 100fr, Air France Boeing 707, first Air France flight to Tahiti, 1973. No. 900, 100fr, Air Tahiti Nui Airbus A340-300, first Tahitian airline, 2000.

2005, June 24
897-900 A346 Set of 4   6.50 6.50

Musical Instruments A347

Designs: No. 901, 130fr, Drum. No. 902, 130fr, Nose flutes, horiz.

2005, July 22 **Perf. 13¼x13, 13x13¼**
901-902 A347 Set of 2   5.50 5.50

Polynesian Landscapes — A348

2005, Aug. 26 **Perf. 13**
903 A348 300fr multi   6.25 6.25

Pineapples
A349

Designs: 90fr, Close-up of spines. 130fr, Entire fruit.

2005, Sept. 23   Litho.   Perf. 13¼x13
904-905 A349   Set of 2   4.75 4.50

Nos. 904-905 are impregnated with pineapple scent.

Marae — A350

Marquesan Tohua — A351

2005, Oct. 21   Perf. 13
906 A350 500fr multi   10.00 10.00
907 A351 500fr multi   10.00 10.00

Autonomy, 20th Anniv. (in 2004) — A352

2005, Nov. 10   Perf. 13¼x13
908 A352 60fr multi   4.00 1.75

No. 908 was printed in France and distributed there in June 2004 but was not sold in French Polynesia until 2005, where it was available from the philatelic bureau upon request, and not through standing orders.

O'Parrey Harbor, Tahiti
A353

2005, Nov. 10   Engr.   Perf. 13x12½
909 A353 100fr multi   2.00 2.00

Christmas
A354

2005, Dec. 16   Litho.   Perf. 13x13¼
910 A354 90fr multi   2.00 2.00

Lotus Flower
A355

Litho. & Silk-screened
2006, Jan. 30   Perf. 13x13¼
911 A355 130fr multi   2.60 2.60

A356

Hearts
A357

2006, Feb. 14   Photo.   Perf. 13
912 A356 60fr multi   1.25 1.25
913 A357 90fr multi   1.90 1.90

Values are for stamps with surrounding selvage.

Polynesian Women — A358

Woman: 60fr, At water's edge. 90fr, With oil lamp.

2006, Mar. 8   Litho.   Perf. 13¼x13
914-915 A358   Set of 2   3.75 3.25

Maupiti — A359

2006, Apr. 26   Engr.   Perf. 13x13¼
916 A359 500fr multi   11.00 11.00

History of the Marquesas (Washington) Islands — A360

Designs: 60fr, Native man and woman. 130fr, Ships.

2006, May 27   Litho.   Perf. 13¼x13
917-918 A360   Set of 2   4.00 4.00
918a   Souvenir sheet, #917-918   4.00 4.00

Diners and Musicians — A361

2006, June 6   Perf. 13
919 A361 300fr multi   6.50 6.50

Polynesian Ground Dove
A362

Tuamotu Sandpiper
A363

2006, June 21   Perf. 13x13¼
920 A362 250fr multi   5.25 5.25
921 A363 250fr multi   5.25 5.25

Heiva — A364

Designs: 90fr, Canoe race. 130fr, Stone lifting. 190fr, Dancer.

2006, July 19   Perf. 13¼x13
922-924 A364   Set of 3   8.75 8.75

Frangipani Flowers
A365

2006, Aug. 23   Litho.   Perf. 13x13½
925 A365 90fr multi   2.25 1.90

No. 925 is impregnated with frangipani scent.

A366

World Tourism Day
A367

Designs: 40fr, Ruins. No. 927, 90fr, Waterfall, woman and child. 130fr, Clothing at open-air market.

No. 929: a, Dancers with yellow skirts. b, Surfer. c, House and palm tree. d, Pearls. e, Fish and coral. f, Islanders in outrigger canoes.
No. 930: a, Woman in hammock. b, Stilt houses. c, Tower and boats. d, Horses and riders. e, Aerial view of island. f, Diver and sting ray.

2006, Sept. 22   Perf. 13¼x13
926-928 A366   Set of 3   6.00 6.00

Booklet Stamps
Perf. 13x13¼
929   Booklet pane of 6   15.00   —
a.-f.   A367 90fr Any single   2.00 2.00
930   Booklet pane of 6   15.00   —
a.-f.   A367 90fr Any single   2.00 2.00
           Complete booklet, #929-930   30.00

Complete booklet sold for 1200fr.

Paintings
A368

Designs: 60fr, Javelin Throwing, by Monique Garnier Bissol. 90fr, Market Life, by Albert Luzuy, horiz. 100fr, Island Quay, by Gilbert Chaussoy, horiz. 190fr, Vahine, by Olivier Louzé.

2006, Oct. 25   Perf. 13
931-934 A368   Set of 4   9.50 9.50

Engravings by Paul Gauguin (1848-1903) — A369

Engravings depicting: 60fr, Women. 130fr, Cow and man carrying items on stick.

2006, Nov. 8   Engr.   Perf. 13¼
935-936 A369   Set of 2   4.25 4.25

Children's Art
A370

2006, Dec. 13   Litho.   Perf. 13x13¼
937 A370 90fr multi   2.00 2.00

Beach Gear — A371

Designs: 60fr, Flip-flops. 90fr, Surfboards.

Serpentine Die Cut 11x11¼
2007   Photo.
Self-Adhesive
938 A371 60fr multicolored   1.25 1.25
a.   Blue tips of die cutting along left side   1.25 1.25
939 A371 90fr multicolored   2.00 2.00
a.   Light blue tips of die cutting along bottom   2.00 2.00

Issued: Nos. 938a, 939a, 1/24; Nos. 938-939, Feb. Nos. 938a and 939a are from the original printing, and are from sheets having adjacent stamps and die cutting that does not extend through the backing paper. Nos. 938-939, which were distributed to the philatelic trade, are from sheets with selvage around each stamp, and with rouletting that extends through the backing paper that allows the stamps to be removed from the sheet more easily.

New Year 2007 (Year of the Pig) A372

2007, Feb. 19　Litho.　Perf. 13x13¼
940　A372　130fr multi　　　　　3.50　3.50

Portions of the design were applied by a thermographic process producing a shiny, raised effect.

Painting of Polynesian Woman by Mathius — A373

Photograph of Polynesian Woman by John Stember — A374

2007, Mar. 8　Litho.　Perf. 13¼x13
941　A373　60fr multi　　　　　1.50　1.40
Perf. 13x13¼
942　A374　90fr multi　　　　　2.25　2.00

Audit Office, Bicent. A375

2007, Mar. 17　Engr.　Perf. 13¼x13
943　A375　90fr multi　　　　　2.75　2.00

Shells — A376

Designs: 10fr, Lambis crocata pilsbryi. 60fr, Cypraea thomasi. 90fr, Cyrtulus serotinus. 130fr, Chicoreus laqueatus.

2007, Apr. 25　　　　　Litho.
944-947　A376　Set of 4　　　　6.75　6.75
947a　　Souvenir sheet, #944-947　6.75　6.75

Coconut A377

2007, May 23　　　Perf. 13x13¼
948　A377　90fr multi　　　　　2.25　2.00

No. 948 is impregnated with a coconut scent.

Ships — A378

Designs: No. 949, 250fr, Gunboat Zélée. No. 950, 250fr, Passenger and cargo liner Sagittaire.

2007, June 22　　　　　Perf. 13
949-950　A378　Set of 2　　　　12.00　11.50

Heiva Festival — A379

Various women dancers: 65fr, 100fr, 140fr.

2007, July 4　　　　Perf. 13¼x13
951-953　A379　Set of 3　　　　7.50　7.50

Arrival of Kon-Tiki Expedition in Polynesia, 60th Anniv. — A380

Litho. & Silk-screened
2007, Aug. 7　　　　　Perf. 13
954　A380　300fr multi　　　　　7.00　7.00

Arrival of Ship at Papeete Dock — A381

2007, Aug. 29　Litho.　Perf. 13
955　A381　190fr multi　　　　　4.50　4.50

Old and Modern Photos of Papeete — A382

Designs: 65fr, Rue Gauguin, 2007. 100fr, Rue de la Petite-Pologne (now Rue Gauguin), 1907.

2007, Sept. 26
956-957　A382　Set of 2　　　　4.75　4.00

Old Franc and Centime Notes — A383

Designs: 65fr, 1919 2-franc Chamber of Commerce note. 140fr, 1942 2-franc note. 500fr, 1943 50-centime note.

2007, Oct. 26　Engr.　Perf. 13
958-960　A383　Set of 3　　　20.00　17.00

Flowers A384

Designs: 100fr, Hibiscus. 140fr, Bird-of-paradise (Oiseaux de paradis).

Litho. & Silk-screened
2007, Nov. 8　　　　Perf. 13x13¼
961-962　A384　Set of 2　　　　7.50　7.50

Christmas A385

2007, Dec. 6　Litho.　Perf. 13x13¼
963　A385　100fr multi　　　　　2.50　2.50

Marine Life A386

Designs: 10fr, Himantura fai. 20fr, Tursiops truncatus. 40fr, Megaptera novaeangliae. 65fr, Negaprion acutidens.

2008, Jan. 10
964-967　A386　Set of 4　　　　4.00　4.00

New Year 2008 (Year of the Rat) — A387

2008, Feb. 7　Photo.　Perf. 13¼x13
968　A387　140fr multi　　　　　3.75　3.75

Paintings of Women by Bénilde Menghini — A388

Designs: 65fr, Woman picking mangos. 100fr, Women scaling fish.

2008, Mar. 7　　　　　Litho.
969-970　A388　Set of 2　　　　4.25　4.25

Paintings by Polynesian Artists A389

Unnamed paintings depicting: No. 971, 100fr, Boat and reef, by Torea Chan. No. 972, 100fr, Polynesian man, by Raymond Vigor. No. 973, 100fr, Fruit bowl, by Teurarea Prokop, horiz.

2008, Apr. 10　Perf. 13x13¼, 13¼x13
971-973　A389　Set of 3　　　　8.00　8.00

Pouvanaa a Oopa (1895-1977), Politician — A390

2008, May 20　Litho.　Perf. 13
974　A390　500fr multi　　　　13.00　13.00

Island Touring Vehicles — A391

Designs: 65fr, Motor scooter. 100fr, Bus, horiz.

Serpentine Die Cut 11
2008, June 12　　　　　Photo.
Self-Adhesive
975-976　A391　Set of 2　　　　4.50　4.50

Heiva Festival A392

Designs: 65fr, Woman with floral headdress. 140fr, Tattooed man. 190fr, Girl dancing.

2008, July 16   Litho.   Perf. 13
977-979   A392   Set of 3   11.00 11.00

Sports — A393

Designs: No. 980, 140fr, Table tennis. No. 981, 140fr, Weight lifting.

2008, Aug. 8   Litho.   Perf. 13¼x13
980-981   A393   Set of 2   7.00 7.00

End of Tahiti Nui Expedition, 50th Anniv. — A394

2008, Aug. 29   Litho.   Perf. 13
982   A394   190fr multi   4.50 4.50

Eric de Bisschop (1890-1958), expedition leader.

Polynesian Scenes A395

No. 983: a, Woman crouching. b, Woman under shelter. c, Boat in bay near cliffs. d, Orange flowers. e, Red hibiscus flower. f, Island. g, Woman with headdress. h, White flower. i, Woman with headdress and flower garland. j, Pink flower. k, Islands. l, Bay near mountains.

Serpentine Die Cut 11¼x11
2008, Sept. 8
Self-Adhesive
983   Booklet pane of 12   32.50
a.-d.   A395 65fr Any single   1.50   1.50
e.-h.   A395 100fr Any single   2.40   2.40
i.-l.   A395 140fr Any single   3.25   3.25

Gardenia Taitensis in Bottle of Monoi Oil — A396

2008, Sept. 17   Perf. 13¼x13
984   A396   100fr multi   2.40 2.40

No. 984 is impregnated with a gardenia scent.

Aviation Anniversaries — A397

Designs: No. 985, 250fr, Air service between France and French Polynesia, 50th

---

anniv. No. 986, 250fr, Air Tahiti Nui, 10th anniv.

2008, Oct. 15   Litho.   Perf. 13
985-986   A397   Set of 2   11.00 11.00

French Polynesia Postage Stamps, 50th Anniv. — A398

Designs: 65fr, French Polynesia #185. 100fr, Vignette of French Polynesia #C24. 140fr, French Polynesia #J29.

2008, Nov. 6   Engr.   Perf. 13
987-989   A398   Set of 3   6.75   6.75
989a   Sheet of 3, #987-989   6.75   6.75

Boater and Dancer A399

2008, Dec. 5   Litho.   Perf. 13x13¼
990   A399   100fr multi   2.25 2.25

Winning design in children's stamp design contest.

Hypolimnas Bolina A400

Litho. & Silk-screened
2009, Jan. 16   Perf. 13
991   A400   70fr multi   1.50 1.50

Fire Fighters — A401

Designs: 70fr, Fireman on aerial ladder. 140fr, Fireboat.

2009, Feb. 13   Litho.   Perf. 13
992-993   A401   Set of 2   4.50 4.50

Paintings of Polynesian Women — A402

Designs: 70fr, Woman, by Myriam Stroken. 140fr, Woman with Guitar, by Stanley Haumani.

2009, Mar. 30   Litho.   Perf. 13¼x13
994-995   A402   Set of 2   4.00 4.00

Jacques Brel (1929-78), Singer — A403

Colors: 70fr, Blue. 100fr, Brown.

2009, Apr. 8   Engr.
996-997   A403   Set of 2   4.25 4.25

Pareo Fabric A404

Pareo in: (70fr), Blue. (100fr), Red. (140fr), Green.

Serpentine Die Cut 11
2009, May 29   Litho.
Self-Adhesive
998-1000   A404   Set of 3   7.25 7.25

Heiva Celebrations of the Past — A405

Various Heiva dancers: 70fr, 100fr, 140fr. 100fr and 140fr are horiz.

Perf. 13¼x13, 13x13¼
2009, June 19
1001-1003   A405   Set of 3   7.50 7.50

First Man on the Moon, 40th Anniv. A406

2009, July 20   Perf. 13¼
1004   A406   140fr multi   3.50 3.50

Water Activities A407

Designs: 70fr, Surfing. 100fr, Canoeing (pirogue).

Serpentine Die Cut 11x11¼
2009, Aug. 7   Litho.
Self-Adhesive
1005-1006   A407   Set of 2   4.00 4.00

Passion Fruit A408

2009, Aug. 14   Perf. 13x13¼
1007   A408   100fr multi   2.40 2.40

No. 1007 has a scratch-and-sniff coating on the fruit having a passion fruit scent.

Underwater Scenes — A409

Designs: 70fr, Scuba divers. 100fr, Turtles, horiz. 140fr, Whale, horiz.

Litho. & Silk-screened
Perf. 13¼x13, 13x13¼
2009, Sept. 11
1008-1010   A409   Set of 3   7.75   7.75
1010a   Sheet of 3, #1008-1010   7.75   7.75

Fish — A410

No. 1011: a, Chaetodon lunula. b, Chaetodon trichrous. c, Chaetodon ornatissimus. d, Chaetodon pelewensis. e, Pterois antennata. f, Myripristis berndti. g, Priacanthus hamrur. h, Epinephelus polyphekadion. i, Thalassoma lutescens. j, Thalassoma hardwicke. k, Pygoplites diacanthus. l, Coris gaimard.

Serpentine Die Cut 11¼x11
2009, Sept. 11
Self-Adhesive
1011   Booklet pane of 12   31.00
a.-d.   A410 70fr Any single   1.75   1.75
e.-h.   A410 100fr Any single   2.50   2.50
i.-l.   A410 140fr Any single   3.50   3.50

Paintings by Paul Gauguin (1848-1903) — A411

Designs: No. 1012, 250fr, Still Life with a Maori Statuette. No. 1013, 250fr, Still Life with Apples, horiz.

2009, Oct. 16   Litho.   Perf. 13
1012-1013   A411   Set of 2   12.50 12.50

French Polynesia No.
180 — A412

2009, Nov. 5   **Engr.**
1014 A412 500fr multi   12.50 12.50

Legend of the
Coconut
Tree — A413

2009, Dec. 11   **Litho.**   **Perf. 13¼x13**
1015 A413 190fr multi   4.75 4.75

Papeete Post Office, 150th
Anniv. — A414

2010, Jan. 20
1016 A414 70fr multi   1.60 1.60

New Year
2010 (Year
of the
Tiger)
A415

Litho. & Silk-screened
2010, Feb. 15   **Perf. 13x13¼**
1017 A415 140fr multi   3.25 3.25

Woman and
Child — A416

Woman and child: 70fr, Facing forward.
100fr, Facing right.

2010, Mar. 8   **Litho.**   **Perf. 13¼x13**
1018-1019 A416   Set of 2   4.00 4.00

Tattoos
A417

Tattooed: No. 1020, 250fr, Woman (green
background). No. 1021, 250fr, Man (dark red
background).

2010, Apr. 6
1020-1021 A417   Set of 2   11.50 11.50

Tiare
Apetahi
Flower
A418

Litho. & Silk-screened
2010, Apr. 20   **Perf. 13x13¼**
1022 A418 70fr multi   1.50 1.50

Captain Frederick William Beechey
(1796-1856), Explorer — A419

2010, May 5   **Litho.**
1023 A419 140fr multi   3.00 3.00

Corals
A420

Various corals: 70fr, 100fr, 140fr. 140fr is
vert.

Litho. & Silk-screened
2010, June 4   **Perf. 13x13¼, 13¼x13**
1024-1026 A420   Set of 3   6.50 6.50
1026a   Sheet of 3, #1024-1026   6.50 6.50

Heiva
Festival — A421

Various festival participants: 100fr, 140fr,
190fr.

2010, July 20   **Litho.**   **Perf. 13¼x13**
1027-1029 A421   Set of 3   9.50 9.50

Mango
A422

2010, Aug. 8   **Perf. 13x13¼**
1030 A422 100fr multi   2.25 2.25

No. 1030 has a scratch-and-sniff coating on
the fruit having a mango scent.

Phosphate
Mining at
Makatea,
Cent.
A423

Designs: 70fr, Office. 100fr, Train. 140fr,
Mining operations.

2010, Aug. 17   **Litho.**   **Perf. 13x13¼**
1031-1033 A423   Set of 3   6.75 6.75

Honotua Fiber
Optic Submarine
Cable
Project — A424

Serpentine Die Cut 11
2010, Sept. 15   **Photo.**
Self-Adhesive
1034 A424 70fr multi   1.75 1.75

Birds
A425

No. 1035: a, Lori de Kuhl (Kuhl's lorikeet). b,
Bécasseau Sanderling (Sanderling). c,
Carpophade de la Société (Imperial pigeon).
d, Tangara à dos rouge (Crimson-backed tanager). e, Ptilope de Hutton (Rapa fruit dove). f,
Sterne huppée (Great crested tern). g, Gygis
blanche (White tern). h, Lori Nonnette (Blue
lorikeet). i, Chevalier errant (Wandering tattler). j, Martin chasseur des Gambier (Tuamotu
kingfisher). k, Fou brun (Brown booby). l,
Pluvier fauve (Pacific golden plover).

Litho. & Silk-screened
2010, Sept. 15
Self-Adhesive
1035   Booklet pane of 12   28.00
a.-l.   A425 100fr Any single   2.25 2.25

Tahiti Faa'a International Airport, 50th
Anniv. — A426

2010, Oct. 14   **Litho.**   **Perf. 13**
1036 A426 500fr multi   11.50 11.50

Sphinx
Moth
A427

2010, Oct. 14   **Perf. 13x13½**
1037 A427 5fr multi   .20 .20

1948 Air Post Stamps of French
Oceania — A428

Designs: 70fr, #C17. 100fr, #C18. 140fr,
#C19.

2010, Nov. 4   **Engr.**   **Perf. 13**
1038-1040 A428   Set of 3   7.25 7.25

Legend of
Moua Puta
A429

2010, Dec. 9   **Litho.**   **Perf. 13x13¼**
1041 A429 70fr multi   1.60 1.60

SEMI-POSTAL STAMPS

Nos. 55 and 26
Surcharged in Red

1915   **Unwmk.**   **Perf. 14x13½**
B1   A1 10c + 5c red   32.50 32.50
   a.   "e" instead of "c"   87.50 87.50
   b.   Inverted surcharge   225.00 225.00
   c.   Double surcharge   525.00 525.00
B2   A2 10c + 5c rose & org   12.50 12.50
   a.   "e" instead of "c"   65.00 65.00
   b.   "c" inverted   65.00 65.00
   c.   Inverted surcharge   300.00 300.00
   d.   As "a," inverted surcharge   400.00
   e.   As "b," inverted surcharge   400.00

Surcharged in Carmine

B3 A2 10c + 5c rose & org 5.50 5.50
a. "e" instead of "c" 45.00 45.00
b. Inverted surcharge 200.00 200.00
c. Double surcharge 200.00 200.00
d. As "a," inverted surcharge 325.00

Surcharged in Carmine

1916
B4 A2 10c + 5c rose & org 5.50 5.50

Curie Issue
Common Design Type
1938 **Perf. 13**
B5 CD80 1.75fr + 50c brt ultra 20.00 20.00

French Revolution Issue
Common Design Type
1939 **Photo.**
Name and Value Typo. in Black
B6 CD83 45c + 25c grn 17.50 17.50
B7 CD83 70c + 30c brn 17.50 17.50
B8 CD83 90c + 35c red org 17.50 17.50
B9 CD83 1.25fr + 1fr rose pink 17.50 17.50
B10 CD83 2.25fr + 2fr blue 17.50 17.50
Nos. B6-B10 (5) 87.50 87.50
Set, never hinged 145.00

> Catalogue values for unused stamps in this section, from this point to the end of the section, are for Never Hinged items.

Common Design Type and

Marine Officer — SP1

"L'Astrolabe" — SP2

1941 **Photo.** **Perf. 13½**
B11 SP1 1fr + 1fr red 3.50
B12 CD86 1.50fr + 3fr maroon 3.50
B12A SP2 2.50fr + 1fr blue 3.50
Nos. B11-B12A (3) 10.50

Nos. B11-B12A were issued by the Vichy government in France, and were not placed on sale in French Polynesia.

Nos. 125A-125B
Surcharged in Black or Red

1944 **Engr.** **Perf. 12½x12**
B12B 50c + 1.50fr on 2.50fr deep blue (R) 1.75
B12C + 2.50fr on 1fr green 1.75
Colonial Development Fund.
Nos. B12B-B12C were issued by the Vichy government in France, but were not placed on sale in French Polynesia.

Red Cross Issue
Common Design Type
1944 **Photo.** **Perf. 14½x14**
B13 CD90 5fr + 20fr peacock blue 2.00 1.60

The surtax was for the French Red Cross and national relief.

Tropical Medicine Issue
Common Design Type
1950, July 17 **Engr.** **Perf. 13**
B14 CD100 10fr + 2fr dk bl grn & dk grn 10.50 8.00

The surtax was for charitable work.

AIR POST STAMPS

Seaplane in Flight AP1

Perf. 13½
1934, Nov. 5 **Unwmk.** **Photo.**
C1 AP1 5fr green 1.25 1.25

For overprint see No. C2.
For Type AP1 without "RF," see Nos. C1A-C1D.

Type of 1934 without "RF" and

Beach Scene — AP1a

Perf. 13½, 13 (#C1E)
1944 **Photo, Engr. (#C1E)**
C1A AP1 5fr green .70
C1B AP1 10fr black 1.00
C1C AP1 20fr orange 1.10
C1D AP1 50fr gray blue 1.50
C1E AP1a 100fr turquoise blue 2.00
Nos. C1A-C1E (5) 6.30

Nos. C1A-C1E were issued by the Vichy government in France, but were not placed on sale in French Polynesia.

> Catalogue values for unused stamps in this section, from this point to the end of the section, are for Never Hinged items.

No. C1 Overprinted in Red

1941
C2 AP1 5fr green 7.25 4.75

Common Design Type
1942 **Perf. 14½x14**
C3 CD87 1fr dark orange .90 .65
C4 CD87 1.50fr bright red .95 .70
C5 CD87 5fr brown red 1.25 .95
C6 CD87 10fr black 1.90 1.40
C7 CD87 25fr ultra 2.75 2.10
C8 CD87 50fr dark green 3.00 2.10
C9 CD87 100fr plum 3.00 2.10
Nos. C3-C9 (7) 13.75 10.00

Victory Issue
Common Design Type
1946, May 8 **Engr.** **Perf. 12½**
C10 CD92 8fr dark green 2.75 2.00

Chad to Rhine Issue
Common Design Types
1946, June 6
C11 CD93 5fr red orange 2.10 1.60
C12 CD94 10fr dk olive bis 2.10 1.60
C13 CD95 15fr dk yellow grn 2.10 1.60
C14 CD96 20fr carmine 2.75 2.10
C15 CD97 25fr dk rose violet 4.00 3.00
C16 CD98 50fr black 4.50 3.50
Nos. C11-C16 (6) 17.55 13.40

Shearwater and Moorea Landscape — AP2

Fishermen — AP3

Shearwater over Maupiti Shoreline — AP4

1948, Mar. 1 **Unwmk.** **Perf. 13**
C17 AP2 50fr red brown 30.00 11.00
C18 AP3 100fr purple 24.00 8.00
C19 AP4 200fr blue green 52.50 17.50
Nos. C17-C19 (3) 106.50 36.50

UPU Issue
Common Design Type
1949
C20 CD99 10fr deep blue 20.00 15.00

Gauguin's "Nafea faaipoipo" — AP5

1953, Sept. 24
C21 AP5 14fr dk brn, dk gray grn & red 80.00 65.00
50th anniv. of the death of Paul Gauguin.

Liberation Issue
Common Design Type
1954, June 6
C22 CD102 3fr dk grnsh bl & bl grn 10.00 8.00

Bahia Peak, Borabora — AP6

1955, Sept. 26 **Unwmk.** **Perf. 13**
C23 AP6 13fr indigo & blue 10.00 5.50

Mother-of-Pearl Artist — AP7

Designs: 50fr, "Women of Tahiti," Gauguin, horiz. 100fr, "The White Horse," Gauguin. 200fr, Night fishing at Moorea, horiz.

1958, Nov. 3 **Engr.** **Perf. 13**
C24 AP7 13fr multicolored 13.00 4.50
C25 AP7 50fr multicolored 12.00 4.50
C26 AP7 100fr multicolored 20.00 7.25
C27 AP7 200fr lilac & slate 40.00 21.00
Nos. C24-C27 (4) 85.00 37.25

Airport, Papeete — AP8

1960, Nov. 19
C28 AP8 13fr rose lil, vio, & yel grn 3.50 2.40

Telstar Issue
Common Design Type
1962, Dec. 5 **Perf. 13**
C29 CD111 50fr red lil, mar & vio bl 11.50 8.00

Tahitian Dancer — AP10

1964, May 14 **Photo.** **Perf. 13**
C30 AP10 15fr multicolored 4.75 2.00

Map of Tahiti and Free French Emblems — AP11

1964, July 10 **Unwmk.**
C31 AP11 16fr multicolored 15.00 9.00

Issued to commemorate the rallying of French Polynesia to the Free French cause.

Moorea Scene — AP12

1964, Dec. 1   Litho.   Perf. 13
C32 AP12 23fr multicolored   9.50   4.00

ITU Issue
Common Design Type

1965, May 17   Engr.   Perf. 13
C33 CD120 50fr vio, red brn
              & bl   80.00 52.50

Paul Gauguin — AP13

Design: 25fr, Gauguin Museum (stylized).
40fr, Primitive statues at Gauguin Museum.

1965   Engr.   Perf. 13
C34 AP13 25fr olive green   7.50   4.50
C35 AP13 40fr blue green   15.00   8.00
C36 AP13 75fr brt red brown   20.00 15.00
     Nos. C34-C36 (3)   42.50 27.50

Opening of Gauguin Museum, Papeete.
Issued: 25fr, 75fr, 6/13. 40fr, 11/7.

Skin Diver with Spear Gun — AP14

1965, Sept. 1   Engr.   Perf. 13
C37 AP14 50fr red brn, dl bl
              & dk grn   90.00 55.00
World Championships in Underwater Fish-
ing, Tuamotu Archipelago, Sept. 1965.

Painting from a
School Dining
Room — AP15

1965, Nov. 29
C38 AP15 80fr brn, bl, dl bl &
              red   22.50 17.50
School Canteen Program.

Radio Tower,
Globe and
Palm — AP16

1965, Dec. 29   Engr.   Perf. 13
C39 AP16 60fr org, grn & dk
              brn   19.00 15.00
50th anniversary of the first radio link
between Tahiti and France.

French Satellite A-1 Issue
Common Design Type

Designs: 7fr, Diamant Rocket and launching
installations. 10fr, A-1 satellite.

1966, Feb. 7
C40 CD121 7fr choc, dp grn
                & lil   6.75   6.00
C41 CD121 10fr lil, dp grn &
                dk brn   6.75   6.00
   a.   Pair, #C40-C41 + label 14.00 14.00

French Satellite D-1 Issue
Common Design Type

1966, May 10   Engr.   Perf. 13
C42 CD122 20fr multicolored   7.00   4.75

Papeete Harbor — AP17

1966, June 30   Photo.   Perf. 13
C43 AP17 50fr multicolored   15.00 11.00

"Vive Tahiti" by A. Benichou — AP18

1966, Nov. 28   Photo.   Perf. 13
C44 AP18 13fr multicolored   11.00   6.50

Explorer's Ship and Canoe — AP19

Designs: 60fr, Polynesian costume and
ship. 80fr, Louis Antoine de Bougainville, vert.

1968, Apr. 6   Engr.   Perf. 13
C45 AP19 40fr multicolored   8.75   3.25
C46 AP19 60fr multicolored   11.50   6.50
C47 AP19 80fr multicolored   14.50   8.75
   a.   Souv. sheet, #C45-C47 160.00 160.00
     Nos. C45-C47 (3)   34.75 18.50

200th anniv. of the discovery of Tahiti by
Louis Antoine de Bougainville.
Issued: 40fr, 4/6/68.

The Meal, by Paul Gauguin — AP20

1968, July 30   Photo.   Perf. 12x12½
C48 AP20 200fr multicolored   40.00 32.50
See #C63-C67, C78-C82, C89-C93, C98.

Shot Put — AP21

PATA 1970
Poster — AP22

1968, Oct. 12   Engr.   Perf. 13
C49 AP21 35fr dk car rose &
              brt grn   16.00   9.00
19th Olympic Games, Mexico City, 10/12-27.

Concorde Issue
Common Design Type

1969, Apr. 17
C50 CD129 40fr red brn & car
                rose   55.00 35.00

1969, July 9   Photo.   Perf. 12½x13
C51 AP22 25fr blue & multi   17.50   7.25
Issued to publicize PATA 1970 (Pacific Area
Travel Association Congress), Tahiti.

Underwater Fishing — AP23

52fr, Hand holding fish made up of flags,
vert.

1969, Aug. 5   Photo.   Perf. 13
C52 AP23 48fr blk, grnsh bl &
              red lil   35.00 13.50
C53 AP23 52fr bl, blk & red   40.00 22.50
Issued to publicize the World Underwater
Fishing Championships.

Gen. Bonaparte as Commander of the
Army in Italy, by Jean Sebastien
Rouillard — AP24

1969, Oct. 15   Photo.   Perf. 12½x12
C54 AP24 100fr car & multi   80.00 67.50
Bicentenary of the birth of Napoleon Bona-
parte (1769-1821).

Eiffel Tower, Torii
and EXPO
Emblem — AP25

Pearl Diver
Descending, and
Basket — AP26

Design: 30fr, Mount Fuji, Tower of the Sun
and EXPO emblem, horiz.

1970, Sept. 15   Photo.   Perf. 13
C55 AP25 30fr multicolored   20.00   8.00
C56 AP25 50fr multicolored   27.50 12.00
EXPO '70 International Exposition, Osaka,
Japan, Mar. 15-Sept. 13.

1970, Sept. 30   Engr.   Perf. 13
Designs: 5fr, Diver collecting oysters. 18fr,
Implantation into oyster, horiz. 27fr, Open oyster with pearl. 50fr, Woman with mother of
pearl jewelry.

C57 AP26 2fr slate, grnsh bl
               & red brn   1.50   .90
C58 AP26 5fr grnsh blue, ul-
               tra & org   2.75   1.50
C59 AP26 18fr sl, mag & org   3.75   2.75
C60 AP26 27fr brt pink, brn &
               dl lil   9.25   4.75
C61 AP26 50fr gray, red brn &
               org   16.00   7.50
     Nos. C57-C61 (5)   33.25 17.40

Pearl industry of French Polynesia.

The Thinker, by Auguste Rodin and
Education Year Emblem — AP27

1970, Oct. 15   Engr.   Perf. 13
C62 AP27 50fr bl, ind & fawn 17.00 10.50
International Education Year.

Painting Type of 1968

Paintings by Artists Living in Polynesia: 20fr,
Woman on the Beach, by Yves de Saint-Front.
40fr, Abstract, by Frank Fay. 60fr, Woman and
Shells, by Jean Guillois. 80fr, Hut under
Palms, by Jean Masson. 100fr, Polynesian
Girl, by Jean-Charles Bouloc, vert.

Perf. 12x12½, 12½x12
1970, Dec. 14   Photo.
C63 AP20 20fr brn & multi   8.00   4.00
C64 AP20 40fr brn & multi   12.00   7.50
C65 AP20 60fr brn & multi   16.00 11.00
C66 AP20 80fr brn & multi   20.00 16.00
C67 AP20 100fr brn & multi   26.00 22.50
     Nos. C63-C67 (5)   82.00 61.00

South Pacific Games Emblem — AP28

1971, Jan. 26   *Perf. 12½*
C68 AP28 20fr ultra & multi   8.00   5.00
Publicity for 4th South Pacific Games, held in Papeete, Sept. 8-19, 1971.

Memorial Flame — AP29

1971, Mar. 19   Photo.   *Perf. 12½*
C69 AP29 5fr multicolored   8.00   5.00
In memory of Charles de Gaulle.

Soldier and Badge — AP30

1971, Apr. 21
C70 AP30 25fr multicolored   11.00   6.75
30th anniversary of departure of Tahitian volunteers to serve in World War II.

Water Sports Type

Designs: 15fr, Surfing, vert. 16fr, Skin diving, vert. 20fr, Water-skiing with kite.

1971, May 11   Photo.   *Perf. 13*
C71 A44 15fr multicolored   6.50   3.50
C72 A44 16fr multicolored   7.50   3.25
C73 A44 20fr multicolored   11.00   7.75
   Nos. C71-C73 (3)   25.00   14.50

Sailing AP31

1971, Sept. 8   *Perf. 12½*
C74 AP31 15fr shown   6.50   3.50
C75 AP31 18fr Golf   8.00   4.75
C76 AP31 27fr Archery   12.00   7.25
C77 AP31 53fr Tennis   20.00   13.50
  a. Souv. sheet, #C74-C77   190.00   190.00
   Nos. C74-C77 (4)   46.50   29.00
4th So. Pacific Games, Papeete, Sept. 8-19.

Painting Type of 1968

Paintings by Artists Living in Polynesia: 20fr, Hut and Palms, by Isabelle Wolf. 40fr, Palms on Shore, by André Dobrowolski. 60fr, Polynesian Woman, by Françoise Séli, vert. 80fr, Holy Family, by Pierre Heymann, vert. 100fr, Crowd, by Nicolai Michoutouchkine.

1971, Dec. 15   Photo.   *Perf. 13*
C78 AP20 20fr multicolored   7.50   4.50
C79 AP20 40fr multicolored   11.00   7.50
C80 AP20 60fr multicolored   13.00   10.00
C81 AP20 80fr multicolored   18.00   12.50
C82 AP20 100fr multicolored   30.00   22.50
   Nos. C78-C82 (5)   79.50   57.00

Papeete Harbor — AP32

1972, Jan. 13
C83 AP32 28fr violet & multi   11.00   8.00
Free port of Papeete, 10th anniversary.

Figure Skating and Dragon AP33

1972, Jan. 25   Engr.   *Perf. 13*
C84 AP33 20fr ultra, lake & brt grn   9.00   7.00
11th Winter Olympic Games, Sapporo, Japan, Feb. 3-13.

South Pacific Commission Headquarters, Noumea — AP34

1972, Feb. 5   Photo.   *Perf. 13*
C85 AP34 21fr blue & multi   11.00   5.25
South Pacific Commission, 25th anniv.

Festival Emblem — AP35

1972, May 9   Engr.   *Perf. 13*
C86 AP35 36fr orange, bl & grn   8.00   5.25
So. Pacific Festival of Arts, Fiji, May 6-20.

Kon Tiki and Route, Callao to Tahiti — AP36

1972, Aug. 18   Photo.   *Perf. 13*
C87 AP36 16fr dk & lt bl, blk & org   10.00   6.50
25th anniversary of the arrival of the raft Kon Tiki in Tahiti.

Charles de Gaulle and Memorial — AP37

1972, Dec. 9   Engr.   *Perf. 13*
C88 AP37 100fr slate   62.50   42.50

Painting Type of 1968

Paintings by Artists Living in Polynesia: 20fr, Horses, by Georges Bovy. 40fr, Sailboats, by Ruy Juventin, vert. 60fr, Harbor, by André Brooke. 80fr, Farmers, by Daniel Adam, vert. 100fr, Dancers, by Aloysius Pilioko, vert.

1972, Dec. 14   **Photo.**
C89 AP20 20fr gold & multi   9.75   4.25
C90 AP20 40fr gold & multi   12.00   6.75
C91 AP20 60fr gold & multi   21.00   9.50
C92 AP20 80fr dk grn, buff & dk brn   27.50   13.00
C93 AP20 100fr gold & multi   32.50   25.00
   Nos. C89-C93 (5)   102.75   58.50

St. Teresa and Lisieux Basilica AP38

1973, Jan. 23   Engr.   *Perf. 13*
C94 AP38 85fr multicolored   25.00   17.50
Centenary of the birth of St. Teresa of Lisieux (1873-1897), Carmelite nun.

Nicolaus Copernicus — AP39

1973, Mar. 7   Engr.   *Perf. 13*
C95 AP39 100fr brn, vio bl & red lil   30.00   17.50
Copernicus (1473-1543), Polish astronomer.

Plane over Tahiti — AP40

1973, Apr. 3   Photo.   *Perf. 13*
C96 AP40 80fr ultra, gold & lt grn   22.50   16.00
Air France's World Tour via Tahiti.

DC-10 at Papeete Airport — AP41

1973, May 18   Engr.   *Perf. 13*
C97 AP41 20fr bl, ultra & sl grn   16.00   9.00
Start of DC-10 service.

Painting Type of 1968

Design: 200fr, "Ta Matete" (seated women), by Paul Gauguin.

1973, June 7   Photo.   *Perf. 13*
C98 AP20 200fr multicolored   27.50   20.00
Paul Gauguin (1848-1903), painter.

Pierre Loti and Characters from his Books — AP42

1973, July 4   Engr.   *Perf. 13*
C99 AP42 60fr multicolored   40.00   20.00
Pierre Loti (1850-1923), French naval officer and writer.

Woman with Flowers, by Eliane de Gennes AP43

Paintings by Artists Living in Polynesia: 20fr, Sun, by Jean Francois Favre. 60fr, Seascape, by Alain Sidet. 80fr, Crowded Bus, by Francois Ravello. 100fr, Stylized Boats, by Jackie Bourdin, horiz.

1973, Dec. 13   Photo.   *Perf. 13*
C100 AP43 20fr gold & multi   8.00   2.75
C101 AP43 40fr gold & multi   11.50   6.00
C102 AP43 60fr gold & multi   17.00   10.50
C103 AP43 80fr gold & multi   22.50   17.00
C104 AP43 100fr gold & multi   27.50   20.00
   Nos. C100-C104 (5)   86.50   56.25

Bird, Fish, Flower and Water — AP44

Catamaran under Sail — AP45

1974, June 12   Photo.   Perf. 13
C105 AP44 12fr blue & multi   7.50   5.25
Nature protection.

1974, July 22   Engr.   Perf. 13
C106 AP45 100fr multicolored   27.50 16.00
2nd Catamaran World Championships.

Still-life, by Rosine Temarui-Masson — AP46

Paintings by Artists Living in Polynesia: 40fr, Palms and House on Beach, by Marcel Chardon. 60fr, Man, by Marie-Françoise Avril. 80fr, Polynesian Woman, by Henriette Robin. 100fr, Lagoon by Moon-light, by David Farsi, horiz.

1974, Dec. 12   Photo.   Perf. 13
C107 AP46 20fr gold & multi   18.00   8.50
C108 AP46 40fr gold & multi   27.50   9.50
C109 AP46 60fr gold & multi   32.50 12.00
C110 AP46 80fr gold & multi   45.00 16.50
C111 AP46 100fr gold & multi   65.00 27.50
   Nos. C107-C111 (5)   188.00 74.00
See Nos. C122-C126.

Polynesian Gods of Travel — AP47

Designs: 75fr, Tourville hydroplane, 1929. 100fr, Passengers leaving plane.

1975, Feb. 7   Engr.   Perf. 13
C112 AP47 50fr sep, pur &
               brn   11.00   6.00
C113 AP47 75fr grn, bl & red   16.00   8.00
C114 AP47 100fr grn, sep &
               car   25.00 15.00
   Nos. C112-C114 (3)   52.00 29.00
Fifty years of Tahitian aviation.

French Ceres Stamp and Woman — AP48

1975, May 29   Engr.   Perf. 13
C115 AP48 32fr ver, brn & blk   8.00   5.00
ARPHILA 75 International Philatelic Exhibition, Paris, June 6-16.

Shot Put and Games' Emblem AP50

1975, Aug. 1   Photo.   Perf. 13
C117 AP50 25fr shown   4.75   3.00
C118 AP50 30fr Volleyball   7.00   3.75
C119 AP50 40fr Women's
               swimming   9.25   5.25
   Nos. C117-C119 (3)   21.00 12.00
5th South Pacific Games, Guam, Aug. 1-10.

Flowers, Athlete, View of Montreal — AP51

1975, Oct. 15   Engr.   Perf. 13
C120 AP51 44fr brt bl, ver & blk 11.00 6.50
Pre-Olympic Year 1975.

UPU Emblem, Jet and Letters — AP52

1975, Nov. 5   Engr.   Perf. 13
C121 AP52 100fr brn, bl & ol   22.50 13.00
World Universal Postal Union Day.

Paintings Type of 1974

Paintings by Artists Living in Polynesia: 20fr, Beach Scene, by R. Marcel Marius, horiz. 40fr, Roofs with TV antennas, by M. Anglade, horiz. 60fr, Street scene with bus, by J. Day, horiz. 80fr, Tropical waters (fish), by J. Steimetz. 100fr, Women, by A. van der Heyde.

1975, Dec. 17   Litho.   Perf. 13
C122 AP46 20fr gold & multi   3.00   1.75
C123 AP46 40fr gold & multi   6.00   3.00
C124 AP46 60fr gold & multi   9.00   4.50
C125 AP46 80fr gold & multi   12.00   7.50
C126 AP46 100fr gold & multi 14.50 12.00
   Nos. C122-C126 (5)   44.50 28.75

Concorde — AP53

1976, Jan. 21   Engr.   Perf. 13
C127 AP53 100fr car, bl & ind 19.00 13.00
First commercial flight of supersonic jet Concorde from Paris to Rio, Jan. 21.

Adm. Rodney, Count de la Perouse, "Barfleur" and "Triomphant" in Battle — AP54

31fr, Count de Grasse and Lord Graves, "Ville de Paris" & "Le Terible" in Chesapeake Bay Battle.

1976, Apr. 15   Engr.   Perf. 13
C128 AP54 24fr grnsh bl, lt brn &
               blk   5.00   2.50
C129 AP54 31fr mag, red & lt brn 5.75 3.50
American Bicentennial.

King Pomaré I — AP55

Portraits: 21fr, King Pomaré II. 26fr, Queen Pomaré IV. 30fr, King Pomaré V.

1976, Apr. 28   Litho.   Perf. 12½
C130 AP55 18fr olive & multi   1.75   .75
C131 AP55 21fr multicolored   2.00   1.10
C132 AP55 26fr gray & multi   2.75   1.25
C133 AP55 30fr plum & multi   3.00   1.90
   Nos. C130-C133 (4)   9.50   5.00
Pomaré Dynasty. See Nos. C141-C144.

Running and Maple Leaf — AP56

Designs: 34fr, Long jump, vert. 50fr, Olympic flame and flowers.

1976, July 19   Engr.   Perf. 13
C134 AP56 26fr ultra & multi   4.25   2.10
C135 AP56 34fr ultra & multi   6.00   2.75
C136 AP56 50fr ultra & multi 11.50   5.00
   a.   Min. sheet, #C134-C136 90.00 90.00
   Nos. C134-C136 (3)   21.75   9.85
21st Olympic Games, Montreal, Canada, July 17-Aug. 1.

The Dream, by Paul Gauguin — AP57

1976, Oct. 17   Photo.   Perf. 13
C137 AP57 50fr multicolored   11.00   7.25

Murex Steeriae — AP58

Pocillopora AP59

Sea Shells: 27fr, Conus Gauguini. 35fr, Conus marchionatus.

1977, Mar. 14   Photo.   Perf. 12½x13
C138 AP58 25fr vio bl & multi 4.25   1.25
C139 AP58 27fr ultra & multi   4.25   1.50
C140 AP58 35fr blue & multi   5.00   2.00
   Nos. C138-C140 (3)   13.50   4.75
See Nos. C156-C158.

Royalty Type of 1976

19fr, King Maputeoa, Mangareva. 33fr, King Camatoa V, Raiatea. 39fr, Queen Vaekehu, Marquesas. 43fr, King Teurarii III, Rurutu.

1977, Apr. 19   Litho.   Perf. 12½
C141 AP55 19fr dull red & multi 1.25   .95
C142 AP55 33fr dk blue & multi   1.90   1.25
C143 AP55 39fr ultra & multi   1.90   1.25
C144 AP55 43fr green & multi   2.75   1.90
   Nos. C141-C144 (4)   7.80   5.35
Polynesian rulers.

Perf. 13x12½, 12½x13
1977, May 23   Photo.

Design: 25fr, Acropora, horiz.

C145 AP59 25fr multicolored   1.90   1.10
C146 AP59 33fr multicolored   2.75   1.90
3rd Symposium on Coral Reefs, Miami, Fla. See Nos. C162-C163.

De Gaulle Memorial — AP60

Tahitian Dancer — AP61

Photogravure and Embossed
1977, June 18 **Perf. 13**
C147 AP60 40fr gold & multi 7.00 5.00
5th anniversary of dedication of De Gaulle memorial at Colombey-les-Deux-Eglises.

1977, July 14 **Litho.** **Perf. 12½**
C148 AP61 27fr multicolored 4.00 2.50

Charles A. Lindbergh and Spirit of St. Louis — AP62

1977, Aug. 18 **Litho.** **Perf. 12½**
C149 AP62 28fr multicolored 7.00 3.50
Lindbergh's solo transatlantic flight from New York to Paris, 50th anniv.

Mahoe — AP63

Palms on Shore — AP64

1977, Sept. 15 **Photo.** **Perf. 12½x13**
C150 AP63 8fr shown 1.40 .80
C151 AP63 12fr Frangipani 1.75 1.25

1977, Nov. 8 **Photo.** **Perf. 12½x13**
C152 AP64 32fr multicolored 10.00 4.50
Ecology, protection of trees.

Rubens' Son Albert AP65

1977, Nov. 28 **Engr.** **Perf. 13**
C153 AP65 100fr grnsh blk & rose cl 11.00 8.00
Peter Paul Rubens (1577-1640), painter, 400th birth anniversary.

Capt. Cook and "Discovery" — AP66

Design: 39fr, Capt. Cook and "Resolution."

1978, Jan. 20 **Engr.** **Perf. 13**
C154 AP66 33fr multicolored 2.50 3.00
C155 AP66 39fr multicolored 3.00 3.50
Bicentenary of Capt. James Cook's arrival in Hawaii.
For overprints see Nos. C166-C167.

Shell Type of 1977
Sea Shells: 22fr, Erosaria obvelata. 24fr, Cypraea ventriculus. 31fr, Lambis robusta.

1978, Apr. 13 **Photo.** **Perf. 13½x13**
C156 AP58 22fr brt blue & multi 2.25 1.25
C157 AP58 24fr brt blue & multi 2.25 1.50
C158 AP58 31fr brt blue & multi 3.50 2.50
Nos. C156-C158 (3) 8.00 5.25

Tahitian Woman and Boy, by Gauguin AP67

1978, May 7 **Perf. 13**
C159 AP67 50fr multicolored 8.75 5.25
Paul Gauguin (1848-1903).

Antenna and ITU Emblem AP68

1978, May 17 **Litho.** **Perf. 13**
C160 AP68 80fr gray & multi 6.00 3.25
10th World Telecommunications Day.

Soccer and Argentina '78 Emblem — AP69

1978, June 1
C161 AP69 28fr multicolored 3.25 2.10
11th World Cup Soccer Championship, Argentina, June 1-25.

Coral Type of 1977
Designs: 26fr, Fungia, horiz. 34fr, Millepora.

Perf. 13x12½, 12½x13
1978, July 13 **Photo.**
C162 AP59 26fr multicolored 1.75 1.25
C163 AP59 34fr multicolored 2.25 1.60

Radar Antenna, Polynesian Woman — AP70

1978, Sept. 5 **Engr.** **Perf. 13**
C164 AP70 50fr blue & black 3.00 1.75
Papenoo earth station.

Bird and Rainbow over Island — AP71

1978, Oct. 5 **Photo.**
C165 AP71 23fr multicolored 6.00 1.75
Nature protection.

Nos. C154-C155 Overprinted in Black or Violet Blue: "1779-1979 / BICENTENAIRE / DE LA / MORT DE"
1979, Feb. 14 **Engr.** **Perf. 13**
C166 AP66 33fr multi 4.00 2.50
C167 AP66 39fr multi (VBl) 5.00 3.50
Bicentenary of Capt. Cook's death. On No. C167 date is last line of overprint.

Children, Toys and IYC Emblem — AP72

1979, May 3 **Engr.** **Perf. 13**
C168 AP72 150fr multicolored 12.00 7.00
International Year of the Child.

"Do you expect a letter?" by Paul Gauguin — AP73

1979, May 20 **Photo.** **Perf. 13**
C169 AP73 200fr multicolored 16.00 8.00

Shell and Carved Head — AP74

1979, June 30 **Engr.** **Perf. 13**
C170 AP74 44fr multicolored 3.50 2.00
Museum of Tahiti and the Islands.

Conference Emblem over Island AP75

1979, Oct. 6 **Photo.** **Perf. 13**
C171 AP75 23fr multicolored 2.25 1.10
19th South Pacific Conf., Tahiti, Oct. 6-12.

Flying Boat "Bermuda" — AP76

Planes Used in Polynesia: 40fr, DC-4 over Papeete. 60fr, Britten-Norman "Islander." 80fr, Fairchild F-27A. 120fr, DC-8 over Tahiti.

1979, Dec. 19 **Litho.** **Perf. 13**
C172 AP76 24fr multicolored 1.00 .50
C173 AP76 40fr multicolored 1.75 1.00
C174 AP76 60fr multicolored 2.75 1.50
C175 AP76 80fr multicolored 3.50 2.25
C176 AP76 120fr multicolored 6.00 3.00
Nos. C172-C176 (5) 15.00 8.25
See Nos. C180-C183.

Window on Tahiti, by Henri Matisse AP77

1980, Feb. 18 **Photo.**
C177 AP77 150fr multicolored 8.00 5.00

Marshi Metua No Tehamana, by Gauguin AP78

1980, Aug. 24 **Photo.** **Perf. 13**
C178 AP78 500fr multicolored 18.00 13.00

Sydpex '80, Philatelic Exhibition, Sydney Town Hall — AP79

1980, Sept. 29 **Photo.** **Perf. 13**
C179 AP79 70fr multicolored 8.00 5.25

Aviation Type of 1979

1980, Dec. 15   Litho.   Perf. 13

C180	AP76	15fr Catalina	.75	.55
C181	AP76	26fr Twin Otter	1.00	.70
C182	AP76	30fr CAMS 55	1.25	.90
C183	AP76	50fr DC-6	2.00	1.40
		Nos. C180-C183 (4)	5.00	3.55

And The Gold of their Bodies, by Gauguin — AP80

1981, Mar. 15   Photo.   Perf. 13

C184	AP80	100fr multicolored	4.50	2.50

20th Anniv. of Manned Space Flight AP81

1981, June 15   Litho.   Perf. 12½

C185	AP81	300fr multicolored	9.00	7.00

First Intl. Pirogue (6-man Canoe) Championship — AP82

1981, July 25   Litho.   Perf. 13x12½

C186	AP82	200fr multicolored	5.50	4.50

Matavai Bay, by William Hodges — AP83

Paintings: 60fr, Poedea, by John Weber, vert. 80fr, Omai, by Joshua Reynolds, vert. 120fr, Point Venus, by George Tobin.

1981, Dec. 10   Photo.   Perf. 13

C187	AP83	40fr multicolored	1.10	.90
C188	AP83	60fr multicolored	1.75	1.25
C189	AP83	80fr multicolored	2.75	1.75
C190	AP83	120fr multicolored	3.50	2.40
		Nos. C187-C190 (4)	9.10	6.30

See Nos. C194-C197, C202-C205.

TB Bacillus Centenary — AP84

1982, Mar. 24   Engr.   Perf. 13

C191	AP84	200fr multicolored	5.00	3.00

1982 World Cup — AP85

1982, May 18   Litho.   Perf. 13

C192	AP85	250fr multicolored	6.50	4.50

French Overseas Possessions' Week, Sept. 18-25 — AP86

1982, Sept. 17   Engr.

C193	AP86	110fr multicolored	2.75	1.65

Painting Type of 1981

Designs: 50fr, The Tahitian, by M. Radiguet, vert. 70fr, Souvenir of Tahiti, by C. Giraud. 100fr, Beating Cloth Lengths, by Atlas JL the Younger. 160fr, Papeete Harbor, by C.F. Gordon Cumming.

1982, Dec. 15   Photo.   Perf. 13

C194	AP83	50fr multicolored	1.90	1.00
C195	AP83	70fr multicolored	2.25	1.50
C196	AP83	100fr multicolored	2.75	2.00
C197	AP83	160fr multicolored	4.50	2.75
		Nos. C194-C197 (4)	11.40	7.25

Wood Cutter, by Gauguin AP87

Photo. & Engr.

1983, May 8   Perf. 12½x13

C198	AP87	600fr multicolored	16.00	8.00

Voyage of Capt. Bligh — AP88

1983, June 9   Litho.   Perf. 13

C199	AP88	200fr Map, fruit	6.00	3.00

BRASILIANA '83 Intl. Stamp Exhibition, Rio de Janeiro, July 29-Aug. 7 — AP89

1983, July 29   Litho.   Perf. 13x12½

C200	AP89	100fr multicolored	2.50	1.75
a.		Souvenir sheet	3.50	3.50

1983, Aug. 4   Litho.   Perf. 13x12½

C201	AP89	110fr Bangkok '83	3.00	2.00
a.		Souvenir sheet	4.00	4.00

Painting Type of 1981

20th Cent. Paintings: 40fr, View of Moorea, by William Alister MacDonald (1861-1956). 60fr, The Fruit Carrier, by Adrian Herman Gouwe (1875-1965). 80fr, Arrival of the Destroyer Escort, by Nicolas Mordvinoff (1911-1977). 100fr, Women on a Veranda, by Charles Alfred Le Moine (1872-1918).

1983, Dec. 22   Photo.   Perf. 13

C202	AP83	40fr multi	1.00	.75
C203	AP83	60fr multi, vert.	1.50	1.00
C204	AP83	80fr multi, vert.	1.60	1.25
C205	AP83	100fr multi	2.00	1.60
		Nos. C202-C205 (4)	6.10	4.60

ESPANA '84 — AP90

Design: Maori canoers.

1984, Apr. 27   Engr.   Perf. 13

C206	AP90	80fr brn red & dk bl	2.25	1.50

Souvenir Sheet

C207	AP90	200fr dk bl & dk red	7.25	7.25

Woman with Mango, by Gauguin AP91

Photo. & Engr.

1984, May 27   Perf. 12½x13

C208	AP91	400fr multicolored	11.00	6.00

Ausipex '84 — AP92

Details from Human Sacrifice of the Maori in Tahiti, 18th cent. engraving.

1984, Sept. 5   Litho.   Perf. 13x12½

C209	AP92	120fr Worshippers	3.00	2.25
C210	AP92	120fr Preparation	3.00	2.25
a.		Pair, #C209-C210 + label	7.50	7.50

Souvenir Sheet

C211	AP92	200fr Entire	9.50	9.50

Painting by Gauguin (1848-1903) — AP93

Design: Where have we come from? What are we? Where are we going? Illustration reduced.

1985, Mar. 17   Litho.   Perf. 13½x13

C212	AP93	550fr multi	14.00	7.50

4th Pacific Arts Festival Type

1985, July 3   Litho.   Perf. 13

C213	A95	200fr Islander, tiki, artifacts	4.50	3.00

Intl. Youth Year — AP95

1985, Sept. 18   Litho.

C214	AP95	250fr Island youths, frigate bird	5.50	3.25

ITALIA '85 — AP96

Designs: Ship sailing into Papeete Harbor, 19th century print.

1985, Oct. 22   Engr.

C215	AP96	130fr multicolored	2.75	2.50

Souvenir Sheet

C216	AP96	240fr multicolored	7.50	7.50

1st Intl. Marlin Fishing Contest, Feb. 27-Mar. 5 — AP97

1986, Feb. 27   Litho.   Perf. 12½

C217	AP97	300fr multicolored	6.50	4.00

Arrival of a Boat, c.1880 — AP98

1986, June 24   Engr.   Perf. 13
C218 AP98 400fr intense blue   8.75 5.25

STOCKHOLMIA '86 — AP99

Design: Dr. Karl Solander and Anders Sparrmann, Swedish scientists who accompanied Capt. Cook, and map of Tahiti.

1986, Aug. 28   Engr.   Perf. 13
C219 AP99 150fr multicolored   3.25 2.25

Souvenir Sheet
C220 AP99 210fr multicolored   4.75 4.75

Protestant Churches — AP100

1986, Dec. 17   Litho.   Perf. 13
C221 AP100 80fr Tiva, 1955   1.75   .90
C222 AP100 200fr Avera, 1880   4.50 2.10
C223 AP100 300fr Papetoai,
              1822   6.50 3.25
    Nos. C221-C223 (3)   12.75 6.25

Broche Barracks, 120th Anniv. — AP101

1987, Apr. 21   Litho.   Perf. 12½x12
C224 AP101 350fr multicolored   7.75 5.00

CAPEX '87 — AP102

Design: George Vancouver (1757-1798), English navigator and cartographer, chart and excerpt from ship's log.

1987, June 15   Engr.   Perf. 13
C225 AP102 130fr multi   2.90 2.25

Imperf
Size: 143x100mm
C226 AP102 260fr multicolored   5.75 5.75

Soyez Mysterieuses, from a 5-Panel Sculpture by Paul Gauguin, Gauguin Museum — AP103

Illustration reduced.

1987, Nov. 15   Perf. 13
C227 AP103 600fr multicolored 14.00 9.50

AIR POST SEMI-POSTAL STAMPS

> **Catalogue values for unused stamps in this section are for Never Hinged items.**

French Revolution Issue
Common Design Type
Unwmk.
1939, July 5   Photo.   Perf. 13
Name and Value Typo. in Orange
CB1 CD83 5fr + 4fr brn blk   35.00 35.00

Mother & Children on Beach — SPAP1

Perf. 12½x13½
1942, June 22   Engr.
CB2 SPAP1 1.50fr + 3.50fr green 2.00
CB3 SPAP1 2fr + 6fr yellow
              brown   2.00

Native children's welfare fund.
Nos. CB2-CB3 were issued by the Vichy government in France, but were not placed on sale in French Polynesia.

Colonial Education Fund
Common Design Type
1942, June 22
CB4 CD86a 1.20fr + 1.80fr blue
              & red   2.00

No. CB4 was issued by the Vichy government in France, but was not placed on sale in French Polynesia.

POSTAGE DUE STAMPS

Postage Due Stamps of French Colonies, 1894-1906, Overprinted

1926-27   Unwmk.   Perf. 14x13½
J1 D1 5c light blue   .95   .95
J2 D1 10c brown   .95   .95
J3 D1 20c olive green   1.40 1.40
J4 D1 30c dull red   1.40 1.50
J5 D1 40c rose   3.00 3.25
J6 D1 60c blue green   3.00 3.25
J7 D1 1fr red brown, straw 3.00 3.25
J8 D1 3fr magenta ('27)   14.00 17.00

With Additional Surcharge of New Value
J9 D1 2fr on 1fr orange red 4.00 4.75
    Nos. J1-J9 (9)   31.70 36.30

Fautaua Falls, Tahiti — D2   Tahitian Youth — D3

1929   Typo.   Perf. 13½x14
J10 D2 5c lt blue & dk brn   .70   .70
J11 D2 10c vermilion & grn   .70   .70
J12 D2 30c dk brn & dk red   1.60 1.60
J13 D2 50c yel grn & dk brn 1.40 1.40
J14 D2 60c dl vio & yel grn 3.50 3.75
J15 D3 1fr Prus bl & red vio 3.00 3.25
J16 D3 2fr brn red & dk brn 1.90 2.10
J17 D3 3fr bl vio & bl grn   2.10 2.40
    Nos. J10-J17 (8)   14.90 15.90

> **Catalogue values for unused stamps in this section, from this point to the end of the section, are for Never Hinged items.**

D4   Polynesian Club — D5

1948   Engr.   Perf. 14x13
J18 D4 10c brt blue grn   .40   .25
J19 D4 30c black brown   .40   .25
J20 D4 50c dk car rose   .50   .30
J21 D4 1fr ultra   .65   .50
J22 D4 2fr dk blue green   .95   .70
J23 D4 3fr red   1.90 1.40
J24 D4 4fr violet   2.00 1.60
J25 D4 5fr lilac rose   3.00 2.10
J26 D4 10fr slate   4.00 3.00
J27 D4 20fr red brown   5.50 4.25
    Nos. J18-J27 (10)   19.30 14.35

1958   Unwmk.   Perf. 14x13
J28 D5 1fr brn & grn   .65   .65
J29 D5 3fr bluish blk & hn brn .90   .90
J30 D5 5fr brown & ultra   1.10 1.10
    Nos. J28-J30 (3)   2.65 2.65

Tahitian Bowl — D6

1984-87   Litho.   Perf. 13
J31 D6 1fr Mother-of-pearl fish
              hook, vert.   .25   .25
J32 D6 3fr shown   .25   .25
J33 D6 5fr Marquesan fan   .25   .25
J34 D6 10fr Lamp stand, vert. .40   .40
J35 D6 20fr Wood headrest ('87) .55   .55
J36 D6 50fr Wood scoop ('87) 1.25 1.25
    Nos. J31-J36 (6)   2.95 2.95

Issued: #J31-34, 3/15; #J35-J36, 8/18.

OFFICIAL STAMPS

> **Catalogue values for unused stamps in this section are for Never Hinged items.**

Breadfruit O1

Polynesian Fruits: 2fr, 3fr, 5fr, like 1fr. 7fr, 8fr, 10fr, 15fr, "Vi Tahiti." 19fr, 20fr, 25fr, 35fr, Avocados. 50fr, 100fr, 200fr, Mangos.

1977, June 9   Litho.   Perf. 12½
O1 O1 1fr ultra & multi   .40   .65
O2 O1 2fr ultra & multi   .40   .65
O3 O1 3fr ultra & multi   .40   .65
O4 O1 5fr ultra & multi   .40   .65
O5 O1 7fr red & multi   .65   .95
O6 O1 8fr red & multi   .65   .95
O7 O1 10fr red & multi   .95 1.25
O8 O1 15fr red & multi   1.40 1.60
O9 O1 19fr black & multi 1.60 2.00
O10 O1 20fr black & multi 1.75 2.40
O11 O1 25fr black & multi 2.40 2.75
O12 O1 35fr black & multi 3.00 3.50
O13 O1 50fr black & multi 3.00 3.50
O14 O1 100fr red & multi 7.00 8.00
O15 O1 200fr red & multi 13.00 16.00
    Nos. O1-O15 (15)   37.00 45.50

1982-86   Perf. 13
O1a O1 1fr ultra & multi   .70 1.25
O2a O1 2fr ultra & multi   .70 1.25
O3a O1 3fr ultra & multi   .95 1.25
O4a O1 5fr ultra & multi   2.00 2.40
O5a O1 7fr red & multi   2.10 2.50
O6a O1 8fr red & multi   3.00 3.50
O7a O1 10fr red & multi   3.25 3.50
O8a O1 15fr red & multi
              ('84)   3.25 3.50
O10a O1 20fr black & multi 3.25 3.50
O11a O1 25fr black & multi
              ('84)   3.25 3.50
O12a O1 35fr black & multi
              ('84)   8.00 10.50
O13a O1 50fr black & multi
              ('84)   17.00 22.50
O14a O1 100fr red & multi
              ('86)   47.50 60.00
O15a O1 200fr red & multi
              ('86)   65.00 80.00
    Nos. O1a-O15a (14)   159.95 199.15

Nos. O1-O15 have dull finish (matte) gum.
Nos. O1a-O15a have shiny gum.

Stamps and Postmarks — O2

1fr, French Colonies #5. 2fr, French Colonies #27, #12. 3fr, French Colonies #29, 1884 Papeete postmark. 5fr, Newspaper franked with surcharge of Tahiti #2, 1884 Papeete postmark. 9fr, #176. 10fr, #4, 1894 octagonal postmark. 20fr, #6, #8. 46fr, #48. 51fr, #147-148, Vaitepaua-Makatea Island postmark. 70fr, Visit Tahiti postmark on postal card piece. 85fr, #59 with 1921 manuscript cancel, vert. 100fr, #181. 200fr, #C21, 1st day cancel.

Perf. 13¼, 13¼x13 (#O20), 13x13¼ (#O26)

1993-99   Litho.
O16 O2 1fr multicolored   .25   .40
  a. Perf. 13¼x13 ('98)   8.00 9.50
O17 O2 2fr multicolored   .25   .40
  a. Perf. 13¼x13 ('97)   .80 1.25
O18 O2 3fr multicolored   .25   .40
  a. Perf. 13¼x13 ('98)   8.00 9.50
O19 O2 5fr multicolored   .30   .55
  a. Perf. 13¼x13 ('97)   .80 1.25
O20 O2 9fr multicolored   .80 1.25
O21 O2 10fr multicolored   .30   .55
  a. Perf. 13¼x13 ('99)   8.00 9.50
O22 O2 20fr multicolored   .65   .95
  a. Perf. 13¼x13 ('99)   .75   .75
O23 O2 46fr multicolored   1.40 1.60
O24 O2 51fr multicolored   2.40 3.25
O25 O2 70fr multicolored   2.25 2.75
  a. Perf. 13¼x13 ('97)   5.25 6.50
O26 O2 85fr multicolored   2.40 3.25
O27 O2 100fr multicolored 2.75 3.50
  a. Perf. 13¼x13 ('99)   1.90 1.90
O28 O2 200fr multicolored 5.25 6.50
  a. Perf. 13¼x13 ('97)   4.50 4.50
    Nos. O16-O28 (13)   19.25 25.35

Issued: 51fr, 4/6/94; 9fr, 85fr, 4/21/97; others, 1/13/93.

FRENCH SOUTHERN & ANTARCTIC TERRITORY

'french 'sə-thərn and
,ant-ärk-tik 'ter-ə-'tōr-ēs

POP. — 130 staff

Formerly dependencies of Madagascar, these areas, comprising the Kerguelen Archipelago; St. Paul, Amsterdam and Crozet Islands and Adelle Land in Antarctica achieved territorial status on August 6, 1955.

100 Centimes = 1 Franc
100 Cents = 1 Euro (2002)

> Catalogue values for all unused stamps in this country are for Never Hinged items.

Madagascar No. 289 Overprinted in Red:

Unwmk.

			Perf. 13	
1955, Oct. 28		**Engr.**		
1	A25	15f dk grn & dp ultra	14.50	*29.00*

Rockhopper Penguins, Crozet Archipelago — A1

New Amsterdam A2

Design: 10fr, 15fr, Elephant seal.

			Perf. 13	
1956, Apr. 25		**Engr.**		
2	A1	50c dk blue, sepia & yel	.40	.75
3	A1	1fr ultra, org & gray	.40	.75
4	A2	5fr blue & dp ultra	2.75	*3.25*
5	A2	8fr gray vio & dk brn	17.00	*21.00*
6	A2	10fr indigo	6.25	6.25
7	A2	15fr indigo & brn vio	7.50	7.50
		Nos. 2-7 (6)	34.30	39.50

Polar Observation A3

			Perf. 13	
1957, Oct. 11				
8	A3	5fr black & violet	3.00	*5.00*
9	A3	10fr rose red	4.00	5.75
10	A3	15fr dark blue	5.00	*7.50*
		Nos. 8-10 (3)	12.00	18.25

International Geophysical Year, 1957-58.

Imperforates

Most stamps of this French possession exist imperforate in issued and trial colors, and also in small presentation sheets in issued colors.

Flower Issue
Common Design Type
Design: Pringlea, horiz.

			Perf. 12½x12	
1959		**Photo.**		
11	CD104	10fr sal, grn & yel	10.00	8.00

Common Design Types pictured following the introduction.

Light-mantled Sooty Albatross — A4   Coat of Arms — A5

Designs: 40c, Skua, horiz. 12fr, King shag.

			Perf. 13	
1959, Sept. 14		**Engr.**		
12	A4	30c blue, grn & red brn	.50	.75
13	A4	40c blk, dl red brn & bl	.50	.75
14	A4	12fr lt blue & blk	13.50	8.75
		Nos. 12-14 (3)	14.50	10.25

			Perf. 13x14	
1959, Sept. 14		**Typo.**		
15	A5	20fr ultra, lt bl & yel	18.00	11.50

Sheathbills — A6

4fr, Sea leopard, horiz. 25fr, Weddell seal at Kerguélen, horiz. 85fr, King penguin.

			Perf. 13	
1960, Dec. 15		**Engr.**		
16	A6	2fr grnsh bl, gray & choc	1.50	*2.25*
17	A6	4fr bl, dk brn & dk grn	9.00	7.50
18	A6	25fr sl grn, bis brn & blk	90.00	42.50
19	A6	85fr grnsh bl, org & blk	20.00	14.50
		Nos. 16-19 (4)	120.50	66.75

Yves-Joseph de Kerguélen-Trémarec — A7

1960, Nov. 22				
20	A7	25fr red org, dk bl & brn	27.50	22.50

Yves-Joseph de Kerguélen-Trémarec, discoverer of the Kerguélen Archipelago.

Charcot, Compass Rose and "Pourquoi-pas?" — A8

			Perf. 13	
1961, Dec. 26		**Unwmk.**		
21	A8	25fr brn, grn & red	27.50	22.50

25th anniv. of the death of Commander Jean Charcot (1867-1936), Antarctic explorer.

Elephant Seals Fighting A9

			Perf. 13	
1963, Feb. 11		**Engr.**		
22	A9	8fr dk blue, blk & claret	12.00	7.50

See No. C4.

Penguins and Camp on Crozet Island A10

20fr, Research station & IQSY emblem.

			Perf. 13	
1963, Dec. 16		**Unwmk.**		
23	A10	5fr blk, red brn & Prus bl	60.00	35.00
24	A10	20fr vio, sl & red brn	70.00	55.00

Intl. Quiet Sun Year, 1964-65. See #C6.

Great Blue Whale A11

Black-browed Albatross — A12   Aurora Australis, Map of Antarctica and Rocket — A13

10fr, Cape pigeons. 12fr, Phylica trees, Amsterdam Island. 15fr, Killer whale (orca).

			Perf. 13	
1966-69		**Engr.**		
25	A11	5fr brt bl & indigo	20.00	11.50
26	A12	10fr sl, ind & ol brn	30.00	25.00
27	A11	12fr brt bl, sl grn & lemon	21.00	14.00
27A	A11	15fr ol, dk bl & ind	12.00	7.25
28	A12	20fr slate, ol & org	350.00	225.00
		Nos. 25-28 (5)	433.00	282.75

Issued: 5fr, 12/12; 20fr, 1/3/68; 10fr, 12fr, 1/6/69; 15fr, 12/21/69.

			Perf. 13	
1967, Mar. 4		**Engr.**		
29	A13	20fr mag, blue & blk	26.00	22.50

Launching of the 1st space rocket from Adelie Land, Jan., 1967.

Dumont d'Urville A14

1968, Jan. 20				
30	A14	30fr lt ultra, dk bl & dk brn	140.00	80.00

Jules Sébastien César Dumont D'Urville (1790-1842), French naval commander and South Seas explorer.

WHO Anniversary Issue
Common Design Type

			Perf. 13	
1968, May 4				
31	CD126	30fr red, yel & bl	65.00	45.00

Human Rights Year Issue
Common Design Type

			Perf. 13	
1968, Aug. 10		**Engr.**		
32	CD127	30fr grnsh bl, red & brn	60.00	45.00

Polar Camp with Helicopter, Plane and Snocat Tractor — A15

			Perf. 13	
1969, Mar. 17		**Engr.**		
33	A15	25fr Prus bl, lt grnsh bl & brn red	25.00	15.00

20 years of French Polar expeditions.

ILO Issue
Common Design Type

			Perf. 13	
1970, Jan. 1		**Engr.**		
35	CD131	20fr org, dk bl & brn	18.50	11.00

UPU Headquarters Issue
Common Design Type

			Perf. 13	
1970, May 20		**Engr.**		
36	CD133	50fr blue, plum & ol bis	45.00	29.00

Ice Fish A16

Fish: Nos. 38-43, Antarctic cods, various species. 135fr, Zanchlorhynchus spinifer.

1971		Engr.		Perf. 13	
37	A16	5fr brt grn, ind & org		2.00	.85
38	A16	10fr redsh brn & dp vio		2.25	.95
39	A16	20fr dp cl, brt grn & org		4.50	2.10
40	A16	22fr pur, brn ol & mag		5.00	3.25
41	A16	25fr grn, ind & org		6.50	2.75
42	A16	30fr sep, gray & bl vio		8.00	4.25
43	A16	35fr sl grn, dk brn & ocher		7.00	3.25
44	A16	135fr Prus bl, dp org & ol grn		12.00	5.25
		Nos. 37-44 (8)		47.25	22.65

Issued: #37-39, 41-42, 1/1; #40, 43-44, 12/22.

Map of Antarctica A17

Microzetia Mirabilis A18

1971, Dec. 22

| 45 | A17 | 75fr red | | 28.00 | 25.00 |

Antarctic Treaty pledging peaceful uses of and scientific cooperation in Antarctica, 10th anniv.

1972

Insects: 15fr, Christiansenia dreuxi. 22f, Phtirocoris antarcticus. 30fr, Antarctophytosus atriceps. 40fr, Paractora drenxi. 140fr, Pringleophaga Kerguelenensis.

46	A18	15fr cl, org & brn		10.00	6.00
47	A18	22fr vio bl, sl grn & yel		14.50	9.25
48	A18	25fr grn, rose lil & pur		5.75	4.75
49	A18	30fr blue & multi		18.00	10.00
50	A18	40fr dk brn, ocher & blk		8.75	4.75
51	A18	140fr bl, emer & brn		12.50	8.75
		Nos. 46-51 (6)		69.50	43.50

Issued: #48, 50-51, 1/3; #46-47, 49, 12/16.

De Gaulle Issue
Common Design Type

Designs: 50fr, Gen. de Gaulle, 1940. 100fr, Pres. de Gaulle, 1970.

1972, Feb. 1		Engr.		Perf. 13	
52	CD134	50fr brt grn & blk		21.00	13.50
53	CD134	100fr brt grn & blk		26.00	20.00

Kerguelen Cabbage — A19

Designs: 61fr, Azorella selago, horiz. 87fr, Acaena ascendens, horiz.

1972-73

54	A19	45fr multicolored		10.00	5.00
55	A19	61fr multicolored		4.00	2.75
56	A19	87fr multicolored		6.00	4.00
		Nos. 54-56 (3)		20.00	11.75

Issued: 45fr, 12/18; others, 12/13/73.

Mailship Sapmer and Map of Amsterdam Island — A20

1974, Dec. 31		Engr.		Perf. 13	
57	A20	75fr bl, blk & dk brn		7.50	5.25

25th anniversary of postal service.

Antarctic Tern — A21

Designs: 50c, Antarctic petrel. 90c, Sea lioness. 1fr, Weddell seal. 1.20fr, Kerguelen cormorant, vert. 1.40fr, Gentoo penguin, vert.

1976, Jan.		Engr.		Perf. 13	
58	A21	40c multicolored		4.75	3.00
59	A21	50c multicolored		4.75	3.00
60	A21	90c multicolored		7.50	4.00
61	A21	1fr multicolored		12.00	9.25
62	A21	1.20fr multicolored		15.00	11.00
63	A21	1.40fr multicolored		14.00	11.50
		Nos. 58-63 (6)		58.00	41.75

James Clark Ross — A22

James Cook — A23

Design: 30c, Climbing Mount Ross.

1976, Dec. 16		Engr.		Perf. 13	
64	A22	30c multicolored		4.50	3.00
65	A22	3fr multicolored		5.00	3.00

First climbing of Mount Ross, Kerguelen Island, Jan. 5, 1975.

1976, Dec. 16

| 66 | A23 | 70c multicolored | | 13.50 | 10.00 |

Bicentenary of Capt. Cook's voyage past Kerguelen Island. See No. C46.

Commerson's Dolphins — A24

1977, Feb. 1		Engr.		Perf. 13	
67	A24	1.10fr Blue whale		5.75	3.25
68	A24	1.50fr shown		6.25	4.00

Macrocystis Algae — A25

Salmon Hatchery — A26

Magga Dan — A27

Designs: 70c, Durvillea algae. 90c, Albatross. 1fr, Underwater sampling and scientists, vert. 1.40fr, Thala Dan and penguins.

1977, Dec. 20		Engr.		Perf. 13	
69	A25	40c ol brn & bis		1.10	.70
70	A25	50c dk bl & pur		1.40	1.00
71	A25	70c blk, grn & brn		1.60	1.00
72	A26	90c grn, brt bl & brn		1.60	1.00
73	A27	1fr slate		1.40	1.00
74	A27	1.20fr multi		3.25	1.60
75	A27	1.40fr multi		2.00	1.60
		Nos. 69-75 (7)		12.35	7.90

See Nos. 77-79.

A28

A29

Explorer with French and Expedition Flags.

1977, Dec. 24

| 76 | A28 | 1.90fr multicolored | | 7.75 | 5.00 |

French Polar expeditions, 1947-48.

Types of 1977

40c, Forbin, destroyer. 50c Jeanne d'Arc, helicopter carrier. 1.40fr, Kerguelen cormorant.

1979, Jan. 1		Engr.		Perf. 13	
77	A27	40c black & blue		1.40	1.10
78	A27	50c black & blue		1.60	1.10
79	A26	1.40fr multicolored		1.60	1.10
		Nos. 77-79 (3)		4.60	3.30

1979, Jan. 1

| 80 | A29 | 1.20fr citron & indigo | | 1.40 | 1.10 |

R. Rallier du Baty. See Nos. 97, 100, 111, 117, 129, 135, 188.

French Navigators Monument, Hobart — A30

1979, Jan. 1

| 81 | A30 | 1fr multicolored | | .90 | .80 |

French navigators and explorers.

Petrel — A31

1979		Engr.		Perf. 13	
82	A31	70c Rockhopper penguins, vert.		1.25	1.00
83	A31	1fr shown		1.50	1.25

Commandant Bourdais — A32

1979

| 84 | A32 | 1.10fr Doudart de Lagree, vert. | | 1.25 | 1.00 |
| 85 | A32 | 1.50fr shown | | 1.50 | 1.25 |

Adm. Antoine d'Entrecasteaux A33

Sebastian de el Cano A34

1979
86 A33 1.20fr multicolored   1.40 1.10

1979

Discovery of Amsterdam Island, 1522: 4fr, Victoria, horiz.

87 A34 1.40fr multicolored   1.25 .80
88 A34 4fr multicolored   2.25 1.60

Adelie Penguins — A35

Adelie Penguin — A36

Sea Leopard A37

1980, Dec. 15   Engr.   Perf. 13
89 A35 50c rose violet   1.40 1.25
90 A36 60c multicolored   1.40 .90
91 A35 1.20fr multicolored   2.00 1.10
92 A37 1.30fr multicolored   1.40 1.25
93 A37 1.80fr multicolored   1.40 1.25
Nos. 89-93 (5)   7.60 5.75

20th Anniv. of Antarctic Treaty — A38

1981, June 23   Engr.   Perf. 13
94 A38 1.80fr multicolored   4.50 4.50

Alouette II — A39

1981-82   Engr.   Perf. 13
95 A39 55c brown & multi   .65 .45
96 A39 65c blue & multi   .70 .45

Explorer Type of 1979
1981
97 A29 1.40fr Jean Loranchet   .80 .55

Landing Ship Le Gros Ventre, Kerguelen — A41

1983, Jan. 3   Engr.   Perf. 13
98 A41 55c multicolored   .90 .65

Our Lady of the Winds Statue and Church, Kerguelen — A42

1983, Jan. 3
99 A42 1.40fr multicolored   .90 .90

Explorer Type of 1979
Design: Martin de Vivies, Navigator.

1983, Jan. 3
100 A29 1.60fr multicolored   .90 .75

Eaton's Ducks A44

1983, Jan. 3
101 A44 1.50fr multicolored   .90 .60
102 A44 1.80fr multicolored   1.00 .75

Trawler Austral — A45

1983, Jan. 3
103 A45 2.30fr multicolored   1.50 1.10

Freighter Lady Franklin — A46

1983, Aug. 4   Engr.   Perf. 13
104 A46 5fr multicolored   4.00 3.00

Glaciology — A47

Design: Scientists examining glacier, base.

1984, Jan. 1   Engr.   Perf. 13
105 A47 15c multicolored   .45 .30
106 A47 1.70fr multicolored   .85 .55

Crab-eating Seal — A48

Penguins — A49

1984, Jan. 1
107 A48 60c multicolored   .55 .45
108 A49 70c multicolored   .45 .45
109 A49 2fr multicolored   1.25 1.00
110 A48 5.90fr multicolored   2.00 1.75
Nos. 107-110 (4)   4.25 3.65

Explorer Type of 1979

1984, Jan. 1
111 A29 1.80fr Alfred Faure   .90 .70

Biomass — A51

1985, Jan. 1   Engr.   Perf. 13
112 A51 1.80fr multicolored   .80 .55
113 A51 5.20fr multicolored   2.00 1.75

Emperor Penguins — A52

Snowy Petrel — A53

1985, Jan. 1   Engr.   Perf. 13
114 A52 1.70fr multicolored   1.00 .80
115 A53 2.80fr multicolored   1.25 1.10

Port Martin — A54

1985, Jan. 1   Engr.   Perf. 13
116 A54 2.20fr multicolored   1.25 .80

Explorer Type of 1979

1985, Jan. 1   Engr.   Perf. 13
117 A29 2fr Andre-Frank Liotard   .90 .70

Antarctic Fulmar — A56

1986, Jan. 1   Engr.   Perf. 13
118 A56 1fr shown   .55 .45
119 A56 1.70fr Giant petrels   .80 .75
Nos. 118-119,C91 (3)   3.35 2.95

Echinoderms — A57

1986, Jan. 1
120 A57 1.90fr shown   .90 .75

Cotula Plumosa — A58

Shipping — A59

1986, Jan. 1
121 A58 2.30fr shown   .90 .75
122 A58 6.20fr Lycopodium. saururus   2.50 1.90

1986, Jan. 1
123 A59 2.10fr Var research ship   .90 .85
124 A59 3fr Polarbjorn support ship   1.25 1.25

Marine Life — A60

1987, Jan. 1   **Engr.**   **Perf. 13½x13**
125 A60 50c dk blue & org   .60   .50

Flora — A61

1987, Jan. 1
126 A61 1.80fr Poa cookii   .70   .50
127 A61 6.50fr Lichen, Neuro-
         pogon taylori   2.00 1.90

Marret Base, Adelie Land — A62

1987, Jan. 1
128 A62 2fr yel brn, dk ultra &
         lake   .90   .70

Explorer Type of 1979
1987, Jan. 1
129 A29 2.20fr Adm. Mouchez   1.00 .75

Reindeer — A64

1987, Jan. 1
130 A64 2.50fr black   1.25 .80

Transport Ship Eure — A65

1987, Jan. 1
131 A65 3.20fr dk ultra, Prus grn
         & dk grn   1.50 1.00

Macaroni Penguins — A66

1987, Jan. 1   **Perf. 13x12½**
132 A66 4.80fr multicolored   2.50 1.90

Elephant Grass — A67

1988, Jan. 1   **Engr.**   **Perf. 13**
133 A67 1.70fr Prus grn, emer &
         olive   .85   .65

Rev.-Father Lejay,
Explorer — A68

1988, Jan. 1
134 A68 2.20fr vio, ultra & blk   1.00 .80

Explorer Type of 1979
Design: Robert Gessain (1907-86).

1988, Jan. 1
135 A29 3.40fr gray, dk red & blk 1.50 1.10

Le Gros Ventre, 18th Cent. — A70

1988, Jan. 1
136 A70 3.50fr dp ultra, bl grn &
         brn   1.25 1.25

Mermaid and B.A.P. Jules Verne,
Research Vessel — A71

1988, Jan. 1
137 A71 4.90fr gray & dk blue   2.50 1.75

La Fortune, Early
19th Cent. — A72

1988, Jan. 1
138 A72 5fr blk & dull bl grn   2.25 1.75

Wilson's Petrel — A73

1988, Jan. 1
139 A73 6.80fr blk, sepia & dl bl
         grn   2.75 2.25
         See Nos. 143-144.

Mt. Ross Campaign (in 1987) — A74

1988, Jan. 1   **Perf. 13x12½**
140 A74 2.20fr Volcanic rock
         cross-sections   1.00 1.00
141 A74 15.10fr Kerguelen Is.   5.50 5.50
  a. Pair, #140-141 + label   7.50 7.50

Darrieus System Wind Vane Electric
Generator — A75

1988, Jan. 1   **Engr.**   **Perf. 13**
142 A75 1fr dark blue & blue   .50   .35

Fauna Type of 1988
1989, Jan. 1   **Engr.**
143 A73 1.10fr Lithodes   .40   .40
144 A73 3.60fr Blue petrel   1.40 .75

Fern
A76

1989, Jan. 1
145 A76 2.80fr Blechnum penna
         Marina   1.00 .90

Minerals
A77

1989, Jan. 1
146 A77 5.10fr Mesotype   2.00 2.00
147 A77 7.30fr Analcime   3.00 3.00

Henri and
Rene
Bossiere,
Pioneers of
the
Kerguelen
Isls. — A78

1989, Jan. 1
148 A78 2.20fr multicolored   1.10 .75

Kerguelen Is. Sheep — A79

1989, Jan. 1   **Perf. 13½x13**
149 A79 2fr multicolored   .90   .65

Scuba Diver, Adelie Coast — A80

1989, Jan. 1
150 A80 1.70fr dk olive bis, blue &
         dk grn   .80   .60

Map of Kerguelen Island, Protozoa
and Copepod — A81

1990, Jan. 1   **Engr.**   **Perf. 13**
151 A81 1.10fr blk, brt blue & red
         brn   .75   .40
         Study of protista, Kerguelan Is.

Cattle on Farm, Sea Birds — A82

1990, Jan. 1
152 A82 1.70fr Prus blue, grn & brn
         blk   .85   .60
         Rehabilitation of the environment, Amster-
dam Is.

Quoy and   Dumont d'Urville
Copendium   (1790-1842),
decollata — A83   Explorer — A84

1990, Jan. 1   **Perf. 13½x13**
153 A83 2.20fr brt blue, blk & red
         brn   1.00 .75
         Jean Rene C. Quoy (1790-1869), naturalist,
navigator.

1990, Jan. 1
154 A84 3.60fr ultra & blk   1.50 1.10

Yellow-billed Albatross — A85

1990, Jan. 1   **Perf. 13x12½**
155 A85 2.80fr multicolored   2.00 .90

Aragonite
A86

1990, Jan. 1
156 A86 5.10fr deep ultra & dark
yel grn 2.50 1.75

*Ranunculus
pseudo
trullifolius* — A87

1990, Jan. 1 *Perf. 13*
157 A87 8.40fr dp bl, org & emer
grn 3.25 2.75

Penguin Type of Airpost 1974
1991, Jan. 1
158 AP18 50c blue grn, bl & blk .80 .40
Postal Service at Crozet Island, 30th anniv.

Moss — A88

1991, Jan. 1 *Perf. 13x12½*
159 A88 1.70fr gray, brn & blk .90 .65

Adm. Max
Douguet
(1903-1989)
A89

1991, Jan. 1
160 A89 2.30fr org brn, blk & bl 1.25 .90

Lighter L'Aventure — A90

1991, Jan. 1 **Engr.** *Perf. 13*
161 A90 3.20fr brn, grn & bl 1.50 1.25

Sea
Lions — A91

1991, Jan. 1 *Perf. 13*
162 A91 3.60fr blue & ol brn 2.25 1.40

Mordenite — A92

1991, Jan. 1
163 A92 5.20fr blk, grn bl & grn 2.75 2.00

Champsocephalus Gunnari — A93

1991, Jan. 1
164 A93 7.80fr blue & green 3.00 3.00

A94 A95

1991, Jan. 1
165 A94 9.30fr ol grn & rose red 4.00 3.50
Antarctic Treaty, 30th anniv.

1992, Jan. 1 **Engr.** *Perf. 13*
Design: Colobanthus Kerguelensis.
166 A95 1fr bl grn, grn & brn .90 .45

Globe Challenge Yacht Race — A96

1992, Jan. 1 **Litho.**
167 A96 2.20fr multicolored 1.50 1.00

Dissostichus Eleginoides — A97

1992, Jan. 1 **Engr.**
168 A97 2.30fr blue, ol grn & red
brn 1.50 1.00

Paul
Tchernia
A98

1992, Jan. 1 **Engr.** *Perf. 13*
169 A98 2.50fr brown & green 1.00 1.00

Capt. Marion
Dufresne (1724-
1772) — A99

1992, Jan. 1 **Engr.** *Perf. 13*
170 A99 3.70fr red, blk & bl 1.50 1.50

Supply Ship Tottan, 1951 — A100

1992, Jan. 1 **Engr.** *Perf. 13*
171 A100 14fr blue grn, brn & bl 5.75 5.75

WOCE Program — A101

1992, Jan. 1
172 A101 25.40fr multi 12.00 10.50

Coat of
Arms — A102

1992-95 **Engr.** *Perf. 13*
173 A102 10c black .40 .25
174 A102 20c greenish blue .40 .25
175 A102 30c red .40 .25
176 A102 40c green .40 .25
177 A102 50c orange .40 .25
Nos. 173-177 (5) 2.00 1.25
Issued: 10c, 1/1/92; 20c, 30c, 1/1/93; 40c,
1/1/94; 50c, 1/2/95.
See Nos. 295-299.

Garnet
A103

1993, Jan. 1 **Engr.** *Perf. 13*
183 A103 1fr multicolored 1.25 .30
See Nos. 194, 203, 212, 222, 235, 244, 259,
279, 300, 330.

Research Ship
Marion Dufresne,
20th
Anniv. — A104

1993, Jan. 1
184 A104 2.20fr multicolored 1.25 .60

Lyallia
Kerguelensis
A105

1993, Jan. 1
185 A105 2.30fr blue & green 1.25 .60

A106

A107

1993, Jan. 1
186 A106 2.50fr Killer whale 1.50 .70
187 A107 2.50fr Skua 7.00 .70

A108

Design: 2.50fr, Andre Prudhomme (1930-
1959), Meteorologist. 22fr, Weather station,
Adelie Land.

1993, Jan. 1 *Perf. 12½x13*
188 2.50fr blue, blk & org 1.00 .65
189 22fr org, blk & bl 8.50 6.00
a. A108 Pair, #188-189 + label 11.00 11.00
43rd Anniv. of Mèteo France in French
Southern & Antarctic Territory.

Centriscops Obliquus — A109

1993, Jan. 1 *Perf. 13*
190 A109 3.40fr multicolored 1.50 .90

Freighter Italo Marsano — A110

1993, Jan. 1
191 A110 3.70fr multicolored 1.75 1.00

ECOPHY Program A111

1993, Jan. 1
192 A111 14fr black, blue & brn 6.50 4.25

L'Astrolabe on Northeast Route, 1991 A112

1993, Jan. 1
193 A112 22fr multicolored 9.25 5.75

Mineral Type of 1993
1994, Jan. 1 Engr. Perf. 13
194 A103 1fr Cordierite 2.00 .80

Felis Catus — A113

1994, Jan. 1
195 A113 2fr green & black 3.50 1.25

A114

1994, Jan. 1 Engr. Perf. 13
196 A114 2.40fr dk brn, blk & bl 1.50 .65

A115

1994, Jan. 1
197 A115 2.80fr slate blue 1.60 .90

Robert Pommier (1919-61) A116

1994, Jan. 1
198 A116 2.80fr multicolored 1.60 .90

A117

Designs: 2.80fr, C.A. Vincendon Dumoulin (1811-58), hydrographer. 23fr, Measuring Earth's magnetic field.

1994, Jan. 1 Perf. 12½x13
199 2.80fr black & blue 1.40 .70
200 23fr blue & black 8.75 5.75
a. A118 Pair, #199-200 + label 11.00 11.00

Rascasse — A119

1994, Jan. 1 Perf. 13
201 A119 3.70fr bl grn & red brn 1.50 .95

Kerguelen of Tremarec — A120

1994, Jan. 1
202 A120 4.30fr multicolored 1.75 1.10

Mineral Type of 1993
1995, Jan. 2 Engr. Perf. 13
203 A103 1fr Olivine 1.50 .40

Mancoglosse Antarctique — A121

1995, Jan. 2
204 A121 2.40fr ol brn, vio & bl grn 1.50 .95

Andree (1903-90) and Edgar de la Rue (1901-91) A122

1995, Jan. 2
205 A122 2.80fr bl, red brn & mag 1.50 .85

SODAR Station — A123

1995, Jan. 2
206 A123 2.80fr vio, mag & red brn 1.50 .90

Mont D'Alsace — A124

1995, Jan. 2
207 A124 3.70fr dk bl, vio, red brn 1.75 1.10

Balaenoptera Acutorostrata — A125

1995, Jan. 2
208 A125 23fr blue, claret & ind 11.50 7.00

Sailing Ship Tamaris A126

1995, Jan. 2
209 A126 25.80fr multicolored 11.00 7.50

L'Heroine, Crozet Islands Mission, 1837 — A127

1995, Jan. 2
210 A127 27.30fr blue 11.50 7.75

Creation of the Territories, 40th Anniv. — A128

1995, Aug. 7 Litho. Imperf.
Size: 143x84mm
211 A128 30fr multicolored 15.00 15.00

Mineral Type of 1993
1996, Jan. 1 Engr. Perf. 13
212 A103 1fr Amazonite 1.00 .30

White-chinned Petrel — A129

1996, Jan. 1
213 A129 2.40fr blue black 1.50 .75

Expedition Ship Yves de Kerguelen — A130

1996, Jan. 1
214 A130 2.80fr multicolored 1.75 .80

Benedict Point Scientific Research Station, Amsterdam Island — A131

1996, Jan. 1
215 A131 2.80fr multicolored 1.50 .80

Paul-Emile Victor (1907-1995), Polar Explorer — A132

Designs: 2.80fr, Victor crossing Greenland with sled dogs, 1936. 23fr, Victor, penguins, Dumont d'Urville Base, Adélie Land.

1996, Jan. 1
216 A132 2.80fr multicolored 1.50 .90
217 A132 23fr multicolored 12.00 8.00
a. Pair, #216-217 + label 14.00 14.00

Admiral Jacquinot (1796-1879), Antarctic Explorer — A133

1996, Jan. 1
218 A133 3.70fr dark blue & blue 1.75 1.10

Trawler Austral — A134

1996, Jan. 1 Photo. & Engr.
219 A134 4.30fr multicolored 2.25 1.40

Lycopodium Magellanicum — A135

1996, Jan. 1 Engr.
220 A135 7.70fr multicolored 3.25 2.40

Search for Micrometeorites, Cape Prudhomme — A136

1996, Jan. 1
221 A136 15fr vio, blk & grn bl 8.00 5.00

Mineral Type of 1993
1997, Jan. 1 Engr. Perf. 13x12½
222 A103 1fr Amethyst 1.40 .40

Storm Petrel — A137

1997, Jan. 1 Perf. 13
223 A137 2.70fr blue & indigo 1.50 .90

Rene Garcia (1915-95), Windmill A138

1997, Jan. 1
224 A138 3fr multicolored 1.60 1.00

Research Ship Marion Dufresne — A139

Photo. & Engr.
1997, Jan. 1 Perf. 13x12½
225 A139 3fr multicolored 1.75 1.00

A140   A141

1997, Jan. 1 Engr. Perf. 13
226 A140 4fr black & brown 1.75 1.25
Jean Turquet (1867-1945).

1997, Jan. 1
227 A141 5.20fr multicolored 2.40 1.60
Church of Our Lady of Birds, Crozet Island.

A142

1997, Jan. 1
228 A142 8fr multicolored 4.00 2.60
Army Health Service.

A143

1997, Jan. 1
229 A143 29.20fr Poa Kerguelensis 12.50 9.25

French Polar Expeditions, 50th Anniv. — A144

Designs: No. 230, Greenland Expedition. No. 231, Port Martin, 1950-51, Marret Base, 1952, Adélie Land. No. 232, Dumont D'Urville, 1956, Charcot Station, Magnetic Pole, 1957.

Photo. & Engr.
1997, Feb. 28 Perf. 13x12½
230 A144 1fr multicolored 1.25 .80
231 A144 1fr multicolored 1.25 .80
232 A144 1fr multicolored 1.25 .80
a. Strip of 3, #230-232 7.50 3.25

Yves-Joseph de Kerguelen Trémarec (1734-97) — A145

3fr, Portrait. 24fr, Cook's landing at Kerguelen Island, Dec. 1776.

1997, Mar. 3 Engr. Perf. 13
233 3fr multicolored 1.25 .90
234 24fr multicolored 9.75 7.25
a. A145 Pair, #233-234 + label 14.00 10.00
No. 234 is 37x37mm.

Mineral Type of 1993
1998, Jan. 2 Engr. Perf. 13
235 A103 1fr Rock crystal 1.25 .40

Fisheries Management — A146

Designs: No. 236, Fishing boats. No. 237, Examining fish, performing research.

1998, Jan. 2
236 A146 2.60fr multicolored 1.50 .75
237 A146 2.60fr multicolored 1.50 .75
a. Pair, #236-237 + label 4.00 4.00

Gray-headed Albatross — A147

1998, Jan. 2
238 A147 2.70fr multicolored 1.75 .75

Ecology of St. Paul Island — A148

1998, Jan. 2
239 A148 3fr bl, brn & grn 2.50 1.00

A149   A150

1998, Jan. 2 Perf. 13x13½
240 A149 3fr lilac, blue & black 1.75 .85
Etienne Peau, Antarctic explorer.

1998, Jan. 2
241 A150 4fr lt org, blk & red brn 1.75 1.10
Georges Laclavere (1906-94), geographer.

Mole Shark — A151

1998, Jan. 2 Perf. 13
242 A151 27fr multicolored 11.00 7.25

"Le Cancalais" — A152

1998, Jan. 2
243 A152 29.20fr multicolored 12.00 7.75

Mineral Type of 1993
1999, Jan. 1 Engr. Perf. 13
244 A103 1fr Epidote, vert. 1.25 .40

Chinstrap Penguin — A153

1999, Jan. 1
245 A153 2.70fr brn, blk & bl 1.60 .85

Pierre Sicaud (1911-98), Antarctic Explorer, Commander of Outpost at Kerguelen Islands — A154

1999, Jan. 1
246 A154 3fr black & green 1.40 .95

Penguins of Crozet Islands — A155

1999, Jan. 1
247 A155 3fr multicolored 3.00 .85

Jacques-André Martin (1911-49) — A156

1999, Jan. 1
248 A156 4fr multicolored 1.75 1.10

Ray — A157

1999, Jan. 1 Perf. 12½
249 A157 5.20fr mag, bl & brn 2.50 1.50
Value is for stamp with surrounding rectangular selvage.

F.S. Floreal — A158

1999, Jan. 1   **Photo.**   **Perf. 13**
250 A158 5.20fr multicolored   2.50 1.40

No. 250 was printed se-tenant with label. Value is for stamp with label attached.

"Pop Cat" Program, Kerguelen Islands — A159

1999, Jan. 1   **Engr.**
251 A159 8fr multicolored   4.75 2.75

Study of Albatrosses on Artificial Nests A160

1999, Jan. 1
252 A160 16fr olive, grn & blk   7.00 4.50

Amsterdam Base, Kerguelen Base, 50th Anniv. — A161

1999, Jan. 1
253 A161 3fr Amsterdam Base   6.00 .85
254 A161 24fr Kerguelen Base   10.50 6.50
a.   Pair, #253-254 + label   18.00 15.00

Festuca Contracta A162

1999, Jan. 1
255 A162 24fr dk grn, ol & bl grn   10.50 6.50

Geoleta Program — A163

1999, Jan. 1   **Perf. 13x12½**
256 A163 29.20fr blk, bl & red brn   13.00 7.75

Voyage of Marion Dufresne II — A164

a, Docked, Reunion. b, Passengers in dining salon. c, Penguins, Crozet Island. d, Postal manager of Alfred Faure, Crozet Island, vert. e, Port of France, Kerguelen Island. f, Port Couvreux, Kerguelen Island. g, Offloading stores, Port of France, Kerguelen Island. h, Port Jeanne d'arc, Kerguelen Island. i, St. Paul Island. j, Ruins of lobster cannery, St. Paul Island. k, Martin de Vivies Base, Amsterdam Island. l, Offloading cargo, Amsterdam Island.

1999, May 1   **Litho.**   **Perf. 13**
257 A164   Souv. bklt., #a.-l.   92.50

Nos. 257a-257l are all non-denominated. Stamps are valid for 20 gram international letter rate. Each stamp appears on a separate booklet pane showing an enlarged design of the stamp. Booklet sold for 100fr.
See Nos. 294, 329, 359, 390.

Souvenir Sheet

PhilexFrance '99, World Philatelic Exhibition — A165

Antarctic postmarks on stamps: a, Malagasy Republic #280. b, Malagasy Republic #282. c, Malagasy Republic #C42. d, #21.

1999, July 2   **Litho. & Engr.**   **Perf. 13**
258 A165 5.20fr Sheet of 4, #a.-d.   11.50 7.00

Nos. 258b-258c are each 40x52mm.

Mineral Type of 1993

2000, Jan.   **Engr.**   **Perf. 12¾x13**
259 A103 1fr Mica, vert.   1.25 .40

Puffin — A166

2000, Jan.   **Perf. 13x12¾**
260 A166 2.70fr multi   2.00 .80

André Beaugé (1913-97) A167

2000, Jan.   **Perf. 12¾x13**
261 A167 3fr multi   1.40 .70

Abby Jane Morrell — A168   Sled Dog Hobbs — A170

Oceanographic Survey — A169

2000, Jan.   **Perf. 13¼x13**
262 A168 4fr multi   1.75 .95

2000, Jan.   **Perf. 13x12½**
263 A169 4.40fr multi   1.90 1.00

2000, Jan.   **Perf. 12¾x13**
264 A170 5.20fr multi   2.25 1.25

Sleep Study — A171

2000, Jan.   **Photo.**   **Perf. 13x12½**
265 A171 8fr multi + label   3.50 1.90

Ship "La Perouse" — A172

2000, Jan.   **Engr.**   **Perf. 13x12½**
266 A172 16fr multi   7.00 3.75

Lantern Fish — A173

2000, Jan.
267 A173 24fr multi   10.50 5.50

Larose Bay — A174

2000, Jan.
268 A174 27fr multi   12.00 6.25

Explorers A175

#269, Yves Joseph de Kerguelen-Trémarec (1734-97). #270, Jules Sébastien César Dumont D'Urville (1790-1842). #271, Raymond Rallier du Baty (1881-1978). #272, Edgar Aubert de La Rüe (1901-91). #273, Paul-Emile Victor (1907-95).

2000, Jan.   **Perf. 13**

Booklet Stamps

269 A175 3fr multi   1.50 .70
270 A175 3fr multi   1.50 .70
271 A175 3fr multi   1.50 .70
272 A175 3fr multi   1.50 .70
273 A175 3fr multi   1.50 .70
a.   Bklt. pane, #269-273 + 2 labels   8.00
   Complete booklet, #273a   9.50

Souvenir Sheet

The Third Millennium — A176

No. 274: a, Penguins, Crozet Islands. b, Seals, Kerguelen Islands. c, Crustacean, Saint-Paul and Amsterdam Islands. d, Hovering vehicle, Adelie Land.

2000, Jan.   **Photo.**   **Perf. 13**
274 A176 3fr Sheet of 4, #a.-d.   7.50 7.50

Bird Demographic Studies — A177

Designs: 5.20fr, Bird banding. 8fr, Albatross, graph. 16fr, Emperor penguins, graph.

2000, Jan.   **Perf. 13x13¼**
275 A177 5.20fr multi   2.25 1.25

Size: 50x28mm

276 A177   8fr multi   3.50 1.90
277 A177 16fr multi   7.00 3.75
a.   Horiz. strip, #275-277   14.00 14.00

Relocation of Headquarters to Reunion — A178

2000, Aug. 6   **Litho.**   **Perf. 13**
278 A178 27fr multi   12.00 5.50

Mineral Type of 1993

2001, Jan. 1   **Engr.**   **Perf. 13x12¾**
279 A103 1fr Magnetite   1.25 .40

Diving Petrel — A179

2001, Jan. 1 *Perf. 13x13¼*
280 A179 2.70fr multi 1.50 .60

High Mountain Military Group A180

2001, Jan. 1 *Perf. 13¼x13*
281 A180 3fr multi 1.40 .65

Kerguelen Arch — A181

2001, Jan. 1 *Perf. 13*
282 A181 3fr blue gray 2.00 .70

Xavier-Charles Richert (1913-92) A182

Jean Coulomb A183

2001, Jan. 1
283 A182 3fr multi 1.40 .65

2001, Jan. 1
284 A183 4fr multi 1.75 .85

Memorial to 1874 Astronomical Observation, St. Paul Island — A184

2001, Jan. 1
285 A184 8fr brn & blk 3.50 1.75

Frigate La Fayette — A185

2001, Jan. 1 *Perf. 13x13¼*
286 A185 16fr multi 7.00 3.50

Squid — A186

2001, Jan. 1
287 A186 24fr multi 10.50 5.00

Amateur Radio Link Between Space Station Mir and Crozet Island — A187

2001, Jan. 1 *Litho.* *Perf. 13*
288 A187 27fr multi 12.00 5.50

Bryum Laevigatum — A188

2001, Jan. 1 *Engr.* *Perf. 13x12½*
289 A188 29.20fr multi 13.00 6.00

Souvenir Sheet

Ships — A189

No. 290: a, Carmen. b, Austral. c, Ramuntcho. d, Samper 1.

2001, Jan. 1 *Perf. 13x13½*
290 A189 5.20fr Sheet of 4, #a-d 9.00 4.50

Souvenir Sheet

Wildlife — A190

No. 291: a, Albatrosses. b, Emperor penguins, horiz. c, Sea lions, horiz. d, Whales.

2001, Jan. 1 *Litho.* *Perf. 13*
291 A190 3fr Sheet of 4, #a-d 10.50 5.00

Antarctic Treaty, 40th Anniv. — A191

2001, June 23 *Engr.* *Perf. 13x12¾*
292 A191 5.20fr dark & sky blue 3.25 1.00

Commission for the Conservation of Antarctic Marine Living Resources, 20th Anniv. — A192

2001, Oct. 22 *Litho.* *Perf. 13*
293 A192 5.20fr multi 5.00 2.00

Voyage Booklet Type of 1999

Adélie Land: a, Boat in pack ice. b, Dumont d'Urville Base. c, Adélie penguin rookery. d, L'Astrolabe Glacier. e, Pointe Géologie Archipelago. f, Release of meteorological balloon. g, Equipment convoy. h, Helicopter transport of fresh supplies. i, Arrival of emperor penguins. j, Telecommunications center. k, Looking towards the Antarctic. l, Cape Prud'homme. m, Ship L'Astrolabe anchored. n, Dispatch of mail.

2001, Oct. 29 *Perf. 13*
294 A164 Souvenir booklet, 2 each #a-n 95.00

Nos. 294a-294n are all non-denominated. Stamps are valid for 20 gram international letter rate. Each stamp appears on a separate booklet pane showing an enlarged design of the stamp and on one pane with all of the stamps and four labels found at the center of the booklet. the booklet sold for 196.78fr.

100 Cents = 1 Euro (€)
Arms Type of 1992-95 with Euro Denominations

2002, Jan. 2 *Engr.* *Perf. 13*
295 A102 1c black .20 .20
296 A102 2c greenish blue .25 .20
297 A102 5c red .30 .20
298 A102 10c green .40 .20
299 A102 20c orange .70 .20
Nos. 295-299 (5) 1.85 1.00

Mineral Type of 1993 with Euro Denomination

2002, Jan. 2 *Engr.* *Perf. 12¾x13*
300 A103 15c Nepheline, vert. 1.00 .40

Albatross A193

2002, Jan. 2 *Perf. 13¼x13*
301 A193 41c multi 3.00 .80

Ship "Marion Dufresne" — A194

2002, Jan. 2 *Perf. 13x13¼*
302 A194 46c multi 1.40 .60

1963-83 Telegraph Station, Crozet Island A195

2002, Jan. 2 *Litho.* *Perf. 13*
303 A195 46c multi 1.50 .60

Jacques Dubois (1920-2000) A196

2002, Jan. 2 *Engr.*
304 A196 61c multi 2.25 .90

Engraved Rock, Saint Paul Island — A197

2002, Jan. 2 *Perf. 13x13¼*
305 A197 79c multi 2.40 1.25

Kerguelen Cabbage A198

2002, Jan. 2 *Perf. 12¼*
306 A198 €1.22 multi 3.50 1.75

Passage of the Ship "Gauss," Cent. — A199

2002, Jan. 2 *Perf. 13x12¼*
307 A199 €2.44 multi 7.25 3.50

Crab — A200

2002, Jan. 2 **Perf. 13x13¼**
308 A200 €3.66 multi 11.00 5.25

Pack Ice Diatoms — A201

2002, Jan. 2 **Litho.** **Perf. 13**
309 A201 €4.12 multi 12.50 6.00

French Geographic Society Building, Paris — A202

2002, Jan. 2 **Engr.** **Perf. 13¼x13**
310 A202 €4.45 multi + label 13.50 8.00

Cartoker Program — A203

No. 311: a, 46c, Diagram of plate tectonics. b, €3.66, Geological map of Kerguelen Island.

2002, Jan. 2 **Perf. 13x12¼**
311 A203 Horiz. pair, #a-b, + central label 12.50 12.50

Souvenir Sheet

Olympic Games for Antarctic Animals — A204

No. 312: a, Albatrosses flying marathon. b, Langoustines diving, vert. c, Penguins riding

bobsled course, vert. d, Killer whales performing synchronized swimming, vert.

2002, Jan. 2 **Litho.** **Perf. 13**
312 A204 46c Sheet of 4, #a-d 6.50 5.50

Souvenir Sheet

Animals and Their Young — A205

No. 313: a, Penguins. b, Sea lions. c, Albatrosses. d, Elephant seals.

2002, Jan. 2
313 A205 79c Sheet of 4, #a-d 10.50 9.50

Introduction of the Euro A206

2002, Feb. 17
314 A206 46c blue & black 3.50 .60

Mineral Type of 1993
2003, Jan. **Engr.** **Perf. 13¼**
315 A103 15c Apatite, vert. 1.25 .40

Lobster Processing Plant, Saint-Paul — A207

2003, Jan. **Perf. 13x13¼**
316 A207 41c multi 1.25 .65

Luc Marie Bayle (1914-2000), Painter — A208

2003, Jan. **Litho.** **Perf. 13**
317 A208 46c multi 1.50 .70

Emperor Penguins — A209

2003, Jan.
318 A209 46c multi 2.75 .80

Otice Hydroacoustic Station — A210

2003, Jan. **Engr.** **Perf. 13x13¼**
319 A210 61c multi 1.90 1.00

Restoration of Port Jeanne d'Arc — A211

2003, Jan. **Perf. 13x12¼**
320 A211 79c multi 2.40 1.25

Phylica — A212

2003, Jan. **Perf. 13x13¼**
321 A212 €1.22 multi 4.50 2.25

Ship "Bougainville" A213

2003, Jan. **Perf. 13¼x13**
322 A213 €2.44 multi 7.25 4.25

Chub — A214

2003, Jan. **Engr.** **Perf. 13x13¼**
323 A214 €3.66 multi 11.00 6.50

Ile aux Pingouins — A215

2003, Jan. **Perf. 13x12¼**
324 A215 €3.66 black 11.00 6.50

Super Darn Antenna Array — A216

2003, Jan. **Perf. 13**
325 A216 €4.12 multi 12.50 7.00

Souvenir Sheet

Paintings Revised to Reflect a Less Southerly Antarctica — A217

No. 326: a, Triumph of Venus with fish and lobsters. b, King Louis XV and wife with penguins, vert. c, Jules Dumont d'Urville and wife in a grassy Adélie Land. d, Chevalier Yves de Kerguelin under umbrella, seal in pool, vert.

2003, Jan. **Litho.**
326 A217 46c Sheet of 4, #a-d 6.50 6.50

Protective Clothing — A218

Cold-weather outerwear from: a, 1898. b, 1912. c, 2002. d, 1980, e, 1996.

2003, Jan. **Photo.** **Perf. 13¼x13**
327 Booklet pane of 5 12.00 —
a.-e. A218 79c Any single 2.40 1.25
Booklet, #327 12.00

Voyage of the Ship "Français," Cent. — A219

2003, Aug. 31 **Engr.** **Perf. 13x13¼**
328 Horiz. strip of 3 15.00 13.50
a. A219 79c Capt. J.-B. Charcot 2.50 1.25
b. A219 €1.22 Ship in ice, horiz. 4.00 2.00
c. A219 €2.44 Ship in harbor, horiz. 7.50 4.25

Stamp size: Nos. 328b-328c, 49x29mm.

Voyage Booklet Type of 1999

Recipes: a, Truite aus deux citrons (trout and waterfall). b, Veau d'Amsterdam à la savoyarde (cattle). c, Lapin "Volage" à la cannelle (rabbits, penguins). d, Rôti de légine de l'ile de l'est (fish). e, Civet de renne "Volcan du diable," (reindeer). f, Iles antarctiques flottantes. g, Langouste à la mode de Saint-Paul (lobster). h, Gigot de mouflon aux 5 épices et aux pommes (sheep). i, Cabot tropical (fish, ship). j, Tagine d'agneau aux épices de la Réunion (sheep). k, Moules au pastis (mussels). l, Glace à la menthe sauvage d'Amsterdam (mint plant).

2003, Nov. 6   Litho.   Perf. 13
329 A164   Souvenir booklet,
              #a-l   50.00

Nos. 329a-329l are all non-denominated. Stamps are valid for 20 gram international letter rate. Each stamp appears on a separate booklet pane showing an enlarged design of the stamp. The booklet sold for €17.

Mineral Type of 1993

2004, Jan. 1   Engr.   Perf. 13¼
330 A103   15c Chalcedony, vert.   1.25   .40

A220

A221

2004, Jan. 1   Engr.   Perf. 13x13¼
331 A220   45c multi   1.40   .85

Mario Marret, director of film "Terre Adélie."

2004, Jan. 1
332 A221   50c multi   1.75   .95

Col. Robert Genty (1910-2001).

Albert Faure Base, Crozet Island, 40th Anniv. — A222

2004, Jan. 1   Litho. & Engr.
333 A222   50c multi   1.50   .95

Péron's Dolphins — A223

2004, Jan. 1   Litho.   Perf. 13
334 A223   75c multi   3.00   1.50

Twin Otter Flights
A224

2004, Jan. 1   Photo.   Perf. 12¾
335 A224   90c multi   2.75   1.75

Values are for stamps with surrounding selvage.

Iceberg — A225

2004, Jan. 1   Engr.   Perf. 13x13¼
336 A225   €1.30 multi   4.00   2.40

Grave of Sailors from the Volage — A226

2004, Jan. 1   Perf. 13¼x13
337 A226   €2.50 multi   7.50   5.00

Krill — A227

2004, Jan. 1   Perf. 13x13¼
338 A227   €4 multi   12.00   8.00

Ship "Dives" — A228

2004, Jan. 1
339 A228   €4.50 multi   13.50   9.25

Souvenir Sheet

Hydrological Surveys, Adélie Land — A229

2004, Jan. 1   Litho.   Perf. 13
340 A229   €4.90 multi   15.00 10.50

Souvenir Sheet

Imaginary "TAAFland" Theme Park — A230

No. 341: a, Whale statue, pyramidal entrance structure. b, Showgirls, seals, vert. c, Boy and girl with ice cream cones, vert. d, Woman in swimsuit, penguins.

2004, Jan. 1
341 A230   50c Sheet of 4, #a-d   8.00   8.00

Souvenir Sheet

Post Offices — A231

No. 342: a, Amsterdam Island. b, Crozet Island. c, Kerguelen Island. d, Adélie Land.

2004, Jan. 1
342 A231   90c Sheet of 4, #a-d   12.00 12.00

Penguin and Liberty Cap — A232

2004, June 26   Engr.   Perf. 13¼x13
343 A232   €4.50 multi   15.00   7.00

Mineral Type of 1993

2005, Jan. 1   Engr.   Perf. 13¼
344 A103   15c Agate   .80   .50

Albert Bauer (1916-2003), Glaciologist — A233

2005, Jan. 1   Perf. 13x13¼
345 A233   45c multi   2.00   1.75

Roger Barberot (1915-2002), Administrator A234

2005, Jan. 1
346 A234   50c multi   2.00   2.00

Ship "Cap Horn" — A235

2005, Jan. 1
347 A235   50c multi   2.00   2.00

Seal Pot A236

2005, Jan. 1   Litho.   Perf. 13
348 A236   50c multi   2.25   2.25

Macgillivray's Prion — A237

2005, Jan. 1   Engr.   Perf. 13x13¼
349 A237   75c multi   2.75   2.75

Studer Valley — A238

2005, Jan. 1   Perf. 13x12½
350 A238   90c multi   3.00   3.00

Peigne des Néréides A239

2005, Jan. 1   Perf. 12¼
351 A239   €2.50 multi   8.00   7.50

Harpovoluta Charcoti — A240

2005, Jan. 1   **Perf. 13x12½**
352 A240 €4 multi   14.00 14.00

Murray's Ray — A241

2005, Jan. 1   Litho.   Perf. 13
353 A241 €4.50 multi   14.00 14.00

Elephant Seal and Oceanographic Chart — A242

2005, Jan. 1   Engr.
354 A242 €4.90 multi   16.00 16.00

Concordia Station — A243

2005, Jan. 3   Litho.   Perf. 13
355 A243 50c multi   1.75 1.75

Return of the Ship "Français," Cent. — A244

2005, Mar. 4   Engr.   Perf. 13x13¼
356 A244 €4.50 multi + label   15.00 15.00

Disappearance of Paul-Emile Victor, 10th Anniv. — A245

2005, Mar. 7   Litho.   Perf. 13
357 A245 50c multi   2.50 2.50

50th Anniversary Coat of Arms — A246

2005, Aug. 6
358 A246 (90c) multi   3.00 3.00
   a.   Booklet pane of 1   4.00   —
      No. 358a is found in No. 359.

Voyage Booklet Type of 1999

History: a, Discovery of Amsterdam Island, 1522. b, Discovery of Crozet Island, 1772. c, Discovery of Kerguelen Island, 1772, vert. d, Discovery of Adélie Land, 1840. e, Astronomers viewing 1874 transit of Venus on St. Paul Island. f, Wreck of the Strathmore, 1875. g, Port Jeanne d'Arc, 1908. h, Port-Couvreux, 1925. i, Building of Port-Martin, 1950. j, Antarctic Treaty, 1959. k, Building of fourth base, 1963-64.

2005, Aug. 6   Litho.   Perf. 13
359 A164   Souvenir booklet,
         #a-k, 358a   65.00

Nos. 359a-359k are all non-denominated. Stamps are valid for 90c, the 20 gram international letter rate. Each stamp appears on a separate booklet pane showing an enlarged design of the stamp. The booklet sold for €18.

Penguins and No. 1 — A247

2005, Nov. 2
360 A247 90c multi   3.25 3.25
   French Southern & Antarctic Territories, 50th anniv.

Souvenir Sheet

Maps — A248

Maps of: a, Crozet Archipelago. b, Amsterdam and St. Paul Islands. c, Kerguelen Island. d, Adélie Land.

Litho. & Engr.
2005, Nov. 10   Perf. 13x13¼
361 A248 50c Sheet of 4, #a-d   6.50 6.50
   French Southern & Antarctic Territories, 50th anniv.

Rutile A249

2006, Jan. 1   Engr.   Perf. 13x12½
362 A249 15c multi   .80 .80

A250   A251

2006, Jan. 1   Perf. 13x13¼
363 A250 48c pur & red   1.60 1.60
   Charles Vélain (1845-1925), geologist.

2006, Jan. 1
364 A251 53c multi   1.60 1.60
   Albert Seyrolle (1887-1919), mariner.

Amsterdam Island Garden — A252

2006, Jan. 1   Litho.   Perf. 13
365 A252 53c multi   1.60 1.60

Ship "Osiris" — A253

2006, Jan. 1   Photo.   Perf. 13x13¼
366 A253 90c multi   3.00 3.00

Dumont d'Urville Base, 50th Anniv. — A254

2006, Jan. 1   Engr.   Perf. 13x12½
367 A254 90c multi   2.75 2.75

Virgin of the Seal Hunters — A255

2006, Jan. 1   Perf. 12½x13
368 A255 €2.50 multi   7.50 7.50

Lagenorhynchus Cruciger — A256

2006, Jan. 1   Perf. 13x13¼
369 A256 €4 multi   12.00 12.00

Keguelen Hake — A257

2006, Jan. 1
370 A257 €4.53 multi   13.50 13.50

Amsterdam Island Carbon Dioxide Measurements, 25th Anniv. — A258

2006, Jan. 1
371 A258 €4.90 multi   15.00 15.00

Miniature Sheet

Penguins — A259

No. 372 — Penguin (background color): a, Emperor penguin (lilac, 22x36mm). b, King penguin (pale yellow green, 22x36mm). c, Gentoo penguin (green, 22x27mm). d, Adélie penguin (pink, 22x27mm). e, Macaroni penguin (orange, 22x27mm). f, Rockhopper penguin (blue, 22x27mm).

Litho. & Engr.
2006, Jan. 1   Perf. 13
372 A259 53c Sheet of 6, #a-f 12.00 12.00

Souvenir Sheet

Albatross — A260

Litho. & Engr.

2006, June 1   **Perf. 13**
373 A260 €4.53 multi   14.50 14.50

Souvenir Sheet

Albatross — A261

Litho. & Engr.

2006, Nov. 8   **Perf. 13**
374 A261 90c multi   3.50 3.50

Corundum
A262

2007, Jan. 1   **Engr.**   **Perf. 13¼**
375 A262 15c multi   1.25 1.25

A263   A264

2007, Jan. 1   **Perf. 13x13¼**
376 A263 49c multi   1.50 1.50

Louis-Francois Aleno de Saint Aloüarn (1738-72), explorer who claimed Australia for France.

2007, Jan. 1
377 A264 54c multi   1.60 1.60

Marthe Emmanuel (1901-97), assistant to explorer Jean Charcot.

Cattle, Amsterdam Island — A265

2007, Jan. 1   **Perf. 13x12½**
378 A265 54c multi   1.50 1.50

Ship Tonkinois — A266

2007, Jan. 1   **Perf. 13x13¼**
379 A266 90c multi   2.50 2.50

Ile de la Baleine — A267

2007, Jan. 1   **Perf. 13x12½**
380 A267 90c multi   2.50 2.50

Archaeology on
Saint Paul
Island — A268

2007, Jan. 1   **Perf. 12½x13**
381 A268 €2.50 multi   7.00 7.00

Lampris Immaculatus — A269

2007, Jan. 1   **Perf. 13x12½**
382 A269 €4 multi   11.00 11.00

Astonomy at Concordia — A270

Litho. & Engr.

2007, Jan. 1   **Perf. 13**
383 A270 €4.90 multi   14.00 14.00

French Polar Expeditions, 60th
Anniv. — A271

No. 384: a, Expedition headquarters, Paris, men shaking hands over globe. b, Expedition headquarters.

2007, Jan. 1   **Engr.**   **Perf. 13x13¼**
384   Horiz. pair + central label   13.50 13.50
   a. A271 54c multi   1.75 1.75
   b. A271 €4 multi   11.00 11.00

Miniature Sheet

Albatrosses — A272

No. 385: a, Amsterdam albatross. b, Great albatross (Grand albatros). c, Black-browed albatross (Albatros à sourcils noir). d, Yellow-beaked albatross (Albatros à bec jaune). e, Sooty albatross (Albatros fuligineux).

Litho. & Engr.

2007, Jan. 1   **Perf. 13**
385 A272 54c Sheet of 5, #a-e   8.00 8.00

Intl. Polar Year — A273

No. 386: a, Penguins. b, Map of Antarctica, French Southern & Antarctic Territories #9.

2007, Mar. 1   **Litho.**   **Perf. 13**
386   Horiz. pair + central label   15.00 15.00
   a. A273 90c multi   2.75 2.75
   b. A273 €4 multi   12.00 12.00

Audit
Office,
Bicent.
A274

2007 Mar. 19   **Engr.**   **Perf. 13¼**
387 A274 90c multi   4.50 4.50

Miniature Sheet

Indian Ocean Islands — A275

No. 388: a, Ile Tromelin. b, Iles Glorieuses. c, Ile Juan de Nova. d, Ile Bassas da India. e, Ile Europa.

2007, May 10   **Photo.**   **Perf. 13x13¼**
388 A275 54c Sheet of 5, #a-e   9.00 9.00

Path of Sun on June 21 Over Dumont
d'Urville Base — A276

2007, June 21
389 A276 90c multi   3.00 3.00

Voyage Booklet Type of 1999

No. 390 — Photographs of land features: a, Apostle Island, Crozet Archipelago. b, Chamonix Lake, Kerguelen Island. c, Phylicia forest, Amsterdam Island. d, Gulf of Morbihan, Kerguelen Islands. e, Mount Cook, Chamonix Lake and glacier, Kerguelen Islands. f, Tourbiéres Plateau, Amsterdam Island. g, Nuageuses Islands, Kerguelen Islands. h, Caldera, Amsterdam Island. i, Mount Cook, Kerguelen Island. j, Central Plateau, Kerguelen Island. k, Isle of Penguins, Crozet Archipelago. l, Antonelli Crater, Amsterdam Island. m, Lake on Possession Island, Crozet Archipelago. n, Rocks off Apostle Island, Crozet Archipelago. o, Geographic Society Peninsula, Kerguelen Island. p, Ronarch Peninsula, Kerguelen Island.

2007, Nov. 8   **Litho.**   **Perf. 13**
390 A164 (90c) Souvenir booklet, #a-p   70.00

No. 390 sold for €20, and contains four panes, consisting of a block of four stamps of Nos. 390a-390d, 390e-390h, 390i-390l, and 390m-390p.

French Southern
and Antarctic
Territories
Flag — A277

2008, Jan. 1   **Litho.**   **Perf. 13**
Background Color
391 A277 1c black   .25 .25
392 A277 2c blue   .35 .35
393 A277 5c red   .40 .40
394 A277 10c green   .40 .40
395 A277 20c brn orange   .80 .80
   Nos. 391-395 (5)   2.20 2.20

Spinel — A278

2008, Jan. 1   **Engr.**   **Perf. 13¼**
396 A278 15c multi   .80 .45

Samivel (1907-
92),
Writer — A279   St. Paul
Island — A280

2008, Jan. 1   **Perf. 13x13¼**
397 A279 54c grn & brown   1.60 1.60

2008, Jan. 1
398 A280 54c blue & dk blue   1.60 1.60

Construction of Port Jeanne d'Arc, Cent. — A281

2008, Jan. 1 Perf. 13x12¾
399 A281 90c multi 2.75 2.75

Rockhopper Penguins — A282

2008, Jan. 1 Perf. 13x12½
400 A282 90c multi 2.75 2.75

Shipwreck of L'Esperance — A283

2008, Jan. 1 Litho. Perf. 13x12¾
401 A283 90c multi 2.75 2.75

Macrourus Carinatus — A284

2008, Jan. 1 Engr. Perf. 13x12½
402 A284 €4 multi 12.00 12.00

Galium Antarcticum A285

2008, Jan. 1 Perf. 12½x13
403 A285 €4.54 multi 13.50 13.50

Adélie Land Coastal Ichthyology Program A286

2008, Jan. 1 Litho. Perf. 13
404 A286 €4.90 multi 14.50 14.50

Souvenir Sheet

Kerguelen Fish Biomass Evaluation Project (POKER) — A287

2008, Jan. 1 Litho. & Engr.
405 A287 €2.50 multi 7.50 7.50

Souvenir Sheet

Elephant Seals — A288

No. 406: a, Head of adult female. b, Seals initiating combat. c, Juvenile seal. d, Head of adult male.

2008, Jan. 1
406 A288 54c Sheet of 4, #a-d 6.50 6.50

Gérard Mégie (1946-2004), Ozone Researcher — A289

2008, Feb. 15 Engr. Perf. 13x13¼
407 A289 54c multi 1.75 1.75

Miniature Sheet

Birds — A290

No. 408: a, Sooty tern (Sterne fulgineuse). b, Red-footed booby (Fou a pieds rouges), vert. c, Masked booby (Fou masque), vert. d, Great frigatebird (Fregate du Pacifique), vert. e, Tropicbird (Paille en queue).

Perf. 13¼x13 (#408a, 408e), 13x13¼
2008, June 1 Litho. & Engr.
408 A290 54c Sheet of 5, #a-e 8.50 8.50

Earth and Birds — A291

2008, June 14 Photo. Perf. 13
409 A291 €4.54 multi 14.50 14.50

Ship Marion Dufresne — A292

2008, Nov. 6 Litho. Perf. 13
410 A292 (55c) multi 1.75 1.75
Compare with type A194.

Pyrite A293

2009, Jan. 1 Engr. Perf. 13¼
411 A293 15c multi .60 .60

A294 A295

2009, Jan. 1 Perf. 13x13¼
412 A294 55c multi 1.60 1.60
Henri Paschal de Rochegude (1741-1834), naval officer.

2009, Jan. 1 Perf. 13
413 A295 55c multi 1.60 1.60
Charles Gaston Rouillon (1915-2007), director of French polar scientific expeditions.

Residence de France Seal of Kerguelen Islands, Cent. — A296

2009, Jan. 1 Litho.
414 A296 90c multi 2.50 2.50

Shark With Dorsal Spines — A297

2009, Jan. 1 Engr. Perf. 13x12½
415 A297 €2.50 multi 7.00 7.00

Ship Jeanne d'Arc — A298

2009, Jan. 1
416 A298 €4 multi 11.00 11.00

MACARBI Program Scallop Research A299

2009, Jan. 1 Perf. 12½x13
417 A299 €4.55 multi 13.00 13.00

Seaweed — A300

No. 418: a, Himantothallus grandifolius and iceberg. b, Laminaria pallida and seals.

2009, Jan. 1 Perf. 13x13¼
418 Horiz. pair + central
  label 13.50 13.50
  a. A300 90c multi 2.50 2.50
  b. A300 €4 multi 11.00 11.00

Miniature Sheet

Petrels — A301

No. 419: a, Soft-plumaged petrel (Petrel soyeux). b, Wilson's petrel (Petrel de Wilson). c, Gray petrel (Petrel gris). d, Diving petrel (Petrel plongeur). e, Snow petrel (Petrel des neiges).

Litho. & Engr.
2009, Jan. 1 Perf. 13¼x13
419 A301 55c Sheet of 5, #a-e 7.75 7.75

Voyage Booklet Type of 1999

No. 420 — Photographs: a, Frigatebirds, Europa Island. b, Beach on north coast of Europa Island. c, Mangroves, Europa Island. d, Flagpole, palm trees, Europa Island. e, Turtle on beach, Juan de Nova Island. f, Sandbanks off Juan de Nova Island. g, Tree, Juan de Nova Island. h, Grounded ship, Juan de Nova Island. i, Brown noddies, Glorioso Islands. j, Flower, Glorioso Islands. k, Pool of water, Glorioso Islands. l, Tree on islet, Glorioso Islands. m, Birds, Tromelin Island. n, Meteorological station, Tromelin Island. o, Coral fossil, Tromelin Island. p, Anchor, Tromelin Island.

2009, Nov. 5 Litho. Perf. 13
420 A164 (90c) Souvenir booklet, #a-p 65.00

No. 420 sold for €21.50, and contains four panes, consisting of a block of four stamps of Nos. 420a-420d, 420e-420h, 420i-4290l, and 420m-420p.

Antarctic Treaty, 50th Anniv. — A302

2009, Dec. 1   Engr.   Perf. 13x13¼
421   A302   56c multi   1.75 1.75

Tourmaline
A303

2010, Jan. 2   Engr.   Perf. 13¼
422   A303   28c multi   .80   .80

Dr. Jean Rivolier (1923-2007), Medical
Researcher — A304

2010, Jan. 2   Litho.   Perf. 13
423   A304   56c multi   1.60 1.60

Birds on Ile du Lys — A305

2010, Jan. 2   Engr.   Perf. 13x13¼
424   A305   56c multi   1.60 1.60

Patureau House, Juan de Nova
Island — A306

2010, Jan. 2
425   A306   56c multi   1.60 1.60

Program Crac-ice — A307

2010, Jan. 2
426   A307   90c multi   2.50 2.50

Supply Ship Ile St. Paul — A308

2010, Jan. 2
427   A308   €1.35 multi   3.75 3.75

Crozet Orca — A309

2010, Jan. 2
428   A309   €2.80 multi   7.75 7.75

Kerguelen Terns — A310

2010, Jan. 2
429   A310   €4.30 multi   12.00 12.00

Miniature Sheet

Sea Lions of Amsterdam
Island — A311

No. 430: a, Sea lion and ship. b, Two sea
lions on rocks, denomination at UR in black,
horiz. c, Sea lion, denomination at UL in black,
horiz. d, Two sea lions near water, denomination in white at UR, horiz. e, Two sea lions,
denomination at LL in black, horiz.

Litho. & Engr.
2010, Jan. 2   Perf. 13
430   A311   56c Sheet of 5, #a-e   7.75 7.75

Miniature Sheet

Polar Transportation — A312

No. 431: a, Team of dogs pulling sled. b,
Weasel M29C. c, Sno-cat 743. d, HB40-
Castor. e, Challenger 65. f, PB 330.

2010, Jan. 2
431   A312   90c Sheet of 6, #a-f   15.00 15.00

Gabriel Pavilion, Paris — A313

2010, May 28   Litho.   Perf. 13
432   A313   56c multi   1.40 1.40
Second Elysée Philatelic Club Show, Paris.

Miniature Sheet

Albatross Protection — A314

No. 433: a, Albatross and chick on nest. b,
Albatross facing left. c, Albatross facing right.
d, Two juvenile albatrosses.

Litho. & Engr.
2010, June 12   Perf. 13
433   A314   56c Sheet of 4, #a-d   5.75 5.75

French Southern & Antarctic Territories
Booth at Espace Champerret Stamp
Show — A315

2010, Nov. 5   Litho.   Perf. 13
434   A315   56c multi   1.60 1.60

Self-Adhesive
Serpentine Die Cut 11
435   A315   56c multi   1.60 1.60

AIR POST STAMPS

Emperor Penguins and Map of
Antarctica — AP1

Unwmk.
1956, Apr. 25   Engr.   Perf. 13
C1   AP1   50fr lt ol grn & dk
                           grn   42.50 29.00
C2   AP1   100fr dl bl & indigo   35.00 25.00

Wandering Albatross — AP2

1959, Sept. 14
C3   AP2   200fr brn red, bl &
                           blk   40.00 27.50

Adélie Penguins — AP3

1963, Feb. 11   Unwmk.   Perf. 13
C4   AP3   50fr blk, dk bl & dp cl   42.50 32.50

Telstar Issue
Common Design Type
1963, Feb. 11
C5   CD111 50fr dp bl, ol & grn   29.00 21.00

Radio Towers,
Adelie Penguins
and IQSY
Emblem — AP4

1963, Dec. 16   Engr.
C6   AP4   100fr bl, ver & blk   110.00 87.50
International Quiet Sun Year, 1964-65.

Discovery of Adelie Land — AP5

1965, Jan. 20   Engr.   Perf. 13
C7   AP5   50fr blue & indigo   125.00 87.50
125th anniversary of the discovery of Adelie
Land by Dumont d'Urville.

ITU Issue
Common Design Type
1965, May 17   Unwmk.   Perf. 13
C8   CD120 30fr multi   200.00 160.00

French Satellite A-1 Issue
Common Design Type

Designs: 25fr, Diamant rocket and launching
installations. 30fr, A-1 satellite.

1966, Mar. 2   Engr.   Perf. 13
C9   CD121 25fr dk grn, choc
                           & sl   13.50 10.00
C10 CD121 30fr choc, sl & dk
                           grn   13.50 10.00
 a.   Pair, #C9-C10 + label   29.00 24.00

French Satellite D-1 Issue
Common Design Type
1966, Mar. 27
C11 CD122 50fr dk pur, lil &
                           org   57.50 40.00

Ionospheric
Research Pylon,
Adelie
Land — AP6

1966, Dec. 12
C12 AP6   25fr plum, bl & dk
                           brn   32.50 17.50

Port aux Français, Emperor Penguin and Explorer — AP7

40fr, Aerial view of Saint Paul Island.

1968-69		Engr.		Perf. 13
C13	AP7	40fr brt bl & dk gray	42.50	27.50
C14	AP7	50fr lt ultra, dk grn & blk	175.00	110.00

Issue dates: 50fr, Jan. 21; 40fr, Jan. 5, 1969.

Kerguelen Island and Rocket — AP8

Design: 30fr, Adelie Land.

1968, Apr. 22		Engr.		Perf. 13
C15	AP8	25fr sl grn, dk brn & Prus bl	19.00	14.00
C16	AP8	30fr dk brn, sl grn & Prus bl	19.00	14.00
a.		Pair, #C15-C16 + label	40.00	30.00

Space explorations with Dragon rockets, 1967-68.

Eiffel Tower, Antarctic Research Station, Ship from Paris Arms and Albatross AP9

1969, Jan. 13				
C17	AP9	50fr bright blue	45.00	35.00

5th Consultative Meeting of the Antarctic Treaty Powers, Paris, Nov. 18, 1968.

Concorde Issue
Common Design Type

1969, Apr. 17				
C18	CD129	85fr indigo & blue	55.00	37.50

Prepared but not issued with 87fr denomination. Value $7,000.

Map of Amsterdam Island AP10

Map of Kerguelen Island — AP11

Coat of Arms AP12

Designs: 50fr, Possession Island. 200fr, Point Geology Archipelago.

1969-71		Engr.		Perf. 13
C19	AP10	30fr brown	19.00	12.50
C20	AP11	50fr sl grn, bl & dk red	21.00	14.00
C21	AP11	100fr blue & blk	85.00	40.00
C22	AP10	200fr sl grn, brn & Prus bl	70.00	42.50
C23	AP12	500fr peacock blue	20.00	15.00
		Nos. C19-C23 (5)	215.00	124.00

30fr for the 20th anniv. of the Amsterdam Island Meteorological Station.
Issued: 100fr, 500fr, 12/21; 30fr, 3/27/70; 50fr, 12/22/70; 200fr, 1/1/71.

Port-aux-Français, 1970 — AP13

Design: 40fr, Port-aux-Français, 1950.

1971, Mar. 9		Engr.		Perf. 13
C24	AP13	40fr bl, ocher & sl grn	19.00	12.00
C25	AP13	50fr bl, grn ol & sl grn	19.00	12.00
a.		Pair, #C24-C25 + label	40.00	27.50

20th anniversary of Port-aux-Français on Kerguelen Island.

Marquis de Castries Taking Possession of Crozet Island, 1772 — AP14

250fr, Fleur-de-lis flag raising on Kerguelen Is.

1972		Engr.		Perf. 13
C26	AP14	100fr black	45.00	29.00
C27	AP14	250fr black & dk brn	100.00	45.00

Bicentenary of the discovery of the Crozet and Kerguelen Islands.
Issue dates: 100fr, Jan. 24; 250fr, Feb. 23.

M. S. Galliéni — AP15

1973, Jan. 25		Engr.		Perf. 13
C28	AP15	100fr black & blue	25.00	17.50

Exploration voyages of the Galliéni.

"Le Mascarin," 1772 — AP16

Sailing Ships: 145fr, "L'Astrolabe," 1840. 150fr, "Le Rolland," 1774. 185fr, "La Victoire," 1522.

1973, Dec. 13		Engr.		Perf. 13
C29	AP16	120fr brown olive	6.75	4.75
C30	AP16	145fr brt ultra	6.75	4.75
C31	AP16	150fr slate	8.00	8.00
C32	AP16	185fr ocher	10.50	8.00
		Nos. C29-C32 (4)	32.00	25.50

Ships used in exploring Antarctica.
See Nos. C37-C38.

Alfred Faure Base — AP17

Design: Nos. C33-C35 show panoramic view of Alfred Faure Base.

1974, Jan. 7		Engr.		Perf. 13
C33	AP17	75fr Prus bl, ultra & brn	8.00	5.25
C34	AP17	110fr Prus bl, ultra & brn	11.00	8.00
C35	AP17	150fr Prus bl, ultra & brn	14.00	8.00
a.		Triptych, Nos. C33-C35	37.50	30.00

Alfred Faure Antarctic Base, 10th anniv.

Penguin, Map of Antarctica, Letters — AP18

1974, Oct. 9		Engr.		Perf. 13
C36	AP18	150fr multicolored	7.00	5.50

Centenary of Universal Postal Union.

Ship Type of 1973
100fr, "Le Français." 200fr, "Pourquoi-pas?"

1974, Dec. 16		Engr.		Perf. 13
C37	AP16	100fr brt blue	5.50	3.00
C38	AP16	200fr dk car rose	9.00	4.50

Ships used in exploring Antarctica.

Rockets over Kerguelen Islands — AP19

Design: 90fr, Northern lights over map of northern coast of Russia.

1975, Jan. 26		Engr.		Perf. 13
C39	AP19	45fr purple & multi	7.00	4.00
C40	AP19	90fr purple & multi	9.00	5.25
a.		Pair, #C39-C40 + label	19.00	13.00

Franco-Soviet magnetosphere research.

"La Curieuse" — AP20

Ships: 2.70fr, Commandant Charcot. 4fr, Marion-Dufresne.

1976, Jan.		Engr.		Perf. 13
C41	AP20	1.90fr multicolored	3.25	2.00
C42	AP20	2.70fr multicolored	5.00	3.25
C43	AP20	4fr red & multi	9.00	4.25
		Nos. C41-C43 (3)	17.25	9.50

Dumont d'Urville Base, 1956 — AP21

4fr, Dumont d'Urville Base, 1976, Adelie Land.

1976, Jan.				
C44	AP21	1.20fr multicolored	9.00	4.00
C45	AP21	4fr multicolored	11.00	7.25
a.		Pair, #C44-C45 + label	24.00	16.00

Dumont d'Urville Antarctic Base, 20th anniv.

Capt. Cook's Ships Passing Kerguelen Island — AP22

1976, Dec. 31		Engr.		Perf. 13
C46	AP22	3.50fr slate & blue	13.00	8.00

Bicentenary of Capt. Cook's voyage past Kerguelen Island.

Sea Lion and Cub AP23

1977-79   **Engr.**   *Perf. 13*
C47 AP23 4fr dk blue, grn ('79)   3.00   2.50
C48 AP23 10fr multicolored   10.00   9.00

Satellite Survey, Kerguelen — AP24

Designs: 50c, 2.70fr, Satellites, Kerguelen. 70c, Geophysical laboratory. 1.90fr, Satellite and Kerguelen tracking station. 3fr, Satellites, Adelie Land.

1977-79   **Engr.**   *Perf. 13*
C49 AP24 50c multi ('79)   .90   .70
C50 AP24 70c multi ('79)   .90   .70
C51 AP24 1.90fr multi ('79)   1.60   1.40
C52 AP24 2.70fr multi ('78)   2.75   2.00
C53 AP24 3fr multicolored   4.25   3.25
    Nos. C49-C53 (5)   10.40   8.05

Elephant Seals — AP25

1979, Jan. 1
C54 AP25 10fr multicolored   5.50   4.50

Challenger — AP26

1979, Jan. 1
C55 AP26 2.70fr black & blue   2.25   1.75
Antarctic expeditions to Crozet and Kerguelen Islands, 1872-1876.

La Recherche and L'Esperance — AP27

1979
C56 AP27 1.90fr deep blue   1.50   1.10
Arrival of d'Entrecasteaux and Kermadec at Amsterdam Island, Mar. 28, 1792.

Lion Rock — AP28

1979
C57 AP28 90c multicolored   1.10   .70

Natural Arch, Kerguelen Island, 1840 — AP29

1979
C58 AP29 2.70fr multicolored   1.25   1.10

Phylica Nitida, Amsterdam Island — AP30

1979
C59 AP30 10fr multicolored   4.00   3.25

Charles de Gaulle, 10th Anniversary of Death AP31

1980, Nov. 9   **Engr.**   *Perf. 13*
C60 AP31 5.40fr multicolored   11.00   8.00

HB-40 Castor Truck and Trailer — AP32

1980, Dec. 15
C61 AP32 2.40fr multicolored   1.25   1.00

Supply Ship Saint Marcouf — AP33

1980, Dec. 15
C62 AP33 3.50fr shown   1.60   1.10
C63 AP33 7.30fr Icebreaker Norsel   2.50   2.00

Glacial Landscape, Dumont d'Urville Sea — AP34

Chionis — AP35

Adele Dumont d'Urville (1798-1842) — AP36

Arcad III — AP37

25th Anniv. of Charcot Station — AP38

Antares — AP39

1981   **Engr.**   *Perf. 13, 12½x13 (2fr)*
C64 AP34 1.30fr multicolored   .70   .45
C65 AP35 1.50fr black   .70   .50
C66 AP36 2fr black & lt brn   .90   .85
C67 AP37 3.85fr multicolored   1.60   1.25
C68 AP38 5fr multicolored   1.75   1.50
C69 AP39 8.40fr multicolored   2.75   2.25
    Nos. C64-C69 (6)   8.40   6.80

PHILEXFRANCE '82 Stamp Exhibition, Paris, June 11-21 — AP40

1982, June 11   **Engr.**   *Perf. 13*
C70 AP40 8fr multicolored   5.50   5.25

French Overseas Possessions Week, Sept. 18-25 — AP41

1982, Sept. 17   **Engr.**   *Perf. 13*
C71 AP41 5fr Commandant Charcot   1.75   1.75

Apostle Islands — AP42

1983, Jan. 3   **Engr.**   *Perf. 13*
C72 AP42 65c multicolored   .55   .35

Sputnik I, 25th Anniv. of Intl. Geophysical Year — AP43

Orange Bay Base, Cape Horn, 1883, Cent. — AP44

5.20fr, Scoresby Sound Base, Greenland, 50th anniv.

1983, Jan. 3
C73 AP43 1.50fr multicolored   .60   .60
C74 AP44 3.30fr multicolored   1.75   1.75
C75 AP44 5.20fr multicolored   2.00   2.00
    a.   Strip of 3, #C73-C75   4.50   4.50

AP45

1983, Jan. 3
C76 AP45 4.55fr dark blue   4.00   3.00

Abstract, by G. Mathieu — AP46

Illustration reduced.

1983, Jan. 3   **Photo.**   *Perf. 13x13½*
C77 AP46 25fr multicolored   10.00   8.00

Erebus off Antarctic Ice Cap, 1842 — AP47

Port of Joan of Arc, 1930 — AP48

1984, Jan. 1   **Engr.**   **Perf. 13**
C78 AP47 2.60fr ultra & dk blue   1.10 1.00
C79 AP48 4.70fr multicolored   1.75 1.75

Aurora Polaris — AP49

1984, Jan. 1   **Photo.**
C80 AP49 3.50fr multicolored   2.00 1.25

Manned Flight Bicentenary (1983) — AP50

Various balloons and airships.

1984, Jan. 1   **Engr.**
C81 AP50 3.50fr multicolored   1.75 1.75
C82 AP50 7.80fr multicolored   2.75 2.75
  a.   Pair, #C81-C82 + label   5.00 5.00

Patrol Boat Albatros — AP51

1984, July 2   **Engr.**   **Perf. 13**
C83 AP51 11.30fr multi   4.25 4.25

NORDPOSTA Exhibition — AP52

1984, Nov. 3   **Engr.**   **Perf. 13**
C84 AP52 9fr Scientific Vessel Gauss   4.50 3.50
Issued se-tenant with label.

Corsican Sheep — AP53

Amsterdam Albatross AP54

1985, Jan. 1   **Engr.**   **Perf. 13**
C85 AP53 70c Mouflons   .70 .40
C86 AP54 3.90fr Diomedia amsterdamensis   1.60 1.25

La Novara, Frigate AP55

1985, Jan. 1   **Engr.**   **Perf. 13**
C87 AP55 12.80fr La Novara at St. Paul   5.00 4.50

Explorer and Seal, by Tremois — AP56

Design: Explorer, seal, names of territories. Illustration reduced.

1985, Jan. 1   **Photo.**   **Perf. 13x12½**
C88 AP56 30fr + label   11.00 8.50

Sailing Ships, Ropes, Flora & Fauna — AP57

1985, Aug. 6   **Engr.**   **Perf. 13**
C89 AP57   2fr blk, brt bl & ol grn   .70 .55
C90 AP57 12.80fr blk, ol grn & brt bl   3.75 3.75
  a.   Pair, #C89-C90 + label   5.50 5.50
French Southern & Antarctic Territories, 30th anniv. No. C90a has continuous design with center label.

Bird Type of 1986
1986, Jan. 1   **Engr.**   **Perf. 13½x13**
C91 A56 4.60fr Sea Gulls   2.00 1.75

Antarctic Atmospheric Research, 10th Anniv. — AP58

1986, Jan. 1
C92 AP58 14fr blk, dk red & brt org   5.00 4.00

Jean Charcot (1867-1936), Explorer — AP59

1986, Jan. 1
C93 AP59 2.10fr Ship Pourquoi Pas   .90 .60
C94 AP59   14fr Ship in storm   4.50 4.25
  a.   Pair, #C93-C94 + label   6.25 6.25

SPOT Satellite over the Antarctic — AP60

1986, May 26   **Engr.**   **Perf. 13**
C95 AP60 8fr dp ultra, sep & dk ol grn   3.25 2.50

J.B. Charcot — AP61

1987, Jan. 1   **Engr.**   **Perf. 13x13½**
C96 AP61 14.60fr multi   5.00 4.50

Ocean Drilling Program — AP62

1987, Jan. 1   **Perf. 13½x13**
C97 AP62 16.80fr lem, dk ultra & bluish blk   5.50 4.50

INMARSAT — AP63

1987, Mar. 2   **Engr.**   **Perf. 13**
C98 AP63 16.80fr multi   8.00 7.50

French Polar Expeditions, 40th Anniv. — AP64

1988, Jan. 1
C99 AP64 20fr lake, ol grn & plum   8.00 6.75

Views of Penguin Is. — AP65

1988, Jan. 1
C100 AP65 3.90fr dk bl & sep   1.75 1.50
C101 AP65 15.10fr dp grn, choc brn & dk bl   5.50 5.00
See Nos. C103, C109.

Founding of Permanent Settlements in the Territories, 40th Anniv. — AP66

1989, Jan. 1   **Engr.**   **Perf. 13½x13**
C102 AP66 15.50fr black   5.00 4.75

Island View Type
1989, Jan. 1
C103 AP65 8.40fr Apostle Islands 2.75 2.50

La Curieuse — AP68

1989, Jan. 1   **Perf. 13x12½**
C104 AP68 2.20fr multicolored   .80 .70
C105 AP68 15.50fr multi, diff.   5.00 5.00
  a.   Pair, #C104-C105 + label   6.00 6.00
No. C105a label continues the design.

French Revolution, Bicent. — AP69

1989, July 14　Engr.　*Perf. 13x12½*
C106　AP69　5fr pink, dark olive
　　　　　grn & dark
　　　　　blue　　　　　5.50　3.50

Souvenir Sheet
Perf. 13
C107　　　　Sheet of 4　10.00　10.00
　a.　AP69 5fr Prus green, brt ul-
　　　tra & dark red　　2.50　2.50
　No. C107 for PHILEXFRANCE '89.

15th Antarctic Treaty Summit
Conference — AP70

1989, Oct. 9　Engr.　*Perf. 13*
C108　AP70　17.70fr multicolored　6.00　5.75

Island View Type
1990, Jan. 1　Engr.　*Perf. 13*
C109　AP65　7.30fr Isle of Pigs,
　　　　　Crozet Isls.　3.00　2.40

L'Astrolabe, Expedition Team — AP72

1990, Jan. 1
C110　AP72　15.50fr dk red vio &
　　　　　blk　　　　5.00　5.00
　Discovery of Adelie Land by Dumont
D'Urville, 150th anniv.

L'Astrolabe, Commanded by Dumont
D'Urville, 1840 — AP73

1990, Jan. 1
C111　AP73　2.20fr *L'Astrolabe,*
　　　　　1988　　　　.80　.75
C112　AP73　15.50fr shown　5.00　5.00
　a.　Pair, #C111-C112 + label　6.50　6.50

Bird, by Folon — AP74

Illustration reduced.

1990, Jan. 1　Litho.　*Perf. 12½x13*
C113　AP74　30fr multicolored　10.00　9.50

Albatross,
Argos
Satellite
AP75

1991, Jan. 1
C114　AP75　2.10fr red brn, bl &
　　　　　brn　　　　1.50　.95

Climatological Research — AP76

1991, Jan. 1　Engr.　*Perf. 13*
C115　AP76　3.60fr Weather bal-
　　　　　loons, in-
　　　　　struments　1.40　1.40
C116　AP76　20fr Research
　　　　　ship　　　7.75　7.75
　a.　Pair, #C115-C116 + label　10.00　10.00

Charles de Gaulle (1890-
1970) — AP77

1991, Jan. 1
C117　AP77　18.80fr blk, red & bl　7.75　7.75

Cape
Petrel — AP78

1992, Jan. 1　Engr.　*Perf. 13*
C118　AP78　3.40fr multicolored　2.25　1.40

French Institute of Polar Research and
Technology — AP79

#C120, Polar bear with man offering flowers.

1991, Dec. 16　Engr.　*Perf. 13x12*
C119　AP79　15fr multicolored　5.75　5.75
C120　AP79　15fr multicolored　5.75　5.75
　a.　Strip, #C119-C120 + label　12.00　12.00

Christopher Columbus and Discovery
of America — AP80

1992, Jan. 1　　　　*Perf. 13*
C121　AP80　22fr multicolored　9.75　9.75

Mapping Satellite Poseidon — AP81

1992, Jan. 1　Engr.　*Perf. 13*
C122　AP81　24.50fr multi　11.00　10.50

Dumont d'Urville Base, Adelie
Land — AP82

Illustration reduced.

1992, Jan. 1　Litho.　*Perf. 13x12½*
C123　AP82　25.70fr multi　12.00　10.50

Amateur Radio — AP83

1993, Jan. 1　Engr.　*Perf. 13*
C124　AP83　2fr multicolored　2.00　.75

New Animal Biology Laboratory, Adelie
Land — AP84

1993, Jan. 1
C125　AP84　25.40fr multicolored　11.00　6.75

Support Base D10 — AP85

1993, Jan. 1
C126　AP85　25.70fr ol, red & bl　11.00　7.00

Opening of Adelie Land
Airfield — AP86

1993, Jan. 1
C127　AP86　30fr multicolored　13.00　8.75

Krill — AP87

1994, Jan. 1　Engr.　*Perf. 13*
C128　AP87　15fr black　6.50　4.00

Fishery Management — AP88

1994, Jan. 1
C129　AP88　23fr multicolored　10.00　6.00

Satellite, Ground Station — AP89

Design: 27.30fr, Lidar Station.

1994, Jan. 1
C130　AP89　26.70fr multicolored　12.00　7.00
C131　AP89　27.30fr multicolored　12.00　7.25

Arrival of Emperor Penguins — AP90

Illustration reduced.

1994, Jan. 1　　　　*Perf. 13x12½*
C132　AP90　28fr blue & black　13.00　8.00

Erebus Mission — AP91

1995, Jan. 2　Engr.　*Perf. 13*
C133　AP91　4.30fr bl, vio & slate　2.25　1.50

Moving of Winter Station,
Charcot — AP92

1995, Jan. 2   **Litho.**
C134 AP92 15fr multicolored   6.50 4.25

G. Lesquin (1803-30) — AP93

Illustration reduced.

1995, Jan. 2
C135 AP93 28fr multicolored   12.00 8.00

Map of East Island — AP94

1996, Jan. 1   **Engr.**   **Perf. 13**
C136 AP94 20fr multicolored   8.50 6.00

Expedition to Dome/C — AP95

1996, Jan. 1
C137 AP95 23fr dark blue   10.00 7.00

Blue Whale, Southern Whale
Sanctuary — AP96

1996, Jan. 1
C138 AP96 26.70fr multicolored   12.00 8.00

Port-Couvreux — AP97

1996, Jan. 1
C139 AP97 27.30fr multicolored   12.00 8.50

Jasus Paulensis
AP98

1997, Jan. 1   **Engr.**   **Perf. 12½x13**
C140 AP98 5.20fr multicolored   3.00 1.75

Racing
Yacht
Charentes
2 — AP99

1997, Jan. 1   **Litho.**   **Perf. 13**
C141 AP99 16fr multicolored   8.00 5.50

John Nunn, Shipwrecked 1825-29,
Hope Cottage — AP100

1997, Jan. 1   **Engr.**
C142 AP100 20fr multicolored   8.75 6.25

ICOTA Program — AP101

1997, Jan. 1
C143 AP101 24fr multicolored   10.50 7.50

Harpagifer Spinosus — AP102

1997, Jan. 1
C144 AP102 27fr multicolored   12.00 8.50

EPICA Program — AP103

1998, Jan. 2   **Engr.**   **Perf. 13**
C145 AP103 5.20fr dk brn & lil   2.50 1.40

First Radio Meteorological Station,
Port Aux Francais — AP104

1998, Jan. 2
C146 AP104 8fr black, blue & red 4.25 2.25

King
Penguin,
Argos
Satellite
AP105

1998, Jan. 2   **Perf. 12½x13**
C147 AP105 16fr multicolored   7.00 4.75

Ranunculas
Moseleyi
AP106

1998, Jan. 2
C148 AP106 24fr multicolored   10.50 6.50

Intl. Geophysical Year, 40th
Anniv. — AP107

Illustration reduced.

1998, Oct.   **Engr.**   **Perf. 13x12½**
C149 AP107 5.20fr dk bl, blk &
             brick red   3.00 1.50

FRENCH SUDAN

'french sü-'dan

LOCATION — In northwest Africa,
north of French Guinea and Ivory
Coast
GOVT. — French Colony
AREA — 590,966 sq. mi.
POP. — 3,794,270 (1941)
CAPITAL — Bamako

In 1899 French Sudan was abolished
as a separate colony and was divided
among Dahomey, French Guinea, Ivory
Coast, Senegal and Senegambia and
Niger. Issues for French Sudan were
resumed in 1921.

From 1906 to 1921 a part of this territory was known as Upper Senegal and
Niger. A part of Upper Volta was added
in 1933. See Mali.

100 Centimes = 1 Franc

See French West Africa No. 70 for
stamp inscribed "Soudan Francais" and
"Afrique Occidentale Francaise."

Navigation and
Commerce
A1   A2
Stamps of French Colonies,
Surcharged in Black

Perf. 14x13½

1894, Apr. 12			**Unwmk.**	
1	A1	15c on 75c car, *rose*	*4,600.*	*2,300.*
2	A1	25c on 1fr brnz grn, *straw*	*5,000.*	*1,700.*

The imperforate stamp like No. 1 was made
privately in Paris from a fragment of the lithographic stone which had been used in the Colony for surcharging No. 1.

Counterfeit surcharges exist.

1894-1900	**Typo.**	**Perf. 14x13½**		
Name of colony in Blue or Carmine				
3	A2	1c blk, *lil bl*	1.75	1.75
4	A2	2c brn, *buff*	2.50	2.50
5	A2	4c claret, *lav*	6.00	6.00
6	A2	5c grn, *grnsh*	9.50	9.50
7	A2	10c blk, *lav*	21.00	21.00
8	A2	10c red ('00)	7.25	7.25
9	A2	15c blue, quadrille pa-		
		per	6.50	6.50
10	A2	15c gray, *lt gray* ('00)	7.50	7.50
11	A2	20c red, *grn*	32.50	32.50
12	A2	25c blk, *rose*	27.50	27.50
13	A2	25c blue ('00)	8.50	8.50
14	A2	30c brn, *bister*	40.00	40.00
15	A2	40c red, *straw*	35.00	35.00
16	A2	50c car, *rose*	57.50	57.50
17	A2	50c brn, *az* ('00)	15.00	15.00
18	A2	75c dp vio, *org*	52.50	52.50
19	A2	1fr brnz grn, *straw*	11.00	11.00
		Nos. 3-19 (17)	341.50	341.50

Perf. 13½x14 stamps are counterfeits.
Nos. 8, 10, 13, 17 were issued in error. They
were accepted for use in the other colonies.

Camel and
Rider — A3

Stamps of Upper Senegal and Niger
Overprinted in Black

1921-30			**Perf. 13½x14**	
21	A3	1c brn vio & vio	.25	.40
22	A3	2c dk gray & dl vio	.30	.50
23	A3	4c blk & blue	.30	.50
24	A3	5c ol brn & dk brn	.30	.40
25	A3	10c yel grn & bl grn	1.00	.55
26	A3	10c red vio & bl		
		('25)	.40	.50
27	A3	15c red brn & org	.50	.55
28	A3	15c yel grn & dp		
		grn ('25)	.40	.40
29	A3	15c org brn & vio		
		('27)	1.60	1.60
30	A3	20c brn vio & blk	.50	.55
31	A3	25c blk & bl grn	1.25	.80
a.		Booklet pane of 4	—	
		Complete booklet, 5 #31a	575.00	
32	A3	30c red org & rose	1.60	1.60
33	A3	30c bl grn & blk		
		('26)	.80	.70
34	A3	30c dl grn & bl grn		
		('28)	2.00	2.00
35	A3	35c rose & vio	.40	.55
36	A3	40c gray & rose	1.25	1.25
37	A3	45c bl & ol brn	1.25	1.25
38	A3	50c ultra & bl	1.60	1.25
39	A3	50c red org & bl		
		('26)	1.25	1.25
40	A3	60c vio, *pnksh* ('26)	1.25	1.25
41	A3	65c bis & pale bl		
		('28)	1.60	1.60
42	A3	75c org & ol brn	1.60	2.00
43	A3	90c brn red & pink		
		('30)	5.50	5.50
44	A3	1fr dk brn & dl vio	1.60	2.00
45	A3	1.10fr gray lil & red		
		vio ('28)	2.75	3.50
46	A3	1.50fr dp bl & bl ('30)	5.50	5.50
47	A3	2fr grn & bl	2.40	2.75
48	A3	3fr red vio ('30)	12.00	12.00
a.		Double overprint	190.00	
49	A3	5fr vio & blk	6.75	6.75
		Nos. 21-49 (29)	57.90	59.45

Type of 1921
Surcharged

1922, Sept. 28
50 A3 60c on 75c vio, *pnksh* .80 .80

Stamps and Type of 1921-30
Surcharged with New Values and Bars
1925-27
51	A3	25c on 45c	.80	.80
52	A3	65c on 75c	2.00	2.40
53	A3	85c on 2fr	2.00	2.40
54	A3	85c on 5fr	2.00	2.40
55	A3	90c on 75c brn red & sal pink ('27)	2.40	2.75
56	A3	1.25fr on 1fr dp bl & lt bl (R) ('26)	1.25	1.60
57	A3	1.50fr on 1fr dp bl & ultra ('27)	1.60	2.00
58	A3	3fr on 5fr dl red & brn org ('27)	6.50	5.50
59	A3	10fr on 5fr brn red & bl grn ('27)	24.00	21.00
60	A3	20fr on 5fr vio & ver ('27)	29.00	29.00
		Nos. 51-60 (10)	71.55	69.85

Sudanese
Woman — A4

Entrance to the
Residency at
Djenné — A5

Sudanese
Boatman — A6

1931-40 Typo. Perf. 13x14
61	A4	1c dk red & blk	.25	.25
62	A4	2c dp blue & org	.25	.25
63	A4	3c dk red & blk ('40)	.25	.25
64	A4	4c gray lil & rose	.25	.25
65	A4	5c indigo & grn	.25	.25
66	A4	10c ol grn & rose	.25	.25
67	A4	15c blk & brt vio	.30	.30
68	A4	20c hn brn & lt bl	.30	.30
69	A4	25c red vio & lt red	.30	.30
70	A5	30c grn & lt grn	.75	.50
71	A5	30c dk bl & red org ('40)	.30	.30
72	A5	35c ol grn & grn ('38)	.50	.50
73	A5	40c ol grn & pink	.30	.30
74	A5	45c dk bl & red org	.95	.65
75	A5	45c ol grn & grn ('40)	.50	.50
76	A5	50c red & black	.30	.30
77	A5	55c ultra & car ('38)	.55	.55
78	A5	60c brt bl & brn ('40)	1.20	1.20
79	A5	65c brt vio & blk	.65	.55
80	A5	70c vio bl & car rose ('40)	.80	.80
81	A5	75c brt bl & ol brn	2.40	2.00
82	A5	80c car & brn ('38)	.55	.55
83	A5	90c dp red & red org	1.60	.80
84	A5	90c brt vio & sl blk ('39)	.90	1.00
85	A5	1fr indigo & grn	8.00	2.40
86	A5	1fr rose red ('38)	4.75	2.40
87	A5	1fr car & brn ('40)	.80	.80
88	A6	1.25fr vio & dl vio ('33)	.80	.80
89	A6	1.25fr red ('39)	.90	1.00
90	A6	1.40fr brt vio & blk ('40)	1.25	.90
91	A6	1.50fr dk bl & ultra	.65	.55
92	A6	1.60fr brn & dp bl ('40)	.90	.90
93	A6	1.75fr dk brn & dp bl ('33)	.80	.80
94	A6	1.75fr vio bl ('38)	.80	.80
95	A6	2fr org brn & grn	.75	.55
96	A6	2.25fr vio bl & ultra ('39)	1.00	1.10
97	A6	2.50fr lt brown ('40)	1.60	1.60
98	A6	3fr Prus grn & brn	.75	.40
99	A6	5fr red & blk	2.00	1.20
100	A6	10fr dull bl & grn	2.00	2.00
101	A6	20fr red vio & brn	2.40	2.40
		Nos. 61-101 (41)	44.80	33.50

For surcharges see Nos. B7-B10.
For 10c and 30c, without "RF," see Nos. 120-121.

Common Design Types
pictured following the introduction.

Colonial Exposition Issue
Common Design Types
1931, Apr. 13 Engr. Perf. 12½
Name of Country Printed in Black
102	CD70	40c deep green	4.75	4.75
103	CD71	50c violet	4.75	4.75
104	CD72	90c red orange	4.75	4.75
105	CD73	1.50fr dull blue	4.75	4.75
		Nos. 102-105 (4)	19.00	19.00

Paris International Exposition Issue
Common Design Types
1937, Apr. 15 Perf. 13
106	CD74	20c deep violet	2.00	2.00
107	CD75	30c dark green	2.00	2.00
108	CD76	40c carmine rose	2.00	2.00
109	CD77	50c dark brown	1.60	1.60
110	CD78	90c red	1.60	1.60
111	CD79	1.50fr ultra	2.00	2.00
		Nos. 106-111 (6)	11.20	11.20

Colonial Arts Exhibition Issue
Souvenir Sheet
Common Design Type
1937 Engr. Imperf.
112 CD77 3fr magenta & blk 8.75 10.50

Caillie Issue
Common Design Type
1939, Apr. 5 Perf. 12½x12
113	CD81	90c org brn & org	.95	.95
114	CD81	2fr brt violet	1.10	1.10
115	CD81	2.25fr ultra & dk bl	1.10	1.10
		Nos. 113-115 (3)	3.15	3.15

New York World's Fair Issue
Common Design Type
1939, May 10
116	CD82	1.25fr car lake	1.20	1.20
117	CD82	2.25fr ultra	1.20	1.20

Entrance to the
Residency at
Djenné and Marshal
Pétain — A7

1941 Engr. Perf. 12x12½
118	A7	1fr green	.80	—
119	A7	2.50fr blue	.80	—

For surcharges, see Nos. B14-B15.

Types of 1931-40 without "RF"
1943-44 Typo. Perf. 13½x14
120	A4	10c ol green & rose	.65	
121	A5	30c dk bl & red org	.95	

Nos. 120-121 were issued by the Vichy government in France, but were not placed on sale in French Sudan.

Stamps of French Sudan were superseded by those of French West Africa.

SEMI-POSTAL STAMPS

Curie Issue
Common Design Type
Unwmk.
1938, Oct. 24 Engr. Perf. 13
B1 CD80 1.75fr + 50c brt ultra 12.50 12.50

French Revolution Issue
Common Design Type
1939, July 5 Photo.
Name and Value Typo. in Black
B2	CD83	45c + 25c green	10.00	10.00
B3	CD83	70c + 30c brown	10.00	10.00
B4	CD83	90c + 35c red org	10.00	10.00
B5	CD83	1.25fr + 1fr rose pink	10.00	10.00
B6	CD83	2.25fr + 2fr blue	10.00	10.00
		Nos. B2-B6 (5)	50.00	50.00

Stamps of 1931-40,
Surcharged in Black
or Red

1941 Perf. 13x14
B7	A5	50c + 1fr red & blk (R)	3.25	3.25
B8	A5	80c + 2fr car & brn	7.25	7.25
B9	A6	1.50fr + 2fr dk bl & ultra	7.25	7.25
B10	A6	2fr + 3fr org brn & grn	7.25	7.25
		Nos. B7-B10 (4)	25.00	25.00

Common Design Type and

Native
Officer — SP1

Aviation
Officer — SP2

1941 Photo. Perf. 13½
B11	SP1	1fr + 1fr red	1.25
B12	CD86	1.50fr + 3fr claret	1.40
B13	SP2	2.50fr + 1fr blue	1.40
		Nos. B11-B13 (3)	4.05

Surtax for the defense of the colonies.
Issued by the Vichy government in France, but not placed on sale in French Sudan.

Petain Type of 1941
Surcharged in Black or Red

1944 Engr. Perf. 12x12½
B14		50c + 1.50fr on 2.50fr deep blue (R)	.80	
B15		+ 2.50fr on 1fr green	.80	

Colonial Development Fund.
Nos. B14-B15 were issued by the Vichy government in France, but were not placed on sale in French Sudan.

AIR POST STAMPS

Common Design Type
Perf. 12½x12
1940, Feb. 8 Unwmk. Engr.
C1	CD85	1.90fr ultra	.40	.40
C2	CD85	2.90fr dark red	.55	.55
C3	CD85	4.50fr dk gray green	.95	.95
C4	CD85	4.90fr yellow bister	.95	.95
C5	CD85	6.90fr deep orange	1.10	1.10
		Nos. C1-C5 (5)	3.95	3.95

Common Design Types
1942, Oct. 19
C6	CD88	50c carmine & bl	.30
C7	CD88	1fr brown & blk	.40
C8	CD88	2fr dk grn & red brn	.65
C9	CD88	3fr dk blue & scar	.80
C10	CD88	5fr vio & brn red	.80

Frame Engr., Center Typo.
C11	CD89	10fr ultra, ind & gray blk	1.20
C12	CD89	20fr rose car, mag & lt vio	1.40
C13	CD89	50fr yel grn, dl grn & dl bl	2.40
		Nos. C6-C13 (8)	7.95

There is doubt whether Nos. C7-C12 were officially placed in use.

AIR POST SEMI-POSTAL STAMPS

Types of Dahomey Air Post Semi-
Postal Issue
Perf. 13½x12½, 13 (#CB3)
Photo, Engr. (#CB3)
1942, June 22
CB1	SPAP1	1.50fr + 3.50fr green	.80	5.50
CB2	SPAP2	2fr + 6fr brown	.80	5.50
CB3	SPAP2	3fr + 9fr car red	.80	5.50
		Nos. CB1-CB3 (3)	2.40	16.50

Native children's welfare fund.

Colonial Education Fund
Common Design Type
Perf. 12½x13½
1942, June 22 Engr.
CB4 CD86a 1.20fr + 1.80fr blue & red .80 5.50

POSTAGE DUE STAMPS

D1

D2

Postage Due Stamps of Upper
Senegal and Niger Overprinted
Perf. 14x13½
1921, Dec. Unwmk. Typo.
J1	D1	5c green	.50	.65
J2	D1	10c rose	.65	.80
J3	D1	15c gray	.80	.95
J4	D1	20c brown	1.10	1.25
J5	D1	30c blue	1.10	1.25
J6	D1	50c black	1.90	2.10
J7	D1	60c orange	2.00	2.25
J8	D1	1fr violet	2.40	2.60
		Nos. J1-J8 (8)	10.45	11.85

Type of 1921 Issue
Surcharged

1927, Oct. 10
J9	D1	2fr on 1fr lilac rose	7.25	8.00
J10	D1	3fr on 1fr org brown	7.25	8.00

1931, Mar. 9
J11	D2	5c green	.25	.30
J12	D2	10c rose	.25	.30
J13	D2	15c gray	.30	.50
J14	D2	20c dark brown	.30	.50
J15	D2	30c dark blue	.50	.55
J16	D2	50c black	.55	.65

J17	D2	60c deep orange	.70	.80
J18	D2	1fr violet	1.10	1.20
J19	D2	2fr lilac rose	1.60	1.60
J20	D2	3fr red brown	1.60	1.60
		Nos. J11-J20 (10)	7.15	8.00

FRENCH WEST AFRICA

'french 'west 'a-fri-kə

LOCATION — Northwestern Africa
GOVT. — French colonial administrative unit
AREA — 1,821,768 sq. mi.
POP. — 18,777,163 (est.)
CAPITAL — Dakar

French West Africa comprised the former colonies of Senegal, French Guinea, Ivory Coast, Dahomey, French Sudan, Mauritania, Niger and Upper Volta.

In 1958, these former colonies became republics, eventually issuing their own stamps. Until the republic issues appeared, stamps of French West Africa continued in use. The Senegal and Sudanese Republics issued stamps jointly as the Federation of Mali, starting in 1959.

> Catalogue values for all unused stamps in this country are for Never Hinged items.

Many stamps other than Nos. 65-72 and 77 are inscribed "Afrique Occidentale Francaise" and the name of one of the former colonies. See listings in these colonies for such stamps.

Senegal No. 156 Surcharged in Red

1943		**Unwmk.**	**Perf. 12½x12**	
1	A30	1.50fr on 65c dk vio	1.10	.95
2	A30	5.50fr on 65c dk vio	1.40	.80
3	A30	50fr on 65c dk vio	3.50	2.00

Mauritania No. 91 Surcharged in Red

1943			**Perf. 13**	
4	A7	3.50fr on 65c dp grn	.75	.55
5	A7	4fr on 65c dp grn	.75	.55
6	A7	5fr on 65c dp grn	1.40	1.10
7	A7	10fr on 65c dp grn	1.40	1.10
		Nos. 1-7 (7)	10.30	7.05

Senegal No. 143, 148 and 188 Surcharged with New Values in Black and Orange

1944			**Perf. 12½x12**	
8	A29	1.50fr on 15c blk (O)	.80	.65
9	A29	4.50fr on 15c blk (O)	1.10	.90
10	A29	5.50fr on 2c brn	2.40	1.60
11	A29	10fr on 15c blk (O)	3.50	1.75
12	CD81	20fr on 90c org brn & org	2.40	1.75
13	CD81	50fr on 90c org brn & org	6.00	3.25

Mauritania No. 109 Surcharged in Black

14	CD81	15fr on 90c org brn & org	2.25	1.60
		Nos. 8-14 (7)	18.45	11.50

Common Design Types pictured following the introduction.

Eboue Issue
Common Design Type

1945		**Engr.**	**Perf. 13**	
15	CD91	2fr black	.95	.70
16	CD91	25fr Prussian green	2.25	1.60

Nos. 15 and 16 exist imperforate.

Colonial Soldier — A1

1945		**Litho.**	**Perf. 12½x12, 12**	
17	A1	10c indigo & buff	.40	.25
18	A1	30c olive & yel	.40	.25
19	A1	40c blue & buff	.65	.50
20	A1	50c red org & gray	.65	.50
21	A1	60c ol brn & bl	.65	.50
22	A1	70c mag & cit	.65	.50
23	A1	80c bl grn & pale lem	.65	.50
24	A1	1fr brn vio & cit	.75	.55
25	A1	1.20fr gray brn & cit	4.25	2.40
26	A1	1.50fr choc & pink	.75	.50
27	A1	2fr ocher and gray	.90	.50
28	A1	2.40fr red & gray	1.25	.95
29	A1	3fr brn red & yelsh	.75	.40
30	A1	4fr ultra & pink	.75	.40
31	A1	4.50fr org brn & yelsh	.75	.40
32	A1	5fr dk pur & yelsh	.75	.40
33	A1	10fr ol grn & pink	1.40	1.00
34	A1	15fr orange & yel	2.50	1.40
35	A1	20fr sl grn & grnsh	2.90	1.60
		Nos. 17-35 (19)	21.75	13.50

Rifle Dance, Mauritania — A2

Shelling Coconuts, Togo — A6

Bamako Dike, French Sudan — A3

Trading Canoe, Niger River — A4

Oasis of Bilma, Niger — A5

Kouandé Weaving, Dahomey A7

Donkey Caravan, Senegal A8

Crocodile and Hippopotamus, Ivory Coast — A9

Gathering Coconuts, French Guinea — A10

Peul Woman of Dienné — A12

Bamako Fountain, French Sudan A11

Bamako Market — A13

Dahomey Laborer — A14

Woman of Mauritania A15

Fula Woman, French Guinea A16

Djenné Mosque, French Sudan A17

Monorail Train, Senegal A18

Agni Woman, Ivory Coast — A19

Azwa Women at Niger River — A20

1947		**Engr. Unwmk.**	**Perf. 12½**	
36	A2	10c blue	.40	.25
37	A3	30c red brn	.40	.25
38	A4	40c gray grn	.65	.25
39	A5	50c red brn	.50	.25
40	A6	60c gray blk	.90	.50
41	A7	80c brown vio	.90	.50
42	A8	1fr maroon	.65	.30
43	A9	1.20fr dk blue grn	1.90	1.40
44	A10	1.50fr ultra	1.90	1.10
45	A11	2fr red orange	.90	.25
46	A12	3fr chocolate	.90	.30
47	A13	3.60fr brown red	1.75	1.40
48	A14	4fr deep blue	.65	.30
49	A15	5fr gray green	.65	.25
50	A16	6fr dark blue	.90	.30
51	A17	10fr brn red	1.40	.25
52	A18	15fr sepia	2.60	.30
53	A19	20fr chocolate	1.60	.30
54	A20	25fr grnsh blk	3.00	.50
		Nos. 36-54 (19)	22.55	8.95

Types of 1947

1948		**Re-engraved**		
55	A6	60c brown olive	1.20	.80
56	A12	3fr chocolate	1.20	.55

Nos. 40 and 46 are inscribed "TOGO" in lower margin. Inscription omitted on Nos. 55 and 56.

Imperforates
Most stamps of French West Africa from 1949 onward exist imperforate in issued and trial colors, and also in small presentation sheets in issued colors.

Military Medal Issue
Common Design Type
Engraved and Typographed

1952, Dec. 1			**Perf. 13**	
57	CD101	15fr multicolored	8.75	6.50

Treich Laplène and Map — A21

1952, Dec. 1			**Engr.**	
58	A21	40fr brown lake	2.40	.40

Marcel Treich Laplène, a leading contributor to the development of Ivory Coast.

Medical Laboratory A22

1953, Nov. 18				
59	A22	15fr brn, dk bl grn & blk brn	1.60	.40

Couple Feeding Antelopes A23

1954, Sept. 20				
60	A23	25fr multicolored	2.00	.40

Gov. Noel Eugène Ballay A24

1954, Nov. 29				
61	A24	8fr indigo & brown	2.00	.80

Chimpanzee — A25

Giant
Pangolin
A26

1955, May 2   Unwmk.   Perf. 13
62 A25 5fr gray & dk brn   2.00   .80
63 A26 8fr brn & bl grn   2.00   .80
International Exhibition for Wildlife Protection, Paris, May 1955.

Map,
Symbols of
Industry,
Rotary
Emblem
A27

1955, July 4
64 A27 15fr dark blue   2.40   .80
50th anniv. of the founding of Rotary Intl.

FIDES Issue
Common Design Type

Designs: 1fr, Date grove, Mauritania. 2fr, Milo Bridge, French Guinea. 3fr, Mossi Railroad, Upper Volta. 4fr, Cattle raising, Niger. 15fr, Farm machinery and landscape, Senegal. 17fr, Woman and Niger River, French Sudan. 20fr, Palm oil production, Dahomey. 30fr, Road construction, Ivory Coast.

1956   Engr.   Perf. 13x12½
65 CD103 1fr dk grn & dk bl
                 grn   1.10   .65
66 CD103 2fr dk bl grn & bl   1.50   .65
67 CD103 3fr dk brn & red
                 brn   1.60   1.00
68 CD103 4fr dk car rose   2.00   1.10
69 CD103 15fr ind & ultra   1.60   .55
70 CD103 17fr dk bl & ind   1.75   .75
71 CD103 20fr rose lake   2.00   .65
72 CD103 30fr dk pur & claret 2.00   1.00
        Nos. 65-72 (8)   13.55   6.35

Coffee
A28a

1956, Oct. 22   Perf. 13
73 A28a 15fr dk blue green   1.60   .80

Mobile
Leprosy
Clinic and
Maltese
Cross
A29

1957, Mar. 11
74 A29 15fr dk red brn, pur & red 2.40   .80
Issued in honor of the Knights of Malta.

Map of Africa — A30

1958, Feb.   Unwmk.   Perf. 13
75 A30 20fr multicolored   1.60   .80
6h Intl.Cong. for African Tourism at Dakar.

"Africa" and Communications
Symbols — A31

1958, Mar. 15   Engr.
76 A31 15fr org, ultra & choc 2.00   .80
Stamp Day. See No. 86.

Abidjan
Bridge
A32

1958, Mar. 15
77 A32 20fr dk sl grn & grnsh bl 2.00   .80

Bananas
A33

1958, May 19   Perf. 13
78 A33 20fr rose lil, dk grn & ol-
              ive   1.60   .40

Flower Issue
Common Design Type

10fr, Gloriosa. 25fr, Adenopus. 30fr, Cyrtosperma. 40fr, Cistanche. 65fr, Crinum Moorei.

1958-59   Photo.   Perf. 12x12½
79 CD104 10fr multicolored   .95   .40
80 CD104 25fr red, yel & grn 1.50   .75
81 CD104 30fr multicolored   1.75 1.00
82 CD104 40fr blk brn, grn &
                 yel   2.25 1.40
83 CD104 65fr multicolored   2.40 1.20
        Nos. 79-83 (5)   8.85 4.75
Issued: 25fr, 40fr, 1/5/59; others, 7/7/58.

Moro Naba
Sagha and
Map — A34

1958, Nov. 1   Engr.   Perf. 13
84 A34 20fr ol brn, car & vio 1.60   .80
10th anniv. of the reestablishment of the Upper Volta territory.

Human Rights Issue
Common Design Type

1958, Dec. 10
85 CD105 20fr maroon & dk bl   2.40 2.00

Type of 1958 Redrawn

1959, Mar. 21   Engr.   Perf. 13
86 A31 20fr red, grnsh bl & sl grn 3.00 3.00
Name of country omitted on No. 86; "RF" replaced by "CF," inscribed "Dakar-Abidjan." Stamp Day.

SEMI-POSTAL STAMPS

Red Cross Issue
Common Design Type
Perf. 14½x14

1944, Dec.   Photo.   Unwmk.
B1 CD90 5fr + 20fr plum   6.50 4.75
The surtax was for the French Red Cross and national relief.

Type of
France,
1945,
Overprinted
in Black

1945, Oct. 13   Engr.   Perf. 13
B2 SP150 2fr + 3fr orange red 1.20   .80

Tropical Medicine Issue
Common Design Type

1950, May 15   Perf. 13
B3 CD100 10fr +2fr red brn &
                 sep   9.50 7.25
The surtax was for charitable work.

AIR POST STAMPS

Common Design Type

1945   Photo.   Unwmk.   Perf. 14½x14
C1 CD87 5.50fr ultra   2.00 1.00
C2 CD87 50fr dark green   3.50 1.40
C3 CD87 100fr plum   4.00 1.50
        Nos. C1-C3 (3)   9.50 3.90

Victory Issue
Common Design Type

1946, May 8   Engr.   Perf. 12½
C4 CD92 8fr violet   1.60 1.20

Chad to Rhine Issue
Common Design Types

1946, June 6
C5   CD93 5fr brown car   1.90 1.40
C6   CD94 10fr deep blue   1.90 1.40
C7   CD95 15fr brt violet   2.10 1.60
C8   CD96 20fr dk slate grn   2.40 1.90
C9   CD97 25fr olive brn   2.60 2.25
C10 CD98 50fr brown   3.50 2.75
        Nos. C5-C10 (6)   14.40 11.30

Antoine de Saint-
Exupéry, Map
and
Natives — AP1

Plane over Dakar — AP2

Great White Egrets in Flight — AP3

Natives and Phantom Plane — AP4

1947, Mar. 24   Engr.
C11 AP1 8fr red brown   1.60   .80
C12 AP2 50fr rose violet   3.50 1.20
C13 AP3 100fr ultra   16.00 4.75
C14 AP4 200fr slate gray   14.00 5.25
        Nos. C11-C14 (4)   35.10 12.00

UPU Issue
Common Design Type

1949, July 4   Perf. 13
C15 CD99 25fr multicolored 12.50 8.75

Vridi Canal, Abidjan — AP5

1951, Nov. 5   Unwmk.   Perf. 13
C16 AP5 500fr red org, bl grn
              & dp ultra   32.50 4.75

Liberation Issue
Common Design Type

1954, June 6
C17 CD102 15fr indigo & ultra 9.50 5.50

Logging — AP6

Designs: 100fr, Radiotelephone exchange. 200fr, Baobab trees.

1954, Sept. 20
C18 AP6 50fr ol grn & org
              brn   4.00   .80
C19 AP6 100fr ind, dk brn &
              dk grn   6.50 1.20
C20 AP6 200fr bl grn, grnsh
              blk & brn lake 17.50 2.75
        Nos. C18-C20 (3)   28.00 4.75

Gen. Louis
Faidherbé and
African
Sharpshooter
AP7

1957, July 20   Unwmk.   Perf. 13
C21 AP7 15fr indigo & blue 2.00 1.60
Centenary of French African troops.

Gorée Island and Woman — AP8

Designs: 20fr, Map with planes and ships. 25fr, Village and modern city. 40fr, Seat of

Council of French West Africa. 50fr, Worker, ship and peanut plant. 100fr, Bay of N'Gor.

1958, Mar. 15   **Engr.**

C22	AP8	15fr blk brn, grn & vio	1.40	.80
C23	AP8	20fr blk brn, dk bl & red brn	1.40	.80
C24	AP8	25fr blk vio, bis & grn	1.40	1.00
C25	AP8	40fr dk bl, brn & grn	1.60	1.00
C26	AP8	50fr violet, brn & grn	2.50	1.40
C27	AP8	100fr brown, bl & grn	6.75	2.10
a.		Souvenir sheet of 6, #C22-C27	17.50	13.50
		Nos. C22-C27 (6)	15.05	7.10

Centenary of Dakar.

Woman Playing Native Harp — AP9

1958, Dec. 1   **Unwmk.**   **Perf. 13**

C28	AP9	20fr red brn, blk & gray	1.60	.80

Inauguration of Nouakchott as capital of Mauritania.

POSTAGE DUE STAMPS

D1

1947   **Engr.**   **Unwmk.**   **Perf. 13**

J1	D1	10c red	.40	.25
J2	D1	30c deep orange	.40	.25
J3	D1	50c greenish blk	.40	.25
J4	D1	1fr carmine	.40	.25
J5	D1	2fr emerald	.50	.30
J6	D1	3fr red lilac	.90	.65
J7	D1	4fr deep ultra	1.10	.80
J8	D1	5fr red brown	2.25	1.60
J9	D1	10fr peacock blue	2.90	2.25
J10	D1	20fr sepia	5.25	3.75
		Nos. J1-J10 (10)	14.50	10.35

OFFICIAL STAMPS

Mask — O1

Designs: Various masks.

Perf. 14x13

1958, June 2   **Typo.**   **Unwmk.**

O1	O1	1fr dk brn red	1.10	1.00
O2	O1	3fr brt green	.65	.55
O3	O1	5fr crim rose	.65	.50
O4	O1	10fr light ultra	.80	.65
O5	O1	20fr bright red	1.60	.80
O6	O1	25fr purple	1.60	.80
O7	O1	30fr green	2.75	1.60
O8	O1	45fr gray black	3.25	1.60
O9	O1	50fr dark red	3.25	1.60
O10	O1	65fr brt ultra	4.50	1.60
O11	O1	100fr olive bister	10.50	2.75
O12	O1	200fr deep green	21.00	5.50
		Nos. O1-O12 (12)	51.65	18.95

FUJEIRA

fü-'jī-rə

LOCATION — Oman Peninsula, Arabia, on Persian Gulf
GOVT. — Sheikdom under British protection

Fujeira is one of six Persian Gulf sheikdoms to join the United Arab Emirates which proclaimed independence Dec. 2, 1971. See United Arab Emirates.

100 Naye Paise = 1 Rupee

> **Catalogue values for all unused stamps in this country are for Never Hinged items.**

Sheik Hamad bin Mohammed al Sharqi and Grebe — A1

Sheik and: 2np, 50np, Arabian oryx. 3np, 70np, Hoopoe. 4np, 1r, Wild ass. 5np, 1.50r, Herons in flight. 10np, 2r, Arabian horses. 15np, 3r, Leopard. 20np, 5r, Camels. 30np, 10r, Hawks.

Photo. & Litho.
1964   **Unwmk.**   **Perf. 14**
Size: 36x24mm

1	A1	1np gold & multi	.20	.20
2	A1	2np gold & multi	.20	.20
3	A1	3np gold & multi	.20	.20
4	A1	4np gold & multi	.20	.20
5	A1	5np gold & multi	.20	.20
6	A1	10np gold & multi	.20	.20
7	A1	15np gold & multi	.20	.20
8	A1	20np gold & multi	.20	.20
9	A1	30np gold & multi	.20	.20

Size: 43x28mm

10	A1	40np gold & multi	.30	.20
11	A1	50np gold & multi	.30	.20
12	A1	70np gold & multi	.35	.20
13	A1	1r gold & multi	.50	.20
14	A1	1.50r gold & multi	.75	.20
15	A1	2r gold & multi	1.00	.20

Size: 53½x35mm

16	A1	3r gold & multi	1.75	.25
17	A1	5r gold & multi	2.25	.35
18	A1	10r gold & multi	5.75	.50
		Nos. 1-18 (18)	14.75	4.10

Issued: 20np, 30np, 70np, 1.50r, 3r, 10r, Nov. 14; others, Sept. 22.
Exist imperf. Value, set $30.

Sheik Hamad and Shot Put A2

1964, Dec. 6   **Perf. 14**
Size: 43x28mm

19	A2	25np shown	.20	.20
20	A2	50np Discus	.20	.20
21	A2	75np Fencing	.25	.25
22	A2	1r Boxing	.30	.30
23	A2	1.50r Relay race	.40	.35
24	A2	2r Soccer	.50	.40

Size: 53½x35mm

25	A2	3r Pole vaulting	1.00	.50
26	A2	5r Hurdling	2.50	.75
27	A2	7.50r Equestrian	3.75	.90
		Nos. 19-27 (9)	9.10	3.85

18th Olympic Games, Tokyo, 10/10-25/64.
Exist imperf. Value, set $12.

John F. Kennedy — A3

Kennedy: 10np, As sailor in the Pacific. 15np, As naval lieutenant. 20np, On speaker's rostrum. 25np, Sailing with family. 50np, With crowd of people. 1r, With Mrs. Kennedy, Lyndon B. Johnson. 2r, With Eisenhower on

White House porch. 3r, With Mrs. Kennedy & Caroline. 5r, Portrait.

1965, Feb. 23   **Photo.**   **Perf. 13½**
Size: 29x44mm
Black Design with Gold Inscriptions

28	A3	5np pale gray	.20	.20
29	A3	10np pale yellow	.20	.20
30	A3	15np pink	.20	.20
31	A3	20np pale greenish gray	.20	.20
32	A3	25np pale blue	.25	.20
33	A3	50np pale rose	.30	.20

Size: 33x51mm

34	A3	1r pale gray	.75	.30
35	A3	2r pale green	1.25	.40
36	A3	3r pale gray	2.25	.50
37	A3	5r pale yellow	3.00	.80
		Nos. 28-37 (10)	8.60	3.20

Pres. John F. Kennedy (1917-1963). A souvenir sheet contains 2 29x44mm stamps similar to Nos. 36-37 with pale blue (3r) and pale rose (5r) backgrounds. Value (unused): perf $7; imperf $9.
Nos. 28-37 exist imperf. Value $14.

AIR POST STAMPS

Wild Ass AP1

Photo. & Litho.
1965, Aug. 16   **Unwmk.**   **Perf. 13½**
Size: 43x28mm

C1	AP1	15np Grebe	.25	.20
C2	AP1	25np Arabian oryx	.25	.20
C3	AP1	35np Hoopoe	.35	.20
C4	AP1	50np Wild ass	.40	.20
C5	AP1	75np Herons in flight	.45	.20
C6	AP1	1r Arabian horses	.50	.20

Size: 53½x35mm

C7	AP1	2r Leopard	1.00	.20
C8	AP1	3r Camels	2.00	.25
C9	AP1	5r Hawks	4.00	.50
		Nos. C1-C9 (9)	9.20	2.15

Exist imperf. Value, set $11.

AIR POST OFFICIAL STAMPS

Type of Air Post Issue, 1965
Photo. & Litho.
1965, Nov. 10   **Unwmk.**   **Perf. 13½**
Size: 43x28mm

CO1	AP1	75np Arabian horses	.50	.25

Perf. 13
Size: 53½x35mm

CO2	AP1	2r Leopard	1.25	.40
CO3	AP1	3r Camels	2.00	.60
CO4	AP1	5r Hawks	4.00	1.00
		Nos. CO1-CO4 (4)	7.75	2.25

Exist imperf. Values same as perf.

OFFICIAL STAMPS

Type of Air Post Issue, 1965
Photo. & Litho.
1965, Oct. 14   **Unwmk.**   **Perf. 13½**
Size: 43x28mm

O1	AP1	25np Grebe	.20	.20
O2	AP1	40np Arabian oryx	.20	.20
O3	AP1	50np Hoopoe	.25	.20
O4	AP1	75np Wild ass	.40	.20
O5	AP1	1r Herons in flight	1.00	.20
		Nos. O1-O5 (5)	2.05	1.00

Exist imperf. Values same as perf.

FUNCHAL

fün-'shäl

LOCATION — A city and administrative district in the Madeira island group in the Atlantic Ocean northwest of Africa
GOVT. — A part of the Republic of Portugal
POP. — 150,574 (1900)

Postage stamps of Funchal were superseded by those of Portugal.

1000 Reis = 1 Milreis

King Carlos
A1   A2

1892-93   **Typo.**   **Unwmk.**
Perf. 11½, 12½, 13½

1	A1	5r yellow	3.00	2.00
a.		Half used as 2½r on entire newspaper		17.50
b.		Perf. 11½	4.00	2.75
2	A1	10r red violet	2.50	2.00
3	A1	15r chocolate	3.50	2.50
4	A1	20r lavender	3.75	2.50
a.		Perf. 13½	9.00	7.50
5a	A1	25r dark green	6.00	1.00
6	A1	50r ultramarine	6.00	2.50
a.		Perf. 13½	8.75	5.50
7	A1	75r carmine	7.50	6.00
8	A1	80r yellow green	14.00	11.00
a.		Perf. 13½	17.50	12.00
9	A1	100r brn, yel ('93)	9.00	5.00
a.		Diagonal half used as 50r on cover		37.50
10	A1	150r car, rose ('93)	52.50	30.00
11	A1	200r dk bl, bl ('93)	60.00	45.00
12	A1	300r dk bl, sal ('93)	70.00	55.00
		Nos. 1-12 (12)	237.75	164.50

Nos. 1-12 were printed on both enamel-surfaced and chalky papers. Values are for the most common varieties. For detailed listings, see the *Scott Classic Specialized Catalogue*.

The reprints of this issue have shiny white gum and clean-cut perforation 13½. The shades differ from those of the originals and the uncolored paper is thin.

1897-1905   **Perf. 11¾**
Name and Value in Black except Nos. 25 and 34

13	A2	2½r gray	.50	.35
14	A2	5r orange	.50	.35
15	A2	10r light green	.50	.35
16	A2	15r brown	5.50	5.00
17	A2	15r gray grn ('99)	3.75	2.75
18	A2	20r gray vio	1.40	.75
19	A2	25r sea green	2.75	.75
20	A2	25r car rose ('99)	1.40	.55
a.		Booklet pane of 6		
21	A2	50r dark blue	6.00	5.00
a.		Perf. 12½	21.00	9.00
22	A2	50r ultra ('05)	1.50	.90
23	A2	65r slate blue ('98)	1.25	.90
24	A2	75r rose	1.40	.90
25	A2	75r brn & red, yel ('05)	4.00	1.40
26	A2	80r violet	1.40	1.10
27	A2	100r dark blue, blue	1.40	1.10
a.		Diagonal half used as 50r on cover		—
28	A2	115r org brn, pink ('98)	2.25	1.40
29	A2	130r gray brown, buff ('98)	2.25	1.40
30	A2	150r lt brn, buff	3.00	1.25
31	A2	180r sl, pnksh ('98)	2.25	1.40
32	A2	200r red vio, pale lil	3.00	2.10
33	A2	300r blue, rose	3.00	2.10
34	A2	500r blk & red, bl	5.00	2.40
a.		Perf. 12½	15.00	7.75
		Nos. 13-34 (22)	54.00	34.25

Cover Supplies

COVER SLEEVES

Protect your covers with clear polyethylene sleeves.
Sold in packages of 100.

U.S. POSTAL CARD

3¾"

5⅞"

Item	Retail	AA*
CV005	$3.95	$2.99

U.S. FIRST DAY COVER #6

4"

6¾"

Item	Retail	AA*
CV006	$3.95	$3.10

CONTINENTAL POSTCARD

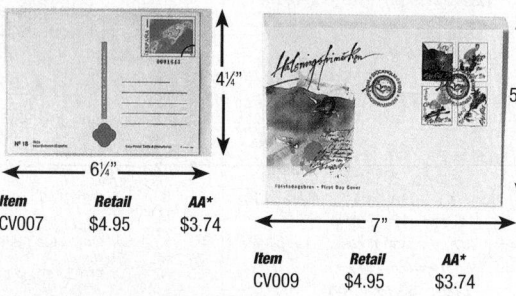

4¼"

6¼"

Item	Retail	AA*
CV007	$4.95	$3.74

EUROPEAN FIRST DAY COVER

5⅞"

7"

Item	Retail	AA*
CV009	$4.95	$3.74

#10 BUSINESS ENVELOPE

4¾"

10"

Item	Retail	AA*
CV010	$5.95	$4.49

COVER BINDERS AND PAGES

Padded, durable, 3-ring binders will hold up to 100 covers. Features the "D" ring mechanism on the right hand side of album so you don't have to worry about creasing or wrinkling covers when opening or closing binder. Cover pages sold separately. Available in black with 1 or 2 pockets. Sold in packages of 10.

Item		Retail	AA*
CBRD	Burgundy	$11.99	$9.59
CBBL	Blue	$11.99	$9.59
CBCA	Candy Apple	$11.99	$9.59
CBGY	Gray	$11.99	$9.59
CBBK	Black	$11.99	$9.59
SS2PGB	Pgs. 2-Pock.	$4.95	$4.50
SS2PG1B	Pgs. 1-Pock.	$4.95	$4.50

MINT SHEET BINDERS & PAGES

Keep those mint sheets intact in a handsome, 3-ring binder. Just like the cover album, the Mint Sheet album features the "D" ring mechanism on the right hand side of binder so you don't have to worry about damagaing your stamps when turning the pages.

Item		Retail	AA*
MBRD	Red (Burgundy)	$18.99	$15.25
MBBL	Blue	$18.99	$15.25
MBGY	Gray	$18.99	$15.25
MBBK	Black	$18.99	$15.25
SSMP3B	Mint Sheet Pages (Black 12 per pack)	$8.75	$7.95
SSMP3C	Mint Sheet Pages (Clear 12 per pack)	$8.75	$7.95

PRINZ CORNER MOUNTS

Clear, self-adhesive corner mounts are ideal for postal cards and covers. Mounts measure ⅞" each side and are made from transparent glass foil. There are 250 mounts in each pack.

Item	Retail	AA*
ACC176	$9.95	**$7.96**

1. AA* prices apply to paid subscribers of *Scott Stamp Monthly* and *Linn's* and orders placed online.

2. Prices, terms and product availability subject to change.

3. **Shipping & Handling:**
   United States: 10% of order total. Minimum charge $6.99 Maximum charge $45.00.
   Canada: 15% of order total. Minimum charge $19.99 Maximum charge $50.00.
   Foreign orders are shipped via DHL and billed actual freight. Credit cards only.

Call 1-800-572-6885
www.amosadvantage.com

Pronunciation Symbols

ə .... banana, collide, abut

ˈə, ˌə .... humdrum, abut

ə .... immediately preceding \l\, \n\, \m\, \ŋ\, as in battle, mitten, eaten, and sometimes open \ˈō-pᵊm\, lock and key \-ᵊŋ-\; immediately following \l\, \m\, \r\, as often in French table, prisme, titre

ər .... further, merger, bird

ˈər-
ˈə-r   } .... as in two different pronunciations of hurry \ˈhər-ē, ˈhə-rē\

a .... mat, map, mad, gag, snap, patch

ā .... day, fade, date, aorta, drape, cape

ä .... bother, cot, and, with most American speakers, father, cart

à .... father as pronunced by speakers who do not rhyme it with bother; French patte

aù .... now, loud, out

b .... baby, rib

ch .... chin, nature \ˈnā-chər\

d .... did, adder

e .... bet, bed, peck

ˈē, ˌē .... beat, nosebleed, evenly, easy

ē .... easy, mealy

f .... fifty, cuff

g .... go, big, gift

h .... hat, ahead

hw .... whale as pronounced by those who do not have the same pronunciation for both whale and wail

i .... tip, banish, active

ī .... site, side, buy, tripe

j .... job, gem, edge, join, judge

k .... kin, cook, ache

ḵ .... German ich, Buch; one pronunciation of loch

l .... lily, pool

m .... murmur, dim, nymph

n .... no, own

ⁿ .... indicates that a preceding vowel or diphthong is pronounced with the nasal passages open, as in French un bon vin blanc \œⁿ -bōⁿ -vaⁿ -bläⁿ\

ŋ .... sing \ˈsiŋ\, singer \ˈsiŋ-ər\, finger \ˈfiŋ-gər\, ink \ˈiŋk \

ō .... bone, know, beau

ȯ .... saw, all, gnaw, caught

œ .... French boeuf, German Hölle

œ̄ .... French feu, German Höhle

ȯi .... coin, destroy

p .... pepper, lip

r .... red, car, rarity

s .... source, less

sh .... as in shy, mission, machine, special (actually, this is a single sound, not two); with a hyphen between, two sounds as in grasshopper \ˈgras-ˌhä-pər\

t .... tie, attack, late, later, latter

th .... as in thin, ether (actually, this is a single sound, not two); with a hyphen between, two sounds as in knighthood \ˈnīt-ˌhùd\

th .... then, either, this (actually, this is a single sound, not two)

ü .... rule, youth, union \ˈyün-yən\, few \ˈfyü\

ù .... pull, wood, book, curable \ˈkyùr-ə-bəl\, fury \ˈfyùr-ē\

ue .... German füllen, hübsch

ūe .... French rue, German fühlen

v .... vivid, give

w .... we, away

y .... yard, young, cue \ˈkyü\, mute \ˈmyüt\, union \ˈyün-yən\

y .... indicates that during the articulation of the sound represented by the preceding character the front of the tongue has substantially the position it has for the articulation of the first sound of yard, as in French digne \dēnʸ\

z .... zone, raise

zh .... as in vision, azure \ˈa-zhər\ (actually, this is a single sound, not two); with a hyphen between, two sounds as in hogshead \ˈhȯgz-ˌhed, ˈhägz-\

\ .... slant line used in pairs to mark the beginning and end of a transcription: \ˈpen\

ˈ .... mark preceding a syllable with primary (strongest) stress: \ˈpen-mən-ˌship\

ˌ .... mark preceding a syllable with secondary (medium) stress: \ˈpen-mən-ˌship\

- .... mark of syllable division

( ) .... indicate that what is symbolized between is present in some utterances but not in others: factory \ˈfak-t(ə-)rē\

÷ .... indicates that many regard as unacceptable the pronunciation variant immediately following: cupola \ˈkyü-pə-lə, ÷-ˌlō\

The system of pronunciation is used by permission from Merriam-Webster's Collegiate® Dictionary, Tenth Edition ©1993 by Merriam-Webster Inc., publisher of the Merriam-Webster® dictionaries.

Illustrated Identifier

This section pictures stamps or parts of stamp designs that will help identify postage stamps that do not have English words on them.

Many of the symbols that identify stamps of countries are shown here as well as typical examples of their stamps.

See the Index and Identifier on the previous pages for stamps with inscriptions such as "sen," "posta," "Baja Porto," "Helvetia," "K.S.A.," etc.

Linn's Stamp Identifier is now available. The 144 pages include more 2,000 inscriptions and over 500 large stamp illustrations. Available from Linn's Stamp News, P.O. Box 29, Sidney, OH 45365-0029.

1. HEADS, PICTURES AND NUMERALS

GREAT BRITAIN

Great Britain stamps never show the country name, but, except for postage dues, show a picture of the reigning monarch.

Victoria

Edward VII   George V   Edward VIII

George VI

Elizabeth II

Some George VI and Elizabeth II stamps are surcharged in annas, new paisa or rupees. These are listed under Oman.

Silhouette (sometimes facing right, generally at the top of stamp)

The silhouette indicates this is a British stamp. It is not a U.S. stamp.

VICTORIA

Queen Victoria

INDIA

Other stamps of India show this portrait of Queen Victoria and the words "Service" and "Annas."

AUSTRIA

YUGOSLAVIA

(Also BOSNIA & HERZEGOVINA if imperf.)

BOSNIA & HERZEGOVINA

Denominations also appear in top corners instead of bottom corners.

HUNGARY

Another stamp has posthorn facing left

BRAZIL

AUSTRALIA

Kangaroo and Emu

GERMANY

Mecklenburg-Vorpommern

SWITZERLAND

PALAU

2. ORIENTAL INSCRIPTIONS

CHINA

Any stamp with this one character is from China (Imperial, Republic or People's Republic). This character appears in a four-character overprint on stamps of Manchukuo. These stamps are local provisionals, which are unlisted. Other overprinted Manchukuo stamps show this character, but have more than four characters in the overprints. These are listed in People's Republic of China.

Some Chinese stamps show the Sun.

Most stamps of Republic of China show this series of characters.

Stamps with the China character and this character are from People's Republic of China.

Calligraphic form of People's Republic of China

(一)	(二)	(三)	(四)	(五)	(六)
1	2	3	4	5	6
(七)	(八)	(九)	(十)	(一十)	(二十)
7	8	9	10	11	12

Chinese stamps
without China character

REPUBLIC OF CHINA

PEOPLE'S REPUBLIC OF CHINA

Mao Tse-tung

MANCHUKUO

Temple   Emperor Pu-Yi

The first 3 characters are common to
many Manchukuo stamps.

The last 3 characters are common
to other Manchukuo stamps.

Orchid Crest

Manchukuo
stamp with-
out these
elements

JAPAN

Chrysanthemum Crest   Country Name

Japanese stamps without these elements

The number of characters in the center and the
design of dragons on the sides will vary.

RYUKYU ISLANDS

Country Name

PHILIPPINES
(Japanese Occupation)

Country Name

NETHERLANDS INDIES
(Japanese Occupation)

JAVA   SUMATRA

Java   Sumatra

MOLUCCAS, CELEBES AND
SOUTH BORNEO

NORTH BORNEO
(Japanese Occupation)

Indicates Japanese   Country
Occupation   Name

MALAYA
(Japanese Occupation)

Indicates Japanese Occupation   Country Name

BURMA
Union of Myanmar

Union of Myanmar

(Japanese Occupation)

Indicates Japanese Occupation   Country Name

Other Burma Japanese Occupation stamps
without these elements

Burmese Script

KOREA

These two characters, in any order, are common
to stamps from the Republic of Korea (South
Korea) or of the People's Democratic
Republic of Korea (North Korea).

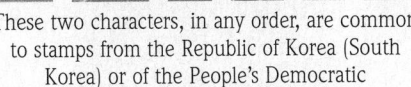

This series of four characters can be found
on the stamps of both Koreas.
Most stamps of the Democratic People's
Republic of Korea (North Korea)
have just this inscription.

Indicates Republic of Korea (South Korea)

South Korean postage stamps issed after 1952
do not show currency expressed in Latin letters.
Stamps wiith "HW," "HWAN," "WON,"
"WN," "W" or "W" with two lines through it, if
not illustrated in listings of stamps
before this date, are revenues.
North Korean postage stamps do not have
currency expressed in Latin letters.

Yin Yang appears on some stamps.

South Korean stamps show Yin Yang and starting
in 1966, 'KOREA' in Latin letters

Example of South Korean stamps lacking Latin
text, Yin Yang and standard Korean text of country name. North Korean stamps never show Yin
Yang and starting in 1976 are inscribed "DPRK"
or "DPR KOREA" in Latin letters.

THAILAND

Country Name

King Chulalongkorn

King Prajadhipok and
Chao P'ya Chakri

3. CENTRAL AND EASTERN ASIAN INSCRIPTIONS

INDIA - FEUDATORY STATES

Alwar

Bhor

Bundi

Similar stamps come with
different designs in corners
and differently drawn daggers
(at center of circle).

Dhar   Duttia

Faridkot

Hyderabad

Similar stamps exist with different central
design which is inscribed "Postage"
or "Post & Receipt."

Indore

Jammu & Kashmir

Text varies.

Jasdan

Jhalawar

Kotah

Size and text varies

Nandgaon

Nowanuggur

Poonch

Similar stamps exist
in various sizes with different text

Rajasthan

Rajpeepla

Soruth

Tonk

BANGLADESH

Country Name

NEPAL

Similar stamps are smaller, have squares in
upper corners and have five or nine
characters in central bottom panel.

TANNU TUVA   ISRAEL

GEORGIA

This inscription is found on
other pictorial stamps.

Country Name

ARMENIA

The four characters are found somewhere
on pictorial stamps. On some stamps only
the middle two are found.

4. AFRICAN INSCRIPTIONS

ETHIOPIA

5. ARABIC INSCRIPTIONS

The four characters are found somewhere on pictorial stamps. On some stamps only the middle two are found.

١ ٢ ٣ ٤ ٥
1 2 3 4 5

٦ ٧ ٨ ٩ ٠
6 7 8 9 0

AFGHANISTAN

Many early Afghanistan stamps show Tiger's head, many of these have ornaments protruding from outer ring, others show inscriptions in black.

Crest of King Amanullah

Arabic Script

BAHRAIN

Mosque Gate & Crossed Cannons

EGYPT

Postage

IRAN

Country Name

Royal Crown

Lion with Sword

Symbol

IRAQ

JORDAN

LEBANON

Similar types have
denominations at top and
slightly different design.

LIBYA

Country Name in various styles

Other Libya stamps show Eagle and Shield (head
facing either direction) or Red, White and Black
Shield (with or without eagle in center).

Without Country Name

SAUDI ARABIA

Tughra (Central design)

→ Palm Tree and Swords

SYRIA

ARAB GOVERNMENT ISSUES

THRACE   YEMEN

PAKISTAN

PAKISTAN - BAHAWALPUR

Country Name in top panel, star and crescent

TURKEY

Star & Crescent is a device found on many Turkish stamps, but is also found on stamps from other Arabic areas (see Pakistan-Bahawalpur)

Tughra (similar tughras can be
found on stamps of Turkey in
Asia, Afghanistan and Saudi
Arabia)

Mohammed V

Mustafa Kemal

Plane, Star and Crescent

TURKEY IN ASIA

Other Turkey in Asia pictorials show
star & crescent.
Other stamps show tughra shown under Turkey.

6. GREEK INSCRIPTIONS

GREECE

Country Name in various styles
(Some Crete stamps overprinted with the
Greece country name are listed in Crete.)

Lepta

Drachma   Drachmas   Lepton

Abbreviated Country Name

Other forms of Country Name

No country name

CRETE

Country Name

Crete stamps with a surcharge that have the year "1922" are listed under Greeece.

EPIRUS

Similar stamps have text above the eagle.

IONIAN IS.

7. CYRILLIC INSCRIPTIONS

RUSSIA

Postage Stamp

Imperial Eagle

Postage in various styles

Abbreviation for Kopeck   Abbreviation for Ruble   Russia

Abbreviation for Russian Soviet Federated Socialist Republic
RSFSR stamps were overprinted (see below)

Abbreviation for Union of Soviet Socialist Republics

This item is footnoted in Latvia

RUSSIA - Army of the North

"OKCA"

RUSSIA - Wenden

RUSSIAN OFFICES IN THE TURKISH EMPIRE

These letters appear on other stamps of the Russian offices.

The unoverprinted version of this stamp and a similar stamp were overprinted by various countries (see below).

ARMENIA

BELARUS

FAR EASTERN REPUBLIC

Country Name

SOUTH RUSSIA

Country Name

FINLAND

Circles and Dots
on stamps similar
to Imperial
Russia issues

BATUM

Forms of Country Name

TRANSCAUCASIAN FEDERATED REPUBLICS

 Abbreviation for
Country Name

KAZAKHSTAN

КАЗАКСТАН

Country Name

KYRGYZSTAN

КЫРГЫЗСТАН

КЫРГЫЗСТАН

Country
Name

ROMANIA

TADJIKISTAN

Country Name & Abbreviation

UKRAINE

Country Name in various forms

The trident appears
on many stamps,
usually as an overprint.

Abbreviation for
Ukrainian Soviet
Socialist Republic

WESTERN UKRAINE

Abbreviation for
Country Name

AZERBAIJAN

 AZƏRBAYCAN

Country Name

Abbreviation for Azerbaijan
Soviet Socialist Republic

MONTENEGRO

ЦРНА ГОРА

Country Name in various forms

Abbreviation for country name   No country name (A similar Montenegro stamp without country name has same vignette.)

SERBIA

Country Name in various forms

Abbreviation for country name

No country name

SERBIA & MONTENEGRO

YUGOSLAVIA

Showing country name

No Country Name

MACEDONIA

Country Name

Different form of Country Name

BOSNIA & HERZEGOVINA
(Serb Administration)

РЕПУБЛИКА СРПСКА

Country Name

Different form of Country Name

No Country Name

BULGARIA

Country Name   Postage

Stotinka

Stotinki (plural)

Abbreviation for Stotinki

Country Name in various forms and styles

No country name

Abbreviation for Lev, leva

MONGOLIA

Country name in one word

Tugrik in Cyrillic

Country name in two words

Mung in Cyrillic

Mung in Mongolian

Tugrik in Mongolian

Arms

No Country Name

INDEX AND IDENTIFIER

All page numbers shown are those in this Volume.

Postage stamps that do not have English words on them are shown in the Illustrated Identifier.

INDEX TO ADVERTISERS
2012 VOLUME 2

2012
VOLUME 2
DEALER DIRECTORY
YELLOW PAGE LISTINGS

This section of your Scott Catalogue contains advertisements to help you conveniently find what you need, when you need it...!

Accessories

BROOKLYN GALLERY COIN & STAMP, INC.
8725 4th Ave.
Brooklyn, NY 11209
PH: 718-745-5701
FAX: 718-745-2775
info@brooklyngallery.com
www.brooklyngallery.com

Appraisals

PHILIP WEISS AUCTIONS
1 Neil Ct.
Oceanside, NY 11572
PH: 516-594-0731
FAX: 516-594-9414
phil@prwauctions.com
www.prwauctions.com

Asia

MICHAEL ROGERS, INC.
Suite 4-1
415 S. Orlando Ave.
Winter Park, FL 32789-3683
PH: 407-644-2290
PH: 800-843-3751
FAX: 407-645-4434
Stamps@michaelrogersinc.com
www.michaelrogersinc.com

THE STAMP ACT
PO Box 1136
Belmont, CA 94002
PH: 650-703-2342
PH: 650-592-3315
FAX: 650-508-8104
thestampact@sbcglobal.net
www.thestampact.com

Auctions

DANIEL F. KELLEHER AUCTIONS LLC
PMB 44
60 Newtown Rd
Danbury, CT 06810
PH: 203-297-6056
FAX: 203-297-6059
info@kelleherauctions.com
www.kelleherauctions.com

JACQUES C. SCHIFF, JR., INC.
195 Main St.
Ridgefield Park, NJ 07660
PH: 201-641-5566
FAX: 201-641-5705

MICHAEL ROGERS, INC.
Suite 4-1
415 S. Orlando Ave.
Winter Park, FL 32789-3683
PH: 407-644-2290
PH: 800-843-3751
FAX: 407-645-4434
Stamps@michaelrogersinc.com
www.michaelrogersinc.com

PHILIP WEISS AUCTIONS
1 Neil Ct.
Oceanside, NY 11572
PH: 516-594-0731
FAX: 516-594-9414
phil@prwauctions.com
www.prwauctions.com

R. MARESCH & SON LTD.
5th Floor - 6075 Yonge St.
Toronto, ON M2M 3W2
CANADA
PH: 416-363-7777
FAX: 416-363-6511
www.maresch.com

Auctions

THE STAMP CENTER DUTCH COUNTRY AUCTIONS
4115 Concord Pike
Wilmington, DE 19803
PH: 302-478-8740
FAX: 302-478-8779
auctions@thestampcenter.com
www.thestampcenter.com

Auctions - Public

ALAN BLAIR AUCTIONS, L.L.C.
Suite 1
5405 Lakeside Ave.
Richmond, VA 23228-6060
PH: 800-689-5602
FAX: 804-262-9307
alanblair@verizon.net
www.alanblairstamps.com

British Commonwealth

ARON R. HALBERSTAM PHILATELISTS, LTD.
PO Box 150168
Van Brunt Station
Brooklyn, NY 11215-0168
PH: 718-788-3978
FAX: 718-965-3099
arh@arhstamps.com
www.arhstamps.com

Central America

GUY SHAW
PO Box 27138
San Diego, CA 92198
PH/FAX: 858-485-8269
guyshaw@guyshaw.com
www.guyshaw.com

China

MICHAEL ROGERS, INC.
Suite 4-1
415 S. Orlando Ave.
Winter Park, FL 32789-3683
PH: 407-644-2290
PH: 800-843-3751
FAX: 407-645-4434
Stamps@michaelrogersinc.com
www.michaelrogersinc.com

THE STAMP ACT
PO Box 1136
Belmont, CA 94002
PH: 650-703-2342
PH: 650-592-3315
FAX: 650-508-8104
thestampact@sbcglobal.net
www.thestampact.com

China - PRC

MICHAEL ROGERS, INC.
Suite 4-1
415 S. Orlando Ave.
Winter Park, FL 32789-3683
PH: 407-644-2290
PH: 800-843-3751
FAX: 407-645-4434
Stamps@michaelrogersinc.com
www.michaelrogersinc.com

China - PRC

MR. GUANLUN HONG
Jade Crown International
Stamp Company
PO Box 118
Blaine, WA 98231 USA
PH: 1-604-288-8815
PH: 1-888-482-6586
FAX: 1-604-288-8815
guanlun@hotmail.com
guanlun@shaw.ca

THE STAMP ACT
PO Box 1136
Belmont, CA 94002
PH: 650-703-2342
PH: 650-592-3315
FAX: 650-508-8104
thestampact@sbcglobal.net
www.thestampact.com

Ducks

MICHAEL JAFFE
PO Box 61484
Vancouver, WA 98666
PH: 360-695-6161
PH: 800-782-6770
FAX: 360-695-1616
mjaffe@brookmanstamps.com
www.brookmanstamps.com

Falkland Islands

**ARON R. HALBERSTAM
PHILATELISTS, LTD.**
PO Box 150168
Van Brunt Station
Brooklyn, NY 11215-0168
PH: 718-788-3978
FAX: 718-965-3099
arh@arhstamps.com
www.arhstamps.com

France

WULFF'S STAMPS
PO Box 661746
Sacramento, CA 95866
PH/FAX: 800-884-0656
PH/FAX: 916-489-0656
service@wulffstamps.com
www.wulffstamps.com

WWW.WORLDSTAMPS.COM
PO Box 4743
Pinehurst, NC 28374
PH: 910-295-2048
FAX: 910-295-2049
by mail:
Frank Geiger Philatelists
info@WorldStamps.com
www.WorldStamps.com

France & Colonies

E. JOSEPH McCONNELL, INC.
PO Box 683
Monroe, NY 10949
PH: 845-783-9791
FAX: 845-782-0347
ejstamps@gmail.com
www.EJMcConnell.com

WULFF'S STAMPS
PO Box 661746
Sacramento, CA 95866
PH/FAX: 800-884-0656
PH/FAX: 916-489-0656
service@wulffstamps.com
www.wulffstamps.com

French S. Antarctic

E. JOSEPH McCONNELL, INC.
PO Box 683
Monroe, NY 10949
PH: 845-783-9791
FAX: 845-782-0347
ejstamps@gmail.com
www.EJMcConnell.com

Japan

MICHAEL ROGERS, INC.
Suite 4-1
415 S. Orlando Ave.
Winter Park, FL 32789-3683
PH: 407-644-2290
PH: 800-843-3751
FAX: 407-645-4434
Stamps@michaelrogersinc.com
www.michaelrogersinc.com

Korea

MICHAEL ROGERS, INC.
Suite 4-1
415 S. Orlando Ave.
Winter Park, FL 32789-3683
PH: 407-644-2290
PH: 800-843-3751
FAX: 407-645-4434
Stamps@michaelrogersinc.com
www.michaelrogersinc.com

Latin America

GUY SHAW
PO Box 27138
San Diego, CA 92198
PH/FAX: 858-485-8269
guyshaw@guyshaw.com
www.guyshaw.com

Manchukuo

MICHAEL ROGERS, INC.
Suite 4-1
415 S. Orlando Ave.
Winter Park, FL 32789-3683
PH: 407-644-2290
PH: 800-843-3751
FAX: 407-644-4434
Stamps@michaelrogersinc.com
www.michaelrogersinc.com

New Issues

**DAVIDSON'S STAMP
SERVICE**
PO Box 36355
Indianapolis, IN 46236-0355
PH: 317-826-2620
ed-davidson@earthlink.net
www.newstampissues.com

New Issues - Retail

BOMBAY PHILATELIC INC.
PO Box 301
Wake Forest, NC 27588
PH: 561-499-7990
FAX: 561-499-7553
sales@bombaystamps.com
www.bombaystamps.com

South America

GUY SHAW
PO Box 27138
San Diego, CA 92198
PH/FAX: 858-485-8269
guyshaw@guyshaw.com
www.guyshaw.com

STAMP STORES

Arizona

A TO Z STAMPS & COINS
4950 E. Thomas Rd.
Phoenix, AZ 85018
OFFICE: 480-844-9878
CELL: 248-709-8939
michael@azstampcoin.com
www.WorldwideStamps.com

California

**BROSIUS STAMP, COIN &
SUPPLIES**
2105 Main St.
Santa Monica, CA 90405
PH: 310-396-7480
FAX: 310-396-7455
brosius.stamp.coin@hotmail
.com

STAMP STORES

California

**COLONIAL STAMP CO./
BRITISH EMPIRE
SPECIALIST**
5757 Wilshire Blvd. PH #8
(by appt.)
Los Angeles, CA 90036
PH: 323-933-9435
FAX: 323-939-9930
Toll Free in North America
PH: 877-272-6693
FAX: 877-272-6694
info@colonialstampcompany.com
www.colonialstampcompany.com

**FISCHER-WOLK
PHILATELICS**
Suite 211
22762 Aspan St.
Lake Forest, CA 92630
PH: 949-837-2932
fischerwolk@fw.occoxmail.com

NATICK STAMPS & HOBBIES
PO Box 80613
San Marino, CA 91118
PH: 626-285-1384
natickco@att.net
Ebay ID: attickmwj

Connecticut

SILVER CITY COIN & STAMP
41 Colony St.
Meriden, CT 06451
PH: 203-235-7634
FAX: 203-237-4915

Georgia

**STAMPS UNLIMITED OF
GEORGIA, INC.**
Suite 1460
100 Peachtree St.
Atlanta, GA 30303
PH: 404-688-9161
tonyroozen@yahoo.com

Illinois

**DR. ROBERT FRIEDMAN &
SONS**
2029 W. 75th St.
Woodridge, IL 60517
PH: 800-588-8100
FAX: 630-985-1588
drbobstamps@yahoo.com
www.drbobfriedmanstamps.com

British Commonwealth

Stamp Shows

STAMP STORES

Indiana

KNIGHT STAMP & COIN CO.
237 Main St.
Hobart, IN 46342
PH: 219-942-4341
PH: 800-634-2646
knight@knightcoin.com
www.knightcoin.com

Missouri

DAVID SEMSROTT STAMPS
11235 Manchester Rd.
St. Louis (Kirkwood), MO 63122
PH: 314-984-8361
fixodine@sbcglobal.net
www.DavidSemsrott.com

New Jersey

BERGEN STAMPS & COLLECTIBLES
306 Queen Anne Rd.
Teaneck, NJ 07666
PH: 201-836-8987

TRENTON STAMP & COIN CO.
Thomas DeLuca
Store: Forest Glen Plaza
1804 Route 33
Hamilton Square, NJ 08690
Mail: PO Box 8574
Trenton, NJ 08650
PH: 800-446-8664
PH: 609-584-8100
FAX: 609-587-8664
TOMD4TSC@aol.com

New York

CHAMPION STAMP CO., INC.
432 W. 54th St.
New York, NY 10019
PH: 212-489-8130
FAX: 212-581-8130
championstamp@aol.com
www.championstamp.com

Ohio

HILLTOP STAMP SERVICE
Richard A. Peterson
PO Box 626
Wooster, OH 44691
PH: 330-262-8907 (O)
PH: 330-262-5378
hilltop@bright.net

Ohio

THE LINK STAMP CO.
3461 E. Livingston Ave.
Columbus, OH 43227
PH/FAX: 614-237-4125
PH/FAX: 800-546-5726

Virginia

KENNEDY'S STAMPS & COINS, INC.
7059 Brookfield Plaza
Springfield, VA 22150
PH: 703-569-7300
FAX: 703-569-7644
j.w.kennedy@verizon.net

LATHEROW & CO., INC.
5054 Lee Hwy.
Arlington, VA 22207
PH: 703-538-2727
PH: 800-647-4624
FAX: 703-538-5210
latherow@filatco.com

Topicals

E. JOSEPH McCONNELL, INC.
PO Box 683
Monroe, NY 10949
PH: 845-783-9791
FAX: 845-782-0347
ejstamps@gmail.com
www.EJMcConnell.com

WWW.WORLDSTAMPS.COM
PO Box 4743
Pinehurst, NC 28374
PH: 910-295-2048
FAX: 910-295-2049
by mail:
Frank Geiger Philatelists
info@WorldStamps.com
www.WorldStamps.com

Topicals-Columbus

MR. COLUMBUS
PO Box 1492
Fennville, MI 49408
PH: 269-543-4755
Mr.Columbus1492@gmail.com

United States

ACS STAMP COMPANY
10831 Chambers Way
Commerce City, CO 80022
PH: 303-841-8666
ACS@ACSStamp.com
www.acsstamp.com

A TO Z STAMPS & COINS
4950 E. Thomas Rd.
Phoenix, AZ 85018
OFFICE: 480-844-9878
CELL: 248-709-8939
michael@azstampcoin.com
www.WorldwideStamps.com

BROOKMAN STAMP CO.
PO Box 90
Vancouver, WA 98666
PH: 360-695-1391
PH: 800-545-4871
FAX: 360-695-1616
larry@brookmanstamps.com
www.brookmanstamps.com

U.S.-Collections Wanted

DR. ROBERT FRIEDMAN & SONS
2029 W. 75th St.
Woodridge, IL 60517
PH: 800-588-8100
FAX: 630-985-1588
drbobstamps@yahoo.com
www.drbobfriedmanstamps.com

Want Lists

CHARLES P. SCHWARTZ
PO Box 165
Mora, MN 55051
PH: 320-679-4705
cpschw@yahoo.com

Wanted-Worldwide Collections

A TO Z STAMPS & COINS
4950 E. Thomas Rd.
Phoenix, AZ 85018
OFFICE: 480-844-9878
CELL: 248-709-8939
michael@azstampcoin.com
www.WorldwideStamps.com

Wanted-Worldwide Collections

DANIEL F. KELLEHER AUCTIONS LLC
PMB 44
60 Newtown Rd
Danbury, CT 06810
PH: 203-297-6056
FAX: 203-297-6059
info@kelleherauctions.com
www.kelleherauctions.com

DR. ROBERT FRIEDMAN & SONS
2029 W. 75th St.
Woodridge, IL 60517
PH: 800-588-8100
FAX: 630-985-1588
drbobstamps@yahoo.com
www.drbobfriedmanstamps.com

THE STAMP CENTER DUTCH COUNTRY AUCTIONS
4115 Concord Pike
Wilmington, DE 19803
PH: 302-478-8740
FAX: 302-478-8779
auctions@thestampcenter.com
www.thestampcenter.com

Websites

ACS STAMP COMPANY
10831 Chambers Way
Commerce City, CO 80022
PH: 303-841-8666
ACS@ACSStamp.com
www.acsstamp.com

Worldwide

A TO Z STAMPS & COINS
4950 E. Thomas Rd.
Phoenix, AZ 85018
OFFICE: 480-844-9878
CELL: 248-709-8939
michael@azstampcoin.com
www.WorldwideStamps.com

WWW.WORLDSTAMPS.COM
PO Box 4743
Pinehurst, NC 28374
PH: 910-295-2048
FAX: 910-295-2049
by mail:
Frank Geiger Philatelists
info@WorldStamps.com
www.WorldStamps.com

SCOTT
Specialty Series

Embark on a new collecting journey. There are Specialty pages available for more than 140 countries with some of them back in print after many years thanks to on-demand printing technology. Start a new collecting adventure with countries featured in Volume 2 of the new Scott Standard Postage Stamp Catalogue!

Specialty Series pages are sold as page units only. Binders, labels and slipcases are sold separately.

ALBUM SETS

These money-saving album sets include pages, binders and self-adhesive binder labels. Some set contents may vary, please call or visit or web site for specific information.

Item		# of Pgs.	Retail	AA
CANADA				
240CAN1	1851-1952	64	$34.99	$26.99
240CAN2	1953-1978	57	$42.50	$33.99
240CAN3	1979-1990	54	$42.50	$33.99
240CAN4	1991-1995	39	$34.99	$26.66
240CAN5	1996-2000	60	$34.99	$26.99
240CAN6	2001-2006	88	$39.99	$29.99
240S007	2007 #59	14	$12.99	$10.99
*240S008	2008 #60	9	$9.99	$7.99
240S009	2009 #61	16	$15.99	$12.99
LB012	Label: Canada		$2.29	$1.69
240BLANK	Blank Pages	20	$16.99	$13.99
240SET	Album Set	376	$347.99	$259.99
Supplemented in May.				
CAYMAN ISLANDS				
261CYI0	1900-1995	78	$45.95	$32.99
261CYI2	1996-2006	42	$29.99	$23.99
261CI07	2007 #11	4	$4.99	$3.99
*261CI08	2008 #12	7	$7.99	$6.99
*261CI09	2009 #13	4	$5.99	$4.99
LB150	Label: Cayman Islands		$2.29	$1.69
*CAYBLANK	Blank Pages	20	$16.99	$13.99
261CISET	Album Set	137	$155.99	$118.99
Supplemented in June.				
CHILE				
645CHL1	1853-1977	73	$49.95	$27.99
645CHL2	1978-1993	74	$49.95	$27.99
645CHL3	1994-1997	25	$18.95	$10.99
645CHL4	1998-2006	49	$49.99	$39.99
*645S007	2007 #13	5	$5.99	$4.99
*645S008	2008 #14	10	$10.99	$8.99
LB193	Label: Chile		$2.29	$1.69
*645BLANK	Blank Pages	20	$16.99	$13.99
645SET	Album Sets	236	$229.99	$149.99
Supplemented in September.				

Item		# of Pgs.	Retail	AA
CHINA				
480CHN1	1878-1949	91	$59.99	$47.99
480CHN2	1865-1950	101	$64.99	$51.99
LB094	Label: China		$2.29	$1.69
480SET	Album Set	192	$174.99	$134.99
CHINASET	Complete Parts 480, 520 and 530	999	$799.99	$574.99
COLOMBIA				
646COL1	1856-1976	151	$89.95	$49.99
646COL2	1977-1994	58	$39.95	$21.99
646COL3	1995-1997	15	$12.95	$7.99
646COL4	1998-2006	58	$42.50	$33.99
*646S007	2007 #13	7	$7.99	$6.99
LB194	Label: Colombia		$2.29	$1.69
646SET	Album Set	282	264.99	169.99
Supplemented in September.				
CYPRUS				
203CYP0	1880-1997	85	$42.95	$27.99
203CYP2	1998-2006	33	$31.99	$25.99
203CY07	2007 #9	3	$3.99	$3.29
*203CY08	2008 #10	5	$5.99	$4.99
*203CY09	2009 #11	4	$5.99	$4.99
LB188	Label: Cyprus		$2.29	$1.69
*CYPBLANK	Blank Pages:	20	$16.99	$13.99
203CYPSET	Album Set	126	$157.90	$107.59
Supplemented in May.				

Item		# of Pgs.	Retail	AA
CZECHOSLOVAKIA				
307CZH1	1918-1959	121	$69.99	$55.99
307CZH2	1960-1972	89	$59.99	$47.99
307CZH3	1973-1986	82	$59.99	$47.99
307CZH4	1987-1994	47	$34.99	$27.99
307CZH5	1995-1999	37	$27.99	$22.99
307CZH6	2000-2006	58	$42.50	$33.99
*307S007	2007 #58	10	$10.99	$8.99
*307S008	2008 #59	10	$10.99	$8.99
*307S009	2009 #60	13	$14.99	$11.99
LB014	Label: Czechoslovakia		$2.29	$1.69
*CZEBLANK	Blank Pages	20	$16.99	$13.99
307SET	Album Set	454	$429.99	$319.99
DENMARK				
345DEN1	1851-1995	81	$49.99	$37.99
345DEN2	1996-2004	48	$39.99	$29.99
345DM05	2005 #10	15	$12.99	$10.99
345DM06	2006 #11	13	$11.99	$9.99
345DM07	2007 #12	6	$5.99	$4.99
*345DM08	2008 #13	7	$7.99	$6.99
345DM09	2009 #14	13	$14.99	$11.99
LB157	Label: Denmark		$2.29	$1.69
*DENBLANK	Blank Pages	20	$16.99	$13.99
345DENSET	Album Set	212	$209.99	$159.99
Supplemented in June.				
DOMINICA				
261DMN1	1874-1982	112	$59.95	$32.99
261DMN2	1983-1990	85	$45.95	$25.99
261DMN3	1991-1993	75	$39.95	$21.99
261DMN4	1994-1995	56	$29.95	$16.99
261DM96	1996 #1	16	$12.95	$10.36
*261DM97	1997 #2	39	$28.99	$23.99
261DM98	1998 #3	18	$13.95	$11.16
261DM99	1999 #4	27	$17.95	$14.36
261DM00	2000 #5	4	$4.99	$3.99
261DM01	2001 #6	3	$3.99	$3.29
*261DM03	2002-2003 #7	4	$5.99	$4.99
261DM04	2004 #8	8	$7.99	$6.99
261DM06	2005-06 #9	4	$4.99	$3.99
*261DM08	2008 #10	5	$5.99	$4.99
LB153	Label: Dominica		$2.29	$1.69
261DOMSET	Album Set	461	$419.99	$249.99
Supplemented in September.				
DOMINICAN REPUBLIC				
648DMR1	1865-1994	169	$99.99	$79.99
648DMR2	1995-2008	49	$46.99	$37.99
*648BLANK	Blank Pages:	20	$16.99	$13.99
LB205	Label: Dominican Rep.		$2.29	$1.69
FALKLAND ISLANDS				
261FAI0	1878-1995	100	$69.99	$55.99
261FAI2	1996-2006	66	$44.99	$35.99
*261FI07	2007 #12	9	$9.99	$7.99
*261FI08	2008 #13	7	$7.99	$6.99
*261FI09	2009	8	$8.99	$7.99
LB170	Label: Falkland Islands		$2.29	$1.69
Supplemented in July.				
FAROE ISLANDS				
345FIS0	1919-1995	30	$21.99	$16.99
345FIS2	1996-1999	16	$14.99	$11.99
345FIS3	2000-2006	34	$29.99	$23.75
*345FI07	2007 #11	5	$5.99	$4.99
*345FI08	2008 #12	5	$5.99	$4.99
*345FI09	2009 #13	4	$5.99	$4.99
LB158	Label: Faroe Islands		$2.29	$1.69
*FAROBLANK	Blank Pages	20	$16.99	$13.99
345FAISET	Album Set	80	$129.99	$99.99
Supplemented in June.				

Item		# of Pgs.	Retail	AA
FIJI				
624FJI1	1870-1993	64	$44.99	$35.99
624FJI2	1994-1997	16	$19.95	$10.99
624FJI3	1998-2006	49	$39.99	$31.99
*624S007	2007 #14	7	$7.99	$6.99
*624S008	2008 #15	5	$5.99	$4.99
*624S009	2009 #16	3	$4.99	$3.99
LB130	Label: Fiji		$2.29	$1.69
FIJISET	Album Set	136	164.95	119.95
FINLAND				
345FIN1	1856-1995	108	$59.99	$44.99
345FIN2	1996-2003	45	$24.99	$18.99
345FN04	2004 #9	10	$9.99	$7.99
*345FN05	2005 #10	9	$9.99	$7.99
345FN06	2006 #11	8	$7.99	$6.99
*345FN07	2007 #12	9	$9.99	$7.99
*345FN08	2008 #13	14	$14.99	$11.99
345FN09	2009 #14	7	$7.99	$6.99
LB017	Label: Finland		$2.29	$1.69
345FINSET	Album Set	218	$219.99	$159.99
Supplemented in June.				
FRANCE				
310FRN1	1849-1958	70	$49.99	$39.99
310FRN2	1959-1976	66	$44.99	$33.99
310FRN3	1977-1987	59	$43.99	$32.99
310FRN4	1988-1994	54	$39.99	$29.99
310FRN5	1995-2000	55	$39.99	$29.99
310FRN6	2001-2005	98	$59.99	$49.99
310S006	2006 #41	30	$19.99	$15.99
*310S007	2007 #42	19	$16.99	$13.99
*310S008	2008 #43	24	$17.99	$14.99
*310S009	2009 #44	34	$25.99	$20.99
LB018	Label: France		$2.29	$1.69
*310BLANK	Blank Pages	20	$16.99	$13.99
310SET	Album Set	475	$429.99	$324.99
Supplemented in May.				
FRENCH AFRICA				
310FRA1	1886-1977	244	$139.99	$104.99
310FRA2	1888-1974	222	$119.99	$89.99
LB073	Label: French Africa		$2.29	$1.69
FRENCH COLONIES				
310FCP0	1859-1956	126	$72.50	$57.99
LB020	Label: French Colonies		$2.29	$1.69
FRENCH OFFICES ABROAD				
310FOA0	1885-1941	40	$28.99	$23.99
FRENCH POLYNESIA				
625FRP1	1892-1994	108	$69.99	$55.99
625FRP2	1995-2006	40	$28.99	$23.99
625S007	2007 #13	5	$5.99	$4.99
*625S008	2008 #14	6	$6.99	$5.99
LB136	Label: French Polynesia		$2.29	$1.69
FRPOSET	Album Set	159	$159.99	$119.95
Supplemented in August.				
FRENCH SOUTHERN & ANTARCTIC TERRITORIES				
626FSA1	1955-1994	38	$27.99	$22.99
626FSA2	1995-2007	37	$27.99	$22.99
*626S007	2007 #10	6	$6.99	$5.99
*626S008	2008 #11	6	$6.99	$5.99
LB141	Label: French & Antarctic Territories		$2.29	$1.69
FSASET	Album Set	87	$118.99	$92.50
Supplemented in August.				

SPECIALTY/NATIONAL SERIES BINDERS

3-RING BINDERS & SLIPCASES

With the three ring binder, pages lay flat and the rings make turning the pages easy. The locking mechanism insure that the rings won't pop open even when the binder is full.

Item		Retail	AA
ACBR01	Small 3-Ring Binder Holds up to 100 pages	$39.99	$32.99
ACBR03	Large 3-Ring Binder Holds up to 250 pages	$39.99	$32.99
ACSR01	Small 3-Ring Slipcase	$37.50	$26.99
ACSR03	Large 3-Ring Slipcase	$37.50	$26.99

ORDER ONLINE Get the AMOS ADVANTAGE Discount

* Indicates special order item. May take 4-6 weeks for delivery.

ORDERING INFORMATION

*AA prices apply to paid subscribers of Amos Hobby titles and orders placed online.

Prices, terms and product availability subject to change.

Shipping & Handling:
United States: 10% of order total. Minimum charge $6.99 Maximum charge $45.00.
Canada: 15% of order total. Minimum charge $19.99 Maximum charge $50.00.
Foreign orders are shipped via FedEx Economy Intl. and billed actual freight.

To Order

Call **1-800-572-6885**

Visit **www.amosadvantage.com**